CHORAL MUSIC IN PRINT

Volume I:
SACRED CHORAL MUSIC

Edited By:

Thomas R. Nardone

James H. Nye

Mark Resnick

MUSICDATA, INC.
Philadelphia, 1974

International Standard Book Numbers:

0-88478-000-7 (library binding)
0-88478-001-5 (paperbound)
0-88478-004-X (library binding set, *Sacred Choral Music* and *Secular Choral Music*)
0-88478-005-8 (paperbound set, *Sacred Choral Music* and *Secular Choral Music*)

Library of Congress Catalog Card Number: 73-87918

Manufactured in the United States of America by Port City Press

Musicdata, Inc.
18 West Chelten Avenue
Philadelphia, Pennsylvania 19144

Contents

Preface

While the need for an in-print service in the field of music has been a longstanding one acknowledged by musicians, the music industry, and librarians, the only catalog which gives comprehensive coverage of a field of music, and which has been updated on a regular basis, is *String Music In Print,* by Margaret Farish. For most areas of music, the scope of the task demands the use of data processing equipment. Musicdata, Inc. has developed a system for doing this, and *Choral Music In Print* is the first product of this system. The catalog is an attempt at an exhaustive listing of the offerings of music publishers throughout the world.

Publishers' catalogs have served as the primary source of material. However, there is a great deal of unevenness from publisher to publisher in the quality of the catalogs of published choral music. They range from accurate and complete to a lower extreme. In certain catalogs composers are identified by surname only, some titles appear in truncated form and other titles, particularly English titles of works by German composers, are not properly connected with a uniform title. A good deal of this ambiguity has been preserved in our index entries. Where possible, *Baker's Biographical Dictionary* has been used as a standard for the spelling of composers' names, and for their dates of birth and death. Duplicate entries for the same edition occur frequently within publishers' catalogs, and in the catalogs of agents. We have attempted to eliminate this duplication, but inevitably some remains.

We have made a few departures from usual bibliographic conventions. In alphabetizing, titles beginning with the abbreviation "St." will be found alphabetized in the position accorded by those two letters rather than under the proper "Saint." Additionally, the articles of foreign titles have not been transposed, although those of English titles have been. The newness of the system we have developed will account for some other oddities. When discovered, we will be pleased if users draw them to our attention for revision in future supplements and editions.

Our thanks are due to a number of people who have been particularly helpful in the shaping and execution of this project. Margaret Farish has been of great assistance in providing a prototype and in helping us establish relations with publishers. Arnold Broido, President of Theodore Presser Co. and of the Music Publishers Association, was freely available with probing questions and important comment during the development of our concept of a Music-in-Print series. Both Elizabeth Hartman and Frederick Kent of the Free Library of Philadelphia, Music Department, offered significant feedback on the format of entries and types of information to be included. Our staff of coders and proofreaders who performed the task of encoding materials from the publishers' catalogs for data processing and checking for accuracy deserve special credit. They are: Carter R. Boynton, Nancy Caldwell, Ellon D. Carpenter, Timothy Flaherty, Joanne S. Godeck, Yvette C. Hammond, Charles E. King, Stuart B. Leigh, Nancy Nardone, Maria E. Portone, Allen A. Prebus, Eileen A. Regan, Mary Ann Resnick, Janeth R. Rouzer, Suzanne M. Sharrock, Susan Simon. Translation assistance was given by: John Huneke, Rudolf Kroha, Franco Nardone, Tamas Strasser. The typists who served as our link with the computer for data entry were: Helene Farrell, Judy Mellon, Rose Phillips. And thanks to the publishers for their cooperation and assistance.

The Editors

Philadelphia
May, 1974

v

Guide to Use

GENERAL ARRANGEMENT

Within *Choral Music In Print* the user will find a comprehensive listing of the choral works of over 300 music publishers throughout the world. The arrangement of this listing is a single alphabetic interfiling of composers names, titles of works, and cross references. The title under the composer's name serves as the focus for major information on each composition. In the absence of a composer the title in the main list is the focal point.

For each title there are two types of information: a) generic information about the composition and b) specific information pertaining to the editions which are in print. Included in the generic information category are the uniform title of the composition, a structured title for the work (e.g., Cantata 140), a thematic catalog number or opus and number designation, the larger source from which the work was taken, and remarks. The remarks are a series of codes or abbreviations giving information on the seasonal or other usage of the piece, the type of music, and the national origin and century for folk or anonymous pieces. (These codes also make it possible to retrieve from the data base developed for *Choral Music In Print* specialized listings of music for particular seasons, types, etc.)

Following the generic information about the piece is the information about the individual editions. This information includes the arranger, the published title of the edition if different from the uniform title, the language of the text, voicing for the chorus and soli, instrumentation required for performance, a difficulty rating assigned for the edition by the publisher, the format of the publication, publisher, publisher's number, price, and information on the availability of music for rental or the availability of orchestral parts.

Following is a typical entry under a composer:

AHLE, JOHANN RUDOLPH (1625-1673)
Furchtet Euch Nicht *Xmas, cant
(Lillehaug, L.) "Be Not Afraid" [Eng/Ger]
dbl cor,cont,4trom sc CONCORDIA 97-6407
$1.50, cor pts CONCORDIA 97-6430 $.40,
ipa   (A316)

In this entry, the title, "Furchtet Euch Nicht" is shown in the section for the composer, Johann Rudolph Ahle. "Xmas" and "cant" are remark codes indicating that the piece is a contata appropriate for Christmas use. (The asterisk before Xmas merely serves to set off the remarks from the title.) The piece has only one edition, arranged by L. Lillehaug. The English title is "Be Not Afraid." The text is in English and German. The piece is scored for double chorus, continuo and four trombones. Both score and choral parts may be obtained from Concordia at the prices shown. 97-6407 and 97-6430 are the publisher's order numbers. The code "ipa" indicates that instrumental parts are available, but we have not undertaken to list the prices of these.

SACRED-SECULAR DESIGNATIONS

With few exceptions, we have relied upon the sacred-secular distinctions made for us by the publishers. Where publishers have not made the distinction, for the purpose of this index we have taken choral music with a scriptural text or which is appropriate for religious usage or church service to be sacred.

SEQUENCE NUMBERS

An alphanumeric number, appearing on the right margin, has been assigned to each edition represented in this catalog. These are for the purpose of easing identification and location when corrections are made in our updating service. Annual supplements to the catalog are planned.

PRICES

We can give no assurances of the accuracy of stated prices. The prices of editions have been increasing steadily over the last few years, yet we have thought it helpful to give the user a U.S. dollar figure, where available, for comparative purposes. The publishers should be consulted directly for current prices.

CROSS REFERENCES

In order to provide the user with as many points of access as possible, *Choral Music In Print* has been heavily cross-referenced. For example, the piece by Ahle, illustrated above, may be located under either its German or English title in the main alphabet, as well as under the composer. Therefore, the following cross references exist in the main alphabet:

FURCHTET EUCH NICHT see Ahle, Johann Rudolph

and

BE NOT AFRAID see Ahle, Johann Rudolph, Furchtet Euch Nicht

and in addition, the following cross reference will be found under the composer's name:

Be Not Afraid *see Furchtet Euch Nicht

CHORAL COLLECTIONS

An attempt has been made to provide the user with access to pieces contained within choral collections, while still keeping the work within reasonable bounds of time and space. Accordingly, the following practices have been adopted:

If the members of a collection are published separately, they are listed individually, regardless of the number of pieces involved. If the collection is only published as a whole, the members are listed only if they do not exceed six in number. For larger collections, a code is given indicating the number of pieces and whether or not the contents are listed in the publisher's catalog. For example,

CC18L indicates a collection of 18 pieces which are *listed* in the publisher's catalog

CC101U indicates a collection of 101 pieces which are *unlisted* in the publisher's catalog

CCU indicated a collection of an unknown number of pieces

Whenever the members are listed, they are also cross-referenced to the collection. For example, consider the following entry:

BACH, JOHANN SEBASTIAN (1685-1750)
Two Bach Chorales For Christmas *Xmas, chorale oct SATB PRO ART 1440 $.30; SAB PRO ART 1816 $.30; SSA PRO ART 1106 $.30; 2pt PRO ART 1817 $.30
contains: Break Forth, O Beauteous, Heavenly Light; Child Is Born In Bethlehem, A

(B2013)

This collection contains two members, which are not published separately. Under each of the members there is a cross reference saying 'see Two Bach Chorales For Christmas'.

If the members were also published separately, the cross references in both directions would say 'see also'. If the members were *only* published separately (i.e., the collection were not published as a whole) then the cross reference under the collection would read 'see' and under the members, 'see from'. Thus, 'see' and 'see also' direct the user to information concerning publication, while 'see from' provides access to the collection of which a given publication is a part.

Another problem is the cataloging of untitled choral collections. These are collections of several pieces published as a whole, but having no overall title. In this case, the publication information is given under the first piece listed, together with the cross reference 'contains also', followed by the titles of the other members. Under each of the other members, the cross reference 'see' directs the user to the entry for the first member.

List of Abbreviations

The following is a general list of abbreviations developed for the Music-in-Print series. Therefore, all of the abbreviations do not necessarily occur in the present volume. Also, it should be noted that terms spelled out in full in the catalog, e.g., winds, tuba, Easter, Passover, folk, Swiss, do not appear in this list.

A	alto	Eng	English	mot	motet
acap	a cappella	Epiph	Epiphany		
Adv	Advent	eq voices	equal voices	Neth	Netherlands
Afr	African	Eur	European	NJ	Name of Jesus
Agnus	Agnus Dei	evang	evangelistic	No.	Number
Allelu	Alleluia	Eve	Evening	Nor Am	North American
anti	antiphonal			Norw	Norwegian
anti cor	antiphonal chorus	fac ed	facsimile edition	Nunc	Nunc Dimittis
Asc	Ascension	Fest	festivals		
ASD	All Saints' Day	fing. cym.	finger cymbals	ob	oboe
Aus	Austrian	Finn	Finnish	oct	octavo
Austral	Australian	fl	flute	Offer	Offertory
		Fr	French	Op.	Opus
B	bass			opt	optional, ad lib
Bar	baritone	Gd.Fri.	Good Friday	ora	oratorio
Baroq	Baroque	Gen	general	orch	orchestra
bass inst	bass instruments	Ger	German	org	organ
bds	boards	girl cor	girls' chorus		
Belg	Belgian	Greg	Gregorian chant	Palm	Palm Sunday
Bene	Benediction, Benedictus	gtr	guitar	pap	paperbound
Bibl	Biblical			Pent	Pentecost
Boh	Bohemian	Harv	Harvest	perc	percussion
boy cor	boys' chorus	Heb	Hebrew	pic	piccolo
Braz	Brazilian	hndbl	handbells	pno	piano
bsn	bassoon	Holywk	Holy Week	Pol	Polish
bvl	bass viol	horn	French horn	Polynes	Polynesian
BVM	Blessed Virgin Mary	hpsd	harpsichord	pop	popular
		Hung	Hungarian	Port	Portuguese
camb	cambiata			PreClass	Pre-Classical
cant	cantata	Impres	Impressionist	Proces	processional
Carib	Caribbean	Ind	Indian	Psntd	Passiontide
CC	choral collection	inst	instruments	pt	part
CCU	choral collection, unlisted	ipa	instrumental parts available		
CCUL	choral collection, partially listed	ipr	instrumental parts for rent	Quinqua	Quinquagesima
Cen Am	Central American	Ir	Irish		
cent	century	Isr	Israeli	rec	recorder
Chin	Chinese	It	Italian	Reces	recessional
Circum	Circumcision			Refm	Reformation
clar	clarinet	Jap	Japanese	Rembrnc	Remembrance
Class	Classical	Jew	Jewish	Renais	Renaissance
cloth	clothbound	jr cor	junior chorus	Req	Requiem
cmplt ed	complete edition	Jubil	Jubilate Deo	Romant	Romantic
Cnfrm	Confirmation			Royal	royal occasion
Commun	Communion	K.	Köchel-Verzeichnis	Rum	Rumanian
cong	congregation	kbd	keyboard	Russ	Russian
cont	continuo	Kor	Korean		
contemp	contemporary			S	soprano
cor	chorus	L	listed	S.	Schmieder (BWV, or Bach-Werke-Verzeichnis)
cor pts	choral parts	Lat	Latin		
cor-resp	choral response	liturg	liturgical	s.p.	separately published
Corpus	Corpus Christi			Sab	Sabbath
cradle	cradle song	Magnif	Magnificat	sac	sacred
		med	medium	sc	score
Dan	Danish	med diff	medium difficult	Scot	Scottish
dbl cor	double chorus	Mediev	Medieval	sec	secular
Ded	Dedication	men cor	men's chorus	Septua	Septuagesima
desc	descant	Mex	Mexican	Sexa	Sexagesima
diff	difficult	Mez	mezzo-soprano	Slav	Slavic
Doxol	Doxology	min sc	miniature score	So Am	South American
Dut	Dutch	mix cor	mixed chorus	Span	Spanish
		Morav	Moravian	speak cor	speaking chorus
ECY	End of Church Year	Morn	Morning	spir	spiritual
Ember	Ember Days				

sr cor	senior chorus	treb inst	treble instruments	vcl	violoncello
study sc	study score	Trin	Trinity	vla	viola
Swed	Swedish	trom	trombone	vln	violin
SWV	Schütz-Werke-Verzeichnis	trp	trumpet	voc pt	vocal part
				voc sc	vocal score
T	tenor	U	unlisted		
tamb	tambourine	UL	partially listed	wom cor	women's chorus
Thanks	Thanksgiving	unis	unison		
timp	timpani	unis cor	unison chorus	Xmas	Christmas
treb cor	treble chorus	US	United States		

A

A BEKAKIRALY see Dobos, K.

A BELEN see Gomis

A CAPPELLA SACRED CHOIR *CC10L,Gen
SATB,acap oct PRO ART 359 $1.25 (A1)

A CAPPELLA SINGER, THE, VOL. I *sac/sec,CCU
(Clough-Leighter, H.) SSA,acap SCHIRM.EC 1545
$3.00 (A2)

A CAPPELLA SINGER, THE-VOL. II *sac/sec,CCU
(Clough-Leighter, H.) SATB,acap SCHIRM.EC
1682 $3.00 (A3)

A CAPPELLA SINGER, THE, VOL. III *sac/sec,CCU
(Clough-Leighter, H.) TTBB,acap SCHIRM.EC 557
$3.00 (A4)

A FESTIVAL OF FOLK CAROLS see Mendoza, Anne

A FIKK JEG KUN VAERE DEN MINSTE KVIST see
Karlsen, Rolf

A FIKK JEG KUN VAERE DEN MINSTE KVIST see
Lindhjelm, Nils

A GESU BAMBINO see Chiesa, Federico

A, JESUS STORE GUD see Gulbranson, Eilif

A KOM, A KOM IMMANUEL see Helmore, T.

A KOM, LIVSENS BROD see Nystedt, Knut

A KRISTI, SOM I BRYLLAUP GJESTA see Nystedt,
Knut

A KUM BACHUR ATSEL
see Rounds Of Israel

A LA CHIVIRIBUELA see Martin Pompey

A LA CLAIRE FONTAINE
(Archer, Violet) SA,pno oct BERANDOL 877A7A1
$.35 (A5)

A LA FONTAINE DU PREZ see Clemens, Jacobus

A LA LA DEG TIRILILL see Nystedt, Knut

A LA NANITA NANA *Xmas,carol/cradle,Pol/Span
(Glover, R.F.) "Virgin's Lullaby" SSST,
opt fl,vcl,vln,vla oct KERBY 6224 $.55 (A6)
(Luboff, Norman) SATB WALTON 3016 $.25 (A7)
(Luboff, Norman) SSA oct WALTON 5000 $.25 (A8)

A LA NANITA NANA see Ehret, Walter

A LA NANITA NANA see Glover, R.F.

A LA NATIVITE see Darcieux, [F.]

A LA NATIVITE see Parozai, Gui

A LA NOEL see Dauly, G.

A LA PUERTA DE TU CASA see Martin Pompey

A LA SAINT-MEDARD see Revil, H.

A LA VENUE DE NOEL
see Five French Noels

A LA VENUE DE NOEL see Migot, Georges

A L'ECHELLE DE JACOB see We Am Clim'in Jacobs's
Ladder

A L'EGLISE see Lowell, Gene

A L'EGLISE see Tchaikovsky, Piotr Ilyitch

A LEVA see Olsen, Sparre

A MARIA IMMACOLATA see Ascenso, Antonio

A MINUET FUT FAIT UN REVEIL
see Five French Noels

A MUNKA HIMNUSZA see Liszt, Franz

A REGGEL see Palestrina, Giovanni

A-ROCKIN' ALL NIGHT *Xmas
(Ehret) SATB BOSTON 13777 $.40 (A9)

A-ROCKIN ALL NIGHT see Wilson, H.

A S. CECILIA see Bottazzo, Luigi

A S. GIUSEPPE see Magri, Pietro

A S. GIUSEPPE *CC3U,ASD
[Lat] unis,org ZANIBON 2718 s.p. contains
works by: Ascenso; Bottazzo; Volpi (A10)

A S. GIUSEPPE *CC2U,ASD
[Lat] 2 eq voices,org ZANIBON 2720 s.p.
contains works by: Moioli; Volpi (A11)

A S. LUIGI see Ascenso, Antonio

A S. LUIGI see Gerli, Giovanni

A S. LUIGI GONZAGA see Bottazzo, Luigi

A S. TERESA DEL BAMBINO GESU see Ravanello,
Oreste

A SANT'ANTONIO "LA CANZONCINA DEI GIGLI" see
Zimarino, Settimio

A SAVING HEALTH TO US IS BROUGHT see Brahms,
Johannes, Es Ist Das Heil

A SOLIS ORTUS CARDINE see Binchois, Gilles

A TOI, MON DIEU (Psalm 26) 16th cent
(Geveart, F.-A.) [Fr] 4pt mix cor,acap (med
easy) cor pts LEMOINE s.p. see from

Collection De Choeurs, septieme Fascicule (A12)

A TOI, MON DIEU, MON COEUR MONTE see Goudimel,
Claude

A TOI, MON DIEU, MON COEUR MONTE see Jannequin,
Clement

A TRISTRIA SECLA PRIORA see Joubert, John

A UN ARROYO ME BAJE see Martin Pompey

A UN NINO IIORANDO see Guerrero, Francisco

AAGAARD, THOMAS
David Og Goliat (from Olaf Ring)
SATB HANSEN-DEN 121 s.p. see also Otte
Salmer Og Sange (A13)

Det Mulmer Mod Den Morke Nat (from Olaf Ring)
SATB HANSEN-DEN 119 s.p. see also Otte
Salmer Og Sange (A14)

Horer Du Rosten (from Olaf Ring)
SATB HANSEN-DEN 120 s.p. see also Otte
Salmer Og Sange (A15)

Otte Salmer Og Sange (from Olaf Ring) sac/
sec,CC8L
SATB cmplt ed HANSEN-DEN 24797 s.p.
see also: David Og Goliat (from Olaf
Ring); Det Mulmer Mod Den Morke Nat
(from Olaf Ring); Horer Du Rosten (from
Olaf Ring) (A16)

AAMODT, THORLEIF
Herre Du, Har Vaert Oss En Bolig
[Norw] cor,org LYCHE 25 s.p. (A17)

AAMODT, VALTER
Gud Singe Vart Folk
mix cor MUSIKK 149 s.p. (A18)

Songarbon
mix cor MUSIKK 37 s.p. (A19)
men cor MUSIKK 51 s.p. (A20)

AAN BETHLEHEM'S POORTE see Hoogerwerf, N.

AAN BETHLEHEMS STERRE see Pennartz, P.

AAN DE KRIBBE TE BETHLEHEM see Bach, Johann
Sebastian

AAN DE STROMEN BABYLON see Vaal, O. de

AB ORIENTE see Gallus, Jacobus

AB ORIENTE VENERUNT MAGI see Gallus, Jacobus

AB ORIENTE VENERUNT MAGI IN BETHLEHEM see
Gallus, Jacobus

ABBEY, H.
Behold, A Star *Xmas
SATB oct PRESSER MC274 $.30 (A21)

No Room In The Inn *Xmas
SATB oct PRESSER MC269 $.30 (A22)

Sleep, Sweet Jesus, Sleep *Xmas
SATB oct PRESSER MC191 $.25 (A23)
SSA oct PRESSER MC285 $.25 (A24)

ABBI PIETA DI ME, O DIO! see Giannini, Vincenzo

ABBOT
Alleluia
SATB,org/pno BOSTON 13130 $.35 (A25)

ABBOTT
Exalt The Lord
SATB,org/pno BOSTON 12946 $.35 (A26)

ABEL, J.T.
My God, My Father
SA,pno (easy) oct WILLIS 3426 $.15 (A27)

O Make Me Love Thee
SA,pno (easy) oct WILLIS 3427 $.16 (A28)

ABEND KOMMT, DER TAG SICH NEIGET see Weber,
Karl-Heinz

ABEND WARD, BALD KOMMT DIE NACHT see Trubel,
Gerhard

ABENDLIED see Schieri, Fritz

ABENDLIED ZU GOTT see Haydn, (Franz) Joseph

ABENDMAHL see Bruckner, Anton

ABENDMAHL-MESSE see Rehmann, Theodor Bernhard,
Coena Domini

ABER DAS KIND WUCHS see Vulpius, Melchior

ABER DER GERECHTEN SEELEN see Gwinner, Volker

ABER DER TROSTER, DER HEILIGE GEIST see
Hufschmidt, Wolfgang

ABER DES HERRN WORT BLEIBT see Zipp, Friedrich

ABER GOTT SPRACH ZU IHM, DU NARR! see
Driessler, Johannes

ABER MIT SEINEM VOLKE see Handel, George
Frideric, But As For His People

ABER WER GLAUBT UNSERER PREDIGT see Franck,
Melchior

ABERG, JAN H.
Den Kristliga Dagvisan
(Romson, J.) mix cor NORDISKA 2120 s.p. (A29)

I Himmelen, I Himmelen
mix cor NORDISKA 2121 s.p. (A30)

ABIDE IN MY LOVE see Clare, Edwyn A.

ABIDE, O DEAREST JESUS see Vulpius, Melchior

ABIDE, O DEAREST JESUS see Wolff, S. Drummond

ABIDE WITH ME *hymn
(Gardner) SSA (med easy) OXFORD 44.224 $.25,
ipr see from Five Hymns In Popular Style (A31)

ABIDE WITH ME see Barnby, Sir Joseph

ABIDE WITH ME see Bennett

ABIDE WITH ME see Gardner, John [Linton]

ABIDE WITH ME see Gratton, Frank L.

ABIDE WITH ME see Hirt, L.

ABIDE WITH ME see Monk

ABIDE WITH ME see Seymour, H.

ABIDE WITH ME see Wilson

ABIDE WITH ME, 'TIS EVENTIDE
SSA oct BELWIN 2016 $.30 (A32)

ABIDE WITH US OUR SAVIOUR see Wetzler, Robert

ABIDING JOY see Byles, B. D.

ABIDING PRESENCE, THE see Sateren, Leland
Bernhard

ABOVE A STAR see Graham, Robert [V.]

ABOVE ALL ELSE LOVE GOD ALONE see Blakley

ABOVE ALL PRAISE see Mendelssohn-Bartholdy,
Felix

ABOVE HIM STOOD THE SERAPHIM see Deering,
Richard

ABOVE, ON THE MOUNTAIN *Xmas,carol,Aus
(Ehret, Walter) SATB oct WALTON 2521 $.30 (A33)

ABOVE THE CLEAR BLUE SKY see Emerson, John

ABOVE THE CLEAR BLUE SKY see Wolff, S. Drummond

ABOVE THE HILLS OF TIME see Hughes, Robert J.

ABOVE THE HILLS THE ADVENT LIGHT see Hutson,
Wihla

ABOVE THE STARS see Tomkins, Thomas

ABRAHAM see Kramer, Gottfried

ABRAHAM AND ISAAC see Pfautsch, Lloyd

ABRIL
Missa *Mass
SATB HANSEN-US C596 $.40 (A34)

ABROAD THE REGAL BANNERS FLY see Pergolesi,
Giovanni Battista

ABROAD THE ROYAL BANNERS FLY *hymn
SATB oct ST.MARTIN s.p. (A35)

ABSALOM see Tomkins, Thomas

ABSALOM, ABSALOM! see Johnson, Carl

ABSALOM, OH, MY SON see Des Prez, Josquin,
Absalon, Fili Mi

ABSALON, FILI MI see Des Prez, Josquin

ABSIL, [JEAN] (1893-   )
Colindas *CC9L,Xmas,Rum
3pt,acap LEMOINE s.p. (A36)

Colindas (Chants De Noel) *CC8L,Xmas
[Fr] 3pt jr cor,acap LEMOINE s.p. (A37)

ABT, FRANZ (1819-1885)
Ave Maria
men cor,acap ERDMANN 103 s.p. (A38)
(Ehret) "O Lord Most Holy" SAB,S solo oct
PRO ART 1431 $.20 (A39)
(Sheppard) SA,org/pno BOSTON 12345 $.35 (A40)

Boven De Sterren
men cor sc ALSBACH&D s.p. see also Vier
Geestelijke Liederen (A41)

Living Light, The *Xmas
SATB oct LORENZ C263 $.25 (A42)

O Lord Most Holy *see Ave Maria

Vier Geestelijke Liederen *see Boven De
Sterren (A43)

ABUNDANT LIFE see Mc Lellan

ACCEDITE GENTES see Buxtehude, Dietrich

ACCEPT, ALMIGHTY FATHER
see Offertory Hymns

ACCEPT MY HEART see Sateren, Leland Bernhard

ACCEPT OUR THANKS see Sibelius, Jean

ACCLAMATIONS see Anonymous, Christus Vincit

ACCLAMATIONS see Englert, Eugene

ACCOMPANIED CHRISTMAS CAROLS *CCU,Xmas,carol
(Cope) SA&SSA,acap BOOSEY $.60 (A44)

ACCOMPANIMENTS FOR UNISON HYMN-SINGING *CC50U,
hymn
unis,pno/org oct ROYAL 85402 017 9 s.p. (A45)

ACCORDI, CARLO
Per La S. Comunione *Commun
[Lat] 2 eq voices,org ZANIBON 179 s.p. (A46)

ACCORDING TO HIS PROMISE see Rose

ACCORRI A BETLEMME see Moioli, Romano

ACCURSED TREE, THE see Posegate

ACH, ARME WELT see Brahms, Johannes

AD TE LEVAVI see Rheinberger, Josef

AD TE LEVAVI OCULOS MEOS see Palestrina, Giovanni

AD TE LEVAVI OCULOS MEOS; MISERE NOSTRI, DOMINE see Palestrina, Giovanni

AD VESPERAS see Wiklund, Gustav

ADAGIO see Geitvik, S.H.

ADAIR
Praise And Give Thanks
(O'Hare) SATB oct HUNTZINGER 4013 $.20 (A68)

ADAM see Le Sueur, [Jean Francois]

ADAM, ADOLPHE-CHARLES (1803-1856)
Cantique De Noel *Xmas,anthem/carol
SATB oct LORENZ 4362 $.30 (A69)
SAB oct LORENZ 7350 $.30 (A70)
2pt oct LORENZ 5708 $.30 (A71)
"Christmas Song" SATB oct PRESSER 312-20369 $.25 (A72)
"O Holy Night" SATB ALLANS 373 s.p. (A73)
"O Holy Night" SATB oct PRESSER 312-20369 $.25 (A74)
"O Holy Night" 2pt,S solo oct NOVELLO 47.0414.02 s.p. (A75)
"O Holy Night" unis,pno (easy) oct WILLIS 1761 $.10 (A76)
"O Holy Night" 4pt mix cor,A/Bar solo,pno (med) oct WILLIS 2611 $.10 (A77)
"O Holy Night" SATB KJOS P1707 $.30 (A78)
"O Holy Night" SSA KJOS P1720 $.30 (A79)
"O Holy Night" SA KJOS P1735 $.30 (A80)
"O Holy Night" SSAA KJOS P1765 $.30 (A81)
"O Holy Night" men cor KJOS P1734 $.30 (A82)
(Andrews) "O Holy Night" SATB oct GRAY GCMR 233 $.25 (A83)
(Barlow) "O Holy Night" TTBB,acap oct FISCHER,J 5185 $.30 (A84)
(Biederman) "O Holy Night" SATB oct FISCHER,J 1160 $.35 (A85)
(Breck) "O Holy Night" SATB oct FISCHER,C CM-6263 $.25 (A86)
(Breck) "O Holy Night" SA oct FISCHER,C CM-6567 $.25 (A87)
(Breck) "O Holy Night" SSA oct FISCHER,C CM-6568 $.25 (A88)
(Brewer) "O Holy Night" 4pt men cor oct SCHIRM.G 5897 $.40 (A89)
(Buck) "O Holy Night" mix cor,ST soli oct SCHIRM.G 10018 $.30 (A90)
(Buck) "O Holy Night" 4pt mix cor,high solo oct SCHIRM.G 3002 $.30 (A91)
(Deis) "On Holy Night" [Eng/Fr] 3pt mix cor oct SCHIRM.G 9980 $.40 (A92)
(Downing) "Christmas Song" 3pt wom cor oct SCHIRM.G 8877 $.30 (A93)
(Dressler, W.) "O Holy Night" SATB oct PRESSER 332-01196 $.30 (A94)
(Duey) "O Holy Night" TTBB BOSTON 12061 $.30 (A95)
(Ehret) "O Holy Night" SAB oct BOOSEY 5547 $.30 (A96)
(Gaines; McKinney) "O Holy Night" SA oct FISCHER,J 8433 $.30 (A97)
(Gaines; McKinney) "O Holy Night" SAB oct FISCHER,J 9684 $.30 (A98)
(Gaines; McKinney) "O Holy Night" SSA oct FISCHER,J 8434 $.30 (A99)
(Giffe, W.) "O Holy Night" SATB oct PRESSER 332-07337 $.30 (A100)
(Gilchrist, W.) "O Holy Night" SATB oct PRESSER 332-10181 $.35 (A101)
(Hallett) "O Holy Night" SA/SAB/SSA/TTBB/SATB oct WORD CS-2227 $.30 (A102)
(Harris) "O Holy Night" SSATBB ALFRED 6403 $.30 (A103)
(Heller) "O Holy Night" SATB/unis/jr cor SCHMITT 1679 $.30 (A104)
(Holmes) "O Holy Night" TTBB oct PRO ART 1963 $.30 (A105)
(Hustad) "O Holy Night" SATB,opt trp oct AGAPE F 938 $.30 (A106)
(Leist) "O Holy Night" SATB,S solo,chimes/pno, vibraphone oct FOX $.22 (A107)
(Moore) "O Holy Night" SAB KJOS P1766 $.30 (A108)
(Peery, R.) "O Holy Night" SAB oct PRESSER 312-40404 $.30 (A109)
(Richardson) "O Holy Night" SSA oct SPRATT 628 $.30 (A110)
(Richardson) "O Holy Night" SATB oct SPRATT 627 $.30 (A111)
(Riegger) "O Holy Night" SATB SHAWNEE A 5218 $.35 (A112)
(Riegger) "O Holy Night" SSA FLAMMER B 5078 $.30 (A113)
(Riegger) "O Holy Night" SAB FLAMMER D5057 $.30 (A114)
(Ringwald) "O Holy Night" SATB SHAWNEE A 332 $.40 (A115)
(Rix) "O Holy Night" 3pt boy cor/SAA oct SCHIRM.G 5847 $.25 (A116)
(Ryder, A.) "O Holy Night" SSA oct PRESSER 332-12225 $.35 (A117)
(Seymour) "O Holy Night" 3pt wom cor,pno (easy) oct WILLIS 1766 $.12 (A118)
(Simon) "O Holy Night" SATB oct FISCHER,C CM-7225 $.25 (A119)
(Spicker) "O Holy Night" 2pt wom cor oct SCHIRM.G 5806 $.25 (A120)
(Stickles) "O Holy Night" jr cor&sr cor oct SCHIRM.G 10322 $.25 (A121)
(Stone) "O Holy Night" SATB oct PRO ART 1251 $.30 (A122)
(Stone) "O Holy Night" SAB oct PRO ART 1252 $.25 (A123)
(Stone) "O Holy Night" SSA oct PRO ART 1320 $.25 (A124)
(Stone) "O Holy Night" 2pt oct PRO ART 1558 $.25 (A125)
(Strickling) "O Holy Night" SSA SCHMITT 2537 $.35 (A126)
(Swift, Frederic F.) "O Holy Night" SSA oct BELWIN 1058 $.25 (A127)
(Swift, Frederic F.) "O Holy Night" SAB oct BELWIN 1059 $.30 (A128)
(Swift, Frederic F.) "O Holy Night" SATB oct BELWIN 911 $.25 (A129)
(West, John E.) "O Holy Night" mix cor,S/T solo oct NOVELLO 28.0982.06 s.p. (A130)
(Wetzler) "O Holy Night" SATB,opt inst SCHMITT 8030 $.35, ipa (A131)

ADAM, ADOLPHE-CHARLES (cont'd.)

Christmas Song *see Cantique De Noel

Christmas Song, The *Xmas
SATB oct LORENZ 995 $.30 (A132)

Julsang
[Swed] mix cor LUNDQUIST 56 s.p. (A133)

Minuit Chretien, C'est L'heure Solennelle *Xmas
[Fr] cor,S/T solo,org,opt vln cor pts s.p., ipa, voc sc s.p. LEMOINE (A134)
[Fr] cor,A/Bar solo,org,opt vln cor pts s.p., ipa, voc sc s.p. LEMOINE (A135)

Noel No. 4 *Xmas,carol
[Fr] 4pt men cor,S/T solo oct DURAND s.p. (A136)

Noel No. 5 *Xmas,carol
[Fr] 4pt mix cor,A/Bar solo oct DURAND s.p. (A137)

O Holy Night *see Cantique De Noel

Oh, Holy Night! *Xmas
(Whitman) SATB oct LILLENAS AN-2284 $.30 (A138)

On Holy Night *see Cantique De Noel

Ring On, Sweet Angels *Xmas,carol
3pt wom cor,pno (easy) oct WILLIS 5224 $.12 (A139)

Sing Of Mary, Pure And Lowly *BVM
SSA oct PRO ART 1897 $.25 (A140)

ADAM, J.
O, Day Of Rest And Gladness *Easter
SATB oct PRESSER 312-40432 $.30 (A141)

ADAM LAY I-BOWNDYN see Green, Ray

ADAM LAY Y-BOUNDEN see Bartow

ADAM LAY Y BOUNDEN see Scandrett, Robert

ADAM LAY YBOUNDEN see Heseltine, Philip

ADAM LAY YBOUNDEN see Ord, B.

ADAM LAY YBOUNDEN see Spencer, W.

ADAM DE LA HALE (ca. 1240-1287)
Det Gamla Ar Framganget Ar *Bibl
(Hallnas, Hilding) [Swed] SATB,acap GEHRMANS KRB 161 (A142)

Oeuvres Completes *CCU
(Coussemaker, Edmond de) cor GREGG ISBN 0:576 28409 2 s.p. (A143)

ADAMS, CARRIE
Adeste Fideles *Xmas,carol
(Seymour) "O Come, All Ye Faithful" 3pt wom cor,pno (easy) oct WILLIS 1765 $.12 (A144)

O Come, All Ye Faithful *see Adeste Fideles

ADAMS, J.T.
Time Out! *cant
SATB voc sc WORD 37502 $2.95 (A145)

ADAMS, JOSEPH
Sun Of My Soul *anthem
mix cor,S/T solo oct NOVELLO 28.1042.05 s.p. (A146)

ADAMS KLAGE see Fehres, Wilhelm

ADAMS, STEPHEN
Christmas Story, The *Xmas
SATB oct LORENZ 4054 $.30 (A147)

Den Heliga Staden
NORDISKA U394 s.p. (A148)
mix cor,solo,org/pno,orch HANSEN-DEN sc s.p., ipa, voc sc s.p., cor pts s.p. (A149)

Holy City
SA oct BELWIN 737 $.25 (A150)
SSA oct BELWIN 738 $.25 (A151)
SAB oct BELWIN 739 $.25 (A152)
SATB oct BELWIN 740 $.30 (A153)

Holy City, The *Xmas/Easter/Lent
SATB oct LORENZ 9350 $.30 (A154)
SATB (very easy) oct LORENZ A168 $.25 (A155)
SA oct LORENZ 5321 $.30 (A156)
SSA oct LORENZ 6224 $.30 (A157)
SAB oct LORENZ 7322 $.30 (A158)
unis oct LORENZ 8556 $.30 (A159)
SATB oct FISCHER,C CM-653 $.30 (A160)
(Arnold) SATB,S solo oct BOOSEY 1601 $.40 (A161)
(Arnold) TTBB,B solo,band,org oct BOOSEY 1600 $.40 (A162)
(Breck) SSA oct FISCHER,C CM-652 $.25 (A163)
(Ehret) SSA oct SPRATT 519 $.25 (A164)
(Fletcher) 2pt oct PRO ART 1127 $.30 (A165)
(Gilbert) SAB FLAMMER D5052 $.30 (A166)
(Gray) SSA oct PRO ART 1284 $.30 (A167)
(Gray) SATB oct PRO ART 1283 $.35 (A168)
(Gray) SAB oct PRO ART 1616 $.35 (A169)
(Howorth) SAB oct BOOSEY 1616 $.35 (A170)
(Huntley) SAB BOSTON 11340 $.40 (A171)
(Jones) SATB oct WORD CS-2058 $.30 (A172)
(Page, N.) SATB oct PRESSER 332-15250 $.40 (A173)
(Ringwald) SATB SHAWNEE A 89 $.40 (A174)
(Ringwald) SSA SHAWNEE B 82 $.40 (A175)
(Salter) SATB,SAT soli oct BOOSEY 1355 $.40 (A176)
(Samuelson) SA/TB oct BOOSEY 1526 $.35 (A177)
(Samuelson) SSA oct BOOSEY 1521 $.35 (A178)
(Treharne) SSA BOSTON 10479 $.40 (A179)
(Treharne) SATB BOSTON 10066 $.45 (A180)
(Treharne) TTBB BOSTON 10067 $.45 (A181)
(Treharne) sr cor&jr cor,org/pno BOSTON 10103 $.40 (A182)
(van den Dyck) TTBB,band oct BOOSEY 1411 $.35, ipa (A183)
(Verrall) SA,org/pno BOSTON 2678 $.35 (A184)

I Met My Master Face To Face
SATB oct LORENZ 4188 $.30 (A185)

ADAMS, STEPHEN (cont'd.)

Remember Now Thy Creator
SATB oct LORENZ 513 $.30 (A186)
SAB oct LORENZ 7016 $.30 (A187)

They That Trust In The Lord
SATB oct LORENZ 1134 $.30 (A188)

ADAMS, THOMAS (1785-1858)
Holy Child, The *Xmas,Bibl/cant/hymn
SATB,STB soli voc sc NOVELLO rental (A189)

Lift Up Your Heads, Ye Gates (from Story Of Calvary, The) Easter/Lent/Psntd
SATB oct NOVELLO 28.1203.07 s.p. (A190)

ADASKIN
Hymn Of Thanks *Thanks,hymn
unis BOOSEY-CAN s.p. (A191)

ADATH ISRAEL see Fromm, Herbert

ADELL, ARTHUR
Evige Konung Och Hell Jerusalem
mix cor NORDISKA 3017 s.p. (A192)

ADES
Christ Child, Christ Child
SA/TB SHAWNEE E66 $.30 (A193)

ADESTE see Noble, O. de

ADESTE FIDELES *Xmas,carol
see Tanti Auguri
see Silent Night
see Silent Night
"O Come, All Ye Faithful" see Many Moods Of Christmas, The, Suite One
"O Come All Ye Faithful" see Gruber, Franz Xaver, Silent Night
"O Come All Ye Faithful" SATB CHARTER $.35 (A194)
"O Come, All Ye Faithful" jr cor&sr cor oct SCHIRM.G 10323 $.25 (A195)
(Cassler, G. Winston) "O Come, All Ye Faithful" SATB (easy) cor pts AUGSBURG 1434 $.25, ipa (A196)
(Foote) SSATB (very easy) OXFORD 42.037 $.35 (A197)
(Heller) "O Come, All Ye Faithful" SATB (Wade's Cantus Diversi) SCHMITT 1650 $.30 (A198)
(Luboff, Norman) "O Come All Ye Faithful" SATB,opt winds,perc oct WALTON 2750 $.35, cmplt ed WALTON 2750A $6.00 (A199)
(Novello) [Eng/Lat] 4pt mix cor oct SCHIRM.G 3334 $.25 (A200)
(Seymour) "O Come All Ye Faithful" 3pt wom cor,pno (easy) oct WILLIS 1765 $.10 (A201)
(Sharpe) "O Come, All Ye Faithful" cor&desc CRAMER 54 s.p. (A202)
(Shaw; Parker) "O Come, All Ye Faithful" SATB,acap oct LAWSON 716 $.30 (A203)
(Van Koert, Han) "O Come All Ye Faithful" SA&SATB,opt solo,acap oct WORLD AC-257-8 $.60 (A204)
(Whitman) "Oh, Come, All Ye Faithful" SATB oct LILLENAS AN-2280 $.30 (A205)

ADESTE FIDELES see Adams, Carrie

ADESTE FIDELES see Anonymous

ADESTE FIDELES see Baumann, Max

ADESTE FIDELES see Bottazzo, Luigi

ADESTE FIDELES see Casimiri, Raffaele Casimiro

ADESTE FIDELES see Dubois, Theodore

ADESTE FIDELES see Novello, Vincent

ADESTE FIDELES see Reading, J.

ADESTE FIDELIS *Xmas
(Stickles) "O Come, All Ye Faithful" jr cor&sr cor oct SCHIRM.G 10323 $.25 (A206)

ADESTE FIDELIS see Titcomb, Everett

ADJICIAT DOMINUS see Schmitt, Florent

ADLAM, FRANK
Holy Communion *Commun
SATB (F maj) oct NOVELLO 44.1051.03 s.p. (A207)

ADLER, HUGO CH.
Avodath Habonim *Fest
unis/2pt TRANSCON. TCL 300 $2.50 (A208)

Avodim Hoyinu *Fest/Passover
"We Were Slaves" [Eng/Heb] SATB TRANSCON. TCL 232 $.25 (A209)

Balak And Balaam *Purim,ora
[Heb] TTBB cor pts TRANSCON. TCL 209 $.35, ipa (A210)

Bearers Of Light *cant
mix cor&jr cor,narrator,SBar soli,orch,pno/org TRANSCON. ipr (A211)

Bread Of Affliction, The *see Ho Lachmo Anyo.

Chad Gadyo *Fest/Passover
[Eng] SATB TRANSCON. TCL 794 $.45 (A212)

Early Will I Seek
SATB TRANSCON. TCL 123 $.25 (A213)

El Mole Rachamin
[Heb] SATB,cantor TRANSCON. TCL 675 $.50 (A214)

Gabirol-Schindler *Hanakkah
"Joy Of Dedication, The" [Eng] SATB TRANSCON. TCL 798 $.75 (A215)

Haneros Halolu *Hanakkah
"Lights We Have Kindled, The" [Eng/Heb] SATB TRANSCON. TCL 779 $.40 (A216)

Ho Lachmo Anyo. *Fest/Passover
"Bread Of Affliction, The" [Heb] SATB TRANSCON. TCL 231 $.25 (A217)

ADLER, HUGO CH. (cont'd.)

Joy Of Dedication, The *see Gabirol-
Schindler

Lights We Have Kindled, The *see Haneros
Halolu

Nachlat Israel *Sab-Eve
SATB TRANSCON. TCL 780 $3.00   (A218)

We Were Slaves *see Avodim Hoyinu

Woman Of Valor, A
SATB TRANSCON. TCL 122 $.50   (A219)

ADLER, SAMUEL (1928-   )
Avina Malkaynu Chanayno
4pt mix cor,ST soli,acap oct SCHIRM.G 11911
$.35 see from Hinay Yom Hadin   (A220)

Awake, Do Not Cast Us Off *anthem
mix cor oct OXFORD 94.208 $.30   (A221)

Ayl Melech Yoshayv
4pt mix cor,T solo,acap oct SCHIRM.G 11909
$.35 see from Hinay Yom Hadin   (A222)

Be-Shaaray Tefila *Sab-Eve/Sab-Morn
SATB TRANSCON. TCL 834 $3.50, ipa   (A223)

Binding, The *ora
SATB,SSATB soli,orch (med) voc sc OXFORD
94.604 $3.00, ipr, rental   (A224)

Division
SATB/TTBB,bells oct AGAPE AG 7126 $.75
                                       (A225)

Feast Of Light, The *Hanakkah
4pt mix cor oct SCHIRM.G 11500 $.30   (A226)

Four Responses For Yom Kippur *CC4U,liturg,
Jew
SATB oct PRESSER MC385 $.30   (A227)

God Is My Salvation
see Two Songs Of Hope

Hayom Harat Olam
4pt mix cor,T solo,acap oct SCHIRM.G 11908
$.30 see from Hinay Yom Hadin   (A228)

Hinay Yom Hadin *see Avina Malkaynu
Chanayno; Ayl Melech Yoshayv; Hayom Harat
Olam; Uv' shofar Gadol   (A229)

How Long, O Lord?
2 speak cor,5brass oct AGAPE CY 3336 $.45
                                       (A230)

How Precious Is Thy Lovingkindness (Psalm 36)
Gen
SATB,S solo (med) oct OXFORD 94.202 $.35
                                       (A231)

Hymn Of Praise, A *hymn
SATB,T solo,pno/org oct LAWSON 819 $.25
                                       (A232)

I Will Give Thanks (Psalm 9) Ded/Gen/Thanks
SSATTB (med) oct OXFORD 94.203 $.35   (A233)

Judah's Song Of Praise
4pt mix cor oct SCHIRM.G 11508 $.25   (A234)

Lord Reigneth, The
see Two Psalm Motets

O Lord, Open Thou My Lips
see Two Psalm Motets

Praise The Lord *anthem
SA oct OXFORD 94.401 $.25   (A235)
girl cor SOUTHERN $.25   (A236)

Praised Be The Lord By Day
SATB TRANSCON. TCL 601 $.30   (A237)

Psalm 9 *see I Will Give Thanks

Psalm 24
SATB,opt brass oct PRESSER 312-40476 $.35
                                       (A238)

Psalm 36 *see How Precious Is Thy
Lovingkindness

Psalm 40 *anthem
mix cor oct OXFORD 94.209 $.25   (A239)

Psalm 96 *Bibl
4pt mix cor,org oct SCHIRM.G 11491 $.25
                                       (A240)

Psalm 100 *see Psalm Of Dedication

Psalm 121
see Two Songs Of Hope

Psalm Of Dedication (Psalm 100)
SATB,opt trp TRANSCON. TCL 130 $.30   (A241)

Set Me As A Seal
SATB oct PRESSER MC335 $.30   (A242)

Shir Chadash *Sab-Eve
SA/SAB TRANSCON. TCL 345 $3.00   (A243)

Shiru Ladonoy *Sab-Eve
SATB/unis TRANSCON. TCL 346 $3.00   (A244)

Song Of Exaltation, A
SATB (diff) ABINGDON APM-249 $.60   (A245)

Song Of Hanukkah, A *Hanakkah
4pt mix cor oct SCHIRM.G 11162 $.25   (A246)

Two Psalm Motets *Bibl/mot/Psalm
SATB,org oct LAWSON 51098 $.35
contains: Lord Reigneth, The; O Lord,
Open Thou My Lips   (A247)

Two Songs Of Hope
TTBB oct PRESSER MC430 $.50
contains: God Is My Salvation; Psalm 121
                                       (A248)

Uv' shofar Gadol
4pt mix cor,T solo,acap oct SCHIRM.G 11910
$.35 see from Hinay Yom Hadin   (A249)

Vision Of Isaiah, The *cant
SATB oct SOUTHERN $1.75, ipr   (A250)

ADLER, SAMUEL (cont'd.)

Yom Ha-Shabbat
[Heb] mix cor,fl,vcl TRANSCON. TCL 701 $.35
                                       (A251)

ADON OLAM see Baer, [Charles E.]

ADON OLAM see Gottlieb, J.

ADON OLAM see Rathom, A.

ADON-OLAM see Rossi, Salomone

ADON OLOM see Wuerfel

ADONAI, ELOHIM see Bloch, Ernest

ADONOY, ADONOY see Helfman, Max

ADONOY MOH ODOM see Kellerman

ADORAMUS see Aichinger, Gregor

ADORAMUS see Brahms, Johannes

ADORAMUS see Volpi, Edoardo

ADORAMUS TE see Aichinger, Gregor

ADORAMUS TE see Brahms, Johannes

ADORAMUS TE see Clemens, Jacobus

ADORAMUS TE see Clement

ADORAMUS TE see Clokey

ADORAMUS TE see Corsi

ADORAMUS TE see Gasparini

ADORAMUS TE see Gasparini, Francesco

ADORAMUS TE see Gasparini, Quirino

ADORAMUS TE see Lassus, Roland de (Orlandus)

ADORAMUS TE see Lotti, Antonio

ADORAMUS TE see Martini, Padre

ADORAMUS TE see Monteverdi, Claudio

ADORAMUS TE see Mozart, Wolfgang Amadeus

ADORAMUS TE see Palestrina, Giovanni

ADORAMUS TE see Perti, J.

ADORAMUS TE see Pitoni, Giuseppe Ottavio

ADORAMUS TE see Roselli

ADORAMUS TE see Rosselli, Francesco

ADORAMUS TE see Rossello

ADORAMUS TE see Ruffo, [Vincenzo]

ADORAMUS TE see Zielenski, Nicholas

ADORAMUS TE CHRISTE see Gorlatto, Giacomo

ADORAMUS TE CHRISTE see Aichinger, Gregor

ADORAMUS TE, CHRISTE see Corsi, Giuseppe

ADORAMUS TE, CHRISTE see Dubois, Theodore

ADORAMUS TE, CHRISTE see Escovada, R.

ADORAMUS TE, CHRISTE see Forest

ADORAMUS TE, CHRISTE see Goodman, Joseph

ADORAMUS TE CHRISTE see Hart

ADORAMUS TE, CHRISTE see Hart, Fritz

ADORAMUS TE, CHRISTE see Lassus, Roland de
(Orlandus)

ADORAMUS TE, CHRISTE see Monteverdi, Claudio

ADORAMUS TE CHRISTE see Mozart, Wolfgang
Amadeus

ADORAMUS TE, CHRISTE see Palestrina, Giovanni

ADORAMUS TE CHRISTE see Parthun, Paul

ADORAMUS TE, CHRISTE see Perti, Giacomo Antonio

ADORAMUS TE, CHRISTE see Pitoni, Giuseppe
Ottavio

ADORAMUS TE, CHRISTE see Roselli

ADORAMUS TE, CHRISTE see Ruffo, [Vincenzo]

ADORAMUS TE, CHRISTE see Tenero

ADORAMUS TE, CHRISTE see Vene, Ruggero

ADORAMUS TE, CHRISTE see Viadana, Lodovico
Grossi da

ADORAMUS TE, CHRISTI see Corsi

ADORAMUS TE, JESU CHRISTE see Gallus, Jacobus

ADORAMUS THE CHRISTIE see Slogedal, Bjarne

ADORATE see Villette, P.

ADORATE DEUM see Trexler, Georg

ADORATION *anthem,Heb
(Malmin, Gunnar) SA (easy) oct AUGSBURG 1239
$.18   (A252)

ADORATION see Hovhaness, Alan

ADORATION CAROL see Edmundson

ADORATION DES BERGERS *Xmas,carol
(Geveart, F.-A.) [Fr] 4pt mix cor,acap (med
easy) cor pts LEMOINE s.p. see from
Collection De Choeurs, dixieme Fascicule

ADORATION OF THE MAGI (from Ben-Hur)   (A253)
SSA/SATB BIG3 $.35   (A254)

ADORATION OF THE SHEPHERDS *Xmas
(Molzer, F.) SSA oct PRESSER 332-40112 $.30
                                       (A255)

ADORATION OF THE SHEPHERDS see Manziarly de,
L'Adoration Des Bergers

ADORATION, THE *Xmas
(Russell) SATB&jr cor oct PRO ART 2292 $.25
                                       (A256)
(Russell) SSAA&jr cor oct PRO ART 2295 $.25
                                       (A257)

ADORE ALMIGHTY GOD see Gretchaninov, Alexander
Tikhonovitch

ADORE AND BE STILL see Gounod, Charles Francois

ADOREMOS A JESUS see Santa Cruz, Domingo

ADOREMUS see Cherubini, Luigi

ADOREMUS see Palestrina, Giovanni, Adoremus Te
Christe

ADOREMUS TE see Anerio, Giovanni Francesco

ADOREMUS TE CHRISTE see Bianchini, Carlo

ADOREMUS TE CHRISTE see Palestrina, Giovanni

ADOREMUS TE CHRISTE see Sevim, Giuseppe

ADOREMUS TE CHRISTE see Volpi, Edoardo

ADOREMUSTE see Gallus, Jacobus

ADORIAMO IL SACRAMENTO see Goi, M.

ADORO TE see Mendelssohn-Bartholdy, Felix

ADORO TE DEVOTE see Creston, Paul

ADORO TE DEVOTE see Volpi, Edoardo

ADORO TE DEVOTE see Zaccaria, Vittore

ADORO TE SUPPLEX see Gounod, Charles Francois

ADORO TE SUPPLEX see Dagand, Abbe J.

ADRIESSEN, WILLEM (1887-1964)
Missa In Es Kl Terts *Mass
[Dut] mix cor,SATB soli,org,2fl,2ob,2clar,
2bsn,3trp,4horn,3trom,tuba,strings,timp
DONEMUS min sc s.p., cor pts s.p., voc sc
s.p.   (A258)

ADVENSTHYMN see Wikander, David

ADVENT see Franck, [Johann Wolfgang]

ADVENT see New

ADVENT see Othegraven, August J. von

ADVENT see Schieri, Fritz

ADVENT ANTHEM see Proulx, Richard

ADVENT AR VANTANS TID see Ahlen, Waldemar

ADVENT CAROL see Brandon, G.

ADVENT CAROL see Hamill

ADVENT CAROL see Pfautsch, Lloyd

ADVENT CAROL see Purvis, Richard

ADVENT CHORALE, THE see Mendelssohn-Bartholdy,
Felix

ADVENT-CHRISTMAS CYCLE see Bach

ADVENT GLAD SONG see Toolan, S. Suzanne

ADVENT MOTET 1ST MVT see Schreck

ADVENT MOTET 2ND MVT see Schreck

ADVENT MOTET 3RD MVT see Schreck

ADVENT-MOTTETTEN see Rheinberger, Josef

ADVENT OF OUR GOD see Cassler

ADVENT OF OUR GOD, THE see Leaf, Robert

ADVENT ORATORIO-GOOD TIDINGS OF GREAT JOY see
Bach, Johann Sebastian

ADVENT-PSALM see Jonsson, Josef [Petrus]

ADVENT SONG see Schumann, Robert (Alexander),
Adventlied

ADVENT UND WEIHNACHT, HEFT 1 *Adv/Xmas
mix cor,acap cmplt ed DOBLINGER s.p.
contains & see also: Anonymous, Uns Ist
Geboren Ein Kindelein; Anonymous, Zu
Bethlehem Geboren; Bach, Johann
Sebastian, Lobt Gott, Ihr Christen; Bach,
Johann Sebastian, O Jesulein Suss; Bach,
Johann Sebastian, Von Himmel Hoch Da Komm
Ich Her; Bach, Johann Sebastian, Wie Soll
Ich Dich Empfangen; Burck, Joachim, Nun
Ist Es Zeit Zu Singen; Eccard, Johannes,
O Freude Uber Freude; Eccard, Johannes,
Vom Himmel Hoch Da Komm Ich Her; Franck,
Melchior, Jesu, Du Zartes Kindelein;
Praetorius, Michael, Es Ist Ein Ros
Entsprungen; Praetorius, Michael, Geborn
Ist Uns Emanuel; Praetorius, Michael, In
Dulci Jubilo; Praetorius, Michael, Lobt
Gott, Ihr Christen; Praetorius, Michael,
Quem Pastores Laudavere; Praetorius,
Michael, Singt Und Klingt; Scheidt,
Samuel, O Jesulein Zart; Schutz,
Heinrich, Macht Auf Die Tor   (A259)

ADVENT UND WEIHNACHT, HEFT 2 *Adv/Xmas
mix cor,acap cmplt ed DOBLINGER s.p.
contains & see also: Ammon, Blasius, Grates
Nunc Ominium; Anonymous, Der Tag, Der Ist
So Freudenreich; Battre, H., De Qua Natus
Est; Brahms, Johannes, Gegrusset, Maria;

Brahms, Johannes, O Heiland, Reiss Die
Himmel Auf; Brahms, Johannes, Taublein
Weiss; Bruck, Johann von, Germinavit
Radix; Bruckner, Anton, Virga Jesse;
Dufay, Guillaume, Ave Maris Stella;
Dufay, Guillaume, Christe Redemptor;
Dunstable, John, Alma Redemptoris; Fux,
Johann Joseph, Ecce Virgo Concipiam;
Fux, Johann Joseph, Tollite; Gallus,
Jacobus, Haec Est Dies; Gallus, Jacobus,
Pueri Concinite; Gallus, Jacobus, Resonet
In Laudibus; Stadlmayr, Johann, Conditor
Alme Siderum; Stadlmayr, Johann, Jesu
Redemptor Omnium; Zangius, Nikolaus,
Angelus Ad Pastores Ait; Zangius,
Nikolaus, Congratulamini   (A260)

ADVENT WREATH, THE see Hutson

ADVENTLIED see Schumann, Robert (Alexander)

ADVENTMUSIK see Heiller, Anton

ADVENTS-MUSIK see Lehman, Siegfried

ADVENTS-UND WEIHNACHTSLIEDER *CC8L,Xmas
(Henking, B.) [Ger] wom cor,acap HUG s.p.
(A261)

ADVENTSBON see Ahlen, Waldemar

ADVENTSBON see Runback, Albert

ADVENTSHYMN see Schutz, Heinrich

ADVENTSKANTAT see Olson, Daniel

ADVENTSKANTATE see Maasz, Gerhard

ADVENTSKANTATE NACH ALTEN VOLKS- LIEDERN see
Erdmann, Dietrich

ADVENTSMUSIK see Salonen, Sulo

ADVENTSMUSIK FOR KOR OCH INSTRUMENT
(Ohrwall, Anders) mix cor,inst sc NORDISKA
NMS-6420 s.p., ipa
contains: Bach, Johann Sebastian, Jerusalem
Hav Upp Din Rost; Handel, George
Frideric, Dotter Sion   (A262)

AERA VERE FADEREN see Schutz, Heinrich

AERENS KONGE GOD see Marenzio, Luca, O Rex
Gloriae

AESCHBACHER, WALTHER (1901-1969)
Aufglanzt Der Gottgewollte Tag *Easter,hymn
[Ger] mix cor,2fl,2ob,2clar,2bsn,2horn,
2trp,2trom,timp,strings (after a sequence
of Notkers (840-912)) HUG s.p., ipr
(A263)

Das Schweizerkreuz
[Ger] men cor,2trp HUG s.p.   (A264)
[Ger] mix cor,acap (easy) HUG s.p.   (A265)

Motette (from Eingebungen Des Marianus) mot
[Ger] men cor,acap (diff) HUG s.p.   (A266)

Zur Konfirmation *Cnfrm
[Ger] mix cor,acap (med easy) HUG s.p.
(A267)

AESCHBACKER, C.
Wie Heimlicher Weise
(Morike, E.) [Ger] wom cor,acap (easy, new
year) HUG s.p.   (A268)

AESTIMATUS SUM see Victoria, Tomas Luis de

AETERNA CHRISTI MUNERA see Palestrina, Giovanni

AETERNA FAC see Bononcini, Giovanni Maria

AETERNA MUNERA CHRISTI see Palestrina, Giovanni

AETERNA PAX see Mozart, Wolfgang Amadeus

AFFERTE DOMINO see Buxtehude, Dietrich

AFFICTUS SUM see Nielsen, Carl

AFRICAN MASS, THE see Luboff, Norman

AFRICAN NOEL *Xmas,folk,Afr
(Lewis) SSA oct PLYMOUTH PCS-215 $.25   (A269)
(Lewis) SAB oct PLYMOUTH PCS-407 $.30   (A270)

AFRICAN NOEL see Lewis

AFTENSANG see Weyse, Christoph Ernst Friedrich

AFTER THE HOLIDAYS see Hunt, Reginald

AFTER THE PEOPLE HAD SEEN THE SIGN see Vulpius,
Melchior

AFTERNOON SERVICE FOR THE DAY OF ATONEMENT see
Binder, Abraham Wolfe

AFTONKANTAT see Salonen, Sulo

AFTONPSALM *Psalm
(Carlstedt, Jan) [Swed] SATB,acap GEHRMANS
KRB 370   (A271)

AFTONPSALM see Carlstedt, Gunnemer

AFTONPSALM see Sandberg, Folke

AFTONSANG see Berg

AGAIN AND AGAIN see Paris

AGAIN, THE MORN OF GLADNESS see Thiman, Eric
Harding

AGAINST THE MORN IS COME A KING see Curry, W.
Lawrence

AGAZZARI, AGOSTINO (1578-1640)
Benedicta Sit Sancta Trinitas *Trin,mot
[Lat] SSAB,acap (med) MULLER M 24 s.p.
(A272)
[Lat] SSABar,acap oct NOVELLO DM-24 s.p.
(A273)

Jubilate Deo
(Klaes) [Lat] AA,org SCHOTT voc sc s.p.,
cor pts s.p.   (A274)

AGELESS MIRACLE, THE see Filkins

AGER
Our Thanks To Thee
unis BOSWORTH s.p.   (A275)

AGER, LAURENCE
From The Hill
SS BOSWORTH s.p.   (A276)

In Honour Of A King *Easter
2pt wom cor oct SCHIRM.G 10661 $.20   (A277)

Little Saviour, The *Xmas
4pt mix cor oct SCHIRM.G 11122 $.25   (A278)

AGEY
Behold, We Come, Dear Lord, To Thee
SATB oct LORENZ C256 $.30   (A279)

What Shall We Children Bring? *Xmas
unis/2pt oct PRO ART 2165 $.25   (A280)

AGEY, C. BUELL
All Praise And Thanks To God *Thanks
SATB (med) ABINGDON APM-210 $.32   (A281)

Eternal God, Whose Power Upholds
SA (easy) ABINGDON APM-169 $.25   (A282)

Praise Ye Jehovah
SATB (med) ABINGDON APM-170 $.25   (A283)

AGINCOURT SONG *folk,Eng
(Goodhart) unis jr cor/unis wom cor CURWEN
71671 s.p.   (A284)

AGINCOURT SONG, THE
see Musica Britannica Vol. 4: Set 2

AGNUS DEI *Greg
(Christiansen, Paul) SATB (med) oct AUGSBURG
1533 $.20   (A285)

AGNUS DEI see Bandrier, Yves

AGNUS DEI see Barber, Samuel

AGNUS DEI see Beethoven, Ludwig van

AGNUS DEI see Bizet, Georges

AGNUS DEI see Boulay, J.

AGNUS DEI see Brunner, Adolf

AGNUS DEI see Byrd, William

AGNUS DEI see Caplet, [Lucien]

AGNUS DEI see Chaminade, Cecile

AGNUS DEI see Concone, Giuseppe

AGNUS DEI see Davis, Katherine K.

AGNUS DEI see Faure, Gabriel-Urbain

AGNUS DEI see Felderhof, Jan

AGNUS DEI see Flipse, E.

AGNUS DEI see Franck, Cesar

AGNUS DEI see Gabrieli, Andrea

AGNUS DEI see Gabrieli, Giovanni

AGNUS DEI see Gounod, Charles Francois

AGNUS DEI see Gumpeltzhaimer, A.

AGNUS DEI see Hager, Sister Conleth

AGNUS DEI see Hammarstrom, Hugo

AGNUS DEI see Handel, George Frideric

AGNUS DEI see Hassler, Hans Leo

AGNUS DEI see Haydn, (Franz) Joseph

AGNUS DEI see Jewell

AGNUS DEI see Kalinnikov, Vassili Sergeievitch

AGNUS DEI see Kendrie, Frank E.

AGNUS DEI see Koechlin, Charles

AGNUS DEI see Larsson, Lars-Erik

AGNUS DEI see Lassus, Roland de (Orlandus)

AGNUS DEI see Lotti, Antonio

AGNUS DEI see Morales, Cristobal de

AGNUS DEI see Morley

AGNUS DEI see Morley, Thomas

AGNUS DEI see Mozart, Wolfgang Amadeus

AGNUS DEI see Najera, Edmund

AGNUS DEI see Oscarson, Gun

AGNUS DEI see Palestrina, Giovanni

AGNUS DEI see Pergolesi, Giovanni Battista

AGNUS DEI see Persichetti, Vincent

AGNUS DEI see Reger, Max

AGNUS DEI see Scarlatti, Alessandro

AGNUS DEI see Schubert, Franz (Peter)

AGNUS DEI see Thompson, Randall

AGNUS DEI see Tubb, Monte

AGNUS DEI see Tye, Christopher

AGNUS DEI see Victoria, Tomas Luis de

AGNUS DEI see Webbe, Samuel

AGNUS DEI see Wilson

AGNUS DEI I see Des Prez, Josquin

AGNUS DEI II see Des Prez, Josquin

AGNUS DEI III see Des Prez, Josquin

AGNUS DEI NO. 2 see Palestrina, Giovanni

AGNUS DEI - O CHRIST, THOU LAMB OF GOD see
Willan, Healey

AGNUS DEI, THE see Reger, Max

AGNUS DEI UND DEUTSCHES SANCTUS *CC9L,Agnus/
Sanctus
SATB/SATTB,org sc HANSSLER 15.001 s.p.
contains works by: Poos; Eccard; Schein;
Isaac; Senfl; Hassler; Praetorius   (A286)

AGOSTINI
O Blessed Jesus *see O Bone Jesu

O Bone Jesu
(Greyson) "O Blessed Jesus" SATB oct BOURNE
ES79 $.25   (A287)

AGOSTINI, F.
Noel Des Anges *Xmas,carol
unis/4pt,pno/acap LEMOINE s.p.   (A288)
[Fr] 4pt mix cor/unis,pno/acap (easy) voc
sc LEMOINE s.p.   (A289)

Noel Des Sabots *Xmas,carol
(Devigne, R.) [Fr] 4pt mix cor/unis,pno/
acap (med easy) voc sc LEMOINE s.p.
(A290)

AGOSTINI, PAOLO (1583-1629)
Blessed Sacrament *see Ego Sum Panis Vivus

Ego Sum Panis Vivus *Commun/Fest,mot
[Lat] SSAB,acap (med easy) MULLER M 27 s.p.
(A291)
"Blessed Sacrament" [Lat] SSABar,acap oct
NOVELLO DM-27 s.p.   (A292)

AGREE WITH GOD AND BE AT PEACE see Ford, Virgil
T.

AGRICOLA, ALEXANDER (ca. 1446-1506)
Missa In Myne Zyn
see Opera Omnia Vol. I

Missa Je Ne Demande
see Opera Omnia Vol. I

Missa La Serviteur
see Opera Omnia Vol. I

Missa Malheur Me Bat
see Opera Omnia Vol. I

Opera Omnia Vol. I *Mass
(Lerner, Edward R.) cor AM.INST.MUS. $22.00
contains: Missa In Myne Zyn; Missa Je Ne
Demande; Missa La Serviteur; Missa
Malheur Me Bat   (A293)

Opera Omnia vol. II *CC8L,Mass
(Lerner, Edward R.) cor AM.INST.MUS. $22.00
(A294)

Opera Omnia vol. III *CCU
(Lerner, Edward R.) cor AM.INST.MUS. $18.50
(A295)

Opera Omnia vol. IV *CCU
(Lerner, Edward R.) cor AM.INST.MUS. $16.00
(A296)

AGRICOLA, MARTIN (1486-1556)
Her, Her, Ich Verkund Euch Neue Mar *Xmas
(Funck, Heinz) [Ger] SATB,acap (med) BAREN
BA 535 $1.50   (A297)

Mit Fried Und Freud Ich Fahr Dahin *Gd.Fri.
ATTB,acap voc pt DOBLINGER s.p. see also
TOD UND VERGANGLICHKEIT   (A298)

AGUILAR
Canto De Navidad *Xmas,carol
[Span] cor UNION ESP. 19255 s.p.   (A299)

AGUILERA DE HEREDIA, SEBASTIAN
(ca. 1565-ca. 1627)
Drei Magnificat *CC3U,Magnif
(Hudson) [Lat] 4pt mix cor/5pt mix cor/8pt
mix cor MOSELER s.p.   (A300)

AGUINALDO see Benedito

AGUSTSSON, HERBERT H.
Ave Maria
wom cor,org ICELAND s.p.   (A301)

Prayer *prayer
men cor ICELAND s.p.   (A302)

AH, BLEAK AND CHILL THE WINTRY WIND see Burt,
Alfred

AH, DEAREST JESU CHILD see Hokanson, Margrethe

AH, DEAREST JESU, HOLY CHILD see Wetzler,
Robert

AH! DEAREST JESUS see Bach, Johann Sebastian

AH! DEAREST JESUS see Barnard

AH, GOD, FROM HEAVEN LOOK DOWN see Bach, Johann
Sebastian

AH, HOLY JESUS *anthem
(Cassler, G. Winston) TTBB (easy) oct
AUGSBURG 1388 $.20 contains also: O Lamb Of
God   (A303)

AH HOLY JESUS see Bach, Johann Sebastian

AH, HOLY JESUS see Cruger, Johann

AH, HOLY JESUS see Stucky, Steven

AH, HOLY JESUS, HOW HAST THOU OFFENDED see
Boatwright, Howard

AH, HOLY JESUS, HOW HAST THOU OFFENDED? see Krapf, Gerhard

AH, JESU CHRIST, MY LORD MOST DEAR see Brahms, Johannes, Ach Lieber Herre Jesu Christ

AH, JESUS LORD, THY LOVE TO ME *anthem/folk,US
see Lone, Wild Bird , The
(Johnson, David N.) SSA (easy) oct AUGSBURG 0517 $.25 (A304)
(Johnson, David N.) TTBB (easy) oct AUGSBURG 0525 $.20 contains also: Lone, Wild Bird, The (A305)
(Johnston, David N.) SATB (easy) oct AUGSBURG 0514 $.25 (A306)

AH KNOW DE LORD LAID HIS HANDS ON ME *spir
(Clements) SATB,pno SCHOTT s.p. (A307)

AH! LA BONNE FORTUNE *Xmas,carol,Fr
(Tomasi) [Fr] SMezA LEDUC s.p. see also Douze Noels De Saboly (A308)

AH LORD GOD THE WORLD'S CREATOR see Ebeling, J.

AH, LORD, THY DEAR, SWEET ANGELS SEND see Bach, Johann Sebastian

AH! MY BELOVED JESUS CHILD see Scheidt, Samuel, Ach, Mein Herzliebes Jesulein

AH MY SOUL IS ONWARD PRESSING see Handel, George Frideric

AH! QUAND REVIENDRA-T-IL? see Aubanel, Georges

AH, SOME CHILD JESUS see Bach, Johann Sebastian, Ach, Mein Herzliebes

AH, THOU POOR WORLD see Brahms, Johannes

AHLBERG, VERNER (1926-)
Milde Stjarna, Ren Och Klar
(Ahlen, Waldemar) 3pt wom cor/3pt jr cor, acap NORDISKA 5326 s.p. (A309)

O, Huru Salla Aro Ej De Fromma
(Ahlen, Waldemar) 3pt wom cor/3pt jr cor, pno,inst NORDISKA 5261 s.p. (A310)
(Ahlen, Waldemar) 3pt wom cor/3pt jr cor, acap NORDISKA 5262 s.p. (A311)

AHLE
Blessed Jesus
(Hadley) SATB oct PRO ART 1961 $.30 (A312)

AHLE, JOHANN GEORG (1651-1706)
Die Guldene Sonne Bringt Leben Und Wonne
see Bach, Johann Sebastian, Ich Liebe Jesum Alle Stund
SAT/SAB HANSSLER 6.269 s.p. contains also: Kriger, Adam, Nun Sich Der Tag Geendet Hat (A313)

Morgenglanz Der Ewigkeit
see Konig, Johann Balthasar, Ich Will Dich Lieben Meine Starke

AHLE, JOHANN RUDOLPH (1625-1673)
Be Not Afraid *see Furchtet Euch Nicht

Der Tag Ist Nun Vergangen *Gen
[Ger] SATB,strings,cont (easy) BAREN. BA 197 s.p. (A314)

Es Ist Vollbracht
(Berger, H.L.) "Gott Ist Getreu" TTBB HANSSLER 6.5127 s.p. (A315)

Furchtet Euch Nicht *Xmas,cant
(Lillehaug, L.) "Be Not Afraid" [Eng/Ger] dbl cor,cont,4trom sc CONCORDIA 97-6407 $1.50, cor pts CONCORDIA 97-6430 $.40, ipa (A316)

Gott Ist Getreu *see Es Ist Vollbracht

Jesu, Joyaunce Of My Heart
(Akerman, Martin; Bach, J.S.) 2pt,solo oct NOVELLO 33.0075.07 s.p. (A317)

Wisset, Dass Ihr Nicht Mit Verganglichem *mot
(Hellmann) SSATB HANSSLER 1.092 s.p. (A318)

AHLEN, WALDEMAR
Advent Ar Vantans Tid
wom cor/jr cor NORDISKA 5982 s.p. (A319)

Adventsbon
unis/2pt,opt org NORDISKA 4825 s.p. (A320)
2pt wom cor/2pt jr cor,acap NORDISKA 4826 s.p. (A321)

Barnabon
(Ahlen, Waldemar) unis wom cor/unis jr cor, acap NORDISKA 4070 s.p. (A322)

En Vanlig Gronskas Rika Drakt *Psalm
mix cor NORDISKA 1026 s.p. (A323)
men cor NORDISKA 4901 s.p. (A324)

O, Guds Lamm
mix cor NORDISKA 1326 s.p. (A325)

Paskhymn *Easter,hymn
mix cor NORDISKA 882 s.p. (A326)

Vi Tacka Dig, O Jesu God
mix cor NORDISKA 1885 s.p. (A327)

AHLWIN
He The Pearly Gates Will Open *anthem
(Skiles) SSAT oct LILLENAS AN-1127 $.30 (A328)

AHNFELT
Day By Day
(Widen) SATB oct LILLENAS AN-1623 $.25 (A329)

AHRENS, JOSEPH (1904-)
Auferstehung *Easter
[Ger] SATB,org (med) sc MULLER SM 2449 s.p. (A330)

Beata Es, Virgo Maria *Fest
[Lat] 3-5pt mix cor,acap (med) MULLER SM 2205 s.p. (A331)

AHRENS, JOSEPH (cont'd.)

Christ Ist Erstanden *Easter,mot
[Ger] SATB&jr cor,brass (med) MULLER SM 2421 sc s.p., cor pts s.p. see from Drei Festmotetten (A332)

Das Heilige Jahr, Heft I: Advent *Adv
[Ger] 2-5pt mix cor,acap (med) MULLER SM 2221 s.p. (A333)

Das Heilige Jahr, Heft II: Weihnachten *Xmas
[Ger] 2-4pt mix cor,acap (med) MULLER SM 2222 s.p. (A334)

Das Heilige Jahr, Heft III: Jesu Namen *Gen
[Ger] 2-4pt mix cor,acap (med) MULLER SM 2223 s.p. (A335)

Das Heilige Jahr, Heft IV: Passion *Psntd
[Ger] 2-4pt mix cor,acap (med) MULLER SM 2224 s.p. (A336)

Das Heilige Jahr, Heft V: Ostern *Easter
[Ger] 2-4pt mix cor,acap (med) MULLER SM 2225 s.p. (A337)

Das Heilige Jahr, Heft VI: Pfingsten *Easter/Pent
[Ger] 2-4pt mix cor,acap (med) MULLER SM 2226 s.p. (A338)

Das Heilige Jahr, Heft VII: Eucharistie *Commun
[Ger] 3pt mix cor/4pt mix cor,acap (med) MULLER SM 2227 s.p. (A339)

Das Heilige Jahr, Heft VIII: Marienlob *BVM/Fest
[Ger] 2-5pt mix cor,acap (med) MULLER SM 2228 s.p. (A340)

Das Heilige Jahr, Heft IX: Gotteslob *Gen
[Ger] 2-8pt mix cor,acap (med) MULLER SM 2229 s.p. (A341)

Der Geist Des Herrn Erfullt Den Erdenkreis *hymn
SATB,brass (med) BAREN. SM 2435 sc s.p., cor pts s.p. see from Vier Hymnen (A342)

Die Deutschen Cantica Der Osternacht *Easter
[Ger] SATB,acap (med) MULLER SM 2206 s.p. (A343)

Drei Festmotetten *see Christ Ist Erstanden; Nun Bitten Wir Den Heiligen Geist; Von Edler Art (A344)

Ecce Sacerdos *Fest
[Lat] SATB,org (med) MULLER MS 53 s.p. (A345)
[Ger] SATB,org,brass (med) MULLER SM 2423 sc s.p., cor pts s.p. (A346)

Erde Gottes *Gen,mot
[Ger] SATB,acap (med diff) sc MULLER SM 2432 s.p., cor pts s.p. (A347)

Gnade Euch Und Friede *hymn
SATB,brass (med) BAREN. SM 2433 sc s.p., cor pts s.p. see from Vier Hymnen (A348)

Ich Horte Etwas Wie Eine Stimme *hymn
SATB,brass (med) BAREN. SM2436 sc s.p., cor pts s.p. see from Vier Hymnen (A349)

Jesus, Jesus, Komm Zu Mir *ECY/Gen
[Ger] SSA,acap (med easy) MULLER MS 4 s.p. (A350)
[Ger] SATB,acap (med) MULLER MS 73 s.p. (A351)

Missa Choralis *Mass
[Lat] SAT/SAB SCHOTT s.p. (A352)

Missa Dodekaphonica (1966) *Mass
[Ger] ST&AB,org,fl,ob,clar,bsn,trp,horn, trom,bvl, English horn (med diff) MULLER SM 2448 sc s.p., cor pts s.p. (A353)

Missa Dorica *Mass
[Lat] SATB,org SCHOTT cor pts s.p., sc s.p. (A354)

Missa Hymnica *Mass
[Ger] SATTB,acap (med diff) MULLER SM 2419 sc s.p., cor pts s.p. (A355)

Missa Salvatoris *Mass
[Ger] SATB,acap (med) MULLER SM 2439 sc s.p., cor pts s.p. (A356)

Nun Bitten Wir Den Heiligen Geist *Pent,mot
[Ger] SATB,acap (med) MULLER SM 2422 sc s.p., cor pts s.p. see from Drei Festmotetten (A357)

Passion Nach Dem Evangelisten Johannes *Psntd,evang
[Ger] SATB,B solo,acap (med) MULLER SM 2443 s.p. (A358)

Passion Nach Dem Evangelisten Matthaus *Psntd,evang
[Ger] SSAATTBB,acap (med diff) MULLER SM 2437 sc s.p., cor pts s.p. (A359)

Sechs Lateinische Motetten *CC6U,Gen,mot
[Ger] SATB,acap (med) sc MULLER SM 2230 s.p. (A360)

Sei Uns Willkommen, Herre Christ *Xmas,Bibl/evang
[Ger] 1-12pt mix cor,acap (med diff) MULLER SM 2438 sc s.p., cor pts s.p. (A361)

Siehe! Gekommen Ist Der Herrscher *hymn
SATB,brass (med) BAREN. SM2434 sc s.p., cor pts s.p. see from Vier Hymnen (A362)

Silesius-Motette *Gen
[Ger] SATB,acap (med) MULLER SM 2373 s.p. (A363)

Tantum Ergo I *Gen
[Ger] SATB,org (med easy) MULLER SM 2431A s.p. see also Vier Tantum Ergo (A364)
[Ger] SATB,org (easy) MULLER SM 2431A s.p. (A365)

Tantum Ergo II *Gen
[Ger] SATB,org (med easy) MULLER SM 2431B s.p. see also Vier Tantum Ergo (A366)

AHRENS, JOSEPH (cont'd.)

Tantum Ergo III *Gen
[Ger] SATB,org (med easy) MULLER SM 2431C s.p. see also Vier Tantum Ergo (A367)

Tantum Ergo IV *Gen
[Ger] SATB,org (med easy) MULLER SM 2431D s.p. see also Vier Tantum Ergo (A368)

Vier Hymnen *see Der Geist Des Herrn Erfullt Den Erdenkreis; Gnade Euch Und Friede; Ich Horte Etwas Wie Eine Stimme; Siehe! Gekommen Ist Der Herrscher (A369)

Vier Tantum Ergo *Gen
[Ger] SATB,org (med easy) MULLER SM 2431 s.p.
contains & see also: Tantum Ergo I; Tantum Ergo II; Tantum Ergo III; Tantum Ergo IV (A370)

Von Edler Art *Xmas,mot
[Ger] SATB,acap (med) MULLER SM 2420 sc s.p., cor pts s.p. see from Drei Festmotetten (A371)

AHROLD, FRANK
Bedtime Prayer, A
SATB,acap oct PRESSER 312-40911 $.30 (A372)

Behold The Joy *cant
mix cor BELWIN $1.75 (A373)

Canticle Of Judith
SATB,org,opt 2horn&3trom&perc&2trp oct LAWSON 51728 $.45, ipr (A374)

Crucifixion
SATB FLAMMER A 5331 $.30 (A375)

Garden Hymn, The *hymn
SATB,acap WARNER W3613 $.30 (A376)

He's Gone Away
SAB FLAMMER D5160 $.25 (A377)

Holy Valley
SSA,acap oct PRESSER 312-40912 $.25 (A378)

Legend Of The Stork, The *Xmas
2pt treb cor oct PRESSER 312-40763 $.30 (A379)

Little Family, The *Xmas
SA oct PRESSER 312-40654 $.30 (A380)

Missa Brevis
SA/TB FLAMMER E5121 $.30 (A381)

AIBLINGER, JOHANN KASPAR (1779-1867)
Bei Der Krippe Jesu *Xmas
(Bier, Albert) [Ger] SATB,org (med easy) MULLER SM 110 sc s.p., cor pts s.p. (A382)

I Have Lifted Up My Spirit
(Forest) SATB FLAMMER A 5342 $.30 (A383)

Jubilate Deo *Jubil
men cor sc ALSBACH&D s.p. (A384)
(Cramer) [Eng/Lat] SATB,acap MARKS 4300 $.30 (A385)

Justorium Animae
(Dite, L.) 4pt mix cor,org (contains also: Brosig, Moritz, Timete Dominum) DOBLINGER voc sc s.p., cor pts s.p. see from DER KLEINE KIRCHENCHOR (A386)

Locus Iste *Fest
(Dite, L.) 4pt mix cor,org (contains also: Stuntz, Josef Hartmann, Domine Deus) DOBLINGER voc sc s.p., cor pts s.p. see from DER KLEINE KIRCHENCHOR (A387)

Messe *Mass
(Dite, L.) SSA,org DOBLINGER voc sc s.p., cor pts s.p. see from DER KLEINE KIRCHENCHOR (A388)

Messe C-Dur *Mass
mix cor (C maj) VOLK 107 sc s.p., cor pts s.p. (A389)

AICHINGER, GREGOR (1564-1628)
Adoramus *Lent,mot
[Lat] SSAT/SSABar,acap oct NOVELLO DM-16 s.p. (A390)

Adoramus Te *Easter/Lent
"We Adore Thee" SATB oct WALTON 6000 $.30 (A391)

Adoramus Te Christe *Psntd
[Lat] SSA&men cor,acap (med) MULLER M 16 s.p. (A392)

Alleluja
see Proprium Von Kirchweihfest

Assumpta Est Maria
girl cor SOUTHERN $.30 (A393)
[Lat] SST/SSA,acap oct SCHIRM.G 6250 $.20 (A394)
(Tillinghast) SSA,acap WARNER W2899 $.30 (A395)

Communio
see Proprium Von Kirchweihfest

Confirm In Us, O God *see Confirma Hoc, Deus

Confirma Hoc, Deus
(Martens, Mason) "Confirm In Us, O God" SATB oct WALTON 6016 $.30 (A396)

Duo Seraphim
(Tillinghast) SSA,acap WARNER W3394 $.30 (A397)

Factus Est Repente *Pent,mot
[Ger] SATB,acap (med) MULLER MS 37 s.p. (A398)
[Lat] mix cor,acap oct NOVELLO MS37 s.p. (A399)
(Payson, A.) "Suddenly There Came A Sound From Heaven" SATB,acap FRANK F-441 $.30 (A400)

He Is Risen *see Regina Coeli

Introitus
see Proprium Von Kirchweihfest

AICHINGER, GREGOR (cont'd.)

Jubilate Deo
(Knight, Gerald) SATB,acap oct FISCHER,C
CM-7588 $.35 (A401)

Jubilate Deo, Part I
SSATB,acap SCHIRM.EC $.30 (A402)

Jubilate Deo, Part II
SSATB,acap SCHIRM.EC $.30 (A403)

King Of Glory, The *see Salve Regina

Lauda Anima Mea *Easter/Pent,mot
[Lat] SATB,acap (med) MULLER M 19 s.p. (A404)

[Lat] mix cor,acap oct NOVELLO DM-19 s.p. (A405)

Lord Is Risen, The *Easter
(Christiansen, P.) SATB SCHMITT 1429 $.35 (A406)

Now, My Tongue, The Mystery Telling *see
Pange Lingua

O Be Joyful *see Regina Coeli

O Lord Of Hosts *Renais
(Ehret, Walter) SATB,acap PEER $.40 (A407)

Pange Lingua *Commun
"Now, My Tongue, The Mystery Telling"
SATTB,acap SCHIRM.EC 1217 $.25 (A408)

Proprium Von Kirchweihfest *Fest
mix cor sc VOLK 143 s.p.
contains: Alleluja; Communio; Introitus (A409)

Regina Caeli Laetare
(Steele, Jonathan) [Lat] SATB CHESTER s.p. (A410)

Regina Coeli *Easter/Psntd
SATB,acap voc pt DOBLINGER s.p. see also
PASSION UND OSTERN (A411)
[Lat] SATB,acap (med easy) MULLER MS 26
s.p. (A412)
"He Is Risen" [Eng/Lat] 4pt mix cor,acap
oct SCHIRM.G 7706 $.25 (A413)
(Tillinghast) [Lat] SSA,acap WARNER W2900
$.30 (A414)
(Vene) boy cor SOUTHERN $.30 (A415)
(Vene) "O Be Joyful" [Lat/Eng] TTB/SSA,acap
oct COLOMBO 1848 $.25 (A416)

Salve Regina
"King Of Glory, The" SATB,acap SCHIRM.EC
1242 (A417)

Sing To The Lord
(McKinney) SSA oct FISCHER,J 8701 $.30 (A418)

Suddenly There Came A Sound From Heaven *see
Factus Est Repente

Ubi Est Abel *Septua,mot
[Lat] SABar,acap oct NOVELLO DM-11 s.p. (A419)

Ubi Est Abel Frater Tuus *Psntd
[Lat] SAB,acap (med) MULLER M 11 s.p. (A420)

We Adore Thee *see Adoramus Te

AIKEN, WALTER H.
For Christ Is Born
(Crawford) SATB,acap (easy) oct WILLIS 7470
$.25 (A421)

AIN'A THAT GOOD NEWS *spir
(Dawson) SATB KJOS T103 $.30 (A422)
(Dawson) men cor KJOS TI04 $.30 (A423)

AINSI QU'ON OIT LE CERF BRUIRE see Goudimel,
Claude

AINSI QU'ON OIT LE CERF BRUIRE see Le Jeune,
Claude

AINT-A THAT GOOD NEWS *spir
(De Cormier) SATB oct LAWSON 51603 $.35 (A424)

AIN'T GOT TIME TO DIE *spir
(Johnson) 4pt mix cor,T solo,acap oct
SCHIRM.G 10301 $.40 (A425)

AIN'T GWINE TO STUDY WAR NO MORE *spir
(Swift) SATB oct SPRATT 114 $.22 (A426)

AIN'T THAT GOOD NEWS *spir
(Cain) SATB,acap oct PRO ART 2127 $.18 (A427)
(Ehret, Walter) SATB oct WALTON 2127 $.35 (A428)

AIR D'EGLISE see Stradella, Alessandro

AIRECILLOS DE BELEN see Balzanelli

AKE THE BODY OF CHRIST see Bachmetiev, Nikolai
I

AKS
Come To Zion, Sin Sick Souls
SATB MARKS 4038 $.30 see from THREE SHAKER
SONGS (A429)

AL HANISSIM *Hanakkah
(Fromm, Herbert) [Heb] SATB TRANSCON. TCL 796
$.60 (A430)

AL MOMENTO DELLA COMMUNIONE see Bottazzo, Luigi

AL SACRO CUORE DI GESU see Bottazzo, Luigi

AL SS. NOME DI MARIA see Firpo, Antonio

ALABAD, NINOS AL SENOR see Gorostidi, Laudate
Pueri Dominum

ALABADO SEA EL SANTISIMO see Comes, Juan
Bautista

ALABANZAS DEL ADVIENTO see Santa Cruz, Domingo

ALAIN, A.
There With His Mother In A Manger *Xmas
(Bedell, R.) TTB oct PRESSER 312-40286 $.25
(A431)
(Bedell, R.) SSA oct PRESSER 312-40286 $.25
(A432)

ALALA DE MONTFORTE see Benedito

ALAS, AND DID MY SAVIOR BLEED see Hughes

ALAS! AND DID MY SAVIOR BLEED see Martin, G.

ALAS! AND DID MY SAVIOR BLEED see Wilson

ALAS, AND DID MY SAVIOUR BLEED see Work

ALAS, MY GOD see Jannequin, Clement, Hellas,
Mon Dieu

ALAS!THEY HAVE TAKEN JESUS see Morley, Thomas,
Eheu! Sustulerunt Dominum

ALBANUS see Fayrfax, Robert

ALBERT, HEINRICH (1604-1651)
Du Mein Einzig Licht *Bibl
SAT/SAB HANSSLER 6.275 s.p. contains also:
Gumpeltzhaimer, Adam, Der Herr Ist Mein
Treuer Hirt (SAT/SAB) (A433)

Gott Des Himmels Und Der Erden
see Trubel, Gerhard, Gott Des Himmels Und
Der Erden

Lobet Gott In Seinem Heiligtum *mot
(Hellmann) SSATB HANSSLER 1.110 s.p. (A434)

Rise, My Soul, And Praise God's Kindness
*Gen
unis,kbd (med easy) oct CONCORDIA 98-1481
$.20 (A435)

Selig Sind, Dei Leide Tragen
SSATB HANSSLER 6.166 s.p. (A436)

ALBERT-ROMAN
Jesu, Lar Mig Ratt Betanka
mix cor NORDISKA 3360 s.p. (A437)

ALBERTI, GIUSEPPE MATTEO (1685-1750)
Is It Nothing To You? *Lent
SATB SCHMITT 1713 $.25 (A438)

ALBINONI, TOMASO (1671-1750)
Magnificat *Magnif
[Lat] min sc PETERS E1074 $2.00, ipa (A439)

ALBRECHT, K.
Earth Feared And Was Silent, The *Easter,
anthem
SATB (med easy) oct GIA G1206 $.25 (A440)

ALBRECHTSBERGER, JOHANN GEORG (1736-1809)
Gloria (from Messe In F-Dur) Gloria
(Dite, L.) 4pt mix cor,acap DOBLINGER sc
s.p., cor pts s.p. (A441)

Messe In Es-Dur *Mass
mix cor,org (E flat maj, contains also:
Messe In F-Dur) DOBLINGER voc sc s.p.,
cor pts s.p. see from OSTERREICHISCHE
KIRCHENMUSIK (A442)

Messe In F-Dur *Adv/Lent,Mass
unis,acap (F maj, contains also: Messe In
Es-Dur) DOBLINGER voc sc s.p., cor pts
s.p. see from OSTERREICHISCHE
KIRCHENMUSIK (A443)
(Pfannhauser, K.) 4pt mix cor,opt org (F
maj) DOBLINGER sc s.p., cor pts s.p. see
from OSTERREICHISCHE KIRCHENMUSIK (A444)

ALBUM see Victoria, Tomas Luis de

ALCOCK
There Were Shepherds In The Fields
SATB oct BOOSEY 431 $.30 (A445)

ALCOCK, STANLEY
Missa Brevis Secunda *Mass/mot
[Lat] mix cor oct NOVELLO 03.0108.06 s.p. (A446)

ALCOCK, WALTER G.
Te Deum *Te Deum
SATB (B flat maj) oct NOVELLO 44.0652.04
s.p. (A447)

ALDERFER
In A Manger Gently Lay *Xmas
SATB,acap,opt pno oct PRO ART 1377 $.25 (A448)

Sing Forth His Praise
SATB,acap,opt pno oct PRO ART 2161 $.25 (A449)

ALDERSHAW see Duckworth, Arthur

ALDRICH
O Praise The Lord, All Ye Nations
(Kingsbury, John) SATB ALFRED 6407 $.30 (A450)

ALDRICH, HENRY (1647-1710)
Classic Anthems *CCU,anthem
SATB oct PRESSER 352-00061 $.55 (A451)

ALDRIDGE, RICHARD
Fill Thou My Life
mix cor LENGNICK s.p. (A452)

ALEATORY PSALM see Lamb, Gordon H.

ALEINU (VAANACHU V'HAYA ADONAI) see Gottlieb,
J.

ALELUIA see Handel, George Frideric

ALELUYA see Mozart, Wolfgang Amadeus

ALEXANDER
God Be Merciful (Psalm 67)
SSAATTBB oct PRO ART 1612 $.25 (A453)

Psalm 67 *see God Be Merciful

ALEXANDER, JOHANN
Once In Royal David's City *Xmas
(Gauntlett) unis oct BELWIN 60549 $.25 (A454)

ALEXANDER, JOSEF (1910-)
Hosanna
SATB,acap oct LAWSON 51607 $.40 (A455)

New Psalm, A *Psalm
mix cor oct LAWSON 51267 $.45 (A456)

ALEXANDER, JOSEF (cont'd.)
O Sing Unto The Lord
SATB (diff) ABINGDON APM-562 $.90 (A457)

Song Of Captivity
SSA oct SHAPIRO SK 3007 $.85 (A458)

ALEXANDRE, GEORGES
Ave Maria *BVM
[Lat] unis,pno/org,opt vln&harp LEMOINE
s.p. (A459)

ALFONSO, JOSE
Seven Last Words Of Our Lord Jesus Christ,
The *Holywk,cant,Span
SATB SCHIRM.EC 1243 (A460)

ALFRED BURT CAROLS see Burt, Alfred

ALFRED BURT CAROLS, SET 1 see Burt, Alfred

ALFRED BURT CAROLS, SET 2 see Burt, Alfred

ALFRED BURT CAROLS, SET 3 see Burt, Alfred

ALFVEN, HUGO (1872-1960)
Motett *mot
[Swed] SATB,acap GEHRMANS KRB 183 (A461)

Saeterjentens Sondag
mix cor NORDISKA 1072 s.p. (A462)

ALGAZI, LEON
Aschivenu
[Heb] SATB,pno/org oct SALABERT-US $.65 (A463)

Psalm 27
[Fr/Heb] SATB,B solo,pno/org oct SALABERT-
US $4.25 (A464)

Service Sacre *Sab-Eve/Sab-Morn
SATB TRANSCON. TCL 805 $3.50 (A465)

ALIX, RENE (1907-)
Messe De Notre-Dame De L'assomption *Mass
4pt mix cor,soli,org CHOUDENS voc sc s.p.,
voc pt s.p. (A466)

O Quam Suavis Est
[Lat] 4pt mix cor,acap oct DURAND (A467)

ALL AS GOD WILLS see Ford, Virgil T.

ALL BEAUTIFUL THE MARCH OF DAYS
SATB oct BELWIN 60806 $.30 (A468)

ALL BEAUTIFUL THE MARCH OF DAYS see Lapo, Cecil
E.

ALL BELLS IN PARADISE see Hamilton, Alisdair

ALL BLESSED, ALL HOLY, LORD GOD see Kastalsky,
Alexander Dmitrievitch

ALL BLESSING, HONOR, THANKS AND PRAISE
(Luvaas) men cor KJOS 2504 $.30 (A469)

ALL BLESSING, HONOR, THANKS, AND PRAISE see
Luvaas

ALL BREATHING LIFE see Bach, Johann Sebastian

ALL BY OURSELVES see Martin, Gilbert M.

ALL CREATION SING see Fautch, Magdalen

ALL CREATURES NOW see Bennet, Lasst Diesen Tag
Uns Alle Preisen

ALL CREATURES NOW WITH HEARTS REJOICE see
Heseltine, Philip

ALL CREATURES OF OUR GOD see Cain, Noble

**ALL CREATURES OF OUR GOD AND KING (from
Geistliche Kirchengesange)**
(Shaw) mix cor,acap,opt org oct SCHIRM.G 9909
$.30 (A470)

ALL CREATURES OF OUR GOD AND KING see Chapman

ALL CREATURES OF OUR GOD AND KING see Darst, W.
Glenn

ALL CREATURES OF OUR GOD AND KING see Gibbs,
[Cecil] Armstrong

ALL CREATURES OF OUR GOD AND KING see Harris,
William Henry

ALL CREATURES OF OUR GOD AND KING see Lorenz

ALL CREATURES OF OUR GOD AND KING see
Matterling

ALL CREATURES OF OUR GOD AND KING see Robertson

ALL CRY GLORY see Ford

ALL DARKNESS FLIES see Bach, Johann Sebastian

ALL DEN HELGA KRISTENHET see Blom, Oscar

ALL DING AUF ERDEN see Schrader, Oswald

ALL EARTH BE GLAD see Rodby

ALL EHR UND LOB SOLL GOTTES SEIN see Schutz,
Heinrich

ALL FLESH IS GRASS see Berger, Jean

ALL FLESH IS GRASS see Monaco, Richard A.

ALL FLESH IS GRASS see Pinkham, Daniel

ALL FOR JESUS see Moffatt

ALL FROM SABA SHALL COME see Schroth, Gerhard

ALL FROM THE SUN'S UPRISE see Tomblings, Philip

ALL GLORIOUS GOD see Rorem, Ned

ALL GLORY BE TO GOD see Vivaldi, Antonio,
Gloria In Excelsis Deo

ALL GLORY BE TO GOD ON HIGH *Xmas
(Whitford) SATB SCHMITT 1767 $.25   (A471)

ALL GLORY BE TO GOD ON HIGH see Cruger, Johann

ALL GLORY BE TO GOD ON HIGH see Decius, Nicolaus

ALL GLORY BE TO GOD ON HIGH see Kugelmann, Johann

ALL GLORY BE TO GOD ON HIGH see Lundquist, Matthew Nathanael

ALL GLORY BE TO GOD ON HIGH see Praetorius, Michael

ALL GLORY BE TO GOD ON HIGH see Schroeter, Leonhardt

ALL GLORY BE TO GOD ON HIGH see Schroter, L.

ALL GLORY BE TO GOD ON HIGH see Schumann

ALL GLORY BE TO GOD ON HIGH see Wienhorst, Richard

ALL GLORY BE TO THEE, MOST HIGH see Eccard, Johannes

ALL GLORY LAUD AND HONOR *Easter/Lent
(Couper) SA oct FISCHER,C CM-7676 $.30 (A472)

ALL GLORY, LAUD AND HONOR see Angell, Warren M.

ALL GLORY, LAUD AND HONOR see Bach, Johann Sebastian

ALL GLORY, LAUD, AND HONOR see Bunjes, Paul G.

ALL GLORY, LAUD, AND HONOR see Markworth, Henry

ALL GLORY, LAUD, AND HONOR see Neale

ALL GLORY, LAUD, AND HONOR see Purvis, Richard

ALL GLORY, LAUD AND HONOR see Rossel, Denton

ALL GLORY, LAUD AND HONOR see Schreiner, Alexander

ALL GLORY, LAUD AND HONOR see Sjolund, Paul

ALL GLORY, LAUD AND HONOR see Teschner, Wie Soll Ich Dich Empfangen

ALL GLORY, LAUD, AND HONOR see Wilson

ALL GLORY, LAUD AND HONOUR see Bach, Johann Sebastian

ALL GLORY ON HIGH see Lynn, George

ALL GLORY, PRAISE AND MAJESTY see Bach, Johann Sebastian

ALL GLORY TO GOD IN THE HIGHEST see Beethoven, Ludwig van

ALL GOD'S CHILLUN' see Stewart

ALL GODS CHILLUN GOT WINGS *spir,US
(Aubanel, Georges) "Les Enfants De Dieu Ont Des Ailes" [Eng/Fr] 3 eq voices OUVRIERES s.p.   (A473)

ALL GOOD GIFTS see Warner

ALL HAIL, ADORED TRINITY see Sowerby, Leo

ALL HAIL, STAR OF THE SEA see Anerio, Giovanni Francesco, Ave Maris Stella

ALL HAIL THE POWER *hymn
(Thompson, Van Denman) SATB ALLANS 428 s.p.   (A474)

ALL HAIL THE POWER see Goldsworthy, William Arthur

ALL HAIL THE POWER see Greenhill, Harold

ALL HAIL THE POWER see Mueller, Carl F.

ALL HAIL THE POWER see Shrubsole

ALL HAIL THE POWER see Vaughan Williams, Ralph

ALL HAIL THE POWER OF JESUS' NAME *hymn
see Choral Hymn, A
SATB oct ST.MARTIN SMP6410 s.p.   (A475)
(Beebe) SATB LUDWIG L-1151 $.40   (A476)

ALL HAIL THE POWER OF JESUS NAME see Barnard, Park

ALL HAIL THE POWER OF JESUS' NAME see Darst, W. Glenn

ALL HAIL THE POWER OF JESUS' NAME see Ellor

ALL HAIL THE POWER OF JESUS' NAME see Galbraith, J.

ALL HAIL THE POWER OF JESUS' NAME see Hamer

ALL HAIL THE POWER OF JESUS' NAME see Holden, [Oliver]

ALL HAIL THE POWER OF JESUS NAME see Hughes, Robert J.

ALL HAIL THE POWER OF JESUS' NAME see Johnston

ALL HAIL THE POWER OF JESUS' NAME see Shrubsole

ALL HAIL THE POWER OF JESUS' NAME see Thompson

ALL HAIL THE POWER OF JESUS' NAME see Wilson

ALL HAIL THE POWER OF JESUS' NAME see Young, G.

ALL HAIL THE POWER OF JESUS' NAME see Young, Gordon

ALL HAIL THIS RESURRECTION DAY see Wald, George

ALL HAIL THOU NOBLE GUEST see Tallis, Thomas

ALL HAIL TO THEE, BLESSED MORN see Bach, Johann Sebastian

ALL HAIL TRUE BODY see Byrd, William, Ave Verum Corpus

ALL HAS BEEN HEARD see Boyd, Jack

ALL HIS MERCIES SHALL ENDURE see Handel, George Frideric

ALL HOLY LORD see Santa Maria, Thomas de

ALL I WANT
(Work) SATB oct LORENZ 9908 $.30   (A477)

ALL IN THE APRIL EVENING see Diack, [John Michael]

ALL IN THE APRIL EVENING see Roberton, Hugh S.

ALL IN THE MORNING *Xmas,carol,Eng
(Barrow, R.) "It Was On Christmas Day" TTBB, org SCHIRM.EC 2304   (A478)

ALL IN THE MORNING see Marryott, Ralph E.

ALL IS WELL
(Wilson) SATB oct LORENZ C186 $.30   (A479)

ALL KNEW HE WAS THERE see Turner

ALL-KNOWING GOD see Johnson, David N.

ALL LANDS AND PEOPLES see Lovelace, Austin C.

ALL-LIGHT-CREATING GOOD *hymn
SATB oct ST.MARTIN s.p.   (A480)

ALL MEN, ALL THINGS, PRAISE THOU THE LORD see Mendelssohn-Bartholdy, Felix

ALL MEN ARE LIST'NING see Stanton

ALL MEN LIVE AND THRIVE BRIEFLY see Reger, Max

ALL MEN LIVING ARE BUT MORTAL see Rosenmuller, Johann

ALL MEN NOW SING, REJOICE see Krone

ALL MEN SEEK GOD see Track, Gerhard

ALL MEN SHALL HONOR AND ADORE THEE see Bach, Johann Sebastian

ALL MEN SING NOEL! see Peninger, David

ALL MORGAN IST GANZ FRISCH UND NEU see Bornefeld, Helmut

ALL MORGAN IST GANZ FRISCH UND NEU see Walter (Walther), Johann

ALL MORGEN IST GANZ FRISCH UND NEU see Eglin, Arthur

ALL MORGEN IST GANZ FRISCH UND NEU see Kretzschmar, Gunther

ALL MORGEN IST GANZ FRISCH UND NEU see Kubler, Emil

ALL MORGEN IST GANZ FRISCH UND NEU see Stern, Hermann

ALL' MUSSEN WIR STERBEN
(Steiner, Lois; Uray, Ernst L.) mix cor,acap oct DOBLINGER s.p. see from Vier Totenlieder Aus St. Lambrecht   (A481)

ALL MY FRIENDS FORSAKE ME see Haydn, (Johann) Michael, Omnes Amici Mei Dereliquerunt Me

ALL MY HEART see Cruger, Johann

ALL MY HEART AND SOUL see Liszt, Franz

ALL MY HEART, INFLAMED AND BURNING see Dvorak, Antonin, Inflammatus

ALL MY HEART REJOICES see Lockwood, Normand

ALL MY HEART THIS NIGHT REJOICES *Xmas
SATB CHARTER $.30   (A482)
(Thompson, R.) SAB LEONARD-US 08001120 $.25   (A483)

ALL MY HEART THIS NIGHT REJOICES see Cartford, Gerhard M.

ALL MY HEART THIS NIGHT REJOICES see Cashmore, Donald

ALL MY HEART THIS NIGHT REJOICES see Cruger, Johann

ALL MY HEART THIS NIGHT REJOICES see Durston, D.

ALL MY HEART THIS NIGHT REJOICES see Ebeling, J.

ALL MY HEART THIS NIGHT REJOICES see Emig, Lois

ALL MY HEART THIS NIGHT REJOICES see Erdlen, Hermann

ALL MY HEART THIS NIGHT REJOICES see Goode, J.

ALL MY HEART THIS NIGHT REJOICES see Goode, Jack C.

ALL MY HEART THIS NIGHT REJOICES see Graham, Robert [V.]

ALL MY HEART THIS NIGHT REJOICES see Lovelace, Austin C.

ALL MY HEART THIS NIGHT REJOICES see Mueller, Carl F.

ALL MY HEART THIS NIGHT REJOICES see Roff, Joseph

ALL MY HEART THIS NIGHT REJOICES see Thiman, Eric Harding

ALL MY HEART TODAY REJOICES see Harris

ALL MY HEART TODAY REJOICES see Peeters, Flor

ALL MY HOPE ON GOD IS FOUNDED see Howells, Herbert Norman

ALL MY TRIALS *spir
(Luboff, Norman) SATB oct WALTON 3065 $.30   (A484)

ALL MY TRIALS, LORD *folk/spir,Carib
(Hopkins, Ewart) SATB,acap ROBERTON   (A485)
(Hopkins, Ewart) mix cor ROBERTON s.p.   (A486)

ALL NATURE'S WORK HIS PRAISE DECLARE see Ehret, Walter

ALL NATURE'S WORKS HIS PRAISE DECLARE see Butler, Eugene

ALL NATURE'S WORKS HIS PRAISE DECLARE see Fink

ALL NATURE'S WORKS HIS PRAISE DECLARE see Fink, G.

ALL NATURE'S WORK'S HIS PRAISE DECLARE see Rogers

ALL NATURE'S WORKS HIS PRAISE DECLARE see Young, C.

ALL NIGHT, ALL DAY *spir
(Barton, Clement A.) SATB oct WALTON 2022 $.30   (A487)
(Hallett) SA oct WORD CS-2423 $.25   (A488)

ALL NIGHT, ALL DAY see Howorth, Wayne

ALL NIGHT, ALL DAY see Swift, R.A.

ALL OUR JOYS see Bristol, Lee H., Jr.

ALL PEOPLE CLAP YOUR HANDS see Weelkes, Thomas

ALL PEOPLE SING PRAISES see Hokanson, M.

ALL PEOPLE THAT ON EARTH see Farnes

ALL PEOPLE THAT ON EARTH DO DWELL see Bach, Johann Sebastian

ALL PEOPLE THAT ON EARTH DO DWELL see Bourgeois, Loys (Louis)

ALL PEOPLE THAT ON EARTH DO DWELL see Grieb

ALL PEOPLE THAT ON EARTH DO DWELL see Gustafson, Dwight

ALL PEOPLE THAT ON EARTH DO DWELL see Holst, Gustav

ALL PEOPLE THAT ON EARTH DO DWELL see Sweelinck, Jan Pieterszoon, Or Sus, Serviteurs

ALL PEOPLE THAT ON EARTH DO DWELL see Tallis, Thomas

ALL PEOPLE THAT ON EARTH DO DWELL see Young

ALL PEOPLE THAT ON EARTH DO WELL see Tallis, Thomas

ALL POOR MEN see Prentice, Fred

ALL POOR MEN AND HUMBLE *carol,Welsh
(Wetzler, Robert) SATBB (med) oct AUGSBURG 1506 $.25   (A489)

ALL POOR MEN AND HUMBLE see Kelly

ALL POW'R IN HEAVEN ABOVE see Handel, George Frideric

ALL PRAISE AND THANKS TO GOD see Agey, C. Buell

ALL PRAISE TO GOD see Caldwell, Mary [Elizabeth]

ALL PRAISE TO GOD see Caldwell

ALL PRAISE TO GOD ETERNAL see Gaul, Harvey Bartlet

ALL PRAISE TO GOD, IN LIGHT ARRAYED see Wagner, Richard

ALL PRAISE TO GOD, WHO REIGNS ABOVE see Bunjes, Paul G.

ALL PRAISE TO GOD, WHO REIGNS ABOVE see Lenel, Ludwig

ALL PRAISE TO GOD, WHO REIGNS ABOVE see Markworth, Henry

ALL PRAISE TO GOD WHO REIGNS ABOVE see Vulpius, Melchior

ALL PRAISE TO GOD, WHO REIGNS ABOVE see Wolff, S. Drummond

ALL PRAISE TO JESUS' HALLOWED NAME see Bunjes, Paul G.

ALL PRAISE TO MUSIC see Nelson, Ronald A.

ALL PRAISE TO OUR REDEEMING LORD see Ford, Virgil T.

ALL PRAISE TO OUR REDEEMING LORD see Peninger, David

ALL PRAISE TO OUR REDEEMING LORD see Wyatt

ALL PRAISE TO THEE see Bach

ALL PRAISE TO THEE see Boatwright, Howard

ALL PRAISE TO THEE see Lassus, Roland de (Orlandus)

ALL PRAISE TO THEE see Mueller, Carl F.

ALL PRAISE TO THEE see Pitcher, Gladys, Tallis Canon

ALL PRAISE TO THEE see Powell

ALL PRAISE TO THEE see Tallis, Thomas

ALL PRAISE TO THEE, ETERNAL GOD see Anonymous

ALL PRAISE TO THEE, ETERNAL GOD see Darst, W. Glenn

ALL PRAISE TO THEE, ETERNAL GOD see Johnson

ALL PRAISE TO THEE, ETERNAL GOD see Lenel, Ludwig

ALL PRAISE TO THEE, ETERNAL LORD *Easter/Gen
(Peery, R.) SA oct PRESSER 312-40003 $.25
(A490)

ALL PRAISE TO THEE, MY GOD, THIS NIGHT see Tallis, Thomas

ALL PRAISE TO THY GREAT MERIT see Bach, Johann Sebastian, Ehr' Sei In's Himmels Thron

ALL 'ROUN' DE GLORY MANGER *Xmas
(Ehret, W.) SATB LEONARD-US 08001600 $.25
(A491)
(Ehret, W.) SSA LEONARD-US 08001680 $.30
(A492)

ALL SHALL BE WELL see Wilson

ALL SO STILL see Lloyd, Richard H.

ALL SOLCH DEIN GUET WIR PREISEN see Buxtehude, Dietrich

ALL SOLCH DEIN GUT WIR PREISEN see Buxtehude, Dietrich

ALL THANKS BE TO GOD see Schutz, Heinrich, Danksagen Wir Alle Gott Christo, Der Uns Mit Seinem Wort

ALL THAT HAS LIFE AND BEAUTY see Crawford, John, Tout Ce Qui Prend Naissance

ALL THAT HAS LIFE AND BREATH see Mendelssohn-Bartholdy, Felix

ALL THAT HAS LIFE PRAISE GOD see Schneider, Kent

ALL THAT 'LIEVE IN CHRISTIAN LAY see Edmunds, John

ALL THAT THRILLS MY SOUL see Harris

ALL THAT WE DO see Bock, F.

ALL THAT'S GOOD AND GREAT AND TRUE see Thiman, Eric Harding

ALL THAT'S GOOD AND GREAT AND TRUE see Vick

ALL THE EARTH DOTH WORSHIP THEE see Handel, George Frideric

ALL THE EARTH DOTH WORSHIP THEE see Wetzler, Robert

ALL THE EARTH HID ITSELF *Easter
(Coggin, E.) SATB,acap oct PRESSER 312-40734 $.25
(A493)

ALL THE EARTH IS SINGING see Emig, Lois

ALL THE EARTH SING UNTO THE LORD see McLin

ALL THE ENDS OF THE EARTH see Peloquin, C. Alexander

ALL THE REST IS UP TO YOU see Price, Paul

ALL THE WORLD SHALL SING see Hagen

ALL THEY FROM SABA see Gallus, Jacobus, Omnes De Saba

ALL THEY FROM SABA SHALL COME see Bach, Johann Sebastian

ALL THEY FROM SABA SHALL COME see Powell

ALL THINGS see Lewis

ALL THINGS ARE FULL OF THEE, LORD see Twohig

ALL THINGS ARE THINE see Darst, W. Glenn

ALL THINGS ARE THINE see Jordan, Alice

ALL THINGS ARE THINE see Simon

ALL THINGS BRIGHT AND BEAUTIFUL
see Two Songs Of Praise
(Kinsman, F.) SA LEONARD-US 08001920 $.25
(A494)

ALL THINGS BRIGHT AND BEAUTIFUL see Brown

ALL THINGS BRIGHT AND BEAUTIFUL see Davies, Henry Walford

ALL THINGS BRIGHT AND BEAUTIFUL see Ferguson

ALL THINGS BRIGHT AND BEAUTIFUL see George, Graham

ALL THINGS BRIGHT AND BEAUTIFUL see Grime, William

ALL THINGS BRIGHT AND BEAUTIFUL see Hankey

ALL THINGS BRIGHT AND BEAUTIFUL see Hankey, Mark

ALL THINGS COME OF THEE
see Worship Responses

ALL THINGS THAT RISE WILL FALL see Berger, Jean

ALL THIS NIGHT SHRILL CHANTICLEER *Xmas
(Kinsman) SATB oct PRO ART 1936 $.22 (A495)

ALL THIS NIGHT SHRILL CHANTICLEER see Stevens, Halsey

ALL THROUGH THE NIGHT see Lawson, Malcolm

ALL THROUGH THE WINTRY NIGHT see Kountz

ALL THROUGH THE WIN'TRY NIGHT see Kountz

ALL THROUGH THE YEAR *folk,Welsh
SA/SAB oct LORENZ 7834 $.25
(A496)

ALL THY MERCIES see Williams

ALL THY WORKS PRAISE THEE *Thanks
(Garden, Charlotte L.) SATB oct GRAY
GCMR 1067 $.25
(A497)

ALL THY WORKS PRAISE THEE see Church, H.

ALL THY WORKS SHALL PRAISE THEE see Clare, Edwyn A.

ALL THY WORKS SHALL PRAISE THEE see Mathias, William

ALL WE LIKE SHEEP see Handel, George Frideric

ALL WE LIKE SHEEP see Nelson, Jerry

ALL WE LIKE SHEEP HAVE GONE ASTRAY see Handel, George Frideric

ALL WERE THERE *Xmas
(Lynn, G.) SSA oct PRESSER 332-40086 $.25
(A498)

ALL WERE THERE see Lynn, George

ALL WISDOM COMETH FROM THE LORD see Joubert, John

ALL YE CHRISTIANS, NOW REJOICE
(Lundquist) SATB,pno (diff) oct WILLIS 7480 $.20
(A499)

ALL YE GOOD PEOPLE see Kountz

ALL YE NATIONS
(Brandon) unis/SA&desc oct SUMMY M 2896 $.25
(A500)

ALL YE PEOPLE see Palestrina, Giovanni, O Vos Omnes

ALL YE PEOPLE see Valotti

ALL YE PEOPLE see van Berchem, J., O Vos Omnes

ALL YE PEOPLE see Victoria, Tomas Luis de, O Vos Omnes

ALL YE PEOPLE see Viotti, Giovanni Battista

ALL YE SAINTS BE JOYFUL see Davis, Katherine K.

ALL YE SERVANTS OF THE LORD see Elmore, Robert [Hall]

ALL YE SERVANTS OF THE LORD see Young

ALL YE THAT CRIED UNTO THE LORD see Mendelssohn-Bartholdy, Felix, Lobgesang

ALL YE WHO PASS BY see Morales, Cristobal de, O Vos Omnes

ALL YE WHO SEEK THE LORD see Iden, Raymond

ALL YE WHO WEEP see Gounod, Charles Francois

ALL YOU PEOPLES CLAP YOUR HANDS see Rocherolle

ALL YOU PEOPLES CLAP YOUR HANDS see Roff, Joseph

ALLA B.V. DEL ROSARIO *CC3U,BVM
[Lat] unis,org ZANIBON 2759 s.p. (A501)

ALLA POLACCA SUB TUUM PRAESIDIUM see Milwid, Antoni

ALLA TRINITE *15th cent
(Burney) [Lat] 4pt mix cor,acap oct SCHIRM.G 6252 $.25
(A502)

ALLA VARA DAGR see Grimstad, Johan H.

ALLAIRE, G.
Noel! Noel! Noel! *Xmas,Fr
SATB oct PRESSER 312-40468 $.30 (A503)
SATB oct PRESSER 312-40428 $.30 (A504)

ALLAN
Precious Lord, Take My Hand
(Ringwald) TTBB SHAWNEE C203 $.30 (A505)
(Ringwald) SSAA SHAWNEE B 306 $.30 (A506)

ALLAN, MEA
Bells Of Easter *Easter
SATB WEINBERGER s.p. (A507)

ALLANBROOK
Psalm 130
SATB,org oct BOOSEY 5724 $.40 (A508)

Psalm 131
SATB,org oct BOOSEY 5725 $.35 (A509)

ALLARD, F.M.
Uppvaknen, I Kristne Alla
6pt mix cor NORDISKA 3194 s.p. (A510)

ALLAS OGON VANTA PA DIG, HERRE see Schutz, Heinrich

ALLDIS, JOHN
Festival Te Deum, A *Fest,Bibl/Te Deum
SATB&cong,cantor WEINBERGER s.p. voc sc, cor pts (A511)

ALLE, ALLELUIA see Reinhart

ALLE ENGEL ZU DIESEM FEST see Spitta, Heinrich

ALLE EURE SORGE WERFET AUF IHN see Zipp, Friedrich

ALLE GUTE GABE see Hufschmidt, Wolfgang

ALLE GUTE GABE see Micheelsen, Hans Friedrich

ALLE GUTEN GABEN see Attenhofer, [Karl]

ALLE HELGENS DAG see Groven, Eivind

ALLE JAHRE WEIDER see Burkhart, Franz

ALLE KONIGE WERDEN IHN ANBETEN see Gottschick, Friedemann

ALLE MENNESKER PA JORDEN see Bach, Johann Sebastian, Alle Menschen Mussen Sterben

ALLE MENSCHEN MOETEN STERVEN see Bach, Johann Sebastian

ALLE MENSCHEN MUSSEN STERBEN see Anton, Christoph

ALLE MENSCHEN MUSSEN STERBEN see Bach, Johann Sebastian

ALLE MENSCHEN MUSSEN STERBEN see Graap, Lothar

ALLE MENSCHEN SIND NUN AUFGEWACHT see Ruhl, Herbert

ALLE TAGE SING UND SAGE (from Paradeisvogel Ingolstadt 1613) BVM
SATB,acap (contains also: Ihr Christenmenschen Alle (from Bamberger Gesangbuch 1628)) voc pt DOBLINGER s.p. see also Unsere Liebe Frau (A512)

ALLE VENDER AUGO SINE TIL DEG see Schutz, Heinrich

ALLE WELT SINGE see Bornefeld, Helmut

ALLEGRI, GREGORIO (ca. 1582-1652)
Miserere
mix cor NORDISKA 1651 s.p. (A513)

Miserere Mei, Deus (Psalm 50) Adv/Lent,anti/mot
[Lat] SSATB&SSAB,acap oct SCHIRM.G 6257 $.25 (A514)
[Lat] dbl cor HANSSLER 1.539 s.p. (A515)
SSATB&SSAB SCHIRM.EC $.20 (A516)
(Amman) [Lat] SATTB&SSAB SCHOTT s.p. (A517)
(Atkins, Ivor) [Lat] SATB/SSATB oct NOVELLO 44.1298.02 s.p. (A518)
(Davison, A.) [Lat] TTBB,acap SCHIRM.EC 27 $.25 (A519)

Psalm 50 *see Miserere Mei Deus

Psalm 51 *see Miserere Mei, Deus

Veni Sancte Spiritus *Easter/Pent/Whitsun
SATB,acap voc pt DOBLINGER s.p. see also PFINGSTEN UND EUCHARISTIE (A520)
[Ger] SATB,acap (med) MULLER MS 67 s.p. (A521)

ALLEIN AUF GOTTES WORT see Jeep, Johann

ALLEIN AUF GOTTES WORT WILL ICH see Walter (Walther), Johann

ALLEIN GOTT IN DER HOH see Barbe, Helmut

ALLEIN GOTT IN DER HOH see Schroter, Leonhard

ALLEIN GOTT IN DER HOH see Zipp, Friedrich

ALLEIN GOTT IN DER HOH SEI EHR see Bach, Johann Sebastian

ALLEIN GOTT IN DER HOH SEI EHR see Cruger, Johann

ALLEIN GOTT IN DER HOH SEI EHR see Decius, Nicolaus

ALLEIN GOTT IN DER HOH SEI EHR see Eccard, Johannes

ALLEIN GOTT IN DER HOH SEI EHR see Praetorius, Michael

ALLEIN GOTT IN DER HOH SEI EHR see Schein, Johann Hermann

ALLEIN GOTT IN DER HOH SEI EHR see Schlenker, Manfred

ALLEIN GOTT IN DER HOH SEI EHR see Schroter, Leonhard

ALLEIN GOTT IN DER HOH SEI EHR see Schubert, Gunter

ALLEIN GOTT IN DER HOHE SEI EHR see Cruger, Johann

ALLEIN ZU DIR, HERR JESU CHRIST see Bach, Johann Sebastian

ALLEIN ZU DIR HERR JESU CHRIST see Franck, Melchior

ALLEIN ZU DIR, HERR JESU CHRIST see Lechner, Leonhard

ALLEIN ZU DIR, HERR JESU CHRIST see Micheelsen, Hans Friedrich

ALLEIN ZU DIR, HERR JESU CHRIST see Pahlitzsch, Wolfgang

ALLEIN ZU DIR, HERR JESU CHRIST see Praetorius, Michael

ALLEIN ZU DIR HERR JESU CHRIST see Solter, Heinz

ALLEIN ZU DIR, HERR JESU CHRIST see Witte, Gerd

ALLELUIA see Abbot

ALLELUIA see Bach

ALLELUIA see Bach, Johann Sebastian

ALLELUIA see Beebe, Edward J.

ALLELUIA see Belt, T.

ALLELUIA see Berger, Jean

ALLELUIA see Booth

ALLELUIA! see Boughton, Rutland

ALLELUIA see Boyce

ALLELUIA see Caldara, Antonio

ALLELUIA see Christiansen, Larry A.

ALLELUIA see Coggin, Elwood

ALLELUIA see Creston, Paul

ALLELUIA see Diemer, Emma Lou

ALLELUIA see Ein Frolich Gesang

ALLELUIA see Forcucci, S.L.

ALLELUIA see Franceschini

ALLELUIA see Franck, Cesar

ALLELUIA see Gardner, Maurice

ALLELUIA see Garlick, Anthony

ALLELUIA see Gassman, Clark

ALLELUIA see Handel, George Frideric

ALLELUIA see Hannahs, R.C.

ALLELUIA! see Hawkins, Floyd W.

ALLELUIA! see Hayes

ALLELUIA see Hovhaness, Alan

ALLELUIA see Hughes

ALLELUIA! see Hummel

ALLELUIA see Johns, Donald

ALLELUIA see Kay, Ulysses Simpson

ALLELUIA see Koechlin, Charles

ALLELUIA see Korhonen, J.

ALLELUIA see Kreter

ALLELUIA see Krul

ALLELUIA! see Land, Lois B.

ALLELUIA see Lapo, Cecil E.

ALLELUIA see Lassus, Roland de (Orlandus)

ALLELUIA see Liadoff

ALLELUIA see Lockwood, Normand

ALLELUIA see Luening, Otto

ALLELUIA see Lynn, George

ALLELUIA see McCowen

ALLELUIA see Mailman, [Martin]

ALLELUIA see Marshall

ALLELUIA! see Miranda, A.

ALLELUIA see Morgan

ALLELUIA see Mozart, Wolfgang Amadeus

ALLELUIA see Muczynski, Robert

ALLELUIA see Nees, Staf

ALLELUIA see Palestrina, Giovanni

ALLELUIA see Pergolesi, Giovanni Battista

ALLELUIA see Poch, Gail

ALLELUIA see Price

ALLELUIA see Revicki

ALLELUIA see Rinehart

ALLELUIA see Saint-Saens, Camille

ALLELUIA see Scandello

ALLELUIA see Schutz, Heinrich

ALLELUIA see Shilling, F.

ALLELUIA see Simpson

ALLELUIA see Stewart, Kensey D.

ALLELUIA see Sweeny, Jack

ALLELUIA see Tcherepnin, Alexander

ALLELUIA see Tellep, Leo M.

ALLELUIA see Tgettis, Nicholas

ALLELUIA see Thompson, Randall

ALLELUIA! see Todd, M. Flora

ALLELUIA see Vance, Margaret Shelley

ALLELUIA see Walton, Kenneth

ALLELUIA see Wellesz, Egon

ALLELUIA see Wienhorst, Richard

ALLELUIA see Williams

ALLELUIA see Young

ALLELUIA see Zaumeyer

ALLELUIA, A HOLY DAY see Santa Cruz, Domingo, Alleluia, Dies Sanctificatus

ALLELUIA, ALL GLORY BE TO GOD see Young

ALLELUIA, ALL THE EARTH DOTH WORSHIP THEE see Titcomb, Everett

ALLELUIA, ALLELUIA see Balogh, Louis L.

ALLELUIA, ALLELUIA see Bock, Fred

ALLELUIA, ALLELUIA see Boyce, William

ALLELUIA, ALLELUIA see Buxtehude, Dietrich

ALLELUIA, ALLELUIA see Cain, Noble

ALLELUIA, ALLELUIA see Giannini, Vincenzo

ALLELUIA!ALLELUIA! see Hopkins

ALLELUIA! ALLELUIA! see Kinsman

ALLELUIA! ALLELUIA! see Kopylov, Alexander Alexandrovitch

ALLELUIA, ALLELUIA see Pergolesi, Giovanni Battista

ALLELUIA! ALLELUIA! see Williams

ALLELUIA! ALLELUIA! HEARTS AND VOICES see Bellman

ALLELUIA, AMEN see Hokanson

ALLELUIA, AMEN see Leighton, Kenneth

ALLELUIA, AMEN see Wagner, Georg Gottfried

ALLELUIA, AMEN, AND CHORALE see Wagner, Georg Gottfried

ALLELUIA AND BENEDICTION see Evans

ALLELUIA AND HYMN see Palestrina, Giovanni

ALLELUIA AND VERSE *Easter
SATB&unis&cong oct SUMMY M 2845 $.25
contains: Diemente, Edward, Verse;
   Palestrina, Giovanni, Alleluia   (A522)

ALLELUIA! BEHOLD THE KING see Carnevali

ALLELUIA! CHILD JESUS see Grime, William

ALLELUIA CHOIR BOOK 1 see Hokanson

ALLELUIA! CHRIST HAS TRIUMPHED see Mueller, Carl F.

ALLELUIA, CHRIST IS BORN! see Clothier, Louita

ALLELUIA! CHRIST IS BORN see Porter

ALLELUIA! CHRIST IS BORN see Williams

ALLELUIA! CHRIST IS BORN see Young

ALLELUIA! CHRIST IS RISEN see Diemer, Emma Lou

ALLELUIA! CHRIST IS RISEN see Gillette

ALLELUIA, CHRIST IS RISEN see Jolley, Florence [W.]

ALLELUIA! CHRIST IS RISEN see Kopylov, Alexander Alexandrovitch

ALLELUIA, CHRIST IS RISEN see Lockwood, Normand

ALLELUIA, CHRIST IS RISEN! see Otis

ALLELUIA! CHRIST IS RISEN see Upshur

ALLELUIA! CHRIST IS RISEN see Young

ALLELUIA! CHRIST IS RISEN see Young, Gordon

ALLELUIA! CHRISTUS NATUS EST see Lo Presti

ALLELUIA, COME, GOOD PEOPLE see Davis, Katherine K.

ALLELUIA, DIES SANCTIFICATUS see Santa Cruz, Domingo

ALLELUIA FANFARE see Kennedy, John Brodbin

ALLELUIA FOR ST. FRANCIS see Binkerd, [Gordon]

ALLELUIA! FOR THE LORD, OUR GOD ALMIGHTY, NOW REIGNS see Goemanne, Noel

ALLELUIA! FREUET EUCH, IHR CHRISTEN see Hammerschmidt, Andreas

ALLELUIA, GLORIOUS IS THY NAME see Olson

ALLELUIA! GOD IS GONE UP WITH A MERRY NOISE see Reynolds, Gordon

ALLELUIA HAEC DIES see Donati, I.

ALLELUIA, HAEC DIES see Donati, Ignazio

ALLELUIA! HE AROSE see Judson

ALLELUIA! HE IS RISEN see Giasson

ALLELUIA! HEARTS AND VOICES see Pasquet, Jean

ALLELUIA, HEARTS AND VOICES HEAVENWARD RAISE see Blake, G.

ALLELUIA, HEARTS TO HEAVEN see Stanton, [Walter Kendall]

ALLELUIA, HODIE! see Young, Gordon

ALLELUIA! I BRING YOU GOOD TIDINGS see Goodman, Joseph

ALLELUIA, I HEARD A VOICE see Weelkes, Thomas

ALLELUIA! JESUS CHRIST IS BORN TODAY see Cooper, Irvin

ALLELUIA, JESUS LIVES see Lindeman

ALLELUIA! JESUS LIVES! see Smart, David

ALLELUIA! KING ETERNAL see Wesley

ALLELUIA! LET PRAISES RING! see Wolff, S. Drummond

ALLELUIA LET US SING see Alleluia Psallat

ALLELUIA, LORD GOD see Palestrina, Giovanni, Adoramus Te, Christe

ALLELUIA, MORN OF BEAUTY see Mueller, Carl F.

ALLELUIA! NOEL! see Ball, Albert C.

ALLELUIA! NOW IS THE CHRISTMAS MORN see Irvin

ALLELUIA! O COME, LET US SING see Titcomb

ALLELUIA! O PRAISE THE LORD MOST HOLY see Bach, Johann Sebastian

ALLELUIA! O PRAISE YE THE LORD see Bach

ALLELUIA! O REJOICE YE CHRISTIANS LOUDLY see Hammerschmidt, Andreas

ALLELUIA OF THE BELLS see Marryott, Ralph E.

ALLELUIA! OH, REJOICE YE CHRISTIANS LOUDLY see Hammerschmidt, Andreas

ALLELUIA OUR LORD HAS RISEN see Da Mantua, Alleluia, Surrexit, Dominus

ALLELUIA, PRAISE THE LORD see Kirk, Theron W.

ALLELUIA, PRAYER AND AMEN see Cappadonia

ALLELUIA, PRO VIRGINE MARIA see Aston, Peter

ALLELUIA, PRO VIRGINE MARIA see Davies, Peter Maxwell

ALLELUIA PSALLAT
see English Gothic Music
(Hughes; Grainger) "Alleluia Let Us Sing"
[Eng/Lat] 3pt wom cor/3pt men cor/6pt mix
cor,acap,inst/opt org oct SCHIRM.G 8898
$.20   (A523)

ALLELUIA PSALLAT see Anonymous

ALLELUIA, SING A NEW SONG see Gallus, Jacobus

ALLELUIA! SING HOSANNA! see Glarum, L. Stanley

ALLELUIA, SING NOEL see Templeton

ALLELUIA! SING PRAISE see Bach, Johann Sebastian

ALLELUIA, SING PRAISE TO THE LORD see Bach, Johann Sebastian

ALLELUIA, SING TO JESUS see Darst, W. Glenn

ALLELUIA, SING TO JESUS see Goemanne, Noel

ALLELUIA, SING TO JESUS see Hughes

ALLELUIA, SING TO JESUS! see Pritchard

ALLELUIA, SING TO JESUS see Shea

ALLELUIA, SONG OF GLADNESS *Easter/Lent
(Barthelson) SATB oct PRO ART 1886 $.25
    (A524)

ALLELUIA! SONG OF GLADNESS see Gauntlett, [Henry John]

ALLELUIA, SONG OF GLADNESS see Lundquist, Matthew Nathanael

ALLELUIA, SONG OF GLADNESS see Vick

ALLELUIA, SURRECIT DOMINUS see Jaquet Of Mantua

ALLELUIA, SURREXIT, DOMINUS see Da Mantua

ALLELUIA! THE DISCIPLES WITH WONDERING EYES see Byrd, William

ALLELUIA, THE LORD IS NOW ARISEN see Jaquet Of Mantua, Alleluia, Surrecit Dominus

ALLELUIA, THE LORD SAID UNTO ME see Goodman, Joseph

ALLELUIA! THE STRIFE IS O'ER see Palestrina, Giovanni

ALLELUIA THE STRIFE IS OVER see Palestrina, Giovanni

ALLELUIA TO OUR KING see Graham

ALLELUIA TO THE LORD OF BEING see Fast, Willard S.

ALLELUIA, TODAY IS CHRIST RISEN see Gallus, Jacobus

ALLELUIA! TULERUNT DOMINUM see Palestrina, Giovanni

ALLELUIA VENI SANCTE SPIRITUS see Dufay, Guillaume

ALLELUIA, WE PRAISE THE VIRGIN MARY see Aston, Peter, Alleluia, Pro Virgine Maria

ALLELUIA! WE SING WITH JOY see Gallus, Jacobus

ALLELUJA see Aichinger, Gregor

ALLELUJA! see Bach, Johann Sebastian

ALLELUJA see Koch, Karl

ALLELUJA see Lassus, Roland de (Orlandus)

ALLELUJA! see Mancini, Vincenzo

ALLELUJA see Mozart, Wolfgang Amadeus, Alleluia

ALLELUJA see Senfl, Ludwig

ALLELUJA, ALLELUJA see Buxtehude, Dietrich

ALLELUJA, CHRISTO E RISORTO see Picchi, Luigi

ALLELUJA, DER TOD IST VERSCHLUNGEN see Hanff, Johann Nicolaus

ALLELUJA FUR DIE WEIHNACHTSZEIT see Etti, Karl

ALLELUJA IST EIN FROHLICH GESANG see Grimm, Heinrich

ALLELUJA, LOBET DEN HERRN ALLE HEIDEN see Dedekind, Constantine Christian

ALLELUJA, MAN SINGET MIT FREUDEN VOM SIEG see Scheile, Johann Hermann

ALLELUJA-MELODIEN *CC24U
unis cmplt ed DOBLINGER s.p. contains works by: Bamer, A.; Dopf, H.; Haselbock, H.; Knotzinger, K. (A525)

ALLELUJA, MERK AUF, MEIN HERZ see Hammerschmidt, Andreas

ALLELUJA-PSALM I see Schieri, Fritz

ALLELUJA-PSALM II see Schieri, Fritz

ALLELUJA, SING PRAISES see Vecchi, Orazio

ALLELUJA UND PFINGSTSEQUENZ see Komma, Karl Michael

ALLELUJAH!
(Hallett) SATB,pno/org,hndbl WORD CS-2425 $.25 (A526)

ALLELUJAH see Purcell, Henry

ALLELUJAH, CHRIST IS RISEN see Dressler, Gallus

ALLELUJAH FESTIVAL ANTHEM see Nyvall, David Jr.

ALLELUYA, A NEW WORK see Wishart

ALLELUYA PSALLAT see Anonymous

ALLEN
Christ The Lord Is Risen Again *Easter/Lent
SATB GALLEON GCS2003 (A527)

Christmas Night *Xmas
SATB oct GALLEON GCS1011 (A528)

Far Judean Hills, The *Xmas
SATB oct GALLEON (A529)

Like A Mighty River
SAB SOUTHERN $.30 (A530)

Precious Lord, Take My Hand
(Ringwald) SATB SHAWNEE A 981 $.30 (A531)

ALLEN, CHESTER G.
Praise Him!
(Parker) TTBB,acap oct LAWSON 51296 $.30 (A532)

ALLEN, LANNY
He Lives Today!
SAB oct WORD CS-2563 $.35 (A533)

Like A Mighty River
SAB oct WORD CS-2550 $.35 (A534)

Since Jesus Came Into My Heart
SAB oct WORD CS-2521 $.30 (A535)

ALLENA GUD I HIMMELRIK *Bibl
(Schroter, Leonard) [Swed] SATB,acap GEHRMANS KRB 318 (A536)

ALLENA GUD I HIMMELRIK see Cruger, Johann

ALLENAST HOS GUD see Olson, Daniel

ALLENAST HOS GUD SOKER MIN SJAL SIN RO see Berg, Gottfrid

ALLER AUGEN WARTEN AUF DAS BROT VON DIR see Schlenker, Manfred

ALLER AUGEN WARTEN AUF DICH see Becker-Foss, Jurgen

ALLER AUGEN WARTEN AUF DICH see Grosse-Schware, Hermann

ALLER AUGEN WARTEN AUF DICH see Reda, Siegfried

ALLER AUGEN WARTEN AUF DICH see Schutz, Heinrich

ALLER AUGEN WARTEN AUF DICH, HERRE see Schutz, Heinrich

ALLER AUGEN WARTEN AUF DICH, HERRE see Stern, Hermann

ALLER AUGEN WARTEN, HERR see Bach, Johann Sebastian

ALLERSEELEN see Schieri, Fritz

ALLERSEELEN see Schubert, Franz (Peter)

ALLES FLEISCH IST GRAS see Brunner, Adolf

ALLES FLEISCH IST WIE GRAS see Callhoff, Herbert

ALLES GAB EUCH GOTT see Sturmer, Bruno

ALLES GEBEN DIE GOTTER see Beckerath, Alfred von

ALLES GROSSE MACHT STERBEN UND AUFERSTEHN see Gerhard, Fritz Christian

ALLES IST AN GOTTES SEGEN see Hiller, Johann Adam

ALLES IST AN GOTTES SEGEN see Mendelssohn, Arnold

ALLES IST EITEL see Rothenberg

ALLES NUR NACH GOTTES WILLEN see Bach, Johann Sebastian

ALLES OYNE YOKTER PA DEG see Schutz, Heinrich

ALLES STEHT IN GOTTES HAND see Weismann, Wilhelm

ALLES VERRINNT see Bresgen, Cesar

ALLES WAS IHR TUT see Brunner, Adolf

ALLES, WAS IHR TUT see Buxtehude, Dietrich

ALLES, WAS IHR TUT see Vogel, W.

ALLES, WAS IHR TUT MIT WORTEN see Dedekind, Constantine Christian

ALLES, WAS ODEM HAT, JAUCHZE DEM HERRN see Sweelinck, Jan Pieterszoon

ALLES, WAS ODEM HAT, LOBE DEN HERREN see Schutz, Heinrich

ALLES, WAS ODEM HAT, LOBE DEN HERRN see Etti, Karl

ALLES, WAS ODEM HAT, LOBE DEN HERRN see Schutz, Heinrich

ALLHELGONAMASSA see Hovland, Egil

ALLIED PRINCE, THE see Beethoven, Ludwig van

ALLITSEN
Lord Is My Light
(Howorth) SAB BOOSEY-CAN s.p. (A537)

Lord Is My Light, The
SATB oct LORENZ C116 $.30 (A538)
(Barthelson) SATB oct SPRATT 529 $.25 (A539)

Song Of Thanksgiving *Thanks
(Cain) SSA oct BOOSEY 1577 $.30 (A540)
(Hinkel) SSA oct VOLKWEIN VB259 $.25 (A541)
(Salter) SATB oct BOOSEY 1289 $.30 (A542)

ALLITSEN, FRANCES
Hymn Of Trust *hymn
2pt ENOCH T.P.35 s.p. (A543)

Lord Is My Light
(Cain) SSA oct BOOSEY 1759 $.35 (A544)
(Salter) SATB oct BOOSEY 1339 $.35 (A545)
(Samuelson) TTBB oct BOOSEY 1292 $.35 (A546)
(Samuelson) SSA oct BOOSEY 1470 $.30 (A547)

Lord Is My Light, The
(Stickles) 3pt mix cor oct SCHIRM.G 10287 $.35 (A548)
(Stickles) 4pt mix cor oct SCHIRM.G 10288 $.35 (A549)
(Stickles) 3pt wom cor oct SCHIRM.G 10286 $.35 (A550)
(Stickles) 4pt men cor oct SCHIRM.G 10311 $.35 (A551)
(Wright) SATB FLAMMER A 5049 $.30 (A552)
(Wright) SAB FLAMMER D5118 $.25 (A553)

ALLON, GAY BERGERES see Costeley, Guillaume

ALLONS ECOUTER L'AUBADE see Canteloube de Malaret, Marie-Joseph

ALLONS, GAY BERGERES see Costeley, Guillaume

ALLONS OUIR SUR NOS TETES see Maillard-Verger, P.

ALLONS PASTOUREAUX see Aubanel, Georges

ALLT UNDER HIMMELENS FASTE *folk
(Bruhn, O.) TTB NORDISKA 4842 s.p. (A554)

ALLT VADHELST I GOREN see Buxtehude, Dietrich, Alles Was Ihr Tut

ALMA DEI CREATORIA see Mozart, Wolfgang Amadeus

ALMA DEI CREATORIS see Mozart, Wolfgang Amadeus

ALMA REDEMPTORIS see Bottazzo, Luigi

ALMA REDEMPTORIS see Dunstable, John

ALMA REDEMPTORIS see Ravanello, Oreste

ALMA REDEMPTORIS see Thermignon

ALMA REDEMPTORIS see Victoria, Tomas Luis de

ALMA REDEMPTORIS MATER
see Musica Britannica Vol. 4: Set 1

ALMA REDEMPTORIS MATER see Bernabei, (Giuseppe) Ercole

ALMA REDEMPTORIS MATER see Davies, Peter Maxwell

ALMA REDEMPTORIS MATER see Dufay, Guillaume

ALMA REDEMPTORIS MATER see Ockeghem, Johannes

ALMA REDEMPTORIS MATER see Palestrina, Giovanni

ALMA REDEMPTORIS MATER see Philips, Peter

ALMA REDEMPTORIS MATER see Roger-Ducasse, Jean-Jules Aimable

ALME DEUS see Lassus, Roland de (Orlandus)

ALMIGHTY AND EVERLASTING GOD see Canavati

ALMIGHTY AND EVERLASTING GOD see Ford, Virgil T.

ALMIGHTY AND EVERLASTING GOD see Gibbons, Orlando

ALMIGHTY AND EVERLASTING GOD see Ramsey, Robert

ALMIGHTY AND EVERLASTING GOD see Roff, Joseph

ALMIGHTY AND EVERLASTING GOD see Tomkins, Thomas

ALMIGHTY AND EVERLASTING GOD see Young

ALMIGHTY AND MERCIFUL GOD see Goss, John

ALMIGHTY FATHER see Bernstein, Leonard

ALMIGHTY FATHER see Stradella, Alessandro

ALMIGHTY GOD see Ford

ALMIGHTY GOD see Pedrette

ALMIGHTY GOD, EVER BLESSED see Hopeson

ALMIGHTY GOD, GIVE US GRACE see Stucky, Steven

ALMIGHTY GOD IN TRINITY see Pasquet, Jean

ALMIGHTY GOD OF OUR FATHERS see James

ALMIGHTY GOD, OUR HEAVENLY FATHER see Saar, Louis Victor

ALMIGHTY GOD, THE FOUNTAIN OF ALL WISDOM see Tomkins, Thomas

ALMIGHTY GOD, THY WORD IS CAST see Cawood

ALMIGHTY GOD, THY WORD IS CAST see Wolff, S. Drummond

ALMIGHTY GOD, UNTO WHOM ALL HEARTS ARE OPEN see McAfee, Don

ALMIGHTY GOD, UNTO WHOM ALL HEARTS ARE OPEN see Pears, James R.

ALMIGHTY GOD, WE WORSHIP THEE see Kalinnikov, Vassili Sergeievitch

ALMIGHTY GOD, WHICH HAS ME BROUGHT see Ford, Thomas

ALMIGHTY GOD, WHICH HAST GIVEN see Gibbons, Orlando

ALMIGHTY GOD WHICH HAST ME BROUGHT see Ford, Thomas

ALMIGHTY GOD, WHO BY THE LEADING OF A STAR see Bull, John

ALMIGHTY GOD, WHO BY THY SON see Gibbons, Orlando

ALMIGHTY GOD, WHO HAST GIVEN US GRACE see Whittredge

ALMIGHTY GOD, WHO HAST ME BROUGHT see Ford

ALMIGHTY GOD, WHO HAST ME BROUGHT see Ford, Thomas

ALMIGHTY GOD, WHO HAST ME BROUGHT see Ford, Virgil T.

ALMIGHTY GOD, WHO HAST ME BROUGHT IN SAFETY see Ford

ALMIGHTY GOD, WHO HAST ME BROUGHT IN SAFETY see Ford, Thomas

ALMIGHTY GOD, WHO SAFELY LED US see Ford

ALMIGHTY GOD, WHOSE HAND CAN LEAD
(Roff) SATB oct VOLKWEIN VB104 $.30 (A555)

ALMIGHTY GOD, WHOSE LOVE PROFOUND see Swift

ALMIGHTY LORD see Giles, Nathaniel

ALMIGHTY LORD AND GOD OF LOVE *Gen
SATB,opt inst (easy) oct OXFORD 43.348 $.25
contains: This Is The Day; Giles, Nathaniel, Almighty Lord And God Of Love (A556)

ALMIGHTY LORD AND GOD OF LOVE see Giles, Nathaniel

ALMIGHTY, THE see Schubert, Franz (Peter)

ALMIGHTY WORD see Tallis, Thomas

ALMOST OVER see Kennedy, John Brodbin

ALONE see Moffatt

ALONE IN THE GARDEN see Wilson, Ira B.

ALONE THOU GOEST FORTH, O LORD see Boatwright, Howard

ALONG THE TRAIL *CCUL
(Barrows) SATB voc sc WORD 15017 $1.25 (A557)

ALOYSE, SR. M.
Come, Let Us Sing
SSA SHAWNEE B 305 $.30 (A558)

Shout Amen *CC4U,folk/hymn
unis&SA&SSA,gtr oct SUMMY M 2837 $.30 (A559)

ALS DER GUTIGE GOTT see Praetorius, Michael

ALS DORT DAS KIND ZU BETHLEHEM
see Weihnacht Ist Da

ALS DORT IN BETHLEHEM see Cadow, Paul

ALS GOD MIJN GOD VOOR MIJ IS
(Kuxhaven, J.) mix cor sc ALSBACH&D GEZ.201 s.p. (A560)

ALS ICH BEI MEIN SCHAFEN WACHT see Spitta, Heinrich

ALS ICH BEI MEINEN SCHAFEN WACHT' *Xmas,Aus, 17th cent
(Schemitsch, Hans) [Ger] mix cor,acap oct DOBLINGER s.p. see also Zehn Osterreichische Weihnachtslieder (A561)

ALS ICH BEI MEINEN SCHAFEN WACHT see Kern, Matthais

ALS ICH BEI MEINEN SCHAFEN WACHT see Neumeyer, Fritz

ALS JESUS NAHE HINZUKAM see Vulpius, Melchior

ALS JESUS VON SEINER MUTTER GING see Marx, Karl

ALS JESUS VON SEINER MUTTER GING see Rohwer, Jens

ALS UNSER HERR IN DEN GARTEN GING see Micheelsen, Hans Friedrich

ALSO AUCH SAGE ICH EUCH, WIRD FREUDE SEIN see Raselius, Andreas

ALSO HAT see Bach, Johann Sebastian, Also Hat Gott Die Welt Geliebt

ALSO HAT GOTT DIE WELT GELIEBET see Bach, Johann Sebastian

ALSO HAT GOTT DIE WELT GELIEBET see Distler, Hugo

ALSO HAT GOTT DIE WELT GELIEBET see Dressler, Gallus

ALSO HAT GOTT DIE WELT GELIEBET see Driessler, Johannes

ALSO HAT GOTT DIE WELT GELIEBET see Hufschmidt, Wolfgang

ALSO HAT GOTT DIE WELT GELIEBET see Rosenmuller, Johann

ALSO HAT GOTT DIE WELT GELIEBT see Bach, Johann Sebastian

ALSO HAT GOTT DIE WELT GELIEBT see Franck, Melchior

ALSO HAT GOTT DIE WELT GELIEBT see Knefelius, Johann

ALSO HAT GOTT DIE WELT GELIEBT see Kubizek, Augustinian

ALSO HAT GOTT DIE WELT GELIEBT see Linde, Gerhard

ALSO HAT GOTT DIE WELT GELIEBT see Praetorius, Heironymous

ALSO HAT GOTT DIE WELT GELIEBT see Raselius, Andreas

ALSO HAT GOTT DIE WELT GELIEBT see Schutz, Heinrich

ALSO HAT GOTT DIE WELT GELIEBT see Telemann, Georg Philipp

ALSO LIEBT GOTT DIE ARGE WELT see Schwartz, Gerhard von

ALSO WERDEN DIE LETZTEN DIE ERSTEN SEIN see Raselius, Andreas

ALSO WIRD EUCH MEIN HIMMELICHER VATER AUCH TUN see Driessler, Johannes

ALSO WIRD EUCH MEIN HIMMLISCHER VATER see Raselius, Andreas

ALSO WIRD EUCH MEIN HIMMLISCHER VATER see Vulpius, Melchior

ALT ER FERDIG see Vetter

ALT MORGENSTJERNEN ER OPRUNDEN see Praetorius, Michael

ALTA TRINITA BEATA *Trin,16th cent
   (Ramin, G.) SATB,acap cor pts BREITKOPF-L
   CHB-2833 s.p.   (A562)

ALTA TRINITA BEATA see Anonymous

ALTA TRINITA BEATA see Ramin, Gunther

ALTAR CHOIR BOOK see Peery, [Rob Roy]

ALTAR OF CHRISTMAS, THE see Fuller, [Esther Mary]

ALTAR OF GOD, THE see Bahmann, Marianne Eloise

ALTE ADVENTSLIEDER IN NEUEN SATZEN see Strohbach, Siegfried

ALTE CHORALWEISEN *CCU
   (Wieruszowski, L.) [Ger] mix cor,acap (med)
   HUG s.p.   (A563)

ALTE KANONS *CC40U,Gen,canon,16th cent/17th
   cent
   (Ameln, Konrad) [Ger] 1-7 eq voices,2inst
   (med easy) BAREN. BA 116 s.p. contains 5
   canons by Scheidt, S.   (A564)

ALTE MARIENLIEDER see Knab, Armin

ALTE WEIHNACHTSCHORALE UND KLEINE
   WEIHNACHTSMOTETTEN *CCU,Xmas,chorale/mot
   (Wagner, Hermann) mix cor MOSELER s.p. (A565)

ALTENBURG
   Three Intradas For Advent And Christmas
   *CC3U,Xmas
   [Ger] unis men cor,3vln,vla,2vcl/2bvl sc
   PETERS V82 $3.00, ipa, voc sc PETERS V82
   $.75, ipa   (A566)

ALTENBURG, MICHAEL (1584-1640)
   Drei Intraden *CC3U,Adv/Xmas
   (Egidi, A.) [Ger] men cor,brass,3vln,vla,
   bvl,2vcl VIEWEG sc s.p., voc sc s.p., ipa
                                          (A567)

   Herr Gott, Nun Schleuss Den Himmel Auf
   SSATB HANSSLER 6.136 s.p. contains also:
   Trubel, Gerhard, Wenn Mein Stundlein
   Vorhanden Ist (SAB/SAT)   (A568)

ALTENBURG, MICHAEL (cont'd.)
   Savior Of The Nations, Come *Adv/Xmas
   (Pizarro, D.) unis,org,2rec/2fl/2ob/2vln,
   vcl/bsn sc CONCORDIA 97-4847 $1.25, ipa,
   cor pts CONCORDIA 98-1926 $.10   (A569)

   Verzage Nicht, Du Hauflein Klein
   see Praetorius, Heironymous, O Herre Gott,
   Dein Gottlich Wort

ALTER
   Hodu
   (Barash) [Heb] cor,solo,org TRANSCON.
   TCL 673 $.75   (A570)

ALTER OF GOD see Watt

ALTES WEIHNACHTSLIED *folk,Aus
   (Tittel, Ernst) mix cor,acap oct DOBLINGER
   s.p. see from Geistliche Volkslieder Aus
   Osterreich   (A571)

ALTHOUGH YOU ARE SO TINY *Xmas,carol,Fr
   (Ehret) SATB oct LAWSON 51003 $.25   (A572)
   (Ehret) SA oct LAWSON 51230 $.25   (A573)
   (Ehret) SSA/SAA oct LAWSON 51231 $.25 (A574)
   (Ehret) 3pt mix cor oct LAWSON 51232 $.25
                                          (A575)

ALTMAN, LUDWIG
   Beloved Of The Lord, The *Bibl
   SATB,Bar solo,org oct LAWSON 51642 $.35
                                          (A576)

   Early Will I Seek Thee
   [Eng] SATB TRANSCON. TCL 146 $.25   (A577)

   Lift Up Your Heads *see S'u Sh'orim

   May The Words
   SATB TRANSCON. TCL 147 $.25   (A578)

   Psalm 13 *Bibl
   SATB,opt A solo,org oct LAWSON 51347 $.40
                                          (A579)

   Psalm 47 *Psalm
   [Eng] mix cor TRANSCON. TCL 614 $.50   (A580)

   Psalm 67
   mix cor,A solo,org TRANSCON. TCL 610 $.75
                                          (A581)

   Sabbath Music *Sab-Eve/Sab-Morn
   SATB TRANSCON. TCL 829 $2.50   (A582)

   S'u Sh'orim
   "Lift Up Your Heads" [Eng/Heb] SATB
   TRANSCON. TCL 148 $.25   (A583)

ALTMAN, S.
   Bim-Bam
   SATB,acap oct PRESSER MC227 $.30   (A584)

ALTNIEDERLANDISCHE MOTETTEN *Gen,mot
   (Besseler, Heinrich) [Ger] (med) BAREN.
   BA 267 s.p.
   contains: Compere, [Louis], O Vos Omnes
   (ATB,acap); Des Prez, Josquin, Benedicta
   Es (SATTBB,acap); Des Prez, Josquin, Tu
   Pauperum Refugium (STBB,acap); Ockeghem,
   Johannes, Alma Redemptoris Mater (STBB,
   acap)   (A585)

ALTNIKOL
   Befiehl Du Deine Wege *hymn
   (Frank) "To Him Who Never Faileth" SATB oct
   FOX MM3 $.30   (A586)

   To Him Who Never Faileth *see Befiehl Du
   Deine Wege

ALTNIKOL, JOHANN CHRISTOPH (1719-1759)
   Befiehl Du Deine Wege *mot
   (Schneider, M.) SATB,acap cor pts
   BREITKOPF-L PB-3922 s.p., voc pt
   BREITKOPF-L CHB-2788 s.p.   (A587)

   Nun Danket Alle Gott *mot
   5pt mix cor,acap cor pts BREITKOPF-L
   CHB-2922 s.p.   (A588)

ALTTIROLER WEIHNACHTSLIED *Xmas
   (Schmid, Reinhold) mix cor,acap oct DOBLINGER
   s.p. see from Zwei Alte Weihnachtslieder
                                          (A589)

ALVAREZ
   No Me Abandones, Plegaria A La Virgen
   unis UNION ESP. 3636 s.p.   (A590)

   Plegaria A La Virgen
   unis (texts in Catalan and Italian) UNION
   ESP. 3638 s.p.   (A591)

   Plegaria A La Virgen De Montserrat
   unis (texts in Castellano and Catalan)
   UNION ESP. 3909 s.p.   (A592)

ALVDALSPSALM *Psalm
   (Milveden, Ingmar) [Swed] SATB,acap GEHRMANS
   KRB 206   (A593)

ALVIN, ERIK
   Nu Stige Jublets Ton
   [Swed] SATB,acap GEHRMANS KRB 75   (A594)

   Nyarshymn
   [Swed] SATB,acap GEHRMANS KRB 76   (A595)

   Se, Guds Son Till Doden Skrider
   [Swed] SATB,acap GEHRMANS KRB 77   (A596)

AM ABEND ABER see Bach, Johann Sebastian, Am
   Abend Aber Desselbigen Sabbats

AM ABEND ABER DESSELBIGEN SABBATS see Bach,
   Johann Sebastian

AM ABEND ABER DESSELBIGEN SABBATS see Vulpius,
   Melchior

AM BERG HOCH DROBEN see Anonymous

AM FUNFUNDZWANZIGSTEN DEZEMBER *Span
   (Korda, Viktor) 2pt wom cor,acap oct s.p.
   contains also: Schlafe Mit Ruh (Aus)   (CC)
                                          (A597)

AM I A SOLDIER OF THE CROSS? see Thompson

AM I BORN TO DIE? see Clark, K.

AM JAHRESENDE see Schmid, Walter

AM LETZTEN TAGE DES JAHRES see Schieri, Fritz

AM MORGEN see Lassus, Roland de (Orlandus)

AM TRAUALTAR see Spahr, A.

AM WEIHNACHTSBAUM DIE LICHTER BRENNEN see
   Weber, Bernhard

AM WEIHNACHTSTAGE see Schieri, Fritz

AMATE see Keller, Wilhelm

AMATEUR CHOIR NO. 1 *CCU,anthem
   SATB LORENZ $1.95   (A598)

AMATEUR CHOIR NO. 2 *CCU,anthem
   SATB LORENZ $1.95   (A599)

AMATEUR CHOIR NO. 3 *CCU,anthem
   SATB LORENZ $1.95   (A600)

AMATEUR CHOIR NO. 4 *CCU,anthem
   SATB LORENZ $1.95   (A601)

AMATEUR CHOIR NO. 5 *CCU,anthem
   SATB LORENZ $1.95   (A602)

AMATEUR CHOIR NO. 6 *CCU,anthem
   SATB LORENZ $1.95   (A603)

AMATEUR CHOIR NO. 7 *CCU,anthem
   SATB LORENZ $1.75   (A604)

AMATUCCI, PAOLO
   Ave Maria *BVM
   [Lat] 2 eq voices,org ZANIBON 2645 s.p.
                                          (A605)

   Virgo Fidelis *Mass
   [Lat] TB,org sc ZANIBON 448 s.p., voc pt
   ZANIBON s.p.   (A606)

   Virgo Potens *Mass
   [Lat] ATB,org sc ZANIBON 1645 s.p., voc pt
   ZANIBON 1645A-B-C s.p.   (A607)

AMAZING GRACE *folk/hymn
   (Barthelson) SATB oct PRO ART 1853 $.30
                                          (A608)
   (Barthelson) SAB oct PRO ART 2203 $.30 (A609)
   (Barthelson) SSA oct PRO ART 2199 $.30 (A610)
   (Bock, Fred) SATB (easy) PRESSER G-195 $.35
                                          (A611)
   (Dexter) SATB HANSEN-US C542 $.40   (A612)
   (Edmundson) SA HANSEN-US C540 $.40   (A613)
   (Hafso) jr cor KJOS GC49 $.30   (A614)
   (Hughes, Robert J.) SATB ALLANS 427 s.p.
                                          (A615)
   (Leaman) 3pt HANSEN-US C541 $.40   (A616)
   (Shaw; Parker) mix cor,T solo,acap oct LAWSON
   918 $.30   (A617)
   (Staton) SAB SCHMITT 5534 $.35   (A618)

AMAZING GRACE see Bryan, Charles [Faulkner]

AMAZING GRACE see Coates, Eric

AMAZING GRACE see Dean, T.W.

AMAZING GRACE see Fox, Baynard

AMAZING GRACE see Hustad, Donald P.

AMAZING GRACE see Lynn, George

AMAZING GRACE see McAfee, Don

AMAZING GRACE! see Martin

AMAZING GRACE see Rogers

AMAZING GRACE see Wild, Eric

AMAZING WAS THE SIGHT see Nelson, Ronald A.

AMBROSE
   Come To My Heart, Lord Jesus *Xmas
   SATB oct LORENZ C185 $.30   (A619)
   SA/SAB oct LORENZ 7822 $.25   (A620)

   One Sweetly Solemn Thought
   (Townsend) SATB oct PRO ART 1342 $.20 (A621)

   (Townsend) SSA oct PRO ART 1517 $.16   (A622)

AMBROSE, [PAUL] (1868-1941)
   Come To My Heart, Lord Jesus
   SATB oct PRESSER 332-11408 $.30   (A623)
   (Manney, C.) SA oct PRESSER 332-14838 $.30
                                          (A624)

   Hark, Hark, My Soul *anthem
   SATB ALLANS 138 s.p.   (A625)

   O Come To My Heart, Lord Jesus *Xmas
   SATB oct PRESSER 332-11408 $.30   (A626)
   (Page, N.) SAB oct PRESSER 332-15209 $.30
                                          (A627)

   O Jesus, Thou Art Standing
   SATB ALLANS 81 s.p.   (A628)

   O Love That Will Not Let Me Go *anthem
   SATB ALLANS 86 s.p.   (A629)

   Oh, Come To My Heart, Lord Jesus
   SATB oct LILLENAS AN-2288 $.30   (A630)

   Praise Waiteth For Thee *anthem
   SATB,B solo ALLANS 90 s.p.   (A631)

AMBROSE, R.S.
   One Sweetly Solemn Thought *Bibl
   (Churchill) SATB oct PLYMOUTH CH-103 $.25
                                          (A632)
   (Spicker) 4pt mix cor oct SCHIRM.G 4285
   $.20   (A633)
   (Spicker) 2pt wom cor oct SCHIRM.G 5060
   $.20   (A634)

AMEN *CCUL
   (Carmichael, R.) SATB voc sc WORD 20019 $1.95
                                          (A635)

AMEN *spir
   (Luboff, Norman) SATB oct WALTON 3060 $.30
                                          (A636)

AMEN see Arnestad, Finn

AMEN see Balbo

AMEN see Brown, Charles F.

AMEN see Cherubini, Luigi

AMEN see Crawford, Joseph

AMEN see Grant

AMEN see Handel, George Frideric

AMEN see Joosen, B.

AMEN see Pergolesi, Giovanni Battista

AMEN see Ringwald, [Roy]

AMEN see Tgettis, Nicholas

AMEN see Tittel, Ernst

AMEN see Wilson, John F.

AMEN AND AMEN, ALLELUIA see Thompson, Randall

AMEN CHORUS see Buxtehude, Dietrich

AMEN CHORUS see Handel, George Frideric

AMEN, DAS IST: ES WERDE WAHR see Hassler, Hans
   Leo

AMEN, GOTT VATER UND SOHNE see Micheelsen, Hans
   Friedrich

AMEN, LAUD AND HONOR
   (Ehret) SAB SCHMITT 5542 $.45   (A637)

AMEN-SATZE see Micheelsen, Hans Friedrich

AMEN SO BE IT see Sleeth, Natalie

AMEN WIR FROHLICH SPRECHEN see Schein, Johann
   Hermann

AMENS AND RESPONSES see Filkins

AMENS AND RESPONSES see Matterling

AMENS AND RESPONSES FOR THE CHURCH CHOIR see
   Dieterich

AMERICA THE BEAUTIFUL see Ward

AMERICAN CHRISTMAS TRIPTYCH *Xmas,US
   (Terri) mix cor,acap oct LAWSON 837 $.30
                                              (A638)

AMERICAN DIALOGUE see Johnson, Roy E.

AMERICAN FOLK HYMNS FOR CHRISTMAS see Russell

AMERICAN FOLK HYMNS FOR JUNIOR CHOIR see
   Lovelace, Austin C.

AMERICAN JAZZ MASS see Tirro

AMERICANA COLLECTION *sac/sec,CC85L,Gen
   (Preuss, Theodore) SSA voc sc RUBANK $.50
                                              (A639)

AMERICANA COLLECTION *sac/sec,CC85L,Gen
   (Davis, Henry, W.) SATB voc sc RUBANK $.50
                                              (A640)

AMICA MEA see Steffans

AMICUS
   Our Lady's Song *Xmas,carol
      oct ROYAL 333 s.p.   (A641)

AMICUS MEUS see Ingegneri, Marco Antonio

AMICUS MEUS see Rubbra, Edmund

AMICUS MEUS see Victoria, Tomas Luis de

AMIDST US see Liljestrand, Paul

AMISH CAROL OF THE HILLS see Gaul, Alfred
   Robert

AMMANN, BENNO (1904-   )
   Boy Is Born, A *see Puer Natus Est

   Cinque Salmi *CC5U,Psalm
      [Eng/Ger] mix cor,acap oct ZERBONI 6269
      s.p.   (A642)

   Holy Trinity *see Sancta Trinitas

   O Selige Nacht
      see Schweizer Weihnachtslieder

   O, Wer Kann Dies Wunder Fassen
      see Schweizer Weihnachtslieder

   Puer Natus Est *Xmas
      mix cor SOUTHERN $.25   (A643)
      (Vene) "Boy Is Born, A" [Lat/Eng] SATB,acap
      oct COLOMBO 1855 $.20   (A644)

   Quatre Motets *CC4U,mot
      [Lat] mix cor,acap oct ZERBONI 5476 s.p.
                                              (A645)

   Reich Und Arm Soll Frohlich Sein
      see Schweizer Weihnachtslieder

   Sancta Trinitas
      (Vene) "Holy Trinity" [Eng/Lat] SATB,acap
      oct COLOMBO 1853 $.25   (A646)

   Schlafe, Gottlich Kind
      see Schweizer Weihnachtslieder

   Schweizer Weihnachtslieder *Xmas
      [Ger] mix cor,acap HUG s.p.
      contains: O Selige Nacht (easy); O, Wer
         Kann Dies Wunder Fassen; Reich Und Arm
         Soll Frohlich Sein; Schlafe, Gottlich
         Kind (easy)   (A647)

AMMON, BLASIUS (1558-1590)
   Ave Maria
      (Douglas) SATB,acap oct PRO ART 2280 $.20
                                              (A648)

   Confitemini Domino *Gen/Thanks
      SSAATTBB,acap voc pt DOBLINGER s.p. see
      also LOB UND DANK   (A649)

AMMON, BLASIUS (cont'd.)
   Grates Nunc Omnium *Adv/Xmas
      SATB,acap voc pt DOBLINGER s.p. see also
      ADVENT UND WEIHNACHT, HEFT 2   (A650)

   Spirit Of The Lord, The
      SSATB,acap oct LAWSON 51394 $.30   (A651)

AMNER
   Blessed Be The Lord God
      SATB SOUTHERN $.30   (A652)

   Christ Rising Again
      (Greening) SATB OXFORD   (A653)

   He That Descended
      (Greening) SATB,acap (med diff/diff)
      SOUTHERN $.45   (A654)

   O Ye Little Flock
      (Le Huray) SSAATB (med) OXFORD 42.887
      $1.10, ipr   (A655)

   Sweet Are The Thoughts *Gen
      (Carapetyan) SATB SCHMITT 1406 $.35   (A656)

AMNER, JOHN (1579-1641)
   Blessed Be The Lord God *anthem
      SATB,org/pno NOVELLO AP219 $.30   (A657)
      (Greening, Anthony) mix cor oct NOVELLO
      40.1521.05 s.p.   (A658)

   Christ Rising Again *anthem
      mix cor oct OXFORD 42.341 $.35   (A659)

   Come, Let's Rejoice *Gen,anthem
      mix cor oct OXFORD 42.365 $.45   (A660)
      (Carapetyan) SATB SCHMITT 1404 $.35   (A661)
      (Greening) SATB,acap (med diff/diff)
      SOUTHERN $.45   (A662)
      (Pilgrim) mix cor CURWEN 80833 s.p.   (A663)

   Consider, All Ye Passers By *Lent,anthem
      (Greening, Anthony) SAATB, countertenor-
      solo oct NOVELLO 88.0003.00 s.p.   (A664)

   He That Descended Man To Be *anthem
      mix cor oct OXFORD 43.475 $.45   (A665)

   Hear, O Lord (Psalm 30) Gen
      SSATB (med easy) oct OXFORD   (A666)

   I Will Sing Unto The Lord (Psalm 104) Gen/
      Thanks
      SSATB (med easy) oct OXFORD   (A667)

   Lord, I Am Not High Minded *anthem
      (Greening, Anthony) SAATB oct NOVELLO
      88.0004.09 s.p.   (A668)

   Love We In One Consenting
      SST/SSAT/SSTBar/SSATBar,acap (easy) oct
      OXFORD 43.935 $.25   (A669)

   Magnificat And Nunc Dimittis *Magnif/Nunc
      SSATB,opt inst (med easy) oct OXFORD 42.327
      $1.50   (A670)

   O Come Hither, And Hearken *anthem
      (Greening, Anthony) SSATB oct NOVELLO
      88.0002.02 s.p.   (A671)

   O Come Thou Spirit Divinest *Gen
      (Carapetyan) SAB SCHMITT 1407 $.30   (A672)

   O Sing Unto The Lord (Psalm 149) Fest/Gen/
      Thanks
      SSAATB,opt acap (med) oct OXFORD 43.951
      $1.20   (A673)

   Psalm 30 *see Hear, O Lord

   Psalm 104 *see I Will Sing Unto The Lord

   Psalm 149 *see O Sing Unto The Lord

   Sing, O Heavens *anthem
      mix cor oct OXFORD 43.463 $.35   (A674)

   Woe Is Me *anthem
      mix cor oct OXFORD 43.464 $.35   (A675)

AMO CHRISTUM see Arnaldi, Antonio

AMOR IM NACHEN see Gastoldi, Giovanni Giacomo

AMOR JESU see Schattenberg, Thomas

AMP CONTEMPORARY CHORAL COLLECTION, THE *sac/
   sec,CC26U,20th cent
   SATB AMP A642 $2.50   (A676)

AMPHION see Honegger, Arthur

AMRAM, DAVID WERNER (1930-   )
   By The Rivers Of Babylon
      SSAA,S solo,acap PETERS 6983 $.40   (A677)

   Friday Evening Service *see Shir L'Erev
      Shabbat

   Let Us Remember
      SATB,soli,pno PETERS 66053 rental   (A678)

   May The Words Of The Lord
      see Two Anthems

   Shir L'Erev Shabbat
      "Friday Evening Service" SATB,T solo,org/
      pno PETERS 6683 $3.50   (A679)

   Thou Shalt Love The Lord, Thy God
      see Two Anthems

   Two Anthems *anthem
      PETERS 6684A $.30
      contains: May The Words Of The Lord
         (SATB); Thou Shalt Love The Lord, Thy
         God (SATTBB)   (A680)

AN ANGEL SAID TO MARY see Makarov

AN DEINE LEIDEN DENKEN WIR see Hohlfeld,
   Christoph

AN DEN WASSERFLUSSEN ZU BABEL SASSEN WIR UND
   WEINETEN see Schutz, Heinrich

AN DEN WASSERN ZU BABEL see Thomas, Kurt

AN DIE HEILIGE JUNGFRAU see Keldorfer, Viktor

AN INFANT SWEET AND GENTLE *Xmas,Pol
   (Ehret, Walter) SAB,pno (med easy) PRESSER
   $.35   (A681)

AN SICH see Haller, Hermann

AN WASSERFLUSSEN BABYLON see Schein, Johann
   Hermann

AN WASSERFLUSSEN BABYLON see Wannenmacher,
   Johannes

ANA, D'
   Salvation's Author *see Sapientissimus
      Salutis Auctor

   Sapientissimus Salutis Auctor
      (Zanon; Vene) "Salvation's Author" [Lat/
      Eng] SATB,acap oct COLOMBO 1878 $.25
                                              (A682)

ANABASE see Blomdahl, Karl-Birger

ANABASIS see Hovhaness, Alan

ANBETUNG see Bruckner, Anton

ANBETUNG, EHRE, DANK UND RUHM SEI UNSERM see
   Goudimel, Claude

ANCIENT HILLS see Johansen

ANCIENT MORAVIAN CHRISTMAS CAROL see Gaul,
   Alfred Robert

ANCIENT OF DAYS see Powell

ANCIENT PRAYER see Lipscomb, Helen

ANCILLA see Aston, Hugo

ANCIS, SOLOMON
   Hashkivenu II
      [Heb] SATB,cantor TRANSCON. TCL 295 $.40
                                              (A683)

   He Who Blessed *see Mi Sheberach

   Himotze Lonu (from S'lichot)
      [Heb] TTBB TRANSCON. TCL 355 $.40   (A684)

   L'dor Vodor *Purim
      "To All Generations" [Heb] TTBB TRANSCON.
      TCL 356 $.30   (A685)

   Mi Sheberach *Purim
      "He Who Blessed" [Heb] TTBB TRANSCON.
      TCL 357 $.40   (A686)

   M'nuchon V'simchoh *Purim
      "Rest And Joy" [Heb] TTBB TRANSCON. TCL 358
      $.25   (A687)

   Pis-chu Li (Psalm 118) Purim
      [Heb] TTBB TRANSCON. TCL 351 $.25   (A688)

   Psalm 118 *see Pis-chu Li

   Rest And Joy *see M'nuchon V'simchoh

   To All Generations *see L'dor Vodor

   Umipney Chatoeynu
      [Heb] TTBB TRANSCON. TCL 354 $.50   (A689)

   V'shom'ru
      [Heb] 4pt mix cor,acap oct SCHIRM.G 7588
      $.25   (A690)

AND ALL IN THE MORNING
   (Vaughn Williams, Ralph) SATB/unis,pno GALAXY
   s.p. see also Eight Traditional Carols
                                              (A691)

AND ALL THE BELLS ON EARTH DID RING see Fried

AND ALL THE HILLS ECHOED see Beglarian

AND AS THEY CAME DOWN FROM THE MOUNTAIN see
   Hovhaness, Alan

AND CAN IT BE? see Lynn, George

AND DID THOSE FEET IN ANCIENT TIME see
   Chorbajian, John

AND DIDST THOU LOVE THE RACE see Brown, A.G.Y.

AND GOD SAID, LET THE EARTH see Simper, Caleb

AND GOD SHALL WIPE AWAY ALL TEARS see Coombs,
   Charles Whitney

AND HAVE NOT CHARITY see Malotte, Albert Hay

AND HE NEVER SAID A MUMBLIN' WORD *spir
   SATB KJOS 502 $.30   (A692)
   (Meyerowitz) SATB,acap MARKS 101 $.25   (A693)

AND HE NEVER SAID A MUMBLIN' WORD see
   Meyerowitz, Jan

AND HE SHALL PURIFY see Handel, George Frideric

AND HE SHEWED ME A PURE RIVER see Dalby, Martin

AND HIS NAME WAS CALLED JESUS see Hulse, Camil
   Van

AND I HAVE PEACE WITHIN see Caldwell, Mary
   [Elizabeth]

AND I SAW A NEW HEAVEN see Aston, Peter

AND I SAW A NEW HEAVEN see Bainton, Edgar
   Leslie

AND I SAW ANOTHER ANGEL see Stanford

AND I SAW ANOTHER ANGEL see Stanford, Charles
   Villiers

AND I WILL BETROTH YOU TO ME see Steinberg,
   Ben, V'erastich Li

AND I WILL EXALT HIM see Handel, George
   Frideric

AND IN THAT DAY see Beck

AND IT SHALL COME TO PASS see Berger, Jean

AND JESUS INCREASED IN WISDOM see Hahn, Harvey

AND LO, THE STAR see Pezel, Johann Christoph

AND MARY SAID TO THE ANGEL see Hassler, Hans
Leo, Dixit Maria

AND NOBODY KNOW see Graham

AND NOW ANOTHER DAY IS GONE see Bishop, Jeffrey

AND NOW ANOTHER DAY IS GONE see Blake, Leonard

AND NOW THE LORD TO REST IS LAID see Bach,
Johann Sebastian

AND ON EARTH PEACE *Xmas,cant
   mix cor CHAPPELL 0014324-369 $1.00   (A694)

AND PEACE SHALL REIGN AGAIN see Mabry

AND SING NOWELL TONIGHT *Xmas
   (Nyquist) SATB oct PRO ART 1898 $.22   (A695)

AND SO IT WAS see Rocherolle

AND TAKE HEED TO YOURSELVES see Schutz,
Heinrich

AND THE ANGEL CAME IN UNTO MARY see Kellam

AND THE BEST IS LOVE see Proulx, Richard

AND THE CHILD GREW see Thompson, Randall

AND THE GLORY OF THE LORD see Handel, George
Frideric

AND THE GLORY OF THE LORD see Krone

AND THE INN WAS FULL see Williams

AND THE KING WAS GREATLY MOVED see Deering,
Richard, Contristatus Est Rex David

AND THE KING WAS MOVED see Deering, Richard

AND THE LORD APPEARED TO SOLOMON see Young

AND THE RANSOMED OF THE LORD SHALL RETURN see
Franck, Melchior, Die Erloeseten Des Herrn
Werden Wiederkommen

AND THE SKY NEVER SAW THE MORNING see Martin

AND THE TREES DO MOAN see Gaul, Harvey Bartlet

AND THE WATERS KEEP ON RUNNING THROUGH MY MIND
see Temple, S.

AND THE WORD BECAME FLESH see Zimmermann, Heinz
Werner

AND THE WORD WAS MADE FLESH see Hassler, Hans
Leo

AND THEN SHALL THE LIGHT see Mendelssohn-
Bartholdy, Felix

AND THEN SHALL YOUR LIGHT see Mendelssohn-
Bartholdy, Felix

AND THEN SHALL YOUR LIGHT BREAK FORTH see
Mendelssohn-Bartholdy, Felix

AND THERE SHALL COME FORTH A ROD see Roff,
Joseph

AND THERE WERE SHEPHERDS see Garner

AND THERE WERE SHEPHERDS see Noyes, Charles F.

AND THERE WERE SHEPHERDS see Wilson, Ira B.

AND THERE WILL BE SIGNS see Bender, Jan

AND THEY FELL DOWN AND WORSHIPPED HIM see
Newbury, Kent A.

AND THOU SHALT LOVE see Diercks, John H.

AND THOU SHALT LOVE THE LORD see Gerschefski,
Edwin

AND WHEN THE BUILDERS see Rubbra, Edmund

AND WITH HIS STRIPES see Handel, George
Frideric

AND WITH SONGS I WILL CELEBRATE see Marcello,
Benedetto

AND YOU, O BETHLEHEM see Hillert, Richard

ANDACHT ZUM TODE see Lahusen, Christian

ANDALUSIAN CAROL *Xmas,carol/folk,Span
   (Nienow, Elaine) SAB,pno oct WORLD AC-1711-7
   $.30   (A696)

ANDE, FULL AV NADE *Bibl
   (Olson, Daniel) [Swed] SAB,acap GEHRMANS
   KRB 115   (A697)

ANDE, FULL AV NADE see Berg, Gottfrid

ANDERLUH, ANTON
   Das Gruass Die Got'!
   [Ger] mix cor,acap KRENN 82 s.p.   (A698)

ANDERS, CHARLES
   God Is For Us A Refuge And Strength (Psalm
   46) anthem
   unis&cong (easy) oct AUGSBURG 0630 $.40
                                          (A699)

   O Lord, Support Us *anthem
   SATB (easy) oct AUGSBURG 1514 $.25   (A700)

   Psalm 46 *see God Is For Us A Refuge And
   Strength

   Psalm 119 *see They Are Happy Whose Life Is
   Blameless

ANDERS, CHARLES (cont'd.)
   They Are Happy Whose Life Is Blameless (Psalm
   119) anthem
   unis&cong (easy) oct AUGSBURG 0635 $.30
                                          (A701)

ANDERSEN
   Psalm 103 *Gen
   SATB SCHMITT 1714 $.18   (A702)

ANDERSEN, KARL
   Lullaby For Mary's Son *Xmas
   SSA SCHMITT 320 $.35   (A703)
   SATB SCHMITT 839 $.30   (A704)

ANDERSON
   Beatitudes, The
   SATB THOMP.G G-585 s.p.   (A705)

   Come, I Pray Thee
   SATB oct BELWIN 60628 $.25   (A706)

   In Excelsis *CCU
   SA WARNER $1.00   (A707)

   Lullaby Of The Little Angels
   SSA THOMP.G E.I.1003 s.p.   (A708)

   Softly, Softly Fell The Snow *Xmas
   SSA SCHMITT 2568 $.35   (A709)

ANDERSON, BECKY
   Children's Choir Favorites *CCU
   jr cor oct AGAPE $1.25   (A710)

ANDERSON, MARION
   Dancing Carol, A
   see Three For Christmas

   Mary Sang To Her Baby
   see Three For Christmas

   Three For Christmas *Xmas
   cor CRAMER s.p.
      contains: Dancing Carol, A; Mary Sang To
      Her Baby; Wooden Toys   (A711)

   Wooden Toys
   see Three For Christmas

ANDERSON, R.
   Lord's Prayer, The
   (Heller, A.) SATB oct PRESSER 312-40748
   $.30   (A712)

ANDERSON, ROBERT
   Hodie, Christus Natus Est *Xmas
   [Lat] SATB,acap oct LAWSON 51568 $.35
                                          (A713)

ANDERSON, RUTH
   Holly Carol, The *Xmas
   4pt mix cor,acap oct SCHIRM.G 10824 $.20
                                          (A714)

   Passiontide Carol *Easter
   4pt mix cor,acap oct SCHIRM.G 10811 $.20
                                          (A715)

ANDERSON, [WILLIAM H.]
   Ane Song Of The Birth Of Christ (And Joy
   Fills Our Inmost Heart To-Day)
   SATB oct LESLIE 4034   (A716)

   As I Walked In Bethlehem *Xmas
   SATB oct LESLIE 4057   (A717)

   As Mary Sings *Xmas
   SSA oct LESLIE 3036   (A718)

   Birth Night, The *Xmas
   SA oct LESLIE 1008   (A719)

   Born Of Marie *Xmas
   SATB oct LESLIE 4011   (A720)

   Carol Of Ye Angels *Xmas,carol
   SA oct LESLIE 2012   (A721)

   Children's Friend, The
   SSA oct LESLIE 3007   (A722)

   Child's Prayer, A *prayer
   unis oct LESLIE 1006   (A723)

   Christmas Gifts *Xmas
   SSA oct LESLIE 3022   (A724)

   Christmas Questionings *Xmas
   SATB oct LESLIE 4018   (A725)

   Come, I Pray Thee
   SATB oct LESLIE 4007   (A726)

   Eventide *Eve,Introit
   SATB oct LESLIE 4051 see from Five Introits
   And Vespers   (A727)

   Five Introits And Vespers *see Eventide;
   Lord Is In His Holy Temple, The; O Thou
   That Hearest Prayer; Offering; Our Day Of
   Praise Is Done; Vesper   (A728)

   Give Ear To My Words, O Lord
   SATB oct LESLIE 4035   (A729)

   Long, Long Ago *Xmas
   SSA oct LESLIE 3020   (A730)
   unis oct LESLIE 1030   (A731)

   Lord Is In His Holy Temple, The *Eve,Introit
   SATB oct LESLIE 4051 see from Five Introits
   And Vespers   (A732)

   Lullaby Of The Little Angels
   SSA THOMP.G s.p.   (A733)

   Lullay, My Liking *Xmas
   SSAA oct LESLIE 3030   (A734)

   Mary *Xmas
   SSA oct LESLIE 3042   (A735)
   unis oct LESLIE 1110   (A736)

   O, Brother Man
   (Whittier, J.) SATB,acap oct PRESSER
   312-40067 $.25   (A737)

   O For A Closer Walk With God
   (Mueller) SABar,med solo oct SCHIRM.G 8688
   $.25   (A738)

ANDERSON, [WILLIAM H.] (cont'd.)
   O Thou That Hearest Prayer *Eve,Introit
   SATB oct LESLIE 4051 see from Five Introits
   And Vespers   (A739)

   Offering *Eve,Introit
   SATB oct LESLIE 4051 see from Five Introits
   And Vespers   (A740)

   Our Day Of Praise Is Done *Eve,Introit
   SATB oct LESLIE 4051 see from Five Introits
   And Vespers   (A741)

   Sleep Little Jesus *Xmas
   SSA oct LESLIE 3004   (A742)
   unis (D maj) oct LESLIE 1011   (A743)
   unis (E flat maj) oct LESLIE 1010   (A744)

   'Twas In The Silent Night He Came *Xmas
   unis oct LESLIE 1069   (A745)

   Vesper *Eve,Introit
   SATB oct LESLIE 4051 see from Five Introits
   And Vespers   (A746)

   White Dove, The
   SSA oct LESLIE 3015   (A747)

ANDERSSON, KARL-ERIC
   Du Goda Mane *folk,Ger
   wom cor/jr cor s.p. cor pts NORDISKA 3507,
   voc sc NORDISKA 3175   (A748)

ANDERTON
   How Beautiful Upon The Mountains (from Zion)
   (Fearis) SAT,pno (med) oct WILLIS 6318 $.20
                                          (A749)

ANDREAS, CAROLUS
   Magnificat And Nunc Dimittis *Magnif/Nunc
   oct ROYAL 118 s.p.   (A750)

ANDREP-NORDIN, BIRGER
   Uppstandelsen
   [Swed] SATB&2pt jr cor,org GEHRMANS KRB 153
                                          (A751)

ANDRES
   Christus Factus Est Pro Nobis
   (Zanon; Vene) "Jesus Obedient" SATB,acap
   oct COLOMBO 1850 $.25   (A752)

   Jesus Obedient *see Christus Factus Est Pro
   Nobis

   Missa Brevis *Mass
   cor HANSSLER 27.003 s.p.   (A753)

ANDREW, ISAAC
   Daughter Of Moab *cant/ora
   (easy) oct HART s.p.   (A754)

ANDREWS, C.T.
   Before Dawn
   SATB,acap (easy) OXFORD 42.012 $.25   (A755)

   Earth Feared, The *see Terra Tremuit

   Hail Mary *ASD/BVM,anthem
   SATB (easy) oct GIA G1351 $.25   (A756)
   STB (easy) oct GIA G1353 $.25   (A757)
   SA/TB (easy) oct GIA G1352 $.25   (A758)

   Heavens Rejoiced, The *Xmas,anthem
   SATB (easy) oct GIA G1503 $.25   (A759)
   SA/TB (easy) oct GIA G1500 $.25   (A760)

   Mass Of The Holy Child: Sleep, Holy Babe
   *Xmas/Gen,carol,Mass
   SATB/unis (easy) voc sc GIA G1585 $1.00
                                          (A761)

   New Mass For Congregations, A *Gen,Mass
   unis,kbd (easy) voc sc GIA G1544 $1.25
                                          (A762)
   SATB (easy) voc sc GIA G1571 $1.00   (A763)

   O Glorious Night *see Von Himmel Hoch

   Prayer *Gen,anthem/prayer
   2 eq voices (easy) oct GIA G1536 $.25 (A764)

   Regina Coeli *Easter,anthem
   "Rejoice, O Queen Of Heaven" [Eng/Lat] 2pt
   (easy) oct GIA G1537 $.25   (A765)

   Rejoice, O Queen Of Heaven *see Regina Coeli

   Terra Tremuit *Easter,anthem
   "Earth Feared, The" [Eng/Lat] 2pt (easy)
   oct GIA G1538 $.25   (A766)

   This Was The Day When Christ Was Born *Xmas,
   anthem
   SATB (easy) oct GIA G1491 $.30   (A767)
   SA/TB (easy) oct GIA G1490 $.25   (A768)

   Von Himmel Hoch *Xmas,anthem
   "O Glorious Night" SATB (med) oct GIA G1602
   $.35   (A769)

ANDREWS, H.K.
   O Sing The Glories Of Our Lord *Fest/Harv
   SATB (easy) oct OXFORD 42.987 $.35   (A770)

   Spacious Firmament On High, The *Gen
   SATB/SAB (easy) oct OXFORD 42.802 $.35 (A771)

ANDREWS, HAROLD
   When The Herds Were Watching
   jr cor LEONARD-ENG 35 s.p.   (A772)

ANDREWS, MARK (1875-1939)
   Build Thee More Stately Mansions
   4pt mix cor,Bar solo oct SCHIRM.G 6862 $.30
                                          (A773)
   (Downing) 3pt mix cor oct SCHIRM.G 9548
   $.30   (A774)
   (Downing) 3pt wom cor oct SCHIRM.G 9547
   $.25   (A775)

   Lauda Anima *Bibl
   "Praise, My Soul" [Eng] 4pt mix cor oct
   SCHIRM.G 7406 $.25   (A776)
   (Sacco) "Praise, My Soul" 3pt mix cor,org
   oct SCHIRM.G 10635 $.25   (A777)

   Lord Of All Being
   SATB oct GRAY GCMR 424 $.30   (A778)

ANDREWS, MARK (cont'd.)

Praise, My Soul *see Lauda Anima

Shadows Of Thy Wings
SATB oct GRAY GCMR 264 $.25 (A779)

ANDRIESSEN, HENDRIK (1892-1964)
Christus Stervende
men cor ALSBACH&D sc s.p., cor pts s.p.
(A780)

Driekoningenlied *Xmas
mix cor ALSBACH&D sc s.p., cor pts s.p.
(A781)

Magnificat *Magnif
[Lat/Eng] SATB,org SCHIRM.EC 2288 $.50
(A782)
[Lat] mix cor,org BANK (A783)

O Lord, With Wondrous Mystery *Commun
SATB,org oct WORLD ESA-204-8 $.30 (A784)
3 eq voices,org oct WORLD $.30 (A785)
2 eq voices,opt org oct WORLD ESA-205-2
$.30 (A786)

Psalm 9
[Dut] mix cor,T solo,pno,3fl,2ob,2clar,
2bsn,4trp,4horn,3trom,tuba,strings,perc,
timp DONEMUS min sc s.p., cor pts s.p.
(A787)

Qui Habitat *mot
mix cor ALSBACH&D sc s.p., cor pts s.p.
(A788)

Te Deum Laudamus *Te Deum
[Lat] mix cor,3fl,2ob,2clar,2bsn,3trp,
4horn,3trom,tuba,strings,timp min sc
DONEMUS s.p., cor pts ROSSUM s.p., voc sc
ROSSUM s.p. (A789)
[Lat] mix cor,org ROSSUM (A790)

Te Deum Laudamus II
[Lat] mix cor,3fl,2ob,2clar,2bsn,3trp,
4horn,3trom,tuba,strings,timp DONEMUS min
sc s.p., cor pts s.p. (A791)

Veni Creator
[Lat] mix cor,3fl,2ob,2clar,2bsn,3trp,
4horn,3trom,tuba,strings,perc,harp
DONEMUS min sc s.p., cor pts s.p. (A792)
[Lat] mix cor,org DONEMUS sc s.p., cor pts
s.p. (A793)

ANDRIESSEN, JURIAAN (1925-   )
Magnificat *Magnif
[Lat] mix cor,S solo,2fl,2ob,2clar,2bsn,
3trp,4horn,3trom,tuba,strings,timp
DONEMUS min sc s.p., cor pts s.p. (A794)

Sequentia Veni Sancte Spiritus
[Lat] wom cor,SB soli,org sc DONEMUS s.p.
(A795)

ANDRIESSEN, N.H.
Psalm 84
men cor ALSBACH&D sc s.p., cor pts s.p.
(A796)

ANDRISELLI, OTTAVIO EUGENIO
Te Deum *Greg/Te Deum
[Lat] 3pt mix cor/4pt mix cor,org sc
ZANIBON 2432 s.p., cor pts ZANIBON 2433
s.p. (A797)

ANDROZZO
If I Can Help Somebody
(Ehret) SSA/SSAA oct MCA (A798)
(Ehret) SATB oct MCA (A799)
(Ehret) TTBB oct MCA (A800)

ANE SONG OF THE BIRTH OF CHRIST (AND JOY FILLS
OUR INMOST HEART TO-DAY) see Anderson,
[William H.]

ANERIO, FELICE (ca. 1560-1614)
Angel Of The Lord Descended, The *see
Angelus Autem Domini

Angelus Autem, Domini *Easter
[Lat] SATB,acap (med easy) MULLER MS 40
s.p. (A801)
"Angel Of The Lord Descended, The" SATB,
acap SCHIRM.EC 1244 $.25 (A802)

Christus Factus Est *Xmas/Commun/Easter/
Holywk/Lent/Psntd,anthem
mix cor sc ALSBACH&D s.p. (A803)
[Lat] SATB,acap (med) MULLER MS72 s.p.
(A804)
SATB,acap oct PRESSER 312-40175 $.30 (A805)
"Jesus Once For Our Salvation" SATB oct
GRAY GCMR 3094 $.30 (A806)
"Jesus Once For Our Salvation" SATB,acap
SCHIRM.EC 349 $.30 (A807)
"Jesus, Once For Our Salvation" [Eng/Lat]
mix cor oct NOVELLO 40.0735.02 s.p.
(A808)
(Davison, A.) [Lat] TTBB,acap SCHIRM.EC 922
$.16 (A809)
(Hines) "Jesus, Who For Our Salvation"
[Eng/Lat] 4pt mix cor,acap oct SCHIRM.G
11866 $.25 (A810)
(Marshall, Charles) "Jesus, Once For Our
Salvation" SATB FRANK F-580 $.35 (A811)
(Richardson) "Jesus Christ For Our
Salvation" SATB oct SPRATT 2011 $.25
(A812)

Christus Factus Est Pro Nobis
SATB,acap RICORDI-ENG SY197 s.p. (A813)

Crux Fidelis *Easter/Lent
(Martens, Mason) "Faithful Cross" SATB oct
WALTON 2090 $.25 (A814)

Earth Feared, The
see FOUR SHORT ANTHEMS FOR LENT AND EASTER

Ego Dixi *mot
[Lat] mix cor,acap oct NOVELLO DM-35 s.p.
(A815)

Ego Dixi: Domine Miserere Mei *Gen
[Lat] SATB,acap (med diff) MULLER M 35 s.p.
(A816)

Faithful Cross *see Crux Fidelis

Hor Le Tue Forze Adopra *Mass
(Bauerle, H.) SATB,acap cor pts BREITKOPF-L
PB-3393 s.p., voc pt BREITKOPF-L CHB-2771
s.p. (A817)

ANERIO, FELICE (cont'd.)
Jesus Christ For Our Salvation *see Christus
Factus Est

Jesus, Once For Our Salvation *see Christus
Factus Est

Jesus, Who For Our Salvation *see Christus
Factus Est

Kristus Ble For Skyld Lydig
(Nielsen, Ludvig) [Norw] SATB LYCHE 54 s.p.
(A818)

O Blessed Jesus *see O Bone Jesu

O Bone Jesu *Easter/Lent
(Marshall, Charles) "O Blessed Jesus" SATB
FRANK F-602 $.30 (A819)

O Salutaris Hostia
(Ruiz) [Lat] SATB,soli RICORDI-ARG s.p.
(A820)

Sicut Cedrus
see Anerio, Felice, Vidi Speciosam
see Anerio, Felice, Vidi Speciosam

Twenty-Two Canzonettes *CC22U
4pt mix cor,acap sc HINRICHSEN N4790 s.p.
(A821)

Vidi Speciosam *BVM/Fest,mot
[Lat] SATB,acap (med) MULLER M 48 s.p.
contains also: Sicut Cedrus (A822)
[Lat] mix cor,acap oct NOVELLO DM-48 s.p.
contains also: Sicut Cedrus (A823)

ANERIO, GIOVANNI FRANCESCO (1567-1630)
Adoremus Te
(Greyson) "We Adore Thee" SATB oct BOURNE
ES112 $.30 (A824)

All Hail, Star Of The Sea *see Ave Maris
Stella

Ave Maris Stella *mot
[Lat] dbl cor,narrator,acap oct GIA G557
$.25 (A825)
(Greyson) "All Hail, Star Of The Sea" SATB
oct BOURNE ES55 $.25 (A826)

Cantate Domino *Bibl
(Stephens) "O Sing Unto The Lord" [Eng/Lat]
4pt mix cor,acap oct SCHIRM.G 11273 $.35
(A827)

Christus Factus Est *Easter/Psntd,mot
SATB,acap voc pt DOBLINGER s.p. see also
PASSION UND OSTERN (A828)
(Collins, B.C.) [Lat] SATB CHESTER s.p.
(A829)

Jesus, Once For Salvation
(Marshall) mix cor SOUTHERN $.35 (A830)

Kristus Blev For Var Skull Lydig
mix cor NORDISKA 2739 s.p. (A831)

Missa Brevis *Mass
(Bauerle, H.) SATB,acap cor pts BREITKOPF-L
PB-3394 s.p., voc pt BREITKOPF-L CHB-2772
s.p. (A832)

Missa Pro Defunctis, Cum Sequentia Et
Responsorio Libera Me *Mass/Req
(Petti, Anthony G.) [Lat] SATB,opt org
CHESTER s.p. (A833)

O Jesu Mi Dulcissime
(Vene) "O Jesu, Name Most Sweet" [Lat/Eng]
SSA,acap oct COLOMBO 2183 $.20 (A834)

O Jesu, Name Most Sweet *see O Jesu Mi
Dulcissime

O Sing Unto The Lord *see Cantate Domino

We Adore Thee *see Adoremus Te

ANGEL
Cradle Song *cradle
SA (easy) OXFORD 44.105 $.25 (A835)

ANGEL AND THE SHEPHERDS, THE see Trusler, Ivan

ANGEL AND THE STRANGER, THE see Anne, Freda

ANGEL BAND, THE see Bampton, R.

ANGEL BAND, THE see Page, R.

ANGEL BANDS see Saint-Saens, Camille, Ave Verum
Corpus

ANGEL CHOIRS ON HIGH DO SING see Bedell,
[Robert Leech]

ANGEL FROM HEAVEN see Bragg

ANGEL GABRIEL see Diemer, Emma Lou

ANGEL GABRIEL FROM GOD, THE
(Oxley) unis&desc (very easy) OXFORD 81.107
$.30 (A836)
(Oxley) unis/SATB (very easy) OXFORD 08.037
$.15 (A837)

ANGEL GABRIEL, THE
(Vaughn Williams, Ralph) SATB/unis,pno GALAXY
s.p. see also Twelve Traditional Carols
From Herefordshire (A838)

ANGEL HOSTS DECLARE, THE see Monteverdi,
Claudio, Angelus Ad Pastores Ait

ANGEL OF TEARS see Ozolins, V.

ANGEL OF THE LORD, AN see Sterne, Colin

ANGEL OF THE LORD DESCENDED, THE see Anerio,
Felice, Angelus Autem Domini

ANGEL OF THE LORD, THE see Roff, Joseph

ANGEL ROLLED THE STONE AWAY, THE see Boatner,
[Edward H.]

ANGEL SAID TO MARY, AN see Makarov

ANGEL SAID UNTO THE SHEPHERDS, THE see Hassler,
Hans Leo, Angelus Ad Pastores

ANGEL SONGS AND THE STAR see Davison, John

ANGEL, THE see Rubinstein, Anton, Engel, Der

ANGEL TO THE SHEPHERDS see Topff, J.

ANGEL TO THE SHEPHERDS, THE see Goodale, R.L.

ANGEL VOICES EVER SINGING *carol,Fr
SATB,acap SCHIRM.EC 2270 $.18 (A839)

ANGEL VOICES EVER SINGING see Bortniansky,
Dimitri Stepanovitch

ANGEL VOICES EVER SINGING see Hall, E. Vine

ANGEL-VOICES EVER SINGING see Rapley

ANGELI, ARCHANGELI see Gabrieli, Andrea

ANGELI E PASTORI see De Luca, Alessandro

ANGELIC GREETING, THE see Brahms, Johannes, Der
Engelische Gruss

ANGELICAL SALUTATION "HAIL MARY" see Humpherys,
Henry

ANGELINI, LUCIO
La Messa Dei Giovani *see Vianello, Lino

ANGELIS SUIS DEUS see Fux, Johann Joseph

ANGELIS SUIS MANDAVIT see Cardoso, Manuel

ANGELL
Children Of God
(Graff) SATB oct PRO ART 1984 $.25 (A840)

Christmas Means Thinking Of Jesus *Xmas
(O'Hara) SATB oct FISCHER,C SIG. $.25
(A841)

Earth Is The Lord's, The (Psalm 24) Bibl
SATB oct PRO ART 1968 $.25 (A842)
SAB oct PRO ART 2370 $.30 (A843)
SSA oct PRO ART 2545 $.30 (A844)

I Will Extol Thee
SATB oct FISCHER,C SIG. $.25 (A845)

Jesus Name Of Wondrous Love
SATB oct FISCHER,C R-6049 $.25 (A846)
SA oct FISCHER,C R-43 $.35 (A847)
SAB oct FISCHER,C R-6059 $.25 (A848)
SSAA oct FISCHER,C R-42 $.25 (A849)

Mary Had A Baby *Xmas
SATB oct FISCHER,C SIG. $.25 (A850)

Pilgrim's Song Of Thanksgiving *Thanks
SATB oct FISCHER,C CM-7533 $.30 (A851)

Praise To The Lord The Almighty
(Cooper) SATB oct FISCHER,C R-6048 $.25 (A852)

Psalm 24 *see Earth Is The Lord's, The

This Is The Day *anthem
(Cooper) SATB oct FISCHER,C CM-7107 $.25
(A853)

Thy Name We Praise *anthem
SATB oct FISCHER,C CC-141 $.25 (A854)

ANGELL, WARREN M. (1907-   )
All Glory, Laud And Honor *Easter/Lent
SATB oct WALTON 2027 $.25 (A855)

Be Thou Exalted, O My God
SATB SHAWNEE A 703 $.30 (A856)

Brotherhood Of Man
SATB,opt brass&perc oct BOURNE A2 $.25, ipa
(A857)

Christmas Roundelay *Xmas
2pt jr cor FISCHER,C SIG $.18 (A858)

Glorious Things Of Thee Are Spoken
4pt jr cor/SATB (very easy) FISCHER,C SIG
$.25 (A859)
mix cor,pno/org oct FISCHER,C SIG. 151 $.25
(A860)

God's Moments
4pt mix cor oct SCHIRM.G 10881 $.25 (A861)

How Excellent Is Thy Name
SATB SHAWNEE A 701 $.30 (A862)

I Lift Up My Eyes To The Hills
4pt jr cor/SATB (very easy) FISCHER,C SIG
$.22 (A863)

I Will Lift Up Mine Eyes
unis jr cor FISCHER,C SIG. $.25 (A864)

Jesus, Name Of Wondrous Love
3pt jr cor/SAB (easy) FISCHER,C R 6059 $.22
(A865)
2pt jr cor FISCHER,C R 43 $.25 (A866)

Jesus Stand Among Us
3pt jr cor/SAB (very easy) FISCHER,C R 6075
$.22 (A867)

Love Divine
SATB SHAWNEE A 419 $.25 (A868)

O Be Joyful
SATB SHAWNEE A 561 $.30 (A869)

O Day Of Resurrection *Easter/Lent
SATB oct WALTON 2026 $.25 (A870)

O Sing A New Song
SATB SHAWNEE A 485 $.30 (A871)

Our God Is One God
SATB SHAWNEE A 795 $.30 (A872)

Ye Servants Of God
SATB oct PLYMOUTH HA-2 $.25 (A873)

ANGELORUM ESCA see Faccin, Gian Domenico

ANGELS AND SHEPHERDS *Xmas,Boh
(Dickinson, C.) SATB oct GRAY GSC 111 $.25
(A874)

ANGEL'S AND SHEPHERD'S SONG, THE see It Came
Upon The Midnight Clear

ANGELS AND THE SHEPHERDS see Kodaly, Zoltan

ANGELS AND THE SHEPHERDS, THE *Xmas
see Three Old Bohemian Christmas Carols
(Trevor) SATB,acap (easy) OXFORD 84.078 $.20
(A875)
(Trevor) SA/SSA,acap (easy) OXFORD 83.049
$.20
(A876)

ANGELS AND THE SHEPHERDS, THE see Kodaly,
Zoltan, Angyalok Es Pasztorok

ANGELS ARE BRIGHT AND FAIR see Handel, George
Frideric

ANGELS ARE FLYING, THE see Goodale, R.L.

ANGELS ARE SINGING *Xmas
(Coggin) SATB oct PRO ART 2686 $.30　　(A877)

ANGELS ARE SINGING see Coggin

ANGELS ARE SINGING see Langstroth, Ivan Shed

ANGELS ARE STOOPING, THE see Besly, Maurice

ANGELS CAME CAROLING see Walton

ANGEL'S CAROL, THE see Pennell

ANGEL'S CAROL, THE see Billings, William

ANGEL'S CHORUS see Jenkins, Cyril

ANGELS, EVER BRIGHT AND FAIR see Handel, George
Frideric

ANGELS FROM THE REALM OF GLORY see Praetorius,
Michael

ANGELS FROM THE REALMS *Xmas,carol,Ger
(Van Koert, Han) SA&SATB,Mez/Bar solo,org oct
WORLD AC-592-8 $.30　　(A878)

ANGELS FROM THE REALMS OF GLORY *Xmas,carol/
folk,Fr
unis/SATB (very easy) OXFORD 08.118 $.15
(A879)
oct HART s.p.　　(A880)
(Davies, L.H.) 2pt jr cor/2pt wom cor CURWEN
72661 s.p.　　(A881)
(Trant) SSAA,acap (easy) OXFORD 83.070 $.25
contains also: First Nowell, The　　(A882)

ANGELS FROM THE REALMS OF GLORY see Bliss, Paul

ANGELS FROM THE REALMS OF GLORY see Burroughs,
Bob

ANGELS FROM THE REALMS OF GLORY see Gardner

ANGELS FROM THE REALMS OF GLORY see Maunder,
J.H.

ANGELS FROM THE REALMS OF GLORY see Montgomery

ANGELS FROM THE REALMS OF GLORY see Roberts, J.

ANGELS FROM THE REALMS OF GLORY see Smart

ANGELS FROM THE REALMS OF GLORY see Smart,
Henry Thomas

ANGELS GUARD THEE see Godard, Benjamin Louis
Paul

ANGELS HIGH AND HOLY see Pyle, Francis
[Johnson]

ANGELS HIGH AND LOWLY see Gore, Richard T.

ANGELS HOLY, HIGH AND LOVELY see Thiman, Eric
Harding

ANGELS HOLY, HIGH AND LOWLY see Brandon, George

ANGELS, HOLY, HIGH AND LOWLY see Thiman, Eric
Harding

ANGELS HOVERED 'ROUND *Xmas,carol,Fr
(Christiansen, P.) SATB SCHMITT 900 $.35
(A883)

ANGELS IN HEAVEN *Xmas,carol,Hung
(Gordon) SATB oct SHAPIRO SK 2003 $.25 (A884)
(Gordon) SAB oct SHAPIRO SK 5001 $.25 (A885)
(Gordon) SSA oct SHAPIRO SK 3001 $.25 (A886)
(Gordon) 2pt oct SHAPIRO SK 4001 $.25 (A887)
(Gordon, Phillip) SATB voc sc WEINBERGER s.p.
(A888)
(Gordon, Phillip) SAB voc sc WEINBERGER s.p.
(A889)
(Gordon, Phillip) SA voc sc WEINBERGER s.p.
(A890)

ANGELS IN THE SKIES ARE SINGING see Catterick,
J.

ANGELS LULLABY *Xmas,carol,Fr
2pt ENOCH TP164 s.p. contains also: Heavenly
Bud　　(A891)

ANGEL'S MESSAGE, THE see Gevaert, Francois
Auguste, Le Message Des Anges

ANGEL'S MESSAGE, THE see Kuehnhausen, J.G.

ANGELS O'ER THE FIELDS see Les Anges Dans Nos
Campagnes

ANGELS O'ER THE FIELDS WERE FLYING see Les
Anges Dans Nos Campagnes

ANGELS OF THE CROWN see Roff, Joseph

ANGELS, ROLL THE ROCK AWAY see Darst, W. Glenn

ANGELS ROLL THE ROCK AWAY see Newton

ANGELS, ROLL THE ROCK AWAY see Scott, John
Prindle

ANGELS, ROLL THE ROCK AWAY see Willan, Healey

ANGELS, ROLL THE STONE AWAY see Whitney, M.

ANGELS ROLLED DE STONE AWAY see Hairston,
Jester

ANGELS ROLLED THE STONE AWAY see Anonymous

ANGELS SANG IT THEN see Nelson, Ronald A.

ANGELS SANG THAT CHRISTMAS MORN see Cockshott,
Gerald Wilfred

ANGELS SING ON HIGH *Xmas,carol,Pol
(Kropczynski, Thaddeus) SATB oct WALTON 2039
$.25　　(A892)

ANGEL'S SONG, THE see Baynon, Arthur

ANGEL'S SONG, THE *Xmas,carol,Fr
(Grieb) 4pt mix cor oct SCHIRM.G 10930 $.30
(A893)

ANGELS' SONG, THE see Johnson

ANGELS' SONG, THE see Pasquet, Jean

ANGEL'S SONG, THE see Stickles, William

ANGELS' SONG, THE see Tchesnokov, Pavel
Grigorievitch

ANGEL'S SONG, THE see Tschesnokoff, P.I.

ANGEL'S SONG, THE (SCHOOL SONG) see Bollinger,
A.E.

ANGELS SPIRITS OF SLEEP see Willan, Healey

ANGELS, THEN TO THE SHEPHERDS SAYING see
Hassler, Hans Leo, Angelus Ad Pastores Ait

ANGELS TO THE SHEPHERDS SAY see Kozinski,
[David B.]

ANGELS TO THE SHEPHERDS, THE see Topff, J.

ANGELS WE HAVE HEARD ON HIGH see Freed

ANGELS WE HAVE HEARD ON HIGH see Les Anges Dans
Nos Campagnes

ANGELS WE HAVE HEARD ON HIGH see Markworth,
Henry

ANGELS WERE WATCHING *Xmas/Pageant
LORENZ $.75　　(A894)

ANGELUS see Chaminade, Cecile

ANGELUS AD PASTORES see Gabrieli, Giovanni

ANGELUS AD PASTORES see Hassler, Hans Leo

ANGELUS AD PASTORES see Vulpius, Melchior

ANGELUS AD PASTORES AIT see Franck, Cesar

ANGELUS AD PASTORES AIT see Gabrieli, Giovanni

ANGELUS AD PASTORES AIT see Hassler, Hans Leo

ANGELUS AD PASTORES AIT see Lassus, Roland de
(Orlandus)

ANGELUS AD PASTORES AIT see Monteverdi, Claudio

ANGELUS AD PASTORES AIT see Scheidt, Samuel

ANGELUS AD PASTORES AIT see Sweelinck, Jan
Pieterszoon

ANGELUS AD PASTORES AIT see Zangius, Nikolaus

ANGELUS AD VIRGINEM (from Anthology Of Carols,
An) carol,14th cent
see English Gothic Music
see Cherry Tree Carol, The
unis/SATB (easy) OXFORD 08.050 $.15　　(A895)
"Quoth An Angel" [Lat/Eng] SSA,acap oct
COLOMBO 2184 $.25　　(A896)
(Leppard, Raymond) 3 eq voices oct FABER
F0101 $.35　　(A897)

ANGELUS AD VIRGINEM see Spencer, Williametta

ANGELUS AUTEM DOMINI see Anerio, Felice

ANGELUS DOMINI see Verdelot, Phillippe

ANGELUS ET PASTORES AIT see Soderholm, Valdemar

ANGELUS PASTORIBUS see Magri, Pietro

ANGELUS SUIS MANDAVIT see Cardoso, Manuel

ANGELUS, THE see Kammenoi

ANGER, ERHARD (1928-   )
Wo Willst Du Hin Weils Abend Ist　*Gen,mot
[Ger] SATB,acap (med easy) DEUTSCHER
DV 7622 s.p.　　(A898)
[Ger] 4pt mix cor oct DEUTSCHER 7622 $.90
(A899)

ANGERRI
O Crucis Victoria　*Easter,Mass
dbl cor voc sc UNION ESP. 18063 s.p., cor
pts UNION ESP. 18063-B s.p.　　(A900)

ANGLARNA OCH HERDARNA see Runback, Albert

D'ANGLEBERT, JEAN-HENRI (1628-1691)
Kyrie　*Kyrie
[Lat] 4pt mix cor HEUGEL s.p. see from LA
MAITRISE　　(A901)
[Lat] 4pt mix cor,opt pno/org HEUGEL s.p.
(A902)

ANGLICAN FOLK MASS see Shaw, Martin

ANGLICAN FOLK MASS, AN see Shaw, Martin

ANGLICAN FOLK MASS, SERIES 3 see Shaw, Martin

ANGYALOK ES PASZTOROK see Kodaly, Zoltan

ANIMA CHRISTI see Gerald, T.J.

ANIMA CHRISTI see Roff, Joseph

ANIMA CHRISTI see Vranken, Alph.

ANIMAL'S CAROL, THE see Dunhill, Thomas
Frederick

ANIMALS CHRISTMAS CAROL, THE see Grime, William

ANIMALS' CHRISTMAS ORATORIO, THE see Bacon,
Ernst

ANIMALS OF CHRISTMAS, THE see Fargo

ANIMALS OF CHRISTMAS, THE see Wilson

ANIMAM MEAM DILECTAM see Victoria, Tomas Luis
de

ANIMUCCIA, GIOVANNI (ca. 1514-1571)
Ben Venga Amore
(Schinelli, A.) [It/Eng/Ger] 4pt mix cor
CURCI 6494 s.p. see also Collana Di
Composizioni Polifoniche Vocali Sacre E
Profane, Vol. 1　　(A903)
Collana Di Composizioni Polifoniche Vocali
Sacre E Profane, Vol. 1 *see Ben Venga
Amore　　(A904)
Kyrie (from Messa Ave Maris Stella) Kyrie
4pt mix cor SANTIS 1013 s.p.　　(A905)
Missarum Liber Primus　*CCU,Mass
(Dart, Thurston) 4-6pt fac ed GREGG s.p.
(A906)
Misse Ave Maris Stella　*Mass
(Somma, B.) 4pt mix cor voc sc SANTIS 570 s.p.,
cor pts SANTIS 570A-B s.p.　　(A907)

ANKUNFT DES HERRN see Baumann, Max

ANKUNFT DES HERRN see Baumann, Max

ANMUT SPARET NICHT NOCH MUHE see Spies, Leo

ANNE, FREDA
Angel And The Stranger, The　*carol
SATB PROWSE s.p.　　(A908)
TTBB PROWSE s.p.　　(A909)

ANNOINTING OF SOLOMON, THE see Whitmer, Thomas
Carl

ANNONCIATION see Lesur, Daniel

ANNUCIATION, THE see Schutz, Heinrich

ANNUNCIATE GENTES see Carissimi, Giacomo

ANNUNCIATE GENTES see Carissimi, Giacomo

ANNUNCIATION see Brahms, Johannes

ANNUNCIATION see Pfautsch, Lloyd

ANNUNCIATION, THE see Warren, Raymond

ANNUNCIATION ACCORDING TO ST. LUKE, THE see
Schutz, Heinrich, Lukaspassion

ANNUNCIATION CAROL see Rodgers, John

ANNUNCIATION CAROL see Thiman, Eric Harding

ANNUNCIATION CAROL, THE see Thiman, Eric
Harding

ANNUNCIATION, THE see Christiansen, Paul

ANNUNCIATION, THE see Morales, Cristobal de,
Missas Est Gabriel

ANNUNCIATO CONCEPTIONIS
(Paget, Michael) SATB,acap LENGNICK s.p.
(A910)

ANNUNTIO VOBIS see Moioli, Romano

ANOINTING OF SOLOMON, THE see Whitmer, Thomas
Carl

ANONYMOUS
Acclamations　*see Christus Vincit

Ach Lieber Herre Jesu Christ　*see Wir Danken
Dir, Herr Jesu Christ

Adeste Fideles　*Xmas,carol
(Burroughs, Bob) "O Come, All Ye Faithful"
SSAB (easy) oct AGAPE A 416 $.30　　(A911)
(Novello, V.) "O Come All Ye Faithful"
[Lat] SATB oct JUSKO 181 $.25　　(A912)

All Praise To Thee, Eternal God
(Lundquist) SATB,acap (med) oct WILLIS 8465
$.25　　(A913)

Alleluia Psallat
see Three Early Liturgical Settings

Alleluya Psallat　*mot
(Stevens, Denis) [Lat] SSS/TTT/STT oct
NOVELLO 40.1463.04 s.p.　　(A914)

Alta Trinita Beata
see Bach, Johann Sebastian, Gloria Sei Dir
Gesungen
see Victoria, Tomas Luis de, Hosianna,
Davids Sohn, Lob Sei Dem

Am Berg Hoch Droben　*19th cent
(Lehner, Walter) mix cor,acap oct DOBLINGER
s.p.　　(A915)

Angels Rolled The Stone Away　*Easter
(Hustad, Don) SATB oct AGAPE HO 1803 $.30
(A916)

Ave Maria　*BVM,mot
[Lat] 4pt mix cor oct DURAND s.p.　　(A917)

Ave Maris Stella　*Fest
[Ger] SATB,acap (med easy) MULLER MS 16
s.p.　　(A918)

Ay, Santa Maria　*16th cent
(Kaplan, A.) [Span/Eng] SATB/SAB BROUDE,A.
142 $.30　　(A919)

Beautiful Saviour, (Old Crusaders Hymn)
(Treharne) 3pt wom cor,acap (med) oct
WILLIS 6240 $.16　　(A920)

Carol Of The Birds　*carol/folk
TTBB,acap (med) oct WILLIS 4971 $.15 (A921)

ANONYMOUS (cont'd.)

Carol Of The Nuns (from Chester Mystery Plays) Xmas,carol
(Sellew, D.E.) SATB,S solo,acap (med) oct WILLIS 6161 $.10 (A922)

Carol Of The Shepherds, The *Xmas,carol,Fr
(Allen) SATB oct GALLEON GCS1015 (A923)

Carol Of The Stable *Xmas,carol,It
(Ehret) SATB WARNER WB-139 $.30 (A924)

Ceska Polyfonni Tvorba *CC19L,mot,16-17th cent
(Snizkova, J.) [Czech] cor SUPRAPHON s.p. (A925)

Charge To Keep I Have, A *hymn,US
(Barnes, E.S.) SA,pno (easy) oct WILLIS 6125 $.12 (A926)

Children's Carols For All Occasions *sac/sec,CCU,Xmas/Easter/Epiph/Gen,carol
(Marzo, E.) unis&opt SA,pno (easy) oct WILLIS $.50 (A927)

Christians, Sing Alleluia *Easter,16th cent
(Candlyn) SAB WARNER W3732 $.30 (A928)
(Candlyn) SATB WARNER W3660 $.30 (A929)

Christians, To The Paschal Victim *Easter
unis,kbd (med easy) oct CONCORDIA 98-1812 $.25 contains also: Hassler, Hans Leo, Christ Is Arisen (SATB,kbd) (A930)

Christum Wir Sollen Loben Schon *Xmas
[Ger] SATB,acap (med easy) MULLER K 13 s.p. (A931)

Christus Vincit
"Acclamations" [Lat] ST.MARTIN voc sc s.p., cor pts s.p. (A932)

Collana Di Composizioni Polifoniche Vocali Sacre E Profane, Vol. 1 *see Intorno Al Fanciullin Gesu (A933)

Come Rejoicing, Faithful Men *Greg
(Lundquist) SATB&boy cor (med) oct WILLIS 8462 $.25 (A934)

Coventry Carol *carol/hymn
(Terry) SATB oct ST.MARTIN s.p. (A935)

Danket Dem Herrn, Denn Er Ist Freundlich *Thanks,mot
(Mall) SATB HANSSLER 1.226 s.p. (A936)

Der Tag, Der Ist So Freudenreich *Adv/Xmas
ATB,acap voc pt DOBLINGER s.p. see also ADVENT UND WEIHNACHT, HEFT 2 (A937)

Die Glashutter Passion
(Sachsens; Steude) [Ger] 5pt mix cor,soli, cont voc sc DEUTSCHER 7903 s.p. (A938)

Dies Ist Der Tag, Den Der Herr Macht *Bibl/mot
(Mall) SATB HANSSLER 1.121 s.p. (A939)

Dona Nobis Pacem
see THREE FAMOUS CANONS

Drei Weihnachts-Magnificat *CC3U,Xmas,Magnif
(Kirsch) [Ger/Lat] 4pt mix cor MOSELER s.p. (A940)

Drei Weihnachtsleider *see Es Ist Ein Ros' Entsprungen; Es Steht Ein Lind; In Dulci Jubilo (A941)

Du Hast, O Jesulein, Kein Bett Und Keine Wiegen *Xmas,18th cent
4pt mix cor MOSELER LB-346 s.p. (A942)

Es Ist Ein Ros' Entsprungen *Xmas,16th cent
(Kramer, Gerhard) mix cor,acap oct DOBLINGER s.p. see from Drei Weihnachtsleider (A943)

Es Steht Ein Lind *Xmas,15th cent
(Kramer, Gerhard) mix cor,acap oct DOBLINGER s.p. see from Drei Weihnachtsleider (A944)

Fairest Child Of Fairest Mother
(Young, Carlton R.) unis oct AGAPE AG 7130 $.30 (A945)

Fear Born Of The Evils Of Human Life *see Przestrach Na Zte Sprawy Ludzkiego Zywota

Glad Dig O Kristenhet
wom cor/jr cor NORDISKA 1692 s.p. (A946)

Glorious Things Of Thee Are Spoken (from Austria hymn tune) hymn
(Surant, C.) SATB&opt unis,opt S/A solo, pno/org (med) oct WILLIS 6262 $.16 (A947)

Gott, Der Heilige Geist *mot
(Hellmann) SATB HANSSLER 1.095 s.p. (A948)

Her, Da Du Vormals Hast Dein Land
see Frank, Michael, Ach Wie Fluchtig, Ach Wie Nichtig

Herr, Bleibe Bei Uns
see Bach, Johann Sebastian, Der Lieben Sonne Licht Und Pracht

Herr Gott, Dich Loben Alle Wir
see Hassler, Hans Leo, Aus Tiefer Not Schrei Ich Zu Dir

Herr Jesu Christ, Dich Zu Uns Wend
see Neander, Joachim, Gott Ist Gegenwartig, Lasset Uns

Herr, Unser Herrscher, Wie Herrlich *mot
(Mall) SATB HANSSLER 1.227 s.p. (A949)

Holy God, We Praise Thy Name
(Mytych) SAB oct JUSKO 108 $.20 (A950)

Il Est Ne Le Divin Enfant
(Brun, L'abbe F.) [Fr] 4pt mix cor,solo oct DURAND (A951)

In Dulci Jubilo *Xmas,14th cent
(Kramer, Gerhard) mix cor,acap oct DOBLINGER s.p. see from Drei Weihnachtsleider (A952)

In Gottes Namen Fahren Wir *Gen,mot
(Gutmann, Peter) [Ger] SSSAATBB (med) BAREN. BA 2917 $1.00 (A953)

In The Midst Of Earthly Life *16th cent
(Hirsch, C.) SSAATTBB,acap (med) oct WILLIS 6175 $.10 (A954)

Intorno Al Fanciullin Gesu *16th cent
(Schinelli, A.) [It/Eng/Ger] 3 eq voices CURCI 6086 s.p. see also Collana Di Composizioni Polifoniche Vocali Sacre E Profane, Vol. 1 (A955)

It's Up To You And Me
(Rodby, Walter) SATB oct AGAPE BR 2004 $.40 (A956)

Jauchzet, Ihr Himmel *Gen
[Ger] SATB,cont (med easy) MULLER MS 50 s.p. (A957)

Jesus Christ Is Risen Today *Easter,carol/Greg
(Lundquist) SATB,acap oct WILLIS 8464 $.25 (A958)

Jesus Is A Wonderful Saviour
see TEMPO CHORAL PACKAGE NO. 2

Jesus Is Our Joy, Our Treasure *Easter/Gen
SATB,acap (med easy) oct CONCORDIA 98-1071 $.25 (A959)

Johannespassion 1534 *Psntd
(Attaignant, Pierre; Schmidt-Mannheim, H.) SATB HANSSLER 2.021 s.p. (A960)

Komm, Herr Jesu, Sei Du Unser Gast
see Schutz, Heinrich, Aller Augen Warten Auf Dich

Kyrie
see Three Early Liturgical Settings

Lasst Uns Das Kindelein Wiegen
see Praetorius, Michael, Der Spiegel Der Dreifaltigkeit

Le Messie Est Ne *Xmas,carol
4pt mix cor,acap oct DURAND s.p. (A961)

Les Anges Dans Nos Campagnes
(Brun, L'abbe F.) [Fr] 4pt mix cor,solo oct DURAND s.p. (A962)

Libera Me *Gen,mot,16th cent
[Lat] 4pt mix cor,org oct DURAND s.p. (A963)

Litanies De La Sainte Vierge *CCU,BVM,Greg/mot
[Lat] cor,Mez solo oct DURAND s.p. (A964)

Lob, Preis Und Dank Sei Dir *Xmas
SATB HANSSLER 6.2663 s.p. contains also: Erythraus, Gotthard, Verleih Uns Frieden Gnadiglich; Bach, Johann Sebastian, Helft Mir, Gott's Gute Preisen (from Gottlob! Nun Geht Das Jahr Zu Ende) (A965)

Lobe Den Herrn, Meine Seele *Thanks,mot
(Horn) SATB HANSSLER 1.317 s.p. (A966)

Lobet Den Herrn, Alle Heiden *mot
(Mall) SATB HANSSLER 1.228 s.p. (A967)

Magnificat (from Fourteen Ancient Fauxbourdons)
mix cor NORDISKA 4897 s.p. (A968)

Mass In Honor Of The Blessed Virgin Mary (from Codex Las Huelgas) BVM,Mass
(Stevens) [Lat] ATB,ATB soli,org/opt inst AMP N22 $.50 (A969)

Messa Vergine E Madre *Mass,14th cent
(Argenti, G.; Beltrame, T.) [It] unis/dbl cor,solo sc ZANIBON 4881 s.p., cor pts ZANIBON 4882 s.p. (A970)

Never Alone
see TEMPO CHORAL PACKAGE NO. 1

Nun Komm, Der Heiden Heiland *Adv
[Ger] SATBB,acap (med easy) MULLER K 12 s.p. (A971)

O Bone Jesu *mot,Eng,16th cent
(Collins, H.B.) [Lat] TTBarB/AABarB CHESTER s.p. (A972)

O Come All Ye Faithful *see Adeste Fideles

O Crux Benedictus *mot
[Lat] SATTBB,acap MUSICUS 1033 $.15 (A973)

O Little Town Of Bethlehem *Xmas,carol
(Bliss, P.) 3pt wom cor,pno (med) oct WILLIS 1760 $.16 (A974)

O Lord, The Maker Of All Thing *Eve,16th cent
SATB,acap (easy) oct OXFORD 43.250 (A975)

O Salutaris *Commun,mot,15th cent
(Kunc, P.) [Lat] 4pt/4pt mix cor oct DURAND s.p. (A976)

Of The Father's Love Begotten
(Wohlgemuth, Paul) SATB oct AGAPE A 454 $.30 (A977)

Praise And Prayer *CCU
SATB&mix cor oct FOX $1.50 (A978)

Przestrach Na Zte Sprawy Ludzkiego Zywota *Pol,16th cent
"Fear Born Of The Evils Of Human Life" mix cor,acap POLSKIE s.p. (A979)

Psalm 118 *see This Is The Day

ANONYMOUS (cont'd.)

Quarante Noels Anciens *CC40L,Xmas,carol
(Roques, L.) [Fr] 1-2pt,pno/org oct DURAND s.p. (A980)

Regina Caeli *mot,16th cent
[Lat] STTB,acap MUSICUS 1029 $.15 (A981)

Regina Coeli *mot,16th cent
[Lat] boy cor&TTB,acap oct GIA G660 $.25 (A982)

Rejoice In The Lord Alway *Adv/Gen,anthem/Bibl,16th cent
SATB,opt inst (med easy) oct OXFORD $.35 (A983)

Resonet In Laudibus *Xmas,hymn,16th cent
[Lat] 6pt mix cor,acap sc SKAND. SMF5357 s.p. (A984)

Sanctus And Benedictus *Bene/Sanctus,13th cent
(Stevens, D.) [Lat] unis BROUDE,A. 213 $.30 (A985)

Sanctus & Benedictus
see Three Early Liturgical Settings

Santa Lucia
(Martini) 4pt wom cor/4pt men cor/4pt mix cor,pno RICORDI-ARG sc s.p., cor pts s.p. (A986)

Schau Auf, Mein Herz, In Ephrata *mot
(Mall) SATB HANSSLER 1.122 s.p. (A987)

Seligkeiten, Freudenzeiten Kamen Fur Uns
see Praetorius, Michael, Geboren Ist Immanuel, Der Herr Christ

Sende Dein Licht Und Deine Wahrheit
see Vulpius, Melchior, Die Helle Sonn Leucht Jetzt Herfur

Singt Und Klingt (Psallite) *Xmas
[Ger] SATB,acap (easy) BAREN. BA 1174 s.p. (A988)

Sixty Carols Of All Nations *CC60U,Xmas/Easter/Epiph/Gen,carol
(Marzo, E.) unis/SATB,pno oct WILLIS (A989)

So Wahr Ich Lebe, Spricht Dein
SATB HANSSLER 6.161 s.p. contains also: Staden, Johann, Ach Bleib Bei Uns, Herr Jesu Christ (SAB/SAT) (A990)

There Is No Rose Of Such Virtue *Xmas,carol,Renais
(Stevens, John E.) ATB/TTB/ATT,acap STAINER F16 $.25 (A991)

This Is The Day (Psalm 118) Easter/Gen
SATB,acap (easy) oct OXFORD $.25 contains also: Giles, Nathaniel, Almighty Lord (A992)

This Joyful Eastertide *Easter,carol,Dut
(Laloux) [Eng] SAB/SA oct ST.MARTIN SMP653 s.p. (A993)

Three Early Liturgical Settings *13-14th cent
(Stevens, D.) BROUDE,A. 212 $.40
contains: Alleluia Psallat (TTT) (Allelu); Kyrie (AAT) (Kyrie); Sanctus & Benedictus (ATT) (Bene/Sanctus) (A994)

Two Medieval Alleluias *CC2U,Allelu/mot
(Bent, Ian D.) [Lat] TT/2pt,acap oct NOVELLO 40.1523.01 s.p. (A995)

Uns Ist Geboren Ein Kindelein *Adv/Xmas
SATB,acap (contains also: Bach, Johann Sebastian, Von Himmel Hoch Da Komm Ich Her) voc pt DOBLINGER s.p. see also ADVENT UND WEIHNACHT, HEFT 1 (A996)

Vamos Pastorcitos *So Am
(Martini) [Span] 3pt mix cor/3 eq voices, acap RICORDI-ARG BA 12261 s.p. (A997)

Verbum Caro Factum Est *16th cent
(Kaplan, A.) [Lat/Span/Eng] SATB BROUDE,A. 143 $.30 (A998)

Weihnachtliches Krippenlied *Xmas
(Schultz; Hauser) [Ger] 2pt,2vln,pno/org/cembalo sc VIEWEG s.p. (A999)

Wir Danken Dir, Herr Jesu
SATB HANSSLER 6.243 s.p. contains also: Lassus, Roland de (Orlandus), Preis Und Ehre Sei Dir, O Gott (A1000)

Wir Danken Dir, Herr Jesu Christ (from Johannes-Passion)
see Trubel, Gerhard, Der Morgenstern Ist Aufgedrungen
"Ach Lieber Herre Jesu Christ" SATB HANSSLER 6.118 s.p. contains also: Vulpius, Melchior, Wir Danken Dir Fur Deinen Tod (A1001)

Wir Fahr'n Dahin, Wirf Helles Licht
see Schutz, Heinrich, Lasst Uns Den Herren Loben

Zambita De Navidad *Xmas
(Martini) [Span] 3pt mix cor/3 eq voices, acap RICORDI-ARG BA12262 s.p. (A1002)

Zu Bethlehem Geboren *Adv/Xmas
SATB,acap (contains also: Bach, Johann Sebastian, O Jesulein Suss) voc pt DOBLINGER s.p. see also ADVENT UND WEIHNACHT, HEFT 1 (A1003)

ANOTHER BLESSED EASTER see Shelley

ANOTHER YEAR IS DAWNING see Vulpius, Melchior

ANREP-NORDIN, BIRGER
Det Ar En Ros Utsprungen
3pt mix cor,org NORDISKA 2537 s.p., ipa (A1004)

ANRUF see Heilmann, Harald

ANRUFUNG see Haus, Karl

ANSWER, THE *CC8UL
SATB,kbd,gtr cmplt ed LILLENAS MB-003 $1.75 (A1005)

ANSWER, THE see Red, Buryl

ANSWER, THE see Skillings, Otis

ANTES, JOHN (1740-1811)
Go, Congregation, Go *Gen/Lent,Morav
(Dickinson) SATB oct GRAY GMCM 6 $.30
(A1006)

(McCorkle) SATB,S solo,strings/org oct
MORAVIAN 5303 $.40, ipa contains also:
Surely He Has Borne Our Griefs (A1007)

How Beautiful Upon The Mountains
(Nolte) SATB,org oct MORAVIAN 5677 $.40
(A1008)

I Will Mention The Loving Kindnesses
(McCorkle) SA/SS,org oct MORAVIAN 5485 $.40
(A1009)

Surely He Has Borne Our Griefs
see Antes, John, Go, Congregation, Go

Twelve Moravian Chorales *CC12U,chorale,
Morav
(Johnson; McCorkle) SATB,acap oct MORAVIAN
5201 $.45 (A1010)

What Splendid Rays
(Lenel) SA oct BOOSEY 5533 $.30 (A1011)

ANTHEM see Pitfield, Thomas Baron

ANTHEM FOR A HARVEST FESTIVAL see Ley, Henry
George

ANTHEM FOR ALL SAINTS' DAY see Gill

ANTHEM FOR CHRISTMAS see Bach

ANTHEM FOR CHRISTMAS DAY see Greene, Maurice

ANTHEM FOR CHRISTMASTIDE see Nicholson, S.H.

ANTHEM FOR EASTER AND OTHER FESTIVALS see
Nicholson, S.H.

ANTHEM FOR PEACE see Davidson, C.

ANTHEM FOR PENETENTIAL SEASONS see Nicholson,
S.H.

ANTHEM FOR SPRING see Mascagni, Pietro

ANTHEM FOR SPRINGTIME see Wells, Dana F.

ANTHEM FOR THANKSGIVING, AN see Billings,
William

ANTHEM FOR THANKSGIVING DAY see Billings,
William

ANTHEM FOR THE CENTENNIAL OF CANADIAN
CONFEDERATION see Willan, Healey

ANTHEM GLORY *CCU
SATB oct PRESSER $.75 (A1012)

ANTHEM IV see Handel, George Frideric, O Sing
Unto The Lord

ANTHEM OF DEDICATION see Martin, Warren

ANTHEM OF FAITH see Diemer, Emma Lou

ANTHEM OF PRAISE see Dvorak, Antonin

ANTHEM OF THE AGES see Hawkins, Floyd W.

ANTHEM OF UNITY see Beck, John Ness

ANTHEM OF WISDOM see Linn, Robert

ANTHEM OFFERING *CCU
SATB oct PRESSER $.75 (A1013)

ANTHEM ON ST. HELLEN'S TUNE see Law

ANTHEM (ST. LUKE XXI) see King, Harold C.

ANTHEM TO THE TRINITY see Fissinger, Edwin

ANTHEM TREASURY *CCU
SATB oct PRESSER $1.25 (A1014)

ANTHEM VOICES *CCU
SATB oct PRESSER $.75 (A1015)

ANTHEMS see Gorczycki, Gregor Gervasius

ANTHEMS FOR JUNIOR CHORISTERS see Lovelace,
Austin C.

ANTHEMS FOR LIMITED CHOIRS NO. 1 *CCU,anthem
SAB/SA/unis LORENZ $1.75 (A1016)

ANTHEMS FOR LIMITED CHOIRS NO. 2 *CCU,anthem
SAB/SA/unis LORENZ $1.75 (A1017)

ANTHEMS FOR MALE VOICES *CC10L,Gen,anthem
(Holmes) TTBB PRO ART 214 $1.25 (A1018)

ANTHEMS FOR MEN'S VOICES, BOOK I *CCU,anthem
(LeHuray) ATTB (med) OXFORD $3.50 (A1019)

ANTHEMS FOR MEN'S VOICES, BOOK II *CCU,anthem
(LeHuray) TTBB (med) OXFORD $3.50 (A1020)

ANTHEMS FOR MEN'S VOICES, VOLUME I *CCU,anthem
(Le Huray, Peter; Temperley, Nicholas;
Tranchell, Peter; Willcocks, Davis) ATB oct
OXFORD $3.50 (A1021)

ANTHEMS FOR MEN'S VOICES, VOLUME II *CCU,
anthem
(Le Huray, Peter; Temperley, Nicholas;
Tranchell, Peter; Willcocks, Davis) TB oct
OXFORD $3.50 (A1022)

ANTHEMS FOR MIXED VOICES *CCU
mix cor SCHMITT 4 $.50 (A1023)

ANTHEMS FOR PRAISE AND WORSHIP see Coggin

ANTHEMS FOR S.A.B. *CCU
SAB SCHMITT 9182 $1.25 (A1024)

ANTHEMS FOR TREBLE AND JUNIOR CHOIRS (BOOK 1)
*CCU,anthem
treb cor&jr cor BELWIN $1.25 (A1025)

ANTHEMS FOR TREBLE VOICES *CCU,anthem
treb cor oct OXFORD 48.028 $2.95 (A1026)

ANTHEMS FOR UNISON OR TWO PART SINGING
*CC17UL,Gen,anthem
unis/SS,acap/pno voc sc ROYAL s.p.
see also: Bach, Johann Sebastian, Come Let
Us All This Day; Bach, Johann Sebastian,
Prepare Thyself Zion; Brewer, Sir Alfred
Herbert, O Lord God, Thou Strength Of My
Health; Greene, Maurice, Gentiles Shall
Come By, The; Greene, Maurice, O Praise
The Lord; Harris, William Henry, Vox
Ultima Crucis; Holman, Derek, Jesus
Christ The Apple Tree; Lloyd, Charles
Harford, Grieve Not The Holy Spirit;
Long, K., Fight The Good Fight; Mawby,
C., By The Waters Of Babylon; Middleton,
Sanctify, O Lord; Nares, James, In The
Sight Of The Unwise; Nicholson, S.H., Be
Strong In The Lord; Parry, Charles Hubert
Hastings, He Delivered The Poor; Travers,
John, O Worship The Lord; Wesley, Samuel
Sebastian Jr., Love One Another (A1027)

ANTHEMS FOR WOMEN'S VOICES *CCU,anthem
SSA/SSAA LORENZ $1.75 (A1028)

ANTHEMS FOR YOUTH *CCU,anthem
(Malin) SAB MARKS $1.50 (A1029)

ANTHEMS FROM SCRIPTURE see McCormick

ANTHEMS OF PRAISE see Schroth

ANTHEMS WITH DESCANTS see Curry

ANTHEMS see Aston, Hugo

ANTHEMS see Aston, Hugo

ANTHES
Come Unto Me
(Harris) SATB oct PRO ART 1665 $.20 (A1030)

ANTHOLOGY OF 65 POLYPHONIC WORKS BY ITALIAN
MASTERS OF THE 16TH AND 17TH CENTURIES
*CC65U,It,16-17th cent
(Garbelotto, Antonio) [Lat/It] 2-4pt,acap
HINRICHSEN N5075 s.p. (A1031)

ANTHOLOGY OF CAROLS, AN *CC31L,carol/liturg
(Wulstan, David) [Eng/Lat] mix cor CHESTER
s.p. (A1032)

ANTHOLOGY OF ENGLISH CHURCH MUSIC, AN *CC16L,
Eng
(Wulstan, David) [Eng] mix cor CHESTER s.p.
contains works by: Byrd; Gibbons; Tallis;
and others (A1033)

ANTHOLOGY OF OFFERTORIES AND MOTETS *CC21UL,
Gen,anthem/mot/Offer,17th cent
(Meyer, V.; Selner, J.) [Eng/Lat] eq voices,
inst (med easy) cmplt ed GIA G 1268 $2.00
contains works by Bottazzo; Carturan;
Casciolini; Gastroium; Grassi; Isaac;
Palestrina; Polleri; Praetorius; Ravanello;
Remondi (A1034)

ANTHOLOGY OF POLYPHONIC MASTERS, BOOK 1 *CCU,
mot
[Lat] SATB,acap oct GIA G646 $1.50 (A1035)

ANTHOLOGY OF POLYPHONIC MASTERS, BOOK 2 *CCU,
mot
[Lat] 2 eq voices/3 eq voices cmplt ed GIA
G640 $1.00 contains works by: Aichinger;
Lassus; Palestrina; Vittoria; Williaert
(A1036)

ANTI-BLUES see Ford, Delvine

ANTIENNE A SAINTE JEANNE D'ARC see Ropartz,
Joseph Guy

ANTIFONE MARIANE see Bottazzo, Luigi

ANTIPHON see Britten, Benjamin

ANTIPHON see Bruckner, Anton

ANTIPHON see Kirk

ANTIPHON see Vaughan Williams, Ralph

ANTIPHON I see Palestrina, Giovanni

ANTIPHON II see Lassus, Roland de (Orlandus)

ANTIPHON III see Victoria, Tomas Luis de

ANTIPHON OF SPRING see Titcomb

ANTIPHONA DE MORTE see Mengelberg, Rudolf

ANTIPHONA DE MORTE see Slogedal, Bjarne

ANTIPHONAL ALLELUIA see Kirk, T.

ANTIPHONAL CAROL *anti/anthem/carol,Ger
(Manz, Paul) unis treb cor (easy) oct
AUGSBURG 0406 $.20 (A1037)

ANTIPHONAL GLORIA see Bright, Houston

ANTIPHONAL HOSANNA see Ringwald, [Roy]

ANTIPHONAL PSALM see Pfohl

ANTIPHONALS FOR JUNIOR CHOIR *CC9L,Gen,anti
(Gillam, R.C.) 2pt jr cor PRO ART 1241 $1.00
(A1038)

ANTIPHONE OF PRAISE see Nosse

ANTIPHONS see Mueller, Carl F.

ANTIPHONS IN HONOR OF THE BLESSED VIRGIN *BVM
PETERS WM61 $4.00
contains & see also: Lassus, Roland de
(Orlandus), Antiphon II; Palestrina,
Giovanni, Antiphon I; Victoria, Tomas
Luis de, Antiphon III (A1039)

ANTIQUA CHORBUCH: 171 SACRED CHORUSES BY GERMAN
MASTERS, BOOK 1 *CCU
(Monkemeyer) 2-8pt SCHOTT 4251 s.p. contains
works by: Isaac; Finck; Stoltzer and others
(A1040)

ANTIQUA CHORBUCH: 171 SACRED CHORUSES BY GERMAN
MASTERS, BOOK 2 *CCU
(Monkemeyer) 2-8pt SCHOTT 4252 s.p. contains
works by: Forster; Von Bruck; Walther
(A1041)

ANTIQUA CHORBUCH: 171 SACRED CHORUSES BY GERMAN
MASTERS, BOOK 3 *CCU
(Monkemeyer) 2-8pt SCHOTT 4253 s.p. contains
works by: Lasso; Gallus and others (A1042)

ANTIQUA CHORBUCH: 171 SACRED CHORUSES BY GERMAN
MASTERS, BOOK 4 *CCU
(Monkemeyer) 2-8pt SCHOTT 4254 s.p. contains
works by: Hassler; Aichinger; Praetorius
and others (A1043)

ANTIQUA CHORBUCH: 171 SACRED CHORUSES BY GERMAN
MASTERS, BOOK 5 *CCU
(Monkemeyer) 2-8pt SCHOTT 4255 s.p. contains
works by: Shutz; Bach; Schein and others
(A1044)

ANTOLOGIA CORAL, FASCICULO I *sac/sec,CC16L
(Graetzer) 1-4pt,acap (very easy) RICORDI-ARG
BA 11456 s.p. contains works by:
Palestrina; Schutz; Bach; and others
(A1045)

ANTOLOGIA CORAL, FASCICULO II *sac/sec,CC15L
(Graetzer) 1-4pt,acap (easy) RICORDI-ARG
BA 11457 s.p. contains works by:
Palestrina; De Victoria; Mozart; Bach;
Gumpeltzhaimer; and others (A1046)

ANTOLOGIA CORAL, FASCICULO III *sac/sec,CC14L
(Graetzer) 1-4pt,acap (med) RICORDI-ARG
BA 11458 s.p. contains works by: Hassler;
Schutz; Bach; Mozart; and others (A1047)

ANTOLOGIA CORAL, FASCICULO IV *sac/sec,CC14L
(Graetzer) 1-5pt,acap (med diff) RICORDI-ARG
BA 11459 s.p. contains works by: Des Pres;
Palestrina; Lasso; De Victoria; Haydn; and
others (A1048)

ANTOLOGIA CORAL, FASCICULO V *sac/sec,CC14L
(Graetzer) 1-5pt,acap (diff) RICORDI-ARG
BA 11460 s.p. contains works by: Dufay;
Okeghem; Purcell; Bach; Scarlatti, A.;
Graetzer; and others (A1049)

ANTOLOGIA DI BRANI POLIFONICI see Garbelotto,
Antonio

ANTON, CHRISTOPH
Alle Menschen Mussen Sterben
see Hiller, Johann Adam, Alles Ist An
Gottes Segen

ANTONIOL, ANTONIO
Messa Ss. Vitorre E Corona *Mass
[It] unis sc ZANIBON 4870 s.p., cor pts
ZANIBON 4871 s.p. (A1050)

ANTONIUSGESANGE see Rauch, Joseph

ANTWERPEN, P.A. VON
Een Kindeke Is Ons Gheboren *Xmas
men cor sc ALSBACH&D s.p. (A1051)

ANTWORT AUF ALLE FRAGEN see Carl, Michael

ANY DREAM WILL DO see Webber, Andrew

APERGHIS, GEORGES
Oratorio
SMezATBar,inst AMPHION s.p. (A1052)

APERITE MIHI PORTAS see Buxtehude, Dietrich

APERITE MIHI PORTAS JUSTITAE see Buxtehude,
Dietrich

APOCALYPS see Monnikendam, Marius

APOCALYPS, ORATORIUM OP TEKSTEN UIT DE
OPENBARING VAN JOHANNES see Badings, Henk

APOKALYPSE see Thiele, Siegfried

APOLLO CANTICLE see Hokanson, Margrethe

APOSTLES, THE see Elgar, Edward

APOSTLE'S CREED see Bodycombe, [Aneurin]

APOSTLES' CREED see Elaine, Sister M.
(Gentemann)

APOSTLES' CREED, THE see Genuchi, Ivan

APOSTOLO GLORIOSO see Dufay, Guillaume

APOSTROPHE TO THE HEAVENLY HOSTS, AN see
Willan, Healey

APPALACHIAN MASS see Hunkins, Eusebia Simpson

APPAREBIT REPENTINA DIES see Hindemith, Paul

APPEAL OF THE CRUCIFIED, THE see Stainer, John

APPEAR THOU LIGHT DIVINE see Morrison, C.P.

APPELDOORN, [DINA] (1884-1938)
Joseph Ginck Van Nazareth
see Twee Kerstliederen

Twee Kerstliederen
wom cor,pno/acap sc ALSBACH&D s.p.
contains: Joseph Ginck Van Nazareth;
Zoete Kindetje, Weet Gij Wel (A1053)

Zoete Kindetje, Weet Gij Wel
see Twee Kerstliederen

APPLACHIAN NATIVITY, AN see Horton, [Lewis
Henry]

APPLE TREE CAROL, THE see Lovelace, Austin C.

APPLEFORD, REV. PATRICK
Mass Of Five Melodies *Commun,Mass
SATB WEINBERGER s.p. voc sc, cor pts
(A1054)

Raise The Cross *hymn
cong,pno/org WEINBERGER s.p. (A1055)

Six Hymns For All Seasons *CC6U,hymn
cong,pno/org cmplt ed WEINBERGER $1.00
(A1056)

AQUILIUS, JACOBUS (1590-1654)
Sions Dottre
"Ye Daughters Of Zion" 4pt mix cor,acap sc SKAND. SMF5374 s.p. (A1057)

Ye Daughters Of Zion *see Sions Dottre

AR HALSAD SKONA MORGONSTUND see Bond, Anders

AR HYD YNOS *Welsh,19th cent
"Gently, Lord, O Lead Us" SATB,org (easy) oct WILLIS 163 $.12 (A1058)
(Porter) "Gently, Lord, O Lead Us" SSAA,pno (easy) oct WILLIS 1628 $.10 (A1059)

ARA SKE DIG KRISTUS see Schutz, Heinrich

ARA SKE GUD, SA OCK HANS KRIST see Vulpius, Melchior

ARA SKE GUD, SOM FRAN SIN TRON *Bibl
(Bjarnegard, Gustaf) [Swed] SATB,acap GEHRMANS KRB 324 (A1060)

ARA VARE GUD, LOTSCHER *Xmas,hymn
(Wikander, David) mix cor NORDISKA 945 s.p. (A1061)

ARBATSKY, [YURY] (1911-1963)
Psalm 92
3pt wom cor,pno/org voc sc ZIMMER. s.p. (A1062)

ARCADELT, JACOB (ca. 1505-ca. 1560)
Ave Maria *ASD/BVM,anthem/Bibl/mot/prayer, 16th cent
see PRACTICAL POLOPHONY
see THREE WEDDING MOTETS
2pt ASHDOWN E.A.248 s.p. (A1063)
[Lat] SATBar oct DURAND s.p. (A1064)
mix cor ALSBACH&D sc s.p., cor pts s.p. (A1065)
SATB,acap oct PRESSER 332-00284 $.25 (A1066)
SSA oct STAFF 548 $.25 (A1067)
SATB,acap RICORDI-ENG SY138 s.p. (A1068)
[Lat] 4pt mix cor,acap LEMOINE s.p. (A1069)
"Give Ear Unto My Prayer" [Eng/Lat] mix cor oct NOVELLO 50.0060.02 s.p. (A1070)
"Give Ear Unto My Prayer" mix cor SOUTHERN $.30 (A1071)
"Give Ear Unto My Prayer" SATB,acap oct BELWIN 64132 $.25 (A1072)
"Hear My Prayer, O God" SATB,acap SCHIRM.EC 371 $.30 (A1073)
(Andersen) SSA SCHMITT 2504 $.30 (A1074)
(Craig) SATB oct PLYMOUTH DC-118 $.25 (A1075)
(Damrosch, Fr.) [Lat] 4pt men cor,acap oct SCHIRM.G 6242 $.25 (A1076)
(Davis, K.) "Hear Thou My Prayer, O Lord" SSAA,acap SCHIRM.EC 1540 $.25 (A1077)
(Davis, K.) "Hear Thou My Prayer, O Lord" SA,pno/org SCHIRM.EC 1559 $.18 (A1078)
(Greyson) "Give Ear Unto My Prayer" SSA oct BOURNE ES3 $.30 (A1079)
(Greyson) "Give Ear Unto My Prayer" TTBB oct BOURNE ES3A $.30 (A1080)
(Klein, M.) "Hail Mary" [Eng/Lat] SATB (easy) oct GIA G1528 $.25 (A1081)
(Lammers, H.) [Lat] 4pt mix cor,acap (easy) cor pts LEMOINE s.p. see from Collection De Musique Ancienne Premiere Recueli (A1082)
(Montani) [Eng/Lat] 4pt mix cor,acap oct SCHIRM.G 5503 $.25 (A1083)
(Mueller) "Give Ear Unto My Prayer" 3pt jr cor/SAB (easy) FISCHER,C CM 7336 $.20 (A1084)
(Pearce) "Remember Not, Lord" [Eng/Lat] 4pt mix cor,acap oct SCHIRM.G 3488 $.25 (A1085)
(Pisano) SAB oct PLYMOUTH SC-404 $.25 (A1086)
(Steele, Jonathan) [Lat] SATB CHESTER s.p. (A1087)
(Trusler) "Hear Thou My Pray'r" SAB oct SPRATT 573 $.25 (A1088)

Ave Maria, Gratia Plena
[Lat] SCHOTT s.p. (A1089)

Collection De Musique Ancienne Premiere Recueli *see Ave Maria (A1090)

Deh Come Trista
SATB,acap oct PRESSER 352-00081 $.30 (A1091)

D'ou Vient L'ejouissance *Xmas,16th cent
(Honegger, Marc; Pidoux, Pierre) [Fr] SSSA/SSST OUVRIERES E0562 s.p. (A1092)

Give Ear Unto My Prayer *see Ave Maria

Haec Dies, Quam Fecit Dominus *mot
(Collins, H.B.) [Lat] SATB CHESTER s.p. (A1093)

Hail Mary *see Ave Maria

Hear My Prayer, O God *see Ave Maria

Hear Thou My Prayer, O Lord *see Ave Maria

Hear Thou My Pray'r *see Ave Maria

Holy Redeemer
(Peery, R.) SAB oct PRESSER 312-40531 $.25 (A1094)

Jesus, Lover Of My Soul
SATB,acap oct PRESSER 312-40141 $.30 (A1095)

Missa Ave Regina Caelorum
see Opera Omnia Vol. I

Missa De Beata Virgine
see Opera Omnia Vol. I

Missa Noe Noe
see Opera Omnia Vol. I

O, Kom, Guds Ande God
mix cor NORDISKA 2533 s.p. (A1096)

O Lord, I Cry To Thee
see Casciolini, Claudio, Lamb Of God

Opera Omnia Vol. I *Mass
(Seay, Albert) cor AM.INST.MUS. $16.00 contains: Missa Ave Regina Caelorum; Missa De Beata Virgine; Missa Noe Noe (A1097)

ARCADELT, JACOB (cont'd.)

Opera Omnia vol. X *CCU,mot
(Seay, Albert) cor AM.INST.MUS. $21.50 (A1098)

Remember Not, Lord *see Ave Maria

ARCHANGELSKY
Praise The Name Of The Lord
(Cramer) SATB,acap MARKS 4144 $.30 (A1099)

ARCHER, FREDERICK (1838-1901)
Sweet Jesu, King Of Bliss *anthem
SA oct OXFORD 02.001 $.25 (A1100)

ARCHER, VIOLET (1913-)
Christmas
SSA,pno/ob&harp THOMP.G s.p. (A1101)
SSA,pno&ob/harp THOMP.G E.I.1014 s.p. (A1102)

Introit And Choral Prayer
SATB,org oct BERANDOL 917A7AH $.35 (A1103)

Mater Admirabilis Chapel, The
SSA,pno&ob/harp THOMP.G E.I.1015 s.p. (A1104)

ARCHIVES DU CHANT, QUARTIEME VOLUME *CC26L,4-13th cent
(Delsarte, Francios) [Lat] 1-6pt CHOUDENS s.p. contains works by: Charlemagne; Palestrina; Handel; and others (A1105)

ARDIA LA ZARZA see Benedito

ARE WE NOT RISEN WITH CHRIST see Elliot, Robert

"ARE YE ABLE", SAID THE MASTER see Wilson

ARE YOU RUNNING WITH ME LORD
SATB HANSEN-US T9503 $.40 (A1106)
SSA HANSEN-US T9504 $.40 (A1107)

ARE YOU WEARY? see Artman

ARENSKY, ANTON STEPANOVITCH (1861-1906)
Bow Down Thine Ear
SATB oct FISCHER,J 4162 $.30 (A1108)

Bow Down Thine Ear, O Lord
(Davis, K.) SA,pno SCHIRM.EC 1551 (A1109)

Dear Master, In Whose Life I See
(Barrie) SATB,acap oct LAWSON 808 $.25 (A1110)

Easter Day *see Jour De Paques

I Want A Heart To Pray *19th cent
SATB oct WALTON 2113 $.25 (A1111)

Jour De Paques *Op.59,No.6, Easter
"Easter Day" [Eng/Fr] unis,pno CHESTER s.p. (A1112)

O God, We Pray
SATB,acap SCHIRM.EC 1126 $.25 (A1113)

Our Lord Is Risen *Easter,anthem
[Eng] SSA CHESTER s.p. (A1114)

Peace With Our Fellow Men *Gen/Lent,anthem
FOSTER MF 144 $.30 (A1115)

Praise The Lord, We Praise Thee
(Douglas) SATB oct GRAY GAC 7 $.30 (A1116)

Praise Ye The Lord In Heaven
SATB,opt pno BOSTON 5437 $.30 (A1117)

Short Communion Service *Adv/Lent,Mass
[Lat/Eng] SATB,acap SCHIRM.EC 1245 $.50 (A1118)

ARESHES see Helfman, Max

ARFKEN, ERNST
Gib Dich Zufrieden Und Sei Stille
SATB,bvl/vcl, or lute HANSSLER 7.108 s.p. (A1119)

Verleih Uns Frieden Gnadiglich *mot
SSA/TTB HANSSLER 7.003 s.p. (A1120)

ARGENTO, DOMINICK
Revelation Of Saint John The Divine
men cor,T solo,brass,perc BOOSEY voc sc $6.00, sc rental, ipr (A1121)

ARG'RE DICH, O SEELE, NICHT see Bach, Johann Sebastian

ARIEL (VISIONS OF ISAIAH) see Starer, Robert

ARISE AND BE NOT AFRAID see Lenel, Ludwig

ARISE, ARISE, THIS DAY REJOICE see Walther

ARISE, FOR THY LIGHT IS A-COMIN'
SATB oct STAFF 681 $.30 (A1122)

ARISE IN US see Shaw, Martin

ARISE, MY LOVE see Christiansen

ARISE, MY LOVE, MY FAIR ONE see Near, Gerald

ARISE, MY SOUL, ARISE see Edson, [Lewis]

ARISE, MY SOUL, ARISE see Schroth

ARISE, MY SOUL, ARISE! see Wood, Dale

ARISE, O GOD, AND SHINE see Pelz, Walter L.

ARISE O GOD AND SHINE see Young

ARISE, O GOD, AND SHOW THY MIGHT see Morgan

ARISE, O LORD see Beadell, Robert M.

ARISE, O LORD see Brandon, G.

ARISE, O LORD! see Hoffmeister, L.A.

ARISE, O LORD see Rohlig, Harald

ARISE, O YE SERVANTS see Sweelinck, Jan Pieterszoon, Or Sus, Serviteurs

ARISE, O YE SERVANTS OF GOD see Floreen, John

ARISE, O YE SERVANTS OF GOD see Sweelinck, Jan Pieterszoon

ARISE, REJOICE, AND PRAISE THE LORD see Beetz, C.J.

ARISE, SHINE see Berger, Jean

ARISE, SHINE see Elvey, George Job

ARISE, SHINE see Maker, [Frederick Charles]

ARISE, SHINE see Martin

ARISE, SHINE see Naylor, Bernard

ARISE, SHINE see Roseingrave, Thomas

ARISE, SHINE see Scott, John Prindle

ARISE, SHINE see Warren, David

ARISE, SHINE, FOR THY LIGHT HAS COME see Jennings, Kenneth L.

ARISE, SHINE FOR THY LIGHT IS COME
SATB CHAPPELL 0014357-358 $.40 (A1123)

ARISE SHINE, FOR THY LIGHT IS COME see Boyd

ARISE, SHINE FOR THY LIGHT IS COME see Elvey, George Job

ARISE, SHINE, FOR THY LIGHT IS COME see Gordon, Philip

ARISE, SHINE, FOR THY LIGHT IS COME see Willan, Healey

ARISE, SHINE FORTH IN SPLENDOR see Byrd, William

ARISE, SONS OF THE KINGDOM see Gesius, Bartholomaus

ARISE, SONS OF THE KINGDOM see Strube, Adolf

ARISE, YE WHO SERVE THE LORD see Sweelinck, Jan Pieterszoon

ARKHANGELSKY
Lend Thine Ear To My Prayer *prayer
(Wilhousky) SATB,acap oct FISCHER,C CM-613 $.30 (A1124)
(Wilhousky) SSA oct FISCHER,C CM-646 $.25 (A1125)

Nunc Dimittis
SAB KJOS 5718 $.30 (A1126)

O Gladsome Light
(Spiro) SATB,acap oct PRO ART 1480 $.25 (A1127)

ARKHANGELSKY, ALEXANDER (1846-1924)
Cherubim Song
(Ehret) SATB oct BOURNE BL3035 $.30 (A1128)

Hear My Prayer, O Lord
(Ehret, W.) SATB oct PRESSER MC258 $.30 (A1129)

O Light Divine
SATB,acap oct PRESSER 332-14588 $.25 (A1130)

Praise Ye The Name Of The Lord
(Ehret) SSA,acap oct BOOSEY 5348 $.30 (A1131)
(Ehret) SAB,acap oct BOOSEY 5539 $.30 (A1132)
(Ehret) SATB,acap oct BOOSEY 5126 $.30 (A1133)
(Ehret) TTBB oct BOOSEY 5559 $.30 (A1134)
(Norden) SATB,acap SHAWNEE A 345 $.25 (A1135)

ARKHANGELSKY, G.
Blessings Of Peace
(Krone) SSA,acap WARNER W3219 $.30 (A1136)
(Krone) SATB,acap WARNER W2766 $.35 (A1137)

Cherubic Hymn
(Ehret) SATB,acap oct BELWIN 60146 $.25 (A1138)

Day Of Judgment, The
SATB oct FISCHER,J 4120 $.35 (A1139)
(Gaines) TTBB oct FISCHER,J 7471 $.30 (A1140)

Go To Dark Gethsemane
(Howorth) SATB FLAMMER A 5445 $.35 (A1141)

Hear My Prayer
SATB oct FISCHER,J 4468 $.30 (A1142)

Hear My Prayer, O Lord
(Ehret, W.) SSA oct PRESSER MC471 $.30 (A1143)
(Spence) SATB oct PLYMOUTH SC-22 $.25 (A1144)
(Trusler) SAB WARNER W3719 $.30 (A1145)

Hear My Supplication
(Krone) SATB,acap WARNER W2727 $.35 (A1146)

Incline Thine Ear, Oh Lord
2pt WARNER W3702 $.30 (A1147)
SATB,acap WARNER W2689 $.30 (A1148)

Lord Most Holy And Righteous
SATB oct WALTON 2102 $.25 (A1149)

Praise Ye The Lord Of Hosts
(Trusler) SAB,acap WARNER W3675 $.30 (A1150)

To Thee We Sing *Gen
(Tellep) SATB SCHMITT 857 $.25 (A1151)

ARMBRUSTER
Lord, God Of Our Fathers
3pt jr cor/SSA (med) FISCHER,C CM 7146 $.30 (A1152)

ARMITAGE, ELLEN M.
Sing Hosanna *anthem
SAB&unis treb cor,org,opt 3trp (med) oct AUGSBURG 1587 $.40 (A1153)

ARMOR DEI see Reda, Siegfried

ARMOUR OF GOD, THE see Liljestrand, Paul

ARMOUR OF LIGHT, THE see Naylor, Bernard

ARMSTRONG, THOMAS
Christ, Whose Glory Fills The Skies *Morn
SATB (med) oct OXFORD 46.106 $.30   (A1154)

Never Weather-Beaten Sail *anthem/mot
mix cor oct NOVELLO 45.1484.10 s.p. (A1155)

ARNALDI, ANTONIO
Amo Christum
see Duo Motecta

Ave Maria
see In Honorem B. Mariae Virginis-Tre
Motteti

Ave Maris
see Quattro Inni Per La Feste Principali
Dell'anno

Cantibus Organis *Op.13, ASD,mot
[Lat] ATTB,org sc ZANIBON 2465 s.p., cor
pts ZANIBON 2466 s.p.   (A1156)

Canzoncina
see Due Mottetti In Onore Di S. Antonio

[Cinque] Litanie
see In Honorem B. Mariae Virginis-Tre
Motteti

Cor Jesu Flagrans
see Tre Canti Al Sacro Cuore Di Gesu

Da Pacem Domine *Op.11
[Lat] ATB,org sc ZANIBON 2455 s.p. (A1157)

Decora Lux
see Per La Festa Del Papa

Deus Tuorum Militum
see Quattro Inni Del Comune Dei Santi

Dolce Cuor
see Tre Canti Al Sacro Cuore Di Gesu

Due Canti Trionfali Per Processione
Eucharistica *Op.51, Commun
[Lat] 4pt mix cor/unis,opt org ZANIBON 2357
s.p.
contains: O Pane Celeste; Osanna O
Signore   (A1158)

Due Mottetti In Onore Di S. Antonio *Op.27,
ASD,mot
[Lat] unis/4pt mix cor,org ZANIBON 2366
s.p.
contains: Canzoncina; Si Quaeris (A1159)

Due Mottetti Pasquali *Easter,mot
[Lat] ATB,org sc ZANIBON 3045 s.p., cor pts
ZANIBON 3046 s.p.
contains: Haec Dies; Surrexit Pastor
Bonus   (A1160)

Due Mottetti Per La Visita Pastorale *Op.18,
mot
[Lat] SATTB,org ZANIBON 2530 s.p.
contains: Ecce Sacerdos Magnus; Sacerdos
Et Pontifex   (A1161)

Due Tantum Ergo *Op.58, CC2U,Commun
[Lat] 1-3pt,org (easy) ZANIBON 2336 s.p.
(A1162)

Duo Motecta *Op.15, mot
[Lat] 2pt jr cor,org ZANIBON 2434 s.p.
contains: Amo Christum; Veni Sponsa
Christi   (A1163)

Ecce Fidelis Servus
see Tre Mottetti Per Messa Novella,
Ingresso E Festa Parrocchiale

Ecce Sacerdos Magnus
see Due Mottetti Per La Visita Pastorale

Egli E Il Messia *Op.40, Xmas
[It] unis/SATB,opt org ZANIBON 3221 s.p.
(A1164)

Ego Sum Pastor Bonus
see Tre Mottetti Per Messa Novella,
Ingresso E Festa Parrocchiale

Eucaristica *Op.10, CC8L,Commun
[Lat] ATTB,org sc ZANIBON 2520 s.p., voc pt
ZANIBON s.p.   (A1165)

Exultet Orbis
see Quattro Inni Del Comune Dei Santi

Haec Dies
see Due Mottetti Pasquali

In Honorem B. Mariae Virginis-Tre Motteti
*Op.12, BVM
[Lat] ATB,org sc ZANIBON 3055 s.p.
contains: Ave Maria; [Cinque] Litanie;
Regina Coeli; Salve Regina (A1166)

In Onore Di S. Giuseppe *Op.59, CC2U,ASD
[Lat] unis&4pt mix cor,opt org ZANIBON 2397
s.p.   (A1167)

Infensus Hostis, In Onore Die S. Luigi
*Op.45, ASD,hymn
[Lat] unis/3pt mix cor,org ZANIBON 2407
s.p.   (A1168)

Iste Confessor
see Quattro Inni Del Comune Dei Santi

Jesu Corona Virginum
see Quattro Inni Del Comune Dei Santi

Jesu Mitis
see Tre Canti Al Sacro Cuore Di Gesu

Jesu Redemptor
see Quattro Inni Per La Feste Principali
Dell'anno

Lauda Sion *Op.8, Mass
"Messa Solenne" [Lat] ATTB,org,opt strings
sc ZANIBON 3105 s.p., voc pt ZANIBON
s.p., ipr   (A1169)

Magnificat Solenne *Op.23, Magnif
[Lat] ATTB,org sc ZANIBON 2449 s.p., voc pt
ZANIBON 2449A-B-C-D s.p. (A1170)

ARNALDI, ANTONIO (cont'd.)

Messa Solenne *see Lauda Sion

O Biondo Piccino! *Op.35, Xmas
[It] ATB,org ZANIBON 3222 s.p.   (A1171)

O Pane Celeste
see Due Canti Trionfali Per Processione
Eucharistica

Osanna O Signore
see Due Canti Trionfali Per Processione
Eucharistica

Per La Festa Del Papa *Op.57
[Lat] 3-4pt mix cor,org ZANIBON 2421 s.p.
contains: Decora Lux; Tu Es Petrus
(A1172)

Quattro Inni Del Comune Dei Santi *Op.55,
hymn
[Lat] unis mix cor/4pt mix cor,opt org
ZANIBON 2351 s.p.
contains: Deus Tuorum Militum; Exultet
Orbis; Iste Confessor; Jesu Corona
Virginum   (A1173)

Quattro Inni Per La Feste Principali
Dell'anno *Op.56, hymn
[Lat] unis mix cor/4pt mix cor,opt org
ZANIBON 2354 s.p.
contains: Ave Maris; Jesu Redemptor; Veni
Creator; Vexilla Regis   (A1174)

Regina Coeli
see In Honorem B. Mariae Virginis-Tre
Motteti

Sacerdos Et Pontifex
see Due Mottetti Per La Visita Pastorale

Salve Regina
see In Honorem B. Mariae Virginis-Tre
Motteti

Salve S. Pater In Onore Di S. Francesco
*Op.33, ASD,anti
[Lat] 3pt mix cor,org ZANIBON 2402 s.p.
(A1175)

Si Quaeris
see Due Mottetti In Onore Di S. Antonio

Sia Gloria Al Divin Pargolo! *Op.38
[Lat] unis/2pt,pno/org ZANIBON 3223 s.p.
(A1176)

Sonno Divino *Op.41, Xmas
[Lat] unis/SATB,opt org ZANIBON 3220 s.p.
(A1177)

Surrexit Pastor Bonus
see Due Mottetti Pasquali

Te Deum Solenne *Te Deum
[Lat] unis/SATB ZANIBON 3458 s.p. (A1178)

Tre Canti Al Sacro Cuore Di Gesu *Op.34
[Lat] unis/ATB ZANIBON 2347 s.p.
contains: Cor Jesu Flagrans; Dolce Cuor;
Jesu Mitis   (A1179)

Tre Mottetti Per Messa Novella, Ingresso E
Festa Parrocchiale *Op.9, mot
[Lat] 3pt mix cor,org voc pt ZANIBON
2533-35 s.p., sc ZANIBON 2532 s.p.
contains: Ecce Fidelis Servus; Ego Sum
Pastor Bonus; Tu Es Sacerdos (A1180)

Tu Es Petrus
see Per La Festa Del Papa

Tu Es Sacerdos
see Tre Mottetti Per Messa Novella,
Ingresso E Festa Parrocchiale

Veni Creator
see Quattro Inni Per La Feste Principali
Dell'anno

Veni Sponsa Christi
see Duo Motecta

Vexilla Regis
see Quattro Inni Per La Feste Principali
Dell'anno

ARNATT, RONALD (1930-   )
Blessed City, Heavenly Salem
SATB,acap oct PRESSER MC470 $.30   (A1181)

Coventry Anthem *Xmas,anthem
SATB,brass oct WALTON 2190 $.50, ipa
(A1182)

Four Christmas Carols *CC4U,Xmas,carol
SSA oct GRAY GCMR 2949 $.30   (A1183)

God Is Our Hope And Strength
SATB,opt 2trp&2trom&tuba oct GRAY GCMR 3219
$.35   (A1184)

I Waited Patiently For The Lord
boy cor oct PRESSER MC419 $.35   (A1185)
boy cor oct PRESSER MC419 $.35   (A1186)

Lord, Thou Hast Been Our Dwelling Place
SATB oct PRESSER MC266 $.30   (A1187)

O Praise The Lords From The Heavens
SATB (med) PRESSER 312-40991 $.45   (A1188)

On Christmas Night *Xmas
SATB,acap oct PRESSER MC250 $.25   (A1189)

Virgin Most Pure, A *Xmas
SATB,acap oct GRAY GCMR 3220 $.35   (A1190)

ARNE (ca. 1490-1556)
Awake, The Trumpet
(Pisano) SATB,acap oct PRO ART 2518 $.25
(A1191)

Libera Me *funeral/mot
[Lat] SATTB,STB soli,org PETERS H112 $.90
(A1192)

ARNE, THOMAS AUGUSTINE (1710-1778)
Water Parted From The Sea
unis,pno SCHIRM.EC 1020 $.12   (A1193)

ARNESTAD, FINN
Amen
[Eng] mix cor LYCHE 52 s.p.   (A1194)

ARNOLD
Evening Service *see Magnificat And Nunc
Dimittis

Magnificat And Nunc Dimittis *Magnif/Nunc
"Evening Service" TTB/SSA,acap (very easy)
OXFORD 40.010 $.20   (A1195)

My Prayer For Today *see Van Alstyne

Pilgrim Caravan, The (from Song Of Simeon)
SATB,acap (easy) OXFORD 43.339 $.20 (A1196)
unis/desc (easy) OXFORD 81.100 $.25 (A1197)

Song Of Praise
unis jr cor&desc FISCHER,C PT 1761 $.24
(A1198)

Song Of Simeon
SATB (diff) voc sc OXFORD 46.510 $3.65, ipr
(A1199)

Two Ceremonial Psalms *CC2U,Thanks,Psalm
3pt jr cor/SSA (med diff) FISCHER,C PT 1863
$.36   (A1200)

ARNOLD, J.H.
Benedicite Omnia Opera
SAT/SATB (very easy) oct OXFORD 43.921 $.25
(A1201)

Great Advent Antiphons On Magnificat, The
*CCU,Adv,anti/Magnif
oct OXFORD 45.060 $.50   (A1202)

Simple 3-Part Evening Canticles
SSA/TTB,acap (very easy) oct OXFORD 40.014
$.65   (A1203)

ARNOLD, MALCOLM (1921-   )
Laudate Dominum
SATB,org LENGNICK s.p.   (A1204)

This Christmas Night *Xmas,carol
SATB oct FABER F0229 $.35   (A1205)

ARNOLD, SAMUEL (1740-1802)
Magnificat And Nunc Dimittis *Magnif/Nunc
(Ley, H.G.) SATB (A maj) oct NOVELLO
44.1316.04 s.p.   (A1206)

AROUND THE MANGER see Strimer

ARP, KLAUS-MICHAEL
Nehmt Und Esst, Das Ist Mein Leib
see Schweizer, Rolf, Deutsches Sanctus

ARROW AND THE SONG, THE see Wilson, John F.

ARS CONTRAPUNCTICA see Mulder, Ernest W.

ARS NOVA TO RENNAISSANCE VOL. 1-1200 TO ABOUT
1500 *sac/sec,CCU
mix cor min sc KALMUS 701 $1.30 contains
works by: Dufay; Binchois; Obrecht;
Ockeghem; Compere   (A1207)

ARS NOVA TO RENNAISSANCE VOL. 2-1200 TO ABOUT
1500
mix cor min sc KALMUS 703 $1.30
contains: de la Rue, Pierre, Requiem Moter
(Req); Finck, Heinrich, Missa In Summis
(Mass); Fulda, Adam von, Baptistae;
Fulda, Adam von, In Decollatione St.
Johannis; Fulda, Adam von, In Festo
Pentecostis (Pent); Isaac, Heinrich,
Missa Carminium (Mass)   (A1208)

ARS NOVA TO RENNAISSANCE VOL. 3-1200 TO ABOUT
1500 see Des Prez, Josquin

ARS NOVA TO RENNAISSANCE VOL. 4-1200 TO ABOUT
1500 *sac/sec,CCU
mix cor min sc KALMUS 704 $1.30 contains
works by: Jannequin; Clemens Non Papa;
Arcadelt; Gabrieli, G.; Gabrieli, A.
(A1209)

ARS NOVA TO RENNAISSANCE VOL. 5-1200 TO ABOUT
1500 *sac/sec,CC10UL
mix cor min sc KALMUS 705 $1.30 contains
works by zarlino; marenzio; vecchi; bertani
(A1210)

ARS NOVA TO RENNAISSANCE VOL. 6-1200 TO ABOUT
1500 see Palestrina, Giovanni

ARS NOVA TO RENNAISSANCE VOL.7-1200 TO ABOUT
1500 see Lassus, Roland de (Orlandus)

ARS NOVA TO RENNAISSANCE VOL. 8-1200 TO ABOUT
1500 *CCUL,Span
mix cor min sc KALMUS 708 $1.30 contains
works by: Vittoria; Morales; Guerrero;
Vivanco; Esquival   (A1211)

ART THOU A KING, THEN? see Roff, Joseph

ART THOU THE CHRIST see O'Hara, Geoffrey

ART THOU WEARY see Leighton, E.I.

ART THOU WEARY, ART THOU LADEN see Gehring,
Philip

ART THOU WITH ME see Bach, Johann Sebastian,
Bist Du Bei Mir

ARTE CORAL. VOL III see Benedito

ARTE CORAL. VOL. IV see Benedito

ARTE CORAL. VOL. V see Benedito

ARTE CORAL. VOL. VI
[Span] mix cor,acap UNION ESP. 19114 s.p.
contains: Beethoven, Ludwig van, Canto A La
Noche; Benedito, Alala De Montforte;
Benedito, El Triquitri; Benedito, Gloria
A Maria; Benedito, Las Torras; Benedito,
Me Dices Que No Me Quieres (A1212)

ARTEGA, [ESTEBAN DE] (1747-1799)
Everyone Must Have A Friend (composed with
Donnelly)
(Ehret) SSA/SSAA oct MCA   (A1213)
(Ehret) SAB oct MCA   (A1214)
(Ehret) SATB oct MCA   (A1215)

ARTHUR, JAN
How Abundant Is Thy Goodness
SATB oct FISCHER,J 9859 $.35   (A1216)

How Long Wilt Thou Forget Me
SATB oct FISCHER,J 8783 $.30   (A1217)

ARTMAN
Are You Weary? *Xmas
SATB&desc SCHMITT 235 $.25   (A1218)

Baby Jesus *Xmas
unis/SATB WARNER W7-1013 $.35   (A1219)

Do You Hear The Angels Singing? *Xmas
SAB WARNER R3473 $.30   (A1220)

He Has No Hands *Gen
SATB SCHMITT 7034 $.35   (A1221)

I Am Just A Little Child *Xmas
unis SCHMITT 239 $.30   (A1222)

I Have Only One Life To Live
SATB FLAMMER A 5616 $.30   (A1223)

I'll Walk Beside You, Gentle Jesus
2pt&desc WARNER WB-141 $.35   (A1224)

Light, The Love, The *Gen
SATB SCHMITT 7040 $.35   (A1225)

Little Lamb
unis WARNER W7-1044 $.30   (A1226)
2pt WARNER W7-1044 $.30   (A1227)

Lord, Walk With Me
SAB WARNER WB-270 $.35   (A1228)

Shepherds And The Angels, The *Xmas
SSA,opt perc WARNER W7-1043 $.30   (A1229)

ARUNDEL-TIMMS, T.
Sweet Was The Song The Virgin Sang
PROWSE s.p.   (A1230)

ARVIT L'ROSH HASHANAH V'YOM KIPPUR see Binder,
Abraham Wolfe

ARVIT L'SHABBAT see Jacobi, Frederick

AS A CHILD see White

AS A HART see Lockwood, Normand

AS A HART LONGS FOR THE BROOKLET see Goudimel,
Claude

AS A LAMB see Victoria, Tomas Luis de, Tanquam
Agnus

AS A LITTLE CHILD see Kaiser, Kurt

AS BOUNTIFUL AS MAY see Bull, John

AS BY THE STREAMS OF BABYLON see Campion,
[Thomas]

AS BY THE STREAMS OF BABYLON see Dett, Robert
Nathaniel

AS CANDLES GLOW *anthem/carol,Ger
(Bender, Jan) unis treb cor (easy) oct
AUGSBURG 0403 $.18   (A1231)

AS CHILDREN, WALK YE IN GOD'S LOVE see Dett,
Robert Nathaniel

AS DEW IN APRIL (from Anthology Of Carols, An)
Xmas
(Wulstan, David) SATB,B solo CHESTER s.p.
                                      (A1232)

AS DEW IN APRIL see Britten, Benjamin

AS DEW IN APRIL see Collins, Anthony

AS DEW IN APRILLE see Gifford

AS EVENING'S SHADOW FALLS see Stanislaus

AS FOR MAN, HIS DAYS ARE AS GRASS see
Willmington

AS GOD THE LORD HATH SPOKEN see Klein

AS I OUT RODE THIS ENDERS NIGHT see Rimmer,
Frederick

AS I RODE OUT ON A WINTER'S NIGHT see Davies,
Lawrence H.

AS I RODE OUT THIS ENDERES NIGHT see Stevens,
Halsey

AS I RODE OUT THIS ENDERS NIGHT see Spencer, W.

AS I SAT ON A SUNNY BANK see Friedell, Harold
W.

AS I SAT UNDER A HOLLY TREE *Xmas
(Holst, Imogen) 3pt boy cor/3pt wom cor,acap
oct SCHIRM.G 11634 $.30   (A1233)

AS I SAT UNDER A SYCAMORE TREE see Gordon

AS I SAT UNDER A SYCAMORE TREE see Spencer, W.

AS I WALKED IN BETHLEHEM see Anderson, [William
H.]

AS I WATCHED BESIDE MY SHEEP *Xmas
(Fuller) SATB oct PRO ART 1226 $.25   (A1234)
(Fuller) SAB oct PRO ART 1174 $.25   (A1235)
(Fuller) SSA oct PRO ART 1319 $.20   (A1236)

AS IT BEGAN TO DAWN see Coombs, Charles Whitney

AS IT BEGAN TO DAWN see Foster, Myles Birket

AS IT BEGAN TO DAWN see Harker, F. Flaxington

AS IT BEGAN TO DAWN see Martin, George Clement

AS IT BEGAN TO DAWN see Moffatt

AS IT BEGAN TO DAWN see Stoughton, R.

AS IT BEGAN TO DAWN see Vincent, Charles John

AS IT FELL UPON A NIGHT see Davis, Katherine K.

AS JESUS WENT TO CALVARY see Ratcliffe, Desmond

AS JOSEPH WAS A WALKING *Xmas,carol,Eng
oct HART s.p.   (A1237)
(Chambers) SATB oct BOOSEY 5253 $.30 (A1238)
(Davis) SATB oct PRO ART 2078 $.22   (A1239)
(Ehret) SSA oct SPRATT 632 $.30   (A1240)
(Ehret) SA oct SPRATT 601 $.30   (A1241)
(Hicks, Mary) 2pt ENOCH TP264 s.p.   (A1242)
(Johnstone) unis (easy) OXFORD 45.035 $.25
                                      (A1243)
(Montgomery) SATB,S solo (med easy) OXFORD
42.203 $.35   (A1244)
(Sharpe, E.) cor&desc CRAMER 40 $.30 (A1245)
(Vaughan Williams) TTBB,acap (easy, contains
also: Mummer's Carol) OXFORD 41.901 $.30
see from Nine Carols   (A1246)

AS JOSEPH WAS A-WALKING see Ehret, Walter

AS JOSEPH WAS A-WALKING see Geoffrey

AS JOSEPH WAS A-WALKING see Gordon, Philip

AS JOSEPH WAS A-WALKING see Grieb, Herbert [C.]

AS JOSEPH WAS A-WALKING see Hallstrom, Henry

AS JOSEPH WAS A WALKING see Jenkins, [Joseph
Willcox]

AS JOSEPH WAS A-WALKING see Jerrett, Jack

AS JOSEPH WAS A WALKING see Moe, Daniel

AS LATELY WE WATCHED *Xmas,anthem/carol,Aus
(Black, Charles) SATB&jr cor&sr cor oct GRAY
GCMR 1358 $.30   (A1247)
(Ehret) SATB oct FOX S124 $.30   (A1248)
(Ehret) SSA oct FOX S137 $.30   (A1249)
(Ehret) SA oct FOX S142 $.30   (A1250)
(Ehret) SAB oct FOX S138 $.30   (A1251)
(Ehret, W.) SSA PROWSE s.p.   (A1252)
(Ehret, W.) 2pt PROWSE s.p.   (A1253)
(Ehret, W.) SATB PROWSE s.p.   (A1254)
(Ehret, W.) SAB PROWSE s.p.   (A1255)
(Griffith, Allen) SA/SATB oct BELWIN 1458 $.25
                                      (A1256)
(Kirk) SATB oct PRO ART 1306 $.30   (A1257)
(Kirk) SAB oct PRO ART 1393 $.30   (A1258)
(Kirk) SSA oct PRO ART 1394 $.30   (A1259)
(Kirk) 2pt oct PRO ART 1711 $.30   (A1260)
(Kirk) TTB oct PRO ART 1883 $.30   (A1261)
(Pooler, Marie) SATB (very easy) oct AUGSBURG
1269 $.18 contains also: While By My Sheep
(carol,17th cent)   (A1262)
(Tkach) SATB SCHMITT 856 $.30   (A1263)

AS LATELY WE WATCHED see Cain, Noble

AS LATELY WE WATCHED see Hillert, Richard

AS LONG AS CHILDREN PRAY see Crawford

AS LONGS THE HART FOR FLOWING STREAMS see
Handel, George Frideric, As Pants The Hart

AS MANY AS RECEIVED HIM see Brown, Leon F.

AS MARY SINGS see Anderson, [William H.]

AS MARY WALKED IN THE GARDEN GREEN see Voris,
W.R.

AS MEN OF OLD THEIR FIRST FRUITS BROUGHT see
Sateren, Leland Bernhard

AS ON THE CROSS *hymn,US
(Pfautsch) SATB,acap oct LAWSON 51299 $.25
                                      (A1264)

AS PANTS THE HART see Handel, George Frideric

AS PANTS THE HART see Lassus, Roland de
(Orlandus)

AS PANTS THE HART see Powell

AS PANTS THE HART see Spohr, Ludwig (Louis)

AS PANTS THE HART see Thiman, Eric Harding

AS PANTS THE HART FOR COOLING STREAMS see
MacDonald

AS PANTS THE HEART see Handel, George Frideric

AS PANTS THE WEARIED HART see Bach, Johann
Sebastian

AS SHEPHERDS WERE GUARDING THEIR SHEEP see
Billings, William

AS SMOKE IS DRIVEN AWAY see McCormick

AS THE BRANCH IS TO THE VINE see Day, Peggy

AS THE DISCIPLES see Bristol, L.

AS THE HART see Lombardo

AS THE HART LONGS see Mendelssohn-Bartholdy,
Felix

AS THE HART PANTETH see Hawkins, Gordon

AS THE HART PANTETH see Imbrie, Andrew Welsh

AS THE HART PANTETH see Lombardo, Robert

AS THE HART PANTETH see Marcello, Benedetto

AS THE HART PANTETH see Young, G.

AS THE HART PANTS see Mendelssohn-Bartholdy,
Felix, Wie Der Hirsch Schreit

AS THE HART PANTS see Palestrina, Giovanni,
Sicut Cervus

AS THE HEART see Mendelssohn-Bartholdy, Felix

AS THE HEART LONGS see Diemer, Emma Lou

AS THE HEART PANTETH see Marcello, Benedetto

AS THE SUN DOTH DAILY RISE see Barker

AS TORRENTS IN SUMMER see Elgar, Edward

AS WITH GLADNESS see Williams, David H.

AS WITH GLADNESS MEN OF OLD see Cocher

AS WITH GLADNESS MEN OF OLD see Hokanson,
Margrethe

AS WITH GLADNESS MEN OF OLD see Kocher

ASCENDENS CHRISTUS see Gallus, Jacobus

ASCENDIT CHRISTUS HODIE (from Anthology Of
Carols, An)
see Immortal Babe

ASCENDIT DEUS *cant
mix cor voc sc CHAPPELL 0021857-3691 $1.50,
cor pts CHAPPELL 0021857-3692 $.35   (A1265)

ASCENDIT DEUS see Burkhart, Franz

ASCENDIT DEUS see Gallus, Jacobus

ASCENDIT DEUS see Hutchings, Arthur

ASCENDIT DEUS see Palestrina, Giovanni

ASCENDIT DEUS see Philips, Peter

ASCENDO AD PATREM see Palestrina, Giovanni

ASCENDO AD PATREM MEUM see Scheidt, Samuel

ASCENSION see Sateren, Leland Bernhard

ASCENSION HYMN see Schicht, Johann Gottfried

ASCENSION HYMN see Schlicht, Johann Gottfried

ASCENSION, THE see Dello Joio, Norman

ASCENSION, THE see Naylor, Bernard, In
Ascensione Domine

ASCENSIONTIDE see Giasson

ASCENSO, ANTONIO
A Maria Immacolata (composed with Gerli,
Giovanni) *CC2U,BVM
[Lat] unis,org ZANIBON 2752 s.p.   (A1266)

A S. Luigi *ASD
[Lat] unis,org ZANIBON 2728 s.p.   (A1267)

Ave Maria
see CINQUE AVE MARIA

Due Canzoncine Pastorali *CC2U,Xmas/Epiph
[Lat] unis ZANIBON 2667 s.p.   (A1268)

Due Motteto Per S. Giuseppe *ASD,mot
[Lat] ZANIBON 2722 s.p.
contains: Te Joseph (unis&dbl cor,org);
Vir Fidelis (2 eq voices,org)   (A1269)

Ecce Sacerdos
see AD REC. EPISCOPUM

Inno Alla S. Infanzia *hymn
unis ZANIBON 2808 s.p.   (A1270)

O Crux Benedicta
see PER LA SETTIMANA SANTA

O Salutaris
see SEI MOTTETTI EUCARISTICI

Pel S. Natale E L'Epifania *Xmas
unis&unis ZANIBON 2667 s.p.   (A1271)

Quam Dilecta
see SEI MOTTETTI EUCARISTICI

Salve Regina Coelitum *BVM
[Lat] unis ZANIBON 2967 s.p.   (A1272)

Te Joseph
see Due Motteto Per S. Giuseppe

Tre Canti A Maria *CC3U,BVM
[Lat] unis,org ZANIBON 2754 s.p.   (A1273)

Vir Fidelis
see Due Motteto Per S. Giuseppe

ASCENTION see Hoiby, Lee

ASCHAFFENBURG, [WALTER] (1927-   )
Psalm 23 *see Twenty-Third Psalme, The

Twenty-Third Psalme, The (Psalm 23)
SATB,T solo,org,ob oct PRESSER 312-40692
$.40   (A1274)

ASCHIVENU see Algazi, Leon

ASCRIBE UNTO THE LORD see Travers, John

ASCRIBE UNTO THE LORD see Wesley, Samuel
Sebastian Jr.

ASCRIBE UNTO THE LORD(FIRST SECTION) see
Travers, John

ASCRIPTION OF PRAISE, AN see Sateren, Leland
Bernhard

ASH GROVE, THE *folk,Welsh
(Luboff, Norman) SATTBB oct WALTON 3047 $.30
                                      (A1275)

ASH GROVE, THE see Sharpe, Evelyn

ASHBY, BERTRAND
Unto Thee O Lord *anthem,Austral
SATB,S solo ALLANS 305 s.p.   (A1276)

ASHFIELD, ROBERT
Benedicite
SATB (F maj) oct NOVELLO 44.1339.03 s.p.
                                      (A1277)

Divinum Mysterium *Xmas,anthem
"Of The Father's Love Begotten" mix cor,B
solo oct NOVELLO 28.1456.00 s.p.   (A1278)

ASHFIELD, ROBERT (cont'd.)

"Of The Father's Love Begotten" 4pt mix
cor,org oct SCHIRM.G 11373 $.25   (A1279)

Holy Communion *Commun
2pt NOVELLO 44.1409.08 s.p.   (A1280)

Magnificat And Nunc Dimittis Minor *Magnif/
Nunc
unis (D maj) NOVELLO 44.1423.03 s.p. (A1281)

Of The Father's Love Begotten *see Divinum
Mysterium

ASHFORD
Lift Up Your Heads
SATB oct LORENZ 175 $.30   (A1282)
SATB (very easy) oct LORENZ 4382 $.30 (A1283)
SAB oct LORENZ 7401 $.35   (A1284)
SATB oct LILLENAS AN-2258 $.30   (A1285)

Lift Up Your Heads, O Ye Gates *anthem
SATB ALLANS 357 s.p.   (A1286)

Mother's Task
SATB oct LORENZ 9331 $.25   (A1287)

My Task
SATB oct LORENZ 1036 $.30   (A1288)
SSAA oct LORENZ 3524 $.30   (A1289)
SA oct LORENZ 5073 $.30   (A1290)
SSA oct LORENZ 6050 $.30   (A1291)
SAB oct LORENZ 7012 $.30   (A1292)
(Ehret) SATB oct PRO ART 1988 $.30   (A1293)
(Ehret) SAB oct PRO ART 2066 $.30   (A1294)
(Ehret) SSA oct PRO ART 1989 $.25   (A1295)
(Ehret) 2pt oct PRO ART 2263 $.25   (A1296)

ASHFORD, E.L.
Joyous Morn, The *Easter
SATB,SB soli,pno (easy) oct WILLIS 6324
$.12   (A1297)

Lift Up Your Heads
(Thompson) SATB oct BOURNE D5 $.30   (A1298)

Rest In The Lord
SATB,ST soli,pno (easy) oct WILLIS 6331
$.15   (A1299)

ASHIRA LADONAI *Fest
(Jospe, Erwin) "Sing Unto The Lord" [Eng/Heb]
SATB TRANSCON. TCL 703 $.30   (A1300)

ASHTON
Together With God *anthem
SATB oct FISCHER,C ASH. $.35   (A1301)

We Shall All Be Changed *anthem
SATB oct FISCHER,C ASH. $.25   (A1302)

Wonderful Love *Xmas,cant
SATB FISCHER,C ASH. $1.25   (A1303)

ASHTON, BOB
Hand Of God, The
(Carmichael) SATB oct WORD CS-2416 $.30 (A1304)

Songs Of Living Faith *CCUL
(Carmichael, Ralph) SATB voc sc WORD 20023
$1.95   (A1305)

Songs Of Living Hope *CCUL
(Carmichael, Ralph) SATB voc sc WORD 30036
(A1306)

ASHWORTH-HOPE, H.
Comrades And Brothers *carol
unis (scout song) CRAMER 4   (A1307)

ASK see Burroughs, B.

ASK, AND IT SHALL BE GIVEN YOU see Glarum, L.
Stanley

ASK THE FATHER see Englert, Eugene

ASK YE WHAT GREAT THING I KNOW see Blakley, D.

ASOLA, GIOVANNI MATTEO (ca. 1530-1609)
Christ Our Passover
see FOUR SHORT ANTHEMS FOR LENT AND EASTER

Christus Factus Est *Lent/Psntd,mot
[Lat] SATB,acap (med) MULLER M 15 s.p. (A1308)

[Lat] mix cor,acap oct NOVELLO DM-15 s.p. (A1309)

Decem Sacrae Laudes *CC10U
(Della Ragione, Ferdinando) [Lat] ATB
ZANIBON 4451 s.p.   (A1310)

Dieci Laudi Sacre *CC10U
[Lat] STB PETERS ZA4451 $1.50   (A1311)

Grant Us Thy Truth
(Coggin) SATB oct PRO ART 2586 $.30 (A1312)
(Coggin) SAB oct PRO ART 2589 $.30   (A1313)

Make My Steps Steadfast
see FOUR SHORT ANTHEMS FOR LENT AND EASTER

Pange Lingua
(Lammers, H.) [Lat] 4pt mix cor,acap (med)
cor pts LEMOINE s.p. see from COLLECTION
DE MUSIQUE ANCIENNE, PREMIERE RECUEIL
(A1314)

Tantum Ergo
mix cor,acap ERDMANN 541 s.p.   (A1315)

ASPERGES ME see Casciolini, Claudio

ASPERGES ME see Demerath, F.

ASPERGES ME see Haydn, (Johann) Michael

ASPICE DOMINE see Palestrina, Giovanni

ASPICE DOMINE (WITH CREQUILLON'S CHANSON) see
Merulo, Claudio

ASPICE, PATER see Schutz, Heinrich

ASPIENS A LONGE see Gallus, Jacobus

ASSOCIATE CRUSADES CHOIR BOOK *CC26L
(Chambers, Irv; Bledsoe, Tom) SATB voc sc
WORD 37604 $1.95   (A1316)

ASSUMPTA EST see Oltrassi, Giuseppe

ASSUMPTA EST MARIA see Aichinger, Gregor

ASSUMPTA EST MARIA see Baronchelli, Nestore

ASSUMPTA EST MARIA see Byrd, William

ASSUMPTA EST MARIA see Cerquetelli, Giuseppe

ASSUMPTA EST MARIA see Lovato, Zeno

ASSUMPTA EST MARIA see Palestrina, Giovanni

ASSUMPTA EST MARIA see Prenner, Georg

ASSUMPTA EST MARIA see Trexler, Georg

ASSURANCE SONGS *CC52U
cong cmplt ed LILLENAS MB-004 $.25   (A1317)

ASTITERUNT REGES see Victoria, Tomas Luis de

ASTON, HUGO (ca. 1480-ca. 1522)
Ancilla
see Anthems

Anthems *anthem
mix cor,acap voc sc KALMUS 6651 $1.00
contains: Ancilla; Ave Maria; Gaude
Virgo; Te Deum   (A1318)

Anthems *anthem
mix cor,acap voc sc KALMUS 6652 $1.00
contains: Ave Maria; O Baptista (A1319)

Ave Maria
see Anthems
see Anthems

Gaude Virgo
see Anthems

Mass Te Deum *Te Deum
mix cor,acap voc sc KALMUS 6659 $1.35
(A1320)

O Baptista
see Anthems

Te Deum
see Anthems

Videte Manus Meas *Mass
mix cor,acap voc sc KALMUS 6650 $1.50 (A1321)

ASTON, PETER
Alleluia, Pro Virgine Maria
"Alleluia, We Praise The Virgin Mary" see
Three Hymns To The Virgin

Alleluia, We Praise The Virgin Mary *see
Alleluia, Pro Virgine Maria

And I Saw A New Heaven *anthem
mix cor,S solo oct NOVELLO 29.0007.06 s.p.
(A1322)

Balulalow *Xmas
4pt mix cor,org oct SCHIRM.G 11546 $.25
(A1323)

Dormi, Jesu
"Sleep, Sweet Jesu" see Three Hymns To The
Virgin

For I Went With The Multitude *anthem
mix cor oct NOVELLO 29.0012.02 s.p. (A1324)

God Be Merciful Unto Us *anthem
mix cor oct NOVELLO 40.1494.04 s.p. (A1325)

Haec Dies *Easter
[Lat] SATB,org voc sc NOVELLO s.p.   (A1326)

O Queen Of Heaven We Praise Thee *see Regina
Coeli, Laetare

Praise Ye The Lord *anthem
SATB,org/brass oct NOVELLO 29.0014.09 s.p.,
ipr   (A1327)

Regina Coeli, Laetare
"O Queen Of Heaven We Praise Thee" see
Three Hymns To The Virgin

Sleep, Sweet Jesu *see Dormi, Jesu

Three Hymns To The Virgin *BVM,anthem/hymn
[Lat] mix cor,acap oct NOVELLO 40.1440.05
s.p.
contains: Alleluia, Pro Virgine Maria,
"Alleluia, We Praise The Virgin Mary";
Dormi, Jesu, "Sleep, Sweet Jesu";
Regina Coeli, Laetare, "O Queen Of
Heaven We Praise Thee"   (A1328)

D'ASTORGA, EMANUELLE (1680-ca. 1757)
Christ, Now At Thy Passion *see Christe,
Quum Sit Jam Exire

Christe, Quum Sit Jam Exire (from Stabat
Mater)
"Christ, Now At Thy Passion" SATB,org
SCHIRM.EC 2400 $.35   (A1329)
(Clough-Leighter, H.) "Christ, Now At Thy
Passion" SATB,org (abridged) SCHIRM.EC
2620 $.40   (A1330)
(Glaser, V.; Clough-Leighter, H.) "Christ,
Now At Thy Passion" SSA,org (abridged)
SCHIRM.EC 1983 $.35   (A1331)

Oh! What Sorrow!
(Barrie) SATB oct LAWSON 898 $.25   (A1332)

Stabat Mater
[Lat] SATB,acap PETERS HU1614 $2.00, ipr
(A1333)

ASULAE, I.M.
Le Vergine
(Vecchi, I.) 3pt quarto FORNI 26 s.p. (A1334)

AT ASSEMBLY (O LORD OF ALL) see White, Robert

AT CALVARY see Towner, Daniel B.

AT CALVARY see Wilson

AT CHRISTMAS TIME WAS BORN A KING see Charles

AT EASTER MORN see Blake, G.

AT EVEN ERE THE SUN see Turner, Edmund (Edmond)

AT EVEN WHEN THE SUN DID SET see Wolff, S.
Drummond

AT GOD'S RIGHT HAND HE DOTH STAND see Bach

AT GOLDEN DAWN OF CHRISTMAS see Ehret, Walter

AT HER FEET see Castaldo

AT HIS CRADLE see Lefebvre

AT LAST WE'RE IN THE TOWN see Nous Voici Dans
La Ville

AT LENGTH THERE DAWNS THE GLORIOUS DAY see
Cutler

AT MONTSERRAT see Nicolau, [Antonio]

AT PENTECOST see Ortlip, Stephen

AT THE CRADLE see Franck, Cesar, La Vierge A La
Creche

AT THE CROSS see Lundquist, Matthew Nathanael

AT THE CROSS, HER STATION KEEPING see Wood

AT THE CROSS OF GOD see Coots

AT THE CROSS, REMEMBER ME see Christiansen,
Olaf Christian

AT THE CROSSING see Lister, Mosie

AT THE CRY OF THE FIRST BIRD see Guion, David
Wendall Fentress

AT THE CRY OF THE FIRST BIRD see Morgan

AT THE CRY OF THE FIRST BIRD see Wilson

AT THE END OF EIGHT DAYS see Hillert, Richard

AT THE FEET OF JESUS see Ferguson

AT THE FOOT OF THE CROSS see Dvorak, Antonin,
Stabat Mater

AT THE GATE OF THE YEAR see Ross

AT THE GATES OF HEAVEN see Kjelson

AT THE GATES OF HEAVEN see Zaninelli, Luigi

AT THE HOUR OF MIDNIGHT *Xmas,carol,Carib
(Ehret, Walter) SATB,opt inst WALTON 2527
$.30   (A1335)

AT THE JOURNEY'S END see Lister, Mosie

AT THE LAMB'S HIGH FEAST see Edmundson, Garth

AT THE LAMB'S HIGH FEAST see Glasson

AT THE LAMB'S HIGH FEAST WE SING *hymn
SATB oct ST.MARTIN s.p.   (A1336)

AT THE LAMB'S HIGH FEAST WE SING see Blake, G.

AT THE LAMB'S HIGH FEAST WE SING see Mudde,
Willem

AT THE LAMB'S HIGH FEAST WE SING see Ratcliffe,
Desmond

AT THE LAMB'S HIGH FEAST WE SING see Wadely,
F.W.

AT THE MANGER *Xmas,carol
(Pearson) 4pt mix cor,acap oct CURWEN 11182
$.25
contains: Away In A Manger (Fr); Bethlehem
(Span); Gabriel's Message (Span);
Virgin's Cradle Song   (A1337)

AT THE MANGER see Gibbs

AT THE NAME OF JESUS see Gallus, Jacobus, In
Nomine Jesu

AT THE NAME OF JESUS see Hughes

AT THE NAME OF JESUS see Malin, Don

AT THE NAME OF JESUS see Marryott, Ralph E.

AT THE NAME OF JESUS see Roff, Joseph

AT THE NAME OF JESUS see Vaughan Williams,
Ralph

AT THE RIVER *US
(Copland; White-Wilding) TTBB oct BOOSEY 5514
$.30 see from Old American Songs (A1338)
(Copland; White-Wilding) SA oct BOOSEY 5511
$.30 see from Old American Songs (A1339)
(Copland; White-Wilding) SSA oct BOOSEY 5512
$.30 see from Old American Songs (A1340)
(Copland; White-Wilding) SATB oct BOOSEY 5513
$.30 see from Old American Songs (A1341)

AT THE ROUND EARTH'S IMAGIN'D CORNERS see
Hewitt-Jones, Tony

AT THE ROUND EARTH'S IMAGINED CORNERS see
Spencer, W.

AT THE SEPULCHRE see Johnson, Robert Sherlaw

AT THE SWEET BIRTH OF OUR LORD see Praetorius,
Michael, In Natali Domini

AT THE TIME OF THE BANQUET see Krapf, Gerhard

AT THE TURNING OF THE NARROW ROAD see Lewis

AT THY FEET see Bach

AT THY FEET see Edmundson, Garth

AT THY FEET COME GRACIOUS SPIRIT see Bach

AT THY FEET, OUR GOD AND FATHER see Ford,
Virgil T.

AT THY FEET, OUR GOD AND FATHER see Larson

ATHALIA see Handel, George Frideric

ATKINSON
Door, The *Xmas
SATB SCHMITT 8063 $.35 (A1342)

I Sing The Mighty Power Of God *Gen
SATB SCHMITT 1802 $.40 (A1343)

Two Introits *anthem/Introit
mix cor oct OXFORD 02.017 $.20 (A1344)

ATKINSON, CONDIT R.
One In Christ
SATB oct AGAPE CF 124 $.35 (A1345)

Ring Out, Wild Bells
SATB,opt chimes/hndbl oct AGAPE F 933 $.30
(A1346)

We Plow The Fields
SATB oct AGAPE CF 150 $.30 (A1347)

ATKINSON, THELMA
First Nowell, The *Xmas,anthem
SATB,opt SATB soli oct HARRIS HC 4007 $.35
(A1348)

ATONEMENT MUSIC see Fromm, Herbert

ATONEMENT, THE see Peters, Sidney

ATT BEDJA GUD, HAN SJALV OSS BJOD see
Hammarstrom, Hugo

ATT VARA KRISTEN AR NA'T MER'
see Klippa Du Som Brast For Mig

ATTEND OUR PRAYERS see Williams

ATTENHOFER, [KARL] (1837-1914)
Alle Guten Gaben *Xmas
(Schonholzer, G.) [Ger] wom cor,acap (easy)
HUG s.p. (A1349)

Gott Schutze Die Reben Am Sonnigen Rhein
*Op.116,No.3
[Ger] men cor,acap (easy) HUG s.p. (A1350)

ATTIOFEM KORKORALER see Bach, Johann Sebastian

ATTWOOD, THOMAS (1765-1838)
Come Holy Ghost *Fest/Gen/Marriage/Whitsun,
anthem/Bibl
SATB ALLANS 206 s.p. (A1351)
SA ALLANS 271 s.p. (A1352)
mix cor,S solo oct NOVELLO 40.0170.02 s.p.
(A1353)
(Hines) SAB SCHMITT SD5535 $.30 (A1354)
(Knight) 3pt mix cor,org oct CURWEN 11026
$.20 (A1355)
(Noble) 4pt mix cor,S solo oct SCHIRM.G
6511 $.25 (A1356)
(Wyton) SATB oct FISCHER,C CM-7693 $.25
(A1357)
Come, Holy Ghost Our Souls Inspire *Whitsun
SSA,S solo oct NOVELLO 33.0050.01 s.p.
(A1358)
Enter Not Into Judgment *anthem
mix cor oct NOVELLO 40.0217.02 s.p. (A1359)

God That Madest Earth And Heaven
(Bridge, Sir Fredk.) SATB,S solo oct BOSWORTH
s.p. (A1360)

O God, Who By The Leading Of A Star *Epiph/
Gen
SATB (easy) oct OXFORD 43.305 $.35 (A1361)

Songs Of Praise The Angels Sang *Xmas
2pt oct NOVELLO 33.0027.07 s.p. (A1362)

Teach Me O Lord *anthem/Bibl
SATB ALLANS 240 s.p. (A1363)
4pt mix cor oct SCHIRM.G 4488 $.25 (A1364)
mix cor oct NOVELLO 40.0221.00 s.p. (A1365)
(Davis, K.) SA,org,pno SCHIRM.EC 1576 $.20
(A1366)
(Gillespie, J.) SSA,acap oct NOVELLO
51.0611.07 s.p. (A1367)
(Harris) 3pt jr cor/SSA (med easy) FISCHER,
C CM 7468 $.20 (A1368)
(Harris) SSA,acap oct FISCHER,C CM-7468
$.25 (A1369)
(Knight) SAB CURWEN 80806 s.p. (A1370)
(Mueller) SABar oct SCHIRM.G 8689 $.25
(A1371)
(Talmadge, A.) SSAA,acap SCHIRM.EC 2534
$.25 (A1372)
(Trusler) SATB oct PLYMOUTH TR-121 $.25
(A1373)
Teach Me, O Lord, The Way Of Thy Statutes
SATB,org SCHIRM.EC 372 $.30 (A1374)

Turn Thee, Again, O Lord *Gen,anthem
SATB,org SCHIRM.EC 1721 $.35 (A1375)
mix cor oct NOVELLO 40.0431.00 s.p. (A1376)
SATB BOSWORTH s.p. (A1377)
(Davis, K.) SSA SCHIRM.EC 1879 $.35 (A1378)
(Hines) SATB SCHMITT 1927 $.35 (A1379)

Turn Thy Face From My Sins *anthem/Bibl
4pt mix cor,high solo oct SCHIRM.G 4489
$.25 (A1380)
mix cor,S solo oct NOVELLO 40.0155.09 s.p.
(A1381)
SATB oct LESLIE 4030 (A1382)
(Ehret) SATB,S/T solo oct PRO ART 1491 $.18
(A1383)
(Mueller) SABar oct SCHIRM.G 9748 $.25
(A1384)
(Pitcher, Gladys) 3pt wom cor,pno (med) oct
WILLIS 8487 $.20 (A1385)

Unclouded Day, The
(Clements) SATB oct AGAPE GC 801 $.30
(A1386)

ATZEY ZEYDIM OMDIM *Fest
(Helfman, Max) "Olive Trees" [Heb] SATB
TRANSCON. TCL 715 $.30 (A1387)

AU CHRIST-ROI see Mercenier, P.

AU CHRIST-ROI DANS LA SAINTE EUCHARISTIE see
Renaud, E.

AU MOINS, MON DIEU, NE M'ABANDONNE PAS see
Goudimel, Claude

AU PIED DU TRONE CELESTE see Mendelssohn-
Bartholdy, Felix, Periti Autem

AU ROI DES ROIS, IMMORTEL, INVISIBLE see
Sermisy, Claude de

AU SAINT-NAU see Inghelbrecht, Desire Emile

AU SAINT NAU see Migot, Georges

AUBANEL, GEORGES
Ah! Quand Reviendra-t-Il? *Xmas
[Fr] 4pt mix cor,opt pno/org HEUGEL s.p.
see from Quatre Noels (A1388)

Allons Pastoureaux
[Fr] 4pt mix cor,acap oct DURAND (A1389)

Ave Maria
[Lat] SATB,acap oct SALABERT-US $.65
(A1390)

Ave Verum
[Lat] SATB,org oct SALABERT-US $.65 (A1391)

Caille, Pauvre Caille
see Aubanel, Georges, Jesus Christ
S'Habille En Pauvre

C'est Le Bon Lever *Xmas
[Fr] 4pt mix cor,SB soli,opt pno/org HEUGEL
s.p. see from Quatre Noels (A1392)

Chantons Noel *Xmas
[Fr] 4pt mix cor,acap oct DURAND (A1393)

En Sortant De L'etable *Xmas
[Fr] 4pt mix cor,acap oct DURAND (A1394)

Jesus Christ S'Habille En Pauvre *Fr
[Fr] 4pt mix cor CHAPPELL-FR s.p. contains
also: Caille, Pauvre Caille (A1395)
[Fr] 3 eq voices CHAPPELL-FR s.p. contains
also: Kyriole Lorrain; Voici La Saint-
Jean (A1396)

Kyriole Lorrain
see Aubanel, Georges, Jesus-Christ
S'Habille En Pauvre
see Aubanel, Georges, Quand Mon Mari Se
Fachera

Noel De La Marche Des Rois *Xmas,carol,Fr
[Fr] mix cor,acap cor pts LEMOINE s.p.
(A1397)
[Fr] 4pt men cor,acap (med easy) cor pts
LEMOINE s.p. (A1398)

Noels Pittoresques De France (Vol. 1a) *CCU,
Xmas,carol,Fr
[Fr] CHAPPELL-FR 3 eq voices s.p.; 4pt mix
cor s.p. (A1399)

Nuit De Felicite *Xmas
[Fr] 4pt mix cor,opt pno/org HEUGEL s.p.
see from Quatre Noels (A1400)

O Salutaris
[Lat] SATB,acap oct SALABERT-US $.65
(A1401)

O Up! As-Tu Entendu
see Aubanel, Georges, Voici La Saint-Jean

Quand Mon Mari Se Fachera *Fr
[Fr] 4pt mix cor CHAPPELL-FR s.p. contains
also: Kyriole Lorrain (A1402)

Quatre Noels *see Ah! Quand Reviendra-t-Il?;
C'est Le Bon Lever; Nuit De Felicite;
Sont Trois Hommes Fort Sages (A1403)

Sont Trois Hommes Fort Sages *Xmas
[Fr] 4pt mix cor,opt pno/org HEUGEL s.p.
see from Quatre Noels (A1404)

Tantum Ergo
[Lat] SATB,acap oct SALABERT-US $.65
(A1405)

Voici La Saint-Jean
see Aubanel, Georges, Jesus-Christ
S'Habille En Pauvre
[Fr] 4pt mix cor CHAPPELL-FR s.p. contains
also: O Up! As-Tu Entendu (A1406)

AUBER, DANIEL-FRANCOIS-ESPRIT (1782-1871)
O Loving Savior *Gen/Lent
(Dickinson) SATB oct GRAY GSC 61 $.30
(A1407)

AUBERT, [LOUIS-FRANCOIS-MARIE] (1877-1968)
Ave Maria
[Lat] 4pt mix cor,acap oct DURAND (A1408)

O Salutaris *Commun,mot
[Lat] SATBar,T/S solo,org,vln DURAND s.p.
(A1409)
[Lat/Fr] SATB,S/T solo,org,vln,harp oct
DURAND s.p. (A1410)

AUBERT, PIERRE FRANCOIS OLIVER
(ca. 1763-ca. 1830)
O God Who By The Leading Of A Star
see Byrd, William, Prevent Us, O Lord

AUBRY, F.
Invocation Pour Une Messe De Mariage
*Marriage
[Lat/Fr] unis,opt vln LEMOINE s.p. (A1411)

AUDI BENIGNE CONDITOR see Hamel, M.-R.

AUDI, BENIGNE CONDITOR see Washington, Henry

AUDI FILIA see Goudimel, Claude

AUDI FILIA see Jackson, Francis

AUDI FILIA see Scarlatti, Alessandro

AUDITE MORTALES see Pekiel, Bertlomiej

AUDITE NOVA see Lassus, Roland de (Orlandus)

AUDITOR IN OPPORTUNITATIBUS see Eberlin,
Johann Ernst

AUDIVI, MEDIA NOCTE see Tallis, Thomas

AUDIVI VOCEM DE CAELO see Tallis, Thomas

AUDRAN, EDMOND (1840-1901)
Petite Noel Avec Mystere (from La Cigale)
Xmas,carol
[Fr] 2-3pt CHOUDENS s.p. see also CHOEURS
POUR DISTRIBUTIONS DE PRIX OU POUR
ENFANTS (A1412)

AUERBACH, N.
Bells Ring Out Joyfully *Xmas
SSAA oct HERITAGE $.40 (A1413)

Prince Of Peace Is Born Today *Xmas
SSA oct HERITAGE H6005 $.35 (A1414)

AUF! AUF! ERGREIFET DEN VERRATER! see
Beethoven, Ludwig van

AUF, AUF IHR BUBEN! see Brautigam, Helmut

AUF, AUF, IHR HIRTEN
(Strobl, Otto) mix cor,acap oct DOBLINGER
s.p. (A1415)

AUF, AUF, IHR HIRTEN see Barthel, Ursula

AUF, AUF, IHR HIRTEN ALLZUGLEICH see Werner,
Gregor Joseph

AUF, AUF, IHR REICHSGENOSSEN see Bausznern,
Dietrich von

AUF, AUF, MEIN HERZ see Geisel, Gustav

AUF, AUF, MEIN HERZ see Neubert, Gottfried

AUF, AUF, MEIN HERZ MIT FREUDEN see Bach,
Johann Sebastian

AUF, AUF, MEIN HERZ, MIT FREUDEN see Cruger,
Johann

AUF, AUF, MEIN HERZ, MIT FREUDEN see Ebeling,
Johann Georg

AUF, AUF, MEIN HERZ, MIT FREUDEN see Fiebig,
Kurt

AUF, AUF, MEIN HERZ, MIT FREUDEN see Gadsch,
Herbert

AUF, AUF, MEIN HERZ, MIT FREUDEN see
Hufschmidt, Wolfgang

AUF, AUF, MEIN HERZ, MIT FREUDEN see Reimerdes,
Friedrich

AUF, AUF, MOSES see Go Down, Moses

AUF, BLEIBET TREU *CCU,Cnfrm/Marriage,funeral
(Reich, Philipp) [Ger] men cor BAREN. EM 335
s.p. or Baptism (A1416)

AUF BLEIBET TREU, AUSGABE A *CCU,Cnfrm/
Marriage,funeral
(Reich, Philipp) [Ger] 4pt mix cor BAREN.
EM 333 s.p. or Baptism (A1417)

AUF, BLEIBET TREU, AUSGABE B *CCU,Cnfrm/
Marriage,funeral
(Reich, Philipp) [Ger] 3pt mix cor BAREN.
EM 334 s.p. or Baptism (A1418)

AUF, BLEIBET TREU, AUSGABE D *Cnfrm,funeral/
Gradual
(Reich, Philipp) [Ger] 3 eq voices,acap
BAREN. EM336 s.p. or Baptism (A1419)

AUF CHRISTI HIMMELFAHRT ALLEIN see Bach, Johann
Sebastian

AUF DAS CHRISTFEST see Weyrauch, Johannes

AUF DEIN WORT WILL ICH TRAUEN see Schutz,
Heinrich

AUF DEM BERGE, DA GEHET DER WIND see Grofe

AUF DEM BERGE DA WEHET DER WIND see Knab, Armin

AUF DEM GEBIRGE HAT MAN EIN GESCHREI GEHORET
see Schutz, Heinrich

AUF DEM GEBIRGE HAT MAN EIN GESCHREI GEHORT see
Schutz, Heinrich

AUF DER ANDACHT HEIL'GEN FLUGELN see Mozart,
Wolfgang Amadeus

AUF DICH ALLEIN, DU TREUER GOTT see Hartmann,
Heinrich

AUF DICH, HERR, HAB' ICH GEHOFFET see
Buxtehude, Dietrich

AUF DICH, HERR, STEHT MEIN VERTRAUEN see
Poschio, Isaac

AUF DICH, HERR, TRAU ICH ALLEZEIT see Schutz,
Heinrich

AUF DIESEN TAG BEDENKEN WIR see Heilmann,
Harald

AUF DIESEN TAG BEDENKEN WIR see Ruppel, Paul
Ernst

AUF, HALTET EUER HERZ BEREIT see Rein, Walter

AUF IHN WILL ICH VERTRAUEN see Kurig, Hans-
Hermann

AUF, LOBET DEN HERREN see Telemann, Georg
Philipp, Laudate Jehovam

AUF, LOBET DEN HERRN, ALLE HEIDEN see Telemann,
Georg Philipp

AUF, MEIN HERZ see Bach, Johann Sebastian, Auf,
Mein Herz, Des Herren Tag

AUF MEIN HERZ! DES HERREN TAG see Bach, Johann
Sebastian

AUF MEINEN LIEBEN GOTT see Pepping, Ernst

AUF MEINEN LIEBEN GOTT see Schein, Johann Hermann

AUF MEINEN LIEBEN GOTT TRAU ICH see Regnart, Jacob

AUF MEINEN LIEBEN GOTT, TRAU ICH see Schein, Johann Hermann

AUF MEINEN LIEBEN GOTT TRAU ICH see Stern, Hermann

AUF PFINGSTEN see Pfirstinger, F.

AUF, SEELE DES HERREN LOB ERKLINGEN see Mareschall, Samuel

AUFBLICK see Wolf, Hugo

AUFBLICK: VERGEHT MIR DER HIMMEL see Wolf, Hugo

AUFDEMBERGE, EDGAR
    Christ Is Our Cornerstone *Gen
        SATB,kbd (med easy) oct CONCORDIA 98-1591
        $.25   (A1420)

AUFERSTANDEN, AUFERSTANDEN see Reger, Max

AUFERSTANDEN BIN ICH see Marx, Karl

AUFERSTANDEN BIST DU see Kloft, Gerhard

AUFERSTEHUNG see Ahrens, Joseph

AUFERSTEHUNGS-ORATORIUM see Thomas, Kurt

AUFGLANZT DER GOTTGEWOLLTE TAG see Aeschbacher, Walther

AUFLICK see Wolf, Hugo

AUFS NEUE JAHR I: GEISTLICHE LIEDER (from
        Cantionale Sacrum) CCU
    (Pass, Walter) 4-5pt DOBLINGER s.p. contains
        works by Aldenburger, M.; Franck, M.;
        Helder, B.; Lindemann, J.; Vecchi, O.
                                                  (A1421)

AULBACH
    Cast Thy Burden Upon The Lord
        SATB,acap oct FISCHER,C CM-6741 $.25
                                                  (A1422)

    Hear My Prayer *anthem/prayer
        SATB,acap oct FISCHER,C CM-7205 $.25
                                                  (A1423)

    King Of Peace
        SATB oct FISCHER,C CM-7120 $.25 (A1424)

    Unto Thee O Lord
        4pt jr cor/SATB (easy) FISCHER,C CM 6824
        $.25   (A1425)

AULEN
    Dreistimmige Messe *Mass
        (Birtner) 3pt mix cor MOSELER s.p. (A1426)

    Missa *Mass
        3pt,acap voc sc KALMUS 6000 $1.25 (A1427)

AULEN, GUSTAF
    Fadernas Kyrka
        men cor NORDISKA 4199 s.p.   (A1428)

AUPRES D'AQUEL ESTABLE see Saboly, Nicholas

AURICHER SINGBUCHLEIN, HEFT 1 see Bender, Jan

AURICHER SINGBUCHLEIN, HEFT 2 see Bender, Jan

AURICHER SINGBUCHLEIN, HEFT 3 see Bender, Jan

AURICHER-SINGBUCHLEIN, HEFT 4 see Bender, Jan

AUS DEM DUNKEL DER WELT see Huber, P.

AUS DEM ENGLISCHEN see Gebhard, Hans

AUS DEN TIEFEN SCHREIE ICH ZU DIR, O HERR see
    Philipp, Franz, Friedensmesse

AUS DER TIEFE see Bach, Johann Sebastian, Aus
    Der Tiefe Rufe Ich, Herr, Zu Dir

AUS DER TIEFE see Gattermayer, Heinrich

AUS DER TIEFE see Romanovsky, Erich

AUS DER TIEFE RUF ICH, HERR, ZU DIR see Selle,
    Thomas

AUS DER TIEFE RUFE ICH see Klein, Richard
    Rudolf

AUS DER TIEFE RUFE ICH see Lissmann, Kurt

AUS DER TIEFE RUFE ICH see Schutz, Heinrich

AUS DER TIEFE RUFE ICH see Stockmeier, Wolfgang

AUS DER TIEFE RUFE ICH, HERR see Beck, Conrad

AUS DER TIEFE RUFE ICH, HERR see Marks, Gunther

AUS DER TIEFE RUFE ICH, HERR, ZU DIR see Bach,
    Johann Sebastian

AUS DER TIEFE RUFE ICH, HERR, ZU DIR see
    Hartmann, Heinrich

AUS GEIST ENTSTAND DIE WELT see Gerhard, Fritz
    Christian

AUS HARTEM WEH see Sendt, Willy

AUS HARTEM WEH DIE MENSCHHEIT KLAGT see
    Pepping, Ernst

AUS HARTEN WEH' DIE MENSCHEIT KLAGT see Lehner,
    F.X.

AUS MEINER SUNDEN TIEFE see Lassus, Roland de
    (Orlandus)

AUS MEINES HERZENS GRUNDE see Bach, Johann
    Sebastian

AUS MEINES HERZENS GRUNDE see Hassler, Hans Leo

AUS MEINES HERZENS GRUNDE see Micheelsen, Hans
    Friedrich

AUS MEINES HERZENS GRUNDE see Schlenker,
    Manfred

AUS MEINES HERZENS GRUNDE see Schutz, Heinrich

AUS MEINES HERZENS GRUNDE see Stern, Hermann

AUS MEINES HERZENS GRUNDE see Trubel, Gerhard,
    Nun Jauchzet, All Ihr Frommen

AUS MEINES HERZENS GRUNDE SAG ICH DIR see
    Praetorius, Michael

AUS MEINES HERZENS GRUNDE see Schutz, Heinrich

AUS MEINES JAMMERS TIEFE see Stier, Alfred

AUS MEINS JAMMERS TIEFE RUF ICH see Goudimel,
    Claude

AUS TIEFER NOT see Bach, Johann Sebastian, Aus
    Tiefer Not Schrei Ich Zu Dir

AUS TIEFER NOT see Brown, R.

AUS TIEFER NOT see Fischer-Dieskau, Klaus

AUS TIEFER NOT see Hassler, Hans Leo

AUS TIEFER NOT see Hellingk, Lupus

AUS TIEFER NOT see Resinarius, Balthasar

AUS TIEFER NOT see Rohwer, Jens

AUS TIEFER NOT see Schutz, Heinrich

AUS TIEFER NOT see Thomas, Kurt

AUS TIEFER NOT see Walter (Walther), Johann

AUS TIEFER NOT see Zeuner, Martin

AUS TIEFER NOT NOT SCHREI ICH ZU DIR see
    Franck, Melchior

AUS TIEFER NOT SCHREI ICH ZU DIR see Bach,
    Johann Sebastian

AUS TIEFER NOT SCHREI ICH ZU DIR see Distler,
    Hugo

AUS TIEFER NOT SCHREI ICH ZU DIR see Ducis,
    Benedictus

AUS TIEFER NOT SCHREI ICH ZU DIR see Franck,
    Melchior

AUS TIEFER NOT SCHREI ICH ZU DIR see Hassler,
    Hans Leo

AUS TIEFER NOT SCHREI ICH ZU DIR see Hemmel,
    Sigmund

AUS TIEFER NOT SCHREI ICH ZU DIR see
    Hufschmidt, Wolfgang

AUS TIEFER NOT SCHREI ICH ZU DIR see Kukuck,
    Felicitas

AUS TIEFER NOT SCHREI ICH ZU DIR see
    Mendelssohn-Bartholdy, Felix

AUS TIEFER NOT SCHREI ICH ZU DIR see
    Praetorius, Michael

AUS TIEFER NOT SCHREI ICH ZU DIR see Reda,
    Siegfried

AUS TIEFER NOT SCHREI ICH ZU DIR see Schein,
    Johann Hermann

AUS TIEFER NOT SCHREI ICH ZU DIR see Schutz,
    Heinrich

AUS TIEFER NOT SCHREI'ICH ZU DIR [CHORALE] see
    Bach, Johann Sebastian

AUSGEWAHLTE CHORALSATZE see Bach, Johann
    Sebastian

AUSGEWAHLTE KIRCHENLIEDER see Franck, Melchior

AUSGEWAHLTE KIRCHENMUSIK see Selle, Thomas

AUSGEWAHLTE KIRCHENMUSIK see Hammerschmidt,
    Andreas

AUSKLANG see Jacot, Andre

AUSTIN
    Beggar Baby, The *Xmas
        unis BOOSEY-CAN s.p.   (A1429)

    Carol
        (Smith) SATB oct FISCHER,C CM-7536 $.25
                                           (A1430)

    Let All The World In Ev'ry Corner Sing
        SATB oct SUMMY 5833 $.30   (A1431)

    One Winter Night *Xmas
        unis BOOSEY-CAN s.p.   (A1432)

AUSTIN, ERNEST (1874-1947)
    Christmas Bells *Xmas,carol
        unis ASHDOWN U.31 s.p.   (A1433)

    God's Way
        SATB ENOCH EC237 s.p.   (A1434)

    When Thou Passest Through The Waters
        SATB ENOCH EC239 s.p.   (A1435)

AUSTIN, R.
    Twenty Popular Anthems For General Use
        *CC20U
        SATB oct PRESSER $1.25   (A1436)

AUSTRALIAN CAROL, AN *Xmas,carol,Austral
    (Grainer; Meaghan) SSA ALLANS 348 s.p.
                                           (A1437)

AUSTRALIAN CAROLS see Young, K.

AUSTRALIAN CHRISTMAS CAROL, AN see Jones

AUSTRIAN SHEPHERD'S CAROL see Wood, Dale

AUSTRO TERRIS INFLUENTE see Lybbert, Donald

AUTHOR OF LIFE DIVINE see Cope, Cecil

AUTHOR OF LIFE DIVINE see Thiman, Eric Harding

AUTHOR OF LIGHT see Cook, John

AUTHOR OF LIVE DIVINE see Thompson, Alan

AUTUMN REVERIE see Young, Gordon

AV DJUPETS NOD *Bibl
    (Lunden, Lennart) [Swed] SAB,opt fl GEHRMANS
    TKS 4   (A1438)

AV DJUPETS NOD see Berg, Gottfrid

AV DJUPETS NOD, O GUD, TILL DIG see Luther,
    Martin

AV HIMLENS HOJD see Olson, Daniel

AV HIMLENS HOJD see Runback, Albert

AV HIMLENS HOJD OSS KOMMET AR see Berg,
    Gottfrid

AV HIMLENS HOJD OSS KOMMET AR see Scheidt,
    Samuel

AV HJARTAT VILL JAG PRISA see Praetorius,
    Michael

AVALONE
    Sing Praise To His Name
        (Boersma) SAB oct WORD CS-2422 $.30 (A1439)

AVALOS
    Mariachi Mass *folk/Mass,Mex
        [Eng] unis/2pt/SATB,opt trp,bvl,perc,gtr
        PRO ART 1194 $1.50   (A1440)

    O Lord, Increase My Faith
        SATB oct PRO ART 1867 $.22   (A1441)

AVE, AVE MARIA, DICH LOBT DIE SUSSE MUSICA see
    Woll, Erna

AVE CHRISTE IMMOLATE see Des Prez, Josquin

AVE CRUX see Moren, John

AVE DOMINE JESU CHRISTE see Senfl, Ludwig

AVE GRATIA PLENA see Verdonck, Cornelius

AVE MARIA (from Bamberger Gesangbuch 1628) BVM
    SATB,acap (contains also: Eine Jungfrau Zart
        (from Psalteriolum 1642)) voc pt DOBLINGER
        s.p. see also Unsere Liebe Frau   (A1442)
    "Mother Of All" SSA CHAPPELL 0016105-354 $.40
                                           (A1443)
    "Mother Of All" SATB CHAPPELL 0016105-358
        $.40   (A1444)
    (Arcadelt, J.) "Hear My Prayer, O God" TTBB,
        acap SCHIRM.EC 526 $.20   (A1445)
    (Racine, C.; Geveart, F.-A.) "La Salutation
        Angelique" [Lat/Fr] 3pt wom cor,acap (med
        easy) cor pts LEMOINE s.p. see from
        Collection De Choeurs, premiere Facsimile
                                           (A1446)

AVE MARIA see Abt, Franz

AVE MARIA see Agustsson, Herbert H.

AVE MARIA see Alexandre, Georges

AVE MARIA see Amatucci, Paolo

AVE MARIA see Ammon, Blasius

AVE MARIA see Anonymous

AVE MARIA see Arcadelt, Jacob

AVE MARIA see Arnaldi, Antonio

AVE MARIA see Ascenso, Antonio

AVE MARIA see Aston, Hugo

AVE MARIA see Aubanel, Georges

AVE MARIA see Aubert, [Louis-Francois-Marie]

AVE MARIA see Bach

AVE MARIA see Bach, Johann Sebastian

AVE MARIA see Baden, Conrad

AVE MARIA see Batiste, Antoine-Edouard

AVE MARIA see Bauernfiend, Hans

AVE MARIA see Becker, Peter

AVE MARIA see Bernard, William

AVE MARIA see Binkerd, [Gordon]

AVE MARIA see Bizet, Georges

AVE MARIA see Borsieri, C.

AVE MARIA see Bottazzo, Luigi

AVE MARIA see Bottigliero, Eduardo

AVE MARIA see Brahms, Johannes

AVE MARIA see Brahms, Johannes, Ave Maria

AVE MARIA see Breville, Pierre-Onfroy de

AVE MARIA see Bruckner, Anton

AVE MARIA see Buissart-Moriseaux

AVE MARIA see Busser, [Henri-Paul]

AVE MARIA see Byrd, William

AVE MARIA see Campbell-Watson, Frank

AVE MARIA see Canniciari, D. Pompeo

AVE MARIA see Cerquetelli, Giuseppe

AVE MARIA see Champagne, Claude

AVE MARIA see Cherubini, Luigi

AVE MARIA see Choisnel, G.

AVE MARIA see Cline

AVE MARIA see Constantini, Artemio

AVE MARIA see Cory, George

AVE MARIA see Curran, E.L.

AVE MARIA see Dall'Adria, Giovanni

AVE MARIA see Davies

AVE MARIA see Davies, Peter Maxwell

AVE MARIA see Delvincourt, Claude

AVE MARIA see Des Prez, Josquin

AVE MARIA see Dexter

AVE MARIA see Dietsch, Pierre Louis Philippe

AVE MARIA see Donizetti, Gaetano

AVE MARIA see Dubois, Theodore

AVE MARIA see Du Caurroy, Francoise-Eustache

AVE MARIA see Eccher

AVE MARIA see Egaddi

AVE MARIA see Escovada, R.

AVE MARIA see Eulalia, Sister

AVE MARIA see Fabiani, Angelo

AVE MARIA see Faure, Gabriel-Urbain

AVE MARIA see Fevin, Antoine de

AVE MARIA see Fogliano

AVE MARIA see Franck, Cesar

AVE MARIA see Franz

AVE MARIA see Fuser, Ireneo

AVE MARIA see Gaburo, Kenneth

AVE MARIA see Gibilaro

AVE MARIA see Gigout, [Eugene]

AVE MARIA see Gluck, Christoph Willibald Ritter von

AVE MARIA see Gombert, Nicolas

AVE MARIA see Gounod, Charles Francois

AVE MARIA see Grassi, Ciro

AVE MARIA see Head, Michael (Dewar)

AVE MARIA see Heiller, Anton

AVE MARIA see Holst, Gustav

AVE MARIA see Hovhaness, Alan

AVE MARIA see Ketelbey, Albert William

AVE MARIA see Kodaly, Zoltan

AVE MARIA see Large

AVE MARIA see Lefebure-Wely, Louis James Alfred

AVE MARIA see Leoncini, Lorenzo

AVE MARIA see Luzzi, Luigi

AVE MARIA see Mangon, Johannes

AVE MARIA see Mangone, Gioacchino

AVE MARIA see Martinz, Alfredo

AVE MARIA see Mascagni, Pietro

AVE MARIA see Massenet, Jules

AVE MARIA see Mattoni, Filippo

AVE MARIA see Mazellier, J.

AVE MARIA see Mendelssohn-Bartholdy, Felix

AVE MARIA see Merkx, C.J.E.

AVE MARIA see Meyerowitz, Jan

AVE MARIA see Morassutti, Dino

AVE MARIA see Mouton, Jean

AVE MARIA see Mozart, Wolfgang Amadeus

AVE MARIA see Muller, A.M.

AVE MARIA see Niedermeyer, Louis

AVE MARIA see Oltrassi, Giuseppe

AVE MARIA see Paisiello, Giovanni

AVE MARIA see Palestrina, Giovanni

AVE MARIA see Parente, Sister Elizabeth

AVE MARIA see Parodi, Lorenzo

AVE MARIA see Peeters, Flor

AVE MARIA see Philipp, Franz

AVE MARIA see Picchi, Luigi

AVE MARIA see Pierobon, Giuseppe

AVE MARIA see Pinkham, Daniel

AVE MARIA see Poulenc, Francis

AVE MARIA see Rachmaninoff, Sergey Vassilievitch

AVE MARIA see Ramella

AVE MARIA see Ravagnan, Bice

AVE MARIA see Ravanello, Oreste

AVE MARIA see Renzi, Angelo

AVE MARIA see Rheinberger, Josef

AVE MARIA see Ridout

AVE MARIA see Rodrigo

AVE MARIA see Rouher, M.

AVE MARIA see Saint-Saens, Camille

AVE MARIA see Schubert, Franz (Peter)

AVE MARIA see Schutz, Heinrich

AVE MARIA see Sermisy, Claude de

AVE MARIA see Shaffer, Sherwood M.

AVE MARIA see Smith, Gregg

AVE MARIA see Stibbe, A.

AVE MARIA see Stravinsky, Igor

AVE MARIA see Tebaldini, Giovanni

AVE MARIA see Tesoriero

AVE MARIA see Tocchi, [Gian-Luca]

AVE MARIA see Trexler, Georg

AVE MARIA see Vene, Ruggero

AVE MARIA see Verdi, Giuseppe

AVE MARIA see Verdonck, Cornelius

AVE MARIA see Viardot-Garcia, Pauline

AVE MARIA see Victoria, Tomas Luis de

AVE MARIA see Vittoria, Ludovico

AVE MARIA see Volpi, Edoardo

AVE MARIA see Wilson

AVE MARIA see Witt, Friedrich

AVE MARIA see Wolff, A.

AVE MARIA see Yung, Alf.

AVE MARIA see Zuchino

AVE MARIA see Bottigliero, Eduardo

AVE MARIA DE L'ENFANT see Gounod, Charles Francois

AVE MARIA, DICH LOBT MUSICA see Muller, A.M.

AVE MARIA, DU HIMMELSKONIGIN (from Psalteriolum 1642) BVM
SATB,acap voc pt DOBLINGER s.p. see also Unsere Liebe Frau   (A1447)

AVE MARIA, EN LA see Saint-Saens, Camille

AVE MARIA, GRATIA PLENA see Arcadelt, Jacob

AVE MARIA, GRATIA PLENA see Des Prez, Josquin

AVE MARIA GRATIA PLENA see Michels, Josef

AVE MARIA GRATIA PLENA see Palestrina, Giovanni

AVE MARIA, GRATIA PLENA see Schubert, Heino

AVE MARIA, GRATIA PLENA see Schutz, Heinrich

AVE MARIA, GRATIA PLENE see Senfl, Ludwig

AVE MARIA KLARE (from Psalteriolum 1642) BVM
SATB,acap voc pt DOBLINGER s.p. see also Unsere Liebe Frau   (A1448)

AVE MARIA, ROS' OHNE DORN *16th cent
(Katt, Leopold) wom cor,acap oct DOBLINGER s.p.   (A1449)

AVE MARIA STELLA see Linden, N. v.d.

AVE MARIA ZART (from Echo Hymnodia Caelestis) BVM
(Burkhart, Franz) mix cor,acap oct DOBLINGER s.p.   (A1450)

AVE, MARIA ZART see Fegers, Karl

AVE MARIA ZART see Margenburg, Erich

AVE MARIA see Palestrina, Giovanni

AVE MARIS see Arnaldi, Antonio

AVE, MARIS STELLA (from Anthology Of Carols, An) Xmas,Greg/hymn
unis oct ST.MARTIN s.p.   (A1451)
4pt mix cor&4pt mix cor,cont,opt inst MOSELER s.p.   (A1452)
(Wulstan, David) unis CHESTER s.p. contains also: Eia, Novus Annus Est (unis) (New Year); Omnes Gentes Plaudite (unis) (Easter); Chaucher's Carol (TTB)   (A1453)

AVE MARIS STELLA see Anerio, Giovanni Francesco

AVE MARIS STELLA see Anonymous

AVE MARIS STELLA see Bach, Johann Sebastian

AVE MARIS STELLA see Badings, Henk

AVE MARIS STELLA see Bardos, Lajos

AVE MARIS STELLA see Bottazzo, Luigi

AVE MARIS STELLA see Des Prez, Josquin

AVE MARIS STELLA see Dufay, Guillaume

AVE MARIS STELLA see Firpo, Antonio

AVE MARIS STELLA see Grieg, Edvard Hagerup

AVE MARIS STELLA see Handel, George Frideric

AVE MARIS STELLA see Hassler, Hans Leo

AVE MARIS STELLA see Heidet, Le R. P.

AVE MARIS STELLA see Massenet, Jules

AVE MARIS STELLA see Meyerowitz, Jan

AVE MARIS STELLA see Monteverdi, Claudio

AVE MARIS STELLA see Olsson, Otto Emmanuel

AVE MARIS STELLA see Palestrina, Giovanni

AVE MARIS STELLA see Torsten, Stenius

AVE MARIS STELLA see Vasinis, Giusseppe

AVE MARIS STELLA see Visona', Gino

AVE MARIS STELLA see Volpi, Edoardo

AVE MUNDI SPES MARIA see Plautz, Gabriel

AVE PLENA GRACIA see Davies

AVE REGINA see Bottazzo, Luigi

AVE REGINA see Busser, [Henri-Paul]

AVE REGINA see Byrd, William

AVE REGINA see Nicolosi, Salvatore

AVE REGINA see Perti, Giacomo Antonio

AVE REGINA see Philips, Peter

AVE REGINA see Schmitt, Florent

AVE REGINA see Suriano, Francesco

AVE REGINA see Webbe, Samuel

AVE REGINA CAELORUM see Binkerd, [Gordon]

AVE REGINA CAELORUM see Byrd, William

AVE REGINA CAELORUM see Power, Lyonel

AVE REGINA CAELORUM see Smith, Frank H.

AVE REGINA CAELORUM see Suriano, Francesco

AVE REGINA CAELORUM see Torres, Eduardo

AVE REGINA CAELORUM see Willaert, Adrian

AVE REGINA COELORUM see Dufay, Guillaume

AVE REGINA COELORUM see Lassus, Roland de (Orlandus)

AVE REGINA COELORUM see Paladilhe, [Emile]

AVE REGINA COELORUM see Palestrina, Giovanni

AVE REGINA COELORUM see Ravanello, Oreste

AVE REGINA COELORUM; GAUDE VIRGO GLORIOSA see Palestrina, Giovanni

AVE REGINAE COELORUM see Dufay, Guillaume

AVE REX NOSTER see Mercenier, P.

AVE SANCTISSIMA see Isaac, Heinrich

AVE SPES ET SALUS see Koerppen, Alfred

AVE VERA VIRGINITAS see Des Prez, Josquin

AVE VERUM see Aubanel, Georges

AVE VERUM see Bach, Johann Sebastian

AVE VERUM see Beethoven, Ludwig van

AVE VERUM see Breville, Pierre-Onfroy de

AVE VERUM see Bruckner, Anton

AVE VERUM see Busser, [Henri-Paul]

AVE VERUM see Delvincourt, Claude

AVE VERUM see Des Prez, Josquin

AVE VERUM see Dubois, Theodore

AVE VERUM see Elgar, Edward

AVE VERUM see Franck, Cesar

AVE VERUM see Gounod, Charles Francois

AVE VERUM see Guilmant, Alexandre

AVE VERUM see Haydn, (Franz) Joseph

AVE VERUM see Leoncini, Lorenzo

AVE VERUM see Liszt, Franz

AVE VERUM see Magri, Pietro

AVE VERUM see Maugeri, Giuseppe

AVE VERUM see Mendelssohn-Bartholdy, Felix

AVE VERUM see Mercadante, G. Saverio

AVE VERUM see Mozart, Wolfgang Amadeus

AVE VERUM see Rabaud, H.

AVE VERUM see Ropartz, Joseph Guy

AVE VERUM see Saint-Saens, Camille

AVE VERUM see Schmitt, Florent

AVE VERUM see Schubert, Franz (Peter)

AVE VERUM see Volpi, Edoardo

AVE VERUM see Welsh, W.A.

AVE VERUM see Willan, Healey

AVE VERUM see Zaccaria, Vittore

AVE VERUM CORPUS see Beveridge, Thomas G.

AVE VERUM CORPUS see Bottigliero, Eduardo

AVE VERUM CORPUS see Byrd, William

AVE VERUM CORPUS see Deering, Richard

AVE, VERUM CORPUS see Des Prez, Josquin

AVE VERUM CORPUS see Elgar

AVE VERUM CORPUS see Escovada, R.

AVE, VERUM CORPUS see Faure, Gabriel-Urbain

AVE VERUM CORPUS see Fortig, Peter

AVE VERUM CORPUS see Franco

AVE VERUM CORPUS see Gounod, Charles Francois

AVE VERUM CORPUS see La Forge

AVE, VERUM CORPUS see Lassus, Roland de (Orlandus)

AVE VERUM CORPUS see Liszt, Franz

AVE VERUM CORPUS see Magin, Charles

AVE VERUM CORPUS see Mercatali, A.

AVE VERUM CORPUS see Moren, John

AVE VERUM CORPUS see Mozart, Wolfgang Amadeus

AVE VERUM CORPUS see Parthun, Paul

AVE VERUM CORPUS see Poulenc, Francis

AVE VERUM CORPUS see Quilici, Abbe F.

AVE VERUM CORPUS see Rodella, Sante

AVE VERUM CORPUS see Saint-Saens, Camille

AVE VERUM CORPUS see Viadana, Lodovico Grossi da

AVE VERUM CORPUS see Victoria, Tomas Luis de

AVE VERUM CORPUS see Wills, Arthur

AVE VERUM CORPUS, AND OTHER WORKS see Mozart, Wolfgang Amadeus

AVE VERUM CORPUS CHRISTE see Des Prez, Josquin

AVE VERUM see Mozart, Wolfgang Amadeus

AVE VIRGO see Franchois

AVE VIRGO GLORIOSA see Lherittier, Jean.

AVE VIRGO SANCTISSIMA see Guerrero, Francisco

AVE VIVENS HOSTIA! see Campion, M.

AVERRE, R.
    Christ Thou Art The Sure Foundation
        SATB oct PRESSER 312-40430 $.30   (A1454)

    Clap Your Hands, All Ye People
        SATB,acap oct PRESSER 312-40429 $.30
                                            (A1455)
    Did Mary Know? *Xmas
        SATB,acap oct PRESSER 312-40289 $.30
                                            (A1456)
    Gifts, The *Xmas
        SATB,acap oct PRESSER 312-40431 $.30
                                            (A1457)
    Rise Up, Shepard, And Follow *Xmas
        SATB,acap oct PRESSER 312-40343 $.35
                                            (A1458)

AVERY
    Born Again (composed with Marsh)
        (Roff) 2 eq voices oct AGAPE AG 7116 $.35
                                            (A1459)
    Choir Sings Hymns Hot And Carols Cool, The
        (composed with Marsh) *CCU,carol/hymn
        (Young) mix cor oct AGAPE $1.50   (A1460)
    Christ The Lord Is Risen (composed with
        Marsh) *Easter
        (Ehret) mix cor oct AGAPE AG 7122 $.35
                                            (A1461)
    Come As A Child (composed with Marsh)
        (Rogers) 2pt oct AGAPE AG 7134 $.35 (A1462)
    Doxology And Gloria Patri (composed with
        Marsh)
        (Young) mix cor oct AGAPE AG 7121 $.35
                                            (A1463)
    Here We Go A-Caroling (composed with Marsh)
        *Xmas,carol
        (Pfautsch) SATB oct AGAPE AG 7105 $.35
                                            (A1464)
    Hey! Hey! Anybody Listening? (composed with
        Marsh) *Xmas
        (Young) mix cor oct AGAPE AG 7120 $.35
                                            (A1465)

AVERY (cont'd.)
    I Was Glad (composed with Marsh)
        (Red) SATB oct AGAPE AG 7131 $.40   (A1466)
    I Wonder Why? (composed with Marsh)
        (Pfautsch) SATB oct AGAPE AG 7104 $.35
                                            (A1467)
    If There Is A Holy Spirit (composed with
        Marsh)
        (McAfee) SATB oct AGAPE AG 7108 $.40 (A1468)
    Jesus, White Boy (composed with Marsh)
        (Young) mix cor oct AGAPE AG 7106 $.35
                                            (A1469)
    Join The Revolution (composed with Marsh)
        (McAfee) SATB oct AGAPE AG 7112 $.35 (A1470)
    Little Baby Boy (composed with Marsh)
        (Young) mix cor oct AGAPE AG 7102 $.35
                                            (A1471)
    O Let's Get On (composed with Marsh)
        (Wilson) SATB oct AGAPE AG 7115 $.40 (A1472)
    Possibly, Probably (composed with Marsh)
        (Dietterich) SATB,soli oct AGAPE AG 7114
        $.40   (A1473)
    Put Down Your Guns (composed with Marsh)
        (Red) SATB oct AGAPE AG 7132 $.40   (A1474)
    Rebel, The (composed with Marsh)
        (Burroughs) SATB oct AGAPE AG 7107 $.40
                                            (A1475)
    Star Light, Star Bright (composed with Marsh)
        (Young) 2pt mix cor oct AGAPE AG 7103 $.30
                                            (A1476)
    Take Time (composed with Marsh)
        (Young) mix cor oct AGAPE AG 7117 $.35
                                            (A1477)
    Taste The New Wine (composed with Marsh)
        (Young) mix cor oct AGAPE AG 7118 $.35
                                            (A1478)
    Thank You, Thank You (composed with Marsh)
        (Hustad) mix cor oct AGAPE AG 7123 $.40
                                            (A1479)
    We're Here To Be Happy And Go And Be Happy
        (composed with Marsh)
        (Bock) 2pt oct AGAPE AG 7136 $.35   (A1480)
    What Makes The Wind Blow? (composed with
        Marsh)
        (Young) mix cor oct AGAPE AG 7109 $.35
                                            (A1481)
    When I'm Feeling Lonely (composed with Marsh)
        (Young) mix cor oct AGAPE AG 7110 $.35
                                            (A1482)
    Who's That Guy With The Beard (composed with
        Marsh)
        (Young) mix cor oct AGAPE AG 7119 $.35
                                            (A1483)

AVERY, S.R.
    I Called Upon The Lord
        4pt mix cor,acap oct SCHIRM.G 10357 $.25
                                            (A1484)

AVEZ-VOUS VU JESUS-CHRIST? *Xmas,carol,17th
        cent
        (Geveart, F.-A.) [Fr] 4pt mix cor,acap (med
        easy) cor pts LEMOINE s.p. see from
        Collection De Choeurs, dixieme Fascicule
                                            (A1485)

AVIDOM, MENACHEM (1908-   )
    Psalm Cantata *see Psalmenkantate

    Psalmenkantate *cant/Psalm,Heb
        "Psalm Cantata" SATB,acap ISRAELI 309 s.p.
                                            (A1486)

AVINA MALKAYNU CHANAYNO see Adler, Samuel

AVODAH L'AMI see Wurman, Hans

AVODAT ISRAEL see Goldfarb, Samuel E.

AVODAT SHABBAT see Berlinski, [Herman]

AVODAT SHABBAT see Fromm, Herbert

AVODATH HABONIM see Adler, Hugo Ch.

AVODATH HAKODESH see Bloch, Ernest

AVODATH HAKODESH see Janowski, Max

AVODIM HOYINU see Adler, Hugo Ch.

AVONDRUST see Rennes, Cath. v.

AVSHALOMOV, JACOB (1919-   )
    Praises From The Corners Of The Earth
        mix cor,org,perc voc sc MCA $1.25, ipa
                                            (A1487)
    Prophecy
        SATB,T solo,org SCHIRM.EC 2704 $.50, ipa
                                            (A1488)

AWAKE! see Wagner, Richard, Wach Auf!

AWAKE! ARISE! see Edwards, Clara

AWAKE, ARISE, GO FORTH AND REJOICE see Leaf,
    Robert

AWAKE, AWAKE GOOD PEOPLE ALL see Morgan

AWAKE, AWAKE, PUT ON THY STRENGTH see Naylor,
    Bernard

AWAKE, DO NOT CAST US OFF see Adler, Samuel

AWAKE! DRAWS NIGH THE BREAK OF DAY see Wagner,
    Richard, Wach' Auf! Es Nahet Gen Den Tag

AWAKE MY HEART see Bach, Johann Sebastian

AWAKE, MY HEART see Cruger, Johann

AWAKE, MY HEART see Marshall, Jane M.

AWAKE MY HEART WITH GLADNESS see Bach, Johann
    Sebastian

AWAKE, MY HEART, WITH GLADNESS see Cruger,
    Johann

AWAKE, MY SOUL see Bach, Johann Sebastian

AWAKE, MY SOUL see Frackenpohl, Arthur

AWAKE MY SOUL see Gomolka, Mikolaj

AWAKE MY SOUL see Herman

AWAKE, MY SOUL see Kirk

AWAKE, MY SOUL see Macpherson, Charles

AWAKE, MY SOUL! see Martin

AWAKE, MY SOUL see Whitecotton, Shirley

AWAKE MY SOUL see Wolff

AWAKE, MY SOUL see Wolff, S. Drummond

AWAKE, MY SOUL, AND SING YE see Bach, Johann
    Sebastian

AWAKE, MY SOUL, AND WITH THE SUN see Tallis,
    Thomas

AWAKE, MY SOUL, STRETCH EVERY NERVE see Hilty,
    Everett Jay

AWAKE, MY TONGUE see Blakley

AWAKE, O CHURCH OF CHRIST see Gould, Morton

AWAKE, O SHEPHERDS see Sacco

AWAKE, OUR SOULS see Brandon, George

AWAKE, PSALTRY AND HARP see Young, Gordon

AWAKE, PUT ON STRENGTH! see Warren, Elinor
    Remick

AWAKE THE HARP see Haydn, (Franz) Joseph

AWAKE THE HARP see Kjelson

AWAKE, THE JOYOUS DAY IS HERE see Opitz

AWAKE, THE TRUMPET see Arne

AWAKE, THE TRUMPET'S LOFTY SOUND see Handel,
    George Frideric

AWAKE, THOU SPIRIT BOLD AND DARING see Schalk,
    Carl

AWAKE, THOU SPIRIT OF THE WATCHMEN see Lenel,
    Ludwig

AWAKE, THOU SPIRIT, WHO DIDST FIRE see Bender,
    Jan

AWAKE, THOU THAT SLEEPEST see Maker

AWAKE, THOU THAT SLEEPEST see Maker, [Frederick
    Charles]

AWAKE, THOU THAT SLEEPEST see Newbury

AWAKE, THOU WINTRY EARTH *Dut,17th cent
    (Davis, K.) SA,pno/org SCHIRM.EC 1550 $.25
                                            (A1489)
    (Davis, K.) SSAA,acap SCHIRM.EC 1591 $.18
                                            (A1490)

AWAKE, THOU WINTRY EARTH see Bach, Dem Wir Das
    Heilig Itzt

AWAKE, THOU WINTRY EARTH see Bach, Johann
    Sebastian, Dem Wir Das Heilig Itzt

AWAKE UP, MY GLORY see Barnby

AWAKE UP, MY GLORY see Barnby, Sir Joseph

AWAKE US, LORD, AND HASTEN see Bach, Johann
    Sebastian

AWAKE WERE THEY ONLY *Xmas,carol
    unis/SATB (very easy) OXFORD 08.034 $.15
                                            (A1491)

AWAKENING, AN see Robson, R. Walker

AWAY IN A MANGER *Xmas,carol,Eng/Span
    see Many Moods Of Christmas, The, Suite Two
    see Three Christmas Carols
    see Three Christmas Carols
    see At The Manger
    SATB BIG3 $.25   (A1492)
    (Cashmore) SATB FRANCIS s.p.   (A1493)
    (Ehret) SAB,opt vcl oct FOX CC10 $.25   (A1494)
    (Ehret, W.) SAB,opt vcl PROWSE CC10 s.p.
                                            (A1495)
    (George) unis (very easy) OXFORD 94.502 $.25
                                            (A1496)
    (Hustad, Don) SATB ALLANS 403 s.p.   (A1497)
    (Iseler, E.) SATB THOMP.G E.I.1004 s.p. (A1498)
    (Long) 2pt jr cor oct LILLENAS AN-4019 $.25
                                            (A1499)
    (Manson) SA FRANCIS s.p.   (A1500)
    (Ossewaarde, Jack) SATB oct GRAY GCMR 2665
        $.25   (A1501)
    (Ross) SATB oct GALAXY 1.1306.1 $.30   (A1502)
    (Rotermund, M.) unis,inst (easy) oct
        CONCORDIA 98-1929 $.25   (A1503)
    (Sharpe, E.) cor&desc CRAMER 42   (A1504)
    (Shaw; Parker) SATB,acap oct LAWSON 719 $.30
                                            (A1505)
    (Terri) SSA/SAA,acap,opt pno/harp oct LAWSON
        666 $.30   (A1506)
    (Terri) SSA ALLANS 461 s.p.   (A1507)

AWAY IN A MANGER see Brandon, Phyllis

AWAY IN A MANGER see Giasson

AWAY IN A MANGER see Hallstrom, Henry

AWAY IN A MANGER see Hijman, Julius

AWAY IN A MANGER see Kirkpatrick

AWAY IN A MANGER see Kirkpatrick W.

AWAY IN A MANGER see Luther, Martin

AWAY IN A MANGER see Pasquet, Jean

AWAY IN A MANGER see Plettner, A.

AWAY IN A MANGER see Spilman

AWAY IN A MANGER see Van Dyke

AWAY IN A MANGER see Vorse, R.

AWAY IN THE MANGER see Luther, Martin

AWAY WITH GLOOM see Holman, Derek

AXENFELD, FRITZ
    Te Deum Fur Liturg *Te Deum
      4pt mix cor&cong,org MOSELER s.p.   (A1508)

AY, SANTA MARIA see Anonymous

AYL MELECH YOSHAYV see Adler, Samuel

AYLEWARD, RICHARD (1626-1669)
    Preces And Responses
      (Gittens, John) SATB oct NOVELLO 88.0006.05
      s.p.   (A1509)

    Preces And Responses, The
      SATB,acap PETERS H1475 $.40   (A1510)

    Short Evening Service
      (Gittens, John) SATB oct NOVELLO 88.0008.01
      s.p.   (A1511)

AZNAVOUR, [CHARLES] (1924-   )
    Yerushalaim
      [Fr] 4pt mix cor,soli CHAPPELL-FR s.p.
                                           (A1512)

B

B MINOR MASS see Bach, Johann Sebastian, Messe
    H-Moll

BABE DIVINE see Christiansen, Olaf Christian

BABE FROM HEAVEN, A see Caurroy, Eustache du

BABE HOLDS COURT IN BETHLEHEM , A see Tatton

BABE IN A MANGER see Le Lachuer

BABE IN A MANGER BORN see Bronson, Margaret

BABE IN BETHLEHEM'S MANGER LAID see Hopkins

BABE IN BETHLEHEM'S MANGER LAID, THE *Xmas,
    carol,Eng
    unis/SATB (easy) OXFORD 08.069 $.15   (B1)
    (Collins) SATB,acap oct PRO ART 1618 $.20
                                             (B2)
    (Collins) SSA,acap,opt pno oct PRO ART 1472
      $.22   (B3)
    (Kinsman) SATB oct SPRATT 588 $.30   (B4)

BABE IN BETHLEHEM'S MANGER LAID, THE see
    Buebendorf

BABE IS BORN *Xmas
    (Chambers) SATB,acap oct BOOSEY 5255 $.30
                                             (B5)

BABE IS BORN see Praetorius, Michael

BABE IS BORN, A *Xmas,carol,Eng
    unis/SATB (easy) OXFORD 08.107 $.15   (B6)
    (Bouman, P.) SATB,acap (med easy) oct
      CONCORDIA 98-1058 $.25   (B7)
    (Forsblad) SATB oct PRO ART 1847 $.25   (B8)
    (Glarum) SATB SCHMITT SD6222 $.25   (B9)

BABE IS BORN, A see Diemer, Emma Lou

BABE IS BORN, A see Malin, Don

BABE IS BORN, A see Moe, Daniel

BABE IS BORN, A see Rose

BABE IS BORN, A see Routh, Francis

BABE IS BORN, A see Spencer, W.

BABE IS BORN ALL OF A MAY, A see Edmunds, John

BABE IS BORN IN BETHLEHEM, A see Bach, Johann
    Sebastian, Puer Natus In Bethlehem

BABE IS BORN IN BETHLEHEM, A see Van Dyke

BABE LIES IN A MANGER, A see Piggott, H.E.

BABE LIES IN THE CRADLE, A see Droste, Doreen

BABE LIES IN THE CRADLE, A see Elmore, Robert
    [Hall]

BABE LIES IN THE CRADLE, A see Lockwood,
    Normand

BABE OF BEAUTY see Boda, John

BABE OF BETHLEHEM see Bacon, Ernst

BABE OF BETHLEHEM see Bornschein, [Franz Carl]

BABE OF BETHLEHEM see Ehret, Walter

BABE OF BETHLEHEM see Gaul, Harvey Bartlet

BABE OF BETHLEHEM, THE *Xmas,cant/carol/folk,
    US
    mix cor CHAPPELL 0017889-3691 $1.00   (B10)
    SSA CHAPPELL 0017889-3692 $1.00   (B11)
    (McAfee) SATB, southern harmony oct BOURNE
      840 $.35   (B12)
    (Noble) SATB oct SPRATT 571 $.25   (B13)

BABE OF BETHLEHEM, THE see Rogers, S.E.

BABE SO TENDER *Xmas
    (Dickinson) SSA oct FISCHER,C CM-7223 $.25
                                            (B14)

BABE, SO TENDER, A *carol,Belg
    (Davis, K.K.) mix cor SCHIRM.EC 1159 $.30
                                            (B15)
    (Manton, R.) TTBB,acap SCHIRM.EC 543 $.18
                                            (B16)

BABE SO TENDER, A see Dickinson, Clarence

BABE, THE see El Rorro

BABEL see Smith, Gregg

BABEL see Stravinsky, Igor

BABER, JOSEPH
    Snowflakes *carol
      SATB oct KERBY 7104 $.25   (B17)

BABST
    My Soul, Now Bless Thy Maker
      (Kirk) SATB,acap oct PRO ART 1666 $.20
                                            (B18)

BABY BETHLEHEM see Boatner, [Edward H.]

BABY BOY see Rocherolle

BABY BOY, SO WONDERFUL, A see Schroter, L., Ein
    Kindelein So Lobelich

BABY JESU see Crow

BABY JESUS see Artman

BABY JESUS see Cochrane, Naomi

BABY JESUS see Scull

BABY JESUS STIRRED IN SLEEP see Reed

BABY, WHAT YOU GOIN' TO BE see Sleeth, Natalie

BABYLON IS FALLEN see Cain, Noble

BABYLON'S FALLING
    (Follett) SSA oct PRO ART 2435 $.25   (B19)

BACH
    Advent-Christmas Cycle *CCU,Adv/Xmas
      (Otto) SATB KJOS $1.25   (B20)

    All Praise To Thee
      SATB (easy) oct AUGSBURG 1353 $.20   (B21)

    Alleluia
      (Narvik) SATB KJOS 5133 $.30   (B22)
      (Ramsey) SATB KJOS 5381 $.30   (B23)

    Alleluia! O Praise Ye The Lord *Xmas
      (Black) SATB oct SACRED E57 $.35   (B24)

    Anthem For Christmas *Xmas
      (Mason) SATB WORD CS-357 $.30   (B25)

    At God's Right Hand He Doth Stand
      (Best) SA/TB SHAWNEE E57 $.25   (B26)

    At Thy Feet
      SATB oct BELWIN 64023 $.30   (B27)

    At Thy Feet Come Gracious Spirit
      (Ottesen) SAB FLAMMER D5153 $.25   (B28)

    Ave Maria
      (Gounod; Ehret) "Father To Thee We Pray"
      2pt oct PRO ART 1630 $.18   (B29)
      (Gounod; Ehret) "Father To Thee We Pray"
      SATB oct PRO ART 1488 $.30   (B30)

    Awake, The Joyous Day Is Here *see Opitz

    Awake, Thou Wintry Earth *see Dem Wir Das
      Heilig Itzt

    Bach Anthem Book *CCU,anthem
      (Holler, John) mix cor BELWIN $.75   (B31)

    Be Calm And Peaceful
      (Kemmer) SATB oct GRAY GCMR 1934 $.30   (B32)

    Beside Thy Cradle Here I Stand
      SATB KJOS 17 $.30   (B33)

    Blessing, Glory And Wisdom
      (Tkach) men cor KJOS 7503 $.30   (B34)
      (Wagner) SATB oct GRAY GCMR 1502 $.60   (B35)

    Blessing, Glory And Wisdom, And Thanks
      (Fricker) SATB oct FOX AN2006 $.30   (B36)

    Come And Abide
      SATB oct LORENZ C269 $.30   (B37)

    Come And Thank Him *anthem
      SA oct OXFORD 44.231 $.65   (B38)

    Come, Blessed Rest
      (Luvaas) SATB KJOS 2004 $.30   (B39)

    Come, Dearest Lord
      (Holler) SATB oct GRAY GCMR 1438 $.30   (B40)

    Come, Souls, Behold Today *anthem
      (Nelson) SAB (easy) oct AUGSBURG 1171 $.20
                                             (B41)

    Come Unto Me
      (Hall) SATB oct GALAXY 1.0592.1 $.35   (B42)

    Dem Wir Das Heilig Itzt
      "Awake, Thou Wintry Earth" SATB oct BELWIN
      64022 $.30   (B43)

    Father To Thee We Pray *see Ave Maria

    Favorite Anthems From Bach *CCU,anthem
      SATB LORENZ $1.50   (B44)

    Gloria In Excelsis Deo
      (Krone) SATB KJOS 505 $.30   (B45)

    Glory And Honor Are Before Him
      men cor KJOS 7504 $.30   (B46)

    God Is Life
      (Davis) SSA oct GALAXY 1.1898.1 $.30   (B47)
      (Davis) SATB oct GALAXY 1.1833.1 $.30   (B48)

    God Is Our Life
      (Fargo) SATB oct KENDOR $.25   (B49)

    God, My Shepherd
      (Dickinson) SATB oct GRAY GSC 216 $.30
                                             (B50)

    God Of Mercy
      (McCurdy) SSA oct BOOSEY 1741 $.30   (B51)
      (McCurdy) SATB oct BOOSEY 1742 $.30   (B52)

    Grant Us To Do With Zeal
      SATB,acap oct BOSTON 70 $.30   (B53)
      (Treharne) TTBB,opt pno BOSTON 1937 $.30
                                             (B54)

    Hear The Joyful News *Xmas
      SATB oct GALAXY 1.2174.1 $.35   (B55)

    Holy Communion *Commun
      (Lethbridge) SATB oct NOVELLO 44.1342.03
      s.p.   (B56)

    Holy, Holy, Holy
      (Field) SATB,acap oct BOOSEY 5491 $.30
                                             (B57)

    Holy Morn
      (Gounod; Bronson) SATB oct HUNTZINGER 4046
      $.18   (B58)

    How Brightly Shines The Morning Star *Xmas
      (Palmer) SATB ALFRED 6351 $.30   (B59)

    Hush My Dear *Xmas
      (Krumnach) SA SCHMITT 236 $.25   (B60)

    In Faith I Calmly Rest
      (Dickinson) SATB oct GRAY GSC 188 $.30
                                             (B61)

    In Steadfast Faith I Stand *Gen
      (Heller) SATB SCHMITT 1696 $.25   (B62)

    It Is Finished *Easter/Lent
      (Brooks) SATB oct SPRATT 584 $.25   (B63)

BACH (cont'd.)

Jesus In Gethsemane *Lent
(Kemmer) SATB oct GRAY GCMR 1738 $.25   (B64)

Live Your Life For Him *anthem
mix cor oct OXFORD 43.456 $.25   (B65)

Lord, Above All Other
(Bitgood) unis oct GRAY GCM 2998 $.30   (B66)

Lord And Savior, True And Kind
(Lovelace) SA/TB FLAMMER E5048 $.25   (B67)

Lord God, Thy Praise We Sing *Gen
(Buszin) SATB SCHMITT 8015 $.22   (B68)

Lord, Grant Us Peace
(Roff) SSA,A/Bar solo,opt vln MARKS 4040
$.30   (B69)

Lord Of Life *Gen
(Christiansen, P.) SATB SCHMITT 1430 $.30   (B70)

Lord Will Not Suffer
SATB oct FISCHER,C PT-1567 $.25   (B71)

Lord's Prayer, The
(Gounod) SATB oct LORENZ 9526 $.30   (B72)

Master Of Peace And Love
(Lorenz) SATB oct LORENZ C289 $.25   (B73)

My Jesus *anthem
(Christiansen, Paul) SATB (med) oct
AUGSBURG 1114 $.25   (B74)

My Lord, How Brightly Shines Thy Glory
(Kinsman) SATB oct BOURNE SB109 $.30   (B75)

Now At Thy Feet Creation Lies *Gen
(Olds) SSAA SCHMITT 2501 $.20   (B76)

O Christ The Heavens *Easter/Lent
(Holler) unis/SA oct GRAY GCMR 1373 $.30   (B77)

O Come, Holy Spirit
SATB KJOS 5090 $.30   (B78)

O Savior Sweet *Gen/Lent
(Dickinson) SATB oct GRAY GSC 82 $.30   (B79)
(Dickinson) unis oct GRAY GSC 198 $.30   (B80)
(Holler) SAB oct GRAY GSC 201 $.30   (B81)

Our God, To Whom We Turn
(Blake) SATB oct GRAY GCMR 3061 $.25   (B82)

Praise Him
SATB oct FISCHER,C PT-1590 $.25   (B83)

Praise We His Name *Thanks
(Hadley) SATB oct PRO ART 2298 $.25   (B84)

Praise We The Name Of God
(Coggin) SAB oct PRO ART 2680 $.30   (B85)

Psalm 121
(Atkins; Diack) SSAATTBB FISCHER,C PT-220
$1.25   (B86)

Rejoice And Sing
SATB KJOS 20 $.30   (B87)

Sanctus
(M.T.K.) SATB KJOS 509 $.30   (B88)

Scene Of The Wise Men, The *Xmas
(Palmer) SATB ALFRED 6423 $.30   (B89)

Sing Praise To Christ *Easter
(Strube) SATB oct SOUTHERN $.25   (B90)

Sing Praise To God
(Coggin) SAB SHAWNEE D85 $.40   (B91)

Thanks Be For The Wonderful Things *Baroq
(Kingsbury, John) SATB ALFRED 6438   (B92)

Thee With Tender Care
(Christiansen, O.) SATB KJOS 27 $.30   (B93)

This Night *Xmas
(Grant) SSA oct BELWIN 2047 $.25   (B94)

We Love The Place O God *anthem/hymn
(Wolff) SATB oct SPRATT 590 $.22   (B95)

What Tongue Can Tell Thy Greatness, Lord
(Ehret) SSA oct BOOSEY 5292 $.30   (B96)
(Ehret) SATB oct BOOSEY 5090 $.30   (B97)

BACH, J.C.
Magnificat *Magnif
[Lat] SATB PETERS HU1448 $2.00, ipr   (B98)

Shepherds Sang In Jubilation *Xmas
SATB oct WALTON 2174 $.30   (B99)
SAB oct WALTON 2175 $.30   (B100)

BACH, JOHANN CHRISTIAN (1735-1782)
Kyrie In D *Kyrie
(Vos, M.A.) mix cor,4 soli,strings,2ob,
2horn,cont CONCORDIA 97-5043 $1.50, ipr   (B101)

Unsers Herzens Freude
mix cor oct OXFORD 46.155 $2.50   (B102)

BACH, JOHANN CHRISTOPH (1642-1703)
Der Gerechte *Bibl/mot
(Geiringer) "Righteous, The" SATTB,acap,opt
org oct SCHIRM.G 8426 $.35   (B103)
(Schneider, M.) 5pt mix cor,org/pno voc pt
BREITKOPF-L CHB-2845 s.p.   (B104)

Der Mensch, Vom Weibe Geboren *mot
(Schneider) SSATB,cont HANSSLER 1.258 s.p.   (B105)

Dir, Jesu, Gottes Sohn
"Thou, Jesu, Son Of God" see Bach, Johann
Christoph, Ich Lasse Dich Nicht
"O Jesu, Son Of God" SATB,acap SCHIRM.EC
366 $.25   (B106)

Drei Motetten *see Furchte Dich Nicht; Herr,
Nun Lassest Du Deinen Deiner In Friede
Fahren; Lieber Herr Gott, Wecke Uns Auf!   (B107)

BACH, JOHANN CHRISTOPH (cont'd.)

Furchte Dich Nicht *mot
see Motetten
(Junk, Viktor) SATBB,opt cont cor pts
BREITKOPF-W PB-2544A s.p. see from Drei
Motetten   (B108)

Herr, Nun Lassest Du Deinen Diener In Friede
Fahren *mot
see Motetten
(Junk, Viktor) SATB&SATB,opt cont cor pts
voc pt BREITKOPF-W PB-2544C CHB-2489 s.p.
s.p. see from Drei Motetten   (B109)

I Will Not Let Thee Go *see Ich Lasse Dich
Nicht

Ich Lasse Dich Nicht *Holywk/Lent,Bibl/mot
"I'll Loose Thee, Lord, Not!" dbl cor,acap
SCHIRM.EC 1240 $.60 contains also: Dir,
Jesu, Gottes Sohn, "Thou, Jesu, Son Of
God" (SATB,acap) (Holywk/Lent,chorale)   (B110)
(Ameln; Wolters) 4pt mix cor&4pt mix cor
MOSELER s.p.   (B111)
(Geiringer) "I Will Not Let Thee Go" [Eng/
Ger] 8pt mix cor,acap,opt org oct
SCHIRM.G 8427 $.40   (B112)

Ich Lasse Dich Nicht, Du Segnest Mich Denn
*mot
cor HANSSLER 30.068 s.p.   (B113)
8pt mix cor,acap cor pts BREITKOPF-L
PB-3919 s.p., voc pt BREITKOPF-L CHB-542
s.p. contains also: Bach, Johann
Sebastian, Dir Jesu Gottes Sohn   (B114)
(Kruger) dbl cor,cont HANSSLER 30.068 s.p.   (B115)

I'll Loose Thee, Lord, Not! *see Ich Lasse
Dich Nicht

Lieber Herr Gott, Wecke Uns Auf! *mot
see Motetten
(Junk, Viktor) SATB&SATB,opt cont cor pts
BREITKOPF-W PB-2544B s.p. see from Drei
Motetten   (B116)

Man Born Of A Woman, A
see Three Songs Of Mourning

Mit Weinen Hebt Sichs An
(Schneider, M.) SATB,acap cor pts
BREITKOPF-L PB-3477 s.p.   (B117)

Motetten *mot
(Junk, V.) cor pts BREITKOPF-L PB-2544 s.p.
contains: Furchte Dich Nicht (5pt mix
cor,acap); Herr, Nun Lassest Du Deinen
Diener In Friede Fahren (dbl cor,acap);
Lieber Herr Gott, Wecke Uns Auf! (dbl
cor,acap)   (B118)

My Time Is Come
see Three Songs Of Mourning

O Jesu, Son Of God *see Dir, Jesu, Gottes
Sohn

Righteous, The *see Der Gerechte

Sei Getreu Bis In Den Tod *mot
(Schneider) SSATB,cont HANSSLER 1.259 s.p.   (B119)

Thou, Jesu, Son Of God *see Dir, Jesu,
Gottes Sohn

Three Songs Of Mourning
[Eng/Ger] SATB,org/pno&vcl/bvl BROUDE BR.
$.50, ipa
contains: Man Born Of A Woman, A; My Time
Is Come; With Weeping Life Begins   (B120)

With Weeping Life Begins
see Three Songs Of Mourning

BACH, JOHANN CHRISTOPH FRIEDRICH (1732-1795)
Die Auferweckung Des Lazarus *Bibl/ora
(Schunemann, G.) mix cor,SATB soli,2fl,2ob,
bsn,2horn,strings,cembalo sc BREITKOPF-L
rental   (B121)
(Schunemann, G.) mix cor,SATB soli,2fl,2ob,
2horn,strings BREITKOPF-W rental   (B122)

Die Kindheit Jesu *Gen,Bibl
[Ger] SATB,acap (med diff) cor pts MULLER
SM 1931 s.p.   (B123)
(Schunemann, G.) mix cor,SATB soli,2fl,
2bsn,2horn,strings,cembalo sc BREITKOPF-L
rental   (B124)
(Schunemann, G.) mix cor,SATB soli,cembalo,
fl,horn,strings BREITKOPF-W rental   (B125)

Ehre Sei Gott In Der Hohe (from Die Kindheit
Jesu) Xmas
(Martens, Mason) "Glory To God" SATB,orch
WALTON 2117 sc rental, oct $.25   (B126)
(Martens, Mason) "Glory To God" SATB,inst
oct WALTON 2117 $.15, sc WALTON rental   (B127)
(Martens, Mason) "Glory To God In The
Highest" SATB,opt org,2fl,2horn,strings
voc sc WALTON 2117 $.25, ipr, sc WALTON
rental   (B128)

Es Erhub Sich Ein Streit *cant
(Kruger) SATBB&SATBB,cont,4trp,3vln,3vla,
vcl,timp HANSSLER 10.075 s.p., voc sc
s.p., ipa   (B129)

Glory To God *see Ehre Sei Gott In Der Hohe

Glory To God In The Highest *see Ehre Sei
Gott In Der Hohe

Night Of Wonder
(Herder) [Ger/Eng] SATB,kbd BROUDE,A. 146
$.30   (B130)

BACH, JOHANN ERNST (1722-1777)
O Du Mauer Der Tochter Zion
(Clough-Leighter, H.) "O Thou Fortress Of
Zion's Daughter" SATB,org SCHIRM.EC 2629
$.35   (B131)

O Thou Fortress Of Zion's Daughter *see O Du
Mauer Der Tochter Zion

BACH, JOHANN ERNST (cont'd.)

Passionsoratorium *Psntd,ora
(Kromolicki, Joseph) mix cor,SATB soli,
cembalo,2fl,2ob,2bsn,2trom,strings sc
BREITKOPF-W DDT-48 s.p., ipr, cor pts
BREITKOPF-W rental   (B132)

BACH, JOHANN (HANS) (1604-1673)
Our Days Are As A Shadow
cor voc sc KALMUS 6068 $1.00   (B133)

Unser Leben Ist Ein Schatten *mot
SSATTB&ATB,opt org sc BREITKOPF-W PB-3761
s.p., cor pts BREITKOPF-W CHB-3533 s.p.   (B134)
"We Must Vanish Like A Shadow" [Eng/Ger]
SSATTB&ATB,org sc HANSSLER 30.031 $1.50   (B135)
(Straube, K.) [Eng/Ger] SATB,acap cor pts
BREITKOPF-L PB-2681 s.p., voc pt
BREITKOPF-L CHB-2426 s.p.   (B136)

We Must Vanish Like A Shadow *see Unser
Leben Ist Ein Schatten

Weint Nicht Um Meinen Tod *mot
(Schneider) SATB,cont HANSSLER 1.253 s.p.   (B137)

BACH, JOHANN LUDWIG (1677-1741)
Behold, I Will Send My Angel Before Me *see
Siehe, Ich Will Meinen Engel Senden

Die Mit Tranen Saen *cant/Jubil
(Owen, A.M.) "They That Sow In Tears" [Eng/
Ger] mix cor,soli,strings,cont voc sc
CONCORDIA 97-6361 $2.50, cor pts
CONCORDIA 97-6397 $.40, ipr   (B138)

Siehe, Ich Will Meinen Engel Senden *cant
(Owen, A.M.) "Behold, I Will Send My Angel
Before Me" [Eng/Ger] mix cor,soli,2ob,
strings,cont voc sc CONCORDIA 97-6359
$2.50, cor pts CONCORDIA 97-6443 $.50,
ipr   (B139)

They That Sow In Tears *see Die Mit Tranen
Saen

Zwei Motetten *CC2U,mot
(Geiringer) 6pt mix cor&8pt mix cor MOSELER
s.p.   (B140)

BACH, JOHANN MICHAEL (1648-1694)
Ach Bleib Bei Uns, Herr Jesu Christ *cant
mix cor,org,bsn,strings sc BREITKOPF-L
rental   (B141)

Be Not Afraid *see Feurchtet Euch Nicht

Blood Of Christ Jesus, The *see Das Blut
Jesu Christi

Das Blut Jesu Christi *Easter/Lent,mot
(Martens, Mason) "Blood Of Christ Jesus,
The" SATTB oct WALTON 2099 $.30   (B142)
(Schneider) SATTB,cont HANSSLER 1.100 s.p.   (B143)
(Schneider, M.) 5pt mix cor,org/brass cor
pts BREITKOPF-L CHB-2842 s.p.   (B144)

Dem Menschen Ist Gesetzt Einmal *mot
(Schneider) dbl cor,cont HANSSLER 1.257
s.p.   (B145)
(Videro, Finn) "Hvert Menneske Pa Jord"
[Ger/Dan] SATB&ATTB,cont HANSEN-DEN 453
s.p. see also Tre Motetter   (B146)

Den Kananeiska Kvinnan
(Soderholm, Valdemar) [Swed] SATB,soli,org,
strings GEHRMANS KRB sc s.p., cor pts
s.p., ipa   (B147)

Feurchtet Euch Nicht
(Ehret) "Be Not Afraid" dbl cor oct COLOMBO
2429 $.40   (B148)

Furchtet Euch Nicht *mot
(Schneider) dbl cor,cont HANSSLER 1.102
s.p.   (B149)
(Schneider, M.) 8pt mix cor,acap cor pts
BREITKOPF-L CHB-2849 s.p.   (B150)

Gud, Ma Jeg Kun Dig Have *see Herr, Wenn Ich
Nur Dich Habe

Halt, Was Du Hast *mot
SATB&SATB BREITKOPF-W rental   (B151)
(Schneider, M.) 4pt mix cor,acap voc sc
BREITKOPF-L CHB-2844 s.p.   (B152)

Herr, Du Lassest Mich Erfahren *mot
(Schneider) dbl cor,cont HANSSLER 1.256
s.p.   (B153)

Herr Ich Warte Auf Dein Heil *mot
(Schneider) dbl cor,cont HANSSLER 1.103
s.p.   (B154)

Herr Wenn Ich Nur Dich Habe *mot
(Schneider) SATTB,cont HANSSLER 1.101 s.p.   (B155)
(Schneider, M.) 5pt mix cor,acap voc sc
BREITKOPF-L CHB-2843 s.p.   (B156)
(Videro, Finn) "Gud, Ma Jeg Kun Dig Have"
[Ger/Dan] SATTB,cont HANSEN-DEN 452 s.p.
see also Tre Motetter   (B157)

Hvert Menneske Pa Jord *see Dem Menschen Ist
Gesetzt Einmal

I Know That My Redeemer Lives *see Ich
Weiss, Dass Mein Erloser Lebt

Ich Weiss, Dass Mein Erloser Lebt *Easter/
Gen/Rembrnc,Bibl/chorale/liturg/mot
men cor,acap TONGER s.p.   (B158)
4pt men cor&desc ERDMANN 145 s.p.   (B159)
"I Know That My Redeemer Lives" SATBB,acap
(med easy) oct OXFORD 43.936 $.30   (B160)
(Berger) SATTB HANSSLER 1.073 s.p.   (B161)
(Geiringer) "I Know That My Redeemer Lives"
[Eng/Ger] SATTB,acap oct SCHIRM.G 8418
$.25   (B162)
(Wolters, Gottfried) men cor,inst cor pts
TONGER s.p., ipa   (B163)

BACH, JOHANN MICHAEL (cont'd.)

Now All My Woes Are Over *Gen
dbl cor,kbd (med easy) oct CONCORDIA 98-1427 $.35 (B164)

Nu Ligger Satan Under *see Nun Hab Ich Uberwunden

Nun Hab Ich Uberwunden *mot
(Schneider) dbl cor,cont HANSSLER 1.255 s.p. (B165)
(Videro, Finn) "Nu Ligger Satan Under" [Ger/Dan] SATB&SATB,cont HANSEN-DEN 451 s.p. see also Tre Motetter (B166)

O Dearest Day, Thou'rt Welcome *see Sei Lieber Tag Willkommen

Sei Lieber Tag Willkommen *mot
(Ehret) "O Dearest Day, Thou'rt Welcome" [Ger/Eng] SSATTB oct COLOMBO 2428 $.55 (B167)
(Schneider) SSATTB,cont HANSSLER 1.104 s.p. (B168)

Tre Motetter *mot
(Videro, Finn) [Ger/Dan] HANSEN-DEN 28744 s.p.
contains & see also: Dem Menschen Ist Gesetzt Einmal, "Hvert Menneske Pa Jord"; Herr, Wenn Ich Nur Dich Habe, "Gud, Ma Jeg Kun Dig Have"; Nun Hab Ich Uberwunden, "Nu Ligger Satan Under" (B169)

Unser Leben Ist Ein Schatten *mot
"What Can Life Be But A Shadow?" [Eng/Ger] SSATTB&opt ATB,acap oct SCHIRM.G 8135 $.35 (B170)

Unser Leben Wahret Siebenzig Jahr *mot
(Schneider) SATTB,cont HANSSLER 1.254 s.p. (B171)

What Can Life Be But A Shadow? *see Unser Leben Ist Ein Schatten

BACH, JOHANN SEBASTIAN (1685-1750)

Aan De Kribbe Te Bethlehem *Xmas
mix cor sc ALSBACH&D s.p. (B172)

Ach Bleib Bei Uns, Herr Jesu Christ
see Kurig, Hans-Hermann, Ich Will Dem Herren Singen
SATB HANSSLER 6.6108 s.p. (B173)

Ach Blijf Met Uw Genade
mix cor sc ALSBACH&D s.p. (B174)

Ach Gott Und Herr (from Cantata 48) chorale
(Mishkin, H.) "Now Praise We Great And Famous Men" TTBB,acap SCHIRM.EC 2108 $.20 (B175)

Ach Gott, Vom Himmel Sieh' Darein (Cantata 2) S.2, Trin,cant/mot
mix cor,ATB soli,cont,2ob,4trom,strings cor pts BREITKOPF-W CHB-4502 s.p., ipr, sc BREITKOPF-W rental (B176)
(Ameln; Wolters) 4pt mix cor,cont MOSELER sc s.p., cor pts s.p. (B177)
(Raphael, G.) [Eng/Ger] mix cor,ATB soli, org,2ob,bsn,4trom,strings,cembalo voc sc BREITKOPF-L EB-7002 s.p., ipr (B178)

Ach Gott, Wie Manches Herzeleid (Cantata 3) S.3, cant
mix cor,SATB soli,cont,2ob,trom,strings,opt horn cor pts BREITKOPF-W CHB-4503 s.p., ipr, sc BREITKOPF-W rental (B179)

Ach Gott, Wie Manches Herzeleid [Chorale] (from Ach Gott, Wie Manches Herzeleid)
"O God, How Grievous Is The Woe" SATB,pno SCHIRM.EC 1613 $.50, ipr contains also: Wie Schwerlich Lasst Sich Fleischh Und Blut, "How Hard To Teach Our Flesh And Blood"; Erhalt' Mein Herz Im Glauben Rein, "Uphold My Heart With Faith In Thee" (B180)

Ach Gott, Wie Manches Herzeleid *S.3, Epiph, cant
(Raphael, G.) [Eng/Ger] mix cor,SATB soli, org,2ob,bsn,horn,trom,strings,cembalo cor pts BREITKOPF-L CHB-1604 s.p., voc sc BREITKOPF-L EB-7003 s.p., ipr (B181)

Ach Gott, Wie Manches Herzeleid *S.58, cant
[Ger] cor voc sc KALMUS 6542 $1.25 (B182)

Ach Herr, Lasz Dein' Lieb Engelein (from Johannes Passion)
mix cor sc ALSBACH&D s.p. (B183)

Ach Herr, Mich Armen Sunder (Cantata 135) S.135, Trin,cant
mix cor,ATB soli,org,2ob,bsn,trp,trom, strings,cembalo voc sc BREITKOPF-L EB-7135 s.p., ipr (B184)
mix cor,ATB soli,cont,2ob,trp,trom,strings cor pts BREITKOPF-W CHB-4635 s.p., ipr, sc BREITKOPF-W rental (B185)
[Ger] cor voc sc KALMUS 6591 $1.25 (B186)
(Jones, Ifor) "O Lord, This Grieving Spirit" [Eng/Ger] mix cor,soli,pno voc sc SCHIRM.G $1.00 (B187)

Ach Herr, Mich Armen Sunder [Chorale] (from Ach Herr, Mich Armen Sunder)
"O Lord, Relent, I Pray Thee" SATB,pno SCHIRM.EC 1724 $.50, ipr contains also: Ehr' Sei In's Himmels Thron, "All Praise To Thy Great Merit" (B188)

Ach, Ich Sehe, Ietzt (Cantata 162) S.162, cant
mix cor,SATB soli,cont,bsn,horn,strings cor pts BREITKOPF-W CHB-4662 s.p., ipr, sc BREITKOPF-W rental (B189)
"Ach Ich Sehe, Ietzt" [Ger] cor voc sc KALMUS 6608 $1.25 (B190)

Ach Ich Sehe, Ietzt *see Ach, Ich Sehe, Ietzt

Ach, Ich Sehe, Itzt *S.162, Trin,cant
(Todt, B.) mix cor,SATB soli,org,bsn,trp, strings,cembalo voc sc BREITKOPF-L EB-7162 s.p., ipr (B191)

BACH, JOHANN SEBASTIAN (cont'd.)

Ach Jezus Wat Is Door U Misdreven?
mix cor ALSBACH&D s.p. (B192)

Ach Lieben Christen *see Ach, Lieben Christen, Seid Getrost

Ach, Lieben Christen, Seid Getrost (Cantata 114) S.114, Trin,cant
mix cor,SATB soli,cont,fl,2ob,horn,strings cor pts BREITKOPF-W CHB-4614 s.p., ipr, sc BREITKOPF-W rental (B193)
mix cor,SATB soli,org,fl,2ob,horn,strings, cembalo sc BREITKOPF-L PB-2964 s.p., voc pt BREITKOPF-L CHB-1856 s.p., voc sc BREITKOPF-L EB-7114 s.p., ipr (B194)
"Ach Lieben Christen" [Ger] cor voc sc KALMUS 6579 $1.25 (B195)

Ach, Mein Herzliebes
"Ah, Some Child Jesus" SATB,pno oct WILLIS (B196)

Ach Wie Fluchtig
see Bach, Johann Sebastian, Aus Tiefer Not Schrei Ich Zu Dir

Ach Wie Fluchtig, Ach Wie Nichtig (Cantata 26) S.26, Trin,cant
mix cor,SATB soli,cont,fl,3ob,horn,strings sc BREITKOPF-W PB-4526 s.p., cor pts BREITKOPF-W CHB-4526 s.p., ipa (B197)
"Ach Wie Flueschtig" [Eng] cor voc sc KALMUS 6022 $1.00 (B198)
(Raphael, G.) [Eng/Fr/Ger] mix cor,SATB soli,org,fl,3ob,horn,strings,cembalo voc pt BREITKOPF-L CHB-867 s.p., voc sc BREITKOPF-L EB-7026 s.p., ipr (B199)

Ach Wie Fluchtig, Ach Wie Nichtig [Chorale] (from Ach Wie Fluchtig, Ach Wie Nichtig)
see Trubel, Gerhard, Ach Wie Fluchtig, Ach Wie Nichtig

Ach Wie Flueschtig *see Ach Wie Fluchtig, Ach Wie Nichtig

Advent Oratorio-Good Tidings Of Great Joy *Adv,ora
(Gore, R.T.) cor,4 soli,orch/org/pno sc CONCORDIA 97-4809 $25.00, ipa, voc sc CONCORDIA 97-4810 $4.00, cor pts CONCORDIA 97-4993 $1.75 (B200)

Ah! Dearest Jesus (from Christmas Oratorio, The)
see Three Chorales
see Two Chorales

Ah, God, From Heaven Look Down *chorale
(Talmadge, A.) SSAA,acap SCHIRM.EC 2524 $.35 (B201)

Ah Holy Jesus *Easter/Lent
SATB oct WALTON 2129 $.25 (B202)

Ah, Lord, Thy Dear, Sweet Angels Send (from St. John Passion) Easter
(Shaw; Parker) 4pt mix cor,acap oct SCHIRM.G 9960 $.30 contains also: O Sacred Head, Now Wounded (from St. Matthew Passion) (B203)

Ah, Some Child Jesus *see Ach, Mein Herzliebes

All Breathing Life (from Sing Ye To The Lord)
(Williamson) 4pt mix cor,acap oct SCHIRM.G 7470 $.35 (B204)

All Darkness Flies (from Christmas Oratorio) Xmas,anthem/chorale
SATB oct NOVELLO 50.0242.07 s.p. contains also: Rejoice And Sing (B205)
mix cor oct NOVELLO 50.0242.07 s.p. (B206)

All Glory, Laud And Honor (from Christus Der Ist Mein Leben) Proces,chorale
(Bement, G.) TTBB,acap SCHIRM.EC 2135 $.30 (B207)
(Davis, K.) SA&desc,pno/org SCHIRM.EC 1547 $.20 (B208)
(Geer, E.) SSAA,org SCHIRM.EC 870 $.20 (B209)
(Glaser, V.) SSA,org SCHIRM.EC 2543 (B210)

All Glory, Laud And Honour (from Cantata 95) Palm
SATB,S solo (very easy) oct OXFORD 42.312 $.30 (B211)

All Glory, Praise And Majesty (from Cantata 106)
(Coggin) 4pt men cor,org/pno oct SCHIRM.G 11703 $.35 (B212)

All Hail To Thee, Blessed Morn
(Lundquist) SATB,acap (easy) oct WILLIS 8463 $.20 (B213)

All Men Shall Honor And Adore Thee
(Barrie) SSATB oct KENDOR $.40 (B214)

All People That On Earth Do Dwell (from Gottlob! Nun Geht Das Jahr Zu Ende)
(Barnes) 4pt mix cor,org oct SCHIRM.G 8610 $.35 (B215)

All Praise To Thy Great Merit *see Ehr' Sei In's Himmels Thron

All They From Saba Shall Come (Cantata 165) Epiph
4pt mix cor,TB soli oct SCHIRM.G 2029 $.50 (B216)
(Jones, Ifor) mix cor,soli,pno oct SCHIRM.G $.35 (B217)

Alle Mennesker Pa Jorden *see Alle Menschen Mussen Sterben

Alle Menschen Moeten Sterven
mix cor ALSBACH&D s.p. (B218)

Alle Menschen Mussen Sterben
(Hamburger, Povl) "Alle Mennesker Pa Jorden" [Ger/Dan] SATB,acap HANSEN-DEN 153 s.p. see also Otte Koraludsaettelser (B219)

BACH, JOHANN SEBASTIAN (cont'd.)

Allein Gott In Der Hoh Sei Ehr *S.104 (from Cantata 104)
see Eine Deutsche Messe In Kirchenliedsatzen
SATB (E flat maj) HANSSLER 6.144 s.p.
contains also:
Franck, Melchior, Der Brautigam Wird Bald Rufen (SSTTB) (B220)
(Treharne) "Lord My Shepherd E'er Shall Be, The" [Eng/Ger] 4pt men cor,acap oct SCHIRM.G 8343 $.25 (B221)

Allein Zu Dir, Herr Jesu Christ (Cantata 33) S.33, Trin,cant
mix cor,ATB soli,cont,2ob,strings sc BREITKOPF-W PB-4533 s.p., cor pts BREITKOPF-W CHB-4533 s.p., ipa (B222)
(Bernstein, W.H.) [Eng/Ger] mix cor,ATB soli,org,2ob,strings,cembalo voc pt BREITKOPF-L CHB-2137 s.p., voc sc BREITKOPF-L EB-7033 s.p., ipr (B223)

Alleluia (from Motet VI) Xmas,Allelu/cant
SATB,cont PETERS 6106A $.20 (B224)
4pt mix cor oct SCHIRM.G 11170 $.30 (B225)
mix cor SOUTHERN $.30 (B226)
(Cramer) SATB MARKS 4280 $.25 (B227)
(Ehret) [Eng/Ger] SA MARKS 4311 $.25 (B228)
(Ehret) [Eng/Ger] SAB MARKS 4312 $.30 (B229)
(Ehret) [Eng/Ger] SSA MARKS 4267 $.25 (B230)
(Ehret) [Eng/Ger] TTBB MARKS 4264 $.25 (B231)
(Ehret) [Eng/Ger] SATB MARKS 4215 $.25 (B232)
(Kirk) SAB oct PRO ART 2094 $.30 (B233)
(Kirk) SATB oct PRO ART 2220 $.30 (B234)
(Kirk) SSA oct PRO ART 2223 $.25 (B235)
(Lefebvre) SATB oct GALAXY 1.2729.1 $.30 (B236)
(Lefebvre) SA oct GALAXY 1.1129.1 $.30 (B237)
(Lefebvre) TTBB/TTB oct GALAXY 1.1057.1 $.25 (B238)
(Lefebvre) SSA oct GALAXY 1.1056.1 $.25 (B239)
(Magnani, Quinto) SATB MUSICUS 017 $.20 (B240)
(Trusler) SATB oct PLYMOUTH TR-114 $.25 (B241)

Alleluia! O Praise The Lord Most Holy *S.207a (from Auf Schmetternde Tone) Easter
SATB,orch/org sc CONCORDIA 97-5048 $1.50, cor pts CONCORDIA 98-2101 $.40, ipa (B242)
(Thomas) SATB,opt orch/strings/brass&timp oct SOUTHERN $.40 (B243)

Alleluia! Sing Praise (from Cantata 142)
(Hirt) SATB,opt strings oct FISCHER,C CM-7140 $.30, ipa (B244)

Alleluia, Sing Praise To The Lord
(Kjelson) SA/TB oct BELWIN 2020 $.30 (B245)

Alleluja! (from Uns Ist Ein Kind Geboren) chorale
[Ger/Eng] SATB,pno SCHIRM.EC 2249 $.30, ipr (B246)
[Ger/Eng] SSA,pno SCHIRM.EC 1840 $.25, ipr (B247)
(Bement, G.) [Ger/Eng] TTBB,pno SCHIRM.EC 2121 $.25 (B248)
(Glaser, V.) [Ger/Eng] SAB,pno SCHIRM.EC 2249 $.30, ipr (B249)

Aller Augen Warten, Herr (from Du Wahrer Gott Und Davids Sohn)
"On Thee Mortal Eyes Wait, Lord" SATB,pno SCHIRM.EC 1615 $.50, ipr contains also: Christe, Du Lamm Gottes, "Lamb Of God, Our Savior" (B250)

Alles Nur Nach Gottes Willen (Cantata 72) S.72, Epiph,cant
mix cor,SAB soli,cont,2ob,strings sc BREITKOPF-W PB-4572 s.p., cor pts BREITKOPF-W CHB-4572 s.p., ipa (B251)
(Raphael, G.) [Eng/Ger] mix cor,SAB soli, org,2ob,bsn,strings,cembalo voc pt BREITKOPF-L CHB-1653 s.p., voc sc BREITKOPF-L EB-7072 s.p., ipr (B252)

Also Hat *see Also Hat Gott Die Welt Geliebt

Also Hat Gott Die Welt Geliebet *S.68, Pent/Whitsun,cant
(Grischkat) SATB,SB soli,cont,2ob,horn, 3trom,2vln,vla,vcl, English horn HANSSLER 10.216 sc $5.00, voc sc $4.00, ipa (B253)

Also Hat Gott Die Welt Geliebt (Cantata 68) S.68, Pent/Whitsun,cant
mix cor,SB soli,cont,3ob,horn,trp,3trom, strings sc BREITKOPF-W PB-4568 s.p., cor pts BREITKOPF-W CHB-4568 s.p., ipa (B254)
"Also Hat" cor,orch/org sc KALMUS $3.50, ipa (B255)
"Also Hat" [Eng] cor voc sc KALMUS 6040 $1.00 (B256)
"God So Loved The World" SATB,SB soli,org, 3ob,trp,3trom,strings voc sc NOVELLO s.p., ipr (B257)
(Durr, Alfred) [Ger] SATB,SB soli,org,cont, 2vln,vla, cello piccolo sc BAREN. BA 5124 $4.50, cor pts BAREN. BA 1524 $.75, voc sc BAREN. BA 5124A $2.75, min sc BAREN. TP 182 $2.75, ipa (B258)
(Raphael, G.) [Eng/Ger] mix cor,SB soli, org,3ob,bsn,horn,3trom,strings,cembalo sc BREITKOPF-L PB-2918 s.p., voc pt BREITKOPF-L CHB-547 s.p., voc sc BREITKOPF-L EB-7068 s.p., ipa (B259)

Alt Er Ferdig *see Vetter

Am Abend Aber *see Am Abend Aber Desselbigen Sabbats

Am Abend Aber Desselbigen Sabbats (Cantata 42) S.42, Gen,cant
mix cor,SATB soli,cont,2ob,bsn,strings sc BREITKOPF-W PB-4542 s.p., cor pts BREITKOPF-W CHB-4542 s.p., ipa (B260)
"Am Abend Aber" [Ger] cor voc sc KALMUS

BACH, JOHANN SEBASTIAN (cont'd.)

6537 $1.25 (B261)
(Todt, B.) [Fr/Ger] mix cor,SATB soli,org, 2ob,bsn,strings,cembalo sc BREITKOPF-L PB-2892 s.p., voc pt BREITKOPF-L CHB-2440 s.p., voc sc BREITKOPF-L EB-7042 s.p., ipr (B262)

And Now The Lord To Rest Is Laid (from St. Matthew Passion)
SATB,solo,pno SCHIRM.EC 1121 $.30, ipr (B263)

Argre Dich, O Seele, Nicht (Cantata 186) S.186, Trin,cant
mix cor,SATB soli,cont,3ob,bsn,strings cor pts BREITKOPF-W CHB-4686 s.p., ipr, sc BREITKOPF-W rental (B264)
[Ger] cor voc sc KALMUS 6627 $1.25 (B265)
(Hellmann) SATB,SATB soli,cont,bsn,2vln, vla,opt 2ob HANSSLER 10.176 sc $4.00, cor pts $.90, ipa (B266)
(Todt, B) mix cor,SATB soli,org,3ob,bsn, strings,cembalo voc sc BREITKOPF-L EB-7186 s.p., ipr (B267)

Art Thou With Me *see Bist Du Bei Mir

As Pants The Wearied Hart
(Troxell) SATB,SBar/ST soli oct FOX R190 $.25 (B268)

Attiofem Korkoraler *CC81U,chorale
[Swed] cor NORDISKA 1090 s.p., ipa (B269)

Auf, Auf, Mein Herz Mit Freuden *Easter, chorale
SATB HANSSLER 6.242 s.p. contains also: Erythraus, Gotthard, Erschienen Ist Der Herrlich Tag (B270)
"Up, Up! My Heart, With Gladness" SATB,acap SCHIRM.EC 1640 $.25 (B271)
"Up, Up, My Heart With Gladness" 2pt wom cor,pno (easy) oct WILLIS 1114 $.12 (B272)

Auf Christi Himmelfahrt Allein (Cantata 128) S.128, Asc,cant
mix cor,ATB soli,cont,4ob,2horn,trp,strings sc BREITKOPF-W PB-4628 s.p., cor pts BREITKOPF-W CHB-4628 s.p., ipa (B273)
(Raphael, G.) [Eng/Ger] mix cor,ATB soli, org,3ob,bsn,trp,trp,2horn,strings, cembalo, English horn voc sc BREITKOPF-L EB-7128 s.p., ipr (B274)

Auf, Mein Herz *see Auf, Mein Herz, Des Herren Tag

Auf, Mein Herz, Des Herren Tag (Cantata 145) S.145, Easter,cant
mix cor,STB soli,cont,fl,2ob,trp,strings cor pts BREITKOPF-W CHB-4645 s.p., ipr, sc BREITKOPF-W rental (B275)
mix cor,STB soli,org,fl,2ob,trp,strings, cembalo voc pt BREITKOPF-L CHB-2183 s.p., voc sc BREITKOPF-L EB-7145 s.p., ipr (B276)
"Auf, Mein Herz" [Ger] cor voc sc KALMUS 6598 $1.25 (B277)
(Hamburger, Povl) "Op Min Sjael! En Morgen Klar" [Ger/Dan] SATB,acap HANSEN-DEN 159 s.p. see also Otte Koraludsaettelser (B278)

Aus Der Tiefe *see Aus Der Tiefe Rufe Ich, Herr, Zu Dir

Aus Der Tiefe Rufe Ich, Herr, Zu Dir (Cantata 131) S.131, Gen,cant
mix cor,SATB soli,cont,ob,bsn,strings voc pt BREITKOPF-W CHB-4631 s.p., ipr, sc BREITKOPF-W rental (B279)
"Aus Der Tiefe" cor,orch sc KALMUS $6.00, ipa (B280)
(Grischkat) [Ger/Eng] SATB,SB soli,cont,ob, bsn,vln,2vla HANSSLER 10.029 sc $5.00, cor pts $1.50, ipa, voc sc s.p. (B281)
(Raphael, G.) [Eng/Ger] mix cor,SATB soli, org,ob,bsn,strings,cembalo voc pt BREITKOPF-L CHB-992 s.p., voc sc BREITKOPF-L EB-7131 s.p., ipr (B282)

Aus Meines Herzens Grunde
"Jeg Vil Din Pris Udsjunge" [Ger/Dan] SATB HANSEN-DEN 186 s.p. see also Otte Koraludsaettelser (B283)

Aus Tiefer Not *see Aus Tiefer Not Schrei Ich Zu Dir

Aus Tiefer Not Schrei Ich Zu Dir (Cantata 38) S.38, Lent/Trin,cant/mot
4pt mix cor MOSELER LB-211 s.p. contains also: Ach Wie Fluchtig; Gott Lebet Noch (B284)
mix cor,SATB soli,cont,2ob,4trom,strings cor pts BREITKOPF-W CHB-4538 s.p., ipr, sc BREITKOPF-W rental (B285)
"Aus Tiefer Not" [Eng] cor voc sc KALMUS 6027 $1.00 (B286)
(Ameln; Wolters) 4pt mix cor,cont MOSELER sc s.p., cor pts s.p. (B287)
(Raphael, G.) [Eng/Ger] mix cor,SATB soli, org,2ob,4trom,strings,cembalo sc BREITKOPF-L PB-2888 s.p., voc pt BREITKOPF-L CHB-544 s.p., voc sc BREITKOPF-L EB-7038 s.p., ipr (B288)
(West, John E.) "From Depths Of Woe I Call On Thee" SATB,SATB soli,2ob,4trom,strings voc sc NOVELLO rental (B289)

Aus Tiefer Not Schrei'ich Zu Dir [Chorale] (from Aus Tiefer Not) chorale
"Out Of The Depths I Cry To Thee" see Three Chorales
"Out Of The Depths I Cry To Thee" SATB,org SCHIRM.EC 1246 $.40, ipr contains also: Ob Bei Uns Is Der Sunden Viel, "Though Great Our Sins And Sore Our Woes" (SATB, opt inst) (B290)
"Out Of The Depths I Cry To Thee" SATB,acap SCHIRM.EC 1636 $.20 (B291)
(Glaser, V.) "Out Of The Depths I Cry To Thee" SATB,acap SCHIRM.EC 2243 $.16 (B292)
(Woodworth, G.) "Out Of The Depths I Cry To Thee" TTBB,acap SCHIRM.EC 904 $.20 (B293)

BACH, JOHANN SEBASTIAN (cont'd.)

Ausgewahlte Choralsatze *CCU,Gen
(Burkhardt, Hans; Lipphardt, Walther) [Ger] SATB,opt inst (med) BAREN. BA 873 $2.25 (B294)

Ave Maria *BVM
(Gounod) 2pt ENOCH T.P.141 s.p. (B295)
(Gounod) SATB oct FISCHER,C CM-97 $.30 (B296)
(Gounod) SATB ENOCH EC134 s.p. (B297)
(Gounod) SATB,band oct STAFF 243 $.25, ipa (B298)
(Gounod) TTBB oct FISCHER,C CM-6720 $.25 (B299)
(Gounod, C; Cotton, W.J.) TTBB LEONARD-ENG 41 s.p. (B300)
(Gounod; Cain) wom cor HIGHLAND 5101 $.25 (B301)
(Gounod, Charles; Downing) "Father, To Thee We Pray" [Eng/Lat] 3pt wom cor oct SCHIRM.G 9608 $.30 (B302)
(Gounod, Charles; Downing) "Father, To Thee We Pray" [Eng/Lat] SAB oct SCHIRM.G 9450 $.20 (B303)
(Gounod, Charles; Livingston, H.) [Eng/Lat] 2pt wom cor/2pt men cor oct SCHIRM.G 10427 $.25 (B304)
(Gounod, Charles; Shelley) "Father, To Thee, We Pray" [Eng/Lat] 4pt mix cor,S solo oct SCHIRM.G 3275 $.30 (B305)
(Gounod; Cooper) SSB&camb oct BOURNE C508 $.25 (B306)
(Gounod; Ganschow) SATB SCHMITT 1524 $.30 (B307)
(Gounod; McCarthy) SATB oct BOURNE 867 $.30 (B308)
(Gounod; Ringwald) SATB SHAWNEE A 112 $.35 (B309)

Ave Maris Stella *BVM,mot
see SIX MOTETS A L'UNISSON
[Lat] 4pt mix cor oct DURAND s.p. (B310)

Ave Verum
[Lat] unis/2pt CHOUDENS s.p. (B311)

Awake My Heart *anthem
mix cor oct OXFORD 43.457 $.25 (B312)

Awake My Heart With Gladness *Easter
(Davies) SATB oct SOUTHERN $.30 (B313)

Awake, My Soul *Whitsun,anthem
(Buck, P.C.) SATB oct ROYAL 201 s.p. (B314)

Awake, My Soul, And Sing Ye *chorale
(Davis) SAB oct BELWIN 64161 $.25 (B315)

Awake, The Joyous Day Is Here *see Opitz

Awake, Thou Wintry Earth *see Dem Wir Das Heilig Itzt

Awake Us, Lord, And Hasten (from Jesus Called Him To The Twelve) Gen,anthem/chorale
SATB oct NOVELLO 40.1083.03 s.p. (B316)
mix cor,orch oct NOVELLO 40.1083.03 s.p., ipr (B317)
(Knight, G.H.) SATB oct ROYAL 231 s.p. (B318)

B Minor Mass *see Messe H-Moll

Babe Is Born In Bethlehem, A *see Puer Natus In Bethlehem

Bach Cantatas Vol. 1 *S.1-4, cant
cor,org/orch min sc KALMUS 805 $1.30 (B319)

Bach Cantatas Vol. 2 *S.5-8, cant
cor,org/orch min sc KALMUS 806 $1.30 (B320)

Bach Cantatas Vol. 3 *S.9-11, cant
cor,org/orch min sc KALMUS 807 $1.30 (B321)

Bach Cantatas Vol. 4 *S.12-15, cant
cor,org/orch min sc KALMUS 808 $1.30 (B322)

Bach Cantatas Vol. 5 *S.16-19, cant
cor,org/orch min sc KALMUS 809 $1.30 (B323)

Bach Cantatas Vol. 6 *S.20-22, cant
cor,org/orch min sc KALMUS 810 $1.30 (B324)

Bach Cantatas Vol. 7 *S.23-26, cant
cor,org/orch min sc KALMUS 811 $1.30 (B325)

Bach Cantatas Vol. 8 *S.27-29, cant
cor,org/orch min sc KALMUS 812 $1.30 (B326)

Bach Cantatas Vol. 9 *S.30-31, cant
cor,org/orch min sc KALMUS 813 $1.30 (B327)

Bach Cantatas Vol. 10 *S.32-34, cant
cor,org/orch min sc KALMUS 814 $1.30 (B328)

Bach Cantatas Vol. 11 *S.35-37, cant
cor,org/orch min sc KALMUS 815 $1.30 (B329)

Bach Cantatas Vol. 12 *S.38-40, cant
cor,org/orch min sc KALMUS 816 $1.30 (B330)

Bach Cantatas Vol. 13 *S.41-43, cant
cor,org/orch min sc KALMUS 817 $1.30 (B331)

Bach Cantatas Vol. 14 *S.44-46, cant
cor,org/orch min sc KALMUS 818 $1.30 (B332)

Bach Cantatas Vol. 15 *S.47-50, cant
cor,org/orch min sc KALMUS 819 $1.30 (B333)

Bach Cantatas Vol. 16 *S.51-57, cant
cor,org/orch min sc KALMUS 820 $1.30 (B334)

Bach Cantatas Vol. 17 *S.58-62, cant
cor,org/orch min sc KALMUS 821 $1.30 (B335)

Bach Cantatas Vol. 18 *S.63-65, cant
cor,org/orch min sc KALMUS 822 $1.30 (B336)

Bach Cantatas Vol. 19 *S.66-68, cant
cor,org/orch min sc KALMUS 823 $1.30 (B337)

Bach Cantatas Vol. 20 *S.69-70, cant
cor,org/orch min sc KALMUS 824 $1.30 (B338)

Bach Cantatas Vol. 21 *S.71-73, cant
cor,org/orch min sc KALMUS 825 $1.30 (B339)

BACH, JOHANN SEBASTIAN (cont'd.)

Bach Cantatas Vol. 22 *S.74-76, cant
cor,org/orch min sc KALMUS 826 $1.30 (B340)

Bach Cantatas Vol. 23 *S.77-79, cant
cor,org/orch min sc KALMUS 827 $1.30 (B341)

Bach Cantatas Vol. 24 *S.80-82, cant
cor,org/orch min sc KALMUS 828 $1.30 (B342)

Bach Cantatas Vol. 25 *S.83-88, cant
cor,org/orch min sc KALMUS 829 $1.30 (B343)

Bach Cantatas Vol. 26 *S.89-93, cant
cor,org/orch min sc KALMUS 830 $1.30 (B344)

Bach Cantatas Vol. 27 *S.94-96, cant
cor,org/orch min sc KALMUS 831 $1.30 (B345)

Bach Cantatas Vol. 28 *S.97-99, cant
cor,org/orch min sc KALMUS 832 $1.30 (B346)

Bach Cantatas Vol. 29 *S.100-102, cant
cor,org/orch min sc KALMUS 833 $1.30 (B347)

Bach Cantatas Vol. 30 *S.103-106, cant
cor,org/orch min sc KALMUS 834 $1.30 (B348)

Bach Cantatas Vol. 31 *S.107-109, cant
cor,org/orch min sc KALMUS 835 $1.30 (B349)

Bach Cantatas Vol. 32 *S.110-112, cant
cor,org/orch min sc KALMUS 836 $1.30 (B350)

Bach Cantatas Vol. 33 *S.113-116, cant
cor,org/orch min sc KALMUS 837 $1.30 (B351)

Bach Cantatas Vol. 34 *S.117-120, cant
cor,org/orch min sc KALMUS 838 $1.30 (B352)

Bach Cantatas Vol. 35 *S.121-125, cant
cor,org/orch min sc KALMUS 839 $1.30 (B353)

Bach Cantatas Vol. 36 *S.126-129, cant
cor,org/orch min sc KALMUS 840 $1.30 (B354)

Bach Cantatas Vol. 37 *S.130-133, cant
cor,org/orch min sc KALMUS 841 $1.30 (B355)

Bach Cantatas Vol. 38 *S.134-137, cant
cor,org/orch min sc KALMUS 842 $1.30 (B356)

Bach Cantatas Vol. 39 *S.138-143, cant
cor,org/orch min sc KALMUS 843 $1.30 (B357)

Bach Cantatas Vol. 40 *S.142-145, cant
cor,org/orch min sc KALMUS 844 $1.30 (B358)

Bach Cantatas Vol. 41 *S.146-147, cant
cor,org/orch min sc KALMUS 845 $1.30 (B359)

Bach Cantatas Vol. 42 *S.148-150, cant
cor,org/orch min sc KALMUS 846 $1.30 (B360)

Bach Cantatas Vol. 43 *S.151-156, cant
cor,org/orch min sc KALMUS 847 $1.30 (B361)

Bach Cantatas Vol. 44 *S.157-162, cant
cor,org/orch min sc KALMUS 848 $1.30 (B362)

Bach Cantatas Vol. 45 *S.163-168, cant
cor,org/orch min sc KALMUS 849 $1.30 (B363)

Bach Cantatas Vol. 46 *S.169-172, cant
cor,org/orch min sc KALMUS 850 $1.30 (B364)

Bach Cantatas Vol. 47 *S.173-175, cant
cor,org/orch min sc KALMUS 851 $1.30 (B365)

Bach Cantatas Vol. 48 *S.176-179, cant
cor,org/orch min sc KALMUS 852 $1.30 (B366)

Bach Cantatas Vol. 49 *S.180-183, cant
cor,org/orch min sc KALMUS 853 $1.30 (B367)

Bach Cantatas Vol. 50 *S.184-187, cant
cor,org/orch min sc KALMUS 854 $1.30 (B368)

Bach Cantatas Vol. 51 *S.188-190, cant
cor,org/orch min sc KALMUS 855 $1.30 (B369)

Bach Cantatas Vol. 52 *S.191-193, cant
cor,org/orch min sc KALMUS 856 $1.30 (B370)

Bach Cantatas Vol. 53 *S.194-195, cant
cor,org/orch min sc KALMUS 857 $1.30 (B371)

Bach Cantatas Vol. 54 *S.196-197, cant
cor,org/orch min sc KALMUS 858 $1.30 (B372)

Bach Cantatas Vol. 55 *see Lass, Furstin, Lass Noch Einen Strahl

Bach Cantatas Vol. 56 *S.201-203, cant
cor,org/orch min sc KALMUS 860 $1.30 (B373)

Bach Cantatas Vol. 57 *S.204-205, cant
cor,org/orch min sc KALMUS 861 $1.30 (B374)

Bach Cantatas Vol. 58 *S.206, cant
cor,org/orch min sc KALMUS 862 $1.30 (B375)

Bach Cantatas Vol. 59 *S.207-208, cant
cor,org/orch min sc KALMUS 863 $1.30 (B376)

Bach Cantatas Vol. 60 *S.209-211, cant
cor,org/orch min sc KALMUS 864 $1.30 (B377)

Bach Cantatas Vol. 61 *S.212-213, cant
cor,org/orch min sc KALMUS 865 $1.30 (B378)

Bach Cantatas Vol. 62 *S.214, cant
cor,org/orch min sc KALMUS 866 $1.30 (B379)

Bach Cantatas Vol. 63 *S.215, cant
cor,org/orch min sc KALMUS 867 $1.30 (B380)

Bach Cantatas Vol. 64 *S.217-220, cant
cor,org/orch min sc KALMUS 868 $1.30 (B381)

Bach Cantatas Vol. 65 *cant
cor,org/orch min sc KALMUS 869 $1.30 (B382)

Bach Cantatas Vol. 66 *cant
cor,org/orch min sc KALMUS 870 $1.30 (B383)

BACH, JOHANN SEBASTIAN (cont'd.)

Bach Cantatas Vol. 67 *cant
cor,org/orch min sc KALMUS 871 $1.30 (B384)

Bach Chorale Responses
(Ferguson, Howard) SATB FLAMMER A 5239 $.35
(B385)

Bach Chorales *CCU,chorale
mix cor SCHMITT 5 $.50 (B386)

Bach Chorales (from Passion, The) chorale
(Hoffman) SATB FLAMMER A5503 $.85 (B387)

Barmherziges Herze *see Barmherziges Herze
Der Ewigen Liebe

Barmherziges Herze Der Ewigen Liebe (Cantata
185) S.185, Trin,cant
mix cor,SATB soli,org,ob,bsn,trp,strings,
cembalo voc sc BREITKOPF-L EB-7185 s.p.,
ipr (B388)
mix cor,SATB soli,cont,ob,bsn,trp,strings
sc BREITKOPF-W PB-4685 s.p., cor pts
BREITKOPF-W CHB-4685 s.p., ipa (B389)
"Barmherziges Herze" [Ger] cor voc sc
KALMUS 6626 $1.25 (B390)

Be Not Afraid *see Furchte Dich Nicht

Be Not Downcast *see Nicht So Traurig

Be Our Guide Through Life, Dear Lord
(Buszin) SATB SCHMITT 1700 $.20 (B391)

Be Thou Contented
2pt wom cor,pno (med) oct WILLIS 1113 $.10
(B392)
(Ehret, W.) SATB oct PRESSER 312-40920 $.30
(B393)

Be Ye Glad And Rejoice *see Freuet Euch Und
Jubilirt

Beautify Thyself, My Spirit *see Schmucke
Dich, O Liebe Seele

Befiehl Du Deine Wege *S.272
see Lassus, Roland de (Orlandus), Kyrie
Eleison, Christe Eleison

Before Thine Altar
(Davis) SATB oct GALAXY 1.2158.1 $.30
(B394)

Before Thy Cradle *Xmas
(Gordon) SATB oct SHAPIRO SK 2062 $.25
(B395)
(Gordon) 2pt oct SHAPIRO SK 4008 $.25
(B396)
(Gordon) SSA oct SHAPIRO SK 3017 $.25
(B397)
(Gordon) SAB oct SHAPIRO SK 5006 $.25
(B398)

Bereite Dich, Zion (from Christmas Oratorio)
Xmas/Gen,anthem
"Prepare Thyself Zion" unis,opt pno
(contains also: Come Let Us All This Day)
oct ROYAL 244 s.p. see also ANTHEMS FOR
UNISON OR TWO PART SINGING (B399)
"Prepare Thyself, Zion" unis,pno SCHIRM.EC
1032 $.25, ipr (B400)
"Prepare Thyself, Zion" unis,pno (abridged)
SCHIRM.EC 1521 $.25, ipr (B401)
"Prepare Thyself, Zion" unis,orch oct
NOVELLO 48.1161.05 s.p. (B402)

Bereitet Die Wege *see Bereitet Die Wege,
Bereitet Die Bahn

Bereitet Die Wege, Bereitet Die Bahn (Cantata
132) S.132, Adv,cant
mix cor,SATB soli,ob,bsn,strings cor pts
BREITKOPF-W CHB-4632 s.p., ipr, sc
BREITKOPF-W rental (B403)
"Bereitet Die Wege" [Ger] cor voc sc KALMUS
6589 $1.25 (B404)
(Raphael, Gunter) [Ger] SATB,SATB soli,org,
cont,ob,bsn,2vln,vla sc BAREN. BA 5104
$3.25, cor pts BAREN. BA 5104 $.25, ipa,
voc sc BAREN. BA 5104A $2.00, min sc
BAREN. TP 53 $2.25 (B405)
(Todt, B.) mix cor,SATB soli,org,ob,bsn,
strings,cembalo voc pt BREITKOPF-L
CHB-2200 s.p., voc sc BREITKOPF-L EB-7132
s.p., ipr (B406)

Beside The Flood Of Babylon *hymn
PATERSON s.p. see also English Hymns
Adapted To Bach's Chorales (B407)

Beside Thy Cradle *see Ich Steh An Deiner
Krippen Hier

Beside Thy Cradle Here I Stand *see Ich
Steh' An Deiner Krippen Hier

Beside Thy Manger Here I Stand *Xmas/Epiph
SATB,kbd (med easy) oct CONCORDIA 98-1390
$.25 (B408)
(Strube, A.) SAB,kbd (med easy) oct
CONCORDIA 98-1107 $.20 (B409)

Bide With Us *see Bleib' Bei Uns

Bide With Us *see Bleib' Bei Uns, Denn Es
Will Abend Werden

Bis Hieher Hat Mich Gott Gebracht (from Du
Hirte Israel Hore) Easter
SATB HANSSLER 6.0998 s.p. contains also:
Hassler, Hans Leo, O Mensch, Bewein Dein
Sunde Gross (B410)

Bischer Habt Ihr Nichts Gebeten *see Bisher
Habt Ihr Nichts Gebeten

Bischer Habt Ihr Nichts Gebeten In Meinem
Namen *S.87, Gen,cant
mix cor,ATB soli,org,4ob,bsn,strings,
cembalo voc sc BREITKOPF-L EB-7087 s.p.,
ipr (B411)

Bisher Habt Ihr Nichts Gebeten (Cantata 87)
S.87, cant
mix cor,ATB soli,cont,4ob,strings cor pts
BREITKOPF-W CHB-4587 s.p., ipr, sc
BREITKOPF-W rental (B412)
"Bischer Habt Ihr Nichts Gebeten" [Ger] cor
voc sc KALMUS 6556 $1.25 (B413)

BACH, JOHANN SEBASTIAN (cont'd.)

Bist Du Bei Mir (from Anna Magdalena
Notebook) anthem
"If Thou Wert Near" see Two Songs
(Davis, K.) "If Thou Wert Near" SSA
SCHIRM.EC 1835 $.25 (B414)
(Davis, K.K.) "If Thou Wert Near" SATB,pno
SCHIRM.EC 1766 $.30 (B415)
(Frost) "Art Thou With Me" SATB,opt org
BROUDE.A. 706 $.30 (B416)
(Harris, William, H.) "If Thou Art Near"
mix cor oct NOVELLO 40.1277.01 s.p.
(B417)
(Kemmer) "When Thou Art Near" SATB&opt jr
cor oct GRAY GCMR 1513 $.30 (B418)

Bleib' Bei Uns (Cantata 6) Easter
"Bide With Us" SATB,SATB soli voc sc
NOVELLO s.p. (B419)

Bleib Bei Uns *see Bleib' Bei Uns, Denn Es
Will Abend Werden

Bleib' Bei Uns, Denn Es Will Abend Werden
(Cantata 6) S.6, Easter,cant
mix cor,SATB soli,cont,3ob,strings sc
BREITKOPF-W PB-4506 s.p., cor pts
BREITKOPF-W CHB-4506 s.p., ipa (B420)
"Bide With Us" BELWIN $1.00 (B421)
"Bide With Us" [Eng] cor voc sc KALMUS 6013
$1.00 (B422)
"Bleib Bei Uns" cor,orch sc KALMUS $5.00,
ipa (B423)
(Durr, Alfred) [Ger] SATB,SATB soli,org,
cont,2ob,2vln,vla, oboe da caccia or
English horn,cello piccolo or cello sc
BAREN. BA 5117 $5.50, cor pts BAREN.
BA 5117 $.75, voc sc BAREN. BA 5117A
$2.75, min sc BAREN. TP 60 $2.00, ipa
(B424)
(Horn) SATB,SATB soli,cont,2ob,2vln,vla,
English horn HANSSLER 10.114 sc $5.00,
voc sc $1.00, ipa (B425)
(Raphael, G.) [Eng/Ger] mix cor,SATB soli,
org,3ob,bsn,strings,cembalo sc BREITKOPF-
L PB-2856 s.p., cor pts BREITKOPF-L
CHB-260 s.p., voc sc BREITKOPF-L EB-7006
s.p., ipa (B426)

Bless'd Are They Who In Jesus Live
(Talmadge, A.) SSAA,acap SCHIRM.EC 1951
$.25 (B427)

Blessed Jesus, At Thy Word *Gen
SATB,kbd (med easy) oct CONCORDIA 98-1740
$.25 (B428)

Blessing, Glory And Wisdom *liturg,Jew
(Ehret, W.) SAB,opt brass oct PRESSER
362-03118 $.30 (B429)
(Tillinghast) SSA/SSA&SSA WARNER W2975 $.25
(B430)

Break Forth (from Christmas Oratorio)
see Two Chorales

Break Forth, O Beauteous Heavenly Light (from
Christmas Oratorio, The) Xmas/Gen,anthem/
chorale
see Four Christmas Chorales
see Two Bach Chorales For Christmas
see Two Chorales
see Two Two-Part Bach Chorales
SATB,kbd (med easy) oct CONCORDIA 98-1069
$.25 (B431)
SATB (very easy) oct AUGSBURG 1044 $.15
(B432)
SATB ALLANS 413 s.p. (B433)
SATB oct PRESSER 332-13744 $.25 (B434)
SATB oct BELWIN 64009 $.25 (B435)
SATB oct GRAY GCMR 1479 $.30 (B436)
SATB,opt org SCHIRM.EC 302 $.25, ipr (B437)
SATB oct NOVELLO 50.0167.06 s.p. (B438)
mix cor oct NOVELLO 50.0167.06 s.p. (B439)
SATB SCHMITT 1905 $.30 (B440)
SATB KJOS 5002 $.30 (B441)
(Davison, A.) TTBB,org SCHIRM.EC 53 $.30,
ipr (B442)
(Glaser, V.) SAB,org SCHIRM.EC 2473 $.25,
ipr (B443)
(Lowden) SAB FLAMMER D5089 $.25 (B444)
(Pitcher, Gladys) 3pt mix cor,pno (med) oct
WILLIS 8497 $.20 (B445)
(Scott) SATB oct FOX R111 $.30 (B446)
(Shaw; Parker) 4pt mix cor,acap,opt org oct
SCHIRM.G 10180 $.25 (B447)

Break Forth, O Beauteous Heav'nly Light (from
Christmas Oratorio) chorale
SATB BOSTON 1659 $.30 (B448)
(Davis, K.) SA SCHIRM.EC 1552 ipr (B449)
(Davison, A.) SSAA,pno SCHIRM.EC 803 $.25,
ipr (B450)
(Davison, A.) SSAA,pno SCHIRM.EC 803 $.25,
ipr (B451)
(Lowden) SA/TB FLAMMER E5080 $.25 (B452)

Break Forth O Beauteous Light
SSA oct STAFF 314 $.25 (B453)

Brich An, Du Schones Morgenlicht (from
Weihnachts-Oratorium)
see Bach, Johann Sebastian, Ich Will Beten,
Gott Wird Horen

Brich Dem Hungrigen *see Brich Dem
Hungrigen Dein Brot

Brich Dem Hungrigen Dein Brot (Cantata 39)
S.39, Trin,cant
mix cor,SAB soli,cont,2fl/2rec,2ob,strings
sc BREITKOPF-W PB-4539 s.p., cor pts
BREITKOPF-W CHB-4539 s.p., ipa (B454)
"Brich Dem Hungriegen" cor,orch sc KALMUS
$5.00, ipa (B455)
(Raphael, G.) [Eng/Ger] mix cor,SAB soli,
org,2fl,2ob,strings,cembalo sc BREITKOPF-
L PB-2889 s.p., voc pt BREITKOPF-L
CHB-437 s.p., voc sc BREITKOPF-L EB-7039
s.p., ipr (B456)
(West, John E.) "Give The Hungry Man Thy
Bread" SATB,SATB soli,org,2fl,2ob,strings
voc sc NOVELLO rental (B457)

Brich Entzwei, Mein Armes Herze *S.444
SATB (A flat maj) HANSSLER 6.1965 s.p.
contains also: Schop, Johann, O
Traurigkeit, O Herzelied (B458)

BACH, JOHANN SEBASTIAN (cont'd.)

Brightest And Best *hymn
PATERSON s.p. see also English Hymns
Adapted To Bach's Chorales (B459)

Bringet Dem Herrn *see Bringet Dem Herrn
Ehre Seines Namens

Bringet Dem Herrn Ehre Seines Namens (Cantata
148) S.148 (from Cantata No. 148) Trin,
cant
mix cor,AT soli,cont,3ob,strings sc
BREITKOPF-W PB-4648 s.p., cor pts
BREITKOPF-W CHB-4648 s.p., ipr (B460)
"Bringet Dem Herrn" [Ger] cor voc sc KALMUS
6601 $1.25 (B461)
(Jode) 4pt mix cor,cont,brass,strings
MOSELER sc s.p., cor pts s.p., ipa (B462)
(Todt, B.) mix cor,AT soli,org,3ob,bsn,trp,
strings,cembalo voc sc BREITKOPF-L
EB-7148 s.p., ipr (B463)

By The Waters Of Babylon
(Cornelius) SATB,acap BROUDE BR. $.35 see
from Two Choral Songs (B464)

Calm And Tranquil Lie The Sheepfolds
(Roper) SATB (med) OXFORD 42.083 $.35
(B465)
(Whittaker) SSA (med) OXFORD 54.110 $.40
(B466)
(Whittaker) SA (med) OXFORD 54.111 $.35
(B467)

Cantata 1 *see Wie Schon Leuchtet Der
Morgenstern

Cantata 2 *see Ach Gott, Vom Himmel Sieh'
Darein

Cantata 3 *see Ach Gott, Wie Manches
Herzeleid

Cantata 4 *see Christ Lag In Todesbanden

Cantata 5 *see Wo Soll Ich Fliehen Hin

Cantata 6 *see Bleib' Bei Uns

Cantata 6 *see Bleib' Bei Uns, Denn Es Will
Abend Werden

Cantata 7 *see Christ Unser Herr, Zum Jordan
Kam

Cantata 8 *see Liebster Gott, Wann Werd' Ich
Sterben?

Cantata 9 *see Es Ist Das Heil Uns Kommen
Her

Cantata 10 *see Mein Seel' Erhebt Den Herren

Cantata 11 *see Lobet Gott In Seinen Reichen

Cantata 11 *see Lobet Gott In Seinen Richen

Cantata 12 *see Weinen, Klagen, Sorgen,
Zagen

Cantata 13 *see Meine Seufzer, Meine Tranen

Cantata 14 *see War' Gott Nicht Mit Uns
Diese Zeit

Cantata 15 *see Denn Du Wirst Meine Seele
Nicht In Der Holle Lassen

Cantata 16 *see Herr Gott, Dich Loben Wir

Cantata 17 *see Wer Dank Opfert, Der Preiset
Mich

Cantata 18 *see Gleich Wie Der Regen

Cantata 18 *see Gleich Wie Der Regen Und
Schnee

Cantata 19 *see Es Erhub Sich Ein Streit

Cantata 20 *see O Ewigkeit, Du Donnerwort

Cantata 21 *see Ich Hatte Veil Bekummernis

Cantata 21 *see Ich Hatte Viel Bekummernis

Cantata 22 *see Jesus Nahm Zu Sich Die
Zwolfe

Cantata 23 *see Du Wahrer Gott Und Davids
Sohn

Cantata 24 *see Ein Ungefarbt Gemute

Cantata 25 *see Es Ist Nichts Gesundes An
Meinem Leibe

Cantata 26 *see Ach Wie Fluchtig, Ach Wie
Nichtig

Cantata 27 *see Wer Weiss, Wie Nahe Mir Mein
Ende

Cantata 28 *see Gottlob, Nun Geht Das Jahr
Zu Ende

Cantata 30 *see Freue Dich, Erloste Schar

Cantata 31 *see Der Himmel Lacht, Die Erde
Jubilieret

Cantata 31 *see Der Himmel Lacht, Die Erde
Jubiliert

Cantata 32 *see Liebster Jesu, Mein
Verlangen

Cantata 33 *see Allein Zu Dir, Herr Jesu
Christ

Cantata 34 *see O Ewiges Feuer, O Ursprung
Der Liebe

Cantata 36 *see Schwingt Freudig Euch Empor

Cantata 37 *see Wer Da Glaubet Und Getauft
Wird

BACH, JOHANN SEBASTIAN (cont'd.)

Cantata 38 *see Aus Tiefer Not Schrei' Ich
Zu Dir

Cantata 39 *see Brich Dem Hungrigen Dein
Brot

Cantata 40 *see Dazu Ist Erschienen Der Sohn
Gottes

Cantata 41 *see Jesu, Nun Sei Gepreiset

Cantata 41 *see Jesu, Nun Sie Gepreiset

Cantata 42 *see Am Abend Aber Desselbigen
Sabbats

Cantata 43 *see Gott Fahret Auf Mit Jauchzen

Cantata 44 *see Sie Werden Euch In Den Bann
Tun

Cantata 45 *see Es Ist Dir Gesagt, Mensch,
Was Gut Ist

Cantata 46 *see Schauet Doch Und Sehet

Cantata 47 *see Wer Sich Selbst Erhohet

Cantata 48 *see Ich Elender Mensch Wer Wird
Mich Erlosen

Cantata 50 *see Nun Ist Das Heil

Cantata 50 *see Nun Ist Das Heil Und Die
Kraft

Cantata 51 *see Jauchzet Gott In Allen
Landen

Cantata 52 *see Falsche Welt, Dir Trau' Ich
Nicht

Cantata 53 *see Strike Thou Hour

Cantata 55 *see Ich Armer Mensch, Ich
Sundenknecht

Cantata 56 *see Ich Will Den Kreuzstab Gerne
Tragen

Cantata 57 *see Selig Ist Der Mann

Cantata 59 *see Wer Mich Liebet, Der Wird
Mein Wort Halten

Cantata 60 *see O Ewigkeit, Du Donnerwort

Cantata 61 *see Nun Komm', Der Heiden
Heiland

Cantata 61 *see Nun Komm, Der Heiden Heiland

Cantata 62 *see Nun Komm, Der Heiden Heiland

Cantata 63 *see Christen, Atzet Diesen Tag

Cantata 64 *see Sehet, Welch Eine Liebe

Cantata 65 *see Sie Werden Aus Saba Alle
Kommen

Cantata 66 *see Erfreuet Euch, Ihr Herzen

Cantata 67 *see Halt Im Gedachtnis Jesum
Christ

Cantata 68 *see Also Hat Gott Die Welt
Geliebt

Cantata 69 *see Lobe Den Herrn, Meine Seele

Cantata 70 *see Wachet, Betet, Seid Bereit
Allezeit

Cantata 71 *see Gott Ist Mein Konig

Cantata 72 *see Alles Nur Nach Gottes Willen

Cantata 73 *see Herr, Wie Du Willt, So
Schicks Mit Mir

Cantata 74 *see Wer Mich Liebet, Der Wird
Mein Wort Halten

Cantata 75 *see Die Elenden Sollen Essen

Cantata 76 *see Die Himmel Erzahlen Die Ehre
Gottes

Cantata 77 *see Du Sollst Gott, Deinen
Herren, Lieben

Cantata 78 *see Jesu, Der Du Meine Seele

Cantata 79 *see Gott, Der Herr, Ist Sonn Und
Schild

Cantata 80 *see Ein' Feste Burg Ist Unser
Gott

Cantata 81 *see Jesus Schlaft, Was Soll Ich
Hoffen?

Cantata 82 *see Ich Habe

Cantata 83 *see Erfreute Zeit Im Neuen Bunde

Cantata 84 *see Ich Bin Vergnugt Mit Meinem
Glucke

Cantata 85 *see Ich Bin Ein Guter Hirt

Cantata 86 *see Wahrlich, Wahrlich, Ich Sage
Euch

Cantata 87 *see Bisher Habt Ihr Nichts
Gebeten

Cantata 88 *see Siehe, Ich Will Viel Fischer
Aussenden

Cantata 89 *see Was Soll Ich Aus Dir Machen,
Ephraim?

Cantata 90 *see Es Reifet Euch Ein
Schrecklich Ende

BACH, JOHANN SEBASTIAN (cont'd.)

Cantata 91 *see Gelobet Seist Du, Jesu
Christ

Cantata 92 *see Ich Hab In Gottes Herz Und
Sinn

Cantata 93 *see Wer Nur Den Lieben Gott
Lasst Walten

Cantata 94 *see Was Frag Ich Nach Der Welt

Cantata 95 *see Christus Der Ist Mein Leben

Cantata 96 *see Herr Christ, Der Ein'ge
Gottes-Sohn

Cantata 97 *see In Allen Meinen Taten

Cantata 98 *see Was Gott Tut, Das Ist
Wohlgetan

Cantata 99 *see Was Gott Tut, Das Ist
Wohlgetan

Cantata 100 *see Was Gott Tut, Das Ist
Wohlgetan

Cantata 101 *see Nimm Von Uns, Herr, Du
Treuer Gott

Cantata 102 *see Herr, Deine Augen Sehen
Nach Dem Glauben

Cantata 103 *see Ihr Werdet Weinen Und
Heulen

Cantata 104 *see Du Hirte Israel, Hore

Cantata 105 *see Herr, Gehe Nicht Ins
Gericht

Cantata 106 *see Gottes Zeit Ist Die
Allerbeste Zeit

Cantata 107 *see Was Willst Du Dich Betruben

Cantata 108 *see Es Ist Euch Gut, Dass Ich
Hingehe

Cantata 109 *see Ich Glaube, Lieber Herr,
Hilf Meinem Unglauben

Cantata 110 *see Unser Mund Sei Voll Lachens

Cantata 111 *see Was Mein Gott Will, Das
G'scheh' Allzeit

Cantata 112 *see Der Herr Ist Mein Getreuer
Hirt

Cantata 113 *see Herr Jesu Christ, Du
Hochstes Gut

Cantata 114 *see Ach, Lieben Christen, Seid
Getrost

Cantata 115 *see Mache Dich, Mein Geist,
Bereit

Cantata 116 *see Du Friedefurst, Herr Jesu
Christ

Cantata 117 *see Sei Lob Und Ehr' Dem
Hochsten Gut

Cantata 118 *see O Jesu Christ, Mein's
Lebens Licht

Cantata 119 *see Preise, Jerusalem, Den
Herrn

Cantata 120 *see Gott, Man Lobet Dich In Der
Stille

Cantata 121 *see Christum, Wir Sollen Loben
Schon

Cantata 122 *see Das Neugebor'ne Kindelein

Cantata 123 *see Liebster Immanuel

Cantata 124 *see Meinen Jesum Lass Ich Nicht

Cantata 125 *see Mit Fried' Und Freud' Ich
Fahr' Dahin

Cantata 126 *see Erhalt' Uns, Herr, Bei
Deinem Wort

Cantata 127 *see Herr Jesu Christ, Wahr'r
Mensch Und Gott

Cantata 128 *see Auf Christi Himmelfahrt
Allein

Cantata 129 *see Gelobet Sei Der Herr, Mein
Gott

Cantata 130 *see Herr Gott, Dich Loben Alle
Wir

Cantata 131 *see Aus Der Tiefe Rufe Ich,
Herr, Zu Dir

Cantata 132 *see Bereitet Die Wege, Bereitet
Die Bahn

Cantata 133 *see Ich Freue Mich In Dir

Cantata 134 *see Ein Herz, Das Seinen Jesum
Lebend Weiss

Cantata 135 *see Ach Herr, Mich Armen Sunder

Cantata 136 *see Erforsche Mich, Gott, Und
Erfahre Mein Herz

Cantata 137 *see Lobe Den Herren, Den
Machtigen Konig Der Ehren

Cantata 138 *see Warum Betrubst Du Dich,
Mein Herz

Cantata 139 *see Wohl Dem, Der Sich Auf
Seinen Gott

BACH, JOHANN SEBASTIAN (cont'd.)

Cantata 140 *see Wachet Auf

Cantata 140 *see Wachet Auf, Ruft Uns Die
Stimme

Cantata 141 *see Das Ist Je Gewisslich Wahr

Cantata 142 *see Uns Ist Ein Kind Geboren

Cantata 143 *see Lobe Den Herrn, Meine Seele

Cantata 144 *see Nimm, Was Dein Ist, Und
Gehe Hin

Cantata 145 *see Auf, Mein Herz, Des Herren
Tag

Cantata 146 *see Wir Mussen Durch Viel
Trubsal

Cantata 147 *see Herz Und Mund Und Tat Und
Leben

Cantata 148 *see Bringet Dem Herrn Ehre
Seines Namens

Cantata 149 *see Man Singet Mit Freuden

Cantata 149 *see Man Singet Mit Freuden Vom
Sieg

Cantata 150 *see Nach Dir, Herr, Verlanget
Mich

Cantata 151 *see Mein Susser Trost

Cantata 151 *see Susser Trost, Mein Jesus
Kommt

Cantata 153 *see Schau, Lieber Gott, Wie
Meine Feind'

Cantata 154 *see Mein Liebster Jesus Ist
Verloren

Cantata 155 *see Mein Gott, Wie Lang', Ach
Lange

Cantata 156 *see Ich Steh' Mit Einem Fuss Im
Grabe

Cantata 157 *see Ich Lasse Dich Nicht Du
Segnest Mich Denn

Cantata 158 *see Der Friede Sei Mit Dir

Cantata 159 *see Sehet, Wir Gehn Hinauf Gen
Jerusalem

Cantata 160 *see I Know That My Redeemer
Lives

Cantata 161 *see Komm Du Susse Todesstunde

Cantata 162 *see Ach, Ich Sehe, Ietzt

Cantata 163 *see Nur Jedem Das Seine

Cantata 164 *see Ihr, Die Ihr Euch Von
Christo Nennet

Cantata 165 *see O Heil'ges Geist- Und
Wasserbad

Cantata 166 *see Wo Gehest Du Hin?

Cantata 167 *see Ihr Menschen, Ruhmet Gottes
Liebe

Cantata 168 *see Tue Rechnung, Donnerwort

Cantata 169 *see Gott Soll Allein Mein Herze
Haben

Cantata 171 *see Gott, Wie Dein Name

Cantata 172 *see Erschallet, Ihr Lieder

Cantata 173 *see Erhohtes Fleisch Und Blut

Cantata 174 *see Ich Liebe Den Hochsten

Cantata 175 *see Er Rufet Seinen Schafen Mit
Namen

Cantata 176 *see Es Ist Ein Trotzig Und
Verzagt Ding

Cantata 177 *see Ich Ruf' Zu Dir, Herr Jesu
Christ

Cantata 178 *see Wo Gott, Der Herr, Nicht
Bei Uns Halt

Cantata 179 *see Siehe Zu, Dass Deine
Gottesfurcht

Cantata 180 *see Schmucke Dich, O Liebe
Seele

Cantata 181 *see Leichtgesinnte
Flattergeister

Cantata 182 *see Himmelskonig, Sei
Willkommen

Cantata 183 *see Sie Werden Euch In Den Bann
Tun

Cantata 184 *see Erwunschtes Freudenlicht

Cantata 185 *see Barmherziges Herze Der
Ewigen Liebe

Cantata 186 *see Argre Dich, O Seele, Nicht

Cantata 187 *see Es Wartet Alles Auf Dich

Cantata 188 *see Ich Habe Meine Zuversicht

Cantata 190 *see Singet Dem Herrn Ein Neues
Lied

Cantata 191 *see Gloria In Excelsis Deo

BACH, JOHANN SEBASTIAN (cont'd.)

Cantata 192 *see Nun Danket Alle Gott

Cantata 193 *see Ihr Pforten Zu Zion

Cantata 194 *see Hochsterwunschtes Freudenfest

Cantata 196 *see Der Herr Denket An Uns

Cantata 197 *see Gott Ist Unsre Zuversicht

Cantata 198 *see Lass, Furstin, Lass Noch Einen Strahl

Cantata 208 *see Was Mir Behast, Ist Mur Die Muntre Jagd

Cantata 216 *see Vergnugte Pleissenstadt

Cantate, Pour La Fete De La Pentecote *Pent, cant
SATB,TB soli CHOUDENS voc sc s.p., cor pts s.p. (B468)

Cantate, Pour La Fete De L'ascension *see Lobet Gott In Seinen Reichen

Cantate, Pour La Fete De Saint-Jean- Baptiste *see Christ Unser Herr, Zum Jordan Kam

Cantate, Pour Le Dimanche De La Sexagesime *see Erhalt' Uns, Herr, Bei Deinem Wort

Cantate, Pour Le Jour De L'ascension *Asc, cant
SATB,SATB soli CHOUDENS voc sc s.p., cor pts s.p. (B469)

Cantate, Pour Le Jour De Paques *Easter,cant
SATB CHOUDENS voc sc s.p., cor pts s.p. (B470)

Cantate, Pour Le Neuvieme Dimanche Apres La Trinite *see Tue Rechnung, Donnerwort

Cantate, Pour Le Premiere Jour De Noel *Xmas,cant
SATB CHOUDENS voc sc s.p., cor pts s.p. (B471)

Cantate, Pour Le Seizieme Dimanche Apres La Trinite *see Wer Weiss, Wie Nahe Mir Mein Ende

Cantate, Pour Le Troisieme Dimanche Apres Epiphanie *see Ich Steh' Mit Einem Fuss Im Grabe

Cantate, Pour Le Troisieme Jour Apres Noel *see Sehet, Welch Eine Liebe

Cantate, Pour Tous Le Temps *cant
SATB,SATB soli CHOUDENS voc sc s.p., cor pts s.p. (B472)

Cantique De Pentecote *Pent
(Geveart, F.-A.) [Fr] 4pt mix cor,acap (med) cor pts LEMOINE s.p. see from Collection De Choeurs, cinquieme Fascicule (B473)

Chant De Paques *see Surexit Christus Hodie

Chantez Au Seigneur *S.225, mot
(Barre, J.) [Fr] 4pt mix cor,acap voc sc DURAND see from Motets (B474)

Child Is Born In Bethlehem, A *Xmas/Epiph
see Four Christmas Chorales
see Two Bach Chorales For Christmas
SATB,acap (med easy) oct CONCORDIA 98-1803 $.25 (B475)

Childhood Of Christ, The *cant
(Beveridge) mix cor BELWIN $1.50 (B476)
(Talmadge) wom cor BELWIN $1.50 (B477)

Choral Duets From Cantatas [Nos. 3, 91, 163], Vol. 4
[Eng/Ger] HINRICHSEN G313 sc s.p., voc pt s.p. (B478)

Choral Duets From Cantatas [Nos. 4, 37, 78, 124], Vol. 1
[Ger] SA,orch HINRICHSEN G310 sc s.p., voc pt s.p. (B479)

Choral Duets From Cantatas [Nos. 9, 184], Vol 2.
[Ger] HINRICHSEN G311 sc s.p., voc pt s.p. (B480)

Choral Duets From Cantatas [Nos. 88, 93, 168], Vol. 3
[Eng/Ger] HINRICHSEN G312 sc s.p., voc pt s.p. (B481)

Choral Music *CC7L
cor min sc KALMUS 909 $1.30 (B482)

Chorale (from Christmas Oratorio) chorale
see Bach, Johann Sebastian, Pastoral Symphony
SATB,band oct STAFF 460 $.30, ipa (B483)

Chorale 10 *see Dans Ma Profonde Detresse, Je Crie Vers Toi

Chorale 74 *see Front Couronne D'epines

Chorale 179 *see Leuez-Vous! Une Voix Vous Appelle

Chorale From St. Matthew Passion
see Two Choruses

Chorale-Heft 1 *CC21U,chorale
(Berger) SATB HANSSLER 4.001 s.p. (B484)

Chorale-Heft 2 *CC20U,chorale
(Berger) SATB HANSSLER 4.005 s.p. (B485)

Chorale Mass *CC12U,anthem/chorale/hymn/Mass
(Roff, J) SATB/cong (easy) cmplt ed GIA G1367 $1.00 (B486)

Chorales (from Passion According To St. John, The) CCU,chorale
oct LAWSON $.60 (B487)

BACH, JOHANN SEBASTIAN (cont'd.)

Chorales (from St. John Passion) CCU,Lent, chorale
SATB oct GRAY GCMR 2261 $.25 (B488)

Chorales, Book I *CC91U
(Boyd, Charles N.; Riemenschneider, Albert) [Ger/Eng] 4pt mix cor/5pt mix cor SCHIRM.G $4.00 contains: Chorales Nos. 1-91 (B489)

Chorales, Book II *CC28U
(Boyd, Charles; Riemenschneider, Albert) mix cor sc SCHIRM.G $2.50 contains: Chorales Nos. 92-120 (B490)

Chorales (from St. Matthew Passion) CCU,Lent, chorale
SATB oct GRAY GCMR 2249 $.25 (B491)

Choralgesange *CC90U,chorale
[Ger] 4pt mix cor cloth BAREN. EM 331 s.p. (B492)

Choralgesange *CC389U,chorale
mix cor cor pts BREITKOPF-W EB-3765 s.p. (B493)

Choralgesange
[Ger] mix cor,acap (med easy) HUG s.p. contains: Wenn Ich Einmal Soll Scheiden; Wenn Mein Stundlein Vorhanden Ist (B494)

Choralsatze (from Jesu, Meine Freude) CCU
SATB/SSATB,cont HANSSLER 31.227-1 s.p. (B495)

Christ Is The World's True Light *anthem
(Cook, John) mix cor oct NOVELLO 40.1339.05 s.p. (B496)

Christ Lag In Todesbanden (Cantata 4) S.4, Easter/Gd.Fri./Psntd,cant
see Bach, Johann Sebastian, Dir, Dir Jehova
cor,orch sc KALMUS $4.50, ipa (B497)
mix cor,SATB soli,cont,trp,3trom,strings sc BREITKOPF-W PB-4504 s.p., cor pts BREITKOPF-W CHB-4504 s.p., ipa (B498)
"Christ Lay In Death's Dark Prison" BELWIN $1.00 (B499)
"Christ Lay In Death's Dark Prison" [Eng] cor voc sc KALMUS 6012 $1.00 (B500)
(Schreck, G.) mix cor,SATB soli,org,trp, 3trom,strings cor pts BREITKOPF-L CHB-550 s.p., voc sc BREITKOPF-L EB-7004 s.p., ipr (B501)
(Stephens, Norris L.) "Christ Lay In Death's Dark Prison" [Eng/Ger] mix cor, soli,org SCHIRM.G voc sc $1.00, sc $3.50 (B502)
(West, John E.) "Christ Lay In Death's Dark Prison" SATB,SATB soli,trp,3trom,strings voc sc NOVELLO s.p., ipr (B503)

Christ Lag In Todesbanden [Chorale]
(McKinney) "Christ Lay In Death's Dark Prison" SATB oct FISCHER,J 6593 $.30 (B504)

Christ Lay In Death's Dark Prison *see Christ Lag In Todesbanden

Christ Lay In Death's Dark Prison *see Christ Lag In Todesbanden [Chorale]

Christ Unser Herr *see Christ Unser Herr, Zum Jordan Kam

Christ Unser Herr, Zum Jordan Kam (Cantata 7) S.7, ASD,cant
mix cor,ATB soli,cont,2ob,strings cor pts BREITKOPF-W CHB-4507 s.p., ipr, sc BREITKOPF-W rental (B505)
"Cantate, Pour La Fete De Saint-Jean-Baptiste" SATB,SATB soli CHOUDENS voc sc s.p., cor pts s.p. (B506)
"Christ Unser Herr" [Ger] cor voc sc KALMUS 6524 $1.25 (B507)
"Vor Herre Kom Til Jordans Flod" [Ger/Dan] SATB HANSEN-DEN 189 s.p. see also Otte Koraludsaettelser (B508)
(Raphael, G.) [Eng/Ger] mix cor,ATB soli, org,2ob,2bsn,strings,cembalo cor pts BREITKOPF-L CHB-2136 s.p., voc sc BREITKOPF-L EB-7007 s.p., ipr (B509)

Christe, Du Lamm Gottes *S.233a (from Du Wahrer Gott Und Davids Sohn) Psntd,Kyrie
"Lamb Of God, Our Savior" see Bach, Johann Sebastian, Aller Augen Warten, Herr
"Lamb Of God" SATB,pno SCHIRM.EC 1165 $.40, ipr (B510)
(Wolff) [Ger] 5pt mix cor,vcl&bvl/bsn&bvl BAREN. EM 511 sc s.p., cor pts s.p., ipa (B511)

Christen, Atzet Diesen Tag (Cantata 63) S.63, Xmas,cant
mix cor,SATB soli,cont,3ob,bsn,4trp, strings,timp cor pts BREITKOPF-W CHB-4563 s.p., ipr, sc BREITKOPF-W rental (B512)
(Raphael, G.) [Eng/Ger] mix cor,SATB soli, org,3ob,bsn,4trp,strings,timp,cembalo voc pt BREITKOPF-L CHB-450 s.p., voc sc BREITKOPF-L EB-7063 s.p., ipr (B513)
(West, John E.) "Christians, Grave Ye This Glad Day" SATB,SATB soli,2ob,bsn,4trp, timp,strings voc sc NOVELLO s.p., ipr (B514)

Christians, Be Joyful (from Christmas Oratorio)
SATB oct BELWIN 64140 $.40 (B515)

Christians, Grave Ye This Glad Day *see Christen, Atzet Diesen Tag

Christians, Shout For Joy *Easter,anthem
(Buck, P.C.) SATB oct ROYAL 202 s.p. (B516)

Christmas Chorales (from Christmas Oratorio) CCU,Xmas,chorale
[Eng/Ger] SATB oct BOONIN 147 $.60 (B517)

Christmas Oratorio *see Oratorio Di Natale

Christmas Oratorio, Part I *see Oratorio Di Natale

Christmas Oratorio, Part II *see Oratorio Di Natale

BACH, JOHANN SEBASTIAN (cont'd.)

Christmas Oratorio, Parts I & II *see Oratorio Di Natale

Christmas Program Of Bach Chorales *CCU, Xmas,chorale
(Gordon) SATB&jr cor,opt brass WARNER $1.00, ipa (B518)

Christmas Sequence, A *Xmas
(Whittaker) SSATB (med easy) OXFORD 42.082 $.75 (B519)

Christum Wir Sollen *see Christum, Wir Sollen Loben Schon

Christum, Wir Sollen Loben Schon (Cantata 121) S.121, Xmas,cant
mix cor,SATB soli,cont,ob,trp,3trom,strings cor pts BREITKOPF-W CHB-4621 s.p., ipr, sc BREITKOPF-W rental (B520)
"Christum Wir Sollen" [Ger] cor voc sc KALMUS 6583 $1.25 (B521)
(Todt, B.) mix cor,SATB soli,org,ob,trp, 3trom,strings,cembalo voc sc BREITKOPF-L EB-7121 s.p., ipr (B522)

Christus, Der Ist *see Christus, Der Ist Mein Leben

Christus, Der Ist Mein Leben (Cantata 95) S.95, Trin,cant
SATB HANSSLER 6.014 s.p. contains also: Was Gott Tut, Das Ist Wohlgetan [Chorale] (B523)
mix cor,STB soli,cont,4ob,trp,strings sc BREITKOPF-W PB-4595 s.p., cor pts BREITKOPF-W CHB-4595 s.p., ipa (B524)
"Christus, Der Ist" cor,orch/org sc KALMUS $3.00, ipa (B525)
"Christus, Der Ist Mein Leben" [Ger] cor voc sc KALMUS 6563 $1.25 (B526)
(Raphael, G.) [Eng/Ger] mix cor,STB soli, org,2ob,2bsn,horn,strings,cembalo, 2 English horns sc BREITKOPF-L PB-2945 s.p., voc pt BREITKOPF-L CHB-848 s.p., voc sc BREITKOPF-L EB-7095 s.p., ipr (B527)
(West, John E.) "O Christ, My All In Living" SATB,STB soli,4ob,horn,strings voc sc NOVELLO s.p., ipr (B528)

Christus, Der Ist Mein Leben *see Christus, Der Ist Mein Leben

Christus, Der Uns Selig Macht (from Johannes-Passion) Easter
SATB (F min) HANSSLER 6.115 s.p. contains also: Werner, Fritz, Christus, Der Uns Selig Macht (B529)

Cincuenta Corales *CC50U,chorale
(Obermuller, Carambula) [Ger/Span] SATB, acap RICORDI-ARG BA10698 s.p. (B530)

Collection De Choeurs, Cinquieme Fascicule
(Geveart, F.-A.) [Fr/Lat] 4pt mix cor,acap cmplt ed LEMOINE s.p. (B531)

Collection De Choeurs, cinquieme Fascicule
*see Cantique De Pentecote; Confiance En Dieu; Hymne Du Matin; Jesus, Corona Virginum, "Hymne Des Vierges"; La Brebis Egaree; Le Calvaire; Paix Du Ciel; Sanctus; Soleil Couchant; Surexit Christus Hodie, "Chant De Paques"; Tristesse; Veni Creator Spiritus, "Hymne De La Pentecote" (B532)

Come And Thank Him (from Christmas Oratorio) Xmas,anthem
SATB oct NOVELLO 34.0538.09 s.p. (B533)
(Whitford) SATB,org BOSTON 3030 $.35 (B534)

Come, Come, My Voice
(Whitehead) 4pt mix cor oct CURWEN 10768 $.20 (B535)

Come, Gracious Spirit, Heav'nly Dove
see Four Chorale Harmonizations

Come, Jesu, Come *see Komm, Jesu, Komm

Come, Jesus, Come *see Komm, Jesu, Komm

Come, Kindly Death
2pt wom cor (med) oct WILLIS 1113 $.10 (B536)

Come, Let Us All This Day *see Kommt, Seelen, Dieser Tag

Come My Heart And Ponder Well *chorale
(Luvaas) SATB oct VOLKWEIN VB135 $.25 (B537)

Come Now Good Christians
(Bedell) 2pt jr cor,pno,org,vln,vcl FISCHER,C R 423 $.22 (B538)

Come Peaceful Death
(Martin, C.) SSAATTBB,acap oct PRESSER 312-40104 $.30 (B539)

Come, Redeemer *Adv,cant
BELWIN $.75 (B540)

Come, Redeemer Of Our Race *see Nun Komm', Der Heiden Heiland

Come, Soothing Death *see Komm, Susser Tod

Come, Spirits, 'Tis His Day
(Luvaas) SSAA,acap WARNER G1078 $.30 (B541)

Come, Thou Holy Paraclete *hymn
PATERSON s.p. see also English Hymns Adapted To Bach's Chorales (B542)

Come Thou, O Saviour
(Thoburn) SATB oct SUMMY 5203 $.35 (B543)

Come Thou, Oh, Come (from O Ewigkeit, Du Donnerwort)
(Davison, A.) TTBB,acap SCHIRM.EC 28 $.20 (B544)

Come Thou, Sweet Death *see Komm', Susser Tod

BACH, JOHANN SEBASTIAN (cont'd.)

Come, Together Let Us Sing *see Liebster Jesu, Wir Sind Hier

Comfort, Comfort Ye My People *Adv/Gen SATB,2vln,vla,cont (med easy) oct CONCORDIA 98-2045 $.35, ipa (B545)

Comfort Ye, My People (Aufdenberge) SSA FLAMMER B 5032 $.30 (B546)

Communion Service (McGowan, H.) unis/SATB (easy) oct OXFORD 43.316 $.40 (B547)

Confiance En Dieu (Geveart, F.-A.) [Fr] 4pt mix cor,acap (med easy) cor pts LEMOINE s.p. see from Collection De Choeurs, cinquieme Fascicule (B548)

Crucifixus (from Mass In B-Minor) Easter/ Lent,anthem
see Bach, Johann Sebastian, Et Incarnatus Est
[Lat] SATB/SSATB oct NOVELLO 34.0720.09 s.p. contains also: Et Resurrexit (B549)
SATB,pno SCHIRM.EC 1174 $.30, ipr (B550)
(Brooks) SATB oct PLYMOUTH CC-8 $.25 (B551)
(Churchill) SATB oct BOURNE 750 $.30 (B552)
(Damrosch) 4pt mix cor oct SCHIRM.G 8861 $.25 (B553)
(Davison, A.) [Lat] TTBB,pno SCHIRM.EC 54 $.22, ipr (B554)

Cum Sancto Spiritu (from Mass In B Minor) (Davison, A.) [Lat] TTBB,pno SCHIRM.EC 55 $.50, ipr (B555)

Dankt, Dankt Nu Allen God mix cor sc ALSBACH&D s.p. (B556)

Dans Ma Profonde Detresse, Je Crie Vers Toi (Chorale 10)
(Doyen, A.) [Fr] SATB/SMezTB voc sc LEDUC CC7 s.p. (B557)

Das Alte Jahr [Chorale] see Weihnachtschorale-II

Das Grosse Gloria (from Messe In A) Gloria (Jode) 4pt mix cor,cont,inst MOSELER sc s.p., cor pts s.p., ipa (B558)

Das Ist Je Gewisslich Wahr (Cantata 141) S.141, cant
[Ger] cor voc sc KALMUS 6595 $1.25 (B559)
mix cor,cont,2ob,strings cor pts BREITKOPF-W CHB-4641 s.p., ipr, sc BREITKOPF-W rental (B560)

Das Kirchenjahr Und Seine Chorale *CCU (Kubli, Matthaus) [Ger] mix cor,acap cloth HUG s.p. (B561)

Das Neugebor'ne Kindelein (Cantata 122) S.122 (from Cant122) Xmas,cant
[Ger] cor voc sc KALMUS 6584 $1.25 (B562)
mix cor,SATB soli,cont,3fl/3rec,3ob,strings cor pts BREITKOPF-W CHB-4622 s.p., ipr, sc BREITKOPF-W rental (B563)
"New-Born Babe, The" [Eng] 4pt mix cor,SATB soli,pno voc sc SCHIRM.G $1.00 (B564)
"Sing We The Birth" SATB (med) OXFORD 46.028 $1.35 (B565)
"Unto The World This Happy Morn" [Ger/Eng] cor,orch SCHIRM.EC 2536 ipr (B566)
(Talmadge, A.) "Unto The World This Happy Morn" [Ger/Eng] SSAA,org (contains choral selections from Cantata No. 122) SCHIRM.EC 2536 $.40, ipr contains also: Ist Gott Versohnt Und Unser Freund, "When God On Us His Love Bestows"; Es Bringt Das Rechte Jubeljahr, "Sing Out, Ye Voices, Loud And Clear" (B567)
(Todt, B.) mix cor,SATB soli,org,3fl,2ob, strings,cembalo, English horn voc pt BREITKOPF-L CHB-2134 s.p., voc sc BREITKOPF-L EB-7122 s.p., ipr (B568)
(Whittaker) "Sing We The Birth" SATB,SAB soli (med) OXFORD 46.028 $1.35, ipr (B569)

Das Neugeborne Kindelein [Chorale] see Weihnachtschorale-II

Das Neugebor'ne Kindelein, Das Herzensliebe see Praetorius, Michael, Das Alte Jahr Ist Nun Dahin

Day Is Done, The *see Der Tag Ist Hin

Dazu Ist Erschienen Der Sohn Gottes (Cantata 40) S.40, Xmas,cant
mix cor,ATB soli,cont,2ob,2horn,strings cor pts BREITKOPF-W CHB-4540 s.p., ipr, sc BREITKOPF-W rental (B570)
(Raphael, G.) [Eng/Ger] mix cor,ATB soli, org,2ob,bsn,2horn,strings,cembalo voc pt BREITKOPF-L CHB-1418 s.p., voc sc BREITKOPF-L EB-7040 s.p., ipr (B571)

Dearest Lord Jesus (Saar, L.) SSA oct PRESSER 332-14200 $.30 (B572)

Death, I Do Not Fear Thee (from Jesu, Priceless Treasure)
mix cor SOUTHERN $.30 (B573)
(Damrosch) 5pt mix cor,acap oct SCHIRM.G 9991 $.30 (B574)

Deck Thyself, My Soul *see Schmucke Dich, O Liebe Seele [Chorale]

Dem Wir Das Heilig Itzt (from Gelobet Sei Der Herr) Easter,chorale
"Awake, Thou Wintry Earth" SATB,org SCHIRM.EC 1169 $.30, ipr (B575)
(Glaser, V.) "Awake, Thou Wintry Earth" SSA,pno SCHIRM.EC 1931 $.25 (B576)

Den Tod Niemand Zwingen Kunnt (from Christ Lag In Todesbanden) Easter
[Ger] SA,org/cont BAREN. EM 6 s.p. (B577)

Denn Du Wirst *see Denn Du Wirst Meine Seele Nicht In Der Holle Lassen

Denn Du Wirst Meine Seele Nicht In Der Holle Lassen (Cantata 15) S.15, cant
mix cor,SATB soli,cont,3trp,strings,timp cor pts BREITKOPF-W CHB-4515 s.p., ipr, sc BREITKOPF-W rental (B578)
"Denn Du Wirst" [Ger] cor voc sc KALMUS 6528 $1.25 (B579)

Denn Du Wirst Meine Seele Nicht In Die Holle Lassen *S.15, Easter,cant
mix cor,SATB soli,org,bsn,3trp,strings, perc,cembalo voc pt BREITKOPF-L CHB-1454 s.p., voc sc BREITKOPF-L EB-7015 s.p., ipr (B580)

Der Friede *see Der Friede Sei Mit Dir

Der Friede Sei Mit Dir (Cantata 158) S.158, BVM/Easter,cant
mix cor,B solo,org,ob,strings,cembalo sc BREITKOPF-L PB-3008 s.p., voc pt BREITKOPF-L CHB-863 s.p., voc sc BREITKOPF-L EB-7158 s.p., ipa (B581)
[Ger] cor voc sc KALMUS 6607 $1.25 (B582)
mix cor,SB soli,cont,ob,vln sc BREITKOPF-W PB-4658 s.p., cor pts BREITKOPF-W CHB-4658 s.p., ipa (B583)
"Der Friede" cor,orch/org sc KALMUS $2.25, ipa (B584)
(Durr, Alfred) [Ger] SATB,B solo,org,cont, ob,vln sc BAREN. BA 5122 $3.75, cor pts BAREN. BA 5122 $.35, voc sc BAREN. BA 5122 A $2.25, min sc BAREN. TP 79 $2.00 (B585)
(Grischkat) [Ger/Eng] SATB,SB soli,cont,ob, vln HANSSLER 10.028 sc $3.50, cor pts $.50, ipa, voc sc s.p. (B586)

Der Geist Hilft *mot
(Neumann-Buszin) "Spirit Also Helpeth Us, The" [Eng/Ger] SATB&SATB,cont PETERS 6102 $.90, ipa see from Six Motets (B587)

Der Geist Hilft Unser Schwachheit Auf (Motet 2) S.226, Gen
(Ameln, Konrad) [Ger] SATB&SATB,org,3ob, bsn,2vln,vla,vcl,bvl sc BAREN. BA 5130 $5.25, cor pts BAREN. BA 5131 $1.50, ipa (B588)

Der Geist Hilft Unsrer Schwachheit Auf (Motet 2) S.226, Bibl/mot
8pt mix cor,2ob,bsn,strings, English horn cor pts BREITKOPF-L EB-7226 s.p., voc pt BREITKOPF-L CHB-537 s.p., ipr (B589)
dbl cor,org,3ob,bsn,strings voc pt BREITKOPF-L CHB-537 s.p., voc sc BREITKOPF-L EB-7226 s.p., ipr (B590)
dbl cor sc BREITKOPF-W EB-6292 s.p. (B591)
(Ameln; Wolters) SATB&SATB,cont,strings,opt 2ob&bsn, 2 English horns cor pts MOSELER s.p., ipa (B592)
(West, John E.) "Spirit Also Helpeth Us, The" dbl cor,acap voc sc NOVELLO s.p. (B593)

Der Helle Weg
(Thurer, G.) [Ger] mix cor,acap (med easy) HUG s.p. (B594)

Der Herr *see Der Herr Ist Mein Getreuer Hirt

Der Herr Denket An Uns (Cantata 196) S.196, Marriage,cant
[Ger] cor voc sc KALMUS 6635 $1.25 (B595)
mix cor,STB soli,org,cont,strings sc BREITKOPF-W PB-4696 s.p., cor pts BREITKOPF-W CHB-4696 s.p., ipa (B596)
(Todt, B.) mix cor,STB soli,org,strings, cembalo voc pt BREITKOPF-L CHB-2219 s.p., voc sc BREITKOPF-L EB-7196 s.p., ipr (B597)

Der Herr Ist Mein Getreuer Hirt (Cantata 112) S.112 (from Du Hirte Israel, Hore) Easter/Gen,cant
SATB HANSSLER 6.203 s.p. contains also: Schutz, Heinrich, Des Heilgen Geistes Gnade Gross, SWV 204; Schutz, Heinrich, Danket Dem Herrn (B598)
mix cor,SATB soli,cont,2ob,2horn,strings cor pts BREITKOPF-W CHB-4612 s.p., ipr, sc BREITKOPF-W rental (B599)
"Der Herr" [Eng] cor voc sc KALMUS 6048 $1.00 (B600)
(Pointer, John) "Lord Is My Shepherd, The" SATB,SATB soli,4ob,2clar,2horn,strings voc sc NOVELLO s.p., ipr (B601)
(Raphael, G.) [Eng/Ger] mix cor,SATB soli, org,2ob,bsn,2horn,strings,cembalo voc pt BREITKOPF-L CHB-1973 s.p., voc sc BREITKOPF-L EB-7112 s.p., ipr (B602)

Der Herr Ist Mein Getreuer Hirt' [Chorale] (from Du Hirte Israel)
"Lord My Guide, The [Chorale]" SATB,opt inst SCHIRM.EC 2232 $.16 (B603)

Der Herr Segne Euch (from Wedding Cantata No. 196) Marriage
"May God Smile On You" [Eng/Ger] TB,pno/org PETERS 6079 $.30 (B604)
"May God Smile On You" boy cor SOUTHERN $.30 (B605)

Der Himmel Lacht, Die Erde Jubilieret (Cantata 31) S.31, cant
mix cor,STB soli,cont,4ob,bsn,3trp,strings, timp sc BREITKOPF-W PB-4531 s.p., cor pts BREITKOPF-W CHB-4531 s.p., ipa (B606)
"Heavens Laugh, The" [Eng] cor voc sc KALMUS 6025 $1.00 (B607)

Der Himmel Lacht, Die Erde Jubiliert (Cantata 31) S.31, Easter,cant
"Heavens Laugh, The Earth Exults, The" [Eng/Ger] mix cor,soli,pno voc sc SCHIRM.G $1.00 (B608)
(Raphael, G.) [Eng/Ger] mix cor,STB soli, org,4ob,bsn,3trp,strings,timp,cembalo sc BREITKOPF-L PB-2881 s.p., voc pt BREITKOPF-L CHB-1457 s.p., voc sc BREITKOPF-L EB-7031 s.p., ipa (B609)

Der Leib Zwar In Der Erden (from Komm, Du Susse Todesstunde)
"Though Worms Destroy My Body" see Bach, Johann Sebastian, Wenn Es Meines Gottes Wille
"My Soul, There Is A Country" SATB,pno SCHIRM.EC 1164 $.25, ipr (B610)

Der Lieben Sonne Licht Und Pracht *S.446
see Funf Geistliche Lieder Aus Schemellis Gesangbuch
SATB (A flat maj) HANSSLER 6.2512 s.p. contains also: Vulpius, Melchior, Hinunter Ist Der Sonnen Schein (SATB); Anonymous, Herr, Bleibe Bei Uns (3pt) (canon); Haydn, (Franz) Joseph, Tod Ist Ein Langer Schlaf (3pt) (canon) (B611)
(Berger, H.L.) TTBB HANSSLER 6.5066 s.p. contains also: Regnart, Jacob, Auf Meinen Lieben Gott Trau Ich (B612)

Der Tag, Der Ist So Freudenreich [Chorale] see Weihnachtschorale-III

Der Tag Ist Hin
(Mattfeld, V.) "Day Is Done, The" [Ger/Eng] unis,org SCHIRM.EC 2555 see from Six Sacred Songs (B613)

Det Livsens Ord Vi Bygger Pa *see Wohl Dem, Der Sich Auf Seinen Gott [Chorale]

Dich Bet' Ich An
(Mattfeld, V.) "Exalted Lord, Thee I Adore" [Ger/Eng] unis,org SCHIRM.EC 2555 see from Six Sacred Songs (B614)

Die Chorale Der Matthaus-Passion *CC10L, chorale
SATB HANSSLER 6.258 s.p. (B615)

Die Elenden Sollen Essen (Cantata 75) S.75, Trin,cant
mix cor,SATB soli,org,2ob,bsn,trp,strings, cembalo voc pt BREITKOPF-L CHB-1432 s.p., voc sc BREITKOPF-L EB-7075 s.p., ipr (B616)
[Ger] cor voc sc KALMUS 6550 $1.25 (B617)
mix cor,SATB soli,cont,3ob,bsn,trp,strings cor pts BREITKOPF-W CHB-4575 s.p., ipr, sc BREITKOPF-W rental (B618)

Die Gold'ne Sonne, Voll Freud' Und Wonne see Funf Geistliche Lieder Aus Schemellis Gesangbuch

Die Himmel Erzahlen Die Ehre Gottes (Cantata 76) S.76, Trin,cant
mix cor,SATB soli,cont,3ob,trp,strings sc BREITKOPF-W PB-4576 s.p., cor pts BREITKOPF-W CHB-4576 s.p., ipa (B619)
(Raphael, G.) [Eng/Ger] mix cor,SATB soli, org,2ob,trp,strings,cembalo, English horn voc pt BREITKOPF-L CHB-1460 s.p., voc sc BREITKOPF-L EB-7076 s.p., ipr (B620)

Die Nacht Ist Kommen
see Bach, Johann Sebastian, Nun Ruhen Alle Walder

Die Sonn Hat Sich Mit Ihren Glanz Gewendet see Kurig, Hans-Hermann, Jauchzet, Alle Lande, Gott Zu Ehren

Dig Skall Ditt Sion Sjunga *see Gottlob, Nun Geht Das Jahr Zu Ende

Dig Skall Ditt Sion Sjunga [Chorale] (from Cantata 29) chorale
mix cor NORDISKA 831 s.p. (B621)

Dir, Dir Jehova *Holywk
4pt MOSELER LB-319 s.p. contains also: Christ Lag In Todesbanden (B622)

Dir, Dir, Jehova Will Ich Singen *cant
see Bach, Johann Sebastian, Kommt, Seelen, Dieser Tag
[Ger] 4pt mix cor,acap BAREN. EM 3 s.p. (B623)
SATB HANSSLER 6.0732 s.p. contains also: Berger, Hans Ludwig, Lobt Gott In Allen Landen (B624)
SATB HANSSLER 6.0574 s.p. (B625)
mix cor sc ALSBACH&D s.p. (B626)
wom cor sc ALSBACH&D s.p. (B627)
(Mattfeld, V.) "To Thee, Jehovah, I Am Singing" [Ger/Eng] unis,org SCHIRM.EC 2555 see from Six Sacred Songs (B628)
(Vogel, Moritz; Nagler, Franciscus) [Ger] wom cor&jr cor,org,opt strings HUG 22B s.p. (B629)

Dir Jesu Gottes Sohn
see Bach, Johann Christoph, Ich Lasse Dich Nicht, Du Segnest Mich Denn

Dit Is De Dag Die God Ons Schenkt
mix cor sc ALSBACH&D s.p. (B630)

Ditt Namn, Jehova, Vill Jag Sjunga
mix cor NORDISKA 3618 s.p. (B631)

Dix Chorals *CC10L,chorale
(Bariller, R.) [Ger/Fr] 3 eq voices,pno voc sc LEDUC s.p. (B632)

Dona Nobis Pacem (from Mass In B Minor) anthem/Mass
[Lat] SATB oct NOVELLO 34.0829.09 s.p. (B633)

Drei Chorsatze Zum Magnificat *Xmas,Magnif
(Keller, Hermann) [Ger] (med) BAREN. BA 299 $1.50
contains: Freut Euch Und Jubiliert (SSAT, cont); Gloria In Excelsis (SSATB,cont, vln); Vom Himmel Hoch (SATB) (B634)

Dreihundertneunundachtzig Choralgesange *CC389U,anthem
(Richter, B.F.) SATB,acap cor pts BREITKOPF-L EB-3765 s.p. (B635)

Du Aller Menschen Vater, Du Helfer
SATB HANSSLER 6.162 s.p. contains also: Gumpeltzhaimer, Adam, Wie Lang, O Gott, In Meiner Not (B636)

BACH, JOHANN SEBASTIAN (cont'd.)

Du Friedefurst, Herr Jesu Christ (Cantata 116) S.116 (from Halt' In Gedachtnis Jesum Christ) Trin,cant
see Bach, Johann Sebastian, Nun Danket Alle Gott
SATB HANSSLER 6.006 s.p. contains also: Gesius, Bartholomaus, Du Friedefurst, Herr Jesu Christ (SSATB) (B637)
mix cor,SATB soli,cont,2ob,horn,strings cor pts BREITKOPF-W CHB-4616 s.p., ipr, sc BREITKOPF-W rental (B638)
"Du Friedensfuerst" [Ger] cor voc sc KALMUS 6580 $1.25 (B639)
"Fredsfyrste, Herre Jesus Krist" [Ger/Dan] SATB HANSEN-DEN 185 s.p. see also Otte Koraludsaettelser (B640)
(Raphael, G.) [Eng/Ger] mix cor,SATB soli, org,2ob,horn,strings,cembalo sc BREITKOPF-L PB-2966 s.p., voc pt BREITKOPF-L CHB-1952 s.p., voc sc BREITKOPF-L EB-7116 s.p., ipr (B641)

Du Friedensfuerst *see Du Friedefurst, Herr Jesu Christ

Du Gabst Uns Unser Taglich Brot *Fest
[Ger] SATB,acap (med) BAREN. BA 198 s.p. (B642)

Du Heilige Brunst (from Der Geist Hilft Unsrer Schwachheit Auf)
(Williamson) "Thou Sanctified Fire" [Eng/Ger] 4pt mix cor,acap oct SCHIRM.G 8897 $.20 (B643)

Du Herzog Meiner Seligkeit, Herr Jesu (from Halt' Im Gedachtnis Jesum Christ)
see Praetorius, Michael, Erweckt Hat Mir Das Herz Zu Dir

Du Hirte Israel *see Du Hirte Israel, Hore

Du Hirte Israel, Hore (Cantata 104) S.104, Easter/Gen,cant
mix cor,TB soli,cont,5ob,strings sc BREITKOPF-W PB-4604 s.p., cor pts BREITKOPF-W CHB-4604 s.p., ipa (B644)
"Du Hirte Israel" cor,orch sc KALMUS $5.00, ipa (B645)
"Thou Guide" cor voc sc KALMUS 6046 $1.00 (B646)
"Thou Guide Of Israel" SATB,TB soli,3ob, strings voc sc NOVELLO rental (B647)
"Thou Guide Of Israel" BELWIN $1.00 (B648)
(Naumann, E.) mix cor,TB soli,org,4ob,bsn, strings,cembalo, English horn voc pt BREITKOPF-L CHB-685 s.p., voc sc BREITKOPF-L EB-7104 s.p., ipr (B649)

Du Hirte Israels, Hore *S.104, cant
(Horn) SATB,TB soli,cont,2ob,2vln,vla, English horn HANSSLER 10.116 sc $5.00, cor pts $1.00, ipa (B650)

Du Lebensfurst, Herr Jesu Christ
see Vulpius, Melchior, O Heiliger Geist, Du Gottlich Feur

Du Sollst Gott *see Du Sollst Gott, Deinen Herren, Lieben

Du Sollst Gott, Deinen Herren, Lieben (Cantata 77) S.77, cant
mix cor,SATB soli,cont,2ob,trp,strings cor pts BREITKOPF-W CHB-4577 s.p., ipr, sc BREITKOPF-W rental (B651)
"Du Sollst Gott" [Ger] cor voc sc KALMUS 6551 $1.25 (B652)

Du Sollt Gott, Deinen Herren, Lieben *S.77, Trin,cant
(Bernstein, W.H.) [Eng/Ger] mix cor,SATB soli,org,2ob,trp,strings,cembalo voc pt BREITKOPF-L CHB-2147 s.p., voc sc BREITKOPF-L EB-7077 s.p., ipr (B653)

Du Wahrer Gott *see Du Wahrer Gott Und Davids Sohn

Du Wahrer Gott Und Davids Sohn (Cantata 23) S.23, Gen,cant
mix cor,SAT soli,cont,2ob,trp,3trom,strings sc BREITKOPF-W PB-4523 s.p., cor pts BREITKOPF-W CHB-4523 s.p., ipa (B654)
"Du Wahrer Gott" cor,orch sc KALMUS $4.00, ipa (B655)
(Grischkat) [Ger/Eng] SATB&SA,SAT soli, cont,2ob,2vln,vla,trp,3trom HANSSLER 10.026 sc $4.50, cor pts $1.50, ipa (B656)
(Jones, Ifor) "Thou Very God And David's Son" [Eng/Ger] mix cor,soli,pno voc sc SCHIRM.G $1.00 (B657)
(Raphael, G.) [Eng/Ger] mix cor,SAT soli, org,2ob,2bsn,trp,3trom,strings,cembalo sc BREITKOPF-L PB-2873 s.p., voc pt BREITKOPF-L CHB-1605 s.p., voc sc BREITKOPF-L EB-7023 s.p., ipr (B658)

Durch Adams Fall Ist Ganz Verderbt (from Gleich Wie Der Regen Und Schnee) Sexa, Bibl
SATB (A maj) HANSSLER 6.155 s.p. contains also: Schein, Johann Hermann, Durch Adams Fall Ist Ganz Verderbt (B659)

Durch Adams Fall Ist Ganz Verderbt *S.705, mot
(Hellmann) SATB HANSSLER 1.309 s.p. (B660)

Easter Chorales *CCU,Easter,chorale
(McKinney) SATB oct FISCHER,J 6594 $.30 (B661)

Easter Oratorio *Easter,ora
cor sc KALMUS $10.00 (B662)
cor,orch sc KALMUS $10.00, ipa (B663)
(Hunt) [Eng/Ger] SATB,SATB soli,orch voc sc SCHOTT 10290 s.p., ipr, cor pts SCHOTT 10290 s.p., ipr (B664)

Een Vaste Burg *see Ein Feste Burg Ist Unser Gott

Eet Er Nodigt *see Eins Ist Noth

Ehr' Sei In's Himmels Thron (from Ach Herr, Mich Armen Sunder)
"All Praise To Thy Great Merit" see Bach, Johann Sebastian, Ach Herr, Mich Armen Sunder [Chorale]

Ehre Und Preis Sei Gott (from Magnificat)
5pt mix cor MOSELER LB-65 s.p. (B665)

Ehre Und Preis Sei Gott Dem Herrn (from Magnificat)
(Fischer, H.) [Ger] 5pt mix cor,pno/cembalo VIEWEG voc sc s.p., cor pts s.p. (B666)

Ein Feste Burg Ist Unser Gott (Cantata 80) S.80, Refm,cant/hymn
see Bach, Johann Sebastian, Wachet Auf, Ruft Uns Die Stimme
cor sc KALMUS $5.00 (B667)
mix cor,SATB soli,cont,5ob,3trp,strings, timp sc BREITKOPF-W PB-4580 s.p., cor pts BREITKOPF-W CHB-4580 s.p., ipa (B668)
"Een Vaste Burg" mix cor ALSBACH&D s.p. (B669)
"Eine Feste Burg" cor,orch sc KALMUS $6.00, ipa (B670)
"Stronghold Sure, A" cor voc sc KALMUS 6044 $1.25 (B671)
"Stronghold Sure, A" PATERSON s.p. see also English Hymns Adapted To Bach's Chorales (B672)
"Stronghold Sure, A" SATB,SATB soli,5ob, 3trp,strings,timp voc sc NOVELLO s.p., ipr (B673)
"Var Gud Ar Oss En Valdig Borg" cor pts NORDISKA 837 s.p. (B674)
(Horn) SATB,SATB soli,cont,2ob,3trp,2vln, vla,vcl,timp HANSSLER 10.126 sc $7.50, cor pts $1.50, ipa (B675)
(Schreck, G.) [Eng/Ger] mix cor,SATB soli, org,4ob,2bsn,3trp,strings,cembalo, English horn sc BREITKOPF-L PB-2930 s.p., voc pt BREITKOPF-L CHB-1AB s.p., voc sc BREITKOPF-L EB-7080 s.p., ipr (B676)

Ein Herz *see Ein Herz, Das Seinen Jesum Lebend Weiss

Ein Herz, Das Seinen Jesum Lebend Weiss (Cantata 134) S.134, Easter,cant
mix cor,AT soli,org,2ob,strings,cembalo voc sc BREITKOPF-L EB-7134 s.p., ipr (B677)
mix cor,AT soli,cont,2ob,strings sc BREITKOPF-W PB-4634 s.p., cor pts BREITKOPF-W CHB-4634 s.p., ipa (B678)
"Ein Herz" [Ger] cor voc sc KALMUS 6590 $1.25 (B679)
(Raphael, Gunter) [Ger] SATB,AT soli,org, cont,2ob,bsn,2vln,vla sc BAREN. BA 5107 $7.75, cor pts BAREN. BA 5107 $.65, voc sc BAREN. BA 5107A $5.50, min sc BAREN. TP 55 $2.25 (B680)

Ein Kind Geborn [Chorale]
see Weihnachtschorale-III

Ein Ungefarbt Gemute (Cantata 24) S.24, Trin, cant
mix cor,SATB soli,org,4ob,bsn,trp,strings, cembalo voc pt BREITKOPF-L CHB-2146 s.p., voc sc BREITKOPF-L EB-7024 s.p., ipr (B681)
mix cor,ATB soli,cont,4ob,trp,strings sc BREITKOPF-W PB-4524 s.p., cor pts BREITKOPF-W CHB-4524 s.p., ipa (B682)

Ein Ungelfarbt Gemute *S.24, cant
[Ger] cor voc sc KALMUS 6534 $1.25 (B683)

Eine Deutsche Messe In Kirchenliedsatzen *Mass
mix cor HANSSLER 6.308 s.p.
contains: Allein Gott In Der Hoh Sei Ehr, S.260; Heilig, Heilig, Heilig Ist Der Herre Zebaoth, S.325; Kyrie, Gott Vater In Ewigkeit, S.371; O Lamm Gottes, Unschuldig, S.401; Wir Glauben All An Einen Gott, S.437 (B684)

Eine Feste Burg *see Ein Feste Burg Ist Unser Gott

Eins Ist Noth
"Eet Er Nodigt" [Ger/Dan] SATB HANSEN-DEN 188 s.p. see also Otte Koraludsaettelser (B685)

Einstimmige Chorale, Heft 1: 7 Choralbearbeitungen Aus Kantaten *CC7U, Gen,chorale
(Reinhart Walther) [Ger] unis,ob,vln,vla, vcl,bvl (med) sc BAREN. BA 462 $4.25, cor pts $.55, ipa (B686)

Einstimmige Chorale, Heft 2: 6 Choralbearbeitungen Aus Kantaten *CC6U, Gen,chorale
(Reinhart, Walter) [Ger] unis,2ob,2vln,vcl, bvl (med) sc BAREN. BA 463 $4.25, cor pts $.40, ipa (B687)

English Hymns Adapted To Bach's Chorales *CC12L,chorale/hymn
PATERSON s.p.
see also: Beside The Flood Of Babylon; Brightest And Best; Come, Thou Holy Paraclete; Father, In High Heaven Dwelling; For The Beauty Of The Earth; From All That Dwell Below The Skies; Hallelujah; Holy, Holy; Hosanna To The Living Lord; Jesus Lives; Jesus, Master, Whose Am I; King Of Love My Shepherd Is, The; Love Divine, All Loves Excelling; O Light Of Life, O Saviour Dear; O Sacred Head; O Saviour, Bless Us Ere We Go; Quiet Lord, My Froward Heart; Rise, My Soul, Adore Thy Maker; Show Pity, Lord; Strife Is O'er The Battle Done, The; Stronghold Sure, A; Through The Day Thy Love Has Spared Us; To Thee, O Lord, Our Hearts We Raise; Wake! The Welcome Day Appeareth (B688)

Er Rufet Seinen Schafen *see Er Rufet Seinen Schafen Mit Namen

Er Rufet Seinen Schafen Mit Namen (Cantata 175) S.175, cant
mix cor,ATB soli,cont,3fl/3rec,2trp,strings cor pts BREITKOPF-W CHB-4675 s.p., ipr, sc BREITKOPF-W rental (B689)
"Er Rufet Seinen Schafen" [Ger] cor voc sc KALMUS 6617 $1.25 (B690)
(Durr; Mendel) mix cor voc sc DEUTSCHER 5019 s.p., sc DEUTSCHER 5138A s.p. (B691)
(Todt, B.) mix cor,ATB soli,org,3fl,2trp, strings,cembalo voc pt BREITKOPF-L CHB-2205 s.p., voc sc BREITKOPF-L EB-7175 s.p., ipr (B692)

Erforsche Mich, Gott *see Erforsche Mich, Gott, Und Erfahre Mein Herz

Erforsche Mich, Gott, Und Erfahre Mein Herz (Cantata 136) S.136, Trin,cant
mix cor,ATB soli,org,2ob,bsn,horn,strings, cembalo, English horn voc sc BREITKOPF-L EB-7136 s.p., ipr (B693)
mix cor,ATB soli,cont,2ob,horn,strings cor pts BREITKOPF-W CHB-4636 s.p., ipr, sc BREITKOPF-W rental (B694)
"Erforsche Mich, Gott" [Ger] cor voc sc KALMUS 6592 $1.25 (B695)

Erfreuet Euch, Ihr Herzen (Cantata 66) S.66, cant
mix cor,ATB soli,cont,2ob,bsn,trp,strings cor pts BREITKOPF-W CHB-4566 s.p., ipr, sc BREITKOPF-W rental (B696)

Erfreut Euch, Ihr Herzen *S.66, Easter,cant
[Ger] cor voc sc KALMUS 6546 $1.25 (B697)
(Schreck, G.) [Eng/Ger] mix cor,ATB soli, org,2ob,bsn,trp,strings,cembalo voc sc BREITKOPF-L EB-7066 s.p., ipr (B698)

Erfreute Zeit Im *see Erfreute Zeit Im Neuen Bunde

Erfreute Zeit Im Neuen Bunde (Cantata 83) S.83, BVM,cant
mix cor,ATB soli,cont,2ob,2horn,strings cor pts BREITKOPF-W CHB-4583 s.p., ipr, sc BREITKOPF-W rental (B699)
"Erfreute Zeit Im" [Ger] cor voc sc KALMUS 6552 $1.25 (B700)
(Todt, B.) mix cor,ATB soli,org,2ob,2horn, strings,cembalo voc pt BREITKOPF-L CHB-2190 s.p., voc sc BREITKOPF-L EB-7083 s.p., ipr (B701)

Erhalt' Mein Herz Im Glauben Rein (from Ach Gott, Wie Manches Herzeleid)
"Uphold My Heart With Faith In Thee" see Bach, Johann Sebastian, Ach Gott, Wie Manches Herzeleid [Chorale]

Erhalt Uns Herr, Bei Deinem Wort (Cantata 126) S.416 (from Bleib' Bei Uns Denn Es Will Abend Werden) Refm/Sexa,cant/chorale
see Vulpius, Melchior, Erhalt Uns, Herr, Bei Deinem Wort
mix cor,ATB soli,cont,2ob,trp,strings cor pts BREITKOPF-W CHB-4626 s.p., ipr, sc BREITKOPF-W rental (B702)
[Ger] mix cor,acap (easy) HUG s.p. (B703)
"Cantate, Pour Le Dimanche De La Sexagesime" SATB CHOUDENS voc sc s.p., cor pts s.p. (B704)
(Bernstein, W.H.) [Eng/Ger] mix cor,ATB soli,org,2ob,bsn,trp,strings,cembalo voc pt BREITKOPF-L CHB-2125 s.p., voc sc BREITKOPF-L EB-7126 s.p., ipr (B705)

Erhalt Uns In Der Wahrheit
SATB HANSSLER 6.1069 s.p. contains also: Gott Der Vater Wohn' Uns Bei, S.317 (B706)

Erhohtes Fleisch Und Blut (Cantata 173) S.173, Pent/Whitsun,cant
mix cor,SATB soli,org,2fl,strings,cembalo voc sc BREITKOPF-L EB-7173 s.p., ipr (B707)
[Ger] cor voc sc KALMUS 6615 $1.25 (B708)
mix cor,SATB soli,cont,2fl,strings cor pts BREITKOPF-W CHB-4673 s.p., ipr, sc BREITKOPF-W s.p. (B709)

Ermuntre Dich, Mein Schwacher Geist *S.377 (from Gott Fahret Auf Mit Jauchzen) Adv/Asc/Xmas
SATB HANSSLER 6.098 s.p. contains also: Wir Christenleut Han Jetzund Freud (B710)
SATB (F maj) HANSSLER 6.1495 s.p. contains also: Mach's Mit Mir, Gott, Nach Deiner Gut' (B711)
(Mattfeld, V.) "My Fainting Soul, Awaken Now" [Ger/Eng] unis,org SCHIRM.EC 2554 see from Songs For The Advent And Christmas Seasons (B712)

Ermuntre Dich, Mein Schwacher Geist [Chorale]
see Weihnachtschorale-IV

Erschallet, Ihr Lieder (Cantata 172) S.172, Pent/Whitsun,cant
[Ger] cor voc sc KALMUS 6614 $1.25 (B713)
cor,orch sc KALMUS $3.75, ipa (B714)
mix cor,SATB soli,org,cont,bsn,3trp, strings,timp sc BREITKOPF-W PB-4672 s.p., cor pts BREITKOPF-W CHB-4672 s.p., ipa (B715)
(Bernstein, W.H.) [Eng/Ger] mix cor,SATB soli,org,bsn,3trp,strings,timp,cembalo sc BREITKOPF-L PB-3022 s.p., voc pt BREITKOPF-L CHB-1377 s.p., voc sc BREITKOPF-L EB-7172 s.p., ipr (B716)
(Kilian, Dietrich) [Ger] SATB,SATB soli, org,cont,fl,ob,3trp,2vln,2vla,drums voc sc BA 5126 $.65, min sc BA 5126A $3.50, TP 78 $2.75 (B717)

Erschallet, Ihr Lieder [Chorale] (from Cantata 172) Ded/Gen/Pent
"Sing Praises, Ye Faithful" SATB,kbd (med diff) oct CONCORDIA 98-1823 $.50 (B718)
"Sing Praises, Ye Faithful" mix cor SOUTHERN $.50 (B719)

Erschienen Ist Der Herrlich Tag
(Hamburger, Povl) "Oprundet Er Den Skonne Dag" [Ger/Dan] SATB,acap HANSEN-DEN 160 s.p. see also Otte Koraludsaettelser (B720)

Erwunschtes Freudenlicht (Cantata 184) S.184, Pent/Whitsun,cant
mix cor,SAT soli,cont,2fl,strings cor pts BREITKOPF-W CHB-4684 s.p., ipa, sc

BACH, JOHANN SEBASTIAN (cont'd.)

BREITKOPF-W rental (B721)
(Notzoldt, W.) [Eng/Ger] mix cor,SAT soli,
org,2fl,strings,cembalo voc sc BREITKOPF-
L EB-7184 s.p., ipr (B722)

Es Bringt Das Rechte Jubeljahr (from Cant122)
"Sing Out, Ye Voices, Loud And Clear" see
Bach, Johann Sebastian, Das Neugeborne
Kindelein

Es Erhub Sich Ein Streit (Cantata 19) S.19,
ASD,cant
[Ger] cor voc sc KALMUS 6531 $1.25 (B723)
mix cor,STB soli,cont,5ob,3trp,strings,timp
cor pts BREITKOPF-W CHB-4519 s.p., ipr,
sc BREITKOPF-W rental (B724)
"Es Erhub Such" cor,orch sc KALMUS $4.50,
ipa (B725)
(Jones, Ifor) "There Uprose A Great Strife"
[Eng/Ger] mix cor,soli,pno voc sc
SCHIRM.G $.75 (B726)
(Schreck, B.; Todt, B.) mix cor,STB soli,
org,3ob,3trp,strings,timp,cembalo sc
BREITKOPF-L PB-2869 s.p., voc pt
BREITKOPF-L CHB-1639 s.p., ipr
BREITKOPF-L EB-7019 s.p., ipa (B727)

Es Erhub Such *see Es Erhub Sich Ein Streit

Es Fahret Heute Gottes Sohn
see Praetorius, Michael, Wir Wollen Alle
Frohlich Sein

Es Ist Das Heil *see Es Ist Das Heil Uns
Kommen Her

Es Ist Das Heil Uns Kommen Her (Cantata 9)
S.9, Trin,cant
mix cor,SATB soli,org,fl,ob,strings,cembalo
cor pts BREITKOPF-L CHB-2144 s.p., voc sc
BREITKOPF-L EB-7009 s.p., ipr (B728)
mix cor,SATB soli,cont,fl,ob,strings sc
BREITKOPF-W PB-4509 s.p., cor pts
BREITKOPF-W CHB-4509 s.p., ipa (B729)
"Es Ist Das Heil" [Ger] cor voc sc KALMUS
6525 $1.25 (B730)

Es Ist Das Heil Uns Kommen Her [Chorale]
(from Es Ist Das Heil Uns Kommen Her)
SATB HANSSLER 6.148 s.p. contains also:
Schein, Johann Hermann, Es Ist Das Heil
Uns Kommen Her (B731)

Es Ist Dir Gesagt, Mensch, Was Gut Ist
(Cantata 45) S.45, Trin,cant
mix cor,ATB soli,cont,2fl,2ob,strings cor
pts BREITKOPF-W CHB-4545 s.p., ipr, sc
BREITKOPF-W rental (B732)
"Es Ist Gesagt" [Eng] cor voc sc KALMUS
6029 $1.00 (B733)
(Durr, Alfred) [Ger] SATB,ATB soli,org,
cont&2fl&2ob&2vln&vla/2fl&bsn&2vln&vla&
vcl&bvl cor pts BAREN. BA 5127 s.p., voc
sc BAREN. BA 5127A s.p., min sc BAREN.
TP 189 s.p. (B734)
(Naumann, E.) mix cor,ATB soli,org,2fl,2ob,
bsn,strings,cembalo voc pt BREITKOPF-L
CHB-988 s.p., voc sc BREITKOPF-L EB-7045
s.p., ipr (B735)

Es Ist Ein Kind Geboren [Chorale] (from Es
Ist Ein Kind Geboren) Xmas
(Ehret) "To Us A Child Is Born" [Eng/Ger]
SSA MARKS 4268 $.35 (B736)
(Ehret) "To Us A Child Is Born" [Eng/Ger]
SATB MARKS 4213 $.25 (B737)
(Ehret) "To Us A Child Is Born" [Eng/Ger]
TTBB MARKS 4265 $.30 (B738)

Es Ist Ein Trotzig *see Es Ist Ein Trotzig
Und Verzagt Ding

Es Ist Ein Trotzig Und Verzagt Ding (Cantata
176) S.176, Trin,cant
mix cor,SAB soli,org,3ob,2bsn,strings,
cembalo sc BREITKOPF-L PB-3026 s.p., voc
pt BREITKOPF-L CHB-2038 s.p., voc sc
BREITKOPF-L EB-7176 s.p., ipr (B739)
mix cor,SAB soli,cont,3ob,strings cor pts
BREITKOPF-W CHB-4676 s.p., ipr, sc
BREITKOPF-W rental (B740)
"Es Ist Ein Trotzig" [Ger] cor voc sc
KALMUS 6618 $1.25 (B741)
"Es Ist Ein Trotzig" cor,orch/org sc KALMUS
$3.50, ipa (B742)
(Horn) SATB,SAB soli,org,2ob,2vln,vla,
English horn HANSSLER 10.133 sc $4.00,
cor pts $.60, ipa (B743)

Es Ist Euch Gut *see Es Ist Euch Gut, Dass
Ich Hingehe

Es Ist Euch Gut, Dass Ich Hingehe (Cantata
108) S.108, Gen,cant
mix cor,ATB soli,cont,2ob,strings sc
BREITKOPF-W PB-4608 s.p., cor pts
BREITKOPF-W CHB-4608 s.p., ipa (B744)
"Es Ist Euch Gut" [Ger] cor voc sc KALMUS
6574 $1.25 (B745)
(Todt, B.) mix cor,ATB soli,org,2ob,strings,
cembalo voc pt BREITKOPF-L CHB-1947 s.p.,
CHB-1947 s.p., voc sc BREITKOPF-L EB-7108
s.p., ipr (B746)

Es Ist Genug! *Gd.Fri.
SATB,acap voc pt DOBLINGER s.p. see also
TOD UND VERGANGLICHKEIT (B747)

Es Ist Genug, Herr, Wenn Es Dir (from O
Ewigkeit, Du Donnerswort)
see Praetorius, Michael, Wenn Mein
Stundlein Vorhanden Ist

Es Ist Gesagt *see Es Ist Dir Gesagt,
Mensch, Was Gut Ist

Es Ist Gewisslich An Der Zeit *S.307
see Demantius, Christoph, Wenn Mein
Stundlein Vorhanden Ist

Es Ist Nichts *see Es Ist Nichts Gesundes An
Meinem Leibe

Es Ist Nichts Gesundes An Meinem Leibe
(Cantata 25) S.25, Trin,cant
mix cor,STB soli,cont,3fl,2ob,trp,3trom,
strings cor pts BREITKOPF-W CHB-4525

s.p., ipr, sc BREITKOPF-W rental (B748)
"Es Ist Nichts" [Eng] cor voc sc KALMUS
6021 $1.00 (B749)
(Todt, B.) mix cor,STB soli,org,3fl,2ob,
3trom,strings,cembalo, cornet voc pt
BREITKOPF-L CHB-1910 s.p., voc sc
BREITKOPF-L EB-7025 s.p. (B750)
(West, John E.) "There Is Nought Of
Soundness In All My Body" SATB,STB soli,
3fl,2ob,trp,3trom,strings voc sc NOVELLO
s.p., ipr (B751)

Es Ist Vollbracht!
see Funf Geistliche Lieder Aus Schemellis
Gesangbuch

Es Ist Vollbracht! Vergiss Ja Nicht Dies Wort
*S.458
SATB HANSSLER 6.289 s.p. contains also:
Schutz, Heinrich, Wohl Denen, Die Da
Wandeln, SWV 219 (B752)

Es Reifet Euch Ein Schrecklich Ende (Cantata
90) S.90, cant
mix cor,ATB soli,cont,trp,strings cor pts
BREITKOPF-W CHB-4590 s.p., ipr, sc
BREITKOPF-W rental (B753)
"Es Riefet Euch" [Ger] cor voc sc KALMUS
6559 $1.25 (B754)

Es Reisset Euch Ein Schrecklich Ende *S.90,
Trin,cant
(Todt, B.) mix cor,ATB soli,org,strings,
cembalo voc pt BREITKOPF-L CHB-2192 s.p.,
voc sc BREITKOPF-L EB-7090 s.p., ipr (B755)

Es Riefet Euch *see Es Reifet Euch Ein
Schrecklich Ende

Es Wartet Alles Auf Dich (Cantata 187) S.187,
Trin,cant
mix cor,SAB soli,org,2ob,bsn,strings,
cembalo voc pt BREITKOPF-L CHB-1954 s.p.,
voc sc BREITKOPF-L EB-7187 s.p., ipa, ipr (B756)
[Ger] cor voc sc KALMUS 6628 $1.25 (B757)
mix cor,SAB soli,cont,2ob,strings voc pt
BREITKOPF-W CHB-4687 s.p., ipr, sc
BREITKOPF-W rental (B758)

Es Woll Uns Gott Genadig Sein
"Nu Vaer Os, Gud, Miskundelig" [Ger/Dan]
SATB HANSEN-DEN s.p. see also Otte
Koraludsaettelser (B759)

Es Wolle Gott Uns Gnadig Sein *S.311
see Praetorius, Michael, Ach Gott, Vom
Himmelreiche

Et Exultavit (from Magnificat, The) Gen
(Whittaker) [Lat/Eng] unis (med diff)
OXFORD 45.276 $.30, ipr (B760)
(Whittaker, W. Gillies) "My Soul Rejoices"
unis (med) oct OXFORD $.30, ipr (B761)

Et Exultavit Spiritus Meus
(Harris) SSA oct BELWIN 64327 $.35 (B762)

Et Incarnatus Est (from Mass In B-Minor) Xmas
SSATB,pno SCHIRM.EC 1179 $.35, ipr contains
also: Crucifixus
SSATB,pno SCHIRM.EC 1176 $.30, ipr (B763)
"He Was Incarnate" SSATB oct WALTON 6009
$.30 (B764)
(B765)

Et Misericordia (from Magnificat, The) Gen
(Whittaker, W. Gillies) "His Mercy" SS
(med) oct OXFORD $.35, ipr (B766)

Et Resurrexit (from Mass In B Minor)
see Bach, Johann Sebastian, Crucifixus

Eternity, Thou Awful Word (Cantata 60)
study sc UNIVER. PH. 105 $1.15 (B767)

Ever Faithful I Remain
(Kinsman) SATB oct BOURNE SB101 $.30 (B768)

Everlasting Joy *Xmas,cant
(Lorenz) SATB oct LORENZ $1.95 (B769)

Exalted Lord, Thee I Adore *see Dich Bet'
Ich An

Falsche Welt *see Falsche Welt, Dir Trau'
Ich Nicht

Falsche Welt, Dir Trau' Ich Nicht (Cantata
52) S.52, Trin,cant
mix cor,S solo,cont,3ob,bsn,2horn,strings
sc BREITKOPF-W PB-4552 s.p., cor pts
BREITKOPF-W CHB-4552 s.p., ipa (B770)
"Falsche Welt" [Ger] cor voc sc KALMUS 6541
$1.25 (B771)
(Todt, B.) mix cor,S solo,org,3ob,bsn,
2horn,strings,cembalo voc pt BREITKOPF-L
CHB-2209 s.p., voc sc BREITKOPF-L EB-7052
s.p., ipr (B772)

Father, In High Heaven Dwelling *hymn
PATERSON s.p. see also English Hymns
Adapted To Bach's Chorales (B773)

Father, To Thee We Pray *see Ave Maria

Fear Not, Thou Faithful Christian Flock *Gen
(Worp; Olds) SATB (Strassburg psalter)
SCHMITT 1621 $.30 (B774)

Fifty Sacred Songs, Volume II *CC50U
(Scott) SATB,S solo,acap (easy) OXFORD
43.259 $1.25 (B775)

Five Choral Settings
[Ger] SATB,org/pno,fl,3trp,3vln,2vla,vcl/
bvl,timp,opt ob voc sc PETERS 4872 $1.00,
ipa, cor pts PETERS 4872 $.50, ipa (B776)

Five Chorales (from St. John's Passion) CC5U,
chorale
(Carlton) SATB,acap oct BOOSEY 5271 $.30 (B777)

Five Chorales (from St. John's Passion) CC5U,
Lent,chorale
(Carlton) SATB oct SOUTHERN $.30 (B778)

BACH, JOHANN SEBASTIAN (cont'd.)

Flocks By Shepherds Safe Attended
(Jacobson) mix cor CURWEN 61425 s.p. (B779)

Flocks In Pastures Green
(James) unis (easy) OXFORD 55.007 $.25 (B780)

Flocks In Pastures Green Abiding (from
Cantata No. 208) Gen
(Roper, E. Stanley) SATB (med easy) oct
OXFORD 42.150 $.30, ipa (B781)

Flocks May Graze *anthem
(Chambers, H.A.) mix cor,orch oct NOVELLO
45.1592.05 s.p., ipr (B782)

Flocks May Safely Graze *Xmas
unis oct NOVELLO 40.1238.00 s.p. (B783)

For As The Snow And Rain From Heaven Fall
*see Gleich Wie Der Regen Und Schnee

For The Beauty Of The Earth *hymn
PATERSON s.p. see also English Hymns
Adapted To Bach's Chorales (B784)

For Us A Child Is Born *see Uns Ist Ein Kind
Geboren

Forlan Oss, Herre Gud
mix cor NORDISKA 1965 s.p. (B785)

Four Chorale Harmonizations *Gen,chorale
SATB,kbd (med easy) oct CONCORDIA 98-1896
$.25
contains: Come, Gracious Spirit, Heav'nly
Dove; If Thou But Suffer God To Guide
Thee; Lord Hath Helped Me Hitherto,
The; Our Father, Thou In Heaven Above (B786)

Four Chorales For Easter *CC4U,Easter/Lent,
chorale
(Marshall, Charles) SATB FRANK F-545 $.30 (B787)

Four Chorales (from St. Matthew Passion)
CC4U,Easter/Lent,chorale
(Dawes) SATB oct SPRATT 512 $.25 (B788)

Four Chorales *chorale
(Damrosch) oct SCHIRM.G 7603 $.35
contains: Hence, All Fears And Sadness
(4pt mix cor,acap); Hence With Earthly
Treasure (4pt mix cor,acap); In Thine
Arm I Rest Me (SSATB,acap); Jesu,
Priceless Treasure (4pt mix cor,acap) (B789)

Four Chorales (from St. Matthew Passion)
CC4U,chorale
(Ehret) SATB,acap oct LAWSON 686 $.25 (B790)

Four Christmas Chorales *Xmas,anthem/chorale
(Lee, J.) SATB (med easy) oct GIA G1570
$.50
contains: Break Forth, O Beauteous
Heavenly Light; Child Is Born In
Bethlehem, A; From Heaven Above To
Earth I Come; O Infant Sweet, O Infant
Mild (B791)

Fredsfyrste, Herre Jesus Krist *see Du
Friedefurst, Herr Jesu Christ

Freu' Dich Sehr, O Meine Seele (from Es Erhub
Sich Ein Streit)
SATB,3trp,timp (B maj) HANSSLER 6.236 s.p.
contains also: Nun Lasst Uns Gott Den
Herren (from Gott, Der Herr, Ist Sonn'
Und Schild) (SATB,2horn,timp) (A flat
maj) (B792)

Freue Dich, Erloste Schar (Cantata 30) S.30,
ASD,cant
mix cor,SATB soli,cont,2fl,2ob,3trp,
strings,timp cor pts BREITKOPF-W CHB-4530
s.p., ipr, sc BREITKOPF-W rental (B793)
(Raphael, G.) [Eng/Ger] mix cor,SATB soli,
org,2fl,3ob,2bsn,3trp,strings,timp,
cembalo voc pt BREITKOPF-L CHB-1640 s.p.,
voc sc BREITKOPF-L EB-7030 s.p. (B794)

Freuet Euch Ihr Christen Alle (from Dazu Ist
Erschienen Der Sohn Gottes)
SATB HANSSLER 6.254 s.p. contains also:
Schroeter, Leonhardt, Freut Euch Ihr
Lieben Christen (B795)

Freuet Euch Und Jubilirt (from Magnificat)
(Talmadge, A.; Wright, E.) "Be Ye Glad And
Rejoice" [Ger/Eng] SSAA,org/pno SCHIRM.EC
2547 (B796)

Freut Euch Und Jubiliert
see Drei Chorsatze Zum Magnificat

Freut Euch Und Jubilirt (from Christmas
Oratorio, The) Xmas,anthem/chorale
"Rejoice And Sing" see Three Chorales
"Rejoice And Sing" see Two Christmas
Chorales
"Rejoice And Sing" see Bach, Johann
Sebastian, All Darkness Flies
"Rejoice And Sing" SSATB oct WALTON 2120
$.25 (B797)
"Rejoice And Sing" mix cor oct NOVELLO
50.0242.07 s.p. (B798)

Friede Uber Israel! (from O Ewiges Feuer)
"Peace Be Unto Israel!" see Bach, Johann
Sebastian, O Ewiges Feuer [Chorale]
"Peace Be Unto Israel!" SATB,pno SCHIRM.EC
1673 $.18, ipr (B799)

Frohlich Soll Mein Herze Springen [Chorale]
see Weihnachtschorale-IV

Frojda Dig Du Kopta Hjord (from Cantata 30)
(Ahlen, David) [Swed] cor pts NORDISKA 2232
s.p., ipa (B800)

From All That Dwell Below The Skies *hymn
PATERSON s.p. see also English Hymns
Adapted To Bach's Chorales (B801)

From Depths Of Woe I Call On Thee *see Aus
Tiefer Not Schrei Ich Zu Dir

BACH, JOHANN SEBASTIAN (cont'd.)

From Depths Of Woe I Call To Thee (Cantata 38) Trin
BELWIN $1.00 (B802)

From Heaven Above *see Vom Himmel Hoch

From Heaven Above To Earth I Come
see Four Christmas Chorales
(Frackenpohl) SATB,acap SHAWNEE A 461 $.30 (B803)

From Heav'n Above *see Vom Himmel Hoch

Front Couronne D'epines (Chorale 74)
(Doyen, A.) [Fr] SATB/SMezTB voc sc LEDUC CC8 s.p. (B804)

Funf Geistliche Lieder Aus Schemellis Gesangbuch
(Wipf, R.) [Ger] wom cor,acap HUG s.p.
contains: Der Lieben Sonne Licht Und Pracht (med easy); Die Gold'ne Sonne, Voll Freud' Und Wonne (med easy); Es Ist Vollbracht! (med); Jesus, Unser Trost Und Leben (med easy); Komm, Susser Tod! (med) (B805)

Fur Freuden Lasst Uns Springen [Chorale]
see Weihnachtschorale-IV

Furchte Dich Nicht (Motet 4) mot
"Be Not Afraid" 8pt mix cor,acap oct SCHIRM.G 7806 $.40 (B806)
"Be Not Afraid" cor voc sc KALMUS 6066 $1.00 (B807)
"Be Not Afraid" dbl cor voc sc NOVELLO rental (B808)
(Neumann-Buszin) "Be Not Afraid" [Eng/Ger] SATB&SATB,cont PETERS 6104 $.90, ipa see from Six Motets (B809)

Furchte Dich Nicht, Ich Bin Bei Dir (Motet 4) S.228, Gen,mot
[Eng/Ger] 8pt mix cor,acap cor pts BREITKOPF-L EB-7228 s.p., voc pt BREITKOPF-L CHB-539 s.p. (B810)
(Ameln, Konrad) [Ger] SATB&SATB,org,2ob, bsn,2vln,vla,vcl,bvl (med diff) cor pts BAREN. BA 5133 $1.50, ipa (B811)
(Ameln; Wolters) SATB&SATB,cont,strings,opt 2ob&bsn, 2 English horns cor pts MOSELER s.p., ipa (B812)

Gebed Des Herren
mix cor ALSBACH&D s.p. (B813)

Geist Und Seele *see Geist Und Seele Wird Verwirret

Geist Und Seele Wird Verwirret *S.35, Trin, cant
mix cor,A solo,org,3ob,bsn,strings,cembalo voc sc BREITKOPF-L EB-7035 s.p., ipr (B814)
"Geist Und Seele" [Ger] cor voc sc KALMUS 6535 $1.25 (B815)

Gelobet Sei Der Herr
(Hamburger, Povl) "Hojlovet Vaere Gud" [Ger/Dan] SATB,acap HANSEN-DEN 154 s.p. see also Otte Koraludsaettelser (B816)

Gelobet Sei Der Herr *see Gelobet Sei Der Herr, Mein Gott

Gelobet Sei Der Herr, Mein Gott (Cantata 129) S.129, Trin,cant
mix cor,SAB soli,cont,fl,3ob,3trp,strings, timp cor pts BREITKOPF-W CHB-4629 s.p., ipr, sc BREITKOPF-W rental (B817)
"Gelobet Sei Der Herr" [Ger] cor voc sc KALMUS 6588 $1.25 (B818)
(Todt, B.) mix cor,SAB soli,org,fl,2ob, 3trp,strings,timp,cembalo voc pt BREITKOPF-L CHB-2140 s.p., voc sc BREITKOPF-L EB-7130 s.p., ipr (B819)

Gelobet Seist Du *see Gelobet Seist Du, Jesu Christ

Gelobet Seist Du, Jesu Christ (Cantata 91) S.91 (from Sehet Welch' Eine Liebe) Xmas, cant
see Bach, Johann Sebastian, Lobt Gott, Ihr Christen Allzugleich
see Bach, Johann Sebastian, Uns Ist Ein Kindlein Heut Geborn
SATB HANSSLER 6.2171 s.p. (B820)
mix cor,SATB soli,org,3ob,bsn,2horn, strings,timp,cembalo voc sc BREITKOPF-L EB-7091 s.p., ipr (B821)
mix cor,SATB soli,cont,3ob,2horn,strings, timp cor pts BREITKOPF-W CHB-4591 s.p., ipr, sc BREITKOPF-W rental (B822)
"Gelobet Seist Du" [Ger] cor voc sc KALMUS 6560 $1.25 (B823)
(Raphael, Gunter) [Ger] SATB,SATB soli,org, cont,3ob,bsn,2horn,trom,2vln,vla sc BAREN. BA 5114 $5.50, cor pts BAREN. BA5114 $.65, voc sc BAREN. BA 5114A $3.00, min sc BAREN. TP 54 $2.25, ipa (B824)

Gelobet Seist Du, Jesu Christ [Chorale]
see Weihnachtschorale-IV

Geloofsroem (Jezus, Mijn Verblijden)
mix cor ALSBACH&D s.p. (B825)

Give Praise To Our God *Easter
SATB oct PRESSER 352-00401 $.30 (B826)

Give The Hungry Man Thy Bread *see Brich Dem Hungrigen Dein Brot

Glaube Liebet *see Ich Glaube, Lieber Herr, Hilf Meinem Unglauben

Gleich Wie Der Regen (Cantata 18) S.18, cant
mix cor,STB soli,cont,2fl,bsn,4vla,vcl sc BREITKOPF-W PB-4518 s.p., cor pts BREITKOPF-W CHB-4518 s.p., ipa (B827)

Gleich Wie Der Regen Und Schnee (Cantata 18) S.18, Psntd/Sexa,cant
[Ger] SATB,STB soli,org,cont,2fl,bsn,4vla (med diff) min sc BAREN. BA 5137 $2.25, ipa (B828)
(Jones, Ifor) "For As The Snow And Rain From Heaven Fall" [Eng/Ger] mix cor,soli, pno voc sc SCHIRM.G $1.00 (B829)
(Neumann) [Ger] mix cor voc sc DEUTSCHER 5137A s.p. (B830)

Gleich Wie Der Regen Und Schnee Vom Himmel Fallt *S.18, Sexa,cant
(Schroder, O.) [Eng/Ger] mix cor,STB soli, org,2fl,bsn,strings,cembalo voc pt BREITKOPF-L CHB-1789 s.p., voc sc BREITKOPF-L EB-7018 s.p., ipr (B831)

Gloire, Louange, Honneur A Dieu *S.230, mot
(Barre, J.) [Fr] 4pt mix cor,acap voc sc DURAND see from Motets (B832)

Gloria *see Gloria In Excelsis Deo

Gloria In Excelsis *Gloria
see Drei Chorsatze Zum Magnificat
5pt mix cor MOSELER LB 278 s.p. (B833)
(Ehret) [Lat] SSATB oct BOOSEY 5332 $.30 (B834)

Gloria In Excelsis Deo (Cantata 191) S.191 (from Magnificat) Xmas,cant
[Lat] 5pt mix cor,ST soli,pno voc sc SCHIRM.G $1.00 (B835)
SSATB oct PRESSER 312-21512 $.45 (B836)
[Lat] mix cor,ST soli,org,2fl,2ob,bsn,3trp, strings,timp,cembalo voc sc BREITKOPF-L EB-7191 s.p., ipr (B837)
mix cor,ST soli,cont,2fl,2ob,3trp,strings, timp cor pts BREITKOPF-W CHB-4691 s.p., ipr, sc BREITKOPF-W rental (B838)
"Gloria" [Ger] cor voc sc KALMUS 6631 $1.25 (B839)
(Beveridge) "Glory To God In The Highest" SATB oct FISCHER,J 8525 $.30 (B840)
(Ehret) "Glory To God In The Highest" SSA oct AGAPE A 415 $.35 (B841)
(Pierce, R.B.) "Glory To God In The Highest" SSATB,org SCHIRM.EC 1796 $.35 (B842)

Gloria In Excelsis Deo! [Chorale] *Xmas
(Wilson) SATB oct SPRATT 583 $.25 (B843)

Gloria Sei Dir Gesungen (from Wachet Auf, Ruft Uns Die Stimme) Trin,chorale
see Bach, Johann Sebastian, Ich Will Den Namen Gottes Loben
SATB HANSSLER 6.0755B s.p. contains also: Cruger, Johann, Wie Soll Ich Dich Empfangen (B844)
SATB HANSSLER 6.315 s.p. contains also: Anonymous, Alta Trinita Beata (16th cent) (B845)
""Gloria" Sing All Our Voices" [Eng/Ger] 4pt mix cor,pno/org oct SCHIRM.G 10242 $.25 (B846)

"Gloria" Sing All Our Voices *see Gloria Sei Dir Gesungen

Glory And Worship
(Ehret, W.) SSAATTBB oct PRESSER 312-40729 $.35 (B847)

Glory Be To God Almighty
(Hudson) men cor CURWEN 50825 s.p. (B848)

Glory Be To The Father *see Lob Und Preis Sei Gott Dem Vater

Glory Now To Thee Be Given (from Sleepers, Wake)
see Bach, Johann Sebastian, Zion Hears Her Watchmen's Voices

Glory To God *Gen
(Christiansen, P.) SSATB SCHMITT 1436 $.35 (B849)
(Wilson) SA/TB,band oct COLOMBO 1810 $.25, ipa (B850)
(Wilson) SSA,band oct COLOMBO 1642 $.30, ipa (B851)
(Wilson) SAB,band oct COLOMBO 1811 $.30, ipa (B852)
(Wilson) SATB,band oct COLOMBO 1397 $.30, ipa (B853)
(Wilson) TTBB,band oct COLOMBO 1501 $.30, ipa (B854)

Glory To God In The Highest *see Gloria In Excelsis Deo

God Goeth Up *see Gott Fahret Auf Mit Jauchzen

God Goeth Up With Shouting [Chorale] (from Gott Fahret Auf Mit Jauchzen) Asc,anthem
SATB oct NOVELLO 34.0838.08 s.p. (B855)

God Is Living, God Is Here! *Gen
see Two Chorales
(Davies, Laurence H.) SATB (easy) oct OXFORD 43.954 $.25 (B856)

God Is My Sovereign *see Gott Ist Mein Konig

God Is Our Hope And Strength (from Ein Ungefarbt Gemute)
SATB,org SCHIRM.EC 355 $.30, ipr (B857)

God Is Our Refuge
(Stone) SAB,pno BOSTON 13714 $.35 (B858)

God Liveth Still *Gen,anthem
SATB oct ROYAL 219 s.p. (B859)

God, My King
2pt WARNER W3703 $.30 (B860)
SSA WARNER W2993 $.30 (B861)

God, My King, Thy Might Confessing *chorale
mix cor SCHIRM.EC 368 $.20 (B862)

God So Loved The World *see Also Hat Gott Die Welt Geliebt

God, The Lord, Is Sun And Shield *see Gott, Der Herr, Ist Sonn Und Schild

God's Own Time (Cantata 106)
study sc UNIVER. PH.106 $1.30 (B863)

Gods Time *see Gottes Zeit Ist Die Allerbeste Zeit

God's Time Is The Best *see Gottes Zeit Ist Die Allerbeste Zeit

Good Christian Men, Rejoice *Xmas
(Gaul, H.) SATB,acap oct PRESSER 332-15089 $.30 (B864)

Good News From Heaven (from Christmas Oratorio) Xmas
mix cor SCHIRM.EC 1123 $.25, ipr (B865)
(Woodworth, G.) TTBB,pno SCHIRM.EC 900 $.25, ipr (B866)

Gott Der Herr *see Gott, Der Herr, Ist Sonn' Und Schild

Gott, Der Herr, Ist Sonn Und Schild (Cantata 79) S.79, Fest/Refm,cant
cor sc KALMUS $5.00 (B867)
mix cor,SAB soli,cont,2fl,2ob,2horn, strings,timp sc BREITKOPF-W PB-4579 s.p., cor pts BREITKOPF-W CHB-4579 s.p., ipa (B868)
"God, The Lord, Is Sun And Shield" [Eng/Ger] mix cor,soli,pno voc sc SCHIRM.G $1.00 (B869)
"Gott Der Herr" cor,orch sc KALMUS $3.75, ipa (B870)
"Herren Gud Ar Sol Och Skold" cor pts NORDISKA 832 s.p. (B871)
"Lord Is A Sun, The" cor voc sc KALMUS 6043 $1.00 (B872)
(Atkins, Ivor) "Lord Is A Sun And Shield, The" [Eng/Ger] SATB,SAB soli,org,2fl,2ob, 2horn,2trp,strings,timp voc sc NOVELLO s.p., ipr (B873)
(Horn) SATB,SAB soli,cont,2fl,2ob,2horn, 2vln,vla,timp HANSSLER 10.115 sc $5.00, cor pts $1.00, ipa (B874)
(Raphael, G.; Schreck, G.) [Eng/Ger] mix cor,SAB soli,org,2fl,2ob,2horn,strings, timp,cembalo sc BREITKOPF-L PB-2929 s.p., voc pt BREITKOPF-L CHB-2AC s.p., voc sc BREITKOPF-L EB-7079 s.p., ipr (B875)

Gott Der Vater Wohn' Uns Bei *S.317
see Bach, Johann Sebastian, Erhalt Uns In Der Wahrheit

Gott Faehret *see Gott Fahret Auf Mit Jauchzen

Gott Fahret Auf Mit Jauchzen (Cantata 43) S.43, Asc,cant
mix cor,SATB soli,cont,2ob,3trp,strings, timp cor pts BREITKOPF-W CHB-4543 s.p., ipr, sc BREITKOPF-W rental (B876)
"God Goeth Up" SATB,SATB soli,org,2ob,3trp, 2trom,strings voc sc NOVELLO s.p., ipr (B877)
"Gott Faehret" [Eng] cor voc sc KALMUS 6031 $1.00 (B878)
(Todt, B.) mix cor,SATB soli,org,2ob,bsn, 3trp,strings,timp,cembalo voc pt BREITKOPF-L CHB-545 s.p., voc sc BREITKOPF-L EB-7043 s.p., ipr (B879)

Gott Hat Die Erd Schon Zugericht't
see Bodenschatz, Erhard, Danket Dem Herrn Heut Und Allzeit

Gott Ist *see Gott Ist Mein Konig

Gott Ist Mein Konig (Cantata 71) S.71, Gen, cant
mix cor,SATB soli,cont,2fl/2rec,2ob,bsn, 3trp,strings,timp voc pt BREITKOPF-W CHB-4571 s.p., ipr, sc BREITKOPF-W rental (B880)
"Gott Ist" [Eng] cor voc sc KALMUS 6041 $1.00 (B881)
(Frank) "God Is My Sovereign" SATB oct FOX MM25 $.35 (B882)
(Schroder, O.) [Eng/Ger] mix cor,SATB soli, org,2fl,2ob,bsn,3trp,strings,timp,cembalo voc pt BREITKOPF-L CHB-1648 s.p., voc sc BREITKOPF-L EB-7071 s.p., ipr (B883)

Gott Ist Und Bleibt Getreu
(Berger, H.L.) TTBB HANSSLER 6.5122 s.p. contains also: Goudimel, Claude, Freu Dich Sehr, O Meine Seele (B884)

Gott Ist Unsre *see Gott Ist Unsre Zuversicht

Gott Ist Unsre Zuversicht (Cantata 197) S.197, Marriage,cant
mix cor,SAB soli,org,2ob,bsn,3trp,strings, timp,cembalo voc pt BREITKOPF-L CHB-2216 s.p., voc sc BREITKOPF-L EB-7197 s.p., ipr (B885)
mix cor,SAB soli,cont,4ob,bsn,3trp,strings, timp cor pts BREITKOPF-W CHB-4697 s.p., ipr, sc BREITKOPF-W rental (B886)
"Gott Ist Unsre" [Ger] cor voc sc KALMUS 6636 $1.25 (B887)

Gott Lebet Noch
see Bach, Johann Sebastian, Aus Tiefer Not Schrei Ich Zu Dir
mix cor ALSBACH&D s.p. (B888)

Gott Lebet Noch! Seele, Was Verzagst Du *Holywk/Psntd
SATB HANSSLER 6.0210 s.p. contains also: Bach, Wilhelm Friedemann, Kein Halmlein Wachst Auf Erden (B889)

Gott, Man Lobet Dich *see Gott, Man Lobet Dich In Der Stille

Gott, Man Lobet Dich In Der Stille (Cantata 120) S.120, Gen,cant
mix cor,SATB soli,cont,2ob,3trom,strings, timp cor pts BREITKOPF-W CHB-4620 s.p., ipr, sc BREITKOPF-W rental (B890)
"Gott, Man Lobet Dich" [Ger] cor voc sc KALMUS 6582 $1.25 (B891)
(Raphael, G.) [Eng/Ger] mix cor,SATB soli, org,2ob,bsn,3trp,strings,timp,cembalo sc BREITKOPF-L PB-2970 s.p., voc sc BREITKOPF-L EB-7120 s.p., ipr (B892)

BACH, JOHANN SEBASTIAN (cont'd.)

Gott Soll *see Gott Soll Allein Mein Herze Haben

Gott Soll Allein *see Gott Soll Allein Mein Herze Haben

Gott Soll Allein Mein Herze Haben (Cantata 169) S.169, Trin,cant
mix cor,A solo,org,cont,3ob,strings sc BREITKOPF-W PB-4669 s.p., cor pts BREITKOPF-W CHB-4669 s.p., ipa (B893)
"Gott Soll" [Eng] cor voc sc KALMUS 6058 $1.00 (B894)
"Gott Soll Allein" cor,orch/org sc KALMUS $3.50, ipa (B895)
(Raphael, G.) [Eng/Ger] mix cor,A solo,org, 4ob,bsn,strings,cembalo voc pt BREITKOPF-L CHB-1989 s.p., voc sc BREITKOPF-L EB-7169 s.p., ipr (B896)

Gott Vater, Sende Deine Geist
see Kurig, Hans-Hermann, Herr, Warst Du Nur Ein Mensch

Gott, Wie Dein Name (Cantata 171) S.171, cant
mix cor,SATB soli,cont,2ob,3trp,strings, timp cor pts BREITKOPF-W CHB-4671 s.p., ipr, sc BREITKOPF-W rental (B897)

Gott, Wie Dein Name, So Ist Auch Dein Ruhm *S.171, Gen,cant
(Raphael, G.) [Eng/Ger] mix cor,SATB soli, org,2ob,3trp,strings,timp,cembalo voc pt BREITKOPF-L CHB-2141 s.p., voc sc BREITKOPF-L EB-7171 s.p., ipr (B898)

Gottes Seit (Actus Tragicus) (Cantata 106)
(Genetay, Claude) cor,org,vla,vcl,bvl,2fl/ 2vln cor pts NORDISKA s.p., ipa (B899)

Gottes Sohn Ist Kommen *S.318
SATB (F maj) HANSSLER 6.087 s.p. contains also: Gesius, Bartholomaus, Nun Jauchzet, All Ihr Frommen (B900)

Gottes Zeit *see Gottes Zeit Ist Die Allerbeste Zeit

Gottes Zeit Ist Die Allerbeste Zeit (Cantata 106) S.106, Lent/Trin,cant
cor sc KALMUS $4.00 (B901)
mix cor,AB soli,cont,2fl/2rec,strings sc BREITKOPF-W PB-4606 s.p., cor pts BREITKOPF-W CHB-4606 s.p., ipa (B902)
"Gods Time" cor voc sc KALMUS 6047 $1.00 (B903)
"God's Time Is The Best" BELWIN $.75 (B904)
"God's Time Is The Best" SATB,AB soli,2fl, vla,vcl,bvl voc sc NOVELLO s.p., ipr (B905)
"Gottes Zeit" cor,orch sc KALMUS $4.00, ipa (B906)
"Se, Guds Tid Ar For Oss Den Basta" cor pts NORDISKA 797 s.p. (B907)
(Damrosch, F.) "God's Time Is The Best" mix cor,soli,pno voc sc SCHIRM.G $1.00 (B908)
(Schroder, O.) [Eng/Ger] mix cor,AB soli, org,2fl,bsn,strings,cembalo sc BREITKOPF-L PB-2956 s.p., voc pt BREITKOPF-L CHB-655 s.p., voc sc BREITKOPF-L EB-7106 s.p., ipr (B909)

Gottlob *see Gottlob! Nun Geht Das Jahr Zu Ende

Gottlob! Nun Geht Das Jahr Zu Ende (Cantata 28) S.28, Xmas,cant
mix cor,SATB soli,cont,3ob,brass,strings sc BREITKOPF-W PB-4528 s.p., cor pts BREITKOPF-W CHB-4528 s.p., ipa (B910)
"Dig Skall Ditt Sion Sjunga" cor pts NORDISKA 829 s.p. (B911)
"Gottlob" [Eng] cor voc sc KALMUS 6024 $1.00 (B912)
"O Praise The Lord For All His Mercies" BELWIN $1.00 (B913)
(Pointer, John) "O Praise The Lord For All His Mercies" SATB,SATB soli,org,3ob,trp, 3trom,strings voc sc NOVELLO s.p., ipr (B914)
(Schreck, G.) mix cor,SATB soli,org,3ob, trp,3trom,strings,cembalo voc pt BREITKOPF-L CHB-622 s.p., voc sc BREITKOPF-L EB-7028 s.p., ipr (B915)

Gottlob! Nun Geht Das Jahr Zu Ende [Chorale] (from Gottlob! Nun Geht Das Jahr Zu Ende)
(Rigby, W) "O Praise The Lord For All His Mercies" SSA oct NOVELLO 51.0529.03 s.p. (B916)

Gracious Lord Of All Our Being (from Herz Und Mund Und Tat Und Leben)
(Chambers, H.A.) SSA,orch oct NOVELLO 51.0531.05 s.p., ipr (B917)

Grant Me True Courage, Lord (from Es Ist Dir Gesagt)
mix cor SCHIRM.EC 313 $.25, ipr (B918)

Grant Me True Courage, Lord *see Fritzsch, Ahaseurus

Grant Us To Do With Zeal (from Es Ist Dir Gesagt)
(Davison, A.) TTBB,pno SCHIRM.EC 29 $.20 (B919)

Guds Rena Lamm, Oskyldig
mix cor NORDISKA 1010 s.p. (B920)

Hallelujah (from Christ Lay In Bonds Of Death) hymn
PATERSON s.p. see also English Hymns Adapted To Bach's Chorales (B921)
(Krone) SATB WARNER W2740 $.30 (B922)

Halt Im Gedachtis Jesum Christ *S.67, Gen, cant
(Raphael, G.) [Eng/Fr/Ger] mix cor,ATB soli,org,fl,2ob,trp,strings,cembalo voc pt BREITKOPF-L CHB-548 s.p., voc sc BREITKOPF-L EB-7067 s.p., ipa (B923)

Halt Im Gedachtnis Jesum Christ (Cantata 67) S.67, Easter,cant
mix cor,ATB soli,cont,2ob,horn,strings sc BREITKOPF-W PB-4567 s.p., cor pts BREITKOPF-W CHB-4567 s.p., ipa (B924)

BACH, JOHANN SEBASTIAN (cont'd.)

"Halt In, Gedachtnis" [Ger] cor voc sc KALMUS 6547 $1.25 (B925)
(Pointer John) "Hold In Affection Jesus Christ" SATB,ATB soli,org,fl,2ob,2clar, trp,strings,cembalo voc sc NOVELLO s.p., ipr (B926)

Halt In, Gedachtnis *see Halt Im Gedachtnis Jesum Christ

Happy Flocks In Safety Wander *see Schafe Konnen Sicher Weiden

Hast Du Denn, Jesu, Dein Angesicht Ganzlich (from Selig Ist Der Mann) Xmas
SATB HANSSLER 6.1024 s.p. contains also: Vor Deinen Thron Tret Ich Hiermit (B927)

He Lives!
(Brewer) SATB FLAMMER A 5560 $.30 (B928)

He Was Incarnate *see Et Incarnatus Est

Heavens Laugh, The *see Der Himmel Lacht, Die Erde Jubilieret

Heavens Laugh, The Earth Exults, The *see Der Himmel Lacht, Die Erde Jubiliert

Heilig, Heilig, Heilig Ist Der Herre Zebaoth
see Eine Deutsche Messe In Kirchenliedsatzen

Helft Mir, Gott's Gute Preisen (from Gottlob! Nun Geht Das Jahr Zu Ende)
see Anonymous, Lob, Preis Und Dank Sei Dir

Helft Mir, Gott's Gute Preisen [Chorale]
see Weihnachtschorale-II

Helig, Helig, Helig
mix cor,org NORDISKA 3274 s.p. (B929)

Hell Morgonstjarna, Mild Och Ren *see Wie Schon Leuchtet Der Morgenstern

Hence, All Fears And Sadness
see Four Chorales

Hence With Earthly Treasure
see Four Chorales

Here Yet Awhile (from St. Matthew's Passion) Lent,anti/anthem
SSSSAA WARNER W2994 $.40 (B930)
dbl cor WARNER W2531 (B931)
dbl cor oct SCHIRM.G 8464 $.35 (B932)
SSAATTBB oct BELWIN 64087 $.35 (B933)
SATB,acap oct FISCHER,C CM-7618 $.30 (B934)
SATB,pno SCHIRM.EC 362 $.35, ipr (B935)
SATB oct NOVELLO 34.0337.08 s.p. (B936)
(Wilson) SATB oct BOOSEY 5057 $.30 (B937)

Herr Christ *see Herr Christ, Der Ein'ge Gottes-Sohn

Herr Christ, Der Ein'ge Gottes-Sohn (Cantata 96) S.96, cant
mix cor ALSBACH&D s.p. (B938)
mix cor,SATB soli,cont,fl,pic,2ob,horn,trp, strings cor pts BREITKOPF-W CHB-4596 s.p., ipr, sc BREITKOPF-W rental (B939)
"Herr Christ" [Ger] cor voc sc KALMUS 6564 $1.25 (B940)

Herr Christ, Der Ein'ge Gottessohn *S.96, Trin,cant
(Todt, B.) mix cor,SATB soli,org,fl,2ob, bsn,horn,trom,strings,cembalo voc pt BREITKOPF-L CHB-2133 s.p., voc sc BREITKOPF-L EB-7096 s.p., ipr (B941)

Herr Christ, Der Einig Gotts Sohn [Chorale] (from Herr Christ, Der Ein'ge Gottessohn) Trin
SATB (G min) HANSSLER 6.108 s.p. contains also:
Stern, Hermann, Wie Schon Leuchtet Der Morgenstern (SAT/SAB) (CC) (B942)

Herr, Deine Augen *see Herr, Deine Augen Sehen Nach Dem Glauben

Herr, Deine Augen Sehen Nach Dem Glauben (Cantata 102) S.102, Trin,cant
mix cor,ATB soli,cont,fl,2ob,strings cor pts BREITKOPF-W CHB-4602 s.p., ipr, sc BREITKOPF-W rental (B943)
"Herr, Deine Augen" [Ger] cor voc sc KALMUS 6570 $1.25 (B944)
"Herr, Deine Augen" cor,orch/org sc KALMUS $4.50, ipa (B945)
(Raphael, G.) [Eng/Ger] mix cor,ATB soli, org,fl,2ob,2bsn,strings,cembalo sc BREITKOPF-L PB-2952 s.p., voc pt BREITKOPF-L CHB-1431 s.p., voc sc BREITKOPF-L EB-7102 s.p., ipr (B946)

Herr, Gehe Nicht *see Herr, Gehe Nicht Ins Gericht

Herr, Gehe Nicht Ins Gericht (Cantata 105) S.105, Trin,cant
mix cor,SATB soli,cont,2ob,horn,strings sc BREITKOPF-W PB-4605 s.p., cor pts BREITKOPF-W CHB-4605 s.p., ipa (B947)
"Herr, Gehe Nicht" cor,orch sc KALMUS $2.25, ipa (B948)
"Herr, Gehe Nicht" [Ger] cor voc sc KALMUS 6572 $1.25 (B949)
(Horn) SATB,SATB soli,cont,2ob,horn,2vln, vla HANSSLER 10.127 sc $5.00, cor pts $1.25, ipa (B950)
(Raphael, G.) [Eng/Ger] mix cor,SATB soli, org,2ob,2bsn,horn,strings,cembalo sc BREITKOPF-L PB-2955 s.p., voc pt BREITKOPF-L CHB-654 s.p., voc sc BREITKOPF-L EB-7105 s.p., ipr (B951)

Herr, Gehe Nicht Ins Gericht [Chorale] (from Herr, Gehe Nicht Ins Gericht)
"Lord, Enter Not Into Wrath" SATB,pno SCHIRM.EC 1675 $.65, ipr contains also: Nun, Ich Weiss, Du Wirst Mir Stillen, "Now I Know That Thou Art Loving" (B952)

BACH, JOHANN SEBASTIAN (cont'd.)

Herr Gott, Dich Loben Alle Wir (Cantata 130) S.130, ASD,cant
mix cor,SATB soli,cont,fl,3ob,3trp,strings, timp sc BREITKOPF-W PB-4630 s.p., cor pts BREITKOPF-W CHB-4630 s.p., ipa (B953)
(Raphael, G.) [Eng/Ger] mix cor,SATB soli, org,fl,3ob,3trp,strings,timp,cembalo voc pt BREITKOPF-L CHB-1961 s.p., voc sc BREITKOPF-L EB-7129 s.p., ipr (B954)

Herr Gott, Dich Loben Wir (Cantata 16) S.16, Fest,cant
mix cor,ATB soli,org,3ob,horn,strings, cembalo voc pt BREITKOPF-L CHB-2130 s.p., voc sc BREITKOPF-L EB-7016 s.p., ipr (B955)
[Ger] cor voc sc KALMUS 6529 $1.25 (B956)
mix cor,ATB soli,cont,3ob,horn,strings, English horn cor pts BREITKOPF-W CHB-4516 s.p., ipr, sc BREITKOPF-W rental (B957)

Herr Jesu Christ *see Herr Jesu Christ, Du Hochstes Gut

Herr Jesu Christ, Dich Zu Uns Wend *S.332
see Stobaeus, Johann, Ich Hab Ein Herzlich Freud
[Ger] SATB,acap (med) BAREN. BA 793 s.p. (B958)

Herr Jesu Christ, Du Hochstes Gut (Cantata 113) S.113, Trin,cant
mix cor,SATB soli,cont,fl,2ob,strings cor pts BREITKOPF-W CHB-4613 s.p., ipr, sc BREITKOPF-W rental (B959)
"Herr, Jesu Christ" cor,orch/org sc KALMUS $3.00, ipa (B960)
"Herr Jesu Christ" [Ger] cor voc sc KALMUS 6578 $1.25 (B961)
(Todt, B.) mix cor,SATB soli,org,fl,2ob, bsn,strings,cembalo, 2 English horns sc BREITKOPF-L PB-2963 s.p., voc pt BREITKOPF-L CHB-2065 s.p., voc sc BREITKOPF-L EB-7113 s.p., ipa (B962)

Herr Jesu Christ, Wahr' Mensch Und Gott *S.127, Gen,cant
(Grischkat) SATB,STB soli,cont,2ob,trp, 2vln,vla,2rec HANSSLER 10.221 sc $5.00, cor pts $.80, ipa (B963)
(Raphael, G.) [Eng/Ger] mix cor,STB soli, org,2fl,2ob,bsn,trp,strings,cembalo voc pt BREITKOPF-L CHB-2135 s.p., voc sc BREITKOPF-L EB-7127 s.p., ipr (B964)

Herr Jesu Christ, Wahr'r Mensch Und Gott (Cantata 127) S.127, cant
mix cor,STB soli,cont,2fl/2rec,2ob,trp, strings sc BREITKOPF-W PB-4627 s.p., cor pts BREITKOPF-W CHB-4627 s.p., ipa (B965)

Herr, Wie Du Willt, So Schicks Mit Mir (Cantata 73) S.73, Epiph,cant
mix cor,STB soli,org,cont,2ob,horn,strings sc BREITKOPF-W PB-4573 s.p., cor pts BREITKOPF-W CHB-4573 s.p., ipa (B966)
(Raphael, G.) [Eng/Fr/Ger] mix cor,STB soli,org,2ob,bsn,horn,strings,cembalo voc pt BREITKOPF-L CHB-868 s.p., voc sc BREITKOPF-L EB-7073 s.p., ipr (B967)

Herren Ar Min Herde God
mix cor NORDISKA 4207 s.p. (B968)

Herren Gud Ar Sol Och Skold *see Gott, Der Herr, Ist Sonn' Und Schild

Herrscher Des Himmels (from Weihnachts Oratorium)
(Vogel, Moritz; Nagler, Franciscus) [Ger] wom cor&jr cor,org,opt strings HUG 82 s.p. (B969)

Herrscher Uber Tod Und Leben (from Liebster Jesu, Wann Werd' Ich Sterben)
"Thou That Life And Death Ordainst" see Bach, Johann Sebastian, Liebster Gott, Wann Werd' Ich Sterben [Chorale]

Herz Und Mund *see Herz Und Mund Und Tat Und Leben

Herz Und Mund Und Tat Und Leben (Cantata 147) S.147, BVM,cant
mix cor,SATB soli,cont,5ob,bsn,trp,strings sc BREITKOPF-W PB-4647 s.p., cor pts BREITKOPF-W CHB-4647 s.p. (B970)
"Herz Und Mund" [Ger] cor voc sc KALMUS 6600 $1.25 (B971)
"Herz Und Mund" cor sc KALMUS $5.00 (B972)
(Todt, B.) mix cor,SATB soli,org,3ob,bsn, trp,strings,cembalo voc sc BREITKOPF-L EB-7147 s.p., ipr (B973)

Herzlich Lieb Hab Ich Dich, O Herr (from Ich Liebe Den Hochsten Vor Ganzem Gemute) Whitsun
see Goudimel, Claude, Mein Leben Ist Ein Pilgrimstand
SATB HANSSLER 6.1022 s.p. (B974)

Herzliebster Jesu *Easter/Psntd
SATB,acap (contains also: Ingegneri, Marco Antonio, O Bone Jesu) voc pt DOBLINGER s.p. see also PASSION UND OSTERN (B975)

Herzliebster Jesu, Was Hast Du Verbrochen (from Matthaus-Passion) Psntd
see Bach, Johann Sebastian, O Haupt Voll Blut Und Wunden
4pt mix cor MOSELER LB-83 s.p. (B976)
SATB HANSSLER 6.113 s.p. contains also: Vopelius, Gottfried, Du Grosser Schmerzensmann (B977)

Het Is Volbracht
mix cor ALSBACH&D s.p. (B978)

Het Lam Gods
mix cor ALSBACH&D s.p. (B979)

Heut Trimphieret Gottes Sohn *S.342, Easter
SATB (G min) HANSSLER 6.125 s.p. contains also: Vulpius, Melchior, Erstanden Ist Der Heilig Christ; Helder, Bartholomaeus, Du Starker Held, Herr Jesu Christ (B980)

BACH, JOHANN SEBASTIAN (cont'd.)

Himmelskoenig *see Himmelskonig, Sei Willkommen

Himmelskonig, Sei Willkommen (Cantata 182) S.182, Palm,cant
[Ger] cor voc sc KALMUS 6623 $1.25 (B981)
mix cor,ATB soli,cont,fl/rec,strings sc BREITKOPF-W PB-4682 s.p., cor pts BREITKOPF-W CHB-4682 s.p., ipa (B982)
"Himmelskoenig" cor,orch sc KALMUS $4.50, ipa (B983)
(Todt, B.) [Fr/Ger] mix cor,ATB soli,org, fl,strings,cembalo voc pt BREITKOPF-L CHB-1751 s.p., voc sc BREITKOPF-L EB-7182 s.p., ipr (B984)

Himmelskonig, Sei Willkommen [Chorale] (from Himmelskonig, Sei Willkommen)
"King Of Heaven, Come In Triumph" SATB,pno SCHIRM.EC 1196 $.80, ipr contains also: Jesu, Deine Passion, "Jesu, By Thy Suffering"; So Lasset Uns Gehen In Salem, "With Joy We March Onward To Zion" (B985)

His Mercy *see Et Misericordia

His Servant Israel *see Suscepit Israel

Hochsterwunschtes Freudenfest (Cantata 194) S.194, Trin,cant
[Ger] cor voc sc KALMUS 6634 $1.25 (B986)
mix cor,STB soli,cont,3ob,bsn,strings cor pts BREITKOPF-W CHB-4694 s.p., ipr, sc BREITKOPF-W rental (B987)
(Todt, B.) mix cor,STB soli,org,3ob,bsn, strings,cembalo voc pt BREITKOPF-L CHB-2215 s.p., voc sc BREITKOPF-L EB-7194 s.p., ipr (B988)

Hojlovet Vaere Gud *see Gelobet Sei Der Herr

Hold In Affection Jesus Christ *see Halt Im Gedachtnis Jesum Christ

Holy Ghost, Dispel Our Sadness *Whitsun, anthem
mix cor oct NOVELLO 40.1202.10 s.p. (B989)

Holy, Holy *hymn
PATERSON s.p. see also English Hymns Adapted To Bach's Chorales (B990)

Honor And Glory
(Ehret) SATB oct PLYMOUTH SC-10 $.25 (B991)

Hope And Light Of Man's Endeavour *see Jesus Bleibet Meine Freude

Hosanna To The Living Lord *hymn
PATERSON s.p. see also English Hymns Adapted To Bach's Chorales (B992)

Hosianna, Davids Sohn (from Ich Lasse Dich Nicht, Du Segnest Mich Denn) BVM
SATB HANSSLER 6.240 s.p. contains also: Kommst Du, Kommst Du, Licht Der Heiden, S.259; Nun Komm, Der Heiden Heiland [Chorale] (from Schwingt Freudig Euch Empor) (Adv) (B993)

How Brightly Beams The Morning Star
(Davies) 1-2pt jr cor/1-2pt wom cor CURWEN 72638 s.p. contains also: O Jesu So Dear (B994)

How Brightly Shines Yon Morning Star *see Wie Schon Leuchtet Der Morgenstern [Chorale]

How Brightly Shines Yon Star Of Morn (Cantata 1) Fest
(West, John E.) SATB,STB soli,2ob,2horn, strings voc sc NOVELLO rental (B995)

How Hard To Teach Our Flesh And Blood *see Wie Schwerlich Lasst Sich Fleishch Und Blut

How Shall I Fitly Meet Thee (from Christmas Oratorio, The) Xmas,anthem/chorale
see Three Chorales
see Two Chorales
see Two Two-Part Bach Chorales
SATB,org SCHIRM.EC 353 $.25, ipr (B996)
SATB oct NOVELLO 50.0319.09 s.p. contains also: This Proud Heart (B997)
mix cor oct NOVELLO 50.0319.09 s.p. (B998)

Huit Cantiques *CC8U
(Gevaert) [Fr] unis,kbd LEMOINE voc sc s.p., voc pt s.p. (B999)

Hush, My Dear, Lie Still And Slumber *Xmas, chorale
(Glaser, V.) SSA,acap SCHIRM.EC 2548 $.25 (B1000)

Hvo Ikkun Lader Herren Rade *see Wer Nur Den Lieben Gott Lasst Walten [Chorale]

Hymn Of Praise *Gen,anthem
(Mythch, J.F.) SA (med easy) oct GIA G1479 $.25 (B1001)

Hymne De La Pentecote *see Veni Creator Spiritus

Hymne Des Vierges *see Jesus, Corona Virginum

Hymne Du Matin *Morn,hymn
(Geveart, F.-A.) [Fr] 4pt mix cor,acap (med) cor pts LEMOINE s.p. see from Collection De Choeurs, cinquieme Fascicule (B1002)

I Call To Thee
(Lautner, L.) SAB oct PRESSER MC340 $.30 (B1003)

I Kneel Beside Thy Cradle Here *Xmas
(Kinsman) SATB oct BOURNE SB102 $.30 (B1004)

I Know In Whom I Trust (from Cant 129)
(Follett) SATB oct PRO ART 2358 $.25 (B1005)

I Know That My Redeemer Lives (Cantata 160) S.160, Easter/Lent,cant
(Allen) SATB,ST soli GALLEON (B1006)
(Allen) SATB FISCHER,C GALLEON $1.25 (B1007)

BACH, JOHANN SEBASTIAN (cont'd.)

I Know That My Redeemer Lives [Chorale]
(Kingsbury, John) SATBB ALFRED 6356 $.30 (B1008)

I Suffered With Great Heaviness *see Ich Hatte Veil Bekummernis

I Will Lift Up Mine Eyes (Cantata 37)
SATB PATERSON 1578 s.p. (B1009)

I Would Beside My Lord (from St. Matthew Passion)
SATB,T solo,pno SCHIRM.EC 1119 $.40, ipr (B1010)

Ich Armer Mensch *see Ich Armer Mensch, Ich Sundenknecht

Ich Armer Mensch, Ich Sundenknecht (Cantata 55) S.55, Trin,cant
mix cor,T solo,cont,fl,ob,strings sc BREITKOPF-W PB-4555 s.p., cor pts BREITKOPF-W CHB-4555 s.p., ipa (B1011)
"Ich Armer Mensch" [Eng] cor voc sc KALMUS 6037 $1.25 (B1012)
(Raphael, G.) [Eng/Ger] mix cor,T solo,org, fl,ob,strings,cembalo voc pt BREITKOPF-L CHB-1982 s.p., voc sc BREITKOPF-L EB-7055 s.p., ipr (B1013)

Ich Bin *see Ich Bin Ein Guter Hirt

Ich Bin Ein Guter Hirt (Cantata 85) S.85, Gen,cant
mix cor,SATB soli,cont,2ob,strings cor pts BREITKOPF-W CHB-4585 s.p., ipr, sc BREITKOPF-W rental (B1014)
"Ich Bin" [Ger] cor voc sc KALMUS 6554 $1.25 (B1015)
(Schneider, M.) mix cor,SATB soli,org,2ob, bsn,strings,cembalo voc pt BREITKOPF-L CHB-1951 s.p., voc sc BREITKOPF-L EB-7085 s.p., ipr (B1016)

Ich Bin Vergnuegt *see Ich Bin Vergnugt Mit Meinem Glucke

Ich Bin Vergnugt *see Ich Bin Vergnugt Mit Meinem Glucke

Ich Bin Vergnugt Mit Meinem Glucke (Cantata 84) S.84, Septua,cant
mix cor,S solo,ob,strings,cembalo voc pt BREITKOPF-L CHB-2198 s.p., voc sc BREITKOPF-L EB-7084 s.p., ipr (B1017)
mix cor,S solo,cont,ob,strings sc BREITKOPF-W PB-4584 s.p., cor pts BREITKOPF-W CHB-4584 s.p., ipa (B1018)
"Ich Bin Vergnuegt" cor,orch/org sc KALMUS $3.50, ipa (B1019)
"Ich Bin Vergnugt" [Ger] cor voc sc KALMUS 6553 $1.25 (B1020)

Ich Elender Mensch *see Ich Elender Mensch Wer Wird Mich Erlosen

Ich Elender Mensch Wer Wird Mich Erlosen (Cantata 48) S.48, Trin,cant
mix cor,AT soli,cont,2ob,trp,strings cor pts BREITKOPF-W CHB-4548 s.p., ipr, sc BREITKOPF-W rental (B1021)
"Ich Elender Mensch" [Ger] cor voc sc KALMUS 6539 $1.25 (B1022)
(Raphael, G.) [Eng/Ger] mix cor,AT soli, org,2ob,trp,strings,cembalo voc pt BREITKOPF-L CHB-1854 s.p., voc sc BREITKOPF-L EB-7048 s.p., ipr (B1023)

Ich Freue Mich Im Herrn *S.220,No.5
SATB (C maj) HANSSLER 6.197 s.p. (B1024)

Ich Freue Mich In Dir (Cantata 133) S.133, Adv/Xmas,cant
mix cor,SATB soli,org,2ob,bsn,trp,strings, cembalo voc sc BREITKOPF-L PB-2983 s.p., voc pt BREITKOPF-L CHB-1482 s.p., voc sc BREITKOPF-L EB-7133 s.p. (B1025)
mix cor,SATB soli,cont,2ob,trp,strings sc BREITKOPF-W PB-4633 s.p., cor pts BREITKOPF-W CHB-4633 s.p., ipa (B1026)
(Hamburger, Povl) "Jeg Fryder Mig I Dig" [Ger/Dan] SATB,acap HANSEN-DEN 156 s.p. see also Otte Koraludsaettelser (B1027)
(Mattfeld, V.) "With Joy I Welcome Thee" [Ger/Eng] unis,org SCHIRM.EC 2554 see from Songs For The Advent And Christmas Seasons (B1028)

Ich Geh' Und Suche *see Ich Geh' Und Suche Mit Verlangen

Ich Geh' Und Suche Mit Verlangen *S.49, Trin,cant
mix cor,SB soli,org/cembalo,ob,strings voc sc BREITKOPF-L EB-7049 s.p., ipr (B1029)
"Ich Geh' Und Suche" [Ger] cor voc sc KALMUS 6540 $1.25 (B1030)

Ich Glaube, Lieber Herr, Hilf Meinem Unglauben (Cantata 109) S.109, Trin,cant
mix cor,AT soli,org,2ob,horn,strings, cembalo voc pt BREITKOPF-L CHB-2217 s.p., voc sc BREITKOPF-L EB-7109 s.p., ipr (B1031)
mix cor,AT soli,cont,2ob,horn,strings sc BREITKOPF-W PB-4609 s.p., cor pts BREITKOPF-W CHB-4609 s.p., ipr (B1032)
"Glaube Liebet" [Ger] cor voc sc KALMUS 6575 $1.25 (B1033)

Ich Hab Genug *S.82, cant
[Eng] cor voc sc KALMUS 6033 $1.00 (B1034)

Ich Hab' In Gottes Herz Und Sinn (Cantata 92) S.92, Septua,cant
mix cor,SATB soli,org,2ob,bsn,strings, cembalo voc pt BREITKOPF-L CHB-1863 s.p., voc sc BREITKOPF-L EB-7092 s.p., ipr (B1035)
[Ger] cor voc sc KALMUS 6561 $1.25 (B1036)
mix cor,SATB soli,cont,2ob,strings cor pts BREITKOPF-W CHB-4592 s.p., ipr, sc BREITKOPF-W rental (B1037)

Ich Habe (Cantata 82) S.82, cant
cor sc KALMUS $3.00 (B1038)
cor,orch sc KALMUS $3.00, ipa (B1039)

BACH, JOHANN SEBASTIAN (cont'd.)

Ich Habe Meine Zuversicht (Cantata 188) S.188, Trin,cant
mix cor,SATB soli,org,2ob,bsn,strings, cembalo voc pt BREITKOPF-L CHB-2218 s.p., voc sc BREITKOPF-L EB-7188 s.p., ipr (B1040)
[Ger] cor voc sc KALMUS 6629 $1.25 (B1041)
mix cor,SATB soli,org,cont,ob,strings cor pts BREITKOPF-W CHB-4688 s.p., ipr, sc BREITKOPF-W rental (B1042)

Ich Hatte *see Ich Hatte Viel Bekummernis

Ich Hatte Veil Bekummernis (Cantata 21)
(Jones, Ifor) "I Suffered With Great Heaviness" [Eng/Ger] mix cor,soli,pno voc sc SCHIRM.G $1.50 (B1043)

Ich Hatte Viel Bekummernis (Cantata 21) S.21, Gen/Trin,cant
cor sc KALMUS $6.50 (B1044)
mix cor,STB soli,cont,ob,bsn,3trp,4trom, strings,timp sc BREITKOPF-W PB-4521 s.p., cor pts BREITKOPF-W CHB-4521 s.p., ipa (B1045)
"Ich Hatte" cor,orch sc KALMUS $6.00, ipa (B1046)
"My Spirit" [Eng] cor voc sc KALMUS 6020 $1.25 (B1047)
"My Spirit Was In Heaviness" SATB,STB soli, org,ob,2clar,2bsn,2horn,3trp,4trom, strings voc sc NOVELLO s.p., ipr (B1048)
(Raphael, G.) [Eng/Ger] mix cor,SATB soli, org,ob,bsn,3trp,4trom,strings,timp, cembalo sc BREITKOPF-L PB-2871 s.p., voc pt BREITKOPF-L CHB-257 s.p., voc sc BREITKOPF-L EB-7021 s.p., ipa (B1049)

Ich Jauchze, Ich Lache *Easter/Gen
"With Loudest Rejoicing" SA,kbd (med easy) oct CONCORDIA 98-1846 $.25 (B1050)

Ich Lass Dich Nicht, Du Musst Mein Jesus Bleiben
SATB HANSSLER 6.0597 s.p. contains also: Jesus, Unser Trost Und Leben (B1051)

Ich Lasse Dich Nicht *S.157, cant
[Ger] cor voc sc KALMUS 6606 $1.25 (B1052)

Ich Lasse Dich Nicht, Du Segnest Mich Denn (Cantata 157) S.157, BVM,cant
mix cor,TB soli,org,fl,ob,strings,cembalo voc pt BREITKOPF-L CHB-2195 s.p., voc sc BREITKOPF-L EB-7157 s.p., ipr (B1053)
mix cor,TB soli,cont,fl,ob,strings cor pts BREITKOPF-W CHB-4657 s.p., ipr, sc BREITKOPF-W rental (B1054)

Ich Liebe Den Hochsten (Cantata 174) S.174, cant
mix cor,ATB soli,3ob,bsn,horn,3vln,3vla cor pts BREITKOPF-W CHB-4674 s.p., ipr, sc BREITKOPF-W rental (B1055)
"Ich Liebe Den Hochsten" [Ger] cor voc sc KALMUS 6616 $1.25 (B1056)

Ich Liebe Den Hochsten *see Ich Liebe Den Hochsten

Ich Liebe Den Hochsten Von Ganzem Gemute *S.174, Pent/Whitsun,cant
mix cor,ATB soli,org,2ob,bsn,2horn,strings, cembalo, English horn voc pt BREITKOPF-L CHB-2204 s.p., voc sc BREITKOPF-L EB-7174 s.p., ipr (B1057)

Ich Liebe Jesum Alle Stund *S.468
SAT/SAB HANSSLER 6.276 s.p. contains also: Ruppel, Paul Ernst, Suchet Den Herrn (4pt) (canon); Ahle, Johann Georg, Die Guldene Sonne Bringt Leben Und Wonne (SAT/SAB) (CC) (B1058)
SATB (A maj) HANSSLER 6.2596 s.p. (B1059)

Ich Ruf' Zu Dir *see Ich Ruf' Zu Dir, Herr Jesu Christ

Ich Ruf' Zu Dir, Herr Jesu Christ (Cantata 177) S.177, Trin,cant
mix cor,SAT soli,cont,4ob,bsn,strings cor pts BREITKOPF-W CHB-4677 s.p., ipr, sc BREITKOPF-W rental (B1060)
"Ich Ruf' Zu Dir" [Ger] cor voc sc KALMUS 6619 $1.25 (B1061)
(Todt, B.) mix cor,SAT soli,org,3ob,2bsn, strings,cembalo voc sc BREITKOPF-L EB-7177 s.p., ipr, ipa (B1062)

Ich Steh' *see Ich Steh' Mit Einem Fuss Im Grabe

Ich Steh An Deiner Krippen Hier (from Weihnachts-Oratorium) Adv/Xmas,anthem/ chorale
see Bach, Johann Sebastian, Lobt Gott, Ihr Christen Allzugleich
see Bach, Johann Sebastian, Lobt Gott Ihr Christen
"Beside Thy Cradle" see Two Christmas Chorales
SATB HANSSLER 6.297 s.p. contains also: In Allen Meinen Taten, S.367 (B1063)
"Beside Thy Cradle" SATB ALLANS 394 s.p. (B1064)
"Beside Thy Cradle" unis oct NOVELLO 48.1631.05 s.p. (B1065)
"Beside Thy Cradle" mix cor oct NOVELLO 50.0204.04 s.p. (B1066)
"Beside Thy Cradle" unis ALLANS 395 s.p. (B1067)
"Beside Thy Cradle" SATB oct NOVELLO 50.0204.04 s.p. (B1068)
"Beside Thy Cradle" mix cor,pno SCHIRM.EC 1601 $.30, ipr (B1069)
"Beside Thy Cradle Here I Stand" SAB oct BELWIN 64002 $.25 (B1070)
"Beside Thy Cradle Here I Stand" SATB oct FISCHER,C CM-6798 $.25 (B1071)
(Etti, K.) men cor,acap voc pt DOBLINGER s.p. (B1072)
(Krumnach) "Beside Thy Cradle Here I Stand" SAB SCHMITT 5531 $.25 (B1073)
(Mattfeld, V.) "O Christ Child, Now I Come To Thee" [Ger/Eng] unis,org SCHIRM.EC 2554 see from Songs For The Advent And

BACH, JOHANN SEBASTIAN (cont'd.)

Christmas Seasons (B1074)
(Richardson) "Beside Thy Cradle Here I Stand" SATB,orch oct SPRATT 526 $.25, ipa (B1075)
(Warren, B.) "Beside Thy Cradle Here I Stand" SA,pno SCHIRM.EC 1938 $.25 (B1076)
(Webb) "Beside Thy Cradle Here I Stand" SA/TB FLAMMER E5108 $.30 (B1077)

Ich Steh An Deiner Krippen Hier [Chorale]
see Weihnachtschorale-I

Ich Steh In Meines Herren Hand (from Matthaus-Passion)
see Bach, Johann Sebastian, Nun Ruhen Alle Walder, Vieh, Menschen

Ich Steh Mit Einem Fuss Im Grabe (Cantata 156) S.156, Epiph,cant
mix cor,ATB soli,org,ob,strings,cembalo voc pt BREITKOPF-L CHB-2186 s.p., voc sc BREITKOPF-L EB-7156 s.p., ipr (B1078)
mix cor,ATB soli,cont,ob,strings sc BREITKOPF-W PB-4656 s.p., cor pts BREITKOPF-W CHB-4656 s.p., ipa (B1079)
"Cantate, Pour Le Troisieme Dimanche Apres Epiphanie" SATB,SAB soli CHOUDENS voc sc s.p., cor pts s.p. (B1080)
"Ich Steh'" [Ger] cor voc sc KALMUS 6605 $1.25 (B1081)

Ich Will Beten, Gott Wird Horen (from Matthas-Passion) Easter
SATB (A flat maj) HANSSLER 6.238 s.p. contains also: Brich An, Du Schones Morgenlicht (from Weihnachts-Oratorium) (Xmas) (B1082)

Ich Will Den Kreuzstab *see Ich Will Den Kreuzstab Gerne Tragen

Ich Will Den Kreuzstab Gerne Tragen (Cantata 56) S.56, Trin,cant
[Eng/Ger] SATB,B solo voc sc HINRICHSEN P1664A s.p. (B1083)
study sc UNIVER. PH. 104 $1.15 (B1084)
mix cor,B solo,cont,4ob,strings sc BREITKOPF-W PB-4556 s.p., cor pts BREITKOPF-W CHB-4556 s.p., ipa (B1085)
"Ich Will Den Kreuzstab" [Eng] cor voc sc KALMUS 6017 $1.00 (B1086)
"Ich Will Den Kreuzstab" cor,orch sc KALMUS $3.50, ipa (B1087)
(Ropartz, J. Guy) "O Croix Je T'accepte Avec Joie!" [Fr] cor,org,2vln,2vla,2vcl, 2bvl,2ob, English horn ENOCH cor pts s.p., sc s.p. (B1088)
(Taubmann, O.) [Eng/Ger] mix cor,B solo, org,3ob,strings,cembalo sc BREITKOPF-L PB-2906 s.p., voc pt BREITKOPF-L CHB-1450 s.p., voc sc BREITKOPF-L EB-7056 s.p., ipr (B1089)

Ich Will Den Namen Gottes Loben (from Uns Ist Ein Kind Geboren) Xmas
SATB,cont HANSSLER 6.255 s.p. contains also: Gloria Sei Dir Gesungen (from Wachet Auf, Ruft Uns Die Stimme) (SATB) (Trin) (CC,Thanks) (B1090)

If By His Spirit (from Jesu, Priceless Treasure)
(Carlton) SSATB oct BOOSEY 5254 $.30 (B1091)
(Damrosch) SSATB,acap oct SCHIRM.G 7605 $.30 (B1092)

If It Be God's Will And Pleasure *see Wenn Es Meines Gottes Wille

If Perchance The Final Hour
(Kinsman) SATB oct BOURNE SB103 $.30 (B1093)

If Thou Art Near *see Bist Du Bei Mir

If Thou But Suffer God To Guide Thee
see Four Chorale Harmonizations
see Three Chorales

If Thou Wert Near *see Bist Du Bei Mir

If Thou Wilt Suffer God To Guide Thee *see Wer Nur Den Lieben Gott Lasst Walten

Ihr, Die Ihr Euch *see Ihr, Die Ihr Euch Von Christo Nennet

Ihr, Die Ihr Euch Von Christo Nennet (Cantata 164) S.164, Trin,cant
mix cor,SATB soli,org,2fl,2ob,strings, cembalo voc sc BREITKOPF-L EB-7164 s.p., ipr (B1094)
mix cor,SATB soli,cont,2fl,2ob,strings sc BREITKOPF-W PB-4664 s.p., cor pts BREITKOPF-W CHB-4664 s.p., ipa (B1095)
"Ihr, Die Ihr Euch" [Ger] cor voc sc KALMUS 6610 $1.25 (B1096)

Ihr Gestirn', Ihr Hohen Lufte *Adv/Xmas
(Mattfeld, V.) "O Ye Stars And Highest Heavens" [Ger/Eng] unis,org SCHIRM.EC 2554 see from Songs For The Advent And Christmas Seasons (B1097)

Ihr Menschen, Ruhmet Gottes Liebe (Cantata 167) S.167, ASD,cant
mix cor,SATB soli,cont,2ob,trp,strings cor pts BREITKOPF-W CHB-4667 s.p., ipr, sc BREITKOPF-W rental (B1098)
(Raphael, G.) [Eng/Ger] mix cor,SATB soli, org,2ob,trp,strings,cembalo voc sc BREITKOPF-L EB-7167 s.p., ipr (B1099)

Ihr Pforten Zu Zion (Cantata 193) S.193, cant
mix cor,SA soli (incomplete) voc sc BREITKOPF-L EB-7193 s.p. (B1100)
[Ger] cor voc sc KALMUS 6633 $1.25 (B1101)
mix cor,SA soli,cont,2ob,strings cor pts BREITKOPF-W CHB-4693 s.p., ipr, sc BREITKOPF-W rental (B1102)

Ihr Werdet, Weinen *see Ihr Werdet Weinen Und Heulen

Ihr Werdet Weinen Und Heulen (Cantata 103) S.103, Fest,cant
[Eng/Fr] mix cor,AT soli,org,2fl,2ob,bsn, trp,strings,cembalo voc pt BREITKOPF-L CHB-1416 s.p., voc sc BREITKOPF-L EB-7103 s.p., ipr (B1103)
mix cor,AT soli,cont,fl,pic,2ob,trp,strings cor pts BREITKOPF-W CHB-4603 s.p., ipr, sc BREITKOPF-W rental (B1104)
"Ihr Werdet, Weinen" [Ger] cor voc sc KALMUS 6571 $1.25 (B1105)

In Allen Meinen Taten (Cantata 97) S.367, Gen,cant
see Bach, Johann Sebastian, Ich Steh An Deiner Krippen Hier
[Ger] cor voc sc KALMUS 6565 $1.25 (B1106)
mix cor,SATB soli,org,cont,2ob,bsn,strings cor pts BREITKOPF-W CHB-4597 s.p., ipr, sc BREITKOPF-W rental (B1107)
(Todt, B.) mix cor,SATB soli,2ob,2bsn, strings,cembalo voc pt BREITKOPF-L CHB-2211 s.p., voc sc BREITKOPF-L EB-7097 s.p., ipr (B1108)

In Death's Strong Grasp The Saviour Lay (from Christ Lag In Todesbanden) chorale
(Barrow, R.) TTBB,acap SCHIRM.EC 2116 $.22 (B1109)

In Dulci Jubilo [Chorale]
see Weihnachtschorale-III

In Exultation My Soul Rejoices
(Jacobson) unis jr cor/unis wom cor CURWEN 72209 s.p. (B1110)
(Jacobson) mix cor CURWEN 61426 s.p. (B1111)
(Jacobson) men cor CURWEN 50821 s.p. (B1112)

In Tears Of Grief (from St. Matthew Passion) Easter/Lent/Psntd
(Canavati) SATB oct PRO ART 2343 $.30 (B1113)
(Canavati) SAB oct PRO ART 2007 $.25 (B1114)
(Canavati) SSA oct PRO ART 2320 $.20 (B1115)
(Dawes, Eric) SATB (med) oct OXFORD 42.966 $.35 (B1116)

In The Midst Of Earthly Life *ECY/Gen
SATB,kbd (med easy) oct CONCORDIA 98-1720 $.25 (B1117)

In Thine Arm I Rest Me
see Four Chorales

Ingen Af Gud Blev Sveget *see Keinen Hat Gott Verlassen

Ist Gott Mein Schild Und Helfersmann (from Ich Bin Ein Guter Nacht)
see Bach, Johann Sebastian, Lob Und Preis Sei Gott Dem Vater

Ist Gott Versohnt Und Unser Freund (from Cant122)
"When God On Us His Love Bestows" see Bach, Johann Sebastian, Das Neugeborne Kindelein

It Is Finished *Easter/Lent
(Kinsman) SATB oct BOURNE SB104 $.30 (B1118)

Jag Star Infor Din Krubba Har
unis,pno NORDISKA 1878 s.p. (B1119)

Jauchzet Gott *see Jauchzet Gott In Allen Landen

Jauchzet Gott In Allen Landen (Cantata 51) S.51, Trin,cant
cor sc KALMUS $3.25 (B1120)
"Jauchzet Gott" cor,orch sc KALMUS $3.25, ipa (B1121)
(Raphael, G.; Seiffert, M.) [Eng/Fr/Ger] wom cor,S solo,trp,strings,cembalo sc BREITKOPF-L PB-2901 s.p., voc pt BREITKOPF-L CHB-2220 s.p., voc sc BREITKOPF-L EB-7051 s.p., ipr (B1122)

Jeg Fryder Mig I Dig *see Ich Freue Mich In Dir

Jeg Vil Din Pris Udsjunge *see Aus Meines Herzens Grunde

Jehovah, Let Me Now Adore Thee
(Lundquist) SATB,acap oct WILLIS 8403 $.18 (B1123)

Jerusalem Hav Upp Din Rost
see ADVENTSMUSIK FOR KOR OCH INSTRUMENT

Jesu, Be Thou Here Beside Us
(Fargo) SA/jr cor oct KENDOR $.25 (B1124)
(Fargo) SSA oct KENDOR $.25 (B1125)
(Fargo) SAB oct KENDOR $.30 (B1126)
(Fargo) SATB oct KENDOR $.25 (B1127)

Jesu Bleibet Meine Freude (from Cantata 147)
mix cor ALSBACH&D s.p. (B1128)

Jesu, Bread Of Life *see Jesu, Wahres Brot Des Lebens

Jesu, By Thy Suffering *see Jesu, Deine Passion

Jesu, Comfort Of My Heart
(Kinsman) SATB oct BOURNE SB105 $.30 (B1129)

Jesu, Deine Passion (from Himmelskonig, Sei Willkommen)
"Jesu, By Thy Suffering" see Bach, Johann Sebastian, Himmelskonig, Sei Willkommen [Chorale]

Jesu, Der Du *see Jesu, Der Du Meine Seele

Jesu, Der Du Meine Seele (Cantata 78) S.78, Trin,cant
cor sc KALMUS $5.00 (B1130)
mix cor,SATB soli,cont,fl,2ob,horn,strings sc BREITKOPF-W PB-4578 s.p., cor pts BREITKOPF-W CHB-4578 s.p., ipa (B1131)
"Jesu, Der Du" cor,orch sc KALMUS $4.25, ipa (B1132)
(Jones, Ifor) "Jesus, Thou My Wearied Spirit" [Eng/Ger] mix cor,soli,pno voc sc SCHIRM.G $1.25 (B1133)
(Neumann) [Ger] mix cor voc sc DEUTSCHER 5013 s.p., sc DEUTSCHER 5139A s.p. (B1134)
(Raphael, G.) [Eng/Ger] mix cor,SATB soli, org,fl,2ob,horn,strings,cembalo voc pt BREITKOPF-L CHB-1451 s.p., voc sc BREITKOPF-L EB-7078 s.p., ipr (B1135)

Jesu, Der Du Meine Selle *S.78, Trin,cant
(Horn) SATB,SATB soli,cont,fl,2ob,2vln,vla HANSSLER 10.125 sc $5.00, cor pts $.80, ipa (B1136)

Jesu, Fount Of Joy *Commun/Marriage,anthem
SATB ALLANS 157 s.p. (B1137)
SSA ALLANS 158 s.p. (B1138)
SATB ALLANS 157 s.p. (B1139)
SA ALLANS 257 s.p. (B1140)

Jesu, Glory Of My Life
(Kinsman) SATB oct BOURNE SB106 $.30 (B1141)

Jesu, Jesu, Du Ar Min
mix cor NORDISKA 3730 s.p. (B1142)

Jesu, Jesu, Thou Art Mine
(Kinsman) SATB oct BOURNE SB107 $.30 (B1143)

Jesu, Joy And Treasure *see Jesu, Meine Freude

Jesu, Joy Of Man's Desiring (from Cantata 147) Xmas/Gen,anthem
SATB oct LORENZ B141 $.30 (B1144)
SAB oct LORENZ 7374 $.25 (B1145)
SATB (very easy) oct OXFORD 42.311 $.35 (B1146)
SATB oct PRO ART 1210 $.30 (B1147)
unis WARNER R3417 $.30 (B1148)
2pt WARNER R3134 $.30 (B1149)
SSA WARNER G1552 $.30 (B1150)
SATB,org SCHIRM.EC 317 $.30, ipr (B1151)
SATB oct STAFF 642 $.30 (B1152)
(Andersen) SATB SCHMITT 1578 $.45 (B1153)
(Appel, R.) SSA oct PRESSER 332-14727 $.30 (B1154)
(Appel, R.) SATB oct PRESSER 332-14703 $.30 (B1155)
(Breck) 4pt jr cor/SATB (easy) FISCHER,C CM 6211 $.25 (B1156)
(Breck) SATB oct FISCHER,C CM-6211 $.25 (B1157)
(Davies, E.T.) TTBB (easy) oct OXFORD 41.120 $.35 (B1158)
(Davison, A.) TTBB,pno SCHIRM.EC 96 $.30, ipr (B1159)
(Deis) 3pt mix cor oct SCHIRM.G 10023 $.30 (B1160)
(Glaser, V.) SAB,org SCHIRM.EC 2258 $.35, ipr (B1161)
(Holler) SSA oct GRAY GCMR 1459 $.25 (B1162)
(Holler) SAB oct GRAY GCMR 1435 $.25 (B1163)
(Holler) SATB oct GRAY GCMR 1238 $.35 (B1164)
(Holler) unis/2pt oct GRAY GCMR 2934 $.25 (B1165)
(Howorth) SA/TB oct BELWIN 937 $.30 (B1166)
(Howorth) SSA oct BELWIN 788 $.30 (B1167)
(Howorth) SAB oct BELWIN 1290 $.30 (B1168)
(Howorth) SATB oct BELWIN 747 $.25 (B1169)
(Keating) SA oct SPRATT 581 $.30 (B1170)
(Keating) SSA oct SPRATT 580 $.25 (B1171)
(Keating) SAB oct SPRATT 635 $.30 (B1172)
(Keating) SATB oct SPRATT 528 $.25 (B1173)
(Klotman) SAB oct BELWIN 60848 $.35 (B1174)
(Klotman) SATB oct BELWIN 64027 $.35 (B1175)
(Lee, J) SATB,org (easy) oct GIA G1620 $.40 (B1176)
(Lee, J.) 2 eq voices,kbd,opt treb inst (easy) oct GIA G1638 $.35 (B1177)
(Lefebvre) 2pt oct GALAXY 1.1223.1 $.30 (B1178)
(Mueller) 3pt jr cor/SAB (easy) FISCHER,C CM 6884 $.25 (B1179)
(Mueller) SAB oct FISCHER,C CM-6884 $.25 (B1180)
(Palmer) SATB ALFRED 6360 $.30 (B1181)
(Riegger) SATB FLAMMER A 5019 $.30 (B1182)
(Riegger) SSA FLAMMER B 5025 $.30 (B1183)
(Riegger) TTBB FLAMMER C5020 $.30 (B1184)
(Riegger) SA/TB FLAMMER E5052 $.25 (B1185)
(Riegger) SAB FLAMMER D5047 $.25 (B1186)
(Titus) SATB oct VOLKWEIN VB196 $.25 (B1187)
(Treharne) [Eng/Ger] 4pt mix cor oct SCHIRM.G 8823 $.35 (B1188)
(Treharne) [Eng/Ger] 4pt mix cor,org oct SCHIRM.G 8387 $.35 (B1189)
(Treharne) [Eng/Ger] 4pt men cor oct SCHIRM.G 8389 $.25 (B1190)
(Treharne) [Eng/Ger] 3pt wom cor oct SCHIRM.G 8388 $.30 (B1191)
(Whittaker, W.G.) 2pt (easy) oct OXFORD 44.052 $.30, ipr (B1192)
(Whittaker, W.G.) SSA (easy) oct OXFORD 44.054 $.35, ipr (B1193)
(Whittaker, W.G.) unis (easy) oct OXFORD 45.406 $.30, ipr (B1194)

Jesu, Joyance Of My Heart
(Ahle; Dickinson) SATB oct GRAY GSC 253 $.30 (B1195)

Jesu, Joyaunce Of My Heart
(Field) SATB oct BOOSEY 5529 $.30 (B1196)

Jesu, Meine Freude (Motet 3) S.227, Psntd, anthem/chorale/mot
"Jesu, Priceless Treasure" see Four Chorales
[Ger] mix cor,acap (diff) HUG s.p. (B1197)
mix cor ALSBACH&D s.p. (B1198)
mix cor sc HANSSLER 31.227 s.p. (B1199)
5pt mix cor,acap cor pts BREITKOPF-L EB-7227 s.p., voc pt BREITKOPF-L CHB-538 s.p. (B1200)
mix cor sc BREITKOPF-W EB-6293 s.p., cor pts BREITKOPF-W CHB-583 s.p. (B1201)
"Jesu, Priceless Treasure" SSATB,acap voc sc NOVELLO s.p. (B1202)
"Jesu, Priceless Treasure" SATB (very easy) oct AUGSBURG 1041 $.14 (B1203)
"Jesu, Priceless Treasure" SATB oct SUMMY 5100 $.40 (B1204)

BACH, JOHANN SEBASTIAN (cont'd.)

"Jesu, Priceless Treasure" BELWIN $1.25
(B1205)

"Jesu, Priceless Treasure" cor voc sc
KALMUS 6065 $1.00
(B1206)

(Ahlen, David) wom cor NORDISKA 1480 s.p.
(B1207)

(Ameln, Konrad) [Ger] SSATB,org,2ob,bsn,
3vln,vla,vcl,bvl (med diff) cor pts
BAREN. BA 5132 $2.00, ipa
(B1208)

(Ameln; Wolters) SSATB,org,cor,strings cor pts
MOSELER s.p., ipa
(B1209)

(Damrosch, F.) "Jesu, Priceless Treasure"
5pt voc sc SCHIRM.G $1.00
(B1210)

(Gray) "Jesu, Priceless Treasure" SATB,
kbd oct PRO ART 1273 $.20
(B1211)

(Neumann-Buszin) "Jesus, My Great Pleasure"
[Eng/Ger] SSATB,cont PETERS 6103 $.90,
ipa see from Six Motets
(B1212)

(Peery, R.) "Jesu, Priceless Treasure" SAB
oct PRESSER 312-40463 $.25
(B1213)

(Whittaker, W.G.) "Jesu, Joy And Treasure"
SSATB,acap (diff) voc OXFORD 42.033
$2.00, rental
(B1214)

Jesu, Meine Freude [Chorale] (from Jesu,
Meine Freude) anthem/chorale
"Jesu, Priceless Treasure" SATB KJOS 5025
$.30
(B1215)

"Jesu, Priceless Treasure" mix cor oct
NOVELLO 50.0279.05 s.p.
(B1216)

(Peery) "Jesu Priceless Treasure" SSA oct
BELWIN 1045 $.30
(B1217)

(Peery) "Jesu Priceless Treasure" SATB oct
BELWIN 1095 $.25
(B1218)

Jesu, Meine Freude, Meines Herzens [Chorale]
(from Jesu, Meine Freude)
see Burck, Joachim, Nun Lasst Uns Gott Dem
Herren
SATB HANSSLER 6.245 s.p. contains also:
Goudimel, Claude, Jauchzt, Alle Lande,
Gott Zu Ehren; Franck, Melchior, Kommt
Her Zu Mir, Spricht Gottes Sohn
(B1219)

Jesu, Meines Herzens Freud' *Adv/Xmas
(Mattfeld, V.) "Thou, O Lord, Joy Of My
Heart" [Ger/Eng] unis,org SCHIRM.EC 2554
see from Songs For The Advent And
Christmas Seasons
(B1220)

Jesu Min Herre Till Dig Jag Langtar
mix cor NORDISKA 3435 s.p.
(B1221)

Jesu, Nun *see Jesu, Nun Sei Gepreiset

Jesu, Nun Sei Gepreiset (Cantata 41) S.41,
Gen,cant
mix cor,SATB soli,org,cont,3ob,3trp,
strings,timp cor pts BREITKOPF-W CHB-4541
s.p., ipr, sc BREITKOPF-W CHB-4541
(B1222)
"Jesu, Nun" [Eng] cor voc sc KALMUS 6028
$1.00
(B1223)
(Todt, B.) mix cor,SATB soli,org,3ob,bsn,
3trp,strings,timp,cembalo voc pt
BREITKOPF-L CHB-1965 s.p., voc sc
BREITKOPF-L EB-7041 s.p., ipr
(B1224)

Jesu, Nun Sei Gepreiset [Chorale] (from
Cantata No. 41) chorale
see Weihnachtschorale-II
(Davison, A.T.) "To God On High Be Glory"
SATB,org SCHIRM.EC 1684 $.25
(B1225)

Jesu, Nun Sie Gepreiset (Cantata 41)
"Jesus, Now Will We Praise Thee" SATB,SATB
soli,org,3ob,3trp,strings,timp voc sc
NOVELLO rental
(B1226)

Jesu, Priceless Treasure *see Jesu, Meine
Freude

Jesu, Priceless Treasure [Chorale] (from
Jesu, Meine Freude) anthem/chorale
SATB oct NOVELLO 50.0279.06 s.p.
(B1227)

Jesu, Priceless Treasure *see Jesu, Meine
Freude [Chorale]

Jesu Son Of God Most High
(Pollock; Ahle; Coggin) SA oct BELWIN 64386
$.30
(B1228)

Jesu Sweet *Xmas
(Geer) SATB,acap oct FISCHER,C CM-6822 $.25
(B1229)

(Geer) SSAA oct FISCHER,C CM-377 $.25
(B1230)

Jesu, Thou My Constant Gladness *cant
BELWIN $1.25
(B1231)

Jesu, Thou My Heart's Delight *anthem
(Sateren) SATB (easy) oct AUGSBURG 1254
$.22
(B1232)

Jesu, Wahres Brot Des Lebens (from Schmucke
Dich, O Liebe Seele)
"Jesu, Bread Of Life" see Bach, Johann
Sebastian, Schmucke Dich, O Liebe Seele
[Chorale]

Jesu, Who My Soul Eternal (Cantata 78)
(Steinitz) [Eng/Ger] mix cor,SATB soli,
cont,fl,2ob,strings CURWEN sc rental,
ipr, voc sc rental
(B1233)

Jesus Bleibet Meine Freude
mix cor HANSEN-DEN s.p.
(B1234)
"Hope And Light Of Man's Endeavour" 2pt
ASHDOWN E.A.242 s.p.
(B1235)

Jesus, Corona Virginum *chorale/hymn
(Geveart, F.-A.) "Hymne Des Vierges" [Lat]
4pt mix cor,acap (med) cor pts LEMOINE
s.p. see from Collection De Choeurs,
cinquieme Fascicule
(B1236)

Jesus Fount Of Consolation *anthem
(Davis) SATB oct GALAXY 1.2004.1 $.30
(B1237)
(Field) SATB oct BOOSEY 5531 $.30
(B1238)
(Sampson, Godfrey) mix cor oct NOVELLO
40.1180.05 s.p.
(B1239)

Jesus Is My Heart's Delight *Gen
SATB,kbd (med easy) oct CONCORDIA 98-1191
$.25
(B1240)

BACH, JOHANN SEBASTIAN (cont'd.)

Jesus Is My Joy, My All *chorale
SATB,acap oct SCHIRM.EC 2214 $.30
(B1241)

Jesus, Jesus, Thou Art Mine *Easter
(Aslanoff, A.) SATB,acap oct PRESSER
312-21437 $.30
(B1242)

Jesus, Joy Of Loving Hearts
(Coggin) SAB FLAMMER D5147 $.25
(B1243)

Jesus, Joy Of Man's Desiring *Gen
SATB,kbd (med easy) oct CONCORDIA 98-1124
$.35
(B1244)

Jesus, Joy Of My Endeavor
(Scott) SATB SHAWNEE A 33 $.35
(B1245)
(Scott) SSA FLAMMER B 28 $.25
(B1246)

Jesus Lives *hymn
PATERSON s.p. see also English Hymns
Adapted To Bach's Chorales
(B1247)

Jesus, Master, Whose Am I *hymn
PATERSON s.p. see also English Hymns
Adapted To Bach's Chorales
(B1248)

Jesus, My Great Pleasure *see Jesu, Meine
Freude

Jesus, My Lord, My God
(Hilton, Arthur) (med easy) PRESSER
352-00462 $.35
(B1249)

Jesus, My Lord, My God, My All
(Hilton, A.) SATB oct PRESSER 352-00376
$.25
(B1250)

Jesus Nahm Zu Sich Die Zwolfe (Cantata 22)
S.22, Gen,cant
[Ger] cor voc sc KALMUS 6533 $1.25 (B1251)
mix cor,ATB soli,cont,chzt,strings sc
BREITKOPF-W PB-4522 s.p., cor pts
BREITKOPF-W CHB-4522 s.p., ipa (B1252)
(Todt, B.) mix cor,ATB soli,org,ob,strings,
cembalo voc pt BREITKOPF-L CHB-1892 s.p.,
voc sc BREITKOPF-L EB-7022 s.p., ipr
(B1253)

Jesus, Now Will We Praise Thee *see Jesu,
Nun Sie Gepreiset

Jesus, Priceless Treasure *Gen
SATB,kbd (med easy) oct CONCORDIA 98-1043
$.25 contains also: Lord, Thee I Love
With All My Heart
(B1254)

Jesus Que Ma Joie Demure
(Depelsenaire, J.M.) oct TRANSAT. $.50
(B1255)

Jesus, Refuge Of The Weary *Gen/Lent
SATB,acap (med easy) oct CONCORDIA 98-1774
$.25
(B1256)
(Bunjes) girl cor SOUTHERN $.20
(B1257)

Jesus Schlaeft *see Jesus Schlaft, Was Soll
Ich Hoffen

Jesus Schlaft, Was Soll Ich Hoffen (Cantata
81) S.81, Epiph,cant
mix cor,ATB soli,org,2fl,2ob,bsn,strings,
cembalo voc pt BREITKOPF-L CHB-2189 s.p.,
voc sc BREITKOPF-L EB-7081 s.p., ipr
(B1258)
mix cor,ATB soli,cont,2fl/2rec,2ob,strings
cor pts BREITKOPF-W CHB-4581 s.p., ipr,
sc BREITKOPF-W rental
(B1259)
"Jesus Schlaeft" [Eng] cor voc sc KALMUS
6045 $1.00
(B1260)
"Jesus Schlaeft" cor,orch sc KALMUS $3.50,
ipa
(B1261)
(Atkins, Ivor) "Jesus Sleeps, What Hope
Remaineth?" SATB,ATB soli,org,2fl,2ob,
strings voc sc NOVELLO s.p., ipr
(B1262)

Jesus Sleeps, What Hope Remaineth? *see
Jesus Schlaft, Was Soll Ich Hoffen?

Jesus, Thou My Wearied Spirit *see Jesu, Der
Du Meine Seele

Jesus, Thy Blood And Righteousness *Commun/
Gen/Lent
SATB,kbd (med easy, or Ash Wednesday) oct
CONCORDIA 98-2052 $.25
(B1263)

Jesus, Toi Mon Bonheur *S.227, mot
(Barre, J.) [Fr] 4pt mix cor,acap voc sc
DURAND see from Motets
(B1264)

Jesus, Trostaren Och Livet
mix cor NORDISKA 5087 s.p.
(B1265)

Jesus, Unser Trost Und Leben
see Funf Geistliche Lieder Aus Schemellis
Gesangbuch
see Bach, Johann Sebastian, Ich Lass Dich
Nicht, Du Musst Mein Jesus Bleiben
TTBB HANSSLER 6.0572 s.p.
(B1266)

Jesus Who Did Ever Guide Me
(Frackenpohl) SATB SHAWNEE A 462 $.25
(B1267)

Jesus, Who Hast Ever Led Me (from Christmas
Oratorio) Gen
(Hines) SAB,kbd (med easy) oct CONCORDIA
98-1878 $.25
(B1268)

Jezus Is Ons Licht En Leven
mix cor ALSBACH&D s.p.
(B1269)

Johannespassion *S.245, Lent/Psntd,cant/
chorale/ora
mix cor,SATB soli,org,2fl,4ob,bsn,strings
cor pts BREITKOPF-L CHB-102 s.p., voc sc
BREITKOPF-L EB-480 s.p., ipr
(B1270)
mix cor (includes text and chorales)
MOSELER s.p.
(B1271)
"La Passion Selon Saint Jean" SATB,SATB
soli CHOUDENS s.p., ipr
(B1272)
"St. John's Passion" BELWIN $3.00 (B1273)
(Sievers, Gerd) mix cor,SATB soli,org,2fl,
2ob,bsn,strings, lute sc BREITKOPF-W
PB-3792 s.p., voc sc BREITKOPF-W EB-6280
s.p., cor pt BREITKOPF-W CHB-3000 s.p.,
study sc BREITKOPF-W PB-3811 s.p., ipa
(B1274)

BACH, JOHANN SEBASTIAN (cont'd.)

Johannespassionen *see La Passione Di N.S.
Gesu Cristo Secondo Giovanni

Keinen Hat Gott Verlassen
(Hamburger, Povl) "Ingen Af Gud Blev
Sveget" [Ger/Dan] SATB,acap HANSEN-DEN
155 s.p. see also Otte Koraludsaettelser
(B1275)

Kerstlied (Gij, Al Ons Heil, Ons Hoogste
Goed)
mix cor ALSBACH&D s.p.
(B1276)

Kerstlied (Hoe Zal Ik U Ontvangen)
mix cor ALSBACH&D s.p.
(B1277)

King Of Glory *chorale
SATB oct STAFF 485 $.25
(B1278)
SATB,band oct STAFF 485 $.25, ipa
(B1279)
SAB oct STAFF 593 $.25
(B1280)
SA/TB oct STAFF 594 $.25
(B1281)

King Of Glory, King Of Peace *Gen,chorale
(Harris, W.H.) SATB (easy) oct OXFORD
42.209 $.30
(B1282)
(Lock) SATB,acap (med easy) oct CONCORDIA
98-1845 $.25
(B1283)

King Of Heaven, Come In Triumph *see
Himmelskonig, Sei Willkommen [Chorale]

King Of Love My Shepherd Is, The *hymn
PATERSON s.p. see also English Hymns
Adapted To Bach's Chorales
(B1284)

Kleines Magnificat *S.21, Magnif
cor,orch sc KALMUS $3.00, ipa
(B1285)

Kom, Stilla Dod
mix cor NORDISKA 1713 s.p.
(B1286)

Komm, Du Susse Todesstunde (Cantata 161)
S.161, BVM/Trin,cant
mix cor,AT soli,cont,2fl/2rec,strings sc
BREITKOPF-W PB-4661 s.p., cor pts
BREITKOPF-W CHB-4661 s.p., ipa (B1287)
(Gui, Vittorio) [Eng/Ger] mix cor,AT soli,
2fl,2bsn,2horn,strings cmplt ed BOOSEY
rental
(B1288)
(Raphael, G.) [Eng/Ger] mix cor,AT soli,
org,2fl,strings,cembalo voc pt BREITKOPF-
L CHB-1650 s.p., voc sc BREITKOPF-L
EB-7161 s.p., ipr
(B1289)

Komm, Gott Schopfer, Heiliger Geist *S.370
see Trubel, Gerhard, Nun Bitten Wir Den
Heiligen Geist
SATB HANSSLER 6.246 s.p. contains also:
Kurig, Hans-Hermann, Komm, Gott Schopfer,
Heiliger Geist (SA/TB); Schutz, Heinrich,
Kommt Her, Des Konigs Aufgebot (SATB);
Kurig, Hans-Hermann, Kommt Her, Des
Konigs Aufgebot (SS/TT); Kurig, Hans-
Hermann, Fur Alle Gute Sei Gepreist
(SATB&SS/TT)
(B1290)

Komm, Heiliger Geist *Pent/Whitsun
SATB,acap voc pt DOBLINGER s.p. see also
PFINGSTEN UND EUCHARISTIE
(B1291)

Komm, Jesu, Komm (Motet 5) S.229, Gen,mot
[Eng/Ger] 8pt mix cor,acap cor pts
BREITKOPF-W EB-7229 s.p., voc pt
BREITKOPF-L CHB-540 s.p.
(B1292)
"Come Jesu, Come" BELWIN $1.00 (B1293)
"Come Jesu, Come" cor voc sc KALMUS 6067
$1.25
(B1294)
(Ameln, Konrad) [Ger] SATB&SATB,org,2ob,
bsn,2vln,vla,vcl,bvl (med diff) cor pts
BAREN. BA 5134 $1.50, ipa
(B1295)
(Ameln; Wolters) SATB&SATB,cont,strings,opt
2ob&bsn, 2 English horns cor pts MOSELER
s.p., ipa
(B1296)
(Neumann-Buszin) "Come, Jesus, Come" [Eng/
Ger] SATB&SATB,cont PETERS 6105 $.90, ipa
see from Six Motets
(B1297)
(West, John E.) "Come, Jesu, Come" [Eng/
Ger] dbl cor,acap voc sc NOVELLO rental
(B1298)

Komm, O Tod
[Ger] SATB,acap (med) BAREN. BCH 74 s.p.
(B1299)

Komm, O Tod, Du Schlafes Bruder
SATB HANSSLER 6.2672 s.p. contains also:
Erythraus, Gotthard, Mitten Wir Im Leben
Sind
(B1300)

Komm, Susser Tod! *anthem
see Funf Geistliche Lieder Aus Schemellis
Gesangbuch
(Christiansen, F.M.; Christiansen, Paul)
"Come, Soothing Death" SATB (easy) oct
AUGSBURG 1078 $.20
(B1301)
(Christiasen, F.M.) "Come, Soothing Death"
SATB (easy) oct AUGSBURG 0172 $.18
(B1302)
(Davis) "Come, Soothing Death" 4pt wom cor,
acap oct SCHIRM.G 8153 $.25
(B1303)
(Davis; Deis) "Come, Soothing Death" 4pt
mix cor,acap oct SCHIRM.G 9840 $.25
(B1304)
(Mattfeld, V.) "Come Thou, Sweet Death"
[Ger/Eng] unis,org SCHIRM.EC 2555 s.p.
from Six Sacred Songs
(B1305)
(Weaver) SATB FOSTER MF106 $.15
(B1306)

Kommen For Herren Med Tacksamhet
mix cor NORDISKA 1712 s.p.
(B1307)

Kommst Du, Kommst Du, Licht Der Heiden
*S.259
see Bach, Johann Sebastian, Hosianna,
Davids Sohn

Kommt Her Zu Mir, Spricht Gottes Sohn
see Praetorius, Michael, Herr Jesu Christe,
Gottes Sohn

Kommt, Seelen, Dieser Tag (from Schemelli
Gesangbuch) Gen,anthem
SSA HANSSLER 6.111 s.p. contains also: Dir,
Dir, Jehova Will Ich Singen (B1308)
"Come Let Us All This Day" unis,opt pno
(contains also: Prepare Thyself, Zion)
oct ROYAL 244 s.p. see also ANTHEMS FOR
UNISON OR TWO PART SINGING
(B1309)
"Come, Let Us All This Day" unis oct GRAY
GCMR 2939 $.30
(B1310)

BACH, JOHANN SEBASTIAN (cont'd.)

"Come, Let Us All This Day" unis,pno
SCHIRM.EC 500 $.20 (B1311)
(Chambers) "Come, Let Us All This Day" SAB,
S solo,org oct BOOSEY 5469 $.30 (B1312)
(Chambers) "Come, Let Us All This Day"
SATB,ST soli,org oct BOOSEY 5364 $.30
(B1313)
(Franz, Robert) "Come Let Us All This Day"
unis oct NOVELLO 48.1162.03 s.p., ipr
(B1314)

Kommt, Seelen, Dieser Tag Muss Heilig *S.479
SATB HANSSLER 6.0113 s.p. contains also:
Vulpius, Melchior, Lobet Den Herrn, Ihr
Heiden (B1315)

Koralen *CC20U,chorale
mix cor ALSBACH&D s.p. (B1316)

Kriste Konung I Guds Rike
mix cor NORDISKA 3619 s.p. (B1317)

Kunst Des Chorals *CCU,chorale
4pt mix cor,opt inst MOSELER s.p. (B1318)

Kyrie Eleison
(Denny, James) SATB BOSWORTH s.p. (B1319)

Kyrie Eleison I (from B Minor Mass)
5pt mix cor oct SCHIRM.G 7803 $.30 (B1320)

Kyrie, Gott Vater In Ewigkeit
see Eine Deutsche Messe In
Kirchenliedsatzen

Kyrie In D Minor *Kyrie
(Jones, I.) SSATB,cont,opt org voc sc
SCHIRM.G $.75 (B1321)

La Brebis Egaree
(Geveart, F.-A.) [Fr] 4pt mix cor,acap
(med) cor pts LEMOINE s.p. see from
Collection De Choeurs, cinquieme
Fascicule (B1322)

La Passion De N. S. Jesucristo, Segun San
Mateo *see Matthaus Passione

La Passion Selon Saint Jean *see
Johannespassion

La Passione Di N.S. Gesu Cristo Secondo
Giovanni *S.245, Easter,cant
"Johannespassionen" mix cor NORDISKA 3549
s.p. (B1323)
"St. John's Passion" [Ger] cor voc sc
PETERS 39 $3.00, ipr (B1324)
"St. John's Passion" [Ger] cor cloth PETERS
39 $7.50, ipr (B1325)
"St. John's Passion" [Ger/Eng] cor voc sc
KALMUS 6006 $4.00 (B1326)
"St. Johns' Passion" cor study sc KALMUS
F316 $3.00 (B1327)
"St. Johns Passion" cor (Bach Ges.
Edition) min sc KALMUS 406 $5.00 (B1328)
"St. Johns Passion" cor,orch/org sc KALMUS
$18.00, ipa (B1329)
"St. Johns Passion" cor sc KALMUS $18.00
(B1330)
(Atkins, Avor) "St. John's Passion" SATB,
SATB soli,org,2fl,2ob,2clar,2bsn,strings
bds,voc sc NOVELLO s.p., ipr (B1331)
(Mendel, Arthur) "Passion According To St.
John, The" SCHIRM.G voc sc $4.00, cor pts
$1.50 (B1332)
(Schering) "St. John's Passion" [Ger] cor
min sc PETERS E965 $6.50, ipr (B1333)
(Schering) "St. John's Passion" [Ger] cor
min sc-cloth PETERS E965 $10.00, ipr
(B1334)
(Zanon) [It/Ger] cor,pno RICORDI-ENG ER2445
s.p. (B1335)

La Passione Di N.S. Gesu Cristo Secondo
Matteo *S.244, Easter/Lent,cant/ora
"Passion Of Our Lord According To St.
Matthew" voc sc SCHIRM.G $3.00 (B1336)
"Passion Of Our Lord, According To St.
Matthew" SCHIRM.G voc sc $3.50, cloth
$5.00 (B1337)
"St. Matthew Passion" [Ger] SATB,orch voc
sc BROUDE BR. $3.50 (B1338)
"St. Matthews Passion" cor,orch/org sc
KALMUS $22.00, ipa (B1339)
"St. Matthew's Passion" [Ger] voc sc PETERS
4503 $3.00, ipr, cloth PETERS 4503 $7.50,
ipr, min sc PETERS E953 $7.50, ipr, min
sc-cloth PETERS E953 $10.00, ipr (B1340)
"St. Matthew's Passion" SATB,SATB soli,org,
cembalo,2orch (abridged edition) voc sc
NOVELLO rental (B1341)
"St. Matthew's Passion" cor voc sc KALMUS
6005 $3.50 (B1342)
"St. Matthews' Passion" cor (Bach Ges.
Edition) min sc KALMUS 407 $6.50 (B1343)
"St. Matthews' Passion" cor sc KALMUS
$22.00 (B1344)
(Elgar, Edward; Atkins, Ivor) "St.
Matthew's Passion" SATB,SATB soli,org,
cembalo,2orch bds,voc sc NOVELLO s.p.,
ipr (B1345)
(Read) "St. Matthew Passion, Part I" SSA
voc sc FISCHER,C PT-2703 $1.50, voc pt
FISCHER,C PT-2704 $1.00 (B1346)
(Read) "St. Matthew Passion, Part II" SSA
voc sc FISCHER,C PT-2744 $1.50, voc pt
FISCHER,C PT-2745 $1.00 (B1347)
(Williams) "St. Matthew's Passion" BELWIN
$1.50 (B1348)
(Zanon) [It/Ger] cor,pno RICORDI-ENG ER2070
s.p. (B1349)

Lad Haende Kun, Som Herren Vil *see Was Gott
Tut, Das Ist Wohlgetan [Chorale]

Lad Os Til Gud, Vor Herre *see Nun Lasst Uns
Gott, Dem Herren

Lamb Goes Forth *Lent
(Christiansen) SATB oct SOUTHERN $.25
(B1350)

Lamb Goes Forth, A *Lent
(Christiansen, P.) SATB SCHMITT 1431 $.25
(B1351)

Lamb Of God *see Christe, Du Lamm Gottes

BACH, JOHANN SEBASTIAN (cont'd.)

Lamb Of God, Lord Jesus
(Frackenpohl) SATB SHAWNEE A 459 $.30
(B1352)

Lamb Of God, Our Savior *see Christe, Du
Lamm Gottes

Lamb That For Us Was Slain, The (from Cantata
No. 21)
(Jones) [Eng/Ger] 4pt mix cor oct SCHIRM.G
11028 $.30 (B1353)

Lamb That Was Sacrificed, The *Easter
(Lockwood, N.) SATB oct PRESSER 312-40065
$.35 (B1354)

Lass, Furstin, Lass Noch Einen Strahl
(Cantata 198) S.198, cant
mix cor,SATB soli,cont,2fl,4ob,strings, 2
lutes cor pts BREITKOPF-W CHB-4698 s.p.,
ipr, sc BREITKOPF-W rental (B1355)
"Bach Cantatas Vol. 55" cor,org/orch min sc
KALMUS 859 $1.30 (B1356)
(Tombeau) "Trauermusik" [Eng] cor voc sc
KALMUS 6062 $1.50 (B1357)

Lass Furstin, Lass Noch Einen Strahl
Trauerode
mix cor,SATB soli,org,2fl,2ob,bsn,strings,
cembalo, 2 lutes BREITKOPF-L rental see
also Trauermusik (B1358)

Lass Hochster, Lass Der Hoffnung Strahl
see Trauermusik

Latom Oss Med Jesus Draga *see Hassler, Hans
Leo

Laud We The Name
(Davis) SSA oct GALAXY 1.2054.1 $.30 (B1359)

Le Calvaire
(Geveart, F.-A.) [Fr] 4pt mix cor,acap
(med) cor pts LEMOINE s.p. see from
Collection De Choeurs, cinquieme
Fascicule (B1360)

Lead Me, O Father
(Luvaas) SATB oct VOLKWEIN VB203 $.25
(B1361)

Leichtgesinnte Flattergeister (Cantata 181)
S.181, Sexa,cant
mix cor,SATB soli,org,fl,ob,trp,strings,
cembalo voc pt BREITKOPF-L CHB-2213 s.p.,
voc sc BREITKOPF-L EB-7181 s.p., ipr
(B1362)
[Ger] cor voc sc KALMUS 6622 $1.25 (B1363)
mix cor,SATB soli,cont,fl,ob,trp strings
cor pts BREITKOPF-W CHB-4681 s.p., ipr,
sc BREITKOPF-W rental (B1364)

L'esprit Soutient *S.226, mot
(Barre, J.) [Fr] 4pt mix cor,acap voc sc
DURAND see from Motets (B1365)

Let All The Multitudes Of Light *Adv/Easter/
Gen
SA,kbd (med easy) oct CONCORDIA 98-1766
$.20 (B1366)

Let Now Every Tongue Adore Thee
(Stanford) SATB oct BOOSEY 4039 $.30 (B1367)

Let Songs Of Rejoicing Be Raised *see Man
Singet Mit Freuden

Let Us Walk As Jesus Willeth (from
Schemellischen Gesangbuch)
(Wullner, Franz) 4pt mix cor cor pts
BREITKOPF-W CHB-3482 s.p. (B1368)

Leuez-Vous! Une Voix Vous Appelle (Chorale
179)
(Doyen, A.) [Fr] SATB/SMezTB voc sc LEDUC
CC9 s.p. (B1369)

Liebster Gott *see Liebster Gott, Wann Werd'
Ich Sterben

Liebster Gott, Wann Werd' Ich Sterben
(Cantata 8) S.8, Trin,cant
mix cor,SATB soli,cont,fl,ob,horn,strings
sc BREITKOPF-W PB-4508 s.p., cor pts
BREITKOPF-W CHB-4508 s.p., ipa (B1370)
"Liebster Gott" [Eng] cor voc sc KALMUS
6014 $1.00 (B1371)
"When Will God Recall My Spirit?" SATB,SATB
soli,org,fl,2ob,strings voc sc NOVELLO
rental (B1372)
(Raphael, G.) [Eng/Ger] mix cor,SATB soli,
org,2fl,2ob,2bsn,horn,strings,cembalo cor
pts BREITKOPF-L CHB-948 s.p., voc sc
BREITKOPF-L EB-7008 s.p., ipr (B1373)

Liebster Gott, Wann Werd' Ich Sterben
[Chorale] (from Liebster Jesu, Wann Werd'
Ich Sterben)
"When Will God Recall My Spirit?" SATB,pno
SCHIRM.EC 1674 $.50, ipr contains also:
Herrscher Uber Tod Und Leben, "Thou That
Life And Death Ordainst" (B1374)

Liebster Herr Jesu, Wo Bleibst
(Berger, H.L.) TTBB HANSSLER 6.5062 s.p.
contains also: Lowenstern, Matthaus
Appelles von, Nun Preiset Alle Gottes
Barmherzigkett (B1375)

Liebster Immanuel (Cantata 123) S.123, cant
mix cor,ATB soli,cont,2fl,2ob,strings cor
pts BREITKOPF-W CHB-4623 s.p., ipr, sc
BREITKOPF-W rental (B1376)
"Liebster Immanuel" [Ger] cor voc sc KALMUS
6585 $1.25 (B1377)

Liebster Immanuel *see Liebster Immanuel

Liebster Immanuel, Herzog Der Frommen
*S.123, Epiph,cant
(Todt, B.) mix cor,ATB soli,org,2fl,2ob,
bsn,strings,cembalo voc pt BREITKOPF-L
CHB-1864 s.p., voc sc BREITKOPF-L EB-7123
s.p., ipr (B1378)

Liebster Jesu, Mein Verlangen (Cantata 32)
S.32, Epiph,cant
mix cor,SB soli,cont,ob,strings sc
BREITKOPF-W PB-4532 s.p., cor pts

BACH, JOHANN SEBASTIAN (cont'd.)

BREITKOPF-W CHB-4532 s.p., ipa (B1379)
(Grischkat) SATB,SB soli,cont,ob,2vln,vla
HANSSLER 10.215 sc $5.00, cor pts $.40,
ipa (B1380)
(Raphael, G.) [Eng/Fr/Ger] mix cor,SB soli,
org,ob,strings,cembalo voc pt BREITKOPF-L
CHB-2008 s.p., voc sc BREITKOPF-L EB-7032
s.p., ipa (B1381)

Liebster Jesu, Wir Sind Hier *chorale
"Come, Together Let Us Sing" girl cor
SOUTHERN $.25 (B1382)
"Come, Together Let Us Sing" unis,pno
SCHIRM.EC 1001 $.25 (B1383)
(Glaser, V.) "Come, Together Let Us Sing"
SAB,org SCHIRM.EC 2475 $.30 (B1384)

Liebster Jesu, Wir Sind Hier, Dich Und Dein
Wort Anzuhoren
[Ger] SATB,acap (med) BAREN. BA 793 s.p.
(B1385)

Lift Your Heads *Asc,anthem
(Buck, P.C.) SATB oct ROYAL 203 s.p.
(B1386)

Live Your Life For Him
(Davies) SS/SA (easy) OXFORD 44.227 $.25
see also Two Chorales (B1387)

Live Your Life For Him Always
see Two Chorales

Lo, There Is None
(Jacobson) men cor CURWEN 50822 s.p.
(B1388)

Lob, Ehr Und Preis Sei Gott
(Clough-Leighter, H.) "Praise And Renown To
God" SATB,org SCHIRM.EC 2632 $.45 (B1389)

Lob, Ehr Und Preis Sei Gott Dem Vater (from
Magnificat)
SSATB,cont HANSSLER 31.243-1 s.p. (B1390)

Lob Und Ehre Und Weisheit Und Dank (from Ach
Ich Sehe Itzt) Trin
SATB HANSSLER 6.0100 s.p. contains also:
Nun Last Uns Gott, Dem Herren (from O
Heil'ges Geist-Und Wasserbad) (B1391)
TTBB HANSSLER 6.0136 s.p. (B1392)

Lob Und Preis Sei Gott Dem Vater (from Meine
Seel' Erhebt Den Herren) BVM
"Glory Be To The Father" see Bach, Johann
Sebastian, Meine Seel' Erhebt Den Herren
[Chorale]
SATB HANSSLER 6.202 s.p. contains also: Ist
Gott Mein Schild Und Helfersmann (from
Ich Bin Ein Guter Nacht) (Easter,B min)
(B1393)

Lobe Den Herren, Den Machtigen Konig Der
Ehren (Cantata 137) S.137, Trin,cant
mix cor,SATB soli,cont,2ob,3trp,strings,
timp sc BREITKOPF-W PB-4637 s.p., cor pts
BREITKOPF-W CHB-4637 s.p., ipa (B1394)
"Lobet Den Herrn" cor,orch sc KALMUS $3.75,
ipa (B1395)
(Grischkat) SATB,SATB soli,cont,2ob,3trp,
2vln,vla,timp HANSSLER 10.144 sc $6.50,
cor pts $.90, ipa (B1396)
(Raphael, G.) mix cor,SATB soli,org,2ob,
bsn,3trp,strings,timp,cembalo voc pt
BREITKOPF-L CHB-546 s.p., voc sc
BREITKOPF-L EB-7137 s.p., ipr (B1397)

Lobe Den Herren, Den Machtigen Konig Der
Ehren [Chorale] (from Lobe Den Herren,
Den Machtigen Konig Der Ehren) Xmas/
Thanks
see Bach, Johann Sebastian, Nun Danket Alle
Gott
SATB,3trp,timp (A flat maj) HANSSLER 6.284
s.p. contains also:
Nun Danket Alle Gott, S.252 (SATB,
2horn) (F maj) (B1398)
SATB HANSSLER 6.0759B s.p. contains also:
Nun Lasst Uns Gehn Und Treten (B1399)
SSA HANSSLER 6.1864 s.p. contains also:
Hassler, Hans Leo, Wo Gott Zum Haus Nicht
Gibt Sein Gunst (ST/SS) (B1400)

Lobe Den Herrn *see Lobe Den Herrn, Meine
Seele

Lobe Den Herrn, Meine Seele (Cantata 69)
S.69, Fest/Trin,cant
mix cor,SATB soli,cont,4ob,bsn,3trp,
strings,timp cor pts BREITKOPF-W CHB-4569
s.p., ipr, sc BREITKOPF-W rental (B1401)
mix cor,STB soli,cont,bsn,3horn,strings,
timp cor pts BREITKOPF-W CHB-4643 s.p.,
ipr, sc BREITKOPF-W rental (B1402)
"Lobe Den Herrn" [Ger] cor voc sc KALMUS
6548 $1.25 (B1403)
"Lobe Den Herrn" [Ger] cor voc sc KALMUS
6596 $1.25 (B1404)
(Raphael, G.) [Eng/Ger] mix cor,SATB soli,
org,3ob,bsn,3trp,strings,timp,cembalo voc
pt BREITKOPF-L CHB-2132 s.p., voc sc
BREITKOPF-L EB-7069 s.p., ipr (B1405)
(Todt, B.) mix cor,STB soli,cont,bsn,3horn,
strings,timp,cembalo voc pt BREITKOPF-L
CHB-2182 s.p., voc sc BREITKOPF-L EB-7143
s.p., ipr (B1406)

Lobe Den Herrn *see Lobe Den Herrn, Meine
Seele

Lobet Den Herrn *see Lobe Den Herren, Den
Machtigen Konig Der Ehren

Lobet Den Herrn, Alle Heiden (Psalm 117)
S.230, Gen,Bibl/mot
SATB,cont sc HANSSLER 31.234 s.p., ipr
(B1407)
SATB,opt cont,4inst sc HANSSLER 31.230 s.p.
(B1408)
mix cor,org voc sc BREITKOPF-L EB-7230
s.p., cor pts BREITKOPF-L CHB-541 s.p.
(B1409)
"O Praise The Lord, All Ye Nations" SATB
voc sc NOVELLO s.p. (B1410)
(Ameln, Konrad) [Ger] SATB,org,2vln,vla,vcl
(med) cor pts BAREN. BA 5135 $1.10, ipa
(B1411)
(Ameln; Wolters) SATB&SATB cont,strings,opt
2ob&bsn, 2 English horns cor pts MOSELER
s.p., ipa (B1412)
(Grove, H.) "O Praise The Lord, All Ye

Nations" SATB,acap oct PRESSER 312-40261 $.40 (B1413)
(Kruger, D.) mix cor sc BREITKOPF-W EB-6296 s.p., cor pts BREITKOPF-W CHB-3539 s.p. (B1414)
(Neumann-Buszin) "Praise The Lord, All Ye Nations" [Eng/Ger] SATB,cont PETERS 6106 $.75, ipa see from Six Motets (B1415)

Lobet Gott *see Lobet Gott In Seinen Reichen

Lobet Gott In Seinen Reichen (Cantata 11) S.11 (from Cantata No. 11) Asc,cant/ora
mix cor,SATB soli,cont,2fl,2ob,3trp, strings,timp sc BREITKOPF-W PB-4511 s.p., cor pts BREITKOPF-W CHB-4511 s.p., ipa (B1416)
"Cantate, Pour La Fete De L'ascension" SATB CHOUDENS voc sc s.p., cor pts s.p. (B1417)
"Lobet Gott" [Eng] cor voc sc KALMUS 6018 $1.00 (B1418)
"Lobet Gott" cor,orch sc KALMUS $5.00, ipa (B1419)
(Horn) SATB,SATB soli,cont,2fl,2ob,3trp, 2vln,vla,timp HANSSLER 10.118 sc $6.50, cor pts $1.00, ipa (B1420)
(Naumann, E.) mix cor,SATB soli,org,2fl, 2ob,bsn,3trp,strings,timp,cembalo cor pts BREITKOPF-L CHB-272 s.p., voc sc BREITKOPF-L EB-7011 s.p., ipr (B1421)
(Tillinghast) "Praise Our God Who Reigns In Heaven" SSA WARNER W2855 $.50 (B1422)
(West, John E.) "Praise Our God Who Reigns In Heaven" SATB,SATB soli,2fl,2ob,3trp, strings,timp,cembalo voc sc NOVELLO s.p., ipr (B1423)

Lobet Gott In Seinen Richen (Cantata 11)
(Jones, Ifor) "Praise Our God In All His Splendor" [Eng/Ger] mix cor,soli,pno voc sc SCHIRM.G $1.00 (B1424)

Lobt Gott, Ihr Christen *Adv/Xmas
SATB,acap (contains also: Burck, Joachim, Nun Ist Es Zeit Zu Singen) voc pt DOBLINGER s.p. see also ADVENT UND WEIHNACHT, HEFT 1 (B1425)
SATB HANSSLER 6.257 s.p. contains also: Cruger, Johann, Frohlich Soll Mein Herze Springen; Bodenschatz, Erhard, Gelobet Seist Du, Jesu Christ; Jeep, Johann, Mit Ernst, O Menschenkinder; Bach, Johann Sebastian, Ich Steh An Deiner Krippen Hier (from Weihnachts-Oratorium) (Xmas); Praetorius, Jakob, Vom Himmel Hoch, Da Komm (B1426)

Lobt Gott, Ihr Christen Allzugleich (from Susser Trost, Mein Jesus Kommt)
see Bach, Johann Sebastian, Uns Ist Ein Kindlein Heut Geborn
SATB HANSSLER 6.288 s.p. contains also: Ich Steh An Deiner Krippen Hier; Vom Himmel Hoch, Da Komm Ich Her (from Weihnachts-Oratorium); Gelobet Seist Du, Jesu Christ (B1427)

Lobt Gott, Ihr Christen [Chorale]
see Weihnachtschorale-III
see Weihnachtschorale-I

Loflied (Den Hogen God Alleen Zij Eer)
mix cor ALSBACH&D s.p. (B1428)

Lofpsalm (Looft, Looft Nu Aller Heeren Heer)
mix cor ALSBACH&D s.p. (B1429)

Lofzegging (Lof Zij Den Heer)
mix cor ALSBACH&D s.p. (B1430)

Look Down, O Holy Dove (from Spirit Also Helpeth Us, The)
(Cain) SATB,opt kbd oct PRO ART 1339 $.18 (B1431)

Lord Bless You, The *Gen,anthem
SA/TB,kbd (med easy) oct CONCORDIA 98-1474 $.25 (B1432)
(Becker, Arthur C.) SATB (easy) oct GIA G1539 $.25 (B1433)

Lord, Enter Not Into Wrath *see Herr, Gehe Nicht Ins Gericht [Chorale]

Lord God, Great Master Of Creation *Marriage,cant
(Hudson) [Eng/Ger] mix cor,SATB soli,cont, 3trp,strings,timp, 2 oboe d'amores voc sc CURWEN C03734 s.p., sc CURWEN rental, ipr (B1434)

Lord Hath Helped Me Hitherto, The
see Four Chorale Harmonizations

Lord Is A Sun, The *see Gott, Der Herr, Ist Sonn' Und Schild

Lord Is A Sun And Shield, The *see Gott Der Herr Ist Sonn' Und Schild

Lord Is Merciful, The *see Suscepit Israel

Lord Is My Shepherd, The *see Der Herr Ist Mein Getreuer Hirt

Lord Jesus Christ, Thou Prince Of Peace *Epiph/Gen/Lent
SATB,vln,vcl (med easy) oct CONCORDIA 98-1955 $.30, ipa (B1435)

Lord Jesus Thy Dear Angel Send (from St. John Passion) chorale
(Barrow, R.) TTBB,acap SCHIRM.EC 2143 $.22 (B1436)

Lord My Faithful Shepherd Is, The *anthem
(Jennings) SATB (med) oct AUGSBURG 1538 $.35 (B1437)

Lord My Guide, The [Chorale] *see Der Herr Ist Mein Getreuer Hirt' [Chorale]

Lord My Shepherd E'er Shall Be, The *see Allein Gott In Der Hoh' Sei Ehr'

Lord Our Redeemer (from St. John Passion)
SATB,pno SCHIRM.EC 1117 $.40, ipr (B1438)

Lord, Thee I Love With All My Heart
see Bach, Johann Sebastian, Jesus, Priceless Treasure

Lord, Thou Light Of All My Being
(Kinsman) SATB oct BOURNE SB108 $.30 (B1439)

Lord Will Not Suffer, The
SATB PATERSON 1567 s.p. (B1440)

Love Divine, All Loves Excelling *hymn
PATERSON s.p. see also English Hymns Adapted To Bach's Chorales (B1441)
(Northcote, Sydney) unis oct CURWEN 10401 $.25 (B1442)

Lukas-Passion *S.246, Psntd
mix cor,SATB soli,org,2fl,2ob,bsn,strings, English horn BREITKOPF-L rental (B1443)
"St. Lukes' Passion" cor min sc KALMUS 902 $1.30 (B1444)

Lukaspassion *Psntd
(Radeke, Winfried) mix cor,SATB soli,org, 2fl,2ob,2bsn,strings voc sc BREITKOPF-W EB-6574 s.p., voc pt BREITKOPF-W CHB-3468 s.p., ipr, sc BREITKOPF-W rental (B1445)

Luther's Cradle Hymn *hymn
unis oct NOVELLO 48.1631.05 s.p. (B1446)

Mache Dich *see Mache Dich, Mein Geist, Bereit

Mache Dich, Mein Geist, Bereit (Cantata 115) S.115, Trin,cant
mix cor,SATB soli,cont,fl,ob,horn,strings voc pt BREITKOPF-W CHB-4615 s.p., ipr, sc BREITKOPF-W rental (B1447)
"Mache Dich" [Eng] cor voc sc KALMUS 6049 $1.00 (B1448)
(Atkins, Ivor) "Ready Be, My Soul, Alway" SATB,SATB soli,org,2fl,2ob,trp,strings voc sc NOVELLO s.p., ipr (B1449)
(Raphael, G.) [Eng/Ger] mix cor,SATB soli, org,fl,ob,horn,strings,cembalo sc BREITKOPF-L PB-2965 s.p., voc sc BREITKOPF-L EB-7115 s.p., ipr (B1450)

Machet Die Tore Weit (Psalm 24) Adv,cant
[Ger] men cor,S/T solo,org/orch HUG s.p., ipr (B1451)
[Ger] mix cor,A solo,org/orch HUG s.p., ipr (B1452)

Mach's Mit Mir, Gott, Nach Deiner Gut'
see Bach, Johann Sebastian, Ermuntre Dich, Mein Schwacher Geist

Magnificat *cant/Magnif
[Eng/Lat] 5pt mix cor,SSATB soli,org/pno voc sc SCHIRM.G $1.00 (B1453)
study sc UNIVER. PH.99 $1.30 (B1454)
BELWIN $1.25 (B1455)
SATB (urtext) SCHIRM.EC $.75 (B1456)
[Lat] cor,SATB soli,orch cor pts SALABERT-US $1.25 (B1457)
cor voc sc KALMUS 6003 $1.00 (B1458)
cor sc KALMUS $8.00 (B1459)
cor,orch/org sc KALMUS $8.00, ipa (B1460)
(Ehret, Walter) 4pt mix cor,pno/2ob&2horn& strings LAWSON $1.75, ipr (B1461)
(Schering) SSATB,ATB soli min sc PETERS E964 $2.00 (B1462)
(Straube-Roth) SSATB,ATB soli voc sc PETERS 40 $1.00 (B1463)
(Straube-Roth) SSATB,ATB soli sc PETERS 29A $8.00, ipa (B1464)

Magnificat D-Dur *S.243, Magnif
[Ger] min sc BAREN. TP 2 $2.25 (B1465)
[Ger] (D maj) DEUTSCHER 5003B min sc-pap $1.25, min sc-cloth $2.00 (B1466)
(Durr, Alfred) [Ger] SSATB,SSATB soli,org, cont,2vln,vla (D maj,med) sc BAREN. BA 5103 $12.00, cor pts BAREN. BA 5103 $1.10, voc sc BAREN. BA 5103A $3.25, ipa contains also: Vier Einlagesatzen Der Es-Dur Fassung, S.243a (B1467)
(Jadassohn, S.) 5pt mix cor,SSATB soli,org, 2fl,2ob,2bsn,3trp,strings,timp,cembalo, 2 English horns (D maj) voc pt BREITKOPF-L CHB-261 s.p., voc sc BREITKOPF-L EB-3360 s.p., ipr (B1468)

Magnificat Es-Dur *S.243a
[Ger] min sc BAREN. TP 58 s.p. (B1469)

Magnificat In D *Magnif
[Eng/Lat] SSATB,SMezATB soli,org,2fl,3ob, 2bsn,3trp,strings,timp,cembalo voc sc NOVELLO s.p., ipr (B1470)

Make A Joyful Noise
(Nelhybel, V.) SATB,org oct KERBY 6 $.40 (B1471)
(Nelhybel, V.) SATB oct KERBY 678 $.40 (B1472)

Man Singet Mit Freuden (Cantata 149)
(Pointer, John) "Let Songs Of Rejoicing Be Raised" SATB,SATB soli,3ob,bsn,3trp, strings,timp voc sc NOVELLO rental (B1473)

Man Singet Mit Freuden *see Man Singet Mit Freuden Vom Sieg

Man Singet Mit Freuden Vom Sieg (Cantata 149) S.149, ASD,cant
mix cor,SATB soli,cont,3ob,bsn,3trp, strings,timp sc BREITKOPF-W PB-4649 s.p., cor pts BREITKOPF-W CHB-4649 s.p., ipa (B1474)
"Man Singet Mit Freuden" [Ger] cor voc sc KALMUS 6602 $1.25 (B1475)
(Todt, B.) mix cor,SATB soli,org,3ob,2bsn, 3trp,strings,timp,cembalo sc BREITKOPF-L PB-2999 s.p., voc pt BREITKOPF-L CHB-2026 s.p., voc sc BREITKOPF-L EB-7149 s.p., ipa (B1476)

Markuspassion *S.247, Psntd
(Hellmann) "St. Mark's Passion" [Eng/Ger] SATB,SAT soli,cont,2fl,bsn,2vln,vla,vcl, bvl, 2-English horns, 2-lutes HANSSLER 10.209 cor pts $.60, ipa, sc $15.00, cor pts $1.25, ipa (B1477)

Mass, B Minor *Mass
(Damrosch) [Lat] mix cor,soli,pno SCHIRM.G voc sc $3.00, cloth $4.50 (B1478)

Mass In A *see Messe A-Dur

Mass In B Minor *see Messe H-Moll

Mass In F *see Messe F-Dur

Mass In G *see Messe G-Dur

Mass In G Minor *see Messe G-Moll

Matthaus Passione
(Zanon, M.) "La Passion De N. S. Jesucristo, Segun San Mateo" [Ger/Span] dbl cor,soli,orch RICORDI-ARG BA 10221 s.p. (B1479)

Matthauspassion *S.244, Lent/Psntd,cant/ chorale
mix cor (includes text and chorales) MOSELER s.p. (B1480)
"Passion Selon Saint Mathieu" SATB CHOUDENS voc sc s.p., cor pts s.p. (B1481)
"St. Matthew's Passion" BELWIN $2.25 (B1482)
(Schneider, M.) dbl cor,SSAATTBB soli,2org, 4fl,4ob,2bsn,strings voc pt BREITKOPF-L CHB-2800 s.p., voc sc BREITKOPF-L EB-5700 s.p., ipa (B1483)
(Schneider, Max) mix cor&mix cor,SATB soli, 1-2org,cont,2fl,2rec,6ob,2vln,2vla,vcl, bvl,bsn sc BREITKOPF-W PB-4950 s.p., ipa (B1484)

May God Grant You Peace
(Vree) TB,pno oct LAWSON 51636 $.30 (B1485)

May God Smile On You *see Der Herr Segne Euch

Mein Gott *see Mein Gott, Wie Lang', Ach Lange

Mein Gott, Wie Lang *S.155, Epiph,cant
(Horn) SATB,SATB soli,cont,bsn,2vln,vla HANSSLER 10.132 sc $3.50, cor pts $.60, ipa (B1486)

Mein Gott, Wie Lang', Ach Lange (Cantata 155) S.155, Epiph,cant
mix cor,SATB soli,cont,bsn,strings cor pts BREITKOPF-W CHB-4655 s.p., ipr, sc BREITKOPF-W rental (B1487)
"Mein Gott" cor,orch sc KALMUS $4.00, ipa (B1488)
(Raphael, G.) [Eng/Ger] mix cor,SATB soli, org,bsn,strings,cembalo voc pt BREITKOPF-L CHB-1953 s.p., voc sc BREITKOPF-L EB-7155 s.p., ipr (B1489)

Mein Liebster Jesus *see Mein Liebster Jesus Ist Verloren

Mein Liebster Jesus Ist Verloren (Cantata 154) S.154, Epiph,cant
[Fr/Ger] mix cor,ATB soli,org,2ob,strings, cembalo, 2 English horns voc pt BREITKOPF-L CHB-1968 s.p., voc sc BREITKOPF-L EB-7154 s.p., ipr (B1490)
mix cor,ATB soli,cont,4ob,strings cor pts BREITKOPF-W CHB-4654 s.p., ipr, sc BREITKOPF-W rental (B1491)
"Mein Liebster Jesus" [Ger] cor voc sc KALMUS 6604 $1.25 (B1492)

Mein Seel' Erhebt Den Herren (Cantata 10) S.10, cant/Magnif
mix cor,SATB soli,cont,2ob,trp,strings sc BREITKOPF-W PB-4510 s.p., cor pts BREITKOPF-W CHB-4510 s.p., ipa (B1493)
"My Soul Doth Magnify The Lord" [Eng/Ger] mix cor,SATB soli,cont,2ob,trp,strings voc sc CURWEN C03741 s.p., sc CURWEN rental, ipr (B1494)

Mein Susser Trost (Cantata 151)
(Gui, Vittorio) [Eng/Ger] mix cor,soli,org, 2fl,2ob,strings cmplt ed BOOSEY rental (B1495)

Meine Seel' Erhebt Den Herren *S.10, BVM, cant
(Raphael, G.) mix cor,SATB soli,org,2ob, bsn,trp,strings,cembalo cor pts BREITKOPF-L CHB-1783 s.p., voc sc BREITKOPF-L EB-7010 s.p., ipr (B1496)

Meine Seel' Erhebt Den Herren [Chorale] (from Meine Seel' Erhebt Den Herren)
"My Soul Doth Magnify The Lord" SATB,pno SCHIRM.EC 1614 $.45, ipr contains also: Lob Und Preis Sei Gott Dem Vater, "Glory Be To The Father" (B1497)

Meine Seele Ruhmt *S.189, cant
[Ger] cor voc sc KALMUS 6630 $1.25 (B1498)

Meine Seufzer *see Meine Seufzer, Meine Tranen

Meine Seufzer, Meine Tranen (Cantata 13) S.13, Epiph,cant
mix cor,SATB soli,cont,2fl,ob,strings cor pts BREITKOPF-W CHB-4513 s.p., ipr, sc BREITKOPF-W rental (B1499)
"Meine Seufzer" [Ger] cor voc sc KALMUS 6526 $1.25 (B1500)
(Todt, B.) mix cor,SATB soli,org,2fl,ob, bsn,strings,cembalo voc pt BREITKOPF-L CHB-2188 s.p., voc sc BREITKOPF-L EB-7013 s.p., ipr (B1501)

Meinen Jesum Lass Ich Nicht (Cantata 124) S.124 (from Ich Lasse Dich Nicht, Du Segnest Mich Denn) BVM/Epiph,cant
SATB HANSSLER 6.321 s.p. contains also: Bach, Johann Sebastian, Meinen Jesum Lass Ich Nicht (Kurig, Hans) (SA& SATB);
Kurig, Hans-Hermann, Denn Ist Das Jahr, Dein Ist Die Ziet (SATB/unis&SATB);
Kurig, Hans-Hermann, Lobet Den Herren, Alle, Die Ihn Ehren (unis&SATB);
Kurig, Hans-Hermann, Meinen Jesum Lass Ich Nicht (SA) (B1502)
mix cor,SATB soli,cont,ob,horn,strings sc

BACH, JOHANN SEBASTIAN (cont'd.)

BREITKOPF-W PB-4624 s.p., cor pts
BREITKOPF-W CHB-4624 s.p., ipa (B1503)
(Raphael, G.) [Eng/Ger] mix cor,SATB soli,
org,ob,bsn,horn,strings,cembalo voc pt
BREITKOPF-L CHB-549 s.p., voc sc
BREITKOPF-L EB-7124 s.p., ipr (B1504)

Meinen Jesum Lass Ich Nicht
see Bach, Johann Sebastian, Meinen Jesum
Lass Ich Nicht

Men And Angels Now Adore Thee (from Cantata
140)
4pt mix cor oct CURWEN 11129 $.25 (B1505)
mix cor CURWEN 61496 s.p. (B1506)

Mer Hahn En Neue Oberkeet (from Peasant
Cantata)
"Spring Song" [Ger/Eng] SATB,pno SCHIRM.EC
1116 (B1507)

Messe A-Dur *S.234, Mass
mix cor,SAB soli,org,2ob,strings (A maj)
cor pts BREITKOPF-W CHB-3477 s.p., ipr,
sc BREITKOPF-W rental (B1508)
"Mass In A" [Lat] SATB,SAB soli,orch cor
pts PETERS 1018B $2.00, sc PETERS 25B
$10.00 (B1509)
(Jadassohn, S.) mix cor,SAB soli,org,2fl,
strings,cembalo (A maj) voc pt BREITKOPF-
L CHB-708 s.p., voc sc BREITKOPF-L
EB-4063 s.p. (B1510)

Messe F-Dur *S.233, Mass
mix cor,SAB soli,org,2fl,2bsn,2horn,
strings,cembalo (F maj) voc sc BREITKOPF-
L EB-4062 s.p., ipr (B1511)
mix cor,SAB soli,org,2ob,2bsn,2horn,strings
(F maj) voc pt BREITKOPF-W CHB-707 s.p.,
ipr, sc BREITKOPF-W rental (B1512)
"Mass In F" [Lat] SATB,SAB soli,orch cor
pts PETERS 1018A $2.00, sc PETERS 25A
$10.00, ipa (B1513)

Messe G-Dur *S.236, Mass
mix cor,SATB soli,org,2ob,strings,cembalo
(G maj) sc BREITKOPF-L rental (B1514)
mix cor,SATB soli,2ob,strings (G maj)
BREITKOPF-W rental (B1515)
"Mass In G" [Lat] SATB,SATB soli,orch cor
pts PETERS 1018D $2.00, sc PETERS 25D
$10.00, ipa (B1516)

Messe G-Moll *S.235, Mass
mix cor,ATB soli,2ob,strings (G min) sc
BREITKOPF-L rental (B1517)
"Mass In G Minor" [Lat] SATB,ATB soli,orch
cor pts PETERS 1018C $2.00, sc PETERS 25C
$10.00 (B1518)

Messe H-Moll *S.232, Mass
[Ger] (B min) DEUTSCHER 5001B min sc-pap
$4.50, min sc-cloth $6.00 (B1519)
"B Minor Mass" cor sc KALMUS $26.00 (B1520)
"Mass In B Minor" [Lat] voc sc PETERS 37
$3.00, ipr, cloth PETERS 37 $7.50, ipr,
min sc PETERS E959 $7.50, min sc-cloth
PETERS E959 $10.00 (B1521)
"Mass In B Minor" BELWIN $2.25 (B1522)
"Mass In B Minor" [Lat] SSATB,SSATB soli,
org,2fl,3ob,2clar,2bsn,horn,3trp,strings,
timp,cembalo bds,voc sc NOVELLO s.p., ipr
(B1523)
"Mass In B Minor" cor voc sc KALMUS 6004
$3.00 (B1524)
"Mass In B Minor" cor,orch/org (B min) sc
KALMUS $26.00, ipa (B1525)
(Kretzschmar, H.) mix cor,SATB soli,org,
2fl,3ob,2bsn,3trp,horn,timp,strings, 2
English horns (B min) sc BREITKOPF-L
PB-629 s.p., voc pt BREITKOPF-L CHB-26
s.p., voc sc BREITKOPF-L EB-3105 s.p. (B1526)
(Smend) mix cor,org/cont/orch (B min) sc
DEUTSCHER 5001 s.p., voc sc DEUTSCHER
5001A s.p., study sc DEUTSCHER 5001B
s.p., ipa, cmplt ed DEUTSCHER 5502 s.p.
(B1527)
(Smend, Friedrich) [Ger] SSATB&SATB&SATB,
SSATB soli,org,cont,2vln,vla (B min,diff)
sc BAREN. BA 5001 $30.75, voc sc BAREN.
BA 5102 $3.60, ipa, voc sc BAREN.
BA 5102A $5.50, min sc BAREN. TP 1 $8.25
(B1528)

Mighty Fortress Is Our God, A *Fest/Gen/Refm
see Three Chorales
SATB,acap (med easy) oct CONCORDIA 98-1036
$.15 (B1529)
(Damrosch) SATB WARNER W2835 $.30 (B1530)
(Maddy, J.E.) SATB CRESCENDO $.20 (B1531)

Missa Brevis *Mass
(G maj) BELWIN $2.00 (B1532)

Missa Brevis In A Major *Mass
cor voc sc KALMUS 6009 $1.25 (B1533)
cor,orch sc KALMUS $5.00, ipa (B1534)

Missa Brevis In F Major *Mass
cor voc sc KALMUS 6008 $1.25 (B1535)
cor,orch sc KALMUS $5.00, ipa (B1536)

Missa Brevis In G Major *Mass
cor voc sc KALMUS 6010 $1.25 (B1537)
cor,orch sc KALMUS $8.00, ipa (B1538)

Missa Brevis In G Minor *Mass
cor voc sc KALMUS 60077 $1.25 (B1539)
cor,orch sc KALMUS $5.00, ipa (B1540)

Mistletoe And Holly Bright *Xmas
(Whitford) 3pt wom cor oct SCHIRM.G 9825
$.25 (B1541)

Mit Fried' Und Freud *see Mit Fried' Und
Freud' Ich Fahr' Dahin

Mit Fried Und Freud Ich Fahr Dahin (Cantata
125) S.125, BVM,cant
mix cor,ATB soli,org,fl,ob,horn,strings,
cembalo voc pt BREITKOPF-L CHB-1481 s.p.,
voc sc BREITKOPF-L EB-7125 s.p., ipr (B1542)
mix cor,ATB soli,cont,fl,2ob,horn,strings
cor pts BREITKOPF-W CHB-4625 s.p., ipr,
sc BREITKOPF-W rental (B1543)
"Mit Fried' Und Freud" [Ger] cor voc sc
KALMUS 6587 $1.25 (B1544)

Mit Fried Und Freud Ich Fahr Dahin [Chorale]
(from Mit Fried' Und Freud' Ich Fahr'
Dahin)
see Bach, Johann Sebastian, Wie Schon
Leuchtet Der Morgenstern [Chorale]

Morgengebed
mix cor ALSBACH&D s.p. (B1545)

Morgenlied (Hoe Glansrijk Aller Heemlen Heer)
mix cor ALSBACH&D s.p. (B1546)

Motet 1 *see Singet Dem Herrn Ein Neues Lied

Motet 2 *see Der Geist Hilft Unser
Schwachheit Auf

Motet 2 *see Der Geist Hilft Unsrer
Schwachheit Auf

Motet 3 *see Jesu, Meine Freude

Motet 4 *see Furchte Dich Nicht

Motet 4 *see Furchte Dich Nicht, Ich Bin Bei
Dir

Motet 5 *see Komm, Jesu, Komm

Motet 6 *see Lobet Den Herrn, Alle Heiden

Motets *see Chantez Au Seigneur, S.225;
Gloire, Louange, Honneur A Dieu, S.230;
Jesus, Toi Mon Bonheur, S.227; L'esprit
Soutient, S.226; Ne Crains Pas, Je Suis
Tout Pres De Toi, S.228; Viens, Jesus,
Viens!, S.229 (B1547)

Motets And Chorale "Sei Lob Und Preis"
*CC7U,mot
[Ger] SATB/SSATB,acap HINRICHSEN P4592 cor
pts s.p., voc pt s.p. (B1548)

My Chosen King (from Christmas Oratorio)
see Two Chorales

My Fainting Soul, Awaken Now *see Ermuntre
Dich, Mein Schwacher Geist

My Faith Is Still Secure
(Mueller) 2pt jr cor FISCHER,C CM 6890 $.20
(B1549)

My Heart Ever Faithful (from Also Hat Gott
Die Welt Geliebt) Xmas/Gen
SA oct LORENZ 5367 $.30 (B1550)
unis,org SCHIRM.EC 1009 $.25 (B1551)
unis,orch oct NOVELLO 48.1069.04 s.p., ipr
(B1552)
(Bampton, R.) SA oct PRESSER 312-40474 $.30
(B1553)
(Cain) SATB oct FOX R178 $.30 (B1554)
(Cain) SSA oct FOX R107 $.30 (B1555)
(Rigby, W.) SSA oct NOVELLO 51.0542.00 s.p.
(B1556)
(Scarmolin) SATB oct PRO ART 1569 $.25
(B1557)
(Whittaker, W. Gillies) unis (med) oct
OXFORD 45.279 $.30 (B1558)

My Saviour Dear, What Woe Of Soul *Gen/Lent,
chorale
(Lundquist) SATB,acap (med) oct WILLIS 5503
$.16 (B1559)

My Shepherd
(Hirt) 2pt WARNER $.30 (B1560)

My Soul Awake And Render *chorale
(Fewell, C.M.) SAB,acap SCHIRM.EC 2261 $.20
(B1561)

My Soul Doth Magnify The Lord *see Mein
Seel' Erhebt Den Herren

My Soul Doth Magnify The Lord *see Meine
Seel' Erhebt Den Herren [Chorale]

My Soul Rejoices *see Et Exultavit

My Soul, There Is A Country *see Der Leib
Zwar In Der Erden

My Spirit *see Ich Hatte Viel Bekummernis

My Spirit, Be Joyful *see Wie Will Ich Mich
Freuen

My Spirit Was In Heaviness *see Ich Hatte
Viel Bekummernis

Nach Dir *see Nach Dir, Herr, Verlanget Mich

Nach Dir, Herr, Verlanget Mich (Cantata 150)
S.150, Gen,cant
mix cor,SATB soli,cont,bsn,strings sc
BREITKOPF-W PB-4650 s.p., cor pts
BREITKOPF-W CHB-4650 s.p., ipa (B1562)
"Nach Dir" [Eng] cor voc sc KALMUS 6056
$1.00 (B1563)
(Raphael, G.) [Eng/Ger] mix cor,SATB soli,
org,bsn,strings,cembalo voc pt BREITKOPF-
L CHB-1500 s.p., voc sc BREITKOPF-L
EB-7150 s.p., ipr (B1564)

Ne Crains Pas, Je Suis Tout Pres De Toi
*S.228, mot
(Barre, J.) [Fr] 4pt mix cor,acap voc sc
DURAND see from Motets (B1565)

New-Born Babe, The *see Das Neugebor'ne
Kindelein

Nicht So Traurig
(Mattfeld, V.) "Be Not Downcast" [Ger/Eng]
unis,org SCHIRM.EC 2555 see from Six
Sacred Songs (B1566)

Nimm Von Uns *see Nimm Von Uns, Herr, Du
Treuer Gott

Nimm Von Uns, Herr, Du Treuer Gott (Cantata
101) S.101, Trin,cant
mix cor,SATB soli,cont,fl,3ob,trp,3trom,
strings cor pts BREITKOPF-W CHB-4601
s.p., ipr, sc BREITKOPF-W rental (B1567)
"Nimm Von Uns" [Ger] cor voc sc KALMUS 6569
$1.25 (B1568)
(Todt, B.) mix cor,SATB soli,org,fl,3ob,

BACH, JOHANN SEBASTIAN (cont'd.)

bsn,trp,3trom,strings,cembalo voc sc
BREITKOPF-L EB-7101 s.p., ipr (B1569)

Nimm Was *see Nimm, Was Dein Ist, Und Gehe
Hin

Nimm, Was Dein Ist *see Nimm, Was Dein Ist,
Und Gehe Hin

Nimm, Was Dein Ist, Und Gehe Hin (Cantata
144) S.144, Septua,cant
mix cor,SAT soli,cont,ob,strings cor pts
BREITKOPF-W CHB-4644 s.p., ipr, sc
BREITKOPF-W rental (B1570)
"Nimm Was" cor,orch sc KALMUS $5.00, ipa
(B1571)
"Nimm, Was Dein Ist" [Ger] cor voc sc
KALMUS 6597 $1.25 (B1572)
(Todt, B.) mix cor,SAT soli,org,ob,strings,
cembalo voc pt BREITKOPF-L CHB-1960 s.p.,
voc sc BREITKOPF-L EB-7144 s.p., ipr
(B1573)

Notre Dieu Seul Est Le Maitre Eternel *see
Nun Ist Das Heil Und Die Kraft

Now Come, Let Us Hasten *Easter,cant
[Eng] cor voc sc KALMUS 6016 $2.00 (B1574)

Now Come, The World's Salvation *see Nun
Komm, Der Heiden Heiland

Now I Know That Thou Art Loving *see Nun,
Ich Weiss, Du Wirst Mir Stillen

Now Let All The Heavens Adore Thee (from
Sleeper's Wake) Xmas/Gen
SATB oct PRESSER 332-14563 $.25 (B1575)
SATB oct FISCHER,C CM-6265 $.25 (B1576)
(Hinkle, N.) SSA oct PRESSER 332-14573 $.30
(B1577)
(Runkel) SAB oct PRESSER 332-15058 $.25
(B1578)

Now Let Every Tongue Adore Thee (from Wachet
Auf, Ruft Uns Die Stimme)
TTBB,org/pno BOSTON 2816 $.30 (B1579)
SSA,org/pno BOSTON 11679 $.30 (B1580)
SATB,org/pno BOSTON 1892 $.30 (B1581)
SSA oct BELWIN 1941 $.25 (B1582)
SATB,acap oct BELWIN 779 $.30 (B1583)
SSA,acap oct BELWIN 1941 $.25 (B1584)
SATB,acap oct BELWIN 779 $.25 (B1585)
SATB KJOS 7025 $.30 (B1586)
(Cain) SAB KJOS 5702 $.30 (B1587)
(Pitcher, Gladys) 3pt mix cor,pno (med) oct
WILLIS 8494 $.20 (B1588)
(Scott) SATB oct SPRATT 533 $.25 (B1589)

Now Let Heaven And Earth Adore Thee (from
Wachet Auf, Ruft Uns Die Stimme)
SATB oct BELWIN 64044 $.25 (B1590)

Now Praise We Great And Famous Men *see Ach
Gott Und Herr

Now Rest In Peace
see Two Songs

Now Shall The Grace *see Nun Ist Das Heil

Now Thank We All Our God *see Nun Danket
Alle Gott

Now The Day Is Over
SATB,opt org (easy) oct WILLIS 513 $.10
(B1591)
(Harris) 3pt wom cor,acap,opt pno (easy)
oct WILLIS 5531 $.12 (B1592)

Nu Ar Det Sommar Blid *hymn
mix cor NORDISKA 4258 s.p. (B1593)

Nu Gronskar Det
TTB NORDISKA 4838 s.p. (B1594)

Nu Kom Var Fralsnings Herre *see Nun Komm,
Der Heiden Heiland

Nu Tackar Gud, Allt Folk
mix cor NORDISKA 4141 s.p. (B1595)

Nu Vaer Os, Gud, Miskundelig *see Es Woll
Uns Gott Genadig Sein

Nun Danket Alle Gott (Cantata 192) S.252
(from Gott, Der Herr, Ist Sonn Und
Schild) Ded/Gen/Thanks,anthem/cant/
chorale
see Bach, Johann Sebastian, Lobe Den
Herren, Den Machtigen Konig Der Ehren
[Chorale]
see Bach, Johann Sebastian, O Ewigkeit, Du
Donnerwort
see Fiebig, Kurt, Sollt Ich Meinem Gott
Nicht Singen
SATB,2horn org HANSSLER 6.018 s.p.
contains also:
Nun Lob, Mein Seel, Den Herren (from
Die Himmel Erzahlen Die Ehre Gottes)
(SATB,3trp,timp) (Trin,A flat maj);
Lobe Den Herren, Den Machtigen Konig
Der Ehren [Chorale] (from Lobe Den
Herren, Den Machtigen Konig Der
Ehren) (SATB,3trp,timp) (Circum,A
flat maj);
Du Friedefurst, Herr Jesu Christ (from
Halt' In Gedachtnis Jesum Christ)
(SATB) (Easter,G maj);
Nun Lasst Uns Gott, Dem Herren (from
Gott, Der Herr, Ist Sonn' Und Schild)
(SATB,2horn,timp) (Refm,A flat maj);
Wachet Auf, Ruft Uns Die Stimme
[Chorale] (from Wachet Auf, Ruft Uns
Die Stimme) (SATB) (Trin) (B1596)
mix cor,SB soli,org,2fl,2ob,bsn,strings,
cembalo (incomplete) voc pt BREITKOPF-L
CHB-1966 s.p., voc sc BREITKOPF-L EB-7192
s.p., ipr (B1597)
[Ger] cor voc sc KALMUS 6632 $1.25 (B1598)
mix cor,SB soli,cont,2fl,2ob,strings sc
BREITKOPF-W PB-4692 s.p., cor pts
BREITKOPF-W CHB-4692 s.p., ipa (B1599)
"Now Thank We All Our God" SATB,org,bsn/
vcl,trp,timp (med easy) oct CONCORDIA
98-2102 $.35, ipa (B1600)
"Now Thank We All Our God" mix cor SOUTHERN
$.30 (B1601)
"Now Thank We All Our God" SATB,pno

BACH, JOHANN SEBASTIAN (cont'd.)

SCHIRM.EC 1157 $.30, ipr (B1602)
"Now Thank We All Our God" SATB oct NOVELLO 50.0230.10 s.p. (B1603)
"Now Thank We All Our God" mix cor oct NOVELLO 50.0232.10 s.p. (B1604)
(Chambers) "Now Thank We All Our God" SATB oct LESLIE 4006 (B1605)
(Creston, Paul) "Now Thank We All Our God" SATB oct FISCHER,J 9696 $.35 (B1606)
(Davies, L.H.) "Now Thank We All Our God" 2pt ASHDOWN E.A.318 s.p. (B1607)
(Ferguson) "Now Thank We All Our God" SATB FLAMMER A 5403 $.30 (B1608)
(Frackenpohl) "Now Thank We All Our God" SATB SHAWNEE A 460 $.30 (B1609)
(Geer, E.) "Now Thank We All Our God" SSAA, pno SCHIRM.EC 876 $.18, ipr (B1610)
(Hamill) "Now Thank We All Our God" SSA FLAMMER B 5110 $.25 (B1611)
(Hamill) "Now Thank We All Our God" SAB FLAMMER D5032 $.30 (B1612)
(Hardwicke) "Now Thank We All Our God" SATB oct PRO ART 2413 $.25 (B1613)
(Jones, Ifor) "Now Thank We All Our God" mix cor,soli,pno voc sc SCHIRM.G $1.25 (B1614)
(Sampson, Godfrey) "Now Thank We All Our God" unis&desc oct NOVELLO 40.1176.07 s.p. (B1615)
(Sampson, Godfrey) "Now Thank We All Our God" mix cor oct NOVELLO 40.1176.07 s.p. (B1616)
(Tepper, Albert) "Now Thank We All Our God" SAB oct BELWIN 1754 $.25 (B1617)
(Vogel, Moritz; Nagler, Franciscus) [Ger] wom cor&jr cor,org,opt strings HUG 22A s.p. (B1618)

Nun, Ich Weiss, Du Wirst Mir Stillen (from Herr, Gehe Nicht Ins Gericht)
"Now I Know That Thou Art Loving" see Bach, Johann Sebastian, Herr, Gehe Nicht Ins Gericht [Chorale]
"Now I Know That Thou Art Loving" SATB,pno SCHIRM.EC 1731 $.25, ipr (B1619)

Nun Ist *see Nun Ist Das Heil Und Die Kraft

Nun Ist Das Heil (Cantata 50)
"Now Shall The Grace" dbl cor,org,3ob,3trp, strings,timp voc sc NOVELLO s.p., ipr (B1620)
"Now Shall The Grace" study sc UNIVER. PH. 111 $1.15 (B1621)
"Now Shall The Grace" SATB BELWIN $.60 (B1622)

Nun Ist Das Heil Und Die Kraft (Cantata 50) S.50, ASD,cant
SATB&SATB,cont,3ob,3trp,strings,timp sc BREITKOPF-W PB-4550 s.p., cor pts BREITKOPF-W CHB-4550 s.p., ipa (B1623)
"Notre Dieu Seul Est Le Maitre Eternel" dbl cor CHOUDENS voc sc s.p., cor pts s.p. (B1624)
"Nun Ist" [Eng] cor voc sc KALMUS 6032 $1.00 (B1625)
"Nun Ist" cor,orch sc KALMUS $3.00, ipa (B1626)
(Horn) dbl cor,cont,3ob,3trp,2vln,vla,timp HANSSLER 10. 123 sc $4.50, cor pts $1.25, ipa (B1627)
(Raphael, G.) [Eng/Ger] 8pt mix cor,org, 2ob,3trp,strings,cembalo, English horn voc pt BREITKOPF-L CHB-252 s.p., voc sc BREITKOPF-L EB-7050 s.p., ipr (B1628)

Nun Komm *see Nun Komm, Der Heiden Heiland

Nun Komm', Der Heiden Heiland (Cantata 61) Adv
(Atkins, Ivor) "Come, Redeemer Of Our Race" SATB,STB soli,org,bsn,strings voc sc NOVELLO s.p., ipr (B1629)

Nun Komm, Der Heiden Heiland [Chorale] (from Schwingt Freudig Euch Empor)
see Bach, Johann Sebastian, Hosianna, Davids Sohn

Nun Komm, Der Heiden Heiland (Cantata 61) S.61, Adv,cant
cor sc KALMUS $2.00 (B1630)
mix cor,STB soli,cont,bsn,strings sc BREITKOPF-W PB-4561 s.p., cor pts BREITKOPF-W CHB-4561 s.p., ipa (B1631)
"Nun Komm" [Eng] cor voc sc KALMUS 6038 $1.00 (B1632)
"Nun Komm" cor,orch sc KALMUS $2.00, ipa (B1633)
(Genetay, Claude) "Nu Kom Var Fralsnings Herre" mix cor,org,bsn,strings cor pts NORDISKA 3611 s.p., ipa (B1634)
(Grischkat) [Ger/Eng] SATB,STB soli,cont, bsn,2vln,2vla HANSSLER 10.025 sc $3.50, cor pts $.80, ipa (B1635)
(Raphael, Gunter) [Ger] SATB,STB soli,org, cont,bsn,2vln,2vla (first Sunday in Advent) sc BAREN. BA 5105 $3.25, cor pts BAREN. BA 5105 $.55, ipa, voc sc BAREN. BA 5105A $2.00, min sc BAREN. TP 51 $1.75 (B1636)
(Schreck, G.) [Eng/Ger] mix cor,STB soli, org,bsn,strings,cembalo sc BREITKOPF-L PB-2911 s.p., voc pt BREITKOPF-L CHB-836 s.p., voc sc BREITKOPF-L EB-7061 s.p., ipa (B1637)

Nun Komm, Der Heiden Heiland (Cantata 62) S.62, Adv/Xmas,cant
mix cor,SATB soli,org,2ob,horn,strings, cembalo voc pt BREITKOPF-L CHB-1644 s.p., voc sc BREITKOPF-L EB-7062 s.p., ipr (B1638)
mix cor,SATB soli,cont,2ob,horn,strings sc BREITKOPF-W PB-4562 s.p., cor pts BREITKOPF-W CHB-4562 s.p., ipa (B1639)
"Nun Komm" [Ger] cor voc sc KALMUS 6545 $1.25 (B1640)
"Nun Komm" cor,orch sc KALMUS $4.00, ipa (B1641)
(Boepple, P.) "Now Come, The World's Salvation" SA oct PRESSER 352-00026 $.35 (B1642)
(Grischkat) [Ger/Eng] SATB,TB soli,cont, 2ob,2vln,vla,opt horn HANSSLER 10.030 sc $4.50, cor pts $.80, ipa, voc sc s.p. (B1643)

BACH, JOHANN SEBASTIAN (cont'd.)

(Raphael, Gunter) [Ger] SATB,SATB soli,org, cont,2ob,horn,2vln,vla sc BAREN. BA 5106 $3.50, cor pts BAREN. BA 5106 $.55, ipa, voc sc BAREN. BA 5106A $2.75, min sc BAREN. TP 52 $2.25 (B1644)

Nun Komm *see Nun Komm, Der Heiden Heiland

Nun Komm *see Nun Komm, Der Heiden Heiland

Nun Lasst Uns Gehn Und Treten
see Bach, Johann Sebastian, Lobe Den Herren, Den Machtigen Konig Der Ehren [Chorale]

Nun Lasst Uns Gott, Dem Herren (from Gott, Der Herr, Ist Sonn' Und Schild)
see Bach, Johann Sebastian, Nun Danket Alle Gott
see Bach, Johann Sebastian, Freu' Dich Sehr, O Meine Seele
(Hamburger, Povl) "Lad Os Til Gud, Vor Herre" [Ger/Dan] SATB,acap HANSEN-DEN 158 s.p. see also Otte Koraludsaettelser (B1645)

Nun Last Uns Gott, Dem Herren (from O Heil'ges Geist-Und Wasserbad)
see Bach, Johann Sebastian, Lob Und Ehre Und Weisheit Und Dank

Nun Liebe Seel [Chorale]
see Weihnachtschorale-II

Nun Lob, Mein Seel *Psalm
SATB,acap DOBLINGER s.p. see from PSALMLIEDER (B1646)
mix cor ALSBACH&D s.p. (B1647)

Nun Lob, Mein Seel, Den Herren (from Die Himmel Erzahlen Die Ehre Gottes) mot
see Bach, Johann Sebastian, Nun Danket Alle Gott
(Ameln; Wolters) 4pt mix cor,cont MOSELER sc s.p., cor pts s.p. (B1648)
(Horn) SATB,cont HANSSLER 1.501 s.p. (B1649)

Nun Ruhen Alle Walder
4pt mix cor MOSELER LB-49 s.p. contains also: Die Nacht Ist Kommen (B1650)

Nun Ruhen Alle Walder, Vieh, Menschen (from Matthaus-Passion) Easter,Bibl
SATB HANSSLER 6.316 s.p. contains also: Bach, Johann Sebastian, Ich Steh In Meines Herren Hand (A maj) (B1651)

Nun Singet Und Seid Froh
see Gumpeltzhaimer, Adam, Vom Himmel Hoch, Da Komm Ich Her

Nur Jedem Das Seine (Cantata 163) S.163, Trin,cant
mix cor,SATB soli,org,bsn,strings,cembalo, English horn voc sc BREITKOPF-L EB-7163 s.p., ipr (B1652)
[Ger] cor voc sc KALMUS 6609 $1.25 (B1653)
mix cor,SATB soli,cont,ob,strings cor pts BREITKOPF-W CHB-4663 s.p., ipr, sc BREITKOPF-W rental (B1654)

Nyarsdagen
[Swed] SATB,acap GEHRMANS KRB 149 (B1655)

O Christ Child, Now I Come To Thee *see Ich Steh' An Deiner Krippen Hier

O Christ, My All In Living *see Christus Der Ist Mein Leben

O Croix Je T'accepte Avec Joie! *see Ich Will Den Kreuzstab Gerne Tragen

O Death, None Could Conquer Thee
(Kjelson) girl cor SOUTHERN $.25 (B1656)
(Kjelson) SA/TB oct BELWIN 2131 $.30 (B1657)

O Du Liebe Meiner Liebe
(Mattfeld, V.) "O Thou, Everlasting Virtue" [Ger/Eng] unis,org SCHIRM.EC 2555 see from Six Sacred Songs (B1658)

O Ewiges Feuer *see O Ewiges Feuer, O Ursprung Der Liebe

O Ewiges Feuer [Chorale] (Cantata 34) (from O Ewiges Feuer) Whitsun
"O Light Everlasting" SATB,pno SCHIRM.EC 1195 $.75, ipr contains also: Friede Uber Israel!, "Peace Be Unto Israel!" (B1659)
"O Light Everlasting" SATB,ATB soli,org, 2fl,2ob,3trp,strings,timp voc sc NOVELLO s.p., ipr (B1660)
(Franz) "O Light Everlasting" SATB,ATB soli,org,2fl,2ob,2clar,2bsn,2horn,3trp, strings,timp voc sc NOVELLO s.p., ipr (B1661)

O Ewiges Feuer, O Ursprung Der Liebe (Cantata 34) S.34, Pent/Whitsun,cant
mix cor,ATB soli,cont,2fl,2ob,3trp,strings, timp sc BREITKOPF-W PB-4534 s.p., cor pts BREITKOPF-W CHB-4534 s.p., ipa (B1662)
"O Ewiges Feuer" [Eng] cor voc sc KALMUS 6026 $1.00 (B1663)
"O Ewiges Feuer" cor,orch sc KALMUS $8.00, ipa (B1664)
(Horn) SATB,ATB soli,cont,2ob,2fl,3trp, 2vln,vla,timp HANSSLER 10.120 sc $5.00, cor pts $1.00, ipa (B1665)
(Raphael, G.) [Eng/Ger] mix cor,ATB soli, org,2fl,2ob,bsn,3trp,strings,timp,cembalo voc pt BREITKOPF-L CHB-251 s.p., voc sc BREITKOPF-L EB-7034 s.p., ipr (B1666)

O Ewigkeit, Du Donnerwort *Gd.Fri.
SATB,acap voc pt DOBLINGER s.p. see also TOD UND VERGANGLICHKEIT (B1667)
SATB HANSSLER 6.309 s.p. contains also: Wer Nur Den Lieben Gott Lasst Walten [Chorale] (from Wer Nur Den Lieben Gott Lasst Walten) (SATB) (Trin); Nun Danket Alle Gott, S.252 (SATB, 2horn) (F min) (B1668)
4pt mix cor MOSELER LB-23 s.p. contains also: Wer Nur Den Lieben Gott Lasst Walten; Zwingt Die Saiten In Cythara (B1669)

BACH, JOHANN SEBASTIAN (cont'd.)

O Ewigkeit, Du Donnerwort (Cantata 20) S.20, Trin,cant
[Fr/Ger] mix cor,ATB soli,org,3ob,trp, strings voc pt BREITKOPF-L CHB-1615 s.p., voc sc BREITKOPF-L EB-7020 s.p., ipr (B1670)
[Ger] cor voc sc KALMUS 6532 $1.25 (B1671)
mix cor,ATB soli,cont,3ob,trp,strings cor pts BREITKOPF-W CHB-4520 s.p., ipr, sc BREITKOPF-W rental (B1672)

O Ewigkeit, Du Donnerwort (Cantata 60) S.60, Trin,cant
mix cor,ATB soli,org,2ob,horn,strings, cembalo voc pt BREITKOPF-L CHB-1286 s.p., voc sc BREITKOPF-L EB-7060 s.p., ipr (B1673)
[Ger] cor voc sc KALMUS 6544 $1.25 (B1674)
mix cor,ATB soli,cont,2ob,horn,strings cor pts BREITKOPF-W CHB-4560 s.p., ipr, sc BREITKOPF-W rental (B1675)

O God, How Grievous Is The Woe *see Ach Gott, Wie Manches Herzeleid [Chorale]

O God Of Grace And Goodness (from Cantata 108) anthem
(Jones, P.) SATB ALLANS 238 s.p. (B1676)

O God, Thou Faithful God (from Ein Ungefarbte Gemute) Trin,anthem/chorale
SATB oct NOVELLO 40.1111.02 s.p. (B1677)

O Gott, Du Frommer Gott *S.398
SATB HANSSLER 6.2617 s.p. contains also: Ruppel, Paul Ernst, Wohlan, Alle, Die Ihr Durstig Seid, Kommet Her (SSATB); Stern, Hermann, Ich Freu Mich In Dem Herren (SAB) (B1678)

O Gud, Av Din Barmhartighet
mix cor NORDISKA 5131 s.p. (B1679)

O Haupt Voll Blut Und Wunden (from Matthaus-Passion) Easter/Gd.Fri./Holywk/Psntd
see Schutz, Heinrich, Kommt Her, Des Konigs Aufgebot
SATB,acap voc pt DOBLINGER s.p. see also PASSION UND OSTERN (B1680)
4pt mix cor MOSELER LB-82 s.p. (B1681)
SATB HANSSLER 6.260 s.p. contains also: Herzliebster Jesu, Was Hast Du Verbrochen (G min) (B1682)
SSA HANSSLER 6.1172 s.p. (B1683)
"O Hoved, Hojt Forhanet" [Ger/Dan] SATB HANSEN-DEN 184 s.p. see also Otte Koraludsaettelser (B1684)

O Heil'ge Seelenspeise *Pent/Whitsun
SATB,acap voc pt DOBLINGER s.p. see also PFINGSTEN UND EUCHARISTIE (B1685)

O Heil'ges Geist- Und Wasserbad (Cantata 165) S.165, Trin,cant
mix cor,SATB soli,cont,bsn,strings cor pts BREITKOPF-W CHB-4665 s.p., ipr, sc BREITKOPF-W rental (B1686)
"O Heiliger Geist" [Ger] cor voc sc KALMUS 6611 $1.25 (B1687)
(Todt, B.) mix cor,SATB soli,org,bsn, strings,cembalo voc pt BREITKOPF-L CHB-2212 s.p., voc sc BREITKOPF-L EB-7165 s.p., ipr (B1688)

O Heiliger Geist *see O Heil'ges Geist- Und Wasserbad

O Herrlicher Tag, O Frohilche Zeit *S.493
SATB (A flat maj) HANSSLER 6.128 s.p. contains also: Schutz, Heinrich, Frohlockt Mit Freud', Ihr Volker All, SWV 144 (B1689)

O Holy City
(McCurdy) SATB oct BOOSEY 1740 $.30 (B1690)
(McCurdy) SSA oct BOOSEY 1739 $.30 (B1691)

O Holy City, Seen Of John *see O Mensch, Schau' Jesum Christum An

O Hoofd Bedekt Met Wonden *Gd.Fri.
mix cor ALSBACH&D s.p. (B1692)

O Hoved, Hojt Forhanet *see O Haupt Voll Blut Und Wunden

O Huvud, Blodigt, Sarat
mix cor NORDISKA 1472 s.p. (B1693)

O Infant Sweet, O Infant Mild
see Four Christmas Chorales

O Jesu Christ *see O Jesu Christ, Mein's Lebens Licht

O Jesu Christ, Mein's Lebens Licht (Cantata 118) S.118, cant/mot
mix cor SOUTHERN $.30 (B1694)
mix cor,2horn&trp&3trom/cont&3ob&bsn&2horn& strings sc BREITKOPF-W PB-4617 s.p., cor pts BREITKOPF-W CHB-4617 s.p., ipa (B1695)
"O Jesu Christ" cor voc sc KALMUS 6050 $1.00 (B1696)
"O Jesus, My Light And Life" SATB WEINBERGER s.p. (B1697)
(Jones, Ifor) "O Jesus Christ, My Life And Light" [Eng/Ger] mix cor,pno voc sc SCHIRM.G $.60 (B1698)
(Raphael, G.) [Eng/Ger] mix cor,2horn,trp, 3trom voc pt BREITKOPF-L CHB-122 s.p., voc sc BREITKOPF-L EB-7118 s.p., ipr (B1699)
(Schneider, M.) [Eng/Ger] mix cor,org,3ob, 2bsn,2horn,strings,cembalo sc BREITKOPF-L PB-2825 s.p., voc pt BREITKOPF-L CHB-122 s.p., voc sc BREITKOPF-L EB-7118 s.p., ipr (B1700)

O Jesu, Dir Sei Ewig Dank *Pent/Whitsun
SATB,acap voc pt DOBLINGER s.p. see also PFINGSTEN UND EUCHARISTIE (B1701)

O Jesu God, O Jesu Kar
mix cor NORDISKA 5088 s.p. (B1702)

BACH, JOHANN SEBASTIAN (cont'd.)

O Jesu Most Kind *Xmas,anthem
(Buck, P.C.) SATB oct ROYAL 204 s.p. (B1703)

O Jesu So Dear
see Bach, Johann Sebastian, How Brightly Beams The Morning Star

O Jesu So Sweet *see O Jesulein Suss

O Jesu Sweet
(Geer) girl cor SOUTHERN $.20 (B1704)

O Jesulein Suss (from Schemelli Gesangbuch) Adv/Xmas,Ger
"O Jesu So Sweet" see FOLK-SONGS, BALLADS AND SONGS OF GREAT COMPOSERS (SET V)
SATB,acap (contains also: Anonymous, Zu Bethlehem Geboren) voc pt DOBLINGER s.p. see also ADVENT UND WEIHNACHT, HEFT 1 (B1705)
"O Jesu So Sweet" SATB,acap SCHIRM.EC 2271 $.25 (B1706)
"O Jesu So Sweet" SATB,pno SCHIRM.EC 1593 (B1707)
(Davis, K.) "O Jesu So Sweet" SSAA,acap SCHIRM.EC 1051 $.25 (B1708)
(Davis, K.) "O Jesu So Sweet" SSA,acap SCHIRM.EC 1049 $.30 (B1709)
(Mattfeld, V.) "O Savior Sweet" [Ger/Eng] unis,org SCHIRM.EC 2554 see from Songs For The Advent And Christmas Seasons (B1710)

O Jesulein Suss, O Jesulein Mild *S.493
SATB HANSSLER 6.0614 s.p. contains also: Wessnitzer, Wolfgang, Das Ist Eine Sel'ge Stunde (B1711)

O Jesus Christ, My Life And Light *see O Jesu Christ, Mein's Lebens Licht

O Jesus, Lord, My Light And Life (Cantata 118)
SATB,orch MARKS 6 $.35, ipr (B1712)

O Jesus, My Light And Life *see O Jesu Christ, Mein's Lebens Licht

O, Kindeken Klein
mix cor ALSBACH&D s.p. (B1713)

O, Kom Du Skona Dag
mix cor NORDISKA 1456 s.p. (B1714)

O Lamm Gottes, Unschuldig
see Eine Deutsche Messe In Kirchenliedsatzen

O Light Everlasting *see O Ewiges Feuer [Chorale]

O Light Of Life, O Saviour Dear *hymn
PATERSON s.p. see also English Hymns Adapted To Bach's Chorales (B1715)

O Lord, My God, Forgive Thou Me
(Boepple, P.) SA oct PRESSER 352-00027 $.35 (B1716)

O Lord, Relent, I Pray Thee *see Ach Herr, Mich Armen Sunder [Chorale]

O Lord, This Grieving Spirit *see Ach Herr, Mich Armen Sunder

O Lord, Thou Hast Formed My Every Part *chorale
SATB,acap SCHIRM.EC 369 $.25 (B1717)

O Mensch, Schau' Jesum Christum An *chorale
(Fewell, C.M.) "O Holy City, Seen Of John" SAB,acap SCHIRM.EC 2262 $.18 (B1718)

O My Soul, Be Not Dismayed
(Kinsman) SATB oct BOURNE SB110 $.30 (B1719)

O Praise The Lord (Cantata 160) (from Cantata 160) Easter/Lent,cant
(Allen) SATB,S solo GALLEON GCS2009 (B1720)
(Allen) SATB oct FISCHER,C GCS-2009 $.35 (B1721)

O Praise The Lord, All Ye Nations *see Lobet Den Herrn, Alle Heiden

O Praise The Lord For All His Mercies *see Gottlob! Nun Geht Das Jahr Zu Ende

O Praise The Lord For All His Mercies *see Gottlob! Nun Geht Das Jahr Zu Ende [Chorale]

O Rejoice, Ye Christians, Loudly (from Dazu Ist Erschienen Der Sohn Gottes) chorale
4pt mix cor,acap oct SCHIRM.G 8754 $.25 (B1722)
SATB,acap SCHIRM.EC 367 $.30 (B1723)
men cor KJOS 5539 $.30 (B1724)
SSA KJOS 6029 $.30 (B1725)
(Carlton) SSA,acap oct BOOSEY 5519 $.30 (B1726)
(Carlton) SATB,acap oct BOOSEY 5051 $.30 (B1727)
(Glaser V.) SAB,acap SCHIRM.EC 2238 $.25 (B1728)
(Mueller) 4pt wom cor oct SCHIRM.G 10255 $.25 (B1729)

O Sacred Head *hymn
PATERSON s.p. see also English Hymns Adapted To Bach's Chorales (B1730)

O Sacred Head, Now Wounded (from St. Matthew Passion) Easter/Gen/Lent,chorale
see Bach, Johann Sebastian, Ah, Lord, Thy Dear, Sweet Angels Send
SATB,inst (med easy, or Ash Wednesday) oct CONCORDIA 98-2053 $.25 (B1731)
(Gray) SATB,acap oct PRO ART 1274 $.30 (B1732)
(Kent) SATB oct SPRATT 510 $.25 (B1733)
(Palmer) SATB ALFRED 6408 $.25 (B1734)

O Salutaris *Commun,mot
[Lat] SATBar DURAND s.p. (B1735)
[Lat] unis/2pt CHOUDENS s.p. (B1736)

O Savior Sweet *see O Jesulein Suss

BACH, JOHANN SEBASTIAN (cont'd.)

O Saviour, Bless Us Ere We Go *hymn
PATERSON s.p. see also English Hymns Adapted To Bach's Chorales (B1737)

O Saviour Mine, What Agony
(Field) SATB,acap oct BOOSEY 5530 $.30 (B1738)

O Saviour Sweet *Xmas
(Barthelson) SA oct SPRATT 639 $.30 (B1739)
(Barthelson) SAB oct SPRATT 640 $.30 (B1740)
(Barthelson) SSA oct SPRATT 551 $.25 (B1741)
(Barthelson) SATB oct SPRATT 530 $.30 (B1742)

O Son Of God *Easter
(Henninger, G.) SATB oct PRESSER 312-21588 $.30 (B1743)

O Spotless Lamb *anthem
(Field) SATB,acap oct BOOSEY 5537 $.30 (B1744)
(Thoburn) SATB (med) oct AUGSBURG 1149 $.20 (B1745)

O Teach Me, Lord, My Days To Number *see Wer Weiss, Wie Nahe Mir Mein Ende

O That Heavenly Music *Gen
(Norden) SATB SCHMITT 1128 $.22 (B1746)

O Thou, Everlasting Virtue *see O Du Liebe Meiner Liebe

O Traurigkeit, O Herzelied *S.404 (from Matthaus-Passion)
"So Ruhest Du, O Meine Ruh" see Gesius, Bartholomaus, O Welt, Ich Muss Dich Lassen

O Ye Stars And Highest Heavens *see Ihr Gestirn', Ihr Hohen Lufte

Ob Bei Uns Is Der Sunden Viel (from Aus Tiefer Not)
"Though Great Our Sins And Sore Our Woes" see Bach, Johann Sebastian, Aus Tiefer Not Schrei'ich Zu Dir [Chorale]

Oh, Rejoice, Ye Christians, Loudly (from Cantata 40) chorale
(Saar, L.) TTBB,acap SCHIRM.EC 545 $.18 (B1747)

Old Masters In Settings By J.S. Bach, Vol. I *CC5U
SATB,acap PETERS 4873A $.60 (B1748)

Old Masters In Settings By J.S. Bach, Vol. II *CC4U
SATB,acap PETERS 4873B $.60 (B1749)

Omkring Ditt Kors, O Jesus Kar
mix cor NORDISKA 3731 s.p. (B1750)

On Jesus All My Love Is Cast *see Wie Bin Ich Doch So Herzlich Froh

On Thee Mortal Eyes Wait, Lord *see Aller Augen Warten, Herr

One Hundred Eighty-Five Four Part Chorales *CC185U,chorale
4pt min sc KALMUS 723 $1.30 (B1751)

One Hundred One Chorales Harmonized By J.S. Bach *CC101U,chorale
mix cor SCHMITT 9065 $2.00 (B1752)

Only Son From Heaven, The *Adv/Xmas/Epiph/Gen
SATB,2vln,vla,cont (med easy) oct CONCORDIA 98-2033 $.25, ipa (B1753)

Onverganklijk Levenslicht
mix cor ALSBACH&D s.p. (B1754)

Op Min Sjael! En Morgen Klar *see Auf Mein Herz! Des Herren Tag

Open My Heart *Gen
(Lethbridge, Lionel) SATB,opt S solo (easy) oct OXFORD $.30 (B1755)

Open Now Thy Gates Of Beauty *anthem
(Jennings) SSATB (med) oct AUGSBURG 1497 $.25 (B1756)

Oprundet Er Den Skonne Dag *see Erschienen Ist Der Herrlich Tag

Oratorio De Noel *see Weihnachtsoratorium

Oratorio Di Natale *S.248, Xmas,ora
"Christmas Oratorio" cor KALMUS $2.50 (B1757)
"Christmas Oratorio" cor sc KALMUS $30.00 (B1758)
"Christmas Oratorio" cor,orch/orch sc KALMUS $30.00, ipa (B1759)
"Christmas Oratorio" [Ger] SATB,inst voc sc PETERS 38 $3.00, ipr, cloth PETERS 38 $7.50, ipr, min sc PETERS E962 $7.50, ipr, min sc-cloth PETERS E962 $10.00, ipr (B1760)
"Christmas Oratorio" SATB,SATB soli,org, 2fl,2ob,bsn,2horn,3trp,strings,timp bds, voc sc NOVELLO s.p., ipr, ipa (B1761)
"Christmas Oratorio" cor,opt orch voc sc KALMUS 6001 $2.50, ipa (B1762)
"Christmas Oratorio, Part I" SATB,4 soli oct SCHIRM.G 5713 $.50 (B1763)
"Christmas Oratorio, Part II" SATB,4 soli oct SCHIRM.G 2580 $.40 (B1764)
(Read) "Christmas Oratorio, Part I" SSA FISCHER,C PT-2621 $1.35 (B1765)
(Read) "Christmas Oratorio, Part II" SSA FISCHER,C PT-2622 $1.25 (B1766)
(Read) "Christmas Oratorio, Parts I & II" SSA voc pt FISCHER,C PT-2636 $.75 (B1767)
(Spicker, Max) "Christmas Oratorio" mix cor,soli,pno SCHIRM.G voc sc $2.50, cloth $4.25 (B1768)
(Zanon) [It/Ger] cor,pno RICORDI-ENG ER2436 s.p. (B1769)

Oratorium Festo Paschali *see Osteroratorium

BACH, JOHANN SEBASTIAN (cont'd.)

Osteroratorium *S.249, Easter,ora
"Oratorium Festo Paschali" mix cor,SATB soli,org,cembalo,2fl,2ob,bsn,3trp, strings,timp cor pts BREITKOPF-W CHB-3467 s.p., ipr, voc sc BREITKOPF-W EB-5750 s.p., sc BREITKOPF-W rental (B1770)
(Hellmann) SATB,SATB soli,cont,2fl,2ob, 3trp,2vln,vla,timp HANSSLER 10.135 sc $10.00, cor pts $1.00, ipa (B1771)
(Raphael, G.) [Eng/Ger] mix cor,SATB soli, org,2fl,2ob,bsn,3trp,strings,timp, cembalo, English horn voc sc BREITKOPF-L EB-5750 s.p., ipr (B1772)

Otte Koraludsaettelser
(Hamburger, Povl) [Ger/Dan] SATB,acap cmplt ed HANSEN-DEN 25155 s.p.
contains & see also: Alle Menschen Mussen Sterben, "Alle Mennesker Pa Jorden"; Auf Mein Herz! Des Herren Tag, "Op Min Sjael! En Morgen Klar"; Erschienen Ist Der Herrlich Tag, "Oprundet Er Den Skonne Dag"; Gelobet Sei Der Herr, "Hojlovet Vaere Gud"; Ich Freue Mich In Dir, "Jeg Fryder Mig I Dig"; Keinen Hat Gott Verlassen, "Ingen Af Gud Blev Sveget"; Nun Lasst Uns Gott, Dem Herren, "Lad Os Til Gud, Vor Herre"; Was Gott Tut, Das Ist Wohlgetan [Chorale], "Lad Haende Kun, Som Herren Vil" (B1773)

Otte Koraludsaettelser
[Ger/Dan] SATB cmplt ed HANSEN-DEN 25693 s.p.
contains & see also: Aus Meines Herzens Grunde, "Jeg Vil Din Pris Udsjunge"; Christ Unser Herr Zum Jordan Kam, "Vor Herre Kom Til Jordans Flod"; Du Friedefurst, Herr Jesu Christ, "Fredsfyrste, Herre Jesus Krist"; Eins Ist Noth, "Eet Er Nodigt"; Es Woll Uns Gott Genadig Sein, "Nu Vaer Os, Gud, Miskundelig"; O Haupt Voll Blut Und Wunden, "O Hoved, Hojt Forhanet"; Wer Nur Den Lieben Gott Lasst Walten [Chorale], "Hvo Ikkun Lader Herren Rade"; Wohl Dem, Der Sich Auf Seinen Gott [Chorale], "Det Livsens Ord Vi Bygger Pa" (B1774)

Our Father, Thou In Heaven Above
see Four Chorale Harmonizations

Out Of The Depths I Cry To Thee *see Aus Tiefer Not Schrei'ich Zu Dir [Chorale]

Pa Gud Och Ej Pa Eget Rad
mix cor NORDISKA 2569 s.p. (B1775)

Paix Du Ciel
(Geveart, F.-A.) [Fr] 4pt mix cor,acap (med diff) cor pts LEMOINE s.p. see from Collection De Choeurs, cinquieme Fascicule (B1776)

Paskehymne *Easter,hymn
(Maeland, Lars) [Norw] SATB,org LYCHE 56 s.p. (B1777)

Passion According To St. John, The *see La Passione Di N.S. Gesu Cristo Secondo Giovanni

Passion Chorale (from St. Matthew Passion) CC5U
(Harmon) [Eng/Ger] 4pt mix cor,org/pno oct SCHIRM.G 11861 $.35 (B1778)

Passion Chorale (from Cantata No. 161) chorale
(Bergmann) SATB,pno/org,opt S rec sc SCHOTT CHR5 s.p., ipa (B1779)

Passion Of Our Lord According To St. Matthew *see La Passione Di N.S. Gesu Cristo Secondo Matteo

Passion Selon Saint Mathieu *see Matthauspassion

Passion Song *Easter
(Ehret, W.) SAB (med easy) PRESSER 312-40996 $.35 (B1780)
(Ehret, W.) SATB oct PRESSER 312-40751 $.30 (B1781)

Pastoral Symphony (from Christmas Oratorio) chorale
(Parkinson) SATB (very easy) sc OXFORD 77.993 $2.15, cor pts OXFORD 77.993-42 $.25 contains also: Chorale (B1782)

Peace Be Unto Israel! *see Friede Uber Israel!

Pfingst-Chor
(Schmid, W.) [Ger] mix cor,org/orch HUG s.p., ipr (B1783)

Planets, Stars And Airs Of Space *carol
4pt mix cor oct SCHIRM.G 7554 $.25 (B1784)

Praise And Renown To God *see Lob, Ehr Und Preis Sei Gott

Praise And Thanks *Easter/Lent,ora
SATB,3trp GALLEON GCS2004 ipa (B1785)

Praise Him (from Cantata 207) Harv
SATB PATERSON 1590 s.p. (B1786)
(Barrie) 3pt mix cor,org oct LAWSON 51722 $.30 (B1787)
(Barrie) SATB oct LAWSON 51472 $.30 (B1788)
(Barrie) SSA/SAA oct LAWSON 51471 $.30 (B1789)

Praise Our God In All His Splendor *see Lobet Gott In Seinen Richen

Praise Our God Who Reigns In Heaven *see Lobet Gott In Seinen Reichen

Praise The Lord (Motet 6)
cor voc sc KALMUS 6015 $1.50 (B1790)
(Roberton) SATB oct PLYMOUTH SC-9 $.25 (B1791)

BACH, JOHANN SEBASTIAN (cont'd.)

Praise The Lord, All Ye Nations *see Lobet
Den Herrn, Alle Heiden

Praise Thou The Lord, Jerusalem *see Preise,
Jerusalem, Den Herrn

Praise To The Lord
(Fewell, C.M.) SAB,acap SCHIRM.EC 2263 $.20
(B1792)
(Mendelssohn-Bartholdy, F.; Spiro) SATB oct
PRO ART 1338 $.25 (B1793)

Praise We The Name Of The Lord
(Martin) SATB oct LAWSON 978 $.25 (B1794)

Praise Ye The Lord
(Trusler) SATB oct PLYMOUTH TR-103 $.25
(B1795)

Praises To Our God
(Bampton) SA oct FISCHER,J 9146 $.30
(B1796)

Preise, Jerusalem *see Preise, Jerusalem,
Den Herrn

Preise, Jerusalem, Den Herrn (Cantata 119)
S.119, Fest/Gen,cant
mix cor,SATB soli,org,2fl,3ob,4trp,strings,
timp,cembalo sc BREITKOPF-L PB-2969 s.p.,
voc pt BREITKOPF-L EB-1413 s.p., voc sc
BREITKOPF-L EB-7119 s.p., ipr (B1797)
mix cor,SATB soli,cont,2fl/2rec,5ob,4trp,
strings,timp cor pts BREITKOPF-W CHB-4619
s.p., ipr, sc BREITKOPF-W rental (B1798)
"Preise, Jerusalem" [Ger] cor voc sc KALMUS
6581 $1.25 (B1799)
(Hellmann) SATB,SATB soli,cont,3ob,4trp,
strings,timp,2rec, 2-English horns
HANSSLER 10.293 sc $5.00, cor pts $.80,
ipa (B1800)
(West, John E.) "Praise Thou The Lord,
Jerusalem" SATB,SATB soli voc sc NOVELLO
s.p. (B1801)

Prelude No. 9 (from Well-Tempered Clavichord)
Xmas/Easter,Allelu
(Martino) SATB oct PRO ART 2403 $.25
(B1802)

Prelude No. 11 (from Well-Tempered
Clavichord)
(Martino) SATB oct PRO ART 2399 $.25
(B1803)

Prelude No. 23 (from Well-Tempered
Clavichord)
(Martino) SATB oct PRO ART 2401 $.25
(B1804)

Prelude On Psalms (from Prelude 22; The Well-
Tempered Clavier, Bk. I) Bibl
(Leidzen) mix cor,acap oct SCHIRM.G 10975
$.30 (B1805)

Prepare Thyself, Zion *see Bereite Dich,
Zion

Pris Dig, O Herre
mix cor NORDISKA 1507 s.p. (B1806)

Program Of Six Chorales, A *CC6U
(Zanzig, A.) mix cor SCHIRM.EC 2293 $.30
(B1807)

Psallite Deo Nostro In Laetitia
5pt mix cor MOSELER LB-380 s.p. (B1808)

Psalm 24 *see Machet Die Tore Weit

Psalm 117 *see Lobet Den Herrn, Alle Heiden

Puer Natus In Bethlehem
(Fewell, C.M.) "Babe Is Born In Bethlehem,
A" SAB,opt inst SCHIRM.EC 2260 $.30
(B1809)
(Talmadge, A.) "Babe Is Born In Bethlehem,
A" SSAA,acap SCHIRM.EC 2501 $.25 (B1810)

Quiet Lord, My Froward Heart *hymn
PATERSON s.p. see also English Hymns
Adapted To Bach's Chorales (B1811)

Ready Be, My Soul, Alway *see Mache Dich,
Mein Geist, Bereit

Rejoice And Sing *see Freut Euch Und
Jubilirt

Rejoice In God, Oh Ye Righteous
(Coleman, J.) SSAA,acap oct PRESSER
312-40556 $.30 (B1812)

Rejoice, O My Spirit (from Cantata No. 15)
(Easson) unis jr cor/unis wom cor CURWEN
72322 s.p. (B1813)
(Easson, James) unis oct CURWEN 10319 $.25
(B1814)

Rejoice Ye Christians Loudly
SATB,acap oct FISCHER,C CM-6600 $.25
(B1815)

Rest Here In Peace (from St. John Passion)
SATB,pno SCHIRM.EC 1118 $.35, ipr (B1816)

Rest Well (from St. John Passion)
(Wagner) SATB oct LAWSON 722 $.35 (B1817)

Resurrection And Ascension Of Jesus *cant
(Brewer) SATB SHAWNEE A1058 $2.50 (B1818)

Rise, My Soul, Adore Thy Maker *hymn
PATERSON s.p. see also English Hymns
Adapted To Bach's Chorales (B1819)

Rise, O Soul, This Happy Morning *see
Schmucke Dich, O Liebe Seele

Road To Calvary, The *Bibl
(Cozens, J.) SATB,narrator (med easy) sc
CONCORDIA 98-1629 $1.30, cor pts
CONCORDIA 98-1630 $.35 (B1820)

Sages Of Sheba, The *see Sie Werden Aus Saba
Alle Kommen

Sanctus *S.237 (from B Minor Mass) anthem/
cant/chorale/Sanctus
[Lat] SSAATB SCHIRM.G 5654 $.40 (B1821)
SSAATB,pno SCHIRM.EC 1600 $.40, ipr (B1822)
mix cor,2ob,3trp,strings,timp (C maj) sc
BREITKOPF-L rental (B1823)
[Lat] SATB/SSAATB oct NOVELLO 34.0718.07
s.p. (B1824)

BACH, JOHANN SEBASTIAN (cont'd.)

cor,orch sc KALMUS $3.00, ipa (B1825)
(Cassler) SSAATB,org,timp (diff) oct
AUGSBURG 1541 $.50 (B1826)
(Geveart, F.-A.) [Lat] 4pt mix cor,acap
(med) cor pts LEMOINE s.p. see from
Collection De Choeurs, cinquieme
Fascicule (B1827)
(Luvaas) mix cor SOUTHERN $.25 (B1828)
(Pinkham) [Eng/Lat] SATB,ob/trp,2vln,vla,
vcl,bvl PETERS 66265 $.40, ipa (B1829)

Sanctus In D *Sanctus
mix cor oct OXFORD 46.514 $1.15 (B1830)

Sanctus In D-Dur *S.241, Sanctus
8pt mix cor,cont,2ob,bsn,2vln,3vla,vcl,bvl
(D maj) BREITKOPF-W rental (B1831)

Sanctus In D-Dur *S.241, Sanctus
(Harrassowitz) [Ger/Lat] dbl cor,cont,2ob,
bsn,2vln,3vla HANSSLER 10.187 sc $3.50,
voc sc $.90, ipa (B1832)

Sanctus No. 4 In G *Sanctus
(Ehret) SATB oct BOOSEY 1980 $.40 (B1833)

Sand, Herre, Dina Anglar Ut
mix cor NORDISKA 4116 s.p. (B1834)

Saviour Shepherd (from Cantata 92) Gen/Septua
unis (easy) oct OXFORD 45.281 $.30 (B1835)

Schafe Konnen Sicher Weiden (from Was Mir
Behagt)
"Happy Flocks In Safety Wander" SATB,pno,fl
SCHIRM.EC 2218 $.35 (B1836)

Schau, Lieber Gott *see Schau, Lieber Gott,
Wie Meine Feind'

Schau, Lieber Gott, Wie Meine Feind' (Cantata
153) S.153, Fest,cant
mix cor,ATB soli,org,strings,cembalo voc pt
BREITKOPF-L CHB-2185 s.p., voc sc
BREITKOPF-L EB-7153 s.p., ipr (B1837)
mix cor,ATB soli,cont,strings cor pts
BREITKOPF-W CHB-4653 s.p., ipr, sc
BREITKOPF-W rental (B1838)
"Schau, Lieber Gott" [Ger] cor voc sc
KALMUS 6603 $1.25 (B1839)

Schauet Doch *see Schauet Doch Und Sehet

Schauet Doch Und Sehet (Cantata 46) S.46,
Trin,cant
mix cor,ATB soli,cont,2fl/2rec,2ob,trp,
strings cor pts BREITKOPF-W CHB-4546
s.p., ipr, sc BREITKOPF-W rental (B1840)
"Schauet Doch" cor,orch sc KALMUS $6.00,
ipa (B1841)
(Horn) SATB,ATB soli,cont,2fl,trp,2vln,vla,
2English horn HANSSLER 10.122 sc $5.00,
cor pts $1.00, ipa (B1842)
(Raphael) [Ger] mix cor,ATB soli,
org,2fl,2ob,trp,strings,cembalo voc pt
BREITKOPF-L CHB-1458 s.p., voc sc
BREITKOPF-L EB-7046 s.p., ipr (B1843)

Schlage Doch *S.53, cant
cor,orch sc KALMUS $2.00, ipa (B1844)

Schmucke Dich, O Liebe Seele (Cantata 180)
S.180 (from Schmucke Dich, O Liebe Seele)
Trin,cant
see Vulpius, Melchior, Gott Vater, Hore
Unsre Bitt
mix cor,SATB soli,cont,2fl/2rec,2ob,strings
cor pts BREITKOPF-W CHB-4680 s.p., ipr,
sc BREITKOPF-W rental (B1845)
"Schmuecke Dich" [Eng] cor voc sc KALMUS
6059 $1.50 (B1846)
(Jones, Ifor) "Beautify Thyself, My Spirit"
[Eng/Ger] mix cor,soli,pno voc sc
SCHIRM.G $1.50 (B1847)
(Raphael) [Ger] mix cor,SATB soli,org,2fl,ob,
bsn,strings,cembalo, English horn voc pt
BREITKOPF-L CHB-769 s.p., voc sc
BREITKOPF-L EB-7180 s.p., ipr (B1848)
(West, John E.) "Rise, O Soul, This Happy
Morning" SATB,SATB soli,2fl,2ob,strings,
cembalo voc sc NOVELLO s.p., ipr (B1849)

Schmucke Dich, O Liebe Seele [Chorale] (from
Schmucke Dich, O Liebe Seele)
"Deck Thyself, My Soul" SATB,pno SCHIRM.EC
1197 $.50, ipr contains also: Jesu,
Wahres Brot Des Lebens, "Jesu, Bread Of
Life" (B1850)

Schmuecke Dich *see Schmucke Dich, O Liebe
Seele

Schwingt Freudig *see Schwingt Freudig Euch
Empor

Schwingt Freudig Euch Empor (Cantata 36)
S.36, Adv,cant
mix cor,SATB soli,org,2fl,2ob,strings,
cembalo voc pt BREITKOPF-L CHB-1421 s.p.,
voc sc BREITKOPF-L EB-7036 s.p., ipr
(B1851)
mix cor,SATB soli,cont,3ob,strings cor pts
BREITKOPF-W CHB-4536 s.p., sc BREITKOPF-W
PB-4536 s.p., ipr (B1852)
"Schwingt Freudig" [Ger] cor voc sc KALMUS
6536 $1.25 (B1853)
(Durr, Alfred) [Ger] SATB,SATB soli,org,
cont,4ob,2vln,vla (first Sunday in
Advent) sc BAREN. BA 5101 $5.50, cor pts
BAREN. BA 5101 $1.00, ipa, voc sc BAREN.
BA 5101A $2.75, min sc BAREN. TP 10 $2.25
(B1854)
(Durr; Neumann) [Ger] mix cor,SATB soli,
org,cont,fl,2ob,2vln,vla voc sc BAREN.
5501 s.p., sc DEUTSCH 5501A s.p.
(B1855)

Se, Guds Tid Ar For Oss Den Basta *see
Gottes Zeit Ist Die Allerbeste Zeit

Sechsundvierzig Choralsatze *CC46U,Gen
(Keller, Hermann) [Ger] SATB,acap (easy)
BAREN. BA 257 $2.75 contains settings by:
Bach, J.S. and other old masters to the
chorales of the "Orgelbuchlein" of Bach,
J.S. (B1856)

BACH, JOHANN SEBASTIAN (cont'd.)

Second Book Of Bach Chorales *CCU
mix cor SCHMITT 55 $.50 (B1857)

Sehet *see Sehet, Welch Eine Liebe

Sehet, Welch Ein Liebe *mot
(Ameln; Wolters) 4pt mix cor,cont MOSELER
sc s.p., cor pts s.p. (B1858)

Sehet, Welch Eine Liebe (Cantata 64) S.64,
cant
mix cor,SAB soli,cont,ob,trp,3trom,strings
sc BREITKOPF-W PB-4564 s.p., cor pts
BREITKOPF-W CHB-4564 s.p., ipa (B1859)
"Cantate, Pour Le Troisieme Jour Apres
Noel" SATB CHOUDENS voc sc s.p., cor pts
s.p. (B1860)
"Sehet" [Eng] cor voc sc KALMUS 6030 $1.00
(B1861)

Sehet, Welch Eine Liebe Hat Uns Der Vater
Erzeiget *S.64, Xmas,cant
(Naumann, E.) [Eng/Ger] mix cor,SAB soli,
org,3trom,strings, English
horn sc BREITKOPF-L PB-2914 s.p., voc pt
BREITKOPF-L CHB-695 s.p., voc sc
BREITKOPF-L EB-7064 s.p., ipr (B1862)

Sehet, Wir Gehen Hinauf *see Sehet, Wir Gehn
Hinauf Gen Jerusalem

Sehet, Wir Gehn Hinauf Gen Jerusalem (Cantata
159) S.159, Gen,cant
mix cor,ATB soli,cont,ob,strings sc
BREITKOPF-W PB-4659 s.p., cor pts
BREITKOPF-W CHB-4659 s.p., ipa (B1863)
"Sehet, Wir Gehen Hinauf" cor,orch sc
KALMUS $3.00, ipa (B1864)
(Raphael, G.) [Eng/Ger] mix cor,ATB soli,
org,ob,bsn,strings,cembalo voc sc BREITKOPF-L
PB-3009 s.p., voc pt BREITKOPF-L CHB-1852
s.p., voc sc BREITKOPF-L EB-7159 s.p.,
ipa (B1865)

Sei Gegrusset, Jesu Gutig, Uber Alle Mass
*S.410 (from Matthaus-Passion)
SATB HANSSLER 6.119 s.p. contains also:
Praetorius, Michael, O Christ, Wir Danken
Deiner Gut (B1866)

Sei Lob Und Ehr *see Sei Lob Und Ehr' Dem
Hochsten Gut

Sei Lob Und Ehr Dem Hochsten Gut (Cantata
117) S.117, Gen,cant
[Ger] 4pt mix cor,acap BAREN. EM 35 s.p.
(B1867)
mix cor,ATB soli,cont,2fl,4ob,horn,strings
sc BREITKOPF-W PB-4617 s.p., cor pts
BREITKOPF-W CHB-4617 s.p., ipa (B1868)
"Sei Lob Und Ehr" cor,orch sc KALMUS $4.50,
ipa (B1869)
(Raphael, G.) [Eng/Ger] mix cor,ATB soli,
org,2fl,2ob,bsn,strings,cembalo voc pt
BREITKOPF-L CHB-1442 s.p., voc sc
BREITKOPF-L EB-7117 s.p., ipr (B1870)

Sei Lob Und Preis Mit Ehren *S.231 (from
Jauchzet Dem Herrn Alle Welt) mot
SATB,acap cor pts BREITKOPF-L PB-3902 s.p.,
voc pt BREITKOPF-L CHB-543 s.p., ipr (B1871)
mix cor voc sc BREITKOPF-W EB-6298 s.p.
(B1872)

Seid Froh
mix cor ALSBACH&D s.p. (B1873)

Seid Froh Dieweil [Chorale]
see Weihnachtschorale-III

Selections From St. Luke Passion *Easter/
Lent
(Kelk; Diack) SATB,opt orch FISCHER,C
PT-211 $1.75, ipr (B1874)

Selig Ist Der Mann (Cantata 57) S.57, Xmas,
cant
mix cor,SB soli,cont,3ob,strings sc
BREITKOPF-W PB-4557 s.p., cor pts
BREITKOPF-W CHB-4557 s.p., ipa (B1875)
(Raphael, G.) [Eng/Fr/Ger] SATB soli,
org,3ob,strings,cembalo voc sc BREITKOPF-
L EB-7057 s.p., ipr (B1876)

Senke, O Vater, Herab Deinen Gottlichen
Frieden
see Zwei Lieder Nach Choralsatzen

Seven Lenten Chorales *CC7L,Lent,anthem/
chorale
(Lee, J.) SATB (med easy) oct GIA G1579
$.75 (B1877)

Shall I Not To God Sing Praises *Gen/Refm/
Thanks
SATB,kbd (med diff) oct CONCORDIA 98-1784
$.30 (B1878)

Sheep And Lambs May Safely Graze
see Two Choruses
(Baird) 4pt mix cor oct SCHIRM.G 8860 $.30
(B1879)
(Fletcher) SSA oct PRO ART 1108 $.25
(B1880)
(Treharne) 3pt wom cor oct SCHIRM.G 9529
$.30 (B1881)

Sheep May Graze In Pastures Safely
(Kirk) SATB oct PRO ART 2340 $.25 (B1882)
(Kirk) SAB oct PRO ART 2090 $.25 (B1883)
(Kirk) SSA oct PRO ART 2322 $.30 (B1884)

Sheep May Safely Graze *see Was Mir Behast,
Ist Mur Die Muntre Jagd

Shepherds Keep Their Flocks, The *Xmas
(Kent) SATB,orch oct SPRATT 517 $.25, ipa
(B1885)

Short Passion From St. Matthew's Gospel, A
(from St. Matthew Passion)
(Whittaker, W.G.) [Eng/Welsh] SATB,soli,
orch (med) voc sc OXFORD s.p., ipr,
rental (B1886)

Shout For Joy, Ye Ransomed Band (from Cantata
30)
SATB oct FISCHER,C CM-7314 $.30 (B1887)

BACH, JOHANN SEBASTIAN (cont'd.)

Show Pity, Lord *hymn
PATERSON s.p. see also English Hymns Adapted To Bach's Chorales (B1888)

Sicut Locutus Est (from Magnificat)
(Mishkin, H.) [Lat] TTBB,pno SCHIRM.EC 2109 $.25 (B1889)

Sie Werden *see Sie Werden Aus Saba Alle Kommen

Sie Werden Aus Saba Alle Kommen (Cantata 65) S.65, Epiph,cant
cor sc KALMUS $3.00 (B1890)
mix cor,TB soli,cont,2fl/2rec,2ob,2horn, strings sc BREITKOPF-W PB-4565 s.p., cor pts BREITKOPF-W CHB-4565 s.p., ipr (B1891)
"Sages Of Sheba, The" BELWIN $.75 (B1892)
"Sie Werden" [Eng] cor voc sc KALMUS 6039 $1.00 (B1893)
"Sie Werden" cor,orch sc KALMUS $3.00, ipa (B1894)
(Horn) SATB,TB soli,cont,2fl,2horn,2vln, vla, 2-English horns HANSSLER 10.124 sc $5.00, cor pts $.80, ipa (B1895)
(Naumann, E.) mix cor,TB soli,org,2fl,2ob, 2bsn,2horn,strings,cembalo sc BREITKOPF-L PB-2915 s.p., voc sc BREITKOPF-L EB-7065 s.p., ipr (B1896)
(Pointer, John) "Sages Of Sheba, The" SATB, TB soli,org,2fl,3ob,2horn,strings voc sc NOVELLO rental (B1897)

Sie Werden Euch *see Sie Werden Euch In Den Bann Tun

Sie Werden Euch In Den Bann Tun (Cantata 44) S.44, Fest/Gen,cant
mix cor,SATB soli,cont,2ob,bsn,strings cor pts BREITKOPF-W CHB-4544 s.p., ipr, sc BREITKOPF-W rental (B1898)
mix cor,SATB soli,cont,4ob,strings sc BREITKOPF-W PB-4683 s.p., cor pts BREITKOPF-W CHB-4683 s.p., ipa (B1899)
"Sie Werden Euch" [Ger] cor voc sc KALMUS 6624 $1.25 (B1900)
(Raphael, G.) [Eng/Ger] mix cor,SATB soli, org,2ob,bsn,strings,cembalo voc pt BREITKOPF-L CHB-2131 s.p., voc sc BREITKOPF-L EB-7044 s.p., ipr (B1901)
(Todt, B.) mix cor,SATB soli,org,4ob,bsn, strings,cembalo voc sc BREITKOPF-L EB-7183 s.p., ipr (B1902)

Sieben Choralsatze *CC7L
SATB HANSSLER 6.310 s.p. (B1903)

Siehe, Ich Will *see Siehe, Ich Will Viel Fischer Aussenden

Siehe, Ich Will Viel Fischer Aussenden (Cantata 88) S.88, Trin,cant
mix cor,SATB soli,cont,3ob,2horn,strings cor pts BREITKOPF-W CHB-4588 s.p., ipr, sc BREITKOPF-W rental (B1904)
"Siehe, Ich Will" [Ger] cor voc sc KALMUS 6557 $1.25 (B1905)
(Taubmann, O.; Seiffert, M.) mix cor,SATB soli,org,3ob,bsn,2horn,strings,cembalo voc pt BREITKOPF-L CHB-1901 s.p., voc sc BREITKOPF-L EB-7088 s.p., sc BREITKOPF-L PB-2750 s.p., ipr (B1906)

Siehe Zu *see Siehe Zu, Dass Deine Gottesfurcht

Siehe Zu, Dass Deine Gottesfurcht (Cantata 179) S.179, cant
mix cor,STB soli,cont,4ob,strings cor pts BREITKOPF-W CHB-4679 s.p., ipr, sc BREITKOPF-W rental (B1907)
"Siehe Zu" [Ger] cor voc sc KALMUS 6621 $1.25 (B1908)

Siehe Zu, Dass Deine Gottesfurcht Nicht Heuchelei Sei *S.179, Trin,cant
(Todt, B.) mix cor,STB soli,org,2ob, strings,cembalo, 2 English horn voc sc BREITKOPF-L EB-7179 s.p., ipr (B1909)

Since Thou Art Risen (from Cantata No. 15)
(Easson, James) unis oct CURWEN 10640 $.25 (B1910)

Sing For Joy, Ye Ransomed Band *cant
(Franz) SATB FISCHER,C O-3646 $1.50 (B1911)

Sing His Praises *anthem
SATB ALLANS 88 s.p. (B1912)

Sing Now With Great Rejoicing *Xmas
(Fewell, C.T.) SAB&desc,opt inst SCHIRM.EC 2268 $.25 (B1913)

Sing Out, Ye Voices, Loud And Clear *see Es Bringt Das Rechte Jubeljahr

Sing Praise To Christ *Easter/Gen
SATB,kbd (med easy) oct CONCORDIA 98-1377 $.25 (B1914)
mix cor SOUTHERN $.25 (B1915)

Sing Praise To God *Gen
unis (easy) oct OXFORD 45.288 $.15 (B1916)

Sing Praise To God Who Reigns Above
(Coggin) SATB oct PRO ART 2551 $.30 (B1917)

Sing Praises, Ye Faithful *see Erschallet, Ihr Lieder [Chorale]

Sing To The Lord *see Singet Dem Herrn Ein Neues Lied

Sing To The Lord With Cheerful Voice
(Coggin) SATB WARNER R3495 $.30 (B1918)

Sing We The Birth *see Das Neugeborne Kindelein

Sing We The Praise Of God (from Cantata 142)
(Coggin) 4pt men cor,org/pno oct SCHIRM.G 11471 $.25 (B1919)

Sing Ye To The Lord *see Singet Dem Herrn

BACH, JOHANN SEBASTIAN (cont'd.)

Sing Ye To The Lord *see Singet Dem Herrn Ein Neues Lied

Singet Dem Herrn *Bibl/mot
(Neumann-Buszin) "Sing Ye To The Lord" [Eng/Ger] SATB&SATB,cont PETERS 6101 $1.50, ipa see from Six Motets (B1920)

Singet Dem Herrn Ein Neues Lied (Cantata 190) S.225, Fest/Gen,cant/mot
[Eng/Ger] 8pt mix cor,acap cor pts BREITKOPF-L EB-7225 s.p., voc pt BREITKOPF-L CHB-536 s.p. (B1921)
[Ger] SATB,SATB soli s.p. cor pts HINRICHSEN G290, voc sc HINRICHSEN G290 (B1922)
dbl cor sc BREITKOPF-W EB-6291 s.p. (B1923)
mix cor,ATB soli,cont,4ob,3trp,strings,timp cor pts BREITKOPF-W CHB-4690 s.p., sc BREITKOPF-W PB-4690A s.p., ipr (B1924)
"Sing To The Lord" cor voc sc KALMUS 6060 $1.50 (B1925)
"Sing Ye To The Lord" dbl cor BELWIN $1.75 (B1926)
(Ameln, Konrad) [Ger] SATB&SATB,org,ob,bsn, 2vln,vla,2vcl, 2 English horns (med diff) cor pts BAREN. BA 5129 $2.25, ipa (B1927)
(Ameln; Wolters) SATB&SATB,cont,strings,opt 2ob&bsn, 2 English horns cor pts MOSELER s.p., ipa (B1928)
(Reinhart, Walther) [Ger] cor,soli,org, hpsd,3ob,bsn,3trp,strings,timp HUG s.p. (B1929)
(Stein) SSAATTBB min sc EULENBURG EUL1035 s.p. (B1930)
(Todt, B.) mix cor,ATB soli,org,3ob,3trp, strings,timp voc pt BREITKOPF-L CHB-1471 s.p., voc sc BREITKOPF-L EB-7190 s.p., ipr (B1931)
(West, John E.) "Sing Ye To The Lord" [Eng/Ger] dbl cor,acap voc sc NOVELLO s.p. (B1932)

Singet Dem Herrn (Motet 1)
cor voc sc KALMUS 6070 $1.50 (B1933)

Six Motets *see Der Geist Hilft, "Spirit Also Helpeth Us, The"; Furchte Dich Nicht, "Be Not Afraid"; Jesu, Meine Freude, "Jesus, My Great Pleasure"; Komm, Jesu, Komm, "Come, Jesus, Come"; Lobet Den Herrn, Alle Heiden, "Praise The Lord, All Ye Nations" (Psalm 117); Singet Dem Herrn, "Sing Ye To The Lord" (B1934)

Six Sacred Songs *see Der Tag Ist Hin, "Day Is Done, The"; Dich Bet' Ich An, "Exalted Lord, Thee I Adore"; Dir, Dir, Jehova, Will Ich Singen, "To Thee, Jehovah, I Am Singing"; Komm', Susser Tod, "Come Thou, Sweet Death"; Nicht So Traurig, "Be Not Downcast"; O Du Liebe Meiner Liebe, "O Thou, Everlasting Virtue" (B1935)

Sixteen Chorales *CC16U,chorale
(Lake) [Eng/Ger] 4pt mix cor,winds/strings/ winds&strings oct SCHIRM.G 8212 $.30 (B1936)

Sixty Chorales *CC60U
(Goetschius, P.) SATB oct PRESSER $1.50 (B1937)

Sleepers Awake *see Wachet Auf, Ruft Uns Die Stimme

Sleepers Wake! *see Wachet Auf, Ruft Uns Die Stimme

Slumber, Beloved (from Christmas Oratorio) Xmas
unis,orch oct NOVELLO 48.0795.02 s.p., ipr (B1938)

So Feiern Wir Das Hohe Fest (from Christ Lag In Todesbanden)
"So Keep We All This Holy Feast" see Bach, Johann Sebastian, Wir Essen Und Wir Leben Wohl
"So Keep We All This Holy Feast" SATB,pno SCHIRM.EC 1672 $.30, ipr contains also: Wir Essen Und Wir Leben Wohl, "With Grateful Hearts We All Are Met" (B1939)

So Gibst Du Nun, Mein Jesu, Gute Nacht *S.412
SATB (F min) HANSSLER 6.244 s.p. contains also: Janus, Martin, Du Grosser Schmerzensmann Vom Vater (B1940)

So Keep We All This Holy Feast *see So Feiern Wir Das Hohe Fest

So Lasset Uns Gehen In Salem (from Himmelskonig, Sei Willkommen)
"With Joy We March Onward To Zion" see Bach, Johann Sebastian, Himmelskonig, Sei Willkommen [Chorale]

So Ruhest Du, O Meine Ruh *see O Traurigkeit, O Herzelied

Soleil Couchant
(Geveart, F.-A.) [Fr] 4pt mix cor,acap (med easy) cor pts LEMOINE s.p. see from Collection De Choeurs, cinquieme Fascicule (B1941)

Sollt Ich Meinem Gott Nicht Singen
SATB HANSSLER 6.198 s.p. (B1942)

Song Of Repentance
(Cornelius) SATB,acap BROUDE BR. $.35 see from Two Choral Songs (B1943)

Songs For The Advent And Christmas Seasons *see Ermuntre Dich, Mein Schwacher Geist, "My Fainting Soul, Awaken Now"; Ich Freue Mich In Dir, "With Joy I Welcome Thee"; Ich Steh' An Deiner Krippen Hier, "O Christ Child, Now I Come To Thee"; Ihr Gestirn', Ihr Hohen Lufte, "O Ye Stars And Highest Heavens"; Jesu, Meines Herzens Freud', "Thou, O Lord, Joy Of My Heart"; O Jesulein Suss, "O Savior Sweet" (B1944)

Songs For The Lenten And Easter Seasons *CC7L,Easter/Lent
(Mattfeld, V.) [Ger/Eng] unis,org SCHIRM.EC 2553 (B1945)

BACH, JOHANN SEBASTIAN (cont'd.)

Spirit Also Helpeth, The (Motet 2)
cor voc sc KALMUS 6069 $1.25 (B1946)

Spirit Also Helpeth Us *cant
dbl cor BELWIN $1.25 (B1947)

Spirit Also Helpeth Us, The *see Der Geist Hilft

Spirit Also Helpeth Us, The *see Der Geist Hilft Unsrer Schwachheit Auf

Spring Song *see Mer Hahn En Neue Oberkeet

St. John's Passion *see Johannespassion

St. Johns' Passion *see La Passione Di N.S. Gesu Cristo Secondo Giovanni

St. Lukes' Passion *see Lukas-Passion

St. Mark's Passion *see Markuspassion

St. Matthew Passion *see La Passione Di N.S. Gesu Cristo Secondo Matteo

St. Matthew Passion, Part I *see La Passione Di N.S. Gesu Cristo Secondo Matteo

St. Matthew Passion, Part II *see La Passione Di N.S. Gesu Cristo Secondo Matteo

St. Matthews' Passion *see La Passione Di N.S. Gesu Cristo Secondo Matteo

St. Matthew's Passion *see Matthauspassion

Strife Is O'er The Battle Done, The *hymn
PATERSON s.p. see also English Hymns Adapted To Bach's Chorales (B1948)

Strike Thou Hour (Cantata 53)
study sc UNIVER. PH. 102 $.95 (B1949)

Stronghold Sure *cant
BELWIN $1.25 (B1950)

Stronghold Sure, A *see Ein Feste Burg Ist Unser Gott

Stronghold Sure, A *see Ein' Feste Burg Ist Unser Gott

Stronghold Sure, The (Cantata 80)
mix cor,soli,pno voc sc SCHIRM.G $1.25 (B1951)

Subdue Us By Thy Goodness (from Cantata 22) Gen
(Willan, Healey) SSA (easy) oct OXFORD 44.417 $.30 (B1952)

Subdue Us Through Thy Kindness (from Jesu Nahm Zu Sich Die Zwolfe) chorale
(Donovan, R.) SATB,org SCHIRM.EC 1670 $.25 (B1953)
(Donovan, R.) TTBB,org SCHIRM.EC 529 $.18 (B1954)

Suesser Tod *see Susser Trost, Mein Jesus Kommt

Suesser Trost *see Susser Trost, Mein Jesus Kommt

Surexit Christus Hodie *Easter,chorale
(Geveart, F.-A.) "Chant De Paques" [Lat] 4pt mix cor,acap (med diff) cor pts LEMOINE s.p. see from Collection De Choeurs, cinquieme Fascicule (B1955)

Suscepit Israel (from Magnificat)
"His Servant Israel" SSA oct PRO ART 1307 $.25 (B1956)
(Craig) "Lord Is Merciful, The" SAB oct PLYMOUTH DC-204 $.25 (B1957)

Susser Trost, Mein Jesus Kommt (Cantata 151) S.151, Xmas,cant
mix cor,SATB soli,cont,fl,ob,strings sc BREITKOPF-W PB-4651 s.p., cor pts BREITKOPF-W CHB-4651 s.p., ipa (B1958)
"Suesser Tod" [Eng] cor voc sc KALMUS 6057 $1.00 (B1959)
"Suesser Trost" cor,orch/org sc KALMUS $2.75, ipa (B1960)
(Hellmann) SATB,SATB soli,cont,fl,2vln,vla HANSSLER 10.134 sc $3.50, cor pts $.40, ipa (B1961)
(Raphael, G.) [Eng/Ger] mix cor,SATB soli, org,fl,ob,bsn,strings,cembalo voc pt BREITKOPF-L CHB-2194 s.p., voc sc BREITKOPF-L EB-7151 s.p., ipr (B1962)

Tantum Ergo *Commun,mot
[Lat] 4pt mix cor HEUGEL s.p. see from SAINTE-CECILE (B1963)
SATB,acap RICORDI-ENG SY137 s.p. (B1964)
(Kunc, P.) [Lat] 4pt mix cor,org DURAND s.p. (B1965)

Tantum Ergo, En Si Bemol *Commun,mot
[Lat] SATBar (B flat maj) DURAND s.p. (B1966)

Tantum Ergo, Mi Mineur *Commun,mot
[Lat] SATBar (E min) DURAND s.p. (B1967)

Ten Chorales *CC10U,chorale
(Buszin) mix cor SOUTHERN $.30 (B1968)

Ten Schemelli Chorales *CC10L,chorale
mix cor CONCORDIA 98-1165 $.35 (B1969)

Thank And Praise God, Laud, Extol Him (from Christmas Oratorio) Gen
SATB,kbd (diff) oct CONCORDIA 98-1192 $.36 (B1970)

The Duteous Day Know Closeth
see Bach, Johann Sebastian, Sleepers Wake

Thee We Adore, Eternal Lord (from Uns Ist Ein Kindlein Heut' Geborn)
(Coggin) SATB oct FOX R212 $.25 (B1971)

Thee, With Tender Care (from Christmas Oratorio, The)
see Two Chorales

BACH, JOHANN SEBASTIAN (cont'd.)

There Is Nought Of Soundness In All My Body
*see Es Ist Nichts Gesundes An Meinem
Leibe

There Uprose A Great Strife *see Es Erhub
Sich Ein Streit

Thine Anger Withold
(Easson) unis jr cor/unis wom cor CURWEN
72606 s.p. (B1972)

Thirteen Chorales *CC13L,chorale
mix cor cmplt ed NOVELLO 03.0097.07 s.p. (B1973)

This Proud Heart (from Christmas Oratorio)
Xmas,anthem/chorale
see Bach, Johann Sebastian, How Shall I
Fitly Meet Thee
mix cor oct NOVELLO 50.0319.09 s.p. (B1974)

Thou Guide *see Du Hirte Israel, Hore

Thou Guide Of Israel *see Du Hirte Israel,
Hore

Thou Martyred Lamb, In Darkest Tomb
Imprisoned
(Hardwicke) SATB ALFRED 6633 $.30 (B1975)

Thou, O Lord, Joy Of My Heart *see Jesu,
Meines Herzens Freud'

Thou Sanctified Fire *see Du Heilige Brunst

Thou That Life And Death Ordainst *see
Herrscher Uber Tod Und Leben

Thou Very God And David's Son *see Du Wahrer
Gott Und Davids Sohn

Though Great Our Sins And Sore Our Woes *see
Ob Bei Uns Is Der Sunden Viel

Though Worms Destroy My Body *see Der Leib
Zwar In Der Erden

Three Bach Chorales *CC3U,chorale
TTBB oct FISCHER,J 7561 $.30 (B1976)

Three Chorales, Set I *CC3U,anthem/chorale
(Johnson) SATB (easy) oct AUGSBURG 1413
$.20 (B1977)

Three Chorales, Set II *CC3U,anthem/chorale
SATB (easy) oct AUGSBURG 1415 $.20 (B1978)

Three Chorales (from Christmas Oratorio)
CC3U,Xmas
(Ehret) SATB oct BOURNE WE5 $.40 (B1979)

Three Chorales (from Christmas Oratorio)
CC3U,Xmas,chorale
(Palmer) SATB ALFRED 6634 $.30 (B1980)

Three Chorales *chorale
(Woodworth) 4pt mix cor oct SCHIRM.G 10053
$.35
contains: If Thou But Suffer God To Guide
Thee; Mighty Fortress Is Our God, A;
Out Of The Depths I Cry To Thee (B1981)

Three Chorales (from Christmas Oratorio, The)
Xmas,chorale
(Spicker) 4pt mix cor oct SCHIRM.G 10236
$.30
contains: Ah! Dearest Jesus; How Shall I
Fitly Meet Thee; Rejoice And Sing (B1982)

Three Chorales (from Christmas Oratorio)
CC3U,Xmas,chorale
SATB,opt strings oct SHAPIRO SK 2102 $.25 (B1983)

Three Hundred And Eight-Nine Four Part
Chorales *CC389U,chorale
[Ger] 4pt voc KALMUS 6002 $4.00 (B1984)

Three Hundred Seventeen Chorales And Sacred
Arias, Vol. 1, One Hundred Ninety Five
Chorales And Sacred Arias *CC195U,
chorale
(Erk) SATB,opt org/pno PETERS 4264A $7.50 (B1985)

Three Hundred Seventeen Chorales And Sacred
Arias, Vol. 2, One Hundred Twenty Two
Chorales And Sacred Arias *CC122U,
chorale
(Erk) SATB,opt org/pno PETERS 4264B $7.50 (B1986)

Through The Day Thy Love Has Spared Us *hymn
PATERSON s.p. see also English Hymns
Adapted To Bach's Chorales (B1987)

Thus Then, The Law (from Jesu, Priceless
Treasure)
(Damrosch) 3pt wom cor,acap oct SCHIRM.G
7604 $.25 (B1988)

To God On High Be Glory *see Jesu, Nun Sei
Gepreiset [Chorale]

To Thee Alone Be Glory (from Cantata 41)
chorale
see With Grateful Hearts
(Davison, A.) TTBB,2pno SCHIRM.EC 961 $.18 (B1989)

To Thee Be Praise Forever (from Cantata No.
41)
girl cor SOUTHERN $.30 (B1990)
(Tillinghast) SSA WARNER W2854 $.30 (B1991)

To Thee, Jehovah
SATB oct PRESSER MC336 $.25 (B1992)

To Thee, Jehovah, I Am Singing *see Dir,
Dir, Jehova, Will Ich Singen

To Thee, O Lord, Our Hearts We Raise *hymn
PATERSON s.p. see also English Hymns
Adapted To Bach's Chorales (B1993)

To Thee We Turn
(Lockwood) boy cor SOUTHERN $.25 (B1994)
(Lockwood, N.) TTBB,acap oct PRESSER
312-40090 $.25 (B1995)

BACH, JOHANN SEBASTIAN (cont'd.)

To Us A Child Is Born *see Uns Ist Ein Kind
Geboren

To Us A Child Is Born *see Es Ist Ein Kind
Geboren [Chorale]

To Us A Child Is Given *see Uns Ist Ein Kind
Geboren

Trauermusik *S.198
BREITKOPF-L EB-1942 s.p.
contains: Lass Furstin, Lass Noch Einen
Strahl Trauerode (mix cor,SATB soli,
org,2fl,2ob,bsn,strings,cembalo, 2
lutes); Lass Hochster, Lass Der
Hoffnung Strahl (mix cor,SATB soli,org,
2fl,2ob,2bsn,2horn,3trp,strings,timp,
cembalo, 2 English horns)
see also: Lass Furstin, Lass Noch Einen
Strahl Trauerode (B1996)

Trauermusik *see Lass, Furstin, Lass Noch
Einen Strahl

Tristesse
(Geveart, F.-A.) [Fr] 4pt mix cor,acap (med
easy) cor pts LEMOINE s.p. see from
Collection De Choeurs, cinquieme
Fascicule (B1997)

Tue Rechnung *S.168, cant
[Ger] cor voc sc KALMUS 6613 $1.25 (B1998)

Tue Rechnung, Donnerwort (Cantata 168) S.168,
Trin,cant
mix cor,SATB soli,org,2ob,strings,cembalo
voc sc BREITKOPF-L EB-7168 s.p., ipr (B1999)
mix cor,SATB soli,cont,2ob, strings sc
BREITKOPF-W PB-4668 s.p., cor pts
BREITKOPF-W CHB-4668 s.p., ipa (B2000)
"Cantate, Pour Le Neuvieme Dimanche Apres
La Trinite" SATB,SATB soli CHOUDENS voc
sc s.p., cor pts s.p. (B2001)

Twelve Chorales (from St. Matthew Passion)
CC12U,Easter/Gen
SATB,acap oct PRESSER 332-00923 $.30 (B2002)

Twelve Sacred Duets From Cantatas, Vol. 1
(from Cantatas 4, 37, 78, 124) CC4U
(Reinhart) [Ger] SA,pno/org/hpsd,inst
PETERS A54 sc $5.00, voc sc $4.00, ipa (B2003)

Twelve Sacred Duets From Cantatas, Vol. 2
(from Cantatas 9, 184) CC2U
(Reinhart) [Ger] SA,pno/org/hpsd,inst
PETERS A55 sc $5.00, voc sc $2.00, ipa (B2004)

Twelve Sacred Duets From Cantatas, Vol. 3
(from Cantatas 88, 93, 168) CC3U
(Reinhart) [Eng/Ger] SA,pno/org/hpsd,inst
PETERS A56 sc $5.00, voc sc $3.00, ipa (B2005)

Twelve Sacred Duets From Cantatas, Vol. 4
(from Cantatas 3, 91, 163) CC3U
(Reinhart) [Eng/Ger] SA,pno/org/hpsd,inst
PETERS A57 sc $5.00, voc sc $3.00, ipa (B2006)

Twenty-Eight Chorales, Book II *CC28L
(Clough-Leighter, H.) SATB SCHIRM.EC 615
pap $1.50, ipa, cloth $2.00 (B2007)

Twenty-Five Chorales, Book I *CC25L
(Clough-Leighter, H.) SATB/unis SCHIRM.EC 1
pap $1.50, ipa, cloth $2.00 (B2008)

Twenty-Five Chorales, Book III *CC25L
(Clough-Leighter, H.) SATB SCHIRM.EC 1799
pap $1.50, ipa, cloth $2.00 (B2009)

Twenty-Seven Chorales, Book IV *CC27L
(Clough-Leighter, H.) 4pt wom cor SCHIRM.EC
875 pap $1.50, ipa, cloth $2.00 (B2010)

Twenty-Six Chorales, Book V *CC26L
(Clough-Leighter, H.) 3pt wom cor SCHIRM.EC
878 pap $1.50, ipa, cloth $2.00 (B2011)

Twenty Two Chorales *CC22U
SA FLAMMER GE5018 $.75 (B2012)

Two Bach Chorales For Christmas *Xmas,
chorale
oct SATB PRO ART 1440 $.30; SAB PRO ART
1816 $.30; SSA PRO ART 1106 $.30; 2pt PRO
ART 1817 $.30
contains: Break Forth, O Beauteous,
Heavenly Light; Child Is Born In
Bethlehem, A (B2013)

Two Choral Songs *see By The Waters Of
Babylon; Song Of Repentance (B2014)

Two Chorales *Gen,chorale
(Davies, Laurence H.) 2pt (easy) oct OXFORD
44.277 $.25
contains: God Is Living, God Is Here!;
Live Your Life For Him Always
see also: Live Your Life For Him (B2015)

Two Chorales (from Christmas Oratorio) Xmas,
chorale
(Dickinson) TTBB oct GRAY GSC 98 $.25
contains: Break Forth; My Chosen King (B2016)

Two Chorales (from Jesu Priceless Treasure)
CC2U,mot
SATB oct PRESSER MC346 $.30 (B2017)

Two Chorales (from St. John Passion) CC2U,
Easter
SATB oct PRESSER MC376 $.30 (B2018)

Two Chorales (from Christmas Oratorio) Xmas,
chorale
SATB,acap oct BELWIN 64152 $.25
contains: Ah! Dearest Jesus; How Shall I
Fitly Meet Thee (B2019)

Two Chorales (from Christmas Oratorio) CC2U,
Xmas,chorale
(Ehret) SATB MARKS 881 $.25 (B2020)

Two Chorales (from Motets Nos. 2 And 5) CC2U,
chorale
(Richter) [Eng/Ger] SATB,acap AMP A418 $.25

BACH, JOHANN SEBASTIAN (cont'd.)

(B2021)
Two Chorales (from Christmas Oratorio, The)
Xmas,chorale
4pt mix cor,acap oct SCHIRM.G 7929 $.25
contains: Break Forth, O Beauteous,
Heavenly Light; Thee, With Tender Care
(Deis) (B2022)

Two Chorales (from Christmas Oratorio) CC2U,
Xmas,chorale
(Darwin) SATB oct PLYMOUTH XM-112 $.25 (B2023)

Two Choruses
oct SCHIRM.G 11157 $.35
contains: Chorale From St. Matthew
Passion (Licht) (3pt mix cor,org/pno);
Sheep And Lambs May Safely Graze
(Baird; Mueller) (3pt mix cor,org) (B2024)

Two Christmas Chorales *Xmas,chorale
(Davies) SA (easy) OXFORD 44.074 $.25
contains: Beside Thy Cradle; Rejoice And
Sing (B2025)

Two Festival Chorales *CC2U,Fest,chorale
(Harper) SATB oct PLYMOUTH SC-24 $.25 (B2026)

Two Songs
(Daymond) unis (med) OXFORD 45.285 $.35
contains: If Thou Wert Near; Now Rest In
Peace (B2027)

Two Two-Part Bach Chorales *chorale
(Davies) 2pt jr cor/2pt wom cor CURWEN
72573 $.25
contains: Break Forth, O Beauteous
Heavenly Light; How Shall I Fitly Meet
Thee? (B2028)

Und Wollte Alles Wanken
4pt MOSELER LB-50 s.p. contains also:
Rothenberg, Alles Ist Eitel (3pt mix
cor); Staden, Was Ist Das Menschenleben
(2pt mix cor) (B2029)

Uns Ist *see Uns Ist Ein Kind Geboren

Uns Ist Ein Kind Geboren (Cantata 142) S.142
(from Cantata 142) Xmas,cant
cor sc KALMUS $4.00 (B2030)
mix cor ALSBACH&D sc s.p., cor pts s.p. (B2031)
mix cor,ATB soli,cont,2fl/2rec,2ob,strings
sc BREITKOPF-W PB-4642 s.p., cor pts
BREITKOPF-W CHB-4642 s.p., ipa (B2032)
"For Us A Child Is Born" [Ger/Eng] SSA,orch
GALAXY 1.1841.1 voc sc $.75, ipa, ipr, sc
$3.50 (B2033)
"For Us A Child Is Born" [Ger/Eng] SATB,
orch GALAXY 1.1012.1 voc sc $.75, ipa,
ipr, sc $3.50 (B2034)
"To Us A Child Is Born" [Eng/Ger] SATB,orch
MARKS $1.00, ipr (B2035)
"To Us A Child Is Born" cor voc sc KALMUS
6055 $1.00 (B2036)
"To Us A Child Is Given" [Eng/Ger] 4pt mix
cor,ATB soli,pno voc sc SCHIRM.G $1.00 (B2037)
"Uns Ist" cor,orch sc KALMUS $4.00, ipa (B2038)

Uns Ist Ein Kindlein Heut Geborn
see Weihnachtschorale-I
4pt mix cor MOSELER LB-57 s.p. contains
also: Lobt Gott, Ihr Christen
Allzugleich; Gelobet Seist Du, Jesu
Christ (B2039)

Unser Mund Sei *see Unser Mund Sei Voll
Lachens

Unser Mund Sei Voll Lachens (Cantata 110)
S.110, Xmas,cant
mix cor,SATB soli,org,2fl,4ob,bsn,3trp,
strings,timp,cembalo, English horn voc pt
BREITKOPF-L CHB-1937 s.p., ipr
BREITKOPF-L EB-7110 s.p., ipr (B2040)
mix cor,SATB soli,cont,2fl,5ob,bsn,3trp,
strings,timp sc BREITKOPF-W PB-4610 s.p.,
cor pts BREITKOPF-W CHB-4610 s.p., ipa (B2041)
"Unser Mund Sei" [Ger] cor voc sc KALMUS
6576 $1.25 (B2042)

Unsere Saat, Die Wir Gesaet
see Schutz, Heinrich, Von Gott Will Ich
Nicht Lassen

Unto His Holy Name Sing Praises (from Es Ist
Ein Kind Geboren)
(Ehret) [Eng/Ger] SSA MARKS 4269 $.25 (B2043)
(Ehret) [Eng/Ger] SATB MARKS 4214 $.25 (B2044)
(Ehret) [Eng/Ger] TTBB MARKS 4266 $.25 (B2045)

Unto The World This Happy Morn *see Das
Neugeborne Kindelein

Up, Up! My Heart, With Gladness *see Auf,
Auf! Mein Herz, Mit Freuden

Uphold My Heart With Faith In Thee *see
Erhalt' Mein Herz Im Glauben Rein

Vaknen Upp Hor Rupet Skaller *see Wachet Auf

Var Gud Ar Oss En Valdig Borg *see Ein'
Feste Burg Ist Unser Gott

Vater Unser Im Himmelreich *S.416
see Vulpius, Melchior, Erhalt Uns, Herr,
Bei Deinem Wort

Veni Creator *Gen,mot
(Kunc, P.) [Lat] 4pt mix cor,org oct DURAND
s.p. (B2046)

Veni Creator Spiritus *Pent,chorale/hymn
(Geveart, F.-A.) "Hymne De La Pentecote"
[Lat] 4pt mix cor,acap (med diff) cor pts
LEMOINE s.p. see from Collection De
Choeurs, cinquieme Fascicule (B2047)

Vergnugte Pleissenstadt (Cantata 216)
"Wedding Cantata" SSA,S/A solo,2fl,ob,vcl,
pno cmplt ed SCHIRM.EC P450 $4.80, ipa
(B2048)

BACH, JOHANN SEBASTIAN (cont'd.)

Vertrouwen (Wat God Doet Is Welgedaan)
mix cor ALSBACH&D s.p. (B2049)

Verwunschtes Freudenlicht *S.184, cant
[Ger] cor voc sc KALMUS 6625 $1.25 (B2050)

Vi Tacka Dig, Gud (from Cantata 29)
mix cor,org cor pts NORDISKA 3737 s.p. (B2051)

Viens, Jesus, Viens! *S.229, mot
(Barre, J.) [Fr] 4pt mix cor,acap voc sc DURAND see from Motets (B2052)

Vier Einlagesatzen Der Es-Dur Fassung *S.243a
see Bach, Johann Sebastian, Magnificat D-Dur

Vier Sanctus [BWV 237-240] *CC4U,cant/Sanctus
mix cor,2ob,bsn,3trp,strings,timp,cembalo sc BREITKOPF-L rental (B2053)

Vierstimmige Kirchengesange (from Schemelli'schen Chorale) CCU,chorale
(Bargiel, Woldemar) [Ger] SATB BOTE s.p. (B2054)

Vocal Companion To Bach's Orgelbuchlein, A (Book 1) *CC16L,chorale
(Emery, Walter) [Ger] mix cor cmplt ed NOVELLO 03.0119.01 s.p. (B2055)

Vocal Companion To Bach's Orgelbuchlein, A (Book 2) *CC16L,chorale
(Emery, Walter) [Ger] mix cor cmplt ed NOVELLO 03.0756.04 s.p. (B2056)

Vom Himmel Hoch (from Magnificat) Xmas, chorale
see Drei Chorsatze Zum Magnificat
see Weihnachtschorale-I
"From Heav'n Above" SATB KJOS 506 $.30 (B2057)
"From Heav'n Above" SATB oct WALTON 2121 $.25 (B2058)
(McAfee; Satz) "From Heaven Above" SATB,org oct LAWSON 51377 $.40 (B2059)
(Stravinsky, I.) [Ger] mix cor,orch (choral-variation) BOOSEY cor pts $.30, sc $6.50, ipr, min sc $4.50 (B2060)
(Talmadge, A.) "From Heaven Above" [Ger/Eng] SSAA,acap SCHIRM.EC 2546 $.30 (B2061)

Vom Himmel Hoch, Da Komm Ich Her (from Weihnachts-Oratorium)
see Praetorius, Michael, Lobt Gott, Ihr Christen, Allzugleich
see Bach, Johann Sebastian, Lobt Gott, Ihr Christen Allzugleich

Vom Reiche Gottes *ora
(Grischkat) SATB,SAB soli,cont,3fl,3ob,bsn,3trp,3trom,2vln,vla,timp, English horn HANSSLER 10.001 sc s.p., cor pts s.p., voc sc s.p., ipa (B2062)

Von Dir, Du Gott Der Einigkeit
see Zwei Lieder Nach Choralsatzen

Von Ewigkeit Zu Ewigkeit (from Magnificat)
(Fischer, H.) [Ger] 3pt jr cor/3pt wom cor, ob/vln,pno/cembalo sc VIEWEG s.p. (B2063)

Von Himmel Hoch Da Komm Ich Her *Adv/Xmas
SATB,acap (contains also: Anonymous, Uns Ist Geboren Ein Kindelein) voc pt DOBLINGER s.p. see also ADVENT UND WEIHNACHT, HEFT 1 (B2064)

Vor Deinen Thron Tret Ich Hiermit *mot
see Bach, Johann Sebastian, Hast Du Denn, Jesu, Dein Angesicht Ganzlich
4pt mix cor MOSELER sc s.p., cor pts s.p. (B2065)
4pt men cor MOSELER s.p. (B2066)

Vor Herre Kom Til Jordans Flod *see Christ Unser Herr Zum Jordan Kam

Wach Auf, Mein Herz, Und Singe (from Gott Der Herr Ist Sonn' Und Schild) Gen/Refm
SATB,2horn HANSSLER 6.2191 s.p. contains also: Wie Schon Leucht Uns Der Morgenstern (from Schwingt Freudig Euch Empor) (SATB) (Adv) (B2067)
(Weitemeyer, Herbert) [Ger] 4pt men cor, acap (med) NAGELS NCH 10 s.p. (B2068)

Wachet Auf (Cantata 140)
(Genetay, Claude; Ahlen, David) "Vaknen Upp Hor Rupet Skaller" cor,2ob,2clar,trom, 2vln,vla,bsn/vcl/bvl, English horn cor pts NORDISKA 1046 s.p., ipr (B2069)

Wachet Auf *see Wachet Auf, Ruft Uns Die Stimme

Wachet Auf [Chorale]
see Weihnachtschorale-I

Wachet Auf, Ruft Uns Die Stimme (Cantata 140) S.140 (from Cantata 140) Adv/ECY/Trin, cant/chorale
[Ger] mix cor,acap (easy) HUG s.p. (B2070)
mix cor ALSBACH&D s.p. (B2071)
[Ger] SATB,acap (med) BAREN. BCH 1 s.p. (B2072)
mix cor,STB soli,cont,3ob,horn,strings sc BREITKOPF-W PB-4640 s.p., cor pts BREITKOPF-W CHB-4640 s.p., ipa (B2073)
4pt mix cor,opt inst MOSELER LB-24 s.p. contains also: Ein Feste Burg Ist Unser Gott (B2074)
"Sleepers Awake" cor voc sc KALMUS 6054 $1.00 (B2075)
"Sleepers, Wake!" 3pt wom cor oct SCHIRM.G 7428 $.25 (B2076)
"Sleepers Wake!" 4pt mix cor oct SCHIRM.G 7427 $.25 (B2077)
"Sleepers, Wake" BELWIN $1.00 (B2078)
"Sleepers Wake!" [Eng/Ger] mix cor voc sc SCHIRM.G $1.00 (B2079)
"Sleepers, Wake!" SATB,STB soli,org,3ob, horn,strings,cembalo voc sc NOVELLO s.p., ipr (B2080)
"Wachet Auf" cor,orch sc KALMUS $5.00, ipa (B2081)

BACH, JOHANN SEBASTIAN (cont'd.)

(Davies) "Sleepers Wake" 2pt jr cor/2pt wom cor CURWEN 72627 s.p. contains also: The Duteous Day Hook Closeth (B2082)
(Durr) mix cor voc sc DEUTSCHER 5032 s.p., sc DEUTSCHER 5142A s.p. (B2083)
(Horn) SATB,STB soli,cont,2ob,bsn,2vln,vla HANSSLER 10.113 sc $6.50, voc sc $2.35, ipa (B2084)
(Raphael, G.) [Eng/Fr/Ger] mix cor,STB soli,org,2ob,trp,horn,strings,cembalo, English horn sc BREITKOPF-L PB-2990 s.p., voc pt BREITKOPF-L CHB-275 s.p., voc sc BREITKOPF-L EB-7140 s.p., ipr, ipa (B2085)
(Stanford, Charles Villiers) [Eng/Ger] mix cor,STB soli,3ob,trp,strings cmplt ed BOOSEY rental (B2086)

Wachet Auf, Ruft Uns Die Stimme [Chorale] (from Wachet Auf, Ruft Uns Die Stimme) Adv
see Bach, Johann Sebastian, Nun Danket Alle Gott
SATB HANSSLER 6.279 s.p. (B2087)
(Whittaker, W. Gillies) "Wake, O Wake!" SATB (easy) oct OXFORD 42.084 $.40, ipr (B2088)

Wachet, Betet! *S.70, cant
(Todt, B.) mix cor,SATB soli,org,ob,bsn, trp,strings,cembalo voc pt BREITKOPF-L CHB-857 s.p., voc sc BREITKOPF-L EB-7070 s.p., ipr (B2089)

Wachet, Betet *see Wachet, Betet, Seid Bereit Allezeit

Wachet, Betet, Seid Bereit Allezeit (Cantata 70) S.70, cant
mix cor,SATB soli,cont,ob,bsn,trp,strings sc BREITKOPF-W PB-4570 s.p., cor pts BREITKOPF-W CHB-4570 s.p., ipa (B2090)
"Wachet, Betet" [Eng] cor voc sc KALMUS 6041 $1.00 (B2091)

Wahrlich, Wahrlich *see Wahrlich, Wahrlich, Ich Sage Euch

Wahrlich, Wahrlich, Ich Sage Euch (Cantata 86) S.86, Gen,cant
mix cor,SATB soli,org,2ob,strings,cembalo voc sc BREITKOPF-L EB-7086 s.p., ipr (B2092)
mix cor,SATB soli,cont,2ob,strings sc BREITKOPF-W PB-4586 s.p., cor pts BREITKOPF-W CHB-4586 s.p., ipa (B2093)
"Wahrlich, Wahrlich" [Ger] cor voc sc KALMUS 6555 $1.25 (B2094)

Wailing, Crying, Mourning, Sighing *see Weinen, Klagen, Sorgen, Zagen

Wake, O Wake! *see Wachet Auf, Ruft Uns Die Stimme [Chorale]

Wake! The Welcome Day Appeareth *hymn
PATERSON s.p. see also English Hymns Adapted To Bach's Chorales (B2095)

Walk Humbly With Thy God
(Stone) unis BOSTON 13592 $.30 (B2096)

Wann Ich Einmal Soll Scheiden
mix cor ALSBACH&D s.p. (B2097)

War Gott Nicht *see War' Gott Nicht Mit Uns Diese Zeit

War Gott Nicht Mit Uns *S.14, Epiph,cant/Psalm
SATB,acap DOBLINGER s.p. see from PSALMLIEDER (B2098)
(Todt, B.) mix cor,STB soli,org,2ob,2bsn, trp,strings,cembalo voc pt BREITKOPF-L CHB-2129 s.p., voc sc BREITKOPF-L EB-7014 s.p., ipr (B2099)

War Gott Nicht Mit Uns Diese Zeit (Cantata 14) S.257, cant
SATB HANSSLER 6.185 s.p. contains also: Trubel, Gerhard, War Gott Nicht Mit Uns Diese Zeit (B2100)
mix cor,STB soli,cont,3ob,horn,strings cor pts BREITKOPF-W CHB-4514 s.p., ipr, sc BREITKOPF-W rental (B2101)
"War Gott Nicht" [Ger] cor voc sc KALMUS 6527 $1.25 (B2102)

Warum Betrubst Du Dich *see Warum Betrubst Du Dich, Mein Herz

Warum Betrubst Du Dich, Mein Herz (Cantata 138) S.138, Trin,cant
mix cor,SATB soli,org,2ob,bsn,strings, cembalo voc pt BREITKOPF-L CHB-2193 s.p., voc sc BREITKOPF-L EB-7138 s.p., ipr (B2103)
mix cor,SATB soli,cont,2ob,strings cor pts BREITKOPF-W CHB-4638 s.p., ipr, sc BREITKOPF-W rental (B2104)
"Warum Betrubst Du Dich" [Ger] cor voc sc KALMUS 6593 $1.25 (B2105)

Was Frag' Ich Nach Der Welt (Cantata 94) S.94, Trin,cant
[Ger] cor voc sc KALMUS 6562 $1.25 (B2106)
mix cor,SATB soli,cont,fl,3ob,strings sc BREITKOPF-W PB-4594 s.p., cor pts BREITKOPF-W CHB-4594 s.p., ipa (B2107)
(Todt, B.) mix cor,SATB soli,org,fl,2ob, strings,cembalo, English horn sc BREITKOPF-L PB-2944 s.p., voc pt BREITKOPF-L CHB-2149 s.p., voc sc BREITKOPF-L EB-7094 s.p., ipr (B2108)

Was Gott Tut Das Ist Wohlgetan *Gen
[Ger] SATB,acap (med diff) BAREN. BCH 73 s.p. (B2109)

Was Gott Tut, Das Ist Wohlgetan *S.98, Trin, cant
mix cor,SATB soli,org,3ob,strings,cembalo voc pt BREITKOPF-L CHB-2179 s.p., voc sc BREITKOPF-L EB-7098 s.p., ipr (B2110)

Was Gott Tut, Das Ist Wohlgetan *S.99, Trin, cant
(Todt, B.) mix cor,SATB soli,org,fl,ob,

BACH, JOHANN SEBASTIAN (cont'd.)

horn,strings,cembalo voc pt BREITKOPF-L CHB-2180 s.p., voc sc BREITKOPF-L EB-7099 s.p., ipr (B2111)

Was Gott Tut, Das Ist Wohlgetan *S.100, Trin,cant
mix cor,SATB soli,org,fl,ob,2horn,strings, timp,cembalo voc pt BREITKOPF-L CHB-2199 s.p., voc sc BREITKOPF-L EB-7100 s.p., ipr (B2112)

Was Gott Tut, Das Ist Wohlgetan [Chorale] (from Was Gott Tut, Das Ist Wohlgetan)
see Bach, Johann Sebastian, Christus, Der Ist Mein Leben
see Schroter, Leonhard, Von Gott Will Ich Nicht Lassen
4pt mix cor MOSELER LB-320 s.p. contains also: Wie Schon Leuchtet Der Morgenstern [Chorale] (B2113)
(Hamburger, Povl) "Lad Haende Kun, Som Herren Vil" [Ger/Dan] SATB,acap HANSEN-DEN 157 s.p. see also Otte Koraludsaettelser (B2114)

Was Gott Tut, Das Ist Wohlgetan (Cantata 98) S.98, cant
mix cor,SATB soli,cont,4ob,strings sc BREITKOPF-W PB-4598 s.p., cor pts BREITKOPF-W CHB-4598 s.p., ipa (B2115)
"Was Gott Tut, Das Ist" [Ger] cor voc sc KALMUS 6566 $1.25 (B2116)

Was Gott Tut, Das Ist Wohlgetan (Cantata 99) S.99, cant
mix cor,SATB soli,cont,fl,ob,horn,strings voc pt BREITKOPF-W CHB-4599 s.p. (B2117)
"Was Gott Tut" [Ger] cor voc sc KALMUS 6567 $1.25 (B2118)

Was Gott Tut, Das Ist Wohlgetan (Cantata 100) S.100, cant
mix cor,SATB soli,org,cont,fl,ob,2horn, strings,timp cor pts BREITKOPF-W CHB-4600 s.p., ipr, sc BREITKOPF-W rental (B2119)
"Was Gott Tut" [Ger] cor voc sc KALMUS 6568 $1.25 (B2120)

Was Gott Tut, Das Ist *see Was Gott Tut, Das Ist Wohlgetan

Was Gott Tut *see Was Gott Tut, Das Ist Wohlgetan

Was Gott Tut *see Was Gott Tut, Das Ist Wohlgetan

Was Mein Gott Will (from Matthaus Passion) Trin
mix cor ALSBACH&D s.p. (B2121)
[Ger] SATB,acap (med) BAREN. BCH 73 s.p. (B2122)

Was Mein Gott Will *see Was Mein Gott Will, Das G'scheh' Allzeit

Was Mein Gott Will, Das G'scheh Allzeit (Cantata 111) S.111 (from Nimm Was Dein Ist, Und Gehe Hin) Epiph,cant
mix cor,SATB soli,org,2ob,2bsn,strings, cembalo voc pt BREITKOPF-L CHB-1855 s.p., voc sc BREITKOPF-L EB-7111 s.p., ipr (B2123)
mix cor,SATB soli,cont,2ob,strings cor pts BREITKOPF-W CHB-4611 s.p., ipr, sc BREITKOPF-W rental (B2124)
"Was Mein Gott Will" [Ger] cor voc sc KALMUS 6577 $1.25 (B2125)
"What God Doth, Only That Is Right" SATB, acap SCHIRM.EC 2635 $.25 (B2126)

Was Mir Behast, Ist Mur Die Muntre Jagd (Cantata 208) (from Cantata 208) Xmas, anthem
"Sheep May Safely Graze" SATB oct LORENZ 9669 $.30 (B2127)
"Sheep May Safely Graze" SATB ALLANS 426 s.p. (B2128)
"Sheep May Safely Graze" [Eng] 4pt mix cor, SATB soli,pno voc sc SCHIRM.G $1.00 (B2129)
(Cramer) "Sheep May Safely Graze" SAB MARKS 4120 $.30 (B2130)
(Davis) "Sheep May Safely Graze" SA oct GALAXY 1.1280.1 $.30 (B2131)
(Davis) "Sheep May Safely Graze" SSA oct GALAXY 1.1279.1 $.30 (B2132)
(Davis) "Sheep May Safely Graze" TTBB oct GALAXY 1.1320.1 $.30 (B2133)
(Davis) "Sheep May Safely Graze" SAB oct GALAXY 1.2297.1 $.30 (B2134)
(Davis) "Sheep May Safely Graze" SATB oct GALAXY 1.1278.1 $.30 (B2135)
(Frost) "Sheep May Safely Graze" SATB,2fl, strings voc sc BROUDE,A. 706 $.35, ipr (B2136)
(Wilber) "Sheep May Safely Graze" SATB,opt inst oct KENDOR $.30 (B2137)

Was Sind Das Fur Grosse Schlosser *S.524
(Schneider, Max) 4pt,cont sc BREITKOPF-W EB-6632 s.p., cor pts BREITKOPF-W CHB-3544 s.p. (B2138)

Was Soll Ich Aus Dir Machen *S.89, cant
[Ger] cor voc sc KALMUS 6558 $1.25 (B2139)

Was Soll Ich Aus Dir Machen, Ephraim? (Cantata 89) S.89, Trin,cant
mix cor,SAB soli,cont,2ob,horn,strings cor pts BREITKOPF-W CHB-4589 s.p., ipr, sc BREITKOPF-W rental (B2140)
(Todt, B.) mix cor,SAB soli,org,2ob,horn, strings,cembalo voc pt BREITKOPF-L CHB-2210 s.p., voc sc BREITKOPF-L EB-7089 s.p., ipr (B2141)

Was Willst Du Dich Betruben (Cantata 107) S.107, Trin,cant
[Ger] cor voc sc KALMUS 6573 $1.25 (B2142)
mix cor,STB soli,org,cont,2fl,horn,strings cor pts BREITKOPF-W CHB-4607 s.p., ipr, sc BREITKOPF-W rental (B2143)
(Todt, B.) mix cor,STB soli,org,2fl,2ob, bsn,horn,strings,cembalo voc pt BREITKOPF-L CHB-1946 s.p., voc sc BREITKOPF-L EB-7107 s.p., ipr (B2144)

BACH, JOHANN SEBASTIAN (cont'd.)

Watch Ye, Pray Ye (Cantata 70) Adv,cant
BELWIN $1.00 (B2145)
(Thorne, E.H.) SATB,SATB soli,org,ob,bsn,
trp,strings voc sc NOVELLO rental (B2146)

We Bless Thy Holy Name (from Magnificat)
(Davies) 3pt boy cor/3pt wom cor oct CURWEN
11477 $.25 (B2147)
(Davies) 3pt jr cor/3pt wom cor CURWEN
72624 $.25 (B2148)

We Hasten, O Jesu (from Cantata 78) Gen
(Davies, Laurence H.) 2pt (easy) oct OXFORD
44.077 $.25 (B2149)

We Hasten, O Master
(Rossi) SA oct MCA (B2150)

We Hasten With Eager, Yet Faltering Footsteps
*see Wir Eilen Mit Schwachen, Doch
Emsigen Schritten

We Hope In Thee, O God
(Rodby) SATB oct PLYMOUTH WR-104 $.25
(B2151)

We Must Through Great Tribulation *see Wir
Mussen Durch Viel Trubsal

We Praise Thee, O God *anthem
(Jennings) SATB (med) oct AUGSBURG 1494
$.35 (B2152)

We Thank Thee, God *Gen
(Whittaker, W.G.) unis (easy) oct OXFORD
45.287 $.20 (B2153)

Wedding Cantata *see Vergnugte Pleissenstadt

Weeping *see Weinen, Klagen, Sorgen, Zagen

Weeping, Crying, Sorrow, Sighing *see
Weinen, Klagen, Sorgen, Zagen

Weihnachtschorale *CC8L,Xmas,chorale
SATB HANSSLER 6.207 s.p. (B2154)

Weihnachtschorale-I *Xmas,chorale
mix cor cor pts BREITKOPF-W CHB-3494 s.p.
contains: Ich Steh An Deiner Krippen Hier
[Chorale]; Lobt Gott, Ihr Christen
[Chorale]; Uns Ist Ein Kindlein Heut
Geborn; Vom Himmel Hoch; Wachet Auf
[Chorale]; Wie Schon Leuchtet Der
Morgenstern [Chorale] (B2155)

Weihnachtschorale-II *Xmas,chorale
mix cor cor pts BREITKOPF-W CHB-3495 s.p.
contains: Das Alte Jahr [Chorale]; Das
Neugeborne Kindelein [Chorale]; Helft
Mir, Gott's Gute Preisen [Chorale];
Jesu, Nun Sei Gepreiset [Chorale]; Nun
Liebe Seel [Chorale] (B2156)

Weihnachtschorale-III *Xmas,chorale
mix cor cor pts BREITKOPF-W CHB-3496 s.p.
contains: Der Tag, Der Ist So
Freudenreich [Chorale]; Ein Kind Geborn
[Chorale]; In Dulci Jubilo [Chorale];
Lobt Gott, Ihr Christen [Chorale]; Seid
Froh Dieweil [Chorale]; Wie Soll Ich
Dich Empfangen [Chorale] (B2157)

Weihnachtschorale-IV *Xmas,chorale
mix cor cor pts BREITKOPF-W CHB-3497 s.p.
contains: Ermuntre Dich, Mein Schwacher
Geist [Chorale]; Frohlich Soll Mein
Herze Springen [Chorale]; Fur Freuden
Lasst Uns Springen [Chorale]; Gelobet
Seist Du, Jesu Christ [Chorale] (B2158)

Weihnachtsoratorium *S.248, Xmas,ora
[Ger] DEUTSCHER 5014B min sc-pap $4.50, min
sc-cloth $6.00 (B2159)
mix cor,SATB soli,org,2fl,6ob,bsn,2horn,
3trp,strings,timp sc BREITKOPF-W PB-4949
s.p., voc pt BREITKOPF-W CHB-103 s.p.,
ipa, voc sc BREITKOPF-W EB-13 s.p.
(B2160)
"Oratorio De Noel" [Fr] SATB,SATB soli
CHOUDENS voc sc s.p., voc pt s.p. (B2161)
(Blankenburg, Walter; Durr, Alfred) [Ger]
SATB,SATB soli,org,cont,2vln,vla (med
diff) sc BAREN. BA 5014 $33.00, cor pts
BAREN. BA 5014A $5.50, min sc BAREN. TP 85
$8.75, ipa (B2162)

Weinein, Klagen *see Weinen, Klagen, Sorgen,
Zagen

Weinen, Klagen, Sorgen, Zagen (Cantata 12)
S.12, Easter/Fest,cant
mix cor,ATB soli,cont,ob,bsn,trp,strings sc
BREITKOPF-W PB-4512 s.p., cor pts
BREITKOPF-W CHB-4512 s.p., ipa (B2163)
"Weeping" [Eng] cor voc sc KALMUS 6019
$1.00 (B2164)
"Weeping, Crying, Sorrow, Sighing" [Eng/
Ger] 4pt mix cor voc sc SCHIRM.G $.90
(B2165)
"Weinein, Klagen" cor,orch sc KALMUS $5.00,
ipa (B2166)
(Raphael, G.) [Eng/Fr/Ger] mix cor,ATB
soli,org,ob,bsn,trp,strings,cembalo sc
BREITKOPF-L PB-2862 s.p., cor pts
BREITKOPF-L CHB-1465 s.p., voc sc
BREITKOPF-L EB-7012 s.p., ipa (B2167)
(West, John E.) "Wailing, Crying, Mourning,
Sighing" SATB,ATB soli,org,ob,bsn,trp,
strings voc sc NOVELLO rental (B2168)

Welt Ade, Ich Bin Dein Mude
(Weitemeyer, Herbert) [Ger] 5pt men cor,
acap voc sc NAGELS NCH 4 s.p. (B2169)

Wenn Es Meines Gottes Wille (from Komm, Du
Susse Todesstunde)
"If It Be God's Will And Pleasure" SATB,pno
SCHIRM.EC 1725 $.45, ipr contains also:
Der Leib Zwar In Der Erden, "Though Worms
Destroy My Body" (B2170)

Wenn Ich Einmal Soll Scheiden
see Choralgesange
see Hassler, Hans Leo, Befiehl Du Deine
Wege
see Rosenmuller, Johann, Welt Ade, Ich Bin

BACH, JOHANN SEBASTIAN (cont'd.)

Dein Mude

Wenn Mein Stundlein Vorhanden
see Vulpius, Melchior, Christus, Der Ist
Mein Leben

Wenn Mein Stundlein Vorhanden Ist
see Choralgesange

Wenn Meine Trubsal Als Mit *mot
(Hellmann) SAB,cont HANSSLER 1.249 s.p.
(B2171)

Wenn Wir In Hochsten Noten Sind
mix cor ALSBACH&D s.p. (B2172)

Wer Da Glaubet Und Getauft Wird (Cantata 37)
S.37, Asc,cant
mix cor,SATB soli,cont,2ob,strings sc
BREITKOPF-W PB-4537 s.p., cor pts
BREITKOPF-W CHB-4537 s.p., ipa (B2173)
(Grischkat) SATB,SATB soli,cont,2vln,vla,
English horn HANSSLER 10.218 sc $5.00,
voc sc $1.00, ipa (B2174)
(Raphael, G.) [Eng/Ger] mix cor,SATB soli,
org,2ob,bsn,strings,cembalo voc pt
BREITKOPF-L CHB-448 s.p., ipr
BREITKOPF-L EB-7037 s.p., ipr (B2175)

Wer Dank *see Wer Dank Opfert, Der Preiset
Mich

Wer Dank Opfert *see Wer Dank Opfert, Der
Preiset Mich

Wer Dank Opfert, Der Preiset Mich (Cantata
17) S.17, Trin,cant
mix cor,SATB soli,org,2ob,bsn,strings,
cembalo voc pt BREITKOPF-L CHB-2145 s.p.,
voc sc BREITKOPF-L EB-7017 s.p., ipr
(B2176)
mix cor,SATB soli,cont,2ob,strings cor pts
BREITKOPF-W CHB-4517 s.p., ipr, sc
BREITKOPF-W rental (B2177)
"Wer Dank" cor,orch sc KALMUS $4.00, ipa
(B2178)
"Wer Dank Opfert" [Ger] cor voc sc KALMUS
6530 $1.25 (B2179)
(Grischkat) SATB,SATB soli,cont,2ob,2vln,
vla HANSSLER 10.143 sc $5.00, cor pts
$.90, ipa (B2180)

Wer Mich Liebet *see Wer Mich Liebet, Der
Wird Mein Wort Halten

Wer Mich Liebet, Der Wird Mein Wort Halten
*S.59, Pent/Whitsun,cant
mix cor,SB soli,org,2trp,strings,timp,
cembalo voc sc BREITKOPF-L EB-7059 s.p.,
ipr (B2181)
(Todt, B.) mix cor,SATB soli,org,3ob,bsn,
3trp,strings,timp,cembalo voc sc
BREITKOPF-L EB-7074 s.p., ipr (B2182)

Wer Mich Liebet, Der Wird Mein Wort Halten
(Cantata 59) S.59, cant
mix cor,SB soli,cont,2trp,strings,timp sc
BREITKOPF-W PB-4559 s.p., cor pts
BREITKOPF-W CHB-4559 s.p., ipa (B2183)
"Wer Mich Liebet" [Ger] cor voc sc KALMUS
6543 $1.25 (B2184)

Wer Mich Liebet, Der Wird Mein Wort Halten
(Cantata 74) S.74, cant
mix cor,SATB soli,cont,3ob,3trp,strings,
timp cor pts BREITKOPF-W CHB-4574 s.p.,
ipr, sc BREITKOPF-W rental (B2185)
"Wer Mich Liebet" [Ger] cor voc sc KALMUS
6549 $1.25 (B2186)

Wer Mich Liebet *see Wer Mich Liebet, Der
Wird Mein Wort Halten

Wer Nur *see Wer Nur Den Lieben Gott Lasst
Walten

Wer Nur Den Lieben Gott Lasst Walten (Cantata
93) S.93, Gen/Trin,cant
see Bach, Johann Sebastian, O Ewigkeit, Du
Donnerwort
mix cor,SATB soli,cont,2ob,strings sc
BREITKOPF-W PB-4593 s.p., cor pts
BREITKOPF-W CHB-4593 s.p., ipa (B2187)
mix cor ALSBACH&D s.p. (B2188)
[Ger] SATB,acap (med diff) BAREN. BCH 74
s.p. (B2189)
"Wer Nur" cor,orch/org sc KALMUS $3.00, ipa
(B2190)
(Jones, Ifor) "If Thou Wilt Suffer God To
Guide Thee" [Eng/Ger] mix cor,soli voc sc
SCHIRM.G $1.00 (B2191)
(Raphael, G.; Seiffert, M.) mix cor,SATB
soli,org,2ob,2bsn,strings,cembalo voc pt
BREITKOPF-L PB-2943 s.p., voc pt
BREITKOPF-L CHB-1390 s.p., voc sc
BREITKOPF-L EB-7093 s.p., ipr (B2192)

Wer Nur Den Lieben Gott Lasst Walten
[Chorale] (from Wer Nur Den Lieben Gott
Lasst Walten)
see Bach, Johann Sebastian, O Ewigkeit, Du
Donnerwort
"Hvo Ikkun Lader Herren Rade" [Ger/Dan]
SATB HANSEN-DEN 187 s.p. see also Otte
Koraludsaettelser (B2193)

Wer Sich Selbst Erhohet (Cantata 47) S.47,
cant
mix cor,SB soli,org,cont,2ob,strings cor
pts BREITKOPF-W CHB-4547 s.p., ipr, sc
BREITKOPF-W rental (B2194)
"Wer Sich Selbst Erhohet" [Ger] cor voc sc
KALMUS 6538 $1.25 (B2195)

Wer Sich Selbst Erhohet *see Wer Sich Selbst
Erhohet

Wer Sich Selbst Erhohet, Der Soll Erniedriget
Werden *S.47, Trin,cant
(Todt, B.) mix cor,SB soli,org,2ob,strings,
cembalo voc pt BREITKOPF-L CHB-2208 s.p.,
voc sc BREITKOPF-L EB-7047 s.p., ipr
(B2196)

Wer Weiss *see Wer Weiss, Wie Nahe Mir Mein
Ende

BACH, JOHANN SEBASTIAN (cont'd.)

Wer Weiss, Wie Nahe Mir Mein Ende (Cantata
27) S.27, Trin,cant
mix cor,SATB soli,org,cont,3ob,horn,strings
sc BREITKOPF-W PB-4527 s.p., cor pts
BREITKOPF-W CHB-4527 s.p., ipa (B2197)
"Cantate, Pour Le Seizieme Dimanche Apres
La Trinite" SATB,SATB soli CHOUDENS voc
sc s.p., cor pts s.p. (B2198)
"Wer Weiss" cor,orch sc KALMUS $3.50, ipa
(B2199)
"Wer Weiss" [Eng] cor voc sc KALMUS 6023
$1.00 (B2200)
(Grischkat) [Ger/Eng] SATB,SATB soli,cont,
2ob,horn,2vln,vla, English horn HANSSLER
10.027 sc $5.00, cor pts $.80, ipa
(B2201)
(Raphael, G.) [Eng/Fr/Ger] mix cor,SATB
soli,org,3ob,2bsn,horn,strings,cembalo
voc pt BREITKOPF-L CHB-274 s.p., voc sc
BREITKOPF-L EB-7027 s.p., ipr (B2202)
(West, John E.) "O Teach Me, Lord, My Days
To Number" SATB,SATB soli,org,2ob,horn,
strings voc sc NOVELLO s.p., ipr (B2203)

What Fear Has Death For Me?
(Frackenpohl) SATB SHAWNEE A 463 $.25
(B2204)

What God Doth, Only That Is Right *see Was
Mein Gott Will, Das G'scheh Allzeit

What God Ordains Is Always Good *Gen
SATB,vln,ob,vla,cont (med easy) oct
CONCORDIA 98-3006 $.35, ipa (B2205)

What God Ordains Is Best Of All (from Cantata
75) anthem/chorale
mix cor oct NOVELLO 40.1135.10 s.p. (B2206)

What Tongue Can Tell Thy Greatness, Lord
*chorale
SATB,acap SCHIRM.EC 365 $.20 (B2207)

When God On Us His Love Bestows *see Ist
Gott Versohnt Und Unser Freund

When Thou Art Near *see Bist Du Bei Mir

When Will God Recall My Spirit? *see
Liebster Gott, Wann Werd' Ich Sterben?

When Will God Recall My Spirit? *see
Liebster Gott, Wann Werd' Ich Sterben
[Chorale]

Wherefore, O Saviour, So Long In Returning
*Easter/Gen
(Ehret, W.) SATB oct PRESSER 312-40731 $.25
(B2208)
(Kraft) SSA WARNER G1466 $.30 (B2209)

Whoso Doth Offer Thanks (Cantata 17) Trin
(West, John E.) SATB,SATB soli,2ob,strings
voc sc NOVELLO rental (B2210)

Why Are Thou Cast Down, O My Spirit *Gen
(Buszin) SATB SCHMITT 1704 $.22 (B2211)

Widerstehe *S.54, cant
[Eng] cor voc sc KALMUS 6036 $1.00 (B2212)
cor,orch sc KALMUS $2.00, ipa (B2213)

Wie Bin Ich Doch So Herzlich Froh (from Wie
Schon Leuchtet Der Morgenstern)
"On Jesus All My Love Is Cast" see Bach,
Johann Sebastian, Wie Schon Leuchtet Der
Morgenstern [Chorale]

Wie Maar Den Goeden God Laat Zorgen
mix cor ALSBACH&D s.p. (B2214)

Wie Schoen *see Wie Schon Leuchtet Der
Morgenstern

Wie Schon Ist's Doch, Herr Jesu Christ, Im
see Herzogenberg, Heinrich von, Huter
Israels, Behute Uns

Wie Schon Leucht Uns Der Morgenstern (from
Schwingt Freudig Euch Empor)
see Bach, Johann Sebastian, Wach Auf, Mein
Herz, Und Singe

Wie Schon Leuchtet Der Morgenstern (Cantata
1) S.1, BVM/Epiph,cant
[Ger] SATB,acap (med) BAREN. BCH 1 s.p.
(B2215)
mix cor,STB soli,cont,2ob,2horn,strings sc
BREITKOPF-W PB-4051 s.p., cor pts
BREITKOPF-W CHB-4501 s.p., ipa (B2216)
"Hell Morgonstjarna, Mild Och Ren" cor pts
NORDISKA 3617 s.p. (B2217)
"Wie Schoen" [Eng] cor voc sc KALMUS 6011
$1.00 (B2218)
"Wie Schoen" cor,orch sc KALMUS $5.00, ipa
(B2219)
(Raphael, G.) [Eng/Fr/Ger] mix cor,STB
soli,org,2ob,bsn,2horn,strings,cembalo
cor pts BREITKOPF-L EB-688 s.p., voc sc
BREITKOPF-L EB-7001 s.p., ipr (B2220)

Wie Schon Leuchtet Der Morgenstern [Chorale]
(from Schwingt Freudig Euch Empor) Adv
see Weihnachtschorale-I
see Bach, Johann Sebastian, Was Gott Tut,
Das Ist Wohlgetan [Chorale]
SATB HANSSLER 6.109 s.p. contains also: Mit
Fried Und Freud Ich Fahr Dahin [Chorale]
(from Mit Fried' Und Freud' Ich Fahr'
Dahin) (BVM,A maj) (B2221)
"How Brightly Shines Yon Morning Star"
SATB,pno SCHIRM.EC 1247 $.65, ipr
contains also: Wie Bin Ich Doch So
Herzlich Froh, "On Jesus All My Love Is
Cast" (B2222)

Wie Schwerlich Lasst Sich Fleischh Und Blut
(from Ach Gott, Wie Manches Herzeleid)
"How Hard To Teach Our Flesh And Blood" see
Bach, Johann Sebastian, Ach Gott, Wie
Manches Herzeleid [Chorale]

Wie Soll Ich Dich Empfangen *Adv/Xmas
SATB,acap voc pt DOBLINGER s.p. see also
ADVENT UND WEIHNACHT, HEFT 1 (B2223)

BACH, JOHANN SEBASTIAN (cont'd.)

Wie Soll Ich Dich Empfangen [Chorale]
  see Weihnachtschorale-III

Wie Will Ich Mich Freuen (from Cantata 146)
  "My Spirit, Be Joyful" girl cor SOUTHERN
  $.30   (B2224)
  (Davison, A.) "My Spirit, Be Joyful" [Ger/
  Eng] TB,pno SCHIRM.EC 938 $.35   (B2225)

Wir Christenleut Han Jetzund Freud
  see Bach, Johann Sebastian, Ermuntre Dich,
  Mein Schwacher Geist

Wir Danken Dir *see Wir Danken Dir, Gott,
  Wir Danken Dir

Wir Danken Dir, Gott
  4pt mix cor MOSELER LB-350 s.p.   (B2226)

Wir Danken Dir, Gott, Wir Danken (Cantata 29)
  S.29, cant
  mix cor,SATB soli,cont,2ob,3trp,strings,
  timp sc BREITKOPF-W PB-4529 s.p., cor pts
  BREITKOPF-W CHB-4529 s.p., ipr   (B2227)
  "Wir Danken Dir" cor,orch sc KALMUS $5.00,
  ipa   (B2228)
  (Grischkat) SATB,SATB soli,cont,2ob,3trp,
  2vln,vla,timp HANSSLER 10.085 cor pts
  s.p., voc sc s.p., ipa   (B2229)
  (Raphael, G.) [Eng/Ger] mix cor,SATB soli,
  org,2ob,3trp,strings,timp,cembalo voc pt
  BREITKOPF-L CHB-1414 s.p., voc sc
  BREITKOPF-L EB-7029 s.p., ipr   (B2230)

Wir Eilen Mit Schwachen, Doch Emsigen
  Schritten (from Cantata 78)
  (Talmadge, A.) "We Hasten With Eager, Yet
  Faltering Footsteps" SA,org SCHIRM.EC
  2506 $.30   (B2231)

Wir Essen Und Wir Leben Wohl (from Christ Lag
  In Todesbanden)
  "With Grateful Hearts We All Are Met" see
  Bach, Johann Sebastian, So Feiern Wir Das
  Hohe Fest
  "With Grateful Hearts We All Are Met" SATB,
  pno SCHIRM.EC 1672 $.18, ipr contains
  also: So Feiern Wir Das Hohe Fest; "So
  Keep We All This Holy Feast"   (B2232)

Wir Glauben All An Einen Gott
  see Eine Deutsche Messe In
  Kirchenliedsatzen

Wir Mussen. *see Wir Mussen Durch Viel
  Trubsal

Wir Mussen Durch Viel Trubsal (Cantata 146)
  S.146, cant
  mix cor,SATB soli,org,cont,5ob,trp,strings
  sc BREITKOPF-W PB-4646 s.p., cor pts
  BREITKOPF-W CHB-4646 s.p., ipa   (B2233)
  "Wir Mussen" [Ger] cor voc sc KALMUS 6599
  $1.25   (B2234)
  (Jones, Ifor) "We Must Through Great
  Tribulation" [Eng/Ger] mix cor,soli,pno
  voc sc SCHIRM.G $1.25   (B2235)

Wir Mussen Durch Viel Trubsal In Das Reich
  Gottes Eingehen *S.146, Fest,cant
  (Todt, B.) mix cor,SATB soli,org,fl,3ob,
  bsn,strings,cembalo, English horn voc pt
  BREITKOPF-L CHB-1862 s.p., voc sc
  BREITKOPF-L EB-7146 s.p., ipr   (B2236)

Wir Singen Dir In Deinem Heer (from
  Weihnachtsoratorio) chorale
  mix cor ALSBACH&D s.p.   (B2237)

With Grateful Hearts *Easter/Lent,Commun
  (Whitford) SATB oct PRO ART 1852 $.25
  contains: To Thee Alone Be Glory; With
  Grateful Hearts   (B2238)

With Grateful Hearts
  see With Grateful Hearts

With Grateful Hearts We All Are Met *see Wir
  Essen Und Wir Leben Wohl

With Joy I Welcome Thee *see Ich Freue Mich
  In Dir

With Joy We March Onward To Zion *see So
  Lasset Uns Gehen In Salem

With Loudest Rejoicing *see Ich Jauchze, Ich
  Lache

Wo Gehest Du Hin? (Cantata 166) S.166,
  Easter/Gen/Pent,cant
  mix cor,ATB soli,cont,ob,strings voc pt
  BREITKOPF-W CHB-4666 s.p., ipr, sc
  BREITKOPF-W rental   (B2239)
  (Bernstein, W.H.) mix cor,SATB soli,org,ob,
  strings,cembalo voc pt BREITKOPF-L
  CHB-2197 s.p., voc sc BREITKOPF-L EB-7166
  s.p., ipr   (B2240)
  (Durr, Alfred) [Ger] SATB,SATB soli,org,ob,
  bsn,2vln,vla,vcl,bvl (Cantate Sunday) sc
  BAREN. BA 5123 $2.75, cor pts BAREN.
  BA 5123 $.40, voc sc BAREN. BA 5123A
  $2.75, min sc BAREN. TP 81 $2.00, ipa
                                        (B2241)

Wo Gehst Du Hin *S.166, cant
  [Ger] cor voc sc KALMUS 6612 $1.25 (B2242)

Wo Gott, Der Herr *see Wo Gott, Der Herr,
  Nicht Bei Uns Halt

Wo Gott, Der Herr, Nicht Bei Uns Halt
  (Cantata 178) S.178, cant
  mix cor,ATB soli,cont,4ob,horn,strings cor
  pts BREITKOPF-W CHB-4678 s.p., ipr, sc
  BREITKOPF-W rental   (B2243)
  "Wo Gott Der Herr" [Ger] cor voc sc KALMUS
  6620 $1.25   (B2244)
  "Wo Gott, Der Herr" cor,orch sc KALMUS
  $3.50, ipa   (B2245)
  (Todt, B.) mix cor,ATB soli,org,2ob,2bsn,
  strings,cembalo voc sc BREITKOPF-L
  EB-7178 s.p., ipr   (B2246)

Wo Soll Ich Fliehen Hin (Cantata 5) S.5,
  Trin,cant
  [Ger] cor voc sc KALMUS 6623 $1.25 (B2247)
  mix cor,SATB soli,cont,2ob,trp,strings cor

BACH, JOHANN SEBASTIAN (cont'd.)

  pts BREITKOPF-W CHB-4505 s.p., ipr, sc
  BREITKOPF-W rental   (B2248)
  (Todt, B.) mix cor,SATB soli,org,2ob,bsn,
  trp,strings,cembalo voc sc BREITKOPF-L
  EB-7005 s.p., ipr   (B2249)

Wohl Dem *see Wohl Dem, Der Sich Auf Seinen
  Gott

Wohl Dem, Der Sich Auf Seinen Gott (Cantata
  139) S.139, Trin,cant
  mix cor,SATB soli,cont,2ob,strings cor pts
  BREITKOPF-W CHB-4639 s.p., ipr, sc
  BREITKOPF-W rental   (B2250)
  "Wohl Dem" [Ger] cor voc sc KALMUS 6594
  $1.25   (B2251)
  (Todt, B.) mix cor,SATB soli,org,2ob,bsn,
  strings,cembalo voc sc BREITKOPF-L
  EB-7139 s.p., ipr   (B2252)

Wohl Dem, Der Sich Auf Seinen Gott [Chorale]
  "Det Livsens Ord Vi Bygger Pa" [Ger/Dan]
  SATB HANSEN-DEN 183 s.p. see also Otte
  Koraludsaettelser   (B2253)

Wohl Mir, Das Ich Jesum Habe (from Cantata
  147)
  mix cor ALSBACH&D s.p.   (B2254)

Ye Are Not Of The Flesh (from Jesu Meine
  Freude)
  (Barrie) 5pt mix cor oct LAWSON 785 $.30
                                        (B2255)

Zion Hears Her Watchmen's Voices (from
  Sleepers, Wake) Adv,anthem/chorale
  SATB oct GRAY GCMR 1486 $.25   (B2256)
  SATB oct NOVELLO 34.0808.06 s.p. contains
  also: Glory Now To Thee Be Given   (B2257)
  (Hardwicke) SATB oct PRO ART 2398 $.25
                                        (B2258)
  (Sampson, Godfrey) mix cor oct NOVELLO
  28.1255.10 s.p.   (B2259)

Zwei Lieder Nach Choralsatzen
  [Ger] mix cor,acap (easy) HUG s.p.
  contains: Senke, O Vater, Herab Deinen
  Gottlichen Frieden; Von Dir, Du Gott
  Der Einigkeit   (B2260)

Zwingt Die Saiten In Cythara
  see Bach, Johann Sebastian, O Ewigkeit, Du
  Donnerwort

BACH, KARL PHILIPP EMANUEL (1714-1788)
Die Israeliten In Der Wuste *ora
  (Steffin, Fritz) [Ger] SATB,soli,orch,opt
  pno BOTE voc sc s.p., cor pts s.p., ipa
                                        (B2261)
Goodness Of The Lord, The
  (Ehret) SATB oct ELKAN-V 362-1253 $.25
                                        (B2262)
Gross Ist Der Herr
  mix cor,acap ERDMANN 536 s.p. contains
  also: Handel, George Frideric, Gebet
                                        (B2263)
Heilig
  (Geiringer, K.) "Holy Is God" [Eng/Ger] mix
  cor,4 soli,org CONCORDIA 97-6226 $1.00,
  ipr   (B2264)
Heilig Ist Gott
  mix cor oct OXFORD 46.158 $2.05   (B2265)
His Holy Place
  SATB oct ELKAN-V 362-1270 $.30   (B2266)
Holy Is God *see Heilig
Humility Before Thee
  SATB oct ELKAN-V 362-1268 $.30   (B2267)
In Whom I Put My Trust
  (Ehret) SATB oct ELKAN-V 362-1269 $.30
                                        (B2268)
Israelites In The Desert, The
  (Darvas) [Ger/Eng] SATB,acap voc sc PETERS
  GM31 $7.50, ipr, sc PETERS 10018 $10.00,
  ipr   (B2269)
Lob Gottes
  (Gellert, C.F.) [Ger] mix cor,acap (easy)
  HUG s.p.   (B2270)
Magnificat *Magnif
  cor,orch rc KALMUS $15.00, ipa   (B2271)
  (Backers) [Lat] SATB,acap voc sc PETERS
  HU1481 4.00, ipr   (B2272)
  (Darvas) [Lat] SATB,acap voc sc PETERS GM53
  $7.50, ipr   (B2273)
  (Darvas) [Lat] SATB,acap sc PETERS 10034
  $10.00, ipr   (B2274)
  (Deis) [Eng/Lat] mix cor,soli,orch/org/pno
  voc sc SCHIRM.G $1.75   (B2275)
  (Graulich) [Lat] mix cor,org,2fl,2ob,bsn,
  2horn,3trp,2vln,vla,vcl/bvl,timp sc
  HANSSLER 33.215 $20.00, voc sc HANSSLER
  33.215A $4.00, ipa   (B2276)
Morgengesang
  cor,orch sc KALMUS $7.00, ipa   (B2277)
Noch Kommt Sie Nicht, Die Sonne *Fest
  mix cor,SS soli,2fl,bsn,strings,cembalo sc
  BREITKOPF-L rental   (B2278)
Search Into Me
  (Ehret) SATB oct ELKAN-V 362-1255 $.30
                                        (B2279)
BACH, WILHELM FRIEDEMANN (1710-1784)
Dies Ist Der Tag *cant
  (Nowack, L.) mix cor,SATB soli,cont,2fl,
  2ob,bsn,2horn,strings BREITKOPF-L sc
  rental, voc pt s.p., ipa   (B2280)
Ehre Sey Gott In Der Hohe *Xmas,cant
  [Ger] sc PETERS V139 $7.50, ipa, voc sc
  PETERS V139 $1.00, ipa   (B2281)
  (Schultz; Hauser) [Ger] mix cor,STB soli,
  cont,strings,opt 2horn VIEWEG s.p.,
  cor pts s.p., ipa   (B2282)
Kein Halmlein Wachst Auf Erden
  see Bach, Johann Sebastian, Gott Lebet
  Noch! Seele, Was Verzagst Du

BACH CANTATAS VOL. 49 see Bach, Johann Sebastian

BACH CANTATAS VOL. 50 see Bach, Johann Sebastian

BACH CANTATAS VOL. 51 see Bach, Johann Sebastian

BACH CANTATAS VOL. 52 see Bach, Johann Sebastian

BACH CANTATAS VOL. 53 see Bach, Johann Sebastian

BACH CANTATAS VOL. 54 see Bach, Johann Sebastian

BACH CANTATAS VOL. 55 see Bach, Johann Sebastian, Lass, Furstin, Lass Noch Einen Strahl

BACH CANTATAS VOL. 56 see Bach, Johann Sebastian

BACH CANTATAS VOL. 57 see Bach, Johann Sebastian

BACH CANTATAS VOL. 58 see Bach, Johann Sebastian

BACH CANTATAS VOL. 59 see Bach, Johann Sebastian

BACH CANTATAS VOL. 60 see Bach, Johann Sebastian

BACH CANTATAS VOL. 61 see Bach, Johann Sebastian

BACH CANTATAS VOL. 62 see Bach, Johann Sebastian

BACH CANTATAS VOL. 63 see Bach, Johann Sebastian

BACH CANTATAS VOL. 64 see Bach, Johann Sebastian

BACH CANTATAS VOL. 65 see Bach, Johann Sebastian

BACH CANTATAS VOL. 66 see Bach, Johann Sebastian

BACH CANTATAS VOL. 67 see Bach, Johann Sebastian

BACH CHORALE RESPONSES see Bach, Johann Sebastian

BACH CHORALES see Bach, Johann Sebastian

BACH CHORALES see Bach, Johann Sebastian

BACH FAVORITE CHORALES *CCU,chorale
(Schroth) SATB KJOS $1.25 (B2283)

BACHMAN
Lil Ol' Train *spir
TTBB SCHMITT 407 $.18 (B2284)

BACHMANN, F.
Miserere *Op.7
8pt mix cor BIRNBACH s.p. (B2285)

Psalm 100 *Op.8
8pt mix cor BIRNBACH s.p. (B2286)

BACHMETIEV, NIKOLAI I (1807-1891)
Ake The Body Of Christ *Commun
SATB,acap SCHIRM.EC 1202 $.20 (B2287)

BACK HOME see Price, Flo

BACK, SVEN-ERICK (1919-)
Behold I Am Making All Things New
mix cor NORDISKA 10111 s.p. (B2288)
[Eng] SATB NORDISKA 10.111 s.p. (B2289)

Darkness Is Soon Over *see Nox Praecessit

Domine Memento Mei *Gd.Fri.,mot
"Jesu, Think Of Me" [Eng/Lat] 4pt mix cor, acap oct SCHIRM.G 11838 $.30 (B2290)
"Jesu, Think Of Me" [Lat/Eng] SATB NORDISKA 10.103 s.p. (B2291)

Ecce Ascendimus Jerosolymam *Quinqua,mot
"Lo, We Go Up To Jerusalem" [Eng/Lat] 4pt mix cor,acap oct SCHIRM.G 11836 $.30 (B2292)
"Lo, We Go Up To Jerusalem" [Lat/Eng] SATB NORDISKA 10.039 s.p. (B2293)

Ego Sum Panis Vitae *Lent,mot
"I Am The Bread Of Life" [Eng/Lat] 4pt mix cor,acap oct SCHIRM.G 11837 $.30 (B2294)
"I Am The Bread Of Life" [Lat/Eng] SATB NORDISKA 10.040 s.p. (B2295)

Et Verbum Caro Factum Est *Xmas,mot
"Word Was Made Flesh, The" [Eng/Lat] 4pt mix cor,acap oct SCHIRM.G 11840 $.30 (B2296)
"Word Was Made Flesh, The" [Lat/Eng] SATB NORDISKA 10.038 s.p. (B2297)

Herr, Zu Wem Sollen Wir Gehen?
[Ger] SATB NORDISKA 10.056 s.p. (B2298)

I Am The Bread Of Life *see Ego Sum Panis Vitae

Jesu, Think Of Me *see Domine Memento Mei

Lo, We Go Up To Jerusalem *see Ecce Ascendimus Jerosolymam

Nox Praecessit *Adv
"Darkness Is Soon Over" [Eng/Lat] 4pt mix cor,acap oct SCHIRM.G 11839 $.30 (B2299)
"Darkness Is Soon Over" [Lat/Eng] SATB NORDISKA 10.041 s.p. (B2300)

Transfiguration, The
[Eng] SATB NORDISKA 10.075 s.p. (B2301)

BACK, SVEN-ERICK (cont'd.)

Word Was Made Flesh, The *see Et Verbum Caro Factum Est

BACKERS, [COR] (1910)
Huit Vieilles Chansons De Noel *CC8U,Xmas
3-4pt wom cor BROEKMANS 46 s.p. (B2302)

BACKES, LOTTE
Funf Motetten *CC5U,mot
[Lat] 4pt mix cor oct DEUTSCHER 7629 s.p. (B2303)

BACON, ERNST (1898-)
Animals' Christmas Oratorio, The *Xmas
boy cor/jr cor/wom cor,narrator PRESSER $1.25 (B2304)

Babe Of Bethlehem *Xmas
SATB oct GRAY GCMR 3209 $.35 (B2305)

Carol, A *Xmas,carol
SSA oct GALAXY 1.2132.1 $.30 (B2306)

Christmas Carol, A *Xmas,carol
SATB,pno/org PEER $.40 (B2307)

Give Me Jesus
SA oct GALAXY 1.2136.1 $.25 (B2308)

No Room *Xmas
3pt jr cor/SSA (easy) FISCHER,C CM 6991 $.20 (B2309)
SSA oct FISCHER,C CM-6991 $.25 (B2310)

Pilgrim Hymn *hymn
unis oct SCHIRM.G 11234 $.25 (B2311)

Precepts Of Angelus Silesius
(Scheffer) 3-6pt wom cor BROUDE,A. 208 $.40 (B2312)

BADEN, CONRAD
Ave Maria
[Lat] wom cor/jr cor/eq voices LYCHE s.p. (B2313)

Dropen
mix cor MUSIKK 30 s.p. (B2314)

Ga Varsommt, O Sjel
see Religiose Folketoner, Vol. I

Gloria
[Lat] mix cor LYCHE 60 s.p. (B2315)

Herre Gud, Ditt Dyre Navn Og Aere
see Religiose Folketoner, Vol. I

Hoyr, Kor Kyrkjeklokka Lokkar
see Religiose Folktoner, Vol. II

Ikke Enhver Som Sier Til Meg
[Norw] LYCHE 46 s.p. (B2316)

Ingen Vinner Frem Till Den Evige Ro
see Religiose Folketoner, Vol. I

Introitus Ved Kristi Apenbaring
[Norw] mix cor,org LYCHE 99 s.p. (B2317)

Jeg Ser Dig, O Guds Lam A Sta
see Religiose Folktoner, Vol. II

Jesus, Din Sote Forening A Smake
see Religiose Folktoner, Vol. II

Korset Vil Jeg Aldri Svike
see Religiose Folktoner, Vol. II

Med Jesus Vil Eg Fara
see Religiose Folketoner, Vol. I

Mitt Hjerte Alltid Vanker
see Religiose Folketoner, Vol. I

Pange Lingua
[Lat] mix cor LYCHE 42 s.p. (B2318)

Religiose Folketoner, Vol. I
[Norw] men cor LYCHE 18A s.p.
contains: Ga Varsommt, O Sjel; Herre Gud, Ditt Dyre Navn Og Aere; Ingen Vinner Frem Till Den Evige Ro; Med Jesus Vil Eg Fara; Mitt Hjerte Alltid Vanker (B2319)

Religiose Folktoner, Vol. II
[Norw] men cor LYCHE 18B s.p.
contains: Hoyr, Kor Kyrkjeklokka Lokkar; Jeg Ser Dig, O Guds Lam A Sta; Jesus, Din Sote Forening A Smake; Korset Vil Jeg Aldri Svike; Sjung Amern (B2320)

Sanctus *Sanctus
[Lat] wom cor/jr cor/eq voices LYCHE s.p. (B2321)

Se Jeg Star For Doren
[Norw] LYCHE 67 s.p. (B2322)

Sjung Amern
see Religiose Folktoner, Vol. II

BADINGS, HENK (1907-)
Apocalyps, Oratorium Op Teksten Uit De Openbaring Van Johannes *ora
[Dut] mix cor,SATB soli,pno,3fl,3ob,3clar, 3bsn,4trp,4horn,3trom,tuba,strings,perc, timp,harp, celesta DONEMUS min sc s.p., cor pts s.p., voc sc s.p. (B2323)

Ave Maris Stella
[Dut] wom cor,strings,perc, vibraphone, celeste DONEMUS min sc s.p., cor pts s.p., voc sc s.p. (B2324)

Hi Treur Die Truren Will
see Vier Geestelijke Liederen

Ic Draech Dat Liden Verborghen
see Vier Geestelijke Liederen

Kyrie Eleison
see Vier Geestelijke Liederen

Ons Is Gheboren Een Kindekijn
see Vier Geestelijke Liederen

Psalm 147
[Dut] mix cor&jr cor,3fl,2ob,3clar,2bsn, 3trp,4horn,3trom,tuba,strings,perc,timp, celeste DONEMUS min sc s.p., cor pts s.p.

BADINGS, HENK (cont'd.)
(B2325)

Psalmensymphonie *No.6
[Dut] mix cor,pno,2fl,2ob,3clar,2bsn,3trp, 4horn,3trom,tuba,strings,perc,timp,harp, celeste DONEMUS min sc s.p., cor pts s.p., voc sc s.p. (B2326)

Te Deum *Te Deum
[Lat] men cor,pno,3fl,2ob,2clar,2bsn,4trp, 4horn,3trom,tuba,strings,perc,timp, celeste DONEMUS min sc s.p., cor pts s.p., voc sc s.p. (B2327)

Vier Geestelijke Liederen
BROEKMANS 90 s.p.
contains: Hi Treur Die Truren Will (2pt wom cor); Ic Draech Dat Liden Verborghen (3pt wom cor); Kyrie Eleison (4pt wom cor); Ons Is Gheboren Een Kindekijn (4pt wom cor) (B2328)

BAER, [CHARLES E.] (1870-1962)
Adon Olam
(Davidson) "Eternal Lord" SATB,org oct MCA (B2329)

Eternal Lord *see Adon Olam

BAGNI
Eructavit Cor Meum *cant
SATB&SATB,4trp,4trom MOSELER sc s.p., cor pts s.p., ipa (B2330)

BAGPIPE CAROL *Xmas,carol,It
(Barthelson, Joyce) SATB WEINBERGER s.p. (B2331)
(Barthelson, Joyce) SATB voc sc WEINBERGER s.p. (B2332)

BAGPIPE CAROL, THE *Xmas,carol,It
(Barthelson) SATB,opt 2treb inst oct SHAPIRO SK 2037 $.25, ipa (B2333)
(Barthelson) SAB,opt 2treb inst oct SHAPIRO SK 5015 $.25, ipa (B2334)
(Barthelson) SSA,opt 2treb inst oct SHAPIRO SK 3012 $.25, ipa (B2335)
(Barthelson) 2pt,2treb inst oct SHAPIRO SK 4022 $.25, ipa (B2336)

BAGPIPERS' CAROL see Track, Gerhard

BAHMANN, MARIANNE ELOISE
Altar Of God, The *anthem/Bibl
SATB,solo,pno/org oct FISCHER,C CM-7310 $.25 (B2337)

BAI, [TOMMASO] (ca. 1660-1714)
Bone Jesu
(Ehret) SATB,acap oct FISCHER,C CM-7004 $.25 (B2338)

BAIN
Gathering Clouds *Xmas
SATB oct FISCHER,C CM-6530 $.25 (B2339)
SSA oct FISCHER,C CM-6531 $.25 (B2340)
TTBB,acap oct FISCHER,C CM-6819 $.25 (B2341)

BAIN, J.L. MC BETH
Brother James's Air *Gen
(Davies, E.T.) TTBarB,acap (easy) oct OXFORD 41.110 $.40 (B2342)
(Gibbs, Armstrong) SB/SAB (easy) oct OXFORD 42.954 $.25 (B2343)
(Jacob, Gordon) unis&SATB oct OXFORD $.35 (B2344)
(Jacob, Gordon) SSA (easy) oct OXFORD 44.029 $.35 (B2345)
(Jacob, Gordon) SATB (easy) oct OXFORD 94.316 $.35 (B2346)
(Jacob, Gordon) unis&desc (easy) oct OXFORD 44.047 $.30 (B2347)
(Trew, Arthur) unis (easy) oct OXFORD 45.017 $.25 (B2348)

Great Peace, The *Gen
(Branson, David) unis&opt desc (easy) oct OXFORD 40.008 $.30 (B2349)

BAINES, W.
Bless Ye Our God
SATB oct PRESSER 332-40028 $.30 (B2350)

Easter Dawn *Easter
SATB oct PRESSER 312-21577 $.35 (B2351)

Glorify His Name
SATB oct PRESSER 312-21624 $.35 (B2352)

Our Hearts Shall Rejoice
SATB oct PRESSER 312-21633 $.35 (B2353)

Praise The Lord
SA oct PRESSER 312-20301 $.30 (B2354)

BAINTON, EDGAR LESLIE (1880-1956)
And I Saw A New Heaven *anthem
mix cor oct NOVELLO 28.1155.03 s.p. (B2355)

BAIRSTOW, EDWARD CUTHBERT (1874-1946)
Communion Service In E Flat *Commun,Agnus/Bene/Credo/Gloria/Sanctus
unis (med) oct OXFORD 45.301 $.65 (B2356)

Day Draws On With Golden Light, The *Eve/Gen
SATB/SAB (very easy) oct OXFORD 42.133 $.30 (B2357)

Evening Service In E Flat *Eve,Magnif/Nunc
unis (med easy) oct OXFORD 45.025 $.35 (B2358)

Evening Service In G *Eve
SATB (med easy) oct OXFORD 42.117 $.35 (B2359)

I Sat Down Under His Shadow *Commun/Gen,Bibl
SATB,acap (med easy) oct OXFORD 43.002 $.25 (B2360)
(Davies, Laurence H.) 2pt (easy) oct OXFORD 44.219 $.25 (B2361)

Jesu, The Very Thought Of Thee *Commun/Gen
SATB,acap (med easy) oct OXFORD 43.003 $.25 (B2362)

King Of Love My Shepherd Is, The *Easter/Gen
SATB (easy) oct OXFORD 42.024 $.35 (B2363)

Lamentations *Lent
SATB (med easy) oct OXFORD 42.182 $.30 (B2364)

BAIRSTOW, EDWARD CUTHBERT (cont'd.)

Promise Which Was Made, The *Easter
SATB oct GRAY GCMR 1510 $.35   (B2365)

Save Us O Lord *anthem
SATB oct GRAY GCMR 3179 $.25   (B2366)
mix cor oct NOVELLO 28.0740.08 s.p. (B2367)

Te Deum *Te Deum
unis (med) OXFORD 45.025 $.20   (B2368)

Though I Speak With The Tongues Of Men *Gen/
Quinqua
SATB/SAB (med) oct OXFORD 42.042 $.35
(B2369)

BAKER
Everywhere, Everywhere Christmas Tonight
*Xmas
(Whitman) SAB oct LILLENAS AN-3815 $.25
(B2370)

Give Peace, O God
(Harris) SATB oct PRO ART 1774 $.20 (B2371)

Jesus, Thou Joy Of Loving Hearts
(Swift) SATB,acap oct BOOSEY 1981 $.30
(B2372)

Lord, Guard And Guide The Men Who Fly
(Genuchi) SATB (Official Hymn Of The
U.S.Air Force) LUDWIG SS-010 $.30 (B2373)
(Genuchi) TTBB LUDWIG SS-011 $.30 (B2374)

Three Original Carols For Junior Choir *CC3U
SA oct SACRED S-8630 $.35   (B2375)

BAKER, DALTON
Shadows Of Evening *Eve,anthem
SATB ALLANS 244 s.p.   (B2376)
SATB LESLIE 4021   (B2377)

BAKER, DWIGHT B.
Three Original Carols For Junior Choir
*CC3U,Xmas,anthem/carol
SA oct SACRED S-8630 $.35   (B2378)

BAKER, E.
Christ The Lord Is Risen Again *Easter
SATB,org FISCHER,J 10092 $.30   (B2379)

Christmas Carol Sung To The King, A *Xmas,
carol
SATB,acap FISCHER,J 10090 $.35   (B2380)

BAKER, ROBERT
Let All The World
SATB oct GRAY GCMR 2237 $.35   (B2381)

O Lord God, Unto Whom
SATB oct GRAY GCMR 1741 $.30   (B2382)

BAKSA, R.
My Soul Doth Magnify The Lord
SATB,acap oct PRESSER 352-00398 $.35
(B2383)

BAKSA, ROBERT
Psalm 13
SSATB,T solo,org/pno PEER $.40   (B2384)

BALAK AND BALAAM see Adler, Hugo Ch.

BALAKIREV, MILY ALEXEYEVITCH (1837-1910)
O Send Thy Light
SATB oct FISCHER,J 4163 $.30   (B2385)

O Send Thy Light Forth
(Gillman, W.) SATB,acap oct PRESSER G-4002
$.30   (B2386)

Send Forth Thy Light
(Cain) SAB SCHMITT 5508 $.30   (B2387)
(Cain) SATB SCHMITT 1554 $.30   (B2388)
(Cain) TTBB SCHMITT 3506 $.30   (B2389)

Send Out Thy Light *Gen
(Hallagan, R.) SATB,acap oct PRESSER
312-40444 $.30   (B2390)
(Henderson) SATB oct SPRATT 536 $.25
(B2391)
(Tkach) SATB SCHMITT 855 $.20   (B2392)

BALAMOS, JOHN
In The Shelter Of Thy Wings
SATB oct FISCHER,J 8627 $.30   (B2393)

BALBO
Amen *fugue
SSAATB,acap oct FOX $.40   (B2394)

BALDASAR
O Jesu Dolce
(Sorenson, Soren) "O Jesus Blide" [Lat/Dan]
SATB,acap HANSEN-DEN 268 s.p. see also
MOTETTER OG LAUDER FRA DET 16. ARHUNDREDE
(B2395)

O Jesus Blide *see O Jesu Dolce

BALDWIN
They That Wait Upon The Lord
(Whitman) SATB oct LILLENAS AN-2230 $.30
(B2396)

BALES, [RICHARD] (1915-   )
O Lord From Whom *anthem
mix cor oct OXFORD 02.015 $.25   (B2397)

BALL
Worship The Christ Child
SATB oct LORENZ C337 $.30   (B2398)

BALL, ALBERT C.
Alleluia! Noel! *Xmas
4pt mix cor,B solo oct SCHIRM.G 9769 $.25
(B2399)

BALL, ERIC
Hail To The Lord's Anointed *anthem
SATB,org/brass oct NOVELLO 29.0016.05 s.p.,
ipr   (B2400)

New Creation, A *anthem
SATB (diff) oct LORENZ 9997 $.30   (B2401)
SATB oct LORENZ 9997 $.30   (B2402)

Our Father's Care *anthem
SATB (med diff) oct LORENZ C347 $.30
(B2403)

BALLAD OF CHRISTMAS, A see Burgstahler, Elton

BALLAD OF EASTER see Smith

BALLAD OF JESUS
see Two Folk Carols

BALLAD OF JESUS CHRIST *Xmas,carol,Fr
(Ehret, Walter) SATB,opt inst oct WALTON 2526
$.30   (B2404)

BALLAD OF JUDAS ISCARIOT see Purvis, Richard

BALLAD OF THE BROWN KING, THE see Hughes

BALLAD OF THE HOLY CHILD, THE see Griffith,
Peter

BALLAD OF THE SHEPHERDS see Johnson

BALLAD OF TREES AND THE MASTER see Helyer,
Marjorie

BALLAD OF TREES AND THE MASTER, see Matthews,
Harvey Alexander

BALLADORI, ANGELO
Hodie Christus Natus Est *Xmas
2 eq voices,org ZANIBON 2605 s.p.   (B2405)

BALLANTINE
God Is Near
(Weaver) SATB oct HUNTZINGER 7040 $.20
(B2406)

BALLE, C.
Happy Christmas, The *Xmas
(Pasquet, Jean) SATB,pno/org (easy) PRESSER
$.35   (B2407)

BALLERINO, G.
Come, Let Us Worship *CC12U,Gen,folk/Mass,
Contemp
unis,gtr cmplt ed GIA G1473 $1.00   (B2408)

BALLET'S LULLABY (from Anthology Of Carols, An)
see Christo Paremus Cantica

BALLETT, WILLIAM
Sweet Was The Song The Virgin Sang
(Davies) 2pt jr cor/2pt wom cor CURWEN
72653 s.p.   (B2409)

BALLOU, ESTHER W.
Hear Us *Fest
mix cor,brass,perc oct WORD CS-503 $.50
(B2410)

BALLOU, LAMMY see Cain, Noble

BALLULOW *Xmas
(Kirk) SATB oct PRO ART 2040 $.22   (B2411)

BALM IN GILEAD *spir
(Burleigh) SATB RICORDI-ENG LD456 s.p.
(B2412)
(McLellan) SATB oct LILLENAS AT-1057 $.25
(B2413)
(Whitman) SATB oct LILLENAS AN-2291 $.30
(B2414)

BALM IN GILEAD see Burleigh, Henry Thacker

BALM IN GILEAD see Rogers

BALM IN GILEAD see Wilson

BALOGH, LOUIS L.
Alleluia, Alleluia
SATB LUDWIG L-1155 $.30   (B2415)

Easter Alleluia *Easter
TTBB LUDWIG L-5142 $.35   (B2416)

BALOO LAMMY *Xmas,carol,Scot
see Troll The Ancient Carol
(Kirk) SATB,opt ob/fl oct PRO ART 2132 $.30
(B2417)
(Kirk) SAB,opt ob/fl oct PRO ART 2321 $.30
(B2418)
(Kirk) SSA,opt ob/fl oct PRO ART 2324 $.30
(B2419)
(Kirk) TTB,opt ob/fl oct PRO ART 2323 $.30
(B2420)
(Luboff, Norman) SATB oct WALTON 3030 $.25
(B2421)

BALOO, LAMMY see Rhea

BALSON
Christmas Prayer, A *Xmas
SATB oct LORENZ B85 $.30   (B2422)

Easter Hope *Easter
SATB oct LORENZ A321 $.25   (B2423)

BALULALOW *Xmas,carol
(Brown) SATB,acap (med easy) OXFORD 84.148
$.20   (B2424)
(Lumsden) unis/SATB,acap (very easy) OXFORD
84.108 $.25   (B2425)
(Pasfield, W.R.) 2pt ASHDOWN E.A.331 s.p.
(B2426)
(Warlock) unis (med) OXFORD 45.006 $.25, ipr
see also Three Carols   (B2427)
(Warlock) SATB,S solo (med) OXFORD 42.201
$.25, ipr see also Three Carols   (B2428)

BALULALOW see Aston, Peter

BALULALOW see Bennett, R.

BALULALOW see Britten, Benjamin

BALULALOW see Heseltine, Philip

BALULALOW see Maw

BALULALOW see Tomlins, Greta

BALULALOW see Vene, Ruggero

BALZANELLI
Airecillos De Belen
cor RICORDI-ARG BA 12929 s.p.   (B2429)

BAMER, ALFRED
Deutsches Ordinarium
3 eq voices&cong,cantor,org DOBLINGER voc
sc s.p., cor pts s.p.   (B2430)

Deutsches Ordinarium I
mix cor&cong,cantor,org DOBLINGER voc sc
s.p., cor pts s.p., voc pt s.p., sc s.p.
(B2431)

BAMER, ALFRED (cont'd.)

Deutsches Ordinarium II
wom cor,org DOBLINGER s.p.   (B2432)
wom cor&jr cor,cantor,org voc sc DOBLINGER
s.p.   (B2433)

Deutsches Proprium Der Priester-Messe *Mass
3pt wom cor,acap cor pts DOBLINGER s.p.
(B2434)

Fons Pietatis *Mass
4pt mix cor,acap DOBLINGER sc s.p., cor pts
s.p.   (B2435)

Marienmesse *Mass
4pt mix cor,org/2trp&2trom DOBLINGER voc sc
s.p., cor pts s.p., ipa   (B2436)

BAMPTON, R.
Angel Band, The
unis oct PRESSER 312-40386 $.30   (B2437)

Choral Responses For The Church Year (Group
1) *Gen
SATB SCHMITT 1671 $.25   (B2438)

Glory To God
SAB BOSTON 13052 $.35   (B2439)

Let Us Humbly Walk With Thee
SAB,org/pno BOSTON 12862 $.35   (B2440)

O Bells In The Steeple
unis oct BELWIN 64379 $.30   (B2441)

Praise Him Evermore *see Flint

Song Of Bethlehem *Xmas
SATB/unis/jr cor SCHMITT 1678 $.30 (B2442)

Tidings Of Joy
SA oct FISCHER,J 9147 $.30   (B2443)

Winds Through The Olive Trees *Xmas
SA oct BELWIN 64244 $.30   (B2444)
SSA oct BELWIN 64270 $.30   (B2445)

BANCHIERI, ADRIANO (1568-1634)
Cantate Domino
(Martens, Mason) "O Sing Unto The Lord"
SATB oct WALTON 2152 $.25   (B2446)

O Sing Unto The Lord *see Cantate Domino

BANCROFT, H. HUGH
For Those We Love Within The Veil
SATB oct LESLIE 4066   (B2447)

Good Christians Now Let All Rejoice *Easter
SATB oct LESLIE 4010   (B2448)

I Sing Of A Maiden *Xmas
SATB oct LESLIE 4099   (B2449)

Love Of The Father
SATB oct LESLIE 4009   (B2450)

O Thou Not Made With Hands
SATB oct LESLIE 4101   (B2451)

Temple Of God, The *Ded/Gen
SATB (very easy) oct OXFORD 42.977 $.30
(B2452)

Until The Shadows Lengthen
SATB oct LESLIE 4012   (B2453)

BANCSI, RUTH
Walk Into Your World
SSAA oct AGAPE SP 696 $.35   (B2454)
SATB oct AGAPE SP 697 $.35   (B2455)

BAND OF CHILDREN, THE see McLaughlin, Marian

BANDRIER, YVES
Agnus Dei *Agnus
4pt AMPHION A130 s.p.   (B2456)

BANKS, H.
Christmas Story, The *Xmas,cant
BELWIN $.50   (B2457)

BANKS OF JORDAN see Gardner, Maurice

BANKS, ROBERT
Praise Chorale, The *CCU,chorale
SATB BELWIN $1.50   (B2458)

BANTOCK, GRANVILLE (1868-1946)
By The Rivers Of Babylon *anthem
SATB,org CRAMER B 35 s.p.   (B2459)

Cantique De Paques *Easter,hymn,17th cent
"Easter Hymn" [Eng/Fr] SATB,org CHESTER
s.p.   (B2460)

Easter Hymn *see Cantique De Paques

Praise Ye The Lord *anthem
SATB,org CRAMER B 36 s.p.   (B2461)

BANYON, ARTHUR
Shepherds Carol, A *Xmas,carol
unis jr cor/unis wom cor CURWEN 72117 s.p.
(B2462)

BAOTENG, S. GEOFFREY
I Was Glad
cor oct HART s.p.   (B2463)

BAPTISTAE see Fulda, Adam von

BAR-AM, BENJAMIN
Kedushah *Heb
SATB,cantor,org ISRAELI 229 s.p.   (B2464)

BAR JESU MINNE I DITT BROST see Nilsson, Olle

BARAB
Merry Are The Bells
SATB,acap oct BOOSEY 5282 $.30   (B2465)

BARASH, MORRIS
Marriage Service *Marriage
cor,cantor,org oct TRANSCON. TCL 690 $2.50
(B2466)

BARBE, HELMUT (1927-   )
Allein Gott In Der Hoh
mix cor HANSSLER 14.131 s.p.   (B2467)

BARBE, HELMUT (cont'd.)

Canticum Simeonis *cant
[Lat] SATB,T solo,org,2vln,vla,vcl,bvl,
perc, celeste HANSSLER 10.070 sc $9.00,
voc sc $2.00, ipr (B2468)

Christe, Du Lamm Gottes
mix cor HANSSLER 14.136 s.p. contains also:
Schweppe, Joachim, Verleih Uns Frieden (B2469)

Das Kreuz Ist Aufgerichtet
see Bossler, Kurt, Fragst Du Nach Meiner
Sunde

Das Wort Gottes, Des Allerhochsten *Gen
SATB,acap (med diff) BAREN. BA 4941 $.40 (B2470)

Die Auferweckung Des Lazarus *cant
dbl cor,AT soli,org,ob,trp,3trom,2vln,vla,
vcl,bvl,perc,timp HANSSLER 10.096 sc
s.p., voc sc s.p., ipr, cor pts s.p. (B2471)

Diesen Weg, Herr *Gen
(Gruschwitz, Gunther) [Ger] 3pt mix cor,
kbd,fl,bvl (med) BOSSE BE 248 s.p. (B2472)

Es Kommt Ein Schiff Geladen
SAT/SAB,opt 1-2inst HANSSLER 14.004 s.p.
contains also: Dittmann, Thomas, O
Heiland, Reiss Die Himmel Auf (SAT/SAB,
treb inst) (B2473)

Heiliger Ewiger Gott
see DEUTSCHES SANCTUS UND PSALM 111

Herr Gott, Du Bist Unsre Zuflucht (Psalm 90)
ECY
[Ger] SSATBB,acap (med diff) BAREN. BA 5413
$2.75 (B2474)

Herr, Unser Herrscher (Psalm 8) cant
[Ger] unis mix cor,2ob,bsn,strings,drums
BAREN. EM 504 rental (B2475)

Ich Will Dem Herren Singen *Bibl/cant/mot
[Ger] 6pt mix cor,acap cor pts BAREN.
EM 439 s.p. (B2476)

Jesaja, Dem Propheten
mix cor HANSSLER 14.135 s.p. (B2477)

Kyrie, Gott Vater
mix cor HANSSLER 14.130 s.p. (B2478)

Magnificat *Magnif
SATB,org,2fl,2ob,2bsn,3trp,2trom,vcl,bvl,
timp HANSSLER 10.034 sc s.p., cor pts
s.p., ipr (B2479)

Missa Brevis *Mass
[Lat] SAB,2fl,ob,bsn,vcl, English horn
HANSSLER 10.149 sc $5.00, voc sc $1.25,
ipa (B2480)

Nun Bitten Wir Den Heiligen Geist
see Poser, Hans, Komm, Heiliger Geist,
Herre Gott

Ostergeschichte *Easter,cant
SATB,ABar soli,2ob,3clar,2trp,2trom,tuba,
2vln,vla,vcl,bvl,perc,timp,gtr HANSSLER
10.150 sc s.p., cor pts s.p. (B2481)

Passionsmotette *Psntd,Bibl/mot
[Ger] 5pt mix cor,acap cor pts BAREN.
EM 440 s.p. (B2482)

Psalm 8 *see Herr, Unser Herrscher

Psalm 90 *see Herr Gott, Du Bist Unsre
Zuflucht

Requiem *Req
mix cor,fl,ob,bsn,strings HANSSLER 10.277
sc s.p., cor pts s.p., ipa (B2483)

Wachet Auf, Ruft Uns Die Stimme
SA/ST/SAB,treb inst/bass inst HANSSLER
14.121 s.p. (B2484)

Wir Glauben All An Einen
mix cor HANSSLER 14.132 s.p. (B2485)

Ye Shall Have A Song *cant
[Eng] SSAA,ob,horn,harp sc HANSSLER 10.303
s.p. (B2486)

BARBEE, N.
Judge Me, O God (Psalm 43) Bibl
4pt mix cor,acap oct SCHIRM.G 10337 $.25 (B2487)

Psalm 43 *see Judge Me, O God

BARBER
Easter Chorale *Easter,chorale
mix cor SOUTHERN $.40 (B2488)

BARBER, J.
Snowflakes *carol
SATB,acap oct KERBY 7104C $.25 (B2489)

BARBER, RUBY D.M.
How Far Is It To Bethlehem *carol
unis CRAMER 20 s.p. (B2490)

BARBER, SAMUEL (1910-)
Agnus Dei (from Adagio For Strings) Allelu
[Lat] 4pt mix cor,org/pno oct SCHIRM.G
11486 $.35 (B2491)

Easter Chorale
4pt mix cor,org,brass,timp oct SCHIRM.G
11265 $.40 (B2492)

Lamb Of God (from Adagio For Strings)
4pt mix cor,org/pno oct SCHIRM.G 11495 $.35 (B2493)

Nun Takes The Veil, A
4pt mix cor,acap oct SCHIRM.G 10858 $.25 (B2494)
4pt men cor,acap oct SCHIRM.G 10859 $.25 (B2495)
4pt wom cor,acap oct SCHIRM.G 10860 $.25 (B2496)

Prayers Of Kierkegaard *Op.30
[Eng/Ger] mix cor,S,opt ST/SA soli,orch
SCHIRM.G voc sc $1.50, sc $5.00 (B2497)

BARBIREAU, MAITRE JACQUES (ca. 1408-1491)
Opera Omnia *CCU
(Meier, Bernhard) cor cmplt ed AM.INST.MUS.
$18.00 (B2498)

BARCAROLLE see Offenbach, Jacques

BAR'CHU see Gottlieb, J.

BARCROFTE, THOMAS
Two Anthems *CC2U,anthem
mix cor oct OXFORD 43.460 $.35 (B2499)

BARDOS, LAJOS (1899-)
Ave Maris Stella
[Lat] SSA,acap oct BOOSEY 5757 $.30 (B2500)

Christmas Lullaby *Xmas
SAB FOSTER MF511 $.30 (B2501)

BARDOS, LUDWIG
Ecce Sacerdos *Op.7
[Lat] SATB,org SCHOTT voc sc s.p., cor pts
s.p. (B2502)

Hochzeitsmusik
mix cor (med easy) oct LEUCKART 673 s.p. (B2503)

BAREKHU see Rossi, Salomone

BARKER
As The Sun Doth Daily Rise *Gen/Thanks
4pt jr cor/SATB (easy) FISCHER,C CM 7383
$.25 (B2504)

My Master Was So Very Poor
4pt jr cor/SATB (med easy) FISCHER,C R6047
$.25 (B2505)

This Is The Day
treb cor&SATB,acap oct BELWIN 64267 $.30 (B2506)

Winds Through The Olive Trees
SSA oct BOOSEY 5424 $.30 (B2507)
SATB,acap oct BOOSEY 5251 $.30 (B2508)

BARMHERZIG UND GNADIG IST DER HERR see Schelle,
Johann Hermann

BARMHERZIGER, EWIGER GOTT see Pepping, Ernst

BARMHERZIGES HERZE see Bach, Johann Sebastian,
Barmherziges Herze Der Ewigen Liebe

BARMHERZIGES HERZE DER EWIGEN LIEBE see Bach,
Johann Sebastian

BARN, DU SPEILER HIMLEN AV see Geitvik, S.H.

BARNABON see Ahlen, Waldemar

BARNARD
Ah, Dearest Jesus
SATB SCHMITT 1684 $.22 (B2509)

O Tidings Great And Wondrous
SSA SHAWNEE B 175 $.25 (B2510)

BARNARD, JOHN
First Book Of Selected Church Musick *CCU,
anthem
cor GREGG ISBN 0:576 28200 6 s.p. 10 part-
books bound in 10 volumes; each volume
sold individually (B2511)

Responses
see Gibbons, Orlando, Preces
SAATB,acap (med easy) oct OXFORD $.30
contains also: Gibbons, Orlando, Preces (B2512)

BARNARD, PARK
All Hail The Power Of Jesus Name
SATB,pno (easy) oct WILLIS 7368 $.25 (B2513)

BARNARD, PARKE S.
Veni Emmanuel *Adv
SATB oct GRAY GCMR 3025 $.25 (B2514)

BARNBY
Awake Up, My Glory *Easter/Lent
SATB oct PRO ART 1209 $.30 (B2515)

Cradle Song Of The Blessed Virgin, A *Xmas
(Collins) SSA oct PRO ART 1688 $.20 (B2516)

Jesus, My Lord, My God *Commun
(Wiley) SATB,S solo oct PRO ART 1583 $.25 (B2517)

Just As I Am, Thine Own To Be
(Whitsett) SAB oct LILLENAS AN-2345 $.30 (B2518)

Lord Of Our Life
(Ehret) SATB oct PRO ART 2034 $.22 (B2519)
(Wyatt) SATB oct PRO ART 1587 $.22 (B2520)

Now The Day Is Over
(Ringwald) SSA SHAWNEE B 34 $.25 (B2521)

O God Of Mercy
(Hadley) SATB oct PRO ART 2465 $.25 (B2522)

O Paradise
(Wiley) SATB oct PRO ART 1602 $.18 (B2523)

When Morning Gilds The Skies *Gen
(Olds) SATB SCHMITT 1861 $.25 (B2524)

BARNBY, SIR JOSEPH (1838-1896)
Abide With Me *anthem
SATB CRAMER C 0 s.p. (B2525)

Awake Up, My Glory *Easter,anthem/Bibl
4pt mix cor oct SCHIRM.G 3870 $.25 (B2526)
mix cor oct NOVELLO 40.0576.07 s.p. (B2527)

Break Forth Into Joy *Easter,anthem
mix cor oct NOVELLO 40.0468.10 s.p. (B2528)

Eyes Of All Wait Upon Thee, The
2pt ASHDOWN E.A.240 s.p. (B2529)

King, All Glorious *Bibl
(Squires) 4pt mix cor,high solo,B solo oct
SCHIRM.G 3770 $.30 (B2530)

Now The Day Is Over *Gen
(Norden) SATB SCHMITT 1872 $.25 (B2531)
(Ringwald) SATB,acap SHAWNEE A 35 $.25 (B2532)

BARNBY, SIR JOSEPH (cont'd.)

O How Amiable *anthem
SATB ALLANS 327 s.p. (B2533)

O How Amiable Are Thy Dwellings *Bibl
4pt mix cor oct SCHIRM.G 3836 $.30 (B2534)
(Mueller) SABar,opt Bar solo oct SCHIRM.G
8690 $.25 (B2535)

O Lord, How Manifold *Gen/Harv/Thanks,
anthem/Bibl
SATB ALLANS 324 s.p. (B2536)
4pt mix cor oct SCHIRM.G 3846 $.25 (B2537)

O Lord, How Manifold Are Thy Works *Harv,
anthem
mix cor oct NOVELLO 40.0281.04 s.p. (B2538)

O Perfect Love *Marriage,anthem/Bibl
SATB ALLANS 391 s.p. (B2539)
SA ALLANS 392 s.p. (B2540)
4pt mix cor oct SCHIRM.G 3837 $.30 (B2541)
mix cor oct NOVELLO 28.0380.01 s.p. (B2542)

Praise, O Praise Our God And King *Harv,
anthem
SATB,org CRAMER C 0 s.p. (B2543)

Preces And Responses According To Tallis
(Festal)
SATB oct NOVELLO 02.0002.06 s.p. (B2544)

Preces And Responses With Harmonized
Confession (Ely)
SATB oct NOVELLO 02.0003.04 s.p. (B2545)

Preces And Responses With Litany (Ferial)
SATB oct NOVELLO 02.0001.08 s.p. (B2546)

Sweet Is Thy Mercy *anthem
SATB oct PRESSER 332-00040 $.30 (B2547)
SATB oct PRO ART 1694 $.20 (B2548)
SATB (easy) ALLANS 37 s.p. (B2549)
4pt mix cor,S solo oct SCHIRM.G 3838 $.25 (B2550)
mix cor,S solo oct NOVELLO 40.0368.03 s.p. (B2551)
(Stickles) 3pt mix cor,S solo,org oct
SCHIRM.G 11124 $.25 (B2552)

Ye Shall Go Out With Joy *Harv,anthem
mix cor oct NOVELLO 28.0352.06 s.p. (B2553)

BARNER, A.
Es Ist Etwas, Des Heilands Sein
TTBB HANSSLER 6.2320 s.p. contains also:
Ebeling, Johann Georg, Du Meine Seele,
Singe (TTBB) (B2554)

BARNES
Unto Thee Will I Cry *anthem
mix cor oct OXFORD 43.462 $.65 (B2555)

BARNES, ALBERT F.
Cross, The *anthem/Introit
mix cor oct NOVELLO 50.0286.09 s.p. (B2556)

Missa Brevis *Mass
SA,org/winds oct LAWSON 51160 $.50 (B2557)

BARNES, [EDWARD SHIPPEN] (1887-1958)
Come, We That Love The Lord
SA,pno/org (easy) oct WILLIS 5972 $.15 (B2558)

I Would Walk With You, Lord
(Nichols) SATB FLAMMER A 5580 $.30 (B2559)

Mother's Day Hymn
SSA oct FISCHER,J 8285 $.30 (B2560)
SATB oct FISCHER,J 8087 $.30 (B2561)

O Worship The King *Bibl
4pt mix cor oct SCHIRM.G 7353 $.25 (B2562)

Three Kings *Xmas/Epiph
4pt mix cor oct SCHIRM.G 7053 $.20 (B2563)

Twenty Unison Anthems For Junior Choir
*CC20U
unis oct PRESSER $1.25 sold only in USA (B2564)

Unison Anthem Book *CCU
unis oct PRESSER $2.25 sold only in USA (B2565)

BARNES, H.W.S.
Sun Of My Soul
SATB,S/T solo,org (med) oct WILLIS 3385
$.12 (B2566)

Trust Ye In The Lord
SATB,S/T solo,org (easy) oct WILLIS 4972
$.12 (B2567)

BARNES, M.H.
Three Songs To Children
SA/SSA oct KERBY 7007C $.45 (B2568)

BARNETT, JOHN (1802-1890)
Hunter, The (from Songs Of Mary)
(Granville; Heiberg) SATB,acap oct FOX $.30 (B2569)
(Granville; Heiberg) SSA,acap oct FOX $.30 (B2570)

BARNEY
Psalm Of Exaltation
SATB SHAWNEE A 1016 $.30 (B2571)

BARNEY, MARGARET HIGGINSON
Nativity, The (composed with Warner, Lorraine
D'Oremieulx)
jr cor/wom voc sc SCHIRM.EC 11 $1.00 (B2572)

BARNLIGE SANGER TIL JULENS PRIS see Beck,
Thomas [Ludvigsen]

BARONCHELLI, NESTORE
Assumpta Est Maria *BVM,Offer
[Lat] 3pt mix cor ZANIBON 3759 s.p. (B2573)

BARONI, GIOVANNI
Beate S. Carole *ASD
[Lat] T/S,org ZANIBON 2730 s.p. (B2574)

Elegit Te Dominus
[Lat] T,org ZANIBON 2619 s.p. (B2575)

BARONI, GIOVANNI (cont'd.)

Oremus Pro Antistite
[Lat] 3pt mix cor,org ZANIBON 2704 s.p.
(B2576)

Panis Angelicus
see SEI MOTTETTI EUCARISTICI

Salve Sancta Parens *BVM
[Lat] 3pt mix cor,org ZANIBON 2762 s.p.
(B2577)

Tantum Ergo
see QUATTRO MOTTETTI EUCARISTICI

BAROQUE MASSES *CCU,Mass,Baroq
[Lat] mix cor,acap voc sc KALMUS 6073 $1.25
contains works by: Dunstable; Dufay;
Touron; Obrecht; Finch; Josquin (B2578)

BAROQUE SONG BOOK, THE *CCU
(Murphy, Ernest) 2pt jr cor MCAFEE cor pts
$.50, cmplt ed $2.95 (B2579)

BAROQUE TO THE GREAT CLASSICS, THE VOL. 1-1550
TO 1700 see Byrd, William

BAROQUE TO THE GREAT CLASSICS, THE VOL. 2A-1550
TO 1700 see Schuetky, Joseph

BAROQUE TO THE GREAT CLASSICS, THE VOL. 2B-1550
TO 1700 see Schutz, Heinrich

BAROQUE TO THE GREAT CLASSICS, THE VOL. 3-1550
TO 1700 see Monteverdi, Claudio

BAROQUE TO THE GREAT CLASSICS, THE VOL. 4-1550
TO 1700 see Buxtehude, Dietrich

BAROTI
Caligaverunt Oculi Mei *cant
SATB&SATB,4trp,4trom MOSELER sc s.p., cor
pts s.p., ipa (B2580)

BARR, J.
Magnificat And Nunc Dimittis
unis oct PRESSER MC476 $.40 (B2581)

BARRACLOUGH
Ivory Palaces
(Hustad) SSATB oct AGAPE HA 105 $.30
(B2582)
(Hustad) SSAATTBB oct AGAPE HA 504 $.25
(B2583)
(McCluskey) SATB oct LORENZ B154 $.30
(B2584)
(Vaughn) SATB oct AGAPE GC 803 $.25 (B2585)
(Wilson) SATB oct LORENZ A299 $.25 (B2586)

Trumpet Of God
SATB oct LORENZ C192 $.30 (B2587)

BARRATT, R.
Calm On The Listening Ear Of Night *Xmas
SSAATTBB,pno (diff) oct WILLIS 5589 $.20
(B2588)

BARRAUD, HENRY (1900-)
Homage A Rameau *see Pange Lingua

Le Mystere Des Saints Innocents
"Mystery Of The Holy Innocents, The" [Eng/
Fr] mix cor&jr cor,TBar,narrator,pno,3fl,
3ob,3clar,3bsn,3trp,4horn,3trom,tuba,
strings,2harp,perc,timp cmplt ed BOOSEY
rental (B2589)

Mystery Of The Holy Innocents, The *see Le
Mystere Des Saints Innocents

Noel *Xmas
3pt AMPHION A129 s.p. (B2590)

Pange Lingua
"Homage A Rameau" [Eng/Lat] mix cor,SBar
soli,2fl,2ob,2bsn,2trp,2horn,2trom,
strings cmplt ed BOOSEY rental (B2591)

Te Deum *Te Deum
mix cor,org RICORDI-ENG R1565 s.p. (B2592)
mix cor,acap RICORDI-ENG R1429 s.p. (B2593)
mix cor,org RICORDI-FR R1565 s.p. (B2594)
cor,acap RICORDI-FR R1429 s.p. (B2595)

BARRELL, BERNARD (1919-)
Missa Brevis *Op.35, Mass
[Eng/Lat] unis,org CHESTER sc s.p., voc sc
s.p. (B2596)

BARRETT-AYRES, REGINALD
Holy Communion *Commun
unis (series 3) oct NOVELLO 29.0022.10 s.p.
(B2597)

New Songs For The Church Book 1 *CCU
(Routley) unis,kbd GALLIARD 2.9053.1 $1.75
(B2598)

BARRI, O.
Good Shepherd, The
(Rees) 4pt mix cor,B solo oct SCHIRM.G 3412
$.25 (B2599)
(Spicker) 2pt wom cor oct SCHIRM.G 5062
$.25 (B2600)
(Stevens) SAB oct PRO ART 1624 $.18 (B2601)

BARROW, ROBERT G.
Christians, Awake, Salute The Happy Morn
*Xmas,anthem
TTBB,org SCHIRM.EC 2157 $.18 (B2602)

Hush, My Dear, Lie Still And Slumber *Xmas,
anthem
TTBB,org SCHIRM.EC 2173 $.30 (B2603)

BARTHEL, URSULA (1913-)
Auf, Auf, Ihr Hirten
see Zwei Chore Zur Weihnacht

Heiligste Nacht *Xmas
SSAA,SS soli TONGER s.p. (B2604)

Markt Und Strassen
see Zwei Chore Zur Weihnacht

Zu Bethlehem Geboren *Xmas
SSAA,S solo TONGER s.p. (B2605)

Zwei Chore Zur Weihnacht *Xmas
SSAA,SS soli TONGER s.p.
contains: Auf, Auf, Ihr Hirten; Markt Und
Strassen (B2606)

BARTHELSON
Child's Prayer, A
SA/TB SHAWNEE E35 $.25 (B2607)

Falan Tiding Dio *Xmas,carol,Aus
SSA oct BOURNE 216 $.25 (B2608)
SATB oct BOURNE 771 $.30 (B2609)

Happy Christmas Comes Once More *Xmas
SATB oct VOLKWEIN VB166 $.25 (B2610)

BARTHELSON, JOYCE
Lift Up Your Heads
SATB oct PLYMOUTH HA-6 $.25 (B2611)

O Sons And Daughters
SATB oct PLYMOUTH HA-3 $.25 (B2612)

Praise The Lord With Song *Gen
SATB oct SPRATT 552 $.25 (B2613)

BARTHOLEMEW
Sleep, Little Jesus *Xmas
SATB oct PRO ART 2339 $.25 (B2614)

BARTMUS, RICHARD (1859-1910)
Du Liebes Kind
[Ger] wom cor,solo,org HUG s.p. (B2615)

Uns Ist Ein Kind Geboren *chorale/mot
[Ger] wom cor,org HUG s.p. (B2616)

BARTOCK
Lonely Shepherd, The
SATB oct STAFF 595 $.25 (B2617)

BARTOK, BELA (1881-1945)
Shepherd's Christmas Songs *Xmas
(Arma, Paul) mix cor,acap cor pts BOOSEY
$1.00 (B2618)

BARTOW
Adam Lay Y-Bounden
SATB SHAWNEE A 836 $.25 (B2619)
SSA SHAWNEE B 257 $.25 (B2620)

Christmas Canticle, A
SATB SHAWNEE A809 $.50 (B2621)

King Of Love My Shepherd Is, The
SATB SHAWNEE A 842 $.25 (B2622)

Scene On Easter Morning
SATB SHAWNEE A843 $.75 (B2623)

Thanksgiving Exultation *Thanks
SATB SHAWNEE A 844 $.25 (B2624)

Tower Of Babel, The
SATB SHAWNEE A1002 $1.25 (B2625)

BARUCH see Gotthelf-Levita, Gerard

BAS, GIULIO (1874-1929)
Dodici Canzoncine *CC12U,Xmas
unis,org ZANIBON 321 s.p. (B2626)

Missa Secunda *Mass
[Lat] ATB,org sc ZANIBON 1609 s.p., voc pt
ZANIBON 1609A-B-C s.p. (B2627)

Ventequatro Nuove Canzoncine Spirituali
*CC24U,BVM,Commun/Gen
[Lat] unis,org ZANIBON 322 s.p. (B2628)

BASHAM, ROBERT A.
Fear Thou Not
SATB oct LILLENAS AN-2367 $.30 (B2629)

He Is The King Of Glory (composed with
Basham, Shirley) *Easter,cant
mix cor,narrator&SATB soli,inst voc sc
LILLENAS ME-9 $1.50 (B2630)

Oh, It's Wonderful
(Schubert) SAB oct LILLENAS AN-1177 $.25
(B2631)

Saviour Has Come, The *Xmas,Bibl,cant
mix cor,solo,inst voc sc LILLENAS MC-20
$1.50 (B2632)

Wonderful Story, A (composed with Basham,
Shirley) *Xmas,Bibl/cant
4pt,narrator&SAT/narrator&STBar soli voc sc
LILLENAS MC-11 $1.50 (B2633)

BASHAM, SHIRLEY
He Is The King Of Glory *see Basham, Robert
A.

Wonderful Story, A *see Basham, Robert A.

BASQUE CHRISTMAS CAROL *Xmas,carol,Span
(Kirk, Theron) SATB WEINBERGER s.p. (B2634)

BASS
Name Of Wondrous Love
2pt oct SACRED S-5744 $.30 (B2635)

BASSETT, LESLIE (1923-)
Hear My Prayer, O Lord (Psalm 64)
2pt jr cor,org/pno PETERS 66121 $.25
(B2636)

Psalm 64 *see Hear My Prayer, O Lord

Remembrance
SATB (med) ABINGDON APM-563 $.45 (B2637)

BATEMAN, RONALD
Lord Of Our Life
(Mansfield, P.J.) SATB LEONARD-ENG 78 s.p.
(B2638)

BATISTE, ANTOINE-EDOUARD (1820-1876)
Ave Maria
2pt ENOCH T.P.252 s.p. (B2639)

BATTEN, ADRIAN (ca. 1585-1637)
Deliver Us, O Lord *Lent/Thanks
SATB,acap (easy) oct OXFORD 43.074 $.30
contains also: O Praise The Lord (Epiph/
Thanks) (B2640)

Four Anthems *CC4U,anthem
(Evans, David) 4-6pt,org oct PENN STATE
0-271-09117-7 $3.25 (B2641)

Fourth Evening Service *Eve,Magnif/Nunc
SATB (med easy) oct OXFORD 42.996 $.65
(B2642)

BATTEN, ADRIAN (cont'd.)

Haste Thee, O God *Lent
SATB,acap (easy) oct OXFORD 43.219 $.25
(B2643)

Hear My Prayer, O God *Gen/Lent
(Shaw) SSATB,acap (med) oct OXFORD 43.912
$.35 (B2644)

Hear My Prayer, O Lord *anthem
(Bevan) SATB,B solo,org SCHOTT 10574 s.p.
(B2645)

Hear The Prayers, O Our God *anthem
(Bevan) SAATB SCHOTT s.p. (B2646)

Let My Complaint Come Before Thee (Psalm 119)
Lent
(Bevan) SATB,acap (med easy) oct OXFORD
43.358 $.30 (B2647)

Lord, We Beseech Thee
SATB,acap (easy) oct OXFORD 43.401 $.30
contains: Lord, We Beseech Thee (Asc/
Lent); When The Lord Turned Again
(Easter/Thanks) (B2648)

Lord, We Beseech Thee
see Lord, We Beseech Thee

O Clap Your Hands Together *anthem
(Bevan) SSAATTBB SCHOTT 10642 s.p. (B2649)

O Lord, Thou Hast Searched Me Out *anthem
(Bevan) SATB,AB soli,org SCHOTT s.p.
(B2650)

O Praise The Lord
see Batten, Adrian, Deliver Us, O Lord
(Ehret) mix cor CHAPPELL 0024240-358 $.40
(B2651)

O Sing Joyfully (Psalm 81) Gen/Thanks,anthem
SATB,acap PETERS H1551 $.40 (B2652)
SATB oct ROYAL 228 s.p. (B2653)
(Bevan) SATB,acap oct OXFORD 43.355
$.30 (B2654)

Out Of The Deep *anthem
(Bevan) SATB,S/T solo,org SCHOTT 10573 s.p.
(B2655)

Psalm 81 *see O Sing Joyfully

Psalm 119 *see Let My Complaint Come Before
Thee

Short Communion Service *Commun,Agnus/Bene/
Credo/Gloria/Kyrie/Sanctus
SATB oct OXFORD 43.334 $.50 (B2656)

Short Service For Men *Magnif/Nunc
TTBB (easy) oct OXFORD 41.015 $.65 (B2657)

Sing We Merrily Unto God *anthem
(West, John E.) mix cor oct NOVELLO
28.0856.00 s.p. (B2658)

Third Verse Service *Magnif/Nunc
SATB oct OXFORD (B2659)

Vier Anthems *CCU,Gen
(Evans, David) [Ger] 4-6pt mix cor,org
(med) PENN STATE PSM 17 s.p. (B2660)

We Beseech Thee Almighty God *anthem
(Bevan) SAATB SCHOTT s.p. (B2661)

When The Lord Turned Again
see Lord, We Beseech Thee

BATTER MY HEART, THREE PERSON'D GOD see
Berkeley, Lennox

BATTISHILL, JONATHAN (1738-1801)
How Long Wilt Thou Forget Me
(Holman) mix cor oct SCHIRM.G 10927 $.25
(B2662)

O Lord, Look Down From Heaven *anthem
(Martin, George C.) SSATTB,orch oct NOVELLO
28.0184.01 s.p., ipr (B2663)
(Shaw, Watkins) mix cor oct NOVELLO
88.0001.04 s.p. (B2664)

Oh Remember Not
SAB,org SCHIRM.EC 2615 $.30 (B2665)

BATTLE HYMN OF THE REPUBLIC see Lee

BATTLE HYMN OF THE REPUBLIC see Reed

BATTLE HYMN OF THE REPUBLIC see Steffe,
[William]

BATTLE HYMN OF THE REPUBLIC see Wilson

BATTLE OF JERICHO, THE *spir
(Bartholomew) mix cor,acap oct SCHIRM.G 10081
$.30 (B2666)
(Bartholomew) 4pt men cor,acap oct SCHIRM.G
7390 $.30 (B2667)
(Bartholomew) 2pt men cor,acap oct SCHIRM.G
9776 $.30 (B2668)
(Trant) SSA,acap (med) OXFORD 83.059 $.25
(B2669)

BATTLE O'JERICHO *spir
(Wagner) SATB,acap oct LAWSON 51570 $.35
(B2670)

BATTMANN
Deuxieme Messe *Op.282, Mass
[Fr] 2 eq voices,pno (C maj) LEDUC BL49 voc
sc s.p., voc pt s.p. (B2671)

Premiere Messe *Op.193, Mass
[Fr] 2 eq voices,pno (F maj) LEDUC BL48 voc
sc s.p., voc pt s.p. (B2672)

BATTRE, H.
De Qua Natus Est *Adv/Xmas
ATB,acap voc pt DOBLINGER s.p. see also
ADVENT UND WEIHNACHT, HEFT 2 (B2673)

BAUDACH, ULRICH (1921-)
Christ Fuhr Gen Himmel
SAT/SAB/SA,treb inst HANSSLER 14.090 s.p.
(B2674)

Evangelisches Kirchengesangbuch *Asc/Pent
[Ger] 3pt mix cor,acap BAREN. EM 21 s.p.
contains: Freut Euch Ihr Christen Alle,
No.102; Komm, Heiliger Geist, Herre
Gott, No.98; Und Es Soll Geschehen
(B2675)

BAUDACH, ULRICH (cont'd.)

Freut Euch Ihr Christen Alle
see Evangelisches Kirchengesangbuch

Hilf Herr Jesu, Lass Gelingen
SAT/SAB,treb inst HANSSLER 14.041 (B2676)

Johannes-Passion *see Liedpassion: Jesu
Kreuz, Leiden Und Pein   (B2677)

Johannes-Passion *Psntd
[Ger] SSATB,TB soli,acap (med diff) BAREN.
BA 3882 $4.50   (B2678)

Komm, Heiliger Geist, Herre Gott
see Evangelisches Kirchengesangbuch

Liedpassion: Jesu Kreuz, Leiden Und Pein
*Psntd
[Ger] SSATB,Bar solo,acap (med diff,
choralpartita) BAREN. BA 3883 $2.50 see
from Johannes-Passion   (B2679)

Und Es Soll Geschehen
see Evangelisches Kirchengesangbuch

BAUERNBEGRABNIS see Bella, R.

BAUERNFIEND, HANS (1908-   )
Ave Maria *Mass/mot
mix cor,acap oct DOBLINGER s.p. see from
Drei Motetten   (B2680)
4pt mix cor,acap DOBLINGER sc s.p., cor pts
s.p.   (B2681)

Cantate Domino *mot
mix cor,acap DOBLINGER s.p. see from
Drei Motetten   (B2682)

Christ Ist Erstanden
wom cor,acap oct DOBLINGER s.p. see from
Zwei Geistliche Chore   (B2683)

Da Jesus In Den Garten Ging
wom cor,acap oct DOBLINGER s.p. see from
Zwei Geistliche Chore   (B2684)

Dein Lob, Herr, Ruft Der Himmel Aus
4pt mix cor/3pt wom cor,acap DOBLINGER s.p.
see from Kirchenliedsatze   (B2685)

Der Cherubinische Wandersmann *see Die
Schonheit Kommt Von Lieb; Du Selbst Musst
Sonne Sein; Halt An, Wo Laufst Du Hin;
Mensch, Werde Wesentlich   (B2686)

Deutsches Ordinarium
4pt mix cor&cong,cantor,org DOBLINGER voc
sc s.p., cor pts s.p.   (B2687)

Deutsches Ordinarium II
mix cor&cong,cantor,org DOBLINGER sc s.p.,
cor pts s.p.   (B2688)

Die Schonheit Kommt Von Lieb
wom cor,acap oct DOBLINGER s.p. see from
Der Cherubinische Wandersmann   (B2689)
(Silesius) men cor,acap voc pt DOBLINGER
s.p. see from Der Cherubinische
Wandersmann   (B2690)

Drei Motetten *see Ave Maria; Cantate
Domino; Jubilate Deo   (B2691)

Du Selbst Musst Sonne Sein
wom cor,acap oct DOBLINGER s.p. see from
Der Cherubinische Wandersmann   (B2692)
(Silesius) men cor,acap voc pt DOBLINGER
s.p. see from Der Cherubinische
Wandersmann   (B2693)

Gen Himmel Aufgefahren Ist
4pt mix cor/3pt wom cor,acap DOBLINGER s.p.
see from Kirchenliedsatze   (B2694)

Halt An, Wo Laufst Du Hin
wom cor,acap oct DOBLINGER s.p. see from
Der Cherubinische Wandersmann   (B2695)
(Silesius) men cor,acap voc pt DOBLINGER
s.p. see from Der Cherubinische
Wandersmann   (B2696)

Jubilate Deo *mot
mix cor,acap oct DOBLINGER s.p. see from
Drei Motetten   (B2697)

Kirchenliedsatze *CC7L,Xmas
cor&wom cor voc pt DOBLINGER s.p.
see also: Dein Lob, Herr, Ruft Der Himmel
Aus; Gen Himmel Aufgefahren Ist; Konig
Ist Der Herr; Nun Bitten Wir Den
Heiligen Geist; Nun Danket All Und
Bringet Ehr'; Nun Lobet Gott Im Hohen
Thron; O Jesu Christe, Wahres Licht (B2698)

Konig Ist Der Herr
4pt mix cor/3pt wom cor,acap DOBLINGER see
from Kirchenliedsatze   (B2699)

Macht Hoch Die Tur
"Raise High The Door" SATB,acap AMP A584
$.30   (B2700)

Maria Durch Ein Dornwald Ging
"Once Through A Woodland Mary Walked" [Eng/
Ger] SATB,acap AMP A402 $.25   (B2701)

Mensch, Werde Wesentlich
wom cor,acap DOBLINGER see from Der
Cherubinische Wandersmann   (B2702)
(Silesius) men cor,acap voc pt DOBLINGER
s.p. see from Der Cherubinische
Wandersmann   (B2703)

Missa Salve Regina *Mass
2pt wom cor,org DOBLINGER voc sc s.p., cor
pts s.p.   (B2704)

Nun Bitten Wir Den Heiligen Geist
4pt mix cor/3pt wom cor,acap DOBLINGER s.p.
see from Kirchenliedsatze   (B2705)

Nun Danket All Und Bringet Ehr'
4pt mix cor/3pt wom cor,acap DOBLINGER s.p.
see from Kirchenliedsatze   (B2706)

BAUERNFIEND, HANS (cont'd.)

Nun Lobet Gott Im Hohen Thron
4pt mix cor/3pt wom cor,acap DOBLINGER s.p.
see from Kirchenliedsatze   (B2707)

O Heiland, Reiss Die Himmel Auf
"O Savior, Rend The Heavens Wide" [Eng/Ger]
SATB,acap AMP A585 $.25   (B2708)

O Jesu Christe, Wahres Licht
4pt mix cor/3pt wom cor,acap DOBLINGER s.p.
see from Kirchenliedsatze   (B2709)

O Savior, Rend The Heavens Wide *see O
Heiland, Reiss Die Himmel Auf

Once Through A Woodland Mary Walked *see
Maria Durch Ein Dornwald Ging

Proprium Fur Den Achtzehnten Sonntag Nach
Pfingsten *Trin
4pt mix cor,org DOBLINGER voc sc s.p., cor
pts s.p.   (B2710)

Psalm 12
4pt mix cor,acap DOBLINGER sc s.p., cor pts
s.p.   (B2711)

Raise High The Door *see Macht Hoch Die Tur

Salve Regina *Mass
4pt mix cor,org,opt 2trp&2trom DOBLINGER
voc sc s.p., cor pts s.p., ipa   (B2712)

Zwei Geistliche Chore *see Christ Ist
Erstanden; Da Jesus In Den Garten Ging (B2713)

BAUERNHOCHZEIT see Bella, R.

BAUERNPSALM see Bella, R.

BAUMANN, HERBERT
Psalm 8
see Psalmen-Tryptichon

Psalm 33
see Psalmen-Tryptichon

Psalm 57
see Psalmen-Tryptichon

Psalmen-Tryptichon
mix cor,strings MOSELER sc s.p., cor pts
s.p., ipa
contains: Psalm 8; Psalm 33; Psalm 57 (B2714)

BAUMANN, MAX (1917-   )
Adeste Fideles *Xmas,carol
[Lat] mix cor (med) oct SIRIUS 9 s.p. (B2715)

Ankunft Des Herrn *see Die Geburt Des Herrn,
Op.66,No.1   (B2716)

Ankunft Des Herrn *Op.66, Adv
[Ger] mix cor&boy cor&wom cor,acap
SIRIUS sc s.p., cor pts s.p.   (B2717)

Befiehl Du Deine Wege *Op.56, chorale/mot
[Ger] SATB,acap voc sc SIRIUS s.p.   (B2718)

Communio
see Drei Weihnachtsmotetten

Deutsche Vesper *Op.64
[Ger] mix cor,opt narrator,S solo,winds,
horn,trp,trom,strings SIRIUS voc sc s.p.,
cor pts s.p., ipa   (B2719)

Die Geburt Des Herrn *Op.66,No.1, Adv/Xmas
[Ger] mix cor&boy cor&wom cor cor pts
SIRIUS s.p. see from Ankunft Des Herrn (B2720)

Drei Weihnachtsmotetten *Op.53, Xmas,mot
SATB,acap SIRIUS sc s.p., cor pts s.p.
contains: Communio (Commun); Graduale
(Gradual); Introitus (Introit)   (B2721)

Ecce Sacerdos
[Lat] wom cor&jr cor,acap (med) oct SIRIUS
1 s.p.   (B2722)

Geistliches Lied
[Ger] wom cor&jr cor,acap (med) oct SIRIUS
3 s.p.   (B2723)

Graduale
see Drei Weihnachtsmotetten

Ihr Freunde Gottes Allzugleich
[Ger] mix cor (easy) oct SIRIUS 8 s.p. (B2724)

Introitus
see Drei Weihnachtsmotetten

Kleine Marienmesse *Op.59, Mass
[Ger] wom cor&jr cor,opt org voc sc SIRIUS
s.p.   (B2725)

Lob Und Ehr Sei Gott *BVM
[Ger] wom cor&jr cor,acap (med) oct SIRIUS
4 s.p.   (B2726)

Lobet Den Herrn (Psalm 116)
[Ger] wom cor&jr cor,acap (med) oct SIRIUS
2 s.p.   (B2727)

Marienlied *BVM
[Ger] wom cor&jr cor,acap (med) oct SIRIUS
5 s.p.   (B2728)

Missa *Op.39, Mass
[Lat] SATB,acap SIRIUS sc s.p., cor pts
s.p.   (B2729)

Offertorium Zu Ehren Des Hl. Ludgerus *Offer
[Ger] mix cor (med) oct SIRIUS 7 s.p. (B2730)

Passion *Op.63, Easter
[Ger] mix cor&speak cor,SBar&narrator,2pno,
4fl,2trp,perc,timp,harp SIRIUS sc s.p.,
cor pts s.p., voc sc s.p., ipa   (B2731)

Psalm 116 *see Lobet Den Herrn

Psalm *Op.67, Psalm
[Ger] mix cor,Bar solo,org,pno,3trp,3trom,
tuba,timp,harp cor pts SIRIUS s.p., ipa (B2732)

BAUMANN, MAX (cont'd.)

Salve Regina *Fest
[Ger] SATB,opt org (med) MULLER MS 57 s.p. (B2733)

Schutzengel-Messe *Op.50, Mass
[Ger] SATB,opt org SIRIUS sc s.p., cor pts
s.p.   (B2734)

Tantum Ergo (from Passion) Easter
[Lat] SATB,acap voc sc SIRIUS s.p.   (B2735)

BAUMGARTNER, H. LEROY
His Delight Is In The Law Of The Lord
SATB (med) ABINGDON APM-454 $.30   (B2736)

Remember All The People *ASD
SATB&jr cor (easy) ABINGDON APM-235 $.25 (B2737)
SAB (easy) ABINGDON APM-211 $.25   (B2738)

When, His Salvation Bringing *Palm
SATB (med) ABINGDON APM-453 $.25   (B2739)

BAUSTEINE FUR DEN GOTTESDIENST-HEFT 1 *CC19U
mix cor,inst sc HANSSLER 19.901 s.p. contains
works by: Lotz; Michel; Ruppel; Schauss-
Flake, V; Schwartz; Schwarz; Schweizer (B2740)

BAUSTEINE FUR DEN GOTTESDIENST-HEFT 2 *CC15U
mix cor,inst sc HANSSLER 19.902 s.p. contains
works by: Kretzschmar; Michel; Planzer;
Ruppel; Schauss-Flake; Schwarz; Schweizer (B2741)

BAUSTEINE FUR DEN GOTTESDIENST-HEFT 3 *CC12U
mix cor,inst sc HANSSLER 19.903 s.p. contains
works by: Blarr; Ruppel; Schweizer; Wehnert (B2742)

BAUSTEINE FUR DEN GOTTESDIENST-HEFT 4 *CC9U
mix cor,inst sc HANSSLER 19.904 s.p. contains
works by: Kretzschmar; Michel; Ruppel;
Schweizer   (B2743)

BAUSTEINE FUR DEN GOTTESDIENST-HEFT 5 *CC13U
mix cor,inst sc HANSSLER 19.905 s.p. contains
works by: Blarr; Lotz; Ruppel; Schweizer (B2744)

BAUSZNERN, DIETRICH VON (1928-   )
Auf, Auf, Ihr Reichsgenossen
SAB/SAT,treb inst,bass inst HANSSLER 14.008
s.p.   (B2745)

Europaische Weihnachtslieder, Heft 4 *CCU,
Xmas,Eur
(Strube, Adolf) [Ger] 4pt men cor BAREN.
EM 757 s.p.   (B2746)

BAWDEN, CLARENCE
Benedictus In G
SATB ELKAN,H $.30   (B2747)

BAX, SIR ARNOLD (1883-1953)
Turn Back O Man
(Harter, Harry) SATB oct BELWIN 2139 $.25 (B2748)

BAXTER, F.
Good Christian Men, Rejoice *Xmas
SATB,acap oct PRESSER 312-40505 $.30 (B2749)

In Bethlehem *Xmas
SATB,acap oct PRESSER 312-40424 $.30 (B2750)

BAXTER, T.
English Mass, An *Credo/Mass
cong&opt cor,opt org oct ST.MARTIN SMP666
s.p., ipa   (B2751)

Introit-Motet In Honor Of St Joseph *mot
[Eng] unis&opt cong,org oct ST.MARTIN
SMP669   (B2752)

Parish Choir Book No. 12, The *CCU,Adv,
Allelu/Gradual
cong&opt cor,cantor oct ST.MARTIN SMP6710
s.p.   (B2753)

Psalm 150
[Eng] cor&cong,org oct ST.MARTIN SMP6711
s.p.   (B2754)

BAY BOOK, THE *CC30U,Gen
(Pitcher, G.) SA oct JUSKO $2.00   (B2755)

BAYERISCHE MADRIGALE see Lehner, F.X.

BAYLEY, ROBERT CHARLTON
Blessed Are The Pure In Heart
SATB,acap oct BERANDOL 910B9AC $.35 (B2756)

Child Jesus *carol
SATB,acap oct BERANDOL 910B9AD $.35 (B2757)

None Other Lamb
SA oct AGAPE A 455 $.30   (B2758)

What Makes The Yellow Star To Dance?
SATB,acap oct BERANDOL 910B9AE $.35 (B2759)

Winds Through The Olive Trees
SSA,acap oct BERANDOL 830B9AB $.35   (B2760)

BAYNON, ARTHUR
Angel's Song, The *Xmas
unis oct NOVELLO 48.1881.04 s.p.   (B2761)

Child's Thanksgiving, A *Gen/Thanks
unis (very easy) oct OXFORD 55.004 $.20 (B2762)

BAZIN, [FRANCOIS-EMANUEL-JOSEPH] (1816-1878)
Pater Noster
[Lat] 4pt mix cor,acap LEMOINE s.p. (B2763)

Pie Jesu
[Lat] 3pt men cor,acap LEMOINE s.p. (B2764)

BE A CHILD AGAIN! see Mc Call, Harlo

BE CALM AND PEACEFUL see Bach

BE EXALTED, O LORD see Newbury, Kent A.

BE FOLLOWERS OF GOD see Wiley

BE GLAD AND SING FOR JOY see Johnston

BE GLAD IN THE LORD see Glarum, L. Stanley

BE GLAD THEN AMERICA see Billings, William

BE GLAD THEN AND REJOICE see Roff, Joseph

BE GLAD, YE HEAVENS see Byrd, William, Laetentur Coeli

BE GOOD, BE GENTLE, AND BELIEVE see Myrow, Jerry

BE GRACIOUS UNTO ME see Mozart, Wolfgang Amadeus

BE HONOR TO GOD ETERNAL see Mason

BE IT SO see Cerbus, [Paul]

BE JOYFUL see Glarum, L. Stanley

BE JOYFUL see Monteverdi, Claudio, Laetatus Sum

BE JOYFUL, BE MERRY see Tellep, Leo M.

BE JOYFUL IN GOD see Pond, S.B.

BE JOYFUL IN THE LORD see Couperin

BE JOYFUL IN THE LORD see Couperin, Francois

BE JOYFUL IN THE LORD see Fearis, J.S.

BE JOYFUL IN THE LORD see James

BE JOYFUL IN THE LORD see Peek

BE JOYFUL IN THE LORD see Titcomb

BE JOYFUL, O DAUGHTER OF ZION see Titcomb

BE JOYFUL, O EARTH see Warland, Dale

BE KNOWN TO US see Lovelace, Austin C.

BE KNOWN TO US see Younger, John B.

BE KNOWN TO US IN BREAKING BREAD see Hopkins

BE KNOWN TO US IN BREAKING OF THE BREAD see Kelley

BE MERCIFUL AFTER THY POWER see Winchester, F.

BE MERCIFUL, EVEN AS YOUR FATHER see Hillert, Richard

BE MERCIFUL, EVEN AS YOUR FATHER IS MERCIFUL see Krapf, Gerhard

BE MERCIFUL, LORD see Sternburg, Daniel

BE MERCIFUL TO ME see Roff, Joseph

BE MERCIFUL UNTO ME see Blow, John

BE MERCIFUL UNTO ME, O GOD see Glarum, L. Stanley

BE MERCIFUL UNTO ME, O GOD see Scarmolin, (Anthony) Louis

BE MERCIFUL UNTO ME, O LORD see Williams

BE MERCIFUL UNTO ME, O LORD see Wolff, S. Drummond

BE MERCIFUL UNTO US, O LORD see Butler C.W.

BE MERRY see Childs, Barney

BE MERRY! see Davies

BE MERRY BE MERRY see Edmunds, John

BE NOT AFRAID see Ahle, Johann Rudolph, Furchtet Euch Nicht

BE NOT AFRAID see Bach, Johann Michael, Feurchtet Euch Nicht

BE NOT AFRAID see Bach, Johann Sebastian, Furchte Dich Nicht

BE NOT AFRAID see Mendelssohn-Bartholdy, Felix

BE NOT AFRAID MARY see Victoria, Tomas Luis de, Ne Timeas Maria

BE NOT DOWNCAST see Bach, Johann Sebastian, Nicht So Traurig

BE NOT FAR FROM ME see Zingarelli, Nicola Antonio

BE NOT FOR AUGHT REGRETFUL see Brahms, Johannes, Lass Dich Nur Nichts Dauren

BE NOT SILENT UNTO US see Pergolesi, Giovanni Battista

BE OF THE SAME MIND ONE TOWARD ANOTHER see Daniel, K.

BE OUR GUIDE THROUGH LIFE, DEAR LORD see Bach, Johann Sebastian

BE-SHAARAY TEFILA see Adler, Samuel

BE STILL see Lowe

BE STILL AND KNOW
(Dexter, Harry) 2pt ENOCH TP281 s.p.   (B2765)

BE STILL AND KNOW see Bitgood, Roberta

BE STILL AND KNOW see Brown, Frank Edwin

BE STILL AND KNOW see Byles

BE STILL AND KNOW see Glarum, L. Stanley

BE STILL AND KNOW see McCormick

BE STILL AND KNOW THAT I AM GOD see Morgan

BE STILL AND KNOW THAT I AM GOD see Noe, J.T.

BE STILL, MY SOUL see Darst, W. Glenn

BE STILL MY SOUL see Sibelius, Jean

BE STILL, MY SOUL see Webber, Lloyd

BE STILL, MY SOUL see Whitlock, Percy

BE STRONG see Rowley, Alec

BE STRONG AND OF A GOOD COURAGE see Darke, Harold [Edwin]

BE STRONG AND OF A GOOD COURAGE see Oxley, Harrison

BE STRONG AND OF GOOD COURAGE see Campbell, Sydney S.

BE STRONG IN BATTLE see Victoria, Tomas Luis de, Estote Fortes In Bello

BE STRONG IN THE LORD see Harris

BE STRONG IN THE LORD see Nicholson, S.H.

BE THANKFUL UNTO HIM see Clark

BE THOU CONTENTED see Bach, Johann Sebastian

BE THOU EXALTED, O GOD see Ingegneri, Marco Antonio

BE THOU EXALTED, O GOD see Roff, Joseph

BE THOU EXALTED, O GOD see Williams

BE THOU EXALTED, O MY GOD see Angell, Warren M.

BE THOU FAITHFUL UNTO DEATH see Richter, Willy

BE THOU MY GUIDE see Wheeler, Alfred

BE THOU MY JUDGE O LORD see Morgan, Haydn

BE THOU MY JUDGE, O LORD see Willis

BE THOU MY VISION   *anthem/folk,Ir
(Godfrey, G.) SATB oct PRESSER 332-15116 $.30
(B2766)
(Pooler, Frank; Pooler, Marie) SATB&jr cor
(easy) oct AUGSBURG 1155 $.30   (B2767)
(Pooler, Frank; Pooler, Marie) SA&SATB (easy)
oct AUGSBURG 1155 $.30   (B2768)
(Pooler, Marie) unis treb cor&opt desc (easy)
oct AUGSBURG 1323 $.25   (B2769)

BE THOU MY VISION see Cannon, Jack D.

BE THOU MY VISION see Gillette

BE THOU MY VISION see Middleton, J. Roland

BE THOU MY VISION see Pearson

BE THOU MY VISION see Ward

BE THOU MY VISION see Wetherill

BE THOU MY VISION see Young, C.

BE THOU NEAR ME LORD see Morgan

BE THOU NEAR ME, LORD see Morgan, Haydn

BE THOU NOT STILL, OH LORD see Morgan

BE THOU, O GOD, ON HIGH EXALTED see Graun, Karl Heinrich

BE THOU OUR GUIDE see Sibelius, Jean

BE THOU WITH ME see Franck, Cesar

BE THOU WITH ME see Hiller

BE WITH ME LORD see Roff, Joseph

BE YE GLAD AND REJOICE see Bach, Johann Sebastian, Freuet Euch Und Jubilirt

BE YE GLAD AND REJOICE, O YE RIGHTEOUS see Coggin, Elwood

BE YE JOYFUL, EARTH AND SKY   *Xmas,anthem,Boh
(Bender, Jan) SATB (easy) oct AUGSBURG 1357
$.25   (B2770)
(Liemohn, E.) SATB,acap oct PRESSER 312-40172
$.25   (B2771)

BE YE KIND, ONE TO ANOTHER see Davis, Katherine K.

BE YE LOVING EVEN AS YOUR FATHER HATH LOVED YOU
see Schutz, Heinrich, Seid Barmherzig, Wie
Auch Euer Vater Barmherzig Ist

BE YE RECONCILED TO GOD see Mueller, Carl F.

BE YE SURE THAT THE LORD HE IS GOD see Handel, George Frideric

BE YE THEREFORE FOLLOWERS OF GOD see Rogers, J.H.

BEACH, AMY MARCY CHENEY (1867-1944)
Let This Mind Be In You   *Easter
SATB,acap oct PRESSER 322-35307 $.30
(B2772)

BEADELL, ROBERT M.
Arise, O Lord
SATB oct KERBY 5601C $.25   (B2773)

Five Introits For Two Equal Voices   *Introit
2pt wom cor oct KERBY 6403 $.25   (B2774)

Five Introits For Two Equal Voices   *Introit
SS,acap oct KERBY 6403C $.25   (B2775)

Friendly Beasts, The
SSA SHAWNEE B 235 $.30   (B2776)

Great All In All
SATB oct BELWIN 2210 $.25   (B2777)

Jesus Christ Is Born Today   *Xmas
SATB oct BELWIN 2135 $.30   (B2778)

Out Of The Depths
SATB oct BELWIN 2175 $.25   (B2779)

BEADELL, ROBERT M. (cont'd.)
Royal Proclamation, The
SATB oct KERBY 6702C $.35   (B2780)

Send Down Thy Truth
SAB,acap oct KERBY 6505C $.30   (B2781)

Sing Ye Shepherds
SATB oct BELWIN 2134 $.25   (B2782)

So Great The Light
SATB,acap AMP A388 $.20   (B2783)

Vidi Aquam
SATB STANDARD A27MX4 $.60   (B2784)

BEAMS OF GENTLE LIGHT see Holmes, Robert

BEARD
Christmas Story, A   *Xmas
(Miller) SATB oct FOX R157 $.25   (B2785)

I Believe
(Tucker) SATB (quodlibet with Bach-Gounod
"Ave Marie") SHAWNEE A 1206 $.35   (B2786)

Song Of Mary
SATB SHAWNEE A 1131 $.30   (B2787)

BEARERS OF LIGHT see Adler, Hugo Ch.

BEAT THE DRUM see Peloquin, C. Alexander

BEATA ES see Byrd, William

BEATA ES VIRGO see Gabrieli, Giovanni

BEATA ES VIRGO see Pierobon, Giuseppe

BEATA ES VIRGO see Sevim, Giuseppe

BEATA ES, VIRGO MARIA see Ahrens, Joseph

BEATA ES, VIRGO MARIA see Byrd, William

BEATA VIRGO see Byrd, William

BEATA VISCERA
see English Gothic Music

BEATA VISCERA see Byrd, William

BEATA VISCERA see Riley, Dennis

BEATA VISCERA MARIAE VIRGINIS see Byrd, William

BEATAE MARIAE VIRGINIS see Sermisy, Claude de

BEATE S. CAROLE see Baroni, Giovanni

BEATI ERITIS see Croce, Giovanni

BEATI IMMACULATI see Radulescu, Michael

BEATI IMMACULATI see Victoria, Tomas Luis de

BEATI MORTUI see Mendelssohn-Bartholdy, Felix

BEATI MORTUI see Mendelssohn-Bartholdy, Felix,
Wie Selig Sind Die Toten

BEATI OMNES see Gombert, Nicolas

BEATI OMNES see Purcell, Henry

BEATI OMNES see Roman, Johan Helmich

BEATI OMNES QUI TIMENT DOMINUM see Purcell,
Henry

BEATI QUI see Migot

BEATI QUI LUGENT see Soderholm, Valdemar

BEATI QUORUM VIA see Stanford

BEATITUDE OF JOHN, THE see Pfautsch, Lloyd

BEATITUDES   *Bibl
SSA HANSEN-US T9506 $.40   (B2788)

BEATITUDES see Hopkins

BEATITUDES, THE see Bliss, Sir Arthur

BEATITUDES, THE see Jordan, Alice

BEATITUDES, THE see Lunde, Lawson

BEATITUDES AND THE LORD'S PRAYER, THE see
Dasher, James

BEATITUDES, THE see Anderson

BEATITUDES, THE see Bender, Jan

BEATITUDES, THE see Christiansen, Paul

BEATITUDES, THE see Evans

BEATITUDES, THE see Glarum, L. Stanley

BEATITUDES, THE see Harris, William Henry

BEATITUDES, THE see Hovhaness, Alan

BEATITUDES, THE see Joubert, John

BEATITUDES, THE see McAfee, Don

BEATITUDES, THE see Malotte, Albert Hay

BEATITUDES, THE see Martin

BEATITUDES, THE see Mueller, Carl F.

BEATITUDES, THE see Newbury, Kent A.

BEATITUDES, THE see Pfautsch, Lloyd

BEATITUDES, THE see Rubbra, Edmund

BEATITUDES, THE see Simeone

BEATITUDES, THE see York, D.

BEATO IN VER CHI PUO see Handel, George
  Frideric

BEATTIE, HERBERT
  Burning Babe, The *Xmas
    SATB,acap oct LAWSON 51253 $.25   (B2789)

  Moonless Darkness Stands Between *Xmas
    SATB,acap oct LAWSON 51007 $.25   (B2790)

BEATUS LAURENTIUS see Palestrina, Giovanni

BEATUS VIR see Comes, Juan Bautista

BEATUS VIR see Galuppi, Baldassare

BEATUS VIR see Monteverdi, Claudio

BEATUS VIR see Pergolesi, Giovanni Battista

BEATUS VIR see Stevens, Halsey

BEATUS VIR see Vivaldi, Antonio

BEATUS VIR see Volpi, Edoardo

BEATUS VIR (II) see Vivaldi, Antonio

BEATUS VIR QUI NON ABIIT see Hassler, Hans Leo

BEATUS VIR QUI TIMET DOMINUM see Colonna,
  Giovanni Paolo

BEAUCOUP DE GENS see Saboly, Nicholas, Li A
  Proun De Gent

BEAUMONT
  Twentieth Century Folk Mass *Mass
    unis MARKS $1.50   (B2791)

BEAUMONT, REV. GEOFFREY
  Eleven Hymn Tunes *CC11U,hymn
    cong,pno/org (easy) cmplt ed WEINBERGER
    $1.25   (B2792)

  Three Hymn Tunes (Set 1) *CC3U,hymn,20th
    cent
    SATB oct PAXTON P85380 s.p.   (B2793)

BEAUMONT, REV. GERARD
  Mass Of St. Budeax, The *Commun,Mass
    cong,cantor voc sc WEINBERGER s.p. (B2794)

  Twentieth Century Folk Mass *Commun,hymn/
    Mass
    cong,cantor,opt orch voc sc WEINBERGER
    s.p., ipa   (B2795)

BEAUTIFICATIONS, THE see Edlund, Lars,
  Saligprisningarna

BEAUTIFUL, BEAUTIFUL WORLD see Leyden

BEAUTIFUL CHRISTMAS TIME see Ehret, Walter

BEAUTIFUL GARDEN OF PRAYER, THE
  SATB BIG3 $.25   (B2796)

BEAUTIFUL GARDEN OF PRAYER, THE see Fillmore

BEAUTIFUL ISLE OF SOMEWHERE see Fearis

BEAUTIFUL RIVER see Lowry, [Robert]

BEAUTIFUL SAVIOR *anthem/folk,It
  (Christiansen, F.M.) SSAATTBB,A solo (easy)
    oct AUGSBURG 0051 $.16   (B2797)
  (Christiansen; Wycisk) TTBB (med) oct
    AUGSBURG 0263 $.18   (B2798)

BEAUTIFUL SAVIOR see Christiansen, F. Melius

BEAUTIFUL SAVIOR see Emig, Lois

BEAUTIFUL SAVIOR see Hughes

BEAUTIFUL SAVIOR see Peery

BEAUTIFUL SAVIOR see Schroth

BEAUTIFUL SAVIOUR *Xmas,folk,Czech/It,17th
  cent
  (Collins) SATB oct LILLENAS AT-1047 $.25
                                       (B2799)
  (Duncan) SATB,opt org BOSTON 2179 $.35
                                       (B2800)
  (Fry H) TTBB,acap oct PRESSER 322-35462 $.30
                                       (B2801)
  (Griffith, Allen) SAB oct BELWIN 959 $.30
                                       (B2802)
  (Griffith, Allen) SATB oct BELWIN 1060 $.30
                                       (B2803)
  (Mueller) SA oct FISCHER,C CM-6345 $.25
                                       (B2804)
  (Mueller) SATB oct FISCHER,C CM-6227 $.25
                                       (B2805)
  (Wasner) 4pt mix cor,acap oct SCHIRM.G 8765
    $.25   (B2806)

BEAUTIFUL SAVIOUR see Fry, H.

BEAUTIFUL SAVIOUR see Mueller, Carl F.

BEAUTIFUL SAVIOUR see Riegger, Wallingford

BEAUTIFUL SAVIOUR see Vick, Beryl, Jr.

BEAUTIFUL SAVIOUR, KING OF CREATION (from
  Munster Gesangbuch)
  (Wolff) SATB BOSTON 13411 $.35   (B2807)

BEAUTIFUL SAVIOUR, (OLD CRUSADERS HYMN) see
  Anonymous

BEAUTIFUL VALLEY, THE see Sanders, Robert L.

BEAUTIFUL YULETIDE see Christiansen, F. Melius

BEAUTIFUL ZION FOR ME
  (Cornwall, J.S.) SATB PIONEER 5063 $.20
                                       (B2808)

BEAUTIFY THYSELF, MY SPIRIT see Bach, Johann
  Sebastian, Schmucke Dich, O Liebe Seele

BEAUTY IN HUMILITY see Christiansen, F. Melius

BEAUTY OF THE LORD, THE see Lovelace, Austin C.

BEBER, AMBROSIUS
  Markuspassion *Psntd
  (Beckmann, Klaus) mix cor,soli sc
    BREITKOPF-W PB-4833 s.p., cor pts
    BREITKOPF-W CHB-3668 s.p.   (B2809)
  (Wallon) 5pt mix cor&2-4pt,narrator MOSELER
    s.p.   (B2810)

BECAUD
  L'Enfant A L'Etoile *Xmas,cant
    [Eng/Fr] cor&boy cor,Bar solo,orch
    SALABERT-US cor pts $1.25, voc sc $13.00
                                       (B2811)

BECAUSE OF JESUS' BIRTHDAY *Xmas/Pageant
  LORENZ $.75   (B2812)

BECHLER
  O The Blessedness Is Great *Morav
  (Dickinson) SATB oct GRAY GMCM 12 $.30
                                       (B2813)

  Praise, Thanksgiving, Glory *Morav
  (Dickinson) SATB oct GRAY GMCM 17 $.40
                                       (B2814)

BECK
  And In That Day
    SATB KJOS GC31 $.35   (B2815)

  Benediction
    SATB oct SACRED S-128 $.35   (B2816)

  Holy Festival
    SATB,brass (med diff/diff) SOUTHERN $.50
                                       (B2817)

  Hymn For Easter Day *Easter,hymn
    SATB,trp oct SOUTHERN $.30   (B2818)

  On The Way To Bethlehem *Xmas
    SA oct SACRED S-5389 $.35   (B2819)

  Rejoice In The Lord Always *Gen
    SAB SCHMITT 5541 $.35   (B2820)

  Ye Shall Go Out With Joy
    SATB KJOS GC25 $.30   (B2821)

  Ye Sons Of God
    SATB (med easy) SOUTHERN $.35   (B2822)
    SATB SOUTHERN $.35   (B2823)

BECK, AUDREY D.
  Song Of The Righteous, The (composed with
    Monson, Helen C.)
    SSA PIONEER 1010 $.40   (B2824)

BECK, CONRAD (1901-   )
  Aus Der Tiefe Rufe Ich, Herr *mot
    SAB HANSSLER 7.061 s.p.   (B2825)

  Death Over Basle *see Der Tod Zu Basel

  Der Tod Des Oedipus *cant
    [Ger] SATB,STB soli,2trp,2trom,org,opt timp
    SCHOTT rental   (B2826)

  Der Tod Zu Basel
    "Death Over Basle" [Ger/Eng] SATB,3
    narrators,SB soli,orch voc sc SCHOTT 5058
    s.p., cor pts SCHOTT 5058 s.p.   (B2827)

  Es Ist Ein Kostlich Ding *mot
    see VIER PSALM-MOTETTEN
    SAB HANSSLER 7.060 s.p.   (B2828)

  Lyrische Kantate *cant
    wom cor,SA soli,orch voc sc SCHOTT 3256
    s.p., ipr   (B2829)

  O Lebensbrunnlein Tief Und Gross *mot
    SATB HANSSLER 7.086 s.p.   (B2830)

  Requiem *Req
    [Lat] SATB SCHOTT s.p.   (B2831)

BECK, JOCHEN
  Geistliche Chormusik *CCU
    4pt mix cor MOSELER s.p.   (B2832)

BECK, JOHN NESS (1930-   )
  Anthem Of Unity *Bibl
    4pt mix cor,org/pno oct SCHIRM.G 11872 $.35
                                       (B2833)

  Canticle Of Praise
    SATB oct PRESSER 312-40588 $.40   (B2834)

  Celebration
    mix cor,org/pno oct SCHIRM.G 11779 $.35
                                       (B2835)

  Child's Noel, A *Xmas
    jr cor&sr cor,org/pno oct SCHIRM.G 10432
    $.20   (B2836)

  Hymn For Easter Day *Easter
    SATB oct PRESSER 312-40696 $.35   (B2837)

  Hymn For Our Time (from Hyfrydol)
    mix cor,org/pno oct SCHIRM.G 11575 $.40
                                       (B2838)

  Litany Of Thanksgiving *Thanks
    SATB&cong,narrator,org,brass (easy)
    ABINGDON $.65, ipa   (B2839)

  New Heart Will I Give You, A
    4pt mix cor oct SCHIRM.G 11780 $.40 (B2840)
    4pt men cor oct SCHIRM.G 11781 $.40 (B2841)

  Osanna
    mix cor,acap oct SCHIRM.G 11235 $.35
                                       (B2842)

  Short Communion Service In D *Commun
    cong ROYAL s.p. see from MUSIC FOR THE HOLY
    COMMUNION   (B2843)

  Song Of Exhaltation
    4pt mix cor,org/pno oct SCHIRM.G 11487 $.40
                                       (B2844)

  Upon This Rock
    4pt mix cor,org/pno,opt 6brass oct SCHIRM.G
    11467 $.35   (B2845)

  Variants On An Irish Hymn *hymn
    SATB,pno,drums,opt band/orch (med easy)
    PRESSER BP-1002 $.40, ipa   (B2846)

  Visions Of St. John
    SATB oct PRESSER 312-40604 $.60   (B2847)

  Young Lions, The *Psalm
    SSAATB (med) PRESSER BP-1001 $.40 (B2848)

BECK, THEODORE
  Child Is Born, The Son Of God, A *Xmas
    SAB/SATB,3trp (med easy) oct CONCORDIA
    98-2156 $.45, ipa   (B2849)

  Child So Gentle And Pure *Xmas
    SATB,acap (med easy) oct CONCORDIA 98-1879
    $.20   (B2850)

  Christmas Story, The *Xmas,cant
    SATB acap CONCORDIA 97-6435 $.75   (B2851)

  King Shall Come When Morning Dawns, The
    *Adv/Gen
    SATB,acap (med easy) oct CONCORDIA 98-1882
    $.20   (B2852)

  Little Christmas Concert On "From Heaven
    Above", A *Xmas
    2-3pt treb cor,kbd,rec/inst sc CONCORDIA
    97-4860 $1.75, cor pts CONCORDIA 98-1940
    $.25, ipa   (B2853)

  Lord's My Shepherd, The *Easter/Gen
    SATB,acap (easy) oct CONCORDIA 98-1931 $.25
                                       (B2854)

  Ye Sons Of God *Gen
    SATB/unis&desc,kbd (med easy) oct CONCORDIA
    98-2131 $.35   (B2855)

BECK, THOMAS [LUDVIGSEN] (1899-1963)
  Barnlige Sanger Til Julens Pris
    mix cor MUSIKK 58 s.p.
    contains: Et Barn Er Fodt I Bethlehem; No
    Koma Guds Englar; Saele Jolekveld;
    Varherre Han Hvilte I Krybben Sa Trang
                                       (B2856)

  Det Store Gloria
    mix cor,org cor pts MUSIKK 56 s.p. (B2857)

  Elsk Din Neste, Du Kristensjel
    mix cor MUSIKK 9 s.p.   (B2858)

  Et Barn Er Fodt I Bethlehem
    see Barnlige Sanger Til Julens Pris

  Gammel Maria-Vise
    mix cor MUSIKK 212 s.p.   (B2859)
    men cor MUSIKK 201 s.p.   (B2860)

  Hyrdene Pa Marken *Xmas,cant
    mix cor,solo,org oct MUSIKK 218 s.p.
                                       (B2861)

  Kjaerlighet Fra Gud
    see To Salmetoner

  Ljoset
    see To Salmetoner

  Marimess
    (Krokann, I.) [Norw] mix cor LYCHE 34 s.p.
                                       (B2862)

  No Koma Guds Englar
    see Barnlige Sanger Til Julens Pris

  Saele Jolekveld
    see Barnlige Sanger Til Julens Pris

  This Is The Day
    mix cor SOUTHERN $.30   (B2863)

  To Salmetoner
    mix cor MUSIKK 78 s.p.
    contains: Kjaerlighet Fra Gud; Ljoset
                                       (B2864)

  Varherre Han Hvilte I Krybben Sa Trang
    see Barnlige Sanger Til Julens Pris

BECK, W. LEONARD
  Easter Carillon, An *Easter
    unis (very easy) oct OXFORD 94.503 $.20
                                       (B2865)

BECKER
  One Is Holy
    SATB oct SUMMY M 2884 $.25   (B2866)

BECKER, ALBERT ERNST ANTON (1834-1899)
  Father, Be Thou Ever Near Us
    (Lundquist) SATB,acap (med) oct WILLIS 5485
    $.16   (B2867)

BECKER, J.
  Christ The Lord Is Risen
    SATB,org oct KERBY 5406 $.35   (B2868)
    SATB KERBY 5406C $.35   (B2869)

  Draw Nigh To Thy Jerusalem *Palm
    SATB&2pt jr cor,S solo,org oct KERBY 6001
    $.45   (B2870)
    SATB&jr cor oct KERBY 6001C $.45   (B2871)

  Judge Eternal Throned In Splendor *Epiph
    SATB,org oct KERBY 6202 $.35   (B2872)
    SATB oct KERBY 6202C $.35   (B2873)

  Our Father By Whose Name
    SATB&jr cor,org oct KERBY 6006 $.35 (B2874)
    SATB&jr cor oct KERBY 6006C $.35   (B2875)

BECKER, PETER (1934-   )
  Ave Maria *chorale/mot
    mix cor,acap TONGER s.p.   (B2876)

  Christ Ist Erstanden *Easter,chorale/mot
    mix cor,acap TONGER s.p.   (B2877)

  Der Mensch Lebt
    mix cor,acap TONGER s.p.   (B2878)

BECKER-FOSS, JURGEN (1917-   )
  Aller Augen Warten Auf Dich
    see Kretzschmar, Gunther, Jauchzet Dem
    Herrn

  Brunn Alles Heils
    see Schlenker, Manfred, Allein Gott In Der
    Hoh Sei Ehr

  Die Furcht Des Herrn
    mix cor HANSSLER 5.170 s.p.   (B2879)

  Gelobet Sei Gott
    unis jr cor,org,strings sc HANSSLER 12.506
    s.p.   (B2880)

  Kommt, Lasst Uns Anbeten
    jr cor,org,2vln,opt vcl sc HANSSLER 12.505
    s.p.   (B2881)

BECKER-FOSS, JURGEN (cont'd.)

Laudate Dominum
mix cor HANSSLER 5.171 s.p.   (B2882)

Mache Dich Auf, Werde Licht   *canon
3pt jr cor,org,rec,opt vcl sc HANSSLER
12.507 s.p.   (B2883)

Machet Die Tore Weit
see Tzschoppe, Eberhart, Kleine
Weihnachtskantate

Singet Dem Herrn Ein Neues Lied
jr cor,org,opt treb inst sc HANSSLER 12.508
s.p.   (B2884)

Wie Schon Leuchtet
jr cor,strings HANSSLER 12.215 sc s.p., cor
pts s.p.   (B2885)

BECKERATH, ALFRED VON
Alles Geben Die Gotter
4pt mix cor MOSELER LB-382 s.p.   (B2886)

Deo Patri Sit Gloria
4pt mix cor&4pt mix cor MOSELER s.p.
contains also: Imploratio (4pt mix cor&
4pt mix cor&4pt mix cor)   (B2887)

Der Sperling Und Das Kanguruh
mix cor (med) oct LEUCKART 513 s.p. see
from Drei Christian Morgenstern-Chore   (B2888)

Die Drei Spatzen
mix cor (med) oct LEUCKART 514 s.p. see
from Drei Christian Morgenstern-Chore   (B2889)

Drei Christian Morgenstern-Chore   *see Der
Sperling Und Das Kanguruh; Die Drei
Spatzen; Vor Dem Grossen Elefanten   (B2890)

Gottes Ist Der Orient
4pt mix cor MOSELER LB-318 s.p. contains
also: Zwolf Wurzeln Und Zwolf Fruchte   (B2891)

Imploratio
see Beckerath, Alfred von, Deo Patri Sit
Gloria

In Dulci Jubilo
4-6pt mix cor MOSELER LB-321 s.p.   (B2892)

Jubilate
mix cor&mix cor&mix cor MOSELER s.p.   (B2893)

Oratio Sancti Augustini "Spira In Me"
SATB&SATB TONGER s.p.   (B2894)

Vor Dem Grossen Elefanten
mix cor (med) oct LEUCKART 515 s.p. see
from Drei Christian Morgenstern-Chore   (B2895)

Wachet Auf, Ruft Uns Die Stimme
4pt mix cor,opt S solo MOSELER s.p.   (B2896)

Zwolf Wurzeln Und Zwolf Fruchte
see Beckerath, Alfred von, Gottes Ist Der
Orient

BECKERSCHER PSALTER see Schutz, Heinrich

BECKHARD
Christmas In Bethlehem   *Xmas
SATB oct PRO ART 2265 $.25   (B2897)
SSA oct PRO ART 2118 $.25   (B2898)

Out Of Your Sleep Arise And Wake   *Xmas
SATB oct PRO ART 1341 $.18   (B2899)

See, Amid The Winter's Snow   *Xmas
SATB oct PRO ART 1690 $.22   (B2900)

Thanks Unto The Lord   *Thanks
SATB oct PRO ART 1855 $.22   (B2901)

What Star Is This?   *Xmas
SATB,acap,opt pno oct PRO ART 1285 $.18   (B2902)

BECKONING STAR, THE see Stern, Patricia

BECKWITH, JOHN CHRISTMAS (1750-1809)
Three Blessings
SATB,acap oct BERANDOL 911B2AN $.50 (B2903)

BECLARD D'HARCOURT, M.
Deux Psaumes
LEMOINE voc sc s.p., cor pts s.p.
contains: Psalm 43 (cor) (Lent); Psalm 97
(cor) (Xmas)   (B2904)

Psalm 43
see Deux Psaumes

Psalm 97
see Deux Psaumes

BEDELL, [ROBERT LEECH] (1909-   )
Angel Choirs On High Do Sing
SA/TB,pno/org (med) oct WILLIS 6193 $.12   (B2905)

Come Let Us Unite In A Joyous Noel   *Xmas
SATB,pno/org oct WILLIS 6216 $.12   (B2906)

Come Ye And See The Holy Child   *Xmas
2pt jr cor FISCHER,C CM 6570 $.20   (B2907)

God Is Wisdom, God Is Love
SATB,AB soli,pno oct WILLIS 6164 $.12   (B2908)

Let Us Sing Noel   *Xmas
SA oct PRESSER 312-40285 $.30   (B2909)

Methinks I Hear The Heavens Resound
SATB,org BOSTON 10499 $.40   (B2910)

Regina Coeli
mix cor SOUTHERN $.15   (B2911)

BEDFORDSHIRE MAY DAY
see Six Traditional Carols, Set I

BEDTIME PRAYER, A see Ahrold, Frank

BEEBE
Prayer   *prayer
SATB oct PRO ART 2407 $.25   (B2912)

BEEBE, EDWARD J.
Alleluia
SATB LUDWIG L-1152 $.30   (B2913)

How Long Wilt Thou Forget Me, O Lord? (Psalm
13)
SATB,org/pno LUDWIG L-1130 $.35   (B2914)

O, Lord, Rebuke Me Not
SATB LUDWIG L-1147 $.30   (B2915)

O Praise The Lord (Psalm 117)
SATB LUDWIG L-1131 $.35   (B2916)

Psalm 8
SATB,brass LUDWIG L-1124 $.35, ipa   (B2917)

Psalm 13   *see How Long Wilt Thou Forget Me,
O Lord?

Psalm 117   *see O Praise The Lord

BEEKHUIS, HANNA (1889-   )
Kerstnacht   *Xmas
cor,pno,2fl,vcl BROEKMANS 298 s.p.   (B2918)

BEESON, JACK HAMILTON (1921-   )
Psalm 23   *anthem
mix cor oct OXFORD 94.324 $.35 see from
Three Settings From The Bay Psalm Book   (B2919)

Psalm 47   *anthem
mix cor oct OXFORD 94.323 $.25 see from
Three Settings From The Bay Psalm Book   (B2920)

Psalm 131   *anthem
mix cor oct OXFORD 94.322 $.25 see from
Three Settings From The Bay Psalm Book   (B2921)

Three Settings From The Bay Psalm Book   *see
Psalm 23; Psalm 47; Psalm 131   (B2922)

BEETHOVEN, LUDWIG VAN (1770-1827)
Acht Singkanons   *CC8U
(Hess, W.) [Ger] men cor,acap (med) HUG
s.p.   (B2923)

Agnus Dei   *Agnus
[Lat] 4pt mix cor HEUGEL s.p. see from
SAINTE-CECILE   (B2924)

All Glory To God In The Highest
(Craig) SATB oct PLYMOUTH PCS-64 $.35   (B2925)

Allied Prince, The
see Beethoven, Ludwig van, Consecration Of
The House

Auf! Auf! Ergreifet Den Verrater! (from
Christus Am Olberge) ora
(Etti, K.) [Ger] 4pt men cor,2fl,2ob,2clar,
2bsn,2trp,2horn,strings,timp DOBLINGER
voc sc s.p., cor pts s.p. contains also:
Wir Haben Ihn Gesehen Nach Diesem Berge
Gehen; Hier Ist Er, Der Verbrannte   (B2926)

Ave Verum   *Commun,mot
[Lat] 3 eq voices,SMezA soli DURAND s.p.   (B2927)

Before Thy Altar   *Xmas
(Gordon) 2pt oct SHAPIRO SK 4028 $.25   (B2928)

(Gordon) SSA oct SHAPIRO SK 3034 $.25   (B2929)

(Gordon) SATB oct SHAPIRO SK 2116 $.25   (B2930)

(Gordon) SAB oct SHAPIRO SK 5021 $.25   (B2931)

Bitten
(Gellert, C.F.) [Ger] mix cor,acap (easy)
HUG s.p.   (B2932)
(Gerhold, N.; Gellert, C.F.) 4pt mix cor,
acap voc pt DOBLINGER s.p.   (B2933)

Break, Fair Dawn (from Sonata, Opus 57)
anthem
SATB ALLANS 229 s.p.   (B2934)

Calm Sea And Pleasant Voyage   *Op.112, cant
cor min sc KALMUS 433 $2.50 contains also:
Glorious Moment, The, Op.126   (B2935)

Cantata On The Death Of Emperor Joseph II
  *Op.196, Bibl/cant
[Eng/Ger/Lat] 4pt mix cor,SB soli,pno voc
sc SCHIRM.G $1.25   (B2936)
cor min sc KALMUS 434 $2.50   (B2937)
cor,orch sc KALMUS $10.00, ipa   (B2938)

Canto A La Noche
see ARTE CORAL. VOL. VI

Chant D'offrande No. 1
(Doyen, A.) [Fr] SATB,opt S solo,orch,opt
pno LEDUC CC34 voc sc s.p., voc pt s.p.   (B2939)

Chant D'offrande No. 2
(Doyen, A.) [Fr] SATB LEDUC CC35 voc sc
s.p., voc pt s.p.   (B2940)

Choral Fantasy   *Op.80
[Eng] cor voc sc KALMUS 6074 $1.00   (B2941)
cor,orch sc KALMUS $6.00, ipa   (B2942)

Choral Finale (from Ninth Symphony)
(Krone) SATB KJOS $1.25   (B2943)

Choral Section (from 9th Symphony)
cor voc sc KALMUS 6075 $1.50   (B2944)

Chorus Of Joy (from Ninth Symphony)
(Cain) SATB oct PRO ART 1190 $.35   (B2945)

Christ Am Olberge   *Op.85, Holywk
"Christ On The Mount Of Olives" [Ger] cor,
opt orch voc sc KALMUS 6076 $3.00, ipa   (B2946)
"Christ On The Mount Of Olives" cor KALMUS
$2.50   (B2947)
"Christ On The Mount Of Olives" cor sc
KALMUS $18.00   (B2948)
"Christ On The Mount Of Olives" cor,orch sc
KALMUS $18.00, ipa   (B2949)

Christ On The Mount Of Olives   *see Christ Am
Olberge

BEETHOVEN, LUDWIG VAN (cont'd.)

Christus Am Olberg   *Op.85, ora
6pt mix cor,STB soli,2fl,2ob,2clar,2bsn,
2trp,2horn,3trom,strings,timp sc
BREITKOPF-L rental, ipr   (B2950)

Christus Am Olberge   *Op.85, Bibl/ora
SATTBB,STB soli,2fl,ob,clar,bsn,horn,trp,
3trom,strings,timp sc BREITKOPF-W rental,
voc sc BREITKOPF-W EB-1415 s.p., voc pt
BREITKOPF-W CHB-104 s.p., ipr, ipa   (B2951)
"Le Christ Au Mont Des Oliviers" mix cor,
STB soli CHOUDENS voc sc s.p., cor pts
s.p.   (B2952)
"Mount Of Olives, The" SATB,STB soli,2fl,
2ob,2clar,2bsn,2horn,2trp,3trom,strings,
timp voc sc NOVELLO s.p., ipr   (B2953)

Come To Me (from Moonlight Sonata) Bibl
(Treharne) 4pt mix cor oct SCHIRM.G 7812
$.35   (B2954)

Consecration Of The House
cor min sc KALMUS 1026 $1.30 contains also:
Allied Prince, The; Sacrificial Song;
[Two] Bass Arias   (B2955)

Creation's Hymn   *Gen/Harv/Thanks,anthem/hymn
SATB ALLANS 396 s.p.   (B2956)
TTBB oct FISCHER,C CM-6719 $.25   (B2957)
unis oct NOVELLO 47.0032.05 s.p.   (B2958)
mix cor oct NOVELLO 45.0832.07 s.p.   (B2959)
TTBB oct NOVELLO 43.0330.10 s.p.   (B2960)
unis jr cor/unis wom cor CURWEN 77024 s.p.   (B2961)
(Sargent, Malcolm) SATB,acap (easy) oct
OXFORD 43.353 $.25   (B2962)
(Sargent, Malcolm) TTBB,acap (easy) oct
OXFORD 41.018 $.25   (B2963)

Creation's Praise
(Tomlins, G.) 3pt ASHDOWN V.T.64 s.p.   (B2964)

Devotion   *see Ich Liebe Dich

Die Ehre Gottes
(Lehner, L.) [Ger] mix cor,acap (easy)
KRENN s.p.   (B2965)

Die Ehre Gottes Aus Der Natur   *Op.48,No.1,
Harv
wom cor sc ALSBACH&D s.p.   (B2966)
(Dobler, J.) [Ger] mix cor,winds HUG s.p.   (B2967)
(Dost, Bruno) 4pt mix cor,opt pno voc sc
BREITKOPF-W PB-4762 s.p., cor pts
BREITKOPF-W CHB-4723 s.p.   (B2968)
(Gellert, C.F.) [Ger] mix cor,acap (med
easy) HUG s.p.   (B2969)
(Gerhold, N.; Gellert, C.F.) 4pt mix cor,
acap voc pt DOBLINGER s.p.   (B2970)
(Mottl, F.) men cor,2fl,2ob,2clar,2bsn,
2trp,4horn,3trom,strings,timp BREITKOPF-L
rental   (B2971)

Die Ehre Gottes (Die Himmel Ruhmen Des Ewigen
Ehre)
mix cor ALSBACH&D s.p.   (B2972)

Die Ehre Gottes In Der Natur
(Buck; Deis) "Glory Of God In Nature, The"
4pt mix cor oct SCHIRM.G 8055 $.25   (B2973)
(Giehne) "Glory Of God In Nature, The"
[Eng/Ger] mix cor,acap oct SCHIRM.G 2537
$.25   (B2974)

Die Himmel Ruhmen (Psalm 19)
"Heavens Are Telling, The" SATB,pno
SCHIRM.EC 303 $.30, ipr   (B2975)
"Heavens Are Telling, The" unis,org
SCHIRM.EC 1046 $.25, ipr   (B2976)
"Heavens Are Telling, The" unis,pno
SCHIRM.EC 1046 $.25, ipr   (B2977)
"Heavens Are Telling, The" SATB oct PRESSER
312-10398 $.25   (B2978)
(Glaser, V.) "Heavens Are Telling, The"
SAB,org SCHIRM.EC 2474 $.30   (B2979)
(Saar, L.) "Heavens Are Telling, The" TTBB,
pno SCHIRM.EC 546 $.18, ipr   (B2980)
(Schmidt) men cor,acap TONGER s.p. contains
also: Heilige Nacht, O Giesse Du   (B2981)
(Vogel, Moritz; Nagler, Franciscus) [Ger]
wom cor&jr cor,org,opt strings HUG 8 s.p.   (B2982)

Die Himmel Ruhmen Des Ewigen Ehre
(Schaper) [Ger] men cor,acap HEINRICH. 926
voc sc s.p., cor pts s.p.   (B2983)

Die Liebe Des Nachsten
(Gerhold, N.; Gellert, C.F.) 4pt mix cor,
acap voc pt DOBLINGER s.p.   (B2984)

Die Vesper
mix cor sc ALSBACH&D s.p.   (B2985)

Elegy   *see Sanft Wie Du Lebtest

Finale De La Neuvieme Symphonie (from Ninth
Symphony)
[Fr] mix cor HEUGEL s.p.   (B2986)

Fruh Wolltest Du Mich Mit Deiner Gnade
(Vogel, Moritz; Nagler, Franciscus) [Ger]
wom cor&jr cor,org,opt strings HUG 39
s.p.   (B2987)

Glorious Moment, The   *Op.126
see Beethoven, Ludwig van, Calm Sea And
Pleasant Voyage

Glory Of God In Nature, The
(Palmer) SATB ALFRED 6337 $.25   (B2988)

Glory Of God In Nature, The   *see Die Ehre
Gottes In Der Natur

God In Nature
(Barlow) SSA oct COLOMBO 226 $.25   (B2989)

God Is Love   *see Gott Ist Die Liebe

God Is My Song   *see Gottes Macht Und
Vorsehung

BEETHOVEN, LUDWIG VAN (cont'd.)

God Of My Life
(Kirk) SATB oct PRO ART 1410 $.25   (B2990)

God's Might And Providence
(Ehret, W.) SATB oct PRESSER 362-03125 $.30
(B2991)

Gott Ist Die Liebe *hymn
(Frank) "God Is Love" SATB oct FOX MM20
$.35   (B2992)

Gott Ist Mein Lied
mix cor,acap ERDMANN 501 s.p. contains
also: Veni Creator (Muller, A.M.) (B2993)
(Gerhold, N.; Gellert, C.F.) 4pt mix cor,
acap voc sc DOBLINGER s.p.   (B2994)

Gottes Macht Und Vorsehung
(Frank) "God Is My Song" SATB oct FOX MM20
$.30   (B2995)

Gottes Macht Und Vorsehung. Gott Ist Mein
Lied
(Burkhart, F.) mix cor,opt pno,brass
DOBLINGER sc s.p., voc sc s.p., cor pts
s.p., ipa   (B2996)

Hallelujah (from Mount Of Olives) Easter/
Lent,anthem
SATB oct LORENZ 9788 $.35   (B2997)
SATB,acap oct HARRIS HC4028 $.50   (B2998)
4pt mix cor oct SCHIRM.G 2215 $.35   (B2999)
SATB oct GRAY GCMR 3195 $.30   (B3000)
SATB oct FISCHER,C CM-634 $.30   (B3001)
SATB oct NOVELLO 34.0196.00 s.p.   (B3002)
mix cor,orch oct NOVELLO 34.0196.00 s.p.,
ipr   (B3003)
(Heath) 4pt men cor oct SCHIRM.G 10774 $.35
(B3004)
(Trusler) SATB oct PLYMOUTH TR-117 $.40
(B3005)

Hallelujah Chorus (from Mount Of Olives)
anthem
SATB oct PRO ART 1096 $.35   (B3006)
SATB oct PRESSER 312-20978 $.40   (B3007)
SATB oct BELWIN 64004 $.40   (B3008)
cor sc KALMUS $4.00   (B3009)
(Brown, Frank E.) SA ALLANS 445 s.p.
(B3010)
(Davison, A.) TTBB,pno SCHIRM.EC 56 $.35,
ipr   (B3011)
(Ehret) SATB oct BOOSEY 5180 $.40   (B3012)

Hallelujah Unto God's Almighty Son! *see
Welten Singen Dank Und Ehre

Heavens Are Declaring *anthem
SATB oct FISCHER,C CM-50 $.25   (B3013)
(Ehret) SSA oct BELWIN 1950 $.25   (B3014)

Heavens Are Declaring, The *Xmas/Thanks
(Austin, R.) SAB oct PRESSER 332-14395 $.25
(B3015)
(Barns) unis oct SCHIRM.G 8033 $.25 (B3016)
(Buck) 4pt mix cor,ST soli oct SCHIRM.G
3032 $.30   (B3017)
(Downing) 2pt boy cor/2pt wom cor oct
SCHIRM.G 7951 $.30   (B3018)
(Giffe, W.) SATB oct PRESSER 332-07331 $.25
(B3019)
(Keating) SATB oct SPRATT 537 $.25   (B3020)
(Kountz) SAB WARNER W2565 $.30   (B3021)
(Marsden) SATB,brass oct AGAPE F 907 $.35
(B3022)
(Mueller) 3pt mix cor,org oct SCHIRM.G
10670 $.30   (B3023)

Heavens Are Telling, The *see Die Himmel
Ruhmen

Heavens Declare The Glory Of God, The
(Moulton) SATB FLAMMER A 5245 $.25   (B3024)
(Moulton) SSA FLAMMER B 5098 $.25   (B3025)
(Moulton) TTBB FLAMMER C5016 $.30   (B3026)
(Moulton) SAB FLAMMER D5099 $.25   (B3027)

Heavens Resound, The *Gen,anthem
SATB (easy) oct AUGSBURG 0165 $.20   (B3028)
SATB SCHMITT 1920 $.25   (B3029)
(Pitcher, Gladys) 3pt mix cor,pno (easy)
oct WILLIS 8479 $.20   (B3030)

Heil'ge Nacht, O Giesse Du
(Vogel, Moritz; Nagler, Franciscus) [Ger]
wom cor&jr cor,org,opt strings HUG 57
s.p.   (B3031)

Heilige Nacht, O Giesse Du
see Beethoven, Ludwig van, Die Himmel
Ruhmen

Hier Ist Er, Der Verbrannte (from Christus Am
Olberge)
see Beethoven, Ludwig van, Auf! Auf!
Ergreifet Den Verrater!

Holy, Holy, Holy *see Sanctus

Hymn Of Brotherhood *hymn
SATB oct STAFF 106 $.30   (B3032)
SA/TB oct STAFF 604 $.30   (B3033)
SSA oct STAFF 253 $.30   (B3034)
SAB oct STAFF 606 $.30   (B3035)

Hymn To Joy (from Symphony IX) chorale/hymn
SATB,acap SCHIRM.EC 1656 $.20, ipr   (B3036)
(Henderson) SATB,opt band oct PRO ART 2672
$.30   (B3037)
(Henderson) SAB,opt band oct PRO ART 2537
$.30   (B3038)
(Henderson) SSA,opt band oct PRO ART 2674
$.30   (B3039)
(Henderson) SATB,opt band SOUTHERN $.30
(B3040)

I Bow In Prayer Before Thee
(Douglas) SATB,acap,opt pno oct PRO ART
2574 $.30   (B3041)

Ich Liebe Dich
"Devotion" see FOLK-SONGS, BALLADS AND
SONGS OF GREAT COMPOSERS (SET V)

Jesus Guide Us
(Kirk) SATB KJOS 5841 $.30   (B3042)

Joyful, Joyful We Adore Thee
(Angell) SATB oct PLYMOUTH HA-1 $.25 (B3043)

BEETHOVEN, LUDWIG VAN (cont'd.)

(Sanders, H.) SATB oct PRESSER 332-14893
$.30   (B3044)
(Simeone) SATB SHAWNEE A 781 $.40   (B3045)

Kyrie *Op.123 (from Missa Solemnis) Kyrie
cor fac ed HINRICHSEN D2169 s.p.   (B3046)

Lauda Sion
[Lat] 4pt mix cor,T solo,opt pno/org (C
maj) HEUGEL s.p.   (B3047)

Le Christ Au Mont Des Oliviers *see Christus
Am Olberge

Let Man Exult With Heart And Voice
SATB oct HERITAGE H26 $.35   (B3048)

Lord, Have Mercy Upon Us
(Ehret) mix cor CHAPPELL 0023465-358 $.40
(B3049)

Lord's Prayer, The
(Roper) SATB THOMP.G G-529 s.p.   (B3050)

Love Divine (from Choral Symphony)
(Jenkins) 4pt mix cor,org oct SCHIRM.G
11150 $.30   (B3051)

Mass In C *see Messe C-Dur

Mass In C Major *see Messe C-Dur

Mass In D *see Missa Solemnis

Messe C-Dur *Op.86, Mass
mix cor,SATB soli,org,2fl,2ob,2clar,2bsn,
2trp,2horn,strings,timp (C maj) voc pt
BREITKOPF-L CHB-28A-D s.p., voc sc
BREITKOPF-L EB-1414 s.p., ipa   (B3052)
mix cor,SATB soli,org,2fl,ob,clar,bsn,horn,
trp,strings,timp (C maj) sc BREITKOPF-W
PB-4471 s.p., ipa   (B3053)
"Mass In C" cor sc KALMUS $13.50   (B3054)
"Mass In C" cor sc KALMUS $13.50   (B3055)
"Mass In C" [Lat] SATB,SATB soli,orch min
sc PETERS E996 $7.50, ipr min sc-cloth
PETERS E996 $10.00, ipr, voc sc PETERS
1105 $2.50, ipr   (B3056)
"Mass In C" [Lat] SATB,SATB soli,2fl,2ob,
2clar,2bsn,2horn,2trp,strings,timp voc sc
NOVELLO s.p., ipr   (B3057)
"Mass In C" cor,opt orch voc sc KALMUS 6077
$1.50, ipa   (B3058)
"Mass In C" cor min sc KALMUS 436 $5.50
(B3059)
"Mass In C Major" cor,orch sc KALMUS
$13.50, ipa   (B3060)
"Mass In C Major" [Lat] SATB,orch voc sc
BROUDE BR. $2.50, ipr   (B3061)

Messe D-Dur *Op.123, Mass
"Missa Solemnis" 4pt mix cor,SATB soli,org,
2fl,ob,clar,3bsn,4horn,2trp,3trom,
strings,timp (D maj) sc BREITKOPF-W
PB-4470 s.p., ipa   (B3062)

Miserere *Lent,mot
4pt men cor CHOUDENS s.p.   (B3063)

Missa Solemnis *Op.123, Mass
(D min) study sc UNIVER. PH 74 $6.00 (B3064)
mix cor,SATB soli,org,2fl,2ob,2clar,3bsn,
2trp,4horn,3trom,strings,timp sc
BREITKOPF-L PB-632, cor sc BREITKOPF-L
BREITKOPF-L CHB-29A-D s.p., voc sc
BREITKOPF-L EB-29 s.p., ipr   (B3065)
cor voc sc KALMUS 6078 $2.50   (B3066)
cor min sc KALMUS 432 $6.50   (B3067)
cor sc KALMUS $22.00   (B3068)
cor,orch sc KALMUS $22.00, ipa   (B3069)
"Mass In D" [Lat] SATB,SATB soli,org,2fl,
2ob,2clar,3bsn,4horn,2trp,3trom,strings,
timp voc sc NOVELLO s.p., pr   (B3070)
(Soldan) "Mass In D" [Lat] voc sc PETERS 45
$3.00, ipr, cloth PETERS 45 $10.00, ipr,
min sc PETERS E951 $7.50, ipr, min sc-
cloth PETERS E951 $12.00, ipr   (B3071)
(Stern, Julius) [Lat] cor,4 soli voc sc
SCHIRM.G $1.50   (B3072)

Missa Solemnis *see Messe D-Dur

Mount Of Olives *Holywk/Lent,cant
BELWIN $1.50   (B3073)

Mount Of Olives, The *see Christus Am
Olberge

My Soul, Inspired
(Coggin) SAB oct BELWIN 2074 $.25   (B3074)

Nature's Praise Of God
4pt mix cor,acap oct SCHIRM.G 6566 $.25
(B3075)

Nuit D'azur
[Fr] SB/2 eq voices,pno voc sc LEDUC s.p.
(B3076)

O Du Frohliche *see O Sanctissima

O God, I Offer Thanks To Thee
(Lee) SATB FLAMMER A 5335 $.25   (B3077)
(Lee) SAB FLAMMER D5112 $.25   (B3078)

O God, Thy Goodness Reacheth Far
SATB oct BELWIN 64179 $.30   (B3079)

O Lord, Give Ear
(Goldman) SATB oct LAWSON 51668 $.30 (B3080)

O Lord, Thy Mercy
(Gordon) SSA oct SHAPIRO SK 3032 $.25
(B3081)

O Salutaris
[Lat] 4pt mix cor,S solo,opt pno/org (A
flat maj) HEUGEL s.p.   (B3082)

O Sanctissima *folk,It
girl cor SOUTHERN $.30   (B3083)
SSA/SAB oct FISCHER,J 9547 $.30   (B3084)
"O Du Frohliche" [Ger] 3pt mix cor/men cor/
wom cor,vln,vcl,pno/org/cembalo sc VIEWEG
s.p.   (B3085)

O Triumph, All Ye Ransom'd (from Mount Of
Olives)
(Davison, A.) TTBB,S solo,pno SCHIRM.EC 87
$.50, ipr   (B3086)

BEETHOVEN, LUDWIG VAN (cont'd.)

Oh! God! Thy Bounty Reacheth Wide *prayer
(Holmes) SATB oct PRO ART 1343 $.25 (B3087)

Prayer
(Norman) SSA,org/pno BOSTON 9463 $.30
(B3088)

Psalm 19 *see Die Himmel Ruhmen

Sacrificial Song
see Beethoven, Ludwig van, Consecration Of
The House

Sanctus *Sanctus
[Lat] 4pt mix cor HEUGEL s.p. see from
SAINTE-CECILE   (B3089)
"Holy, Holy, Holy" SATB oct WALTON 6014
$.30   (B3090)

Sanft Wie Du Lebtest *Op.118
mix cor,strings sc BREITKOPF-L rental
(B3091)
"Elegy" SATB oct WALTON 7005 $.30   (B3092)

Shepherd, Hear Our Cry
(Bronson) SATB oct HUNTZINGER 4054 $.20
(B3093)

Song Of Penitence
(Binder) SATB oct PLYMOUTH JR-136 $.30
(B3094)

Symphony Of Easter, The *Easter,cant
SATB LORENZ $1.95   (B3095)

Tantum Ergo, En La Mineur *Commun,mot
[Lat] wom cor,Mez solo (A min) DURAND s.p.
(B3096)

Thee Will I Love
SATB oct PRESSER 312-21566 $.30   (B3097)

'Tis The Evening's Holy Hour *Eve,anthem
SATB (easy) oct AUGSBURG 0050 $.20   (B3098)

To Thee, O Lord
(Ehret) SA oct SPRATT 599 $.25   (B3099)

[Two] Bass Arias
see Beethoven, Ludwig van, Consecration Of
The House

Veni Creator
see Beethoven, Ludwig van, Gott Ist Mein
Lied

We Bring Our Eager Souls To Thee
(Gillam) SAB oct PLYMOUTH PCS-403 $.25
(B3100)

Welten Singen Dank Und Ehre (from Mount Of
Olives)
"Hallelujah Unto God's Almighty Son!" SATB,
pno SCHIRM.EC 1602 $.60, ipa   (B3101)

Wir Haben Ihn Gesehen Nach Diesem Berge Gehen
(from Christus Am Olberge)
see Beethoven, Ludwig van, Auf! Auf!
Ergreifet Den Verrater!

Worship Of God In Nature
4pt men cor,acap oct SCHIRM.G 1428 $.25
(B3102)

BEETZ, C.J.
Arise, Rejoice, And Praise The Lord
SATB AMP A204 $.25   (B3103)

BEFAL DU DINE VEJE see Laub, Thomas

BEFALL DIN VAG AT HERREN see Roman, Johan
Helmich

BEFI YESHARIM see Lidarti, C.G.

BEFIEHL DEM ENGEL, DASS ER KOMM see Buxtehude,
Dietrich

BEFIEHL DEM HERRN DEINE WEGE see Reda,
Siegfried

BEFIEHL DEM HERRN DEINE WEGE see Schauss-Flake,
Magdalene

BEFIEHL DEM HERRN DEINE WEGE see Schmid, Walter

BEFIEHL DU DEINE WEGE see Altnikol

BEFIEHL DU DEINE WEGE see Altnikol, Johann
Christoph

BEFIEHL DU DEINE WEGE see Bach, Johann
Sebastian

BEFIEHL DU DEINE WEGE see Baumann, Max

BEFIEHL DU DEINE WEGE see Enders, Gottfried

BEFIEHL DU DEINE WEGE see Hassler, Hans Leo

BEFIEHL DU DEINE WEGE see Micheelsen, Hans
Friedrich

BEFIEHL DU DEINE WEGE see Muller-Ott, G.

BEFIEHL DU DEINE WEGE see Schwartz, Gerhard von

BEFIEHL DU DEINE WEGE see Stern, Hermann

BEFIEHL DU DEINE WEGE see Weyrauch, Johannes

BEFIEHL DU DEINE WEGE UND see Hanssler,
Friedrich

BEFORE DAWN see Andrews, C.T.

BEFORE DAY CAME AGAIN see Monteverdi, Claudio,
Non Havea Febo Ancora

BEFORE HIM see Nystedt, Knut

BEFORE I MET JESUS see Lawson

BEFORE JEHOVAH'S AWEFULL THRONE see Willan,
Healey

BEFORE THE BREAK OF DAY see Fraser

BEFORE THE CRUCIFIX see LaForge, Frank

BEFORE THE DAWN see Sibelius, Jean

BEHRENS, [JACK] (1935-)
In A Manger *Xmas
SATB oct ELKAN-V 362-1197 $.25 (B3113)

BEHTLEHEM TOWN see Lipscomb, Helen

BEI DER KRIPPE JESU see Aiblinger, Johann Kaspar

BEI DIR, HERR, BIN ICH GEBORGEN see Schweizer, Rolf

BEI DIR IST DIE QUELLE DES LEBENS see Schrader, Oswald

BEI STILLER NACHT see Ruthenberg, Otto

BEIM ABSCHIED ZU SINGE, VERZWEIFLE NICHT see Schumann, Robert (Alexander)

BEIM HEILIGEN SANKT LEONHARD see Lehner, F.X.

BEIM LETZTEN ABENDMAHLE see Doppelbauer, Josef Friedrich

BEIM SCHEIDEN EINES GEISTLICHEN ODER LEHRERS see Nagler, F.

BEKOL ZIMRA see Jochsberger, T.

BELCHER, [SUPPLY] (1751-1836)
Deep North Spirituals *CC9U
(Daniel) 3-4pt mix cor/3-4pt men cor PETERS 66331 (B3114)

Harmony Of Maine, The *sac/sec,CCU
3pt mix cor/4pt mix cor cloth DA CAPO LC 77-169607 $11.00 (B3115)

Who Crucified My Lord? *Easter
SATB SCHMITT 844 $.30 (B3116)

BELFRY BOOK OF CHRISTMAS CAROLS, THE *CCU, Xmas,carol
(Davis, K.K.) SSAA,acap WARNER $.85 (B3117)

BELFRY BOOK, THE *CCU
(Davis, K.K.) jr cor WARNER $1.25 (B3118)

BELGIAN CHRISTMAS SONGS, SET 1 *Xmas,Belg
(Terri) 3pt wom cor/3pt boy cor,S solo,acap, opt inst&perc oct LAWSON 51562 $.45
contains: Child Is Born In Bethlehem, A; Ho, Ho, Ho, Ho, Bendicamus Domino; Let Every Voice Sing Praises; Shepherds Bring Candy And Milk (B3119)

BELGIAN CHRISTMAS SONGS, SET 2 *Xmas,Belg
(Terri) 3pt wom cor/3pt boy cor,S solo,opt inst&perc oct LAWSON 51563 $.45
contains: Let Us Welcome Jesus; Oh, Shepherds, Whisper Softly; Three Kings, The (B3120)

BELL
God, Give Me Understanding
SATB oct LORENZ B58 $.30 (B3121)

God Has A Reason
SATB oct LORENZ A423 $.25 (B3122)

Lord Is In His Holy Temple, The
SAB oct LORENZ 7362 $.30 (B3123)
SATB oct LORENZ C87 $.30 (B3124)

Sleep, Baby, Sleep
(Shaw) SATB,acap SHAWNEE A 46 $.30 (B3125)

Walk With Your God
SATB oct LORENZ B82 $.30 (B3126)

BELL, L.R.
This Is The Day *anthem
SATB ALLANS 242 s.p. (B3127)

BELL, LESLIE
Festival Song Book, The *CCU,Fest
treb cor BELWIN $1.25 (B3128)

BELL CAROL see Wichman

BELL CAROL, THE *carol
unis/SATB (easy) OXFORD 08.161 $.15 (B3129)
(Gilbert) SATB,acap (easy) OXFORD 84.117 $.35 (B3130)

BELL CAROL, THE see Hudson

BELL SONG see Lo Presti

BELL SONG, THE see Young

BELLA, R.
Bauernbegrabnis
see Vier Bauerngedichte

Bauernhochzeit
see Vier Bauerngedichte

Bauernpsalm
see Vier Bauerngedichte

Bestandigkeit
see Vier Bauerngedichte

Vier Bauerngedichte *Op.105
[Ger] men cor,acap HUG s.p.
contains: Bauernbegrabnis (med diff); Bauernhochzeit (med diff); Bauernpsalm (diff); Bestandigkeit (med diff) (B3131)

BELLHOUSE, ALAN
Judah, Long Ago *Xmas,carol
SATB ALLANS 469 s.p. (B3132)

BELLINI, VINCENZO (1801-1835)
Salve Regina
[Lat/Eng] SATB,pno/2fl&2ob&2clar&2bsn&2trp& strings voc sc BROUDE,A. 222 $.50, ipr (B3133)

Tantum Ergo
[Lat] unis HEUGEL s.p. see from SAINTE-CECILE (B3134)

BELLMAN
Alleluia! Alleluia! Hearts And Voices
(Lundquist) SATB,acap oct WILLIS 8467 $.25 (B3135)

BELLS see Diemer, Emma Lou

BELLS ARE RINGING *Xmas
(Kirk) SATB,bells,tamb,rec,fing.cym. oct PRO ART 2737 $.30 (B3136)

BELLS ARE RINGING, THE see Luptin, H.J.

BELLS AT SPEYER, THE see Senfl, Ludwig

BELLS OF BETHLEHEM, THE *Xmas,carol
(Barrie) 2pt jr cor oct KENDOR $.30 (B3137)

BELLS OF CHRISTMAS see Whittlesey

BELLS OF CHRISTMAS, THE see Moschetti, [Giuseppe]

BELLS OF CHRISTMAS, THE see Prokofiev, Serge

BELLS OF EASTER see Allan, Mea

BELLS OF EASTER see Emery, John

BELLS OF HEAVEN see Brandon

BELLS OF HEAVEN, THE see Niles, John Jacob

BELLS OF JOY see Williams

BELLS OF PARADISE see Nyquist

BELLS OF PARADISE, THE *Xmas,carol,Eng
(Walker, D.S.) unis, orff inst (easy) oct CONCORDIA 98-2080 $.25 (B3138)

BELLS OF ST. MICHAEL'S TOWER see Knyvett

BELLS ON EASTER MORN, THE see Rogers, Sharon Elery

BELLS OVER BETHLEHEM *Xmas,carol,Span
(Davies) unis/SA (very easy) OXFORD 82.074 $.25 (B3139)
(Ehret, Walter) SATB,opt inst oct WALTON 2501 $.30 (B3140)
(Ehret, Walter) SSA,opt inst oct WALTON 2532 $.30 (B3141)

BELLS OVER JORDAN
2pt CHAPPELL 0442509-352 $.40 (B3142)
SSA CHAPPELL 0442509-354 $.40 (B3143)
SATB CHAPPELL 0442509-358 $.40 (B3144)

BELLS RING OUT AT CHRISTMAS, THE see William A.

BELLS RING OUT FOR CHRISTMAS, THE see Sacco, John [Charles]

BELLS RING OUT JOYFULLY see Auerbach, N.

BELLS RING OUT NOEL see Hadler, R.

BELLS RING OUT, THE see Blake, Rev. Canon, E.C.

BELLS RING SOFTLY, LULLY LOW see Evans

BELLS, THE see Wilson, H.

BELOVED see Youse, Glad [Robinson]

BELOVED, LET US LOVE see Diack, [John Michael]

BELOVED, LET US LOVE see Thompson, V.D.

BELOVED, LET US LOVE ONE ANOTHER see Mead

BELOVED, LET US LOVE ONE ANOTHER see Mueller, Carl F.

BELOVED LORD, HASTEN THE DAY see Buxtehude, Dietrich, Ei Lieber Herr Ei! Zum Gericht

BELOVED OF THE LORD, THE see Altman, Ludwig

BELSAZAR see Handel, George Frideric, Belshazzar

BELSENER CHORKREIS see Gessinger

BELSHAZZAR see Handel, George Frideric

BELSHAZZAR'S FEAST see Walton, William

BELT, T.
Alleluia *Gen,anthem/folk/hymn
SAB,kbd (easy) oct GIA G1700 $.30 (B3145)
SAB,pno,bvl,gtr (easy) oct GIA G1700 $.30 (B3146)

Joy And Other Sublime Aspirations *CC12U, Gen,folk/hymn,Contemp
(easy) unis,gtr cmplt ed GIA G1558 $1.00; unis,pno,gtr cmplt ed GIA G1559 $2.00; SAB,pno,bvl,tamb,gtr cmplt ed GIA G1560 $2.50 (B3147)

Lord Is Come, The *Xmas/Gen,anthem/carol/ folk
SAB,kbd (easy) oct GIA G1589 $.25 (B3148)
SAB,inst (easy) oct GIA G1589 $.25 (B3149)

Love Divine *Xmas/Gen,anthem/carol/folk
SAB,kbd (easy) oct GIA G1590 $.25 (B3150)
SAB,gtr (easy) oct GIA G1590 $.25 (B3151)

Love Knows No Season *CC12U,Gen,folk/hymn, Contemp
(easy) unis,gtr cmplt ed GIA G1646 $1.00; SAB,gtr cmplt ed GIA G1647 $2.00 (B3152)

Open Up Your Heart *Xmas/Gen,anthem/carol/ folk
SAB,kbd (easy) oct GIA G1699 $.35 (B3153)
SAB,pno,bvl,gtr (easy) oct GIA G1699 $.35 (B3154)

Ride On *CC10U,Gen,folk/hymn,Contemp
(easy) SAB,gtr cmplt ed GIA G1623 $2.00; unis,gtr cmplt ed GIA G1621 $1.00 (B3155)

BELWIN CHORUS ALBUM *sac/sec,CCU
SATB BELWIN $1.00 (B3156)

BEMESST DEN SCHRITT, BEMESST DEN SCHWUNG see Rein, Walter

BEN-HAIM, PAUL (1897-)
Book Of Verses, A (Omar Khayyam) *Heb
SAATTB,acap ISRAELI 308 s.p. (B3157)

Die Vision Des Propheten *cant,Heb
"Vision Of A Prophet, The" cor,T solo,orch voc sc ISRAELI 318 s.p. (B3158)

Hymn From The Desert *see Lobgesang Aus Der Wuste

Kabbalat Shabbat *Sab-Eve,Heb
SATB,cantor,S solo,org/9inst ISRAELI 328 s.p. (B3159)
SATB,ST soli,org/7inst sc SEESAW $7.00 (B3160)

Liturgical Cantata *Heb
cor,Bar solo,org/orch voc sc ISRAELI 312 s.p. (B3161)

Lobgesang Aus Der Wuste *Heb
"Hymn From The Desert" cor,SBar soli,orch voc sc ISRAELI 321 s.p. (B3162)

Ma Tovu (from Liturgical Cantata) Heb
SATB,acap ISRAELI 312-M s.p. (B3163)
[Heb] mix cor,Bar solo,orch,opt pno voc sc HEINRICH. s.p. (B3164)

Psalm 121 *Heb
SATB,acap ISRAELI 302 s.p. (B3165)

Thou Shalt No More Be Termed Forsaken *Heb
SATB,acap ISRAELI 314 s.p. (B3166)

Three Psalms *CC3U,Psalm,Heb
cor,SBar soli,org/orch voc sc ISRAELI 319 s.p. (B3167)

Vision Of A Prophet, The *see Die Vision Des Propheten

BEN JOHNSON'S CAROL see Sellew, Donald E.

BEN VENGA AMORE see Animuccia, Giovanni

BENARY, PETER
Chormusik Zum Pfingstfest *CCU,Pent/Whitsun
3-7pt mix cor MOSELER s.p. (B3168)

Chormusik Zur Passion *CCU,Psntd
4-5pt mix cor,narrator MOSELER s.p. (B3169)

Chormusik Zur Weihnacht *CCU,Xmas
3pt&4-7pt mix cor MOSELER s.p. (B3170)

Das Weihnachtsevangelium Nach Lukas *Xmas, Bibl
3pt mix cor MOSELER s.p. (B3171)

Psalm 124 *Bibl
4pt mix cor MOSELER s.p. (B3172)

BENDA, GEORG (1722-1795)
Erschallet, Ihr Himmel *cant
[Ger] cor,SAB soli,org,strings KISTNER sc s.p., cor pts s.p., ipa (B3173)

BENDENK MENSCH see Rohwer, Jens

BENDER
Come, O Blessed Of My Father
girl cor SOUTHERN $.25 (B3174)

BENDER, JAN (1909-)
And There Will Be Signs *Adv/ECY/Gen
unis,kbd (med easy) oct CONCORDIA 98-2082 $.30 (B3175)

Auricher Singbuchlein, Heft 1 *CC30U,Adv/ Xmas/Gen,chorale
[Ger] 2 eq voices/3 eq voices/mix cor (med easy) BA 742 $3.25 (B3176)

Auricher Singbuchlein, Heft 2 *CC26U,Asc/ Easter/Gen/Pent/Psntd/Whitsun,chorale
[Ger] 2 eq voices/3 eq voices/mix cor,acap (med easy) BAREN. BA 741 $3.25 (B3177)

Auricher Singbuchlein, Heft 3 *CC27U,Gen/ Trin,chorale
[Ger] 2 eq voices/3 eq voices/mix cor,acap BAREN. BA 743 $3.25 (B3178)

Auricher-Singbuchlein, Heft 4 *CC36U,Gen, hymn
[Ger] 2 eq voices/3 eq voices/mix cor,acap (med easy) BAREN. BA 744 $4.50 (B3179)

Awake, Thou Spirit, Who Didst Fire *Gen/Pent
SATB,brass (med diff) oct CONCORDIA 98-1699 $.25, ipa (B3180)

Beatitudes, The *cant
2pt treb cor/2pt jr cor,opt ob&vla&org&vcl sc CONCORDIA 97-4742 $.85, ipa (B3181)

Begone, Satan *Gen/Lent
SA/TB,kbd (med easy) oct CONCORDIA 98-1848 $.25 (B3182)

Built On The Rock, The Church Doth Stand *Ded/Gen/Refm
SA,kbd (easy) oct CONCORDIA 98-1646 $.25 (B3183)

Christ Is Arisen *Easter
SATB,brass (med easy) oct CONCORDIA 98-1657 $.25, ipa (B3184)

Christ Ist Erstanden
SAT/SAB HANSSLER 14.075 s.p. contains also: Gottschick, Friedemann, Christ Ist Erstanden (SS/SSA/SST/SSB,treb inst/bass inst) (B3185)

Come, O Blessed Of My Father *ECY/Gen
SA/TB,kbd (med easy) oct CONCORDIA 98-1834 $.25 (B3186)

Come, Ye Faithful, Raise The Strain *Easter
SA,kbd (med easy) oct CONCORDIA 98-1565 $.25 (B3187)

Der Morgenstern Ist Aufgedrungen *Adv
[Ger] SA&men cor,acap (med easy) BAREN. BA 553 $.25 (B3188)

BENDER, JAN (cont'd.)

Die Weihnachtsgeschichte *Xmas
[Ger] SA&men cor,narrator,acap (med easy)
BAREN. BA 2767 sc $2.50, cor pts $1.00
                                          (B3189)

Do Not Be Amazed *Easter
SA/TB,kbd (med easy) oct CONCORDIA 98-1966
$.30   (B3190)

Es Kommt Ein Schiff, Geladen *Adv
[Ger] 3 eq voices,acap (easy) BAREN.
BCH 175 s.p.   (B3191)

Fear Not: For Behold, I Bring Good Tidings Of
Great Joy *Xmas
unis/SS/SA,kbd (med diff) oct CONCORDIA
98-1962 $.50   (B3192)

From Heaven High I Come To Earth
2pt&cong,soli,ob,vln,org,vcl CONCORDIA
97-6399 $1.00, ipa   (B3193)

Go Into All The World *Asc/Trin
SA/TB,kbd (med easy) oct CONCORDIA 98-1990
$.40   (B3194)

God Is Our Refuge And Strength *anthem
SATB (med) oct AUGSBURG 0608 $.30   (B3195)

God So Loved The World *Gen/Lent
SATB,acap (med diff) oct CONCORDIA 98-1078
$.25   (B3196)
SA,kbd (med easy) oct CONCORDIA 98-1641
$.25   (B3197)

God The Father, Be Our Stay *Gen/Refm/Trin
SATB,brass (med diff) oct CONCORDIA 98-1727
$.30, ipa   (B3198)

He Hath Done All Things Well *Gen
SATB,acap (med easy) oct CONCORDIA 98-1067
$.25   (B3199)

He Which Hath Begun A Good Work In You
*Cnfrm/Gen
SAB,acap (med easy) oct CONCORDIA 98-1068
$.25   (B3200)

Herr Jesu, Deine Angst Und Pein
SST/SSB,bass inst HANSSLER 14.069 s.p.
                                          (B3201)

Hodie Christus Natus Est *Xmas
"Today Christ Is Born" SATB,acap (med diff)
oct CONCORDIA 98-1430 $.35   (B3202)

Hosanna To The Son Of David *Adv/Gen/Palm
SAB,acap (med diff) oct CONCORDIA 98-1870
$.30   (B3203)
SA/TB,kbd (med easy) oct CONCORDIA 98-1964
$.25   (B3204)

I Am The Good Shepherd *Gen
SA/TB,kbd (med easy) oct CONCORDIA 98-1992
$.30   (B3205)

Ich Habe Dich Einen Kleinen Augenblick
Verlassen *mot
SSATTB HANSSLER 7.107 s.p.   (B3206)

If A Man Loves Me *Gen/Pent
SA/TB,kbd (med easy) oct CONCORDIA 98-1697
$.20   (B3207)

If You Ask Anthing Of The Father *Cnfrm/
Easter/Gen
SA/TB,kbd (med easy) oct CONCORDIA 98-1991
$.40   (B3208)

In Thee, O Lord, Do I Put My Trust *anthem
unis (med) oct AUGSBURG 0611 $.25   (B3209)
unis treb cor (med) oct AUGSBURG 0611 $.25
                                          (B3210)

Introits For Lent And Holy Week, The *CCU,
Holywk/Lent,anti/Introit/liturg/mot/Psalm
cor CONCORDIA 98-1365 $1.00   (B3211)

It Is Not Fair *Gen/Lent
SA/TB,kbd (med easy) oct CONCORDIA 98-1847
$.25   (B3212)

Jesus Christus, Unser Heiland *No.77, Easter
[Ger] 3pt mix cor,acap BAREN. EM 69 s.p.
see from EVANGELISCHES KIRCHENGESANGBUCH
                                          (B3213)

Jesus, Son Of David, Have Mercy On Me *Gen
SA/TB,kbd (med easy) oct CONCORDIA 98-1965
$.30   (B3214)

Komm, Heiliger Geist, Erfull Die Herzen
*No.124, Asc/Pent
[Ger] 3pt mix cor,acap BAREN. EM 29 s.p.
see from EVANGELISCHES KIRCHENGESANGBUCH
                                          (B3215)

Like Silver Lamps In A Distant Shrine *Xmas
SATB,kbd (med easy) oct CONCORDIA 98-1967
$.25   (B3216)

Lobt Gott, Ihr Christen Alle Gleich
SA/men cor,treb inst/bass inst HANSSLER
14.021 s.p. contains also: Oertzen,
Rudolf von, Lobt Gott Ihr Christen Alle
Gleich (SAT/SAB,treb inst,bass inst,kbd)
                                          (B3217)

Lobt Gott, Ihr Frommen Christen *Gen
[Ger] 2 eq voices,opt vcl (med easy) BAREN.
BA 3037 s.p.   (B3218)

Lord Is My Light And My Salvation, The *mot
dbl cor CONCORDIA 97-6339 $1.50   (B3219)

Lord, Lord, Open To Us *ECY/Gen
unis,kbd (med easy) oct CONCORDIA 98-1833
$.25   (B3220)

Many Shall Come From The East And West
*Epiph
SAB,acap (med easy) oct CONCORDIA 98-1096
$.25   (B3221)

Now Let All Loudly Sing Praise To God
mix cor,strings,fl,ob,bsn,kbd sc CONCORDIA
97-6376 $2.50, cor pts CONCORDIA 97-6389
$.40, ipa   (B3222)

Now Unto Him That Is Able *Gen
SATB,acap (med easy) oct CONCORDIA 98-1079
$.25   (B3223)

BENDER, JAN (cont'd.)

Nun Bitten Wir Den Heiligen Geist *Pent,cant
[Ger] SATB,4trp,2trom (med) BAREN. BA 2634
sc $2.75, cor pts $.40, ipa   (B3224)

O God, O Lord Of Heaven And Earth *anthem
SATB,org,trp (med) oct AUGSBURG 1554 $.35
                                          (B3225)

O Sing Unto The Lord A New Song *Easter/
Epiph/Gen
SATB,acap (med easy) oct CONCORDIA 98-1876
$.35   (B3226)

Psalm 150
5pt mix cor,3trp,2horn,2trom CONCORDIA
97-6278 $.50, ipa   (B3227)

Salvation Unto Us Has Come *cant
mix cor,2vln,vcl,org/hpsd CONCORDIA 97-6390
$1.25   (B3228)

Sentences For The Seasons *CCU,liturg
SSAB CONCORDIA 98-1461 $.60   (B3229)

Sing To The Lord A New Song *CC10L,anthem/
canon/chant/mot
jr cor/treb cor sc CONCORDIA 97-1420 $2.00,
cor pts CONCORDIA 97-6305 $.75   (B3230)

Singet Dem Herrn Ein Neues Lied *Easter/Pent
[Ger] 3pt mix cor,acap (med) BAREN. BA 3098
s.p.   (B3231)

Sir, Come Down Before My Child Dies *Gen/
Trin
SA/TB,kbd oct CONCORDIA 98-1835 $.25
                                          (B3232)

Son, Why Have You Treated Us So? *Epiph
unis/SS/SA,kbd (med easy) oct CONCORDIA
98-1963 $.25   (B3233)

Te Deum Laudamus
mix cor CONCORDIA 97-6273 $.50   (B3234)

This Is Indeed The Prophet *Gen/Lent
SA/TB,kbd (easy) oct CONCORDIA 98-2054 $.25
                                          (B3235)

Today Christ Is Born *see Hodie Christus
Natus Est

Vesper I *Eve
[Ger] SSATB&cor&cong,org (med easy) BAREN.
BA 2775 sc $3.00, cor pts $1.50   (B3236)

Vesper II "O Wie Selig Seid Ihr Doch, Ihr
Frommen" *Eve
[Ger] SA&men cor&cong&cor,org,2vln,vla,vcl
(med) BAREN. BA 3168 sc $5.25, cor pts
$1.50, ipa   (B3237)

Vom Himmel Hoch, Da Komm Ich Her *Xmas
[Ger] 2 eq voices,acap (easy) BAREN. BA 553
$.25   (B3238)

Word Was Made Flesh, The *Xmas/Epiph
SATB,acap (med diff) oct CONCORDIA 98-1431
$.30   (B3239)

BENDICTION see Bloch, Ernest

BENDICTION see Grieb, Herbert [C.]

BENDICTION HYMNS IN HONOR OF THE MOST HOLY NAME
AND OF OUR HEAVENLY QUEEN see Charity,
Sisters of

BENDICTUS ES see Crandell, R.

BENDITA SABEDORIA see Villa-Lobos, Heitor

BENEATH THE CROSS OF JESUS *Lent
(Nelson) SATB SCHMITT 8043 $.35   (B3240)

BENEATH THE CROSS OF JESUS see Hafso

BENEATH THE CROSS OF JESUS see Hallett, John C.

BENEATH THE CROSS OF JESUS see Maker

BENEATH THE CROSS OF JESUS see Rasley

BENEATH THE CROSS OF JESUS see Wilson

BENEATH THE FORMS OF OUTWARD RITE see Lovelace,
Austin C.

BENEATH THE FORMS OF OUTWARD RITE see Sowerby,
Leo

BENEATH THE GLORY OF THE SKIES see Webber,
Lloyd

BENEATH THE SHADOW see Dickinson, Clarence

BENEDIC. see Bottazzo, Luigi

BENEDIC ANIMA MEA see Muller, Giulio

BENEDICAM DOMINO see Muller, Giulio

BENEDICAM DOMINUM see Croce, Giovanni

BENEDICAM DOMINUM see Gabrieli, Andrea

BENEDICAM DOMINUM see Lassus, Roland de
(Orlandus)

BENEDICAM DOMINUM see Schutz, Heinrich

BENEDICAM DOMINUM see Sermisy, Claude de

BENEDICAM DOMINUM see Victoria, Tomas Luis de

BENEDICAM DOMINUM IN OMNI TEMPORA see Selle,
Thomas

BENEDICAMUS see Neilsen, Ludvig

BENEDICAMUS see Praetorius, Michael

BENEDICAMUS DOMINO see Heseltine, Philip

BENEDICAMUS DOMINO see Perosi, (Dom) Lorenzo

BENEDICAMUS DOMINO see Praetorius, Michael

BENEDICAMUS IN ADVENTU DOMINI see Praetorius,
Michael

BENEDICAMUS IN NATALI DOMINI see Hellmann,
Diethard

BENEDICAMUS PATREM see Lechner, Leonhard

BENEDICITE see Ashfield, Robert

BENEDICITE see Coleman, Henry

BENEDICITE see Harwood, Basil

BENEDICITE see Purcell, Henry

BENEDICITE see Schutz, Heinrich

BENEDICITE see Tallis, Thomas

BENEDICITE see Tomblings, Philip

BENEDICITE see Vaughan Williams, Ralph

BENEDICITE GENTES see La Forge

BENEDICITE IN G see Jackson, Francis

BENEDICITE IN G see Naylor, Edward Woodall

BENEDICITE OMNIA OPERA see Arnold, J.H.

BENEDICITE, OMNIA OPERA DOMINI see Sheppard,
[Joseph] Stanley

BENEDICITE (SHORTENED FORM) see Blake, Leonard

BENEDICITE (SHORTENED FORM) see Dyson, George

BENEDICITE (SHORTENED FORM) see Goldsmith, S.W.

BENEDICITE (SHORTENED FORM) see Lloyd, Charles
Harford

BENEDICITE (SHORTENED FORM) see Powell, C.T.

BENEDICITE (SHORTENED FORM) see Shaw, Martin

BENEDICITE (SHORTENED FORM) see Stanford,
Charles Villiers

BENEDICITE (SHORTENED FORM) see Sumsion,
Herbert

BENEDICITE (SHORTENED FORM) see Willan, Healey

BENEDICT
So Little Time
SATB,acap oct PRO ART 2753 $.30   (B3241)

BENEDICT, OMNIA OPERA see Turner, E.

BENEDICTA ES see Des Prez, Josquin

BENEDICTA ES see Fuser, Ireneo

BENEDICTA ES COELORUM REGINA see Merulo,
Claudio

BENEDICTA ES TU see Chailley

BENEDICTA SIT see Jaeggi, Oswald

BENEDICTA SIT SANCTA TRINITAS see Agazzari,
Agostino

BENEDICTA SIT SANCTA TRINITAS see Lefebure,
Jean

BENEDICTA SIT SANCTA TRINITATIS see Palestrina,
Giovanni

BENEDICTIO ET CLARITAS see Mielczewski, Marcin

BENEDICTION see Beck

BENEDICTION see Berger, Jean

BENEDICTION see Hughes, F.

BENEDICTION see Shaw

BENEDICTION see Soderman, (Johan) August

BENEDICTION, A
SSA CHAPPELL 0017905-354 $.40   (B3242)

BENEDICTION, A see Rowley, Alec

BENEDICTION AVANT LA REPAS see Le Jeune, Claude

BENEDICTION, THE see Nystedt, Knut

BENEDICTUS see Brahms, Johannes

BENEDICTUS see Brunner, Adolf

BENEDICTUS see Byrd, William

BENEDICTUS see Cruft

BENEDICTUS see Dieterich

BENEDICTUS see Durand, A.

BENEDICTUS see Faure, Gabriel-Urbain

BENEDICTUS see Gabrieli, Giovanni

BENEDICTUS see Gagliano

BENEDICTUS see Gounod, Charles Francois

BENEDICTUS see Handel, George Frideric

BENEDICTUS see Howells, Herbert Norman

BENEDICTUS see Kerll, [Johann Caspar]

BENEDICTUS see Kitson, Charles Herbert

BENEDICTUS see Lassus, Roland de (Orlandus)

BENEDICTUS see Lotti, Antonio

BENEDICTUS see Magri, Pietro

BENEDICTUS see Oomes, P.J.

BENEDICTUS see Paladilhe, [Emile]

BENEDICTUS see Palestrina, Giovanni

BENEDICTUS see Rossini, Gioacchino

BENEDICTUS see Rubbra, Edmund

BENEDICTUS see Runback, Albert

BENEDICTUS see Saint-Saens, Camille

BENEDICTUS see Sario, Sebastian

BENEDICTUS see Simon, Paul

BENEDICTUS see Stanford, Charles Villiers

BENEDICTUS see Swann, Donald

BENEDICTUS see Tallis, Thomas

BENEDICTUS see Taverner, John

BENEDICTUS see Thompson, Randall

BENEDICTUS see Tours, Berthold

BENEDICTUS see Viadana, Lodovico Grossi da

BENEDICTUS see Victoria, Tomas Luis de

BENEDICTUS see Warland, Dale

BENEDICTUS AND HOSANNA see Bright, Houston

BENEDICTUS DOMINUS see Nielsen, Carl

BENEDICTUS DOMINUS see Schmitt, Florent

BENEDICTUS DOMINUS DEUS see Fevin, Antoine de

BENEDICTUS DOMINUS DEUS ISRAEL see Gallus, Jacobus

BENEDICTUS ES see Crandell, R.

BENEDICTUS ES see Wyton, Alec

BENEDICTUS ES DOMINE see Croce, Giovanni

BENEDICTUS ES, DOMINE see Marsh

BENEDICTUS ES, DOMINE see Matthews, H.

BENEDICTUS ES, DOMINE see Mead

BENEDICTUS, ES DOMINE see Rogers

BENEDICTUS ES, DOMINE see Schubert, Franz (Peter)

BENEDICTUS ES, DOMINE see Titcomb

BENEDICTUS (HOSIANNA I HOJDEN) see Hallnas, Hilding

BENEDICTUS IN C see Thalben-Ball, George [Thomas]

BENEDICTUS IN G see Bawden, Clarence

BENEDICTUS OG AMEN see Gade, Niels [W.]

BENEDICTUS QUI VENIT see Haydn, (Johann) Michael

BENEDICTUS QUI VENIT see Lassus, Roland de (Orlandus)

BENEDICTUS SIT DEUS see Mozart, Wolfgang Amadeus, Offertorium Pro Omni Tempore

BENEDICTUS SIT DEUS see Palestrina, Giovanni

BENEDICTUS, THE see Bunjes, Paul G.

BENEDITO
  Aguinaldo
    see Navidad, Coleccion De Villancicos
    Populares

  Alala De Montforte
    see ARTE CORAL. VOL. VI

  Ardia La Zarza
    see Navidad, Coleccion De Villancicos
    Populares

  Arte Coral. Vol III *sac/sec
    [Span] mix cor/men cor,acap UNION ESP.
    18065 s.p.
    contains: Danza De Pandero; El Adios De
    Iparraguirre; El Conde Olinos; En Toda
    La Quintana; Giraldilla; Seguidillas
    Manchegas; Ven, Oh Santo Espiritu!
                          (B3243)

  Arte Coral. Vol. IV *sac/sec
    [Span] jr cor,acap UNION ESP. 18365 s.p.
    contains: En El Lavadero; La Noche De San
    Juan; Las Palabras, Amor Mio;
    Pastorcito Que Te Vas; Primavera;
    Virgen Santisima (B3244)

  Arte Coral. Vol. V *sac/sec
    [Span] jr cor,acap UNION ESP. 18654 s.p.
    contains: Cancion Campestre; O Voso Galo,
    Comadre; Ofrenda; Salve, Estrella De
    Los Mares; Senor Zapateritero; Tonada
    De Ronda (B3245)

  Campana De Nochebuena
    see Coleccion De Villancicos Populares

  Cancion Campestre
    see Arte Coral. Vol. V

  Canto De Aguinaldo
    see Coleccion De Villancicos Populares

  Canto De Navidad
    see Coleccion De Villancicos Populares

  Claro Abril Resplandecio
    see Navidad, Coleccion De Villancicos
    Populares

BENEDITO (cont'd.)

  Coleccion De Villancicos Populares *Xmas,
    carol
    [Span] cor UNION ESP. 16585 s.p.
    contains: Campana De Nochebuena; Canto De
    Aguinaldo; Canto De Navidad; El Sueno
    Del Nino Jesus; Los Angeles Y Los
    Pastores; Villancico Popular Frances
                          (B3246)

  Danza De Pandero
    see Arte Coral. Vol III

  El Adios De Iparraguirre
    see Arte Coral. Vol III

  El Conde Olinos
    see Arte Coral. Vol III

  El Sueno Del Nino Jesus
    see Coleccion De Villancicos Populares

  El Triquitri
    see ARTE CORAL. VOL. VI

  En El Lavadero
    see Arte Coral. Vol. IV

  En Toda La Quintana
    see Arte Coral. Vol III

  Giraldilla
    see Arte Coral. Vol III

  Gloria A Maria
    see ARTE CORAL. VOL. VI

  La Cancion De La Zambomba
    see Navidad, Coleccion De Villancicos
    Populares

  La Noche De San Juan
    see Arte Coral. Vol. IV

  Las Palabras, Amor Mio
    see Arte Coral. Vol. IV

  Las Torras
    see ARTE CORAL. VOL. VI

  Los Angeles Y Los Pastores
    see Coleccion De Villancicos Populares

  Me Dices Que No Me Quieres
    see ARTE CORAL. VOL. VI

  Navidad, Coleccion De Villancicos Populares
    *Xmas,carol
    [Span] cor UNION ESP. 17356 s.p.
    contains: Aguinaldo; Ardia La Zarza;
    Claro Abril Resplandecio; La Cancion De
    La Zambomba; Romance Del Naranjel;
    Villancico Montanes (B3247)

  O Voso Galo, Comadre
    see Arte Coral. Vol. V

  Ofrenda
    see Arte Coral. Vol. V

  Pastorcito Que Te Vas
    see Arte Coral. Vol. IV

  Primavera
    see Arte Coral. Vol. IV

  Romance Del Naranjel
    see Navidad, Coleccion De Villancicos
    Populares

  Salve, Estrella De Los Mares
    see Arte Coral. Vol. V

  Seguidillas Manchegas
    see Arte Coral. Vol III

  Senor Zapateritero
    see Arte Coral. Vol. V

  Tonada De Ronda
    see Arte Coral. Vol. V

  Ven, Oh Santo Espiritu!
    see Arte Coral. Vol III

  Villancico Montanes
    see Navidad, Coleccion De Villancicos
    Populares

  Villancico Popular Frances
    see Coleccion De Villancicos Populares

  Virgen Santisima
    see Arte Coral. Vol. IV

BENEDIXISTI see Rheinberger, Josef

BENEDIXISTI, DOMINE see Campbell-Watson, Frank

BENEDIXISTI, DOMINE see Gabrieli, Giovanni

BENEKEN, FRIEDRICH
  Wie Sie So Sanft Ruh'n
    [Ger] men cor,acap cor pts HEINRICH. 937
    s.p. (B3248)

BENEVOLI, ORAZIO (1605-1672)
  Christe
    (Couraud) [Lat] SSSAAATTTBBB oct SALABERT-
    US $.75 (B3249)

  Kyrie 1 *Kyrie
    (Couraud) [Lat] SSSAAATTTBBB oct SALABERT-
    US $1.00 (B3250)

  Kyrie 2 *Kyrie
    (Couraud) [Lat] SSSAAATTTBBB oct SALABERT-
    US $1.25 (B3251)

BENFORD
  Oh Lord! How Excellent Thy Name
    SATB oct PRO ART 2123 $.25 (B3252)

BENGSON, W.J.
  Lamb Of God, I Look To Thee
    unis&opt sr cor oct GRAY GCMR 2635 $.25
                          (B3253)

BENGTSON, F.
  Speak Words Of Praise
    SATB oct PRESSER G-156 $.30 (B3254)

BENGTSSON, [GUSTAV ADOLF TIBURT] (1885)
  Julvisa
    3pt wom cor/3pt jr cor,pno NORDISKA 665
    s.p. (B3255)

  Lovsjungen Herren
    [Swed] 3pt men cor LUNDQUIST 80 s.p.
                          (B3256)

  Troget Vid Ditt Kors
    [Swed] 3pt men cor LUNDQUIST 79 s.p.
                          (B3257)

BENGUEREL, XAVIER
  Old Rugged Cross *hymn
    SATB WEINBERGER s.p. (B3258)

BENISSEZ LE SEIGNEUR *Xmas,carol,18th cent
  (Geveart, F.-A.) [Fr] 4pt mix cor,acap (easy)
  cor pts LEMOINE s.p. see from Collection De
  Choeurs, dixieme Fascicule (B3259)

BENITO
  Misa Pastoril *Mass
    [Lat] 2pt (med easy) UNION ESP. 13127 s.p.
                          (B3260)

BENJAMIN, ARTHUR (1893-1960)
  He Is The Lonely Greatness
    SATB,acap oct BOOSEY 5296 $.30 (B3261)

  I See His Blood Upon The Rose
    SSATB,acap oct BOOSEY 5295 $.35 (B3262)

BENKER, HEINZ (1921-)
  Das Lieben Bringt Gross Freud *folk/mot,
    Finn/Ger/Isr/Neth
    mix cor cor pts BREITKOPF-W CHB-3136 s.p.
                          (B3263)

  Schon Ist Die Welt *folk/mot,Fr/Ger/It/Span
    mix cor cor pts BREITKOPF-W CHB-3126 s.p.
                          (B3264)

BENNARD, GEORGE (1873-1958)
  Old Rugged Cross, The *Easter/Gen,anthem
    SATB ALLANS 386 s.p. (B3265)
    SA ALLANS 260 s.p. (B3266)

  Old Rugged Cross, The *hymn
    2pt ASHDOWN E, A.271 s.p. (B3267)
    (Jones) SATB oct WORD CS-1942 $.30 (B3268)
    (Wilson) SATB oct LORENZ 4450 $.30 (B3269)

  Pentecostal Fire Is Falling
    (Boersma) SATB oct WORD CS-2179 $.25
                          (B3270)

BENNER
  My Jesus, I Love Thee *hymn
    SATB oct LILLENAS AN-2227 $.30 (B3271)

  Prepare Ye The Way Of The Lord
    SATB oct LILLENAS AN-2201 $.35 (B3272)

BENNET
  All Creatures Now *see Lasst Diesen Tag Uns
    Alle Preisen

  Lasst Diesen Tag Uns Alle Preisen
    "All Creatures Now" [Eng/Ger] 5pt mix cor
    MOSELER LB-723 s.p. (B3273)

BENNETT
  Abide With Me *anthem
    SATB ALLANS 419 s.p. (B3274)

  God Is A Spirit *anthem
    SATB,acap oct PRO ART 1084 $.25 (B3275)
    SATB (easy) ALLANS 45 s.p. (B3276)
    (Ehret) 2pt oct PRO ART 1430 $.20 (B3277)
    (Gray) SAB oct PRO ART 1617 $.22 (B3278)
    (Nevin) SAB oct FISCHER,J 7627 $.30 (B3279)
    (Pitcher, Gladys) 3pt mix cor,pno (easy)
    oct WILLIS 8495 $.20 (B3280)

BENNETT, F. ROY
  Bethlehem Lies Sleeping *Xmas,carol
    2pt ASHDOWN E.A.343 s.p. see from Three
    Carols For The Nativity (B3281)

  Come To The Manger *Xmas,carol
    2pt ASHDOWN E.A.343 s.p. see from Three
    Carols For The Nativity (B3282)

  Shepherd And The Angels, The *Xmas,carol
    2pt ASHDOWN E.A.343 s.p. see from Three
    Carols For The Nativity (B3283)

  Three Carols For Christ's Nativity *CC3U,
    Xmas,carol
    unis ASHDOWN U.87 s.p. (B3284)

  Three Carols For The Nativity *see Bethlehem
    Lies Sleeping; Come To The Manger;
    Shepherd And The Angels, The (B3285)

  Three Christmas Carols *CC3U,Xmas,carol
    unis ASHDOWN U.88 s.p. (B3286)

BENNETT, R.
  Balulalow
    SSA,acap oct PRESSER 312-40606 $.25 (B3287)

  Dormi Jesu *Xmas/Gen
    SSA,acap oct PRESSER 312-40605 $.25 (B3288)

BENNETT, RICHARD RODNEY (1936-)
  Sorrows Of Mary, The *Psntd
    SSATB,acap (med easy) oct OXFORD 84.135
    $.25 (B3289)

BENNETT, S.
  God Is A Spirit
    cor cor HART s.p. (B3290)

BENNETT, SIR WILLIAM STERNDALE (1816-1875)
  God Is A Spirit (from Woman Of Samaria)
    Easter/Lent/Whitsun,anthem/Bibl
    2pt ASHDOWN E.A.212 s.p. (B3291)
    4pt mix cor,acap oct SCHIRM.G 2477 $.25
                          (B3292)
    SATB oct NOVELLO 28.0967.02 $.35 (B3293)
    2pt oct NOVELLO 33.0068.04 s.p. (B3294)
    SATB oct LESLIE 4022 (B3295)
    (Martin) SATB oct SPRATT 522 $.25 (B3296)
    (Stickles) 3pt mix cor,org/pno oct SCHIRM.G
    11117 $.25 (B3297)

BENNETT, SIR WILLIAM STERNDALE (cont'd.)

Woman Of Samaria, The　*Bibl/ora
SATB,SATB soli,org,2fl,2ob,2clar,2bsn,
4horn,2trp,3trom,tuba,strings,perc,timp
voc sc NOVELLO s.p., ipr　　　(B3298)

BENOIT, DOM PAUL

Where Charity And Love Prevail
(Vermulst, Jan) SATB,opt org oct WORLD
ESA-1135-8 $.45　　　　　(B3299)
(Vermulst, Jan) SSA,opt org oct WORLD
ESA-1342-3 $.45　　　　　(B3300)

BENSON

Choir Of Bethlehem, The　*Xmas,cant
SA/SATB oct LORENZ $1.95　　　(B3301)

So Great Is His Love　*see Mercer, M.

Sunrise Over Calvary　*Easter,cant
SATB LORENZ $1.95　　　　　(B3302)

BENSON, WARREN

Rejoice In The Lord Always
SATB oct MCA　　　　　　(B3303)

Stabat Mater
(Russell) SATB,org oct MCA　　(B3304)

BENTEL, FRANKLIN

God Be In My Head
SATB (easy) ABINGDON APM-565 $.25　(B3305)

BENTIVOGLIO, GIULIO

Tantum Ergo　*Op.55, Commun
[Lat] 3 eq voices,org (easy) ZANIBON 2642
s.p.　　　　　　　(B3306)

Tu Es Sacerdos
[Lat] 2pt men cor,org ZANIBON 2654 s.p.
　　　　　　　　(B3307)

BENTZ, CECIL

Sparrow And The Swallow, The　*Bibl
SA/TB oct LAWSON 970 $.35　　(B3308)

BEOBIDE, JOSE MARIA (1882-　　)

God, Our Father, Lord Of Heaven　*see Tantum
Ergo

Tantum Ergo　*Commun
"Therefore We, Before Him Bending" SATB,opt
org SCHIRM.EC 1218 $.25　　(B3309)
(Glaser, V.) "God, Our Father, Lord Of
Heaven" SAB SCHIRM.EC 2251 $.25　(B3310)
(Williams, W.) "Therefore We, Before Him
Bending" TB,org SCHIRM.EC 1201 $.18
　　　　　　　　(B3311)
Therefore We, Before Him Bending　*see Tantum
Ergo

BERCEUSE DE L'ENFANT JESUS see Schwaab, Maurice

BERCHEM, JACHET

O Jesu Christe
(Vaal, O. De) mix cor sc ALSBACH&D s.p.
　　　　　　　　(B3312)
Osterhalleluja (Der Herr Ist Wahrhaftig)
*Easter,mot
(Hellmann) SATB HANSSLER 1.094 s.p.　(B3313)

BERCHEM, JACOBUS DE

O Jesu, Jesus Christ　*Renais
(Ehret, Walter) SATB,acap PEER $.40 (B3314)

O Vos Omnes　*Psntd
[Lat] SATB,acap (easy) MULLER MS 44 s.p.
　　　　　　　　(B3315)

BEREDD HALL MIG O JESU KRIST see Berg, Gottfrid

BEREDEN VAG FOR HERRAN see Sporr, Karl

BEREITE DICH, ZION see Bach, Johann Sebastian

BEREITET DEM HERRN DEN WEG see Dedekind,
Constantine Christian

BEREITET DIE WEGE see Bach, Johann Sebastian,
Bereitet Die Wege, Bereitet Die Bahn

BEREITET DIE WEGE, BEREITET DIE BAHN see Bach,
Johann Sebastian

BERESINALIED see Niggli, F.

BERG

Aftonsang
[Swed] 3pt wom cor LUNDQUIST 71 s.p.
　　　　　　　　(B3316)

BERG, GOTTFRID

Ack, Mildaste Jesu
mix cor NORDISKA 5957 s.p.　(B3317)

Allenast Hos Gud Soker Min Sjal Sin Ro　*CCU
2pt wom cor/2pt jr cor,acap NORDISKA 4457
s.p.　　　　　　　(B3318)

Ande, Full Av Nade
wom cor/jr cor NORDISKA 5096 s.p.　(B3319)
(Ahlen, Waldemar) 3pt wom cor/3pt jr cor,
acap NORDISKA 4049 s.p.　　(B3320)

Av Djupets Nod
wom cor/jr cor NORDISKA 5098 s.p.　(B3321)

Av Himlens Hojd Oss Kommet Ar
2pt wom cor/2pt jr cor,acap NORDISKA 4450
s.p.　　　　　　　(B3322)

Beredd Hall Mig O Jesu Krist
mix cor NORDISKA 2812 s.p.　(B3323)

De Finns En Vag
(Ahlen, Waldemar) 2pt wom cor/2pt jr cor,
pno,inst NORDISKA 4053 s.p.　(B3324)
(Ahlen, Waldemar) 2pt wom cor/2pt jr cor,
acap NORDISKA 4054 s.p.　　(B3325)

Den Blida Var Ar Inne
wom cor/jr cor NORDISKA 5184 s.p.　(B3326)

Det Ar En Ros Utsprungen
wom cor/jr cor NORDISKA 5092 s.p.　(B3327)

Det Gar Ett Tyst Och Taligt Lamm
wom cor/jr cor NORDISKA 5094 s.p.　(B3328)

BERG, GOTTFRID (cont'd.)

Dig Tillbedja Vi, Kristi
2pt wom cor/2pt jr cor,acap NORDISKA 4454
s.p.　　　　　　　(B3329)

Du Som Har Kommit Till Var Jord
wom cor/jr cor NORDISKA 5099 s.p.　(B3330)

En Gudomsstrale Mild Och Ren
(Ahlen, Waldemar) 3pt wom cor/3pt jr cor,
acap NORDISKA 4045 s.p.　　(B3331)

En Vanlig Gronskas Rika Drakt
(Ahlen, Waldemar) 3pt wom cor/3pt jr cor,
acap NORDISKA 4050 s.p.　　(B3332)

Frojda Dig Du Dotter Sion
3pt mix cor NORDISKA 1865 s.p.　(B3333)

Giv, O Himmelske Fader
3pt mix cor NORDISKA 5976 s.p.　(B3334)

Glad Dig, Du Helga Kristenhet
mix cor NORDISKA 4241 s.p.　(B3335)

Gud Later Sina Trogna Har
mix cor NORDISKA 3953 s.p.　(B3336)

Gud, Var Mig Nadig
mix cor NORDISKA 4878 s.p.　(B3337)

Guds Vag I Dunkel Ofta Gar
mix cor NORDISKA 3287 s.p.　(B3338)

Helige Ande, Sanningens Ande
2pt wom cor/2pt jr cor,acap NORDISKA 4455
s.p.　　　　　　　(B3339)

Herre Jesu , Du Ar Vagen
(Ahlen, Waldemar) wom cor/jr cor,pno,inst
NORDISKA 4055 s.p.　　　(B3340)
(Ahlen, Waldemar) unis wom cor/unis jr cor,
acap NORDISKA 4056 s.p.　　(B3341)

Herren, Var Gud, Ar En Konung
(Ahlen, Waldemar) 3pt wom cor/3pt jr cor,
acap NORDISKA 4052 s.p.　　(B3342)

I Pingsten Blev Guds Ande Sand
mix cor NORDISKA 4879 s.p.　(B3343)

Jag Beder Dig, O Jesu Kar
mix cor NORDISKA 1303 s.p.　(B3344)

Jerusalem, Hav Upp Din Rost
(Ahlen, Waldemar) 3pt wom cor/3pt jr cor,
acap NORDISKA 4044 s.p.　　(B3345)

Jesu, Lat Din Karleks Laga
(Ahlen, Waldemar) wom cor/jr cor,pno,inst
NORDISKA 4059 s.p.　　　(B3346)
(Ahlen, Waldemar) wom cor/jr cor,acap
NORDISKA 4060 s.p.　　　(B3347)

Jesu Namn Begynna Skall
mix cor NORDISKA 3016 s.p.　(B3348)

Lat Oss Nu Jesus Prisa
2pt wom cor/2pt jr cor,acap NORDISKA 4451
s.p.　　　　　　　(B3349)

Lov, Pris Och Ara Vare Dig, O Gud
wom cor/jr cor NORDISKA 5089 s.p.　(B3350)

Lov Vare Dig, O Jesu Krist
wom cor/jr cor NORDISKA 5093 s.p.　(B3351)

Med Tacksam Rost Och Tacksam Sjal
(Ahlen, Waldemar) 2pt wom cor/2pt jr cor,
acap NORDISKA 4058 s.p.　　(B3352)
(Ahlen, Waldemar) 2pt wom cor/2pt jr cor,
pno,inst NORDISKA 4057 s.p.　(B3353)

Min Sjal, Du Maste Nu Glomma
(Ahlen, Waldemar) 3pt wom cor/3pt jr cor,
acap NORDISKA 4047 s.p.　　(B3354)

Nattlig Madonna
wom cor/jr cor NORDISKA 5035 s.p.　(B3355)

Nu Vilans Dag Forflutit
wom cor/jr cor NORDISKA 5126 s.p.　(B3356)

Nu Vilar Hela Jorden
wom cor/jr cor NORDISKA 5127 s.p.　(B3357)

O, Herre Gud, Gor Nad Meg Mig
mix cor NORDISKA 2716 s.p.　(B3358)

O Herre Gud Oandelig
2pt wom cor/2pt jr cor,acap NORDISKA 4453
s.p.　　　　　　　(B3359)
(Ahlen, Waldemar) 3pt wom cor/3pt jr cor,
acap NORDISKA 4051 s.p.　　(B3360)

O Herre Gud, Vi Bedja Dig
wom cor/jr cor NORDISKA 5097 s.p.　(B3361)

O Huvud, Blodigt Sarat
(Ahlen, Waldemar) 3pt wom cor/3pt jr cor,
acap NORDISKA 4048 s.p.　　(B3362)

O Kriste, Du Som Ljuset Ar
wom cor/jr cor NORDISKA 5125 s.p.　(B3363)

O, Min Jesu, Dit Du Gatt
mix cor NORDISKA 5364 s.p.　(B3364)

Pa Gud Och Je Pa Eget Rad
mix cor NORDISKA 1866 s.p.　(B3365)

Rads Ej Bekanna Kristi Namn
(Ahlen, Waldemar) 2pt wom cor/2pt jr cor,
pno,inst NORDISKA 4061 s.p.　(B3366)
(Ahlen, Waldemar) 2pt wom cor/2pt jr cor,
acap NORDISKA 4062 s.p.　　(B3367)

Sitt Oga Jesus Oppnat Har
wom cor/jr cor NORDISKA 5095 s.p.　(B3368)

Staffansvisa
wom cor/jr cor NORDISKA 5418 s.p.　(B3369)

Uppfaren Ar Var Herre Krist
2pt wom cor/2pt jr cor,acap NORDISKA 4452
s.p.　　　　　　　(B3370)

BERG, GOTTFRID (cont'd.)

Upplat Var Mun Till Ditt Namns Pris
2pt wom cor/2pt jr cor,acap NORDISKA 4456
s.p.　　　　　　　(B3371)

Uppstanden Ar Var Herre Krist
mix cor NORDISKA 5956 s.p.　(B3372)

Vak Upp, Min Sjal, Giv Ara
wom cor/jr cor NORDISKA 5090 s.p.　(B3373)

Var Man Ma Nu Val Gladja Sig
wom cor/jr cor NORDISKA 5091 s.p.　(B3374)

Var Mig Nadig, O Gud
mix cor NORDISKA 4410 s.p.　(B3375)

Varldens Fralsare Kom Har
(Ahlen, Waldemar) 3pt wom cor/3pt jr cor,
acap NORDISKA 4046 s.p.　　(B3376)

Vart Paskalamm, O Jesu Krist
mix cor NORDISKA 4242 s.p.　(B3377)

BERGBAUERNWEIHNACHT see Biebl, Franz

BERGBAUERNWEIHNACHT see Klein, Karl Heinz

BERGER

Behold, The Lord Hath Proclaimed
SATB KJOS 5398 $.30　　　(B3378)

Blessing And Righteousness
SATB KJOS 5388 $.30　　　(B3379)

Christmas Night　*Xmas
(Vene) SSA oct COLOMBO 1296 $.25　(B3380)
(Vene) SATB oct COLOMBO 2008 $.25　(B3381)

Five Songs Of Israel　*CC5U,Isr
SSA KJOS PC518 $.50　　　(B3382)

From The Bay Psalm Book
SATB,acap SHAWNEE A 729 $.40　(B3383)

Happy Are They That Dwell In Thy House
SATB KJOS 5348 $.30　　　(B3384)

I To The Hills Lift Up Mine Eyes
SATB KJOS 5326 $.30　　　(B3385)

Let Us Go Into The House
SATB KJOS 6300 $.40　　　(B3386)

Lift Up Your Heads
SSATBB oct SUMMY 5484 $.50　(B3387)

O Give Thanks Unto The Lord
SSATTB oct SUMMY 5366 $.70　(B3388)

O Sing To The Lord
SATB KJOS 5896 $.40　　　(B3389)

Wake Psaltry, And Harp
SATB,acap SHAWNEE A 820 $.30　(B3390)

We Sanctify Thy Name
SSAATTBB oct SUMMY 5483 $.45　(B3391)

What Strangers Are These?
(Purvis) SSAATTBB oct SUMMY B 1447 $.60
　　　　　　　　(B3392)
(Purvis) unis&desc oct SUMMY B 969 $.40
　　　　　　　　(B3393)

Wisdom Hath Builded Her House
SSAATTBB oct SUMMY 5367 $.60　(B3394)

Your Treasures In Heaven
SATB KJOS 5432 $.30　　　(B3395)

BERGER, HANS LUDWIG (1892-1972)

Das Konigsbanner Zieht Voraus, Ihm
SAB HANSSLER 6.2671 s.p.　(B3396)

Ein Lammlein Geht Und Tragt Die Schuld
(Berger, H.L.) TTBB HANSSLER 6.5101 s.p.
　　　　　　　　(B3397)

Frohlich Wir Nun All Fangen An
SATB HANSSLER 6.230 s.p. contains also:
Kurig, Hans-Hermann, Frohlich Wir Nun All
Fangen An (SA/SAT/SAB); Werner, Fritz,
Freut Euch, Ihr Lieben Christen All (SA/
SATB); Kurig, Hans-Hermann, Nun Jauchzt
Dem Herren Alle Welt (SATB/SS/SA); Kurig,
Hans-Hermann, Singet Dem Herrn Ein Neues
Lied (3pt) (canon)　　　(B3398)

Jauchz, Erd Und Himmel, Juble Hell
SATB HANSSLER 8.015 s.p.　(B3399)

Kommt Her, Des Konigs Aufgebot　*CC8L
SSA HANSSLER 6.292 s.p.　(B3400)

Lobe Den Herren Den Machtigen　*Thanks
SATB HANSSLER 6.239 s.p. contains also:
Cruger, Johann, Lobet Den Herren, Alle,
Die Ihn Ehren　　　　　(B3401)

Lobt Gott Ihr Christen　*CC8L,Xmas
SSA HANSSLER 6.6105 s.p.　(B3402)

Lobt Gott In Allen Landen
see Bach, Johann Sebastian, Dir, Dir,
Jehova, Will Ich Singen

Nur Einen Wunsch, Nur Ein Verlangen Hat Unser
SATB HANSSLER 6.2668 s.p. contains also:
Wohl Einem Haus, Da Jesus Christ　(B3403)

O Heiland, Reiss Die Himmel Auf
SATB HANSSLER 6.010 s.p. contains also:
Jansen, Philipp, Gott Heiliger Schopfer
Aller Stern　　　　　　(B3404)

Sonne Der Gerechtigkeit
see Kurig, Hans-Hermann, Lobt Gott, Ihr
Frommen Christen

Sonne Der Gerechtigkeit, Gehe Auf
SATB/SSA HANSSLER 8.017 s.p.　(B3405)

Wohl Einem Haus, Da Jesus Christ
see Berger, Hans Ludwig, Nur Einen Wunsch,
Nur Ein Verlangen Hat Unser

BERGER, JEAN (1909-)
All Flesh Is Grass *anthem
SATB (med diff) oct AUGSBURG 1419 $.35 (B3406)
SATB (med diff) oct AUGSBURG 1419 $.35 see from From Isaiah (B3407)

All Things That Rise Will Fall
SATB,S solo,acap AMP A327 $.35 see from Two Proverbs (B3408)

Alleluia (from Brazilian Psalm)
mix cor,acap oct SCHIRM.G 9992 $.40 (B3409)
(Heath) 4pt men cor,acap oct SCHIRM.G 11020 $.35 (B3410)

And It Shall Come To Pass
SATB (diff) oct AUGSBURG 1519 $.35 (B3411)

Arise, Shine *anthem
SATB (med diff) oct AUGSBURG 1421 $.35 see from From Isaiah (B3412)

Behold, God Is My Salvation *anthem
SATB (med) oct AUGSBURG 1464 $.30 (B3413)

Behold, O God Our Shield
dbl cor,soli oct SHEPPARD 1017 $.70 see from How Lovely Are Thy Tabernacles (B3414)

Benediction
SATB oct FISCHER,J 9592 $.30 (B3415)

Blessed Are They That Dwell In The House
dbl cor,soli oct SHEPPARD 1016 $.70 see from How Lovely Are Thy Tabernacles (B3416)

Blessed Art Thou, O Lord *hymn
SATB,acap AMP A459 $.30 see from Hymns Of Praise (B3417)

Blessed Is Every One (Psalm 128)
SATB,S solo,pno BROUDE BR. $.50 (B3418)

Blessed Is He *anthem
SATB,S solo,trp AMP A559 $.30 see also Three Anthems (B3419)

Bow Down, O Lord, Thine Ear *Gen
SATB,kbd (med diff) oct CONCORDIA 98-1736 $.25 (B3420)

Brazilian Psalm *see Psalmo Brasileiro

Create In Me A Clean Heart
SATB oct FISCHER,J 9446 $.30 (B3421)

De Profundis Clamavi
[Lat] SATB,opt S solo,acap AMP A416 $.35 (B3422)

Extolled And Hallowed Be The Name Of God
SATB oct FISCHER,J 9591 $.30 (B3423)

Eyes Of All Wait Upon Thee, The *anthem
SATB (med diff) oct AUGSBURG 1264 $.30 (B3424)

Fiery Furnace, The *Bibl/cant
4pt mix cor,soli,acap voc sc SCHIRM.G $1.50 (B3425)

For This Good Company
SATB,pno/org oct SHEPPARD 1014 $.30 (B3426)

Fountain Of Life, A *Bibl
SATB oct SHEPPARD 1012 $.35 (B3427)

From Isaiah *see All Flesh Is Grass; Arise, Shine; When Thou Passest Through The Waters (B3428)

Glorify The Lord With Me (Psalm 34) Bibl
SATB oct SHEPPARD 1007 $.40 (B3429)

Glory Be To God
SATB KJOS 5206A $.35 (B3430)

God Help The Poor
SATB,S solo,acap AMP A328 $.25 see from Two Proverbs (B3431)

Good Of Contentment, The
SATB,acap oct PRESSER 312-40131 $.30 (B3432)

Happy Is The Man *Bibl
4pt mix cor,acap oct SCHIRM.G 10910 $.30 (B3433)

How Amiable Are Thy Tabernacles
SATB (diff) ABINGDON APM-695 $1.25 (B3434)

How Beautiful Upon The Mountains *Bibl
SATB oct SHEPPARD 1002 $.40 (B3435)

How Lovely Are Thy Tabernacles *see Behold, O God Our Shield; Blessed Are They That Dwell In The House; How Lovely Are Thy Tabernacles (B3436)

How Lovely Are Thy Tabernacles
dbl cor,soli oct SHEPPARD 1015 $.80 see from How Lovely Are Thy Tabernacles (B3437)

Hymns Of Praise *see Blessed Art Thou, O Lord; In Thy Covanant Does My Heart Rejoice; Thou Hast Given Abundance To Thy Servant (B3438)

I Lift Up My Eyes (Psalm 121) mot
SATB,acap PETERS 6261 $.30 (B3439)

I Will Extol Thee, My God *anthem
SATB,2trp AMP A558 $.35 see also Three Anthems (B3440)

I Will Greatly Rejoice In The Lord *anthem
SATB (med diff) oct AUGSBURG 1263 $.25 (B3441)

I Will Praise Thee, O Lord *anthem
SATB,2trp AMP A560 $.40 see also Three Anthems (B3442)

In Thy Covanant Does My Heart Rejoice *hymn
SATB,acap AMP A461 $.35 see from Hymns Of Praise (B3443)

It Is Good To Give Thanks *anthem
SATB&jr cor,2fl (easy) oct AUGSBURG 0643 $.40 (B3444)

BERGER, JEAN (cont'd.)

Lift Up Your Eyes On High *Bibl
SATB oct SHEPPARD 1003 $.40 (B3445)

Lord Is My Shepherd, The (Psalm 23) Bibl
SATB,opt S solo BROUDE BR. $.40 (B3446)

Magnificat
SATB,S solo,fl,tamb, triangle oct SHEPPARD 1004 $1.50 (B3447)

O Come Let Us Sing Unto The Lord
SATB,acap BROUDE BR. $.50 (B3448)

O Death Rock Me Asleep
SATB,acap oct PRESSER 312-40590 $.30 (B3449)

O God, The Proud Rose 'Gainst Me *Gen
SATB,kbd (med easy) oct CONCORDIA 98-1738 $.25 (B3450)

O Magnify The Lord
SATB oct FISCHER,J 9416 $.30 (B3451)

O Mortal Man
SATB KJOS 5225 $.30 (B3452)

O Praise The Lord, All Ye Nations (Psalm 117)
SATB,tamb,opt hndbl, castenets oct SHEPPARD 1005 $.70 (B3453)

O Sing All Ye Lands *anthem
SATB (med) oct AUGSBURG 1337 $.30 (B3454)

Of Wisdom And Folly *Bibl
SATB oct SHEPPARD 1001 $.80 (B3455)

Path Of The Just, The *Bibl
SATB oct SHEPPARD 1009 $.40 (B3456)

Praised Be Thou, O Lord
SATB TRANSCON. TCL 635 $.60 (B3457)

Prayer Of Manasseh, The *Bibl
4pt mix cor,T solo,acap oct SCHIRM.G 11064 $.35 (B3458)

Preserve Me, O God (Psalm 16)
[Eng] mix cor,S/T solo TRANSCON. TCL 634 $.60 (B3459)

Psalm 13
SATB oct FISCHER,J 8673 $.30 (B3460)

Psalm 16 *see Preserve Me, O God

Psalm 23 *see Lord Is My Shepherd, The

Psalm 34 *see Glorify The Lord With Me

Psalm 57
SATB,pno/org/4brass PRESSER $1.25 (B3461)

Psalm 100 *see Shout To The Lord

Psalm 117 *see O Praise The Lord, All Ye Nations

Psalm 121 *see I Lift Up My Eyes

Psalm 128 *see Blessed Is Every One

Psalm 140
mix cor,strings (diff) sc AUGSBURG 11-9343 $3.00, ipa, cor pts AUGSBURG 11-9344 $.50 (B3462)

Psalm 146
mix cor,strings (diff) sc AUGSBURG 11-9351 $3.00, ipa, cor pts AUGSBURG 11-9352 $.50 (B3463)

Psalm 150
SATB oct FISCHER,J 8512 $.30 (B3464)

Psalmo Brasileiro *Psalm
"Brazilian Psalm" [Eng/Port] cor voc sc SCHIRM.G $.85 (B3465)

Psalms Of Penitence *CCU,cant/Psalm
mix cor BELWIN $1.00 (B3466)

Rejoice!
SATB oct SHEPPARD 1013 $.50 (B3467)

Rose Touched By The Sun's Warm Rays, A *anthem
SATB (easy) oct AUGSBURG 0953 $.20 (B3468)

Seek Ye The Lord *anthem
SATB (med diff) oct AUGSBURG 1279 $.22 (B3469)

Sermon For Our Time, A
SATB,S/T solo,opt gtr oct PRESSER 312-40941 $.30 (B3470)

Shepherd's Farewell To The Holy Family, The (from Childhood Of Christ, The)
4pt mix cor oct SCHIRM.G 10672 $.25 (B3471)
(Stickles) 3pt wom cor,S solo,org/pno oct SCHIRM.G 11031 $.25 (B3472)
(Stickles) 3pt mix cor,org/pno oct SCHIRM.G 11030 $.30 (B3473)

Shout To The Lord (Psalm 100) mot
SATB,acap PETERS 6250 $.30 (B3474)

Speak To One Another Of Psalms *anthem
SATB (med) oct AUGSBURG 0954 $.35 (B3475)

Take From Us, Lord
SATB,acap BROUDE BR. $.40 (B3476)

They That Wait Upon The Lord *anthem
SATB (med diff) oct AUGSBURG 1467 $.30 (B3477)

Thou Hast Given Abundance To Thy Servant *hymn
SATB,acap AMP A460 $.35 see from Hymns Of Praise (B3478)

Three Anthems *anthem
sc AMP A558A $.50, ipa
contains & see also: Blessed Is He; I Will Extol Thee, My God; I Will Praise Thee, O Lord (B3479)

Three Introits *CC3U,Introit
SATB oct SHEPPARD 1008 $.50 (B3480)

BERGER, JEAN (cont'd.)

Thy Kingdom Come
4pt mix cor oct SCHIRM.G 10165 $.35 (B3481)

Thy Word With Me Shall Always Stay *anthem
SATB (med) oct AUGSBURG 0591 $.30 (B3482)

To Do God's Will *anthem
SATB (med) oct AUGSBURG 0952 $.35 (B3483)

Trust In The Lord *anthem
SATB (med) oct AUGSBURG 1285 $.25 (B3484)

Two Proverbs *see All Things That Rise Will Fall; God Help The Poor (B3485)

Vision Of Peace
SATB,acap BROUDE BR. $1.50 (B3486)

Way Of Charity, The *Bibl
SATB oct SHEPPARD 1010 $.85 (B3487)

When Thou Passest Through The Waters *anthem
SATB,solo (med diff) oct AUGSBURG 1420 $.30 (B3488)
SATB (med diff) oct AUGSBURG 1420 $.30 see from From Isaiah (B3489)

Where Shall Wisdom Be Found? *Bibl
SATB oct SHEPPARD 1006 $.40 (B3490)

Who Is Like Unto Thee, O Lord *anthem
dbl cor (med diff) oct AUGSBURG 1482 $.50 (B3491)

Whom Shall I Send? *anthem
SATB (med diff) oct AUGSBURG 1338 $.30 (B3492)

Why Art Thou Cast Down, O My Soul? *anthem
SATB (med diff) oct AUGSBURG 0616 $.35 (B3493)

Word Of God, The *anthem
SATB,narrator (diff) oct AUGSBURG 9535 $1.00 (B3494)

Ye Shall Go Out With Joy *Bibl
SATB oct SHEPPARD 1011 $.40 (B3495)

BERGERS, BERGERES see Tomasi

BERGERS, IL EST PLUS DE MINUIT see Canteloube de Malaret, Marie-Joseph

BERGERS, SECOUE TON SOMMEIL PROFOND *Xmas, carol,Fr
"Shepherds, Shake Off Your Drowsy Sleep" SATB,acap SCHIRM.EC 2237 $.25 (B3496)
"Shepherds! Shake Off Your Drowsy Sleep" 2pt ENOCH TP255 s.p. (B3497)
(Ehret, W.) "Shepherds, Shake Off Your Drowsy Sleep" SATB oct PRESSER MC347 $.35 (B3498)
(Ehret, W.) "Shepherds, Shake Off Your Drowsy Sleep" SSA oct PRESSER MC268 $.35 (B3499)
(Gray) "Shepherds! Shake Off Your Drowsy Sleep" SATB,acap,opt pno oct PRO ART 1828 $.25 (B3500)
(Rotermund, M.) "Shepherds, Shake Off Your Drowsy Sleep" SA,kbd (med easy) oct CONCORDIA 98-1892 $.25 (B3501)
(Wasner) "Shepherds, Shake Off Your Drowsy Sleep" 6pt mix cor,acap oct SCHIRM.G 8935 $.25 (B3502)
(Wasner) "Shepherds, Shake Off Your Drowsy Sleep" 4pt mix cor,acap oct SCHIRM.G 8934 $.30 (B3503)

BERGGREN
Master, Speak To Me
SATB KJOS 2016 $.30 (B3504)

BERGLUND
Transfiguration *Gen
SATB SCHMITT 15003 $.30 (B3505)

BERGLUND, R.
I Will Praise Thee, O Lord
SATB oct KERBY 6701 $.45 (B3506)
SSAATTBB,acap oct KERBY 82279 $.45 (B3507)

BERGMAN
Sleep, My Little Jesus
(Hoggard) SAB SHAWNEE D59 $.30 (B3508)

BERGMAN, ERIK (1911-)
Missa In Honorem Sancti Henrici *Op.68, Mass
[Lat] mix cor,soli,org oct FAZER s.p. (B3509)

BERGMANN
Sleep, My Little Jesus
(Hoggard) SATB SHAWNEE A 414 $.30 (B3510)

BERGMANN, WALTER
Easter *Easter
unis,rec SCHOTT CHR4 s.p. (B3511)

Matthew, Mark
unis,rec SCHOTT CHR3 s.p. (B3512)

BERGSMA, WILLIAM LAURENCE (1921-)
Confrontation From The Book Of Job *Bibl
SATB,orch voc sc GALAXY $3.50 (B3513)

Let True Love Be Among Us
2pt jr cor FISCHER,C CM 6534 $.30 (B3514)

Praise
SATB oct GALAXY 1.2165.1 $.30 (B3515)

BERKELEY, LENNOX (1903-)
Batter My Heart, Three Person'd God *cant
[Eng] SATB,S solo,org,ob,horn,vcl,bvl sc CHESTER s.p. (B3516)

Christ Is The World's Redeemer *hymn
SATB oct NOVELLO 44.1411.10 s.p. (B3517)

Domini Est Terra *Psalm
[Lat] SATB,orch voc sc CHESTER s.p. (B3518)

Festival Anthem, A *Fest,anthem
[Eng] SATB,ST soli,org sc CHESTER s.p. (B3519)

Jonah *Bibl/ora
[Eng] SATB,TB soli,orch voc sc CHESTER s.p. (B3520)

Justorum Animae *mot
[Lat] SATB CHESTER s.p. (B3521)

BERKELEY, LENNOX (cont'd.)

Look Up, Sweet Babe *Xmas,anthem
[Eng] SATB,S solo,org CHESTER s.p.   (B3522)

Lord, When The Sense Of Thy Sweet Grace
*anthem
[Eng] SATB,org CHESTER s.p.   (B3523)

Magnificat *Magnif
[Eng] SATB,org,orch voc sc CHESTER s.p.   (B3524)

Mass For Five Voices *Mass
[Lat] SSATB CHESTER s.p.   (B3525)

Missa Brevis *Mass
[Lat] SATB,org CHESTER s.p.   (B3526)

Missa Brevis *Mass
[Eng] SATB,org (Anglican usage version)
CHESTER s.p.   (B3527)

Salve Regina *anti
[Lat] unis,org CHESTER s.p.   (B3528)

Sweet Was The Song The Virgin Sang *Xmas,
carol
[Eng] SATB,org CHESTER s.p.   (B3529)

Thou Hast Made Me *anthem
[Eng] SATB,org CHESTER s.p.   (B3530)

BERKOWITZ, S.
Without Words *cant
mix cor,acap CHAPPELL 0017384-368 $1.00
  (B3531)

BERLIN see Billings, William

BERLIN REQUIEM see Weill, Kurt

BERLINSKI, (HERMAN (1910-   )
Avodat Shabbat *liturg,Jew
SATB PRESSER $4.50   (B3532)

Entreat Me Not
SATB oct PRESSER MC380 $.30   (B3533)

BERLINSKI, HERMAN (1910-   )
Forget Thy Affliction
SATB TRANSCON. TCL 604 $.50   (B3534)

BERLINSKI, [HERMAN] (1910-   )
I Sought Him
SSA,pno/harp oct PRESSER MC146 $.30 (B3535)

It Hath Been Told Thee, O Man
SATB oct PRESSER MC550 $.30   (B3536)

Lecho Dodi
SATB,cantor oct PRESSER MC195 $.45 (B3537)

May The Words *liturg,Heb
SATB oct PRESSER MC228 $.30   (B3538)

BERLINSKI, HERMAN (1910-   )
Psalm 30
cor,A solo,org,2trp, shofar TRANSCON.
TCL 618 $.75   (B3539)

BERLINSKI, [HERMAN] (1910-   )
Shofar Service *liturg,Jew
SATB oct PRESSER 451-00390 $2.00
SATB,T/Bar solo,org,trp PRESSER $2.00
  (B3540)
  (B3541)

Sing Joyfully
SATB oct PRESSER 312-40853 $.30   (B3542)

Three Liturgical Amens *CC3U,liturg,Heb
SATB,acap oct PRESSER MC511 $.35   (B3543)

BERLIOZ, HECTOR (1803-1869)
Born Among Us, In The Manger *Xmas
(Cramer) SATB MARKS 4288 $.25   (B3544)

Childhood Of Christ *Eng/Fr/Ger
cor voc sc KALMUS 6091 $3.50   (B3545)

Childhood Of Christ, The
cor min sc KALMUS 505 $3.50   (B3546)

Childhood Of Christ, The *see L'9enfance Du
Christ

Childhood Of Christ, The *see L'enfance Du
Christ

Dearest Saviour, Watch Thou O'er Us
SATB/SA WEINBERGER s.p.   (B3547)
(Gordon) SATB oct SHAPIRO SK 2009 $.25
  (B3548)
(Gordon) 2pt oct SHAPIRO SK 4003 $.25
  (B3549)
(Gordon) SSA oct SHAPIRO SK 3014 $.25
  (B3550)
(Gordon) SAB oct SHAPIRO SK 5003 $.25
  (B3551)

Der Traum Des Herodes
see Des Heilands Kindheit

Des Heilands Kindheit *Bibl
[Eng/Fr/Ger] mix cor,STTBarBBB soli,orch
voc sc BREITKOPF-W EB-1920 s.p., ipr, sc
BREITKOPF-W rental
contains: Der Traum Des Herodes; Die
Ankunft In Sais; Die Flucht Nach
Agypten   (B3552)

Des Heilands Kindheit *Op.25
mix cor,STTBarBBB soli,org,2fl,2ob,2clar,
2bsn,2trp,2horn,3trom,strings,timp, 2
cornets sc BREITKOPF-L rental   (B3553)

Die Ankunft In Sais
see Des Heilands Kindheit

Die Flucht Nach Agypten
see Des Heilands Kindheit

Farewell Of The Shepherds
SATB KJOS 22 $.30   (B3554)

Glory And Triumph
SATB oct PRESSER 352-00049 $.35   (B3555)

Grosse Totenmesse *Op.5
SATTBB,T solo,2fl,2ob,2clar,2bsn,4horn,
4trp,4trom,2tuba,strings,perc,timp,
English horn BREITKOPF-W rental, voc
pt BREITKOPF-W CHB-1375 s.p., ipr, voc sc

BERLIOZ, HECTOR (cont'd.)

BREITKOPF-W EB-1791 s.p.   (B3556)

L'9enfance Du Christ *Op.25
cor,orch sc KALMUS $20.00, ipa   (B3557)
"Childhood Of Christ, The" [Eng] mix cor,
soli,pno voc sc SCHIRM.G $2.50   (B3558)
"Childhood Of Christ, The" cor sc KALMUS
$20.00   (B3559)

L'Adieu Des Bergers (from L'Enfance Du
Christ)
mix cor sc ALSBACH&D s.p.   (B3560)

L'Enfance Du Christ *Op.25
[Fr/Ger/Eng] SATB,orch cmplt ed BROUDE BR.
$17.50   (B3561)
"Childhood Of Christ, The" SATB,STBarB
soli,org,3fl,3ob,2clar,2bsn,2horn,2trp,
3trom,strings,timp,harp voc sc NOVELLO
s.p., ipr   (B3562)

O Mon Ame (from L'enfance Du Christ)
(Brun, L'abbe F.) [Fr] 4pt mix cor,T solo,
pno,org oct DURAND s.p.   (B3563)

Oh, My Spirit (from L'Enfance Du Christ)
[Fr/Eng] SATB,T solo BROUDE,A. 150 $.35 (B3564)

Quartet And Chorus Of Magi
see Berlioz, Hector, Resurrexit

Requiem *Op.5, Mass/Req
[Lat] mix cor,orch voc sc SCHIRM.G $1.50
  (B3565)
[Lat] SATB,orch cmplt ed BROUDE BR.
$15.00   (B3566)
mix cor,2fl,3ob,2clar,2bsn,4trp,4horn,
4trom,2tuba,strings,perc,timp, 4cornets
sc BREITKOPF-L rental   (B3567)
[Ger] cor voc sc KALMUS 6092 $1.50   (B3568)
cor min sc KALMUS 503 $3.50   (B3569)
cor,orch sc KALMUS $12.00, ipa   (B3570)

Resurrexit *Easter
mix cor,SATB soli,2fl,2ob,2clar,2bsn,4trp,
4horn,3trom,2trom,strings,timp sc
BREITKOPF-L PB-1677 s.p.   (B3571)
cor min sc KALMUS 1225 $1.30 contains also:
Quartet And Chorus Of Magi   (B3572)

Shepherd's Farewell
(Jacques) SSA (med) OXFORD 44.207 $.25, ipr
  (B3573)

Shepherd's Farewell, The *Xmas
(Hastings) SSA ALFRED 6224 $.30   (B3574)
(Hastings) SATB ALFRED 6426 $.30   (B3575)

Shepherd's Farewell, The *Xmas
(Hansen) SAB SCHMITT 5537 $.35   (B3576)

Shepherds' Farewell To The Holy Family, The
(from Childhood Of Christ)
SATB,pno SCHIRM.EC 1617 $.35, ipr   (B3577)
(Glaser, V.) SSA,pno SCHIRM.EC 2544 $.25,
ipr   (B3578)
(Ringwald) SATB SHAWNEE A 946 $.25   (B3579)

Te Deum *Op.22, Magnif/Te Deum
[Lat] 3 cor,T solo,pno voc sc SCHIRM.G
$2.00   (B3580)
3 cor,T solo,org,4fl,4ob,4clar,4bsn,2trp,
4horn,6trom,2tuba,strings,perc,timp,harp,
2 cornets sc BREITKOPF-L rental, ipr
  (B3581)
cor voc sc KALMUS 6093 $2.00   (B3582)
cor min sc KALMUS 504 $3.50   (B3583)
cor sc KALMUS $20.00   (B3584)
cor,orch sc KALMUS $20.00, ipa   (B3585)
STB&STB&SA,org,3fl,2ob,2clar,4horn,3trp,
3trom,2tuba,strings,perc,timp,harp,
saxophone sc BREITKOPF-W s.p., ipr, voc
pt BREITKOPF-W CHB-1427 s.p., voc sc
BREITKOPF-W EB-1866 s.p.   (B3586)

Thou Must Leave Thy Lowly Dwelling (from
L'enfance Du Christ) Xmas,anthem
mix cor SOUTHERN $.35   (B3587)
SATB oct SUMMY M 2314 $.25   (B3588)
SATB oct GRAY GCMR 1898 $.25   (B3589)
SATB oct NOVELLO 40.0723.09 s.p.   (B3590)
2pt oct NOVELLO 48.1713.03 s.p.   (B3591)
mix cor,orch oct NOVELLO 40.0723.09 s.p.,
ipr   (B3592)
(Carlton) SSA oct BOOSEY 5409 $.30   (B3593)
(Carlton) SATB oct BOOSEY 5133 $.30   (B3594)
(Ramsey, Basil) SSA oct NOVELLO 51.0639.07
s.p.   (B3595)

Veni Creator *mot
3pt wom cor/3pt jr cor,SSA soli cor pts
BREITKOPF-W   (B3596)

Veni, Creator Spiritus
[Lat] SSA,acap MARKS 13 $.35.   (B3597)

BERMAN, JUDITH M.
Sacred Service, A *Sab-Eve
SATB,solo oct TRANSCON. TCL 347 $2.50
  (B3598)

BERMUDA ANTHEM, THE see Tankard, Geoffrey

BERNABEI, (GIUSEPPE) ERCOLE (ca. 1620-1687)
Alma Redemptoris Mater
(Payson, A.) "Blessed Mother Of The Savior"
SATB,acap FRANK F-569 $.30   (B3599)

Blessed Mother Of The Savior *see Alma
Redemptoris Mater

O Sacred And Holy Feast *see O Sacrum
Convivium

O Sacrum Convivium *Easter/Lent
(Martens, Mason) "O Sacred And Holy Feast"
SATB oct WALTON 6019 $.35   (B3600)

BERNABEI, GIUSEPPE ANTONIO (1649-1732)
Ad Regias Agni Dapes *Mass
(Bauerle, Hermann) SATB,acap cor pts
BREITKOPF-L PB-3444 s.p., voc pt
BREITKOPF-L CHB-2825 s.p.   (B3601)

Missa In D *Mass
(Bauerle, Hermann) SATB,acap cor pts
BREITKOPF-L PB-3131 s.p., voc pt
BREITKOPF-L CHB-2541 s.p.   (B3602)

BERNABEI, GIUSEPPE ANTONIO (cont'd.)

Missa In G *Mass
SATB,acap voc sc KALMUS 6097 $1.00   (B3603)
(Bauerle, Hermann) SATB,acap cor pts
BREITKOPF-L PB-3132 s.p., voc pt
BREITKOPF-L CHB-2542 s.p.   (B3604)

O Blessed Sacrament *see O Sacrum Convivium

O Sacrum Convivium *Fest,mot
[Lat] SATB,acap (med) MULLER M 25 s.p.
  (B3605)
"O Blessed Sacrament" [Lat] mix cor,acap
oct NOVELLO DM-25 s.p.   (B3606)

Veni Creator Spiritus *Mass
(Bauerle, Hermann) SATB,acap cor pts
BREITKOPF-L PB-3133 s.p., voc pt
BREITKOPF-L CHB-2543 s.p.   (B3607)

BERNAL JIMENEZ, MIGUEL
Te Deum Jubilar
[Lat] STB,org sc PEER $1.35   (B3608)

BERNARD
Jesus Is His Name
SATB,acap (med easy) OXFORD 84.162 $.25
  (B3609)

BERNARD, JAMES
Magnificat And Nunc Dimittis *Magnif/Nunc
SATB oct NOVELLO 44.1456.10 s.p.   (B3610)

BERNARD, WILLIAM
Ave Maria
unis,pno (diff) oct WILLIS 6766 $.18
  (B3611)

BERNARDI, STEFFANO (ca. 1576-1636)
Dixit Dominus
cor FABER F0061 s.p.   (B3612)

Dixit Dominus Domino Meo *mot,It
(Roche) "Thus Said The Lord" [Eng/Lat] 4pt
mix cor,S solo,kbd oct FABER 11731 s.p.
  (B3613)
(Roche, Jerome) [Lat] SATB,S solo oct FABER
11731 $.35   (B3614)

Laudate Dominium *Bibl
(Rosenthal) "Praise Ye The Lord" [Eng/Lat]
SSATB,acap oct SCHIRM.G 9234 $.30 (B3615)

Praise Ye The Lord *see Laudate Dominium

Thus Said The Lord *see Dixit Dominus Domino
Meo

BERNASCONI, LUIGI
Dixit
[Lat] 2pt mix cor,org ZANIBON 2700 s.p.
  (B3616)
Domine
[Lat] 3pt mix cor,org ZANIBON 2699 s.p. (B3617)

Tantum Ergo
see QUATTRO MOTTETTI EUCARISTICI

BERNE see Hall

BERNHARD
Missa Brevis
see Thiele, Missa Brevis

BERNHARD, CHRISTOPH (1627-1692)
Eine Kurzmesse *Mass/mot
(Drechsler) [Ger/Lat] 5pt mix cor MOSELER
s.p. contains also: Eine Motette   (B3618)

Eine Motette
see Bernhard, Christoph, Eine Kurzmesse

Zwei Kurzmessen *see Thiele, Siegfried

BERNSTEIN, LEONARD (1918-   )
Almighty Father (from Mass) chorale
SATB,acap (med diff/diff) SOUTHERN $.25
  (B3619)
4pt mix cor,acap oct SCHIRM.G 11948 $.25
  (B3620)

Chichester Psalms *Psalm,Heb
4pt mix cor,A/T solo,orch voc sc SCHIRM.G
$1.50   (B3621)
cor,high solo,org,perc,harp, or boy solo sc
SCHIRM.G $15.00   (B3622)

Haskivenu
[Heb] SATB,cantor&T solo,org WARNER W3250
$.40   (B3623)

Kaddish (from Symphony No. 3)
[Eng/Heb] mix cor&boy cor,S,narrator voc sc
SCHIRM.G $4.00   (B3624)

BERGGREN
One There Is Above All Others
(Lynn) SATB oct SOUTHERN $.25   (B3625)

BERRIDGE, A.
Thou Crownest The Year
oct HART   (B3626)

BERRIMAN, C.
Boy Was Born, A
see BOY WAS BORN, A

BERTHIER, P.
Orate Fratres *Mass
[Lat] 4pt mix cor,pno/org oct DURAND s.p.
  (B3627)

BERTILORENZI
Immacolata Concezione *Mass
SA/TB,org FORLIVESI 14000 s.p.   (B3628)

BERTLESEN, ARNE
Psalm 3
SSATBB oct WALTON 2905 $.35   (B3629)

BESANCON
Shepherds! Shake Off Your Drowsy Sleep *Xmas
(Hruby) 2pt oct PLYMOUTH JR-506 $.30
  (B3630)

Up And Wake Thee, Peter Lad *Xmas
(Caldwell, Mary E.) unis oct GRAY GCMR 2897
$.25   (B3631)
(Caldwell, Mary E.) SAB oct GRAY GCMR 2536
$.30   (B3632)

BESCH
  Rise Up, Shepherd An' Foller *Xmas
    SATB oct PLYMOUTH XM-117 $.25   (B3633)

BESCH, OTTO
  Marienlied (from Maria Durch Ein Dornwald
    Ging) Adv,cant
    [Ger] jr cor,S solo,pno BOTE cor pts s.p.,
    voc sc s.p.   (B3634)

BESCHER UNS, HERR, DAS TAGLICH BROT see
  Micheelsen, Hans Friedrich

BESIDE STILL WATERS see Hamblen

BESIDE STILL WATERS see Hamblen, [Bernard]

BESIDE THE FLOOD OF BABYLON see Bach, Johann
  Sebastian

BESIDE THE SEPULCHRE see Sateren, Leland
  Bernhard

BESIDE THE STILL WATERS see Shields

BESIDE THY CRADLE see Bach, Johann Sebastian,
  Ich Steh An Deiner Krippen Hier

BESIDE THY CRADLE see Soule

BESIDE THY CRADLE HERE I STAND see Bach

BESIDE THY CRADLE HERE I STAND see Bach, Johann
  Sebastian, Ich Steh' An Deiner Krippen Hier

BESIDE THY MANGER HERE I STAND see Bach, Johann
  Sebastian

BESIG
  Children's Prayer *prayer
    unis/2pt oct PRO ART 2727 $.30   (B3635)

  Fanfare And Invocation
    SATB oct PRO ART 2414 $.30   (B3636)

  Lonely Shepherd Boy, The *Xmas
    SATB oct PRO ART 2607 $.35   (B3637)

  Sleep, Little Tiny King *Xmas,cradle
    SATB (calypso style) oct PRO ART 2368 $.35
                                      (B3638)
    SAB (calypso style) oct PRO ART 2593 $.35
                                      (B3639)
    SSA (calypso style) oct PRO ART 2405 $.35
                                      (B3640)
    2pt (calypso style) oct PRO ART 2098 $.30
                                      (B3641)
    boy cor SOUTHERN $.30   (B3642)

  Time For Joy, A *Xmas
    SATB oct PRO ART 2728 $.30   (B3643)

BESINNER DOCK see Roman, Johan Helmich

BESLY, MAURICE (1888-1945)
  Angels Are Stooping, The
    2pt ENOCH T.P.226 s.p.   (B3644)

  Shepherds Had An Angel, The
    4pt mix cor,S solo,vla, or English horn oct
    CURWEN 8475 $.35   (B3645)

BESOZZI, L.D.
  Messe *Mass
    [Fr] unis,pno/org oct DURAND s.p. (B3646)

BEST
  Jennifer
    (Burroughs) SATB oct AGAPE BR 2002 $.30
                                      (B3647)

BEST-LOVED HYMNS *CCU
    mix cor SCHMITT 9060 $1.00   (B3648)

BESTANDIGKEIT see Bella, R.

BESTOR, C.
  Lord Unto Thee
    SATB oct ELKAN-V 362-1118 $.25   (B3649)

  Unto Thee Do I Lift Up My Soul
    SATB oct ELKAN-V 362-1192 $.25   (B3650)

BETE A BON DIEU FAIS MOI-T-UN BEAU DIMANCHE see
  Wissmer

BETH-LEHEM (HAUS DES BROTES) see Lauth,
  Wolfgang

BETHANY CAROL, A see Edmunds, Doris

BETHLEHEM see Billings, William

BETHLEHEM see Bliss, Paul

BETHLEHEM see Boughton, Rutland

BETHLEHEM see Dans Cett' Etable

BETHLEHEM see Dasher, James

BETHLEHEM see Goldsworthy, William Arthur

BETHLEHEM see Gounod, Charles Francois

BETHLEHEM see Maunder, J.H.

BETHLEHEM see Parke

BETHLEHEM see Parke, Dorothy

BETHLEHEM see Webber

BETHLEHEM CAROL see Brandt

BETHLEHEM DOWN see Heseltine, Philip

BETHLEHEM INNKEEPER'S REGRET, THE see Grime,
  William

BETHLEHEM LIES SLEEPING see Bennett, F. Roy

BETHLEHEM NIGHT see Warrell

BETHLEHEM ROAD see Byles, B. D.

BETHLEHEM STAR see Wilhelm

BETHLEHEM STAR, THE see Kenney

BETHLEHEM STAR, THE see Wilhelm

BETHLEHEM'S BABE see Ratcliffe, Desmond

BETHLEHEMS KINDEREN see Lukkien, H.G.

BETHLEHEMS STJARNA
  see Frojda Dig O Kristenhet

BETHLEHEMS STJARNA see Carlsson, Werther

BETHL'EM LAY A-SLEEPING *Xmas,carol,Pol
    (Pelz, W.L.) SATB,kbd (med easy) oct
    CONCORDIA 98-1530 $.25   (B3651)
    (Willan, H.) SA&desc (easy) oct CONCORDIA
    98-1410 $.25   (B3652)

BETLEHEMS STJARNA see Tegner, Alice

BETRUBTES HERZ see Wildgans, Friedrich

BETTAGSLIED see Decker, W.

BETTAGSLIED see Schelling, J.

BETULIA LIBERATA see Mozart, Wolfgang Amadeus

BETULIA LIBERATA see Mozart, Wolfgang Amadeus,
  Betulia Liberata

BETWEEN THE OXEN AND THE SHEEP see Coates

BEUERLE, HERBERT
  Da Christus Geboren War *Xmas
    [Ger] SATB,acap (med) BAREN. BA 1028+1029
    s.p.   (B3653)

  Den Die Hirten Lobeten Sehre *Xmas
    [Ger] SATB,acap (easy) BAREN. BA 1027 s.p.
                                      (B3654)

  Es Kommt Ein Schiff, Geladen *Adv
    [Ger] 4pt men cor,acap (med easy) NAGELS
    NCH 4 s.p.   (B3655)

  Ihr Hirten *anthem
    "O Shepherds" SATB (easy) oct AUGSBURG 1548
    $.18   (B3656)
    "O Shepherds" SSA, inst (easy) oct AUGSBURG
    0303 $.18   (B3657)

  O Heiland Reiss Die Himmel Auf *Adv
    [Ger] 4pt men cor,acap (med) NAGELS NCH 12
    s.p.   (B3658)

  O Shepherds *see Ihr Hirten

BEULAH LAND *spir
    (Roberts) SATB,acap,opt perc oct LAWSON 51691
    $.35   (B3659)

BEVAN, RICHARD T.
  Eternal Ruler
    SATB oct LESLIE 4091   (B3660)

  I Will Lift Up Mine Eyes *anthem
    unis oct LESLIE 1094   (B3661)

  Souls Of The Righteous, The
    SATB oct LESLIE 4081   (B3662)

  Thee We Adore
    SATB oct LESLIE 4065   (B3663)

BEVANS, WILLIAM
  Psalm 24
    SATB (med) ABINGDON APM-677 $.50 (B3664)

BEVENOT, LAURENCE
  Fifteen Psalms To Honour The Holy Eucharist
    *CC15L,liturg/Psalm
    [Eng] cong,org CHESTER sc s.p., voc sc s.p.
                                      (B3665)

  First Mass In English *Credo/Mass
    unis,acap/org oct ST.MARTIN SMP665 s.p.,
    ipa   (B3666)

  Second English Mass *Credo/Mass
    cor&cong, org oct ST.MARTIN SMP676 s.p., ipa
                                      (B3667)

  Two-Part Mass In English *Mass
    2pt,org oct ST.MARTIN SMP684 s.p., ipa
                                      (B3668)

BEVERIDGE, THOMAS G. (1938-   )
  Ave Verum Corpus
    "Hail To Thee" SSA,acap SCHIRM.EC 2559 $.35
                                      (B3669)

  Creation's Song *Eve
    cor,org/pno FOSTER MF138 $.45   (B3670)

  Drop, Drop, Slow Tears
    TTBB,pno SCHIRM.EC 2174 $.30   (B3671)

  Hail To Thee *see Ave Verum Corpus

  I Lift Up Mine Eyes (Psalm 121)
    SATB,acap SCHIRM.EC 2646 $.35   (B3672)

  Light Looked Down
    SATB oct AGAPE SP 710 $.30   (B3673)

  Once: In Memoriam Martin Luther King, Jr.
    SATB FLAMMER A1089 $2.00   (B3674)

  Psalm 121 *see I Lift Up Mine Eyes

  Sing, Christmas Bell *Xmas
    SATB,acap SHAWNEE A 1171 $.30   (B3675)

  Songs Of Praise *CC13U
    SSA/TTB/4 eq voices/unis SCHIRM.EC 2560
    $.75   (B3676)

  St. Francis' Prayer *prayer
    unis,pno/org FOSTER MF 702 $.25   (B3677)

BEVERSDORF, THOMAS (1924-   )
  Mini-Motet From Micah
    SATB oct SOUTHERN $.50   (B3678)

BEVERST
  Gloria In Excelsis Deo *Xmas,Gloria
    SATB oct SACRED S-86 $.35   (B3679)

  One Hundredth Psalm, The (Psalm 100)
    SATB oct SACRED S-123 $.40   (B3680)
    SATB (med diff/diff) SOUTHERN $.35 (B3681)

BEVERST (cont'd.)

  Psalm 100 *see One Hundredth Psalm, The

BEVIN, ELWAY
  Lord, Who Shall Dwell In Thy Tabernacle?
    *Gen
    SAB (med easy) oct OXFORD 43.360 $.25
                                      (B3682)

BEWAHR MICH, HERR, UND SEI NICHT FERN see
  Schede, Paul

BEWAHRE MICH, GOTT, DENN ICH TRAU see Peter,
  Herbert

BEWARE OF FALSE PROPHETS see Telemann, Georg
  Philipp

BEYER, FRANK MICHAEL (1928-   )
  Gloria *Gloria
    [Lat] mix cor (med) oct SIRIUS 1 s.p.
                                      (B3683)

  Lavatio *Psntd,Bibl/mot
    [Ger] SAATB,acap (diff) BAREN. BA 5415
    $3.50   (B3684)

  Manifestatio Christi *Easter/Pent,Bibl/mot
    [Lat] SAATB,acap (diff) BAREN. BA 5415
    $3.50   (B3685)

BEYER, JOHANN SAMUEL (1669-1744)
  Furchtet Euch Nicht *Xmas
    (Fricke, Richard) [Ger] SATB&treb cor,cont,
    3vln,vcl (med) BAREN. NMA 54 sc $2.50,
    cor pts $.40, ipa   (B3686)

BEYOND THE CROSS see Moffatt

BEYOND THE SUNSET
    SSA/SATB BIG3 $.25   (B3687)

BEYOND THE SUNSET see Brock, Blanche [Kerr]

BEYOND THE WHEELING WORLDS OF LIGHT see
  Buettell

BEZZI, ENRICO
  Pange Lingua *Commun
    [Lat] 2pt,org ZANIBON 148 s.p. contains
    also: Tantum Ergo   (B3688)

  Tantum Ergo
    see Bezzi, Enrico, Pange Lingua

BIALAS, GUNTHER (1907-   )
  Da Pacem *Gen,mot
    [Ger] SATB&SATB&cong,SSS soli,org (med
    diff) BAREN. BA 4457 sc $8.25, cor pts
    $2.50   (B3689)

  Ecce, Dominus Veniet *Xmas
    mix cor TONGER s.p.   (B3690)

  Im Anfang. Die Schopfungsgeschichte *Gen
    SSATBB,SSS soli,acap (diff) sc BAREN.
    BA 4349 $16.50   (B3691)
    [Ger] SSATBB,SSS soli,org (diff) cor pts
    BAREN. BA 4349 s.p.   (B3692)
    [Ger] SSATBB,SSS soli,orch (diff) sc BAREN.
    BA 3976 rental   (B3693)

  Symbolum
    [Ger] TTBB,5winds (med diff) BAREN. BA 3930
    sc s.p., cor pts s.p.   (B3694)

BIALIK see Low, Leo

BIANCHI, FRANCESCO (1752-1810)
  Cantico Delle Creature
    5pt mix cor FORLIVESI 14011 s.p. (B3695)

BIANCHINI, CARLO
  Adoremus Te Christe
    see Tre Mottetti Pel Venerdi Santo

  In Jucunda Captivitate *Mass
    3pt mix cor,org sc RICORDI-ENG 127567 s.p.,
    voc pt RICORDI-ENG 12768-70   (B3696)

  O Crux Benedicta
    see Tre Mottetti Pel Venerdi Santo

  Popule Meus
    see Tre Mottetti Pel Venerdi Santo

  Tre Mottetti Pel Venerdi Santo *Gd.Fri.,mot
    [Lat] 2 eq voices ZANIBON 2949 s.p.
    contains: Adoremus Te Christe; O Crux
    Benedicta; Popule Meus   (B3697)

BIBER, C.H.
  Darkness Was All Over *see Tenebrae Factae
    Sunt

  Tenebrae Factae Sunt
    (Pauly) "Darkness Was All Over" [Lat/Eng]
    SATB,acap oct SCHIRM.G 11934 $.30 (B3698)

BIBLE SONGS FOR YOUNG VOICES see Smith, Gregg

BIBLE STORIES AND SONGS see Fuller, [Esther
  Mary]

BIBLE STORIES IN SONG (BK. 1) see Cassell

BIBLE STORIES IN SONG (BK. 2) see Cassell

BIBLE TELLS ME SO, THE
    SATB HANSEN-US F9012 $.40   (B3699)

BIBLISCHE MOTETTEN FUR DAS KIRCHENJAHR, BAND 1:
  ERSTER ADVENT BIS LETZTER SONNTAG NACH
  EPIPHANIAS *CCU,Adv,mot
    (Ameln, Konrad; Kummerling, Harald) [Ger] mix
    cor,acap (med) cloth BAREN. BA 5473 s.p.
                                      (B3700)

BIBLISCHE SPRUCHE see Telemann, Georg Philipp

BICINIEN, HEFT 1: 34 CHORALE see Pepping, Ernst

BICINIEN, HEFT 2: 12 PSALMEN see Pepping, Ernst

BICINIEN, HEFT 3: 9 EVANGELIEN UND EPISTELN see
  Pepping, Ernst

BIDE WITH US see Bach, Johann Sebastian, Bleib'
  Bei Uns

BIDE WITH US see Bach, Johann Sebastian, Bleib' Bei Uns, Denn Es Will Abend Werden

BIDE WITH US, LORD see Praetorius, Michael

BIEBL, FRANZ (1906-)
Bergbauernweihnacht *Xmas,cant
mix cor,gtr,2S rec MOSELER s.p. (B3701)

Drei Segenspruche
mix cor,acap TONGER s.p.
contains: Wenn Gott Das Haus; Wo Glaube, Da Liebe; Wo Gott Zum Haus (B3702)

Freu Dich, O Christenheit
4pt mix cor,narrator,solo,orch DOBLINGER sc s.p., voc sc s.p., cor pts s.p., ipa (B3703)

Gottes Welt Ist Ein Zelt
4pt mix cor MOSELER LB-362 s.p. (B3704)

Jubilate *Xmas
men cor/mix cor TONGER s.p. (B3705)

Schlaf Wohl, Du Himmelsknabe Du *Xmas
men cor TONGER s.p. (B3706)

Wenn Gott Das Haus
see Drei Segenspruche

Wir Danken, Herr
(Baum) mix cor,acap TONGER s.p. (B3707)

Wo Glaube, Da Liebe
see Drei Segenspruche

Wo Gott Zum Haus
see Drei Segenspruche

BIECHTELER, M.S.
Ad Cantus, Ad Choros
(Rosenthal) "To Singing And Dancing" [Eng/Lat] 5pt mix cor,S solo,org/pno oct SCHIRM.G 10391 $.20 (B3708)

To Singing And Dancing *see Ad Cantus, Ad Choros

BIECHTELER, SIGISMUND (ca. 1700-1740)
Christians, Come With Praises *see Victimae Paschali Laudes

Victimae Paschali Laudes *Easter
"Christians, Come With Praises" SATB&SATB, kbd (med easy) oct CONCORDIA 97-5016 $.60 (B3709)
(Pauly, R.) "Christians, Come With Praises" SATB&SATB/SATB&opt cong,opt org&brass CONCORDIA 97-5016 $.60, ipa (B3710)

BIELAWA, HERBERT
Cradle, The *Xmas
4pt boy cor/SSAA,acap oct LAWSON 51364 $.30 (B3711)
Jesus Christ, Our Blessed Saviour *Commun, anthem
SATB,org oct LAWSON 51423 $.30 (B3712)

Sweet Was The Song *Xmas
SATB,acap FOSTER MF507 $.30 (B3713)

BIERLY, A.
Hold Thou My Hand
TTBB,pno (easy) oct WILLIS 6317 $.10 (B3714)

BIESKE, WERNER (1913-)
Vater Unser Im Himmelreich *Easter/Pent,cant
[Ger] SATB,2trp,2trom (med easy) sc BAREN. BA 3595 s.p. (B3715)

BIGGEST LITTLE SONG BOOK, THE *sac/sec,CCU
(Christofer, John) MCAFEE $1.50 (B3716)

BIGGS, JOHN
Christmas Canticle, A *Xmas
SATB oct WALTON 2183-5 $.40 (B3717)

Dirge For The Savior (from Christmas Canticle, A) Xmas
SATB oct WALTON 2183 $.40 (B3718)

Hymn Of Thanksgiving *Thanks,hymn
SATB FOSTER MF115 $.25 (B3719)

Meditabor *Gen/Lent
[Lat] 8pt mix cor,acap oct SCHIRM.G 11159 $.35 (B3720)

Nova, Nova (from Christmas Canticle, A) Xmas
SATB oct WALTON 2184 $.40 (B3721)

Silent Night *Xmas
SATB oct WALTON 2176 $.30 (B3722)

Song To Sing, A (from Christmas Canticle, A) Xmas
SATB oct WALTON 2185 $.40 (B3723)

BIJL, THEO VAN DER (1886-)
Christus Heeft Overwonnen
mix cor sc ALSBACH&D s.p. (B3724)

Jesu Dulcis Memoria
3pt men cor ALSBACH&D sc s.p., cor pts s.p. (B3725)
wom cor ALSBACH&D sc s.p., cor pts s.p. (B3726)

BIJVANCK, HENK (1909-)
Missa In Es Kl. Terts *Mass
[Dut] wom cor,org DONEMUS sc s.p., cor pts s.p. (B3727)

Psalm 21
[Dut] mix cor,T solo,org sc DONEMUS s.p. (B3728)

BILLINGS, WILLIAM (1746-1800)
Angel's Carol, The *Xmas
(Daniel, Oliver) SATBB PETERS 66332 $.60 (B3729)

Anthem For Thanksgiving, An
(Sinzheimer, M.) SATB oct PRESSER MC461 $.35 (B3730)

Anthem For Thanksgiving Day *Thanks
(McAfee) SATB oct BOURNE 839 $.60 (B3731)

As Shepherds Were Guarding Their Sheep *Xmas
(Ehret) SATB ALFRED 6313 $.30 (B3732)

BILLINGS, WILLIAM (cont'd.)

Be Glad Then America
SATB oct PRESSER 352-00101 $.40 (B3733)

Berlin
(Moore) 4pt mix cor,acap oct SCHIRM.G 11678 $.25 (B3734)

Bethlehem *Xmas
see Two Christmas Anthems
(Daniel, Oliver) SAATB PETERS 66333 $.50 (B3735)

Bird, The
(Daniel, Oliver) SATBB,pno PETERS 66335 $.50 (B3736)

Boston
see Two Christmas Anthems

Crucifixion
see Two Easter Anthems

David's Lamentation *Bibl,18th cent
4pt mix cor,acap oct SCHIRM.G 11270 $.25 (B3737)
SATB,acap oct FISCHER,C CM-6572 $.25 (B3738)
SATB oct WALTON 2203 $.30 (B3739)
(Daniel, Oliver) SATBB PETERS 66336 $.50 (B3740)
(Kjelson) SATB oct BELWIN 2264 $.35 (B3741)
(Siegmeister) mix cor SOUTHERN $.25 (B3742)
(Trusler) TTBB oct PLYMOUTH TR-309 $.25 (B3743)
(Warner) SATB oct PLYMOUTH SC-3 $.25 (B3744)
(Wilson) mix cor SOUTHERN $.25 (B3745)

David's Lamentation And Assurance
SATB,acap oct LAWSON 51372 $.30 (B3746)

Easter Anthem *Easter,anthem
(Johnson) SATB FLAMMER A 5386 $.35 (B3747)
(Johnson) SATB oct SOUTHERN $.30 (B3748)
(Shaw) 4pt mix cor,acap oct SCHIRM.G 9949 $.40 (B3749)

From All That Dwell Below The Skies
(McAfee) SATB oct BOURNE 844 $.25 (B3750)

I Am The Rose Of Sharon *anthem
SATB oct WALTON 2201 $.35 (B3751)
(Daniel) 4pt mix cor,acap oct SCHIRM.G 10054 $.40 (B3752)

I Heard A Great Voice
(Daniel, Oliver) SAATBB PETERS 66338 $.50 (B3753)

John's Gone To Hilo
see Billings, William, When Jesus Wept

Kittery
(Lowens) 4pt mix cor,acap oct SCHIRM.G 10309 $.30 (B3754)

Lift Up Your Eyes
(Wienandt) SATB,4brass oct SOUTHERN $.30, ipa (B3755)

Lord Into His Garden Comes, The *hymn
(Russell) SATB oct PRO ART 2750 $.30 (B3756)

Lord Is Risen, The *Easter/Lent
SATB oct WALTON 2206 $.35 (B3757)
(McAfee) SATB oct BOURNE 849 $.40 (B3758)

Lord Is Ris'n Indeed, The *Easter/Lent, anthem
(Daniel, Oliver) SATB,acap PETERS 66496 (B3759)
(Marshall, Charles) SATB FRANK F-581 $.30 (B3760)

Majesty
SATB oct WALTON 2221 $.30 (B3761)

Mariner's Anthem, The
(Moore) 4pt mix cor,acap oct SCHIRM.G 11677 $.35 (B3762)

Morpheus And Paris
SATB,acap MARKS 63 $.30 (B3763)

My Redeemer
mix cor SOUTHERN $.18 (B3764)
(Sanders) SATB oct GALAXY 1.2112.1 $.25 (B3765)

Peace Be On Earth
(Daniel) SATB/4pt men cor/4pt mix cor PETERS 66341 $.90 (B3766)
(Daniel, Oliver) SATB/men cor/4pt mix cor PETERS 66341 $.90 (B3767)

Psalm 23
(Rossi) SSA/SSAA oct MCA (B3768)

Resurrection
see Two Easter Anthems

Shepherd's Carol *Xmas
(Copes) SSA oct GRAY GCMR 3024 $.24 (B3769)
(Copes) SAB oct GRAY GCMR 2667 $.25 (B3770)
(Copes) SATB oct GRAY GCMR 2760 $.30 (B3771)

Shepherd's Carol, The *Xmas,carol
SATB oct SUMMY B 366 $.25 (B3772)
SATB oct WALTON 2209 $.35 (B3773)
(Cramer) SATB,acap MARKS 4296 $.25 (B3774)
(Kaplan) SATB,acap oct LAWSON 51718 $.35 (B3775)

Stockbridge
(Moore) 4pt mix cor,acap oct SCHIRM.G 11679 $.25 (B3776)

Three Fuguing Tunes *CC3U
SATB oct PRESSER 352-00062 $.55 (B3777)

Thus Saith The High, The Lofty One
(McAfee) SATB oct BOURNE 854 $.30 (B3778)

Thus Saith The Lord
SATB oct WALTON 2217 $.30 (B3779)

Truly My Soul
(Dilsner) SAB,acap,opt org BOSTON 13518 $.30 (B3780)

BILLINGS, WILLIAM (cont'd.)

Two Christmas Anthems *Xmas,anthem
SATB oct WALTON 2208 $.30
contains: Bethlehem; Boston (B3781)

Two Easter Anthems *Easter,anthem
(Daniel, Oliver) SATB,acap PETERS 66342 $.60
contains: Crucifixion; Resurrection (B3782)

Two Fuging Tunes *CC2U,fugue
(Wienandt) SATB oct AGAPE US 1771 $.40 (B3783)

Virgin Unspotted, A *Xmas
SATB,acap oct PRESSER 352-00064 $.30 (B3784)
SATB oct SUMMY B 1529 $.45 (B3785)
SATB SCHIRM.EC 2794 $.30 (B3786)
SATB oct WALTON 2207 $.30 (B3787)
(Ehret) SATB,acap oct LAWSON 620 $.25 (B3788)
(Trusler) SAB oct PLYMOUTH TR-403 $.30 (B3789)

When Jesus Wept *Xmas/Easter/Lent,canon/round,US
SATB oct HERITAGE H3 $.35 (B3790)
SATB,acap oct PRESSER 352-00102 $.30 (B3791)
TTBB,acap oct PRESSER 352-00102 $.30 (B3792)
SSAA,acap oct PRESSER 352-00102 $.30 (B3793)
SSAA/SATB oct WALTON 2205 $.30 (B3794)
TTBB oct WALTON 2205 $.30 (B3795)
(Bock) SATB oct WORD CS-672 $.30 (B3796)
(Gustafson) 2pt/3pt/4pt,acap oct SCHIRM.G 11145 $.30 (B3797)
(Mason, Roger) 4pt HEUGEL PJ110 s.p.
contains also: John's Gone To Hilo (B3798)
(Shaw; Parker) SATB,acap oct LAWSON 913 $.30 (B3799)
(Trusler) SATB oct PLYMOUTH TR-105 $.25 (B3800)
(Whatt) SATB oct PRO ART 2234 $.30 (B3801)

While Shepherds Watched Their Flocks By Night *Xmas
(Ehret) SATB ALFRED 6627 $.25 (B3802)

BILLSON (1917-)
Lord's Supper, The *Gen
SATB SCHMITT 1605 $.35 (B3803)

BILLUPS, [W.]
Stand The Storm *spir
SATB oct FOX R210 $.25 (B3804)

BIM-BAM see Altman, S.

BIMBO BIMBO FAI LA NANNA "PIVA, PIVA"
see Tanti Auguri

BINCHOIS, GILLES (ca. 1400-1460)
A Solis Ortus Cardine
(Boepple, P.) SSA,acap oct PRESSER 352-00038 $.30 (B3805)
(Boepple, P.) TBB,acap oct PRESSER 352-00038 $.30 (B3806)

O Solis Ortus Cardine
SATB,acap oct LAWSON 51524 $.25 (B3807)

BINDER
Haleluyah (Of Trees And Brooks)
(Raymond) SATB oct PLYMOUTH JR-119 $.35 (B3808)

BINDER, ABRAHAM WOLFE (1895-)
Afternoon Service For The Day Of Atonement
SATB TRANSCON. TCL 810 $2.50 (B3809)

Arvit L'rosh Hashanah V'yom Kippur *Rosh Hashanah/Yom Kippur
SATB TRANSCON. TCL 875 $5.50 (B3810)

Esther, Queen Of Persia *Purim
[Eng] SATB&cong,narrator TRANSCON. TCL 735 $1.50 (B3811)

Etz Chayim
[Heb] SATB TRANSCON. TCL 857 $.40 (B3812)

Hanukkah Of The Maccabees *Hanakkah
[Eng] mix cor&cong,narrator TRANSCON. TCL 725 $2.00 (B3813)

Hibbath Shabbath *Sab-Eve
SATB TRANSCON. TCL 820 $2.50 (B3814)

Kabbalath Shabbath *Sab-Eve
SATB TRANSCON. TCL 862 $2.50 (B3815)

Legend Of The Ari, The *ora
mix cor,TBar soli,pno/org LAWSON $1.75 (B3816)

Mi Y'mallel *Hanakkah,round
[Heb] SATB TRANSCON. 741 $.25 (B3817)

Morning Service For The New Year *Sab-Morn
SATB TRANSCON. TCL 760 $3.50 (B3818)

N'ilah Service
SATB TRANSCON. TCL 830 $2.00 (B3819)

N'ilhh Kaddish
[Heb] SATB,cantor TRANSCON. TCL 856 $.35 (B3820)

Passover To Freedom *Fest
[Eng] mix cor&cong,narrator TRANSCON. TCL 730 $2.00 (B3821)

Requiem-Yizkor *Yiskor
SATB,Bar solo TRANSCON. TCL 740 $1.75 (B3822)

Sabbath For Israel *Sab-Eve
SATB TRANSCON. TCL 800 $4.00 (B3823)

Three Festival Music Liturgy *Fest
SATB TRANSCON. TCL 850 $4.50 (B3824)

BINDING, THE see Adler, Samuel

BINGHAM
Christmas Child *Xmas
SATB oct GALAXY 1.1526.1 $.30 (B3825)
SSA/SAT oct GALAXY 1.1527.1 $.25 (B3826)

BINGHAM (cont'd.)

Gabriel From The Heav'n Descending *Xmas
SATB&desc SCHMITT 1625 $.25   (B3827)
SSAA SCHMITT 2551 $.18   (B3828)

O Come And Mourn
SATB oct GALAXY 1.1498.1 $.35   (B3829)

Perfect Through Suffering
SATB,org PETERS 66348 $.90   (B3830)

BINKERD, [GORDON] (1916-   )
Ad Te Levavi
"Unto The Father" [Lat/Eng] SATB,acap AMP
A368 $.25   (B3831)

Alleluia For St. Francis
SA/TB/SATB BOOSEY 5687 $.30   (B3832)
SA/TB/SATB,org oct BOOSEY 5686 $.30 (B3833)

Ave Maria
[Lat] SATB,acap oct BOOSEY 5783 $.30
                                     (B3834)

Ave Regina Caelorum *BVM
"Hail Queen Of Heaven" [Lat/Eng] SSATB AMP
A545 $.30   (B3835)

Confitebor Tibi
[Lat] SATB,acap oct BOOSEY 5691 $.30
                                     (B3836)

Feast Of Saint Francis Of Assissi
SA/TTBB,org oct BOOSEY 5827 $.35   (B3837)

From Your Throne, O Lord
men cor oct BOOSEY 5826 $.40   (B3838)

Hail Queen Of Heaven *see Ave Regina
Caelorum

Jesus Weeping
SATBB,acap oct BOOSEY 5715 $.50   (B3839)

Lamb
SATB,acap oct BOOSEY 5797 $.30   (B3840)

Let My Prayer Come Like Incense
TTBB,org oct BOOSEY 5828 $.35   (B3841)

Lord Is King, The (Psalm 93)
SATB,org PETERS 6260 $.60, ipr   (B3842)

Nativitas Est Hodie *Xmas
[Lat] SATB,acap oct BOOSEY 5593 $.35
                                     (B3843)

Octave Day Of Christmas
see Binkerd, [Gordon], Third Mass Of
Christmas

Omnes Gentes
[Lat] SATB BOOSEY-CAN s.p.   (B3844)
[Lat] SATB,acap oct BOOSEY 5684 $.35 (B3845)

Psalm 23
SATB,T solo,org oct BOOSEY 5820 $.45 (B3846)

Psalm 93 *see Lord Is King, The

Remember Now Thy Creator
SATB,S solo,org oct BOOSEY 5644 $.40
                                     (B3847)

There Is In Souls
SATB,acap oct BOOSEY 5794 $.30   (B3848)

Third Mass Of Christmas *Xmas,Mass
SATB,org oct BOOSEY 5829 $.60 contains
also: Octave Day Of Christmas   (B3849)

Unto The Father *see Ad Te Levavi

BIRCSAK
Lord Is Nigh, The
SATB,acap WARNER W7-1046 $.30   (B3850)

BIRD, R.
Let Thy Merciful Ears *mot
SAATTB,acap FISCHER,J 11095 $.30   (B3851)

BIRD, THE see Billings, William

BIRDS AND THE BABE, THE *Xmas,carol,Czech
(Wilson, Harry R.) SSA oct WALTON 5011 $.25
                                     (B3852)

BIRDS AND THE CHRIST CHILD, THE see Krone

BIRDS' NOEL, THE see Davis, Katherine K.

BIRDS PRAISE THE ADVENT OF THE SAVIOR *Xmas
(Molzer, F.) SATB,acap oct PRESSER 332-40113
$.35   (B3853)

BIRDS, THE see Blasdale

BIRGINA GAZTE HOBAT *Xmas,Fr/Span
(Glaser, V.) "Virgin Knelt In Prayer, A"
SATB,acap SCHIRM.EC 2608 $.30   (B3854)
(Glaser, V.) "Virgin Knelt In Prayer, A"
SSAA,acap SCHIRM.EC 1975 $.18   (B3855)

BIRKAT KOHANIM-SSIM SHALOM see Jablonsky,
Stephan

BIRNBAUM
Hashkivenu
(Roskin) SATB,solo HATIKVAH HCL 46 $.35
                                     (B3856)

BIRTH see Sateren, Leland Bernhard

BIRTH NIGHT, THE see Anderson, [William H.]

BIRTH OF A KING see Kunz

BIRTH OF CHRIST see Bliss, Paul

BIRTH OF CHRIST, THE see Bliss, Paul

BIRTH OF CHRIST, THE see Richter

BIRTH OF CHRIST, THE see Schickele, Peter

BIRTH OF MOSES, THE see Lockwood, Normand

BIRTH OF OUR LORD see Martinu, Bohuslav

BIRTHDAY GREETING, A see Kodaly, Zoltan

BIRTHDAY OF A KING see Neidlinger

BIRTHDAY OF A KING see Neidlinger, P.

BIRTHDAY OF A KING, THE see Hardwicke

BIRTHDAY OF A KING, THE see Neidlinger

BIRTHDAY OF A KING, THE see Neidlinger, William
Harold

BIRTHDAY OF A KING, THE see Nelhybel, Vaclav

BIRTHDAY OF OUR GOD AND KING, THE *Xmas,carol,
Eng
(Ehret) SAB,opt clar oct FOX CC14 $.25
                                     (B3857)
(Ehret, W.) SAB,opt clar PROWSE CC14 s.p.
                                     (B3858)

BIS HIEHER HAT MICH GOTT GEBRACHT see Bach,
Johann Sebastian

BIS HIEHER HAT MICH GOTT GEBRACHT see Hennig,
Walter

BIS HIEHER HAT MICH GOTT GEBRACHT see Stern,
Hermann

BIS HIEHER HAT MICH GOTT GEBRACHT see Wydler,
A.

BIS HIERHER HAT MICH GEBRACHT see Sohr,
Peter

BIS HIN AN DES KREUZES STAMM see Hammerschmidt,
Andreas

BISCHER HABT IHR NICHTS GEBETEN see Bach,
Johann Sebastian, Bisher Habt Ihr Nichts
Gebeten

BISCHER HABT IHR NICHTS GEBETEN IN MEINEM NAMEN
see Bach, Johann Sebastian

BISCHOFF, M.
Gott Vater, Gott Sohn, Gott Heiliger Geist
*chorale
[Ger] mix cor,acap (easy) HUG s.p.   (B3859)

BISCHOFF, PAUL (1935-   )
Bitte Um Das Rechte *Gen
unis,acap (easy) BOSSE BE 272 s.p.   (B3860)

If God So Clothe The Grass
(Harding) SATB,org/pno BOSTON 10411 $.40
                                     (B3861)

BISHER HABT IHR NICHTS GEBETEN see Bach, Johann
Sebastian

BISHOP, F.G.
Let All The World *anthem
mix cor oct NOVELLO 50.0347.04 s.p. (B3862)

BISHOP, JANICE G.
My Child
SSA PIONEER 1012 $.40   (B3863)

BISHOP, JEFFREY
And Now Another Day Is Gone *Eve,anthem
mix cor oct NOVELLO 40.1129.05 s.p. (B3864)

In Hevene And Helle *anthem
mix cor oct NOVELLO 40.1528.02 s.p. (B3865)

BISP THOMAS FRIHETSSANG see Hammarstrom, Hugo

BISP THOMAS FRIHETSSANG see Jonsson, Josef
[Petrus]

BISP THOMAS' FRIHETSSANG see Nordqvist, Gustaf

BISSELL, KEITH (1912-   )
Christ Being Raised From The Dead
SATB THOMP.G G-537 s.p.   (B3866)

Christ, Whose Glory Fills The Skies
SATB THOMP.G G-556 s.p.   (B3867)

Dark Hills, The
SATB,acap oct BERANDOL 914B4AF $.35 (B3868)

Earth Is The Lord's, The
SATB,acap oct BERANDOL 914B4AG $.35 (B3869)

Hear Thou My Prayer, O Lord
SATB THOMP.G G-544 s.p.   (B3870)

Let There Be Joy *cant
SATB THOMP.G s.p.   (B3871)

Lord, Dismiss Us With Thy Blessing
SATB THOMP.G G-565 s.p.   (B3872)

O Starry Night *Xmas
SSA oct LESLIE 3040   (B3873)

Two Christmas Songs *CC2U,Xmas
unis THOMP.G G-127 s.p.   (B3874)

BIST DU BEI MIR see Bach, Johann Sebastian

BITGOD, ROB.
Rosa Mystica
(Slogedal, Bjarne) [Norw] mix cor LYCHE 35
s.p.   (B3875)

BITGOOD
Bring A Torch, Jeannette, Isabella *Xmas
SA,opt fl oct SACRED S-5376 $.35   (B3876)

Christ The Lord Is Born *Xmas
SSA oct GALAXY 1.1886.1 $.30   (B3877)
SATB oct GALAXY 1.1943.1 $.30   (B3878)

Good Thing It Is To Give Thanks
SATB oct GALAXY 1.1515.1 $.35   (B3879)

How Excellent Thy Name
SA/TB FLAMMER E5006 $.30   (B3880)

Sons Of God, The
TTBB oct SACRED S-2858 $.30   (B3881)

They Shall Walk
SATB oct SACRED E63 $.35   (B3882)

Wise Men Seeking Jesus *Xmas
unis/jr cor,fl SCHMITT SD6005 $.30   (B3883)

BITGOOD, ROBERTA (1908-   )
Be Still And Know
SATB oct GRAY GCMR 2230 $.30   (B3884)

Choral Benedictions *CCU,Bene
SATB (med) ABINGDON APM-470 $.25   (B3885)

Christmas Candle *Xmas
SATB oct GRAY GCMR 1445 $.30   (B3886)

Except The Lord Build The House
SATB FLAMMER A 5236 $.30   (B3887)

Give Me A Faith
SATB oct GRAY GCMR 2017 $.35   (B3888)

Glory Is Thine, The *Thanks
SATB oct GRAY GCMR 3072 $.35   (B3889)

Grant Us Thy Peace
SATB oct GRAY GCMR 1697 $.25   (B3890)

Greatest Of These
SATB oct GRAY GCMR 1396 $.35   (B3891)

Job *cant
BELWIN $1.00   (B3892)

Let There Be Light *Xmas,cant
jr cor SACRED $1.75   (B3893)

New Meaning For Our Age
SATB FLAMMER A 5259 $.50   (B3894)

Prayer For Communion, A *Commun,prayer
SATB,acap WARNER W3560 $.30   (B3895)

Prayer Is The Soul's Sincere Desire
SATB oct GRAY GCMR 1611 $.25   (B3896)

Sixteen Amens From The Oratorios *CC16U
SATB FLAMMER A 5268 $.25   (B3897)

Song Of Triumph, A
SATB&treb cor oct AGAPE F 924 $.35   (B3898)

Thy Temple Is Not Made With Hands
SATB oct AGAPE A 419 $.30   (B3899)

BITTE see Schmid, E.

BITTE UM DAS RECHTE see Bischoff, Paul

BITTE UM FRIEDEN "DU FRIEDEFURST" see
Buxtehude, Dietrich

BITTE UND VERTRAUEN
SATB,acap cmplt ed DOBLINGER s.p.
contains & see also: Eccard, Johannes,
Herr, Wie Du Willst; Eccard, Johannes,
Was Mein Gott Will, Das G'scheh Allzeit;
Gastoldi, Giovanni Giacomo, In Dir Ist
Freude; Gumpeltzhaimer, Adam, O Herr Jesu
Christe; Hassler, Hans Leo, Warum
Betrubst Du Dich; Hassler, Hans Leo, Wo
Gott Zum Haus Nicht Gibt Sein Gunst;
Lassus, Roland de (Orlandus), Dextera
Domini; Lassus, Roland de (Orlandus),
Selig Ist; Lassus, Roland de (Orlandus),
Wer Gott Vertrauen Tut; Neumark, Georg,
Wer Nur Den Lieben Gott Lasst Walten;
Praetorius, Michael, Wacht Auf Ihr
Christen Alle; Resinarius, Balthasar,
Verleih Uns Frieden Gnadiglich; Schein,
Johann Hermann, Auf Meinen Lieben Gott;
Schein, Johann Hermann, Wenn Wir In
Hochsten Noten Sein; Schutz, Heinrich,
Aus Tiefer Not; Schutz, Heinrich, Der
Herr Ist Mein Hirt; Schutz, Heinrich,
Erhor Mich, Wenn Ich Ruf Zu Dir; Schutz,
Heinrich, Ich Heb Mein Augen Sehnlich
Auf; Schutz, Heinrich, In Dich Hab Ich
Gehoffet, Herr; Schutz, Heinrich, Von
Gott Will Ich Nicht Lassen   (B3900)

BITTEN see Beethoven, Ludwig van

BITTER WITHY, THE
(Niles; Horton) 4pt mix cor,ST&3 soli oct
SCHIRM.G 9897 $.25   (B3901)

BITTET, SO WERDET IHR NEHMEN see Driessler,
Johannes

BITTET, SO WIRD EUCH GEGEBEN see Fischer-
Dieskau, Klaus

BIXBY, A.K.
Junior Choir Collection Volume 1 (composed
with Bliss, Paul) *CC2OU,anthem
2pt jr cor,pno/org (med) voc sc WILLIS $.75
                                     (B3902)
Junior Choir Collection Volume 1, The
(composed with Bliss, Paul) *CCU,Gen,
anthem
unis/2pt oct WILLIS $1.00   (B3903)
Junior Choir Collection Volume 2 (composed
with Bliss, Paul) *CC2OL,anthem
1-2pt jr cor,pno/org (easy) voc sc WILLIS
$.75   (B3904)
Junior Choir Collection Volume 2, The
(composed with Bliss, Paul) *CCU,Gen,
anthem
unis/2pt oct WILLIS $1.00   (B3905)
Junior Choir Collection. Volume 3, Songs Of
Worship *CC12L,anthem
1-2pt jr cor,pno/org (easy) voc sc WILLIS
$.75   (B3906)
Junior Choir Collection Volume 3, The
(composed with Blancks, Edward) *CCU,
Gen,anthem
unis/2pt oct WILLIS $1.00   (B3907)

Lift Up Your Heads *Adv/Gen
2pt jr cor,pno/org (easy) oct WILLIS 5951
$.10   (B3908)

Saviour Like A Shepherd
2pt jr cor,pno/org (easy) oct WILLIS 5949
$.15   (B3909)

Sing Alleluia Forth
2pt jr cor,pno/org (easy) oct WILLIS 5950
$.10   (B3910)

BIXEL, JAMES W.
Fine Pearls
see Four Parables

Four Parables *Bibl
SATB,acap oct WORLD ESA-1888-8 $1.25
contains: Fine Pearls; Harvest, The;
Hidden Treasure; Scattered Seed (B3911)

Harvest, The
see Four Parables

Hidden Treasure
see Four Parables

Scattered Seed
see Four Parables

BIZET, GEORGES (1838-1875)
Agnus Dei *Easter/Lent,Agnus
SATB ENOCH EC305 s.p. (B3912)
2pt ENOCH T.P.222 s.p. (B3913)
SSATB ENOCH EC308 s.p. (B3914)
[Lat] 2-3pt CHOUDENS s.p. see also CHOEURS
POUR DISTRIBUTIONS DE PRIX OU POUR
ENFANTS (B3915)
(Deis) "Lamb Of God" 4pt mix cor,acap,opt
org/pno oct SCHIRM.G 10004 $.30 (B3916)
(Lathrop) "Lamb Of God" SATB oct PRO ART
1027 $.25 (B3917)
(Lathrop) "Lamb Of God" SSA oct PRO ART
1006 $.25 (B3918)
(Lathrop) "Lamb Of God" SAB oct PRO ART
1032 $.25 (B3919)
(Lathrop) "Lamb Of God" 2pt oct PRO ART
1050 $.25 (B3920)
(Linden, N.V.D.) men cor,pno ALSBACH&D sc
s.p., cor pts s.p. (B3921)
(Loam, Arthur S.) "O God Of Love" SA ALLANS
294 s.p. (B3922)
(Ryder, A.) "Lamb Of God" SATB oct PRESSER
332-12246 $.30 (B3923)

Ave Maria *BVM
[Fr] unis/2pt CHOUDENS s.p. (B3924)
unis/2pt,org,vln,vcl CHOUDENS s.p. (B3925)
[Lat] unis/2pt CHOUDENS s.p. (B3926)

Lamb Of God *see Agnus Dei

March Of The Three Kings *Xmas
(Smith, D.S.) SATB oct GRAY GCMR 587 $.35
(B3927)

O God Of Love *see Agnus Dei

On Top Of The Hill (from Carmen)
2pt ASHDOWN E.A.165 s.p. (B3928)

BJAERUM, N.
Bonn
mix cor MUSIKK 121 s.p. (B3929)

BJARNEGARD, GUSTAF
Dig Klad I Helighetens Skrud
(Ahlen, Waldemar) 2pt wom cor/2pt jr cor,
acap NORDISKA 4556 s.p. (B3930)

Epifania
(Ahlen, Waldemar) 2pt wom cor/2pt jr cor,
acap NORDISKA 4976 s.p. (B3931)

Gud Ar Var Tillflykt
(Ahlen, Waldemar) 3pt wom cor/3pt jr cor,
acap NORDISKA 5047 s.p. (B3932)

Gud Var Losta Tunga
(Ahlen, Waldemar) 2pt wom cor/2pt jr cor,
acap NORDISKA 5390 s.p. (B3933)

Han Kommer I Sin Kyrka
wom cor/jr cor NORDISKA 5033 s.p. (B3934)

Hell, Morgonstjarna, Mild Och Ren
(Ahlen, Waldemar) 2pt wom cor/2pt jr cor,
acap NORDISKA 4559 s.p. (B3935)

Herre, Nu Later Du Din Tjanare
wom cor/jr cor NORDISKA 5031 s.p. (B3936)

Jag Hoja Vill Till Gud Min Sang
3pt mix cor NORDISKA 2414 s.p. (B3937)

Jerusalem, Hav Upp Din Rost
(Ahlen, Waldemar) 2pt wom cor/3pt jr cor,
acap NORDISKA 5394 s.p. (B3938)

Jul
[Swed] SATB,acap GEHRMANS KRB 298 (B3939)

Kom, Helge Ande, Till Mig In
(Ahlen, Waldemar) 2pt wom cor/2pt jr cor,
acap NORDISKA 5393 s.p. (B3940)

Korshymn
(Ahlen, Waldemar) 2pt wom cor/2pt jr cor,
org NORDISKA 4975 s.p. (B3941)

Lov Vare Dig, O Jesu Krist
(Ahlen, Waldemar) 3pt wom cor/3pt jr cor,
acap NORDISKA 5395 s.p. (B3942)

Loven Herrens Namn
(Ahlen, Waldemar) 2pt wom cor/2pt jr cor,
acap NORDISKA 5048 s.p. (B3943)

Min Sjal Prisar Storligen Herren
(Ahlen, Waldemar) unis&opt wom cor/unis jr cor,
fl NORDISKA 4558 s.p. (B3944)

Nar Gud Andas
(Ahlen, Waldemar) 2pt wom cor/2pt jr cor,
acap NORDISKA 4557 s.p. (B3945)

Nu Kommen Ar Var Paskafrojd
(Ahlen, Waldemar) 3pt wom cor/3pt jr cor,
acap NORDISKA 4247 s.p. (B3946)

Nu Sjunga Vi Med Gladje Stor
(Ahlen, Waldemar) unis wom cor/unis jr cor,
acap NORDISKA 4977 s.p. (B3947)

O Hubud, Blodigt, Sarat
(Ahlen, Waldemar) 2pt wom cor/2pt jr cor,
vln NORDISKA 5391 s.p. (B3948)

O Kriste, Oss Benada
(Ahlen, Waldemar) 2pt wom cor/2pt jr cor,
vln,fl NORDISKA 5396 s.p. (B3949)

BJARNEGARD, GUSTAF (cont'd.)
Salig Ar Den Stilla Stunden
mix cor NORDISKA 4872 s.p. (B3950)

Sen Pa Faglarna
(Ahlen, Waldemar) 2pt wom cor/2pt jr cor,
acap NORDISKA 5049 s.p. (B3951)

Sta Upp, Var Ljus
wom cor/jr cor NORDISKA 4877 s.p. (B3952)

Via Dolorosa
[Swed] SATB,acap GEHRMANS KRB 296 (B3953)

BJORN, HJELM BORG
Fire Sange Og Tre Motetter *sac/sec,CC7L
SAABar/SATB cmplt ed HANSEN-DEN 27850 s.p.
see also: Halleluja! Ja, Det Er Godt At
Lovsynge Vor Gud; Hvor Elskelige Er
Dine Boliger; Hvor Laenge Vil Du Evigt
Glemme Mig, Herre (B3954)

Halleluja! Ja, Det Er Godt At Lovsynge Vor
Gud
SATB HANSEN-DEN 358 s.p. see also Fire
Sange Og Tre Motetter (B3955)

Hvor Elskelige Er Dine Boliger
SATB HANSEN-DEN 356 s.p. see also Fire
Sange Og Tre Motetter (B3956)

Hvor Laenge Vil Du Evigt Glemme Mig, Herre
SATB HANSEN-DEN 357 s.p. see also Fire
Sange Og Tre Motetter (B3957)

BLACHER, BORIS (1903-)
Requiem *Req
mix cor,SBar soli,orch BOTE voc sc s.p.,
min sc s.p. (B3958)

BLACK
Carol Of The Birds *carol
SATB FLAMMER A 5428 $.25 (B3959)

Friendly Beasts, The
SATB FLAMMER A 5358 $.30 (B3960)
SA/TB FLAMMER E5017 $.25 (B3961)

Jacob's Ladder
SATB SACRED E30 $.35 (B3962)

Mary Had A Baby
SATB FLAMMER A 5051 $.30 (B3963)
SSA FLAMMER B 5056 $.30 (B3964)
SAB FLAMMER D5030 $.30 (B3965)

O Come Let Us Sing
SATB SACRED E39 $.35 (B3966)

O Sing A New Song
SATB SACRED E67 $.40 (B3967)

BLACK, CHARLES
Processional Service, A *Proces,cant
mix cor BELWIN $1.00 (B3968)

To Calvary's Summit *Easter
SATB oct GRAY GCMR 2448 $.25 (B3969)

BLACKMORE
Some Golden Daybreak *Gen,anthem
(Boersma) SAB oct WORD CS-2135 $.30 (B3970)
(McLellan) SATB oct LILLENAS AT-1075 $.25
(B3971)

BLACKWELL, J.
Gracious God! To Thee I Pray
SATB oct PRESSER 312-40639 $.30 (B3972)

BLACKWOOD, EASLEY (1933-)
Lead Me, O Lord
SATB,acap oct FOX R205 $.25 (B3973)

BLAENWERN see Rowlands, W.P.

BLAHNIK, J.
Easter Fanfare *Easter
SATB,org,2trp,2trom oct KERBY 43 $.40, ipa
(B3974)
SATB oct KERBY 4378 $.40, ipa (B3975)

BLAIR, ELIZABETH
Thy Kingdom Come *Fest,anthem,Austral
SATB,S solo ALLANS 159 s.p. (B3976)

BLAIR, F.
O Lamb Of God, I Come *Easter/Gen
SATB oct PRESSER 312-21201 $.30 (B3977)
(Stoughton, R.) SAB oct PRESSER 312-21448
$.25 (B3978)

BLAKE
Child Jesus Comes From Heavenly Height *Xmas
SATB oct GALAXY 1.2170.1 $.30 (B3979)

God, My King
SATB,org/pno BOSTON 12886 $.30 (B3980)

O Be Joyful In The Lord
SATB,org/pno BOSTON 13348 $.35 (B3981)

O Bless The Lord, My Soul
SATB,org BOSTON 12916 $.35 (B3982)

O Come, Loud Anthems Let Us Sing
SATB oct LORENZ C326 $.30 (B3983)

Son Of God, Eternal Savior
SATB oct LORENZ C328 $.30 (B3984)

There Were Three Lights *Xmas
SATB oct LORENZ C296 $.30 (B3985)

Way Of Christ, The
SATB oct LORENZ C290 $.30 (B3986)

BLAKE, REV. CANON, E.C.
Bells Ring Out, The *carol
unis CRAMER 32 s.p. (B3987)

Children Singing *CC8U,hymn
jr cor cmplt ed WEINBERGER s.p. (B3988)

Ever-Open Door, The
jr cor WEINBERGER s.p. (B3989)

King And The Star, The *Epiph
WEINBERGER s.p. (B3990)

BLAKE, REV. CANON, E.C. (cont'd.)
Pops With A Purpose *CC8U,pop
jr cor cmplt ed WEINBERGER s.p. (B3991)

BLAKE, G.
Alleluia, Hearts And Voices Heavenward Raise
*Easter
SATB oct PRESSER 312-40433 $.35 (B3992)

At Easter Morn *Easter
SATB oct PRESSER 312-40624 $.30 (B3993)

At The Lamb's High Feast We Sing *Easter
SATB oct PRESSER 312-40393 $.35 (B3994)

Come Hither, Ye Faithful *Xmas
SATB oct PRESSER 312-40410 $.35 (B3595)

Glory To The King Of Kings *Xmas
SATB oct PRESSER 332-40106 $.30 (B3996)

High O'er The Lonely Hills *Xmas
SATB oct PRESSER 332-40031 $.30 (B3997)

Light Of The World
SATB oct PRESSER 312-40238 $.30 (B3998)

Lo, The Earth Is Risen Again *Easter
SATB oct PRESSER 312-40603 $.30 (B3999)

Lord Is Risen Indeed, The *Easter
SATB oct PRESSER 312-40408 $.35 (B4000)

Ring Out, O Bells Of Gladness *Xmas
SATB oct PRESSER 312-40441 $.35 (B4001)

Ring The Joy-Bells *Easter
SATB oct PRESSER 312-40409 $.35 (B4002)

Sing All Ye Christian People *Easter
SATB,acap oct PRESSER 312-40223 $.30
(B4003)

Sing, With All The Sons Of Glory
SATB oct PRESSER 312-40351 $.30 (B4004)

What Star Is This? *Xmas
SATB oct PRESSER 312-40391 $.30 (B4005)

Who Are These In Bright Array? *Easter
SATB oct PRESSER 312-40373 $.35 (B4006)

BLAKE, GEORGE [M.] (1912-)
Blessing And Honor
4pt mix cor oct SCHIRM.G 10853 $.25 (B4007)

In Heavenly Love *Finn
SATB oct GRAY GCMR 2936 $.25 (B4008)

King's Highway
SATB oct BELWIN 2076 $.25 (B4009)

Love Of Jesus, All Divine
4pt mix cor,opt ST soli,org/pno oct
SCHIRM.G 10568 $.25 (B4010)

O Lord Of Life *anthem
SATB oct GRAY GCMR 3120 $.30 (B4011)

BLAKE, LEONARD
And Now Another Day Is Gone *Eve
unis oct NOVELLO 33.0076.05 s.p. (B4012)

Benedicite (Shortened Form)
SATB (E flat maj) oct NOVELLO 44.1224.09
s.p. (B4013)

Consecration *Gen/Harv
SS (easy) oct OXFORD 82.058 $.30 (B4014)

Holy Communion *Commun
unis&opt desc,org (C maj) s.p., ipa sc
NOVELLO 44.1425.10, voc sc NOVELLO
44.1425.00 (B4015)
SATB (D maj) oct NOVELLO 44.1390.03 s.p.
(B4016)
unis (D maj) oct NOVELLO 02.0033.06 s.p.
(B4017)

Lord Of The Worlds Above
unis oct NOVELLO 33.0107.09 s.p. (B4018)

Short Communion Service, A
SATB (med easy) oct OXFORD 42.970 $.50
(B4019)

Sing To The Lord Of Harvest *Harv,anthem
SATB oct ROYAL 215 s.p. (B4020)

BLAKE, WILLIAM
Cradle Song *Xmas,cradle
(Daubney, Brian) SATB ENOCH EC323 s.p.
contains also: Lullay My Liking (16th
cent) (B4021)

BLAKESLEE
Bless All Mothers, Lord We Pray
SATB KJOS PC730 $.30 (B4022)
SSA KJOS PC620 $.40 (B4023)

Dear Lord, We Offer Thee
SATB KJOS PC750 $.30 (B4024)

In Adoration, Lord We Kneel
SATB KJOS PC733 $.30 (B4025)

BLAKLEY
Above All Else Love God Alone
SATB oct FISCHER,C CM-7594 $.25 (B4026)

Awake, My Tongue
SAB FLAMMER D5208 $.30 (B4027)

Come, Let Us Worship Him
SAB FLAMMER D5210 $.30 (B4028)

Draw Nigh To God *Gen
SATB SCHMITT 15007 $.35 (B4029)

God Is Before Me
SATB oct LORENZ 9956 $.30 (B4030)

Jesus Christ, The Crucified
SATB FLAMMER A1052 $1.00 (B4031)

Search Me, O God *Gen
SATB oct SPRATT 618 $.30 (B4032)

Shepherd Of Souls
SATB oct FISCHER,C CM-7619 $.25 (B4033)

BLAKLEY (cont'd.)

Sing Unto The Lord, O Ye Saints *anthem
SATB oct FISCHER,C CM-7595 $.25   (B4034)

Spirit Of God, This Very Hour
SATB oct LORENZ 9994 $.30   (B4035)

To The Work
SATB oct SACRED S-75 $.35   (B4036)

BLAKLEY, D.
Ask Ye What Great Thing I Know
SATB SHAWNEE A 1057 $.30   (B4037)

Psalm 117
SATB oct PRESSER 312-40653 $.35   (B4038)

With My Whole Heart
SATB,opt brass oct BOURNE 873 $.60   (B4039)

BLAKLEY, D. DUANE
Prayer Of The Publican, The
SATB oct AGAPE A 377 $.30   (B4040)

Standing On Promises
SATB oct AGAPE CH 632 $.30   (B4041)

BLANCHARD
Sleep, Little Jesus *Xmas
SATB oct SACRED S-84 $.35   (B4042)

'Twas In The Silent Night He Came
(Anderson) unis oct BELWIN 60544 $.30
                                    (B4043)

BLANCHARD, [WILLIAM G.] (1905-   )
Fill My Cup, Lord
(Bolks) SATB oct WORD CS-2419 $.30 (B4044)
(Burroughs) SATB,solo oct WORD CS-2500 $.30
                                    (B4045)

Hear My Prayer
SATB,opt org (med) oct WILLIS 5329 $.18
                                    (B4046)

I Will Extol Thee
SATB,opt org (med) oct WILLIS 6267 $.15
                                    (B4047)

BLANCKS, EDWARD
Junior Choir Collection Volume 3, The *see
Bixby, A.K.

When The Roll Is Called Up Yonder
(McLellan) SATB oct LILLENAS AT-1054 $.25
                                    (B4048)

BLANK, ALLAN
Give Ear To My Words, O Lord
TTBB,acap oct PRESSER 342-40019 $.30
                                    (B4049)

Herauf Nun, Du Hellichter Tag
jr cor&men cor (easy) oct LEUCKART 12 s.p.
                                    (B4050)

BLARR, OSKAR GOTTLIEB (1934-   )
Canticum Simeonis "Nunc Dimittus" *Nunc
[Ger] SSAATTBB,acap (med) BOSSE BE 414 s.p.
                                    (B4051)

Einige Leute Loben Den Frieden *Gen
unis,acap (easy) BOSSE BE 269 s.p. (B4052)

Frolocket Mit Handen (Psalm 47) Psalm
SSATB&cong,inst sc HANSSLER 19.106 s.p.
contains also: Ruppel, Paul Ernst, Es
Soll Nicht Durch Heer Oder Kraft
Geschehen (SAT/SAB,3trp,trom,bvl,perc,opt
org)   (B4053)

Hilf, Herr Meines Lebens
see Ruppel, Paul Ernst, Gelobt Sei Der Herr
Taglich

Keiner, Der Die Harfe Schlagt *Gen
unis,acap (easy) BOSSE BE 270 s.p. (B4054)

Lobe Den Herrn, Meine Seele (Psalm 103)
SSATBB HANSSLER 19.105 s.p.   (B4055)

Nun Danket All *Gen
[Ger] 4-5pt mix cor,kbd,fl,bvl,perc (med
easy) BOSSE BE 246 s.p.   (B4056)

Psalm 47 *see Frolocket Mit Handen

Psalm 91 *see Wer Wohnt Unterm Schirm Des
Hochsten

Psalm 98 *see Singet Dem Herrn Ein Neues
Lied

Psalm 103 *see Lobe Den Herrn, Meine Seele

Singet Dem Herrn Ein Neues Lied (Psalm 98)
Gen
[Ger] SSATB&cong,clar,trp,bvl,perc, tenor
saxophone (med) BOSSE BE 240 sc s.p., cor
pts s.p.   (B4057)

Thema Weihnachten *CC3U,Xmas
[Ger] SATB,narrator,soli,pno,trp,bvl, tenor
saxophone, electric guitar (med) BOSSE
BE 289 sc s.p., cor pts s.p., ipa (B4058)

Uberdenk Ich Die Zeit *Gen
unis,acap (easy) BOSSE BE 268 s.p. (B4059)

Vater Unser
[Ger] unis,acap (easy) BOSSE BE 269 s.p.
                                    (B4060)

Vater Unser, Der Du Bist Im Himmel
[Ger] SATB&cong,SA soli,kbd,fl,bvl/gtr (med
diff) BOSSE BE 236 s.p.   (B4061)

Weil Du "Ja" Zu Mir Sagst *Gen
unis,acap (easy) BOSSE BE 253 s.p. (B4062)
[Ger] SA&men cor,kbd (med easy) BOSSE
BE 226 s.p.   (B4063)

Wer Wohnt Unterm Schirm Des Hochsten (Psalm
91) Gen
[Ger] SATB,trp,org/hpsd/bvl/gtr (med easy)
BOSSE BE 601 s.p.   (B4064)

Wo Nehmen Wir Den Stern Her *Xmas
[Ger] unis,acap (easy) cor pts BOSSE BE 270
s.p., cor pts BOSSE BE 258 s.p.   (B4065)

BLASDALE
Birds, The
SATB oct SACRED E47 $.30   (B4066)

BLEIB BEI MIR, HERR see Franck, Melchior

BLEIB' BEI UNS see Bach, Johann Sebastian

BLEIB BEI UNS see Bach, Johann Sebastian,
Bleib' Bei Uns, Denn Es Will Abend Werden

BLEIB' BEI UNS, DENN ES WILL ABEND WERDEN see
Bach, Johann Sebastian

BLEIBE BEI UNS, DENN ES WILL ABEND WERDEN see
Driessler, Johannes

BLEIBE BEI UNS, HERR see Schneider, Martin
Gotthard

BLESS ALL MOTHERS, LORD WE PRAY see Blakeslee

BLESS HIS NAME
SATB CHAPPELL 0014431-358 $.40   (B4067)

BLESS NOW, O LORD see Crotch, William

BLESS, O GOD, THIS GLAD ENDEAVOR see Schmucke
Dich

BLESS O MY SOUL THE LIVING GOD see Wood

BLESS THE HARVEST, O LORD see Chaminade, Cecile

BLESS THE LORD see Ippolitov-Ivanov, Mikhail
Mikhailovitch

BLESS THE LORD see Ivanoff, I.

BLESS THE LORD see Schroth

BLESS THE LORD see Tschesnokoff, P.I.

BLESS THE LORD, ALL WORKS OF THE LORD see
Young, Carlton R.

BLESS THE LORD FOR EVER AND EVER see Mozart,
Wolfgang Amadeus

BLESS THE LORD, O BLESS HIS HOLY NAME see
Corelli, Arcangelo

BLESS THE LORD, O MY SOUL *Gen
(Hadyn; Hines) SSA (Appalachian mountain
song) SCHMITT 2571 $.35   (B4068)

BLESS THE LORD, O MY SOUL see Crook, A.T.

BLESS THE LORD, O MY SOUL see Davis, Katherine
K.

BLESS THE LORD, O MY SOUL see Dittenhaver, S.

BLESS THE LORD, O MY SOUL see Fearis, J.S.

BLESS THE LORD, O MY SOUL see Freed, Isadore

BLESS THE LORD, O MY SOUL see Geisler, Johan C.

BLESS THE LORD, O MY SOUL see Gibbs, [Cecil]
Armstrong

BLESS THE LORD, O MY SOUL see Ippolitov-Ivanov,
Mikhail Mikhailovitch

BLESS THE LORD, O MY SOUL see Littleton

BLESS THE LORD, O MY SOUL see Lotti, Antonio

BLESS THE LORD, O MY SOUL see Rinehart

BLESS THE LORD, O MY SOUL see Stein

BLESS THE LORD, O MY SOUL see Young

BLESS THE LORD OH MY SOUL see Fischer, Clare

BLESS THIS HOUSE see Brahe, [May H.]

BLESS THOU THE LORD see Handel, George Frideric

BLESS THOU THE LORD see Martin, James

BLESS THOU THE LORD see Pasquet, Jean

BLESS THOU THE LORD, O MY SOUL see Glarum, L.
Stanley

BLESS THOU THE LORD, O MY SOUL see Lovelace,
Austin C.

BLESS THOU, THE LORD, O MY SOUL see Young,
Gordon

BLESS US, O LORD see Hamblen

BLESS YE OUR GOD see Baines, W.

BLESS YE THE LORD see De Bailhadc

BLESS YE THE LORD see Ippolitov-Ivanov, Mikhail
Mikhailovitch

BLESS'D ARE THE PURE IN HEART see Blower,
Maurice

BLESS'D ARE THEY WHO IN JESUS LIVE see Bach,
Johann Sebastian

BLESSED ANGEL SPIRITS see Tchaikovsky, Piotr
Ilyitch

BLESSED ARE ALL MEN WHO NAME THEE SAVIOR see
Victoria, Tomas Luis de

BLESSED ARE ALL THEY see Brown, Thomas

BLESSED ARE ALL THEY see Soerensen

BLESSED ARE ALL THEY THAT FEAR see Sowerby, Leo

BLESSED ARE ALL THEY THAT FEAR THE LORD see
Wills, Arthur

BLESSED ARE THE DEAD see Brahms, Johannes

BLESSED ARE THE DEAD see Mendelssohn-Bartholdy,
Felix, Beati Mortui

BLESSED ARE THE DEAD see Schutz, Heinrich,
Selig Sind Die Toten

BLESSED ARE THE FAITHFUL see Graun, Karl
Heinrich

BLESSED ARE THE FAITHFUL see Schutz, Heinrich,
Selig Sind Die Toten

BLESSED ARE THE HEARTS see Scarmolin, (Anthony)
Louis

BLESSED ARE THE MEEK see Porter

BLESSED ARE THE MEEK see Wilson

BLESSED ARE THE MEN WHO FEAR HIM see
Mendelssohn-Bartholdy, Felix

BLESSED ARE THE MERCIFUL see Hiles

BLESSED ARE THE MERCIFUL see Hiles, [Henry]

BLESSED ARE THE MERCIFUL see Menegali, Jesu,
Salvator Mundi

BLESSED ARE THE PEOPLE see Righini, Vincenzo

BLESSED ARE THE POOR IN SPIRIT
SATB BIG3 $.25   (B4069)

BLESSED ARE THE POOR IN SPIRIT see Droste

BLESSED ARE THE POOR IN SPIRIT see Preston

BLESSED ARE THE PURE IN HEART see Bayley,
Robert Charlton

BLESSED ARE THE PURE IN HEART see Carnegie, M.

BLESSED ARE THE PURE IN HEART see Graham

BLESSED ARE THE PURE IN HEART see Jones

BLESSED ARE THE PURE IN HEART see Walter,
Samuel

BLESSED ARE THE UNDEFILED see Victoria, Tomas
Luis de, Beati Immaculati

BLESSED ARE THEY
(Cornwall, J.S.) SATB PIONEER 5052 $.20
                                   (B4070)

BLESSED ARE THEY see Conaway, G. Wilkes

BLESSED ARE THEY see Glarum, L. Stanley

BLESSED ARE THEY see Morgan

BLESSED ARE THEY see Pasquet, Jean

BLESSED ARE THEY see Peter, Johann Friedrich

BLESSED ARE THEY see Snow

BLESSED ARE THEY see Staley

BLESSED ARE THEY see Wesley

BLESSED ARE THEY see Wilkinson

BLESSED ARE THEY THAT ALWAY KEEP JUDGEMENT see
Wesley

BLESSED ARE THEY THAT CONSIDER THE POOR see
Handel, George Frideric, Foundling Hospital
Anthem

BLESSED ARE THEY THAT DWELL IN THE HOUSE see
Berger, Jean

BLESSED ARE THEY THAT DWELL IN THY HOUSE see
Brahms, Johannes, Ave Maria

BLESSED ARE THEY THAT DWELL IN THY HOUSE see
Sumsion, Herbert

BLESSED ARE THEY WHO DO THY WILL see Martini,
Padre, O Salutaris

BLESSED ARE THEY WHO FEAR THE LORD see Morgan,
Haydn

BLESSED ARE THOSE THAT ARE UNDEFILED see
Greene, Maurice

BLESSED ARE THOSE WHO BELIEVE see Newbury, Kent
A.

BLESSED ARE YOU see Diemer, Emma Lou

BLESSED ART THOU see Crandell, R., Bendictus Es

BLESSED ART THOU see Crandell, R., Benedictus
Es

BLESSED ART THOU see Davis, J.

BLESSED ART THOU see Egerton, A.H.

BLESSED ART THOU see Lovelace, Austin C.

BLESSED ART THOU see Mc Guire, Felix

BLESSED ART THOU see Marsh, Benedictus Es,
Domine

BLESSED ART THOU see Mead, Edward G.

BLESSED ART THOU see Pasquet, Jean

BLESSED ART THOU FOREVER see York, D.S.

BLESSED ART THOU, O LORD see Berger, Jean

BLESSED ART THOU, O LORD see Kirk, Theron W.

BLESSED ART THOU, O LORD see Lassus, Roland de
(Orlandus)

BLESSED ART THOU, O LORD see Willan, Healey

BLESSED ART THOU, O LORD GOD see Droste

BLESSED ART THOU, O LORD OF OUR FATHERS see
Shaw, Martin

BLESSED ASSURANCE see Hughes

BLESSED ASSURANCE see Hustad, Donald P.

BLESSED ASSURANCE see Knapp, Lavater

BLESSED ASSURANCE see Wolf

BLESSED ASSURANCE see Young, Carlton R.

BLESSED ASSURANCE, JESUS IS MINE see Wilson

BLESSED BE GOD see Fissinger, Edwin

BLESSED BE GOD see Jacobson

BLESSED BE THAT LORD IN MAJESTY see Edmunds,
John

BLESSED BE THAT MAID MARIE see Ehret, Walter

BLESSED BE THAT MAID MARIE see Hardwicke

BLESSED BE THE GOD see Davison, John

BLESSED BE THE GOD AND FATHER see Wesley,
Samuel Sebastian Jr.

BLESSED BE THE KING see Harter, [Harry]

BLESSED BE THE LORD see Englert, Eugene

BLESSED BE THE LORD see Gibbons, Orlando

BLESSED BE THE LORD see Glarum, L. Stanley

BLESSED BE THE LORD see Gottlieb, J., Bar'chu

BLESSED BE THE LORD see Monaco, Richard A.

BLESSED BE THE LORD see Nelson, Ronald A.

BLESSED BE THE LORD see Purcell, Henry

BLESSED BE THE LORD see Riley, Dennis

BLESSED BE THE LORD see Tallis, Thomas

BLESSED BE THE LORD see Wilson, Ira B.

BLESSED BE THE LORD ALLELUIA see Nelson, R.
Wayne

BLESSED BE THE LORD GOD see Amner

BLESSED BE THE LORD GOD see Amner, John

BLESSED BE THE LORD GOD OF ISRAEL see Shelley

BLESSED BE THE LORD GOD OF ISRAEL see Swann,
Donald, Benedictus

BLESSED BE THE LORD GOD OF SABAOTH see Genuchi,
Ivan

BLESSED BE THE NAME OF GOD see Roff, Joseph

BLESSED BE THE NAME OF THE LORD see Ford,
Virgil T.

BLESSED BE THE NAME OF THE LORD see Maunder,
J.H.

BLESSED BE THE NAME OF THE LORD see Willis

BLESSED BE THOU HEAVENLY QUEEN *BVM
(Andrews, H.K.) 2pt,acap (very easy) oct
OXFORD 44.604 $.30   (B4071)

BLESSED BE THY GLORIOUS NAME see Stevens,
Halsey

BLESSED BE THY NAME see Tallis, Thomas, Mihi
Autem Nimis

BLESSED BE THY NAME FOREVER see Brandon, G.

BLESSED BIRD, THE see Niles, John Jacob

BLESSED BIRTH, THE see Davies, Henry Walford

BLESSED BIRTH, THE see Dretke, L.N.

BLESSED CHILD, THE *Xmas,carol
(Ehret, Walter) SA (flemish) FRANK F-611 $.35
                                     (B4072)

BLESSED CHRISTMAS MORN see O'connor

BLESSED CITY, HEAVENLY SALEM *hymn
oct ROYAL s.p.   (B4073)

BLESSED CITY, HEAVENLY SALEM see Arnatt, Ronald

BLESSED CITY, HEAVENLY SALEM see Wetzler,
Robert

BLESSED, HE see Franck, Cesar

BLESSED INFANT, THOU *Xmas
(Follett) SATB oct PRO ART 2013 $.25 (B4074)

BLESSED IS EVERY ONE see Berger, Jean

BLESSED IS HE see Berger, Jean

BLESSED IS HE see Gagliano

BLESSED IS HE see Harper, M.

BLESSED IS HE see Head, Michael (Dewar)

BLESSED IS HE see Lotti, Antonio, Regina Caeli

BLESSED IS HE see Purcell, Henry

BLESSED IS HE see Victoria, Tomas Luis de

BLESSED IS HE THAT COMES see Cram

BLESSED IS HE THAT COMETH see Brown, Leon F.

BLESSED IS HE THAT COMETH see Luvaas

BLESSED IS HE THAT COMETH see Thompson,
Randall, Benedictus

BLESSED IS HE THAT COMETH see Voris, W.R.

BLESSED IS HE THAT FEARETH THE LORD see
Colonna, Giovanni Paolo, Beatus Vir Qui
Timet Dominum

BLESSED IS HE WHO COMETH see Gounod, Charles
Francois

BLESSED IS HE WHO COMETH see Wienhorst, Richard

BLESSED IS HE WHO WALKS NOT IN THE PATH OF THE
WICKED see Schutz, Heinrich

BLESSED IS THE MAN see Bradley

BLESSED IS THE MAN see Corelli, Arcangelo

BLESSED IS THE MAN see Glarum, L. Stanley

BLESSED IS THE MAN see Jones

BLESSED IS THE MAN see Lekberg, Sven

BLESSED IS THE MAN see Marshall, Jane M.

BLESSED IS THE MAN see Rachmaninoff, Sergey
Vassilievitch

BLESSED IS THE MAN see Stevens, Halsey, Beatus
Vir

BLESSED IS THE MAN see Waring, Peter

BLESSED IS THE MAN see Whitney, M.

BLESSED IS THE NATION see Coggin, Elwood

BLESSED IS THE NATION see Roff, Joseph

BLESSED IS THE NATION see Root

BLESSED IS THE NATION see Tkach

BLESSED IS THE NATION see Wilson, John F.

BLESSED JESU see Cram

BLESSED JESU see Dvorak, Antonin

BLESSED JESU see Elgar

BLESSED JESU see Pergolesi, Giovanni Battista,
Stabat Mater

BLESSED JESU FONT OF MERCY
(Pitcher, Gladys) 3pt mix cor,pno (med) oct
WILLIS 8498 $.25   (B4075)

BLESSED JESU, FOUNT OF MERCY see Dvorak,
Antonin

BLESSED JESU, LORD OF ALL see Cherubini, Luigi

BLESSED JESUS see Ahle

BLESSED JESUS see Bodycombe, [Aneurin]

BLESSED JESUS see Cherubini, Luigi, Pie Jesu

BLESSED JESUS see Cram

BLESSED JESUS see Dvorak, Antonin

BLESSED JESUS see Smith, Alfred M.

BLESSED JESUS, AT THY WORD see Bach, Johann
Sebastian

BLESSED JESUS AT THY WORD see Thiman, Eric
Harding

BLESSED JESUS, AT THY WORD see Wolff

BLESSED LORD see Smith, Norman O.

BLESSED LORD, ALL LOVE EXCELLING see Liszt,
Franz, Ave Verum Corpus

BLESSED LORD JESUS see Buxtehude, Dietrich

BLESSED LORD OF HEAVEN ABOVE see Powell

BLESSED LORD, WILT THOU SUSTAIN US see
Mendelssohn-Bartholdy, Felix, Geistliches
Lied

BLESSED MAN WHOM GOD DOTH AID see Lovelace,
Austin C.

BLESSED MARY (from King Of Kings)
SSA/SATB BIG3 $.30   (B4076)

BLESSED MARY, FAITHFUL JOSEPH see Lindstrom

BLESSED MARY TO THE TEMPLE
cor SCHMITT   (B4077)

BLESSED MIRACLES see Kimmel

BLESSED MOTHER OF HEAVEN see Ingegneri, Marco
Antonio, Santa Madre Del Ciel

BLESSED MOTHER OF THE SAVIOR see Bernabei,
(Giuseppe) Ercole, Alma Redemptoris Mater

BLESSED REDEEMER see Denza, Luigi

BLESSED REDEEMER see Fearis, J.S.

BLESSED REDEEMER see Wilson

BLESSED REDEEMER, AT THY WORD see Mendelssohn-
Bartholdy, Felix

BLESSED SACRAMENT see Agostini, Paolo, Ego Sum
Panis Vivus

BLESSED SACRAMENT see Constantini, Alessandro,
Ego Sum Panis Vivus

BLESSED SAVIOR, NOW BEFORE US see Schubert,
Franz (Peter)

BLESSED SAVIOUR, OUR LORD JESUS see Hassler,
Hans Leo

BLESSED SON OF GOD see Vaughan Williams, Ralph

BLESSED SPIRIT, FONT OF MERCY see Dvorak,
Antonin, Eia Mater, Fons Amoris

BLESSED THE BREAD AND WATER see Robertson,
Leroy

BLESSED THE PEOPLE see Geisler, Johan C.

BLESSED THEY see Brahms, Johannes

BLESSED THROUGHOUT ALL GENERATIONS see
Hovhaness, Alan, Omnes Generationes

BLESSING see Curran, Pearl Gildersleeve

BLESSING, A see Hardt

BLESSING, A see Schroth

BLESSING, A see Shaw, Martin

BLESSING, A (GO FORTH INTO THE WORLD IN PEACE)
see Shaw, Martin

BLESSING AND GLORY see Rachmaninoff, Sergey
Vassilievitch

BLESSING AND HONOR *Easter/Lent
(Hadley) SATB,opt trp oct PRO ART 2357 $.30
                                     (B4078)

BLESSING AND HONOR see Blake, George [M.]

BLESSING AND HONOR see Fitch

BLESSING AND HONOR see Hutson

BLESSING AND HONOR see Mueller, Carl F.

BLESSING AND HONOR see Thompson, V.D.

BLESSING AND HONOR see York, D.

BLESSING AND HONOR AND GLORY AND POWER see
Buebendorf

BLESSING AND RIGHTEOUSNESS see Berger

BLESSING FOR EASTER MORNING, A see Ferguson

BLESSING, GLORY AND WISDOM see Bach

BLESSING, GLORY AND WISDOM see Bach, Johann
Sebastian

BLESSING, GLORY AND WISDOM see Tkach, D.

BLESSING, GLORY, AND WISDOM see Wagner

BLESSING, GLORY AND WISDOM, AND THANKS see Bach

BLESSING, GLORY, WISDOM, AND THANKS see Brewer,
Sir Alfred Herbert

BLESSING, GLORY, WISDOM AND THANKS see Wagner,
Georg Gottfried

BLESSING, HONOR, POW'R AND GLORY see Kent

BLESSING OF AARON, THE see Ramsey

BLESSING OF MARY, THE see Page, R.

BLESSING OF OUR LORD, THE see Rosenmueller, Die
Gnade Unsers Herrn

BLESSING OF SAINT FRANCIS see Vermulst, Jan

BLESSING OF THE TRINITY see Pasquet, Jean

BLESSINGS *Bibl
(Parker) SATB,acap oct LAWSON 51592 $.30
                                     (B4079)

BLESSINGS see Parker, Alice

BLESSINGS OF MARY, THE *Xmas
(Johnson) SATB oct LILLENAS AN-5016 $.25
                                     (B4080)

BLESSINGS OF PEACE see Arkhangelsky, G.

BLEST ARE THE PURE see Darst, W. Glenn

BLEST ARE THE PURE see Thiman, Eric Harding

BLEST ARE THE PURE IN HEART see Dieckmann, C.

BLEST ARE THE PURE IN HEART see Eaton, Richard
S.

BLEST ARE THE PURE IN HEART see Huerter,
[Charles]

BLEST ARE THE PURE IN HEART see Vick, Beryl,
Jr.

BLEST ARE THE PURE IN HEART see Wolff, S.
Drummond

BLEST ARE THEY see Stanton

BLEST ARE THEY see Williams

BLEST ARE THEY THAT MOURN see Brahms, Johannes

BLEST BE THE LORD GOD OF ISRAEL see Grime,
William

BLEST BE THE TIE THAT BINDS see Ringwald, [Roy]

BLEST DAY OF GOD see Ramsfield

BLEST IS THE MAN see Lassus, Roland de
(Orlandus)

BLEST SPIRIT see Wideen, Ivar

BLEST SPIRIT, ONE WITH GOD ABOVE see Brahms,
Johannes

BLIJF BIJ MIJ, HEER (HOUD HOOG UW KRUIS) see
Monk, William Henry

BLIJF MET MIJ, HEER see Monk, William Henry

BLIND AND ALONE see Matthews, Harvey Alexander

BLIND MAN see Simpson, Kenneth

BLINDA FA SIN SYN see Nilsson, Torsten

BLISS, PAUL
Angels From The Realms Of Glory *Xmas
3pt wom cor,opt pno (easy) oct WILLIS 2371
$.10   (B4081)

BLISS, PAUL (cont'd.)

Bethlehem *Xmas,Bibl/cant
  wom cor,soli voc sc WILLIS $.80 (B4082)
  mix cor,SAMez soli,org (easy) voc sc WILLIS
  $.75 (B4083)

Birth Of Christ *Xmas,Bibl/cant
  speak cor voc sc WILLIS $.75 (B4084)

Birth Of Christ, The *Xmas,Bibl
  3pt wom cor/3pt jr cor,opt acap,org/pno
  (easy) voc sc WILLIS $.60 (B4085)

Christ Child, The *Xmas,Bibl/cant
  mix cor,S,B soli,pno/org (easy) oct WILLIS
  $.50 (B4086)
  mix cor voc sc WILLIS $.60 (B4087)

Christ The King *Easter,cant
  mix cor,SATB/SMezTB soli,pno/org (med) oct
  WILLIS $.75 (B4088)

Christmas *Xmas,cant
  mix cor&jr cor,high solo,med solo,pno/org
  (easy) oct WILLIS $.75 (B4089)
  jr cor&mix cor,soli voc sc WILLIS $.80 (B4090)

Consider The Lilies
  3pt wom cor,opt pno (med) oct WILLIS 2410
  $.12 (B4091)
  TTBB,opt org (easy) oct WILLIS 2903 $.12 (B4092)

Early Will I Seek Thee
  SATB,S/T solo,pno (easy) oct WILLIS 2612
  $.15 (B4093)

Eastertide *Easter,Bibl
  3pt wom cor/3pt jr cor,opt acap,pno/org
  (easy) voc sc WILLIS $.60 (B4094)

Hallelujah! 'Tis Done
  see TEMPO CHORAL PACKAGE NO. 1

Hark! What Mean Those Holy Voices *Xmas
  TTBB,opt org (easy) oct WILLIS 3166 $.10 (B4095)

It Is Well With My Soul
  (McLellan) SATB oct LILLENAS AT-1048 $.25 (B4096)

Junior Choir Collection Volume 1 *see Bixby,
  A.K.

Junior Choir Collection Volume 1, The *see
  Bixby, A.K.

Junior Choir Collection Volume 2 *see Bixby,
  A.K.

Junior Choir Collection Volume 2, The *see
  Bixby, A.K.

Let The Lower Lights Be Burning
  TTBB,pno/gtr oct LAWSON 51293 $.30 (B4097)

O'er The Distant Mountains *Xmas/Reces,carol
  SATB,pno (easy) oct WILLIS 3916 $.15 (B4098)

Ring Merry Bells
  see SIX EASTER CAROLS

Sacred Two-Part Choruses For Junior Choirs
  *CCU
  SA/2pt jr cor oct PRESSER $1.25 (B4099)

While Shepherds Watched *Xmas
  3pt wom cor,acap (easy) oct WILLIS 2370
  $.12 (B4100)

BLISS, SIR ARTHUR (1891-)
  Beatitudes, The *Bibl/cant
  SATB,soli,org,2fl,2ob,2clar,2bsn,4horn,
  2trp,3trom,tuba,strings,3perc,timp,harp
  voc sc NOVELLO s.p., ipr (B4101)

He Is The Way *hymn
  SATB oct NOVELLO 44.1444.06 s.p. (B4102)

Lord, Who Shall Abide In Thy Tabernacle?
  *anthem
  mix cor oct NOVELLO 28.1475.07 s.p. (B4103)

Mary Of Magdala *cant
  SATB,A solo,3fl,2ob,clar,bsn,2horn,2trp,
  strings,2perc,timp,harp voc sc NOVELLO
  s.p., ipr (B4104)

O Give Thanks Unto The Lord *Thanks,anthem
  mix cor oct NOVELLO 40.1471.05 s.p. (B4105)

Prayer To The Infant Jesus, A *prayer
  SSAA,acap oct NOVELLO 51.0668.00 s.p. (B4106)

Put Thou Thy Trust In The Lord *anthem
  dbl cor,acap oct NOVELLO 28.1483.08 s.p. (B4107)

Stand Up And Bless The Lord *anthem
  mix cor oct NOVELLO 28.1387.04 s.p. (B4108)

Sweet Day, So Cool *hymn
  SATB oct NOVELLO 44.1445.04 s.p. (B4109)

World Is Charged With The Grandeur Of God,
  The *cant
  SATB,2fl,3trp,4trom voc sc NOVELLO s.p.,
  ipr (B4110)

BLITHEMAN, WILLIAM
  In Pace *anthem/mot
  "In Peace" [Lat] mix cor,acap oct NOVELLO
  40.1439.01 s.p. (B4111)

  In Peace *see In Pace

BLITZSTEIN, MARC (1905-1964)
  This Is The Garden *cant
  mix cor CHAPPELL 0013995-368 $2.50 (B4112)

BLIV KVAR HOS MIG see Runback, Albert

BLIV KVAR HOS OSS see Nilsson, Torsten

BLOCH, ERNEST (1880-1959)
  Adonai, Elohim (from Israel Symphony)
  [Eng/Heb/Fr] SSAAB,SAB soli oct SCHIRM.G
  s.p. (B4113)

  Avodath Hakodesh
  "Sacred Service" [Eng/Heb] SATB,orch BROUDE
  BR. voc sc $4.00, ipr, cor pts $2.50, ipr

BLOCH, ERNEST (cont'd.)
  (B4114)

  Benediction (from Sacred Service)
  [Heb/Eng] SATB,Bar solo,pno BROUDE BR. $.35 (B4115)

  Sacred Service *see Avodath Hakodesh

  Sanctification (from Sacred Service)
  SATB,pno BROUDE BR. $.40 (B4116)

  Silent Devotion And Response (from Sacred
  Service)
  mix cor SOUTHERN $.35 (B4117)
  [Heb/Eng] SATB,pno BROUDE BR. $.40 (B4118)

BLOCH, WALDEMAR (1906-)
  Deutsches Ordinarium
  jr cor&cong,cantor,org DOBLINGER voc sc
  s.p., cor pts s.p. (B4119)

  Du Grosser Schmerzensmann (from Passio
  Domini) chorale
  mix cor,acap oct DOBLINGER s.p. see also
  Sechs Chorale (B4120)

  Missa Brevis *Mass
  3pt wom cor,acap cor pts DOBLINGER s.p. (B4121)

  Missa Carminum Ad Horam Matutinam *Mass
  4pt mix cor,acap voc sc DOBLINGER s.p. (B4122)

  O Haupt Voll Blut Und Wunden (from Passio
  Domini) chorale
  mix cor,acap oct DOBLINGER s.p. see also
  Sechs Chorale (B4123)

  O Lamm Gottes Unschuldig (from Passio Domini)
  chorale
  mix cor,acap oct DOBLINGER s.p. see also
  Sechs Chorale (B4124)

  O Traurigkeit, O Herzeleid (from Passio
  Domini) chorale
  mix cor,acap oct DOBLINGER s.p. see also
  Sechs Chorale (B4125)

  Passio Domini *ora
  mix cor,soli,orch DOBLINGER voc sc s.p.,
  cor pts s.p. (B4126)

  Sechs Chorale (from Passio Domini) chorale
  mix cor,acap cmplt ed DOBLINGER s.p.
  contains & see also: Du Grosser
  Schmerzensmann (from Passio Domini); O
  Haupt Voll Blut Und Wunden (from Passio
  Domini); O Lamm Gottes Unschuldig (from
  Passio Domini); O Traurigkeit, O
  Herzeleid (from Passio Domini); Sei
  Getreu Bis An Das Ende (from Passio
  Domini); Wer Hat Dich So Geschlagen
  (from Passio Domini) (B4127)

  Sei Getreu Bis An Das Ende (from Passio
  Domini) chorale
  mix cor,acap oct DOBLINGER s.p. see also
  Sechs Chorale (B4128)

  Wer Hat Dich So Geschlagen (from Passio
  Domini) chorale
  mix cor,acap oct DOBLINGER s.p. see also
  Sechs Chorale (B4129)

BLOM, OSCAR
  All Den Helga Kristenhet
  mix cor NORDISKA 2316 s.p. (B4130)

  Jesu, Du Som Barnen Alla
  unis jr cor/2pt jr cor/unis wom cor/2pt wom
  cor,org NORDISKA 3969 s.p. (B4131)

  Krist Ar Uppstanden
  mix cor NORDISKA 2937 s.p. (B4132)

  To Realms Of Glory
  (Lundquist) SATB,acap oct WILLIS 8407 $.22 (B4133)

  Vart Hjarta Lyfta Vi, O Gud
  mix cor NORDISKA 2936 s.p. (B4134)

BLOMDAHL, KARL-BIRGER (1916-1968)
  Anabase
  [Fr] SATB,narrator,Bar solo,orch voc sc
  SCHOTT 10644 s.p., ipr (B4135)

BLOMQUIST, R.
  Tidings Of Joy *Xmas
  SATB,med solo,pno (easy) oct WILLIS 6471
  $.12 (B4136)

BLOMSTRE SOM EN ROSENGARD see Sletten, Jacob

BLOOD OF CHRIST JESUS, THE see Bach, Johann
  Michael, Das Blut Jesu Christi

BLOOD THAT STAINED THE OLD RUGGED CROSS, THE
  TTBB BIG3 $.25 (B4137)

BLOOM, C.G.L.
  Jesu, Creator Of The World *Gen,anthem
  1-4pt (med easy) oct GIA G661 $.30 (B4138)

BLOSDALE, DON
  Over The Hills
  SATB,acap SEESAW $1.00 (B4139)

BLOSSOM TIME NOW COMETH see Gesius,
  Bartholomaus

BLOTT DU MIG, JESU, KAN LARA see Sorenson,
  Torsten

BLOW
  Coronation And Verse Anthems *CCU,anthem
  cor STAINER 3.8907.8 $18.00 (B4140)

  In The Time Of Trouble
  (Statham) SATB,opt inst (med easy) oct OXFORD
  43.376 $.35 (B4141)

  My God, My God, Look Upon Me
  (Knight, Gerald) SATB,acap oct FISCHER,C
  CM-7507 $.25 (B4142)

BLOW, BLOW THE CLARION TRUMPET see Purcell,
  Henry

BLOW, GOLDEN TRUMPETS see Wild, W.

BLOW, JOHN (1649-1708)
  Be Merciful Unto Me *Gen/Lent
  SATB (med) oct OXFORD 43.931 $.30 (B4143)

  Behold, O God Our Defender
  SATB,opt org STAINER MB7-1 s.p. contains
  also: Let My Prayer Come Up (B4144)
  (Rasmussen, Henning Bro) SSATB HANSEN-DEN
  474 s.p. see also Four Coronation Anthems (B4145)
  (Rasmussen, Henning Bro) SATB HANSEN-DEN
  475 s.p. see also Four Coronation Anthems (B4146)

  Bow Down Thine Ear, O Lord (Psalm 86) Gen/
  Lent
  (Statham) SATBB,opt inst (med easy) oct
  OXFORD 43.375 $.30 (B4147)

  Four Coronation Anthems
  (Rasmussen, Henning Bro) [Eng] HANSEN-DEN
  28834 s.p.
  contains: Behold, O God, Our Defender
  (SSATB); Behold, O God, Our Defender
  (SATB); Let My Prayer Come Up (SATB);
  Let Thy Hand Be Strengthened (SATB)
  see also: Behold, O God, Our Defender;
  Let My Prayer Come Up; Let Thy Hand Be
  Strengthened (B4148)

  Gloria Patri Qui Creavit Nos *mot
  (Shaw, Watkins) [Lat] SSATB,org SCHOTT
  10694 s.p. (B4149)

  God Spake Sometime In Visions
  SSAATBB,org/strings STAINER D3 s.p. (B4150)

  I Beheld, And Lo! A Great Multitude *ASD,
  Bibl
  (Shaw) SATB, male quartet (med) oct OXFORD
  $.35 (B4151)

  I Will Praise The Name Of God (Psalm 69) Gen/
  Thanks
  (Statham) SATB (med easy) oct OXFORD 43.374
  $.50 (B4152)

  In The Time Of Trouble (Psalm 86) Gen
  SATB,opt inst (med easy) oct OXFORD $.35 (B4153)

  Let My Prayer Come Up
  see Blow, John, Behold, O God Our Defender
  (Ehret) SATB oct ELKAN-V 362-1321 $.30 (B4154)
  (Ehret, W.) SATB oct PRESSER 362-01321 $.30 (B4155)
  (Rasmussen, Henning Bro) SATB HANSEN-DEN
  476 s.p. see also Four Coronation Anthems (B4156)

  Let Thy Hand Be Strengthened *anthem
  (Nicholson, S.H.) mix cor oct NOVELLO
  28.1097.02 s.p. (B4157)
  (Rasmussen, Henning Bro) SATB HANSEN-DEN
  473 s.p. see also Four Coronation Anthems (B4158)
  (Simkins) SATB SCHOTT s.p. (B4159)

  Lift Up Your Heads *anthem/Bibl
  (Shaw, Watkins) mix cor,org,strings oct
  NOVELLO 88.0017.00 s.p. (B4160)

  Magnificat And Nunc Dimittis (from Short
  Service, The (No. 4)) Magnif/Nunc
  (Shaw, Watkins) SATB (G maj) oct NOVELLO
  88.0021.09 s.p. (B4161)

  My Days Are Gone Like A Shadow (Psalm 102)
  Lent
  (Statham) SATB,opt org (med) oct OXFORD
  42.980 $.30 (B4162)

  My God, My God, Look Upon Me *anthem
  SATB,acap BROUDE BR. $.45 (B4163)
  (Simkins, C.F.) [Eng] SATB CHESTER s.p. (B4164)

  O Lord God Of My Salvation *anthem
  (Shaw, Watkins) SSAATTBB,opt org SCHOTT
  s.p. (B4165)

  O Pray For The Peace Of Jerusalem *anthem
  (Shaw, Watkins) mix cor,S solo oct NOVELLO
  28.1286.10 s.p. (B4166)

  Praise The Lord, Ye Servants (Psalm 113) Gen
  (Statham) SATB (med easy) oct OXFORD 43.377
  $.30 (B4167)

  Psalm 38 *see Put Me Not To Rebuke

  Psalm 69 *see I Will Praise The Name Of God

  Psalm 86 *see In The Time Of Trouble

  Psalm 102 *see My Days Are Gone Like A
  Shadow

  Psalm 113 *see Praise The Lord, Ye Servants

  Put Me Not To Rebuke (Psalm 38) Gen
  (Statham) SATB,opt inst (med easy) oct
  OXFORD 43.378 $.35 (B4168)

  Salvator Mundi *anthem
  [Lat] SSATB/SSTB,org/pno PETERS H105 $.40 (B4169)
  [Lat] mix cor oct NOVELLO 03.0126.04 s.p. (B4170)
  (Dearnley, C.) [Lat] SSATB,org BROUDE,A.
  214 $.35 (B4171)

BLOW OUT THE TRUMPET see Peerson, Martin

BLOW UP THE TRUMPET IN SION see Purcell, Henry

BLOW, WINDS, O SOFTLY BLOW *Xmas,Ger
  (Mueller) 3pt wom cor,S solo oct SCHIRM.G
  8159 $.25 (B4172)
  (Mueller) 2pt boy cor/SA,SA soli oct SCHIRM.G
  8436 $.25 (B4173)

BLOW YE THE TRUMPET IN ZION see Jackson,
  Francis

BLOW YE THE TRUMPET IN ZION see Vene, Ruggero,
  Canite Tuba In Sion

BLOW, YE WINDS, SOFTLY see Kennerly

BLOW YO' GOSPEL TRUMPET
see Street Corner Spirituals

BLOWER, MAURICE
Bless'd Are The Pure In Heart
SATB THOMP.G G-542 s.p.   (B4174)

Brighter Dawn Is Breaking, A
SATB THOMP.G G-543 s.p.   (B4175)

BLUE CLOAK, THE see Brown, Dora

BLUH AUF, GEFRORNER CHRIST see Silesius,
Angelus

BLUM, ROBERT (1900-   )
Der Kampf Des Elias (from Muspilli Um 860)
[Ger] men cor,perc HUG s.p.   (B4176)

BLUMENSCHEIN, WILLIAM LEONARD (1849-1916)
My Soul Doth Magnify
4pt mix cor,SBar soli oct SCHIRM.G 3788
$.25   (B4177)

BLYTON, CAREY
Lullaby, A *Xmas,carol
oct ROYAL 344 s.p.   (B4178)

BOALT
Christ Is Born *Xmas,cant
1-2pt jr cor oct LORENZ $1.75   (B4179)
SAB oct LORENZ $1.75   (B4180)

Our Mighty Lord *Easter,cant
SATB LORENZ $1.95   (B4181)

Wonderful Savior *Easter,cant
SATB/SA LORENZ $1.50   (B4182)

BOARDMAN, E.
Christ Is Arisen *Easter
SSA oct PRESSER MC455 $.30   (B4183)

BOAR'S HEAD CAROL *Xmas
unis/SATB (easy) OXFORD 08.019 $.15   (B4184)
(Poston) SATB,acap (med) OXFORD 84.068 $.35
                                           (B4185)
(Sargent) SATB,acap (very easy) OXFORD 43.055
$.35   (B4186)

BOAR'S HEAD CAROL, THE *Xmas,carol,Eng
see Two Old English Christmas Carols
(Shaw; Parker) 4pt men cor,acap oct SCHIRM.G
10179 $.25   (B4187)

BOATNER, [EDWARD H.] (1898-   )
Angel Rolled The Stone Away, The *spir
SATB,acap oct COLOMBO 1657 $.30   (B4188)

Baby Bethlehem *spir
SATB,acap oct COLOMBO 2378 $.30   (B4189)

I Want Jesus To Walk With Me
SATB oct GALAXY 1.1735.1 $.30   (B4190)

Star, The *spir
SATB,acap oct COLOMBO 2379 $.30   (B4191)

BOATWRIGHT, HOWARD (1918-   )
Ah, Holy Jesus, How Hast Thou Offended (from
Passion According To Saint Matthew, The)
SATB,opt org SCHIRM.EC 2662 $.25   (B4192)

All Praise To Thee (from Passion According To
Saint Matthew, The)
SATB,opt org SCHIRM.EC 2665 $.25   (B4193)

Alone Thou Goest Forth, O Lord (from Passion
According To Saint Matthew, The)
SATB,opt org SCHIRM.EC 2666 $.30   (B4194)

Come, Holy Spirit *see Nunc Sancte Nobis
Spiritus

Communion Service (from Mass In C) Commun
SATB (med) OXFORD rental   (B4195)

Creator Of The Stars *Adv,hymn
SATB,acap SCHIRM.EC 2438 $.30   (B4196)

For Sins Of Heedless Word And Deed (from
Passion According To Saint Matthew, The)
SATB,opt org SCHIRM.EC 2664 $.25   (B4197)

Go To Dark Gethsemane (from Passion According
To Saint Matthew, The)
SATB&desc,org SCHIRM.EC 2661 $.30   (B4198)

God Is Our Refuge (Psalm 46)
SATB,acap SCHIRM.EC 2441 $.22   (B4199)

Hear My Cry, O God (Psalm 61)
SATB,acap SCHIRM.EC 2440 $.35   (B4200)

I Will Lift Up Mine Eyes Unto The Hills
(Psalm 121)
SATB,acap SCHIRM.EC 2652 $.45   (B4201)

Jesus, All Thy Labor Vast (from Passion
According To Saint Matthew, The)
SATB,opt org SCHIRM.EC 2670 $.30   (B4202)

Mass In C *Mass
mix cor oct OXFORD rental   (B4203)

Morning Hymn
SATB,acap SCHIRM.EC 2454 $.45   (B4204)

Nunc Sancte Nobis Spiritus
"Come, Holy Spirit" [Lat/Eng] SATB,acap
SCHIRM.EC 2439 $.45   (B4205)

O Sacred Head, Sore Wounded (from Passion
According To Saint Matthew, The)
SATB,opt org SCHIRM.EC 2668 $.25   (B4206)

Passion According To Saint Matthew, The
SATB,soli,org SCHIRM.EC 2660 $1.75   (B4207)

Psalm 46 *see God Is Our Refuge

Psalm 61 *see Hear My Cry, O God

Psalm 121 *see I Will Lift Up Mine Eyes Unto
The Hills

BOATWRIGHT, HOWARD (cont'd.)
Royal Banners Forward Go, The (from Passion
According To Saint Matthew, The)
SATB,opt org SCHIRM.EC 2667 $.25   (B4208)

Sing My Tongue, The Glorious Battle (from
Passion According To Saint Matthew, The)
SATB&desc,org SCHIRM.EC 2671 $.30   (B4209)

Star In The East *Xmas
SATB,acap SCHIRM.EC 2437 $.40   (B4210)

We Sing Of God, The Mighty Source
SATB,org SCHIRM.EC 2742 $.35   (B4211)

When I Survey The Wondrous Cross (from
Passion According To Saint Matthew, The)
SATB,opt org SCHIRM.EC 2669 $.25   (B4212)

Who Was The Guilty (from Passion According To
Saint Matthew, The)
SATB,opt org SCHIRM.EC 2663 $.25   (B4213)

BOBEL, KARL (1931-   )
Es Ist Ein Ros' Entsprungen *Xmas
SAT/SAB HANSSLER 6.094 s.p. contains also:
Bodenschatz, Erhard, Gelobet Seist Du,
Jesu Christ (SATB)   (B4214)

O Lamm Gottes, Unschuldig
SA,treb inst/bass inst HANSSLER 14.055 s.p. (B4215)

BOBERG
Christ Is Born *Xmas
SATB,acap oct FISCHER,C CM-7454 $.30   (B4216)

SSA,acap (med) oct FISCHER,C CM-7455 $.25 (B4217)

BOBROV
I Dreamed It Was The Night *Xmas
(Roff) SATB oct SHAPIRO SCE 2502 $.30   (B4218)

(Roff) SSA oct SHAPIRO SCE 3501 $.30   (B4219)

BOBROWITZ, DAVID
Creation, The (composed with Porter, Steven)
*Xmas,Bibl
cor,pno,drums,gtr (rock cantata) voc sc
WALTON M 114 $2.00, ipa   (B4220)

Requiem For A Friend *Req
(Porter, Steven) SATB,opt brass,drums,gtr
oct WALTON 2136 $.40, ipa   (B4221)

BOCCARD, C.C.
Cycle Of Psalms, A *Psalm
SSA JUSKO 112 voc sc $2.00, cor pts $.80   (B4222)

Praise Ye The Lord *anti
SSA oct JUSKO 246 $.25   (B4223)

BOCCHERINI, LUIGI (1743-1805)
Stabat Mater
(Vecchi, Prof. Giuseppe) 3pt,2vln,vla,vcl
oct FORNI 62 s.p.   (B4224)

BOCK
Hymns In Response *hymn
SATB oct LILLENAS AN-6005 $.35   (B4225)

Joy To The World, The Lord Is Coming *Adv
SATB (med diff/diff) SOUTHERN $.40   (B4226)

Let All Nations Praise The Lord
SATB oct BELWIN 1995 $.25   (B4227)

Praise God!
SATB oct SACRED S-113 $.40   (B4228)

BOCK, F.
All That We Do
SATB oct PLYMOUTH FB-104 $.25   (B4229)

Glory And Honor
SATB oct PLYMOUTH FB-101 $.25   (B4230)

God Is At Work Within You
SA oct PRESSER G-117 $.35   (B4231)

Grateful Heart, A
SATB oct PRESSER G-149 $.35   (B4232)

I Sing The Greatness Of God
SATB oct PRESSER G-120 $.35   (B4233)

If We Could See Beyond Today
SATBB oct PRESSER G-128 $.30   (B4234)

Lord's Prayer, The
SATB oct BOURNE 935 $.35   (B4235)

To You, Blessed Mary
SATB oct PLYMOUTH FB-105 $.25   (B4236)

Tree Of Peace
SATB oct PRESSER G-134 $.35   (B4237)

BOCK, FRED (1939-   )
Alleluia, Alleluia
SSA oct AGAPE SP 706 $.35   (B4238)

Before Thy Cross We Sinners Bend
TTBB WORD CS-2421 $.30   (B4239)

Four Communion Responses *CC4U,Commun
SATB oct AGAPE A 450 $.30   (B4240)

Gloria In Excelsis
SATB oct STAFF 317 $.30   (B4241)

I Will Sing Of My Redeemer
SATB oct WORD CS-655 $.25   (B4242)

Let Your Joy Be Known! *Fest
mix cor&jr cor/treb cor,org oct WORD
CS-2393 $.35   (B4243)

Manger Story, The *Xmas
SATB oct STAFF 385 $.25   (B4244)

O Lord, We Beseech Thee
SATB oct AGAPE A 412 $.30   (B4245)

One Solitary Life
SA (easy) PRESSER G-197 $.40   (B4246)
SATB (med easy) PRESSER G-196 $.40   (B4247)

BOCK, FRED (cont'd.)
Save Me, O Lord
SATB oct STAFF 342 $.25   (B4248)

Set Thy Love
SATB oct WORD CS-320 $.30   (B4249)

Song Of Triumph *Bibl
SATB,SB soli,org voc sc WALTON M 123 $1.50
                                           (B4250)

Such Good Things
SATB oct WORD CS-335 $.30   (B4251)

When He Cometh
SA oct WORD CS-691 $.25   (B4252)

BOCK, H.
O Salutaris
[Lat] Mez LEMOINE s.p.   (B4253)

BODA, JOHN (1922-   )
Babe Of Beauty *Xmas
SA,kbd (med easy) oct CONCORDIA 98-1656
$.25   (B4254)

Before The Paling Of The Stars *Xmas
SA,kbd (med easy) oct CONCORDIA 98-1566
$.25   (B4255)

BODE, ARNOLD G.H.
Hark! The Sound Of Holy Voices *ASD/Gen
SATB,pno/org (med) WILLIS 6260 $.16   (B4256)

BODENSCHATZ, ERHARD (1576-1636)
Danket Dem Herrn Heut Und Allzeit
SATB HANSSLER 6.2542 s.p. contains also:
Cruger, Johann, O Meine Seel, Du Sollst
Den Herren Preisen; Bach, Johann
Sebastian, Gott Hat Die Erd Schon
Zugericht't   (B4257)

Gelobet Seist Du, Jesu Christ
see Bobel, Karl, Es Ist Ein Ros'
Entsprungen
see Bach, Johann Sebastian, Lobt Gott Ihr
Christen

Jesus Christus, Unser Heiland, Der Den Tod
see Praetorius, Michael, Wohlauf, Ihr
Christen, Freuet Euch

Joseph, Kjaere Josef Du
(Nystedt, Knut) [Norw] LYCHE 10 s.p.   (B4258)

Joseph, Lieber Joseph *Xmas
mix cor HANSSLER 6.313 s.p.   (B4259)

Joseph, Lieber Joseph Mein *Xmas
[Ger] SATB,acap (easy) MULLER MS 69 s.p.
                                           (B4260)

Now Christ Our Lord Is Risen Again *see
Surrexit Christus Hodie

Surrexit Christus Hodie *Easter
[Lat] SATB,acap (easy) MULLER MS 40 s.p.
                                           (B4261)
(Granville) "Now Christ Our Lord Is Risen
Again" SATB,acap oct FOX CM5 $.25 (B4262)

Uppstanden Ar Var Herre Krist
see UPPSTANDELSE
mix cor NORDISKA 4566 s.p.   (B4263)

BODYCOMBE, [ANEURIN]
Apostle's Creed
SATB oct VOLKWEIN VB107 $.25   (B4264)

Blessed Jesus
SSA oct VOLKWEIN VB117 $.25   (B4265)
SATB oct VOLKWEIN VB116 $.25   (B4266)

Bread Of The World *Commun
SATB oct VOLKWEIN VB119 $.25   (B4267)

For This Dear Land
SATB,band oct VOLKWEIN VB149 $.30   (B4268)

Give Ear, O Lord, Unto My Prayer *prayer
SATB oct VOLKWEIN VB152 $.25   (B4269)

God Be Merciful Unto Us
SATB oct VOLKWEIN VB157 $.30   (B4270)

Hear The Bells Ring Out With Joy *Xmas
SATB oct VOLKWEIN VB168 $.25   (B4271)

How Sweet To Know The Love Of Jesus
SATB oct VOLKWEIN VB174 $.25   (B4272)

I Met The Master Face To Face
SATB oct VOLKWEIN VB182 $.30   (B4273)

Jesus, My Lord
SATB oct VOLKWEIN VB197 $.25   (B4274)

O Come And Mourn
SATB oct VOLKWEIN VB697 $.30   (B4275)

O Master, Let Me Walk With Thee
4pt mix cor,org/pno oct SCHIRM.G 10453 $.25
                                           (B4276)

O Thou Whose Glory Shone Like Fire
SATB oct VOLKWEIN VB236 $.25   (B4277)

Psalm 23 *Bibl
SATB oct VOLKWEIN VB273 $.25   (B4278)

These Are They
SATB oct VOLKWEIN VB266 $.25   (B4279)

This, Our Prayer *prayer
SATB oct VOLKWEIN VB268 $.25   (B4280)

While Shepherds Watched Their Flocks *Xmas
SATB oct VOLKWEIN VB278 $.30   (B4281)

BOEDIJN, GERARD H. (1893-   )
Hymne Aan De Zang
mix cor ALSBACH&D sc s.p., cor pts s.p.
                                           (B4282)

Jesu Allerliefste Kind
mix cor ALSBACH&D sc s.p., cor pts s.p.   (B4283)

BOEKE, J.D.
Acht Oud-Franse Kerstliederen *CC8U,Xmas
wom cor BROEKMANS 71 s.p.   (B4284)

BOEKE, J.D. (cont'd.)

Acht Oud-Franse Kerstliedjes *CC8U,Xmas
wom cor BROEKMANS 71 s.p. (B4285)

BOELLMANN, LEON (1862-1897)
Tantum Ergo (from Lyra Sacra) mot
[Lat] SATB,T/S solo,opt harp&vln,org LEDUC
SACREE
voc sc s.p., voc pt s.p. see from MUSIQUE
(B4286)

BOERINGER, JAMES
I Will Bless The Lord
SATB oct FISCHER,J 9890 $.30 (B4287)

Jesu, The Very Thought Is Sweet
SATB oct SACRED S-1 $.35 (B4288)

King In The Creche, The *Xmas
jr cor&sr cor oct FISCHER,J 9898 $.40 (B4289)

Morning Of Christ's Nativity *Xmas,cant
mix cor BELWIN $1.50 (B4290)

Thy Testimonies Are Very Sure
4pt mix cor oct SCHIRM.G 11216 $.25 (B4291)

Twelve New Hymns For Children *CC12U,hymn
unis BELWIN $1.00 (B4292)

Upon The Rock Of Faith
see FOUR CONTEMPORARY HYMNS, SET I

What Kind Of King? *Xmas
SATB (med) ABINGDON APM-566 $.35 (B4293)

BOETPSALMEN see Monnikendam, Marius

BOEX, A.J.
Catholic Canticles *CC18L,hymn
(easy) voc sc WILLIS $.40 (B4294)

Mass In Honor Of St. Ignatius *Mass
SA/TB,org (easy) voc sc WILLIS $.60 (B4295)

Mass In Honor Of St. Lawrence *Mass
2pt jr cor,org (easy) voc sc WILLIS $.50 (B4296)

BOHEMIAN CAROL see Hokanson, M.

BOHLEN, D.
Prayer For Strength And Light (Psalm 42) Gen,
anthem/prayer
SATB (med) oct GIA G1029 $.30 (B4297)

Psalm 42 *see Prayer For Strength And Light

BOHM, BRODRE
Jesus, Vor Gud Og Frelser *see Stobaeus,
Johann

BOHM, GEORG (1661-1733)
Mein Freund Ist Mein *cant
(Schroeder) SATB,cont,2vln,2vla
HANSSLER 10.042 sc s.p., cor pts s.p.,
ipa (B4298)

BOHM, JOSEPH (1795-1876)
Mein Freund Ist Mein
[Ger/Dut] voc sc PETERS HU1474 $2.00, ipr (B4299)

BOHRNSTEDT, WAYNE
We Have Builded An House *Bibl
SATB,org/pno,2trp oct WORLD CA-2088-8 $.45 (B4300)

BOISDEFFRE, CHARLES-HENRI-RENE DE (1838-1906)
Cantique *Op.80
[Fr] 2 eq voices,solo ENOCH voc sc s.p.,
cor pts s.p. (B4301)

BOISSIERE
Deuxieme Messe Breve *Mass
[Fr] 2 eq voices,pno (F maj) LEDUC BL144
voc sc s.p., voc pt s.p. (B4302)

Premiere Messe Breve *Mass
[Fr] 2 eq voices,pno (D maj) LEDUC BL66 voc
sc s.p., voc pt s.p. (B4303)

BOJ, O HELLIGAND, OS ALLE see Jeppesen, Knud

BOLAND, KATHLEEN
O Little Star *carol
unis CRAMER 2 (B4304)

BOLD AND FREE see Mullins

BOLD PETER see Huggett

BOLDEMANN, LACI
I De Stora Skogarna
see Nattlig Madonna

Nattlig Madonna
wom cor/jr cor NORDISKA 5987 s.p.
contains: I De Stora Skogarna; Nattlig
Madonna; Portratet; Rosen; Sommar I
Bergen (B4305)

Nattlig Madonna
see Nattlig Madonna

Portratet
see Nattlig Madonna

Rosen
see Nattlig Madonna

Sommar I Bergen
see Nattlig Madonna

BOLDI, N.
Fortem Virili Pectore
see INNI DE COMUNE

BOLLBACK
Ring The Bells *Xmas
(Decou) SATB oct LILLENAS AT-C101 $.30 (B4306)

(Wilson) SATB oct AGAPE F 944 $.30 (B4307)

BOLLINGER, A.E.
Angel's Song, The (School Song) *Xmas
unis,pno (easy) oct WILLIS 4291 $.12 (B4308)

BOLTZE
Let Us Ever Walk With Jesus
(Manz) unis oct SUMMY 1503 $.35 (B4309)

BOLZ
Child Of God
see Two Madrigals For Christmas

Lo! A Brighter Star
see Two Madrigals For Christmas

Two Madrigals For Christmas *Xmas
SA oct FOX PS142 $.30
contains: Child Of God; Lo! A Brighter
Star (B4310)

BON see Heggen, Bodvar

BON see Kjeldaas, Gunnar

BON see Soraas, Lars

BON HOMME see Kenins, Talivaldis

BON KARLEK OCH TRO see Nystedt, Knut

BOND, ANDERS
Ar Halsad Skona Morgonstund (Psalm 55)
mix cor NORDISKA 2864 s.p. (B4311)

I Himmelen Sjunger Kring Lammets Tron
[Swed] SATB,org GEHRMANS KRB 247 (B4312)

Lovad Vare Herren
(Ahlen, Waldemar) 2pt wom cor/2pt jr cor,
acap NORDISKA 4448 s.p. (B4313)

Nu Haver Denna Dag (Psalm 440)
mix cor NORDISKA 2863 s.p. (B4314)

Psalm 55 *see Ar Halsad Skona Morgonstund

Psalm 440 *see Nu Haver Denna Dag

Visa Fran Leksand
mix cor NORDISKA 934 s.p. (B4315)

BONDEVILLE, [EMMANUEL DE] (1898-)
O Salutaris *Commun,mot
[Lat] 4pt mix cor,opt pno/org DURAND s.p. (B4316)

[Lat] 4pt mix cor,acap,opt pno/org oct
DURAND (B4317)

Tantum Ergo
[Lat/Fr] mix cor,org,3trp,3trom voc sc
DURAND s.p., ipa (B4318)

BONDS, [MARGARET] (1913-)
Go Tell It On The Mountains *Xmas
SATB,acap oct PRESSER MC432 $.30 (B4319)

Hold On *spir
SATB oct PRESSER MC427 $.35 (B4320)

BONE JESU see Bai, [Tommaso]

BONE PASTOR see Ramsey

BONEPSALM see Gustafson, John

BONER, SIDNEY
How Lovely Shines The Morning Star *Adv/
Epiph/Gen
SATB,acap (med easy) oct CONCORDIA 98-1924
$.40 (B4321)

BONES, COME A-KNITTIN' *spir
(Bartholomew) 4pt men cor,acap oct SCHIRM.G
7757 $.35 contains also: Ready When He
Comes; Roll, Jordon, Roll (B4322)

BONGIORNO MADONNA see Scandelli, A.

BONHAM, EUGENE
Hymn Descants Vol. I *CCU,hymn
unis (easy) ABINGDON APM-763 $1.00 (B4323)

Hymn Descants Vol. II *CCU,hymn
unis (easy) ABINGDON APM-889 $1.00 (B4324)

Hymn Descants Vol. III *CCU,Xmas,hymn
SATB (easy) ABINGDON APM-870 $1.35 (B4325)

BONN see Bjaerum, N.

BONN see Solberg Lief

BONNAL, ERMEND
Cantique De Noel *Xmas,carol
[Fr] wom cor/4pt mix cor,soli,pno voc sc
DURAND s.p. see from Trois Noels (B4326)

Laissez Paistre Vos Betes, Pastoureaux
*Xmas,carol
[Fr] wom cor/4pt mix cor,soli,pno voc sc
DURAND s.p. see from Trois Noels (B4327)

Noel Nouvelet *Xmas,carol
[Fr] wom cor/4pt mix cor,soli,pno voc sc
DURAND s.p. see from Trois Noels (B4328)

Trois Noels *see Cantique De Noel; Laissez
Paistre Vos Betes, Pastoureaux; Noel
Nouvelet (B4329)

BONNEAU, P.
Tantum Ergo *Commun,mot
[Lat] 4pt mix cor,med solo,org DURAND s.p. (B4330)

Victorious Christmas *Xmas
[Eng/Fr] SATB,acap oct SALABERT-US $.65 (B4331)

BONNEL, L.
O Salutaris
[Lat] cor LEMOINE s.p. (B4332)

BONONCINI, GIOVANNI MARIA (1670-1747)
Aeterna Fac *anthem
(Ford, Anthony) [Lat] SSB oct NOVELLO
40.1529.00 s.p. (B4333)

BONSET, JAC.
Het Kind Der Glorie *Op.100
mix cor,pno ALSBACH&D sc s.p., cor pts s.p. (B4334)

Hymne Aan De Morgen *Op.91
men cor ALSBACH&D sc s.p., cor pts s.p. (B4335)

BONSET, JAC. (cont'd.)

Kerstnacht *Op.68
mix cor ALSBACH&D sc s.p., cor pts s.p. (B4336)

Lente-Geboort' *Op.92
mix cor ALSBACH&D sc s.p., cor pts s.p. (B4337)

Lofzang (Psalm 116) Op.154
mix cor,Mez solo,org/pno ALSBACH&D sc s.p.,
cor pts s.p. (B4338)

Psalm 8 *Op.199
mix cor ALSBACH&D sc s.p., cor pts s.p. (B4339)

Psalm 42 *Op.127
men cor sc ALSBACH&D s.p. (B4340)

Psalm 100 *Op.72
mix cor,org/pno ALSBACH&D sc s.p., cor pts
s.p. (B4341)

Psalm 116 *see Lofzang

Spruyte Davids *Op.218
mix cor ALSBACH&D sc s.p., cor pts s.p. (B4342)

BONTA, STEPHEN
In The Bleak Mid-Winter *Xmas
4pt men cor,acap oct SCHIRM.G 11320 $.30 (B4343)

Sir Christemas *Xmas
4pt mix cor,T solo oct SCHIRM.G 11302 $.25 (B4344)

BONUM EST CONFITERI see Eberlin, Johann Ernst

BONUM EST CONFITERI see Palestrina, Giovanni

BONZORNO, MADONNA see Scandello

BOOK
Christmas Fanfare *Xmas
SATB oct PLYMOUTH FB-106 $.25 (B4345)

BOOK OF DESCANTS *CC50U,carol/hymn
(Russell, Leslie) cor voc sc FABER F0367
$1.50, cor pts FABER F0368 $.60 (B4346)

BOOK OF RESPONSES see Fuller, [Esther Mary]

BOOK OF STORIES, THE see Thiman, Eric Harding

BOOK OF VERSES, A (OMAR KHAYYAM) see Ben-Haim,
Paul

BOON, C.
Propitius Esto, Domine
mix cor ALSBACH&D sc s.p., cor pts s.p. (B4347)

BOOTH
Alleluia
SATB,acap oct BELWIN 60840 $.40 (B4348)

We Saw Him Sleeping *Xmas
SATB,S solo,acap WARNER G1484 $.30 (B4349)

BOOZER, PAT
In Heavenly Love
SATB,2treb inst,org oct MCAFEE M1033 $.35 (B4350)

BOR' CHU see Roskin

BOR'CHENU see Weisgal, A.

BORDESE
L'orpheon De La Jeunesse, premiere Volume
*sac/sec,CC25L
[Fr] 2-3pt jr cor,acap oct CHOUDENS s.p. (B4351)

BORDEWIJK-ROEPMAN, JOHANNA (1892-)
Lofpsalm (Psalm 136)
[Dut] mix cor,ST soli,pno,fl,ob,clar,3trp,
3trom,perc BANK (B4352)

Psalm 136 *see Lofpsalm

BORDI, GIOVANNI
Transfige Dulcissime Domine
[Ger] SATB,acap (med) MULLER M 31 s.p. (B4353)

Transfige Dulcissme Domine *anthem/mot
[Lat] mix cor,acap oct NOVELLO DM-31 s.p. (B4354)

BORGESEN, ERLING
Herre, Fylg Du Med Pa Ferdi (Bon)
mix cor MUSIKK 91 s.p. (B4355)

BORLENGHI
Immagini Iontane
4pt mix cor FORLIVESI 14009 s.p. (B4356)

BORN AGAIN see Avery

BORN AGAIN see Skillings, Otis

BORN AMONG US, IN THE MANGER see Berlioz,
Hector

BORN FOR YOU see Glarum, L. Stanley

BORN IN A MANGER see Rogers

BORN IN BETHLEHEM see Frackenpohl, Arthur

BORN IS HE
see Three French Carols

BORN IS HE see Pitfield, Thomas Baron

BORN IS THE LORD EMANUEL see Praetorius,
Michael, En Natus Est Emanuel

BORN OF MARIE see Anderson, [William H.]

BORN THIS DAY see Christiansen

BORN TO BE KING see McWhertor

BORN TO-DAY! see Sweelinck, Jan Pieterszoon,
Hodie Christus Natus Est

BORN TO THE WORLD IS A SHEPHERD see Leaf,
Robert

BORN TO US IS THE CHRIST CHILD see Seay, A.

BORN TODAY see Eilers

BORN TODAY see Marenzio, Luca

BORN TODAY see Sweelinck, Jan Pieterszoon

BORN TODAY IS CHRIST see Poulenc, Francis,
Hodie Natus Christus Est

BORN TODAY IS CHRIST OUR KING see Brown

BORN TODAY IS THE CHILD DIVINE see Chapman

BORN UNTO US see Regnart, Jacob, Puer Natus Est

BORNE, LE
Messe De La Victoire *Mass
1-4pt,org CHOUDENS s.p.   (B4357)

Noel D'apres L'adeste Fideles *Xmas,carol
opt 3pt,solo,opt vln/ob/fl LEMOINE s.p.,
ipa   (B4358)

BORNEFELD, HELMUT (1932-   )
All Morgen Ist Ganz Frisch Und Neu (Cantata
2) Gen
[Ger] SA/SAB,org,2vln,opt vla&vcl (med
easy) sc BAREN. BA 2226 $2.50   (B4359)

Alle Welt Singe *Xmas
[Ger] 1-3 eq voices,inst (med easy) BAREN.
BA 2448 s.p.   (B4360)

Cantata 1 *see O Glaubig Herz, Gebenedei

Cantata 2 *see All Morgen Ist Ganz Frisch
Und Neu

Cantata 3 *see Lobet Den Herren, Alle Die
Ihn Ehren

Cantata 4 *see Herr Jesu Christ, Dich Zu Uns
Wend

Cantata 5 *see Der Herr Ist Mein Getreuer
Hirt

Cantata 6 *see Mein Seel, O Herr, Muss Loben
Dich

Cantata 7 *see Du Meine Seele, Singe

Cantata 8 *see O Traurigkeit, O Herzeleid

Cantata 10 *see Herr Jesu Christ, Du Hochtes
Gut

Cantata 11 *see Frohlich Soll Mein Herze
Springen

Das Choralwerk, No. 1: Advent Zu Trinitas
*CCU,Adv/Gen/Trin
[Ger] unis&opt cor,org,opt inst (med)
BAREN. BA 2928 $7.25   (B4361)

Das Choralwerk, No. 2 *Gen
[Ger] unis&opt cor,org,opt inst (med)
BAREN. BA 2929 $7.25
contains: Gebete; Kirche; Psalmen;
Sakrament; Wort   (B4362)

Das Choralwerk, No. 3 *Gen
[Ger] unis,org,opt inst (med) BAREN.
BA 2930 $7.25
contains: Glaube; Lob Und Dank;
Tageszeiten; Tod Und Ewigkeit   (B4363)

Der Herr Ist Mein Getreuer Hirt (Cantata 5)
Easter/Pent
[Ger] SATB,S solo,org,fl (med diff) BAREN.
BA 2229 sc $2.75, cor pts $.40   (B4364)

Du Meine Seele, Singe (Cantata 7) Gen
[Ger] unis,4trp,2trom,drums,opt org (med
diff) sc BAREN. BA 2442 $2.50, cor pts
$.40, ipa   (B4365)

Ermuntre Dich, Mein Schwacher Geist (Motet 2)
Xmas
[Ger] SATB,acap (med diff) BAREN. BA 2452
$2.75   (B4366)

Es Wolle Gott Uns Gnadig Sein (Motet 10)
Psntd
[Ger] SATB,acap (med diff) BAREN. BA 2460
$2.00   (B4367)

Frohlich Soll Mein Herze Springen (Cantata
11) Xmas
[Ger] SSATB,S solo,org,fl,vla,vcl (med
diff) BAREN. BA 2446 sc $8.75, cor pts
$1.00, ipa   (B4368)
[Ger] SA,opt inst BAREN. BA 177 $.40
                                 (B4369)

Gebete
see Das Choralwerk, No. 2

Glaube
see Das Choralwerk, No. 3

Heilger Geist, Du Troster Mein (Motet 9)
Pent,mot
[Ger] SATB,acap (med diff) BAREN. BA 2459
$2.00   (B4370)

Herr, Ich Habe Lieb Die Statte
see Zwei Psalm-Motetten

Herr Jesu Christ, Dich Zu Uns Wend (Cantata
4)
[Ger] SSATB&cong,org,2trp,2trom (med diff)
BAREN. BA 2228 sc $1.75, cor pts $.55,
ipa   (B4371)

Herr Jesu Christ, Du Hochtes Gut (Cantata 10)
[Ger] SA&men cor,org (med) sc BAREN.
BA 2445 $2.50   (B4372)

Ich Freue Mich Uber Die, So Mir Sagten
see Zwei Psalm-Motetten

Ich Steh An Deiner Krippe Hier *Xmas
[Ger] SA,opt inst BAREN. BA 3048 $.25
contains also: Nun Jauchzet All Ihr
Frommen (SAA)   (B4373)

Jesu, Geh Voran *Gen
[Ger] unis/4pt mix cor&treb cor,org,opt
inst BAREN. BA 3372 s.p.   (B4374)

BORNEFELD, HELMUT (cont'd.)

Jesu Kreuz, Leiden Und Pein *Psntd
[Ger] 3pt mix cor,opt inst (easy) BAREN.
BA 180 s.p.   (B4375)

Jesus Christus Herrscht Als Konig (Motet 8)
Easter/Pent,mot
[Ger] SATB,acap (med diff) BAREN. BA 2458
$2.50   (B4376)

Jesus Christus, Unser Heiland, Der Den Tod
Uberwand *Easter
[Ger] unis,opt S solo,org (med) BAREN.
BA 3778 $.40   (B4377)

Jesus Soll Die Losung Sein (Motet 3) Xmas
[Ger] SA&men cor,acap (med diff) BAREN.
BA 2453 $2.00   (B4378)

Kantoreisatzer (from Kantoreisatzen) CC43U,
Fest/Gen
[Swed] 2-5 eq voices,opt inst (med easy)
BAREN. BA 2591 s.p.   (B4379)

Kantoreisatze, Heft 1 *CC34U,Adv/Xmas/ECY/
Epiph/Gen
[Ger] 2-5 eq voices,opt inst (med easy)
BAREN. BA 2219 $2.75   (B4380)

Kantoreisatze, Heft 2 *CC36U,Easter/Gen/
Pent/Psntd/Trin/Whitsun
[Ger] 2-5 eq voices,opt inst (med easy)
BAREN. BA 2220 $2.75   (B4381)

Kantoreisatze, Heft 3 *CC33U,Eve/Gen
[Ger] 2-5 eq voices,opt inst (med easy)
BAREN. 2221 $2.75 baptism   (B4382)

Kantoreisatze, Heft 4 *CC28U,Gen,prayer/
Psalm
[Ger] 2-5 eq voices,opt inst (med easy)
BAREN. BA 2222 $2.75   (B4383)

Kantoreisatze, Heft 5 *CC34U,Gen,Credo
[Ger] 2-5 eq voices,opt inst (med easy)
BAREN. BA 2223 $2.75 praise and thanks
                                 (B4384)

Kantoreisatze, Heft 6 *CC34U,Gen
[Ger] 2-5 eq voices,opt inst (med easy)
BAREN. BA 2224 $2.75 hours, office,
death, eternity   (B4385)

Kirche
see Das Choralwerk, No. 2

Lob Und Dank
see Das Choralwerk, No. 3

Lobet Den Herren, Alle Die Ihn Ehren (Cantata
3) Gen
[Ger] SA,org/pno,2fl,vcl,opt vln (med)
BA 2227 sc $2.50, cor pts $.40, ipa
                                 (B4386)

Mein Schonste Zier Und Kleinod
see FUNF ALTE KIRCHENLIEDER IN NEUEN
BEARBEITUNGEN

Mein Seel, O Herr, Muss Loben Dich (Cantata
6)
[Ger] SA/TB&cong,org,opt 2inst (med easy)
BAREN. BA 2441 sc $2.50, cor pts $.50
                                 (B4387)

Mit Freuden Zart (Motet 7) Easter
[Ger] SSATB,acap (med diff) BAREN. BA 2457
$2.25   (B4388)
mix cor HANSSLER 7.146 s.p.   (B4389)

Mitten Wir Im Leben *Trin
[Ger] unis&opt 4pt mix cor,org,vcl&1inst
BAREN. BA 3776 $.40   (B4390)

Motet 1 *see O Heiland, Reiss Die Himmel Auf

Motet 2 *see Ermuntre Dich, Mein Schwacher
Geist

Motet 3 *see Jesus Soll Die Losung Sein

Motet 5 *see Wir Danken Dir, Herr Jesu
Christ, Dass Du Fur Uns Gestorben Bis

Motet 6 *see O Haupt Voll Blut Und Wunden

Motet 7 *see Mit Freuden Zart

Motet 8 *see Jesus Christus Herrscht Als
Konig

Motet 9 *see Heilger Geist, Du Troster Mein

Motet 10 *see Es Wolle Gott Uns Gnadig Sein

Nun Jauchzet All Ihr Frommen
see Bornefeld, Helmut, Ich Steh An Deiner
Krippe Hier

O Glaubig Herz, Gebenedei (Cantata 1) Trin
[Ger] SATB,S solo,org,inst (med) BAREN.
BA 2225 $2.25   (B4391)

O Haupt Voll Blut Und Wunden (Motet 6) Psntd
[Ger] SA&men cor/STB,acap (med diff) BAREN.
BA 2456 $2.00   (B4392)

O Heiland, Reiss Die Himmel Auf (Motet 1)
Adv,mot
[Ger] SSATB,acap (med diff) BAREN. BA 2451
$1.25   (B4393)

O Traurigkeit, O Herzeleid (Cantata 8) Psntd
[Ger] SA&men cor,org,2vln,opt vcl (med)
BAREN. BA 2443 sc $2.75, cor pts $.40,
ipa   (B4394)

Psalm Der Nacht *Psalm
mix cor HANSSLER 25.014 s.p.   (B4395)

Psalmen
see Das Choralwerk, No. 2

Sakrament
see Das Choralwerk, No. 2

Sechsunddreissig Geistliche Spruchkanons
*CC36U,Gen,Bibl
[Ger] 2-8 eq voices,acap (easy/diff) BAREN.
BA 2211 s.p.   (B4396)

BORNEFELD, HELMUT (cont'd.)

Tageszeiten
see Das Choralwerk, No. 3

Tod Und Ewigkeit
see Das Choralwerk, No. 3

Verleih Uns Frieden Gnadiglich
see Das Choralwerk, No. 3
[Ger] unis/4pt mix cor,org BAREN. BA 3778
$.40   (B4397)

Wir Danken Dir, Herr Jesu Christ, Dass Du Fur
Uns Gestorben Bis (Motet 5) Psntd
[Ger] SSATTB,acap (med diff) BAREN. BA 2455
$2.75   (B4398)

Wort
see Das Choralwerk, No. 2

Zwei Psalm-Motetten *Gen,mot/Psalm
(med diff) BAREN. BA 5410 $2.25
contains: Herr, Ich Habe Lieb Die Statte
(SSATB,acap); Ich Freute Mich Uber Die,
So Mir Sagten (SATB,acap)   (B4399)

BORNSCHEIN, [FRANZ CARL] (1879-1948)
Babe Of Bethlehem
SATB THOMP.G CF-482 s.p.   (B4400)

God Be Merciful Unto Us *Gen
SATB SCHMITT 1620 $.18   (B4401)

His Star Shineth Clear *Xmas
SSA oct PRESSER 332-15270 $.30   (B4402)

Let There Be Light *Gen
SATB SCHMITT 1619 $.25   (B4403)

BOROGYIN, A.P.
see BORODIN, ALEXANDER PORFIREVITCH

BORRIS, SIEGFRIED (1906-   )
Der Herr Ist Meine Zuflucht *Op.80,No.2
[Ger] SATB,acap cor pts SIRIUS s.p. (B4404)

Dona Nobis Pacem *Op.63, Mass
[Lat] SATB,acap voc sc SIRIUS s.p. (B4405)

Heilge Nacht Der Unendlichen Liebe *Xmas
[Ger] 4pt men cor,acap (med) NAGELS NCH 208
s.p.   (B4406)

Heut Singt Die Liebe Christenheit
see FUNF ALTE KIRCHENLIEDER IN NEUEN
BEARBEITUNGEN
[Ger] men cor,acap (easy) oct SIRIUS 2 s.p.
                                 (B4407)

Ich Gebe Mich In Deine Hande *Op.80,No.3
[Ger] mix cor,S solo,org/opt inst cor pts
SIRIUS s.p., ipa   (B4408)

Jauchzt, Alle Lande, Gott Zu Ehren
see FUNF ALTE KIRCHENLIEDER IN NEUEN
BEARBEITUNGEN
[Ger] men cor,acap (easy) oct SIRIUS 1 s.p.
                                 (B4409)

Jolanthe *Op.115
[Ger] men cor,S solo voc sc SIRIUS s.p.
                                 (B4410)

Krippenspeil *Op.80,No.1, Xmas
[Ger] wom cor&jr cor,opt inst sc SIRIUS
s.p.   (B4411)

Lobe Den Herren
see FUNF ALTE KIRCHENLIEDER IN NEUEN
BEARBEITUNGEN

Lobe Den Herrn
[Ger] men cor,acap (easy) oct SIRIUS 4 s.p.
                                 (B4412)

Madrigale Fur Frauenchor *Op.76, madrigal
[Ger] wom cor voc sc SIRIUS s.p. (B4413)

Mein Schonste Zier Und Kleinod
[Ger] men cor,acap (easy) oct SIRIUS 3 s.p.
                                 (B4414)

Nun Komm Der Heiden Heiland
SAT/SB,treb inst HANSSLER 14.001 s.p.
contains also: Nun Komm Der Heiden
Heiland (SA,treb inst)   (B4415)

Nun Komm Der Heiden Heiland
see Borris, Siegfried, Nun Komm Der Heiden
Heiland

O Haupt Voll Blut Und Wunden
SA/TB,treb inst HANSSLER 14.063 s.p.
                                 (B4416)

Psalm 135 *Op.111
[Ger] mix cor,SATB soli,winds,2horn,2trp,
2trom,strings,timp,perc SIRIUS voc sc
s.p., cor pts s.p., ipa   (B4417)

Verleih Uns Frieden Gnadiglich
[Ger] men cor,acap (easy) oct SIRIUS 5 s.p.
                                 (B4418)

Weihnachtskantate *Xmas,cant
[Ger] wom cor&jr cor,acap sc SIRIUS s.p.
                                 (B4419)

Weihnachtsmotette *Op.76, Xmas,mot
[Ger] men cor,opt S solo,acap voc sc SIRIUS
s.p.   (B4420)

Wir Wollen Sing'n Ein Lobgesang
SS/SA,treb inst HANSSLER 14.114 s.p.
contains also: Fiebig, Kurt, Herr Gott,
Dich Loben Alle Wir (SA,treb inst/bass
inst)   (B4421)

BORSIERI, C.
Ave Maria
see CINQUE AVE MARIA

Ego Dilecto Meo
see SEI MOTTETTI EUCARISTICI

Tantum Ergo
see SEI MOTTETTI EUCARISTICI

BORTNIANSKY, DIMITRI STEPANOVITCH (1751-1825)
Angel Voices Ever Singing
SA oct BELWIN 64033 $.30   (B4422)
SATB,acap oct BELWIN 64032 $.30 (B4423)

BORTNIANSKY, DIMITRI STEPANOVITCH (cont'd.)

Cherubic Hymn No.7 *hymn
SATB oct LESLIE 4077   (B4424)

Cherubim Song *Xmas
(Bement, G.) TTBB,acap oct PRESSER
332-15088 $.30   (B4425)
(Pitcher, Gladys) 3pt mix cor,pno (med) oct
WILLIS 8481 $.20   (B4426)
(Tchaikovsky) mix cor,acap oct SCHIRM.G
8022 $.27   (B4427)
(Tchaikovsky, P.; Ehret) SATB,acap oct PRO
ART 1512 $.25   (B4428)
(Tchaikovsky, P.; Peery, R.) SAB oct
PRESSER 312-40426 $.30   (B4429)
(Tschaikovsky, P.) SATB,acap oct PRESSER
332-14622 $.30   (B4430)

Cherubim Song #7 *Gen
(Tchaikovsky) SATB SCHMITT 1665 $.35   (B4431)

Cherubim Song No. 7 *see Choirs Of Angels
Praise Thee

Children's Bell Carol *Xmas,carol
(Wienandt) unis,opt hndbl oct PRO ART 2433
$.30   (B4432)

Choirs Of Angels Praise Thee *Xmas/Gen
"Cherubim Song No. 7" SATB KJOS 7006 $.30
(B4433)
"Cherubim Song No. 7" SSA KJOS 6019 $.30
(B4434)
"Cherubim Song No. 7" SATB,acap oct
FISCHER,C CM-6315 $.25   (B4435)
"Cherubim Song No. 7" SSA oct FISCHER,C
CM-6314 $.25   (B4436)
(Breck) "Cherubim Song No. 7" 3pt jr cor/
SSA (med) FISCHER,C CM 6314 $.25   (B4437)
(Downing) "Cherubim-Song No. 7" 4pt men
cor,acap oct SCHIRM.G 8383 $.25   (B4438)
(Ehret) "Cherubim Song No. 7" SAB oct PRO
ART 1578 $.30   (B4439)
(Ehret) "Cherubim Song No. 7" SSA oct PRO
ART 1428 $.30   (B4440)
(Ehret) "Cherubim Song No. 7" 2pt oct PRO
ART 1537 $.30   (B4441)
(Ham) "Cherubim Song (No. 7)" SATB oct
GRAY GCMR 687 $.25   (B4442)
(Osman) "Cherubim Song No. 7" SSA&opt men
cor,acap WARNER G1641 $.30   (B4443)
(Tchaikovsky) "Cherubim-Song No. 7" 5pt mix
cor,acap oct SCHIRM.G 2560 $.25   (B4444)
(Tchaikovsky; Deis) "Cherubim-Song No. 7"
3pt mix cor oct SCHIRM.G 9753 $.30   (B4445)
(Tchaikovsky, P.) "Cherubim Song (No. 7)"
SSA oct PRESSER 332-14948 $.25   (B4446)
(Tchaikovsky, P.) "Cherubim Song No. 7"
SATB oct PRESSER 322-35357 $.30   (B4447)
(Tchaikovsky, P.) "Cherubim Song No. 7"
SATB,acap oct PRO ART 1275 $.25   (B4448)
(Tchaikovsky, Piotr; Chapman) "Cherubim
Song No. 7" SATB oct SPRATT 505 $.30   (B4449)
(Treharne) "Cherubim-Song No. 7" 3pt wom
cor,acap oct SCHIRM.G 8939 $.30   (B4450)

Divine Praise *see Kol Slaven

Du Hirte Israels
"Herder Israel" [Ger/Neth] mix cor sc
ALSBACH&D s.p.   (B4451)

Glory And Praise
(Tkach) SATB KJOS 7052 $.30   (B4452)

Glory To God
(Ehret) SATB oct FOX R145 $.25   (B4453)
(Krone) SATB,acap WARNER W2743 $.30   (B4454)
(Krone) TTBB,acap WARNER W3021 $.30   (B4455)

Glory To God In Heaven *Xmas
(Wilhousky) SATB,acap oct FISCHER,C CM-499
$.25   (B4456)
(Wilhousky) SSA oct FISCHER,C CM-645 $.25
(B4457)

Glory To God In The Highest *Pent
(Lundquist) SATTBB,pno (med) oct WILLIS
5731 $.16   (B4458)

Hear My Prayer *anthem/prayer
(Walton) SATB,acap oct FISCHER,C CM-7428
$.25   (B4459)

Herder Israel *see Du Hirte Israels

How Greatly Thou Art Glorified
(Bement) SSA oct FISCHER,J 7411 $.30   (B4460)

I Will Bless The Lord *Commun
SATB,acap SCHIRM.EC 1210 $.25   (B4461)

Israels Herde
men cor NORDISKA 3121 s.p.   (B4462)

Jesus, I My Cross Have Taken
(Killgrove) SATB WARNER R3392 $.30   (B4463)

Jubilate Amen
"Vespersang" [Ger] men cor sc ALSBACH&D
s.p.   (B4464)

Kol Slaven
"Divine Praise" SATB,acap oct PRESSER
332-12857 $.30   (B4465)

Lo, A Voice To Heaven Sounding
SATB,acap SCHIRM.EC 1102 $.30   (B4466)
(Davis, K.) SSA,acap SCHIRM.EC 1079 $.30
(B4467)
(Davis, K.) SSAA,acap SCHIRM.EC 1080 $.30
(B4468)
(Davis, K.) SA,pno/org SCHIRM.EC 1565 $.25
(B4469)
(Marting, E.) SAB,acap SCHIRM.EC 1758 $.30
(B4470)
(Whitford, H.) TTBB,acap SCHIRM.EC 532 $.25
(B4471)

Lord, Grant Thy Servants *Marriage
SATB,acap SCHIRM.EC 1250 $.18   (B4472)

Lord Our God
SATB KJOS 6536 $.30   (B4473)

Lord's Prayer, The
SATB,acap oct FISCHER,C CM-7426 $.25
(B4474)

BORTNIANSKY, DIMITRI STEPANOVITCH (cont'd.)

O Give Thanks Unto The Lord *Thanks
SATB,acap oct FISCHER,C CM-7427 $.25
(B4475)

O God, Thou Art My God *anthem
(Walton) SATB,acap oct FISCHER,C CM-7430
$.25   (B4476)

O Light, Whose Beams Illumine All *anthem/
hymn
(Noble) SATB oct SPRATT 565 $.25   (B4477)

O Lord, How Excellent Is Thy Name
(Walton) SATB,acap oct FISCHER,C CM-7429
$.25   (B4478)

O Taste And See *Commun
SATB,acap SCHIRM.EC 1211 $.25   (B4479)

Our Father *see Pater Noster

Pater Noster
(Geer, E.) "Our Father" SSAA,acap SCHIRM.EC
866 $.22   (B4480)

Praise Ye The Lord Of Heaven *Gen
(Tkach) SATB SCHMITT 1766 $.20   (B4481)

Short Communion Service
SATB,acap SCHIRM.EC 1249   (B4482)

Thine Is The Greatness *anthem
SATB,acap oct FISCHER,C CM-554 $.25   (B4483)

This Is The Day
SATB,acap SCHIRM.EC 1241 $.25   (B4484)

This Is The Day Which The Lord Hath Made
(Ehret) SATB oct BOURNE BL3041 $.30   (B4485)

Thou Hidden Source
(Kirk) SATB&opt desc oct PRO ART 1290 $.20
(B4486)
(Kirk) SAB&opt desc oct PRO ART 1564 $.25
(B4487)

U Bid Ik Aan, O Macht Der Liefde
men cor sc ALSBACH&D s.p. see also Vier
Geestelijke Liederen   (B4488)

Vespersang *see Jubilate Amen

Vier Geestelijke Liederen *see U Bid Ik Aan,
O Macht Der Liefde   (B4489)

We Sing Thy Praise
SSA KJOS 7750 $.30   (B4490)

We Thank Thee, Lord
SSA KJOS 7751 $.30   (B4491)

BORTOLAN, C.
Vexilla Regis
see RACCOLTA DI SEI INNI

BOSSI, MARCO ENRICO (1861-1925)
Cantate Domino
"Hymn Of Glory" SSAA,org SCHIRM.EC 867
$.30, ipr   (B4492)

Canticum Canticorum *Op.120
[Lat] PETERS 3581 $10.00   (B4493)

Domine Ad Adiuvandum
[Lat] SATB,org sc ZANIBON 3914 s.p., cor
pts ZANIBON 3915 s.p.   (B4494)

Hymn Of Glory *see Cantate Domino

Justus Ut Palma Florebit *ASD,mot
[Lat] 3 eq voices,org sc ZANIBON 3956 s.p.,
cor pts ZANIBON 3957 s.p.   (B4495)

Requiem *Req
[Lat] 4pt men cor,org sc ZANIBON 3958 s.p.,
cor pts ZANIBON 3959 s.p.   (B4496)

Salve Regina *BVM
[Lat] 2pt jr cor,org sc ZANIBON 1560 s.p.,
cor pts ZANIBON 1561 s.p.   (B4497)

Sanctificabis Annum Quinquagesimum *mot
[Lat] SATB,org sc ZANIBON 3954 s.p., cor
pts ZANIBON 3955 s.p.   (B4498)

Surrexit Pastor Bonus *Easter,mot
[Lat] 3pt men cor&opt SA,pno/org sc ZANIBON
1564 s.p., cor pts ZANIBON 1565 s.p.
(B4499)

Tantum Ergo *Commun
[Lat] 3pt,org ZANIBON 3917 s.p.   (B4500)

BOSSLER, KURT (1911-   )
Der Herr Ist Mein Getreuer Hirt *Bibl
SAB HANSSLER 6.229 s.p. contains also: In
Dich Hab Ich Gehoffet   (B4501)

Die Sechs Werke Der Barmherzigkeit *CC6U,mot
SATB HANSSLER 7.031 s.p.   (B4502)

Fragst Du Nach Meiner Sunde
SATB sc HANSSLER 19.409 s.p. contains also:
Michel, Josep, Wir Wissen Nicht, Was
Kommt (unis/2pt,kbd/brass); Trubel,
Gerhard, Dein Tod Gebietet Schweigen
(unis,kbd,opt gtr); Barbe, Helmut, Das
Kreuz Ist Aufgerichtet (unis,kbd)   (B4503)

Herr, Unsern Frieden *Gen
SATB,acap (med diff) BOSSE BE 242 s.p. (B4504)

In Dich Hab Ich Gehoffet
see Bossler, Kurt, Der Herr Ist Mein
Getreuer Hirt

Lob Gott Getrost Mit Singen *Thanks
SATB HANSSLER 6.205 s.p.   (B4505)

Manchmal *Gen
unis,acap (easy) BOSSE BE 271 s.p.   (B4506)

Weh! Wir Treten Auf Den Drachen *Fest
[Ger] SATB,acap (med) MULLER SM 2472 s.p.
(B4507)

BOSTON see Billings, William

**BOSTON MUSIC CO. CHRISTMAS CAROLS *CC30U,Xmas,
carol**
unis/mix cor BOSTON 10463 $.50   (B4508)

BOSWELL, ERIC
Boy From Bethlehem *Xmas
unis ASHDOWN U.85 s.p.   (B4509)
unis BOOSEY-CAN s.p.   (B4510)

BOTGORARPSALM *Psalm
(Carlstedt, Jan) [Swed] SATB,acap GEHRMANS
KRB 369   (B4511)

BOTPSALM *Psalm
(Hallnas, Hilding) [Swed] SATB,acap GEHRMANS
KRB 205   (B4512)

BOTPSALM see Thyrestam, Gunnar

BOTTAZZI, B.
Primo Libro *CCU
(Vecchi, Prof. Giuseppe) cor,org oct FORNI
70 s.p.   (B4513)

BOTTAZZO, ALOYSIUS
Missa In B Flat *Mass
[Lat] SA/TB voc sc SCHIRM.G $.50   (B4514)

BOTTAZZO, LUIGI
A S. Cecilia *Op.265, ASD
[Lat] 2 eq voices ZANIBON 2632 s.p.
contains: Jesu Corona Virginum; Veni
Sponsa Christi   (B4515)

A S. Luigi Gonzaga *ASD,Offer
[Lat] ZANIBON 2631 s.p.
contains: Canzone A S. Luigi (unis,org);
Offertorio Per La Festa Di S. Luigi (2
eq voices,org)   (B4516)

Ad Recipiendum Episcopum *Op.356b, mot
[Lat] unis,org cor pts ZANIBON 1260 s.p.
contains: Ecce Sacerdos Magnus; Oremus
Pro Antistite; Sacerdos Et Pontifex
(B4517)

Adeste Fideles
see Tria Motecta Natalicia

Al Momento Della Communione
see Canzoncine Per La Communione

Al Sacro Cuore Di Gesu *Op.296, CC6U
[Lat] 2pt jr cor,org ZANIBON 692 s.p.
(B4518)

Alma Redemptoris
see Antifone Mariane

Antifone Mariane *Op.187, BVM,anti
[Lat] 2 eq voices,org ZANIBON 2653 s.p.
contains: Alma Redemptoris; Ave Regina;
Regina Coeli; Salve Regina   (B4519)

Ave Maria *Op.310a, BVM
see Due Composizione Sacre In Onore Di
Maria Vergine
see TRE MOTECTA IN HON. B.V.M.
[Lat] S/T,pno,vln ZANIBON 805 s.p.   (B4520)
[Lat] unis,org ZANIBON 4 s.p.   (B4521)
[Lat] S/T,pno ZANIBON 804 s.p.   (B4522)
[Lat] SATB ZANIBON 1098 s.p.   (B4523)
[Lat] 2pt mix cor ZANIBON 2609 s.p.   (B4524)

Ave Maris Stella
see Quattro Compositioni Sacre
see RACCOLTA DI SEI INNI

Ave Regina
see Antifone Mariane

Benedic
see CINQUE MOTTETTI

Canzoncine Per La Communione *Op.211, Commun
[Lat] unis,org ZANIBON 2638 s.p.
contains: Al Momento Della Communione;
Dopo La Communione; Prima Della
Communione   (B4525)

Canzone A S. Luigi
see A S. Luigi Gonzaga

Celebre Ave Maria *BVM
[Lat] Mez/Bar,org (A maj) ZANIBON 4013 s.p.
(B4526)
[Lat] Mez/Bar,strings (A maj) ZANIBON 4014
s.p.   (B4527)
[Lat] S/T,org (D maj) ZANIBON 4015 s.p.
(B4528)
[Lat] S/T,strings (D maj) ZANIBON 4016 s.p.
(B4529)

Circunda Tibi Decorem
see IN SOLEMNI CLERICORUM VESTITIONE

Credo III In Gregoriano *Credo/Greg
[Lat] ATB,opt org sc ZANIBON 449 s.p., voc
pt ZANIBON s.p.   (B4530)
[Lat] 1-2pt,opt org sc ZANIBON 613 s.p.
(B4531)

Credo IV *Op.277
see Bottazzo, Luigi, Missa IX Cum Jubilo

De Profundis *Op.312, Req
[Lat] unis,org sc ZANIBON 877 s.p.   (B4532)

Deus Tuorum Militum
see INNI DE COMUNE

Dieci Motecta In Hon. Mariae V *Op.276,
CC10L,BVM,mot
[Lat] unis,org sc ZANIBON 714 s.p., cor pts
ZANIBON 715 s.p.   (B4533)

Dies Irae Ac Libera *Op.119
see Bottazzo, Luigi, Missa Pro Defunctis

Dio Sia Benedetto *Op.328, Commun
[Lat] unis,org ZANIBON 1025 s.p.   (B4534)

Discite A Me
see TRE CANTICI AL S. CUORE DI GESU

Dodici Litanie Lauretane *Op.299, CC12U
[Lat] unis,org ZANIBON 890 s.p.   (B4535)

Dodici Motecta Sacro Cordi Jesu *Op.345,
CC12L,mot
[Lat] unis mix cor,org ZANIBON 230 s.p.
(B4536)

Domine Ad Adjuvandum E Dixit *Op.290
[Lat] SATB,acap cor,soli,org s.p. sc ZANIBON
2601, cor pts ZANIBON 2602   (B4537)

BOTTAZZO, LUIGI (cont'd.)

Dopo La Communione
see Canzoncine Per La Communione

Dormi Non Piangere
see Due Canzoncine Facili Per Il S. Natale

Due Canzoncine Facili Per Il S. Natale *Xmas
2 eq voices ZANIBON 34 s.p.
contains: Dormi Non Piangere; Venite
Adoriamo   (B4538)

Due Composizione Sacre In Onore Di Maria
Vergine *Op.228, BVM
[Lat] 2 eq voices ZANIBON 429A s.p.
contains: Ave Maria; Sub Tuum Praesidium
                                          (B4539)

Due Mottetti Eucaristici *Op.221, Commun
[Lat] 2 eq voices ZANIBON 422 s.p.
contains: Ego Sum Panis; O Quam Suavis
                                          (B4540)

Due Mottetti In On. Di Maria Vergine *BVM,
mot
[Lat] 2 eq voices ZANIBON 491 s.p.
contains: Inviolata; Tota Pulchra (B4541)

Due Mottetti Pel Venerdi Santo *Gd.Fri.,mot
[Lat] 3 eq voices ZANIBON 452 s.p.
contains: Popule Meus; Vexilla Regis
                                          (B4542)

Ecce Fidelis Servus
see Per L'ingresso Parrochiale

Ecce Sacerdos Magnus
see Per La Visita Pastorale
see Ad Recipiendum Episcopum

Ego Sum Panis
see Due Mottetti Eucaristici

Ego Sum Pastor Bonus
see Per L'ingresso Parrochiale

Elegit Te *Op.125, mot
[Lat] 2 eq voices,org ZANIBON 2629 s.p.
                                          (B4543)

Hodie Christus Natus Est
see Tria Motecta Natalicia

I Toni Della Salmodia *Op.323, Eve,chant
[Lat] unis,org ZANIBON 1026 s.p.   (B4544)

Il Santo Natale *Op.293, CC6U,Xmas
2pt jr cor ZANIBON 1023 s.p.   (B4545)

In Festo Epiphania *Op.333, Epiph,Offer
SATB,acap ZANIBON 1097 s.p.   (B4546)

In Nativitate Domini *Op.278, CC12L,Xmas,mot
[Lat] unis,org sc ZANIBON 726 s.p., cor pts
ZANIBON 727 s.p.   (B4547)

In Onore Di S. Antonio *Op.324, ASD
[Lat] unis mix cor/3pt mix cor,opt org
ZANIBON 1024 s.p.
contains: O Lingua Benedicta; Si Quaeris
                                          (B4548)

Inno Constantiniano *hymn
[Lat] unis,org sc ZANIBON 219 s.p., cor pts
ZANIBON 220 s.p.   (B4549)

Inviolata
see Due Mottetti In On. Di Maria Vergine

Iste Confessor
see Quattro Compositioni Sacre

Jaculatorias Da Imm. Conc. *Op.330, CC2U,BVM
[Port] cor ZANIBON 693 s.p.   (B4550)

Jesu Corona Virginum
see A S. Cecilia

Justus Ut Palma Florebit *Op.221, ASD,Offer
[Lat] 2 eq voices ZANIBON 2958 s.p. (B4551)

La Messa Degli Angeli *Op.208, Greg/Mass
[Lat] unis,org sc ZANIBON 95A s.p., cor pts
ZANIBON s.p.   (B4552)

Litanie Del S. Cuore Di Gesu *Op.342
[Lat] 1-3pt,org ZANIBON 324 s.p.   (B4553)

Messa Breve *Greg/Mass
[Lat] unis,org sc ZANIBON 1544 s.p., cor
pts ZANIBON 1545 s.p.   (B4554)

Messa Breve E Facile In On. De S. Martino
Vesc. *Op.201, Mass
[Lat] ABar,org,opt strings (easy) sc
ZANIBON 9 s.p., voc pt ZANIBON 9A-B s.p.
                                          (B4555)

Messa In On. Di Maria Bambina *Op.283, Mass
2pt jr cor,org,opt strings sc ZANIBON 808
s.p., voc pt ZANIBON s.p., ipr   (B4556)

Messa In On. Di S. Clara V. *Op.262, Mass
[Lat] 2 eq voices,org,opt strings sc
ZANIBON 663 s.p., voc pt ZANIBON s.p.,
ipr   (B4557)

Messa In Onore Di S. Dorotea *Op.309, Mass
[Lat] 2 eq voices,org sc ZANIBON 1116 s.p.,
voc pt ZANIBON s.p.   (B4558)

Messa In Onore Di S. Elia, Protettore Degli
Aviatori *Op.305, Mass
unis,soli,org/strings sc ZANIBON 891 s.p.,
cor pts ZANIBON 892 s.p., ipr   (B4559)

Messa In Onore Di S. Guglielmo Ab. *Op.363,
Mass
[Lat] 2 eq voices,acap sc ZANIBON 1515
s.p., cor pts ZANIBON s.p.   (B4560)

Messa In Onore Di S. Tecla *Op.282, Mass
[Lat] unis,org sc ZANIBON 2634 s.p., cor
pts ZANIBON 2635 s.p.   (B4561)

Messa Pei Defunti *Op.273, Greg/Mass/Req
[Lat] unis,org sc ZANIBON 669 s.p.,
ZANIBON s.p.   (B4562)

Militibus In Tuenda Patria Gloriosa Morte
Peremptis *Op.281, Mass
[Lat] 2 eq voices,org ZANIBON   (B4563)

BOTTAZZO, LUIGI (cont'd.)

Miserere *Op.258, Holywk,Greg
[Lat] 2 eq voices&unis,org ZANIBON 1718
s.p.   (B4564)

Missa In Hon. B. Gregorii Card. Barbarici
*Op.190, Mass
unis,org sc ZANIBON 1408 s.p., cor pts
ZANIBON 1498 s.p.   (B4565)

Missa In Hon. Mariae Assumptae *Op.150, Mass
TB,org,opt strings sc ZANIBON 5 s.p., voc
pt ZANIBON s.p.   (B4566)

Missa In Hon. S. Benedicti AB. *Op.217,
Mass
[Lat] TTB,org/strings sc ZANIBON 96 s.p.,
voc pt ZANIBON 96A-B-C s.p., ipr   (B4567)

Missa In Hon. S. Joannis Baptistae *Op.260,
Mass
2 eq voices,org,opt strings sc ZANIBON 1741
s.p., voc pt ZANIBON s.p.   (B4568)

Missa In Hon. S. Marcellinae V *Mass
[Lat] unis,opt org sc ZANIBON 716 s.p., voc
pt ZANIBON s.p.   (B4569)

Missa In Hon. S. Rosae Vir. Limanae *Op.263,
Mass
[Lat] unis,org,opt strings sc ZANIBON 609
s.p., cor pts ZANIBON 610 s.p., ipr (B4570)

Missa In Hon. Virginis Deiparae *Op.280,
Mass
[Lat] AB,org sc ZANIBON 767 s.p., voc pt
ZANIBON s.p.   (B4571)

Missa IX Cum Jubilo *Op.277, Greg/Mass
[Lat] unis,org voc sc ZANIBON 589 s.p., cor
pts ZANIBON 590 s.p., sc ZANIBON 342
s.p., min sc ZANIBON 341 s.p. contains
also: Credo IV   (B4572)

Missa Pro Defunctis *Op.119, Mass/Req
[Lat] 3pt,org sc ZANIBON 2501 s.p., voc pt
ZANIBON 2501A-B-C s.p. contains also:
Dies Irae Ac Libera   (B4573)
[Lat] unis,org sc ZANIBON 875 s.p., cor pts
ZANIBON 876 s.p.   (B4574)

Nove Inni D'uso Piu Commune *Op.274, CC9L,
Greg
[Lat] unis,org ZANIBON 395 s.p.   (B4575)

O Lingua Benedicta
see In Onore Di S. Antonio

O Quam Suavis
see Due Mottetti Eucaristici

O Salutaris Hostia
see SEI MOTTETTI EUCARISTICI

Offertorio Per La Festa Di S. Luigi
see A S. Luigi Gonzaga

Oremus Pro Antistite
see Ad Recipiendum Episcopum

Otto Cantica Eucaristica *Op.271, CC7L,
Commun
[Lat] unis,org sc ZANIBON 723 s.p., voc pt
ZANIBON 724 s.p.   (B4576)

Otto Tantum Ergo *Op.270, CC8U,Commun
[Lat] 1-4pt ZANIBON 725 s.p.   (B4577)

Pange Lingua
see Quattro Compositioni Sacre

Parti Variabli O Sequenza Della Messa Di
Pasqua *Op.323, Easter
[Lat] unis/3pt mix cor ZANIBON 1092 s.p.
                                          (B4578)

Pater Noster *Op.300, prayer
[Lat] unis,org sc ZANIBON 858 s.p., cor pts
ZANIBON 859 s.p.   (B4579)

Per La Notte Del Santo Natale *Op.242, CC2U,
Xmas,Gloria
unis/2pt,org ZANIBON 528 s.p.   (B4580)

Per La Visita Pastorale
[Lat] 2 eq voices,org ZANIBON 393 s.p.
contains: Ecce Sacerdos Magnus; Sacerdos
Et Pontifex   (B4581)

Per L'ingresso Parrochiale *Op.355, mot
[Lat] unis,org ZANIBON 1247 s.p.
contains: Ecce Fidelis Servus; Ego Sum
Pastor Bonus; Tu Es Sacerdos   (B4582)

Per L'Ora Di Adorazione *Op.292, CC11L,
Commun,mot
[Lat] unis,org sc ZANIBON 826 s.p., cor pts
ZANIBON 827 s.p.   (B4583)

Popule Meus
see Due Mottetti Pel Venerdi Santo

Prima Della Communione
see Canzoncine Per La Communione

Pro Pace Et Gloria *Op.268, Greg/Te Deum
[Lat] 2 eq voices,org sc ZANIBON 587 s.p.,
cor pts ZANIBON 588 s.p. contains also:
Te Deum Laudamus   (B4584)

Proprium Missae *Op.367, BVM
[Lat] unis/3pt mix cor,org ZANIBON 1739
s.p.   (B4585)

Proprium Missae *Op.364, Xmas/Circum/Epiph
unis/ATB,opt org ZANIBON 1519 s.p. (B4586)

Proprium Missarum In Festo Sacratissimi
Cordis Jesu *Op.366
see Bottazzo, Luigi, Proprium Missarum In
Festo SS. Trinitatis

Proprium Missarum In Festo SS. Corpus Christi
*Op.366
see Bottazzo, Luigi, Proprium Missarum In
Festo SS. Trinitatis

BOTTAZZO, LUIGI (cont'd.)

Proprium Missarum In Festo SS. Trinitatis
*Op.366, Corpus/Trin
[Lat] unis/ATB,opt org ZANIBON 1738 s.p.
contains also: Proprium Missarum In Festo
SS. Corpus Christi; Proprium Missarum In
Festo Sacratissimi Cordis Jesu   (B4587)

Quatordici Canzoncine Catechistice *CC14U
[Lat] unis,org ZANIBON 1659 s.p.   (B4588)

Quattro Canzoncine Mariane *Op.251b, CC4U,
BVM
[Lat] 2 eq voices,org ZANIBON 2621 s.p.
                                          (B4589)

Quattro Compositioni Sacre *Op.253
[Lat] 2 eq voices,org ZANIBON 1478 s.p.
contains: Ave Maris Stella; Iste
Confessor; Pange Lingua; Tu Es Sacerdos
                                          (B4590)

Quattro Litanie Lauretane *Op.357, CC4L,Greg
[Lat] TTB,org ZANIBON 1590 s.p.   (B4591)

Quattro Pange Lingua *Op.362, CC4U,Commun
[Lat] 1-3pt ZANIBON 1520 s.p.   (B4592)

Regina Coeli
see Antifone Mariane

Resonet In Laudibus
see Tria Motecta Natalicia

Sacerdos Et Pontifex
see Per La Visita Pastorale
see Ad Recipiendum Episcopum

Salve Regina *Op.252, BVM
see QUATTRO ANTIFONE MARIANE
see Antifone Mariane
[Lat] 2 eq voices ZANIBON 1477 s.p. (B4593)

Sedici Canzoncine A Maria Vergine *Op.215,
CC16U,BVM
[Lat] unis/3pt mix cor ZANIBON 14 s.p.
                                          (B4594)

Sei Litanie Lauretane *Op.351, CC6U
[Lat] 2pt jr cor ZANIBON 1190 s.p. (B4595)

Sette Motetti Eucaristici *Op.287, CC7L,
Commun,mot
[Lat] ABar,org sc ZANIBON 828 s.p., cor pts
ZANIBON 829 s.p.   (B4596)

Sette Motetti Eucaristici *Op.225, CC7L,
Commun,mot
[Lat] 2 eq voices,org ZANIBON 2579 s.p.
                                          (B4597)

Si Quaeris
see In Onore Di S. Antonio

Stellario In Onore Di Maria SS. *Op.230,
CC12U,BVM
[Lat] A/3pt mix cor sc ZANIBON 451 s.p.,
cor pts ZANIBON 484 s.p.   (B4598)

Sub Tuum Praesidium *Op.177, BVM
see Due Composizione Sacre In Onore Di
Maria Vergine
[Lat] 2 eq voices,org ZANIBON 2652 s.p.
                                          (B4599)

Tantum Ergo
see QUATTRO MOTTETTI EUCARISTICI

Tantum Ergo *Op.227, Commun
[Lat] 2 eq voices,org ZANIBON 2651 s.p.
                                          (B4600)

Tantum Ergo *Op.250b, Commun
[Lat] TTB,org ZANIBON 1476 s.p.   (B4601)
[Lat] 2 eq voices,org ZANIBON 1475 s.p.
                                          (B4602)

Te Deum Laudamus *Op.268
see Bottazzo, Luigi, Pro Pace Et Gloria

Tota Pulchra
see Due Mottetti In On. Di Maria Vergine

Tria Motecta Natalicia *Op.295, Xmas,mot
[Lat] ZANIBON 2674 s.p.
contains: Adeste Fideles (2 eq voices);
Hodie Christus Natus Est (unis);
Resonet In Laudibus (2 eq voices)
                                          (B4603)

Tu Es Sacerdos
see IN PRIMA MISSA CELEBRANDA
see Per L'ingresso Parrochiale
see Quattro Compositioni Sacre

Veni Sponsa Christi
see PRO VESTITIONE MONIALIUM
see A S. Cecilia

Venite Adoriamo
see Due Canzoncine Facili Per Il S. Natale

Venite Populi
see DUE MOTTETTI EUCARISTICI

Vespri Della Domenica *Op.372, Eve,Greg
[Lat] unis,opt org ZANIBON 1599 s.p.
                                          (B4604)
"Vespro Della Domenica" [Lat] 1-3pt,opt org
ZANIBON 1599 s.p.   (B4605)

Vespro *Op.298, CC7L
[Lat] 2pt mix cor,org sc ZANIBON 1192 s.p.,
voc pt ZANIBON 1561-62 s.p.   (B4606)

Vespro Della Domenica *Op.359, CC9U,BVM/Eve,
anti/Greg/hymn
[Lat] unis,org sc ZANIBON 1744 s.p., cor
pts ZANIBON 1745 s.p.   (B4607)

Vespro Della Domenica *see Vespri Della
Domenica

Vexilla Regis
see Due Mottetti Pel Venerdi Santo

Victimae Paschali *Op.249, Easter
[Lat] 2 eq voices,org ZANIBON 2648 s.p.
                                          (B4608)

BOTTCHER, GEORG

Drei Alte Hausinschriften
3 eq voices,3vln HANSSLER 7.106 s.p.
contains: Herr Gott, Dies Haus Bewahr;
Ubique Est Omniaque Inspicit Deus; Wilt
Du Geben Sonnenschein   (B4609)

BOTTCHER, GEORG (cont'd.)

Herr Gott, Dies Haus Bewahr
see Drei Alte Hausinschriften

Ubique Est Omniaque Inspicit Deus
see Drei Alte Hausinschriften

Wilt Du Geben Sonnenschein
see Drei Alte Hausinschriften

BOTTENBERG, [WOLFGANG]
God Himself Is With Us
SATB oct LORENZ C272 $.30   (B4610)

Law Of Love, The *Bibl
2 eq voices/2pt mix cor,org oct WORLD
ESA-1817-2 $.45   (B4611)

Power Of Prayer, The *Bibl
2 eq voices/2pt mix cor,org oct WORLD
ESA-1816-2 $.45   (B4612)

BOTTIGLIERO, EDUARDO
Ave Maria *BVM,Offer
[Lat] 3 eq voices ZANIBON 2964 s.p. (B4613)

Ave Maria *Op.102, BVM
[Lat] unis,org ZANIBON 2741 s.p.   (B4614)

Ave Verum Corpus
see Quattro Mottetti Eucaristici

Complete Requiem Mass
(Montani, Nicola A.) [Lat] unis voc sc
SCHIRM.G $.75   (B4615)

Cor Jesu Flagrens
see CINQUE MOTTETTI

Dieci Litanie Facilissime In Onore Della
B.V.M. *Op.57, CC10U
[Lat] 2 eq voices,org (very easy) sc
ZANIBON 1665 s.p., voc pt ZANIBON 1665A-B
s.p.   (B4616)

Dio Sia Benedetto
see Quattro Canti Eucaristici

Domine Non Sum Dignus
see Quattro Canti Eucaristici

Ego Sum Panis
see Quattro Mottetti Eucaristici

Flos Carmeli
see QUATTRO CANTI ALLA MADONNA DEL CARMINE

Gustate Et Vidette
see Quattro Mottetti Eucaristici

Inno Popolare A S. Giuseppe *Op.62, ASD,hymn
[Lat] unis,org ZANIBON 2664 s.p.   (B4617)

Iste Confessor *Op.178
[Lat] 2 eq voices,org ZANIBON 2715 s.p.
                                  (B4618)

Missa In Hon. S. Mauri Abbatis *Op.81, Mass
[Lat] TB,org sc ZANIBON 2571 s.p., cor pts
ZANIBON s.p.   (B4619)

O Salutari
see Quattro Mottetti Eucaristici

Parce Domine
see Quattro Canti Eucaristici

Per L'Ora Santa
see Quattro Canti Eucaristici

Quattro Canti Eucaristici *Op.80, Commun
[Lat] ZANIBON 2959 s.p.
contains: Dio Sia Benedetto (2 eq voices,
org); Domine Non Sum Dignus (S/T,org);
Parce Domine (3 eq voices,org); Per
L'Ora Santa (unis,org)   (B4620)

Quattro Mottetti Eucaristici *Op.114, Commun
[Lat] 2pt,org ZANIBON 2580 s.p.
contains: Ave Verum Corpus; Ego Sum
Panis; Gustate Et Vidette; O Salutari (B4621)

Veritas Mea *ASD,Offer
[Lat] 2 eq voices,org ZANIBON 2717 s.p.
                                  (B4622)

BOTTLE, CAROL
Breton Carol, The
unis sr cor CRAMER 77   (B4623)

Bring The Christmas Log To Town *Xmas
unis sr cor CRAMER 78   (B4624)

BOUGHTON, RUTLAND (1878-1960)
Alleluia! (from Bethlehem) Xmas,Allelu
mix cor CURWEN 80642 s.p.   (B4625)
4pt mix cor oct CURWEN 10692 $.20   (B4626)

Bethlehem *Xmas,cant
(Widdicombe) wom cor,SA soli,fl&ob&2clar&
bsn&2horn&2trp&2trom&strings&timp&bells&
harp/pno&strings CURWEN voc sc rental,
cor pts rental, sc rental   (B4627)

Holly And The Ivy, The *Xmas,carol
SSA ALLANS 434 s.p.   (B4628)

O Come, All Ye Faithful *Xmas,carol
mix cor CURWEN 80625 s.p.   (B4629)

BOUICHERE, EMILE
Cantate Domino
[Lat] 4pt mix cor,opt pno/org HEUGEL s.p.
                                  (B4630)

BOULANGER, LILI (1893-1918)
De Profundis
see Psaume

Du Fond De L'abime
see Psaume

Psaume 24 *see Psaume 24

Psaume *Psalm
[Fr] cor,A solo,orch&org/2pno DURAND oct
s.p., sc s.p., ipa
contains: De Profundis; Du Fond De
L'abime   (B4631)

BOULANGER, LILI (cont'd.)

Psaume 24 (Psalm 24) Psalm
[Fr] cor,orch&org/pno DURAND voc sc s.p.,
sc s.p., ipa   (B4632)
SATB oct ELKAN-V $3.00   (B4633)

BOULAY, J.
Agnus Dei *Agnus
[Lat] SSA,solo,org ENOCH voc sc s.p., cor
pts s.p.   (B4634)

Regina Coeli *BVM,mot
[Lat] SSA,solo,org ENOCH voc sc s.p., cor
pts s.p.   (B4635)

Sub Tuum
[Lat] SS,org ENOCH voc sc s.p., cor pts
s.p.   (B4636)

Tantum Ergo *mot
[Lat] 2 eq voices ENOCH voc sc s.p., cor
pts s.p.   (B4637)

BOUMAN, PAUL
Behold The Lamb Of God *Lent
SA,kbd (easy) oct CONCORDIA 98-1088 $.25
                                  (B4638)

Create In Me A Clean Heart, O God *Gen
SA,kbd (med easy) oct CONCORDIA 98-1143
$.25   (B4639)

Jesus Christ, The Lord Of Joy
mix cor,4brass,org sc CONCORDIA 97-4894
$1.50, ipa, cor pts CONCORDIA 97-4896
$.30   (B4640)

Magnificat, The *Adv/Xmas/Gen
unis,kbd (med easy) oct CONCORDIA 98-1689
$.25   (B4641)

O God, I Thank Thee Heartily *Gen
unis,kbd (easy) oct CONCORDIA 98-1089 $.20
                                  (B4642)

With Shining Face And Bright Array *Epiph/
Gen
SATB,acap (med easy, or Transfiguration)
oct CONCORDIA 98-1420 $.25   (B4643)

BOUND FOR THE PROMISED LAND
(Freed, I.) SATB,acap oct PRESSER 312-40325
$.30   (B4644)

BOUND FOR THE PROMISED LAND see Kjelson

BOUND TO GO see Kennedy, John Brodbin

BOUND UPON THE ACCURSED TREE see Wood

BOUNDLESS MERCY
(Niles; Horton) 4pt mix cor,AT soli,acap oct
SCHIRM.G 9935 $.25   (B4645)

BOUNDLESS MERCY see Hoggard

BOUNDLESS MERCY see Niles, John Jacob

BOURDON
Christmas Tide *Xmas
SSA FLAMMER B 5050 $.50   (B4646)
(Riegger) SAB FLAMMER D5086 $.50   (B4647)

Wonderous Mystery, A *Xmas
(Pooler) SATB,acap,opt pno oct PRO ART 2342
$.25   (B4648)

BOURGEOIS, LOYS (LOUIS) (ca. 1510-1561)
All People That On Earth Do Dwell
(Jolley) mix cor oct LAWSON 623 $.25
                                  (B4649)

God Of The Nations *Gen
(Strohm) SATB SCHMITT 1783 $.25   (B4650)

Psalm 38
(Seay) [Eng/Fr] SATB,acap oct MCA (B4651)

Turn Back, O Man
(Wolff) SATB,org oct LAWSON 51536 $.35
                                  (B4652)

BOUSTEAD, WILLIAM
Souls Of The Righteous, The *Rembrnc,anthem
SATB ALLANS 191 s.p.   (B4653)

BOUTRY
Le Rosaire Des Joies
[Fr] cor,narrator,S solo,orch SALABERT-US
cor pts $2.00, voc sc $13.50   (B4654)

BOUZIGNAC, [GUILLAUME] (fl. ca. 1610-1640)
Vulnerasti Cor Meum *mot
[Lat] SATB,acap MUSICUS 1021 $.15 (B4655)

BOVEN DE STERREN see Abt, Franz

BOVENSI, GIUSTINO
Dio Sia Benedetto *Commun
[Lat] 2 eq voices,org ZANIBON 2702 s.p.
                                  (B4656)

BOW DOWN, O LORD, THINE EAR see Berger, Jean

BOW DOWN THINE EAR see Arensky, Anton
Stepanovitch

BOW DOWN THINE EAR see Brahms, Johannes

BOW DOWN THINE EAR see Deagan, E.

BOW DOWN THINE EAR see Frank, J.L.

BOW DOWN THINE EAR see Handel, George Frideric

BOW DOWN THINE EAR see Mozart, Wolfgang Amadeus

BOW DOWN THINE EAR see Mueller, Carl F.

BOW DOWN THINE EAR see Nelson, R. Wayne

BOW DOWN THINE EAR see Palestrina, Giovanni,
Alma Redemptoris Mater

BOW DOWN THINE EAR see Parker, Horatio William

BOW DOWN THINE EAR see Snyder, J.

BOW DOWN THINE EAR see Tchaikovsky, Piotr
Ilyitch

BOW DOWN THINE EAR see Tkach

BOW DOWN THINE EAR see Todd, M. Flora

BOW DOWN THINE EAR, O LORD see Arensky, Anton
Stepanovitch

BOW DOWN THINE EAR, O LORD see Blow, John

BOW DOWN THINE EAR, O LORD see Graun, Karl
Heinrich

BOW DOWN THINE EAR, O LORD see Handel, George
Frideric

BOW DOWN THINE EAR, O LORD see Morgan, Haydn

BOW DOWN THINE EAR, O LORD see Piston, Walter

BOW DOWN THINE EAR, O LORD see Wickins, F.

BOW DOWN THINE EAR, O LORD see Yeakle, Thomas

BOW MY HEAD, O LORD see Lekberg, Sven

BOW OUR HEARTS see Lotti, Antonio

BOW THINE EAR, O LORD see Byrd, William,
Civitas Sancti Tui

BOW THY HEAVENS, O GOD see Hovdesven, E.A.

BOWEN, CAYLOR
Christmas Carol *Xmas,carol
2 eq voices,S solo,pno oct WORLD AC-1431-2
$.60   (B4657)

I Know What God Is *see Raye

Rejoice In The Lord *Bibl
SATB,acap oct WORLD ESA-1704-8 $.45 (B4658)

BOWIE, [WILLIAM]
Faith *anthem
mix cor oct OXFORD 42.353 $.35   (B4659)

Hast Thou Not Known?
SATB,org oct BOOSEY 5643 $.30   (B4660)

My Rock And My Castle
SATB,org oct BOOSEY 5642 $.30   (B4661)

Welcome, Happy Morning *anthem
mix cor oct OXFORD 42.351 $.50   (B4662)

BOWLES
Come Unto Me *anthem
SATB (easy) ALLANS 246 s.p.   (B4663)

BOWLES, G.
God Is Holy
unis oct LESLIE 1081   (B4664)

BOWMAN, CARL
Festival Of Praise *Te Deum
SATB,org/brass (med) PRESSER G-120 $1.00
                                  (B4665)

BOXBERG, CHRISTIAN LUDWIG
Machet Die Tore Weit *cant
(Hellmann) unis cor,cont,2vln,2rec HANSSLER
10.009 cor pts s.p., voc sc s.p., ipa
                                  (B4666)

BOY FROM BETHLEHEM see Boswell, Eric

BOY IS BORN see Pehkonen

BOY IS BORN, A see Ammann, Benno, Puer Natus
Est

BOY IS BORN, A *Xmas
(Pooler) SATB oct SUMMY 1538 $.40 (B4667)

BOY IS BORN, A see George

BOY IS BORN, A see Scheidt, Samuel, Puer Natus

BOY WAS BORN, A *Xmas,carol
oct ROYAL 343 s.p.
contains: Berriman, C., Boy Was Born, A;
Heys, S., Christ-Child Lay On Mary's Lap,
The   (B4668)

BOY WAS BORN, A see Berriman, C.

BOY WAS BORN, A see Jarret, Jack M.

BOY WAS BORN, A see Puer Natus

BOY WAS BORN, A see Soule

BOY WAS BORN [CHORUS] see Britten, Benjamin

BOY WAS BORN IN BETHLEHEM
see Six Traditional Carols, Set IV

BOY WAS BORN IN BETHLEHEM, A *Xmas
unis/SATB (easy) OXFORD 08.080 $.15 (B4669)

BOY WAS BORN IN BETHLEHEM, A see Forsblad

BOY WHO CAUGHT THE FISH, THE see Coleman, Jack

BOY WHO WANTED TWO DRUMSTICKS, THE see Longman

BOYCE
Alleluia *Allelu
(Kirk) SATB,acap oct PRO ART 2288 $.30
                                  (B4670)
(Kirk) SSA,acap oct PRO ART 2217 $.30
                                  (B4671)
(Kirk) SAB,acap oct PRO ART 2031 $.30
                                  (B4672)
(Kirk) boy cor SOUTHERN $.30   (B4673)
(Kirk) TTBB oct PRO ART 2383 $.30 (B4674)
(Kirk) 2pt oct PRO ART 2381 $.30   (B4675)

BOYCE, WILLIAM (1710-1779)
Alleluia, Alleluia *Allelu
SATB oct HERITAGE H4 $.35   (B4676)

Examine Me, O Lord
(Shaw, Watkins) SS,org/pno oct NOVELLO
33.0100.01 s.p.   (B4677)

Hymn For The New Year *hymn
SATB FLAMMER A 5118 $.25   (B4678)

BOYCE, WILLIAM (cont'd.)

I Have Surely Built Thee An House *anthem/ Bibl
mix cor,ATB soli oct NOVELLO 28.0122.01 s.p. (B4679)

Jubilate *Jubil
(Ehret) "O Be Joyful In The Lord" 4pt mix cor,org/pno oct SCHIRM.G 11877 $.30 (B4680)

Lord Is King, The *anthem
(Nicholson, S.H.) ATB oct NOVELLO 38.0109.08 s.p. (B4681)

O Be Joyful In The Lord *see Jubilate

O Praise The Lord
(Graves) unis jr cor/unis wom cor CURWEN 72275 s.p. (B4682)

O Sing Unto The Lord A New Song *anthem
(Bevan) SATB,SBar soli,org s.p. voc sc SCHOTT 10572, cor pts SCHOTT 10572 (B4683)

O Turn Away Mine Eyes *Gen
unis (med) oct OXFORD 55.603 $.25 (B4684)

O Where Shall Wisdom *anthem/Bibl
mix cor,SSATB soli oct NOVELLO 28.0123.10 s.p. (B4685)

Psalm 25 *see Sorrows Of My Heart, The

Sorrows Of My Heart, The (Psalm 25) Commun/ Gen/Lent
SA/TB,kbd (med easy) oct CONCORDIA 98-1380 $.25 (B4686)
(Shaw) SS (very easy) oct OXFORD 44.073 $.25 (B4687)

BOYD
Arise Shine, For Thy Light Is Come
SATB oct PLYMOUTH PCS-63 $.30 (B4688)

Behold My Servant
SATB,org/pno BOSTON 13274 $.35 (B4689)

Come, Thou Almighty King
SATB,pno/org,2trp cmplt ed STANDARD A19MX1 $.50 (B4690)

God Rest Ye Merry Gentlemen *Xmas
SATB oct PLYMOUTH PCS-56 $.30 (B4691)

How Beautiful
SATB,acap BOSTON 13276 $.35 (B4692)

Infant So Gentle *Xmas,carol
SSA,acap,opt fl WARNER WB-233 $.35 (B4693)

Listen, O Coastlands
SATB,acap BOSTON 13275 $.40 (B4694)

Shall We Gather At The River
SATB STANDARD A21MX1 $.40 (B4695)

When Peace Like A River
SATB,org/pno,2clar cmplt ed STANDARD A20MX1 $.50 (B4696)

BOYD, JACK
All Has Been Heard
SATB,acap oct LAWSON 51384 $.30 (B4697)

Lament For A Dead Son
SATB STANDARD A33MX1 $.50 (B4698)

Let The Day Perish
SATB STANDARD A30MX1 $.50 (B4699)

Man That Is Born Of A Woman
SATB STANDARD A31MX1 $.40 (B4700)

O Earth, Cover Not My Blood
SATB STANDARD A32MX1 $.40 (B4701)

There Was A Man
SATB STANDARD A29MX1 $.35 (B4702)

BOYN
Jesus, Jesus, Rest Your Head *Xmas,carol/ folk,US
SATB,acap WARNER WB234 $.35 (B4703)

BOYS' CAROL, THE see Personet Hodie

BOZZA, EUGENE (1905-)
Messe De Requiem *Mass/Req
[Fr] SATB,acap cor pts LEDUC s.p. (B4704)

Messe De Sa Saintete Pie XII *Mass
[Fr] SATB,acap,opt inst cor pts LEDUC BL774 s.p. (B4705)

Psaumes *Psalm
[Fr] mix cor,orch cor pts LEDUC rental (B4706)

BRAAFLADT, WALTER
Psalm 100
SSATB,opt brass oct AGAPE F 936 $.25 (B4707)

BRAAL, ANDREAS DE (1909)
Drie Psalmen
[Dut] mix cor,3fl,2ob,2clar,3bsn,3trp, 3horn,3trom,strings,perc,timp,harp, celeste min sc DONEMUS s.p.
contains: Psalm 99; Psalm 118; Psalm 137 (B4708)

Profetie, Jesaja 25, 26 *Bibl
[Dut] mix cor,Bar solo,pno,2trp,2horn,2trom min sc DONEMUS s.p., ipa (B4709)

Psalm 23 *see Psalm 23, Een Psalm Van David

Psalm 23, Een Psalm Van David (Psalm 23)
[Dut] mix cor,org ARS NOVA (B4710)

Psalm 99
see Drie Psalmen

Psalm 118
see Drie Psalmen

Psalm 137
see Drie Psalmen

BRAAL, ANDREAS DE (cont'd.)

Te Deum Laudamus *Te Deum
[Lat] mix cor,2fl,2ob,2clar,2bsn,3trp, 4horn,2trom,tuba,strings,timp DONEMUS min sc s.p., cor pts s.p., voc sc s.p. (B4711)

BRACKETT, F.H.
Christ Is Risen *Easter
SATB,SB soli,org (easy) oct WILLIS 1086 $.15 (B4712)

Shout The Glad Tidings *Xmas
SATB,pno (easy) oct WILLIS 1193 $.15 (B4713)

We Would See Jesus *anthem
SATB (easy) ALLANS 96 s.p. (B4714)

BRADBURY
He Leadeth Me
(Harper) SATB oct PRO ART 2189 $.25 (B4715)

He Shall Come Down *anthem
(Sheppherd) SATB oct FISCHER,C R-6121 $.25 (B4716)

Meet And Right *anthem
(Brandon) SAB (easy) oct AUGSBURG 1583 $.35 (B4717)

BRADBURY, WILLIAM BATCHELDER (1816-1868)
He Leadeth Me
(Cain) SATB FLAMMER A 5489 $.25 (B4718)
(Lynn) SATB oct SOUTHERN $.25 (B4719)

Just As I Am
(Parker) TTBB,pno/gtr oct LAWSON 51360 $.25 (B4720)

Oh, Sing Of His Mighty Love
see TEMPO CHORAL PACKAGE NO. 2

Savior, Like A Shepherd Lead Us
(Bock) SATB oct WORD CS-2394 $.30 (B4721)
(Bock) TTBB WORD CS-2407 $.30 (B4722)

Solid Rock, The *hymn
(Whitman) SAB oct LILLENAS AN-1170 $.30 (B4723)

Sweet Hour Of Prayer *hymn
(Parker) TTBB,pno/gtr oct LAWSON 51359 $.30 (B4724)
(Peery, R.) SA oct PRESSER 312-40530 $.30 (B4725)
(Williams) SATB oct LILLENAS AN-2368 $.30 (B4726)

'Tis Midnight
(Ferguson) SATB oct LILLENAS AN-2349 $.25 (B4727)

BRADLEY
Blessed Is The Man
SATB oct FISCHER,C R-6026 $.30 (B4728)

BRADLEY, RUTH
Invocation
SATB,acap SEESAW $1.00 (B4729)

BRADSHAW
Worthy The Lamb
(Shaw; Parker) SATB,acap oct LAWSON 914 $.25 (B4730)

BRAEIN, EDVARD
Forsorgeren, Den Store Gud
men cor MUSIKK 179 s.p. (B4731)

Jeg Ser Dig, O Guds Lam
men cor,T solo MUSIKK 14 s.p. (B4732)

BRAGG
Angel From Heaven *carol,Hung
(Halasz) 3pt/4pt oct MCA (B4733)

Holy Infant, Lowly Infant *Xmas,carol,Pol
(Halasz) 3pt/4pt oct MCA (B4734)

In The Name Of Heaven *carol,Mex
(Halasz) 3pt/4pt oct MCA (B4735)

Little Babe In A Manger Is Born, A *Xmas, carol,Dut
(Halasz) 3pt/4pt oct MCA (B4736)

Noel Nouvelet *Xmas,carol,Fr
(Halasz) [Fr] 3pt/4pt oct MCA (B4737)

Slumber Softly, Jesus Holy *Xmas
(Halasz) treb cor/jr cor oct MCA (B4738)

BRAHE, [MAY H.]
Bless This House
(Cain) SAB oct BOOSEY 1484 $.30, ipa (B4739)
(Ehret) SSA,band/orch oct BOOSEY 5293 $.30, ipa (B4740)
(Janssen) SATB,band/orch oct BOOSEY 1453 $.30, ipa (B4741)
(Ringwald) TTBB SHAWNEE C227 $.35 (B4742)
(Ringwald) SSA SHAWNEE B 358 $.35 (B4743)
(Ringwald) SATB SHAWNEE A 1177 $.35 (B4744)
(Samuelson) TTBB,band/orch oct BOOSEY 1456 $.30, ipa (B4745)
(Samuelson) SSA,band/orch oct BOOSEY 1451 $.30, ipa (B4746)
(Samuelson) SA,band/orch oct BOOSEY 1449 $.30, ipa (B4747)

BRAHMS CHORUSES FOR TREBLE VOICES see Brahms, Johannes

BRAHMS, JOHANNES (1833-1897)
A Saving Health To Us Is Brought *see Es Ist Das Heil

Ach, Arme Welt
see Drei Motetten
"Thou Weary World" SATB,acap SCHIRM.EC 2616 $.30 (B4748)

Ach, Arme Welt, Du Trugest Mich
see Drei Motetten

Ach Lieber Herre Jesu Christ (from Deutsche Volkslieder)
(Geer, E.) "Ah, Jesu Christ, My Lord Most Dear" SSAA,acap SCHIRM.EC 884 $.16 (B4749)

Ack, Kare Jesu Krist *folk
[Swed/Ger] mix cor NORDISKA 5315 s.p. (B4750)

BRAHMS, JOHANNES (cont'd.)

Adoramus
see Drei Geistliche Chore
see Three Sacred Choruses
see Three Sacred Choruses [Op.37]
"We Adore Thee" see Three Sacred Choruses [Op.37]

Adoramus Te
see Drei Geistliche Chore

Ah, Jesu Christ, My Lord Most Dear *see Ach Lieber Herre Jesu Christ

Ah, Thou Poor World *Gen
(Russell, Leslie) SSAA,acap (easy) oct OXFORD 44.210 $.25 (B4751)
(Russell, Leslie) SATB,acap (easy) oct OXFORD 43.046 $.30 (B4752)

Alas, Poor World *see Ach, Arme Welt

Angelic Greeting, The *see Der Engelische Gruss

Annunciation (from Songs Of Mary)
(Granville; Heiberg) SATB,acap oct FOX $.30 (B4753)

Ave Maria *Op.12, BVM
[Eng/Lat] SSAA,pno voc sc PETERS 66136 $.30, ipr (B4754)
girl cor SOUTHERN $.25 (B4755)
wom cor sc ALSBACH&D s.p. (B4756)
SSA oct FISCHER,C CM-6277 $.25 (B4757)
[Eng/Lat] 4pt wom cor oct SCHIRM.G 4 $.30 (B4758)
[Ger/Dan] SSAA,org HANSEN-DEN 28238 s.p. (B4759)
4pt wom cor/4pt jr cor,org/2fl&2ob&2clar& 2bsn&2horn&strings sc BREITKOPF-W PB-3217 s.p., cor pts BREITKOPF-W CHB-3540 s.p., ipr (B4760)
wom cor,orch sc KALMUS $4.00, ipa (B4761)
wom cor voc sc KALMUS 6103 $1.00 (B4762)
SSAA BOSWORTH s.p. see from LAUDY COLLECTION OF MODERN PART SONGS (B4763)
"Ave Maria" cor min sc KALMUS $1.30
contains also: Funeral Song, Op.13; Songs For Female Voices, Op.17; Ellens Song (B4764)
"Ave Maria" [Eng/Lat] SSAA,pno/org PETERS 66136 $.30, ipr (B4765)
"Blessed Are They That Dwell In Thy House" SSAA,pno SCHIRM.EC 2515 $.30 (B4766)
"Blessed Are They That Dwell In Thy House" SSAA,orch oct NOVELLO 33.0002.01 s.p., ipr (B4767)
"Blessed Are They That Dwell In Thy House" girl cor SOUTHERN $.30 (B4768)

Ave Maria *see Ave Maria

Be Not For Aught Regretful *see Lass Dich Nur Nichts Dauren

Benedictus *Bene
(Mueller v. Asow, E.H.) 4pt mix cor,acap voc pt DOBLINGER s.p. (B4769)

Blessed Are The Dead *Op.45,No.7 (from Requiem) anthem
mix cor,orch oct NOVELLO 34.0831.00 s.p., ipr (B4770)

Blessed Are They That Dwell In Thy House *see Ave Maria

Blessed They (from German Requiem)
(Field) SATB oct BOOSEY 5252 $.35 (B4771)

Blest Are They That Mourn *Op.45,No.1 (from Requiem) anthem
mix cor,orch oct NOVELLO 34.0830.02 s.p., ipr (B4772)

Blest Spirit, One With God Above
SATB oct BELWIN 64150 $.30 (B4773)

Bow Down Thine Ear
(Black) SAB&unis jr cor oct FISCHER,J 9152 $.30 (B4774)

Brahms Choruses For Treble Voices *CCU
treb cor SCHMITT 51 $.50 (B4775)

But I Am Afflicted *see Ich Aber Bin Elend

Call To Mary *see Ruf Zur Maria

Chant Magyar
(Doyen, A.) [Fr] SATB/SSTB/SMezTB voc sc LEDUC CC37 s.p. (B4776)

Christmas Lullaby, A *see Geistliches Wiegenlied

Come Away, Come Away, Death! *Op.17,No.2
SSA,pno/2horn&harp SCHIRM.EC 2504 $.25, ipr (B4777)

Come, Away, Death
girl cor SOUTHERN $.25 (B4778)

Come, Holy Spirit *Pent,anthem
(Klein, M.) SATB (easy) oct GIA G1436 $.25 (B4779)

Cradle Song *Xmas
(Cain) SAB SCHMITT 5003 $.20 (B4780)
(Ganschow) SATB SCHMITT 1143 $.18 (B4781)
(Stone) SSA oct PRO ART 1216 $.18 (B4782)

Cradle Song Of The Virgin *see Geistliches Weigenlied

Create In Me, O God (from Schaffe In Mir, Gott)
[Eng/Ger] SATBB,acap (1st mov't) oct SCHIRM.G 7504 $.25 (B4783)

Der Engelische Gruss *Op.22,No.1 (from Marienlieder)
(Geer, E.) "Angelic Greeting, The" SSAA, acap SCHIRM.EC 887 $.25 (B4784)
(Mattfeld, V.) "Angelic Greeting, The" [Ger/Eng] SATB,acap SCHIRM.EC 2477 $.30 (B4785)

Der Englische Gruss *Op.22,No.1, Adv
[Ger] SATB,acap (med easy) MULLER MS 70 s.p. (B4786)

BRAHMS, JOHANNES (cont'd.)

Der Jager *Op.22,No.4 (from Marienlieder)
(Geer, E.) "Hunter, The" [Ger/Eng] SSAA, acap SCHIRM.EC 886 $.30 (B4787)

Drei Geistliche Chore *Op.37
4pt wom cor/4pt jr cor,SA soli,acap cor pts BREITKOPF-L CHB-2656A+B s.p.
contains: Adoramus; O Bone Jesu; Regina Coeli (B4788)

Drei Geistliche Chore *Op.37
cor pts BREITKOPF-W CHB-3414 s.p.
contains: Adoramus Te (4pt wom cor,acap); O Bone Jesu (4pt wom cor/4pt jr cor, acap); Regina Coeli (4pt wom cor/4pt jr cor,SA soli,acap) (B4789)

Drei Motetten *Op.110, mot
4pt mix cor&8pt mix cor voc sc BREITKOPF-L PB-3242 s.p., cor pts BREITKOPF-L CHB-2664 s.p.
contains: Ach, Arme Welt; Ich Aber Bin Elend; Wenn Wir In Hochsten Noten Sein (B4790)

Drei Motetten *Op.110, mot
cor pts BREITKOPF-W CHB-3401 s.p.
contains: Ach, Arme Welt, Du Trugest Mich (SATB,acap); Ich Aber Bin Elend (SATB& SATB,acap); Wenn Wir In Hochsten Noten Sein (SATB&SATB,acap) (B4791)

Ein Deutsches Requiem *Op.45, Bibl/Req
mix cor,SB soli,3fl,2ob,2clar,3bsn,2trp, 4horn,3trom,tuba,strings,timp,2harp,opt org voc pt BREITKOPF-L CHB-2602 s.p., voc sc BREITKOPF-L EB-6071 s.p. (B4792)
4pt mix cor,SBarB soli,2ob,2clar,3bsn, 4horn,2trp,3trom,tuba,strings,timp,harp, opt org sc BREITKOPF-W PB-3218 s.p., study sc BREITKOPF-W PB-3814 s.p., ipa (B4793)
"German Requiem" [Ger] cor,opt orch voc sc KALMUS 6110 $1.50, ipa (B4794)
"German Requiem" [Eng] cor,SBar soli,orch voc sc PETERS 3672A $2.50 (B4795)
"German Requiem" [Ger] cor,SBar soli,orch voc sc PETERS 3672 $2.50, cloth PETERS 3672 $7.50, min sc PETERS E969 $5.00, min sc-cloth PETERS E969 $9.00, sc PETERS 3670 $30.00, ipa (B4796)
"German Requiem" cor min sc KALMUS 482 $4.50 (B4797)
"German Requiem" cor sc KALMUS $12.00 (B4798)
"German Requiem" cor KALMUS $1.75 (B4799)
"German Requiem" cor,orch sc KALMUS $9.00, ipa (B4800)
"German Requiem" cor,soli,orch min sc INTERNAT. $3.75 (B4801)
"Requiem" [Eng] cor,opt orch voc sc KALMUS 6109 $1.50, ipa (B4802)
"Requiem" [Eng] mix cor,soli,orch SCHIRM.G voc sc $1.50, cloth $3.00, sc $5.00 (B4803)
(Brahms; Van Camp, Len) "Requiem" mix cor, 2pno voc sc SCHIRM.G $5.00 (B4804)
(West, John E.) "Requiem" SATB,SB soli,org, 3fl,2ob,2clar,2bsn,4horn,2trp,3trom,tuba, strings,timp,harp voc sc,bds NOVELLO s.p., ipr (B4805)

Ellens Song
see Brahms, Johannes, Ave Maria

Es Ist Das Heil *Op.29,No.1, mot
see Two Motets
5pt mix cor cor pts BREITKOPF-L CHB-2613 s.p. see also Zwei Motetten [Op.29] (B4806)
"A Saving Health To Us Is Brought" [Eng/ Ger] SATB SCHOTT s.p. (B4807)

Es Ist Das Heil Uns Kommen Her *mot
"Son Of God Is Come To Earth, The" [Eng/ Ger] SATB PETERS 66133 $.40 see from Two Motets [Op.29] (B4808)

Ever-Loving Father (from Alto Rhapsody)
(Strickling) 4pt mix cor oct SCHIRM.G 10928 $.30 (B4809)

Father, Ever Loving (from Rhapsody)
SATB,solo PATERSON 1626 s.p. (B4810)

Fest- Und Gedenkspruche *Op.109, Bibl
SATB&SATB,acap sc BREITKOPF-W PB-3241 s.p., voc pt BREITKOPF-W CHB-2663 s.p.
contains: Unsere Vater Hofften Auf Dich; Wenn Ein Starker Gewappneter; Wo Ist Ein So Herrlich Volk (B4811)

Fest- Und Gedenkspruche *Op.109
8pt mix cor,acap voc sc BREITKOPF-L PB-3241 s.p., voc pt BREITKOPF-L CHB-2663 s.p. (B4812)

Five Songs *Op.104 (from Requiem) CC5U
[Ger/Eng] SAATBB,acap oct COLOMBO 386 $.45 (B4813)

Four Folk Songs *CC4U,folk
(Kaplan, A.) SATB oct PRESSER 352-00435 $.30 (B4814)

Funeral Song *see Nun Lasst Uns Den Leib Begraben

Gegrusset, Maria *Adv/Xmas
SATB,acap voc pt DOBLINGER s.p. see also ADVENT UND WEIHNACHT, HEFT 2 (B4815)

Geistliches Lied *see Lass Dich Nur Nichts Dauren, "O Heart Subdued With Grieving" (B4816)

Geistliches Weigenlied *Xmas
(Deis) "Cradle Song Of The Virgin" [Eng/ Ger] 3pt wom cor oct SCHIRM.G 8308 $.40 (B4817)
(Deis) "Cradle Song Of The Virgin" 4pt mix cor oct SCHIRM.G 8307 $.45 (B4818)

Geistliches Wiegenlied *Op.91,No.2, Xmas
(Suchoff) "Christmas Lullaby, A" SATB oct FOX PS191 $.35 (B4819)

German Requiem *see Ein Deutsches Requiem

BRAHMS, JOHANNES (cont'd.)

Grant Me Again The Joy Of Thy Salvation (from Zwei Motetten [Op.29])
see Two Responses

Grant Unto Me (from Schaffe In Mir, Gott)
[Eng/Ger] SAATBB,acap (3rd mov't) oct SCHIRM.G 7506 $.35 (B4820)

Grant Unto Me The Joy Of Thy Salvation
mix cor SOUTHERN $.35 (B4821)
(Carlton) SSATBB oct BOOSEY 5233 $.30 (B4822)

Guten Abend, Gut' Nacht
(Vogel, Moritz; Nagler, Franciscus) [Ger] wom cor&jr cor,vln,vcl HUG 70 s.p. (B4823)

Harvest Song
(Tolmage) SATB oct STAFF 453 $.25 (B4824)

Here On Earth (from Requiem)
4pt mix cor,Bar solo oct SCHIRM.G 8543 $.40 (B4825)

Herr, Wie Lange Willst Du Mein Gar Vergessen (Psalm 13)
(Klein) "Lord, How Long Wilt Thou Forget Me" [Eng/Ger] 3pt wom cor,org oct SCHIRM.G 11604 $.40 (B4826)

Herr, Wie Lange Willst Du Mein So Ganz Vergessen? (Psalm 13) Op.27, Gen,Psalm
3pt wom cor/3pt jr cor,pno/org,opt strings sc BREITKOPF-W PB-3227 s.p., cor pts BREITKOPF-W CHB-3480 s.p., ipr (B4827)
SSA,orch MARKS 104 $.40, ipr (B4828)
SSA oct GALAXY 1.1098.1 $.40 (B4829)
"Lord! How Long Wilt Thou Forget Me" SSA, org PETERS H42 $.60 (B4830)
(Track) SSA/TTBB,opt inst SCHMITT 895 $.45, ipa (B4831)

Holy Child
(Bronson) SSA oct HUNTZINGER 507 $.15 (B4832)

Holy Night
(Wilson) SATB oct LORENZ 4201 $.30 (B4833)

How Long Wilt Thou Forget Me *Bibl
SSA oct SCHIRM.G 174 $.25 (B4834)

How Lovely Are Thy Dwellings *Op.45,No.4 (from Requiem) anthem
mix cor,orch oct NOVELLO 28.0988.05 s.p., ipr (B4835)
(Chambers, H.A.) SSAA,orch oct NOVELLO 51.0550.01 s.p., ipr (B4836)
(Runkel, K.) SAB oct PRESSER 332-15059 $.35 (B4837)
(Wild) SSA oct GRAY GCMR 1833 $.30 (B4838)

How Lovely Is Thy Dwelling Place *Op.45,No.4 (from German Requiem) Gen,Bibl
SATB FLAMMER A 5531 $.40 (B4839)
SATB,pno PETERS 3672B $.40 (B4840)
SATB oct PRO ART 1123 $.35 (B4841)
4pt mix cor oct SCHIRM.G 5124 $.35 (B4842)
SATB oct PRESSER 332-14704 $.35 (B4843)
SATB oct BELWIN 64021 $.25 (B4844)
SATB oct GRAY GCMR 145 $.35 (B4845)
SATB oct FISCHER,C CM-632 $.30 (B4846)
SATB SCHMITT 1925 $.35 (B4847)
SATB,pno (sol-fa edition) voc sc HINRICHSEN P3672C s.p. (B4848)
(Cain) SSA FLAMMER B 5069 $.35 (B4849)
(Carlton) SATB oct BOOSEY 5181 $.40 (B4850)
(Curry, R.) SATB oct PRESSER 312-40033 $.40 (B4851)
(Davison, A.T.) SATB,org SCHIRM.EC 1713 $.45, ipr (B4852)
(King) SATB oct PLYMOUTH PCS-44 $.35 (B4853)
(Pfohl) SAB FLAMMER D5078 $.35 (B4854)
(Tillinghast) SSA WARNER W2897 $.35 (B4855)
(Treharne) SSA,org/pno BOSTON 10262 $.40 (B4856)
(Treharne) TTBB,org/pno BOSTON 9384 $.45 (B4857)
(Wilson) SATB oct COLOMBO 1515 $.30 (B4858)

How Pleasant Are Thy Dwellings (from German Requiem) anthem
SATB oct HARRIS HC4033 $.45 (B4859)

How Still The Night *see In Stiller Nacht

Hunter, The *see Der Jager

Hymn Of Freedom *hymn
SATB,band oct STAFF 123 $.30, ipa (B4860)
(Gardner) SATB oct STAFF 123 $.30 (B4861)
(Gardner) TTBB oct STAFF 626 $.35 (B4862)
(Gardner) SAB oct STAFF 623 $.30 (B4863)
(Gardner) SSA oct STAFF 624 $.30 (B4864)
(Gardner) SA/TB oct STAFF 625 $.35 (B4865)

Hymn Of Praise *Gen,hymn
(Wilson) SATB oct SPRATT 582 $.25 (B4866)

Ich Aber Bin Eland *Op.110,No.1, Bibl
(Klein) "Lord, God I Am Weary" [Eng/Ger] dbl cor,acap oct SCHIRM.G 11950 $.40 (B4867)

Ich Aber Bin Elend
see Drei Motetten
see Drei Motetten

Ihr Habt Nun Traurigkeit (from Deutsches Requiem)
(Geer, E.) "Ye With Sorrow Now Are Filled" [Ger/Eng] SSAA,S solo,pno SCHIRM.EC 873 $.20, ipr (B4868)

In Peace And Joy I Now Depart *see Warum Ist Das Licht Gegeben

In Stiller Nacht
(Track, Gerhard) "How Still The Night" [Eng/Ger] SATB,acap oct WORLD CE-2346 $.30 (B4869)

Is There Nation So Elect *Op.109,No.3
SATB LENGNICK s.p. (B4870)

Jubilant Carol, A *Xmas
(Suchoff) SA oct FOX PS173 $.30 (B4871)
(Suchoff) SATB oct FOX PS171 $.30 (B4872)
(Suchoff) SSA oct FOX PS172 $.30 (B4873)
(Suchoff) SAB oct FOX PS174 $.30 (B4874)

BRAHMS, JOHANNES (cont'd.)

Lass Dich Nur Nichts Dauren *Op.30, anthem
4pt mix cor,org/pno voc sc BREITKOPF-W PB-3231 s.p., cor pts BREITKOPF-W CHB-3542 s.p. (B4875)
"Be Not For Aught Regretful" SATB,org/pno LENGNICK s.p. (B4876)
"Let Nothing Ever Grieve Thee" [Eng/Ger] TTBB,org/pno PETERS 6009 $.25 (B4877)
"O Heart Subdued With Grieving" SATB,org SCHIRM.EC 1115 $.35, ipr (B4878)
"O Heart Subdued With Grieving" mix cor oct NOVELLO 28.0880.03 s.p. (B4879)
(Geer) "O Heart Subdued With Grieving" [Ger/Eng] SSAA,org SCHIRM.EC 874 $.25 see from Geistliches Lied (B4880)

Lass Dich Nur Nichts Nicht Dauren *Op.30
"Let Nothing Ever Grieve Thee" [Eng/Ger] SATB,org/pno PETERS 6093 $.25 (B4881)
(Klein) "Let Not Your Heart Be Troubled" [Eng/Ger] 4pt mix cor,org/pno oct SCHIRM.G 11949 $.35 (B4882)

Let Not Your Heart Be Troubled *see Lass Dich Nur Nichts Nicht Dauren

Let Nothing Ever Grieve Thee *see Lass Dich Nur Nichts Dauren

Let Nothing Ever Grieve Thee *see Lass Dich Nur Nichts Nicht Dauren

Lord, God I Am Weary *see Ich Aber Bin Eland

Lord, How Long Wilt Thou Forget Me *see Herr, Wie Lange Willst Du Mein Gar Vergessen

Lord! How Long Wilt Thou Forget Me *see Herr, Wie Lange Willst Du Mein So Ganz Vergessen?

Lord Is Our Fortress, The
(Branscombe) SATB oct FISCHER,J 8364 $.35 (B4883)

Lord, Lead Us Still
(Dickinson) SATB oct GRAY GSC 60 $.30 (B4884)

Lord, Make Me To Know (from Requiem) Bibl
4pt mix cor,Bar solo oct SCHIRM.G 5123 $.25 (B4885)

Magdalena *Op.22,No.6, Easter
mix cor SOUTHERN $.30 (B4886)
(Shaw) 4pt mix cor,acap oct SCHIRM.G 9953 $.30 (B4887)

Make In Me A Clean Heart (from Zwei Motetten [Op.29])
see Two Responses

Make In Me, O Lord, A Pure Heart
(Ehret) SATBB oct BOOSEY 5178 $.30 (B4888)

Make Me, O Lord
SATB oct GRAY GCMR 1507 $.30 (B4889)

Make Thou In Me, God *see Schaffe In Mir, Gott

Maria Magdalena *Op.22,No.6, Easter
(Geer, E.) [Ger/Eng] SSAA,acap SCHIRM.EC 885 $.25 see also Marienlieder (B4890)

Marias Kirchgang *Op.22,No.2 (from Marienlieder)
(Geer, E.) "Mary's Journey To Church" [Ger/ Eng] SSAA,acap SCHIRM.EC 894 $.25 (B4891)
(Mattfeld, V.) "Mary's Journey To Church" [Ger/Eng] SATB,acap SCHIRM.EC 2478 $.30 (B4892)

Marias Lob *Op.22,No.7 (from Marienlieder)
(Geer, E.) "Praise Of Mary" [Ger/Eng] SSAA, acap SCHIRM.EC 896 $.25 (B4893)
(Mattfeld, V.) "Praise Of Mary" [Ger/Eng] SATB,acap SCHIRM.EC 2481 $.30 (B4894)

Marias Wallfahrt *Op.22,No.3 (from Songs Of Mary)
(Geer, E.) "Mary's Pilgrimage" [Ger/Eng] SSAA,acap SCHIRM.EC 897 $.25 see also Marienlieder (B4895)
(Granville, Heiberg) "Mary's Pilgrimage" SATB,acap oct FOX $.25 (B4896)
(Mattfeld, V.) "Mary's Pilgrimage" [Ger/ Eng] SATB,acap SCHIRM.EC 2479 $.30 (B4897)

Marienlieder *Op.22, CCU,BVM
[Ger/Eng] SATB,acap cmplt ed 3658 $1.50, cmplt ed 6897 $.60 (B4898)

Marienlieder And Motets *Op.22,Op.29,Op.74, Op.110, CCU
cor min sc KALMUS 1165 $1.30 (B4899)

Marienlieder *Op.22, CC7L,BVM
SATB,acap voc sc BREITKOPF-L PB-3228 s.p., cor pts BREITKOPF-L CHB-2665 s.p. (B4900)

Mary Goes To Church (from Songs Of Mary)
(Granville, Heiberg) SATB,acap oct FOX $.25 (B4901)

Mary Magdalene *Op.22,No.6 (from Marienlieder) Easter
SATB,acap SCHIRM.EC 2230 $.30 (B4902)
(Granville, Heiberg) SATB,acap oct FOX $.30 (B4903)

Mary's Journey To Church *see Marias Kirchgang

Mary's Pilgrimage *see Marias Wallfahrt

Mary's Wandering
SATB oct GRAY GCMR 1669 $.30 (B4904)

Motet *see Schaffe In Mir, Gott

Nun Lasst Uns Den Leib Begraben *Op.13, Rembrnc
"Funeral Song" see Brahms, Johannes, Ave Maria
mix cor,2ob,2clar,2bsn,2horn,3trom,tuba, timp sc BREITKOPF-L rental (B4905)

O Bone Jesu
see Drei Geistliche Chore
see Drei Geistliche Chore
see Three Sacred Choruses [Op.37]

BRAHMS, JOHANNES (cont'd.)

see Three Sacred Choruses
"O Gracious Jesu" see Three Sacred Choruses
[Op.37]

O Cast Me Not Away (from Schaffe In Mir,
Gott)
[Eng/Ger] 4pt mix cor,acap (2nd mov't) oct
SCHIRM.G 7505 $.35   (B4906)

O God, Thou Faithful God
(Douglas) SATB oct GRAY GCMR 1647 $.30 (B4907)

O Good Morning, My Fair One! *see
Vergebliches Standchen

O Gracious Jesu *see O Bone Jesu

O Great Is The Lord
(Whitford) SATB oct PRO ART 1948 $.22   (B4908)

O Heart Subdued With Grieving *see Lass Dich
Nur Nichts Dauren

O Heiland, Reiss Die Himmel Auf *Op.74,No.2,
Adv/Xmas,mot
SATB,acap cor pts BREITKOPF-L CHB-2644 s.p.
see also Zwei Motetten [Op.74]   (B4909)
4pt mix cor,acap cor pts sc BREITKOPF-W
CHB-3182 PB-3247 s.p. s.p. see from Zwei
Motetten [Op.74]   (B4910)
SATB,acap voc pt DOBLINGER s.p. see also
ADVENT UND WEIHNACHT, HEFT 2   (B4911)
"O Savior, Rend The Heav'n On High" [Eng/
Ger] SATB,acap PETERS 6560 $.40 see from
Two Motets [Op.74]   (B4912)
"O Savior, Throw The Heavens Wide" [Eng/
Ger] 4pt mix cor,acap oct SCHIRM.G 8545
$.40   (B4913)
"Oh Saviour Let The Skies Be Riv'n" SATB,
acap LENGNICK s.p.   (B4914)
"Wall Of Heaven, O Savior, Rend, The" SATB,
acap SCHIRM.EC 382 $.45   (B4915)

O Jesus, Tender Shepherd, Hear *folk,Ger
(Davison, A.) TTBB,acap SCHIRM.EC 921 $.16
                                    (B4916)
(Hilton, A.) SATB oct PRESSER MC327 $.25
                                    (B4917)

O Savior, Open Heaven Wide *see O Heiland,
Reiss Die Himmel Auf

O Savior, Rend The Heav'n On High *see O
Heiland, Reiss Die Himmel Auf

O Savior, Throw The Heavens Wide *see O
Heiland, Reiss Die Himmel Auf

O Sorrow Deep *Lent
(Douglas) SATB oct GRAY GCMR 1640 $.30 (B4918)
(Liszt) SATB oct BELWIN 60854 $.30   (B4919)

Oh, Loving Jesus *see O Bone Jesu

Oh Saviour Let The Skies Be Riv'n *see O
Heiland, Reiss Die Himmel Auf

Our Fathers Hoped In God *Op.109,No.1
SSAATTBB,acap LENGNICK s.p.   (B4920)

Our God And Our Father
(Thompson) SAB LEONARD-US 08049840 $.25
                                    (B4921)

Our Lady And Queen Of Heaven *see Regina
Coeli

Praise Of Mary *see Marias Lob

Praise To Mary (from Songs Of Mary)
(Granville; Heiberg) SATB,acap oct FOX $.25
                                    (B4922)

Prayer
(Land) SATB oct PLYMOUTH SC-503 $.25
                                    (B4923)
(Land) 2pt oct PLYMOUTH SC-503 $.25
                                    (B4924)

Prayer To Mary (from Songs Of Mary) prayer
(Granville; Heiberg) SATB,acap oct FOX $.25
                                    (B4925)

Psalm 13 *see Herr, Wie Lange Willst Du Mein
Gar Vergessen

Psalm 13 *see Herr, Wie Lange Willst Du Mein
So Ganz Vergessen?

Regina Coeli
see Drei Geistliche Chore
see Drei Geistliche Chore
see Three Sacred Choruses
see Three Sacred Choruses [Op.37]
"Our Lady And Queen Of Heaven" see Three
Sacred Choruses [Op.37]
(Track) TTBB,T/B solo,acap,opt pno oct PRO
ART 2491 $.30   (B4926)

Religious Folk Songs *CCU,folk
SATB,acap MARKS 4081 $.75   (B4927)

Requiem *see Ein Deutsches Requiem

Ruf Zur Maria *Op.22,No.5 (from
Marienlieder)
(Geer, E.) "Call To Mary" SSAA,acap
SCHIRM.EC 895 $.25   (B4928)
(Mattfeld, V.) "Call To Mary" [Ger/Eng]
SATB,acap SCHIRM.EC 2480 $.30   (B4929)

Sacred Choruses, Canons, And Songs *Op.37,
Op.44,Op.113, CCU,canon
cor min sc KALMUS $1.30   (B4930)

Sacred Choruses *CC8UL,Psalm
cor min sc KALMUS 1162 $1.30   (B4931)

Saving Health To Us Brought, A
(Krone) SATB,acap WARNER W2706 $.50 (B4932)

Schaffe In Mir, Gott *Op.29,No.2 (from Psalm
51) mot
see Two Motets
5pt mix cor cor pts BREITKOPF-L CHB-2614
s.p. see also Zwei Motetten [Op.29]
                                    (B4933)
"Make Thou In Me, God" [Eng/Ger] SATBB
PETERS 66123 $.75 see from Two Motets
[Op.29]   (B4934)
(Williamson, J. Finley) "Motet" [Eng/Ger]

BRAHMS, JOHANNES (cont'd.)

6pt mix cor,acap voc sc SCHIRM.G $.75
                                    (B4935)

Schicksalslied *Op.54
"Song Of Fate, The" SATB,pno SCHIRM.EC 1643
$.50, ipr   (B4936)

Sing Praise To God Who Reigns Above *anthem
(Sateren) SATBB (med) oct AUGSBURG 1280
$.30   (B4937)

Son Of God Is Come To Earth, The *see Es Ist
Das Heil Uns Kommen Her

Song Of Destiny *cant
BELWIN $.75   (B4938)
SATB,band oct STAFF 537 $.30, ipa   (B4939)

Song Of Fate, The *see Schicksalslied

Songs For Female Voices *Op.17
see Brahms, Johannes, Ave Maria

Taublein Weiss *Adv/Xmas
SATB,acap voc pt DOBLINGER s.p. see also
ADVENT UND WEIHNACHT, HEFT 2   (B4940)

Thou Weary World *see Ach, Arme Welt

Thou Wretched World, Deceivest Me *Op.110,
No.2
(Buszin) SATB,acap (diff) oct WILLIS 6174
$.15   (B4941)

Three Sacred Choruses [Op.37]
[Lat/Eng] SSAA BROUDE BR. $.50
contains: Adoramus; O Bone Jesu; Regina
Coeli   (B4942)

Three Sacred Choruses [Op.37]
[Eng/Lat] SSAA,acap PETERS 66141 $.30
contains: Adoramus, "We Adore Thee"; O
Bone Jesu, "O Gracious Jesu"; Regina
Coeli, "Our Lady And Queen Of Heaven"
                                    (B4943)

Three Sacred Choruses *CC3U
girl cor SOUTHERN $.30   (B4944)

Three Sacred Choruses *Op.37
[Lat] voc sc HINRICHSEN P3664 s.p.
contains: Adoramus (SSAA); O Bone Jesu
(SSAA); Regina Coeli (SSAA,SA soli,
acap)   (B4945)

To God Be The Glory
SATB oct LORENZ B61 $.30   (B4946)

To Thee, O Jesus Christ, We Cry *Gen
(Buszin) SATB SCHMITT 1694 $.20   (B4947)

To Us Salvation Now Is Come *see Es Ist Das
Heil

Triumphal Hymn *Op.55, Eng/Ger
cor voc sc KALMUS 6102 $1.75   (B4948)
cor,orch sc KALMUS $12.00, ipa   (B4949)

Two Motets [Op.29] *see Es Ist Das Heil Uns
Kommen Her, "Son Of God Is Come To Earth,
The"; Schaffe In Mir, Gott, "Make Thou In
Me, God"   (B4950)

Two Motets [Op.74] *see O Heiland, Reiss Die
Himmel Auf, "O Savior, Rend The Heav'n On
High"; Warum Ist Das Licht Gegeben, "Why
Then Has The Light Been Given"   (B4951)

Two Motets *mot
cor voc sc KALMUS 6105 $1.25
contains: Es Ist Das Heil, Op.29,No.1;
Schaffe In Mir, Gott, Op.29,No.2   (B4952)

Two Responses (from Zwei Motetten [Op.29])
SSA,acap SCHIRM.EC 877 $.18
contains: Grant Me Again The Joy Of Thy
Salvation; Make In Me A Clean Heart
                                    (B4953)

Unsere Vater Hofften Auf Dich
see Fest- Und Gedenkspruche

Vergebliches Standchen
"O Good Morning, My Fair One!" see FOLK-
SONGS, BALLADS AND SONGS OF GREAT
COMPOSERS (SET V)

Wall Of Heaven, O Savior, Rend, The *see O
Heiland, Reiss Die Himmel Auf

Warum Ist Das Licht Gegeban *Op.74,No.1
"Wherefore Is The Light Bestowed" SSATBB,
acap SCHIRM.EC 381 $.55   (B4954)

Warum Ist Das Licht Gegeben *Op.74,No.1, mot
SATB,acap cor pts BREITKOPF-L CHB-2643 s.p.
see also Zwei Motetten [Op.74]   (B4955)
"Wherefore Hath The Light Been Given" SATB,
acap LENGNICK s.p.   (B4956)
"Wherefore Hath The Light Been Granted" mix
cor SOUTHERN $.30   (B4957)
"Wherefore Hath The Light Been Granted"
[Eng/Ger] 6pt mix cor,acap oct SCHIRM.G
8544 $.45   (B4958)
"Why Then Has The Light Been Given" [Eng/
Ger] SATB,acap PETERS 66135 $.40 see from
Two Motets [Op.74]   (B4959)

Warum Ist Das Licht Gegeben Dem Muhseligen?
*Op.74, mot
4pt mix cor,acap cor pts BREITKOPF-W
CHB-3181 s.p. see from Zwei Motetten
[Op.74]   (B4960)

We Adore Thee *see Adoramus

We Adore Thee *see Adoramus Te

We Love The Place Where Thine Honour Dwells
(from Requiem) Ded/Gen
(Atkins, Ivor) SSA (med) oct OXFORD 44.050
$.65   (B4961)

Wenn Ein Starker Gewappneter
see Fest- Und Gedenkspruche

Wenn Wir In Hochsten Noten Sein
see Drei Motetten
see Drei Motetten

BRAHMS, JOHANNES (cont'd.)

When A Strong Man *Op.109,No.2
SSAATTBB LENGNICK s.p.   (B4962)

When We Do Suffer *see Wenn Wir In Hoechsten
Noeten Sein

Wherefore Hath The Light Been Given *see
Warum Ist Das Licht Gegeben

Wherefore Hath The Light Been Granted *see
Warum Ist Das Licht Gegeben

Wherefore Is The Light Bestowed *see Warum
Ist Das Licht Gegeban

Why Then Has The Light Been Given *see Warum
Ist Das Licht Gegeben

Wo Ist Ein So Herrlich Volk
see Fest- Und Gedenkspruche

Ye Who Now Sorrow *Op.45,No.5 (from Requiem)
anthem
SATB,S solo,orch oct NOVELLO 34.0836.01
s.p., ipr   (B4963)

Ye With Sorrow Now Are Filled *see Ihr Habt
Nun Traurigkeit

Zwei Motetten [Op.29] *mot
5pt mix cor voc sc BREITKOPF-L PB-3229 s.p.
contains & see also: Es Ist Das Heil,
Op.29,No.1; Schaffe In Mir, Gott,
Op.29,No.2   (B4964)

Zwei Motetten [Op.74] *mot
SATB,acap voc sc BREITKOPF-L PB-3247 s.p.
contains: O Heiland, Reiss Die Himmel
Auf, Op.74,No.2; Warum Ist Das Licht
Gegeben, Op.74,No.1
see also: O Heiland, Reiss Die Himmel
Auf, Op.74,No.2; Warum Ist Das Licht
Gegeben, Op.74,No.1; Warum Ist Das
Licht Gegeben Dem Muhseligen?, Op.74
                                    (B4965)

BRAMBILLA, E.
Improperium
see PER LA SETTIMANA SANTA

In Monte Olivetti
see IN HEBDOMADA SANCTA

BRAMO MORIR see Festa, Costanza

BRANCH OF PROMISE, THE *Adv/Xmas/Epiph
(Brandon) SATB oct PRO ART 2504 $.30 (B4966)

BRANCHINA, PIETRO
Due Laudi A Gesu Sacr. (composed with Magri,
Pietro) *CC2U,Commun
[Lat] unis,org cor pts ZANIBON 2658 s.p.
                                    (B4967)

Ecce Sacerdos *Op.41
[Lat] AT,org ZANIBON 2647 s.p.   (B4968)

Gioiscano I Cuori! *Op.148, Xmas
unis,pno/org ZANIBON 3205 s.p.   (B4969)

BRAND, FRANZ
Laudate Dominum *Greg
[Lat] men cor,acap voc sc BOTE s.p. (B4970)

BRAND NEW MORNING see Di Novi

BRAND, TH.
Furbitten *see Sankt Antonius; Sankt
Christoph; Sankt Judas Thaddaus; Sankt
Michael   (B4971)

Sankt Antonius
6pt&mix cor (med) oct LEUCKART 682 s.p. see
from Furbitten   (B4972)

Sankt Christoph
7pt&mix cor (med) oct LEUCKART 684 s.p. see
from Furbitten   (B4973)

Sankt Judas Thaddaus
6pt&mix cor (med) oct LEUCKART 683 s.p. see
from Furbitten   (B4974)

Sankt Michael
6pt&mix cor (med easy) oct LEUCKART 681
s.p. see from Furbitten   (B4975)

BRANDON
Bells Of Heaven
(Swain) SATB oct BOURNE 855 $.30   (B4976)

Carol For The Ephiphany Season, A *Epiph
SA/unis oct BELWIN 64376 $.30   (B4977)

Clothed With Strength
SAB,acap oct PRO ART 2626 $.30   (B4978)

Festival Introit *Gen,Introit
SAB/SATB,trp SCHMITT 5526 $.25   (B4979)

Forth In Thy Name
SATB oct VOLKWEIN VB150 $.25   (B4980)

Go Tell It On The Mountain *spir
SAB SCHMITT 5523 $.30   (B4981)

He Has Come
SATB oct SUMMY 5849 $.35   (B4982)

Heaven And Earth, And Sea And Air (from Ives)
hymn
SAB WARNER W7-1056 $.30   (B4983)

He's Got The Whole World In His Hands
SAB oct SHAPIRO SCE 5501 $.25   (B4984)

Holy Spirit, Truth Divine
SATB oct SACRED S-94 $.35   (B4985)

I Thank Thee Lord, For All Thy Care
SAB,org/pno BOSTON 13326 $.35   (B4986)

In Thy Mysterious Presence
SATB oct COLOMBO 2506 $.30   (B4987)

Kind Father, Look With Pity Now
SATB oct VOLKWEIN VB200 $.25   (B4988)

BRANDON (cont'd.)

Let All Men Rejoice
  SAB WARNER W7-1054 $.30   (B4989)

Lord's Day
  SAB (med diff/diff) SOUTHERN $.35   (B4990)

O Bless The Lord O My Soul *anthem
  SATB ALLANS 441 s.p.   (B4991)

Sounding Skies, The *Xmas
  2pt mix cor,org/pno oct SCHIRM.G 11531 $.25
                                             (B4992)

Thanks To God Our Father
  SAB oct BELWIN 64339 $.30   (B4993)

This Is The Day Of Light
  SAB oct VOLKWEIN VB267 $.25   (B4994)
  SATB oct VOLKWEIN VB267 $.25   (B4995)

Thy Majestic Greatness
  SAB oct ELKAN-V 362-1263 $.25   (B4996)

To Thee I Lift Up
  SATB oct VOLKWEIN VB272 $.25   (B4997)

What The Future Hath
  3pt mix cor,org oct SCHIRM.G 11448 $.25
                                             (B4998)

Work Of Consolation
  SATB oct VOLKWEIN VB282 $.30   (B4999)
  SA/unis oct VOLKWEIN VB282 $.30   (B5000)

BRANDON, G.
Advent Carol *Adv,anthem/carol
  unis/SA (easy) oct GIA G1719 $.30   (B5001)

Arise, O Lord
  SATB,org oct KERBY 5601 $.25   (B5002)

Blessed Be Thy Name Forever
  SAB oct BOURNE 3029 $.25   (B5003)

Carol Of The Visitation *Adv,anthem
  SATB (easy) oct GIA G1718 $.40   (B5004)

Lift Up Your Heads
  SATB SHAWNEE A 929 $.30   (B5005)

O God To Me Be Merciful (Psalm 57)
  SATB SHAWNEE A 926 $.25   (B5006)

Praise Him Evermore (Psalm 150) Gen,anthem
  SATB (easy) oct GIA $.35   (B5007)

Psalm 57 *see O God To Me Be Merciful

Psalm 98 *see With Harp And Voice Of Psalms

Psalm 150 *see Praise Him Evermore

Royal Proclamation, The
  SATB,org oct KERBY 6702 $.35   (B5008)

Send Down Thy Truth
  SAB oct KERBY 6505 $.30   (B5009)

We'll All Praise God Together *Gen,anthem/
    hymn
  unis&desc (easy) oct GIA G1575 $.30 (B5010)

With Harp And Voice Of Psalms (Psalm 98) Gen,
    anthem,Scot,17th cent
  SA/SAB (easy) oct GIA G1576 $.40   (B5011)

Word Became Flesh, The
  unis oct KERBY 5201C $.25   (B5012)
  unis oct KERBY 5201 $.25   (B5013)

BRANDON, GEORGE
Angels Holy, High And Lowly *Ded/Gen/Thanks
  unis/SA,kbd,opt org&fl&bells (easy) cor pts
  CONCORDIA 98-1808 $.25, ipa   (B5014)

Awake, Our Souls *Gen
  2pt mix cor,kbd (med easy) oct CONCORDIA
  98-1883 $.30   (B5015)

Carol Of Adam's Fall *Adv/Gen,carol
  SAB/SATB,kbd (med easy) oct CONCORDIA
  98-2118 $.35   (B5016)

Carol Of The Baptism *Epiph/Gen,carol
  SAB/2pt mix cor,kbd (med easy, or
  Transfiguration) oct CONCORDIA 98-2138
  $.30   (B5017)

Easter Canticle *Easter
  SATB,kbd (med easy) oct CONCORDIA 98-1919
  $.30   (B5018)

Eternal God, Whose Power Upholds *Gen/Trin
  SATB/SAB/2pt mix cor,kbd (easy) oct
  CONCORDIA 98-2083 $.40   (B5019)

Grace And Power *Gen
  SATB/2pt mix cor,kbd (med easy) oct
  CONCORDIA 98-1996 $.30   (B5020)

Lord's Day, The *Easter/Gen/Pent
  SAB,kbd (med easy) oct CONCORDIA 98-2043
  $.35   (B5021)

O Come, Creator Spirit, Come *Cnfrm/Gen/Pent
  2pt mix cor,kbd (med easy) oct CONCORDIA
  98-1850 $.25   (B5022)

O My Soul, Jehovah Bless *Gen/Refm/Trin
  SATB,kbd (med easy) oct CONCORDIA 98-1923
  $.30   (B5023)

Send Forth, O God *Cnfrm/Gen
  SAB,kbd (med easy) oct CONCORDIA 98-2000
  $.40   (B5024)

Sing To The Lord With Thanksgiving *Ded/Gen/
    Thanks
  SATB/SAB/2pt mix cor/unis,kbd (med easy)
  oct CONCORDIA 98-2087 $.35   (B5025)

Song Of Mary *anthem
  SAB (easy) oct AUGSBURG 1507 $.25   (B5026)

Songs Of Solemn Joy *Commun/Gen
  SAB,kbd (med easy) oct CONCORDIA 98-1849
  $.25   (B5027)

BRANDON, GEORGE (cont'd.)

There Is A Balm In Gilead
  SAB oct AGAPE A 362 $.35   (B5028)

True Fasting
  SATB (easy) ABINGDON APM-522 $.20   (B5029)

Watch, O Master, O'er Us *Gen
  2pt mix cor (med easy) oct CONCORDIA
  98-1843 $.25   (B5030)

Were You There?
  SSA oct AGAPE A 343 $.30   (B5031)

With One Accord *Ded/Gen/Refm
  SA,kbd (easy) oct CONCORDIA 98-1958 $.25
                                             (B5032)

BRANDON, PHYLLIS
Away In A Manger *Xmas
  cor CRAMER 200 s.p.   (B5033)
  unis jr cor CRAMER 200 s.p.   (B5034)

BRANDS, JOH.
Da Pacem, Domine
  "Geef Vrede, Heer" mix cor ALSBACH&D sc
  s.p., cor pts s.p.   (B5035)

Geef Vrede, Heer *see Da Pacem, Domine

BRANDT
Bethlehem Carol *Xmas
  SAB,acap,opt pno oct PRO ART 2637 $.35
                                             (B5036)
  SATB,acap,opt pno oct PRO ART 2523 $.30
                                             (B5037)
  SSA,acap,opt pno oct PRO ART 2639 $.35
                                             (B5038)

Christmas Lullaby *Xmas
  unis oct PRO ART 2591 $.30   (B5039)

Echoes Of Angels *Xmas
  2pt oct PRO ART 2590 $.30   (B5040)

Frisch Auf In Gottes Namen
  4pt mix cor MOSELER LB-341 s.p.   (B5041)

Hosanna *Xmas
  2pt oct PRO ART 2588 $.30   (B5042)

Sing Ye People
  unis oct PRO ART 2587 $.30   (B5043)

BRANSCOMBE, [GINA] (1881-   )
Prayer For Song
  SSA oct COLOMBO 1268 $.30   (B5044)

BRANT, CYR DE
Christus Factus Est *Easter
  boy cor SOUTHERN $.30   (B5045)
  [Lat] SSA/TTB,acap WARNER W2783 $.30
                                             (B5046)

Collection Of Christmas Carols For Church And
    Home *CCU,Xmas,carol
  TTB/TTBB BELWIN $.75   (B5047)

Collection Of Church Carols For Christmas
    *CCU,Xmas,carol
  unis/mix cor BELWIN $.50   (B5048)

BRANT, JOBST VON
  see BRANDT, JOBST VOM

BRANT, JOHANN VON
Gott Sei Gelobt *Pent/Whitsun
  SATB,acap voc pt DOBLINGER s.p. see also
  PFINGSTEN UND EUCHARISTIE   (B5049)

BRASART, J.
O Flos Flagrans
  (Boepple, P.) SAA/STT,acap oct PRESSER
  352-00028 $.30   (B5050)

BRASSART, JOHANNES
Opera Omnia vol. I *CCU
  (Mixer, Keith E.) cor AM.INST.MUS. mass
  sections   (B5051)

Opera Omnia vol. II *CCU,mot
  (Mixer, Keith E.) cor AM.INST.MUS. $30.00
                                             (B5052)

BRASSENS, G.
La Priere
  (Bereau) [Fr] 4pt mix cor HEUGEL CPJ62 s.p.
                                             (B5053)

BRASSICANUS, JOHANNES
Gott Vater, Herr, Wir Danken Dir *Thanks
  SATB HANSSLER 6.135 s.p. contains also:
  Osiander, Lucas, Gott Der Vater Wohn Uns
  Bei   (B5054)

BRATT, C. GRIFFITH
O Come You Now To Bethlehem *Xmas
  SAB/unis/2pt mix or SA soli,org oct WORLD
  AC-1384-7 $.45   (B5055)

BRAUER, JAMES
Lord, Now Lettest Thou Thy Servant *Epiph/
    Gen
  SATB,T solo,acap (med diff) oct CONCORDIA
  98-1987 $.25   (B5056)

Magnificat, The *Xmas/Gen
  SATB,S solo,acap (med diff) oct CONCORDIA
  98-1899 $.35   (B5057)

BRAUNSCHWEIGER LIEDMESSE see Wagner, Alexander

BRAUTIGAM, HELMUT (1914-1942)
Auf, Auf Ihr Buben! *Xmas,mot
  SATB,acap cor pts BREITKOPF-L CHB-2828 s.p.
  see from Vier Kleine Weihnachtsmotetten
                                             (B5058)

Es Singt Wohl Ein Voglein *Xmas
  mix cor TONGER s.p.   (B5059)

Jesus Stillt Den Seesturm *Epiph,evang/mot
  [Ger] SATB,acap (med diff) BAREN. BA 5406
  $1.75   (B5060)

Kleine Weihnachtsfeier *Xmas,cant
  eq voices,fl,strings voc sc TONGER s.p.,
  ipa   (B5061)

Singet Frisch Und Wohlgemut *Xmas,mot
  SATB,acap cor pts BREITKOPF-L CHB-2829 s.p.
  see from Vier Kleine Weihnachtsmotetten
                                             (B5062)

BRAUTIGAM, HELMUT (cont'd.)

Still, Still, Still *Xmas,mot
  SATB,acap cor pts BREITKOPF-L CHB-2827 s.p.
  see from Vier Kleine Weihnachtsmotetten
                                             (B5063)

Und Unsre Lieben Frauen *Xmas,mot
  SATB,acap cor pts BREITKOPF-L CHB-2826 s.p.
  see from Vier Kleine Weihnachtsmotetten
                                             (B5064)

Vier Kleine Weihnachtsmotetten *see Auf, Auf
  Ihr Buben!; Singet Frisch Und Wohlgemut;
  Still, Still, Still; Und Unsre Lieben
  Frauen   (B5065)

BRAUTIGAM, VOLKER (1939-   )
Drei Seligpreisungen *CC3U,Bibl
  [Ger] mix cor oct DEUTSCHER 7624 s.p.
                                             (B5066)

Johann Sebastian Bach. Epitaph *Gen
  4-7pt mix cor,acap (med diff) DEUTSCHER
  DV 7615 s.p.   (B5067)

BRAVE LITTLE SHEPHERD, THE see Grime, William

BRAY
Christmas Folk Song, A *Xmas
  SATB THOMP.G G-588 s.p.   (B5068)

BRAZ, M.
Three Hebrew Psalms *CC3U,Psalm,Heb
  SATB BELWIN 2284 $.30   (B5069)

BRAZILIAN PSALM see Berger, Jean, Psalmo
  Brasileiro

BREAD IS ONE, THE see Peloquin, C. Alexander

BREAD OF AFFLICTION, THE see Adler, Hugo Ch.,
  Ho Lachmo Anyo

BREAD OF GOD, THE see Cain, Noble

BREAD OF HEAVEN see Des Prez, Josquin, Ave
  Verum Corpus

BREAD OF HEAVEN see Elmore, Robert [Hall]

BREAD OF HEAVEN see France, William E.

BREAD OF HEAVEN see Rasely

BREAD OF HEAVEN see Rasley

BREAD OF HEAVEN see Victoria, Tomas Luis de

BREAD OF HEAVEN, ON THEE WE FEED see German,
  Edward

BREAD OF LIFE see Dann

BREAD OF LIFE see Russell

BREAD OF LIFE, THE see Young, Carlton R.

BREAD OF LIFE, THE see Dixon, Panis Vitae

BREAD OF TEARS see Christiansen, Paul

BREAD OF THE LIVING see Byrd, William, Ego Sum
  Panis Vivus

BREAD OF THE WORLD
  (Blake, G.) SATB oct PRESSER 332-40020 $.30
                                             (B5070)
BREAD OF THE WORLD see Bodycombe, [Aneurin]

BREAD OF THE WORLD see Bush, Florence

BREAD OF THE WORLD see Edmundson, Garth

BREAD OF THE WORLD see Eville

BREAD OF THE WORLD see Garland, Hugh

BREAD OF THE WORLD see Harker, Clifford

BREAD OF THE WORLD see Hodges

BREAD OF THE WORLD see Horder, Mervyn

BREAD OF THE WORLD see Lovelace, Austin C.

BREAD OF THE WORLD see Pears, James R.

BREAD OF THE WORLD see Phelps

BREAD OF THE WORLD see Schmutz, Albert C.

BREAD OF THE WORLD see Schroeder

BREAD OF THE WORLD IN MERCY BROKEN see Franz

BREAD OF THE WORLD IN MERCY BROKEN see Vorse,
  R.

BREAD OF THE WORLD, IN MERCY BROKEN see Young

BREAD OF THE WORLD (SOLEMN INTROIT IN G) see
  Davies, Henry Walford

BREAK, BREAK, BREAK see Macirone, C A.

BREAK, DAY OF GOD! see Butler, Eugene

BREAK, DAY OF GOD see Darwall

BREAK, FAIR DAWN see Beethoven, Ludwig van

BREAK FORTH see Bach, Johann Sebastian

BREAK FORTH INTO JOY see Barnby, Sir Joseph

BREAK FORTH INTO JOY see Newbury, Kent A.

BREAK FORTH INTO JOY see Simper, Caleb

BREAK FORTH INTO JOY see Whitman

BREAK FORTH INTO SINGING see Johnson

BREAK FORTH INTO THANKSGIVING see Shaw, Martin

BREAK FORTH, O BEAUTEOUS HEAVENLY LIGHT
  see Many Moods Of Christmas, The, Suite Four

BREAK FORTH, O BEAUTEOUS HEAVENLY LIGHT see
  Bach, Johann Sebastian

BREAK FORTH, O BEAUTEOUS, HEAV'NLY LIGHT see
Bach, Johann Sebastian

BREAK FORTH, O BEAUTEOUS LIGHT
SATB oct STAFF 313 $.20   (B5071)

BREAK FORTH O BEAUTEOUS LIGHT see Bach, Johann
Sebastian

BREAK FORTH UNTO JOY see Hopson

BREAK THOU THE BREAD OF LIFE see Sherwin

BREAKING OF THE BREAD see Lovelace, Austin C.

BREAST THE WAVE, CHRISTIAN see Shelley, [Harry
Rowe]

BREATH OF GOD see Sateren, Leland Bernhard

BREATHE ON ME
TTBB BIG3 $.25   (B5072)

BREATHE ON ME, BREATH OF GOD see Jackson

BREATHE ON ME, BREATH OF GOD see Jackson,
Robert

BREATHE, ON ME, BREATH OF GOD see Lovelace,
Austin C.

BREATHE ON ME, BREATH OF GOD see Pedrette

BREATHE ON ME, BREATH OF GOD see Price

BREATHE ON ME, BREATH OF GOD see Rees

BREATHE ON ME, BREATH OF GOD see Swain, Freda

BREATHE ON ME, BREATH OF GOD see Thiman, Eric
Harding

BREATHE ON ME, BREATH OF GOD see Thompson, V.D.

BREBEUF, J. DE
Jesous Ahatonhia *Xmas
(McGlinchee) "Jesus Is Born" [Eng] 4pt mix
cor,acap oct SCHIRM.G 8593 $.30   (B5073)

Jesus Is Born *see Jesous Ahatonhia

BRECK
Carl Fischer Carol Book *CC34U,Xmas
unis/4pt mix cor,pno oct FISCHER,C CM-6192
$.40   (B5074)

Christmas In Song And Carol *CC17U,Xmas
oct unis/SA/SSA FISCHER,C CM-6311 $.50; 4pt
men cor,pno/org FISCHER,C CM-6427 $.40
(B5075)

BREIT IST DAS WASSER see Csenki, I.

BREITENDICH, FR. CHR.
Choral-Bog 1764 *CC191U
[Dan] cor,cont quarto FOG 146 s.p.   (B5076)

BRENNER, WALTER (1906-   )
Hashkivenu
[Heb] cor,cantor TRANSCON. TCL 665 $.75
(B5077)

Kol Nidre
[Heb] SATB,cantor TRANSCON. TCL 806 $.50
(B5078)

Memorial Prayer *prayer
SATB TRANSCON. TCL 118 $.40   (B5079)

BRESGEN, CESAR (1913-   )
Alles Verrinnt *mot
4pt mix cor MOSELER s.p. see from
Totenmotetten   (B5080)

Der Grimmig Tod Mit Seinem Pfeil *mot
4pt mix cor MOSELER s.p. see from
Totenmotetten   (B5081)

Es Bluhen Die Maien *Xmas
mix cor TONGER s.p.   (B5082)

Es Fiel Ein Himmelstaue *CC12U,BVM/Fest
[Ger] 4pt mix cor/5pt mix cor,acap (med)
MULLER SM 1483 s.p.   (B5083)

Ich Wollt, Dass Ich Daheime War *mot
4pt mix cor MOSELER s.p. see from
Totenmotetten   (B5084)

Kleine Deutsche Orgelmesse *Mass
4pt mix cor,org DOBLINGER voc sc s.p., cor
pts s.p.   (B5085)

Knecht Rupprecht
see Bresgen, Cesar, So Singen Wir Den
Winter An

Lobet Die Tage
(Luckdorff) mix cor,acap TONGER s.p.
(B5086)

Nulla Vita Sine Musica *mot
[Lat/Ger] SSATBB SCHOTT sc s.p., cor pts
s.p.   (B5087)

Requiem *ECY
[Ger] SATB,soli,acap (med) MULLER SM 2357
s.p.   (B5088)

So Singen Wir Den Winter An *Xmas
wom cor&jr cor TONGER s.p. contains also:
Knecht Rupprecht   (B5089)
mix cor TONGER s.p.   (B5090)

Surrexit Dominus *Easter,cant
dbl cor&wom cor&speak cor,soli,orch
DOBLINGER voc sc rental, cor pts s.p.,
s.p.   (B5091)

Totenmotetten *see Alles Verrinnt; Der
Grimmig Tod Mit Seinem Pfeil; Ich Wollt,
Dass Ich Daheime War   (B5092)

BRETON CAROL, THE see Bottle, Carol

BRETT
Nowell *Xmas
SSA SCHMITT 2545 $.25   (B5093)
SATB SCHMITT 1661 $.25   (B5094)

BREUER, HERBERT (1945-   )
Von Guten Machten *Gen
[Ger] SAB,kbd (med) BOSSE BE 232 s.p.
(B5095)

Weigenlied Der Hirten *Xmas
mix cor,acap ERDMANN 548 s.p.   (B5096)

BREVE REGNUN *Pol,15th cent
[Pol/Lat] men cor,trom POLSKIE s.p.   (B5097)

BREVIAIRE DE PIERRE L'ERMITE *Commun
[Lat] LEMOINE s.p. contains also solo work
contains & see also: Busser, [Henri-Paul],
Hosanna Filio David; Dupre, Marcel,
Tantum Ergo; Hahn, Reynaldo, Tu Es
Petrus; Rabaud, H., Ave Verum   (B5098)

BREVILLE, PIERRE-ONFROY DE (1861-1949)
Ave Maria *BVM,mot
[Lat] mix cor,T solo,org,harp,vln oct
DURAND s.p.   (B5099)
[Lat/Fr] mix cor,T solo,org,harp,vln oct
DURAND s.p.   (B5100)

Ave Verum *Commun,mot
[Lat] 4pt wom cor,Bar solo DURAND s.p. (B5101)

Jubilate
[Fr] 3pt wom cor,SMez soli,pno/org oct
DURAND s.p. contains also: O Salutaris;
Sancta Maria; Tantum Ergo   (B5102)

La Noel *Xmas
[Fr] SATB,acap oct SALABERT-US $.65 (B5103)

O Salutaris
see Breville, Pierre-Onfroy de, Jubilate

Sancta Maria
see Breville, Pierre-Onfroy de, Jubilate

Tantum Ergo *Commun,mot
see Breville, Pierre-Onfroy de, Jubilate
[Lat] 4pt wom cor,Mez solo DURAND s.p. (B5104)

BREVIS see Palestrina, Giovanni

BREWER, JOHN HYATT (1856-1931)
Holy Night, The *Xmas,cant
mix cor,4 soli,org voc sc SCHIRM.G $1.25
(B5105)

BREWER, SIR ALFRED HERBERT (1865-1928)
Blessing, Glory, Wisdom, And Thanks *Fest,
anthem
mix cor oct NOVELLO 28.0950.08 s.p. (B5106)

Magnificat And Nunc Dimittis *Magnif/Nunc
SATB (D maj) oct NOVELLO s.p.   (B5107)
SATB (E flat maj) oct NOVELLO 44.0661.03
s.p.   (B5108)

O Lord God, Thou Strength Of My Health *Gen,
anthem
SS,org pno oct ROYAL s.p. see also ANTHEMS
FOR UNISON OR TWO PART SINGING   (B5109)

BREYDERT, F.M.
Kyrie Eleison *Kyrie
"Lord Have Mercy Upon Us" [Eng/Lat] 2pt,kbd
AMP A348 $.20   (B5110)

Lord Have Mercy Upon Us *see Kyrie Eleison

BRICCETTI, T.
Psalm 150
SSAATTBB,pno/org oct KERBY 6402 $.45
(B5111)

BRICH AN, DU SCHONES MORGENLICHT see Bach,
Johann Sebastian

BRICH DEM HUNGRIEGEN see Bach, Johann
Sebastian, Brich Dem Hungrigen Dein Brot

BRICH DEM HUNGRIGEN DEIN BROT see Bach, Johann
Sebastian

BRICH DEM HUNGRIGEN DEIN BROT see Hindermann,
Walter Felix

BRICH ENTZWEI, MEIN ARMES HERZE see Bach,
Johann Sebastian

BRIDE OF CHRIST see Victoria, Tomas Luis de,
Veni Sponsa Christi

BRIDGE
Child Of God
SATB (jazz) ALFRED 6601 $.35   (B5112)

Sister Awake! Close Not Your Eyes
SA oct BOOSEY 5220 $.30   (B5113)

BRIDGE, [JOHN FREDERICK] (1844-1924)
God's Goodness Hath Been Great To Thee
*anthem/mot
mix cor oct NOVELLO s.p.   (B5114)

BRIEF MASS, A see Moevs

BRIEGEL, WOLFGANG CARL (1629-1712)
Festmusik Zum Ersten Weihnachtstag *Xmas
(Egidi, A.) [Ger] mix cor,2vln&2vla/4vln,
vcl,org,opt bvl&2trp&3trom VIEWEG sc
s.p., cor pts s.p., ipa   (B5115)

Festmusik Zum Zweiten Weihnachtstag *Xmas
(Egidi, A.) [Ger] mix cor,2vln&2vla/4vln,
vcl,org,opt bvl VIEWEG sc s.p., cor pts
s.p., ipa   (B5116)

Ich Will Singen Von Der Gnade Des Herrn
*cant
(Kruger) SATB,SATB soli,cont,2vln/2trp,
2vln/2trom HANSSLER 10.014 cor pts s.p.,
voc sc s.p., ipa   (B5117)

Mein Gott, Mein Gott, Warum Hast Du Mich
Verlassen *Easter/Psntd,cant
(Kruger) SATB,SATB soli,cont,2vln,2vla
HANSSLER 10.015 sc s.p., voc sc s.p., ipa
(B5118)

Singet Dem Herrn Ein Neues Lied *cant
(Kruger) SATB,SATB soli,cont HANSSLER
10.013 cor pts s.p., voc sc s.p., ipa (B5119)

BRIGGS
Hold Thou My Hand
SATB oct BELWIN 64020 $.35   (B5120)
SSA oct BELWIN 64154 $.25   (B5121)
(Wilson) SATB oct LORENZ C162 $.30   (B5122)

BRIGHT
Could Ye Not Watch With Me *Lent
SATB oct SOUTHERN $.30   (B5123)

Four Sacred Songs For The Night *CC4U,Eve
girl cor SOUTHERN $.40   (B5124)

Joyous Christmas Carol *Xmas,carol
SATB,acap,opt bells MARKS 4028 $.25 (B5125)

Kyrie Eleison *Kyrie
mix cor SOUTHERN $.25   (B5126)

Now Sing We All His Praise
SATB,acap MARKS 4032 $.25   (B5127)

Sailor's Alleluia
TTBB,acap MARKS 4026 $.35   (B5128)

Thy Lovely Saints
SSA SHAWNEE B 202 $.30   (B5129)

Vision Of Isaiah, The *cant
SATB SHAWNEE A1001 $1.00   (B5130)

BRIGHT ANGEL HOSTS ARE HEARD ON HIGH see Schulz

BRIGHT CANAAN
(Shaw; Parker) SATB,acap oct LAWSON 919 $.30
(B5131)

BRIGHT CANDLE LIGHT see Fuller, [Esther Mary]

BRIGHT, HOUSTON (1916-   )
Antiphonal Gloria
SATB SHAWNEE A 1099 $.30   (B5132)

Benedictus And Hosanna
SATB,acap SHAWNEE A 589 $.35   (B5133)

Could Ye Not Watch
SATB,acap SHAWNEE A 877 $.35   (B5134)

De Profundis
SATB,acap SHAWNEE A 682 $.35   (B5135)

Four Sacred Songs For The Night *CC4U
SSA,acap SHAWNEE B 190 $.40   (B5136)

Hodie Nobis Coelorum Rex
SATB SHAWNEE A 812 $.40   (B5137)

Is Not The Life More Than Meat
SATB FLAMMER A 5582 $.30   (B5138)

Kyrie Eleison
SATB,acap SHAWNEE A 675 $.30   (B5139)

Now Deck Thyself With Majesty
SATB SHAWNEE A 962 $.40   (B5140)

People That Walked In Darness, The
SATB,acap SHAWNEE A 940 $.35   (B5141)

Sunrise Alleluia
SATB SHAWNEE A 852 $.35   (B5142)

Te Deum Laudamus *Te Deum
[Lat] SSATBB,acap AMP A311 $.35   (B5143)

Thou Wilt Keep Him In Perfect Peace
SATB SHAWNEE A 1100 $.30   (B5144)

Watchman, What Of The Night?
SATB,acap SHAWNEE A 776 $.35   (B5145)

BRIGHT IS THE DAY see Kelly, Bryan

BRIGHT LITTLE STAR
(Grant) SATB oct PRO ART 1967 $.25   (B5146)

BRIGHT STAR *Pol
(Ehret) SA MARKS 4407 $.25   (B5147)
(Ehret) SSA MARKS 4348 $.25   (B5148)

BRIGHT STAR see Dello Joio, Norman

BRIGHT STAR OF HEAVEN *Xmas,Fr
(Kinsman, F.) SATB oct PRESSER 312-40534 $.30
(B5149)

BRIGHTEN THE CORNER see Gabriel

BRIGHTER DAWN IS BREAKING, A see Blower,
Maurice

BRIGHTER THAN SUN see Dungan

BRIGHTEST AND BEST see Bach, Johann Sebastian

BRIGHTEST AND BEST see Coombs, Charles Whitney

BRIGHTEST AND BEST see Fearis, J.S.

BRIGHTEST AND BEST see Wesley

BRIGHTEST AND BEST OF THE SONS *hymn
(Gardner) SSA (med easy) OXFORD 44.221 $.25,
ipr see from Five Hymns In Popular Style
(B5150)

BRIGHTEST AND BEST OF THE SONS OF THE MORNING
see Gardner, John [Linton]

BRIGHTEST AND BEST OF THE SONS OF THE MORNING
see Harding, G.P.

BRIGHTEST AND BEST OF THE SONS OF THE MORNING
see Sjolund, Paul

BRIGITTA, ST.
Prayer To The Holy Spirit (from Ritual Of The
Prayer To The Holy Spirit)
(Lundquist) SATB,acap (med) oct WILLIS 5676
$.12   (B5151)

BRILLO UNA LUCE see Leoni, Leonardo

BRIMHALL
Christmas Night *Xmas
SATB,acap,opt pno oct PRO ART 1986 $.25
(B5152)

BRINDLE, [REGINALD SMITH] (1917-   )
Vivo Sin Vivir *anthem
mix cor oct OXFORD 84.174 $.35   (B5153)

BRING A TORCH *Xmas,carol
see Three Songs For Christmas
(Jennings) SATB KJOS PC792 $.30   (B5154)
(Shaw; Parker) SATB ALLANS 436 s.p.   (B5155)

BRING A TORCH, JANETTE, ISABELLA see Miller, J.

BRING A TORCH, JEANETTE see Young, Carlton R.

BRING A TORCH, JEANETTE ISABELLA *Xmas,carol
see Many Moods Of Christmas, The, Suite Three
(Shaw; Parker) SATB,acap oct LAWSON 713 $.35
                                       (B5156)
(Vance) SATB oct BELWIN 2097 $.25   (B5157)

BRING A TORCH JEANNETTE, ISABELLA *Xmas,carol,
Fr
see Three Christmas Carols
SATB,acap SCHIRM.EC 364 $.25   (B5158)
(Davison, A.) TTBB,acap SCHIRM.EC 97 $.25
                                       (B5159)
(Glaser, V.) SAB,acap SCHIRM.EC 2234 $.20
                                       (B5160)
(Stone) SATB oct PRO ART 1921 $.30   (B5161)
(Stone) SAB oct PRO ART 1916 $.30   (B5162)
(Stone) SSA oct PRO ART 1619 $.30   (B5163)
(Stone) 2pt oct PRO ART 1800 $.30   (B5164)
(Wilson) SSA oct SPRATT 604 $.25   (B5165)

BRING A TORCH, JEANNETTE, ISABELLA see Bitgood

BRING BACK THE SPRINGTIME see Kaiser, Kurt

BRING COSTLY OFFERINGS see Saint-Saens,
Camille, Tollite Hostias

BRING THE CHRISTMAS LOG TO TOWN see Bottle,
Carol

BRING THY GLORY TO US see Tschesnokoff, P.I.

BRING TO US THY PEACE AND CALM see Nyquist

BRING US, O LORD GOD see Harris, William Henry

BRING US TOGETHER, GO FORWARD TOGETHER see
Leyden

BRING YOUR TORCHES see Un Flambeau, Jeannette,
Isabelle

BRING YOUR TORCHES JEANNETTE ISABELLA *carol,
Eng
(Glover, R. F.) SSST,org oct KERBY 6025 $.35
contains also: Gloucestershire Wassail; In
Dulci Jubilo   (B5166)

BRINGET DEM HERRN see Bach, Johann Sebastian,
Bringet Dem Herrn Ehre Seines Namens

BRINGET DEM HERRN EHRE SEINES NAMENS see Bach,
Johann Sebastian

BRINGT EHR UND PREIS DEM HERREN see Schutz,
Heinrich

BRINGT HER DEM HERREN see Schutz, Heinrich

BRISSIO
Come, Let Us Worship *see In Medio Ecclesiae

In Medio Ecclesiae
3pt mix cor,acap RICORDI-ENG SY202 s.p.
                                       (B5167)
(Zanon; Vene) "Come, Let Us Worship" [Lat/
Eng] SAT,acap oct COLOMBO 1880 $.25
                                       (B5168)

BRISTOL, L.
As The Disciples
SATB oct PRESSER 312-40656 $.30   (B5169)

Could Jesus Hear The Sounds To Come
SATB&jr cor,org oct KERBY 813 $.35   (B5170)

Lord Of All Being, Throned Afar
SATB,acap oct PRESSER 312-40540 $.30
                                       (B5171)

Our Father, By Whose Servants
SATB oct PRESSER 312-40663 $.30   (B5172)

Sing Praise To God, Who Spoke Through Man
SATB oct PRESSER 312-40760 $.35   (B5173)

Songs From Luke *CCU
(Demarest, D.) jr cor sc KERBY 5316 $1.00,
cor pts KERBY 5317 $.50   (B5174)

Songs From Matthew *CCU
jr cor jr cor sc KERBY 5316 $1.00; jr cor
cor pts KERBY 5317 $.50   (B5175)

BRISTOL, LEE H., JR. (1923-   )
All Our Joys *carol,Span
SATB oct ELKAN-V 362-1243 $.25   (B5176)

Could Jesus Hear The Sounds To Come? *Palm
SATB oct KERBY 81378 $.35   (B5177)

Let The Children Sing *cant
jr cor (easy) ABINGDON APM-684 $1.50
                                       (B5178)

Lord, Speak To Me That I May Speak
SATB (med) ABINGDON APM-760 $.30   (B5179)

New Songs For The Junior Choir (composed with
Friedell, Harold W.) *CC36L
jr cor CONCORDIA 97-7599 $1.40   (B5180)

O Lord, Support Us
SATB oct ELKAN-V 362-1237 $.25   (B5181)

Songs From Luke
unis voc sc KERBY 5316D $1.00, cor pts
KERBY 5317J $.50   (B5182)

Songs From Matthew
unis voc sc KERBY 5707D $1.00, cor pts
KERBY 5708J $.50   (B5183)

Thirty-Five Sacred Rounds And Canons From
Four Centuries *CC35L,canon/round
treb cor,acap oct KERBY 80481 $.75   (B5184)

BRITAIN, [RADIE] (1903-   )
Prayer
SATB,acap oct COLOMBO 1024 $.25   (B5185)

BRITISH CHILDREN'S PRAYER see Wolfe, Jacques

BRITON'S SING! see Purcell, Henry

BRITTEN, ANTHONY
Christ Is Born Of Maiden Fair (composed with
Yorke, Colin)
see FOUR CHRISTMAS CAROLS

BRITTEN, BENJAMIN (1913-   )
Antiphon *anti
SATB,org oct BOOSEY 5196 $.40   (B5186)

As Dew In April (from Ceremony Of Carols, A)
carol
(Harrison) SATB,pno/harp oct BOOSEY 1829
$.30   (B5187)

Balulalow (from Ceremony Of Carols, A) carol
SSS,S solo,opt harp oct BOOSEY 1916 $.30
                                       (B5188)
(Harrison) SATB,S solo,opt harp oct BOOSEY
1828 $.30   (B5189)

Boy Was Born [Chorus] (from Boy Was Born, A)
Xmas,cant
SSAATTBB,opt inst (med diff) voc sc OXFORD
46.123 $4.00   (B5190)
SATB,acap (med) oct OXFORD 84.092 $.20
                                       (B5191)

Cantata Academica *cant
[Lat] mix cor,SATB soli,orch BOOSEY voc sc
$5.00, cor pts $2.00, sc $15.00, ipr, min
sc $6.00   (B5192)

Ceremony Of Carols *CCU,Xmas,carol
girl cor SOUTHERN $1.75   (B5193)

Ceremony Of Carols, A *carol
treb cor,harp/pno voc sc BOOSEY $1.75, ipa
                                       (B5194)
(Harrison, J.) mix cor voc sc BOOSEY $1.75,
ipa   (B5195)

Corpus Christi Carol (from Boy Was Born, A)
Corpus/Psntd,carol
unis,pno (easy) OXFORD 81.086 $.25   (B5196)
unis (easy) oct OXFORD $.25   (B5197)

Deo Gratias (from Ceremony Of Carols, A)
SSS,S solo,pno/harp oct BOOSEY 5071 $.30
                                       (B5198)
(Harrison) SATB,pno/harp oct BOOSEY 1831
$.30   (B5199)

Festival Te Deum *Te Deum
mix cor,org voc sc BOOSEY $1.00   (B5200)

Hymn Of Columba *hymn
SATB,org oct BOOSEY 5569 $.35   (B5201)

Hymn To St. Peter *hymn
SATB,org, treble solo or semi-chorus voc sc
BOOSEY $.40   (B5202)

Hymn To The Virgin
SSAATTBB,acap oct BOOSEY 1856 $.30   (B5203)

Hymns (Noye's Fludde) *hymn
unis BOOSEY-CAN s.p.   (B5204)

Jesu, As Thou Art Our Savior (from Boy Was
Born, A) Xmas
SSATB,S solo,opt inst (med) OXFORD 46.029
$.25   (B5205)

Jubilate Deo In C *Jubil
(Wood, Robin) SATB&cong (med easy) oct
OXFORD 42.848 $.50   (B5206)

Missa Brevis *Mass
[Lat] SSA BOOSEY-CAN s.p.   (B5207)

Missa Brevis In D *Mass
[Lat] treb cor,org BOOSEY voc sc $1.75, cor
pts $.30   (B5208)

New Year Carol, A *Xmas,carol
unis BOOSEY-CAN s.p.   (B5209)

Noye's Fludde
jr cor&audience,AB soli,orch BOOSEY voc sc
$7.50, cor pts $.30, sc $15.00, ipr, min
sc $7.50   (B5210)

Oxen, The *Xmas,carol
2pt wom cor FABER 11637 $.30   (B5211)

Psalm 150
mix cor SOUTHERN $.30   (B5212)
boy cor/girl cor SOUTHERN $.30   (B5213)
2pt treb cor,inst BOOSEY voc sc $1.50, cor
pts $.30, sc $3.75, ipa   (B5214)

Rejoice In The Lamb
mix cor,SATB soli,org/orch BOOSEY voc sc
$1.75, sc rental, ipr   (B5215)

Shepherd's Carol *Xmas,carol
SATB BELWIN AP18 $.35   (B5216)

Song Of The Women *Xmas
3pt wom cor,acap oct FABER 11638 $.30
                                       (B5217)

Spring Carol (from Ceremony Of Carols, A)
SA oct BOOSEY 1755A $.30   (B5218)

Sweet Was The Song *Xmas
4pt wom cor,acap oct FABER 11639 $.30
                                       (B5219)

Sycamore Tree, The *Xmas
4pt mix cor,acap oct FABER 11640 $.30
                                       (B5220)

Te Deum In C Major *Te Deum
SATB,S solo (diff) oct OXFORD 42.141 $.65,
ipr   (B5221)

There Is No Rose (from Ceremony Of Carols, A)
carol
SSS,opt harp oct BOOSEY 1917 $.30   (B5222)
(Harrison) SATB oct BOOSEY 1827 $.30
                                       (B5223)

This Little Babe (from Ceremony Of Carols, A)
carol
SSS,opt harp oct BOOSEY 5138 $.30   (B5224)

BRITTEN, BENJAMIN (cont'd.)
(Harrison) SATB oct BOOSEY 830 $.30   (B5225)

Voices For Today *Op.75, anthem
men cor&wom cor&jr cor voc sc SCHIRM.G
$1.50   (B5226)

Wolcum Yole (from Ceremony Of Carols, A)
SSA/SSS,opt harp oct BOOSEY 1775B $.30
                                       (B5227)
(Harrison) SATB oct BOOSEY 1826 $.30
                                       (B5228)

BRIXI, FRANZ XAVER (1732-1771)
Pastores Loquebantur *mot
(Hellmann, Diethard) 4pt mix cor,cont,2vln
s.p. sc BREITKOPF-W PB-4844, cor pts
BREITKOPF-W CHB-3567   (B5229)

BRIXI, SIMON
Magnificat
(Belsky, V.) cor,soli,10inst sc SUPRAPHON
s.p.   (B5230)

BROAD IS THE ROAD see Read, Daniel

BROADHEAD, G.F.
Hail, Gladdening Light
cor oct HART s.p.   (B5231)

Jesu The Very Thought Of Thee
cor oct HART s.p.   (B5232)

Spacious Firmament On High, The
oct HART   (B5233)

BROCK, BLANCHE [KERR] (1888-1958)
Beyond The Sunset
(Hustad, D.) SATB ALLANS 402 s.p.   (B5234)

He's A Wonderful Savior To Me
(Boersma) SAB oct WORD CS-2139 $.25   (B5235)

BROCKES-PASSION see Handel, George Frideric,
Der Fur Die Sunden Der Welt Gemarterte Und
Sterbende Jesus

BROCKLESS, BRIAN
Behold Now, Praise The Lord *Fest,anthem
mix cor oct NOVELLO 28.1429.03 s.p.   (B5236)

BRODSZKY
I'll Walk With God
unis,opt orch WARNER H4066 $.30   (B5237)
2pt,opt orch WARNER H4052 $.30   (B5238)
SSA,opt orch WARNER H9042 $.30   (B5239)
SAB,opt orch WARNER H3078 $.30   (B5240)
TTBB,opt orch WARNER H1239 $.30   (B5241)
SATB,opt orch WARNER 6073 $.35   (B5242)

BRODZKY
I'll Walk With God
SATB (easy) ALLANS 303 s.p.   (B5243)
(Ernst, Eileen) SA ALLANS 304 s.p.   (B5244)

BROECHIN, ERNST (1894-   )
Wach Auf Mein Herz Und Singe
[Ger] mix cor,org/winds HUG s.p., ipr
                                       (B5245)

BROECKX
Christmas Carol *Xmas,carol
unis oct BOOSEY 4134 $.30   (B5246)

Easter Carol *Easter,carol
(Peterson) SA&SATB oct BOOSEY 5561 $.30
                                       (B5247)

BROGI
Infant Divine *Xmas
(Howorth) 2pt WARNER W3736 $.30   (B5248)

BROKERING, LOIS
Love, Love, Love *anthem/folk/hymn
see 'Tis The Gift To Be Simple
unis treb cor,kbd (very easy) oct AUGSBURG
3004 $.10 contains also: 'Tis The Gift To
Be Simple (unis treb cor,gtr)   (B5249)
oct AUGSBURG 11-3004 $.10 contains also:
'Tis The Gift To Be Simple   (B5250)

'Tis The Gift To Be Simple
see Brokering, Lois, Love, Love, Love
see Brokering, Lois, Love, Love, Love

BROLLOPSKLADER, UTAN see Weman, Henry

BRONSON, MARGARET
Babe In A Manger Born *Xmas
SATB,pno (med) oct WILLIS 6506 $.16   (B5251)

Guiding Shepherd, The
SATB oct HUNTZINGER 4041 $.15   (B5252)

Wise Men Came, The *Epiph
SATB oct HUNTZINGER 4050 $.16   (B5253)

BROOK
Joy Came Softly
SA (easy) OXFORD 44.004 $.30   (B5254)

O Strong Young Christ
unis (easy) OXFORD 45.951 $.25   (B5255)

Shepherds Go To The Manger, The *Xmas
SA (easy) OXFORD 45.019 $.25   (B5256)

BROOK, HARRY
Father, Hear The Prayer We Offer *prayer
SA,pno/org oct NOVELLO 33.0101.10 s.p.
                                       (B5257)

O Strong Young Christ *Gen
unis (easy) oct OXFORD 45.063 $.25   (B5258)

Starlit Night
2pt (easy) CRAMER 322 ipr   (B5259)

BROOKS
Lord Giveth, The
SATB oct COLOMBO 2349 $.25   (B5260)

Praising Song
SATB oct COLOMBO 2422 $.25   (B5261)

BROOKS, NIGEL
Psalm 23
SATB voc sc WEINBERGER s.p.   (B5262)

BROOME, ED
　Lo! The Tomb Is Empty　*Easter
　　4pt mix cor,low solo&high solo oct SCHIRM.G
　　4404 $.35   (B5263)

B'ROSH HASHONO see Weisgal, A.

BROSIG, MORITZ (1815-1887)
　Timete Dominum
　　(Dite, L.) 4pt mix cor,org (contains also:
　　Aiblinger, Johann Kaspar, Justorium
　　Animae) DOBLINGER voc sc s.p., cor pts
　　s.p. see from DER KLEINE KIRCHENCHOR
　　　　　　　　　　　　　　　　　(B5264)

BROTHER JAMES'S AIR see Bain, J.L. Mc Beth

BROTHERHOOD OF MAN see Angell, Warren M.

BROTHERHOOD OF MAN see Chenoweth, Wilbur

BROTHERHOOD OF MAN, THE see Handel, George
　　Frideric

BROTHERHOOD OF PRAISE, THE see Muller, H.

BROTHERS see Lovelace, Austin C.

BROTHERS ALL REJOICE　*Xmas
　(Kozinski, D.) SATB,acap oct PRESSER
　312-40336 $.30   (B5265)

BROUGHTON, EDWARD
　Go, Tell It On The Mountain　*Xmas,anthem/
　　spir
　　SATB (med easy) oct LORENZ B201 $.30
　　　　　　　　　　　　　　　　　(B5266)
　　SATB oct LORENZ B201 $.30   (B5267)

BROWN
　All Things Bright And Beautiful
　　SA SCHMITT 2569 $.22   (B5268)

　Born Today Is Christ Our King
　　SSAA,acap SHAWNEE B 282 $.25   (B5269)

　Carol Of The Angels　*Xmas
　　(Runkel) SATB SCHMITT 1753 $.25 (B5270)

　Christ, Whose Glory Fills The Skies
　　SATB,org/pno BOSTON 11989 $.35   (B5271)

　Consider The Lilies
　　jr cor oct LILLENAS AN-4023 $.25 (B5272)

　Dormi, Jesu (from New Born King) Xmas
　　SATB,acap (diff) OXFORD 84.149 $.25 (B5273)

　Father, Thou Who Art In Heaven
　　SATB,org BOSTON 13312 $.40   (B5274)
　　(Stickles) SSA,org BOSTON 13311 $.40
　　　　　　　　　　　　　　　　　(B5275)

　Great Is The Lord　*Gen
　　SATB SCHMITT 1739 $.25   (B5276)

　Just As I Am
　　SATB,acap SHAWNEE A 991 $.25   (B5277)

　Make We Joy Now
　　see Three Christmas Carols

　Now Well May We Mirthes Make
　　see Three Christmas Carols

　O What Their Joy And Their Glory
　　SATB oct FISCHER,C CM-7698 $.35 (B5278)

　Of A Rose Sing We
　　see Three Christmas Carols

　On Life's Highway
　　(Bertrand) SATB,org (easy) oct WILLIS 4235
　　$.20   (B5279)

　Sing Noel, Ring Noel　*Xmas
　　SATB oct PRO ART 2630 $.30   (B5280)
　　SAB oct PRO ART 2632 $.30   (B5281)
　　SSA oct PRO ART 2524 $.25   (B5282)
　　2pt oct PRO ART 2702 $.30   (B5283)
　　SA SOUTHERN $.30   (B5284)

　Thee We Adore, O Hidden Savior　*Gen
　　SAB SCHMITT 5530 $.30   (B5285)

　Three Christmas Carols　*Xmas,carol
　　SATB,acap (med easy) OXFORD 43.388 $.35
　　contains: Make We Joy Now; Now Well May
　　We Mirthes Make; Of A Rose Sing We
　　　　　　　　　　　　　　　　　(B5286)

　Under The Stars　*Xmas
　　SATB oct FISCHER,C CM-7048 $.25 (B5287)
　　unis oct FISCHER,C CM-7058 $.25 (B5288)
　　SSA oct FISCHER,C CM-7047 $.25   (B5289)
　　(Simon) 3pt jr cor/SAB (med) FISCHER,C
　　CM 7046 $.25   (B5290)
　　(Wilkinson) unis jr cor FISCHER,C CM 7058
　　$.20   (B5291)

BROWN, A.G.Y.
　And Didst Thou Love The Race　*anthem
　　unis oct OXFORD 02.023 $.25   (B5292)

　Only Begotten Word Of God
　　SATB oct GRAY GCMR 1442 $.30   (B5293)

BROWN, CHARLES F.
　Amen
　　SATB WORD CS-2495 $.25   (B5294)

　Jesus, Of A Maid Thou Wouldst Be Born　*Xmas
　　SATB (easy) ABINGDON APM-798 $.35 (B5295)

　One Night　*Xmas
　　unis/SA oct WORD CS-2487 $.25   (B5296)

　Reach Out And Touch
　　SATB oct WORD CS-2539 $.30   (B5297)

BROWN, CHRISTOPHER
　David　*Bibl/cant
　　[Eng] SATB,MezBar soli,orch voc sc CHESTER
　　s.p.   (B5298)

　Gloria　*Gloria
　　mix cor oct OXFORD 46.513 $1.50 (B5299)

　Hymn To The Holy Innocents, A　*Bibl/cant
　　mix cor,T solo,pno,strings,timp (med) voc
　　sc OXFORD 46.151 $.75, ipr   (B5300)

BROWN, CHRISTOPHER (cont'd.)
　Jubilate Deo　*Jubil
　　SATB (med) oct OXFORD 42.713 $.50 (B5301)

　Laudate Dominum (Psalm 150) Fest/Gen/Thanks
　　SATB (med) oct OXFORD 42.910 $.50 (B5302)

　Laus Creatorum　*anthem
　　mix cor oct OXFORD 42.356 $1.50   (B5303)

　Missa Brevis　*Mass
　　mix cor oct OXFORD rental   (B5304)

　Psalm 150　*see Laudate Dominum

BROWN, DORA
　Blue Cloak, The　*Xmas
　　unis jr cor/unis sr cor CRAMER 76 s.p. (B5305)

BROWN, E. BOULDIN
　Carol Of The Beasties　*Xmas,carol
　　SSA oct VOLKWEIN VB123 $.25   (B5306)

　Holy Child, The　*Xmas
　　3pt wom cor oct SCHIRM.G 10378 $.20 (B5307)

　Once Upon A Starlit Night　*Xmas
　　SATB oct VOLKWEIN VB722 $.25   (B5308)

BROWN, FRANK EDWIN (1908)
　Be Still And Know
　　cor oct HART s.p.   (B5309)

　I Will Extol My God
　　cor oct HART s.p.   (B5310)

　Lord's Prayer, The　*prayer
　　SATB ALLANS 431 s.p.   (B5311)

　O God Of All Creation　*carol
　　unis CRAMER 57 s.p.   (B5312)

　Sing Triumphant Hymns
　　oct HART   (B5313)

BROWN, J.
　Carols For Christmastide　*Xmas,anthem/carol
　　(Descroquettes, Dom. J.H.) SATB/unis (easy)
　　oct GIA 1009 $.25
　　contains: Ringing And Singing; Sheeps
　　Lament, The; Turtle Doves, The (B5314)

　Dawn Of Christmas, The
　　see Three Christmas Carols

　Invitation, Come Watch Awhile
　　see Three Christmas Carols

　Manger Lullaby A
　　see Three Christmas Carols

　Ringing And Singing
　　see Carols For Christmastide

　Sheeps Lament, The
　　see Carols For Christmastide

　Three Christmas Carols　*Xmas,anthem/carol
　　(Descroquettes, Dom. J.H.) SATB/unis (easy)
　　oct GIA G733 $.25
　　contains: Dawn Of Christmas, The;
　　Invitation, Come Watch Awhile; Manger
　　Lullaby A   (B5315)

　Turtle Doves, The
　　see Carols For Christmastide

BROWN, LEON F.
　As Many As Received Him
　　SATB oct BOURNE 659 $.25   (B5316)

　Blessed Is He That Cometh
　　SATB oct SOUTHERN $.30   (B5317)

　God Be Merciful Unto Us
　　cor HIGHLAND 4100 $.25   (B5318)

　O God, How Wonderful Thou Art
　　SATB oct SOUTHERN $.25   (B5319)

　Psalm 98　*see Psalm Of Praise

　Psalm Of Praise (Psalm 98)
　　SATB oct BOURNE 736 $.25   (B5320)

　To God Be The Glory
　　SATB,7brass oct SOUTHERN $.25, ipa (B5321)

BROWN, MARY HELEN
　Night Is Calling
　　SSAA HUNTZINGER 2032 $.15   (B5322)

　On That First Christmas Morning　*Xmas
　　SSA oct HUNTZINGER 505 $.18   (B5323)

BROWN, R.
　Aus Tiefer Not　*cant
　　mix cor,soli,org (diff) oct WESTERN WIM22
　　$1.75   (B5324)

　Carol Cantata　*cant
　　SATB&3pt jr cor,soli,org (med diff) oct
　　AVANT AV94 $2.50   (B5325)

　O Sacred Head
　　SATB,org (med easy) oct WESTERN WIM 11 $.30
　　　　　　　　　　　　　　　　　(B5326)

BROWN, REX P.
　Carol Of Humility, A　*see O Deue D Pob
　　Cristion

　Carol Of Praise, A　*see Nos Galan

　Christmas Is Come　*Xmas,carol,Eng
　　SATB,acap oct SCHIRM.EC 2698   (B5327)

　Nos Galan　*Xmas,carol,Welsh
　　"Carol Of Praise, A" SATB,acap SCHIRM.EC
　　2700   (B5328)

　O Deue D Pob Cristion　*Xmas,carol,Welsh
　　"Carol Of Humility, A" SATB,acap SCHIRM.EC
　　2699   (B5329)

BROWN, THOMAS
　Blessed Are All They (Psalm 128) Gen,18th
　　cent
　　(Smith) SA (easy) oct OXFORD 44.208 $.25
　　　　　　　　　　　　　　　　　(B5330)

　Psalm 128　*see Blessed Are All They

BROWN, WILLIAM DAVID
　Trust In The Word Of The Lord
　　SATB,acap oct WORD CS-2514 $.35 (B5331)

BROWN, WILLIAM [H., JR.]
　Hail, All Hail
　　SATB (med diff) oct WOLF W-M102 $.45 (B5332)

　Hallelujah
　　SATB (med diff) oct WOLF W-M101 $.45
　　　　　　　　　　　　　　　　　(B5333)

　He's Got The Whole World In His Hands
　　SATB (med diff) oct WOLF W-M106 $.60 (B5334)

　Prayer, A　*prayer
　　SATB (med diff) oct WOLF W-M104 $.45 (B5335)

　Psalm 23
　　SATB (med diff) oct WOLF W-M103 $.45
　　　　　　　　　　　　　　　　　(B5336)

　Sermon On The Mount　*Bibl
　　SATB (med diff) oct WOLF W-M105 $.45 (B5337)

　Sing Of Him
　　SATB oct WORD CS-2560 $.35   (B5338)

　Sometimes I Feel Like A Motherless Child
　　SATB (med diff) oct WOLF W-M107 $.45
　　　　　　　　　　　　　　　　　(B5339)

BROWNE
　Folk Hymns With Guitar　*CCU,folk/hymn
　　cor,gtr ALBERT s.p.   (B5340)

　Jesu, Mercy, How May This Be?
　　(Little) SATB CHESTER s.p.   (B5341)

　Song For The Junior School　*CC7U,folk/hymn
　　jr cor,bells,gtr ALBERT s.p.   (B5342)

BROWNE, H.M.
　Day Is Past Over, The
　　3pt wom cor,pno (easy) oct WILLIS 6311 $.12
　　　　　　　　　　　　　　　　　(B5343)

　O Be Joyful　*Fest/Thanks
　　SATB,pno (easy) oct WILLIS 6306 $.15
　　　　　　　　　　　　　　　　　(B5344)

BROWNE, JOHN [LEWIS] (1864-1933)
　Stabat Mater　*anthem
　　SATTB STAINER BM10-2 s.p.   (B5345)

BROWNSON
　Salisbury
　　SATB,acap MARKS 65 $.30   (B5346)

BROZEN, MICHAEL
　Five Alleluias　*CC5U,Easter/Gen
　　SATB&SSAATTBB,acap oct PRESSER MC541 $.50
　　　　　　　　　　　　　　　　　(B5347)

BRUBAKER, GWEN
　Love Is Come Again
　　2pt,inst oct AGAPE JR 201 $.30 (B5348)

　Sing Praise
　　SATB/SAT oct AGAPE A 456 $.30   (B5349)

BRUBECK
　Forty Days
　　SATB SHAWNEE A 996 $.50   (B5350)

　Gates Of Justice, The
　　SATB voc sc FLAMMER A1116 $7.00, rental
　　　　　　　　　　　　　　　　　(B5351)

　Let Not Your Heart Be Troubled
　　SATB SHAWNEE A 998 $.40   (B5352)

　Light In The Wilderness, The
　　SATB voc sc FLAMMER A1000 $7.00, rental
　　　　　　　　　　　　　　　　　(B5353)
　　SATB min sc SHAWNEE LC446 $3.00 (B5354)

　Lord, Lord
　　SATB SHAWNEE A 1102 $.40   (B5355)

　Oh Come Let Us Sing
　　SATB SHAWNEE A 1151 $.45   (B5356)

　Praise Ye The Lord
　　SATB FLAMMER A 999 $.35   (B5357)

　Sermon On The Mount, The
　　SATB SHAWNEE A 997 $.40   (B5358)

BRUBECK, HOWARD (1916-)
　How Glorious Is Thy Name
　　SATB SHAWNEE A 1103 $.35   (B5359)

BRUCH, MAX (1838-1920)
　Die Flucht Der Heiligen Familie
　　mix cor ALSBACH&D sc s.p., cor pts s.p.
　　　　　　　　　　　　　　　　　(B5360)

　Jubilate, Amen　*Op.3
　　4pt mix cor,S solo,2fl,ob,clar,bsn,horn,
　　trp,strings,timp BREITKOPF-W rental
　　　　　　　　　　　　　　　　　(B5361)

　Morning-Song Of Praise
　　SSATBB BOSWORTH s.p. see from LAUDY
　　COLLECTION OF MODERN PART SONGS (B5362)

BRUCK, ARNOLD VON (? -ca. 1554)
　Christ, Der Ist Erstanden　*Easter,mot
　　(Heilman) SATB HANSSLER 1.093 s.p. (B5363)

　Mitten Wir Im Leben Sind　*ECY/Gd.Fri.
　　[Ger] SATB,acap (med) MULLER K 4 s.p.
　　　　　　　　　　　　　　　　　(B5364)
　　SATB,acap voc pt DOBLINGER s.p. see also
　　TOD UND VERGANGLICHKEIT   (B5365)

　Vater Unser Im Himmelreich
　　[Ger] SATB,acap (med) MULLER K 32 s.p.
　　　　　　　　　　　　　　　　　(B5366)

　Wir Glauben All An Einen Gott
　　[Ger] SATB,acap (med) MULLER K 8 s.p.
　　　　　　　　　　　　　　　　　(B5367)

BRUCK, JOHANN VON
　Christ, Der Ist Erstanden　*Easter/Lent
　　(Richardson) "Christ, The Lord, Is Risen"
　　SATB oct SPRATT 2006 $.30   (B5368)

　Christ, The Lord, Is Risen　*see Christ, Der
　　Ist Erstanden

BRUCK, JOHANN VON (cont'd.)

Germinavit Radix *Adv/Xmas
SSATB,acap voc pt DOBLINGER s.p. see also
ADVENT UND WEIHNACHT, HEFT 2 (B5369)

BRUCKHORST, A.M.

Weihnachtsmusik *Xmas
(Egidi, A.) [Ger] mix cor,SAT soli,strings,
2trp,cont VIEWEG sc s.p., cor pts s.p.,
ipa (B5370)

BRUCKNER, ANTON (1824-1896)

Abendmahl
(Graner, G.) 4pt mix cor cor pts LIENAU
s.p. see also Geistliche Gesange Heft 3 (B5371)

Anbetung
SAATTBB cor pts LIENAU s.p. see also Sieben
Motetten (B5372)

Antiphon
[Lat] SATB MARKS 4252 $.30 (B5373)

Ave Maria
see Geistliche Gesange, Heft II
see Geistliche Gesange, Heft II
see Two Marian Compositions
mix cor sc ALSBACH&D s.p. (B5374)
[Lat] SATB,acap MARKS 47 $.25 (B5375)
(Kjelson) SATB acap BELWIN 2259 $.35 (B5376)

Ave Verum *Easter/Lent
(Marshall, Charles) "Jesu, Jesu, God
Incarnate" SATB FRANK F-600 $.30 (B5377)

Christ Is Born For Us *Xmas,mot
SATB MUSICUS 018 $.25 (B5378)

Christ Was Made Obedient *see Christus
Factus Est

Christus Am Kreuz
SATB cor pts LIENAU s.p. see also Sieben
Motetten (B5379)

Christus Factus Est *Easter/Lent,Gradual/mot
see Geistliche Gesange, Heft III
SATB,acap BREITKOPF-L cor pts s.p., voc pt
s.p. (B5380)
4pt mix cor cor pts LIENAU s.p. see also
Four Graduale (B5381)
[Lat] SATB,acap PETERS 6316 $.30 see from
Three Graduals For The Church Year (B5382)
"Christ Was Made Obedient" [Eng/Lat] 4pt
mix cor,acap oct SCHIRM.G 11395 $.35 (B5383)
"Jesus Christ, For Our Salvation" SATB oct
WALTON 2161 $.30 (B5384)
(Randolph) SATB,acap oct LAWSON 748 $.35 (B5385)
(Westlund) SATB oct SUMMY 5249 $.60 (B5386)

Das Heil Der Welt
SATB cor pts LIENAU s.p. see also Sieben
Motetten (B5387)

Das Himmlische Haus
SATB,T solo,opt org cor pts LIENAU s.p. see
also Sieben Motetten (B5388)

Dexterra Domini
mix cor,acap ERDMANN 527 s.p. (B5389)

Diese Statte
see Bruckner, Anton, Locus Iste

Ecce Sacerdos
see Two Motets
[Lat] mix cor,org,3trom sc UNIVER. 4972
$1.50 (B5390)

Entsagen
4pt mix cor,S/T solo,org DOBLINGER voc sc
s.p., cor pts s.p. (B5391)

Eternal Spirit, We Confess
(Ehret, Walter) SATB,acap (med) PRESSER
312-40994 $.35 (B5392)

Fest-Cantate *Fest,cant
(Etti, K.) 4pt men cor,opt org/2fl&2ob&
4clar&2bsn&4horn&3trp&3trom&tuba&timp
DOBLINGER voc sc s.p., cor pts s.p., ipr (B5393)

Forth From Jesse Sprang A Rose
(Carlton) SATB,acap oct BOOSEY 5405 $.35 (B5394)

Four Graduale *Gradual
4pt mix cor sc LIENAU s.p.
contains & see also: Christus Factus Est;
Locus Iste; Os Justi; Virga Jesse
Floruit (B5395)

Gebet
see Geisliche Gesange Heft 1

Geistliche Gesange Heft 1
(Graner, G.) cmplt ed LIENAU s.p.
contains & see also: Barmherzigkeit;
Gebet; Jesus Christus (B5396)

Geistliche Gesange Heft 2
(Graner, G.) 4pt mix cor sc LIENAU s.p.
contains & see also: Ostern; Passion;
Pfingsten (B5397)

Geistliche Gesange Heft 3
(Graner, G.) 4pt mix cor sc LIENAU s.p.
contains & see also: Abendmahl; Jesu Komm (B5398)

Geistliche Gesange, Heft I *CC7L,Gen
(Darmstadt, Georg) [Ger/Lat] SATB,opt org
(med) sc MULLER SM 451 s.p., cor pts s.p. (B5399)

Geistliche Gesange, Heft II *Fest
(Darmstadter, Georg) [Lat] SATB,opt org
(med) MULLER SM 452 sc s.p., cor pts s.p.
contains: Ave Maria; Tota
Pulchra Es Maria (B5400)

Geistliche Gesange, Heft III *Gen
(Darmstadt, Georg) [Ger/Lat] SATB,opt org
(med) sc MULLER SM 453 s.p., cor pts s.p.
contains: Christus Factus Est; Locus
Iste; Os Justi; Vexilla Regis; Virga
Jesse (B5401)

BRUCKNER, ANTON (cont'd.)

Gloria (from Second Mass) Gloria
(Schoette) [Lat] SATB MARKS 4050 $.50 (B5402)

Glory Be To God *Gen,anthem/Doxol
(Klein, M) SATB (med) oct GIA G1440 $.25 (B5403)

God So Loved The World *Gd.Fri./Lent,anthem/
mot
(Klein, M.) SATB (easy) oct GIA G1438 $.25 (B5404)

Grosse Messe F-Moll *Mass
(Nowak, Leopold) [Ger] SATB,SATB soli,orch
(F min,med diff) BAREN. cor pts s.p., min
sc s.p., voc sc s.p., ipr (B5405)

Holy Art Thou *Gen
(Strickling) SATB SCHMITT 1797 $.25 (B5406)

Holy, Holy *see Sanctus

In Gethsemane *Lent
(Nordin) SATB SCHMITT 1441 $.30 (B5407)

In Monte Oliveti *Easter/Holywk/Lent,anthem/
mot,Eng
(Klein, M.) "On The Mount Of Olives" SATB
(easy) oct GIA G1437 $.25 (B5408)
(Marshall, Charles) "On The Mount Of
Olives" SATB FRANK F-548 $.30 (B5409)

Inveni David
[Lat] TTBB,opt 4trom PETERS 6318 $.30, ipa (B5410)

Jesu, Jesu, God Incarnate *see Ave Verum

Jesu Komm
(Graner, G.) 4pt mix cor cor pts LIENAU
s.p. see also Geistliche Gesange Heft 3 (B5411)

Jesus Christ, For Our Salvation *see
Christus Factus Est

Jesus Christus
see Geisliche Gesange Heft 1

Jesus, Once For Our Salvation
(Ehret) mix cor CHAPPELL 0023457-358 $.40 (B5412)

Jesus, Our Saviour
SSATTBB,opt org/pno PETERS 6380 $.25 (B5413)

Just Mouth, The *see Os Justi

Let Us Celebrate God's Name *anthem
(Peek, Richard) SATB,org/3trom (med) oct
AUGSBURG 0626 $.25 (B5414)

Locus Este A Deo Factus Est *Gradual
[Lat] SATB,acap PETERS 6314 $.25 see from
Three Graduals For The Church Year (B5415)

Locus Iste *Gradual
see Geistliche Gesange, Heft III
[Lat/Ger] SATB SCHOTT s.p. contains also:
Diese Statte (hymn) (B5416)
4pt mix cor cor pts LIENAU s.p. see also
Four Graduale (B5417)

Mass II E Minor *Mass
[Lat] voc sc UNIVER. 2915 $2.55, cor pts
UNIVER. 2896A-D $.55 (B5418)

Mass III F Minor *Fest,Mass
[Lat] voc sc UNIVER. 2901 $4.25, cor pts
UNIVER. 2900A-D $.85 (B5419)

Mass In D Minor *see Messe D-Moll

Mass In E Minor *see Messe E-Moll

Mass In F Minor *see Messe F-Moll

Messe D-Moll *Mass
"Mass In D Minor" [Lat] SATB,SATB soli,orch
min sc-cloth PETERS BR26 $1.25, ipr,
PETERS BR26 $7.50, ipr (B5420)
"Mass In D Minor" [Lat] SATB,SATB soli,orch
HINRICHSEN D1194 voc sc s.p., voc pt s.p. (B5421)
"Mass In D Minor" cor voc sc KALMUS 6107
$2.50 (B5422)
(Nowak, Leopold) [Ger] SATB,SATB soli,orch
(D min,med diff) BAREN. cor pts s.p., min
sc s.p. (B5423)
(Nowak, Leopold) SATB,orch (D min)
MUSIKWISS. sc s.p., cor pts s.p., ipa (B5424)

Messe E-Moll *Mass
"Mass In E Minor" [Lat] voc sc PETERS 4114
$2.00, min sc PETERS BR13 $6.50, ipa, voc
pt PETERS BR13 $1.25, voc pt PETERS BR13
$1.25 (B5425)
"Mass In E Minor" cor voc sc KALMUS 6127
$1.50 (B5426)
"Mass In E Minor" [Lat] SATB,orch voc sc
BROUDE BR. $1.50, ipr (B5427)
"Mass In E Minor" study sc UNIVER. PH.204
$2.80 (B5428)
(Haas, R.; Nowak, L.) mix cor,2ob,2clar,
2bsn,2trp,4horn,3trom (E min) sc
BREITKOPF-L rental (B5429)
(Nowak, Leopold) [Ger] SSAATTBB,winds (E
min,med diff, second setting from 1888)
BAREN. cor pts s.p., min sc s.p., ipr (B5430)
(Nowak, Leopold) SATB,orch (E min)
MUSIKWISS. sc s.p., cor pts s.p., ipa (B5431)

Messe F-Moll *Mass
"Mass In F Minor" [Lat] voc sc PETERS 3845
$4.00, ipr, cloth PETERS 3845 $9.00, ipr,
min sc PETERS BR14 $7.50, ipr, voc pt
PETERS BR14 $1.25, ipr (B5432)
"Mass In F Minor" cor voc sc KALMUS 6122
$2.75 (B5433)
"Mass In F Minor" cor,orch sc KALMUS
$25.00, ipa (B5434)
(Geissler, Fritz) mix cor,SATB soli,2fl,
2ob,2clar,2bsn,2trp,2horn,3trom,strings,
timp (F min) sc BREITKOPF-L s.p., voc pt
BREITKOPF-L s.p., voc sc BREITKOPF-L
EB-5758 s.p., study sc BREITKOPF-L
PB-3624 s.p., ipa (B5435)
(Nowak, Leopold) SATB,orch (F min)
MUSIKWISS. sc s.p., cor pts s.p., voc sc
s.p., ipr (B5436)

BRUCKNER, ANTON (cont'd.)

Missa Brevis In F *Mass
(Muller, A.M.) mix cor,acap ERDMANN 539
s.p. (B5437)

Missa Solemnis *Mass
[Lat] PETERS (B5438)
mix cor,SATB soli,2ob,2bsn,2trp,2horn,
3trom,strings,timp (B min) BREITKOPF-L
rental (B5439)

Missa Solemnis B-Moll *Mass
(Haas, Robert) [Ger] SATB,SATB soli,orch (B
flat min,med diff) sc BAREN. rental (B5440)

O How Blessed
(Granville; Heiberg) SATB,acap oct FOX R154
$.30 (B5441)
(Granville; Heiberg) SSA oct FOX R175 $.25 (B5442)

O Lord Most Holy
(Dickinson) SATB oct GRAY GSC 261 $.30 (B5443)
(Dickinson) SAATTBB oct GRAY GSC 34 $.25 (B5444)

Offertorium
see Two Motets

On The Mount Of Olives *see In Monte Oliveti

Os Justi *Gradual
see Geistliche Gesange, Heft III
4pt mix cor cor pts LIENAU s.p. see also
Four Graduale (B5445)
"Just Mouth, The" [Eng/Lat] mix cor,acap
oct SCHIRM.G 8121 $.30 (B5446)

Os Justi Meditabitur Sapientiam *Gradual
[Lat] SATB,acap PETERS 6315 $.30 see from
Three Graduals For The Church Year (B5447)

Ostern
(Graner, G.) 4pt mix cor cor pts LIENAU
s.p. see also Geistliche Gesange Heft 2 (B5448)

Pange Lingua *hymn
[Lat] SATB,acap PETERS 6313 $.25 (B5449)
[Lat/Eng] SATB BROUDE,A. 229 $.35 (B5450)

Passion
(Graner, G.) 4pt mix cor cor pts LIENAU
s.p. see also Geistliche Gesange Heft 2 (B5451)

Peace To Mankind *Xmas
(Stone) SATB oct WORD CRS-11 $.35 (B5452)

Pfingsten
(Graner, G.) 4pt mix cor cor pts LIENAU
s.p. see also Geistliche Gesange Heft 2 (B5453)

Praise Ye The Lord (Psalm 112) Gen,Bibl/Psalm
[Eng/Ger] dbl cor,pno voc sc SCHIRM.G $1.50 (B5454)
[Eng/Ger] 4pt mix cor,pno voc sc SCHIRM.G
$1.00 (B5455)
[Ger] voc sc UNIVER. 2909 $1.50, cor pts
UNIVER. 1908A-D $.30 (B5456)
study sc UNIVER. PH. 205- $1.70 (B5457)
[Ger] study sc PETERS BR30 $8.50, voc pt
PETERS BR30 $1.25, ipr, min sc PETERS
E972 $3.50 (B5458)
[Ger] SATB,S solo,orch (diff) sc s.p., cor
pts s.p., ipr (B5459)
cor sc KALMUS $5.00 (B5460)
(Nowak, Leopold) SATB,orch MUSIKWISS. sc
s.p., cor pts s.p., ipa (B5461)

Psalm 112 *see Praise Ye The Lord

Psalm 150 *see Praise Ye The Lord

Requiem *Req
[Lat] study sc PETERS BR43 $10.00, ipr, voc
pt PETERS BR43 $1.50 (B5462)
cor sc KALMUS $7.50 (B5463)

Requiem D-Moll *ECY,Req
(Berberich, L.) mix cor,SATB soli,org,horn,
3trom,strings (D min) BREITKOPF-L sc
s.p., voc pt s.p., voc sc s.p., ipa (B5464)
(Haas, Robert) [Ger] SATB,SATB soli,orch (D
min,med diff) BAREN. s.p. (B5465)
(Nowak, Leopold) SATB,orch (D min)
MUSIKWISS. sc s.p., cor pts s.p., ipa (B5466)

Rise Up, My Love *Easter,anthem/Bibl
(Klein, M.) SATB (easy) oct GIA G1439 $.25 (B5467)

Rod Of Jesse Hath Blossomed, The *see Virga
Jesse

Royal Banners Forward Go *Palm
(Peek) SATB oct SOUTHERN $.30 (B5468)

Royal Banners Forward Go, The *Lent
SATB,acap (med easy) oct CONCORDIA 98-2039
$.30 (B5469)

Sacred Choruses *CCU
mix cor,acap voc sc KALMUS 6124 $2.50 (B5470)

Sacred Choruses *CC10U
[Lat] 4-8pt,acap/org&opt 2trom voc sc
HINRICHSEN P4185 s.p. (B5471)

Sanctus (from Great Mass No. 3) Sanctus
"Holy, Holy" SATB oct LAWSON 51202 $.30 (B5472)

Save Us, Lord Jesus
(Klein) SATB KJOS 5478 $.30 (B5473)

Seek Ye First The Kingdom Of God *Gen,anthem
(Klein, M.) SATB (med) oct GIA G1529 $.25 (B5474)

Seven Sacred Hymns *CC7U,hymn
mix cor,acap voc sc KALMUS 6125 $1.25 (B5475)

Sieben Motetten
sc LIENAU s.p.
contains & see also: Anbetung; Christus
Am Kreuz; Das Heil Der Welt; Das
Himmlische Haus; Weihe: Tretet Naher;
Weihnachtsmotette; Wer Gott Liebt (B5476)

Six Tantum Ergo *CC6U
mix cor,acap voc sc KALMUS 6123 $1.25 (B5477)

BRUCKNER, ANTON (cont'd.)

Tantum Ergo *CC6L
[Eng/Lat] SATB,acap PETERS 66159 $.40 6 settings in major and phrygian modes (B5478)

Te Deum *Te Deum
[Lat] cor,soli,orch voc sc SCHIRM.G $1.25 (B5479)
[Lat] voc pt PETERS 3843 $1.00, sc PETERS 3844 $12.00, ipa, min sc PETERS E960 $3.50 (B5480)
cor voc sc KALMUS 6126 $1.25 (B5481)
cor sc KALMUS $10.00 (B5482)
cor,orch sc KALMUS $10.00, ipa (B5483)
(Hass, Robert) [Ger] SATB,SATB soli,orch (med diff) sc s.p., voc sc s.p., cor pts s.p., ipr (B5484)
(Nowak, Leopold) SATB,orch MUSIKWISS. sc s.p., voc sc s.p., ipr, cor pts s.p. (B5485)
(Schalk) [Lat] voc sc UNIVER. 429 $2.80, cor pts UNIVER. 8759A-D $.30 (B5486)

Three Graduals For The Church Year *see Christus Factus Est; Locus Este A Deo Factus Est; Os Justi Meditabitur Sapientiam (B5487)

Thy Will Be Done *Gen
(Strickling) SSATTBB SCHMITT 1787 $.30 (B5488)

Tota Pulchra Es Maria
see Geistliche Gesange, Heft II

Tota Pulchra Est
see Two Marian Compositions

Two Marian Compositions *BVM
[Lat] PETERS 6312 $.40
contains: Ave Maria (7pt mix cor,acap); Tota Pulchra Est (6-9pt mix cor,T solo, org/pno) (anti) (B5489)

Two Motets *mot
[Lat] PETERS 6037 $.40
contains: Ecce Sacerdos (SSAATTBB,opt 3trom,org); Offertorium (SATB,opt 3trom) (B5490)

Vexilla Regis
see Geistliche Gesange, Heft III

Vexilla Regis Prodeunt
[Lat] SATB,acap PETERS 6319 $.30 (B5491)

Virga Jesse *Adv/Xmas
see Geistliche Gesange, Heft III
SATB,acap voc pt DOBLINGER s.p. see also ADVENT UND WEIHNACHT, HEFT 2 (B5492)
"Rod Of Jesse Hath Blossomed, The" SATB, acap SCHIRM.EC 1219 $.30 (B5493)

Virga Jesse Floruit *Gradual
[Lat] SATB,acap PETERS 6317 $.30 (B5494)
4pt mix cor cor pts LIENAU s.p. see also Four Graduale (B5495)

Weihe: Tretet Naher
SATB cor pts LIENAU s.p. see also Sieben Motetten (B5496)

Weihnachtsmotette
SSAATTBB,opt 3trom/opt org/opt 3trom&org cor pts LIENAU s.p. see also Sieben Motetten (B5497)

Wer Gott Liebt
SATB cor pts LIENAU s.p. see also Sieben Motetten (B5498)

Worthy Art Thou, O Lord God *anthem
(Peek) SATB,org,opt trom (med diff) oct AUGSBURG 1564 $.35, ipa (B5499)

BRUDER, BOHM
Lobt Gott Getrost Mit Singen
TTBB HANSSLER 6.2385B s.p. (B5500)

BRUDER KOMMT see Muller von Kulm, Walter

BRUGK, HANS MELCHOIR (1909-)
Der Mensch Lebt Und Bestehet *Op.23,No.1, mot
(Claudius, M.) mix cor (med easy) oct LEUCKART 601 s.p. (B5501)

Die Hochzeit Zu Kana *Epiph
[Ger] SATB,MezTBarB soli,acap (med) sc MULLER SM 2131 s.p. (B5502)

Hochzeitslandler
mix cor (easy) oct LEUCKART 637 s.p. (B5503)

Hochzeitslied *Op.23,No.3
mix cor (easy) oct LEUCKART 607 s.p. (B5504)

BRUHNE, J.F.
Eenmaal Bethlehem *Xmas
mix cor sc ALSBACH&D s.p. (B5505)

BRUHNS, NICHOLAUS (1665-1697)
Choral Church Cantatas *see Die Zeit Meines Abschields Ist Vorhanden; Hemmt Eure Trauenflut; Ich Liege Und Schlafe; Muss Nicht Der Mensch Auf Dieser Erden; O Werter Heil'ger Geist (B5506)

Die Zeit Meines Abschieds Ist Vorhanden *cant
(Kruger) SATB,cont,bsn,2vln,2vla HANSSLER 10.045 sc s.p., cor pts s.p., ipa (B5507)

Die Zeit Meines Abschields Ist Vorhanden *cant
(Stein) [Ger] SATB,org/pno,bsn,2vln,2vla, vcl/bvl PETERS 5826 sc $3.50, ipa, cor pts $.40 see from Choral Church Cantatas (B5508)

Hemmt Eure Trauenflut *cant
(Stein) [Ger] SATB,2vln,2vla,vcl,bsn,org PETERS 5836 sc $3.00, ipa, cor pts $.50 see from Choral Church Cantatas (B5509)

Ich Liege Und Schlafe *cant
[Ger] SATB,SATB soli,pno/org,2vln,2vla,vcl, bsn voc sc PETERS HU1647 $2.00, sc PETERS 5833 $3.50, ipa, voc pt PETERS 5833 $.40 (B5510)

BRUHNS, NICHOLAUS (cont'd.)

(Stein) [Ger] SATB,SATB soli,org/pno,2vln, 2vla,vcl/bvl,bsn PETERS 5833 sc $3.50, ipa, cor pts $.40 see from Choral Church Cantatas (B5511)

Muss Nicht Der Mensch Auf Dieser Erden *cant
(Stein) [Ger] SATB,org/pno,bsn,2trp,2vln, 2vla,vcl PETERS 5834 sc $5.00, ipa, cor pts $.50 see from Choral Church Cantatas (B5512)

O Werter Heil'ger Geist *cant
(Stein) [Ger] SATB,SATB soli,pno/org,bsn, 2trp,2vln,2vla,vcl PETERS 5835 sc $5.00, ipa, cor pts $.50 see from Choral Church Cantatas (B5513)

BRUMBAUGH, HARLEY
Drums Of God
2pt oct AGAPE CF 141 $.30 (B5514)

BRUMBELOW, ROY
O Come, Let Us Sing
2pt oct AGAPE CH 648 $.25 (B5515)

BRUMBY
Virgin And The Child, The *Xmas,carol
SATB,acap ALBERT s.p. (B5516)

BRUMEL, ANTOINE (ca. 1475?-ca. 1520?)
Communion Hymn *Commun,Bibl
4pt mix cor oct SCHIRM.G 3772 $.25 (B5517)

Darkly Rose The Guilty Morning *Lent
4pt mix cor,S solo oct SCHIRM.G 3893 $.25 (B5518)

Fear Not Ye, O Israel *Bibl
(Deis) 4pt mix cor oct SCHIRM.G 7375 $.25 (B5519)

Festival Te Deum No. 7, E Flat *Te Deum
4pt mix cor oct SCHIRM.G 10027 $.35 (B5520)

He Shall Come Down Like Rain
SATB oct SCHIRM.G 10028 $.30 (B5521)

Mater Patris Et Filia *mot
boy cor SOUTHERN $.25 (B5522)
(Forbes) [Lat] TBB,acap oct SCHIRM.G 11011 $.25 (B5523)

Missa A L'ombre D'ung Buissonet
see Opera Omnia vol. IV

Missa Berzerette Savoyenne
see Opera Omnia vol. I

Missa Bontemps
see Opera Omnia vol. II

Missa De Beata Virgine
see Opera Omnia vol. IV

Missa De Dringhs
see Opera Omnia vol. IV

Missa Descendi In Hortum
see Opera Omnia vol. II

Missa Dominicalis
see Opera Omnia vol. II

Missa Et Ecce Terrae Motus
(Hudson, Barton) cor cmplt ed AM.INST.MUS. $16.00 see from Opera Omnia vol. III (B5524)

Missa Je Nay Dueul
see Opera Omnia vol. I

Missa L'homme Arme
see Opera Omnia vol. I

Missa Pro Defunctis *Mass
see Opera Omnia vol. IV
(Seay) 4pt mix cor MOSELER s.p. (B5525)

Missa Sine Nomine
see Opera Omnia vol. II

Missa Ut Re Mi Fa Sol
see Opera Omnia vol. I

Missa Victime Paschali
see Opera Omnia vol. I

Morning Invocation
3pt boy cor/3pt wom cor oct SCHIRM.G 4754 $.20 (B5526)

Opera Omnia vol. I *Mass
(Hudson, Barton) cor cmplt ed AM.INST.MUS. $19.00
contains: Missa Berzerette Savoyenne; Missa Je Nay Dueul; Missa L'homme Arme; Missa Ut Re Mi Fa Sol; Missa Victime Paschali (B5527)

Opera Omnia vol. II *Mass
(Hudson, Barton) cor cmplt ed AM.INST.MUS. $18.00
contains: Missa Bontemps; Missa Descendi In Hortum; Missa Dominicalis; Missa Sine Nomine (B5528)

Opera Omnia vol. III *see Missa Et Ecce Terrae Motus (B5529)

Opera Omnia vol. IV
(Hudson, Barton) cor cmplt ed AM.INST.MUS. $22.00
contains: Missa A L'ombre D'ung Buissonet; Missa De Beata Virgine; Missa De Dringhs; Missa Pro Defunctis (B5530)

Opera Omnia vol. V *CCU,mot
(Hudson, Barton) cor cmplt ed AM.INST.MUS. $26.00 (B5531)

Opera Omnia vol. VI *sac/sec,CCU,Magnif
(Hudson, Barton) cor cmplt ed AM.INST.MUS. $24.00 (B5532)

Sicut Lilium
SATB,acap oct PRESSER 352-00041 $.25 (B5533)

Sing Alleluia Forth
4pt mix cor,SSTTBB soli oct SCHIRM.G 10029 $.35 (B5534)

BRUN, ABBE F.
Noel Gregorien *see Puer Natus

Puer Natus *Xmas/Gen,mot
"Noel Gregorien" [Lat/Fr] 4pt mix cor,solo oct DURAND s.p. (B5535)

BRUN, G.
Cantate A Notre-Dame *BVM,cant
cor,narrator,org/pno,opt fl&vln LEMOINE voc sc s.p., cor pts s.p., sc s.p., ipa (B5536)

Golgotha *ora
cor LEMOINE s.p., rental (B5537)

O Salutaris
[Lat] cor LEMOINE s.p. (B5538)

BRUNCKHORST, ARNOLD MELCHOIR
Die Ostergeschichte Nach Dem Evangelisten Markus *Easter,cant
(Hellmann) SATB,SATB soli,cont,trp,2vln,vla HANSSLER 10.012 cor pts s.p., voc sc s.p., ipa (B5539)

Die Weihnachtsgeschichte *Xmas,cant
(Hellmann) SATB,SATB soli,cont,2trp,2vln, vla HANSSLER 10.008 sc s.p., cor pts s.p., ipa (B5540)

BRUNER
Easter Victory, The *Easter
SATB oct LILLENAS AN-2303 $.25 (B5541)

BRUNETTI, DOMENICO
Cantemus Domino
(Wilhelm) "Sing Unto God" 3pt mix cor,org oct LAWSON 51634 $.35 (B5542)

Sing Unto God *see Cantemus Domino

BRUNN ALLES HEILS see Becker-Foss, Jurgen

BRUNN ALLES HEILS see Hufschmidt, Wolfgang

BRUNN ALLES HEILS, BAND 1 *CC114U
(Strube, Adolf) [Ger] 3 eq voices,acap BAREN. EM 328 s.p. on melodies from evangelisches kirchengesangbuch (B5543)

BRUNN ALLES HEILS, BAND 2 *CC100U,canon
(Strube, Adolf) [Ger] 3 eq voices,acap BAREN. EM 328A s.p. (B5544)

BRUNN ALLES HEILS, DICH see Goudimel, Claude

BRUNNER, ADOLF (1901-)
Agnus Dei (from Missa) Agnus
[Ger] SATB,acap (med diff) BAREN. BA 2113E $.55 (B5545)

Alles Fleisch Ist Gras
see Funf Motetten

Alles Was Ihr Tut
see Brunner, Adolf, Unser Anfang Geschehe Im Namen

Benedictus (from Missa)
see Brunner, Adolf, Sanctus

Christus Ist Auferstanden, Er Ist In Wahrheit Auferstanden *Easter
SATB HANSSLER 7.136 s.p. (B5546)

Credo (from Missa) Credo
[Ger] SATB,acap (med diff) BAREN. BA 2113C $1.50 (B5547)

Das Alte Jahre Vergangen Ist *ECY
SATB HANSSLER 7.130 s.p. (B5548)

Das Gleichnis Von Den Zehn Jungfrauen *ECY
[Ger] SATB,horn,2vln,vla,vcl,bvl (med diff) BAREN. BA 1947 voc sc $1.00, cor pts s.p., ipa (B5549)

Das Ist Der Tag, Den Der Herr
SATB HANSSLER 7.129 s.p. (B5550)

Das Weihnachtsevangelium *Xmas,cant
SATB,2vln,vla,vcl,bvl HANSSLER 10.224 sc s.p., voc sc s.p., ipa (B5551)

Der Mensch, Vom Weibe Geboren *Gen,mot
SSATBB,acap (med diff) BAREN. BA 2198 $2.25 (B5552)

Die Versuchung Jesu *Psntd
[Ger] SATB,acap (med diff) BAREN. BA 2122 $2.25 (B5553)

Erhalt Uns Herr, Bei Deinem Wort
SATB HANSSLER 7.141 s.p. (B5554)

Es Ist Dir Gesagt, Mensch, Was Gut Ist
see Funf Motetten

Funf Motetten *Gen,mot
[Ger] SATB,acap (med diff) BAREN. BA 2110 $2.50
contains: Alles Fleisch Ist Gras; Es Ist Dir Gesagt, Mensch, Was Gut Ist; Ich Bin Der Weg; Kommt Und Lasst Uns Wandeln Im Lichte Des Herrn; Leben Wir, So Leben Wir Dem Herrn (B5555)

Gerechtigkeit Erhohet Ein Volk, Aber
SATB HANSSLER 7.139 s.p. (B5556)

Gloria (from Missa) Gloria
[Ger] SATB,acap (med diff) BAREN. BA 2113B $1.25 (B5557)

Gott Ist Geist *Pent
[Ger] SATB,acap (med) BAREN. BA 1995 s.p. (B5558)

Ich Bin Der Weg *Gen
see Funf Motetten
SATB,acap (med diff) BAREN. BA 2110E $.65 (B5559)

Ich Will Meinen Geist Ausgiessen Uber Alles Fleisch
SATB HANSSLER 7.138 s.p. (B5560)

Jesus Und Die Samariterin Am Brunnen *Epiph
[Ger] SATB,STB soli,org,fl,2vln,vla,vcl,bvl (med diff) sc BAREN. BA 2143 $6.50, cor pts BAREN. BA 1995 $.40, ipa (B5561)

BRUNNER, ADOLF (cont'd.)

Kommt Und Lasst Uns Wandeln Im Lichte Des
Herrn
see Funf Motetten

Kyrie (from Missa) Kyrie
[Ger] SATB,acap (med diff) BAREN. BA 2113A
$.45 (B5562)

Leben Wir, So Leben Wir Dem Herrn
see Funf Motetten

Lobe Den Herrn Meine Seele
SATB HANSSLER 7.140 s.p. (B5563)

Machet Die Tore Weit
SATB HANSSLER 7.128 s.p. (B5564)

Missa *Mass
[Ger] SATB,acap (med diff) BAREN. BA 2113
$4.50 (B5565)

Sanctus (from Missa) Bene/Sanctus
[Ger] SATB,acap (med diff) BAREN. BA 2113D
$1.50 contains also: Benedictus (B5566)

Sechzehn Spruchmotetten *CC16U,Fest,mot
4pt mix cor,acap HANSSLER 2.027 s.p.
(B5567)

Sei Getreu Bis In Den Tod
SATB HANSSLER 7.133 s.p. (B5568)

Seid Ihr Nun Mit Christus Auferstanden
*Easter
SATB HANSSLER 7.137 s.p. (B5569)

Siehe, Das Lamm Gottes, Das Der Welt
SATB HANSSLER 7.135 s.p. (B5570)

Spruche Nach Angelus Silesius *CC8L,Gen
[Ger] SATB,acap (med diff) BAREN. BA 2530
$1.75 (B5571)

Unser Anfang Geschehe Im Namen
SATB HANSSLER 7.131 s.p. contains also:
Alles Was Ihr Tut (B5572)

Wachet, Denn Ihr Wisset Nicht Tag Noch Stunde
SATB HANSSLER 7.142 s.p. (B5573)

Wer Mir Nachfolgen Will, Der Verleugne Sich
Selbst
SATB HANSSLER 7.134 s.p. (B5574)

Wie Bin Ich Doch So Herzlich Froh
SATB HANSSLER 7.143 s.p. (B5575)

Wie Schon Leuchtet Der Morgenstern
SATB HANSSLER 7.132 s.p. (B5576)

BRUNSMAN, W.J.
There Is Gladness In The Air *Xmas
(Schehl) SSAA/unis,pno (easy) oct WILLIS
5599 $.12 (B5577)

BRYAN, CHARLES [FAULKNER] (1911-1955)
Amazing Grace
SATB oct FISCHER,J 8764 $.30 (B5578)

I Have A Mother In The Heavens
SATB oct FISCHER,J 8135 $.30 (B5579)

BRYANT
God Is Gone Up
SATB oct MCA $.50 (B5580)

God's Holy Way
SATB,opt org/pno BOSTON 2730 $.35 (B5581)

Hymn Of The City *hymn
(Warren) SATB oct FISCHER,C CM-7704 $.35
(B5582)

BRYDAINE
Les Gaude
[Fr] unis HEUGEL s.p. see from LA MAITRISE
(B5583)

BRYDEN-BROOK, SIMON
Simple English Mass, A *Mass,Eng
[Eng] cong,org CHESTER sc s.p., voc sc s.p.
(B5584)

BRYDSON
Of A Shepherd And A Lamb *Xmas,carol
unis FRANCIS s.p. (B5585)

Rise Up, O Men Of God
unis BOSWORTH s.p. (B5586)

BUCCHI, VALENTINO (1916-)
Cori Della Pieta Morta
mix cor,org/orch voc sc ZERBONI 4689 s.p.
(B5587)

Laudes Evangelii *ora
mix cor,SABarB soli,2fl,3ob,3bsn,4horn,
3trp,3trom,strings,timp,perc,harp CARISH
rental (B5588)

BUCCI, [MARK] (1924-)
Wondrous Kingdom, The (Flora And Fauna)
SATB,acap voc sc MCA $2.25 (B5589)

BUCCINATE see Gabrieli, Giovanni

BUCHANAN, [ANNABEL MORRIS] (1888-)
Store Up Your Riches In Heaven
SATB FLAMMER A 5383 $.30 (B5590)

BUCHNER, PHILIPP FRIEDRICH (1614-1669)
Christmas Cantata *Xmas,cant
(Gottron, A.) mix cor,soli,org CONCORDIA
97-6222 $.60 (B5591)

O Quanta In Coelis
see Weihnachtskantate

O Welche Freude
see Weihnachtskantate

Weihnachtskantate *Xmas
(Gottron, Adam) [Ger] SSATB,SAT soli,cont
(med easy) BAREN. BA 1370 sc s.p., cor
pts s.p.
contains: O Quanta In Coelis; O Welche
Freude (B5592)

BUCHSEL
Kyrie *cant
5pt mix cor&3pt jr cor,org,brass,vcl,bvl
MOSELER sc rental, cor pts s.p., ipr
(B5593)

BUCHTEL
Hail, Land All Glorious
SATB,opt band/orch KJOS 5247 $.30 (B5594)

Lift Up Your Heads
SATB,opt band KJOS 7049 $.30 (B5595)

BUCHTGER, FRITZ (1903-)
Der Mensch *ECY
[Ger] SATB,acap (med) MULLER SM 1001 s.p.
see also Drei Kleine Motetten (B5596)

Der Pilger *ECY
[Ger] SATB,acap (med) MULLER SM 1002 s.p.
see also Drei Kleine Motetten (B5597)

Der Tod *ECY
[Ger] SATB,acap (med) MULLER SM 1003 s.p.
see also Drei Kleine Motetten (B5598)

Die Auferstehung Nach Matthaus *Easter,Bibl
[Eng/Fr/Ger] SATB,org (diff) cor pts BAREN.
BA 2787 s.p., ipr (B5599)

Die Geburt (from Das Weihnachtsoratorium)
Xmas
[Eng/Ger] 4pt mix cor,SATB/SSAATB soli,fl,
ob,strings (med diff) BAREN. BA 3994 sc
$4.75, cor pts $1.00, ipr (B5600)

Die Himmelfahrt Christi *Easter/Pent
[Eng/Ger] SATB,orch (diff) BAREN. BA 3699
sc $3.50, cor pts $1.50, ipr (B5601)

Die Verklarung *Epiph
[Ger] SSAA,Bar solo,strings (diff) sc
BAREN. BA 3647A $1.75, ipr (B5602)

Die Verkundigung (from Das
Weihnachtsoratorium) Xmas
[Eng/Ger] SSA,STB soli,fl,strings (med
diff) BAREN. BA 3992 sc $2.00, cor pts
$.40, ipr (B5603)

Drei Kleine Motetten *ECY
[Ger] SATB,acap (med) cmplt ed MULLER
SM 1001-3 s.p.
contains & see also: Der Mensch; Der
Pilger; Der Tod (B5604)

Drei Konige (from Das Weihnachtsoratorium)
Xmas
[Eng/Ger] 4pt mix cor/6pt mix cor,SATB/
SSAATB soli,fl,ob,strings (diff) BAREN.
BA 3995 sc $4.50, cor pts $.55, ipr (B5605)

Drei Motetten *Op.33,Gen,mot
SATB,acap (med diff) MULLER SM 2359 s.p.
contains: Ein Neu Gebot; Ich Bin Die Tur;
Wer Nicht Von Neuem Geboren Wird
(B5606)

Ein Neu Gebot
see Drei Motetten

Gott Ist Geist *CC5U,Epiph,mot
[Ger] SSATB,org/4vln&vla&vcl&bvl (med diff)
sc BAREN. BA 4465 $3.50, ipa (B5607)

Herr, Unser Herrscher (Psalm 8) Trin
[Ger] SATB,acap (med diff) MULLER SM 2372
sc s.p., cor pts s.p. (B5608)

Ich Bin Die Tur
see Drei Motetten

Johannes Der Taufer *Fest,ora
[Ger] SATB,Bar solo,orch (diff) cor pts
BAREN. BA 3512 $2.25, ipr (B5609)

Pfingsten *Pent
[Ger] SATB,Bar solo,orch (diff) BAREN.
BA 3650 sc $5.25, cor pts $1.50, ipr
(B5610)

Psalm 8 *see Herr, Unser Herrscher

Requiem *Op.7,No.1
men cor (med) oct LEUCKART 230 s.p. (B5611)

Sei Gepriesen
(Du Vinage) mix cor,acap TONGER s.p.
(B5612)

Simeon (from Das Weihnachtsoratorium) Xmas
[Eng/Ger] 4pt mix cor/6pt mix cor,SATB/
SSAATB soli,fl,ob,strings (diff) BAREN.
BA 3996 sc $4.50, cor pts $.55, ipr
(B5613)

Wer Nicht Von Neuem Geboren Wird
see Drei Motetten

BUCK
Holy Easter Morn *Easter/Lent
SATB oct FISCHER,C CM-6461 $.25 (B5614)

Lord, Flood My Soul *anthem
(Trued) SATB oct FOX R186 $.25 (B5615)

March On, O Church Triumphant
(Trued) SATB oct BELWIN 2152 $.25 (B5616)

BUCK, [CARLTON C.] (1907-)
O Holy One *anthem
(Trued, C.) SATB,pno oct BELWIN 2221 $.30
(B5617)

BUCK, DUDLEY (1839-1909)
Coming Of The King, The *Adv/Xmas,cant
mix cor,soli,org voc sc SCHIRM.G $1.50
(B5618)

Festival Te Deum No.7, In E Flat
SATB oct PRESSER 332-00455 $.40 (B5619)

God Is Our Refuge And Strength
SATB oct PRESSER 332-01206 $.30 (B5620)

God Of Abraham, Praise *Easter/Fest
SATB ALLANS 23 s.p. (B5621)

Hark! Hark! My Soul
SATB ENOCH EC248 s.p. (B5622)

He Shall Come Down Like Rain
SATB oct PRESSER 332-00465 $.30 (B5623)

BUCK, DUDLEY (cont'd.)

Lead, Kindly Light *Rembrnc
SATB (easy) ALLANS 100 s.p. (B5624)

Rock Of Ages *Easter/Gen/Rembrnc
SATB oct PRESSER 332-00462 $.30 (B5625)
SATB (easy) ALLANS 105 s.p. (B5626)

Sing Alleluia Forth
SATB oct PRESSER 332-00460 $.30 (B5627)
SATB oct PRO ART 1058 $.25 (B5628)
(Ronaldson) SSA oct PRO ART (B5629)

Story Of The Cross, The *Lent,cant
mix cor,soli,org voc sc SCHIRM.G $1.00
(B5630)

Thou Wilt Keep Him In Perfect Peace
oct FISCHER,J 10012 $.30 (B5631)

BUCK, SIR PERCY CARTER (1871-1947)
Child's Evening Hymn, A
unis ASHDOWN U.27 s.p. (B5632)

Christmas Legend, A *Xmas
2pt ASHDOWN E.A.130 s.p. (B5633)

O Lord God *Sexa
2pt,S solo oct NOVELLO 33.0059.05 s.p.
(B5634)

BUCKNER
Prayer For Man And His World
(Ringwald) SATB SHAWNEE A 1145 $.30 (B5635)
(Ringwald) SAB SHAWNEE D157 $.30 (B5636)

BUEBENDORF
Babe In Bethlehem's Manger Laid, The *Xmas
SATB FLAMMER A 5343 $.35 (B5637)

Blessing And Honor And Glory And Power
SATB FLAMMER A 5241 $.25 (B5638)

BUETTELL
Beyond The Wheeling Worlds Of Light
SATB oct LORENZ C303 $.30 (B5639)

Cross, The *Easter
SATB oct LORENZ C222 $.30 (B5640)

Savior, Make My Heart A Temple
SATB oct LORENZ C188 $.30 (B5641)

BUFFUM
Happier Way, The *anthem
(McLellan) SATB oct LILLENAS AT-1056 $.25
(B5642)

I'm Going Higher Someday
(Kirk) SATB oct LILLENAS AT-1024 $.30
(B5643)

BUGATCH, SAMUEL (1898-)
Jewish Legend, The
SATB TRANSCON. TCL 375 $3.50 (B5644)

Judea *Purim
[Jew/Eng] TTBB TRANSCON. TCL 274 $1.50
(B5645)

Manginot Shabbat *Sab-Eve
SATB TRANSCON. TCL 790 $3.00 (B5646)

BUILD THE MORE STATELY MANSIONS see Williams,
Alice Crane

BUILD THEE MORE STATELY MANSIONS see Andrews,
Mark

BUILD THEE MORE STATELY MANSIONS see Butler,
Eugene

BUILD THEE MORE STATELY MANSIONS see Young,
Gordon

BUILDERS, THE *carol
unis/SATB (easy) OXFORD O8.111 $.15 (B5647)

BUILT ON A ROCK see Cassler, G. Winston

BUILT ON A ROCK see Johnston

BUILT ON A ROCK see Lindeman

BUILT ON A ROCK see Lindeman, Ludvig Mathias

BUILT ON A ROCK THE CHURCH DOTH STAND see
Cassler, G. Winston

BUILT ON A ROCK THE CHURCH DOTH STAND see Kuntz

BUILT ON A ROCK THE CHURCH DOTH STAND see
Nystedt, Knut

BUILT ON THE ROCK see Bunjes, Paul G.

BUILT ON THE ROCK see Frederick, Donald R.

BUILT ON THE ROCK see Hilty

BUILT ON THE ROCK see Lindeman

BUILT ON THE ROCK see Lovelace, Austin C.

BUILT ON THE ROCK, THE CHURCH DOTH STAND see
Bender, Jan

BUILT ON THE ROCK, THE CHURCH DOTH STAND see
Wolff, S. Drummond

BUILT ON THE ROCKS see McAfee, Don

BUISSART-MORISEAUX
Ave Maria *BVM
[Lat] cor,pno LEMOINE s.p. (B5648)

BUISSONS
Thesauri Musici, Heft 11: Cantio Sacra De
Nativitate Domini *Xmas,Renais
(Pass, Walter) 5pt mix cor cmplt ed
DOBLINGER s.p. (B5649)

BUKETOFF, [IGOR] (1915-)
We Praise Thee
mix cor,acap oct SCHIRM.G 9601 $.20 (B5650)

BULL, JOHN (ca. 1562-1628)
Almighty God, Who By The Leading Of A Star
*Epiph
SSAATB (med) oct OXFORD 42.703 $.65 (B5651)

BULL, JOHN (cont'd.)

As Bountiful As May
see SIX SEVENTEENTH CENTURY CAROLS FROM THE NETHERLANDS

In The Departure Of The Lord *anthem
mix cor SOUTHERN $.25
SATB STAINER CC601 s.p. (B5652)
(B5653)

BULLARD, FREDERICK FIELD (1864-1904)
Holy Infant, The *cant
mix cor,soli,org,opt strings voc sc
SCHIRM.G $1.50 (B5654)

BULLOCK, ERNEST
Christ, The Fair Glory Of The Holy Angels
*ASD
SATB (med) oct OXFORD 42.002 $.50 (B5655)

Come, Holy Ghost, In Love *Gen/Whitsun
SAB/unis&desc (easy) oct OXFORD 40.919 $.30 (B5656)

Give Us The Wings Of Faith *ASD
SATB (med easy) oct OXFORD 42.001 $.30 (B5657)
TB (med easy) oct OXFORD 41.016 $.25 (B5658)

God Is A Spirit
see Two Short Introits

Good Christian Men Rejoice And Sing *Easter
SATB (very easy) oct OXFORD 42.124 $.25 (B5659)

Jubilate Deo *Jubil
SATB (med) oct OXFORD 42.876 $.35 (B5660)

Lift Up Your Heads, Great Gates, And Sing
*Asc
SATB (easy) oct OXFORD 42.144 $.35 (B5661)

Love Came Down At Christmas *Xmas
SATB (easy) oct OXFORD 42.845 $.30 (B5662)

O Most Merciful *anthem
mix cor oct NOVELLO 50.0225.07 s.p. (B5663)

O Worship The King *Harv,anthem
mix cor oct NOVELLO 28.1154.05 s.p. (B5664)

Preces And Responses
TTBB,acap (very easy) oct OXFORD 41.019
$.30 (B5665)

Te Deum Laudamus
SATB (med) oct OXFORD 42.885 $.65 (B5666)

They That Wait Upon The Lord
see Two Short Introits

Two Short Introits *Gen,Introit
SATB (easy) oct OXFORD 42.111 $.25
contains: God Is A Spirit; They That Wait
Upon The Lord (B5667)

BUNE
Koom Ba Yah *Xmas,folk
SATB SOUTHERN $.35 (B5668)
SATB SCHMITT 4010 $.35 (B5669)

BUNJES, PAUL G.
All Glory, Laud, And Honor *Gen/Palm
SATB&cong/SATB&jr cor,org,trp (med easy) sc
CONCORDIA 97-4513 $1.25, cor pts
CONCORDIA 98-1544 $.25, ipa (B5670)

All Praise To God, Who Reigns Above *Gen
SATB&cong/SATB&jr cor,org,trp (med easy) sc
CONCORDIA 97-4473 $1.50, cor pts
CONCORDIA 98-1499 $.25, ipa (B5671)

All Praise To Jesus' Hallowed Name
see Chant-Chorale For Christmas

Benedictus, The
see Chant-Chorale For Advent

Built On The Rock *Ded/Gen/Refm
SATB&cong/SATB&jr cor,org,2trp (med easy)
sc CONCORDIA 97-4571 $1.50, cor pts
CONCORDIA 98-1635 $.30, ipa (B5672)

Chant-Chorale For Advent *Adv
unis&SATB,kbd (med easy) oct CONCORDIA
98-1567 $.22, sc CONCORDIA 97-4499 $1.25
contains: Benedictus, The; Let The Earth
Now Praise The Lord (B5673)

Chant-Chorale For Christmas *Xmas
unis&SATB,kbd (med easy) oct CONCORDIA
98-1568 $.22
contains: All Praise To Jesus' Hallowed
Name; Magnificat, The (B5674)

Comfort, Comfort Ye My People *Adv
SATB,2vln,vla,vcl,bvl (med easy) sc
CONCORDIA 98-1371 $1.00, cor pts
CONCORDIA 98-1388 $.30, ipa (B5675)

Confirmation Blessing, A *Gen
SATB,kbd (easy) oct CONCORDIA 98-1419 $.25 (B5676)

God Of The Prophets *Gen
SATB&cong/SATB&jr cor,org,trp (med easy) sc
CONCORDIA 97-4638 $1.25, cor pts
CONCORDIA 98-1647 $.20, ipa (B5677)

Have Mercy On Me, O God *see Miserere Mei

Hear Us, O Lord (Prose For Lent) *Lent
unis,kbd (easy) oct CONCORDIA 98-1540 $.25 (B5678)

Holy Is God The Lord (Isaiah, Mighty Seer)
*Gen
unis&desc (easy) oct CONCORDIA 98-1379 $.25 (B5679)

How Can I Thank Thee, Lord *Cnfrm/Gen
SATB&cong/SATB&jr cor,org,trp (med easy) sc
CONCORDIA 97-4638 $1.25, cor pts
CONCORDIA 98-1698 $.25, ipa (B5680)

I Know That My Redeemer Lives *Easter/Gen
SATB&cong/SATB&jr cor,org,trp (med easy) sc
CONCORDIA 97-4434 $1.50, cor pts
CONCORDIA 98-1462 $.25, ipa (B5681)

Introits For The Church Year, The (from
Service Propers Noted, The) CCU,Introit/
liturg

BUNJES, PAUL G. (cont'd.)

cor,kbd sc,cloth CONCORDIA 97-1455 $5.25,
cor pts,cloth CONCORDIA 97-7613 $2.25 (B5682)

Let The Earth Now Praise The Lord
see Chant-Chorale For Advent

Magnificat And "All Praise To Jesus' Hallowed
Name" *Xmas,chant/chorale/liturg/Magnif
cor sc CONCORDIA 97-4498 $1.25, cor pts
CONCORDIA 98-1568 $.22 (B5683)

Magnificat, The
see Chant-Chorale For Christmas

Mighty Fortress, A *Gen/Refm
SATB&cong/SATB&jr cor,org,3trp (med easy)
sc CONCORDIA 97-1412 $1.50, cor pts
CONCORDIA 98-1417 $.25, ipa (B5684)

Miserere Mei (Psalm 51) Lent
"Have Mercy On Me, O God" unis,kbd (easy)
oct CONCORDIA 98-1541 $.22 (B5685)

Praise To The Lord, The Almighty *Gen
SATB&cong/SATB&jr cor,org,trp (med easy) sc
CONCORDIA 97-4450 $1.25, cor pts
CONCORDIA 98-1473 $.25, ipa (B5686)

Psalm 51 *see Miserere Mei

Service Propers Noted, The *CCU,Gradual/
Introit/liturg/Psalm
cor,org pap CONCORDIA 97-7598 $2.75, cloth
CONCORDIA 97-7600 $4.10, sc CONCORDIA
97-1442, PT. 1 $7.00, sc CONCORDIA
97-1440, PT. 2 $7.00 (B5687)

Shine Forth, O Beauteous Morning Light *Xmas
SAB,acap (med diff) oct CONCORDIA 98-1156
$.22 (B5688)

BUNNETT, EDWARD (1834-1923)
Magnificat And Nunc Dimittis *Magnif/Nunc
unis (F maj) NOVELLO 44.1096.03 s.p. (B5689)

BUONA PASQUA A RENATINA see Tocchi, [Gian-Luca]

BURCK, JOACHIM (1546-1610)
Der Engel Bringt Wahren Bericht *Xmas,mot
(Hellmann) SATB HANSSLER 1.087 s.p. (B5690)

Die Deutsche Passion Nach Johannes *Psntd,
Bibl
(Berger) SATB HANSSLER 2.002 s.p. (B5691)
(Jode) 4pt mix cor MOSELER s.p. (B5692)

Du Rads Min Sjal
[Swed] SATB,acap GEHRMANS KRB 157 (B5693)

Ich Weiss, Dass Mein Erloser Lebt
see Praetorius, Michael, Halleluja Ist Ein
Frohlich Gesang

Now Is The Hour *Xmas
SATB,acap (med easy) oct CONCORDIA 98-2095
$.25 (B5694)

Nun Ist Es Zeit Zu Singen *Adv/Xmas
SATB,acap (contains also: Bach, Johann
Sebastian, Lobt Gott, Ihr Christen) voc
pt DOBLINGER s.p. see also ADVENT UND
WEIHNACHT, HEFT 1 (B5695)

Nun Lasst Uns Gott Dem Herren
SATB HANSSLER 6.192 s.p. contains also:
Bach, Johann Sebastian, Jesu, Meine
Freude, Meines Herzens [Chorale] (from
Jesu, Meine Freude) (D min) (B5696)

Nun Lasst Uns Gott Dem Herren Dank Sagen
*Gen/Thanks
SATB,acap voc pt DOBLINGER s.p. see also
LOB UND DANK (B5697)

Passio Jesu Christi (Psalm 22) Easter
(Hildebrandt) SATB HANSSLER 2.017 s.p. (B5698)

Psalm 22 *see Passio Jesu Christi

Schwer Gehet Uber Mein Haupt
see Hassler, Hans Leo, Ach Gott, Vom Himmel
Sieh Darein
see Palestrina, Giovanni, Finsternis Ward
Uber Das Land

Vom Olberg Zeucht Daher Christus *Palm,mot
SATB HANSSLER 6.2180 s.p. (B5699)
(Berger) SATB HANSSLER 1.116 s.p. (B5700)

BURDETT, E.S.
Du Lieber Herre Jesu Christ
SATB HANSSLER 6.164 s.p. contains also:
Oechsler, Elias, Wach Auf, Meins Herzens
Schone (B5701)

BURGCK, JOACHIM VON
see BURCK, JOACHIM

BURGENLANDISCHE VOLKSLIEDER *CCU,folk
(Strobl, Otto) mix cor,acap cmplt ed
DOBLINGER s.p. (B5702)

BURGESS, FRANCIS
Missa De Angelis *Mass
SATB oct NOVELLO s.p. (B5703)

BURGMANN, J. HARTMUT
Woran Denkst Du, Mein Christus, Jetzt, Im
Tode? *Psntd,mot
SATB HANSSLER 7.166 s.p. (B5704)

BURGSTAHLER, ELTON
Ballad Of Christmas, A *cant/folk
unis/2pt/SATB,opt pno/org/gtr&bvl oct PRO
ART 1212 $1.50 (B5705)
SATB&2pt/unis,acap,opt pno,bvl,gtr PRO ART
$.85 (B5706)

Send Thy Peace
SATB,acap,opt pno oct PRO ART 2166 $.25 (B5707)

Truth About Christmas, The *cant,Contemp
SATB PRO ART 1256 $1.00 (B5708)

BURGWART, K.
Der Einsame Wanderer
see Burgwart, K., Gott Ist

Gott Ist
men cor,acap ERDMANN 186 s.p. contains
also: Der Einsame Wanderer (B5709)

Hochzeits-Standchen
men cor,acap ERDMANN 187 s.p. contains
also: Hymne An Die Allmacht (B5710)

Hymne An Die Allmacht
see Burgwart, K., Hochzeits-Standchen

BURKE, JOHN
Come Heavenly Child *Xmas
jr cor&sr cor (med) ABINGDON APM-430 $.60 (B5711)

Run, Shepherds, Run *Xmas
SATB oct GRAY GCMR 3032 $.25 (B5712)

Saint Patrick's Prayer *prayer
SATB oct STAINER 3.2389.1 $.40 (B5713)

Where Were You, O Shepherd? *Xmas
SATB (med) ABINGDON APM-568 $.35 (B5714)

BURKHARD WILLY (1900-1955)
Acht Spruche Aus Dem "Cherubinischen
Wandersmann" Des A. Silesius *Op.17,
No.2, CC8L,Gen
[Ger] SATB,acap (med diff) BAREN. BA 3637
$2.50 (B5715)

Christi Leidensverkundigung *Op.65, Psntd
[Ger] 2pt mix cor,T solo,org (med) BAREN.
BA 2118 sc $4.50, cor pts $.65 (B5716)

Das Ezzolied: Lux In Tenebris, Das In Unsrer
Mitten Ist *Op.19, Gen,mot
SSAATTBB (diff) BAREN. BA 3949 $7.25 (B5717)

Das Gesicht Des Jesaias
"Isaiah's Vision" [Ger/Eng] voc sc PETERS
A138 $10.00, ipr (B5718)

Das Gesicht Jesaias *Op.41, Gen,ora
[Ger/Eng] SATB,STB soli,org,2fl,2ob,2clar,
2bsn,2horn,2trp,2trom,strings,timp HUG
s.p., ipa (B5719)
[Eng/Ger] SATB,STB soli,orch (diff) BAREN.
BA 3150 rental (B5720)

Der Psalter *see Eile, Gott, Mich Zu
Erretten (Psalm 70); Herr, Wie Lange
Willst Du Mein So Gar Vergessen (Psalm
13); Ich Hebe Meine Augen Auf Zu Den
Bergen (Psalm 121); Wie Lieblich Sind
Deine Wohnungen (Psalm 84) (B5721)

Die Sintflut *Gen,cant
[Ger] SATB,acap (med diff) BAREN. BA 3167
$4.25 (B5722)

Die Verkundigung Mariae *mot
[Ger] mix cor,acap (diff) HUG s.p. (B5723)

Eile, Gott, Mich Zu Erretten (Psalm 70) Trin
[Ger] SATB,acap (med diff) BAREN. BA 2502
$.40 see also Der Psalter (B5724)

Es Ist Ein Wort Ergangen *Gen
3pt mix cor,acap (med) BAREN. BA 3770 s.p.
contains also: Steh Auf, Herr Gott (B5725)

Herr, Du Weisst, Wie Arm Wir Wandern *Gen
SATB,acap (med diff) BAREN. BA 3769 s.p. (B5726)

Herr, Mein Herz Ist Nicht Hoffartig (Psalm
131) (from Der Psalter) Gen
SATB,acap (med diff) BAREN. BA 2504 $.25 (B5727)

Herr, Wie Lange Willst Du Mein So Gar
Vergessen (Psalm 13) Trin
[Ger] SATB,acap BAREN. BA 2505 $.40 see
also Der Psalter (B5728)

Ich Hebe Meine Augen Auf Zu Den Bergen (Psalm
121) Xmas
[Ger] SATB,acap (med diff) BAREN. BA 2503
$.40 see also Der Psalter (B5729)

Ich Liege, Herr, In Deiner Hut *Gen
SATB,acap (med) BAREN. BA 3768 s.p. (B5730)

Ich Singe Dir Mit Herz Und Mund *Gen
SATB,acap (med) BAREN. BA 3769 s.p. (B5731)

Isaiah's Vision *see Das Gesicht Des Jesaias

Kleiner Psalter *Op.82, CCU,Gen
[Ger] SATB,acap (med diff) BAREN. BA 2500
s.p. (B5732)

Lobet Im Himmel Den Herrn (Psalm 148) Easter/
Pent
[Ger] unis,vln,vla,vcl,bvl,drums (med)
BAREN. BA 3981 sc $2.50, cor pts $.40,
ipa (B5733)

Messe *Op.85, Mass
[Ger] SATB,SB soli,orch (med diff) cor pts
BAREN. BA 2486 $2.75, voc sc BAREN.
BA 2486A $13.25, ipr (B5734)

Musikalische Ubung, Teil 1 *Op.39, Trin
[Ger] 2pt,org cor pts BAREN. BA 4421A $1.10 (B5735)

Musikalische Ubung, Teil 2 *Op.39, Trin
[Ger] 3pt,org cor pts BAREN. BA 4421B $1.00 (B5736)

Musikalische Ubung, Teil 3 *Op.39, Trin
[Ger] 4-8pt,org cor pts BAREN. BA 4421C
$1.50 (B5737)

Musikalische Ubung Uber Den Zwolften Psalm
*Op.39, Trin
[Ger] 2-8pt mix cor,org (easy/diff) cmplt
ed BAREN. BA 4421 $13.25 (B5738)

Nun Ist Vorbei Die Finstre Nacht *Gen
SATB,acap (med) BAREN. BA 3768 s.p. (B5739)

Psalm 13 *see Herr, Wie Lange Willst Du Mein
So Gar Vergessen

BURKHARD WILLY (cont'd.)

Psalm 70 *see Eile, Gott, Mich Zu Erretten

Psalm 84 *see Wie Lieblich Sind Deine
  Wohnungen

Psalm 96 *see Singet Dem Herrn Ein Neues
  Lied

Psalm 121 *see Ich Hebe Meine Augen Auf Zu
  Den Bergen

Psalm 131 *see Herr, Mein Herz Ist Nicht
  Hoffartig

Psalm 148 *see Lobet Im Himmel Den Herrn

Psalmenkantate *Gen,cant/Psalm
  [Ger] SSATB,S solo,org,3trp,trom,strings,
  drums (diff) cor pts BAREN. BA 2496
  $1.75, ipr, voc sc BAREN. BA 2496A $4.50
  (B5740)

Singet Dem Herrn Ein Neues Lied (Psalm 96)
  (from Der Psalter) Gen
  [Ger] SATB,acap (med diff) BAREN. BA 2506
  $.65
  (B5741)

Steh Auf, Herr Gott
  see Burkhard Willy, Es Ist Ein Wort
  Ergangen

Te Deum *Op.33, Te Deum
  [Lat] 2pt mix cor,trp,trom,timp,org sc
  SCHOTT 3318 s.p., ipa, cor pts SCHOTT
  3318 s.p., ipa
  (B5742)

Wie Lieblich Sind Deine Wohnungen (Psalm 84)
  Trin
  [Ger] SATB,acap (med diff) BAREN. BA 2501
  $.40 see also Der Psalter
  (B5743)

BURKHART, C.
  'Twas On One Sunday Morning *spir
  SATB,acap oct PRESSER MC360 $.30
  (B5744)

BURKHART, FRANZ (1902-   )
  Alle Jahre Weider
  see Drei Weihnachtslieder

Ascendit Deus *Asc,mot
  men cor,acap DOBLINGER s.p. see also
  Cantate Domino
  (B5745)

Cantate Domino *mot
  men cor,acap cmplt ed DOBLINGER s.p.
  contains & see also: Ascendit Deus;
  Cantate Domino; Caro Mea; Dextera
  Domini; Dies Sanctificatus; Emitte
  Spiritum Tuum; Exsultavit; Justorum
  Animae; Laudate Dominum; O Vos Omnes;
  Tres Sunt; Tu Es Petrus
  (B5746)

Cantate Domino *BVM/Xmas,mot
  men cor,acap DOBLINGER s.p. see also
  Cantate Domino
  (B5747)

Caro Mea *Commun,mot
  men cor,acap DOBLINGER s.p. see also
  Cantate Domino
  (B5748)
  wom cor,acap oct DOBLINGER s.p. see also
  Sechs Motetten
  (B5749)

Das Grosse Licht
  (Dach, S.) 4pt men cor,4trp,4horn,3trom,
  tuba,timp DOBLINGER voc sc s.p., cor pts
  s.p., ipr
  (B5750)

Das Schone Engele
  see Drei Weihnachtslieder

Dass Zwei Sich Herzlich Lieben *Marriage
  mix cor,acap oct DOBLINGER s.p. see from
  Zwei Hochzeitslieder
  (B5751)

Deutsches Ordinarium
  mix cor&cong,cantor,opt org DOBLINGER sc
  s.p., voc sc s.p.
  (B5752)

Dextera Domini *Lent,mot
  men cor,acap DOBLINGER s.p. see also
  Cantate Domino
  (B5753)
  wom cor,acap oct DOBLINGER s.p. see also
  Sechs Motetten
  (B5754)

Dies Sanctificatus *Xmas,mot
  men cor,acap DOBLINGER s.p. see also
  Cantate Domino
  (B5755)

Drei Weihnachtslieder *Xmas
  wom cor,acap cmplt ed DOBLINGER s.p.
  contains: Alle Jahre Weider; Das Schone
  Engele; Ihr Kinderlein Kommet
  (B5756)

Ein Getreues Herz Zu Wissen *Marriage
  mix cor,acap oct DOBLINGER s.p. see from
  Zwei Hochzeitslieder
  (B5757)

Emitte Spiritum Tuum *Pent/Trin,mot
  men cor,acap DOBLINGER s.p. see also
  Cantate Domino
  (B5758)

Exsultavit *Adv/BVM,mot
  men cor,acap DOBLINGER s.p. see also
  Cantate Domino
  (B5759)
  wom cor,acap oct DOBLINGER s.p. see also
  Sechs Motetten
  (B5760)

Geh' Aus, Mein Herz
  (Gerhardt, P; Muller, A.E.) mix cor,acap
  oct DOBLINGER
  (B5761)

Ihr Kinderlein Kommet
  see Drei Weihnachtslieder

Justorum Animae *Trin,mot
  men cor,acap DOBLINGER s.p. see also
  Cantate Domino
  (B5762)
  wom cor,acap oct DOBLINGER s.p. see also
  Sechs Motetten
  (B5763)

Laudate Dominum *Easter,mot
  men cor,acap DOBLINGER s.p. see also
  Cantate Domino
  (B5764)

Lobt Gott, Ihr Christen, Allzugleich *mot
  mix cor,acap oct DOBLINGER s.p. see from
  Zwei Choralmotetten
  (B5765)

BURKHART, FRANZ (cont'd.)

O Freude Uber Freude *CC12U,Xmas
  1-2pt wom cor,org,2vln,vcl,opt bsn,fl,clar,
  rec voc sc DOBLINGER s.p., ipa
  (B5766)

O Heiland, Reiss Die Himmel Auf
  mix cor,acap oct DOBLINGER s.p.
  (B5767)

O Vos Omnes *Easter,mot
  men cor,acap DOBLINGER s.p. see also
  Cantate Domino
  (B5768)
  wom cor,acap oct DOBLINGER s.p. see also
  Sechs Motetten
  (B5769)

Sechs Motetten *mot
  wom cor,acap cmplt ed DOBLINGER s.p.
  contains & see also: Caro Mea; Dextera
  Domini; Exsultavit; Justorum Animae; O
  Vos Omnes; Tu Es Petrus
  (B5770)

Tres Sunt *Trin,mot
  men cor,acap DOBLINGER s.p. see also
  Cantate Domino
  (B5771)

Tu Es Petrus *Trin,mot
  men cor,acap DOBLINGER s.p. see also
  Cantate Domino
  (B5772)
  wom cor,acap oct DOBLINGER s.p. see also
  Sechs Motetten
  (B5773)

Wer Nur Den Lieben Gott Lasst Walten *mot
  mix cor,acap oct DOBLINGER s.p. see from
  Zwei Choralmotetten
  (B5774)

Zwei Choralmotetten *mot
  DOBLINGER s.p.
  contains: Lobt Gott, Ihr Christen,
  Allzugleich (mix cor); Wer Nur Den
  Lieben Gott Lasst Walten (mix cor)
  see also: Lobt Gott, Ihr Christen,
  Allzugleich; Wer Nur Den Lieben Gott
  Lasst Walten
  (B5775)

Zwei Hochzeitslieder *see Dass Zwei Sich
  Herzlich Lieben; Ein Getreues Herz Zu
  Wissen
  (B5776)

BURLEIGH, HENRY THACKER (1866-1949)
  Balm In Gilead *spir
  (Vene) SSA oct COLOMBO 1682 $.25 (B5777)
  (Vene) TTBB oct COLOMBO 1724 $.25 (B5778)
  (Vene) SATB oct COLOMBO 1654 $.25 (B5779)
  (Vene) SAB oct COLOMBO 1729 $.25 (B5780)

Behold That Star *Xmas,spir
  SSA oct COLOMBO 1298 $.25 (B5781)
  SATB oct COLOMBO 785 $.30 (B5782)
  SAB oct COLOMBO 2167 $.25 (B5783)

Deep River
  (Burleigh) TTBB,acap oct COLOMBO 1647 $.25
  (B5784)
  (MacCarthy) SA/TB oct COLOMBO 568 $.20
  (B5785)
  (Page) SSA oct COLOMBO 1576 $.25 (B5786)
  (Vene) SAB oct COLOMBO 1616 $.25 (B5787)
  (Vene) SATB oct COLOMBO 1615 $.25 (B5788)

Ezekiel Saw De Wheel *spir
  SSA,acap oct COLOMBO 699 $.30 (B5789)
  SATB oct COLOMBO 768 $.30 (B5790)
  TTBB,acap oct COLOMBO 700 $.30 (B5791)
  (Vene) SAB,acap oct COLOMBO 1783 $.30
  (B5792)

Give Me Jesus *spir
  (Vene) SATB oct COLOMBO 1734 $.25 (B5793)

Go Down, Moses *spir
  (Brewer) TTBB oct COLOMBO 51 $.25 (B5794)
  (Howorth, Wayne) SA/TB oct BELWIN 2115 $.25
  (B5795)
  (Howorth, Wayne) SATB oct BELWIN 2218 $.30
  (B5796)
  (Kemmer) SATB,acap oct COLOMBO 1004 $.25
  (B5797)
  (MacCarthy) SA/TB oct COLOMBO 562 $.25
  (B5798)
  (Page) SSA oct COLOMBO 1659 $.25 (B5799)
  (Page) SATB oct COLOMBO 1597 $.25 (B5800)
  (Vene) SAB oct COLOMBO 1986 $.25 (B5801)

Go Tell It On De Mountains *spir
  SATB oct COLOMBO 817 $.25 (B5802)

Go Tell It On The Mountains *spir
  (Vene) SSA oct COLOMBO 1961 $.25 (B5803)

Gospel Train, De *spir
  SATB oct COLOMBO 659 $.25 (B5804)
  TTBB oct COLOMBO 210 $.25 (B5805)
  (MacCarthy) SA/TB oct COLOMBO 566 $.25
  (B5806)
  (Taylor) SSA oct COLOMBO 169 $.25 (B5807)
  (Vene) SAB oct COLOMBO 2155 $.30 (B5808)

Hear De Lambs A-Cryin' *spir
  SATB,A solo oct COLOMBO 658 $.30 (B5809)
  (Vene) SSAA oct COLOMBO 1987 $.30 (B5810)

Heav'n, Heav'n *spir
  SATB oct COLOMBO 122 $.35 (B5811)
  TTBB,acap oct COLOMBO 224 $.30 (B5812)
  (MacCarthy) SA/TB oct COLOMBO 567 $.25
  (B5813)
  (Taylor) SSA oct COLOMBO 170 $.25 (B5814)
  (Vene) SAB oct COLOMBO 2156 $.30 (B5815)

I Know De Lord's Laid His Hands On Me *spir
  (Vene) SSA oct COLOMBO 2147 $.25 (B5816)
  (Vene) SSA oct COLOMBO 2148 $.25 (B5817)
  (Vene) SATB oct COLOMBO 1801 $.25 (B5818)

I Stood On De Ribber Ob Jerdon *spir
  (Vene) SSA oct COLOMBO 2146 $.25 (B5819)
  (Vene) SSA oct COLOMBO 2145 $.25 (B5820)
  (Vene) SATB oct COLOMBO 1726 $.25 (B5821)

I Want To Be Ready *spir
  (Page) SSA oct COLOMBO 1649 $.25 (B5822)
  (Stone) SATB oct BELWIN 2069 $.25 (B5823)
  (Vene) SAB oct COLOMBO 2157 $.25 (B5824)
  (Vene) SAB oct COLOMBO 2158 $.25 (B5825)

Little Child Of Mary *Xmas
  SATB,S solo,acap oct COLOMBO 1141 $.25
  (B5826)
  (Pickering) SSA,S solo oct COLOMBO 1227
  $.25 (B5827)

BURLEIGH, HENRY THACKER (cont'd.)

O Lord Have Mercy On Me *spir
  (Vene) SSA,acap oct COLOMBO 1972 $.25
  (B5828)
  (Vene) SATB,acap oct COLOMBO 1960 $.25
  (B5829)

Promised Land, The *hymn
  SATB,solo oct COLOMBO 831 $.25 (B5830)
  (Bryan, Charles F.) SATB oct FISCHER,J 8134
  $.30 (B5831)

Ride On, King Jesus *spir
  (Boatner) SATB,acap oct COLOMBO 2225 $.30
  (B5832)
  (Vene) SSA oct COLOMBO 1969 $.25 (B5833)
  (Vene) SSA oct COLOMBO 1970 $.25 (B5834)
  (Vene) SATB oct COLOMBO 1735 $.25 (B5835)

'Tis Me, O Lord *spir
  TTBB oct COLOMBO 424 $.25 (B5836)
  (Kemmer) SATB,acap oct COLOMBO 1133 $.25
  (B5837)
  (MacCarthy) SA/TB oct COLOMBO 565 $.20
  (B5838)
  (Vene) SSA oct COLOMBO 2137 $.25 (B5839)
  (Vene) SAB oct COLOMBO 2138 $.25 (B5840)
  (Vene) SATB oct COLOMBO 1971 $.25 (B5841)

Weepin' Mary *spir
  (Page) SSA oct COLOMBO 2112 $.20 (B5842)
  (Vene) SAB oct COLOMBO 2165 $.25 (B5843)
  (Vene) SATB oct COLOMBO 1784 $.25 (B5844)

Were You There? *spir
  SSA,acap oct COLOMBO 693 $.25 (B5845)
  SATB,acap oct COLOMBO 592 $.25 (B5846)
  TTBB,acap oct COLOMBO 454 $.25 (B5847)
  SSATTBB,acap oct COLOMBO 423 $.25 (B5848)
  (Hall, William) SATB oct FISCHER,J 9314
  $.30 (B5849)
  (Howorth, Wayne) SA/TB oct BELWIN 1337 $.30
  (B5850)
  (Howorth, Wayne) SSA oct BELWIN 777 $.25
  (B5851)
  (Howorth, Wayne) SAB oct BELWIN 1662 $.25
  (B5852)
  (Howorth, Wayne) SATB oct BELWIN 778 $.30
  (B5853)
  (MacCarthy) SA/TB oct COLOMBO 563 $.25
  (B5854)
  (Vene) SAB oct COLOMBO 1494 $.25 (B5855)

BURNELL, I.
  For Us Men *Psntd,cant
  SATB,MezTB soli,org voc sc NOVELLO s.p.,
  ipr
  (B5856)

Surely The Lord Is In This Place *anthem
  SATB BELWIN AP 23 $.30 (B5857)
  mix cor oct NOVELLO 50.0264.08 s.p. (B5858)

BURNHAM
  Christmas Fanfare *Xmas
  SATB oct HERITAGE H45 $.40 (B5859)
  mix cor SOUTHERN $.35 (B5860)

Halaluah!
  SATB oct HERITAGE H73 $.35 (B5861)

Manger Carol, A *Xmas,carol
  SATB oct LORENZ 7416 $.30 (B5862)

Sometimes I Feel Like A Motherless Child
  SATB oct HERITAGE H49 $.40 (B5863)

BURNHAM, CARDON
  Manger Carol, A *Xmas,anthem
  SAB/SA,opt bells&drums oct LORENZ 7416 $.30
  (B5864)
  Thanksgiving To God For His House, A
  mix cor (med) HERITAGE H2874 $.35 (B5865)

BURNING BABE, THE see Beattie, Herbert

BURNS
  Carol Of The Bells *Xmas
  SSA oct LORENZ 6230 $.25 (B5866)

Deepen My Music
  SATB oct VOLKWEIN VB692 $.25 (B5867)

BURNS, W.
  Common Prayer, A
  1-3pt BOSWORTH s.p. (B5868)

BURNS, WILLIAM K.
  Behold! I Stand At The Door And Knock
  SATB (easy/med) ABINGDON APM-239 $.25
  (B5869)

O Man, Rejoice *Xmas
  SATB,org,2trp (easy) ABINGDON APM-428 $.25
  (B5870)

Seek Ye The Lord
  mix cor oct AGAPE CF 144 $.30 (B5871)

BURRELL
  Mass
  SA sc OXFORD 46.164 $6.20, ipa, cor pts
  OXFORD $.65, ipa (B5872)

BURRONI, G.
  see BARONI, GIOVANNI

BURROUGHS
  Drop, Drop Slow Tears
  SATB oct SACRED S-2 $.35 (B5873)

How Far Is It To Bethlehem? *Xmas
  SATB oct SACRED E60 $.30 (B5874)
  SSA oct SACRED S-6256 $.30 (B5875)

In Memory Of The Saviour's Love
  SATB (med easy) SOUTHERN $.35 (B5876)

O Christ, I Look To Thee
  SA oct SACRED S-5752 $.30 (B5877)

O Come And Mourn With Me *Easter
  SATB oct LORENZ C340 $.25 (B5878)

O Lord Of Life
  SATB oct SACRED S-56 $.35 (B5879)

Praise The Lord His Glories Show
  SATB (med easy) SOUTHERN $.35 (B5880)

BURROUGHS (cont'd.)

Safe In The Arms Of Jesus
SATB oct LORENZ C237 $.30 (B5881)

Seek Ye The Lord
SATB oct SACRED S-130 $.35 (B5882)

Sing Unto The Lord *anthem
SATB oct FISCHER,C CM-7730 $.25 (B5883)

Swing Low
SATB oct HERITAGE H2150 $.30 (B5884)

This Little Babe *Xmas
SATB oct FISCHER,C CM-7740 $.25 (B5885)

Treasures In Heaven
SSAATTBB oct SACRED S-103 $.35 (B5886)

We Thank Thee, Lord
SATB oct LORENZ 9969 $.30 (B5887)

BURROUGHS, B.
Ask
SATB oct PRESSER G-152 $.40 (B5888)

Give Peace, O God
SATB LEONARD-US 08017900 $.30 (B5889)

New Song, A
SA&TB oct PRESSER G-126 $.30 (B5890)

O Lord, Thou Hast Searched Me
SATB,org oct KERBY 7005 $.35 (B5891)
SATB oct KERBY 7005C $.35 (B5892)

O Sing Unto The Lord A New Song
SATB LEONARD-US 08059360 $.30 (B5893)

There Is A Land Of Pleasure
SATB LEONARD-US 08064720 $.30 (B5894)

Ye Servants Of God
SATB oct BOURNE 940 $.50 (B5895)

BURROUGHS, BOB
Angels From The Realms Of Glory *Xmas
SATB,acap (easy) PRESSER $.30 (B5896)

Christmas Wonder (composed with Burroughs, Ester) *Xmas,cant
1-2pt jr cor,kbd,opt fl&gtr voc sc WORD 20052 $1.50, ipa (B5897)

Easter Alleluia, An *Easter
SSATB,acap oct WORD CS-694 $.25 (B5898)

Freedom
unis,inst oct AGAPE SP 691 $.30 (B5899)

Gloria! *anthem/Gloria
unis treb cor (easy) oct AUGSBURG 1611 $.30 (B5900)

Go To Dark Gethsemane
SATB,acap SHAWNEE A 793 $.30 (B5901)

God Of The Galaxies
SATB,acap (easy) PRESSER 362-03139 $.30 (B5902)

Great Is The Lord *Thanks
SATB&cong,narrator,org,trp (easy) PRESSER 312-40986 $.45 (B5903)

I Love My God
SATB oct WORD CS-2541 $.35 (B5904)

In Memory Of The Savior's Love *Commun
SATB (med) ABINGDON APM-656 $.35 (B5905)

In Our Work And In Our Play
SA,pno,hndbl oct WORD CS-2435 $.30 (B5906)

My Lord, My Love, Is Crucified! *Holywk/Lent
LORENZ $1.50 (B5907)

New Commandment, A *anthem
SATB,acap (easy) oct MCAFEE M1010 $.35 (B5908)

New Song, A
(Bock, Fred) SA (easy) PRESSER G-4503 $.35 (B5909)

None Other Lamb *anthem
SATB (easy) oct AUGSBURG 1509 $.20 (B5910)

Now Thank We All Our God
SATB (med) ABINGDON APM-655 $.35 (B5911)

O Little Town Of Bethlehem *Xmas,carol
SATB,pno,gtr (easy) PRESSER $.35 (B5912)

Praise The Lord, His Glories Show
SATB (med) ABINGDON APM-654 $.55 (B5913)

Psalm 8
SATB oct WORD CS-2474 $.25 (B5914)

Psalm 100
SATB oct WORD CS-2562 $.35 (B5915)

Rise, O Lord
2pt mix cor (easy) PRESSER 312-41007 $.35 (B5916)

Variations On "Twinkle, Twinkle"
SSA oct AGAPE SP 713 $.35 (B5917)

Wake Sons Of Earth Awake
SATB oct WORD CS-2561 $.35 (B5918)

You Better Mind!
SATB,T solo (med easy) PRESSER 312-40990 $.35 (B5919)

BURROUGHS, ESTER
Christmas Wonder *see Burroughs, Bob

BURT
Eternal Spirit, The
(Hutson) SATB,org/pno BOSTON 13161 $.35 (B5920)

BURT, ALFRED
Ah, Bleak And Chill The Wintry Wind
(Ades) SA/TB SHAWNEE E78 $.30 (B5921)

Alfred Burt Carols *sac/sec,CCU
(Ades) jr cor voc sc SHAWNEE GF57 $3.00, cor pts SHAWNEE GF58 $.40 (B5922)

BURT, ALFRED (cont'd.)

Alfred Burt Carols, Set 1 *sac/sec,CCU,carol
(Ades) SAB SHAWNEE D113 $.35 (B5923)

Alfred Burt Carols, Set 1 *sac/sec,CCU,carol
SATB,acap SHAWNEE A 449 $.35; TTBB,acap SHAWNEE C 156 $.35; SSA,acap SHAWNEE B 161 $.40 (B5924)

Alfred Burt Carols, Set 2 *sac/sec,CCU,carol
(Ades) SAB SHAWNEE D114 $.35 (B5925)

Alfred Burt Carols, Set 2 *sac/sec,CCU,carol
SATB,acap SHAWNEE A 450 $.35; SAB,acap SHAWNEE D 114 $.35; SSA,acap SHAWNEE B 160 $.40 (B5926)

Alfred Burt Carols, Set 3 *sac/sec,CCU,carol
(Ades) SAB SHAWNEE D115 $.35 (B5927)

Alfred Burt Carols, Set 3 *sac/sec,CCU,carol
SATB,acap SHAWNEE A 451 $.35; TTBB,acap SHAWNEE C 208 $.35; SSA,acap SHAWNEE B 318 $.35 (B5928)

Caroling, Caroling
(Ades) SA/TB SHAWNEE E74 $.35 (B5929)

O Hearken Ye
(Ades) SA/TB SHAWNEE E79 $.30 (B5930)

Some Children See Him
(Ades) SA/TB SHAWNEE E77 $.35 (B5931)

Star Carol
(Ades) SA/TB SHAWNEE E75 $.30 (B5932)

This Is Christmas *sac/sec,cant
SATB SHAWNEE A458 $1.00 (B5933)

BURT, [FRANCIS] (1926-)
Fanfare For A Festive Day *Easter
SATB,org,trp SCHMITT 1930 $.35 (B5934)

BURTHEL, JAKOB (1926-)
Ich Weiss Ein Feins Brauns Magdelein *folk, 16th cent
4pt men cor&4pt wom cor cor pts BREITKOPF-W CHB-3614 s.p. (B5935)

BURTON, PETER
Simple Communion Service In F *Commun
cor,pno/org (F maj) sc ROYAL s.p. (B5936)
oct ROYAL 114 s.p. (B5937)

BURY
Sing Noel *Xmas
unis BOOSEY-CAN s.p. (B5938)

BUSAROW, DONALD
Five Christmas Carols On Traditional Texts *CC5U,Xmas,carol
unis,opt inst oct AGAPE F 921 $.35 (B5939)

If You Continue In My Word *anthem
SATB,opt trp (med) oct AUGSBURG 1537 $.30 (B5940)

Seven Words Of Christ, The
mix cor,4 soli,4strings sc CONCORDIA 97-4744 $.85, ipa (B5941)

Te Deum Laudamus *liturg/Te Deum
mix cor,org,brass,opt timp sc CONCORDIA 97-6426 $1.25, cor pts CONCORDIA 97-6444 $.30, ipa (B5942)
"We Praise Thee, O God" mix cor,brass,opt timp,org/pno sc CONCORDIA 97-6426 $1.25, cor pts CONCORDIA 97-6444 $.30, ipa (B5943)

We Praise Thee, O God *see Te Deum Laudamus

BUSCA
Himno Al Sagrado Corazon De Jesus
4pt UNION ESP. 12739 s.p. (B5944)

Himno Oficial Del Congreso Eucaristico
4pt UNION ESP. 14427 s.p. (B5945)

Misa De Pastorela *Mass
unis,2 soli (easy) voc sc UNION ESP. 13133 s.p., cor pts UNION ESP. 19540-A s.p., cor pts UNION ESP. 19540-B s.p. (B5946)

BUSH
Child Of Bethlehem
unis THOMP.G G-153 s.p. (B5947)

Christmas Night *Xmas
SSATBB,acap (med diff) OXFORD 84.011 $.50 (B5948)

BUSH, FLORENCE
Bread Of The World *Commun,anthem
SATB oct AGAPE A 387 (B5949)

Five Songs From Foreign Lands *CC5U
unis/2pt oct AGAPE CH 652 $.40 (B5950)

BUSH, G.B.
We Give Thanks *Thanks
SATB,org oct KERBY 5208 $.35 (B5951)
SATB oct KERBY 5208C $.35 (B5952)

BUSH, GEOFFREY (1920-)
Christmas Cantata, A *Xmas,cant
SATB,S solo,ob,strings voc sc NOVELLO s.p., ipr (B5953)

Earth Is The Lord's, The (Psalm 24) anthem
mix cor,org,2trp,2trom,timp oct NOVELLO 86.0028.07 s.p., ipr (B5954)

Magnificat And Nunc Dimittis *Magnif/Nunc
SATB oct NOVELLO 86.0024.04 s.p. (B5955)

Missa Brevis Salisburiensis *Mass
SATB oct NOVELLO 86.0025.02 s.p. (B5956)

O Love, How Deep *anthem
mix cor oct NOVELLO 40.1360.03 s.p. (B5957)

O Salutaris Hostia
see Two Latin Hymns

Praise The Lord, O My Soul *Thanks,anthem
mix cor,ST soli oct NOVELLO 28.1344.00 s.p. (B5958)

BUSH, GEOFFREY (cont'd.)

Psalm 24 *see Earth Is The Lord's, The

Tantum Ergo
see Two Latin Hymns

Two Latin Hymns *anthem/hymn
[Lat] mix cor oct NOVELLO 40.1448.00 s.p.
contains: O Salutaris Hostia; Tantum Ergo (B5959)

BUSKIRK
Acquaint Thyself With Him
SATB oct SACRED S-9 $.35 (B5960)

BUSSER, [HENRI-PAUL] (1872-)
Ave Maria *BVM,mot
see Salut Au Saint-Sacrement
[Lat] 4 eq voices oct DURAND s.p. (B5961)

Ave Regina *BVM,anthem
[Lat] 4 eq voices,acap oct DURAND see from Trois Antiennes A La Sainte Vierge (B5962)

Ave Verum *Commun,mot
[Lat] 4 eq voices DURAND s.p. (B5963)

Deus Abraham *mot
[Lat] 4pt mix cor,S/T solo,org,opt vln&vcl&bvl&harp LEMOINE s.p. (B5964)
[Lat] cor,acap LEMOINE s.p. (B5965)

Deux Antiennes Pour La Fete De Sainte Jeanne D'arc *see Joanna Sponsa Christi

Ecce Panis
[Lat] opt mix cor,Mez/Bar solo (E flat maj) LEMOINE s.p. (B5966)
[Lat] cor,acap LEMOINE s.p. (B5967)

Haec Est Joanna *Op.123
see Busser, [Henri-Paul], Joanna Sponsa Christi

Hosanna Filio David *Commun
[Lat] 4pt mix cor,org (contains also solo work) LEMOINE s.p. see also BREVIAIRE DE PIERRE L'ERMITE (B5968)
[Lat] 4pt mix cor,org LEMOINE voc sc s.p., cor pts s.p. see from LE BREVIAIRE DE PIERRE L'ERMITE (B5969)

Joanna Sponsa Christi *Op.123, Gen,anthem/mot
"Deux Antiennes Pour La Fete De Sainte Jeanne D'arc" [Lat] 4pt mix cor,opt org, trp sc DURAND s.p., ipa contains also: Haec Est Joanna (B5970)

Laudate Dominum *mot
[Lat] SATB,orch (F maj) LEDUC MS480 voc sc s.p., voc pt s.p. see from MUSIQUE SACREE (B5971)

Magnificat *Magnif
[Lat] mix cor,Bar solo LEMOINE s.p. (B5972)

Messe De Domremy A La Gloire De Sainte Jeanne D'arc *Op.122, anti/Mass
[Fr] 4pt mix cor,opt org,4trp sc DURAND s.p., ipa (B5973)

Messe De Noel *Op.27, Xmas,Mass
2 eq voices/4pt mix cor,org,opt harp,opt 5strings LEMOINE voc sc s.p., cor pts s.p., ipa (B5974)

Messe De Saint-Bertrand De Comminges *Mass
4pt mix cor,soli,opt org LEMOINE s.p. (B5975)

Messe Solennelle De Saint-Etienne *Op.97, Mass
4pt mix cor,org,brass,opt harp&drums LEMOINE voc sc s.p., cor pts s.p., voc pt s.p., ipa (B5976)

O Salutaris
see Salut Au Saint-Sacrement

Priere Au Redempteur
[Lat/Fr] SMezA,solo ENOCH cor pts s.p., voc sc s.p. (B5977)

Regina Coeli *BVM,anthem
[Lat] 4 eq voices,acap oct DURAND see from Trois Antiennes A La Sainte Vierge (B5978)

Salut Au Saint-Sacrement *mot
[Lat] 4pt mix cor,opt org LEMOINE s.p.
contains: Ave Maria; O Salutaris; Tantum Ergo; Tu Es Petrus (B5979)

Salve Regina *BVM,anthem
[Lat] 4 eq voices,acap oct DURAND see from Trois Antiennes A La Sainte Vierge (B5980)

Tantum Ergo
see Salut Au Saint-Sacrement

Trois Antiennes A La Sainte Vierge *see Ave Regina; Regina Coeli; Salve Regina (B5981)

Tu Es Petrus *Gen,mot
see Salut Au Saint-Sacrement
[Lat] opt 4pt men cor/mix cor,orch oct DURAND s.p., ipr (B5982)

BUSZIN
From Heaven On High Hear Angels Sing *Xmas
SATB SCHMITT 8014 $.20 (B5983)

Motets And Chorales For Treble Choirs *CCU, chorale/mot
treb cor SOUTHERN $.50 (B5984)

BUT AS FOR HIS PEOPLE see Handel, George Frideric

BUT FOR THE GRACE OF GOD
SATB BIG3 $.25 (B5985)

BUT I HAVE TRUSTED IN THY MERCY see Liszt, Franz

BUT IN THE LAST DAYS see Mason

BUT LET'S SING A NEW SONG! *CCU,anthem/pop
(Martin, Gilbert M.) SB/SAB/SATB/unis LORENZ $1.75 (B5986)

BUT OUR GOD ABIDETH IN HEAVEN see Mendelssohn-Bartholdy, Felix

BUT THE LORD IS FAITHFUL see Roff, Joseph

BUT THE LORD IS MINDFUL OF HIS OWN see Mendelssohn-Bartholdy, Felix

BUT THESE ARE THEY THAT FORSAKE THE LORD see Thompson, Randall

BUTCHER, F.
Let All Mortal Flesh Keep Silence *Xmas
SATB oct PRESSER 332-14928 $.30 (B5987)

BUTLER
Christ Crucified
SATB FLAMMER A5287 $1.50 (B5988)

Come, Peace Of God
SATB oct SACRED E56 $.35 (B5989)

Exalt The Name Of The Lord
SA oct HERITAGE H5007 $.35 (B5990)

Glory To Our Risen King *Easter
SATB oct SACRED S-64 $.35 (B5991)

Great God Attend While Zion Sings *anthem
SATB oct FISCHER,C CM-7761 $.30 (B5992)

I Will Lift Up Mine Eyes
SATB oct SACRED S-144 $.35 (B5993)

Jesus Is Born, Alleluia *Xmas
SATB,opt inst SCHMITT 8040 $.35, ipa (B5994)

Jesus Joy Of Every Soul *Gen
SATB SCHMITT 8051 $.30 (B5995)

Late Have I Loved Thee
SATBB,acap WARNER W7-1033 $.30 (B5996)

Let All Mortal Flesh Keep Silence
SATB oct SACRED S-15 $.35 (B5997)

Lift Up Our Hearts
SATB oct GALAXY 1.2332.1 $.30 (B5998)

Lift Up Your Hearts, Ye People *Gen
SAB oct SPRATT 615 $.25 (B5999)

Lord Is Good, The
SATB oct SACRED S-23 $.35 (B6000)

Lord Of All Being
SATB oct GALAXY 1.2301.1 $.25 (B6001)

Lord Reigns, The
SATB oct SACRED S-42 $.35 (B6002)

Make Me A Captive, O Lord
SATB oct GALAXY 1.2410.1 $.30 (B6003)

Night Hymn *Eve,hymn
SATB oct FISCHER,C CM-7763 $.25 (B6004)

O Come, Let Us Sing
SAB oct SACRED S-7382 $.35 (B6005)

O Day Of God, Draw Nigh
SATB oct SACRED E78 $.35 (B6006)

O Holy City Seen Of John
SATB oct SACRED S-9952 $.35 (B6007)

O Men Of God Arise
SATB oct GALAXY 1.2447.1 $.30 (B6008)

O Men Of God, Be Strong! S-76
SATB oct SACRED $.35 (B6009)

O Spirit Of The Living God
SAB oct BOURNE 3027 $.30 (B6010)

Out Of The Depths
SATB oct SACRED S-44 $.35 (B6011)

Praise Christ, Alleluia
SATB oct FISCHER,C CM-7754 $.30 (B6012)

Prayer Of St. Chrysostom *prayer
SATB WARNER W7-1034 $.30 (B6013)

Prophecy Of Joel
SATB SOUTHERN $.35 (B6014)

Prophesy Of Joel *Bibl
SATB oct FISCHER,C CM-7789 $.35 (B6015)

Rejoice, Ye Hearts, Be Glad And Sing *Gen
SATB SCHMITT 8020 $.35 (B6016)

Rise, My Soul *Gen
SATB SCHMITT 8017 $.35 (B6017)

Save Me, O God
SATB oct SACRED S-47 $.35 (B6018)

Sing Aloud To God, Our Strength
SAB oct GALAXY 1.2373.1 $.30 (B6019)

Sing, Men And Angels, Sing
mix cor SOUTHERN $.35 (B6020)

Sing O Sing This Blessed Morn *Xmas
SATB oct GALAXY 1.2348.1 $.30 (B6021)

Song Of Daniel *anthem/Bibl
SATB oct FISCHER,C CM-7766 $.30 (B6022)

Supplication And Alleluia *Easter
SATB oct GALAXY 1.2431.1 $.30 (B6023)

Thanksgiving Hymn, A
SA/TB FLAMMER E5023 $.25 (B6024)

BUTLER C.W.
Be Merciful Unto Us, O Lord
see Farrant, Richard, Lord For Thy Tender Mercies Sake

BUTLER, EUGENE
All Nature's Works His Praise Declare
SATB (easy) oct AGAPE CH 627 $.30 (B6025)

Break, Day Of God!
SATB oct AGAPE CH 618 $.30 (B6026)

BUTLER, EUGENE (cont'd.)

Build Thee More Stately Mansions
TBB LEONARD-US 08005280 $.25 (B6027)

Choral Psalmist, The (composed with Powell, Robert J.; McAfee, Don)
SACRED $1.75 (B6028)

Come, Peace Of God *anthem
TTBB oct SACRED S-2859 $.35 (B6029)

Creator Of The Stars Of Night
SATB FLAMMER A 5084 $.25 (B6030)

Dark The Night
SATB FLAMMER A 5205 $.25 (B6031)

Forth In Thy Name, O Lord
SATB (easy) ABINGDON APM-259 $.18 (B6032)

Gather Ye Rosebuds While Ye May
SATB oct PRESSER G-105 $.30 (B6033)

Great And Mighty Wonder, A
SATB oct AGAPE A 368 $.30 (B6034)

Hark! A Thrilling Voice *Xmas
SATB (med) ABINGDON APM-570 $.30 (B6035)

How Excellent Is Thy Name
SATB (prepack, 25 copies) oct BOURNE 837 $10.00 (B6036)

How Long O Lord
SATB oct BOURNE 859 $.30 (B6037)

Hymn Of Wisdom
SATB oct AGAPE A 438 $.30 (B6038)

Let Us With A Gladsome Mind
SATB (easy) ABINGDON APM-659 $.25 (B6039)

Lord Reigneth, The
SAB oct AGAPE A 381 $.30 (B6040)

Make Some Sort Of Joyful Noise
SATB oct WORD CS-2451 $.30 (B6041)

Mexican Psalm, A *Psalm
SATB LEONARD-US 08043200 $.35 (B6042)

My Heart Is Steadfast, O God (Psalm 57) Bibl
SAB oct AGAPE A 378 $.35 (B6043)

Nature's Hymn Of Praise *hymn
SATB,opt fl oct AGAPE F 917 $.30 (B6044)

O Come, O Come, Immanuel *Xmas
SATB oct WORD CS-690 $.25 (B6045)

O God Of All Above, Below
SATB (med) ABINGDON APM-605 $.25 (B6046)

O God Our Strength And Refuge Sure
SATB oct WORD CS-303 $.30 (B6047)

Ode To Music
SATB oct AGAPE F 941 $.40 (B6048)

Paean Of Brotherhood
SATB oct PRESSER 312-40658 $.35 (B6049)

Praise And Sing
SATB oct AGAPE CF 108 $.30 (B6050)

Praise Ye The Lord
SATB (easy/med) ABINGDON APM-212 $.30 (B6051)

Psalm 57 *see My Heart Is Steadfast, O God

Ride On, Ride On In Majesty *Palm
(Milman) SATB WARNER R3471 $.30 (B6052)

Seek Ye The Lord
SATB FLAMMER A 5063 $.25 (B6053)

Shall I Compare Thee To A Summer's Day?
SATB oct AGAPE SP 698 $.30 (B6054)

Sing To The Lord A Marvelous Song
SATB oct AGAPE A 451 $.35 (B6055)

Singer Of The Universe
SATB (med) ABINGDON APM-606 $.25 (B6056)

Sound Over All Waters
SATB,acap WARNER W7-1026 $.30 (B6057)

Tell Abroad His Rising *Easter
SATB,org,2trp (easy) PRESSER G-198 $.35 (B6058)

That Bethlehem's Babe
SATB FLAMMER A 5290 $.25 (B6059)

Three Contemporary Madrigals *CC3U,madrigal
SATB oct AGAPE SP 687 $.35 (B6060)

'Tis Finished, The Messiah Dies *Easter/Lent
SATB oct WORD CS-337 $.30 (B6061)

Weep You No More, Sad Fountains
SATB oct AGAPE SP 682 $.30 (B6062)

You Are The Salt Of The Earth
SATB oct WORD CS-2452 $.30 (B6063)

BUTT
Knock Down The Wall
(Henderson) SATB BOSTON 12984 $.40 (B6064)
(Henderson) TTBB BOSTON 13233 $.40 (B6065)

BUTTOLPH
He Is Born, The Beloved Child *Xmas
SSA oct GALAXY 1.2339.1 $.30 (B6066)

BUTTON, H.E.
Jesu, Whom Thy Children Love
unis oct GRAY GCMR 1506 $.30 (B6067)

BUXTEHUDE, DIETRICH (ca. 1637-1707)
Accedite Gentes
see Fire Latinske Kantater

Ad Faciem "Illustra Faciem Tuam" *No.7 (from Membra Jesu Nostri) Psntd,cant
(Grusnick, Bruno) [Lat] SSATB,ATB soli, cont,2vln,vcl (med diff) BAREN. BA 3462 sc $3.75, cor pts $1.00 (B6068)

BUXTEHUDE, DIETRICH (cont'd.)

Ad Genua "Ad Ubera Portabimini" *No.2 (from Membra Jesu Nostri) Psntd,cant
(Grusnick, Bruno) [Lat] SATB,SSATB soli, cont,2vln,vcl (med diff) BAREN. BA 3457 sc $3.00, cor pts $.55, ipa (B6069)

Ad Latus "Surge, Amica Mea" *No.4 (from Membra Jesu Nostri) Psntd,cant
(Grusnick, Bruno) [Lat] SSATB,SSATB soli, cont,2vln,vcl (med diff) BAREN. BA 3459 sc $3.00, cor pts $.55, ipa (B6070)

Ad Manus "Quid Sunt Plagae Istae" *No.3 (from Membra Jesu Nostri) Psntd,cant
(Grusnick, Bruno) [Lat] SSATB,SSATB soli, cont,2vln,vcl (med diff) cor pts BAREN. BA 3458 $.40 (B6071)

Ad Pedes "Ecce Super Montes" *No.1 (from Membra Jesu Nostri) Psntd,cant
(Grusnick, Bruno) [Lat] SSATB,SSB soli, cont,2vln,vcl (med diff) sc BAREN. BA 3456 $3.75 (B6072)

Afferte Domino (Psalm 95) cant
[Lat] 3pt,cont SKAND. s.p. (B6073)

All Solch Dein Guet Wir Preisen
[Ger] SSATB,org/pno,2vln,2vla,vcl sc PETERS EM956 $4.00, ipa, voc sc PETERS EM956 $.80, ipa (B6074)

All Solch Dein Gut Wir Preisen *Gen
(Grusnick, Bruno) [Ger] SSATB,cont,2vln, 2vla,vcl (med) sc BAREN. BA 3197 $3.50, cor pts $.65, ipa (B6075)

Alleluia, Alleluia *Easter/Gen
(Ehret, W.) SSATB oct PRESSER 312-40668 $.30 (B6076)

Alleluja, Alleluja *cant
(Ehrlinger) SSATB,cont,2trp,2vln,2vla,vcl HANSSLER 10.004 sc s.p., cor pts s.p., ipa (B6077)

Alles Was Ihr Tut *cant
mix cor,SB soli,org,strings voc pt BREITKOPF-L CHB-2269A+B s.p., ipr (B6078)
[Ger] SATB,SB soli,org,strings KISTNER sc s.p., cor pts s.p., ipa (B6079)
[Eng/Ger] SATB,cont,strings HANSSLER 36.001 sc $3.00, cor pts $1.00, ipa (B6080)
[Ger] SATB,org,2vln,2vla,vcl,bvl sc PETERS EM911 $4.00, ipa, voc sc PETERS EM911 $.80, ipa (B6081)
"Allt Vadhelst I Goren" cor,soli,org,2vln, 2vla,vcl,bvl NORDISKA 5403 cor pts s.p., voc sc s.p., ipa (B6082)
(Bunjes, P.) "Every Word And Thought" [Eng/Ger] mix cor,org&bvl/strings voc sc CONCORDIA 97-6279 $1.00 (B6083)
(Bunjes, P.) "Every Word And Thought" [Ger] mix cor,org&bvl/strings sc CONCORDIA 97-4227 $3.50, ipa (B6084)
(Ehret, Walter) "Whatsoe'er Ye Do" mix cor, SB soli,orch/pno LAWSON $1.50 (B6085)
(Sorenson, Soren) "Eders Hele Vaerk" [Ger/Dan] SATB,soli,org,2vln,2vla,vcl,bvl HANSEN-DEN 26718 s.p., ipa (B6086)

Allt Vadhelst I Goren *see Alles Was Ihr Tut

Amen Chorus (from Befiehl Dem Engel)
(Granville) SATB oct FOX CM9 $.25 (B6087)

Aperite Mihi Portas (Psalm 118) cant
"Open To Me Gates Of Justice" [Eng/Lat] ATB/TTB,org/pno,opt 2vln PETERS 6050 $.60, ipa (B6088)
"Open To Me Gates Of Justice" [Eng/Lat] ATB/TTB,org/pno,2vln PETERS 6050 $.60, ipa (B6089)

Aperite Mihi Portas Justitae *cant
(Hedar) ATB,2vln,cont HANSEN-DEN cor pts s.p., voc sc s.p., ipa (B6090)

Auf Dich, Herr, Hab' Ich Gehoffet *cant/mot
(Liechti, Paul) "In Te, Domine, Speravi" [Ger/Lat] SAB,org KROMPHOLZ s.p. (B6091)
(Trubel) SAB,cont HANSSLER 10.036 sc s.p., cor pts s.p. (B6092)

Baroque To The Great Classics, The Vol. 4- 1550 To 1700
mix cor min sc KALMUS 884 $1.30
contains: In Dulci Jubilo; My Hearts Treasure (B6093)

Befiehl Dem Engel, Dass Er Komm *Gen,cant
"Command Thine Angel That He Come" [Ger/Eng] SATB,org/pno,vln,vln,vcl,bvl BROUDE BR. $.60, ipa (B6094)
(Adell, A.) "Sand Ut Din Angel, Fader Kar" [Swed] cor,strings,cont cor pts NORDISKA U282 s.p., ipa (B6095)
(Grusnick, Bruno) [Eng/Ger] SATB,cont,2vln, vcl (med) sc BAREN. BA 541 $2.50, cor pts $.55, ipa (B6096)
(Grytter, Rud.) "Send Hid Din Engel, Herre From" [Ger/Dan/Swed] SATB,cont,strings HANSEN-DEN 24728 s.p., ipa (B6097)

Behold, He Bore All Our Infirmities
see Sacred Choruses

Behold, He Bore Our Infirmities
cor voc sc KALMUS 6129 $1.25, ipa (B6098)

Beloved Lord, Hasten The Day *see Ei Lieber Herr Eil Zum Gericht

Bitte Um Frieden "Du Friedefurst" *Gen
(Gruswick, Bruno) [Eng/Ger] SSB,cont,2vln, 2vla,bsn (med) BAREN. BA 1737 sc $4.50, cor pts $.65, ipa (B6099)

Blessed Lord Jesus
mix cor SOUTHERN $.30 (B6100)
(Hunter) [Eng/Ger] SSATB,orch MARKS 4508 $.30, ipr (B6101)

Cantate Domini (Psalm 96)
mix cor,acap voc sc KALMUS 6128 $1.00 (B6102)

BUXTEHUDE, DIETRICH (cont'd.)

Cantate Domino *mot
3pt mix cor,solo cor pts NORDISKA 2865 s.p. (B6103)
mix cor,cont sc HANSSLER 36.007 s.p., ipa (B6104)
"Sing To God The Lord" [Lat/Eng] SSB,org CONCORDIA 97-6246 $.75 (B6105)
(Sorenson, Soren) SSB,org HANSEN-DEN 28906 s.p. (B6106)

Cantate Domino *see Lobsinget Gott, Dem Herrn

Child Was Born, A *Xmas
(Stone) unis,kbd/brass oct WORD CRS-14 $.30 (B6107)

Christmas Canon *Xmas,canon
girl cor SOUTHERN $.30 (B6108)

Christmas Canon, A *Xmas,canon
SSA,kbd (med easy) oct CONCORDIA 98-1780 $.30 (B6109)

Command Thine Angel That He Come *see Befiehl Dem Engel, Dass Er Komm

Das Neugeborne Kindelein *Xmas,cant
"Newborn Babe, The" see Sacred Choruses
[Eng/Ger] SATB,3vln,vcl,bvl HANSSLER 36.002 sc $3.00, cor pts $2.00, ipa (B6110)
"Infant Jesus, The" mix cor,strings,cont sc CONCORDIA 97-6341 $1.50, cor pts CONCORDIA 97-6364 $.50, ipa (B6111)
"Newborn Babe, The" cor voc sc KALMUS 6133 $1.25, ipa (B6112)
(Ehret, Walter) "Little Newborn Jesus Child, The" mix cor,orch,org LAWSON $.75 (B6113)
(Grusnick, Bruno) [Eng/Ger] SATB,3vln,vcl (med) BAREN. BA 717 sc $3.75, cor pts $.75, ipa (B6114)

Dearest Lord Jesus *see Liebster Herr Jesu

Dein Edles Herz *Psntd,cant
(Kilian) [Ger] SATB,cont,2vln,2vla, violone BAREN. EM 960 sc s.p., cor pts s.p., ipa (B6115)

Dein Edles Herz, Der Liebe Thron *Psntd,cant
(Grusnick, Bruno) [Ger] SATB,SATB soli,org, cont,2vln,2vla,vcl,bvl (med) BAREN. BA 3364 sc $3.75, cor pts $.55, ipa (B6116)

Der Herr Ist Mit Mir *Gen,cant
"Min Gud Er Med Mig" [Ger/Dan] cor,org SAMFUNDET sc s.p., voc sc s.p., ipa (B6117)
"Min Gud Er Med Mig" [Dan/Ger] SATB,cont, 2vln,vcl FOG III, 89 sc s.p., cor pts s.p., ipa (B6118)
(Grusnick, Bruno) [Ger] SATB,cont,2vln,vcl (med) BAREN. BA 3198 sc $4.50, cor pts $1.00, ipa (B6119)

Derr Herr Erhor Dich
[Ger/Swed] SATB,pno/org,2vln,vcl sc PETERS EM955 $4.00, ipa, voc sc PETERS EM955 $.80, ipa (B6120)

Domine Salvum Fac Regem
see Fire Latinske Kantater

Du Friedefurst, Herr Jesu Christ *Gen
[Ger] voc sc PETERS HU1907 $2.50, ipr (B6121)
(Grusnick, Bruno) [Ger] SSATB,cont,2vln,vcl (med) BAREN. BA 3362 sc $3.75, cor pts $.65, ipa (B6122)

Du Lebensfurst, Herr Jesu Christ *Easter/Pent
(Grusnick, Bruno) [Ger] SATB,SATB soli,org BAREN. BA 3363 sc $4.00, cor pts $.65, ipa (B6123)

Ecce Nunc Benedicite Domino *cant
see Fire Latinske Kantater
(Kilian, Dietrich) [Lat] SATB,ATTB soli, cont,strings HINRICHSEN EM971 s.p. (B6124)

Ecce Nunc Benedicite Domino *see Siehe, Lobet Den Herrn

Eders Hele Vaerk *see Alles, Was Ihr Tut

Eet Onsker Jeg Til Gud *see Eins Bitte Ich Vom Herrn

Ei Lieber Herr Eil Zum Gericht
"Beloved Lord, Hasten The Day" mix cor SOUTHERN $.25 (B6125)
(Granville) "Beloved Lord, Hasten The Day" SSATB oct FOX CM15 $.30 (B6126)

Eins Bitte Ich Vom Herrn *Trin,cant
mix cor,org,2fl,strings,cembalo sc BREITKOPF-L rental (B6127)
(Sorenson, Soren) "Eet Onsker Jeg Til Gud" [Ger/Dan] SSATB,soli,org,opt 2fl,2vln, 2vla,vcl,bvl HANSEN-DEN 27641 s.p., ipa (B6128)

Erbarm Dich Mein, O Herre Gott *ECY
(Grusnick, Bruno) [Ger] SATB,opt SB soli, cont&bsn&2vln&2vla/2vln&2vla&bvl (med) BAREN. BA 1137 sc $3.25, cor pts $.40, ipa (B6129)

Erfreue Dich, Erde
see Buxtehude, Dietrich, Schlagt, Kunstler, Die Pauken

Erhalt Uns, Herr, Bei Deinem Wort *Fest,cant
[Ger] SATB,org/pno,2vln,vcl,bvl sc PETERS EM954 $4.00, ipa, voc sc PETERS EM954 $.80, ipa (B6130)
"Lord, Keep Us Steadfast In Thy Word" mix cor,2vln,cont CONCORDIA 97-6331 $.75, ipa (B6131)
(Grusnick, Bruno) [Eng/Ger/Swed] SATB,cont, 2vln&vcl/2vln, violone (med) BAREN. BA 3196 sc $3.50, cor pts $.65, ipa, cor pts $.65, ipa (B6132)

Erstanden Ist Der Heilig Christ *Easter,cant
(Hellmann) [Ger] SAB/SAT,cont,bsn,3vln HANSSLER 10.011 voc sc $2.00, cor pts $.50, ipa (B6133)

BUXTEHUDE, DIETRICH (cont'd.)

Every Word And Thought *see Alles, Was Ihr Tut

Fire Latinske Kantater *cant,Lat
[Lat] FOG III, 183 sc s.p., cor pts s.p., ipa
contains: Accedite Gentes (SSATB,cont, 2vln); Domine Salvum Fac Regem (SSATB, cont,2vln,2vla,vcl); Ecce Nunc Benedicite Domino (ATTB,cont,2vln); Pange Lingua Gloriosi (SSAB,org,2vln, 2vla,vcl) (B6134)

Fire Latinske Kantater *CC4U,cant
sc SAMFUNDET s.p. vocal score and string score available for each cantata (B6135)

Frohlocket Mit Handen
see Funf Chorkantaten

Funf Chorkantaten
HANSEN-DEN 29145 s.p., ipa
contains: Frohlocket Mit Handen (SSATB, cont,2trp,4vln); Man Singet Mit Freuden Vom Sieg (SSATB,cont,2trp,2vln,2vla); Nun Danket Alle Gott (SSATB,cont,2trom, 2vln, 2 cornetti); O Gott Wir Danken Deiner Gut (SSATB,cont,2vln); Wie Wird Erneuet, Wie Wird Erfreuet (SSATTB, cont,3trp,3trom,3vln) (B6136)

Furchtet Euch Nicht *Xmas,cant
(Goebel, Georg) [Ger] SATB,cont,2vln (med) MULLER SM 940 sc s.p., cor pts s.p. (B6137)

Furwahr, Er Trug Unsere Krankheit *Psntd, cant
mix cor,2vln,2vla,vcl HANSSLER 36.004 sc s.p., cor pts s.p., ipa (B6138)
(Grusnick, Bruno) [Eng/Ger] SSATB,SB soli, cont,2vln,vcl,bvl, 2 viola da gamba (med) BAREN. BA 1093 sc $4.50, cor pts $.65, ipa (B6139)

Gloria (from Missa Brevis)
see Buxtehude, Dietrich, Kyrie

God Shall Do My Advising *Gen
SATB,kbd (med easy) oct CONCORDIA 98-1449 $.30 (B6140)

God's Counsel Is My Wisdom
(Kjelson) SATB oct BELWIN 2235 $.30 (B6141)

Good Christian Men, Rejoice *Xmas
(Stone) SAB/SATB oct WORD CRS-15 $.35 (B6142)

Good Christian Men, With Joy Draw Near *see Ihr Lieben Christen, Freut Euch Nun

Gott Hilf Mir *cant
(Fedtke) 5 cor,2vln,2vla,vcl,bvl,cont HANSSLER 36.006 sc s.p., cor pts s.p., ipa (B6143)
(Sorenson, Soren) "Gud, Hjaelp Mig" [Ger/Dan] SSATB,B solo,org,2vln,2vla,vcl,bvl HANSEN-DEN 28424 s.p., ipa (B6144)

Gud, Hjaelp Mig *see Gott, Hilf Mir

Hark Ye! The Lord Comes With His Thousands *see Siehe! Der Herr Kommt Mit Viel Tausend

Herzlich Lieb Hab Ich Dich, O Herr *Trin, cant
(Grusnick, Bruno) [Ger] SSATB,cont,2trp, 2vln,2vla,vcl,bvl/2trp,2vln,2vla,vcl, violone (med) BAREN. BA 544 sc $5.25, cor pts $2.25, ipa (B6145)

Heut Triumphieret Gottes Sohn *Easter,cant
(Fedtke, Traugott) [Ger] SSATB,SSATB soli, org,cont,2trp,trom,2vln,2vla,vcl,bvl (med) BAREN. BA 1736 sc $9.75, cor pts $1.50, ipa (B6146)

Hva Trengsel Vi Pa Jorden Vet *cant
[Norw] mix cor,org/strings LYCHE 45 s.p. (B6147)

Ich Habe Lust, Abzuscheiden *ECY,cant
(Grusnick, Bruno) [Ger] SSB,cont&2vln&vcl& bvl/2vln&2vcl&bvl/cont&2vln, violone (med) BAREN. BA 894 sc $3.00, cor pts $.65, ipa (B6148)

Ich Halte Es Dafur, Dass Dieser Zeit Leiden *cant
(Trubel) SB,cont,vln,vla,vcl HANSSLER 10.037 sc s.p., cor pts s.p., ipa (B6149)

Ihr Lieben Christen, Freut Euch Nun *Adv/Gen,cant
[Ger] SSATB,B solo,org,orch KISTNER sc s.p., cor pts s.p., ipa (B6150)
(Gore, R.T.) "Good Christian Men, With Joy Draw Near" [Eng/Ger] SSATB,bvl,org/orch voc sc CONCORDIA 97-4724 $1.25 (B6151)
(Gore, R.T.) "Good Christian Men, With Joy Draw Near" [Ger] SSATB,bvl,org/orch sc CONCORDIA 97-4205 $3.00, ipa (B6152)
(Seiffert) SSATB,SB soli,cont,bsn,5trp, 3trom,3vln,2vla HANSSLER 10.018 cor pts s.p., voc sc s.p., ipa (B6153)

In Dulci Jubilo *Xmas,cant/mot
see Sacred Choruses
see Baroque To The Great Classics, The Vol. 4-1550 To 1700
[Swed] 3pt mix cor,org,2vln cor pts NORDISKA 1650 s.p., ipa (B6154)
[Eng/Ger] SAB,2vln,vcl,bvl HANSSLER 36.003 sc $2.50, cor pts $2.00, ipa (B6155)
cor voc sc KALMUS 6131 $1.25 (B6156)
AAB/SAB MUSICUS 011 $.30 (B6157)
"Now Sing We, Now Rejoice" SAB,2vln,cont sc CONCORDIA 98-1500 $1.00, cor pts CONCORDIA 98-1501 $.30, ipa (B6158)
"Now Sing We, Now Rejoice" SAB,kbd (med easy) sc CONCORDIA 98-1500 $1.00, cor pts CONCORDIA 98-1501 $.30 (B6159)
(Grusnick, Bruno) [Eng/Ger] SAB,cont&2vln/ 2vln&vcl (med easy) BAREN. BA 620 sc $2.75, cor pts $.65, ipa (B6160)

BUXTEHUDE, DIETRICH (cont'd.)

In Te Domine Speravi *cant
[Lat] voc sc PETERS HU1900 $1.00, ipr (B6161)
(Hedar) SAB,cont HANSEN-DEN sc s.p., cor pts s.p. (B6162)

In Te, Domine, Speravi *see Auf Dich, Herr, Hab' Ich Gehoffet

Infant Jesus, The *see Das Neugeborne Kindelein

Instruments, Waken And Publish Your Gladness *Easter/Gen
SAB,kbd (med easy) oct CONCORDIA 98-1422 $.25 (B6163)

Ist Es Recht, Dass Man Dem Kaiser Zinse Gebe Oder Nicht? *Trin,cant
(Grusnick, Bruno) [Ger] SSATB,ATB soli, cont&2vln&2vla&vcl&bvl/2vln&2vla&vcl, violone (med) BAREN. BA 1738 sc $4.25, cor pts $.75, ipa (B6164)

Jesu, Joy And Treasure *cant
SATB,SB/TB soli,org/pno,opt 2vln&vcl/bsn PETERS 6158 $.60, ipa (B6165)
SATB,S/TB soli,pno/pno&strings/strings voc sc HINRICHSEN H118 s.p. (B6166)

Jesu, Meine Freude *Psntd,cant
(Grusnick, Bruno) [Eng/Ger] SSB,opt SB soli,cont&bsn&2vln/cont&2vln&vcl (med easy) BAREN. BA 487 sc $3.25, cor pts $.40, ipa (B6167)
(Illing) SSB,kbd,cont,2vln,bsn ALBERT s.p. (B6168)

Jesu, Meines Lebens Leben *Psntd
(Kilian) [Ger] SATB,2fl,2vln,2vla,vcl (aria) BAREN. EM 959 sc s.p., cor pts s.p., ipa (B6169)
(Kilian, Dietrich) [Ger] SATB,fl,strings, cont HINRICHSEN EM959 voc sc s.p., sc s.p. (B6170)

Jesu, My Heart's Treasure
cor voc sc KALMUS 6130 $1.25, ipa (B6171)

Kantaten *cant
(Sachsens; Steude) [Ger] cor,org,brass, strings voc sc DEUTSCHER 7902 s.p., cor pts DEUTSCHER 7902A s.p. (B6172)

Kommst Du, Kommst Du, Licht Der Heiden *cant
(Hedar) SSB,org,strings HANSEN-DEN sc s.p., ipa, cor pts s.p. (B6173)
(Horn) SAB/SSB,cont,2vln,2vla HANSSLER 10.005 sc s.p., cor pts s.p., ipa (B6174)

Kyrie (from Missa Brevis) Gloria/Kyrie/Mass
(Gurlitt, Wilibald) [Lat] SSATB,cont (med) BAREN. BA 265 $3.25 contains also: Gloria (B6175)

Kyrie Eleison *Kyrie
(Granville) "Lord, Have Mercy Upon Us" SSATB,acap oct FOX CM6 $.30 (B6176)

Lauda Sion
[Lat] voc sc PETERS HU1909 $1.00, ipr (B6177)

Lauda Sion Salvatorem *Xmas,cant
HANSEN-DEN sc s.p., cor pts s.p. (B6178)
(Grusnick, Bruno) [Eng/Lat] SSB,opt SB soli,cont,2vln,2vcl (med) BAREN. BA 481A sc $2.50, cor pts $1.50, ipa (B6179)

Liebster Herr Jesu *Gen
(Ehret) "Dearest Lord Jesus" SSATB SCHMITT 1418 $.30 (B6180)

Little Newborn Jesus Child, The *see Das Neugeborne Kindelein

Lobet, Christen, Euren Heiland *Xmas,cant
(Grusnick, Bruno) [Ger] SSB,opt SB soli, cont,2vln,2vla (med) BAREN. BA 481 sc $2.50, cor pts $1.50, ipa (B6181)

Lobsinget Gott, Dem Herrn *Easter/Pent,mot
"Cantate Domino" see Sacred Choruses
(Grusnick, Bruno) "Cantate Domino" [Ger/Lat] SSB,opt SB soli,cont (med) BAREN. BA 542 sc $2.50, cor pts $.65 (B6182)

Lord, Have Mercy Upon Us *see Kyrie Eleison

Lord, Keep Us Steadfast In Thy Word *see Erhalt Uns, Herr, Bei Deinem Wort

Magnificat *Magnif
[Eng/Lat] SSATB (med) PRESSER 312-40987 $.60 (B6183)
mix cor,2vln,2vla,vcl HANSSLER 36.005 sc s.p., voc sc s.p., ipa (B6184)
(Pinkham) SSATB,org/pno voc sc PETERS 66288 $.75, ipa, ipr (B6185)
(Sahlin, Ingvar) [Swed] cor pts NORDISKA 1476 s.p., ipa (B6186)

Magnificat Anima Mea *Magnif
cor,strings voc sc KALMUS 6134 $1.25, ipa (B6187)
(Grusnick, Bruno) [Lat] SSATB,3vln,vla,1-2vcl,bvl,opt cont (med) BAREN. BA 543 sc $4.00, cor pts $.65, ipa (B6188)

Man Singet Mit Freuden Vom Sieg *cant
see Funf Chorkantaten
(Fedtke) SSATB,org,bsn,2trp,2vln,opt 2vla/trom&vcl,bvl HANSSLER 10.200 sc s.p., voc sc s.p., ipa (B6189)

Membra Jesu Nostri *Psntd,cant
(Grusnick, Bruno) [Lat] SSATB,SSATB soli, cont,strings (med diff, cyclically composed for Passiontide) sc BAREN. BA 3463 $13.25 (B6190)
(Kilian) [Lat] 5pt mix cor,SSATB soli,3vln, 2vla,vcl sc BAREN. EM 989 s.p., voc sc BAREN. EM 990 s.p., cor pts BAREN. EM 991 s.p., ipa (B6191)

Min Gud Er Med Mig *see Der Herr Ist Mit Mir

Missa Brevis
SSATB oct PRESSER 352-00023 $.50 (B6192)
cor voc sc KALMUS 6132 $1.25 (B6193)

BUXTEHUDE, DIETRICH (cont'd.)

Mit Fried Und Freud Ich Fahr Dahin *cant
(Fedtke, Traugott) [Ger] AB,cont&vln&2vla&bvl/ob&2bsn, English horn (med easy) BAREN. BA 1735 sc $3.50, cor pts $.50, ipa (B6194)

My Hearts Treasure
see Sacred Choruses
see Baroque To The Great Classics, The Vol. 4-1550 To 1700

My Jesus Is My Lasting Joy
(Bitgood) unis oct GRAY GCMR 2727 $.25 (B6195)

Neun Kantaten *CC9U,cant
(Kilian) [Ger] mix cor,soli,cont,strings voc sc DEUTSCHER 4753 FSP s.p. (B6196)

Newborn Babe, The *see Das Neugeborne Kindelein

Nicht Soll Uns Scheiden Von Der Liebe Gottes *cant
(Liechti, Paul) SSA,org,cont/kbd,2vln,vcl KROMPHOLZ s.p., ipa (B6197)

Nichts Soll Uns Scheiden Von Der Liebe Gottes *cant
(Hjorth, Gunnar) "Vad Kan Oss Skilja Fran Guds Karlek" [Swed/Ger] 3pt mix cor, strings,org NORDISKA 3553 voc sc s.p., ipa, cor pts s.p. (B6198)
(Trubel) SAT/SAB,SABar soli,cont,vln/2vln HANSSLER 10.020 cor pts s.p., voc sc s.p., ipa (B6199)

Nimm Von Uns, Herr, Du Treuer Gott *ECY/Trin,cant
(Grusnick, Bruno) [Ger] SATB,cont&bsn&2vln&2vla/2vln&2vla&vcl&bvl (med) BAREN. BA 776 sc $3.75, cor pts $1.50, ipa (B6200)
(Grusnick, Bruno) [Ger] SATB,cont&bsn&2vln&2vla/2vln&2vla&2vcl&bvl (med) BAREN. BA 776 sc $3.75, cor pts $1.50, ipa (B6201)

Now Sing We, Now Rejoice *see In Dulci Jubilo

Nun Danket Alle Gott
see Funf Chorkantaten

Nun Lasst Uns Gott, Dem Herren, Dank Sagen
[Ger] SATB,org/pno,2vln,vcl sc PETERS EM951 $4.00, ipa, voc sc PETERS EM951 $.80, ipa (B6202)

O Frohliche Stunden, O Herrliche Zeit *Easter,cant
(Kilian) [Ger] SSAB,2vln,2vla,bvl BAREN. EM 961 sc s.p., cor pts s.p., ipa (B6203)

O Gott Wir Danken Deiner Gut
see Funf Chorkantaten

Oh, How Blessed *Commun/Gen
TB/ATB,2vln,vcl (med easy) oct CONCORDIA 98-1485 $.30, ipa (B6204)

Open To Me Gates Of Justice *see Aperite Mihi Portas

Pange Lingua Gloriosi
see Fire Latinske Kantater

Psalm 95 *see Afferte Domino

Psalm 96 *see Cantate Domini

Psalm 118 *see Aperite Mihi Portas

Psalm 134 *see Siehe, Lobet Den Herrn

Rejoice, Beloved Christians *Adv,cant
cor,2vln,vcl BELWIN $1.25, ipa (B6205)

Rejoice, Earth And Heaven *cant
SATB,org/pno,2trp,2vln,vcl/bvl/bsn voc sc PETERS 6633 $.60, ipa (B6206)

Sacred Choruses
cor min sc KALMUS 884 $1.30
contains: Behold, He Bore All Our Infirmities; Cantate Domino; In Dulci Jubilo; My Hearts Treasure; Newborn Babe, The (B6207)

Salve, Jesu, Patris *cant
[Lat] mix cor,strings HANSSLER 10.284 sc s.p., cor pts s.p., ipa (B6208)

Sand Ut Din Angel, Fader Kar *see Befiehl Dem Engel, Dass Er Komm

Schlagt, Kunstler, Die Pauken *Xmas/Easter/Marriage,cant
(Kilian) [Ger] SSAB,SSAB soli,bsn&2trp&2vln&vcl&drums/2trp&2vla&vcl, violone BAREN. EM 976 sc s.p., cor pts s.p. contains also: Erfreue Dich, Erde (B6209)

Schwinget Euch Himmelan, Herzen Und Sinne *Fest/Gen,cant
(Grusnick, Bruno) [Ger] SATB,SSATB soli, cont,org,3vln (med) BAREN. BA 3366 sc $4.75, cor pts $1.50, ipa (B6210)

Send Hid Din Engel, Herre From *see Befiehl Dem Engel, Dass Er Komm

Siehe! Der Herr Kommt Mit Viel Tausend *Adv/Xmas
(Granville) "Hark Ye! The Lord Comes With His Thousands" SATB oct FOX CM23 $.35 (B6211)

Siehe, Lobet Den Herrn (Psalm 134) cant
(Kilian) "Ecce Nunc Benedicite Domino" [Ger/Lat] ATTB,ATTB soli,2vln,vla,vcl BAREN. EM 971 sc s.p., cor pts s.p., ipa (B6212)

Sing To God The Lord *see Cantate Domino

Vad Kan Oss Skilja Fran Guds Karlek *see Nichts Soll Uns Scheiden Von Der Liebe Gottes

BUXTEHUDE, DIETRICH (cont'd.)

Wachet Auf, Ruft Uns Die Stimme *Adv/ECY/Gen,cant
SAB,SB soli,cont,bsn,4vln HANSSLER 10.189 sc s.p., voc sc s.p., ipa (B6213)
"Wake, Awake, For Night Is Flying" [Ger/Eng] SAB,4vln,cont sc CONCORDIA 97-4714 $2.25, cor pts CONCORDIA 97-4765 $.75, ipa (B6214)
(Breshears, D.L.) "Wake, Awake For Night Is Flying" SAB,opt soli,4vln,bsn,bvl,cont (med) sc AUGSBURG 11-9530 $2.25, ipa, cor pts AUGSBURG 11-9531 $.50 (B6215)
(Fedtke, Traugott) [Ger] ATB,2vln,vcl,bvl (med) BAREN. BA 1734 sc $6.50, cor pts $1.50, ipa (B6216)

Wake, Awake, For Night Is Flying *see Wachet Auf, Ruft Uns Die Stimme

Walts Gott, Mein Werk Ich Lasse
[Ger] SATB,org/pno,2vln,vcl sc PETERS EM953 $4.00, ipa, voc sc PETERS EM953 $.80, ipa (B6217)

War Gott Nicht Mit Uns Diese Zeit
[Ger] SATB,org/pno,2vln,vcl sc PETERS EM952 $4.00, ipa, voc sc PETERS EM952 $.80, ipa (B6218)

Was Frag' Ich Nach Der Welt
(Wunderlich, R.) "What Is The World To Me" SAB,org CONCORDIA 97-6357 $1.25, ipr (B6219)

Was Frag' Ich Ncah Der Welt *cant
(Trubel) SAB,cont,2vln,vcl HANSSLER 10.111 sc s.p., voc sc s.p., ipa (B6220)

What Is The World To Me *see Was Frag' Ich Nach Der Welt

Whatsoe'er Ye Do *see Alles, Was Ihr Tut

Wie Soll Ich Dich Empfangen *cant
[Ger] SSB,org/pno,2vln,vcl,bsn sc PETERS EM921 $3.50, ipa, voc sc PETERS EM921 $.80, ipa (B6221)

Wie Wird Erneuet, Wie Wird Erfreuet
see Funf Chorkantaten

Wo Soll Ich Fliehen Hin *cant
(Kilian, Dietrich) [Ger] SATB,SATB soli, org,strings HINRICHSEN EM914 voc sc s.p., sc s.p. (B6222)

Zion Hears The Watchmen Singing *see Zion Hort Die Wachter Singen

Zion Hort Die Wachter Singen (from Wachet Auf)
"Zion Hears The Watchmen Singing" boy cor SOUTHERN $.30 (B6223)
(Clough-Leighter, H.) "Zion Hears The Watchmen Singing" TB,org/pno SCHIRM.EC 538 $.25 (B6224)
(Track, G.) 2pt wom cor,opt pno/org DOBLINGER voc sc s.p., cor pts s.p. (B6225)
(Wiedemann, M.) [Ger] men cor,pno/org HUG s.p. (B6226)

BY BABEL'S STREAM WE SAT AND WEPT see Hopkins

BY BABYLON'S WAVE see Gounod, Charles Francois

BY-BY-BABY, LULLAY see Nixon

BY CHRIST REDEEMED see Lovelace, Austin C.

BY COOL SILOAM
(Roberton, H.S.) TTBB PATERSON 1653 s.p. (B6227)

BY COOL SILOAM'S SHADY RILL see Woodbury

BY EARLY MORNING LIGHT see Reimann, [Johann Balthasar]

BY THE MANGER see Rogers, David

BY THE NAME WE BOW BEFORE see Schalk, Carl

BY THE RIVER OF BABYLON see Lassus, Roland de (Orlandus), Super Flumina Babylonis

BY THE RIVERS OF BABYLON
(Young, R.; Weinandt, E.) SATB,acap oct FISCHER,J 10006 $.35 (B6228)

BY THE RIVERS OF BABYLON see Amram, David Werner

BY THE RIVERS OF BABYLON see Bantock, Granville

BY THE RIVERS OF BABYLON see Henning, Ervin Arthur

BY THE RIVERS OF BABYLON see Kantor, J.

BY THE RIVERS OF BABYLON see Loeffler, Charles Martin

BY THE RIVERS OF BABYLON see Noyes, E.P.

BY THE SEPULCHRE see Krenek, Ernst

BY THE SHORES OF THE JORDAN see Engel, J.

BY THE WATERS OF BABYLON see Bach, Johann Sebastian

BY THE WATERS OF BABYLON see Dvorak, Antonin

BY THE WATERS OF BABYLON see Howell, C.

BY THE WATERS OF BABYLON see Humfrey, Pelham

BY THE WATERS OF BABYLON see James, Philip

BY THE WATERS OF BABYLON see McCormick

BY THE WATERS OF BABYLON see Mawby, C.

BY THE WATERS OF BABYLON see Muller, H.

BY THE WATERS OF BABYLON see Nares, James

BY THE WATERS OF BABYLON see Palestrina, Giovanni

BY THE WATERS OF BABYLON see Wills, Arthur

BY THE WATERS OF BABYLON see Young

BY THEE WITH BLISS see Haydn, (Franz) Joseph

BY THY BIRTH THOU BLESSED LORD see Hubicki

BY THY WOUNDS AND THORNCROWNED HEAD see Schalk, Carl

BY WHAT MASTER HAND see Palestrina, Giovanni, Da Cosi Dotta Man

BYE AN' BYE
(Turner, E.) SSA,acap oct PRESSER 312-40677 $.25 (B6229)

BYE AND BYE *spir
(Luboff, Norman) SSATTB oct WALTON 3044 $.30 (B6230)

BYLES
Be Still And Know
SATB oct LORENZ C23 $.25 (B6231)

I Walk With God
SA oct LORENZ 5351 $.25 (B6232)

We Thank Thee
unis oct LORENZ 8620 $.25 (B6233)

BYLES, B. D.
Abiding Joy
3pt mix cor oct SCHIRM.G 10908 $.25 (B6234)

Before The Paling Of The Stars *Xmas
4pt mix cor oct SCHIRM.G 11189 $.25 (B6235)

Bethlehem Road *Xmas
2pt wom cor oct SCHIRM.G 10756 $.20 (B6236)
3pt wom cor oct SCHIRM.G 10775 $.25 (B6237)

Carol, A *Xmas
unis oct SCHIRM.G 10514 $.20 (B6238)
3pt wom cor oct SCHIRM.G 10842 $.20 (B6239)

Child's Present To His Savior, A *Xmas
unis oct SCHIRM.G 11140 $.25 (B6240)
4pt mix cor oct SCHIRM.G 11141 $.25 (B6241)
3pt wom cor oct SCHIRM.G 11142 $.25 (B6242)

Christmas Folk Song, A *Xmas
2pt boy cor/2pt wom cor oct SCHIRM.G 10513 $.25 (B6243)

De Promis' Lan'
4pt mix cor oct SCHIRM.G 10655 $.25 (B6244)

Desert Shall Rejoice, The *Gen
SATB,A solo SCHMITT 1699 $.25 (B6245)

Easter Carol *Easter
2pt wom cor oct SCHIRM.G 10407 $.20 (B6246)

God Bless The Little Things
3pt wom cor,org/pno oct SCHIRM.G 10363 $.20 (B6247)
3pt mix cor,org/pno oct SCHIRM.G 10364 $.20 (B6248)
4pt mix cor,org/pno oct SCHIRM.G 10365 $.25 (B6249)
2pt boy cor oct SCHIRM.G 10209 $.25 (B6250)

Page's Road Song, A
unis oct SCHIRM.G 11139 $.25 (B6251)

BY'M BY see Lockwood, Normand

BYRD, WILLIAM (1543-1623)
Agnus Dei (from Mass For Five Voices)
SATTB,acap SCHIRM.EC $.20 (B6252)
(Mishkin, H.) [Lat] TTBB,acap SCHIRM.EC 2145 $.20 (B6253)

All Hail True Body *see Ave Verum Corpus

Alleluia! The Disciples With Wondering Eyes *anthem
(Terry, R.R.) mix cor oct NOVELLO 88.0001.04 s.p. (B6254)

Arise, Shine Forth In Splendor *anthem
(Terry, R.R.) mix cor oct NOVELLO 52.0006.07 s.p. (B6255)

Assumpta Est Maria *Offer
SATBB,acap SCHIRM.EC $.16 (B6256)
(Collins, H.B.) [Lat] SATTB/SATBarB CHESTER s.p. (B6257)

Ave Maria *mot
SATBB,acap SCHIRM.EC $.16 (B6258)
(Knight, Gerald) SATB,acap oct FISCHER,C CM-7500 $.25 (B6259)
(Steele, Jonathan) [Lat] SATB/SATBarB CHESTER s.p. (B6260)

Ave Regina
SATB,acap SCHIRM.EC $.25 (B6261)

Ave Regina Caelorum *mot
see TRE ENGELSKA MOTETTER
(Collins, H.B.) [Lat] SATB CHESTER s.p. (B6262)

Ave Verum Corpus (from Gradualia, Liber I) Commun/Corpus/Easter/Lent/Psntd,anthem
4pt mix cor MOSELER LB-727 s.p. (B6263)
mix cor SOUTHERN $.30 (B6264)
"All Hail True Body" SATB STAINER CC520 s.p. (B6265)
"Hail, O Hail" SATB,acap (med) OXFORD 43.232 $.35 (B6266)
"Hail, O Hail, True Body" SATB,acap (med) oct OXFORD 43.232 $.35 (B6267)
"Hail, Oh Hail, True Body" SATB,acap SCHIRM.EC 393 $.30 (B6268)
"Hail True Body" [Lat/Eng] SATB,acap PETERS H1552 (B6269)
(Davison, A.) [Lat] TTBB,acap SCHIRM.EC 919 $.30 (B6270)
(Greenberg) [Eng/Lat] SATB,acap AMP N7 $.35 (B6271)
(Greyson) "O Lord, Great Creator" SATB oct BOURNE ES44 $.35 (B6272)
(Morehen, J.) [Lat] SATB BROUDE,A. 215 $.30 (B6273)

Baroque To The Great Classics, The Vol. 1-1550 To 1700 *CCU
mix cor min sc KALMUS 709 $1.30 contains

BYRD, WILLIAM (cont'd.)

keyboard & choral works　　　(B6274)

Be Glad, Ye Heavens　*see Laetentur Coeli

Beata Es
SATTB,acap SCHIRM.EC $.25　　(B6275)

Beata Es, Virgo Maria　*Offer
(Collins, H.B.) [Lat] SATTB/SATBarB CHESTER
s.p.　　　(B6276)

Beata Virgo　*Fest
[Lat] SATB,acap (med easy) MULLER MS 19
s.p.　　　(B6277)

Beata Viscera　*Adv
SATBB,acap SCHIRM.EC $.25　　(B6278)

Beata Viscera Mariae Virginis　*anti
(Petti, Anthony G.) [Lat] SATTB/SATBarB
CHESTER s.p.　　　(B6279)

Benedictus (from Great Service)
see Byrd, William, Te Deum

Bow Thine Ear, O Lord　*see Civitas Sancti
Tui

Bread Of The Living　*see Ego Sum Panis Vivus

Cantate Domino (from Sacrarum Cantionum,
Liber II) anthem
mix cor oct OXFORD 43.246 $.35　(B6280)
"With Voice Of Melody" OXFORD　(B6281)
"With Voice Of Melody" SSATBB,acap
SCHIRM.EC 392 $.20　　(B6282)

Cantiones Quatuor Vocum Vol. 1　*CCU,anthem
mix cor,acap voc sc KALMUS 6665 $1.35
　　　(B6283)

Cantiones Quatuor Vocum Vol. 2　*CCU
mix cor,acap voc sc KALMUS 6666 $1.35
　　　(B6284)

Cantiones Quinque Vocum　*CCU,anthem
5pt mix cor,acap voc sc KALMUS 6659 $.80
　　　(B6285)

Cast Off Doubtful Care　*anthem
SSAT STAINER CC246 s.p.　　(B6286)

Christe Qui Lux　*Eve/Lent
"O Christ, Who Art The Light And Day"
SATBB,acap (med easy) oct OXFORD 43.253
$.30　　　(B6287)

Christe, Qui Lux Es
"O Christ Who Art" SATBB,acap (med) OXFORD
43.253 $.30　　(B6288)

Christe, Qui Lux Es Et Dies
"O Christ, Who Art The Light And Day" [Lat/
Eng] SATBB,acap PETERS H1504 $.40　(B6289)

Christus Resurgens Ex Mortuis　*Easter,mot
SATB,acap SCHIRM.EC $.25　　(B6290)
(Collins, H.B.) [Lat] SATTB/SATBarB CHESTER
s.p.　　　(B6291)

Civitas Sancti Tui　*Lent/Psntd,mot
SATBB,acap SCHIRM.EC $.25　　(B6292)
"Bow Thine Ear, O Lord" SATTB (med) oct
OXFORD 43.346 $.65　　(B6293)
(Petti, Anthony G.) "Holy City, The" [Eng/
Lat] SATBarB CHESTER s.p.　(B6294)

Come Thou Holy Spirit　*mot
SSATB STAINER CC418 s.p.　　(B6295)

Come Ye With Psalmody　*Introit
SSATB STAINER CC417 s.p.　　(B6296)

Communion Service (from Mass For Three
Voices) Commun
ATB STAINER CS235 s.p.　　(B6297)

Confirma Hoc, Deus　*Cnfrm/Whitsun,Offer
SSATB,acap SCHIRM.EC $.16　　(B6298)
(Collins, H.B.) [Lat] SSATB CHESTER s.p.
　　　(B6299)

Cradle Song　*Xmas,carol/cradle
SSA,pno STAINER PS276 s.p.　(B6300)
SATB,org STAINER CC477 s.p.　(B6301)
(Fellowes, Edmund H.) SATB,pno STAINER
CC477 $.25　　(B6302)

Cristmas Carols　*CCU,Xmas,carol
[Eng/Ger] 5-6pt mix cor,opt inst cor pts
HANSEN-DEN s.p.　　(B6303)

Day Most Holy　*see Dies Sanctificatus

Dies Sanctificatus　*Xmas
(Ehret) "Day Most Holy" SATB,acap,opt pno
oct PRO ART 2277 $.25　　(B6304)

Earthly Tree, A Heavenly Fruit, An
SS,org STAINER CC246 s.p.　(B6305)

Ego Sum Panis Vivus　*Commun/Easter/Lent,mot
SATB,acap SCHIRM.EC $.30　　(B6306)
(Collins, H.B.) [Lat] SATB CHESTER s.p.
　　　(B6307)
(Greyson) "Bread Of The Living" SATB oct
BOURNE ES89 $.25　　(B6308)

Emendemus In Melius　*anthem
SATTB STAINER CC521 s.p.　　(B6309)

Exsurge, Domine (Psalm 44) Gen/Sexa
SATTB,opt inst oct OXFORD 43.074 $.50
　　　(B6310)

First And Second Preces And Psalms　*Psalm
mix cor,acap KALMUS 6653 $1.00　(B6311)

From Depth Of Sin
(Greyson) SATB oct BOURNE ES77 $.30　(B6312)

Gradualia, Liber I　*CCU,anthem
mix cor,acap voc sc KALMUS 6658 $.80
　　　(B6313)

Gradualia, Liber II　*CC11U,anthem
3pt mix cor,acap voc sc KALMUS 6667 $.84　(B6314)

Great Service　*Credo/Kyrie/Mass
SSAATTBB,acap (diff) oct OXFORD 43.601
$2.60　　　(B6315)
mix cor,acap KALMUS 6657 $1.75　(B6316)

BYRD, WILLIAM (cont'd.)

Haec Dies　*Ded/Easter/Fest,anthem
"Sing Praises To God This Holy Day" SSATTB,
acap (diff) oct CONCORDIA 98-2091 $.50
　　　(B6317)
"This Glad Day" SSATTBB,acap (diff) OXFORD
43.078 $.35　　(B6318)
"This Glad Day" SSATTB,acap (med) oct
OXFORD 43.078 $.35　　(B6319)
"This Is The Day" SATB oct GRAY GCMR 3093
$.25　　　(B6320)
(Nott) "Sing Praises To God This Holy Day"
SATB oct SOUTHERN $.50　(B6321)
(Terry, R.R.) [Lat] SSATTB oct NOVELLO
52.0024.05 s.p.　　(B6322)
(Terry, R.R.) "This Is The Day" SSATTB oct
NOVELLO 52.0024.05 s.p.　(B6323)

Hail, O Hail　*see Ave, Verum Corpus

Hail, O Hail, True Body　*see Ave Verum
Corpus

Hail, Oh Hail, True Body　*see Ave Verum
Corpus

Hail True Body　*see Ave Verum Corpus

Hodie Beata Virgo　*anthem
[Lat] mix cor oct NOVELLO 28.1415.03 s.p.
　　　(B6324)
(Rose, Bernard) "On This Day" mix cor oct
NOVELLO 28.1415.03 s.p.　(B6325)

Holy City, The　*see Civitas Sancti Tui

I Have Longed For Thy Saving Health
(Whitehead) SATB oct GRAY GCMR 1679 $.30
　　　(B6326)

I Laid Me Down To Rest
SSAATB,acap PETERS H1553 $.40　(B6327)

I Will Not Leave You Comfortless　*see Non
Vos Relinquam

If Ye Love Me Keep My Commandments　*anthem
mix cor,acap NOVELLO 40.1230.05 s.p.　(B6328)

In Annuntiatione B. Mariae
see Byrd, William, Post Septuagesima

In Ascensione Domini　*Asc
5pt mix cor,acap voc sc KALMUS 6671 $.80
　　　(B6329)

In Assumptione B. Mariae Virginis
mix cor,acap voc sc KALMUS 6664 $1.00
contains also: In Festo Omnium Sanctorum
　　　(B6330)

In Epiphania Domini
mix cor,acap voc sc KALMUS 6669 $1.00
contains also: Post Pascha　(B6331)

In Festo Omnium Sanctorum
see Byrd, William, In Assumptione B. Mariae
Virginis

In Festo Penecostes　*Pent
5pt mix cor,acap voc sc KALMUS 6672 $.80
　　　(B6332)

In Festo Purificationis
mix cor,acap voc sc KALMUS 6660 $.80　(B6333)

In Manus Tuas　*Psntd,anthem
[Lat] SATB,acap PETERS WM38 $.50　(B6334)
[Lat] SATB,acap (med) MULLER MS 38 s.p.
　　　(B6335)
[Lat] mix cor,acap oct NOVELLO MS-38 s.p.
　　　(B6336)

In Nativitate Domini　*Xmas
4pt mix cor,acap voc sc KALMUS 6668 $.80
　　　(B6337)

In Nativitate Mariae Virginis　*Xmas
mix cor,acap voc sc KALMUS 6661 $.80
　　　(B6338)

In Tempore Paschali　*Easter
5pt mix cor,acap voc sc KALMUS 6670 $1.00
　　　(B6339)

In The Temple Do The Priests　*anthem
SATB STAINER CC415 s.p.　　(B6340)

Iustorum Animae　*anthem
SSATB STAINER CC312 s.p.　　(B6341)
"Souls Of The Righteous, The" SSATB,acap
SCHIRM.EC 327 $.22　　(B6342)
(Bement, G.) "Souls Of The Righteous, The"
SSAA,acap SCHIRM.EC 1891 $.25　(B6343)
(Davison, A.) "Souls Of The Righteous The"
[Lat/Eng] TTBB,acap SCHIRM.EC 90 $.18
　　　(B6344)

Laetentur Coeli　*Adv
"Be Glad, Ye Heavens" SATBB,acap (med) oct
OXFORD $.50　　(B6345)
(Fellows) "Be Glad, Ye Heavens" SATBB,acap
(diff) OXFORD 43.704 $.50　(B6346)

Laudibus In Sanctis　*anthem
SSATB STAINER CC528 s.p.　　(B6347)

Look Down, O Lord　*Easter/Lent
SATB SCHIRM.EC 2431 $.30　　(B6348)
(Greyson) SATB oct BOURNE ES58 $.25　(B6349)
(Mattfeld, V.) SATB,acap SCHIRM.EC 2431
$.30　　　(B6350)
(Wulstan) AATB CHESTER s.p.　(B6351)

Look On Him, Man Of Sorrows
(Ehret) SATB oct SHAPIRO SK 2112 $.25
　　　(B6352)

Looke Downe, O Lord　*anthem
(Bridge, J.F.) mix cor oct NOVELLO
40.1213.05 s.p.　　(B6353)

Lord, Do Not Crush Us With Thy Wrath　*see Ne
Irascaris Domine

Lord God Almighty　*anthem
SSATB STAINER CC407 s.p.　　(B6354)

Lord, Hear My Prayer
(Greyson) SATB oct BOURNE ES107 $.30
　　　(B6355)

Lord In Thy Rage
(Greenberg) STB/SAT/SATB/SSA/TTB,acap AMP
N5 $.30　　　(B6356)

Lord Now Lettest Thou Thy Servant Depart In
Peace
(Ehret) SATB oct SHAPIRO SK 2115 $.25

BYRD, WILLIAM (cont'd.)

　　　(B6357)

Lullaby, My Sweet Little Baby-Parts 1 & 2
*cradle
SATB STAINER M14-32 s.p.　(B6358)

Magnificat And Nunc Dimittis　*Magnif/Nunc
SATB oct NOVELLO 44.0892.06 s.p.　(B6359)
SAATTB,acap (med) oct OXFORD 43.280 $.65
see from Short Service　(B6360)

Mass For Five Voices　*Mass
[Lat] SATB min sc PETERS E999 $3.50　(B6361)
[Lat] SATTB STAINER CS357 s.p.　(B6362)
(Terry) 5pt voc sc CURWEN C03706 s.p.
　　　(B6363)
(Washington, Henry) [Lat] SATTB CHESTER
s.p.　　　(B6364)

Mass For Four Voices　*Mass
[Lat] SATB,opt org min sc PETERS E997 $3.50
　　　(B6365)
[Lat] SATB STAINER CS231 s.p.　(B6366)
(Washington, Henry) [Lat] SATB CHESTER s.p.
　　　(B6367)

Mass For Three Voices　*Mass
[Lat] STB/ATB,opt org min sc PETERS E998
$3.50　　　(B6368)
[Lat] ATB STAINER CS230 s.p.　(B6369)
(Washington, Henry) [Lat] STB CHESTER s.p.
　　　(B6370)

Ne Irascaris
(Le Huray, P.) "O Lord, Turn Thy Wrath"
[Lat/Eng] SATTB,org BROUDE.A. 216 $.35
　　　(B6371)

Ne Irascaris Domine　*mot
(Petti, Anthony G.) "Lord, Do Not Crush Us
With Thy Wrath" [Eng/Lat] SATTB/SATBarB
CHESTER s.p.　　(B6372)

Non Nobis Domine
see THREE FAMOUS CANONS
"Not Unto Us, O Lord" see RESPONSES FROM
THE WORKS OF OLD MASTERS
[Lat] TTB ALLANS 178 s.p.　(B6373)
SAB STAINER s.p.　　(B6374)
[Lat] SSA,acap oct NOVELLO 48.1895.04 s.p.
　　　(B6375)

Non Vos Relinquam (from Gradulia, Liber II)
Asc/Easter/Lent/Pent,anthem
"I Will Not Leave You Comfortless" SATB
BELWIN AP 27 $.35　　(B6376)
"I Will Not Leave You Comfortless" SSATB,
acap SCHIRM.EC 1676 $.25　(B6377)
(Davison, A.) "I Will Not Leave You
Comfortless" TTBB,acap SCHIRM.EC 951 $.20
　　　(B6378)
(Marshall) "I Will Not Leave You
Comfortless" SATB oct SOUTHERN $.35
　　　(B6379)
(Marshall, Charles) "I Will Not Leave You
Comfortless" SSATB FRANK F-578 $.35
　　　(B6380)
(McKie, W.) "I Will Not Leave You
Comfortless" SSATB oct NOVELLO 28.0790.04
s.p.　　　(B6381)

Non Vos Relinquam Orphanos　*Whitsun,anti
SSATB,acap SCHIRM.EC 2431 $.18　(B6382)
(Collins, H.B.) [Lat] SSATB/SSTTB CHESTER
s.p.　　　(B6383)

Not Unto Us, O Lord　*see Non Nobis Domine

Now Amend We Our Sinful Lives　*anthem
SATTB STAINER CC521 s.p.　(B6384)

O Blessed Nativity　*see O Magnum Mysterium

O Christ Who Art　*see Christe, Qui Lux Es

O Christ, Who Art The Light And Day　*see
Christe Qui Lux

O Christ, Who Art The Light And Day　*see
Christe, Qui Lux Es Et Dies

O Come, Let Us Sing Unto The Lord　*see
Venite

O Holy And Heavenly Feast　*anthem
(Terry, R.R.) mix cor oct NOVELLO
52.0017.02 s.p.　　(B6385)

O Jesu Blessed Lord, To Thee　*Gen
(Brown) SATB SCHMITT 1685 $.35　(B6386)

O Lord, Great Creator　*see Ave Verum Corpus

O Lord, Make Thy Servant, Elizabeth　*Royal
SATTB,acap (med) oct OXFORD 43.324 $.35
　　　(B6387)

O Lord Our God
(Davis, K.K.) SATB ALFRED 6702 $.25　(B6388)

O Lord, Turn Thy Wrath　*see Ne Irascaris

O Magnum Mysterium　*Xmas,anthem/mot
SATB STAINER CC330 s.p.　(B6389)
SATB,acap SCHIRM.EC $.25　(B6390)
(Collins, H.B.) [Lat] SATB CHESTER s.p.
　　　(B6391)
(Payson, A.) "O Blessed Nativity" SATB,acap
FRANK F-540 $.35　　(B6392)

O Quam Gloriosum　*ASD
"Who Can Tell The Glory" SSATB,acap (med
diff) OXFORD 43.298 $.65　(B6393)
"Who Can Tell The Glory" SSATB,acap (med)
oct OXFORD 43.298 $.65　(B6394)

O Quam Suavis　*Commun
SATB,acap SCHIRM.EC $.25　(B6395)

O Quam Suavis Est, Domine　*anti
(Collins, H.B.) [Lat] SATB CHESTER s.p.
　　　(B6396)

O Rex Gloria
SSATB,acap SCHIRM.EC $.16　(B6397)

O Rex Gloriae　*anti
(Collins, H.B.) [Lat] SSATB CHESTER s.p.
　　　(B6398)

O Sacrum Convivium　*Commun,anti/anthem
SATB,acap SCHIRM.EC $.25　(B6399)
(Collins, H.B.) [Lat] SATB CHESTER s.p.
　　　(B6400)
(Terry, R.R.) [Lat] mix cor oct NOVELLO

BYRD, WILLIAM (cont'd.)

52.0017.02 s.p.   (B6401)

On This Day *see Hodie Beata Virgo

Out Of The Orient *Xmas,carol
(Dart, Thurston) S/SA,pno/org STAINER CC599
$.35   (B6402)

Passion According To St. John, The
SAB,narrator/soli sc CONCORDIA 97-4868
$2.00, cor pts CONCORDIA 97-4818 $.75
                                                (B6403)

Post Nativitatem Domini
see Byrd, William, Pro Adventu

Post Pascha
see Byrd, William, In Epiphania Domini

Post Septuagesima
mix cor,acap voc sc KALMUS 6663 $.80
contains also: In Annuntiatione B. Mariae
                                                (B6404)

Praise Our Lord All Ye Gentiles *anthem
SSATBB STAINER CC242 s.p.   (B6405)

Praise The Lord Among His Holy Ones *anthem
SSATB STAINER CC528 s.p.   (B6406)

Prevent Us, O Lord
SATB,opt inst (med easy) OXFORD 43.305 $.35
contains also: Aubert, Pierre Francois
Oliver, O God Who By The Leading Of A
Star   (B6407)

Prevent Us O Lord, In All Our Doings *Gen
SAATB,acap (med) oct OXFORD 43.238 $.30
                                                (B6408)
SATB (easy) oct OXFORD 43.235 $.35   (B6409)

Pro Adventu
mix cor,acap voc sc KALMUS 6662 $1.00
contains also: Post Nativitatem Domini
                                                (B6410)

Psallite Domini *anthem
SSATB STAINER CC417 s.p.   (B6411)

Psalm 44 *see Exsurge, Domine

Psalm 119 *see Teach Me, O Lord

Rejoice! Rejoice! Christmas
(Geer, E.) SSAA,A solo,org/strings
SCHIRM.EC 855 $.30, ipr   (B6412)

Rejoice With Heart And Voice
girl cor SOUTHERN $.25   (B6413)

Rorate Coeli *Adv
"Sing, Heaven Imperial" SAATB,acap (diff)
OXFORD 43.233 $.50   (B6414)
"Sing, Heaven Imperial" SAATB,acap (med)
oct OXFORD 43.233 $.50   (B6415)

Sacerdotes Domini (from Gradulia, Liber II)
Commun/Ded/Ember,anthem,Lat
SATB STAINER CC415 s.p.   (B6416)
SATB,acap SCHIRM.EC 399 $.25   (B6417)
"Then Did Priests Make Offering" SATB,acap
(med easy) oct OXFORD 43.245 $.25   (B6418)
"Then Did The Priests" SATB (med diff)
OXFORD 43.245 $.25   (B6419)
(Woodworth) [Lat] TTBB,acap SCHIRM.EC 906
$.25   (B6420)
(Woodworth, G.) SSAA,acap SCHIRM.EC 815
$.25   (B6421)

Salve Regina *anti
SATB,acap SCHIRM.EC $.25   (B6422)
(Collins, H.B.) [Lat] SATB CHESTER s.p.   (B6423)

Salve Sancta Parens (from Feasts Of The
Virgin Mary) mot
SATBB,acap SCHIRM.EC $.16   (B6424)
(Collins, H.B.) [Lat] SATBarB CHESTER s.p.   (B6425)

Sanctus (from Mass For Four Voices) Sanctus
SATB oct WALTON 6030 $.30   (B6426)

Second Service *Magnif/Mass/Nunc
SSAATB (med) oct OXFORD 43.707 $.65   (B6427)
mix cor,acap KALMUS 6655 $1.00   (B6428)

Senex Puerum Portabat *anti
SATB,acap SCHIRM.EC $.16   (B6429)
(Collins, H.B.) [Lat] SATB CHESTER s.p.
                                                (B6430)

Short Service *see Magnificat And Nunc
Dimittis; Te Deum And Benedictus   (B6431)

Short Service *Mass
mix cor,acap KALMUS 6654 $1.35   (B6432)

Siderum Rector *anthem
SSATB STAINER CC407 s.p.   (B6433)

Sing, Heaven Imperial *see Rorate Coeli

Sing Joyfully *anthem
SSAATB STAINER CC5559 s.p.   (B6434)

Sing Joyfully Unto God *anthem
(Bantock) mix cor CURWEN 80531 s.p.   (B6435)
(Bennett, G.J.) SSATTB oct NOVELLO
28.1108.01 s.p.   (B6436)

Sing Praises To God This Holy Day *see Haec
Dies

Souls Of The Righteous *anthem/funeral
SSATB STAINER CC312 s.p.   (B6437)

Souls Of The Righteous, The *see Iustorum
Animae

Surge Illuminare *anthem
(Terry, R.R.) [Lat] mix cor oct NOVELLO
52.0006.07 s.p.   (B6438)

Te Deum (from Great Service) Bene/Te Deum
SATB,acap (med) OXFORD 43.282 $.90 contains
also: Benedictus   (B6439)

Te Deum And Benedictus *Bene/Te Deum
SAATTB,acap (med) oct OXFORD 43.706 $.65
see from Short Service   (B6440)

BYRD, WILLIAM (cont'd.)

Teach Me, O Lord (Psalm 119) Adv/Gen/Sexa
SSATB,acap (easy) oct OXFORD 42.314 $.25
                                                (B6441)

Then Did Priests Make Offering *see
Sacerdotes Domini

Then Did The Priests *see Sacerdotes Domini

Third Service *Magnif/Nunc
SAATB,acap (med) oct OXFORD 43.279 $.65
                                                (B6442)

Third Service *Mass
mix cor,acap KALMUS 6656 $1.00   (B6443)

This Day Christ Was Born *Xmas,carol
SSAATB,acap STAINER M1627 $.45   (B6444)

This Glad Day *see Haec Dies

This Is The Day *see Haec Dies

This Little Babe *Xmas
(Lethbridge) SATB,acap (very easy) OXFORD
43.356 $.15   (B6445)

Tu Es Pastor Ovium
SSATB,acap SCHIRM.EC $.25   (B6446)

Tu Es Petrus
SSATTB STAINER CC322 s.p.   (B6447)

Turn Our Captivity, O Lord *anthem
SSTTBB STAINER M16-30 s.p.   (B6448)

Twenty-Two Anthems Vol. 1 *CCU,anthem
6pt mix cor,acap voc sc KALMUS 6674 $1.00
                                                (B6449)

Twenty-Two Anthems Vol. 2 *CCU,anthem
6pt mix cor,acap voc sc KALMUS 6675 $1.00
                                                (B6450)

Twenty-Two Anthems Vol. 3 *CCU,anthem
6pt mix cor,acap voc sc KALMUS 6676 $1.00
                                                (B6451)

Twenty-Two Anthems Vol. 4 *CCU,anthem
6pt mix cor,acap voc sc KALMUS 6677 $1.00
                                                (B6452)

Two Sacred Songs In Five Parts *CC2U,Easter
SSATB,acap oct PRESSER 352-00092 $.35
                                                (B6453)

Two Sacred Songs *CC2U
SATB,acap oct PRESSER 352-00051 $.30   (B6454)

Unto Christ The Victim *see Victimae
Paschali

Veni Sanctie Spiritus *mot
SSATB STAINER CC418 s.p.   (B6455)

Venite *Adv/Easter/Gen
"O Come, Let Us Sing Unto The Lord" SATB,
kbd (med easy) oct CONCORDIA 98-1972 $.30
                                                (B6456)

Victimae Paschali *Easter
"Unto Christ The Victim" SSATB,acap (med
diff) OXFORD 43.236 $.35   (B6457)
"Unto Christ The Victim" SSATB,acap (med)
oct OXFORD 43.236 $.35   (B6458)

Victimae Paschali Laudes *Easter
(Berger) [Ger] 5pt mix cor,acap cor pts
BAREN. EM 554 s.p.   (B6459)

Who Can Tell The Glory *see O Quam Gloriosum

With Voice Of Melody *see Cantate Domino

BYRT, JOHN C.
Magnificat And Nunc Dimittis In D *Magnif/
Nunc
SATB (med) oct OXFORD 42.861 $.30   (B6460)

BYZANTINISCHES PASSIONS see Constantinescu,
Paul

BYZANTINISCHES WEIHNACHTS-ORATORIUM see
Constantinescu, Paul

C

CAAMANO
Psalm 6 *see Salmo VI

Psalm 114 *Op.10
[Lat] SATB,acap oct BOOSEY BAR $.75   (C1)

Salmo VI (Psalm 6) Op.12
[Lat] SATB,soli,acap RICORDI-ARG BA 11625
s.p.   (C2)
[Lat] SATB,acap RICORDI-ARG BA 11625 s.p.   (C3)

CABENA, BARRIE
Congregational Mass In Dorian Mode *Mass
unis/SATB (Roman Catholic text) oct OXFORD
42.322 $.50   (C4)

Congregational Mass In The Dorian Mode
unis/SATB (easy) oct OXFORD 42.322 $.50
                                                (C5)

Jubilate Deo
mix cor oct OXFORD 02.003 $.40   (C6)

Lobe Den Herrn
"Praise To The Lord" SATB oct GRAY
GCMR 2850 $.30   (C7)

Loving Shepherd Of Thy Sheep *anthem
unis oct OXFORD 02.004 $.25   (C8)

O Lord Of Life *anthem
unis oct OXFORD 02.005 $.20   (C9)

Praise To The Lord *see Lobe Den Herrn

Psalm 150 *anthem
mix cor oct OXFORD 02.021 $.35   (C10)

Te Deum *Te Deum
mix cor&cong,org sc OXFORD 02.012 $2.00
                                                (C11)

Twelve Benediction Amens *CC12U,Bene
2pt oct OXFORD 02.022 $.30   (C12)

CABEZON, ANTONIO DE (1510-1566)
Jesu Christe, Gottes Lamm *mot
(Hellmann) SATB HANSSLER 1.091 s.p.   (C13)

CABRA MASS see Illing

CACAVAS, [JOHN] (1930-   )
Love One Another
SA BELWIN 2281 $.40   (C14)

Psalm Of Praise, A *Psalm
SSAATTBB oct BOURNE 779 $.25   (C15)

CADMAN, [CHARLES WAKEFIELD] (1881-1946)
Glory
SATB oct GALAXY 1.0547.1 $.35   (C16)

CADOW, PAUL (1908-   )
Als Dort In Bethlehem *Xmas,It
mix cor,acap, or triangle, glockenspiel and
xylophone cor pts BREITKOPF-W CHB-3526
s.p.   (C17)

Die Heiligen Drei Konige
see Zwei Weihnachtslieder

Ein Kleines Requiem *Req
men cor,org/strings sc BREITKOPF-W PB-4828
s.p., cor pts BREITKOPF-W CHB-3666 s.p.,
ipa   (C18)

Kommet, Ihr Hirten *Xmas,Boh
mix cor,acap, or triangle , glockenspiel
and xylophone cor pts BREITKOPF-W
CHB-3525 s.p.   (C19)

O Heilig Kind
see Zwei Weihnachtslieder

Zwei Weihnachtslieder *Xmas
men cor,acap/perc cor pts BREITKOPF-W
CHB-3608 s.p.
contains: Die Heiligen Drei Konige; O
Heilig Kind   (C20)

CADZOW, D.
Lord's Prayer, The
SATB oct PRESSER MC187 $.30   (C21)

CAECILIA VIRGO see Phillips

CAECILIEN-ODE see Mozart, Wolfgang Amadeus

CAECILIENODE see Handel, George Frideric

CAECILLIAM CANTATA see Marenzio, Luca

CAEDMON'S HYMN OF CREATION see Cotton

CAELESTIS URBS JERUSALEM see Diepenbrock,
Alfons

CAFARELLA
Come Down, O Lord
SATB,org/pno BOSTON 13250 $.40   (C22)

I Will Praise The Lord
SATB oct LORENZ 9980 $.30   (C23)

Lamb Of God
SATB,pno/org BOSTON 13729 $.40   (C24)

Let All Praise Thee
SATB oct PRO ART 2285 $.30   (C25)

CAILLE, PAUVRE CAILLE see Aubanel, Georges

CAIN, NOBLE (1896-   )
All Creatures Of Our God
cor HIGHLAND 4105 $.25   (C26)

Alleluia, Alleluia
SATB FLAMMER A 5102 $.30   (C27)
SAB FLAMMER D5151 $.30   (C28)

As Lately We Watched
SAB FLAMMER D5127 $.30   (C29)

CAIN, NOBLE (cont'd.)

Babylon Is Fallen
SATB FLAMMER A 5219 $.30 (C30)

Ballou, Lammy *Xmas
SATB oct LORENZ 9958 $.30 (C31)

Behold! I Stand At The Door
SATB FLAMMER A 5280 $.25 (C32)

Bread Of God, The
SATB FLAMMER A 5319 $.30 (C33)

Calvary *Easter,spir
(Shaw) 4pt mix cor,Bar solo,acap oct SCHIRM.G 9948 $.30 (C34)

Carol Of The Birds *Xmas
SATB SCHMITT 1507 $.25 (C35)

Celestial Vistor, The *Xmas,cant
SATB oct LORENZ $1.95 (C36)

Child Was Born In Bethlehem *Xmas
SATB FLAMMER A 5246 $.25 (C37)
SSA FLAMMER B 5040 $.25 (C38)

Chorus And Nocturne For Advent *Adv
SATB FLAMMER A 5146 $.30 (C39)

Christ Triumphant
SATB SHAWNEE A5160 $.30 (C40)
SAB FLAMMER D5124 $.30 (C41)

Come, Thou Long Expected Jesus
SATB FLAMMER A 5395 $.30 (C42)
SAB FLAMMER D5037 $.25 (C43)

Communion With God
SATB oct LORENZ C190 $.30 (C44)

Day Star, The *cant
SATB FLAMMER A5486 $1.10 (C45)

Everlasting Life
SATB FLAMMER A 5397 $.25 (C46)

Fight The Good Fight
cor HIGHLAND 4120 $.30 (C47)

Gloria In Excelsis Deo *Xmas
SATB oct PLYMOUTH XM-103 $.25 (C48)

Glorious Things Of Thee Are Spoken
SATB FLAMMER A 5321 $.30 (C49)

Glory To God
SATB oct FOX R216 $.30 (C50)

God Of Our Fathers
SATB FLAMMER A 5429 $.30 (C51)
SAB FLAMMER D5091 $.25 (C52)

God Of The Open Air
TTBB oct BOOSEY 1571 $.30 (C53)
SATB oct BOOSEY 1572 $.30 (C54)

Good News
TTBB FLAMMER C5034 $.25 (C55)

Hail, Heavenly Light *Xmas,cant
cor HIGHLAND CM-101 $2.00 (C56)

Hail Thou Once Despised Jesus
SATB FLAMMER A 5432 $.30 (C57)

Hark, Ten Thousand Harps And Voices
SATB oct LORENZ 9904 $.35 (C58)

Holy Lord God
SATB FLAMMER A 5026 $.25 (C59)
TTBB FLAMMER C5025 $.30 (C60)
SSA FLAMMER B 5022 $.25 (C61)
SAB FLAMMER D5098 $.25 (C62)
boy cor SOUTHERN $.30 (C63)

Hosanna, Loud Hosanna
SAB KJOS 8022 $.30 (C64)

I Heard The Voice Of Jesus Say
SATB FLAMMER A 5543 $.35 (C65)

I Will Arise And Go To Jesus
SATB SHAWNEE A 559 $.30 (C66)

I Will Praise The Name Of God
SATB FLAMMER A 5576 $.30 (C67)

Improperium (composed with Casali, Giovanni Battista)
cor HIGHLAND 4103 $.25 (C68)

In The Night, Christ Came Walking *Bibl
mix cor,acap oct SCHIRM.G 11139 $.25 (C69)

Introits And Opening Sentences
SATB FLAMMER A 5461 $.30 (C70)

Jesus Boy Lullaby
SSA FLAMMER B 5047 $.25 (C71)

King Of Love My Shepherd Is, The
SATB FLAMMER A 5360 $.35 (C72)

Let Us Break Bread Together
SATB FLAMMER A 5078 $.30 (C73)
SSA FLAMMER B 5130 $.25 (C74)
SAB FLAMMER D5044 $.25 (C75)

Lord Is My Shepherd
boy cor SOUTHERN $.30 (C76)

Lord Is My Shepherd, The
SATB FLAMMER A 5028 $.30 (C77)
SSA FLAMMER B 5136 $.30 (C78)
TTBB FLAMMER C5027 $.25 (C79)
SAB FLAMMER D5171 $.25 (C80)

Lord, Our Creator
SATB oct LORENZ E29 $.30 (C81)

Lord, Speak To Me
SATB FLAMMER A 5080 $.30 (C82)
SSA FLAMMER B 5155 $.30 (C83)

Make A Joyful Noise
SATB FLAMMER A 5318 $.30 (C84)

CAIN, NOBLE (cont'd.)

March Of The Kings *see Marche Des Rois

Marche Des Rois *Xmas
"March Of The Kings" [Eng/Fr] 3pt mix cor oct SCHIRM.G 10943 $.30 (C85)
"March Of The Kings" [Eng/Fr] 4pt mix cor oct SCHIRM.G 10769 $.30 (C86)

Mass In Honor Of The Most Blessed Trinity *Mass
[Lat/Eng] SATB oct JUSKO 217 $.80 (C87)

My Soul Doth Magnify The Lord
SAB KJOS 8021 $.30 (C88)

Name Is Jesus, The
cor HIGHLAND 4119 $.30 (C89)

New King, The *Xmas,cant
SATB oct FOX $1.50 (C90)

No Room At The Inn *Xmas
SATB FLAMMER A 5324 $.25 (C91)
SSA FLAMMER B 5093 $.25 (C92)
SAB FLAMMER D5156 $.25 (C93)

Noel Chorus
SATB FLAMMER A 5225 $.25 (C94)

Noel! Noel!
SATB FLAMMER A5031 $1.10 (C95)
SAB FLAMMER D5012 $1.10 (C96)

O Lord Most Holy
SAB KJOS 5701 $.30 (C97)

O Sing Your Songs
SAB FLAMMER D5184 $.25 (C98)

On This Good Christmas Morn *Xmas
SATB FLAMMER A 5056 $.30 (C99)
SSA FLAMMER B 5076 $.30 (C100)
TTBB FLAMMER C5021 $.30 (C101)
TTBB FLAMMER C5021 $.30 (C102)
SAB FLAMMER D5040 $.25 (C103)

Our Father Who Art In Heaven
SATB FLAMMER A 5328 $.30 (C104)

Psalm 103
SATB FLAMMER A 5033 $.35 (C105)
SSA FLAMMER B 5043 $.30 (C106)
SAB FLAMMER D5019 $.30 (C107)

Radiant Christ, The
SATB FLAMMER A5142 $1.75 (C108)

Resurrection Song, The
SATB FLAMMER A5228 $1.25 (C109)

Rise Up, O Men Of God
SATB KJOS 5391 $.30 (C110)

Rocka My Soul! *spir
SATB FLAMMER A 5359 $.40 (C111)

Seven Joys Of Mary *Xmas
SATB oct PLYMOUTH XM-110 $.25 (C112)

Shepherd And The Stone, The
SATB FLAMMER A5485 $1.00 (C113)

Song Anthems *CCU,anthem
2pt treb cor KJOS $.60 (C114)

Song Of The Garo Christians
4pt mix cor,B solo oct SCHIRM.G 10891 $.30 (C115)

To Be A Pilgrim
SATB FLAMMER A 5202 $.30 (C116)

Triumphant Christ, The *Easter,cant
(Buck) oct FOX $1.50 (C117)

Twelve Responses For General Use *CC2U
SATB FLAMMER A 5088 $.30 (C118)

Watchman, Tell Us Of The Night
SAB FLAMMER D5064 $.25 (C119)

Water Of Life
SATB FLAMMER A 5210 $.25 (C120)

CALABRO, LOUIS
Child Sleeps, The *Xmas
SAB oct ELKAN-V 362-1317 $.30 (C121)
SAB oct PRESSER 362-01317 $.30 (C122)

CALAGAVERUNT OCULI MEI see Victoria, Tomas Luis de

CALCOTT
Hymn Of Peace *hymn
SATB (easy) ALLANS 203 s.p. (C123)

CALDARA, ANTONIO (1670-1736)
Alleluia *Allelu
[Lat] SATB MUSICUS 019 $.40 (C124)

Giuseppe *ora
(Frazzim V.; Orecchia, E.R.) mix cor, SATTTBar soli,org,ob,strings CARISH rental (C125)

Il Re Del Dolore *ora
(Frazzim, V.; Orecchia, E. Riccioli) mix cor,SSMezTB soli,org,hpsd,2ob,2bsn,2trom, strings CARISH rental (C126)

Laudate, Pueri, Dominum (Psalm 112) Bibl
mix cor,S solo,strings VOLK 131 sc s.p., voc sc s.p. (C127)

Magnificat C-Dur *Magnif
(Wolff, Christoph) [Lat] SATB,A solo,cont, 4trp,2vln,vla,drums (C maj,med) BAREN. BA 3518 sc s.p., cor pts s.p., ipa (C128)

Missa In G *Mass
(Furlinger) SATB,SATB soli,cont,2vln HANSSLER 10.208 sc $3.50, voc sc $1.00, ipa (C129)

Missa Venerationis In C Minor *Mass
(Drechsler, Otto) mix cor,soli,orch BOTE study sc s.p., oct s.p., ipa (C130)

CALDARA, ANTONIO (cont'd.)

Prager *see Te Deum

Praise Him, Praise Ye The Lord
(Ehret, Walter) SATB (med diff) PRESSER 362-03145 $.40 (C131)

Psalm 112 *see Laudate, Pueri, Dominum

Regina Coeli
(Hengartner) 4pt mix cor,acap sc RICORDI-ENG SY105 s.p., voc pt RICORDI-ENG SY106-109 s.p. (C132)

Stabat Mater *Psntd
[Eng/Lat] SATB,orch voc sc BROUDE BR. $1.50, ipr (C133)
[Lat] SATB,cont (med) MULLER MS 20 s.p. (C134)
[Ger] mix cor,org,orch MULLER (C135)

Te Deum *Te Deum
"Prager" [Ger] 2pt mix cor,SATB soli,org, orch MULLER (C136)

Te Deum Laudamus *ora
(Frazzi, V.; Orecchia, E. Riccioli) 8pt, org,4trp,2trom,strings,timp CARISH rental (C137)

CALDICOTT, ALFRED JAMES (1842-1897)
Out On The Waters
ATTB CRAMER C 0 s.p. (C138)

CALDWELL
All Praise To God
SATB oct SACRED S-67 $.35 (C139)

Come Child Of God *Xmas
SAB WARNER W7-1042 $.30 (C140)

Garden *Easter
unis oct SOUTHERN $.20 (C141)

Gifts
unis SOUTHERN $.30 (C142)

God's Open Road
unis WARNER R3315 $.30 (C143)

God's World
unis WARNER R3316 $.30 (C144)

Hear Us, Our Father
unis&opt desc,opt solo oct SACRED S-8616 $.35 (C145)

I Am The Good Shepherd
SATB oct SACRED E44 $.40 (C146)

Jesu, Friend Of My Delight
unis/SA,opt solo oct SACRED $.35 (C147)

Little Lamb, The
unis,opt fl oct SUMMY 5640 $.30 (C148)

Lo, How A Rose E'er Blooming *Xmas
SA oct SACRED S-5381 $.35 (C149)

Manger Carol, The *Xmas,carol,Aus
SA SCHMITT 2555 $.35 (C150)
SAB SCHMITT 5516 $.35 (C151)
SATB SCHMITT 8023 $.25 (C152)

Morning Prayer
SATB oct SACRED S-108 $.35 (C153)

My Constant Joy
unis/SA oct SACRED S-8615 $.35 (C154)

O Lovely Christmas Rose *Xmas
SATB SCHMITT 875 $.22 (C155)

Polish Easter Carol *Easter,carol,Pol
SA oct SOUTHERN $.25 (C156)

Risen Christ! *Easter
SA/SATB oct SACRED S-104 $.35 (C157)

Rose, The
SATB oct SACRED S-71 $.30 (C158)

Shepherds Come *Xmas
SAB oct FISCHER,C CM-7736 $.25 (C159)

Shine Lovely Christmas Star
SSA&desc oct BOOSEY 5685 $.45, ipa (C160)
unis&desc oct BOOSEY 5535 $.45, ipa (C161)
SA&desc oct BOOSEY 5525 $.45, ipa (C162)

Sing With Joy *Easter/Gen
2pt WARNER R3383 $.30 (C163)

Spring Prayer
unis oct SUMMY B 2113 $.30 (C164)

Three Calls To Worship For Juniors *CC3U
unis oct BELWIN 64377 $.30 (C165)

Welcome, Gay Kolyada *Xmas
SATB oct SACRED S-57 $.35 (C166)
unis/SA oct SACRED S-8618 $.35 (C167)

What Trees Were In Gethsemane *Lent
SA oct SOUTHERN $.30 (C168)

CALDWELL, MARY [ELIZABETH] (1909-)
All Praise To God *CCU,anthem
jr cor SACRED $1.75 (C169)

And I Have Peace Within
SAB oct WORD CS-2503 $.25 (C170)

Carol For Easter, A *Easter
SATB oct WORD CS-341 $.30 (C171)

Carol For Lent, A *Lent
SA,fl oct WORD CS-674 $.25 (C172)

Carol Of The Little King *Xmas,carol
SA oct GRAY GCMR 2260 $.25 (C173)
SAB oct GRAY GCMR 2399 $.25 (C174)
SATB oct GRAY GCMR 2102 $.30 (C175)

Carol Of The Lonely Shepherd *Xmas,carol
SATB oct GRAY GCMR 2418 $.30 (C176)

CALDWELL, MARY [ELIZABETH] (cont'd.)

Come Let Us Sing
SATB (med easy) PRESSER G-219 $.40   (C177)

Enter This Door
SATB oct GRAY GCMR 3051 $.25   (C178)

Festival Of Carols For The Church Year, The
*CCU,Adv/Xmas/Easter/Lent
unis&2pt,org,opt inst voc sc WORD 10014
$1.25   (C179)

Glory Of God, The
SA oct WORD CS-2547 $.30   (C180)

How Far To Bethlehem!
SS oct GRAY GCMR 3029 $.30   (C181)

I Am The One
SATB oct PRESSER G-153 $.40   (C182)

I Know A Lovely Garden *Easter/Lent
SAB oct GRAY GCMR 3077 $.30   (C183)

In Praise Of Spring And Easter *Easter
unis (easy) PRESSER G-192 $.35   (C184)

In Thy Way
SA oct WORD CS-2548 $.30   (C185)

Jesu, My Son *Xmas,So Am
SATB oct GRAY GCMR 2592 $.30   (C186)

Lute Carol, A
SAB oct GRAY GCMR 2808 $.30   (C187)

Now The Prince Of Peace Is Come *Xmas
SATB oct WORD CS-328 $.30   (C188)

O Daniel! *Xmas
unis/SA oct WORD CS-2453 $.30   (C189)

Ring In Noel *Xmas
SAB oct GRAY GCMR 2993 $.25   (C190)

Shepherd, The
SA oct PRESSER G-148 $.35   (C191)

Singing Faith, A *CCUL
jr cor voc sc WORD 20048 $1.50   (C192)

Singing Faith, A
SA oct WORD CS-2544 $.30   (C193)

Song Of Praise
SAB oct GRAY GCMR 2661 $.30   (C194)

Such A Solitary Star *Xmas
SATB oct GRAY GCMR 3031 $.30   (C195)

Sweet Holy Child *Xmas
SATB oct GRAY GCMR 2717 $.30   (C196)
unis oct GRAY GCMR 2612 $.25   (C197)

We Walk With God
unis oct GRAY GCMR 2930 $.30   (C198)

What Trees Were In Gethsemane? *Easter
unis oct GRAY G-122 $.30   (C199)

Who Shall Come? *Xmas
SATB oct WORD CS-345 $.30   (C200)

CALICEM SALUTARIS see Schutz, Heinrich

CALIGAVERUNT OCULI ME see Victoria, Tomas Luis
de

CALIGAVERUNT OCULI MEI see Baroti

CALIGAVERUNT OCULI MEI see Goodman, Joseph

CALIGAVERUNT OCULI MEI see Ingegneri, Marco
Antonio

CALIGAVERUNT OCULI MEI see Victoria, Tomas Luis
de

CALL, THE see Toolan, S. Suzanne

CALL HIS NAME JESUS see Moffatt

CALL OF ISAIAH, THE see Pinkham, Daniel

CALL TO MARY see Brahms, Johannes, Ruf Zur
Maria

CALL TO REMEMBRANCE see Farrant, Richard

CALL TO REMEMBRANCE see Hilton

CALL TO REMEMBRANCE see Hilton, John (The
Elder)

CALL TO REMEMBRANCE see Lepke, C.

CALL TO REMEMBRANCE O LORD see Farrant, Richard

CALL TO REMEMBRANCE O LORD see Graham

CALL TO SONG, THE see Thompson, Randall

CALL TO THE SHEPHERDS, THE
(Malin) SSA oct BELWIN 64317 $.25   (C201)

CALL TO WORSHIP see Gratton, Frank L.

CALLHOFF, HERBERT (1933-   )
Alles Fleisch Ist Wie Gras
see Funf Motetten

Cantate Domino *Easter/Pent
[Lat] SATB,acap (med easy) MULLER SM 732
s.p.   (C202)

Christus Ist Gehorsam Geworden *mot
5pt mix cor MOSELER s.p.   (C203)

Confirma Hoc Deus
see Drei Geistliche Motetten

Der Mensch Lebt Und Besteht *mot
4pt mix cor MOSELER s.p.   (C204)

Die Versuchung Jesu *Bibl
4-8pt mix cor,narrator,T solo,acap voc sc
GERIG 655 s.p.   (C205)

CALLHOFF, HERBERT (cont'd.)

Drei Geistliche Motetten *mot
3-4pt mix cor MOSELER s.p.
contains: Confirma Hoc Deus; Im Namen
Jesu; Terra Tremuit   (C206)

Funf Motetten *mot
4pt mix cor MOSELER s.p.
contains: Alles Fleisch Ist Wie Gras;
Jubelt, Ihr Himmel; Meine Gedanken; So
Spricht Gott Der Herr; Tauet, Ihr
Himmel   (C207)

Im Namen Jesu
see Drei Geistliche Motetten

Jubelt, Ihr Himmel
see Funf Motetten

Maria Aufgenommen Ist *BVM/Fest,cant
[Ger] SATB&cong,org (med) MULLER SM 2472
s.p.   (C208)

Meine Gedanken
see Funf Motetten

Missa *Mass
3pt mix cor,org MOSELER sc s.p., cor pts
s.p.   (C209)

Missa Brevis *Mass
4pt mix cor MOSELER s.p.   (C210)

Nun Bitten Wir Den Heiligen Geist *Pent,cant
[Ger] SATB&cong,org (med) MULLER SM 2473
s.p.   (C211)

Psalm 50 *Bibl
6-8pt MOSELER s.p.   (C212)

Psalm 127
see Psalmentriptychon

Psalm 128
see Psalmentriptychon

Psalmentriptychon *Bibl
mix cor,SSB soli,org,3bvl,perc GERIG 823
rental
contains: Psalm 127; Psalm 128   (C213)

So Spricht Gott Der Herr
see Funf Motetten

Tauet, Ihr Himmel
see Funf Motetten

Terra Tremuit
see Drei Geistliche Motetten

CALLS TO PRAISE AND PRAYER see Lovelace, Austin
C.

CALM AND TRANQUIL LIE THE SHEEPFOLDS see Bach,
Johann Sebastian

CALM IS THE STORM see Smith

CALM ON THE LISTENING EAR OF NIGHT *Xmas
(Kinsman) SATB&desc oct PRO ART 1938 $.22
(C214)
(Kinsman) SSA&desc oct PRO ART 2109 $.22
(C215)

CALM ON THE LISTENING EAR OF NIGHT see Barratt,
R.

CALM ON THE LIST'NING EAR see Worthing, Richard

CALM ON THE LIST'NING EAR OF NIGHT see Harker,
F. Flaxington

CALM ON THE LIST'NING EAR OF NIGHT see Sears

CALM SEA AND PLEASANT VOYAGE see Beethoven,
Ludwig van

CALM THE HILLSIDE see Stanton, Royal [W.]

CALVAIRE see Calvary

CALVARY *Easter/Lent,spir,US
(Aubanel, Georges) "Calvaire" [Eng/Fr] 3pt
mix cor OUVRIERES s.p.   (C216)
(Ehret, Walter) SATB oct WALTON 2016 $.25
(C217)

CALVARY see Cain, Noble

CALVARY see Jenkins, Cyril

CALVARY see Martin, Warren

CALVARY see Maunder, J.H.

CALVARY see Rodney

CALVARY see Rodney, Paul

CALVARY see Wessel, Henry

CALVARY see Westbrook, Francis B.

CALVARY ROAD, THE see Lillenas, Haldor

CALVARY'S LOVE see Correll

CALVARY'S MOUNTAIN *anthem
(Parker) SATB,acap oct LAWSON 51341 $.30
(C218)
(Pooler, Marie) SATB,S solo (easy) oct
AUGSBURG 1105 $.22   (C219)

CALVARY'S MOUNTAIN see Ehret, Walter

CALVISIUS, SETHUS (1556-1615)
Das Alte Jahr Vergangen Ist *ECY,mot
(Tunger) dbl cor,cont HANSSLER 1.192 s.p.
(C220)
Ein Kindelen, So Lobelich *Xmas/Easter
(Weitemeyr, Herbert) [Ger] 4pt men cor,acap
NAGELS NCH 11 s.p.   (C221)

Four Christmas Motets *Xmas,mot
[Ger/Lat] SSATTB PETERS H1512 $.40
contains: Freut Euch Und Jubiliert;
Gloria In Excelsis Deo; Joseph, Lieber
Joseph Mein; Von Himmel Hoch   (C222)

CALVISIUS, SETHUS (cont'd.)

Freut Euch Und Jubiliert *Xmas,mot
see Four Christmas Motets
(Granville) "Rejoice Exultantly" SSATBB,
acap oct FOX CM17 $.40   (C223)
(Tunger) [Ger] SSATTB HANSSLER 1.187 s.p.
see also Vier Weihnachtsmotetten   (C224)

Geistliche Chormusik *CC10U,mot
(Tunger) [Ger] 6-8pt HANSSLER 4.013 $6.00
(C225)

Gloria In Excelsis Deo *Xmas,mot
see Four Christmas Motets
(Tunger) [Lat] SSATTB HANSSLER 1.188 s.p.
see also Vier Weihnachtsmotetten   (C226)

Joseph Dear, Oh Joseph Mild
SSATTB,acap AMP A396 $.25   (C227)

Joseph, Lieber Joseph Mein *Xmas,mot
see Four Christmas Motets
(Straube, K.) 6pt mix cor,acap cor pts
BREITKOPF-L PB-2687 s.p.   (C228)
(Tunger) [Ger] SSATTB HANSSLER 1.189 s.p.
see also Vier Weihnachtsmotetten   (C229)

Lobet Den Herrn (Psalm 150) BREITKOPF-L
12pt mix cor,acap cor pts
PB-2340 s.p., voc pt BREITKOPF-L CHB-2043
s.p.   (C230)

Mit Meinem Gott Geh Ich Zur Ruh
see Praetorius, Michael, Ich Dank Dir Schon
Durch Deinen Sohn

Musiken Klang, Lieblicher G'sang *mot
(Hellmann) SAB HANSSLER 1.244 s.p.   (C231)

Ninety And Nine, The
(Hadley) SATB oct PRO ART 1360 $.30   (C232)

Now Sing We, Now Rejoice
(Ehret) SATB,acap MARKS 4137 $.30   (C233)

Praeter Rerum Seriem *mot
(Tunger) [Lat] SAATBB HANSSLER 1.190 $.80
(C234)

Psalm 150 *see Lobet Den Herrn

Quaerite Primum Regnum Dei *mot
(Tunger) dbl cor,cont HANSSLER 1.191 s.p.
(C235)

Rejoice Exultantly *see Freut Euch Und
Jubiliert

Singet Dem Herrn Ein Neues Lied *Bibl/mot
(Tunger) dbl cor,cont HANSSLER 1.195 s.p.
(C236)

Till Dig Allena, Jesu Krist
mix cor NORDISKA 1258 s.p.   (C237)

Unser Leben Wahret Siebzig Jahr *mot
8pt mix cor,acap cor pts BREITKOPF-L
PB-1433 s.p., voc pt BREITKOPF-L CHB-852
s.p.   (C238)
(Langenbeck) SSAT&ATTB HANSSLER 1.037 s.p.
(C239)
(Tunger) SSAB&ATTB,cont HANSSLER 1.193 s.p.
(C240)

Vier Weihnachtsmotetten *Xmas,mot
(Tunger) SSATTB cmplt ed HANSSLER $1.50
contains & see also: Freut Euch Und
Jubiliert; Gloria In Excelsis Deo;
Joseph, Lieber Joseph Mein; Vom Himmel
Hoch, Da Komm Ich Her   (C241)

Vom Himmel Hoch, Da Komm Ich Her *Xmas,mot
(Tunger) [Ger] SSATTB HANSSLER 1.186 s.p.
see also Vier Weihnachtsmotetten   (C242)

Von Himmel Hoch
see Four Christmas Motets

Zion Spricht: Der Herr Hat Mich Verlassen
*mot
(Tunger) dbl cor,cont HANSSLER 1.194 s.p.
(C243)

CAME THE NEWS TO HUMBLE SHEPHERDS *Xmas,carol
(Wheeler) SATB ALLANS 182 s.p.   (C244)

CAME THE WISE MEN see Posegate

CAMILIERI, L.
Lord's Prayer
unis oct GRAY GCMR 1580 $.25   (C245)

CAMINO DE BELEN
see Villancicos Tradicionales

CAMINO DE BELEN see Martin Pompey

CAMMAROTA, CARLO
Dominus Regnat
SATB oct ZANIBON 5276 s.p.   (C246)

Venite, Exsultemus Domino *Xmas
SATB oct ZANIBON 5275 s.p.   (C247)

CAMPANA DE NOCHEBUENA see Benedito

CAMPANAS DE NAVIDAD see Vivalo

CAMPBELL
He'll Understand, And Say, "Well Done"
SATB oct LORENZ B183 $.25   (C248)

Hiding Place
3pt jr cor/SSA (med) FISCHER,C CM 7280 $.25
(C249)

If Thou O Lord Shouldst Mark Iniquities
(Watson) SATB oct FISCHER,C CM-7727 $.25
(C250)

Jesus Christ Is Risen Today *Easter
(Watson) SATB oct GRAY GCMR 2848 $.40   (C251)

Magnum Nomen Domini *Xmas,mot
(Watson) girl cor SOUTHERN $.30   (C252)
(Watson) [Lat] SSA,acap WARNER W3481 $.30
(C253)

Whither Shall I Go *Gen
SATB SCHMITT SD6215 $.25   (C254)

CAMPBELL, H.A.J.
Christmas Day *Xmas
ASHDOWN E.A.130 s.p.   (C255)

CAMPBELL, MADGE E.
  Spanish Lullaby *carol
    unis CRAMER 19 s.p.   (C256)

  Woolly Lamb At The Manger *Xmas,carol
    unis CRAMER 14   (C257)

CAMPBELL, SYDNEY S.
  Be Strong And Of Good Courage *anthem
    mix cor oct NOVELLO 40.1394.08 s.p.   (C258)

  Fanfare For Michaelmas Day *anthem
    mix cor,Bar solo,acap oct NOVELLO
    40.1422.07 s.p.   (C259)

  Jubilate *Jubil
    SATB oct NOVELLO 40.1492.08 s.p.   (C260)

  King's Call To Greatheart, The *anthem
    mix cor&cong,solo,org oct NOVELLO
    03.0114.00 s.p.   (C261)

  Preces And Responses (Canterbury)
    SATB oct NOVELLO 44.1365.02 s.p.   (C262)

  Preces And Responses (Windsor)
    SATB oct NOVELLO 44.1431.04 s.p.   (C263)

  Sing We Merrily Unto God Our Strength
    *anthem
    mix cor oct NOVELLO 40.1438.03 s.p.   (C264)

  Te Deum *Te Deum
    SATB (B flat maj) oct NOVELLO 44.1394.06
    s.p.   (C265)

CAMPBELL-TIPTON, [LOUIS] (1877-1921)
  I Will Give Thanks Unto The Lord *Bibl
    4pt mix cor oct SCHIRM.G 8006 $.25   (C266)

CAMPBELL-WATSON, FRANK (1898-   )
  Ad Te Levavi *Adv,Offer
    [Lat/Eng] SATB,acap AMP A221 $.20 see from
    Offertories For The Sundays Of Advent
                                                  (C267)
  Ave Maria *Adv,Offer
    [Lat/Eng] SATB,acap AMP A224 $.20 see from
    Offertories For The Sundays Of Advent
                                                  (C268)
  Benedixisti, Domine *Adv,Offer
    [Lat/Eng] SATB,org AMP A223 $.20 see from
    Offertories For The Sundays Of Advent
                                                  (C269)
  Deus, Tu Conversus *Adv,Offer
    [Lat/Eng] SATB,acap AMP A222 $.20 see from
    Offertories For The Sundays Of Advent
                                                  (C270)
  Offertories For The Sundays Of Advent *see
    Ad Te Levavi; Ave Maria; Benedixisti,
    Domine; Deus, Tu Conversus   (C271)

CAMPION
  Jerusalem
    (Davis, K.) 2pt WARNER R3478 $.30   (C272)

CAMPION, M.
  Ave Vivens Hostia!
    unis,org SCHIRM.EC $.16   (C273)

  Cor Jesu, Fons Vitae
    SSA,2 soli,org SCHIRM.EC $.25   (C274)

CAMPION, [THOMAS] (1567-1620)
  As By The Streams Of Babylon *Bibl
    (Dett) 4pt mix cor,high solo,acap oct
    SCHIRM.G 7713 $.25   (C275)

CAN THIS BE THY CRADLE see Franck, Cesar

CAN YOU COUNT THE STARS?
  (Sowerby, Leo) unis&desc oct GRAY GCMR 2775
  $.25   (C276)

CAN YOU COUNT THE STARS see Powell, R.

CAN YOU COUNT THE STARS? see Powell, Robert J.

CAN YOU HEAR THE CHOIRS OF ANGELS
  (Graves) SA FRANCIS s.p.   (C277)

CANAVATI
  Almighty And Everlasting God
    SATB oct PRO ART 2247 $.25   (C278)

  Hear My Prayer
    SATB oct PRO ART 1661 $.25   (C279)

  How Lovely Are Thy Dwellings
    SATB oct PRO ART 1820 $.22   (C280)

  I Will Praise Thee (from Book Of Psalms)
    SATB oct PRO ART 1824 $.25   (C281)

  Psalm 24
    SATB,S/T solo oct PRO ART 1664 $.20   (C282)

  Unto Thee Lift I Up Mine Eyes
    SATB oct PRO ART 1663 $.30   (C283)
    SAB oct PRO ART 2016 $.25   (C284)
    SSA oct PRO ART 1877 $.25   (C285)

CANCION CAMPESTRE see Benedito

CANCION DE LO DIVINO see Gonzalez Barron

CANCION DE NAVIDAD see Guastavino

CANCIONES: CUADERNO I see Escudero

CANCIONES: CUADERNO II see Escudero

CANCIONES DUARUM VOCUM see Lassus, Roland de
  (Orlandus)

CANCO A LA VERGE see Casals, Pablo

CANDLE IN THE WINDOW see Lynn, George

CANDLELIGHT CAROL SERVICE, A see Hamill

CANDLES FOR CHRISTMAS see Graham, Robert [V.]

CANDLES LIKE STARS *Xmas
  (McKelvy, J.) SATB,acap FOSTER MF501 $.20
                                                  (C286)
  (McKelvy, J.) SA/unis,kbd cor pts FOSTER
  MF701 $.24, voc pt FOSTER MF701A $.06
                                                  (C287)

CANDLYN
  Christ, Whose Glory Fills The Skies
    SATB oct FISCHER,C CM-622 $.25   (C288)

  Christians, Sing Alleluia *Easter
    SATB oct SOUTHERN $.30   (C289)

  My God And King
    SAB FLAMMER D5182 $.25   (C290)

  Road To The Lamb, The *Pent
    SAB,opt T solo WARNER W3542 $.30   (C291)

  Thee We Adore *anthem
    SATB oct FISCHER,C CM-492 $.25   (C292)

CANDLYN, T. FREDERICK H. (1892-1964)
  Drop, Drop Slow Tears
    SATB oct GALAXY 1.1630.1 $.25   (C293)

  Endless Alleluia, An
    SAB/SA/TB oct FISCHER,J 8922 $.30   (C294)

  Fierce Raged The Tempest *Bibl
    4pt mix cor oct SCHIRM.G 7041 $.25   (C295)

  Forth In Thy Name I Go
    3pt jr cor/SAB (very easy) FISCHER,C
    CM 7123 $.25   (C296)

  Love Of The Father, The *Xmas
    SAB,opt T solo WARNER W3529 $.30   (C297)

  Ride On, Ride On *Easter/Lent/Palm
    SATB oct GRAY GCMR 643 $.35   (C298)

  Ride On, Ride On In Majesty *Palm
    SATB,kbd (med easy) oct CONCORDIA 98-1064
    $.30   (C299)

  Song Of Rejoicing, A
    SATB (med) ABINGDON APM-128 $.24   (C300)

  Song Of The Crib *Xmas
    jr cor&sr cor (med) FISCHER,C CM 6748 $.20
                                          (C301)
  Thee We Adore *Commun
    3pt jr cor/SSA (easy) FISCHER,C CM 7354
    $.25   (C302)

  To God All Praise And Glory And The Lord
    Ascendeth *Asc/Gen
    SAB WARNER W3659 $.30   (C303)

  What Child Is This *Xmas
    unis jr cor&desc FISCHER,C CM6162 $.20 (C304)

CANITE TUBA IN SION see Palestrina, Giovanni

CANITE TUBA IN SION see Vene, Ruggero

CANNICIARI, D. POMPEO (1670-1744)
  Ave Maria *BVM/Fest,mot
    [Lat] SATB,acap (med) MULLER M 2 s.p. (C305)
    [Lat] mix cor,acap oct NOVELLO DM-2 s.p.
                                          (C306)
  Credo Quod Redemptor *Easter,Req
    "I Know That My Redeemer Liveth" SATB,acap
    SCHIRM.EC 1120 $.16   (C307)

  I Know That My Redeemer Liveth *see Credo
    Quod Redemptor

  Missa A-Moll *Mass
    (Bauerle, Hermann) SATB,acap (A min) cor
    pts BREITKOPF-L CHB-2544 s.p.   (C308)

  Missa Prygia *Mass
    (Bauerle, Hermann) SATB,acap cor pts
    BREITKOPF-L CHB-2797 s.p.   (C309)

CANNING, THOMAS
  John Wesley Covenant Service, The
    cor,2trp,2trom,timp sc ABINGDON APM-335
    $9.00, voc sc ABINGDON APM-315 $2.00, ipa
                                          (C310)

CANNON, JACK D.
  Be Thou My Vision
    SATB (easy) ABINGDON APM-261 $.25   (C311)

CANNON, PHILIP (1929-   )
  Son Of God *CC3U,mot
    SATB&dbl cor,acap voc sc NOVELLO s.p.
                                          (C312)

CANON DE NAVIDAD see Carambula

CANON LAW FOR NEWLYWEDS see Mechem, Kirke

CANON LAW FOR NEWLYWEDS see Mechem, Kirke

CANONIC LITANIES see Schalk, Carl

CANONS see Mozart, Wolfgang Amadeus

CANONS IN THE TRENT CODICES *CCU,canon
  (Loyan, Richard) cor AM.INST.MUS. $16.00 (C313)

CAN'T YO' HEAH ME MOANIN', LORD see James

CAN'T YOU HEAR WHAT MY LORD SAID
  see Street Corner Spirituals

CANT YOU LIVE HUMBLE *spir,US
  (Aubanel, Georges) "Pour Rester Humble" [Eng/
  Fr] 3pt mix cor OUVRIERES s.p.   (C314)

CANTABO DOMINO see Lewkovitch

CANTABO DOMINO see Lewkovitch, Bernhard

CANTABO DOMINO see Vecchi, Orazio

CANTABO DOMINO see Viadana, Lodovico Grossi da

CANTAD, PASTORCITOS see Martin Pompey

CANTANTIBUS ORGANIS see Philips, Peter

CANTARES DE PASCUA see Santa Cruz, Domingo

CANTARES DI PASCUA see Santa Cruz, Domingo

CANTATA see Hjorleifsson, Sigguringi E.

CANTATA ACADEMICA see Britten, Benjamin

CANTATA BREVE see Davico, Vincenzo

CANTATA DI NATALE see Malipiero, Riccardo

CANTATA DIR SELLE DES WELTALLS see Mozart,
  Wolfgang Amadeus

CANTATA DOMINO see Croce, Giovanni

CANTATA DOMINO see Viadana, Lodovico Grossi da

CANTATA DOMINUM see Schutz, Heinrich

CANTATA EBRAICA IN DIALOGO see Grossi, Carlo

CANTATA FOR CHRISTMAS see Gardner

CANTATA FOR THE NATIVITY see Hannahs, R.C.

CANTATA FROM JOB see Milhaud, Darius

CANTATA II see Riley, Dennis

CANTATA, IN HONOREM MARIAE MATRIS DEI see
  Rubbra, Edmund, In Honorem Mariae Matris
  Dei

CANTATA LIRICA see Farkas, Ferenc

CANTATA MECUM DOMINO see Carissimi, Giacomo

CANTATA NIGRA see Szokalay

CANTATA OF PEACE see Moe, Daniel

CANTATA OF ST. JOHN see Surinach, Carlos

CANTATA ON APPALACHIAN CHRISTMAS CAROLS see
  Niles, David

CANTATA ON THE DEATH OF EMPEROR JOSEPH II see
  Beethoven, Ludwig van

CANTATA PACIS see Nelhybel, Vaclav

CANTATA SACRA see Malipiero, Riccardo

CANTATAS ON TEXTS BY FRANZ WERFEL see Orff,
  Carl

CANTATE A NOTRE-DAME see Brun, G.

CANTATE DE JOANNE see Kubizek, Augustinian

CANTATE DE LA CROIX DE CHARITE see Milhaud,
  Darius

CANTATE DE L'INITIATION see Milhaud, Darius

CANTATE DE NOEL see Harsanyi, Tibor

CANTATE DE PSAUMES see Milhaud, Darius

CANTATE DEO see Cooper, Irvin

CANTATE DOMINE see Schutz, Heinrich

CANTATE DOMINI see Buxtehude, Dietrich

CANTATE, DOMINI CANTICUM NOVUM see Schutz,
  Heinrich

CANTATE DOMINO see Burkhart, Franz

CANTATE DOMINO see Anerio, Giovanni Francesco

CANTATE DOMINO see Banchieri, Adriano

CANTATE DOMINO see Bauernfiend, Hans

CANTATE DOMINO see Bossi, Marco Enrico

CANTATE DOMINO see Bouichere, Emile

CANTATE DOMINO see Burkhart, Franz

CANTATE DOMINO see Buxtehude, Dietrich

CANTATE DOMINO see Buxtehude, Dietrich,
  Lobsinget Gott, Dem Herrn

CANTATE DOMINO see Byrd, William

CANTATE DOMINO see Callhoff, Herbert

CANTATE DOMINO see Croce, Giovanni

CANTATE DOMINO see Cruger, Johann

CANTATE DOMINO see Deering, Richard

CANTATE DOMINO see Gabrieli, Giovanni

CANTATE DOMINO see Harris, Jerry Weseley

CANTATE DOMINO see Hassler, Hans Leo

CANTATE DOMINO see Heiberg

CANTATE DOMINO see Indy, Vincent d'

CANTATE DOMINO see Monteverdi, Claudio

CANTATE DOMINO see Naylor, Edward Woodall

CANTATE DOMINO see Pitoni, Giuseppe Ottavio

CANTATE DOMINO see Schroth

CANTATE DOMINI see Schutz, Heinrich

CANTATE DOMINO see Short, Michael

CANTATE DOMINO see Slogedal, Bjarne

CANTATE DOMINO see Spencer, W.

CANTATE DOMINO see Staden, Johann

CANTATE DOMINO see Staden, Johann, Singet Ein
  Neues Lied

CANTATE DOMINO see Sweelinck, Jan Pieterszoon

CANTATE DOMINO see Vecchi, Orazio

CANTATE DOMINO see Williamson, Malcolm

CANTATE DOMINO CANTICUM NOVUM see Doppelbauer, Josef Friedrich

CANTATE DOMINO CANTICUM NOVUM see Manicke, Dietrich

CANTATE DOMINO CANTICUM NOVUM see Nicolson, R.

CANTATE DOMINO CANTICUM NOVUM see Staden, Johann

CANTATE DOMINO CANTICUM NOVUM see Strohbach, Siegfried

CANTATE, POUR LA FETE DE LA PENTECOTE see Bach, Johann Sebastian

CANTATE, POUR LA FETE DE L'ASCENSION see Bach, Johann Sebastian, Lobet Gott In Seinen Reichen

CANTATE, POUR LA FETE DE SAINT-JEAN- BAPTISTE see Bach, Johann Sebastian, Christ Unser Herr, Zum Jordan Kam

CANTATE, POUR LE DIMANCHE DE LA SEXAGESIME see Bach, Johann Sebastian, Erhalt' Uns, Herr, Bei Deinem Wort

CANTATE, POUR LE JOUR DE L'ASCENSION see Bach, Johann Sebastian

CANTATE, POUR LE JOUR DE PAQUES see Bach, Johann Sebastian

CANTATE, POUR LE NEUVIEME DIMANCHE APRES LA TRINITE see Bach, Johann Sebastian, Tue Rechnung, Donnerwort

CANTATE, POUR LE PREMIERE JOUR DE NOEL see Bach, Johann Sebastian

CANTATE, POUR LE SEIZIEME DIMANCHE APRES LA TRINITE see Bach, Johann Sebastian, Wer Weiss, Wie Nahe Mir Mein Ende

CANTATE POUR LE TEMPS DE LA NATIVITE see Rosenthal, Manuel

CANTATE, POUR LE TROISIEME DIMANCHE APRES EPIPHANIE see Bach, Johann Sebastian, Ich Steh' Mit Einem Fuss Im Grabe

CANTATE, POUR LE TROISIEME JOUR APRES NOEL see Bach, Johann Sebastian, Sehet, Welch Eine Liebe

CANTATE, POUR TOUS LE TEMPS see Bach, Johann Sebastian

CANTATE SUR TROIS PSAUMES see DuBois, Pierre Max

CANTATO DOMINO see Franck, Cesar

CANTATO DOMINO IN VITA MEA see Franck, Cesar

CANTAVA LA PIU VAGA PASTORELLA see Marenzio, Luca

CANTELOUBE DE MALARET, MARIE-JOSEPH (1879-1957)
   Allons Ecouter L'Aubade *Xmas
      [Fr] 4pt mix cor,opt pno/org HEUGEL s.p.
                                              (C315)
   Bergers, Il Est Plus De Minuit *Xmas
      [Fr] 4pt mix cor,opt pno/org HEUGEL s.p.
                                              (C316)
   Dans Une Humble Masure *Xmas
      [Fr] 4pt mix cor,opt pno/org HEUGEL s.p.
                                              (C317)
   Je Vous Souhaite *Xmas
      [Fr] 4pt mix cor,opt pno/org HEUGEL s.p.
                                              (C318)
   La Vierge Marie Va A Bethleem *Xmas
      [Fr] 4pt mix cor,opt pno/org HEUGEL s.p.
                                              (C319)
   Leve-Toi Vite Mon Ami *Xmas
      [Fr] 4pt mix cor,opt pno/org HEUGEL s.p.
                                              (C320)
   Noels D'Europe *CC8L,Xmas,carol,Belg/Czech/
      Fr/It/Rum/Span/Swiss
      [Fr] 1-4pt,solo,pno voc sc DURAND s.p.
                                              (C321)
   Qual Tust Oyci? *Xmas
      "Qui Frappe Ici?" [Fr] 4pt mix cor,opt pno/
      org HEUGEL s.p.   (C322)
   Quand Dieu Naquit A Noel *Xmas
      [Fr] 4pt mix cor,opt pno/org HEUGEL s.p.
                                              (C323)
   Qui Frappe Ici? *see Qual Tust Oyci?

CANTEMUS DOMINO see Brunetti, Domenico

CANTEMUS DOMINO see Delalande, Michel-Richard

CANTEMUS OMNES DOMINA see Carissimi, Giacomo

CANTEMUS OMNES DOMINO see Carissimi, Giacomo

CANTEMUS OMNIS DOMINA see Carissimi, Giacomo

CANTEN NOUVE SUS LA MUSETO see Hughes

CANTI LITURGICI EBRAICI DI RITO ITALIANO
   [Heb/It/Eng] cor SANTIS 1068 s.p.   (C324)

CANTI PER LA S. MESSA LETTA E LAUDI SACRE DEVOZIONALE see Virgili, Lavinio

CANTIBUS ORGANIS see Arnaldi, Antonio

CANTIBUS ORGANIS see Marenzio, Luca

CANTICA DAVIDI REGIS see Wagner-Regeny, Rudolf

CANTICA IN HON. S. ANTONII TAUMAT see Ravanello, Oreste

CANTICA NOVA see Driessler, Johannes

CANTICA SACRA see Jochum, Otto

CANTICE OF CAROLS, A *Xmas
   SSA CHAPPELL 0014522-354 $.40   (C325)

CANTICLE FOR COMMUNION see Marshall

CANTICLE FOR EASTER, A see Peninger, David

CANTICLE FOR EASTER, A see Young

CANTICLE FOR GOD'S KINGDOM ON EARTH, A see Purvis, Richard

CANTICLE FROM THE PSALMS see Williams

CANTICLE IN MEDITATION see Kingery

CANTICLE OF BROTHERHOOD see White, John

CANTICLE OF BROTHERHOOD, A see Purvis, Richard

CANTICLE OF CELEBRATION see Young, Gordon

CANTICLE OF CHRISTMAS see Giannini, V.

CANTICLE OF COMMEMORATION, A see Pfautsch, Lloyd

CANTICLE OF CREATION, A see Young

CANTICLE OF JOY, A see Purvis, Richard

CANTICLE OF JUDITH see Ahrold, Frank

CANTICLE OF LIGHT, A see Purvis, Richard

CANTICLE OF LOVE, A see Thompson

CANTICLE OF MAN, A see Rawsthorne

CANTICLE OF MARY see Glarum, L. Stanley, Magnificat

CANTICLE OF PEACE, A see Clokey

CANTICLE OF PRAISE
   (Jurey) SSA,orch oct BELWIN 60385 $.30, ipa
                                              (C326)
   (Jurey) SAB,orch oct BELWIN 60529 $.30, ipa
                                              (C327)
   (Jurey) SATB,orch oct BELWIN 60228 $.25, ipa
                                              (C328)

CANTICLE OF PRAISE see Beck, John Ness

CANTICLE OF PRAISE see Charpentier, Marc-Antoine

CANTICLE OF PRAISE see Clokey, Joseph Waddell

CANTICLE OF PRAISE see Hopson

CANTICLE OF PRAISE see McAfee, Don

CANTICLE OF PRAISE see Pinkham, Daniel

CANTICLE OF PRAISE see Purvis, Richard

CANTICLE OF PRAISE, A see Handel, George Frideric

CANTICLE OF PRAISE, A see Rasley

CANTICLE OF ST. FRANCIS see Tyler

CANTICLE OF THANKSGIVING, A see Pfautsch, Lloyd

CANTICLE OF THE LAMP see Rorem, Ned

CANTICLE OF THE MARTYRS see Giannini, V.

CANTICLE OF THE ROSE see Searle, Humphrey

CANTICLE OF THE SUN, THE see Goemanne, Noel

CANTICLE OF THE WISE MEN see Gretchaninov, Alexander Tikhonovitch

CANTICLE TO HOPE see Hindemith, Paul

CANTICLES FOR CHRISTMAS see Polifrone, J.J.

CANTICLES FOR SALISBURY (1966) see Mc Cabe, John

CANTICLES OF CHRISTMAS see Dean, T.W.

CANTICLES OF THE VIRGIN MARY see Hurd, Michael

CANTICLES, SET I see Rorem, Ned

CANTICLES, SET II see Rorem, Ned

CANTICO DEL SOLE see Somma, Bonaventura

CANTICO DELLE CREATURE see Bianchi, Francesco

CANTICO DI FRATE SOLE see Gorlatto, Giacomo

CANTICO DI MOSE see Renzi, Armando

CANTICUM CANTICORUM see Bossi, Marco Enrico

CANTICUM EPISCOPALE (LAUDATE EPISCOPUM) see Socal, Pietro

CANTICUM EZECHIAE see Kern, Matthias

CANTICUM FESTIVUM see Kelly

CANTICUM FRATIS SOLIS see Sigtenhorst-Meyer, [Bernhard van den]

CANTICUM GAUDII see Peeters, Flor

CANTICUM HEBRAICUM see Saladin, Louis

CANTICUM I-GELOBT SEI DER HERR see Jacob, Werner

CANTICUM PSALMI RESURRECTIONIS see Schonbach, [Dieter]

CANTICUM PSALMORUM see Hemel, Oscar van

CANTICUM SAPIENTIAE see Wellesz, Egon

CANTICUM SIMEONIS see Barbe, Helmut

CANTICUM SIMEONIS see Olsson, Otto Emmanuel

CANTICUM SIMEONIS "NUNC DIMITTUS" see Blarr, Oskar Gottlieb

CANTICUM ZACHARIAE see Johansson, Bengt

CANTILLATION CHORALE see Gottlieb, J.

CANTIONAL ODER GESANGBUCH AUGSBURGISCHER KONFESSION, TEIL I see Schein, Johann Hermann

CANTIONAL ODER GESANGBUCH AUGSBURGISCHER KONFESSION, TEIL II see Schein, Johann Hermann

CANTIONES DUARUM VOCUM see Lassus, Roland de (Orlandus)

CANTIONES QUATUOR VOCUM VOL. 1 see Byrd, William

CANTIONES QUATUOR VOCUM VOL. 2 see Byrd, William

CANTIONES QUINQUE VOCUM see Byrd, William

CANTIONES SACRAE see Heiberg

CANTIONES SACRAE see Gardner, John [Linton]

CANTIONES SACRAE [36] see Schutz, Heinrich

CANTIONES SACRAE [41] see Schutz, Heinrich

CANTIONES SACRAE [42] see Schutz, Heinrich

CANTIONES SACRAE [43] see Schutz, Heinrich

CANTIONES SACRAE [44] see Schutz, Heinrich

CANTIONES SACRAE 1625, BAND 1 see Schutz, Heinrich

CANTIONES SACRAE 1625 BAND 1 [NR. 1-3] see Schutz, Heinrich

CANTIONES SACRAE 1625 BAND 1 [NR. 4-8] see Schutz, Heinrich

CANTIONES SACRAE 1625 BAND 1 [NR. 9-10] see Schutz, Heinrich

CANTIONES SACRAE 1625 BAND 1 [NR. 11-12] see Schutz, Heinrich

CANTIONES SACRAE 1625 BAND 1 [NR. 13-14] see Schutz, Heinrich

CANTIONES SACRAE 1625 BAND 1 [NR. 15] see Schutz, Heinrich

CANTIONES SACRAE 1625 BAND 1 [NR. 17-18] see Schutz, Heinrich

CANTIONES SACRAE 1625 BAND 1 [NR. 19-20] see Schutz, Heinrich

CANTIONES SACRAE 1625, BAND 2 see Schutz, Heinrich

CANTIONES SACRAE 1625 BAND 2 [NR. 16] see Schutz, Heinrich

CANTIONES SACRAE 1625 BAND 2 [NR. 21-23] see Schutz, Heinrich

CANTIONES SACRAE 1625 BAND 2 [NR. 24-25] see Schutz, Heinrich

CANTIONES SACRAE 1625 BAND 2 [NR. 26-28] see Schutz, Heinrich

CANTIONES SACRAE 1625 BAND 2 [NR. 29] see Schutz, Heinrich

CANTIONES SACRAE 1625 BAND 2 [NR. 30] see Schutz, Heinrich

CANTIONES SACRAE 1625 BAND 2 [NR. 31] see Schutz, Heinrich

CANTIONES SACRAE 1625 BAND 2 [NR. 32] see Schutz, Heinrich

CANTIONES SACRAE 1625 BAND 2 [NR. 33-35] see Schutz, Heinrich

CANTIONES SACRAE 1625 BAND 2 [NR. 36-40] see Schutz, Heinrich

CANTIONES SACRAE DE ADVENTU DOMINI-HEFT 1 *CCU,Renais
   (Pass, Walter) 4pt&5pt DOBLINGER s.p.   (C329)

CANTIONES SACRAE HEBDOMADAE SANCTAE see Ferrari, Giovanni

CANTIONES SACRAE IN QUADRAGESIMA, E "NOVI ATQUE CATHOLICI THESAURI MUSICI *CCU
   (Pass, Walter) 4-5pt DOBLINGER s.p. contains works by: Zaphelius, M.; Di Lasso, O.
                                              (C330)

CANTIONES SACRAE see Sweelinck, Jan Pieterszoon

CANTIONES SINE TEXTU see Lassus, Roland de (Orlandus)

CANTIQUE see Boisdeffre, Charles-Henri-Rene de

CANTIQUE A LA VIERGE MARIE see Gigout, [Eugene]

CANTIQUE DE JEAN RACINE see Faure, Gabriel-Urbain

CANTIQUE DE LA SAINTE VIERGE see Magnificat

CANTIQUE DE NOEL see Adam, Adolphe-Charles

CANTIQUE DE NOEL see Bonnal, Ermend

CANTIQUE DE NOEL see Gevaert, Francois Auguste

CANTIQUE DE PAQUES see Bantock, Granville

CANTIQUE DE PAQUES see Honegger, Arthur

CANTIQUE DE PENTECOTE see Bach, Johann Sebastian

CANTIQUE DE RACINE SUR LE BONHEUR DES JUSTES ET LE MALHEUR DES REPROUVES see Hahn, Reynaldo

CANTIQUE DE SIMEON see Nunc Dimitis

CANTIQUE DE SIMEON see Schmitt, Florent

CANTIQUE NUPTIAL see Mazellier, J.

CANTIQUE POUR LA PREMIERE COMMUNION see Gounod, Charles Francois

CANTIQUE POUR L'ADORATION DU SAINT-SACREMENT see Gounod, Charles Francois

CANTIQUE POUR MESSE DE MARRIAGE see Yung, Alf.

CANTO A LA NOCHE see Beethoven, Ludwig van

CANTO ANTIBLASFEMO see Visona', Gino

CANTO DE AGUINALDO see Benedito

CANTO DE NAVIDAD see Aguilar

CANTO DE NAVIDAD see Benedito

CANTO DEL ANGEL see Ciria

CANTO DI NATALE see Zuccoli, Gastone

CANTO DI NATALE E VOCALIZZO see Guerrini, Guido

CANTOR, J.
    Where Shall My Soul Repose?
        SATB,acap oct PRESSER MC378 $.30   (C331)

CANTU
    Immacolata *ora
        cor RICORDI-ENG s.p.   (C332)

CANTUS-FIRMUS-SATZE see Orff, Carl

CANTUS PANNONICUS see Farkas, Ferenc

CANTUS SACRI IN HON. D. ANTONII PAT. COLLECTIO I see Ravanello, Oreste

CANTUS SACRI IN HON. D. ANTONII PAT. COLLECTIO II see Ravanello, Oreste

CANYON HYMNAL FOR BOYS AND GIRLS, THE *CC109U, hymn
    SATB cmplt ed KERBY 5808C $3.00, pap KERBY 5809C $1.50, cloth KERBY 5809 $2.50, voc pt KERBY 5811C $.75   (C333)

CANZONCINA see Arnaldi, Antonio

CANZONCINE PER LA COMMUNIONE see Bottazzo, Luigi

CANZONE A S. FRANCESCO see Moioli, Romano

CANZONE A S. LUIGI see Bottazzo, Luigi

CANZONIERE MARIANO see Tonetti, Ottone

CAPERTON, FLORENCE
    Two Anthems For Children's Voices *Xmas, anthem
        SA (med) ABINGDON APM-681 $.30   (C334)

CAPLET, ADRIEN (1878-1925)
    Oraison Domenicale (from Les Prieres)
        (Charpentier, J.) [Fr] mix cor,org oct DURAND s.p.   (C335)

    Salutation Angelique (from Les Prieres)
        (Charpentier, J.) [Fr] mix cor,org oct DURAND s.p.   (C336)

CAPLET, [LUCIEN] (1873-1928)
    Agnus Dei
        see Trois Chants D'eglise

    Le Miroir De Jesus, Mysteres Du Rosaires
        [Fr] wom cor,solo,harp,strings voc sc DURAND s.p., ipr   (C337)

    Messe Des Petits De Saint-Eustache-La- Foret *Mass
        [Fr] 3pt,opt inst oct DURAND s.p., ipa (C338)

    Panis Angelicus *Commun,mot
        [Lat] opt cor,solo,org,vln/fl,vcl DURAND s.p.   (C339)

    Pie Jesu *Gen,mot
        [Lat] cor,opt org oct DURAND s.p., ipa (C340)

    Sanctus
        see Trois Chants D'eglise
        see Trois Chants D'eglise

    Trois Chants D'eglise
        [Lat] 3pt,acap oct DURAND s.p.
        contains: Agnus Dei; Sanctus; Sanctus (C341)

CAPPADONIA
    Alleluia, Prayer And Amen
        SATB KJOS 5829 $.30   (C342)

CAPPADONIA, ANTHONY
    Litany For A Penitent
        SATB oct AGAPE CE 4324 $.30   (C343)

CAPRA
    O Bambino (composed with Velona) *Xmas
        (Simeone) SSA SHAWNEE B 242 $.30   (C344)
        (Velona; Simeone) TTBB SHAWNEE C200 $.30 (C345)
        (Velona; Simeone) SAB SHAWNEE D97 $.35 (C346)

CAPRICORNUS, SAMEUEL (1628-1665)
    Der Gerechten Seelen Sind In Gottes Hand *ECY
        (Grusnick, Bruno) [Ger] SATB,cont,strings (med easy) BAREN. BA 957 sc s.p., cor pts s.p., ipa   (C347)

CAPTIVE MAID OF ISRAEL see Guest, J.

CAPTIVES OF BABYLON see Shinn, G.

CAPUT see Dufay, Guillaume

CARA LA VITA MIA see Sermisy, Claude de

CARACTACUS see Elgar, Edward

CARAMBULA
    Canon De Navidad *Xmas,canon
        [Span] 8pt,acap RICORDI-ARG BA 11678 s.p. (C348)

CARDELUS, F.-L. DE
    O Salutaris
        [Lat] 4pt mix cor,org LEMOINE s.p.   (C349)
        [Lat] 4pt mix cor,acap LEMOINE s.p.   (C350)

    Regina Coeli (from Messe Pascale) BVM
        [Lat] 4pt mix cor,soli,org LEMOINE s.p. (C351)
        [Lat] 4pt mix cor,soli,acap LEMOINE   (C352)

CARDEW, CORNELIUS (1936-   )
    Great Learning, The *CC7U,20th cent
        cor,inst EXPERIMENTAL s.p.   (C353)

    Great Learning, The *CC2U,20th cent
        cor,inst EXPERIMENTAL s.p. revised version (C354)

CARDOSO, MANUEL
    Angelis Suis Mandavit *Lent,mot
        [Lat] mix cor,acap oct NOVELLO DM-13 s.p. (C355)

    Angelus Suis Mandavit *Psntd
        [Lat] SATB,acap (med) MULLER M 13 s.p. (C356)

    Cum Audisset Joannes *Adv,mot
        [Lat] SATB,acap (med) MULLER M 4 s.p. (C357)
        [Lat] mix cor,acap oct NOVELLO DM-4 s.p. (C358)

CARETTI, G.M.
    Credo
        (Vecchi, Prof. Giuseppe) unis&2pt,opt org quarto FORNI 89 s.p.   (C359)

CAREY, [HENRY] (1692-1743)
    Christ The Lord Is Risen Today *Easter
        (Ringwald) SATB,acap SHAWNEE A 23 $.35 (C360)

CAREY, LEWIS
    Naemere Dig, Min Gud
        (Beck, Thomas) mix cor/men cor,pno/org cor pts MUSIKK 100 s.p.   (C361)

    Naermere Dig, Min Gud
        (Beck, Thomas) men cor,pno/org MUSIKK 100 s.p.   (C362)

CARILLO, GOMEZ
    Huaynito De Navidad *Xmas
        (Martini) [Span] SATB,acap RICORDI-ARG BA 12259 s.p.   (C363)

    La Guagua De Nochebuena
        (Martini) [Span] SATB,acap RICORDI-ARG BA 12258 s.p.   (C364)

CARILLON see Fraser, Shena

CARILLON CAROL see Williams

CARILLON FOR CHRISTMAS see Young, Gordon

CARILLON (GLORIA IN EXCELSIS DEO) see Hopkins, Anthony

CARILLON, HEIGH HO! see Noe, J.T.

CARILLON HEIGH-HO see Perry

CARISSIMI, GIACOMO (1605?-1674)
    Annunciate Gentes *see O Quam Dulcis Est Deus Noster; Omnes Adorate Dominum (C365)

    Annunciate Gentes
        (Jensen, N.M.) [Lat] SSATB,cont oct MUSIKHOJ 3 $2.00   (C366)

    Cantata Mecum Domino (from Jephtha)
        "Praise Ye, With Me, The Lord Our God" see Carissimi, Giacomo, Hymnus Cantemus Domino

    Cantemus Omnes Domina
        (Richardson) mix cor SOUTHERN $.25   (C367)

    Cantemus Omnes Domino (from Jephtha)
        "Let Us Praise The Lord Our God" see Carissimi, Giacomo, Hymnus Cantemus Domino

    Cantemus Omnis Domina
        (Richardson) "We To The Lord Sing Joyfully" SSATBB oct SPRATT 2003 $.25   (C368)

    Children Of Bethlehem *see O Felix Anima

    Christus Factus Est
        ATB,org SCHIRM.EC 2266 $.16   (C369)

    Final Chorus From 'Jephte'
        (Vlasto) SSATBB,acap (med) OXFORD 43.328 $.25   (C370)

    Historia Di Jephte *Bibl
        (Wolters) 6pt mix cor MOSELER sc s.p., cor pts s.p.   (C371)

    Historia Jonae *Bibl/ora
        (Rudelle) 4pt mix cor&4pt mix cor,4 soli, cont MOSELER s.p.   (C372)

    Hymnus Cantemus Domino (from Jephtha)
        (Beveridge) "Sing Hymns Of Praise To The Host" SS SCHIRM.EC 1968 $.40 contains also: Cantata Mecum Domino, "Praise Ye, With Me, The Lord Our God" (SSA,S solo); Cantemus Omnes Domino, "Let Us Praise The Lord Our God" (SSSAAA) (C373)

    Jephta *ora
        cor voc sc KALMUS 6135 $1.00   (C374)
        (Woldike, Mogens) SSATTB,soli,cont HANSEN-DEN 25325 s.p.   (C375)

    Jephte *ora
        mix cor,4 soli,strings BELWIN $1.50   (C376)
        (Gui) [Lat] voc sc UNIVER. 8314 $5.45, cor pts UNIVER. 8789A-F $.85   (C377)

    Jephthah *ora
        ,[Eng/Lat] SSSATB,SATB soli,org/pno voc sc NOVELLO s.p., ipr   (C378)

CARISSIMI, GIACOMO (cont'd.)
    Jeptha *Bibl/cant
        [Eng/Lat] BELWIN $1.00   (C379)
        cor,orch sc KALMUS $12.00, ipa   (C380)

    Judicium Salomonis *Bibl/ora
        (Egidi, A.) "Konig Salomons Urteil" [Ger/Lat] mix cor,SSTB soli,strings,org/pno/cembalo VIEWEG sc s.p., cor pts s.p., ipa (C381)

    Konig Salomons Urteil *see Judicium Salomonis

    Lament Ye Children Of Israel *see Plorate, Filii Israel

    Let Us Praise The Lord Our God *see Cantemus Omnes Domino

    Magnificat *Magnif
        (Drechsler) 4pt mix cor&4pt mix cor,cont MOSELER sc s.p., cor pts s.p.   (C382)

    O Come Little Children *see O Felix Anima

    O Come Ye To The Cross *Lent
        (Lovelace, Austin C.) SSAATB,acap (med) ABINGDON $.25   (C383)

    O Felix Anima *Xmas
        (Greyson) mix cor SOUTHERN $.25   (C384)
        (Greyson) "O Come Little Children" SAB oct BOURNE ES59 $.25   (C385)
        (Zanon-Vene) "Children Of Bethlehem" [Lat/Eng] ATB,acap oct COLOMBO 1874 $.50 (C386)

    O Quam Dulcis Est Deus Noster
        [Lat] SSATB,kbd (contains also solo works) voc sc cor pts HINRICHSEN D2412 s.p. see from Annunciate Gentes   (C387)

    O Sacra Convivium *mot
        [Lat] SAT,acap MUSICUS 1015 $.15   (C388)

    O Weep, Ye Daughters Of Israel (from Jephte) Gen
        SSATBB,acap (med easy) oct OXFORD $.25 (C389)

    Omnes Adorate Dominum
        [Lat] SSATB,kbd (contains also solo works) voc sc cor pts HINRICHSEN D2412 s.p. see from Annunciate Gentes   (C390)

    Plorate, Filii Israel (from Jephtha)
        mix cor SOUTHERN $.35   (C391)
        SATB KJOS 29 $.30   (C392)
        [Lat] 6pt mix cor MOSELER LB-730 s.p. (C393)
        "Lament, Ye Children Of Israel" SSATTB SCHIRM.EC 1172 $.30   (C394)
        (Davison, A.) [Lat] TTBB,pno/org SCHIRM.EC 32 $.25   (C395)
        (Greyson) "Lament Ye Children Of Israel" SSATBB oct BOURNE ES34 $.40   (C396)

    Praise Ye, With Me, The Lord Our God *see Cantata Mecum Domino

    Sing Hymns Of Praise To The Host *see Hymnus Cantemus Domino

    We To The Lord Sing Joyfully *see Cantemus Omnis Domina

CARL FISCHER CAROL BOOK see Breck

CARL FISCHER SACRED CHORAL COLLECTION *CCU
    SATB FISCHER,C O-4467 $1.25   (C397)

CARL, MICHAEL (1911-   )
    Antwort Auf Alle Fragen *Gen
        [Ger] 3pt mix cor,acap (med easy) BOSSE BE 228 s.p.   (C398)

CARLETON
    Memories Of Christmas *Xmas
        SATB oct LORENZ A318 $.30   (C399)

    My Christmas Prayer *Xmas
        SATB oct LORENZ B9 $.30   (C400)

    Night Of The Star *Xmas,cant
        SATB oct LORENZ $1.95   (C401)
        SSA oct LORENZ $1.75   (C402)

    Risen King *Easter,cant
        SATB LORENZ $1.95   (C403)

    Star In The Sky, A *Xmas,cant
        SAB oct LORENZ $1.75   (C404)
        SATB oct LORENZ $1.95   (C405)

    Wonder Of The Star, The *Xmas,cant
        SATB oct LORENZ $1.95   (C406)

CARLEY, ISABEL M.
    Flemish Dance Carol *Xmas,carol,Fr
        unis, orff inst (easy) oct CONCORDIA 98-2159 $.30   (C407)

    Gentle Mary Laid Her Child *Xmas
        unis, orff inst (easy) oct CONCORDIA 98-2158 $.30   (C408)

    Sing For The Joy Of Easter *Easter
        SSA/SSAA,opt brass, Orff inst (med easy) oct CONCORDIA 98-2148 $.25   (C409)

CARLMAN, GUSTAF
    Elie Himmelsfard
        3pt mix cor NORDISKA 4947 s.p.   (C410)

CARLOS V
    Ecce Sic Benedicetur Homo
        (Rubio) [Lat] 4pt mix cor,acap UNION ESP. 21553 s.p.   (C411)

CARLSON, J. BERT
    Chosen Ones *anthem
        SATB (med) oct AUGSBURG 1614 $.25   (C412)

    Mary's Lament *anthem
        unis (easy) oct AUGSBURG 0533 $.20   (C413)
        unis treb cor (easy) oct AUGSBURG 0533 $.20 (C414)

CARLSON, R.
I Heard The Bells On Christmas Day *Xmas
jr cor,acap oct PRESSER 312-40547 $.30
(C415)

CARLSSON, WERTHER
Bethlehems Stjarna
mix cor,solo,pno/org/orch cor pts NORDISKA
1237 s.p., voc sc NORDISKA 3374 s.p.
(C416)

CARLSTEDT, GUNNEMER
Aftonpsalm *Psalm
3pt mix cor NORDISKA 4805 s.p.
(C417)

Hoppas Pa Herren, Israel *mot
mix cor NORDISKA 6116 s.p.
(C418)

Jesu Tank Pa Mig
3pt mix cor NORDISKA 5783 s.p.
(C419)

Kommen Till Mig *Refm,mot
3pt mix cor NORDISKA 6117 s.p.
(C420)

Lova Herren, Min Sjal *mot
3pt mix cor NORDISKA 6118 s.p.
(C421)

O Jesus Krist, Dig Till Oss Vand
mix cor NORDISKA 3793 s.p.
(C422)

Och Du Betlehem *mot
mix cor NORDISKA 6119 s.p.
(C423)

Saliga Aro De Renhjartade
3pt mix cor NORDISKA 5784 s.p.
(C424)

Se, Vi Ga Nu Upp Till Jerusalem
3pt mix cor NORDISKA 5785 s.p.
(C425)

Till Dig, Herre, Upplyfter Jag Min Sjal
mix cor NORDISKA 4899 s.p.
(C426)

CARMEL, DOV
Festival Cantata *Heb
SATB,MezT soli,orch voc sc ISRAELI 335 s.p.
(C427)

CARMEN FINALE "ALLELUIA" see Monnikendam,
Marius

CARMEN FUNEBRAE see Wesley, Samuel Sr.

CARMEN PASCHALE see Wellesz, Egon

CARMEN VERNALE see Foss, Julius

CARMEN VITALE see Rawsthorne, Alan

CARMICHAEL
He Keeps Me Singing
(Bridges) SATB oct WORD CS-2484 $.35 (C428)

Over In Bethlehem *Xmas
(Hearn) unis/SA oct WORD CS-2428 $.30
(C429)

We Are More Than Conquerors
SATB oct WORD CS-354 $.30
(C430)

CARMICHAEL, CAROL
Carol Carmichael Song Book *CC10L
jr cor voc sc WORD 37543 $1.95
(C431)

CARMICHAEL, P.L.
Lord Is My Light, The
SATB,S solo,pno (easy) oct WILLIS 6457 $.12
(C432)

CARMICHAEL, RALPH
Cross And The Switchblade, The *CCUL
SATB voc sc WORD 30075 $1.95, ipa (C433)

Harvest Celebration *Thanks
SATB,kbd,winds,4trp,4trom,5vln,2vla,2vcl,
bvl,gtr voc sc WORD 37531 $2.95, ipa
(C434)

He's Everything To Me
SATB oct WORD CS-321 $.30
(C435)

He's There Waiting
SATB oct WORD CS-2478 $.40
(C436)

I Believe God Is Real
SATB oct WORD CS-2477 $.35
(C437)

Is There Not A Cause
SATB oct WORD CS-2483 $.30
(C438)

Love Is Surrender
SATB oct WORD CS-2475 $.35
(C439)

Man, The
SATB oct WORD CS-2512 $.35
(C440)

My Master
SATB oct WORD CS-342 $.30
(C441)

Natural High *see Kaiser, Kurt

New Mind, A
SATB oct WORD CS-2480 $.35
(C442)

New Twenty-Third, The
SATB oct WORD CS-362 $.30
(C443)

New Wine *folk
SATB voc sc WORD 37551 $2.95
(C444)

Not With A Sword
SATB oct WORD CS-2482 $.35
(C445)

Ralph Carmichael Choir #1, The *CCUL
SATB voc sc WORD 15016 $1.50
(C446)

Restless Ones, The
SATB oct WORD CS-356 $.30
(C447)

Savior Is Waiting, The
SATB oct WORD CS-650 $.25
(C448)

There Is More To Life
SATB oct WORD CS-355 $.30
(C449)

To Our God Give Praise
SATB oct WORD CS-2513 $.30
(C450)

CARMINA DE MORTUIS see Twardowski, Romuald

CARMINALIA see Sibelius, Jean

CARMONY
Behold The Crucified!
SATB oct LORENZ A409 $.60
(C451)

Jesus Speaks From The Cross
SATB oct LORENZ A442 $.60
(C452)

Kneel At The Manger *Xmas,cant
SATB oct LORENZ A398 $.60
(C453)

CARMONY, BRYAN M.
Mine Is A Risen Saviour *Easter,cant
mix cor&opt speak cor,opt narrator voc sc
LILLENAS ME-207 $.60
(C454)

Stones Cry Out, The *Palm,cant
wom cor&men cor,narrator,soli voc sc
LILLENAS ME-216 $.60
(C455)

CARNEGIE, M.
Blessed Are The Pure In Heart *Bibl
SATB PATERSON 1641 s.p.
(C456)

CARNEVALI
Alleluia! Behold The King
SA/SATB oct SUMMY M 2903 $.25
(C457)

CARO MEA see Burkhart, Franz

CARO MEA see Cervi, Luigi

CARO MEA see Clemens, Jacobus

CARO MEA see Gabrieli, Andrea

CARO MEA see Matelart, Johannes

CARO MEA see Scarlatti, Alessandro

CARO MEA see Volpi, Edoardo

CARO MEA VERE EST CIBUS see Gascongne, Mathieu

CARO MIA EST CIBUS see Gascogne

CAROL
Holly Tree *Xmas
(Christiansen, P.) SATB SCHMITT 1804 $.30
(C458)

CAROL
see Colonial Christmas Carols

CAROL see Austin

CAROL see Hannay

CAROL see Smit

CAROL see Taylor, H. Stanley

CAROL, A see Graham

CAROL, A see Bacon, Ernst

CAROL, A see Byles, B. D.

CAROL, A see Farjeon, [Harry]

CAROL BASED ON "THE FIRST NOEL" see Cory, G.

CAROL BERRY TREE see Van Voorhis

CAROL, BROTHERS, CAROL see Fast, Willard S.

CAROL CANTATA see Brown, R.

CAROL CARMICHAEL SONG BOOK see Carmichael,
Carol

CAROL FOR A NEW-BORN KING see Thomas, Mansel

CAROL FOR A WASSEL BOWL, A see Gordon, P.

CAROL FOR CHILDREN see Pfautsch, Lloyd

CAROL FOR CHILDREN, A see Pfautsch, Lloyd

CAROL FOR CHRISTMAS, A see Demuth

CAROL FOR EASTER, A see Caldwell, Mary
[Elizabeth]

CAROL FOR EASTERTIDE, A see Rasley

CAROL FOR EPIPHANY see Hunnicutt, Judy

CAROL FOR JOY see Hunnicutt, Judy

CAROL FOR LENT, A see Caldwell, Mary
[Elizabeth]

CAROL FOR NEW YEAR'S DAY *Xmas,carol
SATB ALLANS 224 s.p.
(C459)

CAROL FOR THE CHRIST-CHILD, A see Rasley

CAROL FOR THE EPIPHANY SEASON, A see Brandon

CAROL FOR THE HOME see Wood

CAROL FOR THE KING see Pooler, Marie

CAROL FOR THE UNITY OF ALL MANKIND, A see
Purvis, Richard

CAROL FOR THE WATCHERS see Musgrave, Thea

CAROL FOR TWO SEASONS, A see Lovelace, Austin
C.

CAROL FROM AN IRISH CABIN see Wood

CAROL IS BORN, A see Heinrich

CAROL, M.
Christmas Folk Song *Xmas
(Reese, L.) SSA,acap oct PRESSER 312-40119
$.30
(C460)

CAROL, N.
Three Holy Women *Easter
(Gaul, H.) SATB oct PRESSER 332-12597 $.25
(C461)

CAROL-NOEL see Wilhousky

CAROL O YE ANGELS *Xmas,carol
(Anderson, W.H.) SATB oct LESLIE 4015 see
from Two Christmas Carols, Set 1 (C462)

CAROL OF A ROSE see Daniels, Mabel Wheeler

CAROL OF ADAM'S FALL see Brandon, George

CAROL OF BEAUTY *Gen/Thanks,carol
unis (easy) OXFORD 08.164 $.15 (C463)
(Sargent, Malcolm) SSAATTBB (med) oct OXFORD
43.319 $.25 (C464)
(Warrell) SATB,acap (med) OXFORD 43. 206 $.50
(C465)

CAROL OF HOPE, A see Swift, B.

CAROL OF HUMILITY, A see Brown, Rex P., O Deue
D Pob Cristion

CAROL OF HUMILITY, A see O Deue D Pob Cristion

CAROL OF KING CANUTE, THE see Wills, Arthur

CAROL OF MARY see Goode, Jack C.

CAROL OF PRAISE, A see Brown, Rex P., Nos Galan

CAROL OF PRAISE, A see Nos Galan

CAROL OF SERVICE
unis/SATB (easy) OXFORD 08.106 $.15 (C466)

CAROL OF TH FRIENDLY BEASTS see Crissman, J.

CAROL OF THANKSGIVING see Wetzler, Robert

CAROL OF THE ADVENT *Adv
unis/SATB (easy) OXFORD 08.132 $.15 (C467)

CAROL OF THE ADVENT see Dietterich, Philip R.

CAROL OF THE ANGELS see Brown

CAROL OF THE ANGELS see Giasson

CAROL OF THE ANGELS, THE see Niles, John Jacob

CAROL OF THE ANIMALS see Strilko, Anthony

CAROL OF THE BAGPIPER
see Christ Is Born, Little Infant King

CAROL OF THE BAGPIPES see Glover, R.F.

CAROL OF THE BAMBOO FLUTE see Purvis, Richard

CAROL OF THE BAPTISM see Brandon, George

CAROL OF THE BEASTIES see Brown, E. Bouldin

CAROL OF THE BELLS *Xmas,carol
oct HART s.p. (C468)
(Wilhousky) SATB,acap oct FISCHER,C CM-4604
$.25 (C469)
(Wilhousky) SSA,acap oct FISCHER,C CM-5276
$.25 (C470)
(Wilhousky) TTBB oct FISCHER,C CM-2270 $.25
(C471)

CAROL OF THE BELLS see Burns

CAROL OF THE BELLS see Jenkyns, Peter

CAROL OF THE BELLS see Leontovich, M.

CAROL OF THE BELLS see Rogers

CAROL OF THE BELLS, A see Watson, D.

CAROL OF THE BIRDS *Xmas,carol,Fr/Span
(Carter) SSA oct BELWIN 60811 $.30 (C472)
(Ehret) SA oct SPRATT 642 $.30 (C473)
(Kinsman, Franklin) SATB oct WALTON 2001 $.30
(C474)
(Shaw; Parker) mix cor,S solo,acap oct
SCHIRM.G 10173 $.35 (C475)
(Walton) SSA oct BOOSEY 5004 $.30 (C476)
(Walton) SAB oct BOOSEY 5131 $.30 (C477)
(Weiss, Donn) SATB,acap FOSTER MF505 $.30
(C478)

CAROL OF THE BIRDS see Anonymous

CAROL OF THE BIRDS see Black

CAROL OF THE BIRDS see Cain, Noble

CAROL OF THE BIRDS see Malin

CAROL OF THE BIRDS see Thiman, Eric Harding

CAROL OF THE BIRDS see Wallace, William

CAROL OF THE BIRDS AND THE CHRIST CHILD *Xmas,
carol,Czech
(Ehret) SAB,opt fl oct FOX CC2 $.25 (C479)
(Ehret, W.) SAB,opt fl PROWSE CC2 s.p. (C480)

CAROL OF THE BIRDS, THE *Xmas,carol,Span
(Higdon, George) SSA,S solo,opt pno/org oct
WORLD AC-1924-3 $.45 (C481)

CAROL OF THE BIRDS, THE see Niles, John Jacob

CAROL OF THE BOHEMIAN BRETHREN see Gaul, Alfred
Robert

CAROL OF THE CHILDREN see Priesing

CAROL OF THE CHRISTMAS CHIMES see Kountz

CAROL OF THE DANCING SHEPHERDS see Davis,
Katherine K.

CAROL OF THE DRUM see Davis, J.

CAROL OF THE FLOWERS *Xmas,carol,Fr
(Bolz) treb cor oct FOX S165 $.25 (C482)

CAROL OF THE FRIENDLY BEASTS *Xmas
(Caldwell) SATB SCHMITT 1741 $.35 (C483)

CAROL OF THE GOOD THIEF *Xmas,carol
(Whitehead, Alfred) SATB oct LESLIE 4008 see
from Three Christmas Carols, Set 2 (C484)

CAROL OF THE HAY *Xmas,carol,Pol
(Ehret, Walter) SATB,opt inst oct WALTON 2512
$.30 (C485)
(Ehret, Walter) SSA oct WALTON 2540 $.30
(C486)

CAROL OF THE HEAVENLY HOSTS see Kountz

CAROL OF THE HOLY ROSE
see Two European Folk Carols

CAROL OF THE INCARNATION see Sjolund, Paul

CAROL OF THE ITALIAN PIPERS see Zgodava

CAROL OF THE LITTLE KING see Caldwell, Mary
[Elizabeth]

CAROL OF THE LITTLEST ANGEL see Taylor, Dorthy
J.

CAROL OF THE LONELY SHEPHERD see Caldwell, Mary
[Elizabeth]

CAROL OF THE MANGER *Xmas
(Wood) SATB&jr cor SCHMITT SD6212 $.40 (C487)

CAROL OF THE MANGER see Hafso

CAROL OF THE NEW YEAR see McAfee, Don

CAROL OF THE NORTHERN LIGHTS *Xmas,carol
(Bancroft, H.H.) SATB oct LESLIE 4020 see
from Two Christmas Carols, Set 2   (C488)

CAROL OF THE NUNS see Anonymous

CAROL OF THE PIFFERARI *Xmas,hymn,It
(Van Christy) mix cor oct BELWIN 2190 $.30
(C489)

CAROL OF THE QUESTIONING CHILD see Kountz,
Richard

CAROL OF THE ROSES see Kountz, Richard

CAROL OF THE RUSSIAN CHILDREN *Xmas
(Gaul) mix cor,acap oct SCHIRM.G 6770 $.25
(C490)
(Gaul) 3pt mix cor,acap oct SCHIRM.G 8618
$.25   (C491)
(Gaul) 4pt men cor,acap oct SCHIRM.G 7363
$.25   (C492)
(Gaul) 4pt wom cor,acap oct SCHIRM.G 7364
$.25   (C493)
(Treharne) 3pt boy cor,acap oct SCHIRM.G 7878
$.25   (C494)

CAROL OF THE SHEEP BELLS see Kountz

CAROL OF THE SHEEPFOLD see Johnson

CAROL OF THE SHEPHERD LAD see Nitske, F.

CAROL OF THE SHEPHERDS *carol
(Ehret) SATB oct BOOSEY 5470 $.30   (C495)

CAROL OF THE SHEPHERDS see Couperin, Francois

CAROL OF THE SHEPHERDS see Dunn, T.

CAROL OF THE SHEPHERDS see Moller, Friedrich

CAROL OF THE SHEPHERDS, THE see Anonymous

CAROL OF THE SIMPLE SHEPHERD
see Two European Folk Carols

CAROL OF THE STABLE see Anonymous

CAROL OF THE STAR *Xmas,carol
oct HART s.p.   (C496)

CAROL OF THE STAR see Noble, Thomas Tertius

CAROL OF THE STAR see Simeone

CAROL OF THE STAR, THE see Simeone

CAROL OF THE STARS *Xmas,carol,Ger
(Ehret) SSA oct SHAPIRO SK 3039 $.30   (C497)

CAROL OF THE STORK see Ossewaarde, Jack

CAROL OF THE STORK see Rickard

CAROL OF THE THREE KINGS see Gesangbuch

CAROL OF THE TRANSFIGURATION *carol
(Brandon) SA oct BOURNE 2031 $.25   (C498)

CAROL OF THE TREES see Wetherill

CAROL OF THE VISITATION see Brandon, G.

CAROL OF THE WIND see Reed, Elmore M.G.

CAROL OF WONDER see Staley

CAROL OF YE ANGELS see Anderson, [William H.]

CAROL ON GREENSLEEVES
see Coventry Carol, The

CAROL ON ST. STEVEN see Davies, Peter Maxwell

CAROL SERVICE FOR CHILDREN, A see Grieb,
Herbert [C.]

CAROL SERVICE WITH NINE LESSONS see Kirk,
Theron W.

CAROL, SWEETLY CAROL *Xmas,carol
(Ehret) SA BOOSEY-CAN s.p.   (C499)

CAROL, SWEETLY CAROL see Hall

CAROL TO THE NEW BORN KING see Ketterer, Laura,
Noel, Nouvelet, Noel Provencal

CAROL TRILOGY, A see Frackenpohl, Arthur

CAROL YE see Wilson

CAROLERS, THE see Matheson

CAROLINE TE DEUM see Handel, George Frideric

CAROLING, CAROLING *CC13L,Xmas,carol
(Luboff, Norman) oct men cor WALTON M 112
$1.75; mix cor WALTON M113 $1.75   (C500)

CAROLING, CAROLING see Burt, Alfred

CAROLS AND SONGS FOR CHRISTMASTIDE see Verrall,
John

CAROLS FOR CHOIRS *CCU,carol
(Jacques; Willcocks) SATB (med) OXFORD pap
$1.80, bds $3.00   (C501)

CAROLS FOR CHRISTMASTIDE see Brown, J.

CAROLS FOR SINGING AND PLAYING *CCU,carol
(Galloway) unis,opt acap (easy) OXFORD 58.632
$1.90   (C502)

CAROLS FOR THE SEASONS see Willan, Healey

CAROLS FROM MANY LANDS *CCU,Xmas,carol
SATB/unis LORENZ C115 $.35   (C503)

CAROLS OF CHRISTMAS see Lorenz

CAROLS OF KING DAVID see Williamson, Malcolm

CAROLS OF TODAY *CCU,carol
SATB (diff) pap OXFORD $2.95   (C504)

CAROLS OLD AND NEW see Peery, [Rob Roy]

CARON, [PHILIPPE]
Da Pacem *15th cent
(Cartier, Anita) [Lat] 4pt mix cor LEMOINE
s.p.   (C505)

CAROSIO
Hymnus Anni Sancti
[It/Fr/Span/Ger/Esperanto] cor,pno s.p. voc
sc RICORDI-ENG 128094, cor pts RICORDI-
ENG 128095   (C506)

CARPANI
Missa In F *Mass
mix cor,acap voc sc KALMUS 6136 $1.00
(C507)

CARPENTER, S.M.
Christmas Pastorale *Xmas
2pt jr cor/3pt jr cor oct KENDOR $.25 (C508)

Sleep Little Jesus *Xmas,Bene
2pt jr cor oct KENDOR $.25   (C509)
SSA oct KENDOR $.25   (C510)

Time For All Things, A *Bibl
SATB oct KENDOR $.25   (C511)

CARR
Were You There? *Lent
dbl cor SCHMITT 7015 $.25   (C512)

CARR, ALBERT LEE
Christo Paremus Canticum
[Lat] mix cor,acap oct LAWSON 51037 $.25
(C513)

CARRIER
While Standing At The Cross
SATB oct LORENZ B104 $.30   (C514)

CARRILLO, JULIAN (1875-1965)
Messe a S.S. Jean XXIII *see Misa a S.S.
Juan XXIII

Misa a S.S. Juan XXIII
"Messe a S.S. Jean XXIII" men cor,acap
JOBERT voc sc s.p., voc rental   (C515)

CARRINGTON
Song And A Prayer, A
SATB oct LORENZ A282 $.30   (C516)

CARRINGTON, O.M.
Behold I Stand At The Door And Knock *carol
3pt wom cor,acap (med) oct WILLIS 7030 $.20
(C517)

Come Unto Me *carol
3pt wom cor,pno (easy) oct WILLIS 7187 $.20
(C518)

Let Not Your Heart Be Troubled *carol
3pt wom cor,acap (med) oct WILLIS 6225 $.15
(C519)

Shepherds *carol
3pt wom cor,acap (med) oct WILLIS 6574 $.18
(C520)

CARROLL, A see Harris, Jerry Weseley

CARROLL, A see Jacobson

CARROLL, J.R.
Come, Let Us Worship *Gen,anthem
SATB (easy) oct GIA G1739 $.30   (C521)

Four Offertories For The Sundays In Advent
*CC4U,Adv,anthem/Offer
SSA/TTB (med) oct GIA G1276 $.60   (C522)

God Grant You Many Years *Gen,anthem
SATB (easy) oct GIA G1740 $.30   (C523)

Music For The Ordinary Of The Mass *Gen,Mass
unis (med) voc sc GIA G1573 $1.25   (C524)
3 eq voices (med) voc sc GIA G1645 $1.00
(C525)

Music For Wedding Services *CCU,Gen/
Marriage/Proces/Reces,anthem/Mass
TTB (med) cmplt ed GIA G1252 $1.25   (C526)

Receive Now The Body Of Christ *Commun,
anthem
SATB (easy) oct GIA G1741 $.30   (C527)

CARRY CANDLES TO THE MANGER see Emig, Lois

CARTAN
Pater *cant
[Lat] cor,SAT soli,orch voc sc SALABERT-US
$20.00   (C528)

CARTER
Every Star Shall Sing A Carol *Xmas
(Davis) SATB oct GALAXY 1.2521.1 $.30
(C529)

Star Carol
SA/TB FLAMMER E5003 $.25   (C530)

CARTER, CHARLES
God's Loving Care *Austral
SATB (easy) ALLANS 139 s.p.   (C531)

O Worship The King *Fest,Austral
SATB ALLANS 188 s.p.   (C532)

CARTER, ELLIOTT COOK, JR. (1908-   )
Thy Giving Power
SATB,acap FRANK F-631 $.30   (C533)

CARTFORD, GERHARD M.
All My Heart This Night Rejoices
see Descants On Six Hymn Tunes

Come, Thou Almighty King
see Descants On Six Hymn Tunes

Descants On Six Hymn Tunes *hymn
cor&cong oct AUGSBURG 11-1550 $.40
contains: All My Heart This Night
Rejoices; Come, Thou Almighty King;
Good Christian Men, Rejoice And Sing!;
Jesus Shall Reign; Joy To The World;
Strife Is O'er, The   (C534)

Eight Descants *CC8L
cor&cong oct AUGSBURG 11-9155 $.75   (C535)

Good Christian Men, Rejoice And Sing!
see Descants On Six Hymn Tunes

Great God Our Source
see FOUR CONTEMPORARY HYMNS, SET I

Ideo Gloria - On This Day Earth Shall Ring
*Xmas
SATB,3trp (med easy) oct CONCORDIA 98-2157
$.35   (C536)

Jesus Shall Reign
see Descants On Six Hymn Tunes

Joy To The World
see Descants On Six Hymn Tunes

Strife Is O'er, The
see Descants On Six Hymn Tunes

CARULLI
Jesus Is Born Today *Xmas
(Harris) SATB,acap,opt pno oct PRO ART 2616
$.35   (C537)

CARVER, R.
Gaude Flore Virginali
(Stevens, D.) [Lat] SATTB BROUDE,A. 217
$.50   (C538)

CARVER, ROBERT (1487-ca. 1546)
Guade Flore Virginali
see Two Extant Motets, The

O Bone Jesu
see Two Extant Motets, The

Two Extant Motets, The *mot
(Stevens, Denis) cmplt ed AM.INST.MUS.
$7.00
contains: Guade Flore Virginali (cor); O
Bone Jesu (19pt)   (C539)

CASAGRADE, A.
Il Pianto Della Madonna *ora
cor,soli,2fl,2ob,2clar,2bsn,4horn,3trp,
3trom,tuba,strings,timp,perc,harp CARISH
rental   (C540)

CASAJUS, VINCENTE
Communion Service In D-Major *see Missa
Lauda Sion

Missa Lauda Sion
"Communion Service In D-Major" mix cor
SCHIRM.EC 1251   (C541)

CASALI, GIOVANNI BATTISTA (1715-1792)
Exaltabo Te *Psntd
[Ger] SATB,acap (med easy) MULLER MS 74
s.p.   (C542)

Gaudens Gaudebo *cant
4pt mix cor&4pt mix cor,4trp,4trom MOSELER
sc s.p., cor pts s.p., ipa   (C543)

Improperium *see Cain, Noble

Missa G-Dur *Mass
(Bauerle, Hermann) SATB,acap (G maj) cor
pts BREITKOPF-L PB-3135 s.p., voc pt
BREITKOPF-L CHB-2545 s.p.   (C544)

CASALS, PABLO (1876-1973)
Canco A La Verge
girl cor SOUTHERN $.30   (C545)

Eucharistica
[Span/Eng] treb cor,pno/org BROUDE,A. 155
$.30   (C546)

O Vos Omnes
mix cor SOUTHERN $.30   (C547)
[Lat/Eng] SATB BROUDE,A. 128 $.30   (C548)
[Lat/Eng] TTBB BROUDE,A. 242 $.30   (C549)

Recordare, Virgo Mater
[Lat/Eng] SATB,pno/org BROUDE,A. 121 $.30
(C550)

Salve Montserratina
[Lat/Eng] SATB,org BROUDE,A. 151 $.35
(C551)

Tota Pulchra
[Lat/Eng] SATB,opt T solo BROUDE,A. 122
$.30   (C552)

CASATI
Messa Concertata *Mass
4pt mix cor MOSELER s.p.   (C553)

CASCIOLINI, CLAUDIO (ca. 1650- ?)
Asperges Me
(Kaplan, A.) [Lat/Eng] SATB BROUDE,A. 124
$.30   (C554)

Istorum Est *ASD
"To Them Hath Been Given" SATB,acap
SCHIRM.EC 1221 $.16   (C555)

Komm, Heiliger Geist, Erfull Die Herzen
see Kaufmann, Diethelm, Komm, Gott
Schopfer, Heiliger Geist

Lamb Of God *Gen/Lent
SATB,acap (med easy) oct CONCORDIA 98-1771
$.22 contains also: Arcadelt, Jacob, O
Lord, I Cry To Thee   (C556)

CASCIOLINI, CLAUDIO (cont'd.)

Magnificat Septimi Toni
(Washington, Henry) [Lat] SATB CHESTER s.p.
(C557)

Missa In G *Mass
SSA voc sc KALMUS 6138 $1.25 (C558)

Missa Pro Defunctis *Mass/Req
mix cor,acap voc sc KALMUS 6137 $1.25 (C559)

(Bauerle, Hermann) SATB,acap voc sc
BREITKOPF-L PB-3446 s.p., cor pts
BREITKOPF-L CHB-2798 s.p. (C560)

Panis Angelicus *Commun,mot
(Brun, L'abbe F.) [Lat] 4pt mix cor,opt
pno/org DURAND s.p. (C561)

Stabat Mater
(Kaplan, A.) [Lat/Eng] SATB BROUDE,A. 125
$.40 (C562)

To Them Hath Been Given *see Istorum Est

Veni Creator Spiritus
(Lavater, H.) [Lat] men cor,acap (med) HUG
s.p. (C563)

CASELLA, ALFREDO (1883-1947)
Pro Pace *Op.71
[Lat] voc sc UNIVER. 11728 $11.25 (C564)

CASHMORE, DONALD
All My Heart This Night Rejoices *Xmas,
mix cor,orch oct NOVELLO 40.1412.10 s.p.
(C565)

Father Most Holy *anthem
mix cor oct NOVELLO 40.1421.09 s.p. (C566)

Five Festal Introits *CC5U,Asc/Xmas/Easter/
Trin/Whitsun,Introit
SATB cmplt ed NOVELLO 03.0099.03 s.p. (C567)

Give Unto The Lord, O Ye Mighty *anthem
mix cor oct NOVELLO 40.1400.06 s.p. (C568)

God Is Ascended Up On High *Asc,anthem
mix cor oct NOVELLO 28.1403.10 s.p. (C569)

Jesus Comes With All His Grace *Adv/Gen,
anthem
mix cor,acap oct NOVELLO 40.1406.05 s.p. (C570)

Let All Mortal Flesh Keep Silence *anthem/
hymn
mix cor oct NOVELLO 28.1380.07 s.p. (C571)

Lord Of Life Is Risen Indeed, The *Easter,
anthem
mix cor oct NOVELLO 28.1406.04 s.p. (C572)

O God The King Of Glory *anthem
mix cor oct NOVELLO 40.1429.04 s.p. (C573)

O How Amiable Are Thy Dwellings
mix cor CURWEN 80854 s.p. (C574)

Prayer For Epiphany, A *Epiph,anthem/prayer
mix cor oct NOVELLO 50.0334.02 s.p. (C575)

Rejoice And Be Merry *Xmas
SATB BOOSEY-CAN s.p. (C576)

Royal Banners Forward Go, The *Gen/Lent,
anthem
mix cor oct NOVELLO 28.1418.08 s.p. (C577)

Strife Is O'er, The *Easter,anthem
SATB,org/pno NOVELLO AP217 $.35 (C578)
mix cor oct NOVELLO 40.1416.02 s.p. (C579)

This Child Behold *Xmas,cant
SATB,SATB soli,org,strings voc sc NOVELLO
s.p., ipr (C580)

Twenty Introits For General Use *CC20U,Gen,
Introit
mix cor cmplt ed NOVELLO 03.0098.05 s.p. (C581)

CASIMIR, HEINRICH (1873-1946)
Nun Ruhe In Frieden *funeral
[Ger] SATB,acap (easy) MULLER SM 385B sc
s.p., cor pts s.p. (C582)

CASIMIRI, RAFFAELE CASIMIRO (1880-1943)
Adeste Fideles
see Due Mottetti Pel S. Natale

Due Mottetti Pel S. Natale *Xmas,mot
[Lat] 2pt,org ZANIBON 612 s.p.
contains: Adeste Fideles; Jesu Redemptor
Omnium (C583)

Jesu Redemptor Omnium
see Due Mottetti Pel S. Natale

CASINI, GIOVANNI MARIA (ca. 1670-1715)
Missa D-Dur *Mass
(Bauerle, Hermann) SATB,acap (D maj) cor
pts BREITKOPF-L PB-3136 s.p., voc sc
BREITKOPF-L CHB-2546 s.p. (C584)

Omnes Gentes Plaudite *Asc/Easter/Pent,mot
[Lat] SATB,acap (med) MULLER M 21 s.p. (C585)
[Lat] mix cor,acap oct NOVELLO DM-21 s.p. (C586)

CASNER, MYRON D.
O Jesus, I Have Promised *Cnfrm/Gen
unis,kbd (easy) CONCORDIA 98-1459 $.25 (C587)

Only-Begotten, Word Of God *Gen
unis,trp (med easy) oct CONCORDIA 98-1598
$.30, ipa (C588)

CASSELL
Bible Stories In Song (Bk. 1) (composed with
Frederickson, Carl) *CCU
jr cor FISCHER,C R 48 $1.25 (C589)

Bible Stories In Song (Bk. 2) (composed with
Frederickson, Carl) *CCU
jr cor FISCHER,C R 49 $1.25 (C590)

CASSERES, A.
Hamesiach Ilemim
see Lidarti, C.G., Nora Elohim

Hishki Hizki *Heb
(Adler, I.) STB,opt inst ISRAELI 707 ipa (C591)

CASSEY
Faith
SATB HANSEN-US E9845 $.40 (C592)

Lord Make Me An Instrument *Bibl
SATB HANSEN-US E9302 $.40 (C593)

CASSLER
Advent Of Our God
SATB KJOS 5299 $.30 (C594)

CASSLER, G. WINSTON
Built On A Rock
SATB&cong,org,opt 5brass sc AUGSBURG
11-9090 $1.25, cor pts AUGSBURG 11-9091
$.25, ipa (C595)

Built On A Rock The Church Doth Stand
cor&cong,org,trp,trom sc AUGSBURG 11-9087
$1.50, cor pts AUGSBURG 11-9089 $.10, ipa (C596)

Cradled All Lowly *Xmas
SA (easy) ABINGDON APM-130 $.26 (C597)

Credo *anthem/Credo
SATB (med) oct AUGSBURG 1300 $.20 (C598)

Drop Down, Ye Heavens From Above *anthem
SATB (med) oct AUGSBURG 1342 $.22 (C599)

Godly Stranger, The *anthem
SATB (med) oct AUGSBURG 1144 $.22 (C600)

Gospel Trumpet, The
SATB (med) ABINGDON APM-672 $.45 (C601)

Hills Of The North, Rejoice
4pt men cor,acap oct CURWEN 10599 $.30 (C602)
4pt mix cor,acap oct CURWEN 11625 $.30 (C603)
mix cor CURWEN 61569 s.p. (C604)

Holy, Holy, Holy
SATB&cong (med) ABINGDON APM-129 $.35 (C605)

Hymns For Men *CC45U,hymn
4pt men cor oct AUGSBURG 11-9199 $1.75 (C606)

Infant Jesus *Xmas
TTBB (easy) ABINGDON APM-162 $.25 (C607)

Now Thank We All Our God
SATB&cong,org,2trp,1trom (easy) sc AUGSBURG
11-9311 $.85, ipa, cor pts AUGSBURG
11-9313 $.10 (C608)

O God Our Help In Ages Past
SATB&cong,org,2trp,1trom (easy) sc AUGSBURG
11-9315 $.85, ipa, cor pts AUGSBURG
11-9317 $.10 (C609)

O Trinity Of Blessed Light *anthem
SATB (med) oct AUGSBURG 1436 $.30 (C610)

Praise The Savior *Easter
SATB (med) ABINGDON APM-437 $.25 (C611)

Praise To The Lord
SATB&cong,org,2trp,1trom (easy) sc AUGSBURG
11-9328 $.85, ipa, cor pts AUGSBURG
11-9329 $.20 (C612)

Six Sacred Anthems For Male Voices *CC6U,
anthem
TTBB,opt acap (med) ABINGDON APM-240 $.75 (C613)

CAST AWAY ALL YOUR TRANSGRESSIONS see Williams

CAST ME NOT AWAY FROM THY PRESENCE see Wesley,
Samuel Sebastian Jr.

CAST OFF DOUBTFUL CARE see Byrd, William

CAST THY BREAD ON THE WATERS see Roeckel, J.L.

CAST THY BURDEN
2pt CHAPPELL 0021949-352 $.40 (C614)
SSA CHAPPELL 0021949-354 $.40 (C615)
SATB CHAPPELL 0021949-358 $.40 (C616)

CAST THY BURDEN see Mendelssohn-Bartholdy,
Felix

CAST THY BURDEN UPON THE LORD see Aulbach

CAST THY BURDEN UPON THE LORD see Mendelssohn-
Bartholdy, Felix

CAST THY GARMENTS see Goodale, R.L.

CASTALDI, PAOLO (1930-   )
Dieci Discanti *CC10U
mix cor,10inst oct ZERBONI 6985 s.p. (C617)

CASTALDO
At Her Feet
SATB oct ELKAN-V 362-1186 $.25 (C618)

CASTELLAZZI, GIUSEPPE
Magnificat *Magnif
[Lat] unis,org ZANIBON 2583 s.p. (C619)

CASTELLINI, J.
In Paradisum *mot
"May All The Angels" [Lat/Eng] SATB,acap
AMP A358 $.35 (C620)

May All The Angels *see In Paradisum

CASTELNUOVO-TEDESCO, MARIO (1895-1968)
Fiery Furnace, The *cant
wom cor,Bar solo BELWIN $1.50 (C621)

Lo, The Messiah *Xmas
SSA oct GALAXY 1.1192.1 $.40 (C622)
SATB oct GALAXY 1.1404.1 $.40 (C623)

Mary, Star Of The Sea
SSA oct GALAXY 1.1191.1 $.35 (C624)

CASTILLO
O Altitude Divitiarum *mot,16th cent
[Lat] 5pt mix cor,acap UNION ESP. 19347
s.p. (C625)

CASWELL
Sleep Holy Babe (composed with Field)
(Ehret) SAB LUDWIG L-9139 $.35 (C626)

CATALAN FOLK-SONG
(McFeeters) 3pt wom cor oct SCHIRM.G 9670
$.25 (C627)

CATALONIAN CHRISTMAS CAROL *Xmas,carol,Span
(Cramer) SAB MARKS (C628)
(Ericksen, F.) SATB oct GRAY GCMR 989 $.25 (C629)

CATHEDRAL ANTHEMS *CC10L,anthem
mix cor FISCHER,C HO-525 $1.25 contains works
by: Ford; Byrd; Tallis; Palestrina; Tye;
Wesley; Weelkes (C630)

CATHEDRAL AT SENS, THE see Maganini, Quinto

CATHEDRAL CHOIR BOOK see Ehret, Walter

CATHOLIC CANTICLES see Boex, A.J.

CATHOLIC MASS IN ENGLISH, THE see Henriksen,
Josef

CATHOLIC MASS, THE see Dalmaine, Cyril C.

CATTERICK, J.
Angels In The Skies Are Singing
(Kjelson, Lee) SA/TB oct BELWIN 2228 $.30 (C631)

CAULERY, JEAN
Fils De Dieu Qui Es Tout-Puissant *16th cent
(Honegger, Marc; Pidoux, Pierre) [Fr] SATB
OUVRIERES EO496 s.p. (C632)

Mon Dieu Veuille Ma Voix Ouir *16th cent
(Honegger, Marc; Pidoux, Pierre) [Fr] SATB
OUVRIERES EO497 s.p. (C633)

Pere De Nous Qui Es La-Haut *16th cent
(Honegger, Marc; Pidoux, Pierre) [Fr] SATB
OUVRIERES EO495 s.p. (C634)

CAURROY, EUSTACHE DU
Babe From Heaven, A *Xmas
(Couper, A.) SATB oct PRESSER 352-00395
$.35 (C635)

Noel *Xmas
(Lammers, H.) [Fr] 4pt mix cor,acap (med)
cor pts LEMOINE s.p. see from COLLECTION
DE MUSIQUE ANCIENNE PREMIERE RECUEIL (C636)

CAUSE OF OUR JOY see Wallace, William

CAUSE US, O LORD see Nelson, Ronald A.

CAUSE US, O LORD see Scandrett, Robert

CAUSE US, O LORD OUR GOD see Gottlieb, J.,
Hashkivenu

CAUSTON, THOMAS
Magnificat And Nunc Dimittis *Magnif/Nunc
(Shore, Royle) SATB oct NOVELLO s.p. (C637)

CAUSTUN, THOMAS (? -1569)
Evening Service For Four Voices *Eve
SATB (med) oct OXFORD 43.277 $.50 (C638)

Rejoice In The Lord Alway *Adv/Gen
TTBB (med easy) oct CONCORDIA 98-1534
$.25 (C639)

CAVALIERI
Lauds From The Court Of Heaven *Easter/Lent
SATB oct PRO ART 2225 $.25 (C640)

Mary's Baby *Xmas
SATB oct PRO ART 1901 $.25 (C641)

On This Holy Night *Xmas
SATB oct PRO ART 2102 $.25 (C642)
2pt oct PRO ART 1892 $.25 (C643)
SAB oct PRO ART 2153 $.30 (C644)
SSA oct PRO ART 2097 $.25 (C645)

Thousand Stars, A *Xmas
2pt oct PRO ART 2715 $.30 (C646)

CAVALIERI, EMILIO DEL (ca. 1550-1602)
Lamentationes Jeremiae Prophetae *Easter
(Mantica, Rev. F.) [Lat] cor,soli,org sc
ZANIBON 4373 s.p., cor pts ZANIBON 4374
s.p. (C647)

Lamentazione Di Geremia
(Maselli) [Lat] SATB,SSTB soli,org sc
SCHOTT AV23 s.p. (C648)

CAVALLI, FRANCESCO
Laetatus Sum
cor,orch FABER F0244 s.p. (C649)
(Leppard, Raymond) [Lat] ATB,cont,strings
voc sc FABER FO 244 $1.25 (C650)

Laudate Dominum
cor,orch FABER F0239 s.p. (C651)
(Leppard, Raymond) [Lat] dbl cor,hpsd,2org,
2trp,3trom,strings FABER FO 239 voc sc
$1.25, sc rental, ipr, cor pts rental (C652)

Magnificat *Magnif
(Leppard, Raymond) [Lat] dbl cor,SSAATTBB
soli,hpsd,org/2org,3trom,strings,ob,
2clar/trp FABER rental, ipa (C653)

Messa Concertata *Mass
cor,orch FABER F0023 s.p. (C654)
(Leppard, Raymond) dbl cor,8 soli,org voc
sc SCHIRM.G $1.50 (C655)
(Leppard, Raymond) dbl cor,SSAATTBB soli,
hpsd,3trom,strings,org/2org,ob&clar/2trp
FABER ED 2737 voc sc $1.50, sc rental,
ipr, cor pts rental (C656)

Salve Regina *mot,It
cor FABER F0354 s.p. (C657)
(Leppard, Raymond) [Lat] ATTB oct FABER
11735 $.35 (C658)

CAVALLI, FRANCESCO (cont'd.)

  Tre Magnificat (from Vesperi) CC3U
    dbl cor,orch CURCI 7025 s.p.   (C659)

CAVALLI, PIER FRANCESCO (1602-1676)
  Salve Regina
    (Leppard) [Lat] ATTB,kbd oct SCHIRM.G 11735
    $.35   (C660)

CAWOOD
  Almighty God, Thy Word Is Cast
    (Brown) SATB oct BOURNE 733 $.25   (C661)

CE QU'IL FAUT A MON AME see Gounod, Charles
  Francois

CE TRAIN see Same Train

CECCATO, ARNALDO
  Ecce Sacerdos Magnus
    [Lat] ATBarB,org ZANIBON 3299 s.p.   (C662)

CECCHERINI
  Sanctus-Benedictus *Bene/Sanctus
    [Lat] men cor voc sc PETERS HU1490 $1.50,
    ipr   (C663)

CECHVALA, AL
  Lord Help Us
    SATB oct PRO ART 2581 $.30   (C664)

  Saviour Of Mankind
    SATB oct PRO ART 2534 $.25   (C665)

CECILIA LIED EN OCULUS NON VINDIT see
  Sweelinck, D.J.

CECILIA, SISTER
  Eight Bible Songs For Young People *CC8U,
    Gen,Bibl/folk
    unis,gtr (easy) cmplt ed GIA G1401 $.50   (C666)

CECILIA, VIRGIN see Phillips, Caecilia Virgo

CEILLIER, L.
  Choral-Obstinato *Gen,mot
    [Lat/Fr] jr cor&2pt men cor,org oct DURAND
    s.p.   (C667)

CELEBRATE see Perkins, Phil

CELEBRATE THIS HOLY ONE see Sateren, Leland
  Bernhard

CELEBRATION see Beck, John Ness

CELEBRATION see Draesel, Lederhouse

CELEBRATION see Krane, David

CELEBRATION OF EASTER, A see Ringwald, [Roy]

CELEBRATION OF UNITY see Hebble, R.

CELEBRE AVE MARIA see Bottazzo, Luigi

CELEBRONS see Nelhybel, Vaclav

CELEBRONS LA NAISSANCE *Fr
  (Fitzgerald, J.) "Sing Praises To Our Savior"
  [Fr/Eng] SSAA,acap SCHIRM.EC 1896 $.25 (C668)

CELESTIAL CITY, THE see McCormick

CELESTIAL SPRING see Christiansen, F. Melius

CELESTIAL VISION, THE see Creston

CELESTIAL VISTOR, THE see Cain, Noble

CELESTIS URBS see Grassi, Ciro

CELLER PASSION 1637 NACH DEM EVANGELISTEN
  MATTHAUS see Mancinus, Thomas

CELSI, CESARE
  Missa SS. Trinitas *Mass
    [Lat] TTB,org sc ZANIBON 3477 s.p., voc pt
    ZANIBON s.p.   (C669)

CENTRONE
  I Wonder *Xmas
    SSA oct KENDOR $.25   (C670)

  You Know Who! *Xmas
    unis/2pt oct PRO ART 2525 $.25   (C671)

CENTURION, THE see Coleman, Jack

CERBUS, [PAUL] (1919-   )
  Be It So
    (Ohl) SATB oct PLYMOUTH FO-106 $.25 (C672)

  How Lovely Is Thy Dwelling Place
    (Ohl) SATB oct PLYMOUTH FO-102 $.25 (C673)

CEREMONY OF CAROLS see Britten, Benjamin

CEREMONY OF CAROLS, A see Britten, Benjamin

CERIANA, ANGELO
  Tota Pulchra *BVM
    [Lat] unis,org ZANIBON 2443 s.p.   (C674)

CERQUETELLI, GIUSEPPE
  Assumpta Est Maria *BVM
    [Lat] 3pt mix cor,org ZANIBON 2758 s.p.
      (C675)

  Ave Maria *BVM
    [Lat] S/T,org ZANIBON 2742 s.p.   (C676)

  Laudate Dominum
    [Lat] 2 eq voices,org ZANIBON 2693 s.p.
      (C677)

  Si Quaeris *ASD
    [Lat] A,Bar solo,org ZANIBON 2724 s.p.
      (C678)

  Tantum Ergo
    see SEI MOTTETTI EUCARISTICI

CERTAINLY LORD
  (Kirk) SATB oct PRO ART 1291 $.25   (C679)
  (Kirk) SAB oct PRO ART 1834 $.25   (C680)
  (Kirk) SSA oct PRO ART 1710 $.22   (C681)
  (Kirk) TTB oct PRO ART 2377 $.30   (C682)

CERT'NLY LORD, CERT'NLY LORD see McLin

CERT'N'Y LORD *spir
  (Kemmer) SSAA,acap oct COLOMBO 1320 $.25
      (C683)
  (Kemmer) SATB,acap oct COLOMBO 1167 $.25
      (C684)

CERTON, [PIERRE] (ca. 1510-1572)
  Magnificat *Magnif
    (Agnel, A.) [Lat] 4pt mix cor,acap HEUGEL
    CPJ9 s.p.   (C685)

  Mass Sus Le Pont D'Avignon *Mass
    [Lat] SATTB,acap voc sc HINRICHSEN SP7 s.p.
      (C686)

  Sus Le Pont D'Avignon *Mass
    (Somma, B.; Bianchi, Lino) 3pt SANTIS 1064
    s.p.   (C687)

CERVI, LUIGI
  Caro Mea
    see Tre Mottetti Eucaristici

  Cibavit Eos
    see Tre Mottetti Eucaristici

  O Esca Viatorum
    see Tre Mottetti Eucaristici

  Tre Mottetti Eucaristici *Commun,mot
    [Lat] unis,org ZANIBON 2656 s.p.
    contains: Caro Mea; Cibavit Eos; O Esca
    Viatorum   (C688)

CERVIANA see Perosi, (Dom) Lorenzo

CESKA POLYFONNI TVORBA see Anonymous

C'EST LE BON LEVER see Aubanel, Georges

C'EST LE JOUR DE LA NOEL *Xmas
  (Grimbert, J.) [Fr] 3 eq voices HEUGEL PJ45
  s.p.   (C689)

C'EST L'ETERNEL (Psalm 49) 16th cent
  (Geveart, F.-A.) [Fr] 4pt mix cor,acap (med
  easy) cor pts LEMOINE s.p. see from
  Collection De Choeurs, septieme Fascicule
    (C690)

C'EST MOI SEIGNEUR see It's Me, O Lord

C'EST NOEL see Rhoda, H.

C'EST PAS MOI QUE SUIS LE BON DIEU see Wissmer

CEVALLOS
  Exaudiat *mot,16th cent
    [Lat] 4pt mix cor UNION ESP. 19355 s.p. (C691)

CHAD GADYO see Adler, Hugo Ch.

CHADWICK, GEORGE WHITEFIELD (1854-1931)
  Judith *Bibl/ora
    cor,soli,orch cloth DA CAPO LC 70-169727
    $13.50   (C692)

CHADWYCK
  That Holy Thing (composed with Healey, H.P.)
    *Xmas,carol
    oct ROYAL 332 s.p.   (C693)

CHAFFIN, L. G.
  Holy Father, Hear My Cry
    (Mueller) SABar,Bar solo oct SCHIRM.G 8692
    $.25   (C694)

CHAILLEY
  Benedicta Es Tu
    [Lat] SSA oct SALABERT-US $.65   (C695)

  Jacob's Ladder
    [Eng/Fr] SATB,T/B solo oct SALABERT-US $.65
      (C696)

  Messe Breve De Angelis *Mass
    [Lat] SATB,acap oct SALABERT-US $1.25 (C697)

  Missa Solemnis *Mass
    [Lat] SATB,acap oct SALABERT-US $2.75
      (C698)

  O Vos Omnes
    [Lat] SATB,acap oct SALABERT-US $.65 (C699)

CHAJES, JULIUS (1910-   )
  Promised Land, The *Fest,cant
    unis/2pt TRANSCON. TCL 325 $2.25   (C700)

  Psalm 114 *see When Yisrael Left Mitzrayim

  Psalm 142
    [Eng] SATB TRANSCON. TCL 215 $.50, ipa
      (C701)

  Shabbat Shalom *Sab-Eve
    SATB TRANSCON. TCL 770 $2.00   (C702)

  We Strode Through The Waves *Fest
    [Eng] SATB TRANSCON. TCL 626 $.50 (C703)

  When Yisrael Left Mitzrayim (Psalm 114) Fest
    [Eng] SATB TRANSCON. TCL 625 $.50 (C704)

CHALET GIRL'S SUNDAY see Saeterjentens Sondag

CHAMBER CANTATA see Fromm, Herbert

CHAMBER MASS see Vivaldi, Antonio

CHAMBERS, H.A.
  Day Thou Gavest, Lord, Is Ended, The
    *anthem/hymn
    mix cor oct NOVELLO 28.1384.10 s.p. (C705)

  Day Thou Gavest, The
    SATB ALLANS 276 s.p.   (C706)
    SA ALLANS 277 s.p.   (C707)
    2pt oct NOVELLO 28.1168.05 s.p.   (C708)

  Holy Communion *Commun
    unis (G maj) NOVELLO 44.0966.03 s.p. (C709)

  Lead Me Lord
    (Wesley) SATB ALLANS 281 s.p.   (C710)

  Now Let The Heavens Be Joyful *Easter
    SATB oct SOUTHERN $.30   (C711)

  Now Thank We All Our God *Fest/Marriage
    SATB ALLANS 243 s.p.   (C712)

CHAMBERS, H.A. (cont'd.)

  Save Us, O Lord, Waking *anthem
    mix cor oct NOVELLO 40.1224.00 s.p. (C713)

  Spirit Of Mercy, Truth, And Love *Whitsun,
    anthem
    mix cor oct NOVELLO 50.0220.06 s.p. (C714)

  True Love's The Gift *Marriage
    SATB oct LESLIE 4093   (C715)

CHAMINADE, CECILE (1857-1944)
  Agnus Dei (from Messe Pour Deux Voix Egales)
    Agnus
    [Lat] 2 eq voices,acap cor pts ENOCH s.p.
      (C716)
    [Lat] 2 eq voices,org voc sc ENOCH s.p.
      (C717)

  Angelus
    2pt/MezBar ENOCH T.P.1 s.p.   (C718)

  Bless The Harvest, O Lord *Harv
    SATB oct BOOSEY 2218 $.30   (C719)

  Gloria (from Messe Pour Deux Voix Egales)
    Gloria
    [Lat] 2 eq voices,org voc sc ENOCH s.p.
      (C720)
    [Lat] 2 eq voices,acap cor pts ENOCH s.p.
      (C721)

  Kyrie (from Messe Pour Deux Voix Egales)
    Kyrie
    [Lat] 2 eq voices,acap cor pts ENOCH s.p.
      (C722)
    [Lat] 2 eq voices,org voc sc ENOCH s.p.
      (C723)

  La Jeune Fille *Op.99
    [Fr] SSAA,solo voc sc cor pts ENOCH s.p.
    s.p. see from Six Poemes Evangeliques
      (C724)

  Laus Mea Dominus *CC20U
    [Fr] cor ENOCH voc sc s.p., cor pts s.p.
      (C725)

  Les Feux De La Saint Jean *Op.44
    [Fr] SSAA,solo ENOCH voc sc s.p., cor pts
    s.p.   (C726)

  Les Humbles *Op.99
    [Fr] SSAA voc sc cor pts ENOCH s.p. s.p.
    see from Six Poemes Evangeliques (C727)

  Les Pecheurs *Op.99
    [Fr] SSAA voc sc cor pts ENOCH s.p. s.p.
    see from Six Poemes Evangeliques (C728)

  Les Petits Enfants *Op.99
    [Fr] SSAA voc sc cor pts ENOCH s.p. s.p.
    see from Six Poemes Evangeliques (C729)

  L'etoile *Op.99
    [Fr] SSAA,soli voc sc cor pts ENOCH s.p.
    s.p. see from Six Poemes Evangeliques (C730)

  Messe Pour Deux Voix Egales *Op.167, Mass
    [Lat] 2 eq voices,org voc sc ENOCH s.p.
      (C731)
    [Lat] 2 eq voices,acap cor pts ENOCH s.p.
      (C732)

  O Salutaris (from Messe Pour Deux Voix
    Egales)
    [Lat] 2 eq voices,org voc sc ENOCH s.p.
      (C733)
    [Lat] 2 eq voices,acap cor pts ENOCH s.p.
      (C734)

  Sainte Madeleine *Op.99
    [Fr] SSAA voc sc cor pts ENOCH s.p. s.p.
    see from Six Poemes Evangeliques (C735)

  Sanctus Et Benedictus (from Messe Pour Deux
    Voix Egales) Bene/Sanctus
    [Lat] 2 eq voices,acap cor pts ENOCH s.p.
      (C736)
    [Lat] 2 eq voices,org voc sc ENOCH s.p.
      (C737)

  Six Poemes Evangeliques *see La Jeune Fille,
    Op.99; Les Humbles, Op.99; Les Pecheurs,
    Op.99; Les Petits Enfants, Op.99;
    L'etoile, Op.99; Sainte Madeleine, Op.99
      (C738)

CHAMPAGNE, CLAUDE (1891-1965)
  Ave Maria
    TTB,acap oct BERANDOL 844C3AG $.35 (C739)

  Missa Brevis
    SSA,acap oct BERANDOL 830C3AF $.50 (C740)

CHAMPION, THOMAS
  D'ou Vient Cela, Seigneur, Je Te Supplie
    (Psalm 10) 16th cent
    (Honegger, Marc; Pidoux, Pierre) [Fr] SATB
    OUVRIERES E0521 s.p.   (C741)

  Or Sus, Serviteurs Du Seigneur (Psalm 134)
    16th cent
    (Honegger, Marc; Pidoux, Pierre) [Fr] SATB
    OUVRIERES E0522 s.p.   (C742)

  Psalm 10 *see D'ou Vient Cela, Seigneur, Je
    Te Supplie

  Psalm 134 *see Or Sus, Serviteurs Du
    Seigneur

CHANCE, NANCY
  Motet *mot
    dbl cor sc SEESAW $7.00   (C743)

CHANCEL CHOIR *CCU,anthem
  SATB LORENZ $1.95   (C744)

CHANCEL CHOIR BOOK see Peery, [Rob Roy]

CHANDLER, MARY
  I Love All Beauteous Things
    unis&desc oct NOVELLO 48.2054 s.p. (C745)

  Prayer For Rejoicing, A *anthem/prayer
    mix cor oct NOVELLO 28.1431.05 s.p. (C746)

CHANDOS ANTHEMS *see Handel, George Frideric,
  As Pants The Hart, "As Longs The Hart For
  Flowing Streams" (Psalm 42); Handel, George
  Frideric, Have Mercy Upon Me, "Have Mercy
  On Me"; Handel, George Frideric, I Will
  Magnify Thee; Handel, George Frideric, In
  The Lord Put I My Trust, "In The Lord I Put
  My Trust"; Handel, George Frideric, Lord Is
  My Light, The; Handel, George Frideric, My

Song Shall Be Alway (Psalm 89); Handel,
George Frideric, O Be Joyful In The Lord;
Handel, George Frideric, O Praise The Lord
With One Consent; Handel, George Frideric,
O Sing Unto The Lord (Psalm 96); Handel,
George Frideric, Oh, Be Joyful In The Lord;
Handel, George Frideric, O Praise The Lord
With One Consent, "Oh, Praise The Lord"
(Psalm 135); Handel, George Frideric, With
Cheerful Notek (C747)

CHANDOS ANTHEMS see Handel, George Frideric

CHANDOS TE DEUM see Handel, George Frideric

CHANGES see Crosse, Gordon

CHANGING VOICES IN JUNIOR HIGH see Cooper,
Irvin

CHANSON DES ANGES see Vidal, Paul

CHANSON JOYEUSE DE NOEL see Gevaert, Francois
Auguste

CHANSON SATYRIQUE
(Geveart, F.-A.) [Fr] 4pt mix cor,acap (easy)
cor pts LEMOINE s.p. see from Collection De
Choeurs, quatrieme Fascicule (C748)

CHANSONS SPIRITUELLES (from Jardin Musical) CCU
(Pass, Walter) 4pt mix cor DOBLINGER s.p.
contains works by: Bacchius, J. de;
Crecquillon, Th.; Non Papa, Clemens;
Maillart, J.; Waelrant, H. (C749)

CHANT-CHORALE FOR ADVENT see Bunjes, Paul G.

CHANT-CHORALE FOR CHRISTMAS see Bunjes, Paul G.

CHANT DE FETE see Lacome, Paul, Laudate Dominum

CHANT DE LA NATIVITE see Roger-Ducasse, Jean-
Jules Aimable

CHANT DE PAIX see Stekke, Leon

CHANT DE PAQUES see Bach, Johann Sebastian,
Surexit Christus Hodie

CHANT DE TRIOMPHE DU ROI DAVID see Hindemith,
Paul

CHANT D'OFFRANDE NO. 1 see Beethoven, Ludwig
van

CHANT D'OFFRANDE NO. 2 see Beethoven, Ludwig
van

CHANT DU CREPUSCULE see Franck, Cesar

CHANT MAGYAR see Brahms, Johannes

CHANT OF GLORY AND PRAISE see Rogers

CHANT PASTORALE see Jongen, [Joseph-Marie-
Alphonse-Nicholas]

CHANTEZ A DIEU see Sweelinck, Jan Pieterszoon

CHANTEZ A DIEU CHANSON NOUVELLE see Lupi II,
Didier

CHANTEZ A DIEU CHANSON NOUVELLE see Sweelinck,
Jan Pieterszoon

CHANTEZ A DIEU NOUVEAU CANTIQUE see Goudimel,
Claude

CHANTEZ AU SEIGNEUR see Bach, Johann Sebastian

CHANTEZ DU SEIGNEUR (Psalm 80) 16th cent
(Geveart, F.-A.) [Fr] 4pt mix cor,acap (med
easy) cor pts LEMOINE s.p. see from
Collection De Choeurs, septieme Fascicule
(C750)

CHANTEZ GAYEMENT A DIEU see Sweelinck, Jan
Pieterszoon

CHANTEZ, VOIX BENIES see Gounod, Charles
Francois

CHANTONS, JE VOUS EN PRIE see Migot, Georges

CHANTONS JOYEUSEMENT see Migot, Georges

CHANTONS NOEL *CC3U,Xmas,carol,Fr
(Phillips, John C.) [Eng/Fr] SSA,pno,opt
strings voc NOVELLO 05.0028.03 s.p., ipr
(C751)

CHANTONS NOEL see Aubanel, Georges

CHANTS DE MARS see Wissmer

CHANTS FOR CERTAIN PSALMS see Davies, Henry
Walford

CHANTS FOR THE ORDINARY OF THE MASS see Milner,
Anthony

CHANTS RELIGIEUX *see Faure, Jean-Baptist,
Charite; Faure, Jean-Baptist, Credo; Faure,
Jean-Baptist, Crucifix; Faure, Jean-
Baptist, Notre Pere; Faure, Jean-Baptist, O
Salutaris; Faure, Jean-Baptist, Sancta
Maria; Gounod, Charles Francois, Ave Maria;
Gounod, Charles Francois, Notre-Dame De
France; Lefebure-Wely, Louis James Alfred,
O Salutaris; Mascagni, Pietro, Ave Maria;
Massenet, Jules, Ave Maria; Massenet,
Jules, Souvenez-Vous Vierge Marie;
Niedermeyer, Louis, Pater Noster;
Stradella, Alessandro, Air D'Eglise (C752)

CHANTS RELIGIEUX see Faure, Jean-Baptist

CHANTS RELIGIEUX see Gounod, Charles Francois

CHANTS RELIGIEUX see Lefebure-Wely, Louis James
Alfred

CHANTS RELIGIEUX see Mascagni, Pietro

CHANTS RELIGIEUX see Massenet, Jules

CHANTS RELIGIEUX see Niedermeyer, Louis

CHANTS RELIGIEUX see Stradella, Alessandro

CHANUKAH FESTIVAL OVERTURE see Wernick

CHAPEL CHOIR *CCU,anthem
SATB LORENZ $1.95 (C753)

CHAPEL CHOIR, THE see Coupe, Alinda B.

CHAPEL CHOIR ANTHEM BOOK see Holler, John

CHAPEL CHORISTER BOOK see Peery, Robert Roy

CHAPEL CHORISTER see Ehret, Walter

CHAPEL SERVICE NO. 1 see Freed, Isadore

CHAPEL SERVICE NO. 2 see Freed, Isadore

CHAPIN, AMZI
Lord, In The Morning *Bibl
(Taylor) 3pt mix cor,pno/org oct LAWSON
51317 $.25 (C754)

CHAPLIN, [MARIAN WOOD] (1914-)
Noel! Noel! A Saviour Is Born *Xmas
4pt mix cor,SBar soli,org/pno oct SCHIRM.G
10833 $.25 (C755)

Sing We To Christ The King *Xmas
(Niles) SATB,A solo oct SCHIRM.G 10486 $.25
(C756)

CHAPLIN, N.W.
Christ Child, Christ Child
(Ades) SAB SHAWNEE D135 $.30 (C757)

Sing Hosanna
(Zaninelli) SATB SHAWNEE A 698 $.30 (C758)

CHAPMAN
All Creatures Of Our God And King
SATB oct SUMMY B 1191 $.60 (C759)

Born Today Is The Child Divine *Xmas
SATB,acap (med) OXFORD 84.052 $.35 (C760)

I Heard Two Soldiers Talking *Easter
SATB oct GALAXY 1.1817.1 $.30 (C761)

CHAPMAN, EDWARD T.
Crowned With The Thorn *Lent
SATB,acap (easy) oct OXFORD 84.036 $.25
(C762)

God Be In My Head *prayer,Eng
4pt mix cor,acap oct SCHIRM.G 11481 $.25
(C763)

Now From Every Christian Steeple *Easter
SATB (very easy) oct OXFORD 84.020 $.25
(C764)

SSA (very easy) oct OXFORD 83.023 $.25
(C765)

Thou Spirit Of Love Divine
mix cor CURWEN 65177 s.p. (C766)

CHAPMAN, M.B.
Pilgrim Way, The
SATB oct SOUTHERN $.25 (C767)

CHAPPELL
Song Of The Dove
(Cole) SATB (med easy) SOUTHERN $.40 (C768)

CHAPPELL, HERBERT
Christmas Jazz, The *Xmas
unis MARKS $1.25 (C769)

Daniel Jazz, The *cant/pop
unis,pno voc sc NOVELLO 20.0001.06 s.p.
(C770)
unis MARKS $1.00 (C771)

Goliath Jazz, The
unis MARKS $1.00 (C772)

Jericho Jazz, The
unis MARKS $1.25 (C773)

Magnificat And Nunc Dimittis *Magnif/Nunc
unis (G maj) NOVELLO 33.0119.02 s.p. (C774)

Noah Jazz, The
unis MARKS $1.25 (C775)

Prodigal Jazz, The
unis MARKS $1.25 (C776)

Red Sea Jazz, The
unis MARKS $1.25 (C777)

Song Of The Dove
(Cole) SA MARKS 4577 $.40 (C778)

CHAPPELL'S SACRED *CCU
SSA CHAPPELL 0014555-374 $1.95; SATB CHAPPELL
0017566-374 $1.95 (C779)

CHARGE TO KEEP I HAVE, A *hymn
(Parker) 5pt mix cor,acap oct LAWSON 51311
$.25 (C780)

CHARGE TO KEEP I HAVE, A see Anonymous

CHARITE see Faure, Jean-Baptist

CHARITY, SISTERS OF
Bendiction Hymns In Honor Of The Most Holy
Name And Of Our Heavenly Queen
mix cor,pno/org (easy) oct WILLIS 4836 $.20
(C781)

CHARLAP
His Love Is Born Anew *see Lehmeier, J.F.

CHARLES
At Christmas Time Was Born A King *Xmas
SAB (easy) OXFORD 42.123 $.35 (C782)
SA (med easy) OXFORD 44.009 $.35 (C783)

CHARLES, ERNEST (1895-)
Festival Jubilate
SATB oct HUNTZINGER 4035 $.16 (C784)

Greatness Of The Lord, The *Bibl
mix cor,S/T/A/B solo,org/pno oct SCHIRM.G
10446 $.25 (C785)

Lord Of The Years
(Treharne) 4pt mix cor oct SCHIRM.G 8712
$.25 (C786)

CHARLES, RAY
Ezekial Saw De Wheel
SATB oct STAFF 143 $.30 (C787)

CHARPENTIER, MARC-ANTOINE (1634?-1704)
Canticle Of Praise
(Phillips) SATB oct SUMMY M 2476 $.40
(C788)

Come, Holy Ghost *anthem
(Riedel) SATB (very easy) oct AUGSBURG 1326
$.20 (C789)

Extremum Dei Judicium
[Lat] SATB,TT/AA soli,cont,2trp,2vln sc
MUSIKHOJ 6 $5.00 (C790)

Glory To God In The Highest
see Three Hymns Of The Church

I Was Glad *see Laetatus Sum

In Nativitatem Domini Nostri Jesu Christi
Canticum *Xmas
(Hitchcock, H.W.) "Song Of The Birth Of Our
Lord Jesus Christ" mix cor,soli,2vln,cont
CONCORDIA 97-6307 $1.50, ipa (C791)

Laetatus Sum
(Dunn, J.P.) "I Was Glad" mix cor,soli,
strings,2fl,cont CONCORDIA 97-6425 $2.00,
ipa (C792)

Laissez Paitre Vos Betes *Offer
cor (use with Messe De Minuit Pour Noel) sc
CONCORDIA 97-4955 $1.25, ipa (C793)

Laudate Dominum (Psalm 116) Psalm
(Hitchcock) SSA/TTB MARKS 4603 $.45 (C794)
(Phillips) TTB/STB/SSB oct SUMMY M 2338
$.60 (C795)

Little Christmas Cantata *Xmas,cant
SATB,trp STAFF 602 $.30 (C796)

Magnificat
[Lat] SAB/TTB,2vln,cont SCHIRM.EC 2151 voc
sc $3.50, cor pts $.75, ipr (C797)
TTB/SAB,2vln,vcl SCHIRM.EC 2151 voc sc
$3.50, ipa, cor pts $.75, ipa (C798)

Magnificat In G
(Bichsel) cor,strings,fl,org voc sc
CONCORDIA 97-6343 $1.50, ipr (C799)

Mass *Mass
mix cor voc sc OXFORD 46.168 $13.00, cor
pts OXFORD 46.169 $3.15 (C800)

Messe De Minuit (composed with Day, W.)
"Midnight Mass For Christmas" SATB oct
ELKAN-V $1.50 (C801)

Messe De Minuit Pour Noel *Xmas,Mass
(Hitchcock, H.W.) "Midnight Mass For
Christmas Based On French Carols" mix
cor,soli,fl,strings,org voc sc CONCORDIA
97-6372 $1.75, ipa (C802)

Messe De Minuit Sur Des Airs De Noel *Xmas,
Mass
(Letocart, H; Marc, E) mix cor,org,orch
(credo not included in choral part. it is
available separately) LEMOINE voc sc
s.p., cor pts s.p., ipa (C803)

Midnight Mass For Christmas *see Messe De
Minuit

Midnight Mass For Christmas Based On French
Carols *see Messe De Minuit Pour Noel

Now, My Tongue The Mystery Telling
see Three Hymns Of The Church

O Come, Creator Spirit, Come
see Three Hymns Of The Church

O Come Ye Unto Me *see Venite Ad Me

Out Of The Depths (Psalm 130) Gen/Lent
SATB,kbd (med easy) oct CONCORDIA 98-1521
$.25 (C804)

Pie Jesu
SSB,2vln,cont SCHIRM.EC 2292 voc sc $2.50,
cor pts $.40, ipa (C805)

Psalm 116 *see Laudate Dominum

Psalm 130 *see Out Of The Depths

Song Of The Birth Of Our Lord Jesus Christ
*see In Nativitatem Domini Nostri Jesu
Christi Canticum

Te Deum *Te Deum
[Lat] dbl cor,2orch HEUGEL s.p., ipr see
from LE PUPITRE (C806)
(Kolneder) study sc UNIVER. PH. 604 $3.15
(C807)
(Kolneder) [Lat] SATB,org voc sc PETERS
WM124 $1.50 (C808)
(Kolneder, W.) [Lat] voc sc UNIVER. 12778
$6.75, cor pts UNIVER. 12779 $2.00 (C809)
(Kolneder, Walter) [Lat] SATB,SSATB soli,
org (med) voc sc MULLER SM 2458 s.p. (C810)
(Lambert, Guy) [Ger] SATB,SATB soli,org,
2vln,vla,vcl,bvl (med diff) MULLER sc
s.p., cor pts s.p., voc sc s.p. (C811)

Three Hymns Of The Church *Xmas/Gen,hymn
unis,kbd (med easy) oct CONCORDIA 98-1779
$.25
contains: Glory To God In The Highest;
Now, My Tongue The Mystery Telling; O
Come, Creator Spirit, Come (C812)

Three Sacred Motets *CC3U,mot
mix cor,acap voc sc KALMUS 6139 $1.25
(C813)

Venite Ad Me
(Dunn, James) "O Come Ye Unto Me" [Eng/Lat]
mix cor,soli,org/pno voc sc SCHIRM.G $.75
(C814)

CHASE
Strangers In The Streets
SA/TB SHAWNEE E108 $.30 (C815)

CHASHOUDIAN, MARSHALL G.
How Lovely Is Thy Dwelling Place *carol
SATB,pno (med) oct WILLIS 7004 $.22 (C816)

Lord Once More Is Come, The *carol
SATB,SA soli,pno (med) oct WILLIS 6951 $.25 (C817)

CHASSIDIC SABBATH EVE SERVICE see Mills, Edgar

CHASSIDIC SABBATH MORNING SERVICE see Mills, Edgar

CHAUCHER'S CAROL (from Anthology Of Carols, An) see Ave Maris Stella

CHAUSSON, ERNEST (1855-1899)
Le Legende De Ste Cecile
[Fr] wom cor,S solo,orch SALABERT-US voc sc $9.25, voc pt $.65 (C818)

CHE POICH'A MORTAL RISCHIO see Monte, de

CHEATHAM
My Soul Is A Witness
SATB SHAWNEE A 1191 $.30 (C819)

CHEER THE WEARY TRAVELLER see Smith

CHEER UP, FRIENDS AND NEIGHBORS see Wilson

CHELSEA UNISON CHOIR BOOK, THE see Williams

CHEMDAT YAMIN see Fromm, Herbert

CHEMIN DE CROIX see Georges, Alexandre

CHEMIN DE CROIX see Jean-Baptiiste, L.

CHEMIN-PETIT, HANS (1902-)
Evangelisches Kirchengesangbuch *cant
[Ger] 3pt mix cor,acap BAREN. EM 19 s.p.
cantate sunday
contains: Nun Freut Euch, Lieben Christen Gmein, No.239; Singt, Singt Jehova Neue Lieder, No.186; Wenn Aber Jener, Der Geist Der Wahrheit Kommen Wird (C820)

Freut Euch, Ihr Leiben Christen All
SAT/SAB,2treb inst,bass inst HANSSLER 14.040 (C821)

Now Let All Loudly Sing Praise *Gen
SAB,kbd (med easy) oct CONCORDIA 98-1106 $.20 (C822)

Nun Freut Euch, Lieben Christen Gmein
see Evangelisches Kirchengesangbuch

Psalm 90
[Ger] mix cor,Bar solo,orch voc sc BOTE s.p. (C823)

Psalm 98
[Ger] mix cor,orch voc sc BOTE s.p. (C824)

Psalm 150
[Ger] mix cor,orch voc sc BOTE s.p. (C825)

Singt, Singt Jehova Neue Lieder
see Evangelisches Kirchengesangbuch

Symphonische Kantate *Bibl/cant
[Ger] mix cor,A solo,orch,opt pno voc sc BOTE s.p. (C826)

Wenn Aber Jener, Der Geist Der Wahrheit Kommen Wird
see Evangelisches Kirchengesangbuch

CHENOWETH, WILBUR (1899-)
Brotherhood Of Man
SATB oct FISCHER,C CM-7450 $.25 (C827)

Come Let Us Sing *Proces,anthem
4pt mix cor oct SCHIRM.G 8670 $.25 (C828)

Do You Know The Newborn Child
SATB,org oct LAWSON 51689 $.30 (C829)

God Of Comfort, God Of Courage
SATB,S/T solo oct LAWSON 51117 $.35 (C830)

Noel, Noel *Xmas
SSA oct SCHIRM.G 10274 $.25 (C831)

Noel! Noel! Bells Are Ringing *Xmas
unis,opt bells oct SCHIRM.G 10586 $.25 (C832)
2pt&opt desc oct SCHIRM.G 10587 $.25 (C833)

Of The Father's Love Begotten
SATB,pno/org oct LAWSON 51038 $.35 (C834)

CHERRY-TREE CAROL see Nelson, Ronald A.

CHERRY TREE CAROL, THE see Lewis

CHERRY-TREE CAROL, THE (from Anthology Of Carols, An) Xmas/Easter/Psntd,carol/folk,US
(McGill; Shaw; Parker) mix cor,T solo,acap oct SCHIRM.G 10170 $.35 (C835)
(Wulstan, David) unis CHESTER s.p. contains also: Angelus Ad Virginem (ATB,S solo) (CC, Xmas) (C836)

CHERUB CAROL, THE see Coates, D.

CHERUB HYMNS see Guess

CHERUBIC HYMN see Arkhangelsky, G.

CHERUBIC HYMN see Hanson

CHERUBIC HYMN see Musicescu, Gavriil

CHERUBIC HYMN see Rachmaninoff, Sergey Vassilievitch

CHERUBIC HYMN see Sarti

CHERUBIC HYMN see Tchesnokov, Pavel Grigorievitch

CHERUBIC HYMN, THE see Gretchaninov, Alexander Tikhonovitch

CHERUBIC HYMN NO.7 see Bortniansky, Dimitri Stepanovitch

CHERUBIC HYMN, THE see Gretchaninov, Alexander Tikhonovitch

CHERUBIC HYMN, THE see Tchaikovsky, Piotr Ilyitch

CHERUBIM COLLECTION, THE *CC22L,Xmas/Easter/Fest/Lent/Thanks
(Harris) jr cor/2pt jr cor PRO ART 216 $1.00 (C837)

CHERUBIM HYMN see Lomakin

CHERUBIM HYMN see Rachmaninoff, Sergey Vassilievitch

CHERUBIM SONG see Arkhangelsky, Alexander

CHERUBIM SONG see Bortniansky, Dimitri Stepanovitch

CHERUBIM SONG see Davis, Katherine K.

CHERUBIM SONG see Glinka, Mikhail Ivanovitch

CHERUBIM SONG see Gretchaninov, Alexander Tikhonovitch

CHERUBIM SONG see Muzicheski

CHERUBIM SONG see Tchaikovsky, Piotr Ilyitch

CHERUBIM SONG see Tcherepnin, Alexander

CHERUBIM SONG #7 see Bortniansky, Dimitri Stepanovitch

CHERUBIM SONG NO. 7 see Bortniansky, Dimitri Stepanovitch, Choirs Of Angels Praise Thee

CHERUBINI, LUIGI (1760-1842)
Adoremus
[Lat] 3pt HEUGEL s.p. see from SAINTE-CECILE (C838)

Amen (from Mass In E)
SATB,acap RICORDI-ENG SY156 s.p. (C839)

Ave Maria *BVM
[Lat] A/Bar ZANIBON 3609 s.p. (C840)
[Lat] S/T ZANIBON 3608 s.p. (C841)

Blessed Jesu, Lord Of All
(Weaver) SATB FOSTER MF102 $.30 (C842)

Blessed Jesus *see Pie Jesu

Come, O Jesus, Come To Me *see Veni Jesu

Come, O Jesus, Saviour Mine *see Veni Jesus

Day Of Mourning *see Lacrymosa

Deuxieme Messe De Requiem *Mass/Req
[Lat] TTBB,opt pno/org (D min) HEUGEL s.p. (C843)

Deuxieme Messe Solennelle *Mass
(Vecchi, Prof. Giuseppe) 4pt,orch FORNI 103 s.p. (C844)

Fourth Mass *Mass
[Lat] cor (C maj) voc sc KALMUS 6143 $2.00 (C845)
cor,orch (C maj) sc KALMUS $18.00, ipa (C846)

Give Unto The Humble
(Barker) 4pt mix cor oct SCHIRM.G 11108 $.25 (C847)

God Of Mercy *see Pie Jesu

Hear Us, Holy Jesus
(Roff) unis/SA oct ELKAN-V 362-128 $.25 (C848)

Holy, Holy, Holy *see Sanctus

Holy, Holy Lord God Of Hosts
(Ehret) SATB oct PLYMOUTH SC-17 $.25 (C849)

In Paradisum
SATB,acap RICORDI-ENG SY160 s.p. (C850)

Jesus, Jesus, We Adore Thee
(Coggin) SATB SHAWNEE A 893 $.30 (C851)

Jesus, Now To Thee I Turn Me
(Lundquist) SATB oct ELKAN-V 362-1159 $.25 (C852)

Kyrie (from Mass In E) Kyrie
SATB,acap RICORDI-ENG SY178 s.p. (C853)

Lacrymosa (from Requiem Mass)
(Ehret) "Day Of Mourning" [Eng/Lat] SATB MARKS 4179 $.25 (C854)
(Lannom) SATB oct PLYMOUTH AL-101 $.25 (C855)
(Tolmage) mix cor SOUTHERN $.20 (C856)
(Tolmage) SATB oct STAFF 455 $.25 (C857)
(Tolmage) SAB oct STAFF 506 $.20 (C858)
(Tolmage) SSA oct STAFF 513 $.25 (C859)

Like As A Father
SSA oct SUMMY 5297 $.40 (C860)

Lord God Of Saboath
(Hilton, A.) SATB oct PRESSER 352-00446 $.30 (C861)

Messe
(Vecchi, Prof. Giuseppe) cor,3 soli,kbd FORNI 106 s.p. (C862)

Messe Du Sacre *Mass
[Lat] STB,org,orch (A maj) HEUGEL voc sc s.p., voc pt s.p., ipa (C863)

Milde Jesu, Herre Gud (from Requiem)
cor,org cor pts NORDISKA 3439 s.p. (C864)

Missa Pro Defunctis *Req
"Requiem C-Moll" 4pt mix cor,2ob,clar,bsn, horn,trp,3trom,strings,perc,timp (C min) voc pt BREITKOPF-W CHB-33 s.p., voc sc BREITKOPF-W EB-299 s.p., ipr, sc BREITKOPF-W rental (C865)
"Requiem Mass In C Minor" [Eng/Lat] SATB, 2ob,2clar,2bsn,2horn,2trp,3trom,strings, timp,perc voc sc NOVELLO rental (C866)
(Confalonieri, G.) "Requiem" mix cor,orch (C min) voc sc ZERBONI 4146 s.p., ipr

CHERUBINI, LUIGI (cont'd.)

(C867)

Missa Pro Defunctus *Req
"Requiem" [Lat] SATB,orch (C min) voc sc PETERS 52 $2.50, ipr, min sc PETERS E993 $6.00, ipr, min sc PETERS E993 $9.00, ipr (C868)

Missa Solemnis *Mass
[Lat] SATB voc pt PETERS 47B $1.50, ipr (C869)

O Salutaris Hostia *mot
[Lat] TTBB RICORDI-ENG SY140 s.p. (C870)
SATB,acap RICORDI-ENG SY143 s.p. (C871)
4pt men cor,acap RICORDI-ENG SY140 s.p. (C872)

Pie Jesu (from Requiem Mass)
(Cramer) "God Of Mercy" [Eng/Lat] SATB MARKS 4180 $.25 (C873)
(Hines) boy cor SOUTHERN $.30 (C874)
(Hines) "Blessed Jesus" [Eng/Lat] TTBB oct LAWSON 51465 $.30 (C875)
(Marzo) "God Of Mercy" [Eng/Lat] 4pt mix cor,ST soli oct SCHIRM.G 11541 $.25 (C876)

Praise Ye The Lord *Bibl
(Messiter) 4pt mix cor,S solo oct SCHIRM.G 3518 $.30 (C877)

Premiere Messe De Ste Cecile *Mass
[Lat] cor,STB soli (F maj) HEUGEL s.p. (C878)

Quatrieme Messe Solennelle *Mass
(Vecchi, Prof. Giuseppe) cor,4-5 soli,orch quarto FORNI 108 s.p. (C879)

Requiem *see Missa Pro Defunctis

Requiem Aeternam *mot
TTB,acap MUSICUS 1013 $.15 (C880)

Requiem C-Moll *Mass
mix cor,2ob,2clar,2bsn,2trp,2horn,3trom, strings,timp (C min) voc sc BREITKOPF-L EB-299 s.p., ipr (C881)

Requiem C-Moll *see Missa Pro Defunctis

Requiem D-Moll *see Requiem

Requiem In C Minor *Mass/Req
cor voc sc KALMUS 6141 $1.50 (C882)
cor sc KALMUS $18.00 (C883)
cor,orch sc KALMUS $18.00, ipa (C884)
(Marzo, Ed) [Eng/Lat] mix cor voc sc SCHIRM.G $1.50 (C885)

Requiem In D Minor *see Requiem

Requiem Mass In C Minor *see Missa Pro Defunctis

Requiem *see Missa Pro Defunctus

Requiem *Req
"Requiem D-Moll" men cor,2fl,2ob,2clar, 2bsn,2trp,4horn,3trom,strings,timp (D min) voc sc BREITKOPF-L EB-298 s.p., ipr (C886)
"Requiem In D Minor" men cor voc sc KALMUS 6140 $1.75 (C887)
"Requiem In D Minor" men cor,orch sc KALMUS $18.00, ipa (C888)
"Requiem" [Lat] TTB,orch (D min) voc sc PETERS 51 $2.50, ipr, sc PETERS 2005 $15.00, ipr, min sc PETERS E992 $6.00, ipr, min sc-cloth PETERS E992 $9.00, ipr (C889)

Requiem *see Requiem

Sanctus (from Requiem) Sanctus
(Coggin) SATB oct FOX R209 $.25 (C890)
(Hines) "Holy, Holy, Holy" [Eng/Lat] TTBB oct LAWSON 51307 $.25 (C891)

Send Some Message From Thy Word
(Hammond; Coggin) SATB WARNER WB-171 $.30 (C892)

Troisieme Messe Solennelle *Mass
(Vecchi, Prof. Giuseppe) 3pt,orch quarto FORNI 109 s.p. (C893)

Twenty-Four Canons *CC24U,canon
2pt&3pt voc sc KALMUS 6142 $1.75 (C894)

Veni Jesu
boy cor SOUTHERN $.30 (C895)
(Ehret) "Come, O Jesus, Come To Me" SATB oct PLYMOUTH SC-16 $.25 (C896)
(Ehret) "Come, O Jesus, Come To Me" SAB oct PLYMOUTH SC-201 $.25 (C897)
(Ehret) "Come, O Jesus, Come To Me" SAB oct PLYMOUTH SC-401 $.25 (C898)
(Ehret) "Come, O Jesus, Come To Me" 2pt oct PLYMOUTH SC-501 $.25 (C899)
(Ehret) "Come, O Jesus, Come To Me" TTBB oct PLYMOUTH SC-301 $.25 (C900)
(Marsh) TTBB FLAMMER C5004 $.30 (C901)
(Marsh) boy cor SOUTHERN $.30 (C902)
(Riegger) SSA FLAMMER B 5090 $.25 (C903)

Veni Jesus
(Riegger) "Come, O Jesus, Saviour Mine" SATB FLAMMER A 5105 $.30 (C904)

CHESNOKOFF
see TCHESNOKOV, PAVEL GRIGORIEVITCH

CHESTERTON
Christ Child, The
(Platt) SATB oct PLYMOUTH SC-31 $.30 (C905)

CHEVALIER, HAROLD
My Peace I Give Unto You *anthem
SATB CRAMER A 17 s.p. (C906)

CHEYETTE
Dese Bones Shall Rise Again *spir
SATB oct BOURNE 683 $.30 (C907)

CHIAPPANI, CARLO
Dodici Canzoncine Alla Vergine *CC12U,BVM
[Lat] unis (easy) ZANIBON 2924 s.p. (C908)

Padre Nostro *prayer
4pt men cor ZANIBON 1284 s.p. (C909)

CHICAGO FOLK SERVICE see Gorman

CHICHESTER PSALMS see Bernstein, Leonard

CHIESA, CESARE
　Praesepe　*Xmas
　　2pt,org ZANIBON 2606 s.p.　　　(C910)

CHIESA, FEDERICO
　A Gesu Bambino　*Xmas
　　unis,org ZANIBON 2665 s.p.　　　(C911)

　Due Canti Al SS. Cuore　*CC2U
　　[Lat] unis,org ZANIBON 2655 s.p.　(C912)

　Inno A Maria　*BVM,cant
　　2 eq voices/4pt mix cor ZANIBON 2804 s.p.
　　　　　　　　　　　　　　　(C913)

CHIHARA, PAUL (1938-)
　Kyrie Eleison　*Kyrie
　　SATB oct HERITAGE H52 $.35　　　(C914)

　Magnificat　*Magnif
　　SSSAA oct SUMMY 5842 $.50　　　(C915)

　Psalm 90
　　SATB FLAMMER A1098 $2.00　　　(C916)

CHILD
　Praise The Lord, O My Soul
　　(Knight, Gerald) SATB,acap oct FISCHER,C
　　CM-7509 $.25　　　　　　　(C917)

CHILD DIVINE, A see Sharpe, Evelyn

CHILD IN THE MANGER　*Xmas
　(Douglas) SAB oct PRO ART 2068 $.22　(C918)
　(Douglas) SSA oct PRO ART 2051 $.22　(C919)

CHILD IS BORN, A　*Xmas/Epiph,carol,Dut
　(Rotermund, M.) SA,kbd (med easy) oct
　CONCORDIA 98-1889 $.25　　　(C920)

CHILD IS BORN, A see Elmore, Robert [Hall]

CHILD IS BORN, A see Praetorius, Michael

CHILD IS BORN, A see Self

CHILD IS BORN IN BETHLEHEM　*Xmas
　(Chambers) SATB,AB soli oct BOOSEY 5362 $.30
　　　　　　　　　　　　　　　(C921)
　(Chambers) TTBB oct BOOSEY 5471 $.30　(C922)

CHILD IS BORN IN BETHLEHEM, A see Bach, Johann
　Sebastian

CHILD IS BORN IN BETHLEHEM, A see Et Barn Er
　Fodt I Bethlehem

CHILD IS BORN IN BETHLEHEM, A see Praetorius,
　Michael

CHILD IS BORN IN BETHLEHEM, A see Scheidt,
　Samuel

CHILD IS BORN IN BETHLEHEM, A see Williams,
　David H.

CHILD IS BORN, THE SON OF GOD, A see Beck,
　Theodore

CHILD JESUS　*Xmas,carol,Dan
　(Ehret, Walter) SATB,opt inst oct WALTON 2513
　$.30　　　　　　　　　　　(C923)

CHILD JESUS see Bayley, Robert Charlton

CHILD JESUS see Gade, Niels [W.]

CHILD JESUS see Tchaikovsky, Piotr Ilyitch

CHILD JESUS see Thygerson

CHILD JESUS CAME TO EARTH see James

CHILD JESUS COMES FROM HEAVENLY HEIGHT see
　Blake

CHILD LIES IN THE MANGER, THE　*Xmas
　(Graves) SATB,acap (easy) OXFORD 84.151 $.20
　　　　　　　　　　　　　　　(C924)

CHILD MY CHOICE, A see Dirksen, Richard W.

CHILD MY CHOICE, A see Williams, David H.

CHILD MY CHOICE, A see Webber, Lloyd

CHILD OF BEAUTY　*Dut
　(Ehret) SSA MARKS 4168 $.30　　　(C925)
　(Ehret) SAB MARKS 4170 $.30　　　(C926)

CHILD OF BEAUTY WAS BORN TO US, A　*Xmas,carol
　(Ehret) SA MARKS 4065 $.30　　　(C927)

CHILD OF BETHLEHEM see Bush

CHILD OF BETHLEHEM, THE see Hankinson, Richard

CHILD OF BETHLEHEM, THE see Walter

CHILD OF BLISS see Fraser, Shena

CHILD OF FAITH see Wehr

CHILD OF GOD　*spir
　(Bridge) SATB ALFRED 6601 $.35　　(C928)

CHILD OF GOD see Bolz

CHILD OF GOD see Bridge

CHILD OF GOD see Ehret, Walter

CHILD OF GOD see Emig, Lois

CHILD OF HEAVEN see Schroth, Elizabeth

CHILD OF HEAVEN see Wilson

CHILD OF HEAVEN, THE see Williams, David H.

CHILD OF HOPE, A see Smith

CHILD OF LOVE see Grimm

CHILD OF LOVE, THE see Grimm, Jeff

CHILD OF OUR TIME, A see Tippett, Michael

CHILD OF PROMISE see Hunkins, Eusebia Simpson

CHILD OF THE WORLD, THE see Sykes

CHILD OF WONDER see Forcucci, S.L.

CHILD, SIMON
　O Bone Jesu
　　[Lat/Eng] SATB,org PETERS H1512 $.40 (C929)

CHILD SLEEPS, THE see Calabro, Louis

CHILD SO GENTLE AND PURE see Beck, Theodore

CHILD THIS DAY, A
　unis/SATB (easy) OXFORD 08.002 $.15　(C930)

CHILD THIS DAY IS BORN, A　*Xmas,carol,Eng
　(Barrow, R.) TTBB,org SCHIRM.EC 2305　(C931)

CHILD THIS DAY IS BORN, A see Herrmann, William

CHILD THIS DAY IS BORN, A see Hughes

CHILD THIS DAY IS BORN, A see Ilse, H.L.

CHILD THIS DAY IS BORN, A see Isle, H.L.

CHILD THIS DAY IS BORN, A see Washburn, Robert

CHILD TO US IS BORN, A see Schutz, Heinrich,
　Ein Kind Ist Uns Geboren

CHILD WAS BORN, A　*Xmas,Dan
　(Blyton) unis,rec/treb inst,vcl/bass inst oct
　FABER 11631 $.30　　　　　　(C932)

CHILD WAS BORN, A see Buxtehude, Dietrich

CHILD WAS BORN IN BETHLEHEM! see Cain, Noble

CHILD WAS BORN IN BETHLEHEM see Gesius,
　Bartholomaus

CHILD WAS BORN IN BETHLEHEM, A see Puer Natus

CHILD, WILLIAM (1606-1697)
　Evening Service　*Eve
　　SATB,acap PETERS H1517　　　(C933)

　O God, Wherefore Art Thou Absent From Us
　　(Le Huray, P.) SATB BROUDE,A. 218 $.30
　　　　　　　　　　　　　　　(C934)

　Praise The Lord, O My Soul　*Gen,anthem
　　SATB oct ROYAL 227 s.p.　　　(C935)
　　(Wienandt) SATB oct SOUTHERN $.25　(C936)

　Turn Thou Us, O Good Lord　*Gen/Lent
　　SSAATBB (med) oct OXFORD 42.886 $.50 (C937)

CHILDE JESUS see Clokey

CHILDHOOD OF CHRIST see Berlioz, Hector

CHILDHOOD OF CHRIST, THE see Berlioz, Hector

CHILDHOOD OF CHRIST, THE see Bach, Johann
　Sebastian

CHILDHOOD OF CHRIST, THE see Berlioz, Hector,
　L'9enfance Du Christ

CHILDHOOD OF CHRIST, THE see Berlioz, Hector,
　L'enfance Du Christ

CHILDING SLEPT, A see Naylor, Bernard

CHILDREN AT CHRISTMAS see Verkaaik

CHILDREN, CLAP YOUR HANDS　*spir
　(Davenport) SATB MARKS 866 $.25　(C938)

CHILDREN DON'T GET WEARY see Smith

CHILDREN OF BETHLEHEM see Carissimi, Giacomo, O
　Felix Anima

CHILDREN OF GOD see Angell

CHILDREN OF GOD, THE see Wilson

CHILDREN OF GOD, SING ON see Yahres

CHILDREN OF JERUSALEM, THE see Hurley

CHILDREN OF THE CHAPEL see Nicholson, S.H.

CHILDREN OF THE FAITHFUL see Johnson, Sidney

CHILDREN OF THE HEAVENLY FATHER　*Gen,anthem/
　folk,Swed
　see Three More General Choruses
　(Christiansen, P.) SATB SCHMITT 912 $.35
　　　　　　　　　　　　　　　(C939)
　(Ehret) SA oct BOOSEY 5387 $.30　(C940)
　(Hustad, Don) SATB ALLANS 404 s.p.　(C941)
　(Myrvik, Norman) SSAATB (med) oct AUGSBURG
　$.22　　　　　　　　　　　(C942)
　(Pooler) unis treb cor&desc (easy) oct
　AUGSBURG 1503 $.25　　　　　(C943)

CHILDREN OF THE HEAVENLY FATHER see Gustafson,
　D.

CHILDREN OF THE HEAVENLY FATHER see Hustad,
　Donald P.

CHILDREN OF THE HEAVENLY FATHER see Larson

CHILDREN OF THE HEAVENLY FATHER see Liemohn

CHILDREN OF THE HEAVENLY FATHER see Lundquist

CHILDREN OF THE HEAVENLY FATHER see Pooler,
　Marie

CHILDREN OF THE HEAVENLY FATHER see Riegger,
　Wallingford

CHILDREN OF THE HEAVENLY FATHER see Schnieder

CHILDREN OF THE HEAVENLY FATHER see Young

CHILDREN OF THE HEAVENLY KING see Pleyel, Ignaz
　Joseph

CHILDREN OF THE HEAVENLY KING see Weimer

CHILDREN OF THE HEBREWS, THE see Schubert,
　Franz (Peter)

CHILDREN OF THE HEBREWS, THE see Zorita,
　Nicosia, Pueri Hebraeorum

CHILDREN OF THE KING see Young, Robert H.

CHILDREN PRAISING　*CC102U,hymn
　(Wiseman) 1-2pt jr cor (easy) OXFORD 48.275
　$3.35　　　　　　　　　　(C944)

CHILDREN SANG THEIR PRAISES, THE see Malin, Don

CHILDREN SING, THE see Fuller, [Esther Mary]

CHILDREN SINGING see Blake, Rev. Canon, E.C.

CHILDREN WHO HAVE SAID THEIR PRAYERS see
　Mueller, Carl F.

CHILDREN'S ALLELUIA see Emig, Lois

CHILDREN'S BELL CAROL see Bortniansky, Dimitri
　Stepanovitch

CHILDREN'S BLESSING see Wasner, Franz,
　Kindersegen

CHILDREN'S CAROLS FOR ALL OCCASIONS see
　Anonymous

CHILDREN'S CHOIR BOOK see Pooler, Marie

CHILDREN'S CHOIR FAVORITES see Anderson, Becky

CHILDREN'S CHOIR NO. 1　*CCU,anthem
　unis LORENZ $1.75　　　　　(C945)

CHILDREN'S CHOIR NO. 2　*CCU,anthem
　unis LORENZ $1.75　　　　　(C946)

CHILDREN'S CHOIR NO. 3　*CCU,anthem
　unis LORENZ $1.75　　　　　(C947)

CHILDREN'S CHRISTMAS CAROLS　*CCU,Xmas,carol
　unis LORENZ $.35　　　　　(C948)

CHILDREN'S CHRISTMAS SONG see Vaughan Williams,
　Ralph

CHILDREN'S CRUSADE, THE see Pierne, Gabriel

CHILDREN'S FIRST CHOIR　*CC15U
　jr cor,opt inst oct LILLENAS MB-010 $.75 gen
　& seasonal　　　　　　　　(C949)

CHILDREN'S FRIEND, THE see Anderson, [William
　H.]

CHILDREN'S HOSANNA, THE see Emig, Lois

CHILDREN'S HYMN OF PRAISE, THE see Rasley

CHILDREN'S PRAISES　*CC200U
　(Latham, Joy) jr cor, autoharp cloth LILLENAS
　MB-011 $1.50, pap LILLENAS MB-012 $.85
　　　　　　　　　　　　　　　(C950)

CHILDREN'S PRAYER　*anthem/folk,Ger
　(Leaf, Robert) unis treb cor (easy) oct
　AUGSBURG 1615 $.25　　　　　(C951)

CHILDREN'S PRAYER see Besig

CHILDREN'S PRAYER see Egoroff, A.

CHILDREN'S PRAYER see Harder

CHILDREN'S PRAYER, THE
　(Treharne) SA (lithuanian) BOSTON 6828 $.35
　　　　　　　　　　　　　　　(C952)

CHILDREN'S PRAYER, THE see Humperdinck,
　Engelbert

CHILDREN'S SONG OF THE NATIVITY　*Xmas,carol
　unis (easy) OXFORD 08.141 $.15　(C953)

CHILDREN'S STORY OF CHRISTMAS, A see Noona,
　Walter

CHILDREN'S TE DEUM, A see Le Fleming,
　Christopher (Kaye)

CHILDREN'S VOICES see Larson

CHILDREN'S VOICES JOYFULLY SING see Leaf,
　Robert

CHILDREN'S WORSHIP IN CHURCH, SERIES 1 see
　Grime, William

CHILDS, BARNEY (1926-)
　Be Merry
　　see Three Carols On Old Texts

　Now We Make Merry
　　see Three Carols On Old Texts

　There Is No Rose
　　see Three Carols On Old Texts

　Three Carols On Old Texts　*carol
　　SATB,acap oct LAWSON 51121 $.35
　　contains: Be Merry; Now We Make Merry;
　　There Is No Rose　　　　　(C954)

CHILD'S BOOK OF ANTHEMS see Fuller, [Esther
　Mary]

CHILD'S CAROL, A see Sharpe, Evelyn

CHILD'S CHRISTMAS PRAYER, A see Silver,
　Frederick

CHILD'S EVENING HYMN, A see Buck, Sir Percy
　Carter

CHILD'S HYMN OF PRAISE see Sharpe, Evelyn

CHILD'S NOEL, A see Beck, John Ness

CHILD'S PRAYER, A see Anderson, [William H.]

CHILD'S PRAYER, A see Barthelson

CHILD'S PRAYER, A see Jones, Marjorie

CHILD'S PRAYER, A see Klemm, Gustav

CHILD'S PRAYER, A see Roff, Joseph

CHILD'S PRAYER, A see Shaw, Geoffrey [Turton]

CHILD'S PRAYER, A see Taylor, Colin

CHILD'S PRAYER, A see White, Michael

CHILD'S PRESENT TO HIS SAVIOR, A see Byles, B. D.

CHILD'S SONG OF CHRISTMAS, A see Graves, Richard

CHILD'S SONG OF CHRISTMAS, A see Pasfield, W.R.

CHILD'S THANKSGIVING, A see Baynon, Arthur

CHILLUN see Kropczynski

CHILLY WATERS *spir
(Roberton) 4pt mix cor ROBERTON 61420 s.p.
(C955)

CHIME, HAPPY CHRISTMAS BELLS see Hokanson, Margrethe

CHIMES OF THE HOLY NIGHT see Holton

CHINESE CHRISTMAS CAROL, A see Wiant, Bliss

CHIQUIRRIQUITIN *Xmas,carol,Span
(Ehret, Walter) "O My Loveliest One" SATB oct
WALTON 2507 $.30
(C956)

CHITI, G.
Sub Tuum Praesidium
(Beichert) [Lat] cor,opt org SCHOTT voc sc
s.p., cor pts s.p.
(C957)

CHIUDER GL'OCCHI VORREI see Fonteijo, Giovanni

CHO-TUNG TANG, JORDAN
Psalm 117 *see Psalm Of Praise

Psalm Of Praise (Psalm 117) Bibl
SATB,2trp,2trom,timp oct WORLD CA-2458-8
$.75, ipa
(C958)

CHOER FINAL see Thiriet, [Maurice]

CHOEUR DE BETHLEMITES ET STROPHES see Franck, Cesar

CHOEUR DE MOABITES see Franck, Cesar

CHOEUR DE MOISONNEURS see Franck, Cesar

CHOEUR DES CHAMELIERS see Franck, Cesar

CHOEUR DES FUGITIFS see Gounod, Charles Francois

CHOEUR DES JEUNES FILLES see Franck, Cesar

CHOEUR DES OLIVETTES see Paladilhe, [Emile]

CHOEUR DES ROMAINS see Massenet, Jules

CHOEUR DES SERVANTES see Massenet, Jules

CHOEUR DES SOLDATS see Gounod, Charles Francois

CHOEUR TRIOMPHAL see Saint-Saens, Camille

CHOEURS POUR DISTRIBUTIONS DE PRIX OU POUR
ENFANTS *sac/sec,CC50L
[Fr/Lat] 2-3pt quarto CHOUDENS s.p. contains
sacred works by: Gounod; Audran; Paladilhe;
Bizet
see also: Audran, Edmond, Petite Noel Avec
Mystere (from La Cigale); Bizet, Georges,
Agnus Dei; Gounod, Charles Francois,
Gloire Immortelle De Nos Aieux (from
Faust); Paladilhe, [Emile], O Salutaris
(C959)

CHOIR OF BETHLEHEM, THE see Benson

CHOIR SING! VOLUME 1 *CCUL
(Mickelson, Paul) cor cmplt ed LILLENAS
MB-013 $1.50
(C960)

CHOIR SING! VOLUME 2 *CCUL,hymn
(Mickelson, Paul) cor cmplt ed LILLENAS
MB-014 $1.50
(C961)

CHOIR SING! VOLUME 3 *CC10UL,gospel
(Mickelson, Paul) cor cmplt ed LILLENAS
MB-015 $1.50
(C962)

CHOIR SINGS HYMNS HOT AND CAROLS COOL, THE see
Avery

CHOIR WORSHIP *CCU
(Hallett, J.) SATB voc sc WORD 20040 $1.50
(C963)

CHOIRISTER'S SING *sac/sec,CC15L
(Ehret; Siegmeister) SSA PRO ART 126 $1.25
(C964)

CHOIRS OF ANGELS *Xmas
(Follett) SATB oct PRO ART 2012 $.25 (C965)
(Follett) SSA oct PRO ART 2326 $.25 (C966)

CHOIRS OF ANGELS see Clare, Edwyn A.

CHOIRS OF ANGELS PRAISE THEE see Bortniansky,
Dimitri Stepanovitch

CHOIRS OF HERALD ANGELS SINGING *Xmas,carol,
Pol
(Ehret) SAB,opt ob oct FOX CC1 $.25 (C967)
(Ehret, W.) SAB,opt ob PROWSE CC1 s.p. (C968)

CHOISNEL, G.
Ave Maria *BVM,mot
[Lat] SATBar oct DURAND s.p. (C969)

O Salutaris *Commun,mot
[Lat] SATBar oct DURAND s.p. (C970)
[Lat] 2 eq voices oct DURAND s.p. (C971)

Tantum Ergo *Commun,mot
[Lat] SATBar oct DURAND s.p. (C972)

CHOJNACKI, J.
Six Motets In Polish And English *CC6U,Gen,
anthem/mot
SATB (easy) cmplt ed GIA G1312 $2.00 (C973)

CHOLLET, A.
Christ Est Ressuscite *Easter
[Fr] 4pt mix cor,acap LEMOINE s.p. (C974)

CHOPIN, FREDERIC (1810-1849)
God's Gift Of Love *Xmas
SATB oct LORENZ C320 $.30 (C975)

Lamb Of God *Commun/Lent,anthem
(Howorth) SATB,acap oct FOX PS145 $.30
(C976)

O Lord, We Adore Thee (from Etude, Op. 10,
No. 3)
(Mahenbrock) jr cor,pno/org (med) oct
WILLIS 6103 $.15 (C977)

O Lovely Hour
SA oct LORENZ 5174 $.25 (C978)
SSA oct LORENZ 6106 $.30 (C979)
SAB oct LORENZ 7119 $.25 (C980)

Speak, Lord To Me *Easter/Gen
(Peery) SATB oct PRESSER 332-40035 $.30
(C981)

Unto Thee Will I Call
(Fearis, S.S.) SATB,SAT soli,pno (med) oct
WILLIS 6336 $.15 (C982)

CHOR IM KIRCHENJAHR-HEFT I UND II see Kern,
Matthias

CHORAL see Iten, Walter

CHORAL see Matthes, Rene

CHORAL ALBUM (BOOK 2) *CC9UL,anthem/hymn
(Gerig, Richard E.) SAB cmplt ed LILLENAS
MB-017 $1.00 (C983)

CHORAL ASCRIPTION OF PRAISE, A see Marshall,
Jane M.

CHORAL BENEDICTIONS see Bitgood, Roberta

CHORAL-BOG 1764 see Breitendich, Fr. Chr.

CHORAL CALLS TO WORSHIP see Fuller, [Esther
Mary]

CHORAL CANTATA NO. 4 see Reger, Max, Meinem
Jesu Lass Ich Nicht

CHORAL CHRISTMAS PRESENT, A *CC10U,Xmas,anthem
(Bock, Fred) SATB (med easy) PRESSER $1.50
(C984)

CHORAL CHURCH CANTATAS see Bruhns, Nicholaus

CHORAL CHURCH YEAR, THE *CCU,anthem
SATB LORENZ $1.75 (C985)

CHORAL DEVOTIONS *CCU
(Granville) SAB oct FOX $1.50 (C986)

CHORAL DUETS FROM CANTATAS [NOS. 3, 91, 163],
VOL. 4 see Bach, Johann Sebastian

CHORAL DUETS FROM CANTATAS [NOS. 4, 37, 78,
124], VOL. 1 see Bach, Johann Sebastian

CHORAL DUETS FROM CANTATAS [NOS. 9, 184], VOL
2. see Bach, Johann Sebastian

CHORAL DUETS FROM CANTATAS [NOS. 88, 93, 168],
VOL. 3 see Bach, Johann Sebastian

CHORAL FANFARE FOR CHRISTMAS see Hartley,
Gerald

CHORAL FANFARE FOR CHRISTMAS see Nelson, Ronald
A.

CHORAL FANFARE ON "HOLY, HOLY, HOLY" see Rasley

CHORAL FANTASIA, A see Holst, Gustav

CHORAL FANTASY see Beethoven, Ludwig van

CHORAL-FESTMESSE see Eschmann, Hanns

CHORAL FINALE see Beethoven, Ludwig van

CHORAL FLOURISH, A see Vaughan Williams, Ralph

CHORAL GOSPEL HYMN ARRANGEMENTS NO. 1 *CCU,
anthem
SATB LORENZ $1.75 (C987)

CHORAL GOSPEL HYMN ARRANGEMENTS NO. 2 *CCU,
anthem
SATB LORENZ $1.75 (C988)

CHORAL GRACE see Stitt, Margaret McClure

CHORAL HYMN, A *Adv/Asc
(Ley, Henry G.) SATB (easy) oct OXFORD 42.167
$.30
contains: All Hail The Power Of Jesus'
Name; Lord Will Come And Not Be Slow, The
(C989)

CHORAL HYMNS *CC11UL,hymn
(Ortlund, Anne) cor,kbd (easy) cmplt ed
LILLENAS MB-018 $1.50 (C990)

CHORAL INTROIT AND SEVENFOLD AMEN see Hartley,
Walter [S.]

CHORAL INTROITS FOR THE CHURCH YEAR see
Mueller, Carl F.

CHORAL MASS see Lee, J.

CHORAL MASTERWORKS *CC7L,Gen
SATB oct PRO ART 358 $1.25 (C991)

CHORAL MEDITATIONS see Wilkinson

CHORAL MUSIC see Bach, Johann Sebastian

CHORAL MUSIC OF TODAY NO. 1 *CCU
SATB HANSEN-US P080 $1.45; TTBB HANSEN-US
P084 $1.95 (C992)

CHORAL MUSIC THROUGH THE CENTURIES *CCU
mix cor SCHMITT 9061 $2.00 (C993)

CHORAL-OBSTINATO see Ceillier, L.

CHORAL PRAISE *CCU,anthem
SATB LORENZ $1.95 (C994)

CHORAL PRAYER see Thompson, V.D.

CHORAL PRAYER, A see Glarum, L. Stanley

CHORAL PRIMER, THE see Wilson, John F.

CHORAL PSALMIST, THE see Butler, Eugene

CHORAL RESPONSES *CCU,cor-resp
SATB LORENZ 4454 $.30 (C995)

CHORAL RESPONSES FOR THE CHRISTMAS SEASON
*CCU,Xmas,cor-resp
SATB LORENZ B92 $.30 (C996)

CHORAL RESPONSES FOR THE CHURCH YEAR (GROUP 1)
see Bampton, R.

CHORAL RESPONSES FOR THE EASTER SEASON *CCU,
Easter,cor-resp
SATB LORENZ B93 $.30 (C997)

CHORAL SAMPLER, THE *sac/sec,CCU
(Berger, M.) SAB oct FOX $1.50 (C998)

CHORAL SECTION see Beethoven, Ludwig van

CHORAL SELECTIONS FROM "GODSPELL" see Schwartz,
Stephen

CHORAL SENTENCES FOR THE WORSHIP SERVICE see
Webb

CHORAL SENTENCES FOR WORSHIP see Wood, Dale

CHORAL SERVICE FOR THANKSGIVING, A see Wilson

CHORAL SERVICE FOR WATCH NIGHT, A see Wilson

CHORAL SETTINGS *CCU
mix cor SCHMITT 9109 $1.35 (C999)

CHORAL SONGBOOK *sac/sec,CCU,Eng/Ger/Neth/
Span,Renais
(Greenberg) SATB,acap AMP N25 $2.00 (C1000)

CHORAL SONGS FOR CHRISTMAS see Hannahs, R.C.

CHORAL SUITE see Rimsky-Korsakov, Nikolai

CHORAL THANKSGIVING, A see Powell, Robert J.

CHORAL TRIPTYCH see Kay, Ulysses Simpson

CHORAL TUNES FOR TEENS *CCU,anthem
LORENZ SATB&SAB&SA $1.50; $1.50 (C1001)

CHORAL VARIATIONS ON "AH, HOLY JESUS" see
Petrich, Roger, Herzliebster Jesu

CHORAL WEDDING SERVICE BOOK *CCU
ROYAL 85402 019 5 s.p. (C1002)

CHORALBUCH *CC90U,chorale
(Doerffel) SATB,acap PETERS 1423 $2.00
(C1003)

CHORALBUCH FUR KINDERCHOR see Weber, Hans

CHORALE see Bach, Johann Sebastian

CHORALE see Rodby, John

CHORALE see Saint-Saens, Camille

CHORALE ANTHEMS BASED ON CHORALE PRELUDES, VOL.
II see Pasquet, Jean

CHORALE CLASSICS *CCU,chorale
(Ehret) SATB MARKS $1.25 (C1004)

CHORALE CLASSICS *CC16L,Gen,chorale
(Whistler, Harvey, S. And Hummel, Herman, A.)
SATB,inst voc sc RUBANK $.50 contains works
by: Bach, J.S; Brahms, Johannes; Gounod,
Charles; Handel, George Frederic; Luther,
Martin; Mason, Lowell; Mendelssohn-
Bartholdy, Felix; Palestrina; Giovanni;
Praetorius, Michael; Saint-Saens, Camille;
Schubert, Franz Joseph; Schumann, Robert
(C1005)

CHORALE FOR EASTER see Davis, J.R.

CHORALE FROM ST. MATTHEW PASSION see Bach,
Johann Sebastian

CHORALE HARMONIZATION IN THE CHURCH MODES see
Hamburger

CHORALE HARMONIZATIONS see Mendelssohn-
Bartholdy, Felix

CHORALE-HEFT 1 see Bach, Johann Sebastian

CHORALE-HEFT 2 see Bach, Johann Sebastian

CHORALE MASS see Bach, Johann Sebastian

CHORALES see Bach, Johann Sebastian

CHORALES AND MOTETS *CC17U,chorale/mot
(Lundquist, Matthew) SATB oct WILLIS $1.25
(C1006)

CHORALES, BOOK I see Bach, Johann Sebastian

CHORALES, BOOK II see Bach, Johann Sebastian

CHORALES FOR UNCHANGED VOICES *CCU,chorale
mix cor SCHMITT 12 $.50 (C1007)

CHORALES FROM THE CRUCIFIXION see Stainer, John

CHORALES see Bach, Johann Sebastian

CHORALFANTASIE UBER "ICH WOLLT', DASS ICH
DAHEIME WAR'" see Kurz, Walter

CHORALGESANGE see Bach, Johann Sebastian

CHORALGESANGE see Bach, Johann Sebastian

CHORALGESANGE see Bach, Johann Sebastian

CHORALMOTETTE see Distler, Hugo

CHORALMOTETTEN see Praetorius, Michael

CHORALMOTETTEN see Micheelsen, Hans Friedrich

CHORALPASSION NACH DEN VIER EVANGELIEN see Distler, Hugo

CHORALS see Goemanne, Noel

CHORALSATZE see Bach, Johann Sebastian

CHORALSATZE-HEFT 1 see Praetorius, Michael

CHORALSATZE-HEFT 2 see Praetorius, Michael

CHORALSINGBUCH *CCU,Gen
    (Brodde, Otto) [Ger] unis,org BAREN. BA 671
    $11.50   (C1008)

CHORALSINGBUCH *CC95U,Gen,Contemp
    (Mahrenholz, Christhard) [Ger] 3 eq voices,
    acap (med easy) BAREN. BA 1590 $4.75
                                                 (C1009)

CHORALSINGBUCH *CC101U,Gen
    (Schmidt, Ferdinand) [Ger] SA&men cor,acap
    (med) BAREN. BA 1589 $4.75   (C1010)

CHORBAJIAN, JOHN (1936-   )
    And Did Those Feet In Ancient Time
    mix cor,acap oct SCHIRM.G 11925 $.30   (C1011)

    De Profundis
    "Out Of The Depths" [Eng/Lat] mix cor,acap
    oct SCHIRM.G 11740 $.30   (C1012)

    Lamb
    mix cor SOUTHERN $.30   (C1013)

    Lamb, The
    mix cor,acap oct SCHIRM.G 11790 $.30   (C1014)

    Out Of The Depths *see De Profundis

CHORBUCH ALTER MEISTER BAND 1 *CCU
    (Jode) 3-4 eq voices MOSELER s.p. contains
    works by: Eccard; Hassler; Isaac; Lasso;
    and others   (C1015)

CHORBUCH FUR GLEICHE STIMMEN *CCU
    (Striebel, Martin; Stern, Hermann) eq voices
    HANSSLER 2.030 s.p.   (C1016)

CHORE ZUR WEIHNACHT *Xmas
    men cor TONGER s.p.
    contains: Lang, Hans, Vom Himmel Hoch;
    Praetorius, Michael, Es Ist Ein Ros'
    Entsprungen; Rein, Walter, Auf, Haltet
    Euer Herz Bereit; Sendt, Willy, In Dulci
    Jubilo; Sturmer, Bruno, Kommet, Ihr
    Hirten   (C1017)

CHORGESANGBUCH see Golz, Richard

CHORGESANGE see Eccard, Johannes

CHORGESANGE FUR DEN GOTTESDIENST *CCU
    mix cor sc BREITKOPF-W CHB-3050 s.p. contains
    works by: Praetorius; Eccard; Vulpius and
    others   (C1018)

CHORGESANGE ZUM GOTTESDIENSTLICHEN UND
    SONSTIGEN GEBRAUCH *CCU
    mix cor HANSSLER 2.022 s.p. in 9 parts
                                                 (C1019)
CHORGESANGE ZUM GOTTESDIENSTLICHEN *CCU
    mix cor HANSSLER 2.039 s.p.   (C1020)

CHORGESANGE ZUM GOTTESDIENSTLICHEN *CCU
    mix cor HANSSLER 2.049 s.p.   (C1021)

CHORGESANGE ZUM KARFREITAG see Fiebig, Kurt

CHORHEFT *CCU
    mix cor HANSSLER 2.047 s.p.   (C1022)

CHORHEFT ZUM SCHUTZJAHR 1972 see Schutz,
    Heinrich

CHORIC PSALM, A see McAfee, Don

CHORISTER SERIES *CC14L
    (Read, Ernest) unis&SSA,solo PATERSON
    contains works by: Bach; Handel; Haydn;
    Mendelssohn; Smart   (C1023)

CHORISTERS OF LIGHT see Davis, Katherine K.

CHORLIEDER ZUR WEIHNACHT see Gotsch, Georg

CHORMUSIK AUF DEN NAMEN ISRAEL see Hufschmidt,
    Wolfgang

CHORMUSIK ZUM PFINGSTFEST see Benary, Peter

CHORMUSIK ZUR PASSION see Benary, Peter

CHORMUSIK ZUR WEIHNACHT see Benary, Peter

CHOROS III, PSALMUS 45 see Horst, Anthon van
    der

CHOROS VII see Horst, Anthon van der

CHORSATZE ALTER MEISTER *CCU
    (Wagner, Hermann) [Eng/Ger/Fr/It] mix cor
    MOSELER s.p.   (C1024)

CHORUS AND NOCTURNE FOR ADVENT see Cain, Noble

CHORUS CHOIR VOICES NO. 1 *CC34UL,hymn
    cor (easy) cmplt ed LILLENAS MB-019 $1.25
                                                 (C1025)
CHORUS CHOIR VOICES NO. 2 *CC34UL,hymn
    cor (easy) cmplt ed LILLENAS MB-020 $1.25
                                                 (C1026)
CHORUS CHOIR VOICES NO. 3 *CC40UL,hymn
    cor cmplt ed LILLENAS MB-021 $1.25   (C1027)

CHORUS CHOIR VOICES NO. 4 *CC40UL
    (Stringfield, R.W.) cor cmplt ed LILLENAS
    MB-022 $1.25   (C1028)

CHORUS CHOIR VOICES NO. 5 *CCUL
    (Hawkins, Floyd) SATB cmplt ed LILLENAS
    MB-023 $1.25   (C1029)

CHORUS CHOIR VOICES NO. 6 *CC45UL,hymn/spir
    (Stringfield, R.W.) cor (easy) cmplt ed
    LILLENAS MB-024 $1.25   (C1030)

CHORUS CHOIR VOICES NO. 7 *CCUL,hymn
    (Hawkins, Floyd) 4pt (easy) cmplt ed LILLENAS
    MB-025 $1.25   (C1031)

CHORUS OF ANGELS see Schutz, Heinrich

CHORUS OF ANGELS (CHRIST IS A-RISEN) see
    Schubert, Franz (Peter)

CHORUS OF BETHLEMITES AND STROPHES see Franck,
    Cesar, Choeur De Bethlemites Et Strophes

CHORUS OF HARVESTERS see Franck, Cesar, Choeur
    De Moisonneurs

CHORUS OF JOY see Beethoven, Ludwig van

CHORUS OF MOABITES see Franck, Cesar, Choeur De
    Moabites

CHORUS OF THE SKIES see Holton

CHORUSES FOR CHANGING VOICES *CCU
    camb SCHMITT 10 $.50   (C1032)

CHORUSES FOR OUR DAY *CC17UL
    jr cor/sr cor cmplt ed LILLENAS MB-026 $.50
                                                 (C1033)
CHORUSES FOR STUDY AND PERFORMANCE see Handel,
    George Frideric

CHORVARIATIONEN UBER DIE SONNENGESANGE DES
    FRANZISKUS VON ASSISI see Herrmann, Hugo

CHORVARIATIONEN UBER EIN THEMA VON HUGO DISTLER
    ("NURNBERGER GROSSES GLORIA") see
    Zimmermann, Heinz Werner

CHOSEN ONES see Carlson, J. Bert

CHRIST ALSO SUFFERED FOR US see Davies, Henry
    Walford

CHRIST AM OLBERGE see Beethoven, Ludwig van

CHRIST AND SINFUL MAN see Hoddinott, Alun

CHRIST AROSE! see Hughes

CHRIST AROSE see Peery

CHRIST ATONED FOR OUR TRANSGRESSIONS see
    Eberlin

CHRIST ATONED FOR OUR TRANSGRESSIONS see
    Eberlin, Johann Ernst, Christus Factus Est

CHRIST, BE THINE THE GLORY! see Schutz,
    Heinrich, Ehre Sei Dir Christe

CHRIST BECAME OBEDIENT FOR US UNTO DEATH see
    Lee, J.

CHRIST BECAME OBEDIENT FOR US UNTO DEATH see
    Sanders, Robert L.

CHRIST BEING RAISED see Thiman, Eric Harding

CHRIST BEING RAISED FROM THE DEAD see Bissell,
    Keith

CHRIST BEING RAISED FROM THE DEAD see Cook,
    E.T.

CHRIST BEING RAISED FROM THE DEAD see Stewart,
    C. Hylton

CHRIST CAME TO BETHLEHEM see Frederickson, Carl

CHRIST CAME TO BETHLEHEM see Williams, David H.

CHRIST CHILD see Harries

CHRIST CHILD see Hawley, [Charles Beach]

CHRIST CHILD, THE see Matthews

CHRIST CHILD, CHRIST CHILD see Ades

CHRIST CHILD, CHRIST CHILD see Chaplin, N.W.

CHRIST CHILD, DIVINE see Shumaker

CHRIST CHILD LAY ON MARY'S LAP *Xmas
    unis/SATB (easy) OXFORD 08.143 $.15   (C1034)

CHRIST-CHILD LAY ON MARY'S LAP, THE see Heys,
    S.

CHRIST-CHILD LAY ON MARY'S LAP, THE see Lee, J.

CHRIST CHILD SLEEPS, THE see Sharpe, Evelyn

CHRIST CHILD SMILES
    see Three Christmas Carols

CHRIST-CHILD SMILES, THE *Xmas,carol
    (Whitehead, Alfred) SATB oct LESLIE 4004 see
    from Three Christmas Carols, Set 1   (C1035)

CHRIST CHILD, THE *Xmas
    SSA CHAPPELL 0014597-354 $.40   (C1036)
    SATB CHAPPELL 0014597-358 $.40   (C1037)

CHRIST CHILD, THE see Bliss, Paul

CHRIST CHILD, THE see Chesterton

CHRIST CHILD, THE see Cornelius, Peter

CHRIST CHILD, THE see Huston, Scott

CHRIST CHILD, THE see Strickland, Lily Teresa

CHRIST CHILD, THE see Whitney, Maurice C.

CHRIST-CHILD'S LULLABY, THE *Xmas,17th cent
    (Mueller, Carl F.) 4pt mix cor oct SCHIRM.G
    7730 $.25   (C1038)

CHRIST CONQUERETH see Clokey, Joseph Waddell

CHRIST CRUCIFIED see Butler

CHRIST, DER DU BIST DIE HELLE TAG see Lechner,
    Leonhard

CHRIST, DER DU BIST TAG UND LICHT see Koch,
    Johannes H.E.

CHRIST, DER HERR, KOMMT IN DIE WELT see Linek,
    Jiri Ignatz

CHRIST, DER IST ERSTANDEN see Bruck, Arnold von

CHRIST, DER IST ERSTANDEN see Bruck, Johann von

CHRIST, DU BIST DER HELLE TAG see Distler, Hugo

CHRIST, DU LAMM GOTTES see Stern, Hermann

CHRIST EST RESSUSCITE see Chollet, A.

CHRIST EVERLASTING see Wilson

CHRIST: FOUNDATION, HEAD AND CORNERSTONE see
    Pfautsch, Lloyd

CHRIST, FROM WHOM ALL BLESSINGS FLOW see
    Westbrook, Francis B.

CHRIST FUHR GEN HIMMEL see Baudach, Ulrich

CHRIST FUHR GEN HIMMEL see Thomas, Kurt

CHRIST HAS ARISEN see Gabrieli, Giovanni,
    Surrexit Christus

CHRIST HAS ARISEN see Luvaas

CHRIST HAS RISEN see Schubert, Franz (Peter)

CHRIST HAS RISEN ON EASTER DAY see Elrich, D.

CHRIST HATH A GARDEN see Holman, Derek

CHRIST HATH A GARDEN see Near, Gerald

CHRIST HATH A GARDEN see Thiman, Eric Harding

CHRIST HATH ARISEN see Lassus, Roland de
    (Orlandus), Christ Ist Erstanden

CHRIST HATH HUMBLED HIMSELF see Slater, Richard
    W.

CHRIST HATH HUMBLED HIMSELF see Willan, Healey

CHRIST HATH TRIUMPHED, ALLELUIA see Darst, W.
    Glenn

CHRIST HATH TRIUMPHED, ALLELUIA! see Hughes

CHRIST HATH WON THE VICTORY see Van Woert

CHRIST IN ME *Fest,medley
    (Thompson, E.D.) SATB&opt jr cor,opt soli,opt
    trp (med diff) THOMP. C008 $.50   (C1039)

CHRIST IN THE UNIVERSE see Davies, Henry
    Walford

CHRIST INDEED IS RISEN TODAY! see Ehret, Walter

CHRIST IS ARISEN see Bender, Jan

CHRIST IS ARISEN see Boardman, E.

CHRIST IS ARISEN see Couperin, Francois

CHRIST IS ARISEN see Deixeii Lo Dol

CHRIST IS ARISEN see Eccard, Johannes

CHRIST IS ARISEN see Harris

CHRIST IS ARISEN see Hassler, Hans Leo, Christ
    Ist Erstanden

CHRIST IS ARISEN see Hirsch, Christ Ist
    Erstanden

CHRIST IS ARISEN see Kukuck, Felicitas

CHRIST IS ARISEN see Lenel, Ludwig

CHRIST IS ARISEN see Lindquist, M.

CHRIST IS ARISEN see Lotti, Antonio

CHRIST IS ARISEN! see Pfautsch, Lloyd

CHRIST IS ARISEN see Rohlig, Harald

CHRIST IS ARISEN see Schubert, Franz (Peter),
    Christ Ist Erstanden

CHRIST IS ARISEN see Schutz, Heinrich

CHRIST IS ARISEN see Young

CHRIST IS ARISEN see Young, G.

CHRIST IS ARISEN FROM THE GRAVE see Hirsch,
    Carl

CHRIST IS BORN see Glover, R.F.

CHRIST IS BORN *Xmas
    (Vree, M.) SAB oct PRESSER 312-40764 $.25
                                                 (C1040)
    (Vree, M.) SATB,acap oct PRESSER 312-40416
    $.30   (C1041)

CHRIST IS BORN see Boalt

CHRIST IS BORN see Boberg

CHRIST IS BORN see Davenport, David

CHRIST IS BORN see Ebeling

CHRIST IS BORN see Newbury

CHRIST IS BORN see O'connor

CHRIST IS BORN see Richolson

CHRIST IS BORN! see Wilson

CHRIST IS BORN FOR US see Bruckner, Anton

CHRIST IS BORN IN A MANGER BED *Xmas,carol,Fr
 (Van Koert, Han) SA&SATB,org oct WORLD
    AC-256-8 $.30   (C1042)

CHRIST IS BORN IN BETHLEHEM see Smith, Paul

CHRIST IS BORN, LITTLE INFANT KING *Xmas,carol
 (Glover, R.F.) SS,org oct KERBY 6023 $.40
    contains also: Carol Of The Bagpiper; From
    Shining Stars Descending   (C1043)

CHRIST IS BORN OF MAIDEN FAIR *carol,Eng
 TTBB,acap SCHIRM.EC 930 $.18   (C1044)

CHRIST IS BORN OF MAIDEN FAIR see Britten,
 Anthony

CHRIST IS BORN OF MAIDEN FAIR see Matthews,
 David

CHRIST IS BORN TO YOU TODAY *Xmas,Ger
 (Ehret) SA,opt vln MARKS 4408 $.25   (C1045)
 (Ehret) SSA,opt vln MARKS 4349 $.25   (C1046)

CHRIST IS BORN TODAY *Xmas
 (Nyquist) SATB,acap oct PRO ART 1589 $.25
                                              (C1047)
 (Nyquist) SAB oct PRO ART 1721 $.25   (C1048)
 (Nyquist) SSA oct PRO ART 1737 $.25   (C1049)
 (Perle) SATB,acap oct BOOSEY 5235 $.30
                                              (C1050)

CHRIST IS BORN TODAY see Christiansen

CHRIST IS BORN TODAY see Leazer

CHRIST IS BORN TODAY see Leazer, Carl W., Hodie
 Christus Natus Est

CHRIST IS BORN TODAY! see Litten, Jack

CHRIST IS BORN TODAY see Marenzio, Luca, Hodie
 Christus Natus Est

CHRIST IS BORN TODAY see Nanini (Nanino),
 Giovanni Maria, Hodie Christus Natus Est

CHRIST IS ERSTANDEN VON DER MARTER see Eccard,
 Johannes

CHRIST IS KING see Peloquin, C. Alexander

CHRIST IS MADE THE SURE FOUNDATION see Englert,
 Eugene

CHRIST IS MADE THE SURE FOUNDATION see Marsh

CHRIST IS MADE THE SURE FOUNDATION see Newbury,
 Kent A.

CHRIST IS MADE THE SURE FOUNDATION see Owens,
 Dewley

CHRIST IS MADE THE SURE FOUNDATION see Purcell,
 Henry

CHRIST IS MADE THE SURE FOUNDATION see Wood

CHRIST IS MADE THE SURE FOUNDATION see York, D.

CHRIST IS NOW RISEN AGAIN *Easter
 (Vree, Marion) SATB&SATB,acap FOSTER MF 410
    $.25   (C1051)

CHRIST IS NOW RISEN AGAIN see Dean

CHRIST IS NOW RISEN AGAIN see Lenel, Ludwig

CHRIST IS NOW RIS'N AGAIN see Lenel

CHRIST IS OUR CORNER-STONE see Shaw, Martin

CHRIST IS OUR CORNER-STONE see Thiman, Eric
 Harding

CHRIST IS OUR CORNER STONE see Wadely, F.W.

CHRIST IS OUR CORNERSTONE see Aufdemberge,
 Edgar

CHRIST IS OUR CORNERSTONE see Cook, John

CHRIST IS OUR CORNERSTONE see Darst, W. Glenn

CHRIST IS OUR CORNERSTONE see Greaves, Terence

CHRIST IS OUR CORNERSTONE see Powell, Robert J.

CHRIST IS RISEN see Brackett, F.H.

CHRIST IS RISEN see Christus Ist Auferstanden

CHRIST IS RISEN see Elvey, George Job

CHRIST IS RISEN see Emerson

CHRIST IS RISEN see Felts

CHRIST IS RISEN see Goemanne, Noel

CHRIST IS RISEN see Handel, George Frideric

CHRIST IS RISEN see Hernried

CHRIST IS RISEN see Jenkins

CHRIST IS RISEN see Joubert, John

CHRIST IS RISEN! see Lovelace, Austin C.

CHRIST IS RISEN see McAfee, D.

CHRIST IS RISEN see Martens

CHRIST IS RISEN see Maunder, J.H.

CHRIST IS RISEN see Monaco, Robert A.

CHRIST IS RISEN see Newton

CHRIST IS RISEN! see Peery

CHRIST IS RISEN see Sanborn, Jan

CHRIST IS RISEN see Sjolund, Paul

CHRIST IS RISEN see Turner, Edmund (Edmond)

CHRIST IS RISEN see Williams

CHRIST IS RISEN! ALLELUIA *Easter
 SATB oct SOUTHERN $.30   (C1052)

CHRIST IS RISEN! ALLELUIA! see Maker

CHRIST IS RISEN! ALLELUIA! see Maker,
 [Frederick Charles]

CHRIST IS RISEN, ALLELUIA see Trusselle,
 Stanley

CHRIST IS RISEN, ALLELUIA see Whittredge

CHRIST IS RISEN! ALLELUIA! see Wilson

CHRIST IS RISEN! ALLELUIA! see Wilson, John F.

CHRIST IS RISEN, ALLELUIA (CHRIST IS BORN,
 ALLELUIA) see Newbury, Kent A.

CHRIST IS RISEN FROM THE DEAD see Duncan, C.

CHRIST IS RISEN FROM THE DEAD see Elvey

CHRIST IS RISEN FROM THE DEAD see Pattison, Lee

CHRIST IS RISEN FROM THE DEAD see Wadely, F.W.

CHRIST IS RISEN TODAY see Davis, Katherine K.

CHRIST IS THE WORLD'S LIGHT see Thiman, Eric
 Harding

CHRIST IS THE WORLD'S REDEEMER *Asc,Ir
 (Vine, John) SATB (med easy) oct OXFORD
    42.073 $.50   (C1053)

CHRIST IS THE WORLD'S REDEEMER see Berkeley,
 Lennox

CHRIST IS THE WORLD'S REDEEMER see Lovelace,
 Austin C.

CHRIST IS THE WORLD'S TRUE LIGHT see Bach,
 Johann Sebastian

CHRIST IS THE WORLD'S TRUE LIGHT see Powell,
 Robert J.

CHRIST IS THE WORLD'S TRUE LIGHT see Sateren,
 Leland Bernhard

CHRIST IS THE WORLD'S TRUE LIGHT see Stanton,
 [Walter Kendall]

CHRIST IS THE WORLD'S TRUE LIGHT see Walter,
 Samuel

CHRIST IST ERSTANDEN *CC8U,Easter,chorale
 (Schmid, Ernst Fritz) [Ger] 3-5pt mix cor,
    acap (med easy) BAREN. BA 136 $1.50
    contains works by: Praetorius; Erythraus;
    Triller; Gesius; Calvisius; Bodenschatz;
    Eccard   (C1054)

CHRIST IST ERSTANDEN *Easter
 (Tittel, Ernst) mix cor,acap oct DOBLINGER
    s.p.   (C1055)

CHRIST IST ERSTANDEN see Ahrens, Joseph

CHRIST IST ERSTANDEN see Bauernfiend, Hans

CHRIST IST ERSTANDEN see Becker, Peter

CHRIST IST ERSTANDEN see Bender, Jan

CHRIST IST ERSTANDEN see David, Johann Nepomuk

CHRIST IST ERSTANDEN see Eglin, Arthur

CHRIST IST ERSTANDEN see Gottschick, Friedemann

CHRIST IST ERSTANDEN see Hassler, Hans Leo

CHRIST IST ERSTANDEN see Hirsch

CHRIST IST ERSTANDEN see Kaufmann, Diethelm

CHRIST IST ERSTANDEN see Lassus, Roland de
 (Orlandus)

CHRIST IST ERSTANDEN see Micheelsen, Hans
 Friedrich

CHRIST IST ERSTANDEN see Praetorius, Michael

CHRIST IST ERSTANDEN see Schubert, Franz
 (Peter)

CHRIST IST ERSTANDEN see Seitz, Rudiger

CHRIST IST ERSTANDEN see Selle, Thomas

CHRIST IST ERSTANDEN see Sendt, Willy

CHRIST IST ERSTANDEN see Unger, Hermann

CHRIST IST ERSTANDEN see Walther, Johann
 Gottfried

CHRIST IST ERSTANDEN see Weismann, Wilhelm

CHRIST IST ERSTANDEN VON DER MARTER see Eccard,
 Johannes

CHRIST IST ERSTANDEN VON DER MARTER see Trubel,
 Gerhard

CHRIST JESUS LAY IN DEATH'S STRONG BANDS see
 Wienhorst, Richard

CHRIST JESUS LAY IN DEATH'S STRONG BONDS see
 Kuhnau, Johann, Christ Lag In Todesbanden

CHRIST JESUS RODE TO JERUSALEM see Hutson,
 Wihla

CHRIST LAG IN TODES BANDEN see Koch, Johannes
 H.E.

CHRIST LAG IN TODES BANDEN see Pachelbel,
 Johann

CHRIST LAG IN TODESBANDEN see Bach, Johann
 Sebastian

CHRIST LAG IN TODESBANDEN see Cruger, Johann

CHRIST LAG IN TODESBANDEN see Gwinner, Volker

CHRIST LAG IN TODESBANDEN see Hessenberg, Kurt

CHRIST LAG IN TODESBANDEN see Kuhnau, Johann

CHRIST LAG IN TODESBANDEN see Pachelbel, Johann

CHRIST LAG IN TODESBANDEN see Praetorius,
 Michael

CHRIST LAG IN TODESBANDEN see Scheidt, Samuel

CHRIST LAG IN TODESBANDEN see Schein, Johann
 Hermann

CHRIST LAG IN TODESBANDEN see Walter

CHRIST LAG IN TODESBANDEN see Weinreich,
 Waltraut

CHRIST LAG IN TODESBANDEN [CHORALE] see Bach,
 Johann Sebastian

CHRIST LAG IN TODESBANDEN, FUR UNSRE see
 Eccard, Johannes

CHRIST LAG IN TODESBANDEN, FUR UNSRE SUND see
 Metzger, Hans-Arnold

CHRIST LAY IN DEATH'S DARK PRISON see Bach,
 Johann Sebastian, Christ Lag In Todesbanden

CHRIST LAY IN DEATH'S DARK PRISON see Walter

CHRIST LAY IN DEATH'S DARK PRISON see Bach,
 Johann Sebastian, Christ Lag In Todesbanden
 [Chorale]

CHRIST LAY IN GRIM DEATH'S PRISON see
 Pachelbel, Johann, Christ Lag In
 Todesbanden

CHRIST MUST LIVE IN ME see Mc Call, Harlo

CHRIST, MY BELOVED see Holman, Derek

CHRIST, MY MASTER
 SATB BIG3 $.25   (C1056)

CHRIST, NOW AT THY PASSION see d'Astorga,
 Emanuelle, Christe, Quum Sit Jam Exire

CHRIST, OF ALL MY HOPES THE GROUND see Handel,
 George Frideric

CHRIST OF EVERY CRISIS, THE see Fischer, L.

CHRIST OF THE SNOW, THE see Gaul, Alfred Robert

CHRIST OF THE UPWARD WAY see Mueller, Carl F.

CHRIST ON THE MOUNT OF OLIVES see Beethoven,
 Ludwig van, Christ Am Olberge

CHRIST, OUR BLESSED SAVIOR see Schutz,
 Heinrich, Ehre Sei Dir, Christe

CHRIST, OUR CAPTAIN see Rossel, Denton

CHRIST OUR LORD see Hallagan, [Robert H.]

CHRIST, OUR LORD, HAS RISEN see Couper

CHRIST, OUR LORD, WHO DIED TO SAVE US see
 Praetorius, Michael, Christ Lag In
 Todesbanden

CHRIST, OUR PASCHAL LAMB see Roff, Joseph

CHRIST OUR PASSOVER see Asola, Giovanni Matteo

CHRIST, OUR PASSOVER see Gibbs, Alan

CHRIST, OUR PASSOVER see Goss, John

CHRIST, OUR PASSOVER see Hall, E. Vine

CHRIST OUR PASSOVER see Macfarlane, William
 Charles

CHRIST OUR PASSOVER see Roth, R.N.

CHRIST OUR PASSOVER see Titcomb

CHRIST, OUR PASSOVER see Willan, Healey

CHRIST OUR PASSOVER IS SACRIFICED FOR US see
 Harwood, Basil

CHRIST OUR SAVIOR see Palestrina, Giovanni,
 Crucifixus

CHRIST OUR SAVIOUR IS BORN see Leland, H.

CHRIST, QUI LUX ES ET DIES see Victory, Gerard

CHRIST REBORN see Sowerby, Leo

CHRIST RISING AGAIN see Amner

CHRIST RISING AGAIN see Amner, John

CHRIST RISING AGAIN see Tye, Christopher

CHRIST SHALL GIVE THEE LIGHT see Clare, Edwyn
 A.

CHRIST, THE CHRIST IS RISEN see Kettering,
 Eunice Lea

CHRIST, THE FAIR GLORY OF THE HOLY ANGELS see
 Bullock, Ernest

CHRIST, THE FLEUR-DE-LIS see Van Iderstine,
 A.P.

CHRIST THE KING see Bliss, Paul

CHRIST THE KING NOW IS BORN see Rimsky-
 Korsakov, Nikolai

CHRIST, THE LIFE OF ALL THE LIVING see
 Kuehnhausen, J.G.

CHRIST, THE LIGHT OF THE NATIONS see Peloquin,
C. Alexander

CHRIST THE LORD HATH RISEN (from Piae
Cantiones) Xmas/Easter,12th cent
see Four Easter Carols
(Geer, E.) SSA,acap SCHIRM.EC 1919 $.25
(C1057)
(Shaw; Parker) 2pt men cor,acap oct SCHIRM.G
9945 $.25
(C1058)

CHRIST THE LORD HATH RISEN see Lang

CHRIST THE LORD HATH RISEN see Lang, C.S.

CHRIST THE LORD HATH RISEN see Shaw

CHRIST THE LORD IN SILENCE COMING see Hughes,
H.

CHRIST THE LORD IS BORN see Bitgood

CHRIST THE LORD IS BORN see Goodale, R.L.

CHRIST, THE LORD IS BORN see Staley

CHRIST THE LORD IS BORN see Walter

CHRIST, THE LORD IS BORN see Williams

CHRIST THE LORD IS RISEN *Easter
unis/SATB (easy) OXFORD 08.147 $.15 (C1059)

CHRIST THE LORD IS RISEN see Avery

CHRIST THE LORD IS RISEN see Becker, J.

CHRIST, THE, LORD, IS RISEN see Bruck, Johann
von, Christ, Der Ist Erstanden

CHRIST THE LORD IS RISEN see Eichorn, Hermene
Warlick

CHRIST THE LORD IS RISEN see Fisher, Herbert R.

CHRIST THE LORD IS RISEN see Garlick, Anthony

CHRIST THE LORD IS RISEN see Gears

CHRIST THE LORD IS RISEN! see Gilbert, Norman

CHRIST THE LORD IS RISEN see Haydn, (Franz)
Joseph

CHRIST, THE LORD IS RISEN see Hochella

CHRIST THE LORD IS RISEN see Pelz, Walter L.

CHRIST THE LORD IS RISEN see Rutter

CHRIST THE LORD IS RISEN see Wehr, David A.

CHRIST THE LORD IS RISEN see Wild, Eric

CHRIST THE LORD IS RISEN see Williams, David H.

CHRIST, THE LORD, IS RISEN see Williams, R.

CHRIST THE LORD IS RISEN AGAIN *Easter,anthem/
carol,Ger
SATB BIG3 $.25
(C1060)
(Johnson, David N.) SATB (easy) oct AUGSBURG
1400 $.30
(C1061)

CHRIST THE LORD IS RISEN AGAIN see Allen

CHRIST THE LORD IS RISEN AGAIN see Baker, E.

CHRIST THE LORD IS RISEN AGAIN see Couperin,
Francois

CHRIST, THE LORD, IS RISEN AGAIN see Moschetti,
[Giuseppe]

CHRIST THE LORD, IS RISEN AGAIN see Powell,
Robert J.

CHRIST THE LORD IS RISEN AGAIN see Proulx,
Richard

CHRIST THE LORD IS RISEN AGAIN see Schalk, Carl

CHRIST THE LORD IS RISEN AGAIN see Smith

CHRIST THE LORD IS RISEN AGAIN see Thiman, Eric
Harding

CHRIST THE LORD IS RISEN AGAIN see Vulpius,
Melchior

CHRIST THE LORD IS RISEN AGAIN see Wetzler,
Robert

CHRIST THE LORD IS RISEN AGAIN see Williams,
David H.

CHRIST THE LORD IS RISEN TO-DAY see Wolff

CHRIST, THE LORD, IS RISEN TODAY (from Lyra
Davidica) Easter/Lent
(Dawson) SATB oct PRO ART 1408 $.25   (C1062)
(Dawson) SSA oct PRO ART 1840 $.25   (C1063)
(Shaw; Parker) SATB,acap oct SCHIRM.G 9951
$.25
(C1064)
(Vree) SAB oct FISCHER,C CM-7724 $.25 (C1065)
(Whitman) SATB oct LILLENAS AN-2275 $.30
(C1066)

CHRIST THE LORD IS RISEN TODAY see Carey,
[Henry]

CHRIST THE LORD IS RISEN TODAY see Church

CHRIST THE LORD IS RISEN TODAY see Davis,
Katherine K.

CHRIST THE LORD IS RISEN TODAY see Denton,
James

CHRIST THE LORD IS RISEN TODAY see Ehret,
Walter

CHRIST THE LORD IS RISEN TODAY see Fiske,
Milton

CHRIST, THE, LORD, IS RISEN TODAY see Foelber,
Paul

CHRIST THE LORD IS RISEN TODAY see Grayson

CHRIST THE LORD IS RISEN TODAY see Hallstrom,
Henry

CHRIST THE LORD IS RISEN TODAY see Hughes

CHRIST THE LORD IS RISEN TODAY see Krone

CHRIST THE LORD IS RISEN TODAY see Legler,
Robert C.

CHRIST THE LORD IS RISEN TODAY see Markworth,
Henry

CHRIST THE LORD IS RISEN TODAY see Martini,
Padre

CHRIST THE LORD IS RISEN TODAY see Ridgeway

CHRIST THE LORD IS RISEN TODAY see Rogers

CHRIST THE LORD IS RISEN TODAY see Rowley, Alec

CHRIST THE LORD IS RISEN TODAY see Titcomb,
Everett

CHRIST THE LORD IS RISEN TODAY see Wilson

CHRIST THE LORD IS RISEN TODAY see Wolff, S.
Drummond

CHRIST THE LORD IS RISEN TODAY see Worthing,
Richard

CHRIST THE LORD IS RIS'N TODAY see Rorem, Ned

CHRIST THE LORD IS RIS'N TODAY see Vree

CHRIST, THE, LORD, TO US IS BORN *Xmas,carol,
Span
(Ehret) SSA oct SHAPIRO SK 3038 $.30   (C1067)

CHRIST, THE NEW-BORN KING see Darst, W. Glenn

CHRIST, THE RISEN LORD see Williams

CHRIST, THE SURE FOUNDATION *anthem,Swed,17th
cent
(Sateren, Leland) SATB (very easy) oct
AUGSBURG 1218 $.20
(C1068)

CHRIST THEME (from Ben Hur)
SATB BIG3 $.35
(C1069)
TTBB BIG3 $.30
(C1070)

CHRIST THOU ART THE SURE FOUNDATION see Averre,
R.

CHRIST, TO THEE BE GLORY see Schutz, Heinrich

CHRIST TRIUMPHANT see Cain, Noble

CHRIST TRIUMPHANT see Koop, Ol.

CHRIST TRIUMPHANT see Wilson, John F.

CHRIST UNSER HERR see Bach, Johann Sebastian,
Christ Unser Herr, Zum Jordan Kam

CHRIST UNSER HERR ZUM JORDAN KAM see Bach,
Johann Sebastian

CHRIST UNSER HERR ZUM JORDAN KAM see
Praetorius, Michael

CHRIST UNSER HERR ZUM JORDAN KAM see Schein,
Johann Hermann

CHRIST, VON DEN TOTEN ERWECKT see Reger, Max

CHRIST WALKED THIS WAY BEFORE see Norman

CHRIST WAS BORN ON CHRISTMAS DAY *Xmas,carol,
Ger
(Davids, Dean) SA oct BELWIN 1931 $.30
(C1071)
(Kirk) SATB,acap oct PRO ART 2741 $.35
(C1072)
(Shaw; Parker) 4pt mix cor,SBar soli,acap oct
SCHIRM.G 10181 $.35
(C1073)

CHRIST WAS BORN ON CHRISTMAS DAY see Freestone,
G.S.

CHRIST WAS BORN ON CHRISTMAS DAY see Roff,
Joseph

CHRIST WAS BORN ON CHRISTMAS-DAY see Veitch,
William.

CHRIST WAS BORN TO SAVE see Hadler

CHRIST WAS BORN TODAY see Gallus, Jacobus,
Hodie Christus Natus Est

CHRIST WAS BORN TODAY see Rockwood, Gay
Hylander

CHRIST WAS BORN TODAY see Rogers, Christus
Natus Hodie

CHRIST WAS CRUCIFIED see Larson, Donald J.

CHRIST WAS MADE OBEDIENT see Bruckner, Anton,
Christus Factus Est

CHRIST WAS MADE OBEDIENT see Goicoechea,
Vincente, Christus Factus Est

CHRIST WAS MADE OBEDIENT see Ripolles,
Vincente, Christus Factus Est

CHRIST, WE ADORE THEE see Dubois, Theodore,
Adoramus Te, Christe

CHRIST WE ADORE THY NAME see Monteverdi,
Claudio

CHRIST WENT UP INTO THE HILLS see Hageman

CHRIST, WHEN A CHILD see Tchaikovsky, Piotr
Ilyitch

CHRIST, WHEN A CHILD, A GARDEN MADE see
Tchaikovsky, Piotr Ilyitch

CHRIST, WHO ALONE ART LIGHT OF DAY see Distler,
Hugo, Christ, Du Bist Der Helle Tag

CHRIST, WHO KNOWS ALL HIS SHEEP see Holman,
Derek

CHRIST, WHO KNOWS ALL HIS SHEEP see Rose,
Michael

CHRIST WHO KNOWS ALL HIS SHEEP see Thiman, Eric
Harding

CHRIST WHO SET ME FREE, THE see Mc Call, Harlo

CHRIST, WHOSE GLORY FILLS THE SKIES see
Armstrong, Thomas

CHRIST, WHOSE GLORY FILLS THE SKIES see
Bissell, Keith

CHRIST, WHOSE GLORY FILLS THE SKIES see Brown

CHRIST, WHOSE GLORY FILLS THE SKIES see Candlyn

CHRIST, WHOSE GLORY FILLS THE SKIES see Gover

CHRIST, WHOSE GLORY FILLS THE SKIES see Graves,
John

CHRIST, WHOSE GLORY FILLS THE SKIES see Knight,
Gerald H.

CHRIST WHOSE GLORY FILLS THE SKIES see
Lovelace, Austin C.

CHRIST WHOSE GLORY FILLS THE SKIES see Mead

CHRIST, WHOSE GLORY FILLS THE SKIES see Peek,
Richard

CHRIST, WHOSE GLORY FILLS THE SKIES see Thiman,
Eric Harding

CHRIST WHOSE GLORY FILLS THE SKIES see Wesley

CHRIST, WHOSE GLORY FILLS THE SKIES see Willan,
Healey

CHRIST, WHOSE GLORY FILLS THE SKIES see Wolff,
S. Drummond

CHRIST WHOSE GLORY FILLS THE SKY see
Kilpatrick, Jack F.

CHRISTE see Benevoli, Orazio

CHRISTE, ADORAMUS TE see Monteverdi, Claudio

CHRISTE, DER DU BIST TAG UND LICHT see Eccard,
Johannes

CHRISTE, DER DU BIST TAG UND LICHT see Hassler,
Hans Leo

CHRISTE, DER DU BIST TAG UND LICHT see Kuhnau,
Johann

CHRISTE, DER DU BIST TAG UND LICHT see
Praetorius, Michael

CHRISTE, DER DU BIST TAG UND LICHT see Scheidt,
Samuel

CHRISTE, DER DU BIST TAG UND LICHT see Schein,
Johann Hermann

CHRISTE, DU BEISTAND DEINER KREUZGEMEINDE see
Lowenstern, Matthaus Appelles von

CHRISTE, DU BIST DER HELLE TAG see Distler.
Hugo

CHRISTE, DU BIST DER HELLE TAG see Gerhardt,
Carl

CHRISTE, DU BIST DER HELLE TAG see Hassler,
Hans Leo

CHRISTE, DU BIST DER HELLE TAG see Kukuck,
Felicitas

CHRISTE DU BIST DER HELLE TAG see Poos,
Heinrich

CHRISTE, DU BIST DER HELLE TAG see Stern,
Hermann

CHRISTE, DU BIST DER HELLE TAG see Wiemer,
Wolfgang

CHRISTE, DU LAMM GOTTES see Bach, Johann
Sebastian

CHRISTE, DU LAMM GOTTES see Barbe, Helmut

CHRISTE, DU LAMM GOTTES see Doppelbauer, Josef
Friedrich

CHRISTE, DU LAMM GOTTES see Micheelsen, Hans
Friedrich

CHRISTE, DU LAMM GOTTES see Schweizer, Rolf

CHRISTE, DU SCHOPFER ALLER WELT see Poser, Hans

CHRISTE, DU SCHOPFER ALLER WELT see
Wapenhensch, W.

CHRISTE ELEISON see Driessler, Johannes

CHRISTE ELEISON see Durante, Francesco

CHRISTE ELEISON see Schutz, Heinrich

CHRISTE, FAC UT SAPIAM see Schutz, Heinrich

CHRISTE JESU see Taverner, John

CHRISTE JESU, PASTOR BONE see Taverner, John

CHRISTE PATRIS VERBUM see Lassus, Roland de
(Orlandus)

CHRISTE QUI LUX see Byrd, William

CHRISTE, QUI LUX ES see Byrd, William

CHRISTE, QUI LUX ES ET DIES see Byrd, William

CHRISTE, QUI LUX ES ET DIES see White, Robert

CHRISTE, QUI LUX ES ET DIES see Whyte, Robert

CHRISTE, QUUM SIT JAM EXIRE see d'Astorga, Emanuele

CHRISTE REDEMPTOR see Dufay, Guillaume

CHRISTE SANCTOREM
(Follett) "Praise Ye The Father" SATB oct PRO
ART 2038 $.22   (C1074)

CHRISTEN, ATZET DIESEN TAG see Bach, Johann
Sebastian

CHRISTEN PEOPLE, CHRISTMAS MORN *It
(Glaser, V.) SSA,acap SCHIRM.EC 2511 $.22
                                           (C1075)

CHRISTEN UND HEIDEN see Eglin, Arthur

CHRISTENIUS, JOHANN
Kommet Her Zu Mir Alle *Pent/Whitsun
SATB,acap voc pt DOBLINGER s.p. see also
PFINGSTEN UND EUCHARISTIE   (C1076)

CHRISTGEBURT see Weber, Ludwig

CHRISTI DOD see Schulz, Joh. Abraham Peter,
Death Of Christ, The

CHRISTI HIMMELFAHRT see Schieri, Fritz

CHRISTI LEIDENSVERKUNDIGUNG see Burkhard Willy

CHRISTIAN CHURCH YEAR IN CHORALS, THE see
Pfatteicher, Karl Friedrich

CHRISTIAN! DOST THOU SEE THEM see Pfautsch,
Lloyd

CHRISTIAN FELLOWSHIP see James

CHRISTIAN LIFE IN SONG: THE CHRISTIAN YEAR
*sac/sec,CCU
(Ladd) unis/SA/SATB SUMMY $1.00   (C1077)

CHRISTIAN RISE! see Coggin

CHRISTIAN, SEEK NOT YE REPOSE see Hankey, Mark

CHRISTIAN, THE MORN BREAKS SWEETLY O'ER THEE
see Shelley

CHRISTIAN, THE MORN BREAKS SWEETLY O'ER THEE
see Shelley, [Harry Rowe]

CHRISTIANS AND PAGANS see Young, Carlton R.

CHRISTIANS AWAKE see Purvis, Richard

CHRISTIANS, AWAKE see Rathbone, George

CHRISTIANS, AWAKE, SALUTE THE HAPPY MORN see
Barrow, Robert G.

CHRISTIANS, AWAKE, SALUTE THE HAPPY MORN see
Maunder, J.H.

CHRISTIANS, BE JOYFUL see Bach, Johann
Sebastian

CHRISTIANS, BE JOYFUL see Wadely, F.W.

CHRISTIANS, COME WITH PRAISES see Biechteler,
Sigismund, Victimae Paschali Laudes

CHRISTIANS, GRAVE YE THIS GLAD DAY see Bach,
Johann Sebastian, Christen, Atzet Diesen
Tag

CHRISTIANS PRAISE THE PASCHAL VICTIM see
Victoria, Victimae Paschali Laudes

CHRISTIAN'S PRAYER see Nosse

CHRISTIANS, SHOUT FOR JOY see Bach, Johann
Sebastian

CHRISTIANS, SING ALLELUIA see Anonymous

CHRISTIANS, SING ALLELUIA see Candlyn

CHRISTIANS, SING JOYFULLY see Emig, Lois

CHRISTIANS, SING OUT WITH EXULTATION see Wolff,
S. Drummond

CHRISTIANS, TO THE PASCHAL VICTIM see Anonymous

CHRISTIANSEN
Arise, My Love *Bibl
TTBB STANDARD B311M1 $.35   (C1078)

Born This Day *Xmas
SATB oct SUMMY 5872 $.30   (C1079)

Christ Is Born Today *Xmas
SATB STANDARD A14MX3 $.45   (C1080)

Come By Here, My Lord
SATB KJOS 5392 $.30   (C1081)

Exultate, Justi
SATB STANDARD A18MX1 $.45   (C1082)

Gloria
see Two Latin Choruses
SATB STANDARD A15MX3 $.40   (C1083)

Lamb Of God *Agnus
mix cor SOUTHERN $.20   (C1084)

Lullaby On Christmas Eve *anthem
(Overby) SSAA,S solo (med) oct AUGSBURG
1011 $.20   (C1085)

O Clap Your Hands *Fest,anthem
SATB oct FOX R218 $.35   (C1086)

O Magnum Mysterium
see Two Latin Choruses

Psalm 117 *Bibl
SATB oct VOLKWEIN VB698 $.30   (C1087)

CHRISTIANSEN (cont'd.)
Two Latin Choruses
[Lat] SATB STANDARD A16MX3 $.45
contains: Gloria; O Magnum Mysterium
                                       (C1088)

We Thank Thee, O God
(Wallace) 3pt wom cor,pno (med) oct WILLIS
6681 $.18   (C1089)

Wondrous Love
mix cor SOUTHERN $.22   (C1090)

CHRISTIANSEN, F. MELIUS (1871-1955)
Beautiful Savior *anthem/hymn
(Christiansen, O.C.) SSA,solo (easy) oct
AUGSBURG 1447 $.20   (C1091)
(Christiansen, O.C.) SSAB,solo (easy) oct
AUGSBURG 1446 $.20   (C1092)
(Overby) SSAA,A solo (med) oct AUGSBURG
1035 $.25   (C1093)
(Peery, R.) SA oct PRESSER 312-21601 $.25
                                       (C1094)

Beautiful Yuletide *anthem
SA&SATB (easy) oct AUGSBURG 0149 $.20
                                       (C1095)
SATB&jr cor (easy) oct AUGSBURG 0149 $.20
                                       (C1096)

Beauty In Humility *anthem
SATB (diff) oct AUGSBURG 0185 $.25   (C1097)

Celestial Spring *see Exaltation;
Glorification; Regeneration; Spirit's
Yearning, The   (C1098)

Christmas Symbol, The *Xmas,anthem
SSATBB (easy) oct AUGSBURG 0235 $.25
                                       (C1099)

Clap Your Hands *anthem
(Christiansen, Paul J.) SSAATBB (diff) oct
AUGSBURG 0110 $.30   (C1100)

Cradle Hymn, A *anthem/hymn
SSATB (med) oct AUGSBURG 0187 $.25   (C1101)

Dayspring Of Eternity *anthem
SSAATB,B solo (med) oct AUGSBURG 0055 $.25
                                       (C1102)

Exaltation *anthem/mot
SSAATTBB (diff) oct AUGSBURG 0126 $.30 see
from Celestial Spring   (C1103)

From Grief To Glory *anthem
SSAATTBB (diff) oct AUGSBURG $.25
contains: Love In Grief; Spring Returns
see also: Love In Grief   (C1104)

Glorification *anthem/mot
SATB (diff) oct AUGSBURG 0128 $.25 see from
Celestial Spring   (C1105)

Hallelujah To The Lord *anthem
SATB (med) oct AUGSBURG 0131 $.20   (C1106)

Have Mercy And Spare *anthem
SATB (med) oct AUGSBURG 0199 $.20   (C1107)

Hosanna *anthem
SAATBB (med diff) oct AUGSBURG 0057 $.35
                                       (C1108)

Immortal Love *anthem
SATB (easy) oct AUGSBURG 0186 $.25   (C1109)

Kingdom Of God *anthem,16th cent
SATB (diff) oct AUGSBURG 0150 $.25   (C1110)

Lamb Of God *anthem
SATB (easy) oct AUGSBURG 0133 $.20   (C1111)

Lost In The Night *anthem/folk,Finn
SSAATTBB,S solo (diff) oct AUGSBURG 0119
$.25   (C1112)

Love In Grief *anthem
SSAATTBB (diff) oct AUGSBURG 0175 $.25 see
also From Grief To Glory   (C1113)

Lullaby On Christmas Eve *anthem
SATB,S solo (med) oct AUGSBURG 0136 $.25
                                       (C1114)
(Overby) SA (very easy) oct AUGSBURG 1115
$.25   (C1115)

My God, How Wonderful Thou Art *anthem
SATB (med) oct AUGSBURG 0178 $.35   (C1116)

Offer Unto God (Psalm 50) anthem
SATB (med) oct AUGSBURG 0264 $.35   (C1117)
SSAATTBB (diff) oct AUGSBURG 0082 $.50
                                       (C1118)

Praise To The Lord *anthem/chorale,Ger
SSAATTBB (diff) oct AUGSBURG 0076 $.25
                                       (C1119)

Psalm 50 *see Offer Unto God

Regeneration *anthem/mot
SSAATTB (diff) oct AUGSBURG 0127 $.35 see
from Celestial Spring   (C1120)

Song Of Mary *BVM
SATB KJOS 5053 $.30   (C1121)

Spirit's Yearning, The *anthem/mot
SSATB (diff) oct AUGSBURG 0125 $.25 see
from Celestial Spring   (C1122)

Spring Returns
see From Grief To Glory

Sunbeam Out Of Heaven *anthem
SATB (med) oct AUGSBURG 0140 $.22   (C1123)

Temples Eternal *anthem
SATB,S solo (med) oct AUGSBURG 0145 $.30
                                       (C1124)

Thy Kingdom Come, O Lord *anthem
SATB (easy) oct AUGSBURG 0209 $.22   (C1125)

Today There Is Ringing *anthem
SATB (easy) oct AUGSBURG 0063 $.30   (C1126)

Vigil *anthem
SATB (easy) oct AUGSBURG 0130 $.25   (C1127)

CHRISTIANSEN, LARRY A.
Alleluia
SATB (med) oct AUGSBURG 1595 $.30   (C1128)

CHRISTIANSEN, LARRY A. (cont'd.)
Hodie, Christus Natus Est
see Two Christmas Choruses

Lord Of Light, The *Gen
SATB SCHMITT 8047 $.25   (C1129)

Lord Of Spirits *anthem
SATB,A/Mez solo (easy) oct AUGSBURG 0265
$.35   (C1130)

O Magnum Mysterium
see Two Christmas Choruses

Paper Reeds *Gen
SAB SCHMITT 5022 $.30   (C1131)

Praise The Lord With Joyful Song *Gen
SATB SCHMITT 7038 $.35   (C1132)

Two Christmas Choruses *Xmas
TTBB,org,4brass cmplt ed STANDARD A34M3-EN
$.60
contains: Hodie, Christus Natus Est; O
Magnum Mysterium   (C1133)

CHRISTIANSEN, OLAF CHRISTIAN (1901)
At The Cross, Remember Me
SATB KJOS 82 $.30   (C1134)

Babe Divine
SATB KJOS 50 $.30   (C1135)

Crown Him King Of Glory
SATB KJOS 76 $.30   (C1136)

God Is My Salvation
SATB KJOS 62 $.30   (C1137)

God's Wondrous Love
SATB KJOS 51 $.30   (C1138)

Guiding Star Carol *carol
SATB KJOS 5146 $.30   (C1139)

Hodie Christus Natus Est
SATB KJOS 33 $.40   (C1140)

If By His Spirit
SATB KJOS 75 $.30   (C1141)

Light Everlasting
SATB KJOS 5110 $.30   (C1142)

Lord Is A Mighty God
SATB KJOS 9 $.30   (C1143)

Now Is Born Emmanuel
SATB KJOS 77 $.30   (C1144)

O Be Joyful, All Ye Lands
SATB KJOS 5 $.30   (C1145)

O Brother Man
SATB KJOS 54 $.30   (C1146)

Praise Him In Gladness
SATB KJOS 70 $.30   (C1147)

Prelude To Christmas *Xmas
SATB KJOS 58 $.30   (C1148)

Resurrection *Easter
SATB KJOS 67 $.30   (C1149)

Sing Nowell, Sing Gloria!
SATB KJOS 49 $.30   (C1150)

Song Of Peace
SATB KJOS 66 $.30   (C1151)

Song Of Simeon
SATB KJOS 5220A $.30   (C1152)

Tenebrae Factae Sunt
SATB KJOS 14 $.30   (C1153)

There Shall A Star From Jacob
SATB,opt band KJOS 13 $.30   (C1154)

Trumpets Of Zion
SATB KJOS 68 $.30   (C1155)

We Need Thee O Lord
SATB KJOS 63 $.30   (C1156)

We've Been A While A'Wandering
SATB KJOS 5105 $.30   (C1157)

Who Shall Ascend
SATB KJOS 37 $.30   (C1158)

CHRISTIANSEN, P.
Easter Carol *Easter,carol
SATB KJOS 44 $.30   (C1159)

How Far Is It To Bethlehem? *Xmas
SATB SCHMITT 15002 $.30   (C1160)
SATB KJOS 42 $.30   (C1161)

Jesus Encounters John The Baptist
SATB KJOS 85 $.30   (C1162)

Lord, Have Mercy
SATB KJOS 74 $.30   (C1163)

O Be Joyful
SATB KJOS 83 $.30   (C1164)

O Ground Of Faith
SATB KJOS 81 $.30   (C1165)

Pilgrim's Chorus
SATB KJOS 71 $.30   (C1166)

Sing Unto The Lord
SATB KJOS 43 $.30   (C1167)

What Child Is This *Xmas
SATB KJOS 69 $.30   (C1168)

CHRISTIANSEN, PAUL
Annunciation, The *anthem
SATB (med diff) oct AUGSBURG 1124 $.22 see
from Four Prophecies   (C1169)

CHRISTIANSEN, PAUL (cont'd.)

Beatitudes, The *anthem/Bibl
SATB&cong,narrator (easy) oct AUGSBURG 1627
$.25   (C1170)
(Ensrud, Paul) SATB&cong,narrator (easy)
AUGSBURG 1627 $.25 see from Service Music
(C1171)

Bread Of Tears *anthem
SSAATB (med) oct AUGSBURG 1058 $.22 (C1172)

Desert Shall Blossom, The (from Four
Prophecies) anthem
SATB (diff) oct AUGSBURG 1123 $.22 (C1173)

Easter Morning *Easter,anthem
SATB (med) oct AUGSBURG 1057 $.25 (C1174)

Four Prophecies *see Annunciation, The;
Solitary City, The   (C1175)

He Cometh With The Clouds (from Revelation Of
Saint John) Gen
SATB SCHMITT 8033 $.25   (C1176)

I Heard A Great Voice *anthem
SATB (med diff) oct AUGSBURG 1189 $.25 see
from Sketches From Revelation   (C1177)

King Of Love, The
SATB KJOS 84 $.30   (C1178)

Kol Nidre *Gen,Heb
SATB SCHMITT 1203 $.35   (C1179)

Kyrie (Psalm 23) anthem/Bibl/Kyrie
SATB&cong,narrator oct AUGSBURG 1625 $.25
(C1180)
(Ensrud, Paul) SATB&cong,narrator (easy)
AUGSBURG 1625 1626 $.25 $.25 see from
Service Music   (C1181)

Kyrie Mass XI *Gen
SATB SCHMITT 1420 $.30   (C1182)

Lilies White And Fair *Gen
SATB SCHMITT 907 $.35   (C1183)

Lord Jesus By Thy Passion *anthem
SATB (med) oct AUGSBURG 1636 $.25 (C1184)

Lord's Prayer, The *anthem/Bibl/prayer
SATB,narrator (easy) oct AUGSBURG 1628 $.25
(C1185)
(Ensrud, Paul) SATB&cong,narrator (easy)
AUGSBURG 1628 $.25 see from Service Music
(C1186)

Make Us One *anthem
SATB (med) oct AUGSBURG 1568 $.35 (C1187)

O Sing To God *Gen
SATB SCHMITT 924 $.35   (C1188)

O Thou Most High
mix cor,acap oct SCHIRM.G 8466 $.25 (C1189)

One Holy Church *see Una Sancta

Praise Ye *anthem
SATB (med) oct AUGSBURG 1275 $.20 (C1190)

Prayers Of Steel *anthem
SATB (diff) oct AUGSBURG 1079 $.30 (C1191)

Psalm 23 *see Twenty-Third Psalm, The

Psalm 92 *Gen
SATB,opt inst SCHMITT SD6214 $.35, ipa
(C1192)

Salutation (from Revelation Of St. John) Gen
SATB SCHMITT 8032 $.35   (C1193)

Service Music *see Beatitudes, The; Kyrie
(Psalm 23); Lord's Prayer, The   (C1194)

Sketches From Revelation *see I Heard A
Great Voice   (C1195)

Solitary City, The *anthem
SATB (diff) oct AUGSBURG 1122 $.20 see from
Four Prophecies   (C1196)

This Is The Day *anthem
SATB (diff) oct AUGSBURG 1092 $.30 (C1197)

Time And Space *anthem
SATB (diff) oct AUGSBURG 0502 $.25 (C1198)

To Him That Overcometh (from Revelation Of
Saint John) Gen
SATB SCHMITT 8035 $.25   (C1199)

Twenty-Third Psalm, The (Psalm 23) anthem
SATB,narrator (easy) oct AUGSBURG 1626 $.25
(C1200)

Una Sancta *cant
"One Holy Church" mix cor,Bar solo,org/pno/
band (med diff) voc sc AUGSBURG 11-9511
$1.35, ipr   (C1201)

Vidi Aquam
mix cor,acap (med) oct AUGSBURG 11-0532
$.35   (C1202)

Vision Of Saint John, The (from Revealtion Of
Saint John) Gen
SATB SCHMITT 8034 $.50   (C1203)

While Shepherds Watched Their Flocks *Xmas
SATB SCHMITT 908 $.35   (C1204)

Winds Through The Olive Trees *Xmas
SATB SCHMITT 1884 $.35   (C1205)

CHRISTKINDL-WIEGENLIED see Pommer, Helmut

CHRISTMAS *Xmas
(Coleman, Satis N.) voc sc SCHIRM.G $1.25
(C1206)

CHRISTMAS see Archer, Violet

CHRISTMAS see Bliss, Paul

CHRISTMAS see Giannini, V.

CHRISTMAS see Hadler

CHRISTMAS see Holden, [Oliver]

CHRISTMAS see Krenek, Ernst

CHRISTMAS see Lehman, Evangeline, Noel

CHRISTMAS see Lovelock, William

CHRISTMAS see Munson

CHRISTMAS ALL YEAR 'ROUND see Russell

CHRISTMAS ASSEMBLY *Xmas
(Kiser) SATB/SSA/TTBB,opt band oct PRO ART
2286 $.30, ipa   (C1207)

CHRISTMAS AT THE CLOISTERS see Corigliano, John

CHRISTMAS BELL CAROL *Xmas
(West) SAB SCHMITT 5529 $.35   (C1208)

CHRISTMAS BELL CAROL see Davies

CHRISTMAS BELL CAROL see Kolyada

CHRISTMAS BELLS see Austin, Ernest

CHRISTMAS BELLS see Coward, J.M.

CHRISTMAS BELLS see Fitzsimons, H.T.

CHRISTMAS BELLS see Graham, M.E.

CHRISTMAS BELLS see Haydn, (Franz) Joseph

CHRISTMAS BELLS see McCormick

CHRISTMAS BELLS see Paul

CHRISTMAS BELLS see Track, Gerhard

CHRISTMAS BELLS ARE RINGING *Xmas
2pt CHAPPELL 0017939-352 $.40   (C1209)
SSA CHAPPELL 0017939-354 $.40   (C1210)
SATB CHAPPELL 0017939-358 $.40   (C1211)

CHRISTMAS BELLS ARE RINGING see Howell, Dorothy

CHRISTMAS BELLS, THE see Talmadge

CHRISTMAS BLESSING see Scholin, C. Albert

CHRISTMAS BLESSING, A see Kraehenbuehl, D.

CHRISTMAS BYE-LO see La Nana

CHRISTMAS CALL TO WORSHIP see Grosvenor

CHRISTMAS CALL TO WORSHIP see Hallett, John C.

CHRISTMAS CANDLE see Bitgood, Roberta

CHRISTMAS CANDLE see Warren, Elinor Remick

CHRISTMAS CANDLELIGHT PROCESSION, A see Orland,
Henry

CHRISTMAS CANON see Buxtehude, Dietrich

CHRISTMAS CANON, A see Buxtehude, Dietrich

CHRISTMAS CANTATA see Buchner, Philipp
Friedrich

CHRISTMAS CANTATA see George, Thomas Ritter

CHRISTMAS CANTATA see Harrison, Julius Allen
Greenway

CHRISTMAS CANTATA see Marx, Karl

CHRISTMAS CANTATA see Rohlfing, Richard T.

CHRISTMAS CANTATA see Runolfsson, Karl Otto

CHRISTMAS CANTATA, A see Bush, Geoffrey

CHRISTMAS CANTICLE see Williams

CHRISTMAS CANTICLE, A see Bartow

CHRISTMAS CANTICLE, A see Biggs, John

CHRISTMAS CARAVAN see Filkins

CHRISTMAS CARAVAN see Summerside, Frank

CHRISTMAS CAROL see Bowen, Caylor

CHRISTMAS CAROL see Broeckx

CHRISTMAS CAROL see Kay, Ulysses Simpson

CHRISTMAS CAROL see Smit, Leo

CHRISTMAS CAROL, A see Williamson, Malcolm

CHRISTMAS CAROL, A *Xmas,carol
(Hangen) SATB oct PRO ART 2219 $.25 (C1212)

CHRISTMAS CAROL, A see Bacon, Ernst

CHRISTMAS CAROL, A see Dello Joio, Norman

CHRISTMAS CAROL, A see Diemer, Emma Lou

CHRISTMAS CAROL, A see Fast, Willard S.

CHRISTMAS CAROL, A see Hill

CHRISTMAS CAROL, A see Kodaly, Zoltan

CHRISTMAS CAROL, A see Lee, Dorothy

CHRISTMAS CAROL, A see Schaefer, Christopher

CHRISTMAS CAROL, A see Whitecotton, Shirley

CHRISTMAS CAROL ANTHEM, A see Williams, Donald
O.

CHRISTMAS CAROL COLLECTION *CCU,Xmas,carol
cor/cong/unis/mix cor BELWIN $.50 (C1213)

CHRISTMAS CAROL FANTASY see Davies

CHRISTMAS CAROL FROM LAPLAND *Xmas,carol
(Dickinson, C.) SATB oct GRAY GSC 101 $.25
(C1214)

CHRISTMAS CAROL PAGEANT, A see Diller, Angela

CHRISTMAS CAROL SERVICE BOOK *CCU,Xmas,carol
unis (easy) OXFORD 48.105 $.75   (C1215)

CHRISTMAS CAROL SONG SHEETS *CCU,Xmas,carol
LORENZ $4.00 per hundred   (C1216)

CHRISTMAS CAROL SUNG TO THE KING, A see Baker,
E.

CHRISTMAS CAROLER'S BOOK IN SONG AND STORY
*CCU,Xmas
mix cor SCHMITT 9075 $1.00   (C1217)

CHRISTMAS CAROLS *CCU,Xmas,carol
(Massey, V.; Massey, J.) SATB ALLANS 133 s.p.
(C1218)

CHRISTMAS CAROLS *CCU,Xmas,carol
(Malin) unis/2pt oct BELWIN 64291 $.40
(C1219)

CHRISTMAS CAROLS AND CHORALES *CCU,Xmas,carol/
chorale
SATB/unis LORENZ 9360 $.30   (C1220)

CHRISTMAS CAROLS AND CHORUSES *CCU,Xmas
mix cor SCHMITT 9076 $.39   (C1221)

CHRISTMAS CAROLS AND FOLK SONGS *CCU,Xmas
mix cor SCHMITT 9077 $.75   (C1222)

CHRISTMAS CAROLS FOR CHOIR, CHORUS OR COMMUNITY
SINGING *CCU,Xmas,carol
unis/mix cor BOSTON 8362 $.45   (C1223)

CHRISTMAS CAROLS FOR MALE VOICES *CCU,Xmas
men cor SCHMITT 43 $.50   (C1224)

CHRISTMAS CAROLS FOR TREBLE CHOIRS *CCU,Xmas
treb cor SCHMITT 56 $.50   (C1225)

CHRISTMAS CAROLS FOR TREBLE VOICES *CCU,Xmas,
carol
SA oct BELWIN 64187 $.35   (C1226)

CHRISTMAS CAROLS FROM MANY COUNTRIES *CCU,
Xmas,carol
(Coleman; Jorgensen) SA ALLANS 371 s.p.
(C1227)

CHRISTMAS CAROLS FROM THE MASTERS *CCU,Xmas,
carol
SATB/unis LORENZ $.30   (C1228)

CHRISTMAS CAROLS NEW AND OLD *CC56U,Xmas,carol
cong cmplt ed LILLENAS MC-5 $1.00 (C1229)

CHRISTMAS CAROLS, SERIES 1 see Grime, William

CHRISTMAS CAROLS, SERIES 2 see Grime, William

CHRISTMAS CAROLS, SERIES 3 see Grime, William

CHRISTMAS CAROLS, SERIES 4 see Grime, William

CHRISTMAS CAROLS, SERIES 5 see Grime, William

CHRISTMAS CAROLS WE LOVE TO SING *CCU,Xmas,
carol
(Reading, J.) SATB,acap oct PRESSER 312-21130
$.60   (C1230)

CHRISTMAS CAROLS WITH DESCANTS see Krones

CHRISTMAS CHANTERS, THE see Harris, A.

CHRISTMAS CHILD see Bingham

CHRISTMAS CHIMES *Xmas
2pt CHAPPELL 0017947-352 $.40   (C1231)
SSA CHAPPELL 0017947-354 $.40   (C1232)
SATB CHAPPELL 0017947-358 $.40   (C1233)

CHRISTMAS CHIMES see Malloch, J. David

CHRISTMAS CHOIR NO. I *CC14UL,Xmas
mix cor,soli BIG3 $.60   (C1234)

CHRISTMAS CHOIR NO. II *CC10UL,Xmas
mix cor,soli BIG3 $.60   (C1235)

CHRISTMAS CHORAL FESTIVAL NO. 1 see McCluskey

CHRISTMAS CHORALE see Luther, Martin

CHRISTMAS CHORALE see Schein, Johann Hermann

CHRISTMAS CHORALES see Bach, Johann Sebastian

CHRISTMAS CHORUSES *see Come Ye To Bethlehem
Apace; Gentle Christ, My Lord Above; Mary
Sat Spinning; O Happiness, O Gladness
(C1236)

CHRISTMAS! CHRISTMAS! see Palmer

CHRISTMAS COLLAGE
(Hunter) SATB MARKS 4585 $.40   (C1237)

CHRISTMAS COMES AGAIN *Xmas
(Hansen) SATB SCHMITT 902 $.30   (C1238)

CHRISTMAS COMES AGAIN see Hopkins

CHRISTMAS COMES IN THE MORNING see Lovelace,
Austin C.

CHRISTMAS CRADLE SONG *Xmas,cradle
2pt CHAPPELL 0017954-352 $.40   (C1239)
SSA CHAPPELL 0017954-354 $.40   (C1240)
SATB CHAPPELL 0017954-358 $.40   (C1241)
(Barthelson) SSA oct PRO ART 2467 $.25
(C1242)

CHRISTMAS CRADLE SONG see Luvaas

CHRISTMAS CRADLE SONG see Sutcliffe, James H.

CHRISTMAS CRADLE SONG see Track, Gerhard

CHRISTMAS CRIB, THE see Ringwald, [Roy]

CHRISTMAS DANCE OF THE SHEPHERDS see Kodaly,
Zoltan, Karasconyi Pasztortanc

CHRISTMAS DARKNESS see Lovelace, Austin C.

CHRISTMAS DAY *Xmas
SATB oct BELWIN 60035 $.30   (C1243)

CHRISTMAS DAY see Campbell, H.A.J.

CHRISTMAS DAY see Fraser, Norman

CHRISTMAS DAY see Gibbons, Orlando

CHRISTMAS DAY see Gibbs, [Cecil] Armstrong

CHRISTMAS DAY see Holst, Gustav

CHRISTMAS DAY see Stimer

CHRISTMAS DAY IN THE MORNING see Foster

CHRISTMAS DAY IN THE MORNING see Moeran

CHRISTMAS DAY IN THE MORNING see Semmler

CHRISTMAS DAY IS COME see Davis, Katherine K.

CHRISTMAS EVE   *Xmas
   unis/SATB (easy) OXFORD 08.001 $.15   (C1244)

CHRISTMAS EVE see Cromie, M.

CHRISTMAS EVE see Ferguson

CHRISTMAS EVE see Fulton

CHRISTMAS EVE see Luboff, Norman

CHRISTMAS EVE see McWhertor

CHRISTMAS EVE see Mellers, Wilfrid Howard

CHRISTMAS EVE see Ottesen, [Milton F.]

CHRISTMAS EVE see Smit, Johannes

CHRISTMAS EVE CAROL (from Anthology Of Carols,
   An)
   see Coventry Carol

CHRISTMAS EVE IS HERE
   (Warner) 2pt boy cor/2pt wom cor oct SCHIRM.G
   10759 $.25   (C1245)

CHRISTMAS EVE IS HERE see Grundman

CHRISTMAS EVE IS HERE see Warner, Richard

CHRISTMAS EVE (THE SNOW LIES CRISP) see
   Pinkham, Daniel

CHRISTMAS EXULTATION, A see Ferguson

CHRISTMAS FABLE see Douglas, James

CHRISTMAS FANFARE see Book

CHRISTMAS FANFARE see Burnham

CHRISTMAS FANFARE see Hart, A.W.

CHRISTMAS FANFARE see Van Dyke

CHRISTMAS FANTASY see Verrall, John

CHRISTMAS FANTASY, A see Vinter, Gilbert

CHRISTMAS FANTASY, A see Wade, Walter

CHRISTMAS FOLK SONG   *Xmas
   (Graham) SSA,S solo,acap oct COLOMBO 1144
   $.30   (C1246)
   (Kjelson) SATB oct BELWIN 2260 $.35   (C1247)
   (Vance, Margaret Shelley) SA/TB oct BELWIN
   2133 $.30   (C1248)

CHRISTMAS FOLK SONG see Carol, M.

CHRISTMAS FOLK SONG see Sjolund, Paul

CHRISTMAS FOLK SONG, A see Bray

CHRISTMAS FOLK SONG, A see Byles, B. D.

CHRISTMAS FOLK SONG, A see Ellsworth, A. Eugene

CHRISTMAS FOLK SONG, A see Gardner

CHRISTMAS FOLK SONG, A see Sjolund, Paul

CHRISTMAS GARLAND, A see Dyson, George

CHRISTMAS GIFT, A   *Xmas,Carib
   (Cramer) SSA MARKS 4393 $.30   (C1249)
   (Cramer) SAB MARKS 4203 $.25   (C1250)
   (Cramer) SATB MARKS 4395 $.30   (C1251)

CHRISTMAS GIFTS see Anderson, [William H.]

CHRISTMAS GLORIA see Davies

CHRISTMAS GLORIA see Gardner, Grace

CHRISTMAS GLORIA see Lovelace, Austin C.

CHRISTMAS GLORIA see Pevernage, Andries, Gloria
   In Excelsis Deo

CHRISTMAS GLORIA, A see Johnston

CHRISTMAS GLORY see Posegate

CHRISTMAS GOSPEL, THE see Mayer, Martin

CHRISTMAS GRADUAL see Needham, Lucien

CHRISTMAS GREETING, A see Gieschen, Thomas

CHRISTMAS HAIKU see Olson, Robert G.

CHRISTMAS HAPPENING, A see Wilson, John F.

CHRISTMAS HATH MADE AN END   *Xmas
   (Treacher) unis (easy) OXFORD 81.076 $.20,
   ipa   (C1252)

CHRISTMAS HISTORY see Schutz, Heinrich,
   Weihnachtsgeschicte

CHRISTMAS HYMN   *Xmas,17th cent
   (Jungst) 4pt mix cor,acap oct SCHIRM.G 2532
   $.25   (C1253)
   (Jungst) 4pt men cor,acap oct SCHIRM.G 1414
   $.20   (C1254)
   (Jungst; Deis) 2pt boy cor,acap oct SCHIRM.G
   10214 $.25   (C1255)

(Jungst; Deis) 3pt wom cor,acap oct SCHIRM.G
   9890 $.25   (C1256)
(Jungst; Deis) 3pt mix cor,acap oct SCHIRM.G
   9891 $.25   (C1257)

CHRISTMAS HYMN see Forsblad

CHRISTMAS HYMN see Grundman

CHRISTMAS HYMN see Pierce, T.C.

CHRISTMAS HYMN see Vaughan Williams, Ralph

CHRISTMAS HYMNS, SET 1 see Ringwald, [Roy]

CHRISTMAS HYMNS, SET 2 see Ringwald, [Roy]

CHRISTMAS HYMNS, SET 3 see Ringwald, [Roy]

CHRISTMAS HYMNS, SET 4 see Ringwald, [Roy]

CHRISTMAS IN BETHLEHEM see Beckhard

CHRISTMAS IN DAYS OF YORE see Hutson

CHRISTMAS IN SONG   *CC108L,Xmas/Gen,carol/hymn
   (Preuss, Theodore) SATB/unis voc sc RUBANK
   $.90   (C1258)

CHRISTMAS IN SONG AND CAROL see Breck

CHRISTMAS IN THE STRAW see Pfautsch, Lloyd

CHRISTMAS INTROIT see Starks

CHRISTMAS INVITATION, THE see Lorenz

CHRISTMAS IS A BEAUTIFUL WORD see Rawls,
   Kathryn H.

CHRISTMAS IS A BIRTHDAY see Manning

CHRISTMAS IS A COMIN' see Pickell

CHRISTMAS IS A-COMING see Simpson, Kenneth

CHRISTMAS IS A TIME FOR HAPPINESS see Kunz,
   Jack

CHRISTMAS IS A TIME FOR SINGING see Schaefer,
   Christopher

CHRISTMAS IS A TIME FOR YOU see Kunz, Jack

CHRISTMAS IS COME see Brown, Rex P.

CHRISTMAS IS COMING
   see Four Songs For Christmas

CHRISTMAS IS COMING see Milkey, E.T.

CHRISTMAS IS COMING see Siegmeister, Elie

CHRISTMAS IS COMING AGAIN see Krunnfusz

CHRISTMAS IS HERE   *Xmas
   (Wood) SATB/unis,solo,harp SCHMITT SD6223
   $.30   (C1259)

CHRISTMAS IS HERE see Weyse, Christoph Ernst
   Friedrich

CHRISTMAS - IS HERE see Wood

CHRISTMAS - ITS CAROLS, CUSTOMS AND LEGENDS
   *CCU,Xmas
   mix cor SCHMITT 9078 $1.25   (C1260)

CHRISTMAS JAZZ, THE see Chappell, Herbert

CHRISTMAS JOY see Couper, Alinda B.

CHRISTMAS JUBILATE   *Xmas,Russ
   SATB oct LORENZ A407 $.25   (C1261)

CHRISTMAS KING, THE see Holton

CHRISTMAS LEGEND see Orland, Henry

CHRISTMAS LEGEND see Weigl, Karl

CHRISTMAS LEGEND, A see Buck, Sir Percy Carter

CHRISTMAS LEGEND, A see Plank, David L.

CHRISTMAS LIGHTS, THE see Grime, William

CHRISTMAS LULLABY   *Xmas,carol/medley,Aus
   (Ehret) SSA MARKS 4350 $.25   (C1262)
   (Gabrid; Wilson) SATB ALLANS 295 s.p. (C1263)
   (Graf) SATB oct LILLENAS AN-3836 $.30 (C1264)

CHRISTMAS LULLABY see Bardos, Lajos

CHRISTMAS LULLABY see Brandt

CHRISTMAS LULLABY see Dirksen, Richard W.

CHRISTMAS LULLABY see Gabriel

CHRISTMAS LULLABY see Lapo, Cecil E.

CHRISTMAS LULLABY see Lovelock, William

CHRISTMAS LULLABY see Mozart, Wolfgang Amadeus

CHRISTMAS LULLABY see Pooler, Frank

CHRISTMAS LULLABY see Seidel

CHRISTMAS LULLABY see Vaughan

CHRISTMAS LULLABY, A see Brahms, Johannes,
   Geistliches Wiegenlied

CHRISTMAS LULLABY, A see Etler, Alvin [Derald]

CHRISTMAS LULLABY, A see Grieb, Herbert [C.]

CHRISTMAS LULLABY, A see Kosteck, G.

CHRISTMAS LULLABY, A see Porter

CHRISTMAS LULLABY, A see Rodgers, Irene

CHRISTMAS LULLABY, A see Schubert, Franz
   (Peter)

CHRISTMAS LULLABY, A see Willan, Healey

CHRISTMAS LULLABY FROM CHINA, A see Graham

CHRISTMAS MADRIGAL, A see Klein

CHRISTMAS MASS OF PEACE AND JOY   *Xmas,Mass
   unis HANSEN-US C611 $.40   (C1265)

CHRISTMAS MEANS THINKING OF JESUS see Angell

CHRISTMAS MEDITATION see Lapo, Cecil E.

CHRISTMAS MEDITATION see Sullivan, Sir Arthur
   Seymour

CHRISTMAS MEDITATIONS see Lapo, Cecil E.

CHRISTMAS MEDLEY   *CC7L,Xmas,medley
   (Collins) unis/SA/SAB PRO ART 84 $.85 (C1266)

CHRISTMAS MEDLEY see Clark

CHRISTMAS MESSIAH see Handel, George Frideric,
   Messiah

CHRISTMAS MESSIAH, THE see Handel, George
   Frideric, Messiah

CHRISTMAS MINSTREL, THE see Turner, Olive

CHRISTMAS MORN   *Xmas,Fr
   (Allen) SATB oct GALLEON GCS1004   (C1267)

CHRISTMAS MORN IS DAWNING see Nar Juldagsmorgon
   Glimmar

CHRISTMAS MORNING see Higgs, R.

CHRISTMAS MORNING see Hutson, Wihla

CHRISTMAS MORNING CAROL CANTATA see Maconchy,
   Elizabeth

CHRISTMAS MOTET see Paminger, Leonhard

CHRISTMAS MOTETS see Stoltzer, Thomas

CHRISTMAS MOTETS OF PRE-PALESTRINA DAYS   *Xmas,
   mot
   [Eng/Lat/Ger] PETERS
   contains & see also: Clemens, Jacobus,
      Parvulus Filius; Senfl, Ludwig, Et Filius
      Datus Est Nobis; Stoltzer, Thomas, Dies
      Sanctificatus; Stoltzer, Thomas, Grates
      Nun Omnes; Verdelot, Phillippe, Angelus
      Domini; Willaert, Adrian, Mirabile
      Mysterium   (C1268)

CHRISTMAS MUSIC see Handel, George Frideric

CHRISTMAS NIGHT see Allen

CHRISTMAS NIGHT see Berger

CHRISTMAS NIGHT see Brimhall

CHRISTMAS NIGHT see Bush

CHRISTMAS NIGHT see Lovelace, Austin C.

CHRISTMAS NIGHT see Ralph, Alan

CHRISTMAS NIGHT see Stille Nacht

CHRISTMAS NIGHT see Whitney, Maurice C.

CHRISTMAS NIGHT see Wolf, Hugo

CHRISTMAS NIGHTINGALE, THE see Die
   Weihnachtsnachtigall

CHRISTMAS NIGHTINGALE, THE see Wasner, Franz

CHRISTMAS NOEL, A see Wetzler, Robert

CHRISTMAS ORATORIO see Bach, Johann Sebastian,
   Oratorio Di Natale

CHRISTMAS ORATORIO see Saint-Saens, Camille,
   Oratorio De Noel

CHRISTMAS ORATORIO see Schutz, Heinrich,
   Weinachts-Oratorium

CHRISTMAS ORATORIO, PART I see Bach, Johann
   Sebastian, Oratorio Di Natale

CHRISTMAS ORATORIO, PART II see Bach, Johann
   Sebastian, Oratorio Di Natale

CHRISTMAS ORATORIO, PARTS I & II see Bach,
   Johann Sebastian, Oratorio Di Natale

CHRISTMAS PASTORAL see Palmer, Anthony

CHRISTMAS PASTORALE see Carpenter, S.M.

CHRISTMAS PASTORALE, A   *Xmas,folk
   (Johnson) SATB (Armenian) oct PLYMOUTH WR-108
   $.25   (C1269)
   (Johnson) SSA (Armenian) oct PLYMOUTH WR-201
   $.25   (C1270)

CHRISTMAS PASTORALE, A see Gubby, Roy

CHRISTMAS PLAINSONG, A see Kihlken, Henry

CHRISTMAS PRAISE see Willan, Healey

CHRISTMAS PRAYER see Mead, Edward G.

CHRISTMAS PRAYER, A see Balson

CHRISTMAS PRAYER, A see Jenkins

CHRISTMAS PRAYER, A see Und Wieder Ist
   Wiehnacht

CHRISTMAS PROCESSIONAL see Proulx, Richard

CHRISTMAS PROGRAM OF BACH CHORALES see Bach,
   Johann Sebastian

CHRISTMAS QUESTIONINGS see Anderson, [William
   H.]

CHRISTMAS READING, A see Shaw, Martin

CHRISTMAS RHAPSODY, A see Thiman, Eric Harding

CHRISTMAS RITE see Walton, Kenneth

CHRISTMAS ROSE, THE see Dunhill, Thomas Frederick

CHRISTMAS ROSE, THE see Knoble, W.

CHRISTMAS ROUNDELAY see Angell, Warren M.

CHRISTMAS SAMPLER, A *CC7U,Xmas,medley (Hartley) SATB&girl cor,pno PRO ART 1270 $.85 (C1271)

CHRISTMAS SCRIPTURE IN SONG see Filkins

CHRISTMAS SEASON see Lohr, Al

CHRISTMAS SECTION see Handel, George Frideric

CHRISTMAS SECTION, THE see Handel, George Frideric, Messiah

CHRISTMAS SELECTIONS see Handel, George Frideric

CHRISTMAS SEQUENCE see Pritchard

CHRISTMAS SEQUENCE, A see Bach, Johann Sebastian

CHRISTMAS SERMON, A *Xmas,cant mix cor CHAPPELL 0014621-3692 $1.00 (C1272)

CHRISTMAS SET, A see Kubik, Gail

CHRISTMAS SO WONDERFUL FAIR see Czajanck, [Victor], Weihnacht, Wie Bist So Schon!

CHRISTMAS SONG see Adam, Adolphe-Charles, Cantique De Noel

CHRISTMAS SONG see Cornelius, Peter

CHRISTMAS SONG see Gevaert, Francois Auguste, Cantique De Noel

CHRISTMAS SONG see Herzogenberg, Heinrich von

CHRISTMAS SONG see Personet Hodie

CHRISTMAS SONG see Sibelius, Jean, Weihnachtslied

CHRISTMAS SONG see Werner, Weihnachtslied

CHRISTMAS SONG see Williams, David H.

CHRISTMAS SONG, A *Xmas (Dinn) unis,opt rec,pno,strings,perc sc SCHOTT RS33 s.p., ipa contains also: Virgin Mary's Lullaby, The (C1273)

CHRISTMAS SONG, A see Manhire, Wilson

CHRISTMAS SONG, A see Praetorius, Michael

CHRISTMAS SONG, A see Statham, Heathcote (Dicken)

CHRISTMAS SONG (NEAR JESUS IN THE MANGER STAND) see Gieschen, Thomas

CHRISTMAS SONG OF PEACE see Lovelace, Austin C.

CHRISTMAS SONG OF SONGS see Wilson, Ira B.

CHRISTMAS SONG OF THE AGES *Xmas/Pageant,cant oct LORENZ $1.00 (C1274)

CHRISTMAS SONG, THE see Adam, Adolphe-Charles

CHRISTMAS SONGS see Weismann, Wilhelm

CHRISTMAS SPIRIT see Scholin, C. Albert

CHRISTMAS SPIRITUAL *Xmas (Higgins, C.) SATB,acap oct PRESSER 312-40687 $.30 (C1275) (Poston) 4pt mix cor,T solo oct CURWEN 10962 $.25 (C1276)

CHRISTMAS STANDS FOR LOVE see Huntington

CHRISTMAS STAR see Constantine, J.

CHRISTMAS STAR, THE see Licht

CHRISTMAS STAR, THE see Matesky, Ralph

CHRISTMAS STAR, THE see Roff, Joseph

CHRISTMAS STARS ARE SHINING BRIGHT see Swaffield, Ronald

CHRISTMAS STORY see Mitchel, William

CHRISTMAS STORY see Titcomb, Everett

CHRISTMAS STORY, THE see Banks, H.

CHRISTMAS STORY, THE see Goldsworthy, William Arthur

CHRISTMAS STORY, THE see Graham, Robert [V.]

CHRISTMAS STORY, THE see Nordholm, H.

CHRISTMAS STORY, A see Beard

CHRISTMAS STORY ACCORDING TO ST. LUKE, THE see Hillert, Richard

CHRISTMAS STORY IN CANDLELIGHT CAROLS, THE see Hustad, Donald P.

CHRISTMAS STORY, THE *CC13L,Xmas (Stone) unis PRO ART 215 $.85 (C1277)

CHRISTMAS STORY, THE see Ford

CHRISTMAS STORY, THE see Adams, Stephen

CHRISTMAS STORY, THE see Beck, Theodore

CHRISTMAS STORY, THE see Distler, Hugo, Die Weihnachtsgeschichte

CHRISTMAS STORY, THE see Drischner, Max

CHRISTMAS STORY, THE see Mennin, Peter (Mennini)

CHRISTMAS STORY, THE see Nelson, Ronald A.

CHRISTMAS STORY, THE see Pezel, Johann Christoph

CHRISTMAS STORY, THE see Schutz, Heinrich

CHRISTMAS STORY, THE see Sheeby

CHRISTMAS SUITE see Gossec, Francois Joseph

CHRISTMAS SYMBOL, THE see Rawls, Kathryn H.

CHRISTMAS SYMBOL, THE see Christiansen, F. Melius

CHRISTMAS SYMBOL, THE see Haupt

CHRISTMAS SYMBOL, THE see Newbury, Kent A.

CHRISTMAS THE WORLD AROUND *CCU,Xmas mix cor SCHMITT 9204 $.60 (C1278)

CHRISTMAS TIDE see Bourdon

CHRISTMAS-TIDE see Hannay

CHRISTMAS TIME see Lavender, William

CHRISTMAS TIME see Scholin, C. Albert

CHRISTMAS TIME AT THE PILGRIM INN see Lewis

CHRISTMAS TIME IS HERE see Lehmeier, J.F.

CHRISTMAS TREE SONG see Grieg, Edvard Hagerup

CHRISTMAS TREE, THE *CCU,Xmas,carol,20th cent jr cor cmplt ed WEINBERGER $1.25 (C1279)

CHRISTMAS TREE, THE *Xmas unis (easy) OXFORD 08.191 $.15 (C1280)

CHRISTMAS TREE, THE see Cornelius, Peter

CHRISTMAS TREE WITH ITS CANDLES GLEAMING, THE *Xmas,carol,Ger (Ehret, Walter) SATB,opt inst oct WALTON 2524 $.30 (C1281)

CHRISTMAS TRIBUTE, THE see Garlick, Anthony

CHRISTMAS TRIPTYCH, A see Mainville

CHRISTMAS VISION see Macaulay

CHRISTMAS WISH, A see Keese

CHRISTMAS WONDER see Burroughs, Bob

CHRISTMASTIDE *Xmas,carol (Van Christy) mix cor oct BELWIN 2179 $.30 (C1282)

CHRISTMETTE see Waldbroel, Wilhelm

CHRISTO, DEM OSTERLAMMLEIN see Scheidt, Samuel

CHRISTO PAREMUS CANTICA (from Anthology Of Carols, An) Xmas,carol (Wulstan, David) SATB CHESTER s.p. contains also: Ballet's Lullaby (SATB); Echo Carol (SATB) (C1283)

CHRISTO PAREMUS CANTICUM see Carr, Albert Lee

CHRISTOPHER, CYRIL S. (1897-   ) Via Crucis *Lent,cant "Way Of The Cross" SATB,SATB soli,org voc sc PETERS H1955 $3.00, ipr (C1284)

Way Of The Cross *see Via Crucis

CHRISTOPHER, DON God Is Alive *see Fanelli, Joseph

CHRIST'S BIRTHDAY see Montgomery, Bruce

CHRIST'S CAROL see Vale, Charles

CHRIST'S ENTRY see Martin

CHRIST'S FLOCK see Shaw, Martin

CHRIST'S SACRIFICE COMPLETE see Young

CHRISTUM WIR SOLLEN see Bach, Johann Sebastian, Christum, Wir Sollen Loben Schon

CHRISTUM WIR SOLLEN LOBEN see Gesius, Bartholomaus

CHRISTUM WIR SOLLEN LOBEN SCHON see Anonymous

CHRISTUM, WIR SOLLEN LOBEN SCHON see Bach, Johann Sebastian

CHRISTUM WIR SOLLEN LOBEN SCHON see Collum, Herbert

CHRISTUM WIR SOLLEN LOBEN SCHON see Eccard, Johannes

CHRISTUM WIR SOLLEN LOBEN SCHON see Gesius, Bartholomaus

CHRISTUM WIR SOLLEN LOBEN SCHON see Peter, Herbert

CHRISTUM WIR SOLLEN LOBEN SCHON see Resinarius, Balthasar

CHRISTUM WIR SOLLEN LOBEN SCHON see Walter (Walther), Johann

CHRISTUM WIR WOLLEN LOBEN see Spitta, Heinrich

CHRISTUS see Kraft, Walter

CHRISTUS see Liszt, Franz

CHRISTUS see Mendelssohn-Bartholdy, Felix

CHRISTUS see Mendelssohn-Bartholdy, Felix, Christus

CHRISTUS see Rosso, R.

CHRISTUS see Volpi, Edoardo

CHRISTUS AM KREUZ see Bruckner, Anton

CHRISTUS AM OLBERG see Beethoven, Ludwig van

CHRISTUS AM OLBERGE see Beethoven, Ludwig van

CHRISTUS DER HERR SATB,acap cmplt ed DOBLINGER s.p. contains & see also: Herr Des Himmels; Cruger, Johann, Jesu, Meine Freude; Cruger, Johann, Jesus, Meine Zuversicht; Eccard, Johannes, Herr Christe, Tu Mir Geben; Franck, Melchior, Ach, Treuer Heiland Jesu Christ; Gesius, Bartholomaus, Christum Wir Sollen Loben; Gesius, Bartholomaus, Mir Nach, Spricht Christus; Gesius, Bartholomaus, O Christe, Morgenstern; Gumpeltzhaimer, Adam, O Herr Jesu Christe; Hammerschmidt, Andreas, Das Ist Je Gewisslich Wahr; Hassler, Hans Leo, Christe, Der Du Bist Tag Und Licht; Hassler, Hans Leo, Christe, Du Bist Der Helle Tag; Isaac, Heinrich, Salva Nos-Heft 3; Kropfreiter, Augustinius Franz, Laudate Dominum; Lechner, Leonhard, Allein Zu Dir, Herr Jesu Christ; Palestrina, Giovanni, Jesu Nostra Redemptio; Praetorius, Michael, Herr Jesu Christe, Gottes Sohn; Schein, Johann Hermann, O Christe, Schopfer Aller Welt; Schutz, Heinrich, Also Hat Gott Die Welt Geliebt; Senfl, Ludwig, Ave Domine Jesu Christe; Staden, Johann, O Jesu Christe; Vulpius, Melchior, Christus, Der Ist Mein Leben; Zangius, Nikolaus, Jesus Dulcis Memoria (C1285)

CHRISTUS, DER IST see Bach, Johann Sebastian, Christus, Der Ist Mein Leben

CHRISTUS, DER IST MEIN LEBEN see Bach, Johann Sebastian

CHRISTUS, DER IST MEIN LEBEN see Bach, Johann Sebastian, Christus, Der Ist Mein Leben

CHRISTUS, DER IST MEIN LEBEN see Hollfelder, Waldram

CHRISTUS, DER IST MEIN LEBEN see Stern, Hermann

CHRISTUS, DER IST MEIN LEBEN see Vulpius, Melchior

CHRISTUS, DER UNS SELIG MACHT see Bach, Johann Sebastian

CHRISTUS, DER UNS SELIG MACHT see David, Johann Nepomuk

CHRISTUS, DER UNS SELIG MACHT see Eccard, Johannes

CHRISTUS, DER UNS SELIG MACHT see Peter, Herbert

CHRISTUS, DER UNS SELIG MACHT see Praetorius, Michael

CHRISTUS, DER UNS SELIG MACHT see Werner, Fritz

CHRISTUS E MISERERE see Zingarelli, Nicola Antonio

CHRISTUS FACTUS EST see Anerio, Felice

CHRISTUS FACTUS EST see Anerio, Giovanni Francesco

CHRISTUS FACTUS EST see Asola, Giovanni Matteo

CHRISTUS FACTUS EST see Brant, Cyr de

CHRISTUS FACTUS EST see Bruckner, Anton

CHRISTUS FACTUS EST see Carissimi, Giacomo

CHRISTUS FACTUS EST see Comes, Juan Bautista

CHRISTUS FACTUS EST see Eberlin, Johann Ernst

CHRISTUS FACTUS EST see Gallus, Jacobus

CHRISTUS FACTUS EST see Goicoechea, Vincente

CHRISTUS FACTUS EST see Lewkovitch, Bernhard

CHRISTUS FACTUS EST see Magri, Pietro

CHRISTUS FACTUS EST see Palestrina, Giovanni

CHRISTUS FACTUS EST see Pitoni, Giuseppe Ottavio

CHRISTUS FACTUS EST see Ripolles, Vincente

CHRISTUS FACTUS EST see Sartori, Baldasaro

CHRISTUS FACTUS EST see Waldbroel, Wilhelm

CHRISTUS FACTUS EST see Zingarelli, Nicola Antonio

CHRISTUS FACTUS EST PRO NOBIS see Andres

CHRISTUS FACTUS EST PRO NOBIS see Anerio, Felice

CHRISTUS FACTUS EST PRO NOBIS see Pitoni, Giuseppe Ottavio

CHRISTUS' GEBOORTE see Schafstall, Joh.

CHRISTUS GIBT DURCH DEN TOD DAS LEBEN see Jacobi, Samuel

CHRISTUS HAT DEM TODE DIE MACHT GENOMMEN see Kretzschmar, Gunther

CHRISTUS HAT DEM TODE DIE MACHT GENOMMEN see
  Weinreich, Waltraut

CHRISTUS HAT UNSERE SUNDE SELBST HINAUFGETRAGEN
  see Hufschmidt, Wolfgang

CHRISTUS HEEFT OVERWONNEN see Bijl, Theo van
  der

CHRISTUS HERI ET HODIE see Kockelmans, Gerard

CHRISTUS-HYMNUS see Ruppel, Paul Ernst

CHRISTUS IN DIE WELT see Poos, Heinrich

CHRISTUS IS OPGESTANDEN see Diepenbrock, Alfons

CHRISTUS IS OPGESTANDEN see Noble, Felix de

CHRISTUS IST AUFERSTANDEN *Easter,Boh
  "Christ Is Risen!" jr cor&sr cor,SA soli oct
  SCHIRM.G 7817 $.25   (C1286)

CHRISTUS IST AUFERSTANDEN see Michel, Josep

CHRISTUS IST AUFERSTANDEN, ER IST IN WAHRHEIT
  AUFERSTANDEN see Brunner, Adolf

CHRISTUS IST AUFERSTANDEN, FREUD IST IN see
  Kretzschmar, Gunther

CHRISTUS IST DES GESETZES ENDE see Schelle,
  Johann Hermann

CHRISTUS IST GEHORSAM GEWORDEN see Callhoff,
  Herbert

CHRISTUS IST GEKOMMEN see Reda, Siegfried

CHRISTUS LEBET, CHRISTUS SIEGET see
  Mendelssohn, Arnold

CHRISTUS NATUS EST see Franck, Cesar

CHRISTUS NATUS EST, ALLELUIA see Rimmer

CHRISTUS NATUS HODIE see Rogers

CHRISTUS, ONZE HEER VERREES see Davidica, L.

CHRISTUS RESURGENS see Viadana, Lodovico Grossi
  da

CHRISTUS RESURGENS EX MORTUIS see Byrd, William

CHRISTUS RESURGENS EX MORTUIS see Lassus,
  Roland de (Orlandus)

CHRISTUS RESURREXIT see Dubois, Theodore

CHRISTUS RESURREXIT see Young

CHRISTUS REX see Ryelandt, Joseph

CHRISTUS SPRICHT: SELIG SIND, DIE DAS WORT
  GOTTES see Fiebig, Kurt

CHRISTUS SPRICHT: WER MEIN WORT HORET see
  Gottschick, Friedemann

CHRISTUS STERVENDE see Andriessen, Hendrik

CHRISTUS SURREXIT see Gallus, Jacobus

CHRISTUS TRIUMPHATOR see Rohwer, Jens

CHRISTUS, UNSER HEIL see Gerhold, Norbert, I'm
  A Rolling

CHRISTUS VICTOR see Roe, Betty

CHRISTUS VINCIT see Anonymous

CHRISTUS WARD FUR UNS GEHORSAM see Pitoni,
  Giuseppe Ottavio, Christus Factus Est Pro
  Nobis

CHRISTUSKIND see Oort, H.C.v.

CHRISTVESPER see Klimpel, Heinrich

CHRISTY
  Lullaby Of The Christ Child *Xmas
  SATB SCHMITT 1698 $.25   (C1287)

  Were You There? *Lent
  TTBB SCHMITT 3514 $.20   (C1288)

CHRYSANTEN see Herwaarden, J.G.

CHRYSOSTOM-KOPPES, SISTER M.
  O Little Stars Shine Out *Xmas
  SA,pno (easy) oct WILLIS 6172 $.10 (C1289)

CHTIC ABY SPAL (from Anthology Of Carols, An)
  carol,Czech
  "Sleep, Baby, Sleep" see Czech Christmas
  Carols
  "Sleep, Baby, Sleep" see First Nowell, The
  (Bement, G.S.) "Sleep, Baby, Sleep" SATB,acap
  SCHIRM.EC 1785 $.25   (C1290)

CHUBB, F.
  O Send Out Thy Light
  SATB oct LESLIE 4090   (C1291)

CHURCH
  Christ The Lord Is Risen Today
  SATB oct PLYMOUTH JR-142 $.30   (C1292)

  Hodie (composed with Clarke, H.)
  (Raymond) "Today Christ Is Born" SATB oct
  PLYMOUTH JR-125 $.25   (C1293)

  Prayer To Jesus *Gen
  SATB SCHMITT 7035 $.25   (C1294)

  Rise Up, O Men Of God
  (Walter) SATB oct PLYMOUTH JR-143 $.30
                                   (C1295)
  Today Christ Is Born *see Hodie

CHURCH A MIGHTY REFUGE IS, THE see Fraser

CHURCH ANTHEM BOOK, THE *CCU,anthem
  (Davies; Ley) mix cor (med) OXFORD $4.50
                                   (C1296)

CHURCH ANTHEM BOOK, THE *CC100U,anthem
  (Davies, Walford; Ley, Henry G.) cloth OXFORD
  $4.50   (C1297)

CHURCH CHOIR ANTHEM BOOK see Holler, John

CHURCH CHOIR BOOK, THE *CC32L
  (Thomas, P.) mix cor CONCORDIA 97-6320 $1.35
  contains works by: Willan; Arcadelt;
  Staden; Lutkin; Scheidemann, D.; Roff;
  Mendelssohn-Bartholdy; Handel; Praetorius;
  Bach; Juengst; Franck; Schultz; Gastoldi;
  Tye; Franck, M.; Gumpeltzhaimer;
  Casciolini; Lotti; Vulpius; Schutz;
  Shrubsole; Wagner; Bunjes; Crueger (C1298)

CHURCH CHORISTER *CCU
  mix cor SCHMITT 9062 $1.00   (C1299)

CHURCH, DARRELL G.
  Magic Of Christmas, The *sac/sec
  SATB oct AGAPE BR 2001 $.30   (C1300)

CHURCH, H.
  All Thy Works Praise Thee
  cor oct HART s.p.   (C1301)

CHURCH IN THE WILDWOOD, THE
  (Carmichael) SATB oct WORD CS-304 $.30
                                     (C1302)

CHURCH IN THE WILDWOOD, THE see Pitts

CHURCH MUSIC see Mendelssohn-Bartholdy, Felix

CHURCH OF GOD see Davis, Katherine K.

CHURCH SERVICE see West, Haydn

CHURCH, THE see Landgrave, Phillip

CHURCH TRIUMPHANT, THE (TUNE OF ST.MAGNUS)
  see Two Processional Hymns

CHURCH WITH JOY ACLAIMS HER LORD, THE see
  Webber, Lloyd

CHURCH WITHIN US, THE see Schneider, Kent

CHURCH YEAR, THE *CCU,Adv/Xmas/Easter/Epiph/
  Lent/Palm/Thanks/Whitsun
  (Holmes) 2pt jr cor PRO ART 133 $1.25 (C1303)

CHURCH YEAR, THE see Gillette

CHURCHILL
  Give Praise To Him *see Wolf

  Rejoice Ye Pure In Heart
  SATB oct BELWIN 1990 $.35   (C1304)

  Vesper Hymn *hymn
  SATB oct PLYMOUTH CH-105 $.25   (C1305)

CHURCHILL, NORMAN
  Behold I Bring You Good Tidings *Xmas,anthem
  mix cor oct NOVELLO 28.1257.06 s.p. (C1306)

CHURCH'S ONE FOUNDATION, THE see Duro, John

CHURCH'S ONE FOUNDATION, THE see Lorenz

CHURCH'S ONE FOUNDATION, THE see Rasely

CHURCH'S ONE FOUNDATION, THE see Wesley

CHURCH'S YEAR IN MUSIC, THE see Gibbin, L.D.

CHUT! TAISEZ-VOUS see Saboly, Nicholas, Chut!
  Teisas-Vous

CHUT! TEISAS-VOUS see Saboly, Nicholas

CIBAVIT see Schieri, Fritz

CIBAVIT EOS see Cervi, Luigi

CIBAVIT EOS see Jaeggi, Oswald

CIBAVIT EOS see Muller, Giulio

CICOGNANI, GINO
  Sei Canzoni Alla B.V. Maria *Op.82, CC6U,BVM
  [Lat] unis/2pt ZANIBON 500 s.p.   (C1307)

CIMAROSA, DOMENICO (1749-1801)
  Te Deum *Te Deum
  [Lat] voc sc PETERS HU1447 $2.00, ipr
                                     (C1308)

CIMBRO, A.
  O Vos Omnes
  see IN HEBDOMADA SANCTA

CINCUENTA CORALES see Bach, Johann Sebastian

CINQ CHOEURS RELIGIEUX see Rossi, Salomone

CINQUE AVE MARIA *BVM
  [Lat] ZANIBON 2746 s.p.
  contains: Ascenso, Antonio, Ave Maria (2 eq
  voices); Borsieri, C., Ave Maria (2 eq
  voices); Leoncini, Lorenzo, Ave Maria
  (3pt mix cor); Mangone, Gioacchino, Ave
  Maria (A/Bar); Oltrassi, Giuseppe, Ave
  Maria (2 eq voices)   (C1309)

CINQUE CANTI PASQUALI see Picchi, Luigi

CINQUE LAUDE see Dinerstein, N.

[CINQUE] LITANIE see Arnaldi, Antonio

CINQUE MOTECTA IN HON. B.V.M. *BVM,mot
  [Lat] S/T,org ZANIBON 740 s.p.
  contains: Gerli, Giovanni, Salve Regina;
  Leoncini, Lorenzo, Tota Pulchra;
  Oltrassi, Giuseppe, Salve Regina;
  Tebaldini, Giovanni, Ave Maria; Volpi,
  Edoardo, Ave Maria   (C1310)

CINQUE MOTECTA IN HON. B.V.M. *BVM,mot
  [Lat] 2 eq voices,org ZANIBON 2745 s.p.
  contains: Mattoni, Filippo, Ave Maria;
  Muller, J., Tota Pulchra; Oltrassi,
  Giuseppe, Salve Regina; Sevim, Giuseppe,
  Beata Es Virgo; Volpi, Edoardo, Ave Maria
                                     (C1311)

CINQUE MOTTETTI *mot
  [Lat] ZANIBON 2767 s.p.
  contains: Bottazzo, Luigi, Benedic. (2 eq

voices,org); Bottigliero, Eduardo, Cor
  Jesu Flagrens (T,org); Fabiani, Angelo,
  Cor Jesu Sacratissimum (unis,org);
  Leoncini, Lorenzo, Cor Arca (unis,org);
  Volpi, Edoardo, Cor Jesu Flagrens (2 eq
  voices,org)   (C1312)

CINQUE MOTTETTI EUCARISTICI see Zaccaria,
  Vittore

CINQUE SALMI see Ammann, Benno

CIRCUNDA TIBI DECOREM see Bottazzo, Luigi

CIRCUNDA TIBI DECOREM see Giachetti, Enrico

CIRELLA
  Earth Feared, The
  SATB oct SUMMY M 2764 $.35   (C1313)

CIRIA
  Canto Del Angel *Xmas,Mass
  [Span] cor,solo UNION ESP. 14463 s.p.
                                     (C1314)

CISNEROS
  Gaudeamus Igitur *hymn
  [Lat] cor,acap UNION ESP. 20772 s.p.
                                     (C1315)

CITIZENS OF CHATRES see Pitfield, Thomas Baron

CITTA DI DIO see Palestrina, Giovanni

CITY AND THE TOWER, THE see Tate, Toby

CITY CALLED HEAVEN *spir
  (Kemmer) SATB,A solo,acap oct COLOMBO 1285
  $.25   (C1316)

CITY NOT FORSAKEN, THE see Mellers, Wilfrid
  Howard

CITY OF DESOLATION, THE see Mellers, Wilfrid
  Howard

CITY OF GOD see Cope

CITY OF GOD see Palestrina, Giovanni, Citta Di
  Dio

CITY OF GOD, THE see Matthews, Harvey Alexander

CITY OF THE KING, A see Coleman, Jack

CITY OF THE LORD, THE see Fox, Daniel H.

CIVIL
  Sant Josep I La Mare Dedeu
  [Span] 4 eq voices,solo,acap UNION ESP.
  19487 s.p.   (C1317)

CIVITAS SANCTI TUI see Byrd, William

CLAP YOUR HANDS see Christiansen, F. Melius

CLAP YOUR HANDS see Diercks, John H.

CLAP YOUR HANDS see Falling

CLAP YOUR HANDS see Glarum, L. Stanley

CLAP YOUR HANDS see Lynn, George

CLAP YOUR HANDS, ALL YE CHILDREN see Hunnicutt,
  Judy

CLAP YOUR HANDS, ALL YE PEOPLE see Averre, R.

CLAP YOUR HANDS, SING PRAISES see Dunford

CLAP YOUR HANDS, YE PEOPLE see Harris

CLAP YOUR HANDS, YE PEOPLE see Kiplinger, John

CLAPISSON, ANTOINE
  Gloria
  [Fr] 2pt,opt pno/org HEUGEL s.p.   (C1318)

CLARE, EDWYN A.
  Abide In My Love *Whitsun,anthem
  mix cor oct NOVELLO s.p.   (C1319)

  All Thy Works Shall Praise Thee *Harv,anthem
  mix cor oct NOVELLO s.p.   (C1320)

  Behold, I Bring You Good Tidings *anthem
  mix cor oct NOVELLO s.p.   (C1321)

  Choirs Of Angels *Xmas,anthem
  mix cor oct NOVELLO s.p.   (C1322)

  Christ Shall Give Thee Light *Easter,anthem
  mix cor oct NOVELLO s.p.   (C1323)

  Eyes Of All Wait Upon Thee, The *Harv,anthem
  mix cor oct NOVELLO s.p.   (C1324)

  Fear Not, O Land *Harv,anthem
  mix cor oct NOVELLO s.p.   (C1325)

  Fruit Of Thy Works, The *Harv,anthem
  mix cor oct NOVELLO s.p.   (C1326)

  Goodwill To Men *Xmas,anthem
  mix cor oct NOVELLO s.p.   (C1327)

  Hallelujah, Christ Is Risen *Easter,anthem
  mix cor oct NOVELLO s.p.   (C1328)

  Hallelujah! King Of Kings *Easter,anthem
  mix cor oct NOVELLO s.p.   (C1329)

  He Gives Us Fruitful Seasons *Harv,anthem
  mix cor oct NOVELLO s.p.   (C1330)

  He Is Risen *Easter,anthem
  mix cor oct NOVELLO s.p.   (C1331)

  He Will Guide You *Whitsun,anthem
  mix cor oct NOVELLO s.p.   (C1332)

  How Great Is His Goodness *Harv,anthem
  mix cor oct NOVELLO s.p.   (C1333)

  Lord Reigneth, The *anthem
  mix cor oct NOVELLO s.p.   (C1334)

  Now Is Christ Risen *Easter,anthem
  mix cor oct NOVELLO s.p.   (C1335)

CLARE, EDWYN A. (cont'd.)

Peace I Leave With You *Whitsun,anthem
  mix cor oct NOVELLO s.p.   (C1336)

Praise The Lord, O Jerusalem *anthem
  mix cor oct NOVELLO s.p.   (C1337)

Prince Of Peace, The *Xmas,anthem
  mix cor oct NOVELLO s.p.   (C1338)

Saviour, Christ The Lord, A *Xmas,anthem
  mix cor oct NOVELLO s.p.   (C1339)

Sing, O Heavens *Xmas,anthem
  mix cor oct NOVELLO s.p.   (C1340)

Sing Praises *Harv,anthem
  mix cor oct NOVELLO s.p.   (C1341)

Sing Unto God *Harv,anthem
  mix cor oct NOVELLO s.p.   (C1342)

Thanks Be To God *Easter,anthem
  mix cor oct NOVELLO s.p.   (C1343)

Thou Crownest The Year *anthem
  mix cor oct NOVELLO s.p.   (C1344)

Why Seek Ye The Living *Easter,anthem
  mix cor,B solo oct NOVELLO s.p.   (C1345)

CLARK
Be Thankful Unto Him
  SATB oct LORENZ A140 $.25   (C1346)

Christmas Medley *Xmas,medley
  SATB oct LILLENAS AT-C102 $.30   (C1347)

Da8ATBeALDANSi881 s.p.   (C1348)

O Give Thanks Unto The Lord
  SATB oct LORENZ 4395 $.30   (C1349)

O Trinity Of Blessed Light *Trin
  (Stevens) SATB oct PRO ART 1751 $.20
                                              (C1350)

Song Of Judea
  SATB SHAWNEE A 634 $.25   (C1351)

CLARK, GEORGE B.
Draw Nigh To Thy Jerusalem *Palm
  SATB oct GRAY GCMR 3038 $.30   (C1352)

CLARK, HENRY A.
Jubilate Deo *anthem
  "O Be Joyful In The Lord" [Eng] SATB oct
  HARRIS HC4011 $.35   (C1353)

Let Not Your Heart Be Troubled *anthem
  SATB,acap oct HARRIS HC4012 $.35   (C1354)

O Be Joyful In The Lord *see Jubilate Deo

Worthy Art Thou
  SATB oct LESLIE 4105   (C1355)

CLARK, K.
Am I Born To Die?
  SATB,acap oct PRESSER 312-40919 $.30
                                              (C1356)

Behold How Good And Pleasant
  SATB oct PRESSER G-141 $.35   (C1357)
  SATB oct FISCHER,J 10035 $.25   (C1358)

Gentle Psalm, A
  SATB,acap oct PRESSER 312-40932 $.30
                                              (C1359)

One Wint'ry Night
  unis jr cor oct FISCHER,J 9868 $.30   (C1360)

CLARK, KEITH
Happy Is The Man Who Finds Wisdom *Bibl
  SATB,acap oct LAWSON 51679 $.30   (C1361)

Mercy, O Thou Son Of David
  SATB oct WORD CS-2415 $.30   (C1362)

O Had I Wings Of A Dove *Bibl
  SATB,acap oct LAWSON 51482 $.35   (C1363)

O That My Head Were Waters *Bibl
  SATB,acap oct LAWSON 51698 $.35   (C1364)

Restore Our Fortunes, O God
  SATB oct WORD CS-2418 $.30   (C1365)

Sing Unto The Lord
  SATB,acap oct LAWSON 51238 $.25   (C1366)

Weeping Savior
  SATB oct WORD CS-2413 $.30   (C1367)

What Sweeter Music *Xmas
  SATB oct WORD CS-2414 $.30   (C1368)

CLARK, THOMAS (1775-1859)
Daughter Of Zion
  cor oct HART s.p.   (C1369)

CLARKE
Day After Day
  SAB oct LORENZ 7813 $.30   (C1370)

Head That Once Was Crowned With Thorns, The
  *anthem
  (Johns) SSA (easy) oct AUGSBURG 1393 $.22
                                              (C1371)

CLARKE, H.
Hodie *see Church

CLARKE, HENRY LELAND (1907-   )
He Is Risen *Easter,anthem
  SATB LESLIE 4108 s.p.   (C1372)

Praise To God Immortal Praise
  cor,opt gtr LESLIE 4109 s.p.   (C1373)

CLARKE, IRMA A.
Crib At Greccio, The *Xmas
  jr cor,pno voc sc SCHIRM.G $1.00   (C1374)

CLARKE, JEREMIAH (ca. 1673-1707)
Praise The Lord, O My Soul *Gen
  SAB,kbd (med easy) oct CONCORDIA 98-1785
  $.20   (C1375)

CLARKE, THOMAS (ca. 1700)
I Will Magnify Thee, O Lord *Gen
  unis,kbd (med easy) oct CONCORDIA 98-1796
  $.25   (C1376)

CLARKE-WITFIELD, DR. J.
Behold, How Good And Joyful
  SATB ALLANS 31 s.p.   (C1377)

I Will Lift Up Mine Eyes
  SATB,B solo ALLANS 58 s.p.   (C1378)

CLARO ABRIL RESPLANDECIO see Benedito

CLARY
Where Shall I Go?
  SATB,acap WARNER W7-1030 $.30   (C1379)

CLASSIC ANTHEMS see Aldrich, Henry

CLASSIC ANTHEMS see Tallis, Thomas

CLASSIC CHORALES, CAROLS, AND HYMNS *CC20L,
  Xmas,carol/hymn
  (Ford; Hadley) unis/SATB,opt band oct PRO ART
  776 $1.00, ipa   (C1380)

CLASSIC CHORALES, CAROLS AND HYMNS *CCU,carol/
  chorale/hymn
  (Ford; Hadley) SATB/unis,opt inst oct PRO ART
  776 $1.00, ipa   (C1381)

CLAUSETTI
San Giovanni Latterano
  [It/Ger/Eng] SATB,acap RICORDI-ENG 128077
  s.p.   (C1382)

CLAUSSMANN, A.
Laudate3DomongmLEMOONE voc sc s.p., cor pts
  [Lat] see also Quatre Motets   (C1383)

Panis Angelicus *mot
  [Lat] 2pt,org LEMOINE voc sc s.p., cor pts
  s.p. see also Quatre Motets   (C1384)

Quatre Motets *see Laudate Dominum; Panis
  Angelicus; Sub Tuum; Tantum Ergo   (C1385)

Sub Tuum *mot
  [Lat] 3pt,org LEMOINE voc sc s.p., cor pts
  s.p. see also Quatre Motets   (C1386)

Tantum Ergo *mot
  [Lat] 2pt,org LEMOINE voc sc s.p., cor pts
  s.p. see also Quatre Motets   (C1387)

CLAYTON
Every Moment Of Every Day
  (Boersma) SAB oct WORD CS-2343 $.30 (C1388)

For All My Sin
  (Boersma) SATB oct WORD CS-2247 $.35
                                              (C1389)

Now I Belong To Jesus
  SATB oct LORENZ A474 $.30   (C1390)

CLEANSE ME *Polynes
  (Yarborough) SATB oct LILLENAS AN-1174 $.30
                                              (C1391)

CLEMENS, JACOBUS (ca. 1510-ca. 1556)
A La Fontaine Du Prez
  see Opera Omnia vol. VII

Adoramus Te
  SATB,acap oct PRESSER 352-00126 $.30
                                              (C1392)
  men cor sc ALSBACH&D s.p.   (C1393)
  mix cor SOUTHERN $.25   (C1394)
  (Davison, A.) [Lat] TTBB,acap SCHIRM.EC 948
  $.25   (C1395)

Caro Mea
  see Opera Omnia vol. VI

Credo (A8)
  see Opera Omnia vol. VIII

Drei Motetten *CC3U,mot
  (Meier) [Ger/Lat] 4-5pt mix cor MOSELER
  s.p.   (C1396)

Ecce Quam Bonum
  see Opera Omnia Vol. I

En Sepoir
  see Opera Omnia Vol. I

Gauda Lux Donatiane
  see Opera Omnia Vol. V

Gloria Tibi
  (Seay) "Glory To Thee" SATB oct FOX R165
  $.30   (C1397)

Glory To Thee *see Gloria Tibi

Helas Mamour *Fr
  (Forbes) 4pt wom cor,acap oct SCHIRM.G
  11435 $.30   (C1398)

Holy Innocents *see Vox In Rama Audita Est

In Bethlehem This Christmas Morn *Xmas
  SATB,acap (med easy) oct CONCORDIA 98-1664
  $.25   (C1399)

Jay Veu Le Cerf
  see Opera Omnia vol. VI

Kyrie Paschale
  see Opera Omnia vol. VIII

Languir My Fault
  see Opera Omnia Vol. V

Misericorde
  see Opera Omnia Vol. I

Missa Defunctorum
  see Opera Omnia vol. VIII

O Maria, Vernans Rosa *mot
  (Collins, H.B.) [Lat] SAATB CHESTER s.p.
                                              (C1400)

Opera Omnia Vol. I *Mass
  (Kempers, K. Ph. Bernet) cor cmplt ed
  AM.INST.MUS. $18.00
  contains: Ecce Quam Bonum; En Sepoir;

CLEMENS, JACOBUS (cont'd.)

Misericorde; Virtute Magna   (C1401)

Opera Omnia vol. II *CCU,Psalm
  (Kempers, K. Ph. Bernet)
  AM.INST.MUS. $17.00 Souterliedekens
                                              (C1402)

Opera Omnia vol. III *CCU,mot
  (Kempers, K. Ph. Bernet) cor cmplt ed
  AM.INST.MUS. $16.00   (C1403)

Opera Omnia vol. IV *CCU,Magnif
  (Kempers, K. Ph. Bernet) cor cmplt ed
  AM.INST.MUS. $17.00   (C1404)

Opera Omnia Vol. V *Mass
  (Kempers, K. Ph. Bernet) cor cmplt ed
  AM.INST.MUS. $16.00
  contains: Gauda Lux Donatiane; Languir My
  Fault; Spes Salutis   (C1405)

Opera Omnia vol. VI *Mass
  (Kempers, K. Ph. Bernet) cor cmplt ed
  AM.INST.MUS. $18.00
  contains: Caro Mea; Jay Veu Le Cerf;
  Pastores Quidnam Vidistis   (C1406)

Opera Omnia vol. VII *Mass
  (Kempers, K. Ph. Bernet) cor cmplt ed
  AM.INST.MUS. $19.50
  contains: A La Fontaine Du Prez; Or
  Combien Est; Panis Quem Ego Dabo; Quam
  Pulchra Es   (C1407)

Opera Omnia vol. VIII
  (Kempers, K. Ph. Bernet) cor cmplt ed
  AM.INST.MUS. $7.00
  cMnssanDefOnedorqm8); Kyrie Paschale(C1408)

Opera Omnia vol. IX *CCU,mot
  (Kempers, K. Ph. Bernet) cor cmplt ed
  AM.INST.MUS. $20.00   (C1409)

Opera Omnia Vol. XII *CCU,mot
  (Kempers, K. Ph. Bernet) cor cmplt ed
  AM.INST.MUS. $19.00   (C1410)

Opera Omnia Vol. XIII *CCU,mot
  (Kempers, K. Ph. Bernet) cor cmplt ed
  AM.INST.MUS. $20.00   (C1411)

Opera Omnia vol. XIV *CCU,mot
  (Kempers, K. Ph. Bernet) cor cmplt ed
  AM.INST.MUS. $17.50   (C1412)

Opera Omnia vol. XV *CCU,mot
  (Kempers, K. Ph. Bernet) cor cmplt ed
  AM.INST.MUS. $14.50   (C1413)

Opera Omnia vol. XVI *CCU,mot
  (Kempers, K. Ph. Bernet) cor cmplt ed
  AM.INST.MUS. $19.50   (C1414)

Opera Omnia vol. XVII *CCU,mot
  (Kempers, K. Ph. Bernet) cor cmplt ed
  AM.INST.MUS. $17.00   (C1415)

Opera Omnia vol. XVIII *CCU,mot
  (Kempers, K. Ph. Bernet) cor cmplt ed
  AM.INST.MUS. $17.50   (C1416)

Opera Omnia vol. XIX *CCU,mot
  (Kempers, K. Ph. Bernet) cor cmplt ed
  AM.INST.MUS. $14.00   (C1417)

Opera Omnia vol. XX *CCU,mot
  (Kempers, K. Ph. Bernet) cor cmplt ed
  AM.INST.MUS. $17.00   (C1418)

Or Combien Est
  see Opera Omnia vol. VII

Panis Quem Ego Dabo
  see Opera Omnia vol. VII

Parvulus Filius *Xmas,mot
  [Eng/Lat/Ger] PETERS V117 $.75 see also
  CHRISTMAS MOTETS OF PRE-PALESTRINA DAYS
                                              (C1419)
  (Egidi, A.) [Eng/Ger/Lat] mix cor cor pts
  VIEWEG s.p. see from SECHS
  WEIHNACHTSMOTETTEN   (C1420)

Pastores Quidnam Vidistis
  see Opera Omnia vol. VI

Quam Pulchra Es
  see Opera Omnia vol. VII

Sanctus, Sanctus, Sanctus
  see Stern, Hermann, Lobt Gott, Ihr Frommen
  Christen

Sing Out With Joy
  SATB oct STAFF 674 $.30   (C1421)

Spes Salutis
  see Opera Omnia Vol. V

St. Peter *see Tu Es Petrus

Tu Es Petrus *Fest,mot
  [Lat] SATB,acap (med easy) MULLER M 37 s.p.
                                              (C1422)
  "St. Peter" [Lat] mix cor,acap oct NOVELLO
  DM-37 s.p.   (C1423)

Virtute Magna
  see Opera Omnia Vol. I

Vox Dicentis: Clama *Adv
  SAATB,acap (penitential seasons) SCHIRM.EC
  $.30   (C1424)

Vox In Rama Audita Est *mot
  "Holy Innocents" [Lat] mix cor,acap oct
  NOVELLO DM-6 s.p.   (C1425)

Vox In Roma Audita Est *Xmas
  [Lat] SATB,acap (med) MULLER M6 s.p.
                                              (C1426)

CLEMENT
Adoramus Te *Easter/Lent
  (Greyson) "We Adore Thee" SATB oct BOURNE
  ES2 $.30   (C1427)

CLEMENT (cont'd.)

O Loving Saviour
SATB FLAMMER A 5436 $.30   (C1428)

We Adore Thee *see Adoramus Te

CLEMENT, [JACOBUS]
see CLEMENS, JACOBUS

CLEMENTS
Come, We That Love The Lord
SATB oct LORENZ C311 $.30   (C1429)

Golden Star, The
unis (easy) OXFORD 81.048 $.25   (C1430)
SATB (easy) OXFORD 84.051 $.25   (C1431)
unis/desc (easy) OXFORD 50.109 $.25 (C1432)

CLEMENTS, FRED
My Gracious Lord, I Own Thy Right
SATB oct AGAPE CH 639 $.25   (C1433)

CLEMENTS, JOHN
Lord's Prayer, The *Gen
unis (very easy) oct OXFORD 45.062 $.20
                                   (C1434)

CLERAMBAULT, DE
He Is Born, Christ Is Born Today *Xmas
SA&SATB oct SACRED S-100 $.40   (C1435)

CLERAMBAULT, LOUIS NICOLAS (1676-1749)
Hodie Christus Natus Est *Xmas
(Phillips) unis/SATB,solo oct SUMMY M 2330
$.20   (C1436)
(Pizarro) "On This Day Christ Is Born" SATB
oct GRAY GCMR 2768 $.30   (C1437)

On This Day Christ Is Born *see Hodie
Christus Natus Est

CLERGUE, J.
Le Repos En Egypte
[Fr] 4pt mix cor,SAT soli,opt orch LEMOINE
s.p., ipr   (C1438)

Oraison Dominicale
[Fr] cor LEMOINE s.p.   (C1439)

Salutation Angelique
[Fr] cor LEMOINE s.p.   (C1440)

CLICHE SUITE see Newbury, Kent A.

CLIFF BARROWS "NOW" *CCUL
(Carmichael, Ralph; Kaiser, Kurt) SATB voc sc
WORD 30061 $1.95   (C1441)

CLIMBIN' UP THE MOUNTAIN *spir
(Douglas) SAB oct PRO ART 2262 $.30 (C1442)
(Douglas) SSA oct PRO ART 2048 $.25 (C1443)
(Douglas) SATB oct PRO ART 2069 $.25 (C1444)
(Kone) eq voices KJOS 4225 $.30   (C1445)
(Smith) SATB KJOS 1001 $.30   (C1446)
(Smith) men cor KJOS 1101 $.30   (C1447)

CLINE
Ave Maria *BVM
[Lat] Mez/Bar,opt vln LEMOINE s.p. (C1448)

Christmas Rose, The *see Knoble, W.

Hush Ye, 'Tis Mary *Xmas
SATB SCHMITT 830 $.25   (C1449)

Tantum Ergo
[Lat] opt cor,Mez/Bar solo LEMOINE voc sc
s.p., cor pts s.p.   (C1450)

CLOCK CAROL see Swann

CLOKEY
Adoramus Te *cant
(Miller) SATB oct SUMMY $1.95   (C1451)

Canticle Of Peace, A
unis,inst oct SUMMY B 340 $.30, ipa (C1452)

Childe Jesus *cant
(Kirk) SATB,inst sc SUMMY $1.50, ipa
                                   (C1453)
(Kirk) SSA cor pts SUMMY $.75   (C1454)

Hosanna, Lord
SA/TB FLAMMER E5049 $.25   (C1455)

Jehovah's Throne
SA/TB FLAMMER E5103 $.25   (C1456)

King Of Kings
SATB oct SUMMY B 2030 $.50   (C1457)

Let Us With A Gladsome Mind
SA/TB FLAMMER E5085 $.25   (C1458)

O Make Our Hearts To Blossom (from For He Is
Risen)
SSAATTBB oct SUMMY B 2065 $.35   (C1459)

Praise, My Soul, The King Of Heaven
SA/TB FLAMMER E5072 $.25   (C1460)

Treasures In Heaven
SATB oct SUMMY B 2010 $.25   (C1461)

When Christ The Child Came *Xmas,cant
(Portor) SATB,orch/inst oct SUMMY $2.00,
ipa   (C1462)

CLOKEY, JOSEPH WADDELL (1890-1960)
Canticle Of Praise *cant
BELWIN $1.00   (C1463)

Christ Conquereth
SATB oct FISCHER,J 7235 $.30   (C1464)

Daughter Of Zion *Xmas/Gen
SATB oct PRESSER 312-21295 $.25   (C1465)

Divine Commission, The *cant
mix cor BELWIN $1.75   (C1466)

I Sing As I Arise Today *Gen/Trin
SATB, or any combination (easy) oct
CONCORDIA 98-2017 $.30   (C1467)

Immortal Love
SATB oct FISCHER,J 9577 $.30   (C1468)

CLOKEY, JOSEPH WADDELL (cont'd.)
Let Hearts Awaken
SATB oct GRAY GCMR 1597 $.30   (C1469)

Light Shines Forth, A
SATB SHAWNEE A 407 $.30   (C1470)

Lord Is My Shepherd
SATB oct GRAY GCMR 1960 $.30   (C1471)

No Lullaby Need Mary Sing
SSA oct FISCHER,J 8465 $.30   (C1472)

Out Of The Depths *cant
mix cor BELWIN $1.50   (C1473)

Steadfast In Faith *cant
mix cor BELWIN $1.50   (C1474)

Te Deum *Te Deum
SATB oct FISCHER,J 7389 $.50   (C1475)

Temple, The *cant
mix cor BELWIN $1.75   (C1476)

To Thee, O Jesu
SAB oct FISCHER,J 9803 $.30   (C1477)
SATB oct FISCHER,J 9576 $.30   (C1478)

To Thee, Our God, We Fly *Gen
SATB,kbd, or any combination chorus (easy)
oct CONCORDIA 98-2015 $.25   (C1479)

Twelve Hymn-Anthems *CC12U,anthem/hymn
unis BELWIN $.60   (C1480)

Two Kings
SAB oct FISCHER,J 9235 $.30   (C1481)
SATB,org oct FISCHER,J 8639 $.30   (C1482)
SATB,trp,trom oct FISCHER,J 7211 $.30
                                   (C1483)
TTBB,acap oct FISCHER,J 8481 $.30 (C1484)

Two Short Motets For Easter *CC2U,Easter,mot
SATB oct FISCHER,J 8009 $.30   (C1485)

Word Made Flesh, The *cant
mix cor BELWIN $1.50   (C1486)

Ye Holy Angels Bright *Gen
SATB,kbd (easy) oct CONCORDIA 98-2016 $.30
                                   (C1487)

CLOSE EVERY DOOR TO ME see Webber, Andrew

CLOSE THINE EYES see Rees-Davies, Ieuan, Cyn
Cau Llygaid

CLOSER STILL WITH THEE see Rolfe

CLOSER WALK WITH GOD, A see Darst, W. Glenn

CLOSING DOXOLOGY, THE see Lockwood, Normand

CLOTHED WITH STRENGTH see Brandon

CLOTHIER, LOUITA
Alleluia, Christ Is Born!
SATB oct FISCHER,J 9712 $.30   (C1488)
SAB oct FISCHER,J 9924 $.30   (C1489)

Hymn For Winter *hymn
SATB (med) ABINGDON APM-756 $.35   (C1490)

Lord Of The Winds
SATB,acap oct WORLD ESA-1633-8 $.30 (C1491)

Sing, Soul Of Mine! The Lord Is Risen
*anthem
SATB (easy) oct AUGSBURG 1480 $.30 (C1492)

CLOTHING OF MY MIND, THE see Lovelace, Austin
C.

CLOTHS OF HEAVEN, THE see Dunhill

CLOTHS OF HEAVEN, THE see Roberton, Hugh S.

CLOUDS OF NIGHT ARE PASSED AWAY see Praetorius,
Michael

CLOUDS OF NIGHT ARE PASSED AWAY, THE see
Praetorius, Michael

CLOUGH-LEIGHTER, HENRY (1874-1956)
Let The Merry Bells Ring Out
(Cain, N.) SATB oct PRESSER 332-15014 $.30
                                   (C1493)
Thy Light Is Come *Xmas
SATB,org SCHIRM.EC 2424 $.35   (C1494)

CLOUZOT
Deux Noels Anciens *see Noel Anciens; Noel
Provencal De Saboly   (C1495)

Noel Anciens *Xmas,carol
[Fr] SMezA cor pts LEDUC s.p. see from Deux
Noels Anciens   (C1496)

Noel Provencal De Saboly *Xmas,carol
[Fr] SATB cor pts LEDUC s.p. see from Deux
Noels Anciens   (C1497)

CLUCAS, HUMPHREY
Preces And Responses, The
SATB,acap (easy) oct OXFORD 43.372 $.25
                                   (C1498)

CLUCK
O Saviour, Hear Me
(Riegger) SAB FLAMMER D5165 $.35   (C1499)

CLUTSAM, G.H.
Ma Curly Headed Baby *Xmas
2pt ASHDOWN E.A.169 s.p.   (C1500)

CLUWEN, P.
Lentelied
mix cor ALSBACH&D sc s.p., cor pts s.p.
                                   (C1501)

CLYMER
Canticle In Meditation *see Kingery

COAT
In The Lord Put I My Faith
(Raymond) SATB oct PLYMOUTH JR-127 $.25
                                   (C1502)

COATES
Between The Oxen And The Sheep *Xmas
unis (very easy) OXFORD 45.022 $.25 (C1503)

COATES, D.
Cherub Carol, The
unis BOSWORTH s.p.   (C1504)

COATES, ERIC (1886-1957)
Amazing Grace
TTBB SHAWNEE C222 $.30   (C1505)
SATB SHAWNEE A 1130 $.30   (C1506)
SA/TB SHAWNEE E102 $.30   (C1507)
SSA SHAWNEE B 362 $.30   (C1508)
SAB SHAWNEE D143 $.30   (C1509)

God's Great Love Abiding
unis&desc PROWSE s.p.   (C1510)
SATB PROWSE s.p.   (C1511)

New Year's Day *Xmas
cor CRAMER 144 s.p.   (C1512)

COATES, HENRY
Pilgrim's Song, The
ASHDOWN 32 s.p.   (C1513)

COCHER
As With Gladness Men Of Old
(Ferrin) SATB oct LILLENAS AN-3829 $.30
                                   (C1514)

COCHRANE, NAOMI
Baby Jesus *Xmas
(Ehret) SATB oct WORD CS-2552 $.25 (C1515)

COCKSHOTT, GERALD WILFRED (1915-   )
Angels Sang That Christmas Morn
SATB,acap RONGWEN $.35   (C1516)

Gloria In Excelsis
SSAATTBB RONGWEN $.45   (C1517)

I Will Be Glad *anthem
SATB oct FOX PS139 $.22   (C1518)

In Praise Of A Lady
SATB,acap oct FOX PS133 $.25   (C1519)

Magnificat And Nunc Dimittis Minor *Magnif/
Nunc
unis (C maj) NOVELLO 33.0120.06 s.p.
                                   (C1520)

Psalmus *Psalm
SSATBB,acap oct FOX R168 $.25   (C1521)

COELI ENARRANT see Saint-Saens, Camille

COELI ENARRANT INTRODUCTION see Saint-Saens,
Camille

COELI ENARRANT NO. 1 see Saint-Saens, Camille

COELOS ASCENDIT HODIE see Stanford

COENA DOMINI see Rehmann, Theodor Bernhard

COENAM CUM DISCIPULIS see Gumpeltzhaimer, Adam

COENEN, W.
Come Unto Me *Bibl
(Rees) 4pt mix cor oct SCHIRM.G 3448 $.25
                                   (C1522)

COEURS DESOLEZ see Des Prez, Josquin

COGGIN
Angels Are Singing
SATB (med diff/diff) SOUTHERN $.30 (C1523)

Anthems For Praise And Worship *CCU
SAB FLAMMER GD5002 $1.10   (C1524)

Christian Rise!
SATB oct PRO ART 2685 $.30   (C1525)

Gracious Spirit, Dove Divine
SATB oct SACRED S-73 $.35   (C1526)

Hymns And Anthems For Youth Choir, Vol. 1
*CCU
SAB FLAMMER GD5009 $1.25   (C1527)

Hymns And Anthems For Youth Choir, Vol. 2
*CCU
SAB FLAMMER GD5010 $1.00   (C1528)

It Is A Thing Most Wonderful
unis oct SACRED S-8868 $.30   (C1529)

Jesus, Gentlest Saviour
SATB FLAMMER A 5574 $.25   (C1530)

Jesus, Most Holy
SATB FLAMMER A 5224 $.25   (C1531)

King Of Love My Shepherd Is, The
SAB oct FISCHER,C CM-7741 $.25   (C1532)

Lord Of Glory Came To Earth, The
SATB SHAWNEE A 1037 $.30   (C1533)
2pt oct PRO ART 2318 $.20   (C1534)

O Come Let Us Worship
SATB oct PRO ART 2550 $.30   (C1535)

Praise Him, Ye People
SATB KJOS 5869 $.30   (C1536)

Praise The God, Whose Great Salvation
SAB KJOS 5724 $.30   (C1537)

Sing Aloud, All Nations *Gen
SATB SCHMITT 1442 $.45   (C1538)

Sing, O Sing This Blessed Morn *Gen
SATB SCHMITT SD6221 $.35   (C1539)

Thanks Be To God
SATB KJOS 5857 $.35   (C1540)

When I Can Read My Title Clear
SATB oct PLYMOUTH PCS-28 $.25   (C1541)

Yea Though I Walk
SAB oct BELWIN 2151 $.25   (C1542)

COGGIN, ELWOOD
  Alleluia
    SSAB oct AGAPE A 360 $.30   (C1543)

  Be Ye Glad And Rejoice, O Ye Righteous *Bibl
    4pt mix cor,org/pno oct SCHIRM.G 11558 $.30
                                       (C1544)

  Blessed Is The Nation
    SATB oct PRESSER 312-40736 $.35   (C1545)

  From The Rising Of The Sun
    SATB,org/pno FISCHER,J 10083 $.35 (C1546)

  Glorious Things Of Thee Are Spoken
    4pt mix cor oct SCHIRM.G 11512 $.30 (C1547)

  Glory To God On High
    SATB FLAMMER A 5333 $.25   (C1548)

  He Was Despised *Xmas
    SSA oct AGAPE A 352 $.30   (C1549)

  Stand Up, And Bless The Lord
    SAB oct AGAPE CH 602 $.30   (C1550)

  Thou Wilt Keep Him In Perfect Peace *Bibl
    4pt mix cor,org/pno oct SCHIRM.G 11513 $.25
                                       (C1551)

COGITATIONES CORDIS EIUS see Jaeggi, Oswald

COGITATIONES CORDIS EJUS see Pfiffner, Ernst

COHEN, D.
  En Kelohenu *hymn,Jew
    "O'er Us But One God" SATB oct PLYMOUTH
    PCS-57 $.25   (C1552)

  Hinach, Yafa
    SATB oct PLYMOUTH PCS-55 $.30   (C1553)

  O'er Us But One God *see En Kelohenu

COHEN, JOEL I.
  Sabbath Evening Service
    [Eng/Heb] 4pt mix cor,Bar solo,org
    SCHIRM.EC 2743   (C1554)

COKE, NORMAN
  Saint Thomas Church Descant Book *CCU
    (Jephcott) BELWIN $.75   (C1555)

  Surely The Lord Is In This Place
    (Jephcott) SATB oct GRAY GCMR 1974 $.35
                                       (C1556)

  Variants For St. Anne
    (Jephcott) SATB oct GRAY GCMR 2493 $.40
                                       (C1557)

COKER, [WILSON] (1928-   )
  Paean
    SATB,orch oct PRESSER 312-40650 $1.25, ipr
                                       (C1558)

COLD, COLD DAY see Leddy

COLE
  When All Thy Mercies, O My God
    (Klauss) SATB oct PRO ART 1969 $.22 (C1559)

COLE, HUGO (1917-   )
  Of The Nativitie Of Christ *Xmas,anthem/mot
    mix cor,acap oct NOVELLO 45.1585.04 s.p.
                                       (C1560)

COLECCION DE VILLANCICOS POPULARES see Benedito

COLEMAN, HENRY
  Benedicite
    SATB (easy) oct OXFORD 43.947 $.25 (C1561)

  Communion Service In C
    SATB,opt org (easy) oct OXFORD 43.536 $.35
                                       (C1562)

  King Of Love(On St. Columbia)
    SATB oct HART s.p.   (C1563)

  Lobe Den Herren *anthem/hymn
    "Praise To The Lord" mix cor oct NOVELLO
    28.1375.00 s.p.   (C1564)

  O God, Unseen Yet Ever Near *anthem/Introit
    mix cor oct NOVELLO 50.0262.01 s.p. (C1565)

  Praise To The Lord *see Lobe Den Herren

  To Thee, O Lord Our Hearts We Raise *Harv
    SATB/SABarB/STB/SBarB (easy) oct OXFORD
    42.902 $.30   (C1566)

COLEMAN, JACK
  Boy Who Caught The Fish, The
    jr cor, rhythm band voc sc WORD 37538 $1.95
                                       (C1567)

  Centurion, The *Easter,cant
    SATB voc sc WORD 37505 $2.95, ipa (C1568)

  City Of The King, A *Xmas,cant
    cor,kbd,3trp,3trom,horn,5vln,2vla,2vcl,bvl,
    drums,perc,harp voc sc WORD 37503 $2.95,
    ipa   (C1569)

  Thus Was He Born *Xmas
    SATB oct WORD CS-2412 $.30   (C1570)

COLERIDGE
  Lift Up Your Heads (Psalm 24) (composed with
    Taylor) Adv
    SATB oct PRO ART 1326 $.25   (C1571)
    (Collins) SAB oct PRO ART 1546 $.25 (C1572)
    (Ehret) SAB oct PRO ART 1631 $.25 (C1573)

  Psalm 24 *see Lift Up Your Heads

COLERIDGE-TAYLOR, SAMUEL (1875-1912)
  Lift Up Your Heads *Fest,anthem
    SATB oct GRAY GCMR 1460 $.75   (C1574)
    mix cor oct NOVELLO 28.0409.03 s.p. (C1575)

  Lord Is My Strength, The *Easter,anthem
    mix cor oct NOVELLO 28.0398.04 s.p. (C1576)

  O Ye That Love The Lord *Lent,anthem
    mix cor oct NOVELLO 40.0882.00 s.p. (C1577)

COLINDAS see Absil, [Jean]

COLINDAS (CHANTS DE NOEL) see Absil, [Jean]

COLLANA DI 20 MOTTETTI EUCARISTICI see
  Gubinelli, Oderisio

COLLANA DI COMPOSIZIONI POLIFONICHE VOCALE
  SACRE E PROFANE, VOL. 1 *see Festa,
  Costanza, Bramo Morir; Ingegneri, Marco
  Antonio, Plange Quasi; Palestrina,
  Giovanni, O Bone Jesu; Palestrina,
  Giovanni, Recordata; Palestrina, Giovanni,
  Vergine Chiara   (C1578)

COLLANA DI COMPOSIZIONI POLIFONICHE VOCALE
  SACRE E PROFANE, VOL. 1 see Festa, Costanza

COLLANA DI COMPOSIZIONI POLIFONICHE VOCALE
  SACRE E PROFANE, VOL. 1 see Ingegneri,
  Marco Antonio

COLLANA DI COMPOSIZIONI POLIFONICHE VOCALE
  SACRE E PROFANE, VOL. 1 see Palestrina,
  Giovanni

COLLANA DI COMPOSIZIONI POLIFONICHE VOCALI
  SACRE E PROFANE, VOL. 1 see Schinelli,
  Achille

COLLE, GIUSEPPE
  Per L'ingresso Del Parroco *hymn
    [Lat] unis,org sc ZANIBON 19 s.p., cor pts
    ZANIBON 19A s.p.   (C1579)

COLLECT see Conway

COLLECT see Rohrer

COLLECT, A see Darlow, Denys

COLLECT FOR PEACE, A see York, W.W.

COLLECTED ANTHEMS see Weelkes

COLLECTED WORKS VOL. I see Fayrfax, Robert

COLLECTED WORKS VOL. II see Fayrfax, Robert

COLLECTED WORKS VOL. I see Genet, Elzear

COLLECTED WORKS VOL. II see Genet, Elzear

COLLECTED WORKS VOL. III see Genet, Elzear

COLLECTED WORKS VOL. IV see Genet, Elzear

COLLECTED WORKS VOL. V see Genet, Elzear

COLLECTED WORKS see Hele, George de la

COLLECTED WORKS VOL. I see Jaquet Of Mantua

COLLECTED WORKS VOL. II see Jaquet Of Mantua

COLLECTED WORKS see Lescurel, Jehan

COLLECTED WORKS VOL. I see Ludford, Nicolas

COLLECTED WORKS VOL. I see Manchicourt, Pierre
  De

COLLECTED WORKS VOL.I see Power, Lyonel

COLLECTED WORKS see Vincentino, Nicola

COLLECTED WORKS II: PSALMS see Sweelinck, Jan
  Pieterszoon

COLLECTED WORKS III: PSALMS see Sweelinck, Jan
  Pieterszoon

COLLECTED WORKS IV: PSALMS see Sweelinck, Jan
  Pieterszoon

COLLECTED WORKS V: PSALMS see Sweelinck, Jan
  Pieterszoon

COLLECTED WORKS VI: CANTIONES SACRAE see
  Sweelinck, Jan Pieterszoon

COLLECTED WORKS GESELLSCHAFT ED. VOL. 38: LATIN
  CHRUCH MUSIC see Handel, George Frideric

COLLECTED WORKS GESELLSCHAFT ED. VOL. 37: THREE
  TE DEUMS see Handel, George Frideric

COLLECTED WORKS GESELLSCHAFT ED. VOLUMES 11 &
  31 see Handel, George Frideric

COLLECTED WORKS GESELLSCHAFT ED. 34: ANTHEMS
  VOL. 1 see Handel, George Frideric

COLLECTED WORKS GESELLSCHAFT ED. 35: ANTHEMS
  VOL. 2 see Handel, George Frideric

COLLECTED WORKS GESELLSCHAFT ED. 36: ANTHEMS
  VOL. 3 see Handel, George Frideric

COLLECTED WORKS GESELLSCHAFT ED. 40 & 41 see
  Handel, George Frideric

COLLECTED WORKS GESELLSCHAFT EDITION 15 see
  Handel, George Frideric

COLLECTED WORKS :MISCELLANEOUS SACRED MUSIC see
  Mendelssohn-Bartholdy, Felix

COLLECTED WORKS : PSALMS see Mendelssohn-
  Bartholdy, Felix

COLLECTED WORKS IN SEVEN VOLUMES see Obrecht,
  Jacob

COLLECTED WORKS: VOL. 1 see Ockeghem, Johannes

COLLECTED WORKS: VOL. 2 see Ockeghem, Johannes

COLLECTED WORKS VOL. 3: MASSES see Obrecht,
  Jacob

COLLECTED WORKS VOL. 1: MASSES see Obrecht,
  Jacob

COLLECTED WORKS VOL. 2:MASSES see Obrecht,
  Jacob

COLLECTED WORKS VOL. 4: MASSES see Obrecht,
  Jacob

COLLECTED WORKS VOL. 5: MASSES see Obrecht,
  Jacob

COLLECTED WORKS VOL. 6: MOTETS see Obrecht,
  Jacob

COLLECTED WORKS VOL. 7: ST. MATTHEW PASSION AND
  MISCELLANEOUS WORKS see Obrecht, Jacob

COLLECTED WORKS VOL. 1: MOTETS see Palestrina,
  Giovanni

COLLECTED WORKS VOL. 2: MOTETS see Palestrina,
  Giovanni

COLLECTED WORKS VOL. 3: MOTETS see Palestrina,
  Giovanni

COLLECTED WORKS VOL. 4: MOTETS see Palestrina,
  Giovanni

COLLECTED WORKS VOL. 5: MOTETS see Palestrina,
  Giovanni

COLLECTED WORKS VOL. 6: MOTETS see Palestrina,
  Giovanni

COLLECTED WORKS VOL. 7: MOTETS see Palestrina,
  Giovanni

COLLECTED WORKS VOL. 8: HYMNS see Palestrina,
  Giovanni

COLLECTED WORKS VOL. 9: MASSES see Palestrina,
  Giovanni

COLLECTED WORKS VOL. 10: MASSES see Palestrina,
  Giovanni

COLLECTED WORKS VOL. 11: MASSES see Palestrina,
  Giovanni

COLLECTED WORKS VOL. 12: MASSES see Palestrina,
  Giovanni

COLLECTED WORKS VOL. 13: MASSES see Palestrina,
  Giovanni

COLLECTED WORKS VOL. 14: MASSES see Palestrina,
  Giovanni

COLLECTED WORKS VOL. 15: MASSES see Palestrina,
  Giovanni

COLLECTED WORKS VOL. 16: MASSES see Palestrina,
  Giovanni

COLLECTED WORKS VOL. 17: MASSES see Palestrina,
  Giovanni

COLLECTED WORKS VOL. 18: MASSES see Palestrina,
  Giovanni

COLLECTED WORKS VOL. 19: MASSES see Palestrina,
  Giovanni

COLLECTED WORKS VOL. 20: MASSES see Palestrina,
  Giovanni

COLLECTED WORKS VOL. 21: MASSES see Palestrina,
  Giovanni

COLLECTED WORKS VOL. 22: MASSES see Palestrina,
  Giovanni

COLLECTED WORKS VOL. 23: MASSES see Palestrina,
  Giovanni

COLLECTED WORKS VOL. 24: MASSES see Palestrina,
  Giovanni

COLLECTED WORKS VOL. 25: LAMENTATION OF
  JEREMIAH see Palestrina, Giovanni

COLLECTED WORKS VOL. 26: LITANIES, MOTETS,
  PSALMS see Palestrina, Giovanni

COLLECTED WORKS VOL. 27: MAGNIFICATS see
  Palestrina, Giovanni

COLLECTION DE CHOEURS, PREMIERE FASCICULE
  (Geveart, F.-A.; Racine, C.) [Lat/Fr] 3pt wom
  cor,acap cmplt ed LEMOINE s.p.   (C1580)

COLLECTION DE CHOEURS, PREMIERE FACSIMILE *see
  Ave Maria, "La Salutation Angelique";
  L'oiseau Vigilant Nous Reveille; O Filii Et
  Filiae, "Prose De La Fete De Paques"; Pater
  Noster, "L'oraison Dominicale"; Source
  Eternelle De Lumiere; Stabat Mater
  Dolorosa, "Prose De La Fete Des Sept
  Douleurs"; Tandis Que Le Sommeil   (C1581)

COLLECTION DE CHOEURS, DEUXIEME FASCICULE
  (Geveart, F.-A.) [Fr] 4pt mix cor,acap cmplt
  ed LEMOINE s.p.   (C1582)

COLLECTION DE CHOEURS, DEUXIEME FASCICULE *see
  La Charmante Etoile; Le Petit Jesus,
  Sauveur Adorable; Les Rois Mages (Nous
  Sommes Trois Souverains); O Dieu! Que
  N'etais-Je En Vie; Si Dieu Vient Au Monde
                                       (C1583)

COLLECTION DE CHOEURS, TROISIEME FASCICULE
  (Geveart, F.-A.) [Lat/Fr] 4pt mix cor,acap
  cmplt ed LEMOINE s.p.   (C1584)

COLLECTION DE CHOEURS, TROISIEME FASCICULE
  *see Dieu, Mon Seul Bien (Psalm 7); Heureux
  Celui Qui Fuit (Psalm 1); Jesu Dulcis,
  "Pour La Fete Du Saint Nom De Jesus";
  Magnificat, "Cantique De La Sainte Vierge";
  Nunc Dimilis, "Cantique De Simeon"; O Qu'il
  Est Doux (Psalm 132); Pater Noster,
  "L'oraison Dominicale"; Puer Natus In
  Bethleem, "Pour Le Jour De Noel"; Surexit
  Christus Hodie, "Pour Le Jour De Pacques";
  Veni Creator, "Pour La Fete De La
  Pentecote"; Veni Redemptor Gentium, "Pour
  Le Temps De L'avent"; Vers Les Monts (Psalm
  120)   (C1585)

COLLECTION DE CHOEURS, QUATRIEME FASCICULE
  (Geveart, F.-A.) [Fr] 4pt mix cor,acap cmplt
  ed LEMOINE s.p.   (C1586)

COLLECTION DE CHOEURS, QUATRIEME FASCICULE
  *see Chanson Satyrique; Gentils Galants De
  France; Il Fait Beau Voir Ces Hommes
  D'armes; Le Bel Ange Du Ciel; O Nuit,
  Heureuse Nuit; Peuples, Chantez (Psalm 97);
  Que Dieu Se Montre Seulement (Psalm 67);
  Super Flumina Babylonis, "U Assis Au Bord
  De Ce Superbe Fleuve" (Psalm 126)   (C1587)

COLLECTION DE CHOEURS, CINQUIEME FASCICULE see Bach, Johann Sebastian

COLLECTION DE CHOEURS, CINQUIEME FASCICULE see Bach, Johann Sebastian

COLLECTION DE CHOEURS, SEPTIEME FASCICULE (Geveart, F.-A.) [Fr] 4pt mix cor,acap cmplt ed LEMOINE s.p.   (C1588)

COLLECTION DE CHOEURS, SEPTIEME FASCICULE *see A Toi, Mon Dieu (Psalm 26); C'est L'eternel (Psalm 49); Chantez Du Seigneur (Psalm 80); Dieu Tout Puissant (Psalm 137); Dieu, Tu Nous Tiens (Psalm 73); Le Message De Anges; Le Sommeil De L'enfant Jesus; Les Voisins; Musette   (C1589)

COLLECTION DE CHOEURS, DIXIEME FASCICULE (Geveart, F.; Du Bois, L.) [Fr] 4pt mix cor,acap cmplt ed LEMOINE s.p.   (C1590)

COLLECTION DE CHOEURS, DIXIEME FASCICULE *see Adoration Des Bergers; Avez-Vous Vu Jesus-Christ?; Benissez Le Seigneur; Dans Cette Etable; Laissez Paitre Vos Betes; Les Bergerettes; Noel Nantais; Noel Wallon; Or Sus, Sortez Bergers; Priere Des Albigeois   (C1591)

COLLECTION DE MUSIQUE ANCIENNE, PREMIERE RECUEIL *sac/sec,CC12L,16th cent/17th cent (Lammers, H) [Lat/Fr] 4-5pt mix cor,acap cmplt ed LEMOINE s.p. contains works by: Arcadelt; Asola; Du Caurroy; and others   (C1592)

COLLECTION DE MUSIQUE ANCIENNE, DEUXIEME RECUEIL *sac/sec,CC9L,16th cent/17th cent (Lammers, H.) [Fr] 4-5pt mix cor,acap cmplt ed LEMOINE s.p. contains works by: Le Jeune; Aux Cousteaux; Jannequin; De Beau Joyeux   (C1593)

COLLECTION DE MUSIQUE ANCIENNE, PREMIERE RECUEIL *see Asola, Giovanni Matteo, Pange Lingua; Caurroy, Eustache du, Noel   (C1594)

COLLECTION DE MUSIQUE ANCIENNE, PREMIERE RECUEIL see Asola, Giovanni Matteo

COLLECTION DE MUSIQUE ANCIENNE PREMIERE RECUEIL see Caurroy, Eustache du

COLLECTION DE MUSIQUE ANCIENNE PREMIERE RECUELI see Arcadelt, Jacob

COLLECTION FOR SOPRANO, ALTO AND TENOR see Lovelace, Austin C.

COLLECTION FOR SOPRANO, ALTO, TENOR *CCU (Lovelace, A.C.) SAT oct KERBY 6410 $1.50   (C1595)

COLLECTION OF CHORALES AND MOTETS *CC17L,Xmas, mot (Lundquist, Matthew) voc sc WILLIS $1.00   (C1596)

COLLECTION OF CHRISTMAS CAROLS FOR CHURCH AND HOME see Brant, Cyr de

COLLECTION OF CHURCH CAROLS FOR CHRISTMAS see Brant, Cyr de

COLLECTION OF SACRED CHORUSES-VOL. 1 *CCU SAB FLAMMER GD5004 $1.25; SA FLAMMER GE5017 $.85   (C1597)

COLLECTION OF TWO-PART SACRED AND SECULAR CHORUSES *CCU (Howorth, W.) 2pt BELWIN $1.00   (C1598)

COLLECTION, VOL. 4 *CCU SATB FLAMMER GA5008 $1.75   (C1599)

COLLEEN, HARALD Psalm 145 mix cor NORDISKA 1502 s.p.   (C1600)

COLLINGWOOD, A. God Be Merciful SATB PATERSON 1636 s.p.   (C1601)

I Will Magnify Thee SATB PATERSON 1638 s.p.   (C1602)

COLLINS Mary's Lullaby *Xmas 3pt jr cor/SSA (med) FISCHER,C R 6117 $.20   (C1603)

Pentecostal Medley *Pent,medley SSATB oct LILLENAS AT-1002 $.30   (C1604)

Susanni *Xmas 3pt jr cor/SSA FISCHER,C R 6118 $.25   (C1605)

COLLINS, ANTHONY As Dew In April SATB PROWSE s.p.   (C1606)

COLLINS, R. Holy, Holy, Holy SATB oct SOUTHERN $.25   (C1607)

COLLUM, HERBERT (1914-   ) Christum Wir Sollen Loben Schon *Xmas,mot [Ger] SATB,acap (med) MULLER MS 32 s.p.   (C1608)
Nun Bitten Wir Den Heiligen Geist *Pent,mot [Ger] SATB,acap (med) MULLER MS 34 s.p.   (C1609)
O Domine Jesu Christe *Psntd,mot [Lat] SATB,acap (med) MULLER MS 33 s.p.   (C1610)

COLN Ye Watchers And Ye Holy Ones (Christiansen, O.) SATB KJOS 28 $.30   (C1611)

COLOMA Lo, The Good Shepherd Riseth *see Surrexit Paston Bonus

Surrexit Paston Bonus (Martens) "Lo, The Good Shepherd Riseth" [Lat/Eng] SATB,acap oct MCA   (C1612)

COLONIAL CHRISTMAS CAROLS *Xmas (McKay) SATB SCHMITT 8065 $.35 contains: Carol; Hark, Hark, Hark; If Angels Sung A Saviour's Birth; Methinks I See An Heavenly Host; Virgin Unspotted, A   (C1613)

COLONIAL REQUIEM, A see Mc Kay, David Phares

COLONNA, GIOVANNI PAOLO (1637-1695) Beatus Vir Qui Timet Dominum (Psalm 112) (Smithers, Don) "Blessed Is He That Feareth The Lord" 5pt mix cor,org/pno voc sc SCHIRM.G $1.00   (C1614)

Blessed Is He That Feareth The Lord *see Beatus Vir Qui Timet Dominum

May The Holy Ghost *Cnfrm/Whitsun mix cor,acap (ordination) SCHIRM.EC 1222 $.50   (C1615)

Psalm 112 *see Beatus Vir Qui Timet Dominum

Tantum Ergo *Gen [Ger] SATB,acap (easy) MULLER MS 48 s.p.   (C1616)

COMBATTI I NEMICI DI DIO see Pozza, Ettore

COME ALIVE *CCU unis MARKS $1.50   (C1617)

COME, ALL YE CHILDREN TO BETHLEHEM STALL see Mozart, Wolfgang Amadeus

COME, ALL YE FAITHFUL see Lorenz

COME, ALL YE FAITHFUL see Novello, Vincent, Adeste Fideles

COME ALL YE PEOPLE, HASTEN NEAR see Wetton, H. Davon

COME, ALL YE SAINTS see Telemann, Georg Philipp

COME ALL YE SHEPHERDS *Xmas,carol/folk,Boh (Roberts, J.) SATB,acap oct PRESSER G-102 $.35   (C1618)
(Track) SA (Tyrolean) SCHMITT 221 $.25 (C1619)
(Trusler) SAB oct PLYMOUTH TR-402 $.25 (C1620)

COME ALL YOU CHILDREN, JOIN AND SING see Piggott, H.E.

COME, ALL YOU FAITHFUL CHRISTIANS see Russell

COME, ALL YOU WEARY TRAVELERS see Elkins

COME, ALL YOU WORTHY GENTLEMEN *Xmas,carol,Eng (Casner, M.D.) SATB,kbd (med easy) oct CONCORDIA 98-1393 $.25   (C1621)

COME ALONG WITH ME see Skillings, Otis

COME AND ABIDE see Bach

COME AND ADORE see Malin, Don

COME AND ADORE HIM see Rasley

COME AND GO WITH ME see Street Corner Spirituals

COME AND HEAR see Roff, Joseph

COME, AND LET US RETURN see Demarest, A.

COME, AND LET US WORSHIP see Gretchaninov, Alexander Tikhonovitch

COME AND LET YOURSELVES BE BUILT see Orr, Robin

COME AND LISTEN see Sully

COME AND MOURN WITH US see Kirkwood

COME AND SEE THE CHRIST CHILD see Wetzler

COME AND SEE THE CHRIST CHILD see Wetzler, Robert

COME AND TASTE (Parker) SATB,acap oct LAWSON 51342 $.30   (C1622)

COME AND THANK HIM see Bach

COME AND THANK HIM see Bach, Johann Sebastian

COME AS A CHILD see Avery

COME AS THE KINGS OF THE EAST see Hovdesven, E.A.

COME AWAY, COME AWAY, DEATH! see Brahms, Johannes

COME, AWAY, DEATH see Brahms, Johannes

COME AWAY TO THE SKIES (Parker) SATB,acap oct LAWSON 51334 $.30   (C1623)

COME BEFORE HIS PRESENCE see Moore

COME, BELOVED MONARCH see Paraissez Monarque Aimable

COME, BLESS THE LORD see Howard

COME, BLESSED MASTER see Pallma

COME, BLESSED PEACE see Norman

COME, BLESSED REST see Bach

COME BY HERE see Kum Ba Yah

COME BY HERE, MY LORD see Christiansen

COME, CELESTIAL FIRE see Gesualdo, Don Carlo, Sancti Spiritus

COME CHILD OF GOD see Caldwell

COME, CHILDREN, HEAR ME see Sowerby, Leo

COME CHILDREN, JOIN TO SING (Tapscott, Carl) SA,pno oct BERANDOL 790T5AB $.35   (C1624)

COME, CHILDREN, JOIN TO SING see Larson

COME, CHILDREN, PRAISE OUR LORD see Haydn, (Johann) Michael, Laudate Pueri

COME, CHILDREN, RUN! see Fraser

COME, CHRISTIANS, JOIN TO SING (Mueller) SATB oct FISCHER,C CM-7470 $.30   (C1625)
(Mueller) SA oct FISCHER,C CM-6326 $.25   (C1626)
(Mueller) SAB oct FISCHER,C CM-7086 $.25   (C1627)

COME, CHRISTIANS, JOIN TO SING see Lundquist

COME CHRISTIANS JOIN TO SING see Mueller, Carl F.

COME, CHRISTIANS, JOIN TO SING see Randall

COME CHRISTIANS, JOIN TO SING see Young

COME, CHRISTIANS, JOIN TO SING ALLELUIA (Gillette) SATB oct SUMMY 1361 $.45   (C1628)

COME CHRISTMAS MORNING see Ehret, Walter

COME, COME AWAY see Pendleton

COME, COME, MY VOICE see Bach, Johann Sebastian

COME, COME YE SAINTS (Cornwall, J.S.) SATB PIONEER 5054 $.20   (C1629)
(Cornwall, J.S.) SSAA PIONEER 5062 $.25   (C1630)
(Davis, Frederick) SSAATTBB oct WALTON 2013 $.30   (C1631)

COME, COME YE SAINTS see Madsen, Florence Jefferson

COME, COME YE SAINTS see Robertson

COME, DANCE AND SING *anthem,US (McKay) 4pt mix cor,org/brass oct SCHIRM.G 11660 $.30   (C1632)

COME, DEAREST LORD see Bach

COME, DEAREST LORD see Naylor, Peter

COME DOWN, ANGELS see King, Betty J.

COME DOWN, O LORD see Cafarella

COME DOWN, O LOVE DIVINE see Dietterich, Philip R.

COME DOWN, O LOVE DIVINE see Francis, W. Douglas

COME DOWN, O LOVE DIVINE see Harris, William Henry

COME DOWN, O LOVE DIVINE see Schroth, Gerhard

COME DOWN, O LOVE DIVINE see Williams

COME, EVER-GRACIOUS SON OF GOD see Handel, George Frideric

COME, FAITHFUL PEOPLE see Darst, W. Glenn

COME, FAITHFUL PEOPLE, COME AWAY see Peek, Richard

COME, FOLLOW, FOLLOW, FOLLOW, ME see Two Old English Christmas Carols

COME FOLLOW THE STAR see Lehmeier, J.F.

COME, GENTLE SHEPHERDS *Xmas (Ley) unis (very easy) OXFORD 45.059 $.25   (C1633)

COME GOD CREATOR (Van Wyatt) SATB,acap oct PRO ART 1460 $.20   (C1634)

COME, GRACIOUS SPIRIT *anthem/hymn,Scot (Wood, Dale) SATB (med) oct AUGSBURG 1571 $.30   (C1635)

COME, GRACIOUS SPIRIT, HEAV'NLY DOVE see Bach, Johann Sebastian

COME, HASTEN, YE SHEPHERDS *Xmas (Ehret) 4pt mix cor oct SCHIRM.G 10441 $.30   (C1636)
(Ehret) 3pt mix cor oct SCHIRM.G 10658 $.25   (C1637)
(Ehret) 3pt wom cor oct SCHIRM.G 10695 $.30   (C1638)
(Ehret) 2pt wom cor oct SCHIRM.G 10847 $.25   (C1639)

COME, HASTEN, YE SHEPHERDS see Zipp, Friedrich

COME HEAVENLY CHILD see Burke, John

COME, HEAVY SOULS see Elmore, Robert [Hall]

COME HERE, LORD (Hancock, E.) SATB,solo,acap FISCHER,J 10078 $.35   (C1640)

COME HITHER, ALL YE WEARY SOULS see Shvedof, C.

COME HITHER, YE FAITHFUL see Blake, G.

COME HOLY GHOST see Attwood, Thomas

COME, HOLY GHOST see Charpentier, Marc-Antoine

COME HOLY GHOST see Dowland, John

COME HOLY GHOST see Duddy, [John H.]

COME HOLY GHOST see Ford, Thomas

COME, HOLY GHOST see Gibbons, Orlando, Veni Creator

COME HOLY GHOST see Kirk, Veni Sancte Spiritus

COME HOLY GHOST see Means, Claude

COME, HOLY GHOST see Palestrina, Giovanni

COME, HOLY GHOST see Pasquet, Jean

COME, HOLY GHOST see Thiman, Eric Harding

COME, HOLY GHOST see Warren, Raymond

COME, HOLY GHOST see Willan, Healey

COME HOLY GHOST, CREATOR BLEST
(Lindquist, M.) SATB oct PRESSER MC232 $.25
(C1641)

COME, HOLY GHOST, CREATOR BLEST see Droste,
Doreen

COME, HOLY GHOST, CREATOR BLEST see Markworth,
Henry

COME, HOLY GHOST, CREATOR BLEST see Resinarius,
Balthasar

COME, HOLY GHOST, DRAW NEAR US see Sowerby, Leo

COME HOLY GHOST, ETERNAL GOD see Naylor,
Bernard

COME, HOLY GHOST, GOD AND LORD see Lenel,
Ludwig

COME, HOLY GHOST, GOD AND LORD see Vulpius,
Melchior

COME, HOLY GHOST, GOD AND LORD! see Walther,
Johann Gottfried

COME, HOLY GHOST, GOD AND LORD see Wienhorst,
Richard

COME, HOLY GHOST, IN LOVE see Bullock, Ernest

COME, HOLY GHOST, IN LOVE see Running, Arnold

COME, HOLY GHOST IN LOVE see Sateren, Leland
Bernhard

COME, HOLY GHOST, IN LOVE see Whitehead, Alfred

COME, HOLY GHOST OUR SOULS INSPIRE see Attwood,
Thomas

COME, HOLY LIGHT, GUIDE DIVINE see Handel,
George Frideric

COME, HOLY SPIRIT see Boatwright, Howard, Nunc
Sancte Nobis Spiritus

COME, HOLY SPIRIT see Brahms, Johannes

COME HOLY SPIRIT see Flagler, [Robert S.]

COME HOLY SPIRIT see Gibbons, Orlando, Veni,
Creator Spiritus

COME, HOLY SPIRIT see Handel, George Frideric

COME, HOLY SPIRIT see Mueller, Luise

COME, HOLY SPIRIT see Najera, Edmund

COME, HOLY SPIRIT see Tans'ur, William

COME, HOLY SPIRIT see Thiman, Eric Harding

COME, HOLY SPIRIT see Young, Gordon

COME, HOLY SPIRIT, COME see Franconia

COME, HOLY SPIRIT, COME see Wolff, S. Drummond

COME, HOLY SPIRIT, GOD AND LORD see Zachau

COME HOME TO GOD see Pallock

COME, I PRAY THEE see Anderson

COME, I PRAY THEE see Anderson, [William H.]

COME, I PRAY THEE, DWELL WITHIN ME see Schutz,
Heinrich, Veni, Rogo, In Cor Meum

COME IN, DEAR ANGELS *Xmas,carol
see Three Christmas Carols
(Whitehead, Alfred) SATB oct LESLIE 4004 see
from Three Christmas Carols, Set 1 (C1642)

COME IN, YOU ANGELS FAIR *Xmas
(Track) SA SCHMITT 336 $.25 (C1643)

COME INTO MY HEART, LORD JESUS see Lowell

COME JESU, COME see Bach, Johann Sebastian,
Komm, Jesu, Komm

COME, JESUS, COME see Bach, Johann Sebastian,
Komm, Jesu, Komm

COME, JESUS HOLY CHILD see Wienhorst, Richard

COME, JESUS, HOLY CHILD see Willan, Healey

COME, JESUS, HOLY CHILD, TO ME see Wolff, S.
Drummond

COME, JESUS, HOLY SON OF GOD see Handel, George
Frideric

COME, KINDLY DEATH see Bach, Johann Sebastian

COME KINGDOM OF OUR GOD see Thiman, Eric
Harding

COME LET US ALL see Handel, George Frideric

COME LET US ALL THIS DAY see Bach, Johann
Sebastian, Kommt, Seelen, Dieser Tag

COME, LET US BOW DOWN see Wapen, Francis A.

COME, LET US JOIN *CCU,hymn
(Parker, Alice) oct LAWSON $1.25 (C1644)

COME, LET US JOIN see Darst, S. Glen

COME, LET US JOIN see Nicholson, S.H.

COME, LET US JOIN see Pelz, Walter L.

COME LET US JOIN OUR CHEERFUL SONGS
(Coggin) SA KJOS 6111 $.30 (C1645)

COME, LET US JOIN OUR CHEERFUL SONGS see
Stanley, John

COME LET US JOIN OUR CHEERFUL SONGS see Wolff

COME, LET US JOIN WITH FAITHFUL ONES
(Coggin) 2pt oct PRO ART 2428 $.25 see from
Hirchberg Gesangbuch (C1646)

COME, LET US PRAISE THE LORD see Halmos,
Ladislas

COME, LET US REJOICE see Sweelinck, Jan
Pieterszoon, Venite, Exultemus Domino

COME, LET US SING see Aloyse, Sr. M.

COME LET US SING see Caldwell, Mary [Elizabeth]

COME LET US SING see Chenoweth, Wilbur

COME LET US SING see Mendelssohn-Bartholdy,
Felix, Kommt, Lasst Uns Anbeten

COME LET US SING see Mueller, Carl F.

COME, LET US SING OF HIS GLORY see Young

COME, LET US SING TO THE LORD see Theophane,
Sister M. (Hytrek)

COME, LET US SING UNTO THE LORD see Couperin,
Francois

COME, LET US SING UNTO THE LORD see Schubert,
Franz (Peter)

COME, LET US SING UNTO THE LORD see Williams,
R.

COME LET US START A JOYFUL SONG see Hassler,
Hans Leo

COME, LET US TO THE LORD
(Roberton, H.S.) TTBB PATERSON 1651 s.p.
(C1647)

COME, LET US TUNE OUR LOFTIEST SONG see Ford,
Virgil T.

COME, LET US TUNE OUR LOFTIEST SONG see Wyatt

COME LET US UNITE IN A JOYOUS NOEL see Bedell,
[Robert Leech]

COME, LET US USE THE GRACE DIVINE see Lynn,
George

COME, LET US WORSHIP see Ballerino, G.

COME, LET US WORSHIP see Brissio, In Medio
Ecclesiae

COME, LET US WORSHIP see Carroll, J.R.

COME, LET US WORSHIP see Palestrina, Giovanni

COME, LET US WORSHIP HIM see Blakley

COME LET'S BE MERRY see Smith

COME, LET'S REJOICE see Amner, John

COME, LISTEN TO MY STORY *Xmas,carol
cor/cong oct MOWBRAY 65019 0 s.p. see also
Cowley Carol Book, The (C1648)

COME LITTLE JESUS *Xmas,carol,Fr
2pt ENOCH TP165 s.p. contains also: Holly Red
And Mistletoe (C1649)

COME, LORD, AND RULE THE EARTH see Thiman, Eric
Harding

COME, LORD JESUS! see Young, Carlton R.

COME, LORD OF LIFE see Trued, Clarence

COME, LOVE WE GOD
SATB (easy) OXFORD 08.009 $.15 (C1650)

COME, MIGHTY FATHER, MIGHTY LORD see Handel,
George Frideric

COME, MY DEAR OLD LADY *Xmas,carol,Span
(Ehret, Walter) SATB,opt inst oct WALTON 2510
$.30 (C1651)
(Ehret, Walter) SSA oct WALTON 2538 $.30
(C1652)

COME MY HEART AND PONDER WELL see Bach, Johann
Sebastian

COME, MY SOUL see Elmore, Robert [Hall]

COME, MY SOUL, THOU MUST BE WAKING see Franz

COME, MY WAY, MY TRUTH see Harker, Clifford

COME, MY WAY, MY TRUTH, MY LIFE see Dietterich,
Philip R.

COME, MY WAY, MY TRUTH, MY LIFE see Friedell,
Harold W.

COME, MY WAY, MY TRUTH, MY LIFE see Graves,
Richard

COME, MY WAY, MY TRUTH, MY LIFE see Harris,
William Henry

COME MY WAY, MY TRUTH, MY LIFE see Jacobson,
Maurice

COME, MY WAY, MY TRUTH, MY LIFE see Piggott,
H.E.

COME, MY WAY, MY TRUTH, MY LIFE see Roff,
Joseph

COME, MY WAY, MY TRUTH, MY LIFE see Sampson,
Godfrey

COME, MY WAY, MY TRUTH, MY LIFE see Tomblings,
Philip

COME NEAR TO ME, JESUS see Johnson, Sidney

COME NEARER see Peloquin, C. Alexander

COME NOW GOOD CHRISTIANS see Bach, Johann
Sebastian

COME NOW, HAPPY SHEPHERDS see Costeley, R.

COME, NOW LET US BE JOYFUL see Vecchi

COME NOW, LET US REASON TOGETHER see Grieb,
Herbert [C.]

COME, NOW SING see Franck, Cesar

COME NOW TO BETHLEHEM see Graham, Robert [V.]

COME NOW TO HIS TABLE see Trued

COME, O BLESSED OF MY FATHER see Bender

COME, O BLESSED OF MY FATHER see Bender, Jan

COME, O CHILDREN, LET US GATHER see Hayde

COME, O COME see Hughes

COME, O COME MY BELOVED see Grandi, Alessandro,
Veniat Dilectus Meus

COME, O COME, MY LIFE'S DELIGHT see Osborne, W.
H.

COME, O COME THOU QUICKENING SPIRIT see Marks,
H.

COME, O CREATOR SPIRIT see Franck, Cesar

COME, O CREATOR SPIRIT, COME see Des Prez,
Josquin

COME, O ENLIGHTENING SPIRIT see Willaert,
Adrian, Ave Regina Caelorum

COME O HOLY GHOST, GOD AND LORD see Osiander,
Lucas, Komm, Heiliger Geist, Herre Gott

COME, O JESUS, COME TO ME see Cherubini, Luigi,
Veni Jesu

COME, O JESUS, SAVIOUR MINE see Cherubini,
Luigi, Veni Jesus

COME, O LONG AWAITED SAVIOR see Korhonen, J.

COME, O THOU GOD OF GRACE see Ford, Virgil T.

COME ON DOWN, ZACCHAEUS see Leaf, Robert

COME, PASTORES *Xmas,carol,Span
(Kirk) SATB oct SHAPIRO SK 2073 $.25 (C1653)

COME, PEACE OF GOD see Butler

COME, PEACE OF GOD see Butler, Eugene

COME PEACEFUL DEATH see Bach, Johann Sebastian

COME, PRAISE HIM see Sweelinck, Jan
Pieterszoon, Venite, Exultemus Domino

COME, PRAISE THE LORD see Young

COME, PRAISE THE LORD see Young, Carlton R.

COME PRAISE THE LORD see Young, G.

COME, PRAISE YOUR LORD AND SAVIOUR see Webber,
Lloyd

COME, READY LYRE see Willan, Healey

COME, REDEEMER see Bach, Johann Sebastian

COME, REDEEMER OF OUR RACE see Bach, Johann
Sebastian, Nun Komm', Der Heiden Heiland

COME REJOICING, FAITHFUL MEN see Anonymous

COME, RISEN LORD see Near, Gerald

COME, RISEN LORD see Sowerby, Leo

COME RUNNING, YOU SHEPHERDS *Xmas,carol,Ger
(Ehret, Walter) SATB,opt inst oct WALTON 2523
$.30 (C1654)

COME, SEE THE PLACE see Mueller, Carl F.

COME, SHEPHERDS, COME *Xmas,carol
(Jewell, Kenneth W.) SSA,org oct WORLD
AC-750-3 $.45 (C1655)

COME, SILENT NIGHT see Johnson, Noel

COME SING see Leaf, Robert

COME SING AND RING see Ramseth, Ann

COME SING TO THE GLORY OF THE LORD see Wild,
Eric

COME SING, YE CHOIRS EXULTANT see Lewis, John
Leo

COME, SINGING NOEL see Davis, Katherine K.

COME, SOOTHING DEATH see Bach, Johann
Sebastian, Komm, Susser Tod

COME, SOULS, BEHOLD TODAY see Bach

COME, SOUND HIS PRAISE ABROAD see Ford, Virgil
T.

COME, SOUND HIS PRAISE ABROAD see Harris

COME, SOUND HIS PRAISE ABROAD see Watts, W.

COME, SPIRIT OF THE LIVING GOD see Speaks,
[Oley]

COME, SPIRITS, 'TIS HIS DAY see Bach, Johann
Sebastian

COME, SWEET PEACE see Edmunds, John

COME, THEN, O HOLY BREATH OF GOD see
Palestrina, Giovanni, Dunque Divin
Spiracolo

COME, THOU ALMIGHTY KING see Boyd

COME, THOU ALMIGHTY KING see Cartford, Gerhard
M.

COME, THOU ALMIGHTY KING see Giardini, Felice de'

COME THOU ALMIGHTY KING see Giardino, Di

COME, THOU ALMIGHTY KING see Landon

COME, THOU ALMIGHTY KING see Ringwald, [Roy]

COME THOU BELOVED OF CHRIST see Willan, Healey

COME, THOU FAITHFUL SERVANT see Monteverdi, Claudio, Veni Sponsa Christi

COME THOU FONT see Ellis, Mary

COME, THOU FOUNT see Wyeth

COME, THOU FOUNT see Wyeth, John

COME THOU FOUNT OF EVERY BLESSING
   (Cornwall, J.S.) SAB PIONEER 4001 $.20
                                            (C1656)
   (Pfautsch) SATB,acap oct LAWSON 51074 $.35
                                            (C1657)
COME, THOU FOUNT OF EVERY BLESSING see Gluck, Christoph Willibald Ritter von

COME, THOU FOUNT OF EVERY BLESSING see Peek, Richard

COME THOU FOUNT OF EVERY BLESSING see Wyeth

COME THOU FOUNT OF EVERY BLESSING see Young, C.

COME, THOU FOUNT OF EV'RY BLESSING see Reynolds, Roger

COME, THOU HOLY PARACLETE see Bach, Johann Sebastian

COME THOU HOLY SPIRIT
   (Tkach) KJOS 7502 $.30   (C1658)

COME THOU HOLY SPIRIT see Byrd, William

COME THOU, HOLY SPIRIT see Tkach

COME THOU HOLY SPIRIT see Tschesnokoff, P.I.

COME, THOU HOLY SPIRIT see Wadely, F.W.

COME, THOU HOLY SPIRIT, COME *Ember/Whitsun, anthem
   (Ley) SATB,acap (easy) OXFORD 43.067 $.25 see from Six Short Anthems   (C1659)
   (Ley, Henry G.) SATB,acap (easy) oct OXFORD $.25   (C1660)
COME THOU HOLY SPIRIT COME see Hunt, Reginald

COME, THOU HOLY SPIRIT, COME see Palestrina, Giovanni, Veni Sancte Spiritus

COME, THOU LONG-EXPECTED see Warner, Richard

COME, THOU LONG EXPECTED JESUS *anthem
   (Pooler, Marie) SA/unis treb cor (easy) oct AUGSBURG 1362 $.25   (C1661)
COME, THOU LONG EXPECTED JESUS see Cain, Noble

COME, THOU LONG-EXPECTED JESUS see Darst, S. Glen

COME, THOU LONG EXPECTED JESUS see Hopkins

COME, THOU LONG-EXPECTED JESUS see Lewis, John Leo

COME, THOU LONG EXPECTED JESUS see Ley, Henry George

COME, THOU LONG EXPECTED JESUS see Lovelace, Austin C.

COME, THOU LONG EXPECTED JESUS see Near, Gerald

COME, THOU LONG-EXPECTED JESUS see Pritchard

COME, THOU LONG EXPECTED JESUS see Rameau, Jean-Philippe

COME, THOU LONG EXPECTED JESUS see Sateren, Leland Bernhard

COME, THOU LONG EXPECTED JESUS see Tyler, Don

COME, THOU MORNING STAR see Gibbons, Orlando

COME THOU, O LOVER OF MY SOUL see Young, Carlton R.

COME THOU, O SAVIOUR see Bach, Johann Sebastian

COME THOU, OH, COME see Bach, Johann Sebastian

COME, THOU QUICKENING SPIRIT see Lundquist

COME, THOU REDEEMER OF THE EARTH see Praetorius, Michael

COME, THOU REDEEMER OF THE EARTH see Willan, Healey

COME THOU, SWEET DEATH see Bach, Johann Sebastian, Komm', Susser Tod

COME THOU TO DWELL WITHIN US see Pasquet, Jean

COME TO BETHLEHEM see Emig, Lois

COME TO BETHLEHEM see Heseltine, Philip

COME TO CALVARY'S HOLY MOUNTAIN see Elmore, Robert [Hall]

COME TO ME see Beethoven, Ludwig van

COME TO ME see Darst, W. Glen

COME TO ME, ALL YE THAT LABOUR see Roff, Joseph

COME TO ME AND REST see Sjolund, Paul

COME TO MY HEART, LORD JESUS see Ambrose

COME TO MY HEART, LORD JESUS see Ambrose, [Paul]

COME TO REIGN LORD JESUS see Gounod, Charles Francois

COME TO THE MANGER see Bennett, F. Roy

COME TO THE MANGER see Kling, Glockchen

COME TO THE MANGER see Kountz

COME TO THE MANGER see Schroth

COME TO THE MANGER see Van Wormer, G.

COME TO THE SAVIOUR, MAKE NO DELAY see Root

COME TO THE STABLE see Klein

COME TO THE STABLE WITH JESUS see O'Hara, Geoffrey

COME TO THE TOMB see Lovelace, Austin C.

COME TO THE WATER see Lister, Mosie

COME TO THE WATERS see Victoria, Tomas Luis de, Sitientes, Venite Ad Aquas

COME TO ZION, SIN SICK SOULS see Aks

COME TOGETHER see Owens, Carol

COME, TOGETHER LET US SING see Bach, Johann Sebastian, Liebster Jesu, Wir Sind Hier

COME UNTO HIM see Gounod, Charles Francois

COME UNTO HIM see Handel, George Frideric

COME UNTO HIM see Maschoff

COME UNTO HIM see Mendelssohn-Bartholdy, Felix

COME UNTO ME see Anthes

COME UNTO ME see Bach

COME UNTO ME see Bowles

COME UNTO ME see Carrington, O.M.

COME UNTO ME see Coenen, W.

COME UNTO ME see Cutler

COME UNTO ME see Glarum, L. Stanley

COME UNTO ME see Henderson, H.

COME UNTO ME see Kirk, T.

COME UNTO ME see Lister, Mosie

COME UNTO ME see Liszt, Franz

COME UNTO ME see Moffatt

COME UNTO ME see Schubert, Franz (Peter)

COME UNTO ME see Wilson, John F.

COME UNTO ME ALL YE THAT LABOUR see Pears, James R.

COME UNTO ME ALL YE WHO WEARY see Lassus, Roland de (Orlandus), Venite Ad Me Omnes

COME UNTO ME, YE WEARY see Lloyd

COME UNTO ME, YE WEARY see Pike, Harry Hale

COME UNTO ME YE WEARY see Smith

COME UNTO ME, YE WEARY see Williams

COME, WE THAT LOVE THE LORD see Barnes, [Edward Shippen]

COME, WE THAT LOVE THE LORD see Clements

COME, WE THAT LOVE THE LORD see Gustafson, Dwight

COME WHERE THE CHRIST CHILD IS SLEEPING see McLaughlin, Marian

COME WITH REJOICING see Leaf, Robert

COME, WORSHIP THE CHILD see Tucker

COME WORSHIP THE KING see Jenkins, Thomas

COME YE see Franck, Melchior, Kommt Her

COME YE AND SEE THE HOLY CHILD see Bedell, [Robert Leech]

COME, YE BLESSED see Scott, John Prindle

COME, YE BLESSED CHILDREN see Emerson

COME YE BLESSED OF MY FATHER see Madsen, Florence Jefferson

COME, YE CHILDREN, AND HARKEN TO ME see Steffani, Agostino

COME, YE CHILDREN, PRAISE THE SAVIOR see Wienhorst, Richard

COME, YE CHILDREN, SWEETLY SINGING see Rasley

COME YE, COME ALL YE PEOPLE see Koepke

COME, YE DISCONSOLATE see Darst, W. Glenn

COME, YE DISCONSOLATE see Webbe

COME YE DISCONSOLATE see Webbe, Samuel

COME, YE FAITHFUL see Denton

COME, YE FAITHFUL see Ford

COME, YE FAITHFUL see Sullivan, Sir Arthur Seymour

COME, YE FAITHFUL see Thatcher, R.S.

COME, YE FAITHFUL see Titcomb

COME YE FAITHFUL, RAISE THE STRAIN see Bender, Jan

COME YE FAITHFUL, RAISE THE STRAIN see Darst, W. Glenn

COME YE FAITHFUL, RAISE THE STRAIN see Graham, George

COME YE FAITHFUL, RAISE THE STRAIN see Lenel, Ludwig

COME YE FAITHFUL, RAISE THE STRAIN see Lindeman

COME YE FAITHFUL, RAISE THE STRAIN see Lundquist

COME YE FAITHFUL, RAISE THE STRAIN see Sullivan, Sir Arthur Seymour

COME YE FAITHFUL, RAISE THE STRAIN see Thiman, Eric Harding

COME YE FAITHFUL, RAISE THE STRAIN see Wolff, S. Drummond

COME YE FATHFUL see Thiman, Eric Harding

COME YE GAY SHEPHERDS see Costeley, Guillaume, Allon, Gay Bergeres

COME, YE LOFTY *Xmas,carol,Fr
   (Leonard, G.) SATB,acap (easy) oct CONCORDIA 98-1435 $.20   (C1662)
COME, YE LOFTY, COME, YE LOWLY *Xmas,carol oct HART s.p.   (C1663)

COME YE LOFTY, COME YE LOWLY see Gurney

COME, YE PEOPLE see Perti, Giacomo Antonio, O Vos Omnes

COME YE, SEE THE SAVIOR see Dagand, Abbe J., Veni Sponsa Christi

COME YE SERVANTS see Garden, Charlotte L.

COME YE SHEPHERDS *Xmas
   (Avalos) SATB oct PRO ART 2250 $.25   (C1664)
COME, YE SINNERS, POOR AND NEEDY *folk/hymn,US
   (Hooper, William L.) SATB oct WALTON 2067 $.25   (C1665)
COME YE SINNERS, POOR AND NEEDY see Ehret, Walter

COME, YE SINNERS, POOR AND NEEDY see McCluskey

COME, YE SINNERS, POOR AND NEEDY see Young, Carlton R.

COME, YE THANKFUL PEOPLE see Elvey

COME, YE THANKFUL PEOPLE see Elvey, George Job

COME, YE THANKFUL PEOPLE see Goldsworthy, William Arthur

COME, YE THANKFUL PEOPLE see Thompson

COME YE THANKFUL PEOPLE COME
   see Three Thanksgiving Hymns
   (Ehret, W.) SATB LEONARD-US 08010240 $.25   (C1666)
COME, YE THANKFUL PEOPLE, COME see Elvey

COME, YE THANKFUL PEOPLE, COME see Elvey, George Job

COME, YE THANKFUL PEOPLE, COME see Williamson, Malcolm

COME, YE THAT LOVE THE LORD *hymn
   (Parker) SATB,acap oct LAWSON 51309 $.25   (C1667)
COME YE THAT LOVE THE LORD see Hopeson

COME, YE THAT LOVE THE LORD see Young, Carlton R.

COME YE TO BETHLEHEM see Davis, Katherine K.

COME YE TO BETHLEHEM APACE *Xmas
   (Kranz, A.) SATB,acap AMP A573 $.25 see from Christmas Choruses   (C1668)
COME YE TO THE LORD see Kantor, J.

COME YE UNTO ME see Danielsen

COME YE WITH CAROLS see Felts

COME YE WITH PSALMODY see Byrd, William

COME, YOUR HEARTS AND VOICES RAISING see Jaeckel, Daniel, Quem Pastores

COME, YOUR HEARTS AND VOICES RAISING see Stellhorn, August W.

COME, YOUR HEARTS AND VOICES RAISING see Strube, Adolf

COMER
   Fight The Good Fight
      SATB THOMP.G E.A.2 s.p.   (C1669)

   Psalm 23
      SATB THOMP.G G-547 s.p.   (C1670)

COMES, AT TIMES, A STILLNESS see Woodward, H.H.

COMES, JUAN BAUTISTA (1568-1643)
   Alabado Sea El Santisimo
      (Kaplan, A.) [Span/Eng] SATB BROUDE,A. 141 $.30   (C1671)

   Beatus Vir
      (Goodale, Robert L.) [Lat] SSAT&SATB,acap voc sc SCHIRM.G $1.25   (C1672)

COMES, JUAN BAUTISTA (cont'd.)

Christus Factus Est *Lat
(Martens) "Jesus Christ Was Made Obediant"
[Lat/Eng] SATB oct MCA (C1673)

Jesus Christ Was Made Obediant *see Christus
Factus Est

Lamentacion
(Goodale, Robert L.) [Lat] 5pt mix cor voc
sc SCHIRM.G $1.00 (C1674)

Magnificat *Magnif
(Goodale) [Lat] SSAT&SATB,acap voc sc
SCHIRM.G $1.25 (C1675)

COMFORT, COMFORT YE MY PEOPLE see Bach, Johann
Sebastian

COMFORT, COMFORT YE MY PEOPLE see Bunjes, Paul
G.

COMFORT, O LORD see Crotch

COMFORT, O LORD see Crotch, William

COMFORT O LORD THE SOUL see Crotch, William

COMFORT, O LORD, THE SOUL OF THY SERVANT see
Crotch

COMFORT, O LORD THE SOUL OF THY SERVANT see
Crotch, William

COMFORT THEM, O LORD (FROM TIME AND TRUTH) see
Handel, George Frideric

COMFORT YE see Davis, Katherine K.

COMFORT YE, MY PEOPLE see Bach, Johann
Sebastian

COMFORT YE MY PEOPLE see Schmidt

COMFORT YE MY PEOPLE see Schutz, Heinrich,
Troset Troset Mein Volk

COMFORT YE MY PEOPLE see Thalben-Ball, George
[Thomas]

COMFORTABLE WORDS OF JESUS, THE see Kevan, G.

COMFORTER HAS COME, THE see Kirkpatrick

COMING OF CHRIST, THE see Holst, Gustav

COMING OF GOD TO MAN, THE see Nelson, Ronald A.

COMING OF THE KING, THE see Buck, Dudley

COMING OF THE KING, THE see Roeckel, J.L.

COMING OF THE PRINCE OF PEACE see Dickinson

COMINI
Sweet Baby King *Xmas
(Simeone) SSA SHAWNEE B 281 $.25 (C1676)

COMINO
Savior Is Born, The *Xmas
(Cornelio) SATB oct JUSKO 239 $.25 (C1677)

COMMAND THINE ANGEL THAT HE COME see Buxtehude,
Dietrich, Befiehl Dem Engel, Dass Er Komm

COMME LES ANGES AU PARADIS see Wissmer

COMMIT THY WAY UNTO THE LORD see Liebhold

COMMIT THY WAYS AND GRANT US TO DO THY ZEAL see
Hassler, Hans Leo

COMMIT YOUR WAY UNTO THE LORD see Russel,
Eleanor

COMMITMENT see Pfautsch, Lloyd

COMMON PRAYER, A see Burns, W.

COMMON THINGS see Jones, Marjorie

COMMUNE DOCTORUM see Lerperger, Kurt

COMMUNIO see Aichinger, Gregor

COMMUNIO see Baumann, Max

COMMUNIO see Lassus, Roland de (Orlandus)

COMMUNIO see Ravanello, Oreste

COMMUNIO see Senfl, Ludwig

COMMUNION see Kodaly, Zoltan

COMMUNION see Ridout

COMMUNION HYMN see Brumel, Antoine

COMMUNION HYMN see Opie, M.P.

COMMUNION HYMN SEQUENCE FOR CHOIR see James

COMMUNION HYMNS
LITURGICAL $.50
contains: Merciful Saviour; O Jesus, We
Adore Thee; Sing With Joy The Saviour's
Glory (C1678)

COMMUNION PSALMS see Krenek, Ernst

COMMUNION SERVICE see Bach, Johann Sebastian

COMMUNION SERVICE see Boatwright, Howard

COMMUNION SERVICE see Byrd, William

COMMUNION SERVICE see Davison, John

COMMUNION SERVICE see Dilsner, L.

COMMUNION SERVICE see Greiner, Allen

COMMUNION SERVICE see Merbecke, John

COMMUNION SERVICE see Piggott, H.E.

COMMUNION SERVICE see Titcomb, Missa Salve
Regina

COMMUNION SERVICE see White, L.J.

COMMUNION SERVICE see Willan, Healey, Missa De
Sancta Maria Magdalena

COMMUNION SERVICE FOR PENITENTIAL SEASONS see
Goicoechea, Vincente, Missa Pro Dominicis
Adventus Et Quadrigestimae

COMMUNION SERVICE IN A see Franck, Cesar, Messa
A Troix Voix

COMMUNION SERVICE IN A MINOR see Darke, Harold
[Edwin]

COMMUNION SERVICE IN C see Coleman, Henry

COMMUNION SERVICE IN C see Mathias, William

COMMUNION SERVICE IN C see Wills, Arthur

COMMUNION SERVICE IN C MAJOR see Ripolles,
Vincente, Missa Sacratissimi Cordis Jesu

COMMUNION SERVICE IN D see Leighton, Kenneth

COMMUNION SERVICE IN D see Statham, Heathcote
(Dicken)

COMMUNION SERVICE IN D see Titcomb

COMMUNION SERVICE IN D-MAJOR see Casajus,
Vincente, Missa Lauda Sion

COMMUNION SERVICE IN D MINOR see Vaughan
Williams, Ralph

COMMUNION SERVICE IN E see Darke, Harold
[Edwin]

COMMUNION SERVICE IN E FLAT see Bairstow,
Edward Cuthbert

COMMUNION SERVICE IN E FLAT MAJOR see Kevan

COMMUNION SERVICE IN F see Darke, Harold
[Edwin]

COMMUNION SERVICE IN F see Watson, Sydney

COMMUNION SERVICE IN F see Wood, Charles, Missa
Sancti Patricii

COMMUNION SERVICE IN F MINOR see Kevan

COMMUNION SERVICE IN G see Jackson, Francis

COMMUNION SERVICE IN G see Schubert, Franz
(Peter)

COMMUNION SERVICE IN G see Wadely, F.W.

COMMUNION SERVICE IN G MAJOR see Goicoechea,
Vincente, Missa In Hon. Immac. Concep.
B.V.M.

COMMUNION SERVICE IN G MAJOR see Vocht,
Lodewijk de, Missa In Honorem Angelorum

COMMUNION SERVICE ON A ROMAN TONE see Heredia,
Piedro, Missa Super Cantu Romano

COMMUNION SERVICE (ST. CECILIA) see Gounod,
Charles Francois, Messe Solennelle

COMMUNION SERVICE: THE "MASS OF THE QUIET HOUR"
see Oldroyd, George

COMMUNION SONG see Salsbury, Sonny

COMMUNION TRILOGY, A see Ratcliffe, Desmond

COMMUNION WITH GOD see Cain, Noble

COMMUNITY ANTHEMS OF EARLY AMERICA *CCU,
anthem,US
(Lindsley) 3-4pt mix cor,acap AMP A654 $1.25
(C1679)
COMMUNITY ANTHEMS OF EARLY AMERICA *CCU,
anthem,US
(Linsley) TTB,acap AMP A654 $1.25 (C1680)

COMMUNITY MASS see Lee, J.

COMMUNITY MASS, A see Proulx, Richard

COMPANIONS ALL SING LOUDLY *Xmas,carol,Span
(Ehret) SSA oct BOOSEY 5498 $.30 (C1681)
(Gray) SATB oct PRO ART 1757 $.22 (C1682)
(Kinsman, Franklin) SATB oct WALTON 2002 $.25
(C1683)
(Kirk) SATB oct SHAPIRO SK 2027 $.25 (C1684)
(Kirk) SSA oct SHAPIRO SK 3021 $.30 (C1685)
(Kirk) 2pt oct SHAPIRO SK 4017 $.25 (C1686)
(Kirk) SAB oct SHAPIRO SK 5010 $.30 (C1687)
(Kirk, Theron) SATB voc sc WEINBERGER s.p.
(C1688)

COMPASSION
2pt CHAPPELL 0017962-352 $.40 (C1689)
SSA CHAPPELL 0017962-354 $.40 (C1690)
SATB CHAPPELL 0017962-358 $.40 (C1691)

COMPERE, [LOUIS] (ca. 1455-1518)
Missa "Alles Regrets" *Mass
(Finscher) 4pt mix cor MOSELER s.p. (C1692)

Nu La Oss Takke Gud
(Sundberg, Ove. K.) mix cor,org MUSIKK 234
s.p. (C1693)

O Bone Jesu *Lat
mix cor SOUTHERN $.30 (C1694)
SATB oct SUMMY 5397 $.45 (C1695)
(Seay) [Lat/Eng] SATB,acap oct MCA (C1696)

O Vos Omnes
see ALTNIEDERLANDISCHE MOTETTEN

Opera Omnia vol. I *CCU,Mass
(Finscher, Ludwig) cor cmplt ed
AM.INST.MUS. $13.50 (C1697)

Opera Omnia vol. II *CC24U
(Finscher, Ludwig) cor cmplt ed
AM.INST.MUS. $12.50 (C1698)

COMPERE, [LOUIS] (cont'd.)

Opera Omnia vol. III *CC23U
(Finscher, Ludwig) cor cmplt ed
AM.INST.MUS. $11.00 (C1699)

Opera Omnia vol. IV *CCU,mot
(Finscher, Ludwig) cor cmplt ed
AM.INST.MUS. $11.00 (C1700)

Opera Omnia vol. V *sac/sec,CC58U
(Finscher, Ludwig) cor cmplt ed
AM.INST.MUS. $18.50 (C1701)

COMPLETE CHURCH MUSIC see Humfrey, Pelham

COMPLETE CHURCH MUSIC 2 see Humfrey, Pelham

COMPLETE EDITIONS VOL. 1 see Palestrina,
Giovanni

COMPLETE EDITIONS VOL. 2 see Palestrina,
Giovanni

COMPLETE EDITIONS VOL. 3 see Palestrina,
Giovanni

COMPLETE EDITIONS VOL. 6: THIRTY-SIX MOTETS see
Palestrina, Giovanni

COMPLETE EDITIONS VOL. 7: THIRTY-SIX MOTETS see
Palestrina, Giovanni

COMPLETE EDITIONS VOL. 8 see Palestrina,
Giovanni

COMPLETE EDITIONS VOL. 9 see Palestrina,
Giovanni

COMPLETE EDITIONS VOL. 10 see Palestrina,
Giovanni

COMPLETE EDITIONS VOL. 11: FORTY-THREE MOTETS
see Palestrina, Giovanni

COMPLETE EDITIONS VOL. 12: FORTY-THREE MOTETS
see Palestrina, Giovanni

COMPLETE EDITIONS VOL. 13: FORTY-THREE MOTETS
see Palestrina, Giovanni

COMPLETE EDITIONS VOL. 14 see Palestrina,
Giovanni

COMPLETE EDITIONS VOL. 15 see Palestrina,
Giovanni

COMPLETE EDITIONS VOL. 16 see Palestrina,
Giovanni

COMPLETE EDITIONS VOL. 17: EIGHTY-EIGHT MOTETS
see Palestrina, Giovanni

COMPLETE EDITIONS VOL. 18: EIGHTY- EIGHT MOTETS
see Palestrina, Giovanni

COMPLETE EDITIONS VOL. 19: EIGHTY-EIGHT MOTETS
see Palestrina, Giovanni

COMPLETE EDITIONS VOL. 20: EIGHTY-EIGHT MOTETS
see Palestrina, Giovanni

COMPLETE EDITIONS VOL. 21: EIGHTY-EIGHT MOTETS
see Palestrina, Giovanni

COMPLETE EDITIONS VOL. 22: EIGHTY-EIGHT MOTETS
see Palestrina, Giovanni

COMPLETE EDITIONS VOL. 23: THIRTY-NINE SECULAR
AND SACRED MADRIGALS see Palestrina,
Giovanni

COMPLETE EDITIONS VOL. 24: THIRTY-NINE SECULAR
AND SACRED MADRIGALS see Palestrina,
Giovanni

COMPLETE EDITIONS VOL. 25 see Palestrina,
Giovanni

COMPLETE EDITIONS VOL. 26 see Palestrina,
Giovanni

COMPLETE EDITIONS VOL. 27: TWENTY-NINE MOTETS
see Palestrina, Giovanni

COMPLETE EDITIONS VOL. 28: TWENTY-NINE MOTETS
see Palestrina, Giovanni

COMPLETE EDITIONS VOL. 29: TWENTY-NINE MOTETS
see Palestrina, Giovanni

COMPLETE EDITIONS VOL. 30: TWENTY-EIGHT MOTETS
see Palestrina, Giovanni

COMPLETE EDITIONS VOL. 31: TWENTY-EIGHT MOTETS
see Palestrina, Giovanni

COMPLETE EDITIONS VOL. 32: LAMENTATIONES see
Palestrina, Giovanni

COMPLETE EDITIONS VOL. 33: LAMENTATIONES see
Palestrina, Giovanni

COMPLETE EDITIONS VOL. 34: LAMENTATIONES see
Palestrina, Giovanni

COMPLETE EDITIONS VOL. 35: LAMENTATIONES see
Palestrina, Giovanni

COMPLETE EDITIONS VOL. 36: FORTY-FIVE HYMNS see
Palestrina, Giovanni

COMPLETE EDITIONS VOL. 37: FORTY-FIVE HYMNS see
Palestrina, Giovanni

COMPLETE EDITIONS VOL. 38: FORTY-FIVE HYMNS see
Palestrina, Giovanni

COMPLETE EDITIONS VOL. 39 see Palestrina,
Giovanni

COMPLETE EDITIONS VOL. 40 see Palestrina,
Giovanni

COMPLETE EDITIONS VOL. 41: THIRTY-FIVE
MAGNIFICATS see Palestrina, Giovanni

COMPLETE EDITIONS VOL. 42: THIRTY-FIVE MAGNIFICATS see Palestrina, Giovanni

COMPLETE EDITIONS VOL. 43: THIRTY-FIVE MAGNIFICATS see Palestrina, Giovanni

COMPLETE EDITIONS VOL. 44: THIRTY-FIVE MAGNIFICATS see Palestrina, Giovanni

COMPLETE EDITIONS VOL. 45: SIXTY-EIGHT OFFERTORIES see Palestrina, Giovanni

COMPLETE EDITIONS VOL. 46: SIXTY-EIGHT OFFERTORIES see Palestrina, Giovanni

COMPLETE EDITIONS VOL. 47: SIXTY-EIGHT OFFERTORIES see Palestrina, Giovanni

COMPLETE EDITIONS VOL. 48 see Palestrina, Giovanni

COMPLETE EDITIONS VOL. 49 see Palestrina, Giovanni

COMPLETE EDITIONS VOL. 50 see Palestrina, Giovanni

COMPLETE EDITIONS VOL. 51 see Palestrina, Giovanni

COMPLETE EDITIONS VOL. 52: THIRTY SACRED MADRIGALS see Palestrina, Giovanni

COMPLETE EDITIONS VOL. 53 see Palestrina, Giovanni

COMPLETE EDITIONS VOL. 55 see Palestrina, Giovanni

COMPLETE EDITIONS VOL. 56 see Palestrina, Giovanni

COMPLETE EDITIONS VOL. 57 see Palestrina, Giovanni

COMPLETE EDITIONS VOL. 58 see Palestrina, Giovanni

COMPLETE EDITIONS VOL. 59 see Palestrina, Giovanni

COMPLETE EDITIONS VOL. 61 see Palestrina, Giovanni

COMPLETE EDITIONS VOL. 63 see Palestrina, Giovanni

COMPLETE EDITIONS VOL. 64 see Palestrina, Giovanni

COMPLETE EDITIONS VOL. 65 see Palestrina, Giovanni

COMPLETE EDITIONS VOL. 66 see Palestrina, Giovanni

COMPLETE EDITIONS VOL. 67 see Palestrina, Giovanni

COMPLETE EDITIONS VOL. 68 see Palestrina, Giovanni

COMPLETE EDITIONS VOL. 69 see Palestrina, Giovanni

COMPLETE EDITIONS VOL. 70 see Palestrina, Giovanni

COMPLETE EDITIONS VOL. 71 see Palestrina, Giovanni

COMPLETE EDITIONS VOL. 72 see Palestrina, Giovanni

COMPLETE EDITIONS VOL. 73 see Palestrina, Giovanni

COMPLETE REQUIEM MASS see Bottigliero, Eduardo

COMPLETE SERVICE see Davies, Henry Walford

COMPLETE SERVICE see Maunder, J.H.

COMPLETE WORKS IN 61 VOLUMES see Mendelssohn-Bartholdy, Felix

COMPLETORIUM see Gorczycki, Gregor Gervasius

COMPREHENDING THE OTHER PERSON see Powell, Robert J.

COMRADES AND BROTHERS see Ashworth-Hope, H.

COMUNIONE see Grassi, Ciro

CONAWAY, G. WILKES
Blessed Are They *Bibl
4pt mix cor oct SCHIRM.G 9308 $.25 (C1702)

CONCENTI DI VOCI see Orff, Carl

CONCENTUS EUCHARISTICI see Santini, Alessandro

CONCEPTIO TUA see Marenzio, Luca

CONCEPTIO TUA see Porta, Costanzo

CONCERT ARIAS see Mozart, Wolfgang Amadeus

CONCERT CHORAL COLLECTION *sac/sec,CC22L
SSA SOUTHERN $1.50 contains works by: Shaw;
Glarum; Williams and others (C1703)

CONCERT MASS see Suderburg, R.

CONCERTO SACRO see Fuga, Sandro

CONCERTO SPIRITUALE see Ghedini, Giorgio Federico

CONCIERTO DE NAVIDAD see Csonka, Paul

CONCONE, GIUSEPPE (1801-1861)
Agnus Dei (from Mass In F)
"Lamb Of God" (easy) oct WILLIS 5168 $.10
contains also: Handel, George Frideric,
Hope Thou In God [Largo] (from Xerxes)
(C1704)

CONCONE, GIUSEPPE (cont'd.)

Lamb Of God *see Agnus Dei

O Lord Most Merciful
SATB oct LORENZ 346 $.30 (C1705)
SSA oct LORENZ 6208 $.25 (C1706)
SATB,pno (med) oct WILLIS 5060 $.10 (C1707)

CONCORD ANTHEM BOOK, THE *CC40U
(Davison, A.; Foote, H.) mix cor cloth
SCHIRM.EC 13 $3.50 (C1708)

CONCORD HYMN see Mailman, [Martin]

CONCORD HYMN see Ward, Robert

CONCORD JUNIOR SONG AND CHORUS BOOK *CCU
(Davison; Surette; Zanzig) SATB cmplt ed,
cloth SCHIRM.EC 15 $6.00, voc sc,cloth
SCHIRM.EC 16 $4.00 (C1709)

CONCUPISCENDO CONCUPISCIT ANIMA MEA see Lassus,
Roland de (Orlandus)

CONDITIONES see Werner, Sven Erik

CONDITOR ALME SIDERUM see Stadlmayr, Johann

CONFIANCE EN DIEU see Bach, Johann Sebastian

CONFIRM IN US, O GOD see Aichinger, Gregor,
Confirma Hoc, Deus

CONFIRM, O GOD see Kline

CONFIRMA HOC see Palestrina, Giovanni

CONFIRMA HOC, DEUS see Aichinger, Gregor

CONFIRMA HOC, DEUS see Byrd, William

CONFIRMA HOC DEUS see Callhoff, Herbert

CONFIRMA HOC, DEUS see Heiller, Anton

CONFIRMA HOC DEUS see Salieri, Antonio

CONFIRMA HOC DEUS see Wiltberger

CONFIRMATION BLESSING, A see Bunjes, Paul G.

CONFIRMATION PRAYER see Davidson, Charles

CONFITEANUR TIBI see Willaert, Adrian

CONFITEBIMUR TIBI DEUS see Lalande, Michel
Richard de

CONFITEBOR see Kaufmann, Ferdinand

CONFITEBOR see Pergolesi, Giovanni Battista

CONFITEBOR see Rozycki, (Jacek) Hyacinthus

CONFITEBOR TIBI see Binkerd, [Gordon]

CONFITEBOR TIBI see Krapf, Gerhard

CONFITEBOR TIBI DOMINE see Palestrina, Giovanni

CONFITEMI DOMINO see Haydn, (Johann) Michael

CONFITEMINI DOMINI see Constantini

CONFITEMINI DOMINI see Constantini, Alessandro

CONFITEMINI DOMINO see Ammon, Blasius

CONFITEMINI DOMINO see Constantini

CONFITEMINI DOMINO see Constantini, Alessandro

CONFITEMINI DOMINO see Haydn, (Johann) Michael

CONFITEMINI DOMINO see Palestrina, Giovanni

CONFITEMINI DOMINO see Schutz, Heinrich

CONFITEMINI DOMINO ET INVOCATE NOMEN EJUS see
Selle, Thomas

CONFRONTATION FROM THE BOOK OF JOB see Bergsma,
William Laurence

CONGAUDEAT
unis/SATB (easy) OXFORD 08.030 $.15 (C1710)

CONGRATULAMINI see Zangius, Nikolaus

CONGREGATIONAL MASS see Johnson, Robert Sherlaw

CONGREGATIONAL MASS see Lee, J.

CONGREGATIONAL MASS see Sherlaw-Johnson, Robert

CONGREGATIONAL MASS IN DORIAN MODE see Cabena,
Barrie

CONGREGATIONAL MASS IN THE DORIAN MODE see
Cabena, Barrie

CONLEY, D.
Crucifixion *Gd.Fri.
SATB oct SOUTHERN $.25 (C1711)

My Faith Looks Up To Thee
SATB oct SOUTHERN $.25 (C1712)

CONQUERING KINGS THEIR TITLES TAKE see Maunder,
J.H.

CONRADI, J.G.
Solnedgang
(Sorass, Lars) mix cor MUSIKK 156 s.p. see
from RELIGIOSE KORSANGER (C1713)

CONSECRATION see Blake, Leonard

CONSECRATION see Lorenz

CONSECRATION OF THE HOUSE see Beethoven, Ludwig
van

CONSERVA ME see Parsley, Osbert

CONSIDER, ALL YE PASSERS BY see Amner, John

CONSIDER AND HEAR ME see Pflueger, Carl

CONSIDER AND HEAR ME see Purcell, Henry

CONSIDER AND HEAR ME see Wooler, A.

CONSIDER MY MEDITATION see Glarum, L. Stanley

CONSIDER MY MEDITATION see Kirk, T.

CONSIDER THE LILIES see Bliss, Paul

CONSIDER THE LILIES see Brown

CONSIDER THE LILIES see Ogden, W.A.

CONSIDER THE LILIES see Posegate

CONSIDER THE LILIES see Scott, John Prindle

CONSIDER THE LILIES see Thygerson

CONSIDER THE LILIES see Willaert, Adrian, O
Gemma Clarissima

CONSIDER THE LILIES see Winslow, R.K.

CONSIDER THE LILIES OF THE FIELD see McCormick

CONSOLATIO see Petzold, Rudolf

CONSTANTINE, J.
Christmas Star *Xmas
SSA oct PRESSER 312-40767 $.35 (C1714)

CONSTANTINESCU, PAUL (1909-1963)
Byzantinisches Passions *Easter,ora
[Ger] SATB,SATBarB soli,orch (diff) BAREN.
BA 6030 rental contains also: Oster-
Oratorium (C1715)

Byzantinisches Weihnachts-Oratorium *Xmas,
ora
[Ger] SATB,SATB soli,orch (diff) BAREN.
BA 6029 rental (C1716)

Oster-Oratorium
see Constantinescu, Paul, Byzantinisches
Passions

CONSTANTINI
Confitemini Domini
(Field) [Lat/Eng] SSA,acap oct BOOSEY 5543
$.30 (C1717)

Confitemini Domino
3pt men cor sc ALSBACH&D s.p. (C1718)

CONSTANTINI, ALESSANDRO
Blessed Sacrament *see Ego Sum Panis Vivus

Confitemini Domini
girl cor SOUTHERN $.30 (C1719)

Confitemini Domino
"Now With One Accord" boy cor SOUTHERN $.25
(C1720)
(Stroud, Ray) "Now With One Accord" SSA/
TBB/SSATBB FOSTER MF 902 $.25 (C1721)

Ego Sum Panis Vivus *Commun/Fest,mot
[Lat] SATB,acap (med) MULLER M 26 s.p.
(C1722)
"Blessed Sacrament" [Lat] mix cor,acap oct
NOVELLO DM-26 s.p. (C1723)

Now With One Accord *see Confitemini Domino

CONSTANTINI, ARTEMIO
Ave Maria *BVM
[Lat] Mez,org ZANIBON 16 s.p. (C1724)

CONSTANTINI, FABIO
Hodie Beata Virgo *Fest,mot
[Lat] SATB,acap (med) MULLER M 50 s.p.
(C1725)
[Lat] mix cor,acap oct NOVELLO DM-50 s.p.
(C1726)
O Admirabile Commercium *Xmas/Circum,mot
[Lat] SATB,acap (med) MULLER M 7 s.p.
(C1727)
[Lat] mix cor,acap oct NOVELLO DM-7 s.p.
(C1728)

CONSTANTINO
Oxen, The *Xmas
SATB,acap WARNER W3754 $.30 (C1729)

CONSTITUES see Janacek, Leos

CONTEMPORARY CHRISTMAS CAROLS see McAfee, Don

CONTEMPORARY HYMN ANTHEMS *CC8UL,anthem/hymn,
Contemp
(Pottenger, Harold) cor,opt inst cmplt ed
LILLENAS MB-252 $1.50 (C1730)

CONTEMPORARY NOEL, A see Rogers

CONTEMPORARY SETTINGS OF PSALM TEXTS *CC13U,
Psalm,20th cent
SATB AMP A644 $2.00 contains works by:
Binkerd; Cowell; Ives; Nystedt; Piston; and
others (C1731)

CONTEMPORARY WORSHIP 1 *CC21UL,hymn
jr cor,kbd,gtr oct AUGSBURG 12-1157 $.50
(C1732)
CONTEMPORARY WORSHIP 1 - HYMNS *CC47U
cor,org CONCORDIA 3-1083 $.50 (C1733)

CONTEMPORARY WORSHIP 2 - THE HOLY COMMUNION
cor,org (setting 1, contemporary) CONCORDIA
3-1101 $.40, ipa (C1734)

CONTEMPORARY WORSHIP 2 - THE HOLY COMMUNION
cor,org (setting 2, hymnic) CONCORDIA 3-1102
$.40, ipa (C1735)

CONTEMPORARY WORSHIP 2 - THE HOLY COMMUNION
cor,org (setting 3, chant) CONCORDIA 3-1103
$.40 (C1736)

CONTEMPORARY WORSHIP 2 - THE HOLY COMMUNION
cor,org (setting 4, folk) CONCORDIA 3-1104
$.40 (C1737)

CONTEMPORARY WORSHIP 2 - THE HOLY COMMUNION
cor,org cmplt ed CONCORDIA 3-1089 $1.00
(C1738)

CONTEMPORARY WORSHIP 3 *Marriage
  cor,org (marriage rite with Holy Communion
  and a short marriage rite) CONCORDIA 3-1094
  $1.00   (C1739)

CONTEMPORARY WORSHIP 4 - HYMNS FOR BAPTISM AND
  HOLY COMMUNION *CC31U,hymn
  cor,org cor pts CONCORDIA 3-1100 $.40, sc
  CONCORDIA 3-1099 $1.25   (C1740)

CONTEMPORARY WORSHIP 5 - SERVICES OF THE WORD
  *Adv/Xmas/Easter/Gen/Lent
  cor,org cor pts CONCORDIA 3-1096 $.20   (C1741)
  cor,org cor pts CONCORDIA 3-1097 $.20   (C1742)
  cor,org cor pts CONCORDIA 3-1098 $.20   (C1743)
  cor,org cor pts sc CONCORDIA 3-1095 $1.75
                                          (C1744)

CONTENTMENT see Mozart, Wolfgang Amadeus

CONTRISTATUS EST REX DAVID see Deering, Richard

CONVERSE
  What A Friend We Have In Jesus
  (Harper) SATB oct PRO ART 1766 $.22 (C1745)

CONVERSE, CHARLES CROZAT (1832-1918)
  What A Friend We Have In Jesus
  (Boersma) SATB oct WORD CS-1999 $.30
                                          (C1746)
  (Lynn, G.) SAB oct PRESSER MC257 $.30
                                          (C1747)

CONVERTERE ANIMA MEA see Vene, Ruggero

CONWAY
  Collect
  SSA oct VOLKWEIN VB131 $.25   (C1748)

  He That Keepeth Israel
  SSA oct VOLKWEIN VB169 $.25   (C1749)

COOK
  Gentle Mary
  (Perrin) SSA THOMP.G G-124 s.p.   (C1750)
  (Rollinson) SATB THOMP.G G-534 s.p.   (C1751)

COOK, CLAUDE KARON
  Hallelujah For Christmas, A *Xmas
  SATB,org SCHIRM.EC 18 $.35 contains also:
  Perdue-Davis, Vernon, O How Amiable
                                          (C1752)

COOK, CLIFFORD A.
  Gentle Mary
  SATB,acap oct FISCHER,C CM-7074 $.25   (C1753)

COOK, E.T.
  Christ Being Raised From The Dead *Easter/
  Gen
  SATB/SAB (easy) oct OXFORD 42.126 $.25
                                          (C1754)
  Magnificat And Nunc Dimittis *Magnif/Nunc
  mix cor oct OXFORD 43.465 $.25   (C1755)

  Qui Creavit Coelum *carol
  unis CRAMER 33 s.p.   (C1756)

COOK, JOHN
  Author Of Light *Gen
  SATB,acap (med) oct OXFORD 43.341 $.25
                                          (C1757)

  Christ Is Our Cornerstone *anthem
  mix cor oct NOVELLO 28.1313.00 s.p. (C1758)

  Te Deum Laudamus *Te Deum
  unis&cong (G maj) NOVELLO 44.1314.08 s.p.
                                          (C1759)

COOKE
  Gentle Saviour, Hold My Hand *Eve
  (Lynn) SATB oct SOUTHERN $.25   (C1760)

  O Men From The Fields
  unis (very easy) OXFORD 81.087 $.20 (C1761)

  Ode On St. Cecilia's Day
  SATB,STB soli (diff) voc sc OXFORD 56.578
  $4.45, cor pts OXFORD 56.579 $1.20
                                          (C1762)

COOKE, ARNOLD (1906-   )
  Lord, Thou Hast Been Our Refuge *Psalm
  SATB,acap (diff) voc sc OXFORD 43.910 $1.25
                                          (C1763)

  Loving Shepherd Of Thy Sheep *Gen
  SSATB,acap (easy) oct OXFORD 43.389 $.35
                                          (C1764)

  Magnificat And Nunc Dimittis (composed with
  Tucker) *Magnif/Nunc
  oct ROYAL 112 s.p.   (C1765)

  O Sing Unto The Lord *anthem
  mix cor oct NOVELLO 28.1412.09 s.p. (C1766)

  Three Wise Kings *Epiph
  unis (very easy) OXFORD 81.073 $.25 (C1767)
  unis (easy) oct OXFORD $.25   (C1768)
  (Sargent) SSAATTBB,acap (easy) OXFORD
  84.154 $.25   (C1769)

  While Shepherds Watched *Xmas
  SA/SS (very easy) OXFORD 44.022 $.30
                                          (C1770)

COOKE, [BENJAMIN] (1734-1793)
  Magnificat And Nunc Dimittis *Magnif/Nunc
  SATB (G maj) oct NOVELLO 02.0634.02 s.p.
                                          (C1771)

COOKE, S.C.
  Fear Not, O Land
  2pt ASHDOWN E.A.224 s.p.   (C1772)
  SATB ENOCH EC242 s.p.   (C1773)

  Glory To God In The Highest
  SATB ENOCH EC197 s.p.   (C1774)

  This Is The Day *Easter
  SATB,org (easy) oct WILLIS 941 $.12 (C1775)

  Why Seek Ye The Living?
  SATB ENOCH EC99 s.p.   (C1776)

COOMBS, CHARLES WHITNEY (1859-1940)
  And God Shall Wipe Away All Tears *Bibl
  4pt mix cor,A solo oct SCHIRM.G 3879 $.25
                                          (C1777)

  As It Began To Dawn *Easter,Bibl
  SSSABar oct SCHIRM.G 3759 $.25   (C1778)

  Brightest And Best *Xmas,Bibl
  4pt mix cor,ST soli,vln,harp oct SCHIRM.G
  6590 $.30   (C1779)

COOMBS, FRANCIS
  If Ye Love Me *Gen/Pent
  SATB,kbd (med easy) oct CONCORDIA 98-1215
  $.25   (C1780)

COOPER
  Great Is The Lord
  (Angell) SATB SHAWNEE A 606 $.30   (C1781)

  He's For Real *Xmas
  SATB oct PRO ART 2720 $.35   (C1782)

  Hymns To The Trinity *hymn
  2pt jr cor FISCHER,C CM 7345 $.20   (C1783)

  Let Us Break Bread Together *Commun
  SATB oct FISCHER,C SIG.$.25   (C1784)

  Lord Reigneth, The (Psalm 93)
  (Angell) SATB SHAWNEE A 641 $.25   (C1785)

  Once In Royal David's City *Xmas
  unis jr cor oct FISCHER,C CM-7342 $.25
                                          (C1786)

  Psalm 93 *see Lord Reigneth, The

  Yuletide For Teentime *CC18U,Xmas
  jr cor oct FISCHER,C O-3881 $1.25   (C1787)

COOPER, DAVID S.
  Sancta Maria *BVM
  SSSSAAAA,acap PEER $.35   (C1788)

COOPER, IRVIN
  Alleluia! Jesus Christ Is Born Today *Xmas
  SSATTBB FISCHER,C CM-6909 $.20   (C1789)

  Cantate Deo *CCU,hymn/mot
  S&camb&Bar FISCHER,C O 4149 $1.00 contains
  works by: Arcadelt; Cooper; Mozart;
  Palestrina; and others   (C1790)

  Changing Voices In Junior High *CCU
  jr cor FISCHER,C O 3875 $1.50   (C1791)

  Festival Processional *Fest/Proces
  SATB,opt brass voc sc FISCHER,C O-4490
  $1.00, ipa   (C1792)

  God Gave Us Song
  SATB,orch/band (med diff) FISCHER,C CM-7298
  $.30   (C1793)

  Ring The Bells *Xmas
  SATB FISCHER,C CM-7350 $.25   (C1794)

  Sing, Boys, Sing *CC10U
  S&camb&Bar FISCHER,C O 4029 $.85   (C1795)

  Songs For Pre-Teen Time *CC23U
  jr cor FISCHER,C O 3953 $1.00   (C1796)

  Turn Ye To Me
  SATB,acap FISCHER,C CM-7479 $.25   (C1797)

  Yuletime For Teentime *CC18U
  S&camb&Bar/unis jr cor FISCHER,C O 3881
  $1.00   (C1798)

COOPER, J.
  Exaudi Domine *Easter
  SATB oct PRESSER MC478 $1.00   (C1799)

  He Is Risen *Easter
  SS (easy) OXFORD 42.401 $.25   (C1800)

COOPER, JOHN
  see COPERARIO, GIOVANNI

COOPER, R.
  Gloria In Excelsis Deo *Xmas,mot
  (Collins, H.B.) [Lat] SSSA CHESTER s.p.
                                          (C1801)

COOPER, ROBERT
  Gloria In Excelsis Deo
  SSAA,acap SCHIRM.EC $.20   (C1802)

COOPER, ROSE MARIE (1937-   )
  Morning Star *Xmas,cant
  unis FISCHER,C O-4845 $1.00   (C1803)

COOPER SQUARE CHORISTER, THE see Whitner, Mary
  Elizabeth

COOPERSMITH, HARRY (1902-   )
  High Holiday Services
  2pt TRANSCON. TCL 340 $3.75   (C1804)

  Mi-Shirey Beth Ha-Kneseth *Sab-Eve
  2pt TRANSCON. TCL 330 $2.50   (C1805)

COOTS
  At The Cross Of God
  (Adams) SATB oct HUNTZINGER 7008 $.20
                                          (C1806)

COPE
  City Of God
  SATB THOMP.G G-558 s.p.   (C1807)

  Jubilate (Psalm 100)
  SATB,org oct BOOSEY 5761 $.35   (C1808)

  Psalm 100 *see Jubilate

COPE, CECIL
  Author Of Life Divine *Commun/Gen
  SATB,acap (easy) oct OXFORD 43.042 $.25
                                          (C1809)

  He Is Risen *Easter
  2-4pt oct OXFORD $.25   (C1810)

  Pleasure It Is *Gen/Harv
  1-2pt (very easy) oct OXFORD $.25   (C1811)

COPES, V. EARLE
  Eternal God
  SATB&speak cor (med) ABINGDON APM-413 $.25
                                          (C1812)

  For The Bread *Commun
  SATB (easy) ABINGDON APM-115 $.22   (C1813)

  Go Tell It In The City
  SATB (diff) ABINGDON APM-880 $.45   (C1814)

  Harvest Carol
  4pt mix cor,acap oct SCHIRM.G 10894 $.25
                                          (C1815)

COPES, V. EARLE (cont'd.)
  Hope Of The World
  SAB (easy) ABINGDON APM-612 $.25   (C1816)

  I Thank Thee, O Lord *Thanks
  SATB (easy) ABINGDON APM-167 $.24   (C1817)

  New Song, A
  SATB (diff) ABINGDON APM-195 $.25   (C1818)

  Psalm 121
  SATB,acap (med) ABINGDON APM-480 $.25
                                          (C1819)

  Turn Back, O Man
  SAB/SATB (easy) ABINGDON APM-327 $.25
                                          (C1820)

  When I Survey The Wondrous Cross *Lent
  4pt mix cor oct SCHIRM.G 10843 $.25 (C1821)

COPLAND, AARON (1900-   )
  Goin' My Way
  (Wilson) SSA oct AGAPE JW 7776 $.30 (C1822)

  I Wonder Why
  (Wilson) SATB oct AGAPE JW 7775 $.30
                                          (C1823)

  In The Beginning
  mix cor,Mez solo,acap voc sc BOOSEY $2.00
                                          (C1824)

  Love Came Down At Christmas *Xmas
  (Wilson) unis oct AGAPE CF 134 $.25 (C1825)

  Reach Out To Your Neighbor
  (Wilson) 2pt mix cor oct AGAPE CF 157 $.30
                                          (C1826)

COPLAS see Taverner, John

COPLEY
  Good Christian Men, Rejoice And Sing
  SAB oct BELWIN 60536 $.30   (C1827)

  King's Men, The
  unis oct BELWIN 05786 $.30   (C1828)

  Let Thy Mercy Be Upon Us *Gen
  SATB GALLEON GCS3001   (C1829)

  Psalm 150
  SATB&unis,pno/org LENGNICK s.p.   (C1830)

  Twelve Short Introits *CC12U,Introit
  1-3pt treb cor LENGNICK s.p.   (C1831)

COPLEY, I.A.
  First Christmas Day, The *Xmas
  2pt ASHDOWN E.A.307 s.p.   (C1832)

  Little Child There Is Yborn, A *Xmas
  unis jr cor/unis wom cor CURWEN 72594 s.p.
                                          (C1833)

COPLEY, R. EVAN
  Four Anthems For Treble Voices *CC4U,anthem
  unis/SA (easy) ABINGDON APM-213 $.35
                                          (C1834)

  Glory To God In The Highest
  SATB (med) ABINGDON APM-287 $.50   (C1835)

  Jesus Christ Is Risen Today *Easter
  SATB (med) ABINGDON APM-831 $1.25, ipa
                                          (C1836)

  Salvation Belongeth Unto The Lord
  SATB,acap (med) ABINGDON APM-145 $.22
                                          (C1837)

  Seven General Anthems For Unison- Treble
  Voices *CC7U,anthem
  unis treb cor (med easy) ABINGDON APM-341
  $.60   (C1838)

  Seven Treble Choir Anthems For The Christian
  Year *CC7U,Adv/Xmas/Easter/Lent/Palm/
  Pent/Trin,anthem
  unis (easy) ABINGDON APM-332 $.75   (C1839)

COR ARCA see Leoncini, Lorenzo

COR JESU see Gounod, Charles Francois

COR JESU see La Rosa, J.

COR JESU see Mangone, Gioacchino

COR JESU see Moioli, Romano

COR JESU see Volpi, Edoardo

COR JESU FLAGRANS see Arnaldi, Antonio

COR JESU FLAGRANS see Nicolosi, Salvatore

COR JESU FLAGRENS see Bottigliero, Eduardo

COR JESU FLAGRENS see Volpi, Edoardo

COR JESU, FONS VITAE see Campion, M.

COR JESU SACRATISSIMUM see Fabiani, Angelo

COR MUNDUM CREA IN ME, DEUS see Ecchienus,
  Caspar

CORALE E ARIA see Peragallo, Mario

CORALE E ARIA see Peragallo, Mario

CORALE E ARIA see Peragallo, Mario

CORBEIL, PIERRE DE
  Little Lyking, The *Xmas,13th cent
  (Niles) 4pt mix cor,SMez soli,acap oct
  SCHIRM.G 10110 $.20   (C1840)

CORBITT
  O Praise The Lord
  SATB oct SACRED S-81 $.35   (C1841)

CORDE NATUS see Thiman, Eric Harding

CORELLI, ARCANGELO (1653-1713)
  Bless The Lord, O Bless His Holy Name
  (Stone) SAB,org/pno BOSTON 13133 $.30
                                          (C1842)

  Blessed Is The Man
  (Stone) SATB,org/pno BOSTON 13593 $.35
                                          (C1843)
  (Stone) SAB,org/pno BOSTON 12465 $.40
                                          (C1844)

CORFE, JOSEPH (1740-1820)
I Will Magnify Thee, O Lord
(Holman, Derek) 2pt oct NOVELLO 33.0112.05
s.p.   (C1845)

My Voice Shalt Thou Hear
(Holman, Derek) unis oct NOVELLO 33.0111.07
s.p.   (C1846)

Psalm 65   *see Thou, O God, Art Praised In
Sion

Thou, O God, Art Praised In Sion (Psalm 65)
Harv/Thanks
(Harker, Clifford) 2pt (easy) oct OXFORD
44.418 $.25   (C1847)

CORI DELLA PIETA MORTA see Bucchi, Valentino

CORIGLIANO, JOHN (1938-   )
Christmas At The Cloisters *Xmas
4pt mix cor,acap oct SCHIRM.G 11593 $.30
(C1848)

CORINA, JOHN
He That Would Love Life
SATB (med) ABINGDON APM-604 $.35   (C1849)

Psalm 118
SATB,brass (med) ABINGDON APM-552 $.60, ipa
(C1850)

CORINTHIANS 13 *Bibl
SATB CHARTER $.35   (C1851)

CORINTHIANS, THE see Rorem, Ned

CORK, PETER
Holly Is Up, The *Xmas
4pt mix cor,S solo oct CURWEN 11126 $.25
(C1852)

CORNELIUS
Three Kings, The *Xmas
(Collins) SATB,acap oct PRO ART 1534 $.25
(C1853)

CORNELIUS, PETER (1824-1874)
Christ Child, The *Xmas
(Allen) SATB&opt jr cor,opt S solo oct
GALLEON GCS 1006   (C1854)
(Heiberg) SATB&jr cor,opt S solo oct FOX
R156 $.30   (C1855)

Christmas Song *Xmas
(Damrosch) mix cor,med solo,acap oct
SCHIRM.G 2557 $.25   (C1856)

Christmas Tree, The
(Fredrickson) 3pt jr cor/SSA (med) FISCHER,
C R 6080 $.22   (C1857)

Das Grosse Domine
(Hasse) [Lat] SATB,T solo,orch SCHOTT
rental   (C1858)

Der Tod, Das Ist Die Kuhle Nacht *Op.11,No.1
8pt mix cor,acap cor pts BREITKOPF-W
CHB-4853 rental   (C1859)

Die Konige *Xmas
(Jochum, Otto) [Ger] SATB,acap (med) MULLER
SM 511 sc s.p., cor pts s.p.   (C1860)

I Kneel In Adoration
(Frank) SATB oct FOX PS176 $.35   (C1861)

Infant Christ, The *Xmas
(Hall) 4pt mix cor,high solo oct SCHIRM.G
8719 $.25   (C1862)

Kings, The *Xmas
(Davies L H) 2pt ASHDOWN E.A.316 s.p.
(C1863)

Liebe Dir Ergeb' Ich Mich!
(Frank) "Lord Of Love, To Thee I Flee" oct
FOX MM26 $.25   (C1864)

Lord Of Love, To Thee I Flee *see Liebe Dir
Ergeb' Ich Mich!

Requiem Aeternam *Req
[Lat] TTBB SCHOTT s.p.   (C1865)
boy cor SOUTHERN $.30   (C1866)
men cor sc ALSBACH&D s.p.   (C1867)
[Lat/Eng] TTBB BROUDE,A. 184 $.30   (C1868)

Seele, Vergiss Sie Nicht *Req
6pt mix cor,opt strings sc BREITKOPF-L
rental   (C1869)

Stabat Mater
[Lat] SATB&men cor,SATB soli,orch SCHOTT
rental   (C1870)

Three Kings From Persian Lands (composed with
Nicolai, Philipp) *Xmas
(Wolff) SATB,med solo,org oct LAWSON 51373
$.25   (C1871)

Three Kings From Persian Lands Afar *Xmas
(Paget) mix cor CURWEN 80903 s.p.   (C1872)

Three Kings, The *Epiph
(Atkins, Ivor) SATB,solo,acap (easy) oct
OXFORD 43.200 $.35   (C1873)
(Hugh-Jones, Enid) SSAA,solo,acap (med) oct
OXFORD 44.420 $.25   (C1874)

Tu Es Petrus
SATB,acap RICORDI-ENG SY154 s.p.   (C1875)

CORNELL
I Will Sing Unto The Lord
SATB,acap oct PRO ART 2487 $.30   (C1876)

CORNER'S CRADLE SONG (HE SMILES WITHIN HIS
CRADLE) *Xmas,carol,Ger
(Reuter, J.F.) unis&desc (easy) oct CONCORDIA
98-1529 $.22   (C1877)

CORNISH CAROLS *CC17L,Xmas,carol,Eng
(Davey, J.L.) SATB ALLANS 335 s.p.   (C1878)

CORNYSH
Woefully Arrayed
(Wulstan) SATB CHESTER s.p.   (C1879)

CORONA DI SACRE CANZONE see Ghedini, Giorgio
Federico

CORONA DI SACRE CANZONE see Ghedini, Giorgio
Federico

CORONA HARMONICA see Demantius, Christoph

CORONA SPINEA see Taverner, John

CORONARO, ANTONIO
Divo Antonio *Mass
[Lat] TTB,org sc ZANIBON 3477 s.p., voc pt
ZANIBON s.p.   (C1880)

Vademecum Per Le Funzioni Religiose *CCU,
hymn/mot
[Lat] 3 eq voices ZANIBON 338 s.p.   (C1881)

CORONARO, BENVENUTO GELLIO (1863-1916)
Inno A S. Luigi Gonzaga *ASD
[Lat] unis,org sc ZANIBON 672 s.p., cor pts
ZANIBON 673 FSP   (C1882)

CORONATION AND VERSE ANTHEMS see Blow

CORONATION ANTHEMS see Handel, George Frideric

CORONATION MASS see Liszt, Franz

CORONATION MASS see Mozart, Wolfgang Amadeus

CORONATION MASS see Mozart, Wolfgang Amadeus,
Coronation Mass

CORONATION TE DEUM see Walton, William

CORPORIS MYSTERIUM see Palestrina, Giovanni

CORPUS CHRISTI see Green, Ray

CORPUS CHRISTI see Heseltine, Philip

CORPUS CHRISTI see Jillett, David

CORPUS CHRISTI CAROL see Britten, Benjamin

CORPUS CHRISTI CAROL see Hesford, Brian

CORPUS CHRISTI MASS see Waters, Peter

CORPUS CHRISTI MYSTICUM see Kronsteiner, Herman

CORPUS DOMINI see Gerli, Giovanni

CORRADINI, VASCO LODOVICO
Dopo La Communione
see Due Canzoncine

Due Canti Al SS. Sacramento *CC2U,Commun
[Lat] unis ZANIBON 48 s.p.   (C1883)

Due Canzoncine *Commun,hymn
[Lat] unis sc ZANIBON 54 s.p.
contains: Dopo La Communione; Prima Della
Communione   (C1884)

Due "Tu Es Sacerdos"
[Lat] sc ZANIBON 50 s.p., cor pts ZANIBON
51 s.p.
contains: Tu Es Sacerdos (3 eq voices,
org); Tu Es Sacerdos (3pt mix cor,org)
(C1885)

Ecce Panis
see SEI MOTTETTI EUCARISTICI

Popule Meus *Easter
[Lat] 3 eq voices,acap ZANIBON 1251 s.p.
(C1886)

Prima Della Communione
see Due Canzoncine

Proprium Missae In Festo S. Benedicti Abatis
*ASD
[Lat] unis ZANIBON 52 s.p.   (C1887)

Tu Es Sacerdos
see Due "Tu Es Sacerdos"
see Due "Tu Es Sacerdos"

CORRE AL SUO FIN MIA VITA see Fonteijo,
Giovanni

CORREA, CARLOS (1680-ca. 1747)
O Vos Omnes
see Two Motets

Plorans Ploravit
see Two Motets

Two Motets *mot
(med easy) oct OXFORD 42.893 $.35
contains: O Vos Omnes (SATB,acap)
(Psntd); Plorans Ploravit (SATB) (Gen)
(C1888)

CORRELL
Calvary's Love *Easter
(Collins) SATB oct LILLENAS AT-1025 $.30
(C1889)

CORSI
Adoramus Te
(Christiansen, O.) SATB KJOS 2 $.30   (C1890)

Adoramus Te, Christi *mot
[Lat] SATB RICORDI-ENG SY176 s.p.   (C1891)

CORSI, GIUSEPPE (fl. 1659-1681)
Adoramus Te, Christe *Easter/Lent,mot
[Lat] SATB,acap oct GIA G555 $.25   (C1892)
4pt mix cor,acap oct SCHIRM.G 6259 $.25
(C1893)
(Cain) SATB oct FOX R181 $.25   (C1894)
(Cain) TTBB oct FOX R180 $.25   (C1895)
(Greyson) "We Adore Thee" SATB oct BOURNE
ES15 $.30   (C1896)
(Scott) SSA oct FOX R117 $.30   (C1897)
(Scott) girl cor SOUTHERN $.25   (C1898)

We Adore Thee *see Adoramus Te, Christe

CORTES, RAMIRO (1933-   )
Missa Brevis
SSA oct PRESSER 312-40300 $.35, ipr   (C1899)

CORTESE, LUIGI (1899-   )
David *Bibl/ora
mix cor,BarS/BarMez soli,org/orch voc sc
ZERBONI 4505 s.p., ipr   (C1900)

Inclina, Domine, Aurem Tuam
mix cor,org/orch voc sc ZERBONI 6795 s.p.,
ipr   (C1901)

CORWIN
Sleep Now On Thy Natal Day (from Miracle,
The) (composed with Murray, Bain) Xmas
SATB oct MCA   (C1902)
(Murray) 2pt oct MCA   (C1903)

Sleep On Thy Natal Day (from Miracle, The)
Xmas
(Murray) SSA/SSAA oct MCA   (C1904)

CORY
Carol Based On "The First Noel" *Xmas,carol
SATBB,acap AMP A167 $.25   (C1905)

CORY, GEORGE
Ave Maria
SATB GENERAL CH169 $.25   (C1906)

Lord's Prayer, The *Bibl/prayer
SATB GENERAL CH76 $.40   (C1907)

COSSETTI, GIO. BATTA.
Exultet Orbis
see INNI DE COMUNE

Inno Eucaristico Dei Cattolici D'Italia
*Commun/Proces,hymn
[It] unis,org/inst sc ZANIBON 1382BIS s.p.,
voc sc ZANIBON 1380 s.p., cor pts ZANIBON
1381 s.p., ipa   (C1908)

Missa In Hon. Mariae SS. Auxiliatricis *Mass
[Lat] 2pt,org sc ZANIBON 3939 s.p., voc pt
ZANIBON s.p.   (C1909)

Missa In Hon. S. Hilarii Martyris Carniae
Patroni *Mass
[Lat] 3 eq voices,org sc ZANIBON 3935 s.p.,
voc pt ZANIBON s.p.   (C1910)

O Bone Jesu
see TRE CANTICI AL S. CUORE DI GESU

Pei Nostri Soldati
cor ZANIBON 607 s.p.   (C1911)

Preghiera Dei Bimbi D'Italia
unis ZANIBON 606 s.p.   (C1912)

COSTA
I Will Extol Thee *Bibl
(Rees) 4pt mix cor oct SCHIRM.G 3612 $.30
(C1913)
I Will Extol Thee, O Lord (from Eli)
(Ehret) SATB,S solo oct PRO ART 1565 $.22
(C1914)

COSTANTINI, MARIO
Inno Ceciliano *ASD,hymn
unis,org ZANIBON 3258 s.p.   (C1915)

COSTELEY
Noel: Sus, Debout, Gentilz Pasteurs
(Expert) [Fr] SATB,acap oct SALABERT-US
$.65   (C1916)

Shepherds Come Away
(Expert) [Eng/Fr] SATB,acap oct SALABERT-US
$.35   (C1917)

COSTELEY, GUILLAUME (1531-1606)
Allon, Gay Bergeres
(Cramer) "Come Ye Gay Shepherds" [Eng/Fr]
SSA,acap MARKS 4482 $.30   (C1918)
(Cramer) "Come Ye Gay Shepherds" [Eng/Fr]
SATB,acap MARKS 4292 $.30   (C1919)

Allons, Gay Bergeres
(Shaw; Parker) [Eng/Fr] 4pt mix cor,acap
oct SCHIRM.G 10178 $.35   (C1920)

Come Ye Gay Shepherds *see Allon, Gay
Bergeres

Noel *Xmas,carol
(Brun, L'abbe) 4pt mix cor,acap oct DURAND
(C1921)

Now, Arise Ye Shepherd's Mild *see Sus,
Debout Gentilz Pasteurs

Sus, Debout Gentilz Pasteurs *Xmas
(Klein) "Now, Arise Ye Shepherd's Mild"
[Eng/Fr] 4pt mix cor,acap oct SCHIRM.G
11860 $.40   (C1922)

COSTELEY, R.
Come Now, Happy Shepherds *Xmas
(Rossi, N.) SATB,acap oct PRESSER 312-40500
$.30   (C1923)

COTTON
Caedmon's Hymn Of Creation *hymn
unis (easy) OXFORD 81.129 $.25   (C1924)

COUILLART
Viri Galilalei *16th cent
(Cartier, Anita; Carol, Henri; Gagnepain,
Bernard) [Lat] SATB OUVRIERES s.p.
(C1925)

COULD JESUS HEAR THE SOUNDS TO COME see
Bristol, L.

COULD JESUS HEAR THE SOUNDS TO COME? see
Bristol, Lee H., Jr.

COULD THIS BE A SPECIAL NIGHT? see Martin

COULD YE NOT WATCH see Bright, Houston

COULD YE NOT WATCH? see Stainer, John

COULD YE NOT WATCH WITH ME see Bright

COULDN'T HEAR NOBODY PRAY *spir
(Bartholomew) 4pt mix cor,T solo,acap oct
SCHIRM.G 8914 $.25   (C1926)
(Burleigh) SSA RICORDI-ENG LD462 s.p. (C1927)
(Burleigh; Vene) SAB,S/B solo oct COLOMBO
1985 $.25   (C1928)
(Burleigh; Vene) SSA,S solo oct COLOMBO 1978
$.25   (C1929)
(Burleigh; Vene) SATB,S/T solo oct COLOMBO
278 $.25   (C1930)
(Cain) 8pt mix cor,acap oct SCHIRM.G 7765
$.30   (C1931)
(Sowande) SATB,S solo,acap oct COLOMBO 1895
$.35   (C1932)

COULTHARD, JEAN (1908-   )
Signature Of God, The
SA,pno oct BERANDOL 915C6AS $.50   (C1933)

COUNT DOWN OR COVENANT see Piket, Frederick

COUNT IT ALL JOY see Goode, J.

COUNT IT ALL JOY see Goode, Jack C.

COUNT YOUR BLESSINGS see O'Hara, Geoffrey

COUNTRY GIRL'S FAREWELL see Jacob, Gordon

COUPE, ALINDA B.
Chapel Choir, The *CCU
SA/jr cor BELWIN $1.50   (C1934)

COUPER
Christ, Our Lord, Has Risen *Easter
SATB oct SOUTHERN $.25   (C1935)

I Saw Three Ships *Xmas
2pt jr cor,hndbl FISCHER,C CM 7598 $.20   (C1936)

In Christ There Is No East Or West
SA,oct bells oct SACRED S-5378 $.35 (C1937)

Let All Mortal Flesh Keep Silence
SATB FLAMMER A 5323 $.30   (C1938)

Of The Father's Love Begotten *Adv
jr cor&sr cor,hndbl (med easy) FISCHER,C
CM 7400 $.25   (C1939)
SATB oct FISCHER,C CM-7400 $.30   (C1940)

Rejoice In The Lord, O You Righteous
SA/TB FLAMMER E5088 $.30   (C1941)

COUPER, ALINDA B.
Christmas Joy *Xmas
SA (med) ABINGDON APM-571 $.35   (C1942)

Festival Introits *CCU,Easter/Fest/Palm,
Introit
SATB (med) ABINGDON APM-780 $.50   (C1943)

Praise And Supplication
SATB (med) ABINGDON APM-854 $.35   (C1944)

COUPER, BERT F.
For All The Saints *ASD/Rembrnc
SATB ALLANS 248 s.p.   (C1945)

COUPERIN
Be Joyful In The Lord
(Jewell) girl cor SOUTHERN $.25   (C1946)

Earth Is The Lord's, The *anthem
(Nelson) unis treb cor,cont,inst (med) oct
AUGSBURG 0304 $.30   (C1947)

COUPERIN, ARMAND-LOUIS (1725-1789)
In Thee, O Lord, Is Fullness Of Joy
(Vree) SA SOUTHERN $.30   (C1948)

COUPERIN, FRANCOIS (1668-1733)
Be Joyful In The Lord *Gen
SS,kbd (med easy) oct CONCORDIA 98-1734
$.25   (C1949)

Carol Of The Shepherds
(Jewell) SA/TB FLAMMER E5042 $.25   (C1950)

Christ Is Arisen *Easter
SS,kbd (med diff) oct CONCORDIA 98-1733
$.30   (C1951)

Christ The Lord Is Risen Again *Easter
SS/SA,kbd (med easy) oct CONCORDIA 98-1893
$.25   (C1952)

Come Let Us Sing Unto The Lord
(Vree) 2pt boy cor/SA,pno/org oct LAWSON
51346 $.30   (C1953)

In Thee, O Lord, Is Fullness Of Joy *Cnfrm/
Commun/Gen/Trin
SA,kbd (med easy) oct CONCORDIA 98-2059
$.30   (C1954)

Lamentations Of Jeremiah
(Boepple, P.) SSAA oct PRESSER 352-00014
$.50   (C1955)

Make A Joyful Noise Unto The Lord *Cnfrm/
Ded/Epiph/Gen
SAB,kbd (med easy) oct CONCORDIA 98-2041
$.40   (C1956)

O Clap Your Hands *Asc/Gen
SA,kbd (med diff) oct CONCORDIA 98-1821
$.30   (C1957)
SAB,kbd (med diff) oct CONCORDIA 98-1822
$.30   (C1958)

O Come Let Us Sing (Psalm 95)
(Jewell, Kenneth W.) SA,org/pno oct WORLD
ESA-1923-2 $.45   (C1959)

Psalm 95 *see O Come Let Us Sing

Sing Unto The Lord A New Song *Ded/Gen
SA,kbd (easy/med diff) oct CONCORDIA
98-1709 $.25   (C1960)

Star Carol, A (Saw You Never In The Twilight)
*Xmas/Epiph,carol
SA,kbd (med easy) oct CONCORDIA 98-1711
$.25   (C1961)

COURAGE, BROTHER see Mendelssohn-Bartholdy,
Felix

COVENANT OF THE RAINBOW see Crosse, Gordon

COVENTRY ANTHEM see Arnatt, Ronald

COVENTRY ANTIPHON see Howells, Herbert Norman

COVENTRY CAROL (from Anthology Of Carols, An)
Xmas,carol,Eng
see Six Christmas Carols, Set III
see Three Early Christmas Carols
unis/SAB (very easy) OXFORD 08.020 $.15   (C1962)
SATB ALLANS 258 s.p.   (C1963)
(Davis, K.) SA,pno SCHIRM.EC 1037 $.20   (C1964)

(Davis, K.K.) SATB,acap SCHIRM.EC 1199 $.20   (C1965)
(Gilbert) TTBB,acap (med easy) OXFORD 85.002
$.25   (C1966)
(Goodman, Joseph) 2pt,drums (med) PRESSER
$.30   (C1967)
(Luboff, Norman) SSATB oct WALTON 3010 $.30   (C1968)
(Rowley) SA BOOSEY-CAN s.p.   (C1969)
(Smith) 4pt mix cor,high solo,acap oct
SCHIRM.G 11560 $.30   (C1970)
(Stone) SSA oct PRO ART 1786 $.30   (C1971)
(Stone) SATB,acap oct PRO ART 1407 $.30   (C1972)
(Stone) SAB oct PRO ART 2195 $.30   (C1973)
(Terri) SATB,opt pno/harp,opt fl/vln oct
LAWSON 673 $.35   (C1974)
(Terri) SATB,opt fl&vln ALLANS 462 s.p.   (C1975)
(Vaughan Williams) TTB,acap (easy, contains
also: Lord At First, The) OXFORD 41.907
$.25 see from Nine Carols   (C1976)
(Warland, D.) SATB,acap (med easy) oct
CONCORDIA 98-1928 $.25   (C1977)
(Wilson) men cor oct SPRATT 610 $.30   (C1978)
(Wulstan, David) SAB CHESTER s.p. contains
also: Christmas Eve Carol (unis,S solo);
Festa Dies Agitur (unis)   (C1979)

COVENTRY CAROL see Anonymous

COVENTRY CAROL see Kirk

COVENTRY CAROL see Mc Cabe

COVENTRY CAROL see Schroth, G.

COVENTRY CAROL see Stone, L.

COVENTRY CAROL see Wallace

COVENTRY CAROL, THE *Xmas,carol
(Geehl, Henry) SATB ENOCH EC215 s.p.   (C1980)
(Rowley, Alec) 2pt ENOCH TP151 s.p. contains
also: Carol On Greensleeves; Furry Day
Carol, The   (C1981)
(Sharpe) cor&desc CRAMER 55 s.p.   (C1982)

COVENTRY CAROL, THE see Riegger, Wallingford

COVENTRY CAROL, THE see Scott

COVENTRY MASS, THE see Howells, Herbert Norman

COVENTRY MASS, THE *Mass
cong ROYAL s.p. see from Music For The Holy
Communion   (C1983)

COVERDALE'S CAROL (from Anthology Of Carols,
An)
see Quem Pastores
see Three Christmas Carols

COVERDALE'S CAROL see Pfautsch, Lloyd

COWARD, J.M.
Christmas Bells *Xmas
cor oct HART s.p.   (C1984)

COWELL, HENRY DIXON (1897-1965)
Creator, The
SSAATTBB,inst voc sc PETERS 66084 rental,
ipr   (C1985)

Edson Hymns And Fuguing Tunes, Part I *CCU,
hymn
SSAATB,org/opt orch AMP A375 $.35   (C1986)

Edson Hymns And Fuguing Tunes, Part II *CCU,
hymn
SSAATB,org/opt orch AMP A376 $.40   (C1987)

Garden Hymn For Easter *Easter
SATB,acap oct PRESSER 312-40224 $.30   (C1988)

Luther's Carol For His Son *Xmas
TTBB,acap oct MCA   (C1989)

Psalm 121
SATB,acap AMP A280 $.25   (C1990)

Road Leads Into Tommorow, The
SSAATTBB AMP A151 $.20   (C1991)

Supplication
unis wom cor,org,2trp,2trom,opt timp sc
PETERS 6322 $3.50   (C1992)

Sweet Was The Song The Virgin Sung
SATB AMP A335 $.25   (C1993)

COWLEY CAROL BOOK, THE *CCUL,Asc/Xmas/Easter
(Woodward, G.R.; Wood, Charles) cor/cong oct
MOWBRAY 65016 6 s.p.
see also: Come, Listen To My Story; Earth
Today Rejoices; Noble Stem Of Jesse, The;
Shepherds In The Field Abiding; This
Joyful Easter-Tide; Up! Good Christen
Folk, And Listen; Virin Most Pure, A   (C1994)

COWPER
O For A Closer Walk With God
(Horsky) SATB oct KENDOR $.25   (C1995)

COX
It's Real
(McLellan) SATB oct LILLENAS AN-1631 $.25   (C1996)
(Skillings) SSATB oct LILLENAS AT-1079 $.25   (C1997)

COX, A.
O, Be Joyful In The Lord
SATB,acap oct PRESSER 312-40216 $.30   (C1998)

This Child Of Life *Xmas,cant
SSA,S solo (med) voc sc OXFORD 46.126
$1.60, ipr   (C1999)

COZENS, J.
Christ Is Arisen *see Lotti, Antonio

CRADLE CAROL *Xmas
(Deale) SSATB,acap (med easy) OXFORD 84.016
$.30 see from Four Old Carols   (C2000)

CRADLE CAROL see Deale

CRADLE CAROL, A see Purvis, Richard

CRADLE HYMN *Xmas,carol,US
(Anderson, W.H.) SATB oct LESLIE 4016 see
from Two Christmas Carols, Set 2   (C2001)
(Walker, D.S.) unis, Orff inst (med easy) oct
CONCORDIA 98-2077 $.30   (C2002)

CRADLE HYMN see Ehret, Walter, Harmonica Sacra

CRADLE HYMN see Frackenpohl

CRADLE HYMN, A see Christiansen, F. Melius

CRADLE HYMN, A see Fovargue, Eva

CRADLE HYMN, A see France, William E.

CRADLE HYMN, A see Lavarque

CRADLE HYMN OF THE VIRGIN see Harris, Mater
Doloroso

CRADLE IN BETHLEHEM see Quilter, Roger

CRADLE SONG *Xmas,carol
see Three Polish Carols
(Bancroft, H.H.) unis oct LESLIE 4020 see
from Two Christmas Carols, Set 2   (C2003)

CRADLE SONG see Angel

CRADLE SONG see Blake, William

CRADLE SONG see Brahms, Johannes

CRADLE SONG see Byrd, William

CRADLE SONG see Gibbs, [Cecil] Armstrong

CRADLE SONG see Grams, Werner P.

CRADLE SONG see Loring

CRADLE SONG, A see Crane, R.

CRADLE SONG AND ALLELUIA (from Harmonia Sacra)
(Kirk) SSA oct PRO ART 1850 $.20   (C2004)

CRADLE SONG OF THE BLESSED VIRGIN, A see Barnby

CRADLE SONG OF THE NUNS OF CHESTER see Crosse,
Gordon

CRADLE-SONG OF THE SHEPHERDS see Glatz,
Wiegenlied Der Hirten

CRADLE-SONG OF THE SHEPHERDS see Wiegenlied Der
Hirten

CRADLE SONG OF THE VIRGIN see Brahms, Johannes,
Geistliches Weigenlied

CRADLE SONG, SCHUBERT'S see Schubert, Franz
(Peter)

CRADLE, THE *Xmas,anthem/carol/folk,Aus
unis/SATB (easy) OXFORD 08.084 $.15, ipr   (C2005)
(Christiansen, Paul) SATB (easy) oct AUGSBURG
1091 $.18   (C2006)

CRADLE, THE see Bielawa, Herbert

CRADLE, THE see Kelly

CRADLED ALL LOWLY see Cassler, G. Winston

CRADLED IN A MANGER see Lovelace, Austin C.

CRADLED IN A MANGER see Myers, J.C.

CRADLED IN A MANGER see Smith, Bernard

CRADLES, THE see Faure, Gabriel-Urbain

CRAIG
Oh Lord And Father Of Us All
SATB oct PLYMOUTH DC-110 $.25   (C2007)

CRAM
Blessed Is He That Comes
2pt oct SACRED S-5753 $.30   (C2008)

Blessed Jesu
SA oct FISCHER,C CM-7764 $.25   (C2009)

Blessed Jesus
SA/TB SOUTHERN $.25   (C2010)

God, Who Made The Earth
SA oct SACRED S-5386 $.35   (C2011)

I Love Thee, My Lord
SATB SHAWNEE A 605 $.25   (C2012)

Let Our Joys Be Known
SATB oct FISCHER,C CM-7765 $.25   (C2013)

This Is My Song
SSA oct HERITAGE H6006 $.35   (C2014)

To God Be The Glory *anthem
SATB oct FISCHER,C SIG. $.25   (C2015)

CRAM, JAMES D. (1931-   )
Deep River
SATB oct AGAPE JW 7777 $.30   (C2016)

I Love Thy Kingdom, Lord
SATB,opt brass oct AGAPE F 935 $.35 (C2017)

CRAMER
Joyous Praise *CCU
SA MARKS $1.50   (C2018)

Praise The Lord
(Wiley) SATB oct PRO ART 2549 $.30 (C2019)

CRAMPTON, T.
I Was Glad *anthem
(easy) oct HART see from Three Easy Anthems   (C2020)

O Cast Thy Burden *anthem
(easy) oct HART see from Three Easy Anthems   (C2021)

O Praise God *anthem
(easy) oct HART see from Three Easy Anthems   (C2022)

CRAMPTON, T. (cont'd.)

Three Easy Anthems *see I Was Glad; O Cast
Thy Burden; O Praise God   (C2023)

CRANDALL, ROBERT
I Sing The Mighty Power Of God
unis&unis oct GRAY GCMR 2885 $.25   (C2024)

CRANDELL, R.
Benedictus Es
"Blessed Art Thou" SATB/SA/TB,org oct KERBY
5104 $.45   (C2025)

Benedictus Es
"Blessed Art Thou" SATB/SA oct KERBY 5104C
$.45   (C2026)

Blessed Art Thou *see Benedictus Es

Blessed Art Thou *see Benedictus Es

January Carol *Xmas,carol
SATB oct KERBY 5112 $.25   (C2027)
SATB,acap oct KERBY 5112C $.25   (C2028)

Laudate Dominum
2 anti cor,org oct KERBY 6304 $.30 (C2029)
2pt oct KERBY 6304C $.30   (C2030)

Second Beatitude, The
SATB,org oct KERBY 5206 $.55   (C2031)
SATB oct KERBY 5206C $.55   (C2032)

CRANE, R.
Cradle Song, A
SATB,acap oct PRESSER 312-40310 $.35
(C2033)

CRANMER, PHILIP
Jesu Dulcis Memoria
[Lat] SSS,acap oct NOVELLO 51.0633.08 s.p.
(C2034)

Teach Us, Good Lord *anthem
mix cor,acap oct NOVELLO 40.1433.02 s.p.
(C2035)

CRASTON, E.S.
Far From My Heavenly Home
SATB ALLANS 181 s.p.   (C2036)

Lord Is My Shepherd
SATB ALLANS 93 s.p.   (C2037)

Lord Reigneth, The *Fest
SATB ALLANS 69 s.p.   (C2038)

CRAVE AS NEWBORN BABES see Sterne, Colin

CRAWFORD
As Long As Children Pray
(Youse) SA oct BOURNE 2006 $.25   (C2039)
(Youse) SSA oct BOURNE 125 $.25   (C2040)

Psalm 98 *anthem
TTBB,brass oct OXFORD 94.102 $.70, ipa
(C2041)

CRAWFORD, JOHN
All That Has Life And Beauty *see Tout Ce
Qui Prend Naissance

Fairest Maid, The *see Je Suis Aime

Here Is The God Who Looks Both Ways *see
Voici Le Pere Au Double Front

I Have Lost All That Once I Was *see Plus Ne
Suis Ce Que J'ai Ete

Je Suis Aime *No.2 (from Amour, Tu As Ete
Mon Maitre)
"Fairest Maid, The" [Fr/Eng] TBB,acap
SCHIRM.EC 2177 $.30   (C2042)

Magnificat
SATB,pno,strings SCHIRM.EC 2520 $.90, ipr
(C2043)

Plus Ne Suis Ce Que J'ai Ete *No.1 (from
Amour, Tu As Ete Mon Maitre)
"I Have Lost All That Once I Was" [Fr/Eng]
TBB,acap SCHIRM.EC 2176 $.30   (C2044)

Tout Ce Qui Prend Naissance *No.4 (from
Amour Tu As Ete Mon Maitre)
"All That Has Life And Beauty" [Fr/Eng]
TBB,acap SCHIRM.EC 2179 $.35   (C2045)

Voici Le Pere Au Double Front *No.3 (from
Amour, Tu As Ete Mon Maitre)
"Here Is The God Who Looks Both Ways" [Fr/
Eng] TBB,acap SCHIRM.EC 2178 $.50 (C2046)

CRAWFORD, JOSEPH
Amen
(De Cormier) SATB,T solo oct LAWSON 51275
$.40   (C2047)

CRAWFORD, T.J.
Good Neighbours Then *Xmas
SATB oct LESLIE 4083   (C2048)

St. Nicolas At Christmas Time *Xmas
SATB oct LESLIE 4085   (C2049)

CREATE IN ME A CLEAN HEART see Berger, Jean

CREATE IN ME A CLEAN HEART see Kirk, Theron W.

CREATE IN ME A CLEAN HEART see Lahmer, [Ruel]

CREATE IN ME A CLEAN HEART see Pasquet, Jean

CREATE IN ME A CLEAN HEART see Wilson

CREATE IN ME A CLEAN HEART, O GOD
see Worship Responses

CREATE IN ME A CLEAN HEART, O GOD see Bouman,
Paul

CREATE IN ME A CLEAN HEART, O GOD see Glarum,
L. Stanley

CREATE IN ME A CLEAN HEART O GOD see Gluck,
H.H.

CREATE IN ME A CLEAN HEART, O GOD see Mueller,
Carl F.

CREATE IN ME A CLEAN HEART, O GOD see
Wendelburg, Norma

CREATE IN ME, O GOD see Brahms, Johannes

CREATION , see Haydn, (Franz) Joseph

CREATION, THE see Hanks, Sybil A.

CREATION, THE see Haydn, (Franz) Joseph

CREATION, THE see Richter

CREATION, THE see Smart, David

CREATION LOCKED see Winslow, R.K.

CREATION SPEAKS THAT GOD IS HERE see Hopson

CREATION, THE see Bobrowitz, David

CREATION, THE see Haydn, (Franz) Joseph, Die
Schopfung

CREATION, THE see Hennagin, Michael

CREATION, THE see Scott, T.

CREATION, THE see Waterman, Frances

CREATION'S CHRISTMAS SONG see Grime, William

CREATION'S HYMN see Beethoven, Ludwig van

CREATION'S PRAISE see Beethoven, Ludwig van

CREATION'S SONG see Beveridge, Thomas G.

CREATOR, THE see Cowell, Henry Dixon

CREATOR ALME SIDERUM see Washington, Henry

CREATOR OF THE EARTH AND SKY see Ratcliffe,
Desmond

CREATOR OF THE STARS see Boatwright, Howard

CREATOR OF THE STARS see Wood, Dale

CREATOR OF THE STARS OF NIGHT *anthem
(Johnson, David N.) SATB (med) oct AUGSBURG
1473 $.30   (C2050)

CREATOR OF THE STARS OF NIGHT see Butler,
Eugene

CREATOR OF THE STARS OF NIGHT see Powell, R.

CREATOR SPIRIT see Stout, Alan

CREATOR SPIRIT see Waters, Charles F.

CREATOR SPIRIT, BY WHOSE AID see Kindermann,
Johann Erasmus

CREATOR, SUPREME see Lewis, J.

CREATURE-SONGS TO HEAVEN see Rubbra, Edmund

CREATURES GREAT AND SMALL *hymn
(Brandon) SAB oct BOURNE 3026 $.30   (C2051)

CRECHE CAROL, THE see Hutson

CRECHE LULLABY *Xmas
2pt CHAPPELL 0014795-352 $.40   (C2052)
SSA CHAPPELL 0014795-354 $.40   (C2053)
SATB CHAPPELL 0014795-358 $.40 (C2054)

CRECQUILLON, THOMAS (? -1557)
Vidit Jacob Scalam *mot
(Collins, H.B.) [Lat] SATTB CHESTER s.p.
(C2055)

CREDIDI see Porpora, Nicola Antonio

CREDIDI PROPTER see Lassus, Roland de
(Orlandus)

CREDIDI PROPTER see Stadler, Maximillian (Abbe)

CREDO see Brunner, Adolf

CREDO see Caretti, G.M.

CREDO see Cassler, G. Winston

CREDO see Dixon

CREDO see Dumont, [Henri]

CREDO see Faure, Jean-Baptist

CREDO see Gombert, Nicolas

CREDO see Gretchaninov, Alexander Tikhonovitch

CREDO see Hassler, Hans Leo

CREDO see Haydn, (Franz) Joseph

CREDO see Latham, [William P.]

CREDO see Lundborg, Gosta

CREDO see Magri, Pietro

CREDO see Palestrina, Giovanni

CREDO see Scarlatti, Alessandro

CREDO see Schubert, Franz (Peter)

CREDO see Stravinsky, Igor

CREDO see Tchaikovsky, Piotr Ilyitch

CREDO see Thompson, Randall

CREDO see Vivaldi, Antonio

CREDO (A8) see Clemens, Jacobus

CREDO AND GLORIA see Palestrina, Giovanni

CREDO CONCERTATO A QUATTRO VOCI see Scarlatti,
Alessandro

CREDO, DAS IST, ICH GLAUBE, HERR see Michel,
Josep

CREDO DE SANCTA JOHANNES EVANGELISTA see
Pipelare, Mathaes

CREDO III IN GREGORIANO see Bottazzo, Luigi

CREDO IV see Bottazzo, Luigi

CREDO MESSE see Mozart, Wolfgang Amadeus, Messa
In C-Dur

CREDO-MESSE see Mozart, Wolfgang Amadeus, Messe
C-Dur

CREDO-PSALM ENLIGT APOSTOLICUM see Nyvall,
Jacob

CREDO QUOD REDEMPTOR see Canniciari, D. Pompeo

CREED see Gretchaninov, Alexander Tikhonovitch

CREED see Jackson, Francis

CREED see Lee, J.

CREED see Palestrina, Giovanni

CREED, LORD'S PRAYER AND RESPONSES, THE see
Swann, Donald

CREED, THE see Duddy, [John H.]

CRESPO
La Estrella De Belen *Xmas
[Span] cor,solo UNION ESP. 14464 s.p.
(C2056)

CRESTON
Celestial Vision, The *cant
TTBB,acap SHAWNEE C166 $1.00   (C2057)

CRESTON, PAUL (1906-   )
Adoro Te Devote
"Devoutly I Adore Thee" see Two Motets

Alleluia (from Isaiah's Prophecy)
SATB oct COLOMBO 2321 $.40   (C2058)

Devoutly I Adore Thee *see Adoro Te Devote

Glory To God In The Highest (from Isaiah's
Prophecy)
SATB oct COLOMBO 2329 $.35   (C2059)

Hail, Holy Queen *see Salve Regina

Isaiah's Prophecy *Xmas,ora
SATB BELWIN $5.00   (C2060)

Lambs To The Lamb *Xmas
3pt jr cor/SSA (med) FISCHER,C CM 6649 $.25
(C2061)
SSA oct FISCHER,C CM-6649 $.25 (C2062)

Lillium Regis
SATB oct COLOMBO 1998 $.40   (C2063)

Missa Cum Jubilo *liturg/Mass
SATB voc sc KERBY 8478 $4.00, ipr (C2064)

O Come, O Come Emmanuel (from Isaiah's
Prophecy)
SATB oct COLOMBO 2327 $.25   (C2065)
(Elmore, Robert) SATB oct FISCHER,J 7715
$.30   (C2066)
(Grant, Louise) SSA oct BELWIN 1696 $.30
(C2067)
(Grant, Louise) SATB oct BELWIN 1705 $.30
(C2068)

Praise The Lord
SATB,acap oct COLOMBO 195 $.25 (C2069)

Psalm 23 *Op.37, Bibl
4pt mix cor,S solo oct SCHIRM.G 10145 $.30
(C2070)

Salve Regina
"Hail, Holy Queen" see Two Motets

Sleep, Holy Babe (from Isaiah's Prophecy)
Xmas
SATB,S solo oct COLOMBO 2330 $.25 (C2071)

Two Motets *mot
[Eng/Lat] 4pt men cor,TTBar soli,org oct
SCHIRM.G 9912 $.45
contains: Adoro Te Devote, "Devoutly I
Adore Thee"; Salve Regina, "Hail, Holy
Queen"   (C2072)

CRIB, THE see Shaw, Martin

CRIB AT GRECCIO, THE see Clarke, Irma A.

CRIB IN BETHLEHEM, A see Williams, Ralph E.

CRIB, THE see Shaw, Martin

CRIMOND *Marriage,Psalm,Scot
(Ross, B.) desc PATERSON s.p.   (C2073)

CRIMOND see Grant, David, Lord's My Shepherd,
The

CRIMP, HERBERT E.
Our Master Hath A Garden *anthem/hymn
mix cor oct NOVELLO 40.0930.04 s.p. (C2074)

CRIS DU MONDE see Honegger, Arthur

CRISPO, E.
Sancta Mater
see TRIA MOTECTA IN FESTO SEPTEM DOL.
B.V.M.

CRISSMAN, J.
Carol Of Th Friendly Beasts *Xmas,carol
SATB&jr cor&sr cor oct GRAY GCMR 2959 $.30
(C2075)

CRIST, [BAINBRIDGE] (1883-1969)
Heavenly Light
SATB,pno (med) oct WILLIS 7039 $.20 (C2076)

CRISTMAS CAROLS see Byrd, William

CRIVELLI, GIOVANNI BATTISTA (? -1682)
O Maria Mater Gratiae *BVM,mot,It
cor FABER F0060 s.p. (C2077)
(Roche) [Eng/Lat] SATTB,kbd oct SCHIRM.G
11730 $.35 (C2078)
(Roche, Jerome) [Lat] SATTB oct FABER 11730
$.35 (C2079)

CROCE, GIOVANNI (ca. 1560-1609)
Beati Eritis
(Martens, Mason) "Yea, Blessed Shall Ye Be"
SATB oct WALTON 2156 $.25 (C2080)

Benedicam Dominum
[Lat] men cor,acap (med) HUG s.p. (C2081)

Benedictus Es Domine *cant
SATB&SATB,4trp,4trom MOSELER sc s.p., cor
pts s.p., ipa (C2082)

Cantata Domino
(Martens) mix cor SOUTHERN $.25 (C2083)

Cantate Domino *mot
[Lat] TTBB,acap MUSICUS 1020 $.15 (C2084)
(Klein) "O Sing Ye To The Lord" [Eng/Lat]
4pt mix cor,acap oct SCHIRM.G 11419 $.35 (C2085)
(Martens, Mason) "O Sing Unto The Lord"
SATB oct WALTON 2095 $.25 (C2086)
(Ruiz) [Lat] SATB,acap RICORDI-ARG BA10087
s.p. (C2087)

Darkness Was Over All *see Tenebrae Factae
Sunt

Ego Sum Pauper Et Dolens *Commun/Gd.Fri.
"When I Was Poor And In Heaviness" SSAA,
acap SCHIRM.EC 1282 $.18 (C2088)
"When I Was Poor And In Heaviness" [Lat/
Eng] TTBB,acap SCHIRM.EC 1252 $.25 (C2089)

Exaltabo Te, Domine *mot
(Steele, Jonathan) [Lat] SATB CHESTER s.p. (C2090)

Exaudi Deus
men cor sc ALSBACH&D s.p. (C2091)

In Monte Oliveti *Easter/Holywk/Lent
(Campbell; Watson) [Eng/Lat] SATB,acap
WARNER W3355 $.30 (C2092)
(Martens, Mason) "Upon The Mt. Of Olives"
SATB oct WALTON 2052 $.25 (C2093)
(Watson) mix cor SOUTHERN $.30 (C2094)

Is It Nothing, All Of You Who Pass By Me
*see O Vos Omnes

Laudate Dominum *cant
SATB&SATB,4trp,4trom MOSELER sc s.p., cor
pts s.p., ipa (C2095)

O Sacrum Convivium *Fest/Pent/Whitsun,mot
[Lat] SATB,acap (med easy) MULLER MS 29
s.p. (C2096)
SATB,acap voc pt DOBLINGER s.p. see also
PFINGSTEN UND EUCHARISTIE (C2097)
(Washington, Henry) [Lat] SATB/ATBarB
CHESTER s.p. (C2098)

O Sing Unto The Lord *see Cantate Domino

O Sing Unto The Lord A New Song
SATB oct WORD CS-310 $.30 (C2099)

O Sing Ye To The Lord *see Cantate Domino

O Vos Omnes *Lent
SATB,acap RICORDI-ENG SY111 s.p. (C2100)
(Kjelson) mix cor SOUTHERN $.30 (C2101)
(Kjelson) SATB oct SOUTHERN $.30 (C2102)
(Kjelson) SATB oct BELWIN 2149 $.25 (C2103)
(Klein) "Is It Nothing, All Of You Who Pass
By Me" [Eng/Lat] 4pt mix cor,acap oct
SCHIRM.G 11418 $.25 (C2104)
(Ruiz) [Lat] SATB,acap RICORDI-ARG BA 10482
s.p. (C2105)
(Schaller; Vene) "Ye Who Pass Me" [Lat/Eng]
SATB,acap oct COLOMBO 1884 $.20 (C2106)

Psalm 96 *see Sing Unto The Lord

Sing Unto The Lord (Psalm 96)
(Cain) SATB oct PRO ART 1333 $.18 (C2107)

Tenebrae Factae Sunt *Easter/Lent
(Martens, Mason) "Darkness Was Over All"
SATB oct WALTON 2051 $.25 (C2108)

Upon The Mt. Of Olives *see In Monte Oliveti

Virtute Magna *Easter/Pent,mot
[Lat] SATB,acap (med) MULLER M 18 s.p. (C2109)
[Lat] mix cor,acap oct NOVELLO DM-18 s.p. (C2110)

When I Was Poor And In Heaviness *see Ego
Sum Pauper Et Dolens

Ye Who Pass Me *see O Vos Omnes

Yea, Blessed Shall Ye Be *see Beati Eritis

CROCKER
Our Lord And Comforter
SATB oct VOLKWEIN VB237 $.25 (C2111)

CROFT
O Give Thanks Unto The Lord *Thanks
mix cor SOUTHERN $.22 (C2112)

Ye Servants Of God
(Coggin) SATB,org/pno BOSTON 13315 $.30 (C2113)
(Coggin) SAB,org/pno BOSTON 13314 $.35 (C2114)

CROFT, W.
O, God Our Help
men cor sc ALSBACH&D s.p. (C2115)

O God Our Help In Ages Past *anthem/hymn
(Christiansen, Paul) SATB (med diff) oct
AUGSBURG 1213 $.22 (C2116)
(Hollis) SATB FLAMMER A 5351 $.30 (C2117)
(Hollis) SAB FLAMMER D5149 $.25 (C2118)
(Kinsman) SATB oct SPRATT 567 $.25 (C2119)
(Martin, R.) SATB oct PRESSER 332-40115
$.30 (C2120)
(Wiley) SATB&desc oct PRO ART 1363 $.25

CROFT, W. (cont'd.)
O Praise The Lord, All Ye Heathen (C2121)
(Bryant) SATB oct MCA (C2122)

O Worship The King
(Lindquist, M.) SATB,acap oct PRESSER MC234
$.30 (C2123)

Ye Servants Of God
(Howorth) SATB,opt acap oct FOX PS192 $.30 (C2124)

CROFT, WILLIAM (1678-1727)
Deliver Us, O Lord, Our God *Gen
ATB&SATB,kbd (med diff) oct CONCORDIA
98-1692 $.50 (C2125)

God Is Gone Up With A Merry Noise *anthem
mix cor,SSAATB soli oct NOVELLO 28.0128.00
s.p. (C2126)

O Give Thanks Unto The Lord *Ded/Gen/Thanks
SAB,kbd (med easy) oct CONCORDIA 98-1788
$.25 (C2127)

O God, Our Help In Ages Past
mix cor oct LAWSON 771 $.25 (C2128)

Oh God, Our Help In Ages Past *hymn
(Gerig) SSATB oct LILLENAS AN-2274 $.30 (C2129)

Our God, Our Help In Ages Past *anthem/hymn
(Frackenpohl, Arthur) SATB/4pt jr cor,pno/
org oct FISCHER,C CM-7459 $.25 (C2130)

Turn Thee, O Lord *anthem
(Carpenter, Adrian) SSATTB oct NOVELLO
40.1537.01 s.p. (C2131)

CROLY
Spirit Of God *see Ford

CROMIE, M.
Christmas Eve *Xmas
[Eng/Lat] SAB,acap (med easy) PRESSER $.40 (C2132)

Ring More Brightly *Xmas,carol
SSATB,pno (med easy) PRESSER $.35 (C2133)

CRONE, R.
Behold A Great Priest
see Three Vernacular Motets

Lord Hath Sworn, The
see Three Vernacular Motets

O Priest And Bishop
see Three Vernacular Motets

Te Deum Laudamus *Gen,anthem
"We Praise Thee, O God" [Eng/Lat] SSA/TTB,
opt brass (med) oct GIA G974 $.60 (C2134)

Three Vernacular Motets *Gen,anthem/mot
[Eng/Lat] SSA/TTB/SSB (med easy) cmplt ed
GIA G1198 $.50 (C2135)
contains: Behold A Great Priest; Lord
Hath Sworn, The; O Priest And Bishop

We Praise Thee, O God *see Te Deum Laudamus

CRONHAM
Opening Sentences, Responses And Amens *CCU,
cor-resp
SATB oct FISCHER,C CM-7573 $.50 (C2136)

Twelve Amens *CC12U
SATB FLAMMER A 5477 $.30 (C2137)

CROO, R.
Lully, Thou Little Tiny Child *Xmas,carol,
Eng
(Vance, M.) SA/SSA oct BELWIN 2230 $.30 (C2138)

CROOK, A.T.
Bless The Lord, O My Soul *Austral
SATB (easy) ALLANS 9 s.p. (C2139)

Lord Is My Shepherd, The *Austral
SATB ALLANS 10 s.p. (C2140)

O Love Divine, How Sweet *Austral
SATB (easy) ALLANS 38 s.p. (C2141)

Sun Of My Soul *Austral
SATB (easy) ALLANS 27 s.p. (C2142)

Teach Me Thy Way *Austral
SATB ALLANS 36 s.p. (C2143)

Teach Me Thy Way, O Lord
SA ALLANS 280 s.p. (C2144)

CROOK, JONN
Kingdom Of Heaven *anthem
SATB,org CRAMER C O s.p. (C2145)

CROOKS, MACK
December Carol *Xmas,carol
SATB,acap oct LAWSON 51430 $.30 (C2146)

CROON CAROL *Xmas
(Whitehead) SATB oct FISCHER,C CM-354 $.25 (C2147)
(Whitehead) unis&desc oct FISCHER,C CM-6151
$.25 (C2148)
(Whitehead) SAB oct FISCHER,C CM-417 $.25 (C2149)

CROON CAROL, THE see Whitehead, Alfred

CROSATO, ONOFRIO
Missa S. Pius X *Mass
[Lat] ATB,org sc ZANIBON 3970 s.p., voc pt
ZANIBON s.p. (C2150)

CROSS, THE see Elmore, Robert [Hall]

CROSS AND THE SWITCHBLADE, THE see Carmichael,
Ralph

CROSS BEARING CHILD, THE see Kunz

CROSS OF CALVARY, THE see Gounod, Charles
Francois

CROSS OF CHRIST see Landon

CROSS OF CHRIST, THE see Romme, Donald R.

CROSS OF CHRIST, THE *Psntd
cor&cong ROYAL s.p. (C2151)

CROSS OF JESUS see Siegl, O Crux Ave

CROSS OF JESUS see Wilson

CROSS OF JESUS see Wilson, John F.

CROSS OF JESUS, CROSS OF SORROW see Lovelace,
Austin C.

CROSS OF REDEMPTION see Norman

CROSS SHINES FORTH, THE see Hoffman

CROSS THAT HELD THEE see Jean IV, Roi De
Portugal, Crux Fidelis

CROSS, THE see Barnes, Albert F.

CROSS, THE see Buettell

CROSS, THE see Harker, F. Flaxington

CROSS, THE see Winchester, E.C.

CROSS TRIUMPHANT see Wilson, Ira B.

CROSS WAS HIS OWN, THE see Floering

CROSS WAS HIS OWN, THE see Heller

CROSS WAS HIS OWN, THE see Willcoxon, Larry

CROSS WAS NOT THE END, THE see Johnson

CROSSE, GORDON
Changes *cant
unis&SATB,SBar soli,inst (diff) OXFORD
46.149 $4.50, ipr (C2152)

Covenant Of The Rainbow
mix cor voc sc OXFORD 46.165 $7.35, cor pts
OXFORD 46.166 $1.50 (C2153)

Cradle Song Of The Nuns Of Chester
see Two Christmas Songs

Laetabundus *Xmas
see Two Christmas Songs
SA/TB,acap (med) OXFORD 82.069 $.35 see
also Two Christmas Songs (C2154)

O Blessed Lord *Gen/Lent
SATB,bass inst/org (med) oct OXFORD 42.896
$.35 (C2155)

Two Christmas Songs *see Laetabundus (C2156)

Two Christmas Songs *Xmas
[Lat] SA,acap (med) OXFORD 82.069 $.25
contains: Cradle Song Of The Nuns Of
Chester; Laetabundus (C2157)

CROSSING THE BAR see Fearis, J.S.

CROSSING THE BAR see Todd, M. Flora

CROTCH
Comfort, O Lord *Lent
SATB ALLANS 332 s.p. (C2158)
(Douglas) SATB,acap oct PRO ART 1614 $.30 (C2159)

Comfort, O Lord, The Soul Of Thy Servant
(Pisano) SATB oct PLYMOUTH PCS-25 $.25 (C2160)

CROTCH, WILLIAM (1775-1847)
Bless Now, O Lord
(Goggin) 3pt mix cor,org/pno oct SCHIRM.G
11659 $.25 (C2161)

Comfort, O Lord
(Knight) 3pt mix cor oct CURWEN 11199 $.25 (C2162)

Comfort O Lord The Soul
(Bridge, Sir Fredk.) SATB BOSWORTH s.p. (C2163)

Comfort, O Lord The Soul Of Thy Servant
*anthem
SA,org SCHIRM.EC 1005 $.18 (C2164)
mix cor oct NOVELLO 40.0320.09 s.p. (C2165)
(Davis, K.) SA SCHIRM.EC 1554 (C2166)
(Goss, J.) SATB SCHIRM.EC 2220 $.30 (C2167)
(Goss, J.) SATB,org oct SCHIRM.EC 2220 $.30 (C2168)

How Dear Art Thy Counsels *anthem
mix cor oct NOVELLO 40.0224.05 s.p. (C2169)

Lo! Star-Led Chiefs (from Palestine) Xmas/
Epiph,anthem
SATB oct NOVELLO 34.0687.03 s.p. (C2170)
(Davies, Laurence H.) 2pt (easy) oct OXFORD
44.075 $.35 (C2171)

Methinks I Hear The Full Celestial Choir
(Hammar) SATBarB,acap oct LAWSON 51671 $.35 (C2172)

CROUCH, ANDRAE
Keep On Singin' *CCUL
SATB voc sc WORD 37528 $1.95 (C2173)

Soulfully *CCUL
SATB voc sc WORD 37546 $1.95 (C2174)

CROW
Baby Jesu *Xmas
SSATB,acap,opt pno oct PRO ART 1910 $.25 (C2175)

My Prayer
SATB oct PRO ART 1943 $.22 (C2176)

CROWDED INN AT BETHLEHEM, A *Xmas,carol,US
(Ehret) SATB,opt ob oct FOX CC16 $.30 (C2177)
(Ehret) SAB,opt ob oct FOX CC13 $.30 (C2178)
(Ehret, W.) SAB,opt ob oct PROWSE CC13 s.p. (C2179)

CROWDED INN, THE see Sharpe, Evelyn

CROWE
Let The People Praise Thee
SATB oct PRO ART 43 $.15 (C2180)

Psalm 121
SATB oct PRO ART 44 $.15 (C2181)

CROWELL, M.
In The Beginning God
(Foltz) SATB,acap oct BELWIN 60106 $.30
(C2182)

Sleep Of The Child Jesus *Xmas
SAB oct PRESSER 312-40447 $.25 (C2183)

This Would I Keep
(Youse) SSA/SSAA oct MCA (C2184)

CROWN CHOIR BOOK, THE see Schalk, Carl

CROWN ETERNAL, THE see Palestrina, Giovanni,
Veni Sponsa Christi

CROWN HIM! see Gieschen, Thomas

CROWN HIM KING see Hawkins, Floyd W.

CROWN HIM KING OF GLORY see Christiansen, Olaf
Christian

CROWN HIM KING OF GLORY see Tchaikovsky, Piotr
Ilyitch

CROWN HIM LORD OF ALL! see Rasley

CROWN HIM LORD OF ALL see Richardson

CROWN HIM LORD OF ALL see Thygerson

CROWN HIM LORD OF ALL see Wetzler, Robert

CROWN HIM WITH MANY CROWNS see Elvey

CROWN HIM WITH MANY CROWNS see Elvey, George
Job

CROWN HIM WITH MANY CROWNS see Pelz, Walter L.

CROWN HIM WITH MANY CROWNS see Thygerson

CROWN HIM WITH MANY CROWNS see Waddington

CROWN HIM WITH MANY CROWNS see Williamson,
Malcolm

CROWN HIM WITH MANY CROWNS see Wilson, John F.

CROWN OF LIFE see Neff, James

CROWN OF ROSES, THE
unis/SATB (very easy) OXFORD 08.197 $.15, ipr
(C2185)

CROWN OF THORNS see Naylor, Bernard, De Corona
Spinea

CROWNED WITH THE THORN see Chapman, Edward T.

CROZE
Noel D'enfant *Xmas
(Darcieux, F.; Missa, E.) [Fr] 4pt mix cor,
acap (easy) cor pts LEMOINE s.p. (C2186)

CRUCEM SANCTAM SUBIIT see Palestrina, Giovanni

CRUCEM TUAM see Doebler, Curt

CRUCEM TUAM ADORAMUS see Goodman, Joseph

CRUCIFIED see Durante, Francesco, Crucifixus

CRUCIFIED see Lotti, Antonio, Crucifixus

CRUCIFIED see Monteverdi, Claudio, Crucifixus

CRUCIFIED see Nevin, Gordon Balch

CRUCIFIED ALSO FOR US see Hassler, Hans Leo,
Crucifixus Etiam Pro Nobis

CRUCIFIX see Faure, Jean-Baptist

CRUCIFIXION see Ahrold, Frank

CRUCIFIXION see Billings, William

CRUCIFIXION see Conley, D.

CRUCIFIXION see Koshetz

CRUCIFIXION see Lynn, George

CRUCIFIXION see Morawetz

CRUCIFIXION see Zimmermann, Heinz Werner

CRUCIFIXION, THE see Kemmer, [George W.]

CRUCIFIXION, THE see Kihlken, Henry

CRUCIFIXION, THE see Stainer, John

CRUCIFIXION, THE see Stainer, John

CRUCIFIXUS see Bach, Johann Sebastian

CRUCIFIXUS see Durante, Francesco

CRUCIFIXUS see Gabrieli, Giovanni

CRUCIFIXUS see Hassler, Hans Leo

CRUCIFIXUS see Lotti, Antonio

CRUCIFIXUS see Monteverdi, Claudio

CRUCIFIXUS see Palestrina, Giovanni

CRUCIFIXUS see Talmadge, Charles L.

CRUCIFIXUS see Vivaldi, Antonio

CRUCIFIXUS see Young

CRUCIFIXUS see Lotti, Antonio

CRUCIFIXUS ETIAM see Hassler, Hans Leo

CRUCIFIXUS ETIAM PRO NOBIS see Hassler, Hans
Leo

CRUCIFIXUS PRO NOBIS see Leighton, Kenneth

CRUCIFIXUS PRO NOBIS see Rubbra, Edmund

CRUCIFIXUS SURREXIT see Rohaczewski, Andriej

CRUCIFIXUS see Lotti, Antonio

CRUCIFIXUS see Lotti, Antonio

CRUEGER
see CRUGER, JOHANN

CRUFT
Benedictus
SATB,org oct BOOSEY 5641 $.40 (C2187)

Hymne Of Heavenly Love, An
mix cor&2pt boy cor,Bar solo,org,strings,
perc,harp voc sc MCA $1.50, ipr (C2188)

I Bring Ye Love
SSAATTBB,acap oct BELWIN 07053 $.50 (C2189)

CRUFT, ADRIAN (1921-   )
How Shall I Find Him
SATB,acap LENGNICK s.p. (C2190)

Magnificat
[Eng/Lat] mix cor,3fl,2ob,2clar,2bsn,3trp,
4horn,3trom,bsn,strings,timp cmplt ed
BOOSEY rental contains also: Nunc
Dimittis (C2191)

Mass For St. Michael
[Lat/Eng] mix cor,fl,ob,clar,bsn,horn,vcl,
bvl cmplt ed BOOSEY rental (C2192)

Nunc Dimittis
see Cruft, Adrian, Magnificat

Welcome *Xmas,anthem
mix cor,acap oct NOVELLO 40.1518.05 s.p.
(C2193)

Ye Are No More Strangers
SSAATTBB,acap oct BOOSEY 5640 $.30 (C2194)

CRUGER, JOHANN (1598-1662)
Ach Herr, Ach Herr, Ich Bin Umfangen *mot
(Hildebrandt) SAT/SAB HANSSLER 1.358 s.p.
(C2195)

Ach, Lass Dir's, Herr, Gefallen, Zu Wenden
*mot
(Hildebrandt) SAT/SAB HANSSLER 1.359 s.p.
(C2196)

Ah, Holy Jesus *anthem
(Jennings) SA,vcl (med) oct AUGSBURG 0302
$.25 (C2197)
(Malmin) SSA (easy) oct AUGSBURG 1236 $.18
(C2198)
(Nelson) SSAB (easy) oct AUGSBURG 1134 $.25
(C2199)

All Glory Be To God On High
see Four Christmas Chorales

All My Heart
(Jennings) SATB,2fl/rec (med) oct AUGSBURG
1597 $.30 (C2200)

All My Heart This Night Rejoices
see Four Christmas Chorales

Allein Gott In Der Hoh Sei Ehr
[Ger] 4pt mix cor,2vln,opt cont BAREN.
BA 163 $.40 (C2201)

Allein Gott In Der Hohe Sei Ehr
see Cruger, Johann, Nun Lob, Mein Seel, Den
Herren

Allena Gud I Himmelrik
(Wessman, Sven A.) mix cor,2fl/2vln cor pts
NORDISKA 5594 s.p. (C2202)

Auf, Auf, Mein Herz, Mit Freuden *No.86,
Easter
see Ebeling, Johann Georg, Warum Sollt Ich
Mich Denn Gramen
[Ger] 4pt mix cor,cont,2vln BAREN. EM 71
s.p. see from EVANGELISCHES
KIRCHENGESANGBUCH (C2203)
(Berger, H.L.) TTBB HANSSLER 6.5063 s.p.
contains also: Janus, Martin, Du Grosser
Schmerzensmann Vom Vater (C2204)

Awake, My Heart *Easter
(Wohlfeil) SATB SCHMITT 1730 $.22 (C2205)

Awake, My Heart, With Gladness
see Three Easter Chorales

Cantate Domino *mot
(Hildebrant) [Lat] SAT/SAB HANSSLER 1.366
$.30 (C2206)

Christ Lag In Todesbanden *Easter
[Ger] 4pt mix cor,2vln,opt cont BAREN.
BA 161 $.25 contains also: Nun Komm, Der
Heiden Heiland (C2207)

Dankt, Dankt Nu Allen God
men cor sc ALSBACH&D s.p. (C2208)
mix cor sc ALSBACH&D s.p. (C2209)

Deck Thyself, My Soul, With Gladness
*chorale
(Bach, J.S.; Barrow, R.) TTBB,org SCHIRM.EC
2170 $.25 (C2210)
(Bach, J.S.; Davis, K.) SSA,pno SCHIRM.EC
1857 (C2211)

Den Tro Som Jesum Favner
(Nystedt, Knut) [Norw] mix cor,inst LYCHE
29 s.p. (C2212)

Der Herr Hat In Sein Handen *mot
(Hildebrandt) SAT/SAB HANSSLER 1.361 s.p.
(C2213)

Der Hochste Herrscht In Majestat Und Pracht
(Psalm 93)
SATB,opt 2treb inst LAUDINELLA LR 59 s.p.
contains also: Ich Erhebe Mein Gemute
(Psalm 25); O Hochster, Deine Gutigkeit
(Psalm 93) (C2214)

Domine, Labia Mea Aperies *mot
(Hildebrandt) [Lat] SAT/SAB HANSSLER 1.355
s.p. (C2215)

Du Friedefurst, Herr Jesu Christ
SATB LAUDINELLA LR 19 s.p. contains also:
Ein Feste Burg Ist Unser Gott (SATB,
5trom); Wer Gott Vertraut (SATB) (C2216)

CRUGER, JOHANN (cont'd.)
Ein Feste Burg Ist Unser Gott
see Cruger, Johann, Du Friedefurst, Herr
Jesu Christ
SATB,2inst HANSSLER 6.038 s.p. contains
also: Frohlich Soll Mein Herze Springen
(C2217)

Exsultate Deo Adjutori Nostro *mot
(Hildebrandt) [Lat] SAT/SAB HANSSLER 1.364
$.30 (C2218)

Father Most Holy *anthem
(Christiansen, F.M.) SSAATBB (med) oct
AUGSBURG 0071 $.25 (C2219)
(Hadley) SATB oct PRO ART 1933 $.25 (C2220)

Four Christmas Chorales *Xmas,chorale
SATB,inst (med easy) oct CONCORDIA 98-2115
$.45
contains: All Glory Be To God On High;
All My Heart This Night Rejoices; From
Heaven Above; Only Son From Heaven, The
(C2221)

Frohlich Soll Mein Herze Springen
see Cruger, Johann, Ein Feste Burg Ist
Unser Gott
see Bach, Johann Sebastian, Lobt Gott Ihr
Christen
TTBB HANSSLER 6.2383 s.p. contains also:
Franck, Melchior, Mit Freuden Hor Es Alle
Welt (C2222)

From Heaven Above
see Four Christmas Chorales

Geistliche Chormusik *CC17U,mot
(Hildebrandt) [Ger] SAT/SAB HANSSLER 4.011
$2.50 (C2223)

Gelobet Seist Du, Jesu Christ *Xmas
[Ger] SATB,2vln,opt cont (easy) BAREN.
BA 594 s.p. contains also: Vom Himmel
Hoch, Da Komm Ich Her (C2224)

God On High
(Hadley) SATB oct PRO ART 2462 $.25 (C2225)

Heiliger Geist, Du Troster Mein
SATB LAUDINELLA LR 51 s.p. contains also:
Komm, Heiliger Geist, Herre Gott (SATB,
5trom); Nun Freut Euch, Gottes Kinder All
(SATB) (C2226)

Herr, Wenn Ich Dich Nur Festiglich, In Meinem
*mot
(Hildebrandt) SAT/SAB HANSSLER 1.356 s.p.
(C2227)

I Dodens Band Lag Herren Krist
(Wessman, Sven A.) mix cor,2fl/2vln cor pts
NORDISKA 5595 s.p. (C2228)

Ich Erhebe Mein Gemute (Psalm 25)
see Cruger, Johann, Der Hochste Herrscht In
Majestat Und Pracht

Ich Muss Ja, Herr, Bekennen Frei *mot
(Hildebrandt) SAT/SAB HANSSLER 1.363 s.p.
(C2229)

Ich Singe Dir Mit Herz Und Mund *Gen
[Ger] SATB,acap (easy) BAREN. BA 989 s.p.
(C2230)

Ich Will Bei Meinem Leben Ruhmen Den Herren
*mot
(Hildebrandt) SMezA/SAB HANSSLER 1.352 s.p.
(C2231)

Ich Will Den Zorn Des Herren Mein *mot
(Hildebrandt) SAT/SAB HANSSLER 1.353 s.p.
(C2232)

Jesu, Meine Freude
(Schabasser, Josef) mix cor,acap oct
DOBLINGER s.p. see also CHRISTUS, DER
HERR (C2233)

Jesu, Priceless Treasure
(Bach, J.S.) SATB,acap oct PRESSER
332-14424 $.35 (C2234)
(Bach; Pietatis) SATB FLAMMER A 5169 $.30
(C2235)

Jesus Christ, My Sure Defense *Easter
see Three Easter Chorales
SATB,acap oct PRESSER 312-40144 $.25
(C2236)
(Marks, H.) SATB oct PRESSER 332-15344 $.30
(C2237)

Jesus Is Well And Alive Today
(Boyd) SATB FRANK 13799 $.35 (C2238)

Jesus, Mein Zuversicht Und Mein Heiland
SATB,2inst HANSSLER 6.039 s.p. contains
also: Ebeling, Johann Georg, Du Meine
Seele, Singe, Wohlauf (C2239)

Jesus, Meine Zuversicht
(Schabasser, Josef) mix cor,acap oct
DOBLINGER s.p. see also CHRISTUS, DER
HERR (C2240)

Jesus, Priceless Treasure
(Ehret) SATB,acap MARKS 4112 $.30 (C2241)

Jubla Hogt, Min Sjal Och Tunga
cor pts NORDISKA 1695 s.p., ipa (C2242)

Komm, Heiliger Geist, Herre Gott
see Cruger, Johann, Heiliger Geist, Du
Troster Mein

Kommt Herr Zu Mir Alle, Die Ihr Muhselig
*Bibl/mot
(Hildebrandt) SAT/SAB HANSSLER 1.360 s.p.
(C2243)

Lobet Den Herren, Alle, Die Ihn Ehren
see Weber, Karl-Heinz, Abend Kommt, Der Tag
Sich Neiget
see Berger, Hans Ludwig, Lobe Den Herren
Den Machtigen
see Vulpius, Melchior, Ich Hab Mein Sach
Gott Heimgestellt
TTBB HANSSLER 6.1279 s.p. (C2244)

Lord, In This, Thy Mercy's Day *Easter/Gen/
Lent
(Hastings) SATB oct BOURNE HA8 $.30 (C2245)
(Walton) SATB SCHMITT 1778 $.25 (C2246)

Mein Hoffnung, Trost Und Zuversicht *mot
(Hildebrandt) SAT/SAB HANSSLER 1.460 s.p.
(C2247)

CRUGER, JOHANN (cont'd.)

Neun Geistliche Lieder *CCU,Gen
(Mahrenholz, Christhard) [Ger] SATB,2vln,
opt cont (med easy) BAREN. BA 1114 $1.75
(C2248)

Now Thank We All Our God *Gen/Thanks,anthem/
chorale/hymn
SATB oct STAFF 308 $.20 (C2249)
(Bach, J.S.) SATB oct GRAY GCMR 1497 $.30
(C2250)
(Bach, J.S.; Holler) SS oct GRAY GCMR 1206
$.30 (C2251)
(Bach, J.S.; Holler) SATB&opt jr cor oct
GRAY GCMR 1499 $.25 (C2252)
(Barrow, R.) TTBB,acap SCHIRM.EC 2115 $.22
(C2253)
(Cailliet) SATB,band oct BOOSEY 1790 $.30,
ipa (C2254)
(Cailliet) SSA,band oct BOOSEY 1789 $.30,
ipa (C2255)
(Cain) TTBB FLAMMER C5028 $.25 (C2256)
(Cain) boy cor SOUTHERN $.30 (C2257)
(Cooper) SSB&camb oct BOURNE C510 $.25
(C2258)
(Curry) SATB FLAMMER A 5401 $.30 (C2259)
(Duey) TTBB,acap BOSTON 12607 $.30 (C2260)
(Farron) SATB oct SPRATT 508 $.25 (C2261)
(Goemanne, Noel) SSA/TTB,opt org,opt 2trp
oct WORLD ESA-1809-3 $.45 (C2262)
(Lee, J.) SATB (med) oct GIA G1391 $.30
(C2263)
(Mendelssohn-Bartholdy, Felix) TTBB,opt
4brass oct PRESSER MC371 $.25 (C2264)
(Mendelssohn-Bartholdy, Felix; Cain) SATB&
opt jr cor oct PRO ART 1510 $.25 (C2265)
(Mendelssohn, F.; Cramer) SATB MARKS 4079
$.25 (C2266)
(Pooler) SATB SCHMITT 8018 $.35 (C2267)
(Scott) SATB oct FOX R108 $.25 (C2268)
(Serio, Joseph M.) SATB,org,opt horn&2trp&
trom/2trp/3trp/3trp&trom oct WORLD
ESA-901-8 $.90 (C2269)
(Shaw; Parker) SATB oct LAWSON 753 $.30
(C2270)
(Smart) unis jr cor,trp,org oct AGAPE F 906
$.30 (C2271)

Nun Danket All
see Selnecker, N.A., Nun Lasst Uns Gott Dem
Herren

Nun Danket Alle Gott *Thanks
TTBB HANSSLER 6.2329 s.p. contains also:
Lobe Den Herren, O Meine Seele (C2272)
men cor,acap ERDMANN 133 s.p. (C2273)

Nun Freut Euch, Gottes Kinder All
see Cruger, Johann, Heiliger Geist, Du
Troster Mein

Nun Jauchzet All, Ihr Frommen *Adv
[Ger] SATB,2vln,opt cont (easy) BAREN.
BA 3042 s.p. contains also: Wie Soll Ich
Dich Empfangen (C2274)
(Hellmann) SA,cont,2rec HANSSLER 5.037 s.p.
(C2275)

Nun Komm, Der Heiden Heiland *Adv
see Cruger, Johann, Christ Lag In
Todesbanden
SATB,2inst HANSSLER 6.042 s.p. contains
also: Nun Lasst Uns Gehn Und Treten
(C2276)
[Ger] 4pt mix cor,2vln,opt cont BAREN.
BA 161 $.25 (C2277)

Nun Lasst Uns Gehn Und Treten
see Cruger, Johann, Nun Komm, Der Heiden
Heiland
(Hellmann) SA,cont,2rec HANSSLER 5.043 s.p.
(C2278)

Nun Lasst Uns Gott Dem Herren
see Praetorius, Michael, O Gott, Wir Danken
Deiner Gut

Nun Lob, Mein Seel, Den Herren *Trin
[Ger] 4pt mix cor,2vln,opt cont BAREN.
BA 163 $.40 contains also: Allein Gott In
Der Hohe Sei Ehr; Was Mein Gott Will, Das
Gscheh Allzeit (C2279)

O Boundless Goodness
(Brandon) SAB,opt kbd oct PRO ART 2431 $.25
(C2280)

O Hochster, Deine Gutigkeit (Psalm 36)
see Cruger, Johann, Der Hochste Herrscht In
Majestat Und Pracht

O Jesu Christ, Dein Kripplein Ist *Xmas
(Hellmann) SA,cont,2rec HANSSLER 5.040 s.p.
(C2281)

O Lord, How Shall I Meet Thee
see Three Advent Chorales

O Meine Seel, Du Sollst Den Herren Preisen
see Hassler, Hans Leo, Ich Grusse Dich Am
Kreuzesstamm
see Bodenschatz, Erhard, Danket Dem Herrn
Heut Und Allzeit

O Sacred Head, Now Wounded *Lent
SATB,acap (med easy) oct CONCORDIA 98-1242
$.18 (C2282)

Only Son From Heaven, The
see Four Christmas Chorales

Psalm 25 *see Ich Erhebe Mein Gemute

Psalm 36 *see O Hochster, Deine Gutigkeit

Psalm 93 *see Der Hochste Herrscht In
Majestat Und Pracht

Salig, Salig Den Som Kande
mix cor NORDISKA 3509 s.p. (C2283)

Savior Of The Nations Come
see Three Advent Chorales

Schweigt Gott Ein Zeit So Meinst Du *mot
(Hildebrandt) SAT/SAB HANSSLER 1354 s.p.
(C2284)

Sei Lob Und Ehr Dem Hochsten Gut *Thanks
SATB,2inst HANSSLER 6.040 s.p. contains
also: Wie Soll Ich Dich Empfangen (C2285)
SATB HANSSLER 6.196 s.p. contains also:
Trubel, Gerhard, Sei Lob Und Ehr Dem
Hochsten Gut (SAB/SAT); Kubler, Emil, Sei

CRUGER, JOHANN (cont'd.)

Lob Und Ehr Dem Hochsten Gut (SATB)
(C2286)
(Berger, H.L.) TTBB HANSSLER 6.5133 s.p.
(C2287)

So Wahr Ich Leb, Spricht Gott Der Herr *mot
(Hildebrandt) SMezA/SAB HANSSLER 1.461 s.p.
(C2288)

Sumite Psalmum, Et Date Tympanum *mot
(Hildebrandt) [Lat] SAT/SAB HANSSLER 1.365
$.30 (C2289)

Tauet, Himmel, Den Gerechten
(Hellmann) SA,cont,2rec HANSSLER 5.038 s.p.
(C2290)

That Easter Day With Joy Was Bright
see Three Easter Chorales

Three Advent Chorales *Adv,chorale
SATB,inst (med easy) oct CONCORDIA 98-2114
$.30
contains: O Lord, How Shall I Meet Thee;
Savior Of The Nations Come; Ye Sons Of
Men, Oh, Hearken (C2291)

Three Easter Chorales *Easter,chorale
SATB,inst (med easy) oct CONCORDIA 98-2116
$.30
contains: Awake, My Heart, With Gladness;
Jesus Christ, My Sure Defense; That
Easter Day With Joy Was Bright (C2292)

Trachtet Am Ersten Nach Dem Reiche Gottes
*mot
(Hildebrandt) SAT/SAB HANSSLER 1.357 s.p.
(C2293)

Up, Up, My Heart *chorale
(Bach, J.S.; Davis, K.) SSA,acap SCHIRM.EC
1880 (C2294)

Vad Min Gud Vill, Det Alltid Sker
(Wessman, Sven A.) mix cor,2fl/2vln cor pts
NORDISKA 5591 s.p. (C2295)

Var Gud Ar Oss En Valdig Borg
(Wessman, Sven A.) mix cor,2fl/2vln cor pts
NORDISKA 5589 s.p. (C2296)

Venite, Exultemus Domino *mot
(Hildebrandt) [Lat] SAT/SAB HANSSLER 1.362
$.30 (C2297)

Vom Himmel Hoch, Da Komm Ich Her
see Cruger, Johann, Gelobet Seist Du, Jesu
Christ

Was Mein Gott Will, Das Gscheh Allzeit
see Cruger, Johann, Nun Lob, Mein Seel, Den
Herren

Wer Gott Vertraut
see Cruger, Johann, Du Friedefurst, Herr
Jesu Christ

Wie Soll Ich Dich Empfangen
see Cruger, Johann, Nun Jauchzet All, Ihr
Frommen
see Cruger, Johann, Sei Lob Und Ehr Dem
Hochsten Gut
see Bach, Johann Sebastian, Gloria Sei Dir
Gesungen

Ye Sons Of Men, Oh, Hearken
see Three Advent Chorales

CRUICIFIED, THE
see Negro Spirituals

CRUSADE see Wilson

CRUSADE CHOIR, THE *CC38UL
(Barrows, Cliff) cor (easy) cmplt ed LILLENAS
MB-027 $1.25 (C2298)

CRUSADE CHOIR SING! *CC12UL,hymn
(Mickelson, Paul) cor,kbd (med) cmplt ed
LILLENAS MB-028 $1.50 (C2299)

CRUSADER'S HYMN see Reger, Max

CRUSADER'S HYMN see Wilson

CRUSADER'S SONG see Marcus, Sister Mary

CRUSIUS, O.E.
Hymne I: Geh Unter, Schone Sonne
4-6pt&mix cor (med) cor pts LEUCKART 21 C
s.p. (C2300)

CRUX AVE see Muller, J.

CRUX AVE see Palestrina, Giovanni

CRUX FIDELIS see Anerio, Felice

CRUX FIDELIS see Jean IV, Roi De Portugal

CRUX FIDELIS see Mozart, Wolfgang Amadeus

CRUX FIDELIS see Plum, P.-J.-M.

CRUX FIDELIS see Roger-Ducasse, Jean-Jules
Aimable

CRUXIFIXION, THE see Stainer, John

CRUZIFIXION see Ruppel, Paul Ernst

CRY AND SHOUT see Nystedt, Knut

CRY HOSANNA see Stanton

CRY OUT AND SHOUT see Ludlow

CRYSTAL FOUNTAIN, THE see Hawkins, Floyd W.

CSENKI, I.
Breit Ist Das Wasser
see Hochzeit In Siebenburgen

Cymbalschlagen
see Hochzeit In Siebenburgen

Hochzeit In Siebenburgen
mix cor (med) oct LEUCKART 620 s.p.
contains: Breit Ist Das Wasser;
Cymbalschlagen; Springtanz; Vogel
Kuckuck (C2301)

CSENKI, I. (cont'd.)

Springtanz
see Hochzeit In Siebenburgen

Vogel Kuckuck
see Hochzeit In Siebenburgen

CSONAKON see Schumann, Robert (Alexander)

CSONKA, PAUL
Concierto De Navidad *Xmas
[Span/Eng] SSAA,harp PEER $2.65 (C2302)

CUATRO VILLANCICOS see Lopez, Almagro

CUCCHI, COLLEONI G.
Foderunt Manus Meas
see PER LA SETTIMANA SANTA

CUCKOO CAROL, THE *folk,Czech
(Glaser) 4pt wom cor,acap oct SCHIRM.G 9282
$.25 (C2303)

CUGLEY
Make We Joy *Xmas,carol
unis,pno/org ALBERT s.p. (C2304)

CUI COMPARABO see Volpi, Edoardo

CUM AUDISSET JOANNES see Cardoso, Manuel

CUM ERGO FLERET, CUM see Scheidt, Samuel

CUM ESSEM PARVULUS see Johansson, Bengt

CUM RIDES MIHI see Lassus, Roland de (Orlandus)

CUM SANCTO SPIRITU see Bach, Johann Sebastian

CUM SANCTO SPIRITU see Vivaldi, Antonio

CUMMING
Lonesome Valley
SATB oct BOOSEY 5804 $.30 (C2305)

CUMMINS, R.
Psalm Of Destiny
SATB FLAMMER A 5608 $.35 (C2306)

Rise Heart, Thy Lord Is Risen *Easter
SSAA oct PRESSER 312-40576 $.35 (C2307)

CUNCTIPOTENS GENITOR DEUS see Gerhard, Fritz
Christian

CUNCTIPOTENS GENITOR DEUS see Schiske, Karl

CUNDICK, ROBERT
We'll Keep A Welcome
mix cor&speak cor PIONEER 5066 $.40 (C2308)

CUNKLE
Behold That Star
SAB,acap SHAWNEE D2 $.35 (C2309)
TB,acap SHAWNEE C71 $.30 (C2310)
TTBB,acap SHAWNEE C69 $.30 (C2311)
SATB,acap SHAWNEE A 84 $.30 (C2312)
SSA,acap SHAWNEE B 50 $.35 (C2313)

CUP OF BLESSING, THE see Englert, Eugene

CUP, THE CROSS, AND THE CROWN, THE see Johnston

CURRAN, E.L.
Ave Maria
SATB PARAGON 1024 $.20 (C2314)

CURRAN, PEARL GILDERSLEEVE (1875-1941)
Blessing *Gen/Thanks
3pt wom cor oct SCHIRM.G 7087 $.25 (C2315)
(Deis) 2pt boy cor oct SCHIRM.G 10222 $.25
(C2316)
(Downing) 4pt mix cor oct SCHIRM.G 9469
$.25 (C2317)
(Stickles) 3pt mix cor oct SCHIRM.G 11098
$.20 (C2318)

Resurrection, The *Easter
(Deis) SATB,T solo oct SCHIRM.G 9868 $.35
(C2319)

CURRIE, E.E.
Masters In This Hall
SAB,org oct KERBY 801 $.35 (C2320)

CURRIE, E.R.
Holly And Ivy, The *Xmas
SSA,opt inst oct KERBY 6903C $.45 (C2321)

Holly And The Ivy, The
SSA,opt inst oct KERBY 6903 $.45 (C2322)

Masters In This Hall
SAB oct KERBY 80175 $.35 (C2323)

CURRY
Anthems With Descants *CCU
SATB&desc FLAMMER GA5018 $1.00 (C2324)

Ding Dong! Merrily On High
SA/TB FLAMMER E5022 $.30 (C2325)

From Bethany The Master Comes
SATB FLAMMER A 5264 $.30 (C2326)

God Is Our Refuge
SATB FLAMMER A 5220 $.30 (C2327)

He Who Would Valiant Be
SATB oct VOLKWEIN VB170 $.30 (C2328)

Heavens Declare The Glory Of God
SATB KJOS PC770 $.30 (C2329)

I Greet Thee, Who My Sure Redeemer Art
SATB oct VOLKWEIN VB175 $.25 (C2330)

I Heard The Bells On Christmas Day *Xmas
SATB,bells oct VOLKWEIN VB176 $.30 (C2331)

I Sing The Mighty Power God
SATB&desc oct VOLKWEIN VB189 $.25 (C2332)

I Sought The Lord
SATB oct VOLKWEIN VB190 $.30 (C2333)

O Brother Man
SATB oct VOLKWEIN VB219 $.25 (C2334)

CURRY (cont'd.)
Tell Out The News
SATB (med) OXFORD 84.113 $.25   (C2335)

CURRY, L.
Once For Us A Child *Xmas
SATB oct GRAY GCMR 2680 $.30   (C2336)

CURRY, R.D.
Put On The Whole Armour Of God *Gen,anthem
SATB (easy) oct GIA G1027 $.25   (C2337)

Whatsoever Things *Gen,anthem
SATB (easy) oct GIA G1032 $.25   (C2338)

CURRY, W. LAWRENCE
Against The Morn Is Come A King *Xmas
4pt mix cor oct SCHIRM.G 10757 $.25   (C2339)
3pt mix cor oct SCHIRM.G 10944 $.25   (C2340)

Great God Of Nations
4pt mix cor oct SCHIRM.G 10844 $.30   (C2341)

Hymn To The Risen Christ, A *Easter,Bibl
4pt mix cor&cong,org oct SCHIRM.G 10988 $.30   (C2342)

In Christ There Is No East Or West
SATB (med) ABINGDON APM-104 $.22   (C2343)

Psalm 150 *Fest/Gen
SATB&opt jr cor oct GRAY $.30   (C2344)

Sing Praise To God
SATB oct GRAY GCMR 2754 $.25   (C2345)

CURTIS, C.
Star Of Beatitude
(Gibb, R.) SSA oct PRESSER G-3502 $.30   (C2346)

CURWIN, CLIFFORD
Lord's Prayer, The *carol
unis CRAMER 46 s.p.   (C2347)

Nativity *Xmas
cor CRAMER 314 s.p.   (C2348)

CUSTODI ME DOMINE see Lassus, Roland de (Orlandus)

CUSTOS QUID DE NOCTE see Hindemith, Paul

CUTLER
At Length There Dawns The Glorious Day
(Lynn) SATB oct SOUTHERN $.25   (C2349)

Come Unto Me
(Young, R.; Weinandt, E.) SATB oct FISCHER,J 10011 $.30   (C2350)

CUYPERS, H.
Te Deum Laudamus
dbl cor,org ALSBACH&D sc s.p., cor pts s.p.   (C2351)

CYBINSKI, J.
Zu Bethlehem Geboren *Xmas
[Ger] wom cor,acap (easy) HUG s.p.   (C2352)

CYCLE FOR CHRISTMAS see Sateren, Leland Bernhard

CYCLE OF PSALMS, A see Boccard, C.C.

CYMBALSCHLAGEN see Csenki, I.

CYN CAU LLYGAID see Rees-Davies, Ieuan

CYPRIOT-FRENCH REPERTORY VOL. I *CCU,Mass
(Hoppin, Richard H.) cor AM.INST.MUS. $17.00
The Polyphony In The Manuscript J. II. 9 Of
The National Library Of Turin   (C2353)

CYPRIOT-FRENCH REPERTORY VOL. II *CCU,mot
(Hoppin, Richard H.) cor AM.INST.MUS. $24.00
The Polyphony In The Manuscript J. II. 9 Of
The National Library Of Turin   (C2354)

CZAJANCK, [VICTOR]
Christmas So Wonderful Fair *see Weihnacht, Wie Bist So Schon!

Weihnacht, Wie Bist So Schon! *Xmas,carol, Aus
(Klein) "Christmas So Wonderful Fair" [Eng/Ger] 4pt mix cor,acap oct SCHIRM.G 11939 $.30   (C2355)

CZECH CHRISTMAS CAROLS *Xmas
(Kricka, J.) SSA&SSAA,acap SCHIRM.EC 854 $.45
contains: Gloria In Excelsis; Harken To Me
Mother Dear; Now The Rarest Day; Sleep,
Baby, Sleep; Strangers Say A King Is Born   (C2356)

CZECH LULLABY CAROL see Jenkyns, Peter

CZECHOSLOVAK CHRISTMAS CAROLS *CC7U,Xmas, carol,Czech
(Tausky; Robertson) [Czech/Eng] unis SCHOTT s.p.   (C2357)

D

DA CHRISTUS GEBOREN WAR see Beuerle, Herbert

DA CHRISTUS GEBOREN WAR see Rohwer, Jens

DA COSI DOTTA MAN see Palestrina, Giovanni

DA DER HERR GEBOREN *see Eia, Du Kleines,
Zartes Kind; Eja Slap Soting; Engel Singen
Frohe Lieder; Es Ist Auf Erden Ein Kindlein
Geboren; Es Ist Fur Uns Eine Zeit
Angekommen; Es War Ein' Jungfrau
Auserkoren; Hirten, Eilt Zur Krippe;
Hirten, Er Ist Geboren; Hort Doch, Liebe
Bruder; Ich Sah Drei Segelschiffe Ziehn;
Welch Frohe Botschaft   (D1)

DA DER HERR GEBOREN. 20 EUROPAISCHE
WEIHNACHTSLIEDER *CC20U,Xmas,Eur
(Doppelbauer, J.F.) 4pt mix cor,acap cmplt ed
DOBLINGER s.p.   (D2)

DA DER SABBAT see Wenzel, Eberhard

DA DER SABBAT VERGANGEN see Wenzel, Eberhard

DA DROBEN VOM BERGE *Xmas,Aus
(Schemitsch, Hans) [Ger] mix cor,acap oct
DOBLINGER s.p. see also Zehn Osterrichische
Weihnachtslieder   (D3)

DA ER NUN AUFERSTANDEN WAR VON DEN TOTEN see
Driessler, Johannes

DA JAKOB VOLLENDET HATTE see Schein, Johann
Hermann

DA JESUS AN DEM KREUZE STUND see Wenzel,
Eberhard

DA JESUS AN DEM KREUZE STUND see Eccard,
Johannes

DA JESUS AN DEM KREUZE STUND see Hoyoul,
Balduin

DA JESUS AN DEM KREUZE STUND see Micheelsen,
Hans Friedrich

DA JESUS AN DEM KREUZE STUND see Poser, Hans

DA JESUS AN DEM KREUZE STUND see Praetorius,
Michael

DA JESUS AN DEM KREUZE STUND see Schein, Johann
Hermann

DA JESUS AN DEM KREUZE STUND see Spitta,
Heinrich

DA JESUS IN DEN GARTEN GING *Easter,mot,17th
cent
(Schiff, Helmut) [Ger] mix cor,acap oct
DOBLINGER s.p. see from Zwei Choralmotetten   (D4)

DA JESUS IN DEN GARTEN GING see Bauernfiend,
Hans

DA JESUS IN DEN GARTEN GING see Lamy, Rudolf

DA JESUS IN DEN GARTEN GING see Zipp, Friedrich

DA JESUS IN DIE GARTEN GING see Weismann,
Wilhelm

DA MANTUA
Alleluia Our Lord Has Risen *see Alleluia,
Surrexit, Dominus

Alleluia, Surrexit, Dominus
(Seay) "Alleluia Our Lord Has Risen" SATB,
acap oct FOX R163 $.30   (D5)

DA NOBIS PACEM see Mendelssohn-Bartholdy, Felix

DA NU MANNISKORNA HADE SETT DET TECKEN see
Nilsson, Torsten

DA NUN DIE MENSCHEN DAS ZEICHEN SAHEN see
Driessler, Johannes

DA NUN DIE MENSCHEN DAS ZEICHEN SAHEN see
Raselius, Andreas

DA NUN JESUS IHREN GLAUBEN SAHE see Vulpius,
Melchior

DA NUN JESUS MERKTE IHRE BOSHEIT see Driessler,
Johannes

DA PACEM see Bialas, Gunther

DA PACEM see Caron, [Philippe]

DA PACEM see Des Prez, Josquin

DA PACEM see Gounod, Charles Francois

DA PACEM see Widor, Charles-Marie

DA PACEM DOMINE see Arnaldi, Antonio

DA PACEM, DOMINE see Brands, Joh.

DA PACEM, DOMINE see Franck, Cesar

DA PACEM DOMINE see Lassus, Roland de
(Orlandus)

DA PACEM, DOMINE see Ruppel, Paul Ernst

DA PACEM, DOMINE, IN DIEBUS NOSTRIS see Schutz,
Heinrich

DA TRATEN DIE JUNGER ZU JESU see Vulpius,
Melchior

D'AANA
Sapientissimus Nostrae Salutis Auctor
mix cor SOUTHERN $.25   (D6)

DACH UND WIESEN SIND VOM FROST SILBERN
UBERZOGEN see Unger, Hermann

DAG OVER NORGE see Elvestrand, Magne

DAGAND, ABBE J.
Adoro Te Supplex
"Sing Alleluia Forth" SA,org/pno SCHIRM.EC
1966 $.25   (D7)

Come Ye, See The Savior *see Veni Sponsa
Christi

Sing Alleluia Forth *see Adoro Te Supplex

Veni Sponsa Christi
"Come Ye, See The Savior" SA,org/pno
SCHIRM.EC 1965 $.16   (D8)

DAGEN IFRAN OSS SKRIDER
see Fem Folkliga Koraler I Sattningar

DAGUES
Now Is Come Our Salvation
SATB oct BELWIN 64092 $.30   (D9)

DAILY, DAILY SING TO MARY see Mytych, J.F.

DAKERS, LIONEL
Missa Exoniensis *Mass
SATB oct NOVELLO 44.1392.10 s.p.   (D10)

DALBY, MARTIN
And He Shewed Me A Pure River
4pt mix cor,org oct SCHIRM.G 11474 $.25   (D11)

Missa Fi-Fi *Mass
[Lat] SATB,SSATTBB soli,opt 5brass CHESTER
s.p.   (D12)

When I Consider Thy Heavens *anthem/Bibl
mix cor oct NOVELLO 40.1490.01 s.p.   (D13)

DALE, A.J.
Story Of Christmas, The *Xmas,cant
1-2pt jr cor,pno voc sc WILLIS $.75   (D14)

DALE, B.J.
Before The Paling Of The Stars *Xmas,hymn
SATB,2fl,2ob,3clar,2bsn,3horn,vcl,strings,
perc,timp,2harp voc sc NOVELLO s.p., ipr   (D15)

DALE, MERVYN
How Sweet The Name Of Jesus Sounds
3pt&opt desc ASHDOWN V.T.65 s.p.   (D16)

DALLA LIBERA
Messa Sancta Maria *Mass
TTB,org s.p. cor pts RICORDI-ENG 129968-69,
voc sc RICORDI-ENG 129384   (D17)

DALLA VECCHIA, WOLFANGO
Messa Antoniana *Mass
[It/Port/Span] unis,org sc ZANIBON 4872
s.p., cor pts ZANIBON 4873 s.p.   (D18)

Tre Canti Di Acclamazione *CC3U
[It] unis ZANIBON 4797 s.p.   (D19)

DALL'ADRIA, GIOVANNI
Ave Maria *BVM
4pt mix cor ZANIBON 2015 s.p.   (D20)

Notte Dolorosa
5pt mix cor ZANIBON 1966 s.p.   (D21)

DALLIER, H.
Pastorale Pour Noel *Xmas
[Fr] STB,acap cor pts LEMOINE s.p.   (D22)
(Runner) [Fr] STB,org,ob,5strings (med)
LEMOINE sc s.p., cor pts s.p., ipa   (D23)

DALLIER-RUNNER
see DALLIER, T.

DALLIN
Songs Of Praise *CCU
SATB oct MCA $.75   (D24)

DALLINGER, FRIDOLIN
Deutsche Messe *Mass
unis,org DOBLINGER voc sc s.p., cor pts
s.p.   (D25)
men cor,org DOBLINGER voc sc s.p., voc pt
s.p.   (D26)
wom cor,org DOBLINGER voc sc s.p., voc pt
s.p.   (D27)
unis,org DOBLINGER voc sc s.p., cor pts
s.p.   (D28)

DALLINGER, GERHARD
Eigengesange Vom Ersten Adventsonntag *Adv
4pt mix cor,org DOBLINGER voc sc s.p., cor
pts s.p.   (D29)

Eigengesange Vom Fest Der Allerheiligsten
Dreifaltigkeit *Trin
mix cor,org/5brass DOBLINGER voc sc s.p.,
cor pts s.p., ipa   (D30)

DALMAINE, CYRIL C.
Catholic Mass, The *Mass
[Eng] unis/SATB oct PAXTON P85388 s.p.   (D31)

DAMASE, JEAN-MICHEL (1928-)
Messe *Mass
mix cor,org LEMOINE s.p.   (D32)

DAME GET UP AND BAKE YOUR CAKE
see Four Songs For Christmas

DAN NUN DIE MENSCHEN DAS ZEICHEN see Vulpius,
Melchior

DANBURG
Let Us Go Forth
SATB KJOS 5410 $.60   (D33)

DANCE OF DEATH see Distler, Hugo

DANCING CAROL, A see Anderson, Marion

DANDELOT, [GEORGES] (1895-)
Pax *ora
cor,soli,orch LEMOINE rental   (D34)

DANGEL, ARTHUR (1931-   )
Das Ist Ein Köstlich Ding *mot
4pt mix cor cor pts BREITKOPF-W CHB-3037
s.p.   (D35)

Es Ist Jetzt So Ein Kalte Nacht
see Magnum Nomen Domini

Geborn Ist Uns Ein Kindelein
see Magnum Nomen Domini

Magnum Nomen Domini
mix cor,acap TONGER s.p.
contains: Es Ist Jetzt So Ein Kalte
Nacht; Geborn Ist Uns Ein Kindelein;
Magnum Nomen Domini; Und Unser Lieben
Frauen Traum   (D36)

Magnum Nomen Domini
see Magnum Nomen Domini

Nun Komm, Der Heiden Heiland
mix cor,acap TONGER s.p.   (D37)

Und Unser Lieben Frauen Traum
see Magnum Nomen Domini

DANHIEUX, G.
Invitation
[Fr] jr cor (easy) BROGNEAUX s.p.   (D38)

L'Escarpolette
[Fr] jr cor (easy) BROGNEAUX s.p.   (D39)

Petit Village
[Fr] jr cor (easy) BROGNEAUX s.p.   (D40)

Petites Hirondelles
[Fr] jr cor (easy) BROGNEAUX s.p.   (D41)

Voici Les Vacaces
[Fr] jr cor (med) BROGNEAUX s.p.   (D42)

DANHOCK, L.
Wings Of Morning, The *Morn
SATB ALLANS 265 s.p.   (D43)

DANIEL JAZZ, THE see Chappell, Herbert

DANIEL, K.
Be Of The Same Mind One Toward Another
SATB,pno (med) oct WILLIS 6427 $.25   (D44)

Fill Your Hearts With Prayer
SSAATBB,pno/org (med) oct WILLIS 6200 $.20
                                            (D45)

DANIEL SAW THE STONE *spir
SATB oct STAFF 639 $.30   (D46)

DANIELS
I Will Dwell In The House Of The Lord
SATB,acap FLAMMER A 5563 $.30   (D47)

Let The Heavens Rejoice
SATB FLAMMER A 5564 $.30   (D48)

Lord Is My Strength, The
TBB STANDARD A10M1 $.40   (D49)

DANIELS, M.
Psalm Of David
SATB oct ELKAN-V 362-1230 $.25   (D50)

DANIELS, M.L.
Let The Trumpet Sound
SATB,2trp oct WORLD CA-2312-8 $.60   (D51)

DANIELS, MABEL WHEELER (1878-1971)
Carol Of A Rose *Xmas
3pt wom cor,acap oct SCHIRM.G 10632 $.25
                                            (D52)

Hail Thee, Day Of Gladness *see Salve,
Festa Dies

Salve, Festa Dies
"Hail Thee, Day Of Gladness" [Lat/Eng]
SATB,acap SCHIRM.EC 2706 $.40   (D53)

Through The Dark The Dreamers Came *Op.32,
No.1, Xmas, anthem
SSATB,pno SCHIRM.EC 2604 $.30   (D54)
SSA,pno SCHIRM.EC 2551 $.30   (D55)

DANIELSEN
Come Ye Unto Me
SATB oct LORENZ C281 $.30   (D56)

DANIELSON, DAVIS G.
Voice In The Wilderness, A *Xmas,cant
oct AGAPE $1.50   (D57)

DANISH CAROL *carol,Dan
(Cockshott, G.) SATB,acap LENGNICK s.p. (D58)

DANISH CHRISTMAS ROUND *Xmas
(Christiansen, P.) SATB SCHMITT 892 $.30
                                            (D59)

DANJOU, F.
Sub Tuum
[Lat] SSTB,B solo,opt pno/org HEUGEL voc sc
s.p., voc pt s.p.   (D60)

DANK SAGEN WIR ALLE see Praetorius, Michael

DANK SAGEN WIR ALLE GOTT see Franck, Melchior

DANK SAGEN WIR ALLE GOTT see Schutz, Heinrich

DANK SEI DIR, HERR see Handel, George Frideric

DANK SEI DIR, HERR see Kern, Matthais

DANK SEI UNSERM HEERN *Ger,17th cent
(Beveridge, L.) "Thanks Be Unto Christ" [Ger/
Eng] TTBB,acap SCHIRM.EC 2198   (D61)

DANK SEI UNSERM HERRN see Schutz, Heinrich

DANK SEI UNSERM HERRN JESU CHRISTO see Schutz,
Heinrich

DANK- UND LOBGESANG see Herbst, Johannes
Andreas

DANKE *CC8U,Gen
[Ger] unis,kbd (med) BOSSE BE 214 s.p. (D62)

DANKE see Schneider, Martin Gotthard

DANKET DEM HERREN see Schutz, Heinrich

DANKET DEM HERREN see Staden, Johann

DANKET DEM HERREN, DENN ER IST FREUNDLICH see
Kurig, Hans-Hermann

DANKET DEM HERREN, DENN ER IST FREUNDLICH see
Schutz, Heinrich

DANKET DEM HERREN, DENN ER IST SHER FREUDLICH
see Schutz, Heinrich

DANKET DEM HERREN, GEBT IHM EHR see Schutz,
Heinrich

DANKET DEM HERREN, LOBT IHN FREI see Kurig,
Hans-Hermann

DANKET DEM HERREN, LOBT IHN FREI see Schutz,
Heinrich

DANKET DEM HERREN see Schutz, Heinrich

DANKET DEM HERRN see Lechner, Leonhard

DANKET DEM HERRN see Meyer-Janson, Burkhard

DANKET DEM HERRN see Rosenmuller, Johann

DANKET DEM HERRN see Schutz, Heinrich

DANKET DEM HERRN see Selle, Thomas

DANKET DEM HERRN see Staden, Johann

DANKET DEM HERRN see Telemann, Georg Philipp

DANKET DEM HERRN ALLEZEIT see Staden, Johann

DANKET DEM HERRN, DENN ER IST see
Hammerschmidt, Andreas

DANKET DEM HERRN, DENN ER IST FREUNDLICH see
Anonymous

DANKET DEM HERRN, DENN ER IST FREUNDLICH see
Reda, Siegfried

DANKET DEM HERRN ERZEIGT IHM EHR see Schutz,
Heinrich

DANKET DEM HERRN HEUT UND ALLZEIT see
Bodenschatz, Erhard

DANKET DEM HERRN UND EHRET see Wieruszowski,
Lili

DANKET DEM HERRN see Schutz, Heinrich

DANKET GOTT UND LOBET IHN see Schweizer, Rolf

DANKS
God Ruleth Over All
(Wiley) SATB oct PRO ART 2548 $.25   (D63)

I Will Magnify Thee, O God
(Harris) SATB oct PRO ART 2640 $.35   (D64)

DANKSAGEN WIR ALLE GOTT (from Sgc)
(Granville) "Now Let All Men Thank Thee" SATB
oct FOX CM18 $.35   (D65)

DANKSAGEN WIR ALLE GOTT see Schutz, Heinrich

DANKSAGEN WIR ALLE GOTT CHRISTO, DER UNS MIT
SEINEM WORT see Schutz, Heinrich

DANKSAGET DEM VATER see Reda, Siegfried

DANKSAGET DEM VATER see Rosenmuller, Johann

DANKT, DANKT NU ALLEN GOD see Bach, Johann
Sebastian

DANKT, DANKT NU ALLEN GOD see Cruger, Johann

DANKT DEM HERRN! see Schmid, Walter

DANKT DEM HERRN UND PREDIGT SEINEN NAMEN see
Ruppel, Paul Ernst

DANKT GOTT *spir
"I Got A Robe" see Four Negro Spirituals
(Dexter, Harry) "I Got A Robe" 2pt ENOCH
TP267 s.p.   (D66)
(Roberton) "I Got A Robe" 3pt jr cor/3pt wom
cor ROBERTON 72106 s.p.   (D67)
(Schmid, Walter) "I Got A Robe" [Eng] mix
cor,acap (easy) HUG s.p.   (D68)
(Widdicombe) "I Got A Robe" 2pt jr cor/2pt
wom cor CURWEN 72560 s.p.   (D69)

DANKT UNSERM GOTT, LOBSINGET IHM see Kurig,
Hans-Hermann

DANN
Bread Of Life
SATB SOUTHERN $.30   (D70)

DANN, H.
Standard Anthems, Vol. 1 *CCU
mix cor BELWIN $2.00   (D71)

Standard Anthems, Vol. 2 *CCU
mix cor BELWIN $2.00   (D72)

DANN SOLLT IHR SEH'N see Handel, George
Frideric, Then Shall They Know

DANN WIRD ZUM GOLD'NEN STERNENZELT see Handel,
George Frideric, Then Round About The
Starry Throne

DANNSTROM
Hur Ljuft Det Ar Att Komma
[Swed] 4pt wom cor LUNDQUIST 75 s.p. (D73)

DANS CETT' ETABLE *Xmas,carol,Fr/Span
"Bethlehem" see Silent Night
"Bethlehem" see At The Manger
"Bethlehem" ASHDOWN 35 s.p.   (D74)
"Bethlehem" unis/SATB (easy) OXFORD O8.074
$.15   (D75)
(Bancroft, H.H.) "Bethlehem" SATB oct LESLIE
4014 see from Two Christmas Carols, Set 1
                                            (D76)

(Barrow, R.) "Bethlehem" [Fr/Eng] TTBB,acap
SCHIRM.EC 2147 $.25   (D77)
(Sargent) "Bethlehem" SATB,acap (easy) OXFORD
43.201 $.25   (D78)

DANS CETTE ETABLE *Xmas,carol
"In That Poor Stable" unis/SATB (easy) OXFORD
08.074 $.15   (D79)
(Du Bois, L.) [Fr] 4pt mix cor (med
easy) cor pts LEMOINE s.p. see from
Collection De Choeurs, dixieme Fascicule
                                            (D80)

DANS LA NUIT DE NOEL see Schmidlin, J.

DANS MA PROFONDE DETRESSE, JE CRIE VERS TOI see
Bach, Johann Sebastian

DANS UNE HUMBLE MASURE see Canteloube de
Malaret, Marie-Joseph

DANSE DE SALOME see Achron, Joseph

DANSKE MOTETTER OG ANDRE KORSTYKKER see
Jeppesen, Knud

DANZA DE PANDERO see Benedito

D'AQUIN, LOUIS-CLAUDE (1694-1772)
Noel We Sing (from Grand Jeu Et Duo) Xmas
(De Cormier; Biggs) SATB,pno/org oct LAWSON
51436 $.40   (D81)

Shepherds, Hark The Song
(Page, N.) SATB oct PRESSER 312-40031 $.30
                                            (D82)

DARAN IST ERSCHIENEN see Thomas, Kurt

DARAN IST ERSCHIENEN DIE LIEBE GOTTES see
Doppelbauer, Josef Friedrich

DARAN IST ERSCHIENEN DIE LIEBE GOTTES see
Rosenmuller, Johann

DARCIEUX, [F.]
A La Nativite *Xmas,carol
[Fr] SSTBarB,opt pno/org (easy) LEMOINE voc
sc s.p., cor pts s.p.   (D83)

Noel *Xmas
(Holmes, A.) [Fr] 3pt jr cor,pno (easy)
LEMOINE cor pts s.p., voc sc s.p.   (D84)

Noel D'enfant *Xmas
(Missa, E.) [Fr] 3pt jr cor,pno (med)
LEMOINE cor pts s.p., voc sc s.p.   (D85)

Noel D'holmes *Xmas,carol
[Fr] 3 eq voices,acap LEMOINE s.p.   (D86)
[Fr] 4pt men cor,acap LEMOINE s.p.   (D87)
[Fr] 4pt mix cor,acap LEMOINE s.p.   (D88)

Noel Dialogue *Xmas
[Fr] 2pt jr cor,acap (easy) LEMOINE s.p.   (D89)

Noel, Ribon, Ribaine *Xmas
[Fr] 2pt jr cor,pno/org (very easy) LEMOINE
voc sc s.p., cor pts s.p.   (D90)

Now Noel Has Come Again
[Eng/Fr] SATB,acap oct SALABERT-US $.35
                                            (D91)

Voici Le Saint Temps, Mes Freres *Xmas
[Fr] mix cor,opt pno/org (easy) LEMOINE voc
sc s.p., cor pts s.p.   (D92)

DARK AND DAWN see Sibelius, Jean

DARK CLOUD, COVER THE SEA see Shure, D.

DARK HILLS, THE see Bissell, Keith

DARK NIGHT OF THE SOUL see Surinach, Carlos,
Noche Oscura Del Alma

DARK THE NIGHT see Butler, Eugene

DARK THE NIGHT see Mead

DARK WAS THE EARTH WITH CLOUDS see Haydn,
(Johann) Michael, Tenebrae Factae Sunt

DARKE, HAROLD [EDWIN] (1888-   )
Be Strong And Of A Good Courage *Fest/Gen,
Bibl
SATB (med) oct OXFORD 42.879 $.50   (D93)

Communion Service In A Minor *Commun,Agnus/
Bene/Credo/Gloria/Kyrie/Sanctus
SATB (med easy) oct OXFORD 42.714 $1.20
                                            (D94)

Communion Service In E *Commun
SATB (med) oct OXFORD 42.847 $.80   (D95)

Communion Service In F *Commun
SATB (med easy) oct OXFORD 42.830 $.75
                                            (D96)

Magnificat And Nunc Dimittis In A Minor
*Magnif/Nunc
SATB,acap CRAMER A3 s.p.   (D97)

Nine-Fold Kyrie (from Communion Service In F)
Kyrie
SATB (med) oct OXFORD 42.972 $.15   (D98)

O God Whose Mighty Works Of Old *Ded/Fest
SATB (med) oct OXFORD 42.858 $.35   (D99)

Psalm Of Thanksgiving, A *Fest/Thanks
SATB (med easy) oct OXFORD 42.995 $.50
                                            (D100)

Responses For Treble Voices
4pt treb cor (easy) oct OXFORD 44.213 $.25
                                            (D101)

Sower, The *cant
SATB,STB soli,pno/org (med) voc sc OXFORD
46.015 $2.25   (D102)

DARKEN'D WAS ALL THE LAND see Haydn, G.

DARKER THE MOUNTAIN *Xmas
(Taylor, V.; Taylor, L.) SATB LEONARD-US
08011520 $.25   (D103)

DARKEST HOUR, THE see Moore, Harold

DARKLY ROSE THE GUILTY MORNING see Brumel,
Antoine

DARKNESS CONCEALED THE EARTH see Haydn, (Franz)
Joseph

DARKNESS FELL ON THE EARTH see Davye, John F.,
Tenebrae Factae Sunt

DARKNESS FELL UPON THE EARTH see Poulenc,
Francis, Tenebrae Factae Sunt

DARKNESS, GROSS DARKNESS DID COVER THE EARTH
see Tenebrae Factae Sunt

DARKNESS IS SOON OVER see Back, Sven-Erick, Nox
Praecessit

DARKNESS MADE DIM THE EARTH see Haydn, (Johann)
Michael

DARKNESS NOW HAS TAKEN FLIGHT, THE see
Lovelace, Austin C.

DARKNESS OBSCURED THE EARTH see Haydn, (Johann)
Michael

DARKNESS OBSCURED THE EARTH see Ingegneri,
Marco Antonio, Tenebrae Factae Sunt

DARKNESS WAS ALL OVER see Biber, C.H., Tenebrae
Factae Sunt

DARKNESS WAS ALL OVER see Haydn, (Johann)
Michael

DARKNESS WAS O'ER THE EARTH see Ingegneri,
Marco Antonio, Tenebrae Factae Sunt

DARKNESS WAS ON THE EARTH see Haydn, (Franz)
Joseph

DARKNESS WAS OVER ALL see Croce, Giovanni,
Tenebrae Factae Sunt

DARKNESS WAS OVER ALL see Haydn, (Franz)
Joseph, Tenebrae Factae Sunt

DARKNESS WAS OVER ALL see Victoria, Tomas Luis
de

DARKNESS WAS OVER THE EARTH see Haydn, (Johann)
Michael, Tenebrae Factae Sunt

DARLOW, DENYS
Collect, A *Gen
SATB,acap (med) oct OXFORD 43.357 $.20
(D104)
Fool Hath Said In His Heart, The *Gen
SATB,acap (med) oct OXFORD 43.351 $.30
(D105)

DARNTON
I Will Sing Of Thy Great Mercies
SATB ALLANS 375 s.p.   (D106)

DARNTON, C.
I Will Sing Of The Mercies Of The Lord
cor oct HART s.p.   (D107)

Praise The Lord And Call Upon His Name
cor oct HART s.p.   (D108)

DARST, S. GLEN
Come, Let Us Join
SATB,org PEER $.35   (D109)

Come, Thou Long-Expected Jesus
SATB,org PEER $.35   (D110)

Lift Up Your Hearts, Ye People
SATB,org PEER $.35   (D111)

Praise The Lord Of Heaven
SATB,org PEER $.40   (D112)

Praise The Saviour
SATB,org PEER $.35   (D113)

Praise Ye The Father
SATB,org PEER $.35   (D114)

Strong Son Of God, Immortal Love
SAB,pno/org PEER $.35   (D115)

DARST THOU NOW see Williams, David McK.

DARST, W. GLEN
Come To Me *Gen
SAB,kbd (med easy) oct CONCORDIA 98-1577
$.25   (D116)

Father, Hear Us Pray
SA,org PEER $.40   (D117)

Heralds Of Christ *Gen
SATB&desc (med easy) oct CONCORDIA 98-1717
$.25   (D118)

To God All Praise And Glory *Gen
2pt mix cor,kbd (med easy) oct CONCORDIA
98-1934 $.30   (D119)

DARST, W. GLENN (1896-)
All Creatures Of Our God And King
SATB oct AGAPE A414 $.35   (D120)

All Hail The Power Of Jesus' Name
SATB oct SACRED S-9926 $.35   (D121)

All Praise To Thee, Eternal God
4pt jr cor/SATB (easy) FISCHER,C CM 7115
$.25   (D122)

All Things Are Thine
SATB oct SACRED E84 $.35   (D123)

Alleluia! Sing To Jesus
SATB oct SACRED S-9919 $.35   (D124)

Angels, Roll The Rock Away *Easter
SATB oct GRAY GCMR 3124 $.30   (D125)

Be Still, My Soul
SATB oct FISCHER,C CM-7658 $.25   (D126)

Blest Are The Pure
SATB oct GRAY GCMR 3052 $.30   (D127)

Christ Hath Triumphed, Alleluia *Easter/Lent
SATB oct WALTON 2020 $.30   (D128)

DARST, W. GLENN (cont'd.)
Christ Is Our Cornerstone
SATB oct GRAY GCMR 3054 $.30   (D129)

Christ, The New-Born King *Xmas
SATB oct ELKAN-V 362-1194 $.25   (D130)

Closer Walk With God, A
2pt jr cor FISCHER,C CM 7243 $.20   (D131)

Come, Faithful People *Palm
SAB oct GRAY GCMR 2630 $.25   (D132)
SATB oct GRAY GCMR 2449 $.30   (D133)

Come, Ye Disconsolate
SAB oct GRAY GCMR 3220 $.30   (D134)

Come Ye Faithful, Raise The Strain *Easter
SATB oct GRAY GCMR 3287 $.30   (D135)

Day Of Resurrection, The
SATB oct ELKAN-V 362-1309 $.30   (D136)

Draw Nigh To Jerusalem *Palm
SATB oct SOUTHERN $.25   (D137)

Draw Nigh To Thy Jerusalem *Palm
SATB oct ELKAN-V 362-1227 $.25   (D138)

Father Almighty
SA GRAY GCMR 3273 $.30   (D139)

Forth In Thy Name
SA/TB FLAMMER E5083 $.25   (D140)

Give Unto The Lord, Ye Mighty
SATB oct FISCHER,C CM-7639 $.30   (D141)

God Is Light
3pt jr cor/SSA (easy) FISCHER,C CM 7435
$.20   (D142)
SSA oct FISCHER,C CM-7435 $.30   (D143)

Gracious Spirit, Holy Spirit
SATB oct SACRED S-9943 $.35   (D144)

Great Is The Holy One *anthem
SATB oct FISCHER,C CM-7114 $.25   (D145)

Hallelujah! Let Praises Ring
SATB oct WALTON 2028 $.30   (D146)

Honor Him Our King *Palm
3pt jr cor/SAB (very easy) FISCHER,C
CM 7597 $.25   (D147)

Hosanna, Loud Hosanna
SATB oct ELKAN-V 362-1114 $.25   (D148)

I Am The Light Of The World
SATB oct SACRED E42 $.35   (D149)

Immortal Love
SATB oct SACRED S-55 $.35   (D150)

Jesus Christ Is Ris'n Today
SATB FLAMMER A 5289 $.35   (D151)

Jesus, Lead Us
unis/SA oct SACRED S-8605 $.30   (D152)

Jesus, The Very Thought Of Thee
SATB oct FISCHER,C CM-7029 $.25   (D153)

Jesus, Thou Joy Of Loving Hearts
SATB oct LORENZ 9983 $.30   (D154)

Lead On, O King Eternal
SAB oct ELKAN-V 362-1251 $.25   (D155)

Let All Mortal Flesh *Xmas
SATB oct GRAY GCMR 2142 $.30   (D156)
(Davis) SAB oct BELWIN 64176 $.30   (D157)

Lord, Teach Us How To Pray
SAB oct ELKAN-V 362-1312 $.30   (D158)

Lord Who Shall Abide
SATB oct PRESSER 362-03121 $.30   (D159)

March On, O Soul, With Strength
SATB oct AGAPE A 439 $.30   (D160)

Now Let Every Tongue Adore
SATB oct GRAY GCMR 3099 $.30   (D161)

O For A Heart To Praise My God
SATB,opt B solo oct GRAY GCMR 3115 $.25
(D162)

O God Of Love *anthem
3pt jr cor/SAB (easy) FISCHER,C CM 7302
$.25   (D163)
SAB oct FISCHER,C CM-7302 $.25   (D164)

O God Of Youth
unis SATB oct GRAY GCMR 2147 $.25   (D165)

O Little One *Xmas
sr cor&jr cor oct ELKAN-V 362-1126 $.25
(D166)

O Sing, All Ye Lands
SAB oct ELKAN-V 362-513 $.30   (D167)

O That I Had A Thousand Voices *anthem
3pt jr cor/SAB (easy) FISCHER,C CM 7467
$.25   (D168)
SAB oct FISCHER,C CM-7467 $.25   (D169)

O Worship The King *Bibl
SATB,opt trp oct AGAPE F 932 $.30   (D170)

Our Lord Is Risen *Easter
SATB oct GRAY GCMR 2926 $.25   (D171)

Praise, My Soul, The King
SATB oct GRAY GCMR 3050 $.30   (D172)

Praise Thou The Lord
SATB oct FOX PS156 $.25   (D173)

Praise To God, Immortal Praise *Thanks
3pt jr cor/SAB (very easy) FISCHER,C
CM 7264 $.20   (D174)

Prayer For Light, A *prayer
SAB GRAY GCMR 3274 $.30   (D175)

DARST, W. GLENN (cont'd.)
Psalm Of Praise *Psalm
SS oct GRAY GCMR 2471 $.25   (D176)

Rejoice And Sing *Easter
SATB oct GRAY GCMR 2875 $.25   (D177)

Rejoice This Happy Morn *Xmas
SATB oct FISCHER,C CM-7674 $.30   (D178)

Rejoice Today
SAB oct GRAY GCMR 2557 $.30   (D179)

Rejoice, Ye Pure In Heart *Easter
SATB oct SOUTHERN $.25   (D180)

Ride On, Ride On *Easter/Lent/Palm
SAB oct GRAY GCMR 2245 $.30   (D181)
SATB oct GRAY GCMR 2120 $.35   (D182)

Ride On! Ride On In Majesty *Palm
SATB oct SOUTHERN $.35   (D183)

Savior Of The World Is Here, The
SATB oct BELWIN 64265 $.35   (D184)

Shepherd Of Tender Youth
SAB oct SUMMY B 2116 $.30   (D185)

Sing And Pray And Keep His Ways
4pt jr cor/SATB (med easy) FISCHER,C
CM 7672 $.25   (D186)

Sing Praise To God
SATB oct SACRED E70 $.35   (D187)

Sing To The Lord
SATB/SAT/SAB oct GRAY GCMR 2053 $.35 (D188)

Song Of Praise
3pt jr cor/SSA (med easy) FISCHER,C CM 7158
$.20   (D189)

Spirit Divine
SAB FLAMMER D5115 $.30   (D190)

Spirt Of God
SATB oct ELKAN-V 362-1264 $.30   (D191)

Stand Up, And Bless The Lord
SA/TB oct GRAY GCMR 2570 $.30   (D192)

Take Thou Our Minds, Dear Lord
SATB oct SACRED S-19 $.35   (D193)

To Thee, O Lord, Our Hearts We Raise
SATB oct WALTON 2034 $.25   (D194)

Unto You Is Born A Saviour *Xmas
SSATB oct WALTON 2032 $.25   (D195)

Variants On "A Mighty Fortress"
SATB oct GRAY GCMR 2746 $.40   (D196)

Walk Humbly With Thy God *anthem
SATB oct FISCHER,C CM-7422 $.25   (D197)

We Need Thy Love *anthem
men cor&wom cor (med diff) oct LORENZ C344
$.30   (D198)
SATB oct LORENZ C344 $.30   (D199)

Ye Holy Angels Bright
unis/SA oct ELKAN-V 362-519 $.25   (D200)

DARTMOUTH MAGNIFICAT, THE see Kendall, John

DARUM SEID BARMHERZIG see Franck, Melchior

DARUM SEID BARMHERZIG see Raselius, Andreas

DARUM SEID BARMHERZIG see Vulpius, Melchior

DARUM SPRICHT DER HERR, HERR see Zipp,
Friedrich

DARUM WACHET see Driessler, Johannes

DARUM WACHET see Koch, Johannes H.E.

DARUM WACHET, DENN IHR WISSET WEDER TAG see
Hammerschmidt, Andreas

DARUM WACHET, DENN IHR WISSET WEDER TAG NOCH
STUNDE see Driessler, Johannes

DARWALL
Break, Day Of God
(Cain) SAB FLAMMER D5062 $.25   (D201)

King Of Glory Praise, The *Easter/Lent/Palm
(Hastings) SATB,opt 2trp oct BOURNE HA9
$.30   (D202)
(Wiley) SATB oct PRO ART 1748 $.22   (D203)

Rejoice
(Kirk) SSA oct BELWIN 1623 $.25   (D204)
(Kirk) SAB oct BELWIN 1172 $.30   (D205)
(Kirk) SATB oct BELWIN 1627 $.30   (D206)

Rejoice, The Lord Is King!
(Gerig) SATB oct LILLENAS AN-2220 $.30
(D207)
(Pfohl) SATB FLAMMER A 5008 $.30   (D208)
(Pfohl) SAB FLAMMER D5093 $.25   (D209)

Ye Holy Angels Bright
(Smith) SATB&opt desc oct PRO ART 2000 $.22
(D210)
(Smith) SAB&opt desc oct PRO ART 2003 $.25
(D211)

DARWELL
Rejoice, The Lord Is King *Gen
(Symonds) SATB,kbd SCHMITT 15014 $.35   (D212)

DAS ABER AUF DEM GUTEN LAND see Raselius,
Andreas

DAS ALTE IST VERGANGEN see Lauth, Wolfgang

DAS ALTE JAHR [CHORALE] see Bach, Johann
Sebastian

DAS ALTE JAHR IST NUN DAHIN see Praetorius,
Michael

DAS ALTE JAHR VERGANGEN IST see Calvisius, Sethus

DAS ALTE JAHR VERGANGEN IST see Dedekind, Constantine Christian

DAS ALTE JAHR VERGANGEN IST see Dulichius, Philippus

DAS ALTE JAHR VERGANGEN IST see Hufschmidt, Wolfgang

DAS ALTE JAHR VERGANGEN IST see Scheidt, Samuel

DAS ALTE JAHR VERGANGEN IST see Schmeel, Dieter

DAS ALTE JAHR VERGANGEN IST see Stern, Hermann

DAS ALTE JAHRE VERGANGEN IST see Brunner, Adolf

DAS APOSTOLICUM "ICH GLAUB AN GOTT VATER" see Kugelmann, Johann

DAS APOSTOLISCHE GLAUBENBEKENNTNIS see Schwartz, Gerhard von

DAS BENEDICITE VOR DEM ESSEN see Schutz, Heinrich

DAS BENEDICITE VOR DEM ESSEN "ALLER AUGEN WARTEN AUF DICH" see Schutz, Heinrich

DAS BLUT JESU CHRISTI see Bach, Johann Michael

DAS BLUT JESU CHRISTI MACHET UNS REIN see Schutz, Heinrich

DAS BROT, HERR, UNS SEGNE see Kurig, Hans-Hermann

DAS CHORALWERK, NO. 1: ADVENT ZU TRINITAS see Bornefeld, Helmut

DAS CHORALWERK, NO. 2 see Bornefeld, Helmut

DAS CHORALWERK, NO. 3 see Bornefeld, Helmut

DAS DEO GRATIAS NACH DEM ESSEN see Schutz, Heinrich

DAS DEUTSCHE ET IN TERRA 1537 *Gen,Gloria/Kyrie,16th cent
(Distler, Hugo) [Lat] SAT&STB,acap (med diff) BAREN. BA 1054 $1.00 (D213)

DAS DEUTSCHE TE DEUM see Praetorius, Michael

DAS EVANGELIUM see Fiebig, Kurt

DAS EVANGELIUM AUF DEN 4. ADVENT see Reda, Siegfried

DAS EWIGE EVANGELIUM see Janacek, Leos

DAS EZZOLIED: LUX IN TENEBRIS, DAS IN UNSRER MITTEN IST see Burkhard Willy

DAS FELD IST WEISS see Rein, Walter

DAS GEBET DES HERRN see Schubert, Franz (Peter)

DAS GESICHT DES JESAJAS see Burkhard Willy

DAS GESICHT JESAJAS see Burkhard Willy

DAS GLAUBENSBEKENNTNIS see Raphael, Gunther

DAS GLEICHNIS VOM SAEMANN see Wenzel, Eberhard

DAS GLEICHNIS VOM UNKRAUT UNTER DEM WEIZEN see Schloemann, Burghard

DAS GLEICHNIS VON DEN ZEHN JUNGFRAUEN see Brunner, Adolf

DAS GOTTLICHE SPIEL, TEIL II; DIE HEIMSUCHUNG see Reda, Siegfried

DAS GRADUALLIED, TEIL I: ADVENT BIS PFINGSTEN see Reda, Siegfried

DAS GRATIAS NACH DEM ESSEN "DANKET DEM HERREN, DENN ER IST SEHR FREUNDLICH" see Schutz, Heinrich

DAS GROSSE DOMINE see Cornelius, Peter

DAS GROSSE GLORIA see Bach, Johann Sebastian

DAS GROSSE HALLELUJA see Handel, George Frideric

DAS GROSSE HALLELUJAH see Schubert, Franz (Peter)

DAS GROSSE LEID see Lehman, Siegfried

DAS GROSSE LICHT see Burkhart, Franz

DAS GRUASS DIE GOT'! see Anderluh, Anton

DAS HEIL DER WELT see Bruckner, Anton

DAS HEILIGE JAHR, HEFT I: ADVENT see Ahrens, Joseph

DAS HEILIGE JAHR, HEFT II: WEIHNACHTEN see Ahrens, Joseph

DAS HEILIGE JAHR, HEFT III: JESU NAMEN see Ahrens, Joseph

DAS HEILIGE JAHR, HEFT IV: PASSION see Ahrens, Joseph

DAS HEILIGE JAHR, HEFT V: OSTERN see Ahrens, Joseph

DAS HEILIGE JAHR, HEFT VI: PFINGSTEN see Ahrens, Joseph

DAS HEILIGE JAHR, HEFT VII: EUCHARISTIE see Ahrens, Joseph

DAS HEILIGE JAHR, HEFT VIII: MARIENLOB see Ahrens, Joseph

DAS HEILIGE JAHR, HEFT IX: GOTTESLOB see Ahrens, Joseph

DAS HIMMELREICH IST GLEICH EINEM KONIGE see Driessler, Johannes

DAS HIMMLISCHE HAUS see Bruckner, Anton

DAS HOHE LIED SALOMONIS see Palestrina, Giovanni

DAS HOHE LIED SALOMONS see David, Karl Heinrich

DAS HOHELIED SALOMONIS see Lechner, Leonhard

DAS IST ABER DAS EWIGE LEBEN see Fischer-Dieskau, Klaus

DAS IST DAS ERSTE ZEICHEN, DAS JESUS TAT see Driessler, Johannes

DAS IST DAS EWIGE LEBEN see Rosenmuller, Johann

DAS IST DER TAG *17th cent
(Strobl, Otto) mix cor,acap oct DOBLINGER s.p. (D214)

DAS IST DER TAG see Kubizek, Augustinian

DAS IST DER TAG, DEN DER HERR see Brunner, Adolf

DAS IST DER TAG DES HERRN see Kreutzer, C.

DAS IST EIN KOSTLICH DING see Dangel, Arthur

DAS IST EIN KOSTLICH DING see Eglin, Arthur

DAS IST EIN KOSTLICH DING see Kubizek, Augustinian

DAS IST EIN KOSTLICH DING see Kukuck, Felicitas

DAS IST EIN KOSTLICH DING see Lisken, Gerd

DAS IST EIN KOSTLICH DING see Reda, Siegfried

DAS IST EIN KOSTLICH DING see Schweizer, Rolf

DAS IST EIN KOSTLICH DING, DEM HERREN DANKEN see Rosenmuller, Johann

DAS IST EINE SEL'GE STUNDE see Wessnitzer, Wolfgang

DAS IST FURWAHR EIN KOSTLICH DING see Gesius, Bartholomaus

DAS IST JE GEWISSLICH WAHR see Bach, Johann Sebastian

DAS IST JE GEWISSLICH WAHR see Distler, Hugo

DAS IST JE GEWISSLICH WAHR see Hammerschmidt, Andreas

DAS IST JE GEWISSLICH WAHR see Hollfelder, Waldram

DAS IST JE GEWISSLICH WAHR see Micheelsen, Hans Friedrich

DAS IST JE GEWISSLICH WAHR see Schutz, Heinrich

DAS IST JE GEWISSLICH WAHR see Telemann, Georg Philipp

DAS IST MEINE FREUDE, DASS ICH MICH ZU GOTT see Kretzschmar, Gunther

DAS IST MIR LIEB see Schutz, Heinrich, Das Ist Mir Lieb, Dass Der Herr Mein Stimm Und Flehen Horet

DAS IST MIR LIEB, DASS DER HERR MEIN STIMM UND FLEHEN HORET see Schutz, Heinrich

DAS JAHR DES HERRN see Micheelsen, Hans Friedrich

DAS JAHR GEHT STILL ZU ENDE see Kammerer, Imanuel Johannes

DAS JAHR GEHT STILL ZU ENDE see Lavater, H.

DAS JUNGE CHORLIED see Rothenberg, Friedrich Samuel

DAS KANANAISCHE WEIB see Jacobi, Samuel

DAS KAROLISSER HEFT *CCU,Xmas,carol
(Stern) [Ger] unis HUG s.p. (D215)

DAS KARTNER PILATUSSPIEL *folk,Aus
(Tittel, Ernst) mix cor,acap oct DOBLINGER s.p. see from Geistliche Volkslieder Aus Osterreich (D216)

DAS KIND RUHT AUS see Vollenwyder, H.

DAS KINDLEIN, DAS MARIA HALT see Spitta, Heinrich

DAS KIRCHENJAHR UND SEINE CHORALE see Bach, Johann Sebastian

DAS KIRCHENLIED IN KLEINER BESETZUNG-HEFT 1 *CC34U
(Stein, Herman) unis,kbd,opt treb inst sc HANSSLER 19.801 s.p. (D217)

DAS KIRCHENLIED IN KLEINER BESETZUNG-HEFT 2 *CC51U
unis,kbd,opt 1-2treb inst sc HANSSLER 19.802 s.p. contains settings by: Freidel; Koch; Kretzschmar; Kukuck; Lotz; Ruppel; Schauss-Flake; Schoof, V.; Schwartz; Schweizer (D218)

DAS KLEINE PSALMENBUCH see Johner, Theodore E.

DAS KOMMENDE REICH see Kukuck, Felicitas

DAS KONIGSBANNER ZIEHT VORAUS see Eccard, Johannes

DAS KONIGSBANNER ZIEHT VORAUS, IHM see Berger, Hans Ludwig

DAS KREUZ CHRISTI see Graap, Lothar

DAS KREUZ IST AUFGERICHTET see Barbe, Helmut

DAS LEBEN IST NUR EIN KOMMEN UND GEHN see Lissmann, Kurt

DAS LICHT BRICHT DURCH see Ruegger, F.

DAS LIEBEN BRINGT GROSS FREUD see Benker, Heinz

DAS LIEBESMAHL DER APOSTEL see Wagner, Richard

DAS LIED DER KIRCHE-HEFT 1 *CC10U,Adv,mot
(Jansen, Philipp) eq voices HANSSLER 9.001 s.p. (D219)

DAS LIED DER KIRCHE-HEFT 2 *CC15U,Psntd,mot
(Jansen, Philipp) 3pt mix cor HANSSLER 9.002 s.p. (D220)

DAS LIED DER KIRCHE-HEFT 4 *CC8U,mot
(Jansen, Philipp) cor,inst HANSSLER 9.004 s.p. (D221)

DAS LIED DER KIRCHE-HEFT 5 *CC7U,Thanks,mot
(Jansen, Philipp) jr cor,inst HANSSLER 9.005 s.p. (D222)

DAS LIED VOM KREUZ see Muller von Kulm, Walter

DAS LIED VOM SCHWEIZERKREUZ see Lavater, H.

DAS LIED VON MOSES see Ettinger, Max

DAS LOB DER FRAU see Hagler, Paul

DAS MAGNIFICAT see Peter, Herbert

DAS MANNERLIED *CC72U,Gen
(Lipphardt, Walther) [Ger] SATB men cor,acap (med easy) BAREN. BA 700 s.p. (D223)

DAS MUSIKWERK see Schmidt-Gorg, Joseph

DAS NAMENSFEST see Sussmayr, Franz Xavier

DAS NEUGEBOR'NE KINDELEIN see Bach, Johann Sebastian

DAS NEUGEBORNE KINDELEIN see Buxtehude, Dietrich

DAS NEUGEBORNE KINDELEIN [CHORALE] see Bach, Johann Sebastian

DAS NEUGEBOR'NE KINDELEIN, DAS HERZENSLIEBE see Bach, Johann Sebastian

DAS NIZANISCHE GLAUBENSBEKENNTNIS see Schwartz, Gerhard von

DAS NIZANISCHE GLAUBENSBEKENNTNIS see Wenzel, Eberhard

DAS NONNCHEN "ALS MICH MEIN MUTTERLEIN ZUM NONNCHEN MACHT" see Strohbach, Siegfried

DAS NONNLEIN UND DER TEUFEL "GING DAS NONNLEIN UND SUCHT IM GARTEN" see Strohbach, Siegfried

DAS PSALMBUCH see Reda, Siegfried

DAS PSALMENBUCH *CC50U,Gen
(Holliger, Hans) [Ger] SATB,acap (med easy) BAREN. BA 2850 $5.25 contains works by: Bourgeois; Jambe De Fer; Goudimel; L'estocart; Claudin Le Jeune; Sweelinck (D224)

DAS QUEMPAS-BUCH *CC98U,Xmas
[Ger] 2 eq voices,acap BAREN. BA 4998 $4.75 (D225)

DAS QUEMPAS-HEFT *CC35U,Xmas
(Ameln, Konrad) [Ger] 2-4 eq voices (med easy) BAREN. BA 1302 $2.75 (D226)

DAS QUEMPAS-HEFT *CC28U,Xmas
(Ameln, Konrad) [Ger] 2-5pt mix cor,acap BAREN. BA 1301 s.p. settings of old and new masters (D227)

DAS SALVE REGINA DEUTSCH *BVM,17th cent
(Dawidowicz, Anton) wom cor,acap (contains also: Ein Ander Schon Bittlied Zur Muttergottes) oct DOBLINGER s.p. see also Acht Marienlieder (D228)

DAS SCHLARAFFENLAND *folk
(Brahms, J.) "Wonderful Inn, The" [Ger/Eng] unis,pno SCHIRM.EC 1047 $.12 (D229)
(Brahms, Johannes) "Wonderful Inn, The" unis, pno SCHIRM.EC 1047 $.12 (D230)

DAS SCHONE ENGELE see Burkhart, Franz

DAS SCHWEIZERKREUZ see Aeschbacher, Walther

DAS TE-DEUM see Kukuck, Felicitas

DAS TE DEUM LAUDAMUS DEUTSCH see Huber, Klaus

DAS TROSTREICHE 53. KAPITEL DES PROPHETEN JESAJA see Franck, Melchior

DAS UNAUFHORLICHE see Hindemith, Paul

DAS VATER UNSER see Poos, Heinrich

DAS VATER UNSER see Resinarius, Balthasar

DAS "VATER UNSER" see Schutz, Heinrich, Vater Unser, Der Du Bist Im Himmel

DAS VATERUNSER see Schutz, Heinrich

DAS VERLANGEN DER ELENDEN HORST DU, HERR see Reda, Siegfried

DAS VOKALWERK see Pachelbel, Johann

DAS VOLK ABER, DAS VORANGING see Vulpius, Melchior

DAS VOLK ABER, DAS VORGING see Vulpius, Melchior

DAS VOLK, SO IM FINSTERN WANDELT see Wenzel,
   Eberhard

DAS VOLK, SO IM FINSTERN WANDELT see Zipp,
   Friedrich

DAS WALT GOTT VATER UND GOTT SOHN see Schlicht,
   Johann Gottfried

DAS WALTE GOTT, DER HELFEN KAN see Knecht,
   [Justin Heinrich]

DAS WEIHNACHTSBEDENKEN see Knorr, Ernst Lother
   von

DAS WEIHNACHTSEVANGELIUM see Brunner, Adolf

DAS WEIHNACHTSEVANGELIUM see Weinreich,
   Waltraut

DAS WEIHNACHTSEVANGELIUM NACH LUKAS see Benary,
   Peter

DAS WEIHNACHTSLIEDERBUCH see Freundt, Cornelius

DAS WELTGERICHT see Pepping, Ernst

DAS WESSOBRUNNER GEBET *mot,9th cent
   (Burkhart, Franz) mix cor,acap DOBLINGER s.p.
   see also In Seiner Handen   (D231)

DAS WESSOBRUNNER GEBET see Weismann, Wilhelm

DAS WOCHENLIED *CC164U,Gen
   (Reich, Philipp) [Ger] 3-5pt mix cor,acap
   (med) BAREN. BA 2208 $7.75 settings by old
   and new masters   (D232)

DAS WOCHENLIED *CC140U,Gen
   (Reich, Philipp) [Ger] 2 eq voices/3 eq
   voices,acap (med) BAREN. BA 2209 $7.75
   contains settings by old and new masters
                                          (D233)

DAS WORT GOTTES, DES ALLERHOCHSTEN see Barbe,
   Helmut

DAS WORT UND DIE MUSIK "EIN STILLES WORT MAG
   TIEF UND WEISE SEIN" see Strohbach,
   Siegfried

DAS WORT WARD FLEISCH see Dedekind, Constantine
   Christian

DAS WORT WARD FLEISCH see Reger, Max

DAS WORT WARD FLEISCH see Schutz, Heinrich, Das
   Wort Ward Fleisch Und Wohnet Unter Uns

DAS WORT WARD FLEISCH UND WOHNET UNTER UNS see
   Schutz, Heinrich

DAS WUNDER DES HEILIGEN JAKOBUS see
   Rovenstrunck, Bernhard, El Miracle De Sant
   Jaume

DASHER, JAMES
   Beatitudes And The Lord's Prayer, The
   mix cor,soli,pno/org (easy) oct WILLIS
   $1.00   (D234)

   Bethlehem *Xmas,cant
   cor voc sc WILLIS $1.00   (D235)

   Joseph In Egypt *cant
   mix cor&men cor,soli,pno/org (med easy,
   operetta) oct WILLIS $1.50   (D236)

   Nativity, The *Xmas,cant
   mix cor,pno/org (med) oct WILLIS $2.00
                                          (D237)
   mix cor,soli (med) voc sc WILLIS $2.00
                                          (D238)

   Olivet To Calvary *cant
   SATB FLAMMER A5293 $1.60   (D239)

   Resurrection, The *Easter,cant
   mix cor,soli,pno/org (med) oct
   WILLIS $1.50   (D240)

DASS ICH WIEDER FROHLICH PREISE see Stier,
   Alfred

DASS WIR GETROSTER see Stier, Alfred

DASS ZWEI SICH HERZLICH LIEBEN see Burkhart,
   Franz

D'ASTORGA, EMMANUELE
   see ASTORGA, EMANUELLE

DATA EST DE LACHRIMIS MIHI VOLUPTAS see Lassus,
   Roland de (Orlandus)

DAUDET
   Mary At The Crib (composed with Frank) *Xmas
   SATB,org/pno oct MCA   (D241)
   (Rossi) SATB,pno/org oct MCA   (D242)

DAUGHTER OF JAIRUS, THE see Stainer, John

DAUGHTER OF MOAB see Andrew, Isaac

DAUGHTER OF ZION see Clark

DAUGHTER OF ZION see Clark, Thomas

DAUGHTER OF ZION see Clokey, Joseph Waddell

DAUGHTER OF ZION, NOW REJOICE see Handel,
   George Frideric

DAUGHTER OF ZION, SHOUT FOR JOY see Handel,
   George Frideric

DAUGHTER ZION, NOW REJOICE! see Handel, George
   Frideric

DAUGHTERS OF ZION see Mendelssohn-Bartholdy,
   Felix

DAULY, G.
   A La Noel *Xmas
   [Fr] mix cor,opt pno/org (med easy) voc sc
   LEMOINE s.p.   (D243)
   [Fr] 4pt mix cor LEMOINE s.p.   (D244)

   Entre Le Boeuf Et L'ane Gris *Xmas
   [Fr] 3 eq voices LEMOINE s.p.   (D245)

DAULY, G. (cont'd.)
   Laissez Paitre Vos Bestes *Xmas
   [Fr] 4pt mix cor LEMOINE s.p.   (D246)

   Noel *Xmas,carol
   [Fr] 4pt mix cor LEMOINE s.p.   (D247)
   [Fr] mix cor,pno/org (med easy) voc sc
   LEMOINE s.p.   (D248)

   Noel En L'honneur De La Sainte Vierge *Xmas
   [Fr] 3pt wom cor LEMOINE s.p.   (D249)

   Nous Etions Trois Pastourelles *Xmas
   [Fr] 3pt wom cor LEMOINE s.p.   (D250)

   Ture, Lure, Lure *Xmas,carol,Fr
   [Fr] 2 eq voices LEMOINE s.p.   (D251)

DAUN
   Sanctus
   SA/TB FLAMMER E5156 $.30   (D252)

DAUNTON, FRANK
   Wise Men, The *Xmas
   SATB,pno cor pts SCHOTT 11007 s.p., ipa
                                          (D253)

DAVENPORT
   Faith Of Our Fathers
   SAB oct LORENZ 7371 $.25   (D254)

   Where He Leads Me
   SATB oct LORENZ B102 $.30   (D255)

DAVENPORT, DAVID
   Christ Is Born *Xmas
   SSA LEONARD-US 08007040 $.25   (D256)

   Follow That Star *Xmas
   SATB oct WALTON 2004 $.30   (D257)

DAVENPORT, G.
   On Christmas Day *Xmas
   unis oct LESLIE 1096   (D258)

DAVICO, VINCENZO (1899-1969)
   Cantata Breve *cant
   [Lat] mix cor,Bar solo,org/orch voc sc
   ZERBONI 4523 s.p.   (D259)

   Requiem Per La Morte Di Un Povero *Req
   mix cor,narrator&SBar soli,org/orch voc sc
   ZERBONI 4928 s.p., ipr   (D260)

DAVID see Brown, Christopher

DAVID see Cortese, Luigi

DAVID see Waterman, Frances

DAVID DANCED BEFORE THE LORD
   SATB,cantor BELWIN $3.00   (D261)

DAVID ES GOLIAT see Handel, George Frideric

DAVID, JOHANN NEPOMUK (1895-   )
   Christ Ist Erstanden *Easter,cant
   SAB,org cor pts BREITKOPF-W CHB-3447 s.p.
   see also Funf Choralkantaten   (D262)

   Christus, Der Uns Selig Macht *Psntd,cant
   SAB,org cor pts BREITKOPF-W CHB-3446 s.p.
   see also Funf Choralkantaten   (D263)

   Deutsche Messe *Mass
   4-5pt mix cor,acap cor pts BREITKOPF-W
   PB-3703 s.p.   (D264)

   Drei Evangelienmotetten *evang/mot
   4pt mix cor,bvl,timp,harp,gong, tam-tam,
   alto flute s.p. sc BREITKOPF-W PB-4857,
   cor pts BREITKOPF-W CHB-3575
   contains: Ihr Habt Gehort, Was Gesagt
   Ist; Und Es Begab Sich Danach; Und Sie
   Kamen Nach Bethsaida   (D265)

   Drei Satze (from Cherubinischen Wandersmann)
   CC3U
   (Scheffler, J.) men cor cor pts BREITKOPF-W
   CHB-4810 s.p.   (D266)

   Ein Lammlein Geht Und Tragt Die Schuld *mot
   SATB,acap cor pts BREITKOPF-L PB-3454 s.p.
                                          (D267)
   4pt mix cor,acap cor pts BREITKOPF-W
   PB-3454 s.p.   (D268)

   Ex Deo Nascimur *mot
   SATB,acap cor pts BREITKOPF-L CHB-2816 s.p.
                                          (D269)
   SATB&SATB,acap cor pts BREITKOPF-W PB-3461
   s.p. contains also: In Christo Morimur;
   Ex Spiritu Sancto Reviviscimus   (D270)

   Ex Spiritu Sancto Reviviscimus
   see David, Johann Nepomuk, Ex Deo Nascimur

   Funf Choralkantaten *cant
   BREITKOPF-W
   contains & see also: Christ Ist
   Erstanden; Christus, Der Uns Selig
   Macht; Gelobet Seist Du, Jesu Christ;
   Komm, Gott Schopfer, Heiliger Geist;
   Nun Komm, Der Heiden Heiland   (D271)

   Gelobet Seist Du, Jesu Christ *Xmas,cant
   SAB,org cor pts BREITKOPF-W CHB-3445 s.p.
   see also Funf Choralkantaten   (D272)

   Herr, Du Erforschest Mich (Psalm 139)
   4pt mix cor,acap cor pts BREITKOPF-W
   CHB-3153 s.p.   (D273)

   Herr, Nun Selbst Den Wagen Halt *mot
   SATB,acap cor pts BREITKOPF-L PB-3455 s.p.
                                          (D274)

   Herre Gott, Erbarme Dich *Kyrie
   "Kyrie" [Ger] 3pt mix cor,acap cor pts
   BREITKOPF-W CHB-3119 s.p.   (D275)

   Ihr Habt Gehort, Was Gesagt Ist
   see Drei Evangelienmotetten

   In Christo Morimur
   see David, Johann Nepomuk, Ex Deo Nascimur

   Komm, Gott Schopfer, Heiliger Geist *Pent/
   Whitsun,cant
   SAB,org cor pts BREITKOPF-W CHB-3448 s.p.

DAVID, JOHANN NEPOMUK (cont'd.)
   see also Funf Choralkantaten   (D276)

   Komm, Heiliger Geist, Herre Gott *cant
   dbl cor,orch voc sc BREITKOPF-W EB-6690
   s.p., sc BREITKOPF-W rental   (D277)

   Kyrie *Kyrie
   3pt wom cor/3pt jr cor,org cor pts
   BREITKOPF-W CHB-3558 s.p.   (D278)

   Kyrie *see Herre Gott, Erbarme Dich

   Maria Durch Den Dornwald Ging *mot
   4pt mix cor,acap cor pts BREITKOPF-W
   CHB-3175 s.p.   (D279)

   Marienpreis "Maget Und Muoter" *mot
   4-6pt mix cor,S solo,acap cor pts
   BREITKOPF-W CHB-3500 s.p.   (D280)

   Messe *Op.6, Mass
   4pt treb cor,acap cor pts BREITKOPF-W
   CHB-3557 s.p.   (D281)

   Missa Choralis *Op.43, Mass
   SATB,acap cor pts BREITKOPF-L PB-3712 s.p.
                                          (D282)

   Now We Beseech The Holy Ghost *see Nun
   Bitten Wir Den Heiligen Geist

   Nun Bitten Wir Den Heiligen Geist *mot
   4pt mix cor,acap cor pts BREITKOPF-L
   PB-3453 s.p.   (D283)
   "Now We Beseech The Holy Ghost" [Eng/Ger]
   SATB,acap AMP A487 $.35   (D284)

   Nun Komm, Der Heiden Heiland *Adv,cant
   SAB,org cor pts BREITKOPF-W CHB-3444 s.p.
   see also Funf Choralkantaten   (D285)

   O Heiland, Reiss Die Himmel Auf *mot
   3pt mix cor,acap cor pts BREITKOPF-W
   CHB-3118 s.p.   (D286)

   Psalm 139 *see Herr, Du Erforschest Mich

   Requiem Chorale *Op.48
   4pt mix cor,SATB soli,2fl,ob,clar,bsn,horn,
   trp,trom,tuba,strings,perc,timp sc
   BREITKOPF-W rental, voc sc BREITKOPF-W
   EB-6276 s.p., voc pt BREITKOPF-W CHB-3029
   s.p., study sc BREITKOPF-W PB-3810 s.p.,
   ipr   (D287)

   Stabat Mater
   6pt mix cor,acap cor pts BREITKOPF-L
   CHB-2904 s.p.   (D288)

   Und Es Begab Sich Danach
   see Drei Evangelienmotetten

   Und Ich Sah Einen Neuen Himmel *mot
   4-5pt mix cor,acap cor pts BREITKOPF-W
   CHB-2879 s.p. see from Zwei Motetten
                                          (D289)
   4pt mix cor&5pt mix cor,acap cor pts
   BREITKOPF-L CHB-2879 s.p. see from Zwei
   Motetten   (D290)

   Und Sie Kamen Nach Bethsaida
   see Drei Evangelienmotetten

   Ut Queant Laxis *Op.35,No.2, hymn
   5pt mix cor,acap cor pts BREITKOPF-L
   CHB-2898 s.p.   (D291)

   Veni Creator Spiritus
   4pt mix cor,acap cor pts BREITKOPF-W
   CHB-3156 s.p.   (D292)

   Victimae Pascali Laudes *Op.35,No.1, Easter,
   mot
   SATB,acap cor pts BREITKOPF-L CHB-2897 s.p.
                                          (D293)

   Wer Ohren Hat Zu Horen, Der Hore *mot
   4pt mix cor&5pt mix cor,acap cor pts
   BREITKOPF-L CHB-2878 s.p. see from Zwei
   Motetten   (D294)
   4pt mix cor,acap cor pts BREITKOPF-W
   CHB-2878 s.p. see from Zwei Motetten
                                          (D295)

   Zwei Motetten *see Und Ich Sah Einen Neuen
   Himmel; Wer Ohren Hat Zu Horen, Der Hore
                                          (D296)
   Zwei Motetten *see Und Ich Sah Einen Neuen
   Himmel; Wer Ohren Hat Zu Horen, Der Hore
                                          (D297)

DAVID, KARL HEINRICH (1884-1951)
   Das Hohe Lied Salomons
   [Ger] wom cor,pic,2fl,2ob,2clar,2bsn,4horn,
   3trp,3trom,tuba,strings,harp,timp,
   English horn, bass clarinet,
   contrabassoon, triangle HUG s.p., ipr (D298)

DAVID OG GOLIAT see Aagaard, Thomas

DAVID PLAYED WITH LIONS see Pinkham, Daniel

DAVID SLEW GOLIATH see Harris, Roy

DAVID, THOMAS [CHRISTIAN] (1925-   )
   Missa In Adventu Christi *Adv
   6pt mix cor DOBLINGER sc s.p., cor pts s.p.
                                          (D299)

   Missa In Honorem Mariae *BVM,Mass
   [Ger] SATB,acap (med diff) BAREN. BA 3932
   $4.25   (D300)

   Wer Ist Es, Der Den Weltenplan Verdunkelt
   *mot
   8pt mix cor voc sc DOBLINGER s.p.   (D301)

DAVID UND GOLIATH see Kretzschmar, Gunther

DAVIDA, SISTER MARY
   Mass In Honor Of Mary Tower Of David *Gen
   SATB/cong SCHMITT 8501 $.80   (D302)

DAVIDDE PENITENTE see Mozart, Wolfgang Amadeus

DAVIDICA, L.
   Christus, Onze Heer Verrees
   mix cor sc ALSBACH&D s.p.   (D303)

DAVIDS 23DJE PSALM see Nordqvist, Gustaf

DAVID'S LAMENT see Seiber, Matyas

DAVID'S LAMENT FOR JONATHAN see Weelkes, Thomas

DAVID'S LAMENT FOR SAUL AND JONATHAN see Hagemann, P.

DAVID'S LAMENT OVER JONATHAN see Ham, Planctus

DAVID'S LAMENTATION see Billings, William

DAVID'S LAMENTATION AND ASSURANCE see Billings, William

DAVIDS PSALM 63 see Ramberg, Paul

DAVID'S SONG see Marshall, Jane M.

DAVID'S SONG FOR JONATHAN see La Rue, Pierre de

DAVIDSON
Did They Crucify My Lord?
SATB oct LORENZ 9913 $.30 (D304)

Three Canticles For Chorus *CC3U
SATB FLAMMER A 5396 $.40 (D305)

Word Made Flesh, The
SATB oct SUMMY M 5919 $.45 (D306)

DAVIDSON, C.
Anthem For Peace
SATB oct PRESSER MC540 $.40 (D307)

Lift Up Your Heads O Ye Gates
SATB oct PRESSER MC433 $.30 (D308)

DAVIDSON, CHARLES (1929-)
Confirmation Prayer
SATB TRANSCON. TCL 149 $.25 (D309)

Hashivenu Adonai
[Heb] SAB/SATB TRANSCON. TCL 688 $.50 (D310)

Sh'ma Kolenu
[Heb] SATB,cantor TRANSCON. TCL 863 $.75 (D311)

DAVIDSON, M.T.
Jesus, Jesus, Rest Your Head
SSA PARAGON 1032 $.35 (D312)

DAVIE, CEDRIC THORPE
Lord Is He Whose Strength Doth Make Me Strong, The *Gen
SATB (med) oct OXFORD 42.061 $.40, ipr (D313)

Rejoice And Be Merry *Xmas,carol
SSA,SSAA soli voc sc OXFORD 46.122 $1.10, ipa (D314)
(med) voc sc OXFORD 46.122 $1.10, ipa (D315)

DAVIES
Ave Maria
SATB,acap SOUTHERN $.30 (D316)

Ave Plena Gracia
SATB,SAT soli,opt inst (med diff) OXFORD 84.157 $.35 (D317)

Be Merry! *Xmas
SA BOOSEY-CAN s.p. (D318)

Christmas Bell Carol
unis FLAMMER E5025 $.25 (D319)
SA FLAMMER E5064 $.30 (D320)

Christmas Carol Fantasy *Xmas
SATB FLAMMER A 5133 $.30 (D321)
SA/TB FLAMMER E5036 $.30 (D322)
SSA FLAMMER B 5026 $.25 (D323)

Christmas Gloria *Xmas
SSA FLAMMER B 5044 $.30 (D324)
SATB FLAMMER A 5116 $.35 (D325)
SAB FLAMMER D5015 $.30 (D326)
SA/TB FLAMMER E5033 $.30 (D327)

Easter Bell Carol *Easter,carol
SATB FLAMMER A 5548 $.30 (D328)
SAB FLAMMER D5087 $.25 (D329)
unis FLAMMER E5009 $.30 (D330)
SA FLAMMER E5097 $.25 (D331)

Easter Song
SA/TB FLAMMER E5132 $.25 (D332)

King Of Kings *Xmas,cant
mix cor,soli voc sc WILLIS $.80 (D333)

O Come To The Manger *Xmas
SA BOOSEY-CAN s.p. (D334)

Praise And Sing *CCU
SA FLAMMER GE5005 $.50 (D335)

Shall I Die For Mannis' Sake *Xmas
SA BOOSEY-CAN s.p. (D336)

When To The Temple *Xmas
SA BOOSEY-CAN s.p. (D337)

DAVIES, G.W.
Hark, The Glad Sound! *Xmas
3pt wom cor,pno (easy) oct WILLIS 3917 $.12 (D338)

King Of Kings *Xmas,cant
mix cor,S,A,T,B soli,pno/org (easy) oct WILLIS $.75 (D339)

DAVIES, HENRY WALFORD (1869-1941)
All Things Bright And Beautiful
unis&opt 2pt oct NOVELLO 37.0017.08 s.p. (D340)
2pt oct NOVELLO 37.0017.08 s.p. (D341)

Blessed Birth, The *Xmas/Epiph
SSA,acap oct NOVELLO s.p. (D342)

Bread Of The World (Solemn Introit In G) *anthem/Introit
mix cor oct NOVELLO s.p. (D343)
mix cor (contains also: Christ Also Suffered For Us; Hour Cometh, The) oct NOVELLO s.p. see also Spiritual Songs (D344)

Chants For Certain Psalms *CCU,chant/Psalm
SATB oct NOVELLO s.p. (D345)

DAVIES, HENRY WALFORD (cont'd.)

Christ Also Suffered For Us *anthem
mix cor (contains also: Bread Of The World; Hour Cometh, The) oct NOVELLO s.p. see also Spiritual Songs (D346)

Christ In The Universe *anthem
mix cor,2 narrators,pno,orch oct NOVELLO s.p., ipr (D347)

Complete Service
SATB (G maj) NOVELLO voc sc s.p., cor pts s.p. (D348)
SATB (F maj) oct NOVELLO s.p. (D349)

God Be In My Head *hymn
SSA,acap oct NOVELLO s.p. (D350)
SATB oct NOVELLO s.p. (D351)
TTBB oct NOVELLO s.p. (D352)
eq voices oct NOVELLO s.p. (D353)

Had We But Hearkened *anthem
unis oct NOVELLO 48.1753.02 s.p. (D354)
(Chambers, H.A.) mix cor oct NOVELLO 40.1112.00 s.p. (D355)

Hark, The Glad Sound! *anthem
mix cor oct NOVELLO s.p. (D356)

Hour Cometh, The *anthem
mix cor (contains also: Bread Of The World; Christ Also Suffered For Us) oct NOVELLO s.p. see also Spiritual Songs (D357)

In Thy Strength, O Lord *anthem
mix cor,solo, or semi-choir oct NOVELLO s.p. (D358)

Introit
see Davies, Henry Walford, Kyrie Eleison

Jubilate *Jubil
SATB (G maj) voc pt NOVELLO s.p. (D359)

King Of Glory *anthem
mix cor oct NOVELLO 50.0292.03 s.p. see also Spiritual Songs (D360)

Kyrie Eleison *Kyrie
SATB (G maj) voc pt NOVELLO s.p. contains also: Introit (D361)

Let Us Now Praise Famous Men *Ded,anthem
mix cor oct NOVELLO s.p. (D362)

Lord, It Belongs Not To My Care *anthem
mix cor oct NOVELLO s.p. see also Spiritual Songs (D363)
(Wilson, John) mix cor,acap oct NOVELLO 50.0348.02 s.p. (D364)

Magnificat And Nunc Dimittis *chant/Magnif/Nunc
SATB,acap (C maj) oct NOVELLO s.p. (D365)
SATB (E flat maj) oct NOVELLO s.p. (D366)
SATB (adapted from Merbecke) oct NOVELLO s.p. (D367)
SATB NOVELLO voc sc s.p., cor pts s.p. (D368)

Magnificat And Nunc Dimittis (Ferial) *Magnif/Nunc
SATB (F maj) oct NOVELLO s.p. (D369)

Magnificat And Nunc Dimittis (Festal) *Magnif/Nunc
SATB (G maj) oct NOVELLO s.p. (D370)

Mine Eyes Have Seen The Glory *anthem
mix cor oct NOVELLO s.p. see also Spiritual Songs (D371)

My Blood, So Red *anthem
mix cor (contains also: O Saviour, With Protecting Care) oct NOVELLO s.p. see also Spiritual Songs (D372)

O Filii Et Filiae *anthem
"O Sons And Daughters" mix cor oct NOVELLO s.p. see also Spiritual Songs (D373)

O Saviour, With Protecting Care *anthem
mix cor (contains also: My Blood, So Red) oct NOVELLO s.p. see also Spiritual Songs (D374)

O Sons And Daughters *see O Filii Et Filiae

O Thou, That Hearest Prayer (from Temple, The) anthem
SATB,S solo oct NOVELLO 40.0824.03 s.p. (D375)
mix cor,S solo,acap oct NOVELLO 40.0824.03 s.p. (D376)

Psalm 121 *chant
SATB oct NOVELLO s.p. (D377)

Sayings Of Jesus (Five) *Op.35, CC5U,anthem
mix cor,T solo oct NOVELLO s.p. (D378)

Sayings Of Jesus (Three) *CC3U,anthem
mix cor,acap oct NOVELLO s.p. (D379)

Sayings Of Our Lord *anthem
men cor oct NOVELLO s.p. (D380)

Souls Of The Righteous, The (from God Created Man) anthem
mix cor oct NOVELLO s.p. see also Spiritual Songs (D381)

Spiritual Songs *CC15L,anthem/Introit
mix cor cmplt ed NOVELLO s.p.
see also: Bread Of The World (Solemn Introit In G); Christ Also Suffered For Us; Hour Cometh, The; King Of Glory; Lord, It Belongs Not To My Care; Mine Eyes Have Seen The Glory; My Blood, So Red; O Filii Et Filiae, "O Sons And Daughters"; O Saviour, With Protecting Care; Souls Of The Righteous, The (from God Created Man); Words Of Comfort (D382)

Te Deum *Te Deum
SATB (G maj) oct NOVELLO s.p. (D383)

Te Deum And Benedictus *Te Deum
mix cor,acap (C maj) oct NOVELLO s.p. (D384)

DAVIES, HENRY WALFORD (cont'd.)

White Paternoster
SATB oct BOOSEY 5344 $.30 (D385)

Words Of Comfort *anthem/Introit
mix cor (contains also: Three Short Introits) oct NOVELLO s.p. see also Spiritual Songs (D386)

DAVIES, IVOR
Immortal, Invisible God *anthem/hymn
mix cor oct NOVELLO s.p. (D387)

May The Grace Of Christ *Marriage
unis oct NOVELLO 33.0073.00 s.p. (D388)

Ye Choirs Of New Jerusalem *Easter,anthem/hymn
mix cor oct NOVELLO s.p. (D389)

DAVIES, JAMES
I Am The Vine
SATB oct AGAPE 373 $.25 (D390)

DAVIES, LAWRENCE H.
As I Rode Out On A Winter's Night *carol
unis CRAMER 53 s.p. (D391)

Rock Him Gently
2pt jr cor LEONARD-ENG 106 s.p. (D392)

What Cheer? Good Cheer *carol
unis CRAMER 52 s.p. (D393)

DAVIES, PETER MAXWELL (1934-)
Alleluia, Pro Virgine Maria (from O Magnum Mysterium)
see Four Carols

Alma Redemptoris Mater (from Four Christmas Carols) Xmas,carol
see Four Christmas Carols On Medieval Texts
4 eq voices SCHOTT s.p. (D394)

Ave Maria
"Hail, Blessed Flower" SATB,acap NOVELLO AP220 $.30 (D395)

Carol On St. Steven
see Four Christmas Carols On Medieval Texts

Ecce Manus Tradentis
[Eng/Lat] mix cor,fl,ob,2bsn,horn,2trom, harp,perc cmplt ed BOOSEY rental (D396)

Fader Of Heaven, The (from O Magnum Mysterium)
see Four Carols

Fader Of Heven, The (from O Magnum Mysterium)
SA SCHOTT s.p. (D397)

Five Carols *CC5U,carol
SSA,acap oct BOOSEY 5672 $.30 (D398)

Four Carols (from O Magnum Mysterium) carol
SCHOTT s.p.
contains: Alleluia, Pro Virgine Maria (SATB,acap); Fader Of Heaven, The (SA, acap); Haylle, Comly And Clene (SATB, acap); O Magnum Mysterium (SATB,SSA soli,acap) (D399)

Four Christmas Carols On Medieval Texts *Xmas,carol
SCHOTT SL s.p.
contains: Alma Redemptoris Mater (4 eq voices); Carol On St. Steven (SATB); Jesus Autem Hodie (SATB); Nowell (SATB) (D400)

Hail, Blessed Flower *see Ave Maria

Haylle, Comly And Clene (from O Magnum Mysterium)
see Four Carols

Jesus Autem Hodie
see Four Christmas Carols On Medieval Texts

Lord's Prayer, The
SATB SCHOTT s.p. (D401)

Nowell
see Four Christmas Carols On Medieval Texts

O Magnum Mysterium *CC9L
[Eng/Lat] SATB,inst,org SCHOTT s.p. (D402)

O Magnum Mysterium (from O Magnum Mysterium)
see Four Carols

Te Lucis Ante Terminum *hymn
SATB,winds,bells,gtr s.p. sc SCHOTT 10817B, cor pts SCHOTT 10817A (D403)
[Lat] SATB,2fl,ob,2clar,trp,2trom,vcl, bells,gtr sc SCHOTT 10871B s.p., cor pts SCHOTT 10871A s.p. (D404)

Veni Sancte Spiritus
[Lat] mix cor,SAB soli,orch BOOSEY voc sc $2.75, cor pts $.40, sc $10.00, ipr, min sc $2.50 (D405)

DAVIS, ALLAN
Psalm Of Praise, A *Psalm
SATB,brass,perc sc SEESAW $12.00 (D406)

Song For Daniel, A
SATB,brass,perc sc SEESAW $7.00 (D407)

DAVIS, CARL
Lullaby *Xmas
SSA/SAA,acap oct LAWSON 51009 $.25 (D408)

There Is No Rose *Xmas
SSA/SAA,S solo,acap oct LAWSON 51011 $.25 (D409)

DAVIS, ELMER L.
Mary's Little Baby *Xmas
4pt mix cor,ST soli,acap oct SCHIRM.G 11076 $.25 (D410)

You Gotta Cross The River When You Die *spir
4pt mix cor,ST soli,acap oct SCHIRM.G 10601 $.25 (D411)

DAVIS, J.
Blessed Art Thou
SATB,acap oct PRESSER 312-40333 $.30 (D412)

Carol Of The Drum
SATB,acap oct BELWIN 64173 $.40 (D413)
SA,acap oct BELWIN 64228 $.25 (D414)
TTBB,acap oct BELWIN 64229 $.35 (D415)
SSAA,acap oct BELWIN 64233 $.35 (D416)
SAB,acap oct BELWIN 64277 $.35 (D417)
SSA,acap oct BELWIN 64268 $.35 (D418)

Fanfare For Palm Sunday, A *Palm
SA oct BELWIN 64330 $.30 (D419)
SATB oct BELWIN 64295 $.35 (D420)

Good Folk Who Dwell On Earth
SA oct BELWIN 64195 $.25 (D421)
SAB oct BELWIN 64230 $.30 (D422)
SSAA oct BELWIN 64180 $.30 (D423)
SATB,acap oct BELWIN 64213 $.30 (D424)

Jesu, The Very Thought Of Thee
SATB oct BELWIN 64361 $.30 (D425)

DAVIS, J.R.
Chorale For Easter *Easter,chorale
SATB,acap AMP A258 $.20 (D426)

Sing Christmas Alleluia *Xmas
SATB oct KERBY 5704 $.45 (D427)

DAVIS, KATHERINE K. (1892-)
Agnus Dei *Lent,Agnus
"Heavenly Father" [Eng/Lat] SAB,acap WARNER
R3484 $.30 (D428)
"Heavenly Father" [Eng/Lat] SATB,acap
WARNER G1751 $.30 (D429)
"Heavenly Father" [Eng/Lat] SSA,acap WARNER
G1534 $.30 (D430)

All Ye Saints Be Joyful
TTBB,acap WARNER R3329 $.30 (D431)
SATB,acap WARNER R3328 $.30 (D432)
SSAA,acap WARNER R3330 $.30 (D433)
boy cor SOUTHERN $.30 (D434)
mix cor SOUTHERN $.30 (D435)

Alleluia, Come Good People *Easter
SSAA oct GALAXY 1.1136.1 $.25 (D436)
SATB oct SOUTHERN $.25 (D437)
SATB oct GALAXY 1.1132.1 $.25 (D438)
TTBB oct GALAXY 1.1135.1 $.25 (D439)

As It Fell Upon A Night *Xmas
SSA/SSAA oct GALAXY 1.1380.1 $.30 (D440)
SA oct GALAXY 1.1395.1 $.30 (D441)
SATB oct GALAXY 1.1291.1 $.30 (D442)
TTBB oct GALAXY 1.1842.1 $.30 (D443)

Be Ye Kind, One To Another
SATB oct GALAXY 1.1644.1 $.30 (D444)

Birds' Noel, The *Xmas
SATB oct GALAXY 1.2336.1 $.35 (D445)

Bless The Lord, O My Soul
SATB oct GALAXY 1.1782.1 $.35 (D446)

Carol Of The Dancing Shepherds *Xmas,carol
SATB oct GALAXY 1.2422.1 $.35 (D447)

Cherubim Song *Xmas
SATB oct GALAXY 1.2191.1 $.30 (D448)

Choristers Of Light
SATB oct GALAXY 1.2494.1 $.25 (D449)

Christ Is Risen Today *Easter
SATB oct GALAXY 1.1979.1 $.30 (D450)
SSA oct GALAXY 1.0941.1 $.25 (D451)

Christ The Lord Is Risen Today *Easter
2pt WARNER G1855 $.30 (D452)
SAB oct SOUTHERN $.30 (D453)

Christmas Day Is Come *Xmas
SATB oct GALAXY 1.1099.1 $.40 (D454)

Church Of God
SA oct GALAXY 1.2405.1 $.30 (D455)
SATB oct GALAXY 1.2338.1 $.30 (D456)

Come, Singing Noel *Xmas
SATB&desc WARNER R3485 $.35 (D457)

Come Ye To Bethlehem *Xmas
SATB oct GALAXY 1.2244.1 $.30 (D458)
TTBB oct GALAXY 1.1996.1 $.30 (D459)
SA oct GALAXY 1.2045.1 $.30 (D460)

Comfort Ye
SATB oct GALAXY 1.2226.1 $.35 (D461)

Ding-Dong! Merrily
4pt mix cor,acap oct SCHIRM.G 8248 $.25 (D462)

Easter Alleluia *Easter,Allelu
girl cor SOUTHERN $.30 (D463)
girl cor SOUTHERN $.30 (D464)
SATB oct SOUTHERN $.30 (D465)

Easter Alleluia, An *Easter
SSA,acap WARNER G1848 $.30 (D466)
SAB,acap WARNER R3506 $.30 (D467)
SATB,acap WARNER G1805 $.30 (D468)

Easter Is A Song *Easter,cant
jr cor,org/pno WARNER W3782 $.75 (D469)
WARNER (D470)

Fanfare For Christmas *Xmas
(Raymond) SATB oct PLYMOUTH JR-108 $.25 (D471)

Fanfare For Palm Sunday *Palm
SATB oct SOUTHERN $.30 (D472)
SA oct SOUTHERN $.25 (D473)

Firmament Of Power
boy cor WARNER $.30 (D474)

Firmament Of Power, The
2pt,acap WARNER W3796 $.30 (D475)
SSA,acap WARNER W3794 $.30 (D476)
SAB,acap WARNER W3795 $.30 (D477)
SATB,acap WARNER W3774 $.30 (D478)
TTB,acap WARNER W3797 $.30 (D479)

DAVIS, KATHERINE K. (cont'd.)

Five Christmas Carols *CC5U,Xmas,carol
SATB oct GALAXY 1.0912.1 $.50 (D480)

For All Men Everywhere
SATB MARKS 4580 $.40 (D481)

Forty Days *see Sheldon

From Far And Wide *Xmas
SAB WARNER R3482 $.35 (D482)
SATB WARNER R3456 $.30 (D483)

Glory Above The Heavens
SATB oct SACRED S-98 $.40 (D484)

Glory Be To God On High
SATB FLAMMER A 5066 $.35 (D485)
SAB FLAMMER D5202 $.30 (D486)

Glory In The Highest
girl cor SOUTHERN $.25 (D487)
SSA oct GALAXY 1.1603.1 $.30 (D488)
SATB oct GALAXY 1.1092.1 $.30 (D489)
SATB&jr cor oct GALAXY 1.2245.1 $.30 (D490)

God Adoring
SATB FLAMMER A 5458 $.30 (D491)

God Is In This Place
SATB oct SACRED S-111 $.35 (D492)

God So Loved The World *Easter
SATB oct GALAXY 1.2214.1 $.30 (D493)

Going To Bethlehem *Xmas
2pt&desc WARNER R3480 $.30 (D494)

Great Is Our God
SATB oct GALAXY 1.2365.1 $.35 (D495)

Hail His Coming, King Of Glory
SAB WARNER WB-259 $.35 (D496)

Have You Seen A Star? *Xmas
SATB&desc WARNER W7-1045 $.35 (D497)

He Is Born (composed with Swift)
cor HIGHLAND 4121 $.25 (D498)

He Is Born, Christ The King
SATB FLAMMER A 5134 $.25 (D499)

He Is Our King
SATB FLAMMER A 5007 $.30 (D500)
SAB FLAMMER D5004 $.30 (D501)

He Was Despised *Lent
SATB oct SOUTHERN $.25 (D502)
SATB,acap MARKS 4380 $.25 (D503)

Heavenly Father *see Agnus Dei

He's Gone Away
SATB oct GALAXY 1.1672.1 $.30 (D504)

Holy Mountain, The
SATB,S solo WARNER R3342 $.30 (D505)

Honor And Praise
SATB&desc&opt jr cor,S solo,org,opt 2trp
WARNER W3770 $.40 (D506)

I Am He That Liveth *Easter,cant
SATB LORENZ $1.95 (D507)

I Sing Of A Maiden *Xmas
SATB,acap SCHIRM.EC 1648 $.20 (D508)

I Sought The Lord
SATB (med) ABINGDON APM-759 $.25 (D509)

I Will Lift Up Mine Eyes
SATB oct FISCHER,C CM-7729 $.25 (D510)

I Will Open My Eyes
SATB (med easy) SOUTHERN $.30 (D511)
SATB oct FISCHER,C CM-7784 $.30 (D512)

If I Were A Shepherd
2pt jr cor FRANK 13801 $.30 (D513)

In The Bleak Midwinter *Xmas
SATB,acap SCHIRM.EC 1647 $.30 (D514)
SSA,acap SCHIRM.EC 1084 $.22 (D515)

Jazz Adoration
SATB (jazz) ALFRED 6703 $.35 (D516)

Jesus Is His Name
unis jr cor FRANK 13790 $.35 (D517)

Joyful News, The *Xmas
SATB oct FISCHER,C CM-7721 $.30 (D518)

Let Thy Merciful Ears, O Lord, Be Open
SATB (med) ABINGDON APM-757 $.20 (D519)

Light Of Heaven, The
SATB ALFRED 6624 $.25 (D520)

Lord All Glorious, Lord Victorious *Easter
SATB oct GALAXY 1.2357.1 $.30 (D521)

Lord God Of Sabaoth
SAB oct SUMMY B 1563 $.20 (D522)

Lord Is God, The
SATB oct GALAXY 1.1951.1 $.25 (D523)

Lord Most Holy
SSA,acap WARNER R3267 $.35 (D524)
SATB,acap WARNER R3439 (D525)

Our God Is A Rock
SATB oct SUMMY B 1517 $.60 (D526)
SAB oct SUMMY B 1581 $.45 (D527)

Out Of Your Sleep Arise And Wake *Xmas
SATB,acap SCHIRM.EC 1659 $.20 (D528)

Poor Mary *Xmas
3pt jr cor/SSA (easy) FISCHER,C CM 6191
$.25 (D529)
4pt jr cor/SATB (easy) FISCHER,C CM 7206
$.25 (D530)

DAVIS, KATHERINE K. (cont'd.)

Praise And Glory
SA oct GALAXY 1.2346.1 $.30 (D531)

Psalm 23
SAB WARNER R3460 $.30 (D532)
SATB WARNER R3183 $.30 (D533)
2pt WARNER R3464 $.30 (D534)
SSA WARNER R3227 $.30 (D535)

Renew A Right Spirit Within Me
4pt mix cor,T solo,acap oct SCHIRM.G 11016
$.20 (D536)
2pt wom cor,S solo,org/pno oct SCHIRM.G
11017 $.20 (D537)

Road To Galilee *Easter
SATB&jr cor,org GALAXY 1.2305.1 $2.50 (D538)

Sanctus *see Schubert, Franz (Peter)

Seasonal Anthems *CCU,anthem
SA BELWIN $1.00 (D539)

Shepherds, Awake *Xmas
girl cor SOUTHERN $.30 (D540)
2pt,acap WARNER R3488 $.30 (D541)
SSA,acap WARNER G1438 $.30 (D542)
SATB,acap WARNER G1752 $.30 (D543)
TTBB,acap WARNER G1580 $.30 (D544)
SATB&jr cor WARNER R3487 $.35 (D545)

Shepherds Came To Bethlehem *Xmas
SATB oct GALAXY 1.2347.1 $.35 (D546)

Sing Gloria *Xmas
girl cor SOUTHERN $.30 (D547)
SATB&jr cor WARNER R3232 $.35 (D548)
unis WARNER R3415 (D549)
2pt WARNER R3416 (D550)
SSA WARNER 3159 (D551)
SAB WARNER R3181 (D552)
SATB WARNER R3158 (D553)
TTBB WARNER R3214 (D554)

Song For Peace *Xmas
SSA oct GALAXY 1.1468.1 $.30 (D555)
SATB oct GALAXY 1.1069.1 $.30 (D556)
TTBB oct GALAXY 1.1560.1 $.30 (D557)

Star At Christmas *Xmas
SSA oct GALAXY 1.2130.1 $.30 (D558)

Star Shone Out, A *Xmas
SATB,S solo,acap SCHIRM.EC 1773 $.25 (D559)

Stone Is Rolled Away, The
SATB FLAMMER A 5180 $.30 (D560)
SSA FLAMMER B 5143 $.30 (D561)
SAB FLAMMER D5129 $.25 (D562)

Thank We The Lord
SATB,S solo MARKS 4398 $.30 (D563)

Thanksgiving Song *Thanks
SSA/SAT/SATB WARNER W7-1009 $.30 (D564)

This Is Noel *Xmas,cant/carol
(Cowley) SATB,org/pno,opt ob WARNER R3194
$1.50 (D565)
(Cowley) SSA,org/pno,opt ob WARNER R3234
$1.50 (D566)

Thou Art Our Bread And Wine
SATB oct GALAXY 1.1757.1 $.20 (D567)

Thou Gracious And Most Holy Lord *folk,Swiss
SSA,acap WARNER R3298 $.30 (D568)

Thou Who Wast God
SSA oct GALAXY 1.2185.1 $.30 (D569)
SAB oct GALAXY 1.2298.1 $.30 (D570)
SATB oct GALAXY 1.2138.1 $.30 (D571)

Three Christmas Carols *CC3U,Xmas,carol
SATB oct GALAXY 1.1084.1 $.50 (D572)

To Shepherds Fast Asleep *Xmas
SSA oct GALAXY 1.1751.1 $.35 (D573)
SATB oct GALAXY 1.1708.1 $.35 (D574)
SATB&jr cor oct GALAXY 1.2243.1 $.35 (D575)

Trust In The Lord
SSA oct GALAXY 1.1478.1 $.30 (D576)

Who Is This Who Comes A-Riding? *Palm
SATB,opt trp WARNER R3509 $.40 (D577)

Wonderful Thing, A *Easter,carol
unis,opt fl,opt hndbl WARNER WB-208 $.30 (D578)

Wonders Of Earth, The
SATB&opt desc,opt trp&timp WARNER WB-102
$.35 (D579)

World Itself Keeps Easter Day *Easter
SSA oct GALAXY 1.0940.1 $.30 (D580)

DAVISON, JOHN
Angel Songs And The Star *Xmas
SATB oct ELKAN-V 362-1207 $.25 (D581)

Blessed Be The God
SATB oct ELKAN-V 362-1240 $.30 (D582)

Communion Service *Commun
unis,org (very easy) PRESSER 312-40981 $.40 (D583)

Hodie Christus Natus Est *Xmas
SATB oct BELWIN 2125 $.25 (D584)

Short Communion Service In C
SATB,opt org SCHIRM.EC 2446 $.65 (D585)

DAVYE
Tenebrae Factae Sunt
boy cor SOUTHERN $.20 (D586)

DAVYE, JOHN F.
Darkness Fell On The Earth *see Tenebrae
Factae Sunt

Spirit Of The Lord, The
SATB FOSTER MF123 $.35 (D587)

Tenebrae Factae Sunt
"Darkness Fell On The Earth" [Lat/Eng]
TTBB,acap AMP A370 $.20 (D588)

DAVYE, JOHN F. (cont'd.)

Thy Glory Dawns, Jerusalem, Awake *Palm
SATB,org oct WORLD CA-2137 -8 $.45   (D589)

DAWIDOWICZ, ALBERT
Deutsches Ordinarium
dbl cor,opt org DOBLINGER voc sc s.p., cor
pts s.p.   (D590)
wom cor&jr cor,opt org DOBLINGER voc sc
s.p., cor pts s.p.   (D591)

DAWN CAROL *Xmas,carol
SATB CHAPPELL 0022137-358 $.40   (D592)

DAWN HAS COME, THE see Whitcomb, Mervin W.

DAWN IN THE GARDEN see Goldsworthy, William
Arthur

DAWN OF CHRISTMAS, THE see Brown, J.

DAWN OF CHRISTMAS, THE see Mueller, Carl F.

DAWN OF CHRISTMAS, THE see Nolte

DAWN VICTORY see Kendell, Iain

DAWNEY, MICHAEL
Lord's Prayer, The
[Eng] SATB oct ST.MARTIN SMP677 s.p.
contains also: Tamblyn, William, Hail
Mary   (D593)

Out Of The Depths (Psalm 129) anthem/Bibl
SATB,acap voc sc WEINBERGER s.p.   (D594)

Psalm 129 *see Out Of The Depths

DAWSON
Behold The Star
SATB KJOS T111 $.35   (D595)

Easter Canticle, An *Easter
SSA,A solo,vln SCHMITT 2543 $.22   (D596)

Hail Mary *BVM
SATB KJOS T112 $.35   (D597)
men cor KJOS T113 $.35   (D598)

Mary Had A Baby *Xmas
SATB KJOS T118 $.30   (D599)
men cor KJOS T119 $.30   (D600)

Oh, What A Beautiful City
SATB KJOS T100 $.35   (D601)

Pilgrim's Chorus
SATB KJOS 5490 $.40   (D602)

Zion's Walls
SATB KJOS T124 $.40   (D603)

DAY
O Praise The Lord In Joyful Song
SATB,org BOSTON 11798 $.40   (D604)

Ring Ye Glad Voices *Xmas,cant
cor&jr cor,soli voc sc WILLIS $.75   (D605)

DAY, THE see Hahn, Reynaldo, Le Jour

DAY AFTER DAY see Clarke

DAY BY DAY see Ahnfelt

DAY BY DAY see Schwartz

DAY BY DAY see Schwartz, Stephen

DAY BY DAY see Smith, Lani

DAY BY DAY, DEAR LORD see Thomas, J.

DAY BY DAY, DEAR LORD see Young, Carlton R.

DAY BY DAY I SEEK THEE see Pasquet, Jean

DAY BY DAY WE MAGNIFY THE see Handel, George
Frideric

DAY BY DAY WE MAGNIFY THEE see Handel, George
Frideric

DAY DRAWS ON WITH GOLDEN LIGHT, THE see
Bairstow, Edward Cuthbert

DAY IN THY COURTS, A see Mac Farren, George
Alexander

DAY IS DONE, THE see Bach, Johann Sebastian,
Der Tag Ist Hin

DAY IS ENDING, THE see White, Robert

DAY IS PAST AND OVER see Marks, J.

DAY IS PAST OVER, THE see Browne, H.M.

DAY LIKE TODAY, A see Vandervalk, Bruce

DAY MOST HOLY see Byrd, William, Dies
Sanctificatus

DAY OF DAWNING BROTHERHOOD see Ream

DAY OF DESOLATION see London, Edwin

DAY OF GLADNESS see Pitcher, Gladys

DAY OF JUDGMENT, THE see Arkhangelsky, G.

DAY OF MIRACLES, THE see Lister, Mosie

DAY OF MOURNING see Cherubini, Luigi, Lacrymosa

DAY OF MOURNING see Mozart, Wolfgang Amadeus,
Lacrymosa

DAY OF PENTECOST, THE see Hawkins, Floyd W.

DAY OF REJOICING see Pelz, Walter L.

DAY OF RESURRECTION *Easter/Lent
(Mueller) SATB oct FISCHER,C CM-6214 $.25
(D606)
(Mueller) SA oct FISCHER,C CM-7266 $.25
(D607)

DAY OF RESURRECTION see Prentice, Fred

DAY OF RESURRECTION, ALLELUIA, THE *Easter,
hymn
(Wolff) SATB,org,opt trp oct LAWSON 51315
$.35   (D608)

DAY OF RESURRECTION, THE *Easter
(Dunsmore) SA SCHMITT 337 $.25   (D609)

DAY OF RESURRECTION, THE see Darst, W. Glenn

DAY OF RESURRECTION, THE see Duncan, C.

DAY OF RESURRECTION, THE see Means, Claude

DAY OF RESURRECTION, THE see Mueller, Carl F.

DAY OF SADNESS see Mozart, Wolfgang Amadeus,
Lacrymosa

DAY OF THE LORD IS AT HAND, THE
(Lynn, G.) SATB,acap oct PRESSER 312-40546
$.30   (D610)

DAY OF TRIUMPH
SATB BIG3 $.25   (D611)

DAY, PEGGY
As The Branch Is To The Vine
(Martindale, James A.G.) unis/2pt,opt gtr
LESLIE 2048 s.p.   (D612)

DAY, R.E.
Fair Christmas Morn *Xmas
3pt wom cor,pno (easy) oct WILLIS 6219 $.20
(D613)

Prayer For Peace
3pt wom cor,S solo,pno/org (easy) oct
WILLIS 6180 $.12   (D614)

Ring Ye Glad Voices
3pt mix cor&jr cor,SMez soli,pno/org oct
WILLIS $.60   (D615)

DAY, STANLEY A. (1894-   )
Jesu, Little Son *Xmas
unis&desc oct GRAY GCMR 2152 $.30   (D616)

DAY STAR, THE see Cain, Noble

DAY THOU GAVEST, LORD, IS ENDED, THE see
Chambers, H.A.

DAY THOU GAVEST, THE see Chambers, H.A.

DAY TO REJOICE, A see Rogers, Ethel Trench

DAY, W.
Messe De Minuit *see Charpentier, Marc-
Antoine

Short Te Deum, A *Te Deum
SATB oct ELKAN-V 362-1226 $.35   (D617)

DAYBREAK CAROL see Gaul, Alfred Robert

DAYLIGHT IS FADING see Passmore, C.M.

DAYS OF CHRISTMAS *CC6L,Xmas
SATB PRO ART 814 $.85   (D618)

DAYS OF MY YOUTH, THE see Lee

DAYSPRING OF ETERNITY see Christiansen, F.
Melius

DAYSTAR see Fryxell, Regina Holmen

DAZU IST ERSCHIENEN DER SOHN GOTTES see Bach,
Johann Sebastian

DE ANGEL ROLL DE STONE AWAY see Rhea

DE ANGELS IN DE HEAB'N *spir,US
(Aubanel, Georges) "Les Anges Dans Le Ciel"
[Eng/Fr] 3 eq voices OUVRIERES s.p.   (D619)

DE ANIMALS A-COMIN' *spir
(Bartholomew) 4pt men cor,acap oct SCHIRM.G
8046 $.30   (D620)
(Bartholomew) 2pt wom cor oct SCHIRM.G 9774
$.30   (D621)
(Bartholomew) 4pt mix cor,acap oct SCHIRM.G
9775 $.35   (D622)
(Stickles) 3pt wom cor oct SCHIRM.G 11034
$.35   (D623)
(Stickles) 3pt mix cor oct SCHIRM.G 11029
$.30   (D624)

DE ARO NU FORGANGNA see Gesius, Bartholomaus

DE BATTLE OB JERICHO *spir
(Roberton) 3pt jr cor/3pt wom cor ROBERTON
72115 s.p.   (D625)
(Roberton) mix cor ROBERTON 61274 s.p. (D626)
(Roberton) 4pt men cor ROBERTON 50710 s.p.
(D627)
(Roberton, Hugh S.) 4pt mix cor,acap oct
CURWEN 8428 $.25   (D628)

DE BEATA VIRGINE see Des Prez, Josquin

DE BEATA VIRGINE see Palestrina, Giovanni

DE BEATA VIRGINE see Palestrina, Giovanni

DE BEATA VIRGINE see Palestrina, Giovanni

DE BON MATIN *Xmas,carol,Fr
(Tomasi) [Fr] 2pt/3pt,pno/orch LEDUC s.p. see
also Douze Noels De Saboly   (D629)

DE CORONA SPINEA see Naylor, Bernard

DE DINA, JESU, NARMA SIG see Vulpius, Melchior

DE DRIE KONINGEN see Zanen, P.

DE DUGUE see Saint-Saens, Camille

DE EMMAUSGANGERS see Pluister, Simon

DE FERIA see Palestrina, Giovanni

DE FINNS EN VAG see Berg, Gottfrid

DE GLORY MANGER *spir
(Schroth, G.) SATB KJOS 5214 $.30   (D630)

DE GOSPEL TRAIN *spir
(Christy) SSA SCHMITT 2062 $.30   (D631)
(Christy) SSATB SCHMITT 1135 $.18   (D632)
(Roberton) mix cor ROBERTON 61421 s.p. (D633)

DE HEER REGEERDE see Olman, Isr, J., Dominus
Regnavit

DE HELIGA MARTYRENA see Runback, Albert

DE HELIGA MARTYRERNA see Runback, Albert

DE JACOB LA NUEVA ESTRELLA see Gallego

DE KOSMOS see Zweers, [Bernard]

DE LEJANAS TIERRAS VENIMOS *Xmas,Carib
(Glaser, V.) "We've Traveled Far" [Span/Eng]
SATB,pno,tamb, castanets SCHIRM.EC 2600
$.25   (D634)

DE LES ARMES see Ghiselin-Verbonnet, Johannes

DE LOS MONTES Y LOS VALLES see Santa Cruz,
Domingo

DE NATIVIATATE DOMINI see Finck

DE OL' ARK'S A-MOVERIN'
SATB CHAPPELL 0022178-358 $.40   (D635)

DE PAASGESCHIEDENIS see Reda, Siegfried, Die
Ostergeschichte

DE PACEM see Gombert, Nicolas

DE PROFONDIS CLAMAVI see De Taeye

DE PROFUNDIS see Bottazzo, Luigi

DE PROFUNDIS see Boulanger, Lili

DE PROFUNDIS see Bright, Houston

DE PROFUNDIS see Chorbajian, John

DE PROFUNDIS see Des Prez, Josquin

DE PROFUNDIS see Driessler, Johannes

DE PROFUNDIS see Dupre, Marcel

DE PROFUNDIS see Espla

DE PROFUNDIS see Etti, Karl

DE PROFUNDIS see Firpo, Antonio

DE PROFUNDIS see Gal, Hans

DE PROFUNDIS see Gluck, Christoph Willibald
Ritter von

DE PROFUNDIS see Gounod, Charles Francois

DE PROFUNDIS see Grassi, Ciro

DE PROFUNDIS see Hahn, Reynaldo

DE PROFUNDIS see Hemel, Oscar van

DE PROFUNDIS see Lalande, Michel Richard de

DE PROFUNDIS see Mozart, Wolfgang Amadeus

DE PROFUNDIS see Mulder, Ernest W.

DE PROFUNDIS see Nystedt, Knut

DE PROFUNDIS see Palestrina, Giovanni

DE PROFUNDIS see Pizzetti, [Ildebrando]

DE PROFUNDIS see Purvis, Richard

DE PROFUNDIS see Ropartz, Joseph Guy

DE PROFUNDIS see Salonen, Sulo

DE PROFUNDIS see Schmitt, Florent

DE PROFUNDIS see Schoenberg, Arnold

DE PROFUNDIS see Thomson, Virgil

DE PROFUNDIS see Thorne, Francis

DE PROFUNDIS see Tittel, Ernst

DE PROFUNDIS see Vlad, Roman

DE PROFUNDIS see Vulpius, Melchior

DE PROFUNDIS see Wellesz, Egon

DE PROFUNDIS see Wordsworth, William

DE PROFUNDIS CLAMAVI see Berger, Jean

DE PROFUNDIS CLAMAVI see De Taeye

DE PROFUNDIS CLAMAVI see Lassus, Roland de
(Orlandus)

DE PROFUNDIS CLAMAVI see Morley, Thomas

DE PROFUNDIS CLAMAVI see Palestrina, Giovanni

DE PROMIS' LAN' *spir
(Byles) 4pt mix cor oct SCHIRM.G 10655 $.25
(D636)
(Byles) 4pt mix cor oct SCHIRM.G 10655 $.25
(D637)

DE PROMIS' LAN' see Byles, B. D.

DE QUA NATUS EST see Battre, H.

DE SALIGE see Hovland, Egil

DE, SOM FORLADER SIG PA HERREN see Jeppesen,
Knud

DE SOM MED TARAR SA see Sorenson, Torsten

DE SPORDE OM SKON SARLING *folk
  (Pergament, Moses) mix cor,T solo NORDISKA
  1081 s.p.   (D638)

DE UNGAS HYMNARIUM *CCU,hymn
  (Eklof, Ejnar; Gustafson, John; and others)
  1-3pt mix cor NORDISKA s.p.   (D639)

DE UNGAS HYMNARIUM *CCU,hymn
  1-3pt mix cor NORDISKA 1100 s.p., ipa
  contains works by: Peters; Ahlen; Eklof;
  and others   (D640)

DE VAUX, JOSEPH
  Rock-a My Soul *spir
  SSA oct BOURNE 195 $.30   (D641)
  SATB oct BOURNE 667 $.30   (D642)

DE VISIONE RESURRECTIONIS EZECHIEL XXXVII see
  Jacob, Werner

DE YDMYKE see Hovland, Egil

DEAGAN, E.
  Bow Down Thine Ear
  SATB,pno (easy) oct WILLIS 7445 $.20 (D643)

DEAL BOUNTIFULLY WITH THY SERVANT see
  Kilpatrick, Jack F.

DEAL WITH ME, THY SERVANT see Morley, Thomas

DEALE
  Cradle Carol
  SSATB,acap (med easy) OXFORD 84.016 $.30
  see from FOUR OLD CAROLS   (D644)

DEAN
  Christ Is Now Risen Again
  SATB oct FOX R166 $.25   (D645)

  Follow Me
  SATB oct FISCHER,C CM-7742 $.25   (D646)

  Joyful Song, The
  SATB oct LILLENAS AN-2366 $.25   (D647)

  Love One Another
  SATB oct FISCHER,C CM-7743 $.25   (D648)

DEAN, T.W.
  Amazing Grace
  SATB oct SOUTHERN $.25   (D649)

  Canticles Of Christmas *Xmas,cant
  SATB oct SOUTHERN $1.25   (D650)

  Let Us Now Praise Famous Men
  SATB oct SOUTHERN $.50   (D651)

  Lord Is My Light, The
  SATB oct SOUTHERN $.25   (D652)

  Music For The Lord's Supper *Holywk
  SATB oct SOUTHERN $.45   (D653)

  Word Was Made Flesh, The *Xmas,cant
  SATB oct SOUTHERN $1.25   (D654)

  Words Of Jesus *cant
  SATB oct SOUTHERN $1.25   (D655)

DEAR BABY JESUS *Xmas
  (Martin) SATB oct LAWSON 51156 $.25 (D656)

DEAR CHRIST OF GALILEE see Kennerly

DEAR CHRISTIANS, LET ONE AND ALL REJOICE see
  Eccard, Johannes

DEAR CHRISTIANS, LET US ALL REJOICE see Ducis

DEAR CHRISTIANS ONE AND ALL see Lundquist,
  Matthew Nathanael

DEAR CHRISTIANS, ONE AND ALL, REJOICE see
  Distler, Hugo

DEAR CHRISTIANS, ONE AND ALL, REJOICE see
  Hassler, Hans Leo

DEAR CHRISTIANS, ONE AND ALL, REJOICE see
  Krapf, Gerhard

DEAR CHRISTIANS, ONE AND ALL, REJOICE see
  Lenel, Ludwig

DEAR CHRISTIANS, ONE AND ALL, REJOICE see
  Praetorius, Michael

DEAR CHRISTIANS, ONE AND ALL, REJOICE see
  Schein, Johann Hermann

DEAR CHRISTIANS, ONE AND ALL, REJOICE see
  Wetzler, Robert

DEAR CHRISTIANS, PRAISE GOD EVERMORE see
  Kindermann, Johann Erasmus

DEAR GOD, O BLESS US see Le Jeune, Claude,
  Benediction Avant La Repas

DEAR JESUS BOY see Wehr, David A.

DEAR LITTLE BABY JESUS see McWhertor

DEAR LORD AND FATHER see Parry, Charles Hubert
  Hastings

DEAR LORD AND FATHER OF MANKIND see Lovelace,
  Austin C.

DEAR LORD AND FATHER OF MANKIND see Maker

DEAR LORD AND FATHER OF MANKIND see Maker,
  [Frederick Charles]

DEAR LORD AND FATHER OF MANKIND see Parry,
  Charles Hubert Hastings

DEAR LORD AND FATHER OF MANKIND see Pedrette

DEAR LORD AND FATHER OF MANKIND see Whittier

DEAR LORD AND FATHER OF MANKIND see Williams

DEAR LORD AND MASTER see Nikolsky

DEAR LORD AND MASTER see Nikolsky, Anton

DEAR LORD AND SAVIOUR see Handel, George
  Frideric

DEAR LORD JESUS, KEEP US see Naumann, Johann
  Gottlieb

DEAR LORD, REMEMBER ME see Roff, Joseph

DEAR LORD TO THEE see Moore

DEAR LORD, WE OFFER THEE see Blakeslee

DEAR LORD, WE PRAISE THEE see Rachmaninoff,
  Sergey Vassilievitch

DEAR LORD, WHO ONCE UPON THE LAKE see Thompson,
  V.D.

DEAR MASTER, IN WHOSE LIFE I SEE see Arensky,
  Anton Stepanovitch

DEAR NAME see Matthews

DEAR NIGHTINGALE AWAKE *Xmas,carol
  see Three Christmas Carols
  (Whitehead, Alfred) SATB oct LESLIE 4004 see
  from Three Christmas Carols, Set 1   (D657)
  (Woodgate) SATB,acap (easy) OXFORD 84.022
  $.35 see from Four Carols   (D658)

DEAR NIGHTINGALE, AWAKE see Track, Gerhard

DEAR SAVIOR BLESS US see Loge

DEAREST JESU DRAW THOU NEAR ME see Glarum, L.
  Stanley

DEAREST JESU, HOLY CHILD see Kirk

DEAREST JESUS, DRAW THOU NEAR ME see Schop

DEAREST LORD AND SAVIOR see Sateren, Leland
  Bernhard

DEAREST LORD JESUS see Bach, Johann Sebastian

DEAREST LORD JESUS see Buxtehude, Dietrich,
  Liebster Herr Jesu

DEAREST SAVIOUR, WATCH THOU O'ER US see
  Berlioz, Hector

DEATH see Sateren, Leland Bernhard

DEATH AND LIFE see Shelley, [Harry Rowe]

DEATH, I DO NOT FEAR THEE see Bach, Johann
  Sebastian

DEATH OF ABSALOM, THE see Sanders, Robert L.

DEATH OF CHRIST, THE see Schulz, Joh. Abraham
  Peter

DEATH OF SAUL see Gaher, J.

DEATH OF SAUL, THE see Gaher, J.

DEATH OF THE BISHOP OF BRINDISI, THE see
  Menotti, Gian Carlo

DEATH OVER BASLE see Beck, Conrad, Der Tod Zu
  Basel

DEATH SHALL NOT DESTROY
  (Shaw; Parker) mix cor,acap oct LAWSON 920
  $.35   (D659)

DE BAILHADC
  Bless Ye The Lord
  (Bedell) unis oct MCA   (D660)

DEBORAH see Lacome, Paul

DEBORAH AND BARAK see Gibbs, [Cecil] Armstrong

DE BRANT
  see BRANT, CYR DE

DEBUSSY, CLAUDE (1862-1918)
  Jesus, Toi Qui Sauvas Le Monde
  (Brun, L'abbe F.) [Fr] 2pt wom cor,org voc
  sc DURAND s.p.   (D661)

  Louez Le Seigneur (from Martyre De Saint
  Sebastien) Bibl
  (Brun, L'abbe F.) [Fr] 4pt mix cor,org oct
  DURAND s.p.   (D662)

DECEM SACRAE LAUDES see Asola, Giovanni Matteo

DECEMBER see Walthew, [Richard Henry]

DECEMBER CAROL see Crooks, Mack

DECEMBER SONG see Pooler, Marie

DECHANT, A.
  Sonntagmorgen
  (Altena, E.) [Ger] mix cor,acap (med easy)
  HUG s.p.   (D663)

DECIUS, NICOLAUS (ca. 1485-ca. 1546)
  All Glory Be To God On High *anthem
  (Johns) SAB (easy) oct AUGSBURG 1391 $.35
                                                 (D664)

  Allein Gott In Der Hoh Sei Ehr
  see O Jesu Christ, Meins Lebens Licht

  Lamb Of God *anthem
  (Pooler) unis treb cor/SA (easy) oct
  AUGSBURG 1383 $.25   (D665)

  Lord My Guide Will Surely Be, The
  (Bach; Ehret) SATB oct SPRATT 570 $.25
                                                 (D666)

  To God On High
  SATB,acap SCHIRM.EC 1127 $.25   (D667)
  (Glaser, V.) SAB,pno SCHIRM.EC 2405 $.20
                                                 (D668)
  (Mendelssohn, F.; Davison, A.) TTBB,opt
  pno/org SCHIRM.EC 61 $.15   (D669)

  To God On High Be Thanks And Praise
  SA,pno/org SCHIRM.EC 1577 $.12   (D670)

DECK THE HALL *Xmas,carol,Welsh
  (Barnard) SATB SCHMITT 1130 $.22   (D671)
  (Heath) 4pt men cor,acap oct SCHIRM.G 10613
  $.35   (D672)
  (Smith) 4pt mix cor,acap oct SCHIRM.G 11051
  $.35   (D673)

DECK THE HALLS *Xmas,carol,Welsh
  see Troll The Ancient Carol
  (Shaw; Parker) SATB,acap oct LAWSON 720 $.30
                                                 (D674)
  (Tellep, L.) SATB,acap oct PRESSER 352-00335
  $.35   (D675)
  (Whitford) TTBB oct GALAXY 1.1087.1 $.25
                                                 (D676)

DECK THE HALLS WITH BOUGHS OF HOLLY
  see Many Moods Of Christmas, The, Suite Four

DECK THYSELF, MY SOUL see Bach, Johann
  Sebastian, Schmucke Dich, O Liebe Seele
  [Chorale]

DECK THYSELF, MY SOUL, WITH GLADNESS see
  Cruger, Johann

DECK THYSELF, MY SOUL, WITH GLADNESS see
  Handel, George Frideric

DECK, THYSELF, MY SOUL, WITH WITH GLADNESS see
  Handel, George Frideric

DECKER, JOACHIM
  Gott Sei Gelobet Und Gebenedeiet
  see Kubler, Emil, Im Frieden Dein, O Herre
  Mein

DECKER, W.
  Bettagslied
  [Ger] mix cor,acap (easy) HUG s.p.   (D677)

  Des Menschen Leben Ist Ein Jahr *Cnfrm
  (Huggenberger, A.) [Ger] wom cor,acap
  (easy) HUG s.p.   (D678)

  Gott Segne Diesen Bund
  [Ger] mix cor,acap (easy) HUG s.p.   (D679)

  Konfirmation *Cnfrm
  [Ger] mix cor,acap (easy) HUG s.p.   (D680)

DECLARE HIS HONOR see Handel, George Frideric

DECLARE HIS HONOR see Purcell, Henry

DECORA LUX see Arnaldi, Antonio

DE CORMIER, ROBERT (1922-   )
  Hallelujah *spir
  SATB,acap oct LAWSON 51272 $.35   (D681)

DE COURSEY
  Make A Joyful Noise Unto The Lord
  SATB oct FOX R192 $.25   (D682)

  Sing Hosannas! *Easter/Lent
  SATB oct PRO ART 2033 $.25   (D683)

DECREE, THE
  unis/SATB (very easy) OXFORD 08.046 $.15
                                                 (D684)

DEDEKIND, CONSTANTINE CHRISTIAN (1628-1725)
  Alleluia, Lobet Den Herrn Alle Heiden *mot
  (Hellmann) SA/SAB,cont HANSSLER 1.445 s.p.
                                                 (D685)

  Alles, Was Ihr Tut Mit Worten *mot
  (Hellmann) SAB/SA,cont HANSSLER 1.252 s.p.
                                                 (D686)

  Bereitet Dem Herrn Den Weg *mot
  (Hellmann) SAB/SAT,cont HANSSLER 1.305 s.p.
                                                 (D687)

  Das Alte Jahr Vergangen Ist *ECY,mot
  (Hellmann) SAB/SAT,cont HANSSLER 1.307 s.p.
                                                 (D688)

  Das Wort Ward Fleisch *Bibl/mot
  (Hellmann) SAB/SA,cont HANSSLER 1.239 s.p.
                                                 (D689)

  Der Herr Ist Nahe Allen *mot
  (Hellmann) SA/SAB,cont HANSSLER 1.446 s.p.
                                                 (D690)

  Der Tod Ist Tot *mot
  (Hellmann) SAB/SA,cont HANSSLER 1.452 s.p.
                                                 (D691)

  Der Tod Ist Verschlungen In Den Sieg *mot
  (Hellmann) SS/SAB,cont HANSSLER 1.453 s.p.
                                                 (D692)

  Du, Tochter Zion, Freue Dich Sehr *Bibl/mot
  (Hellmann) SS,cont HANSSLER 1.304 s.p.
                                                 (D693)

  Furwahr Er Trug Unsre Krankheit *mot
  (Hellmann) SAB/SA,cont HANSSLER 1.451 s.p.
                                                 (D694)

  Gelobet Sei, Der Da Kommt *mot
  2pt wom cor/2pt jr cor,org cor pts
  BREITKOPF-W CHB-3490 s.p.   (D695)
  (Hellmann) SAB/SA,cont HANSSLER 1.237 s.p.
                                                 (D696)

  Gelobet Sei Gott Und Der Vater *mot
  (Hellmann) SAB/SMezA/SA,cont HANSSLER 1.441
  s.p.   (D697)

  Gelobet Seist Du *mot
  (Hellmann) SAB/SA,cont HANSSLER 1.443 s.p.
                                                 (D698)

  Ist Gott Fur Uns, Wer Mag *mot
  (Hellmann) SS,cont HANSSLER 1.440 s.p.
                                                 (D699)

  Komm, Heilig Reiner Geist *mot
  (Hellmann) SAB/SA,cont HANSSLER 1.246 s.p.
                                                 (D700)

  So Du Mit Deinem Munde *mot
  (Hellmann) SAB/SA,cont HANSSLER 1.444 s.p.
                                                 (D701)

  Uns Ist Ein Kind Geboren *Xmas,mot
  (Hellmann) SAB/SAT,cont HANSSLER 1.306 s.p.
                                                 (D702)

  Zu Seinen Zeiten *mot
  (Hellmann) SAB/SA,cont HANSSLER 1.442 s.p.
                                                 (D703)

DEDICATION see Edwards, Clara

DEDICATION see Franz, Robert, Die Widmung

DEDICATION see Kennedy, John Brodbin

DEDICATION see Reske

DEDICATION see Roberton, Hugh S.

DEDICATION FESTIVAL PROCESSION *Ded,Fr
  (Hawkins, H.A.) SATB,org (easy) oct OXFORD
  42.961 $.30   (D704)

DEEGAN, JOHN
  Missa Brevis *Mass
  [Lat] SATB CHESTER s.p.   (D705)

DEEP IN THE BODING NIGHT see Ferguson

DEEP IS THE SILENCE *Xmas,carol,Pol
  (Henninger) SATB SCHMITT 1608 $.30   (D706)

DEEP NORTH SPIRITUALS see Belcher, [Supply]

DEEP RIVER *spir,US
  see Tva Negro Spirituals
  (Aubanel, George) "Fleuve Profond" [Eng/Fr] 3
    eq voices OUVRIERES s.p.   (D707)
  (Aubanel, Georges) "Fleuve Profond" [Eng/Fr]
    4pt mix cor,A solo OUVRIERES s.p.   (D708)
  (Aubanel, Georges) "Fleuve Profond" [Eng/Fr]
    3 eq voices&opt cor,opt A solo OUVRIERES
    s.p.   (D709)
  (Koll, Fritz) 3 eq voices cor pts BREITKOPF-W
    CHB-3648 see from Zwei Negro-Spirituals
                                           (D710)

DEEP RIVER see Burleigh, Henry Thacker

DEEP RIVER see Cram, James D.

DEEP RIVER see Heilger Gott

DEEP WERE HIS WOUNDS *anthem
  (Sateren, Leland) SATB (easy) oct AUGSBURG
  1461 $.25   (D711)

DEEP WITHIN MY SOUL'S RECESSES see Santa Cruz,
  Domingo, Desde El Fondo De Mi Alma

DEEPEN MY MUSIC see Burns

DEEPER, DEEPER see Jones

DEER IS PANTING FOR THE STREAM see Thompson

DEERING, RICHARD (ca. 1580-ca. 1629)
  Above Him Stood The Seraphim *Gen/Trin
  2pt (easy) oct OXFORD 44.709 $.25   (D712)

  And The King Was Greatly Moved *see
    Contristatus Est Rex David

  And The King Was Greatly Moved *Gen,Bibl
  SSATB (med) oct OXFORD 43.391 $.30   (D713)

  Ave Verum Corpus *anthem
  "Hail True Body" SATTB,acap
    PETERS H1555   (D714)
  (Turner) SATTB,org SCHOTT s.p.   (D715)

  Cantate Domino
  "O Sing Unto The Lord" [Lat/Eng] SSATTB,
    acap PETERS H1554 $.40   (D716)

  Contristatus Est Rex David
  "And The King Was Greatly Moved" [Lat/Eng]
    SSATB,acap PETERS H1513 $.40   (D717)

  Factum Est Silentium *cor-resp
  (Simkins, Cyril F.) [Lat] SSATTB CHESTER
    s.p.   (D718)

  Gaudent In Coelis
    see Two Motets

  Hail True Body *see Ave Verum Corpus

  Jesu, Dulcis Memoria
  "Jesus, The Very Thought Is Sweet" [Lat/
    Eng] SATTB,acap PETERS H1514 $.40   (D719)

  Jesu, Summa Benignitas
  (McCarthy) "Lord Of All Kindness" SATTB oct
    BOURNE 903 $.35   (D720)

  Jesus, The Very Thought Is Sweet *see Jesu,
    Dulcis Memoria

  Jubilate Deo
  "Make A Cheerful Noise Unto God" [Lat/Eng]
    SSATTB,acap PETERS H1556   (D721)

  Lord Of All Kindness *see Jesu, Summa
    Benignitas

  Make A Cheerful Noise Unto God *see Jubilate
    Deo

  O All Ye That Pass By
  (Bridge, Sir Fredk.) SSATTB BOSWORTH s.p.
                                           (D722)

  O Bone Jesu
    see Two Motets
  "O Good Jesus" [Lat/Eng] SATTB,acap PETERS
    H1515 $.40   (D723)

  O Good Jesus *see O Bone Jesu

  O Sing Unto The Lord *see Cantate Domino

  O Vos Omnes *Psntd,Bibl
  SSATTB (med) oct OXFORD 43.390 $.35   (D724)

  Quam Vidistis Pastores *anthem
  (Terry, R.R.) [Lat] SSATTB oct NOVELLO
    52.0012.01 s.p.   (D725)

  Quem Vidistis, Pastores? *Xmas,mot
  SSATTB SCHIRM.EC $.25   (D726)
  (Collins, H.B.) [Lat] SSATTB CHESTER s.p.
                                           (D727)

  Say, O Shepherds, Whom Saw Ye? *Xmas,anthem
  (Terry, R.R.) SSATTB oct NOVELLO s.p.
                                           (D728)

  Silence Prevailed In Heaven
  (Bridge, Sir Fredk.) SSATTB BOSWORTH s.p.
                                           (D729)

  Two Motets *mot
  (Turner) SS,org SCHOTT s.p.
    contains: Gaudent In Coelis; O Bone Jesu
                                           (D730)

DEFEND THE POOR AND DESOLATE *Bibl
  (Brandon, George) 2pt mix cor/SAB/SATB,org
  oct WORLD ESA-1857-8 $.45   (D731)

DE FER
  Psalm 25 *see Jambe

DEGEN, HELMUT (1911-   )
  Johannes-Passion *Bibl
  4pt mix cor,ST soli MOSELER s.p.   (D732)

  Osteroratorium *Easter,ora
  [Ger] 2-7pt mix cor,acap (med diff) BAREN.
    BA 634 $4.50   (D733)

DE GRANDIS, VINCENZO (1631-1708)
  L'esodo Di Mose Dall'egitto *Bibl/ora
  (De Grandis, R.) mix cor,SMezTBarB soli,
    orch voc sc ZERBONI 7059 s.p., ipr   (D734)

DEH COME TRISTA see Arcadelt, Jacob

DEI MATER ALMA see Palestrina, Giovanni

DEICI MADRIGALI SACRI see Eccher

DEILIG ER DEN HIMMEL BLAA *anthem
  (Christiansen, Paul) "Oh, How Beautiful The
  Sky" SATB (easy) oct AUGSBURG 0901 $.25 (D735)

DEILIG ER JORDEN *Xmas
  (Beck, Thomas) mix cor MUSIKK 95B s.p.   (D736)

DEIN EDLES HERZ see Buxtehude, Dietrich

DEIN EDLES HERZ, DER LIEBE THRON see Buxtehude,
  Dietrich

DEIN GEIST MEIN LEIB UND SEEL REGIER see Graun,
  Karl Heinrich

DEIN KONIG KOMMT IN NIEDERN HULLEN see
  Schumann, Robert (Alexander)

DEIN KONIG KOMMT IN NIEDERN HULLEN see
  Zillinger, Erwin

DEIN LOB, HERR, RUFT DER HIMMEL AUS see
  Bauernfiend, Hans

DEIN, O HERR, IST DIE KRAFT see Reger, Max

DEIN REICH KOMME see Driessler, Johannes

DEIN TOD GEBIETET SCHWEIGEN see Trubel, Gerhard

DEIN WORT IST MEINES HERZENS FREUDE see
  Schrader, Oswald

DEIN WORT, O HERR, WOHNT WEIT UND EWIG see
  Reger, Max

DEINEM NAMEN GIB EHRE see Graap, Lothar

DEINES LICHTES GLANZ see Pepping, Ernst

DEIXEII LO DOL *Easter,carol,Span
  (Glaser, V.) "Christ Is Arisen" SSAA,
    castanets SCHIRM.EC 2518 $.28   (D737)
  (Glaser, V.) "Christ Is Arisen" SATB,tamb,
    castanets SCHIRM.EC 2491 $.30   (D738)

DE JONG, CONRAD (1934-   )
  Peace Maker
  SATB FOSTER MF121 $.30   (D739)

DE KOVEN, [HENRY LOUIS REGINALD] (1859-1920)
  Recessional
  SATB oct LORENZ 4479 $.30   (D740)
  SSTB oct PRESSER 322-35015 $.25   (D741)
  TTBB&opt wom cor oct PRESSER 322-35017 $.30
                                           (D742)
  SSA oct PRESSER 332-35019 $.30   (D743)
  3pt wom cor,pno (med) oct WILLIS 7808 $.18
                                           (D744)
  TTBB,pno (med) oct WILLIS 7306 $.18   (D745)
  3pt mix cor,pno (med) oct WILLIS 7307 $.18
                                           (D746)
  SATB,pno (easy) oct WILLIS 7309 $.18   (D747)
  (Bliss, P.) SAB oct PRESSER 322-35016 $.30
                                           (D748)

DEL CIELO DE TUS OJUS see Martin Pompey

DEL CIELO SALIA DIOS see Santa Cruz, Domingo

DELALANDE, MICHEL-RICHARD
  Cantemus Domino *mot
  (Husa, Karel) mix cor,ATBar soli,opt orch,
    org,cont LAWSON $2.00, ipa   (D749)

DELAMORINIERE, G.
  Eveillez-Vous *Xmas,Fr
  [Fr] SATBarB cor pts LEDUC RF65 s.p.   (D750)

  Libera Et In Paradisium *Gen,mot
  [Lat] 4pt mix cor oct DURAND s.p.   (D751)

DELANNOY, MARCEL
  O Salutaris
  [Lat] 2pt,opt pno/org HEUGEL s.p.   (D752)

DE LA RUE, PIERRE (1460-1518)
  Gaude Virgo
  (Davison, N.) SATB,acap oct PRESSER
    312-40621 $.45   (D753)

  Lamentations Of Jeremiah, The
  SATB,acap PRESSER $1.75   (D754)

  Motet
    see de la Rue, Pierre, Requiem

  O Jesus, Pa Din Alterfod *see O Salutaris
    Hostia

  O Salutaris Hostia
  (Knight, Gerald) SATB,acap oct FISCHER,C
    CM-7591 $.25   (D755)
  (Sorensen, Soren) "O Jesus, Pa Din
    Alterfod" [Lat/Dan] SATB,acap HANSEN-DEN
    281 s.p. see also MOTETTER OG LAUDER FRA
    DET 16. ARHUNDREDE   (D756)

  Pater De Caelis (from Motets Of Pierre De La
    Rue)
  SATB,acap oct PRESSER 312-40618 $.60   (D757)

  Requiem *mot/Req
  mix cor,acap voc sc KALMUS 6377 $1.25
    contains also: Motet   (D758)

DE LA RUE, PIERRE (cont'd.)

  Requiem Moter
    see ARS NOVA TO RENNAISSANCE VOL. 2-1200 TO
    ABOUT 1500

  Salve Mater Salvatoris
  SATB,acap oct PRESSER 312-40619 $.35 (D759)

  Sicut Cervus Desiderat
  SATB oct PRESSER 352-00036 $.30   (D760)

  Wir Danken Dir, O Gottes Lamm (from Matthaus-
    Passion)
  SATB HANSSLER 6.120 s.p. contains also:
    Trubel, Gerhard, Mit Freuden Zart Zu
    Dieser Fahrt (SAB/SAT)   (D761)

DE LATTRE, [ROLAND]
  O Blessed Jesus *see O Bone Jesu

  O Bone Jesu
  (Seay) "O Blessed Jesus" SSAA oct FOX R164
    $.25   (D762)

DELA VENNA, P.
  Hodie Nobis *Xmas,mot
  "Let Us Sing Noel" SATB,S/T solo,org/pno
    SCHIRM.EC 2281 $.20   (D763)

  Let Us Sing Noel *see Hodie Nobis

DEL CASTILLO
  Monstra Te Esse Matrem *mot,Mex
  (Barwick, S.; Hines, R.S.) SSAT,acap PEER
    $.35   (D764)

DELDEN, LEX VAN
  see VAN DELDEN, LEX

DE LEEUW
  To Us A Little Child Is Born
    see SIX SEVENTEENTH CENTURY CAROLS FROM THE
    NETHERLANDS

DE LEONE, [FRANCESCO B.] (1887-1948)
  Lord Is My Shepherd, The
  SATB oct PRESSER 312-20165 $.30   (D765)

DELICATE CHILD OF ROYAL LINE *Xmas,carol,Ger
  (Schroeder, H.) SATB,inst (med easy) oct
  CONCORDIA 98-2071 $.25   (D766)

DELIG ER JORDEN
  (Wegelius, M.) mix cor MUSIKK 97 s.p.   (D767)

DELIRIO DEL ALMA POR VERA DIOS see Surinach,
  Carlos

DELIUS, FREDERICK (1862-1934)
  Mass For Life, A
  mix cor,soli,3fl,5ob,4clar,4bsn,4trp,6horn,
    3trom,tuba,strings,2harp,perc,timp cmplt
    ed BOOSEY rental   (D768)

  Requiem *Req
  dbl cor,SBar soli,orch BOOSEY cor pts
    $1.50, min sc $3.00, voc sc rental, sc
    rental, ipr   (D769)

DELIVER ME FROM MINE ENEMIES see Parsons,
  Robert

DELIVER US see Harper, M.

DELIVER US, GOOD LORD see Tye, Christopher

DELIVER US, O LORD see Batten, Adrian

DELIVER US, O LORD, OUR GOD see Croft, William

DELIVER US, O LORD OUR GOD see Gibbons, Orlando

DELIVERANCE see Wheelwright, Lorin F.

DELLO JOIO, NORMAN (1913-   )
  Ascension, The *Easter
  SATB oct PRESSER MC420 $.35   (D770)

  Bright Star
  SATB,2pno MARKS 4567 $.50   (D771)
  SA MARKS 4444 $.30   (D772)

  Christmas Carol, A *Xmas,carol
  SATB,2pno MARKS 4566 $.50   (D773)
  SATB MARKS 4237 $.25   (D774)
  SSA MARKS 4323 $.30   (D775)

  Holy Infant's Lullaby *Xmas,cradle
  girl cor SOUTHERN $.25   (D776)

  Holy Infant's Lullaby, The *Xmas
  SSA MARKS 4392 $.30   (D777)
  SATB MARKS 4240 $.25   (D778)
  SATB,2pno MARKS 4572 $.50   (D779)

  Improperium Expectavit
  [Lat] SATB,acap oct COLOMBO 1807 $.25
                                           (D780)

  Mass *Mass
  [Fr] SATB,brass MARKS voc sc $2.50, sc
    $7.50   (D781)

  Prayers Of Cardinal Newman *prayer
  SATB oct FISCHER,C CM-7321 $.30   (D782)

  Psalm Of David *Psalm
  SATB,opt orch/band FISCHER,C O-3723 $2.50
                                           (D783)

  Psalm Of Peace *Psalm
  SATB,org,trp,horn/pno MARKS $3.00   (D784)

  To Saint Cecilia *cant
  SATB,opt brass FISCHER,C O-4119 $1.75, ipr
                                           (D785)

DELMAS, M.
  Messe De Requiem *Mass/Req
  men cor,orch LEMOINE voc sc s.p., cor pts
    s.p., ipr   (D786)

DELMONTE
  Let The Sound Ring
  unis FLAMMER F5002 $.30   (D787)

DEL MONTE
  May We Be Worthy Of Thy Trust
  SATB (med easy) SOUTHERN $.35   (D788)

DELMONTE
  Voices In Worship
    (Peterson) SA oct WORD CS-403 $.40   (D789)

DEL RIEGO
  Star Was His Candle *Xmas,carol
    SATB ALLANS 288 s.p.   (D790)
    SA ALLANS 289 s.p.   (D791)
    SATB oct FISCHER,C CM-504 $.25   (D792)
    SA oct FISCHER,C CM-654 $.25   (D793)
    SAB oct FISCHER,C CM-657 $.25   (D794)
    SSA oct FISCHER,C CM-655 $.25   (D795)
    TTBB oct FISCHER,C CM-656 $.25   (D796)

  Star Was His Candle, A *Xmas
    (Breck) 2pt jr cor FISCHER,C CM 654 $.20   (D797)
    (Breck) 3pt jr cor/SAB (easy) FISCHER,C
      CM 657 $.25   (D798)

DE LUCA, ALESSANDRO
  Angeli E Pastori *Xmas
    unis ZANIBON 1700 s.p.   (D799)

  Sette Invocazioni A Maria *CC7U,BVM
    [Lat] unis,org ZANIBON 1653 s.p.   (D800)

DELVINCOURT, CLAUDE (1888-1954)
  Ave Maria
    see Salut Solennel En Sol

  Ave Verum
    see Salut Solennel En Sol

  Laudate Dominum
    see Salut Solennel En Sol

  Salut Solennel En Sol
    [Lat] cor,soli,orch voc sc DURAND s.p., ipr
      contains: Ave Maria; Ave Verum; Laudate
      Dominum; Tantum Ergo; Tu Es Petrus   (D801)

  Tantum Ergo
    see Salut Solennel En Sol

  Tu Es Petrus
    see Salut Solennel En Sol

DEM BRUDER DIE HAND see Sturmer, Bruno

DEM, DER UNS LIEBT see Tittel, Ernst

DEM DUNKLEN SCHOSS DER HEILGEN ERDE see Rein,
  Walter

DEM EINGEBORNEN KINDELEIN see Gesius,
  Bartholomaus

DEM GEDENKEN EINES TONDICHTERS
  (Etti, Karl) men cor,acap oct DOBLINGER s.p.
    see from Drei Ernste Gesange   (D802)

DEM KONIG ALLER ZEITEN see Heiller, Anton

DEM MENSCHEN IST GESETZT EINMAL see Bach,
  Johann Michael

DEM NEUGEBORNEN KINDELEIN see Praetorius,
  Michael

DEM WIR DAS HEILIG ITZT see Bach

DEM WIR DAS HEILIG ITZT see Bach, Johann
  Sebastian

DEMANTIUS, CHRISTOPH (1567-1643)
  Ach Bleib Bei Uns, Herr Jesu Christ *Easter,
    Bibl
    (Schmidt) [Ger] 6pt mix cor,acap cor pts
      BAREN. EM 483 s.p. see from Corona
      Harmonica   (D803)

  Corona Harmonica *see Ach Bleib Bei Uns,
    Herr Jesu Christ; Erstanden Ist Der
    Heilge Christ; Ich Bin Die Auferstehung
    Und Das Leben   (D804)

  Deutsche Johannes-Passion Und Weissagung Des
    Lebens Und Sterbens Jesu Christi *Bibl
    (Blume) 5pt mix cor MOSELER s.p.   (D805)

  Erstanden Ist Der Heilge Christ *Easter,Bibl
    (Schmidt) [Ger] 6pt mix cor,acap cor pts
      BAREN. EM 482 s.p. see from Corona
      Harmonica   (D806)

  Ich Bin Die Auferstehung Und Das Leben
    *Easter,Bibl
    (Schmidt) [Ger] 6pt mix cor,acap cor pts
      BAREN. EM 484 s.p. see from Corona
      Harmonica   (D807)

  Ich Hab Mein Sach *Gd.Fri.
    SATB,acap voc pt DOBLINGER s.p. see also
      TOD UND VERGANGLICHKEIT   (D808)

  Psalm 116 *Bibl
    (Adrio) 5pt mix cor MOSELER s.p. contains
      also: Schein, Psalm 116   (D809)

  Und Wie Moses In Der Wusten *Psntd
    [Ger] SSATTB,acap (med) MULLER MS 3 s.p.   (D810)

  Vier Deutsche Motetten *CC4U,mot
    6pt mix cor MOSELER s.p.   (D811)

  Wenn Mein Stundlein Vorhanden Ist
    SATBB HANSSLER 6.139 s.p. contains also:
      Bach, Johann Sebastian, Es Ist Gewisslich
      An Der Zeit, S.307 (SATB)   (D812)

DE MARBELLE
  When They Ring The Golden Bells
    (McLellan) SSATB oct LILLENAS AN-1171 $.30
                                                 (D813)

DEMAREST, A.
  Come, And Let Us Return
    SATB,pno/org oct KERBY 5001 $.35   (D814)

  Easter Introit *Easter,Introit
    SATB,org oct KERBY 5405 $.25   (D815)
    SATB oct KERBY 5405C $.25   (D816)

  Habakkuk - The Lord Is My Strength *anthem
    SATB oct KERBY 5002C $.35   (D817)

  He Is Not Here But Is Risen *Easter
    unis,org oct KERBY 5204 $.25   (D818)
    unis oct KERBY 5204C $.25   (D819)

DEMAREST, A. (cont'd.)

  Ho, Every One That Thirsteth
    SATB,org oct KERBY 5005 $.35   (D820)

  Hosea - Come, And Let Us Return Unto The Lord
    *anthem
    SATB oct KERBY 5001C $.35   (D821)

  How Shall I Come Before The Lord
    SATB,pno/org oct KERBY 5003 $.35   (D822)

  Isaia - Ho, Every One That Thirsteth *anthem
    SATB oct KERBY 5005C $.35   (D823)

  Jeremiah - Why Should Thou Be As A Stranger
    In The Land *anthem
    SATB oct KERBY 5004C $.35   (D824)

  Little Lamb *Xmas
    unis,pno/org oct KERBY 5202 $.25   (D825)
    unis oct KERBY 5202C $.25   (D826)

  Lord Is My Strength, The
    SATB,pno/org oct KERBY 5002 $.35   (D827)

  Micah - How Shall I Come Before The Lord
    *anthem
    SATB oct KERBY 5003C $.35   (D828)

  Why Shouldst Thou Be As A Stranger In The
    Land
    SATB,pno/org oct KERBY 5004 $.35   (D829)

DEMAREST, CLIFFORD (1874-1946)
  Shepherds Of Bethlehem, The *Xmas,cant
    mix cor,solo,org voc sc SCHIRM.G $1.00
                                                 (D830)

DEMERATH, F.
  Asperges Me
    mix cor,acap ERDMANN 531 s.p.   (D831)

  Drei Marienlieder
    mix cor,acap ERDMANN 535 s.p.
      contains: Jauchzet Ihr Volker; Maria,
      Wunder Der Gnade; Mutter Der Viel
      Schonen Minne   (D832)

  Jauchzet Ihr Volker
    see Drei Marienlieder

  Maria, Wunder Der Gnade
    see Drei Marienlieder

  Mutter Der Viel Schonen Minne
    see Drei Marienlieder

  Tantum Ergo
    mix cor,acap ERDMANN 516 s.p. contains
      also: Veni Creator   (D833)

  Veni Creator
    see Demerath, F., Tantum Ergo

DEMMING
  Seasonal Introits And Responses *CCU,Xmas/
    Commun/Easter/Gen/Thanks,Bene/Offer
    SATB PRO ART 561 $.50   (D834)

DEMMING, LANSON F. (1902-   )
  God, The Eternal
    SATB oct AGAPE CH 628 $.30   (D835)

DEMUTH
  Carol For Christmas, A *Xmas,carol
    unis (easy) OXFORD 45.049 $.25   (D836)

DEMUTIG WILL ICH MICH DIR ERGEBEN see Schutz,
  Heinrich, Si Non Humiliter Sentiebam

DEN ABER, DER EINE KLEINE ZEIT see Micheelsen,
  Hans Friedrich

DEN APOSTOLISKE TROSBEKJENNELSE see Nilsen,
  Ing. Frederik

DEN BLIDA VAR AR INNE see Berg, Gottfrid

DEN DAG EN WIL NIET VERBORGHEN SIJN see
  Rontgen, [Julius]

DEN DANSKE PSALMEBOG 1569 see Thomisson, Hans

DEN DIE HIRTEN LOBETEN SEHRE see Beuerle,
  Herbert

DEN DIE HIRTEN LOBETEN SEHRE see Klein, Richard
  Rudolf

DEN DIE HIRTEN LOBETEN SEHRE see Praetorius,
  Michael

DEN FRIEDEN LASSE ICH EUCH see Micheelsen, Hans
  Friedrich

DEN FURSTEN DES LEBENS HABT IHR GETOTET see
  Weinreich, Waltraut

DEN GEBOREN HAT EIN MAGD see Distler, Hugo

DEN HEIL'GEN GEISTES GNADE GROSS see Schutz,
  Heinrich

DEN HELIGA NATTEN see Rosenberg, Hilding

DEN HELIGA STADEN see Adams, Stephen

DEN HERREN LOBT MIT FREUDEN see Schutz,
  Heinrich

DEN KANANEISKA KVINNAN see Bach, Johann Michael

DEN KARLEK DU TILL VARLDEN BAR see Erseus,
  Torsten

DEN KRISTI PINA PA HJARTAT LAGT see Schutz,
  Heinrich

DEN KRISTLIGA DAGVISAN see Aberg, Jan H.

DEN LJUSA DAG FRAMGANGEN AR
  see Sex Koraler I Folkton I Sattningar

DEN LYSE DAG FORGANGEN ER see Jeppesen, Knud

DEN, SEG SELV OPPHOYER, SKAL FORNEDRES see
  Nystedt, Knut

DEN SIGNADE DAG *Bibl/Psalm
  see Sex Koraler I Folkton I Sattningar
  (Larsson, Rune) [Swed] SAB,acap GEHRMANS
    TKS 19   (D837)
  (Von Koch, Erland) [Swed] SATB,acap GEHRMANS
    KRB 429   (D838)

DEN SOM BER HAN FAR see Hovland, Egil

DEN STEN SOM BYGGNIGSMANNEN FORKASTADE see
  Nilsson, Torsten

DEN TOD NIEMAND ZWINGEN KUNNT see Bach, Johann
  Sebastian

DEN TOLVARIGE JESUS I TEMPLET see Schutz,
  Heinrich

DEN TRO SOM JESUM FAVNER see Cruger, Johann

DEN TYNGSTE SORG see Nesse, Sigurd

DEN TYNGSTE SORG OG MODA see Groven, Eivind

DEN YNDIGSTE ROSE ER FUNDEN see Hansen, Carl
  Willum

DEN YNDIGSTE ROSE ER FUNNET
  (Solberg, Per) mix cor MUSIKK 200 s.p. (D839)

DENCKE
  Lord Our God *Morav
    (Dickinson) SATB oct GRAY GMCM 8 $.30
                                                 (D840)

DEN HERREN
  Praise To The Lord
    (Hornibrook) SATB SHAWNEE A 534 $.25 (D841)

DENHOFF, JOACHIM (1924-   )
  Freu Dich, Erd- Und Himmelszelt *Xmas
    mix cor TONGER s.p. contains also: Markt
      Und Strassen Sind Verlassen   (D842)

  Markt Und Strassen Sind Verlassen
    see Denhoff, Joachim, Freu Dich, Erd- Und
    Himmelszelt

  O Laufet, Ihr Hirten *Xmas
    mix cor TONGER s.p.   (D843)

DENIZTON, N.
  Esprits Divins *Xmas,carol
    (Brun, L'abbe) 4pt mix cor,acap oct DURAND
                                                 (D844)

DENK ICH DER WALDER see Rohwer, Jens

DENK, MENSCH, WIE DEIN HEILAND DICH LIEBET see
  Pepping, Ernst

DENK NICHT, DER HERR SEI NOCH FERN see
  Kindermann, Johann Erasmus

DENN DEIN IST DAS REICH see Schweizer, Rolf

DENN DEIN LICHT KOMMT see Driessler, Johannes

DENN DER GOTTLOSEN ZEPTER WIRD NICHT see
  Hartmann, Heinrich

DENN DER HERR IST NAHE see Strohbach, Siegfried

DENN DU WIRST see Bach, Johann Sebastian, Denn
  Du Wirst Meine Seele Nicht In Der Holle
  Lassen

DENN DU WIRST MEINE SEELE NICHT IN DER HOLLE
  LASSEN see Bach, Johann Sebastian

DENN DU WIRST MEINE SEELE NICHT IN DIE HOLLE
  LASSEN see Bach, Johann Sebastian

DENN ER HAT SEINEN ENGELN BEFOHLEN UBER DIR see
  Mendelssohn-Bartholdy, Felix

DENN ES IST HIER KEIN UNTERSCHIED see Kukuck,
  Felicitas

DENN ES IST HIER KEIN UNTERSCHIED see Reda,
  Siegfried

DENN GLEICH WIE DER BLITZ AUSGEHT see Raselius,
  Andreas

DENN ICH HALTE ES DAFUR, DASS DIESER WELT
  LEIDEN see Reda, Siegfried

DENN IST DAS JAHR, DEIN IST DIE ZIET see Kurig,
  Hans-Hermann

DENN SIEHE, BEI DIR WOHNEN WILL UNSER HERR UND
  GOTT see Raphael, Gunther

DENN SO WIR GLAUBEN, DASS JESUS GESTORBEN UND
  AUFERSTANDEN IST see Reger, Max

DENN UNSER KEINER LEBT SICH SELBER see Raphael,
  Gunther

DENN VON IHM UND DURCH IHN SIND ALLE DINGE see
  Micheelsen, Hans Friedrich

DENN WER SICH SELBST ERHOHET see Raselius,
  Andreas

DENN WER SICH SELBST ERHOHT see Driessler,
  Johannes

DENN WIR HABEN AUCH EIN OSTERLAMM see
  Hufschmidt, Wolfgang

DENNE JESUS see Soderholm, Valdemar

DENNISON, S.
  Jesu Christes Milde Moder
    SATB,acap AMP A524 $.25   (D845)

DENNOCH BLEIBE ICH STETS AN DIR see Reda,
  Siegfried

DENNOCH BLEIBE ICH STETS AN DIR see Schein,
  Johann Hermann

DENNOCH HAT ISRAEL ZUM TROST see Schutz,
  Heinrich

DENNY, JAMES
Hymn To Christ The King *hymn
mix cor,STB soli,hpsd/pno,org (med) voc sc
OXFORD 46.138 $3.70 (D846)

DE NOON
Little Pine Tree, The *Xmas
(Maxwell) SSATB,opt bvl,perc,gtr oct
SHAPIRO SK 2013 $.25, ipa (D847)
(Maxwell) SATB,opt bvl,perc,gtr oct SHAPIRO
SK 2015 $.25, ipa (D848)
(Maxwell) SSA,opt bvl,perc,gtr oct SHAPIRO
SK 3027 $.25, ipa (D849)

DENTE, JOSEPH
Herre, Var Mig Nadig
mix cor NORDISKA 4248 s.p. (D850)

DENTICE, FABRIZIO
Nunc Dimittis
mix cor SCHIRM.EC 1253 (D851)

DENTON
Come, Ye Faithful
SATB oct LORENZ B186 $.30 (D852)

For All The Saints
SATB oct LORENZ B148 $.30 (D853)

God In A Star *Xmas,cant
SAB oct LORENZ $1.75 (D854)
SATB oct LORENZ $1.95 (D855)

Hymn Of Thanksgiving *hymn
SATB oct LORENZ C211 $.30 (D856)

I Want To Be Ready
SB oct LORENZ 5764 $.30 (D857)

Jesus Is Born The King! *Xmas,cant
SATB oct LORENZ $1.95 (D858)

Joy To All People! *Xmas,cant
SATB oct LORENZ $1.95 (D859)

King Forever *Xmas,cant
SATB/SAB oct LORENZ $1.95 (D860)

Let All Mortal Flesh Keep Silence
SATB oct LORENZ 9985 $.30 (D861)

Long Time Ago
SATB oct LORENZ B189 $.30 (D862)

O For A Thousand Tongues To Sing
SATB oct LORENZ B197 $.30 (D863)

Praise Our God *Easter
SATB oct LORENZ B192 $.30 (D864)

Song Of The Angels *Xmas
SATB oct LORENZ A469 $.30 (D865)

Thorns And Purple *Easter,cant
SATB LORENZ $1.95 (D866)

What Wondrous Love Is This *Easter
SATB oct LORENZ B147 $.30 (D867)

When Morning Gilds The Skies
SAB oct LORENZ 7405 $.25 (D868)

DENTON, JAMES
Christ The Lord Is Risen Today *Easter
SATB oct LORENZ A454 $.30 (D869)

First Noel, The *Xmas,anthem
SATB&opt jr cor (med easy) oct LORENZ B200
$.30 (D870)

Peace *anthem/medley
SATB,med solo (med diff) oct LORENZ C350
$.30 (D871)

DENZA, LUIGI (1846-1922)
Blessed Redeemer
(Fearis) SATB,pno (easy) oct WILLIS 6308
$.10 (D872)

DEO AC VERITATI see Schumann, William Howard

DEO DICAMUS GRATIAS see Homilius, Gottfried
August

DEO DICAMUS GRATIAS see Homilius, Gottfried
August, Herre, Var Gud, Vi Tacka Dig

DEO GRATIAS see Britten, Benjamin

DEO PATRI SIT GLORIA see Beckerath, Alfred von

DEPELSENAIRE, J.M.
Les Sept Dernieres Paroles Du Christ
4pt mix cor,TBarB soli,org/orch voc sc
TRANSAT. $2.80 (D873)

DEPTH OF MERCY see Mueller, Luise

DEPUE
Glory To God In The Highest
SATB KJOS PC789 $.30 (D874)

Hosanna
SATB KJOS PC790 $.50 (D875)
SATB KJOS PC790B $2.50 (D876)

Joy To All Mankind, A *Xmas
SATB oct PLYMOUTH BG-102 $.30 (D877)

Psalm 1
SATB KJOS PC791 $.75 (D878)

DER ANFANG, DAS ENDE see Hohlfeld, Christoph

DER BANKELSANGER "ALS VATER NOAH DIE ARCHE
GEMACHT HAT" see Strohbach, Siegfried

DER BLINDE BARTHIMAUS see Kramer, Gottfried

DER BLINDE VON JERICHO "ES GESCHAH ABER, ALS ER
NAHE AN JERICHO KAM" see Wiemer, Wolfgang

DER BRAUTIGAM WIRD BALD RUFEN see Franck,
Melchior

DER BUND
see Psalmen Und Geistliche Lieder Der
Christenheit

DER CHERUBINISCHE WANDERSMANN see Bauernfiend,
Hans

DER CHORVERS, HEFT 1 see Reich, Phillip

DER CHORVERS, HEFT 2 see Reich, Phillip

DER DA MIT WENIG FISCHEN see Jacobi, Samuel

DER DU AUSSPANNEST DAS HIMMLISCHE ZELT see
Hensel, Walther

DER DU BIST DREY see Praetorius, Michael

DER DU DER MENSCHEN HEILAND BIST see Stadlmair,
Hans

DER DU DIE WELT GESCHAFFEN HAST see Schrader,
Oswald

DER DU DIE ZEIT IN HANDEN HAST see Lambertz,
Johann Sebastian

DER DU IN TODESNACHTEN see Michel, Josep

DER EINSAME WANDERER see Burgwart, K.

DER ENGEL BRINGT WAHREN BERICHT see Burck,
Joachim

DER ENGEL DES HERRN
(Tittel, Ernst) mix cor,acap oct DOBLINGER
s.p. (D879)

DER ENGEL SPRACH ZU DEN HIRTEN see Gabrieli,
Andrea

DER ENGEL SPRACH ZU DEN HIRTEN see Hassler,
Hans Leo, Angelus Ad Pastores Ait

DER ENGEL SPRACH ZU DEN HIRTEN see Praetorius,
Michael

DER ENGEL SPRACH ZU DEN HIRTEN see Schutz,
Heinrich

DER ENGELISCHE GRUSS see Brahms, Johannes

DER ENGLE SPRACH ZU DEN HIRTEN see Schutz,
Heinrich

DER ENGLISCHE GRUSS see Brahms, Johannes

DER ERSTE PSALM see Trubel, Gerhard

DER ERSTE TAG see Lazarof, Henri

DER ESEL see Gebhard, Hans

DER FELDJAGER see Spratte, Hermann

DER FRIEDE see Bach, Johann Sebastian, Der
Friede Sei Mit Dir

DER FRIEDE SEI MIT DIR see Bach, Johann
Sebastian

DER FRIEDEN IST UNTER UNS (from Evangelischen
Kirchentag 1967) CC15U,Gen
[Ger] unis,kbd (med) BOSSE BE 287 s.p. (D880)

DER FUR DIE SUNDEN DER WELT GEMARTERTE UND
STERBENDE JESUS see Handel, George Frideric

DER FURST DES LEBENS see Nagler, F.

DER GEIST DES HERRN ERFULLET DEN ERDKREIS see
Wenzel, Eberhard

DER GEIST DES HERRN ERFULLET DEN ERDKREIS see
Zipp, Friedrich

DER GEIST DES HERRN ERFULLT DEN ERDENKREIS see
Ahrens, Joseph

DER GEIST DES HERRN ERFULLT DEN ERDKREIS see
Micheelsen, Hans Friedrich

DER GEIST GOTTES see Schubert, Franz (Peter)

DER GEIST HILFT see Bach, Johann Sebastian

DER GEIST HILFT UNSER SCHWACHHEIT AUF see Bach,
Johann Sebastian

DER GEIST HILFT UNSRER SCHWACHHEIT AUF see
Bach, Johann Sebastian

DER GERECHTE see Bach, Johann Christoph

DER GERECHTEN SEELEN SIND IN GOTTES HAND see
Capricornus, Samuel

DER GOTT UND DIE BAJADERE see Porena, Boris

DER GOTTESKNECHT see Kukuck, Felicitas

DER GRIMMIG TOD MIT SEINEM PFEIL see Bresgen,
Cesar

DER GRIMMIG TOD MIT SEINEM PFEIL see
Schoendlinger, Anton

DER GUTE MENSCH see Orff, Carl

DER HAUPTMANN GLAUBT, DRUM see Jacobi, Samuel

DER HEILAND IST ERSTANDEN see Heiller, Anton

DER HEILAND IST GEBOREN *Xmas,Aus
(Schemitsch, Hans) [Ger] mix cor,acap oct
DOBLINGER s.p. see also Zehn Osterrichische
Weihnachtslieder (D881)

DER HEILIG GEIST VOM HIMMEL KAM see Eccard,
Johannes

DER HEILIGE GEIST VOM HIMMEL KAM see Eccard,
Johannes

DER HEILIGE GEIST VOM HIMMEL KAM see Stobaeus,
Johann

DER HELLE WEG see Bach, Johann Sebastian

DER HERR see Bach, Johann Sebastian, Der Herr
Ist Mein Getreuer Hirt

DER HERR BEHUTE DICH VOR ALLEM UBEL see
Holsten, Martin

DER HERR BEWAHRET DIE SEELEN SEINER HEILIGEN
see Liszt, Franz

DER HERR DENKET AN UNS see Bach, Johann
Sebastian

DER HERR DENKET AN US see Schein, Johann
Hermann

DER HERR DENKT AN UNS see Ruppel, Paul Ernst

DER HERR ERHOR DICH IN DER NOT see Schutz,
Heinrich

DER HERR GEDENKT AN UNS see Frauenholtz, Johann
Christoph

DER HERR HAT GESAGT ZU MEINEM HERREN see
Raselius, Andreas

DER HERR HAT IN SEIN HANDEN see Cruger, Johann

DER HERR HAT OFFENBARET see Erlebach, Philipp
Heinrich

DER HERR HAT UNS DAS SALZ GENANNT see
Schweizer, Rolf

DER HERR IST AUFERSTANDEN see Schaper, Heinz-
Christian

DER HERR IST DER ARMEN SCHUTZ see Reda,
Siegfried

DER HERR IST GOTT, DER UNS ERLEUCHTET see Reda,
Siegfried

DER HERR IST GROSS see Schutz, Heinrich

DER HERR IST GUT! see Kocher, Konrad

DER HERR IST KONIG see Matthes, Rene

DER HERR IST KONIG see Kaufmann, Otto

DER HERR IST KONIG see Kubizek, Augustinian

DER HERR IST KONIG see Kurig, Hans-Hermann

DER HERR IST KONIG see Matthes, Rene

DER HERR IST KONIG see Micheelsen, Hans
Friedrich

DER HERR IST KONIG see Nicolai, Otto

DER HERR IST KONIG see Pachelbel, Johann

DER HERR IST KONIG see Sweelinck, Jan
Pieterszoon

DER HERR IST KONIG, HERRLICH SCHON see Schutz,
Heinrich

DER HERR IST KONIG, HOCH ERHOHT see Goudimel,
Claude, Es Geht Daher Des Tages Schein

DER HERR IST KONIG UBERALL see Schutz, Heinrich

DER HERR IST KONIG UND REGIERT see Schutz,
Heinrich

DER HERR IST KONIG see Pachelbel, Johann

DER HERR IST KONIG see Pachelbel, Johann

DER HERR IST KONIG see Pachelbel, Johann

DER HERR IST MEIN GETREUER HIRT see Bach,
Johann Sebastian

DER HERR IST MEIN GETREUER HIRT see Bornefeld,
Helmut

DER HERR IST MEIN GETREUER HIRT see Bossler,
Kurt

DER HERR IST MEIN GETREUER HIRT see Franck,
Melchior

DER HERR IST MEIN GETREUER HIRT see
Laitenberger, Theophil

DER HERR IST MEIN GETREUER HIRT see Praetorius,
Michael

DER HERR IST MEIN GETREUER HIRT see Reda,
Siegfried

DER HERR IST MEIN GETREUER HIRT see Schutz,
Heinrich

DER HERR IST MEIN GETREUER HIRT see Stern,
Hermann

DER HERR IST MEIN GETREUER HIRT see Wagner,
Alexander

DER HERR IST MEIN GETREUER HIRT' [CHORALE] see
Bach, Johann Sebastian

DER HERR IST MEIN HIRT see Klein, Richard
Rudolf

DER HERR IST MEIN HIRT see Schutz, Heinrich

DER HERR IST MEIN HIRT see Sweelinck, Jan
Pieterszoon

DER HERR IST MEIN HIRTE see Doernberg, Martin

DER HERR IST MEIN HIRTE see Klein, Bernhard

DER HERR IST MEIN HIRTE see Lavater, H.

DER HERR IST MEIN HIRTE see Meyer-Janson,
Burkhard

DER HERR IST MEIN HIRTE see Micheelsen, Hans
Friedrich

DER HERR IST MEIN HIRTE see Pepping, Ernst

DER HERR IST MEIN HIRTE see Ruppel, Paul Ernst

DER HERR IST MEIN HIRTE see Stern, Hermann

DER HERR IST MEIN HIRTE see Telemann, Georg Philipp

DER HERR IST MEIN HIRTE see Weismann, Wilhelm

DER HERR IST MEIN LICHT see Handel, George Frideric

DER HERR IST MEIN LICHT UND MEIN HEIL see Raphael, Gunther

DER HERR IST MEIN LICHT UND MEIN HEIL see Werner, Fritz

DER HERR IST MEIN TREUER HIRT see Gumpeltzhaimer, Adam

DER HERR IST MEINE MACHT UND MEIN PSALM see Zimmermann, Heinz Werner

DER HERR IST MEINE ZUFLUCHT see Borris, Siegfried

DER HERR IST MIT MIR see Buxtehude, Dietrich

DER HERR IST NAHE see Lehman, Siegfried

DER HERR IST NAHE ALLEN see Dedekind, Constantine Christian

DER HERR JESUS MEIN HIRTE IST see Eccard, Johannes

DER HERR SCHAUET VOM HIMMEL see Schutz, Heinrich

DER HERR SEGNE EUCH see Bach, Johann Sebastian

DER HERR SENDET EINE ERLOSUNG see Rohwer, Jens

DER HERR SPRACH ZU MEIM HERREN see Schutz, Heinrich

DER HERR WARD AUFGEHOBEN GEN HIMMEL see Pezel, Johann Christoph

DER HERR WARD AUFGEHOBEN GEN HIMMEL see Wenzel, Eberhard

DER HERR WARD GEHORSAM BIS ZUM TOD see Weyrauch, Johannes

DER HERR WARD GEHORSAM BIS ZUM TODE see Pezel, Johann Christoph

DER HIMMEL LACHT, DIE ERDE JUBILIERET see Bach, Johann Sebastian

DER HIMMEL LACHT, DIE ERDE JUBILIERT see Bach, Johann Sebastian

DER HIMMEL SENKET SICH see Lang, Hans

DER HIMMEL SOLL SICH HEUTE FREUN see Stadlmair, Hans

DER HOCHSTE HERRSCHT IN MAJESTAT UND PRACHT see Cruger, Johann

DER HOCHSTE HERRSCHT IN MAJESTAT UND PRACHT see Pfiffner, Ernst

DER HUGENOTTENPSALTER see Sweelinck, Jan Pieterszoon

DER JAGER see Brahms, Johannes

DER JAHRKREIS see Distler, Hugo

DER JUNGER IST NICHT UBER SEINEN MEISTER see Driessler, Johannes

DER JUNGLING ZU NAIM see Schieri, Fritz

DER KAMPF DES ELIAS see Blum, Robert

DER KLEINE KIRCHENCHOR *see Aiblinger, Johann Kaspar, Justorium Animae; Aiblinger, Johann Kaspar, Locus Iste; Aiblinger, Johann Kaspar, Messe; Brosig, Moritz, Timete Dominum; Sechter, Simon, Messe In Der Lydischen Tonart; Sechter, Simon, Tenuisti, Improperium, Graduale Und Offertorium Fur Den Palmsonntag; Stuntz, Josef Hartmann, Domine Deus   (D882)

DER KLEINE KIRCHENCHOR see Aiblinger, Johann Kaspar

DER KLEINE KIRCHENCHOR see Brosig, Moritz

DER KLEINE KIRCHENCHOR see Sechter, Simon

DER KLEINE KIRCHENCHOR see Stuntz, Josef Hartmann

DER KONIG IN THULE see Zelter

DER KREUZWEG see Liszt, Franz, Via Crucis

DER KUHLE MAIEN see Schein, Johann Hermann

DER LEBENDIGE see Driessler, Johannes

DER LEIB ZWAR IN DER ERDEN see Bach, Johann Sebastian

DER LIEBEN SONNE LICHT UND PRACHT see Bach, Johann Sebastian

DER LOBGESANG DES SIMEON see Goudimel, Claude

DER LOBGESANG DES SIMEON see Jambe de Fer, Philibert

DER LOBGESANG DES SIMEON see Mareshall, Samuel

DER MAI TRITT EIN MIT FREUDEN see Rhau, Johannes

DER MANN LOT see Koetsier, Jan

DER MENSCH see Buchtger, Fritz

DER MENSCH IST WIE GRAS see Kubizek, Augustinian

DER MENSCH LEBT see Becker, Peter

DER MENSCH LEBT NICHT VOM BROT ALLEIN see Driessler, Johannes

DER MENSCH LEBT NICHT VOM BROT ALLEIN see Werner, Fritz

DER MENSCH LEBT NICHT VOM BROT ALLEIN, ABER AUCH NICHT OHNE see Hindermann, Walter Felix

DER MENSCH LEBT UND BESTEHET see Brugk, Hans Melchoir

DER MENSCH LEBT UND BESTEHET see Nageli, Johann (Hans) Georg

DER MENSCH LEBT UND BESTEHET NUR EINE KLEINE ZEIT see Grot, H.

DER MENSCH LEBT UND BESTEHT see Callhoff, Herbert

DER MENSCH LEBT UND BESTEHT see Erdlen, Hermann

DER MENSCH LEBT UND BESTEHT see Zelter, Carl Friedrich

DER MENSCH, VOM WEIBE GEBOREN see Bach, Johann Christoph

DER MENSCH, VOM WEIBE GEBOREN see Brunner, Adolf

DER MESSIAS see Handel, George Frideric, Messiah

DER MICHAELSKAMPF see Wenzel, Eberhard

DER MOND IST AUFGEGAGEN see Rohwer, Jens

DER MOND IST AUFGEGANGEN see Girnatis, Walter

DER MOND IST AUFGEGANGEN see Graap, Lothar

DER MOND IST AUFGEGANGEN see Henking, Bernhard

DER MOND IST AUFGEGANGEN see Hohlfeld, Christoph

DER MOND IST AUFGEGANGEN see Raphael, Gunther

DER MOND IST AUFGEGANGEN see Schulz, Joh. Abraham Peter

DER MOND IST AUFGEGANGEN see Trubel, Gerhard

DER MORGENSTERN IST AUFGEDRUNGEN see Bender, Jan

DER MORGENSTERN IST AUFGEDRUNGEN see Herzog, Johann Georg

DER MORGENSTERN IST AUFGEDRUNGEN see Kretzschmar, Gunther

DER MORGENSTERN IST AUFGEDRUNGEN see Micheelsen, Hans Friedrich

DER MORGENSTERN IST AUFGEDRUNGEN see Pepping, Ernst

DER MORGENSTERN IST AUFGEDRUNGEN see Praetorius, Michael

DER MORGENSTERN IST AUFGEDRUNGEN see Trubel, Gerhard

DER MORGENSTERN IST AUFGEGANGEN see Praetorius, Michael

DER OSTERKREIS
   see Psalmen Und Geistliche Lieder Der Christenheit

DER PILGER see Buchtger, Fritz

DER PSALTER see Schutz, Heinrich

DER SAME IST DAS WORT GOTTES see Vulpius, Melchior

DER SAS VED NATTETID ET SYN see Jeppesen, Knud

DER SCHONSTE KLANG VON ALL' DEN TAUSEND KLANGEN see Hess, C.

DER SPERLING UND DAS KANGURUH see Beckerath, Alfred von

DER SPIEGEL DER DREIFALTIGKEIT see Praetorius, Michael

DER STARKE GOTT IM HIMMELREICH see Lassus, Roland de (Orlandus)

DER STERN, DER STERN SOLL RUNDHERUM GEHN
   *CC5U, Xmas, canon
   [Ger] 2-4pt, acap (med easy) BAREN. BA 106
   s.p. contains works by: Bornefeld, H.;
   Dietrich, F.; Rein, W.; Vulpius, M. (D883)

DER STERN VON BETHLEHEM see Etti, Karl

DER SUSSE GESANG see Hasselbach, Hans

DER TAG BRICHT AN *CC11U, Gen
   (Ameln, Konrad; Thomas, Wilhelm) [Ger] 3-5pt
   mix cor, acap (med easy) BAREN. BA 483 $1.25
   contains works by: Praetorius; Senfl;
   Kugelmann; Walter; Vulpius; Regnart;
   Cruger; Albert   (D884)

DER TAG BRICHT AN UND ZEIGET SICH see Stern, Hermann

DER TAG BRICHT AN UND ZEIGET SICH see Vulpius, Melchior

DER TAG, DER IST SO FREUDENREICH see Anonymous

DER TAG, DER IST SO FREUDENREICH see Eccard, Johannes

DER TAG, DER IST SO FREUDENREICH see Gallus, Jacobus, Dies Est Laetitia

DER TAG, DER IST SO FREUDENREICH see Grimm, Heinrich

DER TAG, DER IST SO FREUDENREICH see Poos, Heinrich

DER TAG, DER IST SO FREUDENREICH see Praetorius, Michael

DER TAG, DER IST SO FREUDENREICH see Raphael, Gunther

DER TAG, DER IST SO FREUDENREICH see Spitta, Heinrich

DER TAG, DER IST SO FREUDENREICH see Stern, Hermann

DER TAG, DER IST SO FREUDENREICH see Werner, Gregor Joseph

DER TAG, DER IST SO FREUDENREICH [CHORALE] see Bach, Johann Sebastian

DER TAG GEHT MUD VON HINNEN see Trubel, Gerhard

DER TAG HAT SICH GENEIGET see Distler, Hugo

DER TAG IST HIN see Bach, Johann Sebastian

DER TAG IST NUN VERGANGEN see Ahle, Johann Rudolph

DER TAG IST SEINER HOHE NAH see Lohr, Ina

DER TAG IST SO FREUDENREICH
   mix cor sc ALSBACH&D s.p.   (D885)

DER TAG VERTREIBT DIE FINSTRE NACHT see Praetorius, Michael

DER TOD see Buchtger, Fritz

DER TOD, DAS IST DIE KUHLE NACHT see Cornelius, Peter

DER TOD DES OEDIPUS see Beck, Conrad

DER TOD IST DER SUNDE SOLD see Reda, Siegfried

DER TOD IST TOT see Dedekind, Constantine Christian

DER TOD IST VERSCHLUNGEN see Geisel, Gustav

DER TOD IST VERSCHLUNGEN see Hammerschmidt, Andreas

DER TOD IST VERSCHLUNGEN see Thomas, Kurt

DER TOD IST VERSCHLUNGEN IN DEN SIEG see Dedekind, Constantine Christian

DER TOD IST VERSCHLUNGEN IN DEN SIEG see Weinreich, Waltraut

DER TOD JESU see Graun, Karl Heinrich

DER TOD JESU see Niedermann, G.

DER TOD ZU BASEL see Beck, Conrad

DER TRAUM DES HERODES see Berlioz, Hector

DER TURMBAU ZU BABYLON see Kretzschmar, Gunther

DER VERDORRTE FEIGENBAUM see Schieri, Fritz

DER VERLORENE SOHN see Peter, Herbert

DER VERLORENE SOHN see Rudnick, Wilhelm

DER WACHTER AUF DEM TURMLEIN SASS see Dingemann, [Gustav]

DER WEG DER BARMHERZIGKEIT see Schneider, Martin Gotthard

DER WEIHNACHTSKREIS *CCU, Xmas, Psalm
   (Lohr) [Ger] 1-3pt HUG s.p.   (D886)

DER WEIHNACHTSKREIS
   see Psalmen Und Geistliche Lieder Der Christenheit

DER WEIHNACHTSSTERN see Herrmann, Hugo

DER ZWOLFJAHRIGE JESUS see Schutz, Heinrich, Mein Sohn, Warum Hast Du Uns Das Getan?

DERBY, RICHARD
   To Everything There Is A Season *Bibl
   SATB, acap oct LAWSON 51574 $.30   (D887)

DEREINST, MEIN SINN *mot
   (Burkhart, Franz) mix cor, acap DOBLINGER s.p.
   see also In Seiner Handen   (D888)

DERE'S NO HIDIN' PLACE
   (Shaw; Parker) SATB, T solo, acap oct LAWSON
   51110 $.35   (D889)

DERING, RICHARD
   see DEERING, RICHARD

DERR HERR ERHOR DICH see Buxtehude, Dietrich

DERR HERR IST KONIG see Matthes, Rene

DERR HERR VETERINADOKTOR see Lehner, F.X.

DERTIL VI SYNGER see Distler, Hugo, So Singen Wir All Amen

DES HEILANDS KINDHEIT see Berlioz, Hector

DES HEILANDS KINDHEIT see Berlioz, Hector

DES HEILGEN GEISTES GNADE GROSS see Schutz, Heinrich

DES HEILGEN GEISTES GNADE GROSS see Vulpius, Melchior

DES HERREN LOB SEI UNSER LIED see Haydn, (Franz) Joseph

DES HERREN WORT see Graap, Lothar

DES HERRN WORT see Kramer, Gottfried

DES HERRN WORT BLEIBT IN EWIGKEIT see Dietrich, Fritz

DES HIMMELS GEZELT see Valerius

DES HOCHSTEN WORT see Wildgans, Friedrich

DES JAHRES LAUF HAT UNS see Haller, Hans Peter

DES LASST UNS ALLE FORHLICH SEIN *CCU,Xmas,mot
(Hellmann, Diethard) mix cor HANSSLER 2.028 s.p. (D890)

DES MENSCHEN LEBEN IST EIN JAHR see Decker, W.

DES MENSCHEN SOHN IST GEKOMMEN ZU SUCHEN see Lohr, Ina

DES MENSCHEN SOHN IST NICHT GEKOMMEN see Zipp, Friedrich

DES SOMMERS WILL ICH SINGEN see Stier, Alfred

DES STAUBES EITLE SORGEN see Handel, George Frideric, Insanae Et Vanae Curae

DESCANT CHRISTMAS CAROL BOOK *CCU,Xmas,carol
desc BELWIN $.75 (D891)

DESCANTS ON CHRISTMAS CAROLS *CCU,Xmas
mix cor/treb cor SCHMITT 47 $.50 (D892)

DESCANTS ON FAVORITE HYMNS *CCU
mix cor SCHMITT 31 $.50 (D893)

DESCANTS ON FAVORITE SONGS *CCU
mix cor SCHMITT 40 $.50 (D894)

DESCANTS ON NINE CHRISTMAS CAROLS *CC9U,Xmas, carol
(Le Cras) 4pt mix cor&unis oct CURWEN 10978 $.30 (D895)

DESCANTS ON SIX HYMN TUNES see Cartford, Gerhard M.

DESCANTS ON TEN CHRISTMAS HYMNS AND CAROLS see Frothingham

DESCARRIES, AUGUSTE
Magnificat
TTBB,acap oct BERANDOL 842D8AB $.50 (D896)

DESCEND, THOU HEAV'NLY DOVE see Palestrina, Giovanni, Salvete Flores Martyrum

DESCENDIT ANGELUS DOMINI see Palestrina, Giovanni

DESCENDS MOISE see Go Down Moses

DESCENT OF THE CELESTIAL CITY, THE see Hamilton, Iain

DESCH, RUDOLF (1911-)
Kyrie Und Gloria *Gloria/Kyrie
[Lat] men cor,acap BOTE sc s.p., cor pts s.p. (D897)

Lasst Tonen Die Glocken Um Mitternacht *Xmas
men cor/mix cor TONGER s.p. (D898)
wom cor&jr cor/mix cor TONGER s.p. (D899)

DESDE EL FONDO DE MI ALMA see Santa Cruz, Domingo

DESDERI, ETTORE (1892-)
Ad Pueros *Mass
[Lat] unis,org sc ZANIBON 4113 s.p., cor pts ZANIBON 4114 s.p. (D900)

In Natali Domini *Xmas,mot
[Lat] cor pts ZANIBON 4323 s.p., sc ZANIBON 4322 s.p. also contains solo work: Tota Silescit
contains: In Natali Domini (3pt,solo, org); Virgo Parens Christi (2pt,solo, org) (D901)

In Natali Domini
see In Natali Domini

Missa Dona Pacem *Mass
SATB SCHOTT voc sc s.p., cor pts s.p. (D902)

Missa Sinite Parvulo *Mass
[Lat] SSA SCHOTT voc sc s.p., cor pts s.p. (D903)

Virgo Parens Christi
see In Natali Domini

DESE BONES SHALL RISE AGAIN see Cheyette

DESERT SHALL BLOSSOM, THE see Christiansen, Paul

DESERT SHALL REJOICE, THE see Offer, Charles K.

DESERT SHALL REJOICE, THE see Byles, B. D.

DESERT SHALL REJOICE, THE see Wilson

DE SILVA, ANDREAS
Opera Omnia vol. I *CCU,mot
(Kirsch, Winifred) cor AM.INST.MUS. $16.00 (D904)

Opera Omnia vol. II *CCU,mot
(Kirsch, Winifred) 5pt/6pt AM.INST.MUS. $17.00 (D905)

DES MARAIS, PAUL (1920-)
Psalm 121
SATB oct ELKAN-V 362-1218 $.30 (D906)

DESPAIR NOT HEART see Praetorius, Michael

DESPAIR NOT, MY SOUL, NOR TO SORROW GIVE WAY *Gen
(Buszin, W.) SATB,acap (med easy) oct CONCORDIA 98-1177 $.25 (D907)

DES PREZ, JOSQUIN (ca. 1450-1521)
Absalom, Oh, My Son *see Absalon, Fili Mi

Absalon, Fili Mi
(Payson, A.) "Absalom, Oh, My Son" SATB, acap FRANK F-445 $.30 (D908)

Agnus Dei I (from Hercules) Agnus
(Couraud) [Lat] SATB,acap oct SALABERT-US $1.00 contains also: Agnus Dei II (D909)

Agnus Dei II (from Hercules)
see Des Prez, Josquin, Agnus Dei I

Agnus Dei III (from Hercules) Agnus
(Couraud) [Lat] SSATB oct SALABERT-US $1.00 (D910)

Ars Nova To Rennaissance Vol. 3-1200 To About 1500 *CC9UL,Mass/mot/Psalm
mix cor min sc KALMUS 702 $1.30 (D911)

Ave Christe Immolate
(Couraud) [Lat] SSSAAATTTBBB oct SALABERT-US $1.50 (D912)

Ave Maria
see MUSICA RESERVATA, BAND 2
SATB,acap oct PRESSER 352-00044 $.35 (D913)
(Couraud) [Lat] SATB,acap oct SALABERT-US $1.00 (D914)

Ave Maria, Gratia Plena *BVM,mot
(Greenberg) [Lat] SATB,acap (medieval poem) AMP N28 $.35 see from Two Marian Motets (D915)
(Greenberg) [Lat] SATB,acap (from petrucci's "motteti c") AMP N27 $.30 see from Two Marian Motets (D916)

Ave Maris Stella
(White) [Lat] SATB,acap AMP N35 $.50 (D917)

Ave Vera Virginitas *mot
[Lat] SATB,acap oct GIA G565 $.25 (D918)
mix cor SOUTHERN $.25 (D919)
(Greyson) "We Worship Thy Virginity" SATB oct BOURNE ES4 $.30 (D920)

Ave Verum
see LA SCHOLA PALESTRINIENNE PREMIERE CAHIER

Ave, Verum Corpus *Commun/Easter/Lent, anthem/mot
boy cor SOUTHERN $.30 (D921)
SAB,acap WARNER W2970 $.30 (D922)
(Damrosch) "Hail, True Body Born Of Mary" [Eng/Lat] 3pt mix cor,acap oct SCHIRM.G 11606 $.25 (D923)
(Davison, A.) [Lat] TTBB,acap SCHIRM.EC 34 $.30 (D924)
(Geer, E.) "Bread Of Heaven" SSA,acap SCHIRM.EC 2500 $.30 (D925)
(Greyson) "Hail, True Body" SSA oct BOURNE ES88A $.30 (D926)
(Klein) "Hail, True Body" [Eng/Lat] SAB (med) oct GIA G1533 $.25 (D927)
(Scott) SSA oct FOX R101 $.25 (D928)
(Woodworth, G.) [Lat] SSA,acap SCHIRM.EC 816 $.20 (D929)

Ave Verum Corpus Christe
(Expert) [Lat] SATB,acap oct SALABERT-US $.65 (D930)

Benedicta Es
see ALTNIEDERLANDISCHE MOTETTEN

Bread Of Heaven *see Ave Verum Corpus

Coeurs Desolez
SATB,acap oct PRESSER 352-00039 $.25 (D931)

Come, O Creator Spirit, Come *Cnfrm/Gen/Pent
SATB,kbd (med easy) oct CONCORDIA 98-1994 $.25 (D932)

Da Pacem *Mass
(Blume) 4pt mix cor MOSELER s.p. (D933)

De Beata Virgine *Mass
see Des Prez, Josquin, Pange Lingua
(Blume) 4-5pt mix cor MOSELER s.p. (D934)

De Profundis
SATB,acap oct PRESSER 352-00043 $.40 (D935)

Drei Evangelien-Motetten *CC3U,mot
(Blume) [Ger/Lat] 4pt mix cor&6pt mix cor& 8pt mix cor MOSELER s.p. (D936)

Drei Motetten *CC3U,mot
(Osthoff) [Ger/Lat] 4-6pt mix cor MOSELER s.p. (D937)

Drei Psalmen *CC3U,Psalm
(Blume) [Ger/Lat] 4pt mix cor&wom cor&men cor MOSELER s.p. (D938)

Et Incarnatus Est (from Pange Lingua)
see Lassus, Roland de (Orlandus), Agnus Dei

[Four] Motets
see Des Prez, Josquin, Pange Lingua

Four Motets *CC4U,mot
mix cor,acap voc sc KALMUS 6152 $1.75 (D939)

Gloria (from Hercules) Gloria
(Couraud) [Lat] SATB,acap oct SALABERT-US $1.00 (D940)

Hail To The Child *Xmas
SATB oct WORD CRS-13 $.25 (D941)
(Stone) SAB,acap oct WORD CRS-13 $.25 (D942)

Hail, True Body *see Ave, Verum Corpus

Hail, True Body Born Of Mary *see Ave, Verum Corpus

In Pace
see MEISTERWERKE MITTELALTERLICHER MUSIK

Jesu! The Very Thought Is Sweet *Circum/Gen
SATB,acap (med easy) oct CONCORDIA 98-1095 $.25 (D943)

DES PREZ, JOSQUIN (cont'd.)

Jesus, Word Of God Incarnate
(Harris) SAB FLAMMER D5169 $.25 (D944)

Kyrie - Christe - Kyrie (from Hercules) Kyrie
(Couraud) [Lat] SATB,acap oct SALABERT-US $.75 (D945)

Magnificat Quarti Toni *Magnif
(Maderna, B.) mix cor,orch voc sc ZERBONI 6660 s.p., ipr (D946)

Miserere Mei Deus (Psalm 50)
[Lat] 5pt PETERS EM550 $1.50 (D947)
girl cor SOUTHERN $.25 (D948)

Missa Da Pacem *Mass
mix cor,acap voc sc KALMUS 6157 $1.25 (D949)

Missa De Beata Virgine *Mass
mix cor,acap voc sc KALMUS 6149 $2.00 (D950)

Missa Mater Patris *Mass
(Forbes, Elliot) 4pt men cor,acap voc sc SCHIRM.G $1.50 (D951)

Missa Pange Lingua *Mass
mix cor,acap voc sc KALMUS 6148 $1.40 (D952)

Mittit Ad Virginem
(Davies, M.G.) [Eng/Lat] 4pt mix cor,acap voc sc SCHIRM.G $1.00 (D953)

O Christ, Son Of Our God
(Kingsbury, John) SATB ALFRED 6380 $.30 (D954)

O Domine Jesu Christe
(Woodworth) 4pt men cor,acap oct SCHIRM.G 10573 $.35 (D955)

O Jesu, Fili David
(Gronquist, R.) [Lat/Eng] SA,org BROUDE,A. 169 $.30 (D956)

Pange Lingua *Mass/mot/Psalm
cor min sc KALMUS 702 $1.30 contains also: De Beata Virgine; [Four] Motets; [Three] Psalms (D957)
(Blume) 4pt mix cor MOSELER s.p. (D958)

Parting From You
(Expert) [Eng/Fr] SATB,acap oct SALABERT-US $.35 (D959)

Pleni Sunt Coeli
(Boepple, P.) TB,acap oct PRESSER 352-00025 $.30 (D960)
(Boepple, P.) SA,acap oct PRESSER 352-00025 $.30 (D961)
(Expert) [Lat] SA oct SALABERT-US $.65 (D962)

Psalm 50 *see Miserere Mei Deus

Regina Celi Letare *anthem
(Noble, Jeremy) [Lat] SATTBarB,acap oct NOVELLO 40.1542.08 s.p. (D963)

Salve Regina
SAATB,acap oct PRESSER 352-00093 $.45 (D964)

Sanctus *Sanctus
(Couraud) [Lat] SATB,acap oct SALABERT-US $1.00 (D965)

Stabat Mater
(Expert) [Lat] SATB,acap oct SALABERT-US $.65 (D966)

Sun Of My Soul *anthem
(Parkinson, John A.) mix cor oct NOVELLO 44.1327.10 s.p. (D967)

Thou Art Great
SATB oct WORD CS-315 $.30 (D968)

Thou, Lord, The Refuge Of The Meek
(Coggin, E.) SAB FISCHER,J 10085 $.30 (D969)

Thou Refuge Of The Destitute *see Tu Pauperum Refugium

Three Motets *CC3U,mot
mix cor,acap voc sc KALMUS 6150 $1.50 (D970)

[Three] Psalms
see Des Prez, Josquin, Pange Lingua

Three Psalms *CC3U,Psalm
mix cor,acap voc sc KALMUS 6151 $1.50 (D971)

Tu Pauperum Refugium
see ALTNIEDERLANDISCHE MOTETTEN
(Beveridge) mix cor SOUTHERN $.25 (D972)
(Beveridge) "Thou Refuge Of The Destitute" [Eng/Lat] 4pt mix cor,acap oct SCHIRM.G 9565 $.30 (D973)
(Knight) mix cor SOUTHERN $.30 (D974)
(Knight, Gerald) SATB,acap oct FISCHER,C CM-7511 $.25 (D975)
(W.R.S.) [Lat] TTBB,acap SCHIRM.EC 62 $.18 (D976)

Tu Solus *mot
[Lat] STTB,acap MUSICUS 1023 $.20 (D977)

Tu Solus Qui Facis Mirabilla *Easter
SATB,acap oct PRESSER 352-00045 $.30 (D978)

Two Marian Motets *see Ave Maria, Gratia Plena (D979)

Vier Motetten *CC4U,mot
(Blume) [Ger/Lat] 4pt mix cor&6pt mix cor MOSELER s.p. (D980)

We Worship Thy Virginity *see Ave Vera Virginitas

Zwei Psalmen *CC2U,Psalm
(Osthoff) [Ger/Lat] 4-5pt mix cor MOSELER s.p. (D981)

DET AR EN ROS UTSPRUNGEN *Xmas,hymn
see Sex Koraler I Folkton I Sattningar
(Lundvik, Hildor) men cor NORDISKA 1168 s.p. see from Julhymner (D982)
(Wikander, David) mix cor NORDISKA 961 s.p. (D983)

DET AR EN ROS UTSPRUNGEN see Anrep-Nordin, Birger

DET AR EN ROS UTSPRUNGEN see Berg, Gottfrid

DET AR EN ROS UTSPRUNGEN see Norman, Rudolf

DET AR EN ROS UTSPRUNGEN see Praetorius, Michael, Es Ist Ros' Entsprungen

DET GAMLA AR FRAMGANGET AR see Adam de la hale

DET GAR ETT TYST OCH TALIGT LAMM see Berg, Gottfrid

DET HELLIGE KORS see Jeppesen, Knud

DET HEV EI ROSA SPRUNGE *Xmas
(Beck, Thomas) mix cor MUSIKK 95E s.p.
contains also: Med Englar Song Guds Lov

DET LILLE BARN I KRYBBEN TRANG see Praetorius, Michael

DET LIVSENS ORD VI BYGGER PA see Bach, Johann Sebastian, Wohl Dem, Der Sich Auf Seinen Gott [Chorale]

DET MULMER MOD DEN MORKE NAT see Aagaard, Thomas

DET SPIRAR I GUDS ORTAGARD see Hammarstrom, Hugo

DET STORE GLORIA see Beck, Thomas [Ludvigsen]

DET VOLDER HERREN JESULIL see Vulpius, Melchior

DE TAEYE
De Profondis Clamavi
SATB,SATB soli CHOUDENS voc sc s.p., cor pts s.p. (D985)

De Profundis Clamavi *mot
4pt mix cor,ST soli,org CHOUDENS s.p. (D986)

Sancta Maria *BVM,mot
4pt mix cor,ST soli,org CHOUDENS s.p. (D987)

SATB,SATB soli CHOUDENS voc sc s.p., cor pts s.p. (D988)

DETAR
Short Setting Of The Communion Service
SATB (A min) oct GALAXY 1.0600.1 $.30 (D989)

DETHIER
Sixteen Choral Responses *CC16U,cor-resp
SATB oct LORENZ C301 $.30 (D990)

DETT
On That Sabbath Morn *Easter
SATB SCHMITT 1553 $.30 (D991)

Rise Up Shepherds And Follow *Xmas
(Grant, Louise) SSA oct BELWIN 1699 $.30 (D992)
(Grant, Louise) SATB oct BELWIN 1708 $.35 (D993)
(Ross) SSAA oct FISCHER,J 8183 $.30 (D994)

DETT COLLECTION OF NEGRO SPIRITUALS-NO. 1 *CCU,spir
mix cor SCHMITT 13 $.50 (D995)

DETT COLLECTION OF NEGRO SPIRITUALS-NO. 2 *CCU,spir
mix cor SCHMITT 14 $.50 (D996)

DETT COLLECTION OF NEGRO SPIRITUALS-NO. 3 *CCU,spir
mix cor SCHMITT 15 $.50 (D997)

DETT COLLECTION OF NEGRO SPIRITUALS-NO. 4 *CCU,spir
mix cor SCHMITT 16 $.50 (D998)

DETT, ROBERT NATHANIEL (1882-1943)
As By The Streams Of Babylon
(Campian) 4pt mix cor,S solo oct SCHIRM.G 7713 $.25 (D999)

As Children, Walk Ye In God's Love
(Stickles) 4pt mix cor,T solo,acap oct SCHIRM.G 10609 $.25 (D1000)

Don't You Weep No More, Mary
4pt mix cor,acap oct SCHIRM.G 7396 $.25 (D1001)

Let Us Cheer The Weary Traveler
SATB,acap oct PRESSER 332-35044 $.35 (D1002)

Listen To The Lambs
mix cor,STB soli,acap oct SCHIRM.G 5956 $.25 (D1003)
4pt mix cor,S solo,acap oct SCHIRM.G 8010 $.35 (D1004)
4pt men cor,T solo,acap oct SCHIRM.G 7405 $.35 (D1005)
(Harris, V.) SSA/SSAA,S solo,acap oct SCHIRM.G 7028 $.30 (D1006)
(Nash) SAB oct SCHIRM.G 7337 $.30 (D1007)

O Holy Lord
8pt mix cor,acap oct SCHIRM.G 6579 $.25 (D1008)

Ordering Of Moses, The *cant
mix cor BELWIN $3.00 (D1009)

Wasn't That A Mighty Day? *spir
SATBBar,opt ABar soli,acap oct SCHIRM.G 7712 $.30 (D1010)

DETTA SLAKTE SKALL ICKE FORGAS see Nilsson, Torsten

DETTE ER DAGEN see Karlsen, Kjell Mork

DETTE ER DEN DAG SOM HERREN HAR GJORT see Runback, Albert

DETTIGEN TE DEUM see Handel, George Frideric

DETTINGEN TE DEUM see Handel, George Frideric

DETWEILER
Nativity Service Of Nine Lessons And Carols *see Matthews

DEUM LAUDAMUS see Leng

DEUS ABRAHAM see Busser, [Henri-Paul]

DEUS ABRAHAM see Dubois, Theodore

DEUS ABRAHAM see Handel, George Frideric

DEUS ABRAHAM see Saint-Saens, Camille

DEUS ABRAHAM see Wagner, Richard

DEUS, DEUS MEUS see Soegijo, Paul Gutama

DEUS IN ADJUTORIUM see Monteverdi, Claudio

DEUS IN ADJUTORIUM see Pachelbel

DEUS IN ADJUTORIUM MEUM INTENDE see Lalande, Michel Richard de

DEUS MEUS IN SIMPLICITATE CORDIS MEI see Lassus, Roland de (Orlandus)

DEUS MISEREATUR see Naylor, Edward Woodall

DEUS MISEREATUR see Schutz, Heinrich

DEUS MISEREATUR NOSTRI see Hemel, Oscar van

DEUS MISEREATUR NOSTRI see Schutz, Heinrich

DEUS NOSTER see Valen, Fartein

DEUS, TU CONVERSUS see Campbell-Watson, Frank

DEUS TUORUM see Fabiani, Angelo

DEUS TUORUM MILITUM see Arnaldi, Antonio

DEUS TUORUM MILITUM see Bottazzo, Luigi

DEUS TUORUM MILITUM see Monteverdi, Claudio

DEUS TUORUM MILITUM see Tallis, Thomas

DEUS TUORUM MILITUM see Volpi, Edoardo

DEUTSCH, HERBERT
Mutima *Afr
SSAB&audience,fl,perc oct WORLD CA-2154-7 $.95 (D1011)

DEUTSCHE EVANGELIENSPRUCHE see Franck, Melchior

DEUTSCHE EVANGELIENSPRUCHE, 1623 *see Franck, Melchior, Darum Seid Barmherzig; Franck, Melchior, Er Hat Alles Wohl Gemacht; Franck, Melchior, Es Kommt Aber Die Zeit; Franck, Melchior, Gleichwie Der Blitz Ausgehet; Franck, Melchior, Gleichwie Moses In Der Wuste; Franck, Melchior, Herr, Komm Hinab, Eh Denn Mein Kind Stirbet; Franck, Melchior, Ich Habe Euch Noch Viel Zu Sagen; Franck, Melchior, Kommt Her, Ihr Gesegneten Meines Vaters; Franck, Melchior, Nehmet Hin Den Heiligen Geist; Franck, Melchior, Trachtet Am Ersten Nach Dem Reich Gottes; Franck, Melchior, Wahrlich, Ich Sage Euch: So Ihr Den Vater Etwas Bitten Werdet; Franck, Melchior, Warum Denket Ihr So Args In Eurem Herzen?; Franck, Melchior, Wenn Du Geladen Wirst, So Gehe Hin (D1012)

DEUTSCHE EVANGELIENSPRUCHE, 1623 see Franck, Melchior

DEUTSCHE EVANGELIENSPRUCHE FUR DAS KIRCHENJAHR 1623 see Franck, Melchior

DEUTSCHE FESTKREIS-PROPRIEN see Tittel, Ernst

DEUTSCHE GESANGE VOM LEIDEN CHRISTI *CC6U, Psntd,chorale
(Saalfeld, Ralf Von) [Ger] 3pt mix cor/4pt mix cor,acap (med easy) BAREN. BA 135 $1.50 contains works by: Le Maistre; Dressler, A; Burgk; Praetorius; Deder (D1013)

DEUTSCHE JOHANNES-PASSION UND WEISSAGUNG DES LEBENS UND STERBENS JESU CHRISTI see Demantius, Christoph

DEUTSCHE KANONMESSE see Krol, Bernhard

DEUTSCHE KANTIONALSATZE DES 17. JAHRHUNDERTS *CC26U,Gen,chorale
(Burkhardt, Hans; Lipphardt, Walther) [Ger] 4pt mix cor/5pt mix cor,acap (easy) BAREN. BA 2703 $2.25 contains works by: Praetorius; Albert; Schein; Degen; Osiander; Eccard; Gippenbusch; Cruger; Helder; Vulpius; Goudimel; Hassler; Schutz; Gumpelzhaimer (D1014)

DEUTSCHE LIEDER VERGANGENER JAHRHUNDERTE-HEFT 2 see Rein, Walter

DEUTSCHE LIEDLEIN see Sayve

DEUTSCHE LIEDMESSE see Marx, Karl

DEUTSCHE LIEDMESSE see Micheelsen, Hans Friedrich

DEUTSCHE MEISTER DES 15 JAHRHUNDERTS *CC12U, hymn
(Gerber) [Ger/Lat] 3-5pt mix cor,inst MOSELER s.p. (D1015)

DEUTSCHE MESSE see Dallinger, Fridolin

DEUTSCHE MESSE see David, Johann Nepomuk

DEUTSCHE MESSE see Koerppen, Alfred

DEUTSCHE MESSE see Lehner, Walter

DEUTSCHE MESSE see Mendelssohn, Arnold

DEUTSCHE MESSE see Micheelsen, Hans Friedrich

DEUTSCHE MESSE see Poos, Heinrich

DEUTSCHE MESSE see Rechsteiner

DEUTSCHE MESSE see Schubert, Franz (Peter)

DEUTSCHE MESSE see Weiss, Ewald

DEUTSCHE MESSE AUF BIBELWORTE see Zillinger, Erwin

DEUTSCHE MESSE F-DUR see Schubert, Franz (Peter)

DEUTSCHE MESSE IN C see Romanovsky, Erich

DEUTSCHE MESSE (ORDINARIUM) 1968 see Krenek, Ernst

DEUTSCHE PSALMEN: PSALM 1-51 see Lassus, Roland de (Orlandus)

DEUTSCHE SINGMESSE see Jochum, Otto

DEUTSCHE SONNTAGLICHE EVANGELIENSPRUCHE see Raselius, Andreas

DEUTSCHE SONNTAGLICHE EVANGELIENSPRUCHE 1612 see Vulpius, Melchior

DEUTSCHE SONNTAGLICHE EVANGELIENSPRUCHE 1614 see Vulpius, Melchior

DEUTSCHE SONNTAGLICHE EVANGELIENSPRUCHE 1612 & 1614 see Vulpius, Melchior

DEUTSCHE SPRUCHE VON LEBEN UND TOD see Lechner, Leonhard

DEUTSCHE VESPER see Baumann, Max

DEUTSCHE ZWOLFTONMESSE see Radulescu, Michael

DEUTSCHES MAGNIFICAT see Fiebig, Kurt

DEUTSCHES MAGNIFICAT see Praetorius, Michael

DEUTSCHES MAGNIFICAT see Schutz, Heinrich

DEUTSCHES MAGNIFICAT see Tittel, Ernst

DEUTSCHES MAGNIFICAT 1671 see Schutz, Heinrich

DEUTSCHES MESSLIED see Grossmann, Ferdinand

DEUTSCHES MISERERE see Haydn, (Johann) Michael

DEUTSCHES ORDINARIUM see Bamer, Alfred

DEUTSCHES ORDINARIUM see Bauernfiend, Hans

DEUTSCHES ORDINARIUM see Bloch, Waldemar

DEUTSCHES ORDINARIUM see Burkhart, Franz

DEUTSCHES ORDINARIUM see Dawidowicz, Albert

DEUTSCHES ORDINARIUM see Heiller, Anton

DEUTSCHES ORDINARIUM see Kocsis, Stefan

DEUTSCHES ORDINARIUM see Kreig, Franz

DEUTSCHES ORDINARIUM see Kubizek, Augustinian

DEUTSCHES ORDINARIUM see Lambertz, Johann Sebastian

DEUTSCHES ORDINARIUM see Planyavsky, Peter

DEUTSCHES ORDINARIUM see Romanovsky, Erich

DEUTSCHES ORDINARIUM see Strobl, Otto

DEUTSCHES ORDINARIUM see Tittel, Ernst

DEUTSCHES ORDINARIUM see Wolf, Friederich

DEUTSCHES ORDINARIUM-AUSGABE A see Doppelbauer, Josef Friedrich

DEUTSCHES ORDINARIUM-AUSGABE B see Doppelbauer, Josef Friedrich

DEUTSCHES ORDINARIUM-AUSGABE C see Doppelbauer, Josef Friedrich

DEUTSCHES ORDINARIUM I see Bamer, Alfred

DEUTSCHES ORDINARIUM II see Bamer, Alfred

DEUTSCHES ORDINARIUM II see Bauernfiend, Hans

DEUTSCHES PROPRIUM see Heiller, Anton

DEUTSCHES PROPRIUM see Schandl, Ernst

DEUTSCHES PROPRIUM see Tittel, Ernst

DEUTSCHES PROPRIUM DER ERSTEN WEIHNACHTSMESSE see Planyavsky, Peter

DEUTSCHES PROPRIUM DER PRIESTER-MESSE see Bamer, Alfred

DEUTSCHES PROPRIUM FUR DAS DREIFALTIGKEITSFEST see Heiller, Anton

DEUTSCHES PROPRIUM FUR DEN DREIFALTIGKEITSSONNTAG see Heiller, Anton

DEUTSCHES REQUIEM see Tittel, Ernst

DEUTSCHES SANCTUS see Schweizer, Rolf

DEUTSCHES SANCTUS UND PSALM 111 *Mass/Psalm
sc HANSSLER 15.002 s.p.
contains: Barbe, Helmut, Heiliger Ewiger Gott (SATBB); Dietrich, Sixtus, Heilig Ist Gott Der Vater (SATTB); Goudimel, Claude, Jauchzt Halleluja, Lobt Den Herrn; Praetorius, Michael, Gott Dem Vater Im Hochsten Thron (SATB); Schein, Johann Hermann, Ich Danke Gott Dem Herren Mein (SATB,org) (D1016)

DEUTSCHES TE DEUM see Praetorius, Michael

DEUTSCHES TE DEUM see Strohbach, Siegfried, Dich, Gott, Loben Wir

DEUX ANTIENNES POUR LA FETE DE SAINTE JEANNE D'ARC see Busser, [Henri-Paul], Joanna Sponsa Christi

DEUX CANTIQUES see Gigout, [Eugene]

DEUX CHANTS DE NOEL see Roesgen-Champion, Marguerite

DEUX MOTETS A LA TRES SAINTE-VIERGE see Paladilhe, [Emile]

DEUX MOTETS POUR LA CHAPELLE DU ROY see Robert, Pierre

DEUX NOELS see Inghelbrecht, Desire Emile

DEUX NOELS ANCIENS see Clouzot

DEUX PSAUMES see Beclard d'Harcourt, M.

DEUXIEME MESSE see Battmann

DEUXIEME MESSE BREVE see Boissiere

DEUXIEME MESSE BREVE see Niedermeyer, Louis

DEUXIEME MESSE DE REQUIEM see Cherubini, Luigi

DEUXIEME MESSE SOLENNELLE see Cherubini, Luigi

DEUXIEME MESSE SOLENNELLE see Franck, Cesar

DEUXIEME SALUT see Heidet, Le R. P.

DEVANT LA LOI NOUVELLE see Franck, Cesar

DE VICTORIA, TOMAS LUIS
see VICTORIA, TOMAS LUIS DE

DE VITO
Long Ago In Bethlehem *Xmas
SATB oct PLYMOUTH K-4 $.25 (D1017)

DEVON CAROL see McGraw, Cameron

DEVOTION
(Kinsman, F.) SATB LEONARD-US 08012660 $.25
(D1018)

DEVOTION see Beethoven, Ludwig van, Ich Liebe Dich

DEVOTION see Strauss, Richard

DEVOUTLY I ADORE THEE see Creston, Paul, Adoro Te Devote

DEVREESE, GODEFROID
Stabat Mater
[Lat] mix cor,S solo,orch voc sc CBDM s.p.
(D1019)
Te Deum *Te Deum
[Lat] unis mix cor,org,2trp,2trom CBDM sc
s.p., cor pts s.p. (D1020)

DE WERT
Three Motets *CC3U,mot
(De Surcy, Bernard Bailly) 5pt/6pt oct PENN
STATE 0-271-09119-3 $5.75 (D1021)

DEXTER
Ave Maria
SATB FRANCIS s.p. (D1022)
Go, Prayer Of Mine
SATB oct LORENZ B110 $.30 (D1023)
So Quietly He Came
SATB oct LORENZ B123 $.30 (D1024)

DEXTER, HARRY
Give Us, O Lord
2pt ASHDOWN E.A.371 s.p. (D1025)
Rejoice In Life
(Nageli) 3pt jr cor/3pt wom cor CURWEN
72634 s.p. (D1026)
What Can I Do For Thee?
2pt ASHDOWN E.A.344 s.p. (D1027)

DEXTERA DOMINI see Burkhart, Franz

DEXTERA DOMINI see Geoffray, Cesar

DEXTERA DOMINI see Lassus, Roland de (Orlandus)

DEXTERA DOMINI see Palestrina, Giovanni

DEXTERA DOMINI see Volpi, Edoardo

DEXTERRA DOMINI see Bruckner, Anton

DI MAKT see Olsen, Sparre

DI MOI, MALHEUREUX, QUI TE FIES see Goudimel, Claude

DI OCCHI, PIANGETE see Lassus, Roland de (Orlandus)

DIABELLI, ANTON (1781-1858)
Pastoral Mass In F *Mass
cor,orch sc KALMUS ipa (D1028)

DIACK, [JOHN MICHAEL] (1869-1946)
All In The April Evening
(Cain) SA oct BOOSEY 1776 $.30 (D1029)
(Cain) SATB oct BOOSEY 1771 $.30 (D1030)
(Howorth) SSA oct BOOSEY 1677 $.30 (D1031)
Beloved, Let Us Love
SATB PATERSON 1640 s.p. (D1032)
Father, I Know That All My Life
SATB PATERSON 1643 s.p. (D1033)

DIALOGO DE REYES see Santa Cruz, Domingo

DIALOGUE FROM THE BOOK OF JOB see Haines, [Edmund]

DIALOGUE OF THE KINGS see Santa Cruz, Domingo, Dialogo De Reyes

DIAMANT, B.
Kerstlied
mix cor ALSBACH&D sc s.p., cor pts s.p.
(D1034)

DIAMOND, DAVID (1915-)
Martyr, The
TTBB,acap/opt inst PEER $.45, ipr (D1035)
Prayer For Peace *prayer
SATB,acap PEER $.40 (D1036)
Young Joseph
SSA,opt strings oct PRESSER 352-00105 $.40,
ipr (D1037)

DIC NOBIS MARIA, QUID VIDISTI IN VIA? see Manicke, Dietrich

DICH BET' ICH AN see Bach, Johann Sebastian

DICH, FRAU VOM HIMMEL (from Psalteriolum 1642)
BVM
SATB,acap voc pt DOBLINGER s.p. see also
Unsere Liebe Frau (D1038)

DICH, GOTT, LOBEN WIR see Strohbach, Siegfried

DICIE
Now Let The Earth With Joy Resound *Gen
unis SCHMITT 245 $.30 (D1039)
Spring Carol *Gen
SATB SCHMITT 357 $.35 (D1040)

DICIT DOMINUS see Schieri, Fritz

DICKEY, MARK
I Will Lift Up Mine Eyes
3pt jr cor/SAB (very easy) FISCHER,C R 491
$.22 (D1041)
Let Not Your Heart Be Troubled
SAB oct GRAY GCMR 2207 $.30 (D1042)
SATB oct GRAY GCMR 1191 $.25 (D1043)
Sing Alleluia Forth *ASD
SATB (easy) ABINGDON APM-113 $.24 (D1044)

DICKINSON
Coming Of The Prince Of Peace *Xmas,cant
BELWIN $1.00 (D1045)

DICKINSON, CLARENCE (1873-1969)
Babe So Tender, A *Xmas
3pt jr cor/SSA (easy) FISCHER,C CM 7223
$.25 (D1046)
Beneath The Shadow
SATB oct GRAY GSC 85 $.30 (D1047)
Great And Glorious
SATB oct GRAY GSC 215 $.50 (D1048)
List To The Lark *Gen/Thanks
SATB&jr cor&sr cor oct GRAY GSC 68 $.25
(D1049)

DICKINSON, PETER (1934-)
Holy Communion *Commun
SA NOVELLO 86.0021.10 s.p. (D1050)
SA/TB/SATB oct NOVELLO 86.0021.10 s.p.
(D1051)
Jesus Christ Is Risen Today *Easter,anthem/
mot
mix cor,acap oct NOVELLO 40.1464.02 s.p.
(D1052)
John *anthem/mot
ATB,acap oct NOVELLO 38.0145.04 s.p.
(D1053)
Judas Tree, The
SATB,org,horn,2trp,2trom,strings,5perc,timp
voc sc NOVELLO s.p., ipr (D1054)
Magnificat And Nunc Dimittis *Magnif/Nunc
unis NOVELLO 44.1430.06 s.p. (D1055)
Mark *anthem/mot
ATB,acap oct NOVELLO 38.0146.02 s.p.
(D1056)
Martin Of Tours *cant
SATB,TBar soli,pno,org voc sc NOVELLO s.p.,
ipr (D1057)
Mass *Mass
SATB,acap oct NOVELLO 44.1429.02 s.p.
(D1058)

DICKSON
Thanks Be To God
(Cain) SATB oct BOOSEY 1756 $.30 (D1059)
(Ehret) SSAB oct BOOSEY 5361 $.30 (D1060)
(Lucas) SSA oct BOOSEY 2404 $.30 (D1061)
(O'Shea) SA oct BOOSEY 2111 $.30 (D1062)
(Salter) SAB oct BOOSEY 2108 $.30 (D1063)
(Salter) TTBB oct BOOSEY 2512 $.30 (D1064)

DICKSON, STANLEY
Thanks Be To God
2pt ENOCH TP121 s.p. (D1065)
SATB ENOCH EC 57 s.p. (D1066)
TTBB ENOCH EC261 s.p. (D1067)

DID JESUS WEEP FOR ME? see Wilson

DID MARY KNOW? see Averre, R.

DID NOT OUR HEART BURN WITHIN US see Salathiel, Lyndon

DID THEY CRUCIFY MY LORD? see Davidson

DID YOU IN A MANGER LIE? see Rhea, Raymond

DID YOU SEE MY BOY JESUS? see Grime, William

DID YOU STOP TO PRAY THIS MORNING
SATB BIG3 $.30 (D1068)

DIDN'T MA LAWD DELIVER DANIEL
(Bell) SSA oct BELWIN 60338 $.30 (D1069)

DIDN'T MY LORD DELIVER DANIEL? *spir
(Boger) SATB ALFRED 6605 $.35 (D1070)
(Burleigh) 4pt mix cor,acap oct SCHIRM.G 6505
$.30 (D1071)
(Burleigh; Vene) SSA oct COLOMBO 2151 $.30
(D1072)
(Burleigh; Vene) SAB oct COLOMBO 2152 $.30
(D1073)
(Burleigh; Vene) SATB oct COLOMBO 1774 $.30
(D1074)

(Durian, Tim) 4pt men cor,acap BREITKOPF-W
Z-53 s.p. see also Dreizehn Negro-
Spirituals (D1075)
(Genuchi) TTBB LUDWIG SS-008 $.35 (D1076)
(Genuchi) SATB LUDWIG SS-017 $.35 (D1077)
(Heath) 4pt men cor,acap oct SCHIRM.G 11058
$.30 (D1078)
(Hunter) SATB oct LAWSON 957 $.35 (D1079)
(Wiley) SATB oct PRO ART 1825 $.25 (D1080)

DIDN'T MY LORD DELIVER DANIEL see Gottlieb

DIDN'T MY LORD DELIVER DANIEL? see Smith

DIDST THOU SUFFER SHAME? see Telemann, Georg Philipp

DIE ALLMACHT see Lachner, V.

DIE ALLMACHT see Schubert, Franz (Peter)

DIE ALTEN EPISTELLESUNGEN see Reda, Siegfried

DIE ALTEN EPISTELLESUNGEN, TEIL I: ADVENT BIS EPIPHANIAS see Reda, Siegfried

DIE ALTEN EPISTELLESUNGEN, TEIL II: VORFASTEN, PASSION see Reda, Siegfried

DIE ALTEN EPISTELLESUNGEN, TEIL IV: TRINITATISZEIT see Reda, Siegfried

DIE ANKUNFT IN SAIS see Berlioz, Hector

DIE AUF DEN HERREN HOFFEN see Hartmann, Heinrich

DIE AUFERSTANDENE UND DER UNGLAUBIGE THOMAS see Peter, Herbert

DIE AUFERSTEHUNG see Weismann, Wilhelm

DIE AUFERSTEHUNG CHRISTI U FRUHMORGENS, DA DIE SOHN AUFGEHT see Weismann, Wilhelm

DIE AUFERSTEHUNG JESU see Peter, Herbert

DIE AUFERSTEHUNG JESU see Raphael, Gunther

DIE AUFERSTEHUNG NACH MATTHAUS see Buchtger, Fritz

DIE AUFERSTEHUNGSHISTORIE see Scandellus, Antonius

DIE AUFERWECKUNG DES LAZARUS see Bach, Johann Christoph Friedrich

DIE AUFERWECKUNG DES LAZARUS see Barbe, Helmut

DIE AUGEN DES HERRN see Rosenmuller, Johann

DIE AUGEN DES HERRN SEHEN AUF DIE GERECHTEN see Rosenmuller, Johann

DIE BEIDEN SCHACHER see Reda, Siegfried

DIE BERGREDE see Koch, Johannes H.E.

DIE BESTE ZEIT see Heyden, Reinhold

DIE BLINDEN SEHEN see Driessler, Johannes

DIE BURGER ALL VON CHASTRES see Langer, Hans Klaus

DIE CHORALE DER MATTHAUS-PASSION see Bach, Johann Sebastian

DIE DEUTSCHE LITANEI "KYRIE ELEISON" see Schutz, Heinrich

DIE DEUTSCHE PASSION NACH JOHANNES see Burck, Joachim

DIE DEUTSCHEN CANTICA DER OSTERNACHT see Ahrens, Joseph

DIE DREI SPATZEN see Beckerath, Alfred von

DIE EHRE GOTTES see Beethoven, Ludwig van

DIE EHRE GOTTES AUS DER NATUR see Beethoven, Ludwig van

DIE EHRE GOTTES (DIE HIMMEL RUHMEN DES EWIGEN EHRE) see Beethoven, Ludwig van

DIE EHRE GOTTES IN DER NATUR see Beethoven, Ludwig van

DIE EINGANGSSPRUCHE ZUM HAUPTGOTTESDIENST see Egermann, Eberhard

DIE EINSETZUNGSWORTE *Commun
mix cor sc HANSSLER 15.004 s.p. contains
also: Zur Kommunion (D1081)

DIE ELENDEN SOLLEN ESSEN see Bach, Johann Sebastian

DIE ELENDEN SOLLEN ESSEN see Reda, Siegfried

DIE ERD UND WAS SICH AUF IHR REGT see Schutz, Heinrich

DIE ERLOESETEN DES HERRN WERDEN WIEDERKOMMEN see Franck, Melchior

DIE ERLOSETEN DES HERREN WERDEN WIEDERKOMMEN see Franck, Melchior

DIE ERLOSETEN DES HERRN WERDENKOMMEN see Franck, Melchior

DIE ERLOSTEN DES HERRN WERDEN WIEDERKOMMEN see Fussan, Werner

DIE ERNSTE IST GROSS, ABER WENIGE SIND see Ruppel, Paul Ernst

DIE ERNT' IST NUN ZU ENDE see Rein, Walter

DIE ERNT IST NUN ZU ENDE see Wolder, David

DIE ERSTEN CHORE see Mozart, Wolfgang Amadeus

DIE FLUCHT DER HEILIGEN FAMILIE see Bruch, Max

DIE FLUCHT NACH AGYPTEN see Berlioz, Hector

DIE FLUT see Kelterborn, Rudolf

DIE FROHE BOTSCHAFT see Katt, Leopold

DIE FURCHT DES HERREN, GLAUBE MIR see Le
　　Maistre, Mattheus

DIE FURCHT DES HERREN IST DER WEISHEIT ANFANG
　　see Reda, Siegfried

DIE FURCHT DES HERREN IST DER WEISHEIT ANFANG
　　see Schutz, Heinrich

DIE FURCHT DES HERREN see Le Maistre, Mattheus

DIE FURCHT DES HERRN see Becker-Foss, Jurgen

DIE GANZE WELT (from Sirenes Symphoniacae)
　　Easter/Psntd
　　SATB,acap voc pt DOBLINGER s.p. see also
　　Passion Und Ostern　　　　　　　　　　　(D1082)

DIE GEBURT see Buchtger, Fritz

DIE GEBURT DES HERRN see Baumann, Max

DIE GEBURT UNSERES HERRN JESUS CHRISTUS NACH
　　DEM EVANGELISTEN LUKAS see Lohr, Ina

DIE GEBURT UNSRES HERREN JESU CHRISTI, NACH DEN
　　EVANGELISTEN LUKAS UND MATTHAUS 1602 see
　　Michael, Rogier

DIE GERECHTEN see Staden

DIE GERECHTEN WERDEN EWIGLICH LEBEN see Franck,
　　Melchior

DIE GERECHTEN WERDEN WEGGERAFFT see Krieger,
　　Johann Philipp

DIE GLASHUTTER PASSION see Anonymous

DIE GNADE UNSERES HERREN JESU see Rosenmuller,
　　Johann

DIE GNADE UNSERS HERRN see Rosenmueller, Johann

DIE GNADE UNSERS HERRN see Thomas, Kurt

DIE GOLD'NE SONNE, VOLL FREUD' UND WONNE see
　　Bach, Johann Sebastian

DIE GROSSE FLUT see Kretzschmar, Gunther

DIE GULDENE SONNE BRINGT LEBEN UND WONNE see
　　Ahle, Johann Georg

DIE GULDNE SONNE see Schlenker, Manfred

DIE GULDNE SONNE VOLL FREUD UND WONNE see
　　Ebeling, Johann Georg

DIE GULDNE SONNE VOLL FREUD UND WONNE see
　　Trubel, Gerhard

DIE GUTE DES HERRN see Raphael, Gunther

DIE HEILIGEN DREI KONIGE see Cadow, Paul

DIE HEILIGEN DREI KONIGE see Marx, Karl

DIE HEILIGEN DREI KONIGE see Schilling, Hans
　　Ludwig

DIE HEILUNG DER TAUBSTUMMEN see Schieri, Fritz

DIE HEILUNG DES BLINDEN see Gunsenheimer,
　　Gustav

DIE HELLE SONN LEUCHT see Enders, Gottfried

DIE HELLE SONN LEUCHT JETZT HERFUR see Eglin,
　　Arthur

DIE HELLE SONN LEUCHT JETZT HERFUR see Heer,
　　Emil

DIE HELLE SONN LEUCHT JETZT HERFUR see Rohwer,
　　Jens

DIE HELLE SONN LEUCHT' JETZT HERFUR see Stern,
　　Hermann

DIE HELLE SONN LEUCHT' JETZT HERFUR see
　　Vulpius, Melchior

DIE HERRLICHKEIT DER ERDEN see Weyrauch,
　　Johannes

DIE HIMMEL ERZAHLEN see Lau, Heinz

DIE HIMMEL ERZAHLEN DIE EHRE GOTTES see Bach,
　　Johann Sebastian

DIE HIMMEL ERZAHLEN DIE EHRE GOTTES see Haydn,
　　(Franz) Joseph

DIE HIMMEL ERZAHLEN DIE EHRE GOTTES see Schutz,
　　Heinrich

DIE HIMMEL ERZAHLEN DIE EHRE GOTTES see Schutz,
　　Heinrich

DIE HIMMEL ERZAHLEN DIE EHRE GOTTES see Schutz,
　　Heinrich

DIE HIMMEL, HERR, PREISEN SEHR see Schutz,
　　Heinrich

DIE HIMMEL RUHMEN see Beethoven, Ludwig van

DIE HIMMEL RUHMEN DES EWIGEN EHRE see
　　Beethoven, Ludwig van

DIE HIMMEL VERKUNDIGEN SEINE GERECHTIGKEIT see
　　Gottschick, Friedemann

DIE HIMMELERZAHLEN DIE EHRE GOTTES see Haydn,
　　(Franz) Joseph

DIE HIMMELFAHRT CHRISTI see Buchtger, Fritz

DIE HIRTEN　*Xmas,Aus
　　(Seitz, Rudiger) mix cor,acap oct DOBLINGER
　　s.p. see from Zwei Weihnachtslieder (D1083)

DIE HIRTEN see Jochum, Otto

DIE HIRTEN see Sturmer, Bruno

DIE HIRTEN VON BETHLEHEM see Hohlfeld,
　　Christoph

DIE HOCHZEIT IST ZWAR BEREIT see Raselius,
　　Andreas

DIE HOCHZEIT IST ZWAR BEREIT see Vulpius,
　　Melchior

DIE HOCHZEIT ZU KANA see Brugk, Hans Melchoir

DIE INTROITEN FUR DIE FESTTAGE DES
　　KIRCHENJAHRES see Fiebig, Kurt

DIE ISRAELITEN IN DER WUSTE see Bach, Karl
　　Philipp Emanuel

DIE IST DER TAG, DEN DER HERR MACHT see Graap,
　　Lothar

DIE JAHRESZEITEN see Haydn, (Franz) Joseph

DIE KAROLISSER-LAUTE　*CCU,Xmas
　　(Stern) [Ger] cor HUG s.p.　　　　　　(D1084)

DIE KINDHEIT JESU see Bach, Johann Christoph
　　Friedrich

DIE KLEINE PASSION see Wunsch, Hermann

DIE KONIGE see Cornelius, Peter

DIE KREUZFAHRER see Gade, Niels [W.]

DIE KURRENDE-HEFT 1　*CC28U,Easter/Pent/Trin/
　　Whitsun
　　(Kelletat) 3-5pt mix cor HANSSLER 3.001 s.p.
　　settings by old masters　　　　　　　(D1085)

DIE KURRENDE-HEFT 2　*CC25U,Adv/Xmas
　　(Kelletat) 3-5pt mix cor HANSSLER 3.002 s.p.
　　　　　　　　　　　　　　　　　　　　　(D1086)

DIE KURRENDE-HEFT 3　*CC29U,Easter/Psntd
　　(Kelletat) 3-5pt mix cor HANSSLER 3.003 s.p.
　　settings by old masters　　　　　　　(D1087)

DIE KURRENDE-HEFT 4　*CC30U,Fest
　　(Berger) 3-5pt mix cor HANSSLER 3.004 s.p.
　　settings by old masters　　　　　　　(D1088)

DIE KURRENDE-HEFT 5　*CC23U,Gen
　　(Trubel) mix cor HANSSLER 3.005 s.p.　(D1089)

DIE KURRENDE-HEFT 6　*CC44U,Adv/Xmas/ECY/Epiph,
　　Contemp
　　(Trubel) 3-5pt mix cor HANSSLER 3.006 s.p.
　　　　　　　　　　　　　　　　　　　　　(D1090)

DIE KURRENDE-HEFT 7　*CCU,Asc/Easter/ECY/Pent/
　　Psntd/Trin/Whitsun,Contemp
　　(Trubel) 3-5pt mix cor HANSSLER 3.007 s.p.
　　　　　　　　　　　　　　　　　　　　　(D1091)

DIE KURRENDE-HEFT 8　*CCU,Commun,Bibl,Contemp
　　(Trubel) 3-5pt mix cor HANSSLER 3.008 s.p.
　　　　　　　　　　　　　　　　　　　　　(D1092)

DIE KURRENDE-HEFT 9　*CCU,Thanks,Psalm,Contemp
　　(Trubel) 3-5pt mix cor HANSSLER 3.009 s.p.
　　　　　　　　　　　　　　　　　　　　　(D1093)

DIE LIEBE DES NACHSTEN see Beethoven, Ludwig
　　van

DIE LIEBSTE ALS SCHLANGENKOCHIN "WO BIST DU
　　DENN GEWESEN?" see Strohbach, Siegfried

DIE LOR SITZT IM GARTEN see Fassler, G.

DIE MACHT DES GESANGES see Spitta, Heinrich

DIE MESSE see Schmidt-Gorg, Joseph

DIE MESSE DEUTSCH see Kaminski, Heinrich

DIE MIT TRANEN SAEN see Bach, Johann Ludwig

DIE MIT TRANEN SAEN see Franck, Melchior

DIE MIT TRANEN SAEN see Schein, Johann Hermann

DIE MIT TRANEN SAEN see Schutz, Heinrich

DIE MIT TRANEN SAEN see Selle, Thomas

DIE MIT TRANEN SAEN, WERDEN see Hollfelder,
　　Waldram

DIE MUSIK ALLEIN　*CCU
　　(Wagner, Hermann) mix cor MOSELER s.p.
　　　　　　　　　　　　　　　　　　　　　(D1094)

DIE MUTTER JUBELT see Tal, Joseph

DIE MUTTERGOTTES GING UBER DAS LAND see
　　Krietsch, Georg

DIE NACHT IST KOMMEN　*CC30U,Eve
　　(Schmidt-Mannheim, Hans) 3pt mix cor/4pt mix
　　cor HANSSLER 2.023 s.p.　　　　　　　(D1095)

DIE NACHT IST KOMMEN see Bach, Johann Sebastian

DIE NACHT IST KOMMEN see Pepping, Ernst

DIE NACHT IST KOMMEN see Schein, Johann Hermann

DIE NACHT IST KOMMEN, DRIN WIR RUHEN see
　　Schein, Johann Hermann

DIE NACHT IST VIRGERUCKT see Wenzel, Eberhard

DIE NACHT IST VORGEDRUNGEN see Graap, Lothar

DIE NACHT IST VORGEDRUNGEN see Pezel, Johann
　　Christoph

DIE NACHT IST VORGEDRUNGEN see Wenzel, Eberhard

DIE NACHT IST VORGEDRUNGEN, DER TAG see Gesius,
　　Bartholomaus

DIE NACHT IST VORGERUCKT see Michaelsen, Hans
　　Friedrich

DIE NUDELN "BIN EIN ARMER KLEINER BUBE" see
　　Strohbach, Siegfried

DIE OSTERGESCHICHTE see Graap, Lothar

DIE OSTERGESCHICHTE see Heroldt, Bruno

DIE OSTERGESCHICHTE see Kukuck, Felicitas

DIE OSTERGESCHICHTE see Poser, Hans

DIE OSTERGESCHICHTE see Reda, Siegfried

DIE OSTERGESCHICHTE NACH DEM EVANGELISTEN
　　MARKUS see Brunckhorst, Arnold Melchoir

DIE PASSION JESU CHRISTI NACH DEM EVANGELISTEN
　　JOHANNES see Micheelsen, Hans Friedrich

DIE PASSION JESU CHRISTI NACH DEM EVANGELISTEN
　　MARKUS see Micheelsen, Hans Friedrich

DIE PASSION JESU CHRISTI NACH DEM EVANGELISTEN
　　MATTHAUS see Micheelsen, Hans Friedrich

DIE PFINGSTGESCHICHTE see Hufschmidt, Wolfgang

DIE PFINGSTGESCHICHTE see Koch, Johannes H.E.

DIE PFINGSTSCHICHTE see Doernberg, Martin

DIE PREDIGT
　　see Psalmen Und Geistliche Lieder Der
　　Christenheit

DIE PSALMEN
　　see Psalmen Und Geistliche Lieder Der
　　Christenheit

DIE PSALMEN DAVIDS see Schutz, Heinrich

DIE PSALMEN
　　see Psalmen Und Geistliche Lieder Der
　　Christenheit

DIE PSALMEN
　　see Psalmen Und Geistliche Lieder Der
　　Christenheit

DIE RESPONSORIEN DER KARWOCHE see Schroeder,
　　Hermann

DIE SANGER DER VORWELT see Orff, Carl

DIE SCHONHEIT KOMMT VON LIEB see Bauernfiend,
　　Hans

DIE SCHOPFUNG see Haydn, (Franz) Joseph

DIE SECHS WERKE DER BARMHERZIGKEIT see Bossler,
　　Kurt

DIE SEEL' IST EIN KRISTALL see Kratochwill,
　　Heinrich

DIE SELIGPREISUNGEN see Peter, Herbert

DIE SIEBEN BUSSPSALMEN see Gabrieli, Andrea

DIE SIEBEN LETZEN WORTE UNSERES ERLOSERS AM
　　KREUZE see Haydn, (Franz) Joseph

DIE SIEBEN WORTE see Forster, Georg

DIE SIEBEN WORTE see Grunmach, Ulrich

DIE SIEBEN WORTE AM KREUZ see Hufschmidt,
　　Wolfgang

DIE SIEBEN WORTE AM KREUZ see Wenzel, Eberhard

DIE SIEBEN WORTE CHRISTI AM KREUZ see
　　Hessenberg, Kurt

DIE SIEBEN WORTE DES ERLOSERS AM KREUZE see
　　Haydn, (Franz) Joseph

DIE SIEBEN WORTE JESU AM KREUZ see Schuetky,
　　Joseph

DIE SIEBEN WORTE JESU AM KREUZ see Schutz,
　　Heinrich

DIE SINTFLUT see Burkhard Willy

DIE SONN HAT SICH MIT IHREM GLANZ GEWENDET see
　　Kurig, Hans-Hermann

DIE SONN HAT SICH MIT IHREN GLANZ GEWENDET see
　　Bach, Johann Sebastian

DIE SONNE BRENNT see Kern, Matthais

DIE SONNE SINKT VON HINNEN see Distler, Hugo

DIE STARKEN BEDURFEN DES ARZTES NICHT see
　　Hartmann, Heinrich

DIE STILLUNG DES SEESTURMS see Ruppel, Paul
　　Ernst

DIE STUNDEN, DIE TAGE, UND JAHRE see
　　Schallibaum, G.

DIE TOREN SPRECHEN IN IHREN see Wagener, Gregor

DIE TOREN SPRECHEN IN IHREN HERZEN see Reda,
　　Siegfried

DIE TOTEN see Liszt, Franz

DIE VERKLARUNG see Buchtger, Fritz

DIE VERKUNDIGUNG see Buchtger, Fritz

DIE VERKUNDIGUNG MARIAE see Burkhard Willy

DIE VERKUNDINGUNG see Weismann, Wilhelm

DIE VERSUCHUNG JESU see Brunner, Adolf

DIE VERSUCHUNG JESU see Callhoff, Herbert

DIE VERSUCHUNG JESU see Gunsenheimer, Gustav

DIE VERSUCHUNG JESU see Raphael, Gunther

DIE VERSUCHUNG JESU see Stockmeier, Wolfgang

DIE VESPER see Beethoven, Ludwig van

DIE VISION DES PROPHETEN see Ben-Haim, Paul

DIE WEIHNACHTSGESCHICHTE see Bender, Jan

DIE WEIHNACHTSGESCHICHTE see Brunckhorst,
    Arnold Melchoir

DIE WEIHNACHTSGESCHICHTE see Distler, Hugo

DIE WEIHNACHTSGESCHICHTE see Graap, Lothar

DIE WEIHNACHTSGESCHICHTE see Lahusen, Christian

DIE WEIHNACHTSGESCHICHTE see Reda, Siegfried

DIE WEIHNACHTSGESCHICHTE see Rienecker

DIE WEIHNACHTSGESCHICHTE see Schwartz, Gerhard
    von

DIE WEIHNACHTSGESCHICHTE see Tunger, Albrecht

DIE WEIHNACHTSGESCHICHTE see Zipp, Friedrich

DIE WEIHNACHTSGESCHICHTE DES LUKAS see Pepping,
    Ernst

DIE WEIHNACHTSGESCHICHTE NACH LUKAS see
    Wunderlich, Heinz

DIE WEIHNACHTSNACHTIGALL *Xmas,carol,Ger
    (Barthelson) "Christmas Nightingale, The"
        SATB LAWSON 570 $.25   (D1096)
    (Petterssen, B.) "Christmas Nightingale, The"
        SSAA,acap SCHIRM.EC 2542 $.25   (D1097)

DIE WEISSAGUNG DES JESAJA see Martinu, Bohuslav

DIE WELT SINGT GOTTES PREIS see Franck, [Johann
    Wolfgang]

DIE WIDMUNG see Franz, Robert

DIE WOCHENSPRUCHE FUR DAS KIRCHENJAHR *CCU
    mix cor HANSSLER 2.034 s.p.   (D1098)

DIE ZEIT MEINES ABSCHIEDS IST VORHANDEN see
    Bruhns, Nicholaus

DIE ZEIT MEINES ABSCHIELDS IST VORHANDEN see
    Bruhns, Nicholaus

DIE ZWISCHENGESANGE DER MESSFEIER *CC41L,
    liturg/Mass
    (Knotzinger, Kurt) cong,solo,org cmplt ed,voc
        sc DOBLINGER s.p.   (D1099)

DIECI CANTI AL S. CUORE DI GESU *CC10U
    [Lat] unis,org ZANIBON 2768 s.p. contains
        works by: Bottigliero, E.; Brambilla, A.;
        Leoncini, L.; Firpo, A.; Mariani, E.;
        Volpi, E.   (D1100)

DIECI CANTI IN ONORE DELLA B.V.M. *CC10U,BVM
    [Lat] unis,org ZANIBON 2755 s.p. contains
        works by: Branchina, P.; Chiesa, F.; Chiesa
        C.; Leoncini, L.; Magri, P.; Volpi, E.
                                              (D1101)

DIECI CONCERTI ECCLESIASTICI see Viadana,
    Lodovico Grossi da

DIECI DISCANTI see Castaldi, Paolo

DIECI LAUDI SACRE see Asola, Giovanni Matteo

DIECI LITANIE FACILISSIME IN ONORE DELLA B.V.M.
    see Bottigliero, Eduardo

DIECI MOTECTA EUCHARISTICA *CC10L,Commun,mot
    [Lat] 2 eq voices,org ZANIBON 2682 s.p.
        contains work by: Bottazzo; Bianchini;
        Branbille; Jannazzi, C.; Janazzi, G.U.;
        Ferro; Margiotta; Mauri; Volpi   (D1102)

DIECI MOTECTA EUCHARISTICA *CC10L,Commun,mot
    [Lat] unis,org ZANIBON 2683 s.p. contains
        works by: Bentivoglio; Bottigliero;
        Cerquetelli; Muller; Volpi   (D1103)

DIECI MOTECTA IN HON. MARIAE V see Bottazzo,
    Luigi

DIECKMANN, C.
    Blest Are The Pure In Heart
        (Keble, J.) SATB oct PRESSER 312-21279 $.30
                                              (D1104)

DIEMENTE, EDWARD
    Hosanna To The Son Of David
        see MUSIC FOR PALM SUNDAY

    Music For Lauds For The Vigil Of Easter
        *Easter
        SATB,pno/org oct LAWSON 51522 $.40   (D1105)

    Our Father *Gen,anthem
        SATB (med) oct GIA G880 $.25   (D1106)

    Three Motets *CC3U,mot
        mix cor,org sc SEESAW $3.00   (D1107)

    Verse
        see ALLELUIA AND VERSE

DIEMER, EMMA LOU (1927-   )
    Alleluia *Allelu
        3pt jr cor/SSA,acap (med diff) FISCHER,C
            CM 7289 $.25   (D1108)
        girl cor SOUTHERN $.25   (D1109)

    Alleluia! Christ Is Risen *Easter
        SATB,trp oct SOUTHERN $.35   (D1110)
        SATB FLAMMER A 5373 $.40   (D1111)

    Angel Gabriel *Xmas
        SATB oct FISCHER,C CM-7516 $.30   (D1112)

    Anthem Of Faith *anthem
        SATB STANDARD A25MX4 $.60   (D1113)

    As The Heart Longs
        SATB oct GRAY GCMR 2642 $.25   (D1114)

    Babe Is Born, A *Xmas
        SATB oct SACRED S-61 $.40   (D1115)

DIEMER, EMMA LOU (cont'd.)
    Before The Paling Of The Stars *Xmas
        SATB oct ELKAN-V 362-1198 $.30   (D1116)

    Bells
        SATB,2pno oct BOOSEY 5394 $.35   (D1117)

    Blessed Are You
        SATB oct FISCHER,C CM-7755 $.30   (D1118)

    Christmas Carol, A
        3pt jr cor/SSA (med easy) FISCHER,C CM 7262
            $.25   (D1119)

    For Ye Shall Go Out With Joy
        SATB oct FISCHER,C EAST $.35   (D1120)

    Four Carols *CC4U,carol
        girl cor SOUTHERN $.40   (D1121)

    Four Carols *CC4U,Xmas
        SSA oct ELKAN-V 362-3088 $.45   (D1122)

    Fragments From The Mass
        girl cor SOUTHERN $.35   (D1123)
        SSAA,acap MARKS   (D1124)

    How Majestic Is Thy Name
        unis oct GRAY GCMR 2729 $.25   (D1125)

    I Stand Beside The Manger Stall *Xmas
        SATB,acap oct FISCHER,C CM-7263 $.25
                                              (D1126)

    I Will Give Thanks
        SATB oct SACRED S-7 $.40   (D1127)

    Magnificat, The *Magnif
        SA MARKS 99 $.30   (D1128)

    Mary's Lullaby
        SSA oct BOOSEY 5393 $.30   (D1129)

    O Give Thanks To The Lord
        SATB oct COLOMBO 2359 $.30   (D1130)

    O To Praise God Again
        SATB oct FISCHER,C CM-7783 $.40   (D1131)

    Outburst Of Praise
        SATB oct PRESSER G-121 $.50   (D1132)

    Praise Of Created Things
        SATB oct COLOMBO 2360 $.30   (D1133)

    Praise The Lord
        SATB oct GRAY GCMR 2505 $.30   (D1134)

    Praise Ye The Lord
        SATB FLAMMER A 5021 $.30   (D1135)

    Thine, O Lord
        SA/TB FLAMMER E5135 $.25   (D1136)

    To Him All Glory Give
        SATB oct ELKAN-V 362-1162 $.35, ipr   (D1137)

DIENER
    Hofstetter Weihnachtskantate *Xmas,cant
        SSA,fl,ob,clar,bsn,2vln,vcl,bvl,perc
            HANSSLER 10.304 sc s.p., cor pts s.p.,
            ipa   (D1138)

DIENER, THEODOR (1908-   )
    Magnificat *Magnif
        [Ger] wom cor,S solo,org,strings HUG s.p.,
            ipr   (D1139)

DIENET EINAND see Franck, Melchior

DIENET EINANDER see Hufschmidt, Wolfgang

DIENET EINANDER see Ruppel, Paul Ernst

DIEPENBROCK, ALFONS (1862-1921)
    Caelestis Urbs Jerusalem
        mix cor ALSBACH&D sc s.p.   (D1140)

    Christus Is Opgestanden
        mix cor ALSBACH&D sc s.p., cor pts s.p.
                                              (D1141)

    Ecce Quomodo Moritur
        men cor ALSBACH&D sc s.p.   (D1142)

    Hymnus De Spiritu Sancto
        mix cor,org ALSBACH&D sc s.p., cor pts s.p.
                                              (D1143)

    Kyrie En Gloria
        mix cor sc ALSBACH&D s.p.   (D1144)

    Missa *Mass
        men cor,T solo,org ALSBACH&D sc s.p., cor
            pts s.p.   (D1145)

    Stabat Mater Dolorosa
        men cor ALSBACH&D sc s.p., cor pts s.p.
                                              (D1146)
        mix cor ALSBACH&D sc s.p., cor pts s.p.
                                              (D1147)

    Stabat Mater Speciosa
        mix cor ALSBACH&D sc s.p., cor pts s.p.
                                              (D1148)

    Tantum Ergo Sacramentum
        men cor,org ALSBACH&D sc s.p., cor pts s.p.
                                              (D1149)

    Te Deum Laudamus
        mix cor,4 soli,orch ALSBACH&D sc s.p., cor
            pts s.p.   (D1150)

    Tibur
        men cor ALSBACH&D sc s.p., cor pts s.p.
                                              (D1151)

    Veni Creator Spiritus
        men cor ALSBACH&D sc s.p., cor pts s.p.
                                              (D1152)

DIERCKS, JOHN H.
    And Thou Shalt Love
        SATB (med) ABINGDON APM-668 $.45   (D1153)

    Clap Your Hands
        SATB (med) ABINGDON APM-103 $.25   (D1154)

    Dove Of Peace *CCU
        FLAMMER GF5024 $.90   (D1155)

    He Is Risen, Alleluia *Easter
        SATB,opt brass (med) ABINGDON APM-389 $.45,
            ipa   (D1156)

DIERCKS, JOHN H. (cont'd.)
    Lord, I Cry Unto Thee *Lent
        SATB oct ABINGDON APM-303 $.35   (D1157)

    Sweet Was The Song *Xmas
        SSA,acap oct WORLD CA-2332-3 $.30   (D1158)

    Upon A Night *Xmas
        SSAA oct WALTON 5003 $.25   (D1159)

    Why Do The Nations Rage?
        unis (med) ABINGDON APM-572 $.25   (D1160)

DIERCKS, L.H.
    Prayer *prayer
        SATB,acap AMP A126 $.20   (D1161)

DIES EST LAETITIA see Gallus, Jacobus

DIES EST LAETITIAE see Szadek, Tomasz

DIES IRAE see Fellegara, Vittorio

DIES IRAE see Lotti, Antonio

DIES IRAE see Mozart, Wolfgang Amadeus

DIES IRAE see Penderecki, Krzysztof

DIES IRAE see Pergolesi, Giovanni Battista

DIES IRAE see Raphael, Gunther

DIES IRAE see Wellesz, Egon

DIES IRAE AC LIBERA see Bottazzo, Luigi

DIES IRAE AC LIBERA see Magri, Pietro

DIES IST DER TAG see Bach, Wilhelm Friedemann

DIES IST DER TAG see Doebler, Curt

DIES IST DER TAG, DEN DER HERR see Telemann,
    Georg Philipp

DIES IST DER TAG, DEN DER HERR MACHT see
    Anonymous

DIES IST DER TAG, DEN DER HERR MACHT see Reda,
    Siegfried

DIES IST DER TAG, DEN DER HERR MACHT see Rein,
    Walter

DIES IST DER TAG, DEN DER HERR MACHT see
    Schulz, Raimund

DIES IST MEIN LIEBER SOHN see Driessler,
    Johannes

DIES SANCTIFICATUS see Burkhart, Franz

DIES SANCTIFICATUS see Byrd, William

DIES SANCTIFICATUS see Handel, George Frideric

DIES SANCTIFICATUS see Kroeger, Karl

DIES SANCTIFICATUS see Palestrina, Giovanni

DIES SANCTIFICATUS see Stoltzer, Thomas

DIES SANCTIFICATUS ILLUXIT NOBIS see Gallus,
    Jacobus

DIES SANCTIFICATUS, TUI SUNT COELI see Eybler,
    Joseph

DIES SANCTIFICAUS see Stoltzer, Thomas

DIES SANTIFICATUS see Palestrina, Giovanni

DIES SIND DIE HEIL'GEN 10 GEBOT see Le Maistre,
    Mattheus

DIES SIND DIE HEILGEN ZEHN GEBOT see
    Praetorius, Michael

DIES SIND DIE HEILIGEN ZEHN GEBOT see Schein,
    Johann Hermann

DIES ULTIMA see Nelhybel, Vaclav

DIESE STATTE see Bruckner, Anton

DIESEN TAG, HERR see Schneider, Martin Gotthard

DIESEN WEG, HERR see Barbe, Helmut

DIETERICH
    Amens And Responses For The Church Choir
        *CCU
        oct SATB PRO ART 1433 $.25; SSA PRO ART
            1740 $.22   (D1162)

    Benedictus
        [Lat] SATB,acap oct BOOSEY 5083 $.30
                                              (D1163)

    God Of Love
        SATB oct BOOSEY 5132 $.30   (D1164)

    Great Is The Peace
        SATB,acap oct PRO ART 2253 $.25   (D1165)

    In Perfect Peace
        SATB oct PRO ART 1526 $.20   (D1166)

    Keep Us Ever In Thy Mercy
        SATB,opt kbd oct PRO ART 1498 $.18   (D1167)

    Kyrie Eleison *Kyrie
        mix cor SOUTHERN $.30   (D1168)
        [Greek] SATB,acap oct BOOSEY 1931 $.30
                                              (D1169)

    Psalm 84
        SATB,acap oct PRO ART 1643 $.20   (D1170)

    Thy Will Be Done
        SATB,acap,opt pno oct PRO ART 1380 $.22
                                              (D1171)

    When I Think Of Calvary *Easter/Lent
        SSA oct PRO ART 1904 $.25   (D1172)
        SATB,acap,opt pno oct PRO ART 1409 $.30
                                              (D1173)
        SAB oct PRO ART 1720 $.30   (D1174)

DIETERICH, M.
  O God Of Peace
    SATB,acap oct PRESSER MC297 $.30   (D1175)

DIETRICH, FRITZ (1905-1945)
  Des Herrn Wort Bleibt In Ewigkeit *Kyrie
    [Ger] 3-4 eq voices/3-4pt mix cor,acap
    (easy) BAREN. BA 1172 s.p. contains also:
    Kyrie (Herre Gott, Erbarme Dich)   (D1176)

  Dreikonigskantate *Epiph,cant
    [Ger] SA,solo,2fl,2vln,vcl (easy) BAREN.
    BA 1036 sc $2.50, cor pts $.40, ipa   (D1177)

  Kleine Osterkantate *Easter,cant
    [Ger] SA,soli,2fl,2vln,vcl (easy) BAREN. BA 1305
    sc $2.50, cor pts $.40, ipa   (D1178)

  Kleine Passionsmusik *Psntd
    [Ger] SA,solo,2fl,2vln,vcl (easy) BAREN.
    BA 1228 sc $2.50, cor pts $.40, ipa   (D1179)

  Kleine Weihnachtskantate Nach Dem
    Evangelisten Lukas *Xmas,cant
    [Ger] 2pt jr cor/2pt wom cor,narrator,2fl,
    2vln,vcl (easy) BAREN. BA 955 sc $2.75,
    cor pts $.25, ipa   (D1180)

  Kyrie (Herre Gott, Erbarme Dich)
    see Dietrich, Fritz, Des Herrn Wort Bleibt
    In Ewigkeit

  Little Christmas Cantata According To The
    Evangelist St. Luke, A *Xmas,cant
    treb cor/men cor/mix cor/SAB,2fl,2vln,vcl,
    male solo CONCORDIA 97-6277 $.60, ipa
    (D1181)

  O Haupt Voll Blut Und Wunden *Psntd
    [Ger] SATB,acap (easy) BAREN. BA 990, 991
    s.p.   (D1182)

  Three Kings, The *Xmas/Epiph,cant
    treb cor/men cor/mix cor,soli,2fl,2vln,vcl
    CONCORDIA 97-6362 $.75, ipa   (D1183)

DIETRICH, M.
  Fear God And Give Glory To Him
    SATB oct SOUTHERN $.25   (D1184)

DIETRICH, SIXTUS (ca. 1490?-1548)
  Heilig Ist Gott Der Vater
    see DEUTSCHES SANCTUS UND PSALM 111

  Heilig Ist Gott Der Vater (Das Sanctus
    Deutsch) *Mass
    [Ger] SATB/SSATB,acap (med) MULLER K 19
    s.p.   (D1185)

  Hymnen (from Das Erbe Deutscher Musik) CCU
    (Zenck, H.) [Ger] cor cmplt ed CONCORDIA
    97-2040 $15.00   (D1186)

  Novum Ac Insigne Opus Musicum 36
    Antiphonarum, 1541 *anti
    (Albrecht, H.) cor CONCORDIA 97-2026 $7.75
    see also MUSIC OF EARLY LUTHERANISM, THE
    (D1187)

DIETSCH, PIERRE LOUIS PHILIPPE (1808-1865)
  Ave Maria *Fest
    [Lat] SATB,acap (easy) MULLER MS 16 s.p.
    (D1188)

DIETTERICH, PHILIP R.
  Carol Of The Advent *Xmas
    SATB (easy) ABINGDON APM-216 $.30   (D1189)

  Come Down, O Love Divine
    SATB (easy) ABINGDON APM-241 $.18   (D1190)

  Come, My Way, My Truth, My Life
    SATB oct GRAY GCMR 3046 $.30   (D1191)

  Holy God Of Sabaoth
    STB/SATB,acap (med) ABINGDON APM-534 $.18
    (D1192)

  Immortal Love
    SAB (easy) ABINGDON APM-214 $.25   (D1193)

  O Love, How Deep, How Broad, How High *Gen/
    Lent/Thanks
    SA/SATB (easy) ABINGDON APM-583 $.30
    (D1194)

  O Love That Triumphs Over Loss *Lent
    SAB,acap (easy) ABINGDON APM-126 $.22
    (D1195)

  Sanctus, The *Sanctus
    SATB (easy) ABINGDON APM-191 $.40   (D1196)

  Wilt Not Thou Turn Again? *Lent
    SATB (easy) ABINGDON APM-134 $.22   (D1197)

DIEU DANS LA NATURE see Schubert, Franz (Peter)

DIEU EST MON GUIDE see Schubert, Franz (Peter),
  Gott Ist Mein Hirt

DIEU LE VEUT! DIEU LE VEUT! see Gounod, Charles
  Francois

DIEU, MON SEUL BIEN (Psalm 7)
  (Geveart, F.-A.) [Fr] 4pt mix cor,acap (easy)
  cor pts LEMOINE s.p. see from Collection De
  Choeurs, troisieme Fascicule   (D1198)

DIEU PARTOUT see Gounod, Charles Francois

DIEU TOUT PUISSANT (Psalm 137) 16th cent
  (Geveart, F.-A.) [Fr] 4pt mix cor,acap (med
  easy) cor pts LEMOINE s.p. see from
  Collection De Choeurs, septieme Fascicule
  (D1199)

DIEU, TU NOUS TIENS (Psalm 73) 16th cent
  (Geveart, F.-A.) [Fr] 4pt mix cor,acap (med
  easy) cor pts LEMOINE s.p. see from
  Collection De Choeurs, septieme Fascicule
  (D1200)

DIEU VOUS GARD', NOSTRE MESTRE see Saboly,
  Nicholas

DIEU VOUS GARD', NOTRE MAITRE see Saboly,
  Nicholas, Dieu Vous Gard', Nostre Mestre

DIEWEIL AUCH HEUER NACH ADVENT see Thiele,
  Siegfried

DIFFUSA EST GRATIA see Gallus, Jacobus

DIFFUSA EST GRATIA see Nanini

DIFFUSA EST GRATIA see Nanini (Nanino),
  Giovanni Maria

DIG A LITTLE DEEPER IN GOD'S LOVE
  TTBB BIG3 $.25   (D1201)

DIG, GUD LOVER VI see Neilsen, Ludvig, Te Deum

DIG HELGE ANDE, BEDJA VI see Rosenquist, Carl
  E.

DIG, HELGE ANDE, BEDJA VI see Runback, Albert

DIG, HELGE ANDE, BEDJA VI see Staden, Johann

DIG KLAD I HELIGHETENS SKRUD see Bjarnegard,
  Gustaf

DIG KLAD I HELIGHETENS SKRUD see Moren, John

DIG KRISTI KORS VI HALSA see Granstam, Bengt

DIG MY GRAVE *spir
  see Deep River
  see Deep River
  (Burleigh; Deis) 4pt men cor,acap oct
  SCHIPM.G 10069 $.25 contains also: Deep
  River   (D1202)

DIG SKALL DITT SION SJUNGA see Bach, Johann
  Sebastian, Gottlob, Nun Geht Das Jahr Zu
  Ende

DIG SKALL DITT SION SJUNGA [CHORALE] see Bach,
  Johann Sebastian

DIG TILLBEDJA VI, KRISTI see Berg, Gottfrid

DIG VARE LOV OCH PRIS see Ek, Gunnar

DIGGLE, [ROLAND] (1887-1954)
  Grant Us Thy Peace
    SSA WARNER W3208 $.30   (D1203)

  Let All Mortal Flesh Keep Silence *Fr
    4pt mix cor oct SCHIRM.G 10005 $.25   (D1204)

DIGNARE ME see Gesualdo, Don Carlo

DIGNUS EST AGNUS see Jaeggi, Oswald

DI IANNI
  Nightly Prayer *prayer
    SATB oct VOLKWEIN VB216 $.25   (D1205)

DIJK, JAN VAN (1918-   )
  Pros Romaious
    [Dut] mix cor,narrator&TB soli,2fl,2ob,
    2clar,2bsn,2trp,2horn,trom,strings,perc
    DONEMUS min sc s.p., cor pts s.p. (D1206)

DI JULIO, [MAX] (1919-
  Little Children Listen *Xmas
    SATB oct PRESSER MC251 $.30   (D1207)

  Sacred Service, A
    SSATB,gtr/opt pno oct FOX UM123 $1.25
    (D1208)

  Shepherds, Awake *Xmas
    SATB oct PRESSER MC265 $.30   (D1209)

DI LASSO, ORLANDO
  see LASSUS, ROLAND DE (ORLANDUS)

DILETTO SPIRITUALE see Verovio, S.

DILEXI QUONIAM see Palestrina, Giovanni

DILEXISTI JUSTITIAM see Wildgans, Friedrich

DILLER, ANGELA (1877-1968)
  Christmas Carol Pageant, A (composed with
    Paget, Kate; Stearns) *Xmas,carol
    jr cor SCHIRM.G voc sc $1.25, cor pts $.35
    (D1210)

DILSNER, L.
  Communion Service *Commun
    SATB MUSICUS 1034 $.25   (D1211)

DIMMI, DOLCE MARIA
  see Three Christmas Laude

DIN SPIRA, JESU, STRACKES UT
  (Berg, Gottfrid) mix cor NORDISKA 2119 s.p.
  see also Sacrae Cantiones   (D1212)

DINERSTEIN, N.
  Cinque Laude *CC5U
    [Lat] SATB,acap oct BOOSEY 5649 $.35
    (D1213)

  Our Father
    SS/TT,acap AMP A551 $.25   (D1214)

DING-DONG! MERRILY
  (Davis) 4pt mix cor,acap oct SCHIRM.G 8248
  $.25   (D1215)

DING-DONG! MERRILY see Davis, Katherine K.

DING DONG, MERRILY ON HIGH *Xmas,carol,Fr
  (Barthelson) SATB oct LAWSON 572 $.30 (D1216)
  (Barthelson) SA oct LAWSON 51276 $.25 (D1217)
  (Barthelson) SSA/SAA oct LAWSON 767 $.30
  (D1218)
  (Deale) SSA,acap (easy) OXFORD 83.019 $.25
    see from Four Old Carols   (D1219)
  (Deale) SATB,acap (med easy) OXFORD 84.014
    $.35 see from Four Old Carols   (D1220)
  (Reed) unis&desc BOOSEY-CAN s.p.   (D1221)
  (Williamson) 4pt mix cor,acap oct FABER 11371
    $.25   (D1222)

DING DONG! MERRILY ON HIGH see Curry

DING, DONG, MERRILY ON HIGH see Hunt, Reginald

DING, DONG, MERRILY ON HIGH see Wilson

DING, DONG, MERRILY ON HIGH see Woodward

DINGEMANN, [GUSTAV] (1915-   )
  Der Wachter Auf Dem Turmlein Sass *folk
    jr cor&men cor (easy) oct LEUCKART 35 s.p.
    (D1223)

DINN, FREDA
  Except The Lord Build The House (Psalm 127)
    unis,pno SCHOTT 10482 s.p.   (D1224)

DINN, FREDA (cont'd.)
  First Nowell, The
    see Four Christmas Carols

  Four Christmas Carols *Xmas,carol
    (Murray) unis SCHOTT 10857 s.p.
    contains: First Nowell, The; In Dulci
    Jubilo; O Little Town Of Bethlehem;
    Past Three O'clock   (D1225)

  Good King Wenceslas *Xmas
    (Bergmann) unis,pno,strings,perc,rec sc
    SCHOTT RS23 s.p., ipa, cor pts SCHOTT
    RS23 s.p., ipa   (D1226)

  In Dulci Jubilo
    see Four Christmas Carols

  O Little Town Of Bethlehem
    see Four Christmas Carols

  Past Three O'clock
    see Four Christmas Carols

  Psalm 127 *see Except The Lord Build The
    House

  Shepherds By The Manger *Xmas,carol
    2pt jr cor,2vln,perc,rec s.p. sc SCHOTT
    RS28, cor pts SCHOTT RS28   (D1227)

DINNING
  First Palm Sunday, The *Palm
    jr cor&sr cor (med easy) FISCHER,C CM 6378
    $.30   (D1228)

DI NOVI
  Brand New Morning *sec
    (Ades) SATB SHAWNEE A 1110 $.35   (D1229)

DIO SI LODE CIELO, IN TERRA see Handel, George
  Frideric

DIO SIA BENEDETTO see Bottazzo, Luigi

DIO SIA BENEDETTO see Bottigliero, Eduardo

DIO SIA BENEDETTO see Bovensi, Giustino

DIO VI SALVI REGINA see Thomasi, [Henri]

DIPLOCK, CYRIL
  Peace To Every Neighbor *Xmas,carol
    oct ROYAL 340 s.p.   (D1230)

DIR, DIR JEHOVA see Bach, Johann Sebastian

DIR, DIR JEHOVA see Oertzen, Rudolf von

DIR, DIR, JEHOVA, WILL ICH SINGEN see Bach,
  Johann Sebastian

DIR, DIR, JEHOVA, WILL ICH SINGEN see Stern,
  Hermann

DIR, JESU, GOTTES SOHN see Bach, Johann
  Christoph

DIR JESU GOTTES SOHN see Bach, Johann Sebastian

DIR, SEELE DES WELTALLS see Mozart, Wolfgang
  Amadeus

DIR SEI LOB see Lassus, Roland de (Orlandus),
  Tibi Laus

DIRECT OUR STEPS THIS DAY see Wilson

DIRGE FOR THE SAVIOR see Biggs, John

DIRKSEN, RICHARD W.
  Child My Choice, A *Xmas
    SATB oct GRAY GCMR 2489 $.30   (D1231)

  Christmas Lullaby *Xmas
    SATB,acap oct LAWSON 893 $.25   (D1232)

  Hilariter *Easter
    SATB oct GRAY GCMR 2634 $.50   (D1233)

  I Sing The Birth
    SATB FLAMMER A 5612 $.30   (D1234)

  Jubilate Deo *Jubil
    2pt mix cor oct LAWSON 894 $.35   (D1235)

  Nativity, The *Xmas
    SATB oct GRAY GCMR 2944 $.25   (D1236)

  Nowell Sing We
    SATB SHAWNEE A 1120 $.30   (D1237)

DI RORE, CIPRIANO (1516-1565)
  Opera Omnia vol. I *CCU,mot
    (Meier, Bernhard) cor cmplt ed AM.INST.MUS.
    $19.50   (D1238)

  Opera Omnia vol. II *CCU,mot
    (Meier, Bernhard) cor cmplt ed AM.INST.MUS.
    $23.50   (D1239)

  Opera Omnia vol. VII *CCU,Mass/mot
    (Meier, Bernhard) cor cmplt ed AM.INST.MUS.
    $20.00   (D1240)

DISCEDITE A ME see Schutz, Heinrich

DISCITE A ME see Bottazzo, Luigi

DISCITE A ME see Faccin, Gian Domenico

DISCOVERY! see Owens, Jimmy

DISPERSIT see Fernandez de Castilleja

DISPREZZATOR MAGNANIMO see Volpi, Edoardo

DISTLER, HUGO (1908-1942)
  Ach Herr, Vom Himmel Sieh Darein *Trin,mot
    [Ger] 3 eq voices,acap (med diff) BAREN.
    BA 4947 s.p.   (D1241)

  Ach Herr, Ich Bin Nicht Wert *Gen
    [Ger] SATB,acap (med) BAREN. BA 1997 s.p.
    (D1242)

  Also Hat Gott Die Welt Geliebet *Pent
    [Ger] SA&men cor,acap (med) BAREN. BA 3279
    $.25 see also Der Jahrkreis   (D1243)

DISTLER, HUGO (cont'd.)

Aus Tiefer Not Schrei Ich Zu Dir *ECY
[Ger] 5pt mix cor,acap (med) BAREN. BA 4948 $.40 (D1244)

Choralmotette *Op.2, mot
dbl cor,acap cor pts BREITKOPF-L PB-3348 s.p. (D1245)

Choralpassion Nach Den Vier Evangelien *Op.7, Psntd,evang
[Ger] SSATB,TB soli,acap (med diff) BAREN. BA 633 $4.50 (D1246)

Christ, Du Bist Der Helle Tag *Op.6,No.1 (from Little Advent Musik, A) Gen
[Ger] SA&men cor,cont,2vln (med) BAREN. BA 636 sc $2.25, cor pts $.40 (D1247)
(Palmer, L.) "Christ, Who Alone Art Light Of Day" SAB,2vln,kbd CONCORDIA 97-5066 $1.25, ipa (D1248)

Christ, Who Alone Art Light Of Day *see Christ, Du Bist Der Helle Tag

Christe, Du Bist Der Helle Tag *Gen
[Ger] 5pt mix cor,acap (med) BAREN. BA 4948 s.p. (D1249)

Christmas Story, The *see Die Weihnachtsgeschichte

Dance Of Death
(Johns, Malcolm) SATB,narrator FOSTER MF 125 $2.00 (D1250)

Das Ist Je Gewisslich Wahr (Motet 8) Trin
[Ger] SATB,acap (med) BAREN. BA 1801 $2.00 see also Geistliche Chormusik (D1251)

Dear Christians, One And All, Rejoice *Easter/Gen/Refm
SATB,acap (med diff) oct CONCORDIA 98-1901 $.30 (D1252)

Den Geboren Hat Ein Magd *Xmas
[Ger] SATB,acap (med easy) BAREN. BA 1996 s.p. contains also: Vom Himmel Hoch, O Englein Kommt (D1253)

Der Jahrkreis *Op.5, CC52UL,Gen
[Ger] 2pt/3pt,acap (med) BAREN. BA 676 s.p. see also: Also Hat Gott Die Welt Geliebet; Macht Hoch Die Tur; Selig Sind Die Toten; Verleih Uns Frieden Gnadiglich; Wie Der Hirsch Schreiet Nach Frischem Wasser; Wie Schon Leucht' Uns Der Morgenstern (D1254)

Der Tag Hat Sich Geneiget *Gen
[Ger] 4pt men cor,acap (med) BAREN. BCH 124 s.p. (D1255)

Dertil Vi Synger *see So Singen Wir All Amen

Die Sonne Sinkt Von Hinnen *Gen
[Ger] SATB,acap (med) BAREN. BA 940 s.p. (D1256)

Die Weihnachtsgeschichte *Op.10, Xmas
[Ger] SATB,SSTB soli,acap (med diff) BAREN. BA 690 $4.50 (D1257)
(Klein, M.) "Christmas Story, The" cor, SMezTTBarB soli,acap voc sc CONCORDIA 97-4780 $2.00 (D1258)

Ehre Sei Dir, Christe *Psntd/Trin
[Ger] SATB,acap (med) BAREN. BA 3210 $.25 (D1259)
[Ger] SATB,acap BAREN. BA 3210 s.p. (D1260)

Eine Deutsche Choralmesse *Op.3, Mass
6pt mix cor,acap cor pts BREITKOPF-L PB-3407 s.p., voc pt BREITKOPF-L CHB-2760 s.p. (D1261)

En Rose Er Udsprunget *see Es Ist Ein Ros Entsprungen

Es Ist Das Heil Uns Kommen Her *Fest
[Ger] SATB,acap (med) BAREN. BA 586-587 s.p. (D1262)

Es Ist Ein Ros Entsprungen *Op.10 (from Weihnachtsgeschichte) Xmas
(Rasmussen, Henning Bro) [Ger/Dan] SATB, acap HANSEN-DEN 28536 s.p.
contains & see also: Es Ist Ein Ros Entsprungen, "En Rose Er Udsprunget"; Lob, Ehr Sei Gott, Dem Vater, "Lov Pris Og Tak Gud Fader"; So Singen Wir All Amen, "Dertil Vi Synger"; Wir Bitten Dich Von Herzen, "Vi Priser Dig Af Hjerte" (D1263)

Es Ist Ein Ros Entsprungen *Op.10, Xmas
[Ger] SATB,acap (med, choralpartita) BAREN. BA 681 s.p. (D1264)
[Ger] SATB,acap (med, choralpartita) BAREN. BA 681 s.p. (D1265)
[Ger] SATB,acap (med easy) BAREN. BCH 171 s.p. (D1266)
[Ger] 4pt men cor,acap (med diff) NAGELS NCH 207 s.p. (D1267)
(Rasmussen, Henning Bro) "En Rose Er Udsprunget" [Ger/Dan] SATB,acap (contains also: Das Roslein, Das Ich Meine) HANSEN-DEN 406 s.p. see also Es Ist Ein Ros Entsprungen (D1268)

Es Kommt Ein Schiff Geladen
"Et Skib Herhid Mon Komme" see Fem Satser

Et Skib Herhid Mon Komme *see Es Kommt Ein Schiff Geladen

Fem Satser *Adv/Xmas
(Rasmussen, Henning Bro) [Ger/Dan] HANSEN-DEN 28055 s.p.
contains: Es Kommt Ein Schiff Geladen, "Et Skib Herhid Mon Komme" (SSA,acap); Macht Hoch Die Tur, "Oploft Dig, Dor" (SSA,acap); Maria Durch Ein Dornwald Ging, "Maria Gennem Kratskov Gik" (SABar,acap); Nun Komm, Der Heiden Heiland, "Hedningers Genloser, Kom" (SABar,acap); Wie Schon Leucht't Uns Der Morgenstern, "Hvor Skont Lyser I Stralekrans" (SABar,acap) (D1269)

DISTLER, HUGO (cont'd.)

Furwahr, Er Trug Unsere Krankheit *Op.12, No.9, Psntd,mot
[Ger] SATB,acap (med diff) BAREN. BA 1802 $1.75 see also Geistliche Chormusik (D1270)

Geistliche Chormusik *see Das Ist Je Gewisslich Wahr (Motet 8); Furwahr, Er Trug Unsere Krankheit, Op.12,No.9; Ich Wollt, Dass Ich Daheime War, Op.12,No.5; In Der Welt Habt Ihr Angst, Op.12,No.7; Singet Dem Herrn Ein Neues Lied, Op.12, No.1; Singet Frisch Und Wohlgemut, Op.12, No.4; Totentanz, Op.12,No.2; Wach Auf, Du Deutsches Reich, Op.12,No.3; Wachet Auf, Ruft Uns Die Stimme, Op.12,No.6 (D1271)

Gott Der Vater Wohn Uns Bei *Trin
[Ger] 3 eq voices,acap (med easy) BAREN. BA 1998 s.p. (D1272)

Gott Ist Unsre Zuversicht *Gen
[Ger] 3 eq voices,acap (med easy) BAREN. BA 3037 s.p. (D1273)

Hedningers Genloser, Kom *see Nun Komm, Der Heiden Heiland

Hvor Skont Lyser I Stralekrans *see Wie Schon Leucht't Uns Der Morgenstern

I Wish That I Were Going Home *ASD/ECY/Gen
SATB,acap (diff) oct CONCORDIA 98-1832 $.30 (D1274)

Ich Wollt, Dass Ich Daheime War *Op.12,No.5, ECY,mot
[Ger] SATB,acap (med) BAREN. BA 755 s.p. see also Geistliche Chormusik (D1275)

In Der Welt Habt Ihr Angst *Op.12,No.7, ECY, mot
[Ger] SATB,acap (med) BAREN. BA 757 $.55 see also Geistliche Chormusik (D1276)

In The World You Have Fear *ECY/Gen
SATB,acap (diff) oct CONCORDIA 98-2146 $.35 (D1277)

Jesu, Deine Passion (from Choralpassion Nach Den Vier Evangelium) Psntd,evang/mot
[Ger] SSATB,acap (med diff) BAREN. BA 1467 $1.50 (D1278)

Jesus Christus, Gestern Und Heute *Gen
[Ger] 3 eq voices,acap (med easy) BAREN. BA 1608 s.p. (D1279)

Kleine Adventsmusik *Op.4, Adv
mix cor,narrator,org/pno,fl,ob,strings,opt vcl sc BREITKOPF-L PB-3415 s.p., voc pt BREITKOPF-L CHB-2767 s.p., ipa (D1280)
3pt mix cor,narrator,org/pno/cembalo,fl,ob, vln voc sc BREITKOPF-W PB-4967 s.p., voc pt BREITKOPF-W CHB-2767 s.p., ipa (D1281)

Komm, Heiliger Geist *Pent
[Ger/Swed] SATB,acap (med easy) cor pts BAREN. BA 588 s.p. (D1282)

Lamb Goes Uncomplaining Forth, A *Lent
SATB,kbd (med easy, or Ash Wednesday) oct CONCORDIA 98-2076 $.30 (D1283)

Little Advent Music, A
(Palmer, L.) SAB,narrator,kbd,fl,ob,vln,opt vcl (based on the chorale Nun Komm Der Heiden Heiland) sc CONCORDIA 97-6438 $2.25, cor pts CONCORDIA 97-4707 $.40, ipa (D1284)

Lob, Ehr Sei Gott, Dem Vater
(Rasmussen, Henning Bro) "Lov Pris Og Tak Gud Fader" [Ger/Dan] SATB,acap HANSEN-DEN 408 s.p. see also Es Ist Ein Ros Entsprungen (D1285)

Lobe Den Herren, Den Machtigen Konig Der Ehren *Gen
[Ger] SATB,acap (med easy) BAREN. BA 589 s.p. (D1286)

Lobt Gott, Ihr Christen Allzugleich *Xmas
[Ger] SATB,acap (med easy) BAREN. BA 934, 935 s.p. (D1287)

Lov Pris Og Tak Gud Fader *see Lob, Ehr Sei Gott, Dem Vater

Macht Hoch Die Tur *Adv
"Oploft Dig, Dor" see Fem Satser
[Ger] SAA,acap (med easy) BAREN. BA 3010 $.25 see also Der Jahrkreis (D1288)

Maria Durch Ein Dornwald Ging
"Maria Gennem Kratskov Gik" see Fem Satser

Maria Gennem Kratskov Gik *see Maria Durch Ein Dornwald Ging

Motet 8 *see Das Ist Je Gewisslich Wahr

Nun Danket All Und Bringet Ehr *Op.11,No.2, Gen
[Ger] SATB,ST soli,org,2vln,vla,vcl,opt vla&bvl (med) BAREN. BA 758 sc $2.50, cor pts $.40, ipa (D1289)

Nun Freut Euch, Lieben Christen Gmein *Easter/Pent
[Ger] SATB,acap (med easy) BAREN. BA 936, 937 s.p. (D1290)

Nun Komm, Der Heiden Heiland
"Hedningers Genloser, Kom" see Fem Satser

O Heiland, Reiss Die Himmel Auf *Adv
[Ger] SATB,acap (med easy) BAREN. BA 1065 s.p. (D1291)

Oploft Dig, Dor *see Macht Hoch Die Tur

Praise God The Lord, Ye Sons Of Men *Xmas
SATB,acap (med easy) oct CONCORDIA 98-1908 $.25 (D1292)

Salvation Unto Us Has Come *Gen/Refm
SATB,acap (med diff) oct CONCORDIA 98-1943 $.30 (D1293)

DISTLER, HUGO (cont'd.)

Selections From Der Jahrkreis *CC20L
SSA&SST&SAB&SSAA&SSAB CONCORDIA 97-4846 $1.75 (D1294)

Selig Sind Die Toten *ECY
[Ger] SA&men cor,S solo,acap (med) BAREN. BA 3242 $.25 see also Der Jahrkreis (D1295)

Sing With Joy, Glad Voices Lift *Xmas,mot
SATB,acap (diff) oct CONCORDIA 98-5111 $.50 (D1296)
(Palmer, L.) SATB,soli,acap CONCORDIA 97-5111 $.50 (D1297)

Singet Dem Herrn Ein Neues Lied *Op.12,No.1, Easter/Pent,mot
[Ger] SATB,acap (med diff) BAREN. BA 751 $2.00 see also Geistliche Chormusik (D1298)

Singet Frisch Und Wohlgemut *Op.12,No.4, Xmas,mot
[Ger] SATB,acap (med diff) BAREN. BA 754 $2.00 see also Geistliche Chormusik (D1299)

So Singen Wir All Amen
(Rasmussen, Henning Bro) "Dertil Vi Synger" [Ger/Dan] SATB,acap HANSEN-DEN 409 AMEN s.p. see also Es Ist Ein Ros Entsprungen (D1300)

Totentanz *Op.12,No.2, ECY,mot
[Ger] SATB,narrator,acap (med, all souls day) BAREN. BA 752 $2.75 see also Geistliche Chormusik (D1301)

Verleih Uns Frieden Gnadiglich
[Ger] SA&men cor,acap (med) BAREN. BA 3037 $.40 see also Der Jahrkreis (D1302)

Vi Priser Dig Af Hjerte *see Wir Bitten Dich Von Herzen

Vom Himmel Hoch, O Englein Kommt
see Distler, Hugo, Den Geboren Hat Ein Magd

Wach Auf, Du Deutsches Reich *Op.12,No.3, Fest
[Ger] SATB,SS soli,acap (med diff) BAREN. BA 753 $2.25 see also Geistliche Chormusik (D1303)

Wachet Auf, Ruft Uns Die Stimme *Op.12,No.6, ECY,mot
[Ger] SSATB,SS soli,acap (med diff) BAREN. BA 756 $2.25 see also Geistliche Chormusik (D1304)

Wacht Auf, Es Tut Euch Not "Klaglich Ich Schrei" *Gen
[Ger] SATB,acap (med) BAREN. BA 949 s.p. (D1305)

Wer Der Heirsch Schreiet *Gen
[Ger] SAB,acap (med easy) BAREN. BA 3280 $.25 (D1306)

Wie Der Hirsch Schreiet Nach Frischem Wasser *Easter/Pent
[Ger] SA&men cor,acap (med) BAREN. BA 3280 $.25 see also Der Jahrkreis (D1307)

Wie Schon Leucht' Uns Der Morgenstern *Epiph
[Ger] SA&men cor,acap (med) BAREN. BA 579 s.p. see also Der Jahrkreis (D1308)

Wie Schon Leucht't Uns Der Morgenstern
"Hvor Skont Lyser I Stralekrans" see Fem Satser

Wir Bitten Dich Von Herzen
(Rasmussen, Henning Bro) "Vi Priser Dig Af Hjerte" [Ger/Dan] SATB,acap (contains also: Meine Seele Erhebt Gott; Das Blumelein So Kleine; Die Hirten Zu Der Stunden) HANSEN-DEN 407 s.p. see also Es Ist Ein Ros Entsprungen (D1309)

Wo Gott Zu Haus Nit Gibt Sein Gunst *Op.11, No.1, Gen
[Ger] SATB,opt SATB soli,org/pno,2ob,2vln, vla,vcl (med diff) BAREN. BA 750 sc s.p., cor pts s.p., ipa (D1310)

DIT IS DE DAG see Hoogerwerf, N., Haec Dies

DIT IS DE DAG see Vranken, Alph., Haec Dies

DIT IS DE DAG DIE GOD ONS SCHENKT see Bach, Johann Sebastian

DITT LIDANDE HAR NATT SITT SLUT see Holmberg, Simon

DITT NAMN, JEHOVA, VILL JAG SJUNGA see Bach, Johann Sebastian

DITT NAMN, O GUD JAG LOVA VILL see Schutz, Heinrich

DITT ORD, O JESU, BLIVA MA see Nordqvist, Gustaf

DITTENHAVER, S.
Bless The Lord, O My Soul
SATB oct PRESSER 312-40684 $.35 (D1311)

DITTMANN, THOMAS (1931-)
O Heiland, Reiss Die Himmel Auf
see Barbe, Helmut, Es Kommt Ein Schiff Geladen

DIVES AND LAZARUS *carol
(Vaughan Williams) TBB,acap (easy) OXFORD 41.905 $.25 see from Nine Carols (D1312)

DIVES AND LAZARUS see Hoddinott, Alun

DIVINE COMMISSION, THE see Clokey, Joseph Waddell

DIVINE GUEST, THE see France, William E.

DIVINE IMAGE, THE see Hewitt-Jones, Tony

DIVINE INTERCESSION, A see Rowley

DIVINE MYSTERY, THE see Gillette, James Robert

DIVINE PRAISE see Bortniansky, Dimitri
    Stepanovitch, Kol Slaven

DIVINE PRAISES, THE see Murphy, J.A.

DIVINE REDEEMER see Gounod, Charles Francois

DIVINUM MYSTERIUM see Ashfield, Robert

DIVIS ORTE BONIS see Olman, Isr, J.

DIVISION see Adler, Samuel

DIVITIS, [ANTONIUS] (ca. 1475-ca. 1526)
    Missa Quem Dicunt Homines *Mass
        (Lockwood) 2-5pt mix cor MOSELER s.p.
                                              (D1313)

DIVO ANTONIO see Coronaro, Antonio

DIX CHORALS see Bach, Johann Sebastian

DIX MARIA QUID VIDISTI see Plautz, Gabriel

DIXIT see Bernasconi, Luigi

DIXIT see Giorgi, Piero

DIXIT see Margiotta, Giovanni

DIXIT see Muller, Giulio

DIXIT see Vivaldi, Antonio

DIXIT DOMINUM see Lalande, Michel Richard de

DIXIT DOMINUS see Bernardi, Steffano

DIXIT DOMINUS see Handel, George Frideric

DIXIT DOMINUS see Magri, Pietro

DIXIT DOMINUS see Monteverdi, Claudio

DIXIT DOMINUS see Mozart, Wolfgang Amadeus

DIXIT DOMINUS see Pergolesi, Giovanni Battista

DIXIT DOMINUS see Vivaldi, Antonio

DIXIT DOMINUS see Volpi, Edoardo

DIXIT DOMINUS AND MAGNIFICAT see Mozart,
    Wolfgang Amadeus

DIXIT DOMINUS DOMINO MEO see Bernardi, Steffano

DIXIT DOMINUS DOMINO MEO see Handel, George
    Frideric

DIXIT MARIA see Hassler, Hans Leo

DIXIT MARIA AD ANGELUM see Hassler, Hans Leo

DIXITQUE FIAT see Pezzati, Mauro

DIXON
    Bread Of Life, The *see Panis Vitae

    Credo *Credo
        [Lat] SATB,org PETERS H592E $.60   (D1314)

    Go Down, Moses *spir
        TTBB&3pt treb cor SCHMITT 7009 $.18 (D1315)

    Mass In Honor Of St. Paulinus Of York *Mass
        SATB,org voc sc PETERS H592C $1.50 (D1316)

    Panis Vitae *ora
        "Bread Of Life, The" SATB,STB soli,orch,org
        voc sc PETERS H618A $3.50, ipr   (D1317)

    Transfiguration
        SATB,acap PETERS H592D $.40   (D1318)

DLUGOS
    Lord Is Risen, The
        SATB FLAMMER A 5622 $.30   (D1319)

DO-DON'T TOUCH-A MY GARMENT *spir
    (Shaw) 4pt mix cor,Bar solo,acap oct SCHIRM.G
    9954 $.25   (D1320)

DO DON'T TOUCHA MY GARMENT see Rhea

DO I CRUCIFY MY SAVIOR? see York

DO LORD see Murray, Lyn

DO LORD, REMEMBER ME see Wild, Eric

DO NOT BE AMAZED see Bender, Jan

DO NOT BE CONFORMED see Landgrave, Phillip

DO NOT I LOVE THEE, O MY LORD? see Work, John
    [Wesley]

DO WHAT HE WANTS YOU DO see Martin

DO YOU FACE A WALL? see Landgrave, Phillip

DO YOU HEAR THE ANGELS SINGING? see Artman

DO YOU HEAR WHAT I HEAR? see Regney

DO YOU KNOW? see Hughes

DO YOU KNOW MY JESUS? see Ellis

DO YOU KNOW THE LOVE OF JESUS? see Vogler,
    Georg Joseph

DO YOU KNOW THE NEWBORN CHILD see Chenoweth,
    Wilbur

DO YOU KNOW THE ONE see Page, R.

DOANE, [WILLIAM HOWARD] (1832-1915)
    More Love To Thee *hymn
        (Owens) SATB oct LILLENAS AT-1026 $.25
                                            (D1321)

    Nearer The Cross
        (McCall) SATB oct PRO ART 2605 $.30 (D1322)

    Pass Me Not
        (Collins) SATB oct LILLENAS AT-1082 $.30
                                            (D1323)

DOANE, [WILLIAM HOWARD] (cont'd.)

    Though Your Sins Be As Scarlet
        (Whitman) SATB oct LILLENAS AN-1175 $.30
                                            (D1324)

    To God Be The Glory
        (Whitman) SATB oct LILLENAS AN-1144 $.30
                                            (D1325)

DOBBS, J.P.B.
    Garden Of Christ, The
        SAB LENGNICK s.p.   (D1326)

    Once There Came To Earth
        SAB,opt pno LENGNICK s.p.   (D1327)

DOBIAS, VACLAV (1909-   )
    Kdoz Jste Bozi Bojovnici
        men cor,solo,pno SUPRAPHON s.p.   (D1328)

DOBIE
    O Most Merciful Redeemer
        SATB oct PLYMOUTH PCS-13 $.25   (D1329)

DOBLER, W.
    O Land Der Vater
        [Ger] mix cor,acap (easy) HUG s.p. (D1330)

    Schweizer Weihegesang
        [Ger] mix cor,acap (easy) HUG s.p. (D1331)

DOBLINGER MESSE see Romanovsky, Erich, Deutsche
    Messe In C

DOBOS, K.
    A Bekakiraly
        see Harom Madrigal

    Ha Vihar Jo
        see Harom Madrigal

    Harom Madrigal *sac/sec,madrigal
        (Weores, S.) [Hung] 3 eq voices (diff)
        BUDAPEST 3211 s.p.
            contains: A Bekakiraly; Ha Vihar Jo; Kis
            Dal A Szelrol   (D1332)

    Kis Dal A Szelrol
        see Harom Madrigal

DODICI CANTI NATALIZI TRADIZIONALI *CC12U,Xmas
    (Loregian, S.) 1-4pt,org sc ZANIBON 5096
    s.p., cor pts ZANIBON 5097 s.p.   (D1333)

DODICI CANZONCINE see Bas, Giulio

DODICI CANZONCINE ALLA VERGINE see Chiappani,
    Carlo

DODICI LITANIE LAURETANE see Bottazzo, Luigi

DODICI LITANIE LAURETANE see Gorlatto, Giacomo

DODICI LITANIE LAURETANE see Zaccaria, Vittore

DODICI MOTECTA SACRO CORDI JESU see Bottazzo,
    Luigi

DODICI TANTUM ERGO *CC12U,Commun
    [Lat] unis,org sc ZANIBON 1121 s.p., cor pts
    ZANIBON 1122 contains works by: Bottazzo;
    Coronaro; Livieri; Nicolosi; Pasini;
    Rodella; Zamboni; Sangiorgio   (D1334)

DOEBLER, CURT
    Crucem Tuam
        [Lat] mix cor (med) oct SIRIUS 2 s.p.
                                            (D1335)
    Dies Ist Der Tag *Fest
        [Ger] mix cor,org cor pts SIRIUS s.p.
                                            (D1336)
    Kommet Her Und Sehet An Die Taten Gottes
        [Ger] mix cor,org cor pts SIRIUS s.p.
                                            (D1337)
    Lobpreise Den Herrn
        [Ger] mix cor,org cor pts SIRIUS s.p.
                                            (D1338)
    Lourdes-Messe *Mass
        [Ger] SATB,acap voc sc SIRIUS s.p. (D1339)

    Missa Fatima *Mass
        [Lat] 2pt mix cor/3pt mix cor,org SIRIUS sc
        s.p., cor pts s.p.   (D1340)

    Selig Die Toten
        [Ger] mix cor (med) oct SIRIUS 4 s.p.
                                            (D1341)
    Singt Unserm Gott
        [Ger] mix cor (med) oct SIRIUS 3 s.p.
                                            (D1342)
    Wer Nur Den Lieben Gott Lasst Walten
        [Ger] SATB,acap voc sc SIRIUS s.p. (D1343)

DOERNBERG, MARTIN (1920-   )
    Der Herr Ist Mein Hirte *Bibl
        mix cor HANSSLER 7.144 s.p.   (D1344)

    Die Pfingstschichte *Pent/Whitsun
        mix cor HANSSLER 2.040 s.p.   (D1345)

    Lieber Herre Gott, Wecke Uns Auf
        see Doernberg, Martin, Mache Dich Auf,
        Werde Licht

    Mache Dich Auf, Werde Licht
        SAT/SAB HANSSLER 7.162 s.p. contains also:
        Lieber Herre Gott, Wecke Uns Auf   (D1346)

    Psalm 148 *mot
        SATB HANSSLER 7.098 s.p.   (D1347)

    Selig Sind Die Toten
        SATB HANSSLER 7.152 s.p.   (D1348)

DOES IT MAKE ANY DIFFERENCE TO YOU see Roe,
    Gloria [Ann]

DOES JESUS CARE?
    SSA BIG3 $.25   (D1349)

DOES JESUS CARE? see Wilson

DOES THE DAY-STAR RISE? see Naylor, Bernard

DOG'S CAROL, THE see Wallace, William

DOHERTY, CHRISTOPHER
    Follow Me *sac/sec,CC8U
        jr cor cmplt ed WEINBERGER $1.25   (D1350)

    Three Canticles For The Easter Vigil *CC3U,
        Holywk
        TTBB/SATB,cantor oct SUMMY M 2840 $.25
                                            (D1351)

DOHNANYI, ERNST VON (1877-1960)
    Stabat Mater *Op.46
        [Lat] SSMezMezAA/6pt boy cor AMP A219 $1.50
                                            (D1352)

DOIN' HIS TASK see Harrell, Jan

DOLCE CUOR see Arnaldi, Antonio

DOLCISSIMA MARIA see Rossini, Gioacchino

DOLCISSIMA MIA VITA see Gesualdo, Don Carlo

DOLES, JOHANN FRIEDRICH (1715-1797)
    Ein' Feste Burg Ist Unser Gott
        (Schreck, G.) SATB,acap cor pts BREITKOPF-L
        PB-1432 s.p.   (D1353)

DOLF, TH.
    Lebe Wohl, Du Mudes Jahr
        [Ger] mix cor,acap (easy) HUG s.p. (D1354)

DOM IKKE see Hovland, Egil

DOMENICA DI PASQUA see Ravanello, Oreste

DOMENICA DI PENTECOSTE see Mannino, F.

DOMINE see Bernasconi, Luigi

DOMINE see Vivaldi, Antonio

DOMINE AD ADIUVANDUM see Bossi, Marco Enrico

DOMINE, AD ADIUVANDUM see Pergolesi, Giovanni
    Battista

DOMINE AD ADJUVANDUM see Magri, Pietro

DOMINE AD ADJUVANDUM see Volpi, Edoardo

DOMINE AD ADJUVANDUM E DIXIT see Bottazzo,
    Luigi

DOMINE, AD ADJUVANDUM ME see Homilius,
    Gottfried August

DOMINE, AD ADJUVANDUM ME FESTINA see Martini,
    Padre

DOMINE CONVERTERE see Lassus, Roland de
    (Orlandus)

DOMINE DEUS see Gines Perez, Juan

DOMINE DEUS see Stuntz, Josef Hartmann

DOMINE DEUS see Vivaldi, Antonio

DOMINE DEUS, AGNUS DEI see Vivaldi, Antonio

DOMINE DEUS, DEUS VIRTUTUM see Schutz, Heinrich

DOMINE DEUS, PATER COELESTIS see Schutz,
    Heinrich

DOMINE, DOMINUS NOSTER see Hassler, Hans Leo

DOMINE, DOMINUS NOSTER see Lechner, Leonhard

DOMINE, DOMINUS NOSTER see Schmitt, Florent

DOMINE EXAUDI ORATIONEM MEAM see Selle, Thomas

DOMINE FAC MECUM see Morley

DOMINE FAC MECUM see Morley, Thomas

DOMINE FILI UNIGENITE see Vivaldi, Antonio

DOMINE, LABIA MEA APERIES see Cruger, Johann

DOMINE MEMENTO MEI see Back, Sven-Erick

DOMINE, NE IN FURORE TUO see Gabrieli, Andrea

DOMINE, NE IN FURORE TUO see Schutz, Heinrich

DOMINE, NE IN FURORE TUO ARGUAS ME see
    Soderholm, Valdemar

DOMINE, NON EST EXALTATUM see Schutz, Heinrich

DOMINE NON EST EXALTATUM see White, Robert

DOMINE, NON EST EXALTATUM COR MEUM see Schutz,
    Heinrich

DOMINE, NON SECUNDUM PECCATA NOSTRA see
    Manicke, Dietrich

DOMINE NON SUM DIGNUS see Bottigliero, Eduardo

DOMINE NON SUM DIGNUS see Victoria, Tomas Luis
    de

DOMINE NON SUM DIGNUS see Zaccaria, Vittore

DOMINE QUI HABITABIT I see White, Robert

DOMINE QUI HABITABIT II see White, Robert

DOMINE QUI HABITABIT III see White, Robert

DOMINE SALVAM FAC REGINA NOSTRAM see
    Schrijvers, J.

DOMINE SALVUM FAC see Weegenhuise, Johan

DOMINE, SALVUM FAC PASTOREM NOSTRUM see Rioda,
    Umberto

DOMINE SALVUM FAC PASTOREM NOSTRUM see Volpi,
    Edoardo

DOMINE SALVUM FAC REGEM see Buxtehude, Dietrich

DOMINI, DOMINI IN D see Turner, E.

DOMINI, DOMINI IN G see Turner, E.

DOMINI EST TERRA see Berkeley, Lennox

DOMINI EST TERRA see Gallus, Jacobus

DOMINI EST TERRA see Schutz, Heinrich

DOMINI EXAUDI ORATIONEM MEUM see Lassus, Roland de (Orlandus)

DOMINICA IN RAMIS see Padilla

DOMINICUS MESSE see Mozart, Wolfgang Amadeus, Messa In C-Dur

DOMINO NON SUM DIGNUS see Victoria, Tomas Luis de

DOMINUS DABIT BENIGNITATEM see Fux, Johann Joseph

DOMINUS DEUS see Lassus, Roland de (Orlandus)

DOMINUS FORTITUDO PLEBII see Schubert, Heino

DOMINUS ILLUMINATIO MEA see Quack, Erhard

DOMINUS ILLUMINATIO MEA see Revicki

DOMINUS PARS see Rodella, Sante

DOMINUS REGIT ME see Nielsen, Carl

DOMINUS REGNAT see Cammarota, Carlo

DOMINUS REGNAT see Nystedt, Knut

DOMINUS REGNAVIT see Olman, Isr, J.

DOMSONDAGEN SAMT NATTVARDSGUDSTJANSTER *Easter
  (Runback, Albert) 4pt mix cor,acap NORDISKA
  2942 s.p. see from Introitus   (D1355)

DOMSSONDAGEN SAMT NATTVARDGUDSTJANSTER see
  Runback, Albert ~

DOMUS MEA see Zielenski, Mikolaj

DONA NOBIS PACEM *Gen,round
  (Sister M. Elaine) [Lat] SSA,acap AMP A160
    $.20   (D1356)
  (Wilson) "Grant Us Peace" SSA SCHMITT 2520
    $.30   (D1357)
  (Wilson) "Grant Us Peace" TBB SCHMITT 3502
    $.30   (D1358)
  (Wilson) "Grant Us Peace" SAB SCHMITT 5510
    $.30   (D1359)
  (Wilson) "Grant Us Peace" SATB SCHMITT 1722
    $.30   (D1360)

DONA NOBIS PACEM see Anonymous

DONA NOBIS PACEM see Bach, Johann Sebastian

DONA NOBIS PACEM see Borris, Siegfried

DONA NOBIS PACEM see Haydn, (Franz) Joseph

DONA NOBIS PACEM see Lau, Heinz

DONA NOBIS PACEM see Pepping, Ernst

DONA NOBIS PACEM see Vaughan Williams, Ralph

DONA NOBIS PACEM see Weber, Bernhard

DONA NOBIS PACEM see Wilson, Charles

DONATH, J.
  God Of Our Fathers
    SATB oct PRESSER 312-40169 $.25   (D1361)

  Hail Mary
    SSA oct PRESSER 312-40288 $.25   (D1362)

DONATI, I.
  Alleluia Haec Dies
    cor FABER F0062 s.p.   (D1363)

DONATI, IGNAZIO (1585-1638)
  Alleluia, Haec Dies *mot,Eng/It/Lat
    (Roche) 4pt mix cor,opt kbd,vln oct
      SCHIRM.G 11732 $.40   (D1364)
    (Roche, Jerome) [Lat] SATB,opt vln oct
      FABER 11732 $.40   (D1365)

DONATO
  Madonna And Child *Xmas
    girl cor SOUTHERN $.30   (D1366)
    SSA,acap oct BOOSEY 1949 $.30   (D1367)

  Make A Joyful Noise
    SSA KJOS 6099 $.30   (D1368)

  Praiseye The Lord
    SATB,acap oct BOOSEY 5035 $.30   (D1369)

DONATO, ANTHONY (1909-   )
  How Excellent Is Thy Name (Psalm 8)
    SATB,org PEER $.50   (D1370)

  Last Supper, The
    SATB,acap PEER $.50   (D1371)

  Psalm 8 *see How Excellent Is Thy Name

DONATO, BALDASSARE
  Quattro Dee Che'l Mondo Onora *mot,It
    (Stevens, Denis) [It] SATB oct FABER 11834
    $.35   (D1372)

DONE FOUND MY LOST SHEEP *spir
  (Forbes, E.) TTBB,acap SCHIRM.EC 2307 (D1373)

DONE FOUND MY LOST SHEEP see Rhea

DONE IS A BATTELL ON THE DRAGON BLAK see Kelly, Bryan

DONE MADE MY VOW TO THE LORD see McLin

DONE MADE MY VOW TO THE LORD see Work

DONE PAID MY VOW TO THE LORD *spir
  (Dett, R.) SSA,A/Bar solo oct PRESSER
  322-35007 $.30   (D1374)

DONENFELD
  May The Words
    SATB oct PRO ART 2675 $.30   (D1375)

  Psalm 100 *see Shout Unto The Lord

  Shout Unto The Lord (Psalm 100)
    SATB oct PRO ART 2636 $.30   (D1376)

DONIZETTI, GAETANO (1797-1848)
  Ave Maria
    (Townsend, D.) [Lat] SATB,S solo,strings
      voc sc BROUDE,A. 117 $.30, ipa, sc
      BROUDE,A. 117 $1.50   (D1377)

  Vater Im Himmel Hoch (from Maria Stuart)
    prayer
    mix cor,opt S solo,pno cor pts BREITKOPF-W
      CHB-3649 s.p.   (D1378)

DONKEY, THE see Purdy, Hunter

DONNA, CHE IN CIEL see Handel, George Frideric

DONNE-MOI CETTE RELIGION see Gimme Dat Ol'time Religion

DONNELLY
  Everyone Must Have A Friend *see Artega, [Esteban de]

DONOSTIA, [JOSE ANTONIO DE] (1886-   )
  Happy Bethlehem *see Oi Betleem

  Oi Betleem *Xmas
    "Happy Bethlehem" [Span/Eng] SSA oct
      COLOMBO 1055 $.25   (D1379)
    (Schindler) "Happy Bethlehem" [Span/Eng]
      SATB,acap oct COLOMBO 401 $.25   (D1380)

DONOVAN
  Jacques, Come Here *Xmas
    SSA/SSAA oct GALAXY 1.1894.1 $.30   (D1381)
    SATB oct STAINER 3.4196.1 $.30   (D1382)

DONOVAN, RICHARD [FRANK] (1891-   )
  Forever, O Lord
    SATB,org/pno PETERS 6849 $.60   (D1383)

DON'T BE A LOSER *CC8UL
  (Owens, Jimmy) jr cor,pno,bvl,gtr cmplt ed
    LILLENAS MB-040 $1.95   (D1384)

DON'T BE WEARY, TRAVELLER see Kennedy, John Brodbin

DON'T LOOK AT ME, LOOK AT JESUS see Russel, Eleanor

DON'T YOU WEEP NO MORE, MARY *spir
  (Dett) 4pt mix cor,acap oct SCHIRM.G 7396
    $.25   (D1385)

DON'T YOU WEEP NO MORE, MARY see Dett, Robert Nathaniel

DOOMSDAY CAROL, A see Stokes, Eric

DOONER, A.
  Music For Weddings *CCU,Gen/Marriage,anthem/
    hymn
    unis/SA/TB,org (easy) sc GIA G1168 $2.50,
    voc sc GIA G1168A $.60   (D1386)

DOOR IS OPEN, THE see Goldsborough

DOOR, THE see Atkinson

DOPO LA COMMUNIONE see Bottazzo, Luigi

DOPO LA COMMUNIONE see Corradini, Vasco Lodovico

DOPO LA CONSACRAZIONE see Nicolosi, Salvatore

DOPPELBAUER, JOSEF FRIEDRICH (1918-   )
  Beim Letzten Abendmahle
    3-4pt mix cor DOBLINGER s.p. see from
    Kirchenliedsatze   (D1387)

  Cantate Domino Canticum Novum *mot
    [Ger] mix cor DOBLINGER s.p.   (D1388)

  Christe, Du Lamm Gottes
    3-4pt mix cor DOBLINGER s.p. see from
    Kirchenliedsatze   (D1389)

  Daran Ist Erschienen Die Liebe Gottes *Xmas,
    Bibl/mot
    [Ger] mix cor,acap oct DOBLINGER s.p. see
    from Drei Kleine Weihnachtsmotetten (D1390)

  Deutsches Ordinarium-Ausgabe A *CCU
    unis/mix cor&cong,opt org voc sc DOBLINGER
    s.p.   (D1391)

  Deutsches Ordinarium-Ausgabe B *CCU
    cong,opt org DOBLINGER voc sc s.p., cor pts
    s.p.   (D1392)

  Deutsches Ordinarium-Ausgabe C *CCU
    mix cor&cong,opt org DOBLINGER voc sc s.p.,
    cor pts s.p.   (D1393)

  Drei Kleine Weihnachtsmotetten *see Daran
    Ist Erschienen Die Liebe Gottes; Mache
    Dich Auf, Werde Licht; Und Das Wort Ward
    Fleisch   (D1394)

  Du Hast, O Herr, Dein Leben
    3-4pt mix cor DOBLINGER s.p. see from
    Kirchenliedsatze   (D1395)

  Gott In Der Hoh' Sei Preis Und Ehr'
    3-4pt mix cor DOBLINGER s.p. see from
    Kirchenliedsatze   (D1396)

  Heilig, Heilig
    3-4pt mix cor DOBLINGER s.p. see from
    Kirchenliedsatze   (D1397)

  Im Frieden Dein
    3-4pt mix cor DOBLINGER s.p. see from
    Kirchenliedsatze   (D1398)

  In Dulci Jubilo *Mass
    4pt mix cor,acap voc sc DOBLINGER s.p.
                                         (D1399)

DOPPELBAUER, JOSEF FRIEDRICH (cont'd.)

  Kirchenliedsatze *see Beim Letzten
    Abendmahle; Christe, Du Lamm Gottes; Du
    Hast, O Herr, Dein Leben; Gott In Der
    Hoh' Sei Preis Und Ehr'; Heilig, Heilig;
    Im Frieden Dein; Nun Jauchzt Dem Herren
    Alle Welt; Sonne Der Gerechtigkeit
                                         (D1400)

  Mache Dich Auf, Werde Licht *Xmas,Bibl/mot
    [Ger] mix cor,acap oct DOBLINGER s.p. see
    from Drei Kleine Weihnachtsmotetten (D1401)

  Missa Psalmodica *Mass/Psalm
    4pt mix cor,acap voc sc DOBLINGER s.p.
                                         (D1402)

  Nun Jauchzt Dem Herren Alle Welt
    3-4pt mix cor DOBLINGER s.p. see from
    Kirchenliedsatze   (D1403)

  Sonne Der Gerechtigkeit
    3-4pt mix cor DOBLINGER s.p. see from
    Kirchenliedsatze   (D1404)

  Und Das Wort Ward Fleisch *Xmas,Bibl/mot
    [Ger] mix cor,acap oct DOBLINGER s.p. see
    from Drei Kleine Weihnachtsmotetten (D1405)

  Vier Kleine Motetten *CC4U,mot
    mix cor DOBLINGER s.p.   (D1406)

  Vier Kleine Weihnachtsmotetten *CC4U,Xmas,
    mot
    [Ger] mix cor,acap oct DOBLINGER s.p.
                                         (D1407)

DORAN
  Sing! Rejoice Together!
    (Butler) jr cor&unis oct VOLKWEIN VB721
                                         (D1408)

DORIAN ANTHEM OF PRAISE, A see Matthews, [Timothy Richard]

DORMEZ DIVIN ENFANT see Gounod, Charles Francois

DORMI JESU *Xmas,Mediev
  (Daubney, Brian) "Slumber Jesu" SATB ENOCH
    EC324 s.p. contains also: Puer Natus, "Boy
    Was Born, A" (Arr,16th cent)   (D1409)

DORMI, JESU see Aston, Peter

DORMI JESU see Bennett, R.

DORMI, JESU see Brown

DORMI, JESU see Hannahs, R.C.

DORMI, JESU! see Tuttle, Stephen

DORMI JESUS see Haus, Karl

DORMI NON PIANGERE see Bottazzo, Luigi

DORMI NON PIANGERE see Volpi, Edoardo

DORMID, MI BUEN JESUS see Frigola

DORMIVA DOLCEMENTE see Gabrieli, Giovanni

DORTCH
  Jesus, Tender Shepherd
    2pt jr cor,org/pno BOSTON 2904 $.30 (D1410)

DOS MOTETES
  [Lat] SATB,acap sc RICORDI-ARG BA 11357 s.p.,
    cor pts RICORDI-ARG BA 11358 s.p.
    contains: Pahissa, [Jaime], Quomodo Sedet
    Sola; Victoria, Tomas Luis de, Sitientes,
    Venite Ad Aquas   (D1411)

DOSONGE, R.
  Let All On Earth *Epiph,anthem
    SATB (med) oct GIA G1563 $.30   (D1412)

DOST THOU IN A MANGER LIE? see Hallstrom, Henry

DOST THOU IN A MANGER LIE see Held, Wilbur

DOST THOU IN A MANGER LIE see Posegate

DOST THOU IN A MANGER LIE? see Van Dyke

DOSWELL, MICHAEL
  Lead Us, O Father *anthem
    mix cor,acap oct NOVELLO 28.1295.09 s.p.
                                         (D1413)

DOTH NOT WISDOM CRY see Rogers, J.H.

DOTTER SION see Handel, George Frideric

DOTTER SION, FROJDA DIG see Handel, George Frideric

DOTTIM, G.
  La Vierge Marie Va A Bethleem *Xmas
    [Fr] 4pt mix cor MOSELER s.p.   (D1414)

D'OU VIENS-TU BERGERE see Favre, Georges

D'OU VIENS-TU, BERGERE? see Moineau, G.

D'OU VIENT CELA, SEIGNEUR, JE TE SUPPLIE see
  Champion, Thomas

D'OU VIENT L'EJOUISSANCE see Arcadelt, Jacob

DOUBLE ALLELUIA see Felciano, Richard

DOUBT NOT THY FATHER'S CARE see Elgar, Edward

DOUBTING THOMAS see Hourdeaux

DOUGHERTY, CELIUS (1902-   )
  First Christmas, The *Xmas
    4pt men cor,acap oct SCHIRM.G 10616 $.25
                                         (D1415)

DOUGLAS
  O Come, Let Us Sing Unto The Lord *Gen
    SA SCHMITT 2550 $.25   (D1416)

  Wake Up! Jacob
    SAB oct PRO ART 2429 $.25   (D1417)

DOUGLAS, [CHARLES] WINIFRED (1867-1944)
  He Who Would Valiant Be *anthem
    (Near, Gerald) SATB (easy) oct AUGSBURG
    1468 $.25   (D1418)

DOUGLAS, JAMES
  Christmas Fable *Xmas
    mix cor CURWEN 63002 s.p.   (D1419)

DOULCE MEMOIRE see Lassus, Roland de (Orlandus)

DOUZE NOELS DE SABOLY *Xmas,carol,Fr
  (Tomasi) [Fr] 2pt/3pt,pno/orch LEDUC BL872
    voc sc s.p., cor prts s.p.
    contains & see also: Ah! La Bonne Fortune;
    De Bon Matin; Guillaume, Toinet, Pierre;
    Le Noir Taudis De La Mauvaise Etable; Les
    Pastoureaux Ont Fait Une Assemblee; Les
    Plus Sages; O Bergers, Dans La Montagne;
    Quand La Minuit Sonnait; Saint Joseph M'a
    Dit; Trois Rois Sont En Campagne; Ture-
    Lure-Lure; Venez, Enfants Du Seigneur
                                         (D1420)

DOUZE NOELS PROVENCAUX see Saboly, Nicholas

DOVE FLEW DOWN FROM HEAVEN, A *Adv/Xmas,carol,
  Ger
  (Schroeder, H.) SATB,inst (med easy) oct
    CONCORDIA 98-2061 $.25   (D1421)

DOVE FLIES LOW ON WHITSUNDAY, THE see Kopylov,
  Alexander Alexandrovitch

DOVE OF PEACE see Diercks, John H.

DOVE OF PEACE, THE
  (Forsblad) SAB oct PRO ART 2722 $.30 (D1422)
  (Forsblad) SATB oct PRO ART 2699 $.30 (D1423)
  (Forsblad) SSA oct PRO ART 2645 $.30 (D1424)

DOVE, THE see Licht, Myrtha B.

DOVENSPIKE
  This Is The Day Which The Lord Hath Made
    SATB oct VOLKWEIN VB715 $.35   (D1425)

DOVENSPIKE, WILLIAM
  Listen My Heart
    SATB oct AGAPE SP 701 $.35   (D1426)

DOWDY
  Easter Song *Easter
    SATB oct SACRED E75 $.35   (D1427)

DOWLAND, JOHN (1563-1626)
  Come Holy Ghost *Whitsun,anthem
    mix cor oct NOVELLO 40.0125.07 s.p. (D1428)

  Everlasting Arms Of Love
    (Davis, K.K.) 2pt WARNER R3503 $.30 (D1429)

  Insult Has Broken My Heart
    see FOUR SHORT ANTHEMS FOR LENT AND EASTER

  Psalm 130
    (Weaver) SATB FOSTER MF107 $.25   (D1430)

  Seven Hymn Tunes, Part I *CCU,anthem
    mix cor oct OXFORD 43.239 $.55   (D1431)

  Seven Hymn Tunes, Part II *CCU,anthem
    mix cor oct OXFORD 43.240 $.45   (D1432)

DOWN BY THE RIVER *spir
  (Kinsman, F.) SATB LUDWIG L-1116 $.30 (D1433)

DOWN BY THE RIVERSIDE *spir
  see Folio Of Sacred Music (Volume 3)
  (Kinsman, F.) SATB LEONARD-US 08013440 $.25
                                         (D1434)
  (Kinsman, F.) SAB LEONARD-US 08013120 $.25
                                         (D1435)

DOWN EAST SPIRITUALS see Kimball

DOWN IN ADORATION FALLING see Tartini, Giuseppe

DOWN IN THE MEADOWS see Kirk

DOWN IN YON FOREST *Xmas,folk,US
  (Niles; Brant) 4pt mix cor,acap oct SCHIRM.G
    8024 $.20   (D1436)
  (Niles; Brant) 3pt wom cor,acap oct SCHIRM.G
    8025 $.20   (D1437)
  (Vaughn Williams, Ralph) SATB/unis,pno GALAXY
    s.p. see also Eight Traditional Carols
                                         (D1438)

DOWN IN YON FOREST see Niles, John Jacob

DOWN TO EARTH see Lovelace, Austin C.

DOXOLOGY see Leidzen

DOXOLOGY see Wetzler, Robert

DOXOLOGY see Young

DOXOLOGY AND GLORIA PATRI see Avery

DRAESEL, LEDERHOUSE
  Celebration
    unis,pno/org MARKS $1.00, ipa   (D1439)

  God Who Made The Earth
    (Cole) SATB,opt perc&gtr MARKS 4548 $.40
                                         (D1440)

  Lamb Of God
    (Hutson) unis MARKS 4561 $.30   (D1441)

  Now Hymns For Young People *CCU,hymn
    unis MARKS $1.50   (D1442)

  Praise And Jubilee
    unis,inst MARKS $1.00, ipa   (D1443)

  Rejoice
    unis MARKS $1.00, ipa   (D1444)

  Six Hymns (from Rejoice) CC6U,hymn
    SATB MARKS $.50, ipa   (D1445)

  They Cast Their Nets In Galilee
    (Hutson) MARKS 4487 $.30   (D1446)

DRAKEFORD, RICHARD
  Magnificat And Nunc Dimittis *Magnif/Nunc
    SATB (E min) oct NOVELLO 44.1379.02 s.p.
                                         (D1447)
    unis oct NOVELLO 33.0109.05 s.p.   (D1448)

DRAUSSEN VOR DER KIRCHENTUR see Lehmann,
  Andreas

DRAW NEAR AND HEAR MY PRAYER see Morgan

DRAW NEAR, O LORD *Lent,hymn
  (Vermulst, Jan) 3 eq voices&cong,opt org oct
    WORLD LE-737-3 $.30   (D1449)

DRAW NIGH AND TAKE THE BODY OF THE LORD see
  Thiman, Eric Harding

DRAW NIGH AND TAKE THE BODY OF THE LORD see
  Wolff

DRAW NIGH TO GOD see Blakley

DRAW NIGH TO JERUSALEM see Darst, W. Glenn

DRAW NIGH TO JERUSALEM see Williams

DRAW NIGH TO JERUSALEM see Williams, David H.

DRAW NIGH TO THY JERUSALEM *anthem
  (Johnson) SAB (easy) oct AUGSBURG 1616 $.25
                                         (D1450)

DRAW NIGH TO THY JERUSALEM see Becker, J.

DRAW NIGH TO THY JERUSALEM see Clark, George B.

DRAW NIGH TO THY JERUSALEM see Darst, W. Glenn

DRAW US IN THE SPIRIT'S TETHER see Friedell,
  Harold W.

DRAW US IN THE SPIRIT'S TETHER see Ossewaarde,
  Jack

DRAW US TO THEE see Wolff, S. Drummond

DRAW YE WATERS JOYFULLY see Pugatchov, E.,
  Ush'avtem Mayim

DRAWN TO THE CROSS see Schroth

DRAYTON
  Jesu, Dulcis Memoria *anthem
    mix cor oct OXFORD 84.188 $.30   (D1451)

  Spacious Firmament *anthem
    mix cor oct OXFORD 42.366 $.70   (D1452)

DRAYTON, PAUL
  How Like An Angel Came I Down *anthem
    mix cor oct NOVELLO 86.0035.10 s.p. (D1453)

DREAM see Mellnas, Arne

DREAM BETHLEHEM see Dryhaug

DREAM, LOVELY BABE see Sharpe, Evelyn

DREAM OF CHRISTMAS, A see Holst, Gustav

DREAM OF GERONTIUS, THE see Elgar, Edward

DREAM OF LACE see Torrans, Richard

DREAM OF PARADISE see Gray, Hamilton

DREAMERS BEFORE THE DAWN *Adv
  SATB CHAPPELL 0014894-358 $.40   (D1454)

DRECHSLER, [JOSEPH] (1782-1852)
  Hallelujah
    (Roskin) SATB HATIKVAH HCL 9 $.30   (D1455)

DREI ALTE HAUSINSCHRIFTEN see Bottcher, Georg

DREI BAROCK-LIEDER see Haller, Hermann

DREI CHORE see Schubert, Franz (Peter)

DREI CHORSATZE ZUM MAGNIFICAT see Bach, Johann
  Sebastian

DREI CHRISTIAN MORGENSTERN-CHORE see Beckerath,
  Alfred von

DREI DEUTSCHE PSALMEN see Koler, Martin

DREI ERNSTE GESANGE *see Dem Gedenken Eines
  Tondichters; Eucharistisches Gebet; Widmung
  An Gott   (D1456)

DREI EVANGELIEN-MOTETTEN see Des Prez, Josquin

DREI EVANGELIENMOTETTEN see David, Johann
  Nepomuk

DREI FESTMOTETTEN see Ahrens, Joseph

DREI, FRANCESCO
  Musica Vocale Esequita In Occasione
    Dell'apertura Della Nuovo Scuola Di
    Siena, 1786 *see Gallichi, Volunio

  Musique Pour L'Inauguration D'une Synagogue
    *see Gallichi, Volunio

DREI GEBETE see Keller, Wilhelm

DREI GEISTLICHE CHORE see Brahms, Johannes

DREI GEISTLICHE CHORE see Brahms, Johannes

DREI GEISTLICHE GESANGE see Martini

DREI GEISTLICHE GESANGE FUR MANNERCHOR see
  Micheelsen, Hans Friedrich

DREI GEISTLICHE KONZERTE see Strohbach,
  Siegfried

DREI GEISTLICHE MOTETTEN see Callhoff, Herbert

DREI GEISTLICHE MOTETTEN see Kubizek,
  Augustinian

DREI GEMISCHTE CHORE see Silesius, Angelus

DREI GESANGE AUS DER GEHEIMEN OFFENBARUNG see
  Tittel, Ernst

DREI GLEICHNISSE JESU see Kern, Matthias

DREI INTRADEN see Altenburg, Michael

DREI KLEINE GEISTLICHE CHORE see Heiller, Anton

DREI KLEINE GEISTLICHE MOTETTEN see Wildgans,
  Friedrich

DREI KLEINE MOTETTEN see Kubizek, Augustinian

DREI KLEINE MOTETTEN see Buchtger, Fritz

DREI KLEINE WEIHNACHTSMOTETTEN see Doppelbauer,
  Josef Friedrich

DREI KONIG VON SABA KOMMEN see Spitta, Heinrich

DREI KONIGE see Buchtger, Fritz

DREI KONIGE AUS DEM MOHRENLAND see Koerppen,
  Alfred

DREI KONZERTIERENDE MOTETTEN see Grandi,
  Alessandro

DREI LIEDER AUF TEXTE DES ABRAHAM A SANCTA
  CLARA see Wildgans, Friedrich

DREI LIEDER IM VOLKSTON see Schulz, Joh.
  Abraham Peter

DREI MAGNIFICAT see Aguilera de Heredia,
  Sebastian

DREI MARIENLIEDER *see Es Bluh'n Drei Rosen
  Auf Einem Strauch; Es Bluht Den Engeln
  Wohlbekannt; Gegrusset Seist Du, Konigin
                                         (D1457)

DREI MARIENLIEDER see Demerath, F.

DREI MOTETTEN see Bach, Johann Christoph

DREI MOTETTEN AUS PSALMEN see Jacot, Andre

DREI MOTETTEN I see Gabrieli, Giovanni

DREI MOTETTEN II see Gabrieli, Giovanni

DREI MOTETTEN [OP.22C] see Kubizek, Augustinian

DREI MOTETTEN [OP.22D] see Kubizek, Augustinian

DREI MOTETTEN UND EIN GEISTLICHES MADRIGAL see
  Zarlino, [Gioseffo]

DREI MOTETTEN ZU EHREN DES HERRN see Etti, Karl

DREI MOTETTEN see Buchtger, Fritz

DREI MOTETTEN see Bauernfiend, Hans

DREI MOTETTEN see Brahms, Johannes

DREI MOTETTEN see Brahms, Johannes

DREI MOTETTEN see Des Prez, Josquin

DREI MOTETTEN *Easter,mot
  SATB HANSSLER 7.094 s.p.
    contains: Hessenberg, Kurt, Die Sieben
    Worte Christi Am Kreuz; Marx, Karl, Herr,
    Du Hast Alles, Himmel; Pezel, Johann
    Christoph, Der Herr Ward Gehorsam Bis Zum
    Tode   (D1458)

DREI MOTETTEN *CC3U,mot
  (Brennecke) [Ger/Lat] 5-6pt mix cor MOSELER
    s.p. contains works by: Hemmerley and other
    German masters   (D1459)

DREI MOTETTEN see Gabrieli, Andrea

DREI MOTETTEN see Lassus, Roland de (Orlandus)

DREI MOTETTEN see Mendelssohn-Bartholdy, Felix

DREI MOTETTEN see Clemens, Jacobus

DREI MOTETTEN see Palestrina, Giovanni

DREI MOTETTEN see Radulescu, Michael

DREI MOTETTEN see Reger, Max

DREI MOTETTEN see Sturmer, Bruno

DREI MOTETTEN see Wert, Giaches de

DREI MOTETTEN see Willaert, Adrian

DREI PSALMEN see Des Prez, Josquin

DREI PSALMEN DAVIDS see Hashagen, Klaus

DREI PSALMEN see Mendelssohn-Bartholdy, Felix

DREI PSALMEN see Studer, Hans

DREI QUODLIBETS see Franck, Cesar

DREI SATZE see David, Johann Nepomuk

DREI SCHONE DINGE SIND see Schein, Johann
  Hermann

DREI SEGENSPRUCHE see Biebl, Franz

DREI SELIGPREISUNGEN see Brautigam, Volker

DREI SPRUCHTEXTE AUF DAS EVANGELIUM see Jacobi,
  Samuel

DREI TE DEUM-KOMPOSITIONEN DES 16. JAHRHUNDERTS
  *CC3U,Te Deum,16th cent
  (Kirsch) [Ger/Lat] 4pt mix cor&5pt mix cor
    MOSELER s.p.   (D1460)

DREI WEIHNACHTLICHE LIEDSATZE see Praetorius,
  Michael

DREI WEIHNACHTS-MAGNIFICAT see Anonymous

DREI WEIHNACHTSLIEDER see Anonymous

DREI WEIHNACHTSLIEDER *see Es Ist Ein Ros'
  Entsprungen; Es Steht Ein Lind; In Dulci
  Jubilo   (D1461)

DREI WEIHNACHTSLIEDER see Burkhart, Franz

DREI WEIHNACHTSMOTETTEN see Baumann, Max

DREIHUNDERTNEUNUNDACHTZIG CHORALGESANGE see
Bach, Johann Sebastian

DREIKONIGSKANTATE see Dietrich, Fritz

DREIKONIGSLIED see Poschl, A.

DREIMALIGES KYRIE MARTIN LUTHERS 1526 *Kyrie
(Distler, Hugo) [Ger] SA&men cor,acap (med)
BAREN. BA 1048 $.40 see also Liturgische
Satze   (D1462)
(Distler, Hugo) [Ger] SSATB,acap (easy)
BAREN. BA 1044 $.25 see also Liturgische
Satze   (D1463)

DREIMALIGES KYRIE NURNBERG 1525 *Kyrie
(Distler, Hugo) [Ger] SATB,acap (easy) BAREN.
BA 1044 $.25 see also Liturgische Satze (D1464)

DREIMALIGES KYRIE STRASSBURG 1525 *Kyrie
(Distler, Hugo) [Ger] SATB,acap (easy) BAREN.
BA 1044 $.25 see also Liturgische Satze (D1465)
(Distler, Hugo) [Ger] unis&SSATB,acap (med
diff) BAREN. BA 1047 $.65 see also
Liturgische Satze   (D1466)

DREIMALIGES KYRIE STRASSBURG 1525 UND NURNBERG
1525 *Kyrie
(Distler, Hugo) [Ger] 2 eq voices/3 eq
voices,acap (med) BAREN. BA 1043 $.25 see
also Liturgische Satze   (D1467)

DREISSIG GEISTLICHE LIEDER, CHORALE, UND
HYMNEN-HEFT 1 see Weismann, Wilhelm

DREISSIG GEISTLICHE LIEDER, CHORALE, UND
HYMNEN-HEFT 2 see Weismann, Wilhelm

DREISSIG GEISTLICHE LIEDER, CHORALE, UND
HYMNEN-HEFT 3 see Weismann, Wilhelm

DREISSIG GEISTLICHE LIEDER, CHORALE, UND
HYMNEN-HEFT 4 see Weismann, Wilhelm

DREISSIG GEISTLICHE LIEDER, CHORALE, UND
HYMNEN-HEFT 5 see Weismann, Wilhelm

DREISSIG GEISTLICHE LIEDER, CHORALE, UND
HYMNEN-HEFT 6 see Weismann, Wilhelm

DREISSIG GEISTLICHE LIEDER, CHORALE, UND
HYMNEN-HEFT 7 see Weismann, Wilhelm

DREISSIG GEISTLICHE LIEDER, CHORALE, UND
HYMNEN-HEFT 8 see Weismann, Wilhelm

DREISSIG GEISTLICHE LIEDER, CHORALE, UND
HYMNEN-HEFT 9 see Weismann, Wilhelm

DREISSIG KANON UND ANDERE LIEDER see Scholl

DREISTIMMIGE GESANGE NACH ANGELUS SILESIUS see
Heiss, Hermann

DREISTIMMIGE KIRCHENLIEDSATZE see Micheelsen,
Hans Friedrich

DREISTIMMIGE MESSE see Aulen

DREISTIMMIGE OSTERLIEGER see Praetorius,
Michael

DREIZEHN GEESTELIJKE LIEDEREN see Smit, H.J.

DREIZEHN NEGRO-SPIRITUALS *CC13L,spir
(Durian, Tim) 4pt men cor,acap BREITKOPF-W
see also: Deep River; Didn't My Lord
Deliver Daniel; Ezekiel Saw The Wheel;
Get On Board; Go Down, Moses; Go, Tell It
On The Mountain; Joshua Fit De Battle Of
Jericho; Little David, Play On Your Harp;
Nobody Knows De Trouble I've Seen; Roll,
Jordan; Somebody's Knocking; Swing Low,
Sweet Chariot; Wade In The Water   (D1468)

DRE'S NO HIDIN' PLACE
see Negro Spirituals

DRESDEN, SEM (1881-1957)
Memoria Judaeorum
men cor ALSBACH&D sc s.p., cor pts s.p.
(D1469)
Psalm 99
[Dut] mix cor,org,4trom KON BOND   (D1470)

Sankt Antonius *ora
SSATB,2 narrators,SSATBar soli,pno,3fl,2ob,
4clar,2bsn,4horn,3trp,trom,tuba,strings,
perc,timp,harp, English horn, saxophone
and celeste BREITKOPF-W sc s.p., ipa, voc
sc s.p., voc pt s.p.   (D1471)

DRESSLER, GALLUS (1533-1585)
Alleluja, Christ Is Risen
SSA FLAMMER E 5086 $.25   (D1472)

Also Hat Gott Die Welt Geliebet *Pent
[Ger] SATB,acap (easy) BAREN. BA 1028, 1029
s.p.   (D1473)

Eins Bitte Ich Vom Herren *Gen
[Ger] SATB,acap (easy) BAREN. BA 3258 s.p.
(D1474)

Five Motets *CC5U,mot
mix cor,acap voc sc KALMUS 6157 $1.25 (D1475)

Funf Motetten *CC5U,mot
(Ruetz) [Ger/Lat] 4-5pt mix cor MOSELER
s.p.   (D1476)

Furchte Dich Nicht *mot
(Hellmann) SATB HANSSLER 1.105 s.p. (D1477)

Ich Bin Die Auferstehung Und Das Leben
*Gd.Fri./Trin,mot
[Ger] SATB,acap (easy) BAREN. BA 1686 s.p.
(D1478)
[Ger] SATB,acap (med easy) MULLER MS 71
s.p.   (D1479)
SATB,acap voc pt DOBLINGER s.p. see also
TOD UND VERGANGLICHKEIT   (D1480)
(Hellmann) SATB HANSSLER 1.067 s.p. (D1481)

Let All The Peoples Praise The Lord *Gen
(Lindquist) SATB SCHMITT 1528 $.35 (D1482)

DRESSLER, JOHN
Easter Carol *Easter
SATB oct FISCHER,J 8995 $.30   (D1483)

Festival Of Hymns *CCU,hymn
jr cor,inst BELWIN $1.25, ipa   (D1484)

First, The Last, The
SATB (med) ABINGDON APM-396 $.25   (D1485)

God's Greatest Gift *cant
mix cor BELWIN $1.50   (D1486)

God's Greatest Sacrifice *cant
mix cor BELWIN $1.50   (D1487)

Lobe Den Herrn
"Praise To The Lord" SATB oct FISCHER,J
9695 $.30   (D1488)

Lord, Open Thou My Heart
SATB (easy) ABINGDON APM-215 $.24   (D1489)

Not For Ourselves O Lord
SAB,org,fl oct FISCHER,J 10020 $.35 (D1490)

O Fear Thee Not
(Richardson) SATB oct WORD CS-2420 $.30
(D1491)

O Little One Sweet
SA oct FISCHER,J 9154 $.30   (D1492)

Onward Christian Soldiers
unis jr cor oct FISCHER,J 9153 $.30 (D1493)

Praise To The Lord *see Lobe Den Herrn

Reformation Antiphon, A
SATB,brass oct FISCHER,J 10044 $.25 (D1494)

Resurrection Song, The *Easter
SATB oct FISCHER,J 9703 $.30   (D1495)

Ride On, O King!
SATB oct FISCHER,J 9785 $.35   (D1496)

Sing Praise To God
SATB (very easy) ABINGDON APM-107 $.20 (D1497)

Sing To The Lord God
(Ehret) mix cor CHAPPELL 0024265-358 $.40
(D1498)

Singing Christian Children
unis jr cor oct FISCHER,J 9895 $.30 (D1499)

Spirit Of Life
SATB,opt vln (med) ABINGDON APM-414 $.25,
ipa   (D1500)

Three Junior Choir Anthems *CC3U,anthem
jr cor (med) ABINGDON APM-533 $.25 (D1501)

Trumpet Gloria, A
SAB oct FISCHER,J 9544 $.30   (D1502)
SATB oct FISCHER,J 9241 $.30   (D1503)

When Morning Gilds The Skies
SAB (easy) ABINGDON APM-117 $.22   (D1504)

DRESSLER, L.R.
Eight Responses *CC8U
4pt men cor,acap oct SCHIRM.G 7499 $.25
(D1505)

DRETKE, L.N.
Blessed Birth, The *Xmas
SATB oct GRAY GCMR 1897 $.30   (D1506)

In Praise And Adoration *Gen
SATB SCHMITT 1798 $.25   (D1507)

Shout Hosanna!
SATB FLAMMER A 5498 $.25   (D1508)

Sing Allelujah! Christ Is Born *Xmas
4pt mix cor,acap oct SCHIRM.G 10683 $.30
(D1509)
3pt wom cor oct SCHIRM.G 10779 $.25 (D1510)
3pt mix cor oct SCHIRM.G 10778 $.25 (D1511)

Sing We Now For Christ Is King
4pt mix cor oct SCHIRM.G 10846 $.25 (D1512)

DREWES
Great Day *spir
TTBB oct BOURNE WP2 $.25   (D1513)

DREWES, CAPT. BARRY
Rock-a My Soul
TTBB oct BOURNE WP5 $.25   (D1514)

DRIE KERSTLIEDEREN see Oort, H.C.v.

DRIE MANNENKOREN see Vranken, Alph.

DRIE OUD-FRANSE KERSTLIEDEREN see Zanen, P.

DRIE PSALMEN see Braal, Andreas de

DRIEKONINGENLIED see Andriessen, Hendrik

DRIESSEN, RENE
Nobody Knows *spir
[Fr] 4pt men cor sc BROGNEAUX s.p. (D1515)

DRIESSLER, JOHANNES (1921-   )
Aber Gott Sprach Zu Ihm, Du Narr!
see Evangelienspruche Fur Das Kirchenjahr
[20]

Ach, Dass Gott Frieden Zusagte *mot
5pt mix cor,acap cor pts BREITKOPF-W
CHB-3199 s.p.   (D1516)

Ach Herr, Du Sohn Davids, Erbarme Dich Mein
see Evangelienspruche Fur Das Kirchenjahr
[6]

Also Hat Gott Die Welt Geliebet
see Evangelienspruche Fur Das Kirchenjahr
[11]

Also Wird Euch Mein Himmelicher Vater Auch
Tun
see Evangelienspruche Fur Das Kirchenjahr
[18]

Bittet, So Werdet Ihr Nehmen
see Evangelienspruche Fur Das Kirchenjahr
[10]

DRIESSLER, JOHANNES (cont'd.)
Bleibe Bei Uns, Denn Es Will Abend Werden
see Evangelienspruche Fur Das Kirchenjahr
[9]

Cantica Nova *Op.13, CC11L,Gen,Bibl
[Ger] SATB&SATB,acap (diff) BAREN. BA 2540
$6.50   (D1517)

Christe Eleison *Op.9, Psntd,mot
[Lat] SSATB,Bar solo,acap (med diff) BAREN.
BA 2402 $3.75   (D1518)

Da Er Nun Auferstanden War Von Den Toten
see Evangelienspruche Fur Das Kirchenjahr
[20]

Da Nun Die Menschen Das Zeichen Sahen
see Evangelienspruche Fur Das Kirchenjahr
[7]

Da Nun Jesus Merkte Ihre Bosheit
see Evangelienspruche Fur Das Kirchenjahr
[18]

Darum Wachet *Op.43,No.5, ECY,mot
[Ger] SSATB,acap (med) BAREN. BA 3638 $3.00
(D1519)

Darum Wachet, Denn Ihr Wisset Weder Tag Noch
Stunde
see Evangelienspruche Fur Das Kirchenjahr
[19]

Das Himmelreich Ist Gleich Einem Konige
see Evangelienspruche Fur Das Kirchenjahr
[17]

Das Ist Das Erste Zeichen, Das Jesus Tat
see Evangelienspruche Fur Das Kirchenjahr
[3]

De Profundis *Op.22, Gen,Bibl/ora
[Ger] SATB&SATB,STB soli,orch (diff) sc
BAREN. BA 2780 $25.00, cor pts BAREN.
BA 2780 $4.75, voc sc BAREN. BA 2780A
$17.50, ipr   (D1520)

Dein Reich Komme *Op.11, Gen,Bibl/ora
[Ger] SSATB,STBar soli,orch (diff) BAREN.
BA 2531 sc s.p., cor pts s.p., ipr (D1521)

Denn Dein Licht Kommt *Op.4, Gen,cant
[Ger] SATB&SATB,SBar soli,2fl,strings (med
diff) BAREN. BA 2538 rental   (D1522)

Denn Wer Sich Selbst Erhoht
see Evangelienspruche Fur Das Kirchenjahr
[16]

Der Junger Ist Nicht Uber Seinen Meister
see Evangelienspruche Fur Das Kirchenjahr
[13]

Der Lebendige *Op.40, Gen,Bibl/ora
[Ger] SATB,STB soli,orch (diff) sc BAREN.
BA 3656 rental   (D1523)

Der Mensch Lebt Nicht Vom Brot Allein
see Evangelienspruche Fur Das Kirchenjahr
[6]

Die Blinden Sehen
see Evangelienspruche Fur Das Kirchenjahr
[1]

Dies Ist Mein Lieber Sohn
see Evangelienspruche Fur Das Kirchenjahr
[3]
see Evangelienspruche Fur Das Kirchenjahr
[4]

Du Sollst Lieben Gott, Deinen Herrn
see Evangelienspruche Fur Das Kirchenjahr
[17]

Ehre Sei Gott In Der Hohe
see Evangelienspruche Fur Das Kirchenjahr
[2]

Entsetzet Euch Nicht
see Evangelienspruche Fur Das Kirchenjahr
[9]

Er Hat Alles Wohlgemacht
see Evangelienspruche Fur Das Kirchenjahr
[15]

Es Werden Nicht Alle, Die Zu Mir Sagen
see Evangelienspruche Fur Das Kirchenjahr
[14]

Evangelienspruche Fur Das Kirchenjahr [1]
*Op.37, Adv
[Ger] 3pt mix cor,acap (med easy) BAREN.
BA 3601 $.40
contains: Die Blinden Sehen; Hosianna Dem
Sohne Davids; Ich Bin Eine Stimme Eines
Rufers; Wenn Aber Dieses Anfangt
(D1524)

Evangelienspruche Fur Das Kirchenjahr [2]
*Op.37, Xmas
[Ger] 3pt mix cor,acap (med easy) BAREN.
BA 3602 $.40
contains: Ehre Sei Gott In Der Hohe;
Siehe, Dieser Wird Gesetzt; Stehe Auf
Und Nimm Das Kindlein; Und Das Wort
Ward Fleisch   (D1525)

Evangelienspruche Fur Das Kirchenjahr [3]
*Op.37, Epiph
[Ger] 3pt mix cor,acap (med easy) BAREN.
BA 3603 $.40
contains: Das Ist Das Erste Zeichen, Das
Jesus Tat; Dies Ist Mein Lieber Sohn;
Und Du Bethlehem Im Judischen Lande;
Was Ists, Dass Ihr Mich Gesucht Habt
(D1526)

Evangelienspruche Fur Das Kirchenjahr [4]
*Op.37, Epiph
[Ger] 3pt mix cor,acap (med easy) BAREN.
BA 3604 $.40
contains: Dies Ist Mein Lieber Sohn;
Herr! Ich Bin Nicht Wert; Sammelt Zuvor
Das Unkraut; Was Ist Das Fur Ein Mensch
(D1527)

Evangelienspruche Fur Das Kirchenjahr [5]
*Op.37, Psntd/Septua
[Ger] 3pt mix cor,acap (med easy) BAREN.

DRIESSLER, JOHANNES (cont'd.)

BA 3605 $.40
  contains: Jesu, Du Sohn Davids; Mein
    Freund, Ich Tue Dir Nicht Unrecht; Wer
    Ohren Hat Zu Horen   (D1528)

Evangelienspruche Fur Das Kirchenjahr [6]
  *Op.37, Psntd,evang
  [Ger] 3pt mix cor,acap (med easy) BAREN.
  BA 3606 $.40
    contains: Ach Herr, Du Sohn Davids,
      Erbarme Dich Mein; Der Mensch Lebt
      Nicht Vom Brot Allein   (D1529)

Evangelienspruche Fur Das Kirchenjahr [7]
  *Op.37, Psntd,evang
  [Ger] 3pt mix cor,acap (med easy) BAREN.
  BA 3607 $.40
    contains: Da Nun Die Menschen Das Zeichen
      Sahen; Selig Ist Der Leib; Wahrlich,
      Ich Sage Euch   (D1530)

Evangelienspruche Fur Das Kirchenjahr [8]
  *Op.37, Gd.Fri./Palm/Psntd
  [Ger] 3pt mix cor,acap BAREN. BA 3608 $.40
    contains: Hosianna! Gelobt Sei, Der Da
      Kommt; Weib, Siehe, Das Ist Dein Sohn;
      Wisset Ihr, Was Ich Euch Getan Habe
                                           (D1531)

Evangelienspruche Fur Das Kirchenjahr [9]
  *Op.37, Easter/Pent
  [Ger] 3pt mix cor,acap (med easy) BAREN.
  BA 3609 $.40
    contains: Bleibe Bei Uns, Denn Es Will
      Abend Werden; Entsetzet Euch Nicht;
      Friede Sei Mit Euch   (D1532)

Evangelienspruche Fur Das Kirchenjahr [10]
  *Op.37, Easter/Pent
  [Ger] 3pt mix cor,acap (med easy) BAREN.
  BA 3610 $.40
    contains: Bittet, So Werdet Ihr Nehmen;
      Ich Bin Der Gute Hirte; Und Ihr Habt
      Auch Nun Traurigkeit; Wenn Aber Jener
      Geist Der Wahrheit Kommen Wird (D1533)

Evangelienspruche Fur Das Kirchenjahr [11]
  *Op.37, Easter/Pent
  [Ger] 3pt mix cor,acap (med easy) BAREN.
  BA 3611 $.40
    contains: Also Hat Gott Die Welt
      Geliebet; Gehet Hin In Alle Welt; Wenn
      Der Troster Kommen Wird; Wer Mich
      Liebet   (D1534)

Evangelienspruche Fur Das Kirchenjahr [12]
  *Op.37, Trin
  [Ger] 3pt mix cor,acap (med easy) BAREN.
  BA 3612 $.40 until second Sunday
  after Trinity
    contains: Gedenke Sohn, Dass Du Dein
      Gutes Empfangen Hast; Kommt, Denn Es
      Ist Alles Bereit; Wahrlich Ich Sage
      Euch   (D1535)

Evangelienspruche Fur Das Kirchenjahr [13]
  *Op.37, Trin
  [Ger] 3pt mix cor,acap (med easy) BAREN.
  BA 3613 $.40 third to sixth Sunday after
  Trinity
    contains: Der Junger Ist Nicht Uber
      Seinen Meister; Herr, Gehe Von Mir
      Hinaus; Ich Sage Euch, Also Wird Auch
      Freude; Ich Sage Euch, Es Sei Denn Eure
      Gerechtigkeit   (D1536)

Evangelienspruche Fur Das Kirchenjahr [14]
  *Op.37, Trin
  [Ger] 3pt mix cor,acap (med easy) BAREN.
  BA 3614 $.40 seventh to tenth Sunday
  after Trinity
    contains: Es Werden Nicht Alle, Die Zu
      Mir Sagen; Und Der Herr Lobte Den
      Ungerechten Haushalter; Und Er Nahm Die
      Sieben Brote; Wenn Doch Auch Du
      Erkenntest   (D1537)

Evangelienspruche Fur Das Kirchenjahr [15]
  *Op.37, Trin
  [Ger] 3pt mix cor,acap (med easy) BAREN.
  BA 3615 $.40 eleventh to thirteenth
  Sunday after Trinity
    contains: Er Hat Alles Wohlgemacht; Ich
      Danke Dir, Gott, Das Ich Nicht Bin;
      Selig Sind Die Augen   (D1538)

Evangelienspruche Fur Das Kirchenjahr [16]
  *Op.37, Trin
  [Ger] 3pt mix cor,acap (med easy) BAREN.
  BA 3616 $.40 fourteenth to seventeenth
  Sunday after Trinity
    contains: Denn Wer Sich Selbst Erhoht;
      Ist Nicht Das Leben Mehr Denn Die
      Speise; Jesu, Lieber Meister, Erbarme
      Dich Unser; Und Es Kam Sie Alle Eine
      Furcht An   (D1539)

Evangelienspruche Fur Das Kirchenjahr [17]
  *Op.37, Trin
  [Ger] 3pt mix cor,acap (med easy) BAREN.
  BA 3617 $.40 eighteenth to twentieth
  Sunday after Trinity
    contains: Das Himmelreich Ist Gleich
      Einem Konige; Du Sollst Lieben Gott,
      Deinen Herrn; Sei Getrost, Mein Sohn
                                           (D1540)

Evangelienspruche Fur Das Kirchenjahr [18]
  *Op.37, Trin
  [Ger] 3pt mix cor,acap (med easy) BAREN.
  BA 3618 $.40 twenty-first to twenty-
  fourth Sunday after Trinity
    contains: Also Wird Euch Mein Himmelicher
      Vater Auch Tun; Da Nun Jesus Merkte
      Ihre Bosheit; Sei Getrost, Dein Glaube
      Hat Dir Geholfen; Wenn Ihr Nicht
      Zeichen Und Wunder Seht   (D1541)

Evangelienspruche Fur Das Kirchenjahr [19]
  *Op.37, ECY
  [Ger] 3pt mix cor,acap (med easy) BAREN.
  3619 $.40
    contains: Darum Wachet, Denn Ihr Wisset
      Weder Tag Noch Stunde; Und Wo Diese
      Tage Nicht Wurden Verkurzt; Wahrlich
      Ich Sage Euch, Was Ihr Getan Habt;
      Wahrlich Ich Sage Euch, Wer Mein Wort
      Horet   (D1542)

DRIESSLER, JOHANNES (cont'd.)

Evangelienspruche Fur Das Kirchenjahr [20]
  *Op.37, Fest
  [Ger] 3pt mix cor,acap (med easy) BAREN.
  BA 3620 $.40
    contains: Aber Gott Sprach Zu Ihm, Du
      Narr! (Harv) (Harv); Da Er Nun Auferstanden
      War Von Den Toten (Refm); Herr, Lass
      Ihn Noch Dies Jahr (day of national
      prayer); Zachaus, Steig Eilend
      Hernieder (Ded)   (D1543)

Friede Sei Mit Euch
  see Evangelienspruche Fur Das Kirchenjahr
    [9]

Gedenke Sohn, Dass Du Dein Gutes Empfangen
  Hast
  see Evangelienspruche Fur Das Kirchenjahr
    [12]

Gehet Hin In Alle Welt
  see Evangelienspruche Fur Das Kirchenjahr
    [11]

Herr, Gehe Von Mir Hinaus
  see Evangelienspruche Fur Das Kirchenjahr
    [13]

Herr Gott, Du Bist Unsre Zuflucht (Psalm 90)
  Op.25,No.1, Xmas
  [Ger] SSATB,Bar solo,acap (med diff) BAREN.
  BA 2509 $3.00   (D1544)

Herr! Ich Bin Nicht Wert
  see Evangelienspruche Fur Das Kirchenjahr
    [4]

Herr, Lass Ihn Noch Dies Jahr
  [20]

Hosianna Dem Sohne Davids
  [1]

Hosianna! Gelobt Sei, Der Da Kommt
  [8]

Ich Bin Der Gute Hirte
  see Evangelienspruche Fur Das Kirchenjahr
    [10]

Ich Bin Eine Stimme Eines Rufers
  [1]

Ich Danke Dir, Gott, Das Ich Nicht Bin
  see Evangelienspruche Fur Das Kirchenjahr
    [15]

Ich Sage Euch, Also Wird Auch Freude
  see Evangelienspruche Fur Das Kirchenjahr
    [13]

Ich Sage Euch, Es Sei Denn Eure Gerechtigkeit
  see Evangelienspruche Fur Das Kirchenjahr
    [13]

Ist Nicht Das Leben Mehr Denn Die Speise
  see Evangelienspruche Fur Das Kirchenjahr
    [16]

Jesu, Du Sohn Davids
  see Evangelienspruche Fur Das Kirchenjahr
    [5]

Jesu, Lieber Meister, Erbarme Dich Unser
  see Evangelienspruche Fur Das Kirchenjahr
    [16]

Kommt, Denn Es Ist Alles Bereit
  see Evangelienspruche Fur Das Kirchenjahr
    [12]

Markus-Passion *Op.36,No.1, Psntd,evang
  [Ger] SSATB,acap (med diff) BAREN. BA 3641
  $3.00   (D1545)

Mein Freund, Ich Tue Dir Nicht Unrecht
  see Evangelienspruche Fur Das Kirchenjahr
    [5]

Psalm 90 *see Herr Gott, Du Bist Unsre
  Zuflucht

Psalm 124 *see Wo Der Herr Nicht Bei Uns
  Ware

Sammelt Zuvor Das Unkraut
  see Evangelienspruche Fur Das Kirchenjahr
    [4]

Sei Getrost, Dein Glaube Hat Dir Geholfen
  see Evangelienspruche Fur Das Kirchenjahr
    [18]

Sei Getrost, Mein Sohn
  see Evangelienspruche Fur Das Kirchenjahr
    [17]

Selig Ist Der Leib
  see Evangelienspruche Fur Das Kirchenjahr
    [7]

Selig Sind Die Augen
  see Evangelienspruche Fur Das Kirchenjahr
    [15]

Siehe, Dieser Wird Gesetzt
  see Evangelienspruche Fur Das Kirchenjahr
    [2]

Siehe, Ich Bin Bei Euch *mot
  5pt mix cor,acap cor pts BREITKOPF-W
  CHB-3198 s.p.   (D1546)

Sinfonia Sacra *Op.6, Gen,Bibl
  [Ger] SSATBB (med diff) BAREN. BA 2537
  $6.50   (D1547)

Stehe Auf Und Nimm Das Kindlein
  see Evangelienspruche Fur Das Kirchenjahr
    [2]

DRIESSLER, JOHANNES (cont'd.)

Und Das Wort Ward Fleisch
  see Evangelienspruche Fur Das Kirchenjahr
    [2]

Und Der Herr Lobte Den Ungerechten Haushalter
  see Evangelienspruche Fur Das Kirchenjahr
    [14]

Und Du Bethlehem Im Judischen Lande
  see Evangelienspruche Fur Das Kirchenjahr
    [3]

Und Er Nahm Die Sieben Brote
  see Evangelienspruche Fur Das Kirchenjahr
    [14]

Und Es Kam Sie Alle Eine Furcht An
  see Evangelienspruche Fur Das Kirchenjahr
    [16]

Und Ihr Habt Auch Nun Traurigkeit
  see Evangelienspruche Fur Das Kirchenjahr
    [10]

Und Wo Diese Tage Nicht Wurden Verkurzt
  see Evangelienspruche Fur Das Kirchenjahr
    [19]

Wahrlich Ich Sage Euch
  see Evangelienspruche Fur Das Kirchenjahr
    [12]
  see Evangelienspruche Fur Das Kirchenjahr
    [7]

Wahrlich Ich Sage Euch, Was Ihr Getan Habt
  see Evangelienspruche Fur Das Kirchenjahr
    [19]

Wahrlich Ich Sage Euch, Wer Mein Wort Horet
  see Evangelienspruche Fur Das Kirchenjahr
    [19]

Was Ist Das Fur Ein Mensch
  see Evangelienspruche Fur Das Kirchenjahr
    [4]

Was Ists, Dass Ihr Mich Gesucht Habt
  see Evangelienspruche Fur Das Kirchenjahr
    [3]

Weib, Siehe, Das Ist Dein Sohn
  see Evangelienspruche Fur Das Kirchenjahr
    [8]

Wenn Aber Dieses Anfangt
  see Evangelienspruche Fur Das Kirchenjahr
    [1]

Wenn Aber Jener Geist Der Wahrheit Kommen
  Wird
  see Evangelienspruche Fur Das Kirchenjahr
    [10]

Wenn Der Troster Kommen Wird
  see Evangelienspruche Fur Das Kirchenjahr
    [11]

Wenn Doch Auch Du Erkenntest
  see Evangelienspruche Fur Das Kirchenjahr
    [14]

Wenn Ihr Nicht Zeichen Und Wunder Seht
  see Evangelienspruche Fur Das Kirchenjahr
    [18]

Wer Mich Liebet
  see Evangelienspruche Fur Das Kirchenjahr
    [11]

Wer Ohren Hat Zu Horen
  see Evangelienspruche Fur Das Kirchenjahr
    [5]

Wisset Ihr, Was Ich Euch Getan Habe
  see Evangelienspruche Fur Das Kirchenjahr
    [8]

Wo Der Herr Nicht Bei Uns Ware (Psalm 124)
  Op.25,No.2, Gen
  [Ger] SATB,org (med diff) BAREN. BA 2508 sc
  s.p., cor pts s.p.   (D1548)

Zachaus, Steig Eilend Hernieder
  see Evangelienspruche Fur Das Kirchenjahr
    [20]

DRING, [MADELEINE]
  Thank You Lord
    SATB PROWSE s.p.   (D1549)
    SSA PROWSE s.p.   (D1550)

DRISCHNER, MAX
  Christmas Story, The *Xmas
    SATB/unis,org,opt orch HINRICHSEN D1726 voc
    sc s.p., cor pts s.p.   (D1551)

  Make A Joyful Noise *CC25L,carol/hymn
    unis,treb inst,org/hpsd/pno sc CONCORDIA
    97-4684 $2.50, cor pts CONCORDIA 97-4685
    $.50, ipa   (D1552)

DRITTER NACHTRAG ZUR GESAMTAUSGABE-BAND XXXII
  see Palestrina, Giovanni

DRONNING DAGMAR-MESSE see Jeppesen, Knud

DROOP SACRED HEAD see Maunder, J.H.

DROP DOWN DEW see Tye, Christopher

DROP DOWN, YE HEAVENS see Ferris, W.

DROP DOWN YE HEAVENS see Neff, James

DROP DOWN, YE HEAVENS see Statham, Heathcote
  (Dicken)

DROP DOWN, YE HEAVENS FROM ABOVE see Cassler,
  G. Winston

DROP DOWN YOUR DEW, YE HEAVENS see Tye,
  Christopher, Rorate Coeli

DROP, DROP SLOW TEARS *Gen/Psntd
  (Bullock, Ernest) SATB (easy) oct OXFORD
  42.023 $.25   (D1553)

DROP, DROP, SLOW TEARS see Beveridge, Thomas G.

DROP, DROP SLOW TEARS see Burroughs

DROP, DROP SLOW TEARS see Candlyn, T. Frederick H.

DROP, DROP, SLOW TEARS see Elmore, Robert [Hall]

DROP, DROP, SLOW TEARS see Gibbons, Orlando

DROP, DROP, SLOW TEARS see Graham, Robert [V.]

DROP, DROP, SLOW TEARS see Green, R.

DROP, DROP, SLOW TEARS see Johnston, Jack

DROP, DROP, SLOW TEARS see Lapo, Cecil E.

DROP, DROP, SLOW TEARS see Leighton, Kenneth

DROP, DROP SLOW TEARS see Marshall

DROP, DROP, SLOW TEARS see Near, Gerald

DROP, DROP, SLOW TEARS see Pasfield, W.R.

DROP, DROP SLOW TEARS see Powell

DROP, DROP, SLOW TEARS see Young

DROP, DROP SLOW TEARS see Young, Robert H.

DROP, SLOW TEARS see Harris, William Henry

DROPEN see Baden, Conrad

DROSTE
  Blessed Are The Poor In Spirit
    SATB oct PRO ART 2020 $.25   (D1554)

  Blessed Art Thou, O Lord God
    SATB FLAMMER A 5515 $.25   (D1555)

  Hymn Of St. Columba *hymn
    SATB oct FISCHER,C CM-7748 $.25   (D1556)

DROSTE, DOREEN
  Babe Lies In The Cradle, A
    SATB,opt SA soli,acap AMP A462 $.25 (D1557)

  Come, Holy Ghost, Creator Blest
    SATB (med) ABINGDON APM-675 $.40   (D1558)

  Hear My Prayer *anthem
    SATB,org AMP A301 $.20   (D1559)

  Jubilate Deo
    "O Be Joyful In The Lord" 2pt AMP A337 $.25
                                       (D1560)
  O Be Joyful In The Lord *see Jubilate Deo

  Ride On! Ride On In Majesty
    SATB,org oct LAWSON 51510 $.30   (D1561)

DROZDOFF, I.
  O Lord, We Pray
    SATB,acap SCHIRM.EC 1128 $.25   (D1562)

DROZDOV, ANATOL NIKOLAIEVITCH (1883-1950)
  Give Ear, O Lord, Unto My Prayer
    (Ehret) SATB,acap oct PRO ART 1597 $.18
                                       (D1563)

DRUM LASST UNS FROHLICH SEIN see Gattermayer, Heinrich

DRUMS OF GOD see Brumbaugh, Harley

DRUMS OF GOD, THE see Young

DRY BONES
  see Eight Negro Spirituals: Book Ii
    (Kirk) 2pt oct PRO ART 2059 $.35   (D1564)
    (Kirk) TTBB oct PRO ART 2348 $.30   (D1565)
    (Kirk) SATB oct PRO ART 1317 $.35   (D1566)
    (Kirk) SAB oct PRO ART 1833 $.35   (D1567)
    (Kirk) SSA oct PRO ART 1832 $.35   (D1568)

DRYHAUG
  Dream Bethlehem *Xmas
    SSATB SCHMITT 893 $.25   (D1569)

DRYNAN, MARGARET
  Missa Brevis In F Minor
    SATB,acap oct BERANDOL 916D6AB $.35 (D1570)

  Why Do The Bells Of Christmas Ring? *Xmas
    unis,pno oct BERANDOL 916D5AA $.35 (D1571)

DU ABER DANIEL, GEHE HIN see Telemann, Georg Philipp

DU ABER, HERR, BIST UNSER VATER see Zilcher, Hermann

DU ALLER MENSCHEN VATER, DU HELFER see Bach, Johann Sebastian

DU BIST ALS STERN UNS AUFGEGANGEN see Weismann, Wilhelm

DU BIST DER BORN see Kaun, [Hugo]

DU BIST DER GOTT MEINER ZUFLUCHT see Schilling, Hans Ludwig

DU BIST DER HERR, INS AMT GESTELLT see Stier, Alfred

DU BIST DER WEG see Gottschick, Friedemann

DU BIST DIE RUH' see Schubert, Franz (Peter)

DU BIST, O HERR, MEIN SCHIRM UND HORT see Iten, Walter

DU BIST'S, DEM RUHM UND EHRE GEBUHRET see Haydn, (Franz) Joseph

DU DOTTER SION, FROJDA DIG see Thyrestam, Gunnar

DU ER EIN GJEST I DENNE VERD see Geitvik, S.H.

DU FOND DE L'ABIME see Boulanger, Lili

DU FONS DE MA PENSEE see Goudimel, Claude

DU FRIEDEFURST, HERR JESU CHRIST see Bach, Johann Sebastian

DU FRIEDEFURST, HERR JESU CHRIST see Buxtehude, Dietrich

DU FRIEDEFURST, HERR JESU CHRIST see Cruger, Johann

DU FRIEDEFURST, HERR JESU CHRIST see Gesius, Bartholomaus

DU FRIEDENSFUERST see Bach, Johann Sebastian, Du Friedefurst, Herr Jesu Christ

DU GABST UNS UNSER TAGLICH BROT see Bach, Johann Sebastian

DU GLANZ AUS GOTTES HERRLICHKEIT see Henking, Bernhard

DU GODA MANE *folk,Ger
    (Jonsson, Josef) men cor NORDISKA 3650 s.p.
                                       (D1572)
    (Magnison, Thor) mix cor NORDISKA 3718 s.p.
                                       (D1573)

DU GODA MANE see Andersson, Karl-Eric

DU GOTT, DEM ERD' UND HIMMEL SCHWEIGT see Handel, George Frideric, Oh Father, Whose Almighty Pow'r

DU GROSSER SCHMERZENSMANN see Bloch, Waldemar

DU GROSSER SCHMERZENSMANN see Koch, Johannes H.E.

DU GROSSER SCHMERZENSMANN see Vopelius, Gottfried

DU GROSSER SCHMERZENSMANN VOM VATER see Janus, Martin

DU HAST, O HERR, DEIN LEBEN see Doppelbauer, Josef Friedrich

DU HAST, O JESULEIN, KEIN BETT UND KEINE WIEGEN see Anonymous

DU HEILIGE BRUNST see Bach, Johann Sebastian

DU HERZOG MEINER SELIGKEIT, HERR JESU see Bach, Johann Sebastian

DU HIRTE ISRAEL see Bach, Johann Sebastian, Du Hirte Israel, Hore

DU HIRTE ISRAEL, HORE see Bach, Johann Sebastian

DU HIRTE ISRAELS see Bortniansky, Dimitri Stepanovitch

DU HIRTE ISRAELS, HORE see Bach, Johann Sebastian

DU HIRTE ISRAELS, HORE see Wenzel, Eberhard

DU HOCHSTES LICHT, EWIGER SCHEIN see Kurig, Hans-Hermann

DU LEBENSFURST, HERR JESU CHRIST see Bach, Johann Sebastian

DU LEBENSFURST, HERR JESU CHRIST see Buxtehude, Dietrich

DU LIEBER HERRE JESU CHRIST see Burdett, E.S.

DU LIEBES KIND see Bartmus, Richard

DU LIEBSTER HERR, DU ALLERGUTIGSTER, CHRISTE see Schutz, Heinrich, Dulcissime Et Benignissime Christe

DU MAL IN LE MESCHANT VOULOIR see Goudimel, Claude

DU MALIN LE MESCHANT VOULOIR see Goudimel, Claude

DU MEIN EINZIG LICHT see Albert, Heinrich

DU MEINE SEELE, SINGE see Bornefeld, Helmut

DU MEINE SEELE, SINGE see Ebeling, J.

DU MEINE SEELE, SINGE see Ebeling, Johann Georg

DU MEINE SEELE, SINGE see Fronmuller, Frieda

DU MEINE SEELE, SINGE see Oertzen, Rudolf von

DU MEINE SEELE, SINGE see Rein, Walter

DU MEINE SEELE, SINGE, WOHLAUF see Ebeling, Johann Georg

DU MEINE SEELE, SINGE, WOHLAUF see Kubler, Emil

DU MEINE SELLE, SINGE see Peter, Herbert

DU OMME FADERHJERTE see Mendelssohn-Bartholdy, Felix

DU PFINGSTLICH HOHER GEIST DER GNADEN see Peter, Herbert

DU RADS MIN SJAL see Burck, Joachim

DU SCHALKSKNECHT see Schutz, Heinrich

DU SCHALKSKNECHT, ALLE DIESE SCHULD see Schutz, Heinrich

DU SEIGNEUR LES BONTEZ SANS FIN see Goudimel, Claude

DU SELBST MUSST SONNE SEIN see Bauernfiend, Hans

DU SOLLST GOTT see Bach, Johann Sebastian, Du Sollst Gott, Deinen Herren, Lieben

DU SOLLST GOTT, DEINEN HERREN, LIEBEN see Bach, Johann Sebastian

DU SOLLST GOTT, DEINEN HERREN, LIEBEN see Raselius, Andreas

DU SOLLST GOTT, DEINEN HERRN see Ruppel, Paul Ernst

DU SOLLST LIEBEN GOTT, DEINEN HERREN see Vulpius, Melchior

DU SOLLST LIEBEN GOTT, DEINEN HERRN see Driessler, Johannes

DU SOLLT GOTT, DEINEN HERREN, LIEBEN see Bach, Johann Sebastian

DU SOM HAR KOMMIT TILL VAR JORD see Berg, Gottfrid

DU SOM HARLIG STALLDE
    see Sex Koraler I Folkton I Sattningar

DU, TOCHTER ZION, FREUE DICH SEHR see Dedekind, Constantine Christian

DU, TOCHTER ZION, FREUE DICH SEHR see Hessenberg, Kurt

DU TUST VIEL GUTS BEWEISEN see Schutz, Heinrich

DU WAHRER GOTT see Bach, Johann Sebastian, Du Wahrer Gott Und Davids Sohn

DU WAHRER GOTT UND DAVIDS SOHN see Bach, Johann Sebastian

DU WIRST MEINE SEELE NICHT DEM TODE LASSEN see Reda, Siegfried

DU WIRST MEINE SEELE NICHT DEM TODE LASSEN see Schaper, Heinz-Christian

DUBOIS, PIERRE MAX
  Cantate Sur Trois Psaumes
    [Fr] SATB cor pts LEDUC s.p.   (D1574)

  Ver Toi J'aileve Mes Yeux
    [Fr] SATB cor pts LEDUC s.p.   (D1575)

DUBOIS, THEODORE (1837-1924)
  Adeste Fideles
    [Lat] SSTB,vln,vcl,ob HEUGEL sc s.p., cor
      pts s.p., ipa   (D1576)

  Adoramus Te, Christe (from Seven Last Words
    Of Christ, The) Easter/Lent
    [Lat/Eng] SATB oct SOUTHERN $.25   (D1577)
    [Eng] 4pt mix cor oct SCHIRM.G 9749 $.25
                                       (D1578)
    "Christ, We Adore Thee" SATB oct LORENZ
      9748 $.25   (D1579)
    "Christ, We Adore Thee" mix cor SOUTHERN
      $.25   (D1580)
    "Christ, We Adore Thee" SATB oct SOUTHERN
      $.25   (D1581)
    (Marshall, Charles) "We Adore Thee, O
      Christ" SATB,pno/org FRANK F-599 $.30
                                       (D1582)

  Ave Maria
    [Lat] SS,opt pno/org (E min, parts
      available also) HEUGEL s.p.   (D1583)
    [Lat] ST,opt pno/org (G maj) HEUGEL s.p.
                                       (D1584)
    [Lat] SSTB soli,bvl,opt pno/org (A flat
      maj, parts available also) HEUGEL s.p.
                                       (D1585)
    [Lat] 4pt mix cor,S solo,opt pno/org (A
      min, parts available also) HEUGEL s.p.
                                       (D1586)

  Ave Verum
    [Lat] 4pt mix cor,opt pno/org HEUGEL s.p.
                                       (D1587)

  Behold, God Is My Salvation
    SATB oct FISCHER,J 9484 $.30   (D1588)

  Christ, We Adore Thee *see Adoramus Te, Christe

  Christus Resurrexit
    [Lat] 4pt mix cor,opt pno/org HEUGEL s.p.
                                       (D1589)

  Deus Abraham
    [Lat] SSTB,TB soli,opt pno/org HEUGEL s.p.
                                       (D1590)

  Ecce Panis
    [Lat] SS,opt pno/org (E flat maj) HEUGEL
      s.p.   (D1591)
    [Lat] SB,opt pno/org (E flat maj) HEUGEL
      s.p.   (D1592)

  Fulgebunt Justi
    [Lat] SSSS&STB,B solo,opt pno/org HEUGEL
      voc sc s.p., voc pt s.p.   (D1593)

  God, My Father (from Seven Last Words, The)
    (Thompson) SATB oct PLYMOUTH SC-4 $.25
                                       (D1594)

  Hymne Antique *hymn
    [Fr] SSS HEUGEL voc sc s.p., voc pt s.p.
                                       (D1595)

  Illuxit Dies Tertia
    [Lat] SATB,solo,opt pno/org HEUGEL s.p.
                                       (D1596)

  Le Paradis Perdu *ora
    [Fr] SATB,SATB soli,orch LEDUC sc rental,
      cor pts rental   (D1597)

  Les Sept Paroles Du Christ *Easter/Holywk/
    Lent/Psntd,cant/ora
    "Seven Last Words Of Christ, The" 4pt mix
      cor,soli,orch voc sc SCHIRM.G $1.25
                                       (D1598)
    "Seven Last Words Of Christ, The" SATB
      PRESSER $1.25   (D1599)
    "Seven Last Words, The" cor,orch sc KALMUS
      $15.00, ipa   (D1600)
    "Seven Last Words, The" SATB LORENZ $1.95
                                       (D1601)
    "Seven Last Words, The" cor,opt orch voc sc
      KALMUS 6158 $1.25, ipa   (D1602)
    "Seven Last Words, The" cor KALMUS $1.50
                                       (D1603)
    "Seven Words Of Christ" BELWIN $1.50
                                       (D1604)
    (Beidermann) "Seven Last Words Of Christ,
      The" mix cor BELWIN $1.25   (D1605)
    (Cain) "Seven Last Words Of Christ, The".

DUBOIS, THEODORE (cont'd.)

SATB FLAMMER A5320 $1.40 (D1606)
(Dasher) "Seven Last Words Of Christ, The" SATB FLAMMER A5550 $1.75 (D1607)
(Douty, N.) "Seven Last Words Of Christ, The" SATB (sold only in USA) PRESSER $1.25 (D1608)
(Howorth) "Seven Last Words" BELWIN $1.50 (D1609)
(Osborn, A.) "Seven Last Words Of Christ, The" SSAA (sold only in USA) PRESSER $.60 (D1610)
(Stephens, Norris L.) "Seven Last Words Of Christ, The" mix cor,soli,org,timp,harp sc SCHIRM.G $5.00, ipa (D1611)

Messe *Mass
[Lat] STB,org,bvl,opt 5strings&ob (E flat maj) HEUGEL voc sc s.p., voc pt s.p., ipa (D1612)
[Lat] SSTB,org (F maj) HEUGEL voc sc s.p., voc pt s.p. (D1613)
[Lat] TTB/SMezB,org (G maj, parts available also) voc sc HEUGEL s.p. (D1614)
[Lat] ST,org (G maj, parts available also) voc sc HEUGEL s.p. (D1615)
[Lat] STB,opt pno/org (A flat maj) HEUGEL voc sc s.p., voc pt s.p. (D1616)
[Lat] STB,org (B min) HEUGEL voc sc s.p., voc pt s.p. (D1617)

Messe Solennelle Dest Remy *Mass
[Lat] SATB,5strings/orch (E flat maj) HEUGEL voc sc s.p., voc pt s.p. (D1618)

O Quam Suavis
[Lat] SSTB,opt pno/org HEUGEL s.p. (D1619)

Panis Angelicus
[Lat] SSTB,S solo,opt pno/org (B min, parts available also) HEUGEL s.p. (D1620)
[Lat] SSTB,Mez solo,opt pno/org (A min) HEUGEL s.p. (D1621)

Pater Noster
[Lat] SSTB,opt pno/org HEUGEL s.p. (D1622)

Regina Coeli
[Lat] STB,T solo,opt pno/org HEUGEL voc sc s.p., voc pt s.p. (D1623)

Seven Last Words *see Les Sept Paroles Du Christ

Seven Last Words Of Christ, The *see Les Sept Paroles Du Christ

Seven Last Words, The *see Les Sept Paroles Du Christ

Seven Words Of Christ *see Les Sept Paroles Du Christ

Tantum Ergo
[Lat] SSTB,T solo,opt pno/org (B flat maj) HEUGEL s.p. (D1624)
[Lat] TTBB,opt pno/org (G maj) HEUGEL s.p. (D1625)

Thee We Adore *Easter
SSTB oct PRESSER 312-21196 $.25 (D1626)
(Peery, R.) SAB oct PRESSER 312-21449 $.25 (D1627)

Tu Es Petrus
[Lat] SSTB,opt pno/org (F maj, parts available also) HEUGEL s.p. (D1628)
[Lat] SSTB,B solo,opt pno/org (B flat maj, parts available also) HEUGEL s.p. (D1629)
[Lat] STB,vln,vcl,bvl (B maj, parts available also) HEUGEL s.p. (D1630)

We Adore Thee, O Christ *see Adoramus Te, Christe

DU CAURROY, FRANCOISE-EUSTACHE (1549-1609)
Ave Maria *mot
[Lat] SSAA,acap MUSICUS 1017 $.15 (D1631)

Forth From Thy Home On High *see Sors De Ton Lit Pare

Infant Has Come To Earth, An *see Un Enfant Du Ciel Nous Est Ne

Noel, A Child From Heaven Is Born *see Noel, Un Enfant Du Ciel Nous Est Ne

Noel, Un Enfant Du Ciel Nous Est Ne *Xmas
(Greyson) "Noel, A Child From Heaven Is Born" SATB oct BOURNE ES104 $.35 (D1632)

Sors De Ton Lit Pare
"Forth From Thy Home On High" [Eng/Fr] SATB,acap oct SALABERT-US $.35 (D1633)
"Forth From Thy Home On High" [Eng/Fr] SA oct SALABERT-US $.35 (D1634)

Un Enfant Du Ciel Nous Est Ne *Xmas
"Infant Has Come To Earth, An" [Eng/Fr] SATB,acap oct SALABERT-US $.35 (D1635)

DUCIS
Dear Christians, Let Us All Rejoice *Gen
(Lundquist) SATB SCHMITT 1506 $.25 (D1636)

DUCIS, BENEDICTUS (ca. 1490-1544)
Aus Tiefer Not Schrei Ich Zu Dir *mot
(Berger) SATB HANSSLER 1.039 s.p. contains also: Erbarm Dich Mein, O Herre Gott (D1637)

Erbarm Dich Mein, O Herre Gott *ECY
see Ducis, Benedictus, Aus Tiefer Not Schrei Ich Zu Dir
[Ger] SATB,acap (med) MULLER K 30 s.p. (D1638)

Es Woll Uns Gott Gnadig Sein *mot/prayer
(Berger) SATB HANSSLER 1.038 s.p. contains also: Vater Unser Im Himmelreich (D1639)

Herr Jesu Christ, Du Hochstes Gut
see Staden, Johann, Es Ist Ein Kostlich Ding, Dem Herren

Nun Freut Euch, Lieben Christen G'mein
SATB HANSSLER 6.147 s.p. contains also: Stern, Hermann, Nun Freut Euch, Lieben Christen G'mein (SAB) (D1640)

DUCIS, BENEDICTUS (cont'd.)

Vater Unser Im Himmelreich
see Ducis, Benedictus, Es Woll Uns Gott Gnadig Sein

DUCKWORTH, ARTHUR
Aldershaw
SATB PATERSON 1687 s.p. (D1641)

For Those In Peril On The Sea *hymn
mix cor CURWEN 80906 s.p. (D1642)

DUCOUDRAY, B.
Hymne Du Matin *Morn,hymn
wom cor voc sc CHOUDENS s.p. (D1643)

Noel *Xmas
wom cor voc sc CHOUDENS s.p. (D1644)

DUDDY, [JOHN H.] (1904-)
Come, Holy Ghost
SATB,acap oct PRESSER 312-40292 $.30 (D1645)

Creed, The
SATB oct PRESSER 312-40101 $.30 (D1646)

Lay Down Your Staves
SATB,acap oct PRESSER 312-40198 $.30 (D1647)

'Twas On A Quiet Starry Night *Xmas
SATB,acap oct PRESSER 312-40483 $.30 (D1648)

DUE AVE MARIA *BVM
[Lat] 2pt,org ZANIBON 2763 s.p. contains: Mattoni, Filippo, Ave Maria; Picchi, Luigi, Ave Maria (D1649)

DUE CANTI AL SS. CUORE see Chiesa, Federico

DUE CANTI AL SS. SACRAMENTO see Corradini, Vasco Lodovico

DUE CANTI EUCARISTICI see Nicolosi, Salvatore

DUE CANTI PER BAMBINI see Somma

DUE CANTI TRIONFALI PER PROCESSIONE EUCHARISTICA see Arnaldi, Antonio

DUE CANZONCINE see Corradini, Vasco Lodovico

DUE CANZONCINE FACILI PER IL S. NATALE see Bottazzo, Luigi

DUE CANZONCINE PASTORALI see Ascenso, Antonio

DUE COMPOSIZIONE SACRE IN ONORE DI MARIA VERGINE see Bottazzo, Luigi

DUE COMPOSIZIONI SACRE see Maugeri, Giuseppe

DUE CORI FRANCESCANI see Somma

DUE CORI see Tocchi, [Gian-Luca]

DUE GRADUALE ET TRACTUS PRO PALMIS ET PARASCEVE see Eccher

DUE INNI A CRISTO RE see Gubinelli, Oderisio

DUE LAUDI A GESU SACR. see Branchina, Pietro

DUE MOTTETO PER S. GIUSEPPE see Ascenso, Antonio

DUE MOTTETTI see Veretti, Antonio

DUE MOTTETTI EUCARISTICI see Bottazzo, Luigi

DUE MOTTETTI EUCARISTICI *Commun,mot
[Lat] 2 eq voices,org sc ZANIBON 529 s.p. contains: Bottazzo, Luigi, Venite Populi; Grassi, Ciro, Responsorio (D1650)

DUE MOTTETTI EUCARISTICI see Magri, Pietro

DUE MOTTETTI IN ON. DI MARIA VERGINE see Bottazzo, Luigi

DUE MOTTETTI IN ONORE DI S. ANTONIO see Arnaldi, Antonio

DUE MOTTETTI PASQUALI see Arnaldi, Antonio

DUE MOTTETTI PEL S. NATALE see Casimiri, Raffaele Casimiro

DUE MOTTETTI PEL VENERDI SANTO see Bottazzo, Luigi

DUE MOTTETTI PER LA VISITA PASTORALE see Arnaldi, Antonio

DUE "PARCE DOMINE" see Volpi, Edoardo

DUE SALMI see Giannini, Vincenzo

DUE TANTUM ERGO see Arnaldi, Antonio

DUE TOTA PULCHRA see Ravanello, Oreste

DUE "TU ES SACERDOS" see Corradini, Vasco Lodovico

DUERME, NINO MIO see Vivalo

DUFAULT, SHELDON
Life Of Christ, The
unis,pno voc sc MARKS $2.00 (D1651)

DUFAY, GUILLAUME (ca. 1400-1474)
Alleluia Veni Sancte Spiritus
see Opera Omnia Tom. II

Alma Redemptoris Mater *16th cent
(Cartier, Anita; Carol, Henri; Gagnepain, Bernard) [Lat] SAT OUVRIERES EO524 s.p. (D1652)

Apostolo Glorioso
(Cartier, Anita) [Lat] mix cor LEMOINE s.p. (D1653)

Ave Maris Stella *Adv/Xmas
ATT,acap voc pt DOBLINGER s.p. see also ADVENT UND WEIHNACHT, HEFT 2 (D1654)

Ave Regina Coelorum
see MEISTERWERKE MITTELALTERLICHER MUSIK
SATB,acap oct PRESSER 352-00116 $.40 (D1655)

DUFAY, GUILLAUME (cont'd.)

Ave Reginae Coelorum
see Opera Omnia Tom. III

Caput *Mass
see Opera Omnia Tom. II
(Darvas) [Lat] cor voc sc PETERS 10035 $4.50 (D1656)

Christe Redemptor *Adv/Xmas
ATB,acap voc pt DOBLINGER s.p. see also ADVENT UND WEIHNACHT, HEFT 2 (D1657)

Ecce Ancilla Domini
see Opera Omnia Tom. III

Gloria *Gloria
(Cramer) [Lat] SATB&SA/SATB&TB,2brass MARKS 4297 $.30 (D1658)
(Engel) SATB FLAMMER A 5130 $.30 (D1659)

Kyrie Eleison
(Knight, Gerald) SATB,acap oct FISCHER,C CM-7506 $.25 (D1660)

Kyrie II (from Missa Super L'homme Arme)
SATB,opt org/inst BROUDE BR. $.35 (D1661)

La Mort De Saint Gothard
see Opera Omnia Tom. II

L'homme Arme
see Opera Omnia Tom. III

Magnificat In The 8th Mode
3pt mix cor,acap oct PRESSER 352-00029 $.35 (D1662)

Missa Se La Face Ay Pale
see Opera Omnia Tom. III

Opera Omnia tom. I *CCU,mot
(Besseler, H.; de Van) cor AM.INST.MUS. cmplt ed $27.50, cmplt ed $6.50 (D1663)

Opera Omnia Tom. II *Mass
(Besseler, H.) cor cmplt ed AM.INST.MUS. $24.00
contains: Alleluia Veni Sancte Spiritus; Caput; La Mort De Saint Gothard; Sancti Antoni Viennensis; Sancti Iacobi; Sine Monine (D1664)

Opera Omnia Tom. III *Mass
(Besseler, H.) cor cmplt ed AM.INST.MUS. $26.00
contains: Ave Reginae Coelorum; Ecce Ancilla Domini; L'homme Arme; Missa Se La Face Ay Pale (D1665)

Opera Omnia Tom. IV *CC28U,Mass
(Besseler, H.) cor cmplt ed AM.INST.MUS. $22.00 (D1666)

Sacred Hymns *CCU,hymn
mix cor,acap voc sc KALMUS 6160 $2.00 (D1667)

Samtliche Hymnen *CCU,hymn
(Gerber) [Ger/Lat] 3pt mix cor&4pt mix cor MOSELER s.p. (D1668)

Sancti Antoni Viennensis
see Opera Omnia Tom. II

Sancti Iacobi *Mass
see Opera Omnia Tom. II
(de Van) cor cmplt ed AM.INST.MUS. $3.50 (D1669)

Sanctus *Mass
(Graetzer) [Lat] SATB,acap (Joined With Osanna By La Rue) RICORDI-ARG BA 9826 s.p. (D1670)

Se La Face Ay Pale *Mass
(Besseler, Heinrich) [Ger] STTB,acap (med diff) BAREN. BA 1712 $4.25 (D1671)

Sine Monine
see Opera Omnia Tom. II

Sine Nomine *Mass
(de Van) cor cmplt ed AM.INST.MUS. $2.50 (D1672)

Trumpet Gloria *Gloria
SATB/SSAA/SA/TB,2inst FOSTER MF 124 $.35 (D1673)

Vos Qui Secuti
(Stone, Kurt) "Ye Who Have Followed Me" [Lat/Eng] 3pt treb cor oct BOONIN 104 $.25 (D1674)

Ye Who Have Followed Me *see Vos Qui Secuti

Zwolf Geistliche Und Weltliche Werke *sac/sec,CC12U
(Besseler) [Ger/Fr/It/Lat] 3 eq voices/3pt mix cor,inst MOSELER s.p. (D1675)

DUKE
Magnificat
unis,org BOSTON 13722 $.35 (D1676)

DUKE, JOHN (1899-)
O Sing Unto The Lord A New Song
3pt wom cor,org oct SCHIRM.G 10650 $.35 (D1677)

DUKE, VERNON
see DUKELSKY, VLADIMIR

DULCES EXUVIAE see Willaert, Adrian

DULCISSIME ET BENIGNISSIME CHRISTE see Schutz, Heinrich

DULICHIUS, PHILIPPUS (1562-1631)
Das Alte Jahr Vergangen Ist *ECY,mot
(Schreck) SAATTB HANSSLER 1.124 s.p. (D1678)

Gloria Patri *Gen,mot
(Goebel, Georg) [Ger] SATB&ATBB,acap (med) MULLER SM 2165 s.p. (D1679)

Ich Hebe Meine Augen Auf *Gen,mot
(Goebel, Georg) [Ger] SSAT&ATBB,acap (med) MULLER SM 2164 s.p. (D1680)

DULICHIUS, PHILIPPUS (cont'd.)

Zion Spricht: Der Herr Hat Mich Verlassen
*Gen,mot
(Goebel, Georg) [Ger] SAAT&SATB,acap (med)
MULLER SM 2163 s.p. (D1681)

DULL SOUL ASPIRE see Naylor, Bernard

DULOT, FRANCOIS
Maria Magdalenae *Easter,16th cent
(Cartier, Anita; Carol, Henri; Gagnepain,
Bernard) [Lat] SATB OUVRIERES EO 664 s.p. (D1682)

DUM COMPLERENTUR see Palestrina, Giovanni

DUM COMPLERENTUR DIES PENTECOSTES see Victoria,
Tomas Luis de

DUM COMPLERENTUR DIES PENTECOTES see Victoria,
Tomas Luis de

DUM ERGO ESSENT see Palestrina, Giovanni

DUM ERGO ESSENT see Victoria, Tomas Luis de

DUM ESSET SUMMUS PONTIFEX see Palestrina,
Giovanni

DUM TRANSISSET SABBATUM see Johnson, R.

DUM TRANSISSET SABBATUM see Johnson, Robert

DUM TRANSISSET SABBATUM see Tallis, Thomas

DUM TRANSISSET SABBATUM see Taverner, John

DUMONT, [HENRI] (1610-1684)
Credo (from La Messe Royale) Credo/Mass
(L'abbe Brun) [Fr] 4pt mix cor&opt unis,org
voc sc DURAND s.p. (D1683)

Messe Royale Plain Chant *Mass
[Fr] 4pt mix cor&unis,solo,org oct DURAND
s.p. (D1684)

Panis Angelicus *Commun,mot
(Kunc) [Lat] 4pt/4pt mix cor oct DURAND
s.p. (D1685)

DUNCAN
Praise, My Soul, The King Of Heaven
SATB,org/pno BOSTON 10857 $.40 (D1686)

DUNCAN, C.
Christ Is Risen From The Dead *Easter
SATB,pno (med) oct WILLIS 5695 $.15 (D1687)

Day Of Resurrection, The *Easter
SATB,pno (easy) oct WILLIS 5694 $.15 (D1688)

Praise The Lord, O Jerusalem *Fest/Thanks
SATB,A solo,pno (easy) oct WILLIS 5748 $.16 (D1689)

DUNFORD
Clap Your Hands, Sing Praises
SATB,perc (med diff/diff) SOUTHERN $.35 (D1690)

DUNFORD, BENJAMIN
Gideon *cant
mix cor BELWIN $1.25 (D1691)

Promise, The *cant
mix cor BELWIN $1.50 (D1692)

Psalm 103 *cant
mix cor BELWIN $1.25 (D1693)

Unspeakable Gift, The *cant
SAB BELWIN $1.50 (D1694)

DUNGAN
Brighter Than Sun
SATB oct VOLKWEIN VB121 $.25 (D1695)

Faith In Little Things
SATB oct VOLKWEIN VB146 $.25 (D1696)

God Is Everywhere
SATB oct VOLKWEIN VB158 $.25 (D1697)

I Like To Dream *Xmas,carol
SATB oct VOLKWEIN VB178 $.25 (D1698)

Peace I Leave With You
SATB oct VOLKWEIN VB239 $.25 (D1699)

DUNGAN, O.
Eternal Life
TTBB oct PRESSER 322-40040 $.30 (D1700)
SA oct PRESSER 322-40038 $.30 (D1701)
(Bock, Fred) SATB (easy) PRESSER 322-40042
$.35 (D1702)
(Donath, J.) SSA oct PRESSER 322-40019 $.30 (D1703)
(Stickles, W.) SATB oct PRESSER 322-40018
$.30 (D1704)

Song Of The Creatures
SSATB oct PRESSER 312-40707 $.40 (D1705)

DUNHILL
Cloths Of Heaven, The
(Davis) SATB oct GALAXY 1.1415.1 $.30 (D1706)
(Davis) SSA oct GALAXY 1.1386.1 $.30 (D1707)

It Came Upon The Midnight Clear *Xmas
unis jr cor&desc FISCHER,C ARD 19 $.20 (D1708)

Virgin Unspotted, A *Xmas
unis jr cor&desc FISCHER,C ARD 31 $.20 (D1709)

DUNHILL, THOMAS FREDERICK (1877-1946)
Animal's Carol, The
unis sr cor CRAMER 203 (D1710)

Christmas Rose, The *Xmas,cant
unis treb cor&2pt treb cor,opt strings voc
sc NOVELLO 24.0028.06 s.p., ipr (D1711)

Fir Tree
jr cor LEONARD-ENG 74 s.p. (D1712)

Holy Babe *Xmas
SSA CRAMER B44 s.p. (D1713)

DUNHILL, THOMAS FREDERICK (cont'd.)

To The Queen Of Heaven
3pt wom cor oct CURWEN 8449 $.25 (D1714)

DUNKEL WAR'S see Kretzschmar, Gunther

DUNLAP, FERN
My Church Is A Holy Place
4pt mix cor oct SCHIRM.G 10723 $.25 (D1715)

Wedding Prayer *Marriage,prayer
(Stickles) 4pt mix cor oct SCHIRM.G 10889
$.30 (D1716)

DUNN
Oh Thou, Who Camest From Above
(Boyd) SATB,acap,opt pno oct PRO ART 2283
$.25 (D1717)

DUNN, T.
Carol Of The Shepherds *Xmas
SATB,acap oct PRESSER MC341 $.35 (D1718)

DUNQUE DIVIN SPIRACOLO see Palestrina, Giovanni

DUNSTABLE, JOHN (ca. 1385-1453)
Alma Redemptoris *Adv/Xmas
ATT,acap voc pt DOBLINGER s.p. see also
ADVENT UND WEIHNACHT, HEFT 2 (D1719)

Quam Pulchra Es
see MEISTERWERKE MITTELALTERLICHER MUSIK

Veni Sancte Spiritus *mot
[Lat] SAT,org/trom PETERS H1453 $.60 (D1720)

DUO HYMNI see Fabiani, Angelo

DUO HYMNI see Volpi, Edoardo

DUO MOTECTA see Arnaldi, Antonio

DUO MOTECTA see Muller, Giulio

DUO PSALTERII CANTICA see Kersters, Willem

DUO SERAPHIM see Aichinger, Gregor

DUO SERAPHIM see Victoria, Tomas Luis de

DUO SERAPHIM CLAMABANT see Scheidt, Samuel

DUPRE, MARCEL (1886-1971)
De Profundis *Op.18, Mass
[Fr] SATB,STB soli,orch LEDUC BL639 voc sc
s.p., voc pt s.p. (D1721)

Noel De France *Xmas,Fr
[Fr] unis,pno voc sc LEDUC s.p. (D1722)

Tantum Ergo *Commun
[Lat] 4pt mix cor,org (contains also solo
work) LEMOINE s.p. see also BREVIAIRE DE
PIERRE L'ERMITE (D1723)
[Lat] 4pt mix cor,org LEMOINE voc sc s.p.,
cor pts s.p. see from LE BREVIAIRE DE
PIERRE L'ERMITE (D1724)

DURAND, A.
Benedictus *Gen,mot
(Kunc, P.) [Lat] mix cor,org oct DURAND
s.p. (D1725)

Messe *Op.82, Mass
[Fr] 2 eq voices,pno/org oct DURAND s.p. (D1726)

Messe Breve *Op.49, Mass
[Fr] STB,pno/org oct DURAND s.p. (D1727)

Messe Solennelle *Op.55, Mass
[Fr] 4pt mix cor,STB soli,pno/org oct
DURAND s.p. (D1728)

O Salutaris *Commun,mot
[Lat] 2 eq voices oct DURAND s.p. (D1729)

DURAND, F.L.
Veni Creator *Commun/Gen,mot
[Lat] opt mix cor,Bar solo oct DURAND s.p. (D1730)
[Lat] opt SATBar,Mez/Bar solo oct DURAND
s.p. (D1731)

DURANT, C.
Glorious Things Of Thee Are Spoken
4pt mix cor,SAB soli,org/pno (med) oct
WILLIS 6262 $.16 (D1732)

God Of Abraham Praise, The
SATB,S solo,pno/org (med) oct WILLIS 6152
$.15 (D1733)

Lord, God Of Hosts
SATB,pno/org (med) oct WILLIS 5996 $.15 (D1734)

DURANTE
Kyrie *Kyrie
mix cor SOUTHERN $.25 (D1735)

Kyrie Eleison *Kyrie
(Ehret) "Lord Have Mercy Upon Us" SATB,opt
kbd oct PRO ART 2279 $.25 (D1736)

Lord Have Mercy Upon Us *see Kyrie Eleison

Magnificat
cor voc sc KALMUS 6159 $1.25 (D1737)

Thy God Is Great And Mighty
(Hardwicke) SATB oct PRO ART 2611 $.35 (D1738)

DURANTE, FRANCESCO (1684-1755)
Christe Eleison *Kyrie
mix cor SOUTHERN $.25 (D1739)
(Zanon; Vene) "Jesu, Be Merciful" SATB,acap
oct COLOMBO 2003 $.25 (D1740)

Crucified *see Crucifixus

Crucifixus *Easter/Lent
see Two Motets
(Richardson) "Crucified" SATB oct SPRATT
2018 $.25 (D1741)

Et Incarnatus
see Two Motets

DURANTE, FRANCESCO (cont'd.)

For Thy Great Mercy *see Misericordias
Domini

Holy And Merciful Lord *see Misericordias
Domini

Jesu, Be Merciful *see Christe Eleison

Kyrie *Easter/Lent,Kyrie
(Beveridge) [Lat/Eng] SATB,acap oct
SCHIRM.G 9566 $.30 (D1742)
(Harris) [Lat/Eng] 3pt mix cor,acap oct
LAWSON 51326 $.30 (D1743)
(Richardson) "Lord, Have Mercy" SATB oct
SPRATT 2001 $.30 (D1744)

Lord, Have Mercy *see Kyrie

Magnificat *Magnif
(Hellmann) [Lat] SATB,cont,2vln,vla (B flat
maj) HANSSLER 10.270 sc $5.00, voc sc
$1.50, ipa (D1745)

Misericordias Domini
"Holy And Merciful Lord" SATB oct WALTON
2164 $.35 (D1746)
"Holy And Merciful Lord" SATB oct WALTON
2164 $.35 (D1747)
(Damrosch) "For Thy Great Mercy" [Lat/Eng]
dbl cor,acap oct SCHIRM.G 11563 $.40 (D1748)
(Davison, A.) [Lat] dbl cor,acap SCHIRM.EC
941 $.45 (D1749)

Two Motets *mot
[Lat] SATB,acap MUSICUS 1024 $.18
contains: Crucifixus; Et Incarnatus (D1750)

DURCH ADAMS FALL IST GANZ VERDERBT see Bach,
Johann Sebastian

DURCH ADAMS FALL IST GANZ VERDERBT see Franck,
Melchior

DURCH ADAMS FALL IST GANZ VERDERBT see
Praetorius, Michael

DURCH ADAMS FALL IST GANZ VERDERBT see Schein,
Johann Hermann

DURCH ADAMS FALL IST GANZ VERDERBT see Bach,
Johann Sebastian

DURCH DIE HERZLICHE BARMHERZIGKEIT UNSERS
GOTTES see Goldberg, Johann Gottlieb

DURCHS GANZE JAHR *CCU
(Wagner, Hermann) mix cor, male solo MOSELER
s.p. (D1751)

DURCHS KIRCHENJAHR see Stern, Hermann

DURHAM
Ye Heavens Adore Him
SATB,acap BOSTON 10939 $.30 (D1752)

DURO, JOHN
Church's One Foundation, The
4pt mix cor&opt jr cor,opt S solo,org oct
SCHIRM.G 10896 $.35 (D1753)

Joyful Song, A
3pt jr cor/SSA (med easy) FISCHER,C CM 6742
$.35 (D1754)

DURON
O Vos Omnes
(Ehret) "O Ye People" [Lat/Eng] SATB oct
COLOMBO 2388 $.25 (D1755)

O Ye People *see O Vos Omnes

DURRANT
Lullaby
unis FRANCIS s.p. (D1756)

DURRANT, FREDERICK
Rock The Cradle For A King
cor oct HART s.p. (D1757)

DURST, SIDNEY C.
I Was Glad (Psalm 122)
SATB,pno (med) oct WILLIS 1195 $.15 (D1758)

Lo Our Father's Tender Care
SATB,A solo,org (med) oct WILLIS 1524 $.12 (D1759)

Psalm 122 *see I Was Glad

DURSTON, D.
All My Heart This Night Rejoices *carol
4pt/unis oct HART s.p. (D1760)

King Of Love
unis HART s.p. (D1761)
2pt oct HART s.p. (D1762)

O Little One Sweet! *carol
unis/4pt oct HART s.p. (D1763)

On Mary's Heart Her Baby Lay
unis/4pt oct HART s.p. (D1764)

DURUFLE, MAURICE (1902-   )
Four Motets On Gregorian Themes *see Tantum
Ergo; Tota Pulchra Es; Tu Es Petrus; Ubi
Caritas (D1765)

Quatre Motets *see Tantum Ergo (from Les
Themes Gregoriens); Tota Pulchra Es (from
Les Themes Gregoriens); Tu Es Petrus
(from Les Themes Gregoriens); Ubi Caritas
(from Les Themes Gregoriens) (D1766)

Quatre Motets Sur Des Themes Gregoriens *see
Tantum Ergo; Tota Pulchra Es; Tu Es
Petrus; Ubi Caritas (D1767)

Requiem *Op.9, Mass/Req
[Fr] cor,org,5strings,opt harp,trp,drums
voc sc DURAND s.p., ipa (D1768)
[Fr] 4pt mix cor,soli,orch/org voc sc
DURAND s.p., ipr (D1769)

Tantum Ergo (from Les Themes Gregoriens)
Greg/mot
SATB oct ELKAN-V $.35 see from Four Motets

DURUFLE, MAURICE (cont'd.)

On Gregorian Themes (D1770)
[Fr] 4pt mix cor,acap oct DURAND see from Quatre Motets Sur Des Themes Gregoriens (D1771)
[Lat] 3-4pt oct DURAND see from Quatre Motets (D1772)

Tota Pulchra Es (from Les Themes Gregoriens) Greg/mot
SSA oct ELKAN-V $.70 see from Four Motets On Gregorian Themes (D1773)
[Lat] 3-4pt oct DURAND see from Quatre Motets (D1774)
[Fr] 3pt wom cor,acap oct DURAND see from Quatre Motets Sur Des Themes Gregoriens (D1775)

Tu Es Petrus (from Les Themes Gregoriens) Greg/mot
SATB oct ELKAN-V $.50 see from Four Motets On Gregorian Themes (D1776)
[Fr] 4pt mix cor,acap oct DURAND see from Quatre Motets Sur Des Themes Gregoriens (D1777)
[Lat] 3-4pt oct DURAND see from Quatre Motets (D1778)

Ubi Caritas (from Les Themes Gregoriens) Greg/mot
SATB oct ELKAN-V $.70 see from Four Motets On Gregorian Themes (D1779)
[Lat] 3-4pt oct DURAND see from Quatre Motets (D1780)
[Fr] 4pt mix cor,acap oct DURAND see from Quatre Motets Sur Des Themes Gregoriens (D1781)

DUSSEK, JOHANN LADISLAUS (1760-1812)
Sweet Was The Song *Xmas
unis BOOSEY-CAN s.p. (D1782)

DUTCH CHRISTMAS CAROL *Xmas,carol,Dut
(Cockshott, G.) unis,pno LENGNICK s.p. (D1783)

DUTCH CHRISTMAS CAROL, A *Xmas,carol,Dut
(Wolff) SAB THOMP.G M-14 s.p. (D1784)

DUTEOUS DAY NOW CLOSETH, THE see Lang, C.S.

DVORAK, ANTONIN (1841-1904)
All My Heart, Inflamed And Burning *see Inflammatus

Anthem Of Praise (Psalm 149) Op.79
cor voc sc SUPRAPHON s.p. (D1785)
SATB,orch LENGNICK s.p., ipa (D1786)
(Davison, A.) SATB,org (abridged) SCHIRM.EC 1701 $.30 (D1787)

At The Foot Of The Cross *see Stabat Mater

Blessed Jesu (from Stabat Mater)
4pt mix cor oct SCHIRM.G 4490 $.35 (D1788)

Blessed Jesu, Fount Of Mercy (from Stabat Mater) Easter/Lent,anthem
mix cor,orch oct NOVELLO 28.0286.04 s.p., ipr (D1789)
SATB oct GRAY GCMR 3173 $.30 (D1790)
SATB oct PRESSER 332-09915 $.35 (D1791)
SATB oct PRO ART 1313 $.30 (D1792)
(Condie) SATB oct FISCHER,C CM-6392 $.35 (D1793)
(Tillinghast) [Eng/Lat] SSA WARNER W2852 $.30 (D1794)

Blessed Jesus
SATB oct GRAY GCMR 3173 $.30 (D1795)

Blessed Spirit, Font Of Mercy *see Eia Mater, Fons Amoris

By The Waters Of Babylon
(Mansfield, P.J.) SATB,org LENGNICK s.p. (D1796)

Eia Mater, Fons Amoris
"Blessed Spirit, Font Of Mercy" SATB,org SCHIRM.EC 2613 $.35 (D1797)

Father Of All
SATB KJOS 5272 $.35 (D1798)

Gloria (from Mass In D) Gloria
SATB oct FISCHER,C CM-7415 $.35 (D1799)

God Is My Shepherd *anthem/Bibl
(Clokey) SATB oct SUMMY B 949 $.35 (D1800)
(Snow) 3pt jr cor/SSA (med) FISCHER,C HO $.20 (D1801)
(Suchoff) SATB oct PLYMOUTH BS-103 $.25 (D1802)
(Vree, M.) SA,opt fl/ob oct PRESSER 312-40702 $.30 (D1803)
(Vree, M.) SSA,opt ob/fl oct PRESSER 312-40517 $.30 (D1804)
(Younger, John B.) SATB,S solo oct HARRIS HC4021 $.25 (D1805)

Goin' Home (from New World Symphony) anthem
SATB,SAT soli,pno/org oct HARRIS HC4010 $.40 (D1806)
SATB,org/pno LENGNICK s.p. (D1807)
(Fisher, W.) SATB,acap oct PRESSER 332-13674 $.30 (D1808)

Heart Divine
SATB oct LORENZ 9125 $.30 (D1809)

Holy, God Of Sabaoth (from Te Deum)
(Hines) SA oct LAWSON 51389 $.30 (D1810)

I Will Sing New Songs Of Gladness *Op.99, No.5, Bibl
(Black) SATB FLAMMER A 5303 $.25 (D1811)
(Heath) 4pt mix cor oct SCHIRM.G 10382 $.25 (D1812)
(Jewell, Kenneth W.) SA,pno/org oct WORLD ESA-1718-2 $.45 (D1813)
(Ross) 2pt wom cor/2pt men cor oct SCHIRM.G 8646 $.30 (D1814)

Inflammatus (from Stabat Mater)
(Sacco) "All My Heart, Inflamed And Burning" [Eng/Lat] 4pt mix cor,org oct SCHIRM.G 11538 $.35 (D1815)

Lord Is My Shepherd, The
(Macrum) SATB,S solo oct COLOMBO 582 $.30 (D1816)

DVORAK, ANTONIN (cont'd.)

(Mansfield, P.J.) SATB,org LENGNICK s.p. (D1817)

Mass In D *Op.86, Mass
[Lat] SATB,SATB soli,org,2ob,2bsn,3horn, 2trp,3trom,strings,timp voc sc NOVELLO s.p., ipr (D1818)
cor voc sc KALMUS 6165 $2.50 (D1819)
cor,orch sc KALMUS $20.00, ipa (D1820)

Morning Star *Xmas
(Allen) SATB,ABar soli oct GALLEON GCS1024 (D1821)

Oh, Here's A Day For Joyful Singing
mix cor SOUTHERN $.30 (D1822)

Psalm 149 *see Anthem Of Praise

Psalm Of Praise *Psalm
(Gardner) SATB,orch/band oct STAFF 500 $.25 (D1823)
(Gardner) SATB,band oct STAFF 500 $.25, ipa (D1824)

Requiem *Op.89, ECY,Req
mix cor,SATB soli BOOSEY voc sc $8.00, sc $20.00, min sc $10.00 (D1825)
[Ger] SATB,SATB soli,orch (med diff) sc ARTIA AP 344 s.p., cor pts ARTIA AP 344, voc sc ARTIA AP 344A s.p., min sc ARTIA AP 344B s.p., ipr (D1826)
cor voc sc KALMUS 6163 $3.00 (D1827)
cor,orch sc KALMUS $15.00, ipa (D1828)
"Requiem" [Lat] SATB,SATB soli,org,3fl,3ob, 3clar,3bsn,4horn,4trp,3trom,tuba,strings, drums,timp,harp voc sc NOVELLO s.p., ipr (D1829)

Requiem *see Requiem

Sanctus (from Requiem Mass)
(Geer, E.) [Lat/Eng] SSAA,S/A/Bar solo,pno SCHIRM.EC 893 $.45 (D1830)

Sing Ye A Joyful Song
(Woodman) SATB oct WALTON 2012 $.30 (D1831)

Sing Ye A Joyful Song Unto The Lord
(Hesch) SSA BOOSEY-CAN s.p. (D1832)

Stabat Mater *Op.58, Psntd
[Lat] 4pt mix cor,soli,orch voc sc SCHIRM.G $2.00 (D1833)
[Lat/Eng] mix cor,SATB soli BOOSEY voc sc $7.50, sc $12.50, min sc $7.50 (D1834)
[Ger] mix cor,orch LENGNICK s.p., ipa (D1835)
cor voc sc SUPRAPHON s.p. (D1836)
[Lat] SATB,SATB soli,orch (med diff) sc ARTIA AP 159 s.p., cor pts ARTIA AP 159 s.p., voc sc ARTIA AP 1256 s.p. (D1837)
mix cor,SATB soli,orch voc pt BREITKOPF-L CHB-2942A-E s.p., voc sc BREITKOPF-L EB-4005 s.p., ipr (D1838)
[Lat] SATB,SATB soli,org,2fl,2ob,2clar, 2bsn,4horn,2trp,3trom,tuba,strings,timp voc sc NOVELLO s.p., ipr (D1839)
cor voc sc KALMUS 6162 $2.00 (D1840)
cor,orch sc KALMUS $30.00, ipa (D1841)
"At The Foot Of The Cross" [Eng] mix cor, soli,pno voc sc SCHIRM.G $2.00 (D1842)
(Crowe, F.J.W.; Button, H.E.) "At The Foot Of The Cross" SATB,SATB soli,org,2fl,2ob, 2clar,2bsn,4horn,2trp,3trom,tuba,strings, timp voc sc NOVELLO s.p., ipr (D1843)

Svata Ludmila *Op.71
cor voc sc SUPRAPHON s.p. (D1844)

Te Deum *Op.103, cant/Te Deum
[Lat] SATB,SBar soli LENGNICK s.p. (D1845)
cor voc sc SUPRAPHON s.p. (D1846)
[Ger] SATB,SB soli,orch (med diff) sc ARTIA AP 1782 s.p., cor pts ARTIA AP 1782 s.p., voc sc ARTIA AP 1782A s.p. (D1847)
[Lat] BELWIN $1.00 (D1848)
cor voc sc KALMUS 6164 $2.50 (D1849)
cor,orch sc KALMUS $12.00, ipa (D1850)
(Vaugh Williams, R.) SATB,SBar soli LENGNICK s.p. (D1851)

Turn Thee To Me
SATB oct WALTON 2005 $.25 (D1852)

DVORAK, R.
Songs Of Deliverance *CCU,cant
BELWIN $1.75 (D1853)

DYKE, J.B.
Heilig, Heilig, Heilig
mix cor sc ALSBACH&D s.p. (D1854)

DYKES
Behold The Lamb Of God *Easter/Lent
(Kinsman) SATB oct SPRATT 587 $.25 (D1855)

Eternal Father, Strong To Save
(Treharne) TTBB,org/pno BOSTON 10394 $.35 (D1856)
(Treharne) SATB,org/pno BOSTON 10310 $.35 (D1857)

Holy, Holy, Holy *anthem/hymn/Sanctus
(Richardson) SAB oct SPRATT 617 $.25 (D1858)
(Richardson) SATB oct SPRATT 616 $.30 (D1859)
(Townsend) SATB oct PRO ART 1321 $.25 (D1860)
(Townsend) SAB oct PRO ART 1788 $.25 (D1861)
(Townsend) SSA oct PRO ART 1638 $.25 (D1862)
(Townsend) 2pt oct PRO ART 2023 $.25 (D1863)

Hosanna
(Robinson) SATB oct PRO ART 1895 $.22 (D1864)

Hosanna We Sing *Easter
unis oct LORENZ 8856 $.25 (D1865)

I Heard The Voice Of Jesus
(Wiley) SATB oct PRO ART 1860 $.25 (D1866)

Jesus, The Very Thought Of Thee
(Harris) SATB oct PRO ART 1458 $.20 (D1867)

O Come And Mourn With Me Awhile *Easter/Lent
(Ehret) SATB oct FISCHER,C CM-7332 $.25 (D1868)

DYKES (cont'd.)

Sleep, Holy Babe *Xmas
(Grant) SAB oct PRO ART 1927 $.25 (D1869)
(Grant) SSA oct PRO ART 1928 $.25 (D1870)
(Hansen) SAB SCHMITT 5520 $.30 (D1871)
(West) SSA SCHMITT 231 $.25 (D1872)

DYKES, JOHN BACCHUS (1823-1876)
Behold The Lamb Of God! *Easter/Lent
(Ziemer, Charles) SATB oct WALTON 2021 $.25 (D1873)

Holy, Holy, Holy
(Gilbert) SAB FLAMMER D5096 $.25 (D1874)
(Ringwald) SATB SHAWNEE A 36 $.30 (D1875)
(Ringwald) SSA SHAWNEE B 292 $.25 (D1876)

Jesus, Tender Saviour *Gen
(Dunsmore) SA SCHMITT 226 $.20 (D1877)

Jesus, The Very Thought Of Thee *Gen
(Olds) SATB SCHMITT 1866 $.25 (D1878)
(Walton) SATB oct BOOSEY 5143 $.30 (D1879)

King Of Love My Shepherd Is, The *Gen
(Olds) SATB SCHMITT 1856 $.18 (D1880)

Leid, Vriend'lijk Licht
men cor sc ALSBACH&D s.p. see also Vier Geestelijke Liederen (D1881)

My Jesus Lord, I Thee Adore
(Peery, R.) SAB oct PRESSER 312-40532 $.30 (D1882)

Sleep, Holy Babe *Xmas
SSA oct WALTON 5005 $.25 (D1883)
(Ehret) SATB oct FOX PS73 $.25 (D1884)

Vier Geestelijke Liederen *see Leid, Vriend'lijk Licht (D1885)

DYP AV NADE see Sletten, Jacob

DYSERINCK, A.
Kerstcantate *Op.1, cant
2pt wom cor,S solo,pno ALSBACH&D sc s.p., cor pts s.p. (D1886)

Kerstgedachte *Op.21
wom cor,S solo,pno sc ALSBACH&D s.p. (D1887)

Lenteliedje *Op.20
2pt wom cor,pno ALSBACH&D sc s.p., cor pts s.p. (D1888)

DYSON, GEORGE (1883-1964)
Benedicite (Shortened Form)
SATB (F maj) oct NOVELLO 44.1360.01 s.p. (D1889)

Christmas Garland, A *Xmas,cant
SSA,Mez solo,pno,opt strings voc sc NOVELLO 20.0031.08 s.p. (D1890)

Evening Service In C *Eve,Magnif/Nunc
unis (easy) oct OXFORD 42.321 $.35 (D1891)

Hierusalem *hymn
SATB,S solo,opt harp,opt org,strings voc sc NOVELLO s.p., ipr (D1892)

I Will Worship
unis oct NOVELLO 40.1337.09 s.p. (D1893)

Lauds *anthem
mix cor oct NOVELLO 45.1489.00 s.p. (D1894)

Magnificat And Nunc Dimittis *Magnif/Nunc
SATB (F maj) oct NOVELLO 44.1271.00 s.p. (D1895)

Praise
unis jr cor FISCHER,C ARD 29 $.20 (D1896)

Prayer For The Queen, A *prayer
unis oct NOVELLO 48.1778.08 s.p. (D1897)

Ye Choir Above
unis oct NOVELLO 28.1309.02 s.p. (D1898)

Ye That Do Your Master's Will *Gen
SATB (easy) oct OXFORD 42.965 $.30 (D1899)

DZISIAJ W BETLEJEM *carol,Pol
(Bement, G.) "Hark! Bethlehem" SATB,acap SCHIRM.EC 1739 $.25 (D1900)

E

E HEHU KERITO see Jillett, David

E LA DON, DON, SWEET VIRGIN MARY *Xmas,carol,
Span,16th cent
(Greenberg, N.) [Span/Eng] SATB,Bar solo,opt
perc AMP N8 $.30 see from Three Spanish
Christmas Carols   (E1)

E LA DON DON, VERGES MARIA see Greenberg

EAGER, MARY ANNE
Glory Train
SATB oct BOURNE 817 $.25   (E2)

Joyous Bells Of Christmas, The
SATB oct BOURNE 819 $.25   (E3)

Stations, The
SATB oct BOURNE 816 $.25   (E4)

EARLY CHRUCH MUSIC, VOL. 8 *see Passion
According To St. Luke   (E5)

EARLY CHURCH MUSIC, VOL. 8 *see Missa Ferialis   (E6)

EARLY EASTER MORNING see Grieb, Herbert [C.]

EARLY IN THE MORNING see Erb, Donald

EARLY IN THE MORNING see Grimes, Travis

EARLY IN THE MORNING see Hawkins, Ed.

EARLY IN THE MORNING see McCormick

EARLY, O LORD, MY FAINTING SOUL see Purcell,
Henry

EARLY ONE MORNING see Osborne

EARLY ONE MORNING see Schroth

EARLY ONE MORNING see Scott

EARLY SPRING, THE see Eliot

EARLY TUDOR MAGNIFICATS 1 *CCU,Magnif,Eng
cor STAINER 3.8204.8 $11.50   (E7)

EARLY TUDOR MASSES 1 *CCU,Mass
cor STAINER 3.8201.8 $11.50   (E8)

EARLY WILL I SEEK see Adler, Hugo Ch.

EARLY WILL I SEEK THEE see Altman, Ludwig

EARLY WILL I SEEK THEE see Bliss, Paul

EARLY WILL I SEEK THEE see Weelkes, Thomas

EARTH AND ALL STARS
see Four Folksongs And Spirituals

EARTH AND ALL STARS see Johnson, David N.

EARTH AND STARS see Johnson, David N.

EARTH DOES NOT HOLD see Thiman, Eric Harding

EARTH FEARED AND WAS SILENT, THE see Albrecht,
K.

EARTH FEARED AND WAS SILENT, THE see Ferris, W.

EARTH FEARED AND WAS SILENT, THE see Roff,
Joseph

EARTH FEARED, THE see Andrews, C.T., Terra
Tremuit

EARTH FEARED, THE see Anerio, Felice

EARTH FEARED, THE see Cirella

EARTH FEARED, THE see Mc Grath, Joseph J.

EARTH HAS GROWN OLD, THE see Manton, Robert W.

EARTH HAS MANY A NOBLE CITY see Hallstrom,
Henry

EARTH IS FULL OF THY RICHES, THE see Warren,
Raymond

EARTH IS HUSHED IN SILENCE, THE see
Mendelssohn-Bartholdy, Felix

EARTH IS THE LORD'S see Smith, R.A.

EARTH IS THE LORD'S, THE see Schutz, Heinrich

EARTH IS THE LORD'S, THE see Angell

EARTH IS THE LORD'S, THE see Bissell, Keith

EARTH IS THE LORD'S, THE see Bush, Geoffrey

EARTH IS THE LORD'S, THE see Couperin

EARTH IS THE LORD'S, THE see Giordano

EARTH IS THE LORD'S, THE see Harris

EARTH IS THE LORD'S, THE see Hollins, Alfred

EARTH IS THE LORD'S, THE see Kirkpatrick

EARTH IS THE LORD'S THE see Lang, C. Tilghman

EARTH IS THE LORD'S, THE see Lowe, Albert

EARTH IS THE LORD'S, THE see McAfee

EARTH IS THE LORD'S, THE see McCormick

EARTH IS THE LORD'S, THE see McLin

EARTH IS THE LORD'S, THE see Mitcheltree, John
Jr.

EARTH IS THE LORD'S, THE see Nikolsky, A.

EARTH IS THE LORD'S, THE see Rogers

EARTH IS THE LORD'S, THE see Thiman, Eric
Harding

EARTH REJOICES see Mozart, Wolfgang Amadeus

EARTH SHALL BE FAIR see Ward

EARTH SHALL BE FILLED, THE see Roff, Joseph

EARTH SO LOVELY see Lekberg, Sven

EARTH TODAY REJOICES *Xmas,carol
cor/cong oct MOWBRAY 65020 4 s.p. see also
Cowley Carol Book, The   (E9)
unis/SATB (easy) OXFORD 08.141 $.15   (E10)

EARTH WITH WONDERS SWEET AND FAIR see Wiley

EARTHLY FRIENDS WILL CHANGE AND FALTER
unis/SATB (easy) OXFORD 08.134 $.15   (E11)

EARTHLY TREE, A HEAVENLY FRUIT, AN see Byrd,
William

EARTHQUAKE see Peloquin, C. Alexander

EARTH'S JOY
see Two Mexican Carols

EASDALE, BRIAN (1909-   )
Missa Coventrensis *Mass
[Eng] SATB&cong,org sc CHESTER s.p.   (E12)

EAST, MICHAEL (ca. 1580-ca. 1648)
When David First Heard That Absalom Was Slain
SSATTB PETERS H1557 $.40   (E13)

When David Heard *anthem
(Le Huray) SSATBB SCHOTT 10835 s.p.   (E14)

EASTE
see EAST, MICHAEL

EASTER see Bergmann, Walter

EASTER see Giannini, V.

EASTER see Krenek, Ernst

EASTER see Lynn, George

EASTER see Prutting, R.H.

EASTER ALLELUIA see Balogh, Louis L.

EASTER ALLELUIA see Davis, Katherine K.

EASTER ALLELUIA see Larson, Earl R.

EASTER ALLELUIA see Ludlow

EASTER ALLELUIA see Schroeder

EASTER ALLELUIA see Shaw, Martin

EASTER ALLELUIA see Van Dyke

EASTER ALLELUIA, AN see Young, Gordon

EASTER ALLELUIA, AN see Burroughs, Bob

EASTER ALLELUIA, AN see Davis, Katherine K.

EASTER ALLELUIA, AN see Fuhrmann, W.A.

EASTER ALLELUIA, AN see Purvis, Richard

EASTER ALLELUIA, AN see Wilson

EASTER ANTHEM see Billings, William

EASTER ANTHEM see Gantvoort, Arnold Johann

EASTER ANTHEM see Roff, Joseph

EASTER ANTHEM see Young, C.

EASTER ANTHEMS, THE see Shaw, Martin

EASTER ANTIPHON see Kirk, Theron W.

EASTER ANTIPHON (CHRIST BEING RAISED) see
Krapf, Gerhard

EASTER BELL CAROL see Davies

EASTER BELL CAROL see Pfautsch, Lloyd

EASTER BELLS see Larson

EASTER BELLS ARE RINGING see Elmore, Robert
[Hall]

EASTER BELLS, THE see Grime, William

EASTER CALL TO WORSHIP see Grosvenor

EASTER CANTATA see Hovhaness, Alan

EASTER CANTATA see Lundquist, Matthew Nathanael

EASTER CANTATA see Pinkham, Daniel

EASTER CANTICLE see Brandon, George

EASTER CANTICLE see Kirk, Theron W.

EASTER CANTICLE see Moe, Daniel

EASTER CANTICLE, AN see Dawson

EASTER CANTICLE, AN see Towne

EASTER CANTICLE OF PRAISE see Wilson, John F.

EASTER CANTICLE, THE see Hutson

EASTER CARILLON, AN see Beck, W. Leonard

EASTER CAROL *Easter,carol
unis/SATB (very easy) OXFORD 08.147 $.15
                                                   (E15)

EASTER CAROL see Broeckx

EASTER CAROL see Byles, B. D.

EASTER CAROL see Christiansen, P.

EASTER CAROL see Dressler, John

EASTER CAROL see Glarum, L. Stanley

EASTER CAROL see Newton

EASTER CAROL see Reske

EASTER CAROL see Whitney, Maurice C.

EASTER CAROL see Williamson, Malcolm

EASTER CAROL, AN see Holler, John

EASTER CAROL, AN see Thiman, Eric Harding

EASTER CAROL, AN see Lovelace, Austin C.

EASTER CAROL, AN see Rasley

EASTER CAROL, AN see Tisserand

EASTER CAROL OF THE THREE ORPHANS see Gaul,
Alfred Robert

EASTER CAROL SERVICE, AN see Grieb, Herbert
[C.]

EASTER CAROLS NEW AND OLD *CCU,Easter/Gd.Fri./
Palm,carol
cor cmplt ed LILLENAS ME-8 $1.00   (E16)

EASTER CHANT, AN see Young, C.

EASTER CHIMES see Hutson, Wihla

EASTER CHOIR NO. I *CCUL,Easter,anthem
(easy) BIG3 $.75   (E17)

EASTER CHOIR NO. II *CCUL,Easter,anthem
(easy) BIG3 $.75   (E18)

EASTER CHORALE see Barber

EASTER CHORALE see Barber, Samuel

EASTER CHORALES see Bach, Johann Sebastian

EASTER DAWN see Baines, W.

EASTER DAWN see Hine

EASTER DAWN see Krone, B.P.

EASTER DAWN see Nolte

EASTER DAWNING AT THE TOMB see Wetzler, Robert

EASTER DAY see Arensky, Anton Stepanovitch,
Jour De Paques

EASTER DAY see Sharpe, Evelyn

EASTER DAY CAROL see Lovelace, Austin C.

EASTER DAY, NO MAN MAY see Garlick, Anthony

EASTER DIALOGUE see Schutz, Heinrich

EASTER DIALOGUE, AN see Hammerschmidt, Andreas

EASTER EGGS *Easter,folk,Russ
(Shaw) 4pt mix cor,ST/Bar soli oct SCHIRM.G
9956 $.25   (E19)

EASTER FANFARE see Blahnik, J.

EASTER FANFARE see Ferguson, Howard

EASTER FANFARE see Peninger

EASTER FANFARE see Pfautsch, Lloyd

EASTER FANFARE see Walton

EASTER FANFARE: CHRIST THE LORD IS RISEN see
Fetler, Paul

EASTER FLOWERS ARE BLOOMING BRIGHT *Easter/
Lent
(Holmes) SATB oct PRO ART 1761 $.20   (E20)

EASTER FOLK STYLE see Hadler

EASTER HALLELUJAH see Vulpius, Melchior

EASTER HALLELUJAH, AN see Vulpius, Melchior

EASTER HALLELUJAH, THE see Lorenz

EASTER HOPE see Balson

EASTER HYMN see Bantock, Granville, Cantique De
Paques

EASTER HYMN see Lester

EASTER HYMN see Lynn, George

EASTER HYMN see Vaughan Williams, Ralph

EASTER HYMN OF PRAISE see Lapo, Cecil E.

EASTER HYMNS AND CAROLS *CC11L,Easter,carol
(Collins) unis/SA/SAB PRO ART 266 $.60   (E21)

EASTER IN HEAVEN see Lowell

EASTER INTROIT see Demarest, A.

EASTER INTROIT see Wells

EASTER INTROIT see Williams, D.

EASTER INTROIT, AN see Slater

EASTER IS A SONG see Davis, Katherine K.

EASTER JOY see Osterfreude

EASTER LAUD, AN *Easter,Eng
(Pizarro, David) SATB oct GRAY GCMR 2508 $.30
                                                 *(E22)

EASTER LILIES see Walton

EASTER MEDITATION see Heiden, Bernhard

EASTER MEDITATION SONG see Smith, H. Hamilton

EASTER MESSAGE see Scholin, C. Albert

EASTER MESSAGE, AN
SSA CHAPPELL 0017871-354 $.40 (E23)
SATB CHAPPELL 0017871-358 $.40 (E24)

EASTER MESSIAH see Handel, George Frideric

EASTER MIRACLE OF ST. ANNE DE BEAUPRE see Gaul, Harvey Bartlet

EASTER MORN see Plank, David L.

EASTER MORNING see Christiansen, Paul

EASTER MORNING see Kountz

EASTER (MOST GLORIOUS LORD OF LYFE) see Gibbs, [Cecil] Armstrong

EASTER ON EARTH see Roff, Joseph

EASTER ORATORIO see Bach, Johann Sebastian

EASTER PAEAN see Williams

EASTER PASSACAGLIA see Riegger, Wallingford

EASTER PRAISE see Martin

EASTER PRAISES see Wilhelm

EASTER PROCESSIONAL, AN see Near, Gerald

EASTER PSALM see Ruh

EASTER REVELATION, THE *Easter,cant
LORENZ $1.00 (E25)

EASTER SEQUENCE see Leighton, Kenneth

EASTER SEQUENCE see Naylor, Bernard, Sequentia Paschalis

EASTER SERVICE see McKinney, Howard D.

EASTER SONG see Davies

EASTER SONG see Dowdy

EASTER SONG see Fehrmann

EASTER SONG see Gardner, Gloria

EASTER SONG see Howard, Edward F.

EASTER SONG see Owen

EASTER SONG see Steer, Michael

EASTER SONGS FOR COMMUNITY SINGING see Stickles

EASTER STORY, THE see Williams

EASTER STORY, THE see Reed, Robert B.

EASTER STORY, THE see Hustad, Donald P.

EASTER TIDE see Pearson, Edith

EASTER TRIUMPH see Rogers

EASTER VICTORY see Upshur

EASTER VICTORY, THE see Bruner

EASTERN HEAVENS ARE ALL AGLOW, THE see Edwards, Clara

EASTERTIDE see Bliss, Paul

EASTERTIDE see Protheroe, Daniel

EASY ANTHEMS FOR INTERMEDIATE CHOIRS, BOOK 1 see Nevin, Gordon Balch

EASY ANTHEMS FOR INTERMEDIATE CHOIRS, BOOK 2 see Nevin, Gordon Balch

EASY ANTHEMS FOR INTERMEDIATE CHOIRS, BOOK 3 see Nevin, Gordon Balch

EASY ANTHEMS FOR MIX VOICES, BOOK II see Johnson, David N.

EASY ANTHEMS FOR MIXED VOICES, BOOK I see Johnson, David N.

EASY ANTHEMS WITH DESCANTS see Rhea

EASY CHOIR RESPONSES NO. 1 *CCU,cor-resp
SATB LORENZ A171 $.30 (E26)

EASY CHOIR RESPONSES NO. 2 *CCU,cor-resp
SATB LORENZ A399 $.30 (E27)

EASY CHORALE ANTHEMS *CCU,anthem
SATB LORENZ $1.75 (E28)

EASY COMMUNION SERVICE, AN see Willan, Healey, Missa De Sancto Albano In E Flat

EASY HYMN-TUNE ANTHEMS *CCU,anthem
SATB LORENZ $1.75 (E29)

EASY RESPONSES see Walters

EASY STANDARD ANTHEMS NO. 1 *CCU,anthem
SATB LORENZ $1.95 (E30)

EASY STANDARD ANTHEMS NO. 2 *CCU,anthem
SATB LORENZ $1.75 (E31)

EATON, JOHN (1935-)
One Is For The Christ Child *Xmas
SATB,pno/gtr oct FOX UM136 $.45 (E32)

EATON, RICHARD S.
Blest Are The Pure In Heart *Gen
SATB (very easy) oct OXFORD 42.978 $.30 (E33)

EATON, RICHARD S. (cont'd.)

O Holy Spirit, Lord Of Grace
SATB,S/T solo,org oct BERANDOL 910E5AA $.35 (E34)

EBELING
Christ Is Born *Xmas
(Kirk) SATB oct PRO ART 1932 $.25 (E35)

Rejoice This Night
(Christiansen, O.) SATB KJOS 36 $.30 (E36)

EBELING, J.
Ah Lord God The World's Creator
(Roff, J.) SATB oct PRESSER 332-40057 $.25 (E37)

All My Heart This Night Rejoices *anthem
(Bender) SATB (med) oct AUGSBURG 1376 $.25 (E38)
(Bender) unis treb cor,opt inst (easy/med) oct AUGSBURG 1375 $.20 (E39)
(Pooler) unis treb cor&desc (easy) oct AUGSBURG 1504 $.25 (E40)

Du Meine Seele, Singe *Gen
[Ger] SATB,2vln,opt cont BAREN. BA 772 s.p. (E41)

EBELING, JOHANN GEORG (1637-1676)
Auf, Auf, Mein Herz, Mit Freuden
see Ebeling, Johann Georg, Die Guldne Sonne Voll Freud Und Wonne

Die Guldne Sonne Voll Freud Und Wonne
SATB,2inst HANSSLER 6.041 s.p. contains also: Auf, Auf, Mein Herz, Mit Freuden (E42)

Du Meine Seele, Singe
see Barner, A., Es Ist Etwas, Des Heilands Sein

Du Meine Seele, Singe, Wohlauf
see Cruger, Johann, Jesus, Mein Zuversicht Und Mein Heiland

Warum Sollt Ich Mich Denn Gramen
SATB,2inst HANSSLER 6.043 s.p. contains also: Cruger, Johann, Auf, Auf, Mein Herz, Mit Freuden (E43)

Zwolf Geistliche Lieder Paul Gerhardts *CC12U,Gen
(Ameln, Konrad) [Ger] SATB,2vln,opt cont (med) BAREN. BA 775 $2.50 (E44)

EBEN, PETR (1929-)
Ubi Caritas Et Amor Dei *Gen,anti
[Lat] SSATBB,acap (med diff) BAREN. BA 5404 $2.50 (E45)

EBERLIN
Christ Atoned For Our Transgressions
(Pauly) mix cor SOUTHERN $.25 (E46)

Remember Our Savior *Lent
(Pauly) SATB SCHMITT 1422 $.35 (E47)

Remember Our Saviour *Lent
mix cor SOUTHERN $.30 (E48)
(Pauly) SATB oct SOUTHERN $.30 (E49)

EBERLIN, JOHANN ERNST (1702-1762)
Audiutor In Opportunitatibus *Lent
(Pauly) "O Savior, Our Refuge" [Eng/Lat] 4pt mix cor,acap oct SCHIRM.G 10730 $.25 (E50)

Bonum Est Confiteri
(Pauly) "Trust In The Lord" [Eng/Lat] 4pt mix cor,acap oct SCHIRM.G 10728 $.25 (E51)

Christ Atoned For Our Transgressions *see Christus Factus Est

Christus Factus Est *Easter/Lent
(Marshall, Charles) "Jesus Christ, Our Lord, For Our Sake" SATB FRANK F-605 $.30 (E52)
(Pauly) "Christ Atoned For Our Transgressions" SATB SCHMITT 1415 $.35 (E53)

God Is Holy *see Sciant Gentes

God Our Father *see Tu Es Deus

Grief Is In My Heart *see Improperium Exspectavit Cor Meum

Improperium Exspectavit Cor Meum *Palm
(Pauly) "Grief Is In My Heart" [Eng/Lat] 4pt mix cor,acap oct SCHIRM.G 10731 $.25 (E54)

Jesus Christ, Our Lord, For Our Sake *see Christus Factus Est

Let Us Praise Him! *Gen
(Pauly) SATB SCHMITT 1414 $.30 (E55)

O Savior, Our Refuge *see Audiutor In Opportunitatibus

Sciant Gentes *Gen
(Pauly) "God Is Holy" SATB SCHMITT 1413 $.35 (E56)

Trust In The Lord *see Bonum Est Confiteri

Tu Es Deus *Lent
(Pauly) "God Our Father" [Eng/Lat] 4pt mix cor,acap oct SCHIRM.G 10729 $.25 (E57)

ECCARD, JOHANNES (1553-1611)
All Glory Be To Thee, Most High
(Ehret) SATB,acap MARKS 4114 $.30 (E58)

Allein Gott In Der Hoh Sei Ehr
SATTB,opt cont HANSSLER 37.021 s.p. (E59)

Chorgesange *CC29U
(Berger) 4-8pt HANSSLER 4.002 s.p. (E60)

Christ Is Arisen *Easter,mot
(Klein) 5pt mix cor,acap oct SCHIRM.G 13394 $.25 (E61)

Christ Is Erstanden Von Der Marter *Easter
SATTB,opt cont HANSSLER 37.016 s.p. (E62)

Christ Ist Erstanden Von Der Marter *mot
(Berger) SSATB HANSSLER 1.068 s.p. (E63)

ECCARD, JOHANNES (cont'd.)

Christ Lag In Todesbanden, Fur Unsre (from Matthaus-Passion) Holywk/Psntd
SATTB/SAATB HANSSLER 6.121 s.p. (E64)
mix cor,opt cont HANSSLER 37.015 s.p. (E65)

Christe, Der Du Bist Tag Und Licht
SATTB,opt cont HANSSLER 37.009 s.p. (E66)

Christum Wir Sollen Loben Schon
SATTB,opt cont HANSSLER 37.002 s.p. (E67)

Christus, Der Uns Selig Macht
SATTB,opt cont HANSSLER 37.010 s.p. (E68)

Da Jesus An Dem Kreuze Stund *Gd.Fri./Holywk
SATTB,opt cont HANSSLER 37.011 s.p. (E69)

Das Konigsbanner Zieht Voraus
(Berger, H.L.) TTBB HANSSLER 6.5132 s.p. (E70)

Dear Christians, Let One And All Rejoice *Gen
(Buszin) SATBB SCHMITT 1551 $.18 (E71)

Der Heilig Geist Vom Himmel Kam *Easter
SATB HANSSLER 6.262 s.p. contains also: Zu Dieser Osterlichen Zeit (E72)

Der Heilige Geist Vom Himmel Kam
4pt mix cor MOSELER LB-91 s.p. (E73)

Der Herr Jesus Mein Hirte Ist *mot
(Berger) SATB HANSSLER 1.081 s.p. (E74)

Der Tag, Der Ist So Freudenreich
SATTB,opt cont HANSSLER 37.005 s.p. (E75)

Entre Le Beouf Et L'ane Gris
"Ox And Ass He Does Not Shun!" see Eccard, Johannes, When To The Temple Mary Went

Es Kam Ein Engel Hell Und Klar *Xmas
[Ger] SSATB,acap (med easy) MULLER MS 69 s.p. (E76)

Freu Dich, Du Werte Christenheit
SATTB HANSSLER 6.2519 s.p. contains also: Wach Auf, Du Werte Christenheit (SSATTB) (E77)

Freut Euch, Ihr Christen Alle, Gott Schenkt Uns Seinen Sohn
SATTB/SAATB HANSSLER 6.133 s.p. (E78)

Freut Euch, Ihr Lieben Christen
SATB HANSSLER 6.100 s.p. (E79)

Geistliche Lieder 1597 Teil I *CCU
5pt mix cor MOSELER s.p. (E80)

Geistliche Lieder 1597 Teil II *CCU
5pt mix cor MOSELER s.p. (E81)

Gelobet Seist Du, Jesu Christ
SATTB,opt cont HANSSLER 37.003 s.p. (E82)

Gott Der Vater Wohn Uns Bei
SATTB,opt cont HANSSLER 37.020 s.p. (E83)

Guds Riges Evangelium
(Sorensen, Soren) [Dan] SATTB HANSEN-DEN 305 s.p. see also Kirkelige Festsange (E84)

Have Done Dull Care *Easter
SATB,acap oct PRESSER MC202 $.30 (E85)

Herr Christ, Der Einig Gotts Sohn
SATBB HANSSLER 6.107 s.p. (E86)

Herr Christe, Tu Mir Geben
(Schabasser, Josef) mix cor,acap oct DOBLINGER s.p. see also CHRISTUS, DER HERR (E87)

Herr Gott, Dich Loben Wir
SATTB,opt cont HANSSLER 37.023 s.p. (E88)

Herr Jesu Christ, Wahr' Mensch
SATTB,opt cont HANSSLER 37.012 s.p. (E89)

Herr, Wie Du Willst
SATTB,acap DOBLINGER s.p. see also BITTE UND VERTRAUEN (E90)

Herr, Wie Du Willst, So Schicks Mit Mir
SATTB HANSSLER 6.137 s.p. contains also: Osiander, Lucas, Herr, Wie Du Willst, So Schicks Mit Mir (SATB) (E91)

Hosanna To The Living God
mix cor SOUTHERN $.25 (E92)

Ich Lag In Tiefer Todesnacht *Psntd
TTTBB HANSSLER 6.0148 s.p. (E93)

Ich Steh An Deiner Krippen Hier *Xmas
SAATB/SATTB,opt cont HANSSLER 37.037-1 s.p. (E94)

Im Garten Leidet Christus Not *Easter/Psntd
SSATTB,acap voc pt DOBLINGER s.p. see also PASSION UND OSTERN (E95)

In Dulci Jubilo *Xmas
SATBB,acap (med diff) oct CONCORDIA 98-2097 $.25 (E96)
SSTTB HANSSLER 37.007 s.p. (E97)
(Sorensen, Soren) "Om Kristi Fodsel" [Dan] SATTB,acap HANSEN-DEN 299 s.p. see also Kirkelige Festsange (E98)
(Straube, K.) 5pt mix cor,acap cor pts BREITKOPF-L CHB-2433 s.p. (E99)

Jesus Christus, Unser Heiland, Der Den Tod Uberwand
SSATB,opt cont HANSSLER 37.014 s.p. (E100)

Jesus, The Lord, The Mighty God *Easter
SSATTB,acap oct PRESSER 312-40360 $.30 (E101)

Kirkelige Festsange *Fest
(Sorenson, Soren) [Dan] 4-6pt mix cor HANSEN-DEN 27092 s.p.
contains & see also: Guds Riges Evangelium; In Dulci Jubilo, "Om Kristi Fodsel"; Kom, Hedningers Frelsermand; Maria Gar Over Bjergene; O, Jesus! Guds Udkarne; Pa Sct. Michaels Dag (Hvor Lader Gud Sin Kristenhed); Til Mariae

ECCARD, JOHANNES (cont'd.)

Renselsesfest (Maria Gar Sin
Tempelgang); Til Paskefesten (For Denne
Paskemorgens Fryd); Til Pinsefesten
(Den Helligand Fra Himlen Kom)   (E102)

Kom, Hedningers Frelsermand
(Sorensen, Soren) [Dan] SATTB,acap HANSEN-
DEN 298 s.p. see also Kirkelige Festsange
(E103)

Komm, Gott Schopfer, Heiliger Geist
SATTB,opt cont HANSSLER 37.017 s.p.   (E104)

Komm, Heiliger Geist, Herre Gott
SATTB,opt cont HANSSLER 37.018 s.p.   (E105)

Krist Ar Uppstanden
see UPPSTANDELSE

Maria Gar Over Bjergene
(Sorensen, Soren) SSATB,acap HANSEN-
DEN 301 s.p. see also Kirkelige Festsange
(E106)

Maria Wallt Zum Heiligtum *BVM,mot
SSATBB,acap voc pt DOBLINGER s.p. see also
UNSERE LIEBE FRAU   (E107)
(Berger) SAATTB HANSSLER 1.126 s.p.   (E108)

Maria Wallt Zum Heligtum
(Straube, K.) 6pt mix cor,acap cor pts
BREITKOPF-L PB-2683 s.p., voc pt
BREITKOPF-L CHB-2428 s.p.   (E109)

Mary's Salutation *anthem
mix cor oct OXFORD 43.453 $.25   (E110)
(Parkinson) SSATB,acap OXFORD   (E111)
(Parkinson) SSAT,acap OXFORD   (E112)

Meine Seele Erhebt Den Herrn
SATTB,opt cont HANSSLER 37.022 s.p.   (E113)

Missa A 5 Vocibus *Mass/mot
(Hermann) SSATB HANSSLER 1.327 s.p.   (E114)

Mit Ernst, O Menschenkinder
SATTB/SAATB HANSSLER 6.089 s.p.   (E115)

Mit Fried Und Freud Ich Fahr Dahin
SATTB,opt cont HANSSLER 37.008 s.p.   (E116)

Nach Dem Die Sonn Beschlossen
SSATB HANSSLER 6.106 s.p. contains also:
Hassler, Hans Leo, In Gottes Namen Fahren
Wir (SATB)   (E117)

Nun Bitten Wir Den Heiligen Geist
SATTB,opt cont HANSSLER 37.019 s.p.   (E118)

Nun Freut Euch, Lieben Christen Gmein
SATB,opt cont HANSSLER 37.037 s.p.   (E119)

Nun Komm, Der Heiden Heiland *Xmas
SATTB HANSSLER 6.085 s.p. contains also:
Trubel, Gerhard, Nun Komm, Der Heiden
Heiland (SAB)   (E120)
SATTB,opt cont HANSSLER 37.001 s.p.   (E121)
(Richardson) "Saviour Of The Nations, Come"
SATBB oct SPRATT 2010 $.25   (E122)

Nun Singet Und Seid Froh (from In Dulci
Jubilo)
SATTB,opt cont HANSSLER 37.007-1 s.p.
(E123)

O Freude Uber Freud *mot
(Hermann) dbl cor HANSSLER 1.019 s.p.
(E124)
(Payson) "O Joy Above All Joy" mix cor
SOUTHERN $.30   (E125)
(Payson, A.) "O Joy Above All Joy" SSAATTBB
FRANK F-539 $.30   (E126)

O Freude Uber Freude *Adv/Xmas
SATB&SATB,acap voc pt DOBLINGER s.p. see
also ADVENT UND WEIHNACHT, HEFT 1   (E127)

O, Jesus! Guds Udkarne
(Sorensen, Soren) [Dan] SATTB,acap HANSEN-
DEN 297 s.p. see also Kirkelige Festsange
(E128)

O Joy Above All Joy *see O Freude Uber
Freud'

O Kriste, Oss Benada
[Swed] SATB,acap GEHRMANS KRB 319   (E129)

O Lamb Of God *Commun
(Lundquist) SATB,acap oct WILLIS 8405 $.18
(E130)
(Nott, David) SATTB/SATBB (med) ABINGDON
APM-584 $.25   (E131)

O Lamb Of God Most Holy *see O Lamm Gottes
Unschuldig

O Lamm Gottes Unschuldig *Easter/Lent/Psntd
5pt mix cor MOSELER LB-79 s.p.   (E132)
SATTB,acap voc pt DOBLINGER s.p. see also
PASSION UND OSTERN   (E133)
(Klein) "O Lamb Of God Most Holy" [Eng/Ger]
5pt mix cor,acap oct SCHIRM.G 11340 $.30
(E134)
(Marshall, Charles) "O Lamb Of God Most
Holy" SATBB FRANK F-583 $.30   (E135)

O Lamm Gottes, Unschuldig, Am Stamm
SATTB,opt cont HANSSLER 37.013 s.p.   (E136)
SATTB HANSSLER 37.013 s.p.   (E137)

Om Kristi Fodsel *see In Dulci Jubilo

Ostergesang *Easter
[Ger] mix cor,acap (med) HUG s.p.   (E138)

Over The Hills Maria Went *see Uber's Gebirg
Maria Geht

Ox And Ass He Does Not Shun! *see Entre Le
Beouf Et L'ane Gris

Pa Sct. Michaels Dag (Hvor Lader Gud Sin
Kristenhed)
(Sorensen, Soren) [Dan] SSATB HANSEN-DEN
304 s.p. see also Kirkelige Festsange
(E139)

Presentation Of Christ
(Damrosch, F.) SSATBB,acap oct SCHIRM.G
2618 $.30   (E140)

ECCARD, JOHANNES (cont'd.)

Presentation Of Christ In The Temple *anthem
SSATBB oct NOVELLO 03.0123.10 s.p.   (E141)

Resonet In Laudibus
SATTB,opt cont HANSSLER 37.006 s.p.   (E142)

Saviour Of The Nations, Come *see Nun Komm
Der Heiden Heiland

Sei Frohlich Alle Zeit
see Hassler, Hans Leo, Gott, Der Vater,
Wohn Uns Bei

Sweet Mary To The Temple Fares
mix cor SOUTHERN $.25   (E143)

Til Mariae Renselsesfest (Maria Gar Sin
Tempelgang)
(Sorensen, Soren) [Dan] SSATTB,acap HANSEN-
DEN 300 s.p. see also Kirkelige Festsange
(E144)

Til Paskefesten (For Denne Paskemorgens Fryd)
(Sorensen, Soren) [Dan] SSATTB,acap HANSEN-
DEN 302 s.p. see also Kirkelige Festsange
(E145)

Til Pinsefesten (Den Helligand Fra Himlen
Kom)
(Sorensen, Soren) [Dan] SATB,acap HANSEN-
DEN 303 s.p. see also Kirkelige Festsange
(E146)

Till Templet Jesusbarnet Kom
6pt mix cor NORDISKA 1455 s.p.   (E147)

Ubers Gebirg Maria Geht *BVM
SSATB,acap voc pt DOBLINGER s.p. see also
UNSERE LIEBE FRAU   (E148)
(Geiringer) "Over The Hills Maria Went"
[Eng/Ger] SSATB,acap oct SCHIRM.G 8420
$.30   (E149)
(Straube, K.) 5pt mix cor,acap cor pts
BREITKOPF-L CHB-2432 s.p.   (E150)

Ubers Gebirg Maria Geht, Halt Einkehr *BVM
SSATB HANSSLER 6.204 s.p.   (E151)

Vater Unser Im Himmelreich *prayer
[Ger] SATB,acap (med easy) BAREN. BA 6306
s.p.   (E152)
SATTB/SAATB HANSSLER 6.150 s.p. contains
also: Werner, Fritz, Vater Unser Im
Himmelreich (SAB/SAT)   (E153)

Verleih Uns Frieden Gnadiglich
SATTB/SAATB HANSSLER 6.154 s.p. contains
also: Schein, Johann Hermann, Ein Wahrer
Glaube Gotts Zorn Stillt (SATB)   (E154)
SATTB HANSSLER 6.2174 s.p.   (E155)

Vom Himmel Hoch Da Komm Ich Her *Adv/Xmas
SATTB HANSSLER 6.241 s.p.   (E156)
SSATB,opt cont HANSSLER 37.004 s.p.   (E157)
SSATB,acap voc pt DOBLINGER s.p. see also
ADVENT UND WEIHNACHT, HEFT 1   (E158)

Wach Auf, Du Werte Christenheit
see Eccard, Johannes, Freu Dich, Du Werte
Christenheit

Was Mein Gott Will, Das G'scheh Allzeit
SATTB,acap DOBLINGER s.p. see also BITTE
UND VERTRAUEN   (E159)

When To The Temple Mary Went *Xmas
(Davies, L.H.) 2pt ASHDOWN E.A.302 s.p.
contains also: Entre Le Beouf Et L'ane
Gris, "Ox And Ass He Does Not Shun!"   (E160)
(Davies, Laurence H.) SATB ENOCH EC326 s.p.
(E161)
(Davis, K.) SA SCHIRM.EC 1580   (E162)

Wir Singen All Mit Freudenschall *mot
(Hermann) SSAB&ATTB HANSSLER 1.020 s.p.
(E163)

Wo Ist Dein Stachel Nun, O Tod?
SSATTB HANSSLER 6.2518 s.p.   (E164)

Zu Dieser Osterlichen Zeit *Easter/Psntd
see Eccard, Johannes, Der Heilig Geist Vom
Himmel Kam
4pt mix cor MOSELER LB-88 s.p. contains
also: Hassler, Hans Leo, Jesus Christus,
Unser Heiland   (E165)
SSATTB,acap voc pt DOBLINGER s.p. see also
PASSION UND OSTERN   (E166)

Zu Dieser Osterlichen Zeit *Easter
SATB HANSSLER 6.123 s.p. contains also: Zu
Dieser Osterlichen Zeit (SSATTB)   (E167)

Zu Dieser Osterlichen Zeit
see Eccard, Johannes, Zu Dieser Osterlichen
Zeit

ECCE ADVENIT see Jaeggi, Oswald

ECCE ADVOCATUS MEUS see Schutz, Heinrich

ECCE ANCILLA DOMINI see Dufay, Guillaume

ECCE ANNUNTIO VOBIS see Ramella

ECCE ASCENDIMUS JEROSOLYMAM see Back, Sven-
Erick

ECCE CONCIPIES see Gallus, Jacobus

ECCE CONCIPIES see Handel, George Frideric

ECCE, DOMINUS VENIET see Bialas, Gunther

ECCE DOMINUS VENIET see Victoria, Tomas Luis de

ECCE EGO JOANNES see Palestrina, Giovanni

ECCE FIDELIS SERVUS see Arnaldi, Antonio

ECCE FIDELIS SERVUS see Bottazzo, Luigi

ECCE GRATUM see Foss, Julius

ECCE HOMO see Reda, Siegfried

ECCE LIGNUM CRUCISC see Kropfreiter,
Augustinius Franz

ECCE MANUS TRADENTIS see Davies, Peter Maxwell

ECCE MARIA GENUIT NOBIS see Lasso, Rudolph de

ECCE NUNC BENEDICITE DOMINO see Buxtehude,
Dietrich

ECCE NUNC BENEDICITE DOMINO see Buxtehude,
Dietrich, Siehe, Lobet Den Herrn

ECCE NUNC TEMPUS see Guerrero, Francisco

ECCE PANIS see Busser, [Henri-Paul]

ECCE PANIS see Corradini, Vasco Lodovico

ECCE PANIS see Dubois, Theodore

ECCE PANIS see Mendelssohn-Bartholdy, Felix

ECCE PANIS see Reuchsel, L.

ECCE PANIS see Schumann, Robert (Alexander)

ECCE PANIS see Vivet, A.

ECCE PANIS ANGELORUM see Lotti, Antonio

ECCE PRANDIUM see Sweelinck, Jan Pieterszoon

ECCE QUAM BONUM see Clemens, Jacobus

ECCE, QUAM BONUM see Hassler, Hans Leo

ECCE QUOMODO MORITUR see Diepenbrock, Alfons

ECCE QUOMODO MORITUR see Gallus, Jacobus

ECCE QUOMODO MORITUR see Ingegneri, Marco
Antonio

ECCE, QUOMODO MORITUR see Palestrina, Giovanni

ECCE QUOMODO MORITUR see Victoria, Tomas Luis
de

ECCE QUOMODO MORITUR JUSTUS see Gallus, Jacobus

ECCE! QUOMODO MORITUR JUSTUS see Haydn,
(Johann) Michael

ECCE QUOMODO MORITUR JUSTUS see Ingegneri,
Marco Antonio

ECCE QUOMODO MORITUR JUSTUS see Palestrina,
Giovanni

ECCE QUOMODO MORITUS JUSTUS see Gallus, Jacobus

ECCE SACERDOS see Ahrens, Joseph

ECCE SACERDOS see Ascenso, Antonio

ECCE SACERDOS see Bardos, Ludwig

ECCE SACERDOS see Baumann, Max

ECCE SACERDOS see Branchina, Pietro

ECCE SACERDOS see Bruckner, Anton

ECCE SACERDOS see Ferrari, Giuseppe

ECCE SACERDOS see Jochum, Otto

ECCE SACERDOS see Kaufmann, Ferdinand

ECCE SACERDOS see Volpi, Edoardo

ECCE SACERDOS MAGNUS see Arnaldi, Antonio

ECCE SACERDOS MAGNUS see Bottazzo, Luigi

ECCE SACERDOS MAGNUS see Ceccato, Arnaldo

ECCE SACERDOS MAGNUS see Haas, Joseph

ECCE SACERDOS MAGNUS see Palestrina, Giovanni

ECCE SACERDOS MAGNUS see Pasini, Crescenzio

ECCE SACERDOS MAGNUS see Ravanello, Oreste

ECCE SACERDOS MAGNUS see Rioda, Umberto

ECCE SACERDOS MAGNUS see Trexler, Georg

ECCE SACERDOS MAGNUS see Victoria, Tomas Luis
de

ECCE SACERDOS MAGNUS see Waldbroel, Wilhelm

ECCE SIC BENEDICETUR HOMO see Carlos V

ECCE TU PULCHRA ES see Palestrina, Giovanni

ECCE VIDIMUS see Ingegneri, Marco Antonio

ECCE, VIDIMUS EUM see Ingegneri, Marco Antonio

ECCE VIDIMUS EUM see Palestrina, Giovanni

ECCE VIDIMUS EUM see Rubbra, Edmund

ECCE VIRGO CONCIPIENT see Fux, Johann Joseph

ECCE VIRGO CONCIPIET see Morales, Cristobal de

ECCHER
Ave Maria *Mass
4pt men cor/4pt mix cor,org s.p. voc sc
RICORDI-ENG 128181, cor pts RICORDI-ENG
128223-26   (E168)
3-4pt men cor,org s.p. sc RICORDI-ENG
128314, voc pt RICORDI-ENG 128315-18
(E169)
Deici Madrigali Sacri (from Cantico Delle
Creature Di S. Francesco Di Assisi)
CC10U,madrigal
TTBB,acap s.p. sc RICORDI-ENG 128651, voc
pt RICORDI-ENG 128652-55   (E170)

Due Graduale Et Tractus Pro Palmis Et
Parasceve *CC3U,Gradual
4pt men cor,acap cor pts RICORDI-ENG 129048
s.p.   (E171)

ECCHER (cont'd.)

Relaxa Facinora *Mass
TTBB,org s.p. sc RICORDI-ENG 128408, voc pt
RICORDI-ENG 128409-12   (E172)

Requiem Messa E Assoluzione
2 eq voices,org s.p. voc sc RICORDI-ENG
128039, cor pts RICORDI-ENG 128040-41
                                             (E173)

Sei Responsori Per La Settimana Santa *CC6U,
Holywk
4pt men cor sc RICORDI-ENG 129041 s.p.
                                             (E174)

ECCHER, CELESTINO
Missa Stabat Juxta Crucem *Op.205, Mass
4 eq voices,org sc SANTIS 904 s.p., cor pts
SANTIS 905A-B s.p.   (E175)

ECCHIENUS, CASPAR
Cor Mundum Crea In Me, Deus *mot
4pt mix cor,acap sc SKAND. SMF5317 s.p.
                                             (E176)

ECCO'L MESSIA
see Three Christmas Laude

ECELESIASTES see Starer, Robert, Kohelet

ECHO see Smart, David

ECHO ALLELUIA see Gardano, Alessandro

ECHO ALLELUIA see Young

ECHO CAROL (from Anthology Of Carols, An)
see Christo Paremus Cantica

ECHO CAROL see Forsblad

ECHO NOEL see Rhea, A.

ECHO OF CHRISTMAS, THE see Lorenz

ECHO SONG see Lassus, Roland de (Orlandus)

ECHOD HU ELOHENU see Weisgal, A.

ECHOES ARE SOUNDING *carol,Pol
(Barthelson) SATB MARKS 4004 $.25   (E177)

ECHOES OF ANGELS see Brandt

ECHOES OF CHRISTMAS EVE see Lorenz

ECHOING ALLELUIA see James, Allen

ECHOING HOSANNA see James

ECHOS DU MONDE RELIGIEUX *CCU
(Vecchi, Prof. Giuseppe) cor FORNI 28 s.p.
                                             (E178)

ECHOS DU MONDE RELIGIEUX VOL. 1: A LA MESSE
*CCU
[Lat] SATB oct DURAND s.p.   (E179)

ECHOS DU MONDE RELIGIEUX VOL. 2: AUS SALUTS
*CCU,Greg
[Lat] cor,org oct DURAND s.p.   (E180)

ECHOS DU MONDE RELIGIEUX VOL. 6: RECUEIL DE
CANTIQUES *CCU,hymn/liturg
[Fr] cor oct DURAND s.p.   (E181)

EDEN-GETHSEMANE see Marks, Gunther

EDER, HELMUT (1916-   )
Gott, Hulle Dich Nicht In Schweigen (Psalm
83) Gen
[Ger] SATB,acap (med diff) BAREN. BA 5405
s.p.   (E182)

Psalm 83 *see Gott, Hulle Dich Nicht In
Schweigen

EDERS HELE VAERK see Buxtehude, Dietrich,
Alles, Was Ihr Tut

EDLUND, LARS
Beautifications, The *see Saligprisningarna

Gloria *Gloria
mix cor,T solo NORDISKA NMS-10.260 s.p.
                                             (E183)

Helige Fralsare *mot
[Swed] SATB,acap GEHRMANS KRB 316   (E184)

Maria *Xmas
mix cor,TBar soli,acap NORDISKA NMS-6385
s.p.   (E185)

Motett Pa Heliga Trefaldighets Dag *mot
[Swed] ATB,acap GEHRMANS KRB 315   (E186)

Saligprisningarna *Bibl/cant
"Beautifications, The" [Eng/Swed] mix cor,
orch NORDISKA NMS-10.256 s.p., ipa (E187)

EDMONDS
In Peace And Joy I Now Depart
SATB,acap SHAWNEE A 546 $.25   (E188)

EDMONDS, PAUL
Good Master And Mistress *Xmas
cor CRAMER 81 s.p.   (E189)

Holly And Ivy
2pt boy cor CRAMER 97 s.p.   (E190)

EDMUNDH, GEORG
Glad Dig, Du Kristi Brud
mix cor NORDISKA 3655 s.p.   (E191)

EDMUNDS, DORIS
Bethany Carol, A *Xmas
cor CRAMER 115 s.p.   (E192)
unis jr cor CRAMER 115 s.p.   (E193)

EDMUNDS, JOHN (1913-   )
All That 'lieve In Christian Lay
see Son Is Born, A, Five Carols To Old
English Texts

Babe Is Born All Of A May, A
see Son Is Born, A, Five Carols To Old
English Texts

Be Merry Be Merry
see Son Is Born, A, Five Carols To Old
English Texts

EDMUNDS, JOHN (cont'd.)

Blessed Be That Lord In Majesty
see Son Is Born, A, Five Carols To Old
English Texts

Come, Sweet Peace
SATB,pno/org oct LAWSON 51196 $.25   (E194)

Jesus, My Sweet Lover
see Son Is Born, A, Five Carols To Old
English Texts

Lord God Of Hosts
SATB,org oct LAWSON 51257 $.30   (E195)

Son Is Born, A, Five Carols To Old English
Texts *carol,Eng
mix cor CONCORDIA 97-4836 $.85
contains: All That 'lieve In Christian
Lay; Babe Is Born All Of A May, A; Be
Merry Be Merry; Blessed Be That Lord In
Majesty; Jesus, My Sweet Lover (E196)

Twelve Choral Hymns And Carols *CC12U,carol/
hymn
mix cor oct LAWSON 51255 $.60   (E197)

EDMUNDSON
Adoration Carol *Xmas,carol
SATB oct VOLKWEIN VB101 $.25   (E198)

EDMUNDSON, GARTH (1900-   )
At The Lamb's High Feast *Easter
SATB oct SOUTHERN $.30   (E199)

At Thy Feet
SATB oct FISCHER,J 8920 $.30   (E200)

Bread Of The World
SATB oct FISCHER,J 9213 $.30   (E201)

God Be In My Head
SATB oct FISCHER,J 8482 $.30   (E202)

Jesus, The Very Thought Of Thee
SATB oct FISCHER,J 8513 $.30   (E203)

None Other Lamb
SATB oct FISCHER,J 7519 $.30   (E204)

EDSON HYMNS AND FUGUING TUNES, PART I see
Cowell, Henry Dixon

EDSON HYMNS AND FUGUING TUNES, PART II see
Cowell, Henry Dixon

EDSON, [LEWIS] (1748-1820)
Arise, My Soul, Arise
(Gerig) SATB oct LILLENAS AN-2237 $.30
                                             (E205)

O Holy, Holy Lord *see Ware

EDWARD, J.
Men And Angels Sing Hallelujah (composed with
Edwards, T.O.)
(Jones) SATB,S solo,acap WARNER W2936 $.30
                                             (E206)

EDWARDS, CLARA
Awake! Arise! *Easter
(Stickles) 4pt mix cor oct SCHIRM.G 10642
$.25   (E207)

Dedication
4pt mix cor oct SCHIRM.G 10721 $.25   (E208)

Eastern Heavens Are All Aglow, The *Xmas
(Stickles) 4pt mix cor oct SCHIRM.G 10952
$.25   (E209)
(Stickles) 3pt wom cor,S solo oct SCHIRM.G
10954 $.25   (E210)
(Stickles) 3pt mix cor oct SCHIRM.G 10953
$.25   (E211)

I Will Lift Mine Eyes *Easter,Bibl
(Treharne) 4pt mix cor,high solo oct
SCHIRM.G 7862 $.30   (E212)

Lord Is My Light, The (Psalm 27)
(Downing) 4pt mix cor,high solo oct
SCHIRM.G 8520 $.35   (E213)

Psalm 27 *see Lord Is My Light, The

EDWARDS, P.M.H.
O Little One Sweet *Xmas
unis oct LESLIE 1090   (E214)

EDWARDS, T.O.
Men And Angels Sing Hallelujah *see Edward,
J.

EEN KIND IS ONS GHEBOREN see Rontgen, [Julius]

EEN KINDEKE GENADERIJK see Lambrechts-Vos, A.

EEN KINDEKE IS ONS GEBOREN see Antwerpen, P.A.
von

E'EN SO, LORD JESUS, QUICKLY COME see Manz

E'EN SO, LORD JESUS, QUICKLY COME see Manz,
Paul

EEN TING HAR JEG BEGAERET AF HERREN see
Jeppesen, Knud

EEN VASTE BURG see Bach, Johann Sebastian, Ein
Feste Burg Ist Unser Gott

EENMAAL BETHLEHEM see Bruhne, J.F.

EESU BAMBINO see Yon, Pietro Alessandro

EET ER NODIGT see Bach, Johann Sebastian, Eins
Ist Noth

EET ONSKER JEG TIL GUD see Buxtehude, Dietrich,
Eins Bitte Ich Vom Herrn

EFFINGER, CECIL (1914-   )
Behold Thy Brother Man
SATB oct KERBY 6406C $.45   (E215)
SATB,org oct KERBY 6406 $.45   (E216)

Forget Not My Law
TTBB oct GRAY GCMR 3006 $.25   (E217)

EFFINGER, CECIL (cont'd.)

Mary's Soliloquy (from St. Luke Christmas
Story, The) Xmas
4pt mix cor oct SCHIRM.G 10980 $.25   (E218)

Paul Of Tarsus
4pt mix cor,Bar solo,org,strings voc sc
SCHIRM.G $2.00   (E219)

Shepherds In The Field
2pt mix cor oct PRESSER MC238 $.30   (E220)

St. Luke Christmas Story, The *cant
mix cor,soli,org/pno voc sc SCHIRM.G $1.50
                                             (E221)

EFFINGER, S.
I Shall Not Pass Again This Way
(Durst, S.) SAA oct PRESSER 322-35031 $.30
                                             (E222)
(Durst, S.) SATB oct PRESSER 332-35259 $.30
                                             (E223)

EFFUNDERUNT SANGUINEM see Haydn, (Johann)
Michael

EGADDI
Ave Maria
[Lat] SATB,acap RICORDI-ARG BA 11765 s.p.
                                             (E224)

Pater Noster
[Lat] SATB,acap RICORDI-ARG BA11766 s.p.
                                             (E225)

EGERMANN, EBERHARD
Die Eingangsspruche Zum Hauptgottesdienst
*CC26U,Gen,cant
[Ger] unis,org BAREN. s.p.   (E226)

Vier Leitverse Zum Psalm-Singen *CC4U,Gen
[Ger] BAREN. s.p.   (E227)

EGERTON, A.H.
Blessed Art Thou
SATB oct LESLIE 4067   (E228)

Te Deum *Te Deum
SATB (C sharp min) oct LESLIE 4075   (E229)

EGGE, KLAUS (1906-   )
Jole-Salme
mix cor MUSIKK 60 s.p.   (E230)

EGGEN, ARNE (1881-1955)
Hail Thee, Star Of The Ocean *see Heil Deg,
Havsens Stjerne

Heil Deg, Havsens Stjerne
"Hail Thee, Star Of The Ocean" [Eng/Lat/
Norw] SATB,S solo,org cor pts NORSK 7760A
s.p.   (E231)

EGGLESTON, JOHN W.
Sweet Is The Sunlight *Austral
SATB ALLANS 245 s.p.   (E232)
SA ALLANS 278 s.p.   (E233)
SAB ALLANS 335 s.p.   (E234)

EGLI E IL MESSIA see Arnaldi, Antonio

EGLIN, ARTHUR (1932-   )
All Morgen Ist Ganz Frisch Und Neu *canon
1-2pt,opt 2treb inst LAUDINELLA LR 52 s.p.
contains also: Die Helle Sonn Leucht
Jetzt Herfur; Ich Sag Dir Dank, Gott
Vater Gut   (E235)

Christ Ist Erstanden
unis,4trp LAUDINELLA LR 14 s.p. contains
also: Erstanden Ist Der Heilig Christ
(SB,treb inst); Wir Wollen Alle Frohlich
Sein (SB,treb inst)   (E236)

Christen Und Heiden
unis,kbd LAUDINELLA LR 109 s.p. contains
also: Ich Traue Deiner Gnade (4pt)
(canon); In Mir Ist Es Finster (SAA,kbd);
Von Guten Machten Wunderbar Geboren
(unis,kbd)   (E237)

Das Ist Ein Kostlich Ding *canon
2pt,inst LAUDINELLA LR 95 s.p. contains
also: Halleluja, Lobet Den Herrn, Alle
Heiden (3pt mix cor&cong,opt 3inst); Lobe
Den Herrn, Meine Seele (3pt,opt B solo)
(canon); Sende Dein Licht Und Deine
Wahrheit (SATB)   (E238)

Die Helle Sonn Leucht Jetzt Herfur
see Eglin, Arthur, All Morgen Ist Ganz
Frisch Und Neu

Erstanden Ist Der Heilig Christ
see Eglin, Arthur, Christ Ist Erstanden

Es Wird Ein Stern Aus Jakob Aufgehen
SAT/SAB LAUDINELLA LR 81 s.p. contains
also: Meine Seele Erhebt Den Herrn (SAT/
SAB); Und Es Waren Hirten In Derselben
Gegend (SATB)   (E239)

Halleluja, Lobet Den Herrn, Alle Heiden
see Eglin, Arthur, Das Ist Ein Kostlich
Ding

Ich Sag Dir Dank, Gott Vater Gut
see Eglin, Arthur, All Morgen Ist Ganz
Frisch Und Neu

Ich Traue Deiner Gnade
see Eglin, Arthur, Christen Und Heiden

Ihr Knechte Gottes Allzugleich
unis,3treb inst LAUDINELLA LR 116 s.p.
contains also: Mein Ganzes Herz Erhebet
Dich; Singt Mit Froher Stimm; Wie
Lieblich Ist Das Haus Des Herrn   (E240)

In Mir Ist Es Finster
see Eglin, Arthur, Christen Und Heiden

Lieder Und Kanos *sac/sec,CC8L,canon
LAUDINELLA LR 91 s.p.   (E241)

Lobe Den Herrn, Meine Seele
see Eglin, Arthur, Das Ist Ein Kostlich
Ding

Mein Ganzes Herz Erhebet Dich
see Eglin, Arthur, Ihr Knechte Gottes
Allzugleich

EGLIN, ARTHUR (cont'd.)

Meine Seele Erhebt Den Herrn
see Eglin, Arthur, Es Wird Ein Stern Aus
Jakob Aufgehen

Sende Dein Licht Und Deine Wahrheit
see Eglin, Arthur, Das Ist Ein Kostlich
Ding

Singt Mit Froher Stimm
see Eglin, Arthur, Ihr Knechte Gottes
Allzugleich

Und Es Waren Hirten In Derselben Gegend
see Eglin, Arthur, Es Wird Ein Stern Aus
Jakob Aufgehen

Von Guten Machten Wunderbar Geboren
see Eglin, Arthur, Christen Und Heiden

Wie Lieblich Ist Das Haus Des Herrn
see Eglin, Arthur, Ihr Knechte Gottes
Allzugleich

Wir Wollen Alle Frohlich Sein
see Eglin, Arthur, Christ Ist Erstanden

EGO CLAMAVI see Sandvold, Arild

EGO CUBUI ET DORMIVI see Purcell, Henry

EGO DILECTO MEO see Borsieri, C.

EGO DIXI see Anerio, Felice

EGO DIXI: DOMINE MISERERE MEI see Anerio,
Felice

EGO DORMIO see Schutz, Heinrich

EGO ENIM INIQUE EGI see Schutz, Heinrich

EGO IPSE CONSOLABOR VOS see Smith, Frank H.

EGO MATER see Kobierkowicz, Jozef

EGO SUM PANIS see Bottazzo, Luigi

EGO SUM PANIS see Bottigliero, Eduardo

EGO SUM PANIS see Faccin, Gian Domenico

EGO SUM PANIS VITAE see Back, Sven-Erick

EGO SUM PANIS VIVUS see Agostini, Paolo

EGO SUM PANIS VIVUS see Byrd, William

EGO SUM PANIS VIVUS see Constantini, Alessandro

EGO SUM PANIS VIVUS see Palestrina, Giovanni

EGO SUM PANIS VIVUS see Roger-Ducasse, Jean-
Jules Aimable

EGO SUM PASTOR BONUS see Arnaldi, Antonio

EGO SUM PASTOR BONUS see Bottazzo, Luigi

EGO SUM PAUPER ET DOLENS see Croce, Giovanni

EGO SUM TUI PLAGA DOLORIS see Schutz, Heinrich

EGOROFF, A.
Children's Prayer *prayer
SATB&jr cor,acap PEER $.40   (E242)

EGOTIST AND POETS, THE see Newbury, Kent A.

EGREDIETUR VIRGA see Gallus, Jacobus

EGREDITUR VIRGA see Gallus, Jacobus

EGRESSUS JESUS see Wert, Giaches de

EHEU! SUSTULERUNT DOMINUM see Morley, Thomas

EHLERS, ERICH
Wir Danken Dir, Herr Jesu Christ
see Kretzschmar, Gunther, Christus Ist
Auferstanden, Freud Ist In

EHR' SEI IN'S HIMMELS THRON see Bach, Johann
Sebastian

EHRE SEI DEM HERRN
see Gloria

EHRE SEI DEM HOCHERHABENEN see Schubert, Franz
(Peter)

EHRE SEI DEM VATER see Schutz, Heinrich

EHRE SEI DEM VATER UND DEM SOHN see Schutz,
Heinrich

EHRE SEI DEM VATER see Schutz, Heinrich

EHRE SEI DIR, CHRISTE see Distler, Hugo

EHRE SEI DIR, CHRISTE see Micheelsen, Hans
Friedrich

EHRE SEI DIR, CHRISTE see Schutz, Heinrich

EHRE SEI DIR, CHRISTE see Stier, Alfred

EHRE SEI DIR CHRISTE see Wagner, Alexander

EHRE SEI GOTT see Klink, W.

EHRE SEI GOTT see Mozart, Wolfgang Amadeus

EHRE SEI GOTT IN DER HOHE see Bach, Johann
Christoph Friedrich

EHRE SEI GOTT IN DER HOHE see Driessler,
Johannes

EHRE SEI GOTT IN DER HOHE see Friederici,
Daniel

EHRE SEI GOTT IN DER HOHE see Hammerschmidt,
Andreas

EHRE SEI GOTT IN DER HOHE see Hufschmidt,
Wolfgang

EHRE SEI GOTT IN DER HOHE see Lossius, Lukas

EHRE SEI GOTT IN DER HOHE see Nicolai, Otto

EHRE SEI GOTT IN DER HOHE see Schelle, Johann
Hermann

EHRE SEI GOTT IN DER HOHE see Schubert, Franz
(Peter)

EHRE SEI GOTT IN DER HOHE see Schutz, Heinrich

EHRE SEI GOTT IN DER HOHE see Selle, Thomas

EHRE SEI GOTT IN DER HOHE see Telemann, Georg
Philipp

EHRE SEI GOTT IN DER HOHE see Weber, Ludwig

EHRE SEI GOTT IN DER HOHE see Woll, E.

EHRE SEY GOTT IN DER HOHE see Bach, Wilhelm
Friedemann

EHRE UND PREIS SEI GOTT see Bach, Johann
Sebastian

EHRE UND PREIS SEI GOTT DEM HERRN see Bach,
Johann Sebastian

EHRET IN SEINER HERRLICHTKEIT see Handel,
George Frideric, Fix'd In His Everlasting
Seat

EHRET, WALTER (1918-   )
A La Nanita Nana
SSA SHAWNEE B 219 $.30   (E243)
SATB SHAWNEE A 674 $.30   (E244)
SA/TB SHAWNEE E36 $.30   (E245)
SAB SHAWNEE D75 $.30   (E246)

All Nature's Work His Praise Declare
SATB oct LORENZ C191 $.30   (E247)

As Joseph Was A-Walking *carol,Eng
SATB LUDWIG L-1118 $.30   (E248)

At Golden Dawn Of Christmas *Xmas
SAB ALFRED 6501 $.30   (E249)
SA ALFRED 6117 $.30   (E250)

Babe Of Bethlehem *Xmas
SA MARKS 4071 $.30 contains also: O Come,
Little Children   (E251)

Beautiful Christmas Time *Xmas
SA ALFRED 6119 $.25   (E252)

Behold If There Be Any Sorrow
SAB SHAWNEE D101 $.25   (E253)

Blessed Be That Maid Marie *Xmas
SAB,opt vln WARNER WB-296   (E254)
SATB oct PLYMOUTH XM-102 $.25   (E255)

Calvary's Mountain
SATB oct ELKAN-V 362-1210 $.25   (E256)

Cathedral Choir Book *CCU
SAB BELWIN $1.25   (E257)

Chapel Chorister *CCU
SAB BELWIN $1.00   (E258)

Child Of God
SATB SHAWNEE A 1211 $.30   (E259)

Christ Indeed Is Risen Today!
SATB SHAWNEE A1055 $.35   (E260)

Christ The Lord Is Risen Today *Easter
SATB oct LORENZ C266 $.30   (E261)

Come Christmas Morning *Xmas
SATB oct AGAPE AD 1976 $.35   (E262)

Come Ye Sinners, Poor And Needy *anthem/hymn
SATB oct SPRATT 586 $.25   (E263)

Cradle Hymn *see Harmonica Sacra

Eternal Source Of Truth And Light
SATB oct VOLKWEIN VB144 $.25   (E264)

Gracious, Mighty Sovereign Lord
SAB SHAWNEE D100 $.25   (E265)

Grant Us Peace
SATB oct HERITAGE H6 $.35   (E266)

Harmonica Sacra *Xmas
"Cradle Hymn" SATB oct SPRATT 556 $.30
                                   (E267)

Hasten, All Ye Shepherds
SA oct ELKAN-V 362-521 $.25   (E268)

High Over Bethlehem *Xmas,carol,Czech
SA oct ELKAN-V 362-527 $.30   (E269)

Holiday And Holy Day *Xmas
SA oct HERITAGE H5004 $.35   (E270)

Holy, Holy, Holy
3pt jr cor/SAB (very easy) FISCHER,C S $.22
                                   (E271)

Hymn Anthem-Choir Book *CCU,hymn
(Tepper, A.) SA/TB BELWIN $1.00   (E272)

In Fields Not Far From Bethlehem *Xmas
SATB oct ELKAN-V 362-3117 $.30   (E273)

Jacob's Vision *Easter
SATB oct PRESSER 312-40478 $.30   (E274)

Jesus Born In Bethlea *Xmas
SA ALFRED 6136 $.25   (E275)
SSA ALFRED 6213 $.30   (E276)

Jesus' Christmas Lullaby
SSA oct ELKAN-V 362-3070 $.25   (E277)

Joseph And Mary *Xmas,anthem/carol,Fr
SATB,org/pno PETERS 6605 $.30 see from
Three Christmas Anthems   (E278)

Let All Rejoice At Christmas Time *Xmas
SAB WARNER WB-297   (E279)

EHRET, WALTER (cont'd.)

Listen, Lordlings, Unto Me *carol,Fr,16th
cent
SATB oct ELKAN-V 362-1199 $.30   (E280)

Little Child So Lowly, A *Xmas
2pt,opt ob WARNER WB-298   (E281)

Lives Once Again Our Glorious King
SAB FLAMMER D5213 $.30   (E282)

Lullaby For Jesus *Xmas
(Walton) 3pt jr cor/SSA (med easy) FISCHER,
C CM 6913 $.25   (E283)

Make A Joyful Noise *CCU
SAB SHAWNEE GD46 $1.25   (E284)

New Born Again
SATB oct VOLKWEIN VB214 $.25   (E285)

O Come, Little Children
see Ehret, Walter, Babe Of Bethlehem

O, Jerusalem *Xmas
SSA ALFRED 6218 $.30   (E286)
SATB ALFRED 6404 $.30   (E287)

O Lord, How Excellent Is Thy Name
SATB SHAWNEE A 891 $.25   (E288)

O My Soul, Bless God The Father
SATB SHAWNEE A 680 $.30   (E289)

Oh Bethlehem *Xmas,carol
SATB oct ELKAN-V 362-1181 $.30   (E290)

On Christmas Night *Xmas
SATB oct VOLKWEIN VB229 $.25   (E291)

Praise In Song *CCU
SATB BELWIN $1.00   (E292)

Rejoice And Sing
SA BELWIN $1.00   (E293)

Rejoice, Rejoice, Ye Christians *Xmas
SATB oct VOLKWEIN VB248 $.25   (E294)

Rejoice The Lord Is King
SATB oct VOLKWEIN VB250 $.25   (E295)
SAB oct VOLKWEIN VB251 $.25   (E296)

Ride On! Ride On In Majesty *Palm
SAB oct SOUTHERN $.25   (E297)

S.S.A.B. Sacred Collection *CCU
SSAB BELWIN $1.00   (E298)

Saw Ye My Savior?
SATB FLAMMER A 5546 $.30   (E299)

Shepherds Had An Angel, The *Xmas,anthem/
carol,Eng
SATB,org/pno PETERS 6605 $.30 see from
Three Christmas Anthems   (E300)

Shepherds On The Mountain Steeps Afar!
SSA FLAMMER B 5024 $.30   (E301)

Sing To The Lord Of The Harvest
SATB oct PLYMOUTH HA-10 $.25   (E302)

Sing We To God *CCU
SATB&SA FISCHER,C O-4263 $1.25   (E303)

Sinners Come, The Saviour See
SAB SHAWNEE D99 $.25   (E304)

Sister Mary Had-a But One Child
SATB SHAWNEE A 1085 $.30   (E305)
SSA SHAWNEE B 324 $.30   (E306)
SAB SHAWNEE D140 $.30   (E307)
SA/TB SHAWNEE E99 $.30   (E308)

Snow Lay On The Ground, The *Xmas
SSA ALFRED 6229 $.30   (E309)
SA ALFRED 6146 $.30   (E310)

Songs Of Praise, Vol. 1 *CCU
SA FLAMMER GE5013 $1.25   (E311)

Songs Of Praise, Vol. 2 *CCU
SA SHAWNEE GE5014 $1.35   (E312)

Stable Cold And Barren, A *Xmas
SSA ALFRED 6166 $.30   (E313)
SA ALFRED 6113 $.30   (E314)

Star Of Bethlehem
SSA SHAWNEE B 283 $.25   (E315)

Susanni *Xmas
SAB ALFRED 6524 $.35   (E316)

Sweet Lamb
SATB SHAWNEE A 1212 $.30   (E317)

Sweet Mary, Guard Thy Precious Child
SATB FLAMMER A 5567 $.30   (E318)
SA/TB FLAMMER E5158 $.30   (E319)

Sweet Mary Rocks Her Infant
SATB SHAWNEE A 1122 $.30   (E320)

Sweet Mary Tends Her Newborn Son *Xmas
SATB oct ELKAN-V 362-3116 $.30   (E321)

Tender Shepherd
SSA HANSEN-US E9955 $.40   (E322)

That First Christmas Night
SA/TB FLAMMER E5050 $.30   (E323)

Therefore Be Merry
SSA SHAWNEE B 371 $.30   (E324)

Three Christmas Anthems *see Joseph And
Mary; Shepherds Had An Angel, The; Three
Kings, The   (E325)

Three Kings, The *Xmas,anthem/carol,Eng
SATB,org/pno PETERS 6606 $.25 see from
Three Christmas Anthems   (E326)

Turn Ye To Me
SATB FLAMMER A 5524 $.25   (E327)

EHRET, WALTER (cont'd.)

Walking Along To Bethlehem *Xmas
SATB oct ELKAN-V 362-1166 $.25   (E328)

Wasn't That A Mighty Day! *Xmas
SATB SCHMITT 655 $.30   (E329)

What Star Is This? *Xmas
SATB oct VOLKWEIN VB277 $.25   (E330)

When Christ Was Born Of Mary Free *Xmas
SATB oct PLYMOUTH XM-102 $.25   (E331)
SSA oct PLYMOUTH WE-201 $.25   (E332)

With Voices Raised
SSA BELWIN $1.00   (E333)

You Better Mind *spir
SATB SCHMITT 647 $.30   (E334)

EI DU FROMMER UND GETREUER KNECHT see Franck,
Melchior

EI DU GRUN-GRUNES BAUMLEIN see Knab, Armin

EI LIEBER HERR EIL ZUM GERICHT see Buxtehude,
Dietrich

EI WAS GROSSES WUNDER see Spitta, Heinrich

EIA, DU KLEINES, ZARTES KIND *Xmas,Eng/Eur
(Doppelbauer, Josef Friedrich) mix cor,acap
DOBLINGER s.p. see from Da Der Herr Geboren
(E335)

EIA DULCIS ANIMA see Keja, J.F.

EIA MATER, FONS AMORIS see Dvorak, Antonin

EIA, NOVUS ANNUS EST (from Anthology Of Carols,
An)
see Ave Maris Stella

EIA VERBA DICITE see Mauduit, Jacques

EIBL, TH.
Psalm 34
[Ger] mix cor,acap (med) HUG s.p.   (E336)

EICHHORN
O Come Creator Spirit
SAB oct GALAXY 1.2146.1 $.30   (E337)

EICHORN, HERMENE WARLICK (1906-   )
Christ The Lord Is Risen *Easter/Lent
unis&desc oct GRAY GCMR 2124 $.30   (E338)

Mary Magdalene *cant
SSA BELWIN $.80   (E339)
mix cor BELWIN $1.25   (E340)

Song For Easter *Easter
unis oct GRAY GCMR 2057 $.25   (E341)

EIDGENOSSISCHER DANK-, BUSS- UND BETTAG see
Wettstein, H.

EIDSVOOG
Love *Gen
SATB SCHMITT 15018 $.35   (E342)

EIGENGESANGE VOM ERSTEN ADVENTSONNTAG see
Dallinger, Gerhard

EIGENGESANGE VOM FEST DER ALLERHEILIGSTEN
DREIFALTIGKEIT see Dallinger, Gerhard

EIGHT ANTHEMS see Gibbons, Orlando

EIGHT ANTHEMS see White, Robert

EIGHT BIBLE SONGS FOR YOUNG PEOPLE see Cecilia,
Sister

EIGHT CANONS see Hindemith, Paul

EIGHT CANONS FOR EQUAL VOICES see Holst, Gustav

EIGHT CHORAL PRELUDES see Krebs, J.

EIGHT CHORALE SETTINGS FROM OPELLA NOVA see
Schein, Johann Hermann

EIGHT CHRISTMAS CHORUSES FROM THE MESSIAH see
Handel, George Frideric

EIGHT DESCANTS see Cartford, Gerhard M.

EIGHT HYMNS see Finck

EIGHT MADRIGALS AND FOUR PART-SONGS see
Hassler, Hans Leo

EIGHT NEGRO SPIRITUALS *CC8U,spir
(Phillips, John C.) SSA,acap voc sc NOVELLO
20.0139.10 $1.75   (E343)

EIGHT NEGRO SPIRITUALS: BOOK I *spir
(Brown) ST/AB (med) OXFORD 58.621 $.95
contains: Rise Up, Shepherd; Shine, Shine;
Somebody's Knocking; Zion's Children
(E344)

EIGHT NEGRO SPIRITUALS: BOOK II *spir
(Brown) ST/AB (med) OXFORD 58.622 $.95
contains: Dry Bones; Gospel Train; I'm A-
Trav'ling; Oh, Yes!   (E345)

EIGHT OFFERTORY MOTETS AND NOW THANK WE ALL OUR
GOD *CC8L,anthem/mot/Offer
(Lee, J.) SATB (med easy) cmplt ed GIA G 1383
$1.25 contains works by: Carissimi; Cruger;
Lotti; Mozart; Palestrina; Soriano; Tye
(E346)

EIGHT RESPONSES see Dressler, L.R.

EIGHT SENTENCES FOR THE SEVEN SEASONS OF THE
CHRISTIAN CHURCH see Moschetti, [Giuseppe]

EIGHT SONGS TO SING ABOUT CHRISTMAS see Hankey,
Mark

EIGHT STANDARD ANTHEMS *CC8U
mix cor SCHMITT 6 $.50   (E347)

EIGHT TRADITIONAL CAROLS *CC8L,carol,Eng
(Vaughn Williams, Ralph) SATB,unis,pno GALAXY
s.p.
see also: And All In The Morning; Down In
Yon Forest; On Christmas Night; Truth

Sent From Above, The; Wassail Song (E348)

EIGHTEEN RESPONSES *CC18U,cor-resp
SATB LORENZ 9479 $.30   (E349)

EIGHTEEN RESPONSES FOR GENERAL USE see Evans

EIGHTY AMENS *CC80U
(Dickinson, C.) men cor&wom cor BELWIN $.75
(E350)

EILE, GOTT, MICH ZU ERETTEN see Wangenheim,
[Volker]

EILE, GOTT, MICH ZU ERRETTEN see Burkhard Willy

EILE GOTT, MICH ZU ERRETTEN see Zimmermann,
Heinz Werner

EILE, HERR, MIR ZU HELFEN see Zaccariis, Caesar
de

EILE MICH, GOTT, ZU ERRETTEN see Hammerschmidt,
Andreas

EILERS
Born Today *Xmas
SA SCHMITT 2587 $.35   (E351)

Gift, The *Xmas
SA SCHMITT 359 $.35   (E352)

It's Christmas *Xmas
SSA SCHMITT 358 $.35   (E353)
SAB SCHMITT 5021 $.35   (E354)

Oh, What A Wonder *Xmas
SA SCHMITT 242 $.30   (E355)

Star Shone Bright, A *Xmas
2pt oct FISCHER,C CM-7780 $.30   (E356)

Tiny King *Xmas
SAB SCHMITT 5540 $.35   (E357)
SATB SCHMITT 1205 $.35   (E358)
SSA SCHMITT 240 $.35   (E359)
TTBB SCHMITT 3515 $.35   (E360)

EILI, EILI *folk,Jew
(Schindler) [Eng/Jew] mix cor,Mez solo,acap
oct SCHIRM.G 6690 $.35   (E361)

EIN ANDER SCHON BITTLIED ZUR MUTTERGOTTES
*BVM,17th cent
(Dawidowicz, Anton) wom cor,acap (contains
also: Das Salve Regina Deutsch) oct
DOBLINGER s.p. see also Acht Marienleider
(E362)

EIN BAUER STIEG DEN BERG HINAUF *folk
mix cor,acap TONGER s.p.   (E363)

EIN DEUTSCHER PSALTER see Rauch, Joseph

EIN DEUTSCHES REQUIEM see Brahms, Johannes

EIN DRAUM I GUDS HJARTE see Heggen, Bodvar

EIN EDLER SCHATZ DER WEISHEIT see Fiebig, Kurt

EIN ENGEL SCHON AUS GOTTES THRON see
Praetorius, Michael

EIN FESTE BURG see Hassler, Hans Leo

EIN' FESTE BURG see Hunter

EIN FESTE BURG see Rohwer, Jens

EIN FESTE BURG see Schein, Johann Hermann

EIN' FESTE BURG see Thomas, Kurt

EIN' FESTE BURG IST UNSER GOTT see Bach, Johann
Sebastian

EIN FESTE BURG IST UNSER GOTT see Cruger,
Johann

EIN' FESTE BURG IST UNSER GOTT see Doles,
Johann Friedrich

EIN FESTE BURG IST UNSER GOTT see Franck,
Melchior

EIN FESTE BURG IST UNSER GOTT see Herbst,
Johannes Andreas

EIN FESTE BURG IST UNSER GOTT see Krieger,
Johann Philipp

EIN FESTE BURG IST UNSER GOTT see Mahu, Stephen

EIN FESTE BURG IST UNSER GOTT see Praetorius,
Michael

EIN FESTE BURG IST UNSER GOTT see Scheidt,
Samuel

EIN FESTE BURG IST UNSER GOTT see Schein,
Johann Hermann

EIN FESTE BURG IST UNSER GOTT see Stern,
Hermann

EIN FESTE BURG IST UNSER GOTT see Stoll, Helene
Marianne

EIN FESTE BURG IST UNSER GOTT see Telemann,
Georg Philipp

EIN FESTE BURG IST UNSER GOTT see Thomas, Kurt

EIN FESTE BURG IST UNSER GOTT see Vulpius,
Melchior

EIN FESTE BURG IST UNSER GOTT see Walter
(Walther), Johann

EIN FROHES LIED SUR WEIHNACHTSZEIT see Hunger,
J.

EIN FROHES LIED ZUR WEIHNACHTSZEIT see Hunger,
J.

EIN FROLICH GESANG *Easter/Gen,Ger
"Alleluia" 2pt CHAPPELL 0017863-352 $.40
(E364)
"Alleluia" SSA CHAPPELL 0017863-354 $.40
(E365)
(O'Conner; Morris) "Alleluia" SATB,acap oct

BOOSEY 1367 $.35   (E366)
(Coggin, E.) "Alleluia" SATB,acap oct PRESSER
312-40752 $.30   (E367)
(Wagner) "Alleluia" SATB,acap oct LAWSON 558
$.30   (E368)

EIN GETREUES HERZ ZU WISSEN see Burkhart, Franz

EIN GROSSER STERN *CCU,Xmas
(Wagner, Hermann) wom cor MOSELER s.p.   (E369)

EIN HAUS VOLL GLORIE SCHAUET see Mohr, T.W.

EIN HELLES LICHT IST UNS ENTBRANNT see Maasz,
Gerhard

EIN HERZ see Bach, Johann Sebastian, Ein Herz,
Das Seinen Jesum Lebend Weiss

EIN HERZ, DAS SEINEN JESUM LEBEND WEISS see
Bach, Johann Sebastian

EIN JAHRTAUSEND LATEINISCHER HYMNEN DICHTUNG:
BK. 1. HYMNEN BEKANNTER VERFASSER *CCU
(Dreves, G. M.; Blume, C.; Vecchi, Prof.
Giuseppe) oct FORNI $1.72   (E370)

EIN JAHRTAUSEND LATEINISCHER HYMNEN DICHTUNG:
BK. 2. HYMNEN UNBEKANNTER VERFASSER *CCU
(Dreves, G.M.; Blume, C.; Vecchi, Prof.
Giuseppe) oct FORNI $1.72   (E371)

EIN JEDER MENSCH BEDENKE EBEN see Staden,
Johann

EIN JEGLICHER SEI GESINNT see Reda, Siegfried

EIN KIND GEBOREN ZU BETHLEHEM IM STALL see
Wolters, Gottfried

EIN KIND GEBORN [CHORALE] see Bach, Johann
Sebastian

EIN KIND GEBORN ZU BETHLEHEM see Gesius,
Bartholomaus

EIN KIND GEBORN ZU BETHLEHEM see Kaufmann,
Diethelm

EIN KIND GEBORN ZU BETHLEHEM see Praetorius,
Michael

EIN KIND GEBORN ZU BETHLEHEM see Schilling,
Hans Ludwig

EIN KIND GEBORN ZU BETHLEHEM see Schroter,
Leonhard

EIN KIND GEBORN ZU BETHLEHEM see Vulpius,
Melchior

EIN KIND GEBORN ZU BETHLEHEM see Praetorius,
Michael

EIN KIND IST UNS GEBOREN see Schutz, Heinrich

EIN KIND IST UNS GEBOREN HEUT see Pepping,
Ernst

EIN KIND IST UNS GEBOREN see Schutz, Heinrich

EIN KIND IST UNS GEBOREN see Schutz, Heinrich

EIN KIND IST UNS ZUM HEIL GEBORN see Frank,
J.W.

EIN KINDELEIN SO LOBELICH see Hassler, Hans Leo

EIN KINDELEIN SO LOBELICH see Poos, Heinrich

EIN KINDELEIN, SO LOBELICH see Praetorius,
Michael

EIN KINDELEIN SO LOBELICH see Scheidt, Samuel

EIN KINDELEIN SO LOBELICH see Schroter, L.

EIN KINDELEIN SO LOBELICH see Schroter,
Leonhard

EIN KINDELEIN SO LOBELICH see Telemann, Georg
Philipp

EIN KINDELEIN ZU BETHLEHEM see Freundt,
Cornelius

EIN KINDELEN, SO LOBELICH see Calvisius, Sethus

EIN KINDLEIN KLEIN ZU BETHLEHEM see Freundt,
Cornelius

EIN KINDLEIN LIEGT IN DEM ARMEN STALL see
Schneider, Martin Gotthard

EIN KINDLEIN LIEGT IN DEM ARMEN STALL see
Schwartz, Gerhard von

EIN KINDLEIN ZART see Raphael, Gunther

EIN KLEINES REQUIEM see Cadow, Paul

EIN KLEINES WEIHNACHTSORATORIUM see Stier,
Alfred

EIN KRANZLEIN ZU JOHANNI see Weber, Bernhard

EIN LAMMLEIN GEHT UND TRAGT DIE SCHULD see
Berger, Hans Ludwig

EIN LAMMLEIN GEHT UND TRAGT DIE SCHULD see
David, Johann Nepomuk

EIN LAMMLEIN GEHT UND TRAGT DIE SCHULD see
Fiebig, Kurt

EIN LAMMLEIN GEHT UND TRAGT DIE SCHULD see
Grabner, Hermann

EIN LAMMLEIN GEHT UND TRAGT DIE SCHULD see
Hassler, Hans Leo

EIN LEISES, ZARTES SINGEN see Lehman, Siegfried

EIN LICHT IST AUFGEGANGEN see Kammerer, Imanuel
Johannes

EIN LIED AUF OSTERN see Mockel, Franz

EIN LOBGESANG. NEUE LIEDER FUR KIRCHE UND HAUS
see Lahusen, Christian

EIN MENSCH IST IN SEINEM LEBEN WIE GRAS see
Reda, Siegfried

EIN NEU GEBOT see Buchtger, Fritz

EIN RUF HAT UNS GETROFFEN see Stier, Alfred

EIN SCHONES KINDLEIN see Spitta, Heinrich

EIN SEGEN HAT ERGOSSEN SICH see Lehman,
Siegfried

EIN SEGEN HAT ERGOSSEN SICH see Trust, Heinz-
Ewald

EIN SOLCH VERTRAUEN ABER see Hollfelder,
Waldram

EIN SOLCH VERTRAUEN HABEN WIR see Reda,
Siegfried

EIN STERNLEIN IST GEKOMMEN see Wolters,
Gottfried

EIN TAG IN DEINEN VORHOFEN see Rosenmuller,
Johann

EIN TAGESKREIS ALTER GEISTLICHER LIEDER *CCU
[Ger] mix cor,acap (med) HUG s.p.   (E372)

EIN TRAUM *mot
(Burkhart, Franz) mix cor,acap DOBLINGER s.p.
see also In Seiner Handen   (E373)

EIN UNGEFARBT GEMUTE see Bach, Johann
Sebastian

EIN UNGELFARBT GEMUTE see Bach, Johann
Sebastian

EIN WAHRER GLAUBE GOTTS ZORN STILLT see Schein,
Johann Hermann

EIN WENIG NUR, HERR, WENDE DICH UNS ZU see
Schwarz-Schilling, Reinhard

EINE DEUTSCHE CHORALMESSE see Distler, Hugo

EINE DEUTSCHE MESSE IN KIRCHENLIEDSATZEN see
Bach, Johann Sebastian

EINE DEUTSCHE MISSA BREVIS see Selle, Thomas

EINE FESTE BURG see Bach, Johann Sebastian, Ein
Feste Burg Ist Unser Gott

EINE FESTE BURG IST UNSER GOTT see Tunder,
Franz

EINE GROSSE FREUD *Xmas
(Strobl, Otto) mix cor,acap oct DOBLINGER
s.p. contains also: Morgenlied Zu Jesu
(folk)   (E374)

EINE JUNGFRAU ZART (from Psalteriolum 1642) BVM
SATB,acap (contains also: Ave Maria (from
Bamberger Gesangbuch 1628)) voc pt
DOBLINGER s.p. see also Unsere Liebe Frau
(E375)

EINE KURZMESSE see Bernhard, Christoph

EINE MOTETTE see Bernhard, Christoph

EINE MOTETTE see La Rue, Pierre de

EINE STUNDE see Victoria, Tomas Luis de, Una
Hora

EINEM, G.
Hymn *Op.12
[Ger] voc sc UNIVER. 12016 $5.70, cor pts
UNIVER. 12017A-D $1.10   (E376)

EINEN ANDEREN GRUND KANN ZWAR NIEMAND LEGEN see
Raphael, Gunther

EINER TRAGE DES ANDERN LAST see Lohr, Ina

EINER TRAGE DES ANDERN LAST see Reda, Siegfried

EINGEBORNER GOTTESSOHN WAHRER GOTT see Stier,
Alfred

EINIGE LEUTE LOBEN DEN FRIEDEN see Blarr, Oskar
Gottlieb

EINKLANG see Wolf, Hugo

EINKLANG: WEIL JETZO ALLES STILLE IST see Wolf,
Hugo

EINS BITTE ICH VOM HERREN see Dressler, Gallus

EINS BITTE ICH VOM HERREN see Hartmann,
Heinrich

EINS BITTE ICH VOM HERREN see Wenzel, Eberhard

EINS BITTE ICH VOM HERRN see Buxtehude,
Dietrich

EINS IST NOTH see Bach, Johann Sebastian

EINSTIMMIGE CHORALE, HEFT 1: 7
CHORALBEARBEITUNGEN AUS KANTATEN see Bach,
Johann Sebastian

EINSTIMMIGE CHORALE, HEFT 2: 6
CHORALBEARBEITUNGEN AUS KANTATEN see Bach,
Johann Sebastian

EINSTIMMIGE DEUTSCHE ORDINARIUMS-MESSE see
Johner, Theodore E.

EINZUG JESU IN JERUSALEM see Graap, Lothar

EINZUG JESU IN JERUSALEM see Wenzel, Eberhard

EISLEBEN
Sing Praise, Sing Praise
(Harris) SATB oct PRO ART 1580 $.25 (E377)

EIT BARN ER FODD I BETLEHEM see Gjendem, J.J.

EJA SLAP SOTING *Xmas,cradle,Eur
(Doppelbauer, Josef Friedrich) mix cor,acap
(contains also: Welche Frohe Botschaft)

DOBLINGER s.p. see from Da Der Herr Geboren
(E378)

EK, GUNNAR (1900-   )
Dig Vare Lov Och Pris
[Swed] SATB,org,strings sc GEHRMANS s.p.,
cor pts GEHRMANS KRB 323 ipa   (E379)

Harlig Ar Jorden
[Swed] SATB,org,2vln sc GEHRMANS s.p., cor
pts GEHRMANS KRB 156   (E380)

EKESSZOLAS see Haydn, (Franz) Joseph

EKLOF, EJNAR
Visa Mig, Herre Din Vag
mix cor NORDISKA 1473 s.p.   (E381)

EKLUND
Thanks From Earth To Heaven *Gen
SATB SCHMITT 8062 $.35   (E382)

EKMAN, L.
Gloria In Excelsis Deo (composed with Fyffe,
E.) *Xmas
SA oct PRESSER 332-14846 $.25   (E383)

EL ADIOS DE IPARRAGUIRRE see Benedito

EL BUEN RABADAN
see Villancicos Tradicionales

EL CONDE OLINOS see Benedito

EL ESTABLO see Lopez, Almagro

EL HAY'LADIM B'YISRAEL see Salkov, Abraham

EL MIRACLE DE SANT JAUME see Rovenstrunck,
Bernhard

EL MOLE RACHAMIN see Adler, Hugo Ch.

EL NACIMIENTO see Irigaray

EL NINO DIVINO NACE see Santa Cruz, Domingo

EL NOI DE LA MARE *Xmas,carol,Span
(Anderson) "What Shall We Give?" [Eng/Span]
4pt mix cor,acap oct SCHIRM.G 10542 $.30
(E384)

EL PASTORCITO DE BELEN see Viloni

EL RORRO *Xmas,cradle,Mex
(Wasner) "Babe, The" [Eng/Span] 4pt mix cor,
acap oct SCHIRM.G 10618 $.25   (E385)

EL SUENO DEL NINO JESUS see Benedito

EL TRIQUITRI see Benedito

EL VIAJE DE LOS REYES MAGOS see Lopez, Almagro

ELAINE, SISTER M. (GENTEMANN)
Apostles' Creed
see Trilogy

Hail Mary
see Trilogy

I See His Blood Upon The Rose *Lent
SSA SCHMITT 2574 $.25   (E386)

Mass For Two Or Four Voices *Gen,Mass
2pt/4pt (easy) voc sc GIA G1562 $1.00
(E387)

Music For Reception Ceremonies *CCU,Gen,
anthem
1-3pt wom cor (easy) oct GIA G1365 $1.00
(E388)

Our Father
see Trilogy

Rejoice, Queen Of Heaven *Easter,anthem
SSA/unis (med easy) oct GIA D1712 $.40
(E389)

Son Of David *Easter
SATB SCHMITT 890 $.25   (E390)

Trilogy *Gen,anthem
SSAA (easy) oct GIA G882 $.30
contains: Apostles' Creed; Hail Mary; Our
Father   (E391)

ELAM, U.
Jesus Hung And Died
5pt mix cor,TB soli oct LAWSON 829 $.35
(E392)

ELDRIDGE, GUY H.
Let Us, With A Gladsome Mind *Gen/Harv
SATB (med) oct OXFORD 42.958 $.35 (E393)

May The Grace Of Christ *anthem
mix cor oct NOVELLO 50.0325.03 s.p. (E394)

Songs Of Praise The Angels Sang *Gen/Thanks
unis (easy) oct OXFORD 81.001 $.25 (E395)

'Tis The Spring Of Souls
SATB THOMP.G G-545 s.p.   (E396)

ELECT OF GOD see Lorenz, Ellen Jane

ELECTRIC CHURCH, THE see Salsbury, Sonny

ELEGERUNT APOSTOLI see Palestrina, Giovanni

ELEGI ABJECTUS ESSE see Mercatali, A.

ELEGI ABJECTUS ESSE see Philips, Peter

ELEGIT EUM DOMINUS see Theophane, Sister M.
(Hytrek)

ELEGIT TE see Bottazzo, Luigi

ELEGIT TE DOMINUS see Baroni, Giovanni

ELEGY see Beethoven, Ludwig van, Sanft Wie Du
Lebtest

ELEGY (NOW TIME HAS GATHERED TO ITSELF) see
Pinkham, Daniel

ELEVATION see Ollone, Max d'

ELEVEN HYMN TUNES see Beaumont, Rev. Geoffrey

ELEVEN HYMNS (from The Westminster Hymnal)
CC11U, hymn
[Lat/Eng] cor oct ST.MARTIN s.p.   (E397)

ELEVEN MOTETS see Pergolesi, Giovanni Battista

ELGAR
Ave Verum Corpus *Easter/Lent,Commun
(Ehret) "Jesu, Word Of God Incarnate" SATB
oct PRO ART 1940 $.22   (E398)

Blessed Jesu
(Rodby) SA KJOS 6097 $.30   (E399)

Hail, Land All Glorious
(Buchtel) SSA,opt band/orch KJOS 6074 $.30
(E400)

Jesu, Word Of God Incarnate *see Ave Verum
Corpus

Thine Is The Glory
SATB oct LORENZ C141 $.30   (E401)

ELGAR, EDWARD (1857-1934)
Apostles, The *Op.49, Bibl/ora
SATB,SATBBB soli,org,4fl,3ob,3clar,3bsn,
4horn,3trp,3trom,tuba,strings,4perc,timp,
2harp voc sc NOVELLO s.p., ipr   (E402)

As Torrents In Summer
SATB,acap oct PRESSER 332-14675 $.25 (E403)
(Cain) SATB FLAMMER A 5322 $.30   (E404)
(Shepherd) SSAA,acap SHAWNEE B 245 $.25
(E405)

Ave Verum *Op.2,No.1, anthem/mot
[Lat] mix cor oct NOVELLO 03.0127.02 s.p.
(E406)
"Jesu, Word Of God Incarnate" 4pt oct
NOVELLO 51.0530.07 s.p.   (E407)
"Jesu, Word Of God Incarnate" mix cor oct
NOVELLO 30.0036.02 s.p.   (E408)

Caractacus *Op.35, cant
SATB,STBarB soli,org,2fl,2ob,3clar,3bsn,
4horn,4trp,3trom,tuba,strings,perc,timp,
harp voc sc NOVELLO s.p., ipr   (E409)

Doubt Not Thy Father's Care (from Light Of
Life, The)
2pt,orch oct NOVELLO 53.0110.06 s.p., ipr
(E410)

Dream Of Gerontius, The *Op.38, ora
SATB,MezTB soli,org,3fl,3ob,3clar,3bsn,
4horn,3trp,3trom,tuba,strings,perc,timp,
2harp bds,voc sc NOVELLO s.p., ipr (E411)

Fear Not, O Land *Harv,anthem
mix cor oct NOVELLO 28.1050.06 s.p. (E412)

Give Unto The Lord (Psalm 29) Op.74
SATB,org/2fl&2ob&2clar&2bsn&4horn&2trp&
3trom&tuba&strings&timp&harp&perc voc sc
NOVELLO rental   (E413)

Go, Song Of Mine *sac/sec
(Ziemer) SATB (easy) oct AGAPE SP 685 $.35
(E414)

Great Is The Lord (Psalm 48) Op.67
SATB,org/2fl&2ob&2clar&3bsn&4horn&2trp&
3trom&tuba&strings&timp voc sc NOVELLO
rental   (E415)

Hail, Glorious Day
(Schaefer) SATB,band oct BOOSEY 5229 $.40,
ipa   (E416)

How Calmly The Evening *Eve,anthem
2pt,orch oct NOVELLO 53.0289.07 s.p., ipr
(E417)
4pt,orch oct NOVELLO 51.0504.08 s.p., ipr
(E418)
mix cor oct NOVELLO 40.0779.04 s.p. (E419)

I Sing The Birth *anthem
mix cor oct NOVELLO 40.1030.02 s.p. (E420)

Jesu, Meek And Lowly *anthem
mix cor oct NOVELLO 28.0907.09 s.p. (E421)

Jesu, Word Of God Incarnate *see Ave Verum

Kingdom, The *Op.51, Bibl/ora
SATB,SATB soli,org,3fl,3ob,3clar,3bsn,
4horn,3trp,3trom,tuba,strings,perc,timp,
2harp voc sc NOVELLO s.p., ipr   (E422)

Lift Up Your Hearts *see Sursum Corda

Light Of Life, The *see Lux Christi

Light Of The World, We Know Thy Praise (from
Light Of Life, The) anthem
SATB oct NOVELLO 28.0595.02 s.p.   (E423)
mix cor,orch oct NOVELLO 28.0595.02 s.p.,
ipr   (E424)

Lord's Prayer, The (from Kingdom, The)
anthem/Bibl/prayer
SATB oct NOVELLO 28.1201.00 s.p.   (E425)

Lux Christi *Op.29, ora
"Light Of Life, The" SATB,SATBar soli,org,
2fl,2ob,2clar,3bsn,4horn,2trp,3trom,tuba,
strings,perc,timp,harp voc sc NOVELLO
rental   (E426)

March Triumphal Thunders, The (from
Caractacus) anthem
SATB oct NOVELLO 34.0827.02 s.p.   (E427)

Psalm 29 *see Give Unto The Lord

Psalm 48 *see Great Is The Lord

Snow, The
(Ehret) SSA oct FOX S129 $.30   (E428)

Spirit Of The Lord Is Upon Me, The (from
Apostles, The) anthem
SATB oct NOVELLO 34.0805.01 s.p.   (E429)

Sursum Corda *anthem
(Johnson) "Lift Up Your Hearts" SATB oct
FISCHER,C CM-7706 $.40   (E430)

ELGAROY, JAN
Kristenhjerter Alle Steder
mix cor MUSIKK 244 s.p.   (E431)

Mitt Hjerte, Na Ma Du Glemme
mix cor MUSIKK 245 s.p.   (E432)

ELIAS see Mendelssohn-Bartholdy, Felix

ELIASON
Name I Highly Treasure, A
(Beresford) SATB oct LILLENAS AN-1114 $.25
     (E433)

ELIE HIMMELSFARD see Carlman, Gustaf

ELIJAH see Mendelssohn-Bartholdy, Felix

ELIJAH see Mendelssohn-Bartholdy, Felix, Elias

ELIJAH, ROCK *spir
(Johnson) mix cor,acap oct SCHIRM.G 10354
$.40   (E434)

ELIJAH, THE PROPHET *Fest/Passover
(Adler, Hugo Ch.) [Heb] SATB TRANSCON.
TCL 702 $.25   (E435)

ELIOT
Early Spring, The *Easter
SA oct LORENZ 5392 $.25   (E436)

Look Softly, Lord
SATB oct LORENZ B196 $.30   (E437)

O Let Me Fly
SATB oct LORENZ 7840 $.30   (E438)

ELKINS
Come, All You Weary Travelers
SATB oct PLYMOUTH AFH-2 $.25   (E439)

Garden Hymn
SATB oct PLYMOUTH AFH-5 $.25   (E440)

His Voice, As The Sound Of The Dulcimer,
Sweet
SATB oct PLYMOUTH AFH-4 $.25   (E441)

How Firm A Foundation
SATB oct PLYMOUTH AFH-6 $.25   (E442)

Once More, My Soul
SATB oct PLYMOUTH AFH-1 $.25   (E443)

ELLACOMBE
I Sing The Mighty Power Of God *anthem/hymn
(Walton) SATB oct SPRATT 563 $.25   (E444)

ELLENS SONG see Brahms, Johannes

ELLERTON
God The Omnipotent
(Rhea) SATB oct PLYMOUTH UIL-105 $.25
     (E445)

ELLIOT
God Of Mercy, God Of Grace
SATB oct PRO ART 1674 $.22   (E446)

I Look To Thee In Every Need
SATB oct PRO ART 1656 $.20   (E447)

O Praise Our Great And Gracious Lord
SATB oct PRO ART 1654 $.20   (E448)

ELLIOT, DENNIS
O Let Me Fly *Gen,anthem/spir
SA/SAB oct LORENZ 7840 $.30   (E449)

ELLIOT, ROBERT
Are We Not Risen With Christ *Easter,anthem
mix cor oct NOVELLO 44.1354.07 s.p. (E450)

Praise We The Lord *anthem/hymn
SATB/unis&desc oct NOVELLO 28.1343.02 s.p.
     (E451)

ELLIOTT
Father Of Mankind *Gen
SATB oct SPRATT 624 $.25   (E452)

Glory To God In The Highest
SATB,acap oct MCA   (E453)

God Rest Ye Merry, Gentlemen *Xmas
SAB oct LORENZ 7404 $.30   (E454)

House Of The Lord, The
SATB,opt pno/org oct MCA   (E455)

Love One Another *Gen
SATB oct SPRATT 576 $.25   (E456)

Sun Shines In Splendor, The
2pt oct LORENZ 5758 $.30   (E457)

ELLIOTT, KENNETH
Fourteen Psalms *CC14U,Gen,Psalm
(Scotch) SATB/unis (easy) oct OXFORD 48.002
$1.30   (E458)

ELLIS
Do You Know My Jesus?
(Mercer) SATB oct LILLENAS AN-1645 $.30
     (E459)

Let Me Touch Him
(Collins) SATB oct LILLENAS AT-1066 $.25
     (E460)

Light Of The World, The *Xmas
SATB oct LORENZ 4430 $.30   (E461)

Love Is Why
(Mercer) SATB oct LILLENAS AN-1646 $.30
     (E462)

Shall I Crucify Him? *Easter
SATB oct LORENZ 4421 $.30   (E463)

ELLIS, MARY
Come Thou Font
cor HIGHLAND 2006 $.25   (E464)

Father In Heaven
cor HIGHLAND 2004 $.30   (E465)

Sweet Hour Of Prayer
cor HIGHLAND 2001 $.30   (E466)

ELLISON
In Bethle'em Town *Xmas
SSA oct PRO ART 1505 $.18   (E467)

ELLOR
All Hail The Power Of Jesus' Name
(Ehret) SATB,org/pno BOSTON 12908 $.35
     (E468)

ELLSWORTH, A. EUGENE
Christmas Folk Song, A *Xmas
SATB oct PRESSER MC307 $.30   (E469)

Family Benediction, A *Bene
SAB (easy) ABINGDON APM-574 $.25   (E470)

God Be In My Head
SATB,acap (easy) ABINGDON APM-419 $.25
     (E471)

Let Her Own Works Praise Her
SATB oct PRESSER MC507 $.35   (E472)

ELLSWORTH, EUGENE
O Be Joyful
SATB (med) ABINGDON APM-500 $.35   (E473)

Show Me The Way To Thee
SATB (med) ABINGDON APM-573 $.25   (E474)

ELMORE, ROBERT [HALL] (1913-   )
All Ye Servants Of The Lord
SATB oct GALAXY 1.1481.1 $.35   (E475)

Babe Lies In The Cradle, A
SATB FLAMMER A 5136 $.25   (E476)

Bread Of Heaven
SATB oct WORD CS-689 $.25   (E477)

Child Is Born, A
SATB FLAMMER A 5172 $.25   (E478)
SAB FLAMMER D5125 $.30   (E479)

Come, Heavy Souls
SATB FLAMMER A 5156 $.30   (E480)

Come, My Soul
SATB oct GALAXY 1.1790.1 $.35   (E481)

Come To Calvary's Holy Mountain
SATB FLAMMER A 5282 $.30   (E482)

Cross, The *cant
mix cor BELWIN $2.00   (E483)

Drop, Drop, Slow Tears
SATB WARNER W3414 $.30   (E484)

Easter Bells Are Ringing *Easter
SATB oct GALAXY 1.1499.1 $.30   (E485)

God Of Ages
SATB FLAMMER A 5173 $.35   (E486)

Hail, Alpha And Omega
SATB oct SACRED S-53 $.35   (E487)

He Who Would Valiant Be
SATB oct GALAXY 1.1634.1 $.30   (E488)

Incarnate Word, The *cant
(Reed) mix cor BELWIN $2.00   (E489)

Living Christ, The
SATB oct SACRED E89 $.35   (E490)

Lord Jesus Think On Me
SATB oct GRAY GCMR 2096 $.35   (E491)

Now That The Daylight Fills The Sky
SATB oct GALAXY 1.1844.1 $.30   (E492)

O Lord, Support Us
SATB,S solo WARNER W3415 $.30   (E493)

Psalm Of Redemption *cant/Psalm
mix cor BELWIN $1.50   (E494)

Shepherd Of Israel
SACRED $1.75   (E495)

Short Communion Service
SATB oct GALAXY 1.2047.1 $.35   (E496)

Sing A Song Of Gladness
SAB oct GALAXY 1.2302.1 $.30   (E497)

Three Psalms *CC3U,Psalm
SATB FLAMMER A5509 $1.00   (E498)

We Give Thee But Thine Own
SATB oct SACRED E48 $.35   (E499)

Wondrous Child Divine
SATB FLAMMER A5551 $1.25   (E500)

ELRICH, D.
Christ Has Risen On Easter Day *Easter/Lent
SAB oct WORD CS-2396 $.30   (E501)

ELSK DIN NESTE, DU KRISTENSJEL see Beck, Thomas
[Ludvigsen]

ELSMITH, BERTA
Jeannette-Isabella *Xmas,carol,Fr
SSA,pno SCHIRM.EC 623 $1.00   (E502)

Noel In A Forgotten Farmyard *Xmas,carol
SSA,pno SCHIRM.EC 626 $1.00   (E503)

ELVESTRAND, MAGNE
Dag Over Norge
mix cor MUSIKK 41 s.p.   (E504)

No Koma Guds Englar
mix cor MUSIKK 166 s.p.   (E505)

ELVEY
Christ Is Risen From The Dead *Easter/Lent
(Collins) SAB oct PRO ART 1626 $.25 (E506)

Come, Ye Thankful People *Thanks
(Townsend) SSA oct PRO ART 1637 $.25 (E507)
(Townsend) SATB oct PRO ART 1731 $.25
     (E508)
(Townsend) 2pt oct PRO ART 1924 $.25 (E509)
(Townsend) SAB oct PRO ART 1453 $.30 (E510)

ELVEY (cont'd.)
Come, Ye Thankful People, Come *anthem
(Nelson) SATB&jr cor,trp (med) oct AUGSBURG
1526 $.30   (E511)

Crown Him With Many Crowns *anthem
(Johnson) SAB,opt trp (easy) oct AUGSBURG
1574 $.30, ipa   (E512)
(Pelz) cor&cong,org,trp (med) oct AUGSBURG
9093 $.35   (E513)

ELVEY, GEORGE JOB (1816-1893)
Arise, Shine *Xmas,Bibl
4pt mix cor oct SCHIRM.G 4491 $.20 (E514)

Arise, Shine For Thy Light Is Come *Xmas,
anthem
2pt ASHDOWN E.A.243 s.p.   (E515)
SATB ALLANS 209 s.p.   (E516)
SATB oct PRO ART 1727 $.20   (E517)
mix cor oct NOVELLO 40.0225.03 s.p. (E518)

Christ Is Risen *Easter,Bibl
SATB ALLANS 422 s.p.   (E519)
4pt mix cor,acap oct SCHIRM.G 4492 $.20
     (E520)

Come, Ye Thankful People
see THANKSGIVING SONGS

Come, Ye Thankful People, Come *Thanks,
anthem
(Davis) SSA FLAMMER B 5113 $.25 (E521)
(Gerig) SATB oct LILLENAS AN-2346 $.30
     (E522)
(Nelson) unis treb cor&SATB,org,trp (easy)
oct AUGSBURG 1526 $.30   (E523)

Crown Him With Many Crowns *sac/sec,Easter/
Lent,hymn
(Cain) SAB FLAMMER D5035 $.35   (E524)
(Cain) SATB FLAMMER A 5016 $.35   (E525)
(Ehret) sr cor&opt jr cor,opt trp oct
SPRATT 620 $.35   (E526)
(Hustad, Don) SATB/SAB ALLANS 451 s.p.
     (E527)
(Williams) SATB oct LILLENAS AN-2352 $.30
     (E528)

Eyes Of All Wait On Thee, The *Harv,anthem
mix cor oct NOVELLO 28.0547.02 s.p. (E529)

I Was Glad When They Said *anthem/Bibl
mix cor oct NOVELLO 28.0032.02 s.p. (E530)

O Give Thanks Unto The Lord *Gen/Thanks,
anthem
SATB ALLANS 384 s.p.   (E531)
mix cor oct NOVELLO 28.0016.00 s.p. (E532)

Praise The Lord
SATB ALLANS 424 s.p.   (E533)

Praise The Lord And Call Upon His Name
*anthem
mix cor oct NOVELLO 28.0070.05 s.p. (E534)

Rejoice In The Lord
(Knight) 3pt mix cor oct CURWEN 11202 $.20
     (E535)
(Knight) SAB CURWEN 80805 s.p.   (E536)

Souls Of The Righteous *Rembrnc
SATB ALLANS 385 s.p.   (E537)

Thankful People, Raise Your Song
(Zerr, J.) SATB oct PRESSER 312-40201 $.30
     (E538)

Thanksgiving Proclamation *Thanks
(Ringwald) SSAA SHAWNEE B 277 $.30   (E539)

Thanksgiving Proclamation And Harvest Hymn
*Harv/Thanks,hymn
(Ringwald) SATB SHAWNEE A 292 $.40 (E540)

EMENDEMUS see Palestrina, Giovanni

EMENDEMUS IN MELIUS see Byrd, William

EMERSON
Christ Is Risen *Easter
SATB oct LORENZ 518 $.30   (E541)

Come, Ye Blessed Children
(Karlin) girl cor SOUTHERN $.25   (E542)
(Karlin) SSAA,acap oct MCA   (E543)

Father We Thank Thee
(Hurlburt; Wilson) SA oct BOURNE 2008 $.25
     (E544)

He Is Risen
see SIX EASTER CAROLS

Lift Up Your Heads
SSA oct LORENZ 6047 $.25   (E545)
SAB oct LORENZ 7069 $.30   (E546)
SATB oct LORENZ 246 $.30   (E547)

EMERSON, JOHN
Above The Clear Blue Sky
SA/unis,pno oct WILLIS 2958 $.12   (E548)

Grant Us, Oh Our Heavenly Father
SA/unis,pno (easy) oct WILLIS 2959 $.12
     (E549)

King Of Peace *Xmas,cant
mix cor,soli voc sc WILLIS $.80   (E550)

King Of Peace, The *Xmas,cant
mix cor,high solo,med solo,Bar solo,pno/org
(med) oct WILLIS $.75   (E551)

Morning Hymn
SA,pno (easy) oct WILLIS 2711 $.12 (E552)

Morn's Roseate Hues *Easter
3pt wom cor,pno (med) oct WILLIS 2904 $.12
     (E553)

O Jesus, Thou Are Standing *Asc
3pt wom cor,pno (med) oct WILLIS 2861 $.16
     (E554)

Search Me, O God
SA,pno (easy) oct WILLIS 2710 $.12 (E555)

EMERY
What Can I Give Him? *Xmas
SATB oct LORENZ E19 $.30   (E556)

EMERY, DOROTHY R.
So Dark The Night *Xmas
   SSATBB,opt 3trp (med) ABINGDON APM-487
   $.50, ipa   (E557)

EMERY, JOHN
Bells Of Easter *Easter
   2pt jr cor,hndbl FISCHER,C CM 7373 $.25
                                                        (E558)
Make We Joy Now In This Feast *Xmas,carol
   SATB oct FABER 11748 $.35   (E559)
   4pt mix cor,acap oct SCHIRM.G 11748 $.35
                                                        (E560)

EMIG, LOIS
All My Heart This Night Rejoices
   (Hayward) SSA SHAWNEE B 210 $.30   (E561)

All The Earth Is Singing
   SA/TB FLAMMER E5012 $.30   (E562)

Beautiful Savior *Easter,cant
   SATB LORENZ $1.95   (E563)

Carry Candles To The Manger
   SAB FLAMMER D5203 $.30   (E564)

Child Of God
   2pt oct LORENZ 5755 $.30   (E565)

Children's Alleluia *Easter,Allelu
   1-2pt LORENZ $1.75   (E566)

Children's Hosanna, The *Easter
   SATB oct LORENZ 4499 $.30   (E567)

Christians, Sing Joyfully *Easter
   SAB oct LORENZ 7381 $.30   (E568)

Come To Bethlehem *Xmas,cant
   SATB oct LORENZ 4453 $.60   (E569)

Ev'ry Little Lamb Needs A Shepherd
   SSA SHAWNEE B 284 $.25   (E570)

Gather The Harvest
   SATB FLAMMER A 5196 $.35   (E571)

Gentle Shepherd
   unis/2pt oct PRO ART 1990 $.25   (E572)

God Is Great
   unis oct LORENZ 8859 $.25   (E573)

Greatest Blessing, The
   SATB oct LORENZ 4482 $.60   (E574)

He Took A Child
   SATB,acap SHAWNEE A 436 $.30   (E575)

Hosanna! Hosanna! *Easter
   SA oct LORENZ 5379 $.30   (E576)

Hosanna To The King *Easter
   SATB oct LORENZ C283 $.30   (E577)

Hymn At Bethlehem
   SSA SHAWNEE B 228 $.25   (E578)

I Speak Of Thee
   SATB,acap SHAWNEE A 555 $.25   (E579)

King Of Glory, The *Xmas
   SATB oct LORENZ B151 $.30   (E580)

Let Us Sing To The Lord
   SAB oct LORENZ 7378 $.30   (E581)

Lullaby Of The Children *Xmas
   SSA,acap oct PRO ART 1957 $.25   (E582)
   2pt oct PRO ART 1952 $.30   (E583)

Merry Noel, A
   SAB FLAMMER D5211 $.30   (E584)

My Father Walks Beside Me
   SATB oct LORENZ B17 $.30   (E585)

O Come And Mourn With Me Awhile
   SATB FLAMMER A 5412 $.25   (E586)
   SSA FLAMMER B 5066 $.30   (E587)
   SAB FLAMMER D5140 $.25   (E588)

O Sing Noel
   SATB FLAMMER A 5013 $.25   (E589)
   SAB FLAMMER D5002 $.30   (E590)

Our Blessed Savior
   SATB FLAMMER A 5216 $.30   (E591)
   SAB FLAMMER D5054 $.30   (E592)

Round For Christmas, A *Xmas,round
   SATB FLAMMER A 5131 $.30   (E593)
   SSA FLAMMER B 5028 $.25   (E594)
   SAB FLAMMER D5068 $.30   (E595)
   SA/TB FLAMMER E5010 $.30   (E596)

Shepherds' Carol, The *Xmas,cant
   1-2pt jr cor oct LORENZ $1.75   (E597)

Shepherds I Can See You
   SA/TB FLAMMER E5159 $.30   (E598)

Song Of Bethlehem, A *Xmas,cant
   1-2pt jr cor oct LORENZ $1.75   (E599)

Thank Thee, O Lord
   SA oct BELWIN 1609 $.25   (E600)

Thou Who Lovest Little Children
   SS/unis oct PRO ART 1991 $.25   (E601)

Walk With Me
   SATB oct LORENZ B69 $.30   (E602)
   2pt oct LORENZ 5737 $.30   (E603)

Watchman, Tell Us Of The Night *Xmas
   SATB oct LORENZ C205 $.25   (E604)

Wonder Of Easter *cant
   SA FLAMMER E5090 $1.10   (E605)

EMITTE SPIRITUM TUUM see Burkhart, Franz

EMITTE SPIRITUM TUUM see Matterling

EMITTE SPIRITUM TUUM see Schuetky, Franz Joseph

EMMANUEL (GOD WITH US) see Worthing, Richard

EMMAUS ROAD see Smith

EMPIRE ANTHEM BOOK, THE, BOOK 1 *CCU,anthem
   oct HART s.p.   (E606)

EMPIRE ANTHEM BOOK, THE, BOOK 2 *CCU,anthem
   oct HART s.p.   (E607)

EMPIRE ANTHEM BOOK, THE, BOOK 3 *CCU,anthem
   oct HART s.p.   (E608)

EMPIRE CAROL BOOK *CCU,Xmas,carol
   HART oct s.p., pap s.p.   (E609)

EMPTY TOMB, THE
   2pt CHAPPELL 0018002-352 $.40   (E610)
   SSA CHAPPELL 0018002-354 $.40   (E611)
   SATB CHAPPELL 0018002-358 $.40   (E612)

EMPTY TOMB, THE see Posegate

EN BELEN TOCAN A FUEGO see Martin Pompey

EN BORNESANG (BEHOLD OS, HERRE, VED DIT ORD)
   see Pederson, Mogens

EN CE DOUX ASILE see Rameau, Jean-Philippe

EN EL LAVADERO see Benedito

EN EL MONTE MURIO CHRISTO see Sanjuan, Pedro

EN EL PORTAL DE BELEN see Lopez, Almagro

EN GUDOMSSTRALE MILD OCH REN see Berg, Gottfrid

EN JUNGFRU FODDE ETT BARN I DAG *Xmas,hymn
   (Wikander, David) mix cor NORDISKA 2243 s.p.   (E613)

EN KELOHENU see Cohen, D.

EN LITEN JULKANTAT see Norman, Rudolf

EN MORGEN-SANG see Karlsen, Rolf

EN NATUS EST EMANUEL see Praetorius, Michael

EN NATUS EST EMMANUEL see Praetorius, Michael

EN PRIERE see Faure, Gabriel-Urbain

EN ROSE ER UDSPRUNGET see Distler, Hugo, Es Ist
   Ein Ros Entsprungen

EN SALIG FROJD DEN DAG BESKAR see Runback,
   Albert

EN SALME OM KRISTUS see Walther, Johann
   Gottfreid

EN SALME OM VORT FALD OG FORLOSNING see Franck,
   Melchior

EN SANGERS BONN see Reissiger, F.A.

EN SEPOIR see Clemens, Jacobus

EN SLAEGT GAR OG EN SLAEGT KOMMER see Jeppesen,
   Knud

EN SON TEMPLE SACRE see Mauduit, Jacques

EN SORTANT DE L'ETABLE see Aubanel, Georges

EN TODA LA QUINTANA see Benedito

EN VANLIG GRONSKAS RIKA DRAKT see Ahlen,
   Waldemar

EN VANLIG GRONSKAS RIKA DRAKT see Berg,
   Gottfrid

ENATUS EST EMMANUEL see Praetorius, Michael

ENCHITIDION
   Now Praise We Christ, The Holy One *Xmas
   (Avalos) SATB oct PRO ART 2086 $.22   (E614)

END IS THE BEGINNING, THE see Gardner, John
   [Linton]

END OF THE ROAD, THE see Roff, Joseph

ENDERS, GOTTFRIED
   Befiehl Du Deine Wege
      see Tzschoppe, Eberhart, Es Ist Ein
      Kostlich Ding

   Die Helle Sonn Leucht
      see Tzschoppe, Eberhart, Es Ist Ein
      Kostlich Ding

ENDING OF THE YEAR see Wells

ENDLESS ALLELUIA see Van Dyke

ENDLESS ALLELUIA, AN see Candlyn, T. Frederick
   H.

ENDLESS ALLELUIA, AN see Sheppard

ENDLESS ALLELUIA, AN see Wyton, Alex

ENDLESS LIGHT OF DAY see Grigg, W.E.

ENE I GUD see N-N, J.

ENGEL, [A. LEHMAN] (1910-   )
   Lamb
      SSA,acap oct BOOSEY AP37 $.30   (E615)

   Let Us Now Praise Famous Men
      SATB,acap oct PRESSER MC200 $.35   (E616)

   On The Gallows Tree
      SATB FLAMMER A 5170 $.30   (E617)
      SSA FLAMMER B 5036 $.30   (E618)

   Sing Forth The Honor Of His Name
      SATB,acap FLAMMER A 5586 $.30   (E619)

ENGEL, DER see Rubinstein, Anton

ENGEL, J.
   By The Shores Of The Jordan
      SATB,acap PEER $.45   (E620)

ENGEL SINGEN FROHE LIEDER *Xmas,Aus/Eur
   (Doppelbauer, Josef Friedrich) mix cor,acap
   DOBLINGER s.p. see from Da Der Herr Geboren
                                                        (E621)

ENGELBREKT
   I Lay My Sins On Jesus *Lent
      SATB SCHMITT 861 $.35   (E622)

ENGELHART, P.
   Vesper Bell, The
      SATB BOSWORTH s.p.   (E623)

ENGELSKONZERT see Kelling, H.

ENGLERT, EUGENE
   Acclamations
      SATB&cong,org,opt gtr oct WORLD ESA-1885-8
      $.30   (E624)

   Ask The Father
      see Six Scriptural Anthems

   Blessed Be The Lord *anthem
      SATB (med) oct AUGSBURG 1492 $.25   (E625)

   Christ Is Made The Sure Foundation *anthem
      SATB,opt trp,timp (med) oct AUGSBURG 1652
      $.35   (E626)

   Cup Of Blessing, The
      see Six Scriptural Anthems

   I Will Extol You
      see Six Scriptural Anthems

   Law Of The Lord Is Perfect, The
      see Six Scriptural Anthems

   Light Of The World, The
      see Six Scriptural Anthems

   Memorare
      "Remember O Most Gracious Virgin" SSA oct
      JUSKO 282 $.25   (E627)

   Out Of The Depths *Psalm
      SATB,acap oct WORLD ESA-1897-8 $.30   (E628)

   Praise The King Of Glory *anthem
      SATB (easy) oct AUGSBURG 1613 $.25   (E629)

   Remember O Most Gracious Virgin *see
      Memorare

   Shout Joyfully To God
      see Six Scriptural Anthems

   Six Scriptural Anthems *anthem/Bibl
      oct SATB,org WORLD ESA-666-8 $.90; 2 eq
      voices,org WORLD ESA-780-2 $.90; SSA,org
      WORLD ESA-561-3 $.90
      contains: Ask The Father; Cup Of
      Blessing, The; I Will Extol You; Law Of
      The Lord Is Perfect, The; Light Of The
      World, The; Shout Joyfully To God
                                                        (E630)

ENGLISH CAROL BOOK, THE *CCUL,carol,Eng
   (Shaw, Martin; Dearmer, Percy) cor/cong oct
   MOWBRAY 65051 4 s.p.
   see also: O Sisters Too (Coventry Carol);
   Shaw, Geoffrey [Turton], Unto Us Is Born
   A Son   (E631)

ENGLISH CHRISTMAS CAROLS *CC7L,Xmas,Eng
   (Geer, E.) SSA&SSAA,acap SCHIRM.EC 853 $.45   (E632)

ENGLISH GOTHIC MUSIC see Power, Lyonel

ENGLISH GOTHIC MUSIC
   (Hughes, Dom Anselm; Grainger, Percy) [Lat/
   Eng] SCHOTT SSA cmplt ed s.p.; TTB cmplt ed
   s.p.
   contains: Alleluia Psallat; Angelus Ad
   Virginem; Beata Viscera; Puellare Gremium
                                                        (E633)

ENGLISH GOTHIC MUSIC see Power, Lyonel

ENGLISH HYMNAL, THE *CCU,hymn
   SATB (easy) OXFORD $3.55   (E634)

ENGLISH HYMNS ADAPTED TO BACH'S CHORALES see
   Bach, Johann Sebastian

ENGLISH MASS see Goemanne, Noel

ENGLISH MASS see Heiller, Anton

ENGLISH MASS, AN see Howells, Herbert Norman

ENGLISH MASS, AN see Baxter, T.

ENGLISH MASS FOR ST. DOMENIC see Goemanne, Noel

ENGLISH SACRED MUSIC see Ramsey, Robert

ENGLISH TRADITIONAL CAROLS *CC21U,carol
   (Vaughan Williams; Shaw) 1-4pt treb cor,opt
   acap OXFORD 44.992 $1.50   (E635)

ENGLISH UNISON MASS see Jillett, David

ENGRATULEMUR see Ravanello, Oreste

ENLIGHTENMENT IS FROM THE LORD see Norden, Hugo

ENMENDEMUS IN MELIUS see Morales, Cristobal de

ENOSH see Lewandowski, Louis

ENOUGH TO KNOW
   SSA BIG3 $.25   (E636)

ENTER HIS HOUSE WITH PRAISE see Hedges

ENTER NOT INTO JUDGMENT see Attwood, Thomas

ENTER THIS DOOR see Caldwell, Mary [Elizabeth]

ENTRANCE HYMNS
   LITURGICAL $.50
      contains: From All Who Dwell Beneath The
      Skies; Holy, Holy, Holy; Praise To The
      Lord   (E637)

ERK, LUDWIG (cont'd.)

Getan, Mein Volk (dbl cor)   (E668)

ERKEL, FRANZ (1810-1893)
   Himnusz
      (Kolcsey, F.; Forrai, M.) [Hung] SATB
         (easy) BUDAPEST 1403 s.p.   (E669)
      (Kolcsey, F.; Forrai, M.) [Hung] SATB,pno/
         orch (easy) BUDAPEST 1404 s.p.   (E670)
      (Kolcsey, F.; Forrai, M.) [Hung] SATB,pno
         (easy) BUDAPEST 779 s.p.   (E671)
      (Kolcsey, F.; Forrai, M.) [Hung] SATB,orch
         (easy) BUDAPEST 1279 s.p.   (E672)

   Unnepi Kantata *cant
      (Andras; Raics) [Hung] SATB,SATB soli (med
         diff) BUDAPEST 4020 s.p.   (E673)
      (Raics, I.; Andras, B.) [Hung] SATB,pno
         (diff) BUDAPEST 4020 s.p.   (E674)

ERKENNET, DASS CHRISTUS LIEBHABEN see Reda,
   Siegfried

ERLANDSON, AKE
   Herre, Vem Far Bo I Din Hydda? *Bibl
      [Swed] SAB,acap GEHRMANS TKS 130   (E675)

   Jag Har Herren Kar *Bibl
      [Swed] SAB,acap GEHRMANS TKS 129   (E676)

   Led Mig I Din Sanning
      [Swed] SAB,acap GEHRMANS TKS 131   (E677)

   Tranger I Dolda Djupen Ner *Bibl
      [Swed] SAB,acap GEHRMANS TKS 128   (E678)

   Var Sjal Vantar Efter Herren
      3pt mix cor NORDISKA 5574 s.p.   (E679)

ERLEBACH, PHILIPP HEINRICH (1657-1714)
   Der Herr Hat Offenbaret *cant
      [Ger] cor,soli,org,strings KISTNER sc s.p.,
         cor pts s.p., ipa   (E680)

   Give Us Joy For This New Year *see Gott, Gib
      Gluck Zum Neuen Jahr

   Gott, Gib Gluck Zum Neuen Jahr *mot
      (Hunter) "Give Us Joy For This New Year"
         [Eng/Ger] SATTB,acap MARKS 4430 $.30
                                                        (E681)
   Ich Will Wasser Giessen Auf Die Durrsteden
      *cant
      (Steuber) SATB,cont,2vln,2vla HANSSLER
         10.101 sc s.p., voc sc s.p., ipa   (E682)

   Lobe Den Herrn, Meine Seele *Gen
      (Steuber, Otfried V.) [Ger] SATB,TB soli,
         cont,2vln,2vla,vcl,bvl (med) BAREN.
         BA 3453 sc s.p., cor pts s.p., ipa   (E683)

   Sei Lob Und Preis Mit Ehren *Gen
      [Ger] SATB,cont,2vln,opt 2vla (med) BAREN.
         BA 4943 $.40   (E684)

   Siehe, Ich Verkundige Euch Grosse Freude
      *cant
      (Steuber) SATB,SATB soli,cont,bsn,2trp,
         2vln,2vla HANSSLER 10.019 cor pts s.p.,
         voc sc s.p., ipa   (E685)

ERMATINGER, ERHART (1900)
   Furchtet Euch Nicht *mot
      [Ger] mix cor,acap (diff) HUG s.p.   (E686)

ERMUNTRE DICH, MEIN SCHWACHER GEIST see Bach,
   Johann Sebastian

ERMUNTRE DICH, MEIN SCHWACHER GEIST see
   Bornefeld, Helmut

ERMUNTRE DICH, MEIN SCHWACHER GEIST see Kubler,
   Emil

ERMUNTRE DICH, MEIN SCHWACHER GEIST [CHORALE]
   see Bach, Johann Sebastian

ERNEUERT EUCH IM GEIST see Reda, Siegfried

ERNEURE MICH, O EWIGS LICHT see Zipp, Friedrich

ERNTEFEIER see Rein, Walter

ERNTESEGEN: DIE WACHTEL RUFT see Weismann,
   Wilhelm

ERPF, HERMANN (1891-1969)
   Requiem *Req
      6pt mix cor MOSELER s.p.   (E687)

ERRETTE, HERR, MICH VON DEN BOSEN see Le Jeune,
   Claude

ERSCHALLET, IHR HIMMEL see Benda, Georg

ERSCHALLET, IHR LIEDER see Bach, Johann
   Sebastian

ERSCHALLET, IHR LIEDER [CHORALE] see Bach,
   Johann Sebastian

ERSCHALLT, TROMPETEN see Handel, George
   Frideric, Awake The Trumpet's Lofty Sound

ERSCHALT, TROMPETEN see Handel, George Frideric

ERSCHIENEN IST DER HERRLICH TAG see Bach,
   Johann Sebastian

ERSCHIENEN IST DER HERRLICH TAG see Erythraus,
   Gotthard

ERSCHIENEN IST DER HERRLICH TAG see Grabner,
   Hermann

ERSCHIENEN IST DER HERRLICH TAG see Hasselbock,
   Hans

ERSCHIENEN IST DER HERRLICH TAG see Praetorius,
   Michael

ERSCHIENEN IST DER HERRLICH TAG see Schein,
   Johann Hermann

ERSCHIENEN IST DER HERRLICH TAG see Stern,
   Hermann

ERSCHIENEN IST DER HERRLICH TAG see Weber,
   Karl-Heinz

ERSCHIENEN IST DER HERRLICH TAG see Wenzel,
   Eberhard

ERSCHIENEN IST DER HERRLICH TAG see Zipp,
   Friedrich

ERSCHIENEN IST DER HERRLICHE TAG see Schein,
   Johann Hermann

ERSEUS, TORSTEN
   Den Karlek Du Till Varlden Bar *Bibl
      [Swed] SAB,acap GEHRMANS TKS 62   (E688)

   Nar Vi I Hogsta Noden Sta *Bibl
      [Swed] SAB,acap GEHRMANS TKS 63   (E689)

ERSTANDEN IST DER HEILGE CHRIST see Demantius,
   Christoph

ERSTANDEN IST DER HEILIG CHRIST see Buxtehude,
   Dietrich

ERSTANDEN IST DER HEILIG CHRIST see Eglin,
   Arthur

ERSTANDEN IST DER HEILIG CHRIST see Hassler,
   Hans Leo

ERSTANDEN IST DER HEILIG CHRIST see Hufschmidt,
   Wolfgang

ERSTANDEN IST DER HEILIG CHRIST see
   Kretzschmar, Gunther

ERSTANDEN IST DER HEILIG CHRIST see Praetorius,
   Michael

ERSTANDEN IST DER HEILIG CHRIST see Raselius,
   Andreas

ERSTANDEN IST DER HEILIG CHRIST see Stegen,
   Wilfried

ERSTANDEN IST DER HEILIG CHRIST see Vulpius,
   Melchior

ERSTANDEN IST DER HEILIGE CHRIST see Hassler,
   Hans Leo

ERSTANDEN IST DER HEILIGE CHRIST see Koch,
   Johannes H.E.

ERSTANDEN IST DER HERRE CHRIST see Selle,
   Thomas

ERSTER NACHTRAG ZUR GESAMTAUSGABE-BAND XXX see
   Palestrina, Giovanni

ERUCTAVIT COR MEUM see Bagni

ERWECKT HAT MIR DAS HERZ ZU DIR see Praetorius,
   Michael

ERWUNSCHTES FREUDENLICHT see Bach, Johann
   Sebastian

ERYTHRAUS, GOTTHARD
   Erschienen Ist Der Herrlich Tag
      see Bach, Johann Sebastian, Auf, Auf, Mein
         Herz Mit Freuden

   In The Midst Of Earthly Life
      SATB,acap oct PRESSER 312-40152 $.30 (E690)

   Mitten Wir Im Leben Sind
      see Bach, Johann Sebastian, Komm, O Tod, Du
         Schlafes Bruder

   Vater Unser Im Himmelreich *prayer
      SATB HANSSLER 6.1073 s.p.   (E691)

   Verleih Uns Frieden Gnadiglich
      see Anonymous, Lob, Preis Und Dank Sei Dir

ERZUNE DICH NICHT see Stoltzer, Thomas

ERZURNE DICH NICHT UBER DIE see Wagener, Gregor

ES BEGAB SICH ABER ZU DER ZEIT see Selle,
   Thomas

ES BLUHEN DIE MAIEN see Bresgen, Cesar

ES BLUHEN DIE MAIEN see Liebe, Kurt Maria

ES BLUHEN DREI ROSEN *BVM
   (Dawidowicz, Anton) wom cor,acap (contains
      also: Wie Schon Scheint Der Mond) oct
      DOBLINGER s.p. see also Acht Marienlieder
                                                        (E692)
ES BLUH'N DREI ROSEN AUF EINEM STRAUCH *BVM,
   19th cent
   (Miggl, Erwin) wom cor,acap oct DOBLINGER
      s.p. see also Drei Marienlieder   (E693)

ES BLUHN DREI ROSEN AUF EINEM ZWEIG see Rahner,
   Hugo

ES BLUHT DEN ENGELN WOHLBEKANNT *BVM,18th cent
   (Miggl, Erwin) wom cor,acap oct DOBLINGER
      s.p. see also Drei Marienlieder   (E694)

ES BLUHT DER BLUME EINE see Muller, A.M.

ES BRINGT DAS RECHTE JUBELJAHR see Bach, Johann
   Sebastian

ES DUNKELT SCHON BALD see Lang, Hans

ES ERHUB SICH EIN STREIT see Bach, Johann
   Christoph Friedrich

ES ERHUB SICH EIN STREIT see Bach, Johann
   Sebastian

ES ERHUB SICH EIN STREIT, MICHAEL see Schutz,
   Heinrich

ES ERHUB SUCH see Bach, Johann Sebastian, Es
   Erhub Sich Ein Streit

ES FAHRET HEUTE GOTTES SOHN see Bach, Johann
   Sebastian

ES FIEL EIN HIMMELSTAUE see Bresgen, Cesar

ES FLOG EIN TABLEIN WEISSE see Krause, Chr.

ES FLOG EIN TAUBLEIN WEISSE see Michels, Josef

ES FREUEN SICH DIE ENGELEIN see Spitta,
   Heinrich

ES GEHT DAHER DES TAGEN SCHEIN see Schlicht,
   Johann Gottfried

ES GEHT DAHER DES TAGES SCHEIN see Goudimel,
   Claude

ES GEHT DAHER DES TAGES SCHEIN see Heilmann,
   Harald

ES GEHT WOHL ZU DER SOMMERZEIT see Kurig, Hans-
   Hermann

ES GING EIN SAMANN AUS ZU SAEN SEINEN SAMEN see
   Schutz, Heinrich

ES GING EIN SAMANN AUS, ZU SAEN SEINEN SAMEN
   see Schutz, Heinrich, Es Ging Ein Samann
   Aus Zu Saen Seinen Samen

ES GINGEN ZWEENE MENSCHEN see Schutz, Heinrich

ES HAT SICH EROFFNET DAS HIMMLISCHE TOR see
   Polzer, Odo

ES HAT SICH HALT EROFFNET
   (Bauernfeind, Hans) mix cor,acap oct
      DOBLINGER s.p.   (E695)

ES HAT'S KEIN AUG GESEHEN see Franck, Melchior

ES IST AUF ERDEN EIN KINDLEIN GEBOREN *Xmas,
   Dut/Eur
   (Doppelbauer, Josef Friedrich) mix cor,acap
      DOBLINGER s.p. see from Da Der Herr Geboren
                                                        (E696)
ES IST DAS HEIL see Bach, Johann Sebastian, Es
   Ist Das Heil Uns Kommen Her

ES IST DAS HEIL see Brahms, Johannes

ES IST DAS HEIL UNS KOMMEN HER
   see Ich Steh In Meines Herren Hand

ES IST DAS HEIL UNS KOMMEN HER see Bach, Johann
   Sebastian

ES IST DAS HEIL UNS KOMMEN HER see Brahms,
   Johannes

ES IST DAS HEIL UNS KOMMEN HER see Distler,
   Hugo

ES IST DAS HEIL UNS KOMMEN HER see Praetorius,
   Michael

ES IST DAS HEIL UNS KOMMEN HER see Schein,
   Johann Hermann

ES IST DAS HEIL UNS KOMMEN HER see Stern,
   Hermann

ES IST DAS HEIL UNS KOMMEN HER [CHORALE] see
   Bach, Johann Sebastian

ES IST DIR GESAGT, MENSCH, WAS GUT IST see
   Bach, Johann Sebastian

ES IST DIR GESAGT, MENSCH, WAS GUT IST see
   Brunner, Adolf

ES IST DIR GESAGT, MENSCH, WAS GUT IST see
   Peter, Herbert

ES IST EIN FREUD DEM HERZEN MEIN see Schutz,
   Heinrich

ES IST EIN GROSSER PROPHET see Raselius,
   Andreas

ES IST EIN GROSSER PROPHET UNTER UNS see
   Vulpius, Melchior

ES IST EIN KIND GEBOREN [CHORALE] see Bach,
   Johann Sebastian

ES IST EIN KOSTLICH DING see Beck, Conrad

ES IST EIN KOSTLICH DING see Staden, Johann

ES IST EIN KOSTLICH DING see Tzschoppe,
   Eberhart

ES IST EIN KOSTLICH DING, DEM HERREN see
   Staden, Johann

ES IST EIN' ROS'
   see Six Christmas Carols, Set III

ES IST EIN ROS' ENTSPRUGEN see Linkenbach,
   Klaus

ES IST EIN ROS ENTSPRUNGEN see Distler, Hugo

ES IST EIN' ROS' ENTSPRUNGEN *Xmas,carol,16th
   cent
   unis/SATB (very easy) OXFORD 08.074 $.15
                                                        (E697)
   (Kramer, G.) mix cor DOBLINGER s.p. see also
      Drei Weihnachtslieder   (E698)

ES IST EIN ROS' ENTSPRUNGEN see Anonymous

ES IST EIN ROS' ENTSPRUNGEN see Bobel, Karl

ES IST EIN ROS ENTSPRUNGEN see Distler, Hugo

ES IST EIN ROS ENTSPRUNGEN see Knab, Armin

ES IST EIN' ROS' ENTSPRUNGEN see Kranz, Albert

ES IST EIN ROS ENTSPRUNGEN see Praetorius,
   Michael

ES IST EIN ROS ENTSPRUNGEN see Raphael, Gunther

ES IST EIN ROS ENTSPRUNGEN see Stern, Hermann

ES IST EIN ROS ENTSPRUNGEN see Sturmer, Bruno

ES IST EIN ROS ENTSPRUNGEN see Vulpius,
Melchior

ES IST EIN ROS ENTSPRUNGEN see Weiss, Ewald

ES IST EIN ROS ETSPRUNGEN see Koch, Johannes
H.E.

ES IST EIN SCHNITTER, HEISST DER TOD see
Raphael, Gunther

ES IST EIN TROTZIG see Bach, Johann Sebastian,
Es Ist Ein Trotzig Und Verzagt Ding

ES IST EIN TROTZIG UND VERZAGT DING see Bach,
Johann Sebastian

ES IST EIN WORT ERGANGEN see Burkhard Willy

ES IST EINER FUR UNS GESTORBEN see Lotz, Hans-
Georg

ES IST ERSCHIENEN DIE HEILSAME GNADE see
Micheelsen, Hans Friedrich

ES IST ERSCHIENEN DIE HEILSAME GNADE GOTTES see
Reda, Siegfried

ES IST ERSCHIENEN DIE HEILSAME GNADE GOTTES see
Schutz, Heinrich

ES IST ETWAS, DES HEILANDS SEIN see Barner, A.

ES IST EUCH GUT see Bach, Johann Sebastian, Es
Ist Euch Gut, Dass Ich Hingehe

ES IST EUCH GUT, DASS ICH HINGEHE see Bach,
Johann Sebastian

ES IST EUCH GUT, DASS ICH HINGEHE see Vulpius,
Melchior

ES IST FUR UNS EINE ZEIT ANGEKOMMEN *Xmas,Eur/
Swiss
(Doppelbauer, Josef Friedrich) mix cor,acap
DOBLINGER s.p. see from Da Der Herr Geboren
                                            (E699)

ES IST FUR UNS EINE ZEIT ANGEKOMMEN see
Wolters, Gottfried

ES IST GENUG! see Bach, Johann Sebastian

ES IST GENUG, HERR, WENN ES DIR see Bach,
Johann Sebastian

ES IST GESAGT see Bach, Johann Sebastian, Es
Ist Dir Gesagt, Mensch, Was Gut Ist

ES IST GEWISSLICH AN DER ZEIT see Bach, Johann
Sebastian

ES IST GEWISSLICH AN DER ZEIT see Praetorius,
Michael

ES IST GEWISSLICH AN DER ZEIT see Schein,
Johann Hermann

ES IST GEWISSLICH AN DER ZEIT see Stern,
Hermann

ES IST IN KEINEM ANDERN HEIL see Weinreich,
Waltraut

ES IST JETZT SO EIN KALTE NACHT see Dangel,
Arthur

ES IST NICHT FEIN, DASS MAN DEN KINDLEIN IHR
BROT NEHME see Franck, Melchior

ES IST NICHTS see Bach, Johann Sebastian, Es
Ist Nichts Gesundes An Meinem Leibe

ES IST NICHTS GESUNDES AN MEINEM LEIBE see
Bach, Johann Sebastian

ES IST ROS' ENTSPRUNGEN see Praetorius, Michael

ES IST VOLLBRACHT see Ahle, Johann Rudolph

ES IST VOLLBRACHT! see Bach, Johann Sebastian

ES IST VOLLBRACHT see Zipp, Friedrich

ES IST VOLLBRACHT! VERGISS JA NICHT DIES WORT
see Bach, Johann Sebastian

ES KAM EIN ENGEL HELL UND KLAR see Eccard,
Johannes

ES KAM EIN ENGEL, HELL UND KLAR see Praetorius,
Michael

ES KAM EIN ENGEL HELL UND KLAR see Schilling,
Hans Ludwig

ES KOMMT ABER DIE ZEIT see Franck, Melchior

ES KOMMT ABER DIE ZEIT see Vulpius, Melchior

ES KOMMT ALLES DARAUF AN see Hindermann, Walter
Felix

ES KOMMT DER HERR DER HERRLICHKEIT see
Schneider, Herbert

ES KOMMT DER HERR DER HERRLICHKEIT see Woll, E.

ES KOMMT DER TAG see Kratochwill, Heinrich

ES KOMMT DIE ZEIT, SO SPRICHT DER HERR see
Reger, Max

ES KOMMT EIN SCHIFF see Nelhybel, Vaclav

ES KOMMT EIN SCHIFF see Nickel, Eckehardt

ES KOMMT EIN SCHIFF GELADEN see Barbe, Helmut

ES KOMMT EIN SCHIFF, GELADEN see Bender, Jan

ES KOMMT EIN SCHIFF, GELADEN see Beuerle,
Herbert

ES KOMMT EIN SCHIFF GELADEN see Distler, Hugo

ES KOMMT EIN SCHIFF, GELADEN see Friedrichs,
Karl

ES KOMMT EIN SCHIFF, GELADEN see Geiser,
Walther

ES KOMMT EIN SCHIFF GELADEN see Kluge, Manfred

ES KOMMT EIN SCHIFF GELADEN see Lehner, F.X.

ES KOMMT EIN SCHIFF GELADEN see Lissmann, Kurt

ES KOMMT EIN SCHIFF, GELADEN see Lohr, Ina

ES KOMMT EIN SCHIFF GELADEN see Raphael,
Gunther

ES KOMMT EIN SCHIFF, GELADEN see Rein, Walter

ES KOMMT EIN SCHIFF, GELADEN see Spitta,
Heinrich

ES KOMMT EIN SCHIFF, GELADEN see Strohbach,
Siegfried

ES KOMMT EIN SCHIFF, GELADEN see Studer, Hans

ES KOMMT EIN SCHIFF, GELADEN see Tenne, Arno

ES KOMMT EIN SCHIFF GELADEN see Weber, Karl-
Heinz

ES KOMMT EIN SCHIFF, GELADEN see Weiss, Ewald

ES KOMMT EIN SCHIFF, GELADEN see Wunderlich,
Heinz

ES KOMMT EIN SCHIFF GELADEN see Zipp, Friedrich

ES LAGEN IM FELDE DIE HIRTEN see Lahusen,
Christian

ES MAG SEIN, DASS ALLES FALLT see Lahusen,
Christian

ES MUSS EIN ZEICHEN SEIN see Stier, Alfred

ES MUSSEN SICH FREUEN UND FROHLICH SEIN see
Reda, Siegfried

ES REIFET EUCH EIN SCHRECKLICH ENDE see Bach,
Johann Sebastian

ES REISSET EUCH EIN SCHRECKLICH ENDE see Bach,
Johann Sebastian

ES RIEFET EUCH see Bach, Johann Sebastian, Es
Reifet Euch Ein Schrecklich Ende

ES SCHALLE HELL UND FROH see Handel, George
Frideric

ES SIND DREI FRAUEN NACH BOHMEN GEGANGEN see
Krietsch, Georg

ES SINGT WOHL EIN VOGLEIN see Brautigam, Helmut

ES SOLL NICHT DURCH HEER ODER KRAFT GESCHEHEN
see Ruppel, Paul Ernst

ES SPRACH ZU MIR see Ruppel, Paul Ernst

ES SPRICHT DER UNWEISEN MUND see Schein, Johann
Hermann

ES STEH GOTT AUF, DASS SEINE FEIND see Schutz,
Heinrich

ES STEHT EIN LIND *15th cent
(Kramer, G.) mix cor DOBLINGER s.p. see also
Drei Weihnachtslieder   (E700)

ES STEHT EIN LIND see Anonymous

ES STEHT EIN LIND see Lang, Hans

ES STEHT EIN LIND IN JENEM TAL see Othmayr,
Kaspar

ES STRAHLEN HELL DIE GERECHTEN see Mendelssohn-
Bartholdy, Felix

ES SUNGEN DREI ENGEL see Micheelsen, Hans
Friedrich

ES SUNGEN DREI ENGEL see Rothschuh, F.

ES SUNGEN DREI ENGEL see Teuscher, Hans

ES WANDELN SICH DIE REICHE see Stern, Hermann

ES WAR DES EWIGEN VATERS RAT see Praetorius,
Michael

ES WAR EIN' JUNGFRAU AUSERKOREN *Xmas,Dut/Eur
(Doppelbauer, Josef Friedrich) mix cor,acap
DOBLINGER s.p. see from Da Der Herr Geboren
                                            (E701)

ES WAR EIN MENSCH, DER MACHTE EIN GROSSES
ABENDMAHL see Kretzschmar, Gunther

ES WARTET ALLES AUF DICH see Bach, Johann
Sebastian

ES WARTET ALLES AUF DICH see Motte, Diether de
la

ES WERDEN NICHT ALLE, DIE ZU MIR SAGEN see
Driessler, Johannes

ES WERDEN NICHT ALLE, DIE ZU MIR SAGEN see
Raselius, Andreas

ES WERDEN NICHT ALLE, DIE ZU MIR SAGEN see
Selle, Thomas

ES WERDEN NICHT ALLE, DIE ZU MIR SAGEN see
Vulpius, Melchior

ES WIRD ABER DES HERREN TAG KOMMEN see Reda,
Siegfried

ES WIRD DAS SZEPTER VON JUDA NICHT ENTWENDET
WERDEN see Schutz, Heinrich

ES WIRD DAS ZEPTER VON JUDA NICHT ENTWENDET
WERDEN see Schutz, Heinrich

ES WIRD EIN STERN AUS JAKOB AUFGEHEN see Eglin,
Arthur

ES WIRD GESAET VERWESLICH UND WIRD AUFERSTEHEN
see Peter, Herbert

ES WIRD SCHO GLEI DUMPA
(Tittel, Ernst) mix cor,acap oct DOBLINGER
s.p.   (E702)

ES WIRD SCHO GLEI DUMPA see Kropfreiter,
Augustinius Franz

ES WIRD SEIN IN DEN LETZTEN TAGEN see Michel,
Josep

ES WOLL UNS GOTT GENADIG SEIN see Bach, Johann
Sebastian

ES WOLL UNS GOTT GENADIG SEIN see Wannenmacher,
Johannes

ES WOLL UNS GOTT GNADIG SEIN see Ducis,
Benedictus

ES WOLLE GOTT UNS GNADIG SEIN see Bach, Johann
Sebastian

ES WOLLE GOTT UNS GNADIG SEIN see Bornefeld,
Helmut

ES WOLLE GOTT UNS GNADIG SEIN see Franck,
Melchior

ES WOLLE GOTT UNS GNADIG SEIN see Praetorius,
Michael

ES WOLLE GOTT UNS GNADIG SEIN see Reda,
Siegfried

ES WOLLE GOTT UNS GNADIG SEIN see Wagner,
Alexander

ESCHMANN, HANNS (1900-   )
Choral-Festmesse *Fest,Mass
[Ger] SATB&cong,acap (med) MULLER SM 1169
s.p.   (E703)

Missa Gregoriana *Mass
[Ger] SSA&cong/cor (med) sc MULLER SM 1359
s.p.   (E704)

ESCOBEDO, BARTOLOME (ca. 1515-1563)
Exsurge, Quare Obdormis *mot
[Lat] 4pt mix cor,acap UNION ESP. 19353
s.p.   (E705)

Immutemur
[Lat] 4pt mix cor,acap UNION ESP. 19354
s.p.   (E706)

ESCOVADA, R.
Adoramus Te, Christe *mot
SATB,acap AMP A470 $.25 see from Four
Motets   (E707)

Ave Maria *mot
SATB,acap AMP A469 $.25 see from Four
Motets   (E708)

Ave Verum Corpus *mot
SATB,acap AMP A472 $.25 see from Four
Motets   (E709)

Four Motets *see Adoramus Te, Christe; Ave
Maria; Ave Verum Corpus; O Salutaris
Hostia   (E710)

O Salutaris Hostia *mot
SATB,acap AMP A471 $.25 see from Four
Motets   (E711)

Psalm 131
SATB,acap AMP A387 $.20   (E712)

Two Hymns On Poems Of Christopher Smart
*CC2U,hymn
SATB,acap oct MCA   (E713)

What Child Is This?
SATB,acap AMP A547 $.30   (E714)

ESCUDERO
Canciones: Cuaderno I *sac/sec,CC27L
[Span/Lat] cor,acap UNION ESP. 21487 s.p.
                                            (E715)
Canciones: Cuaderno II *sac/sec,CC49L
[Span/Lat] cor,acap UNION ESP. 21488 s.p.
                                            (E716)
Villancicos. Cuaderno II *CC12L,Xmas,carol
[Span] cor UNION ESP. 21505 s.p.   (E717)

Villancicos. Cuaderno I *CC10L,Xmas,carol
[Span] cor UNION ESP. 21504 s.p.   (E718)

ESPECIALLY FOR CHRISTMAS *sac/sec,CC11L,Xmas
SATB PRO ART 112 $1.25   (E719)

ESPLA
De Profundis (Psalm 129)
[Lat] mix cor,4 soli,pno UNION ESP. 21085
s.p.   (E720)
mix cor,4 soli,orch/pno UNION ESP. 21085
s.p.   (E721)

Psalm 129 *see De Profundis

ESPOIR EN DIEU see Rhene-Baton

ESPRITS DIVINS see Denizton, N.

ESQUIVEL, JUAN BARAHONA DE (ca. 1565-ca. 1613)
O How Glorious *see O Quam Gloriosum

O Quam Gloriosum
(Goodale) 4pt mix cor,acap oct SCHIRM.G
11078 $.35   (E722)
(Martens, Mason) "O How Glorious" SATB oct
WALTON 2154 $.25   (E723)

O Vos Omnes *Easter/Gen/Holywk/Lent
(Goodale) [Lat] 4pt mix cor,acap oct
SCHIRM.G 11231 $.30   (E724)
(Martens) [Lat/Eng] SATB oct SOUTHERN $.25
                                            (E725)
(Martens, Mason) "O Ye People" SATB oct
WALTON 2134 $.25   (E726)

O Ye People *see O Vos Omnes

EST-IL RIEN DE PLUS CHARMANT see Migot, Georges

ESTA NOCHE LOS PASTORES
    see Villancicos Tradicionales

ESTA NOCHE NACE EL NINO
    see Villancicos Tradicionales

ESTANS ASSIS AUX RIVES AQUATIQUES see Goudimel,
    Claude

ESTE
    Este's Psalter *Xmas,hymn
        (Shaw, Geoffrey) SATB&desc oct NOVELLO
        44.1117.10 s.p.   (E727)

ESTE'S PSALTER see Este

ESTHER see Handel, George Frideric

ESTHER, QUEEN OF PERSIA see Binder, Abraham
    Wolfe

L'ESTOCART, PASCHAL DE (1539-1584)
    Je Crois En Dieu *16th cent
        (Honegger, Marc; Pidoux, Pierre) [Fr] SATB
        OUVRIERES EO565 s.p.   (E728)

    O Souverain Pasteur Et Maitre *16th cent
        (Honegger, Marc; Pidoux, Pierre) [Fr] SATB
        OUVRIERES EO563-4 s.p. contains also:
        Pere Eternel Qui Nous Ordonnes   (E729)

    Pere De Nous *16th cent
        (Honegger, Marc; Pidoux, Pierre) [Fr] SATB
        OUVRIERES EO566 s.p.   (E730)

    Pere Eternel Qui Nous Ordonnes
        see L'Estocart, Paschal de, O Souverain
        Pasteur Et Maitre

    Psalm 1 *see Marot

    Psalm 57
        (Seay) [Eng/Fr] SATB,acap oct MCA   (E731)

ESTOTE FORTES IN BELLO see Victoria, Tomas Luis
    de

ESURIENTES see Palestrina, Giovanni

ESURIENTES IMPLEVIT see Vivaldi, Antonio

ET ABSTERGET DEUS OMNEM LACRYMAM see Heilmann,
    Harald

ET BARN ER FODT I BETHLEHEM *anthem
    "Child Is Born In Bethlehem, A" see Belgian
        Christmas Songs, Set 1
    (Pooler, Marie) "Child Is Born In Bethlehem,
        A" SATB (easy) oct AUGSBURG 0914 $.30
                                               (E732)
    (Pooler, Marie) "Child Is Born In Bethlehem,
        A" SA (easy) oct AUGSBURG 0915 $.25   (E733)

ET BARN ER FODT I BETHLEHEM see Beck, Thomas
    [Ludvigsen]

ET BARN ER FODT I BETHLEHEM see Vulpius,
    Melchior

ET DICES IN DIE ILLA see Valen

ET DICES IN DIE ILLA see Valen, Fartein

ET EXULTAVIT see Bach, Johann Sebastian

ET EXULTAVIT SPIRITUS MEUS see Bach, Johann
    Sebastian

ET FILIUS DATUS EST NOBIS see Senfl, Ludwig

ET IN TERRA PAX see Vivaldi, Antonio

ET IN TERRA PAX HOMINIBUS see Vivaldi, Antonio

ET INCARNATUS see Durante, Francesco

ET INCARNATUS see Mozart, Wolfgang Amadeus

ET INCARNATUS EST see Bach, Johann Sebastian

ET INCARNATUS EST see Des Prez, Josquin

ET INCARNATUS EST see Hassler, Hans Leo

ET LES CLOCHES SONNAIENT
    SATB CHARTER $.30   (E734)
    SAB CHARTER $.25   (E735)
    SSA CHARTER $.30   (E736)
    SA CHARTER $.30   (E737)

ET LILLE BARN I DAVIDS STAD see Praetorius,
    Michael, Ein Kind Geborn Zu Bethlehem

ET MISERICORDIA see Bach, Johann Sebastian

ET MISERICORDIA see Vivaldi, Antonio

ET NE DESPICIAS see Schutz, Heinrich

ET NUNC, REGES see Moevs, Robert W.

ET RESURREXIT see Bach, Johann Sebastian

ET RESURREXIT see Palestrina, Giovanni

ET SKIB HERHID MON KOMME see Distler, Hugo, Es
    Kommt Ein Schiff Geladen

ET UNAM SANCTAM see Fiebig, Kurt

ET VERBUM CARO FACTUM EST see Back, Sven-Erick

ETENIM SEDERUNT PRINCIPES see Jaeggi, Oswald

ETERNAL FATHER see Holst, Gustav

ETERNAL FATHER-GOD see Hastings

ETERNAL FATHER, STRONG TO SAVE see Dykes

ETERNAL GATES LIFT UP THEIR HEADS see Tye,
    Christopher

ETERNAL GIFTS OF CHRIST THE KING see Marshall

ETERNAL GOD see Copes, V. Earle

ETERNAL GOD see Harris, William Henry

ETERNAL GOD IS THY REFUGE see Williams

ETERNAL GOD IS YOUR DWELLING PLACE, THE see
    Walter

ETERNAL GOD, WHOSE POWER UPHOLDS see Agey, C.
    Buell

ETERNAL GOD, WHOSE POWER UPHOLDS see Brandon,
    George

ETERNAL HEAVENLY KING see Swan

ETERNAL HOPE see Ferguson

ETERNAL KING OF DAY see Todd, M. Flora

ETERNAL LIFE see Dungan, O.

ETERNAL LIGHT see Routley

ETERNAL LIGHT, THE see Matthews, Harvey
    Alexander

ETERNAL LORD see Baer, [Charles E.], Adon Olam

ETERNAL PEACE see Mozart, Wolfgang Amadeus,
    Aeterna Pax

ETERNAL PRAISE see Titcomb

ETERNAL RULER see Bevan, Richard T.

ETERNAL RULER see Ley, Henry George

ETERNAL RULER OF THE CEASELESS ROUND see
    Greenhill, Harold

ETERNAL RULER OF THE CEASELESS ROUND see
    Powell, Robert J.

ETERNAL RULER OF THE CEASELESS ROUND see
    Thiman, Eric Harding

ETERNAL SON OF GOD see Kirk

ETERNAL SONG see Olson

ETERNAL SOURCE OF TRUTH AND LIGHT see Ehret,
    Walter

ETERNAL SPIRIT, THE see Burt

ETERNAL SPIRIT, WE CONFESS see Bruckner, Anton

ETERNAL SPRING OF THE SPIRIT see Lundquist

ETERNAL TRINITY see Trued, Clarence

ETERNITY, THOU AWFUL WORD see Bach, Johann
    Sebastian

ETERNITY TODAY see Lovelace, Austin C.

ETLER, ALVIN [DERALD] (1913-   )
    Christmas Lullaby, A *Xmas
        SATB,acap AMP A333 $.25   (E738)

    Lord God, Hear Our Prayer
        SSA,acap AMP A456 $.25   (E739)

    Peace Be Unto You *anthem
        SATB,acap AMP A303 $.25   (E740)

ETON CHOIRBOOK 1 *CCU
    cor STAINER 3.8910.8 $21.00   (E741)

ETON CHOIRBOOK 3 *CCU
    cor STAINER 3.8912.8 $21.00   (E742)

ETT BARN AR FOTT
    see Frojda Dig O Kristenhet

ETT BARN AR FOTT I BETLEHEM see Praetorius,
    Michael, Ein Kind Geborn Zu Bethlehem

ETT BARN AR FOTT PA DENNA DAG *Xmas,hymn
    (Wikander, David) mix cor NORDISKA 965 s.p.
                                               (E743)

ETT HAR JAG BEGART AV HERREN see Soderholm,
    Valdemar

ETT, [KASPAR] (1788-1847)
    Laudate Dominus
        men cor sc ALSBACH&D s.p.   (E744)

ETT ORD AV GUD see Lindberg, Oskar [Fredrik]

ETTI, KARL (1912-   )
    Alleluja Fur Die Weihnachtszeit *Xmas,Allelu
        mix cor,acap oct DOBLINGER s.p.   (E745)

    Alles, Was Odem Hat, Lobe Den Herrn *Bibl
        men cor,acap oct DOBLINGER s.p. see also
        Drei Motetten Zu Ehren Des Herrn   (E746)

    De Profundis *mot
        men cor,acap oct DOBLINGER s.p.   (E747)

    Der Stern Von Bethlehem *Xmas
        wom cor,acap oct DOBLINGER s.p.   (E748)
        mix cor,acap oct DOBLINGER s.p.   (E749)
        (Stegbauer, J.) men cor,acap oct DOBLINGER
        s.p.   (E750)

    Drei Motetten Zu Ehren Des Herrn *Bibl
        men cor,acap cmplt ed DOBLINGER s.p.
        contains & see also: Alles, Was Odem Hat,
        Lobe Den Herrn; Herr, Bleibe Bei Uns;
        Nun Entlassest Du   (E751)

    Herr, Bleibe Bei Uns *Bibl
        men cor,acap oct DOBLINGER s.p. see also
        Drei Motetten Zu Ehren Des Herrn   (E752)

    Nun Entlassest Du *Bibl
        men cor,acap oct DOBLINGER s.p. see also
        Drei Motetten Zu Ehren Des Herrn   (E753)

    Tantum Ergo
        mix cor,acap oct DOBLINGER s.p.   (E754)

ETTINGER, MAX (1874-1951)
    Das Lied Von Moses *ora,Heb
        "Song Of Moses, The" cor,soli,orch voc sc
        ISRAELI 325 s.p.   (E755)

    Song Of Moses, The *see Das Lied Von Moses

ETZ CHAYIM see Binder, Abraham Wolfe

ETZ CHAYIM see Freed, Isadore

ETZ CHAYIM see Weisgal, A.

EUCARISTICA see Arnaldi, Antonio

EUCARISTICA see Ravanello, Oreste

EUCH ABER, DIE IHR TRUBSAL LEIDET see Reda,
    Siegfried

EUCH IST HEUTE DER HEILAND GEBOREN see Erdlen,
    Hermann

EUCH IST HEUTE DER HEILAND GEBOREN see
    Weyrauch, Johannes

EUCHARIST MUSIC see Wagner, Richard

EUCHARIST OF THE SOUL see McLin

EUCHARISTICA see Casals, Pablo

EUCHARISTISCHES GEBET
    (Etti, Karl) men cor,acap oct DOBLINGER s.p.
        see from Drei Ernste Gesange   (E756)

EUGEN, KARL
    Gluck Auf! Guds Fred! *see Lund, Sundt

EUKARISTI see Norman, Rudolf

EULALIA, SISTER
    Ave Maria *BVM
        SSA,acap/pno SEESAW $1.00   (E757)

EULOGY see Low, Leo, Bialik

EUROPA CANTAT I *CC50U,canon/chorale
    (Wolters) mix cor MOSELER s.p. contains works
        by: Bach; Gastoldi; Isaac; Morley; and
        others   (E758)

EUROPA CANTAT III *CC37U,canon
    (Wolters) mix cor MOSELER s.p. contains works
        by: Von Atteignant; Di Lasso; Dvorak; and
        others   (E759)

EUROPA CANTAT IV *CC36U
    (Wolters) mix cor MOSELER s.p. contains works
        by: Isaac; Schutz; Mozart; Kodaly; and
        others   (E760)

EUROPAISCHE WEIHNACHTSLIEDER, HEFT 1 *CC32U,
    Xmas,Eur
    (Strube, Adolf) [Ger] 3 eq voices,acap BAREN.
        EM 723 s.p.   (E761)

EUROPAISCHE WEIHNACHTSLIEDER, HEFT 2 *CC31U,
    Xmas,Eur
    (Strube, Adolf) [Ger] 3pt mix cor BAREN.
        EM 724 s.p.   (E762)

EUROPAISCHE WEIHNACHTSLIEDER, HEFT 3 *CC16U,
    Xmas,Eur
    (Strube, Adolf) [Ger] 4pt mix cor BAREN.
        EM 737 s.p.   (E763)

EUROPAISCHE WEIHNACHTSLIEDER, HEFT 4 see
    Bausznern, Dietrich von

EUROPEAN STABAT MATER see Nees, Vic

EVANGELIENSPRUCHE FUR DAS KIRCHENJAHR [1] see
    Driessler, Johannes

EVANGELIENSPRUCHE FUR DAS KIRCHENJAHR [2] see
    Driessler, Johannes

EVANGELIENSPRUCHE FUR DAS KIRCHENJAHR [3] see
    Driessler, Johannes

EVANGELIENSPRUCHE FUR DAS KIRCHENJAHR [4] see
    Driessler, Johannes

EVANGELIENSPRUCHE FUR DAS KIRCHENJAHR [5] see
    Driessler, Johannes

EVANGELIENSPRUCHE FUR DAS KIRCHENJAHR [6] see
    Driessler, Johannes

EVANGELIENSPRUCHE FUR DAS KIRCHENJAHR [7] see
    Driessler, Johannes

EVANGELIENSPRUCHE FUR DAS KIRCHENJAHR [8] see
    Driessler, Johannes

EVANGELIENSPRUCHE FUR DAS KIRCHENJAHR [9] see
    Driessler, Johannes

EVANGELIENSPRUCHE FUR DAS KIRCHENJAHR [10] see
    Driessler, Johannes

EVANGELIENSPRUCHE FUR DAS KIRCHENJAHR [11] see
    Driessler, Johannes

EVANGELIENSPRUCHE FUR DAS KIRCHENJAHR [12] see
    Driessler, Johannes

EVANGELIENSPRUCHE FUR DAS KIRCHENJAHR [13] see
    Driessler, Johannes

EVANGELIENSPRUCHE FUR DAS KIRCHENJAHR [14] see
    Driessler, Johannes

EVANGELIENSPRUCHE FUR DAS KIRCHENJAHR [15] see
    Driessler, Johannes

EVANGELIENSPRUCHE FUR DAS KIRCHENJAHR [16] see
    Driessler, Johannes

EVANGELIENSPRUCHE FUR DAS KIRCHENJAHR [17] see
    Driessler, Johannes

EVANGELIENSPRUCHE FUR DAS KIRCHENJAHR [18] see
    Driessler, Johannes

EVANGELIENSPRUCHE FUR DAS KIRCHENJAHR [19] see
    Driessler, Johannes

EVANGELIENSPRUCHE FUR DAS KIRCHENJAHR [20] see
    Driessler, Johannes

EVANGELISCHE MANNERCHORLIEDER *CC163U,Gen,
    evang/mot
    (Jenny, Markus; Odermatt, Arnold) [Ger] 2-5pt
    men cor,acap (med easy) BAREN. BA 3980
    $5.25   (E764)

EVANGELISCHES KALENDARIUM-HEFT 1 see Hohlfeld,
    Christoph

EVANGELISCHES KALENDARIUM-HEFT 2 see Hohlfeld,
    Christoph

EVANGELISCHES KIRCHENGESANGBUCH *see Bender,
    Jan, Jesus Christus, Unser Heiland, No.77;
    Bender, Jan, Komm, Heiliger Geist, Erfull
    Die Herzen, No.124; Cruger, Johann, Auf,
    Auf, Mein Herz, Mit Freuden, No.86;
    Gerhardt, Carl, Nun Bitten Wir Den Heiligen
    Geist, No.99; Grabner, Hermann, Erschienen
    Ist Der Herrlich Tag, No.80; Huth, Alfred,
    Zeuch Ein Zu Deinen Toren, No.105; Neubert,
    Gottfried, Komm, Heiliger Geist, Herre
    Gott, No.98; Poos, Heinrich, Heilger Geist,
    Du Troster Mein, No.101; Poos, Heinrich,
    Wir Wollen Alle Frohlich Sein, No.82;
    Praetorius, Michael, Erstanden Ist Der
    Heilig Christ, No.78; Praetorius, Michael,
    Komm, Heiliger Geist, Herre Gott, No.98;
    Praetorius, Michael, Nun Bitten Wir Den
    Heiligen Geist, No.99; Reimerdes,
    Friedrich, Auf, Auf, Mein Herz, Mit
    Freuden, No.86; Siemoneit, Hans Rudolf, Nun
    Jauchzt Dem Herren, Alle Welt, No.187;
    Spar, Otto, Sei Lob Und Ehr Dem Hochsten
    Gut, No.233; Werner, Fritz, Mit Freuden
    Zart, No.80; Zipp, Friedrich, Lob Gott
    Getrost Mit Singen, No.205   (E765)

EVANGELISCHES KIRCHENGESANGBUCH see Bender, Jan

EVANGELISCHES KIRCHENGESANGBUCH see Cruger,
    Johann

EVANGELISCHES KIRCHENGESANGBUCH see Gerhardt,
    Carl

EVANGELISCHES KIRCHENGESANGBUCH see Grabner,
    Hermann

EVANGELISCHES KIRCHENGESANGBUCH see Huth,
    Alfred

EVANGELISCHES KIRCHENGESANGBUCH see Neubert,
    Gottfried

EVANGELISCHES KIRCHENGESANGBUCH see Poos,
    Heinrich

EVANGELISCHES KIRCHENGESANGBUCH see Praetorius,
    Michael

EVANGELISCHES KIRCHENGESANGBUCH see Reimerdes,
    Friedrich

EVANGELISCHES KIRCHENGESANGBUCH see Siemoneit,
    Hans Rudolf

EVANGELISCHES KIRCHENGESANGBUCH see Spar, Otto

EVANGELISCHES KIRCHENGESANGBUCH see Werner,
    Fritz

EVANGELISCHES KIRCHENGESANGBUCH see Zipp,
    Friedrich

EVANGELISCHES KIRCHENGESANGBUCH see Werner,
    Fritz

EVANGELISCHES KIRCHENGESANGBUCH see Chemin-
    Petit, Hans

EVANGELISCHES KIRCHENGESANGBUCH see Ruppel,
    Paul Ernst

EVANGELISCHES KIRCHENGESANGBUCH see Baudach,
    Ulrich

EVANGELISCHES KIRCHENGESANGBUCH see Grabner,
    Hermann

EVANGELISCHES KIRCHENGESANGBUCH see
    Wapenhensch, W.

EVANGELISCHES KIRCHENGESANGBUCH: AUSGABE FUR
    DIE EVANGELISCHE KIRCHE VON KURHESSEN-
    WALDECK *CCU,Gen,evang
    [Ger] cloth BAREN. s.p.   (E766)

EVANGELISCHES KIRCHENGESANGBUCH: GESANGBUCH FUR
    DIE GLIEDKIRCHEN DER EVANGELISCHEN KIRCHE
    IN DEUTSCHLAND STAMM-AUSGABE *CCU,Gen,
    evang
    [Ger] cloth BAREN. s.p.   (E767)

EVANGELISCHES KIRCHENGESANGBUCH: GROSSDRUCK-
    AUSGABE FUR DIE EVANGELISCHE KIRCHE VON
    KURHESSEN-WALDECK *CCU,Gen,evang
    [Ger] cloth BAREN. s.p.   (E768)

EVANGELISCHES KIRCHENGESANGBUCH: GROSSDRUCK-
    GESCHENKAUSGABE FUR DIE EVANGELISCHE KIRCHE
    VON KURHESSEN UND WALDECK *CCU,Gen,evang
    [Ger] BAREN. s.p.   (E769)

EVANGELISCHES KIRCHENGESANGBUCH:
    JUGENDGESANGBUCH FUR DIE EVANGELISCHE
    KIRCHE VON KURHESSEN-WALDECK *CCU,Gen,
    evang
    [Ger] BAREN. s.p.   (E770)

EVANGELISCHES KIRCHENGESANGBUCH see Hessenberg,
    Kurt

EVANGELISCHES KIRCHENGESANGBUCH see Grabner,
    Hermann

EVANGELISCHES KIRCHENGESANGBUCH see Gadsch,
    Herbert

EVANGELISCHES KIRCHENGESANGBUCH see Reimerdes,
    Friedrich

EVANGELISCHES KIRCHENGESANGBUCH see Stier,
    Alfred

EVANGELISHES KIRCHENGESANGBUCH see Grabner,
    Hermann

EVANGELISTIC CHOIR see Lister, Mosie

EVANS
    Alleluia And Benediction
        SATB FLAMMER A 5286 $.35   (E771)

    Beatitudes, The *Bibl
        SSA,Bar solo WARNER R3496   (E772)
        SATB,Bar solo WARNER G1307 $.35   (E773)

    Bells Ring Softly, Lully Low
        SATB oct FOX R194 $.30   (E774)

    Eighteen Responses For General Use *CC18U
        SATB,acap WARNER R3321 $.30   (E775)

    Gladness Is Ours, Hallelujah!
        SAB FLAMMER D5071 $.30   (E776)

    Glory To His Name
        SATB,SAB soli WARNER G1806 $.30   (E777)

    Lord, Make Us Instruments Of Thy Peace
        SSA,org oct BOOSEY 5504 $.30   (E778)
        SATB,org oct BOOSEY 5505 $.30   (E779)

    Love Faileth Never
        SATB WARNER R3320 $.30   (E780)

    Prayer, A
        SAB FLAMMER D5135 $.25   (E781)

    Prayer For All Nations
        SATB FLAMMER A 5468 $.25   (E782)

    Psalm 91
        SATB WARNER R3272 $.30   (E783)

EVANS, AUBREY
    O Lord, We Bring To Thee
        unis oct NOVELLO 37.0033.10 s.p.   (E784)

    We Are Soldiers Of The King
        unis oct NOVELLO 48.2063.00 s.p.   (E785)

EVANS, RODERICK
    Festival Alleluia *Fest
        SATB,acap oct FOX R207 $.35   (E786)

    Glorious Thy Work, O Lord Of Hosts
        SATB oct FOX R 191 $.25   (E787)

    Joyful Song To God, A
        SATB oct FOX R197 $.25   (E788)

EVE OF GRACE see Matthews, Harvey Alexander

EVEILLEZ-VOUS see Delamoriniere, G.

EVEN FOR ONE see Smith

EVEN ME *Swed
    (Ferguson) SATB oct LILLENAS AN-2375 $.30
                                             (E789)

EVEN ME see Warren, J.

EVEN ME see Warren, John C.

EVEN SO, LORD JESUS, QUICKLY COME see Narum,
    Jeanne

EVENING AND MORNING see Matthews, H.

EVENING AND MORNING see Oakeley

EVENING AND MORNING see Oakeley, Herbert
    Stanley

EVENING CANTICLES WITH FAUX-BOURDONS, NO. 1 see
    Willan, Healey

EVENING CANTICLES WITH FAUX-BOURDONS, NO. 3 see
    Willan, Healey

EVENING CANTICLES WITH FAUX-BOURDONS, NO. 4 see
    Willan, Healey

EVENING CANTICLES WITH FAUX-BOURDONS, NO. 5 see
    Willan, Healey

EVENING HYMN see Gardiner, Henry Balfour

EVENING HYMN see Ley, Henry George

EVENING HYMN see Purcell, Henry

EVENING HYMN see Westbrook, Francis B.

EVENING HYMN, AN see Purcell, Henry

EVENING HYMN, AN see Reger, Max

EVENING HYMN OF KING CHARLES I see Ley, Henry
    George

EVENING MASS OF HOLY THURSDAY see Felciano,
    Richard

EVENING MASS OF HOLY THURSDAY see Woollen

EVENING PASTORAL see Rae, Kenneth

EVENING PASTORALE, AN see Shaw, Wilfred

EVENING PRAYER see Fearis, J.S.

EVENING PRAYER see Humperdinck, Engelbert

EVENING PRAYER see Thorne

EVENING PRAYER AND DREAM PANTOMINE see
    Humperdinck, Engelbert

EVENING PRAYER FOR PEACE see Weisgall, Hugo

EVENING SERVICE see Arnold, Magnificat And Nunc
    Dimittis

EVENING SERVICE see Child, William

EVENING SERVICE see Humfrey, Pelham

EVENING SERVICE see Hyslop, Magnificat And Nunc
    Dimittis

EVENING SERVICE see Pavior

EVENING SERVICE see Purcell, Henry, Magnificat
    Und Nunc Dimittis

EVENING SERVICE see Tye, Christopher

EVENING SERVICE FOR FOUR VOICES see Caustun,
    Thomas

EVENING SERVICE FOR SABBATH AND FESTIVALS see
    Lewandowski, Louis

EVENING SERVICE FOR VERSES see Hooper, Edmund

EVENING SERVICE IN "A RE" see Rogers, Benjamin

EVENING SERVICE IN C see Dyson, George

EVENING SERVICE IN C see Stewart, C. Hylton

EVENING SERVICE IN E see Watson, Sydney

EVENING SERVICE IN E FLAT see Bairstow, Edward
    Cuthbert

EVENING SERVICE IN E FLAT see Hunt, Thomas W.

EVENING SERVICE IN G see Bairstow, Edward
    Cuthbert

EVENING SERVICE IN G MINOR see Purcell, Henry

EVENING SONG see Narvik

EVENING SONG, AN see Schroth

EVENING SONG TO GOD see Haydn, T.

EVENING WATCH, THE see Holst, Gustav

EVENSONG see Haydn, (Franz) Joseph, Abendlied
    Zu Gott

EVENSONG (A CHILD'S PRAYER) see Parke, Dorothy

EVENSONG-A JAZZ LITURGY see Summerlin, Ed.

EVENTIDE see Anderson, [William H.]

EVER FAITHFUL I REMAIN see Bach, Johann
    Sebastian

EVER-LOVING FATHER see Brahms, Johannes

EVER-OPEN DOOR, THE see Blake, Rev. Canon, E.C.

EVERLASTING ARMS OF LOVE see Dowland, John

EVERLASTING GOD
    SATB,acap BIG3 $.30   (E790)

EVERLASTING GOD see Kalinnikoff, Paul

EVERLASTING JOY see Bach, Johann Sebastian

EVERLASTING LIFE see Cain, Noble

EVERLASTING LIGHT *Xmas,cant
    oct LORENZ $1.00   (E791)

EVERLASTING LIGHT see Pooler, Marie

EVERLASTING MERCIES OF OUR LORD, THE see Rhea,
    A.

EVERY MAN'S WORK SHALL BE MADE MANIFEST see
    Hoddinott, Alun

EVERY MOMENT OF EVERY DAY see Clayton

EVERY MORNING MERCIES NEW see Newton

EVERY STAR SHALL SING A CAROL see Carter

EVERY STONE SHALL CRY see Lovelace, Austin C.

EVERY TIME I FEEL DE SPIRIT *spir
    (Murray) SATB oct BOOSEY 1737 $.40   (E792)

EVERY TIME I FEEL THE SPIRIT
    (Trant) SSA (med) OXFORD 83.060 $.25   (E793)

EVERY WIND THAT BLOWS see Lucas, Leighton

EVERY WORD AND THOUGHT see Buxtehude, Dietrich,
    Alles, Was Ihr Tut

EVERYBODY SING see Skillings, Otis

EVERYBODY SINGS! *CCU
    (Carmichael, Ralph; Kaiser, Kurt; Barrows,
    Cliff) SATB voc sc WORD 15011 $1.95   (E794)

EVERYMAN'S PRAYER see Pitfield, Thomas Baron

EVERYONE MUST HAVE A FRIEND see Artega,
    [Esteban de]

EVERYONE SANG see Horrocks

EVERYTHING IS BEAUTIFUL see McAfee, Don

EVERYTIME I FEEL DE SPIRIT *spir
    (Cain) SSAA oct PRO ART 1521 $.30   (E795)
    (Dietrich) SATB oct PRO ART 1570 $.25   (E796)

EVERYTIME I FEEL THE SPIRIT *spir
    (Smith) SATB KJOS 1006 $.30   (E797)

EVERYWHERE, EVERYWHERE CHRISTMAS TONIGHT see
    Baker

EVERYWHERE, EVERYWHERE, CHRISTMAS TONIGHT see
    Redner, Lewis [Henry]

EVIGE KONUNG OCH HELL JERUSALEM see Adell,
    Arthur

EVIL SHALL NOT PREVAIL see Riegger, Wallingford

EVILLE
    Bread Of The World (composed with Herber)
        SATB FLAMMER A 5446 $.30   (E798)

    So Near To God Am I
        (Gillette) SATB oct SUMMY 1410 $.30 (E799)

EV'RY LITTLE LAMB NEEDS A SHEPHERD see Emig,
  Lois

EV'RY TIME I FEEL DE SPIRIT *CC8L,spir
  (Stenzel, Norbert) mix cor,pno/brass, rhythm
  instruments sc BREITKOPF-W Z29 s.p., cor
  pts BREITKOPF-W Z30 s.p., ipa   (E800)

EV'RY TIME I FEEL DE SPIRIT *spir,US
  (Mittergradnegger, Gunther) [Ger] mix cor,
  acap oct DOBLINGER s.p. see also Funf
  Amerikanische Negro-Spirituals   (E801)
  (Roberton) mix cor ROBERTON 61422 s.p.   (E802)
  (Trusler) 7pt mix cor,acap oct SCHIRM.G 10499
  $.40   (E803)

EV'RY TIME I FEEL DE SPIRIT see Gerhold,
  Norbert

EV'RY TIME I FEEL THE SPIRIT *spir
  SATB oct STAFF 304 $.30   (E804)
  (Burleigh) SATB,acap oct COLOMBO 488 $.25
                                              (E805)
  (Burleigh; Vene) SSA oct COLOMBO 1964 $.25
                                              (E806)
  (Burleigh; Vene) SAB oct COLOMBO 1965 $.25
                                              (E807)
  (Dawson) SATB KJOS T117 $.30   (E808)
  (Dawson) SSA KJOS T126 $.30   (E809)
  (Dawson) men cor KJOS T125 $.30   (E810)
  (Diton) mix cor,acap oct SCHIRM.G 6101 $.20
                                              (E811)
  (Hilton) SATB ALFRED 6335 $.35   (E812)
  (Johnson) SATB SCHMITT 7030 $.35   (E813)
  (Widen) SSATTBB oct LILLENAS AN-3825 $.25
                                              (E814)
  (Williamson, W.) SA LEONARD-US 08014560 $.25
                                              (E815)
  (Williamson, W.) SSA LEONARD-US 08014880 $.25
                                              (E816)
  (Williamson, W.) SAB LEONARD-US 08014720 $.25
                                              (E817)

EV'RY TIME I FEEL THE SPIRIT see Scott

EWENS, R.C.
  King Of Love, The *anthem
  mix cor oct NOVELLO s.p.   (E818)

EWIGER GOTT see Senfl, Ludwig

EX ALTARI TUO see Pitoni, Giuseppe Ottavio

EX ALTARI TUO, DOMINE see Pitoni, Giuseppe
  Ottavio

EX DEO NASCIMUR see David, Johann Nepomuk

EX SION see Rheinberger, Josef

EX SPIRITU SANCTO REVIVISCIMUS see David,
  Johann Nepomuk

EXALT THE LORD see Abbott

EXALT THE NAME OF THE LORD see Butler

EXALT WE NOW THY HOLY NAME see Henninger,
  [George R.]

EXALT YE see Glarum, L. Stanley

EXALTABO TE see Casali, Giovanni Battista

EXALTABO TE, DOMINE see Croce, Giovanni

EXALTABO TE, DOMINE see Erbach, Christian

EXALTABO TE, DOMINE see Palestrina, Giovanni

EXALTABO TE, DOMINE see Vulpius, Melchior

EXALTATA EST see Firpo, Antonio

EXALTATION see Christiansen, F. Melius

EXALTATION see Hadler

EXALTATION see Wolf, Hugo, Erhebung

EXALTED LORD, THEE I ADORE see Bach, Johann
  Sebastian, Dich Bet' Ich An

EXAMINE ME, O LORD see Boyce, William

EXAUDI DEUS see Croce, Giovanni

EXAUDI DEUS see Grandi, Alessandro

EXAUDI DEUS DEPRECATIONEM MEAM see
  Nieuwenhoven, H. v.

EXAUDI DEUS ORATIONEM MEAM see Grandi,
  Alessandro

EXAUDI DOMINE see Cooper, J.

EXAUDI, DOMINE see Trexler, Georg

EXAUDI DOMINE see Waldbroel, Wilhelm

EXAUDI DOMINE VOCEM MEAM see Lassus, Roland de
  (Orlandus)

EXAUDIAT see Cevallos

EXCELSUS SUPER OMNES GENTES DOMINUS see
  Pergolesi, Giovanni Battista

EXCEPT THE LORD BUILD THE HOUSE see Bitgood,
  Roberta

EXCEPT THE LORD BUILD THE HOUSE see Dinn, Freda

EXCEPT THE LORD BUILD THE HOUSE see Gilchrist,
  William Wallace

EXCEPT THE LORD BUILD THE HOUSE see Monk, M.J.

EXCEPT THE LORD BUILD THE HOUSE see Moodie,
  James

EXCEPT THE LORD BUILD THE HOUSE see Palmer,
  Peggy Spenser

EXCEPT THE LORD BUILD THE HOUSE see Rubbra,
  Edmund

EXHORTATION TO FAITH see Pfohl

EXIIT EDICTUM see Paminger, Leonhard

EXNER, MAX
  I Have A Dream
    SATB (med) ABINGDON APM-921 $.50   (E819)

  Where Shall I Find The Christ Child? *Xmas
    SATB (med) ABINGDON APM-852 $.70   (E820)

EXPECTANS EXPECTAVI see Wood

EXPECTANS EXSPECTAVI see Lassus, Roland de
  (Orlandus)

EXPERIENCE DOES ME SO INSPIRE see Oldham,
  Arthur

EXSPECTANS EXSPECTAVI see Lassus, Roland de
  (Orlandus)

EXSPECTANS EXSPECTAVI DOMINUM see Vranken,
  Alph.

EXSULTATE DEO see Palestrina, Giovanni

EXSULTATE DEO see Scarlatti, Alessandro

EXSULTATE DEO see Scarlatti, Domenico

EXSULTATE DEO ADJUTORI NOSTRO see Cruger,
  Johann

EXSULTATE DOMINO see Hemel, Oscar van

EXSULTATE IUSTI see Viadana, Lodovico Grossi da

EXSULTATE JUSTI see Viadana, Lodovico Grossi da

EXSULTAVIT see Burkhart, Franz

EXSULTE, JUBILATE see Mozart, Wolfgang Amadeus

EXSULTEMUS OMNES see Rozycki, (Jacek)
  Hyacinthus

EXSURGAT DEUS see Pachelbel, Johann

EXSURGE, DOMINE see Byrd, William

EXSURGE, QUARE OBDORMIS see Escobedo, Bartolome

EXSURGE, QUARE OBDORMIS see Kerle, Jacobus de

EXTOLLED AND HALLOWED BE THE NAME OF GOD see
  Berger, Jean

EXTREMUM DEI JUDICIUM see Charpentier, Marc-
  Antoine

EXTULI ELECTUM DE POPULO see Trexler, Georg

EXULTA ET LAUDA see Faccin, Gian Domenico

EXULTABUNT SANCTI see Haydn, (Johann) Michael

EXULTATE DEO see Palestrina, Giovanni

EXULTATE DEO see Poulenc, Francis

EXULTATE DEO see Scarlatti, Alessandro

EXULTATE DEO see Scarlatti, Domenico

EXULTATE DEO ADJUTORI NOSTRO see Neilsen,
  Ludvig, Pris Gud Var Hjelper

EXULTATE, JUBILATE see Mozart, Wolfgang Amadeus

EXULTATE, JUSTI see Christiansen

EXULTATE JUSTI see Fuller, J.W.

EXULTATE JUSTI see Viadana, Lodovico Grossi da

EXULTATE JUSTI IN DOMINO see Viadana, Lodovico
  Grossi da

EXULTENT ET LAETENTUR see Vulpius, Melchior

EXULTET MUNDUS GAUDIO see Naylor, Bernard

EXULTET ORBIS see Arnaldi, Antonio

EXULTET ORBIS see Cossetti, Gio. Batta.

EXULTET ORBIS see Fabiani, Angelo

EXURGE DOMINE see Teller, Marcus

EYBLER, JOSEPH (1765-1846)
  Dies Sanctificatus, Tui Sunt Coeli *Gradual/
    Offer
    4pt mix cor,org,2clar,2bsn,2trp,2horn,timp,
    strings DOBLINGER voc sc s.p., cor pts
    s.p., ipa see from OSTERREICHISCHE
    KIRCHENMUSIK   (E821)

EYE HATH NOT SEEN see Foster

EYE HATH NOT SEEN see Gaul, Alfred Robert

EYE HATH NOT SEEN see Matthews, Harvey
  Alexander

EYE HATH NOT SEEN see Wade, Walter

EYES OF ALL LOOK HOPEFULLY TO YOU, THE see
  Felciano, Richard

EYES OF ALL, THE see Hutson

EYES OF ALL WAIT ON THEE, THE see Elvey, George
  Job

EYES OF ALL WAIT UPON THEE, O LORD see Titcomb

EYES OF ALL WAIT UPON THEE, O LORD, THE see
  Harris, William Henry

EYES OF ALL WAIT UPON THEE, THE see Barnby, Sir
  Joseph

EYES OF ALL WAIT UPON THEE, THE see Berger,
  Jean

EYES OF ALL WAIT UPON THEE, THE see Clare,
  Edwyn A.

EYES OF FAITH, THE see Lovelace, Austin C.

EYES OF THE LORD ARE UPON THE RIGHTEOUS, THE
  see Johnson, David N.

EYKEN, H. VAN
  Gracious And Long-Suffering
    SSA BOSWORTH s.p. see from LAUDY COLLECTION
    OF MODERN PART SONGS   (E822)

EYRE, ALFRED J.
  Holy Communion *Commun
    SATB (E flat maj) oct NOVELLO 44.1305.04
    s.p.   (E823)

EZEK'EL SAW THE WHEEL
  (Bonds, M.) SATB oct PRESSER MC489 $.30
                                              (E824)

EZEKIAL
  (Gray, Willis James) SATB oct STAFF 465 $.30
                                              (E825)

EZEKIAL SAW DE WHEEL *spir
  (Wilson) SATB SCHMITT 1610 $.30   (E826)

EZEKIAL SAW DE WHEEL see Charles, Ray

EZEKIAL SAW DE WHEEL see Ray, Charles

EZEKIEL SAW DE WHEEL *spir
  (Cain, Noble) SA oct BELWIN 1260 $.30   (E827)
  (Cain, Noble) SAB oct BELWIN 1131 $.25   (E828)
  (Dawson) SATB KJOS T110 $.40   (E829)
  (Kinsman) SATB oct SPRATT 134 $.30   (E830)
  (Large) men cor KJOS 5528 $.30   (E831)
  (Luboff, Norman) SSATTBB oct WALTON 3020 $.35
                                              (E832)

EZEKIEL SAW DE WHEEL see Burleigh, Henry
  Thacker

EZEKIEL SAW DE WWHEEL *spir
  (Swift) SATB,T solo,acap oct PRO ART 1354
  $.25   (E833)

EZEKIEL SAW THE WHEEL *spir
  (Durian, Tim) 4pt men cor,acap BREITKOPF-W
  Z-54 s.p. see also Dreizehn Negro-
  Spirituals   (E834)
  (Ehret, W.) SATB oct PRESSER 312-40326 $.30
                                              (E835)
  (Williamson, W.) SA LEONARD-US 08015040 $.25
                                              (E836)
  (Williamson, W.) SSA LEONARD-US 08015120 $.25
                                              (E837)
  (Williamson, W.) SAB LEONARD-US 08015080 $.25
                                              (E838)

F

FABER
Oh, Come And Mourn With Us *Lent
(Matthews) SATB WARNER WB-174 $.40   (F1)

FABIANI, ANGELO
Ave Maria
see TRE MOTECTA IN HON. B.V.M.

Cor Jesu Sacratissimum
see CINQUE MOTTETTI

Deus Tuorum
see Duo Hymni

Duo Hymni *hymn
[Lat] 2 eq voices,org ZANIBON 2709 s.p.
contains: Deus Tuorum; Exultet Orbis (F2)

Exultet Orbis
see Duo Hymni

Haec Dies
see PER LA SANTA PASQUA

In Dominica Palmarum
see PEL TEMPO PASQUALE

In Festo S. Aloysii - Quis Ascendet *ASD,
Offer
[Lat] 2 eq voices,org ZANIBON 2726 s.p.
(F3)

In Festo S. Ceciliae *ASD,Offer
[Lat] 3pt mix cor,org ZANIBON 2725 s.p.
(F4)

In Me Gratia *BVM
[Lat] 2 eq voices,org ZANIBON 2761 s.p.
contains also: Mariani, Eligio, In Me
Gratia (3 eq voices,org)   (F5)

In Nativitate Domine Ad Tertiam Missam *Xmas
SA ZANIBON 2625 s.p.   (F6)

Infensus Hostis, In Honore Di S. Luigi *ASD
[Lat] 2 eq voices,org ZANIBON 2717 s.p.
(F7)

Oremus Pro Pontifici
[Lat] 2pt,org ZANIBON 2706 s.p.   (F8)

Veni Sponsa Christi
[Lat] 2 eq voices ZANIBON 2734 s.p. (F9)

Vexilla Regis
see PER LA SETTIMANA SANTA

FABODPSALM FRAN SOLLERON
see Klippa Du Som Brast For Mig

FABORDON DEL I TONO see Santa Maria

FAC NOS DOMINE see Mercenier, P.

FAC, UT ARDEAT COR MEUM see Pergolesi, Giovanni
Battista

FACCIN, GIAN DOMENICO
Angelorum Esca
see Quattro Mottetti Sacri

Discite A Me
see Quattro Mottetti Sacri

Ego Sum Panis
see Quattro Mottetti Sacri

Exulta Et Lauda
see Quattro Mottetti Sacri

Missa In Hon. SS. Cordis Jesu *Mass
[Lat] ATB,org,opt strings sc ZANIBON 1314
s.p., voc pt ZANIBON 3.p.   (F10)

Quattro Mottetti Sacri *mot
[Lat] 2 eq voices,org ZANIBON 807 s.p.
contains: Angelorum Esca; Discite A Me;
Ego Sum Panis; Exulta Et Lauda   (F11)

FACE OF MOSES SHONE see Lee, T. Charles

FACE TO FACE see Johnson

FACE TO FACE see Tullar

FACTUM EST see Vulpius, Melchior

FACTUM EST SILENTIUM see Deering, Richard

FACTUS EST REPENTE see Aichinger, Gregor

FADER, FORLAT DEM see Nilsson, Torsten

FADER JEG VIL see Nystedt, Knut

FADER OF HEAVEN, THE see Davies, Peter Maxwell

FADER OF HEVEN, THE see Davies, Peter Maxwell

FADERNAS KYRKA see Aulen, Gustaf

FAGER KVELDSOL see Geitvik, S.H.

FAHR HIN, DU LIEBSTE SEELE MEIN see Staden,
Johann, O Du Lamm Gottes, Jesu Christ

FAHRE SANFT, SCHONER WAGEN see Swing Low, Sweet
Chariot

FAHRET AUF DIE HOHE UND WERFET EUER NETZ AUS
see Ruppel, Paul Ernst

FAHRT HIN IHR, TAG UND JAHR see Krietsch, Georg

FAIGNIENT, NOEL (ca. 1568?)
Ick Sal Den Heer Mijn Godt Ghebenedyen
(Vaal, O. De) mix cor ALSBACH&D sc s.p.,
cor pts s.p.   (F12)

Jamais Ne Cesserai De Magnifier Le Seigneur
(Psalm 34) 16th cent
(Honegger, Marc; Pidoux, Pierre) [Fr] SATB
OUVRIERES EO523 s.p.   (F13)

FAIGNIENT, NOEL (cont'd.)

Psalm 34 *see Jamais Ne Cesserai De
Magnifier Le Seigneur

Que Peut Au Fol Richesse Profiter *16th cent
(Honegger, Marc; Pidoux, Pierre) [Fr] SST
OUVRIERES EO567 s.p.   (F14)

FAIR CHRISTMAS MORN see Day, R.E.

FAIR EASTER see Licht, Myrtha B.

FAIR IN FACE see Willan, Healey

FAIR QUEEN OF HEAVEN see Suriano, Francesco,
Regina Caeli

FAIR WAS THE GARDEN see Tchaikovsky, Piotr
Ilyitch

FAIR WEATHER TODAY! see Martin

FAIREST CHILD *Xmas,anthem
(Warner, R.) SA,org oct GRAY GCMR 3216 $.30
(F15)

FAIREST CHILD OF FAIREST MOTHER see Anonymous

FAIREST LORD JESUS *Gen,folk/hymn,Slav
(Burkhard, S.T.) STB SCHIRM.EC 2247 $.25
(F16)
(Cain) dbl cor SCHMITT 1600 $.22   (F17)
(Gillette) unis&SATB oct SUMMY 1393 $.40
(F18)
(Shaw; Parker) SATB ALLANS 235 s.p. (F19)
(Winans) SATB oct LILLENAS AN-2242 $.25 (F20)

FAIREST LORD JESUS see Hustad, Donald P.

FAIREST LORD JESUS see Krones

FAIREST LORD JESUS see Landon

FAIREST LORD JESUS see Willan, Healey

FAIREST MAID, THE see Crawford, John, Je Suis
Aime

FAIS-MOI OUIR, DES LE MATIN, TA MISERICORDE see
Servin, Jean

FAITH see Bowie, [William]

FAITH see Cassey

FAITH see Malotte, Albert Hay

FAITH, FOLK, AND CLARITY see Smith

FAITH, FOLK, AND FESTIVITY see Smith

FAITH, FOLK, AND NATIVITY see Smith

FAITH IN LITTLE THINGS see Dungan

FAITH OF OUR FATHERS see Davenport

FAITH OF OUR FATHERS see Hemy, [Henri
Frederick]

FAITH OF OUR FATHERS see Westbrook, Francis B.

FAITH-ORBIT see Sateren, Leland Bernhard

FAITH UNLOCKS THE DOOR see Scott

FAITHFUL CROSS see Anerio, Felice, Crux Fidelis

FAITHFUL CROSS see Sateren, Leland Bernhard

FAITHFUL CROSS AND O MY PEOPLE see Jean IV, Roi
De Portugal

FAITHFUL SHEPHERD, GUIDE ME see Stickles,
William

FAITHFUL SHEPHERD IS MY LORD, A see Nageli,
Johann (Hans) Georg

FAITH'S HERITAGE see Whitford

FALAN TIDING DIO see Barthelson

FALL AB, HERZ, VOM BAUM DER ZEIT see Woll, Erna

FALL ON US see Lister, Mosie

FALL ON YOUR KNEES see Townsend, John

FALL SOFTLY, SNOW see Moe, Daniel

FALL WARD SEIN LOS see Handel, George Frideric,
Fall'n Is The Foe

FALLING
Clap Your Hands
SAB SHAWNEE D129 $.35   (F21)
SA/TB SHAWNEE E67 $.35   (F22)

FALL'N IS THE FOE see Handel, George Frideric

FALSCHE WELT see Bach, Johann Sebastian,
Falsche Welt, Dir Trau' Ich Nicht

FALSCHE WELT, DIR TRAU' ICH NICHT see Bach,
Johann Sebastian

FALSIBORDONI-SATZE ZU DEN PROPRIEN DES
KIRCHENJAHRES *CC184L
[Ger/Lat] mix cor/unis,acap/org DOBLINGER
s.p. 88 German settings & 96 Latin
settings, all separately published (F23)

FAMILY see Valley, Jim

FAMILY BENEDICTION, A see Ellsworth, A. Eugene

FAMILY OF MAN, THE see Hennagin, Michael

FAMOUS HYMN-TUNE ANTHEMS, VOL. 1 see Vandre,
Carl W.

FAMOUS HYMN-TUNE ANTHEMS, VOL. 2 see Vandre,
Carl W.

FAMOUS SPIRITUALS *CCU,spir
men cor SCHMITT 2 $.50   (F24)

FANELLI, JOSEPH
God Is Alive (composed with Christopher, Don)
SATB CRITERION $.50   (F25)

FANFARE see Shaw, Martin, Gloria In Excelsis
Deo

FANFARE AND ALLELUIA see Knighton

FANFARE AND ALLELUIAS see Thomas, Paul Lindsley

FANFARE AND CHORAL PROCESSION see Moe, Daniel

FANFARE AND CHORALE FOR EASTER see Kinsman

FANFARE AND INVOCATION see Besig

FANFARE FOR A CHRISTMAS FESTIVAL see McCowen

FANFARE FOR A FESTIVAL see Nelson, Ronald A.

FANFARE FOR A FESTIVE DAY see Burt, [Francis]

FANFARE FOR A HOLY DAY see Young

FANFARE FOR CHRISTMAS *Xmas
SATB CHARTER $.30   (F26)

FANFARE FOR CHRISTMAS see Davis, Katherine K.

FANFARE FOR CHRISTMAS see Pfautsch, Lloyd

FANFARE FOR CHRISTMAS DAY see Plettner, A.

FANFARE FOR CHRISTMAS DAY see Shaw, Martin,
Gloria In Excelsis Deo

FANFARE FOR EASTER see Marshall, Jane M.

FANFARE FOR EASTER see Pfautsch, Lloyd

FANFARE FOR EASTER see Ream, Albert

FANFARE FOR EASTER see Vulpius, Melchior

FANFARE FOR EASTER see Walton, Kenneth

FANFARE FOR EASTER see Wilson, Harry [Robert]

FANFARE FOR EASTER MORN *Easter,anthem
(Nolin, Wallace) SATB,org,opt horn&3trp&
2trom&tuba oct WORLD CA-2330 $.75 (F27)

FANFARE FOR MICHAELMAS DAY see Campbell, Sydney
S.

FANFARE FOR PALM SUNDAY see Davis, Katherine K.

FANFARE FOR PALM SUNDAY, A see Davis, J.

FANFARE FOR THANKSGIVING see Glarum, L. Stanley

FANGET AN see Gattermayer, Heinrich

FANING, EATON (1850-1927)
O How Amiable *anthem
mix cor oct NOVELLO 28.0752.01 s.p. (F28)

When The Lord Turned Again *anthem
mix cor,T solo oct NOVELLO 28.0791.02 s.p.
(F29)

FANNON, DANIEL STEPHEN
Surely The Lord Is In This Place *Gen
SATB,acap (med easy) oct CONCORDIA 98-2149
$.25   (F30)

FANTASIA ON CHRISTMAS CAROLS see Vaughan
Williams, Ralph

FANTASIA ON THE 'OLD 104TH' PSALM TUNE see
Vaughan Williams, Ralph

FAR FROM MY HEAVENLY HOME see Craston, E.S.

FAR FROM MY HEAVENLY HOME see Newton

FAR JUDEAN HILLS, THE see Allen

FARDEMANNENS PSALM see Hannikainen, Ilmari

FARDEMANNES PSALM see Hannikainen, Ilmari

FARE YOU WELL (IN THAT GREAT GETTIN'-UP
MORNING) *spir
(Kent) 3pt mix cor,acap oct LAWSON 51470 $.30
(F31)

FAREFARE FOR THANKSGIVING see Posegate

FAREWELL OF THE SHEPHERDS see Berlioz, Hector

FARGO
Animals Of Christmas, The *Xmas
2pt jr cor/3pt jr cor oct KENDOR $.25 (F32)

Lord's Prayer, The
SAB oct KENDOR $.25   (F33)

Now Tell Us, Gentle Mary *Xmas
SATB oct KENDOR $.25   (F34)

Seek Ye First His Kingdom
SAB oct KENDOR $.25   (F35)
SATB oct KENDOR $.25   (F36)

FARINA
Loving Lord
SSA,acap oct COLOMBO 2585 $.25   (F37)

FARINA, E.
Messa Dei Poveri *Mass
cor,soli,org RICORDI-ENG 130756 s.p. (F38)

FARINA, G.
Vergine Tutto Amor
cor,SSS soli RICORDI-ENG 129039 s.p. (F39)

FARISEEN OCH, PUBLIKANEN see Schutz, Heinrich

FARJEON, [HARRY] (1878-1948)
Carol, A *carol
unis (very easy) OXFORD 45.706 $.25 (F40)

FARJEON, HARRY (1878-1948)
Medley Of Perfume, A
2pt CRAMER 73 s.p.   (F41)

FARKAS, FERENC (1905-   )
Cantata Lirica *cant
[Hung] BarATB (diff) BUDAPEST 3786 s.p.
(F42)

Cantus Pannonicus *cant
[Hung] SATB,S solo (diff) BUDAPEST 3504
(F43)

Gyongyori-Gyongy *CC9L
[Hung] 2 eq voices cmplt ed BUDAPEST 6285
s.p.
(F44)

FARMER
Gloria In Excelsis
(Douglas) "Glorious Be Thy Name Forever"
[Eng/Lat] SATB oct PRO ART 1596 $.30
(F45)

Glorious Be Thy Name Forever *see Gloria In
Excelsis

FARMER, [HENRY GEORGE] (1882-1965)
Gloria (from Mass In B Flat) Gloria
[Eng/Lat] 4pt mix cor oct SCHIRM.G 7203
$.30
(F46)

Lord For Thy Tender Mercies' Sake *Commun/
Lent
4pt mix cor oct SCHIRM.G 4912 $.25
(F47)
(Heckenlively) 4pt men cor,acap oct
SCHIRM.G 8089 $.25
(F48)
(Mueller) SAB oct SCHIRM.G 9747 $.25
(F49)

FARMER, JOHN (fl. 1591-1601)
Lord's Prayer, The *Gen
SATB (easy) oct OXFORD 43.397 $.25
(F50)
SATB (easy) oct OXFORD 43.953 $.25
(F51)
SSAA/ATBB/ATTBB (easy) oct OXFORD 40.017
(F52)

FARMER, JOHN (1836-1901)
Lord's Prayer, The *Bibl/prayer
SATB,acap PETERS H1506 $.40
(F53)

FARNES
All People That On Earth
SATB FLAMMER A 5334 $.30
(F54)

FARRANT, RICHARD (ca. 1530-1581)
Call To Remembrance *Easter/Lent/Rembrnc,
anthem
see Farrant, Richard, Hide Not Thou Thy
Face
SATB oct SUMMY 5258 $.30
(F55)
SATB oct GRAY GCMR 1751 $.30
(F56)
SATB,acap oct BELWIN 64061 $.30
(F57)
mix cor oct NOVELLO 40.0008. 00 s.p.
(F58)
SATB,opt org SCHIRM.EC 1639 $.25
(F59)
(Bantock) mix cor CURWEN 80530 s.p.
(F60)
(Greyson) SSA oct BOURNE ES17A $.30
(F61)
(Greyson) SATB oct BOURNE ES17 $.30
(F62)
(Manney) SATB oct SOUTHERN $.30
(F63)

Call To Remembrance O Lord
(Stone) SATB,acap oct PRO ART 1217 $.30
(F64)
(Stone) SSA,acap oct PRO ART 1415 $.25
(F65)

Hide Not Thou Thy Face *Easter/Gen/Lent,
anthem
see Hilton, Call To Remembrance
SATB (easy) oct OXFORD 42.705 $.30 contains
also: Call To Remembrance
(F66)
SATB oct ROYAL 217 s.p.
(F67)
SATB ALLANS 372 s.p.
(F68)
(Beveridge, L.) TTBB,acap SCHIRM.EC 2196
$.30
(F69)
(Byrd) SATB,acap oct PRO ART 1155 $.22
(F70)
(Holler) TTBB,acap GRAY GCMR 3292 $.30
(F71)
(West, John E.) mix cor oct NOVELLO
50.0123.04 s.p.
(F72)

Hide Not Thou Thy Face From Me, O Lord
*Easter/Lent
(Greyson) SATB oct BOURNE ES71 $.25 (F73)

Hide Not Thou Thy Face From Us
SATB,acap SCHIRM.EC 373 $.30
(F74)

Hide Not Thou Thy Face From Us, O Lord
(Davis, K.) SSAA,acap SCHIRM.EC 1542 $.16
(F75)
(Davis, K.) SA,pno SCHIRM.EC 1560
(F76)

Hide Not Thy Face
(Hallagan, R.) SATB,acap oct PRESSER
312-40445 $.30
(F77)

Lord, For Thy Tender Mercies' Sake *Gen,
anthem
SATB,acap oct PRESSER 332-00792 $.25 (F78)
SATB,acap oct BELWIN 64007 $.30
(F79)
SATB oct GRAY GCMR 3139 $.30
(F80)
SATB,acap oct SCHIRM.EC 374 $.30
(F81)
mix cor oct NOVELLO 40.0029.03 s.p.
(F82)
SATB SCHMITT 1922 $.35
(F83)
SATB oct LESLIE 4031
(F84)
cor oct HART s.p. contains also: Butler
C.W., Be Merciful Unto Us, O Lord (cor)
(F85)
(Beveridge, L.) TTBB,acap SCHIRM.EC 2197
$.30
(F86)
(Byrd) SATB oct PRO ART 1143 $.25
(F87)
(Hallagan) mix cor SOUTHERN $.25
(F88)
(Hallagan, R.) SATB,acap oct PRESSER
312-40437 $.30
(F89)
(Knight) SAB CURWEN 80807 s.p.
(F90)
(Pitcher, Gladys) 3pt mix cor,pno (med) oct
WILLIS 8488 $.20
(F91)

Lord For Thy Tender Mercy's Sake *Commun/
Lent,anthem
SATB ALLANS 190 s.p.
(F92)
(Jones, P.) 2pt ALLANS 232 s.p.
(F93)
(Shaw, Watkins) mix cor oct NOVELLO
50.0321.00 s.p.
(F94)

Magnificat And Nunc Dimittis *Magnif/Nunc
SATB,acap (med) oct OXFORD 43.284 $.50
(F95)

Skjul Ei Ditt Asyn
(Aamodt, Thorleif) [Norw] LYCHE 20 s.p.
(F96)

We Sing Our Praises Now To Thee
(Davies) SAB FLAMMER D5113 $.30
(F97)

FARRAR, H.M.
I Know Of A Lovely And Blessed Place
2pt ENOCH TP251 s.p.
(F98)

Little Child's Prayer, A *prayer
unis ASHDOWN U.69 s.p.
(F99)

Lord's Prayer, The *Bibl/prayer
3pt ASHDOWN V.T.53 s.p.
(F100)

Virgin Mary-Mother Blessed
3pt ASHDOWN V.T.57 s.p.
(F101)

FASCH, JOHANN FRIEDRICH (1688-1758)
Siehe Zu, Dass Deine Gottesfurcht Nicht
Heuchelei Sei *cant
(Egidi, A.) [Ger] mix cor,AT soli,strings,
cont,opt 2ob VIEWEG voc sc s.p., cor pts
s.p., ipa, sc s.p.
(F102)

FASCICULUS MYRRAE see Palestrina, Giovanni

FASSBAENDER, P.
Jauchzet Dem Herrn
[Ger] mix cor,acap (med) HUG s.p.
(F103)

FASSLER, G.
Die Lor Sitzt Im Garten
[Ger] men cor,acap (med) HUG s.p.
(F104)

FAST
Veni Creator Spiritus *Xmas
SATB,acap WARNER WB-114 $.30
(F105)

FAST, WILLARD S.
Alleluia To The Lord Of Being
4pt mix cor,acap oct SCHIRM.G 11937 $.40
(F106)
Carol, Brothers, Carol *Xmas
SATB SCHMITT 8037 $.30
(F107)
Christmas Carol, A *Xmas
SATB,solo SCHMITT 905 $.35
(F108)
If Ye Would Hear The Angels Sing *Xmas
SATB,acap WARNER WB-109 $.30
(F109)
O Thou Whose Pow'r
SATB oct PLYMOUTH PCS-60 $.25
(F110)
Prayer For This House *prayer
SATB,acap AMP A591 $.25
(F111)
To Mercy, Pity, Peace And Love
4pt mix cor,acap oct SCHIRM.G 11905 $.30
(F112)

FATHER ABRAHAM see Haubiel, Charles

FATHER ABRAHAM, HAVE MERCY ON ME see Krapf,
Gerhard

FATHER ABRAHAM, HAVE MERCY ON ME see Schutz,
Heinrich, Vater Abraham, Erbarme Dich Mein

FATHER ALMIGHTY see Darst, W. Glenn

FATHER ALMIGHTY see Franck, Cesar

FATHER ALMIGHTY see Stradella, Alessandro,
Pieta, Signore!

FATHER ALMIGHTY see Vene, Ruggero, Ave Maria

FATHER ALMIGHTY, GRANT OUR PETITION see Vene,
Ruggero, Ave Maria

FATHER, AT THY THRONE WE BOW see Rains, Dorothy

FATHER, BE THOU EVER NEAR US see Becker, Albert
Ernst Anton

FATHER ETERNAL see Franck, Cesar, Ave Maria

FATHER ETERNAL see Handel, George Frideric

FATHER ETERNAL see Williams

FATHER, EVER LOVING see Brahms, Johannes

FATHER, FORGIVE THEM see Osborne, Hayward

FATHER, FORGIVE THEM see Graf, Franz

FATHER, FORGIVE THEM see Lynn, George

FATHER, HEAR OUR PRAYER see Wells

FATHER, HEAR THE PRAYER WE OFFER see Brook,
Harry

FATHER, HEAR US PRAY see Darst, W. Glen

FATHER, HOLY FATHER see Land

FATHER, I KNOW THAT ALL MY LIFE see Diack,
[John Michael]

FATHER, I SING THY WONDROUS GRACE see Karvonen

FATHER I'M COMING HOME see Freeman, Charles

FATHER IN HEAVEN see Ellis, Mary

FATHER IN HEAVEN see Fleming

FATHER IN HEAVEN see Grant, Louise

FATHER IN HEAVEN see Nanini (Nanino), Giovanni
Maria

FATHER IN HEAVEN see Victoria, Tomas Luis de,
Ave Maria

FATHER, IN HIGH HEAVEN DWELLING see Bach,
Johann Sebastian

FATHER, IN THY MYSTERIOUS PRESENCE see
Protheroe, Daniel

FATHER, IN THY MYSTERIOUS PRESENCE see
Thompson, V.D.

FATHER IN THY MYSTERIOUS PRESENCE KNEELING see
Wehr, David A.

FATHER, LEAD ME DAY BY DAY see Strattner, G.

FATHER, LORD OF ALL CREATION see Weber

FATHER LOVES YOU, THE see Salsbury, Sonny

FATHER MOST HOLY see Cashmore, Donald

FATHER MOST HOLY see Cruger, Johann

FATHER MOST HOLY see Lapo, Cecil E.

FATHER MOST MERCIFUL see Franck, Cesar, Panis
Angelicus

FATHER, O FORGIVE THOU ME see Roberts, N.

FATHER, O HEAR ME see Handel, George Frideric

FATHER, O HEAR ME see Strickling, George F.

FATHER, O HEAR US see Palmer, H.

FATHER, O HEAR US see Wehr

FATHER OF ALL see Dvorak, Antonin

FATHER OF ALL see Tye, Christopher

FATHER OF GLORY see Marcello

FATHER OF HEAVEN see Handel, George Frideric

FATHER OF HEAVEN, WHOSE LOVE PROFOUND see
Willan, Healey

FATHER OF MANKIND see Elliott

FATHER OF MERCIES see Pedrette

FATHER OF MERCIES see Waddington

FATHER OF MERCIES, GOD OF LOVE see Hall, E.
Vine

FATHER OF MERCIES, GOD OF LOVE see West, John
Ebenezer

FATHER OF MERCY see Handel, George Frideric

FATHER OF MERCY see Warner, Richard

FATHER OF TRUTH, THE see Pasquet, Jean

FATHER OF US ALL see Thomas, Christopher

FATHER, ONCE MORE WITHIN THY HOLY PLACE see
Matthews, Harvey Alexander

FATHER, OUR FATHER see Verdi, Giuseppe, Pater
Noster

FATHER SEND A CHILD AGAIN
SATB CHARTER $.25
(F113)

FATHER, SON, AND HOLY GHOST see Wolff, S.
Drummond

FATHER TEACH ME HOW TO PRAY see Keese

FATHER TEACH US HOW TO PRAY see Jolley

FATHER, THE HOUR HAS COME see Trued, Clarence

FATHER, THOU THAT HEAREST PRAYER see Lliebster
Jesu

FATHER, THOU WHO ART IN HEAVEN see Brown

FATHER, THY HOLY SPIRIT SEND see Franck,
Melchior, Jesu, Dein' Seel'

FATHER TO THEE WE PRAY see Bach, Ave Maria

FATHER, TO THEE, WE PRAY see Bach, Johann
Sebastian, Ave Maria

FATHER, TO THY THRONE WE BEND see Handel,
George Frideric

FATHER, WE PRAISE THEE see Jennings, Carolyn

FATHER, WE PRAISE THEE see Matthews, Harvey
Alexander

FATHER, WE PRAISE THEE see Pyle, Francis
[Johnson]

FATHER, WE PRAISE THEE see Smith

FATHER, WE PRAISE THEE see Thiman, Eric Harding

FATHER, WE PRAISE THEE see Ward

FATHER, WE PRAISE THEE see Willan, Healey

FATHER WE THANK THEE see Emerson

FATHER WE THANK THEE see Goemanne, Noel

FATHER, WE THANK THEE see Larson

FATHER, WE THANK THEE see Lewis, John Leo

FATHER, WE THANK THEE see Morley, Thomas

FATHER, WE THANK THEE see Pasquet, Jean

FATHER WE THANK THEE see Roff, Joseph

FATHER, WHAT E'ER OF EARTHLY BLISS see Pike,
Harry Hale

FAUCHEY, PAUL
Panis Angelicus
[Lat] SATB,solo,opt org&ob&vln&vcl&bvl
HEUGEL sc s.p., voc sc s.p., cor pts s.p.
(F114)

Premiere Messe Solennelle *Mass
[Lat] STB,STB soli,orch (B flat maj) HEUGEL
voc sc s.p., voc pt s.p.
(F115)

Quatrieme Messe Breve *Mass
[Lat] STB,org,opt 5strings (G min) HEUGEL
voc sc s.p., voc pt s.p.
(F116)

FAULSTICH
Lateinisches Ordinarium
cor HANSSLER 27.005 sc s.p., cor pts s.p.
(F117)

FAURE
Les Rameaux *Palm
(Andrews) "Palms, The" SATB oct GRAY GCMR 375 $.25 (F118)

My Friend Of Calvary
unis oct LORENZ 8536 $.25 (F119)

Palms, The *see Les Rameaux

Palms, The *Easter/Lent
(Gray) SSA oct PRO ART 1280 $.22 (F120)
(Gray) SATB oct PRO ART 1279 $.30 (F121)
(Gray) SAB oct PRO ART 1790 $.30 (F122)

Pie Jesu *Easter/Lent,Req
(Diller) SSA oct PRO ART 1911 $.30 (F123)

FAURE, GABRIEL-URBAIN (1845-1924)
Agnus Dei (from Messe Basse) Agnus
[Lat] SS,opt pno/org HEUGEL voc sc s.p., voc pt s.p. (F124)
(Candlyn) [Lat/Eng] SSA WARNER W3573 $.35 (F125)

Ave Maria
[Lat] SS,org,ob,vln,vcl HEUGEL s.p. (F126)
[Fr] 3pt men cor,org HEUGEL s.p. (F127)
[Lat] 3pt men cor,org HEUGEL s.p. (F128)

Ave, Verum Corpus *Op.65,No.1
"Jesu, Word Of God Incarnate" SA,org SCHIRM.EC 860 $.25 (F129)

Benedictus (from Messe Basse) Bene
[Lat] unis wom cor,Mez solo,opt pno/org HEUGEL voc sc s.p., voc pt s.p. (F130)

Cantique De Jean Racine *Op.11, cant
mix cor BELWIN $.80 (F131)
[Eng/Fr] SATB,org/pno BROUDE BR. $.70 (F132)

Cradles, The *Xmas
(Cain) SSA SCHMITT 2005 $.25 (F133)

En Priere
"Prayer" [Fr/Eng] SATB,pno BROUDE BR. $.40 (F134)

Gentle Jesus Ever Blest
(Kjelson) girl cor SOUTHERN $.25 (F135)
(Kjelson) unis oct BELWIN 2031 $.25 (F136)

Hymn Of Rejoicing
(Gibb) SSA oct FISCHER,J 9077 $.30 (F137)

In Paradisum (from Requiem)
(Candlyn) [Eng/Lat] SSA WARNER W3574 $.30 (F138)

In Prayer
(McClendon) SATB FLAMMER A 5505 $.25 (F139)

Introit And Kyrie (from Requiem) Introit/Kyrie
(Field) [Lat/Eng] SATB oct BOOSEY 5493 $.40 (F140)

Jesu, Word Of God Incarnate *see Ave, Verum Corpus

Kyrie (from Messe Basse) Kyrie
[Lat] unis wom cor,S solo,opt pno/org HEUGEL voc sc s.p., voc pt s.p. (F141)

Libera Me
(Kjelson, Lee) "Save Me, O Lord" SATB oct BELWIN 2032 $.35 (F142)

Mass *Mass
[Eng/Fr/Lat] SATB (med) PRESSER 312-41006 $.50 (F143)

Messe *Mass
(Lambert, C.J.) [Fr] 4pt mix cor HEUGEL s.p. (F144)

Messe Basse *Mass
girl cor SOUTHERN $.75 (F145)
SS oct PRESSER 312-40598 $.75 (F146)
[Lat] SSA,soli HEUGEL voc sc s.p., voc pt s.p. (F147)

Palm Branches *Easter
(Sudds, W.) SATB oct PRESSER 332-09568 $.25 (F148)

Prayer *see En Priere

Religious Music *CC7UL
cor voc sc KALMUS 6177 $2.00 (F149)

Requiem *Op.48, Req
[Eng/Lat] 4pt mix cor,SBar soli voc sc SCHIRM.G $1.00 (F150)
cor,opt orch voc sc KALMUS 6166 $1.25, ipa (F151)
cor min sc KALMUS 403 $4.00 (F152)
cor KALMUS $2.25 (F153)
cor sc KALMUS $14.00 (F154)
cor,orch sc KALMUS $14.00, ipa (F155)
cor min sc INTERNAT. $3.75 (F156)
(Candlyn) SSA,org WARNER $1.50 (F157)
(Field, Robert) mix cor,SBar soli BOOSEY voc sc $1.50, cor pts $.75 (F158)
(Stevens, Norris) mix cor,SBar soli,org sc SCHIRM.G $5.00 (F159)

Sanctus (from Messe Basse) Req/Sanctus
[Lat] SS,opt pno/org HEUGEL voc sc s.p., voc pt s.p. (F160)
(Candlyn) [Eng/Lat] SSA WARNER W3571 $.30 (F161)
(Field) STB oct BOOSEY 5494 $.35 (F162)

Save Me, O Lord *see Libera Me

Tantum Ergo *Op.65,No.2, Commun,mot
girl cor SOUTHERN $.30 (F163)
[Lat/Eng] SSA,org/pno BROUDE BR. $.35 (F164)
[Lat] mix cor,S/T solo oct DURAND s.p. (F165)
cor voc sc KALMUS 6167 $1.00 (F166)
cor,orch sc KALMUS $4.00, ipa (F167)
"Therefore We, Before Him Bending" SSA,org SCHIRM.EC 861 $.25 (F168)

Tantum Ergo, En Fa *Commun,mot
[Lat] opt unis cor,Mez/Bar solo (F maj) oct DURAND s.p. (F169)

FAURE, GABRIEL-URBAIN (cont'd.)

Therefore We, Before Him Bending *see Tantum Ergo

Tu Es Petrus *Gen,mot
[Lat] SATB,Bar solo oct DURAND s.p. (F170)

Virgin And Child, The *Xmas
(Allen) SATB oct GALLEON GCS1005 (F171)

FAURE, JEAN-BAPTIST
Charite
[Fr] unis HEUGEL s.p. see from CHANTS RELIGIEUX (F172)
[Fr] SATB,opt pno/org HEUGEL s.p. (F173)

Credo *Credo
[Lat] unis HEUGEL s.p. see from CHANTS RELIGIEUX (F174)

Crucifix
[Fr] unis HEUGEL s.p. see from CHANTS RELIGIEUX (F175)
[Fr] 2pt HEUGEL s.p. see from CHANTS RELIGIEUX (F176)
[Fr] SSA,med solo,opt pno/org HEUGEL s.p. (F177)

In Dreams I've Heard The Seraphs Fair *see Sancta Maria

Join All And Sing *see Les Rameaux

Les Rameaux *Easter/Lent/Palm
"Palms, The" SA KJOS P736 $.30 (F178)
"Palms, The" SATB&jr cor oct LORENZ 4401 $.25 (F179)
"Palms, The" 2pt oct LORENZ 5701 $.25 (F180)
"Palms, The" SAB oct LORENZ 7070 $.30 (F181)
"Palms, The" unis oct LORENZ 8536 $.25 (F182)
"Palms, The" SATB oct LORENZ 916 $.25 (F183)
"Palms, The" SATB (easy) oct LORENZ A135 $.25 (F184)
(Biedermann) "Palm Trees, The" SATB oct FISCHER,J 965 $.35 (F185)
(Black) "Join All And Sing" SAB&jr cor&sr cor oct FISCHER,J 9767 $.30 (F186)
(Booth) "Palms, The" SATB oct FISCHER,C CM-6390 $.25 (F187)
(Buck) "Palms, The" 4pt mix cor,Bar solo, org oct SCHIRM.G 7397 $.30 (F188)
(Buck; Downing) "Palms, The" SAB,org oct SCHIRM.G 9648 $.35 (F189)
(Cronham) "Palms, The" SATB oct FISCHER,C CM-6533 $.25 (F190)
(Deis) "Palms, The" 3pt wom cor oct SCHIRM.G 9837 $.30 (F191)
(Deis) "Palms, The" 2pt wom cor/2pt men cor oct SCHIRM.G 10213 $.35 (F192)
(Filkins) "Palms, The" 3 cor oct BELWIN 814 $.25 (F193)
(Holmes) "Palms, The" 2pt oct PRO ART 2021 $.22 (F194)
(Howorth, Wayne) "Palms, The" SAB oct BELWIN 1120 $.30 (F195)
(Howorth, Wayne) "Palms, The" SATB oct BELWIN 790 $.30 (F196)
(Howorth, Wayne) "Palms, The" SA/TB oct BELWIN 1013 $.25 (F197)
(Howorth, Wayne) "Palms, The" SSA oct BELWIN 1014 $.25 (F198)
(Kowden) "Palms, The" SATB FLAMMER A 5380 $.25 (F199)
(Prendiville) "Palms, The" SATB oct FISCHER,C CM-6403 $.30 (F200)
(Riegger) "Palms, The" SAB FLAMMER D5130 $.25 (F201)
(Ringwald) "Palms, The" SATB SHAWNEE A 313 $.35 (F202)
(Stickles) "Palms, The" jr cor&sr cor oct SCHIRM.G 10470 $.35 (F203)

Notre Pere
[Fr] TB HEUGEL s.p. see from CHANTS RELIGIEUX (F204)
[Fr] unis HEUGEL s.p. see from CHANTS RELIGIEUX (F205)

O Salutaris
[Lat] unis HEUGEL s.p. see from CHANTS RELIGIEUX (F206)
[Lat] STB,solo,opt pno/org HEUGEL s.p. (F207)

Palm Branches *Easter
(Bruche, C.) SATB oct PRESSER 332-09678 $.30 (F208)

Palm Trees, The *see Les Rameaux

Palms *Palm
(Buck) SATB oct SOUTHERN $.25 (F209)

Palms, The *see Les Rameaux

Palms, The *see Les Rameaux

Panis Angelicus
[Lat] SATB,T/S solo,vln,opt pno/org HEUGEL s.p. (F210)

Sancta Maria
[Lat] unis HEUGEL s.p. see from CHANTS RELIGIEUX (F211)
(Shelly) "In Dreams I've Heard The Seraphs Fair" SSA oct SCHIRM.G 4641 $.25 (F212)

Tu Es Petrus
[Lat] SATB,solo,opt pno/org HEUGEL s.p. (F213)

FAUTCH, MAGDALEN
All Creation Sing
SSA,org oct WORLD CA-2121-3 $.45 (F214)

FAUX BOURDON SERIES OF OLD SCOTTISH PSALM TUNES, THE *CC15L,Psalm,Scot
(Roberton, H.S.) cor PATERSON s.p. (F215)

FAUX-BOURDONS AND HYMN TUNES *CC20L,hymn
(Willan, Healey) cor oct LESLIE (F216)

FAVERO, GINO
In Hora Mortis (from Satana) BVM
[Lat] unis,Bar solo ZANIBON 36 s.p. (F217)

FAVERO, GINO (cont'd.)

Panis Angelicus
see SEI MOTTETTI EUCARISTICI

Tre Invocazioni A Maria *CC3U,BVM
[Lat] unis,org sc ZANIBON 458 s.p., cor pts ZANIBON 456 s.p. (F218)

FAVORITE ANTHEMS CLASSICS NO. 3 *CCU,anthem
SATB LORENZ $1.75 (F219)

FAVORITE ANTHEMS FROM BACH see Bach

FAVORITE ANTHEMS FROM MENDELSSOHN see Mendelssohn-Bartholdy, Felix

FAVORITE CHRISTMAS CAROLS see Selner, J.

FAVORITE CHRISTMAS CAROLS AND CHRISTMAS HYMNS *CC15L,Xmas,carol/hymn
(Read, E.) PATERSON unis/2pt&desc/3pt wom cor/4pt mix cor s.p.; unis s.p.; 2-4pt,pno s.p. (F220)

FAVORITE HYMN FOR WOMEN'S VOICES see Steckel

FAVORITE HYMN-TUNE ANTHEMS NO. 1 *CCU,anthem
SATB LORENZ $1.95 (F221)

FAVORITE HYMN-TUNE ANTHEMS NO. 2 *CCU,anthem
SATB LORENZ $1.75 (F222)

FAVORITE HYMNS AND STORIES *CC99U
BIG3 $1.50 (F223)

FAVRE, GEORGES (1905-)
D'ou Viens-Tu Bergere *Xmas,carol
[Fr] 4pt mix cor,acap oct DURAND see from Trois Noels Francais (F224)

Jacotin *Xmas,carol
[Fr] 4pt mix cor,acap oct DURAND see from Trois Noels Francais (F225)

Je Me Suis Leve *Xmas,carol
[Fr] 4pt mix cor,acap oct DURAND see from Trois Noels Francais (F226)

Saint Joseph Avec Marie
[Fr] 3 eq voices oct DURAND (F227)

Trois Noels Francais *see D'ou Viens-Tu Bergere; Jacotin; Je Me Suis Leve (F228)

FAWCETT, J.
I Was Glad When They Said Unto Me
cor oct HART s.p. (F229)

Lord, What Is Man?
cor oct HART s.p. (F230)

When I Survey The Wondrous Cross
oct HART (F231)

FAX, M.
Go Tell It On The Mountain *Xmas
SATB,acap oct PRESSER 312-21393 $.30 (F232)

FAYRFAX, ROBERT (1464-1521)
Albanus
see Collected Works vol. I

Collected Works vol. I
(Warren, Edwin B.) cor cmplt ed AM.INST.MUS. $23.00
contains: Albanus; O Bone Jesu; O Quam Glorifica; Regnali; Sponsus Amat Sponsam; Tecum Principium (F233)

Collected Works Vol. II *CCU,Magnif/Mass/mot
(Warren, Edwin B.) cor cmplt ed AM.INST.MUS. $18.00 (F234)

Magnificat *Magnif
SATBarB STAINER MB12-4 s.p. (F235)

FAYRFAX, [ROBERT] (1464-1521)
Missa Tecum Principium *Mass
(Stevens) 4pt mix cor MOSELER s.p. (F236)

FAYRFAX, ROBERT (1464-1521)
O Bone Jesu
see Collected Works vol. I

O Quam Glorifica
see Collected Works vol. I

Regnali
see Collected Works vol. I

Sponsus Amat Sponsam
see Collected Works vol. I

Tecum Principium
see Collected Works vol. I

FEAR BORN OF THE EVILS OF HUMAN LIFE see Anonymous, Przestrach Na Zte Sprawy Ludzkiego Zywota

FEAR GOD AND GIVE GLORY TO HIM see Dietrich, M.

FEAR NOT, FOR BEHOLD I BRING GOOD TIDINGS see Hagen

FEAR NOT: FOR BEHOLD, I BRING GOOD TIDINGS OF GREAT JOY see Bender, Jan

FEAR NOT, I AM WITH THEE see Foster, Will

FEAR NOT, O ISRAEL see Spicker, M.

FEAR NOT, O ISRAEL see Young, Gordon

FEAR NOT, O LAND see Clare, Edwyn A.

FEAR NOT, O LAND see Cooke, S.C.

FEAR NOT, O LAND see Elgar, Edward

FEAR NOT, O LAND see Harris, William Henry

FEAR NOT, O LAND see Rogers, J.H.

FEAR NOT, O LAND see Sumsion, Herbert

FEAR NOT, O LAND, BE GLAD AND REJOICE see Goss,
John

FEAR NOT, THOU FAITHFUL CHRISTIAN FLOCK see
Bach, Johann Sebastian

FEAR NOT YE, O ISRAEL see Brumel, Antoine

FEAR THE ALMIGHTY see Schutz, Heinrich

FEAR THOU NOT see Basham, Robert A.

FEAR THOU NOT see Frank, Rene

FEARING, JOHN
Praise Ye The Lord (Psalm 150)
SATB oct LESLIE 4103   (F237)

Psalm 150 *see Praise Ye The Lord

FEARIS
Beautiful Isle Of Somewhere
(Wilson) SATB oct LORENZ A326 $.25   (F238)

FEARIS, J.S.
Be Joyful In The Lord *Fest
SATB,AT soli,pno (med) oct WILLIS 6307 $.12
(F239)
Bless The Lord, O My Soul (composed with
High) *Gen/Thanks
3pt men cor,pno (med) oct WILLIS 7072 $.20
(F240)
SATB,S/T solo,pno (easy) oct WILLIS 6435
$.10   (F241)
Blessed Redeemer
(Denza, L.) SATB,pno (easy) oct WILLIS 6308
$.10   (F242)
Brightest And Best *Xmas
SATB,S/T solo,pno (easy) oct WILLIS 6440
$.10   (F243)
Crossing The Bar
TTBB,opt pno (easy) oct WILLIS 6310 $.15
(F244)
Evening Prayer
unis,pno (easy) oct WILLIS 6312 $.12 (F245)
First Christmas Morn, The *Xmas
3pt wom cor,pno (easy) oct WILLIS 6313 $.10
(F246)
Forget Not All His Benefits
SATB,Mez solo,pno (easy) oct WILLIS 6314
$.15   (F247)
O God, The Rock Of Ages
SATB,SAT soli,pno (med) oct WILLIS 6462
$.12   (F248)
Search Me, O God
SATB,A/B solo,pno (easy) oct WILLIS 6332
$.15   (F249)

FEAST AFTER FEAST see Ford, Virgil T.

FEAST OF CHRISTMAS, THE see Mac Mahon

FEAST OF LIGHT, THE see Adler, Samuel

FEAST OF LIGHTS see Luskin, Samuel

FEAST OF PRAISE, A see Thompson, Randall

FEAST OF SAINT FRANCIS OF ASSISSI see Binkerd,
[Gordon]

FEAST OF THE STAR see Friedell

FEAT OF INGATHERING see Parker

FECIT POTENTIAM see Senfl, Ludwig

FECKERS, ADOLF
Festliche Kantate *Fest,cant
4pt mix cor,solo,strings MOSELER voc sc
s.p., cor pts s.p., ipa   (F250)

Pfingstkantate *Pent,cant
4pt mix cor,opt solo,2fl/S rec&A rec,ob/
clar/T rec,vln,vla,vcl,bvl MOSELER voc sc
s.p., cor pts s.p., ipa   (F251)

FEDERER, R.
Star On The Christmas Tree *Xmas
SA oct PRESSER 312-21523 $.30   (F252)

FEED-A MY SHEEP *spir
(Dawson) SATB KJOS T-34 $.35   (F253)
(Dawson) SSA KJOS TI35 $.35   (F254)
(Dawson) men cor KJOS T133 $.35   (F255)

FEED MY LAMBS see Sleeth

FEED MY LAMBS see Sleeth, Natalie

FEED THY PEOPLE see Miron

FEGERS, KARL
Ave, Maria Zart
see Zwei Weihnachtliche Liedkantaten

Gloria In Excelsis Deo
see Zwei Weihnachtliche Liedkantaten

Kommet Ihr Hirten *Xmas,cant
4pt mix cor/cong,5-6brass MOSELER sc s.p.,
cor pts s.p., ipa contains also: Macht
Noch Die Tur   (F256)

Macht Noch Die Tur
see Fegers, Karl, Kommet Ihr Hirten

Zwei Weihnachtliche Liedkantaten *Xmas,cant
4pt mix cor/cong,5-6brass MOSELER sc s.p.,
cor pts s.p., ipa
contains: Ave, Maria Zart; Gloria In
Excelsis Deo   (F257)

FEGET DEN ALTEN SAUERTEIG AUS UND LASST UNS
OSTERN HALTEN see Schutz, Heinrich

FEHRES, WILHELM
Adams Klage
see Fehres, Wilhelm, Gott Sei Uns Gnadig

Gott Sei Uns Gnadig (Psalm 67) mot
4pt mix cor MOSELER s.p. contains also:
Adams Klage   (F258)

FEHRES, WILHELM (cont'd.)

Psalm 67 *see Gott Sei Uns Gnadig

FEHRMANN
Easter Song *Easter
(Dickinson, C.) SATB oct GRAY GSC 20 $.25
(F259)
FEHRMANN, PAUL (1859-1938)
Osterpsalm *Easter,Psalm
[Ger] mix cor,acap (med) HUG s.p.   (F260)

Psalm 92
[Ger] mix cor,org HUG s.p.   (F261)

FEIBEL
King Of Love My Shepherd Is, The
SATB,org BOSTON 13473 $.40   (F262)

FEIGER GEDANKEN see Lissmann, Kurt

FELCIANO, RICHARD (1930-   )
Double Alleluia *Pent
unis men cor,org,electronic tape oct WORLD
EMP-1532-1 $.45   (F263)
Evening Mass Of Holy Thursday *Eve/Holywk,
Gradual
(Snow, Robert J.) TTB/SSA,acap oct WORLD
EMP-1215-3 $.30   (F264)
Eyes Of All Look Hopefully To You, The
(Snow, Robert J.) TTB/SSA,org oct WORLD
EMP-1854-3 $.90   (F265)
Much Have They Oppressed Me From My Youth
see Felciano, Richard, Rescue Me From My
Enemies, O Lord
No One Who Waits *Adv,Gloria
(Snow, Robert J.) 2 eq voices,org oct WORLD
EMP-1093-2 $.30   (F266)
O Come, O Come, Emmanuel *Adv
girl cor SOUTHERN $.25   (F267)
Out Of Sight (The Ascension That Nobody Saw)
SATB,org,electronic tape (easy) SCHIRM.EC
2909 $.45, ipa   (F268)
Rescue Me From My Enemies, O Lord *Psntd,
Gradual
TB/SA,acap oct WORLD EMP-1170-2 $.30
contains also: Much Have They Oppressed
Me From My Youth (tract)   (F269)
Sic Transit
SSA,org, light sources (easy) SCHIRM.EC
2807 $.45, ipa   (F270)
SAB,org, light sources (easy) SCHIRM.EC
2903 $.45, ipa   (F271)
Three-In-One-In-Three
SAB&SAB,1-2org,electronic tape (easy)
SCHIRM.EC 2910 $.45, ipa   (F272)
Words Of Saint Peter *Bibl
SATB,org,electronic tape oct WORLD
CA-2093-8 $.45   (F273)

FELDERHOF, JAN (1907-   )
Agnus Dei *Agnus
[Dut] mix cor,org DONEMUS sc s.p., cor pts
s.p.   (F274)

Tot Wien Zullen Wij Henengaan *Bibl/cant
[Dut] mix cor,SABar soli,pno,2fl,2ob,2clar,
2bsn,2trp,2horn,trom,tuba,strings,perc,
timp DONEMUS min sc s.p., cor pts s.p.,
voc sc s.p.   (F275)

FELDMAN, JAMES
Glory To God *Xmas
SATB FOSTER MF133 $.30   (F276)

Shout! Shout!
cor FOSTER MF135 $.40   (F277)

FELDMAN, MORTON (1926-   )
Hallelujah
SATB SHAWNEE A 1138 $.30   (F278)

FELIS
Quem Vidistis Pastores
(Hoagland) [Eng/Lat] SSATB MARKS 4491 $.30
(F279)
FELLEGARA, VITTORIO (1927-   )
Dies Irae
mix cor,16inst ZERBONI 5666 s.p.   (F280)

Requiem Di Madrid *Req
mix cor,org/orch voc sc ZERBONI 5607 s.p.,
ipr   (F281)

FELLOWSHIP see Sanders, Robert L.

FELTMATE
Listen! *gospel
(Cable) SATB,drums,gtr BOSTON 13791 $.80
(F282)
Your Work With Love Surrounds You *cant
cor,narrator,solo FRANK $1.85   (F283)

FELTS
Christ Is Risen *Easter/Lent
SSA WORD CS-2347 $.30   (F284)

Come Ye With Carols *Xmas
unis/SA oct WORD CS-2242 $.25   (F285)

Guide Me, O Thou Great Jehovah
SATB oct WORD CS-2311 $.30   (F286)

He That Dwelleth In The Secret Place
SATB oct WORD CS-2120 $.30   (F287)

Onward With Christ
(Boersma) SATB oct WORD CS-2333 $.25   (F288)
(Roe) SATB oct WORD CS-2260 $.30   (F289)

Thanksgiving Hymn, A
SATB oct WORD CS-2279 $.30   (F290)

FEM FOLKLIGA KORALER I SATTNINGAR
(Hahn, Gunnar) mix cor NORDISKA NMS-6382 s.p.
contains: Dagen Ifran Oss Skrider; Gud
Later Sina Trogna; I Himmelen; Jag Lyfter
Mina Hander; O Jesu, Nar Jag Hadan Skall
(F291)

FEM KORKORALER
(Berwald, Franz) mix cor NORDISKA NMS-6379
s.p. contains also: Saliga Heliga (Hemberg,
Eskil); Tva Dopvisor (Hemberg)   (F292)

FEM LATINSKE KIRKEKOR see Sandvold, Arild

FEM SANGE FOR MANDSKOR see Schubert, Franz
(Peter)

FEM SATSER see Distler, Hugo

FEMTEN FEM-SEKS-STEMMIGE SATSER see Pederson,
Mogens

FENWICK
Little Boy Jesus And I
SSA THOMP.G G-118 s.p.   (F293)

FERFIKAROK see Kodaly, Zoltan

FERGUSON
All Things Bright And Beautiful
unis&SA&SAB oct SACRED S-6503 $.35   (F294)

At The Feet Of Jesus
SATB oct HERITAGE H50 $.35   (F295)

Blessing For Easter Morning, A *Easter
SATB oct SACRED S-132 $.35   (F296)

Christmas Eve *Xmas
SATB oct SACRED S-13 $.35   (F297)

Christmas Exultation, A *Xmas
SATB oct SACRED S-60 $.40   (F298)

Deep In The Boding Night *Lent
SATB oct SOUTHERN $.30   (F299)
SATB oct SACRED S-35 $.35   (F300)

Eternal Hope
SATB oct SACRED S-3 $.30   (F301)

Hammering *Lent
SATB oct SACRED E64 $.40   (F302)

Hosanna, Loud Hosanna *Palm
unis&SA&SAB oct SACRED S-6500 $.35   (F303)

Mother's Day Carol
SATB oct SACRED S-40 $.35   (F304)

Resurrection Tidings
SATB FLAMMER A5309 $.80   (F305)

Sing Brothers, Sing
SATB oct SACRED S-122 $.35   (F306)

Twenty Responses In Elizabethan Style
*CC20U,cor-resp
SATB oct SACRED S-10 $.40   (F307)

FERGUSON, EDWIN EARLE
I Have Built A House
SATB oct LAWSON 51161 $.30   (F308)

Paul's Farewell To The Church At Ephesus
*Bibl
SATB,pno/org oct LAWSON 51520 $.40   (F309)

We Pause Beside This Door *anthem
SATB,org oct LAWSON 51291 $.25   (F310)

Ye Followers Of The Lamb
SATB,acap AMP A586 $.35   (F311)

FERGUSON, HOWARD (1908-   )
Easter Fanfare *Easter
SATB FLAMMER A 5025 $.25   (F312)

Give Me Jesus
SATB FLAMMER A 5097 $.25   (F313)

Take, Take And Eat
SATB FLAMMER A 5204 $.25   (F314)
SSA FLAMMER B 5129 $.25   (F315)
SAB FLAMMER D5045 $.25   (F316)

There Dwelt In Old Judea
SATB FLAMMER A 5526 $.25   (F317)

This Hour With Thee
SATB FLAMMER A 5624 $.30   (F318)

We Hear The Angel Gabriel
SATB FLAMMER A 5533 $.25   (F319)

FERIA V. IN COENA DOMINI see Nanini (Nanino),
Giovanni Maria

FERIA VI. IN PARASCEVE see Palestrina, Giovanni

FERIA VI. IN PARASCEVE see Nanini (Nanino),
Giovanni Maria

FERIAL RESPONSES see Winchester, E.C.

FERNANDEZ DE CASTILLEJA
Dispersit *mot,16th cent
[Lat] 4pt mix cor,acap UNION ESP. 19350
s.p.   (F320)

Heu Mihi *mot,16th cent
[Lat] 5pt mix cor,acap UNION ESP. 19351
s.p.   (F321)

FERNEYHOUGH, BRIAN
Missa Brevis *Mass
[Lat] SATB&SATB&SATB,acap sc PETERS 7125
$10.00   (F322)

FERRADINI, ANTONIO (1718-1779)
Stabat Mater
(Bettarini, Luciano) mix cor&mix cor,SSATB
soli,org,2fl,2clar,2bsn,2horn,3trom,
strings BREITKOPF-W rental   (F323)

FERRANTE
Messa In Onore Di S. Caterina Da Siena *Mass
SA/TB,org voc sc RICORDI-ENG 127626,
cor pts RICORDI-ENG 127627-29   (F324)

FERRARI, GIOVANNI
Cantiones Sacrae Hebdomadae Sanctae *Easter
[Lat] 3pt mix cor/4pt mix cor,org ZANIBON
4414 s.p.
contains: Gloria Laus; Ingrediente
Domino; Stabat Mater; Vexilla Regis

FERRARI, GIOVANNI (cont'd.)

(F325)

Gloria Laus
see Cantiones Sacrae Hebdomadae Sanctae

Ingrediente Domino
see Cantiones Sacrae Hebdomadae Sanctae

Stabat Mater
see Cantiones Sacrae Hebdomadae Sanctae

Vexilla Regis
see Cantiones Sacrae Hebdomadae Sanctae

FERRARI, GIUSEPPE
Ad Recipiendum Episcopum *mot
[Lat] SATB,org sc ZANIBON 4412 s.p., cor
pts ZANIBON 4413 s.p.
contains: Ecce Sacerdos; Tu Es Sacerdos
(F326)

Ecce Sacerdos
see Ad Recipiendum Episcopum

Tu Es Sacerdos
see Ad Recipiendum Episcopum

FERRARI-TRECATE, LUIGI (1884-1964)
Missa "Domina Angelorum" *Mass
3pt mix cor,org sc SANTIS 987 s.p., cor pts
SANTIS 988A-C s.p.   (F327)

Missa Sancta Trinitas *Mass
ATB,org s.p. voc sc RICORDI-ENG 128925, cor
pts RICORDI-ENG 129020-22   (F328)

FERRER
Misa Pastoril *Mass
cor,3 soli UNION ESP. 17562 s.p.   (F329)

FERRIS, W.
Drop Down, Ye Heavens
see Five Short Anthems

Earth Feared And Was Silent, The *Easter,
anthem
SATB (med diff) oct GIA G1441 $.40   (F330)

Five Short Anthems *anthem
TB/SB (med) cmplt ed GIA G1511 $.80
contains: Drop Down, Ye Heavens; In Thee,
O Lord, Have I Put My Trust; Lighten
Mine Eyes; O Taste And See; Sorrows Of
My Heart Are Enlarged, The   (F331)

Hail, Noble Flesh *Commun,anthem
SATB (med) oct GIA G1369 $.30   (F332)

In Thee, O Lord, Have I Put My Trust
see Five Short Anthems

Lighten Mine Eyes
see Five Short Anthems

Lord Said To Me, The *Xmas,anthem/Introit/
Mass
SATB,org,2trp,2trom,timp (med easy) oct GIA
G1389 $.60   (F333)

O Taste And See
see Five Short Anthems

Praise The Lord, O My Soul (Psalm 145) Gen,
anthem
SATB (med diff) oct GIA 1368 $.30   (F334)

Psalm 145 *see Praise The Lord, O My Soul

Serene Alleluias *Gen,Allelu/anthem
SA (med) oct GIA G1534 $.30   (F335)

Sorrows Of My Heart Are Enlarged, The
see Five Short Anthems

FERRO, STEFANO
In Solemnitate Paschae *Op.17, Easter
[Lat] ZANIBON 2953 s.p.
contains: Pascha Nostrum (3 eq voices)
(Commun); Resurrexi (unis) (Introit);
Terra Tremuit (2 eq voices) (Offer)
(F336)

Justus Ut Palma Florebit *Op.42, ASD,Offer
[Lat] 3 eq voices,org ZANIBON 2646 s.p.
(F337)

O Salutaris *Op.8, Commun
[Lat] 2pt,org ZANIBON 2666 s.p.   (F338)

Pascha Nostrum
see In Solemnitate Paschae

Resurrexi
see In Solemnitate Paschae

Terra Tremuit
see In Solemnitate Paschae

Tu Es Sacerdos *Op.15
[Lat] TB,org ZANIBON 1625 s.p.   (F339)

FEST-CANTATE see Bruckner, Anton

FEST- UND GEDENKSPRUCHE see Brahms, Johannes

FEST- UND GEDENKSPRUCHE see Brahms, Johannes

FESTA, COSTANZA (ca. 1490-1545)
Bramo Morir *madrigal
(Schinelli, A.) [It/Eng/Ger] 4pt mix cor
CURCI 6493 s.p. see from COLLANA DI
COMPOSIZIONI POLIFONICHE VOCALE SACRE E
PROFANE, VOL. 1   (F340)

Jesus Christ, Our Salvation *see Regem
Archangelorum

O Lord, King Of The Angels *see Regem
Archangelorum

Opera Omnia Vol. I *CC8L,Mass
(Main, Alexander) cor AM.INST.MUS. $18.00
(F341)

Opera Omnia Vol. II *CC14U,Magnif
(Main, Alexander) cor AM.INST.MUS. $22.00
(F342)

Regem Archangelorum
SATB,acap RICORDI-ENG SY179 s.p.   (F343)
(Payson, A.) "O Lord, King Of The Angels"
SATB,acap FRANK F-452 $.30   (F344)
(Zanon; Vene) "Jesus Christ, Our Salvation"

FESTA, COSTANZA (cont'd.)

SATB,acap oct COLOMBO 1889 $.30   (F345)

Ut Queant Laxis *Eve,anthem/hymn
(J.M.D.) [Lat] SATB&unis oct ST.MARTIN
SMP621 s.p.   (F346)

FESTA DIES AGITUR (from Anthology Of Carols,
An)
see Coventry Carol

FESTAL ALLELUIA, A see Lorenz

FESTAL HYMNS see Williams

FESTAL RESPONSES see Tallis, Thomas

FESTAL SONG, A see Wilm, Nicolai von

FESTGESANG see Mendelssohn-Bartholdy, Felix

FESTGESANG see Nagle, W.

FESTIVAL see Haubiel, Charles

FESTIVAL ALLELUIA see Evans, Roderick

FESTIVAL ALLELUIA see Langlais, Jean

FESTIVAL ANTHEM see Mistowski, Alfred

FESTIVAL ANTHEM see Phillips

FESTIVAL ANTHEM see Vaughn

FESTIVAL ANTHEM, A see Berkeley, Lennox

FESTIVAL ANTHEM ON "CROWN HIM WITH MANY CROWNS"
see Proulx, Richard

FESTIVAL ANTHEMS FOR SAB see Powell, Robert J.

FESTIVAL ANTIPHONS see Slater, Richard W.

FESTIVAL BENEDICITE IN D see Sumsion, Herbert

FESTIVAL CANTATA see Carmel, Dov

FESTIVAL CAROL *Fest,carol
unis/SATB (very easy) OXFORD 08.151 $.15
(F347)

FESTIVAL CHIME see Holst, Gustav

FESTIVAL CHORUSES FOR TWO EQUAL VOICES see
Grant, Louise

FESTIVAL GLORIA see Rubbra, Edmund

FESTIVAL HALLELUJAH see Reinagle, [Alexander
Robert]

FESTIVAL HYMN *anthem/folk,Dut
(Christiansen, Paul) SATB (easy) oct AUGSBURG
1100 $.20   (F348)

FESTIVAL HYMNS WITH DESCANTS see Pooler, Marie

FESTIVAL INTROIT see Brandon

FESTIVAL INTROITS see Couper, Alinda B.

FESTIVAL INTROITS [1] see Lovelace, Austin C.

FESTIVAL INTROITS [2] see Lovelace, Austin C.

FESTIVAL JUBILATE see Charles, Ernest

FESTIVAL MAGNIFICAT AND NUNC DIMITTIS see
Pinkham, Daniel

FESTIVAL MAGNIFICAT AND NUNC DIMITTIS see
Spencer, S. Reid

FESTIVAL MASS see Janacek, Leos, Msa Glagskaja

FESTIVAL MASS see Lee, J.

FESTIVAL MATINS see Swann, Donald

FESTIVAL OF CAROLS FOR THE CHURCH YEAR, THE see
Caldwell, Mary [Elizabeth]

FESTIVAL OF CHRISTMAS see Wilson

FESTIVAL OF HYMNS see Dressler, John

FESTIVAL OF HYMNS
(Constantine, J.) SATB,opt band oct PRESSER
312-40770 $.35   (F349)

FESTIVAL OF LIFE, THE see Webber, Lloyd

FESTIVAL OF PRAISE see Bowman, Carl

FESTIVAL PRELUDE see Wagner, Richard

FESTIVAL PROCESSIONAL see Cooper, Irvin

FESTIVAL RESPONSE see Stocker, David

FESTIVAL RESPONSES see Winchester, E.C.

FESTIVAL SONG see Shirat Chag

FESTIVAL SONG BOOK, THE see Bell, Leslie

FESTIVAL SONG OF PRAISE see Mendelssohn-
Bartholdy, Felix

FESTIVAL TE DEUM see Britten, Benjamin

FESTIVAL TE DEUM see Mathias, William

FESTIVAL TE DEUM see Rubbra, Edmund

FESTIVAL TE DEUM see Sanders, John

FESTIVAL TE DEUM see Vaughan Williams, Ralph

FESTIVAL TE DEUM see Willan, Healey

FESTIVAL TE DEUM, A see Alldis, John

FESTIVAL TE DEUM NO. 7, E FLAT see Brumel,
Antoine

FESTIVAL TE DEUM NO.7, IN E FLAT see Buck,
Dudley

FESTIVE ALLELUIA see Mayer

FESTIVE ALLELUIA see Young, Gordon

FESTIVE CAROLS *CCU,carol
(Cope) SSA,acap oct BOOSEY 5002 $.35 (F350)

FESTIVE HALLS OF CHRISTMAS *Xmas
SATB CHARTER $.35   (F351)

FESTIVE ODE see Husa, Karel

FESTLICHE HYMNE "O HEIMAT, SIEH DES MORGENS
HELLE SCHWINGEN" see Sibelius, Jean

FESTLICHE KANTATE see Feckers, Adolf

FESTLICHE SCHULSCHLUSSKANTATE see Kukuck,
Felicitas

FESTLICHES LIED "EINMAL NUR IN UNSERM LEBEN"
see Strohbach, Siegfried

FESTLICHES ORDINARIUM see Track, Gerhard

FESTLICHES PRALUDIUM *Op.100, Fest
(Wellesz, Egon) 4pt mix cor,org voc sc
DOBLINGER s.p.   (F352)

FESTMESSE see Walter, Karl

FESTMUSIK ZUM ERSTEN WEIHNACHTSTAG see Briegel,
Wolfgang Carl

FESTMUSIK ZUM ZWEITEN WEIHNACHTSTAG see
Briegel, Wolfgang Carl

FESTORATORIUM see Handel, George Frideric

FETLER, D.
In Peace And Joy I Now Depart
SATB,acap oct PRESSER 312-40057 $.30 (F353)

FETLER, PAUL
Easter Fanfare: Christ The Lord Is Risen
*Easter,anthem
SATB,3trp (easy) oct AUGSBURG 1591 $.30
(F354)

Great And Mighty Wonder, A *anthem
SATB,opt trp (med) oct AUGSBURG 1487 $.30,
ipa   (F355)

Hosanna *anthem
SATB,opt bvl (med) oct AUGSBURG 1647 $.60
(F356)

Introit And Gradual For Reformation Day
*Refm,Gradual/Introit/liturg,Contemp
SATB WOLF 11-1404 $.22   (F357)

King Shall Come, The *anthem
SATB (med diff) oct AUGSBURG 1250 $.30 (F358)

Make A Joyful Noise *anthem
SATB (med) oct AUGSBURG 1476 $.40   (F359)

Noel *anthem
unis treb cor,hpsd,fl,bells (med) oct
AUGSBURG 9309 $.50   (F360)

O All Ye Works Of The Land *anthem
SATB (med diff) oct AUGSBURG 1408 $.30 (F361)

Praise Ye The Lord
SATB STANDARD A26MX $.60   (F362)

Prayer For Peace *anthem
SATB (easy) oct AUGSBURG 1547 $.20   (F363)

Reformation Day *Refm,anthem/Gradual/Introit
SATB (easy) oct AUGSBURG 1404 $.22   (F364)

Sing Unto God *anthem
SATB (med) oct AUGSBURG 1244 $.30   (F365)

Te Deum *Te Deum,Contemp
mix cor,acap (diff) oct AUGSBURG 11-9494
$1.00   (F366)

Words From The Cross, The *Gd.Fri./Holywk/
Lent
mix cor,narrator,org (med easy) oct
AUGSBURG 11-9536 $1.00   (F367)

You Did Not Miss Jerusalem *anthem
SATB (med diff) oct AUGSBURG 0507 $.25 (F368)

FEUCHTET EUCH NICHT see Bach, Johann Michael

FEVIN, ANTOINE DE (ca. 1474-1512)
Ave Maria
(Brun, L'abbe) [Lat] 4pt mix cor,acap oct
DURAND   (F369)

Benedictus Dominus Deus
see OPERA OMNIA VOL. I

Holy Trinity *see Sancta Trinitas

Laudetur
(Brun, L'abbe) [Lat] 4pt mix cor,acap oct
DURAND   (F370)

Sancta Trinitas *Gen/Trin,mot
"Holy Trinity" SATB (med easy) oct
CONCORDIA 98-1933 $.40   (F371)
(Boorman, Stanley) [Lat] mix cor,acap oct
NOVELLO 40.1525.08 s.p.   (F372)

FEYHL, J.
Osterlied *Easter
[Ger] mix cor,acap (easy) HUG s.p.   (F373)

FHEDOROFF, NIKOLAUS
Heiligenbluter Krippenmesse *see
Mittergradnegger, G.

FICHER, JACOBO (1896-   )
Salmo De Alegria *Op.69, cant/Psalm
cor,SATB soli,orch PEER rental   (F374)

FICHER, TRYGVE
Gud, Du Er Min Gud
[Norw] mix cor LYCHE 39 s.p.   (F375)

FICHTHORN, [CLAUDE L.] (1885-   )
   Out Of The Depths *Easter
      SATB oct PRESSER 332-40013 $.30   (F376)

FIEBIG, KURT (1908-   )
   Auf, Auf, Mein Herz, Mit Freuden
      see Kukuck, Felicitas, Heut Triumphieret
      Gottes Sohn

   Chorgesange Zum Karfreitag *Gd.Fri./Psntd,
      Bibl
      [Ger] 3pt mix cor,acap BAREN. EM 17 s.p.
      contains: Das Evangelium; Ein Lammlein
      Geht Und Tragt Die Schuld   (F377)

   Christus Spricht: Selig Sind, Die Das Wort
      Gottes
      see Fiebig, Kurt, Ich Will Gottes Wort
      Ruhmen

   Das Evangelium
      see Chorgesange Zum Karfreitag

   Deutsches Magnificat *Bibl/liturg/Magnif
      4-6pt&mix cor,S solo (med diff) LEUCKART
      s.p.   (F378)

   Die Introiten Fur Die Festtage Des
      Kirchenjahres *CC16U
      [Ger] 3pt mix cor/4pt mix cor BAREN.
      EM 202
      s.p.   (F379)

   Ein Edler Schatz Der Weisheit
      SA,treb inst&bass inst/bass inst HANSSLER
      14.501 s.p.   (F380)

   Ein Lammlein Geht Und Tragt Die Schuld
      see Chorgesange Zum Karfreitag
      SS/T,2treb inst HANSSLER 14.062 s.p.   (F381)

   Et Unam Sanctam *Asc/Pent,cant
      [Lat] 4-6pt mix cor&cong,STBar soli,org,fl,
      ob,clar,bsn,2trp,trom,strings,drums
      BAREN. EM 525 voc sc rental, s.p.   (F382)

   Freuet Euch, Ihr Christen Alle
      SAT/SAB,treb inst,bass inst HANSSLER 14.025
      s.p.   (F383)

   Frohlich Wir Nun All
      mix cor HANSSLER 14.125 s.p. contains also:
      Werner, Fritz, Frohlich Wir Nun All (mix
      cor)   (F384)

   Gott Sei Dank Durch Alle Welt
      see Poser, Hans, Wie Soll Ich Dich
      Empfangen

   Herr Gott, Dich Loben Alle Wir
      see Borris, Siegfried, Wir Wollen Sing'n
      Ein Lobgesang
      [Ger] mix cor (med) oct SIRIUS 13 s.p.   (F385)

   Ich Will Gottes Wort Ruhmen
      SAT/SAB HANSSLER 14.602 s.p. contains also:
      Christus Spricht: Selig Sind, Die Das
      Wort Gottes   (F386)

   Jauchzet, Ihr Himmel, Frohlocket, Ihr Engel,
      In Choren
      SAT/SAB HANSSLER 14.033 contains also:
      Schwartz, Gerhard von, Also Liebt Gott
      Die Arge Welt (SAT/SAB,treb inst,bass
      inst)   (F387)

   Markus-Passion *Psntd
      [Ger] 4pt mix cor&4pt mix cor,5 soli,acap
      BAREN. EM 430 rental   (F388)

   Missa Media Vita *Mass
      4pt mix cor,acap cor pts BREITKOPF-W
      CHB-3031 s.p.   (F389)

   Sollt Ich Meinem Gott Nicht Singen
      SATB HANSSLER 8.039 s.p. contains also:
      Woehl, Waldemar, Sollt Ich Meinem Gott
      Nicht Singen (SS/SA);
      Schutz, Heinrich, Freut Euch Des Herrn,
      Ihr Christen All (SATB);
      Woehl, Waldemar, Freut Euch Des Herrn,
      Ihr Christen All (SA/TTB);
      Bach, Johann Sebastian, Nun Danket Alle
      Gott, S.252 (SATB) (F maj)   (F390)

FIELD
   Sleep Holy Babe *see Caswell

FIELD, J.T.
   God Shall Wipe Away All Tears
      SATB,org (med) oct WILLIS 714 $.12   (F391)

FIELD, JOHN (1782-1837)
   God Shall Wipe Away All Tears *Bibl
      4pt mix cor oct SCHIRM.G 4649 $.25   (F392)

FIELD, R.
   Venite Adoremus *Xmas
      SATB,org oct KERBY 5706 $.35   (F393)
      SATB oct KERBY 5706C $.35   (F394)

FIELDS
   Open The Gates Of The Temple *see Knapp,
      Lavater

   Way Outside You
      SATB oct HERITAGE H74 $.40   (F395)

FIERCE RAGED THE TEMPEST see Candlyn, T.
   Frederick H.

FIERCE RAGED THE TEMPEST see Jenkins, Cyril

FIERCE RAGED THE TEMPEST see Ryley

FIERCE WAS THE WILD BILLOW see Hewlett, W.H.

FIERCE WAS THE WILD BILLOW see Noble, Thomas
   Tertius

FIERY FURNACE, THE see Castelnuovo-Tedesco,
   Mario

FIERY FURNACE, THE see Berger, Jean

FIFTEEN ANTHEMS VOL. 1 see Tallis, Thomas

FIFTEEN ANTHEMS VOL. 2 see Tallis, Thomas

FIFTEEN CHORAL RESPONSES see Harris

FIFTEEN CHRISTMAS CAROLS *CC15U,Xmas,carol
   (Milford) unis/desc (easy) OXFORD 44.026
   $1.10   (F396)

FIFTEEN ORIGINAL AMENS, SEVENFOLD AMEN see
   Overton, Hall

FIFTEEN PSALMS TO HONOUR THE HOLY EUCHARIST see
   Bevenot, Laurence

FIFTEEN TWO-PART CHRISTMAS CAROLS *CC15L
   (Geer, E.) SA SCHIRM.EC 1976 $.50   (F397)

FIFTEENTH CENTURY LITURGICAL MUSIC 1 *CCU,
   Holywk,anti,Eng,15th cent
   cor STAINER 3.8208.8 $18.00   (F398)

FIFTEENTH CENTURY REPERTORY FROM THE CODEX
   REINA, A *CCU,15th cent
   (Wilkins, E. Nigel) cor AM.INST.MUS. $9.00   (F399)

FIFTH MYSTERY CANTATA, THE see Mader, Clarence

FIFTH SERVICE see Tomkins, Thomas

FIFTY SACRED SONGS, VOLUME II see Bach, Johann
   Sebastian

FIFTY-TWO SACRED MOTETS *CC52U,mot,Lat
   mix cor,acap voc sc KALMUS 6041 $1.75   (F400)

FIGHT THE GOOD FIGHT *hymn
   (Gardner) SSA (med easy) OXFORD 44.225 $.25,
   ipr see from Five Hymns In Popular Style   (F401)

FIGHT THE GOOD FIGHT see Cain, Noble

FIGHT THE GOOD FIGHT see Comer

FIGHT THE GOOD FIGHT see George, Graham

FIGHT THE GOOD FIGHT see Long, K.

FIGHT THE GOOD FIGHT see Martin

FIGHT THE GOOD FIGHT see Rhodes, Harold

FIGHT THE GOOD FIGHT see Thiman, Eric Harding

FIGHT THE GOOD FIGHT see Williams

FIGHT THE GOOD FIGHT WITH ALL THY MIGHT see
   Gardner, John [Linton]

FILA, FILA LUNGA see Somma

FILAS, T.
   O Lord Give Me The Grace
      SATB,acap oct PRESSER 332-40014 $.25   (F402)

FILIAE JERUSALEM, ADJURO VOS see Pizzetti,
   [Ildebrando]

FILITZ, [FRIEDRICH] (1804-1876)
   God Of Love, Who Hearest Prayer
      (Coggin) 2pt WARNER R3492 $.30   (F403)

FILKINS
   Ageless Miracle, The *Easter/Lent
      SATB oct PRO ART 1148 $.30   (F404)

   Amens And Responses *CCU
      SATB BELWIN $.75   (F405)

   Christmas Caravan *Xmas
      SATB oct PRO ART 1214 $.30   (F406)

   Christmas Scripture In Song *CC6L,Xmas,Bibl
      unis PRO ART 42 $.35; SATB PRO ART 82 $.75   (F407)

   Psalm 23 *Bibl/Psalm
      unis oct PRO ART 1161 $.20   (F408)

   Resurrection Morn *Easter/Lent
      SATB,acap oct PRO ART 1197 $.20   (F409)

   Strong Son Of God
      SATB,S solo oct PRO ART 1221 $.22   (F410)

   Sweet Story, The
      unis oct PRO ART 1213 $.25   (F411)

   Te Deum In G *Te Deum
      SATB,soli oct PRO ART 1187 $.22   (F412)

FILL MY CUP, LORD see Blanchard, [William G.]

FILL THE WORLD WITH THY GLORY see Ford

FILL THOU MY LIFE see Aldridge, Richard

FILL THOU MY LIFE, O LORD MY GOD see Thiman,
   Eric Harding

FILL THOU MY LIGHT see Thiman, Eric Harding

FILL YOUR HEARTS WITH PRAYER see Daniel, K.

FILLMORE
   Beautiful Garden Of Prayer, The
      (Wilson) SATB oct LORENZ A292 $.25   (F413)

   I Know That My Redeemer Liveth
      (Whitman) SATB oct LILLENAS AN-2277 $.30   (F414)
      (Whitman) SAB oct LILLENAS AN-2306 $.30   (F415)

FILOMENA see Gombert, Nicolas

FILS DE DIEU QUI ES TOUT-PUISSANT see Caulery,
   Jean

FINAL CHORUS FROM 'JEPHTE' see Carissimi,
   Giacomo

FINAL RESPONSES AT MORNING AND EVENING PRAYER
   see Naylor, Edward Woodall

FINALE DE LA NEUVIEME SYMPHONIE see Beethoven,
   Ludwig van

FINCH, R.
   Wassail Song
      SATB CHESTER s.p.   (F416)

FINCK
   Acht Hymnen *CC8U,hymn
      (Gerber) [Ger/Lat] 4pt mix cor MOSELER s.p.   (F417)

   De Nativitate Domini
      [Lat/Ger] SATB,acap PETERS 4884 $.50   (F418)

   Eight Hymns *CC8U,hymn
      mix cor,acap voc sc KALMUS 6168 $1.50   (F419)

   In Gottes Namen Fahren Wir
      4pt mix cor MOSELER LB-342 s.p.   (F420)

   Missa In Summis *Mass
      mix cor,acap voc sc KALMUS 6169 $2.00   (F421)
      6-7pt mix cor MOSELER s.p.   (F422)

   Sanctus
      see MEISTERWERKE MITTELALTERLICHER MUSIK

FINCK, HEINRICH (1445-1527)
   Erbe Deutscher Musik: Vol. 57 *CCU,Mass/mot
      (Hoffmann-Erbrecht, Lothar) cor,org cloth,
      fac ed PETERS $25.00   (F423)

   Masses And Motets *CCU,Mass/mot
      3-6pt cloth HINRICHSEN P7015A s.p. with
      facsimile reproductions   (F424)

   Missa In Summis
      see ARS NOVA TO RENNAISSANCE VOL. 2-1200 TO
      ABOUT 1500

FINDING CHRISTMAS JOY *Xmas
   (worship program) LORENZ $.75   (F425)

FINDING GOD THROUGH NATURE, SERIES 1 see Grime,
   William

FINDLAY, GEORGE
   Let Songs Of Joy Arise *Austral
      SATB ALLANS 202 s.p.   (F426)

   Sweet Is The Hour *Austral
      SATB ALLANS 195 s.p.   (F427)

FINE PEARLS see Bixel, James W.

FINK
   All Nature's Works His Praise Declare
      (Hadley) SATB oct PRO ART 1734 $.25   (F428)
      (Hadley) SSA oct PRO ART 1884 $.22   (F429)
      (Hadley) SAB oct PRO ART 1541 $.25   (F430)
      (Hadley) 2pt oct PRO ART 2015 $.25   (F431)

   Sanctus (from Missa 6 Vocum) Mass/mot
      SATTBB HANSSLER 1.537 s.p.   (F432)

   Vision Of The Shepherds *Xmas
      (Peninger) SATB (med easy) SOUTHERN $.30   (F433)

   Vision Of The Shepherds, The *Xmas
      (Peninger) SATB oct PRO ART 2660 $.30   (F434)

FINK, CHRISTIAN (1822-1911)
   O Thou, Who By A Star Didst Guide *Xmas
      (Hastings) SATB oct BOURNE HA6 $.30   (F435)

FINK, G.
   All Nature's Works His Praise Declare
      (Randell, B.) SATB LEONARD-US 08001280 $.25   (F436)

FINK, MICHAEL
   O God, We Laud And Praise Thee *see Te Deum

   Sabbath Evening Service, A
      [Heb/Eng] unis,org SCHIRM.EC 2718   (F437)
      [Heb/Eng] unis,org SCHIRM.EC 2718   (F438)

   Septem Angeli *cant
      "Seven Angels" [Lat/Eng] SATB,pno/2pno,
      perc,vcl,bvl, celesta SCHIRM.EC 2659
      $1.35, ipr   (F439)
      "Seven Angels" [Lat/Eng] 4pt mix cor,pno/
      2pno,perc,vcl,bvl SCHIRM.EC 2659 $1.35,
      ipr   (F440)

   Seven Angels *see Septem Angeli

   Te Deum
      [Lat/Eng] 4pt mix cor,T/Bar solo,pno
      SCHIRM.EC 2676 $1.35   (F441)
      "O God, We Laud And Praise Thee" [Lat/Eng]
      SATB,T/Bar solo,pno SCHIRM.EC 2676 $1.35   (F442)

FINLAY
   Hark The Song Of Jubilee
      SATB,org FRANCIS s.p.   (F443)

FINNEY
   Pilgrim Psalms
      SATB&cong,opt orch cmplt ed FISCHER,C
      0-3604 $5.00, voc sc FISCHER,C 0-3640
      $3.00, ipr   (F444)

FINO, GIOCONDO (1867-1950)
   Missa In Hon. Beati J.B. Cottolengo *Mass
      [Lat] 2 eq voices,org sc ZANIBON 1541 s.p.,
      voc pt ZANIBON s.p.   (F445)

   Responsorium In Hon. S. Dominici *ASD
      [Lat] 3 eq voices,org ZANIBON 1189 s.p.   (F446)

FINSTERNIS WARD UBER DAS LAND see Palestrina,
   Giovanni

FINZI
   My Spirit Sang All Day
      SATB,acap (med) OXFORD 53.017 $.25   (F447)

FINZI, GERALD (1901-1956)
   God Is Gone Up
      SSAATTBB,org oct BOOSEY 1926 $.40   (F448)

   Haste On, My Joys!
      SSATB oct BOOSEY 5813 $.35   (F449)

   In Terra Pax
      mix cor,SBar soli,orch/strings&harp, &
      cymbal BOOSEY voc sc $.60, sc rental, ipr   (F450)

   Lo, The Full, Final Sacrifice
      SATB,org/orch BOOSEY voc sc $2.50, sc
      rental, ipr   (F451)

   My Spirit Sang All Day
      SATB oct BOOSEY 5814 $.30   (F452)

FIOR DI CIELO see Tincani, Alceste

FIR TREE see Dunhill, Thomas Frederick

FIRE LATINSKE KANTATER see Buxtehude, Dietrich

FIRE LATINSKE KANTATER see Buxtehude, Dietrich

FIRE SALMER see Grieg, Edvard Hagerup

FIRE SALMETONER see Karlsen, Rolf

FIRE SANGE OG TRE MOTETTER see Bjorn, Hjelm
Borg

FIRMAMENT OF POWER see Davis, Katherine K.

FIRMAMENT OF POWER, THE see Davis, Katherine K.

FIRPO, ANTONIO
Al SS. Nome Di Maria *CC4U,BVM
  [Lat] unis/2pt ZANIBON 2737 s.p.   (F453)

Ave Maris Stella *BVM
  [Lat] 2 eq voices ZANIBON 2749 s.p.
  contains also: Volpi, Edoardo, Ave Maris
  Stella   (F454)

De Profundis *Psalm/Req
  [Lat] 2 eq voices ZANIBON 2774 s.p. (F455)

Exaltata Est *BVM
  [Lat] 3 eq voices,org ZANIBON 2744 s.p.
                                       (F456)

Iste Confessor
  [Lat] unis ZANIBON 2771 s.p.   (F457)

Vespro Domenicale
  [Lat] 2 eq voices,org sc ZANIBON 2690 s.p.
                                       (F458)

FIRST AND SECOND PRECES AND PSALMS see Byrd,
William

FIRST AND SECOND PRECES AND PSALMS see Gibbons,
Orlando

FIRST BOOK OF SELECTED CHURCH MUSICK see
Barnard, John

FIRST CHRISTMAS DAY, THE see Copley, I.A.

FIRST CHRISTMAS MORN *Xmas/Pageant
  oct LORENZ $.75   (F459)

FIRST CHRISTMAS MORN see Newton, Ernest

FIRST CHRISTMAS MORN, THE see Fearis, J.S.

FIRST CHRISTMAS MORN, THE see Mozart, Wolfgang
Amadeus

FIRST CHRISTMAS, THE see Dougherty, Celius

FIRST CHRISTMAS, THE see Lohr

FIRST CHRISTMAS, THE see Woodgate

FIRST EASTER see Wilson, Ira B.

FIRST EASTER, THE see Lillenas, Haldor

FIRST GOOD JOY THAT MARY HAD *Xmas,carol
  unis/SATB (easy) OXFORD 08.067 $.20 (F460)

FIRST LONDON CAROL, THE see Rendall, Honor

FIRST MASS IN C see Mozart, Wolfgang Amadeus,
Missa Brevis

FIRST MASS IN ENGLISH see Bevenot, Laurence

FIRST MASS IN F see Rosewig, A.

FIRST MASS IN F see Schubert, Franz (Peter)

FIRST MERCY see Heseltine, Philip

FIRST MOTET BOOK, A *CC17L,mot
  (Thomas, P.) mix cor CONCORDIA 97-4845 $1.75
  contains works by: Distler; Vaughan
  Williams; Byrd; Schutz; Bender; Goudimel;
  Bach; Mozart; Bodenschatz; De Victoria;
  Hillert; Tye; Willan; Pitoni; Des Prez;
  Gibbons; Gumpeltzhaimer   (F461)

FIRST NOEL
  see Five Christmas Carols

FIRST NOEL, THE *Xmas,carol
  (Swift, Frederic Fay) SA/TB oct BELWIN 1493
  $.25   (F462)
  (Swift, Frederic Fay) SSA oct BELWIN 1535
  $.25   (F463)
  (Swift, Frederic Fay) SAB oct BELWIN 1613
  $.30   (F464)
  (Swift, Frederic Fay) SATB oct BELWIN 1492
  $.25   (F465)

FIRST NOEL, THE *Xmas
  (Heath) 4pt men cor,T solo,acap oct SCHIRM.G
  11489 $.25   (F466)
  (McKelvy, J.) SATB,acap FOSTER MF 502 $.25
                                       (F467)

FIRST NOEL, THE see Denton, James

FIRST NOEL, THE see Groom, Lester H.

FIRST NOEL, THE see Wade

FIRST NOWELL
  see Six Two-Part Carols
  see Two Carols

FIRST NOWELL, THE (from Anthology Of Carols,
An) Xmas,carol,Eng,17th cent
  see Angels From The Realms Of Glory
  see Many Moods Of Christmas, The, Suite Four
  see Tidings Of Comfort And Joy
  unis/SATB (easy) OXFORD 08.027 $.15 (F468)
  (Kaplan) SATB oct LAWSON 51715 $.30 (F469)
  (Sharpe, E.) cor&desc CRAMER 27   (F470)
  (Shaw; Parker) SATB,acap oct LAWSON 714 $.30
                                       (F471)
  (Stevens) SATB oct PRO ART 1421 $.25 (F472)
  (Stevens) SAB oct PRO ART 1550 $.30 (F473)
  (Stevens) 2pt oct PRO ART 1782 $.25 (F474)
  (Van Koert, Han) 2 eq voices,org oct WORLD
  AC-638-2 $.30   (F475)
  (Van Koert, Han) SA&SATB,org oct WORLD

AC-351-8 $.45   (F476)
  (Vaughan Williams) TTBB,acap (easy) OXFORD
  41.902 $.30 see also Nine Carols   (F477)
  (Wulstan, David) SATB CHESTER s.p. contains
  also: Gaudete, Christus Est Natus; Sleep,
  Baby, Sleep   (F478)

FIRST NOWELL, THE see Atkinson, Thelma

FIRST NOWELL, THE see Dinn, Freda

FIRST NOWELL, THE see Lorenz

FIRST NOWELL, THE see Suderburg, R.

FIRST NOWELL, THE see Vaughan Williams, Ralph

FIRST OFFERTORIUM see Schubert, Franz (Peter)

FIRST PALM SUNDAY, THE see Dinning

FIRST PLACE see Spurr

FIRST PSALM see LaForge, Frank

FIRST SERVICE see Tomkins, Thomas

FIRST SERVICE, THE see Ward, John

FIRST, THE LAST, THE see Dressler, John

FIRST WALPURGISNIGHT see Mendelssohn-Bartholdy,
Felix

FIRT NOWEL, THE *Xmas
  cor CRAMER s.p.   (F479)

FIRTH, REV. PETER
  Two Thousand Years Ago *Xmas
  WEINBERGER s.p.   (F480)

FISCHBACH, K.
  Lobe Den Herren, Den Machtigen Konig *cant
  mix cor&cong,org TONGER s.p.   (F481)

FISCHER
  I Longed To Find The Risen Lord *Easter
  (Lynn) SATB oct SOUTHERN $.25   (F482)

  O Come Let Us Sing
  SATB,org BOSTON 13454 $.35   (F483)

  O Worship The Lord
  SATB,org BOSTON 13455 $.40   (F484)

  Teach Me, O Lord, Thy Holy Way
  SATB,org/pno BOSTON 13408 $.40   (F485)

FISCHER, CLARE
  Bless The Lord Oh My Soul
  SATB oct WORD CS-2517 $.45   (F486)

  I Lift Up My Soul
  SATB oct WORD CS-2516 $.35   (F487)

  My Son Forget Not My Law
  SATB oct WORD CS-2515 $.40   (F488)

FISCHER, H.
  Praise My Soul The King Of Heaven
  SATB oct BELWIN 2117 $.25   (F489)

FISCHER, L.
  Christ Of Every Crisis, The
  SATB oct WORD CS-318 $.30   (F490)

FISCHER-DIESKAU, KLAUS
  Aus Tiefer Not *mot
  5pt mix cor MOSELER s.p.   (F491)

  Bittet, So Wird Euch Gegeben
  3 eq voices MOSELER LB-198 s.p.   (F492)

  Das Ist Aber Das Ewige Leben
  5pt mix cor MOSELER s.p. see from Motetten
                                       (F493)

  Ich Bin Gekommen, Zu Rufen
  5pt mix cor MOSELER s.p. see from Motetten
                                       (F494)

  Motetten *see Das Ist Aber Das Ewige Leben;
  Ich Bin Gekommen, Zu Rufen; Nun Bitten
  Wir Den Heiligen Geist   (F495)

  Nun Bitten Wir Den Heiligen Geist
  5pt mix cor MOSELER s.p. see from Motetten
                                       (F496)

  Wachet Und Betet
  3 eq voices MOSELER LB-181 s.p.   (F497)

FISCHERLIED see Schubert, Franz (Peter)

FISCHLI, FR.
  Wach Auf, Mein Herz, Und Singe!
  (Mumenthaler, M.) [Ger] mix cor,acap (med
  easy) HUG s.p.   (F498)

FISCHPREDIGT DES HEILIGEN ANTONIUS see
Schindler, Walter

FISHER
  Hort, Wen Jesus Glucklich Preist *Gen
  [Ger] unis,acap (easy) BOSSE BE 255 s.p.
  contains also: Komm, Sag Es Allen Weiter
  (spir)   (F499)

  Komm, Sag Es Allen Weiter
  see Fisher, Hort, Wen Jesus Glucklich
  Preist

  Light, Light The Candle *Xmas
  SSA WARNER R3326 $.30   (F500)

  Shepherds' Story, The *Xmas
  WARNER $.30   (F501)

  Song Of Mary, The
  (Kranz) SATB,acap oct COLOMBO 784 $.25
                                       (F502)
  (Vene) SSA oct COLOMBO 1309 $.20   (F503)
  (Vene) SAB oct COLOMBO 1990 $.20   (F504)

  Song Of Mary, The *Xmas
  (Kranz; Hansen) SATB SCHMITT 910 $.25
                                       (F505)

FISHER, C.A.
  Song Of Mary, The
  SSATTBB,acap oct SCHIRM.G 7659 $.30 (F506)
  (Williamson; Milkey) 3pt wom cor,acap,opt
  pno oct SCHIRM.G 10090 $.25   (F507)

FISHER, C.A. (cont'd.)
  (Williamson; Milkey) 4pt mix cor,acap,opt
  pno oct SCHIRM.G 10091 $.20   (F508)

FISHER, CARLOTTA
  It's Christmastime Again *Xmas
  SA BOSWORTH s.p.   (F509)

FISHER, HERBERT R.
  Christ The Lord Is Risen *Easter,anthem
  SATB oct BELWIN 2042 $.25   (F510)

  Slumber, Infant Divine *Xmas
  SA/TB oct BELWIN 2118 $.25   (F511)

FISHERMAN PETER
  see Four Folksongs And Spirituals

FISHERMAN, THE *CC17U,Gen,folk
  (easy) unis,gtr cmplt ed GIA G1720 $1.50;
  SATB,gtr cmplt ed GIA G1742 $3.00   (F512)

FISKE, MILTON
  Christ The Lord Is Risen Today *Easter
  SATB,pno PEER $.35   (F513)

  Songs Of Praise The Angels Sang
  SATB,pno PEER $.40   (F514)

FISSINGER, EDWIN
  Anthem To The Trinity *Trin,anthem/Introit/
  Psalm
  (Snow, Robert J.) SATB,org oct WORLD
  CA-4000-8 $.60   (F515)

  Blessed Be God *Trin,Offer/Psalm
  (Snow, Robert J.) SATB,org oct WORLD
  CA-4001-8 $.45   (F516)

  O Make A Joyful Noise
  SATB,acap AMP A515 $.30   (F517)

  O Praise The Lord, All Ye Nations (Psalm 117)
  Bibl
  SATB,acap oct WORLD ESA-515-8 $.45   (F518)

  Psalm 117 *see O Praise The Lord, All Ye
  Nations

  We Bless The God Of Heaven *Commun/Trin,
  Psalm
  (Snow, Robert J.) SATB,org oct WORLD
  CA-4002-8 $.45   (F519)

FITCH
  Blessing And Honor
  SAB,org BOSTON 13533 $.40   (F520)

  My Strength And My Song
  SAB,org BOSTON 13534 $.35   (F521)

  Number Our Days
  SAB,org BOSTON 13537 $.35   (F522)

  Psalm 100
  2pt jr cor,org/pno BOSTON 3111 $.30 (F523)

  Think On These Things
  2pt jr cor,org/pno BOSTON 12883 $.30 (F524)

  Thy Glorious Name
  SAB,org BOSTON 13529 $.30   (F525)

  Voice Of A Psalm, The
  SAB,org BOSTON 13407 $.35   (F526)

FITZGERALD, B.
  Now We Sing Noel *Xmas
  SATB,opt brass oct PRESSER 312-40685 $.30
                                       (F527)

FITZSIMONS, H.T.
  Christmas Bells *Xmas,carol
  SATB,acap (med) oct WILLIS 3951 $.12 (F528)

FIVE ALLELUIAS see Brozen, Michael

FIVE ANTHEMS see Taverner, John

FIVE CANNONS see Mozart, Wolfgang Amadeus

FIVE CAROLS see Davies, Peter Maxwell

FIVE CAROLS FOR NOW see Nelson, Ronald A.

FIVE CENTURIES OF ALLELUIAS AND AMENS, VOL. I
  *CCU
  (Ades) SATB SHAWNEE F 7 $.40   (F529)

FIVE CENTURIES OF ALLELUIAS AND AMENS, VOL. II
  *CCU
  (Ades) SATB SHAWNEE F 8 $.40   (F530)

FIVE CENTURIES OF ALLELUIAS AND AMENS, VOL. III
  *CCU
  (Ades) SATB SHAWNEE F 9 $.50   (F531)

FIVE CENTURIES OF CHORAL MUSIC *sac/sec,CCU
  mix cor SOUTHERN $2.00   (F532)

FIVE CHORAL SETTINGS see Bach, Johann Sebastian

FIVE CHORALES see Bach, Johann Sebastian

FIVE CHORALES see Bach, Johann Sebastian

FIVE CHRISTMAS CAROLS ON TRADITIONAL TEXTS see
Busarow, Donald

FIVE CHRISTMAS CAROLS see Davis, Katherine K.

FIVE CHRISTMAS CAROLS *Xmas,carol
  (Gray) TTBB ALLANS 216 s.p.
  contains: First Noel; God Rest Ye Merry
  Gentlemen; Good King Wenceslas; Silent
  Night; While Shepherds Watched   (F533)

FIVE DUTCH CAROLS *Xmas,carol,Dut
  (Edmunds, J.) SATB,kbd (easy) oct CONCORDIA
  98-1775 $.30
  contains: Let Us Start Upon Our Journey;
  Noble Child To Us Is Born, A; Stork She
  Rose On Christmas Eve, The; This Day Has
  Come For Us To Sing; This Night There
  Comes To Bethlehem   (F534)

FIVE FESTAL INTROITS see Cashmore, Donald

FIVE FRENCH NOELS *Xmas,Fr
(Forbes) [Fr/Eng] oct SCHIRM.G 10835 $.40
contains: A La Venue De Noel (SSATBB,acap); A
Minuet Fut Fait Un Reveil (SSATBB,acap);
Joseph Est Bien Marie (SATBB,acap); Ou
S'en Vont Ces Gais Bergers (SATB,acap);
Tous Les Bourgeois De Chastres (SATB,
acap) (F535)

FIVE HYMN TUNES see Willan, Healey

FIVE HYMNS see Zimmermann, Heinz Werner

FIVE HYMNS FOR EVENING WORSHIP *CC5U,Eve,hymn
(Knight, Gerald) SATB,acap oct FISCHER,C
CM-7585 $.30 contains works by: Schutz;
Calvisius; Schein (F536)

FIVE HYMNS IN POPULAR STYLE *see Abide With
Me; Brightest And Best Of The Sons; Fight
The Good Fight; Nearer, My God, To Thee;
Saviour, Again To Thy Dear Name; Gardner,
John [Linton], Abide With Me; Gardner, John
[Linton], Brightest And Best Of The Sons Of
The Morning; Gardner, John [Linton], Fight
The Good Fight With All Thy Might; Gardner,
John [Linton], Nearer, My God, To Thee;
Gardner, John [Linton], Saviour, Again To
Thy Dear Name We Raise (F537)

FIVE HYMNS IN POPULAR STYLE see Gardner, John
[Linton]

FIVE HYMNS (from Book Of Hymns) CC5U,hymn
[Lat/Eng] cor oct ST.MARTIN s.p. (F538)

FIVE HYMNS see Tallis, Thomas

FIVE INTROITS AND VESPERS see Anderson,
[William H.]

FIVE INTROITS FOR TWO EQUAL VOICES see Beadell,
Robert M.

FIVE LAMENTATIONS see Nanini (Nanino), Giovanni
Maria

FIVE MASTER CHORUSES *CC5U
mix cor SCHMITT 58 $.50 (F539)

FIVE MOTETS see Dressler, Gallus

FIVE MOTETS see Franck, Melchior

FIVE MOUNTAINS TO CLIMB
SATB BIG3 $.40 (F540)

FIVE NARRATIVE CAROLS see Powell, Robert J.

FIVE OPENING ANTHEMS see Fromm, Herbert

FIVE-PART LITANY see Tallis, Thomas

FIVE PRAYERS FOR THE YOUNG see Rorem, Ned

FIVE PSALMS see Le Fleming, Christopher (Kaye)

FIVE PSALMS FROM THE "BECKER PSALTER" see
Schutz, Heinrich

FIVE PSALMS see Le Fleming, Christopher (Kaye)

FIVE SACRED CHORUSES see Purcell, Henry

FIVE SHORT ANTHEMS see Ferris, W.

FIVE SHORT ANTHEMS OR RESPONSES see Nelhybel,
Vaclav

FIVE SONGS FOR FIVE TO TEN see Hankey, Mark

FIVE SONGS FROM FOREIGN LANDS see Bush,
Florence

FIVE SONGS OF ISRAEL see Berger

FIVE SONGS see Brahms, Johannes

FIVE SYMPHONIES see Haydn, (Franz) Joseph

FIX ME, JESUS *spir
(Johnson, Hall) mix cor,S solo,acap oct
SCHIRM.G 10278 $.30 (F541)

FIX'D IN HIS EVERLASTING SEAT see Handel,
George Frideric

FJERSTAD
Shepherds, The *Xmas
SA SCHMITT 9156A $.40 (F542)

FLAGELLO, NICHOLAS (1928-   )
Te Deum *Te Deum
SATB,opt orch FISCHER,C O-4793 $1.25, ipr
(F543)

FLAGLER, [ROBERT S.] (1890-1935)
Come Holy Spirit
SATB oct HUNTZINGER 4026 $.15 (F544)

Jesus, The Very Thought Of Thee
SATB oct HUNTZINGER 4012 $.16 (F545)

O How Plentiful Is Thy Goodness
SATB oct HUNTZINGER 4034 $.20 (F546)

FLAMME EMPORL see Glaser, T.

FLANAGAN
Non Nobis
girl cor SOUTHERN $.30 (F547)

FLANAGAN, WILLIAM (1923-1969)
Psalm 130
SATB,acap BOSTON 13739 $.40 (F548)

FLEISHER, SIMI
Songs Of Israeli Children, Part One
2pt oct AGAPE $.45 (F549)

Songs Of Israeli Children, Part Two
2pt oct AGAPE $.45 (F550)

Tall Tower Tale
unis oct AGAPE JR 200 $.35 (F551)

FLEMING
Father In Heaven
(Davis, K.K.) 2pt WARNER R3501 $.30 (F552)

Lord Of Our Life
(Holler) SATB oct GRAY GCMR 1434 $.30
(F553)

Would That I Were There
SATB,opt inst (med) OXFORD 43.927 $.35
(F554)

FLEMING, CHRISTOPHER LE
see LE FLEMING, CHRISTOPHER (KAYE)

FLEMISH CAROL *carol,Belg
unis/SATB (easy) OXFORD 08.074 $.15 (F555)

FLEMISH CAROL, A *anthem/carol
(Christiansen, Paul) SATB (easy) oct AUGSBURG
1089 $.20 (F556)
(Christiansen, Paul) SSA (med) oct AUGSBURG
1117 $.18 (F557)

FLEMISH DANCE CAROL see Carley, Isabel M.

FLEMMING, F.
Grablied
see Zwei Einfache Grabgesange

Ruhe Sanft
see Zwei Einfache Grabgesange

Zwei Einfache Grabgesange
[Ger] mix cor,acap (easy) HUG s.p.
contains: Grablied; Ruhe Sanft (F558)

FLERSTAMMIGA SATTNIGAR AV FOLKLIGA KORALER
*CC10U
(Kullnes, Ake) mix cor NORDISKA NMS-6295 s.p.
(F559)

FLETCHER
God Of My Salvation, The
SATB KJOS GC47 $.35 (F560)

God So Loved The World
SATB oct SACRED S-69 $.40 (F561)

Noel, A *Xmas
SATB oct HERITAGE H18 $.45 (F562)

Rise Up, My Love
SATB oct SACRED S-31 $.40 (F563)

Thy King Cometh *Easter/Lent,cant
SATB FISCHER,C O-3602 $1.00 (F564)

FLETCHER, PERCY [E.] (1879-1932)
Lord Is My Light
SATB ALLANS 374 s.p. (F565)
cor oct HART s.p. (F566)

Now Once Again Our Hearts We Raise *anthem/
carol
4pt oct NOVELLO 51.0506.04 s.p. (F567)

Passion Of Christ, The *Easter/Lent,cant
SATB,SAB/SATB soli,org/org&2fl&2ob&3clar&
bsn&2horn&2trp&trom&strings&timp voc sc
NOVELLO s.p., ipr (F568)

Ring Out, Wild Bells *Xmas/Fest,anthem/carol
4pt,orch oct NOVELLO 51.0505.06 s.p., ipr
(F569)
2pt,orch oct NOVELLO 53.0217.10 s.p., ipr
(F570)
mix cor,orch oct NOVELLO 28.1053.00 s.p.,
ipr (F571)

FLEUVE PROFOND see Deep River

FLIGHT INTO EGYPT, THE see Thomson, Virgil

FLING WIDE THE GATES see Stainer, John

FLINT
Praise Him Evermore (composed with Bampton,
R.)
cong oct BELWIN 1552 $.30 (F572)

FLIPSE, E.
Agnus Dei
mix cor ALSBACH&D sc s.p., cor pts s.p.
(F573)

Hoe Groot O Heer
mix cor ALSBACH&D sc s.p., cor pts s.p.
(F574)

Sanctus
mix cor ALSBACH&D sc s.p., cor pts s.p.
(F575)

Wie Op God Betrouwt
mix cor sc ALSBACH&D s.p. (F576)

FLITTNER
O How Great Is Thy Compassion
(Harris) SATB oct PRO ART 1562 $.18 (F577)

FLOCKS BY SHEPHERDS SAFE ATTENDED see Bach,
Johann Sebastian

FLOCKS IN PASTURES GREEN see Bach, Johann
Sebastian

FLOCKS IN PASTURES GREEN ABIDING see Bach,
Johann Sebastian

FLOCKS MAY GRAZE see Bach, Johann Sebastian

FLOCKS MAY SAFELY GRAZE see Bach, Johann
Sebastian

FLOERING
Cross Was His Own, The *Easter
unis oct LORENZ 8593 $.25 (F578)

FLOOD, THE see Stravinsky, Igor

FLOR, MISSA IN HON. ST. JOSEPHI see Peeters,
Flor

FLOREEN, JOHN
Arise, O Ye Servants Of God *Fest/Thanks
SATB (easy) oct OXFORD (F579)

FLORIA, [CARYL] (1843-1920)
Godofallofus *CC10L
SATB voc sc WORD 37535 $1.95 (F580)

It's Getting Late *folk
cor,kbd,fl,2trp,horn,2trom,bvl,drums,gtr,
alto saxophone voc sc WORD 37561 $2.95,

FLORIA, [CARYL] (cont'd.)
ipa (F581)

FLOS CARMELI see Bottigliero, Eduardo

FLOS CARMELI see Magri, Pietro

FLOWER O' THE FOREST, THE
(Wiseman) unis/desc (very easy) OXFORD 8L.089
$.20 (F582)

FLOWER OF BETHLEHEM
(Williams) SATB (med) OXFORD 84.040 $.25
(F583)

FLOWER OF BETHLEHEM, THE see Thiman, Eric
Harding

FLOWER OF CHRISTMAS *Xmas/Pageant
LORENZ $.75 (F584)

FLOWER OF JESSE see Niles, John Jacob

FLOWERING THORN, THE *Xmas,Ger
(Britton, Jean) treb cor,acap (easy) PRESSER
$.30 (F585)

FLOWERS OF THE FOREST, THE *carol
(Lawson, Malcolm) unis CRAMER 58 s.p. (F586)

FLOWERS, THE see Wright, Evelyn

FLOYD, ALFRED E.
Love Came Down At Christmas *Xmas,Austral
SATB ALLANS 421 $.40 (F587)

FLOYD, CARLISLE (1926-   )
Martyr, The
cor,inst BELWIN $2.50 (F588)

FLURY, H.
Komm, O Komm, Du Geist Des Lebens *chorale
[Ger] mix cor,acap (easy) HUG s.p. (F589)
[Ger] mix cor,acap (easy) HUG s.p. (F590)

FLUTE GLORIA
(Young, Gordon) SATB,pno,fl (easy) PRESSER
362-03158 $.35 (F591)

FODERUNT MANUS MEAS see Cucchi, Colleoni G.

FOELBER, PAUL
Christ, The Lord, Is Risen Today *Easter
4pt mix cor,acap oct SCHIRM.G 11186 $.25
(F592)

Gradual For Easter *Easter,Gradual
4pt mix cor oct SCHIRM.G 11193 $.30 (F593)

FOGLIANO
Ave Maria
(Greyson) SATB oct BOURNE ES87 $.25 (F594)

FOLD TO THY HEART THY BROTHER see Hovdesven,
E.A.

FOLIO OF SACRED MUSIC (VOLUME 1) *CC7L,anthem
SATB HARRIS $2.50 (F595)

FOLIO OF SACRED MUSIC (VOLUME 3) *anthem
SATB HARRIS $2.50
contains: Down By The Riverside; Isn't It
Strange; Prayer For Peace; Shepherd,
Shepherd; When The Saints Go Marching In
(F596)

FOLK AND SPIRITUAL TIME see Iams

FOLK HYMNS OF AMERICA *CC12L,Gen,folk/hymn
(Hadley) SATB,opt fl,gtr PRO ART 1160 $1.00
(F597)

FOLK HYMNS OF EARLY AMERICA *CCU,anthem
SATB LORENZ $1.75 (F598)

FOLK HYMNS WITH GUITAR see Browne

FOLK LORE CHRISTMAS CANTATA see Shure, R. Deane

FOLK-SONGS, BALLADS AND SONGS OF GREAT
COMPOSERS (SET I) *sac/sec,CC10L
unis&SA&TB&SATB,pno SCHIRM.EC 1035 $.35
(F599)

FOLK-SONGS, BALLADS, AND SONGS OF GREAT
COMPOSERS (SET II) *sac/sec,CC10L
unis&SATB,pno SCHIRM.EC 1061 $.25 (F600)

FOLK-SONGS, BALLADS AND SONGS OF GREAT
COMPOSERS (SET V) *sac/sec
unis&SATB,pno SCHIRM.EC 1593 $.25
contains: Bach, Johann Sebastian, O Jesu So
Sweet; Beethoven, Ludwig van, Ich Liebe
Dich, "Devotion"; Brahms, Johannes,
Vergebliches Standchen, "O Good Morning,
My Fair One!"; Grieg, Edvard Hagerup,
Solvejg's Song (from Peer Gynt); Handel,
George Frideric, Where'er You Walk (from
Semele) (F601)

FOLK SONGS FOR CHOIRS see Hanks, Billie

FOLK SONGS HISTORIC AND CONTEMPORARY see
Johnson, David N.

FOLKEFERELSAR TIL OSS KOM
(Ree, Knut) men cor MUSIKK 206 s.p. (F602)

FOLKLIGA KORALER *CC16U
mix cor NORDISKA NMS-6202 s.p. (F603)

FOLKSONGS OF THE FOUR SEASONS see Vaughan
Williams, Ralph

FOLLOW ME see Doherty, Christopher

FOLLOW ME see Dean

FOLLOW ME see Newbury

FOLLOW ME see Stanphill

FOLLOW ME see Wilson

FOLLOW ON see Lowry, [Robert]

FOLLOW THAT STAR see Davenport, David

FOLLOW THE ROAD see Patterson

FOLLOWERS OF THE STAR see Neidlinger, William
Harold

FOLTZ
Prayer Of St. Francis Of Assisi
SATB,acap oct BELWIN 60595 $.30 (F604)

Send Us Thy Heav'nly Light
SATB oct BELWIN 60211 $.30 (F605)

When Jesus Christ Was Yet A Child
SATB oct BELWIN 60747 $.25 (F606)

FONS PIETATIS see Bamer, Alfred

FONTEIJO, GIOVANNI
Chiuder Gl'occhi Vorrei *madrigal
(Hans, Nielsen) 5pt mix cor,acap SKAND.
SMF5430 s.p. (F607)

Corre Al Suo Fin Mia Vita *madrigal
(Nielsen, Hans) [It] 5pt mix cor,acap sc
SKAND. SMF5428 s.p. (F608)

FOOL HATH SAID IN HIS HEART, THE see Darlow,
Denys

FOOL HATH SAID IN HIS HEART, THE see Townsend,
John

FOOL HATH SAID "THERE IS NO GOD", THE see
O'Hara, Geoffrey

FOOLISHNESS CAROL, THE see Lovelace, Austin C.

FOR A CLOSER WALK WITH GOD see Williams

FOR ALL MANKIND see Hughes

FOR ALL MANKIND WE PRAY see Gale

FOR ALL MEN EVERYWHERE see Davis, Katherine K.

FOR ALL MY SIN see Clayton

FOR ALL THE SAINTS see Thalben-Ball, George
[Thomas]

FOR ALL THE SAINTS *Gen
(Christiansen, P) SATB,opt inst SCHMITT 8041
$.35, ipa (F609)

FOR ALL THE SAINTS see Couper, Bert F.

FOR ALL THE SAINTS see Denton

FOR ALL THE SAINTS see Johnston

FOR ALL THE SAINTS see Vaughan Williams, Ralph,
Sine Nomine

FOR ALL THE SAINTS see Williams

FOR ALL THESE MERCIES WE WILL SING see Handel,
George Frideric

FOR ALLA HELGON *Bibl
(Olson, Daniel) [Swed] SAB,acap GEHRMANS
KRB 116 (F610)

FOR AS THE RAIN COMETH DOWN see Lekberg, Sven

FOR AS THE SNOW AND RAIN FROM HEAVEN FALL see
Bach, Johann Sebastian, Gleich Wie Der
Regen Und Schnee

FOR CHRIST IS BORN see Aiken, Walter H.

FOR CHRISTMAS *sac/sec,CC21L,Xmas
(Kirk) 2pt/3pt PRO ART 667 $1.50 (F611)

FOR COURAGE see Shaw, Martin

FOR DEG, VAR HERRE see Geitvik, S.H.

FOR EVENING see Pitfield, Thomas Baron

FOR EVER, O LORD see Gore, Richard T.

FOR EVER, O LORD see Lewis, John Leo

FOR FRED OCH OVERHET see Schein, Johann Hermann

FOR GOD ALONE see Graham

FOR GOD SO LOVED THE WORLD see Schutz,
Heinrich, Also Hat Gott Die Welt Geliebet

FOR GOD SO LOVED THE WORLD , %ALSO CONTAINS
SOLO WORK: OFFERTORIO see Tchesnokov, Pavel
Grigorievitch

FOR GOD SO LOVED THIS SINFUL WORLD see Schutz,
Heinrich, Also Hat Gott Die Welt Geliebet

FOR HE SHALL GIVE HIS ANGELS see Mendelssohn-
Bartholdy, Felix

FOR HE SHALL GIVE HIS ANGELS CHARGE see
Protheroe, Daniel

FOR HE SHALL GIVE HIS ANGELS CHARGE OVER THEE
see Jennings, Kenneth L.

FOR I WENT WITH THE MULTITUDE see Aston, Peter

FOR IN MY HOUSE ARE MANY MANSIONS see Rogers

FOR IN THIS MOMENT see Lassus, Roland de
(Orlandus), Di Occhi, Piangete

FOR JESUS CHRIST IS BORN see McLin

FOR ME? O LORD see Wolle

FOR MY SOUL THIRSTETH FOR GOD see Mendelssohn-
Bartholdy, Felix

FOR OUR OFFENCES see Mendelssohn-Bartholdy,
Felix

FOR PETE'S SAKE! *CCU
(Carmichael, R.) SATB voc sc WORD 20017 $1.95
(F612)

FOR SABBATH EVE see Kouguell, [Arkadie]

FOR SINS OF HEEDLESS WORD AND DEED see
Boatwright, Howard

FOR SO HATH THE LORD see Mendelssohn-Bartholdy,
Felix

FOR SPACIOUS SKIES see Peery

FOR THE BEAUTY OF THE EARTH see Bach, Johann
Sebastian

FOR THE BEAUTY OF THE EARTH see Joubert, John

FOR THE BEAUTY OF THE EARTH see Kocher

FOR THE BEAUTY OF THE EARTH see Kocher,
[Conrad]

FOR THE BEAUTY OF THE EARTH see Luvaas

FOR THE BEAUTY OF THE EARTH see Pierpont, J.

FOR THE BEAUTY OF THE EARTH see Thiman, Eric
Harding

FOR THE BEAUTY OF THE EARTH see York

FOR THE BLESSINGS OF OUR DAYS
eq voices KJOS 4218 $.30 (F613)

FOR THE BLESSINGS OF OUR DAYS see Krones

FOR THE BREAD see Copes, V. Earle

FOR THE MIGHT OF THINE ARM see Heath, G.

FOR THE PEOPLE OF GOD see Schroth, Gerhard

FOR THE RIGHTEOUS see Staden, Die Gerechten

FOR THE RIGHTEOUS SHALL FLOURISH FOREVER see
Franck, Melchior, Die Gerechten Werden
Ewiglich Leben

FOR THE SINS OF HER PROPHETS see Schalk, Carl

FOR THE TIME BEING see Levy, Marvin David

FOR THEE, O DEAR, DEAR COUNTRY see Gaul, Alfred
Robert

FOR THEIR FAITH IN THE LORD see Victoria, Tomas
Luis de, Iste Sanctus

FOR THEIRS IS THE KINGDOM OF HEAVEN see Nelson,
Paul

FOR THIS CAUSE see Friedell, Harold W.

FOR THIS DEAR LAND see Bodycombe, [Aneurin]

FOR THIS GOOD COMPANY see Berger, Jean

FOR THIS, HIS SON IS BORN
(Nyquist) SATB oct PRO ART 1900 $.22 (F614)

FOR THIS MORTAL MUST PUT ON IMMORTALITY see
Wesley, Samuel Sebastian Jr.

FOR THOSE IN PERIL ON THE SEA see Duckworth,
Arthur

FOR THOSE WE LOVE WITHIN THE VEIL see Bancroft,
H. Hugh

FOR THOU ART POWERFUL see Vivaldi, Antonio, Cum
Sancto Spiritu

FOR THOU ART WORTHY TO BE PRAISED see
Tchaikovsky, Piotr Ilyitch

FOR THY CHURCH WE THANK THEE see Plank, David
L.

FOR THY GREAT MERCY see Durante, Francesco,
Misericordias Domini

FOR THY SAKE see Williams, David H.

FOR TONIGHT A KING IS BORN IN BETHLEHEM see
Roberton, Hugh S.

FOR UNTO US A CHILD IS BORN see Giasson

FOR UNTO US A CHILD IS BORN see Handel, George
Frideric

FOR UNTO US A CHILD IS BORN see Krone

FOR UNTO US IS BORN TODAY *Xmas
(Bedell, R.) jr cor oct PRESSER 312-40197
$.25 (F615)

FOR UNTO US IS BORN TODAY see Quignard, R.

FOR US A CHILD IS BORN see Bach, Johann
Sebastian, Uns Ist Ein Kind Geboren

FOR US A CHILD IS BORN see Krieger, Johann
Philipp

FOR US CHRIST WAS MADE OBEDIENT see Sartori,
Baldasaro, Christus Factus Est

FOR US MEN see Burnell, I.

FOR WE HAVE SEEN HIS STAR see Newbury, Kent A.

FOR YE SHALL GO OUT WITH JOY see Diemer, Emma
Lou

FOR YET A LITTLE WHILE see Ford, Virgil T.

FOR YOU SHALL GO OUT IN JOY see Newbury, Kent
A.

FOR YOUR LIGHT HAS COME see Nelson, Ronald A.

FORBES, SEBASTIAN
Gracious Spirit, Holy Ghost *Whitsun,anthem
mix cor oct NOVELLO 40.1515.00 s.p. (F616)

Pleasure It Is To Hear *anthem
mix cor oct NOVELLO 86.0011.02 s.p.
(F617)

Suddenly Afraid *Lent,anthem
mix cor,acap oct NOVELLO 86.0010.04 s.p.
(F618)

Te Deum *Te Deum
SATB oct NOVELLO 86.0012.00 s.p. (F619)

FORCUCCI, S.L.
Alleluia *Allelu
SATB,acap oct PRO ART 2653 $.35 (F620)

Child Of Wonder *Xmas,cant
SATB,ST soli,pno, 4 hands AMP A634 $1.25
(F621)

Song Of Benediction *Bene
SATB,acap,opt pno oct PRO ART 2654 $.30
(F622)

FORD
All Cry Glory (Psalm 29)
SAB oct PRO ART 2678 $.30 (F623)
SATB,bells oct PRO ART 2530 $.30 (F624)

Almighty God *anthem
SS/SA oct OXFORD 44.229 $.20 (F625)

Almighty God, Who Hast Me Brought
(Collins) SATB,acap oct PRO ART 1531 $.15
(F626)
(Greyson) SATB oct BOURNE ES24 $.25 (F627)
(Greyson) SAB oct BOURNE ES24A $.25 (F628)

Almighty God, Who Hast Me Brought In Safety
(Wolff) SATB,acap (med diff/diff) SOUTHERN
$.30 (F629)

Almighty God, Who Safely Led Us
(Collins) SATB oct PRO ART 2442 $.25 (F630)
(Collins) SAB oct PRO ART 2444 $.25 (F631)

Christmas Story, The *CCU
unis FLAMMER GF5002 $1.25 (F632)

Come, Ye Faithful *Easter/Lent
SATB,acap,opt pno oct PRO ART 2677 $.30
(F633)

Fill The World With Thy Glory
SATB,acap WARNER W7-1032 $.30 (F634)

Give Thy Servant An Understanding Heart
SATB,acap oct FISCHER,C CM-7365 $.25 (F635)

God Be With You *CCU
SA FLAMMER GE5021 $.75 (F636)

God Is My Strong Salvation
SATB,acap WARNER W7-1049 $.30 (F637)

I Can Do All Things Through Christ
SATB oct FISCHER,C CM-7267 $.25 (F638)

I Will Give Peace
SATB oct PRO ART 2708 $.30 (F639)
SATB (med easy) SOUTHERN $.30 (F640)
SATB SOUTHERN $.30 (F641)

I Would Seek God
SATB oct LORENZ C287 $.30 (F642)

In Memory Of The Saviour's Love
SATB,acap WARNER W7-1001 $.30 (F643)

Jesus, Our Saviour
SA/TB FLAMMER E5043 $.25 (F644)

Jesus, We Look To Thee
SATB oct LORENZ C307 $.30 (F645)

Keep My Commandments
SATB,opt kbd oct PRO ART 2676 $.30 (F646)
SATB,acap (med easy) SOUTHERN $.30 (F647)
SATB,acap SOUTHERN $.30 (F648)

My God I Thank Thee *CC12U,hymn/pop
unis,gtr, opt banjo WARNER $.75 (F649)

O Give Thanks
SATB oct LORENZ C258 $.30 (F650)

O Lord, Raise Up Thy Power
SATB,acap WARNER W7-1016 $.30 (F651)

Our Savior's Passion *cant
SATB FLAMMER A5494 $1.00 (F652)

Psalm 29 *see All Cry Glory

Salvation Is For All
SATB oct LORENZ 9906 $.25 (F653)

Speak Low To Me, My Savior
SATB,org BOSTON 12239 $.35 (F654)

Spirit Of God (composed with Croly)
SATB ALFRED 6433 $.25 (F655)

Teach Me, Fill Me, Use Me, Lord
SATB oct LORENZ C313 $.30 (F656)

Tell The Blessed Tidings *Xmas
unis&opt desc,hndbl oct PRO ART 2499 $.30
(F657)

There Shall Be One Fold *Gen
SATB SCHMITT 8028 $.25 (F658)

Twelve Coffee House Songs *CC12U
FLAMMER G5001 $.50 (F659)

Word Became Flesh, The
SATB FLAMMER A5310 $1.10 (F660)

FORD, DELVINE
Anti-Blues *folk
unis/2pt voc sc WORD 37529 $1.95 (F661)

FORD PHILPOT CRUSADE CHOIR *CCU
(Kaiser, Kurt) SATB voc sc WORD 15005 $1.50
(F662)

FORD, THOMAS (ca. 1580-1648)
Almighty God, Which Has Me Brought *Morn
(Steinitz) SATB,opt inst (easy) oct OXFORD
43.364 $.25 (F663)

Almighty God Which Has Me Brought *Gen,
anthem
(Morehen, J.) SATB oct ROYAL 230 s.p.
(F664)

Almighty God, Who Hast Me Brought *anthem
SATB,acap PETERS H1558 $.40 (F665)
mix cor oct NOVELLO 50.0122.06 s.p. (F666)
SATB,acap SCHIRM.EC 1709 $.30 (F667)
(Cashmore, Donald) SAB oct NOVELLO
50.0336.09 s.p. (F668)
(Davis, K.) SA SCHIRM.EC 1548 (F669)

FORD, THOMAS (cont'd.)

Almighty God, Who Hast Me Brought In Safety
*Gen
(Wolff, S.) TTBB,acap (med easy) oct
CONCORDIA 98-2111 $.30   (F670)

Come Holy Ghost
(Trusler) 3pt mix cor,opt pno/org oct
LAWSON 977 $.25   (F671)

FORD, VIRGIL T.
Agree With God And Be At Peace *Bibl
4pt mix cor,acap oct SCHIRM.G 11488 $.30
(F672)

All As God Wills
4pt mix cor,acap oct SCHIRM.G 11906 $.30
(F673)

All Praise To Our Redeeming Lord
4pt mix cor,acap oct SCHIRM.G 11661 $.25
(F674)

Almighty And Everlasting God *prayer
4pt mix cor,acap oct SCHIRM.G 11271 $.25
(F675)

Almighty God, Who Hast Me Brought
SATB oct PLYMOUTH PCS-59 $.25   (F676)

At Thy Feet, Our God And Father
4pt mix cor,acap oct SCHIRM.G 11519 $.25
(F677)

Blessed Be The Name Of The Lord *Bibl
4pt mix cor,acap oct SCHIRM.G 11717 $.30
(F678)

Come, Let Us Tune Our Loftiest Song
4pt mix cor,acap oct SCHIRM.G 11443 $.25
(F679)

Come, O Thou God Of Grace
3pt mix cor,acap oct SCHIRM.G 11849 $.25
(F680)

4pt mix cor,acap oct SCHIRM.G 11613 $.30
(F681)

Come, Sound His Praise Abroad
4pt mix cor,acap oct SCHIRM.G 11884 $.25
(F682)

Feast After Feast
SATB FLAMMER A 5534 $.30   (F683)

For Yet A Little While
SATB FLAMMER A 5545 $.30   (F684)

From The Rising Of The Sun
SATB FLAMMER A 5158 $.25   (F685)

Give Thy Servant An Understanding Heart
4pt jr cor/SATB (med easy) FISCHER,C
CM 6365 $.20   (F686)

Go Ye Into All The World
4pt jr cor/SATB (easy) FISCHER,C CM 7463
$.25   (F687)

God Of The Strong
4pt mix cor,acap oct SCHIRM.G 11697 $.30
(F688)

He Has Risen
SATB FLAMMER A 5109 $.30   (F689)

He Shall Come Down
SATB FLAMMER A 5314 $.30   (F690)

How Can A Sinner Know
4pt mix cor,A solo oct SCHIRM.G 11356 $.25
(F691)

How Can We Show Our Love To Thee?
4pt mix cor,acap oct SCHIRM.G 11664 $.25
(F692)

How Gentle God's Commands
4pt mix cor,acap oct SCHIRM.G 11452 $.25
(F693)

Hymn Of Gratitude *hymn
SATB FLAMMER A 5121 $.30   (F694)

Hymn Of Thanks *hymn
SATB FLAMMER A 5069 $.30   (F695)

I Hide Me, Jesus, In Thy Name
4pt mix cor,acap oct SCHIRM.G 11668 $.25
(F696)

If The Lord Wills
4pt mix cor,acap oct SCHIRM.G 11351 $.25
(F697)

Jesus, Lord And Master
unis,org/pno,hndbl oct GRAY GHCS 16 $.30
(F698)

Jesus, Where'er Thy People Meet
4pt mix cor,acap oct SCHIRM.G 11449 $.25
(F699)

Let All On Earth Their Voices Raise
4pt mix cor,acap oct SCHIRM.G 11458 $.25
(F700)

Let Earth Rejoice *Bibl
4pt mix cor,acap oct SCHIRM.G 11698 $.30
(F701)

Long Years Ago *Xmas
4pt mix cor,acap oct SCHIRM.G 11551 $.30
(F702)

Lord, Dismiss Us With Thy Blessing
4pt mix cor,acap oct SCHIRM.G 11886 $.25
(F703)

Lord Of Our Life
4pt mix cor,acap oct SCHIRM.G 11518 $.25
(F704)

Lord, Our Lord
4pt mix cor,acap oct SCHIRM.G 11214 $.25
(F705)

3pt mix cor,acap oct SCHIRM.G 11502 $.25
(F706)

Lost In Wonder, Love, And Praise *meditation
4pt mix cor,acap oct SCHIRM.G 11641 $.25
(F707)

Make A Joyful Noise
SATB FLAMMER A 5144 $.30   (F708)

Men Of Old *Xmas
4pt mix cor,acap oct SCHIRM.G 11614 $.30
(F709)

O Come, And Dwell In Me *meditation
4pt mix cor,acap oct SCHIRM.G 11514 $.25
(F710)

O Jesus, King Of Gentleness *meditation
4pt mix cor,acap oct SCHIRM.G 11696 $.25
(F711)

On The Christmas Morning *Xmas
unis jr cor FISCHER,C CM 7677 $.25   (F712)

Salvation Is Nearer
SATB FLAMMER A 5047 $.30   (F713)

FORD, VIRGIL T. (cont'd.)

Sounds For Now
unis (easy) ABINGDON APM-871 $.60   (F714)

Talk With Us, Lord *prayer
4pt mix cor,acap oct SCHIRM.G 11515 $.25
(F715)

This Is The Day Which The Lord Hath Made
4pt mix cor,acap oct SCHIRM.G 11272 $.30
(F716)

SAB,acap oct SCHIRM.G 11503 $.30   (F717)

Thy Will Be Done! *meditation
4pt mix cor,acap oct SCHIRM.G 11648 $.25
(F718)

Unto Thee, O Lord *Bibl
4pt mix cor,acap oct SCHIRM.G 11101 $.25
(F719)

SAB,acap oct SCHIRM.G 11506 $.25   (F720)

What Manner Of Love
SATB FLAMMER A 5071 $.30   (F721)

FORDENSKULL JESU LED DU MIG see Moren, John

FOREST
Adoramus Te, Christe *Xmas
SSA FLAMMER B 5045 $.30   (F722)

Little Lamb, Who Made Thee
SSA FLAMMER B 5107 $.20   (F723)
TTBB FLAMMER C5065 $.30   (F724)

FOREST HYMN see Klemm, Gustav

FOREVER BLESSED BE THY NAME see Handel, George
Frideric

FOREVER IS IT MEET AND RIGHT see Shvedof, C.

FOREVER, O LORD see Donovan, Richard [Frank]

FOREVER, O LORD see Maunder, J.H.

FOREVER THY WORD, ALLELUIA see Whear, Paul
William

FOREVER WORTHY IS THY LAMB see Tchaikovsky,
Piotr Ilyitch

FORGET-ME-NOT see Hahn, [Carl]

FORGET NOT ALL HIS BENEFITS see Fearis, J.S.

FORGET NOT MY LAW see Effinger, Cecil

FORGET THY AFFLICTION see Berlinski, Herman

FORGIVE ME see Townsend

FORGIVE ME, LORD
SSA CHAPPELL 1570001-354 $.40   (F725)
SATB CHAPPELL 1570001-358 $.40   (F726)

FORGIVE OUR SINS see Gaul, Alfred Robert

FORGIVE US LORD see Haydn, (Franz) Joseph

FORGIVE US, LORD OF LIFE see Hastings

FORGIVENESS DIVINE see Reed

FORLAN OSS, GUD, DEN HELGA FRID
(Berg, Gottfrid) mix cor NORDISKA 2310 s.p.
see also Sacrae Cantiones   (F727)

FORLAN OSS, HERRE GUD see Bach, Johann
Sebastian

FORLAT OSS, KRIST see Rodseth, Johs.

FORM OF COMPLINE, A see Milner, Anthony

FORM OF SUNDAY VESPERS FOR CONGREGATIONAL USE,
A see Milner, Anthony

FORREST
He's Got The Whole World In His Hands
(Edwards) SSA oct BELWIN 60343 $.25   (F728)
(Edwards) SATB oct BELWIN 60078 $.35   (F729)
(Edwards) TTBB oct BELWIN 60461 $.25   (F730)

FORSAKE ME NOT, O LORD see Mechem, Kirke

FORSAKEN OF MAN see Sowerby, Leo

FORSAMLENS, I TROGNE *Xmas,hymn
(Lundvik, Hildor) men cor NORDISKA 1169 s.p.
see from Julhymner   (F731)

FORSBLAD
Boy Was Born In Bethlehem, A
SATB FLAMMER A 5369 $.30   (F732)

Christmas Hymn *Xmas,hymn
SATB oct PRO ART 2697 $.30   (F733)
SSA oct PRO ART 2644 $.30   (F734)
SATB (med easy) SOUTHERN $.30   (F735)
SAB oct PRO ART 2700 $.30   (F736)

Echo Carol *Xmas,carol
3pt jr cor/SSA (easy) FISCHER,C CM 7307
$.20   (F737)
dbl cor (med easy) FISCHER,C $.20   (F738)
SSA,acap oct FISCHER,C CM-7307 $.25   (F739)
SATB,acap oct FISCHER,C CM-7675 $.25   (F740)

I Wanta Be Ready *spir
SATB LEONARD-US 08031360 $.25   (F741)

In Bethlehem *Xmas,round
SSA,acap oct PRO ART 2237 $.25   (F742)

Lamb, The
SSA oct PRO ART 1652 $.25   (F743)

Lo! New Born Jesus *Xmas
SSA oct PRO ART 1831 $.22   (F744)

Oh, Give Thanks Unto The Lord *Thanks
SATB oct PRO ART 1846 $.25   (F745)

Sing Alleluia *Xmas
SSA,acap,opt pno oct PRO ART 2598 $.30
(F746)
SATB oct PRO ART 1993 $.25   (F747)
SAB,acap,opt pno oct PRO ART 2698 $.30
(F748)

FORSBLAD (cont'd.)

SAB,acap (med easy) SOUTHERN $.30   (F749)

Singing Hills
SATB oct PRO ART 2054 $.25   (F750)

Star Song, The *Xmas
SSA oct PRO ART 1826 $.22   (F751)

Surely He Hath Borne Our Burdens *Lent
3pt jr cor/SSA (med) FISCHER,C CM 7290 $.25
(F752)

FORSEULEMENT see Gombert, Nicolas

FORSORGEREN, DEN STORE GUD see Braein, Edvard

FORSTER, GEORG (ca. 1510-1568)
Die Sieben Worte *Psntd
mix cor,inst HANSSLER 10.290 rental (F753)

To You This Night Is Born A Child *Xmas
(Schalk, C.) SATBB,acap (med easy) oct
CONCORDIA 98-2047 $.25   (F754)

Trost Mich, O Herr
[Ger] SATB,acap (med easy) MULLER K 5 s.p.
(F755)

Vom Himmel Hoch, Da Komm Ich Her *Xmas
[Ger] SATTB,acap (med) MULLER K 13 s.p.
(F756)

SATBB HANSSLER 6.093 s.p.   (F757)

FORSTER, KASPAR
Ad Arma Fideles *cant
(Sorenson, Soren) [Lat] SSB,org HANSEN-DEN
28738 s.p., ipa   (F758)

FORSYTH, [JOSEPHINE] (1889-1940)
Lord's Prayer, The *Bibl
(Kraft) 4pt mix cor oct SCHIRM.G 7491 $.25
(F759)

FORTEM VIRILI see Tebaldini, Giovanni

FORTEM VIRILI PECTORE see Boldi, N.

FORTH FROM JESSE SPRANG A ROSE see Bruckner,
Anton

FORTH FROM THY HOME ON HIGH see Du Caurroy,
Francoise-Eustache, Sors De Ton Lit Pare

FORTH HE CAME see Williams, David H.

FORTH HE CAME AT EASTER see Williams, David H.

FORTH IN THY NAME see Brandon

FORTH IN THY NAME see Darst, W. Glenn

FORTH IN THY NAME see Wadely, F.W.

FORTH IN THY NAME see Young

FORTH IN THY NAME see Young, Gordon

FORTH IN THY NAME I GO see Candlyn, T.
Frederick H.

FORTH IN THY NAME, O LORD see Butler, Eugene

FORTH IN THY NAME, O LORD see Hughes

FORTH IN THY NAME, O LORD see Purvis, Richard

FORTH IN THY NAME, O LORD see Williams

FORTH TO THY NEW YEAR see Young, Gordon

FORTIG, PETER (1934-)
Ave Verum Corpus *Psntd
[Lat] SSAATTBB,ob,2clar,bsn,trp,horn,trom,
English horn (diff) BAREN. BA 4129 rental
(F760)

FORTRESS OF HOPE see Van Iderstine, A.P.

FORTRESS, ROCK OF OUR SALVATION see Weisgall,
Hugo

FORTY DAYS see Brubeck

FORTY DAYS see Sheldon

FORTY DAYS AND FORTY NIGHTS see Herbst

FORTY DAYS HE TARRIED HERE see Williams

FORTY DAYS TO EASTER see Wilson, Roger [C.]

FORTY-TWO POPULAR SPIRITUALS *CC42U,spir
mix cor SCHMITT 45 $.50   (F761)

FORWARD TO CHRIST see O'Hara, Geoffrey

FOSS, JULIUS (1879-)
Carmen Vernale
see Foss, Julius, Som Et Stille Offerlam

Ecce Gratum
see Three Motets

Good Wishes
see Foss, Julius, Som Et Stille Offerlam

In Domum Domini
see Three Motets

Ita Enim Deus
see Foss, Julius, Som Et Stille Offerlam

Mandatum Novum
see Three Motets

Som Et Stille Offerlam *Easter,hymn
4pt mix cor SKAND. SMF5453 s.p. contains
also: Ita Enim Deus (4pt mix cor) (mot);
Carmen Vernale (3pt); Good Wishes (4pt
mix cor) (madrigal)   (F762)

Three Motets *mot
[Lat] SKAND. SMF5500 s.p.
contains: Ecce Gratum (4pt); In Domum
Domini (4pt); Mandatum Novum (5pt)
(F763)

FOSS, LUKAS (1922-)
Behold! I Build An House
SATB oct PRESSER 352-00384 $.45   (F764)

FOSS, LUKAS (cont'd.)

Psalms *CCU,Psalm
SATB FISCHER,C O-4034 $2.00   (F765)

FOSTER
Christmas Day In The Morning *Xmas
unis oct LORENZ 8621 $.25   (F766)

Eye Hath Not Seen
(Ehret) SATB oct SPRATT 568 $.25   (F767)

O! For A Closer Walk With God
SATB oct PRO ART 1059 $.25   (F768)
(Lathrop) SAB/SSA oct PRO ART 1164 $.18   (F769)

Rejoice, For Christ Is Born (composed with
Nowlan)
(Nowlan) SATB&opt jr cor oct FOX R201 $.30
                                                (F770)

FOSTER, MYLES BIRKET (1851-1922)
As It Began To Dawn *Easter
4pt mix cor,Bar&high solo oct SCHIRM.G 7388
$.25   (F771)

O For A Closer Walk With God *Bibl
4pt mix cor,med solo oct SCHIRM.G 3895 $.25   (F772)

Oh, For A Closer Walk With God *Whitsun,
anthem
mix cor,S/T solo,orch oct NOVELLO
40.0495.07 s.p.   (F773)

FOSTER, WILL
Fear Not, I Am With Thee *Bibl
4pt mix cor,S solo oct SCHIRM.G 8711 $.30   (F774)

Hear My Prayer
SATB oct SOUTHERN $.25   (F775)

Thy Will Be Done
4pt mix cor,B solo oct SCHIRM.G 10399 $.30   (F776)

FOSTERLANDSK HYMN see Runback, Albert

FOUNDLING HOSPITAL ANTHEM see Handel, George
Frideric

FOUNTAIN OF LIFE, A see Berger, Jean

FOUR AMERICAN FOLK HYMNS see Wade, Walter

FOUR ANTHEMS see Batten, Adrian

FOUR ANTHEMS FOR TREBLE VOICES see Copley, R.
Evan

FOUR ANTHEMS FOR YOUNG CHOIRS see Nelson,
Ronald A.

FOUR ANTHEMS OF PRAISE see Knight, Vincent

FOUR ANTHEMS see Howells, Herbert Norman

FOUR ANTHEMS see Gibbons, Orlando

FOUR ANTHEMS see Gibbons, Orlando

FOUR ANTHEMS see White, Robert

FOUR CANONS FOR EQUAL VOICES see Hindemith,
Paul

FOUR CANONS *CC4U,anthem/canon
(Riedel) SA/SSA/SSAA (easy) oct AUGSBURG 1332
$.20   (F777)

FOUR CANONS see Mozart, Wolfgang Amadeus

FOUR CANTICLES FOR THE CHRISTMAS SEASON see
Moore

FOUR CAROLS *see Dear Nightingale, Awake;
Joseph Dearest, Joseph Mine; Rocking (F778)

FOUR CAROLS FOR A HOLY NIGHT see Lekberg, Sven

FOUR CAROLS FROM ABROAD *CC4U,carol,Braz/Mex/
Span
(Treacher) unis/SA (easy) OXFORD 44.067 $.35
                                                (F779)

FOUR CAROLS see Diemer, Emma Lou

FOUR CAROLS see Diemer, Emma Lou

FOUR CAROLS see Davies, Peter Maxwell

FOUR CAROLS see Mellers, Wilfrid Howard

FOUR CAROLS see Stevens, Halsey

FOUR CHORALE HARMONIZATIONS see Bach, Johann
Sebastian

FOUR CHORALE HARMONIZATIONS see Praetorius,
Michael

FOUR CHORALES see Mendelssohn-Bartholdy, Felix

FOUR CHORALES FOR CHRISTMAS *CC4U,Xmas,chorale
(Ehret) SATB,acap MARKS 868 $.25   (F780)

FOUR CHORALES FOR COMMUNION see Sjolund, Paul

FOUR CHORALES FOR EASTER see Bach, Johann
Sebastian

FOUR CHORALES see Bach, Johann Sebastian

FOUR CHORALES see Bach, Johann Sebastian

FOUR CHORALES see Bach, Johann Sebastian

FOUR CHORUSES see Schalk

FOUR CHORUSES FOR MORNING WORSHIP *CC4U,Morn
(Greyson) SATB oct BOURNE ES70 $.30 contains
works by: Praetorius; Vulpius; Cruger   (F781)

FOUR CHORUSES FROM THE LAMENTATIONS OF JEREMIAH
see Schalk, Carl

FOUR CHORUSES [NO. 1 & 2], VOL. I see Haydn,
(Franz) Joseph

FOUR CHORUSES [NO. 3 & 4], VOL. II see Haydn,
(Franz) Joseph

FOUR CHRISTMAS CAROLS ON MEDIEVAL TEXTS see
Davies, Peter Maxwell

FOUR CHRISTMAS CAROLS see Arnatt, Ronald

FOUR CHRISTMAS CAROLS see Dinn, Freda

FOUR CHRISTMAS CAROLS *Xmas,carol
LENGNICK s.p.
contains: Britten, Anthony, Christ Is Born
Of Maiden Fair (composed with Yorke,
Colin) (mix cor); Lloyd, Richard H., All
So Still (mix cor,acap); Morris, Reginald
Owen, Love Came Down At Christmas (mix
cor,acap); Smith, Peter, When Christ Was
Born (mix cor,acap)   (F782)

FOUR CHRISTMAS CAROLS see Garlick, Anthony

FOUR CHRISTMAS CHORALES see Bach, Johann
Sebastian

FOUR CHRISTMAS CHORALES see Cruger, Johann

FOUR CHRISTMAS CHORALES see Praetorius, Michael

FOUR CHRISTMAS CHORUSES see Kraehenbuehl, D.

FOUR CHRISTMAS MOTETS see Calvisius, Sethus

FOUR CHRISTMAS SETTINGS see Wienhorst, Richard

FOUR CHRISTMAS SONGS see Praetorius, Michael

FOUR CHRISTMAS SONGS see Praetorius, Michael

FOUR COMMUNION HYMNS *CC4U,Commun,hymn
oct ROYAL 339 s.p.   (F783)

FOUR COMMUNION RESPONSES see Bock, Fred

FOUR CONTEMPORARY HYMNS, SET I *hymn
oct AUGSBURG 11-9193 $.12
contains: Boeringer, James, Upon The Rock
Of Faith; Cartford, Gerhard M., Great God
Our Source; Moe, Daniel, O Jesus Christ,
To Thee May Hymns Be Rising; Sateren,
Leland Bernhard, God Is God   (F784)

FOUR CONTEMPORARY HYMNS, SET II see Moe, Daniel

FOUR CORONATION ANTHEMS see Blow, John

FOUR EASTER CAROLS (from Piae Cantiones)
(Geer, E.) SSAA,acap SCHIRM.EC 859 $.50
contains: Christ The Lord Hath Risen (12th
cent); On Easter Morn, Ere Break Of Day
(Scot); Tell It Out, The Story (Belg);
World Itself Keeps Easter Day, The (F785)

FOUR 18TH-CENTURY ENGLISH ROUNDS see Wienhorst,
Richard

FOUR FLEMISH CHRISTMAS CAROLS see Peeters, Flor

FOUR FOLK SONGS see Brahms, Johannes

FOUR FOLKSONGS AND SPIRITUALS *anthem/folk/
spir
(Johnson, David N.) TBB (easy) oct AUGSBURG
1637 $.35
contains: Earth And All Stars; Fisherman
Peter; Lone, Wild Bird, The; There Is
Balm In Gilead   (F786)

FOUR FREEDOM SONGS see Peloquin, C. Alexander

FOUR FREEDOMS, THE see York, D.

FOUR GOSPEL HYMN ANTHEMS see Lynn, George

FOUR GRACES see Thiman, Eric Harding

FOUR GRADUALE see Bruckner, Anton

FOUR GREAT CHORALS FROM THE MESSIAH see Handel,
George Frideric

FOUR HYMNS FOR CHRISTCHURCH *CC4U,carol/hymn
SCHIRM.EC 12 $.25 contains works by: Beecham,
A.; Hallstrom; Ford, B.S.; Perdue-Davis, V.
                                                (F787)

FOUR INTROITS FOR SEASONAL USE see Waters,
Charles F.

FOUR INTROITS see Webber, Lloyd

FOUR MEDIEVAL SONGS *see Mater Ora Filium
                                                (F788)

FOUR MODERN ANTHEMS see Walls, Dana

FOUR MODERN PSALM TUNES *Bibl
cong cmplt ed WEINBERGER s.p.
contains: Psalm 97; Psalm 98; Psalm 121;
Psalm 122   (F789)

FOUR MOTETS see Escovada, R.

[FOUR] MOTETS see Des Prez, Josquin

FOUR MOTETS ON GREGORIAN THEMES see Durufle,
Maurice

FOUR MOTETS see Des Prez, Josquin

FOUR MOTETS see Palestrina, Giovanni

FOUR MOTETS see Palestrina, Giovanni

FOUR MOTETS see Victoria, Tomas Luis de

FOUR NEGRO SPIRITUALS *spir
(Tate) SA (med) OXFORD 54.932 $.95
contains: I Got A Robe; Joshua Fit The
Battle; My Lord, What A Morning; Swing
Low   (F790)

FOUR NOELS *CC4U,Xmas
(Oldham) SSA,acap (easy) OXFORD 44.072 $.65   (F791)

FOUR OFFERTORIES FOR THE SUNDAYS IN ADVENT see
Carroll, J.R.

FOUR OLD CAROLS *see Cradle Carol; Ding! Dong!
Merrily On High; I Saw Three Ships;
Remember God's Goodnesse; Deale, Cradle
Carol   (F792)

FOUR OLD CAROLS see Deale

FOUR OLD ENGLISH CAROLS see Kirk, Theron W.

FOUR OLD ITALIAN CANTIONES see Sistinius, Truid
Aagesen

FOUR PARABLES see Bixel, James W.

FOUR PATHS TO BETHLEHEM *Xmas
(song and story) LORENZ $.75   (F793)

FOUR PRAYERS FOR CHRISTIAN UNITY see Peloquin,
C. Alexander

FOUR PROPHECIES see Christiansen, Paul

FOUR PROVERBS see London, Edwin

FOUR PSALM SETTINGS see Mawby, C.

FOUR PSALMS see Grieg, Edvard Hagerup

FOUR PSALMS see Schutz, Heinrich

FOUR RESPONSES FOR YOM KIPPUR see Adler, Samuel

FOUR ROUNDS FOR CHRISTMAS see Gore, Richard T.

FOUR SACRED CANONS see Telemann, Georg Philipp

FOUR SACRED PIECES see Verdi, Giuseppe

FOUR SACRED PIECES see Verdi, Giuseppe

FOUR SACRED SONGS see Karkoff, Maurice Ingvar

FOUR SACRED SONGS FOR THE NIGHT see Bright

FOUR SACRED SONGS FOR THE NIGHT see Bright,
Houston

FOUR SELECTIONS FROM THE MASS see Near, Gerald

FOUR SETTINGS OF THE PRECES AND RESPONSES BY
ELIZABETHAN AND EARLY STUART COMPOSERS
*CCU
(Shaw, Watkins; Graves, Richard) SAATB oct
OXFORD 48.005 $1.00 contains works by:
Byrd; Morley; Smith; Tomkins   (F794)

FOUR SHORT ANTHEMS FOR LENT AND EASTER
*Easter/Lent,anthem/Bibl
(Diemente) SATB,org oct LAWSON 51523 $.35
contains: Anerio, Felice, Earth Feared,
The; Asola, Giovanni Matteo, Christ Our
Passover; Asola, Giovanni Matteo, Make My
Steps Steadfast; Dowland, John, Insult
Has Broken My Heart   (F795)

FOUR SHORT INTROITS see Murray

FOUR SLOVAK CHRISTMAS CAROLS *CC4U,Xmas,carol
(Kountz, Richard) oct SSA GRAY GCMR 1197
$.30; SATB GRAY GCMR 725 $.30; TTBB GRAY
GCMR 1530 $.25   (F796)

FOUR SLOVAK CHRISTMAS CAROLS see Kountz

FOUR SONGS FOR CHRISTMAS *Xmas
(De Cormier) 2pt boy cor/SA,org oct LAWSON
51476 $.45
contains: Christmas Is Coming; Dame Get Up
And Bake Your Cake; Merry Christmas;
Welcome Here   (F797)

FOUR SPIRITUAL SONGS, SET 1 see Kennedy, John
Brodbin

FOUR SPIRITUAL SONGS, SET 2 see Kennedy, John
Brodbin

FOUR SPIRITUALS see Gardner

FOUR TRADITIONAL CAROLS *CC4U,Xmas,carol
(Neff) SATB,inst oct SUMMY 5212 $.45, ipa   (F798)

FOUR VESPER HYMNS see Washington, Henry

FOUR-WAY CHORISTER, THE *CCU
2-4pt oct STAFF 700 $1.50   (F799)

FOURTEEN CANTICLES AND RESPONSES see Young,
Carlton R.

FOURTEEN CHORAL RESPONSES see McAfee

FOURTEEN PSALMS see Elliott, Kenneth

FOURTEEN RESPONSES AND AMENS see Savage

FOURTEENTH-CENTURY MASS MUSIC IN FRANCE see
Wert, Giaches de

FOURTEENTH CENTURY REPERTORY FROM THE CODEX
REINA, A *CCU,14th cent
(Wilkins, E. Nigel) cor AM.INST.MUS. $14.00   (F800)

FOURTH COMMUNION SERVICE see Gounod, Charles
Francois, Missa Choralis

FOURTH EVENING SERVICE see Batten, Adrian

FOURTH MASS see Cherubini, Luigi

FOURTH SERVICE see Tomkins, Thomas

FOURTH WISE MAN, THE see Hamill

FOUSER, C.E.
Preface And Sanctus
SATB,pno (med) oct WILLIS 6646 $.16   (F801)

Te Deum
SATB,pno (diff) oct WILLIS 6522 $.25   (F802)

FOVARGUE, EVA
Cradle Hymn, A *cradle/hymn
unis&opt 2pt&desc ASHDOWN U.71 s.p.   (F803)

FOX
Te Deum *Gen
SATB SCHMITT 885 $.25   (F804)

FOX, BAYNARD
Amazing Grace
(Mercer, E.) SATB (easy) PRESSER G-209 $.35   (F805)

FOX, BAYNARD (cont'd.)

I'll Tell The World
(Burroughs, Bob) SA (easy) PRESSER G-190
$.30   (F806)
(Huff, R.) SATB (easy) PRESSER G-189 $.35
                                              (F807)

FOX, DANIEL H.
City Of The Lord, The
SATB oct SHAPIRO SK 2082 $.30   (F808)

FOX, GEORGE
Jesu, My Jesu, Lovely Lord
unis,pno oct BERANDOL 916F8AD $.35   (F809)

Seven Simple Sacred Songs *CC7L,Xmas/Gen,
anthem
unis jr cor,pno/org (easy) voc sc HARRIS
$.95   (F810)

FOX, GREGORY
Suddenly There Came A Sound *Commun/Pent
SATB,org oct WORLD EMP-1846-8 $.30   (F811)

FRA HIMLEM HOJT see Laub, Thomas

FRA HIMLEN HOJT KOM BUDSKAB HER see Othmayr,
Kaspar

FRA HIMLEN KOM EN ENGEL KLAR see Triller,
Valentin

FRACKENPOHL
Cradle Hymn
SATB SHAWNEE A 444 $.25   (F812)

God Of The Earth, The Sky, The Sea
SATB KJOS 6301 $.30   (F813)

My Song Forever Shall Record
SATB,acap MARKS 4308 $.25   (F814)

Not Alone For Mighty Empire
SATB MARKS 4283 $.25   (F815)

FRACKENPOHL, ARTHUR (1924-   )
Awake, My Soul
SATB SHAWNEE A 442 $.25   (F816)

Born In Bethlehem *Xmas
SATB MARKS 4243 $.25   (F817)

Carol Trilogy, A *Xmas
SATB oct PLYMOUTH PCS-68 $.50   (F818)

Give A Cheer For The Lord
SA MARKS 119 $.30   (F819)
SATB,opt T solo MARKS 118 $.35   (F820)

Hallelujah, Praise The Lord! *Easter
SATB SHAWNEE A 993 $.30   (F821)
SA/TB SHAWNEE E54 $.35   (F822)
SATB oct SOUTHERN $.25   (F823)
SA/TB oct SOUTHERN $.25   (F824)

Make A Joyful Noise (Psalm 100)
SATB oct ELKAN-V 362-1187 $.35   (F825)

Merchants' Carol, The
SATB SHAWNEE A 699 $.30   (F826)

O Mary, Where Is Your Baby?
SATB,acap SHAWNEE A 439 $.30   (F827)

Praise, O Praise Our God And King
SA MARKS 4219 $.25   (F828)
SATB MARKS 4220 $.25   (F829)

Psalm 8
SATB,org RONGWEN $.35   (F830)

Psalm 100 *see Make A Joyful Noise

Star Of The East *Xmas
SA oct ELKAN-V 362-512 $.25   (F831)

What Child Is This? *Xmas
SATB SHAWNEE A 440 $.30   (F832)

Whole Bright World Rejoices Now, The
SATB SHAWNEE A 602 $.25   (F833)

World Itself Keeps Easter Day, The
SA/TB SHAWNEE E31 $.25   (F834)

FRAG NUR UMHER see Weelkes

FRAGMENT AF OEHLENSCHLAGERS "JESU
BJERGPRAEDIKEN" see Hartmann, Johan Peder
Emilius

FRAGMENTS FROM THE MASS see Diemer, Emma Lou

FRAGST DU NACH MEINER SUNDE see Bossler, Kurt

FRAGST DU NACH MEINER SUNDE see Ruppel, Paul
Ernst

FRAMMENTI BIBLICI see Pezzati, Mauro

FRAMMENTI DALLE LETTERE DE SANTA CATERINA see
Perry, Julia

FRANCAIX, JEAN (1912-   )
L'apocalypse Selon St. Jean *ora
[Fr] SATB,SATB soli,2orch voc sc SCHOTT
4035 s.p., ipr   (F835)

FRANCE
Little Saviour, Sleep
SATB THOMP.G G-573 s.p.   (F836)

FRANCE, W.
Jesus, Tender Shepherd, Hear Me
unis oct PRESSER 312-21632 $.25   (F837)

FRANCE, WILLIAM E.
Bread Of Heaven
SATB,acap oct BERANDOL 918F2AG $.35   (F838)

Cradle Hymn, A
SSA,acap AMP A226 $.20   (F839)
SSA,acap oct BERANDOL 838F2AE $.35   (F840)

Divine Guest, The
SATB,acap oct BERANDOL 918F2AI $.35   (F841)

FRANCE, WILLIAM E. (cont'd.)

Hymn Of Praise
SATB,acap oct BERANDOL 918F2AH $.35   (F842)

Morning Hymn, A *Morn,anthem/hymn
unis jr cor/SA oct HARRIS HC2002 $.20   (F843)

My Lord, My Master, At Thy Feet Adoring
SATB,acap oct BERANDOL 848F2AF $.35   (F844)

FRANCESCHINI
Alleluia *Mass
TB,org s.p. voc sc RICORDI-ENG 111953, cor
pts RICORDI-ENG 128480-81   (F845)

FRANCHOIS
Ave Virgo *BVM,15th cent
(Cartier, Anita) [Lat] 4pt mix cor LEMOINE
s.p.   (F846)

FRANCIS, J.
O, Come Let Us Sing
SATB oct PRESSER 312-40115 $.35   (F847)

FRANCIS, W. DOUGLAS
Come Down, O Love Divine
SATB oct GRAY GCMR 2605 $.30   (F848)

FRANCK, CESAR (1822-1890)
Agnus Dei *Agnus
"Lamb Most Holy" 2pt ENOCH TP248 s.p.   (F849)

Alleluia
SATB oct LORENZ 9767 $.30   (F850)
SAB oct LORENZ 7364 $.25   (F851)

Angelus Ad Pastores Ait *Xmas,mot
(Gramss) 6pt mix cor MOSELER s.p.   (F852)

At The Cradle *see La Vierge A La Creche

Ave Maria
2pt ASHDOWN E.A.194 s.p.   (F853)
(Cramer) [Lat] SATB MARKS 4290 $.30   (F854)
(Davis, K.) "Father Eternal" SSA SCHIRM.EC
1858   (F855)

Ave Verum *Commun,mot
(Kunc, P.) [Lat] 4pt/4pt mix cor oct DURAND
s.p.   (F856)

Be Thou With Me
(Luvaas) SATB KJOS 2056 $.30   (F857)

Blessed, He (from Beatitudes, The) Bibl
4pt mix cor,B solo oct SCHIRM.G 4930 $.30
                                        (F858)
(Tillinghast) SSA WARNER W3582 $.30   (F859)

Can This Be Thy Cradle *Xmas
(Ehret) SATB oct ELKAN-V 362-1278 $.25 (F860)

Cantato Domino (Psalm 150) mot
(Gramss) mix cor&mix cor MOSELER s.p.   (F861)

Cantato Domino In Vita Mea (Psalm 150) mot
(Gramss) mix cor MOSELER s.p.   (F862)

Chant Du Crepuscule (from Ruth)
[Fr] 4pt mix cor HEUGEL voc sc s.p., voc pt
s.p.   (F863)

Choeur De Bethlemites Et Strophes (from Ruth)
"Chorus Of Bethlemites And Strophes" SSTB,
pno SCHIRM.EC 385 $.25   (F864)

Choeur De Moabites (from Ruth)
"Chorus Of Moabites" SATB,pno SCHIRM.EC 383
$.25   (F865)

Choeur De Moisonneurs (from Ruth)
"Chorus Of Harvesters" SATB,pno SCHIRM.EC
386 $.35   (F866)

Choeur Des Chameliers (from Rebecca)
[Fr] TTBB HEUGEL s.p.   (F867)

Choeur Des Jeunes Filles (from Rebecca)
[Fr] SA,acap HEUGEL s.p.   (F868)

Chorus Of Bethlemites And Strophes *see
Choeur De Bethlemites Et Strophes

Chorus Of Harvesters *see Choeur De
Moisonneurs

Chorus Of Moabites *see Choeur De Moabites

Christus Natus Est *Mass
[Lat] TB,org sc ZANIBON 1617 s.p., voc pt
ZANIBON s.p.   (F869)

Come, Now Sing
(Wiley) SATB,acap oct PRO ART 2747 $.30 (F870)

Come, O Creator Spirit
(Coggin) SAB MARKS 4441 $.25   (F871)

Communion Service In A *see Messa A Troix
Voix

Da Pacem, Domine *mot
(Gramss) 4pt mix cor&4pt mix cor,acap
MOSELER s.p.   (F872)

Deuxieme Messe Solennelle *Mass
3pt men cor,pno/org CHOUDENS s.p.   (F873)

Devant La Loi Nouvelle (from Redemption)
[Fr] 4pt mix cor HEUGEL voc sc s.p., voc pt
s.p.   (F874)

Drei Quodlibets *CC3U
(Gudewill) [Ger/It] 4pt mix cor MOSELER
s.p.   (F875)

Father Almighty
SATB oct LORENZ 4437 $.30   (F876)
SATB oct LORENZ 9166 $.30   (F877)

Father Eternal *see Ave Maria

Father Most Merciful *see Panis Angelicus

Funf Hohelied-Motetten *CC5U,mot
(Abert) 5-6pt mix cor MOSELER s.p.   (F878)

FRANCK, CESAR (cont'd.)

Geh Deinen Weg *mot
(Gramss) 4pt mix cor&4pt mix cor MOSELER
s.p.   (F879)

Gloria In Excelsis (from Mass In A)
[Lat] SATB,T solo,harp,vcl SCHIRM.EC 1154
$.65, ipr   (F880)
(Williams, W.) [Lat/Eng] SATB,T solo,org
SCHIRM.EC 1726 $.35   (F881)

Gloria Patri *mot
(Gramss) 4pt mix cor&5pt mix cor MOSELER
s.p.   (F882)

Great God Of Nations
(Ehret) SATB SHAWNEE A 917 $.30   (F883)

Guardian Angel
SA SCHIRM.EC 498 $.16   (F884)

Halleluja! Lobt Gott (Psalm 150) anthem/Bibl/
Psalm
4pt mix cor,org cor pts BREITKOPF-W
CHB-3481 s.p., voc sc BREITKOPF-W EB-1523
s.p.   (F885)
4pt mix cor,org,2fl,2ob,2clar,2bsn,4horn,
2trp,3trom,perc,timp,harp cor pts
BREITKOPF-W CHB-3481 s.p., ipr, voc sc
BREITKOPF-W EB-1523 s.p., sc BREITKOPF-W
rental   (F886)
SATB oct FISCHER,J 5670 $.30   (F887)
mix cor NOVELLO 28.1254.01 s.p.   (F888)
[Fr/Ger] cor voc sc KALMUS 6215 $1.50   (F889)
cor sc KALMUS $4.00   (F890)
cor,orch sc KALMUS $4.00, ipa   (F891)
"Sing Praise To God" SATB,org SCHIRM.EC 314
$.35, ipr   (F892)
(Breck) SATB oct FISCHER,C CM-6870 $.30 (F893)
(Coke; Jephcott) SATB oct GRAY GCMR 1296
$.35   (F894)
(Ehret) SSA ALFRED 6220 $.35   (F895)
(Gaines) SA oct FISCHER,J 5805 $.30   (F896)
(Gaines) SSA oct FISCHER,J 6822 $.35   (F897)
(Gaines) SSAA oct FISCHER,J 5706 $.30   (F898)
(Gaines) TTBB oct FISCHER,J 5707 $.30   (F899)
(Geer, E.) "Sing Praise To God, The Lord"
SSAA,org SCHIRM.EC 851 $.35, ipr   (F900)
(Jadassohn) SATB,org,opt orch AMP A61 $.30
                                        (F901)
(Jamison) SATB oct PLYMOUTH SC-5 $.25   (F902)
(McKinney) SAB oct FISCHER,J 9207 $.35 (F903)
(Mueller) 4pt mix cor,org oct SCHIRM.G
11013 $.40   (F904)
(Reynolds) SSA,band MARKS 4199 $.30, ipa (F905)
(Reynolds) SATB,band MARKS 4140 $.35, ipa
                                        (F906)

Hallelujah! Lobt Gott In Seiner Veste Macht
(Psalm 150)
[Fr/Ger] mix cor,org,2fl,2ob,2clar,2bsn,
2trp,4horn,3trom,strings,timp,harp voc sc
BREITKOPF-L EB-1523 s.p., voc pt
BREITKOPF-L CHB-689 s.p., ipr   (F907)

Kommt, Ihr G'spielen
4pt mix cor MOSELER LB-97 s.p. contains
also: Praetorius, Michael, Herzlich Tut
Mich Erfreuen   (F908)

Kyrie Eleison (from Mass In A) Greek
SATB,org SCHIRM.EC 1153 $.30   (F909)

La Vierge A La Creche
"At The Cradle" SA,pno SCHIRM.EC 1533 $.30
                                        (F910)
(Noyon, J.) [Fr] SATB voc sc ENOCH s.p. (F911)
(Noyon, J.) [Fr] SATB cor pts ENOCH s.p. (F912)
(Noyon, J.) [Fr] SA voc sc ENOCH s.p.   (F913)
(Noyon, J.) [Fr] SA cor pts ENOCH s.p. (F914)

Lamb Most Holy *see Agnus Dei

Laudate Dominum
(Gramss) 3pt mix cor MOSELER s.p.   (F915)

Les Moissonneurs (from Ruth)
[Fr] 4pt mix cor HEUGEL voc sc s.p., voc pt
s.p.   (F916)

Lord God Of Heaven *see Panis Angelicus

Lord, Thou Art Holy
(Dean) 2pt/unis oct SOUTHERN $.25   (F917)

Lord, We Implore Thee
(Southwick) 4pt mix cor oct SCHIRM.G 3283
$.25   (F918)

Lord, We Thank Thee For Thy Grace *Gen
(Sircom) SATB SCHMITT SD6206 $.25   (F919)

March And Chorus *see Marche Et Choeur

Marche Et Choeur (from Ruth)
"March And Chorus" SATB,pno SCHIRM.EC 384
$.20   (F920)

Mary At The Manger *Xmas
(Tkach) SSA KJOS 6041 $.30   (F921)

Mary's Cradle Song *Xmas
(Goldman) SATB,acap oct LAWSON 51681 $.30 (F922)

Messa A Troix Voix *Op.21
(Williams, W.) "Communion Service In A"
[Lat/Eng] STB/SATB,soli,org SCHIRM.EC
1208 $1.50, ipr   (F923)

Nation's Prayer *see Panis Angelicus

O God Of Life *see Panis Angelicus

O Jesus Grant Me Hope And Comfort *Gen
(Buszin) TTBB SCHMITT 3507 $.25   (F924)
(Buszin) SSAA SCHMITT 2549 $.20   (F925)
(Buszin) SAB SCHMITT 5519 $.30   (F926)
(Stein; Buszin) SATB SCHMITT 1544 $.30 (F927)

FRANCK, CESAR (cont'd.)

O Lord Most Holy *see Panis Angelicus

O Lord, Most Merciful *see Panis Angelicus

O Praise Ye The Lord (Psalm 150)
SATB oct BELWIN 64008 $.35 (F928)
SAB oct BELWIN 64011 $.35 (F929)

O Salutaris
2pt ENOCH TP246 s.p. (F930)

Oh, Praise The Lord, Ye Nations All
SATB WARNER WB-293 $.35 (F931)

Panis Angelicus *Commun/Gen,mot
see THREE WEDDING MOTETS
2pt ASHDOWN E.A.193 s.p. (F932)
3pt ASHDOWN V.T.11 s.p. (F933)
SATB ENOCH EC131 s.p. (F934)
TTBB ENOCH EC307 s.p. (F935)
SSATB ENOCH EC309 s.p. (F936)
[Lat] S oct DURAND s.p. (F937)
[Lat] Mez oct DURAND s.p. (F938)
mix cor NORDISKA 3552 s.p. (F939)
mix cor,pno cor pts NORDISKA 3552 s.p., voc sc NORDISKA 1893 s.p. (F940)
"Lord God Of Heaven" SATB oct BELWIN 641 $.25 (F941)
"O Lord Most Holy" SATB,S solo ALLANS 219 s.p. (F942)
"O Lord Most Holy" [Lat/Eng] SATB,T/S solo, org SCHIRM.EC 2228 $.30, ipr (F943)
"O Lord Most Holy" SATB KJOS 7020 $.30 (F944)
"O Lord Most Holy" SATB oct LESLIE 4049 (F945)
(Barr, George) "Nation's Prayer" SAB oct BELWIN 667 $.25 (F946)
(Barr, George) "Nation's Prayer" SATB oct BELWIN 641 $.25 (F947)
(Barr, George) "Nation's Prayer" SSA oct BELWIN 640 $.25 (F948)
(Bonset, J.) mix cor ALSBACH&D sc s.p., cor pts s.p. (F949)
(Bornschein) "Lord God Of Heaven" SA oct FISCHER,J 6019 $.30 (F950)
(Bornschein) "Lord God Of Heaven" SATB oct FISCHER,J 6020 $.30 (F951)
(Breck) "O Lord Most Holy" SATB oct FISCHER,C CM-6629 $.25 (F952)
(Christy) SSA SCHMITT 2519 $.30 (F953)
(Dale, Phillip) "O Lord Most Holy" SA ALLANS 223 s.p. (F954)
(Davis, K.) "O Lord, Most Merciful" SA,org SCHIRM.EC 1571 $.25 (F955)
(Deis) "Father Most Merciful" [Eng/Lat] 2pt wom cor/2pt men cor,vln/vcl oct SCHIRM.G 7580 $.30 (F956)
(Deis) "Father Most Merciful" [Eng/Lat] SAB oct SCHIRM.G 10024 $.30 (F957)
(Downing,) "Father Most Merciful" [Eng/Lat] 3pt wom cor oct SCHIRM.G 9496 $.25 (F958)
(Downing) "Father Most Merciful" [Eng/Lat] 4pt mix cor oct SCHIRM.G 9637 $.30 (F959)
(Ehret) "O Lord Most Holy" SA oct BOOSEY 5239 $.30 (F960)
(Ehret) "O Lord Most Holy" SAB oct BOOSEY 5548 $.30 (F961)
(Harris, V.) SSA oct PRESSER 332-13651 $.30 (F962)
(Heller) SATB SCHMITT 1639 $.35 (F963)
(Kubik) SATB/2 eq voices,opt pno sc RICORDI-ARG BA9254 s.p., cor pts RICORDI-ARG s.p. (F964)
(Montani) SATB,org BOSTON 2468 $.35 (F965)
(Mueller) "O Lord Most Holy" SA oct FISCHER,C CM-6891 $.25 (F966)
(Mueller) "O Lord Most Holy" SAB oct FISCHER,C CM-6658 $.25 (F967)
(Mueller) "O Lord Most Holy" 3pt jr cor/SAB (easy) FISCHER,C CM 6658 $.25 (F968)
(Page, N.) SATB oct PRESSER 332-14872 $.30 (F969)
(Peery, R.) "O Lord Most Holy" SAB oct PRESSER 312-40244 $.30 (F970)
(Pitcher, Gladys) "O Lord Most Holy" 3pt wom cor,pno (med) oct WILLIS 8489 $.20 (F971)
(Richardson) SSA,org/pno BOSTON 2793 $.35 (F972)
(Ronaldson) "O Lord Most Holy" SATB,acap, opt pno oct PRO ART 1013 $.30 (F973)
(Ronaldson) "O Lord Most Holy" SAB oct PRO ART 1062 $.30 (F974)
(Ronaldson) "O Lord Most Holy" SSA oct PRO ART 1036 $.30 (F975)
(Ronaldson) "O Lord Most Holy" 2pt oct PRO ART 1051 $.30 (F976)
(Runkel, K.) "O Lord Most Holy" SAB oct PRESSER 312-15173 $.30 (F977)
(Ryder) "O Lord Most Holy" SATB,org BOSTON 510 $.35 (F978)
(Ryder) "O Lord Most Holy" TTBB,org BOSTON 477 $.35 (F979)
(Scott) "O Lord Most Holy" SATB oct FISCHER,C CM-6258 $.25 (F980)
(Treharne) "O Lord Most Holy" SA,org/pno BOSTON 10209 $.35 (F981)
(Wilson) "O God Of Life" SAB oct BOURNE T10 $.25 (F982)

Panis Angelicus Hostia *Commun
[Lat] ST ZANIBON 3610 s.p. (F983)
[Lat] Mez/Bar ZANIBON 3611 s.p. (F984)

Pie Jesu
[Lat] cor,solo ENOCH s.p. (F985)

Praise The Lord (Psalm 150)
SATB oct LORENZ C140 $.30 (F986)

Praise Ye The Lord (Psalm 150) Bibl
SATB oct PRESSER 312-20762 $.30 (F987)
SATB oct VOLKWEIN VB246 $.25 (F988)
(Cain) SATB oct PRO ART 1189 $.30 (F989)
(Clough-Leighter, H.) SATB oct PRESSER 332-14082 $.40 (F990)
(Treharne) SATB,org BOSTON 1725 $.40 (F991)

Prayer For Brotherhood, A *prayer
SAB WEINBERGER s.p. (F992)

Prayer For Brotherhood, A
(Frederick) 2pt oct SHAPIRO SK 4010 $.25 (F993)
(Frederick) SAB oct SHAPIRO SK 5002 $.25 (F994)
(Frederick) SSA oct SHAPIRO SK 3004 $.25 (F995)
(Frederick) SATB oct SHAPIRO SK 2061 $.30 (F996)

Premiere Messe Sclennelle *Mass
STBB,pno/org CHOUDENS s.p. (F997)

Psalm 150 *see Halleluja! Lobt Gott

Psalm 150 *see Psaume CL

Psaume CL (Psalm 150)
(Busser, H.) [Fr] 4pt/4pt mix cor,org oct DURAND s.p. (F998)

Redemption
cor,orch sc KALMUS $12.00, ipa (F999)

Revelation Motet *mot
mix cor SOUTHERN $.35 (F1000)

Sanctus (from Messe A Trois Voix) Sanctus
(Cramer) [Eng/Lat] SATB MARKS 4250 $.25 (F1001)

Sing Praise To God *see Halleluja! Lobt Gott

Sing Praise To God, The Lord *see Halleluja! Lobt Gott

Solemn Mass *Mass
[Lat] cor voc sc KALMUS 6179 $2.50 (F1002)
cor,orch sc KALMUS $14.00, ipa (F1003)

Solemn Mass In A *Mass
mix cor BELWIN $1.50 (F1004)

Tantum Ergo
2pt ENOCH TP247 s.p. (F1005)

There Is No Eye For Seeing
(Kingsbury, John) SATB ALFRED 6637 $.30 (F1006)

They Are Ever Blessed (from Beautitudes, The)
SATB,org SCHIRM.EC 1729 $.30 (F1007)

To Us A Son Is Given *Xmas
SATB oct ELKAN-V 362-1236 $.30 (F1008)

Virgin At The Cradle, The *Xmas
SATB oct WALTON 2122 $.25 (F1009)

Virgin By The Manger *Xmas
(Christy) SATB oct BELWIN 2187 $.30 (F1010)

Virgin By The Manger, The *Xmas/Gen
2pt wom cor oct SCHIRM.G 5520 $.20 (F1011)

Welcome, Welcome, Dear Redeemer
SATB oct PRO ART 1725 $.25 (F1012)
(Southwick) 4pt mix cor,B solo oct SCHIRM.G 3284 $.25 (F1013)

Wo Find Ich Denn Dein's Vaters Haus
4pt mix cor&4pt mix cor MOSELER LB-340 s.p. (F1014)

Ye Fields Of Light, Celestial Plains
(Tillinghast) SSA,S solo WARNER W3396 $.30 (F1015)

FRANCK, J.

Jesu Huvud Sjunker Ner
mix cor NORDISKA 1707 s.p. (F1016)

FRANCK, [JOHANN WOLFGANG] (1641-1688)

Advent *Adv
mix cor sc ALSBACH&D s.p. (F1017)

Die Welt Singt Gottes Preis
(Vogel, Moritz; Nagler, Franciscus) [Ger] wom cor&jr cor,org,opt strings HUG 1 s.p. (F1018)

Messe *Op.86, Mass
[Fr] 2 eq voices,soli,pno/org oct DURAND s.p. (F1019)

Messe Facile *Op.191, Mass
[Fr] 2 eq voices,pno LEDUC BL166 voc sc s.p., voc pt s.p. (F1020)

Ostergesang *Easter
(Kuxhaven, D.) mix cor sc ALSBACH&D s.p. (F1021)

Pinksterlied
wom cor sc ALSBACH&D s.p. (F1022)

Soul, Be Still
(Stein) SATBB,acap (med) oct WILLIS 6173 $.10 (F1023)

Tantum Ergo *Commun,mot
[Lat] 3 eq voices,S solo oct DURAND s.p. (F1024)

FRANCK, MELCHIOR (ca. 1579-1639)

Aber Wer Glaubt Unserer Predigt *mot
(Nitsche) SATB HANSSLER 1.086 s.p. (F1025)

Ach Gott, Vom Himmel Sieh Darein *mot
(Stern; Nitsche) SATB HANSSLER 1.294 s.p. (F1026)

Ach, Herr, Ich Bin Nicht Wert *Epiph
[Ger] SATB,acap (med easy) BAREN. BA 1185 $.25 see from Deutsche Evangeliensspruche (F1027)

Ach, Treuer Heiland Jesu Christ
(Schabasser, Josef) mix cor,acap oct DOBLINGER s.p. see also CHRISTUS, DER HERR (F1028)

Allein Zu Dir Herr Jesu Christ *mot
(Henriksen) "Lord Jesus Christ, In Thee Alone" [Eng/Ger] 4pt mix cor,acap oct SCHIRM.G 11173 $.35 (F1029)
(Stern; Nitsche) SATB HANSSLER 1.295 s.p. (F1030)

Also Hat Gott Die Welt Geliebt *Bibl/mot
(Trubel) SATB HANSSLER 1.322 s.p. (F1031)

And The Ransomed Of The Lord Shall Return *see Die Erloeseten Des Herrn Werden Wiederkommen

Aus Tiefer Not Not Schrei Ich Zu Dir *Eng/Ger
(Henriksen) "Out Of The Depths I Cry To Thee" 4pt mix cor,acap oct SCHIRM.G 11175 $.35 (F1032)

FRANCK, MELCHIOR (cont'd.)

Aus Tiefer Not Schrei Ich Zu Dir *mot
SATTB HANSSLER 6.2673 s.p. contains also: Walter (Walther), Johann, Wohlauf, Wohlauf Mit Lauter Stimm (SATB) (F1033)
SATTB/SAATB HANSSLER 6.188 s.p. contains also: Schutz, Heinrich, Lobt Gott, Den Herrn Der Herrlichkeit (SATB) (F1034)
(Stern; Nitsche) SATB HANSSLER 1.292 s.p. (F1035)

Ausgewahlte Kirchenlieder *CCU,mot/Psalm
[Ger] SATB HANSSLER 4.014 $6.00 (F1036)

Bleib Bei Mir, Herr
see Schott, Johann Georg, Singet Dem Herrn Ein Neues Lied Denn Er Tut Grosse Wunder

Come Ye *see Kommt Her

Dank Sagen Wir Alle Gott *Xmas/Gen,mot
(Peters-Marquardt, Franz) [Ger] SSB&ATTB (med diff) BAREN. BA 624 $2.00 (F1037)

Darum Seid Barmherzig *Trin
(Ameln, Konrad) [Ger] SATB/SAAB,acap (med easy) BAREN. BA 1219 $.25 see from DEUTSCHE EVANGELIENSPRUCHE, 1623 (F1038)

Das Trostreiche 53. Kapitel Des Propheten Jesaja *CC7U,mot
(Nitsche) SATB HANSSLER 2.003 s.p. (F1039)

Der Brautigam Wird Bald Rufen
see Bach, Johann Sebastian, Allein Gott In Der Hoh Sei Ehr

Der Herr Ist Mein Getreuer Hirt *mot
(Stern; Nitsche) SATB HANSSLER 1.290 s.p. (F1040)

Deutsche Evangeliensspruche *see Ach, Herr, Ich Bin Nicht Wert; Entsetzet Euch Nicht; Es Ist Nicht Fein, Dass Man Den Kindlein Ihr Brot Nehme; Und Ich Horte Eine Grosse Stimm (F1041)

Deutsche Evangeliensspruche 1623 *see Furchtet Euch Nicht; Siehe, Dieser Wird Gesetzt Zu Einem Fall (F1042)

Deutsche Evangeliensspruche Fur Das Kirchenjahr 1623 *CCU,Gen
(Ameln, Konrad) [Ger] SATB,acap (med easy) BAREN. BA 1180 $8.75 (F1043)

Die Erloeseten Des Herrn Werden Wiederkommen
(Granville) "And The Ransomed Of The Lord Shall Return" SATB oct FOX CM24 $.25 (F1044)
(Granville) "And The Ransomed Of The Lord Shall Return" mix cor SOUTHERN $.25 (F1045)

Die Erloseten Des Herren Werden Wiederkommen
SATB HANSSLER 6.143 s.p. contains also: Rosenmuller, Johann, Welt Ade, Ich Bin Dein Mude (SSATB) (F1046)

Die Erloseten Des Herrn Werdenkommen *mot
(Berger) SATB HANSSLER 1.112 s.p. (F1047)
(Nitsche) SSATBB HANSSLER 1.015 s.p. (F1048)

Die Gerechten Werden Ewiglich Leben *mot
(Granville) "For The Righteous Shall Flourish Forever" SSATB,acap oct FOX CM25 $.30 (F1049)
(Nitsche) SSATB HANSSLER 1.049 s.p. (F1050)

Die Mit Tranen Saen *mot
(Mauersberger, E.) dbl cor,acap cor pts BREITKOPF-L PB-3403 s.p., voc pt BREITKOPF-L CHB-2759 s.p. (F1051)

Dienet Einand
see Schott, Johann Georg, Singet Dem Herrn Ein Neues Lied Denn Er Tut Grosse Wunder

Durch Adams Fall Ist Ganz Verderbt *mot
(Stern; Nitsche) SATB HANSSLER 1.297 s.p. contains also: Praetorius, Michael, Durch Adams Fall Ist Ganz Verderbt (F1052)

Ei Du Frommer Und Getreuer Knecht *mot
(Nitsche) SSAB&ATTB HANSSLER 1.053 s.p. (F1053)

Ein Feste Burg Ist Unser Gott *mot,Eng/Ger
(Hendriksen) "Mighty Fortress Is Our God, A" 4pt mix cor,acap oct SCHIRM.G 11172 $.35 (F1054)
(Stern; Nitsche) SATB HANSSLER 1.298 s.p. contains also: Praetorius, Michael, Ein Feste Burg Ist Unser Gott (F1055)

En Salme Om Vort Fald Og Forlosning *Psalm, 16th cent
(Woldike, Mogens) [Dan] SATTB,acap HANSEN-DEN 83 s.p. see also SALMEMELODIER FRA REFORMATIONSTIDEN (F1056)

Entsetzet Euch Nicht *Easter
[Ger] SATB,acap (med easy) BAREN. BA 1182 $.40 see from Deutsche Evangeliensspruche (F1057)

Er Hat Alles Wohl Gemacht *Trin
(Ameln, Konrad) [Ger] SATB/SAAB,acap (med easy) BAREN. BA 1211 $.25 see from DEUTSCHE EVANGELIENSPRUCHE, 1623 (F1058)

Es Hat's Kein Aug Gesehen *Gen,mot
[Ger] 5pt mix cor,acap (easy) BAREN. BA 6305 s.p. (F1059)
(Nitsche) SSATB HANSSLER 1.048 s.p. (F1060)

Es Ist Nicht Fein, Dass Man Den Kindlein Ihr Brot Nehme *Psntd
[Ger] SATB,acap (med easy, reminiscere) BAREN. BA 2732 $.40 see from Deutsche Evangeliensspruche (F1061)

Es Kommt Aber Die Zeit
(Ameln, Konrad) SATB/SSAB,acap (med easy) BAREN. BA 2734 $.25 see from DEUTSCHE EVANGELIENSPRUCHE, 1623 (F1062)

Es Wolle Gott Uns Gnadig Sein *mot
(Stern; Nitsche) SATB HANSSLER 1.293 s.p. (F1063)

Father, Thy Holy Spirit Send *see Jesu, Dein' Seel'

FRANCK, MELCHIOR (cont'd.)

Five Motets *CC5U,mot
mix cor,acap voc sc KALMUS 6172 $1.50
(F1064)

For The Righteous Shall Flourish Forever
*see Die Gerechten Werden Ewiglich Leben

Fuhrwahr, Er Trug Uns're Krankheit
(Payson, A.) "Surely, He Hath Borne Our
Griefs" SATB,acap FRANK F-446 $.30
(F1065)

Furchtet Euch Nicht *Xmas
(Ameln, Konrad) [Ger] SATB,acap (med easy)
BAREN. BA 2731 $.40 see from Deutsche
Evangelienspruche 1623
(F1066)

Furwahr, Er Trug Unsere Krankheit *mot
(Nitsche) SATB HANSSLER 1.115 s.p.
(F1067)

Furwahr, Er Trug Unsre Krankheit *Easter/
Psntd
SATB,acap voc pt DOBLINGER s.p. see also
PASSION UND OSTERN
(F1068)

Gelobet Sei Gott Und Der Vater *mot
(Nitsche) SSATTB HANSSLER 1.014 s.p.
(F1069)

Gen Himmel Aufgefahren Ist, Halleluja
see Praetorius, Michael, Gott, Dem Vater Im
Hochsten Thron

Gleichwie Der Blitz Ausgehet *Trin
(Ameln, Konrad) [Ger] SATB,acap BAREN.
BA 1575 $.40 see from DEUTSCHE
EVANGELIENSPRUCHE 1623
(F1070)

Gleichwie Moses In Der Wuste *mot
(Ameln, Konrad) [Ger] SATB/SAAB,acap (med
easy) BAREN. BA 1216 $.40 see from
DEUTSCHE EVANGELIENSPRUCHE, 1623
(F1071)

God Hath Done All Things Well *Gen
SATB,kbd (med diff) oct CONCORDIA 98-1721
$.25
(F1072)

Herr Christ, Der Einig Gotts Sohn *mot
(Stern; Nitsche) SATB HANSSLER 1.302 s.p.
(F1073)

Herr, Fur Dein Wort Sei Hoch Gepreist *mot
(Stern; Nitsche) SATB HANSSLER 1.301 s.p.
(F1074)

Herr Gott, Nun Sei Gepreiset *Eng/Ger
(Henriksen) "Lord God, We Praise Thy
Goodness" 4pt mix cor,acap oct SCHIRM.G
11171 $.35
(F1075)

Herr Jesu, Deine Angst Und Pein
see Erk, Ludwig, Wahrlich, All Unsre Qualen

Herr, Komm Hinab, Eh Denn Mein Kind Stirbet
*Trin
(Ameln, Konrad) [Ger] SATB/SAAB,acap (med
easy) BAREN. BA 2735 $.25 see from
DEUTSCHE EVANGELIENSPRUCHE, 1623 (F1076)

Herr, Nun Lassest Du Deinen Diener *Thanks,
mot
(Berger) SATB HANSSLER 1.113 s.p. (F1077)
(Nitsche) SSB&ATTB HANSSLER 1.052 s.p.
(F1078)

Hosianna
mix cor NORDISKA 1652 s.p. (F1079)

I Know That My Redeemer Liveth *see Ich
Weiss, Dass Mein Erloeser Lebt

Ich Habe Euch Noch Viel Zu Sagen *cant
(Ameln, Konrad) SATB/SSAB,acap (med easy)
BAREN. BA 1574 $.25 see from DEUTSCHE
EVANGELIENSPRUCHE, 1623
(F1080)

Ich Halte Es Dafur, Dass Dieser Zeit *mot
(Nitsche) SATB HANSSLER 1.050 s.p. (F1081)

Ich Ruf Zu Dir, Herr Jesu Christ *mot
(Stern; Nitsche) SATB HANSSLER 1.288 s.p.
contains also: Praetorius, Michael, Ich
Ruf Zu Dir, Herr Jesu Christ (Stern;
Nitsche)
(F1082)

Ich Weiss, Dass Mein Erloeser Lebt *Easter
(Granville) "I Know That My Redeemer
Liveth" SATBB,acap oct FOX CM12 $.35
(F1083)

Ich Weiss, Dass Mein Erloser Lebt *Gd.Fri.,
mot
SATTB,acap voc pt DOBLINGER s.p. see also
TOD UND VERGANGLICHKEIT
(F1084)
(Nitsche) SATTB HANSSLER 1.016 s.p. (F1085)

If God Is For Us
(Lindquist, M.) SATB oct PRESSER MC233 $.30
(F1086)

In Den Armen Dein *Gd.Fri.
SSATB,acap voc pt DOBLINGER s.p. see also
TOD UND VERGANGLICHKEIT
(F1087)

In Dich Hab Ich Gehoffet, Herr *mot
(Stern; Nitsche) SATB HANSSLER 1.289 s.p.
(F1088)

Ist Gott Fur Uns *Gen
[Ger] SATB,acap (easy) BAREN. BA 993 s.p.
(F1089)

Ist Gott Fur Uns, Wer Mag Wider Uns Sein
*mot
(Nitsche) SATB HANSSLER 1.055 s.p. (F1090)

Jerusalem, Du Hochgebaute Stadt
SATB HANSSLER 6.0916 s.p. contains also:
Nun Jauchz' Dem Herren Alle Welt (F1091)

Jesu, By Thee *see Jesu, Dein' Seel' Lass
Heilig'n Mich

Jesu, By Thee I Would Be Blessed *see Jesu,
Dein' Seel'lass Heilig'n Mich

Jesu, Dein' Seel *Lent/Pent/Whitsun
SATB,acap voc pt DOBLINGER s.p. see also
PFINGSTEN UND EUCHARISTIE
(F1092)
"Father, Thy Holy Spirit Send" SATB,acap
SCHIRM.EC 1687 $.25
(F1093)

Jesu, Dein Seel' Lass Heil'gen Mich
SATB HANSSLER 6.0828 s.p.
(F1094)

FRANCK, MELCHIOR (cont'd.)

Jesu, Dein' Seel' Lass Heilig'n Mich
(Beveridge, L.) "Jesu, By Thee" [Ger/Eng]
TTBB,acap SCHIRM.EC 2199 $.30 (F1095)

Jesu, Dein' Seel'lass Heilig'n Mich *Eng/Ger
(Beveridge) "Jesu, By Thee I Would Be
Blessed" 4pt mix cor,acap oct SCHIRM.G
8677 $.25
(F1096)

Jesu, Du Zartes Kindelein *Adv/Xmas,mot
SATTB,acap voc pt DOBLINGER s.p. see also
ADVENT UND WEIHNACHT, HEFT 1 (F1097)
(Hellmann) SATTB HANSSLER 1.090 s.p.
(F1098)

Jesus And The Pharisees *Gen/Trin
SATB,acap (med easy) oct CONCORDIA 98-2093
$.30
(F1099)

Jesus, Thou Tender Child Divine
SATB,org/pno PETERS 66031 $.25 (F1100)

Jesus, Thy Blessings Give To Me
(Knight, Gerald) SATB,acap oct FISCHER,C
CM-7505 $.25
(F1101)

Jesus, Thy Cross Redeem My Soul
see Two Anthems

Kommt Her
"Come Ye" [Ger/Eng] SATB,acap BROUDE BR.
$.30
(F1102)

Kommt Her, Ihr Gesegneten Meines Vaters
*Trin
(Ameln, Konrad) [Ger] SATB,acap BAREN.
BA 1212 $.25 see from DEUTSCHE
EVANGELIENSPRUCHE 1623
(F1103)

Kommt Her Zu Mir Alle
SATB HANSSLER 6.172 s.p. (F1104)

Kommt Her Zu Mir, Spricht Gottes Sohn
see Bach, Johann Sebastian, Jesu, Meine
Freude, Meines Herzens [Chorale]

Lobet Den Herren, Alle Heiden *mot
(Nitsche) SSATTB HANSSLER 1.051 s.p. (F1105)

Lord God, We Praise Thy Goodness *see Herr
Gott, Nun Sei Gepreiset

Lord Jesus Christ, In Thee Alone *see Allein
Zu Dir Herr Jesu Christ

Mache Dich Auf, Werde Licht
(Stern; Nitsche) ST,cont,2vln sc HANSSLER
5.071 s.p., ipa
(F1106)

Meine Seele Erhebt Den Herren *mot
(Stern; Nitsche) SATB HANSSLER 1.310 s.p.
(F1107)

Mighty Fortress Is Our God, A *see Ein Feste
Burg Ist Unser Gott

Mit Freuden Hor Es Alle Welt
see Cruger, Johann, Frohlich Soll Mein
Herze Springen

Nehmet Hin Den Heiligen Geist
(Ameln, Konrad) SATB/SSAB,acap (med easy)
BAREN. BA 1218 $.25 see from DEUTSCHE
EVANGELIENSPRUCHE, 1623
(F1108)

Nu Looft Den Heer
wom cor sc ALSBACH&D s.p. (F1109)

Nun Freut Euch, Gottes Kinder All
see Schott, Johann Georg, Singet Dem Herrn
Ein Neues Lied Denn Er Tut Grosse Wunder

Nun Jauchz' Dem Herren Alle Welt
see Franck, Melchior, Jerusalem, Du
Hochgebaute Stadt

O Lord, I Am Not Worthy *Commun/Epiph
SATB,acap (med easy) oct CONCORDIA 98-1636
$.25
(F1110)

O Mensch, Bewein Dein Sunde Gross *mot
(Stern; Nitsche) SATB HANSSLER 1.299 s.p.
(F1111)

Ordnung Einer Christvesper *CCU
(Stern; Nitsche) mix cor HANSSLER 2.015
s.p.
(F1112)

Our Assurance Is In Heaven *see Unser Wandel
Ist Im Himmel

Our Father, Thou In Heaven Above *see Vater
Unser In Himmelreich

Out Of The Depths I Cry To Thee *see Aus
Tiefer Not Not Schrei Ich Zu Dir

Revelation Motet *mot
[Ger/Eng] SATB,acap BROUDE BR. $.40 (F1113)

Siehe, Dieser Wird Gesetzt Zu Einem Fall
*Xmas
(Ameln, Konrad) [Ger] SATB,acap (med easy)
BAREN. BA 2731 $.65 see from Deutsche
Evangelienspruche
(F1114)

Siehe, Eine Jungfrau Ist Schwanger *Xmas
(Stern; Nitsche) SS/TT,cont HANSSLER 5.072
s.p.
(F1115)

Surely, He Hath Borne Our Griefs *see
Fuhrwahr, Er Trug Uns're Krankheit

Thou Goest To Jerusalem *Lent
SATB,acap (med easy, or pre-Lent) oct
CONCORDIA 98-1092 $.25
(F1116)

Trachtet Am Ersten Nach Dem Reich Gottes
*Trin
(Ameln, Konrad) [Ger] SATB/SAAB,acap (med
easy) BAREN. BA 1576 $.40 see from
DEUTSCHE EVANGELIENSPRUCHE, 1623 (F1117)

Two Anthems
SATB,opt pno PETERS 66033 $.30
contains: Jesus, Thy Cross Redeem My
Soul; When Fears Of Death Do Fright Me
(F1118)

FRANCK, MELCHIOR (cont'd.)

Und Ich Horte Eine Grosse Stimm *Fest
[Ger] SATB,acap (med easy, michaelmas)
BAREN. BA 1572 $.40 see from Deutsche
Evangelienspruche
(F1119)

Uns Ist Ein Kind Geboren *Xmas,mot
(Nitsche) SATB HANSSLER 1.080 s.p. (F1120)
(Stern; Nitsche) SATB,cont HANSSLER 1.311
s.p.
(F1121)

Unser Wandel Ist Im Himmel *mot
(Granville) "Our Assurance Is In Heaven"
SATB,acap oct FOX CM10 $.25 (F1122)
(Hellmann) SATB HANSSLER 1.098 s.p. (F1123)

Unseres Herzens Freude Hat Ein Ende *mot
(Mauersberger, E.) ATTB,acap cor pts
BREITKOPF-L PB-3402 s.p., voc pt
BREITKOPF-L CHB-2758 s.p.
(F1124)

Uppfaren Ar Var Herre Krist
mix cor NORDISKA 4869 s.p. (F1125)

Vater Unser Im Himmelreich *mot
(Nitsche) SATB HANSSLER 1.056 s.p. (F1126)
(Stern; Nitsche) SATB HANSSLER 1.287 s.p.
contains also: Praetorius, Michael, In
Dich Hab Ich Gehoffet
(F1127)

Vater Unser In Himmelreich
(Henriksen) "Our Father, Thou In Heaven
Above" [Eng/Ger] 4pt mix cor,acap oct
SCHIRM.G 11174 $.40
(F1128)

Wahrlich, Ich Sage Euch: So Ihr Den Vater
Etwas Bitten Werdet
(Ameln, Konrad) SATB/SSAB,acap (med easy)
BAREN. BA 1215 $.40 see from DEUTSCHE
EVANGELIENSPRUCHE, 1623
(F1129)

War Gott Nicht Mit Uns Diese Zeit *mot
(Stern; Nitsche) SATB HANSSLER 1.296 s.p.
contains also: Praetorius, Michael, War
Gott Nicht Mit Uns Diese Zeit
(F1130)

Warum Denket Ihr So Args In Eurem Herzen?
*Trin
(Ameln, Konrad) [Ger] SATB/SAAB,acap (med
easy) BAREN. BA 2733 $.25 see from
DEUTSCHE EVANGELIENSPRUCHE, 1623 (F1131)

Wenn Du Geladen Wirst, So Gehe Hin *Trin
(Ameln, Konrad) [Ger] SATB/SAAB,acap (med
easy) BAREN. BA 1573 $.40 see from
DEUTSCHE EVANGELIENSPRUCHE, 1623 (F1132)

Wenn Ich In Todesnoten Bin *Gd.Fri.
SATB,acap voc pt DOBLINGER s.p. see also
TOD UND VERGANGLICHKEIT
(F1133)

Wenn Mein Stundlein Vorhanden Ist *mot
(Stern; Nitsche) SATB HANSSLER 1.303 s.p.
contains also: Praetorius, Michael, Wenn
Mein Stundlein Vorhanden Ist
(F1134)

Wer Uberwindet, Dem Will Ich *mot
(Nitsche) SATB HANSSLER 1.079 s.p. (F1135)

When Fears Of Death Do Fright Me
see Two Anthems

Wo Gott Der Herr Nicht Bei Uns Halt *mot
see Praetorius, Michael, Der Morgenstern
Ist Aufgedrungen
(Stern; Nitsche) SATB HANSSLER 1.291 s.p.
(F1136)

Wo Gott Zum Haus Nicht Gibt Sein Gunst *mot
(Nitsche) SATB HANSSLER 1.057 s.p. (F1137)
(Stern; Nitsche) SATB HANSSLER 1.300 s.p.
contains also: Praetorius, Michael, Wo
Gott Zum Haus Nicht Gibt Sein Gunst
(F1138)

FRANCO
Ave Verum Corpus
"Jesu, Word Of God Incarnate" SA/boy cor&
TB,org SCHIRM.EC 2289 $.18 (F1139)

Jesu, Word Of God Incarnate *see Ave Verum
Corpus

Oh Senora *mot,Mex
(Barwick, S.; Hines, R.S.) SATB,acap PEER
$.35
(F1140)

Parce Mihi Domini *mot,Mex
(Barwick, S.; Hines, R.S.) SATB,acap PEER
$.35
(F1141)

Plegaria A La Virgen
mix cor SOUTHERN $.25 (F1142)

Plegaria A La Virgin *mot,Mex
(Barwick, S.; Hines, R.S.) SSATB,acap PEER
$.35
(F1143)

Proverb Of Solomon, A *Bibl
SATB GENERAL 761CH $.60 (F1144)

Salve *mot,Mex
(Barwick, S.; Hines, R.S.) SATB,acap PEER
$.80
(F1145)

Tantum Ergo
"Therefore We Before Him Bending" SA/boy
cor&TB,org SCHIRM.EC 2290 $.18 (F1146)

Therefore We Before Him Bending *see Tantum
Ergo

FRANCO, CESARE
see FRANCK, CESAR

FRANCO, JOHAN (1908-)
God's Love Is Like The Sun
SAB,acap oct WORLD ESA-1621-7 $.30 (F1147)

FRANCONIA
Come, Holy Spirit, Come
(Hastings) SATB oct BOURNE HA13 $.30
(F1148)

FRANGKISER, CARL (1894-)
King Of The World *Xmas
SATB oct SHAPIRO SK 2001 $.30 (F1149)

FRANK
In Silence And Wonder *Xmas
SATB oct GALAXY 1.2115.1 $.30   (F1150)

Mary At The Crib *see Daudet

Now Is Christ Risen *Easter
SATB oct GALAXY 1.1881.1 $.30   (F1151)

Our God
3pt jr cor/SAB (med easy) FISCHER,C CM 7624
$.20   (F1152)

Song Of The Little Lamb
SSA MARKS 4185 $.25   (F1153)

Star Proclaims The King, The *Xmas
(Harris) SATB oct PRO ART 2461 $.25 (F1154)

FRANK, J.L.
Bow Down Thine Ear *Bibl
4pt mix cor,S solo oct SCHIRM.G 3413 $.20
(F1155)

O Lord Most Holy *Gen/Lent
4pt mix cor,T solo oct SCHIRM.G 3415 $.20
(F1156)

FRANK, J.W.
Ein Kind Ist Uns Zum Heil Geborn *Xmas
TTBB HANSSLER 6.0378 s.p.   (F1157)

FRANK, MARCEL [GUSTAVE] (1909-   )
Glorious Creation *cant
mix cor BELWIN $.75   (F1158)

God's Glory And Honour
mix cor oct SCHIRM.G 10722 $.25   (F1159)

Kings Of The Earth And All People (Psalm 148)
Bibl
8pt mix cor,org oct SCHIRM.G 10991 $.25
(F1160)

Let There Be Light, O Lord
SATB oct SHAPIRO SK 2039 $.25   (F1161)

Lord, Make Me An Instrument Of Thy Peace
*prayer
SATB,pno/org PEER $.45   (F1162)

Psalm 148 *see Kings Of The Earth And All
People

FRANK, MICHAEL
Ach Wie Fluchtig, Ach Wie Nichtig
(Berger, H.L.) TTBB HANSSLER 6.5068 s.p.
contains also: Anonymous, Her, Da Du
Vormals Hast Dein Land   (F1163)

FRANK, RENE (1910-1965)
Fear Thou Not
SATB oct AGAPE A 314 $.20   (F1164)

Spite Of Michal, The
[Eng] SSA,Bar solo TRANSCON. TCL 326 $.75,
ipa   (F1165)

Thou Wilt Keep Him In Perfect Peace
SATB oct AGAPE A 337 $.30   (F1166)

FRANKE
Golden Harps Are Sounding
see SIX EASTER CAROLS

FRANZ
Ave Maria
(Suchoff) [Eng] SATB MARKS 4159 $.25
(F1167)

Bread Of The World In Mercy Broken
(Ehret) SATB oct BOURNE WE4 $.25   (F1168)

Come, My Soul, Thou Must Be Waking
(Watson) SSA,acap oct PRO ART 1035 $.20
(F1169)

FRANZ, ROBERT (1815-1892)
Dedication *see Die Widmung

Die Widmung *Op.14,No.1
(Parnell) "Dedication" SSAA SHAWNEE B246
$.25   (F1170)
(Riegger) "Dedication" SATB FLAMMER A 5354
$.30   (F1171)
(Riegger) "Dedication" SSA FLAMMER B 5106
$.30   (F1172)

FRANZ SCHUBERT SONGS FOR TREBLE VOICES see
Schubert, Franz (Peter)

FRANZ, WALTER
So Spricht Der Herr
men cor,acap oct DOBLINGER s.p.   (F1173)

FRANZISKUSMESSE see Tittel, Ernst

FRASER
Before The Break Of Day
SA/TB FLAMMER E5095 $.25   (F1174)

Church A Mighty Refuge Is, The
SATB FLAMMER A 5274 $.25   (F1175)

Come, Children, Run!
SA/TB FLAMMER E5147 $.30   (F1176)

God Be Merciful Unto Us
SATB oct FOX PS129 $.25   (F1177)

God, Creator
SA/TB FLAMMER E5013 $.25   (F1178)

Is Born Today!
SA/TB FLAMMER E5028 $.25   (F1179)

Lord, Thou Hast Been Our Dwelling Place
SATB oct FOX PS127 $.25   (F1180)

Our Blest Redeemer *anthem
mix cor oct OXFORD 43.468 $.20   (F1181)

Sing Praise!
SATB FLAMMER A 5126 $.25   (F1182)

Son Of God Arisen Today
SA/TB FLAMMER E5034 $.25   (F1183)

Token Of His Love, The
SA/TB FLAMMER E5040 $.25   (F1184)

FRASER, NORMAN (1904-   )
Christmas Day *Xmas
SATB CHESTER s.p.   (F1185)

FRASER, SHENA
Carillon *Xmas,cant
SSA,pno,opt strings voc sc CURWEN C03740
s.p., ipr   (F1186)

Child Of Bliss *Xmas,cant/carol
2pt treb cor,pno CURWEN 3748 s.p.   (F1187)

God Be Merciful Unto Us *anthem
SATB PROWSE s.p.   (F1188)

Lord, Thou Hast Been Our Dwelling Place
*anthem
SATB PROWSE s.p.   (F1189)

To Him Give Praise
SSA,pno,opt strings (easy) voc sc OXFORD
46.207 $.80, ipr   (F1190)

FRATRES EGO ENIM ACCEPI see Palestrina,
Giovanni

FRAU NACHTIGALL, WACH AUF see Knab, Armin

FRAU SONNE SITZT IM HIMMELSHAUS see Knab, Armin

FRAUENHOLTZ, JOHANN CHRISTOPH (1684-1757)
Der Herr Gedenkt An Uns *cant
[Eng/Ger] cor,SB soli,org,strings KISTNER
sc s.p., cor pts s.p., ipa   (F1191)
(Wunderlich, R.) "Lord Remembers Us, The"
[Eng/Ger] mix cor,soli,org,opt strings&
cont voc sc CONCORDIA 97-6413 $.75
(F1192)
(Wunderlich, R.) "Lord Remembers Us, The"
[Ger] mix cor,soli,org,opt strings&cont
sc CONCORDIA 97-4255 $2.25, ipa   (F1193)

Jesus, Thanks To Thee We Offer *Asc/Gen
unis,kbd (med easy) oct CONCORDIA 98-1827
$.25   (F1194)

Lord Remembers Us, The *see Der Herr Gedenkt
An Uns

FRAY ANTON TENIA UNA BURA see Martin Pompey

FRE, HUGO
Lord's Prayer, The
SSA BIG3 $.25   (F1195)

FRED VAERE MED EDER see Hovland, Egil

FREDERICK
Lord's Prayer, The
SATB oct LORENZ C278 $.25   (F1196)

O Bless The Lord, My Soul *Gen
SATB SCHMITT 1734 $.25   (F1197)

FREDERICK, DONALD R.
Built On The Rock
SATB,opt inst oct SHAPIRO SK 2031 $.30
(F1198)

If Any Little Word Of Mine
SATB oct SHAPIRO SK 2022 $.25   (F1199)
SAB oct SHAPIRO SK 5005 $.25   (F1200)
SSA oct SHAPIRO SK 3015 $.25   (F1201)
2pt oct SHAPIRO SK 4012 $.25   (F1202)

Prayer Of Dedication, A *prayer
SATB,org,opt orch PEER $.45, ipr   (F1203)

FREDERICKSON, CARL
Bible Stories In Song (Bk. 1) *see Cassell

Bible Stories In Song (Bk. 2) *see Cassell

Christ Came To Bethlehem *Xmas
3pt jr cor/SAB (very easy) FISCHER,C R 6103
$.20   (F1204)
2pt jr cor FISCHER,C R 54 $.20   (F1205)
3pt jr cor/SSA (very easy) FISCHER,C R 634
$.20   (F1206)

Manger Song *Xmas,carol
SATB oct WALTON 2059 $.25   (F1207)

Star Over Bethlehem *cant
jr cor&sr cor,narrator BOSTON $1.50 (F1208)

FREDSFYRSTE, HERRE JESUS KRIST see Bach, Johann
Sebastian, Du Friedefurst, Herr Jesu Christ

FREE AT LAST *spir
(Ehret, Walter) SATB oct WALTON 2008 $.25
(F1209)

FREE ME LORD see Tubb, Monte, Libera Me

FREE, MY LORD, FREE AT LAS' *spir
(De Cormier) SATB oct LAWSON 51743 $.45
(F1210)

FREED
Angels We Have Heard On High
see Three Shepherd Carols

From Out Of A Wood
SATB,acap oct BOOSEY 5745 $.35   (F1211)

Gloria
[Lat] SATB,brass oct BOOSEY 5555 $.45, ipa
(F1212)

How Much Farther Must We Go
SATB HANSEN-US C616 $.40   (F1213)

I Will Make You Fishers Of Men
SATB HANSEN-US C621 $.40   (F1214)

O Come To Bethlehem
see Three Shepherd Carols

Shepherds Shake Off Your Drowsy Sleep
see Three Shepherd Carols

Sing We Of Paschal Joy *Easter
SATB FLAMMER A 5607 $.30   (F1215)

Three Shepherd Carols *Xmas,carol
SATB,acap oct BOOSEY 5680 $.40
contains: Angels We Have Heard On High; O
Come To Bethlehem; Shepherds Shake Off
Your Drowsy Sleep   (F1216)

FREED (cont'd.)
Where Were You Born, O Holy Child?
SATB,pno,opt perc oct BOOSEY 5620 $.30
(F1217)
SSA,pno,opt perc oct BOOSEY 5753 $.30
(F1218)

FREED, ISADORE (1900-1960)
Bless The Lord, O My Soul (Psalm 103)
[Eng] SATB TRANSCON. TCL 113 $.30, ipa
(F1219)

Chapel Service No. 1 *Sab-Eve
SATB&opt unis TRANSCON. TCL 333 $1.00
(F1220)

Chapel Service No. 2 *Sab-Eve
SATB&opt unis TRANSCON.   (F1221)

Etz Chayim
2pt wom cor HATIKVAH HCL 55 $.30   (F1222)

Hassidic Service *Sab-Eve
4pt TRANSCON. TCL 799 $2.50   (F1223)

High Holiday Music
[Eng/Heb] SATB TRANSCON. TCL 815 $2.00
(F1224)

I Will Lift Up Mine Eyes (Psalm 121)
[Eng] SATB TRANSCON. TCL 114 $.25   (F1225)

Make A Joyful Noise (Psalm 100)
[Eng] SATB TRANSCON. TCL 112 $.25   (F1226)

May The Words
see Prayer For Peace

Prayer For Peace
SATB HATIKVAH HCL 54 $.50
contains: May The Words; Prayer For Peace
(F1227)

Prayer For Peace
see Prayer For Peace

Psalm 100 *see Make A Joyful Noise

Psalm 103 *see Bless The Lord, O My Soul

Psalm 121 *see I Will Lift Up Mine Eyes

Sabbath Morning Service *Sab-Morn
2pt TRANSCON. TCL 324 $2.00   (F1228)

Sacred Service For Sabbath Eve *Sab-Eve
SATB TRANSCON. TCL 795 $4.00   (F1229)

Sacred Service For Sabbath Morning *Sab-Morn
SATB TRANSCON. TCL 765 $4.00   (F1230)

Torat Emet. *Sab-Eve
SATB TRANSCON. TCL 824 $1.25   (F1231)

V'shomru
SATB HATIKVAH HCL 51 $.30   (F1232)

Yism' Chu No. 1
SATB HATIKVAH HCL 52 $.30   (F1233)

Yism' Chu No. 2
SATB HATIKVAH HCL 53 $.25   (F1234)

FREEDOM see Burroughs, Bob

FREELY THE LORD GAVE HIS LOVINGKINDNESS see
Fux, Johann Joseph, Dominus Dabit
Benignitatem

FREEMAN
I Am Blessed By God's Love
SATB oct LORENZ A451 $.25   (F1235)

I Know What God Is *see Raye

FREEMAN, CHARLES
Father I'm Coming Home (composed with Mc
Candless, Robert)
SATB,opt bvl,drums,gtr oct WALTON 2980
$.35, ipa   (F1236)

I Found Jesus (composed with Mc Candless,
Robert)
SATB,opt bvl,drums,gtr oct WALTON 2983
$.40, ipa   (F1237)

We'll Kneel At Jesus' Feet (composed with Mc
Candless, Robert)
SATB,opt bvl,drums,gtr oct WALTON 2982
$.35, ipa   (F1238)

FREESTONE
He Shall Comfort Thine Heart
SATB oct LORENZ 9991 $.30   (F1239)

Let Nothing Disturb Thee
SATB oct SACRED S-5746 $.30   (F1240)

Sing We Merrily To God
SATB oct SACRED S-22 $.35   (F1241)

Thou Lovedst Me *Gen
SATB SCHMITT 874 $.20   (F1242)

FREESTONE, G.S.
Christ Was Born On Christmas Day *Xmas
SATB,T solo oct BELWIN 60807 $.25   (F1243)

God Cares For Me
unis jr cor GRAY GCMR 3279 $.30   (F1244)

God, Who Touchest Earth
unis oct GRAY GCMR 2950 $.30   (F1245)

Lord Jesus, Think On Me *Lent
SATB (med) ABINGDON APM-818 $.35   (F1246)

Love Came Down At Christmas *Xmas
SATB oct SACRED S-140 $.35   (F1247)

Oh Lord, Rebuke Me Not
SATB oct ELKAN-V 362-1292 $.30   (F1248)

Trust In The Lord
SATB,pno/org AMP A588 $.30   (F1249)

FREIBURGER MAGNIFICAT see Kropfreiter,
Augustinius Franz

FREIHEITSLIED see Schumann, Robert (Alexander)

FRELSENS DAG see Hovland, Egil

FREMDE SIND WIR see Orff, Carl

FRENCH, JACOB (1754-1817)
Teach Me The Measure Of My Days
(Mason) SATB oct WORD CS-698 $.25   (F1250)

FRENCH MASS, THE see Shepherd, John

FRERE THIBAULT see Lassus, Roland de (Orlandus)

FRESCOBALDI, GIROLAMO (1583-1643)
In Te Domine Speravi *mot
[Lat] 8pt mix cor ZANIBON 535 s.p.   (F1251)

FRET NOT THYSELF see Morgan

FRET NOT THYSELF see Pasquet, Jean

FRET NOT THYSELF see Young

FREU DICH DES WEIBES see Schein, Johann Hermann

FREU DICH, DU HIMMELSKONIGIN see Praetorius,
Michael

FREU DICH, DU WERTE CHRISTENHEIT see Eccard,
Johannes

FREU DICH, ERD- UND HIMMELSZELT see Denhoff,
Joachim

FREU DICH, ERD' UND STERNENZELT see Kubler,
Emil

FREU DICH, ERD' UND STERNENZELT see Rothschuh,
F.

FREU DICH HEUT see Lahusen, Christian

FREU DICH, O CHRISTENHEIT see Biebl, Franz

FREU' DICH SEHR, O MEINE SEELE see Bach, Johann
Sebastian

FREU DICH SEHR, O MEINE SEELE see Goudimel,
Claude

FREUD UND WOLLUST DIESER WELT see Pepping,
Ernst

FREUE DICH, DU TOCHTER ZION, FREUE DICH see
Hammerschmidt, Andreas

FREUE DICH, ERLOSTE SCHAR see Bach, Johann
Sebastian

FREUE DICH SEHR, DU TOCHTER ZION see Zipp,
Friedrich

FREUEN SOLLEN SICH DIE HIMMEL see Strohbach,
Siegfried

FREUET EUCH DES HERREN see Wagener, Gregor

FREUET EUCH IHR CHRISTEN ALLE see Bach, Johann
Sebastian

FREUET EUCH, IHR CHRISTEN ALLE see Fiebig, Kurt

FREUET EUCH, IHR CHRISTEN ALLE see Stern,
Hermann

FREUET EUCH, IHR CHRISTEN ALLE see Wagner,
Alexander

FREUET EUCH IN DEM HERRN see Micheelsen, Hans
Friedrich

FREUET EUCH MIT MIR see Vulpius, Melchior

FREUET EUCH UND JUBILIRT see Bach, Johann
Sebastian

FREUNDE, LASST UNS FROHLICH LOBEN see
Hollfelder, Waldram

FREUNDT, CORNELIUS (1535-1591)
Das Weihnachtsliederbuch *CC28U,Xmas
(Gohler, G; Hellmann, D.) SATB,acap cor pts
BREITKOPF-L CHB-2950 s.p.   (F1252)

Ein Kindelein Zu Bethlehem *Xmas
(Granville) "In Bethlehem, A Tiny Babe"
SATB,acap oct FOX CM21 $.30   (F1253)

Ein Kindlein Klein Zu Bethlehem *Xmas,mot
(Hellmann) SSAB HANSSLER 1.238 s.p.   (F1254)

How Lovely Sings The Angel Choir *Xmas
SATB,acap (med easy) oct CONCORDIA 98-2094
$.40   (F1255)

How Lovely Sings The Angel Host
(Knight, Gerald) SATB,acap oct FISCHER,C
CM-7587 $.30   (F1256)

In Bethlehem, A Tiny Babe *see Ein Kindelein
Zu Bethlehem

Praise God The Lord, Ye Sons Of Men *Xmas
SATB,acap (easy) oct CONCORDIA 98-1247 $.25   (F1257)

Weihnachtsliederbuch *CC26U,Xmas,mot,16th
cent
(Amein, Konrad) [Ger] SATB/SSATB/SSATTB,
acap (med easy) BAREN. BA 1934 $3.00   (F1258)

Wie Schon Singt Uns Der Engel Schar *mot
(Hellmann) SATB HANSSLER 1.513 s.p.   (F1259)

FREUT EUCH DES HERRN, IHR CHRISTEN ALL see
Schutz, Heinrich

FREUT EUCH DES HERRN, IHR CHRISTEN ALL see
Woehl, Waldemar

FREUT EUCH, DIE WEIHNACHTSZEIT BRICHT NUN
HEREIN see Michels, Josef

FREUT EUCH, FREUT EUCH! see Mozart, Wolfgang
Amadeus

FREUT EUCH, FREUT EUCH IN DIESER ZEIT see
Herzog, Johann Georg

FREUT EUCH IHR CHRISTEN ALLE see Baudach,
Ulrich

FREUT EUCH, IHR CHRISTEN ALLE, GOTT SCHENKT UNS
SEINEN SOHN see Eccard, Johannes

FREUT EUCH, IHR LEIBEN CHRISTEN ALL see Chemin-
Petit, Hans

FREUT EUCH, IHR LIEBEN CHRISTEN see Eccard,
Johannes

FREUT EUCH IHR LIEBEN CHRISTEN see Schroeter,
Leonhardt

FREUT EUCH, IHR LIEBEN CHRISTEN see Schroter,
Leonhard

FREUT EUCH, IHR LIEBEN CHRISTEN see Trubel,
Gerhard

FREUT EUCH, IHR LIEBEN CHRISTEN see Zipp,
Friedrich

FREUT EUCH, IHR LIEBEN CHRISTEN ALL see Gesius,
Bartholomaus

FREUT EUCH, IHR LIEBEN CHRISTEN ALL see Stern,
Hermann

FREUT EUCH, IHR LIEBEN CHRISTEN ALL see Werner,
Fritz

FREUT EUCH IM HERRN DENN ER IST NAH'! see
Lehner, F.X.

FREUT EUCH UND JUBILIERT see Bach, Johann
Sebastian

FREUT EUCH UND JUBILIERT see Calvisius, Sethus

FREUT EUCH UND JUBILIRT see Bach, Johann
Sebastian

FREUT EUCH VON HERZEN SEHR see Schroter,
Leonhard

FREY, R.
O Give Thanks To The Lord
SATB,org,opt hndbl,opt fl GRAY GCMR 3280
$.40   (F1260)

FREYDT
When We In Spirit View Thy Passion *Lent
(Nolte, Ewald V.) SATB/SSAB (med easy)
ABINGDON APM-548 $.35   (F1261)

FREYLINGHAUSEN, JOHANN A.
Macht Hoch Die Tur, Die Tor
see Strattner, G., Herr, Wir Stehen Hand In
Hand

FRICKER, PETER RACINE (1920-   )
In Excelsis Gloria
see Two Carols

Mary Is A Lady
see Two Carols

Two Carols *carol
SATB,acap (med) OXFORD 84.029 $.35
contains: In Excelsis Gloria; Mary Is A
Lady   (F1262)

FRID VARE MED EDER see Nilsson, Torsten

FRIDAY EVENING SERVICE see Amram, David Werner,
Shir L'Erev Shabbat

FRIDAY EVENING SERVICE see Glantz, Yehuda Leib

FRIDAY EVENING SERVICE see Wyner, [Yehudi]

FRIDEN HERRENS HELGON FINGO
(Berg, Gottfrid) 3pt mix cor NORDISKA 4392
s.p. see also Sacrae Cantiones   (F1263)

FRIED
And All The Bells On Earth Did Ring *Xmas
(Kennedy) SATB SCHMITT SD6229 $.45   (F1264)

FRIEDE AUF ERDEN see Schoenberg, Arnold

FRIEDE DEN BRUDERN, "DEIN REICH IST NICHT UNSRE
KIRCHE" see Schweizer, Rolf

FRIEDE SEI MIT EUCH see Driessler, Johannes

FRIEDE UBER ISRAEL! see Bach, Johann Sebastian

FRIEDELL
Feast Of The Star *cant
BELWIN $1.00   (F1265)

FRIEDELL, HAROLD W.
As I Sat On A Sunny Bank *Xmas
SATB oct GALAXY 1.0585.1 $.35   (F1266)

Come, My Way, My Truth, My Life
SATB oct GRAY GCMR 2252 $.30   (F1267)

Draw Us In The Spirit's Tether
SATB oct GRAY GCMR 2472 $.30   (F1268)

For This Cause
SATB oct GRAY GCMR 2622 $.35   (F1269)

Jesus So Lowly *Gen/Lent
SATB oct GRAY GCMR 2018 $.30   (F1270)

King Of Glory, King Of Peace
SATB oct GRAY GCMR 1761 $.35   (F1271)

Lute Book Lullaby *Xmas
SATB oct GALAXY 1.0562.1 $.30   (F1272)

New Songs For The Junior Choir *see Bristol,
Lee H., Jr.

Song Of Mary *Xmas
SATB oct GRAY GCMR 2103 $.30   (F1273)

This Is The Day *Easter
SATB oct GRAY GCMR 2457 $.40   (F1274)

Way To Jerusalem *Palm
SATB oct GRAY GCMR 2328 $.40   (F1275)

FRIEDEN TRAGT DER HERR UNS AN see Schweizer,
Rolf

FRIEDENS GUD, OSS FRID FORLANA see Eriksson,
Nils

FRIEDENSMESSE see Philipp, Franz

FRIEDERICI, DANIEL (1584-1638)
Ehre Sei Gott In Der Hohe *Xmas,canon
[Ger] 7pt,acap (easy) BAREN. BCH 178 s.p.   (F1276)

FRIEDRICHS, KARL
Es Kommt Ein Schiff, Geladen
see Friedrichs, Karl, O Heiland Reiss Die
Himmel Auf

Gelobet Seist Du, Jesu Christ
see Friedrichs, Karl, O Heiland Reiss Die
Himmel Auf

Kommt Und Lasst Und Christum Ehren
see Friedrichs, Karl, O Heiland Reiss Die
Himmel Auf

O Heiland Reiss Die Himmel Auf
3pt mix cor MOSELER LB-249 s.p. contains
also: Es Kommt Ein Schiff, Geladen;
Gelobet Seist Du, Jesu Christ; Kommt Und
Lasst Und Christum Ehren   (F1277)

FRIELITZ, C.
Supplication
(Dilsner, L.) SAB,acap oct PRESSER
312-40709 $.25   (F1278)

FRIEND
On My Way To The Hill *Easter
SATB,opt bvl WARNER WB-185 $.50   (F1279)

Sing Alleluia For Your Soul *hymn/pop
SAT&desc/SAB&desc/SATB&desc,pno,tamb,opt
bvl&gtr WARNER WB-132 $.40   (F1280)

FRIENDLY BEASTS *Xmas,carol,Fr
(Ehret) SAB oct SPRATT 644 $.30   (F1281)
(Walton; Ehret) SSA oct FISCHER,C C-6839 $.25   (F1282)

FRIENDLY BEASTS, THE *Xmas
(Dickinson, C.) unis/SA oct GRAY GSC 254 $.25   (F1283)

FRIENDLY BEASTS, THE *Xmas,carol,Eng/Fr,Mediev
(Downing) 4pt mix cor,acap oct SCHIRM.G 8714
$.25   (F1284)
(Parker) SATB,acap oct LAWSON 51505 $.25   (F1285)
(Walton; Ehret) 3pt jr cor/SSA (easy)
FISCHER,C CM 6839 $.25   (F1286)
(Wasner) 4pt mix cor,SAB soli,acap oct
SCHIRM.G 10610 $.25   (F1287)

FRIENDLY BEASTS, THE see Beadell, Robert M.

FRIENDLY BEASTS, THE see Black

FRIENDLY BEASTS, THE see Hutson

FRIENDLY BEASTS, THE see Raymond, Joseph

FRIENDSHIP HYMN see Toolan, S. Suzanne

FRIENDSHIP WITH JESUS see Owens, Jimmy

FRIESEN
Straw Carol, The *Xmas
TTBB WORD CS-349 $.30   (F1288)
SSA WORD CS-348 $.30   (F1289)
SATB oct WORD CS-1050 $.30   (F1290)

FRIGOLA
Dormid, Mi Buen Jesus *Xmas
[Span] 3pt,3 soli UNION ESP. 14646 s.p.   (F1291)

FRISCH AUF IN GOTTES NAMEN see Brandt

FRISCH AUF IN GOTTES NAMEN see Spratte, Hermann

FRISCH AUF, UND LASST UNS SINGEN see
Scheidemann, Heinrich

FRISCH AUF UND LASST UNS SINGEN see Schiedemann

FRITSCH, [MAGDA VON] (1895-   )
Lord God, We Worship Thee *anthem
(Pooler) unis treb cor/SA (easy) oct
AUGSBURG 1425 $.20   (F1292)

FRITSCHEL, JAMES
Make Haste, O God (Psalm 70)
SATB,acap oct WORLD ESA-1544-8 $.60   (F1293)

Psalm 70 *see Make Haste, O God

With Song And Dance *anthem
SATB (diff) oct AUGSBURG 0537 $.50   (F1294)

FRITZSCH, AHASEURUS
Grant Me True Courage, Lord (composed with
Bach, Johann Sebastian) *chorale
unis,pno/org SCHIRM.EC 1897 $.18   (F1295)

FROHE BOTSCHAFT see Weismann, Wilhelm

FROHLICH SOLL MEIN HERZE SPRINGEN see
Bornefeld, Helmut

FROHLICH SOLL MEIN HERZE SPRINGEN see Cruger,
Johann

FROHLICH SOLL MEIN HERZE SPRINGEN see Horn,
Paul

FROHLICH SOLL MEIN HERZE SPRINGEN see Klein,
Karl Heinz

FROHLICH SOLL MEIN HERZE SPRINGEN see
Mendelssohn, Arnold

FROHLICH SOLL MEIN HERZE SPRINGEN see Raphael,
Gunther

FROHLICH SOLL MEIN HERZE SPRINGEN see Reda,
Siegfried

FROHLICH SOLL MEIN HERZE SPRINGEN see Sadler,
Arthur

FROHLICH SOLL MEIN HERZE SPRINGEN see Stern, Hermann

FROHLICH SOLL MEIN HERZE SPRINGEN see Teuscher, Hans

FROHLICH SOLL MEIN HERZE SPRINGEN see Weber, Ludwig

FROHLICH SOLL MEIN HERZE SPRINGEN see Weiss, Ewald

FROHLICH SOLL MEIN HERZE SPRINGEN [CHORALE] see Bach, Johann Sebastian

FROHLICH WIR NUN ALL see Fiebig, Kurt

FROHLICH WIR NUN ALL see Werner, Fritz

FROHLICH WIR NUN ALL FANGEN AN see Berger, Hans Ludwig

FROHLICH WIR NUN ALL FANGEN AN see Kurig, Hans-Hermann

FROHLICH WIR NUN ALL FANGEN AN see Micheelsen, Hans Friedrich

FROHLICH WIR NUN ALL FANGEN AN see Ochs, Volker

FROHLICHE WEIHNACHT UBERALL
see Oh Weihnacht, Du Selige, Frohliche Zeit

FROHLOCK, DU TOCHTER ZION, SEHR UND JAUCHZ see Gesius, Bartholomaus

FROHLOCKE, WEM VERGEBEN see Stier, Alfred

FROHLOCKET MIT HANDEN see Buxtehude, Dietrich

FROHLOCKET MIT HANDEN see Gadsch, Herbert

FROHLOCKET MIT HANDEN ALLE VOLKER see Graap, Lothar

FROHLOCKT MIT FREUD', IHR VOLKER ALL see Schutz, Heinrich

FROHLOCKT UND RUHMT MIT HERZ UND MUND see Pepping, Ernst

FROJDA DIG DU DOTTER SION see Berg, Gottfrid

FROJDA DIG DU KOPTA HJORD see Bach, Johann Sebastian

FROJDA DIG O KRISTENHET *Xmas,hymn
(Sundberg, Sune) 3pt wom cor/3pt jr cor,opt
Bar solo,orch voc sc NORDISKA 3715 s.p.,
cor pts NORDISKA 1893 s.p., ipa
contains: Bethlehems Stjarna; Ett Barn Ar
Fott; Hosianna; O Du Saliga; Stilla Natt
(F1296)

FROLICH SOLL MEIN HERZE SPRINGEN see
Pfannenstiel, Ekkehart

FROLICH SOLL MEIN HERZE SPRINGEN see Wenzel, Eberhard

FROLOCKET MIT HANDEN see Blarr, Oskar Gottlieb

FROLOCKET MIT HANDEN, ALLE VOLKER see Zipp, Friedrich

FROM ABOVE HE HATH SENT FIRE see Schalk, Carl

FROM AFAR *Xmas
(Christiansen, P.) dbl cor SCHMITT 833 $.20
(F1297)

FROM ALL THAT DWELL see Hatton

FROM ALL THAT DWELL see Walmisley, Thomas Attwood

FROM ALL THAT DWELL BELOW SKIES see Lundquist

FROM ALL THAT DWELL BELOW THE SKIES see Bach, Johann Sebastian

FROM ALL THAT DWELL BELOW THE SKIES see Billings, William

FROM ALL THAT DWELL BELOW THE SKIES see Grieb, Herbert [C.]

FROM ALL THAT DWELL BELOW THE SKIES see Walmisley, Thomas Attwood

FROM ALL THAT DWELL BELOW THE SKIES see Watts, W.

FROM ALL THAT DWELL BELOW THE SKIES see Young

FROM ALL THY SAINTS IN WARFARE see Rotermund, Melvin

FROM ALL THY SAINTS IN WARFARE see Williams

FROM ALL WHO DWELL BENEATH THE SKIES
see Entrance Hymns

FROM BETHANY THE MASTER COMES see Curry

FROM DARKNESS TO LIGHT see Ratcliffe, Desmond

FROM DARKNESS TO LIGHT see Tchaikovsky, Piotr Ilyitch

FROM DAY TO DAY
2pt CHAPPELL 0018010 $.40   (F1298)
SSA CHAPPELL 0018010-354 $.40   (F1299)

FROM DEPTH OF SIN see Byrd, William

FROM DEPTHS OF WOE see Schutz, Heinrich

FROM DEPTHS OF WOE I CALL ON THEE see Bach,
Johann Sebastian, Aus Tiefer Not Schrei'
Ich Zu Dir

FROM DEPTHS OF WOE I CALL TO THEE see Bach,
Johann Sebastian

FROM DEPTHS OF WOE I CRY TO THEE see Lenel,
Ludwig

FROM DEPTHS OF WOE I CRY TO THEE see Schein,
Johann Hermann

FROM DEPTHS OF WOE I CRY TO THEE see Schutz,
Heinrich

FROM EAST TO WEST see Lovelace, Austin C.

FROM EGYPT'S BONDAGE COME see Page, Arthur

FROM EVERY STORMY WIND THAT BLOWS see Hastings

FROM FAR AND WIDE see Davis, Katherine K.

FROM FAR AWAY WE COME TO YOU *carol
unis/SATB (easy) OXFORD 08.174 $.15   (F1300)

FROM GLOOM TO GLORY see Jacobus, Dale Asher

FROM GOD SHALL NAUGHT DIVIDE ME see Praetorius,
Michael

FROM GOD SHALL NAUGHT DIVIDE ME see Schutz,
Heinrich, Von Gott Will Ich Nicht Lassen

FROM GRIEF TO GLORY see Christiansen, F. Melius

FROM HEAVEN ABOVE see Bach, Johann Sebastian,
Vom Himmel Hoch

FROM HEAVEN ABOVE see Cruger, Johann

FROM HEAVEN ABOVE see Krapf, Gerhard

FROM HEAVEN ABOVE see Schein, Vom Himmel Hoch

FROM HEAVEN ABOVE see Schein, Johann Hermann,
Vom Himmel Hoch

FROM HEAVEN ABOVE see Schroth, G.

FROM HEAVEN ABOVE see Schumann

FROM HEAVEN ABOVE TO EARTH I COME *anthem
see Three Christmas Carols
(Cassler, G. Winston) TTBB (easy) oct
AUGSBURG 1387 $.20 contains also: What
Child Is This?   (F1301)

FROM HEAVEN ABOVE TO EARTH I COME see Bach,
Johann Sebastian

FROM HEAVEN ABOVE TO EARTH I COME see Pasquet,
Jean

FROM HEAVEN ABOVE TO EARTH I COME see
Praetorius, Michael

FROM HEAVEN ABOVE, YE ANGELS ALL see Spitta,
Heinrich

FROM HEAVEN ABOVE, YE ANGELS ALL see Wienhorst,
Richard

FROM HEAVEN AN ANGEL *Xmas,carol,Hung
(Salama) 4pt mix cor oct SCHIRM.G 7444 $.20
(F1302)

FROM HEAVEN HIGH see Schein, Johann Hermann

FROM HEAVEN HIGH I COME TO EARTH see Bender,
Jan

FROM HEAVEN HIGH I COME TO EARTH see Willan,
Healey

FROM HEAVEN HIGH I COME TO YOU *Xmas
(Vree, M.) SSA,opt perc oct PRESSER 312-40769
$.30   (F1303)
(Vree, M.) SATB,acap oct PRESSER 312-40664
$.30   (F1304)

FROM HEAVEN HIGH, O ANGELS, COME
see Three Carols For SAB

FROM HEAVEN ON HIGH see Praetorius, Michael,
Vom Himmel Kommt

FROM HEAVEN ON HIGH HEAR ANGELS SING see Buszin

FROM HEAVEN THE LORD CAME FORTH see Santa Cruz,
Domingo, Del Cielo Salia Dios

FROM HEAV'N ABOVE see Bach, Johann Sebastian,
Vom Himmel Hoch

FROM HEAV'N ABOVE TO EARTH I COME see
Praetorius, Michael

FROM HEAV'N ON HIGH see Praetorius, Michael

FROM HENCEFORTH, O MY SOUL see Hammerschmidt,
Andreas

FROM ISAIAH see Berger, Jean

FROM OUT MY HEART'S DEEP LONGING see Lassus,
Roland de (Orlandus)

FROM OUT OF A WOOD see Freed

FROM OUT THE EARTH see Rhea, Raymond

FROM OUT THE MORNINGLAND WE CAME *anthem/folk,
Fr
(Beuerle, Herbert) SSA/unis treb cor,inst
(easy) oct AUGSBURG 0310 $.18   (F1305)

FROM REFUSING TO OBEY see Schalk, Carl

FROM SHINING STARS DESCENDING
see Christ Is Born, Little Infant King

FROM SHINING STARS DESCENDING see Glover, R.F.

FROM STARRY SKIES THOU COMEST *Xmas,carol,It
(Ehret, Walter) SATB,opt inst oct WALTON 2505
$.30   (F1306)

FROM THE BAY PSALM BOOK see Berger

FROM THE CROSS see Reiff

FROM THE DEPTHS see Gluck, Christoph Willibald
Ritter von, De Profundis

FROM THE DEPTHS see Lindusky, Eugene

FROM THE DEPTHS see Mozart, Wolfgang Amadeus,
De Profundis

FROM THE DEPTHS OF MY DISTRESS see Wills,
Arthur

FROM THE EAST UNTO THE WEST see Handel, George
Frideric

FROM THE EASTERN MOUNTAINS see Graham, Robert
[V.]

FROM THE EASTERN MOUNTAINS see Hallstrom, Henry

FROM THE END OF THE EARTH see Hovhaness, Alan

FROM THE HILL see Ager, Laurence

FROM THE HILLS AND FROM THE VALES see Santa
Cruz, Domingo, De Los Montes Y Los Valles

FROM THE LANDS THAT SEE THE SUN ARISE see
Sedulius, Tr.

FROM THE MANGER TO THE CROSS
TTBB BIG3 $.25   (F1307)

FROM THE PSALMS see Rogers, E.

FROM THE PSALMS OF DAVID see Penderecki,
Krzysztof

FROM THE RISING OF THE SUN see Coggin, Elwood

FROM THE RISING OF THE SUN see Ford, Virgil T.

FROM THE RISING OF THE SUN see Ouseley,
Frederick Arthur Gore

FROM THE RISING OF THE SUN see Powell, Robert
J.

FROM THE STABLE see Graham

FROM THE TWENTY-THIRD PSALM see Herder, Ronald

FROM THEE ALL SKILL AND SCIENCE FLOW see
Kingsley

FROM YOUR THRONE, O LORD see Binkerd, [Gordon]

FROMM, HERBERT (1905-   )
Adath Israel *Sab-Eve
SATB TRANSCON. TCL 280 $3.00   (F1308)

Atonement Music
SATB TRANSCON. TCL 755 $3.50   (F1309)

Avodat Shabbat *Sab-Eve
SATB TRANSCON. TCL 835 $4.00   (F1310)

Chamber Cantata
[Eng/Heb] SATB,8inst voc sc TRANSCON.
TCL 748 $2.50, ipa   (F1311)

Chemdat Yamin *Sab-Morn
SATB TRANSCON. TCL 865 $4.50, ipa   (F1312)

Five Opening Anthems *CC5U,anthem
SATB TRANSCON. TCL 789 $2.50   (F1313)

Kiddish Through The Jewish Year, The *Fest/
Sab-Eve
SATB TRANSCON. TCL 776 $2.00   (F1314)

New Year's Prayer *prayer
[Eng] SATB TRANSCON. TCL 240 $.25   (F1315)
SATB TRANSCON. TCL 240 $.25   (F1316)

Psalm 23
SATB TRANSCON. TCL 108 $.25   (F1317)
[Eng] SATB TRANSCON. TCL 108 $.25   (F1318)

Psalm Cantata *Psalm
[Eng] SATB,S solo,fl,trp,vla,timp TRANSCON.
TCL 141 $2.50, ipa   (F1319)

Servant Unto Thee, A
[Eng] SATB TRANSCON. TCL 111 $.25   (F1320)

Shofar Service
[Eng] SATB TRANSCON. TCL 754 $.75   (F1321)

Six Madrigals *CC6U,Purim
SATB TRANSCON. TCL 756 $2.50   (F1322)

FROMMEL, GERHARD (1906-   )
Missa In E In Honorem St. Michaelis
Archangeli *Op.31, Mass
[Ger] SATB,acap (med) MULLER SM 892 sc
s.p., cor pts s.p.   (F1323)

FROMMLET, D.
Herbsttag
mix cor (med) oct LEUCKART 600 s.p.   (F1324)

FRONMULLER, FRIEDA
Du Meine Seele, Singe *cant
SATB,trp,4brass HANSSLER 10.046 sc s.p.,
cor pts s.p., ipa   (F1325)

Jerusalem, Du Hochgbaute Stadt *cant
SATB,trp,4brass HANSSLER 10.128 sc s.p.,
cor pts s.p.   (F1326)

Nun Bitten Wir Den Heiligen Geist *cant
mix cor,inst sc HANSSLER 10.291 s.p.
(F1327)

FRONT COURONNE D'EPINES see Bach, Johann
Sebastian

FROST
Lord, Keep Us Steadfast *Gen
unis,trp SCHMITT SD6228 $.35   (F1328)

FROTHINGHAM
Descants On Ten Christmas Hymns And Carols
*CCU,Xmas,carol,hymn
unis&SATB oct SUMMY 1328 $.60   (F1329)

FRUEH
Psalm 100 *Gen
(Paetkau) SATB SCHMITT 1706 $.30   (F1330)

FRUH WOLLTEST DU MICH MIT DEINER GNADE see
Beethoven, Ludwig van

FRUIT OF THY WORKS, THE see Clare, Edwyn A.

FRUKTA ICKE, DU LILLA HJORD see Hedwall,
Lennart

FRY, H.
Beautiful Saviour *Easter/Gen
SATB,acap oct PRESSER 322-35407 $.30
(F1331)

FRYE, WALTER
Opera Omnia *sac/sec,CCU,Mass/mot
(Kenney, S.) cor AM.INST.MUS. $18.00
(F1332)

FRYER
Go Tell It On The Mountain *Xmas
men cor KJOS 5546 $.30   (F1333)

FRYKT IKKE FRA NA AV see Hovland, Egil

FRYLOF, [HARALD LEONARD] (1882-1919)
O Guds Lamm
mix cor NORDISKA 2114 s.p.   (F1334)

O Thou Lamb Of God
see Passion Motet, A

Passion Motet, A *Easter/Lent
(Lundquist) SATB,acap (diff) oct WILLIS
5515 $.25
contains: O Thou Lamb Of God; Praise
Jehovah; Thy Cross, O Jesus Thou Didst
Bear   (F1335)

Praise Jehovah
see Passion Motet, A

Thy Cross, O Jesus Thou Didst Bear
see Passion Motet, A

FRYSON
Give Yourself To Jesus
(Sanford) SATB WARNER WB-275 $.50 (F1336)

FRYXELL, REGINA HOLMEN
Daystar
SATB (med) ABINGDON APM-577 $.35 (F1337)

Lobe Den Herrn
"Praise To The Lord" SATB oct GRAY
GCMR 2285 $.35   (F1338)

Praise My Soul The King Of Heaven
unis jr cor&desc FISCHER,C CM 7312 $.25
(F1339)

Praise To The Lord *see Lobe Den Herrn

Psalm 67
SATB oct GRAY GCMR 2337 $.30   (F1340)

Seven Choral Service Settings *CC7U
SATB (easy) ABINGDON APM-242 $.35 (F1341)

Thou Wilt Keep Him In Perfect Peace *Lent
SATB (easy) ABINGDON APM-121 $.18 (F1342)

To The Hills I Lift Mine Eyes
SATB (med) ABINGDON APM-475 $.30 (F1343)

Unseen Presence, The
SATB (med) ABINGDON APM-474 $.25 (F1344)

FUGA A 4 (ALLELUJA) see Obrecht, Jacob

FUGA, SANDRO (1906-   )
Concerto Sacro
[Lat] mix cor,orch voc sc ZERBONI 4510
s.p., ipr   (F1345)

FUGER
We Christians May Rejoice Today *see Wir
Christenleut

Wir Christenleut *Xmas,chorale
(Bach, J.S.; Barrow, R.) "We Christians May
Rejoice Today" TTBB,acap SCHIRM.EC 2171
$.18   (F1346)

FUGGER-MOTETTEN see Lassus, Roland de
(Orlandus)

FUHRER, ROBERT (1807-1861)
Mass In C *Mass
"Thou Shalt Keep The Sabbath Holy" mix cor,
org,2vln,vcl,bvl,opt fl&2clar&2horn&2trp&
trom&timp WEINBERGER s.p., ipa voc sc,
cor pts   (F1347)

Thou Shalt Keep The Sabbath Holy *see Mass
In C

FUHRMANN, W.A.
Easter Alleluia, An *Easter
SAB WARNER W3727 $.30   (F1348)

Invocation
SATB,S/T solo (easy) oct WILLIS 5695 $.12
(F1349)

FUHRWAHR, ER TRUG UNS'RE KRANKHEIT see Franck,
Melchior

FUIT HOMO see Palestrina, Giovanni

FULDA, ADAM VON (1440-1506)
Baptistae
see ARS NOVA TO RENNAISSANCE VOL. 2-1200 TO
ABOUT 1500

In Decollatione St. Johannis
see ARS NOVA TO RENNAISSANCE VOL. 2-1200 TO
ABOUT 1500

In Festo Pentecostis
see ARS NOVA TO RENNAISSANCE VOL. 2-1200 TO
ABOUT 1500

FULGEBUNT JUSTI see Dubois, Theodore

FULGEBUNT JUSTI see Lassus, Roland de
(Orlandus)

FULL STATURE see Pyle, Francis [Johnson]

FULLER, [ESTHER MARY] (1907-   )
Altar Of Christmas, The (composed with Paul)
*CCU,Xmas
unis PRO ART 486 $.60   (F1350)

Bible Stories And Songs *CC12L,Gen,anthem/
Bibl
unis jr cor PRO ART 846 $.75   (F1351)

Book Of Responses *CCU,Lent/Thanks,Bene/
Introit/Offer
SATB oct PRO ART 259 $.60   (F1352)

FULLER, [ESTHER MARY] (cont'd.)
Bright Candle Light *CC13L,Gen
unis jr cor PRO ART 927 $.75   (F1353)

Children Sing, The (composed with Lewis)
*CC17L,Adv/Xmas/Easter/Palm/Thanks
unis jr cor PRO ART 487 $.85   (F1354)

Child's Book Of Anthems *CCU
SATB oct PRESSER $.85   (F1355)

Choral Calls To Worship *CCU,Commun,Bene/
Introit/prayer
SATB oct PRO ART 698 $1.00   (F1356)

Let's Sing To God (composed with Paul)
*CC14L,Gen,anthem
unis jr cor PRO ART 699 $.85   (F1357)

Lo, The Child *Xmas
SATB oct PRO ART 2056 $.25   (F1358)

Of Such Is The Kingdom *see Paul

Peace (composed with Paul)
SATB,S/T solo oct PRO ART 1286 $.18 (F1359)

Remember Thy Creator (composed with Paul)
SATB oct PRO ART 1229 $.25   (F1360)

Seasonal Songs For Children *see Paul

Shepherds Rejoice *Xmas
TTBB oct PLYMOUTH JR-304 $.25   (F1361)

Song Of Christmas *Xmas
SAB oct PLYMOUTH JR-400 $.25   (F1362)

Thirty-Eight Introits And Responses (composed
with Paul) *CC38UL,Xmas/Easter/Gen
SATB PRO ART 65 $.60   (F1363)

This Wondrous World
(Raymond) SATB oct PLYMOUTH JR-113 $.25
(F1364)

Thou Art My Lamp *see Paul

Three Motets *CC3U,mot
SATB oct SUMMY 5818 $.80   (F1365)

Trust In The Lord
SATB,acap,opt pno oct PRO ART 1863 $.22
(F1366)

We Bow Our Heads *CC16L,Xmas/Easter/Gen/
Thanks
unis jr cor PRO ART 110 $.85   (F1367)

We Give Thee Thanks
(Paul) SATB oct PRO ART 1811 $.18 (F1368)
(Paul) SSAA oct PRO ART 1810 $.18 (F1369)

FULLER, J.W.
Exultate Justi
[Lat] SATB,acap AMP A550 $.25 (F1370)

Now (More Near Ouselves Than We)
SATB,acap AMP A612 $.30   (F1371)

FULLFILLMENT, THE see Graham

FULLNESS OF JOY see Morgan, Haydn

FULTON
Christmas Eve *Xmas
(Rogers) 2pt jr cor/3pt jr cor oct LILLENAS
AN-4003 $.25   (F1372)

FUM, FUM, FUM *Xmas,carol,Span
see Many Moods Of Christmas, The, Suite Two
see Three Spanish Carols
(Kinsman) SA oct SPRATT 593 $.25 (F1373)
(Kinsman) SATB oct SPRATT 543 $.25 (F1374)
(Kird) SATB oct PRO ART 2133 $.30 (F1375)
(Kird) SAB,acap,opt pno oct PRO ART 2330 $.30
(F1376)
(Kird) SSA,acap oct PRO ART 2328 $.30 (F1377)
(Kird) TTBB,acap,opt pno oct PRO ART 2332
$.30   (F1378)
(Shaw; Parker) 3pt wom cor oct SCHIRM.G 11862
$.30   (F1379)
(Shaw; Parker) 4pt mix cor,acap oct SCHIRM.G
10182 $.25   (F1380)
(Shaw; Parker) 3pt mix cor oct SCHIRM.G 11210
$.25   (F1381)
(Stone) SA/TB oct BELWIN 2154 $.30 (F1382)
(Stone) SATB oct BELWIN 2226 $.30 (F1383)
(Vree, M.) SSA,acap oct PRESSER 312-40379
$.30   (F1384)
(Vree, M.) SSAB oct PRESSER 312-40458 $.25
(F1385)
(Vree, M.) SATB,acap oct PRESSER 312-40281
$.30   (F1386)
(Vree, M.) SSAB,acap oct PRESSER 312-40458
$.30   (F1387)

FUM, FUM, FUM see Nin-Culmell, Joaquin

FUM! FUM! FUM! see Walther, Johann Gottfried

FUM, FUM, FUM see Wilson

FUNCKE
Matthaus-Passion *Psntd
(Birke) 4pt mix cor,soli,inst MOSELER s.p.
(F1388)

FUNERAL ANTHEM see Handel, George Frideric,
Trauer-Hymne

FUNERAL ANTHEM FOR QUEEN CAROLINE see Handel,
George Frideric

FUNERAL ANTHEM ON THE DEATH OF QUEEN CAROLINE
see Handel, George Frideric

FUNERAL SENTENCES see Purcell, Henry

FUNERAL SONG see Brahms, Johannes, Nun Lasst
Uns Den Leib Begraben

FUNF ALTE KIRCHENLIEDER IN NEUEN BEARBEITUNGEN
(Heilmann, Harald) [Ger] men cor/mix cor
SIRIUS s.p.
contains: Bornefeld, Helmut, Mein Schonste
Zier Und Kleinod (med); Bornefeld,
Helmut, Verleih Uns Frieden Gnadiglich
(med); Borris, Siegfried, Heut Singt Die
Liebe Christenheit (easy); Borris,
Siegfried, Jauchzt, Alle Lande, Gott Zu

Ehren (easy); Borris, Siegfried, Lobe Den
Herren (easy)   (F1389)

FUNF AMERIKANISCHE NEGRO-SPIRITUALS *spir,US
(Mittergradnegger, Gunther) [Ger] mix cor,
acap cmplt ed DOBLINGER s.p.
contains & see also: Ev'ry Time I Feel De
Spirit; Nobody Knows The Trouble I've
Seen; Steal Away; Swing Low, Sweet
Chariot; Wayfaring Stranger   (F1390)

FUNF CHORALKANTATEN see David, Johann Nepomuk

FUNF CHORKANTATEN see Buxtehude, Dietrich

FUNF GEISTLICHE CHORE see Purcell, Henry

FUNF GEISTLICHE LIEDER AUS SCHEMELLIS
GESANGBUCH see Bach, Johann Sebastian

FUNF GEISTLICHE LIEDSATZE see Stadlmair, Hans

FUNF GEISTLICHE MOTETTEN see Nees, Vic

FUNF GEISTLICHE STUCKE see Stockmeier, Wolfgang

FUNF HOHELIED-MOTETTEN see Franck, Cesar

FUNF KLEINE FESTMOTETTEN see Marx, Karl

FUNF MARIENLIEDER see Raphael, Gunther

FUNF MARTERLN see Stadlmair, Hans

FUNF MOTETTEN see Brunner, Adolf

FUNF MOTETTEN see Backes, Lotte

FUNF MOTETTEN see Callhoff, Herbert

FUNF MOTETTEN see Dressler, Gallus

FUNF MOTETTEN see Mouton, Jean

FUNF NEGRO-SPIRITUALS
mix cor,acap HUG s.p.
contains: Git On Board, "Kommt Herein"; I
Couldn't Hear Nobody Pray, "Ich Konnte
Horen Kein Gebet"; It's Me, O Lord, "Sieh
Mich, O Herr"; Roll, Jordan, Roll,
"Rausch, Jordan, Rausch"; Steal Away,
"Mach Dich Auf"   (F1391)

FUNF PSALMENGESANGE see Warner, Theodore

FUNF SCHWANK- UND SPOTTLIEDER see Schindler,
Walter

FUNF SPRUCHMOTETTEN see Schrader, Oswald

FUNF VERGIL-MOTETTEN *CC5U,mot
(Osthoff) [Lat] 4-7pt mix cor MOSELER s.p.
contains works by: Desprez; Acadelt; De
Rore; Willaert   (F1392)

FUNFUNDDREISSIG MAGNIFICAT-BAND XXVII see
Palestrina, Giovanni

FUNFZEHN MOTETTEN see Victoria, Tomas Luis de

FUNFZIG GEISTLICHE KANONS see Stier, Alfred

FUR ALLE GUTE SEI GEPREIST see Kurig, Hans-
Hermann

FUR DIE ARMEN SEELEN see Schieri, Fritz

FUR FREUDEN LASST UNS SPRINGEN [CHORALE] see
Bach, Johann Sebastian

FUR SOLCH GROSSES MYSTERIUM see Schutz,
Heinrich, Pro Hoc Magno Mysterio

FURA
In A Manger In Bethlehem *Xmas
(Raymond) SATB oct PLYMOUTH JR-161 $.30
(F1393)

FURBITTEN see Brand, Th.

FURCHT STORET, DOCH NICHTS ZERSTORET DEN TROST
see Schutz, Heinrich, Turbabor, Sed Non
Pertubabor

FURCHTE DICH NICHT see Bach, Johann Christoph

FURCHTE DICH NICHT see Bach, Johann Sebastian

FURCHTE DICH NICHT see Dressler, Gallus

FURCHTE DICH NICHT see Stahmer, Klaus

FURCHTE DICH NICHT see Thomas, Kurt

FURCHTE DICH NICHT, ICH BIN BEI DIR see Bach,
Johann Sebastian

FURCHTE DICH NICHT, ICH BIN DER ERSTE UND DER
LETZTE see Kroll, Stephan

FURCHTE GOTT UND HALTE SEINE GEBOTE see Reger,
Max

FURCHTET EUCH NICHT see Ahle, Johann Rudolph

FURCHTET EUCH NICHT see Bach, Johann Michael

FURCHTET EUCH NICHT see Beyer, Johann Samuel

FURCHTET EUCH NICHT see Buxtehude, Dietrich

FURCHTET EUCH NICHT see Ermatinger, Erhart

FURCHTET EUCH NICHT see Franck, Melchior

FURCHTET EUCH NICHT see Schweizer, Rolf

FURCHTET EUCH NICHT, SIEHE, ICH VERKUNDIG see
Raselius, Andreas

FURMAN, JAMES
Go Tell It On The Mountain *anthem/gospel
SATB oct FOX PS183 $.40   (F1394)

Some Glorious Way
SATB,solo,pno/org oct FOX PS185 $.30
(F1395)

FURRY DAY CAROL, THE
see Coventry Carol, The

FURWAHR, ER TRUG UNSERE KRANKHEIT see
  Buxtehude, Dietrich

FURWAHR, ER TRUG UNSERE KRANKHEIT see Distler,
  Hugo

FURWAHR, ER TRUG UNSERE KRANKHEIT see Franck,
  Melchior

FURWAHR, ER TRUG UNSERE KRANKHEIT see
  Hufschmidt, Wolfgang

FURWAHR, ER TRUG UNSERE KRANKHEIT see Koch,
  Johannes H.E.

FURWAHR, ER TRUG UNSERE KRANKHEIT see
  Micheelsen, Hans Friedrich

FURWAHR ER TRUG UNSRE KRANKHEIT see Dedekind,
  Constantine Christian

FURWAHR, ER TRUG UNSRE KRANKHEIT see Franck,
  Melchior

FURWAHR, ER TRUG UNSRE KRANKHEIT see Thomas,
  Kurt

FURWAHR, ER TRUG UNSRE KRANKHEIT see Trust,
  Heinz-Ewald

FURWAHR, ER TRUG UNSRE KRANKHEIT see Wenzel,
  Eberhard

FUSER, IRENEO
  Ave Maria *BVM
    see Tre Motecta Mariana
    [Lat] SATB sc ZANIBON 3934 s.p.   (F1396)

  Benedicta Es
    see Tre Motecta Mariana

  Missa Puerorum In Hon. S.J. Bosco *Mass
    unis,org sc ZANIBON 3548 s.p., cor pts
    ZANIBON 3549 s.p.   (F1397)

  Salve Regina
    see Tre Motecta Mariana

  Tre Motecta Mariana *BVM,mot
    [Lat] unis,org ZANIBON 4038 s.p.
    contains: Ave Maria; Benedicta Es; Salve
    Regina   (F1398)

FUSSAN, WERNER (1912-   )
  Die Erlosten Des Herrn Werden Wiederkommen
    SSATB HANSSLER 7.056 s.p.   (F1399)

  Gott, Dem Ewigen Konige, Dem Unserganglichen
    *mot
    SAB HANSSLER 7.051 s.p.   (F1400)

  Ich Weiss Ein Edlen Weingartn
    mix cor HANSSLER 5.169 s.p.   (F1401)

FUX, JOHANN JOSEPH (1660-1741)
  Angelis Suis Deus *Lent,mot
    "He Shall Give His Angels" SATB,acap
    SCHIRM.EC 1254   (F1402)

  Dominus Dabit Benignitatem
    "Freely The Lord Gave His Lovingkindness"
    SATB,acap SCHIRM.EC 2636 $.25   (F1403)

  Ecce Virgo Concipient *Adv/Xmas
    SATB,acap voc pt DOBLINGER s.p. see also
    ADVENT UND WEIHNACHT, HEFT 2   (F1404)

  Freely The Lord Gave His Lovingkindness *see
    Dominus Dabit Benignitatem

  He Shall Give His Angels *see Angelis Suis
    Deus

  La Fede Sacrilega Nella Morte Del Precursor
    S. Giovanni Battista *Gen,ora
    (Zelzer, Hugo) [It] SATB,SSATB soli,orch
    (med diff) BAREN. sc s.p., sc rental   (F1405)

  Mass In C *Mass
    [Lat] mix cor,org voc sc UNIVER. 4950
    $6.00, cor pts UNIVER. 4951A-D $.85   (F1406)

  Missa Corporis Christi *Mass
    (Federhofer, Hellmut) [Lat] SATB,SATB soli,
    cont,winds,strings (med diff) sc BAREN.
    $24.00, ipr   (F1407)

  Missa Purificationis *Ded,Mass
    (Moder, R.) 4pt mix cor,org,2vln,bvl
    DOBLINGER voc sc s.p., cor pts s.p., ipa
                                            (F1408)

  Missa Quadragesimalisimalis *Mass
    (Bauerle, Hermann) SATB,acap cor pts
    BREITKOPF-L PB-1948 s.p.   (F1409)

  Missa S. Caroli *canon/Mass
    (Bauerle, Hermann) SATB,acap cor pts
    BREITKOPF-L PB-1947 s.p.   (F1410)

  Tollite *Adv/Xmas
    SATB,acap voc pt DOBLINGER s.p. see also
    ADVENT UND WEIHNACHT, HEFT 2   (F1411)

FYFFE, E.
  Gloria In Excelsis Deo *see Ekman, L.

G

GA VARSOMMT, O SJEL see Baden, Conrad

GABIROL-SCHINDLER see Adler, Hugo Ch.

GABRIEL
  Brighten The Corner
    (Roe) SATB oct WORD CS-2380 $.30   (G1)

  Christmas Lullaby
    see Lovelock, William, Christmas

  He Lifted Me
    see TEMPO CHORAL PACKAGE NO. 2

  Higher Ground
    (Boersma) SATB oct WORD CS-2124 $.35   (G2)

  His Eye Is On The Sparrow
    (Jones) SATB oct WORD CS-1976 $.30   (G3)
    (Whitman) SSATB oct LILLENAS AN-1140 $.30
                                            (G4)
    (Wilson) SATB oct LORENZ A294 $.25   (G5)

  If I Have Wounded Any Soul
    SATB oct LORENZ A405 $.25   (G6)
    SATB oct LORENZ B109 $.30   (G7)

  Way Of The Cross Leads Home, The
    (Boersma) SATB oct WORD CS-2140 $.30   (G8)

GABRIEL ANGEL see Kallstenius, Edvin

GABRIEL ANGELUS see La Tombelle, Fernand de

GABRIEL ANGELUS LOCUTUS EST see Massaino,
  Tiburtius

GABRIEL CAME TO MARY see Hassler, Hans Leo,
  Dixit Maria

GABRIEL, FROM THE HEAV'N DESCENDING see Bingham

GABRIEL SAID UNTO THE SHEPHERD see Hassler,
  Hans Leo, Angelus Ad Pastores Ait

GABRIELI, ANDREA (1510-1586)
  Agnus Dei *Agnus
    mix cor NORDISKA 4415 s.p.   (G9)

  Angeli Archangeli *ASD/Fest,mot
    [Lat] mix cor,acap oct NOVELLO DM-41 s.p.
                                            (G10)
    [Lat] SATB,acap (med) MULLER M 41 s.p. (G11)

  Benedicam Dominum *Mass/mot
    (Allaire, Gaston) cor AM.INST.MUS. see from
    OPERA OMNIA VOL. II   (G12)

  Caro Mea
    (Martens, Mason) "My Flesh Is Meat" SATB
    oct WALTON 6017 $.30   (G13)

  Der Engel Sprach Zu Den Hirten *Xmas
    (Schutz; Agey) "Lo, The Angel Said To The
    Shepherds" SATTBB,opt org oct SCHIRM.G
    10865 $.50   (G14)

  Die Sieben Busspsalmen *see Domine, Ne In
    Furore Tuo (Psalm 6)   (G15)

  Domine, Ne In Furore Tuo (Psalm 6) Gen
    (Grusnick, Bruno) [Lat] SAATTB,acap (med
    diff) BAREN. BA 921 $2.00 see from Die
    Sieben Busspsalmen   (G16)

  Drei Motetten *CC3U,mot
    (Arnold) [Ger/Lat] 8pt mix cor MOSELER s.p.
                                            (G17)

  Holy, Holy, Holy *see Sanctus And Hosanna

  Kyrie *Kyrie
    (Ehret, W.) "Mercy, Lord, On Us" [Lat/Eng]
    SSATBB BROUDE,A. 716 $.65   (G18)

  Lamb Of God
    (Richardson) SATB oct WORD CS-113 $.35 (G19)

  Lo, The Angel Said To The Shepherds *see Der
    Engel Sprach Zu Den Hirten

  Magnificat *Magnif
    (Simkins) 12pt mix cor oct CURWEN 10565
    $.35   (G20)
    (Simkins) 3 cor CURWEN 80825 s.p.   (G21)

  Maria Magdalene
    (Ruiz) [Lat] SATB,acap RICORDI-ARG BA 10088
    s.p.   (G22)

  Mercy, Lord, On Us *see Kyrie

  Missa Brevis *Mass
    mix cor,acap voc sc KALMUS 6173 $1.25   (G23)
    (Bauerle, Hermann) SATB,acap cor pts
    BREITKOPF-L CHB-2773 s.p.   (G24)

  My Flesh Is Meat *see Caro Mea

  O Passi Sparsi *madrigal
    [It/Ger] SSAATB&SATTBB,acap PETERS 4811
    $1.25   (G25)

  Psalm 6 *see Domine, Ne In Furore Tuo

  Quem Vidistis, Pastores? *see Wen Denn Sahet
    Ihr, Hirten?

  Sanctus And Hosanna *Sanctus
    (Ehret, W.) "Holy, Holy, Holy" [Lat/Eng]
    SSATBB BROUDE,A. 709 $.50   (G26)

  Te Deum Patrem *Trin,mot
    [Lat] SATB,acap (med) MULLER M 23 s.p. (G27)

    [Lat] mix cor,acap oct NOVELLO DM-23 s.p.
                                            (G28)

  Wen Denn Sahet Ihr, Hirten? *Xmas/Gen,mot
    (Grusnick, Bruno) "Quem Vidistis,
    Pastores?" [Ger/Lat] SSAT&ATTB,acap (med)
    BAREN. BA 2919 sc $1.75, cor pts $1.10 (G29)

GABRIELI, GIOVANNI (1557-1612)
  Agnus Dei *Easter/Lent,Agnus
    (Richardson) "Lamb Of God" SSATB oct SPRATT
    2004 $.25   (G30)

  Angelus Ad Pastores
    (Couraud) [Lat] SSSAAATTTBBB oct SALABERT-
    US $1.50   (G31)

  Angelus Ad Pastores Ait *Xmas,mot
    [Lat] dbl cor/12pt,opt cont PETERS 5930
    $.80   (G32)

  Beata Es Virgo
    (Jergenson; Wolfe) [Lat] 6pt mix cor,opt
    org oct SCHIRM.G 11809 $.45   (G33)

  Benedictus *Bene/mot
    [Lat] SSSAATTTBBBB,acap oct SCHIRM.G 4250
    $.30   (G34)
    (McKelvy, J.) 3 cor FOSTER MF411 $.40   (G35)

  Benedixisti, Domine
    (Lynn) "Thou Hast Been Gracious, Lord"
    [Eng/Lat] 7pt mix cor,opt org oct
    SCHIRM.G 11312 $.35   (G36)

  Buccinate (from Symphoniae Sacre)
    4 cor/19pt,2trp,3trom,vcl/bvl PETERS 4814
    $1.25, ipa   (G37)

  Cantate Domino *Easter/Epiph/Gen,mot
    "Oh, Sing To God, The Lord" SSATTB,acap
    (diff) oct CONCORDIA 98-1897 $.50   (G38)
    (Hofmann) [Lat] SATTBB/SAATBB HANSSLER
    1.521 s.p.   (G39)

  Cantate Domino *see Schutz, Heinrich

  Christ Has Arisen *see Surrexit Christus

  Crucifixus
    (Ehret) [Eng/Lat] SSA,acap MARKS 4332 $.30
                                            (G40)

  Dormiva Dolcemente *mot,It
    mix cor SOUTHERN $.35   (G41)
    (Stevens, Denis) SATB oct FABER 11835 $.35
                                            (G42)

  Drei Motetten I *CC3U,mot
    (Besseler) [Ger/Lat] 4pt mix cor&4pt mix
    cor MOSELER s.p.   (G43)

  Drei Motetten II *CC3U,mot
    (Engelbrecht) [Ger/Lat] 7pt mix cor&8pt mix
    cor,cont MOSELER s.p.   (G44)

  Glorious Mystery Sublime *see O Magnum
    Mysterium

  Hic Est Filius Dei *Gen
    (Engelbrecht, Christiane) [Lat] SSATBB&
    SATTBB&SATTBB,cont,opt inst (med diff)
    BAREN. BA 3361 rental   (G45)

  Hodie Christus Natus Est *Xmas/Gen
    [Lat] SAT,opt kbd/acap oct NOVELLO MS-5
    s.p.   (G46)
    (Goebel, Georg) [Ger] SATB&SATB,acap (med)
    MULLER MS 5 s.p.   (G47)
    (Jergenson; Wolfe) [Lat] 8pt mix cor,org
    oct SCHIRM.G 11811 $.50   (G48)

  Hodie Completi Sunt Dies Pentecostes *mot
    (Hofmann) [Lat] dbl cor HANSSLER 1.429 s.p.
                                            (G49)

  In Ecclesiis *mot
    [Lat] cor/dbl cor,SATB soli,org/pno,3trp/
    clar&vln,3trom/vla&2vcl min sc PETERS
    E1061 $2.50, ipa   (G50)
    cor,orch KALMUS $5.00, ipa   (G51)
    (Damrosch, F.) [Lat] 8pt mix cor oct
    SCHIRM.G 4452 $.40   (G52)
    (Hudson) [Lat] SATB,SATB soli,3trp&3trom&
    org/3vln&vla&2vcl&org voc sc SCHOTT
    EUL1061 s.p., ipa   (G53)
    (Maderna, B.) mix cor,org,orch voc sc
    ZERBONI 6538 s.p., ipr   (G54)
    (Stevens, Denis) SATB,SATB soli,3ob/3trp,
    trom/vla,2trom voc sc NOVELLO s.p., ipr (G55)
    (Stokowski) [Lat] SSAATTBB,org,opt brass
    BROUDE BR. $1.50   (G56)
    (Woodworth) [Lat] 8pt mix cor,opt ST soli,
    org/pno oct SCHIRM.G 10121 $.60   (G57)

  Jubilate Deo (from Sacrae Symphoniae) Jubil
    [Lat] 8pt mix cor,acap oct SCHIRM.G 4245
    $.40   (G58)
    (Davison, A.) [Lat] TTBB,acap SCHIRM.EC 934
    $.40   (G59)
    (Greyson) "Praise The Lord, Jehovah" 2pt
    mix cor oct BOURNE ES72 $1.00   (G60)
    (Woodworth, G.W.) 8pt mix cor,org/pno,brass
    voc sc SCHIRM.G $1.00   (G61)

  Jubilate Deo Omnis Terra (from Symphoniae
    Sacrae) Jubil/mot
    8pt mix cor,acap cor pts BREITKOPF-L
    PB-3685 s.p.   (G62)
    (Hofmann) [Lat] SSAT/ATBB HANSSLER 1.522
    $1.25   (G63)
    (Hudson) [Lat] SSAABarBarBB,org,2trp/2ob,
    7trom/vln&6trom,bsn min sc PETERS 10001
    $3.50, ipa   (G64)
    (Wolters) 8pt mix cor,opt inst sc MOSELER
    s.p., ipa   (G65)

  Jubilemus Singuli
    (Jergenson; Wolfe) 8pt mix cor,org oct
    SCHIRM.G 11810 $.50   (G66)

  Lamb Of God *see Agnus Dei

  Lieto Godea
    (Kaplan, A.) [It/Eng] SSAATTBB BROUDE,A.
    109 $.50   (G67)

  Lord, Give Ear *anthem/mot
    (Rainbow, Bernarr) dbl cor,acap oct NOVELLO
    28.1432.03 s.p.   (G68)

  Mary Magdalene
    (Knight, Gerald) SATB,acap oct FISCHER,C
    CM-7589 $.30   (G69)

  Missa Tornacensis
    (van den Borren, Charles) "Tournai Mass,
    The" cor cmplt ed AM.INST.MUS. $8.00   (G70)

GABRIELI, GIOVANNI (cont'd.)

Nunc Dimittis *Mass/mot
(Hofmann) [Lat] SSSAB&SATB&ATTBB HANSSLER
1.490 s.p.   (G71)

O Domine Jesu Christe Adoro Te *mot
(Hofmann) [Lat] SSAB&ATTB HANSSLER 1.428
$.90   (G72)

O Domine Jesu Christi
(Payson) "O Lord Of Hosts, Jesus, The
Christ" mix cor SOUTHERN $.45   (G73)
(Payson, A.) "O Lord Of Hosts, Jesus, The
Christ" SSAATTBB FRANK F-453 $.45   (G74)

O Jesu Mi Dulcissime
(Woodworth) [Lat] 8pt mix cor oct SCHIRM.G
9898 $.60   (G75)

O Lord Of Hosts, Jesus, The Christ *see O
Domine Jesu Christi

O Lord, With Hands So Holy *see Signor, Le
Tue Man Sante

O Magnum Mysterium
(Clayson, L.) [Lat/Eng] SSAATBarBarB
BROUDE,A. 231 $.50, ipa   (G76)
(Lynn, G.) "Glorious Mystery Sublime" SATB,
acap oct PRESSER 312-40063 $.40   (G77)
(Wolff, S.D.) "O Wondrous Mystery" SSAB&
ATTB,opt org&4brass cor pts CONCORDIA
97-5027 $.50, sc CONCORDIA 97-5030 $2.50 (G78)

O Wondrous Mystery *see O Magnum Mysterium

Oh, Sing To God, The Lord *see Cantate
Domino

Omnes Gentes (from Symphonaie Sacre) mot
[Lat/It] 16pt/4 cor,2trps,3trom,vcl/bvl
PETERS 4813 $1.25, ipa   (G79)

Opera Omnia vol. I *CCU
(Arnold, Denis) cor cmplt ed AM.INST.MUS.
$21.00 motets from: Concerti (1587);
Sacrae Symphoniae (1597)   (G80)

Opera Omnia vol. II (from Sacrae Symphoniae
(1597)) CCU,mot
(Arnold, Denis) cor cmplt ed AM.INST.MUS.
$22.00   (G81)

Opera Omnia vol. III (from Sacrae Symphoniae
(1615)) CCU,mot
(Arnold, Denis) cor cmplt ed AM.INST.MUS.
$23.50   (G82)

Opera Omnia vol. IV (from Sacrae Symphoniae
(1615)) CCU,mot
(Arnold, Denis) cor cmplt ed AM.INST.MUS.
$25.00   (G83)

Opera Omnia vol. V (from Sacrae Symphoniae)
CCU,mot
(Arnold, Denis) cor cmplt ed AM.INST.MUS.
$27.50   (G84)

Plaudite
(Jergenson; Wolfe) [Lat] SSSAATTTTBBB,org
oct SCHIRM.G 11895 $.60   (G85)

Plaudite Omnis Terra *mot
[Lat] 3 cor,opt cont PETERS 8036 $1.50 (G86)

Praise The Lord, Jehovah *see Jubilate Deo

Quem Vidistis, Pastores? (from Symphoniae
Sacrae) mot
(Hudson) [Lat] TTBar/ATTB,trp/ob,2trom,bsn
sc PETERS 10004 $4.50, ipa, voc sc PETERS
$1.50, ipa   (G87)
(Hudson) [Lat] TTBar/TBarBar,org,bsn,trp/
ob,2trom sc PETERS 10004 $4.50, ipa, voc
sc PETERS $1.50, ipa   (G88)

Signor, Le Tue Man Sante (from Musica
Spiritulae)
"O Lord, With Hands So Holy" see Two
Madrigals

Surrexit Christus (from Symphoniae Sacrae)
Easter,mot
"Christ Has Arisen" boy cor SOUTHERN $.50
(Hudson) [Lat] TTB,org,2trp/2ob,4trom,2vln/
vln&vla sc PETERS 10002 $4.00, ipa, voc sc
PETERS 10002 $.80, ipa   (G90)
(Pantaleoni, H.) "Christ Has Arisen" men
cor,org,opt orch voc sc CONCORDIA 97-6370
$.50, ipr   (G91)

Suscipe, Clementissime Deus (from Symphoniae
Sacrae) mot
(Hudson) [Lat] AATTBB/AABarBarBB,6trom,org
sc PETERS 10003 $4.00, ipa, voc sc PETERS
10002 $.80, ipa   (G92)

Thou Hast Been Gracious, Lord *see
Benedixisti, Domine

Three Motets *CC3U,mot
mix cor,acap voc sc KALMUS 6174 $1.50   (G93)

Timor Et Tremor
(Noble, Jeremy) SATTTB oct PENN STATE
0-271-73141-9 $2.75   (G94)

Timor Et Tremor Venerent Super Me *mot
(Goebel) SATBBB/STTBBB HANSSLER 1.506 s.p. (G95)

Tournai Mass, The *see Missa Tornacensis

Two Madrigals (from Musica Spiritulae)
madrigal
(Kenton) 5pt mix cor,acap oct SCHIRM.G
10701 $.30
contains: Signor, Le Tue Man Sante, "O
Lord, With Hands So Holy"; Vergine Il
Cui Figliol, "Virgin Mild, Whose Own
Dear Son"   (G96)

Vergine Il Cui Figliol (from Musica
Spiritulae)
"Virgin Mild, Whose Own Dear Son" see Two
Madrigals

GABRIELI, GIOVANNI (cont'd.)

Virgin Mild, Whose Own Dear Son *see Vergine
Il Cui Figliol

Viva La Musica *mot
4pt mix cor&4pt mix cor MOSELER s.p.   (G97)

GABRIEL'S MESSAGE *Adv/Xmas,carol,Fr
see Three French Carols
see At The Manger
(Schalk, C.) SATB,acap (easy) oct CONCORDIA
98-1694 $.25   (G98)

GABRIEL'S MESSAGE see Niles, John Jacob.

GABRIEL'S MESSAGE see Young, Robert H.

GABRILE ARCHANGLUS see Palestrina, Giovanni

GABURO
Ad Te, Domine
mix cor SOUTHERN $.35   (G99)

GABURO, KENNETH (1927-)
Ave Maria
[Lat] SATB,acap oct WORLD MO-985-8 $.45 (G100)

Laetentur Caeli
[Lat] SATB,acap oct WORLD AC-986-8 $.45 (G101)

Psalm 31
SATB,acap oct WORLD ESA-961-8 $.45   (G102)

Terra Tremuit
[Lat] SATB,acap oct WORLD LE-987-8 $.45 (G103)

GABUS
Laudate, Pueri Dominum
[Lat] SATB,acap oct SALABERT-US $.65 (G104)

GADE, NIELS [W.] (1817-1890)
Benedictus Og Amen
(Schousboe, Torben; Lindholm, Steen) mix
cor,org HANSEN-DEN 28949 s.p.   (G105)

Child Jesus *anthem
(Pooler, Frank) SAB (easy) oct AUGSBURG
0912 $.20   (G106)

Die Kreuzfahrer *Op.50, Psntd
4pt mix cor,STB soli,2fl,2ob,2clar,2bsn,
4horn,2trp,3trom,tuba,strings,perc,timp,
harp BREITKOPF-W rental   (G107)

Lente Boodschap
wom cor sc ALSBACH&D s.p.   (G108)

O Thou Who Art All Loving
(Lundquist) SATB,acap (med) oct WILLIS 5675
$.15   (G109)

GADSBY
I Will Lay Me Down In Peace
SATB oct PRO ART 1722 $.20   (G110)
(Avalos) SSA oct PRO ART 1395 $.16   (G111)

GADSBY, [HENRY ROBERT] (1842-1907)
He Is Risen *Easter
(Mueller) jr cor&sr cor (med easy) FISCHER,
C CM 6286 $.30   (G112)

O Lord, Our Governor *Bibl
4pt mix cor oct SCHIRM.G 4466 $.25   (G113)

GADSCH, HERBERT (1913-)
Auf, Auf, Mein Herz, Mit Freuden
see Evangelisches Kirchengesangbuch

Evangelisches Kirchengesangbuch *Easter,mot
[Ger] 8pt mix cor,acap BAREN. EM 48 s.p.
contains: Auf, Auf, Mein Herz, Mit
Freuden, No.86; Wir Wollen Alle
Frohlich Sein, No.82   (G114)

Frohlocket Mit Handen
mix cor HANSSLER 7.154 s.p.   (G115)

Gebet Um Frieden *Gen
[Ger] SSATBB,acap (med) DEUTSCHER DV 7625
s.p.   (G116)

Gott Schuf Die Sonne *meditation,Afr
mix cor,narrator,org,perc MOSELER s.p. (G117)

Jauchzet Dem Herrn (Psalm 100) *cant
SATB,5brass HANSSLER 10.171 sc s.p., cor
pts s.p., ipa   (G118)

Lobt Gott Den Herrn, Ihr Heiden All *cant
SATB,4brass HANSSLER 10.146 sc s.p., cor
pts s.p.   (G119)

Lobt Gott, Ihr Frommen Christen *cant
SATB,4brass HANSSLER 10.140 sc s.p., cor
pts s.p.   (G120)

Meinem Gott Gehort Die Welt
see Koch, Johannes H.E., Herr Christ, Der
Einig Gotts Sohn

Mitten Wir Im Leben Sind *cant
SATB,4brass HANSSLER 10.147 sc s.p., cor
pts s.p., ipa   (G121)

Psalm 100 *see Jauchzet Dem Herrn

Sei Lob Und Ehr Dem Hochsten Gut *cant
see Kretzschmar, Gunther, Christus Ist
Auferstanden, Freud Ist In
SATB&jr cor,4brass HANSSLER 10.112 sc s.p.,
cor pts s.p.   (G122)

Wenn Meine Sund Mich Kranken
SS/SSA,treb inst/bass inst HANSSLER 14.061
s.p. contains also: Poser, Hans, Wenn
Meine Sund Mich Kranken (SAT/SAB,bass
inst)   (G123)

Wir Wollen Alle Frohlich Sein
see Evangelisches Kirchengesangbuch

GADWOOD, GARY
Hear, Oh Hear *Xmas
4pt mix cor,acap oct SCHIRM.G 11742 $.30
                                         (G124)

GAELIC EASTER CAROL, A see Johnson, Alfred H.

GAELIC PRAYER, A see Swain, Freda

GAFORIO, FRANCHINO (1451-1522)
Masses vol. I
(Finscher, L.) cor cmplt ed AM.INST.MUS.
$4.00
contains: Missa De Carnival; Missa Sexti
Toni Irregularis   (G125)

Masses Vol. II
(Finscher, L.) cor cmplt ed AM.INST.MUS.
$16.50
contains: Missa Brevis Primi Toni; Missa
De O Clara Luce; Missa De Tous Biens
Pleine; Missa (In Nat. D. N. J. C.)
Omnipotens Genitor; Missa Sanctae
Catherinae V. Et M.; Missa (Sine
Nomine)   (G126)

Missa Brevis Primi Toni
see Masses Vol. II

Missa De Carnevale *Mass
(Hammar, Russell A.) [Lat] 4pt mix cor,acap
LAWSON $2.00   (G127)

Missa De Carnival
see Masses vol. I

Missa De O Clara Luce
see Masses Vol. II

Missa De Tous Biens Pleine
see Masses Vol. II

Missa (In Nat. D. N. J. C.) Omnipotens
Genitor
see Masses Vol. II

Missa Sanctae Catherinae V. Et M.
see Masses Vol. II

Missa Sexti Toni Irregularis
see Masses vol. I

Missa (Sine Nomine)
see Masses Vol. II

GAGLIANO
Benedictus *Bene
SATB,acap RICORDI-ENG SY129 s.p.   (G128)

Blessed Is He *Bene
(Zanon; Vene) [Lat/Eng] SATB,acap oct
COLOMBO 2004 $.25   (G129)

GAHER, J.
Death Of Saul
SATB oct PRESSER 352-00438 $1.00   (G130)

Death Of Saul, The
SATB (diff) PRESSER 352-00438 $1.25   (G131)

GAINES, S.
Yonder, Yonder
SATB,acap oct PRESSER 332-15098 $.30   (G132)

"GAK UNDER JESU KORS AT STA" see Moller, Svend-
Ove

GAK UNDER JESU KORS AT STA see Moller, Svend-
Ove, "Gak Under Jesu Kors At Sta"

GAL, HANS (1890-)
De Profundis *cant
4pt mix cor,SATB soli,org,2fl,2ob,2clar,
2bsn,4horn,3trp,3trom,tuba,strings,perc,
timp,harp BREITKOPF-W rental   (G133)

GALBRAITH, J.
All Hail The Power Of Jesus' Name *Easter/
Gen
SATB oct PRESSER 332-12354 $.30   (G134)

How Beautiful Upon The Mountains *Xmas/Gen
SATB oct PRESSER 332-12750 $.30   (G135)

I Will Lift Up Mine Eyes
SATB oct PRESSER 332-13089 $.35   (G136)

Out Of The Silence
SATB oct PRESSER 332-13392 $.30   (G137)

GALE
For All Mankind We Pray
(Frank) SATB oct FOX PS114 $.25   (G138)
(Frank) SA oct FOX PS115 $.25   (G139)

GALILEAN EASTER CAROL see Shure, R. Deane

GALLARDE, SUIT MARGRIET
O Heer Die Daar Des Hemels Tenten
(Lucas, Jan) men cor sc ALSBACH&D s.p. (G140)

GALLEGO
De Jacob La Nueva Estrella *Xmas
[Span] cor,solo UNION ESP. 16021 s.p.   (G141)

GALLERY CAROL, A *Xmas
(Johnson) SATB SCHMITT SD5901 $.25   (G142)
(Johnson) SAB SCHMITT SD6211 $.35   (G143)

GALLIA see Gounod, Charles Francois

GALLICHI, VOLUNIO
Inauguration Of The Siena Synagogue -
Ceremonial Music, 1786 *see Musica
Vocale Esequita In Occasione
Dell'apertura Della Nuovo Scuola Di
Siena, 1786

Music For The Dedication Of A Synagogue *see
Musique Pour L'Inauguration D'une
Synagogue

Musica Vocale Esequita In Occasione
Dell'apertura Della Nuovo Scuola Di
Siena, 1786 (composed with Drei,
Francesco) *Heb
(Adler, Israel) "Inauguration Of The Siena
Synagogue - Ceremonial Music, 1786" cor
ISRAELI 703 s.p.   (G144)

Musique Pour L'Inauguration D'une Synagogue
(from Inauguration Of, The Siena
Synagogue - Ceremonial Music, 1786)
(composed with Drei, Francesco) Heb
(Adler, Israel) "Music For The Dedication
Of A Synagogue" SATB,soli,narrator,orch

GALLICHI, VOLUNIO (cont'd.)

ISRAELI 703-E s.p. (G145)

GALLICULUS, JOHANN
In Natali Domini Clamant *mot
(Hellmann) SATB HANSSLER 1.120 s.p. (G146)

Ostermesse *Easter,Mass
(Blume; Schulze) 4pt mix cor MOSELER s.p. (G147)

GALLUS, JACOBUS (1550-1591)
Ab Oriente
SATB SCHIRM.EC 2785 $.30 (G148)
(Martens) [Lat/Eng] SATB oct MCA (G149)

Ab Oriente Venerunt Magi *Xmas/Epiph,mot, 16th cent
[Lat] SATB,acap (med) MULLER M 10 s.p. (G150)
[Lat/Eng] SATB BROUDE,A. 271 $.30 (G151)
[Lat] mix cor,acap oct NOVELLO DM-10 s.p. (G152)
(Cartier, Anita; Carol, Henri; Gagnepain, Bernard) [Lat] SATB OUVRIERES EO526 s.p. (G153)

Ab Oriente Venerunt Magi In Bethlehem *Xmas
(Cartier, Anita) [Lat] SATB,acap OUVRIERES LEO $.25 (G154)

Adoramus Te, Jesu Christe
anti cor,acap SCHIRM.EC $.30 (G155)

Adoremuste
(Knight, Gerald) SATB,acap oct FISCHER,C CM-7497 $.25 (G156)

All They From Saba *see Omnes De Saba

Alleluia, Sing A New Song
(Weldy) 3 cor (med) oct AUGSBURG 0613 $.40 (G157)

Alleluia, Today Is Christ Risen
dbl cor,acap SCHIRM.EC 931 $.30 (G158)

Alleluia! We Sing With Joy
(Davison, A.) dbl cor,org SCHIRM.EC 1692 $.35 (G159)

Ascendens Christus *Asc/Easter/Pent,mot
[Lat] mix cor,acap oct NOVELLO DM-20 s.p. (G160)
[Lat] SATB,acap (med easy) MULLER M 20 s.p. (G161)

Ascendit Deus
(Burkhart) "God Goes Up On High" [Eng/Lat] SATBB,acap AMP A83 $.30 (G162)

Aspiens A Longe
[Lat/Eng] SATB&SATB,acap PETERS H1521 $.50 (G163)

At The Name Of Jesus *see In Nomine Jesu

Behold, How Doth The Righteous Man *see Ecce, Quomodo Moritur

Behold How The Righteous Perish *see Ecce Quomodo Moritus Justus

Behold Thou Shalt Conceive *Xmas,mot
(Bridge, Sir Fredk.) SATB BOSWORTH s.p. see from Motets (G164)

Benedictus Dominus Deus Israel
(Collins, H.B.) [Lat] SATB CHESTER s.p. (G165)

Christ Was Born Today *see Hodie Christus Natus Est

Christus Factus Est
"Jesus Christ Became For Our Sins, Obedient" see RESPONSES FROM THE WORKS OF OLD MASTERS

Christus Surrexit *Easter
[Lat] SSATTB,acap (med) MULLER MS 63 s.p. (G166)
[Lat] SSATTB,acap oct NOVELLO MS-63 s.p. (G167)

Der Tag, Der Ist So Freudenreich *see Dies Est Laetitia

Dies Est Laetitia *Xmas
(Trotschel, Heinrich Richard) "Der Tag, Der Ist So Freudenreich" [Ger/Lat] SSAATTBB, acap (med) MULLER SM 891 s.p. (G168)

Dies Sanctificatus Illuxit Nobis *16th cent
(Cartier, Anita; Carol, Henri; Gagnepain, Bernard) [Lat] SATB OUVRIERES EO525 s.p. (G169)

Diffusa Est Gratia
(Grossman) [Lat] 5pt mix cor,acap oct SCHIRM.G 10340 $.20 (G170)

Domini Est Terra *Gen
[Ger] SATB&SATB,acap (med easy) MULLER MS 62 s.p. (G171)

Ecce Concipies *mot
(Collins, H.B.) [Lat] SATB CHESTER s.p. (G172)
(Hellmann) "Siehe, Dein Konig Kommt" SATB HANSSLER 1.085 s.p. (G173)

Ecce Quomodo Moritur *Easter/Holywk/Lent/Psntd,anthem
mix cor oct OXFORD 43.474 $.25 (G174)
[Lat] mix cor,acap oct NOVELLO MS-23 s.p. (G175)
[Lat] SATB,acap (med easy) MULLER MS 23 s.p. (G176)
men cor sc ALSBACH&D s.p. (G177)
SATB,acap voc pt DOBLINGER s.p. see also PASSION UND OSTERN (G178)
"Behold, How Doth The Righteous Man" SATB, acap SCHIRM.EC 1226 $.25 (G179)
(Geiringer) "Lo Now, So Is The Death Of The Just Man" [Eng/Lat] 4pt mix cor,acap oct SCHIRM.G 8424 $.30 (G180)
(Marshall, Charles) "See Now, That The Righteous Man Dieth" SATB FRANK F-584 $.30 (G181)

Ecce Quomodo Moritur Justus *mot
SATB,acap RICORDI-ENG SY198 s.p. (G182)
(Parker) SATB,acap (med diff/diff) SOUTHERN $.25 (G183)
(Tunger) SATB HANSSLER 1.312 s.p. (G184)

GALLUS, JACOBUS (cont'd.)

Ecce Quomodo Moritus Justus *mot
(Klein) "Behold How The Righteous Perish" [Eng/Lat] 4pt mix cor,acap oct SCHIRM.G 11586 $.25 (G185)

Egredietur Virga *Adv
[Lat] SATB,acap (med) MULLER M 3 s.p. contains also: Radix Jesse (G186)

Egreditur Virga *Adv/Xmas,mot
[Lat] mix cor,acap oct NOVELLO DM-3 s.p. contains also: Radix Jesse (G187)

God Goes Up On High *see Ascendit Deus

God Of Mercy, God Of Grace
(Windsor) SATB oct PLYMOUTH SC-15 $.25 (G188)

Haec Dies
(Rodby) dbl cor oct SUMMY 5520 $.60 (G189)
(Track) TTBB&TTBB oct PRO ART 2489 $.25 (G190)

Haec East Dies *Easter,mot
"This Is The Day" [Lat/Eng] SATB&SATB,acap PETERS H1523 $.40 (G191)

Haec Est Dies *Adv/Xmas/Easter/Gen,mot, Renais
men cor&men cor MOSELER M-60 s.p. (G192)
eq voices&eq voices MOSELER LB-734 s.p. (G193)
4pt mix cor&4pt mix cor MOSELER s.p. (G194)
SATB&SATB,acap voc pt DOBLINGER s.p. see also ADVENT UND WEIHNACHT, HEFT 2 (G195)
"This Is The Day" dbl cor/opt SATB,opt brass (med easy) oct CONCORDIA 98-1702 $.30 (G196)
(Ehret, Walter) "This Is The Day" SATB,acap PEER $.40 (G197)
(Thoburn, C.) [Lat/Eng] SSAA&SSAA,acap SCHIRM.EC 2590 (G198)
(Thoburn, C.) "This Is The Day" [Lat/Eng] dbl cor,acap SCHIRM.EC 2720 (G199)

Halleluja!
(Ehret) mix cor CHAPPELL 0024216-358 $.40 (G200)

Halleluja! In Deiner Aufstehung *mot
(Berger) dbl cor HANSSLER 1.029 s.p. (G201)

Hodie Christus Natus Est *Xmas
(Harris) "Christ Was Born Today" [Lat] mix cor,acap oct LAWSON 51695 $.30 (G202)

I Ascend Unto My Father *Asc,mot
(Bridge, Sir Fredk.) SSATBB BOSWORTH s.p. see from Motets (G203)

In Nomine Jesu *Circum/Gen/NJ/Palm,mot
men cor sc ALSBACH&D s.p. (G204)
[Lat] men cor,acap BOTE fac ed s.p., cor pts s.p. (G205)
SAATB SCHIRM.EC $.20 (G206)
"At The Name Of Jesus" SATB,acap (med easy) oct CONCORDIA 98-1051 $.25 (G207)
(Collins) boy cor SOUTHERN $.25 (G208)
(Collins, H.B.) [Lat] SAATB CHESTER s.p. (G209)
(Greyson) "In The Name Of Jesus" SATB oct BOURNE ES78 $.25 (G210)
(Klink) [Lat/Ger] TTBB SCHOTT s.p. (G211)
(Ruiz) [Lat] SATB,acap RICORDI-ARG BA 10090 s.p. (G212)

In The Name Of Jesus *see In Nomine Jesu

Jesus Christ Became For Our Sins, Obedient *see Christus Factus Est

Joseph Dearest, Joseph Mine *see Resonet In Laudibus

Joyful Hearts To Heaven *see Resonet In Laudibus

Joyful Hearts To Heaven Raise *see Resonet In Laudibus

Jubilate Deo Omnis Terra (Psalm 99) 16th cent
(Cartier, Anita; Carol, Henri; Gagnepain, Bernard) [Lat] SATB OUVRIERES EO527 s.p. (G213)

Laus Et Perennis Gloria *Gen
[Ger] SSAA&TTBB,acap (med easy) MULLER MS 61 s.p. (G214)

Let The Earth Resound With Praise *see Resonet In Laudibus

Let The Voice Of Praise Resound *Thanks, anthem
TTBB,acap oct NOVELLO 38.0147.00 s.p. (G215)

Lo, I Reveal Unto Thee
(Lundquist) SATB,acap (diff) oct WILLIS 5677 $.12 (G216)

Lo Now, So Is The Death Of The Just Man *see Ecce, Quomodo Moritur

Lord, In Thy Resurrection
8pt mix cor,acap oct SCHIRM.G 8005 $.30 (G217)

Lord Is Risen, The *see Surrexit Dominus

Mirabile Mysterium *mot
SAT/SATB/SABB SCHIRM.EC 2784 $.30 (G218)
(Grossman) [Lat] 5pt mix cor,acap oct SCHIRM.G 10353 $.30 (G219)
(Ramin, G.) 5pt mix cor,acap cor pts BREITKOPF-L CHB-2832 s.p. (G220)

Missa Ad Imitationem Pater Noster *Mass
(Gillesberger, H.) dbl cor DOBLINGER sc s.p., cor pts s.p. (G221)

Missa Ich Stund *Mass
mix cor,acap voc sc KALMUS 6175 $2.50 (G222)

Motets *see All They From Saba; Behold Thou Shalt Conceive; I Ascend Unto My Father; Righteous Perisheth, The (G223)

O Admirabile Commercium
SSAATTBB,acap oct PRESSER 352-00067 $.30 (G224)

GALLUS, JACOBUS (cont'd.)

O Herre Gott *Gd.Fri.
SATB,acap voc pt DOBLINGER s.p. see also TOD UND VERGANGLICHKEIT (G225)

O Salutaris Hostia *Pent/Whitsun
SATB,acap voc pt DOBLINGER s.p. see also PFINGSTEN UND EUCHARISTIE (G226)

Obsecro Domine *Adv,mot
[Lat] mix cor,acap oct NOVELLO DM-1 s.p. (G227)

Observo Domine *Adv
[Lat] SATB,acap (med) MULLER M 1 s.p. (G228)

Omnes De Saba *Epiph,mot
[Lat] SATTB RICORDI-ENG SY223 s.p. (G229)
(Bridge, Sir Fredk.) "All They From Saba" SATTB BOSWORTH s.p. see from Motets (G230)
(Hunn; Vene) "Three Kings" [Lat/Eng] SATTB, acap oct COLOMBO 1857 $.25 (G231)
(Lundquist) "All They From Saba" SATTB,acap (diff) oct WILLIS 5797 $.10 (G232)

Omnes De Saba Venient *Epiph,anthem
[Lat] SATTB,acap (med easy) MULLER MS 45 s.p. (G233)
SATTB SCHIRM.EC 2783 $.30 (G234)
[Lat] SATTB,acap oct NOVELLO MS-45 s.p. (G235)

Omnia Vincit Amor
6pt mix cor MOSELER LB-833 s.p. (G236)

Orietur Stella *Xmas
(Greyson) "Star Of Jacob" SATB oct BOURNE ES91 $.25 (G237)

Our Father *see Pater Noster

Our King Is Born *see Regem Natum

Passion Nach Johannes *Psntd
[Ger/Lat] men cor&wom cor,acap TONGER s.p. (G238)

Pater Noster *Gen,anthem
[Lat] SSAATTBB,acap oct NOVELLO MS-6 s.p. (G239)
"Our Father" [Lat/Eng] SSAATTBB,acap PETERS H1522 $.75 (G240)
(Goebel, Georg) [Ger] SSAA&TTBB,acap (med) MULLER MS 6 s.p. (G241)

Praise Ye The Lord Of Hosts
(Kingsbury, John) SATB ALFRED 6419 $.30 (G242)

Preis, Dank, Lob, Ehr Und Herrlichkeit *mot
(Berger) dbl cor HANSSLER 1.028 s.p. (G243)

Psalm 98 *see Tribulationes Civitatum

Psalm 99 *see Jubilate Deo Omnis Terra

Pueri Concinite *Adv/Xmas
SSAT,acap voc pt DOBLINGER s.p. see also ADVENT UND WEIHNACHT, HEFT 2 (G244)
(Geer) [Eng/Lat] SSAA,acap oct SCHIRM.G 8441 $.25 (G245)
(Simkins) "Sing Ye Choirs" [Eng/Lat/Ger] 4pt jr cor/4pt wom cor CURWEN 72687 s.p. (G246)
(Track) TTBB,acap oct PRO ART 2451 $.25 (G247)
(Track) boy cor SOUTHERN $.25 (G248)

Quem Vidistis, Pastores? *Xmas,16th cent
(Martens, Mason) "Whom Have You Seen, O Shepherds?" SATB&SATB oct WALTON 6023 $.30 (G249)

Radix Jesse
see Gallus, Jacobus, Egredietur Virga
see Gallus, Jacobus, Egreditur Virga

Regem Natum *Xmas
(McCollough) "Our King Is Born" [Eng/Lat] SATB,acap oct LAWSON 51493 $.30 (G250)

Regnum Mundi
(Boepple, P.) 4 eq voices,acap oct PRESSER 352-00033 $.30 (G251)

Regum Mundi
(Boepple, P.) TTBB,acap oct PRESSER 352-00033 $.30 (G252)

Repleti Sunt
8pt oct PRESSER 352-00031 $.30 (G253)
(Boepple, P.) SSAA&SSAA,acap oct PRESSER 352-00031 $.30 (G254)

Repleti Sunt Omnes
8pt,acap oct PRESSER 352-00031 $.30 (G255)

Resonet In Laudibus *Adv/Xmas,anthem/mot
[Lat] TTBB,acap oct NOVELLO 38.0147.00 s.p. (G256)
SATB,acap voc pt DOBLINGER s.p. see also ADVENT UND WEIHNACHT, HEFT 2 (G257)
"Joyful Hearts To Heaven" [Lat/Eng] SATB& opt anti cor,acap SCHIRM.EC 2492 $.30 (G258)
"Joyful Hearts To Heaven Raise" [Eng/Lat] SATB CHESTER s.p. (G259)
(Greyson) mix cor SOUTHERN $.25 (G260)
(Greyson) "Songs Of Joy To Heaven Raise" SATB oct BOURNE ES6 $.25 (G261)
(Martens, Mason) "Let The Earth Resound With Praise" SATB oct WALTON 2151 $.25 (G262)
(Simkins) "Joseph Dearest, Joseph Mine" [Lat/Ger/Eng] 4pt mix cor CURWEN 61578 s.p. (G263)

Righteous Perisheth, The *ASD,mot
(Bridge, Sir Fredk.) SATB BOSWORTH s.p. see from Motets (G264)
(Gillman, W.) SATB oct PRESSER G-4009 $.30 (G265)

See Now, That The Righteous Man Dieth *see Ecce Quomodo Moritur

Siehe, Dein Konig Kommt *see Ecce Concipies

Sing Ye Choirs *see Pueri Concinite

GALLUS, JACOBUS (cont'd.)

Six Sacred Songs
[Lat] 4pt men cor/5pt men cor,acap voc sc
UNIVER. 9306, cor pts UNIVER. 9307A-E
(G266)

Songs Of Joy To Heaven Raise *see Resonet In
Laudibus

Star Of Jacob *see Orietur Stella

Surrexit Dominus *Easter/Lent,mot
[Lat] SATB,acap oct GIA G573 $.25 (G267)
(Martens, Mason) "Lord Is Risen, The" SATB
oct WALTON 2089 $.25 (G268)

Then Round About The Starry Throne
(Thompson) SATB oct BOURNE D8 $.30 (G269)

This Is The Day *see Haec East Dies

This Is The Day *see Haec Est Dies

Three Kings *see Omnes De Saba

Trahe Me Post Te
(Boepple, P.) SSA/SSAA/TTBB,acap oct
PRESSER 352-00032 $.30 (G270)

Tribulationes Civitatum (Psalm 98) 16th cent
(Cartier, Anita; Carol, Henri; Gagnepain,
Bernard) [Lat] SSATB OUVRIERES EO528 s.p.
(G271)

Vespere Autem Sabbati *Easter/Psntd,mot
[Lat] SATB,acap (med) MULLER M 17 s.p.
(G272)
[Lat] mix cor,acap oct NOVELLO DM-17 s.p.
(G273)

Whom Have You Seen, O Shepherds? *see Quem
Vidistis, Pastores?

Worthy Is The Lamb
(Lundquist) SATB,pno (med) oct WILLIS 5798
$.10 (G274)

Zwei Der Seraphim Sie Riefen *mot
(Berger) dbl cor HANSSLER 1.030 s.p. (G275)

GALLUS, W.E.
Glory And Peace And Majesty
(Gallus, W.E.; Ehret) dbl cor oct SHAPIRO
SK 2117 $.25 (G276)

GALUPPI, BALDASSARE (1706-1785)
Beatus Vir (Psalm 62) Heb
[Lat/Heb] mix cor,SA soli,orch,opt pno sc
HEINRICH. s.p. (G277)
(Verona, Gabriella Gentili) SATB,SA soli,
orch voc sc ISRAELI 320 s.p. (G278)

Magnificat *Magnif
(Martens, Mason) SATB,soli,org,cont,ob,
horn,strings voc sc WALTON M 104 $1.75,
ipr, sc WALTON rental (G279)

Missa In C *Mass
(Bauerle, Hermann) SATB,acap cor pts
BREITKOPF-L PB-3137 s.p., voc pt
BREITKOPF-L CHB-2547 s.p. (G280)

Psalm 62 *see Beatus Vir

Psalm 112 *see Beatus Vir

GAMBINO, J.
Jubilate Deo *Jubil
SATB oct SOUTHERN $.25 (G281)

GAMBOLD
One View, Lord Jesus, Of Thy Passion
(Nolte) [Eng/Ger] SSAB/SATB,org oct
MORAVIAN 5718 $.35 (G282)

Unto Jesus' Cross
(Nolte) [Eng/Ger] SSAB/SATB,org oct
MORAVIAN 5717 $.35 (G283)

Who With Weeping Soweth
(Nolte) [Eng/Ger] SSAB/SATB,S solo,org oct
MORAVIAN 5746 $.40 (G284)

GAMMEL MARIA-VISE
(Beck, Thomas) wom cor MUSIKK 44 s.p. (G285)

GAMMEL MARIA-VISE see Beck, Thomas [Ludvigsen]

GANDOLFI
Vergine Bella *BVM
SSTB s.p. voc sc RICORDI-ENG 128894, cor
pts RICORDI-ENG 128895-96 (G286)

GANG ZUM HERRN see Schmid, Walter

GANNE
Hymne De La Jeunesse Chretienne
[Fr] unis ENOCH voc sc s.p., cor pts s.p.
(G287)

GANTVOORT, ARNOLD JOHANN (1857-1937)
Easter Anthem *Easter,anthem
SATB,S solo,pno (med) oct WILLIS 1870 $.15
(G288)

GARBELOTTO, ANTONIO
Antologia Di Brani Polifonici *CCU
2-4pt cmplt ed ZANIBON 5075 s.p. (G289)

Magnificat
see Garbelotto, Antonio, Vespro Domenicale

Missa Festiva In Hon. S. Caroli Borromei
*Mass
[Lat] ATB,org sc ZANIBON 3472 s.p., voc pt
ZANIBON s.p. (G290)

Missa In Honorem SS. Eucharistici Cordis Jesu
*Op.14, Mass
[Lat] ATTB,org,opt strings sc ZANIBON 3121
s.p., voc pt ZANIBON s.p., ipr (G291)

Quattro Pastorali Per Il Santo Natale *CC4U,
Xmas
ATB/unis,org ZANIBON 2847 s.p. (G292)

Vespro Domenicale *Eve
[Lat] 2 eq voices,org (easy) ZANIBON 3448
s.p. contains also: Magnificat (G293)

GARBERS, WILFRIED
Herr, Gott, Mein Heiland, Ich Schreie Tag Und
Nacht
[Ger] mix cor (diff) oct SIRIUS 14 s.p.
(G294)

GARDANE, ANTONIE (ca. 1500-1571)
O Seigneur Dieu, Ta Loi Parfaite Et Sainte
*16th cent
(Honegger, Marc; Pidoux, Pierre) [Fr] SATB
OUVRIERES EO599 s.p. (G295)

GARDANO, ALESSANDRO
Echo Alleluia
SATB oct STAFF 691 $.35 (G296)

GARDEN see Caldwell

GARDEN AND THE CROSS see Rowley, Alec

GARDEN, CHARLOTTE L.
Come Ye Servants
SATB oct GRAY GCMR 2708 $.30 (G297)

GARDEN HYMN *Easter,anthem/folk/hymn,US
(Lipscomb, H.) SATB oct PRESSER 312-40490
$.30 (G298)
(Niles) 4pt mix cor oct SCHIRM.G 10240 $.25
(G299)
(Pooler, Marie) SATB (easy) oct AUGSBURG 1292
$.30 (G300)
(Shaw; Parker) SATB,T solo,acap oct LAWSON
912 $.30 (G301)

GARDEN HYMN see Elkins

GARDEN HYMN see Niles, John Jacob

GARDEN HYMN see Van Iderstine, A.P.

GARDEN HYMN FOR EASTER see Cowell, Henry Dixon

GARDEN HYMN, T see Price

GARDEN HYMN, THE *hymn
(Russell) TTBB,T solo,acap oct LAWSON 51500
$.35 (G302)

GARDEN HYMN, THE see Ahrold, Frank

GARDEN HYMN, THE see Perera, Ronald

GARDEN HYMN, THE see Thompson

GARDEN OF CHRIST, THE see Dobbs, J.P.B.

GARDEN OF EASTER, THE see Hadler

GARDEN OF JESUS, THE *carol
unis/SATB (very easy) OXFORD 08.105 $.15, ipr
(G303)

GARDEN OF MY LORD, THE see Wheelwright, Lorin
F.

GARDINER
Lord Is My Shepherd, The *anthem/hymn
(Dunham) SATB oct SPRATT 560 $.25 (G304)

Lord's My Shepherd, The
(Avalos) SATB oct PRO ART 1518 $.30 (G305)
(Avalos) SAB oct PRO ART 1463 $.30 (G306)
(Avalos) SSA oct PRO ART 1390 $.25 (G307)
(Avalos) 2pt oct PRO ART 1889 $.30 (G308)
(Avalos) TTB oct PRO ART 2061 $.30 (G309)

Where Cross The Crowded Ways Of Life *anthem
(Johnson) SAB (easy) oct AUGSBURG 1496 $.25
(G310)

GARDINER, HENRY BALFOUR (1877-1950)
Evening Hymn *Eve,anthem
[Eng/Lat] mix cor oct NOVELLO 28.1127.08
s.p. (G311)

Te Lucis Ante Terminum *Eve,anthem/hymn
[Lat] mix cor oct NOVELLO 28.1127.08 s.p.
(G312)
"Thee, Lord, Before The Close Of Day" SATB,
org SCHIRM.EC 320 $.25 (G313)

Thee, Lord, Before The Close Of Day *see Te
Lucis Ante Terminum

GARDNER
Angels From The Realms Of Glory *Xmas
3 eq voices,acap (easy) OXFORD 40.103 $.20
(G314)

Cantata For Christmas *Xmas,cant
SATB OXFORD ipr (G315)

Christmas Folk Song, A *Xmas
3pt wom cor,acap oct SCHIRM.G 10777 $.30
(G316)

Easter Song *see Gloria

Four Spirituals *CC4U
SSA oct STAFF 546 $.30 (G317)

Gloria *Easter,Gloria
"Easter Song" SATB oct STAFF 353 $.30 (G318)

Holly And The Ivy, The
SATB oct STAFF 236 $.30 (G319)

How Firm A Foundation
SATB oct STAFF 340 $.25 (G320)

I Believe In One God
SATB oct STAFF 310 $.25 (G321)

Man Shall Not Live By Bread Alone
SATB FLAMMER A 5061 $.25 (G322)
SAB FLAMMER D5167 $.25 (G323)
(Riegger) TTBB FLAMMER C5062 $.25 (G324)

Michael, Row The Boat
SATB oct STAFF 425 $.30 (G325)
TTBB oct STAFF 502 $.30 (G326)
SAB oct STAFF 466 $.35 (G327)
SSA oct STAFF 473 $.30 (G328)

Mighty Fortress Is Our God, A
SATB oct STAFF 268 $.30 (G329)

O Give Thanks
SATB oct STAFF 346 $.25 (G330)

Peter, Go Ring Them Bells
SATB oct STAFF 348 $.30 (G331)

GARDNER (cont'd.)
Rockin' Jerusalem
SATB oct STAFF 495 $.30 (G332)

Singing On The Mountain
SATB oct STAFF 494 $.30 (G333)
SA/TB oct STAFF 565 $.30 (G334)
SSA oct STAFF 563 $.30 (G335)

Ye Shall Go Out With Joy
SATB oct STAFF 592 $.30 (G336)

GARDNER, GRACE
Christmas Gloria *Xmas
SATB,pno/org (easy) oct WILLIS 4980 $.15 (G337)

GARDNER, JOHN [LINTON] (1917-   )
Abide With Me
SSA,orch/2pno/pno voc pt OXFORD 44.224
$.25, ipr see from FIVE HYMNS IN POPULAR
STYLE (G338)
SATB,orch/2pno/pno oct OXFORD 42.873 $.30,
ipr see from FIVE HYMNS IN POPULAR STYLE
(G339)

Brightest And Best Of The Sons Of The Morning
SATB,orch/2pno/pno oct OXFORD 42.870 $.30,
ipr see from FIVE HYMNS IN POPULAR STYLE
(G340)
SSA,orch/2pno/pno voc pt OXFORD 44.221
$.25, ipr see from FIVE HYMNS IN POPULAR
STYLE (G341)

Cantiones Sacrae *Bibl
SATB,S solo,orch (diff) OXFORD $3.50, ipr,
rental (G342)

End Is The Beginning, The *Gen
SATB,acap (med) oct OXFORD 43.950 $.25 (G343)

Fight The Good Fight With All Thy Might
SSA,orch/2pno/pno voc pt OXFORD 42.874
$.25, ipr see from FIVE HYMNS IN POPULAR
STYLE (G344)
SATB,orch/2pno/pno oct OXFORD 44.225 $.30,
ipr see from FIVE HYMNS IN POPULAR STYLE
(G345)

I Will Lift Up Mine Eyes Unto The Hills
(Psalm 121) Gen
SSA,S solo,acap (med easy) oct OXFORD
44.076 $.25 (G346)

Jubilate Deo *Jubil
SATB,acap (med diff) oct OXFORD 43.943 $.65
(G347)

Magnificat (from Cantiones Sacrae) Magnif/
Nunc
SATB oct OXFORD rental (G348)

Mass In C *Agnus/Gloria/Kyrie/Sanctus
[Lat] SSAATTBB,acap (med) oct OXFORD 43.538
$.65 (G349)

Michael Row The Boat
SA/TB oct STAFF 474 $.30 (G350)

Nearer, My God, To Thee
SSA,orch/2pno/pno voc sc OXFORD 42.872
$.25, ipr see from FIVE HYMNS IN POPULAR
STYLE (G351)
SATB,orch/2pno/pno oct OXFORD 42.872 $.50,
ipr see from FIVE HYMNS IN POPULAR STYLE
(G352)

O, Clap Your Hands (Psalm 47) Fest/Gen
SATB (diff) oct OXFORD 42.957 $.30 (G353)

O Give Thanks Unto The Lord
SATB FLAMMER A 5103 $.30 (G354)

O How Amiable Are Thy Dwellings (Psalm 84)
Ded/Gen
SATB (med) oct OXFORD 42.890 $.30 (G355)

Preces And Responses
SATB oct NOVELLO 44.1432.02 s.p. (G356)

Psalm 46 *Gen/Thanks
SSAATTBB (med diff) oct OXFORD 43.367 $.35
(G357)

Psalm 47 *see O, Clap Your Hands

Psalm 84 *see O How Amiable Are Thy
Dwellings

Psalm 121 *see I Will Lift Up Mine Eyes Unto
The Hills

Saviour, Again To Thy Dear Name We Raise
SSA,orch/2pno/pno voc pt OXFORD 42.871
$.25, ipr see from FIVE HYMNS IN POPULAR
STYLE (G358)
SATB,orch/2pno/pno oct OXFORD 42.871 $.30,
ipr see from FIVE HYMNS IN POPULAR STYLE
(G359)

Shout, The *Easter
SSAATTBB,acap (med) oct OXFORD 84.136 $.35
(G360)

We Have A Strong City *Ded/Gen,Bibl
SATB (med) oct OXFORD 42.913 $.35 (G361)

GARDNER, MAURICE (1909-   )
Alleluia
SATB oct STAFF 443 $.30 (G362)

Banks Of Jordan
SATB oct STAFF 409 $.35 (G363)

God Grant Us
SATB oct STAFF 146 $.30 (G364)

I Am A Pilgrim
SATB oct STAFF 490 $.25 (G365)

I Want To Be Ready
SATB oct STAFF 489 $.30 (G366)
SSA oct STAFF 530 $.30 (G367)

I'll Be There
SATB oct STAFF 557 $.30 (G368)
SSA oct STAFF 617 $.30 (G369)
SA/TB oct STAFF 618 $.30 (G370)
SAB oct STAFF 616 $.30 (G371)

I'm Gonna Sing
SATB oct STAFF 499 $.30 (G372)
SA/TB oct STAFF 571 $.35 (G373)

GARDNER, MAURICE (cont'd.)

Jonah
SATB oct STAFF 666 $.30   (G374)

Lord Is My Shepherd, The
SATB oct STAFF 611 $.30   (G375)

Mary And Martha
SATB oct STAFF 315 $.25   (G376)

Mary Had A Baby *Xmas
SATB oct STAFF 338 $.30   (G377)

Mighty Day
SATB oct STAFF 519 $.30   (G378)

No Hiding Place
SAB oct STAFF 469 $.30   (G379)

Noel *Xmas
SATB oct STAFF 384 $.30   (G380)

O Sanctissima
SATB oct STAFF 299 $.25   (G381)

Prayer
SATB oct STAFF 436 $.25   (G382)

Run To Jesus
SATB oct STAFF 435 $.25   (G383)

Shepherd, Shepherd
SA/TB oct STAFF 620 $.35   (G384)

Two Spirituals *CC2U,spir
SSA oct STAFF 547 $.30   (G385)

Where Is Old Elijah
SATB oct STAFF 343 $.25   (G386)

Wondrous Love
SATB oct STAFF 335 $.30   (G387)

GARFUNKEL, ART
Benedictus *see Simon, Paul

GARLAND, HUGH
Bread Of The World
SATB oct LESLIE 4050   (G388)

This Is The Day *carol
SATB oct LESLIE 4074 see from Two Besancon
Carols   (G389)

Two Besancon Carols *see This Is The Day;
With Songs Of Joy   (G390)

With Songs Of Joy *carol
SATB oct LESLIE 4074 see from Two Besancon
Carols   (G391)

GARLAND OF CAROLS, A *CC8L,Xmas,carol,Eng/Fr/
Ger/It/Swed
(Parker) [Eng/Fr/Ger/Lat] 2pt boy cor/SA,pno/
org oct LAWSON 51146 $.40   (G392)

GARLICK
Three Canadian Carols *CC3U,carol
SATB THOMP.G G-567 s.p.   (G393)

GARLICK, ANTHONY
Alleluia
SATB,pno/org sc SEESAW $1.50   (G394)

Christ The Lord Is Risen
see Six Easter Carols

Christmas Tribute, The *cant
SATB SHAWNEE A717 $1.00   (G395)

Easter Day, No Man May
see Six Easter Carols

Four Christmas Carols *CC4U,Xmas,carol
SATB oct FISCHER,J 9933 $.35   (G396)

Glory To God In The Highest
SATB SHAWNEE A 757 $.35   (G397)

Let The Merry Church Bells Ring
see Six Easter Carols

Now Glad Of Heart Be Everyone
see Six Easter Carols

O Lord, We Beseech Thee
SATB,acap SHAWNEE A 819 $.25   (G398)

Praised Be The Lord
SATB WORD CS-2400 $.40   (G399)

Psalm 90
dbl cor sc SEESAW $11.00   (G400)

Psalm 100
dbl cor,acap sc SEESAW $9.00   (G401)

Sing Alleluia *Easter
SATB SHAWNEE A 797 $.30   (G402)
SATB oct SOUTHERN $.30   (G403)

Six Easter Carols *CC6U,Easter,carol
SATB oct SOUTHERN $.25   (G404)

Six Easter Carols *Easter
SATB SCHMITT 6202 $.30
contains: Christ The Lord Is Risen;
Easter Day, No Man May; Let The Merry
Church Bells Ring; Now Glad Of Heart Be
Everyone; Wintertime Hath Past Away;
World Itself Keeps Easter Day, The
                                           (G405)

Wintertime Hath Past Away
see Six Easter Carols

World Itself Keeps Easter Day, The
see Six Easter Carols

GARMENT OF PRAISE, THE see Thompson, Randall

GARNER
And There Were Shepherds *Xmas
SATB oct FISCHER,C CM-7404 $.35   (G406)

GARRETT
In Humble Faith And Holy Love *Trin
SATB,S solo oct PRO ART 1699 $.25   (G407)

GARRETT, G.M.
Lord Is Loving, The *Fest
SATB ALLANS 326 s.p.   (G408)

Prepare Ye The Way Of The Lord *Adv,Bibl
4pt mix cor,T solo oct SCHIRM.G 4256 $.35 (G409)

GARRETT, GEORGE MURSELL (1834-1897)
In Humble Faith And Holy Love *Trin,anthem
mix cor,orch oct NOVELLO 40.0304.07 s.p.   (G410)

Lord Is Loving Unto Every Man, The *anthem
mix cor oct NOVELLO 28.0039.10 s.p.   (G411)

GASCOGNE
Caro Mia Est Cibus
(Knight, Gerald) SATB,acap oct FISCHER,C
CM-7581 $.25   (G412)

GASCONGNE, MATHIEU
Caro Mea Vere Est Cibus *16th cent
(Cartier, Anita; Carol, Henri; Gagnepain,
Bernard) [Lat] SATB OUVRIERES EO 665 s.p.
                                           (G413)

GASPARINI
Adoramus Te
SATB RICORDI-ENG SY112 s.p.   (G414)
(Kjelson) SATB oct BELWIN 2168 $.25   (G415)
(Marshall) "We Adore Thee" mix cor SOUTHERN
$.30   (G416)
(Schaller; Vene) "We Adore Thee" SATB,acap
oct COLOMBO 1849 $.35   (G417)

Behold The Saviour Of The World *Lent
(Ehret) SATB oct KENDOR $.30   (G418)

We Adore Thee *see Adoramus Te

GASPARINI, FRANCESCO (1668-1727)
Adoramus Te *Easter/Gen/Lent,anthem
(Klein, M.) "We Adore You" [Eng/Lat] SATB
(med))ct GIA G1434 $.25   (G419)
(Marshall, Charles) "We Adore Thee" SATB
FRANK F-586 $.30   (G420)

May Thy Spirit Rest Upon Us *anthem
mix cor oct NOVELLO 40.1258.05 s.p.   (G421)

We Adore Thee *see Adoramus Te

We Adore You *see Adoramus Te

GASPARINI, QUIRINO (1749-1770)
Adoramus Te *Easter/Lent,Eng/Lat
"We Adore Thee" SATB oct WALTON 2177 $.30
                                           (G422)
(Davis) "Let Us Bow Before Thee" 4pt wom
cor,acap oct SCHIRM.G 8154 $.25   (G423)
(Deis) "We Adore Thee" [Eng/Lat] 4pt mix
cor,acap oct SCHIRM.G 9932 $.25   (G424)

Let Us Bow Before Thee *see Adoramus Te

O Eternal Lord *Gen/Lent
SATB,acap (med diff) oct CONCORDIA 98-1685
$.25   (G425)

We Adore Thee *see Adoramus Te

GASS, IRENE
I Will Keep Christmas *Xmas,carol
unis CRAMER 8   (G426)

Song For Christmas Day, A *carol
unis CRAMER 5   (G427)

Stars Shed Their Light *carol
unis CRAMER 18 s.p.   (G428)

GASSMAN, CLARK
Alleluia *Easter/Gen
SATB,acap (med) PRESSER G-185 $.35   (G429)

In Christ There Is No East Or West
3 cor,org,pno/orch voc sc WORD 37534 $2.95,
ipa   (G430)

GAST
Macht Hoch Die Tur
see Nickel, Eckehardt, Es Kommt Ein Schiff

GASTOLDI
In Thee Is Gladness *anthem
(Nelson) SAB (easy) oct AUGSBURG 1231 $.30
                                           (G431)

Love's Hope *see Speme Amorosa

Speme Amorosa
"Love's Hope" SSATB oct WALTON 8011 $.25   (G432)

GASTOLDI, GIOVANNI GIACOMO (? -1622)
Amor Im Nachen
men cor,acap ERDMANN 162 s.p. contains
also: Hassler, Hans Leo, Ach, Fraulein
Zart   (G433)

In Dir Ist Freude
SSATB DOBLINGER s.p. see also BITTE UND
VERTRAUEN   (G434)

In Dir Ist Freude, In Allem Leide *Xmas/Gen
see Gesius, Bartholomaus, Das Ist Furwahr
Ein Kostlich Ding
(Bender, J.) "In Thee Is Gladness" SATB,kbd
(med easy, or New Year) oct CONCORDIA
98-1968 $.25   (G435)
(Davis) "In Thee Is Gladness" mix cor
SOUTHERN $.30   (G436)
(Davis, K.) "In Thee Is Gladness" 2pt
WARNER R3500 $.30   (G437)
(Davis, K.) "In Thee Is Gladness" SATB
WARNER R3505 $.30   (G438)

In Thee Is Gladness *see In Dir Ist Freude,
In Allem Leide

Tutti Venite Armati *It
(Woodworth, G.) TTBB,acap SCHIRM.EC 964
$.25   (G439)

GASTORIUS, SEVERIUS
Sommarpsalm (En Vanlig Gronskas Rika Drakt)
(Wallin, Bertil) [Swed] SAB,acap GEHRMANS
TKS 23   (G440)

GASTORIUS, SEVERIUS (cont'd.)
Was Gott Tut Das Ist Wohlgetan
(Berger, H.L.) TTBB HANSSLER 6.5083 s.p.
                                           (G441)

GATATUMBA *Xmas,carol,Span
(Anderson) [Eng/Span] 4pt mix cor,opt clar&
bells&drums&maracas&tamb&gtr oct SCHIRM.G
10511 $.40   (G442)
(Anderson; Stickles) [Eng/Span] 3pt mix cor,
opt clar&bells&drums&maracas&tamb&gtr oct
SCHIRM.G $.40   (G443)

GATE OF HEAVEN, THE see Thompson, Randall

GATE OF THE YEAR see Gillet, [Ernest]

GATE OF THE YEAR, THE see Robson, R. Walker

GATE OF THE YEAR, THE see Warren

GATES OF JERUSALEM, THE
SATB CHAPPELL 0015230-358 $.50   (G444)

GATES OF JERUSALEM, THE see McAfee, Don

GATES OF JERUSALEM, THE see Mussorgsky, Modest

GATES OF JUSTICE, THE see Brubeck

GATEWAY CAROL see Marryott, Ralph E.

GATEWAY CHOIR BOOK, THE *CC20U
(Lundquist, M.) SAB SCHIRM.EC $1.50   (G445)

GATHER 'ROUND THE CHRISTMAS TREE *Xmas
(Bampton, R.) SA oct PRESSER 312-40401 $.25
                                           (G446)

GATHER THE HARVEST see Emig, Lois

GATHER YE ROSEBUDS WHILE YE MAY see Butler,
Eugene

GATHERING CLOUDS see Bain

GATHERING FLOWERS FOR THE MASTER'S BOUQUET
SATB/TTBB BIG3 $.25   (G447)

GATTERMAYER, HEINRICH (1923-   )
Aus Der Tiefe (Psalm 129) Bibl
men cor,acap oct DOBLINGER s.p. see also
Vier Geistliche Mannerchore   (G448)

Drum Lasst Uns Frohlich Sein *Bibl
men cor,acap oct DOBLINGER s.p. see also
Vier Geistliche Mannerchore   (G449)

Fanget An *Bibl
men cor,acap oct DOBLINGER s.p. see also
Vier Geistliche Mannerchore   (G450)

Gottes Liebe Bluht Im Leben
mix cor,acap oct DOBLINGER s.p.   (G451)

Gruss Gott Dich Schoner Maien *folk
[Ger] men cor,acap (easy) cor pts KRENN
s.p.   (G452)

Psalm 129 *see Aus Der Tiefe

Psalm 132 *see Siehe, Wie Gut Ist's

Psalm 148
men cor,acap oct DOBLINGER s.p.   (G453)

Siehe, Wie Gut Ist's (Psalm 132) Bibl
men cor,acap oct DOBLINGER s.p. see also
Vier Geistliche Mannerchore   (G454)

Trost-Aria
men cor,acap oct DOBLINGER s.p.   (G455)

Vier Geistliche Mannerchore *Bibl
men cor,acap cmplt ed DOBLINGER s.p.
contains & see also: Aus Der Tiefe (Psalm
129); Drum Lasst Uns Frohlich Sein;
Fanget An; Siehe, Wie Gut Ist's (Psalm
132)   (G456)

GAUDA LUX DONATIANE see Clemens, Jacobus

GAUDE BARBARA see Palestrina, Giovanni

GAUDE FLORE VIRGINALI see Carver, R.

GAUDE MARIA see Lotti, Antonio

GAUDE MARIA VIRGO see Victoria, Tomas Luis de

GAUDE PLURIMUM see Taverner, John

GAUDE VIRGO see Aston, Hugo

GAUDE VIRGO see de la Rue, Pierre

GAUDEAMUS HODIE see Sleeth, Natalie

GAUDEAMUS IGITUR see Cisneros

GAUDEAMUS OMNES FIDELES see Ramella

GAUDEAMUS OMNES IN DOMINO see Jaeggi, Oswald

GAUDEAMUS OMNES IN DOMINO see Quack, Erhard

GAUDENS GAUDEBO see Casali, Giovanni Battista

GAUDENS GAUDEBO see Mercatali, A.

GAUDENS GAUDEBO see Volpi, Edoardo

GAUDENT IN CAELIS see Victoria, Tomas Luis de

GAUDENT IN COELIS see Deering, Richard

GAUDENT IN COELIS see Victoria, Tomas Luis de

GAUDETE, CHRISTUS EST NATUS (from Anthology Of
Carols, An)
see First Nowell, The

GAUDETE IN DOMINO SEMPER see Giroust, F.

GAUDETE OMNES see Praetorius, Heironymous

GAUDIA MATRIS see Kubizek, Augustinian

GAUDIMEL, CLAUDE
Hold Oppe, Gud
(Sorass, Lars) mix cor MUSIKK 159 s.p. see
from RELIGIOSE KORSANGER   (G457)

GAUGLER, TH.
Gebet
[Ger] mix cor,acap (med diff) HUG s.p.
                                                 (G458)

GAUL, ALFRED ROBERT (1837-1913)
Amish Carol Of The Hills *Xmas,carol,US
SATB oct GALAXY 1.1528.1 $.30   (G459)

Ancient Moravian Christmas Carol *Xmas,
carol,Morav
2pt oct GALAXY 1.1314.1 $.30   (G460)

Carol Of The Bohemian Brethren *Xmas,carol,
Boh
SATB oct GALAXY 1.1402.1 $.30   (G461)

Christ Of The Snow, The *Xmas
SSA WARNER W3195 $.30   (G462)
SATB WARNER W2606 $.30   (G463)

Daybreak Carol *Xmas,carol
SATB oct GALAXY 1.1461.1 $.30   (G464)

Easter Carol Of The Three Orphans *Easter,
carol
SATB oct GALAXY 1.0954.1 $.30   (G465)

Eye Hath Not Seen (from Holy City, The)
(Bliss, P.) SSA oct PRESSER 312-20293 $.30
                                                 (G466)
(Scarmolin) SATB oct PRO ART 1254 $.35   (G467)

For Thee, O Dear, Dear Country (from Holy
City, The)
SATB,pno (easy) oct WILLIS 394 $.10   (G468)

Forgive Our Sins
SATB,S/T solo WARNER W2605 $.30   (G469)

God Is Wisdom, God Is Love (from Ruth)
(Barker) 4pt mix cor,org/pno oct SCHIRM.G
11052 $.25   (G470)

Great And Marvelous (from Holy City, The)
Bibl
mix cor oct SCHIRM.G 4628 $.35   (G471)

Great And Marvelous Are Thy Works (from Holy
City, The) *anthem
SATB oct PRESSER 312-20352 $.35   (G472)
SATB oct FISCHER,C CM-6255 $.30   (G473)

Holy City, The *Op.36, cant
SATB,SATBar soli,org,2fl,2ob,2clar,2bsn,
2horn,2trp,3trom,strings,timp,2harp voc
sc NOVELLO s.p., ipr   (G474)

Holy City, The *Easter,cant
cor,soli,orch voc sc SCHIRM.G $1.50   (G475)
cor (choruses only) voc sc SCHIRM.G $.75   (G476)
BELWIN $1.50   (G477)
cor voc sc KALMUS 6176 $1.50   (G478)
cor,orch sc KALMUS $35.00, ipa   (G479)

It Shall Be Light (from Holy City)
(Wilson) SAB oct BOURNE T7 $.25   (G480)

Jubilate
SATB (B min) oct GALAXY 1.0510.1 $.35   (G481)

Lights Of Easter *Easter
SATB oct GALAXY 1.0756.1 $.35   (G482)

List! The Cherubic Host (from Holy City, The)
Bibl
3pt wom cor,SA/Bar soli,pno (med) oct
WILLIS 4304 $.10   (G483)
(Deis) 4pt mix cor,Bar solo oct SCHIRM.G
7247 $.30   (G484)
(Deis) 4pt wom cor,SB soli oct SCHIRM.G 343
$.35   (G485)
(Ehret, W.) SSA oct FOX R139 $.25   (G486)
(Farron) SATB oct SPRATT 506 $.30   (G487)
(Spiro) SSA oct PRO ART 1331 $.25   (G488)
(Wilson) SSA/unis boy cor,SBar soli WARNER
W2532 $.30   (G489)

Love Not The World (from Holy City, The) Bibl
4pt mix cor,org/pno oct SCHIRM.G 11014 $.20   (G490)

Michael's Day Carol From The Hebrides
SATB,S solo,acap oct COLOMBO 821 $.30   (G491)

New Heaven And A New Earth, A (from Holy
City, The) Gen/Trin,Bibl
mix cor,Bar solo oct SCHIRM.G 5427 $.25   (G492)
SATB,B solo (med) oct WILLIS 395 $.12   (G493)

No Shadows Yonder (from Holy City, The)
4pt mix cor oct SCHIRM.G 4313 $.25   (G494)
SATB,T,SATB soli,pno (easy) oct WILLIS 252
$.10   (G495)

Nova Scotia Noel, A
SATB oct COLOMBO 820 $.30   (G496)

O Gracious Lord, Cast Down Thine Eyes
(Kinsman) SATB oct SPRATT 555 $.25   (G497)

Ruth *Op.34, cant
cor,soli,orch voc sc SCHIRM.G $1.50   (G498)
SATB,SSAB soli,2fl,2ob,2clar,2bsn,2horn,
2trp,3trom,strings,perc,timp voc sc
NOVELLO rental   (G499)

These Are They (from Holy City)
(Ehret) SATB oct FOX R141 $.25   (G500)

They That Sow In Tears (from Holy City, The)
Bibl
4pt mix cor oct SCHIRM.G 6767 $.35   (G501)

Thine Is The Kingdom (from Holy City, The)
Bibl
4pt mix cor oct SCHIRM.G 3822 $.30   (G502)
(Cain) SATB oct PRO ART 1464 $.22   (G503)

GAUL, HARVEY BARTLET (1881-1945)
Ali Praise To God Eternal
SATB oct FISCHER,J 6500 $.30   (G504)

GAUL, HARVEY BARTLET (cont'd.)
And The Trees Do Moan *Xmas
SATB oct PRESSER 332-14319 $.30   (G505)

Babe Of Bethlehem *Xmas,cant
BELWIN $1.75   (G506)

Easter Miracle Of St. Anne De Beaupre
*Easter,cant
BELWIN $1.50   (G507)

Little Jesu Of Braga, The *Xmas
SATB oct PRESSER 332-40603 $.30   (G508)

March Of The Wise Men *Xmas
TTBB oct GRAY GCMR 766 $.30   (G509)
(Rieder) SATB oct GRAY GCMR 2384 $.30   (G510)

Russian Easter Alleluia *Easter,Russ
mix cor oct SCHIRM.G 7105 $.30   (G511)

Russian Easter Carol Of The Trees *Easter
SATB,acap oct PRESSER 332-14551 $.30   (G512)

Stars Lead Us Ever On *Xmas
(Bailey, R.) SSA (Sioux carol) oct PRESSER
332-15130 $.30   (G513)

Three Lilies, The *Easter
mix cor,opt ST soli oct SCHIRM.G 6728 $.25
                                                 (G514)

GAUNTLETT, [HENRY JOHN] (1805-1876)
Alleluia! Song Of Gladness
(Scoggin) 3pt jr cor/SAB (easy) FISCHER,C
CM 7439 $.25   (G515)

Once In Royal David's City *Xmas,hymn
(Mann, A.M.) SATB oct NOVELLO 44.1372.05
s.p.   (G516)

GAUS
God Spoke
(Schubert) ST oct LILLENAS AN-3822 $.30   (G517)

Make A Joyful Noise Unto The Lord
SATB oct LILLENAS AN-2318 $.25   (G518)

GAY, A.
We Tread Upon Thy Carpets
SAB,org oct KERBY 5409 $.30   (G519)

GDY SIE CHRISTUS RODZI *carol,Pol
(Bement, G.) "When The Savior Christ Is Born"
TTBB,acap SCHIRM.EC 2134 $.15   (G520)

GDY SIE CHRYSTUS RODZI *carol,Pol
(Bement, G.) "When The Savior Christ Is Born"
SATB,acap SCHIRM.EC 1784 $.25   (G521)

GEARHART
Hosianna!
SATB SHAWNEE A 392 $.30   (G522)

Thanksgiving Song *Thanks
SATB SHAWNEE A 474 $.25   (G523)
SSA SHAWNEE B 177 $.30   (G524)

GEARS
Christ The Lord Is Risen *Easter
SATB SCHMITT 872 $.25   (G525)

GEBAUER, JOH. CHR.
Julesang *Xmas
(Per Norloff) [Norw] mix cor LYCHE 10 s.p.
                                                 (G526)

GEBED DES HERREN see Bach, Johann Sebastian

GEBED VOOR DE TEMPEL see Roeske, F.J.

GEBET see Bruckner, Anton

GEBET see Gaugler, Th.

GEBET see Haller, Hermann

GEBET see Handel, George Frideric

GEBET see Kubli, M.

GEBET see Lavater, H.

GEBET see Neumann, M.

GEBET see Schmid, Walter

GEBET see Stroh, E.

GEBET DES FRANZ VON ASSISI see Schweizer, Rolf

GEBET DES NIKOLAUS VON DER FLUE "O GOTT, NIMM
VON MIR" see Schweizer, Rolf

GEBET EINER ARMEN SEELE see Klebe, Giselher

GEBET FUR DAS VATERLAND see Schnyder, Ch.

GEBET UM FRIEDEN see Gadsch, Herbert

GEBET, WENN CHRISTUS, DER HERR see Handel,
George Frideric

GEBET ZU GOTT see Haydn, (Franz) Joseph

GEBETE see Bornefeld, Helmut

GEBETE DER DEUTSCHEN see Rohwer, Jens

GEBHARD, HANS
Aus Dem Englischen
mix cor (med easy) oct LEUCKART 645 s.p.
see from Vier Heitere Chore   (G527)

Der Esel
mix cor (easy) oct LEUCKART 645 s.p.
see from Vier Heitere Chore   (G528)

Ich Bin Vergnugt
mix cor (med easy) oct LEUCKART 646 s.p.
see from Vier Heitere Chore   (G529)

In Memoriam *Op.63
SAATTBBB,T solo,2fl,2ob,2clar,2bsn,horn,
trp,trom,tuba,strings,perc,timp,harp cor
pts BREITKOPF-W CHB-3048 s.p., ipr, sc
BREITKOPF-W rental   (G530)

GEBHARD, HANS (cont'd.)
Kuckuck
mix cor (easy) oct LEUCKART 644 s.p. see
from Vier Heitere Chore   (G531)

Missa Gotica *Op.20, Mass
[Lat] SAB,org SCHOTT sc s.p., cor pts s.p.
                                                 (G532)

Vier Heitere Chore *see Aus Dem Englischen;
Der Esel; Ich Bin Vergnugt; Kuckuck   (G533)

GEBOREN IST IMMANUEL, DER HERR CHRIST see
Praetorius, Michael

GEBOREN IST UNS EIN KINDLEIN KLEIN see Spitta,
Heinrich

GEBORN IST DER EMANUEL see Praetorius, Michael

GEBORN IST GOTTES SOHNELEIN see Praetorius,
Michael

GEBORN IST GOTTES SOHNLEIN see Praetorius,
Michael

GEBORN IST UNS EIN KINDELEIN see Dangel, Arthur

GEBORN IST UNS EMANUEL see Praetorius, Michael

GEDENKE AN DEINEN SCHOPFER see Marx, Karl

GEDENKE, HERR, AN DEINE BARMHERZIGKEIT see
Gottschick, Friedemann

GEDENKE, HERR, AN DEINE BARMHERZIGKEIT see
Kretzschmar, Gunther

GEDENKE, HERR, AN DEINE BARMHERZIGKEIT see
Weismann, Wilhelm

GEDENKE NICHT, HERR see Purcell, Henry,
Remember Not, Lord, Our Offences

GEDENKE SOHN, DASS DU DEIN GUTES EMPFANGEN HAST
see Driessler, Johannes

GEEF VREDE, HEER see Brands, Joh., Da Pacem,
Domine

GEEHL, HENRY ERNEST (1881-   )
Hymn At Sunset, A *Eve,hymn
SATB ENOCH EC312 s.p.   (G534)

What Of Thy Flocks, O Shepherd?
2pt ASHDOWN E.A.201 s.p.   (G535)
SATB ENOCH EC256 s.p.   (G536)

GEGRUSSET, MARIA see Brahms, Johannes

GEGRUSSET SEIST DU, EDELSTE KONIGIN (from
Psalteriolum 1642) BVM
SATB,acap voc pt DOBLINGER s.p. see also
Unsere Liebe Frau   (G537)

GEGRUSSET SEIST DU, KONIGIN *BVM,19th cent
(Miggl, Erwin) wom cor,acap oct DOBLINGER
s.p. see also Drei Marienlieder   (G538)

GEGRUSSET SEIST DU, MARIA *Xmas
(Strobl, Otto) mix cor,acap oct DOBLINGER
s.p.   (G539)

GEGRUSSET SEIST DU, MARIA see Tittel, Ernst

GEH AUS AUF DIE LANDSTRASSEN see Raselius,
Andreas

GEH' AUS, MEIN HERZ see Burkhart, Franz

GEH AUS, MEIN HERZ, UND SUCHE FREUD see Kubler,
Emil

GEH AUS, MEIN HERZ, UND SUCHE FREUD see
Schmidlin, J.

GEH AUS, MEIN HERZ, UND SUCHE FREUD see Stern,
Hermann

GEH AUS, MEIN HERZ, UND SUCHE FREUD see Zipp,
Friedrich

GEH DEINEN WEG see Franck, Cesar

GEH HIN NACH GOTTES WILLEN see Marks, Gunther

GEH, RUF ES VOM BERG see Go Tell It On The
Mountain

GEHE AUS AUF DIE LANDSTRASSEN see Vulpius,
Melchior

GEHET HIN IN ALLE WELT see Driessler, Johannes

GEHET HIN IN ALLE WELT see Micheelsen, Hans
Friedrich

GEHET HIN IN ALLE WELT see Raphael, Gunther

GEHET HIN IN ALLE WELT see Reger, Max

GEHLEN, HERMANN (1937-   )
Messe *Mass
[Ger] SSAATTB,narrator,S solo,5trp,3trom, 3
saxophones (med diff) study sc BOSSE
BE 412 s.p., ipr   (G540)

GEHRING, A.
Tantum Ergo
mix cor,acap ERDMANN 509 s.p. contains
also: Veni Creator   (G541)

Veni Creator
see Gehring, A., Tantum Ergo

GEHRING, PHILIP
Art Thou Weary, Art Thou Laden *Gen/Lent,
anti
unis,kbd (easy) oct CONCORDIA 98-1945 $.25
                                                 (G542)

GEHRKE, RALPH
Christ The Lord Is Risen Today *see Martini,
Padre

In Monte Oliveti *see Martini, Padre

Lamb Of God *see Martini, Padre

GEHRKE, RALPH (cont'd.)

Three Lenten And Easter Hymns *see Martini, Padre

GEHT HIN UND SAGET JOHANNES see Raselius, Andreas

GEHT NUN HIN see Weismann, Wilhelm

GEHT NUN MUD DER TAG see Stier, Alfred

GEIBEL
Prayer *Gen
(Hiller; Sircom) SATB SCHMITT 847 $.16
(G543)

GEIJER
Lord Of My Life Whose Tender Care
(Lundquist) SATB,acap (easy) oct WILLIS
8468 $.25 (G544)

GEISEL, GUSTAV
Auf, Auf, Mein Herz
see Geisel, Gustav, Der Tod Ist
Verschlungen

Der Tod Ist Verschlungen
TTBB HANSSLER 25.023 s.p. contains also:
Geisel, Gustav, Auf, Auf, Mein Herz;
Neubert, Gottfried, Man Singt Mit
Freuden; Neubert, Gottfried, Auf, Auf,
Mein Herz (G545)

Mein Schonste Zier Und Kleinod *cant
SAT/SAB,SBar soli,org,fl,2vln,opt vcl
HANSSLER 10.229 sc s.p., cor pts s.p.
(G546)

Zeuch An Die Macht, Du Arm Des Herrn *cant
SATB,4brass,opt timp sc HANSSLER 10.142
s.p. (G547)

GEISER, WALTHER (1897-)
Es Kommt Ein Schiff, Geladen *Op.18, Adv
[Ger] SATB,strings,harp (med diff) BAREN.
BA 3359 rental (G548)

Hymnus *Op.43, Gen,Bibl/hymn
[Ger] SATB,orch (diff) cor pts BAREN.
BA 2784 $1.50, ipr, voc sc BAREN.
BA 2784A $4.00 (G549)

Stabat Mater *Op.23, Psntd
[Lat] 4-6pt mix cor,Bar solo,org,orch
(diff) BAREN. BA 2114 rental, voc sc
BAREN. BA 2114A $13.25 (G550)

Te Deum *Op.54, Te Deum
[Lat] SATB,SATB soli,org,orch (diff) BAREN.
BA 2041 rental (G551)

GEISLER, JOHAN C.
Bless The Lord, O My Soul
(Nolte) [Eng/Ger] SS oct MORAVIAN 5693 $.40
(G552)

Blessed The People
(Nolte) [Eng/Ger] SSAB/SATB oct MORAVIAN
5659 $.35 (G553)

Glory To God In The Highest
(Nolte) [Eng/Ger] SSAB/SATB,org oct MORAVIAN 5660
$.50 (G554)

Grace Of The Lord
(Nolte) [Eng/Ger] SS,org oct MORAVIAN 5678
$.40 (G555)

How Lovely Is Thy Dwelling Place
(Nolte) [Eng/Ger] SSAB/SATB,org oct MORAVIAN
5606 $.50 (G556)

Like As A Father Doth Pity His Children
(Nolte) [Eng/Ger] SS,org oct MORAVIAN 5678
$.35 (G557)

Lord Is Ruler
(Nolte) [Eng/Ger] SSAB oct BOOSEY 5607 $.40
(G558)

Lord Keepeth Thee
(Nolte) [Eng/Ger] SSAB,org oct MORAVIAN
5608 $.40 (G559)

O How Blessed
(Nolte) [Eng/Ger] SSAB,org oct MORAVIAN
5610 $.40 (G560)

O That Salvation For Israel Would Come
(Nolte) [Eng/Ger] SSTB/SATB,org oct
MORAVIAN 5706 $.40 (G561)

O Thou Our Joy
(Nolte) [Eng/Ger] SS/SA,org oct MORAVIAN
5707 $.40 (G562)

Praise Ye The Lord
(Nolte) [Eng/Ger] SSAB/SATB,org oct
MORAVIAN 5655 $.40 (G563)

Prayer Of The Prophet *prayer
SATB oct PRO ART 2679 $.35 (G564)
SSA oct PRO ART 2271 $.35 (G565)

Seraphim On High, The
(Nolte, Ev.) [Ger/Eng] dbl cor/mix cor,SATB
soli,org,strings,horn voc sc BOOSEY $.60,
ipr (G566)

Sing And Rejoice, O Zion
(Nolte) mix cor SOUTHERN $.40 (G567)
(Nolte) [Eng/Ger] SSAB/SATB,org oct
MORAVIAN 5652 $.40 (G568)

Sing To The Lord A New-Made Song
(Nolte) [Eng/Ger] SSAB/SATB,org oct
MORAVIAN 5682 $.50 (G569)

Thank Ye The Lord
(Nolte) [Eng/Ger] SSAB,org oct MORAVIAN
5601 $.50 (G570)

There Is One God And One Saviour
(Nolte) [Eng/Ger] SSAB,org oct MORAVIAN
5600 $.40 (G571)

This Is The Day That The Lord Created
(Nolte) [Eng/Ger] SSAB/SATB,org oct
MORAVIAN 5692 $.35 (G572)

GEISLER, JOHAN C. (cont'd.)

Thou Hast Given Us Bread *Morav
(Dickinson) SATB oct GRAY GMCM 20 $.30
(G573)

Thus Saith The Lord
(Nolte) [Eng/Ger] SSTT,B solo,org oct
MORAVIAN 5604 $.40 (G574)

GEISLICHE GESANGE HEFT 1 see Bruckner, Anton

GEISSEL, J. VON
Kleine Choralmotette Uber "Erde Singe" *mot
(Romanovsky, Erich) [Ger] mix cor,acap oct
DOBLINGER s.p. (G575)

GEIST
O God, Search Me (Psalm 139)
SATB SHAWNEE A 817 $.25 (G576)

Psalm 139 *see O God, Search Me

GEIST, CHRISTIAN (1640-1711)
Erbe Deutscher Musik: Vol. 48 Church
Concertos *CCU
(Lundgren, Bo; Sorenson, Soren) cor,strings
cloth,fac ed PETERS $30.00 (G577)

Laudet Deum Mea Gloria *mot
[Lat] SSB,org,2vln, viola de gamba sc
GEHRMANS s.p., cor pts GEHRMANS KRB 322
(G578)

Verbum Caro
[Lat] SA,strings,cembalo sc PETERS HU1908
$1.00, ipr (G579)

Verbum Caro Factum Est *mot
[Lat] 2pt,cont,2vln,vcl SKAND. SMF5482 s.p.
(G580)

GEIST UND SEELE see Bach, Johann Sebastian,
Geist Und Seele Wird Verwirret

GEIST UND SEELE WIRD VERWIRRET see Bach, Johann
Sebastian

GEISTLICHE ADVENTMUSIK see Monter, Josef

GEISTLICHE CHORGESANGE ALTER MEISTER *CC10L
(Woyrsch, F.) [Ger] mix cor VIEWEG voc sc
s.p., cor pts s.p. contains works by:
Durante, F.; Marcello, B.; Cassini, C.M.;
Canniciari, P.;Otti, A.; Purcell, H.;
Handl, J.; and others (G581)

GEISTLICHE CHORMUSIK see Beck, Jochen

GEISTLICHE CHORMUSIK 1648 see Schutz, Heinrich

GEISTLICHE CHORMUSIK 1648 [BH] see Schutz,
Heinrich

GEISTLICHE CHORMUSIK see Calvisius, Sethus

GEISTLICHE CHORMUSIK see Cruger, Johann

GEISTLICHE CHORMUSIK see Hartmann, Heinrich

GEISTLICHE CHORSATZE see Micheelsen, Hans
Friedrich

GEISTLICHE GESANGE 1 see Gletle, Johann
Melchoir

GEISTLICHE GESANGE FUR MANNERCHOR *CCU
[Ger] men cor BAREN. EM 314 s.p. (G582)

GEISTLICHE GESANGE HEFT 2 see Bruckner, Anton

GEISTLICHE GESANGE HEFT 3 see Bruckner, Anton

GEISTLICHE GESANGE, HEFT I see Bruckner, Anton

GEISTLICHE GESANGE, HEFT II see Bruckner, Anton

GEISTLICHE GESANGE, HEFT III see Bruckner,
Anton

GEISTLICHE GESANGE NACH RELIGIOSEN MOTIVEN AUS
BOLIVIEN see Helfritz, Hans

GEISTLICHE LIEDER see Othmayr, Kaspar

GEISTLICHE LIEDER see Schafer, Walter

GEISTLICHE LIEDER 1597 TEIL I see Eccard,
Johannes

GEISTLICHE LIEDER 1597 TEIL II see Eccard,
Johannes

GEISTLICHE LIEDER-HEFT 13 *CCU,Adv
(Pass, Walter) 4pt&5pt DOBLINGER s.p.
contains works by: Praetorius, M.; Gesius,
B.; Franck, M.; Helder, B. (G583)

GEISTLICHE MUSIK FUR CHOR UND BLASER *CCU
mix cor,brass HANSSLER 2.046 s.p. (G584)

GEISTLICHE UND LITURGISCHE CHORSATZE see Kraft,
Walter

GEISTLICHE UND WELTLICHE LIEDER see Zangius,
Nikolaus

GEISTLICHE VOLKSLIEDER AUS OSTERREICH *see
Altes Weihnachtslied; Das Kartner
Pilatusspiel; Herr Des Himmels (G585)

GEISTLICHE ZWIEGESANGE *CC202U,Gen,Contemp
(Brodde, Otto) [Ger] 2 eq voices,opt inst
(easy) BAREN. BA 3199 $6.50 (G586)

GEISTLICHE ZWIEGESANGE, 32 BICINIEN see
Othmayr, Kaspar

GEISTLICHE ZWIEGESANGE ZUM MORGEN UND ABEND see
Stern, A

GEISTLICHER LIEDERSCHATZ see Prehl-Schmalzried

GEISTLICHES CHORGESANGBUCH, BAND 1 *CCU
mix cor HANSSLER 2.036 s.p. (G587)

GEISTLICHES CHORGESANGBUCH, BAND 2 *CCU
mix cor HANSSLER 2.037 s.p. (G588)

GEISTLICHES CHORGESANGBUCH, BAND 1 & 2 *CCU
mix cor HANSSLER s.p. (G589)

GEISTLICHES CHORLIED, BAND 1 *CC120U
(Grote, Gottfried) [Ger] 2-6pt mix cor BAREN.
EM 321 s.p. by old masters (G590)

GEISTLICHES CHORLIED, BAND 2 *CC103U,15-20th
cent
(Grote, Gottfried) [Ger] 2-8pt mix cor BAREN.
EM 321A s.p. (G591)

GEISTLICHES CHORLIED, VOL. 1: ONE HUNDRED
TWENTY SETTINGS FOR 2 TO 6 VOICES FROM
DUFAY TO BACH *CC120U
(Grote) 2-6pt PETERS EM321 $10.00 (G592)

GEISTLICHES CHORLIED, VOL. 2: ONE HUNDRED THREE
SETTINGS FOR 2 TO 8 VOICES *CC103U
(Grote) 2-8pt PETERS EM321 $10.00 (G593)

GEISTLICHES GESANGBUCHLEIN WITTENBURG 1551,
ERSTER TEIL see Walter (Walther), Johann

GEISTLICHES KONZERT see Heiller, Anton

GEISTLICHES LIED see Brahms, Johannes

GEISTLICHES LIED see Baumann, Max

GEISTLICHES LIED see Mendelssohn-Bartholdy,
Felix

GEISTLICHES WEIGENLIED see Brahms, Johannes

GEISTLICHES WIEGENLIED see Brahms, Johannes

GEITVIK, S.H.
Adagio
men cor MUSIKK 171 s.p. (G594)
mix cor MUSIKK 194 s.p. (G595)

Barn, Du Speiler Himlen Av
mix cor MUSIKK 195 s.p. (G596)

Du Er Ein Gjest I Denne Verd *Psalm
mix cor,solo,org cor pts MUSIKK 131 s.p.
see also Ni Salmetoner, Hefte II (G597)

Fager Kveldsol
mix cor MUSIKK 193 s.p. (G598)

For Deg, Var Herre
mix cor MUSIKK 152 s.p. (G599)

Guds Menighet
mix cor MUSIKK 192 s.p. (G600)

Herre Gud, Ditt Dyre Namn *Psalm
mix cor,solo,org cor pts MUSIKK 135 s.p.
see also Ni Salmetoner, Hefte II (G601)

Herre Gud, Ditt Dyre Navn
men cor MUSIKK 169 s.p. (G602)

Himlane, Herre, Fortelja Di *Psalm
mix cor,solo,org cor pts MUSIKK 132 s.p.
see also Ni Salmetoner, Hefte II (G603)

Himmelske Fader *Psalm
men cor MUSIKK 116 s.p. (G604)
5pt mix cor MUSIKK 182 s.p. (G605)
mix cor,solo,org cor pts MUSIKK 129 s.p.
see also Ni Salmetoner, Hefte I (G606)

Himmelvegen
mix cor MUSIKK 196 s.p. (G607)

Hogt Fra Den Himmelske Klara
mix cor MUSIKK 241 s.p. (G608)

Hvi Skal Je Med Min Broder Stride
mix cor MUSIKK 197 s.p. (G609)

Hvi Skal Jeg Med Min Broder Stride
men cor MUSIKK 172 s.p. (G610)

Hvor Salig Er Den Lille Flokk *Psalm
mix cor,solo,org cor pts MUSIKK 136 s.p.
see also Ni Salmetoner, Hefte I (G611)

Kimer, I Klokker
mix cor MUSIKK 190 s.p. (G612)

Kvi Skjelv Kvart Lauvblad *Psalm
mix cor,solo,org cor pts MUSIKK 133 s.p.
see also Ni Salmetoner, Hefte II (G613)

La Gulne Hvert Et Glad
mix cor MUSIKK 191 s.p. (G614)

Litani *Psalm
mix cor,solo,org cor pts MUSIKK 130 s.p.
see also Ni Salmetoner, Hefte I (G615)

Litle Fuglen
mix cor MUSIKK 154 s.p. (G616)

Nattevakten
mix cor MUSIKK 189 s.p. (G617)

Ni Salmetoner, Hefte I *Psalm
mix cor,solo,org voc sc MUSIKK s.p.
contains & see also: Himmelske Fader;
Hvor Salig Er Den Lille Flokk; Litani;
Sakramentshymne; Seg Jerusalem (G618)

Ni Salmetoner, Hefte II *Psalm
mix cor,solo,org voc sc MUSIKK s.p.
contains & see also: Du Er Ein Gjest I
Denne Verd; Herre Gud, Ditt Dyre Namn;
Himlane, Herre, Fortelja Di; Kvi Skjelv
Kvart Lauvblad (G619)

Sakramentshymne *Psalm
mix cor,solo,org cor pts MUSIKK 135 s.p.
see also Ni Salmetoner, Hefte I (G620)

Seg Jerusalem *Psalm
mix cor,solo,org cor pts MUSIKK 128 s.p.
see also Ni Salmetoner, Hefte I (G621)

GELINEAU, [JOSEPH] (1920-)
My Shepherd Is The Lord *anti/Psalm
(Phillips) SATB oct SUMMY M 2348 $.45
(G622)

GELOBET SEI, DER DA KOMMT see Dedekind,
Constantine Christian

GELOBET SEI DER HERR see Bach, Johann Sebastian

GELOBET SEI DER HERR see Bach, Johann
  Sebastian, Gelobet Sei Der Herr, Mein Gott

GELOBET SEI DER HERR see Marx, Karl

GELOBET SEI DER HERR, MEIN GOTT see Bach,
  Johann Sebastian

GELOBET SEI DER HERR TAEGLICH see Zimmermann,
  Heinz Werner

GELOBET SEI DER HERR TAGLICH see Stier, Alfred

GELOBET SEI GOTT see Becker-Foss, Jurgen

GELOBET SEI GOTT UND DER VATER see Dedekind,
  Constantine Christian

GELOBET SEI GOTT UND DER VATER see Franck,
  Melchior

GELOBET SEIST DU see Bach, Johann Sebastian,
  Gelobet Seist Du, Jesu Christ

GELOBET SEIST DU see Dedekind, Constantine
  Christian

GELOBET SEIST DU see Scandello

GELOBET SEIST DU, CHRISTE see Senfl, Ludwig

GELOBET SEIST DU, JESU CHRIST *Xmas,cant
  see Nun Freut Euch, Lieben Christen Gmein
  (Dahmen, Hermann Josef) [Ger] 2-4pt mix cor,
  org,winds,strings (med, from settings of
  old masters) sc MULLER SM 601 s.p.   (G623)

GELOBET SEIST DU, JESU CHRIST see Bach, Johann
  Sebastian

GELOBET SEIST DU, JESU CHRIST see Bodenschatz,
  Erhard

GELOBET SEIST DU, JESU CHRIST see Cruger,
  Johann

GELOBET SEIST DU, JESU CHRIST see David, Johann
  Nepomuk

GELOBET SEIST DU, JESU CHRIST see Eccard,
  Johannes

GELOBET SEIST DU, JESU CHRIST see Friedrichs,
  Karl

GELOBET SEIST DU, JESU CHRIST see Gottschick,
  Friedemann

GELOBET SEIST DU, JESU CHRIST see
  Gumpeltzhaimer, Adam

GELOBET SEIST DU, JESU CHRIST see Hindermann,
  Walter Felix

GELOBET SEIST DU, JESU CHRIST see Kuhnau,
  Johann

GELOBET SEIST DU, JESU CHRIST see Praetorius,
  Michael

GELOBET SEIST DU, JESU CHRIST see Rabsch, Edgar

GELOBET SEIST DU, JESU CHRIST see Raphael,
  Gunther

GELOBET SEIST DU, JESU CHRIST see Resinarius,
  Balthasar

GELOBET SEIST DU, JESU CHRIST see Scheidt,
  Samuel

GELOBET SEIST DU, JESU CHRIST see Schein,
  Johann Hermann

GELOBET SEIST DU, JESU CHRIST see Schubert,
  Heino

GELOBET SEIST DU JESU CHRIST see Selle, Thomas

GELOBET SEIST DU JESU CHRIST see Thomas, Kurt

GELOBET SEIST DU JESU CHRIST see Walter

GELOBET SEIST DU, JESU CHRIST see Weiss, Ewald

GELOBET SEIST DU, JESU CHRIST see Zipp,
  Friedrich

GELOBET SEIST DU, JESU CHRIST [CHORALE] see
  Bach, Johann Sebastian

GELOBT SEI, DER DA KOMMT see Praetorius,
  Michael, Benedicamus In Adventu Domini

GELOBT SEI DER HERR TAGLICH see Ruppel, Paul
  Ernst

GELOBT SEI GOTT *CC64U,canon/chorale/mot
  (Strube, Adolf) [Ger] 3pt mix cor/4pt mix cor
  cloth BAREN. EM 432 s.p.   (G624)

GELOBT SEI GOTT see Vulpius, Melchior

GELOBT SEI GOTT IM HOCHSTEN THORN see Stern,
  Hermann

GELOBT SEI GOTT IM HOCHSTEN THRON see Linke,
  Norbert

GELOBT SEI GOTT IM HOCHSTEN THRON see Vulpius,
  Melchior

GELOBT SEI MEIN HERR UND GOTT see Tinel, Edgar

GELOOFD ZIJ GOD DEN VADER see Wesley, Samuel
  Sebastian Jr.

GELOOFSROEM (JEZUS, MIJN VERBLIJDEN) see Bach,
  Johann Sebastian

GEMEINDE-RUFE UND FALSOBORDONI ZU 5 PSALMEN see
  Jaeggi, Oswald

GEN HIMMEL AUFGEFAHREN IST see Bauernfeind,
  Hans

GEN HIMMEL AUFGEFAHREN IST see Hufschmidt,
  Wolfgang

GEN HIMMEL AUFGEFAHREN IST see Kretzschmar,
  Gunther

GEN HIMMEL AUFGEFAHREN IST see Marx, Karl

GEN HIMMEL AUFGEFAHREN IST see Ruppel, Paul
  Ernst

GEN HIMMEL AUFGEFAHREN IST see Stern, Hermann

GEN HIMMEL AUFGEFAHREN IST, HALLELUJA see
  Franck, Melchior

GENERAL ANTHEM BOOK 1 see Holler, John

GENERAL ANTHEM BOOK 2 see Holler, John

GENERAL INVITATION TO PRAISE GOD, A see Ridout

GENESIS see Reizenstein, Franz

GENESIS see Wagner-Regeny, Rudolf

GENET, ELZEAR (ca. 1470-1548)
  Collected Works vol. I *Mass
    (Seay, Albert) cor AM.INST.MUS. $22.00 all
    with their model chansons, except in the
    case of the last mass
    contains: Missa A Lombre Dung Buissonet;
    Missa Encore Iray Je Jouer; Missa Fors
    Seulement; Missa Le Cueur Fut Mien- En
    Amour Ne Sinon Bien; Missa Se Mieulx Ne
    Vient   (G625)

  Collected Works vol. II *CCU
    (Seay, Albert) cor AM.INST.MUS. $29.00
    lamentations   (G626)

  Collected Works vol. III *CCU,hymn/mot
    (Seay, Albert) cor AM.INST.MUS. $42.00 (G627)

  Collected Works vol. IV *CCU,Magnif
    (Seay, Albert) cor AM.INST.MUS. $45.00 (G628)

  Collected Works vol. V *sac/sec,CCU,
    madrigal/mot
    (Seay, Albert) cor AM.INST.MUS. $21.00 (G629)

  Missa A Lombre Dung Buissonet
    see Collected Works vol. I

  Missa Encore Iray Je Jouer
    see Collected Works vol. I

  Missa Fors Seulement
    see Collected Works vol. I

  Missa Le Cueur Fut Mien- En Amour Ne Sinon
    Bien
    see Collected Works vol. I

  Missa Se Mieulx Ne Vient
    see Collected Works vol. I

GENTILES SHALL COME BY, THE see Greene, Maurice

GENTILS GALANTS DE FRANCE
  (Geveart, F.-A.) [Fr] 4pt mix cor,acap (easy/
  med easy) cor pts LEMOINE s.p. see from
  Collection De Choeurs, quatrieme Fascicule
                                           (G630)

GENTLE CHRIST, MY LORD ABOVE *Xmas
  (Kranz, A.) SATB,acap AMP A572 $.25 see from
  Christmas Choruses   (G631)

GENTLE DOVE, THE
  (Williams) unis (med) OXFORD 81.034 $.25
                                           (G632)

GENTLE GUIDE see Hunt, Thomas W.

GENTLE JESUS see Moats

GENTLE JESUS EVER BLEST see Faure, Gabriel-
  Urbain

GENTLE JESUS, MEEK AND MILD see Pleyel, Ignaz
  Joseph

GENTLE JESUS, MEEK AND MILD see Trusler

GENTLE JESUS MEEK AND MILD see Weber, Dennis

GENTLE JESUS, MEEK AND MILD see Wesley

GENTLE JESUS, MEEK AND MILD see Young, Robert
  H.

GENTLE MARY *Xmas,carol/folk,Span
  SA/SSA/SA&SSA ALLANS 285 s.p.   (G633)
  SATB ALLANS 286 s.p.   (G634)
  (McFeeters) 3pt wom cor oct SCHIRM.G 9670
  $.25   (G635)

GENTLE MARY see Cook

GENTLE MARY see Cook, Clifford A.

GENTLE MARY see Kent, Richard

GENTLE MARY see Kirby

GENTLE MARY see Means, Claude

GENTLE MARY AND HER CHILD see Lundquist

GENTLE MARY LAID HER CHILD see Carley, Isabel
  M.

GENTLE MOTHER see Turner, Elthea

GENTLE PSALM, A see Clark, K.

GENTLE SAVIOUR, HOLD MY HAND see Cooke

GENTLE SHEPHERD see Emig, Lois

GENTLE STRANGER, THE see Lister, Mosie

GENTLE VISITATION see Rorem, Ned

GENTLY, LORD, O LEAD US see Ar Hyd Ynos

GENUCHI
  I'll Hold Him In My Heart
    SATB oct KENDOR $.30   (G636)

GENUCHI, IVAN
  Apostles' Creed, The
    SATB LUDWIG SS-027 $.30   (G637)

  Blessed Be The Lord God Of Sabaoth
    TTBB LUDWIG SS-002 $.30   (G638)
    SATB LUDWIG SS-001 $.30   (G639)

GENZMER, HARALD (1909-   )
  Ostermesse *Easter,Mass
    [Ger] SSATBB,SBar soli,orch (med diff)
    BAREN. BA 3577 rental   (G640)

GEOFFRAY, CESAR
  Dextera Domini (Psalm 118) Gen
    "Valiantly Doeth The Lord's Right Hand"
    SATB,acap (med) oct OXFORD 84.039 $.25
                                         (G641)

  Psalm 118 *see Dextera Domini

  Valiantly Doeth The Lord's Right Hand *see
    Dextera Domini

GEOFFREY
  As Joseph Was A-Walking *Xmas
    (Shaw) unis jr cor&desc FISCHER,C ARD 120
    $.20   (G642)

GEORGE
  Boy Is Born, A *Xmas
    SSAATTBB,acap (med) OXFORD 94.318 $.35
                                         (G643)

GEORGE, GRAHAM (1912-   )
  All Things Bright And Beautiful *anthem
    unis/SA (easy) oct AUGSBURG 1528 $.20 (G644)

  Fight The Good Fight
    SATB (med) ABINGDON APM-559 $.25   (G645)

  Junior Choir Anthems For The Church Year
    *CC12L,anthem
    unis jr cor/2pt jr cor,org oct AUGSBURG
    11-9240 $1.10   (G646)

  Ride On, Ride On *Easter/Lent/Palm
    SA oct GRAY GCMR 3078 $.25   (G647)
    SATB oct GRAY GCMR 1765 $.30   (G648)

  Stand Up And Bless The Lord *anthem
    SA (easy) oct AUGSBURG 1515 $.20   (G649)

GEORGE, THOMAS RITTER
  Christmas Cantata *Xmas,cant
    cor,ABar soli,strings ROCHESTER study sc
    $.75, sc s.p., ipa   (G650)

GEORGE WASHINGTON'S PRAYER FOR NATION see
  Hastings

GEORGES, ALEXANDRE
  Chemin De Croix *CC12U
    [Fr] mix cor,soli,pno,org,6strings ENOCH
    voc sc s.p., cor pts s.p., sc s.p., ipa
                                         (G651)

  Noel *Xmas
    [Fr] 2 eq voices,solo,pno/org ENOCH voc sc
    s.p., cor pts s.p.   (G652)

GEPRIESEN BIST DU, HERR see Heiller, Anton

GEPRIESEN SEI DIE HEILIGE DREIFALTIGKEIT see
  Heiller, Anton

GEPRIESEN SEI GOTT VATER see Heiller, Anton

GERAEDTS, JAAP (1924-   )
  Onze Vader
    [Dut] mix cor,org sc DONEMUS s.p.   (G653)

GERALD
  Immaculata Conceptio
    (Stephan) "Sister Of Mercy" SA PARAGON 1017
    $.20   (G654)

  Sister Of Mercy *see Immaculata Conceptio

GERALD, M.B.
  Happy Birthday Baby Jesus *Xmas
    unis/2pt PARAGON 1025 $.20   (G655)

GERALD, T.J.
  Anima Christi
    cor,opt acap PARAGON 1016 $.20   (G656)

GERECHTIGKEIT ERHOHET EIN VOLK, ABER see
  Brunner, Adolf

GERHARD, CARL
  see GERHARDT, CARL

GERHARD, FRITZ CHRISTIAN (1911-   )
  Alles Grosse Macht Sterben Und Auferstehn
    *cant
    mix cor,narrator,B solo,orch cor pts TONGER
    s.p., ipa   (G657)

  Aus Geist Entstand Die Welt *cant
    mix cor,pno/strings cor pts TONGER s.p.,
    ipa   (G658)

  Cunctipotens Genitor Deus
    mix cor,org HANSSLER 10.263 sc s.p., cor
    pts s.p.   (G659)

  Jerusalem *cant
    mix cor,TB soli,orch HANSSLER 10.271 voc sc
    s.p., sc rental, ipr   (G660)

GERHARDT
  Lord Of Light, The *Gen
    SATB SCHMITT 8052 $.30   (G661)

  Still And Hushed *Xmas
    SATB SCHMITT 8046 $.25   (G662)

GERHARDT, CARL (1900-1945)
  Christe, Du Bist Der Helle Tag *Gen
    [Ger] SATB,narrator,vln,vla,2vcl (easy)
    BAREN. BA 2156 sc $2.25, cor pts $.40
                                         (G663)

  Nun Bitten Wir Den Heiligen Geist *No.99,
    Asc/Pent,cant
    [Ger] 3pt mix cor,A solo/2vln,bvl
    BAREN. EM 149 sc s.p., cor pts s.p., ipa
    see from EVANGELISCHES KIRCHENGESANGBUCH
                                         (G664)

  What Is The Joyful News? *Xmas
    unis,2rec/2fl,2vln,vcl/kbd sc CONCORDIA
    97-5012 $1.35, cor pts CONCORDIA 98-3024

GERHARDT, CARL (cont'd.)

$.20, ipa (G665)

GERHOLD, NORBERT
Christus, Unser Heil *see I'm A Rolling

Ev'ry Time I Feel De Spirit *spir
"Gottes Odem" mix cor,acap DOBLINGER s.p. see also Zehn Negro-Spirituals (G666)

Go Down, Moses *spir
"Moses" mix cor,acap DOBLINGER s.p. see also Zehn Negro-Spirituals (G667)

Gottes Odem *see Ev'ry Time I Feel De Spirit

Herr Fuhr Uns Deine Wege *see Road Is Rugged But I Must Go

Herr Ich Will Ein Guter Christ Sein *see Lord, I Want To Be A Christian

Hort Die Botschaft *see Way In The Heaven Bye And Bye

I'm A Rolling *spir
"Christus, Unser Heil" mix cor,acap DOBLINGER s.p. see also Zehn Negro-Spirituals (G668)

Komm Doch Herab *see Swing Low Sweet Chariot

Lord, I Want To Be A Christian *spir
"Herr Ich Will Ein Guter Christ Sein" mix cor,acap DOBLINGER s.p. see also Zehn Negro-Spirituals (G669)

Mein Jesus *see Nobody Knows

Moses *see Go Down, Moses

Nobody Knows *spir
"Mein Jesus" mix cor,acap DOBLINGER s.p. see also Zehn Negro-Spirituals (G670)

Ride On, Conquering King *spir
"Wie Gross Ist Deine Liebe" mix cor,acap DOBLINGER s.p. see also Zehn Negro-Spirituals (G671)

Road Is Rugged But I Must Go *spir
"Herr Fuhr Uns Deine Wege" mix cor,acap (contains also: Way In The Heaven Bye And Bye "Hort Die Botschaft") DOBLINGER s.p. see also Zehn Negro-Spirituals (G672)

Swing Low Sweet Chariot *spir
"Komm Doch Herab" mix cor,acap DOBLINGER s.p. see also Zehn Negro-Spirituals (G673)

Warst Du Dort? *see Were You There?

Way In The Heaven Bye And Bye *spir
"Hort Die Botschaft" mix cor,acap (contains also: Road Is Rugged But I Must Go "Herr, Fuhr Uns Deine Wege") DOBLINGER s.p. see also Zehn Negro-Spirituals (G674)

Were You There? *spir
"Warst Du Dort?" mix cor,acap DOBLINGER s.p. see also Zehn Negro-Spirituals (G675)

Wie Gross Ist Deine Liebe *see Ride On, Conquering King

Zehn Negro-Spirituals *spir
mix cor,acap cmplt ed DOBLINGER s.p. contains & see also: Ev'ry Time I Feel De Spirit, "Gottes Odem"; Go Down, Moses, "Moses"; I'm A Rolling, "Christus, Unser Heil"; Lord, I Want To Be A Christian, "Herr Ich Will Ein Guter Christ Sein"; Nobody Knows, "Mein Jesus"; Ride On, Conquering King, "Wie Gross Ist Deine Liebe"; Road Is Rugged But I Must Go, "Herr Fuhr Uns Deine Wege"; Swing Low Sweet Chariot, "Komm Doch Herab"; Way In The Heaven Bye And Bye, "Hort Die Botschaft"; Were You There?, "Warst Du Dort?" (G676)

GERIG
On The Cross Of Calvary
(Schubert) SB oct LILLENAS AN-1197 $.30 (G677)

Shout To God *Gen
SATB SCHMITT 6009 $.30 (G678)

GERLI, GIOVANNI
A Maria Immacolata *see Ascenso, Antonio

A S. Luigi *ASD
[Lat] unis,org ZANIBON 2729 s.p. (G679)

Corpus Domini *Mass
[Lat] unis,org sc ZANIBON 2575 s.p., cor pts ZANIBON 2576 s.p. (G680)

Regina Coeli
see PEL TEMPO PASQUALE
see PEL TEMPO PASQUALE

Salve Regina
see CINQUE MOTECTA IN HON. B.V.M.

GERMAN AGNUS see Praetorius, Michael

GERMAN, EDWARD (1862-1936)
Bread Of Heaven, On Thee We Feed *anthem/Introit
mix cor oct NOVELLO 28.0939.07 s.p. (G681)

Intercessory Hymn *hymn
SATB oct NOVELLO 44.0933.08 s.p. (G682)

GERMAN MAGNIFICAT see Schutz, Heinrich, Deutsches Magnificat

GERMAN MASS IN F see Schubert, Franz (Peter), Deutsche Messe

GERMAN MISERERE see Haydn, (Johann) Michael

GERMAN MOTET see Strauss, Richard

GERMAN REQUIEM see Brahms, Johannes, Ein Deutsches Requiem

GERMAN REQUIEM, A see Schutz, Heinrich

GERMAN SANCTUS see Praetorius, Michael

GERMINAVIT RADIX see Bruck, Johann von

GERN WALLT' ICH MIT DEM VOLKE HIN see Handel, George Frideric

GEROLD, J.K.
Jehova
mix cor sc ALSBACH&D s.p. (G683)

GERRISH, J.
Virgin Most Pure, A
SA AMP A295 $.25 (G684)

GERSBACH, F.
Markt Und Gassen *Xmas
(Eichendorff, J.V.) [Ger] wom cor,acap (easy) HUG s.p. (G685)

GERSCHEFSKI, EDWIN (1909-)
And Thou Shalt Love The Lord
SATB oct PRESSER 342-40018 $.40 (G686)

Lord's Prayer, The
SSA,acap (med) PRESSER 342-40098 $.35 (G687)
(Dooley, J.) SATB,acap oct PRESSER 342-40016 $.30 (G688)

GERSON
He Is Coming *Easter
SATB SCHMITT 1586 $.25 (G689)

GERTRUDE, SR.
Give Thanks To The Lord *Thanks
SSA oct VOLKWEIN VB154 $.30 (G690)

GESANG DER DREI MANNER IM FEURIGEN OFEN see Schutz, Heinrich

GESANG DER GEISSLER *mot
(Burkhart, Franz) mix cor,acap DOBLINGER s.p. see also In Seiner Handen (G691)

GESANG DER JUNGFRAU MARIA see Kremer, Clemens

GESANG DES ABGESCHIEDENEN see Schweppe, Joachim

GESANGBUCH
Carol Of The Three Kings *Xmas,carol
(Canavati) SATB oct PRO ART 1954 $.25 (G692)

Praise Ye The Lord, The Almighty *Gen
(Olds) SAB SCHMITT 5506 $.35 (G693)
(Olds) SATB SCHMITT 1534 $.35 (G694)

Sun Of My Soul *Gen
(Olds) SATB SCHMITT 1864 $.25 (G695)

GESANGBUCH, S.
Quest For The Victorious Life
(Jones, G.) SATB oct PRESSER 332-15081 $.45 (G696)

GESANGE DER BOHMISCHEN BRUDER IN VARIATIONEN, HEFT 2 see Pepping, Ernst

GESANGE DER BOHMISCHEN BRUDER IN VARIATIONEN, HEFT I see Pepping, Ernst

GESANGE DES PROPRIUMS FUR DEN ERNTEDANKTAG see Suthoff-Gross, Rudolf

GESANGE ZUR FEIER DES HEILIGEN OPFERS DER MESSE see Schubert, Franz (Peter)

GESANGSE ZUM KIRCHENJAHR *CC30U,Gen
(Hellmann) [Ger] 1 eq voices/2 eq voices,org& 2rec/vln&opt vcl HANSSLER 2.007 sc $10.00, voc pt $2.00, ipa (G697)

GESCHICHTE VOM VERLORENEN SOHN see Schwartz, Gerhard von

GESIUS, BARTHOLOMAUS (ca. 1555-1613)
Arise, Sons Of The Kingdom *Palm,chorale
SATB WEINBERGER s.p. (G698)
(Ehret) SATB,acap MARKS 4157 $.30 (G699)

Blossom Time Now Cometh
(Lundquist) SATB,acap (diff) oct WILLIS 8421 $.20 (G700)

Child Was Born In Bethlehem *Xmas
(Lundquist) SATB oct VOLKWEIN VB127 $.25 (G701)

Christum Wir Sollen Loben
(Schabasser, Josef) mix cor,acap oct DOBLINGER s.p. see also CHRISTUS, DER HERR (G702)

Christum Wir Sollen Loben Schon *Gen/Thanks
SATB,acap voc pt DOBLINGER s.p. see also LOB UND DANK (G703)

Das Ist Furwahr Ein Kostlich Ding
SATB HANSSLER 6.194 s.p. contains also: Gastoldi, Giovanni Giacomo, In Dir Ist Freude, In Allem Leide (SSATB) (G704)

De Aro Nu Forgangna
(Anrep-Nordin, B.) [Swed] SATB,acap GEHRMANS KRB 131 (G705)

Dem Eingebornen Kindelein *Xmas
TTBB HANSSLER 6.0790 s.p. (G706)

Die Nacht Ist Vorgedrungen, Der Tag
(Berger, H.L.) TTBB HANSSLER 6.5112 s.p. (G707)

Du Friedefurst, Herr Jesu Christ
see Sohr, Peter, Bis Hierher Hat Mich Gott Gebracht
see Bach, Johann Sebastian, Du Friedefurst, Herr Jesu Christ

Ein Kind Geborn Zu Bethlehem *Xmas
4pt mix cor MOSELER LB-67 s.p. contains also: Praetorius, Michael, Ein Kind Geborn Zu Bethlehem (4pt mix cor); Vulpius, Melchior, Ein Kind Geborn Zu Bethlehem (5pt mix cor) (G708)

Freut Euch, Ihr Lieben Christen All
see Praetorius, Michael, Das Alte Jahr Ist Nun Dahin

GESIUS, BARTHOLOMAUS (cont'd.)

Frohlock, Du Tochter Zion, Sehr Und Jauchz
see Praetorius, Michael, Geboren Ist Immanuel, Der Herr Christ

God's Son In Triumph Rose Today *Easter
(Praetorius; Buszin) SATB SCHMITT 1514 $.25 (G709)

Help Us, Eternal God And Lord *Gen
(Lundquist) SSA SCHMITT 2539 $.25 (G710)

Heut Triumphieret Gottes Sohn *Easter
[Ger] SSATB,acap (easy) MULLER MS 79 s.p. (G711)

Hochpreiset Meine Seele Den Gott
SSATB HANSSLER 6.001 s.p. (G712)

Hosanna To The Son Of David *Adv/Gen/Palm
SATB,acap (med easy) oct CONCORDIA 98-1038 $.25 (G713)
mix cor SOUTHERN $.25 (G714)

Ich Bin Ein Gast Auf Erden *Gd.Fri.
SATB,acap voc pt DOBLINGER s.p. see also TOD UND VERGANGLICHKEIT (G715)
"We Walk The Earth As Pilgrims" SATB,acap SCHIRM.EC 1722 $.25 (G716)

Ich Steh An Deiner Krippen Hier *Xmas
SSATB HANSSLER 6.095 s.p. (G717)

In Peace And Joy I Now Depart *see Mit Fried Und Freud Fahr Ich Dahin

Mir Nach, Spricht Christus
(Schabasser, Josef) mix cor,acap (contains also: Schein, Hermann, O Christe, Schopfer Aller Welt) oct DOBLINGER s.p. see also CHRISTUS, DER HERR (G718)

Mit Fried Und Freud Fahr Ich Dahin
(Lundquist) "In Peace And Joy I Now Depart" SATB,acap (med) oct WILLIS 8402 $.18 (G719)
(Richardson) "In Peace And Joy I Now Depart" SATB oct SPRATT 2019 $.30 (G720)

Nun Jauchzet, All Ihr Frommen
see Bach, Johann Sebastian, Gottes Sohn Ist Kommen

O Christe, Morgenstern
(Schabasser, Josef) mix cor,acap oct DOBLINGER s.p. see also CHRISTUS, DER HERR (G721)

O Welt, Ich Muss Dich Lassen (from Matthaus-Passion)
"O Welt, Sieh Hier Dein Leben" SATB HANSSLER 6.114 s.p. contains also: Bach, Johann Sebastian, O Traurigkeit, O Herzelied, "So Ruhest Du, O Meine Ruh", S.404 (G722)

O Welt, Sieh Hier Dein Leben *see O Welt, Ich Muss Dich Lassen

Strife Is O'er, The Battle Done
SSAATTBB,acap oct PRESSER 312-40157 $.30 (G723)

'Tis Finished! So The Savior Cried *anthem
(Sateren) SATB (easy) oct AUGSBURG 1578 $.30 (G724)

Uppfaren Ar Var Herre Krist
mix cor NORDISKA 3589 s.p. (G725)

We Walk The Earth As Pilgrims *see Ich Bin Ein Gast Auf Erden

Wenn Meine Sund' Mich Kranken (from Matthaus-Passion)
see Praetorius, Michael, Jesu, Deine Passion Will Ich Jetzt Bedenken

Wenn Wir In Hochsten Noten Sein
see Goudimel, Claude, Herr Gott, Dich Loben Alle Wir

Wir Danken Dir, Herr Jesu Christ
4pt mix cor MOSELER LB-89 s.p. contains also: Praetorius, Michael, Nun Freut Euch, Gottes Kinder All (G726)

GESSINGER
Belsener Chorkreis
mix cor HANSSLER 25.008 s.p. (G727)

GESU BAMBINO see Yon, Pietro Alessandro

GESUALDO DI VENOSA, CARLO
see GESUALDO, DON CARLO

GESUALDO, DON CARLO (ca. 1560-1613)
Come, Celestial Fire *see Sancti Spiritus

Dignare Me
(Vene) "O Grant Us Grace" [Lat/Eng] SATTB, acap oct COLOMBO 1909 $.25 (G728)

Dolcissima Mia Vita
mix cor sc ALSBACH&D s.p. (G729)

Lord, Remember Me *see Reminiscere

O Grant Us Grace *see Dignare Me

O Vos Omnes *anthem/mot
(Harris, William H.) [Lat] mix cor oct NOVELLO 28.1271.01 s.p. (G730)

Reminiscere
(Vene) "Lord, Remember Me" [Lat/Eng] SATTB, acap oct COLOMBO 1910 $.30 (G731)

Responsoria
(Watkins) 6pt (with facsimile reproductions) HINRICHSEN D2257 s.p. (G732)

Sacrae Cantiones Vol. I *CCU
(Watkins) 5pt HINRICHSEN D2258 s.p. with facsimile reproductions (G733)

Sacrae Cantiones Vol. II *CCU
(Watkins) 6pt/7pt HINRICHSEN D2259 s.p. with facsimile reproductions (G734)

GESUALDO, DON CARLO (cont'd.)

Salmi Della Compiete and Canzonettes *CCUL
[Lat] SATB/SSATB,acap/kbd HINRICHSEN D2260
s.p.   (G735)

Sancti Spiritus
(Vene) "Come, Celestial Fire" [Lat/Eng]
SATTB,acap oct COLOMBO 1908 $.25   (G736)

Tres Sacrae Cantiones *CC3U
(Stravinsky, Igor) [Lat] mix cor,acap voc
sc BOOSEY $2.00   (G737)

GET INTO HEAV'N see McKay

GET IT TOGETHER! *CCU
mix cor SCHMITT 9071 $1.00   (G738)

GET IT TOGETHER see Red, Buryl

GET ON BOARD *spir
(Durian, Tim) 4pt men cor,Bar solo,acap
BREITKOPF-W Z-41 s.p. see also Dreizehn
Negro- Spirituals   (G739)

GET-TOGETHER HYMNS *CCU
LORENZ $1.25   (G740)

GET-TOGETHER SONGS *CCU
LORENZ $1.25   (G741)

GETHSEMANE see Harkness

GETHSEMANE see Martin, Reginald W.

GETHSEMANE see Pooler, Frank

GETHSEMANE see Steel, Christopher [Charles]

GETHSEMANE see Williams, David H.

GETHSEMANE see Young

GETHSEMANE (BLESSED JESU, COME TO ME) see
Young, Gordon

GETHSEMANE TO GOLGOTHA see Matthews, Harvey
Alexander

GETHSEMANE TO GOLGOTHA see Turner, Edmund
(Edmond)

GETTYSBURG ADDRESS, THE see Weinberg, Jacob

GEVAERT, FRANCOIS AUGUSTE (1828-1908)
Angel's Message, The *see Le Message Des
Anges

Cantique De Noel
(Klein) "Christmas Song" [Eng/Fr] 4pt mix
cor,acap oct SCHIRM.G 11483 $.25   (G742)

Chanson Joyeuse De Noel *Xmas,Fr
[Eng/Fr] 4pt mix cor,acap oct SCHIRM.G 5075
$.25   (G743)
(Krone) "Joyous Christmas Song" [Eng/Fr]
SATB,acap WARNER W2636 $.30   (G744)

Christmas Song *see Cantique De Noel

Good Neighbor, Whence Came That Great Sound
*see Voisin, D'ouvenait Ce Grand Bruit?

Grand-Messe De Noel *see Puer Natus Est
Nobis

Joyful Christmas Song, A *Xmas
(Bliss, P.) SATB,acap oct PRESSER 312-20423
$.30   (G745)

Joyous Christmas Song *see Chanson Joyeuse
De Noel

Joyous Christmas Song, A
(Dickinson) [Fr/Eng] SATB oct GRAY GSC 11
$.35   (G746)

Joyous Christmas Song, A *Xmas
[Fr/Eng] SATB,acap oct BELWIN 64089 $.30
(G747)
(Ehret, W.) [Fr/Eng] SSA oct BELWIN 1949
$.30   (G748)
(Ehret, W.) [Fr/Eng] SAB oct BELWIN 1647
$.25   (G749)
(Ehret, W.) [Fr/Eng] SATB oct BELWIN 1414
$.25   (G750)

Le Message Des Anges *Xmas
(Klein) "Angel's Message, The" [Eng/Fr] 4pt
mix cor,acap oct SCHIRM.G 11482 $.25
(G751)

Le Sommeil De L'Enfant Jesus
"Slumber Of The Infant Jesus, The" SATB,
acap SCHIRM.EC 1163 $.30   (G752)
(Davis, K.) "Slumber Of The Infant Jesus"
SSA,acap SCHIRM.EC 1088 $.25   (G753)

Le Somneil De L'enfant Jesus *Xmas
(Lefebvre) "Sleep, Babe Divine" [Fr/Eng]
TTBB oct COLOMBO 773 $.20   (G754)

Lord's Prayer, The *see Pater Noster

O Filii Et Filiae
"O Sons And Daughters" SSA,acap SCHIRM.EC
868 $.30   (G755)

O Sons And Daughters *see O Filii Et Filiae

Pater Noster *prayer
girl cor SOUTHERN $.30   (G756)
"Lord's Prayer, The" SSA,acap SCHIRM.EC
2502 $.35   (G757)

Puer Natus Est Nobis *Xmas,Mass
"Grand-Messe De Noel" 3pt jr cor/3pt wom
cor,org LEMOINE voc sc s.p., cor pts s.p.
(G758)

Sleep, Babe Divine *see Le Somneil De
L'enfant Jesus

Sleep Of The Child Jesus *Xmas
2pt oct LORENZ 5727 $.30   (G759)

Sleep Of The Child Jesus, The *Xmas
(Ehret) SSA oct SPRATT 633 $.30   (G760)

GEVAERT, FRANCOIS AUGUSTE (cont'd.)
Sleep Of The Child Jesus, The *Xmas
SATB,acap oct PRESSER 332-13340 $.25 (G761)
[Eng/Fr] SATB,acap WARNER W2610 $.30 (G762)
(Ehret) SA oct SPRATT 603 $.25   (G763)
(Ehret) SAB oct SPRATT 634 $.30   (G764)
(Gray) SSA oct PRO ART 1554 $.20   (G765)

Slumber Of The Infant Jesus *see Le Sommeil
De L'Enfant Jesus

Slumber Of The Infant Jesus, The *see Le
Sommeil De L'Enfant Jesus

Slumber Song Of The Infant Jesus *Xmas
(Dickinson) SATB oct GRAY GSC 14 $.25
(G766)

Three Kings, The *Xmas
SATB oct WALTON 2054 $.25   (G767)

Voisin, D'ouvenait Ce Grand Bruit?
(Cramer) "Good Neighbor, Whence Came That
Great Sound" [Eng/Fr] SATB,acap MARKS
4294 $.40   (G768)

GHEDINI, GIORGIO FEDERICO (1892-1965)
Concerto Spirituale
treb cor,SS soli,org/9inst voc sc ZERBONI
4246 s.p., ipr   (G769)

Corona Di Sacre Canzone
mix cor,SA soli,pno,strings voc sc ZERBONI
4622 s.p., ipr
contains: Corona Di Sacre Canzone; Laudi
Spirituali   (G770)

Corona Di Sacre Canzone
see Corona Di Sacre Canzone

La Messa Del Venerdi' Santo
[Lat] mix cor,SMezTBarB soli,orch voc sc
ZERBONI 4549 s.p., ipr   (G771)

Laudi Spirituali
see Corona Di Sacre Canzone

Missa Monodica In Honorem St. Gregorii Magni
*Mass
[Lat] unis,opt org,opt harmonium cor pts
SCHOTT s.p.   (G772)

GHILSELIN-VERBONNET, JOHANNES
De Les Armes
see Opera Omnia Vol. II

Ghy Syt Die Werste Boven Al
see Opera Omnia Vol. III

Gratieuse
see Opera Omnia Vol. III

Je Nay Dueul
see Opera Omnia Vol. III

La Belle Se Siet
see Opera Omnia Vol. II

Narayge
see Opera Omnia Vol. II

Opera Omnia Vol. II *Mass
(Gottwald, Clytus) cor AM.INST.MUS. $17.00
contains: De Les Armes; La Belle Se Siet;
Narayge   (G773)

Opera Omnia Vol. III *Mass
(Gottwald, Clytus) cor AM.INST.MUS. $16.00
contains: Ghy Syt Die Werste Boven Al;
Gratieuse; Je Nay Dueul   (G774)

Opera Omnia Vol. IV *sac/sec,CC23U
(Gottwald, Clytus) cor AM.INST.MUS. $12.00
(G775)
Opera Omnia Vol. I *CCU,mot
(Gottwald, Clytus) cor AM.INST.MUS. $12.00
(G776)

GHY SYT DIE WERSTE BOVEN AL see Ghilselin-
Verbonnet, Johannes

GIA FU CHI' M' EBBE CARA see Palestrina,
Giovanni

GIACHETTI, ENRICO
Circunda Tibi Decorem
see IN PRIMA MISSA CELEBRANDA

Missa In Hon. B.M.V. Immaculatae *BVM,Mass
[Lat] unis,org,opt strings sc ZANIBON 777
s.p., cor pts ZANIBON 778 s.p., ipr   (G777)

GIACOMELLO, PIETRO
Tu Es Sacerdos
[Lat] ATB,org ZANIBON 17 s.p.   (G778)

GIANNETTA "SAG MIR, GIANNETTA, WILLST DU
WIRKLICH FREIN?" see Strohbach, Siegfried

GIANNINI, V.
Canticle Of Christmas *Xmas
SATB,Bar solo BELWIN $2.00   (G779)

Canticle Of The Martyrs *cant
BELWIN $1.25   (G780)

Christmas *Xmas
SATB oct COLOMBO 2076 $.30 see from Three
Devotional Motets   (G781)

Easter *Easter
SATB oct COLOMBO 2078 $.35 see from Three
Devotional Motets   (G782)

Good Friday *Gd.Fri.
SATB oct COLOMBO 2077 $.25 see from Three
Devotional Motets   (G783)

Hosanna *Palm
SATB oct GRAY GCMR 2695 $.40   (G784)

Requiem
[Lat] voc sc UNIVER. 10851 $12.50, cor pts
UNIVER. 10859A-D $.85   (G785)

Three Devotional Motets *see Christmas;
Easter; Good Friday   (G786)

GIANNINI, VINCENZO
Abbi Pieta Di Me, O Dio! (Psalm 51)
see Due Salmi

Alleluia, Alleluia (Psalm 150)
see Due Salmi

Due Salmi
SATB sc ZANIBON 3820 s.p., voc pt ZANIBON
3821-22 s.p.
contains: Abbi Pieta Di Me, O Dio! (Psalm
51); Alleluia, Alleluia (Psalm 150)
(G787)

Psalm 51 *see Abbi Pieta Di Me, O Dio!

Psalm 150 *see Alleluia, Alleluia

GIARDINI, FELICE DE' (1716-1796)
Come, Thou Almighty King
(Churchill) SATB oct PLYMOUTH CH-101 $.25
(G788)
(Howorth, Wayne) SATB oct BELWIN 1211 $.25
(G789)
(Wiley) SATB oct PRO ART 1361 $.25   (G790)

GIARDINO, DI
Come Thou Almighty King
(Hastings) SATB oct BOURNE HA14 $.30 (G791)

GIASSON
Alleluia! He Is Risen *Easter/Lent
SATB GALLEON GCS2001   (G792)

Ascensiontide *Asc/Easter/Lent
unis oct FISCHER,C GCS-2008 $.20   (G793)
SA GALLEON GCS2009   (G794)

At The Lamb's High Feast *Easter/Lent
unis oct FISCHER,C GCS-2007 $.20   (G795)
SA GALLEON GCS2007   (G796)

Away In A Manger *Xmas
2pt jr cor FISCHER,C GCS 1008 $.20   (G797)
S/SA oct GALLEON GCS1008   (G798)

Carol Of The Angels *Xmas
SATB oct GALLEON GCS1020   (G799)

For Unto Us A Child Is Born *Xmas
SATB oct GALLEON GCS 1001   (G800)

In Eastern Lands *Easter/Lent/Palm
S/SA GALLEON GCS2002   (G801)
2pt jr cor FISCHER,C GCS 2002 $.25   (G802)

Prelude, Anunciation And Alleluia *Xmas
SATB,ST soli oct GALLEON GCS1023   (G803)

Shepherd's Song *Xmas
jr cor oct GALLEON GCS1016   (G804)
unis jr cor FISCHER,C GCS 1016 $.20   (G805)

Sing Alleluia Now! *Xmas/Easter/Lent
SATB oct GALLEON GCS1022   (G806)
SATB oct FISCHER,C GCS-1022 $.35   (G807)

What Was This Wondrous Thing? *Xmas
SATB,S solo oct GALLEON GCS1014   (G808)

Yule Log Carol *Xmas
SATB,opt hndbl oct GALLEON GCS1010   (G809)

GIB, DASS EIN LICHT UNS WIEDER SCHEIN see
Rohwer, Jens

GIB DICH ZUFRIEDEN UND SEI STILLE see Arfken,
Ernst

GIB DICH ZUFRIEDEN UND SEI STILLE see Hintze,
Jakob

GIB FRIEDEN UNSRER ZEIT, O HERR see Vulpius,
Melchior

GIB UNS FRIEDEN JEDEN TAG see Luders, Rudiger

GIB UNS HEUT UNSER TAGLICH BROT see Scheidt,
Samuel

GIB UNSERN FURSTEN UND ALLER OBRIGKEIT see
Schutz, Heinrich

GIBB
God Of Our Fathers *anthem
TTBB oct FISCHER,C CM-6591 $.25   (G810)

Search Of The Three Kings *Xmas
SSA oct FISCHER,C CM-6495 $.25   (G811)
SATB oct FISCHER,C CM-6932 $.25   (G812)

GIBBIN, L.D.
Church's Year In Music, The
SATB&cong,narrator (easy) OXFORD 46.041
$1.65   (G813)

GIBBONS, ORLANDO (1583-1625)
Almighty And Everlasting God *Gen/Lent,
anthem
SATB,acap (easy) oct OXFORD 43.244 $.25
(G814)
mix cor oct NOVELLO 40.0129.10 s.p.   (G815)
SATB,acap SCHIRM.EC 1686 $.30   (G816)
SATB oct GRAY GCMR 3142 $.30   (G817)
(Fissinger) SATB oct SUMMY 5349 $.45   (G818)
(Greyson) SATB oct BOURNE ES35 $.30   (G819)
(King) SATB oct PLYMOUTH PCS-36 $.25   (G820)

Almighty God, Which Hast Given *Xmas,anthem
(Vining, Paul) mix cor oct NOVELLO
88.0014.06 s.p.   (G821)

Almighty God, Who By Thy Son *Ember
SAATTBB,A/Bar solo (med) oct OXFORD 42.235
$.35   (G822)

Behold, I Bring You Glad Tidings
SSAATB,org oct PETERS H1559   (G823)

Blessed Be The Lord
(Coggin) 4pt mix cor,org/pno oct SCHIRM.G
11667 $.15   (G824)

Christmas Day *Xmas
(Davison, J.) SATB oct PRESSER 362-01318
$.30   (G825)

Come, Holy Ghost *see Veni Creator

GIBBONS, ORLANDO (cont'd.)

Come, Holy Spirit *see Veni, Creator
  Spiritus

Come, Thou Morning Star *Xmas
  (Hovdesven) SATB,fl/vln SCHMITT 8044 $.35
  (G826)

Deliver Us, O Lord Our God *Easter/Lent
  (Martens, Mason) SATB oct WALTON 2091 $.25
  (G827)

Drop, Drop, Slow Tears *madrigal
  SSAATB STAINER CC116 s.p.   (G828)

Eight Anthems *CC8U,anthem
  mix cor,acap voc sc KALMUS 6683 $1.50
  (G829)

First And Second Preces And Psalms *CCU
  mix cor,acap voc sc KALMUS 6678 $1.00
  (G830)

Four Anthems *CC4U,anthem
  mix cor,acap voc sc KALMUS 6681 $1.00
  (G831)

Four Anthems *CC4U,anthem
  mix cor,acap voc sc KALMUS 6682 $1.35
  (G832)

God Is Gone Up
  (Morehen) SSAATTBB,acap (diff) OXFORD
  43.252 $1.50 contains also: O Clap Your
  Hands   (G833)

Holy Communion *Commun
  SATB (F maj) oct NOVELLO s.p.   (G834)

Hosanna Singt Dem Sohne Davids *Bibl/mot
  (Berger) SSAATB HANSSLER 1.072 s.p. (G835)

Hosanna To The Son Of David *Easter/Palm,
  anthem/Bibl
  SATB oct SOUTHERN $.35   (G836)
  SSAATB,acap BELWIN 64024 $.40   (G837)
  SATB oct GRAY GCMR 1983 $.35   (G838)
  SSAATB,acap SCHIRM.EC 1189 $.35 (G839)
  SSAATB (C maj) oct NOVELLO 28.0129.09 s.p.
  (G840)
  SSAATB (E flat maj) oct NOVELLO 28.1015.08
  s.p.   (G841)
  (Bantock, Granville) mix cor,S solo,opt org
  oct CURWEN 10321 $.35   (G842)

Hosannah To The Son Of David *Adv/Easter/
  Lent/Palm
  SSAATTB,acap (med) oct OXFORD 43.079 $.50
  (G843)
  (Marshall, Charles) SSAATB FRANK F-582 $.30
  (G844)

I Am The Resurrection *anthem
  mix cor oct OXFORD 43.476 $.45   (G845)

I Am The Resurrection And The Life *Easter
  (Humphreys) SATB,acap (med diff/diff)
  SOUTHERN $.45   (G846)

If Ye Be Risen Again With Christ *Easter,
  anthem
  mix cor,SSA soli oct NOVELLO 28.1333.05
  s.p.   (G847)

Lift Up Your Heads (Psalm 24) Asc/Gen
  SSAATB,opt org (med) oct OXFORD 43.251 $.50
  (G848)

Lord Grant Grace, We Humbly Beseech Thee
  *Gen/Trin
  SATB,kbd (med diff) oct CONCORDIA 98-1970
  $.30   (G849)

Lord Jesus, Think Of Me
  SATB oct WALTON 2058 $.25   (G850)

Magnificat And Nunc Dimittis (from Short
  Service) Magnif/Nunc
  SATB,acap (med) oct OXFORD 43.410 $.50
  (G851)
  SATB oct NOVELLO 44.0897.07 s.p. (G852)

My God, Accept My Heart This Day *Gen
  (Waugh) SATB SCHMITT 871 $.25   (G853)

O Clap Your Hands (Psalm 47) Asc
  see Gibbons, Orlando, God Is Gone Up
  SSAATTBB (med) oct OXFORD 43.252 $1.50
  (G854)

O For A Heart To Praise My God
  (Davis, K.) SSA,acap SCHIRM.EC 1870 (G855)

O God The King Of Glory *Asc/Gen
  SAATB&SAAT (med) oct OXFORD 42.895 $.50
  (G856)

O Lord How Do My Woes Increase
  see Two Anthems

O Lord I Lift My Heart To Thee
  see Two Anthems

O Lord, I Meditate On Thee
  (Nichols, A.M.) SAB/SATB,kbd oct KERBY 6405
  $.25   (G857)
  (Nichols, A.M.) SATB oct KERBY 6405C $.25
  (G858)
  (Nichols, A.M.) SAB oct KERBY 6405C $.25
  (G859)

O Lord In Thy Wrath *Lent
  SSATB,acap (med) oct OXFORD 43.299 $.35
  (G860)

O Lord, Increase My Faith *anthem
  SATB oct GRAY GCMR 1579 $.30   (G861)
  SATB,acap SCHIRM.EC 375 $.25   (G862)
  mix cor oct NOVELLO 50.01383.02 s.p. (G863)
  (Lyall) SATB,opt pno/org oct LAWSON 725
  $.30   (G864)
  (Manney) mix cor SOUTHERN $.30   (G865)
  (Talmadge, A.) SSAA,acap SCHIRM.EC 1932
  $.25   (G866)

O Thou, The Central Orb
  SAATB,soli,org SCHIRM.EC 352 $.30 (G867)

Preces
  see Barnard, John, Responses
  SAATB,acap (med easy) oct OXFORD 43.387
  $.30 contains also: Barnard, John,
  Responses   (G868)

Psalm 24 *see Lift Up Your Heads

Psalm 47 *see O Clap Your Hands

GIBBONS, ORLANDO (cont'd.)

Second Service, The
  mix cor,acap voc sc KALMUS 6680 $1.60
  (G869)

Short Service *Bene/Magnif/Nunc/Te Deum
  SATB,acap (med) oct OXFORD 43.285 $1.20
  (G870)

Short Service, The
  mix cor,acap voc sc KALMUS 6679 $1.35
  (G871)

So God Loved The World *anthem
  (Vining, Paul) SAATB oct NOVELLO 88.0015.04
  s.p.   (G872)

This Is The Day The Lord Hath Made *Easter
  (Tyler) SATB SCHMITT 1438 $.30   (G873)

This Is The Record Of John *Adv,anthem
  mix cor,T solo,4strings oct LAWSON 550 $.35
  (G874)
  SAATB,T solo (med easy) oct OXFORD 42.676
  $.35, ipr   (G875)
  (Palmer, William) SAATB,A solo oct NOVELLO
  28.1330.00 s.p.   (G876)

Thou, The All-Holy
  (Davis) SSAA,acap oct BELWIN 64163 $.30
  (G877)

Threefold Amen
  see THREE AMENS
  SATB oct NOVELLO 44.0603.06 s.p. (G878)

Twenty-Five Anthems Vol. 1 *CCU,anthem
  mix cor,acap voc sc KALMUS 6684 $1.00
  (G879)

Twenty-Five Anthems Vol. 2 *CCU,anthem
  mix cor,acap voc sc KALMUS 6685 $1.00
  (G880)

Twenty-Five Anthems Vol. 3 *CCU,anthem
  mix cor,acap voc sc KALMUS 6686 $1.00
  (G881)

Twenty-Five Anthems Vol. 4 *CCU,anthem
  mix cor,acap voc sc KALMUS 6687 $1.00
  (G882)

Two Anthems *anthem
  (Wulstan, D.) CHESTER s.p.
  contains: O Lord How Do My Woes Increase
  (SATB); O Lord I Lift My Heart To Thee
  (SAATB)   (G883)

Veni Creator
  (Kaplan, A.) "Come, Holy Ghost" SATB
  BROUDE,A. 106 $.30   (G884)

Veni, Creator Spiritus *Pent,anthem
  (Becker, A.C.) "Come, Holy Spirit" [Eng/
  Lat] SATB (easy) oct GIA G1540 $.25
  (G885)

Verse Anthems 1 *CCU,Eng
  cor STAINER 3.8203.8 $13.00   (G886)

Why Art Thou Heavy, O My Soul?
  (Engel) SATB FLAMMER A 5344 $.25 (G887)

Why Art Thou So Heavy, O My Soul
  SATB,acap BROUDE BR. $.35   (G888)
  (Payson, A.) SATB,acap FRANK F-444 $.35
  (G889)

Ye That Do Your Master's Will
  (Hilton, J.) SATB,acap oct PRESSER MC395
  $.25   (G890)

You That Like Heedless Strangers Pass Along
  *Lent
  SATB,kbd (easy) oct CONCORDIA 98-1580 $.22
  (G891)

GIBBS

At The Manger *Xmas
  SATB,acap oct BOOSEY 1820 $.30   (G892)

Hail, O Sun Of Righteousness
  SATB,acap (med) OXFORD 84.053 $.25 (G893)

I, Therefore, The Prisoner Of The Lord
  SATB,org oct BOOSEY 5192 $.40   (G894)

Laetatus Sum (Psalm 122)
  SATB,acap (med) OXFORD 43.944 $.35 (G895)

Psalm 122 *see Laetatus Sum

Saviour Born, A *Xmas,cant
  SSA voc sc OXFORD 46.500 $1.25   (G896)

Sleep, Little King
  TTBB,acap oct BOOSEY 1929 $.30   (G897)

Stable Door
  SATB,acap oct BOOSEY 3067 $.30   (G898)

This Great Hour
  SA/TB/SATB (easy) OXFORD 86.002 $.35 (G899)

To My Heart On Christmas Day *Xmas
  TTBB,acap (med diff) OXFORD 85.007 $.35
  (G900)

While The Shepherds Were Watching *Xmas
  SATB,acap (easy) OXFORD 84.013 $.35 (G901)

GIBBS, ALAN

Christ Our Passover *Easter,Bibl
  SATB (med easy) oct OXFORD   (G902)

God Hath Spoken *Gen,anthem
  SATB oct ROYAL 229 s.p.   (G903)

Magnificat And Nunc Dimittis *Magnif/Nunc
  SS (D maj) NOVELLO 86.0019.08 s.p. (G904)

Octave Communion Service *Commun
  cong ROYAL s.p. see from MUSIC FOR THE HOLY
  COMMUNION   (G905)

Short Communion Service, A *Commun
  SATB,opt org (med easy) oct OXFORD 43.945
  $.50   (G906)

Thy Word Is Truth *Fest,anthem
  4pt mix cor&opt cong,org voc sc SCHIRM.G
  $.75   (G907)

GIBBS, [CECIL] ARMSTRONG (1889-1960)

All Creatures Of Our God And King *Op.32,
  mot
  dbl cor,acap oct CURWEN 10592 $.25 (G908)

GIBBS, [CECIL] ARMSTRONG (cont'd.)

Behold The Man *Psntd,cant
  SATB,TBar soli,orch/org&strings/pno&strings
  (med easy) OXFORD 46.504 voc sc $3.25,
  ipr, cor pts $.90   (G909)

Bless The Lord, O My Soul (Psalm 104) Harv
  2pt (easy) oct OXFORD 42.116 $.30 (G910)
  SATB (med) oct OXFORD 42.158 $.35 (G911)
  SATB (med) oct OXFORD 42.158 $.35 (G912)

Christmas Day *Xmas
  (Davidson) SATB oct ELKAN-V 362-1318 $.30
  (G913)

Cradle Song *Xmas,cradle
  mix cor,S solo CURWEN 61130 s.p. (G914)

Deborah And Barak
  mix cor,ABar soli,orch BOOSEY voc sc $1.50,
  sc rental   (G915)

Easter (Most Glorious Lord Of Lyfe) *Easter/
  Gen
  SATB,acap (med) oct OXFORD 43.001 $.30
  (G916)

Lord, Thou Hast Been A Refuge Sure *Fest/Gen
  unis&desc (easy) oct OXFORD 82.010 $.25
  (G917)

O God Of Earth And Altar
  unis&opt mix cor,org oct CURWEN 8825 $.25
  (G918)

O Lord, Increase My Faith
  SATB,acap oct BELWIN 64005 $.30 (G919)
  (Kjelson) SATB oct BELWIN 2171 $.25 (G920)

O Praise God In His Holiness (Psalm 150)
  Fest/Thanks
  SAB/SA/TB (med easy) oct OXFORD 44.986
  $.30, ipr   (G921)

Pilgrim Song *Gen
  SAB/2pt (easy) oct OXFORD 80.013 $.30
  (G922)

Psalm 104 *see Bless The Lord, O My Soul

Psalm 150 *see O Praise God In His Holiness

Song Of Worship, A *Gen/Thanks
  SATB (med diff) oct OXFORD 84.018 $.45
  (G923)

Thee Will I Love
  unis&org oct CURWEN 10402 $.25   (G924)

Three Kings, The
  wom cor/mix cor,S solo,pno/org,strings,
  child's voice voc sc BOOSEY $2.50, ipr
  (G925)

GIBILARO

Ave Maria
  SATB FRANCIS s.p.   (G926)

GIDDI-UP! DEAR LITTLE DONKEY see Grime, William

GIDEON see Dunford, Benjamin

GIDEON, MIRIAM (1906-)
How Goodly Are Thy Tents
  SSA oct PRESSER MC162 $.35   (G927)
  SATB,acap oct PRESSER MC350 $.35 (G928)

GIEFER, WILLY (1930-)
Kommet, Ihr Hirten *Xmas
  SATBB TONGER s.p.   (G929)

Maria Durch Ein Dornwald Ging
  see Zwei Chore Zur Weihnacht

O Heiland, Reiss Die Himmel Auf
  see Zwei Chore Zur Weihnacht

Zwei Chore Zur Weihnacht *Xmas
  SSA,S solo,rec,vcl, xylophone, marimba
  TONGER s.p., ipa
  contains: Maria Durch Ein Dornwald Ging;
  O Heiland, Reiss Die Himmel Auf (G930)

GIESCHEN, THOMAS
Christmas Greeting, A *Xmas
  unis,kbd (easy) oct CONCORDIA 98-2160 $.25
  (G931)

Christmas Song (Near Jesus In The Manger
  Stand) *Xmas
  SATB,acap (med easy) oct CONCORDIA 98-1840
  $.25   (G932)

Crown Him! *Adv/Gen
  SATB&cong/SATB&jr cor,org,2trp,2trom,tuba,
  opt timp (easy) sc CONCORDIA 97-5142
  $2.50, cor pts CONCORDIA 98-2152 $.25,
  ipa   (G933)

GIESER, WALTHER
Siehe, Es Kommt Die Zeit *Gen,cant
  [Ger] SATB,B solo,org (diff) BAREN. BA 2116
  rental   (G934)

GIFFORD
As Dew In Aprille *Xmas,carol
  unis ALBERT s.p.   (G935)

GIFT CAROL, THE *Xmas,carol,Span
  (Pfautsch, Lloyd; Pfautsch, Debby) SATB,acap
  oct LAWSON 51348 $.30   (G936)

GIFT HE GAVE, THE see Sateren, Leland Bernhard

GIFT OF CHRISTMAS MORN, THE see Miller, J.

GIFT OF CHRISTMAS, THE see Schirmer, Rudolph
[E.]

GIFT OF LOVE, THE see Hopson, Hal H.

GIFT OF LOVE, THE see Posegate

GIFT OF MADRIGAL AND MOTETS, A VOL. II *sac/
  sec,CC60L,madrigal/mot,Renais
  (Slim, H. Colin) [Eng/It/Lat] SATB cloth
  UNIV.CH ISBN: 0-226-76271-8 $37.50, pap
  UNIV.CH ISBN: 0-226-76272-6 $7.50 (G937)

GIFT SUPREME, THE see Jacobus, Dale Asher

GIFT, THE see Eilers

GIFT, THE see Scherer, George

GIFT TO BE SIMPLE, THE
SATB oct STAFF 374 $.25   (G938)
(Williamson, W.) SA LEONARD-US 08017560 $.25
                                 (G939)

GIFTING, THE see Walton, William

GIFTS see Caldwell

GIFTS, THE see Averre, R.

GIFTS, THE see Thiman, Eric Harding

GIGOUT, [EUGENE] (1844-1925)
Ave Maria *BVM,mot
[Lat] 2pt wom cor oct DURAND s.p.   (G940)

Cantique A La Vierge Marie *BVM,hymn
cor,solo oct DURAND s.p.   (G941)

Deux Cantiques *see Noel; Pour La Fete Des
Voeux D'une Soeur De Charite   (G942)

Noel *Xmas,carol
[Fr] 3 eq voices,solo,pno/org oct DURAND
s.p. see from Deux Cantiques   (G943)

Pour La Fete Des Voeux D'une Soeur De Charite
*hymn
[Fr] 3 eq voices,solo,pno/org oct DURAND
s.p. see from Deux Cantiques   (G944)

Tantum Ergo *Commun,mot
[Lat] 3pt wom cor oct DURAND s.p.   (G945)

GILBERT, ANTHONY
Missa Brevis *Mass
[Lat] SATB SCHOTT 10929 s.p.   (G946)

GILBERT, J.R.
I Sing Of A Maiden
SSA THOMP.G G-304 s.p.   (G947)

One Holy Night
SATB,acap oct FOX PS124 $.25   (G948)

Pastorale
SATB,org,opt fl oct FOX PS165 $.30 (G949)

Psalm 150
SSAA THOMP.G G-306 s.p.   (G950)

Shepherd And The King, The
SSA (easy) OXFORD 83.016 $.35   (G951)

Sir Christemas
SATB,solo oct FOX PS131 $.25   (G952)

St. Francis' Prayer
SAB oct JUSKO 102 $.20   (G953)
(Pitcher, G.) SSA oct JUSKO 272 $.20 (G954)
(Pitcher, G.) SATB oct JUSKO 245 $.20 (G955)

When Christ Was Born
SSA THOMP.G G-305 s.p.   (G956)

GILBERT, NORMAN
Christ The Lord Is Risen! *Easter
SATB (easy) oct OXFORD 42.967 $.25 (G957)

Glory To Thee *Xmas/Epiph
SATB (easy) oct OXFORD 42.869 $.30 (G958)

Let All The World In Every Corner Sing
*Fest/Gen
SATB (easy) oct OXFORD 42.241 $.25 (G959)

O Praise God (Psalm 150) Gen/Thanks
SATB (easy) oct OXFORD 84.155 $.35 (G960)

One Holy Night
SATB PROWSE s.p.   (G961)
unis,pno,opt rec&perc PROWSE s.p.   (G962)

Praise, My Soul, The King Of Heaven *Gen
unis&SSAA oct OXFORD 44.212 $.30   (G963)

Praise To The Lord *Gen/Thanks
SAB (very easy) oct OXFORD 42.992 $.25
                                    (G964)

Psalm 150 *see O Praise God

Rejoice! The Lord Is King *Asc/Gen
2pt (easy) oct OXFORD 82.018 $.25   (G965)

Sir Christemas *Xmas,carol
mix cor,5 soli PROWSE s.p.   (G966)

Turn Back, O Man *Gen
SATB (very easy) oct OXFORD 42.831 $.25
                                    (G967)

GILBOA, JACOB
Jerusalem Chagall Windows, The *Heb
cor,inst sc ISRAELI 8002 s.p.   (G968)

GILCHRIST, WILLIAM WALLACE (1846-1916)
Except The Lord Build The House *Bibl
4pt mix cor,SBar soli oct SCHIRM.G 3127
$.25   (G969)

GILES, NATHANIEL (ca. 1558-1633)
Almighty Lord
see Anonymous, This Is The Day

Almighty Lord And God Of Love
see ALMIGHTY LORD AND GOD OF LOVE

God, Who As At This Time *Whitsun
SSAATB (med) oct OXFORD 42.899 $.65 (G970)

Out Of The Deep (Psalm 130) Gen/Lent
SSAATB (med easy) oct OXFORD 42.894 $.50
                                    (G971)

Psalm 130 *see Out Of The Deep

GILKYSON
Story Of The Creation, The
SSA oct STAFF 278 $.20   (G972)

GILL
Anthem For All Saints' Day *ASD,anthem
SATB oct SACRED S-34 $.35   (G973)

GILLAM
God Is Everywhere
2pt oct PLYMOUTH SC-505 $.25   (G974)

Snow Lay On The Ground, The
2pt oct PLYMOUTH SC-506 $.30   (G975)

GILLAM (cont'd.)
Watchman, Tell Us Of The Night
2pt oct PLYMOUTH SC-507 $.30   (G976)

GILLAM, R.L.
Lord Of All
4pt men cor oct SCHIRM.G 10160 $.25 (G977)

GILLET, [ERNEST] (1856-1940)
Gate Of The Year
SATB FLAMMER A 5090 $.25   (G978)

GILLETTE
Alleluia! Christ Is Risen
SATB KJOS 5085 $.30   (G979)

Be Thou My Vision
SATB KJOS 8006 $.30   (G980)

Church Year, The *CCU
unis FLAMMER GF5004 $1.25   (G981)

Little Shepherd, The
SA FLAMMER E5044 $.60   (G982)

O Sons And Daughters, Let Us Sing! *Easter
SATB/unis jr cor WARNER G1530 $.30 (G983)

On Calvary's Cross *cant
KJOS $1.25   (G984)

On The First Day Of The Week
SA FLAMMER E5068 $.60   (G985)

Resurrection According To Nicodemus, The
*cant
SATB FLAMMER A5189 $1.20   (G986)

Shepherd And His Lamb, The
SATB FLAMMER A5356 $.90   (G987)

Shepherds And Wise Men
SATB FLAMMER 5479 $.85   (G988)

Were You There?
SATB FLAMMER A 5230 $.30   (G989)

GILLETTE, JAMES ROBERT (1886-   )
Divine Mystery, The *Xmas,cant
mix cor&cong,narrator,pno voc sc SCHIRM.G
$.75   (G990)

Joseph Of Arimathea *Easter,cant
cor,narrator,org voc sc SCHIRM.G $.75
                                    (G991)

GILLIAM
Like A Root
(Johnson) SATB oct LILLENAS AN-5008 $.30
                                    (G992)

Mary Had A Boy Child
SSA,acap SHAWNEE B 356 $.30   (G993)

GILLIS, D.
Hymn And Prayer For Peace
SATB CRESCENDO $.30   (G994)

GIMME DAT OL'TIME RELIGION *spir,US
(Aubanel, Georges) "Donne-Moi Cette Religion"
[Eng/Fr] 3pt mix cor OUVRIERES s.p. (G995)

GIMME THAT OLD TIME RELIGION *spir
(Forsblad) SATB oct PRO ART 1861 $.22 (G996)

GINASTERA, ALBERTO (1916-   )
Lamentations Of Jeremiah
SATB,acap oct PRESSER 352-00103 $.60 (G997)

Psalm 150 *Op.5
[Lat] mix cor,orch BOOSEY cor pts $.75, sc
rental, ipr, voc sc $3.50   (G998)

GINES PEREZ, JUAN (1548-1612)
Domine Deus *mot
[Lat] 5pt mix cor,acap UNION ESP. 19342
s.p.   (G999)

Gloria Laus Et Honor *hymn
[Lat] 5pt mix cor,acap UNION ESP. 19341
s.p.   (G1000)

Miseremini Fideles Animarum *mot
[Lat] 5pt mix cor,acap UNION ESP. 19343
s.p.   (G1001)

Parce Mihi, Domine *mot
[Lat] 5pt mix cor,acap UNION ESP. 19344
s.p.   (G1002)

GIOISCANO I CUORI! see Branchina, Pietro

GIORDANO
Earth Is The Lord's, The
SATB,org/pno BOSTON 12129 $.40   (G1003)

GIORDANO, UMBERTO (1867-1948)
Thanks Be To Thee
(Goldman) SATB,T solo oct LAWSON 51744 $.35
                                    (G1004)

GIORGI, GIOVANNI
Gloria Et Honore
(Ehret) "Glory And Honor" [Eng/Lat] 4pt mix
cor,acap oct SCHIRM.G 11923 $.35   (G1005)

Glory And Honor *see Gloria Et Honore

GIORGI, PIERO
Dixit
see Piccola Sinfonia Corale

Magnificat
see Piccola Sinfonia Corale

Piccola Sinfonia Corale
SAT sc ZANIBON 4351 s.p., voc pt ZANIBON
4352-53 s.p.
contains: Dixit; Magnificat; Quasi Oliva
                                    (G1006)

Quasi Oliva
see Piccola Sinfonia Corale

GIOVANE DONNA see Marenzio, Luca

GIOVANELLI, [RUGGERO] (1560-1625)
Of My Soul Thou Delight *see Tu, Mentis
Delectatio

GIOVANELLI, [RUGGERO] (cont'd.)

Tu, Mentis Delectatio
(Roff, J.) "Of My Soul Thou Delight" SSA/
TTB,acap oct PRESSER 312-40239 $.25
                                    (G1007)

GIPPS, RUTH (1921-   )
Magnificat *Magnif
SSATB PROWSE s.p. contains also: Nunc
Dimittus (Nunc)   (G1008)

Nunc Dimittus
see Gipps, Ruth, Magnificat

GIRALDILLA see Benedito

GIRATTO, ALMERIGO
Messa In Onore Della B. Maddalena Di Canossa
*Mass
[Lat] unis,org sc ZANIBON 3546 s.p., cor
pts ZANIBON 3547 s.p.   (G1009)

GIRD ON THY SWORD see Holst, Gustav

GIRD YOURSELF WITH LAMENTATIONS see Pooler,
Frank

GIRNATIS, WALTER
Der Mond Ist Aufgegangen *Eve,cant
4pt mix cor&opt unis men cor,strings
MOSELER sc s.p., cor pts s.p., ipa
                                    (G1010)

GIROUST
Just Are Thy Ways, O Living God *see Watts

GIROUST, F.
Gaudete In Domino Semper *Mass
"Messe Du Sacre De Louis XVI" 3pt jr cor/
wom cor,org,orch LEMOINE voc sc s.p., cor
pts s.p., ipr   (G1011)

Messe Du Sacre De Louis XVI *see Gaudete In
Domino Semper

GIT ON BOARD
"Kommt Herein" see Funf Negro-Spirituals

GIT ON BOARD, LITTLE CHILDREN *spir
(Grant) boy cor oct BELWIN 1688 $.25 (G1012)
(Howorth) SA/TB oct BELWIN 2046 $.30 (G1013)

GIT ON BOARD, LITTLE CHILDREN see Wilson

GITANILLAS EN EL PORTAL DE BELEN see Martin
Pompey

GITTY- TIGGY TOUCHWOOD see Simpson, Kenneth

GIUSEPPE see Caldara, Antonio

GIV, O HIMMELSKE FADER see Berg, Gottfrid

GIVE A CHEER FOR THE LORD see Frackenpohl,
Arthur

GIVE ALMES OF THY GOODS see Tye, Christopher

GIVE EAR, O LORD see Schutz, Heinrich, Erhoere
Mich

GIVE EAR O LORD see Schutz, Heinrich, Erhore
Mich

GIVE EAR, O LORD see Trued, S. Clarence

GIVE EAR, O LORD, UNTO MY PRAYER see Bodycombe,
[Aneurin]

GIVE EAR, O LORD, UNTO MY PRAYER see Drozdov,
Anatol Nikolaievitch

GIVE EAR, O LORD, UNTO MY PRAY'R see Handel,
George Frideric

GIVE EAR, O YE HEAVENS see Shifrin, Seymour J.

GIVE EAR, O YE HEAVENS see Wood

GIVE EAR, OH LORD see Schutz, Heinrich

GIVE EAR TO MY PRAYER see Hovhaness, Alan

GIVE EAR TO MY PRAYER see Lekberg, Sven

GIVE EAR TO MY WORDS see Newbury, Kent A.

GIVE EAR TO MY WORDS, O LORD see Anderson,
[William H.]

GIVE EAR TO MY WORDS, O LORD see Blank, Allan

GIVE EAR TO MY WORDS, O LORD see Kay, Ulysses
Simpson

GIVE EAR TO MY WORDS, O LORD see Williams, R.

GIVE EAR TO OUR PRAYERS see Pasquet, Jean

GIVE EAR UNTO ME see Marcello

GIVE EAR UNTO ME see Marcello, Benedetto

GIVE EAR UNTO ME see Tkach

GIVE EAR UNTO MY PRAYER see Arcadelt, Jacob,
Ave Maria

GIVE EAR UNTO MY PRAYER see Marcello

GIVE GOD A CHANCE see Lister, Mosie

GIVE LAUD UNTO THE LORD *Asc/Thanks
(Bullock, Ernest) SATB (very easy) oct OXFORD
42.140 $.25   (G1014)

GIVE ME A FAITH see Bitgood, Roberta

GIVE ME A PERFECT HEART see Wooler, A.

GIVE ME JESUS
(Work) SATB oct LORENZ 9901 $.30   (G1015)

GIVE ME JESUS see Bacon, Ernst

GIVE ME JESUS see Burleigh, Henry Thacker

GIVE ME JESUS see Ferguson, Howard

GIVE ME JESUS see Williams

GIVE ME THAT OLD TIME RELIGION *spir
  (Ehret) SATB oct SPRATT 115 $.25   (G1016)
  (Richardson) SSA ALFRED 6204 $.35   (G1017)

GIVE ME THAT OLD-TIME RELIGION see Wild, Eric

GIVE ME THE WINGS OF FAITH see Hutchings,
  Arthur

GIVE ME THE WINGS OF FAITH see Leighton,
  Kenneth

GIVE ME THIS DAY see Peery, [Rob Roy]

GIVE ME THIS DAY see Perry, R.

GIVE PEACE, O GOD see Baker

GIVE PEACE, O GOD see Burroughs, B.

GIVE PRAISE ALL EARTHLY MEN see Saint-Saens,
  Camille

GIVE PRAISE TO GOD see Newbury

GIVE PRAISE TO GOD OUR KING
  (Hadley) SATB oct PRO ART 2352 $.25   (G1018)

GIVE PRAISE TO HIM see Wolf

GIVE PRAISE TO OUR GOD see Bach, Johann
  Sebastian

GIVE PRAISE TO THE LORD see Peloquin, C.
  Alexander, Laudate Dominum

GIVE PRAISE TO THE LORD see Van Hulse

GIVE REST, O CHRIST *Rembrnc,anthem
  (Parrat, Walter) mix cor oct NOVELLO
  50.0114.05 s.p.   (G1019)

GIVE THANKS see Lovelace, Austin C.

GIVE THANKS see Williams

GIVE THANKS AND PRAISE see Rogers

GIVE THANKS AND PRAISE TO GOD see Hadley

GIVE THANKS AND SING see Harris

GIVE THANKS TO GOD see Worp

GIVE THANKS TO THE LORD see Gertrude, Sr.

GIVE THANKS TO THE LORD see Roff, Joseph

GIVE THANKS TO THE LORD see Zaninelli, Luigi

GIVE THANKS UNTO OUR GOD see Pachelbel

GIVE THANKS UNTO OUR GOD see Pachelbel, Johann,
  Nun Danket Alle Gott

GIVE THANKS UNTO THE LORD see Mechem, Kirke

GIVE THANKS UNTO THE LORD see Starer, Robert

GIVE THANKS UNTO THE LORD see Tkach, D.

GIVE THE HUNGRY MAN THY BREAD see Bach, Johann
  Sebastian, Brich Dem Hungrigen Dein Brot

GIVE THE KING THY JUDGEMENTS see Weelkes,
  Thomas

GIVE THY SERVANT AN UNDERSTANDING HEART see
  Ford

GIVE THY SERVANT AN UNDERSTANDING HEART see
  Ford, Virgil T.

GIVE TO JEHOVAH see Schutz, Heinrich, Bringt
  Her Dem Herren

GIVE TO OUR GOD IMMORTAL PRAISE see Harris

GIVE TO OUR LEADERS AND ALL RULING POWERS see
  Schutz, Heinrich

GIVE TO THE LORD see Rocherolle

GIVE TO THE WINDS THY FEARS see Marshall, Jane
  M.

GIVE TO THE WORLD THY PEACE see Molitor, J.B.

GIVE TO US PEACE, LORD see Schutz, Heinrich

GIVE UNTO THE HUMBLE see Cherubini, Luigi

GIVE UNTO THE LORD see Elgar, Edward

GIVE UNTO THE LORD see Wilson, James R.

GIVE UNTO THE LORD, O YE MIGHTY see Cashmore,
  Donald

GIVE UNTO THE LORD, YE MIGHTY see Darst, W.
  Glenn

GIVE US FAITH FOR TODAY see Wilson, Harry
  [Robert]

GIVE US JOY FOR THIS NEW YEAR see Erlebach,
  Philipp Heinrich, Gott, Gib Gluck Zum Neuen
  Jahr

GIVE US, O LORD see Dexter, Harry

GIVE US PEACE see Mendelssohn-Bartholdy, Felix

GIVE US THE WINGS OF FAITH see Bullock, Ernest

GIVE US THE WINGS OF FAITH see Ratcliffe,
  Desmond

GIVE US THIS DAY see Leyden

GIVE YOURSELF TO JESUS see Fryson

GIVEN AT HERREN see Nilsson, Christian

GIVER OF ALL, WE THANK THEE see Lovelace,
  Austin C.

GIVER OF LIFE, THE *Gen/Whitsun
  cor&cong ROYAL s.p.   (G1020)

GIVER, THE see Todd, M. Flora

GJENDEM, J.J.
  Eit Barn Er Fodd I Betlehem
  [Norw] 3pt,org/inst LYCHE 21 s.p.   (G1021)

  Seg Til Sions Datter
  [Norw] 2pt LYCHE 15 s.p.   (G1022)

GLAD DIG, DU HELGA KRISTENHET see Berg,
  Gottfrid

GLAD DIG, DU KRISTI BRUD
  (Soderholm, Valdemar) 3pt wom cor/3pt jr cor,
  acap NORDISKA 5267 s.p.   (G1023)

GLAD DIG, DU KRISTI BRUD see Edmundh, Georg

GLAD DIG O KRISTENHET see Anonymous

GLAD HEARTS ADVENTURING see Shaw, Martin

GLAD NOEL, A *Xmas,carol,Fr
  (Ehret, W.) SATB,kbd (med easy) oct CONCORDIA
  98-1758 $.30   (G1024)

GLAD THAT I LIVE AM I see Shaw, Geoffrey
  [Turton]

GLAD THAT I'M A CHRISTIAN see Paris

GLAD TIDINGS see Greenfield, Marjorie H.

GLAD TIDINGS BRINGING *Xmas,carol,Pol
  (Kirk) SATB oct SHAPIRO SK 2069 $.30 (G1025)
  (Kirk) SSA oct SHAPIRO SK 3023 $.30   (G1026)
  (Kirk) 2pt oct SHAPIRO SK 4019 $.25   (G1027)
  (Kirk) SAB oct SHAPIRO SK 5012 $.30   (G1028)

GLAD TIDINGS OF GREAT JOY see Kountz

GLAD TIDINGS OF GREAT JOY see Wiley

GLADE JUL
  (Kjeldaas, Gunnar) [Norw] 3 eq voices,org
  LYCHE 58 s.p.   (G1029)

GLADE JUL see Gruber, Franz Xaver

GLADE JUL, HELLIGE JUL *Xmas
  (Beck, Thomas) mix cor MUSIKK 95C s.p. (G1030)

GLADELIG VIL VI HALLELUJA KVEDE see Kverno,
  Trond

GLADJENS MED MIG see Nilsson, Torsten

GLADLY FOR AYE WE ADORE HIM see Lekberg, Sven

GLADNESS IS OURS, HALLELUJAH! see Evans

GLADNESS OF EASTER, THE see Rogers

GLADSOME HYMN, A see Larson, Donald J.

GLADSOME HYMN OF PRAISE, A see Lovelace, Austin
  C.

GLANDFIELD, JOHN R.
  Let All The World *carol
  unis CRAMER 30 s.p.   (G1031)

GLANER, A.
  Psalm-Motette
  [Ger] mix cor,acap (med diff) HUG s.p.
                                       (G1032)

GLANTZ, YEHUDA LEIB
  Friday Evening Service *Sab-Eve
  (Loeb, D.) mix cor,cantor,org voc sc BOOSEY
  $7.50   (G1033)

  Hallel And Three Festivals
  (Loeb, D.) mix cor,cantor,org voc sc BOOSEY
  $10.00   (G1034)

  Prayer Modes (from Rinat Hakodesh)
  (Zohar Yehoshua) cor,cantor voc sc BOOSEY
  $6.00   (G1035)

GLARUM, L. STANLEY (1908-   )
  Alleluia! Sing Hosanna! *Easter
  SATB SCHMITT 898 $.35   (G1036)

  Ask, And It Shall Be Given You *anthem/Bibl
  4pt mix cor,acap oct SCHIRM.G 11033 $.20
                                       (G1037)
  3pt mix cor,acap oct SCHIRM.G 11344 $.25
                                       (G1038)
  3pt wom cor,acap oct SCHIRM.G 11343 $.25
                                       (G1039)
  Be Glad In The Lord
  SATB oct WALTON 2055 $.25   (G1040)

  Be Joyful
  SATB,acap oct FISCHER,C CM-6550 $.25
                                       (G1041)
  TTBB oct FISCHER,C CM-7249 $.25   (G1042)
  SSAA oct FISCHER,C CM-7442 $.30   (G1043)
  Be Merciful Unto Me, O God *anthem
  SSAB (easy) oct AUGSBURG 1201 $.22   (G1044)
  SATB (easy) oct AUGSBURG 1148 $.25   (G1045)
  Be Still And Know (Psalm 46)
  SATB oct BOURNE SG2 $.25   (G1046)

  Beatitudes, The
  SSAA SCHMITT 2558 $.25   (G1047)
  TTBB SCHMITT 3511 $.25   (G1048)
  dbl cor SCHMITT 1638 $.40   (G1049)
  Behold, Bless Ye The Lord (Psalm 34)
  SSATB oct BOURNE SG5 $.25   (G1050)

  Bless Thou The Lord, O My Soul
  SATB,acap WARNER 3693 $.30   (G1051)

  Blessed Are They
  4pt jr cor/SATB,acap (easy) FISCHER,C
  CM 7431 $.25   (G1052)

  Blessed Be The Lord
  SATB oct FISCHER,C CM-7517 $.25   (G1053)

GLARUM, L. STANLEY (cont'd.)

  Blessed Is The Man *Bibl
  4pt mix cor,acap oct SCHIRM.G 11318 $.30
                                       (G1054)
  3pt wom cor,opt org oct SCHIRM.G 11319 $.25
                                       (G1055)
  3pt mix cor,opt org oct SCHIRM.G 11317 $.25
                                       (G1056)
  Born For You *Xmas
  SATB SCHMITT SD6226 $.25   (G1057)

  Canticle Of Mary *see Magnificat

  Choral Prayer, A
  3pt mix cor,acap oct SCHIRM.G 10937 $.25
                                       (G1058)
  4pt mix cor,acap oct SCHIRM.G 10755 $.25
                                       (G1059)
  3pt wom cor oct SCHIRM.G 11009 $.25 (G1060)
  Clap Your Hands
  3pt jr cor/SAB (med) FISCHER,C CM 7525 $.20
                                       (G1061)
  Come Unto Me
  SATB,acap oct BOOSEY 5270 $.30   (G1062)
  SAB,acap oct BOOSEY 5480 $.30   (G1063)
  SSA,acap oct BOOSEY 5474 $.30   (G1064)
  Consider My Meditation
  SATB oct ELKAN-V 362-1273 $.30   (G1065)

  Create In Me A Clean Heart, O God (Psalm 51)
  Bibl
  SATB oct BOURNE SG4 $.25   (G1066)

  Dearest Jesu Draw Thou Near Me
  SATB,acap oct FISCHER,C CM-7654 $.25
                                       (G1067)
  Easter Carol *Easter
  SATB SCHMITT 6232 $.35   (G1068)

  Exalt Ye *Bibl
  4pt mix cor,acap oct SCHIRM.G 11225 $.25
                                       (G1069)
  Fanfare For Thanksgiving *Gen/Thanks,Bibl
  3pt mix cor,acap oct SCHIRM.G 11347 $.30
                                       (G1070)
  4pt mix cor,acap oct SCHIRM.G 10893 $.25
                                       (G1071)
  3pt wom cor,acap oct SCHIRM.G 11348 $.25
                                       (G1072)
  God Is Our Refuge *Gen
  SATB SCHMITT 1667 $.35   (G1073)

  God Of All Nations
  SATB,opt band KJOS 5116 $.30   (G1074)

  God That Made The World
  SATB oct WALTON 2030 $.25   (G1075)

  Great Is The Lord *Gen
  SATB SCHMITT 15009 $.40   (G1076)

  He That Dwelleth *Gen
  dbl cor SCHMITT 1755 $.30   (G1077)

  I Love The Lord (Psalm 116)
  SATB oct BOURNE SG3 $.25   (G1078)

  I Saw A Stranger Yestreen
  2pt mix cor,acap oct SCHIRM.G 11529 $.25
                                       (G1079)
  I Sought The Lord
  SATB KJOS 5434 $.30   (G1080)

  I Will Extol Thee, O Lord *Gen
  SATB SCHMITT 1726 $.25   (G1081)
  TTBB SCHMITT 3512 $.35   (G1082)
  I Will Lift Mine Eyes (Psalm 121)
  SSAATTBB oct BOURNE SG6 $.25   (G1083)

  I Will Love Thee, O Lord *Bibl
  4pt mix cor,acap oct SCHIRM.G 10992 $.25
                                       (G1084)
  In Thee Lord (Psalm 31)
  SATB oct BOURNE SG1 $.25   (G1085)

  Let All People Praise Thee
  SATB FLAMMER A 5462 $.30   (G1086)

  Let Them Shout For Joy
  SATB,acap oct FISCHER,C CM-7659 $.25
                                       (G1087)
  Little Jesus, Sweetly Sleep *Xmas
  SATB,acap (med easy) SOUTHERN $.35   (G1088)
  SATB SCHMITT 6230 $.35   (G1089)
  Lord Hosanna In The Highest
  4pt mix cor,acap oct SCHIRM.G 10903 $.30
                                       (G1090)
  3pt mix cor,acap,opt org/pno oct SCHIRM.G
  11548 $.25   (G1091)
  Lord Liveth, The
  SATB,acap WARNER W3696 $.30   (G1092)

  Magnificat *Bibl/Magnif
  "Canticle Of Mary" 4pt mix cor,org oct
  SCHIRM.G 11832 $.35   (G1093)
  "Canticle Of Mary" unis,org oct SCHIRM.G
  11831 $.30   (G1094)
  Make A Joyful Noise Unto God *Gen
  SATB SCHMITT 1682 $.45   (G1095)

  Master, Speak! Thy Servant Heareth
  SATB (easy) ABINGDON APM-262 $.18   (G1096)

  My Soul Doth Wait On God
  SATB KJOS 5444 $.30   (G1097)

  O Come, Little Children *Xmas
  SATB/unis/jr cor SCHMITT 1677 $.30   (G1098)

  O Sing Unto The Lord A New Song *Gen
  dbl cor SCHMITT 1791 $.25   (G1099)

  Offer Unto God Thanksgiving *anthem
  SATB (easy) oct AUGSBURG 1242 $.22   (G1100)

  Our Father Who Art In Heaven
  SATB KJOS 5495 $.30   (G1101)

  Peace I Leave With You
  SATB FLAMMER A 5500 $.25   (G1102)

GLARUM, L. STANLEY (cont'd.)

Praise To Him, Alleluia
SATB KJOS 5445 $.35 (G1103)

Praise Ye Forever
SATB KJOS 5496 $.35 (G1104)

Praise Ye The Lord (Psalm 148) Bibl
4pt mix cor,acap oct SCHIRM.G 11588 $.40 (G1105)

SATB,acap oct FISCHER,C CM-7291 $.25 (G1106)

Psalm 31 *see In Thee Lord

Psalm 34 *see Behold, Bless Ye The Lord

Psalm 46 *see Be Still And Know

Psalm 51 *see Create In Me A Clean Heart, O God

Psalm 116 *see I Love The Lord

Psalm 121 *see I Will Lift Mine Eyes

Psalm 148 *see Praise Ye The Lord

Rejoice In The Lord *Bibl
4pt mix cor,org oct SCHIRM.G 11526 $.35 (G1107)

Search Me, O God
SATB oct FISCHER,C CM-7638 $.25 (G1108)

Sing Aloud Unto God
4pt mix cor,acap oct SCHIRM.G 11288 $.25 (G1109)

3pt mix cor,acap oct SCHIRM.G 11289 $.30 (G1110)

3pt wom cor,acap oct SCHIRM.G 11290 $.25 (G1111)

Sing Praises
SSAA SCHMITT 2557 $.35 (G1112)
SAB/SSAB SCHMITT 8013 $.30 (G1113)
SATB SCHMITT 1656 $.35 (G1114)
TTBB SCHMITT 3510 $.35 (G1115)

Sought The Lord
SATB oct ELKAN-V 362-1231 $.25 (G1116)

They That Know Thy Name
SATB,acap oct BELWIN 64247 $.30 (G1117)
TTBB,acap oct BELWIN 64312 $.30 (G1118)
SSAA oct BELWIN 60735 $.25 (G1119)

Thou Shalt Love The Lord Thy God
SATB oct BOURNE SG-7 $.25 (G1120)

Thy Word Is A Lamp *Bibl
4pt mix cor,acap oct SCHIRM.G 11224 $.25 $.25 (G1121)
4pt mix cor,opt org/pno oct SCHIRM.G 11549 $.25 $.25 (G1122)

Unto Thee Will I Sing *Bibl
4pt mix cor,acap oct SCHIRM.G 11053 $.25 (G1123)

3pt mix cor,acap oct SCHIRM.G 11341 $.25 (G1124)

3pt wom cor,acap oct SCHIRM.G 11342 $.25 (G1125)

We Give Thanks To Thee *Bibl
3pt mix cor oct SCHIRM.G 11292 $.25 (G1126)
3pt wom cor oct SCHIRM.G 11293 $.25 (G1127)
4pt mix cor oct SCHIRM.G 11294 $.25 (G1128)

What Is Man?
SATB oct ELKAN-V 362-1246 $.30 (G1129)

When One Knows Thee
4pt mix cor,acap oct SCHIRM.G 11823 $.30 (G1130)

Who Knoweth God
SATB oct WALTON 2162 $.25 (G1131)

GLASER
O For A Thousand Tongues
SATB oct FISCHER,C CM-7424 $.25 (G1132)

GLASER, T.
Flamme Empor!
(Nagel, W.) [Lat] men cor,acap (med) HUG s.p. (G1133)

GLASS, P.
Last Invocation, The
SATB oct ELKAN-V 362-1248 $.25 (G1134)

GLATZ
Cradle-Song Of The Shepherds *see Wiegenlied Der Hirten

Wiegenlied Der Hirten
(Davison, A.) "Cradle-Song Of The Shepherds" SATB,acap SCHIRM.EC 1728 $.30 (G1135)

GLAUBE see Bornefeld, Helmut

GLAUBE IST EIN BAUM see Ruppel, Paul Ernst

GLAUBE LIEBET see Bach, Johann Sebastian, Ich Glaube, Lieber Herr, Hilf Meinem Unglauben

GLAUBIGE SEEL, SCHAU, DEIN HERR UND KONIG WILL KOMMEN see Pepping, Ernst

GLAZER, CARL
O For A Thousand Tongues *hymn
(Hustad, Don) SATB/SAB ALLANS 453 s.p. (G1136)
(Thompson, Van Denman) SATB ALLANS 447 s.p. (G1137)

Oh, For A Thousand Tongues *hymn
(Gerig) SATB oct LILLENAS AN-2317 $.30 (G1138)

GLED EDER I HERREN see Gulliksen, Harald

GLEICH WIE DER REGEN see Bach, Johann Sebastian

GLEICH WIE DER REGEN UND SCHNEE see Bach, Johann Sebastian

GLEICH WIE DER REGEN UND SCHNEE VOM HIMMEL FALLT see Bach, Johann Sebastian

GLEICH WIE MICH MEIN VATER GESANDT HAT see Ruppel, Paul Ernst

GLEICHNIS VOM KONIG, DER RECHNEN WOLLTE see Schieri, Fritz

GLEICHNIS VOM SPLITTER UND BALKEN see Schieri, Fritz

GLEICHNIS VOM VERLORENEN SCHAF UND VOM VERLORENEN GROSCHEN see Wenzel, Eberhard

GLEICHNIS VOM WEINBERG see Schieri, Fritz

GLEICHWIE DER BLITZ AUSGEHET see Franck, Melchior

GLEICHWIE DER BLITZ AUSGEHET see Vulpius, Melchior

GLEICHWIE MOSES IN DER WUSTE see Franck, Melchior

GLETLE, JOHANN MELCHIOR (1626-1683)
Geistliche Gesange 1 *Gen
(Schanzlin, Hans Peter) [Lat] ATB,cont (med) BAREN. BA 3454 sc $1.75, cor pts $1.50
contains: Salve, Regina; Tota Pulchra Es (G1139)

Magnificat *Magnif
(Schanzlin, Hans Peter; Zulauf, Ernst) [Lat] SSATB,opt 5 soli,cont,strings,opt bsn,vcl (med) cor pts BAREN. BA 3452 $1.00, ipr (G1140)

Salve, Regina
see Geistliche Gesange 1

Tota Pulchra Es
see Geistliche Gesange 1

GLINKA, MIKHAIL IVANOVITCH (1804-1857)
Cherubim Song
mix cor,acap oct SCHIRM.G 5216 $.25 (G1141)
(Baldwin) mix cor,acap oct SCHIRM.G 9025 $.25 (G1142)

Holy, Holy, Holy!
(Howorth) SATB,acap oct PRO ART 1016 $.25 (G1143)

Lord To Thee Our Hearts Are Raised *Gen
(Tkach) SSA SCHMITT 323 $.30 (G1144)
(Tkach) SATB SCHMITT 840 $.25 (G1145)

GLOCKENKANTATE see Rein, Walter

GLOCKENSTUNDE see Lehman, Siegfried

GLOIRE A DIEU see Mussorgsky, Modest

GLOIRE AU TRESHAUT see Heidet, Le R. P.

GLOIRE IMMORTELLE DE NOS AIEUX see Gounod, Charles Francois

GLOIRE, LOUANGE, HONNEUR A DIEU see Bach, Johann Sebastian

GLORIA
(Schmid, W.) men cor,acap HUG s.p.
contains: Ehre Sei Dem Herrn; Nobody Knows De Trouble (G1146)

GLORIA *spir
(Schmid, Walter) [Eng] mix cor,acap (easy) HUG s.p. (G1147)

GLORIA see Albrechtsberger, Johann Georg

GLORIA see Bach, Johann Sebastian, Gloria In Excelsis Deo

GLORIA see Baden, Conrad

GLORIA see Beyer, Frank Michael

GLORIA see Brown, Christopher

GLORIA see Bruckner, Anton

GLORIA see Brunner, Adolf

GLORIA! see Burroughs, Bob

GLORIA see Buxtehude, Dietrich

GLORIA see Chaminade, Cecile

GLORIA see Christiansen

GLORIA see Clapisson, Antoine

GLORIA see Des Prez, Josquin

GLORIA see Dufay, Guillaume

GLORIA see Dvorak, Antonin

GLORIA see Edlund, Lars

GLORIA see Farmer, [Henry George]

GLORIA see Freed

GLORIA see Gardner

GLORIA see Gretchaninov, Alexander Tikhonovitch

GLORIA see Hallnas, Hilding

GLORIA see Hassler, Hans Leo

GLORIA see Haydn, (Franz) Joseph

GLORIA see Hoag, Charles K.

GLORIA see Hovhaness, Alan

GLORIA see Johnson, Sidney

GLORIA see Kennedy, John Brodbin

GLORIA see Kerle, Jacobus de

GLORIA see Knighton

GLORIA see Korte, Karl

GLORIA see Kubizek, Augustinian

GLORIA see Larsson, Lars-Erik

GLORIA see Latham, [William P.]

GLORIA see Lee, J.

GLORIA see Lotti, Antonio

GLORIA see Miller

GLORIA see Mouton, Jean

GLORIA see Mozart, Wolfgang Amadeus

GLORIA see Newbury, Kent A.

GLORIA see Nieuwenhoven, H. v.

GLORIA see Palestrina, Giovanni

GLORIA see Palma

GLORIA see Peloquin, C. Alexander

GLORIA see Pepping, Ernst

GLORIA see Persichetti, Vincent

GLORIA see Pfautsch, Lloyd

GLORIA see Poulenc, Francis

GLORIA see Ramirez

GLORIA see Ramirez, Ariel

GLORIA see Rickard, Jeffrey

GLORIA see Runback, Albert

GLORIA see Saint-Saens, Camille

GLORIA see Schaffer, Robert J.

GLORIA see Schubert, Franz (Peter)

GLORIA see Schwartz, Gerhard von

GLORIA see Smith, R.

GLORIA see Somers, Harry Stewart

GLORIA see Soraas, Lars

GLORIA see Swenson

GLORIA see Taylor, Clifford

GLORIA see Thompson, Randall

GLORIA see Track, Gerhard

GLORIA see Vivaldi, Antonio

GLORIA see Walton, William

GLORIA see Washburn, Robert

GLORIA see Williams, D.

GLORIA A DIOS see Lopez, Almagro

GLORIA A MARIA see Benedito

GLORIA CONCERTATA see Monteverdi, Claudio

GLORIA DEO see Willan, Healey

GLORIA DEO, BOOK I see Johnson, David N.

GLORIA DEO, BOOK II see Johnson, David N.

GLORIA DEO PER IMMENSA SAECULA see Willan, Healey

GLORIA ET HONORE see Giorgi, Giovanni

GLORIA "FROM THE MASS" see Ringwald, [Roy]

GLORIA, GLORIA *Xmas
(Caldwell) SSAA SCHMITT 2564 $.35 (G1148)
(Caldwell) SATB SCHMITT 1716 $.45 (G1149)

GLORIA IN EXCELSIS *Xmas,carol,Czech
see Czech Christmas Carols
(Ekman, L.; Tyffe, E.) unis oct PRESSER 332-14846 $.30 (G1150)
(Glaser, V.) "Rumors Are A-Flying" SATB,acap SCHIRM.EC 2606 $.20 (G1151)

GLORIA IN EXCELSIS see Bach, Johann Sebastian

GLORIA IN EXCELSIS see Bock, Fred

GLORIA IN EXCELSIS see Cockshott, Gerald Wilfred

GLORIA IN EXCELSIS see Farmer

GLORIA IN EXCELSIS see Franck, Cesar

GLORIA IN EXCELSIS see Haydn, (Franz) Joseph

GLORIA IN EXCELSIS see Jolley

GLORIA IN EXCELSIS see Lotti, Antonio

GLORIA IN EXCELSIS see Mendelssohn-Bartholdy, Felix

GLORIA IN EXCELSIS see Mozart, Wolfgang Amadeus

GLORIA IN EXCELSIS see Pepping, Ernst

GLORIA IN EXCELSIS see Thiman, Eric Harding

GLORIA IN EXCELSIS see Vivaldi, Antonio

GLORIA IN EXCELSIS see Weelkes, Thomas

GLORIA IN EXCELSIS DEO *Xmas,carol,Pol
(Barthelson) SATB,opt 4brass oct SHAPIRO SK 2040 $.25, ipa (G1152)
(Barthelson) SAB,opt 4brass oct SHAPIRO SK 5016 $.25, ipa (G1153)
(Barthelson) 2pt,opt 4brass oct SHAPIRO SK 4023 $.25, ipa (G1154)
(Barthelson) SSA,opt 4brass oct SHAPIRO SK 3011 $.25, ipa (G1155)

GLORIA IN EXCELSIS DEO see Bach

GLORIA IN EXCELSIS DEO see Bach, Johann Sebastian

GLORIA IN EXCELSIS DEO see Beverst

GLORIA IN EXCELSIS DEO see Cain, Noble

GLORIA IN EXCELSIS DEO see Calvisius, Sethus

GLORIA IN EXCELSIS DEO see Cooper, R.

GLORIA IN EXCELSIS DEO see Cooper, Robert

GLORIA IN EXCELSIS DEO see Ekman, L.

GLORIA IN EXCELSIS DEO see Fegers, Karl

GLORIA IN EXCELSIS DEO see Gounod, Charles Francois

GLORIA IN EXCELSIS DEO see Hallock, Peter

GLORIA IN EXCELSIS DEO see Hovland, Egil

GLORIA IN EXCELSIS DEO see Kreter

GLORIA IN EXCELSIS DEO! see Kropczynski

GLORIA IN EXCELSIS DEO see Lorenz

GLORIA IN EXCELSIS DEO see McCowen

GLORIA IN EXCELSIS DEO see Mozart, Wolfgang Amadeus

GLORIA IN EXCELSIS DEO see Pevernage, Andries

GLORIA IN EXCELSIS DEO see Richolson

GLORIA IN EXCELSIS DEO see Schafstall, Joh.

GLORIA IN EXCELSIS DEO see Shaw, Martin

GLORIA IN EXCELSIS DEO see Spraugue, Richard L.

GLORIA IN EXCELSIS DEO see Stoker

GLORIA IN EXCELSIS DEO see Thiman, Eric Harding

GLORIA IN EXCELSIS DEO see Van Dyke

GLORIA IN EXCELSIS DEO see Victoria, Tomas Luis de

GLORIA IN EXCELSIS DEO see Vivaldi, Antonio

GLORIA IN EXCELSIS DEO see Weelkes, Thomas

GLORIA IN EXCELSIS DEO see Whitney

GLORIA IN EXCELSIS DEO! [CHORALE] see Bach, Johann Sebastian

GLORIA-IN MEMORIAM see Walker, George

GLORIA LAUS see Ferrari, Giovanni

GLORIA LAUS see Rodella, Sante

GLORIA LAUS ET HONOR see Gines Perez, Juan

GLORIA, LAUS ET HONOR see Vulpius, Melchior

GLORIA OF THE BELLS see Peloquin, C. Alexander

GLORIA PATRI see Dulichius, Philippus

GLORIA PATRI see Franck, Cesar

GLORIA PATRI see Lassus, Roland de (Orlandus)

GLORIA PATRI see Luboff, Norman

GLORIA PATRI see Palestrina, Giovanni

GLORIA PATRI see Pergolesi, Giovanni Battista

GLORIA PATRI see Purcell, Henry

GLORIA PATRI see Tallis, Thomas

GLORIA PATRI see Young

GLORIA PATRI see Zagatti, Francesco

GLORIA PATRI QUI CREAVIT NOS see Blow, John

GLORIA SEI DIR GESUNGEN see Bach, Johann Sebastian

GLORIA SEI DIR GESUNGEN see Nicolai, Philipp

"GLORIA" SING ALL OUR VOICES see Bach, Johann Sebastian, Gloria Sei Dir Gesungen

GLORIA! SING GLORIA! see Hood, Boyde W.

GLORIA, SONG OF SIMEON see Sigurbjornsson, Thorkell

GLORIA TIBI see Clemens, Jacobus

GLORIA TIBI, DOMINE see Gordon, Philip

GLORIA TIBI TRINITAS see Taverner, John

GLORIA TO GOD ON HIGH see Thygerson

GLORIFICATION see Christiansen, F. Melius

GLORIFY HIS NAME see Baines, W.

GLORIFY THE LORD see Pergolesi, Giovanni Battista, Gloria Patri

GLORIFY THE LORD WITH ME see Berger, Jean

GLORIOSA VIRGINUM see Pierobon, Giuseppe

GLORIOUS AND POWERFUL GOD see Wood, Charles

GLORIOUS ART THOU see Klaus

GLORIOUS BE THY NAME FOREVER see Farmer, Gloria In Excelsis

GLORIOUS CREATION see Frank, Marcel [Gustave]

GLORIOUS FOREVER see Rachmaninoff, Sergey Vassilievitch

GLORIOUS FOREVER see Young

GLORIOUS FREEDOM *CC129U, hymn
cong cmplt ed LILLENAS MB-053 $.60   (G1156)

GLORIOUS IN HEAVEN ARE THE SOULS OF ALL SAINTS see Victoria, Tomas Luis de

GLORIOUS IS THE LORD ALMIGHTY see Haydn, (Franz) Joseph

GLORIOUS IS THE SON OF MARY see Staley

GLORIOUS IS THY HOLY NAME see Young

GLORIOUS IS THY NAME see Mozart, Wolfgang Amadeus, Gloria In Excelsis

GLORIOUS IS THY NAME see Tschesnokoff, P.I.

GLORIOUS KING TRIUMPHANT TODAY see Kozinski, [David B.]

GLORIOUS MESSAGE, THE see Krieger

GLORIOUS MOMENT, THE see Beethoven, Ludwig van

GLORIOUS MYSTERY SUBLIME see Gabrieli, Giovanni, O Magnum Mysterium

GLORIOUS SONG, THE see Harris

GLORIOUS THINGS OF THEE ARE SPOKEN
(Coggin) 4pt mix cor,acap,org/pno oct
SCHIRM.G 11512 $.25   (G1157)

GLORIOUS THINGS OF THEE ARE SPOKEN see Angell, Warren M.

GLORIOUS THINGS OF THEE ARE SPOKEN see Anonymous

GLORIOUS THINGS OF THEE ARE SPOKEN see Cain, Noble

GLORIOUS THINGS OF THEE ARE SPOKEN see Coggin, Elwood

GLORIOUS THINGS OF THEE ARE SPOKEN see Durant, C.

GLORIOUS THINGS OF THEE ARE SPOKEN see Haydn, (Franz) Joseph

GLORIOUS THY WORK, O LORD OF HOSTS see Evans, Roderick

GLORY see Cadman, [Charles Wakefield]

GLORY see Hassler, Hans Leo, Gloria

GLORY see Rimsky-Korsakov, Nikolai, Slaua

GLORY ABOVE THE HEAVENS see Davis, Katherine K.

GLORY! ALL GLORY IN THE HEAVENS! *Xmas
(Gehring, L.) SATB,acap oct PRESSER MC393
$.25   (G1158)

GLORY AND HONOR see Bock, F.

GLORY AND HONOR see Giorgi, Giovanni, Gloria Et Honore

GLORY AND HONOR see Rachmaninoff, Sergey Vassilievitch

GLORY AND HONOR ARE BEFORE HIM see Bach

GLORY AND HONOR ARE BEFORE HIM see Tkach

GLORY AND PEACE AND MAJESTY see Gallus, W.E.

GLORY AND PRAISE see Bortniansky, Dimitri Stepanovitch

GLORY AND PRAISE AND DOMINION BY THINE see Webber, Lloyd

GLORY AND TRIUMPH see Berlioz, Hector

GLORY AND TRIUMPH see Hammerschmidt, Andreas

GLORY AND WORSHIP see Bach, Johann Sebastian

GLORY AND WORSHIP ARE BEFORE HIM see Purcell, Henry

GLORY AROUND HIS HEAD, THE see Meyerowitz, Jan

GLORY BE see Hathaway, Charles

GLORY BE TO GOD see Berger, Jean

GLORY BE TO GOD see Bruckner, Anton

GLORY BE TO GOD see Pinkham, Daniel

GLORY BE TO GOD see Rachmaninoff, Sergey Vassilievitch

GLORY BE TO GOD see Schubert, Franz (Peter)

GLORY BE TO GOD see Strokine

GLORY BE TO GOD see Tkach, P.

GLORY BE TO GOD ALMIGHTY see Bach, Johann Sebastian

GLORY BE TO GOD ON HIGH see Davis, Katherine K.

GLORY BE TO GOD ON HIGH see Kirk

GLORY BE TO GOD ON HIGH see Latham, [William P.]

GLORY BE TO GOD ON HIGH see Lovelace, Austin C.

GLORY BE TO GOD ON HIGH see Mueller, Carl F.

GLORY BE TO GOD ON HIGH see Thompson, Randall, Gloria

GLORY BE TO GOD ON HIGH see Victoria, Tomas Luis de

GLORY BE TO GOD THE FATHER see Isch

GLORY BE TO GOD THE FATHER see Kirk

GLORY BE TO HIM see Wolf

GLORY BE TO JESUS see Schutz, Heinrich, Ehre Sei Dir, Christe

GLORY BE TO THE FATHER see Bach, Johann Sebastian, Lob Und Preis Sei Gott Dem Vater

GLORY BE TO THE FATHER see Lekberg, Sven

GLORY BE TO THE FATHER see Schutz, Heinrich, Ehre Sei Dem Vater

GLORY BE TO THEE see Pergolesi, Giovanni Battista

GLORY BE TO THEE see Tschesnokoff, P.I.

GLORY, GLORY, HALLELUJAH see McLin

GLORY, HALLELUJAH
see Street Corner Spirituals

GLORY HALLELUJAH JUBILEE see Turner, Lee

GLORY, HALLELUJAH! TO DE NEW BORN KING see Kittleson

GLORY! HEAR THE SONG see Stanton, R.

GLORY IN HIS HOLY NAME see Williams

GLORY IN THE CHURCH see Prentice, Fred

GLORY IN THE HIGHEST see Davis, Katherine K.

GLORY IN THY PERFECT LOVE see Williams

GLORY IS THINE, THE see Bitgood, Roberta

GLORY, LAUD, HONOR see Rockwood, Gay Hyland

GLORY, LOVE AND PRAISE AND HONOUR see Harris, William Henry

GLORY NOW TO THEE BE GIVEN see Bach, Johann Sebastian

GLORY OF GOD IN NATURE, THE see Beethoven, Ludwig van

GLORY OF GOD IN NATURE, THE see Beethoven, Ludwig van, Die Ehre Gottes In Der Natur

GLORY OF GOD, THE see Caldwell, Mary [Elizabeth]

GLORY OF JEHOVAH IS RISEN UPON THEE, THE see Lindroff

GLORY OF OUR KING, THE see Wood, Dale

GLORY OF THE CROSS see Hadler

GLORY OF THE CROSS, THE *Easter/Pageant,cant
LORENZ $1.00   (G1159)

GLORY OF THE LORD see Kiplinger

GLORY OF THE LORD, THE see Goode, Jack C.

GLORY OF THE STAR, THE see Landon

GLORY, PRAISE AND POWER see Mozart, Wolfgang Amadeus, Litanie De Venerabili Altaris Sacramento

GLORY, PRAISE AND POWER see Mozart, Wolfgang Amadeus, Litany In B Flat

GLORY TO GOD see Schroth

GLORY TO GOD *Xmas
see Three Carols
SSA/SATB/SAB/SA/TB BIG3 $.35   (G1160)
(Shoremount) SATB&opt jr cor oct GRAY
GCMR 2050 $.25   (G1161)

GLORY TO GOD see Bach, Johann Christoph Friedrich, Ehre Sei Gott In Der Hohe

GLORY TO GOD see Bach, Johann Sebastian

GLORY TO GOD see Bampton, R.

GLORY TO GOD see Bortniansky, Dimitri Stepanovitch

GLORY TO GOD see Cain, Noble

GLORY TO GOD see Feldman, James

GLORY TO GOD see Goodale, R.L.

GLORY TO GOD see Gounod, Charles Francois

GLORY TO GOD see Gretchaninov, Alexander Tikhonovitch

GLORY TO GOD see Handel, George Frideric

GLORY TO GOD see Heller

GLORY TO GOD see Henderson

GLORY TO GOD see Hovhaness, Alan

GLORY TO GOD see Kimmell

GLORY TO GOD see Kirk, Theron W.

GLORY TO GOD see Lewis, John Leo

GLORY TO GOD see Liebhold

GLORY TO GOD see Mozart, Wolfgang Amadeus, Ehre Sei Gott

GLORY TO GOD see Palestrina, Giovanni, Gloria Patri

GLORY TO GOD see Prentice, Fred

GLORY TO GOD see Purcell, Henry, Gloria Patri

GLORY TO GOD see Rachmaninoff, Sergey Vassilievitch

GLORY TO GOD see Rogers

GLORY TO GOD see Schubert, Franz (Peter), Das Grosse Hallelujah

GLORY TO GOD see Schutz, Heinrich

GLORY TO GOD see Sullivan, Sir Arthur Seymour

GLORY TO GOD see Sutherland

GLORY TO GOD see Tchesnokov, Pavel Grigorievitch

GLORY TO GOD see Whear, Paul William

GLORY TO GOD IN HEAVEN see Bortniansky, Dimitri Stepanovitch

GLORY TO GOD IN HEAVEN see Kozinski, [David B.]

GLORY TO GOD IN HIGHEST see Saint-Saens, Camille

GLORY TO GOD IN THE HIGHEST *Xmas/Fest/Gen
SATB ALLANS 459 s.p.   (G1162)
SATB,opt band KJOS 5379 $.40   (G1163)
(Buszin, W.E.) SSATB,acap (med easy) oct
CONCORDIA 98-1166 $.25   (G1164)

GLORY TO GOD IN THE HIGHEST see Bach, Johann Christoph Friedrich, Ehre Sei Gott In Der Hohe

GLORY TO GOD IN THE HIGHEST see Bach, Johann Sebastian, Gloria In Excelsis Deo

GLORY TO GOD IN THE HIGHEST see Bortniansky, Dimitri Stepanovitch

GLORY TO GOD IN THE HIGHEST see Charpentier, Marc-Antoine

GLORY TO GOD IN THE HIGHEST see Cooke, S.C.

GLORY TO GOD IN THE HIGHEST see Copley, R. Evan

GLORY TO GOD IN THE HIGHEST see Creston, Paul

GLORY TO GOD IN THE HIGHEST see DePue

GLORY TO GOD IN THE HIGHEST see Elliott

GLORY TO GOD IN THE HIGHEST see Garlick, Anthony

GLORY TO GOD IN THE HIGHEST see Geisler, Johan C.

GLORY TO GOD IN THE HIGHEST see Hallett, John C.

GLORY TO GOD IN THE HIGHEST see Hammerschmidt, Andreas

GLORY TO GOD IN THE HIGHEST see Mueller, Carl F.

GLORY TO GOD IN THE HIGHEST see Pergolesi, Giovanni Battista, Gloria Patri

GLORY TO GOD IN THE HIGHEST see Pergolesi, Giovanni Battista, Hosanna In Excelsis

GLORY TO GOD IN THE HIGHEST see Schubert, Franz (Peter)

GLORY TO GOD IN THE HIGHEST see Thiman, Eric Harding

GLORY TO GOD IN THE HIGHEST see Thompson, Randall

GLORY TO GOD IN THE HIGHEST see Track, Gerhard

GLORY TO GOD IN THE HIGHEST see Whitford

GLORY TO GOD IN THE HIGHEST see Willan, Healey

GLORY TO GOD ON HIGH see Coggin, Elwood

GLORY TO GOD ON HIGH see Milgrove

GLORY TO GOD ON HIGH see Prout, [Ebenezer]

GLORY TO GOD ON HIGH see Silcher

GLORY TO GOD (THE CHRISTMAS STORY) see Nelson, Ronald A.

GLORY TO GOD THE CREATOR see Parris, Herman M.

GLORY TO HIS NAME see Evans

GLORY TO OUR KING see Stewart

GLORY TO OUR RISEN KING see Butler

GLORY TO THAT NEW-BORN KING *Xmas
(Work, J.) SATB,acap oct PRESSER 312-21208
$.30   (G1165)

GLORY TO THE FATHER see Pergolesi, Giovanni Battista, Gloria Patri

GLORY TO THE FATHER see Saint-Saens, Camille, Gloria

GLORY TO THE FATHER GIVE
see Three General Choruses

GLORY TO THE FATHER GIVE see Willan, Healey

GLORY TO THE INCARNATE GOD *Xmas,carol,Aus
(Ehret, W.) SAB PROWSE CC3 s.p.   (G1166)

GLORY TO THE INCARNATE LORD
(Ehret) SAB oct FOX CC3 $.25   (G1167)

GLORY TO THE KING OF KINGS *hymn
(Thompson, Van Denman) SATB ALLANS 359 s.p.
(G1168)

GLORY TO THE KING OF KINGS see Blake, G.

GLORY TO THE KING OF KINGS see Thompson

GLORY TO THE NEW-BORN KING *Xmas,carol,Ger
(Ehret, Walter) SA FRANK F-617 $.35   (G1169)

GLORY TO THE NEWBORN KING *Xmas,carol
(Luboff, Norman) SATB,winds,perc oct WALTON
2751 $.50, cmplt ed WALTON 2751A $6.00
contains: Hark The Herald Angels Sing; Joy
To The World; O Little Town Of Bethlehem
(G1170)

GLORY TO THE NEWBORN KING see Pergolesi, Giovanni Battista

GLORY TO THEE see Clemens, Jacobus, Gloria Tibi

GLORY TO THEE see Gilbert, Norman

GLORY TO THEE MY GOD THIS NIGHT see Gounod, Charles Francois

GLORY TO THEE MY GOD THIS NIGHT see Tallis, Thomas

GLORY TO THY HOLY NAME see Pasquet, Jean

GLORY TRAIN see Eager, Mary Anne

GLOSSNER, HERBERT (1932-   )
Singt Dem Herrn Ein Neues Lied *Gen
[Ger] unis,acap (easy) BOSSE BE 259 s.p.   (G1171)

GLOUCESTERSHIRE WASSAIL *Xmas,carol,Eng
see Bring Your Torches Jeannette Isabella
see Six Two-Part Carols
see Two Wassails
unis/SATB (easy) OXFORD 08.031 $.15   (G1172)
(Luboff, Norman) SATB oct WALTON 3049 $.30   (G1173)

GLOVER, R.F.
A La Nanita Nana *Xmas,Pol
"Virgin's Lullaby, The" treb cor,opt fl,
clar,vln,vla oct KERBY 6224C $.55, ipa   (G1174)

Carol Of The Bagpipes
see Christ Is Born

Christ Is Born *Xmas
oct KERBY 6023C $.40
contains: Carol Of The Bagpipes (SS);
From Shining Stars Descending (SS);
Little Infant King (SS)   (G1175)

From Shining Stars Descending
see Christ Is Born

Little Infant King
see Christ Is Born

Shepherds, Up! *Xmas
SS oct KERBY 6021C $.35   (G1176)

Virgin's Lullaby, The *see A La Nanita Nana

GLUCK AUF see Good News

GLUCK AUF! GUDS FRED! see Lund, Sundt

GLUCK, CHRISTOPH WILLIBALD RITTER VON
(1714-1787)
Ave Maria
[Lat] 4pt mix cor HEUGEL s.p. see from
SAINTE-CECILE   (G1177)

Come, Thou Fount Of Every Blessing
(Anderson) SATB oct LESLIE 4037   (G1178)
(Anderson) SA oct LESLIE 2007   (G1179)

De Profundis (Psalm 130) Adv/Easter/Lent
mix cor sc ALSBACH&D s.p.   (G1180)
[Lat] voc sc PETERS HU1619 $1.50   (G1181)
"From The Depths" [Lat/Eng] SATB,pno/org/
inst BROUDE BR. $1.50, ipr   (G1182)
"O, I Cry Unto Thee" SATB oct WALTON 6007
$.30   (G1183)
(Williams, W.) "Out Of The Deep" SATB,acap
(penitential seasons) SCHIRM.EC 1223 $.25
(G1184)

From The Depths *see De Profundis

Hear Me, O Saviour
(Pitcher, Gladys) 3pt mix cor,pno (med) oct
WILLIS 8484 $.20   (G1185)

Lead Us, Oh Father
(Mueller) SATB oct FISCHER,C CM-7519 $.25   (G1186)

Lord, In Thy Tender Mercy
(Howorth) SAB WARNER W3768 $.30   (G1187)

Mater Divina Gratiae
[Lat] cor,solo HEUGEL s.p. see from SAINTE-
CECILE   (G1188)

O, I Cry Unto Thee *see De Profundis

O Saviour Hear Me (from Orpheus)
(Ehret) SA BOOSEY-CAN $.25   (G1189)
(Ehret) SA,pno/org,opt vln oct BOOSEY 5241
$.30   (G1190)
(Peery, R.) SAB oct PRESSER 312-40246 $.25
(G1191)
(Protheroe) SATB WARNER G455 $.35   (G1192)
(Riegger) SATB FLAMMER A 5223 $.35   (G1193)
(Riegger) SSA FLAMMER B 5039 $.30   (G1194)

Out Of The Deep *see De Profundis

Prayer
(Fisher, W.) SATB,acap oct PRESSER
332-14611 $.30   (G1195)

Psalm 130 *see De Profundis

Saviour, Like A Shepherd Lead Us
(Ehret) SATB oct PRO ART 1995 $.30   (G1196)

Tantum Ergo *Commun,mot
[Lat] SATBar oct DURAND s.p.   (G1197)

GLUCK, H.H.
Create In Me A Clean Heart O God
SATB oct VOLKWEIN VB139 $.25   (G1198)
SSA oct VOLKWEIN VB140 $.25   (G1199)

GLUCK, H.H. (cont'd.)
God Be Merciful
SATB oct VOLKWEIN VB156 $.25   (G1200)

God So Loved The World *Bibl
SATB oct VOLKWEIN VB159 $.25   (G1201)

GLUD HAR UPPVAXT KRISTUS JESUS see Runback, Albert

GNADE EUCH UND FRIEDE see Ahrens, Joseph

GNADE EUCH UND FRIEDE see Trexler, Georg

GNADIG UND BARMHERZIG see Grell, Eduard August

GNEIST, VERNER (1898-   )
So Komm Denn, Heilige Nacht *Gen
[Ger] SATB,acap (easy) BAREN. BCH 23 s.p.
(G1202)

GNOTOV
Glory To God *see Bortniansky, Dimitri Stepanovitch

GO AND TELL JOHN see Pfautsch, Lloyd

GO, CONGREGATION, GO see Antes, John

GO DOWN, DEATH *spir
(Blaine, G. Gordon) SATB oct WALTON 2070 $.35
(G1203)

GO DOWN DEATH see Scott, T.

GO DOWN IN DE LONESOME VALLEY see Hairston, Jester

GO DOWN, MOSES *spir,US
see Negro Spirituals
"Auf, Auf, Moses" see Sechs Negro Spirituals, Blatt 2
SAB oct LORENZ 7096 $.25   (G1204)
(Aubanel, Georges) "Descends Moise" [Eng/Fr]
4pt mix cor OUVRIERES s.p.   (G1205)
(Cain) 8pt mix cor,acap oct SCHIRM.G 7575
$.35   (G1206)
(Cain) 3pt mix cor oct SCHIRM.G 10415 $.25
(G1207)
(Cain) 3pt wom cor oct SCHIRM.G 10416 $.25
(G1208)
(Durian, Tim) 4pt men cor,Bar solo,acap
BREITKOPF-W Z-40 s.p. see also Dreizehn
Negro- Spirituals   (G1209)
(Follett) SAB oct PRO ART 2450 $.30   (G1210)
(Hunter) SATB,acap oct LAWSON 51100 $.25
(G1211)
(Palmer) SATB ALFRED 6340 $.30   (G1212)
(Papale, Henry) SATB&opt SSA/3pt jr cor,S/T
solo,acap oct WORLD ESE-733-8 $.60   (G1213)
(Pens) SATB,acap oct PRO ART 1129 $.25   (G1214)
(Roberton) men cor ROBERTON 50802 s.p.
(G1215)
(Rogers) SATB oct STAFF 247 $.30   (G1216)
(Shaw; Parker) SATB,B solo,acap oct LAWSON
51115 $.25   (G1217)
(Wagner) SATB,A/B solo,acap oct LAWSON 51194
$.30   (G1218)
(Wilson) SAB ALFRED 6511 $.30   (G1219)

GO DOWN, MOSES see Burleigh, Henry Thacker

GO DOWN, MOSES see Dixon

GO DOWN, MOSES see Gerhold, Norbert

GO DOWN MOSES see Wild, Eric

GO DOWN MOSES see Willumson, E.

GO FORTH
see Two Noels

GO FORTH INTO THE WORLD see Hunt, Eric J.

GO FORTH TO LIFE, O CHILD OF EARTH see Thompson

GO FORTH TOGETHER BELIEVING see Wheelwright, Lorin F.

GO FORTH UNTO THE WORLD see Shaw, Martin

GO FORTH WITH COURAGE see Victoria, Tomas Luis de, Estote Fortes In Bello

GO FORTH WITH GOD! see Shaw, Martin

GO INTO ALL THE WORLD see Bender, Jan

GO, LABOR ON! see Warner, Richard

GO LITTLE SONG see Wilson, John F.

GO, LOVELY ROSE! see Moore

GO NOT FAR FROM ME, O GOD see Ponsonby, Noel

GO NOT FAR FROM ME, O GOD see Zingarelli, Nicola Antonio, Christus E Miserere

GO NOT FAR FROM ME, O LORD see Morgan

GO NOW AND LIVE FOR THE SAVIOR see Kaiser, Kurt

GO, PRAYER OF MINE see Dexter

GO PRETTY CHILD see Jarret, Jack M.

GO, SHEPHERD BOY see Hallett, John C.

GO, SONG OF MINE see Elgar, Edward

GO, SONG OF MINE! see Wilson, H.

GO TELL IT IN THE CITY see Copes, V. Earle

GO TELL IT ON DE MOUNTAINS *spir
(Burleigh) SATB RICORDI-ENG LD458 s.p.
(G1220)

GO TELL IT ON DE MOUNTAINS see Burleigh, Henry Thacker

GO TELL IT ON THE MOUNTAIN *Xmas,carol/spir
"Geh, Ruf Es Vom Berg" see Sechs Negro
Spirituals, Blatt 3
SATB oct LORENZ B51 $.25   (G1221)
(Barthelson, Joyce) SATB oct BELWIN 2050 $.30
(G1222)
(Barthelson, Joyce) SA/TB oct BELWIN 1833

$.25
(Barthelson, Joyce) SAB oct BELWIN 1957 $.30   (G1223)
                                                             (G1224)
(Caldwell, Mary E.) SAB oct GRAY GCMR 2765
$.25   (G1225)
(Daniels, M.L.) SATB,acap oct WORLD CA-2313-8
$.45   (G1226)
(Durian, Tim) 4pt men cor,acap BREITKOPF-W
Z-57 s.p. see also Dreizehn Negro-
Spirituals   (G1227)
(Fissinger) SATB oct SPRATT 138 $.30   (G1228)
(Krasser) SATB oct FISCHER,C CM-6908 $.25
                                                             (G1229)
(Lynn, G.) SSA oct PRESSER 312-40331 $.30
                                                             (G1230)
(McKelvy, J.) SATB,acap FOSTER MF651 $.25
                                                             (G1231)
(Sjolund) SATB oct WORD CS-2406 $.30   (G1232)
(Stevens) SATB,acap oct PRO ART 1798 $.30
                                                             (G1233)
(Turner, J.) TTBB PROWSE s.p.   (G1234)
(Turner, J.) SATB PROWSE s.p.   (G1235)
(Wilson; Ehret) SSA oct BOOSEY 5118 $.30
                                                             (G1236)
(Wilson; Ehret) TTBB oct BOOSEY 5591 $.30
                                                             (G1237)
(Work) SA oct GALAXY 1.1960.1 $.30   (G1238)
(Work) SATB&jr cor oct GALAXY 1.2044.1 $.35
                                                             (G1239)
(Work) SSA oct GALAXY 1.1753.1 $.35   (G1240)
(Work) SAB oct GALAXY 1.1927.1 $.35   (G1241)
(Work) TTBB oct GALAXY 1.1583.1 $.35   (G1242)
(Work) SATB oct GALAXY 1.1532.1 $.35   (G1243)

GO TELL IT ON THE MOUNTAIN see Brandon

GO, TELL IT ON THE MOUNTAIN see Broughton,
Edward

GO TELL IT ON THE MOUNTAIN see Fax, M.

GO TELL IT ON THE MOUNTAIN see Fryer

GO TELL IT ON THE MOUNTAIN see Furman, James

GO TELL IT ON THE MOUNTAIN see Simeone

GO TELL IT ON THE MOUNTAIN (HE'S GOT THE WHOLE
WORLD) see Hudson

GO TELL IT ON THE MOUNTAINS *Xmas/Gen,spir
(Genuchi) TTBB LUDWIG SS-006 $.30   (G1244)
(Genuchi) SATB LUDWIG SS-007 $.35   (G1245)
(Koll, Fritz) 3 eq voices cor pts BREITKOPF-W
CHB-3648 see from Zwei Negro-Spirituals
                                                (G1246)
(Lynn, G.) SAB oct PRESSER 312-40089 $.30   (G1247)
(Schubert) SATB oct LILLENAS AN-3826 $.25
                                                (G1248)

GO TELL IT ON THE MOUNTAINS see Bonds,
[Margaret]

GO TELL IT ON THE MOUNTAINS see Burleigh, Henry
Thacker

GO TELL IT ON THE MOUNTAINS see Huntley

GO TELL IT ON THE MOUNTAINS see Smith

GO THY WAY see Krenek, Ernst

GO TO BETHLEHEM, SHEPHERDS see Staley

GO TO DARK GETHSEMANE see Arkhangelsky, G.

GO TO DARK GETHSEMANE see Boatwright, Howard

GO TO DARK GETHSEMANE see Burroughs, Bob

GO TO DARK GETHSEMANE see Landon

GO TO DARK GETHSEMANE see Lunde

GO TO DARK GETHSEMANE see Martin, G.

GO TO DARK GETHSEMANE see Noble, Thomas Tertius

GO TO DARK GETHSEMANE see Sateren, Leland
Bernhard

GO TO SLEEP, HOLY CHILD see Gwynne

GO TO SLEEP O CHILD OF MY JOY see Grime,
William

GO WHERE I SEND THEE *Xmas
SATB oct STAFF 418 $.30   (G1249)
SAB oct STAFF 439 $.30   (G1250)
TTBB oct STAFF 440 $.30   (G1251)
SA/TB oct STAFF 445 $.30   (G1252)
SSA oct STAFF 437 $.30   (G1253)
(Douglas) SATB oct PRO ART 2047 $.25   (G1254)
(Douglas) SSA oct PRO ART 2052 $.22   (G1255)

GO WHERE THE PEOPLE ARE see Landgrave, Phillip

GO YE! *medley
(Clark) SATB oct LILLENAS AT-1020 $.30
                                                (G1256)
GO YE AND TEACH ALL NATIONS see Thompson

GO YE FORTH, AMERICA see Newbury, Kent A.

GO YE FORTH WITH MY WORD see Madsden

GO YE INTO ALL THE WORLD see Ford, Virgil T.

GO YE INTO ALL THE WORLD see Gumpeltzhaimer,
Adam

GO YE INTO ALL THE WORLD see McCormick

GO YE INTO ALL THE WORLD see Wetzler, Robert

GO, YE, INTO ALL THE WORLD see York, D.

GO YE THEREFORE see McAfee

GOD ADORING see Davis, Katherine K.

GOD ALL OVER see Rhea, A.

GOD AND GOD ALONE IS LOVE
SATB CHAPPELL 0022277-358 $.40   (G1257)

GOD AND OUR BROTHER see Hutson, Wihla

GOD BE IN BY HEAD see Richolson

GOD BE IN MY HEAD see Bentel, Franklin

GOD BE IN MY HEAD see Chapman, Edward T.

GOD BE IN MY HEAD see Davies, Henry Walford

GOD BE IN MY HEAD see Edmundson, Garth

GOD BE IN MY HEAD see Ellsworth, A. Eugene

GOD BE IN MY HEAD see Graf, Franz

GOD BE IN MY HEAD see Grant

GOD, BE IN MY HEAD see Kevan, G.

GOD BE IN MY HEAD see Le Fleming, Christopher
(Kaye)

GOD BE IN MY HEAD see Pasquet, Jean

GOD BE IN MY HEAD see Robson, R. Walker

GOD BE IN MY HEAD see Rutter

GOD BE IN MY HEAD see Wilson

GOD BE IN MY HEART see Johnston

GOD BE IN MY HEART see Warren, Elinor Remick

GOD BE MERCIFUL
SATB BIG3 $.25   (G1258)

GOD BE MERCIFUL see Alexander

GOD BE MERCIFUL see Collingwood, A.

GOD BE MERCIFUL see Gluck, H.H.

GOD BE MERCIFUL see Loeillet

GOD BE MERCIFUL see Moe, Daniel

GOD BE MERCIFUL see Reynolds, Roger

GOD BE MERCIFUL AND KIND see Graham, Robert
[V.]

GOD BE MERCIFUL UNTO US see Aston, Peter

GOD BE MERCIFUL UNTO US see Bodycombe,
[Aneurin]

GOD BE MERCIFUL UNTO US see Bornschein, [Franz
Carl]

GOD BE MERCIFUL UNTO US see Brown, Leon F.

GOD BE MERCIFUL UNTO US see Fraser

GOD BE MERCIFUL UNTO US see Fraser, Shena

GOD BE MERCIFUL UNTO US see Hastings, Ross

GOD BE MERCIFUL UNTO US see Ives, Charles

GOD BE MERCIFUL UNTO US see Means, Claude

GOD BE MERCIFUL UNTO US see Powell, Robert J.

GOD BE MERCIFUL UNTO US see Roff, Joseph

GOD BE MERCIFUL UNTO US see Staley, F. Broadus

GOD BE MERCIFUL UNTO US see Waring, Peter

GOD BE MERCIFUL UNTO US see West, John Ebenezer

GOD BE MERCIFUL UNTO US see Westrup, Jack Allan

GOD BE MERCIFUL UNTO US see Williams

GOD BE WITH THEE see Grazioli, Giovanni, Pange
Lingua

GOD BE WITH YOU see Ford

GOD BE WITH YOU see Renolds

GOD BE WITH YOU see Rhodes

GOD BLESS ME see Harding, Phyllis

GOD BLESS OUR HOME
2pt CHAPPELL 0018028-352 $.40   (G1259)
SSA CHAPPELL 0018028-354 $.40   (G1260)
SATB CHAPPELL 0018028-358 $.40   (G1261)

GOD BLESS OUR LAND see Kountz, Richard

GOD BLESS OUR NATIVE LAND see Mueller, Carl F.

GOD BLESS THE KING see Vance

GOD BLESS THE LITTLE THINGS see Byles, B. D.

GOD BLESS THE LITTLE THINGS see Hatch, H.

GOD BLESS THE MASTER see Vaughan Williams,
Ralph

GOD BLESS THE MASTER OF THIS HOUSE see
Hallstrom, Henry

GOD BLESS THE MORNING see Oliver, Herbert

GOD BLESS YOU, MOTHER DEAR see Landon

GOD, BRING THY SWORD see Nelson, Ronald A.

GOD BUILDS NO CHURCHES see Kevan

GOD CALLING YET see Nichel, Ekkehart

GOD CARES FOR ME see Freestone, G.S.

GOD CREATED MAN see Young, Carlton R.

GOD, CREATOR see Fraser

GOD, ENKEL LICHT
(Baas, J.) mix cor sc ALSBACH&D GEZ.16 s.p.
                                                (G1262)
GOD ETERNAL IS MY REFUGE see Peninger, David

GOD EVER GLORIOUS see Lwoff

GOD FATHER, BE THOU PRAISED see Mytych, J.F.

GOD FATHER, PRAISE AND GLORY see Goemanne, Noel

GOD FOR MAN IS BORN see Schubert, Franz (Peter)

GOD GAVE US A LOVELY WORLD see Youse, Glad
[Robinson]

GOD GAVE US SONG see Cooper, Irvin

GOD, GIVE ME UNDERSTANDING see Bell

GOD, GIVE US CHRISTIAN HOMES see McKinney

GOD GIVE YE MERRY CHRISTMASTIDE *Xmas
(Beckham) SATB oct PRO ART 2110 $.25 (G1263)

GOD GOES UP ON HIGH see Gallus, Jacobus,
Ascendit Deus

GOD GOETH UP see Bach, Johann Sebastian, Gott
Fahret Auf Mit Jauchzen

GOD GOETH UP WITH SHOUTING [CHORALE] see Bach,
Johann Sebastian

GOD GRANT US see Gardner, Maurice

GOD GRANT US PEACE see Wickham, B.

GOD GRANT YOU MANY YEARS see Carroll, J.R.

GOD GUIDE US HENCE see Reger, Max

GOD GUIDE US HENCE, OUR GUARDIAN BE see Reger,
Max

GOD HAS A REASON see Bell

GOD HAS EARS TO LISTEN see Lewis

GOD HAS GONE UP WITH A SHOUT see Klein

GOD HATH DONE ALL THINGS WELL see Franck,
Melchior

GOD HATH SPOKEN see Gibbs, Alan

GOD HELP THE POOR see Berger, Jean

GOD HIMSELF COMES DOWN FROM HEAVEN see
Lijestrand

GOD HIMSELF IS WITH US see Bottenberg,
[Wolfgang]

GOD IN A STAR see Denton

GOD IN NATURE see Beethoven, Ludwig van

GOD IN NATURE see Schubert, Franz (Peter)

GOD IN THE STORM CLOUD see Schubert, Franz
(Peter), Gott Im Ungewitter

GOD, IN THEE I SEEK MY SALVATION see Haydn,
(Johann) Michael

GOD IS see Skillings, Otis

GOD IS see Young, Carlton R.

GOD IS A FIRE OF LOVE see Temple, S.

GOD IS A GOD!
see Two Negro Spirituals

GOD IS A SPIRIT see Bennett

GOD IS A SPIRIT see Bennett, S.

GOD IS A SPIRIT see Bennett, Sir William
Sterndale

GOD IS A SPIRIT see Bullock, Ernest

GOD IS A SPIRIT see Kopylov, Alexander
Alexandrovitch

GOD IS A SPIRIT see McCormick

GOD IS A SPIRIT see Pinkham, Daniel

GOD IS A SPIRIT see Scholin

GOD IS A SPIRIT see Work, Henry Clay

GOD IS ALIVE see Fanelli, Joseph

GOD IS ALIVE see Rhea

GOD IS ALMIGHTY see Kirk, Theron W.

GOD IS ASCENDED see Graham, Robert [V.]

GOD IS ASCENDED UP ON HIGH *Easter,carol
unis/SATB (very easy) OXFORD 08.126 $.15
                                                (G1264)
GOD IS ASCENDED UP ON HIGH see Cashmore, Donald

GOD IS ASCENDED UP ON HIGH see Hill. E.

GOD IS AT WORK WITHIN YOU see Bock, F.

GOD IS BEFORE ME see Blakley

GOD IS DUE PRAISE see Weisgall, Hugo

GOD IS EVER BESIDE ME
SATB BIG3 $.30   (G1265)
SSA/SAB BIG3 $.25   (G1266)

GOD IS EVERYWHERE see Dungan

GOD IS EVERYWHERE see Gillam

GOD IS EVERYWHERE see Gretchaninov, Alexander
Tikhonovitch

GOD IS EVERYWHERE see Hughes

GOD IS EVERYWHERE see Williams

GOD IS FOR US A REFUGE AND STRENGTH see Anders,
Charles

GOD IS GOD see Sateren, Leland Bernhard

GOD IS GONE UP see Bryant

GOD IS GONE UP see Finzi, Gerald

GOD IS GONE UP see Gibbons, Orlando

GOD IS GONE UP see Hedges, Anthony

GOD IS GONE UP, ALLELUIA see Van Dyke

GOD IS GONE UP WITH A MERRY NOISE see Croft, William

GOD IS GONE UP WITH A MERRY NOISE see Howells, Herbert Norman

GOD IS GONE UP WITH A MERRY NOISE see Hutchings, Arthur, Ascendit Deus

GOD IS GONE UP WITH A SHOUT see Willan, Healey

GOD IS GOOD see Webber, Lloyd

GOD IS GOOD TO US ALL see Kirby

GOD IS GREAT see Emig, Lois

GOD IS HERE - LET'S CELEBRATE! see Leaf, Robert

GOD IS HERE ON EVERY HAND see Jordan

GOD IS HERE WITH US see Stanton, Royal [W.]

GOD IS HOLY see Bowles, G.

GOD IS HOLY see Eberlin, Johann Ernst, Sciant Gentes

GOD IS IN EVERY TOMORROW see Orjala

GOD IS IN HIS HOLY TEMPLE see Lovelace, Austin C.

GOD IS IN HIS HOLY TEMPLE see Mueller, Carl F.

GOD IS IN HIS TEMPLE see Neander, Joachim

GOD IS IN THIS PLACE see Davis, Katherine K.

GOD IS LIFE see Bach

GOD IS LIGHT see Darst, W. Glenn

GOD IS LIVING, GOD IS HERE! see Bach, Johann Sebastian

GOD IS LOVE *anthem,Eng
(George, Graham) SA (easy) oct AUGSBURG 1552 $.25   (G1267)

GOD IS LOVE see Beethoven, Ludwig van, Gott Ist Die Liebe

GOD IS LOVE see Noe, J.T.

GOD IS LOVE see Roff, Joseph

GOD IS LOVE see Shelley

GOD IS LOVE see Shelley, [Harry Rowe]

GOD IS LOVE see Thompson

GOD IS LOVE see Voris, W.R.

GOD IS LOVE: LET HEAV'N ADORE HIM see Howells, Herbert Norman

GOD IS MERCIFUL see Haydn, (Johann) Michael

GOD IS MIJN LICHT see Vulpius, Melchior

GOD IS MY FRIEND
SSA BIG3 $.25   (G1268)

GOD IS MY GUIDE see Schubert, Franz (Peter)

GOD IS MY SALVATION see Adler, Samuel

GOD IS MY SALVATION see Christiansen, Olaf Christian

GOD IS MY SALVATION see Lewis, John Leo

GOD IS MY SHEPHERD see Dvorak, Antonin

GOD IS MY SONG see Beethoven, Ludwig van, Gottes Macht Und Vorsehung

GOD IS MY SONG see Warren

GOD IS MY SOVEREIGN see Bach, Johann Sebastian, Gott Ist Mein Konig

GOD IS MY STRENGTH
SATB CHAPPELL 0018036-358 $.40   (G1269)

GOD IS MY STRONG SALVATION see Ford

GOD IS MY STRONG SALVATION see Klein

GOD IS MY STRONG SALVATION see Lovelace, Austin C.

GOD IS MY STRONG SALVATION see Pfautsch, Lloyd

GOD IS MY STRONG SALVATION see Pool, K.

GOD IS MY STRONG SALVATION see Powell, Robert J.

GOD IS MY STRONG SALVATION see Stevens, Halsey

GOD IS NEAR see Ballantine

GOD IS NEAR see Rogers

GOD IS NOT DEAD see Roff, Joseph

GOD IS OUR HOPE AND STRENGTH see Arnatt, Ronald

GOD IS OUR HOPE AND STRENGTH see Bach, Johann Sebastian

GOD IS OUR HOPE AND STRENGTH see Pears, James R.

GOD IS OUR HOPE AND STRENGTH see Preston, Simon

GOD IS OUR LIFE see Bach

GOD IS OUR REFUGE
SATB CHAPPELL 1750009-358 $.40   (G1270)

GOD IS OUR REFUGE see Bach, Johann Sebastian

GOD IS OUR REFUGE see Boatwright, Howard

GOD IS OUR REFUGE see Curry

GOD IS OUR REFUGE see Glarum, L. Stanley

GOD IS OUR REFUGE see Lundquist, Matthew Nathanael

GOD IS OUR REFUGE see Macfarlane, William Charles

GOD IS OUR REFUGE see Mozart, Wolfgang Amadeus

GOD IS OUR REFUGE see Mozart, Wolfgang Amadeus, God Is Our Refuge

GOD IS OUR REFUGE see Roman, Johan Helmich

GOD IS OUR REFUGE AND STRENGTH see Bender, Jan

GOD IS OUR REFUGE AND STRENGTH see Buck, Dudley

GOD IS OUR REFUGE AND STRENGTH see Hafso

GOD IS OUR REFUGE AND STRENGTH see Hawkins, Floyd W.

GOD IS OUR REFUGE AND STRENGTH see Mueller, Carl F.

GOD IS OUR REFUGE AND STRENGTH see Newbury

GOD IS OUR REFUGE AND STRENGTH see Ouchterlony, David

GOD IS OUR REFUGE AND STRENGTH see Pachelbel, Johann, Gott Ist Unser Zuversicht

GOD IS OUR REFUGE IS OUR STRENGTH see Hopson

GOD IS OUR STRENGTH AND REFUGE see Landgrave, Phillip

GOD IS OUR STRENGTH AND SONG see Peninger, David

GOD IS OUR SUN AND SHIELD see Schalk, Carl

GOD IS PRESENT EVERYWHERE see Mueller, Carl F.

GOD IS SEEN
(Parker) mix cor,acap oct LAWSON 51333 $.30   (G1271)

GOD IS SO WONDERFUL *CC11L,gospel
(Brown, Charles F.; Kaiser, Kurt; Perkins, Phil) SATB voc sc WORD 37616 $1.50 (G1272)

GOD IS SO WONDERFUL see Marshall, Virginia

GOD IS THE BEAUTY OF THE WORLD see Rowley, Alec

GOD IS THE LIGHT OF THE WORLD see Haydn, (Franz) Joseph

GOD IS TRUE see Roesch

GOD IS WATCHING see Whitecotton, Shirley

GOD IS WISDOM, GOD IS LOVE see Bedell, [Robert Leech]

GOD IS WISDOM, GOD IS LOVE see Gaul, Alfred Robert

GOD IS WITH US see Kastalsky, Alexander Dmitrievitch

GOD IS WITH US see Posegate

GOD IS WORKING HIS PURPOSE OUT see Lovelace, Austin C.

GOD IS WORKING HIS PURPOSE OUT see Young, Carlton R.

GOD KNOWS see Hart, A.W.

GOD LEADS, GOD HELPS see Mozart, Wolfgang Amadeus, Justum Deduxit Dominus

GOD LEADS US ALONG see Young

GOD LIVES IN MY HEART see O'Hara, Geoffrey

GOD LIVETH STILL see Bach, Johann Sebastian

GOD LOVE YOU NOW see Erb, Donald

GOD LOVED THE WORLD SO THAT HE GAVE see Vulpius, Melchior

GOD LOVES ME see White

GOD MADE EVERYTHING GOOD see Redmond

GOD MADE OUR HANDS see Miller

GOD MAKE MY LIFE A LITTLE LIGHT see Thiman, Eric Harding

GOD MAKE MY LIFE A SHINING LIGHT see Lovelace, Austin C.

GOD MEANS MORE TO US NOW see Grime, William

GOD MOUNTS HIS THRONE see Peloquin, C. Alexander

GOD MOUNTS HIS THRONE see Sowerby, Leo

GOD MOVES IN A MYSTERIOUS WAY see Krieger

GOD MOVES IN A MYSTERIOUS WAY see Wheelwright, Lorin F.

GOD, MY FATHER see Dubois, Theodore

GOD, MY FATHER, LOVING ME see Wolff, S. Drummond

GOD, MY HELP see Hauptmann

GOD, MY KING see Bach, Johann Sebastian

GOD, MY KING see Blake

GOD, MY KING, THY MIGHT CONFESSING see Bach, Johann Sebastian

GOD, MY KING, THY MIGHT CONFESSING see Lowe

GOD, MY SHEPHERD see Bach

GOD NOW DWELLS AMONG US see Hassler, Hans Leo

GOD OF A UNIVERSE see Held, Wilbur

GOD OF ABRAHAM see Vance, Margaret Shelley

GOD OF ABRAHAM PRAISE *anthem/liturg,Heb
(Marks, H.) TTBB,acap oct PRESSER 332-40022 $.30   (G1273)
(Mueller) SA oct FISCHER,C CM-6303 $.25   (G1274)

GOD OF ABRAHAM, PRAISE see Buck, Dudley

GOD OF ABRAHAM PRAISE, THE see Jacobson, Maurice

GOD OF ABRAHAM PRAISE, THE *anthem/hymn,Heb
(Cassler, G. Winston) TTBB (med) oct AUGSBURG 1226 $.22   (G1275)
(Kirk) SATB oct PRO ART 1934 $.25   (G1276)
(Malmin, Gunnar) SSA (easy) oct AUGSBURG 1238 $.20   (G1277)
(Noble) SATB oct SPRATT 561 $.25   (G1278)

GOD OF ABRAHAM PRAISE, THE see Durant, C.

GOD OF ABRAHAM PRAISE, THE see Gore, Richard T.

GOD OF ABRAHAM PRAISE, THE see Leoni

GOD OF ABRAHAM PRAISE, THE see Mueller, Carl F.

GOD OF ABRAHAM PRAISE, THE see Watts, Harold E.

GOD OF AGES see Elmore, Robert [Hall]

GOD OF ALL GRACE see Van Dyke

GOD OF ALL LOVE AND PITY see Swann, [Frederick Lewis]

GOD OF ALL NATIONS see Glarum, L. Stanley

GOD OF ALL NATIONS see Johnson, David N.

GOD OF COMFORT, GOD OF COURAGE see Chenoweth, Wilbur

GOD OF COMPASSION see Wilson, Keith E.

GOD OF GLORY THUNDERETH, THE see Hovhaness, Alan

GOD OF GRACE AND GOD OF GLORY see La Montaine, John

GOD OF GRACE AND GOD OF GLORY see Lovelace, Austin C.

GOD OF GRACE AND GOD OF GLORY see Price

GOD OF GREAT AND GOD OF SMALL see Sleeth, Natalie

GOD OF HARVEST PRAISE, THE see Heyser, E.K.

GOD OF HARVEST PRAISE, THE see Rawls

GOD OF JUSTICE, SAVE THY PEOPLE see Wilson, John F.

GOD OF LIGHT see Mueller, Carl F.

GOD OF LOVE see Dieterich

GOD OF LOVE AND GOD OF POWER see Lapo, Cecil E.

GOD OF LOVE, KING OF PEACE see Leaf

GOD OF LOVE MY SHEPHERD IS, THE *hymn
SSA CHAPPELL 0018382-354 $.40   (G1279)
SATB CHAPPELL 0018382-358 $.40   (G1280)
SATB oct ST.MARTIN SMP656 s.p.   (G1281)

GOD OF LOVE MY SHEPHERD IS, THE see Handel, George Frideric

GOD OF LOVE MY SHEPHERD IS, THE see Peek, Richard

GOD OF LOVE MY SHEPHERD IS, THE see Sanford

GOD OF LOVE MY SHEPHERD IS, THE see Thompson

GOD OF LOVE MY SHEPHERD IS, THE see Warner, Richard

GOD OF LOVE, WHO HEAREST PRAYER see Filitz, [Friedrich]

GOD OF MERCY see Bach

GOD OF MERCY see Cherubini, Luigi, Pie Jesu

GOD OF MERCY see Willan, Healey

GOD OF MERCY, GOD OF GRACE see Elliot

GOD OF MERCY, GOD OF GRACE see Gallus, Jacobus

GOD OF MERCY, GOD OF GRACE see Handel, George Frideric

GOD OF MERCY, GOD OF GRACE see Schalk, Carl

GOD OF MERCY, GOD OF GRACE see Whitehead, Alfred

GOD OF MERCY GOD OF GRACE see Young

GOD OF MIGHT, WE PRAISE THY NAME see Pfautsch, Lloyd

GOD OF MIRACLES see Nelson, Jerry

GOD OF MY JUSTICE (Psalm 4) Bibl
(Shaw; Parker) SATB,acap oct LAWSON 584 $.25
(G1282)

GOD OF MY LIFE see Beethoven, Ludwig van

GOD OF MY SALVATION, THE see Fletcher

GOD OF MY SHEPHERD IS, THE see Warner

GOD OF OUR FATHERS see Cain, Noble

GOD OF OUR FATHERS see Donath, J.

GOD OF OUR FATHERS see Gibb

GOD OF OUR FATHERS see Hustad, Donald P.

GOD OF OUR FATHERS see Matesky

GOD OF OUR FATHERS see Warren

GOD OF OUR FATHERS see Warren, George William

GOD OF OUR FATHERS see Wilson

GOD OF OUR LIFE see Pasquet, Jean

GOD OF OUR SALVATION see Mueller, Carl F.

GOD OF THE EARTH see Rhea, A.

GOD OF THE EARTH see Young, P.

GOD OF THE EARTH, THE SKY, THE SEA see
Frackenpohl

GOD OF THE GALAXIES see Burroughs, Bob

GOD OF THE NATIONS see Bourgeois, Loys (Louis)

GOD OF THE OPEN AIR see Cain, Noble

GOD OF THE PROPHETS see Bunjes, Paul G.

GOD OF THE STRONG see Ford, Virgil T.

GOD OF THE UNIVERSE see Posegate, Maxcine W.

GOD OF THE WILDERNESS see House

GOD OF THE WORLD see Wise, Judah L.

GOD OF THE WORLD! THY GLORIES SHINE see Root

GOD OF US ALL
SA BIG3 $.30   (G1283)
SSA/SATB BIG3 $.25   (G1284)

GOD OF WISDOM see Schubert, Franz (Peter)

GOD OF YEARS see Hermanson, P.

GOD ON HIGH see Cruger, Johann

GOD, OUR CREATOR, FATHER see Ingegneri, Marco
Antonio

GOD OUR FATHER see Eberlin, Johann Ernst, Tu Es
Deus

GOD, OUR FATHER, LORD OF HEAVEN see Beobide,
Jose Maria, Tantum Ergo

GOD PAINTED A PICTURE
SSA BIG3 $.30   (G1285)
SATB/SAB BIG3 $.25   (G1286)

GOD REIGNS OVER THE NATIONS see Newbury, Kent
A.

GOD REST YE MERRY GENTLEMEN *Xmas,carol,Eng
see Five Christmas Carols
see Tidings Of Comfort And Joy
(de Paur) TTBB oct LAWSON 545 $.30   (G1287)
(Dello Joio) SATB,2pno MARKS 4568 $.50
(G1288)
(Shaw; Parker) SATB,acap oct LAWSON 729 $.25
(G1289)
(Wagner) SATB,acap oct LAWSON 51186 $.30
(G1290)

GOD REST YE MERRY GENTLEMEN see Boyd

GOD REST YE MERRY, GENTLEMEN see Elliott

GOD REST YE MERRY, GENTLEMEN see Van Iderstine,
A.P.

GOD REST YOU MERRIE, GENTLEMEN *Xmas
(Salter) mix cor,TB soli,acap oct SCHIRM.G
6744 $.30   (G1291)

GOD REST YOU MERRY *carol
see Six Traditional Carols, Set II
see Two Christmas Carols
unis/SATB (very easy) OXFORD 08.011 $.15
(G1292)
(Vaughan Williams) TBB,acap (easy) OXFORD
41.903 $.30 see from Nine Carols   (G1293)

GOD REST YOU MERRY see Todd

GOD REST YOU MERRY, GENTLEMEN *Xmas,carol
(Newbury, Kent) SATB,org oct WORLD CA-2318-8
$.60   (G1294)
(Stevens) SATB oct PRO ART 1420 $.25   (G1295)
(Stevens) SSA oct PRO ART 2042 $.25   (G1296)

GOD REST YOU MERRY, GENTLEMEN see Hallstrom,
Henry

GOD REST YOU MERRY GENTLEMEN see Kocher

GOD REST YOU MERRY, GENTLEMEN see Krones

GOD REST YOU MERRY GENTLEMEN see Lefebvre

GOD REST YOU MERRY, GENTLEMEN see Lynn, George

GOD, ROLL THAT ROCK see Young, Carlton R.

GOD RULETH OVER ALL see Danks

GOD SAVE THE QUEEN *anthem
(Elgar, E.) mix cor,orch oct NOVELLO
45.0885.08 s.p., ipr   (G1297)

GOD SEND US MEN see Strickler, David

GOD SEND US PEACE IN GOOD TIME see Niles, John
Jacob

GOD SENDS THE NIGHT see Rathbone, George

GOD SHALL DO MY ADVISING see Buxtehude,
Dietrich

GOD SHALL WIPE AWAY ALL TEARS see Field, J.T.

GOD SHALL WIPE AWAY ALL TEARS see Field, John

GOD SHALL WIPE AWAY ALL TEARS see Harker, F.
Flaxington

GOD SHALL WIPE AWAY ALL TEARS see Sullivan, Sir
Arthur Seymour

GOD SO LOVED see Winans, Winifred Lamb

GOD SO LOVED THE WORLD *Psntd
cor&cong ROYAL s.p.   (G1298)

GOD SO LOVED THE WORLD see Bach, Johann
Sebastian, Also Hat Gott Die Welt Geliebt

GOD SO LOVED THE WORLD see Bender, Jan

GOD SO LOVED THE WORLD see Bruckner, Anton

GOD SO LOVED THE WORLD see Davis, Katherine K.

GOD SO LOVED THE WORLD see Fletcher

GOD SO LOVED THE WORLD see Gluck, H.H.

GOD SO LOVED THE WORLD see Goss, John

GOD SO LOVED THE WORLD see Hodgson, R.A.

GOD SO LOVED THE WORLD see Lanier, Gary

GOD SO LOVED THE WORLD see Marks

GOD SO LOVED THE WORLD see Marks, J.

GOD SO LOVED THE WORLD see Moore, Harold

GOD SO LOVED THE WORLD see Pfautsch, Lloyd

GOD SO LOVED THE WORLD see Pool, K.

GOD SO LOVED THE WORLD see Schroth

GOD SO LOVED THE WORLD see Schutz, Heinrich

GOD SO LOVED THE WORLD see Stainer, John

GOD SO LOVED THE WORLD see Stickles

GOD SO LOVED THE WORLD see Tremper, Fred

GOD SO LOVED THE WORLD see Wilson

GOD SPAKE SOMETIME IN VISIONS see Blow, John

GOD SPEAKS TO ME
SSA BIG3 $.25   (G1299)

GOD SPOKE see Gaus

GOD SPOKE TO ME TODAY see Hughes

GOD THAT MADE THE WORLD see Glarum, L. Stanley

GOD THAT MADEST EARTH AND HEAVEN see Attwood,
Thomas

GOD, THAT MADEST EARTH AND HEAVEN see Thiman,
Eric Harding

GOD THAT MADEST EARTH AND HEAVENS
(Wiley) SATB oct PRO ART 2001 $.22   (G1300)

GOD, THE CREATOR OF THE WORLD see Klein

GOD, THE ETERNAL see Demming, Lanson F.

GOD THE FATHER, BE OUR STAY see Bender, Jan

GOD THE FATHER, BE OUR STAY see Pezel, Johann
Christoph

GOD THE FATHER, GOD THE SON see Schalk, Carl

GOD THE FATHER, SON, AND SPIRIT see Schalk,
Carl

GOD, THE LORD, A KING see Smart

GOD THE LORD IS GRACIOUS see Raffman, Relly,
Jubilate Deo

GOD, THE LORD, IS SUN AND SHIELD see Bach,
Johann Sebastian, Gott, Der Herr, Ist Sonn
Und Schild

GOD THE MASTER OF THIS SCENE see Somers, Harry
Stewart

GOD THE OMNIPOTENT see Ellerton

GOD, THE OMNIPOTENT see Gregory

GOD THE OMNIPOTENT see Lwoff

GOD THRONED ON HIGH see Jacobson, Maurice

GOD WALKS BESIDE THEE see Sateren, Leland
Bernhard

GOD WANTS A MAN see Starks, Howard

GOD WATCHES OVER ALL see Kettring, Donald D.

GOD WHICH HAS PREPARED see Mudd, Thomas

GOD, WHICH HAST PREPARED see Mudd, Thomas

GOD, WHO ALL HIS BLESSING SHED ON US see
Handel, George Frideric

GOD WHO ART PEACE EVERLASTING see Wald, George

GOD, WHO AS AT THIS TIME see Giles, Nathaniel

GOD, WHO AS UPON THIS DAY see Ramsey, Robert

GOD, WHO AT THIS TIME see Tomkins, Thomas

GOD, WHO MADE THE EARTH see Cram

GOD WHO MADE THE EARTH see Draesel, Lederhouse

GOD WHO MADE THE EARTH see Howard, John Tasker

GOD WHO MADE THE EARTH see Lewis, John Leo

GOD WHO MADE THE EARTH see Tapscott, Carl

GOD, WHO MADEST EARTH AND HEAVEN see Newton,
Ernest

GOD, WHO TOUCHEST EARTH see Freestone, G.S.

GOD WHO TOUCHEST EARTH WITH BEAUTY see Jordan,
Alice

GOD WHO TOUCHEST EARTH WITH BEAUTY see Mueller,
Carl F.

GOD WHO WATCHEST O'ER US see O Dieu De Clemence

GOD WILL ANSWER PRAYER see Stewart, C. Hylton

GOD WILL TAKE CARE OF YOU see Landon

GOD WITH ME LYING DOWN see Lekberg, Sven

GOD WITH US see Palmer, Peggy Spenser

GOD WITH US see Pfautsch, Lloyd

GODARD, BENJAMIN LOUIS PAUL (1849-1895)
Angels Guard Thee
(Clements. J) SATB CRAMER B 17 s.p. (G1301)

GODIMEL
see GOUDIMEL, CLAUDE

GODIN, CARL
Gud Ar Var Starkhet Och Vart Stod *Bibl
(Olson, Daniel) [Swed] SATB,acap GEHRMANS
KRB 128   (G1302)

GODLY STRANGER, THE see Cassler, G. Winston

GODOFALLOFUS see Floria, [Caryl]

GOD'S BLACKSMITH see Kodaly, Zoltan

GOD'S BLESSED SON TODAY IS BORN see Praetorius,
Michael

GOD'S COUNSEL IS MY WISDOM see Buxtehude,
Dietrich

GOD'S ETERNAL SON see Paget, Michael

GOD'S GIFT OF LOVE see Chopin, Frederic

GOD'S GIFT OF LOVE see Miller

GOD'S GIFT TO US see Grime, William

GOD'S GLORY AND HONOUR see Frank, Marcel
[Gustave]

GOD'S GONNA BUIL' UP ZION'S WALL see Hairston,
Jester

GOD'S GOODNESS HATH BEEN GREAT TO THEE see
Bridge, [John Frederick]

GOD'S GREAT GRACE see Hawkins, Floyd W.

GOD'S GREAT LOVE ABIDING see Coates, Eric

GOD'S GREATEST GIFT see Dressler, John

GOD'S GREATEST SACRIFICE see Dressler, John

GOD'S HANDIWORK see Wright

GOD'S HOLY WAY see Bryant

GOD'S HOUSE see Loucks

GOD'S INFANT SON see Praetorius, Michael,
Geborn Ist Gottes Sohnlein

GOD'S LIMITLESS LOVE see Russel, Eleanor

GOD'S LITTLE CANDLES *anthem
SATB/TTBB BIG3 $.25   (G1303)

GOD'S LITTLE CHORISTERS *CCU
jr cor LORENZ $1.00   (G1304)

GOD'S LOVE
SATB BIG3 $.30   (G1305)
SSA BIG3 $.25   (G1306)

GOD'S LOVE see Kirby, Charles

GOD'S LOVE IS LIKE THE SUN see Franco, Johan

GOD'S LOVE STAYS THE SAME see Grime, William

GOD'S LOVING CARE see Carter, Charles

GOD'S MIGHT AND PROVIDENCE see Beethoven,
Ludwig van

GOD'S MOMENTS see Angell, Warren M.

GOD'S OPEN ROAD see Caldwell

GOD'S OWN TIME see Bach, Johann Sebastian

GOD'S PATTERN see Loes, [Harry Dixon]

GOD'S PEACE IS PEACE ETERNAL see Grieg, Edvard
Hagerup

GOD'S PEACE IS PEACE ETERNAL see Handel, George
Frideric

GOD'S PLAN see Roff, Joseph

GOD'S PROVIDENCE *Gen
(Jennings) unis SCHMITT 102 $.05   (G1307)

GOD'S SEASONS see Ratcliffe, Desmond

GOD'S SINGING CHILDREN *CCU
jr cor LORENZ $1.00   (G1308)

GOD'S SON HAS MADE ME FREE see Grieg, Edvard
Hagerup

GOD'S SON HATH SET ME FREE see Grieg, Edvard
Hagerup

GOD'S SON IN TRIUMPH ROSE TODAY see Gesius,
Bartholomaus

GOD'S SON IS BORN see Hoffman

GOD'S SON IS BORN see Stanton, Royal [W.]

GOD'S SUNSHINE see Roff, Joseph

GOD'S TASK FOR YOU see Prutting, R.H.

GOD'S TENDER MERCY KNOWS NO BOUNDS see Handel,
George Frideric

GODS TIME see Bach, Johann Sebastian, Gottes
Zeit Ist Die Allerbeste Zeit

GOD'S TIME IS THE BEST see Bach, Johann
Sebastian, Gottes Zeit Ist Die Allerbeste
Zeit

GOD'S TROMBONES see Ringwald, [Roy]

GOD'S WAY see Austin, Ernest

GOD'S WILL BE DONE
SSA BIG3 $.25   (G1309)

GOD'S WISDOM see Ream

GOD'S WONDROUS LOVE see Christiansen, Olaf
Christian

GOD'S WORD IS SURE see Greatorex, Thomas

GOD'S WORLD see Caldwell

GOD'S WORLD see Youse, Glad [Robinson]

GOEDEN NACHT see Rennes, Cath. v.

GOEHR, ALEXANDER (1932-   )
Man Of Life, The
SATB SCHOTT 10860 s.p.   (G1310)

O Gracious God
SATB,org/pno/vcl SCHOTT 10863 s.p. (G1311)

Verse
SATB,pno,perc,opt org,2clar,vcl voc sc
SCHOTT 10858 s.p., sc SCHOTT 10858A s.p.
(G1312)

GOEMANNE, NOEL
Alleluia! For The Lord, Our God Almighty, Now
Reigns
see Songs From The Book Of Revelation

Alleluia, Sing To Jesus *Gen,anthem
SATB&cong,opt 2trp (easy) oct GIA G1727
$.35   (G1313)

Canticle Of The Sun, The
SATB,opt ABar soli,pno/org oct WORLD
ESA-581-8 $.90   (G1314)

Chorals (from Fanfare For Festivals)
SATB,brass,timp oct AGAPE AG 7137 $.30, ipa
(G1315)

Christ Is Risen *Easter,anthem
SSAA/TTBB (easy) oct GIA G936 $.30 (G1316)
SATB (easy) oct GIA G527 $.30   (G1317)

English Mass *Gen,Mass
2 eq voices/2pt mix cor/unis,org,opt fl/ob
(med easy) voc sc GIA G1551 $1.00, ipa
(G1318)

English Mass For St. Domenic *Gen,Mass,
Contemp
SATB (med diff) voc sc GIA G1701 $1.00 (G1319)

Entrata
"Rejoice Unto The Lord" SATB,org oct WORLD
ESA-955-8 $.60   (G1320)

Father We Thank Thee *Gen,anthem
2 eq voices,opt fl,bvl (easy) oct GIA G1726
$.30   (G1321)

God Father, Praise And Glory *Gen,anthem
SATB&cong,opt 2trp (easy) oct GIA G1736
$.35   (G1322)

Great And Marvelous Are Thy Works
see Songs From The Book Of Revelation

Holy, Holy, Holy
see Songs From The Book Of Revelation

Hymns Of Thanks *Gen,anthem
SATB,org,opt 2trp (med easy) oct GIA G1543
$.50
contains: Psalm 135; Psalm 138   (G1323)

Jazz Alleluia, A
cor,pno (jazz) FOSTER MF139 $.40   (G1324)

Let Us Break Bread Together *Gen,anthem
SATB/cong,org,opt ob,vcl (easy) oct GIA
G1732 $.40   (G1325)

Llanfair *Gen,anthem
SATB&desc&cong,org,opt 2trp (easy) oct GIA
G1731 $.35   (G1326)

Mass For S.A.B. Voices *Gen,Mass,Contemp
SAB,org,opt 2trp,2trom,timp (med) voc sc
GIA G1571 $1.00, ipa   (G1327)

Missa Internationalis *Mass
SATB,narrator,org,ob,3trp,timp oct AGAPE
$1.95   (G1328)

My Shepherd Will Supply My Need *Gen,anthem
SATB,fl&vcl/org (easy) oct GIA G1738 $.35
(G1329)

O Most Holy One And Only *Gen,anthem
unis/2 eq voices/SATB&cong,org,opt fl,ob
(easy) oct GIA G1733 $.30   (G1330)

GOEMANNE, NOEL (cont'd.)
Praise The Lord
SATB,opt org/org&brass&timp/brass&timp oct
SUMMY M 5949 $.60   (G1331)

Praise The Lord, All Ye Nations (Psalm 116)
SATB oct SUMMY M 2155 $.45   (G1332)

Prayer For Peace *Gen,anthem
SATB/SAB,narrator (med easy) oct GIA G1714
$.40   (G1333)

Prayer For Peace Of St. Francis *prayer
SATB,Bar solo,pno oct WORLD ESA-1425-8 $.90
(G1334)

Psalm 65 *see Song Of Praise

Psalm 116 *see Praise The Lord, All Ye
Nations

Psalm 135
see Hymns Of Thanks

Psalm 138
see Hymns Of Thanks

Rejoice, The Lord Is King *Gen,anthem
SATB&cong,opt 2trp (easy) oct GIA G1737
$.35   (G1335)

Rejoice Unto The Lord *see Entrata

Rondo For Children
2pt oct AGAPE SP 708 $.50   (G1336)

Song Of Hope *Gen,anthem
unis/2pt,org,opt 2trp,drums,timp (med) oct
GIA G1713 $.50   (G1337)

Song Of Praise (Psalm 65) Bibl
SATB,org oct WORLD ESA-1313-8 $.90 (G1338)

Songs From The Book Of Revelation *Bibl
voc sc WORLD ESA-1619-1 $.45
contains: Alleluia! For The Lord, Our God
Almighty, Now Reigns (cor&cong); Great
And Marvelous Are Thy Works (jr cor&
cor&cong); Holy, Holy, Holy (unis&opt
cong&opt SATB&opt desc,solo); Therefore
They Are Before The Throne Of God
(unis)   (G1339)

Therefore They Are Before The Throne Of God
see Songs From The Book Of Revelation

There's A Wideness In God's Mercy *Gen,
anthem
SATB/unis/2 eq voices,opt fl,ob,vcl,gtr
(easy) oct GIA G1728 $.45   (G1340)

Unto Us A Boy Is Born *Xmas,anthem
SATB&cong,opt org,2fl,ob,drums (easy) oct
GIA G1734 $.30   (G1341)

GOEYVAERTS, CAREL
Improperia *Holywk
dbl cor,A solo,vla,vcl,2ob,2clar,perc CBDM
s.p.   (G1342)

GOI, M.
Adoriamo Il Sacramento
"Let Us Worship The Sacrament" SATB,acap
oct BERBEN EB 1347 $1.20 contains also:
Lodate Il Signore, "Praise The Lord" (G1343)

Let Us Worship The Sacrament *see Adoriamo
Il Sacramento

Lodate Il Signore
"Praise The Lord" see Goi, M., Adoriamo Il
Sacramento

Praise The Lord *see Lodate Il Signore

GOICOECHEA, VINCENTE
Christ Was Made Obedient *see Christus
Factus Est

Christus Factus Est *Commun/Holywk
"Christ Was Made Obedient" SATB,acap
SCHIRM.EC 1255   (G1344)

Communion Service For Penitential Seasons
*see Missa Pro Dominicis Adventus Et
Quadrigestimae

Communion Service In G Major *see Missa In
Hon. Immac. Concep. B.V.M.

Jerusalem, Jerusalem, Convertere *Holywk
"Jerusalem, Jerusalem, Turn Thyself" SATB,
acap SCHIRM.EC 1256   (G1345)

Jerusalem, Jerusalem, Turn Thyself *see
Jerusalem, Jerusalem, Convertere

Missa In Hon. Immac. Concep. B.V.M.
"Communion Service In G Major" TTB
SCHIRM.EC 1257   (G1346)

Missa Pro Dominicis Adventus Et
Quadrigestimae
"Communion Service For Penitential Seasons"
SATB,acap SCHIRM.EC 1224 $.40   (G1347)

GOIN' HOME see Dvorak, Antonin

GOIN' HOME ON A CLOUD see Turner, E.

GOIN' HOME ON A CLOUD see White, Michael

GOIN' MY WAY see Copland, Aaron

GOIN' SOMEWHERE *CCUL
(Kaiser, Kurt) SATB voc sc WORD 30068 $1.95
(G1348)

GOIN' TO HEAVEN ANYHOW see Smith

GOING TO BETHLEHEM see Davis, Katherine K.

GOLDBERG, JOHANN GOTTLIEB (1727-1756)
Durch Die Herzliche Barmherzigkeit Unsers
Gottes *Fest,cant
(Durr, Alfred) [Ger] SSATB,SATB soli,org,
2ob,bsn,2vln,2vla,vcl,bvl (med diff, John
the Baptist festival) BAREN. BA 3442 sc
$8.75, cor pts $3.25, ipa   (G1349)

GOLDBERG, JOHANN GOTTLIEB (cont'd.)
Hilf, Herr, Die Heiligen Haben Abgenommen
(Psalm 12) Gen,cant
(Durr, Alfred) [Ger] (med diff) BAREN.
BA 3443 sc $5.25, cor pts $2.75, ipa
(G1350)

Psalm 12 *see Hilf, Herr, Die Heiligen Haben
Abgenommen

GOLDEN GATES ARE LIFTED see Peter, Johann
Friedrich

GOLDEN GATES OF JOY see Miron, Issachar

GOLDEN HARPS ARE SOUNDING see Franke

GOLDEN HARPS ARE SOUNDING see Sullivan, Sir
Arthur Seymour

GOLDEN STAR, THE see Clements

GOLDFARB, SAMUEL E.
Avodat Israel *Sab-Eve
SATB TRANSCON. TCL 775 $2.50   (G1351)

GOLDMAN
Wither Thou Goest
SSA oct VOLKWEIN VB279 $.30   (G1352)

GOLDMAN, E.
Hymn For Peace, A *hymn
SATB,opt pno oct WORLD ESA-1438-8 (G1353)

I Will Lift Up Mine Eyes (Psalm 121)
SATB oct PRESSER MC513 $.30   (G1354)

Psalm 121 *see I Will Lift Up Mine Eyes

Though The Fig Tree Do Not Blossom
SATB,acap oct WORLD ESA-1476-8 $.45 (G1355)

GOLDMAN, MAURICE
Entreat Me Not To Leave Thee
[Eng] mix cor,S solo TRANSCON. TCL 611 $.60
(G1356)

Hymn Of Praise (Psalm 117)
SATB TRANSCON. TCL 671 $.60   (G1357)

Jerusalem
mix cor,STBar soli TRANSCON. TCL 344 $3.00
(G1358)

Let The Word Go Forth
SATB TRANSCON. TCL 630 $.50   (G1359)

Lift Up Your Heads
SATB CRITERION $.30   (G1360)

Lord Is My Light, The
SATB CRITERION $.50   (G1361)

Psalm 117 *see Hymn Of Praise

Woman Of Valor, A *see Orleans, Ilo

GOLDSBOROUGH
Door Is Open, The
(Frank) SAB oct BOURNE 3028 $.25   (G1362)
(Frank) SSA oct BOURNE 224 $.25   (G1363)
(Frank) SATB oct BOURNE 861 $.25   (G1364)

GOLDSMITH, S.W.
Benedicite (Shortened Form)
SATB (D maj) oct NOVELLO 44.1243.05 s.p.
(G1365)

GOLDSWORTHY, BROUN
Shepherd *cant
SATB BELWIN $1.00   (G1366)

GOLDSWORTHY, WILLIAM ARTHUR (1878-   )
All Hail The Power *Easter/Gen
SATB&jr cor&sr cor oct GRAY GCMR 1860 $.40
(G1367)

Bethlehem *Xmas
jr cor&sr cor oct GRAY GCMR 1680 $.35 (G1368)

Christmas Story, The *Xmas
jr cor&sr cor oct FISCHER,J 7317 $.35
(G1369)

Come, Ye Thankful People
jr cor&sr cor oct GRAY GCMR 1879 $.40 (G1370)

Dawn In The Garden
jr cor&sr cor oct FISCHER,J 7394 $.30
(G1371)

One Night In Bethlehem *cant
mix cor BELWIN $1.25   (G1372)

GOLGOTHA see Brun, G.

GOLGOTHA see Martin, Frank

GOLGOTHA see Wetherill

GOLGOTHA IS A MOUNTAIN see Work

GOLIATH JAZZ, THE see Chappell, Herbert

GOLLE, JURGEN
Psalm 98
4pt mix cor oct DEUTSCHER 7633 s.p. (G1373)

GOLLER, VINCENT
Klosterneuberger Messe (composed with Tittel,
Ernst) *Mass
mix cor&cong,cantor,opt org voc sc
DOBLINGER s.p., ipa   (G1374)
(Knotzinger, Kurt) 3pt mix cor&cong,cantor,
opt org DOBLINGER sc s.p., voc sc s.p.
(G1375)

GOLZ, RICHARD (1887-   )
Chorgesangbuch *CC162U,Gen
[Ger] 2-5pt mix cor,acap (med easy) BAREN.
BA 680 $8.75   (G1376)

GOMBERT, NICOLAS (ca. 1490-1550)
Ave Maria *BVM/Xmas
mix cor SOUTHERN $.20   (G1377)
SSATTB,acap SCHIRM.EC 1225 $.15   (G1378)
(Richardson) mix cor SOUTHERN $.25 (G1379)
(Richardson) SSATBB oct SPRATT 2009 $.30
(G1380)
(Westlund) mix cor SOUTHERN $.20   (G1381)
(Westlund) "Hail Thou Most Glorious" SSATTB
oct SUMMY 5499 $.25   (G1382)

Beati Omnes
see Opera Omnia Vol. I

GOMBERT, NICOLAS (cont'd.)

Credo
see Opera Omnia vol. III

De Pacem
see Opera Omnia Vol. I

Filomena
see Opera Omnia vol. II

Forseulement
see Opera Omnia vol. II

Hail Thou Most Glorious *see Ave Maria

Je Suis Desheritee
see Opera Omnia vol. I

Media Vita
see Opera Omnia vol. II

Opera Omnia Vol. I *Mass
(Schmidt-Gorg, J.) cor cmplt ed
AM.INST.MUS. $16.00
contains: Beati Omnes; De Pacem; Je Suis
Desheritee; Sancta Maria   (G1383)

Opera Omnia vol. II *Mass
(Schmidt-Gorg, J.) 4pt cmplt ed
AM.INST.MUS. $16.50
contains: Filomena; Forseulement; Media
Vita; Sur Tous Regretz   (G1384)

Opera Omnia vol. III *Mass
(Schmidt-Gorg, J.) cmplt ed AM.INST.MUS.
$18.00
contains: Credo (8pt); Quam Pulchra Es Et
Quam Decora (6pt); Tempore Paschali
(6pt&8pt&12pt)   (G1385)

Opera Omnia vol. IV *CCU,Magnif
(Schmidt-Gorg, J.) cor cmplt ed
AM.INST.MUS. $15.00   (G1386)

Opera Omnia vol. V *CCU,mot
(Schmidt-Gorg, J.) cor cmplt ed
AM.INST.MUS. $17.00   (G1387)

Opera Omnia vol. VI *CCU,mot
(Schmidt-Gorg, J.) cor cmplt ed
AM.INST.MUS. $20.00   (G1388)

Opera Omnia vol. VII *CCU,mot
(Schmidt-Gorg, J.) 5pt cmplt ed
AM.INST.MUS. $24.50   (G1389)

Opera Omnia vol. VIII *CCU,mot
(Schmidt-Gorg, J.) 3pt cmplt ed
AM.INST.MUS. $24.00   (G1390)

Quam Pulchra Es Et Quam Decora
see Opera Omnia vol. III

Quem Dicunt Homines
see Richafort, Quem Dicunt Homines

Sancta Maria
see Opera Omnia Vol. I

Sur Tous Regretz
see Opera Omnia vol. II

Tempore Paschali
see Opera Omnia vol. III

GOMEZ CAMARGO
Himno De Santiago Apostol *hymn
[Lat] 4pt mix cor,acap UNION ESP. 19356
s.p.   (G1391)

GOMIS
A Belen *Xmas
[Span] dbl cor,solo UNION ESP. 17591 s.p.
          (G1392)

Ha Nacido El Nino Dios *Xmas
[Span] dbl cor,solo UNION ESP. 17592 s.p.
          (G1393)

La Cancion *Xmas
[Span] dbl cor,solo UNION ESP. 18064 s.p.
          (G1394)

Misa Pastoril *Xmas,Mass
[Span] dbl cor (easy) UNION ESP. 17562 s.p.
          (G1395)
dbl cor/2pt (easy) UNION ESP. s.p. (G1396)

GOMOLKA, MIKOLAJ (ca. 1535-1591)
Awake My Soul (Psalm 108)
see Two Polish Psalms

Let Us Clap Our Hands (Psalm 47)
see Two Polish Psalms

Melodies For Polish Psalter Vol. 1 *CC50U,
Pol
(Perz, M.) mix cor,acap POLSKIE WDMP47 s.p.
contains: Psalms 1-50   (G1397)

Melodies For Polish Psalter Vol. 2 *CC50U,
Pol
(Perz, M.) mix cor,acap POLSKIE WDMP48 s.p.
contains: Psalms 51-100   (G1398)

Melodies For Polish Psalter Vol. 3 *CC50U,
Pol
(Perz, M.) mix cor,acap POLSKIE WDM49 s.p.
contains: Psalms 101-150   (G1399)

Psalm 47 *see Let Us Clap Our Hands

Psalm 108 *see Awake My Soul

Psalm 137 *see Siedzac Po Niskich Brzegach
Babilonskiej Wody

Siedzac Po Niskich Brzegach Babilonskiej Wody
(Psalm 137) Pol
"Sitting By The Low Banks Of The Waters Of
Babylon" mix cor,acap POLSKIE s.p.
          (G1400)
Sitting By The Low Banks Of The Waters Of
Babylon *see Siedzac Po Niskich Brzegach
Babilonskiej Wody

Two Polish Psalms *Gen
(Riedel) SATB SCHMITT 1411 $.30
contains: Awake My Soul (Psalm 108); Let
Us Clap Our Hands (Psalm 47)   (G1401)

GOMOLKA, MIKOLAJ (cont'd.)

With Broken Heart And Contrite Sigh *Gen/
Lent
SATB,acap (med easy) oct CONCORDIA 98-1772
$.20   (G1402)

GONE TO GLORY see Kennedy, John Brodbin

GONNA RIDE THAT HEAVENLY TRAIN see Young

GONNA RIDE UP IN THE CHARIOT *spir
(Ehret) SSA oct SPRATT 180 $.25   (G1403)
(Ehret, W.) SATB LEONARD-US 08018880 $.25
          (G1404)
(Richardson) SAB ALFRED 6512 $.30   (G1405)
(Richardson) SA ALFRED 6160 $.30   (G1406)

GONNA RIDE UP IN THE CHARIOT see Rhea

GONZALEZ BARRON
Cancion De Lo Divino *Xmas,carol
[Span] cor UNION ESP. 21052 s.p.   (G1407)

Himno A San Isidro Labrador, Patron De Madrid
3pt UNION ESP. 18414 s.p.   (G1408)

Misa En Honor De Ntra. Sra. De La Almundena
*Mass
2pt (text in Castellano) voc sc UNION ESP.
20647 s.p., cor pts UNION ESP. 20670 s.p.
          (G1409)

GOOD-BYE, BROTHER see Kennedy, John Brodbin

GOOD-BYE, HALLELUIA see Kennedy, John Brodbin

GOOD CHRISTIAN MEN REJOICE *Xmas,carol,Ger,
14th cent
see Many Moods Of Christmas, The, Suite One
unis&desc SCHIRM.EC 1763 $.25   (G1410)
(Davis, K.) SSA,acap SCHIRM.EC 1011 $.16
          (G1411)
(Gordon, P.) SATB oct PRESSER 312-40231 $.35
          (G1412)
(Hunter) SATB,S solo,org,fl oct LAWSON 51287
$.30   (G1413)
(Mueller) SA oct FISCHER,C CM-5304 $.20
          (G1414)
(Shaw; Parker) mix cor,acap oct SCHIRM.G
10183 $.30   (G1415)
(Terri) SATB,acap oct LAWSON 678 $.30 (G1416)
(Van Koert, Han) SA&SATB,org,opt fl&vln&vla&
vcl&harp oct WORLD AC-553-8 $.45, ipa
          (G1417)

GOOD CHRISTIAN MEN, REJOICE see Bach, Johann
Sebastian

GOOD CHRISTIAN MEN, REJOICE see Baxter, F.

GOOD CHRISTIAN MEN, REJOICE see Buxtehude,
Dietrich

GOOD CHRISTIAN MEN REJOICE! see Hastings, In
Dulci Jubilo

GOOD CHRISTIAN MEN, REJOICE see Lorenz

GOOD CHRISTIAN MEN REJOICE see Mueller, Carl F.

GOOD CHRISTIAN MEN, REJOICE! see Nyquist

GOOD CHRISTIAN MEN, REJOICE see Nystedt, Knut

GOOD CHRISTIAN MEN, REJOICE see Schroth

GOOD CHRISTIAN MEN, REJOICE see Thiman, Eric
Harding

GOOD CHRISTIAN MEN REJOICE see Werner, Gregor
Joseph

GOOD CHRISTIAN MEN, REJOICE see Wilson, John F.

GOOD CHRISTIAN MEN REJOICE AND SING
(Copley, I.A.) SAB LENGNICK s.p.   (G1418)

GOOD CHRISTIAN MEN, REJOICE AND SING see
Bullock, Ernest

GOOD CHRISTIAN MEN, REJOICE AND SING! see
Cartford, Gerhard M.

GOOD CHRISTIAN MEN, REJOICE AND SING see Copley

GOOD CHRISTIAN MEN, REJOICE AND SING see
Lovelace, Austin C.

GOOD CHRISTIAN MEN, REJOICE AND SING see
Vulpius, Melchior

GOOD CHRISTIAN MEN, WITH JOY DRAW NEAR see
Buxtehude, Dietrich, Ihr Lieben Christen,
Freut Euch Nun

GOOD CHRISTIANS ALL *Xmas
(Ehret) SATB SCHMITT 881 $.25   (G1419)

GOOD CHRISTIANS NOW LET ALL REJOICE see
Bancroft, H. Hugh

GOOD CHRISTIANS, NOW REJOICE see Scheidt,
Samuel

GOOD DAY, SIR CHRISTMAS see Terry, Richard
Runciman

GOOD EARTH see Williams, Ralph E.

GOOD EVENING see Hwrayneeyah Day

GOOD FOLK WHO DWELL ON EARTH see Davis, J.

GOOD FRIDAY see Giannini, V.

GOOD FRIDAY see Sateren, Leland Bernhard

GOOD FRIDAY SPIRITUAL *Easter/Gd.Fri.,spir
SATB oct LORENZ 4433 $.30   (G1420)

GOOD KING WENCESLAS *Xmas,carol,Eng
see Five Christmas Carols
(Hallstrom, H.) SSA oct PRESSER 312-40471
$.35   (G1421)
(Hallstrom, H.) SATB oct PRESSER 312-40472
$.40   (G1422)
(Nightingale) SATB oct FISCHER,C CM-7036 $.25
          (G1423)
(Sharpe, E.) cor&desc CRAMER 43   (G1424)
(Shaw; Parker) mix cor,SB soli,acap oct

SCHIRM.G 10184 $.35   (G1425)

GOOD KING WENCESLAS see Dinn, Freda

GOOD LIFE, THE see Red, Buryl

GOOD LORD, SHALL I EVER BE THE ONE see Papp,
Akos G.

GOOD LORD WILLED IT SO, THE see Peter

GOOD MASTER AND MISTRESS see Edmonds, Paul

GOOD MORNING, BROTHER PILGRIM
(Parker) mix cor,acap oct LAWSON 51330 $.30
          (G1426)
GOOD NEIGHBOR, WHENCE CAME THAT GREAT SOUND see
Gevaert, Francois Auguste, Voisin,
D'ouvenait Ce Grand Bruit?

GOOD NEIGHBOURS THEN see Crawford, T.J.

GOOD NEWS *spir
"Gluck Auf" see Sechs Negro Spirituals, Blatt
1
(Gardner, Maurice) SATB oct STAFF 349 $.30
          (G1427)
(Wilson) SSA oct SPRATT 170 $.25   (G1428)

GOOD NEWS see Cain, Noble

GOOD NEWS! see Marshall

GOOD NEWS see Ratcliffe, Desmond

GOOD NEWS see Smith

GOOD NEWS see Wilson

GOOD NEWS, CHARIOT'S COMIN'! *spir
(Curtis; Burlin) 4pt men cor,acap oct
SCHIRM.G 8224 $.25   (G1429)

GOOD NEWS FROM HEAVEN *CCU,Xmas
(Lenel, L.) TTBB,kbd (med easy) oct CONCORDIA
98-1401 $.25 contains works by: Praetorius;
Othmayr; Hassler   (G1430)

GOOD NEWS FROM HEAVEN *spir
(Tkach) SAB KJOS 5716 $.30   (G1431)

GOOD NEWS FROM HEAVEN see Bach, Johann
Sebastian

GOOD NEWS FROM HEAVEN see Klein

GOOD NEWS FROM HEAVEN see Tkach, P.

GOOD NEWS IN THE KINGDOM *spir
unis/SA oct LORENZ 8611 $.25   (G1432)
(Kinsman) SATB oct PRO ART 1974 $.25 (G1433)

GOOD NEWS IN THE KINGDOM see Sanford

GOOD NEWS IS HERE see Sheppard, [Joseph]
Stanley

GOOD NEWS! THE CHARIOT'S COMIN' *spir
(Hadley) SATB oct PRO ART 1819 $.25   (G1434)

GOOD NIGHT, LITTLE JESUS see Page, R.

GOOD OF CONTENTMENT, THE see Berger, Jean

GOOD OLD WAY, THE see Sateren, Leland Bernhard

GOOD PEOPLE, HEAR THE NEWS I BRING *Xmas
(Cockshott) unis oct PRO ART 2131 $.30
          (G1435)
GOOD SAMARITAN, THE see McAfee, Don

GOOD SAMARITAN, THE see Webber, Lloyd

GOOD SAMARITAN, THE see Grime, William

GOOD SHEPHERD, THE see Pooler, Marie

GOOD SHEPHERD OF THE CHILDREN
SA KJOS 6056 $.30   (G1436)

GOOD SHEPHERD, THE see Barri, O.

GOOD SHEPHERD, THE see Thiman, Eric Harding

GOOD SHEPHERDS
see Three French Carols (Noels)

GOOD SHEPHERDS, LEAVE see Gronquist, R.,
Quittez Pasteurs

GOOD THING IT IS TO GIVE THANKS see Bitgood

GOOD TIDINGS OF JOY see Walter

GOOD TIDINGS TO THE MEEK see Thompson, Randall

GOOD TO ME see Hadler

GOOD WISHES see Foss, Julius

GOODALE
Ju Me Leve Un Bel Maitin
mix cor SOUTHERN $.25   (G1437)

GOODALE, R.
Joseph, Now To Thee Is Given *Xmas
SATB oct ELKAN-V 362-1205 $.25   (G1438)

GOODALE, R.L.
Angel To The Shepherds, The *carol,Span,16th
cent
SSA oct ELKAN-V 362-3104 $.30   (G1439)

Angels Are Flying, The *Xmas
SSA oct ELKAN-V 362-3091 $.25   (G1440)

Cast Thy Garments *Palm
SATB oct ELKAN-V 362-1241 $.30   (G1441)

Christ The Lord Is Born *Xmas
SATB oct ELKAN-V 362-1233 $.25   (G1442)

Glory To God *Xmas
SATB oct ELKAN-V 362-1232 $.25   (G1443)

Kings Follow The Star, The *Xmas
SATB oct ELKAN-V 362-1206 $.25   (G1444)
SSA oct ELKAN-V 362-3092 $.30   (G1445)

GOODALE, R.L. (cont'd.)

See The Shepherd's Dancing *Xmas
SSA oct ELKAN-V 362-3093 $.30   (G1446)

Then The Good Shepherd Arose *Easter
SATB oct ELKAN-V 362-1258 $.25   (G1447)

We Adore Thee, Gracious Lord
oct ELKAN-V 362-132 $.35   (G1448)

GOODE, J.
All My Heart This Night Rejoices
SATB, opt pno/org oct KERBY 6007 $.35
(G1449)

Count It All Joy
SATB, kbd oct KERBY 6105 $.40   (G1450)

Psalm 46
SATB, pno/org oct KERBY 6407 $.35   (G1451)

GOODE, JACK C.
All My Heart This Night Rejoices *Xmas
SATB, acap oct KERBY 6007C $.35   (G1452)

Carol Of Mary *Xmas, carol
SA, org/pno GRAY GCMR 3283 $.30   (G1453)

Count It All Joy
SATB oct KERBY 6105C $.40   (G1454)

Glory Of The Lord, The
SATB, org GRAY GCMR 3294 $.35   (G1455)

How Firm A Foundation
SATB, opt trp oct AGAPE F 919 $.30   (G1456)

Nine Introits *CC9L, Introit
SATB, acap GRAY GCMR 3228 $.30   (G1457)

On His Might
SATB (med) ABINGDON APM-217 $.25   (G1458)

Psalm 46
SATB oct KERBY 6407C $.35   (G1459)

Psalm 150
SATB (med) ABINGDON APM-263 $.35   (G1460)

Sing To The Lord
SATB (med) ABINGDON APM-218 $.25   (G1461)

GOODENOUGH, F.
Psalm 91 *see Who So Dwelleth

Thy Giving Power
SATB oct SOUTHERN $.25   (G1462)

Who So Dwelleth (Psalm 91)
SATB oct SOUTHERN $.25   (G1463)

GOODHALL, CLARE
Lamb, The
2pt wom cor oct SCHIRM.G 7652 $.20 (G1464)

GOODHART
Peace, Gentle Peace
SATB, acap oct BOOSEY 5279 $.30   (G1465)

GOODING CAROL see Oliver

GOODLY CHILD, THE see Kobrich

GOODMAN, A.
Psalm 12
SSA, Bar solo oct PRESSER MC230 $.45 (G1466)

GOODMAN, JOSEPH
Adoramus Te, Christe
[Lat/Eng] SATB, acap AMP A392 $.20 (G1467)

Alleluia! I Bring You Good Tidings *Xmas
SA, A solo, acap AMP A449 $.25 see from Three
Alleluias For Christmas   (G1468)

Alleluia, The Lord Said Unto Me *Xmas
SSA, acap AMP A448 $.30 see from Three
Alleluias For Christmas   (G1469)

Before The Ending Of The Day *Easter
SATB, acap oct PRESSER MC485 $.35 (G1470)

Behold The Hand Maid Of The Lord
SSA, acap oct PRESSER MC440 $.30 (G1471)

Caligaverunt Oculi Mei
[Lat/Eng] SATB BROUDE,A. 149 $.35 see from
Three Responsories   (G1472)

Crucem Tuam Adoramus
"We Venerate Thy Cross" [Lat/Eng] SATB, acap
AMP A359 $.25   (G1473)

Jesum Tradidit
[Lat/Eng] SATB BROUDE,A. 148 $.30 see from
Three Responsories   (G1474)

Laudate Dominum
[Lat] SATB, opt S solo, acap AMP A298 $.35
(G1475)

Let The Heavens Rejoice *Xmas
SSA, acap AMP A450 $.20 see from Three
Alleluias For Christmas   (G1476)

Love Came Down At Christmas *Xmas
SA, org BROUDE,A. 181 $.30   (G1477)

O King Enthroned On High
SATB, acap oct PRESSER MC487 $.25 (G1478)

O Trinity Of Blessed Light
SATB, acap oct PRESSER MC484 $.30 (G1479)

Preserve Me, O God
SATB, acap oct PRESSER MC417 $.40 (G1480)

That Easter Day With Joy Was Bright *Easter
SATB, acap oct PRESSER MC486 $.30 (G1481)

Three Alleluias For Christmas *see Alleluia!
I Bring You Good Tidings; Alleluia, The
Lord Said Unto Me; Let The Heavens
Rejoice   (G1482)

Three Motets For Benediction *CC3U, mot
SATB, acap oct PRESSER 352-00053 $.40
(G1483)

GOODMAN, JOSEPH (cont'd.)

Three Responsories *see Caligaverunt Oculi
Mei; Jesum Tradidit; Tradiderunt Me
(G1484)

Thy Rebuke Hath Broken My Heart *Palm
SATB, acap oct PRESSER MC526 $.30 (G1485)

Tradiderunt Me
[Lat/Eng] SATB BROUDE,A. 147 $.30 see from
Three Responsories   (G1486)

We Venerate Thy Cross *see Crucem Tuam
Adoramus

GOODNESS OF THE LORD, THE see Bach, Karl
Philipp Emanuel

GOODNIGHT, GOD BLESS YOU see Wild, Eric

GOODWILL TO MEN see Clare, Edwyn A.

GOODWIN
O Come, O Come Emmanuel *Adv
SATB FLAMMER A 5057 $.30   (G1487)
SSA FLAMMER B 5097 $.25   (G1488)
SAB FLAMMER D5075 $.30   (G1489)
SA/TB FLAMMER E5059 $.25   (G1490)

GOOSSEN, FREDERIC
Hodie
SATB, acap PEER $.30   (G1491)

GOR PORTEN HOG *Bibl
(Olson, Daniel) [Swed] SAB, acap GEHRMANS
KRB 196   (G1492)

GORCZYCKI, GREGOR GERVASIUS (ca. 1664-1734)
Anthems *CCU, Pol
(Kaczorowska) cor, cont, 2vln POLSKIE WDMP71
s.p.   (G1493)

Completorium *CC7L, Pol
(Wecowski) 4pt mix cor, org, inst POLSKIE
ZHMP7 s.p.   (G1494)

Illuxit Sol *mot, Pol
(Chybinski, A.) SSATB, cont, strings POLSKIE
WDMP14 s.p.   (G1495)

Iustus Ut Palma Florebit
see Gorczycki, Gregor Gervasius, Os Iustus
Meditabitur

Laetatus Sum *mot, Pol
(Swierczek, W.) SATB, cont, inst POLSKIE
WDMP37 s.p.   (G1496)

Missa Paschalis *Pol
(Chybinski, A.) mix cor, acap POLSKIE WDMP7
s.p.   (G1497)

Missa Rorate *Pol
(Swierczek, W.) mix cor, acap POLSKIE WDMP65
s.p.   (G1498)

Os Iusti Meditabitur *Pol
(Kaczorowska, M.) 4pt mix cor, cont, 2vln
POLSKIE WDMP63 s.p. contains also: Iustus
Ut Palma Florebit   (G1499)

GORDON
As I Sat Under A Sycamore Tree *Xmas, carol
SATB oct KENDOR $.30   (G1500)

My Jesus, I Love Thee *hymn
(Eleiott; Collins) SATB oct LILLENAS
AT-1018 $.30   (G1501)

Thanks, O Lord
SA KJOS 6104 $.30   (G1502)

Tribute Of Carols, A *Xmas, carol
2pt/SAB/SATB, opt orch/band WARNER W7-1014
$.50, ipa   (G1503)

We Sanctify The Name Of God
SATB WARNER R3453 $.30   (G1504)

Within Thy Light *see Orleans, Ilo

GORDON, A.
My Jesus, I Love Thee *Easter/Gen
(Peery, R.) SA oct PRESSER 312-40528 $.30
(G1505)

Who Is This Boy?
SATB, pno oct KERBY 5805 $.25   (G1506)

GORDON, LOUIS
I Will Lift Up Mine Eyes (Psalm 121)
[Eng] SATB TRANSCON. TCL 126 $.30 (G1507)

Psalm 121 *see I Will Lift Up Mine Eyes

GORDON, P.
Carol For A Wassel Bowl, A *Xmas
SATB, acap oct PRESSER 312-40596 $.30
(G1508)

O Jesu So Sweet, O Jesu So Mild
SATB oct ELKAN-V 362-11060 $.25   (G1509)

Praise The Lord
SATB, pno (diff) oct WILLIS 7270 $.25
(G1510)

Prayer Of Moses' Mother
SATB oct ELKAN-V 362-1131 $.25   (G1511)

Psalm 67 *see Sixty-Seventh Psalm, The

Sixty-Seventh Psalm, The (Psalm 67)
SATB oct PRESSER MC259 $.40   (G1512)

Susani *Xmas, carol, 16th cent
SSA oct ELKAN-V 362-3071 $.30   (G1513)

GORDON, PHILIP (1894-
Arise, Shine, For Thy Light Is Come
SATB oct LAWSON 799 $.30   (G1514)

As Joseph Was A-Walking *Xmas
SSA oct SHAPIRO SK 3003 $.25   (G1515)

Gloria Tibi, Domine *Xmas
SATB oct SHAPIRO SK 2060 $.30   (G1516)

Isaiah's Vision
SATB oct SHAPIRO SK 2005 $.25   (G1517)

GORDON, PHILIP (cont'd.)

Sing Baloo, Sing Balow *Xmas
SSA oct SHAPIRO SK 3033 $.30   (G1518)
SAB oct SHAPIRO SK 5019 $.30   (G1519)
SATB oct SHAPIRO SK 2111 $.30   (G1520)
2pt oct SHAPIRO SK 4026 $.30   (G1521)

What Cheer? Good Cheer! *Xmas
SATB oct SHAPIRO SK 2110 $.30   (G1522)

GORE, RICHARD T.
Angels High And Lowly *Xmas
SATB oct GALAXY 1.2163.1 $.35   (G1523)

For Ever, O Lord
SATB oct GALAXY 1.2457.1 $.30   (G1524)

Four Rounds For Christmas *CC4U, Xmas
oct SSA FISCHER,J 9106 $.30; SSA FISCHER,J
9549 $.30   (G1525)

God Of Abraham Praise, The *cant
SATB (med) ABINGDON APM-860 $1.00 (G1526)

Let God Arise (Psalm 68)
SATB, org SEESAW $1.50   (G1527)

Psalm 68 *see Let God Arise

GOREN PORTARNA HOGA see Wennerberg, Gunnar

GORLATTO, GIACOMO
Adoramus Te Christe *CC3U, mot
[Lat] unis ZANIBON 2831 s.p.   (G1528)

Cantico Di Frate Sole *ASD, Greg
[Lat] unis, org ZANIBON 2445 s.p.   (G1529)

Dodici Litanie Lauretane *CC12U, Greg
[Lat] unis ZANIBON 1920 s.p.   (G1530)

Officium Et Missa In Festo S. Antonii Pat.
*CCU, ASD, Greg
[Lat] unis ZANIBON 2446 s.p.   (G1531)

Quindici Litanae Lauretane *CC15U, Greg
[Lat] unis, org ZANIBON 2444 s.p. (G1532)

S. Antonio Di Padova *ASD, Greg
[Lat] unis, org sc ZANIBON 2127 s.p., cor
pts ZANIBON 2128 s.p.   (G1533)

Sei Inni Antoniani *CC6U, ASD, hymn
[Lat] unis mix cor, org ZANIBON 3032 s.p.
(G1534)

Venti Litanie Laurentane *CC20U, Greg
[Lat] unis, org ZANIBON 3671 s.p.   (G1535)

GORMAN
Chicago Folk Service *folk
SATB, kbd KJOS $2.50   (G1536)

GOROCHOV, Y.
Israel Harvest Song *see Saleynu

Saleynu *Fest
(Helfman, M.) "Israel Harvest Song" [Heb]
SATB TRANSCON. TCL 723 $.25   (G1537)

GOROSTIDI
Alabad, Ninos Al Senor *see Laudate Pueri
Dominum

Laudate Pueri Dominum
"Alabad, Ninos Al Senor" 3-4pt jr cor UNION
ESP. 18280 s.p.   (G1538)

GOSPEL ACCLAMATIONS AND VERSES see Pross, D.

GOSPEL ACCORDING TO JUDAS, THE see Ludlow

GOSPEL BARD, THE see Hustad, Donald P.

GOSPEL CALL FOR MEN *CCU
men cor LORENZ $1.25   (G1539)

GOSPEL CHOIR NO. 1, THE *CCUL, gospel
(Bock, Fred) SATB voc sc WORD 15015 $1.50
(G1540)

GOSPEL CHOIR NO. 2, THE *CCUL, gospel
(Bock, Fred) SATB voc sc WORD 20029 $1.50
(G1541)

GOSPEL CHORISTER, THE see Vaughn, Leslie

GOSPEL FOLK STYLES (BOOK 1) *CC13UL, gospel
(Johnson, Derric) cor, includes chord symbols
and string bass line cmplt ed LILLENAS
MB-054 $1.50   (G1542)

GOSPEL FOLK STYLES (BOOK 2) *CC12UL, gospel
(Johnson, Derric) cor, bvl, tamb, gtr cmplt ed
LILLENAS MB-055 $1.50   (G1543)

GOSPEL HARMONIES FOR TREBLE VOICES *CCU
SSA LORENZ $1.50   (G1544)

GOSPEL QUARTETS FOR MIXED VOICES *CCU
4pt mix cor LORENZ $1.50   (G1545)

GOSPEL SHOWS THE FATHER'S GRACE, THE see
Rotermund, Melvin

GOSPEL SONG, A see Kersters, Willem

GOSPEL SONG ANTHEMS NO. 1 *CCU, anthem
SATB LORENZ $1.95   (G1546)

GOSPEL SONG ANTHEMS NO. 2 *CCU, anthem
SATB LORENZ $1.95   (G1547)

GOSPEL SONG ANTHEMS NO. 3 *CCU, anthem
SATB/SA LORENZ $1.75   (G1548)

GOSPEL SONG ANTHEMS NO. 4 *CCU, anthem
SATB/SA LORENZ $1.75   (G1549)

GOSPEL SONG ANTHEMS NO. 5 *CCU, anthem
SATB/SA LORENZ $1.75   (G1550)

GOSPEL SONG ANTHEMS NO. 6 *CC12UL, anthem/spir
(Wilson, Roger C.) SA/SATB (easy) LORENZ
$1.75   (G1551)

GOSPEL SONG OF CHRISTMAS, THE see Lorenz

GOSPEL SONG OF EASTER, THE see Lorenz

GOSPEL TRAIN *spir
see Eight Negro Spirituals: Book Ii
(Ritz, James) SA&SATB,acap oct WORLD
ESE-736-8 $.60   (G1552)
(Ritz, James) SSA,pno oct WORLD ESE-1312-3
$.45   (G1553)
(Tate) SAB,acap (med easy) OXFORD 86.006 $.35
                                  (G1554)
(Trant) SSA (easy) OXFORD 83.048 $.25 (G1555)

GOSPEL TRAIN, DE see Burleigh, Henry Thacker

GOSPEL TRAIN, THE *spir
(Widdicombe) 2pt jr cor/2pt wom cor CURWEN
72494 s.p.   (G1556)

GOSPEL TRAIN, DE *spir
(Scarmolin) SATB oct PRO ART 1172 $.16
                                  (G1557)
GOSPEL TRAIN, THE *spir
(Ehret) SSA oct FOX PS78 $.25   (G1558)
(Ehret) SATB oct FOX PS79 $.30   (G1559)

GOSPEL TRAIN, THE see Mansfield, Purcell James

GOSPEL TRUMPET, THE see Cassler, G. Winston

GOSS, JOHN (1800-1880)
Almighty And Merciful God *anthem
mix cor oct NOVELLO 40.0200.08 s.p. (G1560)
(Coggin) SAB oct PRO ART 2440 $.25 (G1561)

Behold, I Bring You Good Tidings *Xmas,
anthem
SATB oct LORENZ 9869 $.30   (G1562)
mix cor oct NOVELLO 40.0178.08 s.p. (G1563)

Christ, Our Passover *Easter,anthem
mix cor oct NOVELLO 40.0169.09 s.p. (G1564)

Fear Not, O Land, Be Glad And Rejoice *Harv,
anthem
mix cor oct NOVELLO 28.0028.04 s.p. (G1565)

God So Loved The World *Easter/Lent,anthem/
Bibl
SATB ALLANS 380 s.p.   (G1566)
mix cor oct NOVELLO 40.0459.00 s.p. (G1567)
(Hines) 3pt mix cor,acap,org/pno oct
SCHIRM.G 11762 $.25   (G1568)
(Strickling) SATB oct SPRATT 538 $.25
                                  (G1569)

I Heard A Voice From Heaven *anthem
SATB,acap (burial) SCHIRM.EC 1705 $.18
                                  (G1570)
mix cor oct NOVELLO 28.0396.08 s.p. (G1571)

If We Believe
SATB oct LESLIE 4150   (G1572)

If We Believe That Jesus Died *anthem
mix cor oct NOVELLO 40.0448.05 s.p. (G1573)
SSAATTBB,org BROUDE,A. 219 $.35 (G1574)

Lord Jehovah Reigns, The
(Ehret) SATB oct PRO ART 2566 $.30 (G1575)

O Praise The Lord
(Knight) 3pt mix cor,org oct CURWEN 10628
$.20   (G1576)

O Praise The Lord, Laud Ye The Name *Thanks,
anthem
mix cor oct NOVELLO 40.0168.00 s.p. (G1577)

O Savior Of The World *Commun/Gen/Lent
SATB (easy) ALLANS 49 s.p.   (G1578)
SATB SCHMITT 1907 $.30   (G1579)

O Saviour Of The World *Easter/Lent,anthem
SATB oct PRO ART 1041 $.25   (G1580)
SATB oct SOUTHERN $.30   (G1581)
4pt mix cor,acap oct SCHIRM.G 4257 $.25
                                  (G1582)
SATB oct PRESSER 312-10014 $.30 (G1583)
SATB oct BELWIN 1143 $.25   (G1584)
SA oct BELWIN 64018 $.30   (G1585)
SATB oct BELWIN 64121 $.30   (G1586)
mix cor oct NOVELLO 40.0408.06 s.p. (G1587)
SATB oct LESLIE 4023   (G1588)
(Deis) 2pt wom cor,org oct SCHIRM.G 10215
$.20   (G1589)
(Dews) 3pt wom cor oct SCHIRM.G 9588 $.25
                                  (G1590)
(Griffith) SAB oct PRO ART 1133 $.25
                                  (G1591)
(Mueller) SABar oct SCHIRM.G 8694 $.25
                                  (G1592)
(Stevens) SSA oct PRO ART 1640 $.25 (G1593)
(Stevens) 2pt oct PRO ART 1560 $.16 (G1594)

O Saviour Of The World (O Lord Of All
Mankind)
SATB,acap SCHIRM.EC 1719 $.30 (G1595)

O Taste And See *Commun,anthem/Bibl
SATB,pno oct HARRIS HC4042 $.35 (G1596)
SATB ALLANS 59 s.p.   (G1597)
4pt mix cor oct SCHIRM.G 3864 $.25 (G1598)
mix cor oct NOVELLO 28.0008.10 s.p. (G1599)
SATB oct LESLIE 4032   (G1600)

O Taste, And See, How Gracious The Lord Is
SATB oct PRO ART 1697 $.25   (G1601)

Praise, My Soul, The King Of Heaven
(Grieb) 3pt mix cor,org oct SCHIRM.G 11188
$.25   (G1602)
(Ohl) SATB oct PLYMOUTH FO-109 $.25 (G1603)

Saviour Of The World *Easter/Lent
SATB oct FISCHER,C CM-253 $.25 (G1604)
TTBB oct FISCHER,C CM-386 $.25 (G1605)

See, Amid The Winter's Snow *Xmas
(Coggin, E.) SAB oct PRESSER 312-40792 $.30
                                  (G1606)
(Fraser) SATB,acap oct FOX PS155 $.25
                                  (G1607)
(Willcocks) SATB (med) OXFORD 84.125 $.30,
ipa   (G1608)

Wilderness, The *anthem
mix cor oct NOVELLO 28.0031.04 s.p. (G1609)

GOSSEC, FRANCOIS JOSEPH (1734-1829)
Christmas Suite *CCU,Xmas
[Lat] sc PETERS V145 $5.00, ipa, voc sc
PETERS V145 $.50, ipa   (G1610)

La Nativite *Xmas,ora
(Townsend, D.) [Fr/Eng] mix cor,SATB soli,
kbd/2fl&2ob&2clar&2bsn&4trp&strings voc
sc BROUDE,A. 112 $1.75, ipr   (G1611)

Weihnachtssuite *CCU,Xmas
(Schultz; Hauser) [Ger] mix cor,2ob/2fl,
strings,cont,opt 2horn VIEWEG voc sc
s.p., cor pts s.p., ipa   (G1612)

GOT A HOME IN THAT ROCK *anthem/spir
(Cain) SATB,acap oct PRO ART 1524 $.18
                                  (G1613)
(Ehret) SATB oct FISCHER,C CM-7613 $.25
                                  (G1614)

GOT NO TIME see Lewis

GOTSCH, GEORG
Chorlieder Zur Weihnacht *CCU,Xmas
3 eq voices MOSELER s.p.   (G1615)

GOTT ABER KANN MACHEN, DASS ALLERLEI GNADE see
Micheelsen, Hans Friedrich

GOTT, BEFREI UNS VON DER ANGST see Keller,
Wilhelm

GOTT, DEINE GUTE REICHT SO WEIT see Hauptmann,
Moritz

GOTT, DEM EWIGEN KONIGE see Stockmeier,
Wolfgang

GOTT, DEM EWIGEN KONIGE see Weyrauch, Johannes

GOTT, DEM EWIGEN KONIGE, DEM UNSERGANGLICHEN
see Fussan, Werner

GOTT DEM VATER IM HOCHSTEN THRON see
Praetorius, Michael

GOTT, DEM VATER UND DEM SOHNE see Victoria,
Tomas Luis de

GOTT, DER DA HIESS DAS LICHT see Stiefel, M.V.

GOTT, DER DU ALLES WOHL BEDACHT see Weber,
Bernhard

GOTT, DER HEILIGE GEIST see Anonymous

GOTT DER HERR see Bach, Johann Sebastian, Gott,
Der Herr, Ist Sonn' Und Schild

GOTT, DER HERR, DER MACHTIGE, RUFT DER WELT see
Reda, Siegfried

GOTT, DER HERR, IST SONN UND SCHILD see Bach,
Johann Sebastian

GOTT DER HERR IST SONN UND SCHILD see Reda,
Siegfried

GOTT DER VATER WOHN BEI UNS see Praetorius,
Michael

GOTT, DER VATER WOHN' UNS BEI see Bach, Johann
Sebastian

GOTT DER VATER WOHN UNS BEI see Distler, Hugo

GOTT DER VATER WOHN UNS BEI see Eccard,
Johannes

GOTT, DER VATER, WOHN UNS BEI see Hassler, Hans
Leo

GOTT DER VATER WOHN UNS BEI see Osiander, Lucas

GOTT DER VATER WOHN UNS BEI see Praetorius,
Michael

GOTT DER VATER WOHN UNS BEI see Scheidt, Samuel

GOTT DER VATER WOHN UNS BEI see Schein, Johann
Hermann

GOTT DER VATER WOHN UNS BEI see Werner, Fritz

GOTT DES HIMMELS UND DER ERDEN see Albert,
Heinrich

GOTT DES HIMMELS UND DER ERDEN see Neubert,
Gottfried

GOTT DES HIMMELS UND DER ERDEN see Trubel,
Gerhard

GOTT DES HIMMELS UND DER ERDEN see Wenzel,
Eberhard

GOTT FAEHRET see Bach, Johann Sebastian, Gott
Fahret Auf Mit Jauchzen

GOTT FAHRET AUF see Thomas, Kurt

GOTT FAHRET AUF MIT JAUCHZEN see Bach, Johann
Sebastian

GOTT FAHRT AUF MIT JAUCHZEN see Hohlfeld,
Christoph

GOTT GEHT AN KEINEM VORBEI see Kretzschmar,
Gunther

GOTT, GIB FRIED UNSERM LANDE see Kretzschmar,
Gunther

GOTT, GIB GLUCK ZUM NEUEN JAHR see Erlebach,
Philipp Heinrich

GOTT GRUSSE DICH see Mucke, F.

GOTT HALT FERN VON UNS see Keller, Wilhelm

GOTT HAT DIE ERD SCHON ZUGERICHT'T see Bach,
Johann Sebastian

GOTT HAT JESUM ERWECKET see Ritter, Christian

GOTT HEILGER SCHOPFER ALLER STERN see Jansen,
Philipp

GOTT, HEILGER SCHOPFER ALLER STERN see Kraft,
Walter

GOTT HEIL'GER SCHOPFER ALLER STERN see Lehner,
F.X.

GOTT, HILF MIR see Buxtehude, Dietrich

GOTT, HULLE DICH NICHT IN SCHWEIGEN see Eder,
Helmut

GOTT, ICH ATME DEINE KRAFT see Lissmann, Kurt

GOTT IM HIMMEL see Rohwer, Jens

GOTT IM UNGEWITTER see Schubert, Franz (Peter)

GOTT IN DER HOH' SEI PREIS UND EHR' see
Doppelbauer, Josef Friedrich

GOTT IN DER HOH SEI PREIS UND EHR see Sendt,
Willy

GOTT IST see Bach, Johann Sebastian, Gott Ist
Mein Konig

GOTT IST see Burgwart, K.

GOTT IST BEI UNS, UND WIR SIND SEIN EIGEN see
Schweizer, Rolf

GOTT IST DA *CC18U,Gen
[Ger] unis,kbd (med) BOSSE BE 224 s.p.
                                  (G1616)
GOTT IST DA (ICH HABE LANGE VERZWEIFELT
GEFRAGT) see Zoller, Alfred Hans

GOTT IST DAS GROSSE SCHWEIGEN see Schnitzler,
Heinrich

GOTT IST DER HERR see Planzer, Emanuel

GOTT IST DIE LIEBE see Beethoven, Ludwig van

GOTT IST DIE ZUFLUCHT ALLER FROMMEN see Wolleb,
Johann Jakob

GOTT IST DOCH HERR IN DEISER WELT see
Schweizer, Rolf

GOTT IST EIN EW'GER GEIST see Kratochwill,
Heinrich

GOTT IST GEGENWARTIG, LASSET UNS see Neander,
Joachim

GOTT IST GEIST see Buchtger, Fritz

GOTT IST GEIST see Brunner, Adolf

GOTT IST GETREU see Ahle, Johann Rudolph, Es
Ist Vollbracht

GOTT IST GEWALTIG see Meissner, Gen. Frauenlob

GOTT IST GEWALTIG see Moser, Hans Joachim

GOTT IST LIEBE see Micheelsen, Hans Friedrich

GOTT IST LIEBE see Reda, Siegfried

GOTT IST LIEBE see Zipp, Friedrich

GOTT IST LIEBE, UND WER IN DER LIEBE see
Thiele, Siegfried

GOTT IST MEIN HIRT see Schubert, Franz (Peter)

GOTT IST MEIN HIRTE see Schubert, Franz (Peter)

GOTT IST MEIN KONIG see Bach, Johann Sebastian

GOTT IST MEIN LIED see Beethoven, Ludwig van

GOTT IST MEIN TROST see Vento, Ivo de

GOTT IST UND BLEIBT GETREU see Bach, Johann
Sebastian

GOTT IST UND BLEIBT GETREU see Lang, Hans

GOTT IST UNSER ZUVERSICHT see Pachelbel, Johann

GOTT IST UNSER ZUVERSICHT UND STARKE see
Kukuck, Felicitas

GOTT IST UNSERE ZUVERSICHT see Pachelbel,
Johann

GOTT IST UNSRE see Bach, Johann Sebastian, Gott
Ist Unsre Zuversicht

GOTT IST UNSRE ZUVERSICHT see Bach, Johann
Sebastian

GOTT IST UNSRE ZUVERSICHT see Distler, Hugo

GOTT IST UNSRE ZUVERSICHT see Klein, Richard
Rudolf

GOTT IST UNSRE ZUVERSICHT see Zimmermann, Heinz
Werner

GOTT IST UNSRE ZUVERSICHT UND STARKE see
Wasmuth, Jan Jurgen

GOTT ISTS, AUF DEN WIR IMMER HOFFEN see Lassus,
Roland de (Orlandus)

GOTT, LASS SICH FREUEN ALLE see Hartmann,
Heinrich

GOTT LEBET NOCH see Bach, Johann Sebastian

GOTT LEBET NOCH! SEELE, WAS VERZAGST DU see
Bach, Johann Sebastian

GOTT LIEBT DEN MENSCHEN see Ruppel, Paul Ernst

GOTT LIEBT DIE WELT MIT IHRER SCHULD see
Ruppel, Paul Ernst

GOTT LIEBT DIESE WELT see Ruppel, Paul Ernst

GOTT, MAN LOBET DICH see Bach, Johann
Sebastian, Gott, Man Lobet Dich In Der
Stille

GOTT, MAN LOBET DICH IN DER STILLE see Bach, Johann Sebastian

GOTT MEINE ZUVERSICHT see Schubert, Franz (Peter)

GOTT MEINT ES GUT MIT DIR see Schneider, Martin Gotthard

GOTT RUFET NOCH, SOLLT ICH NICHT see Trubel, Gerhard

GOTT RUFT DICH HEUT DURCH JESUM CHRIST see Stern, Hermann

GOTT SCHENKT FREIHEIT see Ruppel, Paul Ernst

GOTT SCHUF DIE SONNE see Gadsch, Herbert

GOTT SCHUTZE DIE REBEN AM SONNIGEN RHEIN see Attenhofer, [Karl]

GOTT, SCHWEIGE, DOCH NICHT ALSO see Marx, Karl

GOTT SEGNE DIESEN BUND see Decker, W.

GOTT SEGNE DIESEN BUND see Haug, G.

GOTT SEI DANK, DER UNS DEN SIEG GEGEBEM HAT see Schutz, Heinrich

GOTT SEI DANK DURCH ALLE WELT see Fiebig, Kurt

GOTT SEI DANK DURCH ALLE WELT see Lehman, Siegfried

GOTT SEI DANK DURCH ALLE WELT see Raphael, Gunther

GOTT SEI GELOBET see Praetorius, Michael

GOTT SEI GELOBET UND GEBENEDEIET see Decker, Joachim

GOTT SEI GELOBET UND GEBENEDEIET see Hassler, Hans Leo

GOTT SEI GELOBET UND GEBENEDEIET see Schein, Johann Hermann

GOTT SEI GELOBT see Brant, Johann von

GOTT SEI MIR GNADIG see Kuhnau, Johann

GOTT SEI MIR GNADIG see Lisken, Gerd

GOTT SEI MIR GNADIG see Schein, Johann Hermann

GOTT SEI MIR GNADIG see Telemann, Georg Philipp

GOTT SEI MIR GNADIG see Wagener, Gregor

GOTT, SEI MIR GNADIG DIESER ZEIT see Lasso, Rudolph de

GOTT SEI UNS GNADIG see Fehres, Wilhelm

GOTT, SEI UNS GNADIG see Schmid, Walter

GOTT SEINES HERZENS GRUND AUFSCHLOSS see Le Jeune, Claude

GOTT SO WOLLEN WIR LOBEN UND EHREN see Taubert, K.H.

GOTT SOLL see Bach, Johann Sebastian, Gott Soll Allein Mein Herze Haben

GOTT SOLL ALLEIN see Bach, Johann Sebastian, Gott Soll Allein Mein Herze Haben

GOTT SOLL ALLEIN MEIN HERZE HABEN see Bach, Johann Sebastian

GOTT, TU DICH UBER UNS ERBARMEN see Hagius, Conrad

GOTT TUT GROSSE DINGE, DIE NICHT see Metzger, Hans-Arnold

GOTT UNSER HERR, MACHTIG DURCHS WORT see Schutz, Heinrich

GOTT, UNSER SCHILD, SCHAUE DOCH see Kukuck, Felicitas

GOTT VATER, GOTT SOHN, GOTT HEILIGER GEIST see Bischoff, M.

GOTT VATER, HERR, ALLMACHTIG GROSS see Hagius, Conrad

GOTT VATER, HERR, WIR DANKEN DIR see Brassicanus, Johannes

GOTT VATER, HORE UNSRE BITT see Vulpius, Melchior

GOTT VATER, SENDE DEIN GEIST see Kurig, Hans-Hermann

GOTT VATER, SENDE DEINE GEIST see Bach, Johann Sebastian

GOTT VATER, SENDE DEINEN GEIST see Metzger, Hans-Arnold

GOTT VATER SOHN, UND HEILIGER GEIST see Wiemer, Wolfgang

GOTT WIDERSTEHET DEN HOFFARTIGEN see Reda, Siegfried

GOTT, WIE DEIN NAME see Bach, Johann Sebastian

GOTT, WIE DEIN NAME see Lubeck, Vincentius

GOTT, WIE DEIN NAME, SO IST AUCH DEIN RUHM see Bach, Johann Sebastian

GOTT, WIR GEDENKEN DEINER GUTE see Gruschwitz, Gunther

GOTT WIRD ABWISCHEN ALLE TRANEN see Graap, Lothar

GOTT WIRD ABWISCHEN ALLE TRANEN see Thomas, Kurt

GOTT, ZU DIR RUFE ICH see Ruppel, Paul Ernst

GOTTERMAN, G.
Safe In His Care
SATB ALLANS 241 s.p.   (G1617)

GOTTES IST DER ORIENT see Beckerath, Alfred von

GOTTES IST DER ORIENT see Knab, Armin

GOTTES IST DER ORIENT see Lemacher, Heinrich

GOTTES LIEBE BLUHT IM LEBEN see Gattermayer, Heinrich

GOTTES MACHT UND VORSEHUNG see Beethoven, Ludwig van

GOTTES MACHT UND VORSEHUNG. GOTT IST MEIN LIED see Beethoven, Ludwig van

GOTTES MUTTER *mot
(Burkhart, Franz) mix cor,acap DOBLINGER s.p.
see also In Seiner Handen   (G1618)

GOTTES ODEM see Gerhold, Norbert, Ev'ry Time I Feel De Spirit

GOTTES SEIT (ACTUS TRAGICUS) see Bach, Johann Sebastian

GOTTES SOHN IST KOMMEN
mix cor sc ALSBACH&D s.p.   (G1619)

GOTTES SOHN IST KOMMEN see Bach, Johann Sebastian

GOTTES SOHN IST KOMMEN see Koch, Johannes H.E.

GOTTES SOHN IST KOMMEN see Pahlitzsch, Wolfgang

GOTTES SOHN IST KOMMEN see Peter, Herbert

GOTTES SOHN IST KOMMEN see Stern, Hermann

GOTTES SOHN IST KOMMEN see Trubel, Gerhard

GOTTES SOHN IST KOMMEN UNS ALLEN see Horn, Paul

GOTTES SOHN, UNSER LIEBER HERR see Praetorius, Michael, Veni, Redemptor Gentium

GOTTES STIMME LASST UNS SEIN see Stier, Alfred

GOTTES WELT IST EIN ZELT see Biebl, Franz

GOTTES ZEIT see Bach, Johann Sebastian, Gottes Zeit Ist Die Allerbeste Zeit

GOTTES ZEIT IST DIE ALLERBESTE ZEIT see Bach, Johann Sebastian

GOTTESLOB see Erb, Jorg

GOTTHEIT! DIR SEI PREIS UND EHRE see Mozart, Wolfgang Amadeus

GOTTHELF-LEVITA, GERARD
Baruch *cant
[Eng/Lat] SATB TRANSCON. TCL 216 $.60   (G1620)

GOTTLIEB
Didn't My Lord Deliver Daniel
SATB FISCHER,C O-4632 $1.00   (G1621)

GOTTLIEB, J.
Adon Olam *liturg,Jew
"Lord Of All, The" SATB,perc oct PRESSER
312-40783 $.35 see also Love Songs For
Sabbath   (G1622)

Aleinu (Vaanachu V'haya Adonai) *liturg,Jew
SATB,cantor,perc oct PRESSER 312-40784 $.30
see also Love Songs For Sabbath   (G1623)

Bar'chu *liturg,Jew
"Blessed Be The Lord" SATB oct PRESSER
312-40775 $.30 see also Love Songs For
Sabbath   (G1624)

Blessed Be The Lord *see Bar'chu

Cantillation Chorale
SATB,cantor (half Kaddish) oct PRESSER
312-40779 $.35 see also Love Songs For
Sabbath   (G1625)

Cause Us, O Lord Our God *see Hashkivenu

Hashkivenu *liturg,Jew
"Cause Us, O Lord Our God" SATB,cantor oct
PRESSER 312-40777 $.30 see also Love
Songs For Sabbath   (G1626)

How Goodly Are Thy Tents *see Mah Tovu

Kiddush *liturg,Jew
"Sanctification Of The Sabbath" SATB,cantor
oct PRESSER 312-40782 $.30 see also Love
Songs For Sabbath   (G1627)

L'chah Dodi *liturg,Jew
"To You, My Beloved" SATB,cantor oct
PRESSER 312-40773 $.30 see also Love
Songs For Sabbath   (G1628)

Lord Of All, The *see Adon Olam

Love Songs For Sabbath *liturg,Jew
SATB PRESSER rental
contains & see also: Adon Olam, "Lord Of
All, The"; Aleinu (Vaanachu V'haya
Adonai); Bar'chu, "Blessed Be The
Lord"; Cantillation Chorale;
Hashkivenu, "Cause Us, O Lord Our God";
Kiddush, "Sanctification Of The
Sabbath"; L'chah Dodi, "To You, My
Beloved"; Mah Tovu, "How Goodly Are Thy
Tents"; Mi Chamochah, "Who Is Like Unto
You"; Shiru Ladonai (Psalm 96); Sh'ma
Yisrael; Silent Meditation (May The
Words...); Vay' Chulu; V'shamru (G1629)

Mah Tovu *liturg,Jew
"How Goodly Are Thy Tents" SATB,cantor oct
PRESSER 312-40772 $.30 see also Love
Songs For Sabbath   (G1630)

GOTTLIEB, J. (cont'd.)

Mi Chamochah *liturg,Jew
"Who Is Like Unto You" SATB,cantor oct
PRESSER 312-40776 $.30 see also Love
Songs For Sabbath   (G1631)

Psalm 96 *see Shiru Ladonai

Sanctification Of The Sabbath *see Kiddush

Shiru Ladonai (Psalm 96) liturg,Jew
SATB,cantor oct PRESSER 312-40774 $.30 see
also Love Songs For Sabbath   (G1632)

Sh'ma Yisrael *liturg,Jew
SATB,cantor oct PRESSER 312-40775 $.30 see
also Love Songs For Sabbath   (G1633)

Silent Meditation (May The Words...)
*liturg,Jew
SATB oct PRESSER 312-40780 $.30 see also
Love Songs For Sabbath   (G1634)

To You, My Beloved *see L'chah Dodi

Vay' Chulu *liturg,Jew
TB oct PRESSER 312-40781 $.30 see also Love
Songs For Sabbath   (G1635)

V'shamru *liturg,Jew
SA,perc oct PRESSER 312-40778 $.25 see also
Love Songs For Sabbath   (G1636)

Who Is Like Unto You *see Mi Chamochah

GOTTLOB see Bach, Johann Sebastian, Gottlob! Nun Geht Das Jahr Zu Ende

GOTTLOB! NUN GEHT DAS JAHR ZU ENDE see Bach, Johann Sebastian

GOTTLOB! NUN GEHT DAS JAHR ZU ENDE [CHORALE] see Bach, Johann Sebastian

GOTTSCHALK
Lord, We Come Before Thee Now
(Harris) SATB oct PRO ART 2351 $.25 (G1637)

GOTTSCHICK, FRIEDEMANN (1928-   )
Alle Konige Werden Ihn Anbeten *Epiph,Allelu
[Ger] 2 eq voices&opt men cor,acap (med
easy) BAREN. BA 3393 s.p. contains also:
Die Himmel Verkundigen Seine
Gerechtigkeit   (G1638)

Christ Ist Erstanden
see Bender, Jan, Christ Ist Erstanden

Christus Spricht: Wer Mein Wort Horet *Gen
[Ger] SAB,acap (med easy) BAREN. BA 3685
s.p.   (G1639)

Die Himmel Verkundigen Seine Gerechtigkeit
see Gottschick, Friedemann, Alle Konige
Werden Ihn Anbeten

Du Bist Der Weg *Gen
[Ger] SAB,acap (med easy) BAREN. BCH 190
s.p.   (G1640)

Gedenke, Herr, An Deine Barmherzigkeit
*Psntd,Introit
[Ger] SA&men cor,acap (med easy) BAREN.
BA 3243 s.p.   (G1641)

Gelobet Seist Du, Jesu Christ
SAT/SAB,opt treb inst HANSSLER 14.015 s.p.
                                            (G1642)

Ich Glaube An Den Einen Gott
[Ger] SA&men cor,acap (med easy) BAREN.
BA 3674 s.p.   (G1643)

Jauchzet Dem Herrn, Alle Welt *Gen
[Ger] 2 eq voices,acap (med easy) BAREN.
BA 3266 s.p.   (G1644)

Wie Schon Leuchtet Der Morgenstern
SA/men cor,treb inst/bass inst HANSSLER
14.048   (G1645)

Wir Wollen Alle Frohlich Sein
see Marx, Karl, Mit Freuden Zart

GOTTSCHOVIUS, NIKOLAUS (ca. 1575- ?)
Lobt Gott, Ihr Christen Alle Gleich *Thanks,
mot
(Hellmann) SSATB HANSSLER 1.512 s.p.
                                            (G1646)

O Lamb Of God Most Holy *anthem
(Riedel) SATB (med) oct AUGSBURG 1414 $.25
                                            (G1647)

GOTTWALD, CLYTUS (1925-   )
Missa Super Anastaseos Himera *Mass
4pt cor,org voc sc BREITKOPF-W EB-6304
s.p., cor pts BREITKOPF-W CHB-3060 s.p.
                                            (G1648)

Sieben Spruchmotetten *CC7L,mot
4-7pt mix cor,MezTB soli cor pts BREITKOPF-
W CHB-3038 s.p.   (G1649)

GOUDIMEL, C.W.
Psalm 39 *Bibl
[Eng/Fr] 4pt mix cor oct SCHIRM.G 9415 $.20
                                            (G1650)

Towards The Mountains I Lift My Eyes
(Couper, A.) SATB,acap oct PRESSER
352-00442 $.30   (G1651)

GOUDIMEL, CLAUDE (ca. 1505-1572)
A Toi, Mon Dieu, Mon Coeur Monte (Psalm 25)
(Expert) [Fr] SATB,acap oct SALABERT-US
$.65   (G1652)

Ainsi Qu'on Oit Le Cerf Bruire (Psalm 42)
(Expert) [Fr] SATB,acap oct SALABERT-US
$.65   (G1653)

(Lynn) "So My Heart Seeks Ever After" [Eng/
Fr] 4pt mix cor,acap oct SCHIRM.G 11805
$.25   (G1654)

Anbetung, Ehre, Dank Und Ruhm Sei Unserm
"O Hochster, Deine Gutigkeit" SATB HANSSLER
6.1937 s.p.   (G1655)

As A Hart Longs For The Brooklet
(Couper, A.) SATB oct PRESSER 352-00436
$.35   (G1656)

GOUDIMEL, CLAUDE (cont'd.)

Au Moins, Mon Dieu, Ne M'abandonne Pas *16th
cent
(Honegger, Marc; Pidoux, Pierre) [Fr] SATB
OUVRIERES EO601 s.p.   (G1657)

Audi Filia *Mass
(Expert) [Lat] SATB,acap oct SALABERT-US
$1.25   (G1658)

Aus Meins Jammers Tiefe Ruf Ich
see Goudimel, Claude, Wenn Gott Einst Losen
Wird

Brunn Alles Heils, Dich
see Stobaeus, Johann, Ich Hab Ein Herzlich
Freud

Chantez A Dieu Nouveau Cantique (Psalm 98)
(Expert) [Fr] SSAT oct SALABERT-US $.65
                                        (G1659)

Der Herr Ist Konig, Hoch Erhoht *see Es Geht
Daher Des Tages Schein

Der Lobgesang Des Simeon *Nunc
(Wagner) SATB HANSSLER 6.259 s.p. contains
also: Mareshall, Samuel, Der Lobgesang
Des Simeon; Jambe de Fer, Philibert, Der
Lobgesang Des Simeon   (G1660)

Di Moi, Malheureux, Qui Te Fies (Psalm 12)
(Expert) [Fr] SATB,acap oct SALABERT-US
$.65   (G1661)

Du Fons De Ma Pensee (Psalm 130)
(Expert) [Fr] SATB,acap oct SALABERT-US
$.65   (G1662)

Du Mal In Le Meschant Vouloir (Psalm 36)
"Lo, My Transgression And My Sin" SATB,org
SCHIRM.EC 2634 $.30   (G1663)

Du Malin Le Meschant Vouloir (Psalm 36)
(Expert) [Fr] SATB,acap oct SALABERT-US
$.65   (G1664)

Du Seigneur Les Bontez Sans Fin (Psalm 89)
(Expert) [Fr] SATB,acap oct SALABERT-US
$.65   (G1665)

Es Geht Daher Des Tages Schein
SATB HANSSLER 6.080 s.p. contains also:
Praetorius, Michael, Aus Meines Herzens
Grunde Sag Ich Dir (SSAB/SSAT)
"Der Herr Ist Konig, Hoch Erhoht" SSAT/SSAB
HANSSLER 6.271 s.p. contains also:
Trubel, Gerhard, Lobet Gott Mit
Frohlichem Mund (4pt) (canon);
Resinarius, Balthasar, Erhalt Uns Herr
Bei Deinem Wort (SAT/SAB);
Trubel, Gerhard, Liebster Jesu, Wir
Sind Hier (SAT/SAB)   (G1667)

Estans Assis Aux Rives Aquatiques (Psalm 137)
(Expert) [Fr] ATBB oct SALABERT-US $.65
                                        (G1668)

Freu Dich Sehr, O Meine Seele
see Bach, Johann Sebastian, Gott Ist Und
Bleibt Getreu
"Wie Nach Einer Wasserquelle" see Schein,
Johann Hermann, Es Ist Gewisslich An Der
Zeit
SATB HANSSLER 6.1360 s.p. contains also:
Wie Nach Einer Wasserquelle (Fr)   (G1669)

Helas, Seigneur, Je Te Pri' Sauve Moi (Psalm
69)
(Expert) [Fr] SATB,acap oct SALABERT-US
$.65   (G1670)

Herr, Erhore Meine Klagen
SATB LAUDINELLA LR 35 s.p. contains also:
Jauchzt, Alle Lande Nah Und Fern;
Lobsingt, Ihr Volker Allzugleich; Sei
Gnadig Mir, O Gott   (G1671)

Herr Gott, Dich Loben Alle Wir
SATB HANSSLER 6.163 s.p. contains also:
Gesius, Bartholomaus, Wenn Wir In
Hochsten Noten Sein (SSATB/SAATB)   (G1672)

Herr, Wir Stehen Hand In Hand
see Kurig, Hans-Hermann, Lasset Uns
Wahrhaftig Sein In Der Liebe

Ich Schau Nach Jenen Bergen Gern
see Schutz, Heinrich, Du Tust Viel Guts
Beweisen

Jauchz, Erd Und Himmel, Juble Hell
"O Mensch, Bewein Dein Stunde Gross" SATB
HANSSLER 6.131 s.p.   (G1673)

Jauchz, Erd Und Himmel, Juble Hell *mot
SATB HANSSLER 6.132 s.p. contains also:
Vulpius, Melchior, O Heiliger Geist, Du
Gottlich Feur   (G1674)

Jauchzt, Alle Lande, Gott Zu Ehren
see Bach, Johann Sebastian, Jesu, Meine
Freude, Meines Herzens (Chorale)
SAT/SAB HANSSLER 6.179 s.p. contains also:
Wagner, Alexander, Es Wolle Gott Uns
Gnadig Sein   (G1675)

Jauchzt, Alle Lande Nah Und Fern
see Goudimel, Claude, Herr, Erhore Meine
Klagen

Jauchzt Halleluja, Lobt Den Herrn
see DEUTSCHES SANCTUS UND PSALM 111

Jusques A Quand As Establi, Seigneur (Psalm
13)
(Expert) [Fr] SATB,acap oct SALABERT-US
$.65   (G1676)

La Bien Que J'ay *Mass
mix cor,acap voc sc KALMUS 6191 $1.25
                                        (G1677)

Lass Deinen Knecht Nunmehr In Deinem
SATB HANSSLER 6.6102 s.p.   (G1678)

Le Seigneur Ta Priere Entende (Psalm 20)
(Expert) [Fr] SATB,acap oct SALABERT-US
$.65   (G1679)

GOUDIMEL, CLAUDE (cont'd.)

Lo, My Transgression And My Sin *see Du Mal
In Le Meschant Vouloir

Lobsingt, Ihr Volker Allzugleich
see Goudimel, Claude, Herr, Erhore Meine
Klagen

Lobt Den Herrn, Denn Was Er Tut
see Schutz, Heinrich, Lobt Gott Von
Herzensgrunde

Mein Leben Ist Ein Pilgrimstand
SATB (polyphonic) HANSSLER 6.141 s.p.
                                        (G1680)

Mein Leben Ist Ein Pilgrimstand
SATB (homophonic) HANSSLER 6.142 s.p.
contains also:
Bach, Johann Sebastian, Herzlich Lieb
Hab Ich Dich, O Herr (from Ich Liebe
Den Hochsten Vor Ganzem Gemute)
(Whitsun)   (G1681)

Misericorde A Moi Povre Afflige (Psalm 56)
(Expert) [Fr] ATBB,acap oct SALABERT-US
$.65   (G1682)

Mon Ame En Dieu Tant Seulement (Psalm 62)
(Expert) [Fr] SATB,acap oct SALABERT-US
$.65   (G1683)

Mon Dieu Me Paist Sous Sa Puissance Haute
(Psalm 23)
(Expert) [Fr] SATB,acap oct SALABERT-US
$.65   (G1684)

Now Let Us Hear What Israel Hath Said
(Couper, A.) SATB oct PRESSER 352-00437
$.35   (G1685)

Nun Danket Gott, Erhebt Und Preiset
see Schutz, Heinrich, Danket Dem Herren,
Lobt Ihn Frei

O Combien Est Plaisant Et Souhaitable (Psalm
133)
(Expert) [Fr] SATB,acap oct SALABERT-US
$.65   (G1686)

O Dieu Des Armees (Psalm 84)
(Expert) [Fr] STBB oct SALABERT-US $.65
                                        (G1687)

O Dieu, La Glorie Qui T'est Deue (Psalm 65)
(from Ainsworth Psalter Of Colonial
America)
SATB,acap PETERS 6085 $.60   (G1688)
(Expert) [Fr] SATB,acap oct SALABERT-US
$.65   (G1689)

O Dieu, Ou Mon Espoir J'ai Mis (Psalm 70)
(Expert) [Fr] SATB,acap oct SALABERT-US
$.65   (G1690)

O Hochster, Deine Gutigkeit *see Anbetung,
Ehre, Dank Und Ruhm Sei Unserm

O Lord God, Thy Great Renown
(Couper, A.) SATB oct PRESSER 352-00443
$.30   (G1691)

O Magnify And Honour The Lord (Psalm 150)
SATB BOSWORTH s.p.   (G1692)

O Mensch, Bewein Dein Stunde Gross *see
Jauchz, Erd Und Himmel, Juble Hell

O Nostre Dieu Et Seigneur Amiable (Psalm 8)
(Expert) [Fr] SATB,acap oct SALABERT-US
$.65   (G1693)

Or Peut Bien Dire Israel Maintenant (Psalm
124)
(Expert) [Fr] SATB,acap oct SALABERT-US
$.65   (G1694)

Or Sus, Louez Dieu Tout Le Monde (Psalm 66)
(Expert) [Fr] SATB,acap oct SALABERT-US
$.65   (G1695)

Preis, Lob Und Dank Sei Gott Dem Herren
(Berger, H.L.) TTBB HANSSLER 6.5139 s.p.
                                        (G1696)

Psalm 4 *see Quand Je T'Invoque, Helas,
Escoute

Psalm 8 *see O Nostre Dieu Et Seigneur
Amiable

Psalm 12 *see Di Moi, Malheureux, Qui Te
Fies

Psalm 13 *see Jusques A Quand As Establi,
Seigneur

Psalm 19
(Expert) [Fr] SATB,acap oct SALABERT-US
$.65   (G1697)

Psalm 20 *see Le Seigneur Ta Priere Entende

Psalm 23 *see Mon Dieu Me Paist Sous Sa
Puissance Haute

Psalm 25 *see A Toi, Mon Dieu, Mon Coeur
Monte

Psalm 30 *see Seigneur, Puis Que M'as Retire

Psalm 36 *see Du Mal In Le Meschant Vouloir

Psalm 36 *see Du Malin Le Meschant Vouloir

Psalm 42 *see Ainsi Qu'on Oit Le Cerf Bruire

Psalm 56 *see Misericorde A Moi Povre
Afflige

Psalm 62 *see Mon Ame En Dieu Tant Seulement

Psalm 65 *see O Dieu, La Glorie Qui T'est
Deue

Psalm 66 *see Or Sus, Louez Dieu Tout Le
Monde

Psalm 68 *see Que Dieu Se Monstre Seulement

GOUDIMEL, CLAUDE (cont'd.)

Psalm 69 *see Helas, Seigneur, Je Te Pri'
Sauve Moi

Psalm 70 *see O Dieu, Ou Mon Espoir J'ai Mis

Psalm 73 *see Si Est-Ce Que Dieu Est Tres
Doux

Psalm 84 *see O Dieu Des Armees

Psalm 89 *see Du Seigneur Les Bontez Sans
Fin

Psalm 95 *see Sus, Esgaions Au Seigneur

Psalm 98 *see Chantez A Dieu Nouveau
Cantique

Psalm 119
(Expert) [Fr] SATB,acap oct SALABERT-US
$.65   (G1698)

Psalm 124 *see Or Peut Bien Dire Israel
Maintenant

Psalm 130 *see Du Fons De Ma Pensee

Psalm 131 *see Seigneur, Je Ne Point Le
Coeur Fier

Psalm 133 *see O Combien Est Plaisant Et
Souhaitable

Psalm 137 *see Estans Assis Aux Rives
Aquatiques

Psalm 150 *see O Magnify And Honour The Lord

Quand Je T'Invoque, Helas, Escoute (Psalm 4)
(Expert) [Fr] SATB,acap oct SALABERT-US
$.65   (G1699)

Que Dieu Se Monstre Seulement (Psalm 68)
(Expert) [Fr] SATB,acap oct SALABERT-US
$.65   (G1700)

Sei Gnadig Mir, O Gott
see Goudimel, Claude, Herr, Erhore Meine
Klagen

Seigneur, Je Ne Point Le Coeur Fier (Psalm
131)
(Expert) [Fr] SATB,acap oct SALABERT-US
$.65   (G1701)

Seigneur, Puis Que M'as Retire (Psalm 30)
(Expert) [Fr] SATB,acap oct SALABERT-US
$.65   (G1702)

Si Est-Ce Que Dieu Est Tres Doux (Psalm 73)
(Expert) [Fr] SATB,acap oct SALABERT-US
$.65   (G1703)

Singt Mit Froher Stimm
see Kurig, Hans-Hermann, Lasset Uns
Wahrhaftig Sein In Der Liebe
SATB HANSSLER 6.177 s.p. contains also:
Schutz, Heinrich, Ach Gott, Der Du Vor
Dieser Zeit, SWV 157   (G1704)

So My Heart Seeks Ever After *see Ainsi
Qu'on Oit Le Cerf Bruire

Stedfast And Good Is Jehovah
(Coggin) 4pt mix cor,acap oct SCHIRM.G
11553 $.25   (G1705)

Sus, Esgaions Au Seigneur (Psalm 95)
(Expert) [Fr] SATB,acap oct SALABERT-US
$.65   (G1706)

Te Deum - Halleluja *Te Deum
[Lat] LYCHE 41 s.p.   (G1707)

Two Settings Of The Twenty Third Psalm
*Psalm
(Herder, R.) [Fr/Eng] SATB BROUDE,A. 713
$.35   (G1708)

Videntes Stellam Magi *Epiph
"Wise Men, Beholding The Star, The" SATB,
acap SCHIRM.EC 1258 $.35   (G1709)

Vier Festmotetten *CC4U,Fest,mot
(Hausler) [Ger/Lat] 4pt mix cor&6pt mix cor
MOSELER s.p.   (G1710)

Wenn Gott Einst Losen Wird
SATB HANSSLER 6.186 s.p. contains also: Aus
Meins Jammers Tiefe Ruf Ich   (G1711)

Wie Nach Einer Wasserquelle *see Freu Dich
Sehr, O Meine Seele

Wise Men, Beholding The Star, The *see
Videntes Stellam Magi

GOULD, JOHN
Sans Day Carol (from Anthology Of Carols, An)
*Xmas,carol
SATB,S solo CHESTER s.p.   (G1712)

GOULD, MORTON (1913-)
Awake, O Church Of Christ
(Ferguson) SATB FLAMMER A 5188 $.25 (G1713)

GOUNOD, CHARLES FRANCOIS (1818-1893)
Adore And Be Still *Adv/Xmas,anthem
SSA FLAMMER B 5139 $.25   (G1714)
SATB oct LORENZ 7839 $.30   (G1715)
(Cain) SATB FLAMMER A 5217 $.30   (G1716)
(Cain) SAB FLAMMER D5152 $.25   (G1717)
(Cain) dbl cor FLAMMER A5480 $.30   (G1718)
(Dressler, W.) SATB oct PRESSER 332-10159
$.30   (G1719)
(Mueller, E.) SATB oct PRESSER 312-15678
$.30   (G1720)
(Southbridge, James) SA/SAB oct LORENZ 7839
                                        (G1721)

Adoro Te Supplex *CCU,Commun,hymn
[Lat] mix cor LEMOINE s.p.   (G1722)

Agnus Dei (from Requiem) Allelu
[Lat] 2 eq voices,org/pno CHOUDENS s.p.
                                        (G1723)

GOUNOD, CHARLES FRANCOIS (cont'd.)

All Ye Who Weep
(Wheeler) SATB ALLANS 226 s.p. (G1724)

Ave Maria
[Lat] unis HEUGEL s.p. see from CHANTS RELIGIEUX (G1725)
SSAA oct BELWIN 64130 $.30 (G1726)
(Holden, A.) TTBB,S solo oct PRESSER 332-08533 $.40 (G1727)

Ave Maria De L'enfant *BVM
[Lat] LEMOINE s.p. (G1728)

Ave Verum *mot
SMezATB CHOUDENS s.p. (G1729)
"Jesu, Word Of God Incarnate" [Eng/Lat] 4pt mix cor,acap oct SCHIRM.G 3239 $.25 (G1730)

Ave Verum Corpus *anthem/mot
[Lat] 2 eq voices HEUGEL s.p. see from LA MAITRISE (G1731)
"Jesu, Word Of God Incarnate" [Lat/Eng] mix cor oct NOVELLO 40.0339.10 s.p. (G1732)

Benedictus (from St. Cecelia Mass) Bene
see Gounod, Charles Francois, Sanctus
[Lat] ST,pno CHOUDENS s.p. (G1733)
[Lat] 2 eq voices,org,vln,vcl,harp CHOUDENS s.p. (G1734)
[Lat] 2 eq voices,org CHOUDENS s.p. (G1735)
[Lat/Eng] SATTBB,S/T solo,pno (med) oct WILLIS 3953 $.12 (G1736)
3pt wom cor,S solo oct SCHIRM.G 8944 $.40 contains also: Sanctus (Sanctus) (G1737)
[Eng/Lat] 4pt mix cor,T solo oct SCHIRM.G 3768 $.35 contains also: Sanctus (Sanctus) (G1738)
(Reed) mix cor oct SCHIRM.G 5433 $.25 contains also: Sanctus (Sanctus) (G1739)

Bethlehem *Xmas,anthem
cor oct HART s.p. (G1740)
mix cor oct NOVELLO 28.0938.04 s.p. (G1741)
unis oct NOVELLO 47.0198.04 s.p. (G1742)
SAB oct LORENZ 7383 $.30 (G1743)

Blessed Is He Who Cometh *anthem/Bibl
4pt mix cor,high solo oct SCHIRM.G 3423 $.25 (G1744)
SATTBB,S solo (easy) oct AUGSBURG 0031 $.14 (G1745)
SATB,S solo oct PRO ART 1388 $.18 (G1746)
(Morse, C.) SATB oct PRESSER 332-11474 $.25 (G1747)

By Babylon's Wave *Bibl
SATTBB,pno (med) oct WILLIS 736 $.15 (G1748)
SATB ALLANS 50 s.p. (G1749)
(Buck) mix cor oct SCHIRM.G 3045 $.25 (G1750)
(Farnie, H.) SATB oct PRESSER 312-10405 $.35 (G1751)
(Nicholos) mix cor oct SCHIRM.G 2260 $.30 (G1752)

Cantique Pour La Premiere Communion
[Lat] LEMOINE s.p. (G1753)

Cantique Pour L'adoration Du Saint-Sacrement *Commun
[Lat] LEMOINE s.p. (G1754)

Ce Qu'il Faut A Mon Ame
[Fr] LEMOINE s.p. (G1755)

Chantez, Voix Benies
see Recueil De Six Cantiques
[Fr] unis/2pt CHOUDENS s.p. (G1756)

Choeur Des Fugitifs (from Jeanne D'arc)
SATB CHOUDENS voc sc s.p., cor pts s.p. (G1757)

Choeur Des Soldats (from Jeanne D'arc)
SATB voc sc CHOUDENS s.p. (G1758)

Come To Reign Lord Jesus
SATB ALLANS 228 s.p. (G1759)

Come Unto Him *Bibl
SATB ALLANS 225 s.p. (G1760)
(Shelley) 4pt mix cor,acap oct SCHIRM.G 3277 $.25 (G1761)

Communion Service (St. Cecilia) *see Messe Solennelle

Cor Jesu
(Radford) "Sometimes I Catch Sweet Glimpses" [Eng/Lat] 4pt mix cor,high solo oct SCHIRM.G 3422 $.20 (G1762)

Cross Of Calvary, The *Easter/Lent
(Stevens) SATB oct PRO ART 1622 $.18 (G1763)

Da Pacem
[Lat] 2 eq voices HEUGEL s.p. see from LA MAITRISE (G1764)

De Profundis (Psalm 130)
"Psaume CXXX" [Lat] SATB,Bar solo,orch voc sc DURAND s.p. (G1765)

Dieu Le Veut! Dieu Le Veut! (from Jeanne D'arc)
mix cor CHOUDENS voc sc s.p., cor pts s.p. (G1766)

Dieu Partout
3pt wom cor,solo CHOUDENS voc sc s.p., cor pts s.p. (G1767)

Divine Redeemer *Easter,cant
SATB LORENZ $1.95 (G1768)
SAB LORENZ $1.75 (G1769)

Dormez Divin Enfant *Xmas,carol
[Fr] unis/2pt CHOUDENS s.p. (G1770)

Entreat Me Not To Leave Thee *Bibl
(Deis) 4pt mix cor oct SCHIRM.G 10212 $.30 (G1771)

Fourth Communion Service *see Missa Choralis

Gallia *Lent,mot
SATB,S solo,org,2fl,2ob,2clar,2bsn,4horn, 4trp,3trom,tuba,strings,perc,timp,harp voc sc NOVELLO rental (G1772)
BELWIN $.75 (G1773)
cor,orch sc KALMUS $12.00, ipa (G1774)

GOUNOD, CHARLES FRANCOIS (cont'd.)

cor voc sc KALMUS 6194 $1.00 (G1775)
SSAATTBB,S solo,pno (med) oct WILLIS 755 $.35 (G1776)

Gloire Immortelle De Nos Aieux (from Faust)
[Fr] 2-3pt CHOUDENS s.p. see also CHOEURS POUR DISTRIBUTIONS DE PRIX OU POUR ENFANTS (G1777)

Gloria In Excelsis Deo (from St. Cecilia Mass)
(Barker) 4pt mix cor,S/T solo,org/pno,opt 4brass oct SCHIRM.G 11357 $.35 (G1778)

Glory To God *Xmas,cant
SATB oct LORENZ $1.95 (G1779)

Glory To Thee My God This Night
2pt ENOCH TP188 s.p. (G1780)
cor oct HART s.p. (G1781)

Grant Us Thy Peace
4pt mix cor oct SCHIRM.G 3424 $.20 (G1782)

Holy, Holy, Lord (from St. Cecelia) Sanctus
SATB,T/S solo,pno (med) oct WILLIS 5138 $.15 (G1783)

Holy, Holy, Lord God Almighty
(Nevin, G.) TTBB,T solo oct PRESSER 332-11032 $.30 (G1784)

Hosanna In Excelsis Deo *Xmas/Gen
SATB oct PRESSER G-136 $.35 (G1785)

Hymne A Saint-Augustin
LEMOINE s.p. (G1786)

I Will Call On Thee *see Kyrie

Je Te Rends Grace, O Dieu D'Amour
[Fr] SATBar/SATB,opt T/S solo,pno/org/pno& org LEDUC voc sc s.p., cor pts s.p. (G1787)

Jerusalem
[Eng/Lat] SATB oct BELWIN 64128 $.30 (G1788)
(Whitford) SATB,org BOSTON 12454 $.35 (G1789)

Jerusalem, O Turn Thee (from Gallia)
SATTB,S solo,pno (med) oct WILLIS 180 $.12 (G1790)
(Norman) SSAA,pno/org (diff) oct WILLIS 5749 $.12 (G1791)

Jerusalem! O Turn Thee To The Lord (from Gallia) Bibl
SATB oct PRO ART 1327 $.20 (G1792)
mix cor,S solo oct SCHIRM.G 4429 $.25 (G1793)
(Gray) oct PRO ART 1551 $.18 (G1794)
(Rix) 3pt boy cor/3pt wom cor,S solo oct SCHIRM.G 5860 $.25 (G1795)

Jesu, Word Of God Incarnate *see Ave Verum

Jesu, Word Of God Incarnate *see Ave Verum Corpus

Jesus, Word Of God Incarnate *Easter/Lent, Commun
(Douglas) SATB,acap oct PRO ART 1743 $.25 (G1796)

Jeterands Grace, O Dieu D'amour
[Fr] cor,pno LEDUC voc sc s.p., cor pts s.p. (G1797)

Jour De Noel, Epilogue *Xmas
SATB CHOUDENS voc sc s.p., cor pts s.p. (G1798)

Judex (from Mors Et Vita)
"Praise The Lord" SATB ENOCH EC304 s.p. (G1799)

King Of Love My Shepherd Is, The
SATB ENOCH EC152 s.p. (G1800)

Kyrie
(Imig) "I Will Call On Thee" [Eng/Lat] SATB MARKS 4242 $.30 (G1801)

L'anniversaire Des Martyrs
see Recueil De Six Cantiques
[Fr] unis/2pt CHOUDENS s.p. (G1802)

Laudate Dominum *mot
[Lat] SSTB,SSTB soli,orch (C maj) LEDUC MS100 voc sc s.p., voc pt s.p. see from MUSIQUE SACREE (G1803)
[Lat] 2 eq voices,2 soli,orch (C maj) voc sc LEDUC MS52 s.p. see from MUSIQUE SACREE (G1804)

Le Ciel A Visite La Terre
see Recueil De Six Cantiques
[Fr] unis/2pt CHOUDENS s.p. (G1805)

Le Crucifix
[Fr] 6pt mix cor CHOUDENS voc sc s.p., cor pts s.p. (G1806)

Le Depart Des Missionaires
[Fr] unis/2pt CHOUDENS s.p. (G1807)

Le Depart Des Missionnaires
see Recueil De Six Cantiques

Le Nom De Marie
see Recueil De Six Cantiques
[Fr] unis/2pt CHOUDENS s.p. (G1808)

Les Voix De Jeanne D'arc Ou Ave Maria (from Jeanne D'arc)
SATB voc sc CHOUDENS s.p. (G1809)

L'eucharistie
[Fr] LEMOINE s.p. (G1810)

Lord Jesus Christ
(Wyatt) SATB,Bar solo oct PRO ART 2089 $.22 (G1811)

Lord We Pray
(Mueller) 3pt jr cor/SAB (very easy) FISCHER,C CM 7337 $.25 (G1812)

Lovely Appear (from The Redemption) Bibl
mix cor,S solo oct SCHIRM.G 2013 $.35 (G1813)

GOUNOD, CHARLES FRANCOIS (cont'd.)

SA oct PRESSER 332-14840 $.30 (G1814)
SATB oct PRESSER 332-00998 $.35 (G1815)
SATB oct PRESSER 332-14840 $.25 (G1816)
SATB oct FISCHER,C CM-6251 $.30 (G1817)
(Ehret) SSA oct SPRATT 596 $.30 (G1818)
(Rix) wom cor,S solo oct SCHIRM.G 6055 $.35 (G1819)

Mass In C
[Lat] 4pt mix cor/SA,pno voc sc SCHIRM.G $1.00 (G1820)

Mass No. 2 In G Major *Mass
4pt men cor,org voc sc KALMUS 6413 $2.00 (G1821)

Mass No. 6 In G Major *Mass
4pt,solo voc sc KALMUS 6180 $1.50 (G1822)

Mass Of The Sacred Heart *Mass
cor voc sc KALMUS 6195 $1.50 (G1823)

Messe A La Memoire De Jeanne D'arc *Mass
cor,soli,2org LEMOINE sc s.p., cor pts s.p., voc pt s.p. (G1824)

Messe Breve In C Major No. 7 *Mass
cor voc sc KALMUS 6198 $1.50 (G1825)

Messe Breve No. 5, Aux Seminaires *Mass
[Fr] TBB,soli,pno (C maj) voc sc LEDUC BL347 s.p. (G1826)

Messe Breve No. 7, Aux Chapelles *Mass
[Fr] SSTB,SSTB soli,pno (C maj) LEDUC BL451 voc sc s.p., voc pt s.p. (G1827)

Messe Chorale *Mass
[Lat] 4pt mix cor HEUGEL voc sc s.p., voc pt s.p. (G1828)

Messe De Saint-Jean *Greg/Mass
4pt mix cor,org sc CHOUDENS s.p. (G1829)

Messe De Sainte-Cecile *Mass
[Fr] 2 eq voices,soli,orch LEDUC BL424 voc sc s.p., voc pt s.p. (G1830)

Messe Des Anges Gardiens *Mass
4pt,org LEMOINE voc sc s.p., voc pt s.p. (G1831)

Messe Dite De Clovis *Greg/Mass
4pt mix cor,org sc CHOUDENS s.p. (G1832)

Messe Du Sacre-Coeur De Jesus *Mass
[Fr] SATB,orch/org LEMOINE voc sc s.p., voc pt s.p., ipa (G1833)
[Eng] SATB,orch LEMOINE voc sc s.p., voc pt s.p., sc s.p., ipa (G1834)
[Fr] SAB,orch LEMOINE voc sc s.p., voc pt s.p. (G1835)
[Fr] SA,orch LEMOINE voc sc s.p., voc pt s.p. (G1836)

Messe No. 1, Aux Orpheonistes *Mass
[Fr] TTB/SS,SS soli,opt orch (C min) LEDUC voc sc s.p., voc pt s.p. (G1837)

Messe No. 2, Aux Societes Chorales *Mass
[Fr] TTBB,acap (G maj) LEDUC voc sc s.p., voc pt s.p. (G1838)

Messe No. 3, Aux Communautes Religieuses *Mass
[Fr] 3 eq voices,orch (G maj) LEDUC BL436 voc sc s.p., voc pt s.p. (G1839)

Messe No. 4, A La Congregation Des Dames Auxiliatrices De L'Immaculee -Conception *Mass
[Fr] 2 eq voices,pno (C maj) LEDUC BL425 voc sc s.p., voc pt s.p. (G1840)

Messe No. 6, Aux Cathedrales *Mass
[Fr] SSTB,SSTB soli,orch (G maj) LEDUC BL450 voc sc s.p., voc pt s.p. (G1841)

Messe Solennelle *Commun,Mass
cor voc sc KALMUS 6196 $1.50 (G1842)
cor,orch sc KALMUS $25.00, ipa (G1843)
"Communion Service (St. Cecilia)" SSTTBB, STB soli,org,3fl,2ob,3clar,4bsn,4horn, 4trp,3trom,strings,perc,timp,harp voc sc NOVELLO s.p., ipr (G1844)
"Sainte-Cecile" [Fr] SATB,SATB soli,orch LEDUC BL449 voc sc s.p., voc pt s.p. (G1845)
"St. Cecilia" [Lat] SSTTBB,STB soli,org, 3fl,2ob,2clar,4bsn,4horn,4trp,3trom, strings,perc,timp,harp voc sc NOVELLO s.p., ipr (G1846)
"St. Cecilia Mass" BELWIN $1.50 (G1847)
(Barnby) [Eng/Lat] cor,pno voc sc SCHIRM.G $1.50 (G1848)

Missa Choralis
[Lat/Eng] 4pt mix cor,opt org SCHIRM.EC 1260 (G1849)
"Fourth Communion Service" SATB,opt inst SCHIRM.EC 1260 (G1850)

Missa Paschalis
[Lat/Eng] 4pt mix cor,org SCHIRM.EC 1259 (G1851)
"Third Communion Service" SATB SCHIRM.EC 1259 (G1852)

Motet A Saint Jean L'evangeliste *mot
SATB CHOUDENS sc s.p., voc pt s.p. (G1853)

Nazareth *Xmas,anthem
2pt ENOCH TP67 s.p. (G1854)
SATB ALLANS 129 s.p. (G1855)
unis oct NOVELLO 47.0175.05 s.p. (G1856)
mix cor,Bar solo oct NOVELLO 28.0960.05 s.p. (G1857)
(Bliss, P.) SATB oct PRESSER 312-20232 $.30 (G1858)
(Buck) mix cor,Bar solo oct SCHIRM.G 3003 $.25 (G1859)
(Matthews, H.) TTBB oct PRESSER 312-21132 $.30 (G1860)

Noel *Xmas
[Fr] wom cor,SA soli,opt org CHOUDENS voc sc s.p., cor pts s.p. (G1861)

GOUNOD, CHARLES FRANCOIS (cont'd.)

Noel! Noel! (from Jeanne D'arc) Xmas,carol
[Fr] unis/2pt CHOUDENS s.p. (G1862)
mix cor CHOUDENS voc sc s.p., cor pts s.p.
(G1863)

Notre-Dame De France
[Fr] unis HEUGEL s.p. see from CHANTS
RELIGIEUX (G1864)

Notre-Dame Des Petits Enfants
see Recueil De Six Cantiques

O Divine Redeemer *see Repentir

O Little Town Of Bethlehem *Xmas,carol
(Grove, D.E., Jr.) SATB,S solo,pno (med)
oct WILLIS 3187 $.20 (G1865)

O Salutaris Hostia
(Trevor, C.H.) "O Saving Victim" SSAA,acap
oct NOVELLO 33.0128.01 s.p. (G1866)

O Saving Victim *see O Salutaris Hostia

Oeuvers Chretiennes *CC20L
cor quarto CHOUDENS s.p. (G1867)

Out Of Darkness (Psalm 130) cant
cor voc sc KALMUS 6197 $1.50 (G1868)

Pie Jesu *Xmas
2 eq voices,org CHOUDENS s.p. (G1869)

Praise The Lord *see Judex

Praise Ye The Father *Gen/Trin,Bibl
SATB oct LORENZ 186 $.30 (G1870)
SATB oct PRESSER 312-00044 $.30 (G1871)
SATB oct FISCHER,C CM-49 $.25 (G1872)
SATB,pno (easy) oct WILLIS 640 $.10 (G1873)
SSAB,pno (med) oct WILLIS 5027 $.10 (G1874)
(Barnes) unis oct SCHIRM.G 8053 $.25
(G1875)
(Bliss) 3pt wom cor,pno (easy) oct WILLIS
2797 $.10 (G1876)
(Brooks) SATB oct SPRATT 539 $.25 (G1877)
(Coggin) SAB oct FOX R206 $.25 (G1878)
(Deis) 2pt boy cor/2pt wom cor oct SCHIRM.G
7579 $.30 (G1879)
(Deis) SA/SAB oct SCHIRM.G 7029 $.30 (G1880)
(Deis) 3pt wom cor,org/pno oct SCHIRM.G
10220 $.25 (G1881)
(Ehret) SSA oct PRO ART 1489 $.20 (G1882)
(Fearis) SSAA,pno (easy) oct WILLIS 6458
$.10 (G1883)
(Hilton, R.) SA oct PRESSER 332-13031 $.30
(G1884)
(Nevin) TTBB,pno (med) oct WILLIS 1070 $.12
(G1885)
(Pitcher, Gladys) 3pt wom cor,pno (med) oct
WILLIS 8482 $.25 (G1886)
(Rees) mix cor,org/pno oct SCHIRM.G 3325
$.30 (G1887)
(Rhys; Herbert) SA oct FISCHER,J 3759 $.30
(G1888)
(Riegger) SATB FLAMMER 5315 $.30 (G1889)
(Riegger) SAB FLAMMER D5088 $.25 (G1890)
(Siegmeister) SATB oct PRO ART 1621 $.25
(G1891)
(Thompson) SAB oct BOURNE D2 $.25 (G1892)
(Weston, J.) SATB oct PRESSER 332-01593
$.30 (G1893)

Prelude (from Messe A La Memoire De Jeanne
D'arc)
cor,soli,2org,brass voc sc LEMOINE s.p.,
ipa (G1894)

Pres Du Fleuve Etranger (Psalm 136)
[Fr] SATB/SMezTB,pno/org/orch (choral parts
for each arrangement available
separately) voc sc LEDUC s.p. (G1895)
(Moratin) [Fr] 4pt men cor,pno/org/orch
(choral parts for each arrangement
available separately) voc sc LEDUC s.p.
(G1896)

Presso Il Fiume Stranier
SATB,pno RICORDI-ENG 35537 s.p. contains
also: Super Flumina Babylonis (G1897)

Priere (from Jeanne d'arc)
SATB CHOUDENS voc sc s.p., cor pts s.p.
(G1898)

Psalm 130 *see De Profundis

Psalm 136 *see Pres Du Fleuve Etranger

Psaume CXXX *see De Profundis

Quam Dilecta Tabernacula Tua! *Commun,mot
(Busser) [Lat] opt mix cor,Bar/Mez solo,
org,vln,vcl,harp LEMOINE voc sc s.p., cor
pts s.p. (G1899)

Recessional
(Craig) SATB oct PLYMOUTH DC-120 $.30 (G1900)

Recueil De Six Cantiques
unis oct CHOUDENS s.p.
contains: Chantez, Voix Benies;
L'anniversaire Des Martyrs; Le Ciel A
Visite La Terre; Le Depart Des
Missionnaires; Le Nom De Marie; Notre-
Dame Des Petits Enfants (G1901)

Redemption *Lent,cant
BELWIN $1.50 (G1902)

Redemption, The
cor,pno voc sc SCHIRM.G $1.50 (G1903)
cor,orch sc KALMUS $40.00, ipa (G1904)

Repentir *Easter/Gen
"O, Divine Redeemer" SATB oct PRESSER
312-20338 $.35 (G1905)
"O Divine Redeemer" cor oct HART s.p.
(G1906)
"O Divine Redeemer" SATB oct LORENZ 9057
$.30 (G1907)
"O Divine Redeemer" 2pt ENOCH TP152 s.p.
(G1908)
"O Divine Redeemer" SATB oct ENOCH EC144 s.p.
(G1909)
"O Divine Redeemer" SATB ALLANS 356 s.p.
(G1910)
"O Divine Redeemer" mix cor oct SCHIRM.G
3811 $.35 (G1911)

GOUNOD, CHARLES FRANCOIS (cont'd.)

(Cain) "O Divine Redeemer!" SA SCHMITT 2502
$.30 (G1912)
(Cain) "O Divine Redeemer!" SATB SCHMITT
1602 $.35 (G1913)
(Christy) "O Divine Redeemer" SATB oct
BELWIN 2176 $.30 (G1914)
(Ehret) "O Divine Redeemer" SATB oct PRO
ART 1492 $.30 (G1915)
(Milkey) "O Divine Redeemer" 3pt mix cor,
acap oct SCHIRM.G 11240 $.35 (G1916)
(Treharne) "O Divine Redeemer" 3pt wom cor
oct SCHIRM.G 9647 $.40 (G1917)

Requiem *Req
cor,SATB soli,pno/4strings&harp&org/orch
CHOUDENS s.p., ipr (G1918)
2 eq voices,org/4strings&harp&orch CHOUDENS
s.p., ipr (G1919)

Ring Out, Wild Bells *Xmas,Bibl
(Root) mix cor oct SCHIRM.G 2630 $.25 (G1920)

Sainte-Cecile *see Messe Solennelle

Sanctus (from St. Cecilia Mass) Gen,anthem/
mot/Sanctus
see Gounod, Charles Francois, Benedictus
see Gounod, Charles Francois, Benedictus
see Gounod, Charles Francois, Benedictus
SATB WARNER G420 $.30 contains also:
Benedictus (Bene) (G1921)
SSA oct PRO ART 1429 $.35 (G1922)
SATB,S/T solo (med) oct AUGSBURG 0015 $.25
(G1923)
SATB oct LORENZ 9549 $.30 (G1924)
SATB oct PRO ART 2019 $.35 (G1925)
[Lat] SSTB,T solo,orch LEDUC MS414 voc sc
s.p., voc pt s.p. see from MUSIQUE SACREE
(G1926)
(Clark) [Eng/Lat] SAB,acap WARNER G799 $.35
(G1927)
(Ehret) SAB oct PRO ART 2205 $.35 (G1928)
(Goodell) SATB SCHMITT 1561 $.45 (G1929)
(Licht) SAB FLAMMER D5094 $.35 (G1930)
(Swift; Mitzelfelt) SATTB oct BOURNE 813
$.50 (G1931)

Sanctus And Benedictus (from St. Cecilia
Mass) Gen/Trin,Bene/Sanctus
SATB oct PRESSER 312-00030 $.35 (G1932)
SATB oct BELWIN 64126 $.35 (G1933)
SATB,S/T solo,pno (med) oct WILLIS 679 $.12
(G1934)

Sanctus No. 4 (from St. Cecilia Mass) Sanctus
SATB oct FISCHER,C CM-25 $.25 (G1935)

Send Out Thy Light *anthem
SATB oct LORENZ 1710 $.30 (G1936)
SATB oct LORENZ 4301 $.30 (G1937)
SATB oct PRESSER 332-00068 $.35 (G1938)
SATB ALLANS 46 $.30 (G1939)
SATB oct FISCHER,C CM-6256 $.30 (G1940)
mix cor,orch oct NOVELLO 28.0973.07 s.p.,
ipr (G1941)
SATTBB,pno (easy) oct WILLIS 701 $.10
(G1942)
SATB oct LESLIE 4028 (G1943)
oct HART (G1944)
(Pitcher, Gladys) 3pt wom cor,pno (med) oct
WILLIS 8491 $.25 (G1945)
(Stoughton, R.) SSA oct PRESSER 332-14690
$.30 (G1946)
(Swift) SATB oct PRO ART 1038 $.30 (G1947)
(Swift) SSA oct PRO ART 1039 $.25 (G1948)

Seven Words Of Christ *Lent/Psntd,cant
BELWIN $.75 (G1949)

Sicut Servus *mot
SATBarB CHOUDENS s.p. (G1950)

Sometimes I Catch Sweet Glimpses *see Cor
Jesu

St. Cecilia *see Messe Solennelle

St. Cecilia Mass *see Messe Solennelle

Super Flumina Babylonis
see Gounod, Charles Francois, Presso Il
Fiume Stranier

Tantum Ergo
3pt mix cor,org,opt vln&vcl (choral part
available also) LEMOINE s.p. (G1951)
unis,org,opt vln/vcl LEMOINE s.p. (G1952)

There Is A Green Hill
(Chambers) SA oct LESLIE 2021 (G1953)

There Is A Green Hill Far Away *Commun/
Easter/Lent/Psntd,anthem/Bibl
2pt ASHDOWN E.A.205 s.p. (G1954)
SATB ENOCH EC257 s.p. (G1955)
SATB ALLANS 227 s.p. (G1956)
2pt,orch oct NOVELLO 53.0221.08 s.p., ipr
(G1957)
(Bentley, J.M.) mix cor,S/T solo,orch oct
NOVELLO 28.0576.06 s.p., ipr (G1958)
(Dawson) SATB,S solo oct PRO ART 1330 $.30
(G1959)
(Rees) 4pt mix cor oct SCHIRM.G 3302 $.25
(G1960)
(Richardson) SAB oct SPRATT 648 $.35
(G1961)
(Stoughton, R.) SA oct PRESSER 332-14689
$.30 (G1962)
(Treharne) 3pt wom cor oct SCHIRM.G 9646
$.30 (G1963)

Third Communion Service *see Missa Paschalis

Toujours A Toi, Seigneur *hymn
[Fr] cor,pno LEDUC voc sc s.p., cor pts
s.p. (G1964)
[Fr] SATB,TB soli,pno/org/pno&org LEDUC
voc sc s.p., cor pts s.p. (G1965)

Unfold, Ye Portals (from Redemption, The)
Asc/Easter,anthem
SATB oct LORENZ 960 $.30 (G1966)
SATB oct PRESSER 332-00995 $.35 (G1967)
SATB oct PRO ART 1310 $.30 (G1968)
mix cor&S oct SCHIRM.G 2015 $.25 (G1969)
SATB oct BELWIN 64116 $.35 (G1970)
SATB oct FISCHER,C CM-48 $.25 (G1971)
SATB SCHMITT 1911 $.30 (G1972)

GOUNOD, CHARLES FRANCOIS (cont'd.)

(Bliss, P.) SSA oct PRESSER 312-20285 $.30
(G1973)
(Davids) SSA oct BELWIN 1549 $.25 (G1974)
(Deis) SAB oct SCHIRM.G 10257 $.25 (G1975)

We Praise And Bless Thee
(Whitford, H.) SATB oct PRESSER 332-40049
$.30 (G1976)

GOVER
Christ, Whose Glory Fills The Skies
SA BOOSEY-CAN s.p. (G1977)
2pt mix cor oct BOOSEY 5419 $.30 (G1978)

Lord Is My Shepherd, The *spir
SATB,Bar solo RICORDI-ENG LD.376 s.p.
(G1979)

GOWER, R.
Joyfully Sing Unto God
SATB BELWIN 2283 $.35 (G1980)

GOZO A LA FE see Surinach, Carlos

GRAAP, LOTHAR (1933-)
Alle Menschen Mussen Sterben
[Ger] 2 eq voices&opt men cor,acap (easy)
BAREN. BA 3387 s.p. contains also: O Jesu
Christ, Meins Lebens Licht (G1981)

Das Kreuz Christi *Gd.Fri./Holywk
1-3pt mix cor,Bar solo MOSELER s.p. (G1982)

Deinem Namen Gib Ehre *mot
3pt mix cor,Bar solo MOSELER LB-437 s.p.
(G1983)

Der Mond Ist Aufgegangen *cant
SAB,2vln,vcl,rec HANSSLER 10.145 sc s.p.,
voc sc s.p., ipa (G1984)

Des Herren Wort (Psalm 33) Bibl
dbl cor MOSELER s.p. (G1985)

Die Ist Der Tag, Den Der Herr Macht
*Introit/mot
4pt mix cor,4brass sc MOSELER s.p., ipa
(G1986)

Die Nacht Ist Vorgedrungen *Adv
[Ger] SATB,acap (easy) BAREN. BA 4966 s.p.
(G1987)

Die Ostergeschichte *Easter,cant
SAB,cantor HANSSLER 10.086 sc s.p., cor pts
s.p. (G1988)

Die Weihnachtsgeschichte *Xmas
[Ger] 3pt mix cor,cantor,acap (med)
DEUTSCHER DV 7621 s.p. (G1989)
[Ger] 3pt mix cor,T solo oct DEUTSCHER 7621
s.p. (G1990)

Einzug Jesu In Jerusalem *evang/mot
1-8pt mix cor MOSELER s.p. (G1991)

Frohlocket Mit Handen Alle Volker *Bibl/mot
4pt mix cor MOSELER s.p. (G1992)

Gott Wird Abwischen Alle Tranen
see Graap, Lothar, Wir Warten Aber Eines
Neuen Himmels

Herzliebster Jesu, Was Hast Du Verbrochen
*mot
4pt mix cor MOSELER s.p. (G1993)

Ich Freute Mich (Psalm 122) Bibl
4pt mix cor MOSELER s.p. (G1994)

Katechismus-Messe *Mass
5pt mix cor MOSELER s.p. (G1995)

Lobe Den Herrn *mot
4pt mix cor MOSELER s.p. (G1996)

Missa Brevis *Mass
3pt mix cor MOSELER s.p. (G1997)

Nicht Uns, Herr
3pt mix cor,Bar solo MOSELER LB-437 s.p.
(G1998)

O Heiland, Reiss Die Himmel Auf
SSATB HANSSLER 7.116 s.p. (G1999)

O Jesu Christ, Meins Lebens Licht
see Graap, Lothar, Alle Menschen Mussen
Sterben

Psalm 33 *see Des Herren Wort

Psalm 122 *see Ich Freute Mich

Selig Sind Die Toten
see Graap, Lothar, Wir Warten Aber Eines
Neuen Himmels

Spruchkanons *CC20U,Bibl/canon
[Ger] 2-4pt BAREN. EM 431 s.p. (G2000)

Triptychon *Bibl
[Ger] mix cor oct DEUTSCHER 7631 s.p.
(G2001)

Veni Domine, Jesu *mot
4pt mix cor,TBar soli MOSELER s.p. (G2002)

Wir Christenleut Habn Jetzund Freud
see Werner, Fritz, Vom Himmel Hoch Da Komm
Ich Her

Wir Warten Aber Eines Neuen Himmels
4pt mix cor MOSELER LB-363 s.p. contains
also: Selig Sind Die Toten; Gott Wird
Abwischen Alle Tranen (G2003)

Wir Wollen Alle Frohlich Sein *cant
1-4pt mix cor,2trp,2trom MOSELER s.p.
(G2004)

GRABLIED see Flemming, F.

GRABMUSIK see Mozart, Wolfgang Amadeus

GRABNER, HERMANN (1886-1969)
Ein Lammlein Geht Und Tragt Die Schuld
*No.62, Psntd
[Ger] 2-3 eq voices/3-4pt mix cor,acap
BAREN. EM 50 s.p. see from Evangelisches
Kirchengesangbuch (G2005)

GRABNER, HERMANN (cont'd.)

Erschienen Ist Der Herrlich Tag *No.80,
Easter
[Ger] 2-3 eq voices/3-4pt mix cor,acap
BAREN. EM 49 s.p. see from EVANGELISCHES
KIRCHENGESANGBUCH   (G2006)

Evangelisches Kirchengesangbuch *see Ein
Lammlein Geht Und Tragt Die Schuld, No.62
                                             (G2007)

Evangelisches Kirchengesangbuch *see O
Traurigkeit, O Herzeleid, No.73   (G2008)

Evangelishes Kirchengesangbuch *see Wir
Wollen Alle Frohlich Sein, No.82   (G2009)

O Traurigkeit, O Herzeleid *No.73, Psntd
[Ger] 2-3 eq voices/3-4pt mix cor,acap
BAREN. EM 47 s.p. see from Evangelisches
Kirchengesangbuch   (G2010)

Wir Wollen Alle Frohlich Sein *No.82, Easter
[Ger] 2-3 eq voices/3-4pt mix cor,acap
BAREN. EM 47 s.p. see from Evangelishes
Kirchengesangbuch   (G2011)

GRACE AND POWER see Brandon, George

GRACE GREATER THAN OUR SIN see Towner, Daniel
B.

GRACE IS POURED ABROAD see Pinkham, Daniel

GRACE OF THE LORD see Geisler, Johan C.

GRACE OF THE LORD JESUS, THE see Willan, Healey

GRACE OF THY CONSOLATION see Roff, Joseph

GRACE TE RENDS SEIGNEUR DIEU, DE TES BIENS see
Jannequin, Clement

GRACE UNTO US see Pasquet, Jean

GRACIOUS AND LONG-SUFFERING see Eyken, H. van

GRACIOUS GOD! TO THEE I PRAY see Blackwell, J.

GRACIOUS IS THE LORD see Tchesnokov, Pavel
Grigorievitch

GRACIOUS LORD, HAVE MERCY see Mozart, Wolfgang
Amadeus

GRACIOUS LORD OF ALL OUR BEING see Bach, Johann
Sebastian

GRACIOUS, MIGHTY SOVEREIGN LORD see Ehret,
Walter

GRACIOUS SPIRIT see Lundquist

GRACIOUS SPIRIT, DOVE DIVINE see Coggin

GRACIOUS SPIRIT, DWELL WITH ME
(Lovelace) SAB KJOS 5712 $.30   (G2012)

GRACIOUS SPIRIT, DWELL WITH ME see Jolley

GRACIOUS SPIRIT DWELL WITH ME see Redhead

GRACIOUS SPIRIT, HOLY GHOST see Forbes,
Sebastian

GRACIOUS SPIRIT HOLY GHOST see Hankey, Mark

GRACIOUS SPIRIT, HOLY SPIRIT see Darst, W.
Glenn

GRAD DORT see Heiller, Anton

GRADUAL 1699 see Kingo, Thomas

GRADUAL AD FESTUM B.V.M. see Mozart, Wolfgang
Amadeus

GRADUAL FOR EASTER see Foelber, Paul

GRADUAL FOR ST. CECILIA'S DAY see Scarlatti,
Alessandro, Audi Filia

GRADUALE see Baumann, Max

GRADUALE see Grassi, Ciro

GRADUALE see Janacek, Leos

GRADUALE see Lassus, Roland de (Orlandus)

GRADUALE see Ravanello, Oreste

GRADUALE AND OFFERTORY see Skroup, Jan Nepomuk

GRADUALE FOR TREFALDIGHETSSONDAGEN see
Johansson, Bengt

GRADUALE UND OFFERTORIUM ZUM HEILIGEN OSTERFEST
see Kraft, Karl

GRADUALIA, LIBER I see Byrd, William

GRADUALIA, LIBER II see Byrd, William

GRADUALS FOR THE CHURCH YEAR see Willan, Healey

GRADUALS FOR THE CHURCH YEAR, THE *CCU,chant/
Gradual/liturg
(Buszin, W.) cor CONCORDIA 97-7508 $1.50
                                             (G2013)

GRADULE AD FESTUM B.M.V. see Mozart, Wolfgang
Amadeus

GRAF, FRANZ
Father, Forgive Them *Lent
SSAA SCHMITT 2540 $.22   (G2014)

God Be In My Head *Gen
SSAA SCHMITT 2538 $.18   (G2015)

Great Lord Of All *Gen
SATB SCHMITT 1580 $.20   (G2016)

Nativity Carol *Xmas
SSA SCHMITT 2524 $.25   (G2017)

Psalm 97 *see Singet Dem Herrn

GRAF, FRANZ (cont'd.)

Singet Dem Herrn (Psalm 97)
mix cor,acap oct DOBLINGER s.p.   (G2018)

GRAFF
Put Back The Star Of Bethlehem Into Our
Nation's Flag
(O'Hara) SA oct BOURNE 2014 $.25   (G2019)

GRAHAM
Alleluia To Our King *Easter
SA/unis oct LORENZ 8622 $.25   (G2020)

And Nobody Know
SA oct LORENZ 5391 $.25   (G2021)

Blessed Are The Pure In Heart *Bibl
SATB oct FISCHER,C R-6035 $.25   (G2022)

Call To Remembrance O Lord *Rembrnc
SATB oct FISCHER,C R-6034 $.25   (G2023)

Carol, A
SATB,SATB soli,acap oct COLOMBO 922 $.25
                                        (G2024)

Christmas Lullaby From China, A *Xmas
2pt oct SACRED S-5756 $.35   (G2025)

For God Alone
SATB WARNER R3414 $.30   (G2026)

From The Stable
SA FLAMMER E5075 $1.25   (G2027)

Fulfillment, The *Xmas,cant
SATB FISCHER,C R-8014 $1.35   (G2028)

He Walks Beside Us
SATB WARNER R3441 $.30   (G2029)

I Sought The Lord
4pt jr cor/SATB (very easy) FISCHER,C
R 6036 $.22   (G2030)
SATB oct FISCHER,C R-6036 $.25   (G2031)

Lead Us Father, In The Way
2pt jr cor FISCHER,C R 37 $.22   (G2032)

Lead Us Father, In Thy Way
SA oct FISCHER,C R-37 $.25   (G2033)

Long Ago, And Far Away *Xmas
2pt jr cor FISCHER,C R 36 $.25   (G2034)

Long Ago In Bethlehem *Xmas
2pt oct SACRED S-5747 $.30   (G2035)

My Master Was So Very Poor
unis/SA oct LORENZ 5394 $.30   (G2036)

Prayer For Strength *prayer
SATB oct FISCHER,C CM-7273 $.25   (G2037)

Saviour Teach Me Day By Day
2pt jr cor FISCHER,C R 40 $.22   (G2038)

Shout In Joy Unto The Lord
SAB WARNER R3406 $.30   (G2039)

Sing We Now Hasanna *Palm
SA oct SOUTHERN $.30   (G2040)

Sing We Now Hosanna
2pt oct SACRED S-5742 $.35   (G2041)

Sing With Wonder And Delight *Xmas
2pt oct LORENZ 5754 $.25   (G2042)

That First Christmas Morn *Xmas,cant
SATB FISCHER,C R-8070 $1.50   (G2043)

GRAHAM, GEORGE
Come, Ye Faithful, Raise The Strain *anthem
SA (easy) oct AUGSBURG 1516 $.20   (G2044)

Office Of The Holy Communion
SATB,acap oct BERANDOL 911G2AB $.50   (G2045)

Tread Softly, Shepherds
SATB,acap oct BERANDOL 911G2AC $.35   (G2046)

GRAHAM, M.E.
Christmas Bells *Xmas,anthem/carol
SATB,pno (easy) oct WILLIS 3767 $.20
                                        (G2047)

Lord Of Lords *Easter,cant
mix cor,SATB soli,pno/org (med) oct WILLIS
$.60   (G2048)

GRAHAM, R.W.
Praise And Thanksgiving
SAB,org/pno GRAY GCMR 3296 $.30   (G2049)

To Us A Savior *Xmas,cant
SATB BELWIN $1.50   (G2050)

To Us A Savior [Anthem]
SATB oct FISCHER,J 10043 $.25   (G2051)

GRAHAM, ROBERT [V.] (1912-   )
Above A Star *Xmas
SATB oct ELKAN-V 362-1153 $.25   (G2052)

All My Heart This Night Rejoices *Xmas
SATB oct ELKAN-V 362-1127 $.25   (G2053)

Behold, O Daughters Of Zion *Easter/Lent/
Palm
SATB oct WALTON 2087 $.25   (G2054)

Candles For Christmas *Xmas,cant
jr cor BELWIN $1.50   (G2055)

Christmas Story, The *Xmas
jr cor (easy) ABINGDON APM-467 $1.25
                                        (G2056)

Come Now To Bethlehem *Xmas,cant
2pt SACRED $1.75   (G2057)

Drop, Drop, Slow Tears *Lent
SATB,org/pno oct KERBY 808 $.30   (G2058)
SATB oct KERBY 80878 $.30   (G2059)

From The Eastern Mountains
SATB oct ELKAN-V 362-1157 $.25   (G2060)

GRAHAM, ROBERT [V.] (cont'd.)

God Be Merciful And Kind *anthem/prayer
4pt jr cor/SATB,pno/org (very easy) oct
FISCHER,C R-6087 $.25   (G2061)

God Is Ascended
SATB oct ELKAN-V 362-1125 $.25   (G2062)

Grant, Holy Jesus
SATB oct ELKAN-V 362-1138 $.25   (G2063)

Guiding Star, The *Xmas
SATB oct WALTON 2076 $.25   (G2064)

Holy Child, The *Xmas
SSA oct WALTON 5006 $.25   (G2065)

Hush My Dear *Xmas
SATB (med) ABINGDON APM-102 $.22   (G2066)

In The Beginning *Gen/Thanks
jr cor (easy) ABINGDON APM-469 $1.25
                                        (G2067)

In This Thy Mercy's Day
SATB oct ELKAN-V 362-1190 $.25   (G2068)

O Jesus, Crucified For Man *Easter/Lent
SATB oct WALTON 2086 $.25   (G2069)

Rocking Carol *Xmas
SAB oct PRESSER 312-40698 $.30   (G2070)

Saw You Never, In The Twilight *Xmas
SATB oct ELKAN-V 362-1180 $.30   (G2071)

Sing, O Sing, This Blessed Morn *Xmas
SATB oct WALTON 2077 $.25   (G2072)

There Is A Lamb In The Stable *Xmas
SATB oct KERBY 80978 $.40   (G2073)

Time Draws Near, The *Xmas
SATB,pno oct KERBY 6305 $.30   (G2074)
SATB oct KERBY 6305C $.30   (G2075)

We Beseech Thee
SATB oct ELKAN-V 362-1178 $.25   (G2076)

We Lift Our Hearts Unto The Lord
SATB oct WALTON 2063 $.25   (G2077)

When Jesus Was Born *Xmas
SSA oct WALTON 2064 $.25   (G2078)
2pt oct WALTON 5010 $.25   (G2079)
SA oct WALTON 5009 $.25   (G2080)

Year Of Our Lord, The *cant
mix cor BELWIN $1.50   (G2081)

GRAIL
O Give The Lord, You Sons Of God
[Eng] unis oct ST.MARTIN SMP627 s.p.
                                        (G2082)

GRAINER, J.
Hosanna *Easter
(Deis) 3pt mix cor oct SCHIRM.G 9917 $.30
                                        (G2083)
(Martin) 4pt mix cor oct SCHIRM.G 3600 $.30
                                        (G2084)
(Stickles) jr cor&sr cor,org/pno oct
SCHIRM.G 10471 $.25   (G2085)

GRAINGER, PERCY ALDRIDGE (1882-1961)
Only Son, The
opt SATBB,ST soli,inst voc sc SCHOTT s.p.,
ipr   (G2086)

GRAMS, WERNER P.
Cradle Song *Xmas
SA SCHMITT 222 $.20   (G2087)

GRAND, L.
Story Of The First Christmas *Xmas
SATB, opt multimedia BELWIN $2.50   (G2088)

GRAND MASS see Mozart, Wolfgang Amadeus, Grosse
Messe

GRAND MASS IN C MINOR see Mozart, Wolfgang
Amadeus, Grosse Messe

GRAND-MESSE DE NOEL see Gevaert, Francois
Auguste, Puer Natus Est Nobis

GRANDI, ALESSANDRO (? -1630)
Come, O Come My Beloved *see Veniat Dilectus
Meus

Drei Konzertierende Motetten *CC3U,mot
(Blume) [Ger/Lat] 4pt mix cor,cont MOSELER
s.p.   (G2089)

Exaudi Deus
cor FABER F0064 s.p.   (G2090)
(Roche) "Hear Me O Lord" [Eng/Lat] SATTB,
kbd oct SCHIRM.G 11733 $.35   (G2091)

Exaudi Deus Orationem Meam *mot,It
(Roche, Jerome) [Lat] SATTB oct FABER 11733
$.35   (G2092)

Hear Me O Lord *see Exaudi Deus

O Gate Of Heaven *anthem/mot
mix cor oct NOVELLO 40.1557.06 s.p.   (G2093)

O Porta Caeli *anthem
(Roche, Jerome) [Lat] mix cor oct NOVELLO
40.1557.06 s.p.   (C2094)

Three Concert Motets *CC3U,mot
mix cor,acap voc sc KALMUS 6199 $1.25
                                        (G2095)

Veniat Dilectus Meus *mot,It
cor FABER F0065 s.p.   (G2096)
(Roche) "Come, O Come My Beloved" [Eng/Lat]
STTB,kbd oct SCHIRM.G 11734 $.35   (G2097)
(Roche, Jerome) [Lat] STTB oct FABER 11734
$.35   (G2098)

GRANER FESTMESSE see Liszt, Franz

GRANER MASS see Liszt, Franz, Missa Solemnis

GRANIER, J.
Hosanna! *Easter/Lent
SATB oct FISCHER,C CM-389 $.25   (G2099)
TTBB oct FISCHER,C CM-388 $.25   (G2100)
(Adams, C.) SATB oct PRESSER 312-10111 $.30
(G2101)
(Ehret) SATB,S/T solo oct PRO ART 1576 $.18
(G2102)

GRANSTAM, BENGT
Dig Kristi Kors Vi Halsa
mix cor NORDISKA 5968 s.p.   (G2103)

GRANT
Amen
see Six Responses For General Use

God Be In My Head
(Schaefer) SAB FLAMMER D5102 $.25   (G2104)

Hark! The Vesper Hymn Is Stealing *Eve
boy cor SOUTHERN $.25   (G2105)

Introit
see Six Responses For General Use

Invocation
see Six Responses For General Use

Lift Up Your Hearts, Book 1 *CCU
SAB BOSTON $1.25   (G2106)

Lift Up Your Hearts, Book 2 *CCU
SAB BOSTON $1.25   (G2107)

More Choral Gems From The Masters *CCU
2pt BOSTON $1.50   (G2108)

O Breath From Out Th'eternal Silence *anthem
SATB oct FOX R195 $.25   (G2109)

Offertory
see Six Responses For General Use

Old Gaelic Blessing, An *Bene
SATB oct FOX R188 $.22   (G2110)

Prayer *anthem/prayer
SATB oct FOX R189 $.25   (G2111)

Response After Benediction
see Six Responses For General Use

Response After Prayer
see Six Responses For General Use

Sacred Choral Gems From The Masters *CCU
2pt BOSTON $1.50   (G2112)

Six Responses For General Use
oct FOX R193 $.35
contains: Amen; Introit; Invocation;
Offertory Response; Response After
Benediction; Response After Prayer
(G2113)

GRANT, CECIL
Take Up Thy Cross
SATB ENOCH EC4 s.p.   (G2114)
2pt ENOCH TP60 s.p.   (G2115)

GRANT, DAVID (1833-1893)
Crimond *see Lord's My Shepherd, The

Lord Is My Shepherd, The *Bibl/hymn
SATB&desc oct PAXTON P85374 s.p.   (G2116)

Lord's My Shepherd, The
"Crimond" SATB ENOCH EC281 s.p.   (G2117)
"Crimond" 2pt ASHDOWN E.A.251 s.p.   (G2118)
"Crimond" SATB ENOCH EC278 s.p.   (G2119)

GRANT, HOLY JESUS see Graham, Robert [V.]

GRANT, LORD, THY JOY SUPERNAL see Secchi

GRANT, LOUISE
Father In Heaven
SAB oct BELWIN 1800 $.25   (G2120)

Festival Choruses For Two Equal Voices *CCU,
Fest
2 eq voices BELWIN $1.00   (G2121)

Legend Of The Madonna
SATB, opt multimedia BELWIN $1.25   (G2122)

Songs Of Gladness *CCU
2pt treb cor KJOS $1.25   (G2123)

GRANT ME AGAIN THE JOY OF THY SALVATION see
Brahms, Johannes

GRANT ME, DEAR LORD, DEEP PEACE OF MIND see
Stickles, William

GRANT ME, LORD, THY HOLY SPIRIT see Lundquist

GRANT ME TRUE COURAGE, LORD see Bach, Johann
Sebastian

GRANT ME TRUE COURAGE, LORD see Fritzsch,
Ahaseurus

GRANT THY GRACE TO ME, O GOD see Pergolesi,
Giovanni Battista

GRANT TO US THY MERCY, O LORD see Pergolesi,
Giovanni Battista, Miserere Mei

GRANT UNTO ME see Brahms, Johannes

GRANT UNTO ME see Saint-Saens, Camille

GRANT UNTO ME THE JOY OF THY SALVATION see
Brahms, Johannes

GRANT UNTO US THY BLESSING see Nanini (Nanino),
Giovanni Maria, Diffusa Est Gratia

GRANT US LIGHT see Thiman, Eric Harding

GRANT US, OH OUR HEAVENLY FATHER see Emerson,
John

GRANT US PEACE see Dona Nobis Pacem

GRANT US PEACE see Ehret, Walter

GRANT US PEACE see Massenet, Jules

GRANT US PEACE see Mendelssohn-Bartholdy, Felix

GRANT US STRENGTH AND PROTECTION see Roff,
Joseph

GRANT US THY BLESSING see Loewe, C., Salvum Fac
Regem

GRANT US THY GRACE see Pergolesi, Giovanni
Battista, Miserere Mei

GRANT US THY GREAT MERCY see Pergolesi,
Giovanni Battista, Miserere Mei

GRANT US THY HOLY PEACE see Morgan

GRANT US THY LIGHT see Willan, Healey

GRANT US THY PEACE
2pt CHAPPELL 0018044-352 $.40   (G2124)
SSA CHAPPELL 0018044-354 $.40   (G2125)
SATB CHAPPELL 0018044-358 $.40   (G2126)

GRANT US THY PEACE see Bitgood, Roberta

GRANT US THY PEACE see Diggle, [Roland]

GRANT US THY PEACE see Gounod, Charles Francois

GRANT US THY PEACE see Hokanson, Margrethe

GRANT US THY PEACE see Mendelssohn-Bartholdy,
Felix, Da Nobis Pacem

GRANT US THY PEACE see Young

GRANT US THY SPIRIT see Wallace, G.

GRANT US THY TRUTH see Asola, Giovanni Matteo

GRANT US TO DO WITH ZEAL see Bach

GRANT US TO DO WITH ZEAL see Bach, Johann
Sebastian

GRANT US WISDOM, GRANT US COURAGE see Wehr,
David A.

GRANT, WE BESEECH THEE see Harker, F.
Flaxington

GRANT, WE BESEECH THEE see Langlois, H.G.

GRANT, WE BESEECH THEE see Pedrette

GRANT WE BESEECH THEE see Roberts, J. Varley

GRANT, WE BESEECH THEE see Shaw, Martin

GRANT, WE BESEECH THEE see Sternburg, Daniel

GRANT, WE BESEECH THEE, MERCIFUL LORD see
Okeover, John

GRASSI, CIRO
Ave Maria
see Per La Festa Dell'Immacolata Concezione

Celestis Urbs
see RACCOLTA DI SEI INNI

Comunione
see Per La Festa Dell'Immacolata Concezione

De Profundis *Req
[Lat] TTBB,org sc ZANIBON 3605 s.p., voc pt
ZANIBON 3606-07 s.p.   (G2127)

Graduale
see Per La Festa Dell'Immacolata Concezione

O Salutaris Hostia
see Quattro Canti Eucaristici

Offertorio
see Per La Festa Dell'Immacolata Concezione

Pange Lingua
see Quattro Canti Eucaristici
see Tre Mottetti Eucaristici

Panis Angelicus
see Quattro Canti Eucaristici

Per La Festa Dell'Immacolata Concezione
*Op.19, BVM
[Lat] 4 eq voices ZANIBON 536 s.p.
contains: Ave Maria; Comunione; Graduale;
Offertorio   (G2128)

Quattro Canti Eucaristici *Op.36, Commun
[Lat] sc ZANIBON 15 s.p.
contains: O Salutaris Hostia (2pt men
cor,org); Pange Lingua (2pt men cor,
org); Panis Angelicus (unis men cor,
org); Tantum Ergo (3pt men cor,org)
(G2129)

Responsorio
see DUE MOTTETTI EUCARISTICI

Sanctorum Meritis
see INNI DE COMUNE

Si Quaeris *Op.26, ASD
[Lat] 3 eq voices,org ZANIBON 53 s.p.
(G2130)

Tantum Ergo
see Quattro Canti Eucaristici
see Tre Mottetti Eucaristici
see Tre Mottetti Eucaristici

Tre Mottetti Eucaristici *Op.38, Commun,mot
[Lat] sc ZANIBON 1414 s.p.
contains: Pange Lingua (2pt men cor,org);
Tantum Ergo (3pt men cor,org); Tantum
Ergo (unis/4pt mix cor,org)   (G2131)

GRATEFUL HEART, A see Bock, F.

GRATES NUN OMNES see Stoltzer, Thomas

GRATES NUNC OMINIUM see Ammon, Blasius

GRATES NUNC OMNES see Stoltzer, Thomas

GRATES NUNC OMNES REDDAMUS see Pederson, Mogens

GRATIAS AGIMUS TIBI see Schutz, Heinrich

GRATIEUSE see Ghilselin-Verbonnet, Johannes

GRATTON, FRANK L.
Abide With Me *Rembrnc
SATB ALLANS 164 s.p.   (G2132)

Call To Worship *Austral
SATB ALLANS 135 s.p.   (G2133)

Hark The Vesper Hymn *Eve,hymn,Austral
SATB ALLANS 134 s.p.   (G2134)

I Will Lay Me Down In Peace *Austral
SATB ALLANS 143 s.p.   (G2135)

GRAUEL, J.
Why The Chimes Rang *Xmas
SATB oct PRESSER 312-40228 $.50   (G2136)

GRAUN, E.H.
Surely He Hath Borne Our Griefs
(Ehret) SATB,acap oct LAWSON 661 $.30
(G2137)

GRAUN, KARL HEINRICH (1703-1759)
Be Thou, O God, On High Exalted
(Ehret) SAB oct ELKAN-V 362-1307 $.30
(G2138)

Before Thee Bow, Afflicted Sinners (from Der
Tod Jesu) Easter/Lent
SATB oct WALTON 2096 $.30   (G2139)

Blessed Are The Faithful
(Wienandt) SATB oct SOUTHERN $.50   (G2140)

Bow Down Thine Ear, O Lord
(Chambers) SATB oct BOOSEY 5407 $.30
(G2141)

Dein Geist Mein Leib Und Seel Regier *cant
[Ger] cor,soli,org,strings,opt 2ob KISTNER
sc s.p., cor pts s.p., ipa   (G2142)

Der Tod Jesu *Psntd,cant
mix cor,SATB soli,org,2fl,2ob,2bsn,strings
BREITKOPF-L rental   (G2143)
4pt mix cor,SATB soli,org,2fl,2ob,2bsn,
strings,timp voc pt BREITKOPF-W CHB-258
s.p., ipr, sc BREITKOPF-W rental   (G2144)

He Endured The Cross *anthem
(Wetzler) SATB (med) oct AUGSBURG 1351 $.30
(G2145)

He Was Despised *Easter/Lent,Bibl
(Hilton, A.) SSA oct PRESSER 352-00399 $.30
(G2146)
(Hilton, A.) SAB oct PRESSER 352-00400 $.30
(G2147)
(Hilton, A.) SATB oct PRESSER 352-00400
$.30   (G2148)
(Richardson) SAB oct SPRATT 645 $.30 (G2149)
(Wilson) SATB oct SOUTHERN $.25   (G2150)
(Wilson) 4pt mix cor,org oct SCHIRM.G 11391
$.25   (G2151)

Herr, Ich Habe Lieb De Statte
"Lord, We Love The Place" mix cor SOUTHERN
$.30   (G2152)
(Frank) "Lord We Love The Place" SATB oct
FOX MM6 $.30   (G2153)

How Our Spirit Is Weighed Down (from Der Tod
Jesu) Easter/Lent
SATB oct WALTON 2097 $.30   (G2154)

Joyfully Sing, All Ye Faithful
(Wienandt) SATB oct BELWIN 64304 $.30
(G2155)

Let All That Put Their Trust In Thee
(Hilton, A.) SATB,acap oct PRESSER
352-00397 $.30   (G2156)

Lord, I Love The Habitation Of Thy House
(Wienandt) SATB oct SOUTHERN $.25   (G2157)

Lord, I Love The Place
(Harris) SSA,opt kbd oct PRO ART 2597 $.30
(G2158)

Lord, I Love The Place Where Thou Dwellest
(Ehret) mix cor CHAPPELL 0023473-358 $.40
(G2159)

Lord We Love The Place *see Herr, Ich Habe
Lieb De Statte

O Come Let Us Praise The Lord *Thanks
(Siegert; Fryer) KJOS $1.25   (G2160)

O Praise The Lord
(Cramer) SSA MARKS 4477 $.25   (G2161)
(Cramer) SATB MARKS 4281 $.25   (G2162)

Out Of The Depths
(Hilton, A.) SATB oct PRESSER 352-00377
$.30   (G2163)

Passion Of Our Lord *Easter,ora
(Siegert, Fryer) KJOS $2.00   (G2164)

Sing, All Ye Righteous
(Elkins) SATB,pno/org BOSTON 13572 $.30
(G2165)

Sing And Be Joyful (from Der Tod Jesu)
(Mason; Craig) SATB oct PLYMOUTH DC-121
$.35   (G2166)

Surely He Hath Borne Our Griefs *Lent
SATB,acap (med easy) oct CONCORDIA 98-1171
$.25   (G2167)
SATB oct SOUTHERN $.25   (G2168)

To Us A Child Is Given *Xmas
(Wienandt) SATB FISCHER,C O-4492 $.75
(G2169)
(Wienandt) SATB oct FISCHER,C O-4492 $.60
(G2170)

GRAVER
Ye Sons And Daughters Of The King *Easter
3pt jr cor/SSA (med easy) FISCHER,C CM 6233
$.20   (G2171)

GRAVES
Honey In The Rock
(Smith) SATB oct LILLENAS AT-1003 $.30
(G2172)

GRAVES (cont'd.)

I Was Glad When They Said Unto Me
SATB,org FRANCIS s.p.   (G2173)

Jubilate Deo
see Two Offertories

Lux Perpetua
see Two Offertories

Two Offertories *Gen
SATB SCHMITT 8008 $.30
contains: Jubilate Deo; Lux Perpetua
(G2174)

GRAVES, JOHN
Christ, Whose Glory Fills The Skies *Morn
SA (easy) oct OXFORD 44.209 $.25   (G2175)

Spacious Firmament On High, The *anthem
SATB&unis oct NOVELLO 28.1478.01 s.p.
(G2176)

unis oct NOVELLO 28.3478.02 s.p.   (G2177)

GRAVES, RICHARD
Child's Song Of Christmas, A *Xmas
unis oct CURWEN 10495 $.20   (G2178)

Come, My Way, My Truth, My Life *anthem
mix cor oct NOVELLO 29.0023.08 s.p. (G2179)

In Pastures Green (Psalm 23)
1-2pt BOSWORTH s.p.   (G2180)

Judge Eternal, Throned In Splendor *hymn
mix cor CURWEN 80905 s.p.   (G2181)

Psalm 23 *see In Pastures Green

GRAVES, [WILLIAM] (1916-   )
Hear Us, O Lord, From Heaven, Thy Dwelling
Place
SATB oct ELKAN-V 362-1220 $.25   (G2182)

Unto Thee Do We Cry
SSA oct SOUTHERN $.35   (G2183)

GRAVITT
Hallelujah Mass, The *Mass
SATB FLAMMER A5584 $.60   (G2184)

GRAY
Saviour Is Born, The *Xmas,cant
SATB PRO ART 132 $1.25   (G2185)
SSA PRO ART 267 $.75   (G2186)

GRAY, ALAN (1855-1935)
Jerusalem On High *Gen
SATB (easy) oct OXFORD 42.011 $.30   (G2187)

GRAY, HAMILTON
Dream Of Paradise
2pt ENOCH TP145 s.p.   (G2188)

GRAYSON
Christ The Lord Is Risen Today *Easter
SATB KJOS 7032 $.30   (G2189)

Jubilate Deo
SATB KJOS 7007 $.40   (G2190)

GRAZIOLI, GIOVANNI (1755-1820)
God Be With Thee *see Pange Lingua

Pange Lingua
"God Be With Thee" SAB/SAT,acap SCHIRM.EC
1704 $.25   (G2191)
(Whitford, H.) "God Be With Thee" SSA,acap
SCHIRM.EC 1928 $.15   (G2192)
(Whitford, H.) "God Be With Thee" SATB,acap
SCHIRM.EC 2223 $.18   (G2193)

GREAT ADVENT ANTIPHONS ON MAGNIFICAT, THE see
Arnold, J.H.

GREAT ALL IN ALL see Beadell, Robert M.

GREAT AMONG NATIONS see Heaton, [Wallace]

GREAT AND GLORIOUS see Dickinson, Clarence

GREAT AND GLORIOUS see Haydn, (Franz) Joseph

GREAT AND MARVELLOUS see Tomkins, Thomas

GREAT AND MARVELLOUS see Turner, Edmund
(Edmond)

GREAT AND MARVELOUS (from Mass In B Flat)
(Farmer, H.) SATB oct PRESSER 332-00091 $.35
(G2194)

GREAT AND MARVELOUS see Gaul, Alfred Robert

GREAT AND MARVELOUS see Wilson, Ira B.

GREAT AND MARVELOUS ARE THY WORKS see Gaul,
Alfred Robert

GREAT AND MARVELOUS ARE THY WORKS see Goemanne,
Noel

GREAT AND MARVELOUS ARE THY WORKS see Harper,
Marjorie

GREAT AND MIGHTY ARE THY WORKS, OH, LORD see
Lister, Mosie

GREAT AND MIGHTY WONDER, A see Butler, Eugene

GREAT AND MIGHTY WONDER, A see Fetler, Paul

GREAT AND MIGHTY WONDER, A see Pasquet, Jean

GREAT AND MIGHTY WONDER, A see Sateren, Leland
Bernhard

GREAT AND WONDERFUL ARE THY DEEDS see Newbury

GREAT ARE THY TENDER MERCIES, LORD see Handel,
George Frideric

GREAT ART THOU, O GOD see Hoddinott, Alun

GREAT ART THOU, O LORD see Songer

GREAT CHORAL SERIES
(Warnick, Clay) BIG3 $1.25
contains: Someday; Suddenly There's A
Valley; Take My Hand, Precious Lord;

There'll Be A Place In The Valley For Me;
There'll Be No Tomorrow   (G2195)

GREAT CHORAL SERIES
(Warnick, Clay) SATB BIG3 $1.25
contains: Ivory Palaces; Love Of God, The;
Mansion Over The Hilltop; My Desire
(G2196)

GREAT CHRISTMAS CHORUSES see Johnson

GREAT CREATOR OF THE WORLD see Grieb, Herbert
[C.]

GREAT DAY *CCUL,hymn/spir
(Owens, Jimmy) SATB cmplt ed LILLENAS MB-236
$1.95   (G2197)

GREAT DAY! *spir
(Ehret) SATB oct LAWSON 763 $.30   (G2198)
(Ehret) SSA/SAA oct LAWSON 51078 $.30 (G2199)
(Hardwicke) SA ALFRED 6133 $.30   (G2200)
(Hardwicke) SAB ALFRED 6559 $.30   (G2201)
(Johnson, Hall) mix cor,acap oct SCHIRM.G
10345 $.35   (G2202)
(Roberton) mix cor ROBERTON 61406 s.p. (G2203)
(Whitman) SATB oct LILLENAS AN-3803 $.30
(G2204)

GREAT DAY see Drewes

GREAT DAY see Martin, Warren

GREAT DAY OF THE LORD IS NEAR see Martin,
George Clement

GREAT DAY OF THE LORD, THE see Stout, Alan

GREAT FEAR AND TREMBLING HAVE TAKEN HOLD OF ME
see Poulenc, Francis, Timor Et Tremor
Venerunt Super Me

GREAT GOD
see Two Carols

GREAT GOD see Mueller, Carl F.

GREAT GOD ABOVE *Gen
(Christiansen, P.) SATB SCHMITT 8059 $.30
(G2205)

GREAT GOD A'MIGHTY see Hairston, Jester

GREAT GOD AND GOD OF OUR SALVATION see Mueller,
Carl F.

GREAT GOD ATTEND WHILE ZION SINGS see Butler

GREAT GOD OF LOVE see Hutson

GREAT GOD OF NATIONS see Curry, W. Lawrence

GREAT GOD OF NATIONS see Franck, Cesar

GREAT GOD OF OUR SALVATION see Prentice, Fred

GREAT GOD OUR SOURCE see Cartford, Gerhard M.

GREAT GOD, OUR STRENGTH see Tchesnokov, Pavel
Grigorievitch

GREAT GOD, WE SING THAT MIGHTY HAND see
Markworth, Henry

GREAT GOD, WHAT DO I SEE AND HEAR!
(Grieb) 4pt mix cor oct SCHIRM.G 10907 $.25
(G2206)

GREAT GOD, WHO, HID FROM MORTAL SIGHT see
Harwood, Basil

GREAT HYMNS WITH DESCANTS *CCU
mix cor SCHMITT 9063 $.90   (G2207)

GREAT IS JEHOVAH see Schubert, Franz (Peter)

GREAT IS JEHOVAH, THE LORD see Schubert, Franz
(Peter)

GREAT IS OUR GOD see Davis, Katherine K.

GREAT IS OUR LORD see Schutz, Heinrich, Der
Herr Ist Gross

GREAT IS THE FATHER see Handel, George Frideric

GREAT IS THE GRACE see Nanini (Nanino),
Giovanni Maria, Diffusa Est Gratia

GREAT IS THE HOLY ONE see Darst, W. Glenn

GREAT IS THE LORD see Brown

GREAT IS THE LORD see Burroughs, Bob

GREAT IS THE LORD see Cooper

GREAT IS THE LORD see Elgar, Edward

GREAT IS THE LORD see Glarum, L. Stanley

GREAT IS THE LORD see Haydn, (Franz) Joseph

GREAT IS THE LORD see Kirk

GREAT IS THE LORD see Lewis, J.

GREAT IS THE LORD see Marchant, Arthur W.

GREAT IS THE LORD see Matthews, Harvey
Alexander

GREAT IS THE LORD see Newbury, Kent A.

GREAT IS THE LORD see Schutz, Heinrich, Der
Herr Ist Gross

GREAT IS THE LORD see Sowerby, Leo

GREAT IS THE LORD see Steane, Bruce

GREAT IS THE LORD see Sydenham, E.A.

GREAT IS THE LORD see Willan, Healey

GREAT IS THE LORD see Woollen

GREAT IS THE LORD see Young

GREAT IS THE LORD, OUR GOD see Harris

GREAT IS THE LORD OUR MAKER see Haydn, (Johann)
Michael

GREAT IS THE PEACE see Dieterich

GREAT IS THY FAITHFULNESS see Lorenz

GREAT IS THY FAITHFULNESS see Runyan

GREAT IS THY REWARD see Raymond, Joseph

GREAT KING OF GLORY, COME see Marshall, Jane M.

GREAT LEARNING, THE see Cardew, Cornelius

GREAT LEARNING, THE see Cardew, Cornelius

GREAT LORD OF ALL see Graf, Franz

GREAT LORD OF LORDS see Joubert, John

GREAT LORD OF LORDS see Mc Cabe, John

GREAT MOTHER'S LULLABY see Hatch, H.

GREAT MOVER OF ALL HEARTS see Smith, Noel

GREAT O ANTIPHONS OF ADVENT, THE see Willan,
Healey

GREAT PEACE HAVE THEY see Mac Roberts

GREAT PEACE HAVE THEY see Rogers, J.H.

GREAT PEACE HAVE THEY see Steinel

GREAT PEACE, THE see Bain, J.L. Mc Beth

GREAT RULER OVER TIME AND SPACE see Licht

GREAT SERVICE see Byrd, William

GREAT SHEPHERD OF THY PEOPLE, HEAR see
Ratcliffe, Desmond

GREAT SONGS OF FAITH see Krones

GREAT TO BE ALIVE see Skillings, Otis

GREAT TO BE ALIVE see Skillings, Otis

GREAT WHITE HOST, THE see Grieg, Edvard Hagerup

GREAT WOE HATH TOUCHED THIS HOLY MAN see
Palestrina, Giovanni, O Quantus Luctus

GREATER LIGHT, THE see Shaw, Martin

GREATER LOVE HATH NO MAN see Ireland, John

GREATER LOVE HATH NO MAN see Mueller, Carl F.

GREATEST BLESSING, THE see Emig, Lois

GREATEST GIFT, THE see Perkins, Phil

GREATEST IS LOVE see Merman

GREATEST OF THESE see Bitgood, Roberta

GREATEST OF THESE IS LOVE, THE see Lorenz

GREATNESS OF THE LORD, THE see Charles, Ernest

GREATOREX, THOMAS (1758-1831)
God's Word Is Sure
(Rogers) 2pt jr cor oct LILLENAS AN-4006
$.25   (G2208)

GREAVES, RALPH
I Got Me Flowers *Easter
SATB/unis (very easy) oct OXFORD 40.908
$.25   (G2209)

GREAVES, TERENCE
Christ Is Our Cornerstone *Gen
SATB (med easy) oct OXFORD 42.888 $.30
(G2210)

Mother, White As Lily Flower *Xmas
mix cor CURWEN 61567 s.p.   (G2211)

GRECKEL
Silently The Wonderous Gift Is Given *Xmas
SATB oct KENDOR $.30   (G2212)

GREEN
O Lord Of Life
(Ohl) SATB oct PLYMOUTH FO-103 $.25 (G2213)

Shepherds Come, Now Leave Your Sheep
SATB,acap SHAWNEE A 920 $.30   (G2214)

GREEN BLADE RISETH, THE see Wright, S.

GREEN CATHEDRAL see Hahn, [Carl]

GREEN CATHEDRAL, THE see Hahn, [Carl]

GREEN GROW THE LILACS *Gen
(Johnson) SAB SCHMITT 5015 $.30   (G2215)

GREEN GROW THE RUSHES see Maitland, John
Alexander Fuller

GREEN HILL JUNIOR CHOIR AND DUET BOOK *CC35U,
anthem
(Davis, K.) SA,pno SCHIRM.EC 1546 $2.00
(G2216)

GREEN HILL THREE-PART SACRED MUSIC FOR WOMEN'S
VOICES *CC38U,anthem
(Davis, K.) SSA,pno SCHIRM.EC 1838 $2.00
(G2217)

GREEN, J.R.
My Master Hath A Garden
unis/SSA,kbd oct KERBY 6252 $.30   (G2218)
SSA/unis,kbd oct KERBY 6252 $.30   (G2219)

GREEN PASTURES see Sanderson

GREEN, PHILIP
Hear Us, O Lord
SATB oct PRESSER MC391 $.30   (G2220)

GREEN, R.
Drop, Drop, Slow Tears *Lent
SATB,acap GRAY GCMR 3293 $.30   (G2221)

GREEN, RACHEL K.
Immanuel Forever *see Lillenas, Haldor

Living Redeemer, The *see Lillenas, Haldor

GREEN, RAY (1909-)
Adam Lay I-Bowndyn
SATB/TTBB,acap AM.MUS.ED. $.50 (G2222)

Corpus Christi *carol
SATB/TTBB,acap AM.MUS.ED. $.25 (G2223)

Lullay Myn Lykng *Xmas,cradle
SATB AM.MUS.ED. $.15 (G2224)

GREENBERG
E La Don Don, Verges Maria
mix cor SOUTHERN $.25 (G2225)

GREENE
O Praise The Lord
unis BOSWORTH s.p. (G2226)

Sing We Noel
TTBB FLAMMER C5026 $.25 (G2227)

Sun Shall Be No More Thy Light
unis BOSWORTH s.p. (G2228)

Thou Visitest The Earth *Harv,Austral
SATB ALLANS 317 s.p. (G2229)

GREENE, MAURICE (1695-1775)
Acquaint Thyself With God *anthem
(Johnstone, H. Diack) mix cor,A/T solo oct NOVELLO 88.0023.05 s.p. (G2230)

Anthem For Christmas Day *Xmas,anthem/cant
mix cor BELWIN $1.00 (G2231)

Blessed Are Those That Are Undefiled (Psalm 119)
SS,org/pno PETERS H51 $.40 (G2232)

Gentiles Shall Come By, The *Gen,anthem
unis,opt pno (contains also: In The Sight Of The Unwise by Nares, J.N 237) oct ROYAL s.p. see also ANTHEMS FOR UNISON OR TWO PART SINGING (G2233)

Like As The Hart *Gen
2pt (very easy) oct OXFORD 44.217 $.50 (G2234)

Lord, How Long Wilt Thou Be Angry
SSATB,acap PETERS H1560 (G2235)

Lord Is A Light, The *anthem
2pt wom cor oct CURWEN 10491 $.25 (G2236)

Lord Is My Shepherd, The (Psalm 23)
(Graves) 2pt jr cor/2pt wom cor CURWEN 72557 s.p. (G2237)

Lord, Let Me Know Mine End (Psalm 39) Adv/Lent
SSATB (med) oct OXFORD 42.208 $.50 (G2238)
(Martens, Mason) SATB oct WALTON 2180 $.30 (G2239)

Magnificat And Nunc Dimittis In C *Magnif/Nunc
SSAATTBB (med) oct OXFORD 42.914 $1.00 (G2240)

My Lips Shall Speak Of Thy Praise (from Blessed Are They That Are Undefiled) Gen/Thanks
2pt (med easy) oct OXFORD 44.700 $.30 (G2241)

O Praise The Lord *Gen,anthem
(Bosworth) unis,opt pno oct ROYAL s.p. see also ANTHEMS FOR UNISON OR TWO PART SINGING (G2242)

Praised Be The Lord (from O Sing Unto God) Gen/Thanks
unis (easy) oct OXFORD 45.875 $.25 (G2243)

Psalm 23 *see Lord Is My Shepherd, The

Psalm 39 *see Lord, Let Me Know Mine End

Psalm 119 *see Blessed Are Those That Are Undefiled

Show Me Thy Ways, O Lord
(Davies) 2pt wom cor oct CURWEN 11478 $.25 (G2244)
(Davies) 2pt jr cor/2pt wom cor CURWEN 72630 s.p. (G2245)

Sing We Merrily
(Martens, Mason) SATB,SATBar soli,orch,kbd voc sc WALTON M 122 $1.75, ipr, sc WALTON rental (G2246)

Song Of Deborah And Barak *ora
(Dawes) SATB,ATB soli,orch s.p., ipr voc sc SCHOTT 10570, cor pts SCHOTT 10570 (G2247)

Thou Visitest The Earth *Gen/Harv/Thanks, anthem/Bibl
SA,kbd (med easy) oct CONCORDIA 98-1817 $.25 (G2248)
4pt mix cor,T/Mez solo oct SCHIRM.G 5379 $.25 (G2249)
SATB oct GRAY GCMR 3143 $.20 (G2250)
(Jackson, Francis) mix cor oct NOVELLO 88.0013.08 s.p. (G2251)
(Ley, Henry G.) SS (very easy) oct OXFORD 44.028 $.30 (G2252)
(Ratcliffe, Desmond) SSA oct NOVELLO 51.0653.02 s.p. (G2253)

Try Me, O God
(Martens, Mason) SATB oct WALTON 2181 $.30 (G2254)

GREENE, P.
Let Me Bring Love
voc sc BELWIN $1.50 (G2255)

GREENER
Jesus Calls Us
SA oct FISCHER,C CM-7666 $.25 (G2256)

Love Divine
2pt jr cor FISCHER,C CM 7440 $.25 (G2257)

Praise The Lord, His Glories Show
SS/SA oct SUMMY M 2716 $.30 (G2258)

GREENER (cont'd.)

Purer In Heart, O God
SA oct FISCHER,C CM-7665 $.25 (G2259)

Saviour Teach Me Day By Day
2pt jr cor FISCHER,C CM 7186 $.25 (G2260)

GREENER, JOSEPH H.
Jesus Calls Us
SA&treb cor&jr cor,pno,org FISCHER,C CM 7666 $.20 (G2261)

O God, Thy World Is Sweet With Prayer
SATB oct HUNTZINGER 7051 $.20 (G2262)

Purer In Heart, O God
SA&treb cor&jr cor,pno,org FISCHER,C CM 7665 $.20 (G2263)

GREENFIELD, MARJORIE H.
Glad Tidings
(Adair) unis jr cor/unis wom cor,opt rec&bells&chimes CURWEN 72665 s.p. (G2264)

Seven Christmas Carols For Juniors *CC7U, Xmas,carol
unis jr cor CURWEN 72074 s.p. (G2265)

Seven Christmas Carols For Little Children *CC7U,Xmas,carol
unis jr cor CURWEN 71870 s.p. (G2266)

Seven More Christmas Carols For Little Children *CC7U,Xmas,carol
unis jr cor CURWEN 71949 s.p. (G2267)

Sing Nowell *Xmas
unis jr cor/unis wom cor CURWEN 72297 s.p. (G2268)

GREENHILL, HAROLD
All Hail The Power *anthem
mix cor oct NOVELLO 40.1305.00 s.p. (G2269)

Eternal Ruler Of The Ceaseless Round *anthem
mix cor oct NOVELLO 40.1122.08 s.p. (G2270)

O Love Divine
SATB PATERSON 1644 s.p. (G2271)

Praise To The Lord *anthem
mix cor oct NOVELLO 28.1204.05 s.p. (G2272)

GREENSLEEVES *Xmas,carol
(Ehret, W.) SSA LEONARD-US 08020480 $.25 (G2273)
(Lefebvre) SSA oct GALAXY 1.1969.1 $.35 (G2274)
(Lefebvre) TTBB oct GALAXY 1.1961.1 $.30 (G2275)
(Lefebvre) SATB oct GALAXY 1.1968.1 $.25 (G2276)

GREENWOOD
Jesus Child
SA/TB FLAMMER E5150 $.30 (G2277)

GREGOR
Hosanna *Adv/Easter/Palm,Morav
SATB oct LORENZ 9870 $.30 (G2278)
SATB oct LORENZ A514 $.30 (G2279)
SATB oct LORENZ 5723 $.30 (G2280)
(Bitgood) sr cor&jr cor/SATB oct GRAY GCMR 1345 $.30 (G2281)

Hosanna! Blessed Is He That Comes *Easter/Lent/Palm
(Mueller) jr cor&sr cor oct FISCHER,C CM-7017 $.30 (G2282)

In Slumber, Peaceful Slumber
(Nolte) [Eng/Ger] SSAB/SATB,org oct MORAVIAN 5701 $.35 (G2283)

Lord In Thy Presence
(Nolte) SA BOOSEY-CAN s.p. (G2284)
(Nolte) [Eng/Ger] SA/SS,org oct MORAVIAN 5700 $.40 (G2285)

Lord's Temple
(Nolte) mix cor SOUTHERN $.40 (G2286)
(Nolte) [Eng/Ger] SSAB,org oct BOOSEY 5609 $.40 (G2287)

Thou Lord, Art Our Shepherd *Morav
(Dickinson) SATB oct GRAY GMCM 14 $.40 (G2288)

GREGOR, [CHRISTIAN FRIEDRICH] (1723-1801)
Hosanna! (composed with Hoffman, M.) *Xmas/Easter/Gen/Lent/Palm
SAB oct PRESSER 312-40928 $.30 (G2289)
(Douglas) SATB&jr cor oct PRO ART 2072 $.30 (G2290)
(Douglas) SAB&jr cor oct PRO ART 2305 $.30 (G2291)
(Douglas) SSA&jr cor oct PRO ART 2290 $.25 (G2292)
(Trusler) SA oct SOUTHERN $.25 (G2293)
(Trusler) boy cor SOUTHERN $.25 (G2294)
(Trusler) SATB oct PLYMOUTH TR-106 $.25 (G2295)

Hosanna! Blessed Is He That Comes *Palm
(Mueller) jr cor&sr cor (med easy) FISCHER, C CM 7017 $.30 (G2296)

GREGORY
God, The Omnipotent
SATB,opt org/pno BOSTON 13330 $.35 (G2297)

GREGORY, WILLIAM
Jesus, Our Lord, Is Crucified
SATB oct AGAPE A 324 $.30 (G2298)

GREIF, C.
Jubilate Deo
mix cor ALSBACH&D sc s.p., cor pts s.p. (G2299)

GREINER, ALLEN
Communion Service *Commun,Bene/Gloria/Kyrie/Sanctus
unis/cong,org (very easy) PRESSER 312-40978 $.35 (G2300)

Preces And Responses
SATB,acap (med easy) PRESSER 312-41001 $.35 (G2301)

GREITTER, MATTHAEUS (ca. 1490-1550)
Lamb Of God Goes Meekly Forth, The *Lent
SAB,kbd (med easy, or Ash Wednesday) oct CONCORDIA 98-1999 $.40 (G2302)

O Man, Bewail Thy Sin So Great *see O Mensch Bewein' Dein' Sunde Gross

O Mensch Bewein' Dein' Sunde Gross *chorale
(Bach, J.S.; Barrow, R.) "O Man, Bewail Thy Sin So Great" TTBB,org SCHIRM.EC 2169 $.18 (G2303)

GRELL, EDUARD AUGUST (1800-1886)
Erhaben, O Herr, Uber Alles Lob
(Muller, A.M.) mix cor,acap ERDMANN 566 s.p. (G2304)

Gnadig Und Barmherzig *Gradual
(Schulz) [Ger] 8pt mix cor HEINRICH. 763 voc sc s.p., cor pts s.p. (G2305)

GRESENS, WALTER
Our Fathers' God In Years Long Gone *Ded/Gen
SATB&cong/SATB&jr cor,org,2trp,horn,timp (med easy) sc CONCORDIA 97-5135 $1.75, cor pts CONCORDIA 98-2151 $.25, ipa (G2306)

GRESSER, HANS (1921-)
Lasset Uns Das Kindlein Wiegen *Xmas
mix cor TONGER s.p. (G2307)

Was Soll Das Bedeuten? *Xmas
mix cor TONGER s.p. (G2308)

GRETCHANINOV, ALEXANDER TIKHONOVITCH (1864-1956)
Adore Almighty God *Asc
SSAATTBB,acap SCHIRM.EC 1694 $.30 (G2309)
(Glaser, V.) SSAA,acap SCHIRM.EC 1981 $.30 (G2310)

Canticle Of The Wise Men *Xmas
(Beckwith) [Russ/Eng] SSAATTBB,acap oct MCA (G2311)

Cherubic Hymn, The
TTBB oct FISCHER,J 8567 $.30 (G2312)
SSAATTBB oct FISCHER,J 4363 $.30 (G2313)
(Douglas) SATB oct FISCHER,J 6834 $.30 (G2314)
(Douglas) SATB oct GRAY GAC 1 $.30 (G2315)

Cherubic Hymn, The *Xmas
(Howorth) SATB,acap oct PRO ART 1000 $.25 (G2316)
(Howorth) SSA,acap oct PRO ART 1026 $.25 (G2317)
(Howorth) SAB,acap oct PRO ART 1031 $.25 (G2318)

Cherubim Song
(Hilton, A.) SSAATTBB oct PRESSER MC332 $.35 (G2319)

Come, And Let Us Worship
(Harding) SSAATTBB,acap BOSTON 7299 $.35 (G2320)

Credo *Credo
SSAATTBB,acap BOSTON 3930 $.35 (G2321)
(Cyr) SATB BOSTON 2649 $.40 (G2322)
(McKinney) TTBB oct FISCHER,J 7652 $.30 (G2323)

Creed
(Cyr) SATB,pno BOSTON 13522 $.40 (G2324)

Gloria
see Gretchaninov, Alexander Tikhonovitch, Nunc Dimittis

Glory To God
SATB/TTBB WEINBERGER s.p. (G2325)

God Is Everywhere
SA,pno PEER $.35 (G2326)

Holy, Radiant Light
(Cain) mix cor,acap oct SCHIRM.G 8081 $.30 (G2327)

Lift Up Your Hearts, Sing Ye
(Cain) SSAA oct FOX R170 $.25 (G2328)
(Cain) SATB oct FOX R103 $.25 (G2329)

Liturgia Domestica
[Lat] mix cor,TB soli,org,strings,harp cmplt ed BOOSEY rental (G2330)

Lord's Prayer, The *Bibl
(Engel) mix cor,A solo,acap oct SCHIRM.G 7393 $.25 (G2331)

Lullaby On Christmas Morning
(Heiberg) SATB,S solo,acap oct MCA (G2332)

Missa Festivo *Mass
cor voc sc KALMUS 6200 $1.25 (G2333)

Nunc Dimittis *Nunc
SSAATTBB,acap BOSTON 1125 $.30 (G2334)
(Aschenbrenner) SATB,acap WARNER W2778 $.30 contains also: Gloria (Gloria) (G2335)
(Ehret) SATB oct BOURNE BL3036 $.25 (G2336)

O Be Joyful In The Lord
SATB oct FISCHER,J 4522 $.30 (G2337)

O Gladsome Light
SATB oct FISCHER,J 4135 $.30 (G2338)

O Lord, I Have Loved
SATB oct GRAY GCMR 1832 $.25 (G2339)

Our Father
SATB,acap oct PRESSER 332-13000 $.30 (G2340)

Sing All Ye Lands
SSA KJOS 6095 $.30 (G2341)

Sing Alleluia *anthem
(Warland) SA (med) oct AUGSBURG 1426 $.25 (G2342)

Thou, Gracious Lord, Art My Defense
(Ehret) SATB oct BOURNE BL3040 $.25 (G2343)

GRETRY, ANDRE ERNEST MODESTE (1741-1813)
Noel *Xmas
(Gardner) SSA oct STAFF 478 $.25 (G2344)

GRIEB
All People That On Earth Do Dwell
jr cor&sr cor (easy) FISCHER,C CM 7208 $.25
(G2345)

Hail The Day *Easter
jr cor&sr cor (easy) FISCHER,C CM 7209 $.25
(G2346)

He Shall Come Down Like Rain *anthem
SATB oct FISCHER,C CM-7292 $.30   (G2347)

Three Riders, The *Xmas
SATB oct SACRED E85 $.35   (G2348)

GRIEB, HERBERT [C.] (1898-   )
As Joseph Was a-Walking
4pt mix cor oct SCHIRM.G 10764 $.25 (G2349)
(Stickles) 3pt mix cor,S solo,acap oct
SCHIRM.G 11364 $.25   (G2350)

Benediction *Bene
4pt mix cor,acap oct SCHIRM.G 11103 $.20
(G2351)

Carol Service For Children, A *Xmas,Bibl/
carol
jr cor voc sc SCHIRM.G $.60   (G2352)

Christmas Lullaby, A *Xmas
4pt mix cor,acap oct SCHIRM.G 11121 $.25
(G2353)

Come Now, Let Us Reason Together *Bibl
4pt mix cor,org/pno oct SCHIRM.G 10993 $.30
(G2354)

Early Easter Morning *Easter,Bibl
4pt mix cor,Bar solo,org/pno oct SCHIRM.G
10810 $.25   (G2355)

Easter Carol Service, An *Easter
unis jr cor/2pt jr cor voc sc SCHIRM.G $.50
(G2356)

From All That Dwell Below The Skies *Bibl
4pt mix cor,org oct SCHIRM.G 11102 $.20
(G2357)

Great Creator Of The World
3pt mix cor oct SCHIRM.G 10938 $.20 (G2358)
jr cor&sr cor oct SCHIRM.G 10747 $.20
(G2359)
4pt mix cor oct SCHIRM.G 10742 $.20 (G2360)

How Calm And Beautiful The Morn *Easter
4pt mix cor oct SCHIRM.G 10886 $.25 (G2361)

Kings Of The Orient Three *Xmas
4pt mix cor oct SCHIRM.G 10763 $.25 (G2362)
(Stickles) 3pt mix cor,pno oct SCHIRM.G
11326 $.25   (G2363)

Little White Dove *Xmas
4pt mix cor,acap oct SCHIRM.G 11209 $.25
(G2364)

Long Ago A Prophet Sang
SATB (med) ABINGDON APM-607 $.35   (G2365)

Lovely Garden, The *cant
4pt mix cor,org voc sc SCHIRM.G $1.00
(G2366)

Magnificat, The
"Magnify The Lord" mix cor,SA soli,org/pno
voc sc SCHIRM.G $1.25   (G2367)

Magnify The Lord *see Magnificat, The

Morning Grace
2pt boy cor/2pt wom cor oct SCHIRM.G 11063
$.25   (G2368)

No Room In The Inn *Xmas
4pt mix cor oct SCHIRM.G 10696 $.25 (G2369)

Noel! Noel! *Xmas
"This Holy Day" 4pt mix cor oct SCHIRM.G
11035 $.25   (G2370)

O God Of Every Race And Creed
4pt mix cor,pno/org oct SCHIRM.G 11932 $.30
(G2371)

O Love That Wilt Not Let Me Go
3pt mix cor oct SCHIRM.G 11153 $.25 (G2372)

Prince Of Peace Is Come! The *Xmas,Bibl
mix cor,org voc sc SCHIRM.G $1.25   (G2373)

Set Me As A Seal *Bibl
4pt mix cor,Bar solo,org oct SCHIRM.G 11050
$.25   (G2374)

Seven Times He Spake *Lent,cant
4pt mix cor,soli,org/pno voc sc SCHIRM.G
$.75   (G2375)

This Book Of The Law
4pt mix cor,org/pno oct SCHIRM.G 11047 $.25
(G2376)

This Holy Day *see Noel! Noel!

Walk Worthy *Bibl
4pt mix cor,acap/org oct SCHIRM.G 11104
$.25   (G2377)

GRIEF IS IN MY HEART see Eberlin, Johann Ernst,
Improperium Exspectavit Cor Meum

GRIEG, EDVARD HAGERUP (1843-1907)
Ave Maris Stella
[Lat] SATB,acap sc NORSK 8579 s.p. (G2378)
"Hail Thou, King Of Glory" [Eng/Lat] mix
cor,acap oct SCHIRM.G 5160 $.25   (G2379)

Behold The Hand Of God
SATB oct LORENZ 9338 $.30   (G2380)

Christmas Tree Song *Xmas
(Sutton) SSA oct GALAXY 1.2432.1 $.20
(G2381)
(Sutton) SAB oct GALAXY 1.2433.1 $.20
(G2382)

Fire Salmer *Op.74
[Norw] mix cor,Bar solo,acap LYCHE EP3128
s.p.
contains: Guds Son Har Gjort Mig Fri;
Hvad Est Du Dog Skjon; I Himmelen;
Jesus Kristus Er Opfaren   (G2383)

Four Psalms *Psalm
SATB,Bar solo PETERS 3128A $.50
contains: God's Son Hath Set Me Free; How
Fair Is Thy Face; In Heav'n Above;
Jesus Christ Our Lord Is Risen   (G2384)

GRIEG, EDVARD HAGERUP (cont'd.)
God's Peace Is Peace Eternal
4pt mix cor,S solo oct SCHIRM.G 4379 $.25
(G2385)
(Geer, E.) SSA,S solo,org SCHIRM.EC 862
$.25   (G2386)

God's Son Has Made Me Free *anthem
(Overby) SATB (med diff) oct AUGSBURG 1004
$.25   (G2387)
(Overby) SATB (very easy) oct AUGSBURG 1212
$.20   (G2388)

God's Son Hath Set Me Free
see Four Psalms

Great White Host, The *ASD/Gen
(Gaul) 4pt mix cor,Bar solo oct SCHIRM.G
6753 $.25   (G2389)

Guds Son Har Gjort Mig Fri
see Fire Salmer

Hail Thou, King Of Glory *see Ave Maris
Stella

How Fair Is Thy Face
see Four Psalms

Hvad Est Du Dog Skjon
see Fire Salmer

I Himmelen
see Fire Salmer

In Heavenly Love
SATB,B solo,acap (med) oct WILLIS 1047 $.12
(G2390)

In Heav'n Above
see Four Psalms

Jesu, Friend Of Sinners *Gen/Lent
(Dickinson) SAB oct GRAY GSC 226 $.30
(G2391)
(Dickinson) SATB oct GRAY GSC 1 $.30
(G2392)

Jesus, Blest Redeemer
(Black) unis oct GRAY GCMR 1687 $.30
(G2393)

Jesus Christ Our Lord Is Risen
see Four Psalms

Jesus Christ Today Is Risen *Easter/Lent
(Allen) SATB,Bar solo GALLEON GCS2005
(G2394)

Jesus Kristus Er Opfaren
see Fire Salmer

Lo, God Is Here *Ded/Gen
(Coleman, Henry) SATB (very easy) oct
OXFORD 84.047 $.25   (G2395)

Lord Of All, To Thee We Pray
(Hirt) 2pt/opt unis WARNER W3685 $.30
(G2396)

My Lord Has Set Me Free *Easter
SAB oct LORENZ 7379 $.30   (G2397)

Now We Sing A Joyful Song
(Ehret) SATB oct PLYMOUTH SC-28 $.35 (G2398)

O Father Of Life *Op.74,No.1
(Ziemer) SATB,B solo,acap oct LAWSON 51581
$.35   (G2399)

Psalms *Op.74,CC4U,Psalm
[Ger/Norw] SATB,Bar solo,acap HINRICHSEN
P3128 s.p.   (G2400)

Solvejg's Song (from Peer Gynt)
see FOLK-SONGS, BALLADS AND SONGS OF GREAT
COMPOSERS (SET V)

Song Of Christmas, A *Xmas
(Allen) S/SS oct GALLEON GCS1002   (G2401)

GRIEVE NOT THE HOLY SPIRIT see Lloyd, Charles
Harford

GRIEVE NOT THE HOLY SPIRIT see Stainer, John

GRIEVE NOT THE HOLY SPIRIT OF GOD see Pasfield,
W.R.

GRIEVE NOT THE HOLY SPIRIT OF GOD see Stainer,
John

GRIEVE NOT THY HOLY SPIRIT see Noble, Thomas
Tertius

GRIFFIN, JACK
Mountain Of The Lord, The
SATB,org ROBERTON   (G2402)

GRIFFITH, PETER
Ballad Of The Holy Child, The
SATB,acap,opt perc oct COLOMBO 2476 $.30
(G2403)

GRIFFITHS, VERNON
Jesu, Grant Me This, I Pray *anthem
mix cor oct NOVELLO 50.0345.08 s.p. (G2404)

O Clap Your Hands *anthem
STB,org oct NOVELLO 32.0038.08 s.p. (G2405)

GRIGG, W.E.
Endless Light Of Day
SATB PARAGON 1030 $.25   (G2406)

GRIMBERT, JACQUES
Messe Novale *Mass
[Lat] mix cor,org HEUGEL voc sc s.p., voc
pt s.p.   (G2407)

GRIME
Lent And Easter, Series 2 *Easter/Lent
unis oct FISCHER,C CM-6994 $.25   (G2408)

Song Of Simeon, The
(Hanson) unis oct FISCHER,C CM-7655 $.25
(G2409)

Teaching Little Children To Pray *anthem
unis oct FISCHER,C CM-7015 $.30   (G2410)

To Thee, O Christ, We Sing
(Hanson) 2pt jr cor oct LILLENAS AN-4008
$.25   (G2411)

GRIME, G.
Song Of Simeon, The
(Hanson) unis jr cor FISCHER,C CM 7655 $.25
(G2412)

GRIME, WILLIAM
All Things Bright And Beautiful
see Finding God Through Nature, Series 1

Alleluia! Child Jesus
see Christmas Carols, Series 2

Animals Christmas Carol, The
see Christmas Carols, Series 5

Bethlehem Innkeeper's Regret, The
see Christmas Carols, Series 2

Blest Be The Lord God Of Israel
(Hanson) unis jr cor FISCHER,C CM 7570 $.20
(G2413)

Brave Little Shepherd, The
see Christmas Carols, Series 1

Children's Worship In Church, Series 1
*anthem/hymn
jr cor oct FISCHER,C CM 6844 $.25
contains: I Was Glad; Lord, Take Our
Promises; This Is Our Father's House;
We Love Your Altar Here; When We Come
To Worship; When We Hear The Church
Bells   (G2414)

Christmas Carols, Series 1 *Xmas,carol
jr cor oct FISCHER,C CM6792 $.25
contains: Brave Little Shepherd, The;
Creation's Christmas Song; Giddi-Up!
Dear Little Donkey; Off To Bethlehem;
Swing Little Jesus; What Did The Wise
Men Hear?   (G2415)

Christmas Carols, Series 2 *Xmas,carol
jr cor oct FISCHER,C CM6793 $.25
contains: Alleluia! Child Jesus;
Bethlehem Innkeeper's Regret, The; Did
You See My Boy Jesus?; I Can't Bring
Three Kings To Bethlehem; Mary Was
Waiting For You; When Simeon Came To
Worship   (G2416)

Christmas Carols, Series 3 *Xmas,carol
jr cor oct FISCHER,C CM 6846 $.25
contains: God's Gift To Us; Open Wide The
Stable Door; Seen First By Candle-
Light; Shepherd, Blow Your Horn; We
Meet Around The Manger Bed; We're Glad
Jesus Got Home   (G2417)

Christmas Carols, Series 4 *Xmas,carol
jr cor oct FISCHER,C CM 6847 $.25
contains: Christmas Lights, The; Jesus
Came For Love; Merry Christmas Bells,
The; Night After Christmas, The; Pull,
Pull, The Yule Log; Shepherds Watching
Late One Night   (G2418)

Christmas Carols, Series 5 *Xmas,carol
jr cor oct FISCHER,C CM 6848 $.25
contains: Animals Christmas Carol, The;
Go To Sleep O Child Of My Joy; Knock!
Knock! Knock!; Mary's Cradle Song; When
They First Saw Jesus   (G2419)

Christmas Lights, The
see Christmas Carols, Series 4

Creation's Christmas Song
see Christmas Carols, Series 1

Did You See My Boy Jesus?
see Christmas Carols, Series 2

Easter Bells, The
see Lent And Easter, Series 1

Finding God Through Nature, Series 1
*anthem/hymn
jr cor oct FISCHER,C CM 6795 $.25
contains: All Things Bright And
Beautiful; Let's Sing Of Faithful
Friends; Oh God, It Must Be You; Our
Coal And Oil Song; When We See Sunset;
Who Has Seen The Wind?   (G2420)

Giddi-Up! Dear Little Donkey
see Christmas Carols, Series 1

Go To Sleep O Child Of My Joy
see Christmas Carols, Series 5

God Means More To Us Now
see Hymns Of Prayer And Praise, Series 1

God's Gift To Us
see Christmas Carols, Series 3

God's Love Stays The Same
see Teachings Of Jesus, Series 1

Good Samaritan, The
see Teachings Of Jesus, Series 1

Happy Easter
see Lent And Easter, Series 1

Hymns And Anthems For Children's Voices
*CCU,anthem/hymn
SA (easy) ABINGDON APM-621 $1.25   (G2421)

Hymns Of Prayer And Praise, Series 1 *hymn
jr cor oct FISCHER,C CM 6796 $.25
contains: God Means More To Us Now; I
Like To Hear The Bible; I've Tried And
Tried And Tried; O Praise The Lord;
Teach Us Lord About Time; 'Tis God Who
Made Us Free   (G2422)

I Can't Bring Three Kings To Bethlehem
see Christmas Carols, Series 2

I Like To Hear The Bible
see Hymns Of Prayer And Praise, Series 1

I Was Glad
see Children's Worship In Church, Series 1

I've Tried And Tried And Tried
see Hymns Of Prayer And Praise, Series 1

GRIME, WILLIAM (cont'd.)

Jesus Among His Friends
see When Jesus Was A Boy, Series 1

Jesus Came For Love
see Christmas Carols, Series 4

Jesus Learned To Read
see When Jesus Was A Boy, Series 1

Jesus Likes Good Givers
see Teachings Of Jesus, Series 1

Jesus Lived In A Little House
see When Jesus Was A Boy, Series 1

Jesus Worked In A Carpeter Shop
see When Jesus Was A Boy, Series 1

Knock! Knock! Knock! *Xmas
see Christmas Carols, Series 5
(Wilkinson) 2pt jr cor FISCHER,C CM 7151
$.25　　　　　　　　　　　　　　　(G2423)

Lent And Easter, Series 1 *Easter/Lent,
anthem/hymn
jr cor oct FISCHER,C CM 6843 $.25
contains: Easter Bells, The; Happy
Easter; Little Crocus; Mite Box, The;
Once To Jerusalem Jesus Did Come
　　　　　　　　　　　　　　　　　(G2424)

Let's Sing Of Faithful Friends
see Finding God Through Nature, Series 1

Little Crocus
see Lent And Easter, Series 1

Lord, Take Our Promises
see Children's Worship In Church, Series 1

Mary Was Waiting For You
see Christmas Carols, Series 2

Mary's Cradle Song
see Christmas Carols, Series 5

Merry Christmas Bells, The
see Christmas Carols, Series 4

Mite Box, The
see Lent And Easter, Series 1

More Songs And Carols For Children *CCU
unis jr cor FISCHER,C O 4120 $1.00 (G2425)

New Songs And Carols For Children *CCU
jr cor FISCHER,C O 3928 $1.25　　(G2426)

Night After Christmas, The
see Christmas Carols, Series 4

O Praise The Lord
see Hymns Of Prayer And Praise, Series 1

Off To Bethlehem
see Christmas Carols, Series 1

Oh God, It Must Be You
see Finding God Through Nature, Series 1

Once To Jerusalem Jesus Did Come
see Lent And Easter, Series 1

Open Wide The Stable Door
see Christmas Carols, Series 3

Our Coal And Oil Song
see Finding God Through Nature, Series 1

Our Daily Bread
see Teachings Of Jesus, Series 1

Pharisee One Day, The
see Teachings Of Jesus, Series 1

Pull, Pull, The Yule Log
see Christmas Carols, Series 4

Seen First By Candle-Light
see Christmas Carols, Series 3

Shepherd, Blow Your Horn
see Christmas Carols, Series 3

Shepherds Watching Late One Night
see Christmas Carols, Series 4

Sing Unto The Lord Ye Children
SATB/jr cor FISCHER,C O 4395 $1.25 (G2427)

Swing Little Jesus
see Christmas Carols, Series 4

Teach Us Lord About Time
see Hymns Of Prayer And Praise, Series 1

Teachings Of Jesus, Series 1 *anthem/hymn
jr cor oct FISCHER,C CM 6794 $.25
contains: God's Love Stays The Same; Good
Samaritan, The; Jesus Likes Good
Givers; Our Daily Bread; Pharisee One
Day, The; Wise And Foolish Builders,
The　　　　　　　　　　　　　　　(G2428)

This Is Our Father's House
see Children's Worship In Church, Series 1

'Tis God Who Made Us Free
see Hymns Of Prayer And Praise, Series 1

We Love Your Altar Here
see Children's Worship In Church, Series 1

We Meet Around The Manger Bed
see Christmas Carols, Series 3

We're Glad Jesus Got Home
see Christmas Carols, Series 3

What Did The Wise Men Hear?
see Christmas Carols, Series 1

What Games Did Jesus Play?
see When Jesus Was A Boy, Series 1

When Jesus Was A Boy, Series 1 *anthem/hymn
jr cor oct FISCHER,C CM 6845 $.25
contains: Jesus Among His Friends; Jesus

GRIME, WILLIAM (cont'd.)

Learned To Read; Jesus Lived In A
Little House; Jesus Worked In A
Carpeter Shop; What Games Did Jesus
Play?; When Jesus Went To The Well
　　　　　　　　　　　　　　　　　(G2429)

When Jesus Went To The Well
see When Jesus Was A Boy, Series 1

When Simeon Came To Worship
see Christmas Carols, Series 2

When They First Saw Jesus
see Christmas Carols, Series 5

When We Come To Worship
see Children's Worship In Church, Series 1

When We Hear The Church Bells
see Children's Worship In Church, Series 1

When We See Sunset
see Finding God Through Nature, Series 1

Who Has Seen The Wind?
see Finding God Through Nature, Series 1

Wise And Foolish Builders, The
see Teachings Of Jesus, Series 1

GRIMES, TRAVIS
Early In The Morning *Easter/Holywk/Palm,
cant
SA (med diff) SACRED $1.50　　　(G2430)

GRIMM
Child Of Love
SATB (med easy) SOUTHERN $.25　　(G2431)

GRIMM, HEINRICH (ca. 1593-1637)
Alleluja Ist Ein Frohlich Gesang
see Zwei Kleine Osterkonzerte

Der Tag, Der Ist So Freudenreich
see Grimm, Heinrich, Machet Die Tore Weit

Hosianna Dem Sohne David
see Zwei Kleine Weihnachtskonzerte

Jauchzet Dem Herren, Alle Welt *mot
(Braun) SSAB&ATTB HANSSLER 1.314 s.p. (G2432)

Machet Die Tore Weit *Adv
(Lorenzen, Hermann) [Ger] 2pt,cont (med)
BAREN. BA 460 sc $1.75, cor pts s.p.
contains also: Der Tag, Der Ist So
Freudenreich　　　　　　　　　　(G2433)

O Jesus, Show Thy Great Compassion
(Nolte) [Eng/Ger] SA,org oct MORAVIAN 5599
$.40　　　　　　　　　　　　　　　(G2434)

Wohlauf, Wohlauf Zu Dieser Frist
see Zwei Kleine Weihnachtskonzerte

Zu Dieser Osterlichen Zeit
see Zwei Kleine Osterkonzerte

Zwei Kleine Osterkonzerte *Easter
(Lorenzen, Hermann) [Ger] 2 eq voices,cont
(med) BAREN. BA 461 $1.75
contains: Alleluja Ist Ein Frohlich
Gesang; Zu Dieser Osterlichen Zeit
　　　　　　　　　　　　　　　　　(G2435)

Zwei Kleine Weihnachtskonzerte *Xmas
(Lorenzen, Hermann) [Ger] 2pt treb cor,cont
(med) BAREN. BA 458 $1.50
contains: Hosianna Dem Sohne David;
Wohlauf, Wohlauf Zu Dieser Frist
　　　　　　　　　　　　　　　　　(G2436)

GRIMM, JEFF
Child Of Love, The *anthem
SATB (med easy) oct AUGSBURG 1661 $.25
　　　　　　　　　　　　　　　　　(G2437)

GRIMSTAD, JOHAN H.
Alla Vara Dagr
mix cor MUSIKK 251 s.p.　　　　(G2438)

GRISWOLD
Holy Father, Great Creator
(Williams) SATB,acap oct BELWIN 60139 $.30
　　　　　　　　　　　　　　　　　(G2439)

GROFE
Auf Dem Berge, Da Gehet Der Wind
see Zwei Quodlibets

In Dulci Jubilo
see Zwei Quodlibets

Joseph, Lieber Joseph Mein
see Zwei Quodlibets

Vom Himmel Hoch, Ihr Englein Kommt
see Zwei Quodlibets

Zwei Quodlibets *Xmas
mix cor TONGER s.p.
contains: Auf Dem Berge, Da Gehet Der
Wind; In Dulci Jubilo; Joseph, Lieber
Joseph Mein; Vom Himmel Hoch, Ihr
Englein Kommt　　　　　　　　　　(G2440)

GROFF
Vision Of The Shepherds, The
SATB oct BELWIN 60121 $.30　　　(G2441)

GRONOSTAY, UWE (1939-　　)
Herr, Erhore Mein Gebet *prayer
SATB HANSSLER 7.150 s.p.　　　(G2442)

Mit Ernst, O Menschenkinder *cant
SAB,fl,2vln,vcl HANSSLER 10.141 sc s.p.,
cor pts s.p., ipa　　　　　　　(G2443)

Wohl Den Menschen, Die Durch Fur Ihre Starke
Halten
SSATB HANSSLER 7.151 s.p.　　　(G2444)

GRONQUIST, R.
Good Shepherds, Leave *see Quittez Pasteurs

Quittez Pasteurs
"Good Shepherds, Leave" [Fr/Eng] SATB,acap,
opt pic&perc oct KERBY 6578 $.35 (G2445)

This Endris Night *Xmas
SATB,opt soli,acap oct KERBY 6480 $.35
　　　　　　　　　　　　　　　　　(G2446)

GROOM, LESTER H.
First Noel, The *Xmas
SSA/unis oct AGAPE A 320 $.30　　(G2447)

In Thankful Remembrance *Thanks
SATB (easy) ABINGDON APM-264 $.25 (G2448)

Praise To The Lord
SATB (med) ABINGDON APM-840 $.55 (G2449)

Wondrous Love
SA/unis oct AGAPE A 323 $.30　　(G2450)

GROOT IS DE HEER see Roeske, F.J.

GROSS
Reflections On Christmas *CCU
SATB FLAMMER A5474 $1.25　　　　(G2451)

Six Modernistic Carols *CC6U,Xmas,carol
SATB WARNER G1447 $.35　　　　(G2452)

GROSS IST DER HERR see Bach, Karl Philipp
Emanuel

GROSS IST DER HERR see Lassus, Roland de
(Orlandus)

GROSS IST DER HERR see Lissmann, Kurt

GROSS IST DER HERR UND HOCH GEPREIST see
Schutz, Heinrich

GROSS UND WUNDERBAR see Tittel, Ernst

GROSSE MESSE see Mozart, Wolfgang Amadeus

GROSSE MESSE see Mozart, Wolfgang Amadeus,
Missa C-Moll

GROSSE MESSE F-MOLL see Bruckner, Anton

GROSSE ORGELMESSE see Haydn, (Franz) Joseph,
Missa Solennis In Honorem B.M.V. In Es-Dur

GROSSE-SCHWARE, HERMANN (1931-　　)
Aller Augen Warten Auf Dich *prayer
4 eq voices MOSELER M-49 s.p.　　(G2453)

GROSSE TOTENMESSE see Berlioz, Hector

GROSSER GOTT, WIR LOBEN DICH see Koch, Karl

GROSSER GOTT, WIR LOBEN DICH see Schubert,
Heino

GROSSI, CARLO
Cantata Ebraica In Dialogo *Heb
(Adler, Israel) SATB,T solo,cont ISRAELI
701 s.p.　　　　　　　　　　　　　(G2454)

GROSSMANN, FERDINAND (1887-1970)
Deutsches Messlied *Bibl
4pt mix cor,acap DOBLINGER sc s.p., cor pts
s.p.　　　　　　　　　　　　　　　(G2455)

GROSVENOR
Christmas Call To Worship *Xmas
SATB FLAMMER A 5266 $.30　　　　(G2456)

Easter Call To Worship *Easter
SATB FLAMMER A 5017 $.30　　　　(G2457)
(Gilbert) SAB FLAMMER D5031 $.25　(G2458)

GROT, H.
Der Mensch Lebt Und Bestehet Nur Eine Kleine
Zeit
[Ger] mix cor,acap (med diff) HUG s.p.
　　　　　　　　　　　　　　　　　(G2459)

GROVEN, EIVIND (1901-　　)
Alle Helgens Dag
wom cor MUSIKK 10 s.p.　　　　(G2460)

Den Tyngste Sorg Og Moda
mix cor MUSIKK 237 s.p.　　　　(G2461)

Hellige Tone
wom cor MUSIKK 8 s.p.　　　　(G2462)

Hugen
mix cor MUSIKK 238 s.p.　　　　(G2463)

GRUBEN, FR.
Weihnachts Messe *Xmas,Mass
(Franken, P.) mix cor ALSBACH&D sc s.p.,
cor pts s.p.　　　　　　　　　　(G2464)

GRUBER, ERICH
Herr, Wir Stehen Hand In Hand
see Stier, Alfred, Gottes Stimme Lasst Uns
Sein

Wunderbarer Konig, Herrscher Von Uns Allen
see Zipp, Friedrich, Erneure Mich, O Ewigs
Licht

GRUBER, FRANZ XAVER (1787-1863)
Glade Jul *Xmas
(Kjeldass, Gunnar) mix cor,pno/org MUSIKK
87 voc sc rental, cor pts s.p.　(G2465)

Holy Night *Xmas
(Robinson, Stanford) mix cor CURWEN 61355
s.p.　　　　　　　　　　　　　　(G2466)

My Lord Is Waiting In The Garden
SATB oct LORENZ 4444 $.30　　　(G2467)

Noche De Paz *see Stille Nacht, Heil'ge
Nacht

Savior's Eyes, The
SATB oct LORENZ A475 $.25　　　(G2468)

Silent Night *see Stille Nacht, Heilige
Nacht

Silent Night! Holiest Night! *see Stille
Nacht, Heil'ge Nacht

Silent Night, Holy Night *see Stille Nacht,
Heilige Nacht

Stilla Natt
(Ahlen, Waldemar) 3pt wom cor/3pt jr cor,
acap NORDISKA 4230 s.p.　　　　(G2469)

GRUBER, FRANZ XAVER (cont'd.)

Stilla Natt, Heliga Natt
(Jonsson, Josef) men cor&wom cor&mix cor,
org,strings cor pts NORDISKA 4833 s.p.,
sc NORDISKA s.p.   (G2470)

Stille Nacht *see Stille Nacht, Heil'ge
Nacht

Stille Nacht, Heil'ge Nacht *Xmas,carol,Aus/
Ger
see VIER WEIHNACHTSLIEDER
"Stille Nacht" [Neth] men cor sc ALSBACH&D
s.p.   (G2471)
(Martini) "Noche De Paz" [Span] 3pt wom
cor/3pt men cor/3pt mix cor,pno sc
RICORDI-ARG BA11654 s.p., cor pts
RICORDI-ARG BA 11655 s.p.   (G2472)
(Schemitsch, Hans) [Ger] mix cor,acap oct
DOBLINGER s.p. see also ZEHN
OSTERRICHISCHE WEIHNACHTSLIEDER   (G2473)
(Seymour) "Silent Night! Holiest Night!"
[Eng/Ger] 3pt wom cor,acap (easy) oct
WILLIS 1762 $.10   (G2474)

Stille Nacht, Heilige Nacht *Xmas,anthem/
carol,Ger
mix cor TONGER s.p.   (G2475)
"Silent Night" SATB,acap oct PRO ART 1147
$.16 contains also: O Come All Ye
Faithful (Long)   (G2476)
"Silent Night" SATB ALLANS 173 s.p.   (G2477)
"Silent Night, Holy Night" SAB KJOS P1170
$.30   (G2478)
"Silent Night, Holy Night" SATB PROWSE s.p. (G2479)
(Becker) "Silent Night, Holy Night" [Eng/
Ger] TTBB,acap (med) oct WILLIS 1228 $.10 (G2480)
(Becker, V.E.) "Silent Night, Holy Night"
[Ger/Eng] 4pt men cor,acap (med) oct
WILLIS 1228 $.12   (G2481)
(Crowell, M.) "Silent Night" SSA oct
PRESSER 312-40380 $.30   (G2482)
(Curry, L.) "Silent Night, Holy Night"
SATB,acap oct PRESSER 312-21392 $.30   (G2483)
(Dello Joio) "Silent Night" SATB,2pno MARKS
4571 $.50   (G2484)
(Ehret) "Silent Night" SA MARKS 4073 $.30
contains also: Willis, It Came Upon A
Midnight Clear   (G2485)
(Epperson) "Silent Night" SSA oct FISCHER,C
CM-528 $.25   (G2486)
(Gruber) "Silent Night" SATB oct LORENZ
4496 $.30   (G2487)
(Gruber) "Silent Night" SA oct LORENZ 5366
$.30   (G2488)
(Hartley) "Silent Night" SSA&SATB,acap,opt
pno oct PRO ART 2488 $.30   (G2489)
(Hewitt, T.J.) "Silent Night, Holy Night"
PROWSE s.p.   (G2490)
(Johnson) "Silent Night" SSA,inst oct
FISCHER,C CM-6937 $.25, ipa   (G2491)
(Kunz) "Silent Night" SSAATTBB/SATB,acap
oct KENDOR $.25   (G2492)
(Luboff, Norman) "Silent Night" SATB,winds,
perc oct WALTON 2757 $.30, cmplt ed
WALTON 2757A $6.00   (G2493)
(Ratcliffe, Desmond) "Silent Night" 4pt,
acap oct NOVELLO 51.0605.02 s.p.   (G2494)
(Shaw; Parker) "Silent Night" SATB,acap oct
LAWSON 715 $.30   (G2495)
(Simeone) "Silent Night" SATB SHAWNEE A 930
$.25   (G2496)
(Track) "Silent Night" TTBB,acap,opt pno
oct PRO ART 2452 $.25   (G2497)
(Wagner) "Silent Night" SATB,acap,opt pno/
gtr/harp oct LAWSON 665 $.35   (G2498)
(West, J.E.) "Silent Night" mix cor,S solo
oct NOVELLO 40.0861.08 s.p.   (G2499)
(Wetzel) "Silent Night" SATB WARNER G885
$.30   (G2500)
(Wilson) "Silent Night" SATB&desc SCHMITT
1624 $.35   (G2501)
(Wilson) "Silent Night" SA SCHMITT 2534
$.35   (G2502)

GRUNDMAN
Christmas Eve Is Here
see Three Noels

Christmas Hymn
see Three Noels

Little Child Is Born
see Quiet Christmas

Lullaby
see Quiet Christmas

Now We Sing Of Christmas
see Three Noels

Our Master Has A Garden
see Quiet Christmas

Quiet Christmas *Xmas
oct SA,band/orch BOOSEY 5286 $.30, ipa;
SSA,band/orch BOOSEY 5287 $.30, ipa; SAB,
band/orch BOOSEY 5315 $.35, ipa; SATB,
band/orch BOOSEY 5288 $.35, ipa; TTBB,
band/orch BOOSEY 5289 $.35, ipa
contains: Little Child Is Born; Lullaby;
Our Master Has A Garden   (G2503)

Three Carols For Christmas *Xmas
oct SA,band/orch BOOSEY 5580 $.35, ipa;
SSA,band/orch BOOSEY 5581 $.35, ipa; SAB,
band/orch BOOSEY 5582 $.35, ipa   (G2504)

Three Noels *Xmas
(Grundman) oct SA BOOSEY 5734 $.35; SSA
BOOSEY 5735 $.40; SAB BOOSEY 5736 $.40;
SATB BOOSEY 5719 $.40; TTBB BOOSEY 5737
$.00
contains: Christmas Eve Is Here;
Christmas Hymn; Now We Sing Of
Christmas   (G2505)

GRUNDONNERSTAG see Schieri, Fritz

GRUNERT, HAZEL
In A Manger Lowly
SAB oct JUSKO 105 $.15   (G2506)

GRUNET, FELDER *Xmas,Aus
(Schemitsch, Hans) [Ger] mix cor,acap oct
DOBLINGER s.p. see also Zehn Osterreichische
Weihnachtsleider   (G2507)

GRUNET FELDER see Liebe, Kurt Maria

GRUNKE, FRIEDRICH
Meine Augen Sehen Stets Zu Dem Herrn
*Introit
SATB HANSSLER 7.071 s.p.   (G2508)

GRUNMACH, ULRICH (1891-1966)
Die Sieben Worte *Psntd
[Ger] 3pt mix cor,narrator,acap cor pts
BAREN. EM 311 s.p.   (G2509)

GRUNT EIN TANNENBAUM see Wolters, Gottfried

GRUSCHWITZ, GUNTHER (1928-)
Gott, Wir Gedenken Deiner Gute *Gen
[Ger] SATB,pno,bvl (med) BOSSE BE 250 s.p. (G2510)

Kleine Kantate Zum Pfingstfest *Pent/
Whitsun,cant
jr cor&SA&SSA,fl,ob,strings sc HANSSLER
12.502 s.p., ipa   (G2511)

Kleine Liedkantate Zur Weihnacht *Xmas,cant
jr cor/SSA,inst sc HANSSLER 12.501 s.p.,
ipa   (G2512)

Kleine Osterkantate *Easter,cant
1-3pt jr cor,2rec,2vln,vcl sc HANSSLER
12.206 s.p.   (G2513)

Nun Lasst Uns Gott *cant
mix cor sc HANSSLER 10.298 s.p.   (G2514)

O Herr, Hore Mich An *Gen
[Ger] SSATB,bvl (med easy) BOSSE BE 247
s.p.   (G2515)

GRUSS GOTT DICH SCHONER MAIEN see Gattermayer,
Heinrich

GRUSS GOTT, DU SCHONER MAIE see Hessenberg,
Kurt

GRUSS GOTT, DU SCHONER MAIEN see Heyden,
Reinhold

GUADE FLORE VIRGINALI see Carver, Robert

GUARDIAN ANGEL see Franck, Cesar

GUASTAVINO
Cancion De Navidad *Xmas
[Span] SATB,acap RICORDI-ARG BA 10835 s.p. (G2516)

[Span] 2 eq voices,pno RICORDI-ARG BA9924
s.p.   (G2517)

GUBBY, ROY
Christmas Pastorale, A *Xmas
SATB,MezMez soli,vln/ob oct BOURNE 926 $.35 (G2518)

Lullay, Thou Little Child
SATB oct BOURNE 927 $.25   (G2519)

GUBINELLI, ODERISIO
Collana Di 20 Mottetti Eucaristici *CC20L,
Commun,mot
[Lat] 1-2pt ZANIBON 2274 s.p.   (G2520)

Due Inni A Cristo Re *CC2U,hymn
[Lat] unis,org ZANIBON 1850 s.p.   (G2521)

Il Canzoniere Mariano *CC30U,BVM
[Lat] 1-2pt ZANIBON 1159 s.p.   (G2522)

Missa In Hon. S. Justinae M.V. *Mass
[Lat] SAB,org sc ZANIBON 1708 s.p., voc pt
ZANIBON 1709 s.p.   (G2523)

Missa X Alme Pater Et Credo I *Greg/Mass
[Lat] unis,org sc ZANIBON 1746 s.p., cor
pts ZANIBON 1747 s.p.   (G2524)

Raccolta Di 32 Litanie Lauretane *CC32U
[Lat] 1-2pt,org (easy) ZANIBON 700 s.p.   (G2525)

Ventotto Litanie Lauretane *CC28U
[Lat] 1-2pt,org (easy) ZANIBON 2115 s.p. (G2526)

GUD AR VAR STARKHET OCH VART STOD *Bibl
(Olsen, Daniel) [Swed] SATB,acap GEHRMANS
KRB 128   (G2527)

GUD AR VAR STARKHET OCH VART STOD see Godin,
Carl

GUD AR VAR TILLFLYKT see Bjarnegard, Gustaf

GUD AR VAR TILLFLYKT see Roman, Johan Helmich

GUD AR VAR TILLFLYKT see Wikander, David

GUD, DU ER MIN GUD see Ficher, Trygve

GUD ER MIN HYRDE see Schubert, Franz (Peter),
Gott Ist Mein Hirt

GUD ER VAR TILFLUKT see Nyhus, Rolf

GUD FADER BOR I HIMLEN see Lindroth, Henry

GUD FADERS SON, O JESUS KAR
(Berg, Gottfrid) 3pt mix cor NORDISKA 3447
s.p. see also Sacrae Cantiones   (G2528)

GUD, FRELS MIG see Jeppesen, Knud

GUD HAR ICKE SKONAT SIN EGEN SON see Wikander,
David

GUD HAR UPPVACKT KRISTUS JESU see Wikander,
David

GUD, HJAELP MIG see Buxtehude, Dietrich, Gott,
Hilf Mir

GUD, I EN TID see Nystedt, Knut

GUD LATER SINA TROGNA
see Fem Folkliga Koraler I Sattningar

GUD LATER SINA TROGNA HAR see Berg, Gottfrid

GUD, MA JEG KUN DIG HAVE see Bach, Johann
Michael, Herr, Wenn Ich Nur Dich Habe

GUD, NAR DU TIL OPPBRUDD KALLER see Olsen,
Sparre

GUD REGJERER see Pooler, Frank

GUD SIGNE VART FOLK
(Aamodt, Valter) men cor MUSIKK 36 s.p.   (G2529)

GUD SINGE VART FOLK see Aamodt, Valter

GUD TREFALDIG STATT OSS BI see Praetorius,
Michael

GUD TREFALDIG, STATT OSS BI(KORAL22)
(Hallnas, Hilding) [Swed] SATB,acap GEHRMANS
KRB 192   (G2530)

GUD, VAERE MEG NADIG see Saint-Saens, Camille

GUD, VAR GUD, FOR VARLDEN ALL
(Berg, Gottfrid) mix cor NORDISKA 3445 s.p.
see also Sacrae Cantiones   (G2531)

GUD VAR LOSTA TUNGA see Bjarnegard, Gustaf

GUD, VAR MIG NADIG see Berg, Gottfrid

GUD, VEND OREN TIL MIN BON see Jeppesen, Knud

GUDS KIRKES GRUNNVOLL ENE see Praetorius,
Michael

GUDS LOV see Norrman, John

GUDS MENIGHET see Geitvik, S.H.

GUDS NAD VI SKOLA PRISA
(Berg, Gottfrid) mix cor NORDISKA 3446 s.p.
see also Sacrae Cantiones   (G2532)

GUDS RENA LAMM, OSKYLDIG see Bach, Johann
Sebastian

GUDS RIGES EVANGELIUM see Eccard, Johannes

GUDS RIKE see Neilsen, Ludvig

GUDS SON HAR GJORT MIG FRI see Grieg, Edvard
Hagerup

GUDS VAG I DUNKEL OFTA GAR see Berg, Gottfrid

GUENTHER
Praise Ye The Lord
SATB oct PRO ART 2710 $.30   (G2533)

Song Of David, The
SATB oct PRO ART 2709 $.35   (G2534)

GUERRERO, FRANCISCO (1528-1599)
A Un Nino Iiorando
"To Adore A Tiny Infant" see Three
Christmas Carols

Ave Virgo Sanctissima *mot
[Lat] 5pt mix cor,acap UNION ESP. 19340
s.p.   (G2535)

Ecce Nunc Tempus *Gen/Lent,Span
(Goodale) [Lat] 4pt mix cor,acap oct
SCHIRM.G 11230 $.25   (G2536)

Hoy, Jose, Se Os Da En El Suelo *Xmas
(Greyson) "On This Day, Saint Joseph
Brought Us" SATB oct BOURNE ES90 $.30   (G2537)

Missa Puer Qui Natus Est Nobis *Mass
mix cor,acap voc sc KALMUS 6201 $1.25   (G2538)

O Hear The News *see Oyd, Oyd Una Cosa

On This Day, Saint Joseph Brought Us *see
Hoy, Jose, Se Os Da En El Suelo

Oyd, Oyd Una Cosa
"O Hear The News" see Three Christmas
Carols

Tell Us, Mary *see Virgen Sancta

Three Christmas Carols *Xmas,carol
(Petti, Anthony G.) [Eng/Span] SSATB
CHESTER s.p.
contains: A Un Nino Iiorando, "To Adore A
Tiny Infant"; Oyd, Oyd Una Cosa, "O
Hear The News"; Virgen Sancta, "Tell
Us, Mary"   (G2539)

To Adore A Tiny Infant *see A Un Nino
Iiorando

To The Stable Gate *see Vamos Al Portal

Trahe Me Post Te, Virgo Maria *mot
[Lat] 4pt mix cor,acap UNION ESP. 19175
s.p.   (G2540)

Vamos Al Portal *Xmas,Span
(Goodale) "To The Stable Gate" [Span/Eng]
SSATB,acap oct SCHIRM.G 11080 $.40   (G2541)

Villanesca
(Ruiz) [Span] 3pt men cor,acap RICORDI-ARG
BA 10089 s.p.   (G2542)

Virgen Sancta
"Tell Us, Mary" see Three Christmas Carols

GUERRINI, GUIDO (1890-1965)
Canto Di Natale E Vocalizzo
3pt jr cor,acap RICORDI-ENG 128600 s.p.   (G2543)

Missa Pro Defunctis
mix cor,SMezTBar soli,org,orch sc ZERBONI
4073 rental   (G2544)

GUESS
Cherub Hymns *CCU
unis FLAMMER GF5007 $.60   (G2545)

His Praises Sing *CCU
SA FLAMMER GE5009 $.85   (G2546)

GUEST, DOUGLAS
Missa Brevis (Sarisburiensis) *Mass
SATB,acap (diff) oct OXFORD 43.537 $.75
(G2547)

GUEST FROM HEAVEN *anthem,Span
(Overby, Oscar) SAB (easy) oct AUGSBURG 1288
$.22 (G2548)

GUEST, J.
Captive Maid Of Israel *ora
oct HART s.p. (G2549)

GUGLIELMI
Lord, My God, Show Mercy Unto Me
(Ehret) SATB SHAWNEE A 902 $.25 (G2550)

GUIDE AND KEEP ME, O LORD see Lassus, Roland de
(Orlandus), Custodi Me Domine

GUIDE ME, O GREAT JEHOVAH see Sampson, W.

GUIDE ME, O THOU GREAT JEHOVAH see Felts

GUIDE ME, O THOU GREAT JEHOVAH see Hastings

GUIDE ME, O THOU GREAT JEHOVAH see Hughes

GUIDE ME, O THOU GREAT JEHOVAH see Morgan

GUIDE ME, O THOU GREAT JEHOVAH see Mueller,
Carl F.

GUIDE ME, O THOU GREAT JEHOVAH see Sjolund,
Paul

GUIDE ME, O THOU GREAT JEHOVAH see Smith

GUIDE ME, O THOU GREAT JEHOVAH see Young,
Carlton R.

GUIDE ME, O THOU GREAT REDEEMER see Willan,
Healey

GUIDE MY HEAD *spir
(Heath) 4pt men cor,acap oct SCHIRM.G 11868
$.30 (G2551)

GUIDE US THRU THE NIGHT see Williams

GUIDING CHRIST OUR SHEPHERD, THE see Pfautsch,
Lloyd

GUIDING SHEPHERD, THE see Bronson, Margaret

GUIDING STAR *Xmas
(McKelvy, J.) SATB,acap FOSTER MF506 $.25 (G2552)

GUIDING STAR CAROL see Christiansen, Olaf
Christian

GUIDING STAR, THE see Graham, Robert [V.]

GUIHAUME, TONI, PEIRE see Saboly, Nicholas

GUILLAUME, ANTOINE, PIERRE see Saboly,
Nicholas, Guihaume, Toni, Peire

GUILLAUME, TOINET, PIERRE *Xmas,carol,Fr
(Tomasi) [Fr] 2pt/3pt,pno/orch LEDUC s.p. see
also Douze Noels De Saboly (G2553)

GUILMANT, ALEXANDRE (1837-1911)
Ave Verum *Easter/Lent
"Hail, O Hail" SATB oct WALTON 2128 $.30 (G2554)

Hail, O Hail *see Ave Verum

Kyrie Eleison, Alla Palestrina *Op.6 (from
First Mass)
"Ninefold Kyrie" SATB,opt inst SCHIRM.EC
1261 (G2555)

Ninefold Kyrie *see Kyrie Eleison, Alla
Palestrina

GUION, DAVID WENDALL FENTRESS (1895-)
At The Cry Of The First Bird
(Christy) 4pt wom cor oct SCHIRM.G 9423
$.25 (G2556)

I Talked To God Last Night
(Downing) 4pt mix cor oct SCHIRM.G 8735
$.25 (G2557)
(Marlowe) 3pt wom cor oct SCHIRM.G 9495
$.25 (G2558)

Prayer
(Deis) SAB oct SCHIRM.G 10025 $.25 (G2559)
(Downing) 3pt wom cor oct SCHIRM.G 8722
$.30 (G2560)
(Downing) 4pt mix cor oct SCHIRM.G 8399
$.30 (G2561)

GULBINS
Song Of Praise, A *Gen
(Hansen) SATB SCHMITT 909 $.30 (G2562)

GULBRANSON, EILIF
A, Jesus Store Gud
mix cor MUSIKK 21 s.p. (G2563)

GULLBERG, OLOF
Kyrie--Gloria *Agnus/Kyrie
[Swed] SAB,acap GEHRMANS TKS 31 (G2564)

GULLIKSEN, HARALD
Gled Eder I Herren
[Norw] mix cor LYCHE 69 s.p. (G2565)

GUMMA, VICTOR L.
Rise Up, O Men Of God! *Gen,anthem
SATB (med diff) oct LORENZ C334 $.30 (G2566)

GUMPELTZHAIMER, A.
Agnus Dei *canon
[Ger] mix cor,acap (easy) HUG s.p. (G2567)
[Ger] mix cor,acap (med) HUG s.p. (G2568)

Let God Be Praised With Singing
(Ehret) mix cor CHAPPELL 0024117-358 $.40 (G2569)

Lob Gott Getrost Mit Singen
[Ger] mix cor,acap (med diff) HUG s.p. (G2570)

Wenn Mein Stundlein Vorhanden Ist
[Ger] mix cor,acap (easy) HUG s.p. (G2571)
[Ger] mix cor,acap (med) HUG s.p. (G2572)

GUMPELTZHAIMER, ADAM (ca. 1559-1625)
Coenam Cum Discipulis *Easter
(Shaw) 4pt men cor/4pt mix cor oct SCHIRM.G
9961 $.30 (G2573)

Der Herr Ist Mein Treuer Hirt
see Albert, Heinrich, Du Mein Einzig Licht

Gelobet Seist Du, Jesu Christ
4pt mix cor MOSELER LB-55 s.p. contains
also: Praetorius, Michael, Gelobet Seist
Du, Jesu Christ (G2574)

Go Ye Into All The World *Gen/Trin
SA/TB,acap (med easy) oct CONCORDIA 98-1325
$.12 (G2575)

Helft Mir Gotts Gute Preisen *Xmas
[Ger] SATB,acap MULLER K 28 s.p.
contains also: Nun Freuet Euch, Ihr Arm'
Und Reich' (SAB,acap) (G2576)

Herr Gott, Nun Sei Gepreiset *Xmas
[Ger] 4pt mix cor,acap (med easy) MULLER
K 29 s.p. (G2577)

How Long, O Lord
(Knight, Gerald) SATB,acap oct FISCHER,C
CM-7504 $.25 (G2578)

I Thank Thee Heavenly Father *see Ich Danke
Dir Lieber Herre

Ich Danke Dir Lieber Herre
(Guettler) "I Thank Thee Heavenly Father"
[Eng/Ger] SSAA WARNER WB-134 $.30 (G2579)

Jesu Kreuz, Leiden Und Pein *Holywk/Psntd
4pt mix cor MOSELER LB-78 s.p. (G2580)

Jesus' Cross, The Death And Pain *Lent
SATB,acap (med easy) oct CONCORDIA $.25 (G2581)

Lob Gott Getrost Mit Singen *Gen/Thanks,
anthem
SATB HANSSLER 6.251 s.p. (G2582)
(Klein, M.) "Praise Ye The Lord With
Singing" [Eng/Ger] SATB (med) oct GIA
G1435 $.30 (G2583)

Lobet Gott, Unsern Herrn *Gen
[Ger] 3pt mix cor,acap (med) BAREN. BA 989
s.p. (G2584)

Lobet Gott, Usern Herren
SSB HANSSLER 6.201 s.p. contains also:
Praetorius, Michael, Singen Wir Aus
Herzensgrund (SS/ST) (G2585)

Lobt Gott Getrost Mit Singen *Gen/Thanks
[Ger] SATB,acap (med easy) BAREN. BA 156
s.p. (G2586)
SATB,acap voc pt DOBLINGER s.p. see also
LOB UND DANK (G2587)

Make A Joyful Noise Unto The Lord (Psalm 66)
(Ehret) SATB oct PRO ART 2509 $.35 (G2588)

Mein Hoffnung, Trost Und Zuversicht (Psalm
31) Gen
[Ger] SATB,acap (med) MULLER K 23 s.p. (G2589)

Nun Freuet Euch, Ihr Arm' Und Reich'
see Gumpeltzhaimer, Adam, Helft Mir Gotts
Gute Preisen
SSA/TTB HANSSLER 6.294 s.p. contains also:
Pahlitzsch, Wolfgang, Gottes Sohn Ist
Kommen (SSA); Zipp, Friedrich, Freut
Euch, Ihr Lieben Christen (SSA) (G2590)

Nun Freut Euch, Ihr Arm' Und Reich' *Xmas,
mot
3pt wom cor/3pt jr cor,acap cor pts
BREITKOPF-W CHB-3492 s.p. (G2591)

O Fader Var I Himmerik
mix cor MUSIKK 225 s.p. contains also:
Praetorius, Michael, O Fader Var I
Himmerik; Hassler, Hans Leo, O Fader Var
I Hemmerik (G2592)

O Herr Jesu Christe
SSATB,acap DOBLINGER s.p. see also BITTE
UND VERTRAUEN (G2593)
(Schabasser, Josef) mix cor,acap oct
DOBLINGER s.p. see also CHRISTUS, DER
HERR (G2594)

O Lieber Gott Im Hochsten Thron
SAT/SAB HANSSLER 6.273 s.p. contains also:
Weber, Karl-Heinz, Lobe Den Herren, Den
Machtigen Konig (SSAT/SSAB); Trubel,
Gerhard, Herr, Unser Herrscher (3pt) (G2595)

On The Wood His Arms Are Stretched *anthem
(Sateren) SATB (easy) oct AUGSBURG 1532
$.25 (G2596)

Praise Ye The Lord With Singing *see Lob
Gott Getrost Mit Singen

Psalm 31 *see Mein Hoffnung, Trost Und
Zuversicht

Psalm 66 *see Make A Joyful Noise Unto The
Lord

Rejoice, Rejoice, Believers *Adv
SATB,acap (med easy) oct CONCORDIA 98-1469
$.25 (G2597)

Unnepi Zene *canon
(Szabo, M.) [Hung] 5pt (easy) BUDAPEST 188
s.p. (G2598)

Vom Himmel Hoch Da Komm Ich Her *Xmas
[Ger] SATB,acap (med easy) BAREN. BA 997
s.p. (G2599)
SATB HANSSLER 6.013 s.p. contains also:
Bach, Johann Sebastian, Nun Singet Und
Seid Froh (G2600)
SATB HANSSLER 6.2170 s.p. (G2601)
4pt mix cor MOSELER LB-56 s.p. contains
also: Praetorius, Michael, Vom Himmel
Hoch Da Komm Ich Her (G2602)

Was Mein Gott Will, Das Gescheh Allzeit *Gen
[Ger] SATB&SATB,acap (med easy) MULLER K 22
s.p. (G2603)

GUMPELTZHAIMER, ADAM (cont'd.)
We Sing The Praise Of Him Who Died *Lent
SATB,acap (med easy) oct CONCORDIA 98-1360
$.20 (G2604)

Wenn Mein Stundlein Vorhanden Ist *Gd.Fri.
SATB,acap voc pt DOBLINGER s.p. see also
TOD UND VERGANGLICHKEIT (G2605)

When My Last Hour Is Close At Hand *Lent
SATB SCHMITT 1428 $.25 (G2606)

Wie Lang, O Gott, In Meiner Not
see Bach, Johann Sebastian, Du Aller
Menschen Vater, Du Helfer
4pt mix cor MOSELER LB-14 s.p. (G2607)

Wir Danken Dir, Gott, Fur Und Fur *Thanks
SAT/SAB HANSSLER 6.274 s.p. contains also:
Trubel, Gerhard, Lobe Den Herren, Den
Machtigen Konig (SSAT/SSAB); Staden,
Johann, Ein Jeder Mensch Bedenke Eben
(SAT/SAB) (G2608)

Wir Danken Dir, Herr Gott Vater *Gen/Thanks
[Ger] SSATB,acap MULLER K 29 s.p. (G2609)
SSATB voc pt DOBLINGER s.p. see also LOB
UND DANK (G2610)

GUNSENHEIMER, GUSTAV (1934-)
Die Heilung Des Blinden
SATB HANSSLER 7.167 s.p. (G2611)

Die Versuchung Jesu *Bibl
SSATB HANSSLER 7.156 s.p. (G2612)

Ich Bin Das Licht, Ich Leucht Euch Fur
see Gunsenheimer, Gustav, Jesus Und Der
Zwei Junger

Ich Brach Drei Durre Reiselein
SAT/SAB HANSSLER 6.305 s.p. contains also:
Maria Durch Ein Dornwald Ging (SATBB) (G2613)

Jesus Und Der Kanaanaische Weib *Bibl
SSATB HANSSLER 7.168 s.p. (G2614)

Jesus Und Der Zwei Junger
SATB HANSSLER 7.148 s.p. contains also: Ich
Bin Das Licht, Ich Leucht Euch Fur (G2615)

Jesus Und Die Tochter Des Jairus *Bibl
SATB HANSSLER 7.161 s.p. (G2616)

Maria Durch Ein Dornwald Ging
see Gunsenheimer, Gustav, Ich Brach Drei
Durre Reiselein

GURIDI
Misa De Requiem
3pt UNION ESP. 13215-BIS s.p. (G2617)

GURNEY
Come Ye Lofty, Come Ye Lowly *Xmas
(Douglas) SATB oct PRO ART 2128 $.25 (G2618)

GUSTAF
Mina Lefnadstimmar Stupa
[Swed] 3pt men cor LUNDQUIST 4 s.p. (G2619)

GUSTAFSON, D.
Children Of The Heavenly Father
SATB SHAWNEE A 813 $.30 (G2620)

John The Baptist
SATB oct PRESSER 312-40422 $.30 (G2621)

Keep An Eye On Me
SSA oct PRESSER 312-40349 $.30 (G2622)
SAB oct PRESSER 312-40452 $.30 (G2623)
SATB oct PRESSER 312-40284 $.30 (G2624)

Thou Art The Way
SATB SHAWNEE A 1029 $.25 (G2625)

GUSTAFSON, DWIGHT
All People That On Earth Do Dwell
SATB oct FISCHER,J 9857 $.30 (G2626)

Come, We That Love The Lord
SATB oct AGAPE CH 647 $.30 (G2627)

GUSTAFSON, JOHN
Bonepsalm *Psalm
mix cor NORDISKA 4525 s.p. (G2628)

GUSTATE ET VIDETTE see Bottigliero, Eduardo

GUTEN ABEND, GUT' NACHT see Brahms, Johannes

GUTES UND BARMHERZIGKEIT WERDEN MIR FOLGEN MEIN
LEBEN LANG see Schutz, Heinrich

GUTTMAN, OSKAR
Psalm 19 *see Song Of David

Song Of David (Psalm 19)
SATB,opt perc TRANSCON. TCL 773 $.35 (G2629)

GUZMAN
Rejoice In The Lord
SATB oct PRO ART 1247 $.20 (G2630)

GWINE TO LAY DOWN MY BURDEN see Kirk

GWINE UP see Rhea

GWINNER, VOLKER (1916-)
Aber Der Gerechten Seelen
4pt mix cor MOSELER LB-330 s.p. (G2631)

Christ Lag In Todesbanden *Holywk/Psntd
4pt mix cor MOSELER LB-414 s.p. (G2632)

Herr Christ, Der Einig Gotts Sohn *cant
SATB,fl,ob,vln,vcl HANSSLER 10.169 sc s.p.,
voc sc s.p., ipa (G2633)

Kantate Uber Einen Weihnachtspsalm *Xmas,
cant
(Moliis; Mellberg) [Ger] mix cor,S solo,
org,vln oct FAZER s.p. (G2634)

Lobe Den Herren, Den Machtigen Konig *cant
SS/SA,org HANSSLER 10.177 sc s.p., voc sc
s.p. (G2635)

GWINNER, VOLKER (cont'd.)

Psalm 92
mix cor (med) oct LEUCKART 662 s.p. (G2636)

Seid Frohlich In Hoffnung *mot
4-5pt mix cor&jr cor,S solo MOSELER s.p.
(G2637)

Siehe, Ich Stehe Vor Der Tur *mot
4-6pt mix cor MOSELER LB-415 s.p. (G2638)

GWYNNE
Go To Sleep, Holy Child *Xmas
SATB oct VOLKWEIN VB161 $.25 (G2639)

GYERMEKKAROK I *sac/sec,CC12L,canon
[Hung] 4pt jr cor (easy) BUDAPEST 3035 s.p.
contains sacred works by: Haydn, Michael
(G2640)

GYONGYORI-GYONGY see Farkas, Ferenc

GYOZELMI KORUS see Handel, George Frideric

H

HA NACIDO EL NINO DIOS see Gomis

HA VIHAR JO see Dobos, K.

HAAG
In A Manger Long Ago *Xmas
SATB oct LILLENAS AT-C103 $.30 (H1)

HAALAND, INGEBRET
Sa Har Gud Elsket Verden
mix cor MUSIKK 106 s.p. (H2)

HAAS, JOSEPH (1879-1960)
Ecce Sacerdos Magnus *Op.80a
[Lat/Ger] unis,org/brass voc sc SCHOTT 3255
s.p., ipa, cor pts SCHOTT 3255 s.p., ipa
(H3)

Te Deum *Op.100, Te Deum
[Lat] SATB,SB soli,orch,org voc sc SCHOTT
3889 s.p., ipr (H4)

HABAKKUK - THE LORD IS MY STRENGTH see
Demarest, A.

HABE DEINE LUST AM HERREN see Hartmann,
Heinrich

HABEN ENGEL WIR VERNOMMEN see Werner, St.

HABEN WIR GUTES EMPFANGEN VON GOTT see Reger,
Max

HABEN YAKIR LI see Helfman, Max

HACIA BELEN VA UN BORRICO
(Shaw; Parker) [Eng/Span] 4pt mix cor,Bar
solo,acap oct SCHIRM.G 10185 $.40 (H5)

HACOMPLAYNT, ROBERT
Salve Regina *mot
SATTB STAINER MB10-1 s.p. (H6)

HAD WE BUT HEARKENED see Davies, Henry Walford

HADLER
Christ Was Born To Save *Xmas
SATB oct LORENZ 370 $.25 (H7)

Christmas *Xmas,cant/folk
1-2pt jr cor oct LORENZ $1.95 (H8)

Easter Folk Style *Easter,cant/folk
1-2pt LORENZ $1.95 (H9)

Exaltation
SA/SAB oct LORENZ 7836 $.25 (H10)

Garden Of Easter, The *Easter,cant
1-2pt LORENZ $1.75 (H11)

Glory Of The Cross *Easter,cant
SAB LORENZ $1.75 (H12)
SATB LORENZ $1.50 (H13)

Good To Me
unis oct LORENZ 8866 $.25 (H14)

Hosanna, Loud Hosanna! *Easter
2pt oct LORENZ 5735 $.30 (H15)

Merrily On High *Xmas
SATB oct LORENZ E13 $.30 (H16)

Praise The Lord
2pt oct LORENZ 5739 $.30 (H17)

Prepare Him Room *Xmas,cant
SATB oct LORENZ $1.95 (H18)

Quiet Carol, The *Xmas
SATB oct LORENZ C215 $.25 (H19)

Three Bell Carols For Junior Choirs *Xmas/
Easter
unis jr cor oct LORENZ 8583 $.35 (H20)

HADLER, R.
Bells Ring Out Noel *Xmas
(Porter, E.) SA,opt hndbl oct FISCHER,J
10039 $.25 (H21)

HADLEY
Give Thanks And Praise To God
SATB oct PRO ART 1604 $.18 (H22)

In Thee I Trust
SATB,acap oct PRO ART 1417 $.18 (H23)

Let Not Your Heart Be Troubled
SATB oct PRO ART 2507 $.25 (H24)

O Lord Of All
SATB oct PRO ART 2463 $.30 (H25)

O What Their Glory Must Be
SATB oct PRO ART 2192 $.25 (H26)

Sacred Service, A *Gen,folk/pop
SATB,opt bvl,perc,gtr PRO ART 1161 $1.50,
ipa (H27)

Thanks To God For All His Love *Thanks
SATB oct PRO ART 2296 $.30 (H28)

HAEC DIES see Arnaldi, Antonio

HAEC DIES see Aston, Peter

HAEC DIES see Byrd, William

HAEC DIES see Fabiani, Angelo

HAEC DIES see Gallus, Jacobus

HAEC DIES see Hoogerwerf, N.

HAEC DIES see Moioli, Romano

HAEC DIES see Palestrina, Giovanni

HAEC DIES see Volpi, Edoardo

HAEC DIES see Vranken, Alph.

HAEC DIES see Zucchini, Gregorio

HAEC DIES QUAM FECIT see Palestrina, Giovanni

HAEC DIES, QUAM FECIT see Shepherd, John

HAEC DIES, QUAM FECIT DOMINUS see Arcadelt,
Jacob

HAEC DIES QUAM FECIT DOMINUS see Palestrina,
Giovanni

HAEC DIES QUEM FECIT see Palestrina, Giovanni

HAEC EAST DIES see Gallus, Jacobus

HAEC EST DIES see Gallus, Jacobus

HAEC EST DOMUS DOMINI see Rubbra, Edmund

HAEC EST JOANNA see Busser, [Henri-Paul]

HAFSO
Beneath The Cross Of Jesus
SATB KJOS 5889 $.35 (H29)

Carol Of The Manger *carol
SATB KJOS 5823 $.30 (H30)

God Is Our Refuge And Strength
SATB KJOS 5876 $.30 (H31)

Lord Jesus, Think On Me
SATB KJOS 5890 $.30 (H32)

Of Christ We Sing
SATB KJOS 5870 $.30 (H33)

Praise The Lord
SAB KJOS 5732 $.30 (H34)

HAGEMAN
Christ Went Up Into The Hills *Easter/Lent
TTBB oct FISCHER,C CM-2135 $.25 (H35)
SATB oct FISCHER,C CM-4557 $.25 (H36)
(Saar) 3pt jr cor/SSA (med diff) FISCHER,C
CM 5064 $.25 (H37)
(Saar) SSA,S solo oct FISCHER,C CM-5064
$.25 (H38)

Sundown
(Breck) 3pt jr cor/SSA (med diff) FISCHER,C
CM 5302 $.20 (H39)

HAGEMANN, P.
David's Lament For Saul And Jonathan
SATB,acap oct PRESSER MC549 $.45 (H40)

Praise Ye The Lord
SATB oct PRESSER MC479 $.40 (H41)

HAGEN
All The World Shall Sing *Morav
(Dickinson) SATB oct GRAY GMCM 10 $.25 (H42)

Fear Not, For Behold I Bring Good Tidings
(Gombosi) [Eng/Ger] SATB,S solo,org oct
MORAVIAN 5482 $.50 (H43)

Morning Star
(Gombosi; McCorkle) [Eng/Ger] SATB,A solo,
org oct MORAVIAN 5483 $.35 (H44)

HAGER, SISTER CONLETH
Agnus Dei *Agnus/anthem
"Lamb Of God" unis treb cor (easy) oct
AUGSBURG 3003 $.20 (H45)

Holy, Holy, Holy *anthem/Sanctus
unis treb cor,inst (easy) oct AUGSBURG 3002
$.20 (H46)

Lamb Of God *see Agnus Dei

HAGIUS, CARL
Ihr Kreatur Im Himmel Oben *Gen/Thanks
SATB,acap voc pt DOBLINGER s.p. see also
LOB UND DANK (H47)

Nun Lobet Gott Im Hohen Thron *Gen/Thanks
SATB,acap voc pt DOBLINGER s.p. see also
LOB UND DANK (H48)

HAGIUS, CONRAD (ca. 1550-1620)
Gott, Tu Dich Uber Uns Erbarmen *mot
(Haberl) SAAT HANSSLER 1.421 s.p. (H49)

Gott Vater, Herr, Allmachtig Gross *mot
(Haberl) SATB HANSSLER 1.420 s.p. (H50)

Ihr Kreatur Im Himmel Oben *Psalm
SATB,acap DOBLINGER s.p. see from
PSALMLIEDER (H51)

O Mensch, Betracht Deiner Seele *mot
(Hellmann) SAB HANSSLER 1.247 s.p. (H52)

Wer Heimlich Seine Wohnesatt *Psalm
SATB,acap DOBLINGER s.p. see from
PSALMLIEDER (H53)

HAGLER, PAUL (1897-   )
Das Lob Der Frau *CC3U
[Ger] wom cor,S solo,org/2fl&2ob&2clar&
2bsn&2horn&2trp&strings HUG s.p., ipr
(H54)

HAHN
O Praise The Lord, All Nations
SATB,acap (med diff/diff) SOUTHERN $.30
(H55)

HAHN, [CARL] (1874-1929)
Forget-Me-Not
SSAA HUNTZINGER 2010 $.10 (H56)

Green Cathedral
(Montrose, G.) SATB oct PRESSER 322-35447
$.30 (H57)

Green Cathedral, The
SATB oct PRESSER 322-35073 $.35 (H58)
SSA oct PRESSER 322-35038 $.30 (H59)
(Huntley, F.) TTBB oct PRESSER 322-35308
$.40 (H60)
(Montrose, G.) SAB oct PRESSER 322-35467
$.30 (H61)

HAHN, GUNNER
Valkommen, O Jesu *Xmas
mix cor NORDISKA 3998 s.p.   (H62)
(Mansta, Alvaden) unis mix cor,Bar/Mez
solo,org cor pts NORDISKA 3998 s.p., ipa   (H63)

HAHN, HARVEY
And Jesus Increased In Wisdom *Epiph/Gen,
anthem
SAB,acap (med easy) oct CONCORDIA 98-2100
$.30 contains also: Lo, How A Rose E'er
Blooming   (H64)

Lo, How A Rose E'er Blooming
see Hahn, Harvey, And Jesus Increased In
Wisdom

O Praise The Lord, All Nations *Ded/Gen/
Thanks
SATB,acap (med easy) oct CONCORDIA 98-2124
$.30   (H65)

HAHN, REYNALDO (1875-1947)
Cantique De Racine Sur Le Bonheur Des Justes
Et Le Malheur Des Reprouves
[Fr] SA,opt pno/org HEUGEL s.p.   (H66)

Day, The *see Le Jour

De Profundis (from La Carmelite)
[Lat] SSA,opt pno/org HEUGEL s.p.   (H67)

Le Jour
(Boyd) "Day, The" [Eng/Fr] SATB oct LAWSON
51723 $.30   (H68)

Noctem Quietam
[Lat] cor,T solo,opt pno/org HEUGEL s.p.   (H69)

Tu Es Petrus *Commun
[Lat] 4pt mix cor,acap (contains also solo
work) LEMOINE s.p. see also BREVIAIRE DE
PIERRE L'ERMITE   (H70)
[Lat] 4pt mix cor,org LEMOINE voc sc s.p.,
cor pts s.p. see from LE BREVIAIRE DE
PIERRE L'ERMITE   (H71)

HAIL, ALL HAIL see Brown, William [H., Jr.]

HAIL, ALL HAIL THE GLORIOUS MORN *Xmas,carol,
Boh
see Three Old Bohemian Christmas Carols
(Trusler) SATB,opt S solo,acap LAWSON
51031 $.25   (H72)

HAIL, ALPHA AND OMEGA see Elmore, Robert [Hall]

HAIL! BABE OF GOD THE VERY SON *Xmas
(Spencer, W.) SATB,acap oct PRESSER MC334
$.25   (H73)

HAIL, BLESSED FLOWER see Davies, Peter Maxwell,
Ave Maria

HAIL BRIGHT ABODE see Wagner, Richard

HAIL, BRIGHT CECILIA see Purcell, Henry

HAIL, GLADDENING LIGHT see Broadhead, G.F.

HAIL GLADDENING LIGHT see Jones, A.

HAIL, GLADDENING LIGHT see Martin, George
Clement

HAIL, GLADDENING LIGHT see Shaw, Geoffrey
[Turton]

HAIL, GLORIOUS DAY see Elgar, Edward

HAIL, GLORIOUS SPIRITS see Tye, Christopher

HAIL, HEAVENLY LIGHT see Cain, Noble

HAIL HIS COMING, KING OF GLORY see Davis,
Katherine K.

HAIL, HOLY LIGHT! see Kastalsky, Alexander
Dmitrievitch

HAIL, HOLY QUEEN see Creston, Paul, Salve
Regina

HAIL, HOLY QUEEN see Suriano, Francesco

HAIL, HOLY QUEEN ENTHRONED ABOVE see Mytych,
J.F.

HAIL, HOSANNA! see Licht

HAIL JESU BAMBINO see Weaver

HAIL, KING ETERNAL
2pt CHAPPELL 0018051-352 $.40   (H74)

HAIL, KING OF GLORY see Keating, L.

HAIL, LAND ALL GLORIOUS see Buchtel

HAIL, LAND ALL GLORIOUS see Elgar

HAIL MARY see Andrews, C.T.

HAIL MARY see Arcadelt, Jacob, Ave Maria

HAIL MARY see Dawson

HAIL MARY see Donath, J.

HAIL MARY see Elaine, Sister M. (Gentemann)

HAIL MARY see Illing

HAIL MARY see Peeters, Flor, Ave Maria

HAIL MARY see Roff, Joseph

HAIL MARY see Tamblyn, William

HAIL MARY, FULL OF GRACE
"Nowell, Nowell" see Musica Britannica Vol.
4: Set 1
"Nowell, Nowell" see Musica Britannica Vol.
4: Set 8

HAIL, NOBLE FLESH see Ferris, W.

HAIL, O HAIL see Byrd, William, Ave, Verum
Corpus

HAIL, O HAIL see Guilmant, Alexandre, Ave Verum

HAIL, O HAIL TO THEE, MARY see Schutz,
Heinrich, Sei Gegrusset, Maria

HAIL, O HAIL, TRUE BODY see Byrd, William, Ave
Verum Corpus

HAIL, O HAIL, TRUE BODY see La Forge, Ave Verum
Corpus

HAIL, O HAIL TRUE BODY see Viadana, Lodovico
Grossi da

HAIL, O HAIL, TRUE BODY see Victoria, Tomas
Luis de, Ave Verum Corpus

HAIL O QUEEN see Illing

HAIL, O STAR OF WATERS see Meyerowitz, Jan, Ave
Maris Stella

HAIL, O SUN OF RIGHTEOUSNESS see Gibbs

HAIL, OH HAIL, TRUE BODY see Byrd, William, Ave
Verum Corpus

HAIL, OUR REDEEMER see Rhea, A.

HAIL QUEEN OF HEAVEN see Binkerd, [Gordon], Ave
Regina Caelorum

HAIL, QUEEN OF HEAVEN see La Forge, Salve
Regina

HAIL, QUEEN OF HEAVEN see Lotti, Antonio

HAIL, QUEEN OF HEAVEN, BE JOYFUL see Suriano,
Francesco

HAIL QUEEN OF MERCY see Lotti, Antonio, Salve
Regina

HAIL, REDEEMER, KING DIVINE *hymn
SATB oct ST.MARTIN SMP624 s.p.   (H75)

HAIL, SWEET BABE SO PURE *Xmas,carol
oct HART s.p.   (H76)

HAIL THE DAY see Grieb

HAIL THE DAY see Monk, William Henry

HAIL THE DAY THAT SEES HIM RISE see Johns

HAIL THE DAY THAT SEES HIM RISE see Lekberg,
Sven

HAIL THE DAY THAT SEES HIM RISE see Williams

HAIL THE HEAVEN-BORN PRINCE see Mendelssohn-
Bartholdy, Felix

HAIL, THE KING see Patterson, A.E.

HAIL THE KING OF GLORY see Monks

HAIL THE TIDINGS see Hardwicke, Arthur

HAIL THE VICTOR see Stewart

HAIL THE VICTOR see Wooler, A.

HAIL THEE, DAY OF GLADNESS see Daniels, Mabel
Wheeler, Salve, Festa Dies

HAIL THEE, SPIRIT, LORD ETERNAL see Wetzler,
Robert

HAIL THEE, STAR OF THE OCEAN see Eggen, Arne,
Heil Deg, Havsens Stjerne

HAIL THOU, KING OF GLORY see Grieg, Edvard
Hagerup, Ave Maris Stella

HAIL THOU MOST GLORIOUS see Gombert, Nicolas,
Ave Maria

HAIL THOU ONCE DESPISED JESUS see Cain, Noble

HAIL, THOU ONCE DESPISED JESUS see Sateren,
Leland Bernhard

HAIL TO THE CHILD see Des Prez, Josquin

HAIL TO THE KING *Xmas,carol,Pol
(Kropczynski, Thaddeus) SATB oct WALTON 2040
$.25   (H77)

HAIL TO THE LORDS ANNOINTED see Praetorius,
Michael

HAIL TO THE LORD'S ANNOINTED see Schroeter,
Leonhardt

HAIL TO THE LORD'S ANOINTED
(Cain) SATB oct VOLKWEIN VB163 $.25   (H78)
(Hadley) SATB oct PRO ART 2005 $.22   (H79)

HAIL TO THE LORD'S ANOINTED see Ball, Eric

HAIL TO THE LORD'S ANOINTED see Hastings

HAIL TO THE LORD'S ANOINTED see Lovelace,
Austin C.

HAIL TO THE LORD'S ANOINTED see Schroeter

HAIL TO THE LORD'S ANOINTED see Shroeter

HAIL TO THE LORD'S ANOINTED see Tours, Berthold

HAIL TO THEE see Beveridge, Thomas G., Ave
Verum Corpus

HAIL TO THEE, ETERNAL GOD see Young, Gordon

HAIL TO THEE, GLAD DAY see Lockwood, Normand

HAIL TO THEE, LORD GOD see Roux, Abbe M., Salve
Regina

HAIL TRUE BODY see Byrd, William, Ave Verum
Corpus

HAIL TRUE BODY see Deering, Richard, Ave Verum
Corpus

HAIL, TRUE BODY see Des Prez, Josquin, Ave,
Verum Corpus

HAIL, TRUE BODY see Lassus, Roland de
(Orlandus), Ave, Verum Corpus

HAIL, TRUE BODY see Mews, Douglas

HAIL, TRUE BODY see Saint-Saens, Camille, Ave
Verum Corpus

HAIL, TRUE BODY see Viadana, Lodovico Grossi
da, Ave Verum Corpus

HAIL, TRUE BODY see Willan, Healey, Ave Verum

HAIL, TRUE BODY BORN OF MARY see Des Prez,
Josquin, Ave, Verum Corpus

HAIL, TRUE BODY, BORN OF MARY! see Ratcliffe,
Desmond

HAIL, TRUE VIRGINITY see Roff, Joseph

HAIL, VIRGIN MARY see Shaffer, Sherwood M., Ave
Maria

HAIL, VIRGIN MARY see Victoria, Tomas Luis de,
Ave Maria

HAIL, VIRGIN MARY see Vittoria, Ludovico, Ave
Maria

HAIL, YE BELIEVERS ALL! see Schein, Johann
Hermann, Wohl Dir, Du Christenschar

HAINES
Mary Saw Her Son *Xmas
3pt jr cor/SSA (med diff) FISCHER,C CM 6665
$.20   (H80)

HAINES, [EDMUND] (1914-   )
Dialogue From The Book Of Job *Bibl
SSAA,SA soli,pno BROUDE,A. 119 $.50   (H81)

HAIRSTON, JESTER (1901-   )
Angels Rolled De Stone Away *Easter
SSATB oct BOURNE J8 $.30   (H82)

Go Down In De Lonesome Valley
SATB oct BOURNE J-9 $.30   (H83)

God's Gonna Buil' Up Zion's Wall *spir
SATB oct BOURNE J6 $.30   (H84)

Great God A'mighty *spir
SATB oct BOURNE J3 $.35   (H85)

I Can Tell The World *spir
SATB oct BOURNE J2 $.30   (H86)

Mary's Boy Child *Xmas,carol
(Bowsher) SA,vln ALBERT s.p.   (H87)
(Bowsher) SATB ALBERT s.p.   (H88)
(Bowsher) TTBB ALBERT s.p.   (H89)

Nowhere To Lay His Head
SATB,solo,acap MARKS 4556 $.30   (H90)

Our Troubles Was Hard *spir
SSATB oct BOURNE J7 $.35   (H91)

You Better Mind
SATB oct BOURNE J11 $.35   (H92)

HALALUAH! see Burnham

HALALUJOH, HALALU EL B'KOD'SHO see Lewandowski,
Louis

HALELUYAH (OF TREES AND BROOKS) see Binder

HALEVY, [JACQUES-FRANCOIS-FROMENTAL-ELIE]
(1799-1862)
Psalm 122 *see Somachti Beomrim

Somachti Beomrim (Psalm 122)
(Roskin) SATB HATIKVAH HCL 7 $.35   (H93)

HALFFTER, C.
In Expectatione Resurrectionis Domini *cant
study sc UNIVER. PH 13646 $9.60   (H94)

Misa Ducal *Xmas,Mass
[Lat] mix cor,org UNION ESP. 21072 $3.50   (H95)

Regina Coeli *Easter,anti
[Lat] mix cor,4solo,pno UNION ESP. 20456
$3.00   (H96)

HALFFTER, RODOLFO (1900-   )
Pregon Para Una Pascua Pobre *Op.32
[Lat] SATB,3trp,3trom,timp,perc sc ARION
s.p.   (H97)

HALL
Berne
(Lowens) SATB MARKS 64 $.30   (H98)

Carol, Sweetly Carol *Xmas,carol
unis wom cor,pno/org PETERS H805A $.30 see
from Three Carols In Unison   (H99)

Lead My Feet
SATB,org/pno BOSTON 12138 $.35   (H100)

Shepherds Awake
girl cor SOUTHERN $.25   (H101)

Sing, O My Love *Xmas,carol
unis wom cor,pno/org PETERS H8058 $.30 see
from Three Carols In Unison   (H102)

Star-Swing Is High *Xmas,carol
unis wom cor,pno/org PETERS H805C $.30 see
from Three Carols In Unison   (H103)

Three Carols In Unison *Xmas,carol
unis jr cor,pno/org PETERS $.30
contains: Carol, Sweetly Carol; Sing, O
My Love; Star-Swing Is High
see also: Carol, Sweetly Carol; Sing, O
My Love; Star-Swing Is High   (H104)

HALL, ALAN
Short Communion Service *Commun
SATB&cong/unis&cong (very easy) oct OXFORD
40.108 $.35   (H105)

HALL, ARTHUR
Sing With The Spirit
SATB (med) ABINGDON APM-728 $.35   (H106)

HALL, DICKSON
My Soul's Gonna Rise Again (composed with
Romero, Gary)
(Okum) SATB,acap oct LAWSON 51138 $.30   (H107)

HALL, E. VINE
Angel Voices Ever Singing *Harv,anthem
mix cor oct NOVELLO 28.0642.08 s.p.   (H108)

Christ, Our Passover *Easter
SATB,S solo,org (med) oct WILLIS 1087 $.12
                                                    (H109)

Father Of Mercies, God Of Love *Harv,anthem
mix cor oct NOVELLO 28.0768.08 s.p.   (H110)

Is It Nothing To You? *Gd.Fri./Lent,cant
SATB,T solo,org voc sc NOVELLO s.p.   (H111)

Praise, O Praise Our God And King *Harv,
anthem
mix cor oct NOVELLO 40.0582.01 s.p.   (H112)

Praise The Lord, O Jerusalem *Fest/Harv,
anthem
mix cor,S/T solo oct NOVELLO 28.0316.10
s.p.   (H113)

When God Of Old Came Down From Heaven
*Whitsun,anthem
mix cor oct NOVELLO 28.0337.02 s.p.   (H114)

HALL, F.
Lamb And Jesus Slept, The
SATB oct PRESSER 332-40036 $.30   (H115)

HALL, KING
Hear Me When I Call
4pt mix cor,high solo oct SCHIRM.G 4430
$.25   (H116)

O Lord My Trust Is In Thy Mercy *Bibl
4pt mix cor,high solo oct SCHIRM.G 4916
$.25   (H117)

HALL, REGNAL L.
Praise The Lord
cor HIGHLAND 4125 $.30   (H118)

Worthy Is The Lamb
cor HIGHLAND 4109 $.25   (H119)

HALLAGAN, [ROBERT H.] (1926-   )
Christ Our Lord *Easter
SATB,acap oct PRESSER 312-40470 $.30 (H120)

HALLE, ADAM DE LA
see ADAM DE LA HALE

HALLEL AND THREE FESTIVALS see Glantz, Yehuda
Leib

HALLELU, AMEN see Wortley, Howard [S.]

HALLELUHA see Handel, George Frideric

HALLELUIA, AMEN see Handel, George Frideric

HALLELUIA! CHRIST IS RISEN see Mc Granahan

HALLELUIA, SING! see Wilkinson

HALLELUIAH CHORUS see Handel, George Frideric

HALLELUJA *CCU,spir
(Wende, Horst) [Eng/Ger] 4pt mix cor voc sc
POLYPHON 277 s.p.   (H121)

HALLELUJA! see Gallus, Jacobus

HALLELUJA see Handel, George Frideric

HALLELUJA see Handel, George Frideric,
Hallelujah

HALLELUJA see Haus, Karl

HALLELUJA see Mozart, Wolfgang Amadeus

HALLELUJA see Schwartz, Gerhard von

HALLELUJA, AMEN see Kurig, Hans-Hermann

HALLELUJA, DER HERR IST AUFERSTANDEN see Marx,
Karl

HALLELUJA! DER HERR SENDET EINE ERLOSUNG see
Suthoff-Gross, Rudolf

HALLELUJA! DIE RECHTE DES HERRN IST ERHOHT see
Stockmeier, Wolfgang

HALLELUJA, GOTT DER IST HERR SONNE see Marx,
Karl

HALLELUJA, GOTT ZU LOBEN BLEIBE MEINE see
Kappesser, Karl

HALLELUJA: HEFT 2 (NR. 23-45) *CC23U
(Herrmann; Wagner) [Ger] unis jr cor/2pt jr
cor/unis wom cor/2pt wom cor,org VIEWEG voc
sc s.p., cor pts s.p., ipa   (H122)

HALLELUJA! ICH WILL ANBETEN see Stockmeier,
Wolfgang

HALLELUJA! IN DEINER AUFSTEHUNG see Gallus,
Jacobus

HALLELUJA IST EIN FROHLICH GESANG see
Praetorius, Michael

HALLELUJA! JA, DET ER GODT AT LOVSYNGE VOR GUD
see Bjorn, Hjelm Borg

HALLELUJA, LOBET DEN HERRN see Sweelinck, Jan
Pieterszoon

HALLELUJA, LOBET DEN HERRN, ALLE HEIDEN see
Eglin, Arthur

HALLELUJA! LOBT GOTT see Franck, Cesar

HALLELUJA, LOOFT DEN HEER see Maitre Pierre

HALLELUJA OG KORAL see Orheim, Olav

HALLELUJA, PRIS HERREN I HIMLEN see Jeppesen,
Knud

HALLELUJA, SINGT NEUE LIEDER see Sweelinck, Jan
Pieterszoon

HALLELUJAH *spir
(Howorth) TTBB oct PRO ART 1088 $.30   (H123)
(Jones, G.) SATB (choral service) oct PRESSER
332-15123 $.60   (H124)

HALLELUJAH see Bach, Johann Sebastian

HALLELUJAH see Beethoven, Ludwig van

HALLELUJAH see Brown, William [H., Jr.]

HALLELUJAH see De Cormier, Robert

HALLELUJAH see Drechsler, [Joseph]

HALLELUJAH see Feldman, Morton

HALLELUJAH see Handel, George Frideric

HALLELUJAH see Lewandowski

HALLELUJAH see Newbury, Kent A.

HALLELUJAH see Schubert, Franz (Peter), Das
Grosse Hallelujah

HALLELUJAH see Silver, Mark

HALLELUJAH see Sourire, Souer

HALLELUJAH see Telemann, Georg Philipp

HALLELUJAH see Williams

HALLELUJAH see Wise, Judah L.

HALLELUJAH, AMEN see Handel, George Frideric

HALLELUJAH! AMEN! see Kirkpatrick

HALLELUJAH AMEN see Pergolesi, Giovanni
Battista

HALLELUJAH, AMEN see Tkach, D.

HALLELUJAH, AMEN, AND CHORALE see Wagner, Georg
Gottfried

HALLELUJAH CHORUS see Beethoven, Ludwig van

HALLELUJAH CHORUS see Handel, George Frideric,
Hallelujah

HALLELUJAH, CHRIST IS RISEN see Clare, Edwyn A.

HALLELUJAH! CHRIST IS RISEN see Noe, J.T.

HALLELUJAH! CHRIST IS RISEN! see Nyquist

HALLELUJAH! CHRIST IS RISEN see Simper, Caleb

HALLELUJAH, CHRIST IS RISEN see Vincent,
Charles John

HALLELUJAH CHRIST IS RISEN see Winchester, E.C.

HALLELUJAH DAY see Sleeth, Natalie

HALLELUJAH FOR CHRISTMAS, A see Cook, Claude
Karon

HALLELUJAH, JESUS LIVES! see Lindeman

HALLELUJAH! KING OF KINGS see Clare, Edwyn A.

HALLELUJAH! LET PRAISES RING see Darst, W.
Glenn

HALLELUJAH! LOBT GOTT IN SEINER VESTE MACHT see
Franck, Cesar

HALLELUJAH MASS, THE see Gravitt

HALLELUJAH, PRAISE THE LORD see Frackenpohl,
Arthur

HALLELUJAH, PRAISE YE THE LORD see Lewandowski,
Louis, Halalujoh, Halalu El B'kod'sho

HALLELUJAH SIDE, THE see Entwisle

HALLELUJAH! 'TIS DONE see Bliss, Paul

HALLELUJAH TO THE GOD OF ISRAEL see Haydn,
(Franz) Joseph

HALLELUJAH TO THE LORD see Christiansen, F.
Melius

HALLELUJAH UNTO GOD'S ALMIGHTY SON! see
Beethoven, Ludwig van, Welten Singen Dank
Und Ehre

HALLELUJAH! WHAT A SAVIOR! see Wilson

HALLELUJAH see Handel, George Frideric

HALLELUYAH see Magne, Michel

HALLER, HANS PETER (1929-   )
Des Jahres Lauf Hat Uns *Pent/Whitsun,mot
SATB HANSSLER 7.073 s.p.   (H125)

Herr, Hore Meine Stimme, Wenn Ich Rufe *mot
SAB HANSSLER 7.053 s.p.   (H126)

Herr Nun Lassest Du Deinen Diener *mot
SAT/SAB HANSSLER 7.063 s.p.   (H127)

Hochpreiset Meine Seele
SA,org,2rec HANSSLER 5.063 s.p.   (H128)

Nehmt Wahr Das Licht
SA,org,2rec HANSSLER 5.064 s.p.   (H129)

HALLER, HERMANN
An Sich
see Drei Barock-Lieder

Drei Barock-Lieder
[Ger] SATB,acap cor pts SIRIUS s.p.
contains: An Sich; Gebet; Zeuch Hin,
Betrubtes Jahr   (H130)

Gebet
see Drei Barock-Lieder

Zeuch Hin, Betrubtes Jahr
see Drei Barock-Lieder

HALLER, MICHAEL (1840-1915)
Third Mass *Op.7a
[Lat] SA/TB,pno voc sc SCHIRM.G $.75 (H131)

HALLETT, JOHN C.
Beneath The Cross Of Jesus
(Soderstrom) SATB oct WORD CS-2349 $.25 (H132)

Christmas Call To Worship *Xmas
cor,narrator oct WORD CS-2224 $.25   (H133)

Glory To God In The Highest *Xmas
SATB oct WORD CS-2319 $.25   (H134)

Go, Shepherd Boy *Xmas
unis/SA oct WORD CS-2325 $.25   (H135)

Jesus, Draw Near
SATB oct WORD CS-2184 $.25   (H136)

Jesus, Like A Shepherd
SATB oct WORD CS-2424 $.25   (H137)

Praise, My Soul, The King
SATB oct WORD CS-2181 $.25   (H138)

Sing Jesus Christ Is Born *Xmas,cant
SATB oct WORD CS-2375 $.25   (H139)
1-2pt jr cor,soli,narrator voc sc WORD
20050 $1.25   (H140)

So Very Small *Xmas
unis/SA oct WORD CS-2357 $.25   (H141)
SATB oct WORD CS-2381 $.25   (H142)

Thank You, Jesus
(Leidzen) SATB oct WORD CS-2221 $.30 (H143)

Yes, I'll Sing
SATB oct WORD CS-2351 $.25   (H144)

HALLETT, MRS. ROBERT, JR.
Unto You, My Daughter
SSA PIONEER 1017 $.40   (H145)

HALLNAS, HILDING (1903-   )
Benedictus (Hosianna I Hojden) *Bene
[Swed] SATB,acap GEHRMANS KRB 234   (H146)

Gloria *Gloria
[Swed] SATB,acap GEHRMANS KRB 425   (H147)

Kyrie *Kyrie
[Swed] SATB,acap GEHRMANS KRB 335   (H148)

La Kristi Ord Bo Rikelig
[Norw] mix cor,org LYCHE 11 s.p.   (H149)

Lacrymosa
[Swed] SATB,acap GEHRMANS KRB 199   (H150)

HALLOCK, PETER
Gloria In Excelsis Deo
[Lat] cor,pno,org,perc voc sc WALTON M 119
$1.50, sc WALTON M 119A   (H151)
SATB oct WALTON M 119 $1.50   (H152)

HALLORAN, ELLA ROSE
Prince Of Peace, The
(Milkey) SATB,opt S solo AMP A458 $.25
                                                    (H153)

HALLSTROM, HENRY
As Joseph Was A-Walking
SSA,acap SHAWNEE B 118 $.30   (H154)

Away In A Manger *Xmas
SSAA SHAWNEE B 113 $.25   (H155)

Christ The Lord Is Risen Today *Easter
SATB (med) ABINGDON APM-409 $.20 (H156)

Dost Thou In A Manger Lie? *Xmas
SSA,acap oct PRESSER 312-40480 $.30 (H157)

Earth Has Many A Noble City
SSAA,acap SHAWNEE B 128 $.30   (H158)

From The Eastern Mountains
SATB SHAWNEE A 408 $.30   (H159)

God Bless The Master Of This House
SATB,acap SHAWNEE A 409 $.25   (H160)

God Rest You Merry, Gentlemen *Xmas
SSA SHAWNEE B 117 $.30   (H161)

Jesus, Promised Saviour *Xmas
SATB oct ELKAN-V 362-1296 $.25   (H162)

Sing Ye Glory Alleluia
SSAA,acap SHAWNEE B 132 $.25   (H163)

Snow Lay On The Ground, The
SATB SHAWNEE A 362 $.30   (H164)
SSA SHAWNEE B 147 $.30   (H165)

HALMOS, LADISLAS
Come, Let Us Praise The Lord *Gen,anthem
(Bobak, J; Roff, J.) SATB (easy) oct GIA
G1023 $.25   (H166)

Tava Szi Kantata *cant
[Hung] SSATTB (med diff) BUDAPEST 1187 s.p.
                                                    (H167)

HALO, THE see Licht, Myrtha B.

HALT AN, WO LAUFST DU HIN see Bauernfiend, Hans

HALT IM GEDACHTIS JESUM CHRIST see Bach, Johann
Sebastian

HALT IM GEDACHTNIS JESUM CHRIST see Bach,
Johann Sebastian

HALT IM GEDACHTNIS JESUM CHRIST see Ruppel, Paul Ernst

HALT IM GEDACHTNIS JESUM CHRISTUM see Telemann, Georg Philipp

HALT IN, GEDACHTNIS see Bach, Johann Sebastian, Halt Im Gedachtnis Jesum Christ

HALT, WAS DU HAST see Bach, Johann Michael

HALTE FESTE AN BARMHERZIGKEIT see Kurig, Hans-Hermann

HALTER, CARL
Behold The Name Of The Lord *Adv
SATB,acap (med easy) oct CONCORDIA 98-1031 $.16 (H168)

HAM
David's Lament Over Jonathan *see Planctus

Planctus *Bibl
"David's Lament Over Jonathan" [Lat] TB WEINBERGER s.p. (H169)

Ring, O Ring, Ye Christmas Bells *Xmas
(Mueller) SATB oct FISCHER,C CM-7637 $.30 (H170)

HAMBLEN
Beside Still Waters
SA oct BOOSEY 2119 $.30 (H171)
SATB oct BOOSEY 2225 $.30 (H172)
SSA oct BOOSEY 2426 $.30 (H173)
(Ehret) SAB oct BOOSEY 5309 $.30 (H174)
(Howorth) SAB oct BOOSEY 2531 $.30 (H175)
(Howorth) TTBB oct BOOSEY 2532 $.30 (H176)

Bless Us, O Lord
SSA oct BOOSEY 1627 $.30 (H177)
SATB oct BOOSEY 1623 $.30 (H178)

Hear Thou My Prayer
(O'Hare) SATB oct HUNTZINGER 4014 $.25 (H179)

It Is No Secret
(Ehret) SAB oct MCA (H180)
(Walton) SSA/SSAA oct MCA (H181)
(Walton) TTBB oct MCA (H182)
(Walton) SATB oct MCA (H183)

Lord Is Gracious
SAB oct BOOSEY 1770 $.30 (H184)
TTBB oct BOOSEY 1767 $.30 (H185)

These Things Shall Pass
(Ehret) SAB oct MCA (H186)
(Ehret) SSA/SSAA oct MCA (H187)

HAMBLEN, [BERNARD] (1877-1962)
Beside Still Waters
SATB ENOCH EC118 s.p. (H188)

Hear Us, O Saviour *Bibl
4pt mix cor oct SCHIRM.G 7447 $.25 (H189)

Trust In Him
4pt mix cor,high solo oct SCHIRM.G 7549 $.35 (H190)
(Treharne) 3pt wom cor oct SCHIRM.G 8974 $.35 (H191)

HAMBURGER
Chorale Harmonization In The Church Modes *CCU
(Norden) BOSTON $3.75 (H192)

HAMBURGER MOTETTENBUCH see Micheelsen, Hans Friedrich

HAMBURGER MOTETTENBUCH 4 see Micheelsen, Hans Friedrich

HAMBURGER MOTETTENBUCH, HEFT 4 see Micheelsen, Hans Friedrich

HAMBURGER MOTETTENBUCH III see Micheelsen, Hans Friedrich

HAMBURGER MOTETTENBUCH IV see Micheelsen, Hans Friedrich

HAMBURGER MOTETTENBUCH NR. 1: EVANGELIENSPRUCHE see Micheelsen, Hans Friedrich

HAMBURGER MOTETTENBUCH NR. 2: PSALMWORTE see Micheelsen, Hans Friedrich

HAMBURGER MOTETTENBUCH NR. 5 see Micheelsen, Hans Friedrich

HAMBURGER MOTETTENBUCH NR. 6 see Micheelsen, Hans Friedrich

HAMBURGER MOTETTENBUCH NR. 7 see Micheelsen, Hans Friedrich

HAMBURGER MOTETTENBUCH NR. 9 see Micheelsen, Hans Friedrich

HAMBURGER MOTETTENBUCH NR. 10: ZEIT UND EWIGKEIT see Micheelsen, Hans Friedrich

HAMEL, M.-R.
Audi Benigne Conditor
[Lat] 4-5pt mix cor,acap LEMOINE s.p. (H193)

Laudate Pueri Dominum
[Lat] 4pt mix cor,org LEMOINE s.p. (H194)
[Lat] mix cor,acap LEMOINE s.p. (H195)

HAMER
All Hail The Power Of Jesus' Name
SATB THOMP.G G-584 s.p. (H196)

HAMESIACH ILEMIM see Casseres, A.

HAMESIACH ILEMIM see Lidarti, C.G.

HAMILL
Advent Carol *Adv,carol
SATB FLAMMER A 5074 $.25 (H197)

Behold, I Build A House
SATB FLAMMER A 5453 $.30 (H198)

Candlelight Carol Service, A
SAB FLAMMER D5013 $1.00 (H199)
SATB FLAMMER A5039 $1.00 (H200)

HAMILL (cont'd.)

Fourth Wise Man, The
SA FLAMMER E5020 $1.00 (H201)

King's Highway, The
SATB FLAMMER A 5177 $.25 (H202)

Lenten Devotion
SATB FLAMMER A5374 $.60 (H203)

Lord Jesus, Think On Me
SATB FLAMMER A 5297 $.25 (H204)
SAB FLAMMER D5065 $.25 (H205)

O Love, How Deep
SATB FLAMMER A 5390 $.30 (H206)
SAB FLAMMER D5077 $.25 (H207)

Tenebrae
SATB FLAMMER A5010 $.60 (H208)
SAB FLAMMER D5014 $.60 (H209)

These Forty Day
SATB FLAMMER A 5337 $.25 (H210)

HAMILL, PAUL
My Shepherd
SATB (med) ABINGDON APM-608 $.35 (H211)

HAMILTON, ALISDAIR
All Bells In Paradise
SATB,acap ROBERTON (H212)
mix cor ROBERTON s.p. (H213)

HAMILTON, IAIN (1922-)
Descent Of The Celestial City, The *Bibl
SATB (diff) PRESSER 312-41004 $.45 (H214)

HAMMACK, BOBBY
Have A Nice Day *CC10U
(Carmichael, Ralph) SATB voc sc WORD 37545 $1.95 (H215)

HAMMARSTROM, HUGO
Agnus Dei
3pt wom cor/3pt jr cor,acap NORDISKA 4176 s.p. (H216)

Att Bedja Gud, Han Sjalv Oss Bjod
3pt wom cor/3pt jr cor,acap NORDISKA 4175 s.p. (H217)

Bisp Thomas Frihetssang
wom cor/jr cor NORDISKA 4498 s.p. (H218)

Det Spirar I Guds Ortagard
3pt wom cor/3pt jr cor,acap NORDISKA 4177 s.p. (H219)

Herre Gud Fader I Himmelen
mix cor NORDISKA 2539 s.p. (H220)

Herren Ar Min Herde (Psalm 23)
mix cor,Bar solo,org cor pts NORDISKA 982 s.p., ipa (H221)

Jul, Jul, Stralande Jul
wom cor NORDISKA 4117 s.p. (H222)

Kyrie *Kyrie
wom cor NORDISKA 4042 s.p. (H223)

Miserere
mix cor NORDISKA 4949 s.p. (H224)

Missa Brevis Et Simplex *Mass
mix cor NORDISKA 5429 s.p. (H225)

Pa Marie Bebadelsedag
wom cor/jr cor NORDISKA 3662 s.p. (H226)

Psalm 23 *see Herren Ar Min Herde

Saliga
4pt wom cor/4pt jr cor,acap NORDISKA 4178 s.p. (H227)

Tank Icke Pa Min Ungdoms Synder
mix cor NORDISKA 3197 s.p. (H228)

HAMMEL, B.
When Christ Was Born In Bethlehem
SATB,kbd oct KERBY 810 $.35 (H229)
SATB oct KERBY 81178 $.35 (H230)

HAMMERING *Easter,spir
SA/SAB oct LORENZ 7402 $.30 (H231)

HAMMERING see Ferguson

HAMMERSCHMIDT, ANDREAS (1612-1675)
Alleluia! Freuet Euch, Ihr Christen *mot
(Hellmann) SSATB&TTB,cont HANSSLER 1.308 s.p. (H232)

Alleluia! O Rejoice Ye Christians Loudly
SSATTB,org/pno,opt strings PETERS 66306 $.90, ipa, ipr (H233)

Alleluia! Oh, Rejoice Ye Christians Loudly *Xmas
SSATB&TTB,kbd (med easy) oct CONCORDIA 98-1471 $.40 (H234)

Alleluja, Merk Auf, Mein Herz *mot
(Nitsche) SSATBB HANSSLER 1.078 s.p. (H235)

Ausgewahlte Kirchenmusik *CC10U
(Hellmann) [Ger] 2-8pt,acap/inst HANSSLER 4.006 $5.00 (H236)

Bis Hin An Des Kreuzes Stamm *Gd.Fri./Psntd
(Hellmann) SSATB,cont,2vln,2vla HANSSLER 5.076 sc s.p., cor pts s.p., ipa (H237)

Danket Dem Herrn, Denn Er Ist (Psalm 136) mot
(Nitsche) SSATTB HANSSLER 1.076 s.p. (H238)

Darum Wachet, Denn Ihr Wisset Weder Tag
(Mueller, H.) "Therefore Watch That Ye Be Ready" [Eng/Ger] SSATB,2vln,cont CONCORDIA 97-6316 $1.00 (H239)

Das Ist Je Gewisslich Wahr *mot
(Hellmann) SSATTB,cont HANSSLER 1320 s.p. (H240)
(Schabasser, Josef) mix cor,acap oct DOBLINGER s.p. see also CHRISTUS, DER

HAMMERSCHMIDT, ANDREAS (cont'd.)

HERR (H241)

Der Tod Ist Verschlungen
(Lillehaug, L.) "Now Death Is Devoured" [Eng/Ger] mix cor&opt dbl cor,opt 4 soli, 2vln/2fl/2trp/2ob/2clar,cont sc CONCORDIA 97-6404 $1.50, ipa (H242)

Easter Dialogue, An *Easter
SSATTB,org/pno,2trp,4trom,bvl PETERS 66307 $.90, ipa, ipr (H243)

Ehre Sei Gott In Der Hohe *cant/mot
eq voices&mix cor,cont,opt inst MOSELER s.p., ipa (H244)
(Hellmann) SSATB&TTB,cont HANSSLER 1.318 s.p. (H245)

Eile Mich, Gott, Zu Erretten
(Hellmann) SS/TT,cont HANSSLER 5.078 s.p. (H246)

Freue Dich, Du Tochter Zion, Freue Dich *Bibl
(Hildebrandt) SSTB/SATB,cont,2trom HANSSLER 5.166 s.p. (H247)

From Henceforth, O My Soul
(Schaffer, J.) SATB oct KERBY 6602 $.30 (H248)
(Shaffer, J.E.) SATB,acap oct KERBY 6602C $.25 (H249)

Glory And Triumph *Easter
(Pooler) SATB oct SACRED S-136 $.45 (H250)

Glory To God In The Highest *Xmas
TTB&SSATB,kbd (med diff) oct CONCORDIA 98-1811 $.50 (H251)
SSATTB,org/pno,opt strings PETERS 66305 $.90, ipa, ipr (H252)
(Ehret) SATB FLAMMER A 5571 $.35 (H253)
(Ehret) SATB (med diff/diff) SOUTHERN $.35 (H254)
(Tillinghast) [Eng/Ger] SSA,soli WARNER W3395 $.40 (H255)

Heilig Ist Der Herr
"Holy Is The Lord" mix cor SOUTHERN $.75 (H256)
(Mueller, H.) "Holy Is The Lord" [Eng/Ger] SSATB,2trp/2fl/2ob/2rec/2vln,cont CONCORDIA 97-6314 $.75, ipa (H257)

Herr, Du Weissest Alle Dinge
(Mueller, H.) "Lord, Thou Knowest All Our Being" SSATB,2vln,cont CONCORDIA 97-5028 $1.50, ipa (H258)

Herr, Mein Gott, Gross Sind Deine *mot
(Nitsche) SATB HANSSLER 1.130 s.p. (H259)

Herzlich Lieb Hab Ich Dich
(Hellmann) TT/SS,cont,2vln HANSSLER 5.079 sc s.p., cor pts s.p., ipa (H260)

Holy Is The Lord *see Heilig Ist Der Herr

Ihr Lieben Hirten, Furchtet Euch Nicht *Xmas,cant
(Bonhote, Jean Marc) [Fr/Ger] SATB,2ob&vcl/2vln&vcl/vcl, 2 cornet (med easy) BAREN. BA 2741 sc $2.25, cor pts $.75, ipa (H261)

Jauchzet, Ihr Himmel *Gen,cant
(Bonhote, Jean Marc) [Fr/Ger] SSATB,2trp, 3trom,vcl/2vln,2vla,2vcl (med easy) BAREN. BA 2743 sc $1.10, cor pts $.40, ipa (H262)

Jesu, Meine Freude *Psntd,cant
(Bonhote, Jean Marc) [Fr/Ger] SSATB,2vln, 2vla,vcl,bvl (med easy) BAREN. BA 2742 sc $1.50, cor pts s.p. (H263)

Let The People Praise Thee, O God *Gen/Palm
unis,2vln (med easy) oct CONCORDIA 98-1826 $.35, ipa (H264)

Lift Up Your Heads *Easter/Gen
(Lundquist) SSAATB,acap (diff) oct WILLIS 5486 $.15 (H265)

Lord, Most High, Mighty Are Thy Wonders
mix cor SOUTHERN $.40 (H266)
(Ehret) mix cor CHAPPELL 0024224-358 $.40 (H267)

Lord, Thou Knowest All Our Being *see Herr, Du Weissest Alle Dinge

Machet Die Tore Weit *Adv,mot
[Ger] SSATBB,acap (med easy) MULLER K 25 s.p. (H268)
(Wilhelm) SSATBB HANSSLER 1.007 s.p. (H269)

Meine Seele Gott Erhebt *BVM
(Hellmann) SSATB,cont,2vln,2vla HANSSLER 5.075 sc s.p., cor pts s.p., ipa (H270)

Meinen Jesum Lass Ich Nicht
(Hellmann) SSATB,cont,2vln,2vla HANSSLER 5.049 sc s.p., cor pts s.p., ipa (H271)

Note Well, My Heart
(Ehret, W.) SSATBB,opt 6brass oct PRESSER 312-40670 $.40, ipa (H272)

Now Death Is Devoured *see Der Tod Ist Verschlungen

O Barmherziger Vater *Easter/Lent
(Martens, Mason) "O Thou Merciful Father" SATB oct WALTON 2098 $.30 (H273)
(Martens, Mason) "O Thou Merciful Father" SATB oct WALTON 2098 $.30 (H274)

O Barmherziger Vater, Ich Armer *mot
(Hellmann) SATB HANSSLER 1.107 s.p. (H275)

O Beloved Shepherds *see O Ihr Lieben Hirten

O Domine Jesu Christe
mix cor NORDISKA 4416 s.p. (H276)

O Father Of The Faithful *see O Vater Aller Frommen

HAMMERSCHMIDT, ANDREAS (cont'd.)

O Herr Jesu Christe, Der Du Bist *mot
(Nitsche) SATB HANSSLER 1.129 s.p. (H277)

O Ihr Lieben Hirten *cant
(Mueller, H.) "O Beloved Shepherds" [Eng/Ger] mix cor,2inst CONCORDIA 97-6332 $.85, ipa (H278)

O Rejoice Ye Christians Loudly
(Bach J.S.; Hadley) SATB oct PRO ART 1869 $.30 (H279)

O Susser, O Freundlicher, O Gutiger *mot
(Grischkat) SATB HANSSLER 1.046 s.p. (H280)

O Thou Merciful Father *see O Barmherziger Vater

O Vater Aller Frommen *mot
(Ehret) "O Father Of The Faithful" [Ger/Eng] SATB oct COLOMBO 2386 $.30 (H281)
(Grischkat) SSATB HANSSLER 1.045 s.p. (H282)

Oh, Rejoice, Ye Christians Loudly, Alleluia! *Xmas
SSATB&TBB,kbd (med easy) oct CONCORDIA 98-1471 $.40 (H283)

Psalm 136 *see Danket Dem Herrn, Denn Er Ist

Schaffe In Mir, Gott, Ein Reines Herz *mot
(Hermann) SSATBB HANSSLER 1.004 s.p. (H284)

Schmucket Das Fest Mit Maien *Fest/Pent,cant
(Bonhote, Jean Marc) [Ger/Fr] SSATB,2vln, 2vla,vcl,bvl (med easy) BAREN. 2745 sc $1.10, cor pts $1.25, ipa (H285)
(Hellmann) SSATB,cont,2vln,2vla HANSSLER 5.077 sc s.p., cor pts s.p., ipa (H286)

Singet Dem Herrn Ein Neues Lied *mot
(Nitsche) STTB/SATB HANSSLER 1.075 s.p. (H287)

Therefore Watch That Ye Be Ready *see Darum Wachet, Denn Ihr Wisset Weder Tag

Triumph, Triumph, Victoria *Easter,cant
(Bonhote, Jean Marc) [Fr/Ger] SSATB/SATB, 2trp,3trom,vcl/2vln,2vla,2vcl (med easy) BAREN. BA 2744 sc s.p., cor pts s.p., ipa (H288)

Var Valkommen Jesu Kar
(Arner, Gotthard) 6pt mix cor voc sc NORDISKA 2117 s.p. (H289)

Wer Walzet Uns Den Stein Von Des Grabes Tur *Easter
(Hellmann) SSATTB,SSB soli,cont,2trp,4trom HANSSLER 5.080 sc s.p., cor pts s.p., ipa (H290)

Wer Walzet Uns Den Stein Von Des Grabes Tur *Easter
(Hildebrandt) SATTB,cont,2vln HANSSLER 5.074 sc s.p., cor pts s.p., ipa (H291)

Where Is The Newborn King? *see Wo Ist Der Neugeborne Konig Der Juden?

Wie Lieblich Sind Deine Wohnungen *mot
(Grischkat) SSATB,cont HANSSLER 1.047 s.p. (H292)

Wo Ist Der Neugeborne Konig Der Juden *Xmas
(Hildebrandt) SSATB,cont,2vln HANSSLER 5.165 sc s.p., cor pts s.p., ipa (H293)
(Mueller, H.) "Where Is The Newborn King?" SSATB,2vln/2fl/2ob/2rec,vcl/bsn,cont CONCORDIA 97-5038 $1.50, ipa (H294)

Zion Spricht: Der Herr Hat Mich *mot
(Wilhelm) SSATB HANSSLER 1.006 s.p. (H295)

Zweierlei Bitt Ich Von Dir *mot
(Hellmann) SSATB HANSSLER 1.319 s.p. (H296)

HAMPTON, CALVIN
How Excellent Thy Name
girl cor SOUTHERN $.30 (H297)

HAN BORTKALDER FOR SIN VREDESDAG see Krieger, Johann Philipp, Die Gerechten Werden Weggerafft

HAN ER OPPSTANDEN see Nystedt, Knut

HAN KOM TIL SITT EGET see Skauen, Guttorn

HAN KOMMER I SIN KYRKA see Bjarnegard, Gustaf

HANCOCK
Lovely Rose Is Sprung, A *Xmas
SA BOOSEY-CAN s.p. (H298)

HANCOCK, E.W.
Palm Sunday Anthem, A *Palm,anthem
mix cor&jr cor oct GRAY GCMR 3125 $.30 (H299)

HANCOCK, G.
Song To The Lamb, A *Easter/Fest
SATB,org,brass,timp GRAY GCMR 3286 $.35 (H300)

HANCOCK, NORTON
With God Thy Guide
unis ASHDOWN U.70 s.p. (H301)

HAND, COLIN
Magnificat And Nunc Dimittis In E
SAB (easy) oct OXFORD 42.840 $.50 (H302)

Stabat Mater
SSA,pno/2fl,ob,2clar,bsn,2horn,strings,timp voc sc NOVELLO 20.0125.10 s.p., ipr (H303)

Wolcum Yole *Xmas,carol
SA,pno voc sc NOVELLO 20.0016.04 s.p. (H304)

HAND IN HAND WITH GOD see Moore

HAND IN HAND WITH GOD see Rasley

HAND OF GOD DOTH SUPPLY ALL OUR NEEDS, THE see Vivaldi, Antonio

HAND OF GOD, THE see Ashton, Bob

HANDEL, GEORGE FRIDERIC (1685-1759)
Aber Mit Seinem Volke *see But As For His People

Ach Herr, Mich Armen Sunder *cant
[Ger] SATB,soli,org,cembalo,orch KISTNER sc s.p., cor pts s.p., ipa (H305)
[Ger/Dut] voc sc PETERS HU1372 $2.00 (H306)

Acis And Galatea
(Barnby, J.) SATB,STTB soli,2fl,2ob,strings voc sc NOVELLO s.p., ipr (H307)
(Mozart) SATB,STTB soli,2fl,2ob,2clar,2bsn, 2horn,strings voc sc NOVELLO s.p., ipr (H308)

Acis Und Galatea *meditation
(Ameln) 5pt mix cor,4 soli,orch MOSELER sc s.p., cor pts s.p., ipa (H309)

Agnus Dei *Allelu
[Lat] unis/2pt CHOUDENS s.p. (H310)

Ah My Soul Is Onward Pressing (from Passion, The) Lent
SATB oct GRAY GCMR 1670 $.30 (H311)

Aleluia
(Cramer, John) SATB WEINBERGER s.p. (H312)

All His Mercies Shall Endure (from Occasional Oratorio)
(Tillinghast) SSA WARNER W3390 $.30 (H313)

All Pow'r In Heaven Above (from Theodora)
(Malin) SATB,orch MARKS 4542 $.35, ipr (H314)

All The Earth Doth Worship Thee
(Ehret) SSAATB oct COLOMBO 2030 $.30 (H315)

All We Like Sheep (from Messiah) Xmas
SATB ALLANS 136 s.p. (H316)

All We Like Sheep Have Gone Astray (from Messiah)
(Spicker; Noble) 4pt mix cor oct SCHIRM.G 10235 $.30 (H317)

Alleluia (from Messiah) Allelu
TTBB oct FISCHER,J 3483 $.35 (H318)
SATB,org/pno RICORDI-ENG 127673 s.p. (H319)
[Fr] 4pt mix cor,opt pno/org HEUGEL s.p. (H320)
[Lat] mix cor,pno UNION ESP. 18910 s.p. (H321)
(Clough-Leighter, H.) SATB,org SCHIRM.EC 2637 $.35 (H322)
(Cramer) SATB MARKS 4131 $.25 (H323)
(Dawe) 4pt men cor,T/S solo oct SCHIRM.G 9412 $.30 see from Coronation Anthems (H324)

Amen (from Messiah)
see Handel, George Frideric, Worthy Is The Lamb
(Kingsbury, John) SATB ALFRED 6308 $.35 (H325)

Amen Chorus (from Messiah)
SATB oct PRESSER 332-00987 $.30 (H326)

And He Shall Purify (from Messiah) Xmas, anthem
SATB oct NOVELLO 40.0027.07 s.p. (H327)

And I Will Exalt Him *Xmas
SATB oct STAFF 687 $.30 (H328)
(Craig; Mason) SATB oct PLYMOUTH FS-103 $.40 (H329)

And The Glory Of The Lord (from Messiah) Xmas,anthem/Bibl
see Four Great Chorals From The Messiah
SATB FLAMMER A 5496 $.25 (H330)
SATB oct PRO ART 1218 $.35 (H331)
SATB oct LORENZ 9244 $.30 (H332)
4pt mix cor oct SCHIRM.G 3829 $.35 (H333)
SATB ALLANS 8 s.p. (H334)
SATB oct HARRIS HC4039 $.35 (H335)
SATB (med) oct AUGSBURG 0028 $.25 (H336)
cor oct HART s.p. (H337)
SATB oct LESLIE 4024 (H338)
SATB,pno (med) oct WILLIS 2670 $.10 (H339)
SATB oct BELWIN 762 $.25 (H340)
SATB oct BELWIN 762 $.30 (H341)
SATB oct BELWIN 64193 $.35 (H342)
SATB oct PRESSER 332-00897 $.30 (H343)
(Holmes) SAB oct PRO ART 1814 $.35 (H344)
(Holmes) SSA oct PRO ART 1370 $.35 (H345)
(Palmer) SATB ALFRED 6311 $.40 (H346)
(Shaw, Watkins) SATB oct NOVELLO 34.0001.08 s.p. (H347)
(Trusler) SATB oct PLYMOUTH TR-120 $.30 (H348)

And With His Stripes (from Messiah) Xmas, anthem
SATB oct NOVELLO 34.0002.06 s.p. (H349)

Angels Are Bright And Fair
(Cain) SSA oct PRO ART 1467 $.16 (H350)

Angels, Ever Bright And Fair (from Theodora) Xmas
unis,orch oct NOVELLO 48.0799.05 s.p., ipr (H351)
unis,org SCHIRM.EC 1853 $.20 (H352)
(Koppitz, L.) SA,org SCHIRM.EC 1038 $.25 (H353)
(Wilson; Ehret) SSA oct BOOSEY 5218 $.30 (H354)

Anthem IV *see O Sing Unto The Lord

As Longs The Hart For Flowing Streams *see As Pants The Hart

As Pants The Hart (Psalm 42) Xmas,anthem/cant
[Eng/Ger] STB,STB soli,orch HINRICHSEN D1251 voc sc s.p., cor pts s.p. see from CHANDOS ANTHEMS (H355)
"So Wie Der Hirsch" [Eng/Ger] voc sc PETERS EM502 $4.00, sc PETERS EM502A $7.50, ipa see from CHANDOS ANTHEMS (H356)
"So Wie Der Hirsch Nach Wasser Schreit" [Ger] 3pt mix cor,STB soli,org/2ob&bsn& strings sc DEUTSCHER 509 s.p., voc sc DEUTSCHER 510 s.p., cor pts DEUTSCHER 518 s.p., ipa (H357)
"So Wie Der Hirsch Nach Wasser Schreit" mix cor,SATB soli,org,2ob,bsn,strings,cembalo BREITKOPF-L rental (H358)
"With Cheerful Notes Let All The Earth" SATB,pno SCHIRM.EC 1681 $.40, ipr see from CHANDOS ANTHEMS (H359)
"Your Voices Raise" SATB,pno SCHIRM.EC 1774 $.40 see from CHANDOS ANTHEMS (H360)
(Adler, S.) "As Longs The Hart For Flowing Streams" 4pt mix cor,SATB soli,org/pno voc sc SCHIRM.G see from CHANDOS ANTHEMS (H361)
(Ehret, W.) "Your Voices Raise" SATB oct PRESSER MC364 $.35 (H362)
(Tillinghast) "Your Voices Raise" SSA WARNER W3565 $.30 see from CHANDOS ANTHEMS (H363)

HANDEL, GEORGE FRIDERIC (cont'd.)

As Pants The Heart (Psalm 42) Bibl
cor,orch sc KALMUS $5.00, ipa (H364)

Athalia *ora
(Lewis, Anthony) mix cor,soli,orch (med) voc sc OXFORD 46.150 $6.50, ipr, rental (H365)

Ave Maris Stella
[Lat] unis/2pt CHOUDENS s.p. (H366)

Awake The Trumpet's Lofty Sound (from Samson) Xmas/Easter,ora
(Barker) 4pt mix cor,opt trp oct SCHIRM.G 11135 $.40 (H367)
(Burkhart, F.) "Erschallt, Trompeten" [Ger/Eng] 4pt mix cor,cont,2ob,opt bsn,2horn, strings,timp DOBLINGER voc sc s.p., cor pts s.p. (H368)
(Condie) SATB oct FISCHER,C CM-7561 $.30 (H369)
(Cramer) SATB MARKS 4130 $.30 (H370)
(Cramer) SSA MARKS 4527 $.35 (H371)
(Cramer, John) SATB WEINBERGER s.p. (H372)
(Tillinghast) SSA WARNER W2901 $.35 (H373)

Be Ye Sure That The Lord He Is God
(Cramer) SATB MARKS 4133 $.30 (H374)

Beato In Ver Chi Puo
SATB oct PRESSER 352-00030 $.40 (H375)

Behold, Now Is The Acceptable Time
voc sc PETERS HU1795 $1.00, ipr (H376)

Behold The Lamb Of God (from Messiah) Xmas/ Easter,anthem/Bibl
SATB ALLANS 311 s.p. (H377)
SATB,pno (diff) oct WILLIS 2756 $.10 (H378)
SATB oct PRESSER 332-00899 $.25 (H379)
(Noble) 4pt mix cor oct SCHIRM.G 9448 $.25 (H380)
(Palmer) SATB ALFRED 6317 $.30 (H381)
(Shaw, Watkins) SATB oct NOVELLO 34.0016.06 s.p. (H382)

Belsazar *see Belshazzar

Belshazzar *Bibl/ora
SATB,SATB soli,2ob,2trp,strings,timp (abridged) voc sc NOVELLO s.p., ipr (H383)
[Ger] SATB,SATB soli,orch voc sc PETERS 3636 $7.50, ipr (H384)
"Belsazar" mix cor,SATB soli,org,2ob,bsn, 2trp,strings,timp BREITKOPF-L sc rental, voc pt rental, ipr (H385)

Benedictus *Bene
[Lat] unis/2pt CHOUDENS s.p. (H386)

Bless Thou The Lord
(Whitford) SAB oct FISCHER,J 9074 $.30 (H387)
(Whitford) SA oct FISCHER,J 8839 $.30 (H388)
(Whitford) SATB oct FISCHER,J 8410 $.30 (H389)

Blessed Are They That Consider The Poor *see Foundling Hospital Anthem

Bow Down Thine Ear
(Ehret) SATB,org/pno BOSTON 12907 $.35 (H390)
(Frederickson) SATB oct BOOSEY 5312 $.30 (H391)

Bow Down Thine Ear, O Lord *Gen
(Hines) SAB SCHMITT 5521 $.35 (H392)

Brockes-Passion *see Der Fur Die Sunden Der Welt Gemarterte Und Sterbende Jesus

Brotherhood Of Man, The
(Wiley) SATB oct PRO ART 2529 $.30 (H393)
(Wiley) SSA oct PRO ART 2670 $.30 (H394)
(Wiley) SAB oct PRO ART 2668 $.30 (H395)

But As For His People (from Israel In Agypten) ora
(Burkhart, F.) "Aber Mit Seinem Volke" [Ger/Eng] 4pt mix cor,cont,2fl,2ob,2bsn, strings DOBLINGER voc sc s.p., cor pts s.p. (H396)

Caecilienode
mix cor,ST soli,org,fl,2ob,2bsn,2trp, strings,timp, lute BREITKOPF-L rental (H397)

Canticle Of Praise, A *anthem
(Smithers, Don) mix cor,soli,pno/org voc sc SCHIRM.G $1.00, ipr (H398)

Caroline Te Deum *Te Deum
[Eng/Dan] SATB,ATB soli,orch HINRICHSEN D2410 sc s.p., cor pts s.p. (H399)

Chandos Te Deum
"We Praise Thee" cor voc sc KALMUS 6214 $2.00 (H400)

Choruses For Study And Performance
(Stillings, F.S.) SATB oct KERBY $2.25
contains: O Go Your Way Into His Gates With Thanksgiving (from Utrecht Te Deum - Jubilate); Our Lord, Who Chosen Blessings Shed (from Athalia) (H401)

Choruses For Study And Performance *sac/sec, CCU
(Stillings, F.S.) oct KERBY 6420 $2.25 (H402)

Christ Is Risen *Easter
(Emerson) unis oct LORENZ 8545 $.25 (H403)

HANDEL, GEORGE FRIDERIC (cont'd.)

Christ, Of All My Hopes The Ground *anthem
(Chambers, H.A.) mix cor oct NOVELLO 40.1170.08 s.p. (H404)

Christmas Messiah *see Messiah

Christmas Messiah, The *see Messiah

Christmas Music (from Messiah) Xmas
(Read) SSA,opt orch voc pt FISCHER,C PT-2504 $1.25, voc sc FISCHER,C PT-2645 $1.50 (H405)

Christmas Section (from Messiah) Xmas
(Coopersmith) SATB,opt orch voc sc FISCHER, C O-3475 $1.25, ipa, ipr (H406)

Christmas Section, The *see Messiah

Christmas Selections (from Messiah) Xmas
(Diack) SATB,opt orch voc sc FISCHER,C PT-377 $.90 (H407)

Collected Works gesellschaft Ed. Vol. 38: Latin Chruch Music *CCU,Lat
(Chrysander, Friderich) cor sc GREGG ISBN 0:576 28485 8 s.p. (H408)

Collected Works Gesellschaft Ed. Vol. 37: Three Te Deums *CC3U,Te Deum
(Chrysander, Friderich) cor sc GREGG ISBN 0:576 28467 X s.p. (H409)

Collected Works gesellschaft Ed. Volumes 11 & 31
(Chrysander, Friderich) cor sc GREGG ISBN 0:576 28498 X s.p.
contains: Funeral Anthem On The Death Of Queen Caroline; Utrecht Te Deum & Jubilate (H410)

Collected Works Gesellschaft Ed. 34: Anthems Vol. 1 *CCU,anthem
(Chrysander, Friedrich) cor sc GREGG ISBN 0:576 28390 8 s.p. (H411)

Collected Works gesellschaft Ed. 35: Anthems Vol. 2 *CCU,anthem
(Chrysander, Friedrich) cor sc GREGG ISBN 0:576 28391 6 s.p. (H412)

Collected Works gesellschaft Ed. 36: Anthems Vol. 3 *CCU,anthem
(Chrysander, Friedrich) cor sc GREGG ISBN 0:576 28392 4 s.p. (H413)

Collected Works Gesellschaft Ed. 40 & 41 *ora
(Chrysander, Friedrich) cor sc GREGG ISBN 0:576 28355 X s.p.
contains: Esther (1720 version); Esther (1732 version) (H414)

Collected Works Gesellschaft Edition 15
(Chrysander, Friedrich) cor sc GREGG ISBN 0:576 28400 9 s.p.
contains: Passion; Passion According To St. John (H415)

Come, Ever-Gracious Son Of God
(Hines) SA oct ELKAN-V 362-523 $.25 (H416)

Come, Holy Light, Guide Divine (from Judas Maccabeus)
(Wiley) SSA oct PRO ART 2751 $.30 (H417)

Come, Holy Spirit
(Rodby) SATB MARKS 4177 $.25 (H418)

Come, Jesus, Holy Son Of God
(Hopson) SATB FLAMMER A 5623 $.30 (H419)

Come Let Us All
(Diack) mix cor SOUTHERN $.25 (H420)

Come, Mighty Father, Mighty Lord (from Theodora)
(Malin) SATB,orch MARKS 4475 $.30, ipr (H421)

Come Unto Him (from Messiah) Xmas
unis oct NOVELLO 48.1163.01 s.p. (H422)
unis,pno SCHIRM.EC 1930 $.18 (H423)
(Ehret) SAB oct PRO ART 1821 $.25 (H424)
(Ehret) SATB oct PRO ART 1741 $.25 (H425)
(Ehret) SSA oct PRO ART 1427 $.25 (H426)
(Ganschow) SSA SCHMITT 2535 $.25 (H427)

Comfort Them, O Lord (From Time And Truth)
SATB PATERSON 1624 s.p. (H428)

Coronation Anthems *see Alleluia (from King Shall Rejoice, The); King Shall Rejoice, The; Let Thy Hand Be Strengthened; My Hear Is Inditing; Zadok The Priest (H429)

Dank Sei Dir, Herr *Thanks
"Thanks Be To Thee" SSA,A solo,pno SCHIRM.EC 1944 $.18 (H430)
"Thanks Be To Thee" unis,org SCHIRM.EC 959 $.20 (H431)
"Thanks Be To Thee" unis,pno SCHIRM.EC 960 $.30 (H432)
"Thanks Be To Thee" unis,pno SCHIRM.EC 960 $.20 (H433)
"Thanks Be To Thee" unis,org SCHIRM.EC 959 $.30 (H434)
"Thanks Be To Thee" unis oct GRAY GCMR 1422 $.30 (H435)
(Bement, G.) "Thanks Be To Thee" TTBB,Bar solo,pno SCHIRM.EC 2125 $.25 (H436)
(Christiansen, O.) "Thanks Be To Thee" SATB,opt band KJOS 5103 $.30 (H437)
(Davison, A.) "Thanks Be To Thee" unis,pno SCHIRM.EC 960 $.30 (H438)
(Davison, A.) "Thanks Be To Thee" unis,org SCHIRM.EC 959 $.25 (H439)
(Lefebvre) "Thanks Be To Thee" SAB/TBB oct GALAXY 1.1272.1 $.30 (H440)
(Lefebvre) "Thanks Be To Thee" SATB oct GALAXY 1.1228.1 $.30 (H441)
(Lefebvre) "Thanks Be To Thee" SSA oct GALAXY 1.1288.1 $.30 (H442)
(Lefebvre) "Thanks Be To Thee" TTBB oct GALAXY 1.1222.1 $.30 (H443)
(McKinney) "Thanks Be To Thee" SSA oct FISCHER,J 8952 $.30 (H444)
(McKinney) "Thanks Be To Thee" SAB oct FISCHER,J 8828 $.30 (H445)
(McKinney) "Thanks Be To Thee" SA oct FISCHER,J 8827 $.30 (H446)
(McKinney) "Thanks Be To Thee" SATB oct FISCHER,J 8700 $.30 (H447)
(Nichols) "Thanks Be To Thee" SAB oct AGAPE A 457 $.30 (H448)
(Shaw) "Thanks Be To Thee" SATB oct PLYMOUTH SC-13 $.25 (H449)
(Shaw) "Thanks Be To Thee" TTBB oct PLYMOUTH SC 300 $.25 (H450)
(Shaw) "Thanks Be To Thee" 2pt oct PLYMOUTH SC-500 $.25 (H451)
(Shaw) "Thanks Be To Thee" SAB oct PLYMOUTH SC-400 $.25 (H452)
(Spross, C.) "Thanks Be To Thee" SATB oct PRESSER 322-35383 $.30 (H453)
(Stickles) "Thanks Be To Thee" 4pt mix cor, S solo oct SCHIRM.G 10564 $.30 (H454)
(Syre, L.) "Thanks Be To Thee" TTBB oct PRESSER 332-40015 $.30 (H455)
(Wiley) "Thanks Be To Thee" SATB oct PRO ART 2248 $.25 (H456)

Dann Sollt Ihr Seh'n *see Then Shall They Know

Dann Wird Zum Gold'nen Sternenzelt *see Then Round About The Starry Throne

Das Grosse Halleluja (from Der Messias) Xmas/ Easter
SATB,org HANSSLER 6.2162 s.p. (H457)
(Vogel, Moritz; Nagler, Franciscus) [Ger] wom cor&jr cor,org,opt strings HUG 73 s.p. (H458)

Daughter Of Zion, Now Rejoice (from Judas Maccabaeus)
(Warren, B.) SA,pno SCHIRM.EC 1956 $.25 (H459)

Daughter Of Zion, Shout For Joy *Palm
(Davis) SATB&opt jr cor WARNER W7-1053 $.30 (H460)

Daughter Zion, Now Rejoice! (from Judas Maccabaeus)
(Lundquist, M.) SAB,acap SCHIRM.EC 2456 $.25 (H461)

David Es Goliat (from Saul) Bibl
(Lukin, L.) [Hung] SATB,pno (med diff) BUDAPEST 3126 s.p. (H462)

Day By Day We Magnify The (from Dettingen Te Deum)
(Malin) SATB,orch MARKS 4516 $.50, ipr (H463)

Day By Day We Magnify Thee
(Barrie) 5pt mix cor oct LAWSON 797 $.30 (H464)
(Malin) mix cor SOUTHERN $.40 (H465)

Dear Lord And Saviour
(Davis, K.K.) 2pt WARNER R3504 $.30 (H466)

Deck Thyself, My Soul, With Gladness *Commun
(Ehret) SATB oct PRO ART 1896 $.30 (H467)

Deck, Thyself, My Soul, With With Gladness
(Geer) 4pt mix cor oct SCHIRM.G 8468 $.30 (H468)

Declare His Honor *Asc/Gen
SAB,kbd (med diff) oct CONCORDIA 98-1957 $.35 (H469)

Der Fur Die Sunden Der Welt Gemarterte Und Sterbende Jesus *Psntd
(Schroder, Felix) "Passion Nach B.H. Brockes" [Ger] SATB,SAATTBB soli,cont, 2ob,strings (med diff) sc BAREN. BA 4021 $20.50, cor pts BAREN. BA 4021 s.p., voc sc BAREN. BA 4021A s.p., ipr (H470)
(Schroeder; Bernstein) "Brockes-Passion" [Ger] mix cor,SATB soli,cont,2ob,2vln,vla voc sc DEUTSCHER 4021 s.p., sc DEUTSCHER 4021A s.p., cor pts DEUTSCHER 7066 s.p., ipa (H471)

Der Herr Ist Mein Licht (Psalm 27)
(Kreis, O.) [Ger] men cor,cont,ob,strings HUG s.p. (H472)

Der Messias *see Messiah

Des Staubes Eitle Sorgen *see Insanae Et Vanae Curae

Dettigen Te Deum *Te Deum
(Chrysander, Friedrich) cor (Gesallschaftedition Vol. 25) sc GREGG ISBN 0:576 28477 7 s.p. (H473)

Dettingen Te Deum *Te Deum
cor,orch sc KALMUS $15.00, ipa (H474)
cor BELWIN $1.50 (H475)
(Emery, Walter) SATB,SATB soli,2ob,2bsn, 3trp,strings,timp NOVELLO (H476)
(Straube; Seiffert) [Ger] SSATB,B solo,orch voc pt PETERS 3389 $2.50 (H477)
(Straube; Seiffert) [Ger] SSATB,B solo,orch sc PETERS 3337 $15.00, ipa (H478)
(Walker) [Eng/Ger] SSATB,B solo,orch min sc PETERS E945 $9.00 (H479)

Deus Abraham *Gen,mot
[Lat/Fr] mix cor,Bar solo,org,vcl oct DURAND s.p. (H480)
[Lat] mix cor,Bar solo oct DURAND s.p. (H481)

Dies Sanctificatus
(Cramer) [Eng/Lat] SATB,acap MARKS 4302 $.25 (H482)

Dio Si Lode Cielo, In Terra
"Praise To God, Who Rules The Earth" SATB, org SCHIRM.EC 2622 $.35 (H483)
(Glaser, V.) "Praise To God, Who Rules The Earth" SAB,org SCHIRM.EC 2458 $.30 (H484)

Dixit Dominus (Psalm 109) Bibl
cor,orch sc KALMUS $12.00, ipa (H485)
(Wenzel) mix cor,SA soli,orch voc sc DEUTSCHER 4002 s.p., sc DEUTSCHER 4002A s.p., cor pts DEUTSCHER 4002B s.p., ipa (H486)

Dixit Dominus Domino Meo (Psalm 109) Easter/ Pent
(Wenzel, Eberhard) [Lat] SSATB,SSSAATB soli,cont,strings (med diff) sc BAREN. BA 4002 $9.75, cor pts BAREN. BA 4002 $3.00, voc sc BAREN. BA 4002A $7.25, ipr (H487)

Donna, Che In Ciel
"Herrin, Du Strahlst Im Himmel" mix cor,S solo,strings VOLK 130 sc s.p., voc sc s.p., ipa (H488)

Dotter Sion
see ADVENTSMUSIK FOR KOR OCH INSTRUMENT

Dotter Sion, Frojda Dig
3pt wom cor/3pt jr cor,acap NORDISKA 4442 s.p. (H489)
mix cor NORDISKA 4890 s.p. (H490)

Du Gott Dem Erd' Und Himmel Schweigt *see Oh Father, Whose Almighty Pow'r

Easter Messiah *Easter,cant
SATB LORENZ $1.95 (H491)
SSA LORENZ $1.75 (H492)

Ecce Concipies
[Lat] 4pt mix cor HEUGEL s.p. see from LA MAITRISE (H493)

Ehret In Seiner Herrlichtkeit *see Fix'd In His Everlasting Seat

Eight Christmas Choruses From The Messiah (from Messiah) CC8U,Xmas
(Krone) SATB KJOS $1.25 (H494)

Er Erschlug Alle Erstgeburt Agyptens *see He Smote All The Firstborn Of Egypt

Er Sandte Dicke Finsternis *see He Sent A Thick Darkness

Er Weidet Seine Herde (from Messiah)
(Vogel, Moritz; Nagler, Franciscus) [Ger] wom cor&jr cor,org,2vln HUG 50 s.p. (H495)

Erschallt, Trompeten *see Awake The Trumpet's Lofty Sound

Erschalt, Trompeten (from Samson)
(Vogel, Moritz; Nagler, Franciscus) [Ger] wom cor&jr cor,org,opt strings HUG 87 s.p. (H496)

Es Schalle Hell Und Froh (from Alexander Fest) Fest,cant
(Fricke, R.) [Ger] mix cor,SA soli,orch VIEWEG voc sc s.p., cor pts s.p., ipa (H497)

Esther
see Collected Works Gesellschaft Ed. 40 & 41
see Collected Works Gesellschaft Ed. 40 & 41

Fall Ward Sein Los *see Fall'n Is The Foe

Fall'n Is The Foe (from Judas Maccabeus) ora
(Burkhart, F.) "Fall Ward Sein Los" [Ger/ Eng] 4pt mix cor,cont,2ob,opt bsn,strings DOBLINGER voc sc s.p., cor pts s.p. (H498)

Father Eternal
(Tkach) SAB KJOS 5715 $.30 (H499)

Father, O Hear Me *anthem
(Christiansen, F.M.) SATB (very easy) oct AUGSBURG 0164 $.25 (H500)

Father Of Heaven (from Judas Maccabaeus)
(Davison, A.) SATB,org SCHIRM.EC 1710 $.18 (H501)

Father Of Mercy (from Joshua) ora
(Burkhart, F.) "Vater Der Gnade" [Ger/Eng] 4pt mix cor,cont,2ob,opt bsn,strings DOBLINGER voc sc s.p., cor pts s.p. (H502)

Father, To Thy Throne We Bend
(Suchoff) SATB oct PLYMOUTH BS-102 $.25 (H503)

Festoratorium *Fest,ora
4pt,STB soli,org,hpsd,2ob,2bsn,2horn,3trp, 3trom,strings,timp BREITKOPF-W rental (H504)

Fix'd In His Everlasting Seat (from Samson) ora
(Burkhart, F.) "Ehret In Seiner Herrlichtkeit" [Ger/Eng] 4pt mix cor, cont,2ob,opt bsn,2trp,strings,timp DOBLINGER voc sc s.p., cor pts s.p. (H505)

For All These Mercies We Will Sing
(Stillings) 4pt mix cor,org/pno oct SCHIRM.G 11105 $.25 (H506)

For Unto Us A Child Is Born (from Messiah) Xmas,anthem/Bibl
see Four Great Chorals From The Messiah
cor oct HART s.p. (H507)
SATB,pno (diff) oct WILLIS 2973 $.10 (H508)
SATB SCHMITT 1902 $.35 (H509)
SATB oct BELWIN 6415 $.35 (H510)
4pt mix cor oct SCHIRM.G 3580 $.35 (H511)
SATB,org oct HARRIS HC4006 $.40 (H512)
SATB oct PRO ART 1382 $.35 (H513)
SATB oct LORENZ 4431 $.30 (H514)
SATB oct LORENZ 9246 $.30 (H515)
(Bement) SSAA oct GALAXY 1.1174.1 $.30 (H516)
(Harris) SSA oct PRO ART 2130 $.35 (H517)
(Read) SSA BOOSEY-CAN s.p. (H518)
(Shaw, Watkins) SATB oct NOVELLO 34.0030.01 s.p. (H519)

Forever Blessed Be Thy Name
(Perris) unis&desc oct SUMMY B 2128 $.25 (H520)

Foundling Hospital Anthem *anthem
"Blessed Are They That Consider The Poor" SATB,SA/opt TBar soli,pno,2ob,strings voc sc PETERS H50 $1.25, ipr (H521)

Four Great Chorals From The Messiah (from Messiah) Xmas
SATB PRO ART 813 $1.25

HANDEL, GEORGE FRIDERIC (cont'd.)

contains: And The Glory Of The Lord; For Unto Us A Child Is Born; Glory To God; Hallelujah Chorus (H522)

From The East Unto The West *Xmas
SSATB oct GALAXY 1.2461.1 $.40 (H523)

Funeral Anthem *see Trauer-Hymne

Funeral Anthem For Queen Caroline *anthem/funeral
cor voc sc KALMUS 6210 $2.00 (H524)
cor,orch sc KALMUS $12.00, ipa (H525)

Funeral Anthem On The Death Of Queen Caroline *funeral
see Collected Works gesellschaft Ed. Volumes 11 & 31
SATB,orch voc sc BROUDE BR. $2.50, ipr (H526)

Gebet
see Bach, Karl Philipp Emanuel, Gross Ist Der Herr

Gebet. Wenn Christus, Der Herr
mix cor sc ALSBACH&D s.p. (H527)

Gern Wallt' Ich Mit Dem Volke Hin (Psalm 42)
mix cor,pno/org,orch cor pts TONGER s.p., ipa (H528)

Give Ear, O Lord, Unto My Pray'r *Bibl
(Hines) 3pt mix cor,pno oct SCHIRM.G 11663 $.30 (H529)

Glory To God (from Messiah) Xmas,anthem
see Four Great Chorals From The Messiah
SATB oct LORENZ 9247 $.30 (H530)
SATB ALLANS 313 s.p. (H531)
SATB oct PRO ART 1202 $.25 (H532)
cor oct HART s.p. (H533)
SATB,pno (med) oct WILLIS 2871 $.12 (H534)
SATB SCHMITT 1906 $.25 (H535)
4pt mix cor oct SCHIRM.G 7217 $.30 (H536)
(Barrie) 3pt boy cor/SSA/SAA,S solo,pno/org oct LAWSON 51455 $.35 (H537)
(Barrie) SATB oct LAWSON 796 $.25 (H538)
(Cornelio) SAB oct JUSKO 274 $.25 (H539)
(Palmer) SATB ALFRED 6338 $.35 (H540)
(Shaw, Watkins) SATB oct NOVELLO 34.0046.08 s.p. (H541)

God Of Love My Shepherd Is, The (from Solomon) Gen
(Jacques, Reginald) 2pt (easy) oct OXFORD 44.216 $.25 (H542)

God Of Mercy, God Of Grace
(Ehret) SATB oct ELKAN-V 362-1315 $.30 (H543)

God, Who All His Blessing Shed On Us
(Haroutunian) SATB BOSTON 13075 $.35 (H544)

God's Peace Is Peace Eternal
(Grieg, Edvard) SATB,S solo,org SCHIRM.EC 1663 $.22 (H545)

God's Tender Mercy Knows No Bounds *Gen
(Hines) SSA SCHMITT 2577 $.25 (H546)

Great Are Thy Tender Mercies, Lord
(Hines) SAB oct BELWIN 64338 $.30 (H547)

Great Is The Father
SA oct LORENZ 5372 $.25 (H548)

Gyozelmi Korus (from Judas Maccabeus)
(Sulyoik, K.) [Hung] SATB,cont,2fl,2ob,2horn (easy) BUDAPEST 2645 s.p. (H549)

Halleluha (from Saul)
cor,pno cor pts NORDISKA 3440 s.p. (H550)

Halleluia, Amen (from Judas Maccabaeus)
SATB (C maj) oct SUMMY B 868 $.40 (H551)

Halleluiah Chorus (from Messiah) Easter/Gen
SATB,pno (diff) oct WILLIS 2515 $.12 (H552)

Halleluja (from Messiah)
4pt mix cor,org&brass/2fl&2ob&2clar&2bsn&horn&trp&strings&timp sc BREITKOPF-W PB-4917 s.p., ipa, voc sc BREITKOPF-W EB-2419 s.p., cor pts BREITKOPF-W CHB-3549 s.p. (H553)

Halleluja *see Hallelujah

Hallelujah (from Messiah) Xmas/Easter/Fest/Gen/Lent,anthem/Bibl/ora
"Hallelujah Chorus" see Four Great Chorals From The Messiah
SATB oct LORENZ 1934 $.30 (H554)
SATB (very easy) oct LORENZ 4486 $.30 (H555)
SATB WARNER G418 $.30 (H556)
SATB (C maj) oct SUMMY B 1433 $.70 (H557)
SATB,org oct HARRIS HC4009 $.35 (H558)
SAB oct LORENZ 7078 $.35 (H559)
SSA oct LORENZ 6204 $.35 (H560)
SA oct LORENZ 5105 $.30 (H561)
SATB oct LORENZ C45 $.35 (H562)
"Halleluja" [Ger] mix cor,org HUG s.p. (H563)
"Halleluja" mix cor,pno ALSBACH&D sc s.p., cor pts s.p. (H564)
"Halleluja" 4pt mix cor,org sc BREITKOPF-W PB-4917 s.p., cor pts BREITKOPF-W CHB-4936 (H565)
"Hallelujah Chorus" SATB KJOS 806 $.35 (H566)
"Hallelujah Chorus" SATB (D maj) oct VOLKWEIN VB165 $.25 (H567)
"Hallelujah Chorus" SATB oct LESLIE 4025 (H568)
"Hallelujah Chorus" SATB (C maj) oct VOLKWEIN VB164 $.25 (H569)
"Hallelujah Chorus" cor oct HART s.p. (H570)
"Hallelujah Chorus" cor oct HART s.p. contains also: O Father, Whose Almighty Power (H571)
"Hallelujah Chorus" SATB oct LILLENAS AN-2249 $.35 (H572)
"Hallelujah Chorus" SATB (C maj) oct PRESSER 332-11700 $.35 (H573)
"Hallelujah Chorus" [Eng] SATB oct BELWIN 64112 $.40 (H574)
"Hallelujah Chorus" SATB oct BELWIN 976 $.25 (H575)
"Hallelujah Chorus" SATB,org SCHIRM.EC 1193 $.45, ipr (H576)
"Hallelujah Chorus" SATB oct FISCHER,C CM-86 $.30 (H577)
"Hallelujah Chorus" SATB oct PRO ART 1040 $.35 (H578)
"Hallelujah Chorus" SATB (D maj) oct PRESSER 332-00902 $.35 (H579)
"Hallelujah Chorus" 2pt ENOCH TP147 s.p. (H580)
(Bliss, P.) SATB oct PRESSER 312-20222 $.30 (H581)
(Burkhart, F.) "Halleluja" [Ger/Eng] 4pt men cor,cont,2trp,strings,timp voc sc s.p., cor pts s.p., ipa DOBLINGER (H582)
(Burkhart, F.) "Halleluja" [Ger/Eng] 4pt mix cor,cont,2trp,strings,timp voc sc s.p., cor pts s.p., ipa DOBLINGER (H583)
(Cornelio) "Hallelujah Chorus" SAB oct JUSKO 273 $.25 (H584)
(Dale, Philip) "Hallelujah Chorus" SA ALLANS 412 s.p. (H585)
(Dale, Philip) "Hallelujah Chorus" SATB ALLANS 1 s.p. (H586)
(Dasher) "Hallelujah Chorus" SATB FLAMMER A 5151 $.40 (H587)
(Davison, A.) SATB,org SCHIRM.EC 1698 $.30 (H588)
(Deis) "Hallelujah Chorus" 3pt mix cor oct SCHIRM.G 10057 $.40 (H589)
(Ehret) "Hallelujah Chorus" [Eng] SSA oct BELWIN 1486 $.30 (H590)
(Ehret) "Hallelujah Chorus" [Eng] SATB oct BELWIN 976 $.30 (H591)
(Field) SATB oct BOOSEY 5301 $.30 (H592)
(Fuller) "Hallelujah Chorus" SSA oct PRO ART 1097 $.30 (H593)
(Hardwicke) SSA ALFRED 6206 $.30 (H594)
(Heath) "Hallelujah Chorus" 4pt men cor,org oct SCHIRM.G 10424 $.30 (H595)
(Jacobson) "Hallelujah Chorus" 2pt jr cor/2pt wom cor CURWEN 72503 s.p. (H596)
(Johnson, Clair W.) "Hallelujah Chorus" SATB,pno/org/band oct RUBANK 16 $.50, ipa (H597)
(Koppitz, L.) "Hallelujah Chorus" TTBB,pno SCHIRM.EC 528 $.35, ipr (H598)
(Koppitz, L.) "Hallelujah Chorus" SSA,pno SCHIRM.EC 479 $.30, ipr (H599)
(Mozart, W.A.) mix cor,org,2fl,2ob,2clar,2bsn,2trp,2horn,strings,timp sc BREITKOPF-L PB-974 s.p., cor pts BREITKOPF-L CHB-459 s.p., voc sc BREITKOPF-L EB-2419 s.p., ipa (H600)
(Noble; Spicker) "Hallelujah Chorus" 4pt mix cor oct SCHIRM.G 2020 $.30 (H601)
(Oakey) "Hallelujah Chorus" 3pt jr cor/3pt wom cor CURWEN 70263 s.p. (H602)
(Palmer) "Hallelujah Chorus" SATB (C maj) ALFRED 6345 $.50 (H603)
(Riegger) SSA FLAMMER B 5072 $.35 (H604)
(Shaw, Watkins) SATB oct NOVELLO 34.0054.09 s.p. (H605)
(Simeone) "Hallelujah Chorus" SATB SHAWNEE A 1199 $.30 (H606)
(Treharne) "Hallelujah Chorus" 3pt wom cor oct SCHIRM.G 8937 $.35 (H607)
(Vene) "Hallelujah Chorus" [Lat/Eng] TTBB oct COLOMBO 2060 $.40 (H608)

Hallelujah, Amen (from Judas Maccabaeus) anthem
SATB oct PRESSER 332-14570 $.30 (H609)
SATB oct NOVELLO 34.0062.10 s.p. (H610)
SATB,org SCHIRM.EC 304 $.30, ipr (H611)
SATB oct FISCHER,C CM-6657 $.25 (H612)
SATB oct GRAY GCMR 1505 $.30 (H613)
SATB oct BELWIN 64001 $.30 (H614)
(Brooks) SATB oct PLYMOUTH CC-7 $.25 (H615)
(Davids) SATB oct BELWIN 1415 $.25 (H616)
(Davids) SATB oct BELWIN 1415 $.30 (H617)
(Davison, A.) TTBB,pno SCHIRM.EC 38 $.30, ipr (H618)
(Deis) 4pt mix cor oct SCHIRM.G 9835 $.30 (H619)
(Duey) TTBB BOSTON 12078 $.35 (H620)
(Ehret) SAB oct PRO ART 2204 $.30 (H621)
(Ehret) SATB oct BOOSEY 5089 $.30 (H622)
(Ehret) SSA oct PRO ART 1385 $.30 (H623)
(Geer, E.) SSAA,org SCHIRM.EC 872 $.22, ipr (H624)
(Gray) SATB oct PRO ART 1462 $.30 (H625)
(Henderson) SATB oct SPRATT 535 $.30 (H626)
(Krone) SATB,acap WARNER W3026 $.30 (H627)
(Whitford, H.) SSA,org SCHIRM.EC 1915 $.30, ipr (H628)

Hallelujah Chorus *see Hallelujah

Hallelujah (from Saul)
see Handel, George Frideric, How Excellent Thy Name

Handel's Christmas Messiah (from Messiah)
(Dasher) SATB FLAMMER A5041 $1.75 (H629)
(Dasher) SAB FLAMMER D5018 $1.60 (H630)

Handel's Easter Messiah (from Messiah)
(Dasher) SATB FLAMMER A5106 $1.60 (H631)
(Dasher) SAB FLAMMER D5072 $1.60 (H632)

Handel's Largo (from Xerxes)
(Bliss, P.) SS oct PRESSER 312-21373 $.30 (H633)

Harci Dal (from Judas Maccabeus)
(Sulyok, K.) [Hung] SATB,pno (med diff) BUDAPEST 3178 s.p. (H634)

Have Mercy On Me *see Have Mercy Upon Me

Have Mercy Upon Me
cor,orch sc KALMUS $7.00, ipa (H635)
"Have Mercy On Me" cor voc sc KALMUS 6220 $1.00 see from CHANDOS ANTHEMS (H636)

He Sent A Thick Darkness (from Israel In Agypten) ora
(Burkhart, F.) "Er Sandte Dicke Finsternis" [Ger/Eng] 4pt mix cor,cont,2bsn,strings DOBLINGER voc sc s.p., cor pts s.p. contains also: He Smote All The Firstborn Of Egypt, "Er Erschlug Alle Erstgeburt Agyptens" (4pt mix cor,cont,2ob,2bsn,3trom,strings) (H637)

HANDEL, GEORGE FRIDERIC (cont'd.)

He Shall Feed His Flock (from Messiah) Xmas
unis oct NOVELLO 47.0449.05 s.p. (H638)
(Cain) SSA FLAMMER B 5125 $.30 (H639)
(Davis, K.) SSA,pno SCHIRM.EC 1862 (H640)
(Gray) SATB oct PRO ART 1450 $.30 (H641)
(Gray) SAB oct PRO ART 2151 $.25 (H642)
(Gray) SSA oct PRO ART 1920 $.30 (H643)
(Kountz) SSA WARNER W5017 $.30 (H644)
(Swift) SATB oct BELWIN 1308 $.25 (H645)

He Smote All The Firstborn Of Egypt (from Israel In Agypten)
"Er Erschlug Alle Erstgeburt Agyptens" see Handel, George Frideric, He Sent A Thick Darkness

He Trusted In God (from Messiah) Xmas,anthem
(Shaw, Watkins) SATB oct NOVELLO 34.0051.04 s.p. (H646)

He Was Despised (from Messiah)
SATB ALLANS 400 s.p. (H647)
(Barthelson) SATB oct LAWSON 814 $.25 (H648)

He Was Despised And Rejected (from Messiah)
cor oct HART s.p. (H649)

Hear Me, O Lord
(Kirk) SATB oct PRO ART 2475 $.25 (H650)

Hear Us, O Lord (from Xerxes)
(Fray, J.H.) SATB BOSWORTH s.p. (H651)

Here Is Heavenly Joy *Gen
SAB/unis (easy) oct OXFORD 50.110 $.25, ipa (H652)

Herr, Mach Dich Auf *see Let God Arise

Herrin, Du Strahlst Im Himmel *see Donna, Che In Ciel

Holy Art Thou (from Xerxes) anthem
SATB oct FISCHER,C CM-154 $.25 (H653)
mix cor oct NOVELLO 28.1246.00 s.p. (H654)
(Austin, R.) SA oct PRESSER 332-13328 $.30 (H655)
(Bronson) SATB,org BOSTON 1290 $.35 (H656)
(Kingsmill, L.) SATB oct PRESSER 332-11406 $.30 (H657)
(Page, N.) SAB oct PRESSER 332-15239 $.30 (H658)
(Pitcher, Gladys) 3pt mix cor,pno (med) oct WILLIS 8483 $.25 (H659)
(Swift) SATB oct PRO ART 1037 $.25 (H660)

Holy Art Thou [Largo] (from Xerxes)
SATB oct LORENZ 9680 $.30 (H661)
SATB oct LORENZ A402 $.25 (H662)
SA oct LORENZ 5385 $.25 (H663)
SATB oct BELWIN 64122 $.30 (H664)
(Beethoven) SATB oct SPRATT 524 $.30 (H665)
(Richardson) SSA oct SPRATT 553 $.25 (H666)

Holy, Holy *see Sanctus

Holy, Holy, Father Almighty
SATB oct FISCHER,C CM-7212 $.25 (H667)

Holy, Holy, Holy *ASD/Thanks
SATB,S solo (easy) oct OXFORD 42.923 $.30 (H668)

Holy, Holy, Lord God Almighty
(Kinsman) SATB oct PLYMOUTH SC-19 $.25 (H669)

Hope Thou In God [Largo] (from Xerxes)
see Concone, Giuseppe, Agnus Dei

How Beautiful Are The Feet (from Messiah) Xmas
SATB PATERSON 1655 s.p. (H670)
unis oct NOVELLO 33.0084.06 s.p. (H671)
(Ehret) SATB oct COLOMBO 2029 $.30 (H672)
(Elkins) SATB oct PLYMOUTH SC-18 $.25 (H673)

How Beautiful Are The Feet Of Him (from Messiah)
SATB,org SCHIRM.EC 1129 $.25 (H674)
(Davis, K.) SA,pno SCHIRM.EC 1834 $.25 (H675)
(Davis, K.) SSA SCHIRM.EC 1864 ipr (H676)
(Davison, A.) TTBB,org SCHIRM.EC 912 $.30 (H677)

How Excellent Is Thy Name
(Ehret, W.) SATB oct PRESSER MC286 $.40 (H678)

How Excellent Thy Name (from Saul)
SATB PATERSON 1629 s.p. contains also: Hallelujah (from Saul) (H679)
SATB oct FISCHER,C PT-1629 $.30 (H680)
(Davis) SATB WARNER WB-106 $.30 (H681)
(Herrmann) 4pt mix cor,2pno oct SCHIRM.G 11106 $.35 (H682)
(Herrmann) 3pt mix cor,2pno oct SCHIRM.G 11504 $.35 (H683)
(Herrmann) 3pt wom cor,2pno oct SCHIRM.G 11107 $.25 (H684)
(Kirk) SATB oct PRO ART 2472 $.35 (H685)
(Tillinghast) SSA WARNER W3577 $.35 (H686)

How Excellent Thy Name, O Lord
(Davison, A.) SATB,org (abridged) SCHIRM.EC 1699 $.30 (H687)

I Know That My Redeemer Liveth (from Messiah) Xmas/Easter,anthem
SATB oct LORENZ 9216 $.30 (H688)
SAB oct LORENZ 6216 $.30 (H689)
2pt ENOCH TP184 s.p. (H690)
unis oct NOVELLO 33.0052.08 s.p. (H691)
(Christiansen, F.M.) SATB (easy) oct AUGSBURG 0161 $.22 (H692)
(Runkel, K.) SAB oct PRESSER 312-21441 $.30 (H693)
(Warhurst, J.) SSA oct PRESSER 312-21365 $.35 (H694)
(Warhurst, S.) SATB oct PRESSER 312-21118 $.35 (H695)
(Whitford) SATB,org/pno BOSTON 2912 $.40 (H696)

I Sing The Mighty Power Of God *see Watts

I Will Exalt Him (from Israel In Egypt)
(Coggin) 4pt mix cor,org/pno oct SCHIRM.G 11665 $.35 (H697)

HANDEL, GEORGE FRIDERIC (cont'd.)

I Will Extol Thee, My God *Bibl
(Hines) 2pt boy cor/SA,pno/org oct LAWSON 51461 $.30 (H698)

I Will Magnify Thee
cor,orch sc KALMUS $6.00, ipa see from CHANDOS ANTHEMS (H699)

I'll Proclaim (from Esther)
(Goldsbrough) SS (med) OXFORD 54.931 $.25 (H700)

In Te, Domine
"In Thee, O Lord, Have I Trusted" SATB,org SCHIRM.EC 1130 $.25 (H701)
(Davis, K.) "In Thee, O Lord, Have I Trusted" SA,pno SCHIRM.EC 1563 (H702)
(Ehret, W.) "In Thee, O Lord, Have I Trusted" SATB oct PRESSER MC361 $.30 (H703)
(Glaser, V.) "In Thee, O Lord, Have I Trusted" SAB,org SCHIRM.EC 2250 $.20 (H704)
(Hilton, A.) "In Thee, O Lord, Have I Trusted" SAB oct PRESSER 352-00439 $.25 (H705)

In The Lord I Put My Trust *see In The Lord Put I My Trust

In The Lord Put I My Trust
"In The Lord I Put My Trust" cor voc sc KALMUS 6219 $1.00 see from CHANDOS ANTHEMS (H706)
"In The Lord I Put My Trust" cor,orch sc KALMUS $7.00, ipa (H707)

In Thee, O Father, I Put My Trust *Gen
(Whitford) SATB SCHMITT 1796 $.25 (H708)

In Thee, O Lord, Have I Trusted *see In Te, Domine

In Unsere Chore Mischet Euch! Halleluja, Amen! *see Rejoice, Oh Judah! Hallelujah, Amen!

Insanae Et Vanae Curae *mot
(Muller, Paul) "Des Staubes Eitle Sorgen" [Ger] men cor,opt org,fl,2ob,2bsn,2horn, 2trp,2trom,strings,2timp HUG s.p., ipr (H709)

Israel En Egypte *see Israel In Egypt

Israel In Agypten *see Israel In Egypt

Israel In Egypt *Bibl/ora
[Ger] SATB&SATB,SATB soli,orch voc sc PETERS 64 $7.50 (H710)
SATB,SSATBB soli,org,2fl,2ob,2bsn,2trp, 3trom,strings,timp voc sc NOVELLO s.p., ipr (H711)
[Ger] dbl cor,SATB soli,orch HINRICHSEN P3642 voc sc s.p., voc pt s.p. (H712)
mix cor voc sc KALMUS 6205 $2.50 (H713)
cor,orch sc KALMUS $40.00, ipa (H714)
"Israel En Egypte" SATB,SMezATBarB soli CHOUDENS voc sc s.p., voc pt s.p. (H715)
"Israel In Agypten" 2pt mix cor,SSATBB soli,org,2ob,2bsn,2trp,3trom,strings, timp,cembalo BREITKOPF-L rental (H716)
(Chrysander, Friedrich) cor (Gesellschaft Edition 16) sc GREGG ISBN 0:576 28366 6 s.p. (H717)
(McFarren) SATB,SSATB soli,org,2fl,2ob, 2clar,3bsn,4horn,2trp,3trom,strings,timp voc sc NOVELLO s.p., ipr (H718)
(Mendelssohn, F.) mix cor,soli,pno voc sc SCHIRM.G $2.50 (H719)

Israels Klage Ved Samsons Dod *see Ye Sons Of Israel, Now Lament

Jauchze Dem Herrn Alle Welt (Psalm 100)
5pt mix cor,SAB soli,org,2fl,2ob,2trp, 2horn,strings,timp,cembalo voc pt BREITKOPF-L CHB-679A-B s.p., ipr (H720)

Jephtha *Gen,Bibl/ora
SATB,SATTB soli,2fl,2ob,2clar,2bsn,4horn, 2trp,3trom,strings,timp voc sc NOVELLO s.p., ipr (H721)
(Chrysander, Friedrich) cor (Gesellschaft Edition 44) sc GREGG ISBN 0:576 28365 7 s.p. (H722)
(Neher, Caspar; Rennert, Gunther) [Ger] SATB,SATBarB soli,orch (med diff) voc sc BAREN. BA 4097A $30.75 (H723)
(Stephani) mix cor LEUCKART rental (H724)

Jesus Bids Us Shine
(Chambers) unis oct LESLIE 1067 (H725)

Jesus, Lord Of All Creation
(Habash) SSA/SATB/SAB/SA/TB BIG3 $.40 (H726)

Jesus, Sun Of Life, My Splendor *Commun/Gen
SATB,org,strings (med easy) sc CONCORDIA 98-1441 $.60, voc sc CONCORDIA 98-1445 $.25, ipa (H727)
mix cor SOUTHERN $.25 (H728)

Johannespassion *Easter/Lent/Psntd,ora
[Ger] SAATTB,soli,2fl,2ob,bsn,2vln,vla,vcl, bvl (med diff) MULLER SM 2241 voc sc s.p., cor pts s.p., ipa (H729)
"St. John's Passion" cor,orch sc KALMUS $12.00, ipa (H730)
(Agey, C. Buell) "St. John Passion, The" SATB,org,strings sc ABINGDON APM-205 $2.50, voc sc ABINGDON APM-595 $1.50, ipa (H731)

Joseph *ora
(Chrysander, Friedrich) cor (Geslleschaft Edition 42) sc GREGG ISBN 0:576 28396 7 s.p. (H732)

Joshua *Bibl/ora
[Ger/Eng] voc sc PETERS 3641 (H733)
SATB,SATTB soli,2fl,2ob,2bsn,2horn,3trp, strings,timp voc sc NOVELLO rental (H734)
cor,orch sc KALMUS $50.00, ipa (H735)
(Chrysander, Friedrich) cor (Gesellschaft Edition 17) sc GREGG ISBN 0:576 28364 9 s.p. (H736)
(Prout) SATB,SATTB soli,org,2fl,2ob,2clar, 3bsn,2horn,2trp,3trom,strings,timp voc sc NOVELLO rental (H737)

Joy To The World *Xmas,carol
2pt ENOCH TP280 s.p. (H738)
(Dexter) SA BOOSEY-CAN s.p. (H739)
(Holley) 2pt jr cor oct LILLENAS AN-4018 $.25 (H740)
(Kinyon) SA ALFRED 6137 $.25 (H741)
(Matson; Barnard) SATB SCHMITT 1871 $.30 (H742)
(Palmer) SATB ALFRED 6364 $.35 (H743)
(Shaw; Parker) SATB,acap oct LAWSON 712 $.30 (H744)
(Track) SATB,acap,opt pno oct PRO ART 2633 $.30 (H745)
(Whitman) SAB oct LILLENAS AN-3814 $.25 (H746)

Jubilate (Psalm 100) Bibl/cant
cor,orch sc KALMUS $7.00, ipa (H747)
(Muller) [Eng/Ger] SSAATTBB,ATB soli,cont, 2ob,bsn,2trp,2vln,vla HANSSLER 10.179 sc $7.50, voc sc $2.00, ipa (H748)

Judas Maccabaeus *Bibl/ora
[Ger] SATB,SATB soli,orch voc sc PETERS 61 $6.50 (H749)
SATB,SATTTB soli,2fl,2ob,2bsn,2horn,3trp, strings,timp voc sc NOVELLO s.p., ipr (H750)
cor,opt orch voc sc KALMUS 6206 $1.50, ipa (H751)
cor sc KALMUS $25.00 (H752)
cor KALMUS $7.00 (H753)
cor,orch/org,hpsd sc KALMUS $25.00, ipa (H754)
oct HART s.p. (H755)
"Judas Maccabaus" mix cor,SSAAAATTBBBB soli,org,2fl,2ob,2bsn,3trp,2horn,strings, timp,cembalo BREITKOPF-L rental (H756)
(Chrysander, Friedrich) cor (Gesellschaft Edition 22) sc GREGG ISBN 0:576 28363 0 s.p. (H757)
(Novello , Vincent) SATB,SATTTB soli,2fl, 2ob,2clar,2bsn,4horn,3trp,3trom,tuba, strings,timp voc sc NOVELLO s.p., ipr (H758)
(Van Der Stucken, Frank) mix cor,soli,pno voc sc SCHIRM.G $2.50 (H759)

Judas Maccabaus *see Judas Maccabaeus

Kantate Zum Gedenken An Die Gefallenen (from Samson) cant
(Fischer, H.) 4pt mix cor/3pt jr cor/3pt wom cor,SATB soli,cont,strings,opt brass VIEWEG voc sc s.p., cor pts s.p. (H760)

King Shall Rejoice *cant
BELWIN $1.00 (H761)

King Shall Rejoice, The (from Second Coronation Anthem) Royal,anthem
SAATB,pno SCHIRM.EC 1175 $.25, ipr (H762)
SAATBB,2fl,2ob,2clar,2bsn,2horn,3trp,3trom, strings,timp voc sc NOVELLO s.p., ipr (H763)
cor voc sc KALMUS 6213 $1.00 (H764)
(Herrmann, William) 6pt mix cor,org/pno voc sc SCHIRM.G $1.25 see from Coronation Anthems (H765)

Know That The Lord Is God
(Pfautsch) 2pt mix cor oct LAWSON 872 $.30 (H766)

Kroningshymne (Loft Din Arm Den Sejrende) (from Coronation Anthem No. 4) Royal, anthem
"Let Thy Hand Be Strengthened" BELWIN $.60 (H767)
"Let Thy Hand Be Strengthened" SATB,2fl, 2ob,2clar,2bsn,2horn,2trp,strings,timp voc sc NOVELLO s.p., ipr (H768)
"Let Thy Hand Be Strengthened" cor,orch sc KALMUS $5.00, ipa (H769)
(Grytter, Rud.) "Let Thy Hand Be Strengthened" [Eng/Dan] SAATB,orch HANSEN-DEN 24538 s.p., ipa (H770)
(Herrmann) "Let Thy Hand Be Strengthened" SAATB,org/pno oct SCHIRM.G 11333 $.30 (H771)
(Herrmann) "Let Thy Hand Be Strengthened" 3pt wom cor,org/pno oct SCHIRM.G 11332 $.35 (H772)

La Resurreczione *Easter
(Chrysander, Friderich) cor (geslellschaft edition vol. 39) sc GREGG ISBN 0:576 28493 2 s.p. (H773)

L'Allegro, Il Pensieroso, Ed Il Moderato *cant
(Monk, W.H.) SATB,SATB soli,org,2fl,2ob, 2clar,3bsn,2horn,2trp,strings,timp voc sc NOVELLO rental (H774)

Largo (from Xerxes) Gen
SATB ALLANS 131 s.p. (H775)
(Muller, A.M.) mix cor/wom cor,acap/org ERDMANN 510 s.p. (H776)
(Wilson) SAB oct SPRATT 598 $.25 (H777)

Lascia Chio Pianga
"Lord Of The Nations" SATB PATERSON 1639 s.p. (H778)

Latin Church Music I *CCU
cor min sc KALMUS 801 $1.30 (H779)

Latin Church Music II
cor min sc KALMUS 802 $1.30 contains also: Utrecht Jubilate (H780)

Laudate Pueri Dominum (Psalm 112) Bibl
cor,orch sc KALMUS $12.00, ipa (H781)
(Stein) [Lat] SATB,S solo,orch voc pt PETERS 3762 $1.25, sc PETERS 4317 $9.00, ipa (H782)

Laudate Pueridominum *Gen,mot
[Lat] cor,Bar solo oct DURAND s.p. (H783)

Laut Stimme Ein, Du Ganze Himmelsschar *see Let Their Celestial Concerts All Unite

Le Messie *see Messiah

Lenten Cantata (from Messiah and Passion Of Christ, The) Lent/Psntd,cant
SATB,STB soli,2ob,bsn,strings voc sc NOVELLO s.p., ipr (H784)

Let God Arise (Psalm 68) anthem
cor,orch sc KALMUS $8.00, ipa (H785)
"Herr, Mach Dich Auf" mix cor,SATB soli,ob, bsn,strings BREITKOPF-L rental (H786)

Let Justice Reign (from Susanna)
(Frank) SATB oct FOX MM30 $.25 (H787)

Let The Bright Seraphim (from Samson)
unis,pno SCHIRM.EC 1045 $.25 (H788)
unis,orch oct NOVELLO 33.0030.07 s.p., ipr (H789)
2pt oct NOVELLO 53.0378.08 s.p. (H790)

Let The People Sound His Praise
(Hines) SA oct LAWSON 51258 $.30 (H791)

Let Their Celestial Concerts All Unite (from Samson) anthem/ora
SATB oct BELWIN 64003 $.30 (H792)
SATB,pno SCHIRM.EC 312 $.25, ipr (H793)
SATB oct NOVELLO 34.0068.09 s.p. (H794)
(Burkhart, F.) "Laut Stimme Ein, Du Ganze Himmelsschar" [Ger/Eng] 4pt mix cor,cont, 2ob,opt bsn,2trp,strings,timp DOBLINGER voc sc s.p., cor pts s.p. (H795)
(Chambers) SATB oct BOOSEY 5277 $.30 (H796)
(Condie) SATB oct FISCHER,C CM-7650 $.30 (H797)
(Davison, A.) TTBB,pno SCHIRM.EC 39 $.35, ipr (H798)

Let Thy Hand Be Strengthened *anthem
(Herrmann, William) 5pt mix cor,org/pno voc sc SCHIRM.G $1.00 see from Coronation Anthems (H799)

Let Thy Hand Be Strengthened *see Kroningshymne (Loft Din Arm Den Sejrende)

Lift Up Your Hands, O Ye Gates (from Messiah) Bibl
SSATB oct SCHIRM.G 3850 $.35 (H800)

Lift Up Your Heads (from Messiah) Xmas
SATB/SSA ALLANS 315 s.p. (H801)
SATB oct LESLIE 4054 (H802)

Lift Up Your Heads, O Ye Gates! (from Messiah) Adv/Xmas/Gen,anthem
SSATB,pno (diff) oct WILLIS 1957 $.10 (H803)
(Gilbert) SSA FLAMMER B 5083 $.25 (H804)
(Shaw, Watkins) SATB oct NOVELLO 34.0069.07 s.p. (H805)

Lord, I Trust Thee (from Passion Of Christ, The) Gen/Lent/Psntd
SATB (very easy) oct OXFORD 42.711 $.25 (H806)

Lord Is My Light, The
cor,orch sc KALMUS $7.00, ipa see from CHANDOS ANTHEMS (H807)

Lord My Shepherd Is, The (from Judas Maccabaeus) Bibl/Psalm
(Byles) jr cor&sr cor oct SCHIRM.G 11054 $.25 (H808)

Lord Of Our Being *see Sorge Nel Petto

Lord Of The Nations *see Lascia Chio Pianga

Lord, Our Lord, In Power Divine
(Ehret) SAB oct VOLKWEIN VB695 $.25 (H809)

Lord Shall Reign Forever, The (from Israel In Egypt)
(Coggin) SAB oct FOX R202 $.22 (H810)

Lord's Prayer, The
(Lockwood) SATB,acap SHAWNEE A 317 $.25 (H811)

Lovely Peace (from Judas Maccabeus)
SA oct FISCHER,C PT-1553 $.25 (H812)

Lyric Mass On The Handel Theme "Where E'er You Walk", A *Gen,Mass
(Andrews, C.T.) unis/2pt (easy) voc sc GIA G1578 $1.00 (H813)

Make A Joyful Noise Unto God
(Hines) SSA/SAA oct LAWSON 51395 $.35 (H814)

May No Rash Intruder (from Solomon) anthem
SATB oct NOVELLO 34.0081.06 s.p. (H815)

May No Rash Intruder Disturb (from Solomon)
SSATB,pno SCHIRM.EC 1171 $.35, ipr (H816)
(Geer, E.) SSAA,pno SCHIRM.EC 1599 $.20, ipr (H817)

Mein Lied Sing Auf Ewig *see My Song Shall Be Alway

Messiah *Xmas,Bibl/cant/ora
cor,opt orch voc sc KALMUS 6211 $2.00, ipa (H818)
cor min sc KALMUS 159 $5.00 (H819)
cor,orch/org sc KALMUS $20.00, ipa (H820)
oct HART s.p. (H821)
"Christmas Messiah" SATB oct LORENZ $1.95 (H822)
"Christmas Messiah, The" SSA oct LORENZ $1.75 (H823)
"Christmas Messiah, The" SAB oct LORENZ $1.75 (H824)
"Der Messias" [Ger] min sc DEUTSCHER 4012B s.p. (H825)
"Le Messie" [Fr] mix cor,SATB soli CHOUDENS voc sc s.p., cor pts s.p. (H826)
(Chrysander, Friedrich) cor (Gesellschaft Edition 45) sc GREGG ISBN 0:576 28397 5 s.p. (H827)
(Coopersmith) SATB,opt orch voc sc FISCHER, C O-3473 $1.50, ipa, ipr, cor pts FISCHER,C O-3474 $1.25, ipa, ipr (H828)
(Hutton; Robinson) cor,soli,org sc SCHIRM.G $9.00 (H829)
(Mozart) cor KALMUS $2.50 (H830)
(Mozart, W.A.; Brissler, F.) "Der Messias" mix cor,SATB soli,org,2fl,2ob,2clar,2bsn, 2trp,2horn,3trom,strings,timp voc pt BREITKOPF-L CHB-107A-E s.p., voc sc BREITKOPF-L EB-108 s.p., ipr (H831)

HANDEL, GEORGE FRIDERIC (cont'd.)

(Noble, T.Tertius; Spicker, Max) mix cor,
pno SCHIRM.G pap $2.00, bds $3.00, cloth
$4.50, cor pts $1.25 (H832)
(Noble, T. Tertius; Spicker, Max)
"Christmas Section, The" cor voc sc
SCHIRM.G $1.00 (H833)
(Priestman) [Eng/Ger] min sc-cloth PETERS
E956 $12.50 (H834)
(Priestman) [Eng/Ger] cor min sc PETERS
E956 $9.00 (H835)
(Prout) cor,soli,orch BELWIN $1.50, ipa (H836)
(Prout, E.) cor,soli,orch,org BELWIN
$20.00 (H837)
(Prout, Ebenezer) SATB,SATB soli,pno,org,
2fl,2ob,2clar,2bsn,2horn,2trp,3trom,
strings,timp bds,voc sc,cloth NOVELLO
s.p., ipr (H838)
(Schering; Soldan) [Eng/Ger] cor sc PETERS
4500 $20.00, ipa (H839)
(Schering; Soldan) [Eng/Ger] cor voc sc
PETERS 4501 $2.50 (H840)
(Schering; Soldan) [Eng/Ger] cor cloth
PETERS 4501 $7.50 (H841)
(Schneider) "Der Messias" [Ger] voc sc
DEUTSCHER 133 s.p. (H842)
(Shaw, Watkins) SATB,SATB soli,2ob,2bsn,
2trp,strings,timp bds,voc sc NOVELLO
s.p., ipr (H843)
(Stern) [Ger] cor voc sc PETERS 60 $3.00 (H844)

Messiah A La Moog (from Messiah) CC3U
(Bock, F.) SATB oct PRESSER 332-40120 $.50,
ipa (H845)

Music From Semele
(Blower, Maurice) SSA,opt T solo,pno voc sc
NOVELLO 20.0128.04 s.p. (H846)

Music, Spread Thy Voice Around (from Solomon)
SATB,Mez/A solo,pno SCHIRM.EC 1664 s.p.,
ipr (H847)

My Hear Is Inditing *anthem
(Herrmann, William) 5pt mix cor,org/pno voc
sc SCHIRM.G $1.25 see from Coronation
Anthems (H848)

My Heart Is Inditing *Royal,anthem
SAATBB,SAATB soli,2fl,2ob,2clar,2bsn,2horn,
3trp,3trom,strings,timp voc sc NOVELLO
s.p., ipr (H849)
cor,orch sc KALMUS $7.00, ipa (H850)

My Redeemer Liveth *Easter,cant
(Mozart) SATB LORENZ $1.95 (H851)
(Mozart) SA/SAB LORENZ $1.75 (H852)

My Song Shall Be Alway (Psalm 89) anthem/cant
[Eng/Ger] voc sc PETERS EM501 $5.00, sc
PETERS EM501A $10.00, ipa see from
CHANDOS ANTHEMS (H853)
[Eng/Ger] SATB,STB soli orch HINRICHSEN
D1252 voc sc s.p., cor pts s.p. see from
CHANDOS ANTHEMS (H854)
"My Song Shall Be Alway" [Ger] mix cor,STB
soli,cont,ob,strings sc DEUTSCHER 500
s.p., voc sc DEUTSCHER 501 s.p., cor pts
DEUTSCHER 140 s.p. (H855)
(Schneider; Fiebig) "Mein Lied Sing Auf
Ewig" [Ger/Eng] 4pt mix cor,STB soli,ob,
bsn,2vln,vcl,bvl BAREN. EM 501 voc sc
cor pts s.p., ipa (H856)

Nearer My God To Thee
(Newton, E.) cor oct HART s.p. (H857)

Now On Land And Sea Descending (from
Berenice) anthem
2pt oct NOVELLO 48.1596.03 s.p. (H858)
(Chambers, H.A.) mix cor oct NOVELLO
45.1483.01 s.p. (H859)

O Alles Lichtes Quell *see Oh First Created
Beam

O Be Joyful In The Lord *Gen
"O Frohlocke In Dem Herrn" see Handel,
George Frideric, Wir Preisen Dich, O Gott
cor,orch sc KALMUS $7.00, ipa see from
CHANDOS ANTHEMS (H860)
(Cramer) SATB,A solo MARKS 4135 $.30 (H861)
(Ehret) SATB SCHMITT 1419 $.45 (H862)

O Come, Let Us Sing Unto The Lord *anthem
SATB,T solo,org,2fl,2ob,2clar,2bsn,4horn,
2trp,3trom,strings,timp voc sc NOVELLO
s.p., ipr (H863)

O Father, Whose Almighty Power (from Judas
Maccabaeus) anthem
see Handel, George Frideric, Hallelujah
Chorus
4pt mix cor oct SCHIRM.G 4577 $.25 (H864)
SATB oct NOVELLO 34.0090.05 s.p. (H865)
SATB oct LESLIE 4047 (H866)
cor oct HART s.p. (H867)
SATB oct PRO ART 1386 $.20 (H868)
SATB ALLANS 44 s.p. (H869)

O Frohlocke In Dem Herrn (Psalm 100) Bibl
mix cor,AAB soli,org,cembalo,org,2ob,horn,
trp,strings,timp voc sc BREITKOPF-W
EB-6611 s.p., cor pts BREITKOPF-W
CHB-3641 s.p. (H870)

O Frohlocke In Dem Herrn *see O Be Joyful In
The Lord

O, Go Your Way Into His Gates
(Ehret, W.) SATB oct PRESSER MC365 $.40 (H871)

O Go Your Way Into His Gates With
Thanksgiving (from Utrecht Te Deum -
Jubilate)
see Choruses For Study And Performance

O God, Who In Thy Heavenly Hand *Gen
(Stillings) SATB SCHMITT 883 $.25 (H872)

O God, Who In Thy Heav'nly Hand *anthem
mix cor NOVELLO 40.0221.00 s.p. (H873)

O Herr, Auf Dich Steht Mein Hoffen (from
Dettinger Te Deum)
mix cor,org,2ob,bsn,3trp,strings,timp sc
BREITKOPF-L rental (H874)

HANDEL, GEORGE FRIDERIC (cont'd.)

O Hor, Mein Fleh'n! *see Return, Oh God!

O Lord Correct Me
(Carlton) SATB,acap oct BOOSEY 5380 $.30 (H875)

O Lord, In Thee Have I Trusted (from
Dettingen Te Deum)
(Barrie) 5pt mix cor oct LAWSON 795 $.35 (H876)
(Malin) SSATB,orch MARKS 4464 $.35, ipr (H877)

O Lord Of All
(Anderson) SATB oct LESLIE 4043 (H878)

O Lord, We Trust
SATB oct GRAY GCMR 1526 $.30 (H879)

O Lord, We Trust Alone In Thee *anthem/mot
mix cor NOVELLO 40.0094.03 s.p. (H880)

O Lord, Whose Mercies (from Saul) Gen
(Whittaker, W.G.) unis (easy) oct OXFORD
45.031 $.25 (H881)

O Love Divine
(McEwen) SATB,opt strings oct FISCHER,C
ZCM-108 $.25, ipa (H882)

O Lovely Peace (from Judas Maccabaeus)
2pt ASHDOWN E.A.59 s.p. (H883)
SA oct BELWIN 64080 $.30 (H884)
2pt jr cor/2pt wom cor CURWEN 70029 s.p. (H885)
(Jenkins, Cyril) SA ALLANS 161 s.p. (H886)
(Van Christy) SATB oct BELWIN 2244 $.30 (H887)

O Lovely Peace, With Plenty Crown'd (from
Judas Maccabaeus)
SA,pno SCHIRM.EC 1039 $.30 (H888)
2pt oct HART s.p. (H889)
(Glaser, V.) SSA,pno SCHIRM.EC 1978 $.25 (H890)

O Praise The Lord
(Woodgate) men cor CURWEN 50723 s.p. (H891)

O Praise The Lord With One Consent (Psalm
135) anthem/hymn
SATB,SATB soli,2fl,2ob,2clar,2bsn,2horn,
2trp,3trom,strings,timp voc sc NOVELLO
s.p., ipr (H892)
(Seiffert, M.) "O Preist Den Herrn Mit
Einem Mund" mix cor,SATB soli,org,2ob,
bsn,strings,cembalo voc pt BREITKOPF-L
CHB-2599A+B s.p., ipr (H893)
(Zeimer; Rodby) SATB KJOS $2.00 see from
CHANDOS ANTHEMS (H894)
(Ziemer; Rodby) SATB KJOS V57 $2.00 see
from CHANDOS ANTHEMS (H895)

O Praise The Lord, Ye Angels Of His *anthem/
Bibl
[Eng/Ger] voc sc PETERS HU1959 $2.00, ipr (H896)

O Preist Den Herrn Mit Einem Mund *see O
Praise The Lord With One Consent

O Salutaris
[Lat] unis/2pt CHOUDENS s.p. (H897)

O Savior, Friend And Loving Guide
(Fletcher, Percy) SATB ALLANS 338 s.p. (H898)

O Sing Unto The Lord (Psalm 96) anthem
[Eng/Ger] cor sc PETERS EM508 $5.00, voc sc
PETERS EM508 $1.50, ipa, voc sc PETERS
HU1404 $2.00, ipr see from Chandos
Anthems (H899)
[Eng/Ger] SAB,ST soli,orch HINRICHSEN D1242
sc s.p., cor pts s.p. see from Chandos
Anthems (H900)
(Adler, Samuel) 4pt mix cor,ST soli,pno/org
SCHIRM.G $1.50 see from Chandos Anthems (H901)
(Egidi, A.) "Anthem IV" SAB/SATB,ST soli,
pno,ob,bass,strings VIEWEG voc sc from
Chandos Anthems (H902)
(Graf, Harry) "Anthem IV" SATB,ST soli,
cont,2ob,strings HUG cor pts s.p., voc sc
rental see from Chandos Anthems (H903)
(Grote; Elvers) "O Singet Unserm Gott"
[Eng/Ger] 3pt mix cor,ST soli,ob,bass,
2vln,vcl,bvl BAREN. EM508 sc s.p., cor
pts s.p., ipa see from Chandos Anthems (H904)

O Singet Unserm Gott *see O Sing Unto The
Lord

O Tapfrer Furst (from Belsazar)
mix cor,org,2ob,bsn,2trp,strings,timp sc
BREITKOPF-L rental (H905)

O Thou That Tellest (from Messiah) Xmas
SATB ALLANS 130 s.p. (H906)
cor oct HART s.p. (H907)

O Thou That Tellest Good Tidings *Xmas
SATB oct LORENZ B126 $.30 (H908)

O Thou That Tellest Good Tidings To Zion
(from Messiah) Xmas,anthem/Bibl
SATB oct HARRIS HC4040 $.25 (H909)
4pt mix cor,A solo oct SCHIRM.G 7218 $.40 (H910)
SATB,A solo,pno (diff) oct WILLIS 1955 $.10 (H911)
(Harris) SSA oct PRO ART 2129 $.30 (H912)
(Shaw, Watkins) SATB,solo oct NOVELLO
34.0089.01 s.p. (H913)

O, Wie Wonnig (from Acis Und Galathea)
(Vogel, Moritz; Nagler, Franciscus) [Ger]
wom cor&jr cor,org,opt strings HUG 85
s.p. (H914)

Occasional Oratorio *ora
(Chrysander, Friedrich) cor (Gesellschaft
Edition) sc GREGG ISBN 0:576 28398 3 s.p. (H915)

Ode For St. Cecilia's Day
[Ger/Eng] SATB,orch cmplt ed BROUDE BR.
$15.00 (H916)

Ode On St. Cecilia's Day *cant
BELWIN $1.75 (H917)
SATB,ST soli,org,2fl,2ob,2clar,2bsn,2horn,
2trp,strings,timp,lute voc sc NOVELLO
s.p., ipr (H918)

HANDEL, GEORGE FRIDERIC (cont'd.)

Ode To St. Cecilia *ASD
mix cor voc sc KALMUS 6202 $1.75 (H919)
cor,orch sc KALMUS $12.00, ipa (H920)

Oh, Be Joyful In The Lord
cor voc sc KALMUS 6218 $1.00 see from
CHANDOS ANTHEMS (H921)

Oh Father, Whose Almighty Pow'r (from Judas
Maccabeus) ora
(Burkhart, F.) "Du Gott, Dem Erd' Und
Himmel Schweigt" [Ger/Eng] 4pt wom cor,
cont,2ob,2bsn,strings DOBLINGER voc sc
s.p., cor pts s.p. (H922)
(Burkhart, F.) "Du Gott Dem Erd' Und Himmel
Schweigt" [Ger/Eng] 4pt mix cor,cont,2ob,
2bsn,strings DOBLINGER voc sc s.p., cor
pts s.p. (H923)

Oh First Created Beam (from Samson) ora
(Burkhart, F.) "O Alles Lichtes Quell"
[Ger/Eng] 4pt mix cor,cont,2ob,opt bsn,
strings DOBLINGER voc sc s.p., cor pts
s.p. (H924)

Oh! Had I Jubal's Lyre (from Joshua)
unis,pno SCHIRM.EC 1014 $.30 (H925)
unis,orch oct NOVELLO 33.0034.10 s.p., ipr (H926)
(Gibb, R.) SSA oct PRESSER G-3001 $.35 (H927)

Oh Lamb Of God
(Rodby) SATB MARKS 4178 $.25 (H928)

Oh, Let The Merry Bells Ring Round
(Diack) SA oct FISCHER,C PT-1554 $.25 (H929)

Oh Lord Divine (from Theodora)
(Malin) SATB,orch MARKS 4543 $.30, ipr (H930)

Oh, Praise The Lord *see Oh Praise The Lord
With One Consent

Oh Praise The Lord With One Consent (Psalm
135)
"Oh, Praise The Lord" cor voc sc KALMUS
6212 $1.25 see from CHANDOS ANTHEMS (H931)

Our Lord, Who Chosen Blessings Shed (from
Athalia)
see Choruses For Study And Performance

Paean Of Praise, A *Bibl
(Pasquet) 4pt mix cor,org/pno oct SCHIRM.G
11429 $.30 (H932)

Passion
see Collected Works Gesellschaft Edition 15

Passion, The *Psntd
(Prout, E.) SATB,STB,STBB soli,2ob,2bsn,
strings (abridged) voc sc NOVELLO s.p.,
ipr (H933)

Passion According To St. John
see Collected Works Gesellschaft Edition 15

Passion Music (from Messiah) Easter/Lent
(Read) SSA,opt orch voc sc FISCHER,C
PT-2642 $.75, voc sc FISCHER,C PT-2743
$1.50, ipr, ipa (H934)

Passion Nach B.H. Brockes *see Der Fur Die
Sunden Der Welt Gemarterte Und Sterbende
Jesus

Passion Nach Dem Evangelisten Johannes
*Psntd,evang
(Heilmann; Snell) [Eng/Ger] 4-5pt mix cor,
soli,3vln&vcl&bvl/2fl&2ob&vla&vcl&bvl
BAREN. EM 503 sc s.p., voc sc s.p., cor
pts s.p., ipa (H935)

Passion Of Christ, The
cor sc OXFORD 46.142 $1.00 (H936)
(Darlow, Denys) mix cor,SATB soli,orch/org
(med easy) OXFORD voc sc $3.00, ipr, cor
pts $1.00 (H937)

Praise Be To Thee
(Roskin) SATB HATIKVAH HCL 10 $.35 (H938)

Praise The Lord, O My Heart
(Edmunds) SATB,org oct LAWSON 51382 $.30 (H939)

Praise To God, Who Rules The Earth *see Dio
Si Lode Cielo, In Terra

Prepare The Hymn (from Gelegenheitsoratorium)
ora
(Burkhart, F.) "Stimmt An Den Psalm" [Ger/
Eng] 4pt mix cor,B solo,cont,2ob,opt bsn,
3trp,strings,timp DOBLINGER voc sc s.p.,
cor pts s.p. (H940)

Psalm 27 *see Der Herr Ist Mein Licht

Psalm 42 *see As Pants The Hart

Psalm 42 *see Gern Wallt' Ich Mit Dem Volke
Hin

Psalm 68 *see Let God Arise

Psalm 89 *see My Song Shall Be Alway

Psalm 96 *see O Sing Unto The Lord

Psalm 99 *see My Song Shall Be Alway

Psalm 100 *see Jubilate

Psalm 100 *see O Frohlocke In Dem Herrn

Psalm 109 *see Dixit Dominus

Psalm 109 *see Dixit Dominus Domino Meo

Psalm 112 *see Laudate Pueri Dominum

Psalm 135 *see O Praise The Lord With One
Consent

Psalm 135 *see Oh Praise The Lord With One
Consent

HANDEL, GEORGE FRIDERIC (cont'd.)

Rejoice, Oh Judah! Hallelujah, Amen! (from Judas Maccabeus) ora
(Burkhart, F.) "In Unsere Chore Mischet Euch! Halleluja, Amen!" [Ger/Eng] 4pt mix cor,B solo,cont,2ob,opt bsn,3trp,strings DOBLINGER voc sc s.p., cor pts s.p. (H941)

Rest Of The Weary
(Chambers, H.A.) 2pt oct NOVELLO 53.0287.00 s.p. (H942)

Return, Oh God! (from Samson) ora
(Burkhart, F.) "O Hor, Mein Fleh'n!" [Ger/Eng] 4pt mix cor,A solo,2ob,opt bsn, strings DOBLINGER voc sc s.p., cor pts s.p. (H943)

Solomon *ora
(Raphael, G.; Straube, K.) "Salomo" mix cor,SATB soli,org,2fl,2ob,2bsn,2trp, 2horn,strings,timp,cembalo voc pt BREITKOPF-L CHB-2484A-E s.p., voc sc BREITKOPF-L EB-5310 s.p., ipr (H944)

Sampson *Bibl
(Diack) SATB (abridged version) FISCHER,C PT-2549 $2.25 (H945)

Samson *Bibl/ora
cor voc sc SCHIRM.G $2.50 (H946)
mix cor,SATB soli,2fl,2ob,2clar,2bsn,2trp, 3horn,3trom,strings,timp BREITKOPF-L rental (H947)
SATB,SATB soli,2fl,2ob,2bsn,2horn,2trp, 3trom,strings,timp voc sc NOVELLO s.p., ipr (H948)
(Chrysander, Friedrich) cor (Gesellschaft Edition 10) sc GREGG ISBN 0:576 28362 2 s.p. (H949)
(Doerffel) [Ger] cor voc sc PETERS 63 $7.50 (H950)
(Gervinus) [Eng/Ger] cor voc sc PETERS 3645 $7.50 (H951)
(Prout) SATB,SATB soli,org,2fl,2ob,2clar, 3bsn,4horn,2trp,3trom,strings,timp voc sc NOVELLO s.p., ipr (H952)

Sancta Maria
[Lat] unis/2pt CHOUDENS s.p. (H953)

Sanctus *Sanctus
"Holy, Holy" SATB ALLANS 334 s.p. (H954)

Saul *Gen,Bibl/ora
SATB CHOUDENS voc sc s.p., cor pts s.p. (H955)
SATB,SATB soli,2fl,2ob,2bsn,2trp,3trom, strings,bells,timp voc sc NOVELLO s.p., ipr (H956)
(Chrysander, Friedrich) cor (Gesellschaft Edition 13) sc GREGG ISBN 0:576 28361 4 s.p. (H957)
(Prout) SATB,SATB soli,org,2fl,2ob,2clar, 3bsn,2horn,2trp,3trom,strings,bells,timp voc sc NOVELLO s.p., ipr (H958)
(Young) [Ger] DEUTSCHER 4020A pap s.p., cloth s.p. (H959)
(Young, Percy M.) [Eng/Ger] SATB,SSATB soli,orch (diff) sc BAREN. BA 4020 $34.00, voc sc BAREN. BA 4020A s.p., ipr (H960)

Se, Detta Ar Guds Lamm (from Messias)
cor pts NORDISKA 1234 s.p. (H961)

See, The Conquering Hero Comes (from Judas Maccabaeus)
SATB,pno SCHIRM.EC 1186 $.30, ipr (H962)
SSA SCHIRM.EC 1186 $.15 (H963)

See The Conqu'ring Hero Comes (from Judas Maccabeus) anthem
SATB oct NOVELLO 40.0036.06 s.p. (H964)
(Noble) SSA (easy) OXFORD 54.315 $.40, ipa (H965)

Seht, Er Kommt Mit Preis Gekront (from Judas Maccabaus)
mix cor,org,2fl,2ob,2clar,2bsn,2trp,2horn, 3trom,strings,timp sc BREITKOPF-L rental (H966)
4pt mix cor,2fl,2ob,2clar,2bsn,horn,trp, strings,timp BREITKOPF-W rental (H967)
(Vogel, Moritz; Nagler, Franciscus) [Ger] wom cor&jr cor,org,opt strings HUG 88 s.p. (H968)

Selected Choruses (from Saul) CCU
(Arrin, James) mix cor oct LAWSON $2.00 (H969)

Selected Choruses From The Messiah (from Messiah) CC9L
SATB,pno/org (diff) voc sc WILLIS $.50 (H970)

Semele *Bibl/ora
SATB,SAATB soli,2ob,2bsn,2horn,2trp, strings,timp,cont (abridged) voc sc NOVELLO s.p., ipr (H971)
(Chrysander, Friedrich) cor (Gesellschaft Edition 7) sc GREGG ISBN 0:576 28360 6 s.p. (H972)

Serve The Lord With Gladness
(Harris) SSA/SAA,pno/org oct LAWSON 51300 $.25 (H973)

Shine Out, Great Sun (from Samson)
(Jacques) unis OXFORD 55.815 $.25, ipr (H974)

Silent Worship
(Jacobson) 2pt jr cor/2pt wom cor CURWEN 72199 s.p. (H975)
(Jacobson) 3pt jr cor/3pt wom cor CURWEN 72200 s.p. (H976)
(Somervell) jr cor/wom cor CURWEN 72268 s.p. (H977)

Simson
cor pts NORDISKA 927:8 s.p. (H978)

Since By Man Came Death (from Messiah) Xmas/ Easter,anthem/Bibl
SATB oct PRESSER 332-00911 $.25 (H979)
4pt mix cor oct SCHIRM.G 9871 $.30 (H980)
(Shaw, Watkins) SATB oct NOVELLO 34.0099.09 s.p. (H981)

HANDEL, GEORGE FRIDERIC (cont'd.)

Sing, Oh Ye Heav'ns! (from Belsazar) ora
(Burkhart, F.) "Singt, Himmel!" [Ger/Eng] 4pt mix cor,cont,2ob,opt bsn,strings DOBLINGER voc sc s.p., cor pts s.p. (H982)

Sing To The Lord (from Zadok The Priest)
(Cramer) SATB MARKS 4134 $.30 (H983)
(Cramer, John) SATB WEINBERGER s.p. (H984)

Sing Unto God (from Judas Maccabaeus)
mix cor oct OXFORD 46.167 $4.00 (H985)
SATB oct GRAY GCMR 1837 $.25 (H986)
(Condie) mix cor SOUTHERN $.30 (H987)
(Condie) SATB oct FISCHER,C CM-7414 $.30 (H988)
(Ehret, W.) SATB oct PRESSER MC363 $.40 (H989)

Sing Ye To The Lord! (from Israel In Agypten) ora
(Burkhart, F.) "Singet Unserem Gott!" [Ger/Eng] 8pt mix cor,S/T solo,cont,2ob,opt bsn,2trp,3trom,strings,timp DOBLINGER voc sc s.p., cor pts s.p. (H990)

Singet Unserem Gott! *see Sing Ye To The Lord!

Singt, Himmel! *see Sing, Oh Ye Heav'ns!

Singt Unserm Gott, Ihr Reiche Aller Welt *Marriage,anthem/Bibl
"Wedding Anthem" 4pt mix cor,org,2ob,bsn, 2trp,strings,timp BREITKOPF-W sc s.p., voc pt s.p., ipa (H991)

Smiling Dawn Of Happy Days (from Jephtha)
unis,pno SCHIRM.EC 1015 $.15 (H992)

So Wie Der Hirsch *see As Pants The Hart

So Wie Der Hirsch Nach Wasser Schreit *see As Pants The Hart

Solomon *Bibl/ora
SATB,SSSSATBB soli,2fl,2ob,2bsn,2horn,2trp, strings,timp voc sc NOVELLO s.p., ipr (H993)
(Chrysander, Friedrich) cor (Gesellschaft Edition 26) sc GREGG ISBN 0:576 28359 2 s.p. (H994)
(Diack) SATB,opt orch (abridged version) FISCHER,C PT-195 $2.25, ipr (H995)
(Krone) SATB KJOS VK320 $2.50 (H996)

Sorge Nel Petto (from Rinaldo) anthem
"Lord Of Our Being" unis oct NOVELLO 48.1037.06 s.p. (H997)
"Lord Of Our Being" 2pt oct NOVELLO 48.1651.10 s.p. (H998)
"Lord Of Our Being" [Eng/It] mix cor oct NOVELLO 40.1137.06 s.p. (H999)
(Pisano) "Lord Of Our Being" SAB oct PLYMOUTH PCS-202 $.25 (H1000)

Soul, Adorn Thyself With Gladness *Commun/Gen
(Hines) SAB,kbd (med easy) oct CONCORDIA 98-1844 $.25 (H1001)

Soul, Array Thyself
(Coggin) 4pt men cor,org/pno oct SCHIRM.G 11700 $.30 (H1002)

Sound An Alarm (from Messiah)
(Noble) TTBB (easy) OXFORD 51.704 $.65 (H1003)

St. John Passion *Easter/Holywk/Lent
SATB,opt strings FISCHER,C PT-348 $1.75, ipr (H1004)
[Eng/Ger] SATTB,SATB soli,orch HINRICHSEN D1191 voc sc s.p., cor pts s.p. (H1005)
(Heilmann) [Eng/Ger] SATTB,SATB soli,orch voc sc PETERS EM503 $5.00, sc PETERS EM503A $20.00, voc pt PETERS EM503A $1.50, ipa (H1006)

St. John Passion, The *see Johannespassion

St. John's Passion *see Johannespassion

Stimmt An Den Psalm *see Prepare The Hymn

Strengthen Us, O Lord
SATB PATERSON 1634 s.p. (H1007)

Surely He Hath Borne Our Griefs (from Messiah) Xmas/Easter/Lent,anthem/Bibl
SATB oct LORENZ 9245 $.30 (H1008)
SATB oct PRESSER 332-00912 $.25 (H1009)
SATB oct PRO ART 1312 $.25 (H1010)
4pt mix cor oct SCHIRM.G 6598 $.25 (H1011)
SATB oct FISCHER,C CM-518 $.25 (H1012)
(Palmer) SATB ALFRED 6435 $.25 (H1013)
(Shaw, Watkins) SATB oct NOVELLO 34.0098.00 s.p. (H1014)

Sweet Day *anthem
SSA oct FISCHER,C PT-1584 $.25 (H1015)

Sweet Is The Name Of Jesus
unis oct AGAPE A 391 $.25 (H1016)

Swell The Full Chorus (from Solomon)
(Ehret) mix cor CHAPPELL 0023481-358 $.40 (H1017)
(Ohl) TTBB oct PLYMOUTH FO-300 $.25 (H1018)

Tantum Ergo
[Lat] unis/2pt CHOUDENS s.p. (H1019)

Te Deum Laudamus *Te Deum
(Elvers; Grote) "We Praise Thee" [Eng/Ger] cor sc PETERS EM509 $7.50 (H1020)
(Elvers; Grote) "We Praise Thee" [Eng/Ger] cor voc sc PETERS EM509 $1.50, ipa (H1021)
(Kiel) "We Praise Thee" [Eng] cor voc sc PETERS HU1713 $2.00, ipr (H1022)

Tell It Out
(Gillman, W.) SATB oct PRESSER G-4004 $.35 (H1023)

Thanks Be To Thee *see Dank Sei Dir, Herr

Thanks Be To Thee, O Lord! (from Cantata Con Stromenti)
(Saar, L.) SATB,A solo,pno SCHIRM.EC 1732

HANDEL, GEORGE FRIDERIC (cont'd.)

$.30, ipr (H1024)

Thanks To Thee, O Lord *Gen
(Ganschow) SATB SCHMITT 1540 $.35 (H1025)

Theme Sublime Of Endless Praise (from Jephtha)
(Malin) SATB,orch MARKS 4465 $.40 (H1026)

Then Round About The Starry Throne (from Samson) ora
SATB oct PRO ART 1314 $.25 (H1027)
SATB,pno SCHIRM.EC 305 $.35, ipr (H1028)
SATB,org SCHIRM.EC 1702 $.30 (H1029)
oct HART (H1030)
(Burkhart, F.) "Dann Wird Zum Gold'nen Sternenzelt" [Ger/Eng] 4pt mix cor,cont, 2ob,opt bsn,strings DOBLINGER voc sc s.p., cor pts s.p. (H1031)
(Christy) mix cor,acap oct SCHIRM.G 8369 $.35 (H1032)
(Woodworth, G.) TTBB,pno SCHIRM.EC 907 $.25 (H1033)

Then Round The Starry Throne
SATB ALLANS 79 s.p. (H1034)

Then Shall They Know (from Samson) ora
(Burkhart, F.) "Dann Sollt Ihr Seh'n" [Ger/Eng] mix cor,cont,2ob,opt bsn,strings DOBLINGER voc sc s.p., cor pts s.p. (H1035)

Theodora *ora
mix cor,SAATTB soli,org,2fl,2ob,2bsn,2trp, 2horn,strings,timp,cembalo BREITKOPF-L rental (H1036)

They Have Taken Away The Lord
(Davis, K.K.) SATB MARKS 4434 $.30 (H1037)

Thine Is The Glory
SATB oct LORENZ A433 $.25 (H1038)

Thou Art The King Of Glory
(Cramer) SATB,opt B solo MARKS 4282 $.25 (H1039)

Thron'd High In Heaven (from St. John Passion)
SA,pno SCHIRM.EC 1044 $.15 (H1040)

Thy Spirit Floweth Free
(Rodby) SATB MARKS 4218 $.25 (H1041)

To Song And Dance (from Samson) ora
(Burkhart, F.) "Zu Sang Und Tanz" [Ger/Eng] 4pt mix cor,cont,2ob,opt bsn,2trp,strings DOBLINGER voc sc s.p., cor pts s.p. (H1042)

To Thee Cherubin
SATB,trp oct STAFF 673 $.30 (H1043)

Trauer-Hymne *anthem/funeral
(Reich) "Funeral Anthem" [Eng/Ger] SATB, SATB soli,cont,2ob,2vln,vla HANSSLER 10.212 sc $15.00, voc sc $2.50, ipa (H1044)

Trauerhymne *hymn
(Seiffert, M.) mix cor,SATB soli,org,2ob, bsn,strings,cembalo BREITKOPF-L rental (H1045)

Trumpet Shall Sound, The (from Messiah)
(Williams) men cor CURWEN 50727 s.p. (H1046)

Trust In The Lord (from Xerxes)
(Damrosch, F.) 4pt men cor oct SCHIRM.G 1441 $.20 (H1047)
(Jaeger) 3pt wom cor,pno/harp,org oct SCHIRM.G 413 $.25 (H1048)
(Mueller) SABar oct SCHIRM.G 8696 $.25 (H1049)

Uns Hat Gott Den Helden Hergesandt (from Judas Makkabaus)
(Vogel, Moritz; Nagler, Franciscus) [Ger] wom cor&jr cor,org,opt strings HUG 86 s.p. (H1050)

Unto Us A Child Is Born (from Messiah) Xmas, cant
(Shaw, Watkins) 2pt&opt cor voc sc NOVELLO 20.0017.02 s.p. (H1051)

Utrecht Jubilate (Psalm 100) Jubil
[Swed] cor pts NORDISKA 1280 s.p. (H1052)
SATB,ATB soli,org,2fl,2ob,2clar,2bsn,2horn, 2trp,3trom,strings,timp voc sc NOVELLO s.p., ipr (H1053)
cor voc sc KALMUS 6207 $2.00 (H1054)
cor,orch sc KALMUS $8.00, ipa (H1055)

Utrecht Te Deum *Te Deum
[Lat/Eng] SSAATTBB,SSTTB soli,orch voc sc PETERS EM505 $7.50, sc PETERS EM505A $20.00, voc pt PETERS EM505A $1.50, ipa (H1056)
[Eng/Ger] SSAATTB,SSTTB soli,orch HINRICHSEN D1246 voc sc s.p., cor pts s.p. (H1057)
cor,orch sc KALMUS $8.00, ipa (H1058)
(Shaw, Watkins) SATB,fl,2ob,bsn,2trp, strings,cont voc sc NOVELLO s.p., ipr (H1059)

Utrecht Te Deum & Jubilate
see Collected Works gesellschaft Ed. Volumes 11 & 31

Vater Der Gnade *see Father Of Mercy

Verdant Meadows
(Platt) 2pt oct PLYMOUTH PCS-521 $.30 (H1060)

Was Betrubst Du Dich Meine Seele
(Hellmann) SA,cont,2rec HANSSLER 5.067 s.p. (H1061)

We Believe That Thou Shalt Come (from Dettingen Te Deum)
(Herrmann) SSATB,org/pno oct SCHIRM.G 11535 $.25 (H1062)
(Herrmann) 4pt wom cor,org/pno oct SCHIRM.G 11536 $.25 (H1063)

We Come In Bright Array (from Judas Maccabeus) ora
(Burkhart, F.) "Wohlan! Wir Folgen Gern" [Ger/Eng] 4pt mix cor,cont,2ob,opt bsn, strings DOBLINGER voc sc s.p., cor pts s.p. (H1064)

HANDEL, GEORGE FRIDERIC (cont'd.)

We Come To Praise His Name (from Judas
Maccabeus)
(Wiley) SAB oct PRO ART 2742 $.30   (H1065)

We Hear (from Judas Maccabeus)
(Berger) SAB oct FOX PS135 $.25   (H1066)

We Never Will Bow Down (from Judas Maccabeus)
anthem
SATB oct NOVELLO 34.0137.05 s.p.   (H1067)

We Praise Thee *see Chandos Te Deum

We Praise Thee *see Te Deum Laudamus

We Praise Thee, O God
(Ehret) SATB SHAWNEE A 853 $.30   (H1068)

We Will Never Bow Down
SATB,S solo ALLANS 128 s.p.   (H1069)

Wedding Anthem *see Singt Unserm Gott, Ihr
Reiche Aller Welt

Wedding Chorus (from Alceste)
SATB,pno BROUDE BR. $.35   (H1070)

Welcome, Welcome Christmas Morn *Xmas
(Kirk) SSA oct PRO ART 2477 $.25   (H1071)

When His Loud Voice (from Jephtha)
SATB,pno SCHIRM.EC 1122 $.35, ipr   (H1072)
(Davison, A.; Beveridge, L.) TTBB,pno
SCHIRM.EC 937 $.40, ipr   (H1073)

Where'er I Roam Or Linger
(Spross, C.) SATB oct PRESSER 322-35414
$.30   (H1074)

Where'er You Walk (from Semele)
see FOLK-SONGS, BALLADS AND SONGS OF GREAT
COMPOSERS (SET V)
unis,pno SCHIRM.EC 426 $.25, ipr   (H1075)
(Clough-Leighter, H.) SA oct SCHIRM.EC 439
$.25, ipr   (H1076)
(Davis, K.) SSA,pno SCHIRM.EC 1842 $.35
                                   (H1077)

Wir Preisen Dich, O Gott *Jubil/Te Deum
mix cor,SATB soli,org,fl,2ob,bsn,2trp,
strings,cembalo BREITKOPF-L rental
contains also: O Be Joyful In The Lord,
"O Frohlocke In Dem Herrn"   (H1078)

With A Voice Of Praise *anthem
(McEwen) SATB,opt inst oct FISCHER,C
ZCM-106 $.30, ipa   (H1079)

With Cheerful Notek *anthem
SATB oct NOVELLO 28.1188.10 s.p. see from
CHANDOS ANTHEMS   (H1080)

With Cheerful Notes (from Sixth Chandos
Anthem) anthem
mix cor oct NOVELLO 28.1188.10 s.p. (H1081)
(Ehret, W.) SATB oct PRESSER MC351 $.40
                                   (H1082)

With Cheerful Notes Let All The Earth *see
As Pants The Hart

Wohlan! Wir Folgen Gern *see We Come In
Bright Array

Worthy Is The Lamb (from Messiah) Xmas,
anthem/Bibl
SATB ALLANS 112 s.p.   (H1083)
4pt mix cor oct SCHIRM.G 5426 $.30 (H1084)
SATB oct LESLIE 4046   (H1085)
(Shaw, Watkins) SATB oct NOVELLO 34.0134.00
s.p. contains also: Amen   (H1086)

Worthy Is The Lamb, That Was Slain (from
Messiah) Xmas/Easter
SATB oct PRESSER 312-20350 $.30   (H1087)
SATB oct PRO ART 1387 $.25   (H1088)
SATB,pno (diff) oct WILLIS 2686 $.15
                                   (H1089)

oct HART   (H1090)

Xerxes
[Ger] SATB,acap voc sc PETERS 3792 $7.50
                                   (H1091)

Ye Sons Of Israel, Now Lament (from Samson)
(Larsen, Jens Peter) "Israels Klage Ved
Samsons Dod" [Eng/Ger] SATB,soli,orch
HANSEN-DEN 24346 s.p., ipa   (H1092)

Your Voices Raise *see As Pants The Hart

Your Voices Raise, Ye Cherubim
(Davison, A.) TTBB,pno SCHIRM.EC 86 $.35
                                   (H1093)

Zadok Der Priester *see Zadok, The Priest

Zadok The Priest *Fest/Royal,anthem/ora
SATB ALLANS 275 s.p. see from Coronation
Anthems   (H1094)
SATB oct GRAY GCMR 3205 $.35   (H1095)
SSAATBB oct GRAY GCM 2646 $.25   (H1096)
SSAATBB oct NOVELLO 34.0149.09 s.p. (H1097)
SATB oct NOVELLO 34.0822.01 s.p.   (H1098)
SSAATBB oct NOVELLO 34.0149.09 s.p. (H1099)
SATB oct NOVELLO 34.0822.01 s.p.   (H1100)
"Zadok Der Priester" 7pt mix cor,2fl,2ob,
2clar,2bsn,3trp,2horn,3trom,strings,timp
sc BREITKOPF-L rental   (H1101)
(Herrmann, William) 7pt mix cor,org/pno voc
sc SCHIRM.G $1.00 see from Coronation
Anthems   (H1102)

Zu Sang Und Tanz *see To Song And Dance

HANDEL'S CHRISTMAS MESSIAH see Handel, George
Frideric

HANDEL'S EASTER MESSIAH see Handel, George
Frideric

HANDEL'S LARGO see Handel, George Frideric

HANEROS HALOLU see Adler, Hugo Ch.

HANEROT HALALU *Xmas/Hanakkah
(Chass, Blanche) SATB FOSTER MF 677 $.35
                                   (H1103)

HANFF, JOHANN NICOLAUS (1665-1711)
Alleluja, Der Tod Ist Verschlungen *Easter,
cant
(Grote, Gottfried) [Ger] SSB,SSB soli,bsn,
2vln,vcl,bvl BAREN. EM 1002 sc s.p., cor
pts s.p.   (H1104)

HANFORD, GEORGE
Long Have I Lifted Up
SSATB,acap PETERS H1561   (H1105)

HANKEY
All Things Bright And Beautiful
(Cole) SATB,opt gtr (med easy) SOUTHERN
$.40   (H1106)

HANKEY, MARK
All Things Bright And Beautiful *hymn
SATB MARKS 4573 $.40   (H1107)
cong,pno/org WEINBERGER s.p. contains also:
Gracious Spirit Holy Ghost   (H1108)

Christian, Seek Not Ye Repose
(Hutson) unis MARKS 4558 $.30   (H1109)

Eight Songs To Sing About Christmas *CC8U,
Xmas
unis MARKS $1.25   (H1110)

Eight Songs To Sing About Christmas *CC8U,
Xmas
WEINBERGER s.p.   (H1111)

Five Songs For Five To Ten (composed with
Ross, Toni) *CC5U,hymn/pop
jr cor cmplt ed WEINBERGER $1.25   (H1112)

Gracious Spirit Holy Ghost
see Hankey, Mark, All Things Bright And
Beautiful

Magnificat *Bibl/Magnif
voc sc WEINBERGER s.p. contains also: Nunc
Dimittis (Nunc)   (H1113)

Nunc Dimittis
see Hankey, Mark, Magnificat

O Happy Band Of Pilgrims
(Hutson) unis MARKS 4562 $.30   (H1114)

HANKINSON, RICHARD
Child Of Bethlehem, The *Xmas,anthem
SATB,pno (easy) oct MCAFEE M1028 $.35
                                   (H1115)

HANKS
Heavens Declare His Glory, The *Xmas
(Wilson) 2pt mix cor oct AGAPE CF 156 $.25
                                   (H1116)

How Lost Can A Man Be?
(Wilson) SATB oct AGAPE CF 133 $.30 (H1117)

Lonely Voices *see Voces Tristes

Voces Tristes
(Wilson) "Lonely Voices" SSA oct AGAPE
CF137 $.30   (H1118)
(Wilson) "Lonely Voices" SATB oct AGAPE
CF 101 $.30   (H1119)
(Wilson) "Lonely Voices" SAB oct AGAPE
CF 99 $.30   (H1120)
(Wilson) "Lonely Voices" SATB oct AGAPE
CF 135 $.30   (H1121)

Who Are You To Disagree?
(Wilson) SATB oct AGAPE CF 120 $.30 (H1122)

HANKS, BILLIE
Folk Songs For Choirs *CCU,evang/folk
cor oct AGAPE $1.25   (H1123)

HANKS, SYBIL A.
Creation, The *cant
SATB TRANSCON. TCL 116 $1.50, ipa (H1124)

Quiet My Heart
SATB TRANSCON. TCL 115 $.25   (H1125)

HANNAHS, R.C.
Alleluia *Allelu
mix cor&treb cor,org oct ELKAN-V 362-1113
$.30   (H1126)

Cantata For The Nativity *cant
SATB&treb cor oct ELKAN-V $1.25   (H1127)

Choral Songs For Christmas *see Dormi Jesu,
"Manger Song"; Nowell   (H1128)

Dormi Jesu *Xmas
"Manger Song" [Lat] SSA,acap AMP A632 $.30
see from Choral Songs For Christmas (H1129)

Manger Song *see Dormi Jesu

Missa Brevis *Mass
SATB oct ELKAN-V 362-1101 $.60   (H1130)

Nowell *Xmas
SSA,acap AMP A633 $.30 see from Choral
Songs For Christmas   (H1131)

HANNAHS, ROGER
Hosanna To The Son Of David *Palm
SATB oct GRAY GCMR 2631 $.30   (H1132)

O Praise The Lord From The Heavens
SATB,org GRAY GCMR 3270 $.35   (H1133)

HANNAY
Carol *Xmas,carol
SATB oct GALAXY 1.2340.1 $.30   (H1134)

Christmas-Tide *Xmas
TTBB oct GALAXY 1.2341.1 $.35   (H1135)

HANNIKAINEN, ILMARI
Fardemannens Psalm *Psalm
men cor NORDISKA 4224 s.p.   (H1136)

Fardemannens Psalm *Psalm
mix cor NORDISKA 4226 s.p.   (H1137)

HANNUKKAH TIME *Hanakkah
(Schillio) SATB oct PRO ART 2594 $.35 (H1138)

HANSEN
Hymns And Anthems For Male Voices *CCU,
anthem/hymn
men cor KJOS $1.50   (H1139)

I Know The Lord's Laid His Hand On Me *spir
SATB SCHMITT 7041 $.35   (H1140)

I Know The Lord's Laid His Hands On Me *spir
SATB,acap SOUTHERN $.35   (H1141)

HANSEN, CARL WILLUM
Den Yndigste Rose Er Funden *Xmas,cant
[Norw] 2pt mix cor,solo,2vln,org/pno cor
pts LYCHE s.p.   (H1142)

Liten Julkantate *Xmas,cant
[Norw] 2pt,soli LYCHE s.p.   (H1143)

HANSEN'S JR. CHORAL SERIES see McAfee, Don

HANSON
Cherubic Hymn *hymn
SATB,opt orch FISCHER,C O-3659 $1.00, ipr
                                   (H1144)

How Excellent Thy Name
SATB oct FISCHER,C CM-6806 $.30   (H1145)
SSAA oct FISCHER,C CM-6706 $.30   (H1146)

Praise We The Lord (from Merry Mount)
(Campbell; Watson) SATB,2pno WARNER H2041
$.30, ipa   (H1147)

Psalm 121
SATB oct FISCHER,C CM-7700 $.30   (H1148)

Psalm 150
SATB oct FISCHER,C CM-7699 $.30   (H1149)

Streams In The Desert
SATB,opt orch FISCHER,C O-4804 $1.50, ipr
                                   (H1150)

HANSON, WESLEY
Praise Ye The Lord, The Almighty
SATB,opt brass oct AGAPE F 911 $.35 (H1151)

Praise Ye The Triune God
SATB,opt brass oct AGAPE F 902 $.35 (H1152)

HANSSLER, FRIEDRICH (1892-1972)
Befiehl Du Deine Wege Und
TTBB HANSSLER 6.2354 s.p.   (H1153)

Such, Wer Da Will
see Stobaeus, Johann, Such, Wer Da Will,
Ein Ander Ziel

HANUKKAH CANDLES see Sellew, Donald E.

HANUKKAH MADRIGAL see Mi Y'mallel

HANUKKAH OF THE MACCABEES see Binder, Abraham
Wolfe

HANUKKAH SONG see Mi Y'mallel

HANUKKAH SONG see Sellew, Donald E.

HAPPIER WAY, THE see Buffum

HAPPIEST CHRISTMAS DAY see Tucker, Irene

HAPPILY SINGING *Xmas,carol,So Am
(Ehret, Walter) SATB oct WALTON 2528 $.30
                                   (H1154)
(Ehret, Walter) SATB,opt inst oct WALTON 2528
$.30   (H1155)
(Ehret, Walter) SSA,opt inst oct WALTON 2530
$.30   (H1156)

HAPPY AND BLEST ARE THEY see Mendelssohn-
Bartholdy, Felix

HAPPY ARE THEY THAT DWELL IN THY HOUSE see
Berger

HAPPY ARE THY MEN see Poston, Elizabeth

HAPPY BETHLEHEM see Donostia, [Jose Antonio
de], Oi Betleem

HAPPY BIRTHDAY BABY JESUS see Gerald, M.B.

HAPPY CHRISTMAS COMES ONCE MORE *Xmas,Dan
(Barthelson) SSA oct VOLKWEIN VB167 $.25
                                   (H1157)

HAPPY CHRISTMAS COMES ONCE MORE see Barthelson

HAPPY CHRISTMAS EVE *Xmas,Norw
(Barnard) SA SCHMITT 2561 $.20   (H1158)

HAPPY CHRISTMAS, THE see Balle, C.

HAPPY DAY, THE see Shaw, Geoffrey [Turton]

HAPPY EASTER see Grime, William

HAPPY FLOCKS IN SAFETY WANDER see Bach, Johann
Sebastian, Schafe Konnen Sicher Weiden

HAPPY IS THE MAN see Berger, Jean

HAPPY IS THE MAN WHO FINDS WISDOM see Clark,
Keith

HAPPY JOURNEY, THE see Jonson, William

HAPPY JUBILEE, THE see Pace, Robert

HAPPY MEADOW, THE see Mellers, Wilfrid Howard

HAPPY MORNING see Kennedy, John Brodbin

HAPPY SIDE OF LIFE, THE see Smith

HAPPY SIDE, THE *CC8UL
(Skillings, Otis) jr cor,pno,gtr cmplt ed
LILLENAS MB-062 $1.50 contains works by:
Skillings, Otis   (H1159)

HAPPY THE MAN see Temple, S.

HAPPY THE MAN WHO FEARS THE LORD see Proulx,
Richard

HAPPY THE NATION see Sowerby, Leo

HAR AR GUDAGOTT ATT VARA see Wennerberg, Gunnar

HARCI DAL see Handel, George Frideric

D'HARCOURT, [EUGENE] (1859-1918)
O Salutaris Hostia *mot
[Fr/Lat] 3 eq voices,org,vln,vcl,harp
LEMOINE voc sc s.p., cor pts s.p. (H1160)

HARD TRAILS see Still, William Grant

HARDER
Children's Prayer *prayer
(Frank) 2pt treb cor FRANK E-135 $.30
(H1161)

HARDING, G.P.
Brightest And Best Of The Sons Of The Morning
*Xmas/Epiph
(Kinsman) SATB oct PRO ART 2438 $.25
(H1162)

His Arms Are Open To Everyone
SA&unis/SA/unis oct HUNTZINGER 7047 $.20
(H1163)

SATB oct HUNTZINGER 7044 $.20
(H1164)

House Of Prayer, The
(Leighton) SATB oct HUNTZINGER 7054 $.20
(H1165)

HARDING, HARVEY
Jesus, My Lord
SATB oct HUNTZINGER 7045 $.20
(H1166)
SAB oct HUNTZINGER 7046 $.20
(H1167)

O, Be Joyful
SATB oct HUNTZINGER 4052 $.20
(H1168)
SSA oct HUNTZINGER 509 $.18
(H1169)

HARDING, JULIUS DAYLE
Lord Of All Nations, Grant Me Grace *Gen
SATB,kbd (med easy) oct CONCORDIA 98-2128
$.35
(H1170)

HARDING, PHYLLIS
God Bless Me
3pt ASHDOWN V.T.44 s.p.
(H1171)

HARDT
Blessing, A
SSA GENERAL 757CH $.45
(H1172)
SATB GENERAL 758CH $.45
(H1173)

HARDWICKE
Birthday Of A King, The *Xmas
SA ALFRED 6121 $.25
(H1174)

Blessed Be That Maid Marie *Xmas
SAB ALFRED 6502 $.30
(H1175)
SSA ALFRED 6172 $.30
(H1176)

My Shepherd Will Supply My Need
SATB ALFRED 6377 $.30
(H1177)

Shepherds, Shake Off Your Drowsy Sleep *Xmas
SAB ALFRED 6522 $.35
(H1178)
SA ALFRED 6144 $.35
(H1179)

Sing Ye To The Infant King *Xmas
SSA ALFRED 6227 $.30
(H1180)

Sweet Be Thy Slumber *Xmas
SAB ALFRED 6525 $.25
(H1181)
SA ALFRED 6148 $.25
(H1182)

HARDWICKE, ARTHUR
Hail The Tidings *Xmas,anthem,Carib
SA,bells,opt drums,opt tamb HERITAGE H5008
$.35
(H1183)

HARDY
See The Star *see Palmer, William J.

HARDY, B. EDWARD
Keep Me Near Thee
see TWO PRAYER SONGS

HARE, N.
He's Got The Whole World In His Hands
SATB,acap oct PRESSER MC215 $.30 (H1184)

HARK! A THRILLING VOICE see Butler, Eugene

HARK! A THRILLING VOICE IS SOUNDING see Monk

HARK! A THRILLING VOICE IS SOUNDING see Thiman,
Eric Harding

HARK! A THRILLING VOICE IS SOUNDING see
Wetzler, Robert

HARK! ALL AROUND THE WELKIN RINGS *Xmas,carol
(Anderson, W.H.) SATB oct LESLIE 4017 see
from Two Christmas Carols Set 3 (H1185)

HARK, ALL YE LOVELY SAINTS
(Weelkes, T.; Davison, A.) TTBB,acap
SCHIRM.EC 916 $.20 (H1186)

HARK, ALL YE LOVELY SAINTS see Weelkes, Frag
Nur Umher

HARK, ALL YE LOVELY SAINTS ABOVE see Weelkes,
Thomas

HARK! ANGEL CAROLS see Lovelace, Austin C.

HARK! BETHLEHEM see Dzisiaj W Betlejem

HARK FROM THE TOMB see Jonson, William

HARK, HARK, HARK
see Colonial Christmas Carols

HARK, HARK, MY SOUL see Ambrose, [Paul]

HARK! HARK! MY SOUL see Buck, Dudley

HARK, HARK, MY SOUL see Shelley, [Harry Rowe]

HARK! HARK! WHAT NEWS THE ANGELS BRING see
Ratcliffe, Desmond

HARK, I HEAR THE HARPS ETERNAL *hymn
(Parker) mix cor,acap oct LAWSON 51331 $.30
(H1187)

HARK, NOW, O SHEPHERDS
(Luvaas) SSAATTBB oct SUMMY B 840 $.45
(H1188)

HARK, NOW, O SHEPHERDS see Stellhorn, August W.

HARK TEN THOUSAND HARPS *anthem/hymn
(Ehret, W.) SATB ALLANS 438 s.p. (H1189)

HARK, TEN THOUSAND HARPS AND VOICES see Cain,
Noble

HARK! TEN THOUSAND HARPS AND VOICES see
Markworth, Henry

HARK! TEN THOUSAND HARPS AND VOICES see Mason

HARK TEN THOUSAND VOICES *hymn
(Ehret, Walter) SATB ALLANS 438 s.p. (H1190)

HARK! TEN THOUSAND VOICES SOUNDING see
Worthing, Richard

HARK! THE GLAD SOUND *Xmas
(Kinsman) SATB oct PRO ART 1939 $.22 (H1191)

HARK, THE GLAD SOUND! see Davies, G.W.

HARK! THE GLAD SOUND! see Davies, Henry Walford

HARK, THE GLAD SOUND see Powell

HARK, THE GLAD SOUND see Smart, David

HARK THE GLAD SOUND see Stafford, F.J.

HARK THE GLAD SOUND see Thiman, Eric Harding

HARK! THE GLAD TIDINGS *Xmas
(Coggin) SATB oct PRO ART 2578 $.35 (H1192)
(Coggin) SAB oct PRO ART 2430 $.25 (H1193)
(Coggin) SSA oct PRO ART 2583 $.30 (H1194)

HARK THE HERALD ANGELS SING *carol
see Glory To The Newborn King
see Many Moods Of Christmas, The, Suite Three
(Dello Joio) SATB,2pno MARKS 4569 $.50
(H1195)

HARK! THE HERALD ANGELS SING see Harris

HARK! THE HERALD ANGELS SING see Lorenz

HARK! THE HERALD ANGELS SING see Martin

HARK! THE HERALD ANGELS SING see Mendelssohn-
Bartholdy, Felix

HARK THE SONG OF JUBILEE see Finlay

HARK!THE SONG OF JUBILEE see Robson, R. Walker

HARK THE SONG OF JUBILEE see Whitehead

HARK! THE SOUND OF HOLY VOICES see Bode, Arnold
G.H.

HARK! THE SOUND OF HOLY VOICES see Monk

HARK THE VESPER HYMN see Gratton, Frank L.

HARK, THE VESPER HYMN IS STEALING *Russ
(Stevenson) 4pt mix cor,S solo oct SCHIRM.G
2626 $.25 (H1196)

HARK! THE VESPER HYMN IS STEALING see Grant

HARK! THE VESPER HYMN IS STEALING see Stevenson

HARK! 'TIS THE WATCHMAN'S CRY see Parkyn, W.

HARK TO THE ANGELS *Xmas,carol
(Roseberry, Eric) SATB oct FABER F0289 $.35
contains also: Polish Tune, (Pol) (H1197)

HARK TO THE TIDING see Saint-Saens, Camille

HARK! WHAT MEAN THOSE HOLY VOICES *Xmas
(Kinsman) SATB oct PRO ART 1973 $.22 (H1198)
(Kinsman) SSA oct PRO ART 2114 $.22 (H1199)

HARK! WHAT MEAN THOSE HOLY VOICES see Bliss,
Paul

HARK! WHAT MEAN THOSE HOLY VOICES see Mueller,
Carl F.

HARK! WHAT MEAN THOSE HOLY VOICES see Turner-
Maley, F.

HARK! WHAT MEAN THOSE HOLY VOICES? see Warren,
Elinor Remick

HARK YE! THE LORD COMES WITH HIS THOUSANDS see
Buxtehude, Dietrich, Siehe! Der Herr Kommt
Mit Viel Tausend

HARKEN TO ME MOTHER DEAR
see Czech Christmas Carols

HARKEN UNTO ME see Owen, Blythe

HARKER, CLIFFORD
Bread Of The World
see Two Introits

Come, My Way, My Truth
see Two Introits

Magnificat And Nunc Dimittis *Magnif/Nunc
unis (D maj) oct NOVELLO 44.1289.03 s.p.
(H1200)

O Lord God *anthem
SAB/SATB oct NOVELLO 50.0339.03 s.p.
(H1201)

SAT/SAB oct NOVELLO 50.0339.03 s.p. (H1202)

Te Deum *Te Deum
4pt mix cor oct SCHIRM.G 11257 $.30 (H1203)

Two Introits *anthem/Introit
mix cor,acap oct NOVELLO 50.0324.05 s.p.
contains: Bread Of The World; Come, My
Way, My Truth (H1204)

HARKER, F. FLAXINGTON (1876-1936)
As It Began To Dawn *Easter,Bibl
4pt mix cor,high solo oct SCHIRM.G 4535
$.25 (H1205)
3pt wom cor oct SCHIRM.G 5818 $.25 (H1206)

Calm On The List'ning Ear Of Night
3pt wom cor&4pt mix cor,med solo,Bar solo,
vln,vcl oct SCHIRM.G 5246 $.25 (H1207)

HARKER, F. FLAXINGTON (cont'd.)

Cross, The *Op.50, Lent,cant
cor,SATBarB soli,pno voc sc SCHIRM.G $1.00
(H1208)

God Shall Wipe Away All Tears
4pt mix cor oct SCHIRM.G 8638 $.25 (H1209)

Grant, We Beseech Thee *Bibl
4pt mix cor,high solo oct SCHIRM.G 7081
$.25 (H1210)

How Beautiful Upon The Mountains *Bibl
4pt mix cor,SMez soli oct SCHIRM.G 7255
$.35 (H1211)
3pt wom cor,S solo oct SCHIRM.G 7876 $.30
(H1212)
(Sacco) 3pt mix cor oct SCHIRM.G 10634 $.35
(H1213)

Like As The Hart Desireth The Water-Brooks
*Bibl
(Downing) 4pt mix cor oct SCHIRM.G 8637
$.25 (H1214)

O Lord Most Holy
4pt mix cor,S solo oct SCHIRM.G 5291 $.20
(H1215)

Star Of Bethlehem, The *Xmas,cant
mix cor,soli,org voc sc SCHIRM.G $1.00
(H1216)

Turn Ye Even To Me *Bibl
4pt mix cor,low solo oct SCHIRM.G 6425 $.30
(H1217)
(Deis) SAB,A solo oct SCHIRM.G 10026 $.25
(H1218)

HARKER, JEANNE
Old Testament, The *Bibl
mix cor CURWEN 61551 s.p. (H1219)

Old Testament, The
4pt mix cor,opt gtr CURWEN 11543 $.25
(H1220)

HARKNESS
Gethsemane *Easter/Psntd
(Umstead) SATB oct LILLENAS AN-2304 $.25
(H1221)

Such Love
(Williams) SATB oct LILLENAS AN-1139 $.30
(H1222)

When I See My Saviour
(Wilson) SATB oct AGAPE GC 802 $.25 (H1223)

Why Should He Love Me So?
(Collins; Bussell) SATB oct LILLENAS
AT-1040 $.30 (H1224)

HARKNESS, ROBERT
'Tis Jesus
(Husted) SATB ALLANS 458 s.p. (H1225)

HARLIG AR JORDEN *Xmas,hymn
(Wikander, David) mix cor NORDISKA 1268 s.p.
(H1226)

HARLIG AR JORDEN see Ek, Gunnar

HARMAN, C.
Hymn To The Virgin, A *BVM,hymn
SSATB,acap AMP A239 $.25 (H1227)

HARMONICA SACRA see Ehret, Walter

HARMONIE-MESSE see Haydn, (Franz) Joseph, Missa

HARMONIEMESSE see Haydn, (Franz) Joseph

HARMONIEMESSE see Haydn, (Franz) Joseph, Missa

HARMONIEMESSE see Haydn, (Franz) Joseph, Missa
Solennis

HARMONY see Wolf, Hugo, Einklang

HARMONY OF MAINE, THE see Belcher, [Supply]

HARNISCH, OTTO SIEGFRIED (ca. 1568-1630)
Wenn Ich Nur Dich Hab *mot
(Hellmann) SATB HANSSLER 1.109 s.p. (H1228)

HAROLD FLAMMER ANTHEM COLLECTION, VOL. 3 *CCU
SATB FLAMMER GA5015 $1.50 (H1229)

HAROLD FLAMMER OMNIBUS *CCU
FLAMMER G5004 $1.25 (H1230)

HAROM MADRIGAL see Dobos, K.

HARPER, C.
Junior Intermediate Anthem Book *CCU
unis&2pt oct PRESSER $1.50 (H1231)

HARPER, M.
Blessed Is He *Easter
SSA oct PRESSER MC382 $.30 (H1232)
SATB oct PRESSER MC381 $.35 (H1233)

Deliver Us
SATB oct PRESSER MC282 $.35 (H1234)

Rejoice In The Lord
SATB oct PRESSER MC283 $.30 (H1235)

We Have A Strong City
SATB oct PRESSER 312-40759 $.30 (H1236)

HARPER, MARJORIE (1937-)
Great And Marvelous Are Thy Works *Bibl
SATB,S/T solo oct BOURNE 725 $.25 (H1237)

HARRELL, JAN
Doin' His Task
SA oct WORD CS-2440 $.25 (H1238)

In A Cave A Baby Lay *Xmas
unis/SA oct WORD CS-2429 $.30 (H1239)

HARRER
Mein Herz Ist Bereit
(Coggin) "My Heart Sings To Thee" SATB oct
PRO ART 2552 $.30 (H1240)

My Heart Sings To Thee *see Mein Herz Ist
Bereit

My Heart Sings With Joy
(Harris) SSA oct PRO ART 2684 $.30 (H1241)

HARRGOTT, O LUEG, ES VOLCH ISCH DA see Schmalz,
Paul

HARRHY, EDITH
O Virgin Mother Mary Mild *Xmas,Austral
SA ALLANS 382 s.p. (H1242)

Prayer, A *prayer
SATB ALLANS 429 s.p. (H1243)
SA ALLANS 230 s.p. (H1244)

HARRIES
Christ Child *Xmas
SATB,acap (easy) OXFORD 84.160 $.20 (H1245)

I Said To The Man Who Stood At The Gate Of The Year *anthem
TTBB oct OXFORD 41.026 $.20 (H1246)

O Come Let Us Sing *anthem
mix cor oct OXFORD 42.344 $.65 (H1247)

HARRINGTON
There's A Song In The Air
(Cain) SSAATTBB oct FOX S162 $.25 (H1248)

Where'er The Christ Is Known
(Rogers) 2pt jr cor/3pt jr cor oct LILLENAS AN-4010 $.25 (H1249)

HARRINGTON, KARL P.
There's A Song In The Air
jr cor&sr cor oct SCHIRM.G 10905 $.25 (H1250)

HARRIS
All My Heart Today Rejoices
SATB FLAMMER A 5568 $.30 (H1251)

All That Thrills My Soul
(Gerig) SSATTBB oct LILLENAS AN-2219 $.35 (H1252)
(Mickelson) SSATTB oct LILLENAS AN-1158 $.30 (H1253)
(Pottenger) SATB oct LILLENAS AN-2270 $.35 (H1254)

Be Strong In The Lord
SATB KJOS PL7 $.95 (H1255)
SATB KJOS $.95 (H1256)

Behold I Stand At The Door
SATB KJOS PC783 $.30 (H1257)

Christ Is Arisen
SATB FLAMMER A 5295 $.25 (H1258)

Clap Your Hands, Ye People
SATB KJOS PC796 $.35 (H1259)

Come, Sound His Praise Abroad
SATB oct PRO ART 2734 $.30 (H1260)

Cradle Hymn Of The Virgin *see Mater Doloroso

Earth Is The Lord's, The
SATB KJOS PC784 $.35 (H1261)

Fifteen Choral Responses *CC15U
oct SATB PRO ART 1368 $.30; SAB PRO ART 2334 $.30; SSA PRO ART 2336 $.25 (H1262)

Give Thanks And Sing
(Treharne) SATB,org BOSTON 1802 $.35 (H1263)

Give To Our God Immortal Praise *Thanks
SATB oct PRO ART 1496 $.20 (H1264)

Glorious Song, The *Xmas
SATB,solo oct PRO ART 1873 $.22 (H1265)

Great Is The Lord, Our God
SATB oct PRO ART 2455 $.25 (H1266)

Hark! The Herald Angels Sing *Xmas
SSATBB ALFRED 6346 $.35 (H1267)

He Is Born *Xmas
SATB SCHMITT 1742 $.20 (H1268)

Hosanna To The Son Of David
SATB FLAMMER A 5597 $.30 (H1269)

Joyfully Sing We His Praise!
SATB,acap oct PRO ART 2456 $.25 (H1270)
SAB,acap oct PRO ART 2542 $.30 (H1271)
SSA,acap oct PRO ART 2539 $.30 (H1272)

Let All The Earth Rejoice
SATB,acap oct PRO ART 2736 $.30 (H1273)

Let All The World *Thanks
SATB,org BOSTON 13570 $.35 (H1274)

Mater Doloroso *Xmas
"Cradle Hymn Of The Virgin" SATB SCHMITT 1750 $.18 (H1275)

O Come, Emmanuel *Xmas
SSATBB ALFRED 0401 $.30 (H1276)

O Tannenbaum *Xmas
SSATBB ALFRED 6410 $.35 (H1277)

Our Dedication Prayer *Ded,prayer
SATB oct PRO ART 2083 $.25 (H1278)

Praise Ye The Lord *Gen
SSA SCHMITT 2585 $.35 (H1279)

Psalm 67
SATB,acap oct PRO ART 1603 $.18 (H1280)

Shepherds Keeping Watch That Night *Xmas
SATB oct PRO ART 2613 $.35 (H1281)

Sing Praises!
SATB oct PRO ART 1580 $.25 (H1282)

Sing To God
SATB oct PRO ART 2466 $.25 (H1283)

What Star Is This? *Xmas
SATB oct PRO ART 2596 $.30 (H1284)

With All Thine Heart
SATB oct PRO ART 2464 $.25 (H1285)

HARRIS, A.
Christmas Chanters, The *Xmas
SATB,acap oct PRESSER MC209 $.30 (H1286)

HARRIS, A. (cont'd.)

Song Of Koheleth, The
SSA,Bar solo oct PRESSER MC198 $.45 (H1287)

To Jesus On His Birthday
SATB,acap oct PRESSER MC226 $.30 (H1288)

HARRIS, CUTHBERT
Behold I Have Given You Every Herb *Harv, anthem
mix cor oct NOVELLO 28.0713.00 s.p. (H1289)

Heavenly Vision
SATB ALLANS 156 s.p. (H1290)

Sing A Song Of Praise
SATB ALLANS 82 s.p. (H1291)

Supreme Sacrifice *hymn
SATB oct NOVELLO 44.1406.03 s.p. (H1292)

HARRIS, D.S.
O God, Creation's Secret Force
SATB,org GRAY GCMR 3269 $.30 (H1293)

HARRIS, JERRY WESELEY (1933-)
Cantate Domino
SAB KJOS PC1028 $.30 (H1294)

Carroll, A *Xmas,carol
SATB,acap oct LAWSON 51122 $.25 (H1295)

I Beseech Thee, O God
SSA KJOS PCG50 $.30 (H1296)

Lo, In The Time Appointed
SATB,pno/org oct LAWSON 51494 $.35 (H1297)
3pt boy cor/SSA/SAA,pno/org oct LAWSON 51566 $.35 (H1298)

Lord Is Over All The Earth, The *see Misericordia Domini

Mary, Dear Mother Of Jesus
SSA oct AGAPE AD 1970 $.25 (H1299)

Misericordia Domini
"Lord Is Over All The Earth, The" SATB oct WALTON 2171 $.30 (H1300)

O Lord, To Thee We Pray
SSA KJOS PC654 $.30 (H1301)

Ring Out, Ye Bells Of Christmas *Xmas
SATB,acap oct LAWSON 51433 $.30 (H1302)

Thou Art The Lord Of Heaven
SSA KJOS PC653 $.30 (H1303)

HARRIS, ROY (1898-)
David Slew Goliath (from Folk Fantasies For Festivals)
SSAATTBB,narrator,T solo AMP $1.00 (H1304)

HARRIS, WILLIAM HENRY (1883)
All Creatures Of Our God And King *Gen, anthem
SATB oct ROYAL 222 s.p. (H1305)

Beatitudes, The *anthem/Bibl
dbl cor,acap oct NOVELLO 28.1258.04 s.p. (H1306)

Behold Now, Praise The Lord
2pt oct NOVELLO 33.0087.00 s.p. (H1307)

Behold The Tabernacle *Ded,anthem
SATB oct ROYAL 208 s.p. (H1308)

Bring Us, O Lord God *anthem/mot
dbl cor,acap oct NOVELLO 28.1368.08 s.p. (H1309)

Come Down, O Love Divine *anthem/hymn
mix cor oct NOVELLO 28.1449.08 s.p. (H1310)

Come, My Way, My Truth, My Life *anthem
mix cor oct NOVELLO 28.1224.10 s.p. (H1311)
4pt oct NOVELLO 51.0664.08 s.p. (H1312)

Drop, Slow Tears *Easter
SATB,acap oct PRESSER 332-40008 $.30 (H1313)

Eternal God *anthem/mot
mix cor,acap oct NOVELLO 50.0346.06 s.p. (H1314)

Eyes Of All Wait Upon Thee, O Lord, The (Psalm 145) Gen/Harv
SATB (easy) oct OXFORD 42.983 $.25 (H1315)

Fear Not, O Land *Harv,Bibl
SATB (easy) oct OXFORD (H1316)

Glory, Love And Praise And Honour *Harv, anthem
SATB oct ROYAL 236 s.p. (H1317)

Holy Eucharist, The *Commun
SATB,acap (easy) oct OXFORD 43.399 $.20 (H1318)

Holy Is The True Light *anthem
mix cor oct NOVELLO 40.1259.03 s.p. (H1319)

In The Heavenly Kingdom *anthem
mix cor oct NOVELLO 40.1262.03 s.p. (H1320)

Lead, Kindly Light *Gen
(Gritton, Eric) unis&desc/SATB (easy) oct OXFORD 40.920 $.25 (H1321)

Lord My Pasture Shall Prepare, The *anthem
unis oct NOVELLO 33.0116.08 s.p. (H1322)
mix cor oct NOVELLO 40.1222.04 s.p. (H1323)

Lord Of The Worlds Above *anthem
mix cor oct NOVELLO 28.1411.00 s.p. (H1324)

Magnificat And Nunc Dimittis *Magnif/Nunc
SS/SSS (D maj) NOVELLO 33.0105.02 s.p. (H1325)

Magnificat And Nunc Dimittis In A *Magnif/Nunc
SATB (easy) oct OXFORD 41.008 $.40 (H1326)

Most Glorious Lord Of Life *Easter/Gen
STB/SBBar (easy) oct OXFORD 42.125 $.25 (H1327)

O God, The Protector *anthem
mix cor,acap oct NOVELLO 28.1479.10 s.p. (H1328)

HARRIS, WILLIAM HENRY (cont'd.)

O Sing Unto The Lord With Thanksgiving *Harv,anthem
mix cor oct NOVELLO 28.1317.03 s.p. (H1329)

O What Their Joy And Their Glory Must Be *ASD
SSA,pno/org (med) oct OXFORD 44.218 $.65 (H1330)

Praise The Lord, O My Soul (Psalm 103)
dbl cor,acap voc sc NOVELLO s.p. (H1331)

Prelude To A Solemn Music *anthem
mix cor,T solo oct NOVELLO 28.1283.05 s.p. (H1332)

Psalm 103 *see Praise The Lord, O My Soul

Psalm 145 *see Eyes Of All Wait Upon Thee, O Lord, The

Simple Communion Service In F *Commun
oct ROYAL 111 s.p. (H1333)

Sing A Song Of Joy *anthem
mix cor,acap oct NOVELLO 40.1236.04 s.p. (H1334)

Strengthen Ye The Weak Hands *anthem
mix cor oct NOVELLO 28.1275.04 s.p. (H1335)

Thou Hast Made Me *anthem/mot
dbl cor,acap oct NOVELLO 28.1268.03 s.p. (H1336)

Thus Saith God The Lord *anthem
mix cor oct NOVELLO 28.1324.06 s.p. (H1337)

Vox Ultima Crucis *Gen,anthem
unis (very easy) oct OXFORD 45.203 $.20 (H1338)
unis,opt pno oct ROYAL 241 s.p. see also ANTHEMS FOR UNISON OR TWO PART SINGING (H1339)

HARRISON
Joyous Procession And A Solemn Procession, A
cor,trom,tamb,hndbl,drums, Gong PETERS 6543 $1.00 (H1340)

HARRISON, JULIUS ALLEN GREENWAY (1885-1963)
Christmas Cantata *Xmas,cant
SATB,SATBar soli,org voc sc NOVELLO s.p. (H1341)

Mass In C *Mass
SSATBB,solo,orch LENGNICK s.p., ipa (H1342)

Missa Liturgica *Mass
SATB,acap LENGNICK s.p. (H1343)

Open Thy Gates
mix cor CURWEN 80547 s.p. (H1344)

Psalm 100
SATB,org LENGNICK s.p. (H1345)

Requiem Mass *Mass
SATB,solo,orch LENGNICK s.p., ipa (H1346)

HARRISON, LOU (1917-)
Mass To St. Anthony *Mass
mix cor,trp,strings,harp PEER rental (H1347)

HARRY, P.A.
What Wonderous Love Is This
SAB oct KERBY 7103C $.25 (H1348)

What Wondrous Love Is This
SAB,org oct KERBY 7103 $.25 (H1349)

HARSANYI, TIBOR (1898-1954)
Cantate De Noel *Xmas,Bibl/cant
[Eng/Ger/Fr] SMezTBar,fl,strings voc sc HEUGEL s.p., ipr (H1350)

HART
Adoramus Te Christe
mix cor SOUTHERN $.25 (H1351)

I Will Arise And Go To Jesus
(Higgs) 2pt oct SHAPIRO SK 4015 $.25 (H1352)

HART, A.W.
Christmas Fanfare *Xmas
SATB,acap WARNER W7-1010 $.30 (H1353)

God Knows
SATB,pno (med) oct WILLIS 8254 $.20 (H1354)
3pt wom cor,pno (diff) oct WILLIS 8253 $.20 (H1355)
SA,pno (med) oct WILLIS 8252 $.20 (H1356)

He That Hath Clean Hands
3pt wom cor,pno (med) oct WILLIS 8261 $.20 (H1357)
SATB,pno (med) oct WILLIS 8263 $.20 (H1358)

I Walked In God's Garden
3pt wom cor,pno (med) oct WILLIS 8225 $.25 (H1359)
SA,pno (med) oct WILLIS 8226 $.25 (H1360)
SATB,pno (easy) oct WILLIS 8227 $.25 (H1361)

If Christ Should Come Tomorrow
3pt wom cor,pno (med) oct WILLIS 8262 $.20 (H1362)

They Found Him In The Temple
SATB,pno (med) oct WILLIS 8228 $.20 (H1363)
SA,pno (med) oct WILLIS 8229 $.20 (H1364)
3pt wom cor,pno (med) oct WILLIS 8230 $.20 (H1365)

When God Sees Your Garden
3pt wom cor,pno (med) oct WILLIS 8232 $.20 (H1366)

HART, FRITZ
Adoramus Te, Christe
SATB,acap SHAWNEE A 1051 $.25 (H1367)

Night Of Fear Is Over, The *Xmas,carol
SATB ALLANS 111 s.p. (H1368)

HARTER, [HARRY]
Blessed Be The King
SATB FLAMMER A 5441 $.30 (H1369)

He Guides Me In His Way
SATB,acap SHAWNEE A 565 $.25 (H1370)

Let Not Your Hearts Be Troubled
SATB,acap SHAWNEE A 566 $.25 (H1371)

HARTER, [HARRY] (cont'd.)

Praise God Ye Christians All Alike
SATB oct BELWIN 2023 $.25   (H1372)

Psalm 23 *see Twenty-Third Psalm

Twenty-Third Psalm (Psalm 23)
SATB,acap SHAWNEE A 348 $.30   (H1373)

Where Does The Star Shine Brightly
(Kjelson, Lee) unis/2pt oct BELWIN 2231
$.30   (H1374)

HARTLEY, GERALD
Choral Fanfare For Christmas *Xmas
SATB LEONARD-US 08006720 $.30   (H1375)

HARTLEY, WALTER [S.] (1927-   )
Choral Introit And Sevenfold Amen *Introit
cor ROCHESTER $.20   (H1376)

How Excellent Thy Name
SATB oct GALAXY 1.2366.1 $.35   (H1377)

O Sing A New Song
SATB oct MCA   (H1378)

They That Put Their Trust
SATB oct MCA   (H1379)

HARTMANN
Vier Deutsche Motetten *CC4U,mot
(Adrio) 6pt mix cor&8pt mix cor MOSELER
s.p.   (H1380)

HARTMANN, BR.
Weihnacht, Weiss Fest Der Liebe *Xmas
mix cor,acap ERDMANN 91 s.p.   (H1381)
men cor,acap ERDMANN 5 s.p.   (H1382)

HARTMANN, HEINRICH (? -1616)
Auf Dich Allein, Du Treuer Gott *mot
(Holliger) SSATB HANSSLER 1.334 s.p.   (H1383)

Aus Der Tiefe Rufe Ich, Herr, Zu Dir *mot
(Holliger) SSATTB HANSSLER 1.478 s.p.   (H1384)

Denn Der Gottlosen Zepter Wird Nicht *mot
(Holliger) SSATTB HANSSLER 1.484 s.p.   (H1385)

Die Auf Den Herren Hoffen *mot
(Holliger) SSATTB HANSSLER 1.483 s.p.   (H1386)

Die Starken Bedurfen Des Arztes Nicht *mot
(Holliger) SSATTB HANSSLER 1.480 s.p.   (H1387)

Eins Bitte Ich Vom Herren *mot
(Holliger) SSATTB HANSSLER 1.328 s.p.   (H1388)

Geistliche Chormusik *CC26U,mot
(Holliger) [Ger] 5-6pt HANSSLER 4.010 $9.00   (H1389)

Gott, Lass Sich Freuen Alle *mot
(Holliger) SSATTB HANSSLER 1.337 s.p.   (H1390)

Habe Deine Lust Am Herren *mot
(Holliger) SSATTB HANSSLER 1.481 s.p.   (H1391)

Herr, Wie Lang Willst Du Mein *mot
(Holliger) SSATTB HANSSLER 1.338 s.p.
contains also: Wie Lang Soll Sich Mein
Feind; Ich Hoffe Aber Darauf, Dass Du   (H1392)

Herr Zeige Mir Deine Wege *Bibl/mot
(Holliger) SSATTB HANSSLER 1.479 s.p.   (H1393)

Ich Danke Dir Von Ganzem Herzen *Thanks,mot
(Holliger) SATTB HANSSLER 1.336 s.p.   (H1394)

Ich Hoffe Aber Darauf, Dass Du
see Hartmann, Heinrich, Herr, Wie Lang
Willst Du Mein

Ich Lieb Dich, Herr, Von Herzen Sehr *mot
(Holliger) SSATTB HANSSLER 1.335 s.p.   (H1395)

Lass Mich Dein Sein Und Bleiben *mot
[Ger] SSATB,acap (med easy) MULLER K 24
s.p.   (H1396)
SSATB HANSSLER 6.168 s.p.   (H1397)
(Holliger) SSATTB HANSSLER 1.330 s.p.   (H1398)

Lobet Den Herren, Alle Heiden (Psalm 117)
Bibl/mot
(Holliger) SSATTB HANSSLER 1.476 s.p.   (H1399)

Lobet, Ihr Knechte Des Herren *Thanks,mot
(Holliger) SSATTB HANSSLER 1.333 s.p.   (H1400)

Psalm 117 *see Lobet Den Herren, Alle Heiden

Psalm 126 *see Wenn Der Herr Die Gefangenen
Zions

Siehe, Das Ist Der Herr, Auf Den *mot
(Holliger) SSATTB HANSSLER 1.331 s.p.   (H1401)

Siehe Lobet Den Herren, Alle Knechte *mot
(Holliger) SSATTB HANSSLER 1.475 s.p.   (H1402)

Singt Lieblich Und Lobt Den Herrn *Thanks,
mot
(Holliger) SSATTB HANSSLER 1.485 s.p.   (H1403)

Trachtet Am Ersten Nach Dem Reich Gottes
*Bibl/mot
(Holliger) SSATTB HANSSLER 1.474 s.p.   (H1404)

Was Betrubst Du Dich, Meine Seele *mot
(Holliger) SSATTB HANSSLER 1.329 s.p.   (H1405)

Wenn Der Herr Die Gefangenen Zions (Psalm
126) Bibl/mot
(Holliger) SSATTB HANSSLER 1.477 s.p.   (H1406)

Wenn Mir Angst Ist, So Ruf Ich Den Herrn
*mot
(Holliger) SATTB HANSSLER 1.332 s.p.   (H1407)

Wie Lang Soll Sich Mein Feind
see Hartmann, Heinrich, Herr, Wie Lang
Willst Du Mein

Wie Nach Einer Wasserquelle *mot
(Holliger) SSATTB HANSSLER 1.482 s.p.   (H1408)

HARTMANN, HEINRICH (cont'd.)

Zion Spricht: Ach, Mein Herr Und Gott *Bibl/
mot
(Holliger) SSATTB HANSSLER 1.486 s.p.   (H1409)

HARTMANN, JOHAN PEDER EMILIUS (1805-1900)
Fragment Af Oehlenschlagers "Jesu
Bjergpraediken" *Op.49
(Clausen, Karl) TTBB,3 soli,org HANSEN-DEN
28569 s.p.   (H1410)

Nar Mit Legem Doden Moder *see Quando Corpus
Morietur

Quando Corpus Morietur
(Lunn, Sven) "Nar Mit Legem Doden Moder"
[Lat/Dan] SATB,STBar soli,strings HANSEN-
DEN 27319 s.p., ipa   (H1411)

HARTMANN, LUIGI
Tantum Ergo *Commun
[Lat] 2 eq voices,org sc ZANIBON 2686 s.p.,
cor pts ZANIBON 2686BIS s.p.   (H1412)

HART'S CHRISTMAS CAROLS.FIRST SELECTION *CCU,
Xmas,carol
HART oct s.p., pap s.p.   (H1413)

HART'S CHRISTMAS CAROLS.SECOND SELECTION *CCU,
Xmas,carol
HART oct s.p., pap s.p.   (H1414)

HARVEST ANTHEM, A see Lovelock, William

HARVEST BLESSINGS, RICHLY SHOWERED see Maslen,
Benjamin J.

HARVEST CAROL see Copes, V. Earle

HARVEST CELEBRATION see Carmichael, Ralph

HARVEST FESTIVAL MUSIC *CC6U,anthem
ROYAL s.p.   (H1415)

HARVEST HYMN see Ward

HARVEST SONG see Brahms, Johannes

HARVEST, THE see Bixel, James W.

HARVEY
Joyful Easter-Tide, The *Easter/Lent
SA oct FISCHER,C CM-6952 $.25   (H1416)

This Joyful Eastertide *Easter
2pt jr cor FISCHER,C CM 6952 $.25   (H1417)

Virgin's Lullaby, The
SA/TB FLAMMER E5129 $.25   (H1418)

HARWOOD, BASIL (1859-1949)
Benedicite *chant
SATB (D maj) oct NOVELLO s.p.   (H1419)

Christ Our Passover Is Sacrificed For Us
*anthem/chant
mix cor oct NOVELLO s.p.   (H1420)

Great God, Who, Hid From Mortal Sight
*anthem
mix cor oct NOVELLO s.p.   (H1421)

Holy Communion *Commun
SATB (A flat maj) oct NOVELLO s.p.   (H1422)
SATB (E flat maj) oct NOVELLO s.p.   (H1423)

I Am The Living Bread *Commun/Gen
SATB (easy) oct OXFORD 45.048 $.25   (H1424)

Kyrie Eleison And Ninefold Amen *Kyrie
SATB oct NOVELLO s.p.   (H1425)

Let The People Praise Thee *Harv,anthem
mix cor oct NOVELLO 28.1187.01 s.p.   (H1426)

Magnificat And Nunc Dimittis *Magnif/Nunc
SATB (A flat maj) oct NOVELLO s.p.   (H1427)
unis oct NOVELLO s.p.   (H1428)

Missa De Angelis *Mass
SATB oct NOVELLO 44.0835.07 s.p.   (H1429)

O How Plentiful Is Thy Goodness *Op.41,
Harv,anthem
mix cor oct NOVELLO s.p.   (H1430)

O Saving Victim *anthem
mix cor oct NOVELLO s.p.   (H1431)

Sacrifice Triumphant *Op.64, Holywk/Lent,
cant
SATB,STB soli,org voc sc NOVELLO s.p.   (H1432)

Sweet Saviour, Bless Us Ere We Go *anthem
mix cor oct NOVELLO 40.1187.02 s.p.   (H1433)

Te Deum And Benedictus *Te Deum
SATB (A flat maj) oct NOVELLO s.p.   (H1434)
SATB (E min) oct NOVELLO s.p.   (H1435)

When The Son Of Man Shall Come *Adv,anthem
mix cor oct NOVELLO s.p.   (H1436)

HAS ANYBODY SEEN CHRISTMAS? see Marshall, Jane
M.

HASELTON, ROBERT (ca. 1550)
Praise We The Lord *Gen
TTBB,acap (med easy) oct CONCORDIA 98-1682
$.22   (H1437)
boy cor SOUTHERN $.22   (H1438)

HASHAGEN, KLAUS (1924-   )
Drei Psalmen Davids *CC3U,Psalm
4pt mix cor MOSELER s.p.   (H1439)

HASHIVENU ADONAI see Davidson, Charles

HASHKIVENU see Birnbaum

HASHKIVENU see Brenner, Walter

HASHKIVENU see Gottlieb, J.

HASHKIVENU see Rabinowitch

HASHKIVENU see Telpasi

HASHKIVENU see Weisgal, A.

HASHKIVENU II see Ancis, Solomon

HASHKIVENU NO. 2 see Rabinowitch

HASKIVENU see Bernstein, Leonard

HASLAM, [HERBERT] (1928-   )
Special Starlight
mix cor&treb cor,narrator,orch PRESSER
$1.25   (H1440)

HASSE, JOHANN ADOLPH (1699-1783)
Miserere (Psalm 51)
SSAA,SSAA soli org sc SCHIRM.G $1.00   (H1441)

(Schering) [Lat] SSAA,orch sc PETERS FK35
$5.00, ipa, cor pts PETERS FK35 $.80, ipa   (H1442)

Psalm 51 *see Miserere

Te Deum Laudamus *Te Deum
[Lat] voc sc PETERS HU1775 $2.50, ipr   (H1443)

HASSELBOCK, HANS (1928-   )
Der Susse Gesang
mix cor,acap oct DOBLINGER s.p.   (H1444)

Erschienen Ist Der Herrlich Tag
mix cor,acap oct DOBLINGER s.p.   (H1445)

Salzburger Messe *Mass
mix cor&cong/cong,opt cantor,org,opt 5brass
DOBLINGER voc sc $3.00, cor pts s.p., ipa   (H1446)

HASSIDIC SERVICE see Freed, Isadore

HASSLER, HANS LEO (1564-1612)
Ach, Fraulein Zart
see Gastoldi, Giovanni Giacomo, Amor Im
Nachen

Ach Gott, Vom Himmel Sieh Darein
SATB HANSSLER 6.176 s.p. contains also:
Burck, Joachim, Schwer Gehet Uber Mein
Haupt (SATB)   (H1447)

Ach Lieb, Hier Ist Das Herze
SATB LAUDINELLA LR 5 s.p. contains also:
Ach Schatz, Ich Sing Und Lache; Mit Dein
Lieblichen Augen   (H1448)

Ach Schatz, Ich Sing Und Lache
see Hassler, Hans Leo, Ach Lieb, Hier Ist
Das Herze
(Lavater, H.) [Ger] men cor,acap (easy) HUG
s.p.   (H1449)

Ad Dominium Cum Tribularer
(Knight, Gerald) SATB,acap oct FISCHER,C
CM-7578 $.30   (H1450)

Ad Dominum Cum Tribularer
SAATB,acap oct PRESSER 352-00002 $.30   (H1451)

Agnus Dei (from Mass No. 8) Easter/Lent,Agnus
SATB KJOS 5008 $.30   (H1452)
mix cor NORDISKA 3956 s.p.   (H1453)
(Druba) dbl cor ALFRED 6580 $.50   (H1454)
(Greyson) mix cor SOUTHERN $.30   (H1455)
(Greyson) "Lamb Of God" SATB oct BOURNE ES1
$.30   (H1456)
(Pfautsch) "Lamb Of God" SATB,acap oct
LAWSON 800 $.25   (H1457)
(Wiedemann, M.) [Lat] men cor,acap (med)
HUG s.p.   (H1458)

Amen, Das Ist: Es Werde Wahr
SATB HANSSLER 6.153 s.p.   (H1459)

And Mary Said To The Angel *see Dixit Maria

And The Word Was Made Flesh
(Ehret) mix cor CHAPPELL 0024190-358 $.40   (H1460)

Angel Said Unto The Shepherds, The *see
Angelus Ad Pastores

Angels, Then To The Shepherds Saying *see
Angelus Ad Pastores Ait

Angelus Ad Pastores *Xmas
(Williams, W.) "Angel Said Unto The
Shepherds, The" SATB,acap SCHIRM.EC 1227
$.30   (H1461)

Angelus Ad Pastores Ait *Xmas/Gen,mot
"Angels, Then To The Shepherds Saying" SATB
oct WALTON 6002 $.30   (H1462)
"Shepherds Quaked When The Angel Told Them"
[Lat/Eng] SATB,acap AMP A405 $.30   (H1463)
(Grusnick, Bruno) "Der Engel Sprach Zu Den
Hirten" [Ger/Lat] SSAT&SATTB,acap (med
diff) BAREN. BA 2920 sc $2.75, cor pts
$2.00   (H1464)
(Harris) "Gabriel Said Unto The Shepherd"
[Eng/Lat] 4pt mix cor,acap oct SCHIRM.G
8600 $.30   (H1465)

Aus Meines Herzens Grunde *Gen
[Ger] SATB,acap (med easy) BAREN. BA 3053
s.p.   (H1466)

Aus Tiefer Not
see Psalmen Und Christliche Gesang
Fugweiss, Erste Folge

Aus Tiefer Not Schrei Ich Zu Dir
(Berger, H.L.) TTBB HANSSLER 6.5072 s.p.
contains also: Anonymous, Herr Gott, Dich
Loben Alle Wir   (H1467)

Ave Maris Stella *hymn
(Collins, H.B.) [Lat] SATB CHESTER s.p.   (H1468)

Beatus Vir Qui Non Abiit
[Lat/Eng] SATB BROUDE,A. 157 $.35   (H1469)

Befiehl Du Deine Wege
SATB HANSSLER 6.228 s.p. contains also:
Bach, Johann Sebastian, Wenn Ich Einmal
Soll Scheiden   (H1470)

Behold, How Good And Pleasant It Is *see
Ecce Quam Bonum

HASSLER, HANS LEO (cont'd.)

Blessed Saviour, Our Lord Jesus
4pt mix cor,acap oct SCHIRM.G 7563 $.30 (H1471)

Cantate Domino *Gen/Thanks,Bibl/cant/mot, Renais
SSATB SCHOTT 10449 s.p. (H1472)
SSATB,acap voc pt DOBLINGER s.p. see also LOB UND DANK (H1473)
"O Sing Unto The Lord" SATB,acap SCHIRM.EC 1131 $.30 (H1474)
"O Sing Unto The Lord" [Lat/Eng] SSAA,acap SCHIRM.EC 1887 $.25 (H1475)
"O Sing Unto The Lord" SATB,acap SCHIRM.EC 1262 $.25 (H1476)
"O Sing Unto The Lord" SATB FLAMMER A 5553 $.30 (H1477)
(Beveridge, L.) "Oh Sing Unto The Lord" [Lat/Eng] TTBB,acap SCHIRM.EC 2194 $.35 (H1478)
(Couraud) [Lat] SSSAAATTTBBB oct SALABERT-US $2.00 (H1479)
(Davison, A.) [Lat] TTBB,acap SCHIRM.EC 68 $.30 (H1480)
(Ehret, Walter) "O Sing Unto The Lord" SATB,acap PEER $.40 (H1481)
(Glaser, V.) "O Sing Unto The Lord" SAB, acap SCHIRM.EC 2240 $.22 (H1482)
(Greyson) mix cor SOUTHERN $.30 (H1483)
(Greyson) "O Sing Unto The Lord" SSA oct BOURNE ES18A $.30 (H1484)
(Greyson) "O Sing Unto The Lord" SATB oct BOURNE ES18 $.30 (H1485)
(Greyson) "O Sing Unto The Lord" TTBB oct BOURNE ES18B $.25 (H1486)
(Hellmann) "Singet Ein Neus Lied" [Lat/Ger] SATB HANSSLER 1.125 $.50 (H1487)
(Mueller) "O Sing Unto The Lord" 4pt mix cor,acap oct SCHIRM.G 10872 $.30 (H1488)
(Woodworth) 4pt mix cor,acap oct SCHIRM.G 10572 $.30 (H1489)

Christ Is Arisen *see Christ Ist Erstanden

Christ Ist Erstanden *Easter/Lent/Psntd, anthem,12th cent
"Christ Is Arisen" see Anonymous, Christians, To The Paschal Victim
SATB,acap voc pt DOBLINGER s.p. see also PASSION UND OSTERN (H1490)
"Christ Is Arisen" mix cor SOUTHERN $.25 (H1491)
"Christ Is Arisen" SATB,acap oct PRESSER 312-40138 $.30 (H1492)
"Christ Is Arisen" [Eng/Ger] SATB,acap MARKS 26 $.25 (H1493)
(Coggin, Elwood) "Christ Is Arisen" SSA (easy) PRESSER 362-03159 $.30 (H1494)
(Coggin, Elwood) "Christ Is Arisen" SAB (easy) PRESSER 362-03160 $.30 (H1495)
(Klein, M.) "Christ Is Arisen" [Eng/Ger] SATB (easy) oct GIA G1524 $.25 (H1496)
(Marshall) "Christ Is Arisen" SATB oct SOUTHERN $.30 (H1497)
(Marshall, Charles) "Christ Is Arisen" SATB FRANK F-598 $.30 (H1498)

Christe, Der Du Bist Tag Und Licht
(Schabasser, Josef) mix cor,acap oct DOBLINGER s.p. see also CHRISTUS, DER HERR (H1499)

Christe, Du Bist Der Helle Tag
(Schabasser, Josef) mix cor,acap oct DOBLINGER s.p. see also CHRISTUS, DER HERR (H1500)

Come Let Us Start A Joyful Song
(Greyson) girl cor SOUTHERN (H1501)

Commit Thy Ways And Grant Us To Do Thy Zeal
(Bach, J.S.; Cain) SATB oct PRO ART 1465 $.22 (H1502)

Credo (from Mass No. 8) Credo
(Druba) dbl cor ALFRED 6602 $1.00 (H1503)

Crucified Also For Us *see Crucifixus Etiam Pro Nobis

Crucifixus *Easter
[Ger] mix cor,acap (easy) HUG s.p. see also ZWEI OSTERLICHE ZWIEGESANGE (H1504)
(Stern, A.) [Lat] men cor,acap (easy) HUG s.p. (H1505)

Crucifixus Etiam
see ZWEI OSTERLICHE ZWIEGESANGE

Crucifixus Etiam Pro Nobis
"Crucified Also For Us" [Lat/Eng] SA,acap SCHIRM.EC 1918 $.20 (H1506)

Dear Christians, One And All, Rejoice *Easter/Gen/Refm
SATB,acap (med diff) oct CONCORDIA 98-1949 $.50 (H1507)

Der Engel Sprach Zu Den Hirten *see Angelus Ad Pastores Ait

Dixit Maria *Adv/Xmas,Mass/mot
[Lat] SATB,acap (med easy) MULLER MS 77 s.p. (H1508)
mix cor SOUTHERN $.30 (H1509)
mix cor,acap voc sc KALMUS 6221 $1.25 (H1510)
SATB oct FISCHER,C R-297 $.25 (H1511)
"And Mary Said To The Angel" SATB,acap (med diff) oct CONCORDIA 98-1960 $.30 (H1512)
"Gabriel Came To Mary" SATB oct FISCHER,J 9679 $.30 (H1513)
(Bauerle, Hermann) SATB,acap cor pts BREITKOPF-L PB-3396 s.p., voc pt BREITKOPF-L CHB-2774 s.p. (H1514)
(Gano, Peter) SATB oct PENN STATE 0-271-73123-0 $3.25 (H1515)

Dixit Maria Ad Angelum *mot
(Steele, Jonathan) [Lat] SATB CHESTER s.p. (H1516)

Domine, Dominus Noster
(Couraud) [Lat] SSSAAATTTBBB oct SALABERT-US $2.50 (H1517)

Ecce, Quam Bonum *Gen,mot
SSATB SCHOTT sc s.p., cor pts s.p. (H1518)
"Behold, How Good And Pleasant It Is"
SATTB,acap (diff) oct CONCORDIA 98-1874 $.30 (H1519)

Eight Madrigals And Four Part-Songs
[Ger] 5-8pt PETERS 3498 $2.50 (H1520)

Ein Feste Burg
see Psalmen Und Christliche Gesang Fugweiss, Erste Folge

Ein Kindelein So Lobelich
see Praetorius, Michael, Kommt Und Lasst Uns Christum

Ein Lammlein Geht Und Tragt Die Schuld
see Jeep, Johann, O Lamm Gottes, Unschuldig

Erstanden Ist Der Heilig Christ *Easter
4pt mix cor MOSELER LB-84 s.p. contains also: Vulpius, Melchior, Gelobt Sei Gott (4pt mix cor) (H1521)

Erstanden Ist Der Heilige Christ
see Staden, Johann, Danket Dem Herrn

Et Incarnatus Est
men cor sc ALSBACH&D s.p. (H1522)

Gabriel Came To Mary *see Dixit Maria

Gabriel Said Unto The Shepherd *see Angelus Ad Pastores Ait

Gloria (from Mass 2) Gloria
mix cor SOUTHERN $.35 (H1523)
[Eng/Lat] 4pt mix cor oct SCHIRM.G 9410 $.35 (H1524)
(Druba) dbl cor ALFRED 6619 $.85 (H1525)
(Payson) "Glory" mix cor SOUTHERN $.40 (H1526)
(Payson, A.) "Glory" SATB,acap FRANK F-567 $.30 (H1527)

Glory *see Gloria

God Now Dwells Among Us
(Wilhelm, Roger) SAB/TBB,kbd FOSTER MF 129 $.35 (H1528)

Gott, Der Vater, Wohn Uns Bei
SATB HANSSLER 6.2511 s.p. contains also: Eccard, Johannes, Sei Frohlich Alle Zeit (SSATB) (H1529)

Gott Sei Gelobet Und Gebenedeiet
see Psalmen Und Christliche Gesang Fugweiss, Zweite Folge

Herr Gott, Nun Sey Gepreyset
see Psalmen Und Christliche Gesang Fugweiss, Zweite Folge

Herzlich Lieb Hab Ich Dich *mot
(Berger) [Lat] dbl cor HANSSLER 1.035 s.p. (H1530)

Ich Grusse Dich Am Kreuzesstamm *Gd.Fri./Psntd
see Erk, Ludwig, Wahrlich, All Unsre Qualen
SATB HANSSLER 6.311 s.p. contains also: Cruger, Johann, O Meine Seel, Du Sollist Den Herren Preisen (H1531)

In Dulci Jubilo, Nun Singet
TTBB HANSSLER 6.1246 s.p. (H1532)

In Gottes Namen Fahren Wir
see Eccard, Johannes, Nach Dem Die Sonn Beschlossen

Jesus Christus, Unser Heiland
see Eccard, Johannes, Zu Dieser Osterlichen Zeit

Jubilate Deo *Gen
[Lat] SSAT&ATBB,acap (med) MULLER K 35 s.p. (H1533)
(McKelvy, James) SSAB&ATBB,acap FOSTER MF402 $.40 (H1534)

Jungfrau, Dein Schon Gestalt
(Kunz, E.) men cor,acap (med) HUG s.p. (H1535)

Kirchengesang *CC68U,Gen
(Saalfeld, Ralf V.) [Ger] SATB,acap (med easy) BAREN. BA 129 $4.75 (H1536)

Krist Ar Uppstanden
see UPPSTANDELSE

Kyrie (from Missa Secunda) Kyrie
SATB oct HERITAGE H51 $.35 (H1537)
(Druba) dbl cor ALFRED 6618 $.75 (H1538)

Laetentur Coeli *Adv/Gen,anthem
[Lat] TTBB,acap oct NOVELLO 38.0136.05 s.p. (H1539)

Lamb Goes Uncomplaining Forth, A
SATB,acap oct PRESSER 312-40136 $.25 (H1540)

Lamb Of God *see Agnus Dei

Latom Oss Med Jesus Draga (composed with Bach, Johann Sebastian)
mix cor NORDISKA 4586 s.p. (H1541)

Laudate Dominum
(Cramer) "Praise The Lord" [Eng/Lat] SATB, acap MARKS 4287 $.30 (H1542)

Laudate Dominum, Omnes Gentes
(Schalk, C.) "Praise Ye, O Praise The Lord" [Lat/Eng] SSAB&ATTB CONCORDIA 97-4879 $1.00 (H1543)

Lord, Let At Last Thine Angels Come *ECY/Gen
SATB&SATB,acap (diff) oct CONCORDIA 98-1026 $.40 (H1544)
mix cor SOUTHERN $.40 (H1545)

Mass III
(Day) SATB oct ELKAN-V 362-1211 $1.25 (H1546)

Mass No. 5 *Mass
(Bichsel, M.A.) 5pt mix cor (based on motet "Ecce Quam Bonum") CONCORDIA 97-4779 $1.50 (H1547)

Master, Show Thy Mercy Unto Us
SATB,acap SCHIRM.EC 2630 $.25 (H1548)

Mighty Fortress Is Our God
SATB KJOS 811 $.30 (H1549)

Mighty Fortress Is Our God, A *Gen/Refm,hymn
SATB,kbd (med diff) oct CONCORDIA 98-1986 $.40 (H1550)
(Ehret) SATB,acap MARKS 4111 $.30 (H1551)

Missa Octo Vocum *Gen
(Grusnick, Bruno) [Lat] SATB&SATB,acap (med diff) BAREN. BA 2910 sc $4.75, cor pts $4.25 (H1552)

Missa Secunda *Mass
mix cor BELWIN $1.25 (H1553)
(Bauerle, Hermann) SATB,acap cor pts BREITKOPF-L PB-3397 s.p., voc pt BREITKOPF-L CHB-2775 s.p. (H1554)

Mit Dein Lieblichen Augen
see Hassler, Hans Leo, Ach Lieb, Hier Ist Das Herze

My Heart For Joy Is Bounding
(Parkinson) SSATB,acap (easy) OXFORD 53.921 $.25 see from Two Old German Partsongs (H1555)

Nadversalme *Psalm,16th cent
(Woldike, Mogens) [Dan] SATB (contains also: Vulpius, Melchior, Aftensalme) HANSEN-DEN 81 s.p. see also SALMEMELODIER FRA REFORMATIONSTIDEN (H1556)
(Woldike, Mogens) [Dan] SATB HANSEN-DEN 81 s.p. see also SALMEMELODIER FRA REFORMATIONSTIDEN (H1557)

Now Let Us Lift Our Youthful Voices
SATB,acap oct FISCHER,C CM-4646 $.25 (H1558)

Now Sing We All This Day
(Hirt) mix cor SOUTHERN $.30 (H1559)
(Hirt) SAATB,acap oct BELWIN 60157 $.30 (H1560)

Now We Praise Thee *mot
SATB,acap SCHIRM.EC 2215 $.25 (H1561)

Nun Bitten Wir Den Heiligen Geist
SATTB/SAATB HANSSLER 6.129 s.p. (H1562)

Nun Freut Euch, Lieben Christen Gmein
SATB HANSSLER 6.2526 s.p. (H1563)

Nun Lob, Mein Seel, Den Herren
SATB HANSSLER 6.2571 s.p. contains also: Perti, Giacomo Antonio, Preis Und Ehre, Herr Jesu (H1564)

O Fader Var I Hemmerik
see Gumpeltzhaimer, Adam, O Fader Var I Himmerik

O Haupt Voll Blut Und Wunden *Gd.Fri./Psntd
SATTB HANSSLER 6.112 s.p. (H1565)

O Mensch, Bewein Dein Sunde Gross *Psntd
see Bach, Johann Sebastian, Bis Hieher Hat Mich Gott Gebracht
see Psalmen Und Christliche Gesang Fugweiss, Erste Folge
4pt mix cor MOSELER LB-80 s.p. contains also: Praetorius, Michael, O Lamm Gottes (H1566)
(Saalfeld, Ralf V.) [Ger] SATB,acap (med) BAREN. BA 123 s.p. see from Psalmen Und Christliche Gesange Fugweiss (H1567)

O Sacred Head *Easter,anthem
(Bach) SATB oct LORENZ A466 $.25 (H1568)
(Christiansen) SATBB (med) oct AUGSBURG 0075 $.25 (H1569)
(Ehret) SATBB,acap MARKS 4154 $.30 (H1570)

O Sacred Head, Now Wounded *Easter/Lent, chorale
SATBB,acap (med easy) oct CONCORDIA 98-1193 $.16 (H1571)
SATB,acap SCHIRM.EC 2401 $.25 (H1572)
(Bach, J.S.; Davis, K.) SSA SCHIRM.EC 1873 $.15 (H1573)
(Bach, J.S.; Fewell, C.M.) SAB,acap SCHIRM.EC 2259 $.25 (H1574)
(Christiansen) SATB oct SOUTHERN $.25 (H1575)
(Ehret) SATB oct SOUTHERN $.20 (H1576)
(Grauer) [Eng/Ger] SSA/3pt jr cor oct FISCHER,C CM-6305 $.25 (H1577)
(Lundquist) SATB FLAMMER A 5250 $.30 (H1578)

O Sacred Head Surrounded
(Bach, J.S.) SATB oct JUSKO 233 $.25 (H1579)

O Sing Unto The Lord *see Cantate Domino

Oh Sing Unto The Lord *see Cantate Domino

Praise The Lord *see Laudate Dominum

Praise The Lord With Gladness (Psalm 66)
(McKelvy, J.) SSAB&ATBB,acap FOSTER MF402 $.40 (H1580)

Praise Ye, O Praise The Lord *see Laudate Dominum, Omnes Gentes

Psalm 66 *see Praise The Lord With Gladness

Psalmen Und Christliche Gesang Fugweiss, Erste Folge *Gen
(Saalfeld, Ralf V.) [Ger] SATB,acap (med diff) BAREN. BA 95 $2.50
contains: Aus Tiefer Not; Ein Feste Burg; O Mensch, Bewein Dein Sunde Gross; Wenn Mein Stundlein Vorhanden Ist (H1581)

Psalmen Und Christliche Gesang Fugweiss, Zweite Folge *Gen
(Saalfeld, Ralf V.) [Ger] SATB,acap (med diff) BAREN. BA 147 $2.50
contains: Gott Sei Gelobet Und Gebenedeiet; Herr Gott, Nun Sey Gepreyset; Wir Glauben All An Einen Gott (H1582)

HASSLER, HANS LEO (cont'd.)

Psalmen Und Christliche Gesange Fugweiss
*see O Mensch, Bewein Dein Sunde Gross;
Vater Unser Im Himmelreich   (H1583)

Rejoice, Ye Heavens *Adv/Gen,anthem/mot
TTBB,acap oct NOVELLO 38.0136.05 s.p.
(H1584)

Sanctus (from Mass 2) Sanctus
mix cor SOUTHERN $.25   (H1585)

Sanctus And Benedictus (from Mass No. 8)
Bene/Sanctus
(Druba) dbl cor ALFRED 6603 $.75   (H1586)

Shepherds Quaked When The Angel Told Them
*see Angelus Ad Pastores Ait

Singet Ein Neues Lied *Easter/Pent,mot/Psalm
[Ger] men cor,acap (med) HUG s.p.   (H1587)
[Ger] SATB,acap (easy) MULLER K 24 s.p.   (H1588)

SATB,acap DOBLINGER s.p. see from
PSALMLIEDER   (H1589)
(Berger) SATB HANSSLER 1.036 s.p.   (H1590)

Singet Ein Neus Lied *see Cantate Domino

Two Old German Partsongs *see My Heart For
Joy Is Bounding   (H1591)

Var Kristtrogen Frojde Sig
mix cor NORDISKA 5579 s.p.   (H1592)

Vater Unser Im Himmelreich *Easter/Pent
(Saalfeld, Ralf V.) [Ger] SATB,acap (med)
BAREN. BA 670 $2.50 see from Psalmen Und
Christliche Gesange Fugweiss   (H1593)

Verbum Caro Factum Est *Xmas,anthem
[Lat] SSATBB,acap (med) MULLER MS 25 s.p.   (H1594)
[Lat] SSATBarB,acap oct NOVELLO MS-25 s.p.
(H1595)
[Lat/Eng] SSATTB,opt inst voc sc BROUDE,A.
140 $.35, ipa   (H1596)

Warum Betrubst Du Dich
SATB,acap DOBLINGER s.p. see also BITTE UND
VERTRAUEN   (H1597)

We All Believe In One True God
SATB,acap oct PRESSER 312-40139 $.25
(H1598)

Wenn Mein Stundlein Vorhanden Ist (from
Christus Der Herr Ist Mein Leben)
see Vulpius, Melchior, Christus, Der Ist
Mein Leben
see Psalmen Und Christliche Gesang
Fugweiss, Erste Folge

Wir Glauben All An Einen Gott
see Psalmen Und Christliche Gesang
Fugweiss, Zweite Folge

Wo Gott Zum Haus Nicht Gibt Sein Gunst
see Praetorius, Michael, Der Morgenstern
Ist Aufgedrungen
see Bach, Johann Sebastian, Lobe Den
Herren, Den Machtigen Konig Der Ehren
[Chorale]
SATB,acap DOBLINGER s.p. see also BITTE UND
VERTRAUEN   (H1599)

HAST DU DENN, JESU, DEIN ANGESICHT GANZLICH see
Bach, Johann Sebastian

HAST DU GROSS GUT see Jacobi, Samuel

HAST THOU NOT KNOWN? see Bowie, [William]

HAST THOU NOT KNOWN? see Mueller, Carl F.

HAST VERWUNDET MEIN HERZE see Schutz, Heinrich,
Vulnerasti Cor Meum

HASTE NOT! REST NOT! see Preus, Solveig D.

HASTE ON, MY JOYS! see Finzi, Gerald

HASTE THEE see Shepherd, John

HASTE THEE, O GOD see Batten, Adrian

HASTE THEE, O GOD see Lundquist

HASTEN, ALL YE SHEPHERDS see Ehret, Walter

HASTEN SHEPHERDS ON see Pablo, Juan

HASTEN SWIFTLY, HASTEN SOFTLY see Kountz

HASTEN THY KINGDOM see Roff, Joseph

HASTINGS
Eternal Father-God
SATB,acap oct FISCHER,C CM-7323 $.25
(H1600)

Forgive Us, Lord Of Life
SATB KJOS GC18 $.30   (H1601)

From Every Stormy Wind That Blows *Gen
(Olds) SATB SCHMITT 1863 $.20   (H1602)

George Washington's Prayer For Nation
(Craig) SATB oct PLYMOUTH DC-105 $.25   (H1603)

Good Christian Men Rejoice! *see In Dulci
Jubilo

Guide Me, O Thou Great Jehovah
(Whitman) SATB oct LILLENAS AN-2338 $.30
(H1604)

Hail To The Lord's Anointed *Gen
SATB SCHMITT 15016 $.35   (H1605)
SATB SOUTHERN $.35   (H1606)

Holy Day Of Days
SATB KJOS GC13 $.30   (H1607)

How Sweet The Name Of Jesus Sounds
(Whitsett) SATB oct LILLENAS AN-2358 $.30
(H1608)

I Was Glad When They Said Unto Me
(McAfee) SATB oct BOURNE 846 $.35   (H1609)

HASTINGS (cont'd.)

In Dulci Jubilo *Xmas
"Good Christian Men Rejoice!" SATB WARNER
W3707 $.30   (H1610)

In The Grove Of Cedars *Xmas
unis/2pt/SSA WARNER 3755 $.30   (H1611)
SATB,acap WARNER 3742 $.30   (H1612)

Joy Dawned Again On Easter Day (from Cologne
Gesangbuch) Easter/Lent
SATB,opt 2trp&2trom oct BOURNE HA10 $.30   (H1613)

Lord Is A Mighty God, The
SATB oct SACRED S-29 $.35   (H1614)

Meditation On "Lyra Davidica" *Easter,
meditation
SATB WARNER W3717 $.30   (H1615)

O God Who Hast Prepared
SATB KJOS GC14 $.30   (H1616)

Our Father, Help Us
SATB KJOS GC19 $.30   (H1617)

Our Lord Is Risen *anthem
(Riedel) SATB,2trp,trom (easy) cor pts
AUGSBURG 1262 $.20, ipa   (H1618)

Prayer For The United Nations *prayer
WARNER WB-104 $.35   (H1619)

Preserve Us, O Lord
SATB KJOS GC17 $.30   (H1620)

Rock Of Ages *Gen
(Olds) SATB SCHMITT 1853 $.18   (H1621)
(Rasley) SATB oct LORENZ C271 $.30   (H1622)

Watchman, Tell Us Of The Night *Xmas
SATB ALFRED 6625 $.30   (H1623)

We Know The Paths
SATB KJOS GC15 $.30   (H1624)

HASTINGS, E.
Prayer Of St. Francis
(Craig) SATB oct PLYMOUTH DC-107 $.25   (H1625)

Shepherds Psalm
SATB oct PRESSER MC296 $.35   (H1626)

HASTINGS, PAUL
Lift Up Your Heads, O Ye Gates *see
Psalmodia Evangelica

Psalmodia Evangelica
"Lift Up Your Heads, O Ye Gates" SATB oct
BOURNE HA2 $.30   (H1627)

Unto Us A Boy Is Born *Xmas,carol,Eng
SATB oct BOURNE HA4 $.30   (H1628)

HASTINGS, ROSS (1915-   )
God Be Merciful Unto Us
SATB oct GRAY GCMR 2751 $.25   (H1629)

Lobe Den Herrn
"Praise To The Lord" SATB oct GRAY
GCMR 2649 $.25   (H1630)

Praise To The Lord *see Lobe Den Herrn

Prayer Of Saint Patrick
SSAATTBB oct KERBY 6509C $.30   (H1631)

Prayer Of St. Patrick
SSAATTBB,org oct KERBY 6509 $.35   (H1632)

HASTINGS, THOMAS (1784-1872)
Lie Quiet, Soul
SATB,T solo WARNER W3773 $.30   (H1633)

HATCH, H.
God Bless The Little Things
SA/TB FLAMMER E5098 $.30   (H1634)

Great Mother's Lullaby *Xmas
SATB,acap oct PRESSER 332-14958 $.25   (H1635)

HATHAWAY, C.
Praisin' The Lord *spir
SATB oct BOURNE 738 $.25   (H1636)

HATHAWAY, CHARLES (1904-1966)
Glory Be
SATB oct BOURNE 742 $.25   (H1637)

HATRED STIRRETH UP STRIFE see Mechem, Kirke

HATTON
From All That Dwell
(Gerig) SATB oct LILLENAS AN-2361 $.30
(H1638)

Jesus Shall Reign
(Boersma) SATB oct WORD CS-2382 $.35
(H1639)
(Ibbotson) SATB FLAMMER A 5249 $.30   (H1640)

O God Beneath Thy Guiding Hand
(Smith) jr cor&sr cor (easy) FISCHER,C
CM 7513 $.25   (H1641)

HATTON, JOHN [LIPTROT] (1809-1886)
O God, Beneath Thy Guiding Hand *Thanks
(Shaw) mix cor,org oct SCHIRM.G 10099 $.30
(H1642)

HAUBIEL, CHARLES (1892-   )
Father Abraham
SATB,narrator,orch SEESAW $4.00   (H1643)
SATB,pno SEESAW $1.50   (H1644)
TTBB,B soli,pno SEESAW $1.50   (H1645)
TTBB,B solo,pno,vln,opt trp SEESAW $1.50
(H1646)

Festival
SSA,pno SEESAW $1.00   (H1647)

L'Amore Spirituale
SSSSSAA&SSAA,pno SEESAW $4.00   (H1648)

Madonna
SATB,pno SEESAW $1.00   (H1649)
SSAA,pno SEESAW $1.00   (H1650)

Vision Of Saint Joan
SATB&opt boy cor,SA soli,pno/orch SEESAW
$8.00   (H1651)

HAUBIEL, CHARLES (cont'd.)

What Wondrous Sacrifice
SSATB,acap SEESAW $1.00   (H1652)

HAUBLEIN, ERNST
Liedmesse *Mass
4-6pt mix cor MOSELER s.p.   (H1653)

HAUG, G.
Gott Segne Diesen Bund
(Feuerbacher, W.) [Ger] wom cor,acap (easy)
HUG s.p.   (H1654)

Wie Gott Will
[Ger] mix cor,acap (easy) HUG s.p.   (H1655)

HAUG, [HANS] (1900-   )
Wach Auf, Mein Volk
[Ger] mix cor,acap (easy) HUG s.p.   (H1656)

HAUGLAND
Thee, Holy Father, We Adore *Gen
SATB SCHMITT SD6001 $.25   (H1657)

HAUMESSER, A.
Pie Jesu *Gen,mot
[Lat] cor,org oct DURAND s.p.   (H1658)

HAUPT
Christmas Symbol, The *Xmas
SAB oct PLYMOUTH JR-402 $.30   (H1659)
SSA oct PLYMOUTH JR-204 $.30   (H1660)
TTBB oct PLYMOUTH JR-306 $.30   (H1661)

HAUPT, DAVID
Noel, Noel, Noel *Xmas
SATB,pno&org oct FOX UM122 $.35   (H1662)

HAUPTMANN
God, My Help *Gen
(Paekau) SATB SCHMITT 1788 $.20   (H1663)

HAUPTMANN, MORITZ (1792-1868)
Gott, Deine Gute Reicht So Weit *prayer
3pt wom cor,acap cor pts BREITKOPF-W
CHB-4886 s.p.   (H1664)

Noel *Xmas
3pt wom cor BROEKMANS 127 s.p.   (H1665)

HAUS, KARL (1928-   )
Anrufung
see Weihnachtliches Triptychon

Dormi Jesus
see Weihnachtliches Triptychon

Halleluja
see Weihnachtliches Triptychon

Nun Laufet, Ihr Hirten
see Zwei Schlesische Weihnachtslieder

Susani
jr cor&men cor (med easy) oct LEUCKART 42
s.p.   (H1666)

Was Soll Das Bedeuten
see Zwei Schlesische Weihnachtslieder

Weihnachtliches Triptychon *Xmas
SATB,SATB soli,inst cor pts TONGER s.p.,
ipa
contains: Anrufung; Dormi Jesus;
Halleluja   (H1667)

Zwei Schlesische Weihnachtslieder *Xmas
men cor (easy) oct LEUCKART 353 s.p.
contains: Nun Laufet, Ihr Hirten; Was
Soll Das Bedeuten   (H1668)

HAVA NAGILA *folk,Isr
(Beckahrd) SSA oct PRO ART 2200 $.35   (H1669)
(Beckahrd) SATB oct PRO ART 2121 $.35   (H1670)
(Beckahrd) SAB oct PRO ART 2197 $.35   (H1671)

HAVE A NICE DAY see Hammack, Bobby

HAVE COMPASSION ON ME, O LORD see Erbach,
Christian, Miserere Mei, Domine

HAVE DONE DULL CARE see Eccard, Johannes

HAVE FAITH IN GOD see Trued, Clarence

HAVE FAITH IN GOD, MY HEART see Konig

HAVE MERCY AND SPARE see Christiansen, F.
Melius

HAVE MERCY O LORD see Lvovsky, S., Hospodi
Pomilui

HAVE MERCY ON ME see Handel, George Frideric,
Have Mercy Upon Me

HAVE MERCY ON ME see Peloquin, C. Alexander

HAVE MERCY ON ME, O GOD see Bunjes, Paul G.,
Miserere Mei

HAVE MERCY UPON ME see Handel, George Frideric

HAVE MERCY UPON ME, O GOD see Tomkins, Thomas

HAVE MERCY UPON ME, O LORD see Lupo, Thomas,
Miserere Mei Domine

HAVE MERCY UPON ME, O LORD see Ripolles,
Vincente, Miserere Mei, Deus

HAVE MERCY UPON US see Lekberg, Sven

HAVE MERCY UPON US see Palestrina, Giovanni,
Miserere Nostri

HAVE MERCY UPON US see Pergolesi, Giovanni
Battista

HAVE NO FEAR, LITTLE FLOCK see Zimmermann,
Heinz Werner

HAVE THINE OWN WAY LORD
SATB/TTBB BIG3 $.25   (H1672)

HAVE THINE OWN WAY, LORD see Lorenz

HAVE THINE OWN WAY, LORD see Stebbins, George [Coles]

HAVE YE NOT KNOWN see Thompson, Randall

HAVE YOU ANY ROOM FOR JESUS? see Williams

HAVE YOU EVER WONDERED WHY? see White

HAVE YOU HAD AN ENCOUNTER WITH GOD? see Wooley

HAVE YOU HEARD see Ludlow

HAVE YOU SEEN A STAR? see Davis, Katherine K.

HAVEN OF REST, THE see Moore

HAVEN OF REST, THE see Landon

HAVEY, MARGUERITE
O Spirit, Who From Jesus Came
4pt mix cor oct SCHIRM.G 9878 $.25 (H1673)

HAWEIS, [THOMAS] (1734-1820)
I Lift My Soul To Thee
(Cotterill; Rogers) SATB oct BOURNE 834 $.25 (H1674)

HAWKEY
Hear My Prayer, O Lord *Introit
SATB THOMP.G G-582 s.p. see from Two Introits (H1675)

I Lift My Heart To Thee *Introit
SATB THOMP.G G-582 s.p. see from Two Introits (H1676)

Praise Ye The Lord
SATB THOMP.G G-586 s.p. (H1677)

Two Introits *see Hear My Prayer, O Lord; I Lift My Heart To Thee (H1678)

HAWKEY, WILLIAM
Sweet Was The Song The Virgin Sang
SATB,opt org/pno PETERS H462 $.30 (H1679)

HAWKINS
I've Discovered The Way Of Gladness
SATB oct LORENZ B170 $.30 (H1680)
(Decou) SATB oct LILLENAS AN-1621 $.30 (H1681)
(Schubert) ST oct LILLENAS AN-1190 $.30 (H1682)
(Skillings) SSATTB oct LILLENAS AT-1077 $.25 (H1683)

HAWKINS, ED.
Early In The Morning
SATB BIG3 $.40 (H1684)

I'm Going Through
SATB BIG3 $.40 (H1685)

Jesus Lover Of My Soul
SATB BIG3 $.40 (H1686)

Joy, Joy
SATB BIG3 $.40 (H1687)

Let Us Go Into The House Of The Lord
SATB BIG3 $.40 (H1688)

O Happy Day
SSA/SATB,solo BIG3 $.35 (H1689)

To My Father's House
SATB BIG3 $.40 (H1690)

HAWKINS, FLOYD W. (1904-)
Alleluia! (composed with Leech, Lida [Shivers]) *Easter,cant
mix cor,narrator voc sc LILLENAS ME-1 $.60 (H1691)

Anthem Of The Ages *Easter,anthem/cant
mix cor,solo,narrator,inst voc sc LILLENAS ME-2 $1.00 (H1692)

Crown Him King *Easter,cant/hymn
mix cor,narrator voc sc LILLENAS ME-33 $1.50 (H1693)

Crystal Fountain, The
(Higgins) SATB oct LILLENAS AN-1121 $.25 (H1694)

Day Of Pentecost, The *Pent
SATB oct LILLENAS AN-2221 $.35 (H1695)

God Is Our Refuge And Strength
SATB oct LILLENAS AN-2363 $.30 (H1696)

God's Great Grace
(Whitsett) SATB oct LILLENAS AN-1605 $.30 (H1697)

Heavens Declare, The *Xmas,Bibl/cant
cor,narrator,2 med soli voc sc LILLENAS MC-212 $1.00 (H1698)

I Met God In The Morning
(Whitman) SATB oct LILLENAS AN-2311 $.30 (H1699)
(Whitman) SAB oct LILLENAS AN-2316 $.30 (H1700)

King And Saviour (composed with Leech, Lida [Shivers]) *Xmas,Bibl/cant
cor,pno voc sc LILLENAS MC-216 $.60 (H1701)

Let Thy Mantle Fall On Me
SATB oct LILLENAS AN-1130 $.25 (H1702)
(Mickelson) SSATB oct LILLENAS AN-1145 $.25 (H1703)

Song In The Night *Xmas,cant
mix cor,SATBar soli voc sc LILLENAS MC-10 $1.50 (H1704)

HAWKINS, GORDON
As The Hart Panteth (Psalm 42) Gen
SATB,acap oct OXFORD 43.365 $.25 (H1705)

Psalm 42 *see As The Hart Panteth

HAWLEY
Holy Night! Peaceful Night! *Xmas
SATB oct PRESSER 322-35111 $.30 (H1706)

HAWLEY, [CHARLES BEACH] (1858-1915)
Christ Child *Xmas
SATB PRESSER $1.25 (H1707)

Holy Night! Peaceful Night! *Xmas
(Peery, R.) SSA oct PRESSER 322-35359 $.30 (H1708)

HAWTHORNE
Whispering Hope
SATB oct LORENZ A138 $.25 (H1709)
SA oct LORENZ 5331 $.25 (H1710)

HAWTHORNE, ALICE
Whispering Hope
(Landon, S.) SA ALLANS 360 s.p. (H1711)

HAWTHORNE, G.
Lightshine *see Red, Buryl

HAXBY
While I Sup With Thee
SATB oct LORENZ 9583 $.25 (H1712)

HAYDE
Come, O Children, Let Us Gather
SATB&jr cor oct VOLKWEIN VB274 $.25 (H1713)

HAYDN, G.
Darken'd Was All The Land *Easter
(Lynn, G.) SATB,acap oct PRESSER 312-40055 $.30 (H1714)

HAYDN, (FRANZ) JOSEPH (1732-1809)
Abendlied Zu Gott *Eve
(Wagner) "Evensong" [Eng/Ger] SATB oct LAWSON 51067 $.40 (H1715)

Achieved Is The Glorious Work (from Creation, The) Gen,anthem
SATB ALLANS 142 s.p. (H1716)
4pt mix cor oct SCHIRM.G 2358 $.25 (H1717)
SATB oct NOVELLO 34.0152.09, 34.0153.07 s.p. (H1718)
4pt mix cor (second chorus) oct SCHIRM.G 2359 $.30 (H1719)
SATB oct WALTON 6001 $.30 (H1720)
(Davies, Laurence H.) 2pt (easy) oct OXFORD 44.078 $.25 (H1721)

Agnus Dei (from Missa Brevis Sancti Joannis De Deo) Agnus
(Hines) "Lamb Of God" [Lat/Eng] 4pt mix cor,pno/org oct SCHIRM.G 11441 $.30 (H1722)
(Mattfeld, V.) "Lamb Of God" [Lat/Eng] SATB,pno SCHIRM.EC 2453 (H1723)

Ave Verum
(Barnes) "Saviour, Breathe Forgiveness" unis oct SCHIRM.G 8032 $.20 (H1724)

Awake The Harp (from Creation, The) anthem/Bibl
4pt mix cor oct SCHIRM.G 2357 $.30 (H1725)
SATB oct NOVELLO 34.0150.27 s.p. (H1726)

By Thee With Bliss (from The Creation)
SATB oct PRO ART 1207 $.25 (H1727)

Christ The Lord Is Risen *Easter
(Davis, K.K.) SATB WARNER R3141 $.30 (H1728)
(Davis, K.K.) SAB WARNER R3444 $.30 (H1729)

Christmas Bells *Xmas
(Mathews) SATB oct STAFF 139 $.25 (H1730)

Creation, *ora
[Eng/Ger] voc sc PETERS 66 $3.00, ipr, cloth PETERS 66 $7.50, ipr, min sc PETERS E955 $9.00, ipr, min sc-cloth PETERS E955 $12.50, ipr, study sc PETERS 1029A $30.00, ipr (H1731)

Creation, The *Bibl/cant/ora
SATB,STB soli,2fl,2ob,2clar,2bsn,2horn, 2trp,3trom,strings,timp, opt contrabassoon bds,voc sc NOVELLO s.p., ipr (H1732)
(Read) SSA voc pt FISCHER,C PT-2647 $.75 (H1733)

Creation, The *see Die Schopfung

Credo
(Mason) SATB oct WORD CS-116 $.35 (H1734)

Darkness Concealed The Earth *Easter
SATB oct LORENZ C265 $.25 (H1735)

Darkness Was On The Earth *Easter
(Hallagan, R.) SATB,acap oct PRESSER 312-40754 $.30 (H1736)

Darkness Was Over All *see Tenebrae Factae Sunt

Des Herren Lob Sei Unser Lied (from Die Schopfung)
(Vogel, Moritz; Nagler, Franciscus) [Ger] wom cor&jr cor,org,opt strings HUG 74 s.p. (H1737)

Die Himmel Erzahlen Die Ehre Gottes (from Die Schopfung) anthem
SATB,org HANSSLER 6.0860 sc s.p., cor pts s.p. (H1738)
4pt mix cor,STB soli,2fl,2ob,2clar,3bsn, 2horn,2trp,3trom,strings,timp sc BREITKOPF-W PB-4981 s.p., cor pts BREITKOPF-W CHB-4936 s.p., voc sc BREITKOPF-W EB-5663 s.p. (H1739)
"Heavens Are Telling" 4pt mix cor,STB soli, pno/org sc BREITKOPF-W EB-5663 s.p., cor pts BREITKOPF-W CHB-4936 s.p. (H1740)
"Heavens Are Telling" SATB oct FISCHER,C CM-127 $.30 (H1741)
"Heavens Are Telling" cor oct HART s.p. (H1742)
"Heavens Are Telling" SATB oct LESLIE 4026 (H1743)
(Hamma) [Eng/Ger] mix cor,STB soli,org/pno HEINRICH. 930 sc s.p., cor pts s.p. (H1744)
(Noatzsch, R.) mix cor&3 eq voices,2fl,2ob, 2clar,3bsn,2trp,2horn,3trom,strings,timp voc pt BREITKOPF-L CHB-1504 s.p., voc sc BREITKOPF-L EB-5663 s.p., ipr (H1745)

HAYDN, (FRANZ) JOSEPH (cont'd.)

Die Himmelerzahlen Die Ehre Gottes (from Creation) Gen/Harv,anthem/Bibl
"Heavens Are Telling, The" SATB,pno SCHIRM.EC 1188 $.40, ipr (H1746)
"Heavens Are Telling, The" SATB,STB soli oct LAWSON 51147 $.45 (H1747)
"Heavens Are Telling, The" SATB,STB soli, pno (diff) oct WILLIS 795 $.12 (H1748)
"Heavens Are Telling, The" mix cor CURWEN 60223 s.p. (H1749)
"Heavens Are Telling, The" SATB SCHMITT 1921 $.40 (H1750)
"Heavens Are Telling, The" SATB oct NOVELLO 34.0158.08 s.p. (H1751)
"Heavens Are Telling, The" SAB oct BELWIN 1582 $.25 (H1752)
"Heavens Are Telling, The" SATB oct BELWIN 1027 $.25 (H1753)
"Heavens Are Telling, The" SA oct BELWIN 1818 $.25 (H1754)
"Heavens Are Telling, The" SATB oct PRESSER 332-00813 $.40 (H1755)
"Heavens Are Telling, The" SATB ALLANS 2 s.p. (H1756)
"Heavens Are Telling, The" SA ALLANS 444 s.p. (H1757)
"Heavens Are Telling, The" SATB WARNER G462 $.40 (H1758)
"Heavens Are Telling, The" SATB,SATB soli, org oct HARRIS HC4013 $.35 (H1759)
"Heavens Are Telling, The" SA oct OXFORD 44.230 $.70 (H1760)
"Heavens Are Telling, The" SATB oct PRO ART 1043 $.35 (H1761)
"Heavens Are Telling, The" TTBB oct LORENZ 2838 $.35 (H1762)
"Heavens Are Telling, The" SAB oct LORENZ 7020 $.35 (H1763)
"Heavens Are Telling, The" SATB oct LORENZ 488 $.30 (H1764)
"Heavens Are Telling, The" SATB (very easy) oct LORENZ 9226 $.30 (H1765)
(Buck) "Heavens Are Telling, The" 4pt mix cor,STB soli oct SCHIRM.G 3521 $.35 (H1766)
(Byard, Herbert) "Heavens Are Telling, The" SATB oct NOVELLO 34.0869.08 s.p. (H1767)
(Deis) "Heavens Are Telling, The" SABar oct SCHIRM.G 10032 $.40 (H1768)
(Deis) "Heavens Are Telling, The" 2pt wom cor,org/pno oct SCHIRM.G 10072 $.35 (H1769)
(Peery, Rob Roy) "Heavens Are Telling, The" SATB oct BELWIN 1027 $.25 (H1770)
(Peery, Rob Roy) "Heavens Are Telling, The" SAB oct BELWIN 1582 $.25 (H1771)
(Peery, Rob Roy) "Heavens Are Telling, The" SA oct BELWIN 1818 $.30 (H1772)
(Treharne) "Heavens Are Telling, The" 3pt wom cor,pno/org oct SCHIRM.G 8940 $.35 (H1773)
(Watson) "Heavens Are Telling, The" oct PRO ART 1086 $.30 (H1774)
(Whitford) "Heavens Are Telling, The" SATB oct FISCHER,J 9114 $.35 (H1775)

Die Jahreszeiten *ora
4pt mix cor,STB soli,2fl,2ob,2clar,2bsn, 3horn,3trp,3trom,strings,perc,timp sc BREITKOPF-W PB-4382 s.p., ipa (H1776)
(Klengel, P.) mix cor,STB soli,2fl,2ob, 2clar,3bsn,2trp,2horn,3trom,strings,perc, timp voc pt BREITKOPF-L CHB-108A-D s.p., voc sc BREITKOPF-L EB-116 s.p., ipr (H1777)

Die Schopfung *ora
"Creation, The" 4pt mix cor,STB soli,3fl, 2ob,2clar,3bsn,2horn,2trp,3trom,strings, timp sc BREITKOPF-W PB-4381 s.p., ipa (H1778)
"Creation, The" mix cor,STB soli LAWSON $2.00 (H1779)
"Creation, The" cor,opt orch voc sc KALMUS 6236 $2.00, ipa (H1780)
"Creation, The" cor sc KALMUS L383 $13.00 (H1781)
"Creation, The" cor KALMUS $3.50 (H1782)
"Creation, The" cor sc KALMUS $13.00 (H1783)
"Creation, The" cor,orch sc KALMUS $13.00, ipa (H1784)
"Creation, The" oct HART s.p. (H1785)
"La Creation" [Fr] mix cor,SSTB soli CHOUDENS voc sc s.p., cor pts s.p. (H1786)
(Klengel, P.) [Eng/Fr/Ger] mix cor,STB soli,3fl,2ob,2clar,3bsn,2horn,2trp,3trom, strings,timp voc sc BREITKOPF-L EB-118 s.p., ipr (H1787)
(Klengel, P.) [Fr/Ger] mix cor,STB soli, 3fl,2ob,2clar,3bsn,2horn,2trp,3trom, strings,timp voc pt BREITKOPF-L CHB-109A+B s.p. (H1788)
(Novello, Vincent) "Creation, The" cor, soli,pno SCHIRM.G pap $1.50, cloth $4.00, cor pts $1.00 (H1789)

Die Sieben Letzen Worte Unseres Erlosers Am Kreuze *Psntd,ora
(Unverricht, Hubert) [Ger] SATB,SATB soli, orch (med diff) BAREN. BA 4655 s.p., voc sc BAREN. BA 4655A $9.75 (H1790)

Die Sieben Worte Des Erlosers Am Kreuze *Gd.Fri./Lent/Psntd,cant/ora
4pt mix cor,SATB soli,2fl,2ob,2clar,3bsn, 2horn,2trp,2trom,strings,timp voc sc BREITKOPF-W EB-1235 s.p., ipr, sc BREITKOPF-W rental (H1791)
mix cor,SATB soli,2fl,2ob,2clar,3bsn,2trp, 2horn,2trom,strings,timp voc pt BREITKOPF-L CHB-110A-D s.p., ipr (H1792)
"Last Words Of Christ On The Cross" mix cor voc sc KALMUS 6239 $1.50 (H1793)
"Last Words Of The Saviour On The Cross, The" cor,orch sc KALMUS $25.00, ipa (H1794)
"Passion, The" SATB,SATB soli,2fl,2ob, 2clar,2bsn,2horn,2trp,2trom,strings,timp, opt contrabassoon voc sc NOVELLO s.p., ipr (H1795)
"Seven Last Words" [Ger] SATB,SATB soli, orch voc sc PETERS 1371 $2.50 (H1796)
"Seven Last Words Of Christ, The" cor sc KALMUS $25.00 (H1797)
"Seven Last Words Of Christ, The" cor,pno voc sc SCHIRM.G $1.25 (H1798)

HAYDN, (FRANZ) JOSEPH (cont'd.)

"Seven Words Of Christ" BELWIN $1.50 (H1799)

Dona Nobis Pacem (from Theresienmesse)
(Harris) [Lat] SATB oct PRO ART 2745 $.30 (H1800)

Du Bist's, Dem Ruhm Und Ehre Gebuhret
eq voices/mix cor,pno/orch cor pts TONGER s.p., ipa (H1801)
[Ger] mix cor,acap (med) HUG s.p. (H1802)
(Frank) "Thou Art Worthy Of Praise" SATB oct FOX MM13 $.35 (H1803)
(Gellert, C.F.) 4pt mix cor,acap voc pt DOBLINGER s.p. (H1804)

Ekesszolas
(Lessing, G.E.; Lukin, L.) [Hung] SSTB (med diff) BUDAPEST S152 s.p. (H1805)

Evensong *see Abendlied Zu Gott

Five Symphonies
cor min sc KALMUS 401 $3.00 for choral and orchestral usage
contains: Le Midi; Le Soir; Maria Teresia; Passione; Trauer (H1806)

Forgive Us Lord
(Suchoff) SATB oct FOX RM2 $.35 (H1807)

Four Choruses [No. 1 & 2], Vol. I *CC2U
[Ger] SAT/STB,pno voc sc HINRICHSEN P4936A s.p. (H1808)

Four Choruses [No. 3 & 4], Vol. II *CC2U
[Ger] TTB,pno voc sc HINRICHSEN P4936B s.p. (H1809)

Gebet Zu Gott
(Etti, K.) 4pt mix cor,acap voc pt DOBLINGER s.p. (H1810)
(Etti, K.) men cor,acap voc pt DOBLINGER s.p. (H1811)

Gloria (from Heiligmesse, The) Bibl/Gloria
SATB oct WALTON 2031 $.30 (H1812)
SSA oct WALTON 5025 $.35 (H1813)
SAB oct WALTON 4004 $.35 (H1814)
2pt oct WALTON 5030 $.30 (H1815)
"Sing To The Lord" SATB,pno (diff) oct WILLIS 5059 $.10 (H1816)
(Kjelson) SATB oct BELWIN 2237 $.35 (H1817)
(Marzo) "Sing To The Lord" 4pt mix cor oct SCHIRM.G 5414 $.30 (H1818)
(Woodman) mix cor SOUTHERN $.30 (H1819)

Gloria In Excelsis (from Little Organ Mass) Xmas,Gloria
(Ehret) SSA oct PRO ART 2514 $.35 (H1820)
(Ehret, W.) SSA,pno/org oct BOONIN 146 (H1821)

Glorious Is The Lord Almighty (from Mass No. 3)
(Coggin) SAB oct PRO ART 2270 $.35 (H1822)
(Coggin) SATB oct PRO ART 2577 $.30 (H1823)
(Coggin) SSA oct PRO ART 2580 $.30 (H1824)

Glorious Things Of Thee Are Spoken *hymn
(Ehret) 3pt jr cor/SAB (med easy) FISCHER,C CM 7368 $.25 (H1825)
(Ehret) SSA oct FISCHER,C CM-7368 $.25 (H1826)
(Ehret) SATB oct FISCHER,C CM-7117 $.25 (H1827)
(Shaw; Parker) SATB oct LAWSON 756 $.30 (H1828)
(Smith) SATB oct LILLENAS AN-2355 $.30 (H1829)
(Wiley) SATB oct PRO ART 1542 $.25 (H1830)

God Is The Light Of The World
(Morgan) SSA oct BELWIN 64210 $.30 (H1831)
(Morgan) SSATTB,acap oct BELWIN 64204 $.30 (H1832)
(Morgan) TTBB,acap oct BELWIN 64246 $.25 (H1833)

Great And Glorious
TTBB oct BELWIN 64077 $.30 (H1834)
SATB oct BELWIN 64065 $.35 (H1835)

Great Is The Lord
SATB oct PRESSER 332-09589 $.30 (H1836)

Grosse Orgelmesse *see Missa Solennis In Honorem B.M.V. In Es-Dur

Hallelujah To The God Of Israel
(Young, R.; Weinandt. E.) SATB oct FISCHER, J 10008 $.35 (H1837)

Harmonie-Messe *see Missa

Harmoniemesse *Mass
(Lippmann, Friedrich) [Ger] SATB,SATB soli, org,2vln,vla,vcl,bvl (med diff) BA 4659 voc sc BAREN. BA 4659A $11.00, min sc BAREN. TP 97 $14.25, ipa (H1838)

Harmoniemesse *see Missa

Harmoniemesse *see Missa Solennis

Heavens Are Telling *see Die Himmel Erzahlen Die Ehre Gottes

Heavens Are Telling, The *see Die Himmelerzahlen Die Ehre Gottes

Heilig-Messe *see Missa In Honorem B. Bernardi De Offida

Heilig-Messe *see Missa Solemnis

Heiligmesse *see Missa Sancti Bernardi De Offida

Herr! Der Du Mir Das Leben
(Vogel, Moritz; Nagler, Franciscus) [Ger] wom cor&jr cor,org,opt strings HUG 81 s.p. (H1839)

Hier Liegt Vor Deiner Majestat
see Mozart, Wolfgang Amadeus, Auf Der Andacht Heil'gen Flugeln

Holy, Holy, Holy *Xmas
(Coggin, E.) SAB oct PRESSER 312-40735 $.30 (H1840)
(Ehret) SAB oct AGAPE A 405 $.30 (H1841)

HAYDN, (FRANZ) JOSEPH (cont'd.)

Holy Ten Commandments, The
(Boepple, P.) 3-5 eq voices,acap oct PRESSER 352-00010 $.40 (H1842)

Hymn Of Gratitude
(Buck) SSATTBB oct SCHIRM.G 3989 $.25 (H1843)

Imperial Mass *see Missa In Angustiis

In Thee, O Lord
(Williams) SATB oct FOX PS103 $.35 (H1844)
(Williams) SAB oct FOX PS162 $.30 (H1845)
(Williams) SSA oct FOX PS163 $.30 (H1846)

Insanae Et Vanae Curae *anthem
[Lat] SATB oct NOVELLO 34.0359.09 s.p. (H1847)

Insanae Et Vanae Curea *mot
[Lat] mix cor oct NOVELLO 34.0359.09 s.p. (H1848)

Jesus Christ, Our Lord, Is Risen (from St. Anthony Chorale) Easter
SATB,org oct LAWSON 51381 $.30 (H1849)

Jojj, Beke Mnajas Angyala (from Judas Maccabaeus)
(Szedo, D.) [Hung] 2 eq voices,pno (med diff) BUDAPEST 4731 s.p. (H1850)

Jojj, Beke Mnyajas Angyala (from Judas Maccabaeus)
(Szedo, D.) [Hung] 2 eq voices/SA (med diff) BUDAPEST 4732 s.p. (H1851)

Kanonok *sac/sec,CC17L,canon
(Lukin, L.) [Hung] 4pt (easy) BUDAPEST 3021 s.p. (H1852)

Kleine Orgelmesse *see Missa Brevis St. Johannis De Deo

Kyrie (from Harmoniemesse) Kyrie
(Herrmann) 4pt mix cor,org/pno oct SCHIRM.G 11194 $.35 (H1853)
(Herrmann) 3pt wom cor,org/pno oct SCHIRM.G 11303 $.35 (H1854)
(Herrmann) [Lat] 4pt mix cor,org/pno oct SCHIRM.G 11865 $.40 (H1855)
(Hines) [Eng/Lat] 4pt mix cor,org/pno oct SCHIRM.G 11442 $.30 (H1856)

Kyrie Eleison (from Imperial Mass) Gen,Kyrie
SATB oct HERITAGE H94 $.40 (H1857)
(Ehret) SATB SCHMITT 1437 $.35 (H1858)
(Hirt) [Eng/Lat] SATB WARNER W3543 $.35 (H1859)

La Creation *see Die Schopfung

Lamb Of God *see Agnus Dei

Lamb Of God (Father, Forgive Them) (from Seven Words, The)
SATB,soli,org SCHIRM.EC 1776 $.40, ipr (H1860)

Last Words Of Christ On The Cross *see Die Sieben Worte Des Erlosers Am Kreuze

Last Words Of The Saviour On The Cross, The *see Die Sieben Worte Des Erlosers Am Kreuze

Le Midi
see Five Symphonies

Le Soir
see Five Symphonies

Les Cieux Sont Temoins (from La Creation)
[Fr] mix cor,SMezT soli voc sc CHOUDENS s.p. (H1861)

Litaniae De B.M.V. In C-Dur
(Landon, H.C.R.) 4pt mix cor,soli,org,2ob, 2trp,timp,strings (C maj) DOBLINGER sc s.p., voc sc s.p., cor pts s.p., ipa (H1862)

Lo My Shepherd
SATB oct GRAY GCMR 1744 $.25 (H1863)

Lo, My Shepherd Is Divine (from Mass In G)
SATB oct PRO ART 1684 $.30 (H1864)
SATB oct BELWIN 64091 $.35 (H1865)
2pt oct WALTON 5013 $.25 (H1866)
(Barrie) 3pt mix cor oct LAWSON 51565 $.30 (H1867)
(Carlton) SSA BOOSEY-CAN s.p. (H1868)
(Carlton) SATB oct BOOSEY 5150 $.30 (H1869)
(Kraft) 3pt wom cor oct SCHIRM.G 9669 $.30 (H1870)
(Nevins) SA oct GRAY GCMR 1884 $.25 (H1871)

Lo, My Shepherd's Hand Divine (from Mass In G-Major)
(Davison, A.) SATB,org SCHIRM.EC 1715 $.35 (H1872)
(Greene, E.) SSAA,org SCHIRM.EC 1815 $.25 (H1873)

Lord Nelson Mass *see Nelson-Missa

Magnificat *Magnif
girl cor SOUTHERN $.30 (H1874)

Maria Teresia
see Five Symphonies

Maria Theresa Mass *see Theresienmesse

Mariazeller Mass *see Missa Cellensis

Mariazeller Messe *see Missa Cellensis

Mariazellermesse *see Missa Cellensis

Marvelous Work, The
(Davis) SSA oct GALAXY 1.1950.1 $.30 (H1875)

Marv'lous Work, The (from Creation, The) anthem
SATB oct NOVELLO 34.0157.10 s.p. (H1876)

Mass In B-Flat *see Schoepfungsmesse

Mass In B Flat *see Theresienmesse

Mass In Time Of War *see Missa In Tempore Belli

HAYDN, (FRANZ) JOSEPH (cont'd.)

Mass No. 3 In D *see Nelson-Missa

Messe D-Moll *Mass
(Robbins; Landon) "Nelson Mass" [Lat] SATB, SAB soli,orch (D min) voc sc SCHOTT 10808 s.p., min sc EULENBURG EUL995 s.p. (H1877)

Messe D-Moll *see Nelson-Missa

Messe No. 3 *see Nelson-Misse

Messe No. 5 *see Missa Cellensis

Messe No. 6 *see Missa

Messe No. 7 *see Missa Sancti Nicolai

Missa *Mass
"Harmonie-Messe" [Lat] SATB,SATB soli,orch voc sc PETERS 3538 $2.50, ipr (H1878)
"Harmoniemesse" cor voc sc KALMUS 6225 $2.00 (H1879)
"Harmoniemesse" cor,orch sc KALMUS $22.00, ipa (H1880)
"Messe No. 6" mix cor,SATB soli,org,fl,2ob, 2clar,2bsn,2trp,2horn,strings,timp BREITKOPF-L rental (H1881)

Missa Brevis *Mass
(Moder, R.) 4pt mix cor,S solo,org,2vln,bvl (F maj) DOBLINGER voc sc s.p., cor pts s.p., ipa (H1882)

Missa Brevis St. Johannis De Deo *Fest,Mass
mix cor voc sc KALMUS 6240 $2.50 (H1883)
(Robbins Landon, H.C.; Fussel, Karl Heinz; Landon, Christa) "Kleine Orgelmesse" [Ger] SATB,S solo,org,2vln,vcl (med) BA 4653 rental voc sc BAREN. BA 4653A $3.75, min sc BAREN. TP 95 $2.00 (H1884)

Missa Cellensis *Mass
"Mariazeller Mass" cor voc sc KALMUS 6244 $2.00 (H1885)
"Messe No. 5" mix cor,SATB soli,org,2ob, 2clar,2trp,2horn,strings,timp BREITKOPF-L rental (H1886)
(Landon, H.C. Robbins) "Mariazellermesse" 4pt mix cor,pno/org voc sc SCHIRM.G $2.00 (H1887)
(Robbins Landon, H.C.; Fussel, Karl Heinz; Landon, Christa) "Mariazeller Messe" SATB,SATB soli,orch (med diff) BA 4654 rental voc sc BAREN. BA 4654A $9.75, min sc BAREN. TP 96 $4.00 (H1888)

Missa Hispanica *Mass
(Sherman) [Lat] voc sc UNIVER. HMP 208 $15.20, cor pts UNIVER. HMP 210A-B $3.55 (H1889)

Missa In Angustiis *Mass
"Imperial Mass" BELWIN $1.50 (H1890)
"Imperial Mass" [Lat] SATB,SATB soli,fl, 2ob,2bsn,2trp,strings,timp voc sc NOVELLO s.p., ipr (H1891)

Missa In Angustiis *see Nelson-Messe

Missa In Honorem B. Bernardi De Offida *Mass
"Heilig-Messe" mix cor,org,2ob,2clar,2bsn, 2trp,strings,timp sc BREITKOPF-L rental (H1892)
(Robbins Landon, H.C.; Fussel, Karl Heinz; Landon, Christa) "Heilig-Messe" SATB,SATB soli,orch (med diff) voc sc BAREN. BA 4651 rental, min sc BAREN. BA 4651A $11.00, BAREN. TP 93 $5.00 (H1893)

Missa In Tempore Belli *Mass
"Mass In Time Of War" [Lat] SATB,SATB soli, fl,2ob,2clar,2bsn,2horn,2trp,strings,timp voc sc NOVELLO s.p., ipr (H1894)
"Paukenmesse" mix cor,SATB soli,org,fl,2ob, 2clar,2bsn,2trp,2horn,strings,timp BREITKOPF-L rental (H1895)
"Paukenmesse" cor,opt orch voc sc KALMUS 6245 $1.50, ipa (H1896)
"Paukenmesse" cor sc KALMUS L389 $12.00 (H1897)
"Paukenmesse" cor KALMUS $1.75 (H1898)
"Paukenmesse" cor,orch (C maj) sc KALMUS $12.00, ipa (H1899)
(Miller, Michael R.) "Mass In Time Of War" [Lat] 4pt mix cor,soli,pno voc sc SCHIRM.G $1.50 (H1900)
(Robbins Landon, H.C.; Fussel, Karl Heinz; Landon, Christa) "Paukenmesse" SATB,SATB soli,orch (med diff) BA 4652 rental voc sc BAREN. BA 4652A $13.25, min sc BAREN. TP 94 $5.00 (H1901)

Missa Sanctae Caecilie *Mass
[Lat] cmplt ed UNIVER. HMP14 $8.50, cor pts UNIVER. HMP15 $2.70 (H1902)

Missa Sancti Bernardi De Offida *Mass
"Heiligmesse" cor voc sc KALMUS 6246 $1.50 (H1903)
(Landon, H.C. Robbins) "Heiligmesse" 4pt mix cor,pno/org voc sc SCHIRM.G $2.50 (H1904)

Missa Sancti Nicolai *Mass
cor,orch FABER F0177 s.p. (H1905)
"Messe No. 7" mix cor,SATB soli,org,2ob, 2bsn,2trp,strings,timp BREITKOPF-L rental (H1906)
"St. Nicholas Mass" mix cor voc sc KALMUS 6242 $1.50 (H1907)
(Biss, Roderick; Landon, H.C. Robbins) [Lat] 4pt mix cor,4 soli,pno voc sc SCHIRM.G $1.50 (H1908)
(Landon, H.C. Robbins) cor,SATB soli,cont, 2ob,bsn,2horn,strings (easy) voc sc FABER ED 2814 $1.50 (H1909)

Missa Solemnis *Mass
"Heilig-Messe" [Lat] SATB,SATB soli,orch voc sc PETERS 1372 $1.50, ipr (H1910)

Missa Solennis *Mass
"Schopfungsmesse" mix cor,SSATTB soli,org, 2ob,2clar,2bsn,2trp,2horn,strings,timp BREITKOPF-L rental (H1911)
"Shoepfungsmess" mix cor voc sc KALMUS 6238 $2.50 (H1912)
(Herrmann, William) "Harmoniemesse" 4pt mix cor,org/pno voc sc SCHIRM.G $2.00 (H1913)

HAYDN, (FRANZ) JOSEPH (cont'd.)

Missa Solennis In Honorem B.M.V. In Es-Dur *BVM,Mass
(Strassl'a.) "Grosse Orgelmesse" 4pt mix cor,soli,org,2ob,2horn,2trp,timp,strings (E flat maj) DOBLINGER sc s.p., cor pts s.p., ipa (H1914)

My Shepherd Is The Lord Most High
(Morgan) boy cor SOUTHERN $.30 (H1915)

My Soul Shall Cry To You
(Suchoff) SATB oct FOX RM9 $.30 (H1916)

Native Land, God Keep Thee Free
(Wilson) SAB MARKS 4255 $.30 (H1917)

Nelson Mass *see Messe D-Moll

Nelson Mass *see Nelson-Missa

Nelson-Messe *Mass
(Thomas, Gunter) "Missa In Angustiis" SATB, SATB soli,org,2vln,vla,vcl,bvl (med diff) BA 4660 s.p., ipa voc sc BAREN. BA 4660A $9.75, min sc BAREN. TP 98 $10.50 (H1918)

Nelson-Missa *Mass
"Lord Nelson Mass" [Lat] SATB,SATB soli, orch voc sc PETERS 4351 $2.50, sc PETERS 4372 $15.00, ipa (H1919)
"Lord Nelson Mass" [Lat/Eng] cor voc sc SCHIRM.G $1.50 (H1920)
"Lord Nelson Mass" cor KALMUS $2.00 (H1921)
"Mass No. 3 In D" mix cor voc sc KALMUS 6241 $1.50 (H1922)
"Messe D-Moll" 4pt mix cor,org,fl,2ob,bsn, 3trp,strings,timp (D min) voc pt BREITKOPF-W CHB-714 s.p., ipr, sc BREITKOPF-W rental (H1923)
"Nelson Mass" cor sc KALMUS L390 $8.00, ipa (H1924)

Nelson-Misse *Mass
"Messe No. 3" mix cor,SATB soli,org,fl,2ob, 2bsn,3trp,strings,timp (D min) BREITKOPF-L rental (H1925)

Nicht Uns, O Herr, Gib Ehre *mot
[Ger] mix cor,acap (med diff) HUG s.p. contains also: Non Nobis Domine (H1926)

Non Nobis Domine *Gen/Lent
see Haydn, (Franz) Joseph, Nicht Uns, O Herr, Gib Ehre
"We Seek Not, God, Our Lord, For Glory" SATB,kbd (med diff) oct CONCORDIA 98-1515 $.40 (H1927)

O Dearest Jesus *Commun
(Harris) SATB oct PRO ART 1745 $.22 (H1928)
(Harris) SATB oct PRO ART 1745 $.22 (H1929)

O Lord, Give Ear To Me
(Ehret) SSATBB oct KENDOR $.30 (H1930)

O Worship The King
SATB oct STAFF 333 $.20 (H1931)
(Davis, K.K.) 2pt WARNER W3502 $.30 (H1932)
(Ehret, W.) SATB oct PRESSER 312-40597 $.30 (H1933)
(Kirk) SATB oct PRO ART 1528 $.25 (H1934)

Oh, Worship The King *hymn
(Williams) SATB oct LILLENAS AN-2279 $.30 (H1935)

Passion, The *see Die Sieben Worte Des Erlosers Am Kreuze

Passione
see Five Symphonies

Paukenmesse *see Missa In Tempore Belli

Praise The God Of Our Salvation
(Elkins) SATB oct PLYMOUTH SC-14 $.25 (H1936)

Praise The Lord
(Davis, K.) SSA SCHIRM.EC 1874 (H1937)

Praise The Lord! Ye Heavens Adore Him *Gen/Thanks
(Whittaker, W.G.) 2pt&desc (very easy) oct OXFORD 44.601 $.25 (H1938)

Praise We Sing To Thee
SSA KJOS 3006 $.30 (H1939)
(Luvaas) men cor KJOS 2505 $.30 (H1940)

Psalm Of Trust *Psalm
SA/SAB oct LORENZ 7814 $.25 (H1941)

Requiem C-Moll *Req
(Schmid, E.F.) [Ger] mix cor,soli,orch (C min) sc VIEWEG rental (H1942)

Rorate *Mass
[Lat] voc sc UNIVER. HMP 21 $2.25, cor pts UNIVER. HMP 22A-D $.40 (H1943)

Sainte Nuit
3pt wom cor BROEKMANS 126 s.p. (H1944)

Salve Regina
cor,orch sc KALMUS $12.00, ipa (H1945)
(Landon, H.C.R.) 4pt mix cor,soli,org, strings (G min) DOBLINGER sc s.p., voc sc s.p., cor pts s.p., ipa (H1946)

Salve Regina
(Landon, Robbins) [Lat] SATB,org,strings (G min) AMP A489 $1.00 (H1947)

Sanctus (from Sixteenth Mass) Sanctus
(Barrie) [Eng/Lat] SATB,pno/org oct LAWSON 51582 $.30 (H1948)
(Cramer) [Eng/Lat] SATB MARKS 4182 $.25 (H1949)
(Herrmann) [Eng/Lat] 4pt mix cor,org oct SCHIRM.G 10862 $.30 (H1950)
(Herrmann) [Lat/Eng] 3pt wom cor,org/pno oct SCHIRM.G 11863 $.30 (H1951)
(Herrmann) [Lat/Eng] 4pt mix cor,org/pno oct SCHIRM.G 11864 $.30 (H1952)
(Hilton, A.) "Sixteenth Mass" SATB oct PRESSER 352-00332 $.30 (H1953)
(Warner) SATB oct PLYMOUTH SC-12 $.25 (H1954)
(Warner) SSA oct PLYMOUTH SC-202 $.25 (H1955)
(Williams) SATB oct FOX PS104 $.30 (H1956)

HAYDN, (FRANZ) JOSEPH (cont'd.)

Sanctus And Hosanna
(Suchoff) SATB oct BELWIN 1994 $.30 (H1957)

Saviour, Breathe Forgiveness *see Ave Verum

Schoepfungsmesse *Mass
"Mass In B-Flat" cor,orch (B flat maj) sc KALMUS $18.00, ipa (H1958)

Schopfungsmesse *see Missa Solennis

Seasons *ora
[Eng/Ger] voc sc PETERS 67 $3.00, ipr, cloth PETERS 67 $7.50, ipr, min sc PETERS E987 $12.00, ipr, min sc-cloth PETERS E987 $15.00, ipr, study sc PETERS 1447A $30.00, ipr (H1959)
[Eng/Ger/Fr] mix cor voc sc KALMUS 6237 $2.75 (H1960)

Seasons, The *ora
cor,orch sc KALMUS $35.00, ipa (H1961)

Second Mass In C *Mass
BELWIN $1.50 (H1962)

Seven Last Words *see Die Sieben Worte Des Erlosers Am Kreuze

Seven Last Words Of Christ, The *see Die Sieben Worte Des Erlosers Am Kreuze

Seven Words Of Christ *see Die Sieben Worte Des Erlosers Am Kreuze

Shoepfungsmess *see Missa Solennis

Sing Praise To God
(Whitford) SATB,org BOSTON 12999 $.35 (H1963)

Sing To The Lord *see Gloria

Sing With Joy And Gladness
(Cramer) SATB MARKS 4184 $.40 (H1964)

Singt Dem Herren, Alle Stimmen! (from Die Schopfung)
[Ger] mix cor,acap (diff) HUG s.p. (H1965)

Sixteenth Mass *see Sanctus

Spacious Firmament, The
(Ades; Gearhart) SATB SHAWNEE A 792 $.35 (H1966)
(Davis, K.) unis&desc,pno SCHIRM.EC 1829 $.25, ipr (H1967)
(Davis, K.) SSA,pno/org SCHIRM.EC 1877 $.22 (H1968)
(Mathew) TTBB FLAMMER C5051 $.25 (H1969)

St. Antoni [Chorale] *chorale
(Brahms) SATB oct STAFF 208 $.25 (H1970)
(Brahms) SATB/SSA/SAB/2pt,band oct STAFF 208 $.25, ipa (H1971)
(Brahms) SAB oct STAFF 259 $.25 (H1972)
(Brahms) SSA oct STAFF 256 $.25 (H1973)
(Brahms) SA/TB oct STAFF 532 $.25 (H1974)

St. Martin [Chorale] *chorale
(Gardner) SATB oct STAFF 553 $.30 (H1975)

St. Nicholas Mass *see Missa Sancti Nicolai

Stabat Mater
cor voc sc KALMUS 6248 $2.00 (H1976)
cor,orch sc KALMUS $25.00, ipa (H1977)
4pt mix cor,SATB soli,2ob,strings, 2 English horns BREITKOPF-W sc s.p., voc sc s.p., voc pt s.p., ipa (H1978)

Stimmt An Die Saiten (from Die Schopfung)
[Ger] mix cor,acap (diff) HUG s.p. (H1979)

Te Deum (from Esterhazy) Te Deum
study sc UNIVER. PH. 455 (H1980)
(Atkins, Ivor) [Eng/Lat] SATB,org/orch (med) voc sc OXFORD 46.24 $1.30 (H1981)

Te Deum For The Empress Maria Theresa *see Te Deum [II]

Te Deum For The Empress Marie Theresa *Te Deum
[Lat] study sc UNIVER. PH. 454 $3.85 (H1982)

Te Deum Fur Die Kaiserin Marie Theresa *see Tedeum

Te Deum Fur Furst Nicolaus Esterhazy *Te Deum
(Landon, H.C.R.) mix cor,soli,org,2ob,opt bsn,2trp,3trom,timp,strings (C maj) DOBLINGER sc s.p., cor pts s.p., voc sc s.p., min sc s.p., ipa (H1983)

Te Deum [II] *Te Deum
mix cor,org,fl,2ob,2bsn,3trp,2horn,strings, timp sc BREITKOPF-L rental (H1984)
(Landon, Robbins) "Te Deum For The Empress Maria Theresa" [Lat] SATB,orch AMP A488 $1.00 (H1985)

Te Deum Laudamus *cant/Te Deum
BELWIN $1.00 (H1986)
SATB,fl,2ob,2bsn,2horn,2trp,strings,timp voc sc NOVELLO s.p., ipr (H1987)
cor voc sc KALMUS 6247 $1.25 (H1988)
cor,orch sc KALMUS $12.00, ipa (H1989)
4pt mix cor,org,fl,2ob,2bsn,2horn,3trom, strings,timp BREITKOPF-W rental (H1990)

Tedeum *Te Deum
(Landon.H.C.R.) "Te Deum Fur Die Kaiserin Marie Theresa" mix cor,soli,org,fl,2clar, 2bsn,3trp,3trom,2horn,timp,strings (C maj) DOBLINGER sc s.p., cor pts s.p., voc sc s.p., min sc s.p., ipa (H1991)

Tenebrae Factae Sunt *Easter/Lent
SATB,acap RICORDI-ENG SY116 s.p. (H1992)
(Douglas) "Darkness Was Over All" SATB,acap oct PRO ART 2316 $.25 (H1993)

HAYDN, (FRANZ) JOSEPH (cont'd.)

Tenebrae In E Flat *Easter
(Strickling) SSA SCHMITT 2514 $.25 (H1994)
(Strickling) SATB SCHMITT 1536 $.30 (H1995)

Thanks Be To God
SATB PROWSE s.p. (H1996)
(Imig) SATB oct FOX R158 $.35 (H1997)
(Imig) SSA oct FOX R185 $.35 (H1998)

Theresa *see Theresienmesse

Theresa Mass *see Theresienmesse

Theresienmesse *Mass
[Ger] 4pt mix cor,SATB soli,orch voc sc BAREN. BA 4661 s.p., voc sc BAREN. BA 4661A s.p., min sc BAREN. TP 99 s.p. (H1999)
BELWIN $2.00 (H2000)
"Maria Theresa Mass" [Lat] SATB,SATB soli, 2clar,2trp,strings,timp voc sc NOVELLO s.p., ipr (H2001)
"Mass In B Flat" [Lat] SATB,orch voc sc BROUDE BR. $2.25, ipr (H2002)
"Theresa" study sc UNIVER. PH. 121 $4.25 (H2003)
"Theresa Mass" cor,opt orch voc sc KALMUS 6243 $2.50, ipa (H2004)
"Theresa Mass" cor KALMUS $2.25 (H2005)
(Hermann, William) "Mass In B Flat" 4pt mix cor,soli,org/pno voc sc SCHIRM.G $2.50 (H2006)

Thou Art Worthy Of Praise *see Du Bist's Dem Ruhm Und Ehre Gebuhret

Thou, Lord, All Praise And Honor Commandeth
(Ehret) mix cor CHAPPELL 0023499-358 $.40 (H2007)

Thou, Lord, Of Glory And Honour Art Worthy *anthem
(Ramsey, Basil) mix cor oct NOVELLO 28.1374.02 s.p. (H2008)

Thou, Who Art All Holy
(Jacobson) 4pt mix cor oct CURWEN 10105 $.30 (H2009)

'Tis Thou To Whom All Honor
SATB oct PRESSER 352-00084 $.35 (H2010)

To Shepherds In Cold Winter Night *Xmas
(Pauly) SATB SCHMITT 1440 $.30 (H2011)

Tod Ist Ein Langer Schlaf
see Bach, Johann Sebastian, Der Lieben Sonne Licht Und Pracht

Trauer
see Five Symphonies

Try Me O God
(Suchoff) SATB oct PLYMOUTH BS-101 $.25 (H2012)

Twenty Four Canons *CC24U,Bibl/canon
[Ger] 2-8pt PETERS 5999 (H2013)

Von Deiner Gut'o Herr (from Die Schopfung)
(Vogel, Moritz; Nagler, Franciscus) [Ger] wom cor&jr cor,org,opt strings HUG 2 s.p. (H2014)

Water And Wine
(Jacobson, Maurice) 4pt mix cor CURWEN 61448 s.p. (H2015)

We Seek Not, God, Our Lord, For Glory *see Non Nobis, Domine

When I Think Upon Thy Goodness
(Blakley) SA/TB oct BOURNE 2034 $.25 (H2016)

HAYDN, (JOHANN) MICHAEL

All My Friends Forsake Me *see Omnes Amici Mei Dereliquerunt Me

Asperges Me *mot
"Purge Me, O Lord" [Eng/Lat] SATB,org/pno, opt vln PETERS 6298 $.25 (H2017)

Benedictus Qui Venit *Gradual
[Lat] SATB,org,2trp,strings sc PETERS A63 $4.00, ipa, voc sc PETERS A63 $.60, ipa (H2018)
(Graf) "Hochgepriesen, Der Kommt" [Lat/Ger] cor sc HUG s.p. (H2019)

Come, Children, Praise Our Lord *see Laudate Pueri

Confitemi Domino
(Graf) "Lobt Und Preiset Gott, Den Herrn" [Lat/Ger] cor sc HUG s.p. (H2020)

Confitemini Domino
[Lat] mix cor,acap (med easy) HUG s.p. (H2021)
(Graf) [Lat] SATB,opt org PETERS A146 $.50 (H2022)

Dark Was The Earth With Clouds *see Tenebrae Factae Sunt

Darkness Made Dim The Earth *Easter
(Lynn, G.) SATB oct PRESSER MC168 $.30 (H2023)

Darkness Obscured The Earth
(Davids, Dean) SATB oct BELWIN 1860 $.25 (H2024)

Darkness Was All Over
(Pauly) [Eng/Lat] 3pt wom cor oct SCHIRM.G 10532 $.25 (H2025)

Darkness Was Over The Earth *see Tenebrae Factae Sunt

Deutsches Miserere
(Hagler, Paul) [Ger] 2pt wom cor,S solo, cont,strings,opt 2horn HUG s.p., ipr (H2026)

Ecce! Quomodo Moritur Justus
"See How The Righteous One Dieth" see Passion Motets

Effunderunt Sanguinem
(Pauly) "Sing Aloud To God" [Eng/Lat] 3pt wom cor oct SCHIRM.G 10871 $.30 (H2027)

HAYDN, (JOHANN) MICHAEL (cont'd.)

Exultabunt Sancti
(Pauly) "Thou Art Mighty" [Eng/Lat] 4pt mix
cor,org/pno oct SCHIRM.G 11897 $.35
(H2028)

German Miserere
[Ger] SA,S solo,org,strings,opt 2ob&2horn
sc PETERS A69 $4.00, ipr, voc sc PETERS
A69 $1.00, ipr
(H2029)

God, In Thee I Seek My Salvation
(Pauly) [Eng/Lat] 4pt mix cor oct SCHIRM.G
10531 $.40
(H2030)

God Is Merciful
(Pauly) [Eng/Lat] 4pt mix cor oct SCHIRM.G
10525 $.35
(H2031)

Great Is The Lord Our Maker
(Pauly) 4pt mix cor oct SCHIRM.G 10529 $.40
(H2032)

Heiligste Nacht
[Ger] mix cor,acap (easy) HUG s.p. (H2033)

Help Us, O Lord, Deliver Us
(Pauly) [Eng/Lat] 4pt mix cor oct SCHIRM.G
10550 $.25
(H2034)

Hochgepriesen, Der Kommt *see Benedictus Qui
Venit

I Cried To God In Tribulation
(Pauly) [Eng/Lat] 4pt mix cor oct SCHIRM.G
10526 $.25
(H2035)

Kreuzmesse *see Missa Sanctae Crucis In A-
Moll

Laudate
[Lat] T/S HEUGEL s.p. see from LA MAITRISE
(H2036)

Laudate Populi *Offer
(Biba, O.) 4pt mix cor,org,2trp,2vln,bvl,
timp sc BREITKOPF-W PB-4839 s.p., ipa,
cor pts BREITKOPF-W CHB-4805 s.p., voc sc
BREITKOPF-W EB-6655 s.p.
(H2037)

Laudate Pueri *Xmas
(Pauly) "Come, Children, Praise Our Lord"
[Eng/Lat] 3pt wom cor oct SCHIRM.G 10765
$.30
(H2038)

Lauft, Ihr Hirten, Allzugleich
"Run, Ye Shepherds, To The Light" mix cor,S
solo,strings voc sc VOLK 139 s.p. (H2039)

Lobt Und Preiset Gott, Den Herrn *see
Confitemi Domino

Magnificat *Magnif
(Pauly) "Magnify The Lord" [Eng/Lat] 3pt
wom cor oct SCHIRM.G 10911 $.45 (H2040)

Magnify The Lord *see Magnificat

Missa Pro Defunctis *Mass
study sc UNIVER. 25A008 $13.60 (H2041)
[Lat] voc sc UNIVER. 25C008 $10.85, cor pts
UNIVER. 25D008 $2.20 (H2042)

Missa Sanctae Crucis In A-Moll *Mass
(Pfannhauser, K.) "Kreuzmesse" 4pt mix cor,
opt org (A min) DOBLINGER sc s.p., cor
pts s.p. see from OSTERREICHISCHE
KIRCHENMUSIK
(H2043)

Missa Sancti Aloysii *Mass
see Zwei Messen
[Lat] 3pt wom cor/3pt boy cor,org,strings
sc PETERS A67 $10.00, ipa, cor pts PETERS
A67 $1.00, ipa
(H2044)

Missa Sancti Hieronymi *Mass
[Lat] voc sc UNIVER. 25C007 $10.85, cor pts
UNIVER. 25D007 $2.20 (H2045)
study sc UNIVER. 25A007 $13.60 (H2046)

Missa Sancti Leopoldi *Mass
see Zwei Messen
[Lat] 3pt wom cor/3pt boy cor,org,strings,
opt 2horn sc PETERS A68 $10.00, ipa, cor
pts PETERS A68 $1.00, ipa
(H2047)

Missa St. Aloysii *Mass
[Lat] SSA,org,2vln HINRICHSEN D120 voc pt
s.p., sc s.p.
(H2048)
cor,orch sc KALMUS $10.00, ipa (H2049)

Missa St. Leopoldi *Mass
[Lat] SSA,org,2vln,opt 2horn s.p. cor pts
HINRICHSEN G301, sc HINRICHSEN G301
(H2050)

Missa Tempore Quadragesimae *Mass
[Lat] SATB,org/pno PETERS HU1966 $2.50
(H2051)

O Fear The Lord *see Timete Dominum

O Joyful Day! *Xmas,mot
(Pauly) 4pt mix cor,org/pno oct SCHIRM.G
11044 $.40
(H2052)

O Worship The King *Thanks
(Shaw) mix cor oct SCHIRM.G 10096 $.30
(H2053)

O Ye People
see Two Motets

Omnes Amici Mei Dereliquerunt Me
"All My Friends Forsake Me" see Passion
Motets

Passion Motets *Holywk,mot
[Eng/Lat] 4pt mix cor,acap oct SCHIRM.G
$.25
contains: Ecce! Quomodo Moritur Justus,
"See How The Righteous One Dieth";
Omnes Amici Mei Dereliquerunt Me, "All
My Friends Forsake Me"; Tristis Est
Anima Mea, "Sad Is My Soul"
(H2054)

Prope Est Dominus *Gradual
[Lat] SATB,strings,org,opt 2trp sc PETERS
A125 $4.00, ipa, voc sc PETERS A125 $.80,
ipa
(H2055)
(Graf) [Lat] cor sc HUG s.p. (H2056)

HAYDN, (JOHANN) MICHAEL (cont'd.)

Purge Me, O Lord *see Asperges Me

Qui Sedes, Domine *Gradual
[Lat] SATB,org,2trp,strings sc PETERS A101
$4.00, ipa, voc sc PETERS A101 $.60, ipa
(H2057)
(Graff) [Lat] cor sc HUG s.p. (H2058)

Requiem C-Moll *Req
(Peter, Oskar) "Requiem Solemne" 4pt mix
cor,SATB soli,org,2ob,2trp,3trom,strings,
timp (C min) cor pts BREITKOPF-W CHB-3084
s.p., ipr, voc sc BREITKOPF-W EB-6330
s.p., sc BREITKOPF-W EB-6330
(H2059)

Requiem Solemne *see Requiem C-Moll

Run, Ye Shepherds, To The Light *see Lauft,
Ihr Hirten, Allzugleich

Sad Is My Soul *see Tristis Est Anima Mea

Sad Is My Soul Unto Death *see Tristis Est
Anima Mea

Sanctus
(Kjelson, Lee) SATB oct BELWIN 2257 $.35
(H2060)
See How The Righteous One Dieth *see Ecce!
Quomodo Moritur Justus

Sing Aloud To God *see Effunderunt Sanguinem

Sleep In Peace, O Heavenly Child *Xmas
(Pauly) [Eng/Ger] 4pt mix cor,org/pno oct
SCHIRM.G 11043 $.35, ipr
(H2061)

Son Of God
see Two Motets

Te Deum *Te Deum
(Pfannhauser, K.) mix cor,org,2ob, opt
2clar,opt 2bsn,2trp,opt 2trom,timp,
strings (D maj) DOBLINGER voc sc s.p.,
cor pts s.p., ipa see from
OSTERREICHISCHE KIRCHENMUSIK (H2062)

Tecum Principium
(Graf) [Lat] cor sc HUG s.p. (H2063)

Tecum Principum
[Lat] SATB,org,2ob,2horn,strings sc PETERS
A73 $4.00, ipa, voc sc PETERS A73 $.60,
ipa
(H2064)

Tenebrae Factae Sunt *Gd.Fri.,mot
[Lat] SATB RICORDI-ENG SY116 s.p. (H2065)
"Dark Was The Earth With Clouds" SATB,acap
(Maundy Thursday) SCHIRM.EC 1691 $.30
(H2066)
"Darkness Was Over The Earth" [Eng/Lat]
SATB,opt org/pno PETERS 6377 $.25 (H2067)
(Ramsey, W.) SATB oct BOONIN 148 (H2068)

Thou Art Mighty *see Exultabunt Sancti

Timete Dominum *mot
(Pauly, Reinhard G.) "O Fear The Lord"
[Eng/Lat] mix cor,soli,org voc sc
SCHIRM.G $.75
(H2069)

Tres Sunt *Offer
mix cor,soli,org,2vln,vla,bvl WEINBERGER
s.p., ipa voc sc, cor pts
(H2070)

Tristis Est Anima Mea *Easter/Lent
"Sad Is My Soul" see Passion Motets
(Marshall, Charles) "Sad Is My Soul Unto
Death" SATB FRANK F-577 $.35 (H2071)

Two Motets *Lent,mot
(Pauly) [Eng/Lat] 4pt mix cor,acap,opt org/
pno oct SCHIRM.G 11405 $.35
contains: O Ye People; Son Of God (H2072)

Universi Qui Te Expectant
[Lat] SATB,org,strings,opt 2horn sc PETERS
A115 $4.00, ipa, voc sc PETERS A115 $.80,
ipa
(H2073)
(Graf) [Lat] cor sc HUG s.p. (H2074)

Veni, Sancte Spiritus
[Lat] SATB,org,ob,2horn,strings,opt 3trom
sc PETERS A97 $4.00, ipa, voc sc PETERS
A97 $.80, ipa
(H2075)
(Graf) [Lat] cor sc HUG s.p. (H2076)

Vespers No. 3
(Graf) [Lat] SSA,SSA soli,org,strings,opt
2horn sc PETERS A150 $12.50, ipa, cor pts
PETERS A150 $1.00, ipa
(H2077)

Wer Nur Den Lieben Gott Laesst Walten
[Ger] opt SATB,SA soli,pno,2trp PETERS A147
$.40
(H2078)

Zwei Messen *Mass
(Reinhart, Walther) [Lat] HUG s.p.
contains: Missa Sancti Aloysii (SSA/3pt
wom cor/3pt boy cor,SSA soli,org,2vln,
vcl/bvl); Missa Sancti Leopoldi (SSA&
boy cor/wom cor,SSA soli,org,2horn,
2vln,vcl/bvl)
(H2079)

HAYDN, T.
Evening Song To God
SATB oct PRESSER MC260 $.40 (H2080)

HAYES
Alleluia! *Allelu
SATB oct HERITAGE H1 $.35 (H2081)

I Sing Thy Birth *Xmas
unis (easy) OXFORD 81.020 $.25 (H2082)

Love Of God
(Wyatt) SATB,opt S solo oct PRO ART 1443
$.18
(H2083)

Noel *Xmas
SATB,acap oct BOOSEY 5105 $.30 (H2084)

We Sing Of God
(Wiley) SATB oct PRO ART 2474 $.25 (H2085)

HAYFORD
Behold The Living God
(Kirk) SATB oct LILLENAS AT-1084 $.35
(H2086)

HAYLLE, COMLY AND CLENE see Davies, Peter
Maxwell

HAYOM HARAT OLAM see Adler, Samuel

HAYOM TEAMTZENU see Lind, Joshua

HAYWOOD
I'm Bound For The Promised Land
SATB SHAWNEE A 721 $.30 (H2087)

HAZELL, CHRIS
Holy Moses! *cant
unis,pno,opt bvl,drums (jazz) voc sc
NOVELLO 20.0148.09 s.p., ipa (H2088)

HE
SSA/SATB/SAB/SA/TB/TTBB BIG3 $.35 (H2089)

HE ABIDES see Shanks

HE AROSE see Johnson

HE BEARS OUR BURDENS see Lotti, Antonio, Vere
Languores Nostros

HE BEHELD THE CITY see Jeffreys

HE BEHELD THE CITY see Jeffries, George

HE BOUGHT MY SOUL AT CALVARY *anthem
SATB/SAB/SA/TB BIG3 $.25 (H2090)

HE CAME ALL SO STILL see Roberton, Hugh S.

HE CAME HERE FOR ME see Nelson, Ronald A.

HE CAME SO STILL see Rhea, A.

HE CAME TO GIVE LIFE see Parr, Andy

HE CAN OPEN DOORS see Wright

HE CARES FOR ME see Hutson, Wihla

HE CARES FOR ME see Owens, Jimmy

HE CARETH FOR ME see Roff, Joseph

HE COMES! HE COMES! see Santa Cruz, Domingo,
Llego! Llego!

HE COMES TO US see Marshall

HE COMETH WITH THE CLOUDS see Christiansen,
Paul

HE DAWNS UPON US see White, John

HE DELIVERED THE POOR see Parry, Charles Hubert
Hastings

HE DIES, THE FRIEND OF SINNERS DIES see
Stanton, Royal [W.]

HE ENDURED THE CROSS see Graun, Karl Heinrich

HE FELT THE WHIP see Red, Buryl

HE GIVES US FRUITFUL SEASONS see Clare, Edwyn
A.

HE GIVETH MORE GRACE see Mitchell

HE GUIDES ME IN HIS WAY see Harter, [Harry]

HE HAS BORNE OUR WOES see Schroth, Gerhard

HE HAS COME see Brandon

HE HAS NO HANDS see Artman

HE HAS RISEN see Ford, Virgil T.

HE HAS SURELY BORNE OUR SORROW see Lister,
Mosie

HE HATH DONE ALL THINGS WELL see Bender, Jan

HE HATH FILLED THE HUNGRY see Vivaldi, Antonio,
Esurientes Implevit

HE HIDETH MY SOUL see Kirkpatrick

HE HIDETH MY SOUL see Landon

HE IS BLESSED see Palestrina, Giovanni,
Benedictus

HE IS BLESSED see Righini, Vincenzo

HE IS BORN see Davis, Katherine K.

HE IS BORN see Harris

HE IS BORN see Il Est Ne

HE IS BORN, CHRIST IS BORN TODAY see
Clerambault, De

HE IS BORN, CHRIST THE KING see Davis,
Katherine K.

HE IS BORN, THE BELOVED CHILD see Buttolph

HE IS BORN, THE CHILD DIVINE *Xmas,carol,Fr
(Bisbee, B.W.) SSA,org,fl (med easy) oct
CONCORDIA 98-1839 $.25 (H2091)
(Ehret) SAB,opt fl,ob,perc oct FOX CC5 $.35
(H2092)
(Ehret) SSA,opt fl,ob,perc oct FOX CC17 $.35
(H2093)
(Ehret, W.) SAB,opt fl&ob&perc PROWSE CC5
s.p.
(H2094)

HE IS BORN, THIS CHILD DIVINE *Xmas
(Allen) SATB oct GALLEON GCS1018 (H2095)

HE IS COMING see Gerson

HE IS EVERYWHERE (GOD IS LOVE) see Lohr, Al

HE IS MY ROCK
SATB BIG3 $.40 (H2096)

HE IS MY SAVIOR see Sateren, Leland Bernhard

HE IS NOT HERE BUT IS RISEN see Demarest, A.

HE IS OUR KING see Davis, Katherine K.

HE IS RISEN   *Easter/Lent
   (Mueller) SATB oct FISCHER,C CM-6286 $.30
                                          (H2097)

HE IS RISEN see Aichinger, Gregor, Regina Coeli

HE IS RISEN see Clare, Edwyn A.

HE IS RISEN see Clarke, Henry Leland

HE IS RISEN see Cooper, J.

HE IS RISEN see Cope, Cecil

HE IS RISEN see Emerson

HE IS RISEN see Gadsby, [Henry Robert]

HE IS RISEN see Lekberg, Sven

HE IS RISEN see Mueller, Carl F.

HE IS RISEN see Pelz, Walter L.

HE IS RISEN see Philips, Peter, Surgens Jesus

HE IS RISEN see Simper, Caleb

HE IS RISEN see Surdo, Joseph

HE IS RISEN see Trued, Clarence

HE IS RISEN see Whitlock, Percy

HE IS RISEN see Wilson, John F.

HE IS RISEN see Worthing, Richard

HE IS RISEN, ALLELUIA see Diercks, John H.

HE IS SLEEPING IN A MANGER see Wztobie Lezy

HE IS SUCH AN UNDERSTANDING GOD   *anthem
   SAB/SA/TB BIG3 $.30   (H2098)

HE IS THE KING OF GLORY see Basham, Robert A.

HE IS THE KING OF GLORY see Root

HE IS THE LONELY GREATNESS see Benjamin, Arthur

HE IS THE ONE see Roe, Gloria [Ann]

HE IS THE TENDER SHEPHERD see Mendelssohn-
   Bartholdy, Felix, Surrexit Pastor Bonus

HE IS THE WAY see Bliss, Sir Arthur

HE IS THE WAY see Skillings, Otis

HE IS THERE! see Wild, Eric

HE KEEPS ME SINGING see Carmichael

HE! LA MAISON see Saboly, Nicholas, Hou! De
   L'oustau

HE LAID HIS HAND ON ME see Hughes, Robert J.

HE LEADETH ME see Bradbury

HE LEADETH ME see Bradbury, William Batchelder

HE LEADETH ME see Wilson

HE LEADETH ME BESIDE THE STILL WATERS see
   Hovhaness, Alan

HE LIFTED ME see Gabriel

HE LIVES see Ackley

HE LIVES! see Bach, Johann Sebastian

HE LIVES see Hughes

HE LIVES! see Lorenz

HE LIVES AGAIN see Kenney

HE LIVES FOREVERMORE see Williams

HE LIVES TODAY! see Allen, Lanny

HE LIVES TRIUMPHANT see Van Woert

HE LOVES YOU see Wells

HE NEVER SAID A MUMBALIN' WORD *Easter/Lent,
   spir
   (De Vaux) SATB oct SPRATT 117 $.30   (H2099)
   (De Vaux) SAB oct SPRATT 121 $.30   (H2100)
   (Henninger) SATB SCHMITT 1669 $.30   (H2101)
   (Scarmolin) SATB oct PRO ART 1278 $.25
                                          (H2102)

HE NEVER SAID A MUMBALIN' WORD see Siegmeister

HE NEVER SAID A MUMBALIN' WORD see Smith

HE NEVER SAID A MUMBLIN' WORD see Miller, J.

HE, REMEMBERING HIS MERCY see Steele, J.A.

HE ROSE! ALLELUJAH! see Pfautsch, Lloyd

HE ROSE TRIUMPHANTLY see Ackley

HE SENT A THICK DARKNESS see Handel, George
   Frideric

HE SHALL COME DOWN see Bradbury

HE SHALL COME DOWN see Ford, Virgil T.

HE SHALL COME DOWN LIKE RAIN see Brumel,
   Antoine

HE SHALL COME DOWN LIKE RAIN see Buck, Dudley

HE SHALL COME DOWN LIKE RAIN see Grieb

HE SHALL COME DOWN LIKE RAIN see McCormick

HE SHALL COMFORT THINE HEART see Freestone

HE SHALL FEED HIS FLOCK see Handel, George
   Frideric

HE SHALL FEED HIS FLOCK see Wilson, Roger [C.]

HE SHALL GIVE HIS ANGELS see Fux, Johann
   Joseph, Angelis Suis Deus

HE SHALL GIVE HIS ANGELS CHARGE OVER THEE see
   Lang, C.S.

HE SHALL REIGN see Lillenas, Haldor

HE SHALL REIGN FOREVER see Simper, Caleb

HE SHALL RULE FROM SEA TO SEA see Rorem, Ned

HE SHALL RULE FROM SEA TO SEA see Schroth,
   Gerhard

HE SMILED ON ME see O'Hara, Geoffrey

HE SMILES WITHIN HIS CRADLE *Xmas,carol
   see Three Carols
   unis/SATB (very easy) OXFORD 08.084 $.15
                                          (H2103)

HE SMOTE ALL THE FIRSTBORN OF EGYPT see Handel,
   George Frideric

HE STOOPED TO BLESS see Margetson, Edward

HE THAT DESCENDED see Amner

HE THAT DESCENDED MAN TO BE see Amner, John

HE THAT DWELLETH see Glarum, L. Stanley

HE THAT DWELLETH IN THE SECRET PLACE see Felts

HE THAT DWELLETH IN THE SECRET PLACE see
   Scarmolin, (Anthony) Louis

HE THAT HATH CLEAN HANDS see Hart, A.W.

HE THAT IS DOWN NEED FEAR NO FALL see Joubert,
   John

HE THAT IS DOWN NEED FEAR NO FALL see Vaughan
   Williams, Ralph

HE THAT KEEPETH ISRAEL see Conway

HE THAT SHALL ENDURE see Mendelssohn-Bartholdy,
   Felix

HE THAT SHALL ENDURE TO THE END see
   Mendelssohn-Bartholdy, Felix

HE THAT WOULD LOVE LIFE see Corina, John

HE THE PEARLY GATES WILL OPEN see Ahlwin

HE TOOK A CHILD see Emig, Lois

HE TRUSTED IN GOD see Handel, George Frideric

HE WALKS BESIDE US see Graham

HE WALKS WITH GOD see Hughes, Robert J.

HE WANTS YOU TO FLY see Owens, Carol

HE WAS ALONE see Paxson, Theodore

HE WAS DESPISED see Coggin, Elwood

HE WAS DESPISED see Davis, Katherine K.

HE WAS DESPISED see Graun, Karl Heinrich

HE WAS DESPISED see Handel, George Frideric

HE WAS DESPISED see Johnston

HE WAS DESPISED see Stanton, Royal [W.]

HE WAS DESPISED see Wheeler, Alfred

HE WAS DESPISED AND REJECTED see Handel, George
   Frideric

HE WAS INCARNATE see Bach, Johann Sebastian, Et
   Incarnatus Est

HE, WATCHING OVER ALL THE WORLD see
   Mendelssohn-Bartholdy, Felix

HE, WATCHING OVER ISRAEL see Mendelssohn-
   Bartholdy, Felix, Siehe, Der Huter Israels

HE WHICH HATH BEGUN A GOOD WORK IN YOU see
   Bender, Jan

HE WHO BLESSED see Ancis, Solomon, Mi Sheberach

HE WHO FOLLOWS ME see Roff, Joseph

HE WHO GOD'S SUFFERING IN HONOR HOLDS see
   Schutz, Heinrich, Wer Gottes Marter In
   Ehren Hat

HE WHO HATH MADE HEAVEN see Milano, R.

HE WHO SOWETH WEEPING see Peter, Johann
   Friedrich

HE WHO WITH WEEPING SOWETH see Schutz,
   Heinrich, Die Mit Tranen Saen

HE WHO WOULD VALIANT BE see Curry

HE WHO WOULD VALIANT BE see Douglas, [Charles]
   Winifred

HE WHO WOULD VALIANT BE see Elmore, Robert
   [Hall]

HE WHO WOULD VALIANT BE see Jolley, Florence
   [W.]

HE WHO WOULD VALIANT BE see Marshall, Jane M.

HE WHO WOULD VALIANT BE see Williams

HE WHOM JOYOUS SHEPHERDS PRAISED *carol,Ger
   (Glaser, V.) SSA,acap SCHIRM.EC 2537 $.30
                                          (H2104)

HE WHOM JOYOUS SHEPHERDS PRAISED see Hruby,
   Delores

HE WILL GUIDE YOU see Clare, Edwyn A.

HE WILL RECEIVE THE BLESSING OF THE LORD see
   Roff, Joseph

HE WIPES THE TEAR FROM EVERY EYE see Lee,
   Alexander

HEAB'N
   see Negro Spirituals

HEAD, MICHAEL (DEWAR) (1900-   )
   Ave Maria
      SSA oct BOOSEY 5124 $.30   (H2105)

   Blessed Is He (Psalm 32)
      SATB,MezBar/MezB/ABar/AB soli,org oct
         BOOSEY 5673 $.35   (H2106)

   Little Road To Bethlehem
      SA/TB oct BOOSEY 5040 $.30   (H2107)
      SAB,acap oct BOOSEY 5560 $.30   (H2108)
      SATB,acap oct BOOSEY 5342 $.30   (H2109)
      (Cain) SATB oct BOOSEY 1799 $.35   (H2110)
      (Cain) SSA oct BOOSEY 1796 $.35   (H2111)

   Psalm 32 *see Blessed Is He

   Slumber Song Of The Madonna *Xmas
      SSAA BOOSEY-CAN s.p.   (H2112)

   Star Candles
      SA oct BOOSEY 1698 $.30   (H2113)

HEAD THAT ONCE WAS CROWNED WITH THORNS, THE see
   Clarke

HEADINGTON, CHRISTOPHER (1930-   )
   Man's Redemption *Xmas,carol
      SATB oct FABER 11747 $.35   (H2114)
      4pt mix cor,acap oct FABER 11747 $.35
                                          (H2115)

HEALEY, D.
   I Stiller Fastetider
      mix cor NORDISKA 3276 s.p.   (H2116)

   Shepherd Boy's Song, The *Gen,anthem
      SATB oct ROYAL 233 s.p.   (H2117)

HEALEY, H.P.
   That Holy Thing *see Chadwyck

HEAR DE LAMBS A-CRYIN' see Burleigh, Henry
   Thacker

HEAR LORD
   (Tolmage, Gerald) SATB oct STAFF 392 $.20
                                          (H2118)

HEAR, LORD OUR GOD see Tchaikovsky, Piotr
   Ilyitch

HEAR ME CRY, O GOD see Kopylov, Alexander
   Alexandrovitch

HEAR ME, LORD see Klein, M.

HEAR ME LORD see Youse, Glad [Robinson]

HEAR ME O LORD see Grandi, Alessandro, Exaudi
   Deus

HEAR ME, O LORD see Handel, George Frideric

HEAR ME, O LORD see Tkach, D.

HEAR ME, O LORD see Trued, Clarence

HEAR ME, O LORD GOD see Victoria, Tomas Luis
   de, Salve Regina

HEAR ME, O LORD, THE GREAT SUPPORT see Purcell,
   Henry

HEAR ME, O SAVIOUR see Gluck, Christoph
   Willibald Ritter von

HEAR ME WHEN I CALL see Hall, King

HEAR MY CRY see Milligan, H.V.

HEAR MY CRY see Moore

HEAR MY CRY, O GOD see Boatwright, Howard

HEAR MY CRY, O GOD see Henderson

HEAR MY CRY, O GOD see Rhea, A.

HEAR MY CRY, O GOD see Victoria, Tomas Luis de

HEAR MY CRY, O LORD see Kopylov, Alexander
   Alexandrovitch

HEAR MY CRYING see Weldon, John

HEAR MY PRAYER see Arkhangelsky, G.

HEAR MY PRAYER see Aulbach

HEAR MY PRAYER see Blanchard, [William G.]

HEAR MY PRAYER see Bortniansky, Dimitri
   Stepanovitch

HEAR MY PRAYER see Canavati

HEAR MY PRAYER see Droste, Doreen

HEAR MY PRAYER see Foster, Will

HEAR MY PRAYER see James, Will

HEAR MY PRAYER see Kopylov, Alexander
   Alexandrovitch

HEAR MY PRAYER see Mendelssohn-Bartholdy, Felix

HEAR MY PRAYER see Milner, Arthur

HEAR MY PRAYER, O GOD see Arcadelt, Jacob, Ave
   Maria

HEAR MY PRAYER, O GOD see Ave Maria

HEAR MY PRAYER, O GOD see Batten, Adrian

HEAR MY PRAYER, O GOD see Rogers, Bernard

HEAR MY PRAYER, O LORD see Arkhangelsky, Alexander

HEAR MY PRAYER, O LORD see Arkhangelsky, G.

HEAR MY PRAYER, O LORD see Bassett, Leslie

HEAR MY PRAYER, O LORD see Batten, Adrian

HEAR MY PRAYER, O LORD see Hawkey

HEAR MY PRAYER, O LORD see Hovhaness, Alan

HEAR MY PRAYER, O LORD see Jacobson, Marilyn

HEAR MY PRAYER, O LORD see Kevan, G.

HEAR MY PRAYER, O LORD see Lassus, Roland de (Orlandus)

HEAR MY PRAYER, O LORD see Lupo, Thomas

HEAR MY PRAYER, O LORD see Newbury, Kent A.

HEAR MY PRAYER, O LORD see Pike, Harry Hale

HEAR MY PRAYER, O LORD see Purcell, Henry

HEAR MY PRAYER, O LORD see Royse

HEAR MY PRAYER, O LORD see Tomkins, Thomas

HEAR MY PRAYER, O LORD see Williams

HEAR MY PRAYERS, O LORD see Pergolesi, Giovanni Battista

HEAR MY SUPPLICATION see Arkhangelsky, G.

HEAR NOW OUR CRY, ALLELUIA see Keel, Richard

HEAR O HEAVENS see Humfrey, Pelham

HEAR, O ISRAEL see Nelson, Ronald A.

HEAR, O ISRAEL see Schwadron, Sh'ma Yisroeyl

HEAR O ISRAEL see Smolanoff, Michael

HEAR, O LORD see Amner, John

HEAR, O LORD see Newbury

HEAR, O LORD see Wienhorst, Richard

HEAR, O LORD, HEAR MY PRAYER see Lassus, Roland de (Orlandus)

HEAR, O MY PEOPLE see Strickling, Popule Meus

HEAR, O PEOPLE see Nelson, Ronald A.

HEAR, OH HEAR see Gadwood, Gary

HEAR OUR PRAYER
see Worship Responses

HEAR OUR PRAYER see Rubinstein, Anton

HEAR OUR PRAYER see Ryder, Thomas Philander

HEAR OUR PRAYER see Wilson, Ira B.

HEAR OUR PRAYER, O LORD see Mendelssohn-Bartholdy, Felix, Veni Domine

HEAR OUR PRAYER, O LORD see Rhodes

HEAR OUR SUPPLICATION see Mozart, Wolfgang Amadeus

HEAR THE BELLS RING OUT WITH JOY see Bodycombe, [Aneurin]

HEAR THE GOOD NEWS see White

HEAR THE JOYFUL NEWS see Bach

HEAR THE JOYFUL TIDINGS see Klein

HEAR THE LAMBS see Sanford

HEAR THE LAMBS A-CRYIN' *spir
(Holloway) SA oct SPRATT 211 $.25   (H2119)

HEAR THE PRAYER WE RAISE see Purcell, Henry

HEAR THE PRAYERS, O OUR GOD see Batten, Adrian

HEAR THE RIGHT, LORD see Kaiser, Kurt

HEAR THE SOUND OF THE SHEPHERDS PIPING see Rogers

HEAR THE VOICE AND PRAYER see Tallis, Thomas

HEAR THE VOICE THAT ENTREATS YOU see Weaver, Powell

HEAR THOU MY PRAYER see Hamblen

HEAR THOU MY PRAYER, O LORD see Arcadelt, Jacob, Ave Maria

HEAR THOU MY PRAYER, O LORD see Bissell, Keith

HEAR THOU MY PRAY'R see Arcadelt, Jacob, Ave Maria

HEAR THOU OUR PRAYER, O LORD see Tkach

HEAR THOU OUR PRAYER, O LORD see Tkach, P.

HEAR THY PRAISE see Nicolai, Philipp

HEAR US see Ballou, Esther W.

HEAR US AS WE PRAY see Rossini, Gioacchino

HEAR US AS WE PRAY see Smith, Henry

HEAR US, HOLY JESUS see Cherubini, Luigi

HEAR US, HOLY JESUS see Powell, Robert J.

HEAR US, HOLY JESUS see Wood

HEAR US, JESUS, SON OF GOD see Schutz, Heinrich

HEAR US, LORD see Morgan

HEAR US LORD see Mozart, Wolfgang Amadeus, Kyrie In D Minor

HEAR US, LORD see Rossini, Gioacchino

HEAR US, O FATHER   *anthem/folk,Norw
(Nystedt, Knut) SATB (med) oct AUGSBURG 1481
$.20   (H2120)

HEAR US, O JESUS see Schiavone, John

HEAR US, O LORD   *CC13L,Gen
SATB PRO ART 135 $1.50   (H2121)

HEAR US, O LORD see Green, Philip

HEAR US, O LORD see Handel, George Frideric

HEAR US, O LORD see Rogers

HEAR US, O LORD, FROM HEAVEN, THY DWELLING
PLACE see Graves, [William]

HEAR US, O LORD (PROSE FOR LENT) see Bunjes, Paul G.

HEAR US, O SAVIOUR see Hamblen, [Bernard]

HEAR US, OUR FATHER see Caldwell

HEAR US, OUR FATHER see Rhea, A.

HEAR WHAT THE LORD SAYETH see Morgan, Haydn

HEAR, YE CHILDREN see Levy, Ernst

HEAR YE CHILDREN see Mechem, Kirke

HEAR YE, MY PEOPLE see Victoria, Tomas Luis de, O Vos Omnes

HEAR YE NOW THE JOYFUL TIDINGS *Xmas
(Follett) SATB,acap,opt pno oct PRO ART 2039
$.22   (H2122)

HEAR YE, O MOUNTAINS see Williams

HEARE THE VOYCE AND PRAYER OF THY SERVAUNTS see
Tallis, Thomas, Hear The Voice And Prayer

HEARKEN ALL, WHAT HOLY SINGING see Rawls, Kathryn H.

HEARKEN, ALL YE PEOPLE see Stonard, William

HEARKEN, BRETHREN
(Tate) unis (very easy) OXFORD 81.099 $.25
                                       (H2123)

HEARKEN O DAUGHTER see Jackson, Francis, Audi Filia

HEARKEN! STAY CLOSE see Michael

HEARKEN UNTO ME, MY PEOPLE see Sullivan, Sir Arthur Seymour

HEARKEN UNTO MY CRY see Schutz, Heinrich, Verba Mea Auribus Percipe

HEARKEN, YE GOOD SIRS, WE PRAY
(Schroth) SATB KJOS 5893 $.35   (H2124)

HEARKEN, YE SHEPHERDS *Xmas
(Kinsman) SATB oct PRO ART 2180 $.25   (H2125)

HEART AND MIND, POSSESSIONS, LORD see Hilty, Everett Jay

HEART DIVINE see Dvorak, Antonin

HEART OF GOD, THE see McAfee

HEART OF PRAYER, A see Sateren, Leland Bernhard

HEART THAT'S BROKEN AND CONTRITE, AN see
Oldroyd, George

HEART WORSHIPS see Holst, Gustav

HEART WORSHIPS, THE see Holst, Gustav

HEART'S ADORATION see Marcello

HEARTS AND VOICES RAISE see Young, Carlton R.

HEARTS TO HEAVEN AND VOICES RAISE see Walter, Samuel

HEATH, G.
For The Might Of Thine Arm
(Gracie) unis oct LESLIE 1092   (H2126)
(Gracie) unis oct LESLIE 1092   (H2127)

Lift Up Your Hearts
(Gracie) SATB oct LESLIE 4095   (H2128)

HEATH, JOHN (ca. 1550)
Lay Not Up For Yourselves *Gen/Lent
TTBB,acap (med easy, or Ash Wednesday) oct
CONCORDIA 98-1683 $.35   (H2129)

HEATON, [WALLACE] (1914-   )
Great Among Nations
SATB oct PRESSER 312-40229 $.30   (H2130)

Holiness To The Lord
SATB oct PRESSER 312-40766 $.35   (H2131)

Hymn Of Faith, A
SATB,acap oct PRESSER 312-40443 $.30
                                       (H2132)

Psalm Of Peace
SATB oct PRESSER 312-40460 $.35   (H2133)

Yule Song *Xmas
SATB,acap oct PRESSER 312-40387 $.30
                                       (H2134)

HEAVEN AND EARTH, AND SEA AND AIR see Brandon

HEAVEN AND EARTH AND SEA AND AIR see Meloy, Elizabeth

HEAVEN-BOUND SOLDIER see Wright, G.

HEAVEN CAME DOWN see Peterson, John W.

HEAVEN CAME DOWN (AND GLORY FILLED MY SOUL) see
Peterson, John W.

HEAVEN IS THERE see Robson, R. Walker

HEAVENLY BUD
see Angels Lullaby

HEAVENLY CHILD, THE *Xmas,cant
mix cor CHAPPELL 0018077-3691 $1.00   (H2135)
SSA CHAPPELL 0018077-3692 $1.00   (H2136)

HEAVENLY CHOIR, THE see York

HEAVENLY FATHER see Davis, Katherine K., Agnus Dei

HEAVENLY FATHER see Schubert, Franz (Peter)

HEAVENLY FATHER, KING ETERNAL see Johnston

HEAVENLY GUIDE, THE
2pt CHAPPELL 0018093-352 $.40   (H2137)
SSA CHAPPELL 0018093-354 $.40   (H2138)

HEAVENLY LIGHT see Crist, [Bainbridge]

HEAVENLY LIGHT see Kopylov, Alexander Alexandrovitch

HEAVENLY VISION see Harris, Cuthbert

HEAVENLY VOICES see Swift

HEAVENS ARE DECLARING see Beethoven, Ludwig van

HEAVENS ARE DECLARING, THE see Beethoven, Ludwig van

HEAVENS ARE TELLING see Haydn, (Franz) Joseph, Die Himmel Erzahlen Die Ehre Gottes

HEAVENS ARE TELLING, THE see Beethoven, Ludwig van, Die Himmel Ruhmen

HEAVENS ARE TELLING, THE see Haydn, (Franz) Joseph, Die Himmelerzahlen Die Ehre Gottes

HEAVENS ARE THINE, THE see Hilber

HEAVENS DECLARE, THE see Hawkins, Floyd W.

HEAVENS DECLARE HIS GLORY, THE see Hanks

HEAVENS DECLARE, THE see Marcello, I Cieli Immensi

HEAVENS DECLARE THE GLORY OF GOD see Curry

HEAVENS DECLARE THE GLORY OF GOD, THE see
Beethoven, Ludwig van

HEAVENS DECLARE THE GLORY OF GOD, THE see
Marcello

HEAVENS DECLARE THE GLORY OF GOD, THE see
Tomkins, Thomas

HEAVENS DECLARE THE GLORY OF THE LORD, THE see
Schutz, Heinrich, Die Himmel Erzahlen Die
Ehre Gottes

HEAVENS LAUGH, THE see Bach, Johann Sebastian,
Der Himmel Lacht, Die Erde Jubilieret

HEAVENS LAUGH, THE EARTH EXULTS, THE see Bach,
Johann Sebastian, Der Himmel Lacht, Die
Erde Jubiliert

HEAVENS PROCLAIM THE GLORY OF GOD, THE see
Lewis, Anthony

HEAVENS REJOICED, THE see Andrews, C.T.

HEAVENS RESOUND, THE see Beethoven, Ludwig van

HEAV'N BELLS ARE RINGING see Sowande

HEAV'N BOUN, SOLDIER *spir,US
(Aubanel, Georges) "Tiens Ta Lumiere, Soldat"
[Eng/Fr] 4pt mix cor OUVRIERES s.p.   (H2139)

HEAV'N BOUND SOLDIER see Rhea

HEAV'N BOUND SOLDIERS see Howorth, Wayne

HEAV'N DOTH RESOUND see Victoria, Tomas Luis
de, Gaudent In Caelis

HEAV'N, HEAV'N see Burleigh, Henry Thacker

HEAV'N HEAV'N see I Got A Robe

HEAV'NLY CHILD LAY SLEEPING, THE *Xmas,carol,
Ger
(Ehret) SSA oct SHAPIRO SK 3037 $.30   (H2140)

HEB DICH VON MIR, SATAN see Raselius, Andreas

HEB DICH WEG VON MIR, SATAN! see Vulpius,
Melchior

HEBBLE
Lobe Den Herren
"Praise To The Lord, The Almighty" SATB oct
SACRED S-145 $.40   (H2141)

Lonesome Valley
SATB oct HERITAGE H93 $.40   (H2142)

Praise To The Lord, The Almighty *see Lobe
Den Herren

HEBBLE, R.
Celebration Of Unity *Gen,Mass
SATB (med) voc sc GIA G1748 $1.00
                                       (H2143)

My Spirit For Thee
SATB,org GRAY GCMR 3272 $.30   (H2144)

HEBE DEINE AUGEN AUF see Mendelssohn-Bartholdy, Felix

HEBE DICH WEG VON MIR, SATAN see Vulpius, Melchior

HEBET EURE AUGEN AUF see Rosenmuller, Johann

HEBREW BENEDICTION
(Mason, L.) SATB oct LESLIE 4059 contains also: Langdon, R., Lord's Prayer, The; Vesper (H2145)

HEBREW CANTATA see Shapero, Harold

HEBREW CHILDREN
(Niles; Horton; Jackson) 4pt mix cor,acap oct SCHIRM.G 9901 $.20 (H2146)
(Niles; Horton; Jackson) 3pt wom cor,acap oct SCHIRM.G 9916 $.25 (H2147)

HEBREW CHILDREN see Niles, John Jacob

HEBREW CHILDREN, THE
(Parker) SATB,acap oct LAWSON 51323 $.30 (H2148)

HEDGES
Enter His House With Praise
SATB FLAMMER A 5365 $.25 (H2149)

Hosanna, Blessed Is He That Cometh
SATB FLAMMER A 5099 $.30 (H2150)
(Gilbert) SAB FLAMMER D5026 $.30 (H2151)

O Loving Father, Hear My Prayer
SAB FLAMMER D5097 $.25 (H2152)

Supplication
SATB,acap,opt pno oct PRO ART 2658 $.30 (H2153)
SATB,acap (med easy) SOUTHERN $.30 (H2154)

HEDGES, ANTHONY
God Is Gone Up *Asc,anthem
mix cor oct NOVELLO 40.1396.04 s.p. (H2155)

Hold Not Thy Tongue, O God *anthem
mix cor oct NOVELLO 28.1364.05 s.p. (H2156)

I Am Debtor To All *ASD/Rembrnc,anthem
unis/SATB oct NOVELLO 86.0014.07 s.p. (H2157)

Seek Ye The Lord *anthem
SSBar oct NOVELLO 28.1369.06 s.p. (H2158)

HEDGES, H.
Behold, The Star! *Xmas
4pt mix cor,ST soli oct SCHIRM.G 11152 $.25 (H2159)

Psalm Of Praise
mix cor,org/pno oct SCHIRM.G 11920 $.35 (H2160)

HEDNINGAR ALLA, LOVEN GUD see Vulpius, Melchior

HEDNINGERS GENLOSER, KOM see Distler, Hugo, Nun Komm, Der Heiden Heiland

HEDWALL, LENNART
Frukta Icke, Du Lilla Hjord *Bibl
[Swed] SAB,acap GEHRMANS TKS 93 (H2161)

HEER, EMIL (1926-)
Die Helle Sonn Leucht Jetzt Herfur
unis&SAT/unis&SAB,2trp,opt 2trom LAUDINELLA LR11 s.p. contains also: Unser Vater, Der Du Bist In Den Himmeln (SATB) (H2162)

Unser Vater, Der Du Bist In Den Himmeln see Heer, Emil, Die Helle Sonn Leucht Jetzt Herfur

HEGAR, FRIEDRICH (1841-1927)
Schweizergebet
[Ger] mix cor,acap (diff) HUG s.p. (H2163)

Vater Unser
[Ger] mix cor,org HUG cor pts s.p., voc sc rental (H2164)

HEGEDUS, A.
Proper Offertories Of The Sundays In Advent *CCU,Adv,anthem/Offer
SA/TB/SAT/SAB/SATB (med) oct GIA G1269 $.60 (H2165)

Te Deum *Gen,anthem
[Eng/Lat] SATB/unis (med easy) oct GIA G1290 $.25 (H2166)

HEGENBART, ALEX F.
Lord Of All Being
SATB (med) ABINGDON APM-544 $.25 (H2167)

Meditation *Easter
SATB (med) ABINGDON APM-505 $.35 (H2168)

Sing, O Sing *Xmas
SSAATTBB,acap oct SCHIRM.G 11657 $.25 (H2169)

HEGGEN, BODVAR
Bon
mix cor MUSIKK 29 s.p. (H2170)
(Kristoffersen, D.) men cor MUSIKK 191 s.p. (H2171)

Ein Draum I Guds Hjarte
men cor MUSIKK 23 s.p. (H2172)

Heimsens Heilagdom
men cor MUSIKK 14 s.p. (H2173)

Hellige Tone
men cor,T solo MUSIKK 59 s.p. (H2174)

Med Bon Me No Oss Vender
mix cor MUSIKK 127 s.p. (H2175)

Saknad
mix cor MUSIKK 35 s.p. (H2176)

HEGYON LIBI see Isaacson, Michael

HEIBERG
Cantate Domino
(Sweelnick) [Lat/Eng] SSATB oct MCA see from Cantiones Sacrae (H2177)

Cantiones Sacrae *see Cantate Domino; Laudate Dominum; Venite Exultemus Domino (H2178)

HEIBERG (cont'd.)

Laudate Dominum
(Sweelnick) [Lat/Eng] SSATB oct MCA see from Cantiones Sacrae (H2179)

Venite Exultemus Domino
(Sweelnick) [Lat/Eng] SSATB oct MCA see from Cantiones Sacrae (H2180)

HEIDEN, BERNHARD (1910-)
Easter Meditation *Easter,meditation
SSA BROUDE,A. 145 $.30 see from Two Songs Of Spring (H2181)

Two Songs Of Spring *see Easter Meditation (H2182)

HEIDET, LE R. P.
Ave Maris Stella
[Lat] SATB,T solo,org (contains also solo work) voc sc,cor pts ENOCH s.p. see from Premier Salut (H2183)

Deuxieme Salut *see O Salutaris; Sub Tuum Praesidium; Tantum Ergo (H2184)

Gloire Au Treshaut *Xmas,carol
[Fr] mix cor,B solo ENOCH voc sc s.p., cor pts s.p. (H2185)

Justus
[Lat] SATB,org (contains also solo work) voc sc,cor pts ENOCH s.p. see from Troisieme Salut (H2186)

O Quam Suavis
[Lat] SATB,org (contains also solo work) voc sc,cor pts ENOCH s.p. see from Premier Salut (H2187)

O Sacrum
[Lat] SATB,org (contains also solo work) voc sc,cor pts ENOCH s.p. see from Troisieme Salut (H2188)

O Salutaris
[Lat] SATB,org (contains also solo work) voc sc,cor pts ENOCH s.p. see from Deuxieme Salut (H2189)

Premier Salut *see Ave Maris Stella; O Quam Suavis; Tantum Ergo (H2190)

Sub Tuum Praesidium
[Lat] SATB,org (contains also solo work) voc sc,cor pts ENOCH s.p. see from Deuxieme Salut (H2191)

Tantum Ergo
[Lat] SATB,org (contains also solo work) voc sc,cor pts ENOCH s.p. see from Deuxieme Salut (H2192)
[Lat] SATB,org (contains also solo work) voc sc,cor pts ENOCH s.p. see from Premier Salut (H2193)
[Lat] SATB,org (contains also solo work) voc sc,cor pts ENOCH s.p. see from Troisieme Salut (H2194)

Troisieme Salut *see Justus; O Sacrum; Tantum Ergo (H2195)

HEIFETZ, VLADIMIR (1893-)
President's Message, The
SATB TRANSCON. TCL 104 $.50 (H2196)

HEIL DEG, HAVSENS STJERNE see Eggen, Arne

HEIL DEM TAG, DEM DIE NACHT ERLAG see Mozart, Wolfgang Amadeus

HEILAG ER KYRKJA HER see Hovland, Egil

HEILAG VAR see Olsen, Sparre, Ver Sanctum

HEILBUT, P.
Vier Neue Lieder Zum Advent *CC4U,Adv
[Ger] unis HUG s.p. (H2197)

HEILGE NACHT DER EW'GEN LIEBE see Schmid, H.

HEILGE NACHT DER UNENDLICHEN LIEBE see Borris, Siegfried

HEIL'GE NACHT, O GIESSE DU see Beethoven, Ludwig van

HEILGER GEIST, DU TROSTER MEIN see Bornefeld, Helmut

HEILGER GEIST, DU TROSTER MEIN see Metzger, Hans-Arnold

HEILGER GEIST, DU TROSTER MEIN see Muller-Olm, Horst

HEILGER GEIST, DU TROSTER MEIN see Poos, Heinrich

HEIL'GER GEIST, DU TROSTER MEIN see Raphael, Gunther

HEILGER GEIST, DU TROSTER MEIN see Werner, Fritz

HEILGER GOTT *spir
"Deep River" see Dig My Grave
"Deep River" see Two Negro Spirituals
(Burleigh) "Deep River" mix cor,acap oct SCHIRM.G 5815 $.25 contains also: Dig My Grave (H2198)
(Burleigh) "Deep River" SATB RICORDI-ENG LD455 s.p. (H2199)
(Burleigh; Baldwin) "Deep River" mix cor,acap oct SCHIRM.G 9020 $.25 (H2200)
(Burleigh; Deis) "Deep River" 3pt wom cor oct SCHIRM.G 10073 $.30 contains also: Dig My Grave (H2201)
(Christiansen, P.) "Deep River" SATB KJOS 5327 $.30 (H2202)
(Clements, J.) "Deep River" SATB&opt cor PROWSE s.p. (H2203)
(Dett) "Deep River" SATB SCHMITT 1504 $.25 (H2204)
(Durian, Tim) "Deep River" 4pt men cor,Bar solo,acap BREITKOPF-W Z-55 s.p. see also Dreizehn Negro-Spirituals (H2205)
(Luboff, Norman) "Deep River" SATB oct WALTON 3027 $.30 (H2206)
(Pasfield, W.R.) "Deep River" 2pt ASHDOWN E.A.310 s.p. (H2207)
(Roberton) "Deep River" 3pt jr cor/3pt wom cor ROBERTON 72105 s.p. (H2208)
(Schmid, Walter) "Deep River" [Eng] mix cor, acap (easy) HUG s.p. (H2209)
(Shaw; Parker) "Deep River" SATB,acap oct LAWSON 813 $.30 (H2210)

HEILIG see Bach, Karl Philipp Emanuel

HEILIG see Mendelssohn-Bartholdy, Felix

HEILIG see Telemann, Georg Philipp

HEILIG, HEILIG see Doppelbauer, Josef Friedrich

HEILIG, HEILIG see Schubert, Franz (Peter)

HEILIG, HEILIG, HEILIG see Dyke, J.B.

HEILIG, HEILIG, HEILIG see Schubert, Franz (Peter)

HEILIG, HEILIG, HEILIG IST DER HERRE ZEBAOTH see Bach, Johann Sebastian

HEILIG, HEILIG, IST DER HERR see Krieger, Johann Philipp

HEILIG IST DER HERR see Hammerschmidt, Andreas

HEILIG IST DER HERR see Schubert, Franz (Peter)

HEILIG IST DER HERR ZEBAOTH see Schieferdecker, Johann C.

HEILIG IST GOTT see Bach, Karl Philipp Emanuel

HEILIG IST GOTT DER VATER see Dietrich, Sixtus

HEILIG IST GOTT DER VATER (DAS SANCTUS DEUTSCH) see Dietrich, Sixtus

HEILIG-JAHR-MESSE see Polzer, Odo

HEILIG-MESSE see Haydn, (Franz) Joseph, Missa In Honorem B. Bernardi De Offida

HEILIG-MESSE see Haydn, (Franz) Joseph, Missa Solemnis

HEILIG WORT see Muller von Kulm, Walter

HEILIGE NACHT see Reichardt, Johann Friedrich

HEILIGE NACHT, O GIESSE DU see Beethoven, Ludwig van

HEILIGENBLUTER KRIPPENMESSE see Mittergradnegger, G.

HEILIGENKANTATE *cant/folk
(Strobl, Otto) mix cor,strings DOBLINGER voc sc s.p., cor pts s.p., ipa (H2211)

HEILIGER EWIGER GOTT see Barbe, Helmut

HEILIGER GEIST, DU TROSTER MEIN see Cruger, Johann

HEILIGMESSE see Haydn, (Franz) Joseph, Missa Sancti Bernardi De Offida

HEILIGSTE NACHT see Barthel, Ursula

HEILIGSTE NACHT see Haydn, (Johann) Michael

HEILLER, ANTON (1923-)
Adventmusik *Adv
jr cor,org,ob,vln DOBLINGER voc sc s.p., cor pts s.p., ipa (H2212)

Ave Maria
wom cor,acap oct DOBLINGER s.p. (H2213)

Confirma Hoc, Deus
mix cor,acap oct DOBLINGER s.p. (H2214)

Dem Konig Aller Zeiten *mot
mix cor,acap DOBLINGER s.p. see also Drei Kleine Geistliche Chore (H2215)

Der Heiland Ist Erstanden *mot
4pt mix cor,acap DOBLINGER sc s.p., cor pts s.p. (H2216)

Deutsches Ordinarium
mix cor,org/2ob&2clar&2bsn&2horn&strings DOBLINGER voc sc s.p., cor pts s.p., ipa (H2217)

Deutsches Proprium *Trin
cor&cong,org DOBLINGER voc sc s.p., cor pts s.p. (H2218)
3pt wom cor,acap voc pt DOBLINGER s.p. (H2219)

Deutsches Proprium Fur Das Dreifaltigkeitsfest *Trin
mix cor&cong,org DOBLINGER sc s.p., cor pts s.p. (H2220)

Deutsches Proprium Fur Den Dreifaltigkeitssonntag *Trin
4pt mix cor,acap DOBLINGER sc s.p., cor pts s.p. (H2221)

Drei Kleine Geistliche Chore
mix cor,acap cmplt ed DOBLINGER s.p. contains & see also: Dem Konig Aller Zeiten; Schonster Herr Jesus; Seele Christi, Heilige Mich (H2222)

English Mass *Mass
unis/cong&SATB sc SUMMY M 2590 $1.00 (H2223)

Geistliches Konzert
mix cor,2ob,2bsn cor pts DOBLINGER s.p., ipr (H2224)

Gepriesen Bist Du, Herr *Gradual
mix cor,acap oct DOBLINGER s.p. (H2225)

Gepriesen Sei Die Heilige Dreifaltigkeit *Trin
mix cor,acap oct DOBLINGER s.p. (H2226)

Gepriesen Sei Gott Vater *Offer
mix cor,acap oct DOBLINGER (H2227)

HEILLER, ANTON (cont'd.)

Grad Dort
mix cor,acap oct DOBLINGER s.p.   (H2228)

In Principio Erat Verbum *cant
mix cor,T solo,org,orch DOBLINGER voc sc
s.p., cor pts s.p., ipr, min sc s.p.
(H2229)

Kleine Messe Uber Zwolftonmodelle *Mass
4pt mix cor,acap sc DOBLINGER s.p.   (H2230)

Memorare
mix cor,acap oct DOBLINGER s.p.   (H2231)

Missa In Nocte
2pt wom cor,org DOBLINGER voc sc s.p., cor
pts s.p.   (H2232)

Missa Super Modus Duodecimales *Mass
mix cor,2ob,bsn,vln,vla,vcl DOBLINGER sc
s.p., voc sc s.p.   (H2233)

O Jesu, All Mein Leben
(Stein, A.G.) mix cor,acap oct DOBLINGER
s.p.   (H2234)

O Rex Gentium
mix cor,acap oct DOBLINGER s.p.   (H2235)

Proprium Zum Fronleichnamsfest
SAB sc DOBLINGER s.p.   (H2236)

Psalm 37
[Lat] voc sc UNIVER. 13652 $3.60, cor pts
UNIVER. 13653 $1.90   (H2237)

Psalmenkantate
[Lat] voc sc UNIVER. 12409 $9.90, cor pts
UNIVER. 12410 $2.45   (H2238)

Salve Regina *Mass
wom cor/jr cor,acap cor pts DOBLINGER s.p.
contains also: Vater Unser Im Himmelreich
(H2239)

Schonster Herr Jesus
mix cor,acap DOBLINGER s.p. see also Drei
Kleine Geistliche Chore   (H2240)

Seele Christi, Heilige Mich *mot
mix cor,acap DOBLINGER s.p. see also Drei
Kleine Geistliche Chore   (H2241)

Stabat Mater
mix cor,orch DOBLINGER voc sc s.p., cor pts
s.p.   (H2242)
mix cor,orch study sc DOBLINGER s.p.
(H2243)

Tantum Ergo I
mix cor,acap oct DOBLINGER s.p.   (H2244)

Tantum Ergo II
mix cor,acap oct DOBLINGER s.p.   (H2245)

Te Deum *Te Deum
[Lat] sc UNIVER. 12268 $4.55, cor pts
UNIVER. 12269 $1.40   (H2246)

Tentatio Jesu
mix cor,2pno voc sc UNIVER. 12442 $4.50,
cor pts UNIVER. 12443 $1.65   (H2247)

Vater Unser Im Himmelreich
see Heiller, Anton, Salve Regina

Weihnachtslied *Xmas
men cor,acap oct DOBLINGER s.p.   (H2248)

Wir Preisen Den Himmelsgott
mix cor,acap oct DOBLINGER s.p.   (H2249)

HEILMANN, HARALD (1924-   )
Anruf *mot
[Ger] mix cor&men cor cor pts SIRIUS s.p.
(H2250)
[Ger] 8pt mix cor voc sc SIRIUS s.p.
(H2251)

Auf Diesen Tag Bedenken Wir
see Zwei Kleine Choralmotetten

Es Geht Daher Des Tages Schein *Gen,mot
[Ger] SATB,acap (med) MULLER MS 82 s.p.
(H2252)

Et Absterget Deus Omnem Lacrymam
[Ger] men cor,acap (med) oct SIRIUS 6 s.p.
(H2253)
[Lat] mix cor (med) oct SIRIUS 12 s.p.
(H2254)

Herr Gott, Du Bist Unsre Zuflucht
[Ger] mix cor (med) oct SIRIUS 17 s.p.
(H2255)

Hirtenkantate Zur Weihnacht *Xmas,cant
jr cor/SA,rec, glockenspiel sc HANSSLER
12.503 s.p., ipa   (H2256)

Komm, O Komm, Du Geist Des Lebens
see Zwei Kleine Choralmotetten

Missa *Mass
mix cor,2trp,3trom,bvl,timp HANSSLER 10.297
sc s.p., cor pts s.p., ipa   (H2257)

Proprium Zum Grundonnerstag *Holywk
cor HANSSLER 27.001 s.p.   (H2258)

Zwei Kleine Choralmotetten *mot
4pt mix cor,acap cor pts BREITKOPF-W
CHB-3186 s.p.
contains: Auf Diesen Tag Bedenken Wir
(Asc); Komm, O Komm, Du Geist Des
Lebens (Pent/Whitsun)   (H2259)

HEIMSENS HEILAGDOM see Heggen, Bodvar

HEINRICH
Carol Is Born, A
SSA&unis,fl (carol 'drama) BOSTON $1.75
(H2260)

HEISINGER, BRENT
O Praise The Lord
SATB oct BELWIN 2165 $.25   (H2261)

HEISS, HERMANN (1897-1966)
Dreistimmige Gesange Nach Angelus Silesius
*CCU,Gen
[Ger] SAB,acap (med) MULLER SM 2301 s.p.
(H2262)

HELA VARLDEN FROJDES HERRAN see Ostling

HELAS MAMOUR see Clemens, Jacobus

HELAS, MON DIEU see Le Jeune, Claude

HELAS, MON DIEU, TON IRE S'EST TOURNEE see
Jannequin, Clement

HELAS, MON DIEU, TON IRE S'EST TOURNEE see
Maillard, Jean

HELAS, SEIGNEUR! see Le Jeune, Claude

HELAS, SEIGNEUR, JE TE PRI' SAUVE MOI see
Goudimel, Claude

HELD, PAUL
Hymnus *Heb
SATB,acap ISRAELI 329 s.p.   (H2263)

HELD, WILBUR
Dost Thou In A Manger Lie *anthem
unis treb cor (easy) oct AUGSBURG 1524 $.25
(H2264)

God Of A Universe *anthem
SATB (med) oct AUGSBURG 1549 $.30   (H2265)

Jesus! Name Of Wondrous Love *Circum/Commun/
Gen
SATB,S solo,kbd (easy) oct CONCORDIA
98-2075 $.40   (H2266)

Message Came To A Maiden Young, A *anthem
unis treb cor (easy) oct AUGSBURG 1565 $.25
(H2267)

Saw You Never In The Twilight *anthem
unis treb cor (easy) oct AUGSBURG 1525 $.25
(H2268)

HELDER, BARTHOLOMAEUS (1585-1635)
Du Starker Held, Herr Jesu Christ
see Bach, Johann Sebastian, Heut
Trimphieret Gottes Sohn

Ich Freu Mich In Dem Herren
see Kurig, Hans-Hermann, Wer In Mir Bleibet
Und Ich In Ihm
TTBB HANSSLER 6.0470 s.p.   (H2269)
SATB HANSSLER 6.2513 s.p. contains also:
Isaac, Heinrich, O Welt, Sieh Hier Dein
Leben   (H2270)

Mein Konig, Dir Zu Singen
see Schutz, Heinrich, Wohl Denen, Die Da
Wandeln

Sing We Triumphant Hymns *Asc/Easter
SATB,acap (med easy) oct CONCORDIA 98-1039
$.20 contains also: Strife Is O'er, The
(H2271)

Strife Is O'er, The
see Helder, Bartholomaeus, Sing We
Triumphant Hymns

HELE, GEORGE DE LA (1547-1586)
Collected Works *CC10L,Mass/mot
(Wagner, Laverne) cor AM.INST.MUS. $45.00
chanson   (H2272)

HELFER
Lord's Prayer, The
jr cor&SSA,timp (med) FISCHER,C CM 604 $.20
(H2273)

HELFMAN, MAX (1901-1963)
Adonoy, Adonoy
[Heb] SATB TRANSCON. TCL 782 $.40 contains
also: Va-Ani S'filosi   (H2274)

Areshes
[Heb] cor,cantor,org TRANSCON. TCL 676 $.60
(H2275)

Haben Yakir Li
[Heb] cor,cantor,org TRANSCON. TCL 677 $.60
(H2276)

Holy Ark, Torah Service, The *Fest/Sab-Morn
SATB TRANSCON. TCL 750 $2.75   (H2277)

Holy Sabbath, The *see Shabbat Kodesh

Kol Nidre
[Heb] SATB,cantor TRANSCON. TCL 751 $.50
(H2278)

O Merciful God
[Eng] cor,cantor,org TRANSCON. TCL 628 $.40
(H2279)

Shabbat Kodesh *Sab-Eve
"Holy Sabbath, The" SATB TRANSCON. TCL 250
$3.00   (H2280)

Shabbit M'nuchah *Sab-Eve
SATB TRANSCON. TCL 268 $4.50   (H2281)

Uvashofor Godol
[Heb] SATB,cantor TRANSCON. TCL 816 $1.00
(H2282)

Va-Ani S'filosi
see Helfman, Max, Adonoy, Adonoy

HELFRITZ, HANS (1902-   )
Geistliche Gesange Nach Religiosen Motiven
Aus Bolivien *CCU,Gen,So Am
[Ger] SSA,acap (med easy) MULLER SM 2247
s.p.   (H2283)

HELFT MIR GOTTES GUTE PREISEN see Schroter,
Leonhard

HELFT MIR, GOTT'S GUTE PREISEN see Bach, Johann
Sebastian

HELFT MIR GOTTS GUTE PREISEN see
Gumpeltzhaimer, Adam

HELFT MIR, GOTT'S GUTE PREISEN [CHORALE] see
Bach, Johann Sebastian

HELIG, HELIG, HELIG see Bach, Johann Sebastian

HELIG, HELIG, HELIG see Nyvall, Jacob

HELIG, HELIG, HELIG see Schubert, Franz (Peter)

HELIGE ANDE see Sjoberg, Sven-Gosta

HELIGE ANDE, SANNINGENS ANDE see Berg, Gottfrid

HELIGE FRALSARE see Edlund, Lars

HELL DIG, HELL DIG, SANNA KROPP see Moren,
John, Ave Verum Corpus

HELL MORGONSTJARNA, MILD OCH REN see Bach,
Johann Sebastian, Wie Schon Leuchtet Der
Morgenstern

HELL, MORGONSTJARNA, MILD OCH REN see
Bjarnegard, Gustaf

HE'LL OPEN THE WINDOWS OF HEAVEN see Lister,
Mosie

HE'LL UNDERSTAND, AND SAY, "WELL DONE" see
Campbell

HELLAS, MON DIEU see Jannequin, Clement

HELLDEN, DANIEL
Samothrake (from Non Serviam)
(Ekelof, Gunnar) mix cor,soli,orch cor pts
NORDISKA 5043 s.p., ipa   (H2284)

HELLENE, JOHS.
Kyrie *Kyrie
[Norw] mix cor LYCHE 107 s.p.   (H2285)

HELLER
Cross Was His Own, The *Easter
SATB oct LORENZ A444 $.25   (H2286)

Glory To God *Gen
(Rachmaninoff) SATB SCHMITT 1695 $.35
(H2287)

Treble Choir Responses *CCU,Gen
SSA SCHMITT 2541 $.20   (H2288)

HELLER, A.
L'cho Dodi *liturg,Jew
SATB,cantor oct PRESSER MC546 $.60   (H2289)

HELLER, JOACHIM (ca. 1518-1590)
Sie Ist Mir Lieb, Die Werte Magd *Fest
[Ger] 2pt mix cor,acap (med easy) BAREN.
BA 4955 $.40   (H2290)

HELLIG, HELLIG ER HERREN GUD see Runback,
Albert

HELLIGE TONE see Groven, Eivind

HELLIGE TONE see Heggen, Bodvar

HELLINGK, LUPUS (1495-1541)
Ach, Vater Unser, Der Du Bist
[Ger] SATB,acap (med) MULLER K7 s.p. (H2291)

Aus Tiefer Not *ECY
[Ger] SATB,acap (med easy) MULLER K 16 s.p.
(H2292)

Mit Fried Und Freud Ich Fahr Dahin
[Ger] SATB,acap (med easy) MULLER K 14 s.p.
(H2293)

HELLMANN, DIETHARD (1928-   )
Benedicamus In Natali Domini *Bene
"Lasset Uns Danken Dem Herrn Christ" [Lat/
Ger] SAB HANSSLER 7.042 s.p.   (H2294)

Herr, Neige Deine Ohren Und Erhore Mich *mot
SAB HANSSLER 7.054 s.p.   (H2295)

Herzliebster Jesu, Wer Glaubt Und Dein
SSAATTBB HANSSLER 7.076 s.p.   (H2296)

Lasset Uns Danken Dem Herrn Christ *see
Benedicamus In Natali Domini

Nun Bitten Wir Den Heiligen Geist
SA,org,2rec HANSSLER 5.056 s.p.   (H2297)

Singet Dem Herrn Ein Neues Lied *mot
SAB HANSSLER 7.048 s.p.   (H2298)

HELMORE, T.
A Kom, A Kom Immanuel
(Aamodt, Thorleif) [Norw] mix cor,org LYCHE
6 s.p.   (H2299)

HELP ME TEACH WITH INSPIRATION see Wheelwright,
Lorin F.

HELP US, ETERNAL GOD AND LORD see Gesius,
Bartholomaus

HELP US, JESUS CHRIST, GOD'S SON see Schutz,
Heinrich

HELP US, O LORD, DELIVER US see Haydn, (Johann)
Michael

HELP US TO HELP EACH OTHER, LORD see Wolff, S.
Drummond

HELYER, MARJORIE
Ballad Of Trees And The Master
SSA oct LESLIE 3044   (H2300)

HEMBERG, ESKIL
Massa Vid Malaren
mix cor NORDISKA 5872 s.p.   (H2301)

HEMBERG-ESKIL
Messa *Op.23, Mass
mix cor,5 soli NORDISKA NMS-10.245 s.p.
(H2302)

Signposts
4pt mix cor,acap oct SCHIRM.G 11842 $.35
(H2303)

HEMEL, OSCAR VAN (1892-   )
Canticum Psalmorum *Psalm
[Lat] men cor,A solo,2pno,timp DONEMUS min
sc s.p., cor pts s.p., ipa
contains: De Profundis; Deus Misereatur
Nostri; Exsultate Domino; Laudate
Dominum; Quem Ad Modum   (H2304)

De Profundis
see Canticum Psalmorum

Deus Misereatur Nostri
see Canticum Psalmorum

Exsultate Domino
see Canticum Psalmorum

Laudate Dominum
see Canticum Psalmorum

HEMEL, OSCAR VAN (cont'd.)

Les Mysteres Du Christ: Hymne Symphonique
*hymn
[Fr] men cor,ABar soli,2fl,2ob,2clar,3bsn,
4trp,4horn,3trom,tuba,strings,perc,timp,
harp DONEMUS min sc s.p., cor pts s.p.,
voc sc s.p.   (H2305)

Quem Ad Modum
see Canticum Psalmorum

Te Deum *Te Deum
[Dut] mix cor,SATB soli,2fl,2ob,2clar,2bsn,
3trp,4horn,3trom,tuba,strings,timp,harp
DONEMUS min sc s.p., cor pts s.p., voc sc
s.p.   (H2306)

HEMMEL, SIGMUND (? -1564)
Aus Tiefer Not Schrei Ich Zu Dir
SATB LAUDINELLA LR 53 s.p. contains also:
In Dich Hab Ich Gehoffet, Herr   (H2307)

In Dich Hab Ich Gehoffet, Herr
see Hemmel, Sigmund, Aus Tiefer Not Schrei
Ich Zu Dir

HEMMER, [EUGENE] (1929-   )
Hymn Of Youth *hymn
2 eq voices,pno/org AM.MUS.ED. ESA-559-2
$.20   (H2308)

Journey To Bethlehem *Xmas,cant
SATB oct SPIRE $.45   (H2309)
SATB,acap oct WORLD AC-713-8 $.45   (H2310)

Mary's Lullaby *Xmas,cradle
SA,pno/org oct SPIRE $.30   (H2311)
SA&opt jr cor,opt A solo,pno/org oct WORLD
AC-568-2 $.30   (H2312)

Mother's Christmas Song, A *Xmas
unis,pno oct SPIRE $.75   (H2313)

Prayer For Our Children
SATB,pno oct SPIRE $.35   (H2314)

HEMMT EURE TRAUENFLUT see Bruhns, Nicholaus

HEMY, [HENRI FREDERICK] (1818-1888)
Faith Of Our Fathers
(Ringwald) SATB SHAWNEE A 77 $.30   (H2315)

HENCE, ALL FEARS AND SADNESS see Bach, Johann
Sebastian

HENCE WITH EARTHLY TREASURE see Bach, Johann
Sebastian

HENDERSON
Glory To God *Xmas
(Hirt) 4pt jr cor/SATB (easy) FISCHER,C
CM 7437 $.25   (H2316)
(Hirt) SATB,acap oct FISCHER,C CM-7437 $.25   (H2317)

Hear My Cry, O God
SATB,org/pno BOSTON 12987 $.40   (H2318)

Praise Ye The Lord (Psalm 148)
(Stoutamire) SATB oct PRO ART 2731 $.30   (H2319)

Psalm 51
(Stoutamire) SATB FLAMMER A 5304 $.25   (H2320)

Psalm 148 *see Praise Ye The Lord

These Things Shall Be *anthem
SATB oct FISCHER,C CM-7139 $.25   (H2321)

HENDERSON, H.
Come Unto Me *Bibl
4pt mix cor,S solo oct SCHIRM.G 9307 $.25   (H2322)

HENDERSON, R.
Sing Praises To God *Fest,anthem
4pt mix cor,org/pno oct SCHIRM.G 10408 $.25   (H2323)

HENDERSON, RUTH WATSON
Our Father *see Pater Noster

Pater Noster
"Our Father" SATB THOMP.G s.p.   (H2324)

HENKING, BERNHARD (1897-   )
Der Mond Ist Aufgegangen *cant
SATB,fl,2vln,vla,vcl,bvl,opt org HANSSLER
10.244 sc s.p., cor pts s.p., ipa   (H2325)

Du Glanz Aus Gottes Herrlichkeit *cant
SATB,org,trp/vln HANSSLER 10.207 sc s.p.,
voc sc s.p.   (H2326)

Nun Singet Und Seid Froh *cant
SATB,org HANSSLER 10.172 sc s.p., voc sc
s.p.   (H2327)

Psalm 47 *see Singt Mit Froher Stimm

Singt Mit Froher Stimm (Psalm 47)
see Wieruszowski, Lili, Singt Mit Froher
Stimm

HENNAGIN, MICHAEL
Creation, The (from Family Of Man, The)
SATB oct WALTON 2186 $1.00   (H2328)

Family Of Man, The *Xmas
mix cor,pno,perc,electronic tape voc sc
WALTON M 117 $2.50, sc WALTON rental   (H2329)

Psalm 23
SATB oct WALTON 2807 $.35   (H2330)

HENNIG, WALTER (1903-1967)
Bis Hieher Hat Mich Gott Gebracht *cant
SATB,4brass sc HANSSLER 10.051 s.p.   (H2331)

Jesu, Nun Sei Gepreiset
SA,2bass inst HANSSLER 14.039   (H2332)

Jesus Christus, Unser Heiland, Der Den Tod
Uberwand *Easter
SA/SSA/SAT/SAB,treb inst/bass inst HANSSLER
14.077 s.p. contains also: Stegen,
Wilfried, Erstanden Ist Der Heilig Christ
(SST/SSB,treb inst/bass inst)   (H2333)

HENNIG, WALTER (cont'd.)

Psalm 150 *Bibl
SAB&SAB&unis,SB soli,org,3brass,2vln,vcl
HANSSLER 10.182 sc s.p., voc sc s.p., ipa   (H2334)

HENNING, ERVIN ARTHUR (1910-   )
By The Rivers Of Babylon
SA,pno SCHIRM.EC 2556 $.40   (H2335)

HENNINGER, [GEORGE R.] (1895-1953)
Exalt We Now Thy Holy Name
SATB,acap oct PRESSER 332-40016 $.30   (H2336)

HENRICHSEN, ROGER (1876-1926)
Johannisnacht Hymne *Op.9, hymn
"Sct. Hans Hymne" [Dan/Ger] cor,soli,orch
voc sc FOG II, 33 s.p.   (H2337)

Sct. Hans Hymne *see Johannisnacht Hymne

HENRIKSEN, JOSEF
Catholic Mass In English, The *Mass
unis,org voc sc ST.GREG. s.p.   (H2338)
unis voc pt ST.GREG. s.p.   (H2339)
2pt,org voc sc ST.GREG. s.p.   (H2340)

Jack Be Nimble *sac/sec,CCU,round
cor,cont,opt string/gtr ST.GREG. s.p.   (H2341)

HENSCHEL, ISADORE GEORGE (1850-1934)
Morning Hymn *Op.46,No.4
SATB oct PRESSER 332-14702 $.30   (H2342)
SATB,pno SCHIRM.EC 360 $.20, ipr   (H2343)
TTBB,acap SCHIRM.EC 40 $.25, ipr   (H2344)
(Clough-Leighter, H.) SSAA,pno SCHIRM.EC
478 $.15, ipr   (H2345)
(Gibb) TTBB,acap BOSTON 2133 $.30   (H2346)
(Glaser, V.) SSA,pno SCHIRM.EC 1986 $.25,
ipr   (H2347)

HENSEL, WALTHER (1887-1956)
Der Du Ausspannst Das Himmlische Zelt *Gen
[Ger] 3pt mix cor,acap (easy) BAREN. BCH 33
s.p.   (H2348)

Susaninne *Xmas,cant
[Ger] SAB,soli,fl,vln,vla,vcl,gtr (med
easy) sc BAREN. BA 59 $2.25   (H2349)

Wach Auf *sac/sec,CCU,Gen
[Ger] eq voices/2-4pt mix cor,4brass (med
easy) BAREN. BA 470 $5.25   (H2350)

HENZE, HANS WERNER (1926-   )
Novae De Infinite Laudes *cant
[Lat] SATB,SATB soli,orch voc sc SCHOTT
5267 s.p., min sc SCHOTT 5028 s.p.   (H2351)

HER, DA DU VORMALS HAST DEIN LAND see Anonymous

HER, HER, ICH VERKUND EUCH NEUE MAR see
Agricola, Martin

HER KOMMER DINE ARME SMA *Xmas
(Beck, Thomas) mix cor MUSIKK 95D s.p.   (H2352)

HER KOMMER DINE ARME SMAA see Schulz

HERALD OF GOOD TIDINGS see Titcomb, Everett

HERALDS OF CHRIST see Darst, W. Glen

HERALDS OF CHRIST see Warren

HERAUF NUN, DU HELLICHTER TAG see Blank, Allan

HERBECK, JOHANN FRANZ VON (1831-1877)
Pueri Concinite *Xmas
(Pfannhauser, K.) 4pt mix cor,T solo,fl,
2ob,clar,bsn,2horn,strings (contains
also: Redemptor Nobis) DOBLINGER voc sc
s.p., cor pts s.p., ipa see from
OSTERREICHISCHE KIRCHENMUSIK   (H2353)

Redemptor Nobis *Xmas
(Pfannhauser, K.) 4pt mix cor,T solo,fl,
2ob,clar,bsn,2horn,strings (contains
also: Pueri Concinite) DOBLINGER voc sc
s.p., cor pts s.p., ipa see from
OSTERREICHISCHE KIRCHENMUSIK   (H2354)

HERBEK
Search Me, O God, And Know My Heart
SATB FLAMMER A 5604 $.30   (H2355)

HERBER
Bread Of The World *see Eville

HERBERGSSUCHE DER MARIA see Spitta, Heinrich

HERBERT
King Of Glory, King Of Peace
(Schlotel) SATB LUDWIG L-1119 $.30   (H2356)

Let Mount Zion Rejoice
SATB oct LORENZ 71 $.35   (H2357)

HERBERT, PETER
Komm, O Komm, Du Geist Des Lebens
see Muller-Olm, Horst, Heilger Geist, Du
Troster Mein

HERBST
Forty Days And Forty Nights *Gen
(Ehret) SATB SCHMITT 869 $.22   (H2358)

People That In Darkness *Adv,Morav
(Dickinson) SATB oct GRAY GMCM 5 $.40   (H2359)

HERBST, ANDREAS
see HERBST, JOHANNES ANDREAS

HERBST, JOHANNES ANDREAS (1588-1666)
Dank- Und Lobgesang (Psalm 107) Gen
(Gerber, Rudolf) [Ger] SAATBarB,cont,3vln,
5trom (med diff) BAREN. BA 3695 rental   (H2360)

Ein Feste Burg Ist Unser Gott *cant
(Moser, H.J.) SSATB,SSATB soli,cont,2vln,
2vla,vcl,bvl HANSSLER 10.191 sc s.p., voc
sc s.p., ipa   (H2361)

Psalm 107 *see Dank- Und Lobgesang

HERBST, WOLFGANG
Herr Jesu Christ, Dich Zu Uns Wend
see Kretzschmar, Gunther, Jauchzet Dem
Herrn

Wir Wollen Alle Frohlich Sein
see Kretzschmar, Gunther, Christus Ist
Auferstanden, Freud Ist In

Wohl Denen, Die Da Wandeln
see Kretzschmar, Gunther, Nun Danket All
Und Bringet Ehr

HERBSTTAG see Frommlet, D.

HERDARNA SPELA FOR BARNET JESUS see Tegner,
Alice

HERDER ISRAEL see Bortniansky, Dimitri
Stepanovitch, Du Hirte Israels

HERDER, RONALD
From The Twenty-Third Psalm *Psalm
SATB,acap AMP A577 $.25   (H2362)

Job Elegies, The *Bibl
SATB,acap AMP A520 $.30   (H2363)

HERE ARE WE IN BETHLEHEM see Willan, Healey

HERE BEAUTY DWELL AND HOLINESS see Thiman, Eric
Harding

HERE COMES JESUS see Salsbury, Sonny

HERE IN THE SILENCE see Kirk, T.

HERE IN THIS STABLE *Xmas,Fr
(Ehret) SSA,opt 2vln MARKS 4351 $.25   (H2364)

HERE IS A GREAT PRIEST see Roff, Joseph

HERE IS HEAVENLY JOY see Handel, George
Frideric

HERE IS THE GOD WHO LOOKS BOTH WAYS see
Crawford, John, Voici Le Pere Au Double
Front

HERE, MID THE ASS AND OXEN GRAY *Xmas,Fr
(Trusler) SAB oct PLYMOUTH TR-401 $.25   (H2365)

HERE, MID THE ASS AND OXEN MILD *Xmas,carol,Fr
(Shaw; Parker) mix cor,S solo,acap oct
SCHIRM.G 10186 $.30   (H2366)

HERE, O MY LORD see Nyquist

HERE, O MY LORD, I SEE THEE FACE TO FACE see
Whitlock, Percy

HERE ON EARTH see Brahms, Johannes

HERE REPOSE, O BROKEN BODY see Pinkham, Daniel

HERE WE COME A-CAROLING *CCU,Xmas
mix cor SCHMITT 9079 $.75   (H2367)

HERE WE COME A-WASSAILING *Xmas
see Troll The Ancient Carol
(Lefebvre) TTBB oct GALAXY 1.1219.1 $.35   (H2368)

HERE WE GO A-CAROLING see Avery

HERE WE WORSHIP THEE see Palestrina, Giovanni,
Adoramus Te, Christe

HERE YET AWHILE see Bach, Johann Sebastian

HEREDIA, PIEDRO (? -1648)
Communion Service On A Roman Tone *see Missa
Super Cantu Romano

Missa Super Cantu Romano *Commun,Mass
[Lat/Eng] 4pt mix cor,acap SCHIRM.EC 1228   (H2369)
"Communion Service On A Roman Tone" SATB,
acap SCHIRM.EC 1228   (H2370)
(Bauerle, Hermann) SATB,acap cor pts
BREITKOPF-L PB-3138 s.p.   (H2371)

HERE'S ONE
(Still, W.) SATB oct PRESSER 322-40037 $.30 (H2372)

HERFORTH
Voice, The
SATB oct LORENZ A512 $.30   (H2373)

HERITAGE OF AMERICAN SPIRITUALS, A *CCU,spir
SATB oct LORENZ B94 $.60   (H2374)

HERMAN
Awake My Soul
mix cor SOUTHERN $.25   (H2375)

Lo, Round The Throne *anthem
(Ley) SATB (easy) OXFORD 42.801 $.30 see
from SIX SHORT ANTHEMS   (H2376)

HERMAN, N.
Lobt Gott, Ihr Christen Alle Gleich *Thanks
TTBB HANSSLER 6.2385 s.p.   (H2377)

HERMANN, [NIKOLAUS] (ca. 1480-1561)
O Christ, Our Hope *anthem
(Distler) SSA (easy) oct AUGSBURG 1450 $.20 (H2378)

Praise God The Lord, Ye Sons Of Men *Xmas
(Kirk) SATB oct PRO ART 1868 $.25   (H2379)

HERMANSON, P.
God Of Years
SATB oct PRESSER 312-40396 $.35   (H2380)

HERNRIED
Christ Is Risen *Easter
SATB oct GALAXY 1.1134.1 $.25   (H2381)

HEROLD, LOUIS-JOSEPH-FERDINAND (1791-1833)
Regina Coeli
SSTAB,acap SCHIRM.EC $.30   (H2382)

HEROLDT, BRUNO
Die Ostergeschichte *Op.11, Easter
[Ger] 6pt mix cor oct DEUTSCHER 7628 $2.00   (H2383)

[Ger] SSATBB,acap (med diff) DEUTSCHER
DV 7628 s.p.   (H2384)

HEROLDT, BRUNO (cont'd.)

Variationen Uber Drei Weihnachtslieder
*Op.17, Xmas
[Ger] mix cor oct DEUTSCHER 7623 $1.50
(H2385)

HERR, ALLER ENDEN see Stier, Alfred

HERR, AUF DICH TRAUE ICH see Kretzschmar,
Gunther

HERR AUF DICH TRAUE ICH see Kukuck, Felicitas

HERR, AUF DICH TRAUE ICH see Nicolai, Otto

HERR, AUF DICH TRAUE ICH see Schutz, Heinrich

HERR, BLEIBE BEI UNS see Anonymous

HERR, BLEIBE BEI UNS see Etti, Karl

HERR CHRIST see Bach, Johann Sebastian, Herr
Christ, Der Ein'ge Gottes-Sohn

HERR CHRIST, DER EIN'GE GOTTES-SOHN see Bach,
Johann Sebastian

HERR CHRIST, DER EIN'GE GOTTESSOHN see Bach,
Johann Sebastian

HERR CHRIST, DER EINIG GOTTES SOHN see Schein,
Johann Hermann

HERR CHRIST, DER EINIG GOTTS SOHN see Eccard,
Johannes

HERR CHRIST, DER EINIG GOTTS SOHN see Franck,
Melchior

HERR CHRIST, DER EINIG GOTTS SOHN see Gwinner,
Volker

HERR CHRIST, DER EINIG GOTTS SOHN see Koch,
Heinz

HERR CHRIST, DER EINIG GOTTS SOHN see Koch,
Johannes H.E.

HERR CHRIST, DER EINIG GOTTS SOHN see Poos,
Heinrich

HERR CHRIST, DER EINIG GOTTS SOHN see
Praetorius, Michael

HERR CHRIST, DER EINIG GOTTS SOHN see Schein,
Johann Hermann

HERR CHRIST, DER EINIG GOTT'S SOHN see Stern,
Hermann

HERR CHRIST, DER EINIG GOTTS SOHN [CHORALE] see
Bach, Johann Sebastian

HERR CHRIST, DER ENIG GOTTS SOHN see Werner,
Fritz

HERR CHRIST, HILF UNS IN DIESER ZEIT see
Raphael, Gunther

HERR CHRISTE, KOMM IN UNSRE NOT see Weber,
Ludwig

HERR CHRISTE, TREUER HEILAND WERT see Nickel,
Eckehardt

HERR CHRISTE, TU MIR GEBEN see Eccard, Johannes

HERR, DEIN WORT BLEIBT EWIGLICH see Schmid,
Walter

HERR, DEIN WORT IST MEINES FUSSES LEUCHTE see
Poos, Heinrich

HERR, DEINE AUGEN see Bach, Johann Sebastian,
Herr, Deine Augen Sehen Nach Dem Glauben

HERR, DEINE AUGEN SEHEN NACH DEM GLAUBEN see
Bach, Johann Sebastian

HERR, DEINE GUT UND WAHRHEIT STEHT see Lassus,
Roland de (Orlandus)

HERR, DEINE GUTE REICHT SO WEIT DER HIMMEL IST
see Schweizer, Rolf

HERR, DEINE GUTE REICHT SO WEIT DIE WOLKEN
GEHEN see Reda, Siegfried

HERR, DEINE WELT IST ZUM STAUNEN see Ruppel,
Paul Ernst

HERR, DEM ZU EHREN IN HIMMELSHEEREN see Stier,
Alfred

HERR, DER DU MEINE STARKE BIST see Lassus,
Roland de (Orlandus)

HERR! DER DU MIR DAS LEBEN see Haydn, (Franz)
Joseph

HERR, DER DU THRONEST see Mozart, Wolfgang
Amadeus

HERR, DER DU VORMALS GNADIG WARST see Schutz,
Heinrich

HERR DER WELTEN-HERR DER MENSCHEN see Zoll,
Paul

HERR DES HIMMELS *folk,Aus
(Tittel, Ernst) mix cor DOBLINGER s.p. see
also Christus, Der Herr (H2386)
(Tittel, Ernst) mix cor,acap oct DOBLINGER
s.p. see from Geistliche Volkslieder Aus
Osterreich (H2387)

HERR, DIE WASSERSTROME ERHEBEN SICH see Zipp,
Friedrich

HERR, DU BIST WURDIG ZU NEHMEN PREIS see
Raphael, Gunther

HERR, DU ERFORSCHEST MICH see David, Johann
Nepomuk

HERR, DU ERFORSCHEST MICH see Pepping, Ernst

HERR, DU ERFORSCHEST MICH see Reda, Siegfried

HERR, DU ERFORSCHEST MICH see Wenzel, Eberhard

HERR, DU HAST ALLES, HIMMEL see Marx, Karl

HERR, DU HAST DAS FLEHEN VERNOMMEN see
Schubert, Franz (Peter)

HERR, DU HAST WORTE DES EWIGEN LEBENS see Poos,
Heinrich

HERR, DU HAST WORTE DES EWIGEN LEBENS see
Thiele, Siegfried

HERR, DU LASSEST MICH ERFAHREN see Bach, Johann
Michael

HERR, DU WEISSEST ALLE DINGE see Hammerschmidt,
Andreas

HERR, DU WEISST, WIE ARM WIR WANDERN see
Burkhard Willy

HERR, DU WEISST WIE ARM WIR WANDERN see Schmid,
E.

HERR ERHORE MEIN FLEHEN see Selle, Thomas,
Domine Exaudi Orationem Meam

HERR, ERHORE MEIN GEBET see Gronostay, Uwe

HERR, ERHORE MEIN GEBET see Rohwer, Jens

HERR, ERHORE MEINE KLAGEN see Goudimel, Claude

HERR, ERHORE MEINE KLAGEN see Le Jeune, Claude

HERR, ES GESCHEH DEIN WILLE see Schulz, Joh.
Abraham Peter

HERR FUHR UNS DEINE WEGE see Gerhold, Norbert,
Road Is Rugged But I Must Go

HERR, FUHRE MICH AUF DEM PFAD DEINER GEBOTE see
Reger, Max

HERR, FUR DEIN WORT see Wagner, Alexander

HERR, FUR DEIN WORT SEI HOCH GEPREIST see
Franck, Melchior

HERR, FUR DEIN WORT SEI HOCH GEPREIST see
Praetorius, Michael

HERR, FUR DEIN WORT SEI HOCHGEPREISET see
Praetorius, Michael

HERR, GEHE NICHT see Bach, Johann Sebastian,
Herr, Gehe Nicht Ins Gericht

HERR, GEHE NICHT INS GERICHT see Bach, Johann
Sebastian

HERR, GEHE NICHT INS GERICHT [CHORALE] see
Bach, Johann Sebastian

HERR, GEHE VON MIR HINAUS see Driessler,
Johannes

HERR, GIB FRIEDEN DIESER SEELE see Lang, Hans

HERR, GIB UNS FRIEDEN see Lehmann, Andreas

HERR GOTT, AN DESSEN THRON see Stier, Alfred

HERR GOTT, DEIN WILLE see Rohwer, Jens

HERR GOTT, DICH LOBEN ALLE WIR
TTBB HANSSLER 6.2322 s.p. contains also:
Isaac, Heinrich, O Welt, Ich Muss Dich
Lassen (H2388)

HERR GOTT, DICH LOBEN ALLE WIR see Anonymous

HERR GOTT, DICH LOBEN ALLE WIR see Bach, Johann
Sebastian

HERR, GOTT, DICH LOBEN ALLE WIR see Fiebig,
Kurt

HERR GOTT, DICH LOBEN ALLE WIR see Goudimel,
Claude

HERR GOTT, DICH LOBEN ALLE WIR see Raphael,
Gunther

HERR GOTT, DICH LOBEN ALLE WIR see Schein,
Johann Hermann

HERR GOTT, DICH LOBEN ALLE WIR see Thomas, Kurt

HERR GOTT, DICH LOBEN WIR see Bach, Johann
Sebastian

HERR GOTT, DICH LOBEN WIR see Eccard, Johannes

HERR GOTT, DICH LOBEN WIR see Micheelsen, Hans
Friedrich

HERR GOTT, DICH LOBEN WIR see Schein, Johann
Hermann

HERR GOTT, DICH LOBEN WIR see Telemann, Georg
Philipp

HERR GOTT, DIES HAUS BEWAHR see Bottcher, Georg

HERR GOTT, DU BIST UNSERE ZUFLUCHT! see Schmid,
Walter

HERR GOTT, DU BIST UNSRE ZUFLUCHT see Barbe,
Helmut

HERR GOTT, DU BIST UNSRE ZUFLUCHT see
Driessler, Johannes

HERR GOTT, DU BIST UNSRE ZUFLUCHT see Heilmann,
Harald

HERR GOTT, DURCH DEINE SPEIS see Zipp,
Friedrich

HERR GOTT, ERHORE MEIN FLEHEN see Sweelinck,
Jan Pieterszoon

HERR GOTT, ERZEIG MIR HILF UND GNAD see Schutz,
Heinrich

HERR GOTT, HILF see Schutz, Heinrich, Deus
Misereatur Nostri

HERR, GOTT, MEIN HEILAND, ICH SCHREIE TAG UND
NACHT see Garbers, Wilfried

HERR GOTT, NUN SCHLEUSS DEN HIMMEL AUF see
Altenburg, Michael

HERR GOTT, NUN SCHLEUSS DEN HIMMEL AUF see
Kappesser, Karl

HERR GOTT, NUN SEI GEPREISET see Franck,
Melchior

HERR GOTT, NUN SEI GEPREISET see
Gumpeltzhaimer, Adam

HERR GOTT, NUN SEY GEPREYSET see Hassler, Hans
Leo

HERR GOTT, VATER IM HIMMELREICH see Schlicht,
Johann Gottfried

HERR GOTT, WANN OFFENBARST DU DEINE SOHNE see
Ruppel, Paul Ernst

HERR GOTT, WIR SINGEN ZU DEINER EHR *Russ
(Ignatieff, S.) men cor,Bar solo ZIMMER. s.p.
(H2389)

HERR, HILF UNS, WIR VERDERBEN see Raselius,
Andreas

HERR, HORE DOCH see Wolleb, Johann Jakob

HERR, HORE MEINE STIMME see Lassus, Roland de
(Orlandus), Exaudi Domine Vocem Meam

HERR, HORE MEINE STIMME, WENN ICH see Marx,
Karl

HERR, HORE MEINE STIMME, WENN ICH RUFE see
Haller, Hans Peter

HERR, HORE MEINE STIMME, WENN ICH RUFE see
Werner, Fritz

HERR, HORE MEINE WORTE see Wenzel, Eberhard

HERR, ICH BIN DEIN EIGENTUM see Strobl, Otto

HERR! ICH BIN NICHT WERT see Driessler,
Johannes

HERR, ICH BIN NICHT WERT see Vulpius, Melchior

HERR, ICH HABE LIEB DE STATTE see Graun, Karl
Heinrich

HERR, ICH HABE LIEB DIE STATTE see Bornefeld,
Helmut

HERR, ICH HABE LIEB DIE STATTE see Thomas, Kurt

HERR, ICH HABE LIEB DIE STATTE DEINES HAUSES
see Reda, Siegfried

HERR, ICH HOFFE DARAUF see Schutz, Heinrich

HERR ICH WARTE AUF DEIN HEIL see Bach, Johann
Michael

HERR ICH WILL EIN GUTER CHRIST SEIN see
Gerhold, Norbert, Lord, I Want To Be A
Christian

HERR JESU CHRIST see Bach, Johann Sebastian,
Herr Jesu Christ, Du Hochstes Gut

HERR JESU CHRIST, DICH ZU UNS WEND see
Anonymous

HERR JESU CHRIST DICH ZU UNS WEND see Bach,
Johann Sebastian

HERR JESU CHRIST, DICH ZU UNS WEND see
Bornefeld, Helmut

HERR JESU CHRIST, DICH ZU UNS WEND see Herbst,
Wolfgang

HERR JESU CHRIST, DICH ZU UNS WEND see Werner,
Fritz

HERR JESU CHRIST, DICH ZU UNS WEND see Zipp,
Friedrich

HERR JESU CHRIST, DIEWEIL DU BIST see
Praetorius, Michael

HERR JESU CHRIST, DU HOCHSTES GUT see Bach,
Johann Sebastian

HERR JESU CHRIST, DU HOCHSTES GUT see Ducis,
Benedictus

HERR JESU CHRIST, DU HOCHSTES GUT see Reda,
Siegfried

HERR JESU CHRIST, DU HOCHTES GUT see Bornefeld,
Helmut

HERR JESU CHRIST, WAHR' MENSCH see Eccard,
Johannes

HERR JESU CHRIST, WAHR' MENSCH UND GOTT see
Bach, Johann Sebastian

HERR JESU CHRIST, WAHR'R MENSCH UND GOTT see
Bach, Johann Sebastian

HERR JESU CHRISTE, GOTTES SOHN see Praetorius,
Michael

HERR JESU, DEINE ANGST UND PEIN see Bender, Jan

HERR JESU, DEINE ANGST UND PEIN see Franck,
Melchior

HERR JESU, HILF see Kurig, Hans-Hermann

HERR JEZUS HEEFT EEN HOFKE *Neth
(Snel, D.J.) wom cor sc ALSBACH&D s.p.
(H2390)

HERR, KEHRE DICH WIEDER ZU MIR see Praetorius,
Michael

HERR, KOMM HINAB, EH' DENN MEIN KIND see Vulpius, Melchior

HERR, KOMM HINAB, EH DENN MEIN KIND STIRBET see Franck, Melchior

HERR, KOMM HINAB, EHE DENN MEIN KIND see Raselius, Andreas

HERR, LASS DEINE WUNDER SEHEN see Stier, Alfred

HERR, LASS DEINER SICH FREUEN see Wenzel, Eberhard

HERR, LASS IHN DOCH DIES JAHR see Marks, Gunther

HERR, LASS IHN NOCH DIES JAHR see Driessler, Johannes

HERR, LASS MEINE KLAGE see Schein, Johann Hermann

HERR, LASS UNS DICH LOBEN see Zoller, Alfred Hans

HERR, LASS UNS IN DEINEM LICHTE WANDELN see Schweizer, Rolf

HERR, LEHRE DOCH MICH, DASS ES EIN ENDE MIT MIR HABEN MUSS see Reda, Siegfried

HERR, MACH DICH AUF see Handel, George Frideric, Let God Arise

HERR, MACHE MICH ZUM WERKZEUG DEINES FRIEDENS see Zimmermann, Heinz Werner

HERR, MEIN GEBET ERHOR see Schutz, Heinrich

HERR, MEIN GEBET ERHOR IN GNAD see Schutz, Heinrich

HERR, MEIN GOTT, ACH, NICHT IN DEINEM ZORNE see Schutz, Heinrich, Domine, Ne In Furore Tuo

HERR, MEIN GOTT, GROSS SIND DEINE see Hammerschmidt, Andreas

HERR, MEIN GOTT, ICH DANKE DIR see Rosenmuller, Johann

HERR, MEIN GOTT, NICHT VERMESSEN see Schutz, Heinrich, Domine, Non Est Exaltatum

HERR, MEIN GOTT, VERLASS MICH NICHT! "DA DIE TAGE SO VOLL NOT" see Niedermann, G.

HERR, MEIN HERZ IST NICHT HOFFARTIG see Burkhard Willy

HERR, MEIN NACHSTER RUFT MICH see Schweizer, Rolf

HERR, MEINE STARKE see Kubizek, Augustinian

HERR, NEIGE DEINE OHREN see Pepping, Ernst

HERR, NEIGE DEINE OHREN UND ERHORE MICH see Hellmann, Diethard

HERR, NEIGE DEINE OHREN UND ERHORE MICH see Weyrauch, Johannes

HERR, NUN LASSEST DU DEINEN see Selle, Thomas

HERR, NUN LASSEST DU DEINEN DIENER see Franck, Melchior

HERR NUN LASSEST DU DEINEN DIENER see Haller, Hans Peter

HERR, NUN LASSEST DU DEINEN DIENER see Michelsen, Hans Friedrich

HERR, NUN LASSEST DU DEINEN DIENER see Tunder, Franz

HERR, NUN LASSEST DU DEINEN DIENER IN FRIEDE FAHREN see Bach, Johann Christoph

HERR, NUN LASSEST DU DEINEN DIENER IN FRIEDEN FAHREN see Mendelssohn-Bartholdy, Felix

HERR, NUN LASSEST DU DEINEN DIENER see Schutz, Heinrich

HERR, NUN LASSEST DU DEINEN DIENER see Schutz, Heinrich

HERR, NUN LASSEST DU DEINEN DIENER see Schutz, Heinrich

HERR, NUN LASST DU DEINEN DIENER see Praetorius, Michael

HERR, NUN SELBST DEN WAGEN HALT see David, Johann Nepomuk

HERR, NUN SELBST DEN WAGEN HALT see Zwingli, Huldreich

HERR RUSTE UNS VON NEUEM AUS see Michel, Josep

HERR, SCHICKE WAS DU WILLST see Hessenberg, Kurt

HERR, SCHICKE WAS DU WILLST see Honegger, E.

HERR, SCHICKE WAS DU WILLST see Lavater, H.

HERR, SCHICKE WAS DU WILLT see Micheelsen, Hans Friedrich

HERR, SCHICKE WAS DU WILLT see Zack, O.V.

HERR, SEI MIR GNADIG see Thomas, Kurt

HERR, SENDE UNS BOTSCHAFT see Michel, Josep

HERR, TUE MEINE LIPPEN AUF see Reda, Siegfried

HERR, TUE MEINE LIPPEN AUF see Ruppel, Paul Ernst

HERR UNSER GOTT see Schnabel, J.J.

HERR UNSER GOTT see Schubert, Franz (Peter)

HERR, UNSER HERRSCHER see Barbe, Helmut

HERR, UNSER HERRSCHER see Buchtger, Fritz

HERR, UNSER HERRSCHER see Pepping, Ernst

HERR, UNSER HERRSCHER see Reda, Siegfried

HERR, UNSER HERRSCHER see Rommel, Kurt

HERR, UNSER HERRSCHER see Ruppel, Paul Ernst

HERR, UNSER HERRSCHER see Scheidt, Samuel

HERR, UNSER HERRSCHER see Schutz, Heinrich

HERR, UNSER HERRSCHER see Sommer, Vladimir

HERR, UNSER HERRSCHER see Staden

HERR, UNSER HERRSCHER see Trubel, Gerhard

HERR, UNSER HERRSCHER see Weber, Bernhard

HERR, UNSER HERRSCHER, WIE HERRLICH see Anonymous

HERR, UNSERN FRIEDEN see Bossler, Kurt

HERR, VERHERRLICHE DEINEN NAMEN see Raphael, Gunther

HERR, WARST DU NUR EIN MENSCH see Kurig, Hans-Hermann

HERR, WENN ICH DICH NUR FESTIGLICH, IN MEINEM see Cruger, Johann

HERR, WENN ICH NUR DICH HABE see Bach, Johann Michael

HERR, WENN ICH NUR DICH HABE see Pohle, David

HERR, WENN ICH NUR DICH HABE see Schutz, Heinrich

HERR, WENN ICH NUR DICH HABE see Zachow, Friedrich Wilhelm

HERR, WER WIRD WOHNEN IN DEINER HUTTE see Reda, Siegfried

HERR, WIE DU WILLST see Eccard, Johannes

HERR, WIE DU WILLST see Thomas, Kurt

HERR, WIE DU WILLST, SO SCHICKS MIT MIR see Eccard, Johannes

HERR, WIE DU WILLST, SO SCHICKS MIT MIR see Osiander, Lucas

HERR, WIE DU WILLST, SO SCHICKS MIT MIR see Thomas, Kurt

HERR, WIE DU WILLT, SO SCHICKS MIT MIR see Bach, Johann Sebastian

HERR, WIE LANG WILLST DU MEIN see Hartmann, Heinrich

HERR, WIE LANG WILLST DU MEIN see Scheidt, Samuel

HERR, WIE LANGE WILLST DU MEIN GAR VERGESSEN see Brahms, Johannes

HERR, WIE LANGE WILLST DU MEIN SO GANZ VERGESSEN? see Brahms, Johannes

HERR, WIE LANGE WILLST DU MEIN SO GAR VERGESSEN see Burkhard Willy

HERR, WIE LANGE WILLST DU MEIN SO GAR VERGESSEN see Kretzschmar, Gunther

HERR, WIE SIND DEINE WERKE SO GROSS UND VIEL see Reda, Siegfried

HERR, WIR BITTEN (from Evangelischen Kirchentag 1966) CC10U,Gen [Ger] unis,kbd (med) BOSSE BE 222 s.p. (H2391)

HERR, WIR STEHEN HAND IN HAND see Goudimel, Claude

HERR, WIR STEHEN HAND IN HAND see Gruber, Erich

HERR, WIR STEHEN HAND IN HAND see Strattner, G.

HERR, WOHIN SOLLEN WIR GEHEN? see Schweizer, Rolf

HERR, WOHIN SOLLEN WIR GEHN? see Iten, Walter

HERR ZEIGE MIR DEINE WEGE see Hartmann, Heinrich

HERR, ZU WEM SOLLEN WIR GEHEN? see Back, Sven-Erick

HERRE, AR DET DU, SOM NALKAS see Petersen, Gunnar

HERRE, DAVIDS SON, FORBARMA DIG see Nilsson, Torsten

HERRE DU, HAR VAERT OSS EN BOLIG see Aamodt, Thorleif

HERRE, DU HAR VARIT VAR TILLFLYKT see Runback, Albert

HERRE, FYLG DU MED PA FERDI (BON) see Borgesen, Erling

HERRE, GA EJ TILL DOMS see Moren, John

HERRE, GA EJ TILL DOMS MED DIN TJANARE see Soderholm, Valdemar

HERRE GOTT, ERBARME DICH see David, Johann Nepomuk

HERR GOTT, HIMMLISCHER VATER, WIR DANKEN DIR see Schutz, Heinrich

HERRE GUD, DITT DYRE NAMN see Geitvik, S.H.

HERRE GUD, DITT DYRE NAVN see Geitvik, S.H.

HERRE GUD, DITT DYRE NAVN OG AERE (Aamodt, Valter) men cor MUSIKK 37 s.p. (H2392)

HERRE GUD, DITT DYRE NAVN OG AERE see Baden, Conrad

HERRE GUD FADER I HIMMELEN see Hammarstrom, Hugo

HERRE HOR MIN ROST see Moren, John

HERRE! HVOR ER MINE FJENDER MANGE see Jeppesen, Knud

HERRE, JAG AR ICKE VARDIG see Victoria, Tomas Luis de, Domino Non Sum Dignus

HERRE, JAG VILL TACKA DIG BLAND FOLKEN see Rosenberg, Hilding

HERRE, JEG HJERTELIG ONSKER *folk (Elvestrand, Magne) [Norw] LYCHE 18 s.p. (H2393)

HERRE JESU, DU AR VAGEN see Berg, Gottfrid

HERRE, JESU HERDE GOD see Moren, John

HERRE, LAR MIG BETANKA see Soderlundh, Lille Brov

HERRE, NU LADER DU DIN TJENER FARE see Walther, Johann Gottfried

HERRE, NU LATER DU DIN TJANARE see Bjarnegard, Gustaf

HERRE, NUN LASSEST DU DEINEN DIENER see Praetorius, Michael

HERRE, SAND DITT LJUS see Runback, Albert

HERRE, TIL DIG UPPLYFTER JAG MIN SJAL see Moren, John

HERRE, TILL VEM SKULLE VI GA see Nyvall, Jacob

HERRE, TILL VEM SKULLE VI GA? see Olson, Daniel

HERRE, VAR GUD, VI TACKA DIG see Homilius, Gottfried August

HERRE, VAR GUD, VI TACKA DIG see Homilius, Gottfried August, Deo Dicamus Gratias

HERRE, VAR HERRE see Hovland, Egil

HERRE VAR HERRE see Neilsen, Ludvig

HERRE, VAR MIG NADIG see Dente, Joseph

HERRE, VEM FAR BO I DIN HYDDA? see Erlandson, Ake

HERRELL
Unveiled Christ, The
(Collins) SATB oct LILLENAS AT-1062 $.30 (H2394)
(Skiles) SAB oct LILLENAS AN-1161 $.30 (H2395)

HERREMA, ROBERT
Laudate Pueri Dominum
SSA&SAB,brass oct WALTON 2917 $.40, ipa (H2396)

HERREN AR MIN HERDE see Hammarstrom, Hugo

HERREN AR MIN HERDE see Moren, John

HERREN AR MIN HERDE GOD see Bach, Johann Sebastian

HERREN ER BARMHJERTIG see Jeppesen, Knud

HERREN ER MIN HYRDE see Hovland, Egil

HERREN ER STOR see Jeppesen, Knud

HERREN GUD AR SOL OCH SKOLD see Bach, Johann Sebastian, Gott, Der Herr, Ist Sonn' Und Schild

HERREN, MIN GUD, GOR MITT MORKER LJUST see Rosenberg, Hilding

HERREN SKALL UTGJUTA SIN ANDE see Runback, Albert

HERREN, VAR GUD, AR EN KONUNG see Berg, Gottfrid

HERRICK'S LITANIE see Roberton, Hugh S.

HERRIN, DU STRAHLST IM HIMMEL see Handel, George Frideric, Donna, Che In Ciel

HERRMANN, HUGO (1896-1967)
Chorvariationen Uber Die Sonnengesange Des Franziskus Von Assisi *Op.85
(Brenthand, Franz; Lehrs, Max) [Ger] wom cor&opt jr cor,opt T/S solo,harp/pno BOTE s.p. (H2397)

Der Weihnachtsstern *Xmas
4pt wom cor/4pt jr cor (med easy) oct LEUCKART 815 s.p. (H2398)

Johannes-Oratorium "Jesus Und Seine Junger" *Op.80, ora
[Ger] mix cor,soli,orch BOTE voc sc s.p., voc pt s.p. (H2399)

HERRMANN, WILLIAM
Child This Day Is Born, A *Xmas
4pt wom cor,acap oct SCHIRM.G 11405 $.25 (H2400)
4pt mix cor,acap oct SCHIRM.G 11404 $.25 (H2401)

Ye Saints And Servants Of The Lord *Gen
SATB,kbd (med easy) oct CONCORDIA 98-1948 $.30 (H2402)
SSAA,kbd (med easy) oct CONCORDIA 98-1953 $.30 (H2403)

HERRNHUT
Herz Und Herz Vereint Zusammen
(Berger, H.L.) TTBB HANSSLER 6.5074 s.p.
(H2404)

HERRSCHER DES HIMMELS see Bach, Johann
Sebastian

HERRSCHER UBER TOD UND LEBEN see Bach, Johann
Sebastian

HERTOG, H.J. DEN
Kerstlied
3pt wom cor,pno ALSBACH&D sc s.p., cor pts
s.p.
(H2405)
3pt jr cor,pno ALSBACH&D sc s.p., cor pts
s.p.
(H2406)

HERWAARDEN, J.G.
Chrysanten
mix cor ALSBACH&D sc s.p., cor pts s.p.
(H2407)

Juicht Aarde Juicht (Psalm 100)
men cor sc ALSBACH&D s.p.
(H2408)

Lente
wom cor sc ALSBACH&D s.p.
(H2409)

Lente In 't Land
wom cor sc ALSBACH&D s.p.
(H2410)

Lentelied
men cor sc ALSBACH&D s.p.
(H2411)

Lente's Intocht
mix cor ALSBACH&D sc s.p., cor pts s.p.
(H2412)

Psalm 100 *see Juicht Aarde Juicht

Verlangen Naar God
mix cor ALSBACH&D sc s.p.
(H2413)

Voorjaarshymne
mix cor,Bar solo ALSBACH&D sc s.p., cor pts
s.p.
(H2414)

HERZ UND HERZ VEREINT ZUSAMMEN see Herrnhut

HERZ UND MUND see Bach, Johann Sebastian, Herz
Und Mund Und Tat Und Leben

HERZ UND MUND UND TAT UND LEBEN see Bach,
Johann Sebastian

HERZLICH LIEB HAB ICH DICH see Hammerschmidt,
Andreas

HERZLICH LIEB HAB ICH DICH see Hassler, Hans
Leo

HERZLICH LIEB HAB ICH DICH see Scheidt, Samuel

HERZLICH LIEB HAB ICH DICH see Weiss, Ewald

HERZLICH LIEB HAB ICH DICH, O HERR *16th cent
(Berger, H.L.) TTBB HANSSLER 6.5140 s.p.
(H2415)

HERZLICH LIEB HAB ICH DICH, O HERR see Bach,
Johann Sebastian

HERZLICH LIEB HAB ICH DICH, O HERR see
Buxtehude, Dietrich

HERZLICH LIEB HAB ICH DICH, O HERR see Schutz,
Heinrich

HERZLICH LIEB HAB ICH DICH O HERR see
Tzschoppe, Eberhart

HERZLICH LIEB HABE ICH DICH see Wenzel,
Eberhard

HERZLICH TUT MICH ERFREUEN see Praetorius,
Michael

HERZLICH TUT MICH ERFREUEN see Rhau, Johannes

HERZLICH TUT MICH ERFREUEN DIE LIEBE see
Praetorius, Michael

HERZLIEBSTER JESU see Bach, Johann Sebastian

HERZLIEBSTER JESU see Hufschmidt, Wolfgang

HERZLIEBSTER JESU see Micheelsen, Hans
Friedrich

HERZLIEBSTER JESU see Petrich, Roger

HERZLIEBSTER JESU, WAS HAST DU VERBROCHEN see
Bach, Johann Sebastian

HERZLIEBSTER JESU, WAS HAST DU VERBROCHEN see
Graap, Lothar

HERZLIEBSTER JESU, WER GLAUBT UND DEIN see
Hellmann, Diethard

HERZOG, JOHANN GEORG (1822-1909)
Der Morgenstern Ist Aufgedrungen
see Praetorius, Michael, Geboren Ist
Immanuel, Der Herr Christ

Freut Euch, Freut Euch In Dieser Zeit
SATB HANSSLER 6.2664 s.p. contains also:
Palestrina, Giovanni, Preis Und Ehre,
Herr Jesu, Lob
(H2416)

HERZOGENBERG, HEINRICH VON (1843-1900)
Christmas Song *Xmas
SSATBB,acap oct SCHIRM.G 2553 $.35 (H2417)

Huter Israels, Behute Uns
SATB HANSSLER 6.2667 s.p. contains also:
Bach, Johann Sebastian, Wie Schon Ist's
Doch, Herr Jesu Christ, Im
(H2418)

HE'S A WONDERFUL SAVIOR TO ME see Brock,
Blanche [Kerr]

HE'S ALIVE see Wilson, John F.

HE'S CARRIED THE KEY AND GONE HOME
(Jessye) SATB oct SHAPIRO SK 2094 $.30
(H2419)

HE'S EVERYTHING TO ME see Carmichael, Ralph

HE'S FOR REAL see Cooper

HE'S GOING AWAY *anthem
(Niles) SATB,acap oct FISCHER,C CM-6577 $.30
(H2420)

HE'S GONE AWAY *Easter
(Jurey, E.) SSA oct PRESSER 312-40418 $.25
(H2421)
(Siegmeister, E.) SATB,acap oct PRESSER
332-15161 $.30
(H2422)

HE'S GONE AWAY see Ahrold, Frank

HE'S GONE AWAY see Davis, Katherine K.

HE'S GOT THE WHOLE WORLD IN HIS HAND
(Sargent) SSAATTBB,acap (med easy) OXFORD
84.131 $.30
(H2423)

HE'S GOT THE WHOLE WORLD IN HIS HANDS *spir
SA/TB oct LORENZ 7832 $.30
(H2424)
(Ehret) SA oct FOX S135 $.30
(H2425)
(Ehret) SAB oct FOX S134 $.30
(H2426)
(Ehret) TTBB oct FOX S136 $.30
(H2427)
(Ehret) SSA oct FOX S133 $.30
(H2428)
(Ehret) SATB oct FOX S130 $.30
(H2429)
(Heath) 4pt men cor,T solo oct SCHIRM.G 10854
$.25
(H2430)
(Howorth, Wayne) SA/TB oct BELWIN 1777 $.25
(H2431)
(Howorth, Wayne) SSA oct BELWIN 2159 $.25
(H2432)
(Howorth, Wayne) SAB oct BELWIN 2161 $.35
(H2433)
(Howorth, Wayne) SATB oct BELWIN 1790 $.25
(H2434)
(Page, Robert) TTB,S solo STANDARD B302M1
$.50
(H2435)
(Palmer) SATB ALFRED 6349 $.40
(H2436)
(Regier) SATB KJOS 5229 $.30
(H2437)
(Wilson) SSA SCHMITT 2560 $.30
(H2438)
(Wilson) SATB SCHMITT 1746 $.30
(H2439)

HE'S GOT THE WHOLE WORLD IN HIS HANDS see
Brandon

HE'S GOT THE WHOLE WORLD IN HIS HANDS see
Brown, William [H., Jr.]

HE'S GOT THE WHOLE WORLD IN HIS HANDS see
Forrest

HE'S GOT THE WHOLE WORLD IN HIS HANDS see Hare,
N.

HE'S GOT THE WHOLE WORLD IN HIS HANDS see
Ringwald, [Roy]

HE'S MY FRIEND see Rasley

HE'S MY JESUS see Weaver

HE'S ON HIS WAY!
SATB BIG3 $.40
(H2440)

HE'S ONLY A PRAYER AWAY see Lister, Mosie

HE'S RISEN, CHRIST JESUS, THE LORD see Pelz,
Walter L.

HE'S THE LILY OF THE VALLEY
see Two Negro Spirituals

HE'S THE ONE see Mc Call, Harlo

HE'S THERE see Lawson

HE'S THERE WAITING see Carmichael, Ralph

HESCH
You Can Dig My Grave *spir
SAB, autoharp oct BOURNE CH6 $.25 (H2441)

HESELTINE, PHILIP (1894-1930)
Adam Lay Ybounden
unis (easy) OXFORD 45.703 $.25 (H2442)
(Davies) SATB,acap OXFORD 84.094 $.20
(H2443)
(Jacques) SSA (med) OXFORD 83.055 $.25
(H2444)

All Creatures Now With Hearts Rejoice
SSA,acap (med) OXFORD 54.131 $.30 (H2445)

Balulalow
see Three Carols

Benedicamus Domino
[Lat] SATB,acap oct BOOSEY 420 $.30 (H2446)

Bethlehem Down
SATB,acap oct BOOSEY 3246 $.30
(H2447)

Come To Bethlehem (from Capriol Suite) Xmas
unis jr cor/unis wom cor CURWEN 72271 s.p.
(H2448)
(Jacobson) 2pt jr cor/2pt wom cor CURWEN
72401 s.p.
(H2449)
(Murray) 2pt wom cor oct CURWEN 10751 $.25
(H2450)
(Murray) 4pt mix cor,acap oct CURWEN 10752
$.25
(H2451)
(Murray) unis oct CURWEN 10750 $.25 (H2452)
(Murray) mix cor CURWEN 61473 s.p. (H2453)

Corpus Christi *carol,Eng
mix cor,AT soli,acap oct CURWEN 8648 $.30
(H2454)
mix cor,ST/MezT soli CURWEN 61124 s.p.
(H2455)

First Mercy
SSA oct BOOSEY 3262 $.30
(H2456)
(Russell-Smith) SATB oct BOOSEY 5578 $.30
(H2457)

Sycamore Tree
see Three Carols

Three Carols *Xmas,carol
(med) cmplt ed SATB OXFORD 42.202 $.65,
ipr; SSAA OXFORD 44.203 $.65, ipr; TTBB
OXFORD 41.009 $.30, ipr
contains: Balulalow; Sycamore Tree;
Tyrley, Tyrlow
see also: Tyrley, Tyrlow
(H2458)

Tyrley, Tyrlow
unis,inst (med) OXFORD 45.005 $.30, ipr see
also Three Carols
(H2459)

What Cheer? Good Cheer! *Xmas
unis BOOSEY-CAN s.p.
(H2460)

HESFORD, BRIAN
Corpus Christi Carol *Xmas,carol
unis ASHDOWN U.80 s.p. contains also: Love
Came Down At Christmas
(H2461)
unis BOOSEY-CAN s.p.
(H2462)

I Sing Of A Maiden
unis&opt 2pt ASHDOWN U.72 s.p. (H2463)

Love Came Down At Christmas
see Hesford, Brian, Corpus Christi Carol

Song Of The Crib, The *Xmas
unis ASHDOWN U.79 s.p.
(H2464)
unis BOOSEY-CAN s.p.
(H2465)

HESS, C.
Der Schonste Klang Von All' Den Tausend
Klangen *Xmas
(Bruhl, Schulte Vom) [Ger] wom cor,acap
(easy) HUG s.p.
(H2466)

HESS, E.
Schweizergebet
[Ger] mix cor,acap (med easy) HUG s.p.
(H2467)
[Ger] mix cor,acap (easy) HUG s.p. (H2468)

HESS, W.
O Seel, So Tue Dys Turli Uf! *Xmas
(Haller, D.) [Ger] wom cor,acap (easy) HUG
s.p.
(H2469)

HESSENBERG, KURT (1908-)
Christ Lag In Todesbanden
see Evangelisches Kirchengesangbuch
SAT/SAB, treb inst/bass inst HANSSLER 14.076
s.p.
(H2470)

Die Sieben Worte Christi Am Kreuz *Gd.Fri./
Psntd
see DREI MOTETTEN
SATB HANSSLER 7.074 s.p.
(H2471)

Du, Tochter Zion, Freue Dich Sehr *mot
SAB HANSSLER 7.041 s.p.
(H2472)

Entsetzet Euch Nicht
see Evangelisches Kirchengesangbuch

Evangelisches Kirchengesangbuch *Easter
[Ger] 3pt mix cor,acap BAREN 18 s.p.
contains: Christ Lag In Todesbanden,
No.76; Entsetzet Euch Nicht; Wir Wollen
Alle Frohlich Sein, No.82 (H2473)

Gruss Gott, Du Schoner Maie
jr cor&men cor (med easy) oct LEUCKART 39
s.p.
(H2474)

Herr, Schicke Was Du Willst *prayer
mix cor,acap TONGER s.p.
(H2475)

Jesus Und Die Sunderin *Gen,mot
[Ger] SSATBB,acap (med diff) BAREN. BA 3640
$2.50
(H2476)

Sechs Geistliche Lieder *Op.55, CC6U,Gen
[Ger] SATB,acap (med) BAREN. BA 3642 $2.50
(H2477)

Tauet, Himmel, Den Gerechten
SAB HANSSLER 7.040 s.p.
(H2478)

Willkomen, Susser Brautigam
SAT/SAB, treb inst HANSSLER 14.024 s.p.
(H2479)

Wir Wollen Alle Frohlich Sein
see Evangelisches Kirchengesangbuch

HET ANGELUS see Rennes, Cath. v.

HET ANGELUS KLEPT IN DE VERTE see Rennes, Cath.
v.

HET DAGET IN DEN OOSTEN see Vulpius, Melchior

HET GEBED DES HEEREN see Pomper, A.

HET HOOGLIED see Van Lier, Bertus, Song Of
Songs, The

HET IS VOLBRACHT see Bach, Johann Sebastian

HET KIND DER GLORIE see Bonset, Jac.

HET LAM GODS see Bach, Johann Sebastian

HEU MIHE, DOMINE see Schutz, Heinrich

HEU MIHI see Fernandez de Castilleja

HEU MIHI see Schutz, Heinrich

HEU MIHI DOMINE see Schutz, Heinrich

HEUREUX CELUI QUI FUIT (Psalm 1)
(Geveart, F.-A.) [Fr] 4pt mix cor,acap (easy)
cor pts LEMOINE s.p. see from Collection De
Choeurs, troisieme Fascicule (H2480)

HEUREUX QUI DU COEUR DE MARIE see Saint-Saens,
Camille

HEUREUX, TROIS FOIS HEUREUX see Mendelssohn-
Bartholdy, Felix

HEUREUX, TROIS FOIS HEUREUX see Mendelssohn-
Bartholdy, Felix, Beati Mortui

HEUSSENSTAMM, GEORGE
Our Soul Waits For The Lord *Gen
SATB,acap (med diff) oct CONCORDIA 98-1753
$.40
(H2481)

With Jesus Will I Go *Gen
SA,kbd (med easy) oct CONCORDIA 98-1778
$.25
(H2482)

With Rue My Heart Is Laden
SATB,acap oct PRESSER 362-01326 $.30
(H2483)

HEUT GREIFT NACH DEINEM HERZEN see Stier,
Alfred

HEUT IST CHRISTUS, DER HERR, GEBOREN see
Schutz, Heinrich

HEUT IST EIN STERNLEIN VOM HIMMEL GEFALLN see
Wolters, Gottfried

HEUT SEIN DIE LIEBEN ENGELEIN (DER QUEMPAS) see
Praetorius, Michael

HEUT SINGT DIE LIEBE CHRISTENHEIT see Borris,
Siegfried

HEUT SINGT DIE LIEBE CHRISTENHEIT see Krieger,
Johann Philipp

HEUT SINGT DIE LIEBE CHRISTENHEIT see Kukuck,
Felicitas

HEUT SINGT DIE LIEBE CHRISTENHEIT see Pepping,
Ernst

HEUT SINGT DIE LIEBE CHRISTENHEIT, VOL. I
   *CC38U,Gen
   (Fischer, Walter) [Ger] SA&men cor (med)
   BAREN. BA 3900 s.p. choral settings of
   melodies from the Evangelisches
   Kirchengesangbuch   (H2484)

HEUT SINGT DIE LIEBE CHRISTENHEIT, VOL. II
   *CC34U,Gen
   (Fischer, Walter) [Ger] SA&men cor,inst (med)
   BAREN. BA 3750 s.p. choral settings of the
   melodies from the Evangelisches
   Kirchengesangbuch   (H2485)

HEUT TRIMPHIERET GOTTES SOHN see Bach, Johann
Sebastian

HEUT TRIUMPHIERET GOTTES SOHN see Buxtehude,
Dietrich

HEUT TRIUMPHIERET GOTTES SOHN see Gesius,
Bartholomaus

HEUT TRIUMPHIERET GOTTES SOHN see Kukuck,
Felicitas

HEUT TRIUMPHIERET GOTTES SOHN see Praetorius,
Michael

HEUT TRIUMPHIERET GOTTES SOHN see Schein,
Johann Hermann

HEUT TRIUMPHIERT GOTTES SOHN see Praetorius,
Michael

HEUTE CHRISTUS GEBOREN IST see Nanini (Nanino),
Giovanni Maria, Hodie Christus Natus Est

HEUTE IST CHRIST, DER HERR, GEBOREN see Schutz,
Heinrich

HEUTE IST CHRISTUS DER HERR GEBOREN see Schutz,
Heinrich

HEWITT-JONES, TONY
   At The Round Earth's Imagin'd Corners
      *anthem/mot
   mix cor,acap oct NOVELLO 28.1336.10 s.p.
                                                (H2486)

   Divine Image, The
   SATB,acap LENGNICK s.p.   (H2487)

   Mass Of The Reconciliation *Mass
   SATB oct NOVELLO 44.1428.04 s.p.   (H2488)

   O Clap Your Hands Together *anthem/Introit
   mix cor oct NOVELLO 40.1486.03 s.p.   (H2489)

   O Praise God In His Holiness *anthem/Introit
   mix cor oct NOVELLO 50.0342.03 s.p.   (H2490)

   Te Deum *Te Deum
   [Lat/Eng] mix cor&S,ATB soli,org,strings,
   brass,timp BOOSEY voc sc $3.00, sc
   rental, ipr   (H2491)
   [Eng/Lat] SATB&cong,org,brass,timp LENGNICK
   s.p., ipa   (H2492)

   Two Canticles *CC2U,Bibl
   SATB,SBar soli,org,2fl,ob,2clar,bsn,2horn,
   2trp,2trom,strings,2perc,timp,opt clar&
   trp&trom&tuba, opt two E flat tenor horns
   & opt B flat euphonium voc sc NOVELLO
   s.p., ipr   (H2493)

   Versicles And Responses
   SATB oct NOVELLO 44.1414.04 s.p.   (H2494)

HEWLETT, W.H.
   Fierce Was The Wild Billow
   4pt mix cor oct SCHIRM.G 6724 $.25   (H2495)

HEY! HEY! ANYBODY LISTENING? see Avery

HEY, MANGER CHILD see Smith

HEYDEN, REINHOLD
   Die Beste Zeit
   3-4 eq voices MOSELER s.p.   (H2496)

   Gruss Gott, Du Schoner Maien
   3 eq voices MOSELER LB-142 s.p.   (H2497)

HEYS, S.
   Christ-Child Lay On Mary's Lap, The
   see BOY WAS BORN, A

HEYSER, E.K.
   God Of Harvest Praise, The *Harv
   SATB ALLANS 119 s.p.   (H2498)

HEYWARD
   I Need Thee Every Hour
   SATB oct LORENZ B108 $.30   (H2499)

HI TREUR DIE TRUREN WILL see Badings, Henk

HIBBATH SHABBATH see Binder, Abraham Wolfe

HIC EST FILIUS DEI see Gabrieli, Giovanni

HIC VIR DESPICIANS MUNDUM see Victoria, Tomas
Luis de

HICKS, L'ROY E.
   I Couldn't Hear Nobody Pray
   SATB oct AGAPE SP 712 $.30   (H2500)

HICKS, MARY
   O Give Thanks *Thanks
   unis oct NOVELLO 28.1354.08 s.p.   (H2501)

HIDDEN, O LORD see Pilkington, Francis

HIDDEN TREASURE see Bixel, James W.

HIDE NOT THOU THY FACE see Farrant, Richard

HIDE NOT THOU THY FACE FROM ME, O LORD see
Farrant, Richard

HIDE NOT THOU THY FACE FROM US see Farrant,
Richard

HIDE NOT THOU THY FACE FROM US, O LORD see
Farrant, Richard

HIDE NOT THY FACE see Farrant, Richard

HIDE NOT THY FACE see Morgan

HIDE NOT THY FACE, O MY SAVIOUR *folk,Finn
   (Lundquist) SATB,acap (med) oct WILLIS 8469
   $.25   (H2502)

HIDING PLACE see Campbell

HIE KANN NIT SEIN EIN BOSER MUT see Hindemith,
Paul

HIER IST ER, DER VERBRANNTE see Beethoven,
Ludwig van

HIER LIEGT EIN ARMES SUNDENAAS see Stadlmair,
Hans

HIER LIEGT EIN JUNGES OCHSELEIN see Stadlmair,
Hans

HIER LIEGT VOR DEINER MAJESTAT see Haydn,
(Franz) Joseph

HIER RUHET GOTTFRIED STERKEL see Stadlmair,
Hans

HIER RUHT DER BRAUERSEPP see Stadlmair, Hans

HIER RUHT MEIN WEIB, GOTT SEI'S GEDANKT see
Stadlmair, Hans

HIERONIM OF KOPRZYWNICA
   Veni Sancte Spiritus *mot,Pol
   (Bok, J.) 3pt men cor POLSKIE FMA4 s.p.
                                                (H2503)

HIERUSALEM see Dyson, George

HIGDON, GEORGE
   Let God Arise
   SSA,org oct WORLD ESA-1898-3 $.30   (H2504)

HIGGS, R.
   Christmas Morning *Xmas
   unis oct HART s.p.   (H2505)

HIGH
   Bless The Lord, O My Soul *see Fearis, J.S.

HIGH 'BOVE THE STARRY SKY see Weyse, Christoph
Ernst Friedrich

HIGH HOLIDAY MUSIC see Freed, Isadore

HIGH HOLIDAY SERVICES see Coopersmith, Harry

HIGH O'ER THE LONELY HILLS see Blake, G.

HIGH OVER BETHLEHEM see Ehret, Walter

HIGHER GROUND see Gabriel

HIGHER GROUND see Landgrave, Phillip

HIGHEST HILL, THE see Lister, Mosie

HIGHLANDS OF HEAVEN, THE see Wood

HIJMAN, JULIUS (1901-   )
   Away In A Manger *Xmas
   SATB oct PRESSER MC183 $.30   (H2506)

HIL DAG, DU HOJE see Phillipo, Salve, Sacrata

HILARITER *Easter,Ger
   (Shaw; Parker) 4pt mix cor,acap oct SCHIRM.G
   9952 $.30   (H2507)

HILARITER see Dirksen, Richard W.

HILBER
   Heavens Are Thine, The
   (Cambell; Watson) SAB WARNER W3730 $.30
                                                (H2508)
   (Cambell; Watson) TTBB WARNER W3729 $.30
                                                (H2509)
   (Cambell; Watson) SATB WARNER W3728 $.30
                                                (H2510)

HILES
   Blessed Are The Merciful
   (Mueller) 3pt jr cor/SAB (easy) FISCHER,C
   CM 6882 $.25   (H2511)

HILES, [HENRY] (1826-1904)
   Blessed Are The Merciful *Bibl
   4pt mix cor,acap oct SCHIRM.G 4522 $.20
                                                (H2512)

HILF DEINEM VOLK, HERR JESU CHRIST see Luebeck

HILF, HERR, DIE HEILIGEN HABEN ABGENOMMEN see
Goldberg, Johann Gottlieb

HILF HERR JESU, LASS GELINGEN see Baudach,
Ulrich

HILF, HERR MEINES LEBENS see Blarr, Oskar
Gottlieb

HILF, HERR MEINES LEBENS see Puls, Hans

HILF, O HERR see Klein, Richard Rudolf

HILL
   Christmas Carol, A *Xmas,carol
   SATB (easy) OXFORD 42.975 $.25   (H2513)

   O Sing Unto The Lord
   SATB KJOS 5346 $.30   (H2514)

HILL (cont'd.)
   Sion's Daughter *carol
   SATB (easy) OXFORD 42.976 $.25   (H2515)

HILL DIG, FRELSER OG FORSONER see Karlsen, Rolf

HILL, E.
   God Is Ascended Up On High *Easter
   SSATB,acap oct PRESSER MC299 $.30   (H2516)

HILL, EUGENE
   O God Of Earth
   SATB,org oct BERANDOL 915H7AC $.35   (H2517)

HILL, HARRY
   Unto Us A Boy Is Born *Xmas
   SATB oct LESLIE 4074   (H2518)

HILLER
   Be Thou With Me
   (Olds) SSA SCHMITT 2515 $.22   (H2519)

   Unto Thee I Lift My Praises
   (Harris) SSA MARKS 4486 $.25   (H2520)

   Unto Thee I Lift My Spirit
   mix cor SOUTHERN $.30   (H2521)

HILLER, FERDINAND (1811-1885)
   Saul *ora
   (Vecchi, Prof. Giuseppe) [Ger] cor quarto
   FORNI 250 s.p.   (H2522)

HILLER, JOHANN ADAM (1728-1804)
   Alles Ist An Gottes Segen
   (Berger, H.L.) TTBB HANSSLER 6.5069 s.p.
   contains also: Anton, Christoph, Alle
   Menschen Mussen Sterben   (H2523)

HILLERT, RICHARD
   And You, O Bethlehem *Epiph
   SA/TB,fl (med easy) oct CONCORDIA 98-1632
   $.25   (H2524)

   As Lately We Watched *Xmas
   SATB,acap (med easy) oct CONCORDIA 98-1693
   $.25   (H2525)

   At The End Of Eight Days *Circum
   SAB,acap (med diff) oct CONCORDIA 98-1712
   $.25   (H2526)

   Be Merciful, Even As Your Father *Gen/Trin
   SATB,acap (easy) oct CONCORDIA 98-1633 $.25
                                                (H2527)

   Christmas Story According To St. Luke, The
      *Xmas
   unis&2pt,fl,ob,2vln,vcl,org sc CONCORDIA
   97-4812 $3.00, voc sc CONCORDIA 97-4814
   $.90, ipa   (H2528)

   Holy Ghost, With Light Divine *Gen/Pent
   SATB,kbd (med easy) oct CONCORDIA 98-1590
   $.25   (H2529)

   If Anyone Keeps My Word *Gen/Lent
   SATB,acap (med diff) oct CONCORDIA 98-1676
   $.25   (H2530)

   Jesus Heals The Official's Son *Gen/Trin
   SATB,acap (med diff) oct CONCORDIA 98-1713
   $.22   (H2531)

   Lord I Am Not Worthy *Commun/Epiph
   SATB,kbd (med easy) oct CONCORDIA 98-1631
   $.20   (H2532)

   Magnificat, The *Adv/Xmas
   SATB,acap (med easy) oct CONCORDIA 98-1950
                                                (H2533)

   May God Bestow On Us His Grace (Psalm 67)
   mix cor,3trp,2trom sc CONCORDIA 97-4746
   $.85, ipa   (H2534)

   Not Everyone Who Says To Me, "Lord, Lord"
      *Gen/Trin
   SATB,acap (med diff) oct CONCORDIA 98-1707
   $.25   (H2535)

   Psalm 67 *see May God Bestow On Us His Grace

   Receive The Holy Spirit *Epiph/Gen/Pent
   SATB,kbd (med easy) oct CONCORDIA 98-1675
   $.30   (H2536)

   Rise, Take The Child And His Mother *Xmas/
      Gen
   SATB,kbd (med diff) oct CONCORDIA 98-1674
   $.20   (H2537)

   Seasonal Responses For Unison Voices *CCU,
      Gen,liturg
   cong/unis jr cor/cor,kbd/inst CONCORDIA
   97-5120 $.50   (H2538)

   Stilling Of The Storm, The *Epiph/Gen
   SATB,acap (med easy) oct CONCORDIA 98-1634
   $.20   (H2539)

   Surely He Has Borne Our Griefs *Lent
   SATB,acap (med easy) oct CONCORDIA 98-1597
   $.25   (H2540)

   This Is He Of Whom It Is Written *Adv/Gen
   SATB,acap (med diff) oct CONCORDIA 98-1745
   $.30   (H2541)

   When The People Saw The Sign Which He Had
      Done *Gen/Lent
   SAB,acap (med diff) oct CONCORDIA 98-1708
   $.22   (H2542)

   Where'er I Go, Whate'er My Task *Gen
   SATB,acap (med easy) oct CONCORDIA 98-1837
   $.25   (H2543)

   You Shall Love The Lord Your God *Gen/Trin
   SATB,acap (med diff) oct CONCORDIA 98-1677
   $.30   (H2544)

HILLIS
   Shall I Empty-Handed Be?
   (Whitsett) TTBB oct LILLENAS AN-1636 $.30
                                                (H2545)

HILLS, THE see Pitfield, Thomas Baron

HILLS OF BETHLEHEM see Moore

HILLS OF THE NORTH, REJOICE see Cassler, G. Winston

HILLS OF THE NORTH REJOICE see Shaw, Martin

HILLS, THE see Pitfield, Thomas Baron

HILTON
Call To Remembrance *Rembrnc
SATB (med) OXFORD 42.705 $.30 contains also: Farrant, Richard, Hide Not Thou Thy Face (H2546)

This Day A Child Is Born *Xmas
SAB ALFRED 6527 $.30 (H2547)
SSA ALFRED 6231 $.30 (H2548)

When Christ Was Born Of Mary Free *Xmas
SA ALFRED 6157 $.25 (H2549)

HILTON, JOHN (THE ELDER) (? -1608)
Call To Remembrance (Psalm 25) Lent
SSAATBB,opt inst (med) oct OXFORD 43.702 $.50 (H2550)

Lord, For Thy Tender Mercies' Sake *Commun/Gen/Lent
TTBB,kbd (med easy) oct CONCORDIA 98-2088 $.30 (H2551)
SATB,acap (very easy) oct OXFORD 43.307 $.20 (H2552)

Psalm 25 *see Call To Remembrance

HILTON, JOHN (THE YOUNGER) (1599-1657)
Psalm 119 *see Teach Me, O Lord

Teach Me, O Lord (Psalm 119) Gen
SSATB (med) oct OXFORD 42.868 $.50 (H2553)

HILTSCHER, WOLFGANG
Wir Singen Dir, Immanuel *cant
2pt mix cor,org,2vln,opt 2vcl HANSSLER 10.266 sc s.p., cor pts s.p., ipa (H2554)

HILTY
Built On The Rock *anthem
unis oct OXFORD 94.504 $.30 (H2555)

Lord's Prayer *anthem
(Merbecke) unis oct OXFORD 96.202 $.25 (H2556)

O Come Emmanuel *anthem
1-2pt oct OXFORD 94.003 $.25 (H2557)

O Come, O Come, Emmanuel *Adv
SATB (med easy) SOUTHERN $.25 (H2558)

HILTY, EVERETT JAY
Awake, My Soul, Stretch Every Nerve *Gen
unis,kbd (easy) oct CONCORDIA 98-1922 $.25 (H2559)

Heart And Mind, Possessions, Lord *Gen
unis,kbd (med easy) oct CONCORDIA 98-1918 $.25 (H2560)

If You Continue In My Word *Gen/Refm
SATB,kbd oct CONCORDIA 98-1599 $.25 (H2561)

HIMEBAUGH, H.A.
Put Yo' Trust In De Lawd
SATB oct BOURNE 721 $.25 (H2562)

HIMLANE, HERRE, FORTELJA DI see Geitvik, S.H.

HIMLARS RYMD see Peterson-Berger

HIMLARS RYMD SIN KONUNG *hymn
[Swed] men cor LUNDQUIST 54 s.p. (H2563)

HIMLENES RIKE see Nystedt, Knut

HIMMEL
Incline Thine Ear To Me
(Wiley) SSA oct PRO ART 1396 $.25 (H2564)

HIMMEL, ERDE, LUFT UND MEER see Stern, Hermann

HIMMEL, FRIEDRICH HEINRICH (1765-1814)
Inclina Ad Me *Easter/Lent,Bibl
"Incline Thine Ear To Me" [Lat/Eng] SATB,A/B solo,org (easy) oct WILLIS 2869 $.10 (H2565)
"Incline Thine Ear To Me" 4pt mix cor,low solo oct SCHIRM.G 3801 $.25 (H2566)
"Incline Thine Ear To Me" SATB oct PRESSER 312-06213 $.25 (H2567)
(Kent) "Incline Thine Ear To Me" SATB oct SPRATT 525 $.25 (H2568)

Incline Thine Ear *anthem
SATB,B solo (easy) ALLANS 15 s.p. (H2569)
mix cor,B solo oct NOVELLO 40.0116.08 s.p. (H2570)
(Chambers, H.A.) SA ALLANS 273 s.p. (H2571)

Incline Thine Ear To Me *see Inclina Ad Me

HIMMELFAHRT-PFINGSTEN- FRONLEICHNAM *CCU,Asc/Pent/Whitsun
(Wagner, Hermann) mix cor MOSELER s.p. (H2572)

HIMMELSFARDSSANG see Thyrestam, Gunnar

HIMMELSKE FADER see Geitvik, S.H.

HIMMELSKOENIG see Bach, Johann Sebastian, Himmelskonig, Sei Willkommen

HIMMELSKONIG, SEI WILLKOMMEN see Bach, Johann Sebastian

HIMMELSKONIG, SEI WILLKOMMEN [CHORALE] see Bach, Johann Sebastian

HIMMELVEGEN see Geitvik, S.H.

HIMNO A SAN ISIDRO LABRADOR, PATRON DE MADRID see Gonzalez Barron

HIMNO AL SAGRADO CORAZON DE JESUS see Busca

HIMNO DE SANTIAGO APOSTOL see Gomez Camargo

HIMNO OFICIAL DEL CONGRESO EUCARISTICO see Busca

HIMNUSZ see Erkel, Franz

HIMOTZE LONU see Ancis, Solomon

HINACH, YAFA see Cohen, D.

HINAY YOM HADIN see Adler, Samuel

HINDEMITH, PAUL (1895-1963)
Apparebit Repentina Dies
[Lat] SATB,10brass voc sc SCHOTT 4237 s.p., ipr (H2573)

Canticle To Hope
see Ite, Angeli Veloces

Chant De Triomphe Du Roi David (Psalm 17)
see Ite, Angeli Veloces

Custos Quid De Nocte
see Ite, Angeli Veloces

Das Unaufhorliche *ora
[Ger] SATB&boy cor,STB soli,orch voc sc SCHOTT 3258 s.p., ipr (H2574)

Eight Canons *Op.45,No.2, CC8L,canon
[Ger] SS,opt strings sc SCHOTT 1462 s.p., ipa, cor pts SCHOTT 1462 s.p., ipa (H2575)

Four Canons For Equal Voices *canon
SCHOTT s.p.
contains: Hie Kann Nit Sein Ein Boser Mut [Ger] (2pt); Musica Divinas Laudes [Lat] (3pt); Sine Musica Nulla Disciplina [Lat] (3pt); Wer Sich Die Musik Erkiest [Ger] (2pt) (H2576)

Hie Kann Nit Sein Ein Boser Mut
see Four Canons For Equal Voices

Ite, Angeli Veloces *cant
SCHOTT s.p., ipr
contains: Canticle To Hope [Eng/Fr/Ger] (SATB&audience,Mez solo,orch); Chant De Triomphe Du Roi David (Psalm 17) [Fr/Ger] (SATB&audience,AT soli,orch); Custos Quid De Nocte [Fr/Ger] (SATB,T solo,orch) (H2577)

Messe *Mass
[Ger] SATB,acap s.p. sc SCHOTT 5410, cor pts SCHOTT 5410 (H2578)

Musica Divinas Laudes
see Four Canons For Equal Voices
see Hindemith, Paul, Spruch Eines Fahrenden

Psalm 17 *see Chant De Triomphe Du Roi David

Sine Musica Nulla Disciplina
see Four Canons For Equal Voices

Spruch Eines Fahrenden *canon
[Ger] SSS SCHOTT s.p. contains also: Musica Divinas Laudes [Lat] (H2579)

Wer Sich Die Musik Erkiest
see Four Canons For Equal Voices

When Lilacs Last In The Door- Yard Bloom'd *Req
[Eng/Ger] SATB,MezBar soli,orch s.p., ipr voc sc SCHOTT 3800, cor pts SCHOTT 3800 (H2580)

HINDERMANN, WALTER FELIX (1931-)
Brich Dem Hungrigen Dein Brot
SAT/SAB LAUDINELLA LR 97 s.p. contains also: Der Mensch Lebt Nicht Vom Brot Allein, Aber Auch Nicht Ohne (SSAATB); Es Kommt Alles Darauf An (SAT/SAB); Kein Problem Wird Gelost (SATB); Wenn Jemand Weiss, Was Recht Ist (SATB) (H2581)

Der Mensch Lebt Nicht Vom Brot Allein, Aber Auch Nicht Ohne
see Hindermann, Walter Felix, Brich Dem Hungrigen Dein Brot

Es Kommt Alles Darauf An
see Hindermann, Walter Felix, Brich Dem Hungrigen Dein Brot

Gelobet Seist Du, Jesu Christ
ST,treb inst LAUDINELLA LR 69 s.p. contains also: Kommt Und Lasst Uns Christum Ehren (ST,treb inst); Nun Komm, Der Heiden Heiland (ST,treb inst); O Heiland, Reiss Die Himmel Auf (ST,treb inst); Nun Singen Und Seid Froh (men cor) (H2582)

Kein Problem Wird Gelost
see Hindermann, Walter Felix, Brich Dem Hungrigen Dein Brot

Kommt Und Lasst Uns Christum Ehren
see Hindermann, Walter Felix, Gelobet Seist Du, Jesu Christ

Lobt Den Herrn, Denn Was Er Tut
SATB,2trp,2trom LAUDINELLA LR 20 s.p. contains also: Wie Herrlich Gibst Du, Herr, Dich Zu Erkennen (H2583)

Nun Komm, Der Heiden Heiland
see Hindermann, Walter Felix, Gelobet Seist Du, Jesu Christ

Nun Singen Und Seid Froh
see Hindermann, Walter Felix, Gelobet Seist Du, Jesu Christ

O Heiland, Reiss Die Himmel Auf
see Hindermann, Walter Felix, Gelobet Seist Du, Jesu Christ

Wenn Jemand Weiss, Was Recht Ist
see Hindermann, Walter Felix, Brich Dem Hungrigen Dein Brot

Wie Herrlich Gibst Du, Herr, Dich Zu Erkennen
see Hindermann, Walter Felix, Lobt Den Herrn, Denn Was Er Tut

HINE
Easter Dawn *Easter
SAB oct LORENZ 7325 $.30 (H2584)

HINE, K.
How Great Thou Art
(Bock, F.) SA oct PRESSER G-163 $.35 (H2585)
(Bock, F.) SAB oct PRESSER G-162 $.40 (H2586)
(Bock, F.) SATB oct PRESSER G-161 $.40 (H2587)

HINEBAUGH
O Come, Loud Anthems Let Us Sing *Gen
SATB SCHMITT 1630 $.20 (H2588)

HINEY MATOV
see Rounds Of Israel

HINTZE, JAKOB (1622-1702)
Gib Dich Zufrieden Und Sei Stille
see Lowenstern, Matthaus Appelles von, Ich Hab Von Ferne, Herr, Deinen Thron

Take My Life, And Let It Be
(Bach, J.S.; Davis, K.) SA SCHIRM.EC 1575 (H2589)

HINUNTER IST DER SONNE SCHEIN see Micheelsen, Hans Friedrich

HINUNTER IST DER SONNEN SCHEIN see Micheelsen, Hans Friedrich

HINUNTER IST DER SONNEN SCHEIN see Stern, Hermann

HINUNTER IST DER SONNEN SCHEIN see Vulpius, Melchior

HINUNTER IST DER SONNEN SCHEIN see Wiemer, Wolfgang

HIRCHBERG GESANGBUCH *see Come, Let Us Join With Faithful Ones (H2590)

HIRSCH
Christ Is Arisen *see Christ Ist Erstanden

Christ Ist Erstanden *Easter
(Buszin) "Christ Is Arisen" SATB SCHMITT 1558 $.30 (H2591)

To Heaven Ascended Christ, Our King *Easter
(Buszin) SATB SCHMITT 1693 $.30 (H2592)

HIRSCH, CARL
Christ Is Arisen From The Grave *Easter
SSAATTBB,kbd (easy) oct CONCORDIA 98-1172 $.25 (H2593)

HIRSCHBERG
I Look To Thee In Every Need
(Beebe) SAB oct PRO ART 2420 $.25 (H2594)

HIRT, L.
Abide With Me
SATB oct PRESSER G-119 $.30 (H2595)

HIRTEN, EILT ZUR KRIPPE *Xmas,Eur/Pol
(Doppelbauer, Josef Friedrich) mix cor,acap DOBLINGER s.p. see from Da Der Herr Geboren (H2596)

HIRTEN, ER IST GEBOREN *Xmas,Dut/Eur
(Doppelbauer, Josef Friedrich) mix cor,acap DOBLINGER s.p. see from Da Der Herr Geboren (H2597)

HIRTEN, STEHET AUF, EILET IM RASCHEN LAUF see Trust, Heinz-Ewald

HIRTENKANTATE ZUR WEIHNACHT see Heilmann, Harald

HIRTENLIED AN DER KRIPPE
(Etti, Karl) wom cor,acap oct DOBLINGER s.p. (H2598)

HIRTENLIED AUS DEN BURGENLAND
(Takacs, Jeno) mix cor,acap oct DOBLINGER s.p. (H2599)

HIRZEL, ERICH
Lobet Den Herrn (Psalm 117) Bibl
SATB HANSSLER 6.237 s.p. (H2600)

Psalm 117 *see Lobet Den Herrn

HIS ARMS ARE OPEN TO EVERYONE see Harding, G.P.

HIS COMPASSIONS FAIL NOT see Sateren, Leland Bernhard

HIS DELIGHT IS IN THE LAW OF THE LORD see Baumgartner, H. Leroy

HIS EYE IS ON THE SPARROW see Gabriel

HIS GRACE IS SUFFICIENT FOR ME see Lister, Mosie

HIS HOLY PLACE see Bach, Karl Philipp Emanuel

HIS LOVE see Nichols, Ted

HIS LOVE see Robbins

HIS LOVE ALL AROUND see Wilson

HIS LOVE IS BORN ANEW see Lehmeier, J.F.

HIS LOVE WILL SHINE LIKE A LIGHT see King

HIS MERCY see Bach, Johann Sebastian, Et Misericordia

HIS NAME IS EXALTED see Newbury

HIS NAME IS JOHN see Naylor, Peter

HIS NAME SO SWEET *anthem/spir
(Johnson) SATB oct FISCHER,C CM-4580 $.25 (H2601)
(Johnson) SSA oct FISCHER,C CM-5213 $.25 (H2602)

HIS POVERTY AND GRACE
(Brandon) SATB oct VOLKWEIN VB711 $.25 (H2603)

HIS PRAISE SING FORTH see Williams

HIS PRAISES SING see Guess

HIS PRAISES WE'LL SING *Xmas
(Follett) SATB oct PRO ART 2081 $.25 (H2604)
(Follett) SAB oct PRO ART 2179 $.25 (H2605)

HIS PRESENCE see Stansell

HIS SAVING MIGHT *hymn
   (Brandon) SATB,pno/org oct LAWSON 51501 $.40
                                             (H2606)

HIS SERVANT ISRAEL see Bach, Johann Sebastian,
   Suscepit Israel

HIS STAR SHINETH CLEAR see Bornschein, [Franz
   Carl]

HIS STAR STILL SHINES *Xmas/Pageant,cant
   oct LORENZ $1.00   (H2607)

HIS STEADFAST LOVE ENDURES FOREVER see Niehaus,
   Lennie

HIS VOICE *Gen
   (Fleming) SATB SCHMITT 8054 $.35   (H2608)

HIS VOICE AS THE SOUND
   (Shaw; Parker) SATB,acap oct LAWSON 915 $.30
                                             (H2609)

HIS VOICE, AS THE SOUND OF THE DULCIMER, SWEET
   see Elkins

HIS YOKE IS EASY see Hudson

HISHKI HIZKI see Casseres, A.

HISTORIA DER AUFERSTEHUNG JESU CHRISTI 1623 see
   Schutz, Heinrich

HISTORIA DER GEBURT JESU CHRISTI see Schutz,
   Heinrich

HISTORIA DI JEPHTE see Carissimi, Giacomo

HISTORIA JONAE see Carissimi, Giacomo

HIT, O JESU, SAMLOMS VI *Psalm
   (Von Koch, Erland) [Swed] SATB,acap GEHRMANS
   KRB 427   (H2610)

HJALP, HERRE DE HELIGA see Roman, Johan Helmich

HJORLEIFSSON, SIGGURINGI E. (1902-   )
   Cantata *cant
   mix cor ICELAND s.p.   (H2611)

HO, EVERY ONE THAT THIRSTETH see Demarest, A.

HO, EVERY ONE THAT THIRSTETH see Macfarlane,
   William Charles

HO! EVERY ONE THAT THRSTETH see Martin, George
   Clement

HO, EVERYONE THAT THIRSTETH see Young, Gordon

HO, HO, HO, HO, BENDICAMUS DOMINO
   see Belgian Christmas Songs, Set 1

HO LACHMO ANYO. see Adler, Hugo Ch.

HOAG, CHARLES K.
   Gloria *Gloria
   4pt wom cor oct SCHIRM.G 11759 $.30 (H2612)

   May God Have Mercy Upon Us *Bibl
   4pt mix cor,org oct SCHIRM.G 11846 $.30
                                             (H2613)

   O Be Joyful
   6pt mix cor,acap oct SCHIRM.G 11859 $.35
                                             (H2614)

   Sing Softly *Xmas
   2pt boy cor/2pt wom cor,opt org oct
   SCHIRM.G 11845 $.25   (H2615)

   Sing We Merrily Unto God Our Strength *Bibl
   4pt mix cor,org,trp,horn,perc oct SCHIRM.G
   11757 $.40   (H2616)

HOBBS, C.M.
   Joy Dawned Again On Easter Day *Easter
   SAB,opt brass oct KERBY 5313 $.45   (H2617)
   SAB,opt trom,trp oct KERBY 5313C $.45
                                             (H2618)

   Welcome, Welcome, Jesu
   SATB&jr cor,org oct KERBY 5107 $.40 (H2619)

   Welcome, Welcome Jesus *Xmas
   SATB&jr cor oct KERBY 5107C $.40, oct KERBY
   5107J $.10   (H2620)

HOC CORPUS see Kropfreiter, Augustinius Franz

HOC EST PRAECEPTUM MEUM see Wert, Giaches de

HOCH AM HIMMEL FLIEGT EIN FALKE see
   Pfannenstiel, Ekkehart

HOCH TUT EUCH AUF see Klein, B.

HOCH VOM HIMMEL KOMM ICH HER see Weismann,
   Wilhelm

HOCH WEHT DAS KREUZ see Schmid, Walter

HOCHELLA
   Christ, The Lord Is Risen
   SATB oct PLYMOUTH JR-118 $.25   (H2621)

HOCHGEPRIESEN, DER KOMMT see Haydn, (Johann)
   Michael, Benedictus Qui Venit

HOCHPREISET MEINE SEELE see Haller, Hans Peter

HOCHPREISET MEINE SEELE DEN GOTT see Gesius,
   Bartholomaus

HOCHSTERWUNSCHTES FREUDENFEST see Bach, Johann
   Sebastian

HOCHZEIT IN SIEBENBURGEN see Csenki, I.

HOCHZEITS-STANDCHEN see Burgwart, K.

HOCHZEITSLANDLER see Brugk, Hans Melchoir

HOCHZEITSLIED see Brugk, Hans Melchoir

HOCHZEITSMUSIK see Bardos, Ludwig

HODDINOTT, ALUN (1929-   )
   Christ And Sinful Man
   see Three Medieval Songs

HODDINOTT, ALUN (cont'd.)
   Dives And Lazarus *cant
   mix cor,SBar soli,org/orch (med easy) voc
   sc OXFORD 46.140 $1.55, ipr   (H2622)

   Every Man's Work Shall Be Made Manifest
   *Ded,Bibl
   SATB (med easy) oct OXFORD 42.882 $.35
                                             (H2623)

   Great Art Thou, O God *Gen
   SATB,acap (med easy) oct OXFORD 42.853 $.35
                                             (H2624)

   Holy, Holy, Holy *Gen
   SATB,acap (easy) oct OXFORD 43.380 $.15
                                             (H2625)

   In Praise Of Ivy
   see Three Medieval Songs

   Of The New Year
   see Three Medieval Songs

   Three Medieval Songs *Mediev
   SSA/SSAA,acap (diff) OXFORD 83.058 $.35
   contains: Christ And Sinful Man; In
   Praise Of Ivy; Of The New Year   (H2626)

   What Tidings? *Xmas,carol
   SATB,acap (med) OXFORD 84.138 $.25 (H2627)

   Wondrous Night, The *Xmas
   SSA,acap (med diff) OXFORD 83.054 $.25
                                             (H2628)

HODGES
   Bread Of The World
   (Hornibrook) SATB SHAWNEE A 679 $.30
                                             (H2629)

HODGSON, R.A.
   God So Loved The World
   cor,Bar solo BOSWORTH s.p.   (H2630)

HODIE see Church

HODIE see Goossen, Frederic

HODIE see Vaughan Williams, Ralph

HODIE APPARUIT see Lassus, Roland de (Orlandus)

HODIE BEATA VIRGO see Byrd, William

HODIE BEATA VIRGO see Constantini, Fabio

HODIE, CHRISTUS NATUS EST see Anderson, Robert

HODIE CHRISTUS NATUS EST see Balladori, Angelo

HODIE CHRISTUS NATUS EST see Bender, Jan

HODIE CHRISTUS NATUS EST see Bottazzo, Luigi

HODIE, CHRISTUS NATUS EST see Christiansen,
   Larry A.

HODIE CHRISTUS NATUS EST see Christiansen, Olaf
   Christian

HODIE CHRISTUS NATUS EST see Clerambault, Louis
   Nicolas

HODIE CHRISTUS NATUS EST see Davison, John

HODIE CHRISTUS NATUS EST see Gabrieli, Giovanni

HODIE CHRISTUS NATUS EST see Gallus, Jacobus

HODIE CHRISTUS NATUS EST see Kannon, R.V.

HODIE, CHRISTUS NATUS EST see Lamb

HODIE CHRISTUS NATUS EST see Leazer, Carl W.

HODIE CHRISTUS NATUS EST see Lemacher, Heinrich

HODIE CHRISTUS NATUS EST see Marenzio, Luca

HODIE CHRISTUS NATUS EST see Monteverdi,
   Claudio

HODIE CHRISTUS NATUS EST see Nanini (Nanino),
   Giovanni Maria

HODIE CHRISTUS NATUS EST see Palestrina,
   Giovanni

HODIE CHRISTUS NATUS EST see Poulenc, Francis

HODIE CHRISTUS NATUS EST see Rohlig, Harald

HODIE CHRISTUS NATUS EST see Rousseau, Samuel-
   Alexandre

HODIE CHRISTUS NATUS EST see Santa Cruz,
   Domingo

HODIE CHRISTUS NATUS EST see Schutz, Heinrich

HODIE CHRISTUS NATUS EST see Sweelinck, Jan
   Pieterszoon

HODIE, CHRISTUS NATUS EST see Willan, Healey

HODIE CHRISTUS NATUS EST see Young

HODIE COMPLETI SUNT DIES PENTECOSTES see
   Gabrieli, Giovanni

HODIE IN BETHLEHEM see Volpi, Edoardo

HODIE NATUS CHRISTUS EST see Poulenc, Francis

HODIE NOBIS see Dela Venna, P.

HODIE NOBIS CAELORUM REX see Nanini (Nanino),
   Giovanni Bernardino

HODIE NOBIS COELORUM REX see Bright, Houston

HODIE NOBIS COELORUM REX see Nanini (Nanino),
   Giovanni Bernardino

HODIE NOBIS DE CAELO see Porta, Costanzo

HODIE PAULUS APOSTOLUS see Marenzio, Luca

HODU see Alter

HOE GROOT O HEER see Flipse, E.

HOE GROOT, O HEER see Zagwijn, [Henri]

HOELTY-NICKEL, THEODORE
   TTBB Chorale Book, The *CC37L
   TTBB CONCORDIA 97-7602 $1.25   (H2631)

HOFER, A.
   Magnificat *Magnif
   [Lat] voc sc UNIVER. 25C010 $1.65   (H2632)

   Te Deum *Te Deum
   [Lat] voc sc UNIVER. 25C001 $2.75, cor pts
   UNIVER. 25D001 $1.65   (H2633)

HOFFE ISRAEL see Schutz, Heinrich, Speret
   Israel

HOFFELT, ROBERT O.
   Not Alone For Mighty Empire *Thanks
   TTBB (med) ABINGDON APM-944 $.55   (H2634)
   TTBB (med) ABINGDON APM-944 $.55   (H2635)

HOFFMAN
   Cross Shines Forth, The
   SATB FLAMMER A5389 $1.25   (H2636)

   God's Son Is Born *cant
   SATB FLAMMER A5023 $1.25   (H2637)
   SAB FLAMMER D5207 $1.25   (H2638)

   One Step (composed with MacDonald)
   (Ehret) SSA/SSAA oct MCA   (H2639)
   (Ehret) SAB oct MCA   (H2640)

   Rock Of Ages
   SATB oct PLYMOUTH PCS-27 $.25   (H2641)

HOFFMAN, M.
   Hosanna! *see Gregor, [Christian Friedrich]

   Lord Of Our Life
   SAB oct PRESSER 312-40929 $.25   (H2642)

   Sacred Songs *CCU
   SAB oct PRESSER $1.25   (H2643)

   Sacred Songs For Junior Choir *CCU
   SATB oct PRESSER $.90   (H2644)

HOFFMAN, RICHARD (1831-1909)
   Petitions For Help *anthem
   SATB&speak cor,org (med) oct AUGSBURG 3000
   $.10   (H2645)

HOFFMANN
   Praise For The Year *CCU
   SA FLAMMER GE5003 $1.25   (H2646)

   Prayer For Today, A *Gen
   (House) SSA SCHMITT 2567 $.25   (H2647)
   (House) SATB SCHMITT 1732 $.20   (H2648)

   Select Unison Anthems *CCU
   unis FLAMMER GF5001 $1.25   (H2649)

   Ten Select Anthems *CC10U,anthem
   SA FLAMMER GE5015 $.85   (H2650)

   Year Round Anthem Book, The *CCU,anthem
   SATB FLAMMER GA5017 $1.50   (H2651)

HOFFMANN, ERNST THEODOR AMADEUS (1766-1822)
   Miserere B-Moll
   5pt mix cor,SSATB soli,org,2clar,2bsn,2trp,
   3trom,strings (B min) cor pts BREITKOPF-W
   CHB-4809 s.p., ipr, voc sc BREITKOPF-W
   EB-6656 s.p., sc BREITKOPF-W rental
                                             (H2652)

   Nun Schwebt Auf Engelsflugeln *Xmas
   [Ger] wom cor,acap (easy) HUG s.p. (H2653)

   O Sanctissima *Fest
   [Lat] SATB,acap (med easy) MULLER MS 70
   s.p.   (H2654)

   Ostermorgen *Easter
   [Ger] mix cor,acap (easy) HUG   (H2655)

HOFFMEISTER, FRANZ ANTON (1754-1812)
   How Long Will Thou Forget Me
   SATB oct HUNTZINGER 4031 $.20   (H2656)

HOFFMEISTER, L.A.
   Arise, O Lord! *Bibl
   (Deis) 4pt mix cor oct SCHIRM.G 7629 $.25
                                             (H2657)

HOFFRICHTER, B.
   Lord Is My Shepherd, The
   (Duddy, J.) SATB,acap oct PRESSER 312-40572
   $.30   (H2658)

HOFMANN, EBERHARD
   Wach Auf, Wach Auf, S'ist Hohe Zeit *cant
   SAT/SAB,org&opt 3brass/3strings HANSSLER
   10.160 sc s.p., voc sc s.p., ipa   (H2659)

HOFMANN, FRIEDRICH (1910-   )
   Zeitgenossische Kirchenlieder *CCU
   [Ger] unis BAREN. EM 381 s.p.   (H2660)

   Zeitgenossische Kirchenlieder *CC42U
   [Ger] 3pt mix cor/4pt mix cor BAREN. EM 382
   s.p.   (H2661)

HOFSTETTER WEIHNACHTSKANTATE see Diener

HOGGARD
   Boundless Mercy
   SSA,acap SHAWNEE B 60 $.30   (H2662)
   girl cor SOUTHERN $.30   (H2663)

   Three Kings
   TTBB SHAWNEE C76 $.25   (H2664)

HOGNER, FRIEDRICH (1897-   )
   Lobgesang *CCU
   cor&cong&opt unis,opt solo,org voc pt
   BREITKOPF-L CHB-2896 s.p.   (H2665)

   Wie Teuer Ist Deine Gute, Gott *mot
   SSA HANSSLER 7.009 s.p.   (H2666)

HOGT FRA DEN HIMMELSKE KLARA see Geitvik, S.H.

HOGTLOVAD VARE DAVIDS SON see Praetorius,
   Michael

HOHLFELD, CHRISTOPH (1922-)
Acht Kinderchore-Heft 1
cor pts BREITKOPF-W CHB-3162 s.p.
contains: Ich Danke Gott Und Freue Mich (3pt jr cor,acap); Ich Danke Gott Und Freue Mich (3pt jr cor) (canon); Wenn Einer, Der Mit Muhe Kaum (4pt jr cor, acap) (canon); Wohlauf, Ihr Klein Waldvogelein (3pt jr cor,acap); Zwei Augen Hat Die Seel (4pt jr cor,acap) (canon) (H2667)

Acht Kinderchore-Heft 2
cor pts BREITKOPF-W CHB-3163 s.p.
contains: An Deine Leiden Denken Wir (3pt jr cor,org,fl/vln) (Psntd,chorale); Ich Danke Dir, Mein Himmlischer Vater (3pt jr cor,acap) (Morn,prayer); Ich Danke Dir, Mein Himmlischer Vater (3pt jr cor,acap) (Eve,prayer) (H2668)

An Deine Leiden Denken Wir
see Acht Kinderchore-Heft 2

Der Anfang, Das Ende
see Evangelisches Kalendarium-Heft 2

Der Mond Ist Aufgegangen
4pt men cor,opt 4horn sc BREITKOPF-W PB-4754 s.p., cor pts BREITKOPF-W CHB-3515 s.p., ipa (H2669)

Die Hirten Von Bethlehem *Xmas,cant
1-2pt wom cor/1-2pt jr cor,narrator,pno/ 3inst sc BREITKOPF-W MSP-9 s.p. (H2670)

Evangelisches Kalendarium-Heft 1 *CC7L,Adv/ Xmas/Easter/Psntd,evang/liturg/mot
4-5pt,acap cor pts BREITKOPF-W CHB-3180A s.p. (H2671)

Evangelisches Kalendarium-Heft 2 *evang/ liturg/mot
4-5pt mix cor cor pts BREITKOPF-W CHB-3180B s.p.
contains: Der Anfang, Das Ende; Gott Fahrt Auf Mit Jauchzen (Asc); Ich Will Euch Ein Neues Herz, Einen Neuen Geist Auch Geben; Nun Danket All Und Bringet Ehr; So Halten Wir Nun Dafur (Refm) (H2672)

Gott Fahrt Auf Mit Jauchzen
see Evangelisches Kalendarium-Heft 2

Ich Danke Dir, Mein Himmlischer Vater
see Acht Kinderchore-Heft 2
see Acht Kinderchore-Heft 2

Ich Danke Gott Und Freue Mich
see Acht Kinderchore-Heft 1
see Acht Kinderchore-Heft 1

Ich Will Euch Ein Neues Herz, Einen Neuen Geist Auch Geben
see Evangelisches Kalendarium-Heft 2

Nun Danket All Und Bringet Ehr
see Evangelisches Kalendarium-Heft 2

So Halten Wir Nun Dafur
see Evangelisches Kalendarium-Heft 2

Wenn Einer, Der Mit Muhe Kaum
see Acht Kinderchore-Heft 1

Wohlauf, Ihr Klein Waldvogelein
see Acht Kinderchore-Heft 1

Zwei Augen Hat Die Seel
see Acht Kinderchore-Heft 1

HOHMANN
Jesus Put Forth His Hand *Gen
SATB SCHMITT 1676 $.22 (H2673)

HOIBY, LEE (1926-)
Ascention *Easter
SATB oct PRESSER 312-40728 $.60 (H2674)

Hymn Of The Nativity *Xmas,hymn
SATB,SB soli,orch BELWIN $1.75 (H2675)

Inherit The Kingdom
SATB oct PRESSER 312-40725 $.45 (H2676)

Let This Mind Be In You *Easter
SATB oct PRESSER 312-40726 $.40 (H2677)

Offering, The (from Hymn Of The Nativity, A)
SATB oct COLOMBO 2108 $.30 (H2678)

HOJEN JUBEL TILL HERREN ALLA LANDER see Wikander, David

HOJLOVET VAERE GUD see Bach, Johann Sebastian, Gelobet Sei Der Herr

HOJTIDSDAGEN see Jeppesen, Knud

HOKANSON
Alleluia, Amen
SATB KJOS 5353 $.30 (H2679)

Alleluia Choir Book 1 *CCU
(Michelson) treb cor KJOS $1.25 (H2680)

Were I A Bird *Gen
(Norberg) unis SCHMITT 341 $.30 (H2681)

HOKANSON, M.
All People Sing Praises
SATB oct FISCHER,J 8710 $.30 (H2682)
SAB oct FISCHER,J 9798 $.30 (H2683)

Bohemian Carol *Xmas/Easter,carol,Boh
SAB,kbd oct KERBY 6151 $.25 (H2684)
SAB oct KERBY 6151C $.25 (H2685)

In Dulci Jubilo *Xmas
SAB,pno oct KERBY 6052 $.35 (H2686)
SAB oct KERBY 6052C $.35 (H2687)

O Wondrous Night *Xmas
SATB,opt kbd oct KERBY 6604 $.35 (H2688)
SATB,acap oct KERBY 6604C $.35 (H2689)

Rejoice, All Ye Believers
SAB oct FISCHER,J 9929 $.30 (H2690)

HOKANSON, MARGRETHE (1893-)
Ah, Dearest Jesu Child
SATB oct AGAPE A 353 $.30 (H2691)

Apollo Canticle
SATB SCHMITT 663 $.30 (H2692)

As With Gladness Men Of Old *Xmas
SATB (easy) ABINGDON APM-220 $.25 (H2693)

Chime, Happy Christmas Bells *Xmas
unis,fl (easy) oct CONCORDIA 98-1513 $.25 (H2694)

Grant Us Thy Peace
SAB oct AGAPE A 340 $.25 (H2695)

Jesu, Child Of Bethlehem
SATB,opt fl/ob oct AGAPE F 908 $.30 (H2696)

Journey To Bethlehem
SATB oct AGAPE A 428 $.30 (H2697)

Sing To God *Ded/Gen/Refm/Thanks
SATB,trp (med easy) oct CONCORDIA 98-1790 $.25 (H2698)

Song Of Gratitude And Praise
SATB,opt trp oct AGAPE F 912 $.30 (H2699)

HOLD IN AFFECTION JESUS CHRIST see Bach, Johann Sebastian, Halt Im Gedachtnis Jesum Christ

HOLD MY HAND *spir
(De Pue) SATB,acap oct LAWSON 51396 $.30 (H2700)

HOLD NOT AGAINST ME see Iden, Raymond

HOLD NOT THY TONGUE, O GOD see Hedges, Anthony

HOLD ON! *spir
(Howorth) SATB,acap oct PRO ART 1065 $.16 (H2701)
(Roberts) SATB,A/T solo,opt perc oct LAWSON 51666 $.40 (H2702)

HOLD ON see Bonds, [Margaret]

HOLD ON, HOLD ON *spir
(Fox) SATB SCHMITT 659 $.35 (H2703)

HOLD OPPE, GUD see Gaudimel, Claude

HOLD THOU MY HAND see Bierly, A.

HOLD THOU MY HAND see Briggs

HOLD THOU MY HANDS see Wolff, S. Drummond

HOLDEN, [OLIVER] (1765-1844)
All Hail The Power Of Jesus' Name *sac/sec
(Barnard) SATB SCHMITT 1873 $.35 (H2704)
(Barthelson) SATB,opt 4brass oct SPRATT 544 $.30 (H2705)
(Dawson) SSA&desc oct PRO ART 1709 $.25 (H2706)
(Dawson) SAB&desc oct PRO ART 2196 $.25 (H2707)
(Dawson) SATB&desc oct PRO ART 1439 $.25 (H2708)
(Gerig) SSATTBB oct LILLENAS AN-2372 $.35 (H2709)
(Simeone) SATB SHAWNEE A 783 $.30 (H2710)

Cantata On Appalachian Christmas Carols *see Niles, David

Christmas *Xmas
(Pisano) SATB,acap,opt pno oct PRO ART 2559 $.25 (H2711)

Lord Is Good To All, The
(McAfee) SATB oct BOURNE 848 $.25 (H2712)

HOLIDAY AND HOLY DAY see Ehret, Walter

HOLIDAY BELLS! see Martin, Gilbert M.

HOLIDAY MOTETS see Krenek, Ernst

HOLIDAY ROUND *Xmas
(Williamson, W.) SA LEONARD-US 08023840 $.25 (H2713)

HOLIDAY THANKSGIVING SONG see Pullen, Alice M.

HOLIDAY TIME see Iams

HOLIEST NIGHT *Xmas,carol,Ger
(Van Koert, Han) SA&SATB,org oct WORLD AC-544-8 $.45 (H2714)

HOLINESS TO THE LORD see Heaton, [Wallace]

HOLINESS UNTO THE LORD see Marryott

HOLLER, JOHN (1904-)
Chapel Choir Anthem Book *CCU,anthem
men cor BELWIN $1.00 (H2715)

Church Choir Anthem Book *CCU
mix cor BELWIN $1.25 (H2716)

Easter Carol, An *Easter
unis&opt desc oct GRAY GCMR 1946 $.30 (H2717)

General Anthem Book 1 *CCU,anthem
mix cor BELWIN $1.25 (H2718)

General Anthem Book 2 *CCU,anthem
mix cor BELWIN $1.00 (H2719)

Lo' He Comes *Adv
SATB oct GRAY GCMR 2892 $.25 (H2720)

Loving Saviour
unis oct GRAY GCMR 1911 $.20 (H2721)

Risen Christ *Easter
SATB oct SOUTHERN $.25 (H2722)

Risen Christ, The *Easter/Lent
unis/SA oct GRAY GCMR 2872 $.25 (H2723)
SATB oct GRAY GCMR 1954 $.30 (H2724)

Saviour, Teach Me
unis oct GRAY GCMR 1835 $.30 (H2725)

St. Cecilia Anthem Book *CCU,anthem
SSA BELWIN $1.50 (H2726)

HOLLER, JOHN (cont'd.)

Youth Choir Anthem Book 1 *CCU,anthem
SA BELWIN $1.25 (H2727)

Youth Choir Anthem Book 2 *CCU,anthem
unis BELWIN $1.25 (H2728)

Youth Choir Anthem Book 3 *CCU,anthem
SAB BELWIN $1.25 (H2729)

Youth Choir Anthem Book 4 *CCU,anthem
SA BELWIN $1.25 (H2730)

Youth Choir Anthem Book 5 *CCU,anthem
unis BELWIN $1.25 (H2731)

HOLLER, KARL (1907-)
Hymnischer Gesang *Op.13, hymn
mix cor,orch cor pts LEUCKART s.p., ipr (H2732)
Missa Brevis *Bene/Gloria/Kyrie/Mass/Sanctus
[Ger] SATB,soli,acap (med) MULLER SM 1801 sc s.p., cor pts s.p. (H2733)

HOLLFELDER, WALDRAM (1924-)
Christus, Der Ist Mein Leben
see Zwei Grabchorale

Das Ist Je Gewisslich Wahr *mot
SSATBB HANSSLER 7.102 s.p. (H2734)

Die Mit Tranen Saen, Werden *mot
SATB HANSSLER 7.084 s.p. (H2735)

Ein Solch Vertrauen Aber *mot
MOSELER s.p.
contains: Epistelmotette (5pt mix cor); Motettischer Satz (mix cor) (H2736)

Epistelmotette
see Ein Solch Vertrauen Aber

Freunde, Lasst Uns Frohlich Loben *cant
mix cor&jr cor&men cor,2trp,3trom,timp MOSELER sc s.p., cor pts s.p., ipa (H2737)

Johannespassion
SATB&unis,TB soli cor pts HANSSLER 10.174 s.p. (H2738)

Motettischer Satz
see Ein Solch Vertrauen Aber

Nun Bringen Wir Den Leib Zur Ruh
see Zwei Grabchorale

Zwei Grabchorale *chorale
men cor,acap TONGER s.p.
contains: Christus, Der Ist Mein Leben (Vulpius); Nun Bringen Wir Den Leib Zur Ruh (H2739)

HOLLINGSWORTH, STANLEY (1924-)
Stabat Mater
cor,pno voc sc SCHIRM.G $.75 (H2740)

HOLLINS, ALFRED (1865-1942)
Earth Is The Lord's, The *Harv,anthem
mix cor oct NOVELLO 40.0725.05 s.p. (H2741)

O Worship The Lord *anthem
mix cor oct NOVELLO 40.0731.10 s.p. (H2742)

Rejoice In The Lord *Xmas,anthem
mix cor oct NOVELLO 28.0721.01 s.p. (H2743)

HOLLOWAY, LORRAINE
Thou Wilt Keep Him In Perfect Peace
oct FISCHER,J 2984 $.30 (H2744)

HOLLY AND IVY see Edmonds, Paul

HOLLY AND IVY, THE see Currie, E.R.

HOLLY AND THE IVY *Xmas,carol
see Six Traditional Carols, Set I
(Boughton, Rutland) mix cor CURWEN 80626 s.p. (H2745)
(Britten) SATB,acap oct BOOSEY 5259 $.30 (H2746)
(Ehret) TTBB oct BOOSEY 5472 $.30 (H2747)
(Lefebvre) SSA oct GALAXY 1.0594.1 $.35 (H2748)
(Lefebvre) TTBB oct GALAXY 1.0584.1 $.35 (H2749)

HOLLY AND THE IVY, THE *Xmas,carol,Eng
see Three Christmas Carols
unis/SATB (easy) OXFORD 08.037 $.15 (H2750)
2pt ASHDOWN E.A.256 s.p. (H2751)
(Ahrold, F.) SATB,acap oct PRESSER 312-40502 $.30 (H2752)
(Barrow, R.) TTBB,acap SCHIRM.EC 2117 $.25 (H2753)
(Boughton) 4pt mix cor,acap oct CURWEN 8108 $.25 (H2754)
(Boughton; Deis) 3pt wom cor oct CURWEN 10252 $.25 (H2755)
(Boughton; Jacobson) 3pt mix cor,acap oct CURWEN 10404 $.30 (H2756)
(Cashmore) SSAATTBB,acap (med) OXFORD 84.042 $.30 (H2757)
(Davison, A.) unis,pno SCHIRM.EC 1518 $.20 (H2758)
(De Cormier) SATB,pno/org oct LAWSON 51435 $.35 (H2759)
(Dunhill, Thomas F.) unis&desc oct LESLIE 106 (H2760)
(Gardner) SSS (very easy) OXFORD 40.104 $.30 (H2761)
(Russell) SA (very easy) OXFORD 82.054 $.20 (H2762)
(Shaw; Parker) mix cor,acap oct SCHIRM.G 10187 $.35 (H2763)
(Stone) SATB oct PRO ART 1369 $.30 (H2764)
(Stone) SAB oct PRO ART 2028 $.30 (H2765)
(Stone) SSA oct PRO ART 1791 $.30 (H2766)
(Stone) SA oct PRO ART 2025 $.30 (H2767)
(Terri) SATB,acap oct LAWSON 826 $.30 (H2768)

HOLLY AND THE IVY, THE see Boughton, Rutland

HOLLY AND THE IVY, THE see Currie, E.R.

HOLLY AND THE IVY, THE see Gardner

HOLLY AND THE IVY, THE see Swain, Freda

HOLLY AND THE IVY, THE see Thomson, Virgil

HOLLY CAROL *Xmas,carol,Eng
(Ehret) SAB,opt orch,bells oct FOX CC12 $.35
(H2769)
(Ehret) SSA,opt orch,bells oct FOX CC18 $.35
(H2770)
(Ehret, W.) SAB,opt orch&bells PROWSE CC12
s.p.   (H2771)

HOLLY CAROL, THE see Anderson, Ruth

HOLLY IS UP, THE see Cork, Peter

HOLLY RED AND MISTLETOE
see Come Little Jesus

HOLLY TREE see Carol

HOLLY TREE CAROL, THE see Marryott, Ralph E.

HOLMAN, DEREK
Away With Gloom *Easter
4pt mix cor,acap oct SCHIRM.G 10986 $.25
(H2772)
Christ Hath A Garden
4pt mix cor,acap oct SCHIRM.G 10918 $.25
(H2773)
Christ, My Beloved
4pt mix cor,acap oct SCHIRM.G 10924 $.25
(H2774)
Christ, Who Knows All His Sheep *anthem
mix cor oct NOVELLO 28.1300.09 s.p. (H2775)
Jesus Christ The Apple Tree *Gen,anthem
unis,opt pno oct ROYAL 247 s.p. see also
ANTHEMS FOR UNISON OR TWO PART SINGING
(H2776)
Let This Mind Be In You *Gen
SATB (easy) oct OXFORD 42.323 $.50 (H2777)
Magnificat And Nunc Dimittis *Magnif/Nunc
treb cor LENGNICK s.p. (H2778)
Magnificat And Nunc Dimittis In F Minor
*Magnif/Nunc
oct ROYAL 116 s.p. (H2779)
My God And King *anthem
mix cor oct NOVELLO 28.1314.09 s.p. (H2780)
Prevent Us, O Lord
unis oct NOVELLO 33.0098.06 s.p. (H2781)
Sweet Was The Song The Virgin Sang *Xmas,
carol
oct ROYAL 328 s.p. contains also:
Nicholson, S.H., Ode On The Birth Of Our
Saviour, An (H2782)
Thee We Adore *Commun,anthem
unis oct ROYAL 242 s.p. (H2783)
Versicles, Responses And Lord's Prayer *CCU
treb cor LENGNICK s.p. (H2784)

HOLMBERG, SIMON
Ditt Lidande Har Natt Sitt Slut *Bibl
[Swed] SATB,acap GEHRMANS KRB 78 (H2785)

HOLMES
Hymn And Alleluia
SATB,acap SHAWNEE A 644 $.25 (H2786)

HOLMES, AUGUSTA (MARY ANNE) (1847-1903)
Noel *Xmas,carol
(Darcieux, F.) [Fr] 4pt men cor,acap (easy)
cor pts LEMOINE s.p. (H2787)
(Darcieux, F.) [Fr] 4pt mix cor,acap (easy)
cor pts LEMOINE s.p. (H2788)

HOLMES, JOHN
Magnificat And Nunc Dimittis *Magnif/Nunc
mix cor oct NOVELLO 44.0890.10 s.p. (H2789)

HOLMES, ROBERT
Beams Of Gentle Light *Xmas/Hanakkah
TTBB FOSTER MF1076 $.25 (H2790)

HOLSCHER, BERNHARD (1923-   )
In Dulci Jubilo *Xmas
wom cor&jr cor TONGER s.p. (H2791)
Maria Durch Ein Dornwald Ging *Xmas
mix cor TONGER s.p. (H2792)
O Jesulein Zart *Xmas
mix cor TONGER s.p. (H2793)
Seid Nun Frohlich, Jubiliret *Xmas
wom cor&jr cor TONGER s.p. (H2794)
Uff'm Berge, Da Gehet Der Wind *Xmas
mix cor TONGER s.p. (H2795)
Vom Himmel Hoch, O Engelein, Kommt! *Xmas
mix cor TONGER s.p. (H2796)

HOLST, GUSTAV (1874-1934)
All People That On Earth Do Dwell
SATB oct STAINER 3.2154.1 $.50 (H2797)
Ave Maria
girl cor SOUTHERN $.30 (H2798)
SSSSAAAA BOSWORTH s.p. see from LAUDY
COLLECTION OF MODERN PART SONGS (H2799)
Choral Fantasia, A
4pt mix cor,pno voc sc CURWEN $1.00 (H2800)
Christmas Day *Xmas,anthem/carol
SATB BELWIN AP 34 $.75 (H2801)
mix cor,SATB soli,orch oct NOVELLO
28.0983.04 s.p., ipr (H2802)
Coming Of Christ, The *Xmas
cor,SA soli,org,pno,trp voc sc CURWEN $1.25
(H2803)
mix cor,STBarB soli,org,trp,opt pno&strings
CURWEN sc rental, voc sc rental, ipr (H2804)
Dream Of Christmas, A *Xmas
unis/2pt oct CURWEN 8792 $.25 (H2805)
Eight Canons For Equal Voices *CC8U,canon
(Leppard, Raymond) 2 eq voices/3 eq voices
opt pno voc sc FABER ED 2675 $.75 (H2806)

HOLST, GUSTAV (cont'd.)
Eternal Father
mix cor,S solo CURWEN 80658 s.p.   (H2807)
mix cor,org oct CURWEN 8510 $.30   (H2808)
Evening Watch, The
cor FABER F0004 s.p.   (H2809)
Festival Chime
SATB oct STAINER 3.2153.1 $.30   (H2810)
Gird On Thy Sword (from Man Born To Toil)
mix cor CURWEN 80657 s.p.   (H2811)
4pt mix cor,org oct CURWEN 8669 $.25   (H2812)
Heart Worships
SATB oct GALAXY 1.1409.1 $.25   (H2813)
Heart Worships, The *anthem
(Simon) SATB oct FISCHER,C CM-7362 $.25
(H2814)
How Mighty Are The Sabbaths
unis oct BOOSEY 3129 $.30   (H2815)
Hymn Of Jesus *hymn
dbl cor,orch, semi- chorus voc sc STAINER
3.2175 $2.75   (H2816)
In The Bleak Mid-Winter *Xmas
(Wood) SATB/unis,opt harp SCHMITT 6217
$.45, ipr   (H2817)
(Woodgate) 4pt men cor,acap oct CURWEN 8793
$.25   (H2818)
Intercession
boy cor SOUTHERN $.30   (H2819)
Let All Mortal Flesh Keep Silence
SSA oct GALAXY 1.2248.1 $.25   (H2820)
SATB oct STAINER 3.2309.1 $.35   (H2821)
Lord, Who Hast Made Us (Psalm 148)
mix cor SCHIRM.EC 319 $.50, ipr   (H2822)
SATB oct GALLIARD 2.9010.1 $.40   (H2823)
Lord, Who Hast Made Us For Thine Own (Psalm
143)
SSAA SCHIRM.EC 1886 $.50, ipr   (H2824)
SATB oct GALLIARD 2.9005.1 $.35   (H2825)
Lullay My Liking *Xmas,carol
4pt mix cor,acap oct CURWEN 8312 $.25
(H2826)
mix cor CURWEN 80589 s.p.   (H2827)
(Holst, Imogen) 4pt wom cor,acap oct CURWEN
11750 $.25   (H2828)
(Pierce) 4pt men cor,T/A solo,acap oct
CURWEN 11751 $.25   (H2829)
Man Born To Toil
4pt mix cor,org oct CURWEN 8509 $.25   (H2830)
mix cor CURWEN 80656 s.p.   (H2831)
O Sing, As Thrushes
mix cor CURWEN 61237 s.p.   (H2832)
Of One That Is So Fair And Bright *Xmas
mix cor CURWEN 80590 s.p.   (H2833)
Psalm 86 *see To My Humble Supplication,
Lord
Psalm 143 *see Lord, Who Hast Made Us For
Thine Own
Psalm 148 *see Lord, Who Hast Made Us
Savior Of The World Is Born, The *Xmas
SATB/unis,kbd (easy) oct CONCORDIA 98-2184
$.25   (H2834)
Short Festival Te Deum *Te Deum
SATB oct STAINER 3.2211.1 $.50   (H2835)
Sing Me The Men *Op.43,No.2
mix cor,acap oct CURWEN 11827 $.40   (H2836)
mix cor SOUTHERN $.40   (H2837)
mix cor CURWEN 61194 s.p.   (H2838)
To My Humble Supplication, Lord (Psalm 86)
mix cor SCHIRM.EC 318 $.50, ipr   (H2839)
SATB oct GALLIARD 2.9009.1 $.35   (H2840)
Turn Back O Man
SATB oct STAINER 3.2152.1 $.35   (H2841)
SA oct GALAXY 1.2212.1 $.30   (H2842)
TTBB oct GALAXY 1.1934.1 $.30   (H2843)

HOLST, IMOGEN
Out Of Your Sleep Arise And Wake *Xmas/
Easter,carol
SSATTB oct FABER 11756 $.35   (H2844)
SSATTB,acap oct SCHIRM 11756 $.35   (H2845)

HOLSTEN, MARTIN (1935-   )
Der Herr Behute Dich Vor Allem Ubel
see Holsten, Martin, Siehe, Das Ist Gottes
Lamm
Ich Liege, Herr, In Deiner Hut
see Holsten, Martin, Siehe, Das Ist Gottes
Lamm
Siehe, Das Ist Gottes Lamm
SATB HANSSLER 6.283 s.p. contains also: Ich
Liege, Herr, In Deiner Hut; Der Herr
Behute Dich Vor Allem Ubel   (H2846)
Von Guten Machten Treu Und Still Umgeben
*mot
SATB HANSSLER 7.069 s.p.   (H2847)

HOLSWORTHY BELLS see Wesley, Samuel Sebastian
Jr.

HOLT, EVELYN
Nunc Dimittis
SATB,org/pno SEESAW $1.00   (H2848)

HOLTON
Chimes Of The Holy Night *Xmas,cant
SSA oct LORENZ $1.75   (H2849)
SAB oct LORENZ $1.75   (H2850)
SATB oct LORENZ $1.95   (H2851)
SA oct LORENZ $1.75   (H2852)

HOLTON (cont'd.)
Chorus Of The Skies *Xmas,cant
SATB oct LORENZ $1.95   (H2853)
Christmas King, The *Xmas,cant
SATB oct LORENZ $1.95   (H2854)
Life Eternal *Easter,cant
SATB LORENZ $1.95   (H2855)
SSA LORENZ $1.75   (H2856)
Music Of Bethlehem, The *Xmas,cant
SATB oct LORENZ $1.95   (H2857)
SA oct LORENZ $1.75   (H2858)
SSA oct LORENZ $1.75   (H2859)
SAB oct LORENZ $1.75   (H2860)
Prince Of Peace, The *Xmas
SATB oct LORENZ A39 $.25   (H2861)
Redemption's Song *Easter,cant
SATB LORENZ $1.95   (H2862)
SAB LORENZ $1.75   (H2863)
Thorn-Crowned King *Easter,cant
SATB LORENZ $1.95   (H2864)
SAB LORENZ $1.75   (H2865)
SSA LORENZ $1.75   (H2866)
World's Redeemer, The *Xmas,cant
SATB oct LORENZ $1.95   (H2867)

HOLTZ, J.
Psalm 25
see Zwei Psalmen
Psalm 117
see Zwei Psalmen
Zwei Psalmen
[Ger] men cor,acap (med diff) HUG s.p.
contains: Psalm 25; Psalm 117   (H2868)

HOLY see Mendelssohn-Bartholdy, Felix, Heilig

HOLY AND ALL GLORIOUS see Pergolesi, Giovanni
Battista, Sanctum Et Terrible Nomen Ejus

HOLY AND BLESSED SPIRIT see Jenkins, John

HOLY AND MERCIFUL LORD see Durante, Francesco,
Misericordias Domini

HOLY ARK, TORAH SERVICE, THE see Helfman, Max

HOLY ART THOU see Bruckner, Anton

HOLY ART THOU see Handel, George Frideric

HOLY ART THOU [LARGO] see Handel, George
Frideric

HOLY BABE see Dunhill, Thomas Frederick

HOLY BIRTH, THE see Wadely, F.W.

HOLY BIRTH, THE see Morgan

HOLY BLESSED TRINITY see Tchaikovsky, Piotr
Ilyitch

HOLY BOY see Ireland, John

HOLY CHILD see Brahms, Johannes

HOLY CHILD see Martin

HOLY CHILD, THE see Adams, Thomas

HOLY CHILD IS BORN, A see Morales, Puer Natus
Est

HOLY CHILD OF BETHLEHEM *Xmas
SATB CHAPPELL 0015461-358 $.40   (H2869)

HOLY CHILD SLEEPS see Roger

HOLY CHILD, THE *Xmas
(Hruby) SATB,opt fl oct PRO ART 2687 $.30
(H2870)

HOLY CHILD, THE see Brown, E. Bouldin

HOLY CHILD, THE see Graham, Robert [V.]

HOLY CHILD, THE see Martin, Easthope

HOLY CHILD, THE see Parker, Horatio William

HOLY CHILD, THE see Young

HOLY CITY see Adams, Stephen

HOLY CITY, THE see Gaul, Alfred Robert

HOLY CITY, THE see Adams, Stephen

HOLY CITY, THE see Byrd, William, Civitas
Sancti Tui

HOLY CITY, THE see Gaul, Alfred Robert

HOLY CITY, THE see Vaughan Williams, Ralph,
Sancta Civitas

HOLY COMMUNION see Adlam, Frank

HOLY COMMUNION see Ashfield, Robert

HOLY COMMUNION see Bach

HOLY COMMUNION see Barrett-Ayres, Reginald

HOLY COMMUNION see Blake, Leonard

HOLY COMMUNION see Chambers, H.A.

HOLY COMMUNION see Dickinson, Peter

HOLY COMMUNION see Eyre, Alfred J.

HOLY COMMUNION see Gibbons, Orlando

HOLY COMMUNION see Harwood, Basil

HOLY COMMUNION see Howells, Herbert Norman

HOLY COMMUNION see Hurford, Peter

HOLY COMMUNION see Ireland, John

HOLY COMMUNION see Joubert, John

HOLY COMMUNION see Kelly, Bryan

HOLY COMMUNION see Maunder, J.H.

HOLY COMMUNION see Merbecke, John

HOLY COMMUNION see Milner, Anthony

HOLY COMMUNION see Nourse, John

HOLY COMMUNION see Proctor, Charles

HOLY COMMUNION see Ratcliffe, Desmond

HOLY COMMUNION see Shaw, Geoffrey [Turton]

HOLY COMMUNION see Shaw, Martin

HOLY COMMUNION see Smart, Henry Thomas

HOLY COMMUNION see Stanford, Charles Villiers

HOLY COMMUNION see Sumsion, Herbert

HOLY COMMUNION see Tallis, Thomas

HOLY COMMUNION see Webber, Lloyd

HOLY COMMUNION see Woodward, H.H.

HOLY COMMUNION SERVICE IN A see Rubbra, Edmund,
Missa In Honorem Sanctq Dominici

HOLY COMMUNION SERVICE IN G see Hunt, Reginald

HOLY DAY HOLLY CAROL *Xmas,carol
(Lefebvre) SSA oct GALAXY 1.1010.1 $.35
(H2871)
(Lefebvre) SATB oct GALAXY 1.0596.1 $.35
(H2872)

HOLY DAY OF DAYS see Hastings

HOLY EASTER MORN see Buck

HOLY EASTER MORNING see McFarland

HOLY EUCHARIST, THE see Harris, William Henry

HOLY FATHER see Schubert, Franz (Peter)

HOLY FATHER see Zaumeyer

HOLY FATHER, CHEER OUR WAY see Wood, John

HOLY FATHER, GREAT CREATOR see Griswold

HOLY FATHER, GREAT CREATOR see Smart

HOLY FATHER, HEAR MY CRY see Chaffin, L. G.

HOLY FESTIVAL see Beck

HOLY GHOST, DISPEL OUR SADNESS see Bach, Johann
Sebastian

HOLY GHOST, WITH LIGHT DIVINE
SATB CHAPPELL 0015479-358 $.40   (H2873)
(Davids, Dean) SATB oct BELWIN 2113 $.25
(H2874)
HOLY GHOST, WITH LIGHT DIVINE see Hillert,
Richard

HOLY GHOST! WITH LIGHT DIVINE see Kirk

HOLY GHOST, WITH LIGHT DIVINE see Warner,
Richard

HOLY GOD OF SABAOTH see Dietterich, Philip R.

HOLY, GOD OF SABAOTH see Dvorak, Antonin

HOLY GOD, WE PRAISE THY NAME
(Peloquin) SATB&cong oct SUMMY M 2267 $.45
(H2875)
HOLY GOD, WE PRAISE THY NAME see Anonymous

HOLY GOD, WE PRAISE THY NAME see Hustad, Donald
P.

HOLY GOD, WE PRAISE THY NAME see Mytych, J.F.

HOLY GOD, WE PRAISE THY NAME see Pelz, Walter
L.

HOLY GOD, WE PRAISE THY NAME see Scott

HOLY, HOLY
see Street Corner Spirituals

HOLY, HOLY see Bach, Johann Sebastian

HOLY, HOLY see Bruckner, Anton, Sanctus

HOLY, HOLY see Handel, George Frideric, Sanctus

HOLY, HOLY see Mozart, Wolfgang Amadeus,
Sanctus

HOLY, HOLY see Warren, Elinor Remick, Sanctus

HOLY, HOLY, ALMIGHTY GOD see Mozart, Wolfgang
Amadeus

HOLY, HOLY, FATHER ALMIGHTY see Handel, George
Frideric

HOLY, HOLY, HOLY
see Entrance Hymns
(Leidzen) SATB oct BOURNE 677 $.30   (H2876)

HOLY, HOLY, HOLY see Bach

HOLY, HOLY, HOLY see Beethoven, Ludwig van,
Sanctus

HOLY, HOLY, HOLY see Cassler, G. Winston

HOLY, HOLY, HOLY see Cherubini, Luigi, Sanctus

HOLY, HOLY, HOLY see Collins, R.

HOLY, HOLY, HOLY! see Dykes

HOLY, HOLY, HOLY see Dykes, John Bacchus

HOLY, HOLY, HOLY see Ehret, Walter

HOLY, HOLY, HOLY see Gabrieli, Andrea, Sanctus
And Hosanna

HOLY, HOLY, HOLY! see Glinka, Mikhail
Ivanovitch

HOLY, HOLY, HOLY see Goemanne, Noel

HOLY, HOLY, HOLY see Hager, Sister Conleth

HOLY, HOLY, HOLY see Handel, George Frideric

HOLY, HOLY, HOLY see Haydn, (Franz) Joseph

HOLY, HOLY, HOLY see Hoddinott, Alun

HOLY, HOLY, HOLY see Klein, M.

HOLY, HOLY, HOLY see Lotti, Antonio, Sanctus

HOLY, HOLY, HOLY see Matesky, T.

HOLY, HOLY, HOLY see Mendelssohn-Bartholdy,
Felix

HOLY, HOLY, HOLY see Mozart, Wolfgang Amadeus,
Sanctus

HOLY, HOLY, HOLY see Palestrina, Giovanni

HOLY, HOLY, HOLY see Rasley

HOLY, HOLY, HOLY see Scarlatti, Alessandro,
Sanctus

HOLY, HOLY, HOLY see Scarlatti, Domenico

HOLY, HOLY, HOLY see Schubert, Franz (Peter),
Heilig, Heilig, Heilig

HOLY, HOLY, HOLY see Schubert, Franz (Peter),
Sanctus

HOLY, HOLY, HOLY see Spicker, M., Kedushah

HOLY, HOLY, HOLY see Tchaikovsky, Piotr Ilyitch

HOLY, HOLY, HOLY see Thompson, Randall, Sanctus

HOLY, HOLY, HOLY see Tomkins, Thomas

HOLY, HOLY, HOLY see Victoria, Tomas Luis de,
Sanctus

HOLY, HOLY, HOLY see Walter, Samuel

HOLY, HOLY, HOLY see Warren, Raymond

HOLY, HOLY, HOLY IS THE LORD see Willan, Healey

HOLY, HOLY, HOLY LORD see Worthing, Richard

HOLY, HOLY, HOLY LORD GOD ALMIGHTY see Stewart,
Humphrey John

HOLY, HOLY, HOLY! LORD GOD ALMIGHTY see
Tchaikovsky, Piotr Ilyitch

HOLY, HOLY, HOLY, LORD GOD ALMIGHTY see Wolff,
S. Drummond

HOLY, HOLY, HOSANNA IN THE HIGHEST see
Lundquist

HOLY, HOLY, LORD see Gounod, Charles Francois

HOLY, HOLY, LORD GOD ALMIGHTY see Gounod,
Charles Francois

HOLY, HOLY, LORD GOD ALMIGHTY see Handel,
George Frideric

HOLY, HOLY LORD GOD OF HOSTS see Cherubini,
Luigi

HOLY HOUR, THE see Nevin

HOLY INFANT, LOWLY INFANT see Bragg

HOLY INFANT LYING LOWLY see Kountz

HOLY INFANT LYING LOWLY see Kountz

HOLY INFANT OF BETHLEHEM see McAfee

HOLY INFANT REST YOUR HEAD see Ridgeway

HOLY INFANT, SO TENDER AND MILD see Thomson,
Virgil

HOLY INFANT, THE see Bullard, Frederick Field

HOLY INFANT'S LULLABY see Dello Joio, Norman

HOLY INFANT'S LULLABY, THE see Dello Joio,
Norman

HOLY INNOCENTS see Clemens, Jacobus, Vox In
Rama Audita Est

HOLY IS GOD see Bach, Karl Philipp Emanuel,
Heilig

HOLY IS GOD THE LORD see Mendelssohn-Bartholdy,
Felix

HOLY IS GOD THE LORD (ISAIAH, MIGHTY SEER) see
Bunjes, Paul G.

HOLY IS THE ALMIGHTY see Neukomm, Sigismund
Rittervon

HOLY IS THE LORD see Hammerschmidt, Andreas,
Heilig Ist Der Herr

HOLY IS THE LORD see Naumann, Johann Gottlieb,
Sanctus Et Osanna

HOLY IS THE LORD see Schubert, Franz (Peter),
Sanctus

HOLY IS THE LORD, OUR GOD see Vogler

HOLY IS THE TRUE LIGHT see Harris, William
Henry

HOLY IS THY NAME, O LORD see Vogler, Georg
Joseph

HOLY LAMB OF GOD see Mozart, Wolfgang Amadeus

HOLY, LORD GOD see Cain, Noble

HOLY LORD GOD OF HOSTS see Jolley

HOLY LORD GOD OF HOSTS see Young

HOLY LORD, GOD OF ISRAEL see Hummel

HOLY LORD, GOD OF NATIONS see Victoria, Tomas
Luis de

HOLY LORD OF ALL see Isalaw

HOLY, LORD OF HOSTS see Posegate, Maxcine W.

HOLY LORD OF HOSTS see Tchaikovsky, Piotr
Ilyitch

HOLY LORD OF SABAOTH
(Cornwall, J.S.) SSAATTBB PIONEER 5059 $.25
(H2877)
HOLY, LOVING FATHER see Palestrina, Giovanni,
Dei Mater Alma

HOLY MANNA *Gen
(Staton) SAB SCHMITT 5539 $.35   (H2878)

HOLY MORN see Bach

HOLY MOSES! see Hazell, Chris

HOLY MOUNTAIN, THE see Joubert, John

HOLY MOUNTAIN, THE see Davis, Katherine K.

HOLY NIGHT *Xmas,folk
(Roberton) unis jr cor/unis wom cor ROBERTON
71971 s.p.   (H2879)
(Roberton) 2pt jr cor/2pt wom cor ROBERTON
71972 s.p.   (H2880)
(Robinson, Stanford) mix cor CURWEN 61355
s.p.   (H2881)

HOLY NIGHT see Brahms, Johannes

HOLY NIGHT see Gruber, Franz Xaver

HOLY NIGHT! see Schroth

HOLY NIGHT, PEACEFUL NIGHT *carol,Ger
(Hirsch, C.) SATB,opt pno (easy) oct WILLIS
1408 $.10   (H2882)

HOLY NIGHT! PEACEFUL NIGHT! see Hawley

HOLY NIGHT! PEACEFUL NIGHT! see Hawley,
[Charles Beach]

HOLY NIGHT, THE *CC7UL,Xmas,Bibl/medley
(Besig) SATB PRO ART 490 $.75   (H2883)

HOLY NIGHT, THE see Brewer, John Hyatt

HOLY OF HOLIES, THE see Werther, R.T.

HOLY OFFERINGS RICH AND RARE see Redhead,
[Richard]

HOLY, RADIANT LIGHT see Gretchaninov, Alexander
Tikhonovitch

HOLY REDEEMER see Arcadelt, Jacob

HOLY REDEEMER! BE THY REST MOST GLORIOUS see
Latrobe

HOLY SABBATH, THE see Helfman, Max, Shabbat
Kodesh

HOLY SAVIOUR GRANT THY MERCY see Shelley

HOLY SAVIOUR, IN THY KEEPING see Marryott,
Ralph E.

HOLY SON, THE see Hurford, Peter

HOLY SPIRIT, COME, O COME see Martin

HOLY SPIRIT, DON'T YOU LEAVE ME see Still,
William Grant

HOLY SPIRIT, EVER DWELLING see Howells, Herbert
Norman

HOLY SPIRIT, HEAR US see Roff, Joseph

HOLY SPIRIT, HEAR US see Willan, Healey

HOLY SPIRIT, LORD OF GLORY see Victoria, Tomas
Luis de

HOLY SPIRIT, TRUTH DIVINE see Brandon

HOLY SPIRIT, TRUTH DIVINE see Robson, R. Walker

HOLY SPIRIT, TRUTH DIVINE see Williams

HOLY SPIRIT, TRUTH DIVINE see York, D.

HOLY STILLNESS, A see Ream, Albert

HOLY TEN COMMANDMENTS, THE see Haydn, (Franz)
Joseph

HOLY TRINITY see Ammann, Benno, Sancta Trinitas

HOLY TRINITY see Fevin, Antoine de, Sancta
Trinitas

HOLY VALLEY see Ahrold, Frank

HOLZWORTH, A.
More Love O Christ, To Thee
SATB,SAB soli,pno (easy) oct WILLIS 3828
$.15   (H2884)

HOMAGE A RAMEAU see Barraud, Henry, Pange
Lingua

HOMER, SIDNEY (1864-1953)
Sheep And Lambs
(Deis) 4pt mix cor oct SCHIRM.G 7310 $.30
(H2885)

HOMILIUS, GOTTFRIED AUGUST (1714-1785)
Deo Dicamus Gratias
"Herre, Var Gud, Vi Tacka Dig" 6pt mix cor
NORDISKA 2544 s.p.   (H2886)

Deo Dicamus Gratias *see Herre, Var Gud, Vi
Tacka Dig

Domine, Ad Adjuvandum Me *mot
(Berger) SSATBB HANSSLER 1.034 s.p. (H2887)

Herre, Var Gud, Vi Tacka Dig
"Deo Dicamus Gratias" [Lat/Swed] 6pt,acap
GEHRMANS KRB 148A   (H2888)
(Ahlen, David) "Deo Dicamus Gratias" [Lat/
Swed] SATB,acap GEHRMANS KRB 148B (H2889)

Herre, Var Gud, Vi Tacka Dig *see Deo
Dicamus Gratias

I Will Rejoice In The Lord *see Ich Freue
Mich Im Herrn

Ich Freue Mich Im Herrn
(Kaplan) mix cor SOUTHERN $.35   (H2890)
(Kaplan) "I Will Rejoice In The Lord" [Eng/
Ger] SATB,acap oct LAWSON 51456 $.35
(H2891)
(Kaplan) "I Will Rejoice In The Lord" SATB,
acap SOUTHERN $.35   (H2892)

HOMMAGE A HEINRICH SCHUETZ see Kelemen, Milko

HONEGGER, ARTHUR (1892-1955)
Amphion
[Eng/Fr/Ger] cor,5 soli,narrator,orch voc
sc SALABERT-US $13.00   (H2893)

Cantique De Paques *Easter
[Fr] wom cor,soli,orch SALABERT-US voc sc
$5.25, cor pts $.65   (H2894)

Cris Du Monde *ora
[Fr/Ger] cor,SABar soli,orch SALABERT-US
voc sc $25.00, cor pts $2.25   (H2895)

Jeanne D'Arc Au Bucher *ora
[Eng/Fr/Ger] SATB&boy cor,SSATB,high solo,5
narrators SALABERT-US voc sc $32.00, cor
pts $2.25   (H2896)

King David *see Le Roi David

Le Roi David *ora
"King David" 1665 cor pts SCHIRM.EC 1666
$8.00, study sc SCHIRM.EC 1402 $2.00,
SCHIRM.EC $8.00   (H2897)
"King David" [Fr/Ger] SATB,narrator&SAT
soli,orch voc sc CHESTER s.p.   (H2898)
"King David" [Eng] SATB,narrator&SAT soli,
orch cor pts CHESTER s.p.   (H2899)
"King David" [Eng] SATB,narrator&SAT soli,
orch cor pts CHESTER s.p.   (H2900)
"King David" SATB,narrator voc sc 2707 cor
pts SCHIRM.EC 1666 $8.00, study sc
SCHIRM.EC 1402 $2.00, SCHIRM.EC $8.00   (H2901)
"King David" [Fr/Ger/Eng] SATB cor pts
SCHIRM.EC 1666 $2.00, ipr   (H2902)
"King David" [Fr/Ger/Eng] SATB voc sc
SCHIRM.EC 1665 $8.00, ipr   (H2903)
"King David" SATB min sc SCHIRM.EC 1402
$8.00, ipr   (H2904)
"King David" [Fr/Eng] (narrator's part)
SCHIRM.EC 2707 $1.00, ipr   (H2905)

Une Cantate De Noel *Xmas,cant
[Eng/Fr/Ger] cor&jr cor,Bar solo,org,orch
SALABERT-US voc sc $13.50, cor pts $1.50
(H2906)

HONEGGER, E.
Herr Schicke Was Du Willst *prayer
(Morike) [Ger] wom cor,acap (med easy) HUG
s.p.   (H2907)

HONEY, HENRY
Shepherd's Noel, The *Xmas
2pt jr cor/2pt wom cor CURWEN 72570 s.p.
(H2908)
Shepherd's Noel, The *Xmas
2pt wom cor oct CURWEN 11277 $.25 (H2909)

HONEY IN THE ROCK see Graves

HONOM TILLHOR ARAN see Olsen, Daniel

HONOR AND GLORY see Bach, Johann Sebastian

HONOR AND GLORY see Vivaldi, Antonio, Domine
Fili Unigenite

HONOR AND PRAISE see Davis, Katherine K.

HONOR HIM, ALLELUIA see Lehmeier, J.F.

HONOR HIM OUR KING see Darst, W. Glenn

HONOR! HONOR! see Johnson, Hall

HONOR, PRAISE AND GLORY see Praetorius, Michael

HONOR THY FATHER AND THY MOTHER see Thorton

HONOUR A PHYSICIAN see Thalben-Ball, George
[Thomas]

HONUM EST CONFITERI DOMINO see Vranken, Alph.

HOOD, BOYDE W.
Gloria! Sing Gloria! *Xmas
SATB SCHMITT 863 $.30   (H2910)
SSAA SCHMITT 329 $.25   (H2911)

HOOGERWERF, N.
Aan Bethlehem's Poorte *Xmas
men cor ALSBACH&D sc s.p., cor pts s.p.
(H2912)
Dit Is De Dag *see Haec Dies

Haec Dies
"Dit Is De Dag" men cor ALSBACH&D sc s.p.,
cor pts s.p.   (H2913)

HOOGERWERF, N. (cont'd.)
Hymne
mix cor ALSBACH&D sc s.p., cor pts s.p.
(H2914)

Invocatio
mix cor ALSBACH&D sc s.p., cor pts s.p.
(H2915)

Sanctus *Sanctus
mix cor ALSBACH&D sc s.p., cor pts s.p.
(H2916)

HOOPER
Jubilee
SATB,opt orch FISCHER,C O-4841 $2.00, ipr
(H2917)

Litany Of Praise
2pt oct FISCHER,C O-4881 $1.50 (H2918)

My Soul Waiteth In Silence
SATB,acap (med diff/diff) SOUTHERN $.35
(H2919)
SATB SOUTHERN $.35   (H2920)
SATB oct FISCHER,C CM-7785 $.35 (H2921)

HOOPER, EDMUND (ca. 1553-1621)
Behold It Is Christ *anthem
(Le Huray) SAATB SCHOTT s.p.   (H2922)

Evening Service For Verses *Eve
SSAATB (med) oct OXFORD 42.855 $1.30
(H2923)
"Short" Evening Service, The *Eve,Magnif/
Nunc
SAATB,opt inst (med) oct OXFORD 43.385 $.65
(H2924)
Teach Me Thy Way, O Lord *Adv/Gen/Sexa
(Shaw, Watkins) SATB,acap (easy) oct OXFORD
43.344 $.30   (H2925)

HOOPER, WILLIAM L.
Now Praise We Christ, The Holy One *anthem
SATB (easy) oct AUGSBURG 1345 $.25 (H2926)

We Shall Walk Through The Valley In Peace
*folk/hymn,US
SATB oct WALTON 2085 $.25 (H2927)

HOPE see Humphreys, Don

HOPE AND LIGHT OF MAN'S ENDEAVOUR see Bach,
Johann Sebastian, Jesus Bleibet Meine
Freude

HOPE AND PRAY see Young, Peter

HOPE OF THE WORLD see Copes, V. Earle

HOPE OF THE WORLD see Schnecker, P.

HOPE OF THE WORLD see Wetherill

HOPE OF THE WORLD see Wetzler, Robert

HOPE THOU IN GOD see Mendelssohn-Bartholdy,
Felix

HOPE THOU IN GOD see Williams

HOPE THOU IN GOD [LARGO] see Handel, George
Frideric

HOPESON
Almighty God, Ever Blessed
SATB oct PLYMOUTH PCS-45 $.25 (H2928)

Come Ye That Love The Lord
SATB oct PRO ART 2508 $.25 (H2929)

HOPKINS
Alleluia!Alleluia! *Easter
SATB oct VOLKWEIN VB102 $.25 (H2930)

Babe In Bethlehem's Manger Laid *Xmas
SATB oct VOLKWEIN VB109 $.25 (H2931)

Be Known To Us In Breaking Bread *Commun
SATB oct VOLKWEIN VB112 $.30 (H2932)

Beatitudes *Bibl
SATB oct VOLKWEIN VB110 $.30 (H2933)

By Babel's Stream We Sat And Wept (Psalm 137)
*Bibl
SATB oct VOLKWEIN VB122 $.25 (H2934)

Christmas Comes Again *Xmas
SA oct BELWIN 1886 $.30 (H2935)

Come, Thou Long Expected Jesus
SATB oct VOLKWEIN VB137 $.25 (H2936)

How Long Wilt Thou Forget Me
SATB oct VOLKWEIN VB173 $.25 (H2937)

Hymn Of Progress
SATB oct FISCHER,C CM-7796 $.30 (H2938)

I Love Thy Kingdom Lord
SATB oct VOLKWEIN VB180 $.25 (H2939)

I Waited For The Lord
SATB oct VOLKWEIN VB192 $.25 (H2940)

Lead Us, O Father
(Wiley) SATB oct PRO ART 1872 $.25 (H2941)

Let Us Go Now Into Bethlehem *Xmas
SATB ALLANS 318 s.p. (H2942)

Lift Up Your Heads *Easter
SATB (easy) ALLANS 54 s.p. (H2943)

Lord Almighty Is My Light
SATB oct VOLKWEIN VB702 $.30 (H2944)

Lord, Hear Me In My Distress *prayer
SATB oct VOLKWEIN VB209 $.25 (H2945)

Lullaby, Lullaby, Lu *cradle
SATB oct VOLKWEIN VB713 $.30 (H2946)

O God, Our Help In Ages Past
SATB oct VOLKWEIN VB223 $.25 (H2947)

O Wherefore Do The Nations Rage
SATB oct VOLKWEIN VB238 $.25 (H2948)

HOPKINS (cont'd.)
Psalm 96 *see Sing To The Lord

Psalm 137 *see By Babel's Stream We Sat And
Wept

Psalm 148 *Bibl
SATB oct VOLKWEIN VB247 $.30 (H2949)

Shepherd Of Tender Youth
SATB oct VOLKWEIN VB256 $.25 (H2950)

Shepherds Of Tender Youth
SSA oct VOLKWEIN VB256 $.25 (H2951)

Sing To The Lord (Psalm 96)
SATB oct VOLKWEIN VB257 $.25 (H2952)

Throned Upon The Awful Tree *Gd.Fri./Psntd
SATB oct VOLKWEIN VB271 $.25 (H2953)

Thy Kingdom Come *anthem
(Cassler) SATB (easy) oct AUGSBURG 1246
$.22 (H2954)

HOPKINS, ANTHONY (1921-   )
Carillon (Gloria In Excelsis Deo) *anthem
[Eng/Lat] SATB&SATB CHESTER s.p. (H2955)

Lord, As That Hart Which Water Wants (Psalm
42) anthem
[Eng] SATB,org CHESTER s.p. (H2956)

Magnificat And Nunc Dimittis *Magnif/Nunc
[Lat] SSAA,org CHESTER s.p. (H2957)

Psalm 42 *see Lord, As That Hart Which Water
Wants

HOPKINS, H.
When The Infant Jesus *Xmas
SAB oct PRESSER 312-21450 $.25 (H2958)

HOPKINS, JOHN L.
Lift Up Your Heads *Adv/Gen,anthem/Bibl
mix cor oct NOVELLO 28.0018.07 s.p. (H2959)
(Downing) 2pt boy cor/2pt wom cor oct
SCHIRM.G 7952 $.25 (H2960)
(Downing) 4pt mix cor oct SCHIRM.G 4496
$.25 (H2961)

HOPKINS, PAUL
Service Responses (Set 1) *CCU
SATB FOSTER MF 201 $.25 (H2962)

HOPKINSON, [FRANCIS] (1737-1791)
Psalm 23
(Young, R.; Weinandt, E.) SATB oct FISCHER,
J 10003 $.30 (H2963)

HOPPAS PA HERREN, ISRAEL see Carlstedt,
Gunnemer

HOPSON
Break Forth Unto Joy
SATB oct SACRED S-105 $.35 (H2964)

Canticle Of Praise
SATB SHAWNEE A 990 $.30 (H2965)

Creation Speaks That God Is Here
SAB FLAMMER D5212 $.30 (H2966)

God Is Our Refuge, God Is Our Strength (Psalm
46)
SATB&speak cor&opt cong WARNER WB-181 $.40
(H2967)

Make A Joyful Noise
SATB oct SACRED S-125 $.35 (H2968)

O Clap Your Hands
SATB FLAMMER A 5594 $.30 (H2969)

O Jesus, Prince Of Peace
SATB oct PLYMOUTH SC-29 $.25 (H2970)

O Lord, Our Lord, Majestic Is Thy Name
SA/TB FLAMMER E5152 $.30 (H2971)

Prayer For Our Time
SATB FLAMMER A 5613 $.30 (H2972)

Prayer Of The Christmas Animals
SA/TB FLAMMER E5151 $.30 (H2973)

Psalm 46 *see God Is Our Refuge, God Is Our
Strength

Sing To The Lord A Joyful Song
unis FLAMMER FA5001 $.30 (H2974)

HOPSON, HAL H.
Gift Of Love, The
2pt oct AGAPE CF 148 $.30 (H2975)

Praise The Lord!
SAB/SATB oct WORD CS-2529 $.35 (H2976)

Psalm Of Praise, A *Easter
SA/TB (easy) PRESSER G-194 $.35 (H2977)

Teach Us, Good Lord
SA/unis oct WORD CS-2545 $.25 (H2978)

HOR, BRUDER, WAS KUNDET DER ENGEL see Trust,
Heinz-Ewald

HOR LE TUE FORZE ADOPRA see Anerio, Felice

HOR MEIN BITTEN, HERR see Mendelssohn-
Bartholdy, Felix

HOR OSS SVEA see Wennerberg, Gunnar

HOR PA MEG, MITT FOLK see Hovland, Egil

HORA EUCARISTICA see Rodella, Sante

HORA NOVISSIMA see Parker, Horatio William

HORBE, ERNST
Ich Ruf Zu Dir, Herr Jesu Christ
see Kretzschmar, Gunther, Nun Danket All
Und Bringet Ehr

Lobet Den Herren Alle, Die Ihn Ehren
see Kretzschmar, Gunther, Jauchzet Dem
Herrn

HORCH, WIE UBERS WASSER HALLEND see Kampf, [Karl]

HORDER, MERVYN
Bread Of The World *Commun
SATB (easy) ABINGDON APM-434 $.25   (H2979)

HORE GOTT, MEIN SCHREIEN see Zentner, Johannes

HORE, HERR, HORE MEINE WORTE see Rohwer, Jens

HORE MICH, HERR, BEI DEN TOTEN GEDENKT MAN DEINER NICHT see Schutz, Heinrich, Quoniam Non Est In Morte

HORER DU ROSTEN see Aagaard, Thomas

HORN, PAUL (1922-)
Frohlich Soll Mein Herze Springen *cant
SB,org,vln HANSSLER 10.110 sc s.p., voc sc s.p., ipa   (H2980)

Gottes Sohn Ist Kommen Uns Allen
unis/SATB/SSB/SS/TT,org&opt trp/2vln
HANSSLER 8.011 s.p.   (H2981)

Mit Freuden Zart Zu Dieser Fahrt *cant
SATB,cont,2vln HANSSLER 10.057 sc s.p., voc sc s.p., ipa   (H2982)

Nun Danket All Und Bringet Ehr *cant
see Schutz, Heinrich, Lasst Uns Den Herren Loben
SAB,cont,2vln,vla HANSSLER 10.056 sc s.p., voc sc s.p., ipa   (H2983)

Nun Jauchzt Dem Herren, Alle Welt *cant
SATB HANSSLER 6.298 s.p.   (H2984)
SATB,cont,2vln HANSSLER 10.055 sc s.p., voc sc s.p., ipa   (H2985)

Nun Lob, Mein Seel, Den Herren *cant
SATB,cont,3vln,vla HANSSLER 10.054 sc s.p., voc sc s.p., ipa   (H2986)

O Durchbrecher Aller Bande
unis/SATB/SSB/SS/TT,org&opt trp/2vln
HANSSLER 8.010 s.p.   (H2987)

Singt Dem Herrn Ein Neues Lied *cant
3 eq voices,org,2vln,vcl HANSSLER 10.180 sc s.p., voc sc s.p., ipa   (H2988)

Sonne Der Gerechtigkeit *cant
SATB,org,4brass HANSSLER 10.006 sc s.p., cor pts s.p., ipa, voc sc s.p.   (H2989)

Wie Soll Ich Dich Empfangen *cant
SATB,cont,2trp HANSSLER 10.088 sc s.p., voc sc s.p., ipa   (H2990)

Wir Danken Dir, Herr Jesu Christ *Easter, cant
SATB,org,4brass HANSSLER 1.0010 cor pts s.p., voc sc s.p., ipa   (H2991)

HORNIBROOK
Immortal, Invisible
SSAB SHAWNEE D51 $.25   (H2992)

Jesus Walked This Lonesome Valley
SATB FLAMMER A 5609 $.30   (H2993)

Once To Every Man And Nation
SATB SHAWNEE A 736 $.30   (H2994)

We Gather Together
SATB SHAWNEE A 598 $.30   (H2995)

HORROCKS
Everyone Sang
SAATTB,acap (med) OXFORD 84.009 $.30   (H2996)

HORSCHELMANN, OTTMAR
In Stiller Nacht Zur Ersten Wacht *Psntd
SATB HANSSLER 6.2508 s.p.   (H2997)

HORST, ANTHON VAN DER (1899-1965)
Choros III, Psalmus 45 (Psalm 45) Op.72a
[Dut] mix cor,org sc DONEMUS s.p.   (H2998)

Choros VII *Op.80, Bibl
[Dut] mix cor,Bar solo,org sc DONEMUS s.p.   (H2999)

Psalm 45 *see Choros III, Psalmus 45

Twee Fragmenten Uit Het Hooglied *Op.8a
[Dut] wom cor,fl,horn ALSBACH   (H3000)

HORT DIE BOTSCHAFT see Gerhold, Norbert, Way In The Heaven Bye And Bye

HORT DOCH, LIEBE BRUDER *Xmas,Eur/Slav
(Doppelbauer, Josef Friedrich) mix cor,acap DOBLINGER s.p. see from Da Der Herr Geboren   (H3001)

HORT, EINE HELLE STIMME ERKLINGT see Stier, Alfred

HORT, WEN JESUS GLUCKLICH PREIST see Fisher

HORT ZU, IHR LIEBEN LEUTE see Praetorius, Michael

HORTON
Salvation To Our God *Gen
SATB SCHMITT 1757 $.30   (H3002)

Song Of The Lamb, The *Gen
SATB,opt inst SCHMITT 8010 $.22, ipa   (H3003)

HORTON, [LEWIS HENRY] (1898-)
Applachian Nativity, An *Xmas,cant
BELWIN $1.75   (H3004)

HORTON, WILLIAM
How Excellent Is Thy Name
SATB oct WALTON 2080 $.25   (H3005)

HOSANNA *chorale
(Thompson, Ronald) SA oct BELWIN 1895 $.25   (H3006)

HOSANNA see Alexander, Josef

HOSANNA see Brandt

HOSANNA see Christiansen, F. Melius

HOSANNA see DePue

HOSANNA see Dykes

HOSANNA see Fetler, Paul

HOSANNA see Giannini, V.

HOSANNA see Grainer, J.

HOSANNA see Granier, J.

HOSANNA see Gregor

HOSANNA! see Gregor, [Christian Friedrich]

HOSANNA see Jones

HOSANNA see Lockwood, Normand

HOSANNA see Mozart, Wolfgang Amadeus

HOSANNA see Nelson, Ronald A.

HOSANNA see Newbury, Kent A.

HOSANNA see Nolte

HOSANNA see Pooler, Marie

HOSANNA see Posegate

HOSANNA see Rhoden, D.C.

HOSANNA see Thompson, Randall

HOSANNA see Whear, Paul William

HOSANNA see Williams, D.

HOSANNA BE THE CHILDREN'S SONG see Rawls

HOSANNA BE THE CHILDREN'S SONG see Wienhorst, Richard

HOSANNA, BLESSED IS HE see Johnston

HOSANNA, BLESSED IS HE see Marryott, Ralph E.

HOSANNA! BLESSED IS HE see Nystedt, Knut

HOSANNA, BLESSED IS HE see Sydow

HOSANNA! BLESSED IS HE THAT COMES see Gregor

HOSANNA! BLESSED IS HE THAT COMES see Gregor, [Christian Friedrich]

HOSANNA, BLESSED IS HE THAT COMETH see Hedges

HOSANNA, DAVID'S SON! see Jommelli, Niccolo

HOSANNA FILIO DAVID see Busser, [Henri-Paul]

HOSANNA! HOSANNA! see Emig, Lois

HOSANNA! HOSANNA! see Rogers

HOSANNA IN EXCELSIS see Pergolesi, Giovanni Battista

HOSANNA IN EXCELSIS see Soderman, (Johan) August

HOSANNA IN EXCELSIS DEO see Gounod, Charles Francois

HOSANNA IN THE HIGHEST! see McClure

HOSANNA IN THE HIGHEST see Palestrina, Giovanni

HOSANNA IN THE HIGHEST see Scull, Harold [Thomas]

HOSANNA IN THE HIGHEST see Soderman, (Johan) August, Hosanna In Excelsis

HOSANNA IN THE HIGHEST see Wooler, A.

HOSANNA, LORD see Clokey

HOSANNA, LOUD HOSANNA see Cain, Noble

HOSANNA, LOUD HOSANNA see Darst, W. Glenn

HOSANNA, LOUD HOSANNA see Ferguson

HOSANNA, LOUD HOSANNA! see Hadler

HOSANNA, LOUD HOSANNA see Smith

HOSANNA, LOUD HOSANNA see Wilson, John F.

HOSANNA LOUD HOSANNA see Wolff

HOSANNA! MUSIC IS DIVINE see Spedding, Frank

HOSANNA NOW THROUGH ADVENT see Moschetti, [Giuseppe]

HOSANNA NOW THROUGH ADVENT see Pooler, Marie

HOSANNA! O BLESSED IS HE see Nelson, Ronald A.

HOSANNA SINGT DEM SOHNE DAVIDS see Gibbons, Orlando

HOSANNA, SON OF DAVID see Sateren, Leland Bernhard

HOSANNA THE SON OF DAVID see Moe, Daniel

HOSANNA TO OUR KING see White, John

HOSANNA TO THE KING see Emig, Lois

HOSANNA TO THE LIVING GOD see Eccard, Johannes

HOSANNA TO THE LIVING LORD see Bach, Johann Sebastian

HOSANNA TO THE LIVING LORD! see Litten, Jack

HOSANNA TO THE LIVING LORD see Thompson

HOSANNA TO THE LIVING LORD see Willan, Healey

HOSANNA TO THE SON OF DAVID see Bender, Jan

HOSANNA TO THE SON OF DAVID see Diemente, Edward

HOSANNA TO THE SON OF DAVID see Gesius, Bartholomaus

HOSANNA TO THE SON OF DAVID see Gibbons, Orlando

HOSANNA TO THE SON OF DAVID see Hannahs, Roger

HOSANNA TO THE SON OF DAVID see Harris

HOSANNA TO THE SON OF DAVID see Hurley

HOSANNA TO THE SON OF DAVID see Hutchings, Arthur

HOSANNA TO THE SON OF DAVID see Kirk

HOSANNA TO THE SON OF DAVID see Kirk, Theron W.

HOSANNA TO THE SON OF DAVID see Moe, Daniel

HOSANNA TO THE SON OF DAVID see Nelson

HOSANNA TO THE SON OF DAVID see Nelson, Ronald A.

HOSANNA TO THE SON OF DAVID! see Praetorius, Michael, Hosianna In Der Hohe Dem Sohne Davids

HOSANNA TO THE SON OF DAVID see Scheidt, Samuel, Hosianna Filio David

HOSANNA TO THE SON OF DAVID see Titcomb, Everett

HOSANNA TO THE SON OF DAVID see Victoria, Tomas Luis de, Pueri Hebraeorum

HOSANNA TO THE SON OF DAVID see Weelkes, Thomas

HOSANNA TO THE SON OF DAVID see Willan, Healey

HOSANNA TO THE SON OF DAVIS see Sullivan, Sir Arthur Seymour

HOSANNA UNTO DAVID'S SON see Victoria, Tomas Luis de, Pueri Hebraeorum

HOSANNA WE SING see Dykes

HOSANNA, WE SING see Jones, Marjorie

HOSANNAH TO THE SON OF DAVID see Gibbons, Orlando

HOSEA - COME, AND LET US RETURN UNTO THE LORD see Demarest, A.

HOSIANNA *Xmas,hymn
see Frojda Dig O Kristenhet
(Lundvik, Hildor) men cor NORDISKA 1170 s.p. see from Julhymner   (H3007)

HOSIANNA see Franck, Melchior

HOSIANNA! see Gearhart

HOSIANNA see Rosenquist, Carl E.

HOSIANNA see Volger, Abbe

HOSIANNA, DAVIDS SOHN see Bach, Johann Sebastian

HOSIANNA, DAVIDS SOHN, LOB SEI DEM see Victoria, Tomas Luis de

HOSIANNA, DAVIDS SON see Nilsson, Torsten

HOSIANNA, DAVIDS SON see Victoria, Tomas Luis de

HOSIANNA, DEM SOHNE see Scheidt, Samuel, Hosianna, Filio David

HOSIANNA DEM SOHNE DAVID see Grimm, Heinrich

HOSIANNA DEM SOHNE DAVID see Telemann, Georg Philipp

HOSIANNA DEM SOHNE DAVIDS see Driessler, Johannes

HOSIANNA, DEM SOHNE DAVIDS see Raselius, Andreas

HOSIANNA, DEM SOHNE DAVIDS see Selle, Thomas

HOSIANNA DEM SOHNE DAVIDS see Tunder, Franz

HOSIANNA FILIO DAVID see Scheidt, Samuel

HOSIANNA, GELOBT SEI, DE DA KOMMT see Nagler, F.

HOSIANNA! GELOBT SEI, DER DA KOMMT see Driessler, Johannes

HOSIANNA I DET HOYESTE see Hovland, Egil

HOSIANNA IN DER HOHE DEM SOHNE DAVIDS see Praetorius, Michael

HOSIANNA TIL SONN AV DAVID see Slogedal, Bjarne

HOSIANNA, VOGLER *Xmas,hymn
(Wikander, David) mix cor,org NORDISKA 947 s.p.   (H3008)

HOSKINS
I Know The Secret Of His Rest
SATB oct MCA   (H3009)

HOSPODI POMILOI see Slvovsky

HOSPODI POMILUI see Ludusky

HOSPODI POMILUI see Lvov

HOSPODI POMILUI see Lvovsky

HOSPODI POMILUI see Lvovsky, F.V.

HOSPODI POMILUI see Lvovsky, S.

HOSTPSALM see Lindroth, Henry

HOU! DE L'OUSTAU see Saboly, Nicholas

HOUDY
Sainte-Anne-La-Palud
[Fr] SATB cor pts LEDUC s.p. (H3010)

HOUGE
I Himmelen
[Norw] 2pt wom cor/2pt jr cor,S solo LYCHE 59 s.p. (H3011)
Jubilate
[Norw] men cor LYCHE 47 s.p. see from LAT (H3012)
O Store Gud Vi Lover Deg (from Koralkantaten)
[Norw] cor,org LYCHE 4 s.p. (H3013)

HOUND OF HEAVEN, THE see Jacobson, Maurice

HOUR COMETH, THE see Davies, Henry Walford

HOURDEAUX
Doubting Thomas
(McCarthy; Vic) SATB oct BOURNE 887 $.40 (H3014)
It Is A Great Day Of Joy *fugue
(McCarthy; Vic) SATB (prepack, 25 copies) oct BOURNE 885 $12.50 (H3015)
It Is Not Too Late
(McCarthy; Vic) SATB oct BOURNE 890 $.40 (H3016)
Judas, Why?
(McCarthy; Vic) SATB oct BOURNE 895 $.40 (H3017)
Now He Is Born
(McCarthy; Vic) SATB oct BOURNE 888 $.50 (H3018)
On The Mount Of Olive Groves
(McCarthy; Vic) SATB oct BOURNE 889 $.40 (H3019)
Peter, Peter Hear Me
(McCarthy; Vic) SATB oct BOURNE 893 $.40 (H3020)
St.John, The Evangelist
(McCarthy; Vic) SATB oct BOURNE 894 $.40 (H3021)
They Cast Their Nets
(McCarthy; Vic) SATB oct BOURNE 896 $.50 (H3022)
'Tis Christmas This Night
(McCarthy; Vic) SATB oct BOURNE 891 $.50 (H3023)
What Miracles Of Beauty
(McCarthy; Vic) SATB oct BOURNE 892 $.40 (H3024)
Whither Bound, St. James
(McCarthy; Vic) SATB oct BOURNE 886 $.35 (H3025)

HOUSE
God Of The Wilderness
SATB KJOS 5498 $.30 (H3026)

HOUSE IN WHICH I DWELL, THE see Lovelace, Austin C.

HOUSE, L. MARGUERITE
I Never Knew How Great My Lord Could Be
SATB oct BOURNE 780 $.25 (H3027)

HOUSE, M.
Recuerdo
SATB,pno oct FOX UM133 $.35 (H3028)

HOUSE OF DAVID, THE *Adv,carol,It,17th cent
(Glaser, V.) SATB,acap SCHIRM.EC 2489 $.25 (H3029)

HOUSE OF GOD, THE see Lovelace, Austin C.

HOUSE OF GOD, THE see Maslen, Benjamin J.

HOUSE OF PRAYER, THE see Harding, G.P.

HOUSE OF THE LORD, THE see Elliott

HOUSE OF THE LORD, THE see Young, Gordon

HOUSE OF THE MIND see Howells, Herbert Norman

HOVDESVEN, E.A. (1893-)
Bow Thy Heavens, O God
SATB,org/pno BOSTON 13469 $.35 (H3030)
Come As The Kings Of The East
SATB,acap BOSTON 13468 $.35 (H3031)
Fold To Thy Heart Thy Brother
4pt mix cor,acap oct SCHIRM.G 11870 $.30 (H3032)
Lord, Take My Heart *anthem
SATB (easy) oct AUGSBURG 1542 $.25 (H3033)
My Heart Is A Manger *Xmas
4pt mix cor oct SCHIRM.G 10830 $.25 (H3034)
Nightingale Carol *Xmas
4pt mix cor,S solo,opt fl oct SCHIRM.G 11584 $.25 (H3035)
Olive Tree Lullaby *Xmas
4pt mix cor,acap oct SCHIRM.G 11501 $.25 (H3036)
Sleep Holy Child *Xmas
SSA oct ELKAN-V 362-3101 $.25 (H3037)
Who Has Delivered Us? *Gen
SATB SCHMITT 8006 $.25 (H3038)
Wonderful New Tonight, The *Xmas
jr cor&sr cor (med easy) FISCHER,C CM 6912 $.25 (H3039)

HOVHANESS, ALAN (1911-)
Ad Lyram
[Lat] dbl cor,SATB soli PETERS 6119 rental (H3040)
Adoration
wom cor/men cor,SA/TB soli PETERS 66193 rental (H3041)
Alleluia (from Look Toward The Sea)
SATB,org/pno PETERS 6170 $.40 (H3042)

HOVHANESS, ALAN (cont'd.)

Anabasis
SATB,narrator,SB soli PETERS 6881 rental (H3043)
And As They Came Down From The Mountain
SATB,T solo PETERS 6545 $.25 (H3044)
Ave Maria
SSAA,inst sc AMP $3.50, ipa, voc sc AMP A277 $.30 see from Triptych (H3045)
Beatitudes, The
SATB,orch voc sc AMP A310 $1.00, sc AMP $5.50 see from Triptych (H3046)
Behold, God Is My Help
SATB,org/pno PETERS 66190 $.30 (H3047)
Blessed Throughout All Generations *see Omnes Generationes
Easter Cantata *Easter,cant
SATB,S solo,orch AMP voc sc $2.00, sc $12.00 see from Triptych (H3048)
From The End Of The Earth (Psalm 61)
SATB,org/pno PETERS 6255 $.25 (H3049)
Give Ear To My Prayer
SATB,Bar/T solo,org/pno PETERS 66192B $.40, ipa (H3050)
Gloria (from Magnificat)
SATB,org/pno PETERS 6433 $.40, ipr (H3051)
Glory To God *Xmas,cant
voc sc PETERS 6350 $1.25, ipr, min sc PETERS 6048 $3.50, ipr (H3052)
SATB,SA soli,org/pno,opt brass&timp&perc voc sc PETERS 6350 $1.25, ipr, min sc PETERS 6048 $3.50, ipr (H3053)
God Of Glory Thundereth, The *Bibl
SATB,T/S solo,org/pno PETERS 6440 $.40 (H3054)
He Leadeth Me Beside The Still Waters
see Hovhaness, Alan, Lord Is My Shepherd, The
Hear My Prayer, O Lord (Psalm 143)
SSATBB,opt org/pno PETERS 6444 $.40 (H3055)
I Have Seen The Lord
SATB,S solo,trp,org/pno PETERS 6544 $.40 (H3056)
I Will Lift Up Mine Eyes *Op.93, cant
SATB&opt boy cor,opt B solo,org voc sc PETERS 66232 $1.25 (H3057)
SATB&opt boy cor,opt B solo,org PETERS 66232 $1.25 (H3058)
I Will Rejoice In The Lord
SATB,org/pno PETERS 66200 $.30 (H3059)
Immortality
SATB,S solo,org/pno PETERS 6360 $.30 (H3060)
In The Beginning Was The Word *Bibl
SATB,AB soli,org/pno voc sc PETERS 6838 $3.50, ipr (H3061)
Jesus Is Risen Today (from Easter Cantata)
SATB,opt pno&harp&perc, opt celesta cor pts AMP A309 $.35 see from Triptych (H3062)
Jesus, Lover Of My Soul
SATB,S/T/Bar solo,org/pno PETERS 66231 $.30 (H3063)
Keep Not Thou Silence *mot
mix cor SOUTHERN $.25 (H3064)
SATB,acap AMP A207 $.30 (H3065)
Let Them Praise The Name Of The Lord
SATB,org PETERS 6450 $.30 (H3066)
Let Us Love One Another
SATB,opt T/Bar solo,org/pno PETERS 66199 $.30 (H3067)
Look Toward The Sea
SATB,Bar solo,org,trom voc sc PETERS 6156 $2.00, ipa (H3068)
Lord Is My Shepherd, The (Psalm 23)
SATB,org/pno/6vln PETERS 6466 $.30 (H3069)
SATB,org/pno PETERS 6505 $.75 contains also: He Leadeth Me Beside The Still Waters; Thou Preparest A Table (H3070)
Lord Shall Preserve Thee From All Evil, The
SATB,org PETERS 66232B $.40 (H3071)
Lord's Prayer, The *Bibl/prayer
SATB,org/pno PETERS 6988 $.40 (H3072)
Magnificat *Op.157, Magnif
[Lat/Eng] SATB&SATB,SATB soli,orch voc sc PETERS 6108 $2.00, ipr, sc PETERS 6107 $10.00, ipr (H3073)
Make A Joyful Noise *cant
SATB,Bar/T solo,org/pno,2trp,2trom voc sc PETERS 66192 $.90, ipa (H3074)
Make Haste (Psalm 70) mot
SATB,acap PETERS 6288 $.25 (H3075)
Make His Praise Glorious
SATB,org/pno,2trp,2trom PETERS 66192C $.30, ipa (H3076)
Missa Brevis *Mass
[Lat] sc PETERS 6476 $3.50, ipr, voc sc PETERS 6476A $1.50, ipr (H3077)
Mourn, Mourn, Ye Saints (from Easter Cantata)
SATB,S solo AMP A308 $.30 see from Triptych (H3078)
My Help Comes From The Lord
SATB,org PETERS 66232A $.40 (H3079)
O For A Shout Of Sacred Joy
SATB,org/pno PETERS 6148 $.30 (H3080)
O God Our Help In Ages Past
SATB,org/pno PETERS 6363 $.30 (H3081)

HOVHANESS, ALAN (cont'd.)

O Lord, God Of Hosts
SATB,org/pno,opt 2trp&2trom PETERS 66188 $.30, ipa (H3082)
O Lord, Rebuke Me Not
SATB,org/pno PETERS 66191 $.30 (H3083)
Omnes Generationes
"Blessed Throughout All Generations" [Eng/Lat] SSA,S solo,org/pno PETERS 6850 $.25 (H3084)
Out Of The Depths (Psalm 130)
SATB,S solo,org/pno PETERS 6270 $.30 (H3085)
Praise The Lord With Psaltery *cant
SATB,orch voc sc PETERS 66194 $.90 (H3086)
Praise Ye Him, All His Angels (Psalm 148)
SATB,B solo,org/pno PETERS 6141 $.30 (H3087)
Praise Ye The Lord *mot
SATB,acap AMP A208 $.30 (H3088)
Psalm 23 *see Lord Is My Shepherd, The
Psalm 28 *see Unto Thee Will I Cry
Psalm 61 *see From The End Of The Earth
Psalm 70 *see Make Haste
Psalm 81 *see Sing Aloud
Psalm 130 *see Out Of The Depths
Psalm 143 *see Hear My Prayer, O Lord
Psalm 148 *see Praise Ye Him, All His Angels
Save Me, O God
SATB,org/pno,2trp,2trom PETERS 66192A $.90, ipa (H3089)
Sing Aloud (Psalm 81) mot
SATB,acap PETERS 6287 $.30 (H3090)
Thirtieth Ode Of Solomon *Bibl
voc sc PETERS 6120 $1.25 (H3091)
Thou Preparest A Table
see Hovhaness, Alan, Lord Is My Shepherd, The
SATB,org/pno PETERS 6506 $.50, ipr (H3092)
To The God Who Is In The Fire
TTBB,T solo,6perc sc PETERS 6509A $5.00, voc pt PETERS 6509 $.30 (H3093)
Transfiguration *cant
SATB,T solo PETERS 6057 $.60 (H3094)
Triptych *see Ave Maria; Beatitudes, The; Easter Cantata; Jesus Is Risen Today (from Easter Cantata); Mourn, Mourn, Ye Saints (from Easter Cantata) (H3095)
Unto Thee, O God *mot
mix cor SOUTHERN $.25 (H3096)
SATB,acap AMP A206 $.25 (H3097)
Unto Thee Will I Cry (Psalm 28)
SATB,org/pno PETERS 6149 $.30 (H3098)
Watchman, Tell Us Of The Night *Easter
SATB,B solo,org/pno PETERS 6460 $.40, ipr (H3099)
Why Hast Thou Cast Us Off *mot
SATB,acap AMP A205 $.25 (H3100)

HOVLAND, EGIL
Allhelgonamassa
(Hjorth, Gunnar) [Swed] mix cor NORDISKA NMS-6328 s.p. (H3101)
De Salige *mot
[Norw] mix cor LYCHE 40 s.p. (H3102)
De Ydmyke *mot
[Norw] mix cor LYCHE 43 s.p. (H3103)
Den Som Ber Han Far *mot
[Norw] cor,org LYCHE 25 s.p. (H3104)
Dom Ikke *mot
[Norw] mix cor LYCHE 88 s.p. (H3105)
Fred Vaere Med Eder *mot
[Norw] mix cor LYCHE 62 s.p. (H3106)
Frelsens Dag *mot
[Norw] mix cor LYCHE 41 s.p. (H3107)
Frykt Ikke Fra Na Av *mot
[Norw] mix cor LYCHE 96 s.p. (H3108)
Gloria In Excelsis Deo *mot
[Lat] mix cor,org s.p. voc sc LYCHE LY335, cor pts LYCHE (H3109)
Heilag Er Kyrkja Her
mix cor MUSIKK 80 s.p. (H3110)
Herre, Var Herre *mot
[Norw] mix cor LYCHE 51 s.p. (H3111)
Herren Er Min Hyrde *mot
[Norw] mix cor LYCHE 66 s.p. (H3112)
Hor Pa Meg, Mitt Folk *mot
[Norw] mix cor,org LYCHE 92 s.p. (H3113)
Hosianna I Det Hoyeste *mot
[Norw] mix cor LYCHE 47 s.p. (H3114)
How Long, O Lord
SSAATTBB oct WALTON 2901 $.40 (H3115)
Hva Gagner Det Et Menneske *mot
[Norw] mix cor,org LYCHE 81 s.p. (H3116)
Jesus, Kristus Er Den Samme *mot
[Norw] mix cor LYCHE 46 s.p. (H3117)
Jubilate *anthem/Jubil
[Lat] SATB,S/A solo,org PETERS LY472 $.80 (H3118)
SATB,T solo (med diff) oct AUGSBURG 1529

HOVLAND, EGIL (cont'd.)

$.35   (H3119)

Jubilate (Introitus)
[Norw] mix cor,solo,org LYCHE 3 s.p.
(H3120)

Kom Lat Oss Jubla *Introit
[Norw/Swed] mix cor NORDISKA NMO-8759 s.p.
(H3121)

Loft Troens Skjold *mot
[Norw] mix cor LYCHE 95 s.p.   (H3122)

Lover Gud I Himmelkor *Xmas
[Norw] cor,inst s.p. cor pts LYCHE
ED.L.518, voc sc LYCHE ED.L.518 (H3123)

Marias Lovsang
[Norw] cor,soli,opt org LYCHE 13 s.p.
(H3124)

O Store Gud, Vi Lover Deg *cant/mot
[Norw] mix cor,inst LYCHE LY487 s.p.
(H3125)

Og Ordet Blev Kjod *mot
[Norw] mix cor LYCHE 36 s.p.   (H3126)

Salige Er De Som Horer Guds Ord *mot
[Norw] mix cor LYCHE 72 s.p.   (H3127)

Saul!
mix cor NORDISKA NMO-8754 s.p.   (H3128)

Se Din Konge Kommer *mot
[Norw] mix cor LYCHE 93 s.p.   (H3129)

Sok Forst Guds Rike *mot
[Norw] mix cor LYCHE 70 s.p.   (H3130)

Speen Beltet Om Livet
[Norw] LYCHE 47 s.p.   (H3131)

Talsmannen Den Hellige And *mot
[Norw] mix cor,org LYCHE 91 s.p. (H3132)

Til Bords I Guds Rike *mot
[Norw] mix cor LYCHE 67 s.p.   (H3133)

Vaer Tro *mot
[Norw] mix cor LYCHE 39 s.p.   (H3134)

Ver Miskunnsame *mot
[Norw] mix cor LYCHE 71 s.p.   (H3135)

HOW
O Day Of Light And Life And Grace
(Bost; Coggin) SA oct BELWIN 64388 $.25
(H3136)

HOW ABOUT YOU?
TTBB BIG3 $.25   (H3137)

HOW ABOUT YOU? see Skillings, Otis

HOW ABUNDANT IS THY GOODNESS see Arthur, Jan

HOW AMIABLE ARE THY DWELLINGS see Stanford,
Patric

HOW AMIABLE ARE THY TABERNACLES see Berger,
Jean

HOW ARE MY FOES INCREASED, LORD! see Joubert,
John

HOW ARE THY SERVANTS BLESSED, O LORD see
Wagner, Joseph Frederick

HOW ARE THY SERVANTS BLEST see Ippolitov-
Ivanov, Mikhail Mikhailovitch

HOW BEAUTEOUS ARE THEIR FEET see Stanford,
Charles Villiers

HOW BEAUTEOUS ARE THEIR FEET see Thiman, Eric
Harding

HOW BEAUTIFUL see Boyd

HOW BEAUTIFUL ARE THE FEET see Handel, George
Frideric

HOW BEAUTIFUL ARE THE FEET OF HIM see Handel,
George Frideric

HOW BEAUTIFUL ON THE MOUNTAINS see Shelley,
[Harry Rowe]

HOW BEAUTIFUL UPON THE MOUNTAIN see Smith

HOW BEAUTIFUL UPON THE MOUNTAIN see Stainer,
John

HOW BEAUTIFUL UPON THE MOUNTAINS see Anderton

HOW BEAUTIFUL UPON THE MOUNTAINS see Antes,
John

HOW BEAUTIFUL UPON THE MOUNTAINS see Berger,
Jean

HOW BEAUTIFUL UPON THE MOUNTAINS see Galbraith,
J.

HOW BEAUTIFUL UPON THE MOUNTAINS see Harker, F.
Flaxington

HOW BEAUTIFUL UPON THE MOUNTAINS see Lorenz

HOW BEAUTIFUL UPON THE MOUNTAINS see Moe,
Daniel

HOW BEAUTIFUL UPON THE MOUNTAINS see Ogden

HOW BEAUTIFUL UPON THE MOUNTAINS see Stainer,
John

HOW BEAUTIFUL UPON THE MOUNTAINS see Wolcott,
J.

HOW BEAUTIFUL UPON THE MOUNTAINS see Work

HOW BLEST ARE THEY see Purcell, Henry, Beati
Omnes

HOW BLEST ARE THEY see Schalk, Carl

HOW BLEST ARE THEY see Tchaikovsky, Piotr
Ilyitch

HOW BRIGHT AND FAIR THE MORNING STAR see
Praetorius, Michael, Wie Schon Leuchtet Der
Morgenstern

HOW BRIGHT APPEARS THE MORNING STAR see
Nicolai, Philipp, Wie Schon Leucht' Uns Der
Morgenstern

HOW BRIGHTLY BEAMS see Sweelinck, Jan
Pieterszoon

HOW BRIGHTLY BEAMS THE MORNING STAR see
Praetorius, Michael

HOW BRIGHTLY BEAMS THE MORNING STAR *Xmas,
carol
unis/SATB (very easy) OXFORD 08.104 $.15
(H3138)

HOW BRIGHTLY BEAMS THE MORNING STAR see Bach,
Johann Sebastian

HOW BRIGHTLY BEAMS THE MORNING STAR see
Nicolai, Philipp

HOW BRIGHTLY SHINES see Kuhnau, Johann

HOW BRIGHTLY SHINES THE MORNING STAR see Bach

HOW BRIGHTLY SHINES THE MORNING STAR see
Nicolai, Philipp, Wie Schon Leucht' Uns Der
Morgenstern

HOW BRIGHTLY SHINES THE MORNING STAR see
Praetorius, Michael, Wie Schon Leuchtet Der
Morgenstern

HOW BRIGHTLY SHINES THE MORNING STAR see Wie
Schon Leuchtet Der Morgenstern

HOW BRIGHTLY SHINES YON MORNING STAR see Bach,
Johann Sebastian, Wie Schon Leuchtet Der
Morgenstern [Chorale]

HOW BRIGHTLY SHINES YON MORNING STAR see
Nicolai, Philipp, Wie Schon Leucht' Uns Der
Morgenstern [Chorale]

HOW BRIGHTLY SHINES YON STAR OF MORN see Bach,
Johann Sebastian

HOW CALM AND BEAUTIFUL THE MORN see Grieb,
Herbert [C.]

HOW CALMLY THE EVENING see Elgar, Edward

HOW CAN A SINNER KNOW see Ford, Virgil T.

HOW CAN I THANK THEE, LORD see Bunjes, Paul G.

HOW CAN WE SHOW OUR LOVE TO THEE? see Ford,
Virgil T.

HOW CAN WE THANK YOU, LORD see Roff, Joseph

HOW DEAR ART THY COUNSELS see Crotch, William

HOW EXCELLENT IS THY NAME see Angell, Warren M.

HOW EXCELLENT IS THY NAME see Butler, Eugene

HOW EXCELLENT IS THY NAME see Donato, Anthony

HOW EXCELLENT IS THY NAME see Handel, George
Frideric

HOW EXCELLENT IS THY NAME see Horton, William

HOW EXCELLENT IS THY NAME see McAfee

HOW EXCELLENT IS THY NAME see Morgan

HOW EXCELLENT IS THY NAME see Posegate

HOW EXCELLENT IS THY NAME see Uggen

HOW EXCELLENT IS THY NAME see Wilson, James R.

HOW EXCELLENT THY NAME see Bitgood

HOW EXCELLENT THY NAME see Hampton, Calvin

HOW EXCELLENT THY NAME see Handel, George
Frideric

HOW EXCELLENT THY NAME see Hanson

HOW EXCELLENT THY NAME see Hartley, Walter [S.]

HOW EXCELLENT THY NAME, O LORD see Handel,
George Frideric

HOW FAIR IS THY FACE see Grieg, Edvard Hagerup

HOW FAIR THE CHURCH see Schroth, G.

HOW FAIR THE CHURCH OF CHRIST SHALL STAND see
Schumann

HOW FAR IS IT TO BETHLEHEM? *Xmas,anthem/
carol,Eng
unis (very easy) OXFORD 08.141 $.15 (H3139)
(Hedges) SABar oct SCHIRM.G 10951 $.25
(H3140)
(Hedges) 4pt mix cor oct SCHIRM.G 11120 $.25
(H3141)
(Hedges) jr cor&sr cor oct SCHIRM.G 10766
$.25   (H3142)
(Pooler, Marie) unis treb cor/SA (easy) oct
AUGSBURG 1365 $.25   (H3143)
(Russell) unis/SA (very easy) OXFORD 44.988
$.20, ipa   (H3144)
(Shaw; Parker) SATB,acap oct LAWSON 51017
$.30   (H3145)
(Shaw; Parker) SATB ALLANS 401 s.p. (H3146)

HOW FAR IS IT TO BETHLEHEM see Barber, Ruby
D.M.

HOW FAR IS IT TO BETHLEHEM? see Burroughs

HOW FAR IS IT TO BETHLEHEM see Christiansen, P.

HOW FAR IS IT TO BETHLEHEM? see Jerrett, Jack

HOW FAR IS IT TO BETHLEHEM? see Lawson, Gordon

HOW FAR IS IT TO BETHLEHEM see Miller

HOW FAR IS IT TO BETHLEHEM? see Nelson, Ronald
A.

HOW FAR IS IT TO BETHLEHEM? see Pfautsch, Lloyd

HOW FAR IS IT TO BETHLEHEM? see Shaw, Geoffrey
[Turton]

HOW FAR IS IT TO BETHLEHEM see Williams, David
H.

HOW FAR TO BETHLEHEM! see Caldwell, Mary
[Elizabeth]

HOW FIRM A FOUNDATION *hymn
(Brandon) SATB oct PRO ART 2309 $.25 (H3147)
(Forest, John) cor HIGHLAND 4113 $.25 (H3148)
(Niles) 4pt mix cor,org/pno oct SCHIRM.G
11313 $.30   (H3149)
(Niles; Sheppard) 3pt boy cor/3pt wom cor oct
SCHIRM.G 10899 $.25   (H3150)
(Parker) SATB,acap oct LAWSON 51324 $.30
(H3151)
(Prussing, S.) SATB oct WORD CS-2441 $.30
(H3152)
(Skiles) SAB oct LILLENAS AN-1162 $.30
(H3153)
(Thompson, Van Denman) SATB ALLANS 355 s.p.
(H3154)

HOW FIRM A FOUNDATION see Elkins

HOW FIRM A FOUNDATION see Gardner

HOW FIRM A FOUNDATION see Goode, Jack C.

HOW FIRM A FOUNDATION see Niles, John Jacob

HOW FIRM A FOUNDATION see Ohl, [Jeremiah
Franklin]

HOW FIRM A FOUNDATION see Ringwald, [Roy]

HOW FIRM A FOUNDATION see Steele

HOW FIRM A FOUNDATION see Thompson

HOW FIRM A FOUNDATION see Walter, Samuel

HOW FIRM A FOUNDATION see Warner, Richard

HOW FIRM A FOUNDATION see Young

HOW GENTLE GOD'S COMMANDS see Ford, Virgil T.

HOW GENTLY FALLS THE SNOW *Xmas,carol,Span
(Blaine, G.Gordon) SATB oct WALTON 2035 $.30
(H3155)

HOW GLORIOUS IS THY NAME see Brubeck, Howard

HOW GLORIOUS SION'S COURTS APPEAR see Tye,
Christopher

HOW GODLY IS THE HOUSE OF GOD see Meyerowitz,
Jan

HOW GOODLY ARE THY TENTS see Gideon, Miriam

HOW GOODLY ARE THY TENTS see Gottlieb, J., Mah
Tovu

HOW GOODLY ARE THY TENTS see Ouseley, Frederick
Arthur Gore

HOW GOODLY ARE THY TENTS see Pasquet, Jean

HOW GREAT ARE THY WONDERS see Schumann, Georg

HOW GREAT IS HIS GOODNESS see Clare, Edwyn A.

HOW GREAT THE HARVEST IS
unis/SATB (easy) OXFORD 08.151 $.15 (H3156)

HOW GREAT THE WISDOM
(Cornwall, J.S.) SATB PIONEER 5058 $.20
(H3157)

HOW GREAT THOU ART see Hine, K.

HOW GREATLY THOU ART GLORIFIED see Bortniansky,
Dimitri Stepanovitch

HOW HAPPY YOU, WHO FEAR THE LORD
see Two Hymns In The Dorian Mode

HOW HARD TO TEACH OUR FLESH AND BLOOD see Bach,
Johann Sebastian, Wie Schwerlich Lasst Sich
Fleishch Und Blut

HOW LIKE A HOLY TEMPLE *Xmas,Dut
(Van Koert, Han) 2 eq voices,org oct WORLD
AC-649-2 $.30   (H3158)

HOW LIKE AN ANGEL CAME I DOWN see Drayton, Paul

HOW LONG DEAR SAVIOR, O HOW LONG
(Reynolds) SATB oct FISCHER,C CM-7708 $.25
(H3159)

HOW LONG HAS IT BEEN? see Lister, Mosie

HOW LONG, O GOD, IN MY GREAT NEED see
Praetorius, Michael, Wie Lang, O Gott

HOW LONG, O LORD? see Adler, Samuel

HOW LONG O LORD see Butler, Eugene

HOW LONG, O LORD see Gumpeltzhaimer, Adam

HOW LONG, O LORD see Hovland, Egil

HOW LONG, O LORD see Lassus, Roland de
(Orlandus)

HOW LONG WILL THOU FORGET ME see Hoffmeister,
Franz Anton

HOW LONG WILT THOU FORGET ME see Arthur, Jan

HOW LONG WILT THOU FORGET ME see Battishill,
Jonathan

HOW LONG WILT THOU FORGET ME see Brahms,
Johannes

HOW LONG WILT THOU FORGET ME see Hopkins

HOW LONG WILT THOU FORGET ME? see Pflueger,
Carl

HOW LONG WILT THOU FORGET ME? see Ratcliffe, Desmond

HOW LONG WILT THOU FORGET ME? see Scarlatti, Alessandro

HOW LONG WILT THOU FORGET ME see Speaks, [Oley]

HOW LONG WILT THOU FORGET ME, O LORD? see Beebe, Edward J.

HOW LONG WILT THOU FORGET ME, O LORD see Kay, Ulysses Simpson

HOW LONG WILT THOU FORGET ME, O LORD? see Rorem, Ned

HOW LOST CAN A MAN BE? see Hanks

HOW LOVELY ARE see Mendelssohn-Bartholdy, Felix

HOW LOVELY ARE THE MESSENGERS see Mendelssohn-Bartholdy, Felix

HOW LOVELY ARE THE WORDS OF JESUS see Roff, Joseph

HOW LOVELY ARE THY DWELLINGS see Brahms, Johannes

HOW LOVELY ARE THY DWELLINGS see Canavati

HOW LOVELY ARE THY DWELLINGS see Liddle, [Samuel]

HOW LOVELY ARE THY DWELLINGS see Smart, Henry Thomas

HOW LOVELY ARE THY DWELLINGS see Thiman, Eric Harding

HOW LOVELY ARE THY DWELLINGS see Wolcott, J.

HOW LOVELY ARE THY DWELLINGS FAIR see Hunt, Reginald

HOW LOVELY ARE THY DWELLINGS FAIR see Proulx, Richard

HOW LOVELY ARE THY MESSENGERS see Mendelssohn-Bartholdy, Felix

HOW LOVELY ARE THY TABERNACLES see Berger, Jean

HOW LOVELY ARE THY TABERNACLES see Berger, Jean

HOW LOVELY IS THE HOUSE OF GOD see Lovelace, Austin C.

HOW LOVELY IS THIS PLACE see Morgan

HOW LOVELY IS THY DWELLING PLACE see Brahms, Johannes

HOW LOVELY IS THY DWELLING PLACE see Cerbus, [Paul]

HOW LOVELY IS THY DWELLING PLACE see Chashoudian, Marshall G.

HOW LOVELY IS THY DWELLING PLACE see Geisler, Johan C.

HOW LOVELY IS THY DWELLING PLACE see Newbury, Kent A.

HOW LOVELY IS THY DWELLING PLACE see Schutz, Heinrich

HOW LOVELY IS THY DWELLING PLACE see Somary, J.

HOW LOVELY IS YOUR DWELLING PLACE see Peloquin, C. Alexander

HOW LOVELY IS YOUR DWELLING PLACE see Vermulst, Jan

HOW LOVELY SHINES THE MORNING STAR see Boner, Sidney

HOW LOVELY SHINES THE MORNING STAR see Praetorius, Michael

HOW LOVELY SHINES THE MORNING STAR see Rohlig, Harald

HOW LOVELY SHINES THE MORNING STAR see Strube, Adolf

HOW LOVELY SINGS THE ANGEL CHOIR see Freundt, Cornelius

HOW LOVELY SINGS THE ANGEL HOST see Freundt, Cornelius

HOW LOVELY THE MORNING STAR see Nicolai, Philipp, Wie Schon Leucht' Uns Die Morgenstern

HOW MAJESTIC IS THY NAME see Diemer, Emma Lou

HOW MANY TEARS? see Norden

HOW MIGHTY ARE THE SABBATHS see Holst, Gustav

HOW MUCH FARTHER MUST WE GO see Freed

HOW OUR SPIRIT IS WEIGHED DOWN see Graun, Karl Heinrich

HOW PLEASANT ARE THY DWELLINGS see Brahms, Johannes

HOW PRECIOUS IS THY LOVINGKINDNESS see Adler, Samuel

HOW PRECIOUS IS THY LOVINGKINDNESS see Pinkham, Daniel

HOW REAL GOD IS see Wells

HOW SAD IS MY SPIRIT see Kuhnau, Johann

HOW SHALL I COME BEFORE THE LORD see Demarest, A.

HOW SHALL I FIND HIM see Cruft, Adrian

HOW SHALL I FITLY MEET THEE see Bach, Johann Sebastian

HOW STILL AND TINY see Mizerna Cicha

HOW STILL AND TINY see Peloquin, C. Alexander

HOW STILL HE RESTS see Pierce, Brent

HOW STILL, HOW STILL see Thygerson

HOW STILL THE NIGHT see Brahms, Johannes, In Stiller Nacht

HOW SWEET THE BELLS OF CHRISTMAS see Klemm, Gustav

HOW SWEET THE NAME see Peace, F.W.

HOW SWEET THE NAME OF JESUS SOUNDS see Dale, Mervyn

HOW SWEET THE NAME OF JESUS SOUNDS see Hastings

HOW SWEET THE NAME OF JESUS SOUNDS see Wolff, S. Drummond

HOW SWEET TO KNOW THE LOVE OF JESUS see Bodycombe, [Aneurin]

HOW TEDIOUS AND TASTELESS THE HOURS *18th cent (Fuller) SAB oct PLYMOUTH JR-401 $.25 (H3160)

HOW THEY SO SOFTLY REST see Thompson, Alan

HOW THEY SO SOFTLY REST see Williams, D.

HOW UNTO BETHLEHEM *Xmas,carol,It (Shaw; Parker) mix cor,acap oct SCHIRM.G 10169 $.25 (H3161)

HOW WE LONG FOR CHRISTMAS see Maki

HOW WONDERFUL THIS WORLD see Lovelace, Austin C.

HOW WONDROUS AND GREAT (Gray) SATB oct PRO ART 2111 $.25 (H3162)

HOW WONDROUS AND GREAT see Onderdonk

HOW WONDROUS THE SACRAMENT see Pergolesi, Giovanni Battista, O Sacrum Convivium

HOWARD
  Come, Bless The Lord
    SATB,org BOSTON 12608 $.35 (H3163)

HOWARD, EDWARD F.
  Easter Song *Easter
    SATB,opt org/pno oct WORLD CA-1936-8 $.30 (H3164)

HOWARD, JOHN TASKER (1890-1964)
  God Who Made The Earth
    SAB oct GRAY GCMR 2752 $.30 (H3165)

HOWELL, C.
  By The Waters Of Babylon
    SATB oct PRESSER 332-12565 $.30 (H3166)

HOWELL, DOROTHY (1898-)
  Christmas Bells Are Ringing *Xmas,carol
    2pt jr cor LEONARD-ENG 54 s.p. (H3167)

HOWELL, RICHARD D.
  Sleep Of The Child Jesus *Xmas
    SATB,opt kbd (easy) ABINGDON APM-355 $.18 (H3168)

HOWELLS, HERBERT NORMAN (1892-)
  All My Hope On God Is Founded *hymn
    SATB oct NOVELLO 44.1450.00 s.p. (H3169)

  Benedictus *Bene
    SATB oct NOVELLO 44.1442.10 s.p. (H3170)

  Coventry Antiphon *anthem
    mix cor oct NOVELLO 28.1420.10 s.p. (H3171)

  Coventry Mass, The *Mass
    SATB,org voc sc NOVELLO s.p., ipr (H3172)
    SATB BELWIN 19781 $2.00 (H3173)

  English Mass, An *Mass
    SATB,org,fl,ob,strings,timp,harp voc sc
    NOVELLO s.p., ipr (H3174)

  Four Anthems *see Like As The Hart; O Pray
    For The Peace (H3175)

  God Is Gone Up With A Merry Noise *mot
    (Darke, Dr. H.) SATB voc sc NOVELLO s.p.,
    ipr see from Three Motets For Organ (H3176)

  God Is Love: Let Heav'n Adore Him *hymn
    SATB oct NOVELLO 44.1453.05 s.p. (H3177)

  Holy Communion *Commun
    SATB oct NOVELLO 02.0034.04 s.p. (H3178)

  Holy Spirit, Ever Dwelling *hymn
    SATB oct NOVELLO 44.1454.03 s.p. (H3179)

  House Of The Mind (from Three Motets For
    Strings And Organ) mot
    SATB,org,strings voc sc NOVELLO s.p., ipr (H3180)

  Hymn For St. Cecilia, A *anthem
    mix cor oct NOVELLO 40.1426.10 s.p. (H3181)

  Hymnus Paradisi *hymn/liturg
    SATB,ST soli,2fl,2ob,2clar,2bsn,4horn,3trp,
    3trom,tuba,strings,perc,timp,harp,pno,
    pic, English horn, bass clarinet,
    contrabassoon, celesta voc sc NOVELLO
    s.p., ipr (H3182)

  Jubilate *Jubil
    SATB oct NOVELLO 44.1438.01 s.p. (H3183)

  Like As The Hart *anthem
    SATB,S solo (med) OXFORD 42.066 $.50 see
    from Four Anthems (H3184)

  Like As The Hart Desireth The Waterbrooks
    *Gen
    SATB (med) oct OXFORD 42.066 $.35 (H3185)

HOWELLS, HERBERT NORMAN (cont'd.)

  Lord, By Whose Breath *hymn
    SATB oct NOVELLO 44.1455.01 s.p. (H3186)

  Lord Christ, When First Thou Cam'st To Men
    *Xmas,hymn
    SATB oct NOVELLO 44.1452.07 s.p. (H3187)

  Magnificat And Nunc Dimittis *Magnif/Nunc
    SATB oct NOVELLO 86.0032.05 s.p. (H3188)
    SATB oct NOVELLO 44.1461.06 s.p. (H3189)
    SATB oct NOVELLO 44.1439.10 s.p. (H3190)
    SATB oct NOVELLO 44.1279.06 s.p. (H3191)
    SATB oct NOVELLO 44.1280.10 s.p. (H3192)
    SATB oct NOVELLO 44.1375.10 s.p. (H3193)
    SATB oct NOVELLO 44.1322.09 s.p. (H3194)
    SATB oct NOVELLO 44.1367.09 s.p. (H3195)
    SATB oct NOVELLO 44.1440.03 s.p. (H3196)
    SATB oct NOVELLO 44.1441.01 s.p. (H3197)
    SATB (B min) oct NOVELLO 44.1350.04 s.p. (H3198)

  Missa Aedis Christi *Mass
    SATB oct NOVELLO 02.0035.02 s.p. (H3199)

  Missa Sabrinensis *Mass
    SATB,SATBar soli,pno,org,2fl,3ob,3clar,
    3bsn,4horn,3trp,3trom,tuba,strings,perc,
    timp,harp,celesta voc sc NOVELLO s.p.,
    ipr (H3200)

  My Eyes For Beauty Pine *Gen
    SATB (easy) oct OXFORD 42.008 $.25 (H3201)

  O Holy City *hymn
    SATB oct NOVELLO 44.1451.09 s.p. (H3202)

  O Pray For The Peace *anthem
    SATB (med) OXFORD 42.064 $.35 see from Four
    Anthems (H3203)

  O Pray For The Peace Of Jerusalem *Ded/Gen
    SATB (med) oct OXFORD 42.064 $.35 (H3204)

  One Thing Have I Desired *anthem/mot
    mix cor,acap oct NOVELLO 28.1477.03 s.p. (H3205)

  Preces And Responses (Canterbury)
    SATB,acap oct NOVELLO 44.1549.04 s.p. (H3206)

  Sequence For St. Michael, A *anthem/mot
    mix cor oct NOVELLO 03.0068.03 s.p. (H3207)

  Shepherd, The *Xmas
    2pt jr cor/2pt wom cor CURWEN 71484 s.p. (H3208)

  Stabat Mater *cant
    SATB,T solo,pno,org,3fl,3ob,3clar,3bsn,
    4horn,3trp,3trom,tuba,strings,perc,timp,
    harp,celesta voc sc NOVELLO s.p., ipr (H3209)

  Te Deum *Te Deum
    SATB oct NOVELLO 44.1427.06 s.p. (H3210)

  Te Deum And Jubilate *Jubil/Te Deum
    SATB oct NOVELLO 44.1277.10 s.p. (H3211)

  Thee Will I Love *anthem/mot
    mix cor oct NOVELLO 28.1481.01 s.p. (H3212)

  Three Motets For Organ *see God Is Gone Up
    With A Merry Noise (H3213)

  To The Name Of Our Salvation *hymn
    SATB oct NOVELLO 44.1458.06 s.p. (H3214)

HOWL YE see Thompson, Randall

HOWORTH, WAYNE
  All Night, All Day
    SA/TB oct FOX PS144 $.30 (H3215)

  Heav'n Bound Soldiers
    SATB oct FOX PS175 $.30 (H3216)

  Jesus, Jesus, Rest Your Head
    SATB,acap oct FOX PS67 $.30 (H3217)

  My Soul's Been Anchored In De Lord
    SSA oct BELWIN 1764 $.25 (H3218)

  O Sons And Daughters Let Us Sing *Easter
    SSA oct FOX PS177 $.30 (H3219)

  Open Wide, Oh Ye Gates *Palm
    SSAATTBB WARNER R3472 $.30 (H3220)

  Praise To The Lord The Almighty
    SATB oct BELWIN 1739 $.35 (H3221)

  There Is A Balm In Gilead *spir
    SATB oct BELWIN 1762 $.30 (H3222)

HOY, JOSE, SE OS DA EN EL SUELO see Guerrero, Francisco

HOYOUL, BALDUIN (1547-1594)
  Da Jesus An Dem Kreuze Stund *Psntd
    [Ger] 3pt mix cor,acap (med easy) BAREN.
    BA 990, 991 s.p. (H3223)

HOYR KOR KYRKJEKLOKKA LKKR
    (Baldershage, Bernt) wom cor MUSIKK 41 s.p. (H3224)

HOYR, KOR KYRKJEKLOKKA LOKKAR see Baden, Conrad

HRUBY, DELORES
  He Whom Joyous Shepherds Praised *Xmas/
    Cnfrm/Gen
    unis,perc (easy) oct CONCORDIA 98-1969 $.25 (H3225)

  Sweet It Is To Praise The Lord
    SA,opt hndbl oct AGAPE F 930 $.25 (H3226)

HUAYNITO DE NAVIDAD see Carillo, Gomez

HUBER, HANS (1852-1921)
  Schweizerhymne
    [Ger] mix cor,acap (med diff) HUG (H3227)

  St. Johannisnacht
    [Ger] men cor,acap (diff) HUG s.p. (H3228)

HUBER, KLAUS (1924-)
  Das Te Deum Laudamus Deutsch *Te Deum
    [Ger] SATTB,soli,acap (diff) BAREN. BA 3989
    $3.50 (H3229)

HUBER, P. (1918-   )
Aus Dem Dunkel Der Welt *cant
  [Ger] mix cor,org,opt 2vln HUG s.p. (H3230)

HUBER, W.S.
Kanonisches Triptychon Auf Die Weihnachtszeit
  *Xmas
  [Ger] mix cor,acap (med easy) HUG s.p.
                                            (H3231)

HUBICKI
By Thy Birth Thou Blessed Lord
  see Two Songs

Out Of The Orient Crystal Skies
  see Two Songs

Two Songs *Xmas
  unis BOSWORTH s.p.
  contains: By Thy Birth Thou Blessed Lord;
    Out Of The Orient Crystal Skies (H3232)

HUBLE, M.R.
Sicut Cervus
  [Lat] 4pt mix cor,acap oct DURAND (H3233)

HUDSON
Bell Carol, The *Xmas,carol
  unis BOOSEY-CAN s.p. (H3234)

Go Tell It On The Mountain (He's Got The
  Whole World) *Xmas
  SA BOOSEY-CAN s.p. (H3235)

His Yoke Is Easy
  (Rogers) SATB oct LILLENAS AN-2257 $.25
                                            (H3236)

Jesu Is Crying *Xmas
  SA BOOSEY-CAN s.p. (H3237)

HUDSON, HAZEL
Jesu Is Crying *Braz
  2pt ASHDOWN E.A.352 s.p. (H3238)

HUERTER, [CHARLES] (1885-   )
Blest Are The Pure In Heart *Bibl
  4pt mix cor oct SCHIRM.G 7226 $.25 (H3239)

Lord In Thy Presence Lead Us *Commun
  4pt mix cor oct SCHIRM.G 7077 $.25 (H3240)

HUESSENSTAMM, GEORGE
In Thee, O Lord, Do I Hope *anthem
  SSAA (med) oct AUGSBURG 1586 $.30 (H3241)

HUET, FELIX
Hymne A Sainte Cecile *hymn
  [Lat] cor,org,vln,harp sc ENOCH s.p. (H3242)

HUFSCHMIDT, WOLFGANG (1934-   )
Aber Der Troster, Der Heilige Geist *Pent
  [Ger] SATB,acap (med) BAREN. BA 3878 $.75
  see from Epistelmotetten (H3243)

Alle Gute Gabe *Easter/Pent,cant
  [Ger] SATB,acap (med) BAREN. BA 3872 $.40
  see from Epistelmotetten (H3244)

Also Hat Gott Die Welt Geliebet *Pent
  [Ger] SATB,acap (med) BAREN. BA 3903 $.40
  see from Epistelmotetten (H3245)

Auf, Auf, Mein Herz, Mit Freuden *Easter
  [Ger] SA&men cor,acap (med diff) BAREN.
  BA 4951 $.40 (H3246)

Aus Tiefer Not Schrei Ich Zu Dir *ECY
  [Ger] SATB&SAB,acap (med) BAREN. BA 4935
  s.p. (H3247)

Brunn Alles Heils *Gen
  [Ger] SSATTB,acap (med diff) BAREN. BA 4960
  $.40 (H3248)

Chormusik Auf Den Namen Israel (Psalm 1) Gen
  [Ger] 6pt,acap BAREN. BA 4123 s.p. (H3249)

Christus Hat Unsere Sunde Selbst
  Hinaufgetragen *Easter/Pent,mot
  [Ger] SATB,acap (med, misericordias domini)
  BAREN. BA 3876 $.55 see from
  Epistelmotetten (H3250)

Das Alte Jahr Vergangen Ist *Xmas
  [Ger] SAB,acap (med) BAREN. BA 4931 $.25
                                            (H3251)

Denn Wir Haben Auch Ein Osterlamm *Easter
  [Ger] SATB,acap (med) BAREN. BA 3901 $.55
  see from Epistelmotetten (H3252)

Die Pfingstgeschichte *Pent
  [Ger] 4-12pt mix cor,acap (diff) sc BAREN.
  BA 4458 $8.25, ipr (H3253)

Die Sieben Worte Am Kreuz *Psntd
  [Ger] SATB,acap (med diff) BAREN. BA 3979
  $2.75 (H3254)

Dienet Einander *Easter/Pent,mot
  [Ger] SATB,acap (med, exaudi) BAREN.
  BA 3877 $.40 see from Epistelmotetten
                                            (H3255)

Ehre Sei Gott In Der Hohe
  [Ger] 3pt mix cor,acap (med) BAREN. BA 3247
  s.p. (H3256)

Epistelmotetten *see Aber Der Troster, Der
  Heilige Geist; Alle Gute Gabe; Also Hat
  Gott Die Welt Geliebet; Christus Hat
  Unsere Sunde Selbst Hinaufgetragen; Denn
  Wir Haben Auch Ein Osterlamm; Dienet
  Einander; Ihr Wisset Wohl Von Der
  Predigt; Sei Getreu Bis An Den Tod; Seid
  Ihr Nun Mit Christo Auferstanden; Unser
  Glaube Ist Der Sieg, Der Die Welt
  Uberwunden Hat; Vater Unser Im
  Himmelreich (H3257)

Erstanden Ist Der Heilig Christ *Easter
  [Ger] SA&men cor,acap (med diff) BAREN.
  BA 4952 $.40 (H3258)

Furwahr, Er Trug Unsere Krankheit *Psntd
  [Ger] SATB,acap (med diff) BAREN. 3904 $.55
                                            (H3259)

Gen Himmel Aufgefahren Ist *Easter/Pent
  [Ger] SA&men cor,acap (med) BAREN.
  BA 4958 $.40 (H3260)

HUFSCHMIDT, WOLFGANG (cont'd.)
Herzliebster Jesu *Psntd
  [Ger] SA&men cor (med diff) BAREN. BA 4950
  $.40 (H3261)

Ihr Wisset Wohl Von Der Predigt *Easter
  [Ger] SATB,acap (med) BAREN. BA 3875 $.75
  see from Epistelmotetten (H3262)

Komm, Gott Schopfer, Heiliger Geist *Pent
  [Ger] SA&men cor,S solo,acap (med diff)
  BAREN. BA 4959 $.25 (H3263)

Lobt Gott Den Herrn, Ihr Heiden All *Gen
  [Ger] SAB,acap (med) BAREN. BA 4933 s.p.
                                            (H3264)

Messe *Mass
  [Ger] SATB,soli,acap (med diff) BAREN.
  BA 3985 s.p. (H3265)

Nun Jauchzet All Ihr Frommen *Adv,cant
  [Ger] SA&men cor,S solo,org (med diff)
  BAREN. BA 4464 sc $3.75, cor pts $.55
                                            (H3266)

Nun Preiset Alle Gottes Barmherzigkeit *Fest
  [Ger] SA&men cor,acap (med) BAREN. BA 6301
  s.p. (H3267)

O Heiland, Reiss Die Himmel Auf *Xmas
  [Ger] 3pt mix cor,acap (med) BAREN. BA 4936
  $.40 (H3268)

O Heiliger Geist, O Heiliger Gott *Pent
  [Ger] SAB,acap (med) BAREN. BA 4932 s.p.
                                            (H3269)

O Herre Gott, Dein Gottlich Wort *Fest
  [Ger] SA&men cor,acap (med) BAREN. BA 6302
  s.p. (H3270)

O Jesu Christe, Wahres Licht *Gen
  [Ger] SA&men cor,acap (med diff) BAREN.
  BA 4957 $.40 (H3271)

Psalm 1 *see Chormusik Auf Den Namen Israel

Sei Getreu Bis An Den Tod *Easter/Pent,mot
  [Ger] SATB,acap (med, jubilate) BAREN.
  BA 3873 $.25 see from Epistelmotetten
                                            (H3272)

Seid Ihr Nun Mit Christo Auferstanden
  *Easter/Pent,mot
  [Ger] SATB,acap (med, resurrection) BAREN.
  BA 3902 $.40 see from Epistelmotetten
                                            (H3273)

Unser Glaube Ist Der Sieg, Der Die Welt
  Uberwunden Hat *Easter/Pent,mot
  [Ger] SATB,acap (med, low sunday) BAREN.
  BA 3871 $.55 see from Epistelmotetten
                                            (H3274)

Vater Unser Im Himmelreich *Easter/Pent,mot
  [Ger] SATB,acap (med, rogate) BAREN.
  BA 3874 $.55 see from Epistelmotetten
                                            (H3275)

Vier Gleichnisse Von Der Gerechtigkeit Gottes
  *Gen,Bibl
  [Ger] SATB,acap (med diff) BAREN. BA 5411
  $2.50 (H3276)

Wenn Mein Stundlein Vorhanden Ist *mot
  [Ger] SA&men cor,acap (med) BAREN. BA
  5416 s.p. (H3277)

Wir Danken Dir, Herr Jesu Christ *Psntd
  [Ger] SAB,acap (med) BAREN. BA 4934 s.p.
                                            (H3278)

HUGEN see Groven, Eivind

HUGENOTTEN-PSALMEN see Wieruszowski, Lili

HUGG
No, Not One!
  (McLellan) SATB oct LILLENAS AN-1198 $.30
                                            (H3279)

HUGGETT
Bold Peter
  (Mickelson) SATB oct AGAPE CF 149 $.35
                                            (H3280)

HUGH-JONES, LLIFON
Laus Deo
  [Lat] unis oct GALLIARD 2.9004.1 $.30
                                            (H3281)

Prayers
  unis&desc ASHDOWN U.75 s.p. (H3282)

HUGHES
Alas, And Did My Savior Bleed
  SATB oct LORENZ C229 $.30 (H3283)

Alleluia *Easter
  SATB oct LORENZ B160 $.30 (H3284)

Alleluia! Sing To Jesus *Easter
  SATB oct LORENZ B128 $.30 (H3285)

At The Name Of Jesus *Easter
  SATB oct LORENZ C304 $.30 (H3286)

Ballad Of The Brown King, The *Xmas,cant
  (Bonds) SATB oct FOX $2.00 (H3287)

Beautiful Savior
  SATB oct LORENZ A481 $.25 (H3288)

Blessed Assurance
  SATB oct LORENZ B107 $.30 (H3289)

Canten Nouve Sus La Museto
  (Haufrecht) "Noel Of The Bagpipes" SATB oct
  FOX PS157 $.30 (H3290)

Child This Day Is Born, A *Xmas
  SATB oct LORENZ A516 $.30 (H3291)

Christ Arose! *Easter
  SATB oct LORENZ B103 $.30 (H3292)

Christ Hath Triumphed, Alleluia!
  SATB oct LORENZ A478 $.30 (H3293)

Christ The Lord Is Risen Today *Easter
  SATB oct LORENZ 9917 $.30 (H3294)

Come, O Come
  SATB oct LORENZ B178 $.25 (H3295)

Do You Know?
  SATB oct LORENZ B124 $.30 (H3296)

HUGHES (cont'd.)
For All Mankind
  SSATTB oct HERITAGE H55 $.35 (H3297)

Forth In Thy Name, O Lord
  SATB oct LORENZ C280 $.30 (H3298)

God Is Everywhere
  SATB oct LORENZ B118 $.30 (H3299)
  SA oct LORENZ 5380 $.30 (H3300)

God Spoke To Me Today
  SATB oct LORENZ B168 $.30 (H3301)

Guide Me, O Thou Great Jehovah
  SATB oct LORENZ C331 $.30 (H3302)
  (Coggin) SAB oct PRO ART 2541 $.30 (H3303)
  (Hustad) SATB oct AGAPE HA 114 $.25 (H3304)

He Lives *Easter
  SATB oct LORENZ B145 $.30 (H3305)

I Must Tell Jesus
  SATB oct LORENZ A438 $.25 (H3306)

If Ever The Sun Stops Shining
  SATB oct LORENZ A487 $.25 (H3307)

In Jesus
  SATB oct LORENZ B179 $.30 (H3308)

It's A Glorious Alleluia! *Xmas,cant
  SATB oct LORENZ $1.95 (H3309)

Keep Christ In Christmas *Xmas
  SATB oct LORENZ B88 $.30 (H3310)

Lead On, O King Eternal
  SATB oct LORENZ C225 $.30 (H3311)

L'estrange Deluge
  (Haufrecht) "Noel Of The Flood" SATB oct
  FOX PS159 $.30 (H3312)

Little David, Play On Your Harp
  SATB oct LORENZ C346 $.30 (H3313)

Lord Is My Shepherd, The
  SATB oct LORENZ A497 $.25 (H3314)

Lord Jesus, Think On Me
  SATB oct LORENZ 9993 $.30 (H3315)

Love's Awakening! *Easter,cant
  SATB LORENZ $1.95 (H3316)

Man And His World
  SATB oct HERITAGE H2151 $.35 (H3317)
  SAB oct HERITAGE H7000 $.35 (H3318)
  TTBB oct HERITAGE H2869 $.35 (H3319)

March On With Christ
  SATB oct LORENZ B133 $.30 (H3320)

Master Hath Called Us, The
  SATB oct LORENZ B167 $.30 (H3321)

Mighty Fortress Is Our God, A
  SATB oct LORENZ B155 $.30 (H3322)

More Like The Master
  SATB oct LORENZ B98 $.30 (H3323)

No Turning Back
  SATB oct LORENZ C218 $.30 (H3324)

Noel Of The Bagpipes *see Canten Nouve Sus
  La Museto

Noel Of The Flood *see L'estrange Deluge

Nothing But Miracles
  SATB oct LORENZ A482 $.25 (H3325)

Nous Voici Dans La Ville
  (Haufrecht) "T'was Here A King Was Born"
  SATB oct FOX PS158 $.25 (H3326)

O Come, All Ye Faithful *Xmas
  SATB oct LORENZ A446 $.30 (H3327)

O God Of The Quiet Spirit
  SATB oct LORENZ A471 $.25 (H3328)

O Jesus, Thou Art Standing
  2pt oct LORENZ 5733 $.30 (H3329)

O Master, Let Me Walk With Thee
  SATB oct LORENZ C330 $.30 (H3330)
  SATB (med easy) SOUTHERN $.30 (H3331)
  SATB SOUTHERN $.30 (H3332)

Once In Royal David's City *Xmas
  SATB oct LORENZ B142 $.30 (H3333)

One Way
  SATB oct LORENZ C335 $.30 (H3334)
  SATB (med easy) SOUTHERN $.30 (H3335)

Onward, Christian Soldiers
  SATB oct LORENZ 9915 $.30 (H3336)

Open My Eyes, That I May See
  SATB oct LORENZ A457 $.30 (H3337)

Praise To The Lord, The Almighty
  SA/SAB oct LORENZ 7825 $.30 (H3338)

Psalm 148
  [Welsh/Eng] men cor,pno voc sc WESTWOOD
  s.p. (H3339)

Ride On, Ride On In Majesty *Easter
  SATB oct LORENZ A464 $.30 (H3340)

Rise Up, Shepherd, And Follow *Xmas
  SATB oct LORENZ A504 $.25 (H3341)

Savior, Lead Me
  SATB oct LORENZ B195 $.30 (H3342)

Sing Alleluia!
  SATB oct LORENZ A513 $.30 (H3343)

Someone
  SATB oct LORENZ A459 $.25 (H3344)

HUGHES (cont'd.)

Song Of The Angels, The *Xmas
SATB oct LORENZ A479 $.30 (H3345)

Song Of The Shepherd Boy (composed with Thygerson) *Xmas
SATB oct SACRED S-138 $.35 (H3346)

Stand Up For Jesus
SATB oct LORENZ C275 $.30 (H3347)

Story Of Love, The *Xmas,cant
SATB oct LORENZ $1.95 (H3348)

Take My Life And Let It Be
SATB oct LORENZ A527 $.30 (H3349)

Take Up Thy Cross *Easter
SATB oct LORENZ B153 $.30 (H3350)

That Holy Night *Xmas
SATB oct LORENZ A491 $.30 (H3351)

This Is My Father's World
SATB oct LORENZ A473 $.30 (H3352)

This Is The Land I Love
SATB oct LORENZ C332 $.30 (H3353)

This Noble Task
SATB oct HERITAGE H2153 $.35 (H3354)

Thou Art The Christ *Easter,cant
SATB LORENZ $1.95 (H3355)

Thou Wilt Keep Him In Perfect Peace
SATB oct LORENZ B119 $.30 (H3356)

To God Be The Glory
SATB oct LORENZ B138 $.30 (H3357)

To Thee, O Lord, Our Hearts We Raise
SA oct LORENZ 5393 $.30 (H3358)

T'was Here A King Was Born *see Nous Voici Dans La Ville

When Morning Gilds The Skies
SATB oct LORENZ C220 $.30 (H3359)

Wonder Of The Ages *Xmas,cant
SATB oct LORENZ A435 $.60 (H3360)

Wonder Of The Ages, The *Xmas
SATB oct LORENZ A435 $.60 (H3361)

Wonderful Peace
SATB oct LORENZ B84 $.30 (H3362)

HUGHES, F.
Benediction *Bene
SATB oct SOUTHERN $.25 (H3363)

HUGHES, H.
Christ The Lord In Silence Coming *Xmas, anthem
(Wilson, P.) SATB&cong (easy) oct GIA G1756 $.30 (H3364)

Let Earth Rejoice *Gen,anthem
(Wilson, P.) SATB/cong (easy) oct GIA G1755 $.30 (H3365)

Let Us Enter The House Of The Lord *Gen, anthem
(Wilson, P.) SATB/cong (easy) oct GIA G1757 $.30 (H3366)

Palatines Daughter, The
SATB ASHDOWN E.A.284 s.p. (H3367)

HUGHES, J.W.
Open Ye The Gates
SSAA,pno (med) oct WILLIS 6328 $.12 (H3368)

HUGHES, JOHN
Songs Of Praises *Gen/Thanks
(Jones, G.J.) 4pt mix cor,SBar soli,acap oct SCHIRM.G 8036 $.25 (H3369)

HUGHES, MIKI
No Cradle Song *Xmas,anthem
SA/unis oct LORENZ 5397 $.25 (H3370)

HUGHES, RITA MEA
Psalm 34 *see Through All The Changing Scenes Of Life

Through All The Changing Scenes Of Life (Psalm 34) Gen,anthem
SATB (med diff) oct LORENZ C348 $.30 (H3371)

HUGHES, ROBERT J. (1916-)
Above The Hills Of Time *Easter/Gen,anthem
SATB (med diff) oct LORENZ C343 $.30 (H3372)

All Hail The Power Of Jesus Name *Asc/Easter/Gen,anthem
SATB (med easy) oct LORENZ B205 $.30 (H3373)

He Laid His Hand On Me *Gen,anthem
3pt wom cor&SA/3pt wom cor&SATB (easy) oct LORENZ A535 $.25 (H3374)

He Walks With God *Gen,anthem
SATB (med diff) oct LORENZ C338 $.30 (H3375)

I Look To Thee In Every Need *anthem
SATB (diff) oct LORENZ 9995 $.30 (H3376)

Little David, Play On Your Harp *Gen,anthem/spir
SATB,ST soli (med diff) oct LORENZ C346 $.30 (H3377)

O For A Thousand Tongues To Sing *anthem
SATB (med diff) oct LORENZ C336 $.30 (H3378)

Prince Of Peace, The *Xmas
(easy) voc sc LORENZ $1.95 (H3379)

HUGHES, S.M. HOWARD
Music For The Eucharistic Prayer Acclamations *Commun/Gen,Mass
SATB&cong/SSAA&cong/TTB&cong/SSAA&cong/TTBB&cong (easy) sc GIA G1639 $.35 (H3380)

HUGHES, S.M. HOWARD (cont'd.)

Music For The Eucharistic Prayer Acclamations-2 *Commun/Gen,Mass
opt SATB&cong,cantor,org (easy) voc sc GIA G1758 $.30 (H3381)

HUIT CANTIQUES see Bach, Johann Sebastian

HUIT VIEILLES CHANSONS DE NOEL see Backers, [Cor]

HULL, MOLLY
Let Christmas All *Xmas
SATB CRAMER C35 s.p. (H3382)

HULLAH, JOHN [PYKE] (1812-1884)
Song Of The Crib, The
unis ASHDOWN U.79 s.p. (H3383)

HULSE, CAMIL VAN
And His Name Was Called Jesus *Xmas,cant
cor (diff) voc sc WILLIS $2.00 (H3384)

Night Of Wonder *cant
mix cor BELWIN $2.00 (H3385)

HUMANA SINE NOMINE see Penn, William

HUMBLE BIRTH, THE see Kulla, Hans

HUMBLY I ADORE THEE see Lewis

HUMBLY I ADORE THEE see Walter

HUMBLY KNEEL WE BEFORE THEE see Mozart, Wolfgang Amadeus, Adoramus Te, Christe

HUME
Shepherds And The Kings, The
SATB SHAWNEE A 1084 $.30 (H3386)

HUMFREY, PELHAM (1647-1674)
By The Waters Of Babylon (Psalm 137)
(Bryant, G.) SATB,ATB soli,strings,cont CONCORDIA 97-5008 $1.00, ipa (H3387)

Complete Church Music *CCU
cor STAINER 3.8934.8 $25.00 (H3388)

Complete Church Music 2 *CCU
cor STAINER 3.8935.8 $25.00 (H3389)

Evening Service *Eve
mix cor oct OXFORD 42.363 $1.05 (H3390)
SATB,acap PETERS H1511 $.75 (H3391)

Hear O Heavens *Gen/Lent,anthem/Bibl
SATB (med easy) oct OXFORD 42.883 $.40 (H3392)
SATB,ATB soli SCHIRM.EC 2679 $.35 (H3393)
(Pinkham, D.) SATB,ATB soli,org SCHIRM.EC 2679 (H3394)

Jubilate Deo *Cnfrm/Ded/Epiph/Gen
"O Be Joyful" SATB,kbd (med diff) oct CONCORDIA 98-2051 $.40 (H3395)

O Be Joyful *see Jubilate Deo

O Lord My God *anthem
SATB,ATB soli,org,strings SCHIRM.EC 2689 $.60 (H3396)
(Pinkham, D.) SATB,ATB soli,org,strings SCHIRM.EC 2689 ipr (H3397)

Psalm 137 *see By The Waters Of Babylon

Rejoice In The Lord *Thanks
SATB,ATBarB soli (med) oct OXFORD 40.916 $.35 (H3398)

HUMILITY BEFORE THEE see Bach, Karl Philipp Emanuel

HUMMEL
Alleluia!
(Wilson) SATB oct COLOMBO 1679 $.30 (H3399)
(Wilson) SSA oct COLOMBO 2168 $.30 (H3400)

Holy Lord, God Of Israel
(Suchoff) SATB oct FOX RM7 $.30 (H3401)

HUMMEL, JOHANN NEPOMUK (1778-1837)
O Virgo Intemerata
[Lat] cor,solo HEUGEL s.p. see from SAINTE-CECILE (H3402)

HUMMING see Roskin

HUMMING PRAYER see Rachmaninoff, Sergey Vassilievitch

HUMPERDINCK, ENGELBERT (1854-1921)
Children's Prayer, The (from Hansel And Gretel) Gen,anthem/prayer
see Humperdinck, Engelbert, Sand-Man's Song
(Johnson, Clair W.) SATB,band oct RUBANK 2225-PL $.18, ipa (H3403)

Evening Prayer (from Hansel And Gretel) Eve, prayer
SA,pno SCHOTT s.p. (H3404)
SATB oct LESLIE 4045 (H3405)
SSA oct LESLIE 3012 (H3406)
SA oct LESLIE 2003 (H3407)
SATB oct STAFF 250 $.20 (H3408)
(Eckard, W.) jr cor oct PRESSER 312-40370 $.35 (H3409)
(Palmer) SATB ALFRED 6334 $.30 (H3410)
(Tolmage) SSA oct STAFF 286 $.30 (H3411)

Evening Prayer And Dream Pantomine (from Hansel And Gretel) prayer
(Wilhousky) SATB oct FISCHER,C CM-6301 $.30 (H3412)

Prayer (from Hansel And Gretel) prayer
SSA KJOS 1221 $.30 (H3413)
(Riegger) SATB FLAMMER A5269 $.30 (H3414)
(Riegger) SA/TB FLAMMER E5021 $.30 (H3415)

Rock Of Ages
SATB oct LORENZ B180 $.25 (H3416)

Sand-Man's Song (from Hansel And Gretel)
unis,pno SCHIRM.EC 1833 $.22, ipr contains also: Children's Prayer, The (H3417)

HUMPHERYS, HENRY
Angelical Salutation "Hail Mary"
SSA oct JUSKO 279 $.20 (H3418)

HUMPHREYS, DON
Hope
(Stickles) SATB,org/pno BOSTON 12337 $.35 (H3419)

I Know He Cares For Me
(Stickles) SATB,pno (easy) oct WILLIS 7310 $.20 (H3420)

Lord Is My Shepherd, The
(Harding) SATB,pno/org (med) oct WILLIS 6244 $.20 (H3421)
(Stickles) 3pt wom cor,pno (med) oct WILLIS 7205 $.25 (H3422)

My Prayer
(Stickles) SATB,pno (easy) oct WILLIS 7193 $.20 (H3423)
(Stickles) 3pt wom cor,pno (med) oct WILLIS 7194 $.20 (H3424)
(Stickles) 2pt mix cor,pno (med) oct WILLIS 7195 $.20 (H3425)

Praise Ye The Lord
(Stickles) SATB,pno (med) oct WILLIS 7391 $.25 (H3426)

HUNDRED AND EIGHTY-FIVE THOUSAND MEN see Lewis

HUNGARIAN BOYS' EASTER CAROL *Easter,carol, Hung
(Gaul) SATB oct GALAXY 1.1032.1 $.35 (H3427)

HUNGER, J.
Ein Frohes Lied Sur Weihnachtszeit *Xmas
mix cor (med easy) oct LEUCKART 643 s.p. (H3428)

Ein Frohes Lied Zur Weihnachtszeit *Xmas
men cor (med easy) oct LEUCKART 297 s.p. (H3429)

HUNKINS, EUSEBIA SIMPSON (1902-)
Appalachian Mass *Mass
SATB FISCHER,C O-4769 $1.00 (H3430)

Child Of Promise
treb cor,narrator,SA soli,pno FISCHER,C O 4451 $1.50 (H3431)

Libera Nos
[Lat] SATB,org oct BROWN 5704 $.40 (H3432)

Why? (from Wondrous Love) Easter/Lent
3pt jr cor/SSA (med) FISCHER,C CM 6950 $.20 (H3433)
SSA oct FISCHER,C CM-6950 $.25 (H3434)

Wondrous Love
3pt jr cor/SSA FISCHER,C O 4108 $1.50 (H3435)
4pt jr cor/SATB FISCHER,C O 3948 $1.75 (H3436)

HUNNICUTT, JUDY
Carol For Ephiphany *Epiph,anthem/carol
SA (easy) oct AUGSBURG 1619 $.25 (H3437)

Carol For Joy
see Hunnicutt, Judy, I Will Wake Up The Sun

Clap Your Hands, All Ye Children *anthem
unis treb cor (easy) oct AUGSBURG 1632 $.25 (H3438)

I Will Wake Up The Sun *anthem
unis (easy) oct AUGSBURG 1650 $.30 (H3439)
unis SOUTHERN $.30 contains also: Carol For Joy (H3440)
unis SOUTHERN $.30 (H3441)

Midst The Deep Silence *anthem
SATB&unis,org,hndbl (med easy) oct AUGSBURG 1657 $.25 (H3442)
unis treb cor&SATB,org,hndbl (med easy) oct AUGSBURG 1657 $.25 (H3443)
SATB (med easy) SOUTHERN $.25 (H3444)

Now Tell Us, Gentle Mary *anthem
unis treb cor,fl,hndbl/org (easy) oct AUGSBURG 1659 $.25 (H3445)

Sing Gloria *anthem
SA (easy) oct AUGSBURG 1656 $.25 (H3446)
SA SOUTHERN $.25 (H3447)

Surely He Has Borne Our Griefs *anthem
SAB (med) oct AUGSBURG 1643 $.30 (H3448)

HUNT
My Prayer
SATB oct SUMMY M 2720 $.25 (H3449)

HUNT, ERIC J.
Go Forth Into The World
unis oct NOVELLO 50.0326.01 s.p. (H3450)

HUNT, J.E.
Magnificat And Nunc Dimittis *Magnif/Nunc
SATB (C maj) oct NOVELLO s.p. (H3451)

Requiem Mass *Mass/Req
[Eng] SATB oct NOVELLO s.p. (H3452)

HUNT, REGINALD
After The Holidays
unis ASHDOWN U.84 s.p. (H3453)

Behold, I Bring You Good Tidings *Xmas
SA BOOSEY-CAN s.p. (H3454)
2pt&opt SATB ASHDOWN E.A.346 s.p. (H3455)

Come Thou Holy Spirit Come *Whitsun
2pt&opt SATB ASHDOWN E.A.348 s.p. (H3456)

Ding, Dong, Merrily On High *Xmas
SATB BOOSEY-CAN s.p. (H3457)

Holy Communion Service In G *Commun
unis ASHDOWN s.p. (H3458)

How Lovely Are Thy Dwellings Fair
2pt ASHDOWN E.A.356 s.p. (H3459)

Hymn Of Praise *hymn
unis&desc oct NOVELLO 37.0021.06 s.p. (H3460)

Man Of Life Upright, A
cor CRAMER 331 s.p. (H3461)

HUNT, REGINALD (cont'd.)

Other Night, The *Xmas,carol
SA BOOSEY-CAN s.p.   (H3462)
2pt ASHDOWN E.A.350 s.p.   (H3463)

This Blessed Christmastide *Xmas,carol/hymn
cor&cong,narrator,org ENOCH s.p.   (H3464)

Wondrous Cross, The *CC4U,hymn
SATB&cong,TBar soli,org (easy) OXFORD
46.105 voc sc $2.45, cor pts $.75 (H3465)

Ye Choirs Of New Jerusalem *Easter
2pt&opt SATB ASHDOWN E.A.347 s.p. (H3466)

HUNT, THOMAS W.
Evening Service In E Flat *Eve,Magnif/Nunc
SATB,opt inst (med easy) oct OXFORD 42.077
$.50   (H3467)

Gentle Guide
2pt/unis oct SOUTHERN $.25   (H3468)

Morning Service In E Flat *Morn,Bene/Te Deum
SATB,opt inst (med) oct OXFORD 43.020 $1.90
                                               (H3469)

HUNTER
Ein' Feste Burg
"Mighty Fortress, A" SATB,band/orch oct
BELWIN 60773 $.35, ipr   (H3470)

Mighty Fortress, A *see Ein' Feste Burg

O, Lord Of Hosts
SSAA MARKS 4507 $.30   (H3471)

Prayer Of St. Francis, A
SSSAA/SSAA oct SUMMY M 2486 $.45   (H3472)

HUNTER, THE see Barnett, John

HUNTER, THE see Brahms, Johannes, Der Jager

HUNTINGTON
Christmas Stands For Love *Xmas
(Hansen) SSA SCHMITT 345 $.35   (H3473)

HUNTLEY
Go Tell It On The Mountains *Xmas
boy cor SOUTHERN $.20   (H3474)

HUR LJUFT DET AR ATT KOMMA see Dannstrom

HUR LJUV, O GUD HURR SALL DEN LOTT see Runback,
Albert

HURD, MICHAEL
Canticles Of The Virgin Mary *CC4U,carol,
Eng,15th cent
SSA voc sc NOVELLO 20.0034.02 s.p.   (H3475)

Jonah-Man Jazz *cant/pop
unis voc sc NOVELLO 20.0002.04 s.p. (H3476)
unis,narrator MARKS $1.00   (H3477)

Missa Brevis *Mass
[Lat] SSA,pno/org voc sc NOVELLO 20.0035.00
s.p.   (H3478)

O Come, Let Us Sing Unto The Lord *anthem
mix cor oct NOVELLO 29.0020.03 s.p. (H3479)

O Saving Victim *anthem
mix cor oct NOVELLO 28.1461.07 s.p. (H3480)

Praise Ye The Lord *anthem
mix cor oct NOVELLO 28.1464.07 s.p. (H3481)

HURE, [JEAN] (1877-1930)
Te Deum *Te Deum
[Lat] SATB,S solo,org oct SALABERT-US $5.25
                                               (H3482)

HURFORD, PETER
Holy Communion *Commun
SATB (series 3) oct NOVELLO s.p.   (H3483)

Holy Son, The
TTBB,acap (easy) OXFORD 85.012 $.15 (H3484)
SATB,acap (easy) OXFORD 84.071 $.20 (H3485)

Isle Of Dreams, The
see Three Short Anthems For Boy's Voices

Jesu So Lowly
see Three Short Anthems For Boy's Voices

Litany To The Holy Spirit *Gen
unis (easy) oct OXFORD 81.037 $.20   (H3486)

Magdalen, Cease From Sobs *anthem
mix cor oct OXFORD 84.195 $.30   (H3487)

Magnificat And Nunc Dimittis *Magnif/Nunc
SS (A maj) NOVELLO 33.0115.10 s.p.   (H3488)
SATB (G maj) oct NOVELLO 44.1399.07 s.p.
                                               (H3489)

Sing A Song Of Joy
see Three Short Anthems For Boy's Voices

Three Short Anthems For Boy's Voices *anthem
boy cor oct NOVELLO 33.0118.04 s.p.
contains: Isle Of Dreams, The; Jesu So
Lowly; Sing A Song Of Joy   (H3490)

HURLEY
Children Of Jerusalem, The
(Campbell; Watson) SA/TB oct SUMMY M 5934
$.35   (H3491)
(Campbell; Watson) SATB oct SUMMY M 5933
$.45   (H3492)

Hosanna To The Son Of David
(Campbell; Watson) SA/TB oct SUMMY M 5932
$.25   (H3493)
(Campbell; Watson) SATB oct SUMMY M 5931
$.35   (H3494)

HURNIK, ILJA (1922-   )
Weihnachtspastorella Nach Bohmischen
Volkstexten *Xmas
[Ger] 4pt jr cor,2 soli,pno,perc,inst (med)
BAREN. BA 4118 sc s.p., cor pts s.p.
                                               (H3495)

HURON INDIAN CAROL see Lee

HUSA, KAREL (1921-   )
Festive Ode
SATB oct HIGHLAND 7.0059.1 $.35   (H3496)

HUSBAND, [EDWARD] (1843-1908)
Revive Us Again
(Mccall) SATB oct PRO ART 2606 $.30 (H3497)

We Praise Thee, O God *Gen/Thanks
(Bock) SA/TB oct BELWIN 1978 $.25   (H3498)
(Darst, W. Glen) SAB oct GRAY GCMR 2660
$.25   (H3499)

HUSH, LITTLE BABY see Martin

HUSH, MY BABE, LIE STILL AND SLUMBER *Xmas,
anthem/carol/folk,US
(Ehret, Walter) SATB,opt inst oct WALTON 2503
$.30   (H3500)
(Thoburn, Crawford) SATB (easy) oct AUGSBURG
0508 $.25   (H3501)

HUSH MY DEAR *Xmas
(Ehret) SATB (Nettleton carol) SCHMITT 657
$.22   (H3502)

HUSH MY DEAR see Bach

HUSH MY DEAR see Graham, Robert [V.]

HUSH, MY DEAR, LIE STILL AND SLUMBER see Bach,
Johann Sebastian

HUSH, MY DEAR, LIE STILL AND SLUMBER see
Barrow, Robert G.

HUSH MY LITTLE CHILD *Xmas,carol,Pol
(Kropczynski, Thaddeus) SATB oct WALTON 2041
$.25   (H3503)

HUSH YE, 'TIS MARY see Cline

HUSHING CAROL see Kountz, Richard

HUSS
Jesus Christ Our Strong Salvation
(Dickinson) SATB oct GRAY GSC 239 $.25
                                               (H3504)

HUSTAD, DONALD P.
Amazing Grace
SSAATTBB oct AGAPE HA 501 $.30   (H3505)

Blessed Assurance
SSAATTBB oct AGAPE HA 502 $.30   (H3506)

Children Of The Heavenly Father *Swed
SATB oct AGAPE HA 101 $.25   (H3507)

Christmas Story In Candelight Carols, The
*Xmas,cant/carol
SATB oct AGAPE $1.50   (H3508)
SAB oct AGAPE $1.50   (H3509)

Easter Story, The *Easter,cant
mix cor oct AGAPE $1.50   (H3510)

Fairest Lord Jesus
SAB oct AGAPE HA 102 $.25   (H3511)

God Of Our Fathers
SATB,opt brass oct AGAPE F 922 $.35 (H3512)

Gospel Bard, The *CCU
SATB oct AGAPE $1.95   (H3513)

Holy God, We Praise Thy Name *Xmas
SATB,brass oct AGAPE F 904 $.30, ipa
                                               (H3514)

Hymn Arrangements No. 1 *CCU,hymn
SATB oct AGAPE $1.50   (H3515)

Hymn Arrangements No. 2 *CCU,hymn
SATB oct AGAPE $1.50   (H3516)

Hymn Arrangements No. 3 *CCU,hymn
SSA oct AGAPE $1.25   (H3517)

Hymn Arrangements No. 4 *CCU,hymn
jr cor oct AGAPE $1.25   (H3518)

Hymn Arrangements No. 5 *CCU,hymn
jr cor oct AGAPE $1.25   (H3519)

Hymn Arrangements No. 6 *CCU,hymn
men cor oct AGAPE $1.25   (H3520)

Hymn Arrangements No. 7 *CCU,hymn
SATB oct AGAPE $1.50   (H3521)

Hymn Arrangements No. 8 *CCU,hymn
SATB/SAB oct AGAPE $1.50   (H3522)

Hymn Arrangements No. 9 *CCU,hymn
SATB oct AGAPE $1.50   (H3523)

I Saw Three Ships
SATB,hndbl,opt harp oct AGAPE F 914 $.30
                                               (H3524)

I Will Sing Of My Redeemer
SATB oct AGAPE CH 613 $.30   (H3525)

Lord's My Shepherd, The
SATB oct AGAPE HA 110 $.25   (H3526)

New Song, A
SATB oct AGAPE A 437 $.25   (H3527)
TTBB oct AGAPE MM 9003 $.25   (H3528)

On Christ The Solid Rock I Stand
SATB oct AGAPE CH 651 $.30   (H3529)

Prayer Before Singing
SATB oct AGAPE HA 107 $.25   (H3530)
SSAATTBB oct AGAPE HA 507 $.25   (H3531)

Why Do I Sing About Jesus?
SATB oct AGAPE HA 112 $.25   (H3532)

HUSTED, B.
When Christ Was Born Of Mary Free *carol,Eng
SATB oct ELKAN-V 362-1244 $.30   (H3533)

HUSTON, SCOTT
Christ Child, The
SSA oct JUSKO 236 $.25   (H3534)
SATB oct JUSKO 235 $.25   (H3535)

HUSTON, SCOTT (cont'd.)

Lamentations Of Jeremiah, The
SATB oct JUSKO 283 $.30   (H3536)

Paul To The Philippians *Bibl
SATB,org oct KERBY 7003 $.45   (H3537)
SATB oct KERBY 7003C $.45   (H3538)

Rejoice In The Lord
SA&unis/SA/unis oct JUSKO 234 $.20   (H3539)

HUTCHESON
Lord's My Shepherd
(Smith) SA/SATB oct BOOSEY 5170 $.30
                                               (H3540)

My Shepherd Will Supply My Need
(Coggin) SAB,org BOSTON 13318 $.35   (H3541)

HUTCHINGS, ARTHUR
Ascendit Deus *Asc,anthem
"God Is Gone Up With A Merry Noise" mix cor
oct NOVELLO 50.0296.06 s.p.   (H3542)

Give Me The Wings Of Faith *anthem
mix cor oct NOVELLO 28.1433.01 s.p. (H3543)

God Is Gone Up With A Merry Noise *see
Ascendit Deus

Hosanna To The Son Of David *Palm,anthem
mix cor oct NOVELLO 50.0295.08 s.p. (H3544)

St. Oswald's Music For The Parish Communion
unis&cong CURWEN 80901 s.p.   (H3545)

HUTCHINSON, GODFREY
Seven Traditional Carols *CC7L,Xmas,carol
[Eng/Lat] SSA CHESTER s.p.   (H3546)

HUTCHINSON, W.
Praise The Lord (Psalm 135)
SATB,org FISCHER,J 10082 $.35   (H3547)

Psalm 135 *see Praise The Lord

HUTER ISRAELS, BEHUTE UNS see Herzogenberg,
Heinrich von

HUTET EUCH, DASS EURE HERZEN NICHT BESCHWERET
WERDEN see Schutz, Heinrich

HUTH, ALFRED (1892-   )
Zeuch Ein Zu Deinen Toren *No.105, Asc/Pent
[Ger] 3pt mix cor,acap BAREN. EM 29 s.p.
see from EVANGELISCHES KIRCHENGESANGBUCH
                                               (H3548)

HUTSON
Advent Wreath, The *Xmas
SATB oct PLYMOUTH JR-141 $.30   (H3549)

Blessing And Honor
SATB,org BOSTON 13577 $.35   (H3550)

Christmas In Days Of Yore *Xmas
2pt oct PLYMOUTH JR-503 $.25   (H3551)

Creche Carol, The *Xmas,carol
(Raymond) SATB oct PLYMOUTH JR-100 $.25
                                               (H3552)

Easter Canticle, The *Easter
SATB oct PLYMOUTH JR-140 $.25   (H3553)

Eyes Of All, The
SATB oct PLYMOUTH JR-139 $.25   (H3554)

Friendly Beasts, The *Xmas
SATB oct PLYMOUTH JR-154 $.30   (H3555)

Great God Of Love
(Raymond) SATB oct PLYMOUTH JR-121 $.25
                                               (H3556)

I Saw Three Ships *Xmas
SATB oct PLYMOUTH JR-138 $.25   (H3557)

Jesus, In Thy Thirst And Pain
(Raymond) SATB oct PLYMOUTH JR-101 $.25
                                               (H3558)

Mass For The Family Of God, A
(Raymond) 2pt oct PLYMOUTH JR-502 $.25
                                               (H3559)

Not Everyone
(Raymond) 2pt oct PLYMOUTH JR-501 $.25
                                               (H3560)

Prayer For Our Nation's Homes, A
(Raymond) SATB oct PLYMOUTH JR-133 $.25
                                               (H3561)

Psalm 150
2pt oct PLYMOUTH JR-507 $.30   (H3562)

Rejoice, Rejoice, For God Is King
SATB oct PLYMOUTH JR-134 $.30   (H3563)

Roadway, The
(Raymond) SATB oct PLYMOUTH JR-112 $.25
                                               (H3564)

Shepherd's Christmas Song, A *Xmas
SATB oct PLYMOUTH JR-145 $.30   (H3565)

Unto Us A Boy Is Born *Xmas
(Raymond) SATB oct PLYMOUTH JR-164 $.30
                                               (H3566)

HUTSON, WIHLA
Above The Hills The Advent Light *Adv
SATB SHAWNEE A 580 $.30   (H3567)

Christ Jesus Rode To Jerusalem
SATB SHAWNEE A 796 $.30   (H3568)

Christmas Morning *Xmas
TTBB oct PLYMOUTH JR-305 $.25   (H3569)

Easter Chimes
SA/TB FLAMMER E5024 $.30   (H3570)

God And Our Brother
(Ades) SA/TB FLAMMER E5157 $.30   (H3571)

He Cares For Me
SSA FLAMMER B 5153 $.25   (H3572)
SA/TB FLAMMER E5153 $.30   (H3573)

Hymn Of Trust *hymn
SATB SHAWNEE A 1077 $.30   (H3574)

King's Highway
SAB SHAWNEE D119 $.30   (H3575)

HUTSON, WIHLA (cont'd.)

Lift Your Hearts Ye Sons And Daughters
SATB SHAWNEE A 518 $.30   (H3576)

Lo, I Am With You Always
SATB SHAWNEE A 801 $.30   (H3577)

Lovely Star
SA oct WORD CS-2436 $.30   (H3578)

Mighty Is The Lord
SATB SHAWNEE A 608 $.25   (H3579)

My Lord Calls Out To Me
SA/TB SHAWNEE A696 $.25   (H3580)

Now Christ Liveth
SATB SHAWNEE A 557 $.30   (H3581)

O Saviour Blest
SATB SHAWNEE A 604 $.25   (H3582)

O Thou Holy Spirit
SATB SHAWNEE A 649 $.30   (H3583)

One In God
SATB SHAWNEE A 652 $.25   (H3584)

Rise Up, O Men Of God
SATB SHAWNEE A 487 $.25   (H3585)

Sing And Be Glad
SA oct WORD CS-339 $.30   (H3586)

Thine Be The Majesty
SAB SHAWNEE D76 $.30   (H3587)

This We Give
SATB SHAWNEE A 607 $.25   (H3588)

When Jesus Came To Live With Men *Xmas
(Raymond) TTBB oct PLYMOUTH JR-307 $.30
                                          (H3589)

When The World Began To Wake
SATB SHAWNEE A 700 $.30   (H3590)

Youth Praises *CCU
(Zaninelli) unis SHAWNEE GF29 $1.25; unis/
2pt SHAWNEE GE30 $1.25; SA SHAWNEE GE31
$1.25; SA/SSA SHAWNEE GE32 $1.25 (H3591)

HUTTON
Like As The Hart
SATB FLAMMER A 5300 $.30   (H3592)

On Christmas Night
SA/TB FLAMMER E5018 $.25   (H3593)

HUYBRECHTS, AUGUST J.
Shepherds Went Their Hasty Way, The
SATB oct FISCHER,J 9939 $.35   (H3594)

HVA GAGNER DET ET MENNESKE see Hovland, Egil

HVA TRENGSEL VI PA JORDEN VET see Buxtehude,
Dietrich

HVAD ER ET MENNESKE see Jeppesen, Knud

HVAD EST DU DOG SKJON see Grieg, Edvard Hagerup

HVEM ER DEN STORSTE see Skauen, Guttorn

HVERT MENNESKE PA JORD see Bach, Johann
Michael, Dem Menschen Ist Gesetzt Einmal

HVI SKAL JE MED MIN BRODER STRIDE see Geitvik,
S.H.

HVI SKAL JEG MED MIN BRODER STRIDE see Geitvik,
S.H.

HVO IKKUN LADER HERREN RADE see Bach, Johann
Sebastian, Wer Nur Den Lieben Gott Lasst
Walten [Chorale]

HVOR ELSKELIGE ER DINE BOLIGER see Bjorn, Hjelm
Borg

HVOR ER DET GODT A LANDE
(Grinde, Nils) wom cor MUSIKK 36 s.p. (H3595)

HVOR LAENGE VIL DU EVIGT GLEMME MIG, HERRE see
Bjorn, Hjelm Borg

HVOR SALIG ER DEN LILLE FLOKK see Geitvik, S.H.

HVOR SKONT LYSER I STRALEKRANS see Distler,
Hugo, Wie Schon Leucht't Uns Der
Morgenstern

HWRAYNEEYAH DAY *Afr
(Nebo) "Good Evening" SATB,T solo,perc oct
LAWSON 51463 $.35   (H3596)

HYATT
Sing Noel *Xmas
SATB oct BELWIN 608213 $.35   (H3597)

HYMN see Einem, G.

HYMN see Isolfsson, Pall

HYMN see Jacobi, Frederick

HYMN see Mendelssohn-Bartholdy, Felix

HYMN see Piechler, Arthur

HYMN AND ALLELUIA see Holmes

HYMN AND PRAYER FOR PEACE see Gillis, D.

HYMN ANTHEM-CHOIR BOOK see Ehret, Walter

HYMN ANTHEMS *CC7L,Gen,anthem/hymn
SATB PRO ART 360 $1.25   (H3598)

HYMN ANTHEMS see Strickler, David

HYMN ARRANGEMENTS NO. 1 see Hustad, Donald P.

HYMN ARRANGEMENTS NO. 2 see Hustad, Donald P.

HYMN ARRANGEMENTS NO. 3 see Hustad, Donald P.

HYMN ARRANGEMENTS NO. 4 see Hustad, Donald P.

HYMN ARRANGEMENTS NO. 5 see Hustad, Donald P.

HYMN ARRANGEMENTS NO. 6 see Hustad, Donald P.

HYMN ARRANGEMENTS NO. 7 see Hustad, Donald P.

HYMN ARRANGEMENTS NO. 8 see Hustad, Donald P.

HYMN ARRANGEMENTS NO. 9 see Hustad, Donald P.

HYMN AT BETHLEHEM see Emig, Lois

HYMN AT SUNSET, A see Geehl, Henry Ernest

HYMN BEFORE SUNRISE see Miles, P. Nadier

HYMN DESCANTS VOL. I see Bonham, Eugene

HYMN DESCANTS VOL. II see Bonham, Eugene

HYMN DESCANTS VOL. III see Bonham, Eugene

HYMN FOR ASCENSIONTIDE see Purcell, Henry

HYMN FOR CHRISTMAS DAY see Parry, Charles
Hubert Hastings

HYMN FOR EASTER DAY see Beck

HYMN FOR EASTER DAY see Beck, John Ness

HYMN FOR MANKIND see Wills

HYMN FOR OUR TIME see Beck, John Ness

HYMN FOR OUR TIME see Williams, David H.

HYMN FOR PEACE, A see Goldman, E.

HYMN FOR SCHOOLS see Knight, Vincent

HYMN FOR ST. CECILIA, A see Howells, Herbert
Norman

HYMN FOR THANKSGIVING, A see Williams

HYMN FOR THE NEW YEAR see Boyce, William

HYMN FOR WINTER see Clothier, Louita

HYMN FROM THE DESERT see Ben-Haim, Paul,
Lobgesang Aus Der Wuste

HYMN GOTTHEIT see Mozart, Wolfgang Amadeus,
Gottheit! Dir Sei Preis Und Ehre

HYMN I LATINI MEDII AEVI VOL. 3 see Mone, F.J.

HYMN OF BROTHERHOOD *Neth
(Ramsey, V.) SAB oct GRAY GCMR 2255 $.30
                                          (H3599)
(Ramsey, V.) SATB oct GRAY GCMR 1980 $.25
                                          (H3600)

HYMN OF BROTHERHOOD see Beethoven, Ludwig van

HYMN OF BROTHERHOOD, A see Wyton, Alec

HYMN OF COLUMBA see Britten, Benjamin

HYMN OF CONSECRATION see Thiman, Eric Harding

HYMN OF CONSECRATION see Wetherill

HYMN OF DEDICATION see Wordsworth, William

HYMN OF DEDICATION, A see MacDonald

HYMN OF FAITH, A see Heaton, [Wallace]

HYMN OF FREEDOM see Brahms, Johannes

HYMN OF FREEDOM, A see Thiman, Eric Harding

HYMN OF GLORY see Bossi, Marco Enrico, Cantate
Domino

HYMN OF GLORY, A see Taylor

HYMN OF GLORY LET US SING, A see Rawls, Kathryn
H.

HYMN OF GRATITUDE see Ford, Virgil T.

HYMN OF GRATITUDE see Haydn, (Franz) Joseph

HYMN OF GRATITUDE, A *hymn
(Lynn, George) SATB oct WALTON 2038 $.25
                                          (H3601)

HYMN OF HOPE see Nelhybel, Vaclav

HYMN OF JESUS see Holst, Gustav

HYMN OF JOY see Toolan, S. Suzanne

HYMN OF NATIONS see Lovelace, Austin C.

HYMN OF NATIVITY see Serly, Tibor

HYMN OF PARADISE see Lockwood, Normand

HYMN OF PEACE see Calcott

HYMN OF PEACE, A see Jones

HYMN OF PENITENCE see Pitfield, Thomas Baron

HYMN OF PRAISE see Bach, Johann Sebastian

HYMN OF PRAISE see Brahms, Johannes

HYMN OF PRAISE see France, William E.

HYMN OF PRAISE see Goldman, Maurice

HYMN OF PRAISE see Hunt, Reginald

HYMN OF PRAISE see Larson

HYMN OF PRAISE see Luvaas

HYMN OF PRAISE see Mascagni, Pietro

HYMN OF PRAISE see Mendelssohn-Bartholdy, Felix

HYMN OF PRAISE see Mendelssohn-Bartholdy,
Felix, Lobgesang

HYMN OF PRAISE see Mozart, Wolfgang Amadeus,
Ave Verum

HYMN OF PRAISE see Muller, H.

HYMN OF PRAISE see Pasquet, Jean

HYMN OF PRAISE see Smith

HYMN OF PRAISE see Tchaikovsky, Piotr Ilyitch

HYMN OF PRAISE see Thiman, Eric Harding

HYMN OF PRAISE see Vernon, Sister (Verhaalen,
M.)

HYMN OF PRAISE see Wolff, S. Drummond

HYMN OF PRAISE, A see Adler, Samuel

HYMN OF PROGRESS see Hopkins

HYMN OF REJOICING see Faure, Gabriel-Urbain

HYMN OF ST. COLUMBA see Droste

HYMN OF SUPPLICATION see McAfee, Don

HYMN OF THANKS see Adaskin

HYMN OF THANKS see Ford, Virgil T.

HYMN OF THANKSGIVING see Biggs, John

HYMN OF THANKSGIVING see Denton

HYMN OF THE CHERUBIM see Tchaikovsky, Piotr
Ilyitch

HYMN OF THE CITY see Bryant

HYMN OF THE IMMORTALS see Williams, David McK.

HYMN OF THE INITIANTS see Pasquet, Jean

HYMN OF THE LAST SUPPER see Young

HYMN OF THE NATIVITY see Hoiby, Lee

HYMN OF THE NATIVITY, A see Johnson

HYMN OF THE WEEK, PART I, THE *CCU,Adv/Xmas/
Epiph,hymn,16-20th cent
(Thomas, P.) mix cor CONCORDIA 97-7603 $.90;
SAB CONCORDIA 97-4716 $1.00   (H3602)

HYMN OF THE WEEK, PART II, THE *CCU,hymn,16-
20th cent
(Thomas, P.) mix cor CONCORDIA 97-7604 $.90;
SAB CONCORDIA 97-4717 $1.00 Septua to Gdfri
                                          (H3603)

HYMN OF THE WEEK, PART III, THE *CCU,hymn,16-
20th cent
(Thomas, P.) mix cor CONCORDIA 97-7605 $.90;
SAB CONCORDIA 97-4718 $1.00 East to Trin
                                          (H3604)

HYMN OF THE WEEK, PART IV, THE *CCU,hymn,16-
20th cent
(Thomas, P.) mix cor CONCORDIA 97-7606 $.75;
SAB CONCORDIA 97-4719 $1.00 Trin I to Trin
XVI   (H3605)

HYMN OF THE WEEK, PART V, THE *CCU,hymn,16-
20th cent
(Thomas, P.) mix cor CONCORDIA 97-7607 $.75;
SAB CONCORDIA 97-4720 $1.00 St. Michael and
All Angels Day to Last Sunday After Trin
                                          (H3606)

HYMN OF THE WORLD'S CREATOR see White, Louie

HYMN OF TRIUMPH see Traver, James

HYMN OF TRUST see Allitsen, Frances

HYMN OF TRUST see Hutson, Wihla

HYMN OF TRUST see Pitfield, Thomas Baron

HYMN OF TRUST, A see McAfee

HYMN OF TRUST, A: "IONA" see Perrin, Susan F.

HYMN OF UNITY see Toolan, S. Suzanne

HYMN OF WISDOM see Butler, Eugene

HYMN OF YOUTH see Hemmer, [Eugene]

HYMN OF YOUTH see Washburn, Robert

HYMN OF YOUTH, A see Wood, Dale

HYMN PA ADVENTSUNDAGEN see Pitoni, Giuseppe
Ottavio

HYMN PA KYNDELSMASSODAGEN see Praetorius,
Michael

HYMN PA TACKSAGELSEDAGEN see Nyvall, Jacob

HYMN SERVICE OF NINE LESSONS *CCUL,hymn
oct ROYAL 308 s.p.   (H3607)

HYMN SING (VOLUME 1) see Wild, Eric

HYMN TILL JORDEN see Sibelius, Jean

HYMN TILL SANGEN see Wideen, Ivar

HYMN TILL VASTERGOTLAND see Wideen, Ivar

HYMN TO CHRIST THE KING see Denny, James

HYMN TO JOY see Beethoven, Ludwig van

HYMN TO PEACE see Roberton, Hugh S.

HYMN TO ST. PETER see Britten, Benjamin

HYMN TO THE EARTH see Sibelius, Jean

HYMN TO THE GODHEAD *hymn
(Thompson, Van Denman) SATB ALLANS 364 s.p.
                                          (H3608)

HYMN TO THE GODHEAD see Thompson

HYMN TO THE HOLY INNOCENTS, A see Brown,
Christopher

HYMN TO THE NIGHT see Rhea, Raymond

HYMN TO THE RISEN CHRIST, A see Curry, W. Lawrence

HYMN TO THE SAVIOUR see Kremser, [Edward]

HYMN TO THE SOUL see Jenkins, Cyril

HYMN TO THE SUN see Mozart, Wolfgang Amadeus, Dir, Seele Des Weltalls

HYMN TO THE TRINITY *hymn
(Thompson, Van Denman) SATB ALLANS 361 s.p.
(H3609)

HYMN TO THE TRINITY see King

HYMN TO THE TRINITY see Schroth, G.

HYMN TO THE TRINITY see Taylor, Deems (Joseph)

HYMN TO THE TRINITY see Tchaikovsky, Piotr Ilyitch

HYMN TO THE TRINITY see Thompson

HYMN TO THE TRINITY see Witt, Friedrich, Ave Maria

HYMN TO THE VIRGIN see Britten, Benjamin

HYMN TO THE VIRGIN see Verdi, Giuseppe, Laudi Alla Vergine Maria

HYMN TO THE VIRGIN, A see Harman, C.

HYMN TO THE VIRGIN, A see Ward, Rona

HYMN-TUNE ANTHEMS NO. 1 *CCU,anthem
SATB LORENZ $1.95
(H3610)

HYMN-TUNE ANTHEMS NO. 2 *CCU,anthem
SATB LORENZ $1.95
(H3611)

HYMNAL OF CHRISTIAN UNITY *CCU,hymn
(Hume, Paul; Bennett, Clifford) cong cloth
LITURGICAL $1.00 contains works by: Bach;
Isaak; Tallis; and others
(H3612)

HYMNARIUM FOR KIRKE, SKOLE OG HJEM I BIND:
ADVENT *CCU,Adv,hymn
(Karlsen, Rolf; Nielsen, Ludvig) [Norw] wom
cor/men cor/jr cor LYCHE LY257 s.p.
(H3613)

HYMNARIUM FOR KIRKE, SKOLE, OG HJEM III BIND:
EPIFANIA *Epiph,hymn
(Karlsen, Rolf; Nielsen, Ludvig) [Norw] wom
cor/men cor/jr cor LYCHE LY424 s.p.
(H3614)

HYMNARIUM FOR KIRKE, SKOLE OG HJEM IV BIND:
FASTE *Lent,hymn
(Karlsen, Rolf; Nielsen, Ludvig) [Norw] wom
cor/men cor/jr cor LYCHE LY505 s.p.
(H3615)

HYMNARIUM FOR KIRKE, SKOLE OG HJEM V BIND:
PASKE *Easter,hymn
(Karlsen, Rolf; Nielsen, Ludvig) [Norw] wom
cor/men cor/jr cor LYCHE LY527 s.p.
(H3616)

HYMNARIUM FOR KIRKE, SKOLE OG HJEM X BIND:
KORALVESPER *hymn
(Karlsen, Rolf; Nielsen, Ludvig) [Norw] wom
cor/men cor/jr cor LYCHE LY504 s.p.
(H3617)

HYMNARIUM FOR KIRKE, SKOLE, OG HLEM II BIND:
JUL AND NYTTAR *Xmas,hymn
(Karlsen, Rolf; Nielsen, Ludvig) [Norw] wom
cor/men cor/jr cor LYCHE LY272 s.p.
(H3618)

HYMNE see Hoogerwerf, N.

HYMNE see Monnikendam, Marius

HYMNE see Mozart, Wolfgang Amadeus

HYMNE see Nesse, Sigurd

HYMNE see Oser, H.

HYMNE see Schubert, Franz (Peter)

HYMNE A LA VIERGE see Schubert, Franz (Peter)

HYMNE A SAINT-AUGUSTIN see Gounod, Charles Francois

HYMNE A SAINT-NICOLAS DE LORRAINE see Schmitt, Florent

HYMNE A SAINTE CECILE see Huet, Felix

HYMNE AAN DE MORGEN see Bonset, Jac.

HYMNE AAN DE VREDE see Nieuwenhoven, H. v.

HYMNE AAN DE ZANG see Boedijn, Gerard H.

HYMNE AN DEN UNENDLICHEN see Schubert, Franz (Peter)

HYMNE AN DIE ALLMACHT see Burgwart, K.

HYMNE ANTIQUE see Dubois, Theodore

HYMNE DE LA JEUNESSE CHRETIENNE see Ganne

HYMNE DE LA PENTECOTE see Bach, Johann Sebastian, Veni Creator Spiritus

HYMNE DES VIERGES see Bach, Johann Sebastian, Jesus, Corona Virginum

HYMNE DU MATIN see Bach, Johann Sebastian

HYMNE DU MATIN see Ducoudray, B.

HYMNE I: GEH UNTER, SCHONE SONNE see Crusius, O.E.

HYMNE OF HEAVENLY LOVE, AN see Cruft

HYMNE TO GOD THE FATHER, A see Mc Cabe, John

HYMNEN see Dietrich, Sixtus

HYMNEN see Weber, Ludwig

HYMNEN-BAND VIII see Palestrina, Giovanni

HYMNI AD PROCESSIONEM IN FESTO CORPORIS CHRISTI see Schroeder, Hermann

HYMNI ECCLESIASTICI see Rozycki, (Jacek) Hyacinthus

HYMNI LATINI MEDII AEVI VOL. 1 see Mone, F.J.

HYMNI LATINI MEDII AEVI VOL.2 2 see Mone, F.J.

HYMNI MEDIAEVALES see Reuland, Jacques

HYMNISCHER GESANG see Holler, Karl

HYMNS AND ANTHEMS FOR CHILDREN'S VOICES see Grime, William

HYMNS AND ANTHEMS FOR MALE VOICES see Hansen

HYMNS AND ANTHEMS FOR TREBLE CHOIRS *CCU
treb cor SCHMITT 17 $.50
(H3619)

HYMNS AND ANTHEMS FOR YOUTH CHOIR, VOL. 1 see Coggin

HYMNS AND ANTHEMS FOR YOUTH CHOIR, VOL. 2 see Coggin

HYMNS AND ANTHEMS (SET NO. 1) see Jones

HYMNS AND ANTHEMS (SET NO. 2) see Jones

HYMNS AND CAROLS *CCU,carol/hymn
(Parker, Alice; Shaw, Robert) SATB oct LAWSON $2.50
(H3620)

HYMNS AND CAROLS see Licht

HYMNS AND RESPONSES FOR THE CHURCH YEAR see Persichetti, Vincent

HYMNS FOR A NEW AGE *CCU,anthem
unis LORENZ $.75
(H3621)

HYMNS FOR MALE VOICES *CC21L,Gen,hymn
(Engebrecht) men cor PRO ART 996 $.60 (H3622)

HYMNS FOR MEN see Cassler, G. Winston

HYMNS FOR TEACHERS see Wheelwright, Lorin F.

HYMNS FOR TEENTIME *CC54U,hymn
(Cooper, Irvin) boy cor/SSBar&camb FISCHER,C O-4037 $1.50
(H3623)

HYMNS FOR THE AMUSEMENT OF CHILDREN see Oldham, Arthur

HYMNS FROM THE CROSSROADS see Robertson

HYMNS IN RESPONSE see Bock

HYMNS (NOYE'S FLUDDE) see Britten, Benjamin

HYMNS OF FAITH see Robertson, Leroy

HYMNS OF GLORY, SONGS OF PRAISE see Leaf, Robert

HYMNS OF JOY see Wheelwright, Lorin F.

HYMNS OF NATIONS *CC15U,hymn
SATB,pno PETERS ZM1310 $1.50
(H3624)

HYMNS OF PRAISE see Berger, Jean

HYMNS OF PRAYER AND PRAISE, SERIES 1 see Grime, William

HYMNS OF THANKS see Goemanne, Noel

HYMNS TO THE TRINITY see Cooper

HYMNUS see Geiser, Walther

HYMNUS see Held, Paul

HYMNUS see Nystedt, Knut

HYMNUS see Weiss, Ewald

HYMNUS ANNI SANCTI see Carosio

HYMNUS CAELESTIS URBS JERUSALEM see Maessen, Antoon

HYMNUS CANTEMUS DOMINO see Carissimi, Giacomo

HYMNUS CHORALIS see Wagenheim

HYMNUS DE SPIRITU SANCTO see Diepenbrock, Alfons

HYMNUS DE TRINITATE see Weismann, Wilhelm

HYMNUS PARADISI see Howells, Herbert Norman

HYMNUS TE DEUM LAUDAMUS see Viero, Francesco

HYRDENE PA MARKEN see Beck, Thomas [Ludvigsen]

HYSLOP
Evening Service *see Magnificat And Nunc Dimittis

Magnificat And Nunc Dimittis *Magnif/Nunc
"Evening Service" SATB,acap (easy, set to African melodies) OXFORD 43.347 $.25
(H3625)

I

I AIN'T GONNA STUDY WAR *spir
(Luboff, Norman) SATB,opt bvl,drums,gtr oct WALTON 3054 $.35, ipa
(I1)

I AM
SACRED $1.75
(I2)

I AM see Newbury, Kent A.

I AM A PILGRIM see Gardner, Maurice

I AM A POOR WAYFARING STRANGER
SATB oct STAFF 184 $.25
(I3)

I AM A POUR WAYFARING STRANGER *folk
(Bratt, C. Griffith) SATB,soli,acap oct WORLD ESE-978-8 $.45
(I4)

I AM ALPHA AND OMEGA see Stainer, John

I AM BLESSED BY GOD'S LOVE see Freeman

I AM DEBTOR TO ALL see Hedges, Anthony

I AM GLAD see Zimmermann, Heinz Werner

I AM GOING TO SUNDAY SCHOOL see O'Hara, Geoffrey

I AM HE THAT COMFORTETH YOU see Smith, Frank H., Ego Ipse Consolabor Vos

I AM HE THAT LIVETH see Davis, Katherine K.

I AM HE THAT LIVETH see Simper, Caleb

I AM JUST A LITTLE CHILD see Artman

I AM NOT WORTHY, HOLY LORD see Schirrmann

I AM SO GLAD EACH CHRISTMAS EVE see Knudsen, [Peder], Jeg Er Saa Glad

I AM THE ALPHA AND THE OMEGA see Moe, Daniel

I AM THE BOAT see Lewis, John Leo

I AM THE BREAD OF LIFE see Back, Sven-Erick, Ego Sum Panis Vitae

I AM THE BREAD OF LIFE see Roff, Joseph

I AM THE BREAD OF LIFE see Stainer, John

I AM THE BREAD OF LIFE see Toolan, S. Suzanne

I AM THE DOOR see Lewis

I AM THE GOOD SHEPHERD see Bender, Jan

I AM THE GOOD SHEPHERD see Caldwell

I AM THE GOOD SHEPHERD see Matthews, [Timothy Richard]

I AM THE GOOD SHEPHERD see Morgan

I AM THE GOOD SHEPHERD see Rhea, Raymond

I AM THE GOOD SHEPHERD see Vance

I AM THE GOOD SHEPHERD see Wood, Dale

I AM THE GOOD SHEPHERD see Young

I AM THE LIGHT OF THE WORLD see Darst, W. Glenn

I AM THE LIVING BREAD see Harwood, Basil

I AM THE LORD see Pepping, Ernst

I AM THE ONE see Caldwell, Mary [Elizabeth]

I AM THE RESURRECTION see Gibbons, Orlando

I AM THE RESURRECTION see Wolff, S. Drummond

I AM THE RESURRECTION AND THE LIFE see Gibbons, Orlando

I AM THE RESURRECTION AND THE LIFE see Nelson, Ronald A.

I AM THE RESURRECTION AND THE LIFE see Rasley

I AM THE RESURRECTION AND THE LIFE see Schutz, Heinrich

I AM THE RESURRECTION AND THE LIFE see Williams

I AM THE RESURRECTION AND THE TRUE LIFE see Schutz, Heinrich

I AM THE ROOT AND THE BRANCH OF DAVID see Schein, Johann Hermann

I AM THE ROSE OF SHARON see Billings, William

I AM THE VINE see Davies, James

I AM THE VINE see James, Philip

I AM THE VINE see Morgan

I AM THE WAY see Wheeler, Alfred

I AM THE WAY, THE TRUTH, AND THE LIFE see Young

I ANNOUNCED YOUR JUSTICE see Kaderavek, Milan

I AROSE see Kreutz, Robert E.

I ASCEND UNTO MY FATHER see Gallus, Jacobus

I BEEN IN THE STORM SO LONG *spir
(De Cormier) SATB,S solo,acap oct LAWSON 51282 $.30
(I5)

I BEESEECH YOU TO LOOK see Sjolund, Paul

I BEHELD, AND LO! A GREAT MULTITUDE see Blow, John

I BEHELD HER, BEAUTIFUL AS A DOVE see Willan, Healey

I BELIEVE
SACRED $1.75   (I6)

I BELIEVE see Beard

I BELIEVE see Young

I BELIEVE GOD IS REAL see Carmichael, Ralph

I BELIEVE IN MIRACLES see Peterson, John W.

I BELIEVE IN ONE GOD
SATB KJOS 6518 $.35   (I7)

I BELIEVE IN ONE GOD see Gardner

I BELIEVE IN ONE GOD see Rinehart

I BELIEVE IN ONE GOD see Swenson

I BELIEVE IN ONE GOD see Tchaikovsky, Piotr Ilyitch, Credo

I BELIEVE IN ONE GOD see Thompson, Randall, Credo

I BELIEVE THAT MY REDEEMER LIVES see Peloquin, C. Alexander

I BELONG TO THAT BAND (SHOUT) *spir
(Jessye) SATB oct SHAPIRO SK 2091 $.30   (I8)

I BESEECH THEE, O GOD see Harris, Jerry Weseley

I BIND MY HEART see Lovelace, Austin C.

I BOW IN PRAYER BEFORE THEE see Beethoven, Ludwig van

I BOWED ON MY KNEES AND CRIED HOLY
SSA/SATB/TTBB BIG3 $.30   (I9)

I BRING YE LOVE see Cruft

I BRING YOU GOOD NEWS see Newbury, Kent A.

I CALL AND CRY TO THEE see Tallis, Thomas

I CALL HEAVEN AND EARTH see Winslow, R.K.

I CALL ON HIM *anthem
SAB/SA/TB BIG3 $.25   (I10)

I CALL TO THEE see Bach, Johann Sebastian

I CALL WITH MY WHOLE HEART see Powell

I CALLED UPON THE LORD see Avery, S.R.

I CAN BELIEVE see Nyboer, Martha

I CAN BELIEVE see Peterson, John W.

I CAN DO ALL THINGS THROUGH CHRIST see Ford

I CAN GO ANYWHERE see Kah Behneh Kah

I CAN SEE IN A MORNIN' SUNRISE see Leaf

I CAN TELL THE WORLD see Hairston, Jester

I CANNOT OPE MINE EYES see Raffman, Relly, Matins

I CAN'T BRING THREE KINGS TO BETHLEHEM see Grime, William

I CAN'T SPIN A WEB see Lewis

I CAUSED THY GRIEF see Manz, Paul

I CIELI IMMENSI see Marcello

I COME, O LORD, UNTO THEE see Sateren, Leland Bernhard

I COULDN'T HEAR NOBODY PRAY *spir
"Ich Konnte Horen Kein Gebet" see Funf Negro-Spirituals
(Johnson) mix cor,ST soli,acap oct SCHIRM.G
10151 $.45   (I11)
(King) SATB KJOS 5394 $.30   (I12)
(Smith) SATB KJOS 1011 $.30   (I13)
(Wiley) SATB oct PRO ART 2006 $.22   (I14)

I COULDN'T HEAR NOBODY PRAY see Hicks, L'Roy E.

I CRIED TO GOD IN TRIBULATION see Haydn, (Johann) Michael

I DE STORA SKOGARNA see Boldemann, Laci

I DEN GAMLE KONGESTANDEN *carol
[Norw] LYCHE s.p.   (I15)

I DO NOT ASK, O LORD see Roff, Joseph

I DO NOT ASK, O LORD see Verrees, Leon

I DODENS BAND see Laub, Thomas

I DODENS BAND LAG HERREN KRIST see Cruger, Johann

I DODENS BAND LAG HERREN KRIST see Praetorius, Michael

I DODENS BAND LAG HERREN KRIST see Runback, Albert

I DODENS BAND VOR FRELSER LA see Jeppesen, Knud

I DREAMED IT WAS THE NIGHT see Bobrov

I DREAMT I CAME TO NAZARETH see Sharpe, Evelyn

I EVERMORE SHALL SING see Lyman, Ed.

I FEEL LIKE MY TIME AIN'T LONG see Still, William Grant

I FOUN' MY LOS' SHEEP *spir
(Roberton) mix cor ROBERTON 61391 s.p.   (I16)

I FOUND A FRIEND
SATB/TTBB BIG3 $.25   (I17)

I FOUND HIM IN MY HEART see Nyboer, Martha

I FOUND JESUS see Freeman, Charles

I FOUND MY SAVIOR see York

I FOUND THE LORD see Sourire, Souer

I GIVE MYSELF UNTO PRAYER see Young

I GIVE YOU A NEW COMMANDMENT see Shepherd, John

I GO TO BETHLEHEM *Xmas,carol,Czech
(Ehret, Walter) SATB,opt inst oct WALTON 2516
$.30   (I18)

I GO TO PREPARE A PLACE FOR YOU see Marth, Helen Jun

I GOT A HOME IN THAT ROCK see Lynn, George

I GOT A KEY *spir
(Shaw; Parker) SATB,T solo,acap oct LAWSON
51105 $.35   (I19)

I GOT A ROBE *spir
"Er Kronet Mich" see Sechs Negro Spirituals, Blatt 1
(Brevig, Agnes) "Heav'n Heav'n" [Eng] wom
cor/jr cor/eq voices LYCHE 3 s.p.   (I20)

I GOT A ROBE see Dankt Gott

I GOT A SHOE see Wilson, John F.

I GOT ME FLOWERS see Greaves, Ralph

I GOT MY RELIGION IN TIME see White

I GOT RELIGION *spir
(Cain) mix cor,acap oct SCHIRM.G 7698 $.30 (I21)

I GOT SHOES *spir
(Bartholomew) 4pt men cor,acap oct SCHIRM.G
7144 $.25   (I22)
(Shaw; Parker) mix cor,acap oct LAWSON 51116
$.40   (I23)

I GOT THE SPIRIT see Rodby, Walter

I GREET THEE, WHO MY SURE REDEEMER ART see Curry

I HAD A LITTLE HEN see Simpson, Kenneth

I HAIL THEE, MARY see Luzzi, Luigi, Ave Maria

I HAVE A DREAM see Exner, Max

I HAVE A MOTHER IN THE HEAVENS see Bryan, Charles [Faulkner]

I HAVE A PEACE IN MY HEART see Paris

I HAVE BEEN TO THE MOUNTAINTOP see Southbridge

I HAVE BUILT A HOUSE see Ferguson, Edwin Earle

I HAVE CALLED THEE see Sateren, Leland Bernhard

I HAVE LIFTED UP MY SPIRIT see Aiblinger, Johann Kaspar

I HAVE LONGED FOR THY SAVING HEALTH see Byrd, William

I HAVE LOST ALL THAT ONCE I WAS see Crawford, John, Plus Ne Suis Ce Que J'ai Ete

I HAVE ONLY ONE LIFE TO LIVE see Artman

I HAVE QUIETED MY SOUL see Thompson

I HAVE SEEN THE LORD see Hovhaness, Alan

I HAVE SURELY BUILT THEE A HOUSE TO DWELL IN see Milner, Anthony

I HAVE SURELY BUILT THEE AN HOUSE see Boyce, William

I HAVE TRUSTED IN THEE see Roff, Joseph

I HEAR AMERICA SINGING see Kettering, Eunice Lea

I HEAR CHILDREN SINGING see Rhea, A.

I HEAR NO VOICE see Pyle, Francis [Johnson]

I HEAR THE WORDS OF JESUS see Nordman, Chester

I HEAR THY VOICE see Lang

I HEAR THY WELCOME VOICE see Sateren, Leland Bernhard

I HEARD A GREAT VOICE see Billings, William

I HEARD A GREAT VOICE see Christiansen, Paul

I HEARD A GREAT VOICE see Kimball

I HEARD A VOICE see Roberts, J.D.

I HEARD A VOICE see Tallis, Thomas, Audivi Vocem De Caelo

I HEARD A VOICE FROM HEAVEN see Goss, John

I HEARD A VOICE FROM HEAVEN see Tomkins, Thomas

I HEARD THE BELLS see Yuffy

I HEARD THE BELLS ON CHRISTMAS DAY *Xmas
(Andrews) SATB oct GALAXY 1.1276.1 $.30 (I24)

I HEARD THE BELLS ON CHRISTMAS DAY see Carlson, R.

I HEARD THE BELLS ON CHRISTMAS DAY see Curry

I HEARD THE BELLS ON CHRISTMAS DAY see Palmer

I HEARD THE BELLS ON CHRISTMAS DAY see Rhea, A.

I HEARD THE VOICE OF JESUS
SATB BIG3 $.40   (I25)

I HEARD THE VOICE OF JESUS see Dykes

I HEARD THE VOICE OF JESUS see Mendelssohn-Bartholdy, Felix

I HEARD THE VOICE OF JESUS see Tallis, Thomas

I HEARD THE VOICE OF JESUS SAY see Cain, Noble

I HEARD THE VOICE OF JESUS SAY see Leighton, E.I.

I HEARD THE VOICE OF JESUS SAY see Rankin, W.S.

I HEARD THE VOICE OF JESUS SAY see Rathbun, F.

I HEARD THE VOICE OF JESUS SAY see Thompson

I HEARD TWO SOLDIERS TALKING see Chapman

I HIDE ME, JESUS, IN THY NAME see Ford, Virgil T.

I HIMMELEN
see Fem Folkliga Koraler I Sattningar
(Soderholm, Valdemar) 3pt wom cor/3pt jr cor,
acap NORDISKA 5198 s.p.   (I26)

I HIMMELEN see Grieg, Edvard Hagerup

I HIMMELEN see Houge

I HIMMELEN, I HIMMELEN see Aberg, Jan H.

I HIMMELEN, I HIMMELEN see Ree, Knut

I HIMMELEN SJUNGER KRING LAMMETS TRON see Bond, Anders

I HOLD THE KINGDOM see Postel, C.M.

I HOPPET SIG MIN FRALSTA SJAL FORNOJER
see Sex Koraler I Folkton I Sattningar

I, JOHN, SAW THE HOLY NUMBER see Work

I JULETID see Nordqvist, Gustaf

I KNEEL BESIDE THY CRADLE HERE see Bach, Johann Sebastian

I KNEEL IN ADORATION see Cornelius, Peter

I KNELT AT THY ALTAR
SATB CHAPPELL 0015578-358 $.40   (I27)

I KNEW THAT GOD WAS THERE see Moore

I KNOW A BEAUTIFUL THEME see Stoughton, R.

I KNOW A LOVELY GARDEN see Caldwell, Mary [Elizabeth]

I KNOW A NAME see James

I KNOW A NAME see Lillenas, Haldor

I KNOW DE LORD'S LAID HIS HANDS ON ME see Burleigh, Henry Thacker

I KNOW HE CARES FOR ME see Humphreys, Don

I KNOW I HAVE ANOTHER BUILDING see Lynn, George

I KNOW I LOVE THEE, LORD see Underwood

I KNOW IN WHOM I TRUST see Bach, Johann Sebastian

I KNOW IN WHOM I TRUST see Lundquist, Matthew Nathanael

I KNOW MY LORD IS PROMISE see Klein

I KNOW NOT WHERE THE ROAD MAY LEAD see William, David

I KNOW OF A LOVELY AND BLESSED PLACE see Farrar, H.M.

I KNOW THAT MY REDEEMER LIVES see Bach, Johann Michael, Ich Weiss, Dass Mein Erloser Lebt

I KNOW THAT MY REDEEMER LIVES see Bach, Johann Sebastian

I KNOW THAT MY REDEEMER LIVES see Bunjes, Paul G.

I KNOW THAT MY REDEEMER LIVES see Lynn, George

I KNOW THAT MY REDEEMER LIVES see Schutz, Heinrich, Ich Weiss Dass Mein Erloser Lebt

I KNOW THAT MY REDEEMER LIVES see Bach, Johann Sebastian

I KNOW THAT MY REDEEMER LIVES [CHORALE] see Bach, Johann Sebastian

I KNOW THAT MY REDEEMER LIVETH see Canniciari, D. Pompeo, Credo Quod Redemptor

I KNOW THAT MY REDEEMER LIVETH see Fillmore

I KNOW THAT MY REDEEMER LIVETH see Franck, Melchior, Ich Weiss, Dass Mein Erloeser Lebt

I KNOW THAT MY REDEEMER LIVETH see Handel, George Frideric

I KNOW THAT MY REDEEMER LIVETH see Peeters, Flor

I KNOW THE LORD see Norman, Robert

I KNOW THE LORD LAID HIS HANDS ON ME *spir
(Davids, Dean) SATB oct BELWIN 2114 $.25
(I28)
(Kent, Richard) SATB,acap oct WORLD
ESE-1080-8 $.60   (I29)

I KNOW THE LORD'S LAID HIS HAND ON ME see Hansen

I KNOW THE LORD'S LAID HIS HANDS ON ME see Hansen

I KNOW THE SECRET OF HIS REST see Hoskins

I KNOW THE THOUGHTS I THINK see Wienhorst, Richard

I KNOW THE TOUCH OF HIS HAND see Lowell

I KNOW WHAT GOD IS see Raye

I KNOW WHAT GOD IS see Raye, Don

I KNOW WHEN I'M GOING HOME see Kennedy, John Brodbin

I KNOW WHERE I'M GOING see Moffatt, James

I KNOW WHO HOLDS TOMORROW see Stanphill

I KNOW WHOM I HAVE BELIEVED see Mc Granahan

I LAID ME DOWN TO REST see Byrd, William

I LAY MY SINS ON JESUS see Engelbrekt

I LAY MY SINS ON JESUS see Smart, David

I LAY MY SINS ON JESUS see Speaks, [Oley]

I LAY MY SINS ON JESUS see Young, C.

I LIFT MY EYES TO THE HILLS see Kechley, [Gerald]

I LIFT MY HEART TO THEE see Hawkey

I LIFT MY LONGING EYES WITH LOVE see Schutz, Heinrich

I LIFT MY SOUL TO THEE see Haweis, [Thomas]

I LIFT UP MINE EYES see Beveridge, Thomas G.

I LIFT UP MINE EYES see Moe, Daniel

I LIFT UP MY EYES see Berger, Jean

I LIFT UP MY EYES see Moe, Daniel

I LIFT UP MY EYES see Wichmann

I LIFT UP MY EYES TO THE HILLS see Angell, Warren M.

I LIFT UP MY SOUL see Fischer, Clare

I LIKE TO DREAM see Dungan

I LIKE TO HEAR THE BIBLE see Grime, William

I LONG FOR THY SALVATION see Newbury

I LONG FOR THY SALVATION see Newbury, Kent A.

I LONGED TO FIND THE RISEN LORD see Fischer

I LOOK TO THEE IN EVERY NEED see Elliot

I LOOK TO THEE IN EVERY NEED see Hirschberg

I LOOK TO THEE IN EVERY NEED see Hughes, Robert J.

I LOOK TO THEE IN EV'RY NEED see Kinsman

I LOOKED, AND BEHOLD! see Milner, Anthony

I LOOKED, AND BEHOLD A WHITE CLOUD see Willan, Healey

I LOOKED FOR LOVE *CCU
(Carmichael, Ralph) SATB voc sc WORD 30022
$1.95   (I30)

I LOVE ALL BEAUTEOUS THINGS see Chandler, Mary

I LOVE ALL BEAUTEOUS THINGS see Le Fleming, Christopher (Kaye)

I LOVE MY GOD see Burroughs, Bob

I LOVE MY GOD see Roff, Joseph

I LOVE THE CHURCH see Sateren, Leland Bernhard

I LOVE THE LORD see Glarum, L. Stanley

I LOVE THEE
(Posegate) SATB oct VOLKWEIN VB693 $.30 (I31)

I LOVE THEE, MY LORD *Gen
(Fjerstad) unis SCHMITT 237 $.25   (I32)

I LOVE THEE, MY LORD see Cram

I LOVE THY CHURCH, O GOD see Lorenz

I LOVE THY KINGDOM, LORD *Bibl
(Grieb) jr cor&sr cor oct SCHIRM.G 10749 $.25
                                              (I33)

I LOVE THY KINGDOM, LORD see Cram, James D.

I LOVE THY KINGDOM LORD see Hopkins

I LOVE THY KINGDOM LORD see Saint Thomas

I LOVE THY KINGDOM LORD see Weaver

I LOVE THY KINGDOM, LORD see Young

I LOVE THY KINGDON LORD see Rawls, Kathryn H.

I LOVE TO HEAR THE STORY see Matthews

I LOVE TO TELL THE STORY see Wilson

I MANANS SKIMMER see Soderman, (Johan) August

I MET GOD IN THE MORNING see Hawkins, Floyd W.

I MET MY MASTER FACE TO FACE see Adams, Stephen

I MET THE MASTER FACE TO FACE see Bodycombe, [Aneurin]

I MET THE MASTER FACE TO FACE see Schroeder, John

I MUST TELL JESUS see Hughes

I NEED THEE EVERY HOUR see Heyward

I NEED THEE EVERY HOUR see Lowry, Robert

I NEED THEE EVERY HOUR see Wilson, Ira B.

I NEED THEE EV'RY HOUR see Lynn, George

I NEED THEE HEAVENLY FATHER see Lowell

I NEVER KNEW HOW GREAT MY LORD COULD BE see House, L. Marguerite

I NODTIDER see Soderholm, Valdemar

I PASTORI ALLA CAPANNA see Magri, Pietro

I PINGSTEN BLEV GUDS ANDE SAND see Berg, Gottfrid

I PINGSTEN BLEV GUDS ANDE SAND see Runback, Albert

I PRAISED THE EARTH see Thiman, Eric Harding

I PRAISED THE EARTH IN BEAUTY SEEN see Van Dyke

I PRAY THEE, DEAR LORD JESUS see Pelz, Walter L.

I RISE AND SING see Lapo, Cecil E.

I SAID TO THE LORD see Jacob, Gordon

I SAID TO THE MAN WHO STOOD AT THE GATE OF THE YEAR see Harries

I SAT DOWN UNDER HIS SHADOW see Bairstow, Edward Cuthbert

I SAT DOWN UNDER HIS SHADOW see Johansson, Bengt

I SAT DOWN UNDER HIS SHADOW see Near, Gerald

I SAW A STRANGER YESTREEN see Glarum, L. Stanley

I SAW IN THE NIGHT VISIONS see Naylor, Bernard

I SAW THE LORD see Stainer, John

I SAW THREE SHIPS *Xmas,carol/folk,Eng
see To Us Is Born A Little Child
see Many Moods Of Christmas, The, Suite Four
see Six Traditional Carols, Set I
see Three Christmas Carols
unis/SATB (easy) OXFORD 08.009 $.15   (I34)
SATB,acap (med easy) OXFORD 84.001 $.35 (I35)
(Clark, K.) SATB,acap FISCHER,J 10086 $.35
                                              (I36)
(Deale) SATB,acap (med easy) OXFORD 84.001
$.25 see from Four Old Carols   (I37)
(Hinton) unis (very easy) OXFORD 81.092 $.25,
ipa   (I38)
(Holst) unis jr cor/unis wom cor CURWEN 71654
s.p.   (I39)
(Hunter; Weale) SATB,S solo,acap oct LAWSON
51285 $.25   (I40)
(Mead) SATB oct GALAXY 1.1712.1 $.35   (I41)
(Mead) TTBB&jr cor oct GALAXY 1.1722.1 $.35
                                              (I42)
(Shaw; Parker) mix cor,acap oct SCHIRM.G
10188 $.25   (I43)
(Vaughan Williams) TTBB,B solo,acap (easy)
OXFORD 41.908 $.25 see from Nine Carols (I44)
(Williamson, W.) SA LEONARD-US 08029280 $.25
                                              (I45)
(Williamson, W.) SSA LEONARD-US 08029440 $.25
                                              (I46)
(Woodgate) SS (easy) OXFORD 44.057 $.55 see
also Six Two-Part Carols   (I47)

I SAW THREE SHIPS see Couper

I SAW THREE SHIPS see Hustad, Donald P.

I SAW THREE SHIPS see Hutson

I SAW THREE SHIPS see Van Dyke

I SAW THREE SHIPS CAME SAILING *Xmas
(Marth) 3pt mix cor oct SCHIRM.G 1178 $.25
                                              (I48)

I SAY TO ALL MEN FAR AND NEAR see Mueller, Carl F.

I SEE GOD see Leveen

I SEE HIS BLOOD UPON THE ROSE see Benjamin, Arthur

I SEE HIS BLOOD UPON THE ROSE see Elaine, Sister M. (Gentemann)

I SEE HIS BLOOD UPON THE ROSE see Kirkpatrick

I SEE HIS BLOOD UPON THE ROSE see Nelson, Havelock

I SEE HIS BLOOD UPON THE ROSE see Roberton, Hugh S.

I SEE WHITE AND BLACK, LORD see Lewis, John Leo

I SEEK THY PEACE see Lehenbauer, Ruth B.

I SETTE PECCATI MORTALI see Malipiero, Gian Francesco

I SHALL LIVE see Paris

I SHALL MAKE OF MY SPIRIT A CRADLE see Rose

I SHALL NOT BE MOVED
(Parker) TTBB,pno/gtr oct LAWSON 51297 $.35
                                              (I49)
(Parker) SATB,pno/gtr oct LAWSON 51545 $.35
                                              (I50)

I SHALL NOT PASS AGAIN THIS WAY see Effinger, S.

I SING A SONG OF THE SAINTS see Sowerby, Leo

I SING A SONG OF THE SAINTS OF GOD see O'Hara, Geoffrey

I SING AS I ARISE TODAY see Clokey, Joseph Waddell

I SING OF A MAIDEN *Xmas,carol,Eng,15th cent
unis/SATB (easy) OXFORD 08.103 $.15   (I51)
(Jacques) unis (med) OXFORD 81.074 $.20 (I52)
(Rhodes) SSA,acap (easy) OXFORD 44.987 $.25
                                              (I53)
(Wasner) 4pt mix cor,acap oct SCHIRM.G 10611
$.25   (I54)

I SING OF A MAIDEN see Bancroft, H. Hugh

I SING OF A MAIDEN see Davis, Katherine K.

I SING OF A MAIDEN see Gilbert, J.R.

I SING OF A MAIDEN see Hesford, Brian

I SING OF A MAIDEN see Le Fleming

I SING OF A MAIDEN see Maconchy, Elizabeth

I SING OF A MAIDEN see Roff, Joseph

I SING OF A MAIDEN see Wesley, Samuel Sebastian Jr.

I SING OF A MAIDEN see Wishart

I SING OF A MAIDEN see Young, Carlton R.

I SING OF GOD see Price

I SING OF THE GLORY OF THE LORD see Smith

I SING TH'ALMIGHTY POWER OF GOD see Lovelace, Austin C.

I SING THE ALMIGHTY see Klump

I SING THE BIRTH see Dirksen, Richard W.

I SING THE BIRTH see Elgar, Edward

I SING THE GREATNESS OF GOD see Bock, F.

I SING THE MIGHTY POWER GOD see Curry

I SING THE MIGHTY POWER OF GOD *hymn
(Butler) SATB (tune: Halifax) oct PRO ART
2240 $.30   (I55)
(Ehret) SATB oct WORD CS-657 $.30   (I56)

I SING THE MIGHTY POWER OF GOD see Atkinson

I SING THE MIGHTY POWER OF GOD see Crandall, Robert

I SING THE MIGHTY POWER OF GOD see Ellacombe

I SING THE MIGHTY POWER OF GOD see Lipscomb, Helen

I SING THE MIGHTY POWER OF GOD see Peninger

I SING THE MIGHTY POWER OF GOD see Price

I SING THE MIGHTY POWER OF GOD see Watts

I SING THY BIRTH see Hayes

I SING TO THEE see Luvaas

I SOUGHT HIM see Berlinski, [Herman]

I SOUGHT THE LORD see Curry

I SOUGHT THE LORD see Davis, Katherine K.

I SOUGHT THE LORD see Glarum, L. Stanley

I SOUGHT THE LORD see Graham

I SOUGHT THE LORD see Lovelace, Austin C.

I SOUGHT THE LORD see Stevenson, F.

I SOWED THE SEEDS OF LOVE
(Holst, Gustav) men cor CURWEN 50619 s.p.
                                              (I57)

I SPEAK OF THEE see Emig, Lois

I SPEAK THE NAME OF JESUS see Lawson

I STAND BESIDE THE MANGER STALL see Diemer, Emma Lou

I STILLER FASTETIDER see Healey, D.

I STOOD AT THE DOOR OF MY LORD see Wild, Eric

I STOOD BY THE RIVER OF JORDAN see Smith

I STOOD ON DE RIBBER OB JERDON see Burleigh, Henry Thacker

I SUFFERED WITH GREAT HEAVINESS see Bach, Johann Sebastian, Ich Hatte Veil Bekummernis

I SURRENDER ALL see Mac Roberts

I SURRENDER ALL see Weeden

I TALKED TO GOD LAST NIGHT see Guion, David Wendall Fentress

I THANK THEE HEAVENLY FATHER see Gumpeltzhaimer, Adam, Ich Danke Dir Lieber Herre

I THANK THEE LORD, FOR ALL THY CARE see Brandon

I THANK THEE, O LORD see Copes, V. Earle

I THANK THEE, O LORD see Nelson, Myra Hedges

I THANK THEE, O LORD see Schutz, Heinrich

I THANK YOU GOD
SATB CHAPPELL 0015602-358 $.40   (I58)

I THANK YOU GOD see Pfautsch, Lloyd

I THANK YOU, LORD see Roff, Joseph

I, THEREFORE, THE PRISONER OF THE LORD see
Gibbs

I THINK I HEARD HIM SAY see Martin

I THINK ON THEE see Schumann, Robert
(Alexander), Ich Denke Dein

I THOUGHT ON THE LAMB OF GOD see Wilson

I THOUGHT THAT LOVE HAD BEEN A BOY see Kunz,
Jack

I TO THE HILLS LIFT UP MINE EYES see Berger

I TONI DELLA SALMODIA see Bottazzc, Luigi

I TURN THE CORNER OF PRAYER see Thomas

I WAIT FOR THE LORD see Slates, Philip M.

I WAITED FOR THE LORD see Hopkins

I WAITED FOR THE LORD see Mendelssohn-
Bartholdy, Felix

I WAITED FOR THE LORD see Schutz, Heinrich

I WAITED PATIENTLY FOR THE LORD see Arnatt,
Ronald

I WALK WITH GOD see Byles

I WALK WITH THE KING see Ackley

I WALKED IN GOD'S GARDEN see Hart, A.W.

I WALKED IN THE GARDEN see Weaver

I WALKED INTO THE GARDEN see Weaver, Marion

I WALKED TODAY WHERE JESUS WALKED see O'Hara,
Geoffrey

I WAN' JESUS TO WALK WITH ME see Kemmer,
[George W.]

I WAN' TO BE READY *spir
(Dawson) SATB KJOS T127 $.40   (I59)
(Dawson) men cor KJOS T128 $.40   (I60)
(Dawson) SSA KJOS T129 $.40   (I61)

I WANNA BE READY see Miller

I WANT A HEART TO PRAY see Arensky, Anton
Stepanovitch

I WANT A PRINCIPLE WITHIN see Pfautsch, Lloyd

I WANT GOD'S HEAVEN TO BE MINE see King

I WANT JESUS TO WALK WITH ME *spir
(Jonson, William) SATB WEINBERGER s.p. (I62)
(McLin) SATB oct PRO ART 2533 $.30   (I63)
(Roberts) SATB,acap,opt perc oct LAWSON 51572
$.30   (I64)
(Whitman) SATB oct LILLENAS AN-3812 $.30
(I65)

I WANT JESUS TO WALK WITH ME see Boatner,
[Edward H.]

I WANT JESUS TO WALK WITH ME see Jonson,
William

I WANT JESUS TO WALK WITH ME see Lynn, George

I WANT JESUS TO WALK WITH ME see Pisano

I WANT JESUS TO WALK WITH ME see Wehr, David A.

I WANT THAT CROWN *spir
(Johnson) SATB oct LILLENAS AN-5006 $.30
(I66)

I WANT TO BE LIKE JESUS see Ives, Charles

I WANT TO BE READY *spir
(Cain) SSA BOOSEY-CAN s.p.   (I67)
(Cain) SATB oct BOOSEY 5272 $.30   (I68)
(Cain) SSAATTBB,acap oct BOOSEY 1604 $.30
(I69)
(De Coursey) SATB oct FOX S163 $.35   (I70)
(Ehret) SA oct SPRATT 213 $.30   (I71)
(Ehret, Walter) SAB oct WALTON 4002 $.30
(I72)
(Kinsman, F.) SATB oct PRESSER MC414 $.30
(I73)

I WANT TO BE READY see Burleigh, Henry Thacker

I WANT TO BE READY see Denton

I WANT TO BE READY see Gardner, Maurice

I WANT TO CLIMB UP JACOB'S LADDER *spir
(Kinsman, F.) SA LEONARD-US 08029760 $.25
(I74)
(Kinsman, F.) SAB LEONARD-US 08030080 $.25
(I75)
(Kinsman, F.) SATB LEONARD-US 08030400 $.25
(I76)

I WANT TO DIE EASY *spir
(Shaw; Parker) SATB,T solo,acap oct LAWSON
51114 $.35   (I77)

I WANTA BE READY see Forsblad

I WAS GLAD see Avery

I WAS GLAD see Baoteng, S. Geoffrey

I WAS GLAD see Charpentier, Marc-Antoine,
Laetatus Sum

I WAS GLAD see Crampton, T.

I WAS GLAD see Durst, Sidney C.

I WAS GLAD see Grime, William

I WAS GLAD see Orr, Robin

I WAS GLAD see Parry, Charles Hubert Hastings

I WAS GLAD see Slack, Roy

I WAS GLAD see Sowerby, Leo

I WAS GLAD see Wolff, S. Drummond

I WAS GLAD WHEN THEY SAID see Elvey, George Job

I WAS GLAD WHEN THEY SAID UNTO ME *Introit
SATB BIG3 $.25   (I78)

I WAS GLAD WHEN THEY SAID UNTO ME see Fawcett,
J.

I WAS GLAD WHEN THEY SAID UNTO ME see Graves

I WAS GLAD WHEN THEY SAID UNTO ME see Hastings

I WAS GLAD WHEN THEY SAID UNTO ME see Parry,
Charles Hubert Hastings

I WAS GLAD WHEN THEY SAID UNTO ME see Thompson,
Alan

I WAS LIKE AN INNOCENT LAMB see Victoria, Tomas
Luis de, Eram Quasi Agnus

I WAS THE TREE see O'Hara, Geoffrey

I WILL ALWAY GIVE THANKS see King, Robert

I WILL ALWAYS GIVE THANKS see Kelly

I WILL ALWAYS GIVE THANKS see King

I WILL ALWAYS GIVE THANKS see Titcomb

I WILL ARISE
(Byler; Mason) SATB oct WORD CS-699 $.25
(I79)
(Campbell) SATB,S/T solo,acap oct PRO ART
1838 $.25   (I80)
(Shaw; Parker) SATB,acap oct LAWSON 905 $.30
(I81)

I WILL ARISE AND GO TO JESUS
(Williams) SATB oct LILLENAS AN-1152 $.30
(I82)

I WILL ARISE AND GO TO JESUS see Cain, Noble

I WILL ARISE AND GO TO JESUS see Hart

I WILL ARISE AND GO TO MY FATHER see Smith

I WILL BE AS THE DEW see Nystedt, Knut

I WILL BE GLAD see Cockshott, Gerald Wilfred

I WILL BE GLAD AND REJOICE IN THEE see
Pergolesi, Giovanni Battista

I WILL BLESS THE LORD see Boeringer, James

I WILL BLESS THE LORD see Bortniansky, Dimitri
Stepanovitch

I WILL BOW AND BE SIMPLE
see Two Shaker Songs
(Jacobson) 3pt wom cor oct SCHIRM.G 11599
$.30   (I83)

I WILL CALL ON THEE see Gounod, Charles
Francois, Kyrie

I WILL CALL UPON THE LORD see Mozart, Wolfgang
Amadeus

I WILL DWELL IN THE HOUSE OF THE LORD see
Daniels

I WILL EXALT HIM see Handel, George Frideric

I WILL EXALT THEE see Tye, Christopher

I WILL EXTOL MY GOD see Brown, Frank Edwin

I WILL EXTOL THEE see Rogers, E.

I WILL EXTOL THEE see Angell

I WILL EXTOL THEE see Blanchard, [William G.]

I WILL EXTOL THEE see Costa

I WILL EXTOL THEE see Mead, Edward G.

I WILL EXTOL THEE see Moe, Daniel

I WILL EXTOL THEE see Price

I WILL EXTOL THEE see Roff, Joseph

I WILL EXTOL THEE see Wienandt, Elwyn A.

I WILL EXTOL THEE see Wilson

I WILL EXTOL THEE see Young

I WILL EXTOL THEE, MY GOD see Berger, Jean

I WILL EXTOL THEE, MY GOD see Handel, George
Frideric

I WILL EXTOL THEE, MY GOD see Koch, Frederick

I WILL EXTOL THEE, O GOD see Rachmaninoff,
Sergey Vassilievitch

I WILL EXTOL THEE, O LORD see Costa

I WILL EXTOL THEE, O LORD see Erbach,
Christian, Exaltabo Te, Domine

I WILL EXTOL THEE, O LORD see Glarum, L.
Stanley

I WILL EXTOL YOU see Englert, Eugene

I WILL FEED MY FLOCK see Roff, Joseph

I WILL FEED MY FLOCK see Simper, Caleb

I WILL FREELY SACRIFICE TO THEE see Peter

I WILL GIVE PEACE see Ford

I WILL GIVE THANKS see Adler, Samuel

I WILL GIVE THANKS see Diemer, Emma Lou

I WILL GIVE THANKS see Kirk

I WILL GIVE THANKS see Kirk, Theron W.

I WILL GIVE THANKS see Willan, Healey

I WILL GIVE THANKS UNTO THE LORD see Campbell-
Tipton, [Louis]

I WILL GIVE THANKS UNTO THEE, O LORD see
Rossini, Gioacchino

I WILL GIVE THANKS WITH ALL MY HEART see
Lockwood, Normand

I WILL GIVE YOU RAIN IN DUE SEASON see Rowley,
Alec

I WILL GREATLY REJOICE see Rotermund, Donald

I WILL GREATLY REJOICE IN THE LORD see Berger,
Jean

I WILL KEEP CHRISTMAS see Gass, Irene

I WILL LAY ME DOWN IN PEACE see Gadsby

I WILL LAY ME DOWN IN PEACE see Gratton, Frank
L.

I WILL LAY ME DOWN IN PEACE see Lang, C.S.

I WILL LAY ME DOWN IN PEACE see Thiman, Eric
Harding

I WILL LAY ME DOWN IN PEACE see Willan, Healey

I WILL LIFT MINE EYES see Edwards, Clara

I WILL LIFT MINE EYES see Glarum, L. Stanley

I WILL LIFT MINE EYES UNTO THE HILLS see
Joubert, John

I WILL LIFT UP MINE EYES
SATB CHAPPELL 2526259-358 $.40   (I84)

I WILL LIFT UP MINE EYES see Angell, Warren M.

I WILL LIFT UP MINE EYES see Bach, Johann
Sebastian

I WILL LIFT UP MINE EYES see Bevan, Richard T.

I WILL LIFT UP MINE EYES see Butler

I WILL LIFT UP MINE EYES see Clarke-Witfield,
Dr. J.

I WILL LIFT UP MINE EYES see Davis, Katherine
K.

I WILL LIFT UP MINE EYES see Dickey, Mark

I WILL LIFT UP MINE EYES see Freed, Isadore

I WILL LIFT UP MINE EYES see Galbraith, J.

I WILL LIFT UP MINE EYES see Goldman, E.

I WILL LIFT UP MINE EYES see Gordon, Louis

I WILL LIFT UP MINE EYES see Hovhaness, Alan

I WILL LIFT UP MINE EYES see Johnston, E.
Dwight

I WILL LIFT UP MINE EYES see Ledger, Philip

I WILL LIFT UP MINE EYES see Le Fleming,
Christopher (Kaye)

I WILL LIFT UP MINE EYES see Lekberg, Sven

I WILL LIFT UP MINE EYES see Mayer, Eleanor W.

I WILL LIFT UP MINE EYES see Moore

I WILL LIFT UP MINE EYES see Mueller, Carl F.

I WILL LIFT UP MINE EYES see Pfautsch, Lloyd

I WILL LIFT UP MINE EYES see Rogers, J.H.

I WILL LIFT UP MINE EYES see Shure, R. Deane

I WILL LIFT UP MINE EYES see Sowerby, Leo

I WILL LIFT UP MINE EYES see Stanton, Royal
[W.]

I WILL LIFT UP MINE EYES see Thomas, Mansel

I WILL LIFT UP MINE EYES see Vaughan, Rodger

I WILL LIFT UP MINE EYES see Wadely, F.W.

I WILL LIFT UP MINE EYES see Walker, Ernest

I WILL LIFT UP MINE EYES see Wetherill

I WILL LIFT UP MINE EYES see Willan, Healey

I WILL LIFT UP MINE EYES see Williamson,
Malcolm

I WILL LIFT UP MINE EYES see Young

I WILL LIFT UP MINE EYES UNTO THE HILLS see
Boatwright, Howard

I WILL LIFT UP MINE EYES UNTO THE HILLS see
Gardner, John [Linton]

I WILL LIFT UP MINE EYES UNTO THE HILLS see
Surplice, [Reginald] Alwyn

I WILL LIFT UP NOW MINE EYES see Lassus, Roland
de (Orlandus), Levavi Oculos Meos

I WILL LOVE THEE, O LORD see Glarum, L. Stanley

I WILL MAGNIFY see Wheeler, Alfred

I WILL MAGNIFY THEE see Collingwood, A.

I WILL MAGNIFY THEE see Handel, George Frideric

I WILL MAGNIFY THEE see Parry, W.H.

I WILL MAGNIFY THEE see Rogers, J.H.

I WILL MAGNIFY THEE see Vail

I WILL MAGNIFY THEE O GOD
    (Means, Claude) unis oct GRAY GCMR 3227 $.30
                                              (I85)

I WILL MAGNIFY THEE, O GOD see Danks

I WILL MAGNIFY THEE O GOD see Knapp, Lavater

I WILL MAGNIFY THEE, O LORD see Clarke, Thomas

I WILL MAGNIFY THEE, O LORD see Corfe, Joseph

I WILL MAKE A NEW CONVENANT see Lynn

I WILL MAKE YOU FISHERS OF MEN see Freed

I WILL MENTION THE LOVING KINDNESSES see Antes,
    John

I WILL NEVER PASS THIS WAY AGAIN
    (Davidson) SSA/SATB/SAB/TTBB BIG3 $.40   (I86)
    (Simon, Wm.) SSA/SATB/SAB BIG3 $.40   (I87)

I WILL NOT LEAVE YOU COMFORTLESS see Byrd,
    William, Non Vos Relinquam

I WILL NOT LEAVE YOU COMFORTLESS see Nelson,
    Ronald A.

I WILL NOT LEAVE YOU COMFORTLESS see Titcomb

I WILL NOT LET THEE GO see Bach, Johann
    Christoph, Ich Lasse Dich Nicht

I WILL OPEN MY EYES see Davis, Katherine K.

I WILL POUR OUT MY SPIRIT see Naylor, Bernard

I WILL PRAISE GOD WITH A SONG see Newbury, Kent
    A.

I WILL PRAISE THE LORD see Cafarella

I WILL PRAISE THE LORD see Roff, Joseph

I WILL PRAISE THE LORD see Schutz, Heinrich

I WILL PRAISE THE LORD see Telemann, Georg
    Philipp

I WILL PRAISE THE NAME OF GOD see Blow, John

I WILL PRAISE THE NAME OF GOD see Cain, Noble

I WILL PRAISE THEE see Canavati

I WILL PRAISE THEE see Martin, Reginald W.

I WILL PRAISE THEE see Wood, Robin

I WILL PRAISE THEE, O LORD see Berger, Jean

I WILL PRAISE THEE, O LORD see Berglund, R.

I WILL PRAISE THEE, O LORD see Lalande

I WILL PRAISE THEE, O LORD see Lalande, Michel
    Richard de

I WILL PRAISE THEE, O LORD see Nystedt, Knut

I WILL PRAISE THEE WITH MY WHOLE HEART see
    Wienhorst, Richard

I WILL PUBLISH THE NAME OF THE LORD see Smith

I WILL REJOICE IN THE LORD see Homilius,
    Gottfried August, Ich Freue Mich Im Herrn

I WILL REJOICE IN THE LORD see Hovhaness, Alan

I WILL SHOW FORTH THY GLORY see Pasquet, Jean

I WILL SING see Wilson

I WILL SING AND GIVE PRAISE see Newbury, Kent
    A.

I WILL SING MY MAKER'S PRAISES see Schop

I WILL SING NEW SONGS OF GLADNESS see Dvorak,
    Antonin

I WILL SING OF MY REDEEMER   *hymn
    (Hustad, Don) SATB ALLANS 443 s.p.   (I88)

I WILL SING OF MY REDEEMER see Bock, Fred

I WILL SING OF MY REDEEMER see Hustad, Donald
    P.

I WILL SING OF MY REDEEMER see Mc Granahan

I WILL SING OF MY REDEEMER see Moffatt, James

I WILL SING OF THE MERCIES OF THE LORD see
    Darnton, C.

I WILL SING OF THE MERCIES OF THE LORD see
    Powell

I WILL SING OF THY GREAT MERCIES see Darnton

I WILL SING OF THY GREAT MERCIES see
    Mendelssohn-Bartholdy, Felix

I WILL SING OF THY POWER see Sullivan, Sir
    Arthur Seymour

I WILL SING PRAISES see Telemann, Georg Philipp

I WILL SING TO THE LORD see Peter, Johann
    Friedrich

I WILL SING UNTO THE LORD see Amner, John

I WILL SING UNTO THE LORD see Cornell

I WILL SING UNTO THEE see Kirk, Theron W.

I WILL THANK THEE, O LORD see Moir, F.L.

I WILL WAIT ON THY MERCY see Pasquet, Jean

I WILL WAKE UP THE SUN see Hunnicutt, Judy

I WILL WALK BEFORE THE LORD see Roff, Joseph

I WILL WORSHIP see Dyson, George

I WISH THAT I WERE GOING HOME see Distler, Hugo

I WISH WE'D ALL BEEN READY see Norman

I WISH WE'D ALL BEEN READY see Norman, L.

I WONDER see Centrone

I WONDER see Lewis

I WONDER AS I WANDER   *Xmas
    (Niles) 4pt wom cor,S solo,acap oct SCHIRM.G
      8305 $.30   (I89)
    (Niles; Horton) 4pt men cor,med solo,acap oct
      SCHIRM.G 9292 $.25   (I90)
    (Niles; Horton) 2pt boy cor/2pt wom cor,med
      solo oct SCHIRM.G 9787 $.30   (I91)
    (Niles; Horton) 2pt men cor,med solo oct
      SCHIRM.G 9788 $.35   (I92)
    (Niles; Horton) 4pt mix cor,high solo,acap
      oct SCHIRM.G 8708 $.35   (I93)
    (Niles; Horton) 3pt mix cor,med solo oct
      SCHIRM.G 9497 $.30   (I94)
    (Niles; Horton) 4pt wom cor,high solo,acap
      oct SCHIRM.G 9292 $.25   (I95)
    (Niles; Horton) 3pt wom cor oct SCHIRM.G 9630
      $.30   (I96)
    (Niles; Horton) 2pt wom cor,med solo oct
      SCHIRM.G 9498 $.30   (I97)

I WONDER AS I WANDER see Niles, John Jacob

I WONDER WHY? see Avery

I WONDER WHY see Copland, Aaron

I WON'T HAVE TO CROSS JORDAN ALONE
    SATB BIG3 $.25   (I98)

I WORSHIP HIM see Lovelace, Austin C.

I WORSHIP HIM see Marryott, Ralph E.

I WOULD BE TRUE
    see Three General Hymns

I WOULD BE TRUE see Lovelace, Austin C.

I WOULD BE TRUE see Peek

I WOULD BE TRUE see Peery

I WOULD BESIDE MY LORD see Bach, Johann
    Sebastian

I WOULD NOT BE DENIED see Jones

I WOULD, O LORD see Pevernage, Andries, Je
    Veux, Seigneur

I WOULD SEEK GOD see Ford

I WOULD SING, SING, SING see Lovelace, Austin
    C.

I WOULD WALK WITH YOU, LORD see Barnes, [Edward
    Shippen]

IAM CHRISTUS ASTRA ASCENDERAT see Palestrina,
    Giovanni

IAMS
    Folk And Spiritual Time
      (Thygerson) SSA/SAT oct HERITAGE H6502 $.45
                                              (I99)
    Holiday Time   *Xmas
      (Thygerson) SSA/SAT oct HERITAGE H6501 $.55
                                              (I100)
    Peace I Leave With You   *Gen
      SATB SCHMITT 1777 $.30   (I101)

IC DRAECH DAT LIDEN VERBORGHEN see Badings,
    Henk

ICH ABER BIN ELAND see Brahms, Johannes

ICH ABER BIN ELEND see Brahms, Johannes

ICH ARMER MENSCH see Bach, Johann Sebastian,
    Ich Armer Mensch, Ich Sundenknecht

ICH ARMER MENSCH, ICH SUNDENKNECHT see Bach,
    Johann Sebastian

ICH BIN see Bach, Johann Sebastian, Ich Bin Ein
    Guter Hirt

ICH BIN BEI GOTT IN GNADEN see Stoltzer, Thomas

ICH BIN DAS BROT DES LEBENS see Rosenmuller,
    Johann

ICH BIN DAS LICHT, ICH LEUCHT EUCH FUR see
    Gunsenheimer, Gustav

ICH BIN DEIN RECHTER WEINSTOCK see Schutz,
    Heinrich

ICH BIN DER GUTE HIRTE see Driessler, Johannes

ICH BIN DER GUTE HIRTE see Raselius, Andreas

ICH BIN DER GUTE HIRTE see Vulpius, Melchior

ICH BIN DER HERR see Pepping, Ernst

ICH BIN DER WEG see Brunner, Adolf

ICH BIN DER WEG UND DIE WAHRHEIT UND DAS LEBEN
    see Poos, Heinrich

ICH BIN DIE AUFERSTEHUNG see Schutz, Heinrich

ICH BIN DIE AUFERSTEHUNG UND DAS LEBEN see
    Demantius, Christoph

ICH BIN DIE AUFERSTEHUNG UND DAS LEBEN see
    Dressler, Gallus

ICH BIN DIE AUFERSTEHUNG UND DAS LEBEN see
    Schutz, Heinrich

ICH BIN DIE TUR see Buchtger, Fritz

ICH BIN DIE WURZEL DES GESCHLECHTES DAVID see
    Schein, Johann Hermann

ICH BIN EIN GAST AUF ERDEN see Gesius,
    Bartholomaus

ICH BIN EIN GUTER HIRT see Bach, Johann
    Sebastian

ICH BIN EIN RECHTER WEINSTOCK see Schutz,
    Heinrich

ICH BIN EINE RUFENDE STIMME see Schutz,
    Heinrich

ICH BIN EINE RUFENDE STIMME IN DER WUSTEN see
    Schutz, Heinrich

ICH BIN EINE STIMME EINES RUFERS see Driessler,
    Johannes

ICH BIN EINE STIMME EINES RUFERS see Vulpius,
    Melchior

ICH BIN GEKOMMEN, ZU RUFEN see Fischer-Dieskau,
    Klaus

ICH BIN JUNG GEWESEN see Schein, Johann Hermann

ICH BIN VERGNUEGT see Bach, Johann Sebastian,
    Ich Bin Vergnugt Mit Meinem Glucke

ICH BIN VERGNUGT see Bach, Johann Sebastian,
    Ich Bin Vergnugt Mit Meinem Glucke

ICH BIN VERGNUGT see Gebhard, Hans

ICH BIN VERGNUGT MIT MEINEM GLUCKE see Bach,
    Johann Sebastian

ICH BIN VERSTUMMET GANZ UND STILL see Schutz,
    Heinrich

ICH BITTE DICH, HERR, UM DIE GROSSE KRAFT FUR
    DIESEN KLEINEN TAG see Schweizer, Rolf

ICH BRACH DREI DURRE REISELEIN see
    Gunsenheimer, Gustav

ICH BRING DIE NICHT MIT SILBER, GOLD see
    Schein, Johann Hermann

ICH DANK DIR SCHON DURCH DEINEN SOHN see
    Praetorius, Michael

ICH DANKE DEM HERREN see Schutz, Heinrich

ICH DANKE DEM HERRN see Rohwer, Jens

ICH DANKE DEM HERRN VON GANZEM HERZEN see
    Schutz, Heinrich

ICH DANKE DIR, GOTT, DAS ICH NICHT BIN see
    Driessler, Johannes

ICH DANKE DIR LIEBER HERRE see Gumpeltzhaimer,
    Adam

ICH DANKE DIR, MEIN HIMMLISCHER VATER see
    Hohlfeld, Christoph

ICH DANKE DIR VON GANZEM HERZEN see Hartmann,
    Heinrich

ICH DANKE GOTT see Weber, Bernhard

ICH DANKE GOTT DEM HERREN MEIN see Schein,
    Johann Hermann

ICH DANKE GOTT UND FREUE MICH see Hohlfeld,
    Christoph

ICH DANKE MEINEM GOTT see Reda, Siegfried

ICH DENKE DEIN see Schumann, Robert (Alexander)

ICH ELENDER MENSCH see Bach, Johann Sebastian,
    Ich Elender Mensch Wer Wird Mich Erlosen

ICH ELENDER MENSCH WER WIRD MICH ERLOSEN see
    Bach, Johann Sebastian

ICH ERHEBE MEIN GEMUTE see Cruger, Johann

ICH ERHEBE MEIN GEMUTE see Sweelinck, Jan
    Pieterszoon

ICH FREU MICH DES, DAS MIR GEREDT IST see
    Schutz, Heinrich

ICH FREU MICH IN DEM HERREN see Helder,
    Bartholomaeus

ICH FREU MICH IN DEM HERREN see Stern, Hermann

ICH FREUE MICH IM HERREN see Schein, Johann
    Hermann

ICH FREUE MICH IM HERRN see Homilius, Gottfried
    August

ICH FREUE MICH IM HERRN see Bach, Johann
    Sebastian

ICH FREUE MICH IN DIR see Bach, Johann
    Sebastian

ICH FREUE MICH, SO OFT MAN SPRICHT see Wolleb,
    Johann Jakob

ICH FREUTE MICH see Graap, Lothar

ICH FREUTE MICH UBER DIE, SO MIR SAGTEN see
    Bornefeld, Helmut

ICH GEBE MICH IN DEINE HANDE see Borris,
    Siegfried

ICH GEDENKE ALTER ZEITEN see Le Jeune, Claude

ICH GEH' UND SUCHE see Bach, Johann Sebastian, Ich Geh' Und Suche Mit Verlangen

ICH GEH' UND SUCHE MIT VERLANGEN see Bach, Johann Sebastian

ICH GLAUB' AN GOTT
(Bamer, Alfred) wom cor,acap oct DOBLINGER s.p. see also Sechs Geistliche Chore (I102)

ICH GLAUB AN GOTT IN ALLER NOT see Stadlmair, Hans

ICH GLAUBE AN DEN EINEN GOTT see Gottschick, Friedemann

ICH GLAUBE AN EINEN EINIGEN GOTT see Schutz, Heinrich

ICH GLAUBE, LIEBER HERR, HILF MEINEM UNGLAUBEN see Bach, Johann Sebastian

ICH GRUSSE DICH AM KREUZESSTAMM see Hassler, Hans Leo

ICH HAB EIN HERZLICH FREUD see Stobaeus, Johann

ICH HAB EIN HERZLICH FREUD UND GROSS see Trust, Heinz-Ewald

ICH HAB EINEN GUTEN KAMPF GEKAMPFET see Staden, Johann

ICH HAB GENUG see Bach, Johann Sebastian

ICH HAB' IN GOTTES HERZ UND SINN see Bach, Johann Sebastian

ICH HAB MEIN SACH see Demantius, Christoph

ICH HAB MEIN SACH GOTT HEIMGESTELLT see Raphael, Gunther

ICH HAB MEIN SACH GOTT HEIMGESTELLT see Schutz, Heinrich

ICH HAB MEIN SACH GOTT HEIMGESTELLT see Vulpius, Melchior

ICH HAB VON FERNE, HERR, DEINEN THRON see Lowenstern, Matthaus Appelles von

ICH HABE see Bach, Johann Sebastian

ICH HABE ALLES DINGES EIN ENDE GESEHEN see Pepping, Ernst

ICH HABE DICH EINEN KLEINEN AUGENBLICK VERLASSEN see Bender, Jan

ICH HABE EUCH NOCH VIEL ZU SAGEN see Franck, Melchior

ICH HABE EUCH NOCH VIEL ZU SAGEN see Raselius, Andreas

ICH HABE LUST, ABZUSCHEIDEN see Buxtehude, Dietrich

ICH HABE LUST, ABZUSCHEIDEN see Telemann, Georg Philipp

ICH HABE MEINE ZUVERSICHT see Bach, Johann Sebastian

ICH HABE MIR VORGESETZT see Wagener, Gregor

ICH HABE NUN DEN GRUND GEFUNDEN see Stier, Alfred

ICH HALTE ES DAFUR, DASS DIESER ZEIT see Franck, Melchior

ICH HALTE ES DAFUR, DASS DIESER ZEIT LEIDEN see Buxtehude, Dietrich

ICH HARRETE DES HERREN see Schutz, Heinrich

ICH HARRETE DES HERRN see Jacot, Andre

ICH HATTE see Bach, Johann Sebastian, Ich Hatte Viel Bekummernis

ICH HATTE VEIL BEKUMMERNIS see Bach, Johann Sebastian

ICH HATTE VIEL BEKUMMERNIS see Bach, Johann Sebastian

ICH HEB MEIN AUGEN see Schutz, Heinrich

ICH HEB MEIN AUGEN SEHNLICH AUF see Schutz, Heinrich

ICH HEBE MEINE AUGEN AUF see Dulichius, Philippus

ICH HEBE MEINE AUGEN AUF see Scheidt, Samuel

ICH HEBE MEINE AUGEN AUF see Trubel, Gerhard

ICH HEBE MEINE AUGEN AUF see Wangenheim, [Volker]

ICH HEBE MEINE AUGEN AUF ZU DEN BERGEN see Burkhard Willy

ICH HEBE MEINE AUGEN AUF ZU DEN BERGEN see Reda, Siegfried

ICH HEBE MEINE AUGEN AUF ZU DEN BERGEN see Scheidt, Samuel

ICH HEBE MEINE AUGEN AUF ZU DEN BERGEN see Schutz, Heinrich

ICH HEBE MEINE AUGEN AUF ZU DIR see Ruppel, Paul Ernst

ICH HIELTE MICH NICHT DAFUR see Rosenmuller, Johann

ICH HOFFE ABER DARAUF see Scheidt, Samuel

ICH HOFFE ABER DARAUF, DASS DU see Hartmann, Heinrich

ICH HORTE ETWAS WIE DIE STIMME VIELEN VOLKES see Trexler, Georg

ICH HORTE ETWAS WIE EINE STIMME see Ahrens, Joseph

ICH JAUCHZE, ICH LACHE see Bach, Johann Sebastian

ICH KOMM, WEISS NICHT WOHER see Weber, Bernhard

ICH KONNTE HOREN KEIN GEBET see I Couldn't Hear Nobody Pray

ICH LAG IN TIEFER TODESNACHT see Eccard, Johannes

ICH LASS DICH NICHT, DU MUSST MEIN JESUS BLEIBEN see Bach, Johann Sebastian

ICH LASSE DICH NICHT see Bach, Johann Christoph

ICH LASSE DICH NICHT see Bach, Johann Sebastian

ICH LASSE DICH NICHT see Schein, Johann Hermann

ICH LASSE DICH NICHT, DU SEGNEST MICH DENN see Bach, Johann Christoph

ICH LASSE DICH NICHT DU SEGNEST MICH DENN see Bach, Johann Sebastian

ICH LIEB DICH, HERR, VON HERZEN SEHR see Hartmann, Heinrich

ICH LIEB DICH, HERR, VON HERZEN SEHR see Schutz, Heinrich

ICH LIEBE DEN HOCHSTEN see Bach, Johann Sebastian

ICH LIEBE DEN HOCHSTEN see Bach, Johann Sebastian, Ich Liebe Den Hochsten

ICH LIEBE DEN HOCHSTEN VON GANZEM GEMUTE see Bach, Johann Sebastian

ICH LIEBE DICH see Beethoven, Ludwig van

ICH LIEBE JESUM ALLE STUND see Bach, Johann Sebastian

ICH LIEGE, HERR, IN DEINER HUT see Burkhard Willy

ICH LIEGE, HERR, IN DEINER HUT see Holsten, Martin

ICH LIEGE, HERR, IN DEINER HUT see Lohr, Ina

ICH LIEGE UND SCHLAFE see Bruhns, Nicholaus

ICH LIEGE UND SCHLAFE GANZ IN FRIEDEN see Reda, Siegfried

ICH MOCHT, DASS EINER MIT MIR GEHT see Kobler, Hans

ICH MUSS JA, HERR, BEKENNEN FREI see Cruger, Johann

ICH, NUR ICH BIN DER MISSETATER see Schutz, Heinrich, Ego Enim Inique Egi

ICH, O ICH BIN DIE QUAL DEINER SCHMERZEN see Schutz, Heinrich, Ego Sum Tui Plaga Doloris

ICH REDE VON DEINEN ZEUGNISSEN see Raphael, Gunther

ICH REDE, WENN ICH SCHWEIGEN SOLLTE see Lehmann, Andreas

ICH RIEF ZUM HERRN see Schutz, Heinrich, Ad Dominum, Cum Tribularer

ICH RUF' ZU DIR see Bach, Johann Sebastian, Ich Ruf' Zu Dir, Herr Jesu Christ

ICH RUF ZU DIR see Schutz, Heinrich

ICH RUF' ZU DIR, HERR JESU CHRIST see Bach, Johann Sebastian

ICH RUF ZU DIR, HERR JESU CHRIST see Franck, Melchior

ICH RUF ZU DIR, HERR JESU CHRIST see Horbe, Ernst

ICH RUF ZU DIR, HERR JESU CHRIST see Jeep, Johann

ICH RUF ZU DIR, HERR JESU CHRIST see Kraft, Walter

ICH RUF ZU DIR, HERR JESU CHRIST see Linkenbach, Klaus

ICH RUF ZU DIR, HERR JESU CHRIST see Micheelsen, Hans Friedrich

ICH RUF ZU DIR, HERR JESU CHRIST see Praetorius, Michael

ICH RUF ZU DIR, HERR JESU CHRIST see Reda, Siegfried

ICH RUF ZU DIR, HERR JESU CHRIST see Schein, Johann Hermann

ICH SAG DIR DANK, GOTT VATER GUT see Eglin, Arthur

ICH SAGE EUCH, ALSO WIRD AUCH FREUDE see Driessler, Johannes

ICH SAGE EUCH, DIESER GING HINAB see Vulpius, Melchior

ICH SAGE EUCH, ES SEI DENN EURE GERECHTIGKEIT see Driessler, Johannes

ICH SAGE EUCH: VIEL WERDEN KOMMEN see Raselius, Andreas

ICH SAH DREI SEGELSCHIFFE ZIEHN *Xmas,Eng/Eur
(Doppelbauer, Josef Friedrich) mix cor,acap DOBLINGER s.p. see from Da Der Herr Geboren

ICH SCHAU NACH JENEN BERGEN FERN see (I103)
Mareschall, Samuel

ICH SCHAU NACH JENEN BERGEN FERN see Sweelinck, Jan Pieterszoon

ICH SCHAU NACH JENEN BERGEN GERN see Goudimel, Claude

ICH SCHREIE ZUM HERREN see Rab, Valentin

ICH SINGE DIR see Micheelsen, Hans Friedrich

ICH SINGE DIR MIT HERZ UND MUND see Burkhard Willy

ICH SINGE DIR MIT HERZ UND MUND see Cruger, Johann

ICH SINGE DIR MIT HERZ UND MUND see Kurig, Hans-Hermann

ICH SINGE DIR MIT HERZ UND MUND see Raphael, Gunther

ICH SINGE DIR MIT HERZ UND MUND see Stern, Hermann

ICH SINGE DIR MIT HERZ UND MUND see Stoll, Helene Marianne

ICH STEH' see Bach, Johann Sebastian, Ich Steh' Mit Einem Fuss Im Grabe

ICH STEH AN DEINER KRIPPE HIER see Bornefeld, Helmut

ICH STEH AN DEINER KRIPPEN see Koler, Martin

ICH STEH' AN DEINER KRIPPEN HIER see Bach, Johann Sebastian

ICH STEH AN DEINER KRIPPEN HIER see Eccard, Johannes

ICH STEH AN DEINER KRIPPEN HIER see Gesius, Bartholomaus

ICH STEH AN DEINER KRIPPEN HIER see Kukuck, Felicitas

ICH STEH AN DEINER KRIPPEN HIER see Raphael, Gunther

ICH STEH AN DEINER KRIPPEN HIER see Stern, Hermann

ICH STEH AN DEINER KRIPPEN HIER see Weiss, Ewald

ICH STEH AN DEINER KRIPPEN HIER [CHORALE] see Bach, Johann Sebastian

ICH STEH IN MEINES HERREN HAND *16th cent
(Berger, H.L.) TTBB HANSSLER 6.5137 s.p.
contains also: Es Ist Das Heil Uns Kommen Her (I104)

ICH STEH IN MEINES HERREN HAND see Bach, Johann Sebastian

ICH STEH' MIT EINEM FUSS IM GRABE see Bach, Johann Sebastian

ICH TAUFE MIT WASSER see Raselius, Andreas

ICH TRAUE DEINER GNADE see Eglin, Arthur

ICH TRET HINZU see Schwarz-Schilling, Reinhard

ICH WEISS, DASS MEIN ERLOESER LEBT see Franck, Melchior

ICH WEISS, DASS MEIN ERLOSER LEBET see Schutz, Heinrich

ICH WEISS, DASS MEIN ERLOSER LEBET see Schutz, Heinrich

ICH WEISS, DASS MEIN ERLOSER LEBT see Bach, Johann Michael

ICH WEISS, DASS MEIN ERLOSER LEBT see Burck, Joachim

ICH WEISS, DASS MEIN ERLOSER LEBT see Franck, Melchior

ICH WEISS, DASS MEIN ERLOSER LEBT see Reger, Max

ICH WEISS, DASS MEIN ERLOSER LEBT see Schutz, Heinrich

ICH WEISS, DASS MEIN ERLOSER LEBT see Schutz, Heinrich

ICH WEISS, DASS OHNE MICH see Sendt, Willy

ICH WEISS EIN EDLEN WEINGARTN see Fussan, Werner

ICH WEISS EIN FEINS BRAUNS MAGDELEIN see Burthel, Jakob

ICH WEISS EIN LEIBLICH ENGELSPIEL *Xmas
jr cor HANSSLER 12.601 s.p. (I105)

ICH WEISS EIN LIEBLICH ENGELSPIEL see Kraft, Walter

ICH WEISS EIN LIEBLICH ENGELSPIEL see Lang, Hans

ICH WEISS, MEIN GOTT, DASS ALL MEIN TUN see Kurig, Hans-Hermann

ICH WEISS, WORAN ICH GLAUBE see Kubler, Emil

ICH WEISS, WORAN ICH GLAUBE see Schutz, Heinrich

ICH WILL BEI MEINEM LEBEN RUHMEN DEN HERREN see Cruger, Johann

ICH WILL BEI MEINEN LEBEN RUHMEN see Schutz, Heinrich

ICH WILL BETEN, GOTT WIRD HOREN see Bach, Johann Sebastian

ICH WILL DEM HERREN SINGEN see Barbe, Helmut

ICH WILL DEM HERREN SINGEN see Kurig, Hans-Hermann

ICH WILL DEN HERREN LOBEN see Michel, Josep

ICH WILL DEN HERREN LOBEN see Schmid, Walter

ICH WILL DEN HERREN LOBEN ALLEZEIT see Telemann, Georg Philipp

ICH WILL DEN HERRN LOBEN ALLEZEIT see Schweizer, Rolf

ICH WILL DEN HERRN PREISEN ALLEZEIT see Lohr, Ina

ICH WILL DEN KELCH DES HEILES ANNEHMEN see Schutz, Heinrich, Calicem Salutaris

ICH WILL DEN KREUZSTAB see Bach, Johann Sebastian, Ich Will Den Kreuzstab Gerne Tragen

ICH WILL DEN KREUZSTAB GERNE TRAGEN see Bach, Johann Sebastian

ICH WILL DEN NAMEN GOTTES LOBEN see Bach, Johann Sebastian

ICH WILL DEN ZORN DES HERREN MEIN see Cruger, Johann

ICH WILL DICH ERHEBEN see Schmid, Walter

ICH WILL DICH LIEBEN MEINE STARKE see Konig, Johann Balthasar

ICH WILL DICH, MEIN GOTT, ERHOHEN see Rosenmuller, Johann

ICH WILL DIR DANKEN, HERR see Ruppel, Paul Ernst

ICH WILL EUCH EIN NEUES HERZ, EINEN NEUEN GEIST AUCH GEBEN see Hohlfeld, Christoph

ICH WILL GOTTES WORT RUHMEN see Fiebig, Kurt

ICH WILL IN FRIEDEN MICH NIEDERLEGEN ZUM SCHLAF see Reger, Max

ICH WILL MEINEN GEIST AUSGIESSEN UBER ALLES FLEISCH see Brunner, Adolf

ICH WILL MICH FREUEN DES HERRN see Studer, Hans

ICH WILL SEHR HOCH ERHOHEN DICH see Schutz, Heinrich

ICH WILL SINGEN VON DER GNADE DES HERRN see Briegel, Wolfgang Carl

ICH WILL SINGEN VON DER GNADE DES HERRN see Knupfer, Sebastian

ICH WILL, SOLANG ICH LEBE, RUHMEN DEN HERREN MEIN see Schutz, Heinrich

ICH WILL VON HERZEN DANKEN GOTT, DEM HERRN see Schutz, Heinrich

ICH WILL WASSER GIESSEN AUF DIE DURSTEDEN see Erlebach, Philipp Heinrich

ICH WOLLT, DASS ICH DAHEIME WAR see Bresgen, Cesar

ICH WOLLT, DASS ICH DAHEIME WAR see Distler, Hugo

ICH WOLLT, DASS ICH DAHEIME WAR see Kappesser, Karl

ICH WOLLT, DASS ICH DAHEIME WAR see Krams, Peter

ICH WOLLT, DASS ICH DAHEIME WAR see Muller, Paul

ICH WOLLT EIN BAUMLEIN STEIGN see Ruppel, Paul Ernst

ICH ZIEH MEINE DUNKLE STRASSE see Klienau, Klaus

ICK SAL DEN HEER MIJN GODT GHEBENEDYEN see Faignient, Noel

ICK WIL MI GAEN VERTROOSTEN see Rontgen, [Julius]

ICY DECEMBER, THE see Track, Gerhard

IDELSOHN, ABRAHAM ZEVI (1882-1938)
    Yesterday's Bubble *Purim
    (McKelvy, J.) [Eng] SATB TRANSCON. TCL 119
    $.20   (I106)

IDEN, RAYMOND
    All Ye Who Seek The Lord
    SATB,high solo,low solo,pno (easy) oct
    WILLIS 5521 $.16   (I107)

    Hold Not Against Me *prayer
    TTBB,acap (med) oct WILLIS 5699 $.12 (I108)

    Precious Jesus, (Burden Bearer)
    SATB,high solo,pno/org (easy) oct WILLIS
    5682 $.12   (I109)

IDEO GLORIA IN EXCELSIS DEO see Kraehenbuehl, D.

IDEO GLORIA - ON THIS DAY EARTH SHALL RING see Cartford, Gerhard M.

IERLEY, MERRITT
    Make We Joy In This Fest *Xmas
    SATB,acap (med easy) oct CONCORDIA 98-2155
    $.25   (I110)

IF A MAN LOVE ME see Roff, Joseph

IF A MAN LOVES ME see Bender, Jan

IF ANGELS SUNG A SAVIOUR'S BIRTH see Colonial Christmas Carols

IF ANY LITTLE WORD OF MINE see Frederick, Donald R.

IF ANY MAN WOULD COME AFTER ME *Bibl
    (Trued, S.C.) SATB oct BELWIN 2222 $.30
                                            (I111)

IF ANYONE KEEPS MY WORD see Hillert, Richard

IF ANYONE WISHES TO COME AFTER ME see Roff, Joseph

IF BY HIS SPIRIT see Bach, Johann Sebastian

IF BY HIS SPIRIT see Christiansen, Olaf Christian

IF CHRIST CAME BACK see O'Hara, Geoffrey

IF CHRIST SHOULD COME TOMORROW see Hart, A.W.

IF EVER THE SUN STOPS SHINING see Hughes

IF GOD see Jones, Marjorie

IF GOD BE FOR US, WHO SHALL BE AGAINST US? see Schutz, Heinrich, Ist Gott Fur Uns, Wer Mag Wider Uns Sein?

IF GOD BUILD NOT THE HOUSE see Pitfield, Thomas Baron

IF GOD FORGOT
    SATB BIG3 $.25   (I112)

IF GOD IS FOR US see Franck, Melchior

IF GOD SO CLOTHE THE GRASS see Bischoff, Paul

IF I CAN HELP SOMEBODY see Androzzo

IF I GO NOT AWAY see McCormick

IF I GOT MY TICKET, CAN I RIDE?
    (Shaw) mix cor,T solo,acap oct SCHIRM.G 9933
    $.35   (I113)
    (Shaw) 3pt men cor,T solo,acap oct SCHIRM.G
    9852 $.30   (I114)

IF I HAD-A MY WAY *spir
    (Morris) SATB oct LAWSON 51530 $.40   (I115)

IF I HAVE FAITH see Thayer, Pat

IF I HAVE WOUNDED ANY SOUL see Gabriel

IF I SPEAK WITH THE TONGUES OF MEN see Leonard, Clair

IF I TAKE THE WINGS OF THE MORNING see Pooler

IF I WERE A SHEPHERD see Davis, Katherine K.

IF IT BE GOD'S WILL AND PLEASURE see Bach, Johann Sebastian, Wenn Es Meines Gottes Wille

IF MY PEOPLE see Veckruise

IF PERCHANCE THE FINAL HOUR see Bach, Johann Sebastian

IF THE LORD HIMSELF HAD NOT BEEN ON OUR SIDE see Rapley

IF THE LORD WILLS see Ford, Virgil T.

IF THERE IS A HOLY SPIRIT see Avery

IF THOU ART NEAR see Bach, Johann Sebastian, Bist Du Bei Mir

IF THOU BUT SUFFER GOD TO GUIDE THEE
    (Thompson, R.) SATB oct PRESSER 312-40105
    $.30   (I116)

IF THOU BUT SUFFER GOD TO GUIDE THEE see Bach, Johann Sebastian

IF THOU BUT SUFFER GOD TO GUIDE THEE see Lindh

IF THOU BUT SUFFER GOD TO GUIDE THEE see Lindh, Jody W.

IF THOU BUT SUFFER GOD TO GUIDE THEE see Schroth

IF THOU O LORD SHOULDST MARK INIQUITIES see Campbell

IF THOU WERT NEAR see Bach, Johann Sebastian, Bist Du Bei Mir

IF THOU WILT SUFFER GOD TO GUIDE THEE see Bach, Johann Sebastian, Wer Nur Den Lieben Gott Lasst Walten

IF TO GAIN THE WORLD see Lister, Mosie

IF WE BELIEVE see Goss, John

IF WE BELIEVE THAT JESUS DIED see Goss, John

IF WE COULD SEE BEYOND TODAY see Bock, F.

IF WE WALK IN THE LIGHT see McCormick

IF WITH ALL YOUR HEARTS see Mendelssohn-Bartholdy, Felix

IF WITH ALL YOUR HEARTS see Schroth, G.

IF YE BE MERRY see Liljestrand, Paul

IF YE BE RISEN AGAIN WITH CHRIST see Gibbons, Orlando

IF YE BE RISEN AGAIN WITH CHRIST see Jennings, Kenneth L.

IF YE LOVE ME see Coombs, Francis

IF YE LOVE ME see Pinkham, Daniel

IF YE LOVE ME see Roff, Joseph

IF YE LOVE ME see Simper, Caleb

IF YE LOVE ME see Tallis, Thomas

IF YE LOVE ME see Wolff, S. Drummond

IF YE LOVE ME KEEP MY COMMANDMENTS see Byrd, William

IF YE LOVE ME, KEEP MY COMMANDMENTS see Jolley, Florence [W.]

IF YE LOVE ME, KEEP MY COMMANDMENTS see Monk

IF YE LOVE ME, KEEP MY COMMANDMENTS see Tallis, Thomas

IF YE THEN BE RISEN see Poole-Connor, David

IF YE THEN BE RISEN see Powell, Robert J.

IF YE THEN BE RISEN WITH CHRIST see Roff, Joseph

IF YE THEN BE RISEN WITH CHRIST see Wadely, F.W.

IF YE WOULD HEAR THE ANGELS SING see Fast, Willard S.

IF YE WOULD HEAR THE ANGELS SING see Johnson

IF YE WOULD HEAR THE ANGELS SING see Johnson, G.

IF YOU ASK ANTHING OF THE FATHER see Bender, Jan

IF YOU CONTINUE IN MY WORD see Busarow, Donald

IF YOU CONTINUE IN MY WORD see Hilty, Everett Jay

IF YOU KEEP HOLY NIGHT see Staley

IF YOU KNOW THE LORD see Reichner

IF YOU LOVE ME see Kirk

IF YOU WOULD HEAR THE ANGELS SING
    (Butt) unis oct BOOSEY 5566 $.30   (I117)

IF YOUR HEART KEEPS RIGHT see Ackley

IHR CHRISTENMENSCHEN ALLE (from Bamberger Gesangbuch 1628) BVM
    SATB,acap (contains also: Alle Tage Sing Und Sage (from Paradeisvogel Ingolstadt 1613)) voc pt DOBLINGER s.p. see also Unsere Liebe Frau   (I118)

IHR, DIE IHR EUCH see Bach, Johann Sebastian, Ihr, Die Ihr Euch Von Christo Nennet

IHR, DIE IHR EUCH VON CHRISTO NENNET see Bach, Johann Sebastian

IHR FREUNDE GOTTES ALLZUGLEICH see Baumann, Max

IHR GESTIRN', IHR HOHEN LUFTE see Bach, Johann Sebastian

IHR HABT GEHORT, WAS GESAGT IST see David, Johann Nepomuk

IHR HABT NICHT EINEN KNECHTISCHEN GEIST EMPFANGEN see Schwartz, Gerhard von

IHR HABT NUN TRAURIGKEIT see Brahms, Johannes

IHR HEILIGEN, LOBSINGET see Schein, Johann Hermann

IHR HEILIGEN LOBSINGET DEM HERRN see Schutz, Heinrich

IHR HEILIGEN TOTEN see Knapp, Arno

IHR HEUCHLER, WAS VERSUCHT IHR MICH? see Vulpius, Melchior

IHR HIRTEN see Beuerle, Herbert

IHR HIRTEN ERWACHT *Xmas
    (Wolters) 3 eq voices MOSELER s.p.   (I119)

IHR KINDERLEIN KOMMET *Xmas
    (Stanton) "O Come, Little Children" SATB,acap
    oct LAWSON 881 $.30   (I120)
    (Sumerside) "O Come, Little Children" SATB
    SCHMITT 8045 $.35   (I121)
    (Wasner) "O Come Little Children" 3pt mix cor
    oct SCHIRM.G 10612 $.25   (I122)

IHR KINDERLEIN KOMMET see Burkhart, Franz

IHR KINDERLEIN, KOMMET see Schulz, Joh. Abraham Peter

IHR KNECHTE GOTTES see Wolleb, Johann Jakob

IHR KNECHTE GOTTES ALLZUGLEICH see Eglin, Arthur

IHR KNECHTE GOTTES ALLZUGLEICH see Le Jeune, Claude

IHR KREATUR IM HIMMEL OBEN see Hagius, Carl

IHR KREATUR IM HIMMEL OBEN see Hagius, Conrad

IHR LIEBEN CHRISTEN, FREUT EUCH NUN see Buxtehude, Dietrich

IHR LIEBEN CHRISTEN, FREUT EUCH NUN see Schmidt, Walther

IHR LIEBEN CHRISTEN, FREUT EUCH NUN see Stegen, Wilfried

IHR LIEBEN CHRISTEN, FREUT EUCH NUN see Stern, Hermann

IHR LIEBEN HIRTEN, FURCHTET EUCH NICHT see Hammerschmidt, Andreas

IHR MANNER VON GALILAA see Ruppel, Paul Ernst

IHR MENSCHEN, RUHMET GOTTES LIEBE see Bach, Johann Sebastian

IHR PFORTEN, HEBT DAS HAUPT EMPOR see Sweelinck, Jan Pieterszoon

IHR PFORTEN ZU ZION see Bach, Johann Sebastian

IHR SEID ALLE GOTTES KINDER see Reda, Siegfried

IHR SEID DAS LICHT DER WELT see Schweizer, Rolf

IHR VOLKER, BRINGET HER DEM HERRN see Rohwer, Jens

IHR WERDET DIE KRAFT DES HEILIGEN GEISTES EMPFANGEN see Kurig, Hans-Hermann

IHR WERDET KRAFT EMPFANGEN see Schweizer, Rolf

IHR WERDET, WEINEN see Bach, Johann Sebastian, Ihr Werdet Weinen Und Heulen

IHR WERDET WEINEN UND HEULEN see Bach, Johann Sebastian

IHR WERDET WEINEN UND HEULEN see Raselius, Andreas

IHR WISSET WOHL VON DER PREDIGT see Hufschmidt, Wolfgang

IKKE ENHVER SOM SIER TIL MEG see Baden, Conrad

IL CANZONIERE MARIANO see Gubinelli, Oderisio

IL DAVID-DAVIDIS PUGNA ET VICTORIA see Scarlatti, Alessandro

IL EST NE *Xmas,anthem/carol,Fr
"He Is Born" see Two Old French Carols
(Fosblad) "He Is Born" SSA,acap oct PRO ART 2584 $.30 (I123)
(Roseberry, Eric) "He Is Born" SATB oct FABER F0288 $.35 (I124)
(Wagner) "He Is Born" SATB oct LAWSON 663 $.30 (I125)
(Wagner, Roger) "He Is Born" SATB ALLANS 236 s.p. (I126)
(Wetzler, Robert) "He Is Born" SATB (easy) oct AUGSBURG 1411 $.30 (I127)
(Wetzler, Robert) "He Is Born" SSA (easy) oct AUGSBURG 1474 $.25 (I128)

IL EST NE see Ripolles, Vincente

IL EST NE, LE DIVIN ENFANT *Xmas,carol,Fr
(Cross, Richard) "Now The Holy Child Is Born" [Eng/Fr] SA,org,fing.cym.,tamb oct WORLD AC-1843-2 $.60 (I129)

IL EST NE LE DIVIN ENFANT see Anonymous

IL FAIT BEAU VOIR CES HOMMES D'ARMES
(Gevaert, F.-A.) [Fr] 4pt mix cor,acap (easy/med easy) cor pts LEMOINE s.p. see from Collection De Choeurs, quatrieme Fascicule (I130)

IL NATALE DEL REDENTORE see Perosi, (Dom) Lorenzo

IL NATALE IN FAMIGLIA *CC7L,Xmas
(Travaglia, Silvio) cor,pno ZANIBON 1760 s.p. (I131)

IL PIANTO DELLA MADONNA see Casagrade, A.

IL PRIMO OMICIDIO see Scarlatti, Alessandro

IL RE DEL DOLORE see Caldara, Antonio

IL SANTO NATALE see Bottazzo, Luigi

I'LL BE BESIDE YOU *carol,Fr
(Ehret) SATB MARKS 4035 $.25 (I132)

I'LL BE THERE see Gardner, Maurice

I'LL GO TO BETHLEHEM *Xmas,carol,Czech
(Ehret, Walter) SA FRANK F-616 $.35 (I133)

I'LL HOLD HIM IN MY HEART see Genuchi

I'LL LIVE FOR HIM see Lanier

I'LL LOOSE THEE, LORD, NOT! see Bach, Johann Christoph, Ich Lasse Dich Nicht

I'LL PRAISE MY MAKER see Pfautsch, Lloyd

I'LL PROCLAIM see Handel, George Frideric

I'LL TELL THE WORLD see Fox, Baynard

I'LL WALK BESIDE YOU, GENTLE JESUS see Artman

I'LL WALK WITH GOD see Brodszky

I'LL WALK WITH GOD see Brodzky

ILLING
Cabra Mass *Mass
unis,org ALBERT s.p. (I134)

Hail Mary
SSA,acap ALBERT s.p. (I135)

Hail O Queen
SSA,acap ALBERT s.p. (I136)

Let All The World
unis,pno ALBERT s.p. (I137)

Light Of The Church
SSA,acap ALBERT s.p. (I138)

ILLUMINA see Lassus, Roland de (Orlandus)

ILLUMINA OCULOS MEOS see Lassus, Roland de (Orlandus)

ILLUMINA OCULOS MEOS see Palestrina, Giovanni

ILLUMINE ME, LORD see Kaiser, Kurt

ILLUXIT DIES TERTIA see Dubois, Theodore

ILLUXIT SOL see Gorczycki, Gregor Gervasius

ILSE, H.L.
Child This Day Is Born, A
SATB,acap oct KERBY 80380 $.35 (I139)

I'M A PILGRIM see Posegate

I'M A ROLLIN' *spir
(Whitman) SATB oct LILLENAS AN-3818 $.30 (I140)

I'M A ROLLING see Gerhold, Norbert

I'M A-TRAV'LING
see Eight Negro Spirituals: Book Ii

I'M A-TROUBLED IN MY MIND *spir
(Forsblad) SATB SCHMITT 880 $.25 (I141)

IM ANFANG. DIE SCHOPFUNGSGESCHICHTE see Bialas, Gunther

IM ANFANG WAR DAS WORT see Peter, Herbert

IM ANFANG WAR'S AUF ERDEN see Trust, Heinz-Ewald

I'M BOUND FOR THE KINGDOM
SSA BIG3 $.25 (I142)

I'M BOUND FOR THE PROMISED LAND see Haywood

I'M DEPENDING ON JESUS see Lister, Mosie

I'M FEELING FINE see Lister, Mosie

IM FINSTERN STALL, O WUNDER GROSS see Stobaeus, Johann

I'M FREE AT LAST
(Pfautsch, Lloyd) SATB oct AGAPE SP 714 $.30 (I143)

IM FRIEDEN DEIN see Doppelbauer, Josef Friedrich

IM FRIEDEN DEIN see Reda, Siegfried

IM FRIEDEN DEIN, O HERRE MEIN see Kubler, Emil

IM FRIEDEN DEIN, O HERRE MEIN see Mareshall, Samuel

IM GARTEN GING EINE BRAUT see Krietsch, Georg

IM GARTEN LEIDET CHRISTUS NOT see Eccard, Johannes

I'M GOIN' TO SING *spir
(Shaw; Parker) mix cor,acap oct LAWSON 51101 $.30 (I144)

I'M GOING AWAY see Wilson, John F.

I'M GOING HIGHER SOMEDAY see Buffum

I'M GOING THROUGH see Hawkins, Ed.

I'M GONNA LAY MY BURDEN DOWN *spir
(Johnson, S.) SATB KJOS 5879 $.30 (I145)

I'M GONNA SING *spir
(Kirk) SSAB SCHMITT 5536 $.35 (I146)

I'M GONNA SING see Gardner, Maurice

I'M GONNA SING see Kellermeyer, David M.

I'M GONNA WALK MY WAY TO HEAVEN see Tarrell

I'M HIMMEL IST FREUDE VIEL see Pfannenstiel, Ekkehart

I'M IN HIS CARE *spir
(Schubert) SATB oct LILLENAS AN-3828 $.30 (I147)

I'M IN HIS CARE see Ward

I'M JUST A POOR WAYFARING STRANGER see Lehman, Siegfried

IM NAMEN JESU see Callhoff, Herbert

IM NAMEN JESU SOLLEN SICH BEUGEN see Miserocca, Sebastian

I'M NEW BORN AGAIN
(Hustad, Donald P.) TTBB oct AGAPE TB 202 $.30 (I148)

I'M NOT AFRAID see Mc Call, Harlo

I'M PRAISING THE LORD see Russel, Eleanor

I'M SO GLAD see Lehman, Siegfried

I'M SO GLAD TROUBLE DON'T LAST ALWAY
(Dett, R.) SSA oct PRESSER 322-35123 $.25 (I149)

I'M SO GLAD TROUBLE DON'T LAST ALWAYS *spir
(Ehret, Walter) SATB oct WALTON 2048 $.25 (I150)

I'M STANDING IN THE SUN see Meyers, Carmel

I'M SURE HE KNOWS see Jordan

I'M TROUBLED IN MIND see Jones, A.

IM UTNAK INDUL see Schumann, Robert (Alexander)

I'M WEARY LORD see Schroth

IMBRIE, ANDREW WELSH (1921-   )
As The Hart Panteth (Psalm 42)
TBB,org PETERS 6888 $.50 (I151)

Psalm 42 *see As The Hart Panteth

IMIG
Putney Hymn *hymn
(Simon) SATB oct FISCHER,C CM-7552 $.25 (I152)

IMIG, WARNER (1913-   )
Lambs, The
SATB LEONARD-US 08036102 $.25 (I153)

IMMACOLATA see Cantu

IMMACOLATA CONCEZIONE see Bertilorenzi

IMMACULATA CONCEPTIO see Gerald

IMMAGINI IONTANE see Borlenghi

IMMANUEL FOREVER see Lillenas, Haldor

IMMANUEL, WE SING THY PRAISE see Kirk

IMMORTAL BABE (from Anthology Of Carols, An)
Xmas,carol
unis/SATB (easy) OXFORD 08.106 $.15 (I154)
(Wulstan, David) unis CHESTER s.p. contains also: Song Of The Nuns Of Chester (unis,S solo) (Xmas); Ascendit Christus Hodie (unis) (Asc); Veni, Sancte Spiritus (unis) (Whitsun) (I155)

IMMORTAL INVISIBLE *anthem/folk,Welsh
(Cassler, G. Winston) TTBB (med) oct AUGSBURG 1165 $.25 (I156)
(Williams) SATB oct LILLENAS AN-2320 $.30 (I157)

IMMORTAL, INVISIBLE see Hornibrook

IMMORTAL, INVISIBLE see Lorenz, Ellen Jane

IMMORTAL, INVISIBLE see Thiman, Eric Harding

IMMORTAL, INVISIBLE see Wilson

IMMORTAL, INVISIBLE GOD see Davies, Ivor

IMMORTAL, INVISIBLE, GOD ONLY WISE *anthem, Welsh
(Leupold, Ulrich) SAB (easy) oct AUGSBURG 1440 $.20 (I158)

IMMORTAL LOVE see Christiansen, F. Melius

IMMORTAL LOVE see Clokey, Joseph Waddell

IMMORTAL LOVE see Darst, W. Glenn

IMMORTAL LOVE see Dietterich, Philip R.

IMMORTAL LOVE see Marryott, Ralph E.

IMMORTAL LOVE, FOR EVER FULL see Matthews, Harvey Alexander

IMMORTAL LOVE FOREVER FULL see Wallace

IMMORTALITY see Hovhaness, Alan

IMMORTALITY see Stults, R.

IMMUTEMUR see Escobedo, Bartolome

IMPERIAL MASS see Haydn, (Franz) Joseph, Missa In Angustiis

IMPLORATIO see Beckerath, Alfred von

IMPROPERIA see Goeyvaerts, Carel

IMPROPERIA see Palestrina, Giovanni

IMPROPERIUM see Brambilla, E.

IMPROPERIUM see Cain, Noble

IMPROPERIUM EXPECTAVIT see Dello Joio, Norman

IMPROPERIUM EXSPECTAVIT see Palestrina, Giovanni

IMPROPERIUM EXSPECTAVIT COR MEUM see Eberlin, Johann Ernst

IN A CAVE A BABY LAY see Harrell, Jan

IN A DAY OF DANGER see Landgrave, Phillip

IN A HUMBLE CATTLE SHED *Xmas
SSA CHAPPELL 0018119-354 $.40 (I159)
SATB CHAPPELL 0018119-358 $.40 (I160)

IN A HUT LOWLY see Kozinski, [David B.]

IN A MANGER see Behrens, [Jack]

IN A MANGER see Posegate

IN A MANGER see Roff, Joseph

IN A MANGER see Senob

IN A MANGER GENTLY LAY see Alderfer

IN A MANGER HE IS SLEEPING *Xmas,carol,Pol
(Landon) SATB oct LORENZ A359 $.25 (I161)

IN A MANGER IN BETHLEHEM see Fura

IN A MANGER LONG AGO see Haag

IN A MANGER LOWLY see Grunert, Hazel

IN A STABLE MANGER see Wolfe

IN-A-THAT GREAT GITTIN' UP MO'NIN
(Foltz) SATB oct BELWIN 60096 $.25 (I162)

IN A WORLD THAT NEEDS THY LOVE AND CARE see Wallace, G.

IN ADAM WE HAVE ALL BEEN ONE see Schalk, Carl

IN ADORATION, LORD WE KNEEL see Blakeslee

IN ALL THINGS I SOUGHT REST see Pasquet, Jean

IN ALLEN MEINEN TATEN see Bach, Johann Sebastian

IN AMBER LIGHT see Yoshioka, Emmett

IN ANNUNTIATIONE B. MARIAE see Byrd, William

IN ASCENSIONE DOMINE see Naylor, Bernard

IN ASCENSIONE DOMINI see Byrd, William

IN ASCENSIONE DOMINI see Ravanello, Oreste

IN ASSUMPTIONE B. MARIAE VIRGINIS see Byrd, William

IN BETHLE'EM TOWN see Ellison

IN BETHLEHEM see Baxter, F.

IN BETHLEHEM see Forsblad

IN BETHLEHEM see Johnston

IN BETHLEHEM see Ringwald, [Roy]

IN BETHLEHEM see Shimmire

IN BETHLEHEM see Tellep, Leo M.

IN BETHLEHEM, A TINY BABE see Freundt, Cornelius, Ein Kindelein Zu Bethlehem

IN BETHLEHEM A WONDER *Xmas,carol,Fr (Schroeder, H.) SATB,inst (easy) oct CONCORDIA 98-2063 $.25   (I163)

IN BETHLEHEM CITY *Xmas (Follett) SATB,acap,opt pno oct PRO ART 2237 $.25   (I164)

IN BETHLEHEM CITY see Vaughan Williams, Ralph

IN BETHLEHEM EIN KINDELEIN see Raphael, Gunther

IN BETHLEHEM LOVE IS BORN see Zu Bethlehem Geboren

IN BETHLEHEM OF JUDAH see Roth, J.

IN BETHLEHEM, THAT FAIR CITY unis/SATB (easy) OXFORD 08.105 $.15   (I165)

IN BETHLEHEM THAT FAIR CITY see Niles, John Jacob

IN BETHLEHEM THAT NIGHT (Kjelson) SATB oct BELWIN 2101 $.25   (I166)

IN BETHLEHEM, THAT NOBLE PLACE see Nelson, Paul

IN BETHLEHEM, THAT NOBLE PLACE see Rimmer, Frederick

IN BETHLEHEM THIS CHRISTMAS MORN see Clemens, Jacobus

IN BETHLEHEM THIS FAIR MORNING *Xmas (Schroth) SATB SCHMITT 916 $.30   (I167)

IN BETHLEHEM TOWN *Xmas (Fiske) SATB,acap (very easy) OXFORD 84.106 $.25   (I168)
(Fiske) SA (easy) OXFORD 82.068 $.30   (I169)

IN BETHLEHEM TOWN see Traver, James

IN BETHLEHEM'S CRADLE *Xmas,carol (Ehret, Walter) SATB oct WALTON 2515 $.30   (I170)
(Ehret, Walter) SATB,opt inst oct WALTON 2515 $.30   (I171)

IN BETHLEHEM'S LOWLY MANGER see Williams

IN BETHLEHEM'S LOWLY STABLE *Xmas,carol,Ger (Ehret) SAB,opt vla oct FOX CC9 $.25   (I172)
(Ehret, W.) SAB,opt vla PROWSE CC9 s.p.   (I173)

IN BETHLEM see Musica Britannica Vol. 4: Set 1

IN BETH'LEM'S LOWLY STABLE see Kinsman

IN BRIGHT MANSIONS ABOVE *spir (De Paur) 5pt mix cor,acap oct LAWSON 926 $.30   (I174)

IN CHRIST THE LORD see Peloquin, C. Alexander

IN CHRIST THERE IS NO EAST OR WEST see Couper

IN CHRIST THERE IS NO EAST OR WEST see Curry, W. Lawrence

IN CHRIST THERE IS NO EAST OR WEST see Gassman, Clark

IN CHRISTO MORIMUR see David, Johann Nepomuk

IN CONVERTENDO see Rameau, Jean-Philippe

IN DAT GREAT GITTIN' UP MORNIN' (Howorth, Wayne) SATB oct 1633 $.25   (I175)

IN DAVID'S ROYAL CITY see Morgan, Haydn

IN DEATH'S STRONG GRASP see Luther, Martin

IN DEATH'S STRONG GRASP THE SAVIOUR LAY see Bach, Johann Sebastian

IN DECOLLATIONE ST. JOHANNIS see Fulda, Adam von

IN DEEP DESPAIR I CALL TO THEE see Mendelssohn-Bartholdy, Felix, Aus Tiefer Not Schrei Ich Zu Dir

IN DEINE HAND SIND WIR GEGEBEN see Marks, Gunther

IN DEINEM FRIEDEN STILL see Stier, Alfred

IN DEINER HAND, HERR, STEHT see Metzger, Hans-Arnold

IN DEM HERREN FREUET EUCH see Raphael, Gunther

IN DEN ARMEN DEIN see Franck, Melchior

IN DEN ARMEN DES HEILANDES UND HERREN see Schutz, Heinrich, Inter Brachia Salvatoris Mei

IN DEN HEMEL IS ENEN DANS see Noble, Felix de

IN DER WELT HABT IHR ANGST see Distler, Hugo

IN DER WELT HABT IHR ANGST see Stockmeier, Wolfgang

IN DICH, GOTT, HAB ICH GEHOFFET see Schutz, Heinrich, In Te, Domine, Speravi

IN DICH HAB ICH GEHOFFET see Bossler, Kurt

IN DICH HAB ICH GEHOFFET see Praetorius, Michael

IN DICH HAB ICH GEHOFFET, HERR see Franck, Melchior

IN DICH HAB ICH GEHOFFET, HERR see Hemmel, Sigmund

IN DICH HAB ICH GEHOFFET, HERR see Reda, Siegfried

IN DICH HAB ICH GEHOFFET, HERR see Schutz, Heinrich

IN DICH HAB ICH GEHOFFET, HERR see Studer, Hans

IN DICH HAB ICH GEHOFFET, HERR see Vulpius, Melchior

IN DIE TRIBULATIONIS see Lassus, Roland de (Orlandus)

IN DIESER NACHT SEI DU MIR SCHIRM *17th cent (Burkhart, Franz) mix cor,acap oct DOBLINGER s.p.   (I176)

IN DIR IST FREUDE see Gastoldi, Giovanni Giacomo

IN DIR IST FREUDE see Oertzen, Rudolf von

IN DIR IST FREUDE, IN ALLEM LEIDE see Gastoldi, Giovanni Giacomo

IN DIVERS TONGUES SPAKE THE APOSTLES see Palestrina, Giovanni

IN DOMINICA PALMARUM see Fabiani, Angelo

IN DOMUM DOMINI see Foss, Julius

IN DREAMS I'VE HEARD THE SERAPHS FAIR see Faure, Jean-Baptist, Sancta Maria

IN DULCE JUBILO see Tolmage, Gerald

IN DULCI JUBILO *Xmas,anthem/cant/carol/hymn, Ger,17th cent/14th cent
see Bring Your Torches Jeannette Isabella
see Six Traditional Carols, Set II
unis/SATB (very easy) OXFORD 08.084 $.15   (I177)
(Abell, David) [Ger/Lat] 6pt mix cor,acap (from part-books of the royal danish choir, 1541) sc SKAND. SMF5356 s.p.   (I178)
(Christiansen, F.M.) SSAATTBB,S solo (diff) oct AUGSBURG 0090 $.25   (I179)
(Dahmen, Hermann Joseph) [Ger] 2-5pt mix cor, org,winds,strings (med, from settings by old masters) MULLER SM 482A sc s.p., cor pts s.p.   (I180)
(Davies) [Lat] SA BOOSEY-CAN s.p.   (I181)
(Davison, A.) SSAA,acap SCHIRM.EC 818 $.22   (I182)
(Davison, A.) TTBB,acap SCHIRM.EC 25 $.25   (I183)
(Geer, E.) SSAA,acap SCHIRM.EC 856 $.22   (I184)
(Hinton) unis (very easy) OXFORD 81.096 $.35, ipa   (I185)
(Kaplan) SATB oct LAWSON 51714 $.35   (I186)
(Kramer, G.) mix cor DOBLINGER s.p. see also Drei Weihnachtslieder   (I187)
(Kuxhaven, D.) mix cor sc ALSBACH&D s.p.   (I188)
(Larsen, Jens Peter) [Dan] SATB HANSEN-DEN 205 s.p. see also Julesange   (I189)
(Roseberry) [Lat/Eng] unis,pno/gtr,perc oct SCHIRM.G 11627 $.25   (I190)
(Roseberry, Eric) [Lat] unis,opt pno/gtr,perc oct FABER 11627 $.25   (I191)
(Westbrook, W.; Pearsall, R.) SATB,acap SCHIRM.EC 363 $.35   (I192)
(Wikander, David) "Nu Stige Jublets Ton" mix cor NORDISKA 963 s.p.   (I193)
(Williamson, M.) SATB oct PRESSER JW $.35   (I194)

IN DULCI JUBILO see Anonymous

IN DULCI JUBILO see Beckerath, Alfred von

IN DULCI JUBILO see Buxtehude, Dietrich

IN DULCI JUBILO see Dinn, Freda

IN DULCI JUBILO see Doppelbauer, Josef Friedrich

IN DULCI JUBILO see Eccard, Johannes

IN DULCI JUBILO see Grofe

IN DULCI JUBILO see Hastings

IN DULCI JUBILO see Hokanson, M.

IN DULCI JUBILO see Holscher, Bernhard

IN DULCI JUBILO see Klein, Karl Heinz

IN DULCI JUBILO see Lissmann, Kurt

IN DULCI JUBILO see Nitsche, Paul

IN DULCI JUBILO see Pearsall, Robert Lucas de

IN DULCI JUBILO see Praetorius, Michael

IN DULCI JUBILO see Schafstall, Joh.

IN DULCI JUBILO see Scheidt, Samuel

IN DULCI JUBILO see Schroter, Leonhard

IN DULCI JUBILO see Sendt, Willy

IN DULCI JUBILO see Suderburg, R.

IN DULCI JUBILO see Telemann, Georg Philipp

IN DULCI JUBILO see Walter

IN DULCI JUBILO see Weiss, Ewald

IN DULCI JUBILO see Werner, Gregor Joseph

IN DULCI JUBILO see Wideen, Ivar

IN DULCI JUBILO see Williamson, Malcolm

IN DULCI JUBILO [CHORALE] see Bach, Johann Sebastian

IN DULCI JUBILO, NUN SINGET see Hassler, Hans Leo

IN DULCI JUBILO, NUN SINGET see Praetorius, Michael

IN EASTERN LANDS see Giasson

IN ECCLESIIS see Gabrieli, Giovanni

IN EPIPHANIA DOMINI see Byrd, William

IN EVERY CORNER SING see Sateren, Leland Bernhard

IN EVERY HAND BEGIN THE SONG see Peninger, David

IN EXCELSIS see Anderson

IN EXCELSIS DEO *Xmas (Henninger) SSAA SCHMITT 2526 $.25   (I195)
(Henninger) SATB SCHMITT 1792 $.25   (I196)

IN EXCELSIS GLORIA see Fricker, Peter Racine

IN EXCELSIS GLORIA see Paget, Michael

IN EXCELSIS GLORIA see Peeters, Flor

IN EXCELSIS GLORIA see Spencer

IN EXITU ISRAEL see Vivaldi, Antonio

IN EXPECTATIONE RESURRECTIONIS DOMINI see Halffter, C.

IN EXULTATION MY SOUL REJOICES see Bach, Johann Sebastian

IN FAITH I CALMLY REST see Bach

IN FESTIVITATE SANCTAE TRINITATIS see Lualdi

IN FESTO CORPORIS CHRISTE see Victoria, Tomas Luis de

IN FESTO EPIPHANIE see Bottazzo, Luigi

IN FESTO NATALIS DOMINI see Victoria, Tomas Luis de

IN FESTO OMNIUM SANCTORUM see Byrd, William

IN FESTO PENECOSTES see Byrd, William

IN FESTO PENTECOSTIS see Fulda, Adam von

IN FESTO PURIFICATIONIS see Byrd, William

IN FESTO S. ALOYSII - QUIS ASCENDET see Fabiani, Angelo

IN FESTO S. CECILIAE see Fabiani, Angelo

IN FESTO S. CECILIAE see Oltrassi, Giuseppe

IN FESTO S. FRANCISCI see Ravanello, Oreste

IN FIELDS NOT FAR FROM BETHLEHEM *Xmas (Ehret, W.) SATB oct PRESSER 362-03117 $.30   (I197)

IN FIELDS NOT FAR FROM BETHLEHEM see Ehret, Walter

IN FIELDS WITH THEIR FLOCKS (Sharpe) cor&desc CRAMER 53 s.p.   (I198)

IN FRATERNA CARITA see Santucci, Pellegrino

IN GETHSEMANE see Bruckner, Anton

IN GETHSEMANE see Palestrina, Giovanni, Tristis Est Anima Mea

IN GOD IS MY SALVATION see Pfohl

IN GOD WE TRUST *CCUL,Contemp (Skillings, Otis) SATB cmplt ed LILLENAS MB-237 $1.95   (I199)

IN GOD WE TRUST SATB,acap BIG3 $.25   (I200)

IN GOD WE TRUST see Sherman

IN GOTTES NAMEN FAHREN WIR see Anonymous

IN GOTTES NAMEN FAHREN WIR see Finck

IN GOTTES NAMEN FAHREN WIR see Hassler, Hans Leo

IN HAC DIE see Pergolesi, Giovanni Battista

IN HEAVEN ABOVE *Gen,anthem/folk,Norw SATB oct LORENZ C227 $.30   (I201)
(Andersen) SSAA SCHMITT 2509 $.35   (I202)
(Christiansen, F.M.) SATB,S solo (med) oct AUGSBURG 0106 $.25   (I203)

IN HEAVENLY LOVE see Blake, George [M.]

IN HEAVENLY LOVE see Boozer, Pat

IN HEAVENLY LOVE see Grieg, Edvard Hagerup

IN HEAVENLY LOVE see Pritchard, Arthur J.

IN HEAVENLY LOVE ABIDING see McAfee, D.

IN HEAVENLY LOVE ABIDING see Mendelssohn-Bartholdy, Felix

IN HEAVENLY LOVE ABIDING see Speaks, [Oley]

IN HEAVENLY LOVE ABIDING see Swift, Gertrude P.

IN HEAVENLY LOVE ABIDING see Wesley

IN HEAV'N ABOVE see Grieg, Edvard Hagerup

IN HEBDOMADA SANCTA *Easter,mot
[Lat] ZANIBON 2948 s.p.
contains: Brambilla, E., In Monte Olivetti;
Cimbro, A., O Vos Omnes; Muller, J.,
Vexilla Regis; Rosso, R., Christus;
Volpi, Edoardo, Christus; Volpi, Edoardo,
O Vos Omnes   (I204)

IN HEVENE AND HELLE see Bishop, Jeffrey

IN HIM IS LIFE see McCormick

IN HIS HAND see Mendelssohn-Bartholdy, Felix

IN HIS HOLY TEMPLE see Lorenz

IN HIS HOLY TEMPLE see Mauduit, Jacques, En Son
Temple Sacre

IN HOLY GARB THYSELF ARRAY
(Lundquist) SATB,acap (med) oct WILLIS 6624
$.18   (I205)

IN HONOREM B. MARIAE VIRGINIS-TRE MOTTETI see
Arnaldi, Antonio

IN HONOREM MARIAE MATRIS DEI see Rubbra, Edmund

IN HONOUR OF A KING see Ager, Laurence

IN HORA MORTIS see Favero, Gino

IN HORA ULTIMA see Lassus, Roland de (Orlandus)

IN HUMBLE FAITH AND HOLY LOVE see Garrett

IN HUMBLE FAITH AND HOLY LOVE see Garrett,
George Mursell

IN IEIUNIO ET FLETU see Tallis, Thomas

IN IHM SEIS BEGONNEN see Micheelsen, Hans
Friedrich

IN ILLA TEMPORT see Monteverdi, Claudio, Messa
I A 6 Voci

IN ILLO TEMPORA see Monteverdi, Claudio, Messe
I A 6 Voci

IN ILLO TEMPORE see Palestrina, Giovanni

IN JEDER NACHT, DIE MICH BEDROHT see Lohr, Ina

IN JEJUNIO ET FLETU see Tallis, Thomas

IN JESUS see Hughes

IN JOSEPH'S LOVELY GARDEN *Easter/Lent,Span
(Dickinson, C.) 1-4pt oct GRAY GSC 185 $.25
                                         (I206)
(Dickinson, C.) SATB oct GRAY GSC 135 $.35
                                         (I207)

IN JUCUNDA CAPTIVITATE see Bianchini, Carlo

IN LAUTER TRANEN TROPFT DER TAG see Woll, Erna

IN LOUD, EXALTED STRAINS see Markworth, Henry

IN MAJORIBUS DUPLICIBUS see Palestrina,
Giovanni

IN MANUS TUAS see Byrd, William

IN MANUS TUAS see Novello, Vincent

IN MANUS TUAS see Tallis, Thomas

IN ME GRATIA see Fabiani, Angelo

IN ME GRATIA see Mariani, Eligio

IN ME TRANSIERUNT see Lassus, Roland de
(Orlandus)

IN ME TRANSIERUNT IRAE TUAE see Selle, Thomas

IN MEDIO ECCLESIAE see Brissio

IN MEMORIAM see Gebhard, Hans

IN MEMORIAM see Reznicek, Emil Nikolaus von

IN MEMORIAM-BERYL RUBINSTEIN see Smith

IN MEMORY OF THE SAVIOR'S LOVE see Burroughs,
Bob

IN MEMORY OF THE SAVIOUR'S LOVE see Burroughs

IN MEMORY OF THE SAVIOUR'S LOVE see Ford

IN MINORIBUS DUBLICIBIS see Palestrina,
Giovanni

IN MIR IST ES FINSTER see Eglin, Arthur

IN MIRTH AND IN GLADNESS see Neidt, F.E.

IN MONTE OLIVETI see Bruckner, Anton

IN MONTE OLIVETI see Croce, Giovanni

IN MONTE OLIVETI see Ingegneri, Marco Antonio

IN MONTE OLIVETI see Leo, Leonardo

IN MONTE OLIVETI see Martini, Padre

IN MONTE OLIVETI see Palestrina, Giovanni

IN MONTE OLIVETI see Rubbra, Edmund

IN MONTE OLIVETI see Schubert, Franz (Peter)

IN MONTE OLIVETI see Zielenski, Mikolaj

IN MONTE OLIVETTI see Brambilla, E.

IN MY DISTRESS I CALLED TO THE LORD see
Sanders, Robert L.

IN MY FATHER'S HOUSE see Pasquet, Jean

IN MY FATHER'S HOUSE ARE MANY MANSIONS
SATB CHAPPELL 0022459-358 $.40   (I208)

IN MY HEART THERE RINGS A MELODY see Roth

IN NATALI DOMINE
see Two Christmas Carols

IN NATALI DOMINI see Desderi, Ettore

IN NATALI DOMINI see Desderi, Ettore

IN NATALI DOMINI see Praetorius, Michael

IN NATALI DOMINI see Schroter, Leonhard

IN NATALI DOMINI CLAMANT see Galliculus, Johann

IN NATIVITATE DOMINE AD TERTIAM MISSAM see
Fabiani, Angelo

IN NATIVITATE DOMINI *CC9L,Xmas,mot
mix cor,org ZANIBON 2610 s.p. contains works
by: Schinelli, A.; Mauri, V.; Volpi, E.;
Fabiani, A.; Ferro, S.; Cerquetelli, C.;
Sevim, J.; Volpi, E.   (I209)

IN NATIVITATE DOMINI see Byrd, William

IN NATIVITATE DOMINI see Bottazzo, Luigi

IN NATIVITATE DOMINI see Ravanello, Oreste

IN NATIVITATE MARIAE VIRGINIS see Byrd, William

IN NATIVITATEM DOMINI NOSTRI JESU CHRISTI
CANTICUM see Charpentier, Marc-Antoine

IN NOCTE NATIVITATIS see Ravanello, Oreste

IN NOMINE JESU see Gallus, Jacobus

IN NOMINE JESU see Vranken, Alph.

IN ONORE DI S. ANTONIO see Bottazzo, Luigi

IN ONORE DI S. GIUSEPPE see Arnaldi, Antonio

IN OUR WORK AND IN OUR PLAY see Burroughs, Bob

IN PACE see Blitheman, William

IN PACE see Des Prez, Josquin

IN PARADISIUM see Rousseau, Marcel-Samuel

IN PARADISUM see Castellini, J.

IN PARADISUM see Cherubini, Luigi

IN PARADISUM see Faure, Gabriel-Urbain

IN PARADISUM see Krenek, Ernst

IN PARADISUM see Miot, Vittorio

IN PARADISUM see Spies, Claudio

IN PARADISUM see Vranken, Alph.

IN PASTURES GREEN see Graves, Richard

IN PATHS OF BEAUTY see Young

IN PEACE see Blitheman, William, In Pace

IN PEACE AND JOY see Praetorius, Michael

IN PEACE AND JOY I NOW DEPART see Edmonds

IN PEACE AND JOY I NOW DEPART see Fetler, D.

IN PEACE AND JOY I NOW DEPART see Gesius,
Bartholomaus, Mit Fried Und Freud Fahr Ich
Dahin

IN PEACE AND JOY I NOW DEPART see Praetorius,
Jakob

IN PEACEFUL FIELDS see Shaw, Geoffrey [Turton]

IN PERFECT PEACE see Dieterich

IN PRAISE AND ADORATION see Dretke, L.N.

IN PRAISE OF A LADY see Cockshott, Gerald
Wilfred

IN PRAISE OF FRIDAY see Rodby, Walter

IN PRAISE OF GOD see Mueller, Carl F.

IN PRAISE OF IVY see Hoddinott, Alun

IN PRAISE OF MARY'S SON *Xmas,carol,15th cent
(Kurth, Burton) SSA&opt cor,opt solo oct
LESLIE 3046   (I210)

IN PRAISE OF SONG see Weber, Preis Dir O Ton

IN PRAISE OF SPRING AND EASTER see Caldwell,
Mary [Elizabeth]

IN PRAISE WE SING BOOK 1 *CC11L,Gen
(Barthelson) 2pt treb cor PRO ART 668 $.75
                                         (I211)

IN PRAISE WE SING BOOK 2 *CC10L,Gen
(Barthelson) 2pt treb cor PRO ART 669 $.75
                                         (I212)

IN PRAISE WE SING BOOK 3 *CC11L,Gen
(Barthelson) 2pt treb cor PRO ART 670 $.75
                                         (I213)

IN PRAYER see Faure, Gabriel-Urbain

IN PRIMA MISSA CELEBRANDA *mot
[Lat] 2pt mix cor sc ZANIBON 773 s.p., cor
pts ZANIBON 774 s.p.
contains: Bottazzo, Luigi, Tu Es Sacerdos;
Giachetti, Enrico, Circunda Tibi Decorem;
Mercatali, A., Elegi Abjectus Esse (I214)

IN PRINCIPIO ERAT VERBUM see Heiller, Anton

IN PULVEREM MORTIS see Penderecki, Krzysztof

IN SEINER HANDEN *mot
(Burkhart, Franz) mix cor,acap cmplt ed
DOBLINGER s.p.
contains & see also: Das Wessobrunner
Gebet; Dereinst, Mein Sinn; Ein Traum;
Gesang Der Geissler; Gottes Mutter; Leid
Des Einsiedels; Sterbemotette; Vesper
                                         (I215)

IN SEINER TODESNOT see Spohr, Ludwig (Louis)

IN SILENCE AND WONDER see Frank

IN SILENT NIGHT see Southall, Mitchell

IN SLUMBER, PEACEFUL SLUMBER see Gregor

IN SOLEMN SILENCE see Ippolitov-Ivanov, Mikhail
Mikhailovitch

IN SOLEMNI CLERICORUM VESTITIONE *mot
[Lat] 2pt mix cor,org sc ZANIBON 749 s.p.,
cor pts ZANIBON 748 s.p.
contains: Bottazzo, Luigi, Circunda Tibi
Decorem; Mercatali, A., Gaudens Gaudebo;
Rodella, Sante, Dominus Pars   (I216)

IN SOLEMNITATE PASCHAE see Ferro, Stefano

IN SPEECHLESS PRAYER AND REVERENCE see Urhan,
Chretian

IN STEADFAST FAITH I STAND see Bach

IN STILLER NACHT see Brahms, Johannes

IN STILLER NACHT see Liebe, Kurt Maria

IN STILLER NACHT ZUR ERSTEN WACHT see
Horschelmann, Ottmar

IN STILLER NACHT, ZUR ERSTEN WACHT see Sendt,
Willy

IN TE, DOMINE see Handel, George Frideric

IN TE, DOMINE see Mozart, Wolfgang Amadeus

IN TE DOMINE see Schutz, Heinrich

IN TE DOMINE SPERAVI see Buxtehude, Dietrich

IN TE, DOMINE, SPERAVI see Buxtehude, Dietrich,
Auf Dich, Herr, Hab' Ich Gehoffet

IN TE DOMINE SPERAVI see Frescobaldi, Girolamo

IN TE, DOMINE, SPERAVI see Schutz, Heinrich

IN TE DOMINE, SPERAVI see Trexler, Georg

IN TE DOMINE, SPERAVI see Waclaw of Szamotuly

IN TE DOMINE SPERAVI see Palestrina, Giovanni

IN TE DOMINE SPERAVI see Palestrina, Giovanni

IN TE, DOMINI SPERAVI see Stevens

IN TE SPERAVI see Muller, Giulio

IN TEARS OF GRIEF see Bach, Johann Sebastian

IN TEMPORE PASCHALI see Byrd, William

IN TERRA PAX see Finzi, Gerald

IN TERRA PAX see Martin, Frank

IN TERRA PAX see Pfautsch, Lloyd

IN TERRA PAX see Schwarz-Schilling, Reinhard

IN TERTIA MISSA NATIVITATIS see Ravanello,
Oreste

IN THANKFUL REMEMBRANCE see Groom, Lester H.

IN THAT GREAT GETTIN' UP MORNIN'
SATB oct STAFF 355 $.30   (I217)
(Ehret, W.) SATB oct PRESSER 312-40327 $.30
                                         (I218)
(Heath) 4pt men cor,acap oct SCHIRM.G 11867
$.40   (I219)

IN THAT GREAT GETTIN' UP MORNIN' see
Zimmermann, Heinz Werner

IN THAT GREAT GETTIN' UP MORNING *spir
(Harris) SATB oct PRO ART 2244 $.25   (I220)

IN THAT HOUR see Lister, Mosie

IN THAT LOVELY FAR-OFF CITY see Niles, John
Jacob

IN THAT NEW JERUSALEM *spir
(De Cormier) TTBB,acap oct LAWSON 51091 $.35
                                         (I221)

IN THAT POOR STABLE see Dans Cette Etable

IN THE BEAUTY OF HOLINESS see Lekberg, Sven

IN THE BEGINNING see Copland, Aaron

IN THE BEGINNING see Graham, Robert [V.]

IN THE BEGINNING see Kosakoff, Reuven

IN THE BEGINNING see Pasquet, Jean

IN THE BEGINNING see Raffman, Relly

IN THE BEGINNING see Sjolund, Paul

IN THE BEGINNING GOD see Crowell, M.

IN THE BEGINNING, GOD see Williams

IN THE BEGINNING OF CREATION see Pinkham,
Daniel

IN THE BEGINNING WAS GOD see Lamb

IN THE BEGINNING WAS THE WORD see Hovhaness,
Alan

IN THE BEGINNING WAS THE WORD see Moffat

IN THE BLEAK MID-WINTER
see Six Christmas Carols, Set III

IN THE BLEAK MID-WINTER see Bonta, Stephen

IN THE BLEAK MID-WINTER see Holst, Gustav

IN THE BLEAK MIDWINTER
unis/SATB (very easy) OXFORD 08.187 $.15
                            (I222)

IN THE BLEAK MIDWINTER see Davis, Katherine K.

IN THE BLEAK MIDWINTER see Kent, Richard

IN THE BLEAK MIDWINTER see McAfee, Don

IN THE BLEAK MIDWINTER see Smart, David

IN THE CITY OF DAVID see Sheldon

IN THE CROSS OF CHRIST I GLORY
SA KJOS 6115 $.30   (I223)

IN THE DARK OF THE NIGHT *Xmas,carol,Ger
(Halter, C.) SA,kbd (easy) oct CONCORDIA
98-1661 $.25   (I224)
(Halter, C.) SATB,kbd (easy) oct CONCORDIA
98-1704 $.25   (I225)

IN THE DEPARTURE OF THE LORD see Bull, John

IN THE END OF THE SABBATH see Speaks, [Oley]

IN THE FIELDS WITH THEIR FLOCKS ABIDING *Xmas,
carol
oct HART s.p.   (I226)

IN THE GARDEN
SSA/SATB/SA BIG3 $.30   (I227)

IN THE GARDEN see Miles

IN THE GROVE OF CEDARS see Hastings

IN THE HEAVENLY KINGDOM see Harris, William
Henry

IN THE HIGHEST, GLORY see Williams

IN THE HOLLOW OF YOUR HAND see Schmidt

IN THE HOLLOW OF YOUR HAND see Schmidt, Melvin

IN THE INN see Mc Bradd

IN THE LONELY MIDNIGHT see Kechley, [Gerald]

IN THE LONELY MIDNIGHT see Lovelace, Austin C.

IN THE LONELY MIDNIGHT see Whitney, Maurice C.

IN THE LORD I PUT MY TRUST see Handel, George
Frideric, In The Lord Put I My Trust

IN THE LORD PUT I MY FAITH see Coat

IN THE LORD PUT I MY TRUST see Handel, George
Frideric

IN THE MIDST OF EARTHLY LIFE see Anonymous

IN THE MIDST OF EARTHLY LIFE see Bach, Johann
Sebastian

IN THE MIDST OF EARTHLY LIFE see Erythraus,
Gotthard

IN THE MIDST OF LIFE see Purcell, Henry

IN THE MOON OF WINTERTIME see Sateren, Leland
Bernhard

IN THE NAME OF HEAVEN see Bragg

IN THE NAME OF JESUS see Gallus, Jacobus, In
Nomine Jesu

IN THE NAME OF OUR GOD see Willan, Healey

IN THE NAME OF THE LORD see Nelson, Ronald A.

IN THE NIGHT, CHRIST CAME WALKING see Cain,
Noble

IN THE ORIGINAL TONGUE *CCU
(Lovelace, A.C.) jr cor oct KERBY 7009 $1.35
                            (I228)
IN THE ORIGINAL TONGUE see Lovelace, Austin C.

IN THE QUIETNESS see Lorenz

IN THE RIVER OF JORDAN *spir
(Hunter) SATB,acap oct LAWSON 51140 $.30
                            (I229)

IN THE SECRET OF HIS PRESENCE see Stebbins

IN THE SHADOW OF THY WINGS see Russell, Velma
A.

IN THE SHELTER OF THY WINGS see Balamos, John

IN THE SIGHT OF THE UNWISE see Nares, James

IN THE SILENT NIGHT see Rachmaninoff, Sergey
Vassilievitch

IN THE STABLE
(Track, Gerhard) SATB oct AGAPE AD 1974 $.30
                            (I230)
(Track, Gerhard) SSA oct AGAPE AD 1975 $.30
                            (I231)

IN THE STILL NIGHT see Thompson, Alan

IN THE STILLNESS see Marth, Helen Jun

IN THE STILLNESS OF THE NIGHT see Peery

IN THE STILLNESS OF THE NIGHT see Wilson

IN THE TEMPLE DO THE PRIESTS see Byrd, William

IN THE TIME OF TROUBLE see Blow

IN THE TIME OF TROUBLE see Blow, John

IN THE WORLD YOU HAVE FEAR see Distler, Hugo

IN THE YEAR THAT KING USSIAH DIED see Routh,
Francis

IN THE YEAR THAT KING UZZIAH DIED see Naylor,
Bernard

IN THE YEAR THAT KING UZZIAH DIED see Williams,
David McK.

IN THE YEAR THAT KING UZZIAH DIED see Young,
Gordon

IN THEE DO I PUT MY TRUST see Jerome, Frederick

IN THEE, HOLY LORD see Mozart, Wolfgang
Amadeus, In Te, Domine

IN THEE I TRUST see Hadley

IN THEE I TRUST see Sateren, Leland Bernhard

IN THEE IS GLADNESS *Gen
(Ley, Henry G.) SATB (easy) oct OXFORD 42.709
$.35   (I232)

IN THEE IS GLADNESS see Gastoldi

IN THEE IS GLADNESS see Gastoldi, Giovanni
Giacomo, In Dir Ist Freude, In Allem Leide

IN THEE IS GLADNESS see Ley, Henry George

IN THEE IS GLADNESS see Luvaas

IN THEE LORD see Glarum, L. Stanley

IN THEE, O FATHER, I PUT MY TRUST see Handel,
George Frideric

IN THEE, O LORD see Haydn, (Franz) Joseph

IN THEE, O LORD see Mead

IN THEE, O LORD, DO I HOPE see Huessenstamm,
George

IN THEE, O LORD, DO I PUT MY TRUST see Bender,
Jan

IN THEE O LORD DO I PUT MY TRUST see Jordan,
W.C.

IN THEE, O LORD, DO I PUT MY TRUST see Nyquist

IN THEE, O LORD DO I PUT MY TRUST see Schutz,
Heinrich

IN THEE, O LORD, HAVE I PUT MY TRUST see
Ferris, W.

IN THEE, O LORD, HAVE I PUT MY TRUST see
Stevens, In Te, Domini Speravi

IN THEE, O LORD, HAVE I PUT MY TRUST see Tours,
Berthold

IN THEE, O LORD, HAVE I PUT MY TRUST see Handel,
George Frideric, In Te, Domine

IN THEE, O LORD, HAVE I TRUSTED see Handel,
George Frideric, In Te, Domine

IN THEE, O LORD, I PUT MY TRUST see Kirk

IN THEE, O LORD, IS FULLNESS OF JOY see
Couperin, Armand-Louis

IN THEE, O LORD, IS FULLNESS OF JOY see
Couperin, Francois

IN THINE ARM I REST ME see Bach, Johann
Sebastian

IN THIS NIGHT CHRIST WAS BORN see Moschetti,
[Giuseppe]

IN THIS THY MERCY'S DAY see Graham, Robert [V.]

IN THIS WORLD see McLin

IN THY COVANANT DOES MY HEART REJOICE see
Berger, Jean

IN THY MYSTERIOUS PRESENCE see Brandon

IN THY ONE FOLD OF LOVE see Wells

IN THY STRENGTH, O LORD see Davies, Henry
Walford

IN THY WAY see Caldwell, Mary [Elizabeth]

IN TIEFER NOT see Leuthold, W.

IN TIMES LIKE THESE
SATB BIG3 $.25   (I233)

IN TIMES LIKE THESE see Jones

IN TRANSITU SANCTI PATRIS NOSTRI FRANCISCI see
Perosi, (Dom) Lorenzo

IN TRIDUO SACRO MAIORIS HEBDOMADAE see Magri,
Pietro

IN TUA PATIENTIA see Willaert, Adrian

IN UNS WIRD LICHT see Lehner, Walter

IN UNSERE CHORE MISCHET EUCH! HALLELUJA, AMEN!
see Handel, George Frideric, Rejoice, Oh
Judah! Hallelujah, Amen!

IN VOCE EXSULATIONIS see Pitoni, Giuseppe
Ottavio

IN VOCE EXULTATIONIES see Pitoni, Giuseppe
Ottavio

IN WHOM I PUT MY TRUST see Bach, Karl Philipp
Emanuel

IN YOU, O LORD, HAVE I PUT MY TRUST
(Campbell; Watson) SATB oct SUMMY A 5963 $.30
                            (I234)

INAUGURATION OF THE SIENA SYNAGOGUE -
CEREMONIAL MUSIC, 1786 see Gallichi,
Volunio, Musica Vocale Esequita In
Occasione Dell'apertura Della Nuovo Scuola
Di Siena, 1786

INCARNATE WORD, THE see Elmore, Robert [Hall]

INCLINA AD ME see Himmel, Friedrich Heinrich

INCLINA, DOMINE, AUREM TUAM see Cortese, Luigi

INCLINE THINE EAR see Himmel, Friedrich
Heinrich

INCLINE THINE EAR see Ippolitov-Ivanov, Mikhail
Mikhailovitch

INCLINE THINE EAR, OH LORD see Arkhangelsky, G.

INCLINE THINE EAR TO ME see Himmel

INCLINE THINE EAR TO ME see Himmel, Friedrich
Heinrich, Inclina Ad Me

INCLINE THY SPIRIT see Morgan, Haydn

INCLINE YOUR EAR see Wilkes, R.W.

INDIAN CHRISTMAS CAROL *Xmas,carol
(Hunter) TB,opt drums oct LAWSON 934 $.30
                            (I235)
INDIAN HYMN OF PRAISE see Lovelace, Austin C.

INDY, VINCENT D' (1851-1931)
Cantate Domino *Op.22, Gen,mot
[Fr] STB,org oct DURAND s.p.   (I236)
[Lat] STBar,org oct DURAND s.p.   (I237)
[Lat] 3pt men cor,org oct DURAND s.p.
                            (I238)
(Brun, L'abbe F.) [Fr] 3pt men cor,org oct
DURAND s.p.   (I239)

O Salutaris *Commun,mot
(Brun, L'abbe F.) [Lat] 3pt wom cor oct
DURAND s.p.   (I240)

Sainte Marie Magdeleine, Cantate *cant
[Lat/Fr] wom cor,Mez solo,pno/org oct
DURAND s.p.   (I241)

INFANT CHRIST, THE see Cornelius, Peter

INFANT DIVINE see Brogi

INFANT HAS COME TO EARTH, AN see Du Caurroy,
Francoise-Eustache, Un Enfant Du Ciel Nous
Est Ne

INFANT HOLY *Op.121, Xmas,carol,Pol
(Bowlus) 4pt wom cor,acap oct SCHIRM.G 11123
$.20   (I242)
(Church) SSA oct PLYMOUTH JR-203 $.25   (I243)
(Rubbra, E.) SATB,acap LENGNICK s.p.   (I244)
(Shirley) 4pt boy cor/SSAA,acap oct LAWSON
51349 $.30   (I245)

INFANT HOLY see Rubbra, Edmund

INFANT HOLY, INFANT LOWLY *Xmas
(Paget, Michael) mix cor CURWEN 61568 s.p.
                            (I246)
(Willcocks) SATB,acap (very easy) OXFORD
84.123 $.20   (I247)

INFANT HOLY, INFANT LOWLY see Sjolund, Paul

INFANT JESUS see Cassler, G. Winston

INFANT JESUS, THE *Xmas,cant
mix cor CHAPPELL 0018416-3692 $1.00   (I248)

INFANT JESUS, THE see Buxtehude, Dietrich, Das
Neugeborne Kindelein

INFANT KING *Xmas,carol
(Peltman, E.) SATB ALLANS 296 s.p.   (I249)
(Peltman; Wickham) SA/unis ALLANS s.p. (I250)

INFANT SO GENTLE see Boyd

INFANT SO LOWLY *Xmas
(Ehret, W.) SATB oct PRESSER 312-40479 $.30
                            (I251)
INFANT SWEET AND GENTLE, AN *Xmas
(Ehret, W.) SATB oct PRESSER 312-40765 $.30
                            (I252)

INFANTAS, FERNANDO DE LAS (1534-ca. 1607)
Victimae Paschali *Easter
[Lat] 6pt mix cor,acap UNION ESP. 19349
s.p.   (I253)

INFENSUS HOSTIS, IN HONORE DI S. LUIGI see
Fabiani, Angelo

INFENSUS HOSTIS, IN ONORE DIE S. LUIGI see
Arnaldi, Antonio

INFLAMMATUS see Dvorak, Antonin

INFLAMMATUS see Rossini, Gioacchino

INFLAMMATUS ET ACCENSUS see Rossini, Gioacchino

INGALLS
Northfield
SATB,acap MARKS 70 $.30   (I254)

INGEGNERI
Behold How The Righteous Perish
(Klein, M.) SATB KJOS 5452 $.30   (I255)

INGEGNERI, MARCO ANTONIO (1545-1592)
Amicus Meus
see Responsorien Fur Grundonnerstag-Heft II

Be Thou Exalted, O God *anthem
(Coggin) SATB (easy) oct AUGSBURG 1493 $.25
                            (I256)

Behold And See
(Lundquist) SATB,acap (med) oct WILLIS 5504
$.15   (I257)

Blessed Mother Of Heaven *see Santa Madre
Del Ciel

Caligaverunt Oculi Mei *Easter/Lent
(Marshall, Charles) "My Eyes Grow Misty
From Weeping" SATB FRANK F-601 $.30
                            (I258)

Darkness Obscured The Earth *see Tenebrae
Factae Sunt

INGEGNERI, MARCO ANTONIO (cont'd.)

Darkness Was O'er The Earth *see Tenebrae
Factae Sunt

Ecce Quomodo Moritur *Lent
(Graetzer) [Lat] SATB,acap RICORDI-ARG
BA 9832 s.p.   (I259)
(Payson) "See Then, How The Holy Man Dieth"
SATB oct SOUTHERN $.25   (I260)
(Payson, A.) "See Then, How The Holy Man
Dieth" SATB,acap FRANK F-447 $.30   (I261)

Ecce Quomodo Moritur Justus
SATB,acap RICORDI-ENG BA9832 s.p.   (I262)

Ecce Vidimus
4pt men cor,acap RICORDI-ENG BA10085 s.p. (I263)

Ecce, Vidimus Eum
see Responsorien Fur Grundonnerstag-Heft I
(Ruiz) [Lat] 4pt men cor,acap RICORDI-ARG
BA 10085 s.p.   (I264)

Eram Quasi Agnus Innocens
see Responsorien Fur Grundonnerstag-Heft
III

God, Our Creator, Father *anthem
(Coggin) SATB (easy) oct AUGSBURG 1495 $.25 (I265)

In Monte Oliveti
see Responsorien Fur Grundonnerstag-Heft I
4pt men cor,acap RICORDI-ENG BA10483 s.p. (I266)
(Ruiz) [Lat] 4pt men cor,acap RICORDI-ARG
BA 10483 s.p.   (I267)

Jesus, Merciful Saviour
(Coggin) SATB,acap oct FOX R208 $.25 (I268)

Judas Mercator Pessimus
see Responsorien Fur Grundonnerstag-Heft II

Lucis Creator Optime *hymn
SATB,acap SCHIRM.EC $.16   (I269)
(Collins,H.B.) [Lat] SATB CHESTER s.p.   (I270)

My Eyes Grow Misty From Weeping *see
Caligaverunt Oculi Mei

O Bone Jesu *Easter/Gen/Psntd
[Lat] SATB,acap (easy) MULLER MS 19 s.p. (I271)
SATB,acap (contains also: Bach, Johann
Sebastian, Herzliebster Jesu) voc pt
DOBLINGER s.p. see also PASSION UND
OSTERN   (I272)
"O Goede Jezus Ontferm U Onzer" men cor sc
ALSBACH&D s.p.   (I273)
(Buszin) SATB SCHMITT 1692 $.30   (I274)
(Lavater, H.) [Lat] men cor,acap (easy) HUG
s.p.   (I275)

O Goede Jezus Ontferm U Onzer *see O Bone
Jesu

Plange Quasi
(Schinelli, A.) [It/Eng/Ger] 4pt mix cor
CURCI 6075 s.p. see from COLLANA DI
COMPOSIZIONI POLIFONICHE VOCALE SACRE E
PROFANE, VOL. 1   (I276)

Responsorien Fur Grundonnerstag-Heft I
*Holywk,cor-resp
(Walter, Rudolf) 4pt mix cor cor pts
BREITKOPF-W CHB-3635A s.p.
contains: Ecce, Vidimus Eum; In Monte
Oliveti; Tristis Est Anima Mea (I277)

Responsorien Fur Grundonnerstag-Heft II
*Holywk,cor-resp
(Walter, Rudolf) 4pt mix cor cor pts
BREITKOPF-W CHB-3635B s.p.
contains: Amicus Meus; Judas Mercator
Pessimus; Unus Ex Discipulis Meis (I278)

Responsorien Fur Grundonnerstag-Heft III
*Holywk,cor-resp
(Walter, Rudolf) 4pt mix cor cor pts
BREITKOPF-W CHB-3635C s.p.
contains: Eram Quasi Agnus Innocens;
Seniores Populi Consilium Fecerunt; Una
Hora Non Potuistis   (I279)

Santa Madre Del Ciel
(Malin) "Blessed Mother Of Heaven" [Eng/It]
SATB,acap MARKS 4423 $.25   (I280)

See Now, How The Righteous Man Dieth
*Holywk/Lent
SATB,kbd (med easy) oct CONCORDIA 98-1488
$.25   (I281)

See Then, How The Holy Man Dieth *see Ecce
Quomodo Moritur

Seniores Populi Consilium Fecerunt
see Responsorien Fur Grundonnerstag-Heft
III

Tenebrae Factae Sunt *Easter/Holywk/Lent/
Psntd,mot
[Lat] SATB,acap (med easy) MULLER MS 44
s.p.   (I282)
(Castellazzi) [Lat] SATB,acap RICORDI-ARG
BA 9883 s.p.   (I283)
(Klein) "Darkness Was O'er The Earth" [Eng/
Lat] 4pt mix cor,acap oct SCHIRM.G 11612
$.30   (I284)
(Krone) [Lat] SATB,acap WARNER W3028 $.30 (I285)
(Marshall, Charles) "Darkness Obscured The
Earth" SATB FRANK F-550 $.30   (I286)
(Wilson) SATB,acap oct BOOSEY 5052 $.30   (I287)

Tristis Est Anima Mea
see Responsorien Fur Grundonnerstag-Heft I

Una Hora Non Potuistis
see Responsorien Fur Grundonnerstag-Heft
III

Unus Ex Discipulis Meis
see Responsorien Fur Grundonnerstag-Heft II

INGEN AF GUD BLEV SVEGET see Bach, Johann
Sebastian, Keinen Hat Gott Verlassen

INGEN VINNER FREM TILL DEN EVIGE RO see Baden,
Conrad

INGHELBRECHT, DESIRE EMILE (1880-1965)
Au Saint-Nau *Xmas,carol
[Fr] 4pt mix cor,acap oct DURAND see from
Deux Noels   (I288)

Deux Noels *see Au Saint-Nau; Nole Est Venu (I289)

Nole Est Venu *Xmas,carol
[Fr] 4pt mix cor,acap oct DURAND see from
Deux Noels   (I290)

Requiem *Mass
[Fr] cor,soli,orch DURAND voc sc s.p., sc
s.p., ipr   (I291)

INGREDIENTE DOMINO see Ferrari, Giovanni

INHERIT THE EARTH see Red, Buryl

INHERIT THE KINGDOM see Hoiby, Lee

INIMICI AUTEM see Lassus, Roland de (Orlandus)

INMEMORIAM see Stekke, Leon

INMITTEN DER NACHT see Wolters, Gottfried

INN AT BETHLEHEM, THE *Xmas
(Dickinson, C.) SATB oct GRAY GSC 175 $.30 (I292)
(Dickinson, C.) SSA&opt SSB oct GRAY GSC 176
$.30   (I293)

INNI AMBROSIANI *CCU,Eve,chant/hymn
(Amelli, P.; Magri, Pietro) [Lat] unis,org
ZANIBON 2710 s.p.   (I294)

INNI DE COMUNE *hymn
[Lat] 2 eq voices,org sc ZANIBON 378 s.p.
contains: Boldi, N., Fortem Virili Pectore;
Bottazzo, Luigi, Deus Tuorum Militum;
Cossetti, Gio. Batta., Exultet Orbis;
Grassi, Ciro, Sanctorum Meritis;
Mercatali, A., Jesu Corona Virginum;
Nicolosi, Salvatore, Iste Confessor (I295)

INNKEEPER, THE see Lewis

INNKEEPER'S CAROL, THE *Xmas,Pol
(Warner) mix cor&opt jr cor oct SCHIRM.G 9765
$.40   (I296)
(Warner) 3pt wom cor oct SCHIRM.G 9966 $.35 (I297)
(Warner) 4pt men cor oct SCHIRM.G 9967 $.30 (I298)
(Warner; Stickles) 3pt mix cor oct SCHIRM.G
11180 $.35   (I299)

INNO see Santucci, Pellegrino

INNO A MARIA see Chiesa, Federico

INNO A S. CECILIA see Mangone, Gioacchino

INNO A S. FRANCESO D'ASSISI see Travaglia,
Silvio

INNO A S. LUIGI GONZAGA see Coronaro, Benvenuto
Gellio

INNO A SANT'ANTONIO DI PADOVA see Zimarino,
Settimio

INNO ALLA BEATA MADDALENA DI CANOSSA see
Paperini, Pietro

INNO ALLA S. INFANZIA see Ascenso, Antonio

INNO CECILIANO see Costantini, Mario

INNO CONSTANTINIANO see Bottazzo, Luigi

INNO EUCARISTICO DEI CATTOLICI D'ITALIA see
Cossetti, Gio. Batta.

INNO MISSIONARIO see Trevisiol, Mario

INNO POPOLARE A S. GIUSEPPE see Bottigliero,
Eduardo

INNO POPOLARE A S. VINCENZO DE' PAOLI see
Nicolosi, Salvatore

INNOCENTES PRO CHRISTO see Palestrina, Giovanni

INRATA GOTICA see Neilsen, Ludvig

INSANAE ET VANAE CURAE see Handel, George
Frideric

INSANAE ET VANAE CURAE see Haydn, (Franz)
Joseph

INSANAE ET VANAE CUREA see Haydn, (Franz)
Joseph

INSIDE THOSE PEARLY GATES see Stanphill

INSPIRE US, ALMIGHTY GOD see Roff, Joseph

INSTRUMENT OF THY PEACE, AN see Marshall

INSTRUMENT OF THY PEACE, AN see Morgan, Haydn

INSTRUMENTS, WAKEN AND PUBLISH YOUR GLADNESS
see Buxtehude, Dietrich

INSULT HAS BROKEN MY HEART see Dowland, John

INTENDE VOCI ORATIONIS see Schubert, Franz
(Peter)

INTENDE VOCI ORATIONIS MEAE see Schubert, Franz
(Peter)

INTER BRACCHIA see Schutz, Heinrich

INTER BRACHIA SALVATORIS MEI see Schutz,
Heinrich

INTERCESSION see Holst, Gustav

INTERCESSION see Noe, J.T.

INTERCESSORY HYMN see German, Edward

INTERPRETATIONS FOR CHORUS CHOIR *CCUL,hymn
(Skiles, Paul) 3pt&4pt cmplt ed LILLENAS
MB-096 $1.50   (I300)

INTO THE HAND OF GOD see Morgan

INTO THE WOODS MY MASTER WENT see Lutkin, Peter
Christian

INTO THE WOODS MY MASTER WENT see Nevin, George
[Balch]

INTO THE WOODS MY MASTER WENT see Nyquist

INTO THE WOODS MY MASTER WENT see Rowley, Alec

INTO THE WOODS MY MASTER WENT see Wild

INTO THE WOODS MY MASTER WENT see Williams

INTO THY HANDS see Tallis, Thomas, In Manus
Tuas

INTORNO AL FANCIULLIN GESU see Anonymous

INTRA, E.
Messa D'oggi *Mass
CURCI 9359 s.p.   (I301)

INTRATA SOLEMNIS see Neilsen, Ludvig

INTRODUXIT ME REX see Palestrina, Giovanni

INTRODUZE AL GLORIA E GLORIA see Vivaldi,
Antonio

INTROIBO AD ALTARE DEI see Volpi, Edoardo

INTROIT see Davies, Henry Walford

INTROIT see Grant

INTROIT AND BENEDICTION see Nyquist

INTROIT AND CHORAL PRAYER see Archer, Violet

INTROIT AND GRADUAL FOR DEDICATION, THE see
Willan, Healey

INTROIT AND GRADUAL FOR EASTER, THE see Willan,
Healey

INTROIT AND GRADUAL FOR ORDINATION *chant/
Gradual/Introit/liturg
(Bliss, Carolyn) unis WOLF 11-1501 $.15   (I302)

INTROIT AND GRADUAL FOR REFORMATION DAY see
Fetler, Paul

INTROIT AND KYRIE see Faure, Gabriel-Urbain

INTROIT FOR CHRISTMAS see Mc Cray, James

INTROIT FOR EASTER see Nelson, Ronald A.

INTROIT-MOTET IN HONOR OF ST JOSEPH see Baxter,
T.

INTROIT-RESPONSE-KYRIE-AMEN see McCowen

INTROITEN *CCU,Easter/Gen,Introit
mix cor HANSSLER 2.038 s.p.   (I303)

INTROITEN I see Isaac

INTROITEN UND MOTETTEN ZUM KIRCHENJAHR, BAND I
*CC64U,Introit/mot
(Hellmann) 4pt/5pt cloth HANSSLER 2.005 $8.00 (I304)

INTROITEN UND MOTETTEN ZUM KIRCHENJAHR, BAND II
*CC35U,Introit/mot,Contemp
(Hellmann) SATB/SSATB cloth HANSSLER 2.009
$10.00   (I305)

INTROITEN UND MOTETTEN ZUM KIRCHENJAHR, BAND
III *CC50U,Introit/mot,Contemp
(Hellmann) SAT/SAB cloth HANSSLER 2.010 $9.00 (I306)

INTROITEN UND PSALMEN *CCU,Adv/Gd.Fri.,
Introit/Psalm
mix cor HANSSLER 2.033 s.p.   (I307)

INTROITS see Willan, Healey

INTROITS AND GRADUALS FOR THE CHURCH YEAR, THE
see Willan, Healey

INTROITS AND GRADUALS FOR THE LUTHERAN SERVICE,
VOL. A-I *CCU,Adv/Xmas/Epiph,chant/
Gradual/Introit/liturg
(Ensrud, Paul) unis,opt org (easy) voc sc
AUGSBURG 11-9221 $.75   (I308)

INTROITS AND GRADUALS FOR THE LUTHERAN SERVICE,
VOL. A-II *CCU,Easter/Septua,chant/
Gradual/Introit/liturg
(Ensrud, Paul) unis,opt org (easy) voc sc
AUGSBURG 11-9222 $.75   (I309)

INTROITS AND GRADUALS FOR THE LUTHERAN SERVICE,
VOL. A-III *CCU,Easter/Pent,chant/Gradual/
Introit/liturg
(Ensrud, Paul) unis,opt org (easy) voc sc
AUGSBURG 11-9223 $.75   (I310)

INTROITS AND GRADUALS FOR THE LUTHERAN SERVICE,
VOL. A-IV *CCU,Trin,chant/Gradual/Introit/
liturg
(Ensrud, Paul) unis,opt org (easy) voc sc
AUGSBURG 11-9224 $.75   (I311)

INTROITS AND GRADUALS FOR THE LUTHERAN SERVICE,
VOL. A-V *CCU,Trin,chant/Gradual/Introit/
liturg
(Ensrud, Paul) unis,opt org (easy) voc sc
AUGSBURG 11-9225 $.75   (I312)

INTROITS AND GRADUALS FOR THE LUTHERAN SERVICE,
VOL. A-VI *CCU,chant/Gradual/Introit/
liturg
(Ensrud, Paul) unis,opt org voc sc AUGSBURG
119232 $.75   (I313)

INTROITS AND GRADUALS FOR THE LUTHERAN SERVICE,
VOL. B-I *CCU,Adv/Xmas/Epiph,Gradual/
Introit/liturg
(Ensrud, Paul) cor (med diff) voc sc AUGSBURG

11-9226 $1.50   (I314)

INTROITS AND GRADUALS FOR THE LUTHERAN SERVICE,
   VOL. B-IV *CCU,Trin,Gradual/Introit/liturg
   (Ensrud, Paul) cor (med diff) voc sc AUGSBURG
   11-9229 $1.50   (I315)

INTROITS AND GRADUALS FOR THE LUTHERAN SERVICE,
   VOL. B-V *CCU,Trin,Gradual/Introit/liturg
   (Ensrud, Paul) cor (med diff) voc sc AUGSBURG
   11-9230 $1.50   (I316)

INTROITS AND GRADUALS FOR THE PASCHAL SEASON,
   THE see Petrich, Roger

INTROITS AND OPENING SENTENCES see Cain, Noble

INTROITS FOR LENT AND EASTER see Nelson, Ronald
   A.

INTROITS FOR LENT AND HOLY WEEK, THE see
   Bender, Jan

INTROITS FOR THE CHURCH YEAR see Wyton

INTROITS FOR THE CHURCH YEAR, THE see Bunjes,
   Paul G.

INTROITS FOR THE CHURCH YEAR, THE *CCU,chant/
   Introit/liturg
   (Buszin, W.) cor,org CONCORDIA 97-7518 $1.50
                                       (I317)

INTROITS FOR THE CHURCH YEAR, THE see Willan,
   Healey

INTROITS, PART I see Wetzler, Robert

INTROITS, PART II see Wetzler, Robert

INTROITS, PART III see Wetzler, Robert

INTROITS, PART IV see Wetzler, Robert

INTROITS, PART V see Wetzler, Robert

INTROITUS
   (Runback, Albert) unis,org cor pts NORDISKA
   3588 s.p., ipa   (I318)

INTROITUS see Aichinger, Gregor

INTROITUS see Baumann, Max

INTROITUS see Jeppesen, Knud

INTROITUS see Lassus, Roland de (Orlandus)

INTROITUS see Schwartz, Gerhard von

INTROITUS see Senfl, Ludwig

INTROITUS see Runback, Albert

INTROITUS see Runback, Albert

INTROITUS, ALLELUJA, COMMUNIO see Kerle,
   Jacobus de

INTROITUS. DEL 1 see Runback, Albert

INTROITUS. DEL 2 see Runback, Albert

INTROITUS-PSALMEN-HEFT 1 see Preibisch, Hilde

INTROITUS-PSALMEN-HEFT 2 see Preibisch, Hilde

INTROITUS VED KRISTI APENBARING see Baden,
   Conrad

INTROITUS *see Domsondagen Samt
   Nattvardsgudstjanster; Langfredagen (I319)

INVENI DAVID see Bruckner, Anton

INVIOLATA see Bottazzo, Luigi

INVIOLATA see Palestrina, Giovanni

INVISIBLE HANDS
   SSA BIG3 $.25   (I320)

INVITATION see Danhieux, G.

INVITATION, COME WATCH AWHILE see Brown, J.

INVITATION TO MUSIC see Naylor, Bernard

INVOCATIO see Hoogerwerf, N.

INVOCATION see Bradley, Ruth

INVOCATION see Fuhrmann, W.A.

INVOCATION see Grant

INVOCATION see Moore, Marian

INVOCATION see Mozart, Wolfgang Amadeus

INVOCATION A L'ANGE RAPHAEL see Milhaud, Darius

INVOCATION, AN see Koutzen, Boris

INVOCATION OF PEACE see Kodaly, Zoltan

INVOCATION POUR UNE MESSE DE MARIAGE see Aubry,
   F.

INVOCATIONEN see Koerppen, Alfred

INVOCATIONS A SAINTE-THERESE DE L'ENFANT JESUS
   see Mercenier, P.

IO PIANGO see Marenzio, Luca

IOANNIS A CRVCE, CLODIENSIS
   Missa Prima Sexti Toni *Mass
   cor quarto FORNI 255 s.p.   (I321)

IOCUNDARE IERUSALEM see Mouton, Jean

IPPOLITOV-IVANOV, MIKHAIL MIKHAILOVITCH
   (1859-1935)
   Bless The Lord
      SATB oct BELWIN 64131 $.30   (I322)
      (Clough-Leighter, H.) SATB oct PRESSER
      332-13770 $.30   (I323)
      (Clough-Leighter, H.) SA oct PRESSER
      332-14372 $.25   (I324)

IPPOLITOV-IVANOV, MIKHAIL MIKHAILOVITCH
   (cont'd.)
      (McKinney) SAB oct FISCHER,J 9378 $.30
                                       (I325)
   Bless The Lord, O My Soul *Easter/Gen/Lent,
      anthem,Russ
      SATB oct LORENZ 9228 $.25   (I326)
      SATB KJOS 7012 $.30   (I327)
      SATB,acap BOSTON 3928 $.30   (I328)
      (Becker, A.C.) SATB (easy) oct GIA G1541
      $.25   (I329)
      (Dickinson) SATB oct GRAY GSC 200 $.25
                                       (I330)
      (Ehret) SATB oct BOURNE BL3129 $.25 (I331)
      (Ehret) SAB oct SPRATT 527 $.25 (I332)
      (Ehret) SSA oct SPRATT 520 $.25 (I333)
      (Frances) SATB oct SPRATT 504 $.25 (I334)
      (Howorth) SATB,acap oct BELWIN 781 $.30
                                       (I335)
      (Mueller) 3pt mix cor,acap oct SCHIRM.G
      11254 $.25   (I336)
      (Mueller) 4pt mix cor,acap oct SCHIRM.G
      11100 $.30   (I337)
      (Richardson) SAB,acap BOSTON 11660 $.35
                                       (I338)
      (Roepper) SSA BOSTON 1250   (I339)
      (Roepper) TTBB,acap BOSTON 833   (I340)
      (Snow) SATB,acap oct PRO ART 1276 $.25
                                       (I341)
      (Snow) SSA,acap oct PRO ART 1706 $.30
                                       (I342)
      (Snow) SAB oct PRO ART 1815 $.25 (I343)
   Bless Ye The Lord
      (Wilhousky) SATB,acap oct FISCHER,C CM-636
      $.25   (I344)
      (Wilhousky) 3pt jr cor/SSA (easy) FISCHER,C
      CM 639 $.25   (I345)
      (Wilhousky) SSA oct FISCHER,C CM-639 $.25
                                       (I346)
   How Are Thy Servants Blest
      (Ehret) SATB oct BOURNE BL3042 $.25 (I347)
   In Solemn Silence
      (Wilhousky) SATB,acap oct FISCHER,C CM-635
      $.25   (I348)
   Incline Thine Ear
      SATB oct FISCHER,J 6213 $.30   (I349)
   O Praise The Lord, My Soul
      SATB,acap SCHIRM.EC 1743 $.30   (I350)
      (Bement, G.) TTBB,acap SCHIRM.EC 2123 $.25
                                       (I351)
      (Geer, E.) SSAA,acap SCHIRM.EC 883 $.25
                                       (I352)
      (Glaser, V.) SAB,acap SCHIRM.EC 2252 $.18
                                       (I353)
   Russian Christmas Hymn *Xmas
      (Christy) mix cor,acap oct SCHIRM.G 8431
      $.25   (I354)
   Shepherd, The
      SA,pno PEER $.35   (I355)

IPSA TE COGAT PIETAS see Lassus, Roland de
   (Orlandus)

IPSE DEUS SAPIENS see Wenzel, Eberhard

IPSI SUM DESPONSATA see Livieri, C.

IPSI SUM DESPONSATA see Oltrassi, Giuseppe

IRELAND, JOHN (1879-1962)
   Greater Love Hath No Man
      SATB oct STAINER 3.1137.1 $.35   (I356)
   Holy Boy
      SATB,acap/opt strings oct BOOSEY 3365 $.30,
      ipa   (I357)
   Holy Communion *Commun
      SATB (C maj) oct NOVELLO 44.1304.00 s.p.
                                       (I358)
   Jubilate *Jubil
      SATB (F maj) oct NOVELLO 44.0911.06 s.p.
                                       (I359)
      unis (F maj) oct NOVELLO 02.0026.03 s.p.
                                       (I360)
   Magnificat And Nunc Dimittis *Magnif/Nunc
      SATB (C maj) oct NOVELLO 44.1252.04 s.p.
                                       (I361)
      SATB (F maj) oct NOVELLO 44.0916.07 s.p.
                                       (I362)
      unis (F maj) oct NOVELLO 02.0047.06 s.p.
                                       (I363)
   Te Deum *Te Deum
      SATB (C maj) oct NOVELLO 44.1247.08 s.p.
                                       (I364)
      SATB (F maj) oct NOVELLO 44.0750.04 s.p.
                                       (I365)
      unis oct NOVELLO 02.0007.07 s.p. (I366)

IRIGARAY
   El Nacimiento
      see Navidad Criolla
   La Adoracion
      see Navidad Criolla
   La Anunciacion
      see Navidad Criolla
   La Concepcion
      see Navidad Criolla
   La Gloria
      see Navidad Criolla
   Navidad Criolla *Xmas
      cor,pno RICORDI-ARG BA 12696 s.p.
      contains: El Nacimiento; La Adoracion; La
      Anunciacion; La Concepcion; La Gloria
                                       (I367)

IRISH CAROL
   see Three Christmas Carols

IRVIN
   Alleluia! Now Is The Christmas Morn *Xmas
   (Schowalter) SATB oct BELWIN 60213 $.25
                                       (I368)

IRVING
   Let God's Children Come Home
   (Schlein) SATB oct FOX PS150 $.25   (I369)

IS BORN TODAY! see Fraser

IS HE SATISFIED
   TTBB BIG3 $.25   (I370)

IS IT ANY WONDER? see Owens, Jimmy

IS IT NOTHING, ALL OF YOU WHO PASS BY see
   Palestrina, Giovanni, O Vos Omnes

IS IT NOTHING, ALL OF YOU WHO PASS BY ME see
   Croce, Giovanni, O Vos Omnes

IS IT NOTHING TO YOU? see Alberti, Giuseppe
   Matteo

IS IT NOTHING TO YOU? see Hall, E. Vine

IS IT NOTHING TO YOU see Pedrette

IS IT NOTHING TO YOU? see Victoria, Tomas Luis
   de, O Vos Omnes?

IS IT NOTHING TO YOU? see Zilch

IS IT THE CROWNING DAY see Marsh

IS NOT THE LIFE MORE THAN MEAT see Bright,
   Houston

IS THERE ANYBODY HERE *spir
   (Burkhardt, C.) SATB oct PRESSER MC369 $.30
                                       (I371)

IS THERE ANYBODY HERE? see Smith

IS THERE ANYBODY HERE? see Still, William Grant

IS THERE NATION SO ELECT see Brahms, Johannes

IS THERE NOT A CAUSE see Carmichael, Ralph

IS THIS THE WAY TO BETHLEHEM? *Xmas,It
   (Dickinson, C.) SATB oct GRAY GSC 178 $.30
                                       (I372)

IS THIS YOUR LIFE *sac/sec,CCU
   cmplt ed WEINBERGER $1.50   (I373)

ISAAC
   Introiten I *CCU,Introit
      (Just) [Ger/Lat] 6pt mix cor MOSELER s.p.
                                       (I374)
   Missa Carminum *Mass
      (Heyden) 4pt mix cor MOSELER s.p. (I375)
   O Man, List' To His Sighing *Easter
      (Riedel) SATB SCHMITT 1408 $.25 (I376)
   Vier Marienmotetten *CC4U,mot
      (Just) [Ger/Lat] 4pt mix cor&5pt mix cor
      MOSELER s.p.   (I377)

ISAAC, HEINRICH (ca. 1450-1517)
   Ave Sanctissima *mot
      [Lat/Eng] SATB,acap BROUDE BR. $.30 (I378)
   Kaiser Motette *see Virgo Prudentissima; Vos
      Michael   (I379)
   Lauda Sion Salvatorem *Corpus/Fest
      (Lipphardt, Walther) [Ger] SATB,acap (med)
      BAREN. BA 456 s.p.   (I380)
   Missa Carminum
      see ARS NOVA TO RENNAISSANCE VOL. 2-1200 TO
      ABOUT 1500
   Missa Carminum *Mass
      mix cor,acap voc sc KALMUS 6251 $1.50
                                       (I381)
   Now All The Woods Are Sleeping *see Nun
      Ruhen Alle Walder
   Nun Ruhen Alle Walder *chorale
      (Bach, J.S.; Davis, K.) "Now All The Woods
      Are Sleeping" SA,pno/org SCHIRM.EC 1567
      $.20   (I382)
   O Bread Of Life *anthem
      (Christiansen) SATB,B solo (med) oct
      AUGSBURG 0103 $.20   (I383)
   O Heil'ge Seelenspeise *Pent/Whitsun
      SATB,acap voc pt DOBLINGER s.p. see also
      PFINGSTEN UND EUCHARISTIE   (I384)
   O Welt, Ich Muss Dich Lassen
      see Herr Gott, Dich Loben Alle Wir
      (Berger, H.L.) TTBB HANSSLER 6.5082 s.p.
                                       (I385)
      (Geiringer) "O World, I Must Be Parting"
      [Eng/Ger] 4pt mix cor,acap oct SCHIRM.G
      8425 $.25   (I386)
   O Welt, Sieh Hier Dein Leben
      see Helder, Bartholomaeus, Ich Freu Mich In
      Dem Herren
   O World, I Must Be Parting *see O Welt, Ich
      Muss Dich Lassen
   Officium De Corpore Christi *Psntd
      (Lipphardt, Walther) [Lat] SATB,acap (med)
      BAREN. BA 454 $1.00   (I387)
   Officium De Resurrectione Christi *Easter
      (Lipphardt, Walther) [Lat] SATB,acap (med)
      BAREN. BA 455 $1.50   (I388)
   Officium Epiphaniae Domini *Epiph
      (Lipphardt, Walther) [Lat] SATB,acap (med)
      BAREN. BA 2154 $.65   (I389)
   Officium Nativitatis Domini *Xmas
      (Lipphardt, Walther) [Lat] SATB,acap (med)
      BAREN. BA 2153 $.65   (I390)
   Ora Pro Nobis (from Regina Coeli)
      [Lat/Eng] SATTB BROUDE BR. $.30 (I391)
   Salva Nos-Heft 3 *Mass
      (Pass, Walter) 4pt mix cor DOBLINGER s.p. see also
      CHRISTUS, DER HERR   (I392)
   Thesauri Musici, Heft 3: Missa Salva Nos
      *Mass,Renais
      (Pass, Walter) 4pt mix cor,acap cmplt ed
      DOBLINGER s.p.   (I393)

ISAAC, HEINRICH (cont'd.)

Virgo Prudentissima
[Lat/Ger] SSATTB,opt 2trp,opt 3-4trom
PETERS 4817A $1.00, ipa see from Kaiser
Motette   (I394)

Vos Michael
[Lat/Ger] SSATTB,opt 2trp,opt 3-4trom
PETERS 4817B $1.00, ipa see from Kaiser
Motette   (I395)

ISAACSON, MICHAEL
Hegyon Libi   *Sab-Eve
2pt,cantor,org,4strings oct TRANSCON.
TCL 394 $5.00   (I396)

Kol Sason
SATB,cantor,org,vla,perc,S rec/fl oct
TRANSCON. TCL 695 $3.50   (I397)

ISAIA - HO, EVERY ONE THAT THIRSTETH see
Demarest, A.

ISAIAH, MIGHTY SEER see Vulpius, Melchior

ISAIAH, MIGHTY SEER see Willan, Healey

ISAIAH MIGHTY SEER, IN DAYS OF OLD see Luther,
Martin

ISAIAH'S PROPHECY see Creston, Paul

ISAIAH'S VISION see Burkhard Willy, Das Gesicht
Des Jesajas

ISAIAH'S VISION see Gordon, Philip

ISAIAH'S VISION see Orgad, Ben-Zion

ISAIAS see Mancinelli, A.

ISALAW
Holy Lord Of All
(Williams) TTBB FLAMMER C5002 $.25   (I398)
(Williams) SATB FLAMMER A 5012 $.30   (I399)
(Williams) SAB FLAMMER D5016 $.30   (I400)

ISCH
Glory Be To God The Father   *Gen
SATB SCHMITT 1931 $.35   (I401)

ISIAH'S VISION see Luther, Martin

ISLANDSMOEN, SIGURD
Varsalme   *Psalm
mix cor MUSIKK 246 s.p.   (I402)

ISLE, H.L.
Child This Day Is Born, A   *Xmas
SATB&desc oct KERBY 803 $.30   (I403)

ISLE OF DREAMS, THE see Hurford, Peter

ISN'T IT REASSURING see Sleeth, Natalie

ISN'T IT STRANGE
see Folio Of Sacred Music (Volume 3)

ISOLFSSON, PALL (1893-   )
Hymn   *hymn
mix cor,pno ICELAND s.p.   (I404)

ISRAEL EN EGYPTE see Handel, George Frideric,
Israel In Egypt

ISRAEL HARVEST SONG see Gorochov, Y., Saleynu

ISRAEL IN AGYPTEN see Handel, George Frideric,
Israel In Egypt

ISRAEL IN EGYPT see Handel, George Frideric

ISRAEL LIVES TODAY   *liturg,Jew
(Gaul, H.) SATB,acap oct PRESSER 332-14528
$.30   (I405)

ISRAELITES IN THE DESERT, THE see Bach, Karl
Philipp Emanuel

ISRAELS HERDE see Bortniansky, Dimitri
Stepanovitch

ISRAELS KLAGE VED SAMSONS DOD see Handel,
George Frideric, Ye Sons Of Israel, Now
Lament

ISRAELSBRUNNLEIN see Schein, Johann Hermann

IST ES RECHT, DASS MAN DEM KAISER ZINSE GEBE
ODER NICHT? see Buxtehude, Dietrich

IST GOTT FUR MICH see Kurig, Hans-Hermann

IST GOTT FUR MICH see Oertzen, Rudolf von

IST GOTT FUR MICH see Zipp, Friedrich

IST GOTT FUR MICH, SO TRETE see Kretzschmar,
Gunther

IST GOTT FUR MICH, SO TRETE see Zipp, Friedrich

IST GOTT FUR UNS see Franck, Melchior

IST GOTT FUR UNS see Thomas, Kurt

IST GOTT FUR UNS, WER MAG see Dedekind,
Constantine Christian

IST GOTT FUR UNS, WER MAG WIDER UNS SEIN see
Franck, Melchior

IST GOTT FUR UNS, WER MAG WIDER UNS SEIN? see
Schutz, Heinrich

IST GOTT FUR UNS, WER MAG WIDER UNS SEIN see
Zipp, Friedrich

IST GOTT MEIN SCHILD UND HELFERSMANN see Bach,
Johann Sebastian

IST GOTT VERSOHNT UND UNSER FREUND see Bach,
Johann Sebastian

IST NICHT DAS LEBEN MEHR DENN DIE SPEISE see
Driessler, Johannes

IST NICHT EPHRAIM see Schutz, Heinrich

IST NICHT EPHRAIM MEIN TEURER SOHN see Scheidt,
Samuel

IST NICHT EPHRAIM MEIN TEURER SOHN see Schein,
Johann Hermann

IST NICHT EPHRAIM MEIN TEURER SOHN? see Schutz,
Heinrich

...IST NICHTS ZU GROSS UND NICHTS ZU KLEIN see
Ruppel, Paul Ernst

ISTA SICUT FLAMMA see Pergolesi, Giovanni
Battista

ISTE CONFESSOR see Arnaldi, Antonio

ISTE CONFESSOR see Bottazzo, Luigi

ISTE CONFESSOR see Bottigliero, Eduardo

ISTE CONFESSOR see Firpo, Antonio

ISTE CONFESSOR see Nicolosi, Salvatore

ISTE CONFESSOR see Palestrina, Giovanni

ISTE CONFESSOR see Tebaldini, Giovanni

ISTE SANCTUS see Victoria, Tomas Luis de

ISTI SUNT see Palestrina, Giovanni

ISTORUM EST see Casciolini, Claudio

IT ALL DEPENDS see Nelson, Jerry

IT CAME UPON A MIDNIGHT CLEAR   *Xmas,carol
(Dunhill, Thomas F.) unis&desc oct LESLIE 107
                                           (I406)

IT CAME UPON A MIDNIGHT CLEAR see Willis

IT CAME UPON THE MIDNIGHT CLEAR   *Xmas,carol
oct HART s.p.   (I407)
(Johnson) SATB KJOS GC51 $.30   (I408)
(Reed) unis&desc BOOSEY-CAN s.p.   (I409)
(Sharpe, E.) cor&desc CRAMER 38   (I410)
(Weber, Bertha) "Angel's And Shepherd's Song,
The" SATB,S,SA soli,pno (easy) oct WILLIS
6081 $.15   (I411)

IT CAME UPON THE MIDNIGHT CLEAR see Dunhill

IT CAME UPON THE MIDNIGHT CLEAR see Willis,
Richard Storrs

IT CAME UPON THE MIDNIGHT CLEAR see Wills

IT FELL UPON A WINTER'S DAY   *Xmas
(Ehret) 2pt oct PRO ART 2713 $.30   (I412)
(Ehret) SAB oct PRO ART 2717 $.30   (I413)

IT HATH BEEN TOLD THEE, O MAN see Berlinski,
[Herman]

IT IS A GOOD THING TO GIVE THANKS see McCormick

IT IS A GOOD THING TO GIVE THANKS see
Palestrina, Giovanni, Bonum Est Confiteri

IT IS A GOOD TO GIVE THANKS see Lekberg, Sven

IT IS A GREAT DAY OF JOY see Hourdeaux

IT IS A PRECIOUS THING see Peter, Johann
Friedrich

IT IS A THING MOST WONDERFUL see Coggin

IT IS A THING MOST WONDERFUL see Maunder, J.H.

IT IS ALL I HAVE TO BRING TODAY see Kennedy,
John Brodbin

IT IS BETTER TO TAKE REFUGE IN THE LORD see
Kreutz, Robert E.

IT IS CHRISTMAS ANEW   *Xmas,Fr
(Ehret) SA,opt 2vln MARKS 4409 $.25   (I414)
(Ehret) SSA,opt 2vln MARKS 4352 $.25   (I415)
(Ehret) SAB,opt 2vln MARKS 4459 $.30   (I416)

IT IS FINISHED see Bach

IT IS FINISHED see Bach, Johann Sebastian

IT IS GOOD see Kimmel

IT IS GOOD TO GIVE THANKS   *anthem
SATB&jr cor,2fl (easy) oct AUGSBURG 0643 $.40
                                           (I417)

IT IS GOOD TO GIVE THANKS see Berger, Jean

IT IS GOOD TO GIVE THANKS see Lahmer, [Ruel]

IT IS GOOD TO GIVE THANKS see Schwartz, Paul

IT IS GOOD TO SING THY PRAISES see Peek,
Richard

IT IS MEET AND RIGHT IN TRUTH TO BLESS THEE see
Tcherepnin, Nikolay Nikolayevitch

IT IS NO SECRET see Hamblen

IT IS NOT FAIR see Bender, Jan

IT IS NOT TOO LATE see Hourdeaux

IT IS NOTHING TO YOU? see Vaughan Williams,
Ralph, O Vos Omnes

IT IS THE JOYFUL EASTERTIME   *anthem/carol
(George, Graham) SA (easy) oct AUGSBURG 1456
$.20   (I418)

IT IS WELL WITH MY SOUL see Bliss, Paul

IT IS WELL WITH MY SOUL see Landon

IT IS YOU, O LORD see Roff, Joseph

IT SHALL BE LIGHT see Gaul, Alfred Robert

IT SOON WILL BE EVENING see Track, Gerhard

IT TOOK A MIRACLE
SATB BIG3 $.30   (I419)

IT TOOK A MIRACLE see Peterson, John W.

IT WAS A NIGHT OF WONDER see Tellep, Leo M.

IT WAS ON CHRISTMAS DAY see All In The Morning

IT WAS POOR LITTLE JESUS see Page, R.

ITA ENIM DEUS see Foss, Julius

ITALIA SACRA MUSICA-VOLUME 1   *CC23L,It,16th
cent
(Jeppesen, Knud) [Lat] mix cor HANSEN-DEN
s.p. contains works by: Verdelot; Maffoni;
Alberti; and others   (I420)

ITALIA SACRA MUSICA-VOLUME 2   *CC21L,It,16th
cent
(Jeppesen, Knud) [Lat] mix cor HANSEN-DEN
s.p. contains works by: Cara; Bartolucci;
Michel; and others   (I421)

ITALIA SACRA MUSICA-VOLUME 3   *CC17L,It,16th
cent
(Jeppesen, Knud) [Lat] mix cor HANSEN-DEN
s.p. contains works by: Tromboncino;
Pisano; Palestrina; and others   (I422)

ITALIAN MASS see Passamonti, G., Messa Ritmata

ITALIENISCHE MADONNA see Lafite, C.

ITE, ANGELI VELOCES see Hindemith, Paul

ITE RIME DOLENTI see Lassus, Roland de
(Orlandus)

ITEN, WALTER (1900-   )
Choral   *chorale
[Ger] mix cor,acap (med easy) HUG s.p.   (I423)

Du Bist, O Herr, Mein Schirm Und Hort
[Ger] mix cor,opt 4strings HUG s.p.   (I424)
[Ger] wom cor,opt 4strings HUG s.p.   (I425)

Herr, Wohin Sollen Wir Gehn?   *prayer
(Stegmann, J.) [Ger] wom cor,acap (med
easy) HUG s.p.   (I426)

IT'S A GLORIOUS ALLELUIA! see Hughes

IT'S A WIDE, WIDE WORLD see Lawson

IT'S A WONDERFUL DAY see Owens, Jimmy

IT'S ALL ABOUT LOVE see Smith, Lani

IT'S CHRISTMAS see Eilers

IT'S CHRISTMAS TIME see Wyatt

IT'S CHRISTMASTIME AGAIN see Fisher, Carlotta

IT'S GETTING LATE see Floria, [Caryl]

IT'S JUST LIKE HIS GREAT LOVE see Strouse

IT'S ME, O LORD   *spir,US
"Sieh Mich, O Herr" see Funf Negro-Spirituals
(Aubanel, Georges) "C'est Moi Seigneur" [Eng/
Fr] 3pt mix cor OUVRIERES s.p.   (I427)
(Clements, J.) SATB PROWSE s.p.   (I428)

IT'S REAL see Cox

IT'S THE LORD'S THING see Smith, Lani

IT'S THE TIME OF THE YEAR see Pickell

IT'S UP TO YOU AND ME see Anonymous

IUBILATE DEO OMNIS TERRA see Lilius, Franciszek

IUSTORUM ANIMAE see Byrd, William

IUSTORUM ANIMAE see Lassus, Roland de
(Orlandus)

IUSTUS UT PALMA FLOREBIT see Gorczycki, Gregor
Gervasius

IUSTUS UT PALMA FLOREBIT see Zielenski, Mikolaj

IVANOFF
Laud His Name
(Tkach) SATB KJOS 6525 $.30   (I429)

IVANOFF, I.
Bless The Lord
(Peery, R.) SAB oct PRESSER 312-40461 $.25
                                           (I430)

IVANOFF, P.
Praise The Name Of The Lord
SATB oct FISCHER,J 4125 $.30   (I431)
(McKinney) SAB oct FISCHER,J 9149 $.30   (I432)
(McKinney) TTBB oct FISCHER,J 9166 $.30
                                           (I433)

I'VE BEEN 'BUKED   *spir
(Johnson) 4pt mix cor,acap oct SCHIRM.G 9560
$.30   (I434)

I'VE BEEN CHANGED see Lister, Mosie

I'VE BEEN IN THE STORM SO LONG   *spir
(Papale, Henry) SATB,Bar solo,acap oct WORLD
ESE-735-8 $.45   (I435)

I'VE BEEN LISTENING see Work

I'VE DISCOVERED THE WAY OF GLADNESS see Hawkins

I'VE FOUND A FRIEND see Lovelace, Austin C.

I'VE GOT A GLORY see Lipscomb, Edna

I'VE GOT A MELODY see Kerr

I'VE GOT A REASON TO SING see Skillings, Otis

I'VE GOT PEACE LIKE A RIVER   *spir
(Collins) SATB oct LILLENAS AT-1027 $.30
                                           (I436)
(Johnson) SATB oct LILLENAS AN-5003 $.25   (I437)

I'VE TRIED AND TRIED AND TRIED see Grime,
William

IVERSEN
  Make A Joyful Noise Unto The Lord
    SATB,org/pno BOSTON 2933 $.35   (I438)

IVES, CHARLES (1874-1954)
  God Be Merciful Unto Us (Psalm 67)
    8pt mix cor voc sc BOTE s.p.   (I439)
    mix cor SOUTHERN $.30   (I440)
    SATB,acap AMP A274 $.30   (I441)

  I Want To Be Like Jesus
    (Gerig) SATB oct LILLENAS AN-2214 $.30
                          (I442)
    (Schubert) ST oct LILLENAS AN-1625 $.30
                          (I443)

  Psalm 24
    SATB,acap oct PRESSER MC155 $.35   (I444)

  Psalm 54
    (Kirkpatrick, J.; Smith, G.) SATB,acap (med
      diff) PRESSER 342-40025 $.45   (I445)
    (Smith, G.) SATB,acap oct PRESSER 342-40025
      $.30   (I446)

  Psalm 67 *see God Be Merciful Unto Us

  Psalm 90
    SATB,org&bells oct PRESSER 342-40021 $.60
                          (I447)

  Psalm 150
    (Kirkpatrick, J.; Smith, G.) 4pt treb cor&
      SATB (med) PRESSER 342-40027 $.40 (I448)

  Thanksgiving And Forefathers' Day *Thanks
    opt mix cor,orch PEER rental   (I449)

  Three Harvest Home Chorales *CC3U,chorale
    SATB oct PRESSER 352-00361 $.30   (I450)

  Turn Ye, Turn Ye
    SATB oct PRESSER 352-00170 $.30   (I451)

IVORY PALACES
  see Great Choral Series

IVORY PALACES see Barraclough

IVY AND HOLLY *Xmas,Ir
  4pt mix cor,acap oct CURWEN 11184 $.20 (I452)
  (Widdicombe) 3pt wom cor,acap oct CURWEN
    11183 $.20   (I453)

J

JA, GRIASS DIE GOD see Richar, Elsa

JA, SELIG SIND, DIE GOTTES WORT HOREN see
Telemann, Georg Philipp

JABLONSKY, STEPHAN
  Birkat Kohanim-Ssim Shalom *Heb
    "Priesty Blessing, The" SATB,cantor,org
    ISRAELI 230 s.p.   (J1)

  Priesty Blessing, The *see Birkat Kohanim-
    Ssim Shalom

JACHZT, ALLE LANDE, NAH UND FERN see Le Jeune,
Claude

JACK BE NIMBLE see Henriksen, Josef

JACKSON
  Breathe On Me, Breath Of God
    (Pottenger) SATB oct LILLENAS AN-2269 $.30
                         (J2)
    (Walton, K.) SATB BOOSEY-CAN s.p.   (J3)

  Lift Your Glad Voices *anthem
    (Riedel) SATB,fl,clar,bsn (easy) cor pts
    AUGSBURG 1261 $.18, ipa   (J4)

  Mass For A Saint's Day *Mass
    unis BOOSEY-CAN s.p.   (J5)

  Te Deum Laudamus *Easter/Fest
    SATB ALLANS 6 s.p.   (J6)

  Twentieth Century Merbecke
    SATB BOOSEY-CAN s.p.   (J7)

JACKSON, FRANCIS
  Audi Filia (Psalm 45) Gen/Marriage,anthem
    "Hearken O Daughter" SATB (med) oct OXFORD
    42.849 $.50   (J8)

  Benedicite In G *Bene
    SATB (med) oct OXFORD 42.039 $.50 (J9)

  Blow Ye The Trumpet In Zion *Fest,Bibl
    SATB (med) oct OXFORD 42.867 $.65 (J10)

  Communion Service In G *Commun,Agnus/Bene/
    Gloria/Kyrie/Sanctus
    SATB oct OXFORD 42.436 $.65   (J11)

  Creed (from Communion Service In G) Credo
    SATB (med) oct OXFORD 42.435 $.35 (J12)

  Hearken O Daughter *see Audi Filia

  Jubilate Deo In G *Jubil
    SATB (med) oct OXFORD 42.878 $.50 (J13)

  Magnificat And Nunc Dimittis *Magnif/Nunc
    SATB oct NOVELLO 44.1396.02 s.p. (J14)

  Magnificat And Nunc Dimittis In C *Magnif/
    Nunc
    treb cor oct ROYAL 117 s.p.   (J15)

  Psalm 45 *see Audi Filia

  Remember For Good, O Father *Rembrnc,anthem
    mix cor oct NOVELLO 40.1362.10 s.p. (J16)

  Te Deum In G *Te Deum
    SATB (med) oct OXFORD 42.877 $.65 (J17)

JACKSON, NICHOLAS
  Mass For A Saint's Day *Mass
    mix cor,org BOOSEY voc sc $1.50, cor pts
    $.30   (J18)

  Twentieth-Century Merbecke
    unis&opt mix cor,org BOOSEY voc sc $3.75,
    cor pts $.35   (J19)

JACKSON, ROBERT
  Breathe On Me, Breath Of God
    (Kiser) SATB FOSTER MF103 $.20   (J20)

JACKSON, WILLIAM
  Te Deum In F *Te Deum
    (F maj) oct HART   (J21)

JACKSON, WILLIAM I (1730-1803)
  Te Deum *Te Deum
    SATB (F maj) oct NOVELLO 40.0143.05 s.p.
                         (J22)

JACOB, GORDON (1895-   )
  Country Girl's Farewell
    unis (med easy) OXFORD 81.098 $.25 (J23)

  I Said To The Lord *anthem
    mix cor oct NOVELLO 40.1505.03 s.p. (J24)

  Jubilate *Jubil
    SATB (C maj) oct NOVELLO 28.1372.06 s.p.
                         (J25)

  Newborn King, The *Xmas
    SATB (med) voc sc OXFORD 46.125 $2.20, ipr
                         (J26)

  O Be Joyful In The Lord *anthem
    mix cor oct NOVELLO 28.1372.06 s.p. (J27)

  O Lord, I Will Praise Thee *Gen,Bibl
    SATB (easy) oct OXFORD 42.169 $.30 (J28)

  O My Dear Heart (from New Born King) Xmas
    SATB,acap (very easy) OXFORD 84.076 $.15
                         (J29)

  Psalm 23 *see Twenty-Third Psalm, The

  Sing A Song Of Joy *Fest
    SATB (med) oct OXFORD 42.707 $.65 (J30)

  Spacious Firmament On High, The *Gen
    unis (very easy) oct OXFORD 45.051 $.25,
    ipr   (J31)
    2pt (easy) oct OXFORD 44.705 $.25, ipr
                         (J32)

  To My Humble Supplication *anthem
    mix cor oct NOVELLO 40.1228.03 s.p. (J33)

JACOB, GORDON (cont'd.)

  Twenty-Third Psalm, The (Psalm 23) Gen
    SATB (very easy) oct OXFORD 42.166 $.25
                         (J34)

JACOB, WERNER (1938-   )
  Canticum I-Gelobt Sei Der Herr
    mix cor,B solo,7inst sc BREITKOPF-W rental,
    cor pts BREITKOPF-W CHB-3406 s.p., ipr
                         (J35)

  De Visione Resurrectionis Ezechiel XXXVII
    16pt mix cor,Bar solo,2perc,org sc
    BREITKOPF-W s.p., ipa, cor pts BREITKOPF-
    W CHB-3632 s.p., study sc BREITKOPF-W
    PB-4782 s.p.   (J36)

JACOBI, FREDERICK (1891-1952)
  Arvit L'shabbat *Sab-Eve
    SATB TRANSCON. TCL 785 $4.50   (J37)

  Hymn *Purim,hymn
    [Heb] TTBB TRANSCON. TCL 361 $.35 (J38)
    [Heb] SATB TRANSCON. TCL 804 $.35 (J39)

JACOBI, SAMUEL (1652-1725)
  Christus Gibt Durch Den Tod Das Leben *mot
    (Hellmann) SAB,cont HANSSLER 1.245 s.p.
                         (J40)

  Das Kananaische Weib
    see Zwei Spruchtexte Auf Das Evangelium

  Der Da Mit Wenig Fischen
    see Zwei Spruchtexte Auf Das Evangelium

  Der Hauptmann Glaubt, Drum
    see Drei Spruchtexte Auf Das Evangelium

  Drei Spruchtexte Auf Das Evangelium *Bibl/
    mot
    (Hellmann) SAB,cont HANSSLER 1.240 s.p.
    contains: Der Hauptmann Glaubt, Drum; Vor
    Allen Gasten Christum; Vor Seinem
    Sterben Simeon   (J41)

  Hast Du Gross Gut *mot
    (Hellmann) SAB,cont HANSSLER 1.248 s.p.
                         (J42)

  Vor Allen Gasten Christum
    see Drei Spruchtexte Auf Das Evangelium

  Vor Seinem Sterben Simeon
    see Drei Spruchtexte Auf Das Evangelium

  Zwei Spruchtexte Auf Das Evangelium *Bibl/
    mot
    (Hellmann) SAB,cont HANSSLER 1.243 s.p.
    contains: Das Kananaische Weib; Der Da
    Mit Wenig Fischen   (J43)

JACOBI, WOLFGANG
  Laude
    [Ger/It] 4-5pt mix cor MOSELER s.p. (J44)

JACOB'S LADDER *spir
  (Ehret) SA oct SPRATT 178 $.25   (J45)
  (Ehret) SAB oct SPRATT 164 $.25   (J46)
  (Ehret) SSA oct SPRATT 166 $.30   (J47)
  (Ehret) SATB oct SPRATT 175 $.25   (J48)
  (Lynn, G.) SATB,acap oct PRESSER 312-40066
    $.30   (J49)
  (Ritz, James) SSA&SATB,B solo,acap oct WORLD
    ESE-717-8 $.60   (J50)

JACOB'S LADDER see Black

JACOB'S LADDER see Chailley

JACOB'S LADDER see Murray, Lyn

JACOB'S LADDER see Newbury, Kent A.

JACOB'S LADDER see Wilson

JACOB'S VISION *Eng
  1-2pt oct LORENZ 5729 $.30   (J51)

JACOB'S VISION see Ehret, Walter

JACOBSEN, KATHERINE
  Lullaby For The Holy Child *Xmas
    SATB,opt inst oct SHAPIRO SK 2077 $.25
                         (J52)

JACOBSON
  Blessed Be God
    SSATB,inst oct SUMMY 5715 $.40, ipa (J53)

  Carroll, A *carol
    SSA oct SUMMY B 965 $.35   (J54)

JACOBSON, MARILYN
  Hear My Prayer, O Lord
    SSA PIONEER 1016 $.40   (J55)

JACOBSON, MAURICE (1896-   )
  Come My Way, My Truth, My Life
    mix cor CURWEN 61482 s.p.   (J56)

  God Of Abraham Praise, The
    mix cor CURWEN 80902 s.p.   (J57)

  God Throned On High
    unis jr cor/unis wom cor CURWEN 72246 s.p.
                         (J58)

  Hound Of Heaven, The
    mix cor,T solo,orch CURWEN sc rental, voc
    sc rental, ipr   (J59)

  Virtue
    mix cor CURWEN 61483 s.p.   (J60)

JACOBUS
  Mother's Hymns *hymn
    SATB oct LORENZ A102 $.30   (J61)

  Story Of Christmas *Xmas,cant
    unis&2pt&jr cor voc sc WILLIS $.75 (J62)

JACOBUS, DALE ASHER
  From Gloom To Glory *Easter,cant
    mix cor voc sc LILLENAS ME-202 $1.00 (J63)

  Gift Supreme, The *Xmas,Bibl/cant
    men cor/wom cor,solo,narrator voc sc
    LILLENAS MC-209 $1.00   (J64)

  Night Of Nights *Xmas,cant
    mix cor voc sc LILLENAS MC-220 $1.00 (J65)

JACOBUS, DALE ASHER (cont'd.)

Sweet Story Of Old, The
(Holley) 2pt jr cor oct LILLENAS AN-4021
.25   (J66)

JACOT, ANDRE (1906-   )
Ausklang
[Ger] mix cor,acap (med) HUG s.p.   (J67)

Begleit' Uns, Lieber Herre Christ
(Fluckiger, E.) [Ger] wom cor,acap (easy)
HUG s.p.   (J68)

Drei Motetten Aus Psalmen
[Ger] wom cor,acap (med) HUG s.p.
contains: Ich Harrete Des Herrn (Psalm
40); Nach Dir, Nach Dir, Herr (Psalm
25); Singet Frohlich Unserm Gott
(Psalm)   (J69)

Ich Harrete Des Herrn (Psalm 40)
see Drei Motetten Aus Psalmen

Mirjams Gesang   *cant
[Ger] mix cor,S solo,org HUG cor pts s.p.,
voc sc rental   (J70)

Morgenpsalm
[Ger] mix cor,acap (med) HUG s.p.   (J71)

Nach Dir, Nach Dir, Herr (Psalm 25)
see Drei Motetten Aus Psalmen

Psalm 25   *see Nach Dir, Nach Dir, Herr

Psalm 40   *see Ich Harrete Des Herrn

Sing Lob
[Ger] mix cor,acap (med) HUG s.p.   (J72)

Singet Frohlich Unserm Gott
see Drei Motetten Aus Psalmen

Solches Habe Ich Mit Euch Geredet   *mot
[Ger] mix cor,acap (med) HUG s.p.   (J73)

Zum Neuen Jahr
[Ger] mix cor,acap (easy) HUG   (J74)

JACOTIN see Favre, Georges

JACOTIN see Maillard-Verger, P.

JACQUES
When An Angel Host Entuned   *Xmas
unis (very easy) OXFORD 81.018 .25   (J75)

When Christ Was Born   *Xmas
SATB,acap (easy) OXFORD 84.087 .15   (J76)

JACQUES, COME HERE   *Xmas,carol,Fr
(Wilson, Harry R.) SATB oct WALTON 2074 .25
                                              (J77)

JACQUES, COME HERE see Donovan

JACULATORIAS DA IMM. CONC. see Bottazzo, Luigi

JADLOWKER, HERMANN (1878-1953)
V'shomru
(Roskin) SATB HATIKVAH HCL 3 .25   (J78)

JAECKEL, DANIEL
Come, Your Hearts And Voices Raising   *see
Quem Pastores

Quem Pastores   *Xmas
"Come, Your Hearts And Voices Raising"
unis,fl (easy) oct CONCORDIA 98-2040 .25
                                              (J79)

JAEGGI, OSWALD (1913-   )
Benedicta Sit   *Trin
[Lat] SATB,acap (med) MULLER SM 799 s.p.
                                              (J80)

Cibavit Eos   *Corpus/Fest
[Lat] SATB,acap (med) MULLER SM 717 $1.00
                                              (J81)

Cogitationes Cordis Eius   *Fest/Gen
[Lat] SATB,acap (med) MULLER SM 797 s.p.
                                              (J82)

Dignus Est Agnus   *Fest/Gen
[Ger] SATB,acap (med) MULLER SM 780 s.p.
                                              (J83)

Ecce Advenit   *Epiph
[Lat] SATB,acap (med) MULLER SM 704 s.p.
                                              (J84)

Etenim Sederunt Principes   *Xmas
[Lat] SATB,acap (med, festival of St.
Stephen) MULLER SM 796 s.p.   (J85)

Gaudeamus Omnes In Domino   *ASD/ECY
[Lat] SATB,acap MULLER SM 798 s.p.   (J86)

Gemeinde-Rufe Und Falsobordoni Zu 5 Psalmen
*Gen
[Ger] SATB,acap (med easy) MULLER SM 699
s.p.
contains: Psalm 22; Psalm 33; Psalm 80;
Psalm 95; Psalm 148   (J87)

Judica Me, Deus   *Psntd
[Lat] SATB,acap (med) MULLER SM 725 s.p.
                                              (J88)

Psalm 22
see Gemeinde-Rufe Und Falsobordoni Zu 5
Psalmen

Psalm 33
see Gemeinde-Rufe Und Falsobordoni Zu 5
Psalmen

Psalm 80
see Gemeinde-Rufe Und Falsobordoni Zu 5
Psalmen

Psalm 95
see Gemeinde-Rufe Und Falsobordoni Zu 5
Psalmen

Psalm 148
see Gemeinde-Rufe Und Falsobordoni Zu 5
Psalmen

Rex Pacificus   *Xmas
[Lat] SATB,acap (med) MULLER MS 68 s.p.
                                              (J89)

JAFFE
Rounds For Christmas   *CCU,Xmas,round
2pt jr cor FISCHER,C CM 6749 .20   (J90)

JAG AR DEN GODE HERDEN see Nilsson, Torsten

JAG AR ROSTEN AV EN SOM ROPAR see Nilsson,
Torsten

JAG AR UPPSTANDELSEN OCH LIVET see Torlind,
Tore

JAG BEDER DIG, O JESU KAR see Berg, Gottfrid

JAG HAR HERREN KAR see Erlandson, Ake

JAG HOJA VILL TILL GUD MIN SANG see Bjarnegard,
Gustaf

JAG LYFTER MINA HANDER
see Fem Folkliga Koraler I Sattningar

JAG STAR INFOR DIN KRUBBA HAR see Bach, Johann
Sebastian

JAG UNNAR DIG ANDA ALLT GOTT
(Hemberg, Eskil) mix cor NORDISKA NMS-6122
s.p.   (J91)

JAG VET, ATT HERREN JESUS KRIST see Schutz,
Heinrich

JAG VILL LOVA HERREN see Runback, Albert

JAM CHRISTUS ASTRA ASCENDERAT see Palestrina,
Giovanni

JAM CHRISTUS ASTRA ASCENDERAT see Tallis,
Thomas

JAMAIS NE CESSERAI DE MAGNIFIER LE SEIGNEUR see
Faignient, Noel

JAMBE
Psalm 25 (composed with De Fer)
(Seay) [Eng/Fr] SATB,acap oct MCA   (J92)

JAMBE DE FER, PHILIBERT (1520-1572)
Der Lobgesang Des Simeon
see Goudimel, Claude, Der Lobgesang Des
Simeon

JAMES
Almighty God Of Our Fathers
SSAATTBB oct BELWIN 64382 .30   (J93)
TTBB oct BELWIN 64219 .30   (J94)

Be Joyful In The Lord
SATB oct GALAXY 1.1904.1 .30   (J95)

Can't Yo' Heah Me Moanin', Lord
TTBB oct FOX 186 .25   (J96)

Child Jesus Came To Earth
SATB oct GALAXY 1.1183.1 .25   (J97)

Christian Fellowship
SATB oct LORENZ C297 .25   (J98)

Communion Hymn Sequence For Choir
SATB oct LORENZ B41 .35   (J99)

Echoing Hosanna
2pt oct LORENZ 5731 .25   (J100)

I Know A Name
SATB oct LORENZ 9975 .30   (J101)

Lord Is My Light, The
SATB oct LORENZ 9977 .30   (J102)

Love Of God
SATB oct FISCHER,C CM-6705 .25   (J103)

My Soul Thirsteth For God
SATB oct LORENZ C324 .30   (J104)

Negro Bell Carol   *Xmas,carol
SATB,acap oct FISCHER,C CM-6683 .25   (J105)

O God Of Peace
SATB oct LORENZ 9981 .25   (J106)

O Love Divine
SATB,S solo STANDARD A1MX1 .40   (J107)

One Fellowship
SATB oct LORENZ 9973 .30   (J108)

Song Of Deliverance
SATB oct LORENZ 9992 .25   (J109)

Thee We Adore
SATB oct LORENZ E94 .30   (J110)

JAMES, ALLEN
Echoing Alleluia
SATB (med) ABINGDON APM-773 .30   (J111)

Look To Him And Be Radiant
SATB,acap oct GRAY GCMR 3221 .30   (J112)

O Thou Eternal Christ
unis oct AGAPE A 386 .30   (J113)

Omnipresence
SATB (med) ABINGDON APM-775 .35   (J114)

Sing Jehovah's Praise
SATB,opt trp/trom oct AGAPE F 925 .30
                                             (J115)

JAMES, [MARION] (1913-   )
Revelation, A
SATB oct BOURNE 656 .30   (J116)

JAMES, PHILIP (1890-   )
By The Waters Of Babylon   *Gen/Lent
SATB oct GRAY GCMR 636 .40   (J117)

I Am The Vine
SATB oct HUNTZINGER 4009 .25   (J118)

Mass In English   *see Missa Brevis

Missa Brevis   *Mass
"Mass In English" mix cor BELWIN $1.00
                                             (J119)

JAMES, PHILIP (cont'd.)

Praise Jehovah, All Ye Nations (Psalm 117)
Bibl
4pt mix cor,org oct SCHIRM.G 10603 .25
                                             (J120)

Psalm 117   *see Praise Jehovah, All Ye
Nations

JAMES, WILL (1896-   )
Hear My Prayer   *Bibl
4pt men cor,acap oct SCHIRM.G 9422 .30
                                             (J121)
4pt mix cor,acap oct SCHIRM.G 7739 .30
                                             (J122)
(Deis) 3pt mix cor,acap oct SCHIRM.G 10000
.30   (J123)
(Downing) 3pt wom cor,acap oct SCHIRM.G
8943 .30   (J124)
(Hedges) jr cor&sr cor oct SCHIRM.G 11138
.25   (J125)

Jesus, Our Lord, We Adore Thee
mix cor,acap oct SCHIRM.G 8311 .30   (J126)
(Downing) SAB,acap oct SCHIRM.G 8869 .30
                                             (J127)
(Downing) 3pt wom cor,acap oct SCHIRM.G
8870 .25   (J128)

Out Of The Depths I Cry To Thee
TTBB,pno oct WILLIS 5802 .16   (J129)
(High) 3pt mix cor,acap (med) oct WILLIS
7070 .25   (J130)
(Weelkes) 4pt men cor (med) oct WILLIS 6710
.16   (J131)

JANACEK, LEOS (1854-1928)
Constitues
TTBB,acap (med) PRESSER UE 14982 .35   (J132)

Das Ewige Evangelium   *Gen
[Eng/Czech/Ger] SATB,ST soli,orch (diff)
cor pts ARTIA AP 161 s.p., ipr, voc sc
ARTIA AP 300 s.p.   (J133)

Festival Mass   *see Msa Glagskaja

Graduale
SATB,acap (med) PRESSER UE 14983 .30   (J134)

Msa Glagskaja
"Festival Mass" [Eng/Lat] cor voc sc
UNIVER. 9544A $11.35   (J135)
"Festival Mass" [Ger/Czech] cor voc sc
UNIVER. 9544 $11.35   (J136)
"Festival Mass" cor cor pts UNIVER. 9946A-D
$.85   (J137)

Vater Unser
[Czech/Ger] SATB,T solo,orch,harp (med
diff) ARTIA AP 611 s.p.   (J138)

Vecne Evangelium
mix cor,solo,orch SUPRAPHON voc sc s.p.,
cor pts s.p.   (J139)

JANES, OLIVER
My Jesus Who Loves Me
see TWO PRAYER SONGS

O Love That Will Not Let Me Go
SATB WEINBERGER s.p.   (J140)

JANKOVICS, F.
Kanon
see KERESZTOLTES

JANNEQUIN, CLEMENT (ca. 1475-ca. 1560)
A Toi, Mon Dieu, Mon Coeur Monte (Psalm 25)
16th cent
(Honegger, Marc; Pidoux, Pierre) [Fr] SATB
OUVRIERES EO520 s.p.   (J141)

Alas, My God   *see Hellas, Mon Dieu

Grace Te Rends Seigneur Dieu, De Tes Biens
*16th cent
(Honegger, Marc; Pidoux, Pierre) [Fr] SATB
OUVRIERES EO494 s.p.   (J142)

Helas, Mon Dieu, Ton Ire S'Est Tournee
(Expert) [Fr] SATB,acap oct SALABERT-US
.65   (J143)

Hellas, Mon Dieu
(Greyson) "Alas, My God" SATB oct BOURNE
ES110 .30   (J144)

Jusques A Quand As Etabli (Psalm 13) 16th
cent
(Honegger, Marc; Pidoux, Pierre) [Fr] SATB
OUVRIERES EO519 s.p.   (J145)

La Bataille   *Mass
(Expert) [Lat] SATB,acap oct SALABERT-US
$5.00   (J146)

Look Down, O Lord   *Gen
(Seay) SATB SCHMITT 1417 .35   (J147)

Ne Veuille Pas, O Sire (Psalm 6) 16th cent
(Honegger, Marc; Pidoux, Pierre) [Fr] SATB
OUVRIERES EO518 s.p.   (J148)

Psalm 6   *see Ne Veuille Pas, O Sire

Psalm 13   *see Jusques A Quand As Etabli

Psalm 25   *see A Toi, Mon Dieu, Mon Coeur
Monte

JANOWSKI, MAX
Avodath Hakodesh   *Sab-Eve/Sab-Morn
SATB TRANSCON. TCL 270 $2.50   (J149)

JANSEN, PHILIPP (1908-   )
Gott Heilger Schopfer Aller Stern
see Berger, Hans Ludwig, O Heiland, Reiss
Die Himmel Auf

Missa Consolationis In Deo
SATB HANSSLER 7.018 s.p.   (J150)

JANSON, ALFRED
Tema
"Theme" 12pt mix cor,pno,org,perc voc sc
WALTON M115 $1.00   (J151)

JANSON, ALFRED (cont'd.)

Theme *see Tema

JANUARY CAROL see Crandell, R.

JANUS, MARTIN (ca. 1620-1682)
Du Grosser Schmerzensmann Vom Vater
see Bach, Johann Sebastian, So Gibst Du
Nun, Mein Jesu, Gute Nacht
see Cruger, Johann, Auf, Auf Mein Herz Mit
Freuden

JAPANESE CHRISTMAS CAROL, A *Xmas,carol,Jap
(Lee, T. Charles) SSA oct GRAY GCMR 2948 $.30
(J152)

(Lee, T. Charles) SATB oct GRAY GCMR 3105
$.30   (J153)

(Lee, T. Charles) unis oct GRAY GCMR 2767
$.25   (J154)

JAQUET OF MANTUA (? -1559)
Alleluia, Surrecit Dominus *Easter
(Ehret) "Alleluia, The Lord Is Now Arisen"
[Lat/Eng] SATB,acap oct COLOMBO 2387 $.30
(J155)

Alleluia, The Lord Is Now Arisen *see
Alleluia, Surrecit Dominus

Collected Works Vol. I
(Jackson, Philip) cor AM.INST.MUS. $20.00
The Four Masses Of Scotto's Print Of 1554
contains: Missa Anchor Che Col Partire;
Missa Chiare Dolci E Fresche Acque;
Missa In Die Tribulationis; Missa
Peccata Mea   (J156)

Collected Works vol. II *CCU
(Jackson, Philip) cor AM.INST.MUS. $21.00
Vesper Hymns, 1566   (J157)

Missa Anchor Che Col Partire
see Collected Works Vol. I

Missa Chiare Dolci E Fresche Acque
see Collected Works Vol. I

Missa In Die Tribulationis
see Collected Works Vol. I

Missa Peccata Mea
see Collected Works Vol. I

JARRET, JACK M.
Boy Was Born, A *Xmas
3pt mix cor,acap oct LAWSON 51495 $.30
(J158)

Go Pretty Child *Xmas
SATB,acap oct LAWSON 51483 $.35   (J159)

Manger, The *Xmas
3pt mix cor,acap oct LAWSON 51468 $.30
(J160)

JARVIS, CALEB
Mass In E Minor *Mass
cor&cong,org oct ST.MARTIN SMP685 s.p., ipa
(J161)

JASON
Pageant Of Christmas *Xmas
(Anson; Ballantine) KJOS $1.25   (J162)

JAUCHZ, ERD UND HIMMEL see Trubel, Gerhard

JAUCHZ, ERD UND HIMMEL, JUBLE HELL see Berger,
Hans Ludwig

JAUCHZ, ERD UND HIMMEL, JUBLE HELL see
Sultzberger, Johann Ulrich

JAUCHZ, ERD, UND HIMMEL, JUBLE HELL see Weiss,
Ewald

JAUCHZ, ERD UND HIMMEL, JUBLE HELL see
Goudimel, Claude

JAUCHZ, ERD UND HIMMEL, JUBLE HELL see
Goudimel, Claude

JAUCHZE DEM HERRN ALLE WELT see Handel, George
Frideric

JAUCHZET, ALLE LANDE, GOTT ZU EHREN see Kurig,
Hans-Hermann

JAUCHZET, ALLE LANDE, GOTT ZU EHREN see
Tzschoppe, Eberhard

JAUCHZET DEM HERREN see Lissmann, Kurt

JAUCHZET DEM HERREN, ALLE WELT see Grimm,
Heinrich

JAUCHZET DEM HERREN ALLE WELT see Schutz,
Heinrich

JAUCHZET DEM HERREN ALLE WELT see Wagener,
Gregor

JAUCHZET DEM HERRN see Fassbaender, P.

JAUCHZET DEM HERRN see Gadsch, Herbert

JAUCHZET DEM HERRN see Kretzschmar, Gunther

JAUCHZET DEM HERRN see Pachelbel, Johann

JAUCHZET DEM HERRN see Schauss-Flake, Magdalene

JAUCHZET DEM HERRN see Schmid, Walter

JAUCHZET DEM HERRN see Schoendlinger, Anton

JAUCHZET DEM HERRN, ALLE WELT see Gottschick,
Friedemann

JAUCHZET DEM HERRN, ALLE WELT see Kubizek,
Augustinus

JAUCHZET DEM HERRN ALLE WELT see Mendelssohn-
Bartholdy, Felix

JAUCHZET DEM HERRN, ALLE WELT see Pachelbel,
Johann

JAUCHZET DEM HERRN ALLE WELT see Schmid, Walter

JAUCHZET DEM HERRN, ALLE WELT see Schoeck,
Othmar

JAUCHZET DEM HERRN ALLE WELT see Schutz,
Heinrich

JAUCHZET GOTT see Bach, Johann Sebastian,
Jauchzet Gott In Allen Landen

JAUCHZET GOTT see Schmid, Walter

JAUCHZET GOTT, ALLE LAND see Scheidt, Samuel

JAUCHZET GOTT, ALLE LANDE see Koch, Johannes
H.E.

JAUCHZET GOTT, ALLE LANDE see Rabsch, Edgar

JAUCHZET GOTT, ALLE LANDE see Rohwer, Jens

JAUCHZET GOTT, ALLE LANDE see Suthoff-Gross,
Rudolf

JAUCHZET GOTT, ALLE LANDE see Thomas, Kurt

JAUCHZET GOTT, ALLE LANDE see Weiland

JAUCHZET GOTT, ALLE LANDE SEHR see Schutz,
Heinrich

JAUCHZET GOTT IN ALLEN LANDEN see Bach, Johann
Sebastian

JAUCHZET, IHR HIMMEL see Anonymous

JAUCHZET, IHR HIMMEL see Hammerschmidt, Andreas

JAUCHZET, IHR HIMMEL, FROHLOCKET, IHR ENGEL, IN
CHOREN see Fiebig, Kurt

JAUCHZET IHR VOLKER see Demerath, F.

JAUCHZT, ALLE LANDE, GOTT ZU EHREN see Borris,
Siegfried

JAUCHZT, ALLE LANDE, GOTT ZU EHREN see
Goudimel, Claude

JAUCHZT, ALLE LANDE, GOTT ZU EHREN see Pepping,
Ernst

JAUCHZT ALLE LANDE, GOTT ZU EHREN see
Sweelinck, Jan Pieterszoon

JAUCHZT ALLE LANDE, GOTT ZU EHREN see Trubel,
Gerhard

JAUCHZT, ALLE LANDE NAH UND FERN see Goudimel,
Claude

JAUCHZT HALLELUJA, LOBT DEN HERRN see Goudimel,
Claude

JAY
Word, The
SSAA,S solo (very easy, may be preformed
with mime) cmplt ed OXFORD 46.506 $1.25
(J163)

JAY VEU LE CERF see Clemens, Jacobus

JAZZ ADORATION see Davis, Katherine K.

JAZZ ALLELUIA, A see Goemanne, Noel

JE CROIS EN DIEU see L'Estocart, Paschal de

JE ME SUIS LEVE see Favre, Georges

JE NAY DUEUL see Ghiselin-Verbonnet, Johannes

JE SUIS AIME see Crawford, John

JE SUIS DESHERITEE see Gombert, Nicolas

JE TE RENDS GRACE, O DIEU D'AMOUR see Gounod,
Charles Francois

JE VEUX, SEIGNEUR see Pevernage, Andries

JE VOUS SALUE, MARIE see Thiriet, [Maurice]

JE VOUS SOUHAITE see Canteloube de Malaret,
Marie-Joseph

JEAN IV, ROI DE PORTUGAL (1604-1656)
Cross That Held Thee *see Crux Fidelis

Crux Fidelis *Gd.Fri./Psntd,mot
[Lat/Eng] mix cor SCHIRM.EC $.18   (J164)
[Lat] SATB RICORDI-ENG SY181 s.p.   (J165)
"Cross That Held Thee" [Eng/Lat] SATB
CHESTER s.p.   (J166)

Faithful Cross And O My People *Gd.Fri.,mot
(Bridge, Sir Fredk.) SATB BOSWORTH s.p.
(J167)

JEAN-BAPTIISTE, L.
Chemin De Croix
cor CHOUDENS s.p.   (J168)

Le Menuisier Du Roi
3 eq voices,fl,perc CHOUDENS s.p.   (J169)

O Magnum Mysterium
cor CHOUDENS s.p.   (J170)

Tenebrae Factae Sunt
cor CHOUDENS s.p.   (J171)

JEANNE D'ARC A DOMREMY see Ollone, Max d'

JEANNE D'ARC AU BUCHER see Honegger, Arthur

JEANNETTE-ISABELLA see Elsmith, Berta

JEDERMANN GIBT ZUERST DEN GUTEN WEIN see
Raselius, Andreas

JEDERMANN GIBT ZUERST DEN GUTEN WEIN see
Vulpius, Melchior

JEDERMANN GIBT ZUM ERSTEN VOM GUTEN WEIN see
Vulpius, Melchior

JEEP, JOHANN (1581-1644)
Allein Auf Gottes Wort
SAAT/SAAB HANSSLER 6.272 s.p. contains
also:
Ruppel, Paul Ernst, Herr, Tue Meine
Lippen Auf (5pt) (canon);
Staden, Johann, Danket Dem Herren
(Psalm 136) (SAT/SAB)   (J172)

JEEP, JOHANN (cont'd.)
Ich Ruf Zu Dir, Herr Jesu Christ
SATB HANSSLER 6.158 s.p. contains also:
Trubel, Gerhard, Sonne Der Gerechtigkeit,
Gehe Auf   (J173)

Lamb Of God, Most Holy
(Ehret) SATB,acap MARKS 4165 $.30   (J174)

Lamb Of God, Pure And Holy *Lent
SATB,acap (med easy) oct CONCORDIA 98-1378
$.25   (J175)

Mit Ernst, O Menschenkinder
see Bach, Johann Sebastian, Lobt Gott Ihr
Christen

O Lamm Gottes, Unschuldig
SATB HANSSLER 6.111 s.p. contains also:
Hassler, Hans Leo, Ein Lammlein Geht Und
Tragt Die Schuld   (J176)

JEFFREYS
He Beheld The City
(Aston) SATB SOUTHERN $.35   (J177)

JEFFRIES, GEORGE (? -1685)
Erit Gloria Domini (Psalm 104) Gen
SS (easy) oct OXFORD 44.215 $.30   (J178)

He Beheld The City
(Aston, Peter) mix cor oct NOVELLO
40.1517.07 s.p.   (J179)
(Aston, Peter) SATB,org/pno NOVELLO AP225
$.35   (J180)

O Domine Deus *anthem
(Aston, Peter) [Lat] ATTB oct NOVELLO
88.0005.07 s.p.   (J181)

Psalm 104 *see Erit Gloria Domini

JEG ER SAA GLAD *anthem
(Christiansen, Paul) "Joyous Christmas Song"
SATB (med) oct AUGSBURG 0904 $.25   (J182)
(Christiansen, Paul) "Joyous Christmas Song"
TTBB (easy) oct AUGSBURG 0908 $.25   (J183)

JEG ER SAA GLAD see Knudsen, [Peder]

JEG FRYDER MIG I DIG see Bach, Johann
Sebastian, Ich Freue Mich In Dir

JEG HAR HORT HVOR SANGEN GAR see Stenhammar,
[Per Ulrik]

JEG LOFTER OPP TIL GUD MIN SANG *folk,Ger
(Aamodt, Valter) men cor MUSIKK 35 s.p.
(J184)
(Sorass, Lars) mix cor MUSIKK 162 s.p. see
from Religiose Korsanger   (J185)

JEG RABER FAST, O HERRE see Jeppesen, Knud

JEG RABER TIL DIG, O HERRE KRIST see Pederson,
Mogens

JEG SER DIG, O GUDS LAM
(Baldershage, Bernt) wom cor MUSIKK 39 s.p.
(J186)

JEG SER DIG, O GUDS LAM see Braein, Edvard

JEG SER DIG, O GUDS LAM A STA see Baden, Conrad

JEG SLETTED SOM TAGE see Jeppesen, Knud

JEG SYNGER JULEKVAD *Xmas
(Beck, Thomas) mix cor MUSIKK 95A s.p. (J187)

JEG VIL DIN PRIS UDSJUNGE see Bach, Johann
Sebastian, Aus Meines Herzens Grunde

JEHOVA see Gerold, J.K.

JEHOVA, DEINEM NAMEN see Lendvai, Erwin

JEHOVA QUAM MULTI SUNT see Purcell, Henry,
Jehovah, Quam Multi

JEHOVAH DID MAKE THIS HOLY DAY see Palestrina,
Giovanni, Haec Dies Quam Fecit

JEHOVAH, HOW MANY ARE THEY see Purcell, Henry,
Jehovah, Quam Multi

JEHOVAH, LET ME NOW ADORE THEE see Bach, Johann
Sebastian

JEHOVAH, QUAM MULTI see Purcell, Henry

JEHOVAH'S MIGHT see Weyse, Christoph Ernst
Friedrich

JEHOVAH'S THRONE see Clokey

JELIGE see Kodaly, Zoltan

JENER TAG, DER TAG DER ZAHREN see Stadlmair,
Hans

JENKINS
Christ Is Risen
SA/TB FLAMMER E5106 $.25   (J188)

Christmas Prayer, A
(Lowden) SAB FLAMMER D5143 $.25   (J189)

Let Us Rise With Jesus
SA/TB FLAMMER E5089 $.25   (J190)
(Webb) SATB FLAMMER A 5404 $.25   (J191)

Very First Christmas, The (composed with
Shirley) *Xmas
SA HANSEN-US E9966 $.40   (J192)

JENKINS, CYRIL (1885-   )
Angel's Chorus
4pt mix cor oct SCHIRM.G 10289 $.25   (J193)

Calvary *Easter,cant
mix cor,solo,orch voc sc SCHIRM.G $1.00,
ipr   (J194)

Fierce Raged The Tempest
SATB oct LESLIE 4087   (J195)

JENKINS, CYRIL (cont'd.)

Hymn To The Soul
SSATBB,acap oct SCHIRM.G 10313 $.25 (J196)

Light In Darkness
4pt mix cor,ST soli,org oct SCHIRM.G 10290
$.35   (J197)

JENKINS, JOHN (1592-1678)
Holy And Blessed Spirit *Gen
SAB,acap (med easy) oct CONCORDIA 98-2154
$.40   (J198)

JENKINS, [JOSEPH WILLCOX] (1928-)
As Joseph Was A Walking
SATB oct COLOMBO 2788 $.35   (J199)

Joseph Dearest
SATB oct COLOMBO 2787 $.35   (J200)

O Leave Your Sheep *see Quitez Pasteurs

Quitez Pasteurs
"O Leave Your Sheep" [Fr/Eng] SATB,acap oct
COLOMBO 2431 $.30   (J201)

Virgin Unspotted
SATB oct COLOMBO 2786 $.35   (J202)

JENKINS, M.
Wonderful Saviour
SATB oct BOURNE 878 $.30   (J203)

JENKINS, THOMAS
Come Worship The King
SATB oct LESLIE 4094   (J204)

JENKYNS, PETER
Carol Of The Bells *Xmas,carol
unis BOOSEY-CAN s.p.   (J205)
unis ASHDOWN U.68 s.p.   (J206)

Czech Lullaby Carol *carol,Czech
SSA oct GALAXY 1.2364.1 $.30   (J207)

JENNIFER see Best

JENNINGS
With A Voice Of Singing
mix cor SOUTHERN $.30   (J208)

JENNINGS, ARTHUR B.
Springs In The Desert *Adv/Gen
SATB oct GRAY GCMR 580 $.40   (J209)

JENNINGS, CAROLYN
Father, We Praise Thee *anthem,Fr
SSA (med) oct AUGSBURG 1500 $.20   (J210)

JENNINGS, KENNETH L.
Arise, Shine, For Thy Light Has Come *anthem
SATB (med) oct AUGSBURG 1498 $.25   (J211)

For He Shall Give His Angels Charge Over Thee
*anthem
SATB (med) oct AUGSBURG 1499 $.25   (J212)

If Ye Be Risen Again With Christ *Easter/Gen
SATB,acap (med diff) oct CONCORDIA 98-1798
$.25   (J213)

We Adore Thee, Christ Our Lord *anthem
TTBB (med) oct AUGSBURG 1293 $.22   (J214)

With A Voice Of Singing *anthem
SATB (med) oct AUGSBURG 1379 $.30   (J215)

JENNY, ALBERT (1912-)
Te Deum *Te Deum
[Lat] SATB,SATB soli,org,2fl,2ob,2clar,
2bsn,4horn,2trp,3trom,tuba,strings,timp
HUG s.p., ipr   (J216)

J'ENTENDS PAR NOTRE RUE see Parozai, Gui

JEPHTA see Carissimi, Giacomo

JEPHTE see Carissimi, Giacomo

JEPHTHA see Handel, George Frideric

JEPHTHAH see Carissimi, Giacomo

JEPPESEN, KNUD (1892-)
Boj, O Helligand, Os Alle
ST HANSEN-DEN 421 s.p. see also Tolv
Tostemmige Danske Motetter   (J217)

Danske Motetter Og Andre Korstykker
[Dan] 2-6pt mix cor cmplt ed HANSEN-DEN
24557 s.p.
contains & see also: Een Ting Har Jeg
Begaeret Af Herren; Gud, Vend Oren Til
Min Bon; Halleluja, Pris Herren I
Himlen; Herre! Hvor Er Mine Fjender
Mange; Herren Er Barmhjertig; Hvad Er Et Menneske; Jeg
Sletted Som Tage; Min Sjael, Lov
Herren; Min Sjael, Lov Herren Og Glem
Ikke; Nu Rinder Solen Op; Salige De
(J218)

De, Som Forlader Sig Pa Herren
SA HANSEN-DEN 412 s.p. see also Tolv
Tostemmige Danske Motetter   (J219)

Den Lyse Dag Forgangen Er
SA HANSEN-DEN 420 s.p. see also Tolv
Tostemmige Danske Motetter   (J220)

Der Sas Ved Nattetid Et Syn
[Dan] SA/SATB HANSEN-DEN 345 s.p. see also
Motetter Og Korsange   (J221)

Det Hellige Kors
ST HANSEN-DEN 417 s.p. see also Tolv
Tostemmige Danske Motetter   (J222)

Dronning Dagmar Messe *Mass
SATB,acap HANSEN-DEN 29090 s.p.   (J223)
mix cor HANSEN-DEN 29090 s.p.   (J224)

Een Ting Har Jeg Begaeret Af Herren
[Dan] SATB HANSEN-DEN 72 s.p. see also
Danske Motetter Og Andre Korstykker   (J225)

En Slaegt Gar Og En Slaegt Kommer
SA HANSEN-DEN 410 s.p. see also Tolv
Tostemmige Danske Motetter   (J226)

JEPPESEN, KNUD (cont'd.)
Gud, Frels Mig
SA HANSEN-DEN 413 s.p. see also Tolv
Tostemmige Danske Motetter   (J227)

Gud, Vend Oren Til Min Bon
[Dan] SATB HANSEN-DEN 71 s.p. see also
Danske Motetter Og Andre Korstykker   (J228)

Halleluja, Pris Herren I Himlen
[Dan] SATB HANSEN-DEN 78 s.p. see also
Danske Motetter Og Andre Korstykker   (J229)

Herre! Hvor Er Mine Fjender Mange
[Dan] SATB HANSEN-DEN 74 s.p. see also
Danske Motetter Og Andre Korstykker   (J230)

Herren Er Barmhjertig
[Dan] SA (contains also: De, Som Forlader
Sig Pa Herren) HANSEN-DEN 66 s.p. see
also Danske Motetter Og Andre Korstykker   (J231)

Herren Er Stor
SA HANSEN-DEN 414 s.p. see also Tolv
Tostemmige Danske Motetter   (J232)

Hojtidsdagen
[Dan] SATB (contains also: Glaederig Og
Underfuld; Gud Ske Lov For Dag, Der Gar)
HANSEN-DEN 79 s.p. see also Danske
Motetter Og Andre Korstykker   (J233)

Hvad Er Et Menneske
[Dan] SATB HANSEN-DEN 73 s.p. see also
Danske Motetter Og Andre Korstykker   (J234)

I Dodens Band Vor Frelser La
SA HANSEN-DEN 419 s.p. see also Tolv
Tostemmige Danske Motetter   (J235)

Introitus
[Dan] SATB HANSEN-DEN 342 s.p. see also
Motetter Og Korsange   (J236)

Jeg Raber Fast, O Herre
SS HANSEN-DEN 416 s.p. see also Tolv
Tostemmige Danske Motetter   (J237)

Jeg Sletted Som Tage
[Dan] SSATTB HANSEN-DEN 76 s.p. see also
Danske Motetter Og Andre Korstykker   (J238)

Litani
[Dan] SATB HANSEN-DEN 343 s.p. see also
Motetter Og Korsange   (J239)

Lover Herren
SA HANSEN-DEN 411 s.p. see also Tolv
Tostemmige Danske Motetter   (J240)

Lovet Vaere Herren
[Dan] SSA HANSEN-DEN 344 s.p. see also
Motetter Og Korsange   (J241)

Min Sjael, Lov Herren
[Dan] SATB HANSEN-DEN 77 s.p. see also
Danske Motetter Og Andre Korstykker   (J242)

Min Sjael, Lov Herren Og Glem Ikke
[Dan] SATB HANSEN-DEN 75 s.p. see also
Danske Motetter Og Andre Korstykker   (J243)

Motetter Og Korsange *sac/sec,CC11L
[Dan] SA/SATB cmplt ed HANSEN-DEN 27724
s.p.
see also: Der Sas Ved Nattetid Et Syn;
Introitus; Litani; Lovet Vaere Herren
(J244)

Nu Rinder Solen Op
[Dan] SAT HANSEN-DEN 70 s.p. see also
Danske Motetter Og Andre Korstykker   (J245)

Salige De
[Dan] SSA (contains also: Han Har Grundlagt
En Stad) HANSEN-DEN 67 s.p. see also
Danske Motetter Og Andre Korstykker   (J246)

Sig Manen Langsomt Haever
SA HANSEN-DEN 418 s.p. see also Tolv
Tostemmige Danske Motetter   (J247)

Tolv Tostemmige Danske Motetter
cmplt ed HANSEN-DEN 28608 s.p.
contains & see also: Boj, O Helligand, Os
Alle; De, Som Forlader Sig Pa Herren;
Den Lyse Dag Forgangen Er; Det Hellige
Kors; En Slaegt Gar Og En Slaegt
Kommer; Gud, Frels Mig; Herren Er Stor.
I Dodens Band Vor Frelser La; Jeg Raber
Fast, O Herre; Lover Herren; Sig Manen
Langsomt Haever; Vor Gud Han Er Sa Fast
En Borg   (J248)

Vor Gud Han Er Sa Fast En Borg
SA HANSEN-DEN 415 s.p. see also Tolv
Tostemmige Danske Motetter   (J249)

JEPTHA see Carissimi, Giacomo

JEREMIAH - WHY SHOULD THOU BE AS A STRANGER IN
THE LAND see Demarest, A.

JERICHO JAZZ, THE see Chappell, Herbert

JERICHO-SONG. DER WEG HINAB NACH JERICHO *Gen
[Ger] unis,kbd,gtr (easy) BOSSE BE 273 s.p.
(J250)

JEROME, FREDERICK
In Thee Do I Put My Trust
SATB,B solo,pno (easy) oct WILLIS 6320 $.10
(J251)

Like As A Father
SATB,T,SA soli (easy) oct WILLIS 6453 $.12
(J252)

JERRETT, JACK
As Joseph Was A-Walking
see Three Christmas Songs

How Far Is It To Bethlehem?
see Three Christmas Songs

Joy Shall Be Yours
see Three Christmas Songs

Three Christmas Songs *Xmas
SATB STANDARD A37MX3 $.50
contains: As Joseph Was A-Walking; How
Far Is It To Bethlehem?; Joy Shall Be

JERRETT, JACK (cont'd.)
Yours   (J253)

JERSUALEM MORNING *spir
(Bartholomew) 4pt mix cor,opt solo,acap oct
SCHIRM.G 10202 $.25   (J254)

JERUSALEM see Campion

JERUSALEM see Gerhard, Fritz Christian

JERUSALEM see Goldman, Maurice

JERUSALEM see Gounod, Charles Francois

JERUSALEM see Mendelssohn-Bartholdy, Felix

JERUSALEM see Olman, Isr. J.

JERUSALEM see Parker

JERUSALEM see Parker, Henry

JERUSALEM see Parker, Horatio William

JERUSALEM see Parry, Charles Hubert Hastings

JERUSALEM AR ODE *Psalm
(Von Koch, Erland) [Swed] SATB,acap GEHRMANS
KRB 428   (J255)

JERUSALEM CHAGALL WINDOWS, THE see Gilboa,
Jacob

JERUSALEM, DU HOCHGBAUTE STADT see Fronmuller,
Frieda

JERUSALEM, DU HOCHGEBAUTE STADT see Franck,
Melchior

JERUSALEM, DU HOCHGEBAUTE STADT see Schumann,
Georg

JERUSALEM, DU HOCHGEBAUTE STADT see Thomas,
Kurt

JERUSALEM, HAV UPP DIN ROST *Bibl
(Lunden, Lennart) [Swed] SAB,acap GEHRMANS
TKS 5   (J256)

JERUSALEM HAV UPP DIN ROST see Bach, Johann
Sebastian

JERUSALEM, HAV UPP DIN ROST see Berg, Gottfrid

JERUSALEM, HAV UPP DIN ROST see Bjarnegard,
Gustaf

JERUSALEM IN OR see Shemar, N.

JERUSALEM, JERUSALEM, CONVERTERE see
Goicoechea, Vincente

JERUSALEM, JERUSALEM, TURN THYSELF see
Goicoechea, Vincente, Jerusalem, Jerusalem,
Convertere

JERUSALEM-LIED. IHR MACHTIGEN, ICH WILL NICHT
SINGEN *Gen,Isr
[Ger] unis,kbd (easy) BOSSE BE 274 s.p.
(J257)

JERUSALEM, MY GLORIOUS HOME see Mason, Lowell

JERUSALEM, MY HAPPY HOME *anthem,US
(Sateren, Leland) SATB (easy) oct AUGSBURG
1324 $.25   (J258)

JERUSALEM, MY HAPPY HOME see Pfautsch, Lloyd

JERUSALEM MY HAPPY HOME see Rogers

JERUSALEM MY HAPPY HOME see Walter

JERUSALEM, O TURN THEE see Gounod, Charles
Francois

JERUSALEM! O TURN THEE TO THE LORD see Gounod,
Charles Francois

JERUSALEM, OH, THAT THOU HADST KNOWN see
Wienhorst, Richard

JERUSALEM ON HIGH see Gray, Alan

JERUSALEM REMEMBERED see Palestrina, Giovanni,
Recordata

JERUSALEM THE GOLDEN (from Hymn Tune: Ewing)
(Grieb) jr cor&sr cor oct SCHIRM.G 10845 $.25
(J259)

JESAJA, DEM PROPHETEN see Barbe, Helmut

JESAJA IX: 1-6 see Pluister, Simon

JESOUS AHATONHIA see Brebeuf, J. De

JESSOP, CHAS.
Let The Earth Be Glad *Fest,anthem
SATB,pno (med) oct WILLIS 6326 $.12   (J260)

JESU ALLERLIEFSTE KIND see Boedijn, Gerard H.

JESU AR MIN VAN DEN BASTA see Sjoblom, Heimer

JESU, AS THOU ART OUR SAVIOR see Britten,
Benjamin

JESU, BE MERCIFUL see Durante, Francesco,
Christe Eleison

JESU, BE THOU HERE BESIDE US see Bach, Johann
Sebastian

JESU BLEIBET MEINE FREUDE see Bach, Johann
Sebastian

JESU, BREAD OF LIFE see Bach, Johann Sebastian,
Jesu, Wahres Brot Des Lebens

JESU, BRIGHT AND MORNING STAR see Sowerby, Leo

JESU, BY THEE I WOULD BE BLESSED see Franck,
Melchior, Jesu, Dein' Seel' Lass Heilig'n Mich

JESU, BY THEE I WOULD BE BLESSED see Franck,
Melchior, Jesu, Dein' Seel'lass Heilig'n
Mich

JESU, BY THY SUFFERING see Bach, Johann Sebastian, Jesu, Deine Passion

JESU, CHILD OF BETHLEHEM see Hokanson, Margrethe

JESU CHRISTE, GOTTES LAMM see Cabezon, Antonio de

JESU CHRISTES MILDE MODER see Dennison, S.

JESU, CHRIST'S MILD MOTHER STOOD see Rorem, Ned, Mild Mother, The

JESU, COMFORT OF MY HEART see Bach, Johann Sebastian

JESU CORONA VIRGINUM see Arnaldi, Antonio

JESU CORONA VIRGINUM see Bottazzo, Luigi

JESU CORONA VIRGINUM see Mercatali, A.

JESU CORONA VIRGINUM see Rodella, Sante

JESU CORONA, VIRGINUM see Visona', Gino

JESU CORONA VIRGINUM see Volpi, Edoardo

JESU, CREATOR OF THE WORLD see Bloom, C.G.L.

JESU, DEIN' SEEL' see Franck, Melchior

JESU, DEIN SEEL' LASS HEIL'GEN MICH see Franck, Melchior

JESU, DEIN' SEEL' LASS HEILIG'N MICH see Franck, Melchior

JESU, DEIN' SEEL'LASS HEILIG'N MICH see Franck, Melchior

JESU, DEINE PASSION see Bach, Johann Sebastian

JESU, DEINE PASSION see Distler, Hugo

JESU, DEINE PASSION see Micheelsen, Hans Friedrich

JESU, DEINE PASSION see Zeuner, Martin

JESU, DEINE PASSION WILL ICH JETZT BEDENKEN see Oertzen, Rudolf von

JESU, DEINE PASSION WILL ICH JETZT BEDENKEN see Praetorius, Michael

JESU, DER DU see Bach, Johann Sebastian, Jesu, Der Du Meine Seele

JESU, DER DU MEINE SEELE see Bach, Johann Sebastian

JESU, DER DU MEINE SELLE see Bach, Johann Sebastian

JESU, DU SOHN DAVIDS see Driessler, Johannes

JESU, DU SOM BARNEN ALLA see Blom, Oscar

JESU, DU ZARTES KINDELEIN see Franck, Melchior

JESU DULCEDO CORDIUM see Schattenberg, Thomas

JESU DULCIS *NJ
(Geveart, F.-A.) "Pour La Fete Du Saint Nom De Jesus" [Lat/Fr] 4pt mix cor,acap (easy) cor pts LEMOINE s.p. see from Collection De Choeurs, troisieme Fascicule   (J261)

JESU DULCIS see Victoria, Tomas Luis de

JESU DULCIS MEMORIA see Bijl, Theo van der

JESU DULCIS MEMORIA see Cranmer, Philip

JESU, DULCIS MEMORIA see Deering, Richard

JESU, DULCIS MEMORIA see Drayton

JESU DULCIS MEMORIA see Kothe

JESU, DULCIS MEMORIA see Olsson, Otto Emmanuel

JESU, DULCIS MEMORIA see Victoria

JESU DULCIS MEMORIA see Victoria, Tomas Luis de

JESU DULCIS MEMORIA see Volpi, Edoardo

JESU DULCIS MEMORIA see Wertheim, S.L.

JESU EINZUG IN JERUSALEM see Manicke, Dietrich

JESU, FOUNT OF JOY see Bach, Johann Sebastian

JESU, FRIEND OF MY DELIGHT see Caldwell

JESU, FRIEND OF SINNERS see Grieg, Edvard Hagerup

JESU, GEH VORAN see Bornefeld, Helmut

JESU, GEH VORAN see Weber, Bernhard

JESU, GENTLEST SAVIOUR see Saint-Saens, Camille, Sub Tuum

JESU, GLORY OF MY LIFE see Bach, Johann Sebastian

JESU, GOR MIG ANGELAGEN see Thyrestam, Gunnar

JESU, GRANT ME GRACE see Pasquet, Jean

JESU, GRANT ME THIS, I PRAY see Griffiths, Vernon

JESU, GRANT ME THIS I PRAY see Kitson, Charles Herbert

JESU, GRANT ME THIS I PRAY see Whitlock, Percy

JESU, HOLY SPIRIT see Mozart, Wolfgang Amadeus, Ave Verum Corpus

JESU HUVUD SJUNKER NER see Franck, J.

JESU, I WILL PONDER NOW see Schutz, Heinrich

JESU IS CRYING see Hudson

JESU IS CRYING see Hudson, Hazel

JESU, JESU, DU AR MIN see Bach, Johann Sebastian

JESU, JESU, GOD INCARNATE see Bruckner, Anton, Ave Verum

JESU, JESU, GOD, INCARNATE see Mozart, Wolfgang Amadeus, Ave Verum Corpus

JESU, JESU, THOU ART MINE see Bach, Johann Sebastian

JESU, JESU, WHY DID YOU DIE? see Lipscomb, Helen

JESU, JOY AND TREASURE see Bach, Johann Sebastian, Jesu, Meine Freude

JESU, JOY AND TREASURE see Buxtehude, Dietrich

JESU, JOY OF MAN'S DESIRING see Bach, Johann Sebastian

JESU, JOYANCE OF MY HEART see Bach, Johann Sebastian

JESU, JOYAUNCE OF MY HEART see Ahle, Johann Rudolph

JESU, JOYAUNCE OF MY HEART see Bach, Johann Sebastian

JESU KOMM see Bruckner, Anton

JESU KREUZ, LEIDEN UND PEIN see Bornefeld, Helmut

JESU KREUZ, LEIDEN UND PEIN see Gumpeltzhaimer, Adam

JESU KREUZ, LEIDEN UND PEIN see Spar, Otto

JESU KREUZ, LEIDEN UND PEIN see Stern, Hermann

JESU KREUZ, LEIDEN UND PEIN see Stockmeier, Wolfgang

JESU KREUZ, LEIDEN UND PEIN see Wiemer, Wolfgang

JESU KRISTI SJU ORD PA KORSET see Schutz, Heinrich

JESU KRISTI SYV ORD PA KORSET see Schutz, Heinrich

JESU, LAR MIG RATT BETANKA see Albert-Roman

JESU, LAR MIG RATT BETANKA see Soderholm, Valdemar

JESU, LAT DIN KARLEKS LAGA see Berg, Gottfrid

JESU, LAT MIG HJARTAT BOJA see Sandberg, Folke

JESU LEIDEN UNSERE SELIGKEIT see Rohwer, Jens

JESU, LIEBER MEISTER, ERBARME DICH UNSER see Driessler, Johannes

JESU, LITTLE SON see Day, Stanley A.

JESU, LORD OF HEAVENLY GRACE see Rogers

JESU, LOVER OF MY SOUL *Gen
SATB BIG3 $.25   (J262)
(Coleman, Henry) SATB (very easy) oct OXFORD 42.135 $.30   (J263)

JESU, LOVER OF MY SOUL see Williamson, Malcolm

JESU LULLABY see Jones

JESU, MEEK AND LOWLY see Elgar, Edward

JESU, MEINE FREUDE see Bach, Johann Sebastian

JESU, MEINE FREUDE see Buxtehude, Dietrich

JESU, MEINE FREUDE see Cruger, Johann

JESU, MEINE FREUDE see Hammerschmidt, Andreas

JESU, MEINE FREUDE see Kretzschmar, Gunther

JESU, MEINE FREUDE see Trubel, Gerhard

JESU, MEINE FREUDE [CHORALE] see Bach, Johann Sebastian

JESU, MEINE FREUDE, MEINES HERZENS [CHORALE] see Bach, Johann Sebastian

JESU, MEINES HERZENS FREUD' see Bach, Johann Sebastian

JESU, MEINES LEBENS LEBEN see Buxtehude, Dietrich

JESU, MEINES LEBENS LEBEN see Witte, Gerd

JESU, MERCY, HOW MAY THIS BE? see Browne

JESU MIN HERRE TILL DIG JAG LANGTAR see Bach, Johann Sebastian

JESU MITIS see Arnaldi, Antonio

JESU, MY HEART'S TREASURE see Buxtehude, Dietrich

JESU, MY JESU, LOVELY LORD see Fox, George

JESU, MY SON see Caldwell, Mary [Elizabeth]

JESU NAMM BEGYNNA SKALL see Soderholm, Valdemar

JESU NAMN BEGYNNA SKALL see Berg, Gottfrid

JESU NOSTRA REDEMPTIO see Palestrina, Giovanni

JESU NOSTRA REDEMPTIS see Palestrina, Giovanni

JESU, NUN see Bach, Johann Sebastian, Jesu, Nun Sei Gepreiset

JESU, NUN SEI GEPREISET see Bach, Johann Sebastian

JESU, NUN SEI GEPREISET see Hennig, Walter

JESU, NUN SEI GEPREISET [CHORALE] see Bach, Johann Sebastian

JESU, NUN SIE GEPREISET see Bach, Johann Sebastian

JESU, OUR BLESSED HOPE OF HEAVEN see Young, Gordon

JESU, OUR FAITHFUL GUIDE see Wehr, David A.

JESU, OUR HOLY SAVIOR see Menegali, Jesu, Salvator Mundi

JESU PARVULE see Swann

JESU, PRECIOUS LORD see Willaert, Adrian, Dulces Exuviae

JESU, PRICELESS TREASURE see Bach, Johann Sebastian, Jesu, Meine Freude

JESU, PRICELESS TREASURE see Cruger, Johann

JESU, PRICELESS TREASURE see Roberts, J. Varley

JESU, PRICELESS TREASURE [CHORALE] see Bach, Johann Sebastian

JESU PRICELESS TREASURE see Bach, Johann Sebastian, Jesu, Meine Freude [Chorale]

JESU QUEM VELATUM see Wagner, Richard

JESU REDEMPTOR see Arnaldi, Antonio

JESU REDEMPTOR OMNIUM see Casimiri, Raffaele Casimiro

JESU REDEMPTOR OMNIUM see Rodella, Sante

JESU REDEMPTOR OMNIUM see Stadlmayr, Johann

JESU REDEMPTOR OMNIUM see Viero, Francesco

JESU! REX ADMIRABILIS see Palestrina, Giovanni

JESU, SALVATOR MUNDI see Menegali

JESU SALVATOR SAECULI see Tallis, Thomas

JESU SO LOWLY see Hurford, Peter

JESU, SON OF GOD see Mozart, Wolfgang Amadeus

JESU SON OF GOD MOST HIGH see Bach, Johann Sebastian

JESU, SUMMA BENIGNITAS see Deering, Richard

JESU SWEET see Bach, Johann Sebastian

JESU, SWEET ARE ALL THOUGHTS see Victoria, Tomas Luis de, Jesu Dulcis Memoria

JESU TANK PA MIG see Carlstedt, Gunnemer

JESU, THE VERY THOUGHT IS SWEET see Boeringer, James

JESU! THE VERY THOUGHT IS SWEET see Des Prez, Josquin

JESU, THE VERY THOUGHT IS SWEET see Victoria, Jesu, Dulcis Memoria

JESU, THE VERY THOUGHT IS SWEET see Victoria, Tomas Luis de, Jesu Dulcis Memoria

JESU, THE VERY THOUGHT OF THEE see Bairstow, Edward Cuthbert

JESU THE VERY THOUGHT OF THEE see Broadhead, G.F.

JESU, THE VERY THOUGHT OF THEE see Davis, J.

JESU, THE VERY THOUGHT OF THEE see Lang, C.S.

JESU, THE VERY THOUGHT OF THEE see Prouix

JESU, THE VERY THOUGHT OF THEE see Thiman, Eric Harding

JESU, THE VERY THOUGHT OF THEE see Victoria, Tomas Luis de, Jesu, Dulcis Memoria

JESU, THE VERY THOUGHT OF THEE see Ward

JESU, THE VERY THOUGHT OF THEE see Wesley, Samuel Sebastian Jr.

JESU, THINK OF ME see Back, Sven-Erick, Domine Memento Mei

JESU! THOU DEAR BABE DIVINE *Xmas,Haitian
(Dickinson, C.) SSA oct GRAY GSC 96 $.25
(J264)
(Dickinson, C.) SATB oct GRAY GSC 45 $.30
(J265)

JESU, THOU JOY OF LOVING HEARTS see Kirk

JESU, THOU JOY OF LOVING HEARTS see Saylor, B.

JESU, THOU MY CONSTANT GLADNESS see Bach, Johann Sebastian

JESU, THOU MY HEART'S DELIGHT see Bach, Johann Sebastian

JESU, TRANSCENDENT, GLORIOUS KING see Palestrina, Giovanni, Jesu! Rex Admirabilis

JESU, WAHRES BROT DES LEBENS see Bach, Johann Sebastian

JESU, WAS HAST DU VERBROCHEN see Marx, Karl

JESU, WHO MY SOUL ETERNAL see Bach, Johann Sebastian

JESU, WHOM THY CHILDREN LOVE see Button, H.E.

JESU, WOLLST UNS WEISEN see Schein, Johann Hermann

JESU, WORD OF GOD INCARNATE see Elgar, Ave Verum Corpus

JESU, WORD OF GOD INCARNATE see Elgar, Edward, Ave Verum

JESU, WORD OF GOD INCARNATE see Faure, Gabriel-Urbain, Ave, Verum Corpus

JESU, WORD OF GOD INCARNATE see Franco, Ave Verum Corpus

JESU, WORD OF GOD INCARNATE see Gounod, Charles Francois, Ave Verum

JESU, WORD OF GOD INCARNATE see Gounod, Charles Francois, Ave Verum Corpus

JESU, WORD OF GOD INCARNATE see Liszt, Franz

JESU, WORD OF GOD INCARNATE see Magin, Charles, Ave Verum Corpus

JESU, WORD OF GOD INCARNATE see Mozart, Wolfgang Amadeus, Ave Verum

JESU, WORD OF GOD INCARNATE see Mozart, Wolfgang Amadeus, Ave Verum Corpus

JESU, WORD OF GOD INCARNATE see Quilici, Abbe F., Ave Verum Corpus

JESU, WORD OF GOD INCARNATE see Saint-Saens, Camille

JESU, WORD OF GOD INCARNATE see Titcomb

JESU, WORD OF GOD INCARNATE see Welsh, W.A., Ave Verum

JESU, WORK OF GOD see Mozart, Wolfgang Amadeus, Ave Verum

JESUM TRADIDIT see Goodman, Joseph

JESUM TRADIDIT IMPIUS see Victoria, Tomas Luis de

JESUS see Marshall, Jane M.

JESUS, ALL THY LABOR VAST see Boatwright, Howard

JESUS AMONG HIS FRIENDS see Grime, William

JESUS AND THE PHARISEES see Franck, Melchior

JESUS AND THE TRADERS see Kodaly, Zoltan, Jezus Es A Kufarok

JESUS AUTEM HODIE see Davies, Peter Maxwell

JESUS BEFORE PILATE see Williams

JESUS BIDS US SHINE see Handel, George Frideric

JESUS BLEIBET MEINE FREUDE see Bach, Johann Sebastian

JESUS, BLEST REDEEMER see Grieg, Edvard Hagerup

JESUS BORN see Lynn, George

JESUS, BORN IN BETHLEA *Xmas,carol/folk,US
(Ehret) SATB oct SPRATT 611 $.35   (J266)

JESUS BORN IN BETHLEA see Ehret, Walter

JESUS BORN IN BETHLEA see Scott, T.

JESUS, BORN IN BETHLEHEM see Williams

JESUS BOY LULLABY see Cain, Noble

JESUS, BREAD OF LIFE DIVINE see Rogers, E.

JESUS BREAD OF LIFE I PRAY THEE
(Whitehead, A.) SATB oct LESLIE 4003   (J267)

JESUS, BREAD OF LIFE, I PRAY THEE see Whitehead

JESUS CALL US see Macfarlane, William Charles

JESUS CALLED
see Three More General Choruses

JESUS CALLS US see Greener

JESUS CALLS US see Greener, Joseph H.

JESUS CALLS US see Jude, [William Herbert]

JESUS CALLS US see Mozart, Wolfgang Amadeus, Ave Verum

JESUS CALLS US see Sanders, Robert L.

JESUS CALLS US see Wilson

JESUS CALLS US O'ER THE TUMULT see York, D.

JESUS CAME, ALLELUIA see Stoerl

JESUS CAME FOR ALL MEN see Nelson, Ronald A.

JESUS CAME FOR LOVE see Grime, William

JESUS CHILD see Greenwood

JESUS CHRIST BECAME FOR OUR SINS, OBEDIENT see Gallus, Jacobus, Christus Factus Est

JESUS CHRIST FOR OUR SALVATION see Anerio, Felice, Christus Factus Est

JESUS CHRIST, FOR OUR SALVATION see Bruckner, Anton, Christus Factus Est

JESUS CHRIST FROM THE LAW HATH FREED US see Schelle, Johann Hermann, Christus Ist Des Gesetzes Ende

JESUS CHRIST IS BORN *Xmas,carol,Rum
(Salama) SATB oct SCHIRM.G 7443 $.25   (J268)

JESUS CHRIST IS BORN see Salama, A.

JESUS CHRIST IS BORN TODAY *Xmas
(Kirk) SATB oct PRO ART 2695 $.30   (J269)

JESUS CHRIST IS BORN TODAY see Beadell, Robert M.

JESUS CHRIST IS BORN TODAY see Ringwald, [Roy]

JESUS CHRIST IS RISEN see Wesley

JESUS CHRIST IS RISEN TODAY (from Lyra Davidica) Easter/Lent,anthem
(Davis, K.) TBB,acap SCHIRM.EC 574 $.16   (J270)
(Holmes) TTBB oct PRO ART 1781 $.20   (J271)
(Pelz, Walter) cor&cong,org,trp (easy) oct AUGSBURG 1451 $.30   (J272)

JESUS CHRIST IS RISEN TODAY see Anonymous

JESUS CHRIST IS RISEN TODAY see Campbell

JESUS CHRIST IS RISEN TODAY see Copley, R. Evan

JESUS CHRIST IS RISEN TODAY see Dickinson, Peter

JESUS CHRIST IS RISEN TODAY see Kevan

JESUS CHRIST IS RISEN TODAY see Kirk

JESUS CHRIST IS RISEN TODAY see O'connor

JESUS CHRIST IS RISEN TODAY see Pelz, Walter L.

JESUS CHRIST IS RISEN TODAY ALLELUIA see Wolfe

JESUS CHRIST IS RISEN TODAY, ALLELUIA! see Wolff, S. Drummond

JESUS CHRIST IS RISEN TODAY (EASTER SEQUENCE) *Easter,Greg
(Lundquist) SATB,acap (med) oct WILLIS 8464 $.25   (J273)

JESUS CHRIST IS RIS'N TODAY see Darst, W. Glenn

JESUS CHRIST, MY SURE DEFENSE see Cruger, Johann

JESUS CHRIST, OUR BLESSED SAVIOR see Praetorius, Michael

JESUS CHRIST, OUR BLESSED SAVIOUR see Bielawa, Herbert

JESUS CHRIST, OUR LORD see Pitoni, Giuseppe Ottavio, Christus Factus Est

JESUS CHRIST, OUR LORD, FOR OUR SAKE see Eberlin, Johann Ernst, Christus Factus Est

JESUS CHRIST OUR LORD IS BORN see Praetorius, Michael

JESUS CHRIST OUR LORD IS RISEN see Grieg, Edvard Hagerup

JESUS CHRIST, OUR LORD, IS RISEN see Haydn, (Franz) Joseph

JESUS CHRIST, OUR LORD WAS CRUCIFIED see Palestrina, Giovanni, Christus Factus Est

JESUS CHRIST, OUR SALVATION see Festa, Costanza, Regem Archangelorum

JESUS CHRIST OUR SAVIOUR IS BORN
(Gordon, Philip) SA/TB oct BELWIN 1844 $.25   (J274)
(Gordon, Philip) SSA oct BELWIN 1513 $.25   (J275)
(Gordon, Philip) SAB oct BELWIN 1524 $.30   (J276)
(Gordon, Philip) SATB oct BELWIN 1680 $.25   (J277)

JESUS CHRIST OUR STRONG SALVATION see Huss

JESUS-CHRIST S'HABILLE EN PAUVRE see Aubanel, Georges

JESUS CHRIST THE APPLE TREE see Holman, Derek

JESUS CHRIST, THE CRUCIFIED see Blakley

JESUS CHRIST, THE LORD OF JOY see Bouman, Paul

JESUS CHRIST TODAY IS BORN see Praetorius, Michael

JESUS CHRIST TODAY IS RISEN see Grieg, Edvard Hagerup

JESUS CHRIST TRIUMPHANT see Staley

JESUS CHRIST WAS MADE OBEDIANT see Comes, Juan Bautista, Christus Factus Est

JESUS' CHRISTMAS LULLABY see Ehret, Walter

JESUS' CHRISTMAS see Bruckner, Anton

JESUS CHRISTUS ERNIEDRIGTE SICH SELBST see Spar, Otto

JESUS CHRISTUS, GESTERN UND HEUTE see Distler, Hugo

JESUS CHRISTUS HERRSCHT ALS KONIG see Bornefeld, Helmut

JESUS CHRISTUS IST KOMMEN see Telemann, Georg Philipp

JESUS CHRISTUS, KONIG UND HERR see Wenzel, Eberhard

JESUS CHRISTUS NOSTRA SALUS
(Nystedt, Knut) [Lat] mix cor,org LYCHE 27 s.p.   (J278)

JESUS CHRISTUS, UNSER HEILAND see Bender, Jan

JESUS CHRISTUS, UNSER HEILAND see Hassler, Hans Leo

JESUS CHRISTUS, UNSER HEILAND see Koch, Heinz

JESUS CHRISTUS UNSER HEILAND see Praetorius, Michael

JESUS CHRISTUS UNSER HEILAND see Raphael, Gunther

JESUS CHRISTUS UNSER HEILAND see Waldbroel, Wilhelm

JESUS CHRISTUS UNSER HEILAND see Weismann, Wilhelm

JESUS CHRISTUS, UNSER HEILAND, DER DEN TOD see Bodenschatz, Erhard

JESUS CHRISTUS, UNSER HEILAND, DER DEN TOD UBERWAND see Bornefeld, Helmut

JESUS CHRISTUS, UNSER HEILAND, DER DEN TOD UBERWAND see Eccard, Johannes

JESUS CHRISTUS, UNSER HEILAND, DER DEN TOD UBERWAND see Hennig, Walter

JESUS CHRISTUS, UNSER HEILAND, DER DEN TOD UBERWAND see Reda, Siegfried

JESUS CHRISTUS, UNSER HEILAND, DER VON UNS DEN GOTTESZORN see Raselius, Andreas

JESUS CHRSTUS, UNSER HEILAND, DER DEN TOD see Walter (Walther), Johann

JESUS, COME ABIDE WITH ME see Johnston

JESUS COMES WITH ALL HIS GRACE see Cashmore, Donald

JESUS, CORONA VIRGINUM see Bach, Johann Sebastian

JESUS' CROSS, THE DEATH AND PAIN see Gumpeltzhaimer, Adam

JESUS, DEAR JESUS see Webber, W.S. Lloyd

JESUS DEAR SHEPHERD see McWhertor

JESUS, DEAREST JESUS *anthem/folk,Norw
(Hegge) SSA (very easy) oct AUGSBURG 1031 $.18   (J279)

JESUS DIED ON CALVARY'S MOUNTAIN *Easter/Lent, folk,US
(Parker) SATB,B solo,acap oct LAWSON 51512 $.25   (J280)
(Richardson) SAB oct SPRATT 643 $.30   (J281)

JESUS, DIN SOTE FORENING A SMAKE see Baden, Conrad

JESUS, DIN SOTE FORENING A SMAKE see Nystedt, Knut

JESUS, DRAW NEAR see Hallett, John C.

JESUS, DU SANKT DIG DJUPT I NODEN see Moren, John

JESUS DULCIS see Victoria, Tomas Luis de

JESUS DULCIS MEMORIA see Zangius, Nikolaus

JESUS ENCOUNTERS JOHN THE BAPTIST see Christiansen, P.

JESUS FOR US BECAME OBEDIENT see Zingarelli, Nicola Antonio, Christus Factus Est

JESUS, FOUNT OF CONSOLATION see Bach, Johann Sebastian

JESUS FRESTAS I OKNEN see Nilsson, Torsten

JESUS, GENTLE SHEPHERD see Peninger

JESUS, GENTLEST SAVIOUR see Coggin

JESUS GOOD ABOVE ALL THE OTHERS see Willan, Healey

JESUS, GRANT ME THIS I PRAY see Wolff, S. Drummond

JESUS GUIDE US see Beethoven, Ludwig van

JESUS HAD NOT WHERE TO LAY HIS HEAD see Wood, Dale

JESUS HAV I STANDIGT MINNE see Runback, Albert

JESUS HEALS THE OFFICIAL'S SON see Hillert, Richard

JESUS HOLY, BORN SO LOWLY *Xmas,Pol
(Ehret, Walter) SA,pno,fl (very easy) PRESSER $.35   (J282)

JESUS, HOLY CHILD see Schroth

JESUS HUNG AND DIED see Elam, U.

JESUS, I COME see Rasley

JESUS I LOVE see Noe, J.T.

JESUS, I MY CROSS HAVE TAKEN see Bortniansky, Dimitri Stepanovitch

JESUS, I MY CROSS HAVE TAKEN see Mozart, Wolfgang Amadeus

JESUS, I MY CROSS HAVE TAKEN see Stafford, F.J.

JESUS, I WILL PONDER NOW see Vulpius, Melchior

JESUS, I WILL PONDER NOW see Zeuner, Martin

JESUS IN A MANGER see Kirk

JESUS IN BETHLEHEM IS BORN see Smith, Olive [Kent]

JESUS IN GETHSEMANE see Bach

JESUS, IN THY DYING WOES *anthem/hymn,Swed
(Sateren, Leland) SATB (easy) oct AUGSBURG
1172 $.25   (J283)

JESUS, IN THY THIRST AND PAIN see Hutson

JESUS IS A ROCK see Peery

JESUS IS A ROCK IN A WEARY LAND *spir
(Blaine, G. Gordon) SATB oct WALTON 2033 $.30
(J284)

JESUS IS A WONDERFUL SAVIOUR see Anonymous

JESUS IS ALL THE WORLD TO ME see Lorenz

JESUS IS ALL THE WORLD TO ME see Thompson

JESUS IS ALL THE WORLD TO ME see Thompson, W.

JESUS IS BORN *Xmas
(Goemanne, Noel) 2 eq voices/3 eq voices,acap
oct WORLD AC-223-2 $.45   (J285)

JESUS IS BORN see Brebeuf, J. De, Jesous
Ahatonhia

JESUS IS BORN see Martin

JESUS IS BORN see Rogers, Ethel Trench

JESUS IS BORN, ALLELUIA see Butler

JESUS IS BORN IN BETHLEHEM see Newbury, Kent A.

JESUS IS BORN ON THIS HAPPY NEW DAY see Rogers,
Sharon Elery

JESUS IS BORN THE KING! see Denton

JESUS IS BORN TODAY see Carulli

JESUS IS COMING
SSA/SATB/SAB/SA/TB BIG3 $.30   (J286)

JESUS IS HIS NAME see Bernard

JESUS IS HIS NAME see Davis, Katherine K.

JESUS IS HIS NAME see Mercer, M.

JESUS IS LORD OF THE WORLD see Rinck, Johann
Christian Hein.

JESUS IS MY HEART'S DELIGHT see Bach, Johann
Sebastian

JESUS IS MY JOY, MY ALL see Bach, Johann
Sebastian

JESUS IS OUR JOY, OUR TREASURE see Anonymous

JESUS IS RISEN see Mascagni, Pietro

JESUS IS RISEN TODAY see Hovhaness, Alan

JESUS IS THE NAME EXALTED see Roberts

JESUS IS THE SWEETEST NAME I KNOW see Long

JESUS IS WELL AND ALIVE TODAY see Cruger,
Johann

JESUS IST EIN SUSSER NAM' see Praetorius,
Michael

JESUS IST KOMMEN, GRUND EWIGER FREUDE see
Metzger, Hans-Arnold

JESUS IST KOMMEN, GRUND EWIGER FREUDE see
Ruppel, Paul Ernst

JESUS IST MEIN STARKER HELD see Raimund,
Balthasar

JESUS, JESUS, KOMM ZU MIR see Ahrens, Joseph

JESUS, JESUS, REST YOUR HEAD *Xmas
(Ahrold, F.) SATB,acap oct PRESSER 312-40628
$.30   (J287)
(Bement; Niles) 3pt wom cor,S solo,acap oct
SCHIRM.G 9456 $.30   (J288)
(Freng) SATB SCHMITT 906 $.25   (J289)
(Niles; Deis) 2pt wom cor oct SCHIRM.G 10306
$.30   (J290)
(Niles; Fischer) 4pt men cor,T solo oct
SCHIRM.G 10622 $.25   (J291)
(Terri) SATB oct LAWSON 51730 $.35   (J292)
(Warrell; Niles) 4pt mix cor,acap oct
SCHIRM.G 8302 $.30   (J293)

JESUS, JESUS, REST YOUR HEAD see Boyn

JESUS, JESUS, REST YOUR HEAD see Davidson, M.T.

JESUS, JESUS, REST YOUR HEAD see Howorth, Wayne

JESUS, JESUS REST YOUR HEAD see Niles, John
Jacob

JESUS, JESUS, REST YOUR HEAD see Schroth

JESUS, JESUS, THOU ART MINE see Bach, Johann
Sebastian

JESUS, JESUS, WE ADORE THEE see Cherubini,
Luigi

JESUS JOY OF EVERY SOUL see Butler

JESUS, JOY OF LOVING HEARTS see Bach, Johann
Sebastian

JESUS, JOY OF MAN'S DESIRING see Bach, Johann
Sebastian

JESUS, JOY OF MY ENDEAVOR see Bach, Johann
Sebastian

JESUS KRISTUS AR VAR HALSA
(Berg, Gottfrid) mix cor NORDISKA 2304 s.p.
see also Sacrae Cantiones   (J294)

JESUS KRISTUS ER DEN SAMME see Hovland, Egil

JESUS KRISTUS ER OPFAREN see Grieg, Edvard
Hagerup

JESUS KRISTUS-HAN AR VORDEN *Easter
(Moren, John) mix cor NORDISKA 1710 s.p.
(J295)

JESUS KRISTUS SEJREN VANDT see Pederson, Mogens

JESUS KRISTUS VANDT OS FREDEN see Pederson,
Mogens

JESUS, LA ES-TU see Landowski

JESUS LAY YOUR HEAD IN THE WINDOW see Work

JESUS, LEAD THE WAY see Proulx, Richard

JESUS, LEAD THOU ON see Willan, Healey

JESUS, LEAD US see Darst, W. Glenn

JESUS LEARNED TO READ see Grime, William

JESUS LEBTE, MIT IHM AUCH ICH see Tzschoppe,
Eberhart

JESUS, LET OUR SOULS BE FED see Sateren, Leland
Bernhard

JESUS LIES SLEEPING see Matthews

JESUS, LIKE A SHEPHERD see Hallett, John C.

JESUS LIKES GOOD GIVERS see Grime, William

JESUS LITTLE ONE see Tunder, Franz

JESUS LIVED IN A LITTLE HOUSE see Grime,
William

JESUS LIVES see Bach, Johann Sebastian

JESUS, LORD AND MASTER see Ford, Virgil T.

JESUS, LORD OF ALL CREATION see Handel, George
Frideric

JESUS, LOVER OF MY SOUL see Arcadelt, Jacob

JESUS LOVER OF MY SOUL see Hawkins, Ed.

JESUS, LOVER OF MY SOUL see Hovhaness, Alan

JESUS, LOVER OF MY SOUL see Parry, Joseph

JESUS LOVER OF MY SOUL see Ringwald, [Roy]

JESUS, LOVER OF MY SOUL see Wilson

JESUS MAKES MY HEART REJOICE see Mueller, Carl
F.

JESUS, MASTER, WHOSE AM I see Bach, Johann
Sebastian

JESUS, MEIN ZUVERSICHT UND MEIN HEILAND see
Cruger, Johann

JESUS, MEINE ZUVERSICHT see Cruger, Johann

JESUS, MERCIFUL SAVIOUR see Ingegneri, Marco
Antonio

JESUS, MOST HOLY see Coggin

JESUS, MY GREAT PLEASURE see Bach, Johann
Sebastian, Jesu, Meine Freude

JESUS, MY LORD see Bodycombe, [Aneurin]

JESUS, MY LORD see Harding, Harvey

JESUS, MY LORD, MY ALL see Young

JESUS, MY LORD, MY GOD see Bach, Johann
Sebastian

JESUS, MY LORD, MY GOD see Barnby

JESUS, MY LORD, MY GOD, MY ALL
(Coggin) SAB oct BELWIN 64374 $.30   (J296)

JESUS, MY LORD, MY GOD, MY ALL see Bach, Johann
Sebastian

JESUS, MY LORD, MY GOD, MY ALL see Powell

JESUS, MY SAVIOUR, LOOK ON ME see Nevin, George
[Balch]

JESUS, MY SAVIOUR, LOOK ON ME see Pike, Harry
Hale

JESUS, MY SWEET LOVER see Edmunds, John

JESUS NAHM ZU SICH DIE ZWOLFE see Bach, Johann
Sebastian

JESUS, NAME ALL NAMES ABOVE see Schop

JESUS NAME OF WONDROUS LOVE see Angell

JESUS, NAME OF WONDROUS LOVE see Angell, Warren
M.

JESUS! NAME OF WONDROUS LOVE see Held, Wilbur

JESUS! NAME OF WONDROUS LOVE see Powell, Robert
J.

JESUS! NAME OF WONDROUS LOVE see Titcomb

JESUS, NOW TO THEE I TURN ME see Cherubini,
Luigi

JESUS, NOW WILL WE PRAISE THEE see Bach, Johann
Sebastian, Jesu, Nun Sie Gepreiset

JESUS, O PRECIOUS NAME see Lockwood, Normand

JESUS OBEDIENT see Andres, Christus Factus Est
Pro Nobis

JESUS, OF A MAID THOU WOULDST BE BORN see
Brown, Charles F.

JESUS OF NAZARETH, KING!
SSA CHAPPELL 2920007-354 $.40   (J297)

JESUS OF THE MANGER *Xmas,carol
unis/SATB (very easy) OXFORD 08.109 $.15
(J298)

JESUS, ONCE FOR OUR SALVATION see Anerio,
Felice, Christus Factus Est

JESUS, ONCE FOR OUR SALVATION see Bruckner,
Anton

JESUS, ONCE FOR SALVATION see Anerio, Giovanni
Francesco

JESUS ONLY see Rotoli

JESUS, OUR LORD AND SAVIOR *anthem/carol,Eng
(Christiansen, Paul) SATB (easy) oct AUGSBURG
1090 $.16   (J299)

JESUS, OUR LORD AND SAVIOR see Schutz, Heinrich

JESUS, OUR LORD, IS CRUCIFIED see Gregory,
William

JESUS OUR LORD IS CRUCIFIED see Simon, W.

JESUS, OUR LORD IS RISEN TODAY see Vulpius,
Melchior

JESUS, OUR LORD, IS RISEN TODAY! see Young

JESUS, OUR LORD, WE ADORE THEE see James, Will

JESUS, OUR LOVE, IS CRUCIFIED *Easter/Lent
(Ehret, Walter) SATB oct WALTON 2019 $.25
(J300)

JESUS OUR SAVIOR see Schubert, Franz (Peter)

JESUS, OUR SAVIOR FOR US WAS BORN see Schutz,
Heinrich

JESUS, OUR SAVIOR IS BORN see Young, G.

JESUS, OUR SAVIOUR see Bruckner, Anton

JESUS, OUR SAVIOUR see Ford

JESUS, OUR SAVIOUR, FOR US WAS BORN see Schutz,
Heinrich

JESUS, OUR STRENGTH, OUR HOPE see Peninger,
David

JESUS, PRICELESS TREASURE see Bach, Johann
Sebastian

JESUS, PRICELESS TREASURE see Cruger, Johann

JESUS, PROMISED SAVIOUR see Hallstrom, Henry

JESUS PUT FORTH HIS HAND see Hohmann

JESUS QUE MA JOIE DEMURE see Bach, Johann
Sebastian

JESUS, REDEEMER OF THE WORLD see Tallis,
Thomas, O Nata Lux De Lumine

JESUS, REFUGE OF THE WEARY *Easter/Lent,folk/
hymn,US
(Ehret, Walter) SATB oct WALTON 2049 $.25
(J301)
(Marks, H.) SATB,acap oct PRESSER 312-40018
$.30   (J302)
(Schroth) SATB SCHMITT 917 $.30   (J303)

JESUS, REFUGE OF THE WEARY see Bach, Johann
Sebastian

JESUS SAID TO THE BLIND MAN *Bibl
(McCullough) [Eng/Ger] SATB,acap oct LAWSON
51702 $.35   (J304)

JESUS SAID TO THE BLIND MAN see Vulpius,
Melchior, Jesus Sprach Zu Dem Blinden

JESUS SAID TO THE WIDOW, "DO NOT WEEP" see
Krapf, Gerhard

JESUS SAID UNTO THE PEOPLE see Stainer, John

JESUS SAVES see Kirkpatrick

JESUS SAVIOR, EVER MILD see Schalk, Carl

JESUS SAVIOUR see Traver

JESUS SAVIOUR see Voss

JESUS SCHLAEFT see Bach, Johann Sebastian,
Jesus Schlaft, Was Soll Ich Hoffen

JESUS SCHLAFT, WAS SOLL ICH HOFFEN see Bach,
Johann Sebastian

JESUS SHALL REIGN see Cartford, Gerhard M.

JESUS SHALL REIGN see Hatton

JESUS SHALL REIGN WHERE E'ER THE SUN see
Thiman, Eric Harding

JESUS SHALL REIGN WHERE'ER THE SUN see Schalk,
Carl

JESUS SHALL REIGN WHERE'ER THE SUN see Thiman,
Eric Harding

JESUS, SHEPHERD OF THE SHEEP see Schroth

JESUS SJU ORD PA KORSET see Nystedt, Knut

JESUS SLEEPS
see Two Mexican Carols

JESUS SLEEPS, WHAT HOPE REMAINETH? see Bach,
Johann Sebastian, Jesus Schlaft, Was Soll
Ich Hoffen?

JESUS SO LOWLY see Friedell, Harold W.

JESUS SO TENDER see Townsend, John

JESUS SOLL DIE LOSUNG SEIN see Bornefeld,
Helmut

JESUS, SON OF DAVID, HAVE MERCY ON ME see
Bender, Jan

JESUS, SON OF GOD see Sanford

JESUS, SON OF GOD see Schutz, Heinrich

JESUS SPEAKS FROM THE CROSS see Carmony

JESUS SPRACH ZU DEM BLINDEN see Vulpius, Melchior

JESUS SPRACH ZU SEINEN JUNGERN: MICH JAMMERT DES VOLKS see Selle, Thomas

JESUS STAND AMONG US see Angell, Warren M.

JESUS STILLT DEN SEESTURM see Brautigam, Helmut

JESUS, SUN OF LIFE, MY SPLENDOR see Handel, George Frideric

JESUS, TENDER SAVIOUR see Dykes, John Bacchus

JESUS, TENDER SHEPHERD
see Three General Choruses

JESUS, TENDER SHEPHERD see Dortch

JESUS, TENDER SHEPHERD see Strickland, Lily

JESUS, TENDER SHEPHERD, HEAR ME see France, W.

JESUS, THANKS TO THEE WE OFFER see Frauenholtz, Johann Christoph

JESUS, THE CHRIST, IS BORN *Xmas,folk,US
(Ehret, Walter) SSA,pno (easy) PRESSER $.35
(J305)
(Ehret, Walter) SATB,pno (easy) PRESSER $.35
(J306)
(Niles) 4pt mix cor,acap oct SCHIRM.G 8304
$.25 (J307)
(Niles; Talmadge) 4pt wom cor,acap oct
SCHIRM.G 9454 $.25 (J308)
(Warrell; Niles) mix cor,acap oct SCHIRM.G
8301 $.30 (J309)

JESUS THE CHRIST IS BORN see Niles, John Jacob

JESUS THE CHRIST IS BORN see Schroth, Gerhard

JESUS THE CHRIST IS BORN see Steubing

JESUS, THE LORD, THE MIGHTY GOD see Eccard, Johannes

JESUS, THE NEW-BORN BABY *Xmas,carol,It
(Ehret, Walter) SATB oct WALTON 2517 $.30
(J310)

JESUS, THE NEW BORN BABY see Thygerson

JESUS, THE VERY THOUGHT IS SWEET see Deering, Richard, Jesu, Dulcis Memoria

JESUS, THE VERY THOUGHT OF THEE
(Carmichael) SATB oct WORD CS-306 $.30
contains also: Sun Of My Soul (J311)

JESUS, THE VERY THOUGHT OF THEE see Darst, W. Glenn

JESUS, THE VERY THOUGHT OF THEE see Dykes

JESUS, THE VERY THOUGHT OF THEE see Dykes, John Bacchus

JESUS, THE VERY THOUGHT OF THEE see Edmundson, Garth

JESUS, THE VERY THOUGHT OF THEE see Flagler, [Robert S.]

JESUS, THE VERY THOUGHT OF THEE see Newton

JESUS, THE VERY THOUGHT OF THEE see Talmadge, Charles L.

JESUS, THE VERY THOUGHT OF THEE see Titcomb

JESUS, THE VERY THOUGHT OF THEE see Wood, Dale

JESUS THE VERY THOUGHT OF THEE see Young

JESUS, THE VERY THOUGHT OF THEE see Young, Gordon

JESUS THE WAY-MAKER
TTBB BIG3 $.25 (J312)

JESUS, THE WORLD'S REDEEMING LORD see Tallis, Thomas, Jesu Salvator Saeculi

JESUS, THESE EYES HAVE NEVER SEEN see Skeat, Wiliam J.

JESUS, THOU ART STANDING see Speaks, [Oley]

JESUS, THOU BLESSED NAME OF MERCY see Young

JESUS, THOU JOY OF LOVING HEARTS see Baker

JESUS, THOU JOY OF LOVING HEARTS see Darst, W. Glenn

JESUS, THOU JOY OF LOVING HEARTS see Jones, R.W.

JESUS, THOU JOY OF LOVING HEARTS see Neff, James

JESUS, THOU JOY OF LOVING HEARTS see Peninger, David

JESUS, THOU JOY OF LOVING HEARTS see Roberton, Hugh S.

JESUS THOU JOY OF LOVING HEARTS see Talmadge, Charles L.

JESUS, THOU JOY OF LOVING HEARTS see Work, John [Wesley]

JESUS, THOU MIGHTY KING OF HEAVEN see Young, G.

JESUS, THOU MY WEARIED SPIRIT see Bach, Johann Sebastian, Jesu, Der Du Meine Seele

JESUS, THOU TENDER CHILD DIVINE see Franck, Melchior

JESUS, THY BLESSINGS GIVE TO ME see Franck, Melchior

JESUS, THY BLOOD AND RIGHTEOUSNESS see Bach, Johann Sebastian

JESUS, THY BOUNDLESS LOVE TO ME see Vick

JESUS, THY CROSS REDEEM MY SOUL see Franck, Melchior

JESUS, TOI MON BONHEUR see Bach, Johann Sebastian

JESUS, TOI QUI SAUVAS LE MONDE see Debussy, Claude

JESUS, TOT see Leopold I, (Kaiser)

JESUS, TROSTAREN OCH LIVET see Bach, Johann Sebastian

JESUS UND DER KANAANAISCHE WEIB see Gunsenheimer, Gustav

JESUS UND DER ZWEI JUNGER see Gunsenheimer, Gustav

JESUS UND DIE SAMARITERIN AM BRUNNEN see Brunner, Adolf

JESUS UND DIE SUNDERIN see Hessenberg, Kurt

JESUS UND DIE TOCHTER DES JAIRUS see Gunsenheimer, Gustav

JESUS, UNSER TROST UND LEBEN see Bach, Johann Sebastian

JESUS, UNTO THEE BE PRAISE see Praetorius, Michael

JESUS, VOR GUD OG FRELSER see Stobaeus, Johann

JESUS WALKED see Perrin

JESUS WALKED ON THE WATER *spir
(Genuchi) SATB LUDWIG SS-028 $.35 (J313)

JESUS WALKED THIS LONESOME VALLEY
(Kirk) SATB oct PRO ART 2004 $.30 (J314)
(Kirk) SAB oct PRO ART 2218 $.30 (J315)
(Kirk) SSA oct PRO ART 2215 $.30 (J316)
(Wilson; Ehret) SAB,S solo oct BOOSEY 1936
$.30 (J317)

JESUS WALKED THIS LONESOME VALLEY see Hornibrook

JESUS WALKED THIS LONESOME VALLEY see Kjelson

JESUS WALKED THIS LONESOME VALLEY see Krones

JESUS WALKED THIS LONESOME VALLEY see Prentice, Fred

JESUS WAS BORN
SSA/SATB/SAB/SA/TB BIG3 $.30 (J318)

JESUS WAS BORN IN BETHLEHEM see Marshall, Jane M.

JESUS, WE LOOK TO THEE see Ford

JESUS WEEPING see Binkerd, [Gordon]

JESUS, WHERE'ER THY PEOPLE MEET see Ford, Virgil T.

JESUS, WHERE'ER THY PEOPLE MEET see Larson

JESUS, WHERE'RE THY PEOPLE MEET see Webber, Lloyd

JESUS, WHITE BOY see Avery

JESUS WHO DID EVER GUIDE ME see Bach, Johann Sebastian

JESUS, WHO FOR OUR SALVATION see Anerio, Felice, Christus Factus Est

JESUS, WHO HAST EVER LED ME see Bach, Johann Sebastian

JESUS WILL KEINE SCHONEN WORTE see Lehmann, Andreas

JESUS WITH THY CHURCH ABIDE
SATB CHAPPELL 0015701-358 $.40 (J319)

JESUS, WON'T YOU COME BYE-AND-BYE see Kennedy, John Brodbin

JESUS, WORD OF GOD INCARNATE see Des Prez, Josquin

JESUS, WORD OF GOD INCARNATE see Gounod, Charles Francois

JESUS, WORD OF GOD INCARNATE see Mozart, Wolfgang Amadeus, Ave Verum Corpus

JESUS WORD OF GOD INCARNATE see Williams, David H.

JESUS WORKED IN A CARPETER SHOP see Grime, William

JESUSNAVNET see Soraas, Lars

JETERANDS GRACE, O DIEU D'AMOUR see Gounod, Charles Francois

JETZT IST MEIN GANZES LEBEN AUS
(Steiner, Lois; Uray, Ernst L.) mix cor,acap
oct DOBLINGER s.p. see from Vier
Totenlieder Aus St. Lambrecht (J320)

JEWELL
Agnus Dei
SATB oct PLYMOUTH PCS-31 $.25 (J321)

Kyrie *Kyrie
SATB oct PLYMOUTH PCS-32 $.25 (J322)

Praise, O Praise Our God And King *Gen
SA SCHMITT 2575 $.20 (J323)

Shepherd's Carol, The
SATB FLAMMER A 5154 $.25 (J324)
SSA FLAMMER B 5018 $.25 (J325)

JEWELL (cont'd.)
SAB FLAMMER D5046 $.25 (J326)

Song Of Praise, A
SAB FLAMMER D5206 $.30 (J327)

To Jesus From The Ends Of The Earth
girl cor SOUTHERN $.22 (J328)

JEWELL, KENNETH W.
Joyful Tidings *Xmas
SATB,opt pno/org oct WORLD AC-752-8 $.45
(J329)
Manger Carol, A *Xmas,carol,Aus
SATB,acap oct WORLD AC-755-8 $.30 (J330)

Storke, The *Xmas,carol
SATB,opt pno/org oct WORLD AC-759-8 $.45
(J331)

JEWISH LEGEND, THE see Bugatch, Samuel

JEWITT
Teach Me To Pray
SATB WARNER W2625 $.30 (J332)
2pt WARNER W1810 $.30 (J333)
SAB WARNER W3286 $.30 (J334)

JEZUS ES A KUFAROK see Kodaly, Zoltan

JEZUS, GA ONS VOOR
mix cor sc ALSBACH&D s.p. (J335)

JEZUS IS ONS LICHT EN LEVEN see Bach, Johann Sebastian

JEZUS, 'K BEN D'UWE see Kulke, M.

JEZUS' LIJDEN see Westnitzer, W.

JHESU CHRIST SAINT MARY'S SONE see Oldroyd, George

JILLETT, DAVID
Corpus Christi (from Corpus Christi) cant/mot
[Eng/Lat] SATB,soli,org ALBERT s.p. (J336)
ALBERT s.p. (J337)

E Hehu Kerito
"Strong Is Your Love" see Jillett, David, Mo Maria

English Unison Mass *Mass
unis ALBERT s.p. (J338)

Mo Maria
"Mo Maria You Are Near" [Eng] cor,gtr
ALBERT s.p. contains also: E Hehu Kerito,
"Strong Is Your Love" (J339)

Mo Maria You Are Near *see Mo Maria

Our Father *hymn
unis,org/gtr ALBERT s.p. (J340)

Resurrection *Easter,mot
SATB,org ALBERT s.p. (J341)

Strong Is Your Love *see E Hehu Kerito

JIMMY OWENS SINGERS TURN ON THE WORLD OF YOUTH
*CCUL
(Owens, Jimmy) SATB voc sc WORD 20022 $1.95
(J342)

JINGLE BELLS
see Tanti Auguri

JO TINC UN BURRO see Rodrigo

JOACHIM, OTTO (1910-   )
Psalm
[Ger] SATB,acap oct BERANDOL 915J7AH $.50
(J343)

JOANNA SPONSA CHRISTI see Busser, [Henri-Paul]

JOB see Bitgood, Roberta

JOB see Parry, Charles Hubert Hastings

JOB see Rabaud, H.

JOB ELEGIES, THE see Herder, Ronald

JOCHSBERGER, T.
Bekol Zimra *CCU,liturg,Jew
SATB oct PRESSER $2.50 (J344)

Yom Ze Mekhubad *liturg,Heb
SATB,acap oct PRESSER MC545 $.30 (J345)

JOCHUM, OTTO (1898-1969)
Cantica Sacra *Op.167, ora
mix cor,SATBar soli,org/org&orch/org&
strings/orch oct LEUCKART rental (J346)

Deutsche Singmesse *Mass
[Ger] SSA,S solo,org (med) MULLER SM 2096
sc s.p., cor pts s.p. (J347)

Die Hirten *Op.9,No.1, Xmas
[Ger] SSA,Bar solo,org,fl,ob,clar,2vln,vla,
vcl,bvl,harp (med diff) MULLER SM 510 sc
s.p., cor pts s.p. (J348)

Ecce Sacerdos *Fest
[Lat] SATB,acap (med) MULLER MS 46 s.p. (J349)

Marien-Messe *Op.1, Mass
[Ger] SATB,SATB soli,opt org,2vln,vla,vcl,
bvl (med diff) MULLER SM 482B sc rental,
voc sc s.p., cor pts s.p., ipa (J350)

Wem Gott Will Rechte Gunst Erweisen *Op.133,
No.3
jr cor&men cor (easy) oct LEUCKART 18 s.p.
(J351)

Zwolf Weihnachtliche Kanons *Op.86, CC12U,
Xmas,canon
[Ger] 3pt,acap (easy) MULLER SM 2098 sc
s.p., cor pts s.p. (J352)

JOHANN SEBASTIAN BACH. EPITAPH see Brautigam, Volker

JOHANNES 20:26, 27 EN 28 see Keja, J.F.

JOHANNES DER TAUFER see Buchtger, Fritz

JOHANNES DER TAUFER (ECCE MITTO ANGELUM MEUM)
see Pepping, Ernst

JOHANNES-ORATORIUM "JESUS UND SEINE JUNGER" see
Herrmann, Hugo

JOHANNES-PASSION see Baudach, Ulrich

JOHANNES-PASSION see Baudach, Ulrich

JOHANNES-PASSION see Degen, Helmut

JOHANNES-PASSION see Lechner, Leonhard

JOHANNES-PASSION see Resinarius, Balthasar

JOHANNES-PASSION see Richter, Gotthold Ludwig

JOHANNES-PASSION see Rother, Corbinian

JOHANNES-PASSION see Schutz, Heinrich

JOHANNES-PASSION MIT INTERMEDIEN see Selle,
Thomas

JOHANNES SAG SA KLAR EN SYN see Thyrestam,
Gunnar

JOHANNESKONZERT see Kluge, Manfred

JOHANNESPASSION see Bach, Johann Sebastian

JOHANNESPASSION see Handel, George Frideric

JOHANNESPASSION see Hollfelder, Waldram

JOHANNESPASSION see Scandello

JOHANNESPASSION see Scarlatti, Alessandro

JOHANNESPASSION see Schutz, Heinrich

JOHANNESPASSION 1534 see Anonymous

JOHANNESPASSIONEN see Bach, Johann Sebastian,
La Passione Di N.S. Gesu Cristo Secondo
Giovanni

JOHANNISNACHT HYMNE see Henrichsen, Roger

JOHANSEN
Ancient Hills
(Bartholomew) TTBB oct GALAXY 1.1328.1 $.30
(J353)

JOHANSEN, DAVID MONRAD (1888-   )
Pa Gravbakken Vart Dette Songi
mix cor MUSIKK s.p.   (J354)

JOHANSON, SVEN-ERIC
Jordens Ljus *Xmas
mix cor,Mez solo,acap/strings NORDISKA
NMS-6298 s.p.   (J355)

JOHANSSON, BENGT (1914-   )
Canticum Zachariae *Bibl
[Lat] 4pt mix cor,acap oct FAZER s.p.   (J356)

Cum Essem Parvulus *Bibl
[Lat] 3pt wom cor oct FAZER s.p.   (J357)

Graduale For Trefaldighetssondagen *Gradual
SSATTB&SB,Bar solo oct FAZER s.p.   (J358)

I Sat Down Under His Shadow
see Two Extracts From The Songs Of Solomon

Lauda
unis,Bar solo,org oct FAZER s.p.   (J359)

Mina Kunnioitan Sinua Jumilani *Gradual
SB&SSATTB,Bar solo oct FAZER s.p.   (J360)

Miserere Mei (Psalm 51)
[Lat] mix cor,soli,acap oct FAZER s.p.
(J361)

Missa A Quattro Voci *Mass
[Lat] SATB,acap oct FAZER s.p.   (J362)

Pater Noster
[Lat] SSA oct FAZER s.p.   (J363)

Psalm 51 *see Miserere Mei

Set Me As A Seal
see Two Extracts From The Songs Of Solomon

Two Extracts From The Songs Of Solomon *Bibl
SSATTB oct FAZER s.p.
contains: I Sat Down Under His Shadow;
Set Me As A Seal   (J364)

JOHN see Dickinson, Peter

JOHN IV, KING OF PORTUGAL
see JEAN IV, ROI DE PORTUGAL

JOHN SAW DUH NUMBUH *spir
(Shaw; Parker) mix cor,acap oct LAWSON 51109
$.35   (J365)

JOHN THE BAPTIST see Gustafson, D.

JOHN WESLEY COVENANT SERVICE, THE see Canning,
Thomas

JOHNER, THEODORE E.
Das Kleine Psalmenbuch *CC19U,Psalm
[Ger] TTBB HANSSLER 2.006 $2.00   (J366)

Einstimmige Deutsche Ordinariums-Messe *CCU
unis HANSSLER 27.004 s.p.   (J367)

JOHNS
Hail The Day That Sees Him Rise
see SIX EASTER CAROLS

Magnificat *Magnif
mix cor,S solo,org (med diff) oct WESTERN
WIM39 $1.75   (J368)

JOHNS, DONALD
Alleluia *anthem
SAB (easy) oct AUGSBURG 1390 $.30   (J369)

O Praise The Lord, All Ye Nations *anthem
SSAA (med) oct AUGSBURG 0618 $.20   (J370)

JOHN'S GONE TO HILO see Billings, William

JOHNSON
All Praise To Thee, Eternal God *Adv/Gen
4pt jr cor/SATB (easy) FISCHER,C CM 7568
$.20   (J371)
SATB oct FISCHER,C CM-7568 $.30   (J372)

Angels' Song, The
SATB oct SUMMY M 2829 $.35   (J373)

Ballad Of The Shepherds *Xmas
SATB SCHMITT 1768 $.30   (J374)

Break Forth Into Singing
SATB KJOS PC799 $.30   (J375)

Carol Of The Sheepfold *carol
SATB KJOS 5042 $.30   (J376)

Cross Was Not The End, The *Easter
SATB oct LORENZ B136 $.30   (J377)

Face To Face
(Deis) SATB,org/pno BOSTON 11723 $.35
(J378)
(Norman) SAB BOSTON 2145 $.35   (J379)

Great Christmas Choruses *CCU,Xmas
(Rodby) SATB oct AGAPE $1.75   (J380)

He Arose
SATB FLAMMER A 5256 $.30   (J381)

Hymn Of The Nativity, A
(Frank) SATB,pno,opt inst oct FOX PS166
$.30   (J382)

If Ye Would Hear The Angels Sing *Xmas
SATB oct KERBY 6904C $.45   (J383)

Lead On, O King Eternal
SATB oct LORENZ B156 $.30   (J384)
SATB,opt trp (med easy) SOUTHERN $.30   (J385)

Lift Up Your Heads *Xmas
4pt jr cor/SATB (very easy) FISCHER,C
CM 7493 $.25   (J386)

Lord Shall Give You A Sign, The
SATB KJOS PC787 $.30   (J387)

Lord's Prayer, The *Bibl/prayer
SATB HANSEN-US C249B $.40   (J388)

Mass In Honor Of Our Lady, The Queen Of The
Angels *BVM,Mass
unis/cong&SA/SAB sc SUMMY M 2696 $1.00
(J389)
SA/SAB voc sc SUMMY M 2696A $.45   (J390)

Our Daily Bread
SATB FLAMMER A 5535 $.25   (J391)

Palm Sunday Anthem *Palm,anthem
SATB KJOS PC798 $.30   (J392)

Pipers' Carol *Xmas,carol
SAB oct VOLKWEIN VB712 $.30   (J393)

This Is My Father's World
SATB oct LORENZ C308 $.30   (J394)

Thy Blessings, Father
SATB oct GALAXY 1.1026.1 $.30   (J395)

To Light That Shines
(Kay) SAB,org oct MCA   (J396)

To The Blessed Trinity *Gen
SATB SCHMITT 5908 $.35   (J397)

Water For A Thirsty Land
SATB oct HERITAGE H36 $.40   (J398)

Who Built De Ark? *anthem/spir
TTBB,acap oct FISCHER,C CM-7444 $.35 (J399)

JOHNSON, ALFRED H.
Gaelic Easter Carol, A *Easter,carol,Ir
SATB oct FISCHER,J 9975 $.30   (J400)

Midwinter Carol
SATB,acap oct COLOMBO 1030 $.25   (J401)

Not Jerusalem
SATB oct FISCHER,J 10037 $.25   (J402)

They Led My Lord Away
SATB oct FISCHER,J 10031 $.25   (J403)

JOHNSON, CARL
Absalom, Absalom! *mot
[Ger] 8pt mix cor,T solo voc sc BOTE s.p.
(J404)

JOHNSON, DAVID N.
All-Knowing God
SATB oct GRAY GCMR 3062 $.35   (J405)

Earth And All Stars *anthem
unis (easy) oct AUGSBURG 1600 $.25 (J406)
unis sr cor&unis jr cor (easy) oct AUGSBURG
1600 $.25   (J407)
unis treb cor (easy) oct AUGSBURG 1600 $.25
(J408)

Earth And Stars
oct AUGSBURG 11-9158 $.05   (J409)

Easy Anthems For Mix Voices, Book II
*Easter/Gen/Lent/Palm/Trin,anthem
unis/4pt,pno/org,opt inst (easy) oct
AUGSBURG 11-9163 $1.75   (J410)

Easy Anthems For Mixed Voices, Book I *Adv/
ASD/Xmas/Epiph/Gen/Thanks,anthem
unis/4pt,pno/org,opt inst (easy) oct
AUGSBURG 11-9156 $1.75   (J411)

Eyes Of The Lord Are Upon The Righteous, The
SATB oct ELKAN-V 362-1160 $.30   (J412)

Folk Songs Historic And Contemporary *CCU,
folk
SATB oct AGAPE CF 131 $.75   (J413)

Gloria Deo, Book I *CC17L,Adv/Xmas/Epiph/
Gen/Refm/Thanks
SAB,pno,org,opt inst oct AUGSBURG 11-9160
$1.50   (J414)

JOHNSON, DAVID N. (cont'd.)
Gloria Deo, Book II *CC17L,Easter/Gen/Lent/
Palm/Pent
SAB,pno/org,opt inst oct AUGSBURG 11-9161
$1.65   (J415)

God Of All Nations
SATB oct GRAY GCMR 3014 $.30   (J416)

Lord Christ, When First Thou Cam'st To Men
*anthem
SAB (easy) oct AUGSBURG 1617 $.25   (J417)

Lord Jesus , We Give Thanks To Thee *Lent
SATB oct GRAY GCMR 3084 $.30   (J418)

Mighty Fortress Is Our God, A
SATB&cong,org,opt trp sc AUGSBURG 11-1441
$.35   (J419)

New Christmas Carol, A *Xmas,carol
SATB,inst oct AGAPE CF 145 $.35   (J420)

Ride On, Ride On In Majesty *anthem
SAB,opt trp (easy) oct AUGSBURG 1640 $.35
(J421)

Service Of Nine Lessons And Carols, A *Xmas
mix cor&cong&opt jr cor,org,fl (easy) voc
sc AUGSBURG 11-9380 $1.50, ipa   (J422)

Sweet Was The Song The Virgin Sang
SAB oct ELKAN-V 362-1256 $.30   (J423)

Thy Kingdom Come *anthem
SAB,org,opt trp (easy) cor pts AUGSBURG
1629 $.25, ipa   (J424)

JOHNSON, DAVIS
Lo, He Comes
SATB oct AGAPE A 433 $.30   (J425)

JOHNSON, ELWOOD
Little Baby Jesus
SATB&jr cor/unis jr cor oct AGAPE F 905
$.25   (J426)

My Country 'Tis Of Thee
SATB oct AGAPE SP 688 $.30   (J427)

JOHNSON, G.
If Ye Would Hear The Angels Sing
SATB,kbd oct KERBY 6904 $.45   (J428)

JOHNSON, HALL (1887-1970)
Honor! Honor!
3pt jr cor/SSA (med) FISCHER,C CM 5212 $.25
(J429)

Po' Mo'ner Got A Home At Las'
6pt mix cor,acap oct SCHIRM.G 11358 $.30
(J430)

JOHNSON, MARLOWE
On This Day Earth Shall Ring *Xmas/Epiph
SATB,opt hndbl (med easy) oct CONCORDIA
98-2104 $.30   (J431)

JOHNSON, N.F. BYNG
O Worship The King *anthem/hymn
mix cor oct NOVELLO 28.1194.04 s.p. (J432)

JOHNSON, NOEL
Come, Silent Night
2pt ASHDOWN E.A.131 s.p.   (J433)

JOHNSON, PAUL
Last Trumpet, The
SATB oct WORD CS-2431 $.30   (J434)

That The World May Know
SATB oct WORD CS-2434 $.30   (J435)

Trophy Of His Love, A
SATB (med) PRESSER G-124 $.40   (J436)

When I Trust The Savior
SATB (med) PRESSER G-128 $.35   (J437)

JOHNSON, R. (ca. 1490-1595)
Dum Transisset Sabbatum *mot
(Collins, H.B.) [Lat] SATB CHESTER s.p.
(J438)

JOHNSON, ROBERT
Dum Transisset Sabbatum *Easter
SATB,acap SCHIRM.EC $.25   (J439)

JOHNSON, ROBERT SHERLAW
At The Sepulchre *Easter,anthem
mix cor,acap oct NOVELLO 40.1501.00 s.p.
(J440)

Congregational Mass *Mass
cong,org FABER F0296 voc sc $1.50, cor pts
$.30   (J441)

Sedit Angelus *Easter,anthem
[Lat] mix cor,acap oct NOVELLO 40.1501.00
s.p.   (J442)

Veni Sancte Spiritus *hymn
(Leppard, Raymond) [Lat] SATB,opt perc oct
FABER FO 287 $.75   (J443)

JOHNSON, ROY E.
American Dialogue
SATB oct AGAPE BR 2003 $.30   (J444)

JOHNSON, S.
Tho' Your Sins Be As Scarlet
SSA KJOS PC655 $.30   (J445)

JOHNSON, SIDNEY
Children Of The Faithful
SSA KJOS 6128 $.30   (J446)

Come Near To Me, Jesus
SSA KJOS 6129 $.30   (J447)

Gloria
SATB KJOS PC778 $.30   (J448)

Like A Shepherd
SATB KJOS PC788 $.30   (J449)

Lord, I'm Lost
men cor KJOS PC7027 $.40   (J450)

Pray For Love
SSA KJOS 6130 $.30   (J451)

JOHNSON, SIDNEY (cont'd.)

Proverbs Of Love *Bibl
SATB KJOS $2.50   (J452)

Virgin Shall Conceive, A *Xmas
SATB KJOS PC786 $.30   (J453)

Wonderful! A Child Is Born *Xmas
SATB KJOS PC803 $.30   (J454)

Wondrous Day
SSA KJOS 6131 $.30   (J455)

JOHNSTON
All Hail The Power Of Jesus' Name
SATB oct LORENZ C197 $.30   (J456)

Be Glad And Sing For Joy
SATB SHAWNEE A 1040 $.30   (J457)

Built On A Rock
SATB oct LORENZ C295 $.30   (J458)

Christmas Gloria, A *Xmas
SATB oct LORENZ A456 $.30   (J459)

Cup, The Cross, And The Crown, The *Easter,
cant
SATB LORENZ $1.95   (J460)

For All The Saints
SATB SHAWNEE A 686 $.30   (J461)

God Be In My Heart
SATB oct LORENZ 9892 $.25   (J462)

He Was Despised
SATB oct LORENZ B80 $.25   (J463)

Heavenly Father, King Eternal
(Smith) SATB oct LILLENAS AN-2357 $.30
                                                        (J464)

Hosanna, Blessed Is He
SATB oct LORENZ A397 $.25   (J465)

In Bethlehem *Xmas
SATB oct LORENZ B164 $.30   (J466)

Jesus, Come Abide With Me *Easter
SATB oct LORENZ C302 $.30   (J467)

King In The Stable *Xmas,cant
SATB oct LORENZ $1.95   (J468)

Lead, Kindly Light *Rembrnc
SATB ALLANS 62 s.p.   (J469)

Lord, Rally The Righteous
SATB oct LILLENAS AN-1633 $.30   (J470)

Manger King, The *Xmas,cant
SATB oct LORENZ $1.95   (J471)
SA/SAB oct LORENZ $1.75   (J472)

O Master, Let Me Walk With Thee
SATB oct LORENZ B31 $.30   (J473)

On The Other Side Of Time
SATB oct LORENZ B185 $.30   (J474)

One God
SATB oct LORENZ B194 $.30   (J475)

Praise The Lord
SATB,acap BOSTON 13778 $.35   (J476)

Song Of Praise
SATB FLAMMER A 5572 $.30   (J477)

Welcome, Good Sir Christemas *Xmas
SATB SCHMITT 8026 $.30   (J478)

JOHNSTON, E. DWIGHT
I Will Lift Up Mine Eyes
SATB oct HUNTZINGER 4038 $.20   (J479)

JOHNSTON, JACK
Drop, Drop, Slow Tears
see Three Devotional Songs

Litanie, The
see Three Devotional Songs

That Virgin's Child
see Three Devotional Songs

Three Devotional Songs
SATB,acap oct LAWSON 51416 $.30
contains: Drop, Drop, Slow Tears;
Litanie, The; That Virgin's Child   (J480)

JOHNSTONE, A.
There Was A Little Baby
unis (easy) OXFORD 45.036 $.25   (J481)

JOIN ALL AND SING see Faure, Jean-Baptist, Les
Rameaux

JOIN, EVERY TONGUE see Sheppard

JOIN THE REVOLUTION see Avery

JOIN TO REJOICE see Pfautsch, Lloyd

JOJJ, BEKE MNAJAS ANGYALA see Haydn, (Franz)
Joseph

JOJJ, BEKE MNYAJAS ANGYALA see Haydn, (Franz)
Joseph

JOLANTHE see Borris, Siegfried

JOLE-SALME see Egge, Klaus

JOLIVET, ANDRE (1905-   )
Messe, Dite "Pour Le Jour De La Paix" *Mass
[Lat] unis,org,tamb HEUGEL s.p.   (J482)

Uxor Tua *Mass
[Lat/Fr] cor,org/inst BOOSEY voc sc $4.00,
sc rental, ipr   (J483)

JOLLEY
Father Teach Us How To Pray
unis WARNER R3423 $.30   (J484)

JOLLEY (cont'd.)

Gloria In Excelsis
(Hoggard) SATB SHAWNEE A 326 $.35   (J485)

Gracious Spirit, Dwell With Me
SATB SHAWNEE A 340 $.30   (J486)

Holy Lord God Of Hosts
SATB SHAWNEE A 370 $.30   (J487)

Lord's My Shepherd, The
SSA SHAWNEE B 142 $.25   (J488)

Praise The Lord
(Hoggard) SATB,acap SHAWNEE A 331 $.25   (J489)

Swing Low, Sweet Star *Xmas
SATB,S solo WARNER W7-1003 $.30   (J490)

JOLLEY, FLORENCE [W.] (1917-   )
Alleluia, Christ Is Risen *Easter
SATB,pno/org,opt brass oct LAWSON 51002
$.30   (J491)

He Who Would Valiant Be
SATB oct LAWSON 804 $.25   (J492)

If Ye Love Me, Keep My Commandments
SATB oct WALTON 2068 $.25   (J493)

O Lord, Seek Us
SATB,pno/org oct LAWSON 51124 $.25   (J494)

O Splendor Of God's Glory Bright
SATB oct AGAPE A 424 $.30   (J495)

Strife Is O'er, The *Easter,Introit
SATB oct AGAPE A 396 $.25   (J496)

Unto The Hills
SATB oct AGAPE A 325 $.30   (J497)

JOLLY WAT AND CAROL see Shepherd, [Arthur]

JOLY, CAMILLE
O Sacrum Convivium
"Praise The Lord For He Is God" [Lat/Eng]
SATB,org SCHIRM.EC 2286 $.16   (J498)

Praise The Lord For He Is God *see O Sacrum
Convivium

JOM KIPOER (DAG VAN VERZOENING) see Olman, Isr,
J.

JOMMELLI, NICCOLO (1714-1774)
Hosanna, David's Son! *Easter/Lent/Palm
SATB,acap oct FISCHER,C CM-559 $.25   (J499)

La Passione Di Nostro Signore Gesu Cristo
*ora
(Vecchi, Prof. Giuseppe) cor quarto FORNI
256 s.p.   (J500)

Lux Aeterna (from Requiem)
SATB,acap RICORDI-ENG SY135 s.p.   (J501)

Praise The Lord, All Ye Nations
(James, P.) SATB oct PRESSER 332-13343 $.30
                                                        (J502)

JONAH see Berkeley, Lennox

JONAH see Gardner, Maurice

JONAH see Pinkham, Daniel

JONAH-MAN JAZZ see Hurd, Michael

JONES
Australian Christmas Carol, An *Xmas,carol,
Austral
SA ALLANS 397 s.p.   (J503)
SATB ALLANS 398 s.p.   (J504)

Blessed Are The Pure In Heart *Bibl
SATB WARNER G743 $.30   (J505)

Blessed Is The Man (Psalm 1)
SATB,acap oct PRO ART 1232 $.25   (J506)

Deeper, Deeper
(McLellan) SATB oct LILLENAS AT-1032 $.30
                                                        (J507)

Hosanna *Easter/Lent/Palm
SATB oct FISCHER,C CM-401 $.25   (J508)

Hymn Of Peace, A
SSA oct HERITAGE H6002 $.40   (J509)

Hymns And Anthems (Set No. 1) *CCU,anthem/
hymn
jr cor FISCHER,C CM 475 $.25   (J510)

Hymns And Anthems (Set No. 2) *CCU,anthem/
hymn
jr cor FISCHER,C CM 496 $.30   (J511)

I Would Not Be Denied
(McLellan) SATB oct LILLENAS AN-1601 $.25
                                                        (J512)

In Times Like These
SATB oct LORENZ A505 $.30   (J513)

Jesu Lullaby *Xmas
SSA oct GALAXY 1.1388.1 $.25   (J514)

Lament My Soul
mix cor SOUTHERN $.30   (J515)

Lean On His Arms
see TEMPO CHORAL PACKAGE NO. 1

Little Lamb Who Made Thee?
2pt jr cor FISCHER,C CM 460 $.15   (J516)

Nativity Song, A
SATB SHAWNEE A 1083 $.35   (J517)

Now May The Lord Of Peace
SATB oct PRO ART 2079 $.25   (J518)

Pro Nobis Puer Natus Est *Xmas
SATB oct SACRED S-32 $.35   (J519)

Psalm 1 *see Blessed Is The Man

JONES (cont'd.)

Rise Up, O Men Of God
men cor KJOS 5525 $.30   (J520)

Shepherd Boy, The
SA FLAMMER E5032 $.95   (J521)

Word Of Life, Most Pure And Strong
(Coggin) SAB oct BELWIN 2075 $.25   (J522)

JONES, A.
Hail Gladdening Light
SSA oct PRESSER MC447 $.30   (J523)

I'm Troubled In Mind
SATB oct PRESSER MC421 $.30   (J524)

JONES, BRADWIN
O Be Joyful In The Lord
unis oct NOVELLO 28.1321.01 s.p.   (J525)

JONES, DANIEL (1912-   )
O Lord, Have Thou Respect *anthem
mix cor oct NOVELLO 28.1390.04 s.p.   (J526)

St. Peter *Bibl/ora
SATB,STB soli,2fl,2ob,2clar,2bsn,2horn,
2trp,strings voc sc NOVELLO s.p., ipr
                                                        (J527)

JONES, [DAVID HUGH] (1900-   )
Psalm 150 *Bibl
mix cor oct SCHIRM.G 7594 $.30   (J528)

JONES, EDWARD (1752-1824)
Shepherd Of Souls (Sign Of The Cross)
SATB,org CRAMER A 19 s.p.   (J529)

JONES, ELSA LOAKER
Muttersprache
[Ger] SATB,acap ELKAN,H $.15   (J530)

JONES, G.
Out Of The Deep *Easter
SATB,acap oct PRESSER 332-15151 $.30   (J531)

JONES, GEORGE HERBERT
Lamb, The
3pt ASHDOWN V.T.14 s.p.   (J532)

JONES, HILTON KEAN
Three Hymn Tune Anthems *CC3U,anthem/hymn
SAB oct AGAPE CY 3335 $.40   (J533)

JONES, MARJORIE
Child's Prayer, A
SA oct WORD CS-2408 $.25   (J534)

Common Things
SA oct WORD CS-2410 $.25   (J535)

Hosanna, We Sing *Easter/Lent,cant
SA/SAB/SATB voc sc WORD 20049 $1.50   (J536)

If God
SSA WORD CS-344 $.30   (J537)

Sense Of Him, A
SATB oct WORD CS-343 $.30   (J538)

Shine
SA oct WORD CS-696 $.25   (J539)

What Can I Give Him *Xmas
SA oct PRESSER G-138 $.30   (J540)

JONES, R.
Lament My Soul
(Greenberg) SSA/TTB,acap AMP N4 $.30   (J541)

JONES, R.W.
Jesus, Thou Joy Of Loving Hearts
SATB,org oct LAWSON 51467 $.35   (J542)

Psalm 117 *see Psalm Of Praise, A

Psalm Of Praise, A (Psalm 117) Bibl
SATB,org oct LAWSON 51354 $.30   (J543)

To Men Of Good Will *Fest,anthem
SATB,opt orch oct BOURNE 882 $.60, ipr
                                                        (J544)

JONGEN, [JOSEPH-MARIE-ALPHONSE-NICHOLAS]
(1873-1953)
Chant Pastorale
[Fr] SSAA,pno cor pts SALABERT-US $.65
                                                        (J545)

JONSON, WILLIAM
Happy Journey, The
SATB oct SHAPIRO SK 2052 $.25   (J546)

Hark From The Tomb *spir
SATB oct SHAPIRO SK 2047 $.25   (J547)

I Want Jesus To Walk With Me
SATB oct SHAPIRO SK 2048 $.25   (J548)

You Can Tell The World
SATB oct SHAPIRO SK 2049 $.25   (J549)

JONSSON, JOSEF [PETRUS] (1887-1969)
Advent-Psalm *Adv,Psalm
mix cor NORDISKA 1474 s.p.   (J550)
mix cor,org/pno,vln,vcl cor pts NORDISKA
1484 s.p., sc NORDISKA 1487 s.p.   (J551)

Bisp Thomas Frihetssang
unis,pno/org cor pts NORDISKA 1015 s.p.,
voc sc NORDISKA 1014 s.p.   (J552)
unis,orch,pno/org voc sc NORDISKA 1080
s.p., ipa   (J553)

Jubilate
mix cor NORDISKA 1141 s.p.   (J554)

Missa Solemnis *Op.37
voc sc MUSIKAL. s.p.   (J555)

JOOSEN, B.
Amen *spir
men cor,pno BROEKMANS 943 s.p.   (J556)

Roll, Jordan, Roll *spir
men cor BROEKMANS 860 s.p.   (J557)

Set Down *spir
men cor BROEKMANS 929 s.p.   (J558)

JOOSEN, B. (cont'd.)

   Soon Ah Will Be Done *spir
   men cor BROEKMANS 928 s.p.   (J559)

JORD OCH HIMMEL FROJDEN ER *Xmas,hymn
   (Wikander, David) mix cor NORDISKA 962 s.p.   (J560)

JORD OG HIMMEL LOVER see Lassus, Roland de
   (Orlandus), Jubilate Deo

JORDAHL
   Sweet Hymns And Songs
   SATB oct PLYMOUTH SC-33 $.30   (J561)

JORDAN
   God Is Here On Every Hand
   unis oct BELWIN 64385 $.30   (J562)

   I'm Sure He Knows
   (Ehret) SATB oct MCA   (J563)
   (Ehret) SSA/SSAA oct MCA   (J564)
   (Ehret) SAB oct MCA   (J565)

   Only A Manger *Xmas
   SATB oct BELWIN 64316 $.30   (J566)

   Prayer In Winter
   unis oct BELWIN 64231 $.30   (J567)

   Rejoice, The Lord Is King
   SA/SATB oct SACRED S-114 $.35   (J568)

JORDAN, A.
   Prayer Is The Soul's Sincere Desire
   SATB,org oct KERBY 6104 $.35   (J569)
   SATB oct KERBY 6104C $.35   (J570)

JORDAN, ALICE
   All Things Are Thine
   SATB,acap SEESAW $1.00   (J571)

   Beatitudes The *Bibl
   SATB (med) ABINGDON APM-464 $.25   (J572)

   God Who Touchest Earth With Beauty
   SATB oct BELWIN 64258 $.30   (J573)

   Ring, Christmas Bells *Xmas,anthem
   unis,opt bells oct SACRED S-8872 $.30
                                              (J574)

   Suffer The Little Children *Bibl
   unis oct AGAPE A 459 $.30   (J575)

   Time For Singing Has Come, The
   unis (med) ABINGDON APM-799 $.20   (J576)

JORDAN ROAD, THE see Swift, R.A.

JORDAN, W.C.
   In Thee O Lord Do I Put My Trust
   SATB,S/T solo,pno (med) oct WILLIS 6321
   $.12   (J577)

JORDENS LJUS see Johanson, Sven-Eric

JOSEF, LIEBER JOSEF MEIN *Xmas
   (Bauernfeind, Hans) mix cor,acap oct
   DOBLINGER s.p. see also Zwei
   Weihnachtslieder   (J578)

JOSEF, LIEBER JOSEF MEIN see Schroter, Leonhard

JOSEPH see Handel, George Frideric

JOSEPH AND HIS BROTHERS see Starer

JOSEPH AND MARIA *Xmas,folk,So Am
   (Anderson) [Span/Eng] 4pt mix cor,acap,opt
   gtr&perc oct SCHIRM.G 10541 $.30   (J579)

JOSEPH AND MARY see Ehret, Walter

JOSEPH AND THE AMAZING TECHNICOLOR DREAMCOAT
   see Webber, Andrew

JOSEPH AND THE ANGEL see Terry, Richard
   Runciman

JOSEPH AND THE ANGEL see Thomson, Virgil

JOSEPH CAME SEEKING A RESTING PLACE see
   Willoughby

JOSEPH DEAR, OH JOSEPH MILD see Calvisius,
   Sethus

JOSEPH DEAREST
   see Six Traditional Carols, Set II

JOSEPH DEAREST see Jenkins, [Joseph Willcox]

JOSEPH, DEAREST JOSEPH see Lockwood, Normand

JOSEPH DEAREST, JOSEPH MILD *Xmas
   (Saar) SSAA oct FISCHER,C CM-371 $.25   (J580)

JOSEPH, DEAREST JOSEPH MILD see Walther, Johann
   Gottfried, Joseph, Lieber Joseph Mein

JOSEPH DEAREST, JOSEPH MINE *Xmas,carol,Belg/
   Ger
   (Barthelson) SATB,opt vln/fl&vcl oct SHAPIRO
   SK 2036 $.25, ipa   (J581)
   (Barthelson) SAB,vln/fl&vcl oct SHAPIRO
   SK 5017 $.25, ipa   (J582)
   (Barthelson) SSA,opt vln/fl&vcl oct SHAPIRO
   SK 3013 $.25, ipa   (J583)
   (Barthelson) 2pt,opt vln/fl&vcl oct SHAPIRO
   SK 4024 $.25, ipa   (J584)
   (Bodenschatz, E.) SATB,acap (med easy) oct
   CONCORDIA 98-1989 $.25   (J585)
   (Hallstrom, H.) SSA oct PRESSER 312-40481
   $.25   (J586)
   (Hallstrom, H.) SATB oct PRESSER 312-40482
   $.30   (J587)
   (Lenel, L.) SATB,kbd (med easy) oct CONCORDIA
   98-1131 $.25   (J588)
   (Luboff, Norman) SATB oct WALTON 3011 $.30
                                              (J589)
   (Woodgate) SATB,acap (easy) OXFORD 84.023
   $.35 see from Four Carols   (J590)
   (Woodgate) unis,opt acap (easy) OXFORD 84.023
   $.35   (J591)
   (Woodgate) SATB,acap (easy) OXFORD 84.023
   $.35   (J592)

JOSEPH DEAREST, JOSEPH MINE see Gallus,
   Jacobus, Resonet In Laudibus

JOSEPH, DEAREST JOSEPH MINE see Kranz

JOSEPH DEAREST, JOSEPH MINE see Lapo, Cecil E.

JOSEPH DEAREST, JOSEPH MINE see Martin

JOSEPH DEAREST, JOSEPH MINE see Pfautsch, Lloyd

JOSEPH DEAREST, JOSEPH MINE see Turner

JOSEPH DEAREST, JOSEPH MINE see Turner, Michael

JOSEPH EST BIEN MARIE
   see Five French Noels

JOSEPH GINCK VAN NAZARETH see Appeldoorn,
   [Dina]

JOSEPH IN EGYPT see Dasher, James

JOSEPH, KJAERE JOSEF DU see Bodenschatz, Erhard

JOSEPH, LEIBER JOSEPH MEIN see Raphael, Gunther

JOSEPH, LIEBER JOSEPH see Bodenschatz, Erhard

JOSEPH, LIEBER JOSEPH MEIN see Bodenschatz,
   Erhard

JOSEPH, LIEBER JOSEPH, MEIN see Calvisius,
   Sethus

JOSEPH, LIEBER JOSEPH MEIN see Grofe

JOSEPH, LIEBER JOSEPH MEIN see Kaminski,
   Heinrich

JOSEPH, LIEBER JOSEPH MEIN see Schroter,
   Leonhard

JOSEPH, LIEBER JOSEPH MEIN see Walter

JOSEPH, LIEBER JOSEPH MEIN see Walther, Johann
   Gottfried

JOSEPH, NOW TO THEE IS GIVEN see Goodale, R.

JOSEPH OF ARIMATHEA see Gillette, James Robert

JOSEPH SMITH'S FIRST PRAYER
   (Cornwall, J.S.) SATB PIONEER 5061 $.25
                                              (J593)

JOSEPH TENDER, JOSEPH MINE see Schroter,
   Leonhard, Joseph Lieber, Joseph Mein

JOSEPH UND SEINE BRUDER see Koerppen, Alfred

JOSEPH WAS A HAPPY MAN see Sapienza

JOSEPH'S COAT see Webber, Andrew

JOSEPH'S SORROW
   see Three French Carols (Noels)

JOSEPHSON, JACOB AXEL (1818-1880)
   Requiem *Req
   men cor NORDISKA 2693 s.p.   (J594)

JOSHUA *spir
   (Luboff, Norman) SATB,perc oct WALTON 3046
   $.30   (J595)

JOSHUA see Handel, George Frideric

JOSHUA see Mussorgsky, Modest

JOSHUA FIT DE BATTLE OB JERICHO *spir
   (Pens) SATB oct PRO ART 1183 $.25   (J596)

JOSHUA FIT DE BATTLE OB JERICHO see Montague

JOSHUA FIT DE BATTLE OF JERICHO *spir
   (Durian, Tim) 4pt men cor,acap BREITKOPF-W
   Z-37 s.p. see also Dreizehn Negro-
   Spirituals   (J597)

JOSHUA FIT THE BATTLE
   see Four Negro Spirituals

JOSHUA FIT THE BATTLE OF JERICHO *spir
   SATB oct STAFF 345 $.35   (J598)
   (Christy) SSA SCHMITT 2566 $.25   (J599)
   (Christy) SATB SCHMITT 1609 $.35   (J600)
   (Dressler, John) SATB,inst col AGAPE AG 7128
   $.40   (J601)
   (Ehret, W.) SA LEONARD-US 08034400 $.25
                                              (J602)
   (Ehret, W.) SSA LEONARD-US 08034620 $.25
                                              (J603)
   (Ehret, W.) SAB LEONARD-US 08034560 $.25
                                              (J604)
   (Geller) SATB MARKS 4194 $.40   (J605)
   (Olson) SATB oct SUMMY 2126 $.50   (J606)

JOSQUIN
   see DES PREZ, JOSQUIN

JOSUA see Mussorgsky, Modest

JOUBERT, JOHN (1927-   )
   A Tristria Secla Priora (from Three Motets-
   Pro Pace) anthem/mot
   [Lat] mix cor,acap oct NOVELLO 28.1371.08
   s.p.   (J607)

   All Wisdom Cometh From The Lord *anthem
   boy cor/wom cor oct NOVELLO 40.1535.05 s.p.
                                              (J608)
   4pt oct. NOVELLO 40.1535.05 s.p.   (J609)

   Beatitudes, The *anthem/Bibl
   mix cor,ST soli,acap oct NOVELLO 40.1461.08
   s.p.   (J610)

   Christ Is Risen *Easter,anthem
   mix cor oct NOVELLO 28.1417.10 s.p.   (J611)

   For The Beauty Of The Earth *hymn
   SATB oct NOVELLO 44.1457.08 s.p.   (J612)

   Great Lord Of Lords *anthem
   mix cor oct NOVELLO 28.1429.07 s.p.   (J613)

   He That Is Down Need Fear No Fall *hymn
   SATB oct NOVELLO 44.1446.02 s.p. contains
   also: To Mercy, Pity, Peace And Love

JOUBERT, JOHN (cont'd.)
                                              (J614)
   Holy Communion *Commun
   SATB (D maj) oct NOVELLO 02.0036.00 s.p.
                                              (J615)
   unis (D maj) oct NOVELLO 02.0037.09 s.p.
                                              (J616)

   Holy Mountain, The *Op.44
   SATB, four hand piano part voc sc NOVELLO
   s.p., ipr   (J617)

   How Are My Foes Increased, Lord! *anthem
   mix cor oct NOVELLO 86.0029.05 s.p.   (J618)

   I Will Lift Mine Eyes Unto The Hills
   4pt oct NOVELLO 33.0125.07 s.p.   (J619)

   Let There Be Light *Rembrnc,anthem/mot
   mix cor,acap oct NOVELLO 28.1476.05 s.p.
                                              (J620)

   Libera Plebem (from Three Motets-Pro Pace)
   anthem/mot
   [Lat] SAATBB,acap oct NOVELLO 28.1326.02
   s.p.   (J621)

   Little Child There Is Yborn
   SATB,acap (med diff) OXFORD 84.156 $.35
                                              (J622)

   Lord, Thou Hast Been Our Refuge *anthem
   mix cor oct NOVELLO 86.0001.05 s.p.   (J623)

   Magnificat And Nunc Dimittis *Magnif/Nunc
   SATB oct NOVELLO 86.0020.01 s.p.   (J624)

   Missa Beati Loannis *Op.37, Mass
   [Lat] SATB,org voc sc NOVELLO s.p., ipr
                                              (J625)

   Nowell *Xmas
   SATB BELWIN AP 17 $.30   (J626)

   O Lord Our Lord *anthem
   mix cor oct NOVELLO 28.1441.02 s.p.   (J627)

   O Lord, The Maker Of All Things
   SATB BELWIN AP 19 $.35   (J628)

   O Lorde, The Maker Of Al Thing *anthem
   mix cor oct NOVELLO 40.1319.00 s.p.   (J629)

   O Praise God In His Holiness *anthem
   mix cor oct NOVELLO 40.1499.05 s.p.   (J630)

   Solus Ad Victimam *Op.29 (from Three Motets-
   Pro Pace) anthem/mot
   SSATBB,acap voc sc NOVELLO s.p.   (J631)
   [Lat] SSATBB,acap oct NOVELLO 03.0190.04
   s.p.   (J632)

   Te Deum *Te Deum
   SATB (med diff) oct OXFORD 42.962 $.50
                                              (J633)
   SATB oct NOVELLO 44.1418.07 s.p.   (J634)

   There Is No Rose Of Such Virtue *Xmas
   mix cor SOUTHERN $.30   (J635)

   To Mercy, Pity, Peace And Love
   see Joubert, John, He That Is Down Need
   Fear No Fall

   Urbs Beata *Op.42, cant
   [Lat] SATB,TBar soli,org,3fl,3ob,3clar,
   3bsn,4horn,3trp,3trom,tuba,strings,2perc,
   timp,harp voc sc NOVELLO s.p., ipr   (J636)

JOUR DE NOEL, EPILOGUE see Gounod, Charles
   Francois

JOUR DE PAQUES see Arensky, Anton Stepanovitch

JOURNEY TO BETHLEHEM see Hemmer, [Eugene]

JOURNEY TO BETHLEHEM see Hokanson, Margrethe

JOY AND OTHER SUBLIME ASPIRATIONS see Belt, T.

JOY CAME SOFTLY see Brook

JOY DAWNED AGAIN ON EASTER DAY see Hastings

JOY DAWNED AGAIN ON EASTER DAY see Hobbs, C.M.

JOY DAWNED AGAIN ON EASTER DAY see Praetorius,
   Michael

JOY DAWNED AGAIN ON EASTER DAY see Rogers

JOY DAWNED ON EASTER DAY see Lorenz

JOY DAWNS AGAIN *Easter
   (Bitgood, Roberta) SATB&jr cor&sr cor oct
   GRAY GCMR 1416 $.25   (J637)

JOY FILLS THE MORNING see Lotti, Antonio

JOY IN THE FAITH see Surinach, Carlos, Gozo A
   La Fe

JOY, JOY see Hawkins, Ed.

JOY, JOY, JOY see Lorenz

JOY, JOY, JOY see Page, Robert E.

JOY OF CHRISTMAS, THE see Lorenz

JOY OF DEDICATION, THE see Adler, Hugo Ch.,
   Gabirol-Schindler

JOY SEVEN
   see Six Traditional Carols, Set I

JOY SHALL BE YOURS see Jerrett, Jack

JOY SO DELIGHTS MY HEART see Palestrina,
   Giovanni

JOY TO ALL MANKIND, A see DePue

JOY TO ALL PEOPLE! see Denton

JOY TO THE EARTH see Ridgeway

JOY TO THE WORLD *Xmas
   see Glory To The Newborn King
   see Many Moods Of Christmas, The, Suite Two
   3pt HANSEN-US C626 $.40   (J638)
   SATB CHARTER $.40   (J639)

SAB CHARTER $.40   (J640)
SSA CHARTER $.40   (J641)
(Marzo, E.) 3pt wom cor,S solo,org (med) oct
WILLIS 4776 $.20   (J642)

JOY TO THE WORLD see Cartford, Gerhard M.

JOY TO THE WORLD see Handel, George Frideric

JOY TO THE WORLD see Martin

JOY TO THE WORLD see Mason

JOY TO THE WORLD see Nelson, Ronald A.

JOY TO THE WORLD see Suderburg, R.

JOY TO THE WORLD see Watts

JOY TO THE WORLD, THE LORD IS COMING see Bock

JOY, VIRGINIA
    First Easter, The *see Lillenas, Haldor

JOYBELLS see Lawson

JOYFUL ALLELUIA see Young

JOYFUL ALLELUIA, A see Young

JOYFUL BE TO GOD see Roman, Johan Helmich,
    Jubilate Deo

JOYFUL CAROL see Williams

JOYFUL CHRISTMAS SONG, A see Gevaert, Francois
    Auguste

JOYFUL EASTER-TIDE, THE see Harvey

JOYFUL HEARTS TO HEAVEN see Gallus, Jacobus,
    Resonet In Laudibus

JOYFUL HEARTS TO HEAVEN RAISE see Gallus,
    Jacobus, Resonet In Laudibus

JOYFUL HOSANNA see Pasquet, Jean

JOYFUL, JOYFUL WE ADORE THEE see Beethoven,
    Ludwig van

JOYFUL, JOYFUL WE ADORE THEE see Lockwood,
    Normand

JOYFUL, JOYFUL WE ADORE THEE see Lovelace,
    Austin C.

JOYFUL-JUBILATE see Whear, Paul William

JOYFUL MELODY, A see Kirby

JOYFUL NEWS, THE see Davis, Katherine K.

JOYFUL NEWS WE BRING *Xmas
    (Strickland) SATB SCHMITT 1680 $.18   (J643)

JOYFUL PSALMODY see Mueller, Carl F.

JOYFUL SONG, THE see Dean

JOYFUL SONG, A see Duro, John

JOYFUL SONG, A see Leaf, Robert

JOYFUL SONG, A see Rocherolle

JOYFUL SONG TO GOD, A see Evans, Roderick

JOYFUL SOUND, THE *CCUL
    SATB voc sc WORD 30073 $1.95   (J644)

JOYFUL SOUNDS OF PRAISE see Kirby

JOYFUL TIDINGS see Jewell, Kenneth W.

JOYFUL TORAH SONG see V'natan Lanu Torat Emet

JOYFULLY SING! *CCU,carol/folk/gospel/hymn
    unis jr cor&2pt jr cor cmplt ed LILLENAS
    MB-097 $1.70   (J645)

JOYFULLY SING see Powell

JOYFULLY SING, ALL YE FAITHFUL see Graun, Karl
    Heinrich

JOYFULLY SING UNTO GOD see Gower, R.

JOYFULLY SING WE HIS PRAISE! see Harris

JOYOUS ALLELUIA see Rocherolle

JOYOUS BELLS OF CHRISTMAS, THE see Eager, Mary
    Anne

JOYOUS CAROL see Wells

JOYOUS CAROLS see Whitner, Mary Elizabeth

JOYOUS CHRISTMAS CAROL see Bright

JOYOUS CHRISTMAS DAY, THE see Warner, Richard

JOYOUS CHRISTMAS SONG see Gevaert, Francois
    Auguste, Chanson Joyeuse De Noel

JOYOUS CHRISTMAS SONG see Jeg Er Saa Glad

JOYOUS CHRISTMAS SONG, A see Gevaert, Francois
    Auguste

JOYOUS CHRISTMAS SONG, A *Xmas
    (Hokanson) SSAATBB oct SUMMY 1377 $.30 (J646)

JOYOUS CHRISTMAS SONG, A see Gevaert, Francois
    Auguste

JOYOUS DAY, THIS see Shaw, Martin

JOYOUS EASTER DAWNING see Sateren, Leland
    Bernhard

JOYOUS EASTER HYMN *Easter
    (Manney, C.) SATB oct PRESSER 332-13966 $.35
                                             (J647)

JOYOUS EASTER HYMN see Peery, [Rob Roy]

JOYOUS EASTER SONG, A see Moschetti, [Giuseppe]

JOYOUS MORN, THE see Ashford, E.L.

JOYOUS NEWS TO YOU I'M BRINGING see Praetorius,
    Michael

JOYOUS PRAISE see Cramer

JOYOUS PROCESSION AND A SOLEMN PROCESSION, A
    see Harrison

JOYOUS PSALM OF PRAISE, A see Purvis, Richard

JU ME LEVE UN BEL MAITIN see Goodale

JUBELT GOTT! see Schmalz, Paul

JUBELT, IHR HIMMEL see Callhoff, Herbert

JUBILANT CAROL, A see Brahms, Johannes

JUBILATE *Russ
    2pt oct LORENZ 5707 $.30   (J648)
    unis oct LORENZ 8547 $.30   (J649)

JUBILATE see Beckerath, Alfred von

JUBILATE see Biebl, Franz

JUBILATE see Boyce, William

JUBILATE see Breville, Pierre-Onfroy de

JUBILATE see Campbell, Sydney S.

JUBILATE see Cope

JUBILATE see Davies, Henry Walford

JUBILATE see Gaul, Alfred Robert

JUBILATE see Handel, George Frideric

JUBILATE see Houge

JUBILATE see Hovland, Egil

JUBILATE see Howells, Herbert Norman

JUBILATE see Ireland, John

JUBILATE see Jacob, Gordon

JUBILATE see Jonsson, Josef [Petrus]

JUBILATE see Knopfel

JUBILATE see Lang, C.S.

JUBILATE see Lee, E. Markham

JUBILATE see Leighton, Kenneth

JUBILATE see Nourse, John

JUBILATE see Purcell, Henry

JUBILATE see Stanford, Charles Villiers

JUBILATE see Thalben-Ball, George [Thomas]

JUBILATE see Wills, Arthur

JUBILATE AMEN
    mix cor sc ALSBACH&D s.p.   (J650)

JUBILATE AMEN see Bortniansky, Dimitri
    Stepanovitch

JUBILATE, AMEN see Bruch, Max

JUBILATE, AMEN see Kjerulf, [Halfdan]

JUBILATE DEO *CC28U,anthem/hymn/Jubil
    SSAA oct AUGSBURG 11-9231 $1.75   (J651)

JUBILATE DEO see Agazzari, Agostino

JUBILATE DEO see Aiblinger, Johann Kaspar

JUBILATE DEO see Aichinger, Gregor

JUBILATE DEO see Bauernfiend, Hans

JUBILATE DEO see Brown, Christopher

JUBILATE DEO see Bullock, Ernest

JUBILATE DEO see Cabena, Barrie

JUBILATE DEO see Clark, Henry A.

JUBILATE DEO see Deering, Richard

JUBILATE DEO see Dirksen, Richard W.

JUBILATE DEO see Droste, Doreen

JUBILATE DEO see Erbach, Christian

JUBILATE DEO see Gabrieli, Giovanni

JUBILATE DEO see Gambino, J.

JUBILATE DEO see Gardner, John [Linton]

JUBILATE DEO see Graves

JUBILATE DEO see Grayson

JUBILATE DEO see Greif, C.

JUBILATE DEO see Hassler, Hans Leo

JUBILATE DEO see Humfrey, Pelham

JUBILATE DEO see King, Harold C.

JUBILATE DEO see Lacey, David T.

JUBILATE DEO see Lang, Hans

JUBILATE DEO see Lassus, Roland de (Orlandus)

JUBILATE DEO see Mozart, Wolfgang Amadeus

JUBILATE DEO see Mozart, Wolfgang Amadeus,
    Offertorium Pro Omni Tempore

JUBILATE DEO see Noble, Harold

JUBILATE DEO see Owens

JUBILATE DEO see Palestrina, Giovanni

JUBILATE DEO see Pfautsch, Lloyd

JUBILATE DEO see Pinkham, Daniel

JUBILATE DEO see Preston, Simon

JUBILATE DEO see Purcell, Henry

JUBILATE DEO see Purvis, Richard

JUBILATE DEO see Raffman, Relly

JUBILATE DEO see Roe, Betty

JUBILATE DEO see Rogers

JUBILATE DEO see Roman, Johan Helmich

JUBILATE DEO see Rose, Michael

JUBILATE DEO see Roth, R.N.

JUBILATE DEO see Schubert, Franz (Peter)

JUBILATE DEO see Schubert, Heino

JUBILATE DEO see Sleeth, Natalie

JUBILATE DEO see Smart, Henry Thomas

JUBILATE DEO see Tittel, Ernst

JUBILATE DEO see Tomlins, Greta

JUBILATE DEO see Tours, Berthold

JUBILATE DEO see Track, Gerhard

JUBILATE DEO see White, Louie

JUBILATE DEO see Wickens, Dennis [John]

JUBILATE DEO see Wiltberger

JUBILATE DEO see Wood

JUBILATE DEO see Wood, Dale

JUBILATE DEO see Wyton, Alec

JUBILATE DEO see Young

JUBILATE DEO see Zaninelli, Luigi

JUBILATE DEO IN C see Britten, Benjamin

JUBILATE DEO IN G see Jackson, Francis

JUBILATE DEO OMNIS TERRA see Gabrieli, Giovanni

JUBILATE DEO OMNIS TERRA see Gallus, Jacobus

JUBILATE DEO OMNIS TERRA see Lassus, Roland de
    (Orlandus)

JUBILATE DEO OMNIS TERRA see Peeters, Flor

JUBILATE DEO OMNIS TERRA see Sandvold, Arild

JUBILATE DEO OMNIS TERRA see Spalder, Frithjof

JUBILATE DEO, PART I see Aichinger, Gregor

JUBILATE DEO, PART II see Aichinger, Gregor

JUBILATE DOMINO see Swann

JUBILATE IN C see Shilling, F.

JUBILATE, IN F see Tours, Berthold

JUBILATE (INTROITUS) see Hovland, Egil

JUBILATION see Smith, Lani

JUBILAUMS-MESSE see Koch, Karl

JUBILEE see Hooper

JUBILEE CANTATA, THE see Weber, Carl Maria von

JUBILEE MASS IN HONOUR OF ST. NICHOLAS see
    Peeters, Flor

JUBILEMUS DEO - LIBER I *CC33U,Commun,mot
    (Ballarin, R.) [Lat] 2 eq voices sc ZANIBON
    3961 s.p., cor pts ZANIBON 3961A s.p.
                                             (J652)
JUBILEMUS DEO-LIBER II *CC31U,Xmas/Easter/
    Epiph/Psntd,mot
    (Ballarin, R.) [Lat] 2 eq voices sc ZANIBON
    3962 s.p., cor pts ZANIBON 3962A s.p.
                                             (J653)
JUBILEMUS DEO - LIBER III *CC33U,BVM,mot
    (Ballarin, R.) [Lat] 2 eq voices sc ZANIBON
    3963 s.p., cor pts ZANIBON 3963A s.p.
                                             (J654)
JUBILEMUS DEO-LIBER IV *CC29U,hymn/mot/Psalm
    (Ballarin, R.) [Lat] 2 eq voices sc ZANIBON
    3964 s.p., cor pts ZANIBON 3964A s.p.
                                             (J655)
JUBILEMUS DEO - LIBER V *CC35U,anti/mot
    (Ballarin, R.) [Lat] 2pt ZANIBON 3965 sc
    s.p., cor pts s.p.   (J656)
JUBILEMUS DEO - VOL. I-V *CC160U,mot
    (Ballarin, R.) [Lat] 2 eq voices,org cmplt ed
    ZANIBON 3960 s.p.   (J657)

JUBILEMUS SINGULI see Gabrieli, Giovanni

JUBILIERT DEM HERREN see Lassus, Roland de
    (Orlandus), Jubilate Deo

JUBLA HOGT, MIN SJAL OCH TUNGA see Cruger,
    Johann

JUCH-HE! *Aus
    (Bauernfeind, Hans) mix cor,acap oct
    DOBLINGER s.p.   (J658)

JUDAH, LONG AGO see Bellhouse, Alan

JUDAH'S LAND   *anthem/carol,US
   (Johnson, David N.) SATB (easy) oct AUGSBURG
   0523 $.25   (J659)

JUDAH'S SONG OF PRAISE see Adler, Samuel

JUDAS MACCABAEUS see Handel, George Frideric

JUDAS MACCABAUS see Handel, George Frideric,
   Judas Maccabaeus

JUDAS MERCATOR PESSIMUS see Ingegneri, Marco
   Antonio

JUDAS MERCATOR PESSIMUS see Rubbra, Edmund

JUDAS, MERCATOR PESSIMUS see Victoria

JUDAS MERCATOR PESSIMUS see Victoria, Tomas
   Luis de

JUDAS TREE, THE see Dickinson, Peter

JUDAS, WHO DEALT MOST CRUELLY see Victoria,
   Tomas Luis de, Judas, Mercator Pessimus

JUDAS, WHY? see Hourdeaux

JUDD, PERCY
   When Mary Through The Garden Went   *Easter
   SSA (easy) oct OXFORD 83.062 $.25   (J660)

JUDE, [WILLIAM HERBERT] (1851-1922)
   Jesus Calls Us   *Gen
      (Olds) SATB SCHMITT 1860 $.20   (J661)
      (Rogers) 2pt jr cor oct LILLENAS AN-4012
      $.25   (J662)

JUDEA see Bugatch, Samuel

JUDEX see Gounod, Charles Francois

JUDGE ETERNAL see Marchant, Stanley R.

JUDGE ETERNAL THRONED IN SPLENDOR see Becker,
   J.

JUDGE ETERNAL, THRONED IN SPLENDOR see Graves,
   Richard

JUDGE ETERNAL, THRONED IN SPLENDOR see Scull,
   Harold [Thomas]

JUDGE ETERNAL, THRONED IN SPLENDOUR see Wolff

JUDGE ME, GOD OF MY SALVATION see Tinel, Edgar

JUDGE ME, O GOD see Barbee, N.

JUDGE ME, O GOD see Mendelssohn-Bartholdy,
   Felix

JUDGE ME, O GOD see Mueller, Carl F.

JUDGE ME, O GOD see Neidlinger, William Harold

JUDGE ME, O LORD see Vene, Ruggero, Judica Me,
   Domine

JUDICA ME, DEUS see Jaeggi, Oswald

JUDICA ME, DEUS see Purvis, Richard

JUDICA ME, DOMINE see Vene, Ruggero

JUDICIUM SALOMONIS see Carissimi, Giacomo

JUDITH see Chadwick, George Whitefield

JUDITHA TRIUMPHANS see Vivaldi, Antonio

JUDITHA TRIUMPHANS DEVICTA HOLOFERNIS BARBARIE
   see Vivaldi, Antonio

JUDSON
   Alleluia! He Arose   *Easter/Lent
   SATB WORD CS-2095 $.35   (J663)

JUICHT AARDE JUICHT see Herwaarden, J.G.

JUL see Bjarnegard, Gustaf

JUL, JUL, STRALANDE JUL
   [Swed] men cor LUNDQUIST 75 s.p.   (J664)

JUL, JUL, STRALANDE JUL see Hammarstrom, Hugo

JUL, JUL, STRALANDE JUL see Nordqvist, Gustaf

JULAFTEN see Soraas, Lars

JULBON see Runback, Albert

JULENS GAVA see Tegner, Alice

JULEORATORIUM "IN NATIVITATE DOMINI" see
   Kayser, Leif

JULESANG see Gebauer, Joh, Chr.

JULESANGE   *Xmas,17th cent
   (Larsen, Jens Peter) [Dan] SS/TT/STB/SATB
   cmplt ed HANSEN-DEN 25768 s.p.
      contains & see also: In Dulci Jubilo;
      Othmayr, Kaspar, Fra Himlen Hojt Kom
      Budskab Her; Praetorius, Michael, Alt
      Morgenstjernen Er Oprunden; Praetorius,
      Michael, Det Lille Barn I Krybben Trang;
      Praetorius, Michael, Ein Kind Geborn Zu
      Bethlehem, "Et Lille Barn I Davids Stad";
      Triller, Valentin, Fra Himlen Kom En
      Engel Klar; Vulpius, Melchior, Det Volder
      Herren Jesulil; Vulpius, Melchior, Et
      Barn Er Fodt I Bethlehem; Vulpius,
      Melchior, Vi Christum Love   (J665)

JULGRANSLIUS see Pergament, Moses

JULHYMNER   *see Det Ar En Ros Utsprungen;
   Forsamlens, I Trogne; Hosianna; O, Du
   Harliga; Stilla Natt   (J666)

JULKANTAT see Lindberg, Oskar [Fredrik]

JULMORGON see Lindroth, Henry

JULPSALM see Sibelius, Jean

JULSANG
   (Svanholm, Set) mix cor NORDISKA 1153 s.p.
                                          (J667)

JULSANG see Adam, Adolphe-Charles

JULVISA see Bengtsson, [Gustav Adolf Tiburt]

JULVISA see Sibelius, Jean

JUNCTIM-SATZE   *CCU,Gen
   (Ehmann, Wilhelm) [Ger] SATB,3-6brass (easy/
   med) sc BAREN. BA 3550 s.p., cor pts BAREN.
   3550A s.p.   (J668)

JUNGEND-KANTATE see Stern, Hermann

JUNGET
   While By My Sheep   *Xmas
   SATB FLAMMER A 5086 $.30   (J669)

JUNGFRAU, DEIN SCHON GESTALT see Hassler, Hans
   Leo

JUNGFRU MARIAE VAGGVISA see Rangstrom, Ture

JUNGST
   While By My Sheep   *Xmas
   SATB oct PLYMOUTH XM-114 $.25   (J670)
   TTBB oct PLYMOUTH XM-300 $.25   (J671)
   SSA oct PLYMOUTH XM-200 $.25   (J672)
   SAB oct PLYMOUTH XM-400 $.25   (J673)
   2pt oct PLYMOUTH XM-500 $.25   (J674)

   While Shepherds Watched Their Sheep (from
   Isaiah's Prophecy) Xmas
   (Creston) SATB oct COLOMBO 2328 $.30   (J675)
   (Dickinson) SATB oct GRAY GSC 103 $.30
                                          (J676)
   (Ehret) SA/TB oct BELWIN 1485 $.30   (J677)

JUNGST, HUGO (1853-1923)
   While By Our Sleeping Flocks We Lay   *Ger
   (Whitford, H.) SSA,acap SCHIRM.EC 1848 $.25
                                          (J678)
   (Whitford, H.) echo chorus, acap SCHIRM.EC
   1848 $.25   (J679)

JUNIOR AND SENIOR CHOIR BOOK see Scholin, C.
   Albert

JUNIOR ANTHEM ALBUM, THE, VOL. 1 see Scott

JUNIOR ANTHEM BOOK OF SPIRITUALS   *CCU,anthem/
   spir
   SA/unis LORENZ $1.75   (J680)

JUNIOR CHOIR   *CC74U
   (Tripp, Vivian) 1-2pt jr cor voc sc WORD
   20038 $1.50   (J681)

JUNIOR CHOIR ALBUM see Swift, F. F.

JUNIOR CHOIR ANTHEMS see Williams

JUNIOR CHOIR ANTHEMS FOR THE CHURCH YEAR see
   George, Graham

JUNIOR CHOIR BOOK see Keating, L.

JUNIOR CHOIR CHRISTMAS COLLECTION see McKasson,
   M.

JUNIOR CHOIR COLLECTION VOLUME 1 see Bixby,
   A.K.

JUNIOR CHOIR COLLECTION VOLUME 1, THE see
   Bixby, A.K.

JUNIOR CHOIR COLLECTION VOLUME 2 see Bixby,
   A.K.

JUNIOR CHOIR COLLECTION VOLUME 2, THE see
   Bixby, A.K.

JUNIOR CHOIR COLLECTION. VOLUME 3, SONGS OF
   WORSHIP see Bixby, A.K.

JUNIOR CHOIR COLLECTION VOLUME 3, THE see
   Bixby, A.K.

JUNIOR CHOIR PRAISE see Wilson, John F.

JUNIOR CHOIR RESPONSES   *CCU,cor-resp
   jr cor LORENZ 8595 $.30   (J682)

JUNIOR CHORISTER, THE, VOL. 2 see Mueller, Carl
   F.

JUNIOR CLASSIC ANTHEMS   *CCU,anthem
   2pt/unis LORENZ $1.75   (J683)

JUNIOR HYMN ANTHEMS NO. 1   *CCU,anthem
   2pt/unis LORENZ $1.75   (J684)

JUNIOR HYMN ANTHEMS NO. 2   *CCU,anthem
   2pt/unis LORENZ $1.75   (J685)

JUNIOR INTERMEDIATE ANTHEM BOOK see Harper, C.

JUNIOR-SENIOR CHOIR ANTHEMS   *CCU,anthem
   SATB&1-2pt jr cor LORENZ $1.75   (J686)

JURGENS, WM. A., REV.
   Sung Vespers
   cong cloth LITURGICAL $1.00   (J687)

JUSQUES A QUAND AS ESTABLI, SEIGNEUR see
   Goudimel, Claude

JUSQUES A QUAND AS ETABLI see Jannequin,
   Clement

JUST A CLOSER WALK   *Gen
   (Sutherland) SATB SCHMITT 1874 $.35   (J688)

JUST A CLOSER WALK WITH THEE   *folk/hymn,US
   SATB oct LORENZ A406 $.25   (J689)
   SATB/SAB/SA/TB/TTBB BIG3 $.25   (J690)
   (Lojeski, Ed) SATB,pno,opt perc&gtr&bvl
   WESTPORT $.45   (J691)
   (Widen) SATB oct LILLENAS AN-3827 $.25 (J692)

JUST A CLOSER WALK WITH THEE see Williams

JUST A LITTLE see Roff, Joseph

JUST ARE THY WAYS, O LIVING GOD see Watts

JUST AS I AM
   (Parker) TTBB,pno/gtr oct LAWSON 51360 $.25
                                          (J693)

JUST AS I AM see Bradbury, William Batchelder

JUST AS I AM see Brown

JUST AS I AM see Maunder, J.H.

JUST AS I AM see Nolte

JUST AS I AM see Peery

JUST AS I AM see Rubinstein, Anton

JUST AS I AM see Smith

JUST AS I AM see Stafford, F.J.

JUST AS I AM see Stults, R.

JUST AS I AM, THINE OWN TO BE see Barnby

JUST AS I AM, THINE OWN TO BE see Webber, Lloyd

JUST FOR TODAY see Stairs, L.

JUST FOR YOU see Wilson

JUST MAN SHALL FLOURISH, THE see Proulx,
   Richard

JUST MOUTH, THE see Bruckner, Anton, Os Justi

JUST NOW see Kennedy, John Brodbin

JUST ONE DAY AT A TIME see Orton, Irv

JUSTOREM ANIMAE see Skroup, Jan Nepomuk

JUSTORIUM ANIMAE see Aiblinger, Johann Kaspar

JUSTORUM ANIMAE see Berkeley, Lennox

JUSTORUM ANIMAE see Burkhart, Franz

JUSTORUM ANIMAE see Lassus, Roland de
   (Orlandus)

JUSTORUM ANIMAE see Palestrina, Giovanni

JUSTORUM ANIMAE see Saint-Saens, Camille

JUSTORUM ANIMAE see Stanford

JUSTUM DEDUXIT DOMINUS see Mozart, Wolfgang
   Amadeus

JUSTUS see Heidet, Le R.P.

JUSTUS COR SUUM TRADET see Lassus, Roland de
   (Orlandus)

JUSTUS UT PALMA FLOREBIT see Bossi, Marco
   Enrico

JUSTUS UT PALMA FLOREBIT see Bottazzo, Luigi

JUSTUS UT PALMA FLOREBIT see Ferro, Stefano

K

KABBALAT SHABBAT see Ben-Haim, Paul

KABBALATH SHABBATH see Binder, Abraham Wolfe

KADDISH see Bernstein, Leonard

KADERAVEK, MILAN
    I Announced Your Justice *Gradual
        (Snow, Robert J.) SATB,org oct WORLD
        EMP-1645-8 $.75   (K1)

KAH BEHNEH KAH *Afr
    (Nebo) "I Can Go Anywhere" SATB,acap oct
        LAWSON 51464 $.30   (K2)

KAISER, KURT
    As A Little Child
        SA oct WORD CS-333 $.30   (K3)

    Bring Back The Springtime
        SATB oct WORD CS-2439 $.30   (K4)

    Go Now And Live For The Savior
        (Brown) SATB oct WORD CS-2494 $.25 contains
        also: Illumine Me, Lord   (K5)

    Hear The Right, Lord
        SATB oct WORD CS-2501 $.30   (K6)

    Illumine Me, Lord
        see Kaiser, Kurt, Go Now And Live For The
            Savior

    Natural High (composed with Carmichael,
        Ralph) *folk
        SATB,narrator,2trp,2trom,perc,opt gtr voc
        sc WORD 37507 $2.95, ipa   (K7)

    Pass It On
        SATB oct WORD CS-2479 $.35   (K8)

    Plan Of God, The
        SATB oct WORD CS-334 $.30   (K9)

    Tell It Like It Is *cant
        (Carmichael, Ralph) SATB,soli voc sc WORD
        37501 $2.95   (K10)

    That's For Me
        SATB oct WORD CS-2533 $.30   (K11)

    This Is My Father's World
        SATB oct WORD CS-652 $.25   (K12)

    Where Shall I Run?
        SATB oct WORD CS-2526 $.30   (K13)

KAISER MOTETTE see Isaac, Heinrich

KALEIDOSCOPE OF PSALMS IN SIX MOODS see
    Kosakoff, Reuven

KALINNIKOFF, PAUL
    Everlasting God
        SATB oct WALTON 2114 $.25   (K14)

    To Thee, O Lord
        (Christiansen, O.) SATB KJOS 3 $.30   (K15)

KALINNIKOV, VASSILI SERGEIEVITCH (1866-1901)
    Agnus Dei *Agnus
        SATB KJOS 7035 $.30   (K16)
        (Engel) SATB,acap BOSTON 5618 $.30   (K17)
        (Hollis) SATB FLAMMER A 5263 $.25   (K18)
        (Rosewall) TTBB oct SUMMY 5836 $.20   (K19)

    Almighty God, We Worship Thee
        (Douglas) SAB oct PRO ART 2185 $.20   (K20)
        (Douglas) SATB,acap oct PRO ART 2183 $.20
                                                 (K21)

    O Lamb Of God *Easter
        (Ehret) SATB,acap,opt pno oct PRO ART 1513
        $.25   (K22)

    Sing Praises To Our God
        SATB oct WALTON 2112 $.25   (K23)

    Source Eternal Of Joys Divine
        (Ehret) SATB oct BOURNE BL3038 $.25   (K24)

KALLSTENIUS, EDVIN (1881-   )
    Gabriel Angel *Xmas
        wom cor/jr cor voc sc NORDISKA 3366 s.p.,
        cor pts NORDISKA 3359 s.p.   (K25)

KALMANOFF
    O Lord, How Glorious Is Thy Name
        SATB oct FOX R155 $.30   (K26)

    Sermon On The Mount
        SATB oct MCA   (K27)

KALMANOFF, [MARTIN] (1920-   )
    Lion And The Lamb, The
        SATB oct ELKAN-V 362-1313 $.30   (K28)

    Prayer Of St. Francis
        SATB oct BOURNE 811 $.30   (K29)

    Song Of Peace
        SATB oct ELKAN-V 362-1079 $.25   (K30)

KAMEKE, ERNST-ULRICH VON (1926-   )
    Manche Meinen, Du Hast Dich Zur Ruhe Gesetzt
        *prayer
        cor&speak cor,4 soli cor pts BREITKOPF-W
        CHB-3698 s.p.   (K31)

KAMINSKI, HEINRICH (1886-1946)
    Die Messe Deutsch *Mass
        [Ger] SSATB,2 soli,acap (med diff) BAREN.
        BA 2140 $2.50   (K32)

    Joseph, Lieber Joseph Mein
        see Three Christmas Settings

    Lass Uns Das Kindelein Wiegen
        see Three Christmas Settings

KAMINSKI, HEINRICH (cont'd.)
    Maria Durch Ein' Dornewald Ging
        see Three Christmas Settings

    Nun Lasst Uns Gehen Und Treten *Xmas/ECY
        [Ger] SATB,acap (med easy) BAREN. BA 2400
        s.p.   (K33)

    Three Christmas Settings *Xmas
        [Ger] PETERS 4865 $.50
        contains: Joseph, Lieber Joseph Mein
        (SSAA); Lass Uns Das Kindelein Wiegen
        (SSAT); Maria Durch Ein' Dornewald Ging
        (SSATBB)   (K34)

KAMMEIER, HANS
    Ach Lieber Herre Jesu Christ *Ded,mot
        SSATB HANSSLER 7.101 s.p.   (K35)

KAMMENOI
    Angelus, The (composed with Ostrow)
        (Rubinstein; Swift) SATB oct PRO ART 1053
        $.25   (K36)
        (Rubinstein; Swift) SSA oct PRO ART 1054
        $.25   (K37)
        (Rubinstein; Swift) SAB oct PRO ART 1231
        $.25   (K38)
        (Rubinstein; Swift) 2pt oct PRO ART 1121
        $.20   (K39)

KAMMERER, C.
    Mother's Love, A
        SATB oct PRESSER MC199 $.30   (K40)

KAMMERER, IMANUEL JOHANNES (1896-   )
    Das Jahr Geht Still Zu Ende
        (Reuss, Eleonore Furstin) [Lat] wom cor,
        acap (easy) HUG s.p.   (K41)

    Ein Licht Ist Aufgegangen
        [Ger] mix cor,acap (med easy) HUG   (K42)

    Lobt Gott, Ihr Christen, Alle Gleich *Xmas,
        cant
        [Ger] 3pt,2vln,cont HUG s.p.   (K43)

    Psalm 27
        [Ger] mix cor,acap (med easy) HUG s.p.
                                                 (K44)

KAMPF, [KARL] (1874-1950)
    Horch, Wie Ubers Wasser Hallend *folk,Russ
        men cor (med easy) oct LEUCKART 125 s.p.
                                                 (K45)

    Vespergesang *folk,Russ
        men cor (med easy) oct LEUCKART 533 s.p.
                                                 (K46)

KANNON, R.V.
    Hodie Christus Natus Est *Xmas
        [Lat] SATB,org,3trp,2trom,timp AMP A403
        $.25, ipa   (K47)

KANON see Jankovics, F.

KANONISCHES TRIPTYCHON AUF DIE WEIHNACHTSZEIT
    see Huber, W.S.

KANONJAI see Mozart, Wolfgang Amadeus

KANONOK see Haydn, (Franz) Joseph

KANTAT PA DEN HELIGE MIKAELS DAG see Runback,
    Albert

KANTAT VID KYRKOINVIGNING see Moren, John

KANTATE CHORHEFT 1966 *CCU,Xmas,Eur
    (Hofmann, Friedrich) [Ger] 4pt mix cor BAREN.
    EM 766 s.p. includes works by: Schimdt-
    Mannheim; Stern; Weiss; Zipp   (K48)

KANTATE UBER EINEN WEIHNACHTSPSALM see Gwinner,
    Volker

KANTATE ZUM GEDENKEN AN DIE GEFALLENEN see
    Handel, George Frideric

KANTATEN see Buxtehude, Dietrich

KANTOR, J.
    By The Rivers Of Babylon
        SATB,acap AMP A307 $.25   (K49)

    Come Ye To The Lord
        SATB (med diff) oct SCOTT GS 21 $.45   (K50)

    Psalm 121
        SATB,acap oct PRESSER MC431 $.25   (K51)

KANTOREI-SATS NR. 1. FRA HOGE HIMMEL KJEM EG
    HER *CCU
    1-4pt,inst MUSIKK s.p.   (K52)

KANTOREI-SATS NR. 2. HJERTE, LOFT DIN GLEDES
    VINGE
    1-4pt,inst MUSIKK s.p.   (K53)

KANTOREISATSER see Bornefeld, Helmut

KANTOREISATZE, HEFT 1 see Bornefeld, Helmut

KANTOREISATZE, HEFT 2 see Bornefeld, Helmut

KANTOREISATZE, HEFT 3 see Bornefeld, Helmut

KANTOREISATZE, HEFT 4 see Bornefeld, Helmut

KANTOREISATZE, HEFT 5 see Bornefeld, Helmut

KANTOREISATZE, HEFT 6 see Bornefeld, Helmut

KAPPESSER, KARL (1900-   )
    Ach Wie Fluctig, Ach Wie Nichtig *mot
        SATB HANSSLER 6.280 s.p.   (K54)

    Halleluja, Gott Zu Loben Bleibe Meine
        see Kappesser, Karl, Wachet Auf, Ruft Uns
            Die Stimme

    Herr Gott, Nun Schleuss Den Himmel Auf *mot
        SSATB HANSSLER 6.281 s.p. contains also:
        Ich Wollt, Dass Ich Daheime War (SATB)
                                                 (K55)

    Ich Wollt, Dass Ich Daheime War
        see Kappesser, Karl, Herr Gott, Nun
            Schleuss Den Himmel Auf

KAPPESSER, KARL (cont'd.)
    Lobt Gott Ihr Christen Allzugleich *Thanks
        SA&SAT&SAB&SATB HANSSLER 6.009 s.p.   (K56)

    O Heiland, Reiss Die Himmel Auf
        SAT&SAB&SATB&opt ST&SB HANSSLER 6.248 s.p.
                                                 (K57)

    Wachet Auf, Ruft Uns Die Stimme
        ST/SB/SA/SATB HANSSLER 6.235 s.p. contains
        also: Halleluja, Gott Zu Loben Bleibe
        Meine (SA/SAB/SATB)   (K58)

KARAM, FREDERICK
    Praise To The Lord
        SATB,org oct BERANDOL 910K4AE $.35   (K59)

KARASCONYI PASZTORTANC see Kodaly, Zoltan

KARFREITAG DIE LITURGISCHE CHORGESANGE see
    Quack, Erhard

KARFREITAG (TOTENFEST) see Roder, E.

KARG-ELERT, SIGFRID (1877-1933)
    Praise Ye The Lord
        (Elert) SATB oct LORENZ C63 $.30   (K60)

    Prelude, Aria And Chorale *CC3U,chorale
        (Bedell) SATB oct FISCHER,C R-427 $.25
                                                 (K61)

KARKOFF, MAURICE INGVAR (1927-   )
    Four Sacred Songs *CC4U
        SATB oct WALTON 2904 $.35   (K62)

    Natten Ar Framskriden *Bibl
        [Swed] SAB,acap GEHRMANS TKS 96   (K63)

    Och Du Betlehem *Bibl
        [Swed] SATB,acap GEHRMANS KRB 438   (K64)

KARLSEN, KJELL MORK
    Dette Er Dagen *chorale
        [Norw] mix cor,org LYCHE 70 s.p.   (K65)

KARLSEN, ROLF
    A Fikk Jeg Kun Vaere Den Minste Kvist
        mix cor MUSIKK 77 s.p.   (K66)

    En Morgen-Sang
        mix cor MUSIKK 92 s.p.   (K67)

    Fire Salmetoner
        mix cor MUSIKK 76 s.p.
        contains: Hill Dig, Frelser Og Forsoner;
        Lykksalig, Lykksalig; Naermere Dig, Min
        Gud; Var Gud Han Signe Norges Land   (K68)

    Hill Dig, Frelser Og Forsoner
        see Fire Salmetoner

    Lykksalig, Lykksalig
        see Fire Salmetoner

    Min Sjel, Lov Herren
        [Norw] 4-12pt mix cor,brass/org LYCHE
        LY 455 s.p.   (K69)

    Naermere Dig, Min Gud
        see Fire Salmetoner
        mix cor MUSIKK 94 s.p.   (K70)

    Var Gud Han Signe Norges Land
        see Fire Salmetoner

KARSAMSTAG see Schieri, Fritz

KARVONEN
    Father, I Sing Thy Wondrous Grace
        SATB KJOS 5895 $.30   (K71)

    On That Holy Christmas Night *Xmas
        SATB KJOS 5894 $.30   (K72)

KARVONEN, PAUL
    Rejoice, All Ye Believers *Adv
        SATB oct GRAY GCMR 2983 $.30   (K73)

    Temple Of Holiness, The
        SATB,acap oct GRAY GCMR 3073 $.30   (K74)

KASCHUBISCHES WEIHNACHTSLIED see Mielenz, H.

KASTAL
    There Is No Other Comforter (composed with
        Skii)
        SATB oct MCA   (K75)

KASTALSKY, ALEXANDER DMITRIEVITCH (1856-1926)
    All Blessed, All Holy, Lord God
        SATB/SSATTBB,acap SCHIRM.EC 1707 $.22   (K76)

    God Is With Us
        SATB oct FISCHER,J 4138 $.30   (K77)
        (McKinney) SAB oct FISCHER,J 9381 $.30
                                                 (K78)

    Hail, Holy Light!
        SATB,acap SCHIRM.EC 1105 $.30   (K79)
        (Bement, G.) SSAA,acap SCHIRM.EC 1950 $.25
                                                 (K80)
        (Saar, L.) TTBB,acap SCHIRM.EC 544 $.16
                                                 (K81)

    O Tranquil Light
        (Cramer) SATB,acap MARKS 4060 $.30   (K82)

KASTLE
    Whispers Of Heavenly Death
        SATB,acap oct COLOMBO 1796 $.25   (K83)

KATECHISMUS-MESSE see Graap, Lothar

KATT, LEOPOLD (1917-1965)
    Die Frohe Botschaft *Xmas,cant
        2pt jr cor,3 soli,inst cor pts MOSELER
        s.p., ipa   (K84)

    Mein Hirt, Vernahmst Du
        see Zwei Weihnachtsleider

    Mit Dudelsack Und Mit Schalmein
        see Zwei Weihnachtsleider

    Zwei Weihnachtsleider *Xmas
        mix cor,acap cmplt ed DOBLINGER s.p.
        contains: Mein Hirt, Vernahmst Du; Mit
        Dudelsack Und Mit Schalmein   (K85)

KATTER
Sustaining Power
(Collins) SSATB oct LILLENAS AT-1011 $.25 (K86)

KATZ, E.
Quodlibet *canon
SATB,acap AMP A306 $.25 (K87)

KAUFMAN, H.H.
Manginot Beth El *Sab-Eve
(Luskin S.) SATB TRANSCON. TCL 299 $3.00 (K88)

KAUFMANN
Now Thank We All Our God *anthem
(Pasquet) unis (easy) oct AUGSBURG 1363 $.25 (K89)

KAUFMANN, DIETHELM (1934-)
Christ Ist Erstanden *Easter,cant
SSATBB,org/fl&2trp&trom&2vln&vcl&bvl&timp HANSSLER 10.165 sc s.p., voc sc s.p., ipa (K90)

Ein Kind Geborn Zu Bethlehem
see Zwei Choralsatze Fur Advent Und Weihnachten

Komm, Gott Schopfer, Heiliger Geist
SATB HANSSLER 6.6110 s.p. contains also: Casciolini, Claudio, Komm, Heiliger Geist, Erfull Die Herzen (K91)

Lob Sei Dem Allmachtigen Gott
see Zwei Choralsatze Fur Advent Und Weihnachten

Zwei Choralsatze Fur Advent Und Weihnachten *Adv/Xmas
HANSSLER 6.247 s.p.
contains: Ein Kind Geborn Zu Bethlehem (SATB); Lob Sei Dem Allmachtigen Gott (SAT/SAB) (K92)

KAUFMANN, FERDINAND (1921-)
Confitebor *Psntd
[Lat] SATB,acap (med) MULLER MS 59 s.p. (K93)

Ecce Sacerdos *Fest
[Lat] SATB,org (med) MULLER MS 55 s.p. (K94)

Laudate Dominum *Gen
[Ger] SATB,acap (med) MULLER MS 59 s.p. (K95)

Meditabor *Psntd
[Lat] SATB,acap (med) MULLER MS 58 s.p. (K96)

Tantum Ergo *Gen
[Ger] SATB/SSATBB,acap (med) MULLER MS 54 s.p. (K97)

KAUFMANN, OTTO
Der Herr Ist Konig (Psalm 93) Bibl
4pt mix cor&4pt mix cor,2trp,2trom voc sc MOSELER s.p., ipa (K98)

Kleine Liedmotetten *see Kommt Alle; Vernehmt Die Rede; Wir Harren, Christe (K99)

Kommt Alle *mot
cor,inst MOSELER s.p. see from Kleine Liedmotetten (K100)

Psalm 93 *see Der Herr Ist Konig

Sieben Spirituals *CC7U,spir
4pt mix cor MOSELER s.p. (K101)

Sieben Spirituals *CC7U,spir
4pt mix cor MOSELER s.p. (K102)

Vernehmt Die Rede *mot
cor,inst MOSELER s.p. see from Kleine Liedmotetten (K103)

Vier Adventslieder *CC4U,Adv
2-3 eq voices MOSELER s.p. (K104)

Vier Kanonische Adventsmotetten *CC4U,Adv, mot
2-4pt mix cor MOSELER s.p. (K105)

Wir Harren, Christe *mot
cor,inst MOSELER s.p. see from Kleine Liedmotetten (K106)

KAUN, [HUGO] (1863-1932)
Du Bist Der Born
men cor,acap ERDMANN 25 s.p. (K107)

Requiem *Op.116, Req
men cor,A/Mez solo,orch LEUCKART rental (K108)

Wachet Auf! *cant
men cor&jr cor&SSA,Mez solo,orch ERDMANN 82 s.p., ipr (K109)

Weihnacht *Xmas
mix cor,acap ERDMANN 97 s.p. (K110)

KAVOD LA-TORAH see Piket, Frederick

KAY
Like As A Father (Psalm 103) Psalm
SATB,acap PETERS 6222A $.25 see from New Song, A (K111)

New Song, A *see Like As A Father (Psalm 103); O Praise The Lord (Psalm 117); Sing Unto The Lord (Psalm 149) (K112)

O Praise The Lord (Psalm 117) Psalm
SATB,acap PETERS 6229A $.30 see from New Song, A (K113)

O Worship The King *anthem/hymn
SATB,org/pno PETERS 6223 $.25 (K114)

Parables
mix cor,strings voc sc MCA $2.25, ipr (K115)

Psalm 103 *see Like As A Father

Psalm 117 *see O Praise The Lord

Psalm 149 *see Sing Unto The Lord

Sing Unto The Lord (Psalm 149) Psalm
SATB,acap PETERS 6136A $.30 see from New Song, A (K116)

KAY, NORMAN
King Herod *cant
mix cor,SBar soli,orch (med diff) OXFORD 46.143 voc sc $3.00, ipr, cor pts $1.00 (K117)

KAY, ULYSSES SIMPSON (1917-)
Alleluia
SATB,pno/org AMP A497 $.40 see from Choral Triptych (K118)

Choral Triptych *see Alleluia; Give Ear To My Words, O Lord; How Long Wilt Thou Forget Me, O Lord (K119)

Christmas Carol *Xmas,carol
SSA,acap PEER $.40 (K120)

Give Ear To My Words, O Lord
SATB,pno/org AMP A495 $.35 see from Choral Triptych (K121)

How Long Wilt Thou Forget Me, O Lord
SATB,opt SATB soli,pno/org AMP A496 $.35 see from Choral Triptych (K122)

Lully, Lullay *Xmas
SATB,acap AMP A210 $.25 see from Wreath For Waits (K123)

Noel *Xmas
SATB,acap AMP A209 $.20 see from Wreath For Waits (K124)

Welcome Yule *Xmas
SATB,acap AMP A211 $.25 see from Wreath For Waits (K125)

Wreath For Waits *see Lully, Lullay; Noel; Welcome Yule (K126)

KAYSER, LEIF (1919-)
Juleoratorium "In Nativitate Domini" *Xmas, ora
[Lat] SATB,SBarB soli,2fl,2ob,2clar,2bsn, 3trp,3horn,3trom,2vln,vla,vcl,bvl,harp FOG III, 200 sc s.p., voc sc s.p., cor pts s.p., ipa (K127)

Te Deum *Te Deum
[Lat] mix cor,orch SAMFUNDET sc s.p., ipa, voc sc s.p., cor pts s.p. (K128)
[Lat] SATB,3fl,ob,3clar,3bsn,2trp,4horn, 2trom,tuba,2vln,vla,vcl,bvl,perc,timp FOG III, 229 sc s.p., voc sc s.p., ipa (K129)

KAZZE, L.
Little Chillun, Don't You Cry
SATB PARAGON 1011 $.25 (K130)

KDOZ JSTE BOZI BOJOVNICI see Dobias, Vaclav

KEARNEY
Songs Of Brotherhood *CCU,folk
cor,pno,gtr ALBERT s.p. (K131)

KEATING, L.
Hail, King Of Glory *Easter
SATB PRESSER $.90 (K132)

Junior Choir Book *CCU
SA oct PRESSER $1.00 (K133)

Resurrection Morn *Easter
SATB PRESSER $1.25 (K134)

Second Junior Choir Book *CCU
SA/2pt jr cor oct PRESSER $1.25 (K135)

To Him Be Glory
SATB oct PRESSER 312-21579 $.30 (K136)

KECHLEY, [GERALD] (1919-)
I Lift My Eyes To The Hills
SATB,org oct KERBY 6004 $.35 (K137)
SATB oct KERBY 6004C $.35 (K138)

In The Lonely Midnight
SATB,acap oct PRESSER 312-40743 $.30 (K139)

Maker Of All The Earth
SATB,acap oct PRESSER 312-40715 $.35 (K140)

Psalm 121
SATB,acap oct PRESSER 312-40710 $.30 (K141)

Thank We Now The Lord Of Heaven
SATB,acap oct PRESSER 312-40739 $.35 (K142)

We Are Thy Servants, O Lord
SATB,acap oct PRESSER 312-40716 $.30 (K143)

KEDRON
(Niles; Sheppard) 3pt wom cor oct SCHIRM.G 10708 $.25 (K144)
(Niles; Sheppard) 4pt mix cor oct SCHIRM.G 10712 $.25 (K145)
(Niles; Sheppard) 3pt mix cor oct SCHIRM.G 10970 $.25 (K146)

KEDRON see Niles, John Jacob

KEDUSCHA see Rossi, Salomone

KEDUSHAH see Bar-Am, Benjamin

KEDUSHAH see Spicker, M.

KEEGAN
My Soul Shall Be Joyful *folk
ALBERT s.p. (K147)

KEEL
Lullaby *Xmas
(Hales) SSA oct GALAXY 1.2440.1 $.30 (K148)

KEEL, RICHARD
Hear Now Our Cry, Alleluia
4pt mix cor,SB soli oct SCHIRM.G 11276 $.25 (K149)

Resurrection According To St. Matthew, The *Easter
4pt mix cor,org oct SCHIRM.G 11285 $.25 (K150)

KEEP A-INCHIN' ALONG *spir
(Johnson) 4pt mix cor,T solo,acap oct SCHIRM.G 10485 $.30 (K151)

KEEP A QUIET PLACE APART see Schaefer, Christopher

KEEP AN EYE ON ME see Gustafson, D.

KEEP CHRIST IN CHRISTMAS see Hughes

KEEP HIS COMMANDMENTS see Newbury, Kent A.

KEEP IN DE MIDDLE OF DE ROAD *spir
(Swift) SATB,acap oct PRO ART 1269 $.25 (K152)

KEEP IN THE MIDDLE OF THE ROAD *spir
(Barthlomew) 4pt men cor,acap oct SCHIRM.G 7391 $.40 (K153)
(Barthlomew) mix cor,acap oct SCHIRM.G 10080 $.30 (K154)

KEEP ME EVER CLOSE TO THEE see York

KEEP ME NEAR THEE see Hardy, B. Edward

KEEP ME WHERE LOVE IS *CCUL
(Carmichael, Ralph; Floria, Cam) jr cor voc sc WORD 20029 $1.95 (K155)

KEEP MY COMMANDMENTS see Ford

KEEP NOT THOU SILENCE see Hovhaness, Alan

KEEP NOT THY SILENCE see Schwadron

KEEP ON SINGIN' see Crouch, Andrae

KEEP US EVER IN THY MERCY see Dieterich

KEEPING HOLY VIGIL see Schroth

KEESE
Christmas Wish, A *Xmas
SATB SCHMITT 1185 $.35 (K156)
SSA SCHMITT 343 $.35 (K157)
SAB SCHMITT 5019 $.30 (K158)

Father Teach Me How To Pray
SATB oct VOLKWEIN VB148 $.25 (K159)

KEIN HALMLEIN WACHST AUF ERDEN see Bach, Wilhelm Friedemann

KEIN MEISTER FALLT VOM HIMMEL see Schroeder, Hermann

KEIN PROBLEM WIRD GELOST see Hindermann, Walter Felix

KEINEN HAT GOTT VERLASSEN see Bach, Johann Sebastian

KEINER, DER DIE HARFE SCHLAGT see Blarr, Oskar Gottlieb

KEINER WEISS, WIE ARM ER IST see Schubert, Heino

KEISER, REINHARD (1674-1739)
Markus-Passion *Psntd
(Schroeder) SATB,SATB soli,cont,ob,2vln, 2vla HANSSLER 10.152 sc $15.00, voc sc $2.50, ipa (K160)

KEJA, J.F.
Eia Dulcis Anima
mix cor ALSBACH&D sc s.p., cor pts s.p. (K161)

Johannes 20:26, 27 En 28 *liturg
4pt wom cor BROEKMANS 497 s.p. (K162)

Kerstlied
4pt wom cor ALSBACH&D sc s.p., cor pts s.p. (K163)

KELDORFER, ROBERT (1901-)
Maria Und Das Vogelein
wom cor,acap oct DOBLINGER s.p. (K164)

KELDORFER, VIKTOR (1873-1959)
An Die Heilige Jungfrau
[Ger] mix cor,S solo,5strings/org HUG s.p. (K165)

KELEMEN, MILKO (1924-)
Hommage A Heinrich Schuetz (Psalm 120)
[Lat] SATB,SATB soli PETERS 5977 $1.50 (K166)

Psalm 120 *see Hommage A Heinrich Schuetz

KELLAM
And The Angel Came In Unto Mary *anthem
mix cor oct OXFORD 42.342 $.25 (K167)

KELLER, WILHELM
Amate *Bibl
4-6pt mix cor MOSELER s.p. (K168)

Drei Gebete *prayer
6pt mix cor MOSELER LB-523 s.p.
contains: Gott, Befrei Uns Von Der Angst; Gott Halt Fern Von Uns; Wer Du Auch Bist (K169)

Gott, Befrei Uns Von Der Angst
see Drei Gebete

Gott Halt Fern Von Uns
see Drei Gebete

Wer Du Auch Bist
see Drei Gebete

KELLERMAN
Adonoy Moh Odom
(Roskin) [Heb/Eng] SATB HATIKVAH HCL 22 $.35 (K170)

KELLERMEYER, DAVID M.
I'm Gonna Sing *spir
SATB oct BOURNE 806 $.30 (K171)

KELLEY
Be Known To Us In Breaking Of The Bread
SATB,opt org/pno BOSTON 13431 $.30 (K172)

Lord Is King, The
SSA oct SUMMY M 2725 $.25 (K173)

KELLEY, B.
Magnificat And Nunc Dimitis *Magnif/Nunc
SATB BELWIN AP 25 $.50 (K174)

KELLING, H.
Engelskonzert *mot
(Silesius, A.) SSATBB (med) cor pts
LEUCKART s.p.   (K175)

KELLY
All Poor Men And Humble
SATB,acap (easy) OXFORD 84.082 $.20 (K176)
unis/SATB (very easy) OXFORD 08.034 $.15 (K177)

Canticum Festivum *Fest
SATB,T solo (diff) OXFORD 46.134 $2.10, ipr (K178)

Cradle, The *Xmas,carol
SATB,acap (easy) OXFORD 84.115 $.25 (K179)

I Will Always Give Thanks *Thanks
SATB oct PRO ART 2245 $.25   (K180)

KELLY, BRYAN
Bright Is The Day *Gen/Marriage,anthem
mix cor oct NOVELLO 28.1454.04 s.p. (K181)

Done Is A Battell On The Dragon Blak *anthem
mix cor oct NOVELLO 40.1495.02 s.p. (K182)

Holy Communion *Commun
SATB (C maj) oct NOVELLO 44.1434.09 s.p. (K183)

Magnificat And Nunc Dimittis *Magnif/Nunc
SATB oct NOVELLO 44.1419.05 s.p.   (K184)

Missa Brevis *Agnus/Credo/Gloria/Kyrie/
Sanctus
SATB,org/orch (med diff) oct OXFORD 46.134
$2.55, ipr   (K185)

O Be Joyful In The Lord *anthem,Carib
mix cor oct NOVELLO 28.1482.10 s.p. (K186)

Out Of The Deep *anthem
SATB,org/brass oct NOVELLO 29.0013.00 s.p.,
ipr   (K187)

Ponder My Words, O Lord *anthem
mix cor,acap oct NOVELLO 40.1480.04 s.p. (K188)

Rejoice The Lord Is King! *Asc/Gen,anthem
mix cor oct NOVELLO 91.0004.00 s.p. (K189)

Surrexit Hodie *Easter,cant
[Lat] SATB,Bar solo,org,strings,opt perc&
timp voc sc NOVELLO s.p., ipr   (K190)

Tenebrae Nocturnes *Holywk
[Lat] SATB,T solo,pno,strings,2perc,timp
voc sc NOVELLO s.p., ipr   (K191)

Veni Sancte Spiritus *Whitsun,mot
[Lat] mix cor,acap oct NOVELLO 86.0022.08
s.p.   (K192)

KELTERBORN, RUDOLF (1931-   )
Die Flut *Gen,ora
[Ger] SSAATBB,SATBar soli,orch (diff) sc
BAREN. BA 4426 rental, voc sc BAREN.
BA 4426A $22.00   (K193)

Missa *Mass
[Lat] SATB,ST soli,orch (med diff) BAREN.
BA 3984 rental   (K194)

Musica Spei *Adv/Gen
[Ger] SATB,S solo,org (med diff) BAREN.
BA 4128 s.p.   (K195)
[Ger] 4pt mix cor,S solo,org (med diff)
BAREN. BA 4128 s.p.   (K196)

Tres Cantiones Sacrae *CC3U,Gen
[Ger] SSAATBB,acap (diff) BAREN. BA 5414
s.p.   (K197)

KEMMER, [GEORGE W.] (1890-   )
Crucifixion, The *spir
SATB,SATB soli,acap oct COLOMBO 1272 $.25 (K198)

I Wan' Jesus To Walk With Me *spir
SATB oct COLOMBO 1252 $.25   (K199)

There Is A Balm In Gilead
SSA oct GALAXY 1.1990.1 $.30   (K200)

KEMP, JEFFREY
King Is Born, A *Xmas
unis ASHDOWN U.81 s.p.   (K201)
unis BOOSEY-CAN s.p.   (K202)

KEMPINSKI, LEO [A.] (1891-1958)
Teach Us To Pray
4pt mix cor oct SCHIRM.G 9844 $.25   (K203)

We Lift Our Hearts To Thee
4pt mix cor oct SCHIRM.G 9843 $.25   (K204)

KEMPTER, KARL (1819-1871)
Missa Sancta *Op.13, Mass
SA/mix cor,org,opt winds,strings,opt timp
WEINBERGER s.p., ipa voc sc, cor pts (K205)

KENDALL, JOHN
Dartmouth Magnificat, The *Magnif
STBB STAINER CS322 s.p.   (K206)

KENDEL, ADOLF
Sollt Ich Meinem Gott Nicht Singen *cant
SATB,4brass HANSSLER 10.154 sc s.p., cor
pts s.p., ipa   (K207)

KENDELL, IAIN (1931-   )
Dawn Victory *cant
[Eng] SABar,org,orch CHESTER sc s.p., cor
pts s.p., ipa   (K208)

Mass Of St. Thomas Of Canterbury *Mass
[Eng] unis,pno/org,perc,rec CHESTER sc
s.p., voc pt s.p.   (K209)

KENDRIE, FRANK E.
Agnus Dei
"Lamb Of God" SATB,acap SCHIRM.EC 2233 $.30 (K210)

Lamb Of God *see Agnus Dei

KENINS, TALIVALDIS (1919-   )
Bon Homme *anthem
[Fr] SATB,acap oct HARRIS HC4015 $.40 (K211)

KENNEDY
Little Lamb, Who Made Thee?
TB oct BOOSEY 5654 $.30   (K212)
SA oct BOOSEY 5653 $.30   (K213)

Rise, My Soul, And Stretch Thy Wings
SAB,org oct BOOSEY 5705 $.35   (K214)

Shepherd
boy cor SOUTHERN $.30   (K215)

Star Of The East *Xmas
SATB (very easy) oct LORENZ A259 $.25 (K216)
SATB oct LORENZ B36 $.30   (K217)
(Gray) SATB oct PRO ART 1281 $.25   (K218)
(Gray) SSA oct PRO ART 1282 $.22   (K219)
(Worley) SATB oct BELWIN 1148 $.25   (K220)
(Worley) SATB oct BELWIN 1371 $.25   (K221)

KENNEDY, JOHN BRODBIN
Alleluia Fanfare
mix cor,pno,2trp,3trom,timp,perc oct BOURNE
876 $.40, ipr   (K222)

Almost Over
see Kennedy, John Brodbin, Four Spiritual
Songs, Set 2

Bound To Go (from Glistening Shore, The) spir
SATB,acap (easy) oct MCAFEE M1020 $.35 (K223)

Dedication
SATB oct BOURNE 936 $.35   (K224)

Don't Be Weary, Traveller
see Kennedy, John Brodbin, Four Spiritual
Songs, Set 1

Four Spiritual Songs, Set 1 *spir
SATB oct BOURNE 874 $.75 contains also:
Don't Be Weary, Traveller; No Man Can
Hinder Me; Just Now; Good-Bye, Brother (K225)

Four Spiritual Songs, Set 2 *spir
SATB oct BOURNE 875 $.75 contains also:
Happy Morning; Almost Over; Jesus, Won't
You Come Bye-And-Bye; Gone To Glory   (K226)

Gloria (from Unto Us A Child Is Born) Xmas/
Gen,anthem
SATB,pno/org (med) oct MCAFEE M1030 $.50 (K227)

Gone To Glory
see Kennedy, John Brodbin, Four Spiritual
Songs, Set 2

Good-Bye, Brother
see Kennedy, John Brodbin, Four Spiritual
Songs, Set 1

Good-Bye, Halleluia (from Glistening Shore,
The) spir
SATB,acap (easy) oct MCAFEE M1019 $.35 (K228)

Happy Morning
see Kennedy, John Brodbin, Four Spiritual
Songs, Set 2

I Know When I'm Going Home (from Glistening
Shore, The) spir
SATB,acap (easy) oct MCAFEE M1021 $.35 (K229)

It Is All I Have To Bring Today
SSA,acap FISCHER,J 10093 $.30   (K230)

Jesus, Won't You Come Bye-And-Bye
see Kennedy, John Brodbin, Four Spiritual
Songs, Set 2

Just Now
see Kennedy, John Brodbin, Four Spiritual
Songs, Set 1

Lift Up Your Voices Now!
SATB,opt brass oct BOURNE 880 $.35, ipr (K231)

No Man Can Hinder Me
see Kennedy, John Brodbin, Four Spiritual
Songs, Set 1

Unto Us A Child Is Born *CCU
SATB,SB soli MCAFEE $1.50   (K232)

KENNERLY
Blow, Ye Winds, Softly *Xmas
SATB oct LORENZ C37 $.30   (K233)

Dear Christ Of Galilee
SATB oct LORENZ B18 $.30   (K234)

Lord's Prayer, The
SATB oct LORENZ 4445 $.30   (K235)
SA/SAB oct LORENZ 7807 $.25   (K236)

KENNEY
Bethlehem Star, The *Xmas,cant
SATB oct LORENZ $1.95   (K237)

He Lives Again *Easter,cant
SATB LORENZ $1.95   (K238)

KENOTAFIUM see Norholm, Ib

KENSWILL, A.
Lentelicht
wom cor,pno ALSBACH&D sc s.p., cor pts s.p. (K239)

KENT
Blessing, Honor, Pow'r And Glory
(Sheppard) boy cor SOUTHERN $.30   (K240)
(Sheppard) TTBB,acap BOSTON 12346 $.35 (K241)

Thine, O Lord, Is The Greatness *Fest
SATB ALLANS 319 s.p.   (K242)

KENT, J.
Salvation Belongeth Unto The Lord
(Young R.; Weinandt, E.) SATB oct FISCHER,J
10009 $.45   (K243)

Thine, O Lord, Is The Greatness
SATB oct LESLIE 4064   (K244)

KENT, JAMES (1700-1776)
Pater Noster
SATB THOMP.G E.I.1012 s.p.   (K245)

KENT, JAMES (cont'd.)
Thine, O Lord, Is The Greatness *anthem
mix cor oct NOVELLO 40.0023.04 s.p. (K246)

KENT, RICHARD
Gentle Mary *Xmas,carol
SATB,pno oct WORLD AC-1509-8 $.45   (K247)

In The Bleak Midwinter *anthem
SATB (med) oct AUGSBURG 1556 $.25   (K248)

Lord Is My Shepherd, The (Psalm 23) Bibl
SATB,S solo,acap oct WORLD CA-2311-8 $.45 (K249)

Psalm 23 *see Lord Is My Shepherd, The

Reasons For Singing *Bibl
[Eng/Lat] SATB,acap oct LAWSON 51575 $.30 (K250)

KERESZTOLTES
(Farkas, F.) [Hung] 2 eq voices cmplt ed
BUDAPEST 5767 s.p.
contains: Jankovics, F.: Kanon; Weores, S.:
Kereztoltes; Weores, S.: Tancnota   (K251)

KEREZTOLTES see Weores, S.

KERLE, JACOBUS DE (ca. 1531-1591)
Exsurge, Quare Obdormis *Psntd/Sexa,mot
[Lat] SATB,acap (med) MULLER M 12 s.p. (K252)
[Lat] mix cor,acap oct NOVELLO DM-12 s.p. (K253)

Gloria *mot
[Lat] TTBB RICORDI-ENG SY148 s.p.   (K254)

Introitus, Alleluja, Communio
mix cor voc sc VOLK 136 s.p.   (K255)

Lauda Sion Salvatorem
mix cor voc sc VOLK 137 s.p.   (K256)

KERLL, [JOHANN CASPAR] (1627-1693)
Benedictus *Bene
[Swed] men cor,SA soli,org GEHRMANS KRB 231
s.p.   (K257)

KERN
Song Of Mary, The *Xmas
SATB oct PRO ART 1902 $.25   (K258)

KERN, MATTHAIS (1921-   )
Als Ich Bei Meinen Schafen Wacht
4pt mix cor MOSELER LB-439 s.p. contains
also: Dank Sei Dir, Herr (2pt mix cor) (K259)

Canticum Ezechiae
5pt mix cor MOSELER s.p.   (K260)

Chor Im Kirchenjahr-Heft I Und II *CC55U,
liturg
2-6pt mix cor MOSELER s.p.   (K261)

Dank Sei Dir, Herr
see Kern, Matthais, Als Ich Bei Meinen
Schafen Wacht

Die Sonne Brennt
3 eq voices MOSELER LB-189 s.p. see from
Kleiner Tageskreis II   (K262)

Drei Gleichnisse Jesu *CC3U
3-6pt mix cor MOSELER s.p.   (K263)

Kleine Deutsche Liedmesse *Mass
SATB HANSSLER 7.088 s.p.   (K264)

Kleiner Tageskreis I *see Licht, Leuchtendes
Licht   (K265)

Kleiner Tageskreis II *see Die Sonne Brennt (K266)

Kleiner Tageskreis III *see Rotgoldene
Sonnenglut   (K267)

Licht, Leuchtendes Licht
3 eq voices MOSELER LB-188 s.p. see from
Kleiner Tageskreis I   (K268)

Rotgoldene Sonnenglut
3 eq voices MOSELER LB-190 s.p. see from
Kleiner Tageskreis III   (K269)

Sapientia In Christo *ora
mix cor,Bar solo,org/2fl,3ob,clar,2bsn,
3horn,2trp,2trom,strings,4perc sc MOECK
s.p.   (K270)

Vier Spruchmotetten *CC4U,mot
4pt mix cor MOSELER s.p.   (K271)

KERR
I've Got A Melody
(McLellan) SATB oct LILLENAS AT-1055 $.25 (K272)

Love Is Come Again
SATB (med diff/diff) SOUTHERN $.35   (K273)

KERSTCANTATA see Zwart, Jan

KERSTCANTATE see Dyserinck, A.

KERSTCANTATE see Lambrechts-Vos, A.

KERSTERS, WILLEM
Duo Psalterii Cantica *Op.47a, CC2U
[Lat] 4pt mix cor,acap CBDM s.p.   (K274)

Gospel Song, A *Op.35
cor,4 soli,orch CBDM voc sc s.p., cor pts
s.p.   (K275)

Psalm 29 *Op.47b
[Lat] men cor,T solo,acap CBDM s.p. (K276)

KERSTGEDACHTE see Dyserinck, A.

KERSTLIED see Diamant, B.

KERSTLIED see Hertog, H.J. den

KERSTLIED see Keja, J.F.

KERSTLIED see Loots, Ph.

KERSTLIED see Loser, J.H.

KERSTLIED see Oort, H.C.v.

KERSTLIED (GIJ, AL ONS HEIL, ONS HOOGSTE GOED)
see Bach, Johann Sebastian

KERSTLIED (HOE ZAL IK U ONTVANGEN) see Bach,
Johann Sebastian

KERSTLIEDEJE see Rontgen, [Julius]

KERSTLIEDEREN see Noble, Felix de

KERSTLIEDEREN UIT DE 16E, 17E, EN 18E EEUW.
*CC10U,16th cent/17th cent/18th cent
(Hoogerwerf, N.) men cor ALSBACH&D sc s.p.
cor pts s.p.   (K277)

KERSTMIS see Olman, Isr, J.

KERSTNACHT see Beekhuis, Hanna

KERSTNACHT see Bonset, Jac.

KERSTNACHT see Oort, H.C.v.

KERSTVERHAAL see Lijsen, A.

KERSTVERHALL see Lijsen, A.

KESNAR
Peace *Gen
SATB SCHMITT 860 $.16   (K278)

KESSLER, MINUETTA
Peace And Brotherhood Through Music
[Eng] SATB TRANSCON. TCL 339 $2.50   (K279)

KETCHUM, ALBERT
Why Do I Sing About Jesus *hymn
(Hustad, Don) SATB/SAB ALLANS 456 s.p.   (K280)

KETELBEY, ALBERT WILLIAM (1875-1959)
Ave Maria
SATB BOSWORTH s.p.   (K281)

KETSZOLAMU KORUSGYUJTEMENY *sac/sec,CC92L
[Hung] 2pt mix cor (easy) BUDAPEST 1277 s.p.
contains sacred works by: Des Prez, Josquin (K282)

KETTERER, LAURA
Carol To The New Born King *see Noel,
Nouvelet, Noel Provencal

Noel, Nouvelet, Noel Provencal *Xmas,carol
"Carol To The New Born King" SSA,pno (med)
oct WILLIS 7485 $.20   (K283)

KETTERING, EUNICE LEA
Christ, The Christ Is Risen *Easter
SATB,org/pno,opt 3trp FISCHER,J 10091 $.35 (K284)

I Hear America Singing
SATB oct AGAPE SP 694 $.60   (K285)

Sing Unto The Lord *Bibl
SSA,pno/org/harp oct WORLD ESA-1649-3 $.60 (K286)

Song From St. Matthew *Xmas
2pt wom cor,org/pno oct SCHIRM.G 11534 $.25 (K287)

KETTRING, DONALD D.
God Watches Over All
unis oct GRAY GCMR 1935 $.25   (K288)

KEVAN
Communion Service In E Flat Major *Commun
SATB oct PRO ART 1485 $.18   (K289)

Communion Service In F Minor *Commun
SATB oct PRO ART 1447 $.18   (K290)

God Builds No Churches
SATB oct PRO ART 1442 $.18   (K291)

Jesus Christ Is Risen Today *Easter/Lent
jr cor&sr cor oct PRO ART 1650 $.25   (K292)

Marriage Prayer, A
SATB oct PRO ART 1649 $.18   (K293)

KEVAN, G.
Comfortable Words Of Jesus, The
SATB oct PRESSER 312-40344 $.35   (K294)

God, Be In My Head
SATB,acap oct PRESSER 312-40162 $.25   (K295)

Hear My Prayer, O Lord
SATB oct PRESSER 312-40400 $.35   (K296)

KEY, F.S.
Star Spangled Banner, The *anthem
(Pfautsch, Lloyd) SATB oct AGAPE SP 681
$.25   (K297)
(Pfautsch, Lloyd) SSAA oct AGAPE SP 680
$.25   (K298)

KEYS, BALL-IVOR
Road To The Stable *Xmas
unis BELWIN AP 13 $.35   (K299)

KEYS, IVOR
Magnificat And Nunc Dimittis *Magnif/Nunc
SATB oct NOVELLO 86.0013.09 $.19   (K300)

Prayer For Pentecostal Fire *Whitsun
SATB (easy) oct OXFORD 42.844 $.25   (K301)

KEYS OF HEAVEN, THE *folk,Eng
(Ehret, Walter) SAB oct WALTON 4001 $.25   (K302)

KEYS TO THE KINGDOM, THE
SATB BIG3 $.25   (K303)

KI LEKACH TOV see Lewandowski, Louis

KI LEKACH TOV see Richards, Stephen

KI MI TZIYON *folk,Jew
(Luongo; Poch) SATB STANDARD C600MX1 $.35 (K304)

KICKSTAT, PAUL
Stimmt Unserm Gott Ein Loblied An *Thanks
SATB HANSSLER 6.015 s.p.   (K305)

KIDDISH THROUGH THE JEWISH YEAR, THE see Fromm,
Herbert

KIDDUSH see Gottlieb, J.

KIDDUSH see Neuman

KIDDUSH FOR PASSOVER see Weisgal, A.

KIEKBUSCH
Out Of The Depths, O Lord, We Cry *Gen
(Zuberbier) SATB SCHMITT 1740 $.30   (K306)

KIESERLING, RICHARD
Song Of The Reapers
SATB oct HUNTZINGER 4043 $.20   (K307)

KIHLKEN, HENRY
Christmas Plainsong, A
SATB oct GRAY GCMR 3066 $.30   (K308)

Crucifixion, The *Lent
SATB oct GRAY GCMR 3080 $.30   (K309)

Lute Book Lullaby *Xmas,cradle
SAB oct FISCHER,C CM-7760 $.25   (K310)

O Living Bread
SATB,SA soli,org GRAY GCMR 3277 $.30 (K311)

O Saving Victim *Easter/Lent
SATB oct FISCHER,C CM-7678 $.25   (K312)

KILLGROVE
Rejoice The Lord Is King (from Harmonia
Sacra)
SATB WARNER R3345 $.30   (K313)

KILNARWICK
With Contrite Hearts *hymn
(Brandon) SAB oct SHAPIRO SCE 5504 $.30 (K314)

KILPATRICK, JACK F.
Christ Whose Glory Fills The Sky
SATB,acap (easy) oct WILLIS 6989 $.20 (K315)

Deal Bountifully With Thy Servant
SATB,pno (med) oct WILLIS 7058 $.20 (K316)

Prayer For Our Native Land, A
SATB,acap (med) oct WILLIS 6911 $.18 (K317)

KIMBALL
Down East Spirituals *CC11U,spir
(Daniel) 3-4pt mix cor/3-4pt men cor PETERS (K318)

I Heard A Great Voice
(McAfee) SATB oct BOURNE 845 $.25   (K319)

O Come, Sing Unto The Lord
(McAfee) SATB oct BOURNE 852 $.35   (K320)

KIMER, I KLOKKER see Geitvik, S.H.

KIMES
Lord Bless You And Keep You, The
SSA HANSEN-US C248A $.40   (K321)
SATB HANSEN-US C248B $.40   (K322)
SA HANSEN-US C248C $.40   (K323)

KIMMEL
Blessed Miracles
SATB FLAMMER A 5614 $.30   (K324)

It Is Good
SATB FLAMMER A 5588 $.35   (K325)

This Is What We Are
SATB SHAWNEE A 1146 $.30   (K326)

KIMMELL
Glory To God
SATB FLAMMER A 5561 $.30   (K327)

KIND FATHER, LOOK WITH PITY NOW see Brandon

KIND OF MAN I AM! , THE see Mc Call, Harlo

KIND UND GOTTESSOHN see Woll, Erna

KINDEKE JEZUS
(Vaal, O. De) mix cor sc ALSBACH&D s.p.   (K328)

KINDEKEN VAN BETHLEHEM see Kort, Jac

KINDELEIN ZART *Xmas
(Bauernfeind, Hans) mix cor,acap oct
DOBLINGER s.p. see also Zwei
Weihnachtslieder   (K329)

KINDERLOB see Rothenberg, Friedrich Samuel

KINDERMANN, JOHANN ERASMUS (1616-1655)
Creator Spirit, By Whose Aid *Gen/Pent
SA/TB,vln (med easy) oct CONCORDIA 98-1482
$.25   (K330)

Dear Christians, Praise God Evermore *Gen
unis,kbd (med easy) oct CONCORDIA 98-1503
$.20   (K331)

Denk Nicht, Der Herr Sei Noch Fern *Gen
[Ger] 3pt mix cor,cont (med easy) BAREN.
BA 3682 s.p.   (K332)

Nun Lieben Christen Freuet Euch
unis jr cor/unis wom cor,org,2vln sc
BREITKOPF-W CHB-3491 s.p.   (K333)

KINDERSEGEN see Wasner, Franz

KINDIG
Plaintive Carol, A
SATB FLAMMER A 5455 $.25   (K334)

KING
His Love Will Shine Like A Light
(Toti) SATB oct PLYMOUTH JR-149 $.35 (K335)

Hymn To The Trinity *hymn
SATB oct PLYMOUTH PCS-35 $.25   (K336)

I Want God's Heaven To Be Mine
SATB MARKS 4601 $.30   (K337)

I Will Always Give Thanks
boy cor SOUTHERN $.25   (K338)

Psalm 117 *Gen
SATB SCHMITT 850 $.20   (K339)

KING, ALL GLORIOUS see Barnby, Sir Joseph

KING ALL GLORIOUS see Marenzio, Luca, O Rex
Gloriae

KING ALL-GLORIOUS see Nolte

KING ALL GLORIOUS see Stairs, L.

KING ALL-GLORIOUS see Vail

KING, ALVIN
O Clap Your Hands, All Ye People (Psalm 47)
SATB,narrator,org,4trp,horn,2trom,tuba
(med) sc AUGSBURG 11-9336 $1.75, ipa, cor
pts AUGSBURG 11-9335 $.40   (K340)

Psalm 47 *see O Clap Your Hands, All Ye
People

KING AND SAVIOUR see Hawkins, Floyd W.

KING AND THE STAR, THE see Blake, Rev. Canon,
E.C.

KING ASCENDETH INTO HEAVEN, THE see Willan,
Healey

KING, BETTY J.
Come Down, Angels
SATB KJOS 5393 $.30   (K341)

KING COMETH see Stults, R.

KING DAVID see Honegger, Arthur, Le Roi David

KING DAVID'S DELIVERANCE see Kirk, Theron W.

KING ETERNAL see Williams

KING ETERNAL see Wilson, Ira B.

KING FOREVER see Denton

KING, HAROLD C. (1895-   )
Anthem (St. Luke XXI)
see Vier Gezangen Uit De "Morning Service"

Jubilate Deo
see Vier Gezangen Uit De "Morning Service"

Lord Is His Name, The
[Eng] mix cor,3trp,opt org min sc DONEMUS
s.p.   (K342)

Te Deum Laudamus
see Vier Gezangen Uit De "Morning Service"

Two Anthems For Whitsuntide *Whitsun,Bibl/
Psalm
[Dut] mix cor,org DONEMUS sc s.p., cor pts
s.p.   (K343)

Venite, Exultemus Domino
see Vier Gezangen Uit De "Morning Service"

Vier Gezangen Uit De "Morning Service" *Morn
[Lat] mix cor,org,3trp min sc DONEMUS s.p.,
ipa
contains: Anthem (St. Luke XXI); Jubilate
Deo; Te Deum Laudamus; Venite,
Exultemus Domino   (K344)

KING HEROD see Kay, Norman

KING HEROD AND THE COCK
(Britten) unis oct BOOSEY 5612 $.30 (K345)

KING IN BETHLEHEM *Xmas/Pageant
LORENZ $.75   (K346)

KING IN THE CRECHE, THE see Boeringer, James

KING IN THE STABLE see Johnston

KING IS BORN, A see Kemp, Jeffrey

KING IS GIVEN *Xmas,cant
oct LORENZ $1.00   (K347)

KING IS KNOCKING, THE see Sateren, Leland
Bernhard

KING IS RIDING BY, THE see Price

KING JESUS HATH A GARDEN see Wyton, Alex

KING JESUS IS A LISTENIN' *spir
(Cain) SSATB SCHMITT 1664 $.40   (K348)
(Ehret) SATB oct LAWSON 574 $.25   (K349)

KING JESUS IS A-LISTENIN' see Stanton, Royal
[W.]

KING OF GLORY see Bach, Johann Sebastian

KING OF GLORY see Davies, Henry Walford

KING OF GLORY see Lee, E. Markham

KING OF GLORY see Morrison, R.

KING OF GLORY see Parks

KING OF GLORY, KING OF PEACE see Bach, Johann
Sebastian

KING OF GLORY, KING OF PEACE see Friedell,
Harold W.

KING OF GLORY, KING OF PEACE see Herbert

KING OF GLORY, KING OF PEACE see Sheppard

KING OF GLORY, KING OF PEACE see Smith

KING OF GLORY, KING OF PEACE see Thiman, Eric
Harding

KING OF GLORY, KING OF PEACE see Williams, P.

KING OF GLORY PRAISE, THE see Darwall

KING OF GLORY STANDETH, THE see Schubert, Franz
(Peter)

KING OF GLORY, THE see Aichinger, Gregor, Salve
Regina

KING OF GLORY, THE see Emig, Lois

KING OF GLORY, THE see Parks

KING OF HEAVEN, COME IN TRIUMPH see Bach,
    Johann Sebastian, Himmelskonig, Sei
    Willkommen [Chorale]

KING OF KINGS *Easter
    see Two Negro Spirituals
    (Johnson) SATB oct VOLKWEIN VB201 $.25 (K350)

KING OF KINGS see Clokey

KING OF KINGS see Davies

KING OF KINGS see Davies, G.W.

KING OF KINGS see O'Hara, Geoffrey

KING OF KINGS see Simper, Caleb

KING OF KINGS see Van Iderstine, A.P.

KING OF KINGS THEME
    SSA/SATB BIG3 $.35   (K351)

KING OF LOVE see Durston, D.

KING OF LOVE see Young, Gordon

KING OF LOVE IS DEAD, THE see Taylor, Why?

KING OF LOVE MY SHEPHERD IS
    SAB KJOS 8013 $.30   (K352)

KING OF LOVE MY SHEPHERD IS, THE *anthem,Ir
    (Johnson, David N.) SAB (easy) oct AUGSBURG
    1544 $.25   (K353)

KING OF LOVE MY SHEPHERD IS, THE see Bach,
    Johann Sebastian

KING OF LOVE MY SHEPHERD IS, THE see Bairstow,
    Edward Cuthbert

KING OF LOVE MY SHEPHERD IS, THE see Bartow

KING OF LOVE MY SHEPHERD IS, THE see Cain,
    Noble

KING OF LOVE MY SHEPHERD IS, THE see Coggin

KING OF LOVE MY SHEPHERD IS, THE see Dykes,
    John Bacchus

KING OF LOVE MY SHEPHERD IS, THE see Feibel

KING OF LOVE MY SHEPHERD IS, THE see Gounod,
    Charles Francois

KING OF LOVE MY SHEPHERD IS, THE see Lundquist

KING OF LOVE MY SHEPHERD IS, THE see Martin

KING OF LOVE MY SHEPHERD IS, THE see Nolte,
    Edwald Valentin

KING OF LOVE MY SHEPHERD IS, THE see Schalk,
    Carl

KING OF LOVE MY SHEPHERD IS, THE see Shelley

KING OF LOVE MY SHEPHERD IS, THE see Shelley,
    [Harry Rowe]

KING OF LOVE MY SHEPHERD IS, THE see Simper,
    Caleb

KING OF LOVE MY SHEPHERD IS, THE see Westhoff,
    F.W.

KING OF LOVE(ON ST. COLUMBIA) see Coleman,
    Henry

KING OF LOVE, THE see Christiansen, Paul

KING OF LOVE, THE see Ewens, R.C.

KING OF LOVE, THE see Lang, C.S.

KING OF LOVE, THE see Shelley, [Harry Rowe]

KING OF LOVE, THE see Williamson, Malcolm

KING OF LOVE, THE see Wilson

KING OF PEACE see Aulbach

KING OF PEACE see Emerson, John

KING OF PEACE, THE see Emerson, John

KING OF PEACE, THE see Todd, M. Flora

KING OF THE WORLD see Frangkiser, Carl

KING, OLIVER A. (1855-1923)
    Sing We Merrily Unto God Our Strength *Fest/
    Gen,anthem
    mix cor oct NOVELLO 28.0932.10 s.p.   (K354)

KING, ROBERT (ca. 1660-ca. 1720)
    I Will Alway Give Thanks *Gen/Thanks
    SAB,kbd (med easy) oct CONCORDIA 98-1659
    $.25   (K355)

KING SHALL COME, THE see Fetler, Paul

KING SHALL COME, THE see Lockwood, Normand

KING SHALL COME WHEN MORNING DAWNS, THE see
    Beck, Theodore

KING SHALL COME WHEN MORNING DAWNS, THE see
    Lenel, Ludwig

KING SHALL COME WHEN MORNING DAWNS, THE see
    Lovelace, Austin C.

KING SHALL COME WHEN MORNING DAWNS, THE see
    Niles, John Jacob

KING SHALL REJOICE see Handel, George Frideric

KING SHALL REJOICE, THE see Handel, George
    Frideric

KING SOLOMON'S PRAYER see Naylor, Bernard

KINGDOM, THE see Elgar, Edward

KINGDOM OF GOD see Christiansen, F. Melius

KINGDOM OF HEAVEN see Crook, Jonn

KINGDOM OF LOVE AND LIGHT, THE see Nichol

KINGDOM, THE *carol
    unis/SATB (very easy) OXFORD 08.104 $.15
                                              (K356)

KINGERY
    Canticle In Meditation (composed with Clymer)
    *meditation
    (Alexander) unis/2pt WARNER WB-164 $.30
                                              (K357)

KINGO, THOMAS
    Gradual 1699 *CCU,Gradual
    [Dan/Ger] cor FOG 147 s.p.   (K358)

KING'S CALL TO GREATHEART, THE see Campbell,
    Sydney S.

KINGS FOLLOW THE STAR, THE see Goodale, R.L.

KING'S HIGHWAY see Blake, George [M.]

KING'S HIGHWAY see Hutson, Wihla

KING'S HIGHWAY, THE see Williams, David McK.

KING'S HIGHWAY SONGS *CC100U
    cong cmplt ed LILLENAS MB-099 $.60   (K359)

KING'S HIGHWAY, THE see Hamill

KING'S MEN, THE see Copley

KINGS OF BETHLEHEM, THE
    SATB BIG3 $.40   (K360)

KINGS OF THE EARTH AND ALL PEOPLE see Frank,
    Marcel [Gustave]

KINGS OF THE ORIENT THREE see Grieb, Herbert
    [C.]

KINGS, THE see Cornelius, Peter

KING'S WELCOME, THE see Whitehead, Alfred

KINGSBURY, L.
    O Kind Creator *Lent
    SATB oct GRAY GCMR 3012 $.30   (K361)

KINGSLEY
    From Thee All Skill And Science Flow
    (Rhea) TTBB oct PLYMOUTH UIL-108 $.25
                                              (K362)

KINSMAN
    Alleluia! Alleluia!
    SATB oct PLYMOUTH HA-7 $.25   (K363)

    Fanfare And Chorale For Easter *sac/sec,
    Easter/Lent,chorale
    SATB,opt 4brass oct SPRATT 548 $.25   (K364)

    I Look To Thee In Ev'ry Need
    SATB oct VOLKWEIN VB179 $.25   (K365)

    In Beth'lem's Lowly Stable *Xmas
    SATB oct PLYMOUTH XM-105 $.25   (K366)

    Manger Carol *Xmas,carol
    SATB oct PLYMOUTH XM-107 $.25   (K367)

    Mary Had A Baby *Xmas,spir
    SATB oct BOURNE 800 $.30   (K368)

    O Come, O Come Emmanuel *Xmas
    SATB oct PLYMOUTH XM-109 $.25   (K369)

    One Midnight Long Ago *Xmas
    SATB oct VOLKWEIN VB233 $.25   (K370)

    Rise Up, O Men Of God
    SATB oct VOLKWEIN VB253 $.25   (K371)

    Virgin Most Pure, A *Xmas
    SATB oct PLYMOUTH XM-115 $.25   (K372)

KINSMAN, ELMER F.
    To Greet The Babe So Holy *CC2U,Xmas
    SA (easy) ABINGDON APM-418 $.25   (K373)

KINYON
    O Come All Ye Faithful *Xmas
    SA ALFRED 6140 $.25   (K374)

KIPLINGER
    Glory Of The Lord
    SATB oct VOLKWEIN VB155 $.25   (K375)

KIPLINGER, JOHN
    Clap Your Hands, Ye People
    4pt mix cor,org/pno oct SCHIRM.G 11706 $.35
                                              (K376)

KIRBY
    Gentle Mary
    SATB FLAMMER A 5626 $.30   (K377)

    God Is Good To Us All
    SATB,opt drums,gtr, opt clave oct PRO ART
    2664 $.30   (K378)
    SATB,opt drums&gtr, opt clave (med easy)
    SOUTHERN $.30   (K379)

    Joyful Melody, A
    2pt oct LORENZ 5750 $.30   (K380)

    Joyful Sounds Of Praise *CC9L,Gen
    unis jr cor/2pt jr cor,pno,opt inst PRO ART
    1244 $1.25   (K381)

    O God Whose Vast Domain
    SATB FLAMMER A 5635 $.30   (K382)

    Prince Of Peace, The *Xmas,cant/folk
    SATB,opt gtr PRO ART 1258 $1.75, ipa   (K383)

    Psalm 20 *see Some Trust In Chariots

    Rise Up O Youth Of God
    2pt oct PRO ART 2570 $.30   (K384)

KIRBY (cont'd.)
    Service Music For SAB Choir *CCU,Bene/prayer
    SAB PRO ART 1152 $.85   (K385)

    Some Trust In Chariots (Psalm 20)
    SATB oct PRO ART 2543 $.30   (K386)

    When Jesus Came *Xmas,cant
    unis/2pt,opt inst oct PRO ART 1106 $1.00,
    ipa   (K387)

KIRBY, CHARLES
    God's Love
    SATB oct WORD CS-2498 $.30   (K388)

    Sing With One Accord
    SATB oct WORD CS-2443 $.30   (K389)

KIRBY, GEORGE
    O Jesu, Look *Gen/Lent
    SSATB (med easy) oct OXFORD 43.247 $.35
                                              (K390)

KIRBY, L.M. JR.
    Lord At First Did Adam Make, The *Xmas
    SATB,org FISCHER,J 10087 $.30   (K391)

KIRBYE, GEORGE
    Vox In Rama *mot
    SSATTB STAINER CC406 s.p.   (K392)

KIRCHE see Bornefeld, Helmut

KIRCHENGESANG see Hassler, Hans Leo

KIRCHENLIED IM KANON see Stern, Hermann

KIRCHENLIEDSATZE see Bauernfeind, Hans

KIRCHENLIEDSATZE see Doppelbauer, Josef
    Friedrich

KIRK
    Antiphon (Psalm 105)
    SATB,org/pno,opt brass,perc oct PRO ART
    1271 $.85, ipa   (K393)

    Awake, My Soul
    SATB oct PRO ART 2424 $.30   (K394)

    Behold, He Cometh!
    SATB oct LILLENAS AT-1060 $.30   (K395)

    Come Holy Ghost *see Veni Sancte Spiritus

    Coventry Carol *Xmas,carol
    SATB oct PLYMOUTH XM-116 $.25   (K396)

    Dearest Jesu, Holy Child *Xmas
    SATB oct PRO ART 2356 $.25   (K397)

    Down In The Meadows
    SATB oct HERITAGE H29 $.35   (K398)

    Eternal Son Of God
    SSA oct PRO ART 1412 $.30   (K399)
    girl cor SOUTHERN $.25   (K400)

    Glory Be To God On High
    SATB,acap oct PRO ART 1985 $.25   (K401)
    boy cor SOUTHERN $.25   (K402)
    TTB,acap oct PRO ART 2073 $.22   (K403)
    SSA,acap oct PRO ART 1906 $.22   (K404)
    SAB,acap oct PRO ART 1987 $.25   (K405)

    Glory Be To God The Father
    SATB,acap oct PRO ART 1365 $.18   (K406)

    Great Is The Lord
    SATB KJOS 5498A $.35   (K407)

    Gwine To Lay Down My Burden *spir
    SATB oct PRO ART 1545 $.22   (K408)

    Holy Ghost! With Light Divine
    SATB,acap oct PRO ART 1366 $.30   (K409)

    Hosanna To The Son Of David
    SATB KJOS 5807 $.30   (K410)

    I Will Give Thanks
    SATB oct PRO ART 1908 $.20   (K411)

    If You Love Me
    SATB,acap oct PRO ART 1941 $.22   (K412)

    Immanuel, We Sing Thy Praise
    SATB KJOS 5465 $.30   (K413)

    In Thee, O Lord, I Put My Trust (Psalm 31)
    SSA oct PRO ART 2213 $.25   (K414)
    SAB oct PRO ART 2216 $.25   (K415)
    SATB,acap oct PRO ART 1459 $.25   (K416)

    Jesu, Thou Joy Of Loving Hearts
    SATB,acap oct PRO ART 1294 $.25   (K417)

    Jesus Christ Is Risen Today *Easter/Lent
    SAB oct PRO ART 2063 $.22   (K418)
    SATB oct PRO ART 1292 $.25   (K419)
    SSA oct PRO ART 2046 $.25   (K420)

    Jesus In A Manger *Xmas
    SATB KJOS 5834 $.30   (K421)

    Lead Me, Lord
    SSA oct PRO ART 2259 $.30   (K422)
    SATB oct PRO ART 2256 $.30   (K423)

    Let All The People Praise God
    SATB KJOS 5862 $.30   (K424)

    Lord Is With Us, The
    SATB oct SACRED S-25 $.35   (K425)

    Lord, Thou Hast Been Our Refuge (Psalm 90)
    SATB,opt kbd oct PRO ART 2427 $.25   (K426)

    Man Of Galilee *see Procter

    Noel *Xmas
    cor,brass KJOS $1.95, ipa   (K427)

    O Come Loud Anthems Let Us Sing
    mix cor SOUTHERN $.30   (K428)

    O Praise The King Of Glory
    SATB,acap,opt pno oct PRO ART 2423 $.30
                                              (K429)

KIRK (cont'd.)

O Sing Praises
SATB,acap,opt pno oct PRO ART 2426 $.30
(K430)

SAB,acap,opt pno oct PRO ART 2540 $.30
(K431)

SSA,acap,opt pno oct PRO ART 2538 $.30
(K432)

Praise And Thanks Giving
SATB KJOS 5840 $.30
(K433)

Praise His Name
SATB KJOS 5863 $.35
(K434)

Praise, Praise Ye The Lord
SATB KJOS 5464 $.30
(K435)

Praise The Lord
SATB oct PRO ART 2748 $.35
(K436)

Praise Thee, Lord *Thanks
SATB oct PRO ART 1413 $.22
(K437)

Psalm 25
SATB,acap,opt pno oct PRO ART 1425 $.25
(K438)

Psalm 31 *see In Thee, O Lord, I Put My
Trust

Psalm 90 *see Lord, Thou Hast Been Our
Refuge

Psalm 95
SATB,opt kbd oct PRO ART 1415 $.35
(K439)

Psalm 105 *see Antiphon

Rejoice!
SSA oct PRO ART 2671 $.30
(K440)
SATB oct PRO ART 2506 $.30
(K441)
SAB oct PRO ART 2669 $.30
(K442)

Rejoice In The Lord
SATB,2trp MARKS 4428 $.30, ipa
(K443)

Rejoice In The Lord Always
SATB KJOS 5864 $.30
(K444)

Sing For Joy
SATB,org,2trp,2trom MARKS 4474 $.30, ipa
(K445)

Sing To The Lord A New Song
SATB KJOS 6302 $.35
(K446)

Still, Still, Still
SATB,acap (med diff/diff) SOUTHERN $.30
(K447)

Take My Life And Let It Be
SSA oct PRO ART 1486 $.18
(K448)

Temple Of The Living God
SATB,opt inst voc sc FISCHER,C CM-7788
$.40, ipa
(K449)

This Is The Day Which The Lord Hath Made
SATB oct PRO ART 2446 $.25
(K450)

Thou Wilt Keep Him In Peace
SATB KJOS 5865 $.30
(K451)

Thy Word Is A Lamp
SATB oct PRO ART 2443 $.25
(K452)

Veni Sancte Spiritus
"Come Holy Ghost" SSA oct PRO ART 1293 $.18
(K453)

We Turn To Thee
SATB,acap,opt pno oct PRO ART 1747 $.18
(K454)

What Shall We Bring
SATB KJOS 5867 $.30
(K455)

Ye Shall Be Witnesses
SATB oct LILLENAS AT-1017 $.30
(K456)

You Are The Light Of The World
SATB KJOS 5866 $.30
(K457)

KIRK, T.
Antiphonal Alleluia
SATB KJOS 5832 $.30
(K458)

Come Unto Me
SATB KJOS 5806 $.30
(K459)

Consider My Meditation
SATB KJOS 5835 $.30
(K460)

Here In The Silence
SATB KJOS 5827 $.30
(K461)

O Be Joyful In God
SATB KJOS 5836 $.30
(K462)

Sleep, Oh Sleep
SATB KJOS 5815 $.30
(K463)

Three Chorales In Modern Style *CC3U,chorale
SATB oct FISCHER,J 9904 $.30
(K464)

'Tis Now The Glorious Easter Morn *Easter
SATB oct FISCHER,J 9906 $.30
(K465)

KIRK, THERON W. (1919-   )
Alleluia, Praise The Lord
SATB STANDARD A36MX1 $.50
(K466)

Behold, God Is My Salvation *Bibl
SATB LUDWIG L-1126 $.35
(K467)

Blessed Art Thou, O Lord
SATB STANDARD A35MX1 $.50
(K468)

Carol Service With Nine Lessons *cant
mix cor BELWIN $1.50
(K469)

Create In Me A Clean Heart
SATB WARNER W3780 $.30
(K470)

Easter Antiphon *Easter
SATB FLAMMER A 5213 $.40
(K471)

Easter Canticle *Easter,cant
mix cor BELWIN $1.75
(K472)

Four Old English Carols *CC4U,Xmas,carol
SATB oct FISCHER,J 8835 $.35
(K473)

KIRK, THERON W. (cont'd.)

Glory To God *cant
mix cor BELWIN $1.50
(K474)

God Is Almighty
SATB,brass,timp oct BELWIN 60190 $.35, ipr
(K475)

Hosanna To The Son Of David *Palm
SATB oct SOUTHERN $.25
(K476)

I Will Give Thanks
SATB,acap SHAWNEE A 994 $.30
(K477)

I Will Sing Unto Thee
SATB LUDWIG L-1143 $.30
(K478)

King David's Deliverance *cant
mix cor BELWIN $1.50
(K479)

Let Us Now Praise Famous Men *Bibl
SATB oct WALTON 2115 $.35, sc WALTON rental
(K480)
SATB,orch voc sc WALTON 2115 $.35, ipr
(K481)

Lord Is Come, The
SATB SHAWNEE A 437 $.25
(K482)

Lord Is Good, The
SATB LUDWIG L-1134 $.35
(K483)

Night Of Wonder *cant
SATB SHAWNEE A798 $1.50
(K484)

O Clap Your Hands (Psalm 47)
SATB SHAWNEE A 1033 $.30
(K485)

O Come, Let Us Sing
SSATBB,inst oct SUMMY 5295 $.60, ipa
(K486)

O Come Loud Anthems Let Us Sing
SATB,acap SHAWNEE A 397 $.30
(K487)

O Holy Night Of Wonder
SATB oct MCA
(K488)

O Sons And Daughters *Easter
SATB,brass,timp oct SOUTHERN $.35
(K489)
SATB oct FISCHER,J 9903 $.35
(K490)

Praise!
SATB FLAMMER A 5167 $.30
(K491)

Praise To God
cor HIGHLAND 4104 $.25
(K492)

Psalm 47 *see O Clap Your Hands

Sing And Rejoice!
SATB LUDWIG L-1133 $.35
(K493)

Sing To The Lord
SATB LUDWIG L-1144 $.30
(K494)

Sing We Merrily Unto God
SATB oct MCA
(K495)

Songs Of Immortal Praise
SATB SHAWNEE A 687 $.30
(K496)

KIRKELIGE FESTSANGE see Eccard, Johannes

KIRKEN DEN ER ET GAMMELT HUS see Lindeman,
Ludvig Mathias

KIRKPATRICK
Away In A Manger *Xmas
(Sowerby) SATB&opt jr cor oct GRAY
GCMR 2537 $.30
(K497)

Comforter Has Come, The
(Whitsett) SATB oct LILLENAS AN-1602 $.30
(K498)

Earth Is The Lord's, The
SATB oct LORENZ 110 $.30
(K499)

Hallelujah! Amen!
(Whitsett) SATB oct LILLENAS AN-1627 $.30
(K500)

He Hideth My Soul *anthem
(Ferrin) SATB oct LILLENAS AN-1642 $.30
(K501)

I See His Blood Upon The Rose *Easter/Lent
SATB oct FISCHER,C CM-6528 $.30
(K502)

Jesus Saves *hymn
(Crill) SSATB oct LILLENAS AN-1103 $.30
(K503)

(Hustad, Don) SATB ALLANS 408 s.p.
(K504)

Lead Me To Calvary
(Hustad) SATB oct AGAPE HA 117 $.25
(K505)
(Wilson) SATB oct LORENZ A388 $.25
(K506)

My Faith Hath Found A Resting Place *Norw
(Hustad, Don) SATB/SAB ALLANS 52 s.p.
(K507)

(Hustad, Don) SAB ALLANS 452 s.p.
(K508)

Singing I Go
(Mickelson) SATB oct LILLENAS AN-1156 $.30
(K509)

(Williams) SATB oct LILLENAS AN-1618 $.35
(K510)

'Tis So Sweet To Trust In Jesus *hymn
(Hawkins) SATB oct LILLENAS AN-2364 $.25
(K511)

(Rasley) SATB oct LORENZ A413 $.25
(K512)

KIRKPATRICK W.
Away In A Manger *Xmas,anthem
(Brewer, R.) SATB&jr cor oct PRESSER
312-40617 $.30
(K513)
(Pooler) unis treb cor&desc (easy) oct
AUGSBURG 1369 $.22
(K514)

KIRKWOOD
Come And Mourn With Us *Lent
SATB SHAWNEE A 958 $.25
(K515)
SATB oct SOUTHERN $.25
(K516)

KIRSCHNEREIT, KURT
Zuversicht *cant
SATB,narrator,4trom HANSSLER 10.205 sc
s.p., cor pts s.p.
(K517)

KIS DAL A SZERLOL see Dobos, K.

KITSON, CHARLES HERBERT (1874-1944)
Benedictus *Bene
SATB,org CRAMER A7 s.p.
(K518)

Jesu, Grant Me This I Pray *Gen/Lent
SATB (med easy) oct OXFORD 42.041 $.30
(K519)

Magnificat And Nunc Dimittis *Magnif/Nunc
SATB CRAMER A5 s.p.
(K520)

Te Deum *Te Deum
SATB,org CRAMER A8 s.p.
(K521)

KITTERY see Billings, William

KITTLESON
Glory, Hallelujah! To De New Born King *Xmas
SATB SCHMITT 8022 $.35
(K522)

KJAERLIGHET FRA GUD see Beck, Thomas
[Ludvigsen]

KJELDAAS, ARNLJOT
Kristushymne
[Norw] mix cor LYCHE 12 s.p.
(K523)

Norsk Salme
mix cor MUSIKK 73 s.p.
(K524)

KJELDAAS, GUNNAR
Bon
men cor MUSIKK 69 s.p.
(K525)

KJELSON
At The Gates Of Heaven
(Vance) SA/TB oct BELWIN 1963 $.25
(K526)

Awake The Harp
SATB oct BELWIN 2213 $.25
(K527)

Bound For The Promised Land
SATB oct BELWIN 2253 $.25
(K528)

Jesus Walked This Lonesome Valley
(Vance) SSA oct BELWIN 2138 $.30
(K529)
(Vance) SA/TB oct BELWIN 1970 $.30
(K530)

O Lord Most Holy *see Panis Angelicus

Once To Every Man And Nation
4pt jr cor/SATB (med easy) FISCHER,C
CM 7193 $.25
(K531)

Panis Angelicus
(Vance) "O Lord Most Holy" SA/TB oct BELWIN
1971 $.30
(K532)

Psalm 23
(Vance) SA/TB oct BELWIN 1974 $.25
(K533)

Sacred Music For Mixed Voices *CCU
(Vance) SATB BELWIN $1.00
(K534)

Sacred Music For Treble Voices *CCU
(Vance) SSA BELWIN $1.00
(K535)

Standin' In The Need Of Prayer *spir
(Vance) SATB oct BELWIN 2234 $.25
(K536)
(Vance) SA/TB oct BELWIN 1902 $.30
(K537)

Thou Hast Heard My Cry *anthem
SATB,acap oct FISCHER,C CM-7108 $.25
(K538)

When Jesus Wept
(Vance) SATB oct BELWIN 2111 $.25
(K539)
(Vance) SA/TB oct BELWIN 1972 $.30
(K540)

Ye Sons And Daughters Now Shall Sing
SAB oct BELWIN 2025 $.30
(K541)

KJERULF, [HALFDAN] (1815-1868)
Jubilate, Amen
boy cor SOUTHERN $.15
(K542)

KLAUS
Glorious Art Thou
SATB oct PRO ART 1970 $.25
(K543)

KLEBE, GISELHER (1925-   )
Gebet Einer Armen Seele *Mass
[Ger] SSAATTBB,org (diff) BAREN. BA 4115
$7.00
(K544)

Stabat Mater *Op.46
[Lat] mix cor,SMezA soli,orch voc sc BOTE
s.p.
(K545)

KLEIN
As God The Lord Hath Spoken
SATB KJOS 5849 $.30
(K546)

Christmas Madrigal, A *Xmas
SATB SCHMITT SD6205 $.25
(K547)

Come To The Stable *Xmas
SATB oct PLYMOUTH PCS-14 $.25
(K548)

God Has Gone Up With A Shout
SATB SHAWNEE A 346 $.30
(K549)

God Is My Strong Salvation
SATB KJOS 5850 $.30
(K550)

God, The Creator Of The World
SATB KJOS 5280 $.30
(K551)

Good News From Heaven
SATB KJOS 5402 $.30
(K552)

Hear The Joyful Tidings
SATB FLAMMER A 5361 $.25
(K553)

I Know My Lord Is Promise
SATB,acap oct PRO ART 2485 $.25
(K554)

Let All Rejoice This Holy Night *Xmas
SATB oct PLYMOUTH PCS-23 $.25
(K555)

Lord, In Thee Have I Trusted
SATB KJOS 5422 $.30
(K556)

Lord Is My Shepherd, The
(Ehret) SATB oct SPRATT 564 $.25
(K557)

O Lord, In Thee Have I Trusted
SATB KJOS 5481C $.30
(K558)

KLEIN (cont'd.)

Rejoice Beloved Christians
SATB KJOS 5401 $.30   (K559)

Send Forth Thy Light Upon Us
SATB,acap,opt pno oct PRO ART 2486 $.25   (K560)

SAB oct PRO ART 2493 $.25   (K561)

Thou Art The King Of Glory
SATB KJOS 5481A $.30   (K562)

Two Festival Introits *CC2U,Fest,Introit
SATB KJOS 5851 $.30   (K563)

Waken, O Shepherds *Xmas
SATB SCHMITT 889 $.40   (K564)

KLEIN, B.
Hoch Tut Euch Auf *mot
men cor,acap ERDMANN 166 s.p.   (K565)

KLEIN, BERNHARD (1793-1832)
Der Herr Ist Mein Hirte (Psalm 23)
[Ger] mix cor,acap (med easy) HUG s.p.   (K566)

(Vogel, Moritz; Nagler, Franciscus) [Ger]
wom cor&jr cor,org,opt strings HUG 36
s.p.   (K567)

Psalm 23 *see Der Herr Ist Mein Hirte

KLEIN, IVY FRANCES
Tryste Noel *Xmas
cor CRAMER 94 s.p.   (K568)

KLEIN, KARL HEINZ
Bergbauernweihnacht *Xmas,cant
eq voices,inst MOSELER sc s.p., cor pts
s.p., ipa   (K569)

Frohlich Soll Mein Herze Springen
4pt mix cor MOSELER LB-347 s.p.   (K570)

In Dulci Jubilo
4pt mix cor MOSELER LB-348 s.p.   (K571)

KLEIN, LOTHAR (1932-)
Little Book Of Hours *see Nones; Prime;
Sext; Tierce   (K572)

Nones
SATB,acap oct LAWSON 51223 $.25 see from
Little Book Of Hours   (K573)

Prime
SATB,acap oct LAWSON 51220 $.25 see from
Little Book Of Hours   (K574)

Sext
SATB,acap oct LAWSON 51222 $.25 see from
Little Book Of Hours   (K575)

Tierce
SATB,acap oct LAWSON 51221 $.25 see from
Little Book Of Hours   (K576)

KLEIN, M.
Hear Me, Lord
SATB KJOS 5480 $.30   (K577)

Holy, Holy, Holy
SATB KJOS 5481B $.30   (K578)

KLEIN, RICHARD RUDOLF
Aus Der Tiefe Rufe Ich (Psalm 130) Bibl
SATB,clar,2bsn,2horn,2trp,2trom,3timp sc
HANSSLER 25.104 s.p., ipr   (K579)

Den Die Hirten Lobeten Sehre
SA/men cor,2treb inst,bass inst HANSSLER
14.020 s.p.   (K580)

Der Herr Ist Mein Hirt (Psalm 23) Bibl
SATB,clar,2bsn,2horn,strings sc HANSSLER
25.102 s.p., ipr   (K581)

Gott Ist Unsre Zuversicht (Psalm 46) Bibl
SATB,2horn,2trp,2trom sc HANSSLER 25.103
s.p., ipr   (K582)

Hilf, O Herr (Psalm 12) Bibl
SATB,ob,bsn,trp,trom,strings sc HANSSLER
25.101 s.p., ipr   (K583)

Psalm 1 *see Wohl Dem, Der Nicht Dem Rat Der
Gottlosen Folgt

Psalm 12 *see Hilf, O Herr

Psalm 23 *see Der Herr Ist Mein Hirt

Psalm 46 *see Gott Ist Unsre Zuversicht

Psalm 130 *see Aus Der Tiefe Rufe Ich

Wohl Dem, Der Nicht Dem Rat Der Gottlosen
Folgt (Psalm 1) Bibl
SATB,2clar,strings sc HANSSLER 25.100 s.p.,
ipr   (K584)

KLEINE ADVENTSMUSIK see Distler, Hugo

KLEINE CHORALMOTETTE UBER "ERDE SINGE" see
Geissel, J. von

KLEINE CHORALMOTETTE UBER "NUN BITTEN WIR DEN
HEILIGEN GEIST" *mot
(Romanovsky, Erich) [Ger] mix cor,acap oct
DOBLINGER s.p.   (K585)

KLEINE DEUTSCHE LIEDMESSE see Kern, Matthais

KLEINE DEUTSCHE ORGELMESSE see Bresgen, Cesar

KLEINE FESTMESSE see Kronsteiner, Herman

KLEINE GEBURTSTAGSKANTATE see Marks, Gunther

KLEINE GEISTLICHE CHORMUSIK see Thomas, Kurt

KLEINE KANTATE FUR KARFREITAG see Marks,
Gunther

KLEINE KANTATE ZUM PFINGSTFEST see Gruschwitz,
Gunther

KLEINE LIEDKANTATE ZUR WEIHNACHT see
Gruschwitz, Gunther

KLEINE LIEDMOTETTEN see Kaufmann, Otto

KLEINE MARIENMESSE see Baumann, Max

KLEINE MESSE see Pepping, Ernst

KLEINE MESSE see Kugelmann

KLEINE MESSE UBER ZWOLFTONMODELLE see Heiller,
Anton

KLEINE ORGELMESSE see Haydn, (Franz) Joseph,
Missa Brevis St. Johannis De Deo

KLEINE OSTERKANTATE see Dietrich, Fritz

KLEINE OSTERKANTATE see Gruschwitz, Gunther

KLEINE PASSIONS-KANTATE see Schmid, Walter

KLEINE PASSIONSMUSIK see Dietrich, Fritz

KLEINE SPRUCHMOTTE see Zipp, Friedrich

KLEINE WEIHNACHTS-KANTATE see Schmid, Walter

KLEINE WEIHNACHTSFEIER see Brautigam, Helmut

KLEINE WEIHNACHTSKANTATE see Tzschoppe,
Eberhart

KLEINE WEIHNACHTSKANTATE NACH DEM EVANGELISTEN
LUKAS see Dietrich, Fritz

KLEINE WEIHNACHTSKANTATE NACH WORTEN VON K.
MULLER-OSTEN see Schwartz, Gerhard von

KLEINE WEIHNACHTSMUSIK see Thomas, Kurt

KLEINER PSALTER see Burkhard Willy

KLEINER PSALTER see Lahusen, Christian

KLEINER TAGESKREIS I see Kern, Matthais

KLEINER TAGESKREIS II see Kern, Matthais

KLEINER TAGESKREIS III see Kern, Matthais

KLEINES MAGNIFICAT see Bach, Johann Sebastian

KLEINES PSALMEN-CHORBUCH see Micheelsen, Hans
Friedrich

KLEINSINGER, GEORGE (1914-)
There's A Man Goin' Roun' Takin' Names
*folk,US
SATB oct BOURNE 603 $.25   (K586)

KLEMETTI, HEIKKI (1876-1953)
Scribere Proposui
[Lat] wom cor oct FAZER s.p. see from PIAE
CANTIONES   (K587)

KLEMM, GUSTAV (1897-1947)
Child's Prayer, A
(Schirmer) 3pt wom cor oct SCHIRM.G 10038
$.25   (K588)

Forest Hymn
SATB oct FOX PS21 $.25   (K589)
SSA oct FOX PS13 $.25   (K590)

How Sweet The Bells Of Christmas *Xmas
SSA SCHMITT 2521 $.35   (K591)

KLERK, ALBERT DE (1917-)
Laudate Dominum (Psalm 150)
[Lat] mix cor,2fl,2ob,2clar,2bsn,3trp,
2horn,3trom,tuba,strings,timp min sc
DONEMUS s.p.   (K592)

Missa Mater S. Laetitiae *Mass
[Lat] wom cor,fl,bsn, English horn min sc
DONEMUS s.p., ipa   (K593)

Psalm 150 *see Laudate Dominum

Stabat Mater
[Lat] mix cor,AT soli,fl,ob,clar,bsn,trp,
horn,strings,perc,timp DONEMUS min sc
s.p., voc sc s.p.   (K594)

KLIENAU, KLAUS (1927-)
Ich Zieh Meine Dunkle Strasse *Gen
(Gruschwitz, Gunther) [Ger] SATB,kbd,fl,bvl
(med) BOSSE BE 249 s.p.   (K595)

KLIEWER, JONAH
Sunset To Sunrise
SATB FOSTER MF 122 $.25   (K596)

KLIMPEL, HEINRICH
Christvesper *Xmas
SSAB&wom cor&cong,narrator,solo,org MOSELER
s.p.   (K597)

KLINE
Confirm, O God (Psalm 75)
SATB&cong oct SUMMY M 2692 $.50   (K598)

Psalm 67 *see Spirit Of The Lord, The

Psalm 75 *see Confirm, O God

Spirit Of The Lord, The (Psalm 67) anti/Psalm
SATB&cong oct SUMMY M 2691 $.50   (K599)

KLING, GLOCKCHEN *Xmas,anthem/carol,Ger
(Follett) "Come To The Manger" SAB oct PRO
ART 2242 $.30   (K600)
(Gresens, Walter) "Come To The Manger" SATB
(easy) oct AUGSBURG 0416 $.40   (K601)

KLING NO KLOKKA *folk
(Orheim, Olav) [Norw] mix cor LYCHE 30 s.p. (K602)

KLING NO, KLOKKA see Neilsen, Ludvig

KLINGENDE KETTE see Stern, Hermann

KLINK, W.
Ehre Sei Gott
(Schroder, R.A.) men cor (easy) oct
LEUCKART 361 s.p.   (K603)

KLIPPA DU SOM BRAST FOR MIG
(Sjoberg, Per-Anders) mix cor NORDISKA
NMS-6418 s.p. contains also: Tryggare Kan
Ingen Vara; Fabodpsalm Fran Solleron; Att
Vara Kristen Ar Na't Mer'   (K604)

KLOFT, GERHARD (1929-)
Auferstanden Bist Du *Easter
[Ger] unis,acap BOSSE BE 271 s.p.   (K605)

KLOKKEKLANGEN see Sundberg, Ove Kr.

KLOSTERNEUBERGER MESSE see Goller, Vincent

KLUGE, MANFRED (1928-1971)
Es Kommt Ein Schiff Geladen *mot
SSATB,acap cor pts BREITKOPF-W CHB-3407
s.p.   (K606)

Johanneskonzert *Bibl
unis men cor,Bar solo,org sc BREITKOPF-W
PB-3768 s.p.   (K607)

Mariae Verkundigung *BVM,Bibl
unis men cor,ST soli,org sc BREITKOPF-W
PB-3772 s.p., cor pts BREITKOPF-W
CHB-2999 s.p.   (K608)
unis men cor,ST soli,org sc BREITKOPF-W
PB-3772 s.p., voc pt BREITKOPF-W CHB-2999
s.p.   (K609)
unis jr cor/unis wom cor,ST soli,org sc
BREITKOPF-W PB-3772 s.p., voc pt
BREITKOPF-W CHB-2999 s.p.   (K610)

Messe Maienzeit *Mass
4-6pt mix cor,acap cor pts BREITKOPF-W
CHB-3032 s.p.   (K611)

KLUMP
I Sing The Almighty
unis oct FISCHER,C CM-7751 $.25   (K612)

KNAB, ARMIN (1881-1951)
Alte Marienlieder *CCU,BVM
3 eq voices MOSELER s.p.   (K613)

Auf Dem Berge Da Wehet Der Wind *Xmas
wom cor&jr cor TONGER s.p.   (K614)

Ei Du Grun-Grunes Baumlein
see Knab, Armin, Frau Sonne Sitzt Im
Himmelshaus

Es Ist Ein Ros Entsprungen *Xmas
3 eq voices MOSELER LB-126 s.p.   (K615)

Frau Nachtigall, Wach Auf *Xmas
wom cor&jr cor TONGER s.p.   (K616)

Frau Sonne Sitzt Im Himmelshaus *Xmas
wom cor&jr cor TONGER s.p. contains also:
Ei Du Grun-Grunes Baumlein   (K617)

Gottes Ist Der Orient
wom cor&jr cor,acap TONGER s.p.   (K618)

Maria Durch Ein Dornwald Ging *BVM
3 eq voices MOSELER LB-125 s.p.   (K619)

Sechzehn Chorale *CC16L,chorale
3 cor,inst voc pt BREITKOPF-L CHB-2802 s.p. (K620)

Singt Und Klingt *Xmas
[Ger] SATB,pno/strings sc PETERS 4870
$2.00, ipa, voc sc PETERS 4870 $.50, ipa   (K621)

Vom Himmel Hoch, O Englein Kommt *Xmas
3 eq voices MOSELER LB-125 s.p.   (K622)

wom cor&jr cor TONGER s.p.   (K623)

KNAPP, ARNO
Ihr Heiligen Toten
3pt jr cor/3pt wom cor cor pts HEINRICH.
795 s.p.   (K624)

KNAPP, LAVATER
Blessed Assurance *hymn
(Kirk) SATB oct LILLENAS AT-1022 $.30   (K625)

(Skiles) SATB oct LILLENAS AN-1163 $.25   (K626)

I Will Magnify Thee O God
(Young, R.; Weinandt, E.) SATB oct FISCHER,
J 10005 $.30   (K627)

Open The Gates Of The Temple *Easter/Lent
SATB oct LORENZ 4348 $.30   (K628)
SATB (very easy) oct LORENZ A336 $.25   (K629)
SATB&jr cor oct LORENZ C58 $.35   (K630)
SAB oct LORENZ 7336 $.30   (K631)
unis oct LORENZ 8571 $.30   (K632)
SATB ALLANS 146 s.p.   (K633)
SA oct FISCHER,C CM-6386 $.25   (K634)
SSAA oct FISCHER,C CM-6385 $.25   (K635)
TTBB oct FISCHER,C CM-6389 $.25   (K636)
(Churchill) SATB SHAWNEE A 113 $.35   (K637)
(Dressler) SSA oct FISCHER,C CM-6387 $.25 (K638)
(Ehret) 2pt oct PRO ART 1538 $.25   (K639)
(Ehret) SAB oct PRO ART 1713 $.30   (K640)
(Ehret) SSA oct PRO ART 2104 $.25   (K641)
(Ehret) SATB oct PRO ART 1503 $.25   (K642)
(Fields) SSA BOSTON 2685 $.35   (K643)
(Fields) SATB BOSTON 2686 $.35   (K644)
(Fields) TTBB BOSTON 2684 $.35   (K645)
(Fletcher) SATB oct FISCHER,C CM-6388 $.25 (K646)
(Richardson) SAB BOSTON 2747 $.35   (K647)
(Stavely) sr cor&jr cor,org/pno BOSTON
11814 $.40   (K648)
(Stickles) 2pt jr cor,org/pno BOSTON 2961
$.35   (K649)
(Whitman) SATB oct LILLENAS AN-2302 $.30   (K650)

KNECHT
O Jesus, Thou Art Standing
(Husband, John) SAB FLAMMER D5050 $.25   (K651)

(Olds) SATB SCHMITT 1852 $.30   (K652)

KNECHT, [JUSTIN HEINRICH] (1752-1817)
Das Walte Gott, Der Helfen Kan
see Vulpius, Melchior, Christus, Der Ist
Mein Leben

KNECHT RUPPRECHT see Bresgen, Cesar

KNEEL AT THE MANGER see Carmony

KNEFELIUS, JOHANN (ca. 1530-ca. 1592)
Also Hat Gott Die Welt Geliebt *mot
(Hellmann) SSATB HANSSLER 1.088 s.p.   (K653)

KNIERER, HERMANN (1875-1957)
Psalm Der Liebe *Gen
[Ger] SATB,S solo,org (med) MULLER SM 496B
s.p.   (K654)

KNIGHT, GERALD H.
Christ, Whose Glory Fills The Skies *Gen,
anthem
S/SS oct ROYAL 214 s.p.   (K655)

KNIGHT OF BETHLEHEM, THE see Thomson, David
Cleghorn

KNIGHT, VINCENT
Four Anthems Of Praise *see O God Our
Father; Our God Is Love; With Gladness We
Worship; Ye Servants Of God   (K656)

Hymn For Schools *hymn
cor oct HART s.p.   (K657)

O God Our Father *anthem
cor oct HART s.p. see from Four Anthems Of
Praise   (K658)

Our God Is Love *anthem
cor oct HART s.p. see from Four Anthems Of
Praise   (K659)

They Shall Mount Up With Wings
SATB oct ELKAN-V 362-1286 $.30   (K660)

With Gladness We Worship *anthem
cor oct HART s.p. see from Four Anthems Of
Praise   (K661)

Ye Servants Of God *anthem
cor oct HART s.p. see from Four Anthems Of
Praise   (K662)

KNIGHT WITHOUT A SWORD see Pfautsch, Lloyd

KNIGHTON
Fanfare And Alleluia
SATB FLAMMER A 5048 $.30   (K663)
SAB FLAMMER D5070 $.30   (K664)
SSA FLAMMER B 5035 $.25   (K665)

Gloria
SATB FLAMMER A 5284 $.30   (K666)

Overture For Easter *Easter
SATB FLAMMER A 5302 $.30   (K667)
SATB oct SOUTHERN $.30   (K668)

Sing A Joyful Song
SATB FLAMMER A 5060 $.25   (K669)

Star, The
SATB FLAMMER A 5190 $.25   (K670)

KNOBLE, W.
Christmas Rose, The (composed with Cline)
*Xmas
SATB LEONARD-US 08008320 $.25   (K671)

KNOCHE, KEITH
O Praise The Lord, Ye Nations
SATB,opt brass oct WALTON 2189 $.35, ipa (K672)

KNOCK DOWN THE WALL see Butt

KNOCK! KNOCK! KNOCK! see Grime, William

KNOPFEL
Jubilate *Jubil
(Wiley) SATB,opt kbd oct PRO ART 2547 $.30
(K673)

KNORR, ERNST LOTHER VON (1896-   )
Das Weihnachtsbedenken *Xmas,cant
[Ger] SATB/4 eq voices&men cor,opt S solo,
fl,strings (med diff) BAREN. BA 2523 voc
sc $5.00, cor pts $.40, ipr   (K674)

Suchet Gott, So Werdet Ihr Leben *Gen,mot
[Ger] SSAATTBB,ST soli,acap (med diff)
BAREN. BA 3639 $2.50   (K675)

KNOW ALL THAT GOD SO LOVED THE WORLD see
Schutz, Heinrich

KNOW THAT THE LORD IS GOD see Handel, George
Frideric

KNOW THAT THE LORD IS GOD see Pfohl

KNOW YE NOT? see Nosse

KNOWN ONLY TO HIM
TTBB BIG3 $.25   (K676)

KNUDSEN, [PEDER] (1819-1863)
I Am So Glad Each Christmas Eve *see Jeg Er
Saa Glad

Jeg Er Saa Glad *anthem
(Wood) "I Am So Glad Each Christmas Eve"
SAB (easy) oct AUGSBURG 0919 $.25 (K677)

KNUPFER, SEBASTIAN (1633-1676)
Ich Will Singen Von Der Gnade Des Herrn
*cant
(Kruger) SATB,SATB soli,cont,bsn,3vln,2vla
HANSSLER 10.081 sc s.p., voc sc s.p.,
ipa   (K678)
Sende Dein Licht Und Deine Wahrheit *cant
(Kruger) SATB,cont,bsn,3vln,vla,vcl
HANSSLER 10.199 sc s.p., voc sc s.p.,
ipa   (K679)

KNYVETT
Bells Of St. Michael's Tower
(Ehret) SAB oct BOURNE T9 $.25   (K680)

KOBIERKOWICZ, JOZEF
Ego Mater *mot,Pol
(Szweykowski, Z.M.) cor,soli,cont,2vln
POLSKIE WDMP55 s.p.   (K681)

KOBLER, HANS (1930-   )
Ich Mocht, Dass Einer Mit Mir Geht *Gen
[Ger] unis,acap (easy) BOSSE BE 267 s.p.
(K682)

KOBRICH
Goodly Child, The *cant
mix cor CHAPPELL 0015271-368 $1.00   (K683)

KOCH, FREDERICK
I Will Extol Thee, My God *Bibl
SATB,acap oct APOGEE CA-2113-8 $.60   (K684)

Praise Ye The Lord
SATB,brass,perc sc SEESAW $5.00   (K685)

KOCH, HEINZ (1916-   )
Herr Christ, Der Einig Gotts Sohn
SA/SAB/SATB HANSSLER 8.026 s.p.   (K686)

Jesus Christus, Unser Heiland *prayer
SA/SAB/SATB HANSSLER 8.025 s.p. contains
also: Stern, Hermann, Vater Unser Im
Himmelreich (SA/SS); Metzger, Hans-
Arnold, Vater Unser Im Himmelreich (SATB)
(K687)

Mitt Ernst, O Menschenkinder
see Stern, Hermann, Ihr Lieben Christen,
Freut Euch Nun

Sonne Der Gerechtigkeit , Gehe Auf
see Kurig, Hans-Hermann, Lobt Gott, Ihr
Frommen Christen

Wie Soll Ich Dich Empfangen
SATB HANSSLER 6.090 s.p. contains also: Le
Jeune, Claude, Gott Seines Herzens Grund
Aufschloss   (K688)

KOCH, JOHANNES H.E. (1918-   )
Christ, Der Du Bist Tag Und Licht
4pt mix cor,instr MOSELER LB-236 s.p. (K689)

Christ Lag In Todes Banden *Easter,cant
[Ger] SA&men cor,2trp,2trom,bvl (med)
BAREN. BA 2635 sc $3.00, cor pts $.55,
ipa   (K690)

Darum Wachet *ECY,evang
[Ger] SA&men cor,SA soli,org,2trp,2trom
(med) BAREN. BA 2640 sc $4.75, cor pts
$1.50, ipa   (K691)

Die Bergrede *Bibl
"Sermon On The Mount, The" cor,narrator,
org,8winds sc HANSSLER rental, ipa (K692)

Die Pfingstgeschichte *Pent
[Ger] SSATB&2pt men cor,B solo,acap (med
diff) BAREN. BA 3646 $3.75   (K693)

Du Grosser Schmerzensmann
SAT/SAB,bass inst HANSSLER 14.066 s.p.
(K694)

Erstanden Ist Der Heilige Christ *Easter,
cant
[Ger] SSATB,SA soli,org trp&strings (med)
BAREN. BA 1465 $1.75   (K695)

Es Ist Ein Ros Etsprungen
SA HANSSLER 14.023 s.p. contains also:
Wenzel, Eberhard, Frolich Soll Mein Herze
Springen (SAT/SAB)   (K696)

Furwahr, Er Trug Unsere Krankheit *Psntd
[Ger] 3pt mix cor&cong,opt org BAREN.
BA 3638 s.p.   (K697)

Gottes Sohn Ist Kommen *Adv,cant
[Ger] SSATB,3trp,2trom (med) BAREN. BA 5430
sc $3.25, cor pts $.65, ipa   (K698)

Herr Christ, Der Einig Gotts Sohn
jr cor,vcl,bvl,timp,gtr, glockenspiel,
xylophne sc HANSSLER 12.207 s.p. contains
also: Schlenker, Manfred, O Susser Herre
Jesu Christ (jr cor, glockenspiel,
xylophone); Gadsch, Herbert, Meinem Gott
Gehort Die Welt (unis jr cor,2vln,2rec,
glockenspiel)   (K699)

Jauchzet Gott, Alle Lande
jr cor,org sc HANSSLER 12.221 s.p.   (K700)

Komm, Heiliger Geist, Herre Gott *Pent,cant
[Ger] SATB&cong,3trp,2trom (med) BAREN.
BA 3593 sc $3.00, cor pts $.65, ipa
(K701)

Maria Durch Ein Dornwald Ging *Adv
[Ger] 3 eq voices,acap (med easy) BAREN.
BCH 175 s.p.   (K702)

Maria Und Elizabeth *Adv,mot
[Ger] SSATTB,SAT soli,acap (med diff)
BAREN. BA 3982 rental   (K703)

Nun Juble Laut, All Kreator *Xmas
[Ger] SSATB,3fl,3vln,vla,vcl,bvl (med)
BAREN. BA 3983 sc $5.75, cor pts $1.50,
ipa   (K704)

O Heiliger Geist, O Heiliger Gott
(Bordunquinte) SA/S/T/2pt/3pt HANSSLER
14.104 s.p.   (K705)

Sende Dein Licht
jr cor/SA,treb inst,org sc HANSSLER 12.217
s.p.   (K706)

Sermon On The Mount, The *see Die Bergrede

Sollt Ich Meinem Gott Nicht Singen *Gen
[Ger] 3pt mix cor/4pt mix cor,opt 2trp&
2trom (med easy) BAREN. BA 3385 s.p.
(K707)

Steht Auf, Ihr Lieben Kinderlein *Gen,cant
[Ger] SATB&cong,3trp,2trom,opt drums (med)
BAREN. BA 2630 sc $3.00, ipa, cor pts
$.40, ipa   (K708)

Summa Passionis Vom Leiden Und Sterben
Unseres Herrn Jesu Christi
2pt,narrator,org HANSSLER 14.610 s.p.
(K709)

KOCH, KARL
Alleluia
see Koch, Karl, Grosser Gott, Wir Loben
Dich

Grosser Gott, Wir Loben Dich
cong,org,2trp,2trom DOBLINGER sc s.p., voc
pt s.p., ipa contains also: Alleluia (mix
cor,org,2trp,2trom)   (K710)

KOCH, KARL (cont'd.)

Jubilaums-Messe *Mass
5pt mix cor,org,ob,2clar,bsn,2horn,strings
DOBLINGER voc sc s.p., cor pts s.p., ipa
(K711)

Requiem *Op.85, Mass
4pt mix cor,soli,org&fl&2clar&2trp&2horn&
2trom&bvl/fl&2ob&2clar&2bsn&2trp&2horn&
3trom&strings&timp DOBLINGER voc sc s.p.,
cor pts s.p., ipa   (K712)

KOCHER
As With Gladness Men Of Old *Xmas
(Ehret) SA MARKS 4069 $.30 contains also:
God Rest You Merry Gentlemen   (K713)
(Kirk) SATB oct PRO ART 1305 $.25   (K714)
(Kirk) SSA oct PRO ART 1391 $.20   (K715)
(Kirk) SAB oct PRO ART 1392 $.20   (K716)

For The Beauty Of The Earth
(Churchill) SATB oct PLYMOUTH CH-100 $.25
(K717)
(Davis, K.K.) unis&desc WARNER R3418 $.30
(K718)
(Davis, K.K.) SATB&desc WARNER G1850 $.30
(K719)
(Davis, K.K.) 2pt&desc WARNER R3447 $.30
(K720)
(Davis, K.K.) SAB&desc WARNER R3231 $.30
(K721)
(Davis, K.K.) SSA&desc WARNER R3268 $.30
(K722)
(Hastings) SATB oct BOURNE HA1 $.30   (K723)

God Rest You Merry Gentlemen
see Kocher, As With Gladness Men Of Old

Thou Holy, Lord God
(Harris) SATB oct PRO ART 2663 $.30   (K724)

KOCHER, [CONRAD] (1786-1872)
For The Beauty Of The Earth (from Choral)
Thanks,hymn
(Chenoweth) SATB,pno/org oct LAWSON 51397
$.30   (K725)
(Shaw) mix cor&opt jr cor,S solo,org oct
SCHIRM.G 10097 $.25   (K726)

KOCHER, KONRAD
Der Herr Ist Gut!
(Berger, H.L.) TTBB HANSSLER 6.5067 s.p.
(K727)

KOCHVE VOKER see Wohlberg, Max

KOCKELMANS, GERARD (1925-   )
Christus Heri Et Hodie
[Dut] men cor,3trom min sc DONEMUS s.p.
(K728)

KOCSIS, STEFAN
Deutsches Ordinarium
mix cor&cong,org,opt 3trp&trom DOBLINGER
voc sc s.p., cor pts s.p., ipa   (K729)
men cor&cong,org DOBLINGER voc sc s.p., cor
pts s.p.   (K730)
3pt wom cor,acap cor pts DOBLINGER s.p.
(K731)

KODALY, ZOLTAN (1882-1967)
Angels And The Shepherds *Xmas
girl cor SOUTHERN $.40   (K732)

Angels And The Shepherds, The *see Angyalok
Es Pasztorok

Angyalok Es Pasztorok *Xmas
"Angels And The Shepherds, The" SSA,acap
oct PRESSER 312-40593 $.40   (K733)

Ave Maria
SSA,acap oct PRESSER 312-40592 $.25   (K734)

Birthday Greeting, A *Xmas
SATB,acap oct PRESSER 312-40579 $.25 (K735)

Christmas Carol, A *Xmas,carol
SATB,acap (med) OXFORD 84.091 $.30   (K736)
SSAA,acap (med easy) OXFORD 44.721 $.25
(K737)

Christmas Dance Of The Shepherds *see
Karasconyi Pasztortanc

Communion *Commun
mix cor SOUTHERN $.35   (K738)
SSAATB oct BOOSEY 5574 $.35   (K739)

Epiphany *Xmas
SSA,acap oct PRESSER 312-40594 $.40   (K740)

Ferfikarok *sac/sec,CC20L
[Hung] BUDAPEST 5386 s.p.   (K741)

God's Blacksmith
SSA,acap (med easy) OXFORD 54.940 $.25
(K742)

Invocation Of Peace
SATB,acap oct BOOSEY 5822 $.30   (K743)

Jelige
(Jakovich, F.) [Hung] SATB (easy) BUDAPEST
3011 s.p.   (K744)
(Jakovich, F.) [Hung] SAB (easy) BUDAPEST
2984 s.p.   (K745)
(Jankovich, F.) [Hung] TTBB (easy) BUDAPEST
3010 s.p.   (K746)
(Jankovich, F.) [Hung] 3pt (easy) BUDAPEST
3974 s.p.   (K747)

Jesus And The Traders *see Jezus Es A
Kufarok

Jezus Es A Kufarok *Easter
"Jesus And The Traders" SATB,acap oct
PRESSER 312-40578 $.40   (K748)

Karasconyi Pasztortanc *Xmas
"Christmas Dance Of The Shepherds" SA,
piccolo oct PRESSER 312-40573 $.25 (K749)
"Christmas Dance Of The Shepherds" girl cor
SOUTHERN $.25   (K750)

Korusok I: Gyermek - Es Noikarok *sac/sec,
CC57L
[Hung] BUDAPEST 3738 s.p.   (K751)

Korusuk II *sac/sec,CC36L
[Hung] BUDAPEST 2811 s.p.   (K752)

KODALY, ZOLTAN (cont'd.)

Missa Brevis *Mass
[Lat] mix cor,org/orch BOOSEY voc sc $3.00,
cor pts $1.25, sc $7.50, ipr, min sc
$4.00   (K753)

Ode To The Music Makers, An
SATB oct BOOSEY 5833 $.70   (K754)

Pange Lingua
voc sc UNIVER. 7941 $2.50, cor pts UNIVER.
10290A-D $.35   (K755)

Pray For Honor
SATB,acap oct BOOSEY 5832 $.30   (K756)

Psalm 114
SATB,org oct BOOSEY 5328 $.35   (K757)

Psalm 121
SATB,acap oct BOOSEY 5330 $.30   (K758)

Psalm 150 *Fest/Gen/Thanks
SSA,acap (easy) oct OXFORD 83.074 $.25   (K759)
girl cor SOUTHERN $.25   (K760)

Psalmus Hungaricus *Psalm
[Ger/Eng] voc sc UNIVER. 8463 $4.10, cor
pts UNIVER. 8463A $1.15   (K761)
study sc UNIVER. PH.233 $4.50   (K762)

Saint Gregory's Day
SSAA,acap (med easy) OXFORD 83.039 $.35   (K763)

Song Of Faith
SSATTB,acap oct BOOSEY 5563 $.30   (K764)

Te Deum *Te Deum
study sc UNIVER. PH. 276 $3.40   (K765)
[Lat] voc sc UNIVER. 10849 $2.25, cor pts
UNIVER. 10849A $1.35   (K766)

Te Deum Of Sandor Sik *Te Deum
SATB,acap oct BOOSEY 5741 $.30   (K767)

Voice Of Jesus, The
SSA,acap (med) OXFORD 44.059 $.25   (K768)

Whitesuntide *Whitsun
SSA,acap (med) OXFORD 44.720 $.60   (K769)

KOECHLIN, CHARLES (1867-1950)
Agnus Dei *Agnus
[Lat] 6pt mix cor,acap oct SALABERT-US $.65   (K770)

Alleluia
[Lat] 6pt mix cor,acap oct SALABERT-US $.65   (K771)

Kyrie *Kyrie
[Lat] 6pt mix cor,acap oct SALABERT-US $.65   (K772)

KOEHLER
Our God Our Help In Ages Past
(Ormsby) SATB oct BOURNE 784 $.30   (K773)

KOEPKE
Come Ye, Come All Ye People *Xmas
SATB SCHMITT 8503 $.45   (K774)

KOERPPEN, ALFRED (1926-   )
Ave Spes Et Salus (from Invocationen)
4pt mix cor MOSELER LB-419 s.p.   (K775)

Deutsche Messe *Mass
mix cor,acap cor pts BREITKOPF-W CHB-4814   (K776)

Drei Konige Aus Dem Mohrenland *Xmas
3pt mix cor MOSELER LB-428 s.p. contains
also: Wenn Die Weihnachtsnacht Will
Werden   (K777)

Invocationen *CCU
4pt mix cor,cantor,org,fl,ob,strings
MOSELER sc s.p., cor pts s.p., ipa   (K778)

Joseph Und Seine Bruder *Bibl
4pt wom cor&speak cor MOSELER s.p.   (K779)

Missa Pro Fidei Propagatione *Mass
4pt mix cor,acap cor pts BREITKOPF-W
PB-3709 s.p.   (K780)

Wenn Die Weihnachtsnacht Will Werden
see Koerppen, Alfred, Drei Konige Aus Dem
Mohrenland

KOETSIER, JAN (1911-   )
Der Mann Lot *Op.20, Bibl
[Ger] mix cor,pno,2fl,2ob,2clar,2bsn,2trp,
3horn,2trom,strings,perc,timp,harp,
celeste DONEMUS min sc s.p., cor pts s.p.   (K781)

KOHELET see Starer, Robert

KOHLMAN
There's A Cross At The Crossroads
SATB oct VOLKWEIN VB264 $.25   (K782)

KOHN
Three Descants *CC3U
SATB,opt brass FISCHER,C O-4630 $1.50, ipr   (K783)

KOKKOVEN, JOONAS (1921-   )
Laudatio Domini
[Lat] mix cor,S solo oct FAZER s.p.   (K784)

Missa *Mass
[Lat] 6pt mix cor,S solo,acap oct FAZER
s.p.   (K785)

KOL EMUNAH see Schwarz, Herman

KOL NIDRE see Brenner, Walter

KOL NIDRE see Christiansen, Paul

KOL NIDRE see Helfman, Max

KOL NIDRE see Roskin

KOL SASON see Isaacson, Michael

KOL SLAVEN *Russ
(Davison, A.) "Thy Wisdom, Lord, All Thought
Transcendeth" SAB/SAT,org SCHIRM.EC 1703
$.30   (K786)

KOL SLAVEN see Bortniansky, Dimitri
Stepanovitch

KOLBLE, FRITZ (1906-   )
Psalm 104 *Gen
[Ger] SATB,S solo,orch (easy) MULLER
SM 2363 voc sc s.p., cor pts s.p.   (K787)

KOLER, DAVID (1532-1565)
Ach Herre, Wie Sind Meiner Feinde So Viel
(Psalm 3)
4pt mix cor,acap cor pts BREITKOPF-W
CHB-3152 s.p.   (K788)

Psalm 2 *see Warum Toben Die Heide

Psalm 3 *see Ach Herre, Wie Sind Meiner
Feinde So Viel

Warum Toben Die Heide (Psalm 2)
2-4pt mix cor,acap cor pts BREITKOPF-W
CHB-3151 s.p.   (K789)

KOLER, MARTIN (1620-   )
Drei Deutsche Psalmen *CC3U, Psalm
(Hoffmann; Erbrecht) 4pt mix cor&6pt mix
cor MOSELER s.p.   (K790)

Ich Steh An Deiner Krippen *Xmas,cant
mix cor,strings HANSSLER 10.283 sc s.p.,
cor pts s.p., ipa   (K791)

Unser Herr Jesus Christus, In Der Nacht
*Eve,cant
(Haacke, Walter) [Ger] SSB,cont&2vln&2vla,
bsn/vcl (med) BAREN. BA 956 sc s.p., cor
pts s.p., ipa   (K792)

KOLLER
O Take My Hand, Lord
SATB oct LORENZ A448 $.25   (K793)

KOLTRASTEN see Runback, Albert

KOLVADA *Xmas
(Jenkins) SATB,acap oct FISCHER,C CM-7116
$.30   (K794)

KOLYADA
Christmas Bell Carol *Xmas
(Leontovich; Heller) SA SCHMITT 2554 $.30   (K795)
(Leontovich; Heller) SATB SCHMITT 1721 $.35   (K796)

KOM, HEDNINGERS FRELSERMAND see Eccard,
Johannes

KOM HEDNINGERS FRELSERMAND see Videro, Finn

KOM, HELGE ANDE, HERRE GOD see Lundborg, Gosta

KOM, HELGE ANDE, TILL MIG IN *Bibl
(Bjarnegard, Gustaf) [Swed] SATB,acap
GEHRMANS KRB 307   (K797)

KOM, HELGE ANDE, TILL MIG IN see Bjarnegard,
Gustaf

KOM, HELGE ANDE, TILL MIG IN see Thyrestam,
Gunnar

KOM HIT OG HOR DE TI BUDORD see Praetorius,
Michael

KOM LAT OSS JUBLA see Hovland, Egil

KOM, STILLA DOD see Bach, Johann Sebastian

KOMM DOCH HERAB see Gerhold, Norbert, Swing Low
Sweet Chariot

KOMM, DU HERZLICHER TROSTER see Micheelsen,
Hans Friedrich

KOMM, DU SUSSE TODESSTUNDE see Bach, Johann
Sebastian

KOMM, GOTT SCHOPFER *CCU
(Strube, Adolf) [Ger] 3pt mix cor/4pt mix cor
cloth BAREN. EM 344 s.p.   (K798)

KOMM, GOTT SCHOPFER, HEILIGER GEIST see Bach,
Johann Sebastian

KOMM, GOTT SCHOPFER, HEILIGER GEIST see David,
Johann Nepomuk

KOMM, GOTT SCHOPFER, HEILIGER GEIST see Eccard,
Johannes

KOMM, GOTT SCHOPFER, HEILIGER GEIST see
Hufschmidt, Wolfgang

KOMM, GOTT SCHOPFER, HEILIGER GEIST see
Kaufmann, Diethelm

KOMM, GOTT SCHOPFER, HEILIGER GEIST see Kurig,
Hans-Hermann

KOMM, GOTT SCHOPFER, HEILIGER GEIST see
Resinarius, Balthasar

KOMM, GOTT SCHOPFER, HEILIGER GEIST see Wagner,
Alexander

KOMM, GOTT TROSTER, HEILIGER GEIST see Pepping,
Ernst

KOMM, HEIL'GER GEIST see Stiefel, M.V.

KOMM, HEILIG REINER GEIST see Dedekind,
Constantine Christian

KOMM, HEILIGER GEIST see Bach, Johann Sebastian

KOMM, HEILIGER GEIST see Distler, Hugo

KOMM, HEILIGER GEIST see Kretzschmar, Gunther

KOMM, HEILIGER GEIST see Nagler, F.

KOMM, HEILIGER GEIST see Palestrina, Giovanni,
Veni, Creator, Spiritus

KOMM, HEILIGER GEIST see Poos, Heinrich

KOMM, HEILIGER GEIST see Scheidt, Samuel

KOMM HEILIGER GEIST see Schein, Johann Hermann

KOMM, HEILIGER GEIST see Schutz, Heinrich

KOMM, HEILIGER GEIST see Thomas, Kurt

KOMM, HEILIGER GEIST, DU SCHOPFERISCH see
Petzold, Rudolf

KOMM, HEILIGER GEIST, ERFULL DIE HERZEN see
Bender, Jan

KOMM, HEILIGER GEIST, ERFULL DIE HERZEN see
Casciolini, Claudio

KOMM, HEILIGER GEIST, ERFULLE DIE HERZEN see
Raphael, Gunther

KOMM, HEILIGER GEIST, HERRE GOTT see Baudach,
Ulrich

KOMM, HEILIGER GEIST, HERRE GOTT see Cruger,
Johann

KOMM, HEILIGER GEIST, HERRE GOTT see David,
Johann Nepomuk

KOMM, HEILIGER GEIST, HERRE GOTT see Eccard,
Johannes

KOMM, HEILIGER GEIST, HERRE GOTT see Koch,
Johannes H.E.

KOMM, HEILIGER GEIST, HERRE GOTT see Neubert,
Gottfried

KOMM, HEILIGER GEIST, HERRE GOTT see Osiander,
Lucas

KOMM, HEILIGER GEIST, HERRE GOTT see Poser,
Hans

KOMM, HEILIGER GEIST, HERRE GOTT see
Praetorius, Michael

KOMM, HEILIGER GEIST, HERRE GOTT see
Resinarius, Balthasar

KOMM, HEILIGER GEIST, HERRE GOTT see Scheidt,
Samuel

KOMM, HEILIGER GEIST, HERRE GOTT see Schein,
Johann Hermann

KOMM, HEILIGER GEIST, HERRE GOTT see Selle,
Thomas

KOMM, HEILIGER GEIST, HERRE GOTT see Wenzel,
Eberhard

KOMM, HEILIGER GEIST, UND WECKE, DIE DA
SCHLAFEN see Schweizer, Rolf

KOMM, HERR JESU, SEI DU UNSER GAST see
Anonymous

KOMM, ICH BITT DICH, IN MEIN HERZE see Schutz,
Heinrich, Veni, Rogo In Cor Meum

KOMM, JESU, KOMM see Bach, Johann Sebastian

KOMM NUN WIEDER, STILLE ZEIT see Weber,
Bernhard

KOMM, O JESUS, UNSER GAST see Stier, Alfred

KOMM, O KOMM, DU GEIST DES LEBENS see Flury, H.

KOMM, O KOMM, DU GEIST DES LEBENS see Heilmann,
Harald

KOMM, O KOMM, DU GEIST DES LEBENS see Herbert,
Peter

KOMM, O TOD see Bach, Johann Sebastian

KOMM, O TOD, DU SCHLAFES BRUDER see Bach,
Johann Sebastian

KOMM, SAG ES ALLEN WEITER see Fisher

KOMM, SCHOPFER GEIST, KEHR BEI UNS EIN see
Sultzberger, Johann Ulrich

KOMM, SUSSER GAST, O MUSICA see Woll, Erna

KOMM, SUSSER TOD! see Bach, Johann Sebastian

KOMM, TROSTER GEIST see Rohwer, Jens

KOMM UNS NOCH EINMAL SEGNEN see Weismann,
Wilhelm

KOMMA, KARL MICHAEL
Alleluja Und Pfingstsequenz *Pent/Whitsun,
Allelu
cor HANSSLER 25.005 s.p.   (K799)

Matthaus-Passion *Psntd
4-6pt, acap HANSSLER 2.026 s.p.   (K800)

KOMMEN FOR HERREN MED TACKSAMHET see Bach,
Johann Sebastian

KOMMEN TILL EN FADER see Nordqvist, Gustaf

KOMMEN TILL MIG see Carlstedt, Gunnemer

KOMMEN TILL MIG see Nilsson, Torsten

KOMMEN, TY NU AR ALLT REDO see Nilsson, Torsten

KOMMER VEL LYSET INN see Nystedt, Knut

KOMMET HER! HORET see Ruppel, Paul Ernst

KOMMET HER UND SEHET AN DIE TATEN GOTTES see
Doebler, Curt

KOMMET HER UND SEHET DIE STATTE see Schaper,
Heinz-Christian

KOMMET HER ZU MIR ALLE see Christenius, Johann

KOMMET, IHR HIRTEN *CCU, Xmas
(Wolters) 4pt mix cor MOSELER s.p.   (K801)

KOMMET IHR HIRTEN
    see Vier Weihnachtslieder

KOMMET, IHR HIRTEN see Cadow, Paul

KOMMET IHR HIRTEN see Fegers, Karl

KOMMET IHR HIRTEN see Giefer, Willy

KOMMET IHR HIRTEN see Kukuck, Felicitas

KOMMET IHR HIRTEN see Lissmann, Kurt

KOMMET, IHR HIRTEN see Reiter, A.

KOMMET, IHR HIRTEN see Sturmer, Bruno

KOMMET IHR HIRTEN see Trader, Willi

KOMMET, IHR HIRTEN see Weber, Ludwig

KOMMET, IHR HIRTEN see Wegener, H.

KOMMST DU, KOMMST DU, LICHT DER HEIDEN see
    Bach, Johann Sebastian

KOMMST DU, KOMMST DU, LICHT DER HEIDEN see
    Buxtehude, Dietrich

KOMMST DU, LICHT DER HEIDEN? see Mendelssohn,
    Arnold

KOMMT ALLE see Kaufmann, Otto

KOMMT, DENN ES IST ALLES BEREIT see Driessler,
    Johannes

KOMMT HER see Franck, Melchior

KOMMT HER, DES KONIGS AUFGEBOT see Berger, Hans
    Ludwig

KOMMT HER, DES KONIGS AUFGEBOT see Kurig, Hans-
    Hermann

KOMMT HER, DES KONIGS AUFGEBOT see Schutz,
    Heinrich

KOMMT HER, IHR GESEGNETEN MEINES VATERS see
    Franck, Melchior

KOMMT HER, IHR KINDER see Strohbach, Siegfried

KOMMT HER ZU MIR see Vulpius, Melchior

KOMMT HER ZU MIR ALLE see Franck, Melchior

KOMMT HER ZU MIR, SPRICHT GOTTES SOHN see Bach,
    Johann Sebastian

KOMMT HER ZU MIR, SPRICHT GOTTES SOHN see
    Franck, Melchior

KOMMT HER ZU MIR, SPRICHT GOTTES SOHN see
    Metzger, Hans-Arnold

KOMMT HER ZU MIR, SPRICHT GOTTES SOHN see
    Praetorius, Michael

KOMMT HER ZU MIR, SPRICHT GOTTES SOHN see
    Stern, Hermann

KOMMT HER ZU MIR, SPRICHT GOTTES SOHN see
    Thomaschke, Edgar

KOMMT HEREIN see Git On Board

KOMMT HERR ZU MIR ALLE, DIE IHR MUHSELIG see
    Cruger, Johann

KOMMT HERZU, LASST UNS FROHLICH SEIN see
    Schutz, Heinrich

KOMMT HERZU, LASST UNS FROLICHSEIN see Schutz,
    Heinrich

KOMMT, IHR G'SPIELEN see Franck, Cesar

KOMMT KINDER ALL ZUSAMMEN *CC14U
    [Ger] jr cor BAREN. EM 709 s.p.   (K802)

KOMMT, LASST UNS ANBETEN see Becker-Foss,
    Jurgen

KOMMT, LASST UNS ANBETEN see Mendelssohn-
    Bartholdy, Felix

KOMMT, SEELEN, DIESER TAG see Bach, Johann
    Sebastian

KOMMT, SEELEN, DIESER TAG MUSS HEILIG see Bach,
    Johann Sebastian

KOMMT, SINGT UNSEREM HERRN see Zimmermann,
    Heinz Werner

KOMMT UND LASST UND CHRISTUM EHREN see
    Friedrichs, Karl

KOMMT UND LASST UNS CHRISTUM see Praetorius,
    Michael

KOMMT UND LASST UNS CHRISTUM EHREN see
    Hindermann, Walter Felix

KOMMT UND LASST UNS CHRISTUM EHREN see Linke,
    Norbert

KOMMT UND LASST UNS CHRISTUM EHREN see
    Micheelsen, Hans Friedrich

KOMMT, UND LASST UNS CHRISTUM EHREN see
    Pepping, Ernst

KOMMT UND LASST UNS CHRISTUM EHREN see Raphael,
    Gunther

KOMMT UND LASST UNS WANDELN IM LICHTE DES HERRN
    see Brunner, Adolf

KOMT KINDEKENS KOMT
    mix cor sc ALSBACH&D s.p.   (K803)

KONFIRMATION see Decker, W.

KONFIRMATION see Wanner, J.G.

KONFIRMATIONSLIED see Strobl, K.

KONIG
    Have Faith In God, My Heart
    (Lovelace) SATB oct FISCHER,J 9956 $.35
                                          (K804)
    Oh, That I Had A Thousand Voices *anthem
    (Nelson) SAB (easy) oct AUGSBURG 1167 $.25
                                          (K805)
    This Night *anthem
    (Christian, F.M.) SATB&jr cor (easy) oct
        AUGSBURG 0143 $.20   (K806)
    (Christiansen) SA&SATB (easy) oct AUGSBURG
        0143 $.20   (K807)

KONIG, DEM KEIN KONIG GLEICHET see Zipp,
    Friedrich

KONIG IST DER HERR see Bauernfiend, Hans

KONIG IST DER HERR see Mareschall, Samuel

KONIG, JOHANN BALTHASAR (1691-1758)
    Ach, Jesus Geht Zu Seiner Pein *Psntd,cant
    (Adrio) [Ger] 4pt mix cor,SATB soli,2fl,
        2ob,2vln,vla,vcl (estomihi sunday) BAREN.
        EM 901 sc s.p., cor pts s.p., ipa   (K808)

    Ich Will Dich Lieben Meine Starke
    (Berger, H.L.) TTBB HANSSLER 6.5105 s.p.
        contains also: Ahle, Johann Georg,
        Morgenglanz Der Ewigkeit   (K809)

    O Dass Ich Tausend Zungen Hatte
    (Berger, H.L.) TTBB HANSSLER 6.5104 s.p.
                                          (K810)

KONIG SALOMONS URTEIL see Carissimi, Giacomo,
    Judicium Salomonis

KONIGIN IM HIMMELREICH see Schubert, Heino

KOOM BA YAH see Bune

KOOP, OL.
    Christ Triumphant
    SATB oct FISCHER,J 5378 $.35   (K811)

KOPELENT, MAREK
    Mutter *Gen
    [Ger] 14pt mix cor,fl (diff) study sc ARTIA
        AP 1778 s.p.   (K812)

    Vacillat Pes Meus
    mix cor,acap voc sc GERIG 1035 s.p.   (K813)

KOPYLOV, ALEXANDER ALEXANDROVITCH (1854-1911)
    Alleluia! Alleluia!
    (Grant, Louise) SSA oct BELWIN 1774 $.25
                                          (K814)
    Alleluia! Christ Is Risen *Easter
    (Gaul) SATB oct SOUTHERN $.30   (K815)
    (Gaul, H.) SATB oct PRESSER 332-14081 $.30
                                          (K816)
    Dove Flies Low On Whitsunday, The *Easter
    (Gaul, H.) SATB oct PRESSER 332-14158 $.30
                                          (K817)
    God Is A Spirit
    SATB,acap SCHIRM.EC 1132 $.30   (K818)
    (Bement, G.) TTBB,acap SCHIRM.EC 2129 $.16
                                          (K819)
    (Davis, K.) SA,pno/org SCHIRM.EC 1557 $.25
                                          (K820)
    (Talmadge, A.) SSAA SCHIRM.EC 1917 $.18
                                          (K821)
    Hear Me Cry, O God
    (Clough-Leighter, H.) SATB oct PRESSER
        332-13804 $.30   (K822)
    Hear My Cry, O Lord
    (Ehret, Walter) SAB (easy) PRESSER
        312-40985 $.35   (K823)
    (Spence) SATB oct PLYMOUTH SC-23 $.25
                                          (K824)
    Hear My Prayer
    (Ehret) SATB oct FOX R146 $.30   (K825)
    (Ehret) SSA oct FOX R179 $.30   (K826)
    (Engel) SATB,opt pno BOSTON 5503 $.35
                                          (K827)
    Heavenly Light *Xmas
    (Wilhousky) SATB,acap oct FISCHER,C CM-497
        $.25   (K828)
    (Wilhousky) 3pt jr cor/SSA (med easy)
        FISCHER,C $.20   (K829)
    (Wilhousky) TTBB oct FISCHER,C CM-611 $.25
                                          (K830)
    (Wilhousky) SSA oct FISCHER,C CM-640 $.25
                                          (K831)

KORAL see Nystedt, Knut

KORALEN see Bach, Johann Sebastian

KORALMASSA PA MOTIV UR REFORMATIONSTIDENS
    SVENSKA TRADITION FOR JULEN see Wikander,
    David

KORHONEN, J.
    Alleluia *Gen,Allelu/anthem
    SSAA (easy) oct GIA G1730 $.40   (K832)

    Come, O Long Awaited Savior *Adv,anthem
    TTB (easy) oct GIA G1743 $.30   (K833)
    SSA (easy) oct GIA G1729 $.30   (K834)

KORNER, D.
    Lo, Heaven And Earth
    (Newton, E.) cor oct HART s.p.   (K835)

KORSANG VID SKORDE-VESPER see Runback, Albert

KORSET VIL JEG ALDRI SVIKE *folk
    (Maeland, Lars) [Norw] dbl cor LYCHE 26 s.p.
                                          (K836)

KORSET VIL JEG ALDRI SVIKE see Baden, Conrad

KORSHYMN see Bjarnegard, Gustaf

KORT, JAC
    Kindeken Van Bethlehem *Xmas
    mix cor ALSBACH&D sc s.p., cor pts s.p.
                                          (K837)

KORTE, KARL (1928-   )
    Gloria (from Mass For Youth) Gloria
    SSA oct GALAXY 1.2728.1 $.50   (K838)

    Mass For Youth *Mass
    cor,orch voc sc GALAXY 1.2386.1 $3.00
                                          (K839)

KORTE, KARL (cont'd.)
    O Give Thanks
    SATB oct GALAXY 1.2454.1 $.30   (K840)

KORTKAMP
    Lord Is Merciful, The *Easter
    SATB oct LORENZ C323 $.30   (K841)

KORUSOK I: GYERMEK - ES NOIKAROK see Kodaly,
    Zoltan

KORUSUK II see Kodaly, Zoltan

KOSAKOFF, REUVEN (1898-   )
    In The Beginning
    [Eng] SA,Bar solo TRANSCON. TCL 371 $.75
                                          (K842)
    Kaleidoscope Of Psalms In Six Moods *cant
    cor,solo,narrator,pno TRANSCON. TCL 728
        $3.00   (K843)
    Lichvod Shabbath *Sab-Eve
    SATB TRANSCON. TCL 855 $4.00   (K844)
    Ruth And Naomi *Fest
    SA,Bar solo TRANSCON. TCL 370 $.75   (K845)
    [Eng] SA,Bar solo TRANSCON. TCL 370 $.75
                                          (K846)
    Song Of The Wise, A *Fest,cant
    [Eng] SATB TRANSCON. TCL 746 $2.00   (K847)

KOSCHAT
    Lord Is My Shepherd *Marriage
    SA ALLANS 349 s.p.   (K848)

    Lord Is My Shepherd, The *Lent
    SATB ALLANS 415 s.p.   (K849)
    (Emerson, I.) SATB oct PRESSER 332-00609
        $.30   (K850)

KOSHETZ
    Crucifixion *Lent/Psntd
    SATB,acap WARNER W2773 $.30   (K851)

    Resurrection (from Passion Trilogy) Easter
    SATB,acap WARNER W2772 $.30   (K852)

KOSTECK, G.
    Christmas Lullaby, A
    SA oct ELKAN-V 362-520 $.25   (K853)

KOSZONTO ENEK see Palestrina, Giovanni

KOTHE
    Jesu Dulcis Memoria
    men cor sc ALSBACH&D s.p.   (K854)

KOUGUELL, [ARKADIE] (1898-   )
    For Sabbath Eve *liturg,Jew
    SATB,acap oct PRESSER MC211 $.30   (K855)

KOUNTZ
    All Through The Wintry Night *CC2U,Xmas,
        carol
    SATB oct VOLKWEIN VB103 $.25   (K856)

    All Through The Win'try Night
    see Two Christmas Carols

    All Ye Good People *Xmas
    SATB&jr cor oct GALAXY 1.2043.1 $.35 (K857)
    SA oct GALAXY 1.2042.1 $.30   (K858)
    TTBB oct GALAXY 1.2250.1 $.30   (K859)
    SSA oct GALAXY 1.1999.1 $.30   (K860)
    SATB oct GALAXY 1.2000.1 $.35   (K861)

    Carol Of The Christmas Chimes *Xmas,carol
    SATB oct GALAXY 1.1885.1 $.30   (K862)
    TTBB oct GALAXY 1.1781.1 $.30   (K863)
    SSA oct GALAXY 1.1887.1 $.30   (K864)
    SATB&jr cor oct GALAXY 1.2002.1 $.30 (K865)
    SATB oct GALAXY 1.1780.1 $.30   (K866)

    Carol Of The Heavenly Hosts *Xmas,carol
    SATB oct GALAXY 1.1837.1 $.30   (K867)
    SA oct GALAXY 1.2253.1 $.30   (K868)

    Carol Of The Sheep Bells *Xmas,carol
    SSAATTBB oct GALAXY 1.1748.1 $.35   (K869)
    SATB&jr cor oct GALAXY 1.1575.1 $.30 (K870)
    SATB oct GALAXY 1.1080.1 $.30   (K871)
    TTBB oct GALAXY 1.1172.1 $.30   (K872)
    SAB oct GALAXY 1.1281.1 $.30   (K873)
    SSA oct GALAXY 1.1079.1 $.30   (K874)
    SA oct GALAXY 1.1078.1 $.30   (K875)

    Come To The Manger *Xmas
    SA oct GALAXY 1.1997.1 $.30   (K876)
    SATB oct GALAXY 1.1944.1 $.30   (K877)
    SSA oct GALAXY 1.1945.1 $.30   (K878)
    SATB&jr cor oct GALAXY 1.2252.1 $.35 (K879)

    Easter Morning *Easter
    SATB oct GALAXY 1.1740.1 $.30   (K880)

    Four Slovak Christmas Carols *CC4U,Xmas,
        carol,Slav
    girl cor SOUTHERN $.25   (K881)

    Glad Tidings Of Great Joy *Xmas,cant
    (Bellaire) SAB,pno WARNER W2407 $.85 (K882)

    Hasten Swiftly, Hasten Softly *Xmas
    SATB&jr cor oct GALAXY 1.1952.1 $.35 (K883)
    SSA oct GALAXY 1.1752.1 $.35   (K884)
    SA oct GALAXY 1.1776 $.30   (K885)
    SATB oct GALAXY 1.1750.1 $.35   (K886)
    TBB oct GALAXY 1.2251.1 $.35   (K887)

    Holy Infant Lying Lowly *CC2U,Xmas,carol
    SATB oct VOLKWEIN VB103 $.25   (K888)

    Holy Infant Lying Lowly
    see Two Christmas Carols

    Lord Is Great In Zion
    SATB oct GALAXY 1.1633.1 $.35   (K889)

    Palm Sunday *Easter/Palm
    SATB oct GALAXY 1.1877.1 $.30   (K890)
    SATB&jr cor oct GALAXY 1.1987.1 $.30 (K891)

    Prayer For Guidance *prayer
    SATB oct GALAXY 1.1847.1 $.30   (K892)

    Rise Up Early *Easter
    SSA oct GALAXY 1.1664.1 $.30   (K893)
    SATB oct GALAXY 1.1665.1 $.35   (K894)

KOUNTZ (cont'd.)

TTBB oct GALAXY 1.1749.1 $.35   (K895)
SATB&jr cor oct GALAXY 1.1702.1 $.35 (K896)
SSAATTBB oct GALAXY 1.1889.1 $.35   (K897)

Two Christmas Carols *Xmas,carol
SATB oct VOLKWEIN VB103 $.25
contains: All Through The Win'try Night;
Holy Infant Lying Lowly   (K898)

Wondrous Story, The *Xmas,cant
(Bellaire) SA,pno/orch WARNER W2324 $.75,
ipr   (K899)
(Bellaire) SAB,pno/orch WARNER W2497 $.75,
ipr   (K900)
(Bellaire) SATB,pno/orch WARNER W2348 $.75,
ipr   (K901)

KOUNTZ, RICHARD (1896-1950)
Carol Of The Questioning Child *Xmas,carol
4pt mix cor,SS soli oct SCHIRM.G 9893 $.30
(K902)
(Stickles) 3pt wom cor,SS soli oct SCHIRM.G
11090 $.25   (K903)
(Stickles) 3pt mix cor,SS soli oct SCHIRM.G
11179 $.25   (K904)

Carol Of The Roses *Xmas,carol
4pt mix cor oct SCHIRM.G 8622 $.30   (K905)

God Bless Our Land *prayer
3pt mix cor oct SCHIRM.G 8849 $.25   (K906)
4pt mix cor oct SCHIRM.G 8480 $.25   (K907)
2pt wom cor oct SCHIRM.G 8852 $.25   (K908)
3pt wom cor oct SCHIRM.G 8851 $.25   (K909)

Hushing Carol *Xmas
4pt mix cor,acap oct SCHIRM.G 8621 $.30
(K910)

Prayer
SATB oct GRAY GCMR 685 $.30   (K911)

Prayer Of The Norwegian Child
4pt mix cor,opt SA soli,acap oct SCHIRM.G
9569 $.25   (K912)
jr cor&sr cor,SA soli oct SCHIRM.G 9703
$.20   (K913)
(Deis) 3pt wom cor oct SCHIRM.G 9447 $.25
(K914)
(Deis) 2pt wom cor oct SCHIRM.G 8289 $.25
(K915)
(Oncley) 4pt wom cor,S solo,acap oct
SCHIRM.G 8238 $.25   (K916)

Star And The Stable, The *Xmas,cant
mix cor,SATB soli,org/pno voc sc SCHIRM.G
$1.50   (K917)

KOUTZEN, BORIS (1901-   )
Invocation, An
SSA oct PRESSER MC345 $.50   (K918)

KOX, HANS (1930-   )
Litania
[Dut] wom cor,strings,perc,timp min sc
DONEMUS s.p.   (K919)

KOZINSKI, [DAVID B.] (1917-   )
Angels To The Shepherds Say *Xmas
SATB,acap oct PRESSER 312-40252 $.30 (K920)

Glorious King Triumphant Today *Easter
SATB,acap oct PRESSER 312-40278 $.30 (K921)

Glory To God In Heaven *Xmas
SATB,acap oct PRESSER 312-40205 $.30 (K922)

In A Hut Lowly *Xmas,carol,Pol
SATB oct ELKAN-V 362-1176 $.30   (K923)

O Praise The Lord, All Ye Nations
SATB,acap oct PRESSER 312-40382 $.35 (K924)

Raise Your Voices And Rejoice *Xmas
SATB,acap oct PRESSER 312-40383 $.30 (K925)

Shepherd's Chorus *Xmas
SATB,acap oct PRESSER 312-40337 $.30 (K926)

Sing A Carol *Pol
SATB oct ELKAN-V 362-1242 $.30   (K927)

Sing Mary's Lullabye *Xmas
SSA oct ELKAN-V 362-3105 $.25   (K928)

To Bethlehem *Xmas
SATB oct ELKAN-V 362-1295 $.30   (K929)

Wise Men, The *carol,Pol
SATB oct ELKAN-V 362-1200 $.25   (K930)

Wonder, Wonder
SATB,acap oct PRESSER 312-40207 $.30 (K931)

KPRIVSAK
Lacrymosa
"Mournful Day" SATB/TTBB PARAGON 1015 $.25
(K932)

Mournful Day *see Lacrymosa

KRAEHENBUEHL, D.
Christmas Blessing, A *Xmas
SSAA/TTBB,acap AMP A215 $.30   (K933)

Four Christmas Choruses *see Ideo Gloria In
Excelsis Deo; Song Against Bores, A; Star
Song, The; There Is No Rose   (K934)

Ideo Gloria In Excelsis Deo *Xmas
SSATB,acap AMP A193 $.25 see from Four
Christmas Choruses   (K935)

Song Against Bores, A *Xmas
SSATB,acap AMP A195 $.20 see from Four
Christmas Choruses   (K936)

Star Song, The *Xmas
SSATB,acap AMP A192 $.75 see from Four
Christmas Choruses   (K937)

There Is No Rose *Xmas
SSATB,acap AMP A194 $.30 see from Four
Christmas Choruses   (K938)

KRAFT, KARL (1908-   )
Graduale Und Offertorium Zum Heiligen
Osterfest *Easter,Gradual/Offer
mix cor,acap ERDMANN 508 s.p.   (K939)

Lobet Den Herren *Gen
[Ger] SATB,acap (med) MULLER MS 75 s.p.
(K940)

KRAFT, LEO (1922-   )
New Song, A (Psalm 98)
TBB,acap oct PRESSER MC500 $.30   (K941)

Proverb Of Solomon, A
SATB oct PRESSER MC243 $.50   (K942)

Psalm 98 *see New Song, A

Thanksgiving
SATB,acap oct PRESSER MC321 $.35   (K943)

When Israel Came Forth
SATB,acap oct PRESSER 312-40558 $.35 (K944)

KRAFT, WALTER (1905-   )
Christus *Gen
[Ger] SSAATTBB&SSAATTTB&SATB,acap (diff)
BAREN. BA 2120 rental   (K945)

Geistliche Und Liturgische Chorsatze *CCU
mix cor HANSEN-DEN 28971 s.p.   (K946)

Gott, Heiliger Schopfer Aller Stern *Gen
[Ger] SSATTB,S solo,fl,strings (med diff)
sc BAREN. BA 2194 $2.50, ipr   (K947)

Ich Ruf Zu Dir, Herr Jesu Christ
see Kraft, Walter, Laetatus Sum

Ich Weiss Ein Lieblich Engelspiel *Gen,mot
[Ger] SSAATBB,acap (med diff) BAREN.
BA 2408 $2.25   (K948)

Laetatus Sum *Gen,mot
[Ger] SATB,S solo,fl,strings (med diff) sc
BAREN. BA 2117 $3.50, ipa contains also:
Ich Ruf Zu Dir, Herr Jesu Christ   (K949)

Man Singt Mit Freuden Vom Sieg *Gen
[Ger] 4pt mix cor,acap (med) BAREN. BA 1325
s.p.   (K950)

Mit Freuden Zart *Easter/Pent,cant
[Ger] SA&men cor,org,2vln (med) BAREN.
BA 1775 sc $2.25, cor pts $1.75   (K951)

Nun Lasset Uns Den Leib Begrabn *mot
[Ger] 2pt mix cor/SAB,S/T solo,org,2vla
(med diff) sc BAREN. BA 2407 $2.25
contains also: O Welt, Ich Muss Dich
Lassen   (K952)

O Welt, Ich Muss Dich Lassen
see Kraft, Walter, Nun Lasset Uns Den Leib
Begrabn

Religious And Liturgical Choral Works
*CC14L,liturg
(Mathiesen, A.H.) [Eng/Ger] mix cor CHESTER
s.p.   (K953)

KRAMER, A. WALTER (1890-   )
Before The Paling Of The Stars
SATB oct FISCHER,J 3877 $.30   (K954)
SSA oct FISCHER,J 6631 $.30   (K955)

KRAMER, GOTTFRIED
Abraham
see Kramer, Gottfried, Des Herrn Wort

Der Blinde Barthimaus
see Kramer, Gottfried, Des Herrn Wort

Des Herrn Wort *Bibl/canon
3pt jr cor,org sc HANSSLER 12.510 s.p.
contains also: Der Blinde Barthimaus (jr
cor/SSA,pno); O Dass Ich Tausen Zungen
Hatte (unis jr cor,treb inst); Abraham
(unis jr cor,org,bvl/trom,gtr)   (K956)

O Dass Ich Tausen Zungen Hatte
see Kramer, Gottfried, Des Herrn Wort

KRAMS, PETER
Ich Wollt, Dass Ich Daheime War (Psalm 102)
[Ger] mix cor (med easy) oct SIRIUS 19 s.p.
(K957)

O Jesu, All Mein Leben Bist Du
[Ger] mix cor (easy) oct SIRIUS 18 s.p.
(K958)

Psalm 102 *see Ich Wollt, Dass Ich Daheime
War

KRANE, DAVID
Celebration
mix cor,soli,pno PEER $1.25   (K959)

KRANZ
Joseph, Dearest Joseph Mine
(Schreiner) SATB oct FISCHER,J 9465 $.30
(K960)

Mountain Carol, A *Xmas
(Hansen) SATB SCHMITT 899 $.30   (K961)

KRANZ, ALBERT
Es Ist Ein Ros' Entsprungen *Xmas
[Ger] wom cor,acap (med easy) HUG s.p.
(K962)

Kyrie Eleison *Gen/Lent,Kyrie
"Lord, Our God, Have Mercy" SATB,kbd (med
easy) oct CONCORDIA 98-1457 $.25   (K963)

Lord, Our God, Have Mercy *see Kyrie Eleison

Osterhymne *Easter,hymn
[Ger] mix cor,acap (easy) HUG   (K964)

KRAPF, GERHARD (1924-   )
Ah, Holy Jesus, How Hast Thou Offended?
*Lent
SATB,opt ob (med easy) oct CONCORDIA
98-2153 $.25   (K965)

At The Time Of The Banquet *Gen/Trin
unis,kbd (med diff) oct CONCORDIA 98-1977
$.30   (K966)

Be Merciful, Even As Your Father Is Merciful
*Gen/Trin
unis,kbd (med diff) oct CONCORDIA 98-1979

KRAPF, GERHARD (cont'd.)
$.25   (K967)

Confitebor Tibi *Gen/Refm/Trin
"O Lord, I Will Praise Thee" unis,kbd (med
diff) oct CONCORDIA 98-1853 $.30   (K968)

Dear Christians, One And All, Rejoice
*anthem
SATB,trp (med) oct AUGSBURG 1589 $.30 (K969)

Easter Antiphon (Christ Being Raised)
*Easter
SATB,brass (med diff) oct CONCORDIA 98-1751
$.30, ipa   (K970)

Father Abraham, Have Mercy On Me *Gen/Trin
unis,kbd (med diff) oct CONCORDIA 98-1976
$.25   (K971)

From Heaven Above *Xmas
cor,inst sc ABINGDON APM-554 $3.00, voc sc
ABINGDON APM-555 $.45, ipa   (K972)

Jesus Said To The Widow, "Do Not Weep" *Gen/
Trin
unis,kbd (med diff) oct CONCORDIA 98-2031
$.30   (K973)

Lift Up Your Heads *anthem
SAB (med) oct AUGSBURG 1373 $.25   (K974)

Lo, How A Rose E'er Blooming *Xmas
2pt,acap (easy) oct CONCORDIA 98-2105 $.25
contains also: While By My Sheep I
Watched At Night   (K975)

Lord Jesus Christ, With Us Abide *Epiph/Gen
SATB,kbd (med easy) oct CONCORDIA 98-1988
$.30   (K976)

Master, We Toiled All Night *Gen/Trin
unis,kbd (med diff) oct CONCORDIA 98-1980
$.30   (K977)

My Song Is Love Unknown
unis,inst oct AGAPE AG 7138 $.30   (K978)

O Lord, I Will Praise Thee *see Confitebor
Tibi

Praise To The Lord, The Almighty *Gen
SSA,opt fl (med easy) oct CONCORDIA 97-5107
$.35, ipa   (K979)

Psalm 150 *Gen
SSA,opt fl (med easy) oct CONCORDIA 98-2134
$.40   (K980)

Rejoice With Me, For I Have Found My Sheep
*Gen/Trin
unis,kbd (med diff) oct CONCORDIA 98-1978
$.30   (K981)

Rounds For The Christian Year *CC17L,Adv/
Asc/Xmas/Easter/Epiph/Lent/Pent/Thanks/
Trin
jr cor,opt treb inst CONCORDIA 97-4922 $.60
(K982)

Savior Of The Nations, Come *Adv,hymn,
Contemp
mix cor&opt cong,org (med) voc sc AUGSBURG
11-9366 $.25   (K983)

Sing Ye To The Lord
SAB (diff) ABINGDON APM-527 $.20   (K984)

Truly, Truly, I Say To You *Gen/Trin
unis,kbd (med diff) oct CONCORDIA 98-1975
$.30   (K985)

While By My Sheep I Watched At Night
see Krapf, Gerhard, Lo, How A Rose E'er
Blooming

You Have Heard That It Was Said *Gen/Trin
unis,kbd (med diff) oct CONCORDIA 98-1981
$.25   (K986)

KRATOCHWILL, HEINRICH (1933-   )
Die Seel' Ist Ein Kristall
mix cor,acap oct DOBLINGER s.p. see from
Mensch, Werde Wesentlich   (K987)

Es Kommt Der Tag *Bibl
mix cor,acap oct DOBLINGER s.p. see from
Zwei Geistliche Chore   (K988)

Gott Ist Ein Ew'ger Geist
mix cor,acap oct DOBLINGER s.p. see from
Mensch, Werde Wesentlich   (K989)

Lobe Den Herrn (Psalm 103) Bibl
mix cor,acap oct DOBLINGER s.p. see from
Zwei Geistliche Chore   (K990)

Mensch, Werde Wesentlich *see Die Seel' Ist
Ein Kristall; Gott Ist Ein Ew'ger Geist;
Mensch, Werde Wesentlich   (K991)

Mensch, Werde Wesentlich
mix cor,acap oct DOBLINGER s.p. see from
Mensch, Werde Wesentlich   (K992)

Psalm 103 *see Lobe Den Herrn

Psalm 113 *Op.65
mix cor,acap oct DOBLINGER s.p.   (K993)

Zwei Geistliche Chore *see Es Kommt Der Tag;
Lobe Den Herrn (Psalm 103)   (K994)

KRAUSE, CHR.
Es Flog Ein Tablein Weisse
see Singet Dem Kindlein

Leib Nachtigall
see Singet Dem Kindlein

O Jesulein Suss
see Singet Dem Kindlein

Singet Dem Kindlein
wom cor ERDMANN 507 s.p.
contains: Es Flog Ein Tablein Weisse;
Leib Nachtigall; O Jesulein Suss; Vom
Himmel Hoch   (K995)

KRAUSE, CHR. (cont'd.)

Vom Himmel Hoch
see Singet Dem Kindlein

KRAUSE, JOACH.
Weihnachtliche Chorgemeinschaft *CC8L,Xmas
men cor,acap ERDMANN 135 s.p.   (K996)

Weihnachtshymnus *Xmas,hymn
men cor,acap ERDMANN 126 s.p.   (K997)

KRAUSE, JOH. CHR.
Weihnachtshymnus *Xmas
mix cor,acap ERDMANN 505 s.p.   (K998)

KREBS, J.
Eight Choral Preludes *CC8U
unis cor PRESSER 352-00117 $.35   (K999)

KREIG, FRANZ (1780-1849)
Deutsches Ordinarium
mix cor&jr cor,cantor,opt org/2trp&2trom
DOBLINGER voc sc s.p., cor pts s.p., ipa
(K1000)

KREISLER, A.VON
Psalm 117
SATB,4brass oct SOUTHERN $.30, ipa   (K1001)

Whither Shall I Go
SATB,4brass oct SOUTHERN $.30, ipa   (K1002)

KREMENLIEV, BORIS (1911-   )
They Are Slaves
SATB,org FOSTER MF113 $.30   (K1003)

KREMER, CLEMENS (1930-   )
Gesang Der Jungfrau Maria
mix cor,S solo ERDMANN 515 s.p.   (K1004)

KREMSER
Prayer Of Thanksgiving *anthem/hymn/prayer
SATB oct FOX C1506 $.25   (K1005)
(Noble) SATB oct SPRATT 566 $.25   (K1006)
(Shaw; Parker) SATB ALLANS 399 $.25 (K1007)

KREMSER, [EDWARD] (1838-1914)
Hymn To The Saviour
(Spicker) 4pt mix cor,S solo,harp,org/harp,
pno SCHIRM.G 6976 $.30   (K1008)

KRENEK, ERNST (1900-   )
By The Sepulchre
SATB oct BELWIN 60756 $.25   (K1009)

Christmas
see Holiday Motets

Communion Psalms *CCU,Commun,Psalm
[Lat] 2-4pt SCHOTT s.p.   (K1010)

Deutsche Messe (Ordinarium) 1968 *Mass
[Ger] SATB&cong,clar,trp,2trom,drums,perc
(med) BAREN. BA 5417 sc s.p., cor pts
s.p., ipa   (K1011)

Easter
see Holiday Motets

Epiphany
see Holiday Motets

Go Thy Way *Bibl
SATB,acap RONGWEN $.35 see from Three
Sacred Pieces   (K1012)

Holiday Motets
[Lat] BROUDE BR. $.40
contains: Christmas (SSAA) (Xmas); Easter
(SSA) (Easter); Epiphany (SSA) (Epiph);
Lent (SATB,acap) (Lent); Thanksgiving
(SSA) (Thanks)   (K1013)

In Paradisum *mot
[Lat] SSA RONGWEN $.40   (K1014)

Lamentatio Jeremiae Prophetae *Gen
[Lat] 4-9pt mix cor,acap (diff) BAREN.
BA 3648 $7.25   (K1015)

Lent
see Holiday Motets

O Holy Ghost *Pent
SSAATTBB,acap oct KERBY B123 $.40   (K1016)
[Ger] SATB,acap (diff) BAREN. BA 5402 $1.75
(K1017)

Oculi Mei Semper Ad Dominum *mot
[Lat] SAB SCHOTT s.p.   (K1018)

Proprium Fur Das Dreifaltigkeitsfest *Trin
[Ger] SATB&cong/SAB&cor,S solo,org,2trp,
drums (med diff) voc sc BAREN. BA 4122
$1.00   (K1019)

Psalm 126
SATB oct BELWIN 60150 $.30   (K1020)

Thanksgiving
see Holiday Motets

There Be Four Things *Bibl
SATB,acap RONGWEN $.35 see from Three
Sacred Pieces   (K1021)

There Be Three Things *Bibl
SATB,acap RONGWEN $.30 see from Three
Sacred Pieces   (K1022)

Three Sacred Pieces *see Go Thy Way; There
Be Four Things; There Be Three Things
(K1023)

Veni Sanctificator *mot
[Lat] SAB SCHOTT s.p.   (K1024)

KRENGER, R.
Zwei Kreuze
[Ger] mix cor,acap (easy) HUG   (K1025)

KRETER
Alleluia *Allelu
SATB,acap MARKS 4271 $.30   (K1026)

Gloria In Excelsis Deo *Gloria
[Lat] SATB MARKS 4320 $.30   (K1027)

Show Us Thy Ways, O Lord
SAB oct GALAXY 1.2370.1 $.30   (K1028)

KRETZ
Thou Wilt Keep Him In Perfect Peace
(Whitman) SATB oct LILLENAS AN-2296 $.25
(K1029)

KRETZSCHMAR, GUNTHER (1929-   )
All Morgen Ist Ganz Frisch Und Neu
see Schlenker, Manfred, Allein Gott In Der
Hoh Sei Ehr

Christus Hat Dem Tode Die Macht Genommen
*Easter
jr cor,org sc HANSSLER 12.219 s.p.   (K1030)

Christus Ist Auferstanden, Freud Ist In
4pt jr cor/SSAB&opt men cor,bvl,S rec,A
rec,T rec,B rec/trp, glockenspiel,
xylophone sc HANSSLER 12.204 s.p.
contains also: Herbst, Wolfgang, Wir
Wollen Alle Frohlich Sein (jr cor,timp,
glockenspiel, xylophone); Gadsch,
Herbert, Sei Lob Und Ehr Dem Hochsten Gut
(unis jr cor,timp,2S rec, triangle,
xylophone); Kretzschmar, Gunther,
Erstanden Ist Der Heilig Christ (unis jr
cor,A rec,B rec,opt vcl/bvl, glockenspiel, xylophon); Kretzschmar, Gunther,
Gen Himmel Aufgefahren Ist (2pt jr cor,
vcl/bvl,A rec); Ehlers, Erich, Wir Danken
Dir, Herr Jesu Christ (2pt jr cor,bsn/
vcl,2rec)   (K1031)

Das Ist Meine Freude, Dass Ich Mich Zu Gott
see Tzschoppe, Eberhart, Es Ist Ein
Kostlich Ding

David Und Goliath *Bibl
jr cor,opt vcl/bvl,perc,rec,gtr sc HANSSLER
12.231 s.p., ipa   (K1032)

Der Morgenstern Ist Aufgedrungen
see Tzschoppe, Eberhart, Kleine
Weihnachtskantate

Der Turmbau Zu Babylon *Bibl
jr cor,fl,clar,trp,bvl HANSSLER 12.230 sc
s.p., voc sc s.p., ipa   (K1033)

Die Grosse Flut *Bibl/cant
1-3pt jr cor/SSA,narrator,vcl,perc,rec,gtr
HANSSLER 12.210 sc s.p., cor pts s.p.,
ipa   (K1034)

Dunkel War's
jr cor sc HANSSLER 12.701 s.p.   (K1035)

Erhalt Uns, Herr, Bei Deinem Wort
see Schlenker, Manfred, Allein Gott In Der
Hoh Sei Ehr

Erhore Mich, Wenn Ich Rufe (Psalm 4)
SATB,bvl sc HANSSLER 19.104 s.p. contains
also: Schweizer, Rolf, Ich Will Den Herrn
Loben Allezeit (Psalm 34) (unis,bvl,kbd)
(K1036)

Erstanden Ist Der Heilig Christ
see Kretzschmar, Gunther, Christus Ist
Auferstanden, Freud Ist In

Es War Ein Mensch, Der Machte Ein Grosses
Abendmahl *mot
SSATB HANSSLER 7.099 s.p.   (K1037)

Gedenke, Herr, An Deine Barmherzigkeit
unis jr cor,org sc HANSSLER 12.217 s.p.
(K1038)

Gen Himmel Aufgefahren Ist
see Kretzschmar, Gunther, Christus Ist
Auferstanden, Freud Ist In

Gott Geht An Keinem Vorbei
see Michel, Josep, Herr Ruste Uns Von Neuem
Aus

Gott, Gib Fried Unserm Lande
see Ruppel, Paul Ernst, Da Pacem, Domine

Herr, Auf Dich Traue Ich (Psalm 31)
SSAT/SSAB,opt inst HANSSLER 19.107 s.p.
(K1039)

Herr, Wie Lange Willst Du Mein So Gar
Vergessen
(Horn) unis,kbd HANSSLER 5.122 s.p. (K1040)

Ist Gott Fur Mich, So Trete
see Kretzschmar, Gunther, Nun Danket All
Und Bringet Ehr

Jauchzet Dem Herrn *mot
3pt jr cor sc HANSSLER 12.101 s.p. contains
also: Becker-Foss, Jurgen, Aller Augen
Warten Auf Dich (2pt jr cor); Ochs,
Volker, Frohlich Wir Nun All Fangen An
(2pt jr cor); Kretzschmar, Gunther, O
Lebensbrunnlein Tief Und Gross (2pt jr
cor); Horbe, Ernst, Lobet Den Herren
Alle, Die Ihn Ehren (2pt jr cor); Herbst,
Wolfgang, Herr Jesu Christ, Dich Zu Uns
Wend (2-3pt jr cor)   (K1041)

Jesu, Meine Freude
see Tzschoppe, Eberhart, Es Ist Ein
Kostlich Ding

Komm, Heiliger Geist
unis,kbd,bvl,opt fl sc HANSSLER 19.208 s.p.
contains also: Schweizer, Rolf, Das Ist
Ein Kostlich Ding (unis,kbd,bvl,treb
inst)   (K1042)

Nun Bitten Wir Den Heiligen Geist
see Kretzschmar, Gunther, Pfingstruf

Nun Danket All Und Bringet Ehr
2pt jr cor, xylophone, glockenspiel sc
HANSSLER 12.201 s.p. contains also:
Kretzschmar, Gunther, Ist Gott Fur Mich,
So Trete (unis jr cor,2S rec,A rec,
xylophone, glockenspiel); Horbe, Ernst,
Ich Ruf Zu Dir, Herr Jesu Christ (jr cor,
S rec,A rec); Herbst, Wolfgang, Wohl
Denen, Die Da Wandeln (jr cor,2inst)
(K1043)

O Lebensbrunnlein Tief Und Gross
see Kretzschmar, Gunther, Jauchzet Dem
Herrn

Pfingstruf
3pt jr cor/SSA sc HANSSLER 12.107 s.p.
contains also: Kretzschmar, Gunther, Nun

KRETZSCHMAR, GUNTHER (cont'd.)

Bitten Wir Den Heiligen Geist (2pt jr
cor/SA); Neubert, Gottfried, O Komm, Du
Geist Der Wahrheit (2pt jr cor/SA);
Schulz, Raimund, Dies Ist Der Tag, Den
Der Herr Macht (3pt jr cor/SSA); Rabsch,
Edgar, Jauchzet Gott, Alle Lande (3pt jr
cor/SSA); Tzschoppe, Eberhart, Jauchzet,
Alle Lande, Gott Zu Ehren (2pt jr cor/SS)
(K1044)

Psalm 4 *see Erhore Mich, Wenn Ich Rufe

Psalm 31 *see Herr, Auf Dich Traue Ich

Siehe, Dein Konig
jr cor,2vla,vcl,rec HANSSLER 12.212 sc
s.p., voc sc s.p., ipa   (K1045)

Sonne Der Gerechtigkeit
see Tzschoppe, Eberhart, Es Ist Ein
Kostlich Ding

Vier Weihnachtskonzerten *CC4U,Xmas
jr cor,fl,ob,strings HANSSLER 12.213 sc
s.p., cor pts s.p., ipa   (K1046)

Wie Sich Ein Vater Erbarmt
see Ruppel, Paul Ernst, Da Pacem, Domine

KREUTZ
Laudate Dominum
mix cor SOUTHERN $.35   (K1047)

KREUTZ, ROBERT E.
I Arose *Easter,Bibl/Introit
SATB,org oct WORLD CA-2272-8 $.45   (K1048)

It Is Better To Take Refuge In The Lord
*Pent,Gradual
(Snow, Robert J.) 2pt mix cor,org oct WORLD
EMP-1498-5 $.45   (K1049)

Laudate Dominum (Psalm 148) Bibl
"O Praise Him" [Eng/Lat] SATB,acap oct
WORLD MO-1863-8 $.45   (K1050)

Let My Prayer Come Like Incense *Pent
(Snow, Robert J.) SBar,org oct WORLD
EMP-1641-5 $.30   (K1051)

O Lord, We Believe
SATB,acap oct WORLD ESA-1378-8 $.30 (K1052)

O Praise Him *see Laudate Dominum

O You That Pass This Way *Bibl
SATB,acap oct WORLD CA-2271-8 $.45 (K1053)

Psalm 148 *see Laudate Dominum

This Is The Day *Easter,Allelu/Gradual
SATB,org oct WORLD CA-2273-8 $.45   (K1054)

KREUTZER, C.
Das Ist Der Tag Des Herrn
men cor,acap ERDMANN 205 s.p.   (K1055)

KREUTZER, KONRADIN
This Is The Lord's Own Day
(Mueller) 4pt mix cor,acap oct SCHIRM.G
11109 $.25   (K1056)
(Mueller) 3pt mix cor,org/pno oct SCHIRM.G
11110 $.25   (K1057)

KREUZFIDEL see Lohr-Eyle

KREUZMESSE see Haydn, (Johann) Michael, Missa
Sanctae Crucis In A-Moll

KREUZWEG see Metzler, Friedrich

KRIDER, DALE
Prayer *prayer
SATB (med) ABINGDON APM-682 $.20   (K1058)

KRIEG, H.
Psalm 17
men cor ALSBACH&D sc s.p., cor pts s.p.
(K1059)

Psalm 22
men cor ALSBACH&D sc s.p., cor pts s.p.
(K1060)

Psalm 23
men cor ALSBACH&D sc s.p., cor pts s.p.
(K1061)

KRIEGER
Glorious Message, The *Xmas,cant
SATB oct LORENZ $1.50   (K1062)

God Moves In A Mysterious Way
(Hadley) SATB oct PRO ART 1959 $.22 (K1063)

Two Part Stylings *CCU
SB FISCHER,C ASH. $1.25   (K1064)

KRIEGER, JOHANN PHILIPP (1649-1725)
Die Gerechten Werden Weggerafft *cant
[Ger] SATB,soli,org,strings KISTNER sc
s.p., cor pts s.p., ipa   (K1065)
(Moller, Niels) "Han Bortkalder For Sin
Vredesdag" [Ger/Dan] SATB,soli,org,bsn,
strings HANSEN-DEN 27463 s.p., ipa (K1066)

Ein Feste Burg Ist Unser Gott
(Seiffert, M.) mix cor,pno,org,7strings sc
BREITKOPF-L rental   (K1067)

For Us A Child Is Born *Xmas,cant
(Samuel, H.) SAB,SABar soli,2vln,cont sc
CONCORDIA 97-4692 $1.75, ipa   (K1068)

Han Bortkalder For Sin Vredesdag *see Die
Gerechten Werden Weggerafft

Heilig, Heilig, Ist Der Herr *cant
(Grischkat) SATB,cont,ob,2vln,2vla HANSSLER
10.002 sc s.p., cor pts s.p., ipa (K1069)

Heut Singt Die Liebe Christenheit *cant
mix cor,cont,trp,strings HANSSLER 10.288 sc
s.p., cor pts s.p., ipa   (K1070)

Rufet Nicht Die Weisheit *cant
[Ger] SATB,soli,org,strings KISTNER sc
s.p., cor pts s.p., ipa   (K1071)

KRIEGER, JOHANN PHILIPP (cont'd.)

Schaff In Mir, Gott, Ein Reines Herz *Gen
[Ger] 3pt mix cor,cont (med easy) BAREN. BA 3682 s.p. (K1072)

Singet Dem Herrn Ein Neues Lied *cant
(Heinrichs) SATB,SATB soli,cont,bsn,4vln, vla HANSSLER 10.188 sc s.p., voc sc s.p., ipa (K1073)

KRIETSCH, GEORG (1904-1969)
Die Muttergottes Ging Uber Das Land
see Zauber- Und Segensspruche

Es Sind Drei Frauen Nach Bohmen Gegangen
see Zauber- Und Segensspruche

Fahrt Hin Ihr, Tag Und Jahr
men cor,acap TONGER s.p. (K1074)

Im Garten Ging Eine Braut
see Zauber- Und Segensspruche

Wir Haben So Lange Krieg Gesehn
see Zauber- Und Segensspruche

Zauber- Und Segensspruche
wom cor&jr cor,acap TONGER s.p.
contains: Die Muttergottes Ging Uber Das Land; Es Sind Drei Frauen Nach Bohmen Gegangen; Im Garten Ging Eine Braut; Wir Haben So Lange Krieg Gesehn (K1075)

KRIGER, ADAM (1634-1666)
Nun Sich Der Tag Geendet Hat
see Ahle, Johann Georg, Die Guldene Sonne Bringt Leben Und Wonne

KRIPPENSPEIL see Borris, Siegfried

KRIST AR UPPSTANDEN see Blom, Oscar

KRIST AR UPPSTANDEN see Eccard, Johannes

KRIST AR UPPSTANDEN see Hassler, Hans Leo

KRIST ER OPPSTANDEN
(Rasch, Johannes) [Norw] 2 eq voices,3vln LYCHE 55 s.p. (K1076)

KRIST SEGERRIKE see Kullnes, Ake

KRIST SEGERRIKE see Moren, John

KRISTALLEN DEN FINA
(Bruhn, Otto) TTB NORDISKA 4836 s.p. (K1077)

KRISTALLEN DEN FINA see Nordstrom, Carl-Elow

KRISTALLEN DEN FINA see Paulsson, Carl

KRISTE KONUNG I GUDS RIKE see Bach, Johann Sebastian

KRISTENHJERTER ALLE STEDER see Elgaroy, Jan

KRISTI BRUD, KOM, FRYD DIG see Victoria, Tomas Luis de, Veni Sponsa Christi

KRISTI FODSEL see Raasted, Niels Otto

KRISTUS BLE FOR SKYLD LYDIG see Anerio, Felice

KRISTUS BLEV FOR VAR SKULL LYDIG see Anerio, Giovanni Francesco

KRISTUS KOM SELV TIL JORDANS FLOD see Walther

KRISTUSHYMNE see Kjeldaas, Arnljot

KROEGER, KARL (1932-)
Dies Sanctificatus
"This Sacred Day" [Eng/Lat] SATB,acap oct LAWSON 51434 $.35 (K1078)

This Sacred Day *see Dies Sanctificatus

KROL, BERNHARD (1934-)
Deutsche Kanonmesse *canon/Mass
[Ger] 3pt,acap (easy) BOSSE BE 238 s.p. (K1079)

Magnificat *Magnif
[Ger] cor&cong,S solo,org,trp,bvl,gtr,perc (med diff) BOSSE BE 264 sc s.p., cor pts s.p. (K1080)

KROLL, STEPHAN
Furchte Dich Nicht, Ich Bin Der Erste Und Der Letzte *cant
ST/BB&jr cor,org/5-6brass,timp HANSSLER 10.082 sc s.p., voc sc s.p., ipa (K1081)

KRONE
All Men Now Sing, Rejoice
SATB KJOS 507 $.30 (K1082)

And The Glory Of The Lord
SATB KJOS 801 $.30 (K1083)

Birds And The Christ Child, The *Xmas
3pt jr cor/SSA (easy) FISCHER,C CM 5315 $.20 (K1084)

Christ The Lord Is Risen Today *Easter
SSA KJOS 1229 $.30 (K1085)

For Unto Us A Child Is Born *Xmas
SATB KJOS 803 $.35 (K1086)

Now Thank We All Our God
eq voices KJOS 4223 $.30 (K1087)

O Thou That Tellest
SATB KJOS 802 $.30 (K1088)

Old French Christmas Carol *Xmas,carol,Fr
SSA KJOS 1213 $.30 (K1089)

These Things Shall Be
SATB KJOS 813 $.30 (K1090)

Ye Are Not Of The Flesh
SATB KJOS 503 $.40 (K1091)

KRONE, B.P.
Easter Dawn *Easter
SAB KJOS 5737 $.30 (K1092)

KRONE, MAX
Praise The Lord
SATB KJOS 816 $.40 (K1093)

KRONES
Christmas Carols With Descants *CCU,Xmas, carol
2pt treb cor KJOS $1.25 (K1094)

Fairest Lord Jesus
SSA KJOS 4224 $.30 (K1095)

For The Blessings Of Our Days
SATB KJOS 815 $.30 (K1096)

God Rest You Merry, Gentlemen *Xmas
SATB KJOS 1034 $.30 (K1097)
men cor KJOS 1117 $.30 (K1098)
SSA KJOS 4227 $.30 (K1099)

Great Songs Of Faith *CCU
2pt/3pt KJOS $1.25 (K1100)

Jesus Walked This Lonesome Valley
SATB KJOS 1032 $.30 (K1101)

O Come, All Ye Faithful *Xmas
eq voices KJOS 4217 $.30 (K1102)

Pat-A-Pan
SATB KJOS 4005 $.30 (K1103)
SSA KJOS 1236 $.30 (K1104)

Prayer Of Thanksgiving *Thanks,prayer
SATB KJOS 1036 $.30 (K1105)
SSA&desc KJOS 4222 $.30 (K1106)
SSA KJOS 1232 $.30 (K1107)

Song Of Hope
SATB KJOS 1055 $.30 (K1108)

These Things Shall Be
eq voices KJOS 4221 $.30 (K1109)

KRONINGSHYMNE (LOFT DIN ARM DEN SEJRENDE) see Handel, George Frideric

KRONSTEINER, HERMAN (1914-)
Corpus Christi Mysticum *Corpus,Mass
4pt mix cor,acap sc DOBLINGER s.p. (K1110)

Kleine Festmesse *Fest,Mass
mix cor,org,opt 2trp&2trom DOBLINGER voc sc s.p., cor pts s.p., ipa (K1111)

Stille-Nacht-Messe *Xmas,Mass
4pt mix cor,org,opt 2inst DOBLINGER voc sc s.p., cor pts s.p., ipa (K1112)

KRONSTEINER, JOSEF (1910-)
Memorare
mix cor,acap oct DOBLINGER s.p. (K1113)

Misericordia
4pt mix cor,acap DOBLINGER sc s.p., cor pts s.p. (K1114)

Missa Natalis *Mass
3pt wom cor,acap cor pts DOBLINGER s.p. (K1115)

KRONUNGSMESSE see Mozart, Wolfgang Amadeus, Messe C-Dur

KRONUNGSMESSE see Mozart, Wolfgang Amadeus, Missa C-Dur

KROPCZYNSKI
Chillun *spir
SSA,S solo SCHMITT 2061 $.20 (K1116)

Gloria In Excelsis Deo! *Xmas
SATB SCHMITT 1784 $.25 (K1117)

KROPFREITER, AUGUSTINIUS FRANZ (1936-)
Ecce Lignum Crucisc *Psntd,mot
wom cor,acap oct DOBLINGER s.p. see from Zwei Passionmotetten (K1118)

Es Wird Scho Glei Dumpa
wom cor,acap oct DOBLINGER s.p. (K1119)

Freiburger Magnificat *Magnif
4-8pt,org DOBLINGER voc sc s.p., cor pts s.p. (K1120)

Hoc Corpus *Psntd,mot
wom cor,acap oct DOBLINGER s.p. see from Zwei Passionmotetten (K1121)

Laudate Dominum
mix cor DOBLINGER s.p. see also CHRISTUS, DER HERR (K1122)
mix cor,acap oct DOBLINGER (K1123)

Maria Durch Ein Dorwald Ging
wom cor,acap oct DOBLINGER s.p. (K1124)

Missa Pueri Cantores *Mass
unis&mix cor,org DOBLINGER voc sc $3.75, cor pts $1.00 (K1125)

O Jesulein Zart
wom cor,acap oct DOBLINGER s.p. (K1126)

Pueri Cantores *Mass
unis cor&mix cor,org DOBLINGER voc sc s.p., cor pts s.p. (K1127)

Zwei Passionmotetten *see Ecce Lignum Crucisc; Hoc Corpus (K1128)

KRUL
Alleluia
SATB,acap PETERS 6533 $.25 (K1129)

O Come Let Us Sing (Psalm 95)
SATB,org/pno PETERS 6245 $.25 (K1130)

Prayer (from Psalm 102)
SATB MARKS 4080 $.25 (K1131)

Psalm 95 *see O Come Let Us Sing

KRUNNFUSZ
Christmas Is Coming Again *Xmas
SSA oct SHAPIRO SCE 3502 $.30 (K1132)

KUBELIK, RAFAEL (1914-)
Stabat Mater
voc sc PETERS 5948 $2.00 (K1133)

KUBIK, GAIL (1914-)
Christmas Set, A
SATB,orch voc sc MCA $3.95, ipr (K1134)

Litany And Prayer
men cor,brass,perc PEER voc sc $.85, min sc $4.00, ipr (K1135)

Make We Joye Nowe In This Fest *Xmas,hymn
SATB,acap oct BROWN 5688 $1.00 (K1136)

Morning Prayer
SATB,org/pno BOSTON 12665 $.35 (K1137)

Second Choral Suite
BELWIN $1.50 (K1138)

Soon One Mornin' Death Comes Creepin' *folk, US
mix cor,Bar solo,acap oct SCHIRM.G 9855 $.25 (K1139)

KUBIZEK, AUGUSTINIAN (1918-)
Also Hat Gott Die Welt Geliebt *Bibl
mix cor,acap oct DOBLINGER s.p. see from Drei Kleine Motetten (K1140)

Cantate De Joanne *Op.21a, cant
men cor,TBar soli,2pno,pic,2clar,horn,2trp, timp,perc DOBLINGER voc sc s.p., cor pts s.p., ipr (K1141)

Das Ist Der Tag *Bibl/Psalm
mix cor,acap oct DOBLINGER s.p. see from Drei Kleine Motetten (K1142)

Das Ist Ein Kostlich Ding *Bibl/Psalm
mix cor,acap oct DOBLINGER s.p. see from Drei Kleine Motetten (K1143)

Der Herr Ist Konig *mot/Psalm
mix cor,acap oct DOBLINGER s.p. see also Sechs Kleine Psalmenmotten (K1144)

Der Mensch Ist Wie Gras (Psalm 103) mot/Psalm
mix cor,acap oct DOBLINGER s.p. see also Sechs Kleine Psalmenmotten (K1145)

Deutsches Ordinarium *Op.35
4pt mix cor,acap voc sc DOBLINGER s.p. (K1146)
mix cor,acap cor pts DOBLINGER s.p. (K1147)

Drei Geistliche Motetten *see Memento Homo; O Traurigkeit; Psalm 100 (K1148)

Drei Kleine Motetten *see Also Hat Gott Die Welt Geliebt; Das Ist Der Tag; Das Ist Ein Kostlich Ding (K1149)

Drei Motetten [Op.22c] *Op.22c, mot
wom cor,acap cmplt ed DOBLINGER s.p.
contains & see also: Gaudia Matris; Gloria; Laudate (K1150)

Drei Motetten [Op.22d] *Op.22d
mix cor,acap cmplt ed DOBLINGER s.p.
contains & see also: Gaudia Matris; Gloria; Laudate (K1151)

Gaudia Matris *Op.22c, mot
mix cor,acap oct DOBLINGER s.p. see also Drei Motetten [Op.22d] (K1152)
wom cor,acap oct DOBLINGER s.p. see also Drei Motetten [Op.22c] (K1153)
men cor,acap oct DOBLINGER s.p. (K1154)

Gloria *Gloria/mot
wom cor,acap oct DOBLINGER s.p. see also Drei Motetten [Op.22c] (K1155)
mix cor,acap oct DOBLINGER s.p. see also Drei Motetten [Op.22d] (K1156)

Herr, Meine Starke (Psalm 18) mot/Psalm
mix cor,acap oct DOBLINGER s.p. see also Sechs Kleine Psalmenmotten (K1157)

Jauchzet Dem Herrn, Alle Welt (Psalm 100) mot/Psalm
4pt mix cor,acap DOBLINGER sc s.p., cor pts s.p. see also Drei Geistliche Motetten (K1158)
mix cor,acap sc DOBLINGER s.p. see from Drei Geistliche Motetten (K1159)
mix cor,acap oct DOBLINGER s.p. see also Sechs Kleine Psalmenmotten (K1160)

Laudate *mot
mix cor,acap oct DOBLINGER s.p. see also Drei Motetten [Op.22d] (K1161)
wom cor,acap oct DOBLINGER s.p. see also Drei Motetten [Op.22c] (K1162)

Lobe Den Herren, Den Machtigen Konig Der Ehren *cant
mix cor&cong,org,opt brass DOBLINGER voc sc s.p., cor pts s.p. (K1163)

Memento Homo *mot
mix cor,acap sc DOBLINGER s.p. see from Drei Geistliche Motetten (K1164)
4pt mix cor,acap DOBLINGER sc s.p., cor pts s.p. see also Drei Geistliche Motetten (K1165)

Missa Brevis *Mass
4pt mix cor,acap sc DOBLINGER s.p. (K1166)
mix cor,acap sc DOBLINGER s.p. (K1167)

O Herr, Deine Gute (Psalm 36) mot/Psalm
mix cor,acap oct DOBLINGER s.p. see also Sechs Kleine Psalmenmotten (K1168)

O Traurigkeit *mot
4pt mix cor,acap DOBLINGER sc s.p., cor pts s.p. see also Drei Geistliche Motetten (K1169)
mix cor,acap sc DOBLINGER s.p. see from Drei Geistliche Motetten (K1170)

KUBIZEK, AUGUSTINIAN (cont'd.)

Psalm 18 *see Herr, Meine Starke

Psalm 36 *see O Herr, Deine Gute

Psalm 62 *see Sei Stille Zu Gott, Meine
Seele

Psalm 100 *see Jauchzet Dem Herrn, Alle Welt

Psalm 103 *see Der Mensch Ist Wie Gras

Psalm 126 *Op.31,No.3
mix cor (med diff) DOBLINGER s.p.   (K1171)

Sechs Kleine Psalmenmotten *Op.29, mot/Psalm
mix cor,acap cmplt ed DOBLINGER s.p.
contains & see also: Der Herr Ist Konig;
Der Mensch Ist Wie Gras (Psalm 103);
Herr, Meine Starke (Psalm 18); Jauchzet
Dem Herrn, Alle Welt (Psalm 100); O
Herr, Deine Gute (Psalm 36); Sei Stille
Zu Gott, Meine Seele (Psalm 62) (K1172)

Sehet, Der Tag Ist Gekommen
wom cor,acap oct DOBLINGER s.p.   (K1173)

Sei Stille Zu Gott, Meine Seele (Psalm 62)
mot/Psalm
mix cor,acap oct DOBLINGER s.p. see also
Sechs Kleine Psalmenmotten   (K1174)

Und Unser Lieben Frauen
wom cor,acap oct DOBLINGER s.p.   (K1175)

KUBLER, EMIL (1909-   )
All Morgen Ist Ganz Frisch Und Neu
SS/SA/SATB,3inst HANSSLER 8.003 s.p. (K1176)

Du Meine Seele, Singe, Wohlauf *cant
SATB/SAB HANSSLER 8.013 s.p.   (K1177)
SATB,4-8brass HANSSLER 10.117 sc s.p., cor
pts s.p.   (K1178)

Ermuntre Dich, Mein Schwacher Geist
SATB/SSA/TTB/B/T,2vln/fl HANSSLER 8.023
s.p.   (K1179)

Freu Dich, Erd' Und Sternenzelt
SATB HANSSLER 6.2562 s.p. contains also:
Wunderbarber Gnadenthron, Gottes Und
Marien Schon   (K1180)

Geh Aus, Mein Herz, Und Suche Freud *cant
SATB,ST soli,fl,ob,2vln,vcl,bvl HANSSLER
10.089 sc s.p., cor pts s.p., ipa   (K1181)

Ich Weiss, Woran Ich Glaube
SS/SA/SAT/SAB HANSSLER 8.004 s.p. contains
also: Schutz, Heinrich, Ich Weiss, Woran
Ich Glaube (SATB)   (K1182)

Im Frieden Dein, O Herre Mein
SATB HANSSLER 6.170 s.p. contains also:
Decker, Joachim, Gott Sei Gelobet Und
Gebenedeiet   (K1183)

Lob Gott Getrost Mit Singen
see Rosenmuller, Johann, Ich Will Dich,
Mein Gott, Erhohen
ST/SS/SAB/SATB HANSSLER 8.005 s.p. (K1184)

Lobe Den Herren, O Meine Seele *cant
SATB,4-6brass HANSSLER 10.098 sc s.p., cor
pts s.p.   (K1185)

Lobt Gott Getrost Mit Singen *cant
SATB/men cor,org,4-6brass HANSSLER 10.093
sc s.p., cor pts s.p.   (K1186)

Mit Freuden Zart Zu Dieser Fahrt
see Stern, Hermann, Nun Komm, Der Heiden
Heiland

Nun Schlafet Man *prayer
SATB,S solo,inst HANSSLER 7.021 s.p.
(K1187)

O Heiliger Geist, O Heiliger Gott
SATB HANSSLER 8.002 s.p. contains also: Wir
Wollen Alle Frohlich Sein   (K1188)

Preis, Lob Und Dank Sei Gott Dem Herren
SATB/SS/ST,4brass HANSSLER 8.008 s.p.
(K1189)

Sei Lob Und Ehr Dem Hochsten Gut
see Cruger, Johann, Sei Lob Und Ehr Dem
Hochsten Gut
see Schutz, Heinrich, Ich Will Von Herzen
Danken Gott Dem Herrn
SS/SA/SAB/SATB HANSSLER 8.006 s.p. (K1190)

Singet Dem Herrn Ein Neues Lied
see Kubler, Emil, Singt, Singt Jehova Neue
Lieder

Singt, Singt Jehova Neue Lieder
SATB/SS/TT/ST HANSSLER 8.2630 s.p. contains
also: Singet Dem Herrn Ein Neues Lied
(4pt) (canon)   (K1191)

Treuer Wachter Israel *Bibl
SATB,2brass HANSSLER 6.167 s.p. contains
also: Trubel, Gerhard, Gott Rufet Noch,
Sollt Ich Nicht (SATB)   (K1192)

Treuer Wachter Israel, Des Sich Freuet
SATB/SS/TT/SAB/STB,2brass/vln HANSSLER
8.009 s.p.   (K1193)

Wie Lieblich Ist Der Maien
SA/SSA/TTB/SAB/SSAT,3inst/fl/vln HANSSLER
8.007 s.p.   (K1194)

Wir Wollen Alle Frohlich Sein
see Kubler, Emil, O Heiliger Geist, O
Heiliger Gott

Wunderbarber Gnadenthron, Gottes Und Marien
Schon
see Kubler, Emil, Freu Dich, Erd' Und
Sternenzelt

KUBLI, M.
Gebet *prayer
[Ger] mix cor,acap (med) HUG s.p. (K1195)

KUCKUCK see Gebhard, Hans

KUEHNHAUSEN, J.G. (? -1714)
Angel's Message, The *Xmas
SSA oct KENDOR $.25   (K1196)

Christ, The Life Of All The Living *Lent
SA,kbd (med easy) oct CONCORDIA 98-1825
$.20   (K1197)

KUGELMANN
Kleine Messe *Mass
3 eq voices MOSELER s.p.   (K1198)

Love Is Come Again *anthem
(Bliss) SAB (med) oct AUGSBURG 1341 $.25
(K1199)

My Soul, Now Bless Thy Maker *anthem
(Bliss) SSA (med) oct AUGSBURG 1460 $.22
(K1200)

KUGELMANN, JOHANN (? -1542)
All Glory Be To God On High *Gen/Trin
SSA/TBarB,acap (med easy) oct CONCORDIA
98-1253 $.20   (K1201)

Das Apostolicum "Ich Glaub An Gott Vater"
[Ger] SA&men cor,acap (easy) BAREN. BA 4965
$.40   (K1202)

Nun Lob, Mein Seel, Den Herren
see Neander, Joachim, Lobe Den Herren, Den
Machitigen Konig

Vater Unser *prayer
men cor sc ALSBACH&D s.p.   (K1203)

KUGELMANN, PAUL
Vater Unser Im Himmelreich *Easter/Pent
[Ger] 3 eq voices,acap (easy) BAREN. BCH 60
s.p.   (K1204)

KUHNAHAUSEN
Matthaus-Passion *Psntd
(Adrio) 4pt mix cor,soli,cont MOSELER s.p.
(K1205)

KUHNAU, JOHANN (1660-1722)
Christ Jesus Lay In Death's Strong Bonds
*see Christ Lag In Todesbanden

Christ Lag In Todesbanden *cant
(Fishback) "Christ Jesus Lay In Death's
Strong Bonds" [Ger/Eng] mix cor BELWIN
$1.25   (K1206)

Christe, Der Du Bist Tag Und Licht
SATB LAUDINELLA LR 94 s.p. contains also:
Gelobet Seist Du, Jesu Christ; Wir
Christenleut Habn Jetzund Freud   (K1207)

Gelobet Seist Du, Jesu Christ
see Kuhnau, Johann, Christe, Der Du Bist
Tag Und Licht

Gott Sei Mir Gnadig *cant
[Ger] SATB,acap PETERS HU1696 $1.50, ipr
(K1208)
(Egidi, A.) mix cor,SAT soli,strings,org/
cembalo,opt bsn VIEWEG voc sc s.p., cor
pts s.p., ipa   (K1209)
(Kruger) SATB,SATB soli,cont,bsn,2vln,2vla
HANSSLER 10.016 cor pts s.p., voc sc
s.p., ipa   (K1210)

How Brightly Shines *Xmas,cant
BELWIN $1.50   (K1211)

How Sad Is My Spirit
(Kingsbury, John) SATB ALFRED 6352 $.40
(K1212)

Meine Seele Ist *see Tristis Est Anima Mea

Sorrow Doth Vex Now My Spirit *see Tristis
Sacred Anima Mea

Tristis Est Anima Mea *Lent,mot
"Sorrow Doth Vex Now My Spirit" SSATB,acap
(diff) oct CONCORDIA 98-1971 $.30 (K1213)
(Langenbeck) "Meine Seele Ist" [Lat/Ger]
SSATB HANSSLER 1.027 $.80   (K1214)
(Schreck, G.) 5pt mix cor,acap s.p. cor pts
BREITKOPF-L PB-1437, voc pt BREITKOPF-L
CHB-985   (K1215)

Uns Ist Ein Kind Geboren *Xmas,cant
(Schroder, O.) mix cor,ATB soli,org,2fl,
2ob,strings,cembalo (previously
attributed to Bach, J.S. (BWV 142)) sc
BREITKOPF-L PB-2992 s.p., voc pt
BREITKOPF-L CHB-1652 s.p., voc sc
BREITKOPF-L EB-7142 s.p.   (K1216)

Wir Christenleut Habn Jetzund Freud
see Kuhnau, Johann, Christe, Der Du Bist
Tag Und Licht

KUKU, KUKU, CHASO ZHURU *Xmas,carol,Czech
"Strangers Say A King Is Born" see Czech
Christmas Carols
(Glaser, V.) "Strangers Say A King Is Born"
SATB,acap SCHIRM.EC 2602 $.25   (K1217)

KUKUCK, FELICITAS (1914-   )
Aus Tiefer Not Schrei Ich Zu Dir
(Horn) SATB,A/Bar solo,org,vla HANSSLER
13.005 s.p.   (K1218)

Christ Is Arisen *Easter
SAB,kbd (med easy) oct CONCORDIA 98-1723
$.25   (K1219)

Christe, Du Bist Der Helle Tag *cant
SSATB&cong,org,4brass,2rec HANSSLER 10.080
sc s.p., cor pts s.p.   (K1220)

Das Ist Ein Kostlich Ding (Psalm 92)
see Kukuck, Felicitas, Herr Auf Dich Traue
Ich

Das Kommende Reich *ora
SSATB&cong,SBar soli,2fl,ob,2trp,3trom,
2vln,vla,vcl/bvl,timp,glockenspiel,
cymbals, English horn HANSSLER 10.031 sc
s.p., cor pts s.p., ipr   (K1221)

Das Te-Deum *Te Deum
SSATTB,2ob,3-5brass,2rec HANSSLER 10.079 sc
s.p., cor pts s.p.   (K1222)

KUKUCK, FELICITAS (cont'd.)
Denn Es Ist Hier Kein Unterschied *mot
SAB HANSSLER 7.033 s.p.   (K1223)

Der Gottesknecht *Psntd,ora
mix cor,inst cor pts MOSELER s.p. (K1224)

Die Ostergeschichte *Easter,Bibl
[Ger] 3pt mix cor,opt inst cor pts BAREN.
EM 361 s.p.   (K1225)

Festliche Schulschlusskantate *Fest,cant
3 eq voices,inst cor pts MOSELER s.p., ipa
(K1226)

Gott Ist Unser Zuversicht Und Starke *cant
SAB&SAB HANSSLER 7.032 s.p.   (K1227)
SSAATB&cong,Bar solo,org,3ob,3-5brass,3rec
HANSSLER 10.077 sc s.p., cor pts s.p.
(K1228)

Gott, Unser Schild, Schaue Doch *Gen
[Ger] 3pt mix cor,acap (med easy) BAREN.
BA 3680 s.p.   (K1229)

Herr Auf Dich Traue Ich (Psalm 31) Gen,Psalm
[Ger] cong&men cor&wom cor,opt tamb (med
easy) BAREN. BA 4969 s.p. contains also:
Das Ist Ein Kostlich Ding (Psalm 92)
(K1230)

Heut Singt Die Liebe Christenheit
see Werner, Fritz, Gott Der Vater Wohn Uns
Bei

Heut Triumphieret Gottes Sohn
SA/SB/T HANSSLER 14.083 s.p. contains also:
Fiebig, Kurt, Auf, Auf, Mein Herz, Mit
Freuden (SST/SSB,treb inst)   (K1231)

Ich Steh An Deiner Krippen Hier
SAT/SAB,treb HANSSLER 14.028 s.p.
contains also: Linke, Norbert, Kommt Und
Lasst Uns Christum Ehren (SAT/SAB,treb
inst)   (K1232)

Kommet, Ihr Hirten *mot
6pt mix cor MOSELER s.p.   (K1233)

Lobet Den Herren (Psalm 147) Bibl/cant
4-6pt mix cor,S solo,trp,strings,timp
MOSELER sc s.p., cor pts s.p., ipa
(K1234)

Lobt Gott, Ihr Frommen Christen *cant
SATB,org,4-5brass,3rec HANSSLER 10.078 sc
s.p., cor pts s.p.   (K1235)

Manchmal *Gen
[Ger] unis,acap (easy) BOSSE BE 271 s.p.
(K1236)

Maria Verkundigung *BVM,mot
4pt mix cor&4pt mix cor MOSELER s.p.
(K1237)

Nun Wollen Wir Singen Das Abendlied *mot
3-5pt mix cor MOSELER LB-518 s.p. (K1238)

O Wir Armen Sunder
SS/SSA/TT/TTB HANSSLER 14.057 s.p. contains
also: Wagner, Alexander, Ehre Sei Dir
Christe (SAT/SAB)   (K1239)

Osterkantate *Easter,cant
3pt mix cor,strings sc MOSELER s.p. (K1240)

Psalm 31 *see Herr Auf Dich Traue Ich

Psalm 92 *see Das Ist Ein Kostlich Ding

Psalm 147 *see Lobet Den Herren

KULKE, M.
Jezus, 'K Ben D'uwe
wom cor sc ALSBACH&D s.p.   (K1241)

KULLA, HANS
Humble Birth, The *anthem
SSA (easy) oct AUGSBURG 1518 $.25 (K1242)

KULLNES, AKE
Krist Segerrike
mix cor NORDISKA 4870 s.p.   (K1243)

Psalm 24
mix cor,soli,orch,org cor pts NORDISKA 5405
s.p., voc sc NORDISKA s.p., sc NORDISKA
rental, ipr   (K1244)

Utur Djupen Ropar Jag (Psalm 130)
mix cor NORDISKA 2428 s.p.   (K1245)

KUM BA YAH *folk/spir,Afr
(Dexter, Harry) "Come By Here" 2pt ENOCH
TP278 s.p.   (K1246)
(Ehret, Walter) SATB oct WALTON 2036 $.30
(K1247)
(Ehret, Walter) SAB oct WALTON 4000 $.30
(K1248)
(Lojeski, Ed) SATB,opt pno,gtr,opt bvl
WESTPORT $.45   (K1249)
(Paulson) SATB,opt kbd oct PRO ART 2301 $.30
(K1250)
(Paulson) SAB oct PRO ART 2303 $.30 (K1251)
(Saxton) "Come By Here" unis oct LORENZ 8587
$.25   (K1252)
(Wilson, John F.) "Come By Here" SATB oct
AGAPE CF 103 $.30   (K1253)

KUM-BAH-YAH see Martin

KUNDLICH GROSS IST DAS GOTTSELIGE GEHEIMNIS see
Rosenmuller, Johann

KUNDLICH GROSS IST DAS GOTTSELIGE GEHEIMNIS see
Stolzel, Gottfried Heinrich

KUNST DES CHORALS see Bach, Johann Sebastian

KUNTZ
Built On A Rock The Church Doth Stand
SAB oct PRO ART 2726 $.35   (K1254)

KUNZ
Birth Of A King *Xmas
SATB,acap,opt pno oct PRO ART 2554 $.25
(K1255)

Cross Bearing Child, The
STANDARD C602MX1 $.45   (K1256)

KUNZ (cont'd.)

Who Has Seen The Wind?
SATB oct HERITAGE H17 $.35   (K1257)

KUNZ, ERNST (1891)
Weihnachts-Oratorium *Xmas,ora
[Ger] SATB&opt jr cor,soli,org,2fl,ob,
2clar,bsn,2horn,2trp,trom,timp, triangle,
cymbal HUG rental, ipr   (K1258)

KUNZ, JACK
Christmas Is A Time For Happiness *Xmas
SATB LEONARD-US 08007520 $.35   (K1259)

Christmas Is A Time For You *Xmas
SSA oct AGAPE AD 1972 $.30   (K1260)

I Thought That Love Had Been A Boy *madrigal
SSA oct AGAPE WR 1004 $.30   (K1261)

KURA KWA KWA see Lovelace, Austin C.

KURIG, HANS-HERMANN (1914-   )
Auf Ihn Will Ich Vertrauen
see Schutz, Heinrich, Von Gott Will Ich
Nicht Lassen

Danket Dem Herren, Denn Er Ist Freundlich
see Kurig, Hans-Hermann, Wer In Mir Bleibet
Und Ich In Ihm

Danket Dem Herren, Lobt Ihn Frei
see Kurig, Hans-Hermann, Lasset Uns
Wahrhaftig Sein In Der Liebe

Dankt Unserm Gott, Lobsinget Ihm
see Kurig, Hans-Hermann, Zeuch An Die
Macht, Du Arm Des Herrn

Das Brot, Herr, Uns Segne
see Kurig, Hans-Hermann, Ich Will Dem
Herren Singen

Denn Ist Das Jahr, Dein Ist Die Ziet
see Bach, Johann Sebastian, Meinen Jesum
Lass Ich Nicht

Der Herr Ist Konig
see Kurig, Hans-Hermann, Jauchzet, Alle
Lande, Gott Zu Ehren

Die Sonn Hat Sich Mit Ihrem Glanz Gewendet
see Kurig, Hans-Hermann, Jauchzet, Alle
Lande, Gott Zu Ehren

Du Hochstes Licht, Ewiger Schein
see Kurig, Hans-Hermann, O Dass Doch Bald
Dein Feuer Brennte

Erhalt Uns Herr Bei Deinem Wort *CC22U,Fest
TTBB HANSSLER 2.016 s.p.   (K1262)

Es Geht Wohl Zu Der Sommerzeit *CC18U,folk
4-6pt HANSSLER 2.020 s.p.   (K1263)

Frohlich Wir Nun All Fangen An
see Berger, Hans Ludwig, Frohlich Wir Nun
All Fangen An

Fur Alle Gute Sei Gepreist
see Bach, Johann Sebastian, Komm, Gott
Schopfer, Heiliger Geist

Gott Vater, Sende Dein Geist (from Wer Mich
Liebet, Der Wird Mein Work Halten)
see Kurig, Hans-Hermann, Herr, Warst Du Nur
Ein Mensch

Halleluja, Amen
see Kurig, Hans-Hermann, O Dass Doch Bald
Dein Feuer Brennte

Halte Feste An Barmherzigkeit
see Kurig, Hans-Hermann, Ich Will Dem
Herren Singen

Herr Jesu, Hilf
see Kurig, Hans-Hermann, Ich Will Dem
Herren Singen

Herr, Warst Du Nur Ein Mensch
SATB/SS&SATB HANSSLER 6.312 s.p. contains
also:
Kurig, Hans-Hermann, Ist Gott Fur Mich
(SS&SATB);
Bach, Johann Sebastian, Gott Vater,
Sende Deine Geist (SA&SATB);
Kurig, Hans-Hermann, Gott Vater, Sende
Dein Geist (from Wer Mich Liebet, Der
Wird Mein Work Halten) (SA)
(Whitsun);
Kurig, Hans-Hermann, Nehmet Einhander
An (3pt)   (K1264)

Ich Singe Dir Mit Herz Und Mund
see Kurig, Hans-Hermann, O Dass Doch Bald
Dein Feuer Brennte

Ich Weiss, Mein Gott, Dass All Mein Tun
see Kurig, Hans-Hermann, Zeuch An Die
Macht, Du Arm Des Herrn

Ich Will Dem Herren Singen
SATB/SSATB HANSSLER 6.302 s.p. contains
also: Vulpius, Melchior, Des Heilgen
Geistes Gnade Gross (SATB); Bach, Johann
Sebastian, Ach Bleib Bei Uns, Herr Jesu
Christ (SATB) (A flat maj); Kurig, Hans-
Hermann, Herr Jesu, Hilf (mix cor);
Kurig, Hans-Hermann, Halte Feste An
Barmherzigkeit (3pt) (canon); Kurig,
Hans-Hermann, Das Brot, Herr, Uns Segne
(SATB) (CC)   (K1265)

Ihr Werdet Die Kraft Des Heiligen Geistes
Empfangen
see Kurig, Hans-Hermann, Lasset Uns
Wahrhaftig Sein In Der Liebe

Ist Gott Fur Mich
see Kurig, Hans-Hermann, Herr, Warst Du Nur
Ein Mensch

Jauchzet, Alle Lande, Gott Zu Ehren *canon
3pt HANSSLER 6.306 s.p. contains also:
Kurig, Hans-Hermann, Wir Heben An Zu
Singen (SATB/SSATB); Kurig, Hans-Hermann,
Der Herr Ist Konig (mix cor); Kurig,

KURIG, HANS-HERMANN (cont'd.)

Hans-Hermann, Die Sonn Hat Sich Mit Ihrem
Glanz Gewendet (SA); Bach, Johann
Sebastian, Die Sonn Hat Sich Mit Ihren
Glanz Gewendet (SA&SATB); Sartorius,
Eramus, Nun Bitten Wir Den Heiligen Geist
(mix cor) (CC)   (K1266)

Komm, Gott Schopfer, Heiliger Geist
see Bach, Johann Sebastian, Komm, Gott
Schopfer, Heiliger Geist

Kommt Her, Des Konigs Aufgebot
see Bach, Johann Sebastian, Komm, Gott
Schopfer, Heiliger Geist

Lasset Uns Wahrhaftig Sein In Der Liebe
*canon
3pt HANSSLER 6.286 s.p. contains also:
Kurig, Hans-Hermann, Ihr Werdet Die
Kraft Des Heiligen Geistes Empfangen
(3pt) (canon);
Schutz, Heinrich, Danket Dem Herren,
Lobt Ihn Frei, SWV 203 (SATB);
Kurig, Hans-Hermann, Danket Dem Herren,
Lobt Ihn Frei (SA);
Goudimel, Claude, Singt Mit Froher
Stimm (SATB/SA);
Goudimel, Claude, Herr, Wir Stehen Hand
In Hand (SATB/SA)   (K1267)

Lobet Den Herren, Alle, Die Ihn Ehren
see Bach, Johann Sebastian, Meinen Jesum
Lass Ich Nicht

Lobt Gott, Ihr Frommen Christen
SATB/SS/TT HANSSLER 6.199 s.p. contains
also: Metzger, Hans-Arnold, O
Lebensbrunnlein Tief Und Gross (SATB);
Kurig, Hans-Hermann, O Lebensbrunnlein
Gross Und Tief (SS/TT); Koch, Heinz,
Sonne Der Gerechtigkeit , Gehe Auf
(SATB); Berger, Hans Ludwig, Sonne Der
Gerechtigkeit (SSA/TTB)   (K1268)

Meinen Jesum Lass Ich Nicht
see Bach, Johann Sebastian, Meinen Jesum
Lass Ich Nicht

Nehmet Einhander An
see Kurig, Hans-Hermann, Herr, Warst Du Nur
Ein Mensch

Nun Bitten Wir Den Heiligen Geist
see Kurig, Hans-Hermann, O Dass Doch Bald
Dein Feuer Brennte

Nun Jauchzt Dem Herren Alle Welt
see Berger, Hans Ludwig, Frohlich Wir Nun
All Fangen An
see Kurig, Hans-Hermann, Zeuch An Die
Macht, Du Arm Des Herrn

O Dass Doch Bald Dein Feuer Brennte
see Kurig, Hans-Hermann, O Dass Doch Bald
Dein Feuer Brennte
SATB/SS/SA HANSSLER 8.035 s.p. contains
also: Ich Singe Dir Mit Herz Und Mund
(SATB/SS/SA); Du Hochstes Licht, Ewiger
Schein (SATB/SS/SA); O Dass Doch Bald
Dein Feuer Brennte (3pt) (canon); Nun
Bitten Wir Den Heiligen Geist (3pt)
(canon); Halleluja, Amen (3pt) (canon)
(K1269)

O Lebensbrunnlein Gross Und Tief
see Kurig, Hans-Hermann, Lobt Gott, Ihr
Frommen Christen

Singet Dem Herrn Ein Neues Lied
see Berger, Hans Ludwig, Frohlich Wir Nun
All Fangen An
see Schott, Johann Georg, Singet Dem Herrn
Ein Neues Lied Denn Er Tut Grosse Wunder

Such, Wer Da Will Ein Ander Ziel
see Kurig, Hans-Hermann, Wer In Mir Bleibet
Und Ich In Ihm

Wach Auf, Du Deutsches Land
see Schutz, Heinrich, Von Gott Will Ich
Nicht Lassen

Wach Auf, Wach Auf, Du Deutsches Land
see Schutz, Heinrich, Von Gott Will Ich
Nicht Lassen

Wer In Mir Bleibet Und Ich In Ihm *canon
4pt HANSSLER 8.038 s.p. contains also:
Helder, Bartholomaeus, Ich Freu Mich In
Dem Herren (4pt); Schutz, Heinrich,
Singet Dem Herrn Ein Neues Lied, Denn
Durch Ihn Gross Wunder Geschieht (SATB);
Kurig, Hans-Hermann, Such, Wer Da Will
Ein Ander Ziel (SATB/SA); Kurig, Hans-
Hermann, Danket Dem Herren, Denn Er Ist
Freundlich (4pt) (canon)   (K1270)

Wir Heben An Zu Singen
see Kurig, Hans-Hermann, Jauchzet, Alle
Lande, Gott Zu Ehren

Zeuch An Die Macht, Du Arm Des Herrn
SATB/SS/TT HANSSLER 8.034 s.p. contains
also: Dankt Unserm Gott, Lobsinget Ihm
(3pt) (canon); Nun Jauchzt Dem Herren,
Alle Welt (SATB/SS/TT); Ich Weiss, Mein
Gott, Dass All Mein Tun (SATB/SS/SA)
(K1271)

KURRENDE-SAMMELBAND 1 *CC112U,Gen
[Ger] 3-5pt mix cor cloth HANSSLER 3.201
$4.00 contains Die Kurrende Heft 1 through
4; settings by old masters   (K1272)

KURRENDE-SAMMELBAND 2 *CCU,Gen,Contemp
[Ger] 3-5pt mix cor cloth HANSSLER 3.202
$10.00 contains Die Kurrende Heft 5 through
9   (K1273)

KURTH, BURTON
Opening Sentences, Responses And Amens, Set 1
*CCU
SATB oct LESLIE 4061   (K1274)

Opening Sentences, Responses And Amens, Set 2
*CCU
SATB oct LESLIE 4102   (K1275)

KURZ, WALTER
Choralfantasie Uber "Ich Wollt', Dass Ich
Daheime War'"
(Lauffenberg, H.) mix cor,acap oct
DOBLINGER s.p.   (K1276)

KUYKENDALL, F.
New Born Again *spir
SATB,acap oct PRESSER MC204 $.30   (K1277)

One Nation, Under God
(Raymond) SATB oct PLYMOUTH JR-122 $.25
(K1278)

KVAMME
On Calvary's Hill *Easter
SATB SCHMITT 1758 $.25   (K1279)

KVERNO, TROND
Gladelig Vil Vi Halleluja Kvede
[Norw] mix cor,org,trp LYCHE 58 s.p.
(K1280)

KVI SKJELV KVART LAUVBLAD see Geitvik, S.H.

K'VODO VODO O LOM see Weisgal, A.

KYRIE *anthem/Kyrie
(Christiansen, Paul) SATB (med diff) oct
AUGSBURG 1299 $.20   (K1281)

KYRIE see d'Anglebert, Jean-Henri

KYRIE see Animuccia, Giovanni

KYRIE see Anonymous

KYRIE see Beethoven, Ludwig van

KYRIE see Brunner, Adolf

KYRIE see Buchsel

KYRIE see Buxtehude, Dietrich

KYRIE see Chaminade, Cecile

KYRIE see Cherubini, Luigi

KYRIE see Christiansen, Paul

KYRIE see David, Johann Nepomuk

KYRIE see David, Johann Nepomuk, Herre Gott,
Erbarme Dich

KYRIE see Durante

KYRIE see Durante, Francesco

KYRIE see Erb, Donald

KYRIE see Faure, Gabriel-Urbain

KYRIE see Gabrieli, Andrea

KYRIE see Gounod, Charles Francois

KYRIE see Hallnas, Hilding

KYRIE see Hammarstrom, Hugo

KYRIE see Hassler, Hans Leo

KYRIE see Haydn, (Franz) Joseph

KYRIE see Hellene, Johs.

KYRIE see Jewell

KYRIE see Koechlin, Charles

KYRIE see Larsson, Lars-Erik

KYRIE see Linden, N. v.d.

KYRIE see Lotti, Antonio

KYRIE see Luboff, Norman

KYRIE see Mendelssohn-Bartholdy, Felix

KYRIE see Micheelsen, Hans Friedrich

KYRIE see Mozart, Wolfgang Amadeus

KYRIE see Norman, Rudolf

KYRIE see Ockeghem, Johannes

KYRIE see Palestrina, Giovanni

KYRIE see Pepping, Ernst

KYRIE see Pergolesi, Giovanni Battista

KYRIE see Peters, W.C.

KYRIE see Rhodes

KYRIE see Rossini, Gioacchino

KYRIE see Scarlatti, Alessandro

KYRIE see Schubert, Franz (Peter)

KYRIE see Schwartz, Gerhard von

KYRIE see Schweizer, Rolf

KYRIE see Solem, Edvin

KYRIE see Thompson, Randall

KYRIE see Vivaldi, Antonio

KYRIE 1 see Benevoli, Orazio

KYRIE 2 see Benevoli, Orazio

KYRIE A CINQUE CON DIVERSI CANONI see Mozart,
Wolfgang Amadeus

KYRIE AND GLORIA see Pergolesi, Giovanni
Battista

KYRIE - CHRISTE - KYRIE see Des Prez, Josquin

KYRIE D-MOLL see Mozart, Wolfgang Amadeus

KYRIE ELEISON
(Lundquist) "Old Latin Hymn" SATB,acap (med)
oct WILLIS 5500 $.12   (K1282)

KYRIE ELEISON see Bach, Johann Sebastian

KYRIE ELEISON see Badings, Henk

KYRIE ELEISON see Breydert, F.M.

KYRIE ELEISON see Bright

KYRIE ELEISON see Bright, Houston

KYRIE ELEISON see Buxtehude, Dietrich

KYRIE ELEISON see Chihara, Paul

KYRIE ELEISON see Davies, Henry Walford

KYRIE ELEISON see Dieterich

KYRIE ELEISON see Dufay, Guillaume

KYRIE ELEISON see Durante

KYRIE ELEISON see Franck, Cesar

KYRIE ELEISON see Haydn, (Franz) Joseph

KYRIE ELEISON see Kranz, Albert

KYRIE ELEISON see Lotti, Antonio

KYRIE ELEISON see Mozart, Wolfgang Amadeus

KYRIE ELEISON see Palestrina, Giovanni

KYRIE ELEISON see Schutz, Heinrich

KYRIE ELEISON see Soderman, (Johan) August

KYRIE ELEISON see Solberg Lief

KYRIE ELEISON see Tallis, Thomas

KYRIE ELEISON see Thorne

KYRIE ELEISON see Victoria

KYRIE ELEISON see Victoria, Tomas Luis de

KYRIE ELEISON see Vierne, Louis

KYRIE ELEISON see Wikander, David

KYRIE ELEISON, ALLA PALESTRINA see Guilmant,
Alexandre

KYRIE ELEISON AND NINEFOLD AMEN see Harwood,
Basil

KYRIE ELEISON, CHRISTE ELEISON see Lassus,
Roland de (Orlandus)

KYRIE ELEISON, CHRISTE ERHORE UNS see Schutz,
Heinrich

KYRIE ELEISON I see Bach, Johann Sebastian

KYRIE ELEISON, O ERBARMEN GROSS see Stier,
Alfred

KYRIE ELEISON SANCTUS, BENEDICTUS, AND AGNUS
DEI see Palestrina, Giovanni

KYRIE ELEISON see Palestrina, Giovanni

KYRIE EN GLORIA see Diepenbrock, Alfons

KYRIE, FADER I EVIGHET see Praetorius, Michael

KYRIE--GLORIA see Gullberg, Olof

KYRIE, GOD VATER see Schutz, Heinrich, Kyrie,
Gott Vater In Ewigkeit

KYRIE, GOTT VATER see Barbe, Helmut

KYRIE, GOTT VATER IN EWIGKEIT see Bach, Johann
Sebastian

KYRIE, GOTT VATER IN EWIGKEIT see Schutz,
Heinrich

KYRIE (HERRE GOTT, ERBARME DICH) see Dieterich,
Fritz

KYRIE II see Dufay, Guillaume

KYRIE IN D see Bach, Johann Christian

KYRIE IN D MINOR see Bach, Johann Sebastian

KYRIE IN D MINOR see Mozart, Wolfgang Amadeus

KYRIE LE JOUR DE NOEL see Migot, Georges

KYRIE-LITANEI see Schroeder, Hermann

KYRIE MASS XI see Christiansen, Paul

KYRIE MINUS SUMMUM 1612 *Kyrie
(Distler, Hugo) [Ger] SATB,acap (med) BAREN.
BA 1048 $.40 see from Liturgical Satze
(K1283)

KYRIE PASCHALE see Clemens, Jacobus

KYRIE, SURSUM CORDA, CREED AND GLORIA see
Smart, Henry Thomas

KYRIE UND GLORIA see Desch, Rudolf

KYRIES see Mozart, Wolfgang Amadeus

KYRIOLE LORRAIN see Aubanel, Georges

KYRKLIGA SANGER *CCU
(Olson, Daniel; Oldermark, Birger) 2-3pt mix
cor,acap,pno NORDISKA 5320 s.p.   (K1284)

KYRKOKANTAT NR. 2 see Lindberg, Oskar [Fredrik]

KYRKOKANTAT NR. 5 see Soderholm, Valdemar

L

L'9ENFANCE DU CHRIST see Berlioz, Hector

LA ADORACION see Irigaray

LA ANUNCIACION see Irigaray

LA BATAILLE see Jannequin, Clement

LA BELLE SE SIET see Ghilselin-Verbonnet,
Johannes

LA BIEN QUE J'AY see Goudimel, Claude

LA BREBIS EGAREE see Bach, Johann Sebastian

LA CANCION see Gomis

LA CANCION DE LA ZAMBOMBA see Benedito

LA CANTATE DES COMMENCEMENTS see Reveyron,
Joseph

LA CAPTIVITE DE BABYLONE see Lacome, Paul

LA CARITA see Rossini, Gioacchino

LA CHARMANTE ETOILE *Xmas,18th cent
(Geveart, F.-A.) [Fr] 4pt mix cor,acap (med)
cor pts LEMOINE s.p. see from Collection De
Choeurs, deuxieme Fascicule   (L1)

LA CONCEPCION see Irigaray

LA CREATION see Haydn, (Franz) Joseph, Die
Schopfung

LA CRECHE DE NOEL see Roesgen-Champion,
Marguerite

LA DE SMA BARN KOMME TIL MEG see Slogedal,
Bjarne

LA ESTRELLA DE BELEN see Crespo

LA FEDE see Rossini, Gioacchino

LA FEDE SACRILEGA NELLA MORTE DEL PRECURSOR S.
GIOVANNI BATTISTA see Fux, Johann Joseph

LA FILLE DE JEPHTE see Lacome, Paul

LA FILLE DE JEPHTE see Maurice, Pierre

LA GIUDITTA (DI NAPOLI) see Scarlatti,
Alessandro

LA GLORIA see Irigaray

LA GUAGUA DE NOCHEBUENA see Carillo, Gomez

LA GULNE HVERT ET GLAD see Geitvik, S.H.

LA JAMBE ME FAIT MAL see Tomasi

LA JEUNE FILLE see Chaminade, Cecile

LA KRISTI ORD BO RIKELIG see Hallnas, Hilding

LA MAITRISE *see d'Anglebert, Jean-Henri,
Kyrie; Brydaine, Les Gaude; Gounod, Charles
Francois, Ave Verum Corpus; Gounod, Charles
Francois, Da Pacem; Handel, George
Frideric, Ecce Concipies; Haydn, (Johann)
Michael, Laudate; Lefebure-Wely, Louis
James Alfred, O Salutaris; Mozart, Wolfgang
Amadeus, Ave Verum Corpus, K.618;
Niedermeyer, Louis, Pie Jesu; Palestrina,
Giovanni, Adoremus Te Christe, "Adoremus";
Palestrina, Giovanni, O Bone Jesu;
Palestrina, Giovanni, Pleni Sunt Coeli;
Palestrina, Giovanni, Quae Vox; Rossini,
Gioacchino, O Salutaris; Victoria, Tomas
Luis de, O Vos Omnes, Qui Transitis Per
Viam   (L2)

LA MAITRISE see d'Anglebert, Jean-Henri

LA MAITRISE see Brydaine

LA MAITRISE see Gounod, Charles Francois

LA MAITRISE see Handel, George Frideric

LA MAITRISE see Haydn, (Johann) Michael

LA MAITRISE see Lefebure-Wely, Louis James
Alfred

LA MAITRISE see Mozart, Wolfgang Amadeus

LA MAITRISE see Niedermeyer, Louis

LA MAITRISE see Palestrina, Giovanni

LA MAITRISE see Rossini, Gioacchino

LA MAITRISE see Victoria, Tomas Luis de

LA MESSA DEGLI ANGELI see Bottazzo, Luigi

LA MESSA DEI GIOVANI see Vianello, Lino

LA MESSA DEL VENERDI' SANTO see Ghedini,
Giorgio Federico

LA MESSE DE NOSTRE DAME see Machaut, Guillaume
de

LA MESSE DES MORTS A IS see Riley, Terry

LA MORT DE SAINT GOTHARD see Dufay, Guillaume

LA MORTE DI ABEL see Leo, Leonardo

LA NANA *carol/carol,Span
(Csonka) "Christmas Bye-lo" [Eng/Span] 4pt
mix cor oct SCHIRM.G 10282 $.30   (L3)

LA NATIVITE see Gossec, Francois Joseph

LA NATIVITE see Young, G.

LA NATIVITE DE LA TRES SAINTE VIERGE see
Piriou, A.

LA NATIVITE DE N.S. see Migot, Georges

LA NOCHE DE SAN JUAN see Benedito

LA NOEL see Breville, Pierre-Onfroy de

LA NOVENA DI NATALE *CC9U,Xmas
unis sc ZANIBON 728 s.p., cor pts ZANIBON 729
s.p. contains works by: Bottazzo, L.;
Cicogni, C.; Livieri, C.   (L4)

LA NUIT FROIDE ET SOMBRE see Lassus, Roland de
(Orlandus)

LA NUIT OBSCURE DE SAINT-JEAN DE LA CROIX see
Tomasi

LA PASSION see Migot

LA PASSION DE N. S. JESUCRISTO, SEGUN SAN MATEO
see Bach, Johann Sebastian, Matthaus
Passione

LA PASSION SELON SAINT JEAN see Bach, Johann
Sebastian, Johannespassion

LA PASSIONE DI CRISTO SECONDO MARCO see Perosi,
(Dom) Lorenzo

LA PASSIONE DI N.S. GESU CRISTO SECONDO
GIOVANNI see Bach, Johann Sebastian

LA PASSIONE DI N.S. GESU CRISTO SECONDO MATTEO
see Bach, Johann Sebastian

LA PASSIONE DI NOSTRO SIGNORE GESU CRISTO see
Jommelli, Niccolo

LA PASSIONE NELLE INTONAZIONI DEL "LAUDARIO 97"
see Liuzzi, Fernando

LA PASTORELLA see Schubert, Franz (Peter)

LA PASTORELLA DEL POPOLO see Magri, Pietro

LA PREGHIERA DEL MATTINO see Schinelli, Achille

LA PREGHIERA DEL MATTINO see Travaglia, Silvio

LA PREGHIERA DELL' ANNO MARIANO see Somma

LA PREMIERE COMMUNION see La Rose, L.

LA PRIERE see Brassens, G.

LA RESURRECCIONE see Handel, George Frideric

LA RESURREZIONE DI CRISTO see Perosi, (Dom)
Lorenzo

LA ROUTE see Pierne, Gabriel

LA SACRA FAMIGLIA CANTIAMO see Magri, Pietro

LA SALUTATION ANGELIQUE see Ave Maria

LA SCHOLA PALEST RINIENNE TROISIEME CAHIER
*CC7L,mot
(Brun, Abbe F.) [Lat] 4pt mix cor,acap
LEMOINE s.p. contains works by: Clemens;
Victoria; Palestrina; Victoria; Da Viadana;
Vecchi   (L5)

LA SCHOLA PALESTRINIENNE PREMIERE CAHIER
*Commun,mot
(Brun, Abbe F.) [Lat] 4pt mix cor,acap
LEMOINE s.p.
contains: Des Prez, Josquin, Ave Verum; La
Rue, Pierre de, O Salutaris Hostia;
Palestrina, Giovanni, O Bone Jesu;
Palestrina, Giovanni, Verbum Caro; van
Berchem, J., O Jesu Christe; Victoria,
Tomas Luis de, Jesu Dulcis   (L6)

LA SCHOLA PALESTRINIENNE DEUXIEME CAHIER *BVM,
mot
(Brun, Abbe F.) [Lat] 4pt mix cor,acap
LEMOINE s.p.
contains: Lassus, Roland de (Orlandus),
Salve Regina; Lotti, Antonio, Regina
Coeli; Mouton, Jean, Ave Maria;
Palestrina, Giovanni, Alma Redemptoris
Mater; Suriano, Francesco, Ave Regina
Caelorum; Victoria, Tomas Luis de, Ave
Maria   (L7)

LA SCHOLA PALESTRINIENNE QUARTRIEME CAHIER
*CC8L,Psalm
(Brun, Abbe F.) [Lat] 4pt mix cor,acap
LEMOINE s.p. contains works by: Victoria;
Viadana; Vecchi; Ward; Andreas   (L8)

LA SPERANZA see Rossini, Gioacchino

LA STIRPE DI DAVIDE see Mannino, F.

LA TRANSFIGURATION DE NOTRE SEIGNEUR JESUS-
CHRIST see Messiaen, Oliver

LA VIE see Schubert, Franz (Peter)

LA VIE ET L'ASSOMPTION DE LA SAINTE- VIERGE see
Marc, E.

LA VIERGE A LA CRECHE see Franck, Cesar

LA VIERGE MARIE VA A BETHLEEM see Canteloube de
Malaret, Marie-Joseph

LA VIERGE MARIE VA A BETHLEEM see Dottim, G.

LA VIRGEN LAVA PANALES
see Villancicos Tradicionales

LA VIRGEN LAVA PANALES see Nin-Culmell, Joaquin

LA VIRGEN Y SAN JOSE
see Villancicos Tradicionales

LA VIRGIN LAVA PANALES *Xmas,carol,Span
(Shaw; Parker) [Eng/Span] 4pt men cor,A solo,
acap oct SCHIRM.G 10198 $.30   (L9)

LA VISITATION see Roesgen-Champion, Marquerite

LAAR, W. V.
    Psalm 146
        mix cor ALSBACH&D sc s.p., cor pts s.p.
                                                    (L10)

LABORAVI see Rameau, Jean-Philippe

LABORAVI CLAMANS see Rameau, Jean-Philippe

LABORAVI IN GEMITU MEO see Morley, Thomas

LABOURE
    Temporal Cycle, The *CCU,Adv/Xmas
        (Dunn) unis oct SUMMY M 2710 $1.50
                                                    (L11)

LABROCA, MARIO (1896-   )
    Tre Cantate Sulla Passione Di Cristo *CC3U,
        Psntd,cant
        mix cor,B solo,orch voc sc ZERBONI 4777
        s.p., ipr   (L12)

LACEY, DAVID T.
    Jubilate Deo
        "O Be Joyful In The Lord" SATB oct GRAY
        GCMR 3229 $.30   (L13)

    O Be Joyful In The Lord *see Jubilate Deo

LACHNER, V.
    Die Allmacht *Op.51
        men cor (med diff) LEUCKART s.p.   (L14)

LACOME, PAUL (1838-1920)
    Chant De Fete *see Laudate Dominum

    Deborah *No.6
        [Fr] 2 eq voices voc sc cor pts ENOCH s.p.
        s.p. see from Six Duos Bibliques   (L15)

    La Captivite De Babylone *No.3
        [Fr] 2 eq voices ENOCH see from Six Duos
        Bibliques   (L16)

    La Fille De Jephte *No.5
        [Fr] 2 eq voices&opt 3pt/4pt voc sc ENOCH
        s.p. see from Six Duos Bibliques   (L17)

    L'arc-En-Ciel *No.1
        [Fr] 2 eq voices voc sc ENOCH s.p. see from
        Six Duos Bibliques   (L18)

    Laudate Dominum (Psalm 150)
        "Chant De Fete" [Lat] SATB,pno/org ENOCH
        voc sc s.p., cor pts s.p.   (L19)

    Les Fetes Chretiennes *see Les Rois; Les
        Saints Innocents; Paques   (L20)

    Les Rois *ora
        [Fr] eq voices,soli voc sc ENOCH s.p. see
        from Les Fetes Chretiennes   (L21)

    Les Saints Innocents *ora
        [Fr] eq voices,soli voc sc ENOCH s.p. see
        from Les Fetes Chretiennes   (L22)

    Moise *No.2
        [Fr] 2 eq voices voc sc ENOCH s.p. see from
        Six Duos Bibliques   (L23)

    Noel *Xmas,carol
        [Fr] 2 eq voices,org/pno ENOCH cor pts
        s.p., voc sc s.p.   (L24)

    Paques *ora
        [Fr] eq voices,soli voc sc cor pts ENOCH
        s.p. s.p. see from Les Fetes Chretiennes
                                                    (L25)

    Psalm 150 *see Laudate Dominum

    Ruth Et Noemie *No.4
        [Fr] 2 eq voices voc sc ENOCH s.p. see from
        Six Duos Bibliques   (L26)

    Six Duos Bibliques *see Deborah, No.6; La
        Captivite De Babylone, No.3; La Fille De
        Jephte, No.5; L'arc-En-Ciel, No.1; Moise,
        No.2; Ruth Et Noemie, No.4   (L27)

LACRIMAE CHRISTI see Thuille, Ludwig (Wilhelm
    Andreas Maria)

LACRYMOSA see Cherubini, Luigi

LACRYMOSA see Hallnas, Hilding

LACRYMOSA see Kprivsak

LACRYMOSA see Mozart, Wolfgang Amadeus

LAD HAENDE KUN, SOM HERREN VIL see Bach, Johann
    Sebastian, Was Gott Tut, Das Ist Wohlgetan
    [Chorale]

LAD OS TIL GUD, VOR HERRE see Bach, Johann
    Sebastian, Nun Lasst Uns Gott, Dem Herren

L'ADIEU DES BERGERS see Berlioz, Hector

L'ADORATION DES BERGERS see Manziarly de

LAETABUNDUS see Crosse, Gordon

LAETABUNDUS EXULTET FIDELIS see Rodella, Sante

LAETARE see Schwarz-Schilling, Reinhard

LAETATUS see Vivaldi, Antonio

LAETATUS SUM see Cavalli, Francesco

LAETATUS SUM see Charpentier, Marc-Antoine

LAETATUS SUM see Gibbs

LAETATUS SUM see Gorczycki, Gregor Gervasius

LAETATUS SUM see Kraft, Walter

LAETATUS SUM see Monteverdi, Claudio

LAETATUS SUM see Porpora, Nicola Antonio

LAETATUS SUM see Scarlatti, Domenico

LAETENTUR CAELI see Gaburo, Kenneth

LAETENTUR COELI see Byrd, William

LAETENTUR COELI see Hassler, Hans Leo

LAFITE, C.
    Italienische Madonna
        [Ger] mix cor,acap (diff) KRENN s.p. (L28)

LA FORGE
    Ave Verum Corpus
        (Bergstrom) "Hail, O Hail, True Body" [Lat/
        Eng] SSATTB,acap oct COLOMBO 2482 $.30
                                                    (L29)

    Benedicite Gentes
        (Ehret) "O Praise God" [Lat/Eng] SATB,acap
        oct COLOMBO 2384 $.25   (L30)

    Hail, O Hail, True Body *see Ave Verum
        Corpus

    Hail, Queen Of Heaven *see Salve Regina

    O Praise God *see Benedicite Gentes

    Salve Regina
        (Zanon; Vene) "Hail, Queen Of Heaven" [Lat/
        Eng] SATB,acap oct COLOMBO 1851 $.30   (L31)

LAFORGE, FRANK (1879-1953)
    Before The Crucifix *Lent
        (Deis) 4pt mix cor oct SCHIRM.G 10341 $.25
                                                    (L32)

    First Psalm (Psalm 1) Bibl
        4pt mix cor,acap oct SCHIRM.G 7581 $.30
                                                    (L33)
        4pt men cor,acap oct SCHIRM.G 7409 $.25
                                                    (L34)

    Psalm 1 *see First Psalm

LA HALE, A. DE
    see ADAM DE LA HALE

LAHMER, [RUEL] (1912-   )
    Create In Me A Clean Heart
        SATB,acap oct PRESSER 312-40575 $.25 (L35)

    It Is Good To Give Thanks *Pent,Gradual
        (Snow, Robert J.) 2pt mix cor/2 eq voices,
        org oct WORLD EMP-1499-5 $.45   (L36)

LAHUSEN, CHRISTIAN (1886-   )
    Achtzehn Geistliche Kanons *CC18U,Gen,Bibl,
        canon
        [Ger] 3 eq voices/4 eq voices,acap (med
        easy) BAREN. BA 2175 s.p.   (L37)

    Andacht Zum Tode *ECY,mot
        [Ger] SATB,acap BAREN. BA 1485 $.65   (L38)

    Die Weihnachtsgeschichte *Xmas,cant
        [Ger] 3 eq voices (easy) cor pts BAREN.
        BA 557 $.40, ipa   (L39)
        [Ger] 4pt mix cor (easy) cor pts BAREN.
        BA 556 $.40   (L40)
        [Ger] SATB/3 eq voices,pno,3fl,2vln,vla,vcl
        (easy) sc BAREN. BA 2167 $2.50   (L41)

    Ein Lobgesang. Neue Lieder Fur Kirche Und
        Haus *CCU,Gen
        [Ger] unis,acap (easy) BAREN. BA 1835 s.p.
                                                    (L42)

    Es Lagen Im Felde Die Hirten *Xmas
        [Ger] 4pt men cor,acap (med) NAGELS NCH 12
        s.p. contains also: Mit Schall Von Zungen
                                                    (L43)

    Es Mag Sein, Dass Alles Fallt *Gen
        [Ger] SATB,acap (easy) BAREN. BA 195 s.p.
        contains also: Ob Alle Welt   (L44)

    Freu Dich Heut *CC22U,Xmas
        [Ger] 2 eq voices,acap (very easy) BAREN.
        BA 725 $1.50   (L45)

    Kleiner Psalter *CC14U,Gen
        [Ger] SATB,acap (easy) BAREN. BA 2718 $1.50
                                                    (L46)

    Mit Schall Von Zungen
        see Lahusen, Christian, Es Lagen Im Felde
        Die Hirten

    Ob Alle Welt
        see Lahusen, Christian, Es Mag Sein, Dass
        Alles Fallt

    Wir Danken, Herr, Fur Brot Und Kleid *Fest
        [Ger] SATB,acap (easy) BAREN. BCH 166 s.p.
                                                    (L47)

    Wisst Ihr Noch, Wie Es Geschehen *Xmas
        [Ger] 3pt mix cor,acap (easy) BAREN.
        BA 1498 s.p.   (L48)

    Zur Stillen Nacht *Xmas
        [Ger] 3pt men cor,acap (med easy) NAGELS
        NCH 208 s.p.   (L49)

LAISSEZ PAISTRE VOS BETES, PASTOUREAUX see
    Bonnal, Ermend

LAISSEZ PAITRE VOS BESTES *Xmas,carol,16th
    cent
    (Dauly, G.) [Fr] mix cor,pno/org (easy) voc
    sc LEMOINE s.p.   (L50)

LAISSEZ PAITRE VOS BESTES see Dauly, G.

LAISSEZ PAITRE VOS BETES *Xmas,carol,16th cent
    (Geveart, F.-A.) [Fr] 4pt mix cor,acap (med
    easy) cor pts LEMOINE s.p. see from
    Collection De Choeurs, dixieme Fascicule
                                                    (L51)

LAISSEZ PAITRE VOS BETES see Charpentier, Marc-
    Antoine

LAITENBERGER, THEOPHIL (1903-   )
    Der Herr Ist Mein Getreuer Hirt *Bibl
        SAB/SATB/BB/B,org HANSSLER 8.022 s.p. (L52)

LAJTHA, LASZLO (1891-1963)
    Magnificat *Op.60,mot
        [Lat] SSA,org LEDUC voc sc s.p., voc pt
        s.p.   (L53)

    Missa *Op.54, Mass
        [Lat] SATB,org LEDUC voc sc s.p., voc pt
        s.p.   (L54)

    Missa In Tono Phrygio *Op.50, Mass
        [Lat] SATB,org,brass,orch voc pt LEDUC s.p.
                                                    (L55)

LALANDE
    I Will Praise Thee, O Lord
        (Hines) SATB oct ELKAN-V 362-1238 $.25
                                                    (L56)

LALANDE, MICHEL RICHARD DE (1657-1726)
    Confitebimur Tibi Deus
        [Lat] SATBB,STB soli,org,orch SALABERT-US
        voc sc $13.50, cor pts $1.50   (L57)

    De Profundis
        [Lat] SAATBB,SATB soli,org,orch SALABERT-US
        voc sc $10.50, cor pts $.75   (L58)

    Deus In Adjutorium Meum Intende
        [Lat] SATBB,STBar soli,org,orch SALABERT-US
        voc sc $10.50, cor pts $.75   (L59)

    Dixit Dominum (Psalm 109)
        (Gennaro, M.) [Lat] cor,soli,pno/org voc sc
        HEUGEL s.p.   (L60)
        (Sarlit, H.L.) [Lat] cor,soli,orch HEUGEL
        ipr   (L61)

    I Will Praise Thee, O Lord
        (Hines) boy cor/girl cor SOUTHERN $.25
                                                    (L62)

    Lord, Have Mercy Upon Us *Adv/Lent
        3pt mix cor,org/pno oct SCHIRM.G 11428 $.30
                                                    (L63)

    Psalm 109 *see Dixit Dominum

    Quare Fremuerunt Gentes
        [Lat] SATBB,SSTB soli,org,orch SALABERT-US
        voc sc $10.50, cor pts $1.00   (L64)

    Regina Coeli *BVM,mot
        (Spycket) [Lat] cor,soli,orch sc DURAND
        s.p., ipa   (L65)

    Save Me, O God, By Thy Name
        (Hines) 2pt boy cor/SA oct LAWSON 51306
        $.25   (L66)

    Te Deum Laudamus *Te Deum
        (Gennaro, M.) [Lat] cor,soli,pno/org voc sc
        HEUGEL s.p., ipr   (L67)
        (Sarlit, H.L.) [Lat] cor,soli,orch voc sc
        HEUGEL s.p., ipr   (L68)

L'ALLEGRO, IL PENSIEROSO, ED IL MODERATO see
    Handel, George Frideric

LAMB
    Hodie, Christus Natus Est *Xmas
        TTB STANDARD A11M3 $.45   (L69)
        SATB STANDARD A13MX3 $.45   (L70)

    In The Beginning Was God
        SATB,org BOSTON 12901 $.35   (L71)

    Let Not Your Heart Be Troubled
        SATB,org BOSTON 13441 $.35   (L72)

    O That I Had A Thousand Voices
        SATB,org BOSTON 13440 $.35   (L73)

    Sit Down, Lord *spir
        SATB STANDARD C604MX1 $.40   (L74)

LAMB see Binkerd, [Gordon]

LAMB see Chorbajian, John

LAMB see Engel, [A. Lehman]

LAMB see Shaw, C.

LAMB see Smith, C.N.

LAMB, THE see Wood, Dale

LAMB AND JESUS SLEPT, THE see Hall, F.

LAMB GOES FORTH see Bach, Johann Sebastian

LAMB GOES FORTH, A see Bach, Johann Sebastian

LAMB GOES UNCOMPLAINING FORTH, A see Distler,
    Hugo

LAMB GOES UNCOMPLAINING FORTH, A see Hassler,
    Hans Leo

LAMB GOES UNCOMPLAINING FORTH, A see Wienhorst,
    Richard

LAMB, GORDON H.
    Aleatory Psalm (Psalm 150) Bibl
        SATB,acap oct WORLD CA-4003-8 $.60   (L75)

    Psalm 150 *see Aleatory Psalm

LAMB MOST HOLY see Franck, Cesar, Agnus Dei

LAMB OF CALVARY see Reske

LAMB' OF GOD
    (Coggin) SSA oct PRO ART 2582 $.30   (L76)
    (Coggin) SATB,opt kbd oct PRO ART 2579 $.30
                                                    (L77)
    (Coggin) SAB oct PRO ART 2266 $.30   (L78)

LAMB OF GOD see Bach, Johann Sebastian,
    Christe, Du Lamm Gottes

LAMB OF GOD see Barber, Samuel

LAMB OF GOD see Bizet, Georges, Agnus Dei

LAMB OF GOD see Cafarella

LAMB OF GOD see Casciolini, Claudio

LAMB OF GOD see Chopin, Frederic

LAMB OF GOD see Christiansen

LAMB OF GOD see Christiansen, F. Melius

LAMB OF GOD see Concone, Giuseppe, Agnus Dei

LAMB OF GOD see Decius, Nicolaus

LAMB OF GOD see Draesel, Lederhouse

LAMB OF GOD see Gabrieli, Andrea

LAMB OF GOD see Gabrieli, Giovanni, Agnus Dei

LAMB OF GOD see Hager, Sister Conleth, Agnus Dei

LAMB OF GOD see Hassler, Hans Leo, Agnus Dei

LAMB OF GOD see Haydn, (Franz) Joseph, Agnus Dei

LAMB OF GOD see Kendrie, Frank E., Agnus Dei

LAMB OF GOD see Lotti, Antonio, Agnus Dei

LAMB OF GOD see Martini, Padre

LAMB OF GOD see Monteverdi, Claudio

LAMB OF GOD see Morley, Thomas, Agnus Dei

LAMB OF GOD see Mozart, Wolfgang Amadeus, Agnus Dei

LAMB OF GOD see Palestrina, Giovanni, Agnus Dei

LAMB OF GOD see Schroth

LAMB OF GOD see Schutz, Heinrich

LAMB OF GOD see Tubb, Monte, Agnus Dei

LAMB OF GOD see Verdi, Giuseppe

LAMB OF GOD see Victoria, Tomas Luis de, Agnus Dei

LAMB OF GOD see Wesley, Samuel Sebastian Jr.

LAMB OF GOD see Williams, David H.

LAMB OF GOD (FATHER, FORGIVE THEM) see Haydn, (Franz) Joseph

LAMB OF GOD GOES MEEKLY FORTH, THE see Greitter, Matthaeus

LAMB OF GOD, I LOOK TO THEE see Bengson, W.J.

LAMB OF GOD, I LOOK TO THEE see Lewis, John Leo

LAMB OF GOD, LORD JESUS see Bach, Johann Sebastian

LAMB OF GOD MOST HOLY *Easter/Lent,Commun
  (Wiley) SATB,acap,opt pno oct PRO ART 2355
  $.22   (L79)

LAMB OF GOD, MOST HOLY see Jeep, Johann

LAMB OF GOD, OUR SAVIOR see Bach, Johann Sebastian, Christe, Du Lamm Gottes

LAMB OF GOD, PURE AND HOLY see Jeep, Johann

LAMB OF GOD, PURE AND HOLY see Rotermund, Donald

LAMB OF GOD, PURE AND HOLY see Willan, Healey

LAMB THAT FOR US WAS SLAIN, THE see Bach, Johann Sebastian

LAMB THAT WAS SACRIFICED, THE see Bach, Johann Sebastian

LAMB, THE see Chorbajian, John

LAMB, THE see Forsblad

LAMB, THE see Goodhall, Clare

LAMB, THE see Jones, George Herbert

LAMB, THE see Rasely

LAMB, THE see Ross

LAMB, THE see Schwadron

LAMB, THE see Shaw, Geoffrey [Turton]

LAMB, THE see Takacs, Jeno

LAMB, THE see Younger, John B.

LAMBERT
  O Bone Jesu *Easter/Lent,mot
    [Lat] SATB oct PRO ART 1227 $.16   (L80)

LAMBERTZ, JOHANN SEBASTIAN
  Der Du Die Zeit In Handen Hast
    SATB HANSSLER 6.320 s.p.   (L81)

  Deutsches Ordinarium
    cor&cong HANSSLER 27.002 s.p.   (L82)

  Lass Die Wurzel Unseres Handelns Liebe Sein
    SSATB HANSSLER 7.165 s.p.   (L83)

  Mein Volk, Was Tat Ich Dir
    SATB HANSSLER 7.155 s.p.   (L84)

  Nun Lobet Gott Im Hohen Thron
    SATB HANSSLER 7.149 s.p.   (L85)

LAMBIOLLOTTE, LOUIS (1796-1855)
  Messe Pastorale *Mass
    [Lat] 4pt mix cor,org/orch (F maj) HEUGEL
    voc sc s.p., voc pt s.p.   (L86)

  O Salutaris
    [Lat] 4pt mix cor,opt pno/org (D maj)
    HEUGEL s.p.   (L87)

  Pastores Erant Vigilantes
    [Lat] SATB,solo,org/orch HEUGEL s.p.   (L88)

  Tantum Ergo
    [Lat] 3pt,org/pno HEUGEL s.p.   (L89)
    [Lat] 4pt mix cor,opt pno/org (F maj)
    HEUGEL s.p.   (L90)

LAMBRECHTS-VOS, A.
  Een Kindeke Genaderijk
    jr cor sc ALSBACH&D s.p.   (L91)

  Kerstcantate *cant
    jr cor,soli,pno ALSBACH&D sc s.p., cor pts
    s.p.   (L92)

LAMBRECHTS-VOS, A. (cont'd.)

  Lente *cant
    jr cor,opt S solo,pno ALSBACH&D sc s.p.,
    cor pts s.p.   (L93)

LAMBS ALSO LOVE THEE, THE see Ream

LAMBS, THE see Imig, Warner

LAMBS TO THE LAMB see Creston, Paul

L'AME DES FORGERONS see Stekke, Leon

LAMENT AND ALLELUIA see Morgan, Haydn

LAMENT AND WEEP see Von Den Heiligen Wunden

LAMENT FOR A DEAD SON see Boyd, Jack

LAMENT MY SOUL see Jones

LAMENT MY SOUL see Jones, R.

LAMENT YE CHILDREN OF ISRAEL see Carissimi, Giacomo, Plorate, Filii Israel

LAMENTABATUR JACOB see Morales, Cristobal de

LAMENTACION see Comes, Juan Bautista

LAMENTATIO JEREMIAE PROPHETAE see Krenek, Ernst

LAMENTATION DES KARFREITAGS see Palestrina, Giovanni

LAMENTATION SUR LA MORT D'UN JEUNE HEROS see Schubert, Franz (Peter)

LAMENTATIONEN BAND XXV see Palestrina, Giovanni

LAMENTATIONES see Parsley, Osbert

LAMENTATIONES JEREMIAE PROPHETAE see Cavalieri, Emilio del

LAMENTATIONS see Bairstow, Edward Cuthbert

LAMENTATIONS see Tallis, Thomas

LAMENTATIONS see Thompson, Randall

LAMENTATIONS see White, Robert

LAMENTATIONS OF JEREMIAH see Couperin, Francois

LAMENTATIONS OF JEREMIAH see Ginastera, Alberto

LAMENTATIONS OF JEREMIAH see Lassus, Roland de (Orlandus)

LAMENTATIONS OF JEREMIAH see Pinkham, Daniel

LAMENTATIONS OF JEREMIAH, THE see de la Rue, Pierre

LAMENTATIONS OF JEREMIAH, THE see Huston, Scott

LAMENTATIONS OF JEREMIAH, THE see Tallis, Thomas

LAMENTAZIONE DI GEREMIA see Cavalieri, Emilio del

LAMMERS, DEUXIEME RECUEIL see Le Jeune, Claude

LAMONT
  O God Our Help In Ages Past
    SATB KJOS 8014 $.30   (L94)

  Send Out Thy Light
    SATB KJOS 7009 $.30   (L95)

  Who So Dwelleth
    SSA KJOS 8252 $.30   (L96)

LA MONTAINE, JOHN (1920-   )
  God Of Grace And God Of Glory *Op.22, cant
    SATB,org sc SIFLER $5.00   (L97)

  Mass Of Nature *see Missa Naturae

  Missa Naturae *Op.37
    "Mass Of Nature" cor,narrator,orch SIFLER
    voc sc $14.00, sc $35.00   (L98)

  Songs Of The Nativity *CCU,Xmas
    SATB oct GRAY GCMR 2374 $.50   (L99)

  Te Deum *Op.35
    SATB,winds,perc sc SIFLER $3.50, ipr (L100)

  Wonder Tidings *Xmas,cant
    BELWIN $3.50   (L101)

L'AMORE SPIRITUALE see Haubiel, Charles

LAMP UNTO MY FEET see Lekberg, Sven

LA MURE, [PIERRE]
  Lord's Prayer, The
    cor HIGHLAND 2018 $.35   (L102)

  Thanksgiving Chorale *Thanks,chorale
    SATB WARNER R3276 $.30   (L103)

LAMY, RUDOLF (1905-1962)
  Da Jesus In Den Garten Ging *Psntd
    [Ger] SATB,acap (med easy) MULLER MS 15
    s.p.   (L104)

LAND
  Father, Holy Father
    2pt oct PLYMOUTH SC-502 $.25   (L105)

  What Child Is This?
    2pt oct PLYMOUTH SC-504 $.25   (L106)

LAND, HOR HERRENS ORD see Moren, John

LAND, LOIS B.
  Alleluia!
    2pt oct AGAPE A 422 $.25   (L107)

LAND OF ODEN *folk
  (Owens) SATB oct LILLENAS AN-5015 $.35 (L108)

LANDAHL, [CARL WILFRED] (1908-   )
  Lord's My Shepherd, The *Gen
    SATB (Scottish Psalter, 1650) SCHMITT 849
    $.16   (L109)

LANDET HAR GITT SIN GRODE see Nystedt, Knut

LANDFREDAGEN see Runback, Albert

LANDGRAVE, PHILLIP
  Church, The *cant
    SATB,opt inst FISCHER,C O-4779 $1.50, ipa
                                               (L110)

  Do Not Be Conformed
    SATB oct FISCHER,C CM-7756 $.35   (L111)

  Do You Face A Wall?
    SATB oct AGAPE CF 109 $.30   (L112)

  Go Where The People Are
    mix cor oct AGAPE CF 115 $.30   (L113)

  God Is Our Strength And Refuge *Bibl
    unis oct AGAPE CF 110 $.30   (L114)

  Higher Ground *Xmas
    SATB oct AGAPE CF 129 $.30   (L115)

  In A Day Of Danger
    SATB,brass oct WORD CS-2554 $.30, ipa
                                               (L116)

  Peace I Leave With You
    SATB oct WALTON 2056 $.25   (L117)

  Rise Up, O Men Of God
    SATB,opt brass oct AGAPE F 920 $.35   (L118)

  Song Is Not A Song, A *Gen,anthem
    SAB oct WORD CS-2556 $.30   (L119)
    cor WORD CS-2556 $.30   (L120)

  What You Really Need Is Jesus
    SATB oct WORD CS-2555 $.30   (L121)

  Who Will Go?
    unis oct AGAPE CF 114 $.25   (L122)

  Will It Matter That I Was?
    SATB oct AGAPE CF 164 $.30   (L123)

  Ye Christian Heralds! Go Proclaim
    SATB oct AGAPE CH 642 $.30   (L124)

  Yes, God Is Real
    SATB oct AGAPE CF 111 $.30   (L125)

LANDON
  Come, Thou Almighty King
    SAB oct LORENZ 7385 $.25   (L126)

  Cross Of Christ *Easter,cant
    SATB LORENZ $1.95   (L127)

  Fairest Lord Jesus
    SA/SAB oct LORENZ 7823 $.25   (L128)

  Glory Of The Star, The *Xmas,cant
    SATB LORENZ $1.95   (L129)
    SA/SAB oct LORENZ $1.75   (L130)

  Go To Dark Gethsemane
    SATB oct LORENZ A515 $.25   (L131)

  God Bless You, Mother Dear
    SATB oct LORENZ 9331 $.25   (L132)

  God Will Take Care Of You
    SATB oct LORENZ B71 $.30   (L133)

  Haven Of Rest, The
    SATB oct LORENZ A224 $.30   (L134)

  He Hideth My Soul
    SATB oct LORENZ A428 $.25   (L135)

  It Is Well With My Soul
    SATB oct LORENZ A485 $.30   (L136)

  Mary Had A Baby *Xmas
    SATB oct LORENZ A419 $.25   (L137)
    SA/SAB oct LORENZ 7826 $.25   (L138)

  More Like Jesus
    SATB oct LORENZ A511 $.30   (L139)

  Purer In Heart, O God
    SATB oct LORENZ A509 $.25   (L140)

  Shall I Crucify My Savior? *Easter
    SATB oct LORENZ A520 $.25   (L141)

  Sweet Hour Of Prayer
    SATB oct LORENZ A412 $.25   (L142)

  Wonderful Words Of Life
    SATB oct LORENZ A460 $.30   (L143)

  Wondrous Love *Easter
    SATB oct LORENZ A502 $.25   (L144)

LANDOWSKI
  Jesus, La Es-Tu
    wom cor CHOUDENS voc sc s.p., cor pts s.p.
                                               (L145)

LANDRE, WILLEM (1874-1948)
  Requiem In Memoriam Uxoris *Req
    [Lat] mix cor,SATB soli,2fl,2ob,2clar,2bsn,
    3trp,4horn,3trom,tuba,strings,timp,harp
    DONEMUS min sc s.p., cor pts s.p., voc sc
    s.p.   (L146)

LANE, [SPENCER] (1843-1903)
  There Were Ninety And Nine
    SATB oct LORENZ 4237 $.30   (L147)

LANG
  Christ The Lord Hath Risen
    SATB THOMP.G G-541 s.p.   (L148)

  I Hear Thy Voice
    SATB,org BOSTON 4498 $.35   (L149)

  There Is A Love
    SATB oct LORENZ A507 $.30   (L150)

LANG, C.S.
Christ The Lord Hath Risen *Easter,anthem
  unis,orch oct NOVELLO 40.1044.02 s.p., ipr
                                                (L151)
  unis&opt cor oct NOVELLO 40.1044.02 s.p.
                                                (L152)

Duteous Day Now Closeth, The
  see Six Vesper Hymns

He Shall Give His Angels Charge Over Thee
  *anthem
  SSATB,acap oct NOVELLO 28.1247.09 s.p. (L153)

I Will Lay Me Down In Peace
  see Six Vesper Hymns

Jesu, The Very Thought Of Thee *Gen
  2pt (easy) oct OXFORD 44.423 $.25   (L154)

Jubilate *Jubil
  SATB (G maj) oct NOVELLO 44.1160.09 s.p.
                                                (L155)
  unis (G maj) oct NOVELLO 02.0027.01 s.p.
                                                (L156)

King Of Love, The *Gen
  2pt (easy) oct OXFORD 44.424 $.25   (L157)

Let All The World In Every Corner Sing *Gen/
  Thanks
  2pt (easy) oct OXFORD 44.422 $.25   (L158)

Magnificat And Nunc Dimittis *Magnif/Nunc
  SS,org CRAMER A12 s.p.   (L159)
  SATB (B flat maj) oct NOVELLO 44.1400.04
  s.p.   (L160)

O Let My Wish Be Crowned *Gen
  2pt (easy) oct OXFORD 44.425 $.25   (L161)

Rejoice In The Lord Alway *anthem
  TTBB oct NOVELLO 38.0114.04 s.p.   (L162)

Sing Alleluia Forth
  2pt oct NOVELLO 33.0097.08 s.p.   (L163)

Six Vesper Hymns *Eve,hymn
  4pt oct NOVELLO 33.0104.04 s.p.
  contains: Duteous Day Now Closeth, The,
    No.6; I Will Lay Me Down In Peace, No.5
                                                (L164)

Time Draws Near The Birth Of Christ, The
  *Xmas,anthem
  mix cor oct NOVELLO 28.1242.08 s.p. (L165)

LANG, C. TILGHMAM
Earth Is The Lord's The *Bibl
  4pt mix cor,org oct SCHIRM.G 11087 $.25
                                                (L166)

On That First Bright Easter Day *Easter,
  carol
  unis jr cor oct SCHIRM.G 11301 $.25 (L167)

LANG, HANS (1897-1968)
Es Dunkelt Schon Bald *Xmas
  wom cor&jr cor TONGER s.p.   (L168)
  mix cor TONGER s.p.   (L169)

Es Steht Ein Lind
  see Lang, Hans, Macht Hoch Die Tur
  see Lang, Hans, Macht Hoch Die Tur

Gott Ist Und Bleibt Getreu
  see Zwei Trauerchorale
  see Zwei Trauerchorale

Herr, Gib Frieden Dieser Seele
  see Zwei Trauerchorale
  see Zwei Trauerchorale

Ich Weiss Ein Lieblich Engelspiel
  see Lang, Hans, Macht Hoch Die Tur
  see Lang, Hans, Macht Hoch Die Tur

Macht Hoch Die Tur *Xmas
  men cor TONGER s.p. contains also: Ich
    Weiss Ein Lieblich Engelspiel; Es Steht
    Ein Lind   (L170)
  wom cor&jr cor TONGER s.p. contains also:
    Ich Weiss Ein Lieblich Engelspiel; Es
    Steht Ein Lind   (L171)

Vom Himmel Hoch
  see CHORE ZUR WEIHNACHT

Zwei Trauerchorale *chorale
  men cor,acap TONGER s.p.
  contains: Gott Ist Und Bleibt Getreu;
    Herr, Gib Frieden Dieser Seele   (L172)

Zwei Trauerchorale
  mix cor,acap TONGER s.p.
  contains: Gott Ist Und Bleibt Getreu;
    Herr, Gib Frieden Dieser Seele   (L173)

LANG, HANS (1908-)
Der Himmel Senket Sich *Op.4, mot
  5pt men cor,opt clar&vla/opt vln&vla (med)
  oct LEUCKART 192 s.p., ipa   (L174)

Jubilate Deo
  see Two Motets

Laudate Dominum
  see Two Motets

Marien-Litanei II *Op.53
  mix cor,soli (med) cor pts LEUCKART s.p.
                                                (L175)

Two Motets *mot
  [Lat/Ger] SSAA&unis boy cor SCHOTT sc s.p.,
    cor pts s.p.
  contains: Jubilate Deo; Laudate Dominum
                                                (L176)

LANGDON, JONN
Magnificat *Magnif
  ATTB CRAMER A9 s.p.   (L177)

Te Deum And Jubilate *Jubil/Te Deum
  2pt,org CRAMER A13 s.p.   (L178)

LANGDON, R.
Lord's Prayer, The
  see Hebrew Benediction

LANGE, GREGOR (ca. 1540-1587)
Wenn Ich Nur Hab Dich, Herr *mot
  (Hellmann) SAB HANSSLER 1.250 s.p. (L179)

LANGER, HANS KLAUS
Die Burger All Von Chastres
  [Ger] wom cor&jr cor,acap (easy) oct SIRIUS
  6 s.p.   (L180)

LANGFREDAGEN *Adv
  (Runback, Albert) 4pt mix cor, acap NORDISKA
  2705 s.p. see from Introitus   (L181)

LANGIUS, G.
Mein Herz Und Hort
  (Vaal, O. De) wom cor sc ALSBACH&D s.p. (L182)

LANGLAIS, JEAN (1907-)
Festival Alleluia
  SATB oct PRESSER 362-03127 $.50   (L183)

LANGLOIS, H.G.
Grant, We Beseech Thee *Introit
  SATB oct LESLIE 4078 see from Two Introits
                                                (L184)

O Lord, We Beseech Thee *Introit
  SATB oct LESLIE 4040   (L185)

O Lord Who Didst In Olden Time *Introit
  SATB oct LESLIE 4078 see from Two Introits
                                                (L186)

Two Introits *see Grant, We Beseech Thee; O
  Lord Who Didst In Olden Time   (L187)

LANGSTROTH, IVAN SHED (1887-)
Angels Are Singing *Xmas
  SATB WEINBERGER s.p.   (L188)
  SATB oct SHAPIRO SK 2034 $.25   (L189)

Ring, Ring, Ring Ye Bells *Xmas
  SATB oct SHAPIRO SK 2109 $.25   (L190)

Sing Out The News *Xmas
  SATB oct SHAPIRO SK 2122 $.30   (L191)

LANGUIR MY FAULT see Clemens, Jacobus

LANIER
I'll Live For Him
  SATB oct SACRED S-116 $.30   (L192)

Word Was God, The
  SATB oct SACRED S-82 $.35   (L193)

Ye That Stand In The House Of The Lord
  (Mason) SATB oct WORD CS-359 $.30   (L194)

LANIER, GARY
God So Loved The World
  SATB oct AGAPE A 421 $.30   (L195)

Thy Word Is Like A Garden
  unis oct AGAPE CH 644 $.25   (L196)

L'ANNIVERSAIRE DES MARTYRS see Gounod, Charles
  Francois

L'ANNONCIATION see Migot, Georges

L'ANNONCIATION see Roesgen-Champion, Marguerite

L'ANTONIA see Rovenstrunck, Bernhard

LAPIN
Lord's Supper, The
  SATB HANSEN-US C620 $.40   (L197)

Lord's Supper, The *pop
  SATB SOUTHERN $.40   (L198)

LAPO, CECIL E. (1910-)
All Beautiful The March Of Days
  SATB (easy) ABINGDON APM-202 $.25   (L199)

Alleluia
  jr cor&sr cor (easy) FISCHER,C R 454 $.25
                                                (L200)

Christmas Lullaby *Xmas
  jr cor&sr cor (easy) ABINGDON APM-123 $.22
                                                (L201)
  SATB (easy) ABINGDON APM-123 $.22   (L202)

Christmas Meditation *Xmas
  4pt jr cor/SATB (med easy) FISCHER,C R 497
  $.24   (L203)

Christmas Meditations *CCU,Xmas,meditation
  SATB oct FISCHER,C R-495 $.25   (L204)

Drop, Drop, Slow Tears *Lent
  unis (easy) ABINGDON APM-334 $.18   (L205)

Easter Hymn Of Praise *Easter,hymn
  SATB,opt acap (med) ABINGDON APM-357 $.30
                                                (L206)

Father Most Holy
  SSAATTBB,acap oct PRESSER 312-40112 $.30
                                                (L207)

God Of Love And God Of Power
  cor,org,2trp,2trom sc ABINGDON APM-707
  $.50, ipa   (L208)

I Rise And Sing
  4pt jr cor/SATB (easy) FISCHER,C R 6021
  $.30   (L209)

Joseph Dearest, Joseph Mine *Xmas
  jr cor&sr cor,org,hndbl (easy) ABINGDON
  APM-444 $.25   (L210)

Lullaby At Christmas *Xmas
  SATB (easy) ABINGDON APM-465 $.25   (L211)

O Holy Father
  SATB/SATB&jr cor (med) ABINGDON APM-163
  $.24   (L212)

L'APOCALYPSE SELON ST. JEAN see Francaix, Jean

L'APPARIR DEL SOL see Monte, de

LAR MIG DA BESINNA see Salonen, Sulo

LAR OSS BETANKA see Sorenson, Torsten

L'ARC-EN-CIEL see Lacome, Paul

LARGE
Ave Maria
  SAB oct PLYMOUTH DL-201 $.25   (L213)

LARGO see Handel, George Frideric

LA ROSA, J.
Cor Jesu
  SATB PARAGON 1028 $.25   (L214)

LA ROSE, L.
La Premiere Communion
  unis,pno LEMOINE s.p.   (L215)

LARSON
At Thy Feet, Our God And Father
  2pt oct PRO ART 1256 $.20   (L216)

Children Of The Heavenly Father
  SA oct BELWIN 1421 $.25   (L217)
  SATB oct BELWIN 1923 $.25   (L218)

Children's Voices
  SA oct FISCHER,J 9201 $.30   (L219)

Come, Children, Join To Sing *Easter
  SA SCHMITT 216 $.25   (L220)

Easter Bells *Easter/Lent
  SATB&jr cor oct PRO ART 1827 $.25   (L221)

Father, We Thank Thee *Thanks
  2pt oct PRO ART 1461 $.20   (L222)

Hymn Of Praise *Thanks
  SATB oct PRO ART 1484 $.22   (L223)

Jesus, Where'er Thy People Meet
  SATB oct PRO ART 1220 $.25   (L224)

Lord's Own Day, The
  SA oct BELWIN 64262 $.30   (L225)

My Jesus As Thou Wilt!
  SATB oct PRO ART 1241 $.25   (L226)

O Fount Of Life
  SATB FLAMMER A 5311 $.25   (L227)

Oh Lord Of Heaven And Earth And Sea *Gen
  SA SCHMITT 209 $.22   (L228)

Praise, My Soul, The King Of Heaven
  SATB oct PRO ART 1935 $.22   (L229)

We Come With Songs Of Gladness
  SSA oct PRO ART 1315 $.25   (L230)
  2pt oct PRO ART 1138 $.30   (L231)
  boy cor SOUTHERN $.30   (L232)

LARSON, DONALD J.
Christ Was Crucified
  SATB oct FISCHER,J 7923 $.30   (L233)

Gladness Hymn, A
  SA oct BELWIN 64322 $.30   (L234)

LARSON, EARL R.
Easter Alleluia *Easter
  jr cor&sr cor oct FISCHER,J 9189 $.30 (L235)

On Christmas Day
  SATB oct GRAY GCMR 2941 $.25   (L236)

Sing This Joyous Morning
  jr cor&sr cor oct FISCHER,J 9039 $.30
                                                (L237)

LARSON, LEROY
Rainy Days
  SATB oct AGAPE CE 4321 $.30   (L238)

LARSSON, LARS-ERIK (1908-)
Agnus Dei (from Missa Brevis)
  see Larsson, Lars-Erik, Kyrie

Gloria (from Missa Brevis)
  see Larsson, Lars-Erik, Kyrie

Kyrie (from Missa Brevis)
  [Swed] SAB,acap GEHRMANS s.p. contains
  also: Gloria; Sanctus; Agnus Dei   (L239)

Sanctus (from Missa Brevis)
  see Larsson, Lars-Erik, Kyrie

LA RUE, PIERRE DE (? -1518)
David's Song For Jonathan
  SATB,acap BROUDE BR. $.35   (L240)

Eine Motette
  see La Rue, Pierre de, Requiem

Magnificat Quinti Toni *Magnif
  (Davison, Nigel) SATB oct PENN STATE
  0-271-73081-1 $1.50   (L241)

Missa L'homme Arme *Mass
  mix cor MOSELER s.p.   (L242)

O Salutaris Hostia *Commun
  see LA SCHOLA PALESTRINIENNE PREMIERE
    CAHIER
  "O Saving Victim" SATB,acap SCHIRM.EC 1237
    $.10   (L243)
  (Expert) [Lat] SATB,acap oct SALABERT-US
    $.65   (L244)

O Saving Victim *see O Salutaris Hostia

Requiem *mot/Req
  (Blume) [Ger/Lat] 4-5pt mix cor MOSELER
  s.p. contains also: Eine Motette   (L245)

Vier Motetten *CC4U,mot
  (Davison) 4pt mix cor MOSELER s.p.   (L246)

LAS PALABRAS, AMOR MIO see Benedito

LAS TORRAS see Benedito

LASCIA CHIO PIANGA see Handel, George Frideric

LASS ALLES, WAS DU HAST see Lechner, K.

LASS DEINEN KNECHT NUNMEHR IN DEINEM see
  Goudimel, Claude

LASS DICH NUR NICHTS DAUREN see Brahms,
  Johannes

LASS DICH NUR NICHTS NICHT DAUREN see Brahms,
  Johannes

LASS DIE WURZEL UNSERES HANDELNS LIEBE SEIN see Lambertz, Johann Sebastian

LASS DIE WURZEL UNSRES HANDELNS see Weber, Ludwig

LASS DIR AN MEINER GNADE GENUGEN see Reda, Siegfried

LASS, FURSTIN, LASS NOCH EINEN STRAHL see Bach, Johann Sebastian

LASS FURSTIN, LASS NOCH EINEN STRAHL TRAUERODE see Bach, Johann Sebastian

LASS HOCHSTER, LASS DER HOFFNUNG STRAHL see Bach, Johann Sebastian

LASS MICH DEIN SEIN UND BLEIBEN see Hartmann, Heinrich

LASS MICH IN TREUE DEINE WEGE WANDELN see Schwarz-Schilling, Reinhard

LASS UNS DAS KINDELEIN WIEGEN see Kaminski, Heinrich

LASS UNS SPUREN, DASS DU BIST see Zoller, Alfred Hans

LASSET DAS WORT CHRISTI REICHLICH UNTER EUCH WOHNEN see Micheelsen, Hans Friedrich

LASSET DIE KINDLEIN ZU MIR KOMMEN see Schein, Johann Hermann

LASSET EUCH VERSOHNEN MIT GOTT *CC17U,Gen, chorale
(Reich, Philipp) [Ger] 3-4pt mix cor,acap (med easy) BAREN. BA 2948 $2.25 (L247)

LASSET EURE LENDEN UMGURTET SEIN see Studer, Hans

LASSET UNS ABER WAHRHAFTIG SEIN see Ruppel, Paul Ernst

LASSET UNS ABLEGEN DIE SUNDE see Ruppel, Paul Ernst

LASSET UNS DANKEN DEM HERRN CHRIST see Hellmann, Diethard, Benedicamus In Natali Domini

LASSET UNS DAS KINDLEIN WIEGEN see Gresser, Hans

LASSET UNS DEN HERREN PREISEN see Reger, Max

LASSET UNS DOCH DEN HERREN, UNSERN GOTT, LOBEN see Schutz, Heinrich

LASSET UNS RECHTSCHAFFEN SEIN see Micheelsen, Hans Friedrich

LASSET UNS WAHRHAFTIG SEIN IN DER LIEBE see Kurig, Hans-Hermann

LASSO, ORLANDO DI
see LASSUS, ROLAND DE (ORLANDUS)

LASSO, RUDOLPH DE (? -1625)
Deutsche Psalmen: Psalm 1-51 *see Lassus, Roland de (Orlandus)

Ecce Maria Genuit Nobis *Xmas,mot
[Lat] SAB,acap (med) MULLER M 8 s.p. (L248)
[Lat] SABar,acap oct NOVELLO DM-8 s.p. (L249)

Gott, Sei Mir Gnadig Dieser Zeit (Psalm 51) Gen
[Ger] SA&men cor,acap (med easy) BAREN. BA 176 s.p. (L250)

Psalm 51 *see Gott, Sei Mir Gnadig Dieser Zeit

LASST DIESEN TAG UNS ALLE PREISEN see Bennet

LASST TONEN DIE GLOCKEN UM MITTERNACHT see Desch, Rudolf

LASST UNS ALLE FROHLICH SINGEN see Ruhl, Herbert

LASST UNS AUF DIE BERGE GEHN see Wolters, Gottfried

LASST UNS DAS KINDELEIN WIEGEN see Anonymous

LASST UNS DAS KINDELEIN WIEGEN see Trader, Willi

LASST UNS DAS KINDELEIN WIEGEN see Werner, St.

LASST UNS DAS KINDLEIN WIEGEN see Murschhauser, Franz Xaver Anton

LASST UNS DEN HERREN LOBEN see Schutz, Heinrich

LASST UNS EILEN, LASST UNS WALLEN see Mendelssohn, Arnold

LASST UNS ERFREUEN *ASD/Xmas/Easter/Gen, anthem/hymn,Ger,17th cent
(Cassler, G. Winston) "Ye Watchers And Ye Holy Ones" SATB (easy) cor pts AUGSBURG 1240 $.30, ipa (L251)
(Fisher, W.) "Ye Watchers And Ye Holy Ones" SATB,acap oct PRESSER 332-14596 $.30 (L252)
(Glaser, V.) "Ye Watchers And Ye Holy Ones" SAB,org/pno SCHIRM.EC 2493 (L253)
(Gray) "Ye Watchers And Ye Holy Ones" SATB oct PRO ART 1438 $.25 (L254)
(Gray) "Ye Watchers And Ye Holy Ones" SAB oct PRO ART 1559 $.30 (L255)
(Gray) "Ye Watchers And Ye Holy Ones" TTBB oct PRO ART 1780 $.25 (L256)
(Gray) "Ye Watchers And Ye Holy Ones" SSA oct PRO ART 1615 $.25 (L257)
(Gray) "Ye Watchers And Ye Holy Ones" 2pt oct PRO ART 1716 $.05 (L258)
(Howorth) "Ye Watchers And Ye Holy Ones" SAB oct BELWIN 2079 $.25 (L259)
(Kiel, Sr. Piet) "Ye Watchers And Ye Holy Ones" 2 eq voices,org oct WORLD LE-742-2 $.30 (L260)
(Ley, Henry G.) "Ye Watchers And Ye Holy Ones" SSA (easy) oct OXFORD 44.055 $.35 (L261)
(Oldroyd, George) "Ye Watchers And Ye Holy Ones" SATB/2pt (easy) oct OXFORD 40.001 $.25 (L262)
(Treharne) "Ye Watchers And Ye Holy Ones" SAB,org/pno BOSTON 2080 $.35 (L263)

LASST UNS ERFREUEN HERZLICH SEHR see Stier, Alfred

LASST UNS GOTT, UNSERM HERREN see Schutz, Heinrich

LASST UNS LOBEN DEN TREUEN GOTT see Lechner, Leonhard

LASST UNS REISEN see Werner, Hans

LASST UNS ZUSAMMEN see Steffens

LASSUS, ROLAND DE (ORLANDUS) (1532-1594)
Adoramus Te
see PRACTICAL POLOPHONY
see PRACTICAL POLOPHONY
wom cor sc ALSBACH&D s.p. (L264)
SATB,acap oct PRESSER 352-00076 $.30 (L265)
(Castellazzi; Vene) "Thee We Do Adore" [Lat/Eng] TTB/SSA,acap oct COLOMBO 2039 $.25 (L266)

Adoramus Te, Christe *Xmas/Easter/Lent,mot
[Lat] TTT,acap SCHIRM.EC 953 $.18 (L267)
SSA,acap SCHIRM.EC 1508 $.20 (L268)
[Lat] 3pt boy cor/3pt men cor,acap oct SCHIRM.G 5604 $.25 (L269)
"We Adore Thee, O Christ" SSSAA,acap SCHIRM.EC 890 $.25 (L270)
"We Adore Thee, O Christ" TTBB,acap SCHIRM.EC 1263 (L271)
"We Adore Thee, O Christ" SSAA,acap SCHIRM.EC 1263 (L272)
"We Adore Thee, O Christ" SSA,acap SCHIRM.EC 1284 $.25 (L273)
(Ruiz) [Lat] 4pt men cor,acap RICORDI-ARG BA10484 s.p. (L274)
(Scott) SSA oct FOX R137 $.30 (L275)
(Siegmeister; Ehret) SSA oct BOURNE 210 $.25 (L276)
(Strickling, George) SSA,acap (med) ABINGDON APM-248 $.18 (L277)
(Stroud, Ray) SSA FOSTER MF901 $.20 (L278)
(Washington, Henry) [Lat] SATB CHESTER s.p. (L279)

Agnus Dei (from Doulce Memoire)
[Lat] SATB HANSSLER 6.317 s.p. contains also: Des Prez, Josquin, Et Incarnatus Est (from Pange Lingua) (L280)

All Praise To Thee
(Schroth) SATB KJOS 5340 $.30 (L281)

Alleluia
see Proprium Von Fronleichnam

Alleluja
see Proprium Der Dritten Weihnachtsmesse
see Proprium Von Pfingsten
see Proprium Von Ostern

Alme Deus *Gen
SATB,acap (med) oct OXFORD 53.090 $.50 (L282)

Am Morgen
see Othmayr, Kaspar, Es Steht Ein Lind In Jenem Tal

Angelus Ad Pastores Ait
(Cramer) [Eng/Lat] SATB,acap MARKS 4298 $.25 (L283)

Antiphon II *BVM
SSATB/SATBB PETERS WM59 $1.25 see also ANTIPHONS IN HONOR OF THE BLESSED VIRGIN (L284)

Ars Nova To Rennaissance Vol.7-1200 To About 1500 *sac/sec,CCUL
mix cor min sc KALMUS 707 $1.30 (L285)

As Pants The Hart *anthem
(Bliss) SSA (med) oct AUGSBURG 0604 $.25 (L286)

Audite Nova
mix cor NORDISKA 3761 s.p. (L287)

Aus Meiner Sunden Tiefe *mot
(Geiringer) "Though Deep Has Been My Falling" [Eng/Ger] 4pt mix cor,acap oct SCHIRM.G 8423 $.25 (L288)
(Hellmann) SATB HANSSLER 1.106 s.p. (L289)

Ave Regina Coelorum
"Thou Art The Queen Of All Heaven" [Lat/Eng] SATB,acap AMP A406 $.20 (L290)

Ave, Verum Corpus *Commun
"Hail, True Body" SSATTB,acap SCHIRM.EC 1229 $.30 (L291)

Benedicam Dominum *mot
(Steele, Jonathan) [Lat] SATB CHESTER s.p. (L292)

Benedictus *Bene
(Werle, H.) [Lat] men cor,acap (med) HUG s.p. (L293)

Benedictus Qui Venit (from Missa "Amor Coeli") Bene
(Werle, H.) [Lat] wom cor,acap HUG s.p. (L294)

Blessed Art Thou, O Lord
(Ehret) mix cor CHAPPELL 0024208-358 $.40 (L295)

Blest Is The Man *anthem
(Bliss) SSA (med) oct AUGSBURG 0603 $.30 (L296)

By The River Of Babylon *see Super Flumina Babylonis

Canciones Duarum Vocum *CC12U,mot
TB,acap voc sc KALMUS 6263 $1.25 (L297)

Cantiones Duarum Vocum *CC12U,mot
(Boepple, P.) SA,acap oct PRESSER 352-00011 $.50 (L298)

Cantiones Sine Textu
(Boepple, P.) SA,acap oct PRESSER 352-00016 $.50 (L299)

LASSUS, ROLAND DE (ORLANDUS) (cont'd.)

Christ Hath Arisen *see Christ Ist Erstanden

Christ Ist Erstanden *Easter
[Ger] SATB,acap (med easy) MULLER MS 79 s.p. (L300)
(Pizarro) "Christ Hath Arisen" [Eng/Ger] 4pt mix cor,acap oct SCHIRM.G 10808 $.20 (L301)

Christe Patris Verbum *Gen/Lent
SATTB,acap (med) oct OXFORD 53.089 $.65 (L302)

Christus Resurgens Ex Mortuis *Easter
SSATB,acap SCHIRM.EC $.25 (L303)

Come Unto Me All Ye Who Weary *see Venite Ad Me Omnes

Communio
see Proprium Von Ostern
see Proprium Von Pfingsten
see Proprium Der Dritten Weihnachtsmesse

Concupiscendo Concupiscit Anima Mea
see Drei Motetten

Credidi Propter *Mass
(Hermelink, Siegfried) [Lat] SAATB,acap (med diff) BAREN. BA 4384 $3.00 (L304)

Cum Rides Mihi
see Vier Motetten

Custodi Me Domine
(Agey) "Guide And Keep Me, O Lord" [Eng/Lat] 4pt mix cor,acap oct SCHIRM.G 11370 $.30 (L305)

Da Pacem Domine
see Vier Motetten

Data Est De Lachrimis Mihi Voluptas
see Vier Motetten

De Profundis Clamavi (Psalm 129)
(Bauerle, Hermann) 6pt mix cor,acap cor pts BREITKOPF-L PB-1961 s.p. see from Sieben Busspsalmen (L306)

Der Starke Gott Im Himmelreich
see Lassus, Roland de (Orlandus), O Selig, Dem Der Treue Gott

Deus Meus In Simplicitate Cordis Mei
see Drei Motetten

Deutsche Psalmen: Psalm 1-51 (composed with Lasso, Rudolph de) *CC51U,Gen
(Lipphardt, Walther) [Ger] SA&men cor,acap (med) BAREN. BA 1928 $4.50 (L307)

Dextera Domini
SATB,acap DOBLINGER s.p. see also BITTE UND VERTRAUEN (L308)
(Martens, Mason) "Right Hand Of The Lord" SATB oct WALTON 2081 $.25 (L309)

Di Occhi, Piangete
(Herder, R.) "For In This Moment" [It/Eng] SATB BROUDE,A. 714 $.35 (L310)

Dir Sei Lob *see Tibi Laus

Domine Convertere
(Greyson) "O Lord, God, Forgive My Sins" SATB oct BOURNE ES105 $.30 (L311)

Domini Exaudi Orationem Meum (from Magnus Opus Musicum)
(Agey) "Lord, Hear Thou Our Prayer" [Eng/Lat] 4pt mix cor,acap oct SCHIRM.G 11422 $.25 (L312)

Dominus Deus
(Wiedemann, M.) [Lat] men cor,acap (easy) HUG s.p. (L313)

Doulce Memoire *Mass
(Hermelink, Siegfried) [Lat] SATB,acap (med diff) BAREN. BA 4385 $2.75 (L314)

Drei Motetten *mot
(Ewerhart, R.) mix cor VOLK 129 s.p. contains: Concupiscendo Concupiscit Anima Mea; Deus Meus In Simplicitate Cordis Mei; Voce Mea Ad Dominum Clamavi (L315)

Echo Song
(Davison, A.) anti cor,acap SCHIRM.EC 69 $.30 (L316)

Exaudi Domine Vocem Meam *mot/prayer
(Hellmann) "Herr, Hore Meine Stimme" [Lat/Ger] SATTB HANSSLER 1.316 $.50 (L317)

Expectans Exspectavi *Trin
[Lat] SATB,acap (med) MULLER M 33 s.p. (L318)

Exspectans Exspectavi *mot
[Lat] mix cor,acap oct NOVELLO DM-33 s.p. (L319)

For In This Moment *see Di Occhi, Piangete

Frere Thibault *Mass
(Hermelink, Siegfried) [Lat] SATB,acap (med diff) BAREN. BA 4382 $2.75 (L320)

From Out My Heart's Deep Longing
(Knight, Gerald) SATB,acap oct FISCHER,C CM-7502 $.25 (L321)

Fugger-Motetten *CCU,mot
SATB HANSSLER 4.015 s.p. (L322)

Fulgebunt Justi
(Expert) [Lat] SA oct SALABERT-US $.65 (L323)

Gloria Patri
see Vier Motetten

Gott Ists, Auf Den Wir Immer Hoffen *Psalm
SAT,acap DOBLINGER s.p. see from PSALMLIEDER (L324)

Graduale
see Proprium Von Ostern

LASSUS, ROLAND DE (ORLANDUS) (cont'd.)

Gross Ist Der Herr *Psalm
  SAB,acap DOBLINGER s.p. see from
  PSALMLIEDER   (L325)

Guide And Keep Me, O Lord *see Custodi Me
  Domine

Hail, True Body *see Ave, Verum Corpus

Hear My Prayer, O Lord *Bibl
  (Agey) 4pt mix cor,acap oct SCHIRM.G 11406
  $.30   (L326)

Hear, O Lord, Hear My Prayer
  (Lundquist) SATB oct ELKAN-V 362-1110 $.25
                                                   (L327)

Herr, Deine Gut Und Wahrheit Steht (Psalm 36)
  Gen
  [Ger] SSATB,acap (med easy) BAREN. BA 4970
  s.p.   (L328)

Herr, Der Du Meine Starke Bist *Psalm
  SAT,acap DOBLINGER s.p. see from
  PSALMLIEDER   (L329)

Herr, Hore Meine Stimme *see Exaudi Domine
  Vocem Meam

Hodie Apparuit *Xmas
  boy cor SOUTHERN $.30   (L330)
  wom cor sc ALSBACH&D s.p.   (L331)
  "On This Day The Christ Appears" [Eng/Lat]
  SSA/TTB,acap oct SCHIRM.G 11783 $.30   (L332)
  (Williams) "This Glad Day" TTB,acap
  SCHIRM.EC 1230 $.25   (L333)
  (Williams, W.) "This Glad Day He Appeared"
  SSA,acap pap SCHIRM.EC 1285 $.22   (L334)
  (Williams, W.) "This Glad Day He Appeared"
  TTB,acap SCHIRM.EC 1230 $.16   (L335)

How Long, O Lord *Gen
  (Riedel) SATB SCHMITT 1409 $.25   (L336)

I Will Lift Up Now Mine Eyes *see Levavi
  Oculos Meos

Illumina *mot
  [Lat] mix cor,acap oct NOVELLO DM-32 s.p.   (L337)

Illumina Oculos Meos *Trin
  [Lat] SATB,acap (med) MULLER M 32 s.p.   (L338)

In Die Tribulationis *Mass
  [Lat] 5pt,acap voc sc UNIVER. 9310   (L339)

In Hora Ultima
  see MUSICA RESERVATA, BAND 1
  [Eng/Lat] SSATTB,acap oct SCHIRM.G 7618
  $.25   (L340)

In Me Transierunt
  see MUSICA RESERVATA, BAND 1

Inimici Autem *Lent
  [Lat] TTBB,acap SCHIRM.EC 954 $.20   (L341)
  "Lord, To Thee We Turn" SATB,acap SCHIRM.EC
  1688 $.30   (L342)

Introitus
  see Proprium Von Ostern
  see Proprium Von Pfingsten
  see Proprium Der Dritten Weihnachtsmesse
  see Proprium Von Fronleichnam

Ipsa Te Cogat Pietas
  see Sicut Rose

Ite Rime Dolenti *Mass
  (Hermelink, Siegfried) [Lat] SATTB,acap
  (med diff) BAREN. BA 4383 $4.25   (L343)

Iustorum Animae *ASD
  SSATB,acap SCHIRM.EC $.20   (L344)

Jord Og Himmel Lover *see Jubilate Deo

Jubilate Deo (composed with Palestrina,
  Giovanni) *Gen/Thanks,Jubil/mot
  SATB,acap PETERS 4882 $.50 contains also:
  Sicut Cervus (Psalm 42)   (L345)
  SATB,acap oct PRESSER 352-00080 $.30   (L346)
  [Ger] SATB,acap (med) MULLER MS 22 s.p.
                                                   (L347)
  SATB,acap voc pt DOBLINGER s.p. see also
  LOB UND DANK   (L348)
  (Field) [Lat/Eng] SATB,acap oct BOOSEY 5490
  $.30   (L349)
  (Schmidt, H.) "Jubiliert Dem Herren" [Lat/
  Ger] SATB HANSSLER 1.503 s.p.   (L350)
  (Sorenson, Soren) "Jord Og Himmel Lover"
  [Lat/Dan] SATB,acap HANSEN-DEN 285 s.p.
  see also MOTETTER OG LAUDER FRA DET 16.
  ARHUNDREDE   (L351)

Jubilate Deo Omnis Terra *mot
  [Lat] SATB,acap oct GIA G567 $.25   (L352)
  (Agey) "Praise Thy God, Jehovah, All Ye
  Nations" [Eng/Lat] 4pt mix cor,acap oct
  SCHIRM.G 11410 $.30   (L353)

Jubiliert Dem Herren *see Jubilate Deo

Justorum Animae *Gd.Fri.,mot
  SSATB,acap voc pt DOBLINGER s.p. see also
  TOD UND VERGANGLICHKEIT   (L354)
  (Martens, Mason) "Souls Of Righteous Men,
  The" SATB oct WALTON 2155 $.25   (L355)
  (Martens, Mason) "Souls Of Righteous Men,
  The" SATB oct WALTON 2155 $.25   (L356)
  (Petti, Anthony G.) "Souls Of Righteous
  Men, The" [Eng/Lat] SSATB CHESTER s.p.
                                                   (L357)

Justus Cor Suum Tradet
  (Expert) [Lat] SA oct SALABERT-US $.65 (L358)

Kyrie Eleison, Christe Eleison *S.272, Kyrie
  SATB HANSSLER 6.151 s.p. contains also:
  Bach, Johann Sebastian: Befiehl Du Deine
  Wege   (L359)

La Nuit Froide Et Sombre
  (Expert) "Night, Cold And Somber" [Eng/Fr]
  SATB,acap oct SALABERT-US $.35   (L360)

LASSUS, ROLAND DE (ORLANDUS) (cont'd.)

Lamentations Of Jeremiah
  SAATB,acap oct PRESSER 352-00022 $.40 (L361)

Lauda Anima Mea Dominum
  (Agey) "My Soul Shall Ever Glorify The
  Lord" [Eng/Lat] 4pt mix cor,acap oct
  SCHIRM.G 11337 $.35   (L362)

Lauda Sion
  mix cor,acap voc sc KALMUS 6265 $1.25 (L363)

Lauda Sion Salvatorem *Corpus/Fest
  (Boetticher, Wolfgang) [Ger] SAATBB,acap
  (med diff) BAREN. BA 2915 $4.75   (L364)

Laudate Dominum
  mix cor,acap voc sc KALMUS 6255 $1.25 (L365)

Les Lamentations De Job
  (Passaquet, R.) [Fr] 4pt mix cor HEUGEL
  s.p.   (L366)

Let Fair Peace Bless The World
  SATB MUSICUS 020 $.20   (L367)

Levavi Oculos Meos
  (Agey) "I Will Lift Up Now Mine Eyes" 8pt
  mix cor,acap oct SCHIRM.G 11269 $.40   (L368)

Lobet Den Herren *Psalm
  SSATB,acap DOBLINGER s.p. see from
  PSALMLIEDER   (L369)

Lord, Hear My Prayer
  (Kingsbury, John) SATB ALFRED 6370 $.30 (L370)

Lord, Hear Thou Our Prayer *see Domini
  Exaudi Orationem Meum

Lord Of Heaven
  (Cramer, John) SSA WEINBERGER s.p.   (L371)

Lord, To Thee We Turn *see Inimici Autem

Magnificat Octavi Toni
  SATB,acap SCHIRM.EC $.16   (L372)
  (Collins, H.B.) [Lat] SATB CHESTER s.p. (L373)

Magnificat Primi Toni
  SATB,acap SCHIRM.EC $.16   (L374)

Magnificat Quarti Toni
  SATB,acap SCHIRM.EC $.25   (L375)

Matona, Jungfru Kar
  mix cor NORDISKA 4302 s.p.   (L376)

Matona, Lovely Maiden *see Matona, Mia Cara

Matona, Mia Cara
  "Matona, Lovely Maiden" SATB,acap SCHIRM.EC
  1187 $.35   (L377)
  (Castellazzi) [It] SATB,acap RICORDI-ARG
  BA 9885 s.p.   (L378)

Messe De Feria *Mass
  (Hermelink, Siegried) [Lat] SATB,acap (med)
  BAREN. BA 4386 $2.00   (L379)

Messe Pro Defunctis *Mass
  (Hermelink, Siegfried) [Lat] SATB,acap
  (med) BAREN. BA 4387 $3.00   (L380)

Miserere
  men cor sc ALSBACH&D s.p.   (L381)

Miserere Mei, Domine
  mix cor NORDISKA 3407 s.p.   (L382)

Missa Ecce Nunc Benedicite *Mass
  mix cor,acap voc sc KALMUS 6262 $2.50 (L383)

Missa Octavi Toni *Mass
  (Bauerle, Hermann) SATB,acap cor pts
  BREITKOPF-L PB-3279 s.p., voc pt
  BREITKOPF-L CHB-2770 s.p.   (L384)

Missa Quinti Toni *Mass
  mix cor,acap voc sc KALMUS 6266 $1.25 (L385)

Missa Super "Osculetur Me" *Gen
  (Hermelink, Siegfried) [Ger] SATB&SATB,acap
  (med) BAREN. BA 4396 s.p.   (L386)

Missa VIII *Mass
  "Toni Puisque J' Ai Perdu" mix cor BELWIN
  $1.50   (L387)

Musica, Donum Dei Optimi
  see MUSICA RESERVATA, BAND 2

My Soul Shall Ever Glorify The Lord *see
  Lauda Anima Mea Dominum

Night, Cold And Somber *see La Nuit Froide
  Et Sombre

Nos Qui Sumus In Hoc Mundo
  (Agey) "We, Who Mortals Of This Creation"
  [Eng/Lat] 4pt mix cor,acap oct SCHIRM.G
  11267 $.30   (L388)

O God, To Us Show Mercy
  (Lundquist) SATB oct ELKAN-V 362-1112 $.25
                                                   (L389)

O Lord, God, Forgive My Sins *see Domine
  Convertere

O Lord Of Heaven
  (Ehret) SSA,acap MARKS 4151 $.25   (L390)
  (Ehret) SATB,acap MARKS 4062 $.30   (L391)

O Lord Of Heav'n
  girl cor SOUTHERN $.25   (L392)

O Selig, Dem Der Treue Gott *Gen
  [Ger] SAT,acap (med) MULLER K 27 s.p.
  contains also: Straf Mir, Herr, Nicht Im
  Eifermut; Der Starke Gott Im Himmelreich
                                                   (L393)

Oly Szep Ma Minden
  (Rossa, E.) [Hung] SATB (easy) BUDAPEST see
  also NASZDALOK VEGYESKARRA   (L394)

On This Day The Christ Appears *see Hodie
  Apparuit

LASSUS, ROLAND DE (ORLANDUS) (cont'd.)

Ores Que Je Suis Dispos
  SATB oct PRESSER 352-00009 $.25   (L395)

Our Father, Thou In Heav'n Above *Gen
  SSATB,acap (med diff) oct CONCORDIA 98-1649
  $.30   (L396)

Penitential Psalms Vol. I: Domine *CCU,Psalm
  mix cor,acap voc sc KALMUS 6272 $1.00
                                                   (L397)

Penitential Psalms Vol. VI: De Profundis
  *CCU,Psalm
  mix cor,acap voc sc KALMUS 6277 $1.00 (L398)

Penitential Psalms Vol. VII: Domini Exaudi
  *CCU,Psalm
  mix cor,acap voc sc KALMUS 6278 $1.00 (L399)

Penitential Tears Of St. Peter Vol. 1 *CCU
  mix cor,acap voc sc KALMUS 6258 $1.75 (L400)

Penitential Tears Of St. Peter Vol. 2 *CCU
  mix cor,acap voc sc KALMUS 6259 $1.75 (L401)

Penitential Tears Of St. Peter Vol. 3 *CCU
  mix cor,acap voc sc KALMUS 6260 $1.75 (L402)

Praise And Honor Be Thine
  (Douglas) SATB,acap,opt pno oct PRO ART
  2576 $.30   (L403)

Praise Thy God, Jehovah, All Ye Nations *see
  Jubilate Deo Omnis Terra

Preis Und Ehre Sei Dir, O Gott
  see Anonymous, Wir Danken Dir, Herr Jesu

Proba Me Deus
  (Agey) "Search Me, O God" [Lat/Eng] 4pt mix
  cor,acap oct SCHIRM.G 11268 $.30   (L404)

Prophetiae Sibyllarum
  mix cor,acap voc sc KALMUS 6261 $1.50 (L405)

Proprium Der Dritten Weihnachtsmesse *Xmas
  (Ewerhart, R.) mix cor sc VOLK 133 s.p.
  contains: Alleluja; Communio; Introitus
                                                   (L406)

Proprium Von Fronleichnam
  mix cor sc VOLK 140 s.p.
  contains: Alleluia; Introitus   (L407)

Proprium Von Ostern *Easter
  mix cor sc VOLK 141 s.p.
  contains: Alleluja; Communio; Graduale;
  Introitus   (L408)

Proprium Von Pfingsten *Pent/Whitsun
  mix cor sc VOLK 142 s.p.
  contains: Alleluja; Communio; Introitus
                                                   (L409)

Psalm 5
  see Three Psalms

Psalm 25
  see Three Psalms

Psalm 36 *see Herr, Deine Gut Und Wahrheit
  Steht

Psalm 42 *see Sicut Cervus

Psalm 43
  see Three Psalms

Psalm 129 *see De Profundis Clamavi

Quand Io Pens *Mass
  mix cor,acap voc sc KALMUS 6257 $1.25
                                                   (L410)

Quand Io Pens Other Masses And Madrigals
  *CC8L,madrigal/Mass
  cor min sc KALMUS 707 $1.30   (L411)

Quand Mon Mary Vient De Dehors
  (Expert) [Fr] SATB,acap oct SALABERT-US
  $.50   (L412)

Qui Manducat Carnem Meam *Commun/Pent/
  Whitsun
  mix cor VOLK 134 s.p.   (L413)

Qui Sequitur Me
  see Two Motets
  (Expert) [Lat] SA oct SALABERT-US $.65 (L414)

Right Hand Of The Lord *see Dextera Domini

Saliga Aro De
  mix cor NORDISKA 4213 s.p.   (L415)

Salve Regina
  see LA SCHOLA PALESTRINIENNE DEUXIEME
  CAHIER
  SSATTB,acap SCHIRM.EC $.30   (L416)

Scarco Di Doglia *Mass
  (Hermelink, Siegfried) [Lat] SATTB,acap
  (med diff) BAREN. BA 2925 $4.50   (L417)

Scio Enim Quod Redemptor *mot
  (Collins, H.B.) [Lat] SATB CHESTER s.p. (L418)

Search Me, O God *see Proba Me Deus

Sedebit Dominus *Corpus,anti/Commun/Psalm
  (Peacock) [Lat] 2 eq voices oct ST.MARTIN
  SMP627 s.p.   (L419)

Selig Ist
  SATB,acap DOBLINGER s.p. see also BITTE UND
  VERTRAUEN   (L420)

Selig Ist, Der Auf Gott Sein Hoffnung Setzet
  *Gen
  (Metzger, Hans-Arnold) [Ger] SATB,acap
  (med) MULLER K 26 s.p. contains also:
  Wach Auf, O Menschenkind   (L421)

Serve Bone *mot
  [Lat] SA/TB,acap oct GIA G574 $.25   (L422)
  (Stroud, Ray) SA FOSTER MF801 $.16   (L423)

Seven Sacred Motets *CC7U,mot
  mix cor,acap voc sc KALMUS 6264 $1.25
                                                   (L424)

LASSUS, ROLAND DE (ORLANDUS) (cont'd.)

Shepherd Has Arisen, The *see Surrexit
Pastor Bonus

Sicut Cervus (Psalm 42)
see Lassus, Roland de (Orlandus), Jubilate
Deo

Sicut Rosa
see Two Motets

Sicut Rose *mot
[Lat] SA/TB,acap oct GIA G575 $.25
contains: Ipsa Te Cogat Pietas; Sicut
Rose   (L425)

Sicut Rose
see Sicut Rose

Sieben Busspsalmen *see De Profundis Clamavi
(Psalm 129)   (L426)

Sorrowful Now Is My Soul *Renais
(Ehret, Walter) SATB,acap PEER $.40   (L427)

Souls Of Righteous Men, The *see Justorum
Animae

Straf Mir, Herr, Nicht Im Eifermut
see Lassus, Roland de (Orlandus), O Selig,
Dem Der Treue Gott

Super Flumina Babylonis *Lent,anthem
SSATB BOSWORTH s.p.   (L428)
(Klein, M.) "By The River Of Babylon" [Eng/
Lat] SATB (med) oct GIA G1526 $.30 (L429)

Surge Propera *Mass
(Hermelink, Siegfried) [Lat] SSATTB,acap
(med diff) BAREN. BA 4389 $5.00   (L430)

Surrexit Pastor Bonus *Easter,anthem
[Lat] SSATB,acap (med) MULLER MS 21 s.p.
                                              (L431)
[Lat] SSATB,acap oct NOVELLO MS-21 s.p.
                                              (L432)
"Shepherd Has Arisen, The" [Eng/Lat] SSATB,
acap oct SCHIRM.G 7685 $.30   (L433)

Susanne Un Jour *Mass
(Hermelink, Siegfried) [Lat] SATTB,acap
(med diff) BAREN. BA 4388 $4.25   (L434)

Thee We Do Adore *see Adoramus Te

Thee We Praise *anthem
(Wunderlich) SATB (med) oct AUGSBURG 1423
$.25   (L435)

This Glad Day *see Hodie Apparuit

This Glad Day He Appeared *see Hodie
Apparuit

Thou Art The Queen Of All Heaven *see Ave
Regina Coelorum

Though Deep Has Been My Falling *see Aus
Meiner Sunden Tiefe

Three Passion Motets *CC3U,Psntd,mot
mix cor,acap voc sc KALMUS 6256 $1.00   (L436)

Three Psalms
3pt,acap oct PRESSER 352-00021 $.30
contains: Psalm 5; Psalm 25; Psalm 43   (L437)

Tibi Laus *Gen/Thanks,mot
men cor sc ALSBACH&D s.p.   (L438)
mix cor NORDISKA 3955 s.p.   (L439)
SATB,acap voc pt DOBLINGER s.p. see also
LOB UND DANK   (L440)
(Hellmann) "Dir Sei Lob" [Ger/Lat] SATB
HANSSLER 1.097 $.30   (L441)
(Ruiz) [Lat] SATB,acap RICORDI-ARG BA 10091
s.p.   (L442)

Til Dig Jag Ropar, Herre Krist
mix cor NORDISKA 1706 s.p.   (L443)

Toni Puisque J' Ai Perdu *see Missa VIII

Tristis Est Anima Mea
mix cor,acap voc sc KALMUS 6254 $.50   (L444)

Tu Es Petrus *Gen,mot
(Brun, L'abbe) [Lat] 4pt mix cor,opt org
oct DURAND s.p.   (L445)

Two Excerpts From Penitential Psalm *CC2U,
Psalm
girl cor SOUTHERN $.30   (L446)

Two Excerpts From The Penitential Psalm No. V
*CC2U,Lent
(Tillinghast) [Eng/Lat] SSA,acap WARNER
W3997 $.30   (L447)

Two Motets *mot
[Lat] SA,acap MUSICUS 1011 $.18
contains: Qui Sequitur Me; Sicut Rosa   (L448)

Venite Ad Me Omnes
(Agey) "Come Unto Me All Ye Who Weary"
[Eng/Lat] 5pt mix cor,acap oct SCHIRM.G
11399 $.30   (L449)

Vier Motetten *Gen,mot
(Boetticher, Wolfgang) [Ger] (med) BAREN.
BA 2912 $2.50
contains: Cl, Rides Mihi (SSATB,acap); Da
Pacem Domine (SATTB,acap); Data Est De
Lachrimis Mihi Voluptas (SSATB,acap);
Gloria Patri (SSAATB,acap)   (L450)

Voce Mea Ad Dominum Clamavi
see Drei Motetten

Wach Auf, O Menschenkind
see Lassus, Roland de (Orlandus), Selig
Ist, Der Auf Gott Sein Hoffnung Setzet

We Adore Thee
girl cor SOUTHERN $.30   (L451)

We Adore Thee, O Christ *see Adoramus Te,
Christe

LASSUS, ROLAND DE (ORLANDUS) (cont'd.)

We Do Adore Thee *Renais
(Ehret, Walter) SATB,acap PEER $.40   (L452)

We, Who Mortals Of This Creation *see Nos
Qui Sumus In Hoc Mundo

Wer Gott Vertrauen Tut
SATB,acap DOBLINGER s.p. see also BITTE UND
VERTRAUEN   (L453)

Wer Gott Vertrauen Tut, Den *Easter
SATB HANSSLER 6.157 s.p. contains also:
Lowenstern, Matthaus Appelles von,
Christe, Du Beistand Deiner Kreuzgemeinde
                                              (L454)

Who Shall Ascend Unto His Hill *anthem
(Bliss) SSA (med) oct AUGSBURG 0605 $.30
                                              (L455)

Zu Dir Von Herzensgrunde Ruf Ich
SATB HANSSLER 6.187 s.p.   (L456)

LAST INVOCATION, THE see Glass, P.

LAST INVOCATION, THE see Schuman

LAST JUDGMENT, THE see Spohr, Ludwig (Louis)

LAST MONTH OF THE YEAR
SA CHARTER $.30   (L457)
SATB CHARTER $.30   (L458)
SAB CHARTER $.30   (L459)

LAST PRAYER see Wolf, Hugo, Letzte Bitte

LAST PRAYER, THE see Wolf, Hugo, Letzte Bitte

LAST SUPPER, THE see Thiman, Eric Harding

LAST SUPPER, THE see Donato, Anthony

LAST SUPPER, THE see Schickele, Peter

LAST TRUMPET, THE see Johnson, Paul

LAST WORDS OF CHRIST ON THE CROSS see Haydn,
(Franz) Joseph, Die Sieben Worte Des
Erlosers Am Kreuze

LAST WORDS OF DAVID, THE see Thompson, Randall

LAST WORDS OF JESUS, THE see Peery

LAST WORDS OF THE SAVIOUR ON THE CROSS, THE see
Haydn, (Franz) Joseph, Die Sieben Worte Des
Erlosers Am Kreuze

LAT *see Houge, Jubilate; Oscarson, Gun, Agnus
Dei   (L460)

LAT see Houge

LAT see Oscarson, Gun

LAT OSS MED JESUS VANDRA see Palestrina,
Giovanni

LAT OSS NU JESU PRISA see Soderholm, Valdemar

LAT OSS NU JESU PRISA see Berg, Gottfrid

LATE AUTUMN see Newbury, Kent A.

LATE HAVE I LOVED THEE see Butler

LATEINISCHES ORDINARIUM see Faulstich

LATER RENAISSANCE MOTETS *CCU
mix cor SCHMITT 9064 $1.75   (L461)

LATHAM
Shrine, The
SATB oct PRO ART 2229 $.25   (L462)

LATHAM, [WILLIAM P.] (1917-   )
Credo *Gen,Credo
unis oct SPRATT 557 $.25   (L463)
SATB oct SPRATT 558 $.30   (L464)

Gloria *Gloria
SATB oct SUMMY 1577 $.35   (L465)

Glory Be To God On High
SATB,acap oct SHAWNEE A 900 $.35   (L466)

Only Jesus
(McLellan) SSATB oct LILLENAS AT-1046 $.25
                                              (L467)

Psalm 148
SATB,band oct SUMMY 4903 $.90, ipa   (L468)

Te Deum
SATB SHAWNEE A807 $1.50   (L469)

LATIN-AMERICAN CHRISTMAS LULLABY *Xmas,folk,So
Am
(Hunter) SATB,opt perc oct LAWSON 929 $.30
                                              (L470)

LATIN ANTIPHONS AND PSALMS see Mundy

LATIN CHURCH MUSIC I see Handel, George
Frideric

LATIN CHURCH MUSIC II see Handel, George
Frideric

LATIN MASS IN F see Wood, Charles

LATOM OSS MED JESUS DRAGA see Hassler, Hans Leo

LA TOMBELLE, FERNAND DE (1854-1928)
Gabriel Angelus *mot
[Lat] 2 eq voices/4pt mix cor oct GIA G583 $.25 (L471)

Messe Breve *Mass
2 eq voices/4pt mix cor,org CHOUDENS s.p.
                                              (L472)

Noel *Xmas,mot
cor,solo CHOUDENS s.p.   (L473)

LATROBE
Holy Redeemer! Be Thy Rest Most Glorious
*Lent
(Nolte, Ewald) SATB (med) ABINGDON APM-839
$.50   (L474)

LATROBE (cont'd.)

Psalm 51
cor BOOSEY $3.50   (L475)

We Praise Thee, O God
SATB,SATB soli BOOSEY $1.00   (L476)

LAU, HEINZ
Die Himmel Erzahlen *mot
6pt mix cor MOSELER s.p.   (L477)

Dona Nobis Pacem *mot
5pt mix cor&5pt mix cor MOSELER s.p.   (L478)

O Heiland, Reiss Die Himmel Auf *mot
5pt mix cor MOSELER s.p.   (L479)

LAUB, THOMAS
Befal Du Dine Veje
[Dan] 2 eq voices/3 eq voices HANSEN-DEN 20
s.p. see from Salmer Og Folkeviser   (L480)

Fra Himlem Hojt
[Dan] 2 eq voices/3 eq voices HANSEN-DEN 16
s.p. see from Salmer Og Folkeviser   (L481)

I Dodens Band
[Dan] 2 eq voices/3 eq voices HANSEN-DEN 18
s.p. see from Salmer Og Folkeviser   (L482)

Litani
SATB,org HANSEN-DEN 114 s.p. see from
Liturgisk Musik   (L483)

Liturgisk Music *CC8L
SATB,acap HANSEN-DEN 24779 s.p.   (L484)

Liturgisk Musik *see Litani; Te Deum
Laudamus   (L485)

Lovet Vaere Du, Jesus Krist
[Dan] 2 eq voices/3 eq voices HANSEN-DEN 22
s.p. see from Salmer Og Folkeviser   (L486)

Nu Fryde Sig Hver Kristen Mand
[Dan] 2 eq voices/3 eq voices HANSEN-DEN 21
s.p. see from Salmer Og Folkeviser   (L487)

Salme Og Folkeviser *sac/sec,CC7L
[Dan] 2 eq voices/3 eq voices HANSEN-DEN
24324 s.p.   (L488)

Salmer Og Folkeviser *see Befal Du Dine
Veje; Fra Himlem Hojt; I Dodens Band;
Lovet Vaere Du, Jesus Krist; Nu Fryde Sig
Hver Kristen Mand; Sondag Morgen Fra De
Dode; Vor Gud Han Er Sa Fast En Borg
                                              (L489)

Sondag Morgen Fra De Dode
[Dan] 2 eq voices/3 eq voices HANSEN-DEN 17
s.p. see from Salmer Og Folkeviser   (L490)

Te Deum Laudamus
SATB,solo,org HANSEN-DEN 113 s.p. see from
Liturgisk Musik   (L491)

Vor Gud Han Er Sa Fast En Borg
[Dan] 2 eq voices/3 eq voices HANSEN-DEN 19
s.p. see from Salmer Og Folkeviser   (L492)

LAUD HIM see Pepping, Ernst

LAUD HIS NAME see Ivanoff

LAUD HIS NAME see Tkach, P.

'LAUD, MR.' WILLIAM (1573-1594)
Praise The Lord, O My Soul *Ded/Gen/Thanks/
Trin
SATB,kbd (med easy) oct CONCORDIA 98-2042
$.40   (L493)

LAUD TO THE NATIVITY see Respighi, Ottorino

LAUD TO THE TRINITY see Young

LAUD WE THE NAME see Bach, Johann Sebastian

LAUDA see Johansson, Bengt

LAUDA ANIMA see Andrews, Mark

LAUDA ANIMA MEA see Aichinger, Gregor

LAUDA ANIMA MEA DOMINUM see Lassus, Roland de
(Orlandus)

LAUDA ANIMA MEA DOMINUM see Sandvold, Arild

LAUDA DEL CROCIFISSO: GIESU SOMMO CONFORTO see
Savonarola

LAUDA JERUSALEM see Monteverdi, Claudio

LAUDA JERUSALEM see Navarro

LAUDA JERUSALEM see Porpora, Nicola Antonio

LAUDA JERUSALEM see Vivaldi, Antonio

LAUDA SION see Arnaldi, Antonio

LAUDA SION see Beethoven, Ludwig van

LAUDA SION see Buxtehude, Dietrich

LAUDA SION see Lassus, Roland de (Orlandus)

LAUDA SION see Maggio, Giuseppe

LAUDA SION see Mendelssohn-Bartholdy, Felix

LAUDA SION see Palestrina, Giovanni

LAUDA SION see Rubbra, Edmund

LAUDA SION SALVATOREM see Buxtehude, Dietrich

LAUDA SION SALVATOREM see Isaac, Heinrich

LAUDA SION SALVATOREM see Kerle, Jacobus de

LAUDA SION SALVATOREM see Lassus, Roland de
(Orlandus)

LAUDA SION SALVATOREM see Monteverdi, Claudio

LAUDA SION SALVATOREM see Palestrina, Giovanni

LAUDA SION SALVATOREM see Victoria, Tomas Luis de

LAUDA SION *CCU,hymn
(Runback, Albert) mix cor NORDISKA 2063 s.p. (L494)

LAUDAMUS see Lindegren, Johan

LAUDAMUS see Owen

LAUDAMUS TE see Mueller, Carl F.

LAUDAMUS TE see Vivaldi, Antonio

LAUDATE see Haydn, (Johann) Michael

LAUDATE see Kubizek, Augustinian

LAUDATE see Vogler, Georg Joseph

LAUDATE ALLA VIRGINE see Verdi, Giuseppe

LAUDATE DOMINIUM see Bernardi, Steffano

LAUDATE DOMINUM
"O Praise God!" SATB,org,3trp,3trom,perc,timp oct WORD B-101 $7.00 (L495)

LAUDATE DOMINUM see Arnold, Malcolm

LAUDATE DOMINUM see Becker-Foss, Jurgen

LAUDATE DOMINUM see Brand, Franz

LAUDATE DOMINUM see Brown, Christopher

LAUDATE DOMINUM see Burkhart, Franz

LAUDATE DOMINUM see Busser, [Henri-Paul]

LAUDATE DOMINUM see Cavalli, Francesco

LAUDATE DOMINUM see Cerquetelli, Giuseppe

LAUDATE DOMINUM see Charpentier, Marc-Antoine

LAUDATE DOMINUM see Claussmann, A.

LAUDATE DOMINUM see Crandell, R.

LAUDATE DOMINUM see Croce, Giovanni

LAUDATE DOMINUM see Delvincourt, Claude

LAUDATE DOMINUM see Franck, Cesar

LAUDATE DOMINUM see Goodman, Joseph

LAUDATE DOMINUM see Gounod, Charles Francois

LAUDATE DOMINUM see Hassler, Hans Leo

LAUDATE DOMINUM see Heiberg

LAUDATE DOMINUM see Hemel, Oscar van

LAUDATE DOMINUM see Kaufmann, Ferdinand

LAUDATE DOMINUM see Klerk, Albert de

LAUDATE DOMINUM see Kreutz

LAUDATE DOMINUM see Kreutz, Robert E.

LAUDATE DOMINUM see Kropfreiter, Augustinius Franz

LAUDATE DOMINUM see Lacome, Paul

LAUDATE DOMINUM see Lang, Hans

LAUDATE DOMINUM see Lassus, Roland de (Orlandus)

LAUDATE DOMINUM see Monteverdi, Claudio

LAUDATE DOMINUM see Mozart, Wolfgang Amadeus

LAUDATE DOMINUM see Oltrassi, Giuseppe

LAUDATE DOMINUM see Palestrina, Giovanni

LAUDATE DOMINUM see Peloquin, C. Alexander

LAUDATE DOMINUM see Pitoni, Giuseppe Ottavio

LAUDATE DOMINUM see Purvis, Richard

LAUDATE DOMINUM see Rovetta, Giovanni

LAUDATE DOMINUM see Saint-Saens, Camille

LAUDATE DOMINUM see Schmitt, Florent

LAUDATE DOMINUM see Sweelinck, Jan Pieterszoon

LAUDATE DOMINUM see Tallis, Thomas

LAUDATE DOMINUM see Vivaldi, Antonio

LAUDATE DOMINUM see Volpi, Edoardo

LAUDATE DOMINUM see Wildgans, Friedrich

LAUDATE DOMINUM see Young

LAUDATE DOMINUM see Young, Gordon

LAUDATE DOMINUM (BOOK 1) see Thalben-Ball, George [Thomas]

LAUDATE DOMINUM (BOOK 2) see Thalben-Ball, George [Thomas]

LAUDATE DOMINUM DE COELIS see Moioli, Romano

LAUDATE DOMINUM DOMINI see Tye, Christopher

LAUDATE DOMINUM, HEFT I: ADVENT *CC8U,Adv
(Hubsch, Hanns) [Ger] 3-5pt mix cor,acap (med) MULLER SM 1507 s.p. settings by old masters (L496)

LAUDATE DOMINUM, HEFT II: WEINACHTEN *CC17U, Xmas
(Hubsch, Hanns) [Ger] 3-6pt mix cor,acap (med) MULLER SM 1516B s.p. choruses of old

masters (L497)

LAUDATE DOMINUM, HEFT III: FASTENZEIT *CC12U, Psntd
(Hubsch, Hanns) [Lat] 4-6pt mix cor,acap MULLER SM 1509 s.p. choruses by old masters (L498)

LAUDATE DOMINUM, HEFT IV: KARWOCHE *CC12U, Gd.Fri./Psntd
(Hubsch, Hanns) [Lat] 4-6pt mix cor,acap (med) MULLER SM 1517B s.p. choruses by old masters (L499)

LAUDATE DOMINUM, HEFT IX: MARIENGESANGE *CC10U,Fest
(Hubsch, Hanns) [Ger] 3-6pt mix cor,acap (med) MULLER SM 1515 s.p. works by old masters (L500)

LAUDATE DOMINUM, HEFT V: OSTERN *CC14U,Easter
(Hubsch, Hanns) [Lat] 4-6pt mix cor,acap (med) MULLER SM 1511 s.p. by old masters (L501)

LAUDATE DOMINUM, HEFT VIII: DIE MARIANISCHEN ANTIPHONE *CC12U,Fest
(Hubsch, Hanns) [Ger] 4pt mix cor/5pt mix cor,acap (med) cmplt ed MULLER SM 1514 s.p. contains works by: Palestrina; Lasso; Vittoria (L502)

LAUDATE DOMINUM, HEFT VIII, PART 1: DIE MARIANISCHEN ANTIPHONE see Palestrina, Giovanni

LAUDATE DOMINUM, HEFT VIII, PART 2: DIE MARIANISCHEN ANTIPHONE see Palestrina, Giovanni

LAUDATE DOMINUM, HEFT VIII, PART 3: DIE MARIANISCHEN ANTIPHONE see Victoria, Tomas Luis de

LAUDATE DOMINUM IN F see Mozart, Wolfgang Amadeus

LAUDATE DOMINUM IN SANCTIS EJUS see Strohbach, Siegfried

LAUDATE DOMINUM, OMNES GENTES see Hassler, Hans Leo

LAUDATE DOMINUM OMNES GENTES see Scarlatti, Alessandro

LAUDATE DOMINUS see Ett, [Kaspar]

LAUDATE-HEFT 1 *CC36U,Fest
2-3pt wom cor&T/B sc HANSSLER 17.001 s.p. (L503)

LAUDATE JEHOVAM see Telemann, Georg Philipp

LAUDATE JEHOVAM, OMNES GENTES see Telemann, Georg Philipp

LAUDATE NOMEN DOMINI see Tye, Christopher

LAUDATE PEERI *CC34U,16th cent
(Tovey, D.F.) 2-4pt boy cor/2-4pt wom cor STAINER s.p. contains works by: Agosini; Croce; Constantini; Gabrieli; and others (L504)

LAUDATE POPULI see Haydn, (Johann) Michael

LAUDATE PUERI see Haydn, (Johann) Michael

LAUDATE PUERI see Martini, Padre

LAUDATE PUERI see Mendelssohn-Bartholdy, Felix

LAUDATE PUERI see Monteverdi, Claudio

LAUDATE PUERI see Mozart, Wolfgang Amadeus

LAUDATE PUERI see Pergolesi, Giovanni Battista

LAUDATE PUERI see Radulescu, Michael

LAUDATE PUERI see Vivaldi, Antonio

LAUDATE PUERI see Volpi, Edoardo

LAUDATE, PUERI, DOMINUM see Caldara, Antonio

LAUDATE, PUERI DOMINUM see Gabus

LAUDATE PUERI DOMINUM see Gorostidi

LAUDATE PUERI DOMINUM see Hamel, M.-R.

LAUDATE PUERI DOMINUM see Handel, George Frideric

LAUDATE PUERI DOMINUM see Herrema, Robert

LAUDATE PUERI DOMINUM see Mendelssohn-Bartholdy, Felix

LAUDATE, PUERI DOMINUM see Schmitt, Florent

LAUDATE PUERI DOMINUM see Vicari, Carlo

LAUDATE PUERI, LAUDATE NOMEN DOMINI see Pergolesi, Giovanni Battista

LAUDATE PUERIDOMINUM see Handel, George Frideric

LAUDATIO DOMINI see Kokkoven, Joonas

LAUDATIO MUSICAE see Veress, Sandor

LAUDE see Jacobi, Wolfgang

LAUDE POPOL. A S. AGNESE see Visona', Gino

LAUDENT DEUM see Stobaeus, Johann

LAUDES CREATURARUM see Orff, Carl

LAUDES DE ST. ANTOINE DE PADOUE see Poulenc, Francis

LAUDES EVANGELII see Bucchi, Valentino

LAUDET DEUM MEA GLORIA see Geist, Christian

LAUDETUR see Fevin, Antoine de

LAUDI see Lidholm, Ingvar

LAUDI A NOSTRA SIGNORA see Lewkovitch, Bernhard

LAUDI ALLA VERGINE MARIA see Verdi, Giuseppe

LAUDI SPIRITUALI see Ghedini, Giorgio Federico

LAUDIBUS IN SANCTIS see Byrd, William

LAUDS see Dyson, George

LAUDS FROM THE COURT OF HEAVEN see Cavalieri

LAUDY COLLECTION OF MODERN PART SONGS *see
Brahms, Johannes, Ave Maria; Bruch, Max, Morning-Song Of Praise; Eyken, H. van, Gracious And Long-Suffering; Holst, Gustav, Ave Maria; Mistowski, Alfred, Festival Anthem; Tchaikovsky, Piotr Ilyitch, Hymn Of The Cherubim (L505)

LAUDY COLLECTION OF MODERN PART SONGS see Brahms, Johannes

LAUDY COLLECTION OF MODERN PART SONGS see Bruch, Max

LAUDY COLLECTION OF MODERN PART SONGS see Eyken, H. van

LAUDY COLLECTION OF MODERN PART SONGS see Holst, Gustav

LAUDY COLLECTION OF MODERN PART SONGS see Mistowski, Alfred

LAUDY COLLECTION OF MODERN PART SONGS see Tchaikovsky, Piotr Ilyitch

LAUFET, IHR HIRTEN
(Strobl, Otto) mix cor,acap oct DOBLINGER s.p. (L506)

LAUFT, IHR HIRTEN, ALLZUGLEICH see Haydn, (Johann) Michael

LAURENT, L.
Messe Breve *Mass
3 eq voices,org voc sc LEMOINE s.p. (L507)

LAURIDSEN, MORTEN
Praise Ye The Lord *anthem
SATB (med diff) oct AUGSBURG 0624 $.30 (L508)

LAUS CREATORUM see Brown, Christopher

LAUS DEO see Hugh-Jones, Llifon

LAUS DEO see Milford, Robin

LAUS DEO see Rheinberger, Josef

LAUS ET PERENNIS GLORIA see Gallus, Jacobus

LAUS MEA DOMINUS see Chaminade, Cecile

LAUS NOCTURNA see Wellesz, Egon

LAUT STIMME EIN, DU GANZE HIMMELSSCHAR see Handel, George Frideric, Let Their Celestial Concerts All Unite

LAUTH, WOLFGANG (1931-   )
Beth-Lehem (Haus Des Brotes) *Gen
[Ger] SSATB,acap (med) BOSSE BE 606 s.p. (L509)

Das Alte Ist Vergangen *Gen
[Ger] SSATB,acap (med) BOSSE BE 604 s.p. (L510)

LAUTNER, L.
Praise Our God, Ye Sons Of Men *Xma's
SAB oct PRESSER MC303 $.35 (L511)

LAVARQUE
Cradle Hymn, A *Xmas,cradle/hymn
unis BOOSEY-CAN s.p. (L512)

LAVATER, H. (1885-   )
Das Jahr Geht Still Zu Ende
(Reuss, Eleonore Furstin) [Lat] wom cor, acap HUG s.p. (L513)

Das Lied Vom Schweizerkreuz
[Ger] men cor,acap (easy) HUG s.p. (L514)

Der Herr Ist Mein Hirte (Psalm 23)
[Ger] mix cor,acap (med) HUG s.p. (L515)

Gebet *prayer
[Ger] mix cor,acap (easy) HUG s.p. (L516)

Herr, Schicke Was Du Willst *prayer
(Morike, E.) [Ger] wom cor,acap (easy) HUG s.p. (L517)

Psalm 23 *see Der Herr Ist Mein Hirte

Wenn Ins Land Die Wetter Hangen *BVM
[Ger] HUG s.p. (L518)

LAVATER, LOUIS
We Beseech Thee Almighty God *Austral
SATB ALLANS 184 s.p. (L519)

LAVATIO see Beyer, Frank Michael

L'AVE MARIA see Somma

L'AVE MARIA see Travaglia, Silvio

LAVENDER, WILLIAM
Christmas Time *Xmas
SSA LEONARD-US 08008960 $.25 (L520)

LAVERTY
Psalm 100 *Gen
SATB SCHMITT 1719 $.25 (L521)
TTBB SCHMITT 3509 $.35 (L522)

Psalm 117 *Gen
SATB SCHMITT 1727 $.25 (L523)
SSA SCHMITT 2562 $.35 (L524)

LAW
Anthem On St. Hellen's Tune *anthem
(Merrill) SSATB (easy) OXFORD 94.204 $.30 (L525)

LAW (cont'd.)

　Erect Your Heads, Eternal Gates
　　(McAfee) SATB oct BOURNE 843 $.35　(L526)

LAW OF LOVE, THE see Bottenberg, [Wolfgang]

LAW OF THE LORD IS PERFECT, THE see Englert,
　Eugene

LAWHON
　O Come And Praise The Living God　*Thanks
　　SATB oct VOLKWEIN VB220 $.25　(L527)

LAWRENCE
　Merry Christmas Bells　*Xmas
　　SATB SCHMITT 624 $.20　(L528)

LAWRY
　Shall We Gather At The River
　　(Lynn) SATB oct SOUTHERN $.25　(L529)

LAWSON
　Before I Met Jesus
　　(Schubert) SB oct LILLENAS AN-1187 $.30
　　　(L530)

　He's There
　　(Schubert) SAB oct LILLENAS AN-1188 $.30
　　　(L531)

　I Speak The Name Of Jesus
　　(Schubert) SAT oct LILLENAS AN-1640 $.30
　　　(L532)

　It's A Wide, Wide World
　　(Schubert) SB oct LILLENAS AN-1641 $.25
　　　(L533)

　Joybells
　　(Schubert) ST oct LILLENAS AN-1624 $.30
　　　(L534)

　Turn Ye To Me　*Scot
　　(Harris) SSA oct COLOMBO 1650 $.24　(L535)
　　(Vance, Margaret S.) SATB oct BELWIN 2064
　　$.25　(L536)

LAWSON, GORDON
　How Far Is It To Bethlehem?　*Xmas,carol
　　oct ROYAL 341 s.p.　(L537)

　Rejoice Today With One Accord　*anthem
　　mix oct NOVELLO 50.0331.08 s.p.　(L538)

LAWSON, MALCOLM
　All Through The Night
　　ASHDOWN 1 s.p.　(L539)

LAY DOWN YOUR STAFFS　*Xmas,carol,Fr
　(Shaw; Parker) SATB,acap oct SCHIRM.G 10189
　$.25　(L540)

LAY DOWN YOUR STAFFS see Trusler

LAY DOWN YOUR STAFFS, O SHEPHERDS see Quittez,
　Pasteurs

LAY DOWN YOUR STAVES see Duddy, [John H.]

LAY NOT UP FOR YOURSELVES see Heath, John

LAY NOT UP TREASURES see Morrill

LAY UP TREASURES IN HEAVEN see Neff, James

LAYER, J.
　Wohlauf, Wohlan Zum Letzten Gang
　　(Berger, H.L.) TTBB HANSSLER 6.5138 s.p.
　　　(L541)

LAZAROF, HENRI (1932-)
　Der Erste Tag
　　[Eng/Ger/Heb] mix cor,SATB soli,acap cor
　　pts HEINRICH. s.p.　(L542)

LAZARUS see Schubert, Franz (Peter)

L'CHAH DODI see Gottlieb, J.

L'CHO DODI see Heller, A.

L'CHU N'RAN'NOH see Siegel, Benjamin

L'DOR VODOR see Ancis, Solomon

LE BEL ANGE DU CIEL
　(Geveart, F.-A.) [Fr] 4pt mix cor,acap (med
　easy) cor pts LEMOINE s.p. see from
　Collection De Choeurs, quatrieme Fascicule
　　(L543)

LE BON PASTEUR see Ryelandt, Joseph

LE BREVIAIRE DE PIERRE L'ERMITE　*see Busser,
　[Henri-Paul], Hosanna Filio David; Dupre,
　Marcel, Tantum Ergo; Hahn, Reynaldo, Tu Es
　Petrus; Rabaud, H., Ave Verum　(L544)

LE BREVIAIRE DE PIERRE L'ERMITE see Busser,
　[Henri-Paul]

LE BREVIAIRE DE PIERRE L'ERMITE see Dupre,
　Marcel

LE BREVIAIRE DE PIERRE L'ERMITE see Hahn,
　Reynaldo

LE BREVIAIRE DE PIERRE L'ERMITE see Rabaud, H.

LE CABANON DE BETHLEEM see Tomasi

LE CALVAIRE see Bach, Johann Sebastian

LE CHRIST AU MONT DES OLIVIERS see Beethoven,
　Ludwig van, Christus Am Olberge

LE CIEL A VISITE LA TERRE see Gounod, Charles
　Francois

LE CREDO DE LA VICTOIRE see Messager, Andre

LE CRUCIFIX see Gounod, Charles Francois

LE DELUGE see Saint-Saens, Camille

LE DEPART DES MISSIONAIRES see Gounod, Charles
　Francois

LE DEPART DES MISSIONNAIRES see Gounod, Charles
　Francois

LE FILS DU ROI DE GLOIRE see Roques, L.

LE JOUR see Hahn, Reynaldo

LE LAUDI DI SAN FRANCESCO D'ASSISI see Suter,
　Hermann

LE LEGENDE DE STE CECILE see Chausson, Ernest

LE LIS DE SARON see Martinon, Jean

LE MENUISIER DU ROI see Jean-Baptiiste, L.

LE MESSAGE DE ANGES　*Xmas,carol,18th cent
　(Geveart, F.-A.) [Fr] 4pt mix cor,acap (med)
　cor pts LEMOINE s.p. see from Collection De
　Choeurs, septieme Fascicule　(L545)

LE MESSAGE DES ANGES see Gevaert, Francois
　Auguste

LE MESSIE see Handel, George Frideric, Messiah

LE MESSIE EST NE see Anonymous

LE MIDI see Haydn, (Franz) Joseph

LE MIROIR DE JESUS, MYSTERES DU ROSAIRES see
　Caplet, [Lucien]

LE MYSTERE DES SAINTS INNOCENTS see Barraud,
　Henry

LE NOIR TAUDIS DE LA MAUVAISE ETABLE　*Xmas,
　carol,Fr
　(Tomasi) [Fr] SMezA LEDUC s.p. see also Douze
　Noels De Saboly　(L546)

LE NOM DE MARIE see Gounod, Charles Francois

LE PARADIS PERDU see Dubois, Theodore

LE PARADIS PERDU see Markevitch, Igor

LE PETIT JESUS, SAUVEUR ADORABLE　*Xmas
　(Geveart, F.-A.) [Fr] 4pt mix cor,acap (med)
　cor pts LEMOINE s.p. see from Collection De
　Choeurs, deuxieme Fascicule　(L547)

LE PUPITRE　*see Charpentier, Marc-Antoine, Te
　Deum; Le Jeune, Claude, Missa Ad Placitum
　　(L548)

LE PUPITRE see Charpentier, Marc-Antoine

LE PUPITRE see Le Jeune, Claude

LE REPOS EN EGYPTE see Clergue, J.

LE ROI DAVID see Honegger, Arthur

LE ROSAIRE DES JOIES see Boutry

LE ROSSIGNOLET see Tomasi

LE SEIGNEUR TA PRIERE ENTENDE see Goudimel,
　Claude

LE SERMON SUR LA MONTAGNE see Migot

LE SETTE PAROLE DI CRISTO SULLA CROCE see
　Schutz, Heinrich, Die Sieben Worte Jesu Am
　Kreuz

LE SETTE PAROLE DI GESU CRISTO IN CROCE see
　Volpi, Edoardo

LE SOIR see Haydn, (Franz) Joseph

LE SOMMEIL DE L'ENFANT JESUS　*Xmas,carol,18th
　cent
　(Geveart, F.-A.) [Fr] 4pt mix cor,acap (easy)
　cor pts LEMOINE s.p. see from Collection De
　Choeurs, septieme Fascicule　(L549)

LE SOMMEIL DE L'ENFANT JESUS see Gevaert,
　Francois Auguste

LE SOMNEIL DE L'ENFANT JESUS see Gevaert,
　Francois Auguste

·LE TRE ORE DI AGONIA DI N.S.G.C. see Magri,
　Pietro

LE TRE ORE DI AGONIA DI N. S. GESU' CRISTO see
　Mangone, Gioacchino

LE VERGINE see Asulae, I.M.

LEAD, KINDLY LIGHT see Buck, Dudley

LEAD, KINDLY LIGHT see Harris, William Henry

LEAD, KINDLY LIGHT see Johnston

LEAD, KINDLY LIGHT see Pughe-Evans, D.

LEAD ME IN WAYS OF TRUTH see Willaert, Adrian,
　In Tua Patientia

LEAD ME LORD see Chambers, H.A.

LEAD ME, LORD see Kirk

LEAD ME LORD see Wesley

LEAD ME, LORD see Wesley, A.

LEAD ME, LORD see Wesley, Samuel Sebastian Jr.

LEAD ME, LORD, IN THY RIGHTEOUSNESS see Wesley,
　Samuel Sebastian Jr.

LEAD ME, O FATHER see Bach, Johann Sebastian

LEAD ME, O LORD see Blackwood, Easley

LEAD ME, O LORD see Wesley, Samuel Sebastian
　Jr.

LEAD ME, SAVIOR see Wilson

LEAD ME TO CALVARY see Kirkpatrick

LEAD MY FEET see Hall

LEAD ON, O KING ETERNAL see Darst, W. Glenn

LEAD ON, O KING ETERNAL see Hughes

LEAD ON O KING ETERNAL see Johnson

LEAD ON, O KING ETERNAL see Lundquist

LEAD ON, O KING ETERNAL see Rasley

LEAD ON, O KING ETERNAL see Smart

LEAD ON, O KING ETERNAL see Smart, Henry Thomas

LEAD ON, O KING ETERNAL see Thompson

LEAD ON SOFTLY, LORD see Posegate, Maxcine W.

LEAD US, DEAR LORD see Pallma

LEAD US FATHER, IN THE WAY see Graham

LEAD US FATHER, IN THY WAY see Graham

LEAD US, HEAVENLY FATHER see Roff, Joseph

LEAD US, O FATHER see Doswell, Michael

LEAD US, O FATHER see Hopkins

LEAD US, O FATHER see Newton

LEAD US, O FATHER see Nyquist

LEAD US, O FATHER see Stanton, Royal [W.]

LEAD US, OH FATHER see Gluck, Christoph
　Willibald Ritter von

LEAD US UNTO ALL TRUTH see Roff, Joseph

LEAF
　God Of Love, King Of Peace
　　SATB oct SACRED S-101 $.35　(L550)

　I Can See In A Mornin' Sunrise
　　SATB oct HERITAGE H16 $.35　(L551)

　Let The Whole Creation Cry
　　SA SOUTHERN $.30　(L552)

　To Our King Immortal
　　SATB (med diff/diff) SOUTHERN $.40　(L553)

LEAF, ROBERT
　Advent Of Our God, The
　　see Three Anthems For Beginning Choirs

　Awake, Arise, Go Forth And Rejoice　*anthem
　　unis treb cor (easy) oct AUGSBURG 1580 $.25
　　　(L554)

　Born To The World Is A Shepherd
　　see Three Anthems For Beginning Choirs

　Children's Voices Joyfully Sing　*anthem
　　SA (easy) oct AUGSBURG 1502 $.25　(L555)

　Come On Down, Zaccheaus　*anthem
　　unis treb cor,kbd,opt bells,opt tamb (easy)
　　oct AUGSBURG 1654 $.25 contains also: My
　　Faith　(L556)

　Come Sing　*anthem
　　SATB&opt jr cor,opt solo (easy) oct
　　AUGSBURG 1479 $.25　(L557)
　　unis treb cor&SATB (easy) oct AUGSBURG 1479
　　$.25　(L558)

　Come With Rejoicing　*anthem
　　unis (easy) oct AUGSBURG 1598 $.30　(L559)
　　unis treb cor (easy) oct AUGSBURG 1598 $.30
　　　(L560)

　God Is Here - Let's Celebrate!　*anthem
　　SATB (med) oct AUGSBURG 1602 $.40　(L561)

　Hymns Of Glory, Songs Of Praise
　　see Three Anthems For Beginning Choirs

　Joyful Song, A　*anthem
　　SA (easy) oct AUGSBURG 1577 $.30　(L562)

　Let The Whole Creation Cry　*anthem
　　SA (easy) oct AUGSBURG 1588 $.30　(L563)

　Lord Our God Is King Of Kings, The　*anthem
　　SA (easy) oct AUGSBURG 1582 $.25　(L564)

　My Faith
　　see Leaf, Robert, Come On Down, Zaccheaus

　O How Blessed Is This Place　*anthem
　　SATB (med) oct AUGSBURG 1601 $.30　(L565)

　Rejoice, Rejoice, This Glad Easter Day
　　*Easter,anthem
　　SATB,org,3trp (easy) oct AUGSBURG 1553 $.35
　　　(L566)

　Ride On, Eternal King　*anthem
　　SA (easy) oct AUGSBURG 1851 $.25　(L567)

　Singing Alleluia　*anthem
　　unis treb cor (easy) oct AUGSBURG 1429 $.25
　　　(L568)

　Three Anthems For Beginning Choirs　*anthem
　　unis/2pt,kbd (easy) oct AUGSBURG 11-9500
　　$.60
　　　contains: Advent Of Our God, The; Born To
　　　The World Is A Shepherd; Hymns Of
　　　Glory, Songs Of Praise　(L569)

　To Our King Immortal　*anthem
　　SATB&opt jr cor,opt S solo (easy) oct
　　AUGSBURG 1648 $.40　(L570)
　　unis treb cor&SATB (easy) oct AUGSBURG 1648
　　$.40　(L571)

　With A Jubilant Song　*anthem
　　SATB,pno,org,2trp,opt timp (med) oct
　　AUGSBURG 1621 $.70　(L572)

LEAN ON HIS ARMS see Jones

LEANING ON THE EVERLASTING ARMS see Showalter

LEAVE-TAKING, THE see Thompson, Randall

LEAVE US NOT, NEITHER FORSAKE US see Stainer,
　John

LEAZER
Christ Is Born Today *Xmas
mix cor SOUTHERN $.25   (L573)

LEAZER, CARL W.
Christ Is Born Today *see Hodie Christus
Natus Est

Hodie Christus Natus Est *Xmas
"Christ Is Born Today" SATB,kbd (med easy)
oct CONCORDIA 98-1757 $.25   (L574)

LEBE WOHL, DU MUDES JAHR see Dolf, Th.

LEBEN WIR, SO LEBEN WIR DEM HERRN see Brunner,
Adolf

LEBEN WIR, SO LEBEN WIR DEM HERRN see
Micheelsen, Hans Friedrich

LECHNER, K.
Lass Alles, Was Du Hast
mix cor,inst sc HANSSLER 7.145 s.p., ipa
(L575)

LECHNER, KONRAD (1911-   )
Psalmenkantate *cant/Psalm
mix cor,T solo,2pno,perc sc GERIG 574 s.p.
(L576)

LECHNER, LEONHARD (ca. 1550-1606)
Allein Zu Dir, Herr Jesu Christ
(Schabasser, Josef) mix cor,acap oct
DOBLINGER s.p. see also CHRISTUS, DER
HERR   (L577)

Benedicamus Patrem *Gen
[Lat] SATB,acap (med) BAREN. BA 3259 $.55
(L578)
Christ, Der Du Bist Der Helle Tag *Gen,mot
(Lipphardt, Walther) [Ger] SATB,acap (med
easy) BAREN. BA 486 $1.75   (L579)
Danket Dem Herrn *Gen/Thanks
SATB,acap voc pt DOBLINGER s.p. see also
LOB UND DANK   (L580)
Das Hohelied Salomonis *Gen
(Lipphardt, Walther) [Ger] SATB,acap (med
easy) BAREN. BA 253 s.p.   (L581)
Deutsche Spruche Von Leben Und Tod *ECY
(Lipphardt, Walther) [Ger] SATB,acap (med)
BAREN. BA 255 $2.75   (L582)
Domine, Dominus Noster *Mass
[Lat] SSATTB,acap BAREN. BA 2926 $3.00
(L583)
Johannes-Passion *Psntd
(Ameln, Konrad) [Ger] SATB,acap (med)
BAREN. BA 2968 sc $8.25, cor pts $2.75
(L584)
Lasst Uns Loben Den Treuen Gott *Gen
[Ger] SATB,acap (med) MULLER K 32 s.p.
(L585)
Magnificat Primi Toni *Magnif
[Ger] mix cor,acap BAREN. BA 2924 $1.25
(L586)
Magnificat Quinti Toni *Magnif
[Ger] mix cor,acap BAREN. BA 3780 $.40
(L587)
Motectae Sacrae, Quatuor, Quinque Et Sex
Vocum 1575 *CCU,Gen
(Finscher, Ludwig) [Ger] 4-6pt mix cor,acap
(med) BAREN. BA 2931 $16.50   (L588)
Newe Teutsche Lieder 1577 *CC16U,Gen,mot
(Martin, Uwe) [Ger] 4pt mix cor,acap
cor,acap (med) BAREN. BA 2933 $9.75 (L589)
Non E Lasso Martire *Mass
[It] SATTB,acap BAREN. BA 4381 $3.00 (L590)
Non Fu Mai Cervo *Mass
[It] SATTT,acap BAREN. BA 2927 $4.50 (L591)
Nun Schein, Du Glanz Der Herrlichkeit *Gen
[Ger] 5pt mix cor,acap (med) BAREN. BA 3014
s.p.   (L592)
O Welt, Ich Muss Dich Lassen
see Lechner, Leonhard, O Welt, Sieh Hier
Dein Leben

O Welt, Sieh Hier Dein Leben *Easter/Holywk/
Psntd
SAT/SAB HANSSLER 6.265 s.p. contains also:
Lechner, Leonhard, O Welt, Ich Muss Dich
Lassen (SAT/SAB); Staden, Johann, O Du
Lamm Gottes, Jesu Christ, "Fahr Hin, Du
Liebste Seele Mein" (SSAT/SSAB);
Praetorius, Michael, Erstanden Ist Der
Heilig Christ (SAT/SAB)   (L593)
Oh, May God Bless Thee
mix cor SOUTHERN $.30   (L594)
Sacred Concerto
[Ger/Eng] SATB,T solo,org,vcl sc PETERS
5879 $5.00, voc sc PETERS 5879A $.30
(L595)
Sanctissimae Virginis Mariae Canticum 1578
*CC8U,BVM,Magnif
(Lipphardt, Walther) [Ger] SATB,acap (med)
BAREN. BA 2934 $9.75   (L596)
Vom Himmel Durch Die Wolken Ein Neues Jahr
Herdringet *Xmas
[Ger] SAATB,acap (med easy) BAREN. BCH 170
s.p.   (L597)

LECHO DODI see Berlinski, [Herman]

LED BY THE MASTER'S HAND see Lister, Mosie

LED MIG I DIN SANNING see Erlandson, Ake

LEDDY
Cold, Cold Day
(Wilson) SATB oct AGAPE CF 106 $.30 (L598)

Worthy Is The Lamb
(Wilson) SATB oct AGAPE CF 104 $.25 (L599)

LEDGER, PHILIP
I Will Lift Up Mine Eyes *Gen
SATB,acap (med) oct OXFORD 43.368 $.25
(L600)

LEE
Battle Hymn Of The Republic
SATB KJOS LC7 $.30   (L601)

Days Of My Youth, The *sec
(Simeone) SATB SHAWNEE A 950 $.35   (L602)

Huron Indian Carol *Xmas,carol
unis oct SACRED S-8627 $.35   (L603)

Let Us Adore For All Eternity
see THREE MOTETS IN HONOR OF THE BLESSED
SACRAMENT

O Be Joyful In The Lord S-95
SATB oct SACRED $.35   (L604)

Psalm 116
see THREE MOTETS IN HONOR OF THE BLESSED
SACRAMENT

LEE, ALEXANDER
He Wipes The Tear From Every Eye
2pt ASHDOWN E.A.237 s.p.   (L605)

LEE, DOROTHY
Christmas Carol, A *Xmas,carol
2pt PROWSE s.p.   (L606)

LEE, E. MARKHAM
Jubilate
3pt ASHDOWN V.T.15 s.p.   (L607)

King Of Glory
SATB,acap LEONARD-ENG s.p.   (L608)

LEE, J.
Behold, A Simple Tender Babe *Xmas,anthem
SATB (easy) oct GIA G1643 $.30   (L609)
2 eq voices (easy) oct GIA G1644 $.25
(L610)
Choral Mass *Gen,Mass,Contemp
SA/TB (easy) cor pts GIA G1765 $1.00 (L611)
SATB (easy) voc sc GIA G1596 $1.00 (L612)
Christ Became Obedient For Us Unto Death
*Lent,anthem
SATB (med easy) oct GIA G1554 $.25 (L613)
Christ-Child Lay On Mary's Lap, The *Xmas,
anthem
SATB (easy) oct GIA G1497 $.30   (L614)
SA/TB (easy) oct GIA G1498 $.25   (L615)
Community Mass *Gen,Mass,Contemp
unis,opt kbd (easy) voc sc GIA G1648 $1.25
(L616)
Congregational Mass *Gen,Mass,Contemp
unis,opt kbd (easy) voc sc GIA G1552 $1.25
(L617)
Creed *Gen,Mass
SATB/unis (easy) voc sc GIA G1637 $.25
(L618)
Festival Mass *Fest/Gen,Mass
SA/TB (easy) voc sc GIA G1760 $1.00 (L619)
SATB,org (easy) sc GIA G1759 $1.00 (L620)
Gloria (from Communiy Mass) Gen,Mass,Contemp
SATB (easy) voc sc GIA G1650 $.35   (L621)
2pt (easy) cor pts GIA G1649 $.30   (L622)
Mary's Lullaby *Xmas,anthem
SATB (easy) oct GIA G1501 $.25   (L623)
2 eq voices (easy) oct GIA G1667 $.25
(L624)
Misa Popular *Gen,Mass
[Span] unis,kbd (easy) voc sc GIA G1569
$1.25   (L625)
Short Mass *Adv/Gen/Lent,Mass
SATB,org (easy) voc sc GIA G1747 $.50 (L626)
This Is The Day The Lord Has Made *Easter,
anthem
SATB (med easy) oct GIA G1612 $.35 (L627)
2 eq voices (easy) oct GIA G1613 $.35
(L628)
Yours Are The Heavens *Xmas,anthem
SATB (easy) oct GIA G1362 $.25   (L629)

LEE, T. CHARLES
Face Of Moses Shone
SATB oct GRAY GCMR 2092 $.30   (L630)

Psalm 3
SATB oct GRAY GCMR 2454 $.35   (L631)

LEECH, LIDA [SHIVERS] (1873-1962)
Alleluia! *see Hawkins, Floyd W.

King And Saviour *see Hawkins, Floyd W.

LEEF, HARRY GRANVILLE
Psalm 1
SATB,pno/org oct LAWSON 51240 $.30 (L632)

LEER MIJ, O HEER
(Vaal, O. De) mix cor sc ALSBACH&D GEZ.34
s.p.   (L633)

LEEUW, TON DE (1926-   )
Psalm 118
[Dut] mix cor,2trom DONEMUS min sc s.p.,
cor pts s.p., ipa   (L634)

LEFEBURE, JEAN
Benedicta Sit Sancta Trinitas *cant
SATB&SATB,4trp,4trom MOSELER sc s.p., cor
pts s.p., ipa   (L635)

LEFEBURE-WELY, LOUIS JAMES ALFRED (1817-1869)
Ave Maria
[Lat] unis HEUGEL s.p. see from SAINTE-
CECILE   (L636)

O Salutaris
[Lat] unis HEUGEL s.p. see from CHANTS
RELIGIEUX   (L637)
[Lat] BB HEUGEL s.p. see from LA MAITRISE
(L638)

Tantum Ergo
[Lat] unis HEUGEL s.p. see from SAINTE-
CECILE   (L639)

LEFEBVRE
At His Cradle *Xmas
TTBB oct GALAXY 1.1109.1 $.25   (L640)

LEFEBVRE (cont'd.)

God Rest You Merry Gentlemen *Xmas
TTBB,acap oct COLOMBO 681 $.40   (L641)
SATB oct COLOMBO 682 $.35   (L642)

Twelve Days Of Christmas *Xmas
TTBB oct GALAXY 1.1843.1 $.30   (L643)

LE FLEMING
I Sing Of A Maiden
SATB OXFORD   (L644)

LE FLEMING, CHRISTOPHER (KAYE) (1908-   )
Children's Te Deum, A
unis jr cor CRAMER 252 s.p.   (L645)

Five Psalms *see I Will Lift Up Mine Eyes
(Psalm 121); Lord Is My Shepherd, The
(Psalm 23); O Praise God In His Holiness
(Psalm 150)   (L646)

Five Psalms
CHESTER s.p.
contains: I Will Lift Up Mine Eyes (Psalm
121) (SATB,orch); Lord Is My Shepherd,
The (Psalm 23) (unis,orch); O Praise
God In His Holiness (Psalm 150) (SATB,S
solo,orch); They That Go Down To The
Sea In Ships (Psalm 107) (SATB,S solo,
orch); When I Was In Trouble (Psalm
120) (SATB,orch)   (L647)

God Be In My Head *hymn
SATB CHESTER s.p.   (L648)

I Love All Beauteous Things
cor&desc CRAMER 197 ipr   (L649)

I Will Lift Up Mine Eyes (Psalm 121) Bibl
see Five Psalms
SATB,pno CHESTER s.p. see from Five Psalms
(L650)

Lighten Our Darkness
[Eng] SA,pno/org CHESTER s.p.   (L651)
[Eng] TB,pno/org CHESTER s.p.   (L652)

Lord Is My Shepherd, The (Psalm 23)
see Five Psalms
[Eng] unis,pno CHESTER s.p. see from Five
Psalms   (L653)

O Be Joyful
SA CRAMER 318 ipr   (L654)

O Praise God In His Holiness (Psalm 150) Bibl
see Five Psalms
(Davies, L.H.) SATB,S solo,org CHESTER s.p.
see from Five Psalms   (L655)

Prevent Us, O Lord *carol
unis CRAMER 39 s.p.   (L656)

Psalm 23 *see Lord Is My Shepherd, The

Psalm 107 *see They That Go Down To The Sea
In Ships

Psalm 120 *see When I Was In Trouble

Psalm 121 *see I Will Lift Up Mine Eyes

Psalm 150 *see O Praise God In His Holiness

Sing, Happy Child *Xmas
SATB,Mez solo,acap CRAMER s.p.   (L657)

Te Deum *Te Deum
SATB (C maj) oct NOVELLO 44.1384.09 s.p.
(L658)

Te Deum And Benedictus *Te Deum
SATB (C maj) oct NOVELLO 44.1384.09 s.p.
(L659)

They That Go Down To The Sea In Ships (Psalm
107)
see Five Psalms

When I Was In Trouble (Psalm 120)
see Five Psalms

LEGEND see Tchaikovsky, Piotr Ilyitch

LEGEND, A see Tchaikovsky, Piotr Ilyitch

LEGEND (CHRIST IN HIS GARDEN) see Tchaikovsky,
Piotr Ilyitch

LEGEND OF THE ARI, THE see Binder, Abraham
Wolfe

LEGEND OF THE BELLS see Rhodes

LEGEND OF THE DOGWOOD TREE see Marryott, Ralph
E.

LEGEND OF THE LILIES see Lipscomb

LEGEND OF THE MADONNA see Grant, Louise

LEGEND OF THE STORK, THE see Ahrold, Frank

LEGENDARY CHRISTMAS CAROLS *CCU,Xmas,carol
SATB/unis LORENZ 9012 $.30   (L660)

LEGENDE see Tchaikovsky, Piotr Ilyitch

LEGLER, ROBERT C.
Christ The Lord Is Risen Today *Easter
unis,opt brass,strings oct AGAPE F 918 $.35
(L661)

LEHENBAUER, RUTH B.
I Seek Thy Peace
SATB PIONEER 1011 $.40   (L662)

My Cup Of Joy
SSA PIONEER 1008 $.40   (L663)

Rain
SSA PIONEER 1014 $.40   (L664)

LEHMAN, EVANGELINE
Christmas *see Noel

Love Of God, The
(Lundberg) SATB oct LILLENAS AN-2209 $.25
(L665)

Noel *Xmas,cant
"Christmas" [Eng/Fr] mix cor,STBar soli,
org/pno voc sc SCHIRM.G $1.00   (L666)

LEHMAN, SIEGFRIED
Advents-Musik *Adv
[Ger] mix cor,fl,ob,vln,vla,vcl voc sc
SIRIUS 10 s.p., cor pts SIRIUS s.p., ipa
contains: Der Herr Ist Nahe; Ein Segen
Hat Ergossen Sich; Gott Sei Dank Durch
Alle Welt; Nun Jauchzet, All Ihr
Frommen   (L667)

Das Grosse Leid
see Vier Geistliche Lieder

Der Herr Ist Nahe
see Advents-Musik

Ein Leises, Zartes Singen *Xmas
[Ger] mix cor (easy) oct SIRIUS 6 s.p.
                                     (L668)

Ein Segen Hat Ergossen Sich
see Advents-Musik

Glockenstunde
see Vier Geistliche Lieder

Gott Sei Dank Durch Alle Welt
see Advents-Musik

I'm Just A Poor Wayfaring Stranger *spir
[Eng] mix cor (easy) oct SIRIUS 23 s.p.
                                     (L669)

I'm So Glad *spir
[Eng] mix cor (easy) oct SIRIUS 22 s.p.
                                     (L670)

Nie Zu Stillen Ist Die Sehnsucht
see Vier Geistliche Lieder

Nun Jauchzet, All Ihr Frommen
see Advents-Musik

Vier Geistliche Lieder
[Ger] mix cor (easy) oct SIRIUS 21 s.p.
contains: Das Grosse Leid; Glockenstunde;
Nie Zu Stillen Ist Die Sehnsucht; Was
Jesus Ist   (L671)

Was Jesus Ist
see Vier Geistliche Lieder

LEHMANN, ANDREAS (1930-   )
Draussen Vor Der Kirchentur *Gen
[Ger] SSATB,acap (med) BOSSE BE 605 s.p.
                                     (L672)

Herr, Gib Uns Frieden *Gen
[Ger] SATB,acap (med) BOSSE BE 602 s.p.
                                     (L673)

Ich Rede, Wenn Ich Schweigen Sollte *Gen
[Ger] SSATB,kbd,bvl,perc (med) BOSSE BE 243
s.p.   (L674)

Jesus Will Keine Schonen Worte *Gen
[Ger] SSATB,acap (med) BOSSE BE 603 s.p.
                                     (L675)

LEHMEIER, J.F.
Christmas Time Is Here *Xmas
SATB LEONARD-US 08009600 $.25   (L676)
SSA LEONARD-US 08009280 $.25   (L677)

Come Follow The Star *Xmas
SATB LEONARD-US 08010160 $.30   (L678)

His Love Is Born Anew (composed with Charlap)
*Xmas
SATB LEONARD-US 08023720 $.30   (L679)

Honor Him, Alleluia
SATB LEONARD-US 08026240 $.30   (L680)
SSA LEONARD-US 08025920 $.25   (L681)
SAB LEONARD-US 08025600 $.25   (L682)

O Give Thanks
SATB LEONARD-US 08046560 $.25   (L683)

Peace On Earth *Xmas
SATB&SSA LEONARD-US 08051040 $.30 (L684)

Praise Ye The Lord
SATB LEONARD-US 08052480 $.25   (L685)

LEHNER, F.X.
Aus Harten Weh' Die Menscheit Klagt *Adv
[Ger] mix cor,acap KRENN 713 s.p.   (L686)

Bayerische Madrigale *sac/sec,Ger
men cor (med) cor pts LEUCKART 4A s.p.
contains: Beim Heiligen Sankt Leonhard;
Derr Herr Veterinadoktor; Wann Ih
Wieder Auf'n Tanzboden Geh; Was Ih Mir
Heut Fruh Beim Abwasch'n Denkt Hab
                                     (L687)

Beim Heiligen Sankt Leonhard
see Bayerische Madrigale

Derr Herr Veterinadoktor
see Bayerische Madrigale

Es Kommt Ein Schiff Geladen *Adv
[Ger] mix cor,acap KRENN 716 s.p.   (L688)

Freut Euch Im Herrn Denn Er Ist Nah'! *Adv
[Ger] mix cor,acap KRENN 715 s.p.   (L689)

Gott Heil'ger Schopfer Aller Stern *Adv
[Ger] mix cor,acap KRENN 714 s.p.   (L690)

Maria Durch Ein'm Dornwald Ging *Adv
[Ger] mix cor,acap KRENN 718 s.p.   (L691)

Maria Sei Gegrusset *Adv
[Ger] mix cor,acap KRENN 717 s.p.   (L692)

Wann Ih Wieder Auf'n Tanzboden Geh
see Bayerische Madrigale

Was Ih Mir Heut Fruh Beim Abwasch'n Denkt Hab
see Bayerische Madrigale

LEHNER, WALTER
Deutsche Messe *Mass
mix cor,org DOBLINGER voc sc s.p., cor pts
s.p.   (L693)
mix cor,org DOBLINGER voc sc s.p., voc pt
s.p.   (L694)

Erfreut Euch, Ihr Menschen, Auf Erden
mix cor,acap DOBLINGER s.p.   (L695)

In Uns Wird Licht
mix cor,acap oct DOBLINGER s.p.   (L696)

LEHNER, WALTER (cont'd.)
Schau, Schau, Wie Sie Rennen
mix cor,acap oct DOBLINGER s.p.   (L697)

Still, O Erden, Still, O Himmel
mix cor,acap oct DOBLINGER s.p.   (L698)

Und Fried' Den Menschen Auf Der Erd *CC6U,
Xmas
wom cor,2vln&vcl/winds cor pts DOBLINGER
s.p.   (L699)

LEHR, M.
Poem And Alleluia For The Christ Child
SATB oct KERBY 5806 $.35   (L700)
SATB,acap oct KERBY 5806C $.35   (L701)

LEHR MICH see Mohring, John

LEHR, MICHAEL
Mass Of Saints And Sinners *Commun,Mass
cong,org,gtr voc sc WEINBERGER s.p. (L702)

LEHRE UNS BEDENKEN, DASS WIR STERBEN MUSSEN see
Schein, Johann Hermann

LEI PASTOUREU see Saboly, Nicholas

LEIB NACHTIGALL see Krause, Chr.

LEICHTE CHORSATZE see Palestrina, Giovanni

LEICHTE CHORSATZE see Palestrina, Giovanni

LEICHTE LIEDKANTATEN see Spitta, Heinrich

LEICHTE WEIHNACHTSKANTATEN see Spitta, Heinrich

LEICHTGESINNTE FLATTERGEISTER see Bach, Johann
Sebastian

LEICHTLING, ALAN
Motet *mot
mix cor,acap sc SEESAW $5.00   (L703)

Sacred Service Shabbat Shalom
SATB,B solo,org sc SEESAW $20.00   (L704)

LEID DES EINSIEDELS *mot
(Burkhart, Franz) mix cor,acap DOBLINGER s.p.
see also In Seiner Handen   (L705)

LEID, VRIEND'LIJK LICHT see Dykes, John Bacchus

LEIDENSGESCHICHTE see Quack, Erhard

LEIDENSVERKUNDIGUNG UND HEILUNG EINES BLINDEN
see Reda, Siegfried

LEIDZEN
Doxology
SATB,opt band oct MCA   (L706)

LEIGHTON
Nativitie *Xmas
SATB oct FISCHER,C CM-7734 $.40   (L707)

Teares Or Lamentations Of A Sorrowful Soul,
The *CCU,Eng
cor STAINER 3.8211.8 $22.00   (L708)

LEIGHTON, E.I.
Art Thou Weary
SATBB,SAB soli,org (easy) oct WILLIS 1073
$.12   (L709)

I Heard The Voice Of Jesus Say
SATBB,A/B solo,org (easy) oct WILLIS 2628
$.15   (L710)

LEIGHTON FORD CRUSADE CHOIR BOOK *CC26U
(Chambers, Irv) SATB voc sc WORD 37512 $1.95
                                     (L711)

LEIGHTON, KENNETH (1929-   )
Alleluia, Amen *anthem
mix cor,Bar solo oct NOVELLO 28.1416.01
s.p.   (L712)

Communion Service In D *Agnus/Bene/Credo/
Gloria/Kyrie/Sanctus
unis&opt SATB (easy) oct OXFORD 40.105
$1.00   (L713)

Crucifixus Pro Nobis *Op.28, cant
SATB,S/T solo,org voc sc NOVELLO s.p., ipr
                                     (L714)

Drop, Drop, Slow Tears *anthem
mix cor,acap oct NOVELLO 50.0340.07 s.p.
                                     (L715)

Easter Sequence *Easter
SS voc sc OXFORD 46.157 $3.30   (L716)

Give Me The Wings Of Faith *anthem
mix cor,SBar soli oct NOVELLO 28.1422.06
s.p.   (L717)

Jubilate *Jubil
unis/SATB/unis&SATB oct NOVELLO 86.0007.04
s.p.   (L718)
unis,org s.p., ipa voc sc NOVELLO
86.0007.04, cor pts NOVELLO 86.2007.05
                                     (L719)
unis oct NOVELLO 86.2007.05 s.p. (L720)

Let All The World In Every Corner Sing
*anthem
mix cor oct NOVELLO 28.1458.07 s.p. (L721)

Lift Up Your Heads, O Ye Gates *anthem
mix cor,acap oct NOVELLO 28.1463.03 s.p.
                                     (L722)

Light Invisible, The *Op.16
SATB,T solo,3fl,2ob,2clar,3bsn,4horn,3trp,
3trom,strings,2perc,timp,harp voc sc
NOVELLO s.p., ipr   (L723)

Magnificat And Nunc Dimittis *Magnif/Nunc
SATB oct NOVELLO 44.1383.00 s.p. (L724)

Missa Brevis *Mass
SATB oct NOVELLO 86.0002.03 s.p. (L725)

Missa Sancti Thomae *Mass
SATB oct NOVELLO 02.0038.07 s.p. (L726)

O Be Joyful In The Lord *Gen/Thanks
SATB (med) oct OXFORD 42.324 $.50 (L727)

LEIGHTON, KENNETH (cont'd.)
O God, Enfold Me In The Sun
SATB (med) oct OXFORD   (L728)

O How Amiable *see Quam Dilecta!

Preces And Responses
SATB oct NOVELLO 44.1415.02 s.p. (L729)

Quam Dilecta! *anthem/mot
"O How Amiable" [Eng/Lat] mix cor,S solo,
acap oct NOVELLO 28.1471.04 s.p. (L730)

Te Deum *Te Deum
unis/SATB/unis&SATB oct NOVELLO 86.0006.06
s.p.   (L731)
unis oct NOVELLO 86.2006.07 s.p. (L732)

Te Deum Laudamus *Te Deum
unis,org s.p. voc sc NOVELLO 86.0006.06,
cor pts NOVELLO 86.2006.07   (L733)

Venite *Venite
unis,org s.p., ipa voc sc NOVELLO
86.0005.08, cor pts NOVELLO 86.2005.09
                                     (L734)
unis/SATB/unis&SATB oct NOVELLO 86.0005.08
s.p.   (L735)
unis oct NOVELLO 86.2005.09 s.p. (L736)

LEISER WIRD NICHTS VERKUNDIGT see Woll, Erna

LEISRING
Let All The Nations Praise The Lord
(Hoggard) 8pt mix cor,acap SHAWNEE A 94
$.30   (L737)
(Row) SSA oct FISCHER,C R-283 $.25 (L738)

Ye Sons And Daughters Of The King *Easter
(Davis, K.K.) SATB WARNER WB-103 $.30
                                     (L739)
(Dietterich, Philip R.) SAB/SATB (med)
ABINGDON APM-614 $.18   (L740)

LEISRING, VOLKMAR (1588-1637)
Let All Ye Sons And Daughters Sing *see O
Filii Et Filiae

Lift Up Your Heads, Ye Mighty Gates *Adv/Gen
(Lundquist) SSABarTTBB (diff) oct WILLIS
5753 $.12   (L741)

O Filii Et Filiae *Easter/Lent,Lat
[Lat] SATB&TTBB,acap oct SCHIRM.G 6395 $.25
                                     (L742)
anti cor,acap SCHIRM.EC 41 $.35   (L743)
"Ye Sons And Daughters Of The King" SATB&
TTBB,acap SCHIRM.EC 379 $.30   (L744)
"Ye Sons And Daughters Of The King" anti
cor,acap SCHIRM.EC 2272 $.25   (L745)
(Burnsworth, C.) "Ye Sons And Daughters Of
The King" [Lat/Eng] SSAA&SSAA,acap
SCHIRM.EC 2579   (L746)
(Greyson) "Let All Ye Sons And Daughters
Sing" SSA oct BOURNE ES19 $.30   (L747)

Ye Sons And Daughters Of The King *see O
Filii Et Filiae

LEIST, WARREN C.
O Little One Sweet *Xmas
4pt mix cor,Bar solo,acap oct SCHIRM.G
10848 $.25   (L748)

LE JEUNE, CLAUDE (1528-1600)
Ainsi Qu'on Oit Le Cerf Bruire (Psalm 42)
(Expert) [Fr] SATB,acap oct SALABERT-US
$.65   (L749)

Benediction Avant La Repas
(Harris) "Dear God, O Bless Us" [Eng/Fr]
SATB,acap oct SCHIRM.G 8879 $.25 (L750)

Dear God, O Bless Us *see Benediction Avant
La Repas

Errette, Herr, Mich Von Den Bosen
SATB LAUDINELLA LR 15 s.p. contains also:
Ihr Knechte Gottes Allzugleich (SATB);
Nun Freuet Euch In Gott, Ihr Frommen
(SATB&SSATB,4inst)   (L751)

Gott Seines Herzens Grund Aufschloss
see Koch, Heinz, Wie Soll Ich Dich
Empfangen

Helas, Mon Dieu *anthem
mix cor oct OXFORD 84.202 $.75   (L752)

Helas, Seigneur! (Psalm 69)
(Expert) [Fr] SSATB,acap oct SALABERT-US $.65
                                     (L753)

Herr, Erhore Meine Klagen
SATB/SATBB LAUDINELLA LR 90 s.p. contains
also: Ich Gedenke Alter Zeiten (SATB);
Jachzt, Alle Lande, Nah Und Fern (SATBB);
Wie Lieblich Ist Das Haus De Herrn (L754)

Ich Gedenke Alter Zeiten
see Le Jeune, Claude, Herr, Erhore Meine
Klagen

Ihr Knechte Gottes Allzugleich
see Le Jeune, Claude, Errette, Herr, Mich
Von Den Bosen

Jachzt, Alle Lande, Nah Und Fern
see Le Jeune, Claude, Herr, Erhore Meine
Klagen

Lammers, Deuxieme Recueil *see Psalm 51;
Psalm 70   (L755)

Les Cieux En Chacun Lieu (Psalm 19)
(Expert) [Fr] SATB,acap oct SALABERT-US
$.65   (L756)

Missa Ad Placitum *Mass,15th cent
[Lat] 5pt,acap HEUGEL s.p. see from LE
PUPITRE   (L757)

Nun Freuet Euch In Gott, Ihr Frommen
see Le Jeune, Claude, Errette, Herr, Mich
Von Den Bosen

O Seigneur, J'Espars (Psalm 88)
(Expert) [Fr] SATB,acap oct SALABERT-US
$.65   (L758)

LE JEUNE, CLAUDE (cont'd.)

Psalm 9 *see With My Whole Heart

Psalm 15 *see Qui Pourra, Seigneur, En Bonne Pais

Psalm 19 *see Les Cieux En Chacun Lieu

Psalm 42 *see Ainsi Qu'on Oit Le Cerf Bruire

Psalm 51
(Marot, Clement) [Lat] 3pt mix cor,acap
LEMOINE s.p. see from Lammers, Deuxieme
Recueil   (L759)

Psalm 69 *see Helas, Seigneur!

Psalm 70
(Beze, Theodore De) [Lat] 3pt mix cor,acap
LEMOINE s.p. see from Lammers, Deuxieme
Recueil   (L760)

Psalm 88 *see O Seigneur, J'Espars

Psalm 95
see Three-Part Psalms

Psalm 109
see Three-Part Psalms

Psalm 134
see Three-Part Psalms

Qui Pourra, Seigneur, En Bonne Pais (Psalm 15)
(Expert) [Fr] ATBB oct SALABERT-US $.65
(L761)

Three-Part Psalms
(David, H.) SAB,acap oct PRESSER 352-00056
$.40
contains: Psalm 95; Psalm 109; Psalm 134
(L762)

Two Sacred Settings *CC2U
(Kaplan, A.) [Fr/Eng] SATB BROUDE,A. 139
$.30   (L763)

What Is Man
SATB oct STAFF 541 $.25   (L764)

Wie Lieblich Ist Das Haus De Herrn
see Le Jeune, Claude, Herr, Erhore Meine
Klagen

With My Whole Heart (Psalm 9)
(Couper, A.) SATB,acap oct PRESSER
352-00445 $.30   (L765)

LEKBERG
Lord, Thou Hast Been Our Dwelling Place
SATB KJOS 5174 $.30   (L766)

LEKBERG, SVEN (1899-   )
Blessed Is The Man
SATB oct GALAXY 1.2255.1 $.30   (L767)

Bow My Head, O Lord
mix cor,acap oct SCHIRM.G 11499 $.25 (L768)

Earth So Lovely
see Four Carols For A Holy Night

For As The Rain Cometh Down *Bibl
4pt mix cor,acap oct SCHIRM.G 11509 $.30
(L769)

Four Carols For A Holy Night *Xmas
4pt mix cor,acap oct SCHIRM.G 11646 $.40
contains: Earth So Lovely; Little Boy
Jesus, The; Sing Noel; These Are The
Blossoms   (L770)

Give Ear To My Prayer
SATB oct GALAXY 1.2258.1 $.35   (L771)

Gladly For Aye We Adore Him
SATB STANDARD A28MX1 $.60   (L772)

Glory Be To The Father
4pt mix cor,acap oct SCHIRM.G 11561 $.30
(L773)

God With Me Lying Down
4pt mix cor,acap oct SCHIRM.G 11401 $.25
(L774)

Hail The Day That Sees Him Rise *Easter
SATB oct GALAXY 1.2390.1 $.40   (L775)

Have Mercy Upon Us *Bibl
4pt mix cor,acap oct SCHIRM.G 11582 $.30
(L776)

He Is Risen *Easter
SATB oct SOUTHERN $.35   (L777)
SATB oct GALAXY 1.2406.1 $.35   (L778)

I Will Lift Up Mine Eyes
SATB oct GALAXY 1.2259.1 $.35   (L779)

In The Beauty Of Holiness
SATB oct GALAXY 1.2360.1 $.35   (L780)

It Is A Good To Give Thanks *Bibl
4pt mix cor,acap oct SCHIRM.G 11562 $.30
(L781)

Lamp Unto My Feet
SATB oct GALAXY 1.2359.1 $.40   (L782)

Let All The World In Every Corner Sing
4pt mix cor,acap oct SCHIRM.G 11616 $.30
(L783)
4pt wom cor,acap oct SCHIRM.G 11843 $.30
(L784)

Little Boy Jesus, The
see Four Carols For A Holy Night

Lord Is My Shepherd
SATB oct GALAXY 1.2257.1 $.35   (L785)

Lord Of The Earth And Sky *cant
4pt mix cor,SBar/SA soli,pno voc sc
SCHIRM.G $1.25   (L786)

Make A Joyful Noise Unto The Lord
SATB oct GALAXY 1.1873.1 $.35   (L787)

My Heart Is Ready, O God
SATB oct GALAXY 1.2074.1 $.35   (L788)

O God, Thou Art My God
SATB KJOS 5192 $.30   (L789)

LEKBERG, SVEN (cont'd.)

O Wonder Of This Christmas Night
4pt mix cor,acap oct SCHIRM.G 11190 $.30
(L790)

Praise Ye
SATB oct GALAXY 1.2254.1 $.30   (L791)

Praise Ye The Lord
SATB oct GALAXY 1.2261.1 $.35   (L792)

Sing Noel
see Four Carols For A Holy Night

These Are The Blossoms
see Four Carols For A Holy Night

Thou Art All My Treasure Thou
SATB oct GALAXY 1.2093.1 $.35   (L793)

Truth Of The Lord Endureth Forever, The
4pt mix cor,acap oct SCHIRM.G 11874 $.30
(L794)

Walk In The Light
4pt mix cor,acap oct SCHIRM.G 11518 $.25
(L795)

With My Whole Heart I Have Sought Thee
SATB oct GALAXY 1.2256.1 $.25   (L796)

LE LACHUER
Babe In A Manger
(Lashmar) SATB oct MCA   (L797)

LELAND, H.
Christ Our Saviour Is Born *Xmas
SATB,acap oct PRESSER MC344 $.35   (L798)

LEMACHER, HEINRICH (1891-1966)
Gottes Ist Der Orient
mix cor,acap TONGER s.p.   (L799)

Hodie Christus Natus Est *Xmas
[Lat] SATB,acap (med easy) MULLER MS 47
s.p.   (L800)

LE MAISTRE, MATTHEUS (ca. 1505-1577)
Die Furcht Des Herren, Glaube Mir *mot
(Poos) SATB HANSSLER 1.471 s.p.   (L801)

Die Furcht Des Herren *mot
(Poos) SATB HANSSLER 1.466 s.p.   (L802)

Dies Sind Die Heil'gen 10 Gebot *Bibl/mot
(Poos) SATB HANSSLER 1.463 s.p.   (L803)

Lord Jesus Christ, The Son Of God *Gen
SATB,kbd (med easy) oct CONCORDIA 98-2108
$.25   (L804)

Nun Lasst Uns Gott Dem Herren *Trin
[Ger] 3pt mix cor/4pt mix cor,acap (med
easy) BAREN. BA 3053 s.p.   (L805)

O Du Var Jesus Krist
mix cor NORDISKA 4903 s.p.   (L806)

LEND THINE EAR TO MY PRAYER see Arkhangelsky

LENDVAI, ERWIN (1882-1949)
Jehova, Deinem Namen
men cor,acap TONGER s.p.   (L807)

LENEL
Christ Is Now Ris'n Again *Easter
boy cor SOUTHERN $.25   (L808)

LENEL, LUDWIG
All Praise To God, Who Reigns Above *Gen
SA/TB,kbd (easy) oct CONCORDIA 98-1142 $.25
(L809)

All Praise To Thee, Eternal God *Xmas
unis,kbd (easy) oct CONCORDIA 98-1402 $.25
(L810)

Arise And Be Not Afraid *Epiph/Trin
SATB/SSAA/TTBB,kbd (med easy) oct CONCORDIA
98-1504 $.30   (L811)

Awake, Thou Spirit Of The Watchmen *Gen
SAB,acap (easy) oct CONCORDIA 98-1724 $.25
(L812)

Christ Is Arisen *Easter
SATB,kbd (diff) oct CONCORDIA 98-1572 $.40
(L813)

Christ Is Now Risen Again *Easter
TTBB,trp (med easy) oct CONCORDIA 98-1648 $.25
(L814)

Come, Holy Ghost, God And Lord *Ded/Gen/Pent
SATB,acap (med easy) oct CONCORDIA 98-1041
$.30   (L815)
SAB,acap (med easy) oct CONCORDIA 98-1386
$.25   (L816)

Come, Ye Faithful, Raise The Strain *Easter
SAB,kbd (med easy) oct CONCORDIA 98-1384
$.25   (L817)

Dear Christians, One And All, Rejoice
*Commun/Gen/Refm
SAB,kbd (med diff, or New Year) oct
CONCORDIA 98-1818 $.25   (L818)

From Depths Of Woe I Cry To Thee
SATB,acap oct PRESSER 312-40180 $.35 (L819)

King Shall Come When Morning Dawns, The
*Adv/Gen
SA,kbd (med easy) oct CONCORDIA 98-1831
$.25   (L820)

Lord Of Lyfe
mix cor,Bar/T/S solo,harp/pno CONCORDIA
97-4782 $1.80
contains: Mary, Mother, Come And See;
Most Glorious Lord Of Life; Veni
Creator Spirítus; When Christ Was Born
(L821)

Lord, This Day Thy Children Meet *Gen
SA,kbd (easy) oct CONCORDIA 98-1403 $.20
(L822)

Loving Shepherd Of The Sheep *Gen
SA,kbd (easy) oct CONCORDIA 98-1404 $.25
(L823)

Mary, Mother, Come And See
see Lord Of Lyfe

Most Glorious Lord Of Life
see Lord Of Lyfe

LENEL, LUDWIG (cont'd.)

Now Blessed Be Thou, Christ Jesu *Xmas
SATB,kbd (diff) oct CONCORDIA 98-1571 $.40
(L824)

O Morning Star, So Pure, So Bright *Adv/
Epiph/Gen
unis,kbd (med easy) oct CONCORDIA 98-1452
$.25   (L825)

Oh, Come, Oh, Come, Emmanuel *Adv
SAB,kbd (easy) oct CONCORDIA 98-2022 $.25
(L826)

Rejoice In The Lord
SATB oct PRESSER 312-40693 $.45   (L827)

Sing Praise, Part I *CC13L
SAB CONCORDIA 97-7565 $1.50   (L828)

Sing Praise, Part II *CC13L
SAB CONCORDIA 97-7567 $1.50   (L829)

Veni Creator Spiritus
see Lord Of Lyfe

Wake, Awake, For Night Is Flying *Adv/ECY/
Gen
unis,kbd (med easy) oct CONCORDIA 98-1453
$.30   (L830)

We Now Implore God The Holy Ghost *Gen/Pent
SATB,kbd (diff) oct CONCORDIA 98-1573 $.40
(L831)

When Christ Was Born
see Lord Of Lyfe

When I Survey The Wondrous Cross *Lent
SAB,kbd (med easy) oct CONCORDIA 98-1385
$.25   (L832)

With High Delight *Easter/Gen
SA/TB,kbd (med easy) oct CONCORDIA 98-1830
$.25   (L833)

LENEPVEU, [CHARLES (FERDINAND)] (1840-1910)
O Salutaris Hostia
[Lat] unis,org,vcl LEMOINE s.p.   (L834)

L'ENFANCE DU CHRIST see Berlioz, Hector

L'ENFANT A L'ETOILE see Becaud

LENG
Deum Laudamus *Xmas
"We Praise God" SATB,narrator oct FOX PS76
$.30   (L835)

We Praise God *see Deum Laudamus

LENN, JAY
Morning Prayer *Morn,prayer
SATB WEINBERGER s.p.   (L836)

LENT see Krenek, Ernst

LENT AND EASTER, SERIES 1 see Grime, William

LENT AND EASTER, SERIES 2 see Grime

LENTE see Herwaarden, J.G.

LENTE see Lambrechts-Vos, A.

LENTE see Linden, N. v.d.

LENTE see Olman, Isr, J.

LENTE see Rennes, Cath. v.

LENTE see Rheenen, H. v.

LENTE see Tierie, J.F.

LENTE BOODSCHAP see Gade, Niels [W.]

LENTE EN PAASCHLIED see Tierie, J.F.

LENTE-GEBOORT' see Bonset, Jac.

LENTE IN 'T LAND see Herwaarden, J.G.

LENTEAVOND see Posthuma, D.

LENTEBLOEMEN see Vliegh, C.C.A. de

LENTEKONIGIN see Vaal, O. de

LENTELICHT see Kenswill, A.

LENTELICHT see Olman, Isr, J.

LENTELIED see Cluwen, P.

LENTELIED see Herwaarden, J.G.

LENTELIED see Vaal, O. de

LENTELIEDJE see Dyserinck, A.

LENTELIEDJE see Senecaut, Th. J.L.

LENTEN ANTHEM see McCormick

LENTEN CANTATA see Handel, George Frideric

LENTEN CAROL, A see Purvis, Richard

LENTEN DEVOTION see Hamill

LENTEN MEDITATION see Pasquet, Jean

LENTEN MEDITATION see Williams

LENTEN MOTET, A see Purvis, Richard

LENTE'S INTOCHT see Herwaarden, J.G.

LENTESPROOKJE see Wettig Weissenborn, E.

LEO, LEONARDO (1694-1744)
In Monte Oliveti *Lent
"On The Mount Of Olives" SATB,kbd (med
easy) oct CONCORDIA 98-1652 $.30   (L837)

La Morte Di Abel *Gen,ora
[It] SATB,SSATB soli,orch voc sc CARLTON
CM 21445 s.p., ipr   (L838)

LEO, LEONARDO (cont'd.)

(Piccioli, G.) mix cor,SSATB soli,org,hpsd,
2ob,2horn,strings CARISH rental   (L839)

Mass In F   *Mass
(Aslanian, Vahe) [Lat] mix cor,soli LAWSON
$2.50   (L840)

Misere Mei, Deus (Psalm 50)
(Backers) [Lat] SATB&SATB,pno/org voc sc
PETERS HU1684 $2.00   (L841)
(Ewerhart) [Lat] SATB&SATB,pno/org voc sc
PETERS WM64 $4.00   (L842)

Miserere Mei, Deus (Psalm 50) Gen
(Ewerhart, Rudolf) [Lat] SATB&SATB,cont
(med) MULLER SM 1294 s.p.   (L843)

On The Mount Of Olives *see In Monte Oliveti

Psalm 50 *see Miserere Mei, Deus

Tenebrae *Psntd
SATB (med easy) oct OXFORD 46.137 $1.00 (L844)

LEONARD
Prayer For Peace
[Eng/Fr] SSA,org/pno BOSTON 13299 $.30   (L845)

Thanks Be To Thee *Thanks
unis oct VOLKWEIN VB263 $.30   (L846)

LEONARD, CLAIR
If I Speak With The Tongues Of Men
SATB,acap SEESAW $2.00   (L847)

Te Deum *Te Deum
SATB,org SEESAW $2.00   (L848)

LEONARD, HARRY
Power And The Glory, The *anthem
mix cor,orch oct NOVELLO s.p., ipr   (L849)

LEONARD, S.W.
Lo, The Morning Breaks *Easter
(Brandon) 3pt mix cor,org oct LAWSON 51422
$.30   (L850)

LEONARD, W.
Mass In F
[Lat] unis&opt ATB PRESSER $.80   (L851)

LEONCINI, LORENZO
Ave Maria
see CINQUE AVE MARIA

Ave Verum *Commun
[Lat] unis ZANIBON 2777 s.p.   (L852)

Cor Arca
see CINQUE MOTTETTI

Magnificat *Magnif
[Lat] 2 eq voices,org ZANIBON 2696 s.p. (L853)

O Salutaris
see SEI MOTTETTI EUCARISTICI

Tota Pulchra
see CINQUE MOTECTA IN HON. B.V.M.

LEONI
God Of Abraham Praise, The
(Ohl) SATB oct PLYMOUTH FO-110 $.25 (L854)

LEONI, LEONARDO
Brillo Una Luce *Xmas
3pt mix cor,pno ZANIBON 3886 s.p.   (L855)

Tu Sei Sacerdote
[It] 4pt mix cor sc ZANIBON 4892 s.p., cor
pts ZANIBON 4893 s.p.   (L856)

LEONTOVICH, M.
Carol Of The Bells *Xmas
(Wilhousky) 3pt jr cor/SSA (easy) FISCHER,C
CM 5276 $.25   (L857)
(Wilhousky) 3pt jr cor/SAB (easy) FISCHER,C
CM 4747 $.25   (L858)

Ukrainian Bell Carol *Xmas
SATB oct LORENZ 9782 $.30   (L859)
unis oct LORENZ 8604 $.30   (L860)

Ukranian Bell Carol *Xmas,carol,Russ
(Ehret) SSA,acap oct PRO ART 1592 $.30
                                         (L861)
(Ehret) 2pt oct PRO ART 1676 $.30   (L862)
(Ehret) TTBB oct PRO ART 2207 $.30   (L863)
(Ehret) SATB oct PRO ART 1535 $.25   (L864)
(Ehret) SAB,acap oct PRO ART 1590 $.30
                                         (L865)

LEOPOLD I, (KAISER) (1640-1705)
Jesus Tot
(Hunter) unis,orch MARKS 4433 $.25, ipr
                                         (L866)

Missa Pro Defunctis *Mass/Req
(Kramer, G.) 5pt mix cor,soli,org,orch
DOBLINGER sc s.p., cor pts s.p., ipa
                                         (L867)

LEOPOLITA, MARCIN
Missa Paschalis *Pol
(Feicht, H.) 5pt mix cor POLSKIE WDMP35
s.p.   (L868)

LEPKE, C.
Call To Remembrance
SATB oct PRESSER MC516 $.30   (L869)

LEROY KYRIE see Taverner, John

LERPERGER, KURT
Commune Doctorum
4pt mix cor,acap DOBLINGER sc s.p., cor pts
s.p.   (L870)

Sequentia Pro Festo Sancti Augustini
4pt mix cor,acap DOBLINGER sc s.p., cor pts
s.p.   (L871)

LES ANGES DANS LE CIEL see De Angels In De
Heab'n

LES ANGES DANS NOS CAMPAGNES *Xmas,anthem/
carol,Fr
"Angels We Have Heard On High" see Many Moods
Of Christmas, The, Suite Three
"Angels We Have Heard On High" see Three

Christmas Carols
"Angels We Have Heard On High" see Three
Songs For Christmas
"Angels O'er The Fields Were Flying" SATB,
acap SCHIRM.EC 1635 $.25   (L872)
"Angels We Have Heard On High" SATB ALLANS
237 s.p.   (L873)
(Bisbee, B.W.) "Angels We Have Heard On
High" SA,fl,2vln/2clar (easy) oct CONCORDIA
98-1838 $.25   (L874)
(Christiansen, Paul) "Angels We Have Heard On
High" SATB&treb cor (med) oct AUGSBURG 1145
$.25   (L875)
(Christiansen, Paul) "Angels We Have Heard On
High" treb cor&SATB (med) oct AUGSBURG 1145
$.25   (L876)
(Davison, A.) "Angels O'er The Fields" SSA,
acap SCHIRM.EC 844 $.25   (L877)
(Davison, A.) "Angels O'er The Fields" SA,
org/pno SCHIRM.EC 1029 $.22   (L878)
(Davison, A.) "Angels O'er The Fields" SA,pno
SCHIRM.EC 1549 $.25   (L879)
(Davison, A.) "Angels O'er The Fields" TTBB,
acap SCHIRM.EC 926 $.25   (L880)
(Dickinson, C.) "Angels O'er The Fields"
SSAATTBB oct GRAY GSC 129 $.30   (L881)
(Hood) "Angels We Have Heard On High" TTBB
SCHMITT 411 $.30   (L882)
(McKelvy, J.) "Angels We Have Heard On High"
SATB,acap FOSTER MF 503 $.25   (L883)
(Shaw; Parker) "Angels We Have Heard On High"
5pt mix cor,acap oct LAWSON 718 $.30   (L884)
(Stone) "Angels We Have Heard On High" SATB
oct PRO ART 1406 $.30   (L885)
(Stone) "Angels We Have Heard On High" SAB
oct PRO ART 1705 $.30   (L886)
(Stone) "Angels We Have Heard On High" SSA
oct PRO ART 1635 $.30   (L887)
(Stone) "Angels We Have Heard On High" 2pt
oct PRO ART 1783 $.30   (L888)
(Stone) "Angels We Have Heard On High" TTB
oct PRO ART 1925 $.25   (L889)
(Track) "Angels We Have Heard On High" TTBB,
acap,opt pno oct PRO ART 2490 $.30   (L890)
(Vance) "Angels We Have Heard On High" SA/TB
oct BELWIN 2021 $.30   (L891)
(Wagner) "Angels We Have Heard On High" SATB,
acap oct LAWSON 664 $.25   (L892)
(Wasner) "Angels We Have Heard On High" [Eng]
mix cor,acap oct SCHIRM.G 8564 $.25   (L893)

LES ANGES DANS NOS CAMPAGNES see Anonymous

LES ANGES DANS NOS CAMPAGNES see Maillard-
Verger, P.

LES ANGES DANS NOS CAMPAGNES see Roques, L.

LES BERGERETTES *Xmas,carol,17th cent
(Du Bois, L.) [Fr] 4pt mix cor,acap (med
easy) cor pts LEMOINE s.p. see from
Collection De Choeurs, dixieme Fascicule
                                         (L894)

LES CHANTS DU SANCTUAIRE see Yung, Alf.

LES CIEUX EN CHACUN LIEU see Le Jeune, Claude

LES CIEUX SONT TEMOINS see Haydn, (Franz)
Joseph

LES ENFANTS DE DIEU ONT DES AILES see All Gods
Chillun Got Wings

LES FETES CHRETIENNES see Lacome, Paul

LES FEUX DE LA SAINT JEAN see Chaminade, Cecile

LES GAUDE see Brydaine

LES HUMBLES see Chaminade, Cecile

LES LAMENTATIONS DE JOB see Lassus, Roland de
(Orlandus)

LES MOISSONNEURS see Franck, Cesar

LES MYSTERES DU CHRIST: HYMNE SYMPHONIQUE see
Hemel, Oscar van

LES NATIONS SONT DANS TON HERITAGE (Psalm 73)
16th cent
(Geveart, F.-A.) [Fr] 4pt mix cor,acap (med
easy) cor pts LEMOINE s.p. see from
Collection De Choeurs, septieme Fascicule
                                         (L895)

LES NATIVITES see Migot

LES PASTOUREAUX see Saboly, Nicholas, Lei
Pastoureu

LES PASTOUREAUX see Tomasi

LES PASTOUREAUX ONT FAIT UNE ASSEMBLEE *Xmas,
carol,Fr
(Tomasi) [Fr] 2pt/3pt,pno/orch LEDUC s.p. see
also Douze Noels De Saboly   (L896)

LES PECHEURS see Chaminade, Cecile

LES PECHEURS DE SAINT JEAN see Widor, Charles-
Marie

LES PETITS ENFANTS see Chaminade, Cecile

LES PLUS SAGES *Xmas,carol,Fr
(Tomasi) [Fr] 2pt/3pt,pno/orch LEDUC s.p. see
also Douze Noels De Saboly   (L897)

LES PRELUDES see Liszt, Franz

LES RAMEAUX see Faure

LES RAMEAUX see Faure, Jean-Baptist

LES ROIS see Lacome, Paul

LES ROIS MAGES (NOUS SOMMES TROIS SOUVERAINS)
*Xmas
(Geveart, F.-A.) [Fr] 4pt mix cor,acap (med
easy) cor pts LEMOINE s.p. see from
Collection De Choeurs, deuxieme Fascicule
                                         (L898)

LES SAINTES-MARIE DE LA MER see Paladilhe,
[Emile]

LES SAINTS INNOCENTS see Lacome, Paul

LES SEPT DERNIERES PAROLES DU CHRIST see
Depelsenaire, J.M.

LES SEPT PAROLES DU CHRIST see Dubois, Theodore

LES VOISINS *Xmas,carol,18th cent
(Geveart, F.-A.) [Fr] 4pt mix cor,acap (med
easy) cor pts LEMOINE s.p. see from
Collection De Choeurs, septieme Fascicule
                                         (L899)

LES VOIX DE JEANNE D'ARC OU AVE MARIA see
Gounod, Charles Francois

L'ESCARPOLETTE see Danhieux, G.

LESCUREL, JEHAN (? -ca. 1303)
Collected Works *CCU
(Wilkins, Nigel E.) cor AM.INST.MUS. $12.50
                                         (L900)

LESLIE, C.E.
Temperance Anthem *anthem
SATB,kbd FOSTER MF136 $.40   (L901)

LESLIE, H.T.
Lord Is My Shepherd
cor oct HART s.p.   (L902)

L'ESODO DI MOSE DALL'EGITTO see De Grandis,
Vincenzo

L'ESPRIT SOUTIENT see Bach, Johann Sebastian

LESSON FOR LENT see Ringwald, [Roy]

LESTER
Easter Hymn *Easter,hymn
SATB FLAMMER A 5183 $.30   (L903)
SA/TB FLAMMER E5078 $.30   (L904)
SAB FLAMMER D5043 $.30   (L905)

L'ESTRANGE DELUGE see Hughes

LE SUEUR, [JEAN FRANCOIS] (1760-1837)
Adam
(Vecchi, Prof. Giuseppe) cor quarto FORNI
267 s.p.   (L906)

Oratorio De Noel *Xmas,ora
(Vecchi, Prof. Giuseppe) cor quarto FORNI
268 s.p.   (L907)

LESUR, DANIEL (1908-   )
Annonciation
SATB,narrator,T solo,orch/pno voc sc
TRANSAT. $4.80   (L908)
wom cor&men cor cor pts TRANSAT. $1.00
                                         (L909)

Messe Du Jubile *Mass
cor,org RICORDI-FR R2039 s.p.   (L910)

LET ALL GIVE THANKS TO GOD see Rolle, Nun
Danket Alle Gott

LET ALL MEN REJOICE see Brandon

LET ALL MEN SING GOD'S PRAISES
see Three Old Bohemian Christmas Carols

LET ALL MORTAL FLESH *anthem/folk,Fr
(Christiansen, F.M.; Christiansen, Paul) SATB
(med) oct AUGSBURG 1161 $.25   (L911)

LET ALL MORTAL FLESH see Darst, W. Glenn

LET ALL MORTAL FLESH KEE SILENCE see Mechem,
Kirke

LET ALL MORTAL FLESH KEEP SILENCE *hymn,Fr
cor oct ST.MARTIN SMP6411 s.p.   (L912)
(Diggle) 4pt mix cor,org oct SCHIRM.G 10005
$.25   (L913)
(Grieb) 4pt mix cor,org/pno oct SCHIRM.G
10516 $.35   (L914)
(Keese) SATB oct VOLKWEIN VB205 $.25   (L915)
(Vance, Margaret) SATB oct BELWIN 2209 $.30
                                         (L916)

LET ALL MORTAL FLESH KEEP SILENCE see Butcher,
F.

LET ALL MORTAL FLESH KEEP SILENCE see Butler

LET ALL MORTAL FLESH KEEP SILENCE see Cashmore,
Donald

LET ALL MORTAL FLESH KEEP SILENCE see Couper

LET ALL MORTAL FLESH KEEP SILENCE see Denton

LET ALL MORTAL FLESH KEEP SILENCE see Diggle,
[Roland]

LET ALL MORTAL FLESH KEEP SILENCE see Holst,
Gustav

LET ALL MORTAL FLESH KEEP SILENCE see Sateren,
Leland Bernhard

LET ALL MORTAL FLESH KEEP SILENCE see Somary,
J.

LET ALL MORTAL FLESH KEEP SILENCE see Track,
Gerhard

LET ALL MORTAL FLESH KEEP SILENCE see Willan,
Healey

LET ALL MORTAL FLESH KEEP SILENT
(Howorth) SATB oct BELWIN 2087 $.25   (L917)

LET ALL NATIONS PRAISE THE LORD see Bock

LET ALL ON EARTH see Dosonge, R.

LET ALL ON EARTH THEIR VOICES RAISE see Ford,
Virgil T.

LET ALL ON EARTH THEIR VOICES RAISE see
Robinson, Christopher

LET ALL PEOPLE PRAISE THEE *Bibl
(Brandon) SATB,org oct LAWSON 51583 $.35
                                         (L918)

LET ALL PEOPLE PRAISE THEE see Glarum, L.
Stanley

LET ALL PRAISE THEE see Cafarella

LET ALL REJOICE AT CHRISTMAS TIME see Ehret, Walter

LET ALL REJOICE THIS HOLY NIGHT see Klein

LET ALL THAT ARE TO MIRTH INCLINED see Schalk

LET ALL THAT ARE TO MIRTH INCLINED see Schalk, Carl

LET ALL THAT PUT THEIR TRUST IN THEE see Graun, Karl Heinrich

LET ALL THE EARTH REJOICE see Harris

LET ALL THE EARTH SING PRAISE see Warren, David

LET ALL THE MULTITUDES OF LIGHT see Bach, Johann Sebastian

LET ALL THE NATIONS PRAISE THE LORD see Leisring

LET ALL THE NATIONS SHOUT AND SING see Lyte

LET ALL THE PEOPLE PRAISE GOD see Kirk

LET ALL THE PEOPLE PRAISE THEE see Powell, Robert J.

LET ALL THE PEOPLE PRAISE THEE see Whitman, Morris

LET ALL THE PEOPLE PRAISE THEE, O GOD see Shaw, Martin

LET ALL THE PEOPLES PRAISE THE LORD see Dressler, Gallus

LET ALL THE SAINTS see Roff, Joseph

LET ALL THE WORLD *hymn
     cor oct ST.MARTIN SMP647 s.p.   (L919)

LET ALL THE WORLD see Baker, Robert

LET ALL THE WORLD see Bishop, F.G.

LET ALL THE WORLD see Glandfield, John R.

LET ALL THE WORLD see Harris

LET ALL THE WORLD see Illing

LET ALL THE WORLD see Shaw, Geoffrey [Turton]

LET ALL THE WORLD see Williams, David H.

LET ALL THE WORLD IN EVERY CORNER SING
     (Vaughn Williams, Ralph) unis,acap GALAXY
     s.p.   (L920)

LET ALL THE WORLD IN EVERY CORNER SING see Gilbert, Norman

LET ALL THE WORLD IN EVERY CORNER SING see Lang, C.S.

LET ALL THE WORLD IN EVERY CORNER SING see Leighton, Kenneth

LET ALL THE WORLD IN EVERY CORNER SING see Lekberg, Sven

LET ALL THE WORLD IN EVERY CORNER SING see McAfee, Don

LET ALL THE WORLD IN EVERY CORNER SING see Reed

LET ALL THE WORLD IN EVERY CORNER SING see Roberton, Hugh S.

LET ALL THE WORLD IN EVERY CORNER SING see Rowley, Alec

LET ALL THE WORLD IN EVERY CORNER SING see Shaw, Geoffrey [Turton]

LET ALL THE WORLD IN EVERY CORNER SING see Spedding, Frank

LET ALL THE WORLD IN EVERY CORNER SING see Thiman, Eric Harding

LET ALL THE WORLD IN EVERY CORNER SING see Whitehead, Alfred

LET ALL THE WORLD IN EVERY CORNER SING see Willan, Healey

LET ALL THE WORLD IN EVERY CORNER SING see Young, Carlton R.

LET ALL THE WORLD IN EV'RY CORNER SING see Austin

LET ALL THE WORLD IN EV'RY CORNER SING see Whinfield

LET ALL THE WORLD NOW HAIL OUR LORD see Warland, Dale

LET ALL THINGS NOW LIVING *Welsh
     (Glaser, V.) SAB,pno SCHIRM.EC 2476   (L921)

LET ALL TOGETHER PRAISE OUR GOD see Williams, David H.

LET ALL YE SONS AND DAUGHTERS SING see Leisring, Volkmar, O Filii Et Filiae

LET CAROLS RING *Xmas,Swed
     (Black, Charles) SATB oct GRAY GCMR 1524 $.30
                                            (L922)

LET CHILDREN SING see Licht

LET CHRISTIANS ALL WITH JOYFUL MIRTH *carol
     SATB (very easy) OXFORD 08.020 $.15   (L923)

LET CHRISTIANS ALL WITH ONE ACCORD *carol
     SATB (very easy) OXFORD 08.046 $.10   (L924)

LET CHRISTMAS ALL see Hull, Molly

LET EARTH RECEIVE HER KING see Wilson

LET EARTH REJOICE see Ford, Virgil T.

LET EARTH REJOICE see Hughes, H.

LET EARTH REJOICE see Newbury, Kent A.

LET EVERY VOICE RAISE see Steffens, Lasst Uns Zusammen

LET EVERY VOICE SING PRAISES
     see Belgian Christmas Songs, Set 1

LET FAIR PEACE BLESS THE WORLD see Lassus, Roland de (Orlandus)

LET GOD ARISE see Gore, Richard T.

LET GOD ARISE see Handel, George Frideric

LET GOD ARISE see Higdon, George

LET GOD ARISE see Wills, Arthur

LET GOD ARISE see Young

LET GOD BE PRAISED WITH SINGING see Gumpeltzhaimer, A.

LET GOD LEAD THE WAY see Norden, Hugo

LET GOD PLAN FOR YOU see Russel, Eleanor

LET GOD RULE THE WORLD
     SATB 0015792-358 $.40   (L925)

LET GOD'S CHILDREN COME HOME see Irving

LET GOD'S CHILDREN SING *CCU,spir
     (Mother Mary Oswin, S.H.C.J.) jr cor,gtr
     cloth LITURGICAL $1.75   (L926)

LET HEARTS AWAKE AND SING see Young, C.

LET HEARTS AWAKEN see Clokey, Joseph Waddell

LET HEAVEN AND EARTH EXULT see Pasquet, Jean

LET HEAVEN REJOICE AND SING *Xmas,carol,Ger
     (Ehret) SAB,opt clar oct FOX CC7 $.25 (L927)
     (Ehret, W.) SAB,opt fl PROWSE CC7 s.p. (L928)

LET HER OWN WORKS PRAISE HER see Ellsworth, A. Eugene

LET HIM WHO WOULD NOT see Steffens, Wer Leben Will

LET HIS NAME BE SUNG see Murray, Lyn

LET JESUS FILL YOUR HEART see Moore

LET JOY RESOUND see Ray, Don [Brandon]

LET JOY YOUR CAROLS FILL
     (Russell) SSAA,acap (easy) OXFORD 83.050 $.20
                                            (L929)

LET JUSTICE REIGN see Handel, George Frideric

LET LOVE BE GENUINE see Prentice, Fred

LET MAN EXULT WITH HEART AND VOICE see Beethoven, Ludwig van

LET ME BE WITH THEE see Roff, Joseph

LET ME BRING LOVE see Greene, P.

LET ME, GUIDE ME
     SSA/SATB BIG3 $.40   (L930)

LET ME THIS DAY
     SSA/SA BIG3 $.25   (L931)

LET ME TOUCH HIM see Ellis

LET MINE EYES RUN DOWN WITH TEARS see Purcell, Henry

LET MOUNT ZION REJOICE see Herbert

LET MUSIC BREAK ON THIS BLEST MORN see Moschetti, [Giuseppe]

LET MUSIC LIVE see Rhea, Raymond

LET MY COMPLAINT COME BEFORE THEE see Batten, Adrian

LET MY CRY COME BEFORE THEE see Newbury, Kent A.

LET MY HEART FIND PEACE see Riley

LET MY MOUTH BE FILLED see Pasquet, Jean

LET MY PEOPLE GO *spir
     (Gray) SATB oct STAFF 326 $.25   (L932)
     (Roberts) SATB,acap,opt perc oct LAWSON 51556
     $.30   (L933)

LET MY PEOPLE GO see Nelhybel, Vaclav

LET MY PRAYER COME LIKE INCENSE see Binkerd, [Gordon]

LET MY PRAYER COME LIKE INCENSE see Kreutz, Robert E.

LET MY PRAYER COME UP see Blow, John

LET MY PRAYER COME UP see Purcell, Henry

LET MY PRAYER COME UP INTO THY PRESENCE see Purcell, Henry

LET MY SOUL RISE IN SONG see Rhea

LET NOT YOUR HEART BE TROUBLED see Brahms, Johannes, Lass Dich Nur Nichts Nicht Dauren

LET NOT YOUR HEART BE TROUBLED see Brubeck

LET NOT YOUR HEART BE TROUBLED see Carrington, O.M.

LET NOT YOUR HEART BE TROUBLED see Clark, Henry A.

LET NOT YOUR HEART BE TROUBLED see Dickey, Mark

LET NOT YOUR HEART BE TROUBLED see Hadley

LET NOT YOUR HEART BE TROUBLED see Lamb

LET NOT YOUR HEART BE TROUBLED see Mueller, Carl F.

LET NOT YOUR HEART BE TROUBLED see Richolson

LET NOT YOUR HEART BE TROUBLED see Speaks, [Oley]

LET NOT YOUR HEART BE TROUBLED see Wilson, Harry [Robert]

LET NOT YOUR HEART BE TROUBLED see Wolff, S. Drummond

LET NOT YOUR HEARTS BE TROUBLED see Harter, [Harry]

LET NOTHING DISTURB THEE see Freestone

LET NOTHING DISTURB THEE see Lockwood, Normand

LET NOTHING DISTURB THEE see Takacs, Jeno

LET NOTHING EVER GRIEVE THEE see Brahms, Johannes, Lass Dich Nur Nichts Dauren

LET NOTHING EVER GRIEVE THEE see Brahms, Johannes, Lass Dich Nur Nichts Nicht Dauren

LET NOW EVERY TONGUE ADORE THEE see Bach, Johann Sebastian

LET OUR GLADNESS HAVE NO END see Reske

LET OUR GLADNESS KNOW NO END *Xmas/Epiph,
     anthem/carol/folk,Boh/Czech
     (Ehret) SA MARKS 4066 $.30   (L934)
     (Ehret) SATB MARKS 4103 $.25   (L935)
     (Ehret) SATB MARKS 4103 $.25   (L936)
     (Gray) SATB,acap oct PRO ART 1288 $.20 (L937)
     (Harris) SSA oct BELWIN 64283 $.30   (L938)
     (Pooler, Marie) SA (easy) oct AUGSBURG 1442
     $.25   (L939)
     (Schroeder, H.) SATB,inst (med easy) oct
     CONCORDIA 98-2060 $.25   (L940)

LET OUR GLADNESS KNOW NO END see Van Dyke

LET OUR HEARTS BE JOYFUL see Mendelssohn-Bartholdy, Felix

LET OUR JOYS BE KNOWN see Cram

LET PEACE FILL MY HEART see Townsend, John

LET PRAISE DEVOTE THY WORK see Peach

LET SAINTS ON EARTH see Powell, Robert J.

LET SAINTS ON EARTH see Thiman, Eric Harding

LET SONGS OF JOY ARISE see Findlay, George

LET SONGS OF REJOICING BE RAISED see Bach, Johann Sebastian, Man Singet Mit Freuden

LET THE BRIGHT SERAPHIM see Handel, George Frideric

LET THE CAROLS RING
     SATB BIG3 $.30   (L941)

LET THE CHILDREN SING see Bristol, Lee H., Jr.

LET THE CHURCH ROLL ON
     see Street Corner Spirituals

LET THE CHURCH ROLL ON see Wild, Eric

LET THE DAY PERISH see Boyd, Jack

LET THE EARTH BE GLAD see Jessop, Chas.

LET THE EARTH NOW PRAISE THE LORD see Bunjes, Paul G.

LET THE EARTH NOW PRAISE THE LORD see Wienhorst, Richard

LET THE EARTH RESOUND WITH PRAISE see Gallus, Jacobus, Resonet In Laudibus

LET THE EARTH SING see Mozart, Wolfgang Amadeus, Jubilate Deo

LET THE HEAVENS BE GLAD see Roff, Joseph

LET THE HEAVENS REJOICE see Daniels

LET THE HEAVENS REJOICE see Goodman, Joseph

LET THE LIGHT OF THY COUNTENANCE see Roff, Joseph

LET THE LOWER LIGHTS BE BURNING
     (Parker) TTBB,pno/gtr oct LAWSON 51293 $.30
                                            (L942)

LET THE LOWER LIGHTS BE BURNING see Bliss, Paul

LET THE MERRY BELLS RING OUT see Clough-Leighter, Henry

LET THE MERRY CHURCH BELLS RING see Garlick, Anthony

LET THE MOUNTAINS SHOUT FOR JOY see Stephens, Evan

LET THE PEOPLE GIVE THANKS see Schutz, Heinrich

LET THE PEOPLE PRAISE THEE see Crowe

LET THE PEOPLE PRAISE THEE see Harwood, Basil

LET THE PEOPLE PRAISE THEE see McAfee

LET THE PEOPLE PRAISE THEE see Monhardt

LET THE PEOPLE PRAISE THEE see Monhardt, Maurice

LET THE PEOPLE PRAISE THEE see Williams

LET THE PEOPLE PRAISE THEE see Wright, B.

LET THE PEOPLE PRAISE THEE, O GOD see Hammerschmidt, Andreas

LET THE PEOPLE SING PRAISE see McLin

LET THE PEOPLE SOUND HIS PRAISE see Handel, George Frideric

LET THE RAFTERS RING see Smith, Don

LET THE SAVIOR IN *Dut
  unis oct LORENZ 8852 $.30   (L943)

LET THE SHRILL TRUMPET'S WARLIKE VOICE see Swan

LET THE SONG BE BEGUN see Malin, Piae Cantiones

LET THE SONG GO ROUND THE EARTH see Stock

LET THE SOUND RING see Delmonte

LET THE TRUMPET SOUND see Daniels, M.L.

LET THE VOICE OF PRAISE RESOUND see Gallus, Jacobus

LET THE WHOLE CREATION CRY see Leaf

LET THE WHOLE CREATION CRY see Leaf, Robert

LET THE WHOLE CREATION CRY see Wood, Dale

LET THE WHOLE CREATION CRY see Young, Phillip

LET THE WORD GO FORTH see Goldman, Maurice

LET THE WORD GO FORTH see Uhl

LET THE WORD OF CHRIST see Newbury

LET THE WORD OF CHRIST see Newbury, Kent A.

LET THEIR CELESTIAL CONCERTS ALL UNITE see Handel, George Frideric

LET THEM EVER SING FOR JOY see Newbury, Kent A.

LET THEM GIVE THANKS see Williamson, Malcolm

LET THEM PRAISE THE NAME OF THE LORD see Hovhaness, Alan

LET THEM SHOUT FOR JOY see Glarum, L. Stanley

LET THEM THAT SAY THEY LOVE THE LORD see Ouchterlony, David

LET THEM TRUST IN THEE see Roff, Joseph

LET THERE BE JOY see Bissell, Keith

LET THERE BE LIGHT see Bitgood, Roberta

LET THERE BE LIGHT see Bornschein, [Franz Carl]

LET THERE BE LIGHT see Joubert, John

LET THERE BE LIGHT, O LORD see Frank, Marcel [Gustave]

LET THERE BE SONG see Wilson, Harry [Robert]

LET THIS MIND BE IN YOU see Beach, Amy Marcy Cheney

LET THIS MIND BE IN YOU see Hoiby, Lee

LET THIS MIND BE IN YOU see Holman, Derek

LET THIS MIND BE IN YOU see Lovelace, Austin C.

LET THIS MIND BE IN YOU see Mueller, Carl F.

LET THIS MIND BE IN YOU see Wills, Arthur

LET THY BLESSED SPIRIT see Tschesnokoff, P.I.

LET THY BLOOD IN MERCY POURED see Rickard

LET THY HAND BE STRENGTHENED see Blow, John

LET THY HAND BE STRENGTHENED see Handel, George Frideric

LET THY HAND BE STRENGTHENED see Handel, George Frideric, Kroningshymne (Loft Din Arm Den Sejrende)

LET THY HOLY PRESENCE see Tchesnokov, Pavel Grigorievitch

LET THY HOLY PRESENCE see Tschesnokoff, P.I.

LET THY HOLY SPIRIT COME UPON US see Tschesnokoff, P.I.

LET THY LOVE FLOW DOWN see Powell

LET THY LOVINGKINDNESS BE UPON US see Sateren, Leland Bernhard

LET THY MANTLE FALL ON ME see Hawkins, Floyd W.

LET THY MERCIFUL EARS see Bird, R.

LET THY MERCIFUL EARS see Mudd, Thomas

LET THY MERCIFUL EARS see Powell, Robert J.

LET THY MERCIFUL EARS, LORD see Weelkes

LET THY MERCIFUL EARS, O LORD see Mudd, Thomas

LET THY MERCIFUL EARS, O LORD see Weelkes, Thomas

LET THY MERCIFUL EARS, O LORD, BE OPEN see Davis, Katherine K.

LET THY MERCY BE UPON US see Copley

LET THY MERCY, O LORD see Schirrmann

LET THY MERCY, O LORD, BE UPON US see Roff, Joseph

LET THY SOUL BE FULL OF EXCEEDING GLADNESS see Swan

LET THY WORK APPEAR see Nelson, Ronald A.

LET TRUE LOVE BE AMONG US see Bergsma, William Laurence

LET US ADORE FOR ALL ETERNITY see Lee

LET US ADORE JESUS see Santa Cruz, Domingo, Adoremos A Jesus

LET US ALL WITH GLADSOME VOICE see Markworth, Henry

LET US ALL WITH GLADSOME VOICE see Track, Gerhard

LET US ALL WITH VOICES SING see Veitch, William

LET US BOW BEFORE THEE see Gasparini, Quirino, Adoramus Te

LET US BREAK BREAD TOGETHER *Commun/Gen,
  anthem/spir
  SATB oct LORENZ B106 $.30   (L944)
  SATB oct STAFF 359 $.30   (L945)
  (Beck, John Ness) SSA oct AGAPE A 460 $.30
                                                (L946)
  (Beck, John Ness) SATB oct AGAPE A 447 $.30
                                                (L947)
  (Bell) SSAA oct BELWIN 60538 $.25   (L948)
  (Bell) SATB,acap oct BELWIN 60033 $.30   (L949)
  (Boatner) SATB oct COLOMBO 2224 $.25   (L950)
  (Charles, G.) SSA LEONARD-US 08036920 $.25
                                                (L951)
  (Darrell, Peter) SATB oct AGAPE A 389 $.30
                                                (L952)
  (Goemanne, N) SATB,org/vcl&ob (easy) oct GIA
    G1732 $.40   (L953)
  (Haskell) SATB oct LORENZ C104 $.30   (L954)
  (Heath) 4pt men cor,acap oct SCHIRM.G 10607
    $.25   (L955)
  (Higgins) SATB oct LILLENAS AN-3834 $.30
                                                (L956)
  (Howorth, Wayne) SA/TB oct BELWIN 1604 $.30
                                                (L957)
  (Howorth, Wayne) SSA oct BELWIN 1229 $.30
                                                (L958)
  (Howorth, Wayne) SAB oct BELWIN 1461 $.25
                                                (L959)
  (Howorth, Wayne) SATB oct BELWIN 1034 $.30
                                                (L960)
  (Kirk) SATB SCHMITT 1756 $.35   (L961)
  (Lawrence) SATB oct SUMMY M 1522 $.35   (L962)
  (Page, Robert) SSA STANDARD A7F1 $.40   (L963)
  (Ryder, Noah F.) SSA oct FISCHER,J 9065 $.30
                                                (L964)
  (Ryder, Noah F.) SAB oct FISCHER,J 9557 $.30
                                                (L965)
  (Ryder, Noah F.) SATB oct FISCHER,J 8117 $.30
                                                (L966)
  (Ryder, Noah F.) TTBB oct FISCHER,J 8514 $.30
                                                (L967)
  (Sateren, Leland) SATB (easy) oct AUGSBURG
    1143 $.25   (L968)
  (Scherer, George) SSAATTBB oct AGAPE JW 7773
    $.30   (L969)
  (Terri) SATB,low solo,acap oct LAWSON 896
    $.30   (L970)
  (Wilson) TTBB oct BOOSEY 5499 $.30   (L971)
  (Wilson; Ehret) SAB oct BOOSEY 5008 $.30
                                                (L972)
  (Wilson; Ehret) SA oct BOOSEY 5588 $.30
                                                (L973)

LET US BREAK BREAD TOGETHER see Cain, Noble

LET US BREAK BREAD TOGETHER see Cooper

LET US BREAK BREAD TOGETHER see Goemanne, Noel

LET US BREAK BREAD TOGETHER see Montague

LET US BREAK BREAD TOGETHER see Myers, G.

LET US BREAK BREAD TOGETHER see Ringwald, [Roy]

LET US BREAK BREAD TOGETHER see Schroth

LET US CELEBRATE GOD'S NAME see Bruckner, Anton

LET US CHEER THE WEARY TRAVELER *spir
  (Kinsman) SATB oct SPRATT 131 $.25   (L974)

LET US CHEER THE WEARY TRAVELER see Dett, Robert Nathaniel

LET US CLAP OUR HANDS see Gomolka, Mikolaj

LET US DECLARE THE GLORY OF THE LORD, OUR GOD
  see Schutz, Heinrich, Lasset Uns Doch Den Herren, Unsern Gott, Loben

LET US ENTER THE HOUSE OF THE LORD see Hughes, H.

LET US EVER WALK WITH JESUS see Boltze

LET US GO FORTH see Danburg

LET US GO INTO THE HOUSE see Berger

LET US GO INTO THE HOUSE OF THE LORD see Hawkins, Ed.

LET US GO NOW INTO BETHLEHEM see Hopkins

LET US GO TO BETHLEHEM see Ringwald, [Roy]

LET US HOMAGE BRING see Roberton, Hugh S.

LET US HUMBLY WALK WITH THEE see Bampton, R.

LET US LOVE ONE ANOTHER see Hovhaness, Alan

LET US NOW GO EVEN TO BETHLEHEM *Xmas,carol
  SATB ALLANS 318 s.p.   (L975)

LET US NOW GO UNTO BETHLEHEM see Winchester, E.C.

LET US NOW OUR VOICES RAISE see Smart, Henry Thomas

LET US NOW PRAISE FAMOUS MEN see Pinkham, Daniel

LET US NOW PRAISE FAMOUS MEN see Davies, Henry Walford

LET US NOW PRAISE FAMOUS MEN see Dean, T.W.

LET US NOW PRAISE FAMOUS MEN see Engel, [A. Lehman]

LET US NOW PRAISE FAMOUS MEN see Kirk, Theron W.

LET US NOW PRAISE FAMOUS MEN see Rubbra, Edmund

LET US NOW PRAISE FAMOUS MEN see Sowerby, Leo

LET US NOW PRAISE FAMOUS MEN see Vaughan Williams, Ralph

LET US NOW PRAISE FAMOUS MEN see Wells, Dana F.

LET US PLAY A GAY MUSETTE *Xmas
  (Carr) SATB,acap oct LAWSON 51265 $.30 (L976)
  (Carr) SSA/SAA,acap oct LAWSON 51042 $.35
                                                (L977)

LET US PRAISE GOD see Olds, [William Benjamin]

LET US PRAISE HIM! see Eberlin, Johann Ernst

LET US PRAISE THE LORD see Stuart

LET US PRAISE THE LORD OUR GOD see Carissimi, Giacomo, Cantemus Omnes Domino

LET US PRAY see Pasquet, Jean

LET US REJOICE see Pearson, Edith

LET US REMEMBER see Amram, David Werner

LET US, REPRESENTING MYSTIC'LLY, THE CHERUBIM see Tcherepnin, Nikolay Nikolayevitch

LET US RISE WITH JESUS see Jenkins

LET US SECURELY ENTER see Rubbra, Edmund, Entrez-Y Tous En Surete

LET US SING A JOYFUL SONG see Morgan, Haydn

LET US SING NOEL
  (Bedell, R.) SATB oct PRESSER 312-40285 $.25
                                                (L978)

LET US SING NOEL see Bedell, [Robert Leech]

LET US SING NOEL see Dela Venna, P., Hodie Nobis

LET US SING THE NEW SONG see Wyatt

LET US SING TO THE LORD see Rogers, E.

LET US SING TO THE LORD see Emig, Lois

LET US SING TO THE LORD see Niehaus, Lennie

LET US SING TO THE LORD A SONG OF JOY see Trued, Clarence

LET US STAND IN PRAYER see Schroth, Gerhard

LET US START UPON OUR JOURNEY
  see Five Dutch Carols

LET US WALK AS JESUS WILLETH see Bach, Johann Sebastian

LET US WALK IN THE LIGHT OF THE LORD see O'Hara, Geoffrey

LET US WELCOME JESUS
  see Belgian Christmas Songs, Set 2

LET US WITH A GLADSOME MIND see Butler, Eugene

LET US WITH A GLADSOME MIND see Clokey

LET US, WITH A GLADSOME MIND see Eldridge, Guy H.

LET US WITH A GLADSOME MIND see Means, Claude

LET US WITH A GLADSOME MIND see Moe, Daniel

LET US WITH A GLADSOME MIND see Nicholson, S.H.

LET US WITH A GLADSOME MIND see Thiman, Eric Harding

LET US WITH A GLADSOME MIND see Van Dyke

LET US WITH A GLADSOME MIND see Wilson, John F.

LET US WITH A GLADSOME MIND see Wolff

LET US WORSHIP see Willan, Healey

LET US WORSHIP THE SACRAMENT see Goi, M., Adoriamo Il Sacramento

LET US WORSHIP TOGETHER
  SATB BIG3 $.25   (L979)

LET YOUR JOY BE KNOWN! see Bock, Fred

LET YOUR LIGHT GO SHINE
  SATB BIG3 $.25   (L980)

LET YOUR LIGHT SO SHINE see Webber, Lloyd

LET YOUTH SING *CC123U
  (Loes, Harry Dixon) 2pt jr cor cmplt ed
    LILLENAS MB-104 $1.00   (L981)

L'ETOILE see Chaminade, Cecile

LET'S ALL SING *sac/sec,CC15L
  (Stone) SSA PRO ART 114 $1.25   (L982)

LET'S BOW OUR HEADS AND PRAY see Weaver, Marion

LET'S GO CAROLING! *CC22U,Xmas,anthem/carol
  oct LORENZ D-1 $.50   (L983)

LET'S GO CAROLING! *CC20U,Xmas,carol
  cor/cong cmplt ed LILLENAS MC-219   (L984)

LET'S GO CAROLING! *Xmas
  SATB oct LORENZ D1 $.50   (L985)

LET'S GO DOWN *spir
SATB oct STAFF 638 $.30 (L986)

LET'S SAY A ROSARY EACH DAY see Tanous

LET'S SEE WHAT HAPPENS TODAY see Mc Call, Harlo

LET'S SING OF FAITHFUL FRIENDS see Grime, William

LET'S SING TO GOD see Fuller, [Esther Mary]

LETTER TO MOTHER see Lockwood, Normand

LETTEST THOU THY SERVANT DEPART IN PEACE see Taylor, Clifford, Nunc Dimittis

LETZTE BITTE see Wolf, Hugo

LETZTE BITTE: WIE EIN TODESWUNDER STREITER see Wolf, Hugo

LEU, FERD. OSCAR (1887-1943)
Ostermusik *Easter
[Ger] mix cor&boy cor,org,2trp HUG s.p. (L987)

L'EUCHARISTIE see Gounod, Charles Francois

LEUEZ-VOUS! UNE VOIX VOUS APPELLE see Bach, Johann Sebastian

LEUNING, O.
Pilgrims' Hymn
unis oct PRESSER 342-40010 $.30 (L988)

LEUPOLD, ULRICH SIEGFRIED (1909-)
Rejoice In The Lord *CC21L,anthem
SAB (easy) oct AUGSBURG 11-9356 $1.00 (L989)

LEUTHOLD, W.
In Tiefer Not
[Ger] mix cor,acap (med) HUG s.p. (L990)

LEVAVI OCULOS MEOS see Lassus, Roland de (Orlandus)

LEVE-TOI VITE MON AMI see Canteloube de Malaret, Marie-Joseph

LEVEEN
I See God
(Mencher; Wilson) SSA oct BOURNE 164 $.25 (L991)
(Mencher; Wilson) SATB oct BOURNE 674 $.40 (L992)

LEVY
May The Words Of My Mouth
see Levy, Prayer

Prayer
SATB,org oct BOOSEY 5602 $.30 contains also: May The Words Of My Mouth (L993)

LEVY, ERNST (1895-)
Hear, Ye Children
SSMezMezAA BROUDE,A. 209 $.35 (L994)
TBB&TBB BROUDE,A. 209 $.35 (L995)

LEVY, MARVIN DAVID (1932-)
For The Time Being
mix cor,narrator&SSMezTBarB soli,orch BOOSEY voc sc $12.50, sc rental, ipr (L996)

Our Father (from For The Time Being)
SATB oct BOOSEY 5515 $.30 (L997)

LEWANDOWSKI
Hallelujah (Psalm 150) Gen
SATB oct FISCHER,C CM-6753 $.30 (L998)
(Coggin) SAB oct FISCHER,J 9453 $.30 (L999)
(Cummings) SSA oct FOX R147 $.35 (L1000)
(Norden) SATB oct GRAY GCMR 1538 $.40 (L1001)
(Riegger) SATB FLAMMER A 5273 $.35 (L1002)
(Williams) SATB oct PLYMOUTH SC-6 $.30 (L1003)
(Wilson) SAB SCHMITT 5517 $.40 (L1004)
(Wilson) SATB SCHMITT 1640 $.40 (L1005)
(Wilson) SSA SCHMITT 2559 $.30 (L1006)

Psalm 150 *see Hallelujah

LEWANDOWSKI, LOUIS (1821-1904)
Enosh
(Roskin) SATB HATIKVAH HCL 23 $.35 (L1007)

Evening Service For Sabbath And Festivals *Fest/Sab-Eve
(Adler, H. Ch.) SATB TRANSCON. TCL 825 $4.00 (L1008)

Halalujoh, Halalu El B'kod'sho
"Hallelujah, Praise Ye The Lord" [Eng/Heb] 4pt mix cor oct SCHIRM.G 7454 $.30 (L1009)
(Stickles) "Hallelujah, Praise Ye The Lord" [Eng/Heb] 3pt mix cor oct SCHIRM.G 10878 $.30 (L1010)
(Stickles) "Hallelujah, Praise Ye The Lord" [Eng/Heb] 3pt wom cor oct SCHIRM.G 10879 $.30 (L1011)

Hallelujah, Praise Ye The Lord *see Halalujoh, Halalu El B'kod'sho

Ki Lekach Tov
(Roskin) SATB HATIKVAH HCL 15 $.25 (L1012)

Mah Yokor Chasdecho (Psalm 36)
(Roskin) SATB HATIKVAH HCL 6 $.25 (L1013)

Psalm 19 *see Toras Adonoy T'mimoh

Psalm 36 *see Mah Yokor Chasdecho

Shivisi
(Roskin) SATB HATIKVAH HCL 29 $.25 (L1014)

Toras Adonoy T'mimoh (Psalm 19)
(Roskin) SATB HATIKVAH HCL 5 $.35 (L1015)

Tovo Lefonecho
(Roskin) SATB HATIKVAH HCL 24 $.35 (L1016)

Zocharti Loch
(Roskin) SATB HATIKVAH HCL 21 $.35 (L1017)

LEWIN, FRANK
Behold, How Good
SATB oct LAWSON 51130 $.25 (L1018)

Psalm 148
SATB oct PRESSER 342-40017 $.35 (L1019)

LEWIS
African Noel *Xmas
2pt oct PLYMOUTH PCS-501 $.25 (L1020)
SATB oct PLYMOUTH PCS-38 $.30 (L1021)

All Things
unis oct SUMMY B 1629 $.25 (L1022)

At The Turning Of The Narrow Road
SATB oct VOLKWEIN VB108 $.25 (L1023)

Cherry Tree Carol, The
SATB,S solo,harp/pno oct COLOMBO 2487 $.25 (L1024)

Children Sing, The *see Fuller, [Esther Mary]

Christmas Time At The Pilgrim Inn *Xmas
SATB,fl,bells,tamb oct BOOSEY 5831 $.45 (L1025)

God Has Ears To Listen
unis&opt desc oct SACRED $.35 (L1026)

Got No Time *anthem/spir
SATB oct FISCHER,C CM-7542 $.25 (L1027)

Humbly I Adore Thee
SATB oct FISCHER,C CM-7367 $.25 (L1028)

Hundred And Eighty-Five Thousand Men
SATB oct HERITAGE H2146 $.35 (L1029)
TTBB oct HERITAGE H2868 $.35 (L1030)
SA/SAB oct HERITAGE H7821 $.35 (L1031)

I Am The Door
SATB oct SACRED E43 $.35 (L1032)

I Can't Spin A Web
unis/SA oct SACRED S-8623 $.30 (L1033)

I Wonder *Xmas
unis oct GALAXY 1.2379.1 $.25 (L1034)

Innkeeper, The *Xmas
SATB oct SACRED E92 $.35 (L1035)
SAB/SA oct SACRED S-7829 $.35 (L1036)

Mother, I Didn't Bring Home The Fish
SAB oct SACRED S-7833 $.35 (L1037)

My Father's House
2pt oct PLYMOUTH SC-509 $.30 (L1038)

O, Thou In Whose Presence
(Fuller) SAB oct PRO ART 1151 $.30 (L1039)
(Fuller) SSA oct PRO ART 2096 $.22 (L1040)
(Gerig) SATB oct LILLENAS AN-2226 $.30 (L1041)

Our Daily Bread
SA oct SACRED S-5373 $.35 (L1042)

Sing Unto God
SATB oct SACRED E35 $.35 (L1043)

There Is A River
SATB oct SACRED E62 $.35 (L1044)

You Are Righteous, O Lord
SATB oct SACRED E82 $.35 (L1045)

You Don't Need A Sword
SATB oct HERITAGE H2145 $.35 (L1046)

LEWIS, ANTHONY
Heavens Proclaim The Glory Of God, The *anthem
mix cor oct NOVELLO 28.1459.05 s.p. (L1047)

LEWIS, FREEMAN
O Thou, In Whose Presence
(Cain) 8pt mix cor,opt Bar solo oct SCHIRM.G 8007 $.40 (L1048)

LEWIS, J.
Creator, Supreme
SATB oct PRESSER 312-40221 $.25 (L1049)

Great Is The Lord
SATB oct PRESSER 312-40534 $.30 (L1050)

Lord Of All Power And Might
SATB oct PRESSER 312-40328 $.25 (L1051)

O, Call On The Lord
(James, M.) SATB oct PRESSER 312-40220 $.25 (L1052)

Once In Royal David's City *Xmas
SA oct PRESSER 312-40536 $.25 (L1053)

Paschal Paean *Easter
SATB oct PRESSER 312-40222 $.25 (L1054)

Spirit Of Mercy, Truth And Love
SATB oct PRESSER 312-40486 $.30 (L1055)

Unto Thee O Lord
SATB oct PRESSER 312-40730 $.30 (L1056)

Welcome Yule *Xmas
SATB oct PRESSER 312-40321 $.30 (L1057)

LEWIS, J.L.
O Lord, Give Us All *Lent
SATB,acap oct GRAY GCMR 3128 $.30 (L1058)

LEWIS, JESSIE D.
Spirit Of God *anthem/hymn
4pt mix cor,high solo oct SCHIRM.G 9336 $.25 (L1059)

LEWIS, JOHN LEO (1911-)
Come Sing, Ye Choirs Exultant
SATB/unis (med) ABINGDON APM-450 $.25 (L1060)

Come, Thou Long-Expected Jesus *Adv/Gen
4pt mix cor oct SCHIRM.G 10892 $.25 (L1061)

Father, We Thank Thee *Gen
unis,kbd (easy) oct CONCORDIA 98-1497 $.25 (L1062)

LEWIS, JOHN LEO (cont'd.)

For Ever, O Lord
4pt mix cor,org/pno oct SCHIRM.G 10652 $.25 (L1063)

Glory To God
unis oct AGAPE A 442 $.45 (L1064)

God Is My Salvation
SATB oct AGAPE A 426 $.30 (L1065)

God Who Made The Earth
unis jr cor/2pt jr cor oct SCHIRM.G 10534 $.20 (L1066)

I Am The Boat
SATB oct WORD CS-2497 $.30 (L1067)

I See White And Black, Lord
SATB oct AGAPE CF 123 $.25 (L1068)

Lamb Of God, I Look To Thee
2pt wom cor,org/pno oct SCHIRM.G 10652 $.25 (L1069)

Lord, Jesus, Think On Me
4pt mix cor,acap oct SCHIRM.G 10740 $.20 (L1070)

My Little Lamb *Xmas
SATB,acap (med) ABINGDON APM-440 $.25 (L1071)

O God, The Protector
SATB oct WALTON 2062 $.25 (L1072)

O Lord, The Hope Of Israel *Bibl
4pt mix cor oct SCHIRM.G 10849 $.20 (L1073)

O Thou, From Whom All Goodness Flows
4pt mix cor oct SCHIRM.G 10739 $.25 (L1074)

Psalm 54 *see Save Me, O God, By Thy Name

Save Me, O God, By Thy Name (Psalm 54) Bibl
4pt mix cor,org/pno oct SCHIRM.G 10994 $.25 (L1075)

Soldiers Of Christ, Arise
4pt mix cor oct SCHIRM.G 10851 $.25 (L1076)

There Is A Land
4pt mix cor,acap oct SCHIRM.G 11084 $.25 (L1077)

There Might Have Been A Stranger *Xmas
SATB (easy) ABINGDON APM-265 $.24 (L1078)

LEWKOVITCH
Cantabo Domino
mix cor SOUTHERN $.25 (L1079)

LEWKOVITCH, BERNHARD (1927-)
Cantabo Domino (from Ten Latin Motets)
[Lat] 4pt mix cor,acap oct SCHIRM.G 11833 $.25 (L1080)

Christus Factus Est
mix cor NORDISKA U567 s.p. (L1081)

Laudi A Nostra Signora
mix cor NORDISKA WH-29031 s.p. (L1082)
mix cor HANSEN-DEN 29031 s.p. (L1083)

O Bone Jesu
mix cor NORDISKA U566 s.p. (L1084)

Stabat Mater
[Lat] mix cor oct SCHIRM.G 11927 $.35 (L1085)

mix cor HANSEN-DEN 29030 s.p. (L1086)

Sub Vesperum
mix cor HANSEN-DEN 29078 s.p. (L1087)

LEWY, RON
This Is Your Prayer *see VeHi Tehi'latecha

VeHi Tehilatecha *Heb
"This Is Your Prayer" SAT,narrator,S solo, 3vla ISRAELI s.p. (L1088)

LEY, HENRY GEORGE (1887-)
Anthem For A Harvest Festival *Harv,anthem
SATB (easy) oct OXFORD 42.130 $.30 (L1089)

Come, Thou Long Expected Jesus *Adv/Gen
SATB (easy) oct OXFORD 42.137 $.30 (L1090)

Eternal Ruler *Trin,anthem
SATB,opt inst (easy) oct OXFORD $.25, ipr (L1091)
SATB (easy) OXFORD 42.220 $.25 see from SIX SHORT ANTHEMS (L1092)

Evening Hymn *hymn/prayer
"Prayer Of King Charles" SATB,opt acap (easy) OXFORD 42.917 $.20 see from SIX SHORT ANTHEMS (L1093)

Evening Hymn Of King Charles I *Eve,anthem
SATB,opt inst (easy) oct OXFORD 42.917 $.20 (L1094)

In Thee Is Gladness *Gen,anthem
SATB oct ROYAL 213 s.p. (L1095)

O Be Joyful In The Lord *Thanks
SSS (easy) oct OXFORD 44.062 $.35 (L1096)

Prayer Of King Charles *see Evening Hymn

Prayer Of King Henry VI, A *Gen
SATB,acap (easy) oct OXFORD 43.352 $.15 (L1097)

Rejoice In The Lord Alway *Adv/Gen,anthem/Bibl
SS,opt inst (easy) oct OXFORD 44.021 $.25, ipr (L1098)
SATB,opt inst (med easy) oct OXFORD 42.162 $.35 (L1099)

LEYDEN
Beautiful, Beautiful World
SATB HANSEN-US I4005 $.40 (L1100)

Bring Us Together, Go Forward Together
SATB HANSEN-US I4006 $.40 (L1101)

Give Us This Day
SATB HANSEN-US I4020 $.40 (L1102)

O Bless The Lord
SATB HANSEN-US I4031 $.40 (L1103)

LEYDEN (cont'd.)

Prepare Ye The Way Of The Lord
SATB HANSEN-US I4033 $.40 (L1104)

Turn Back O Man
SATB HANSEN-US I4044 $.40 (L1105)

LHERITTIER, JEAN.
Ave Virgo Gloriosa
(Agnel, A.) [Lat] 3pt mix cor HEUGEL PJ130
s.p. (L1106)

L'HOMME ARME see Dufay, Guillaume

L'HOMME ARME see Palestrina, Giovanni

L'HOMME ARME see Palestrina, Giovanni

L'HORA PASSA see Viadana, Lodovico Grossi da

LI A PROUN DE GENT see Saboly, Nicholas

LIADOFF
Alleluia
(Gearhart) SATB SHAWNEE A 202 $.30 (L1107)

LIBER PSALMORUM see Weis, Flemming

LIBERA ET IN PARADISIUM see Delamoriniere, G.

LIBERA ME see Anonymous

LIBERA ME see Arne

LIBERA ME see Faure, Gabriel-Urbain

LIBERA ME see Samuel-Rosseau, Marcel

LIBERA ME see Tubb, Monte

LIBERA ME DOMINE see Volpi, Edoardo

LIBERA NOS see Hunkins, Eusebia Simpson

LIBERA PLEBEM see Joubert, John

LIBRO PRIMO DELLE LAUDI SPIRITUALI see Razzi,
Serafino

LICHT
Christmas Star, The *Xmas
SSA SCHMITT 2532 $.25 (L1108)

Great Ruler Over Time And Space
SATB FLAMMER A 5347 $.30 (L1109)

Hail, Hosanna!
SATB FLAMMER A 5265 $.25 (L1110)

Hymns And Carols *CCU
SA FLAMMER GE5011 $.60 (L1111)

Let Children Sing *CCU
SA FLAMMER GE5001 $.60 (L1112)

Licht Anthem Book, The *CCU,anthem
SA FLAMMER GF5006 $.60 (L1113)

Little Anthem Book For Children, The *CCU
SA FLAMMER GE5006 $.60 (L1114)

Spring Leads Death To Life *Easter/Lent
jr cor&sr cor,hndbl (easy) FISCHER,C
CM 7196 $.25 (L1115)
jr cor&sr cor,opt hndbl oct FISCHER,C
CM-7196 $.25 (L1116)

Your Children's Choir *CCU
SA FLAMMER GE5004 $.60 (L1117)

Your Youth Choir *CCU
SAB FLAMMER GD5013 $.85 (L1118)

LICHT ANTHEM BOOK, THE see Licht

LICHT, LEUCHTENDES LICHT see Kern, Matthais

LICHT MUSS WIEDER WERDEN see Siegl, Otto

LICHT, MYRTHA B.
Dove, The *Xmas
2pt boy cor/2pt wom cor oct SCHIRM.G 10912
$.20 (L1119)

Fair Easter *Easter
3pt mix cor oct SCHIRM.G 10836 $.25 (L1120)
4pt mix cor,org/pno oct SCHIRM.G 10720 $.25
(L1121)

Halo, The *Xmas
2pt boy cor/2pt wom cor,chimes oct SCHIRM.G
10898 $.20 (L1122)

LICHVOD SHABBATH see Kosakoff, Reuven

LIDARTI, C.G.
Befi Yesharim *Heb
(Adler, Israel) SATB,strings ISRAELI 705
ipa contains also: Rathom, A., Adon Olam
(L1123)

Hamesiach Ilemim
see Lidarti, C.G., Nora Elohim

Nora Elohim *Heb
(Adler, Israel) TTB,strings ISRAELI 704 ipa
contains also: Lidarti, C.G., Hamesiach
Ilemim; Casseres, A., Hamesiach Ilemim
(L1124)

LIDDLE, [SAMUEL]
How Lovely Are Thy Dwellings
(Cain) SSA oct BOOSEY 1758 $.30 (L1125)
(Fagge) SATB,S solo oct BOOSEY 1187 $.35
(L1126)
(Howorth) SAB oct BOOSEY 1614 $.35 (L1127)
(Runkel) unis&SAB&SATB,ST soli oct BOOSEY
5221 $.35 (L1128)
(Samuelson) SA/TB oct BOOSEY 1493 $.30
(L1129)

Lord Is My Shepherd
(Salter) SATB oct BOOSEY 1405 $.30 (L1130)

LIDHOLM, INGVAR (1921-)
Laudi *Bibl
[Swed] SATB,acap GEHRMANS KRB 251 (L1131)

LIE QUIET, SOUL see Hastings, Thomas

LIEB NACHTIGALL, WACH AUF see Erdlen, Hermann

LIEB, NACHTIGALL, WACH AUF! see Wegener, H.

LIEBE DIR ERGEB' ICH MICH! see Cornelius, Peter

LIEBE, KURT MARIA (1929-)
Es Bluhen Die Maien
see Zwei Altosterreichische
Weihnachtslieder

Grunet Felder
see Zwei Altosterreichische
Weihnachtslieder

In Stiller Nacht *Psntd
men cor,acap TONGER s.p. (L1132)

Zwei Altosterreichische Weihnachtslieder
*Xmas
wom cor&jr cor TONGER s.p.
contains: Es Bluhen Die Maien; Grunet
Felder (L1133)

LIEBE RAUSCHT DER SILBERBACH see Schubert,
Franz (Peter)

LIEBER HERR GOTT, WECKE UNS AUF! see Bach,
Johann Christoph

LIEBER HERRE GOTT, WECKE UNS AUF see Doernberg,
Martin

LIEBESTRAUME NO. 3 see Liszt, Franz

LIEBHOLD (ca. 1725?)
Commit Thy Way Unto The Lord *Gen
SATB,acap (med easy) oct CONCORDIA 98-1125
$.35 (L1134)

Glory To God *Xmas
(Barnard, P.) SATB,acap oct PRESSER
352-00434 $.35 (L1135)

LIEBLEITNER, K.
Osterlied *Easter
[Ger] 3pt men cor/3pt wom cor KRENN 110
s.p. (L1136)

LIEBLICH UND SCHONE SEIN IST NICHTS see Schein,
Johann Hermann

LIEBLICHE WEIHNACHT see Napiersky, H.

LIEBLICHE WEIHNACHT see Rein, Walter

LIEBSTER GOTT see Bach, Johann Sebastian,
Liebster Gott, Wann Werd' Ich Sterben

LIEBSTER GOTT, WANN WERD' ICH STERBEN see Bach,
Johann Sebastian

LIEBSTER GOTT, WANN WERD' ICH STERBEN [CHORALE]
see Bach, Johann Sebastian

LIEBSTER HERR JESU see Buxtehude, Dietrich

LIEBSTER HERR JESU, WO BLEIBST see Bach, Johann
Sebastian

LIEBSTER IMMANUEL see Bach, Johann Sebastian

LIEBSTER IMMANUEL see Bach, Johann Sebastian,
Liebster Immanuel

LIEBSTER IMMANUEL, HERZOG DER FROMMEN see Bach,
Johann Sebastian

LIEBSTER JESU, MEIN VERLANGEN see Bach, Johann
Sebastian

LIEBSTER JESU, WIR SIND HIER see Bach, Johann
Sebastian

LIEBSTER JESU, WIR SIND HIER see Trubel,
Gerhard

LIEBSTER JESU, WIR SIND HIER, DICH UND DEIN
WORT ANZUHOREN see Bach, Johann Sebastian

LIED DER HIRTEN "ALS ICH BEI MEINEN SCHAFEN
WACHT" see Rahner, Hugo

LIED VAN MARIA MAGDALENA *Xmas,carol,Belg
(Terri) "Song Of Maria Magdalena" SSA/SAA,
acap,opt hndbl&fing.cym. oct LAWSON 51734
$.35 (L1137)

LIEDER FUR DEN KINDERGOTTESDIENST *CC26U,Gen
[Ger] BAREN. BA 2995 $.65 (L1138)

LIEDER UND KANOS see Eglin, Arthur

LIEDER UNSERER ZEIT *CCU
unis HANSSLER s.p. (L1139)

LIEDERHEFT. DEUTSCHER EVANGELISCHER KIRCHENTAG
1969 *CCU,Gen
[Ger] unis,acap (easy) BOSSE BE 800 s.p.
(L1140)

LIEDMESSE see Haublein, Ernst

LIEDMOTETTEN NACH WEISEN DER BOHMISCHEN BRUDER
*see Pepping, Ernst, Ach Wie Gross Ist
Gottes Gut Und Wohltat; Pepping, Ernst,
Denk, Mensch, Wie Dein Heiland Dich Liebet;
Pepping, Ernst, O Ihr Christen, Teuer
Erkauft; Pepping, Ernst, Wunderlich Ding
Hat Sich Ergangen (L1141)

LIEDMOTETTEN NACH WEISEN DER BOHMISCHEN BRUDER
see Pepping, Ernst

LIEDPASSION: JESU KREUZ, LEIDEN UND PEIN see
Baudach, Ulrich

LIEDSTROPHEN NACH DEM CREDO *CC17U,Credo
(Grote, Gottfried) [Ger] 4pt mix cor/5pt mix
cor BAREN. EM 551 sc s.p., cor pts s.p.
settings by old masters (L1142)

LIEMOHN
Children Of The Heavenly Father *Gen
SATB SCHMITT 1723 $.35 (L1143)

LIER, BERTUS VAN (1906-)
see VAN LIER, BERTUS

LIETI CANTIAMO see Molfino, L.

LIETO GODEA see Gabrieli, Giovanni

LIFE ETERNAL see Holton

LIFE EVERLASTING see Petrie

LIFE EVERLASTING, THE see Matthews, Harvey
Alexander

LIFE GIVER IN THE LIGHT REALMS see Lynn, George

LIFE IS A HYMN *CCU,hymn,Contemp
unis MARKS $1.50 (L1144)

LIFE OF AGES see Nyquist

LIFE OF CHRIST, THE see Dufault, Sheldon

LIFE THAT MAKETH ALL THINGS NEW see Longfellow

LIFT HIGH THE CROSS see Sateren, Leland
Bernhard

LIFT HIGH THE TRIUMPH SONG see Lovelace, Austin
C.

LIFT THE STRAIN OF HIGH THANKSGIVING see
Watkinson, J.R.

LIFT THINE EYES see Mendelssohn-Bartholdy,
Felix

LIFT THINE EYES TO THE MOUNTAINS see
Mendelssohn-Bartholdy, Felix

LIFT THYSELF UP O GOD see Morgan

LIFT UP OUR HEARTS see Butler

LIFT UP OUR HEARTS see York, D.

LIFT UP THE EVERLASTING GATES see Tye,
Christopher

LIFT UP THY VOICE, MY HEART, AND PRAISE see
Sateren, Leland Bernhard

LIFT UP YOUR EYES see Billings, William

LIFT UP YOUR EYES ON HIGH see Berger, Jean

LIFT UP YOUR HANDS see Pasquet, Jean

LIFT UP YOUR HANDS, O YE GATES see Handel,
George Frideric

LIFT UP YOUR HEADS see Altman, Ludwig, S'u
Sh'orim

LIFT UP YOUR HEADS see Ashford

LIFT UP YOUR HEADS see Ashford, E.L.

LIFT UP YOUR HEADS see Barthelson, Joyce

LIFT UP YOUR HEADS see Berger

LIFT UP YOUR HEADS see Bixby, A.K.

LIFT UP YOUR HEADS see Blow, John

LIFT UP YOUR HEADS see Brandon, G.

LIFT UP YOUR HEADS see Buchtel

LIFT UP YOUR HEADS see Coleridge

LIFT UP YOUR HEADS see Coleridge-Taylor, Samuel

LIFT UP YOUR HEADS see Emerson

LIFT UP YOUR HEADS see Gibbons, Orlando

LIFT UP YOUR HEADS see Goldman, Maurice

LIFT UP YOUR HEADS see Hammerschmidt, Andreas

LIFT UP YOUR HEADS see Handel, George Frideric

LIFT UP YOUR HEADS see Hopkins

LIFT UP YOUR HEADS see Hopkins, John L.

LIFT UP YOUR HEADS see Johnson

LIFT UP YOUR HEADS see Krapf, Gerhard

LIFT UP YOUR HEADS see Lundquist

LIFT UP YOUR HEADS see Lynn, George

LIFT UP YOUR HEADS see Nelson, Ronald A.

LIFT UP YOUR HEADS see Newbury, Kent A.

LIFT UP YOUR HEADS see Psalmodia Evangelica

LIFT UP YOUR HEADS see Rorem, Ned

LIFT UP YOUR HEADS see Vulpius, Melchior

LIFT UP YOUR HEADS see Wienandt, Elwyn A.

LIFT UP YOUR HEADS, GREAT GATES, AND SING see
Bullock, Ernest

LIFT UP YOUR HEADS, O YE GATES see Ashford

LIFT UP YOUR HEADS O YE GATES see Davidson, C.

LIFT UP YOUR HEADS, O YE GATES see Handel,
George Frideric

LIFT UP YOUR HEADS, O YE GATES see Hastings,
Paul, Psalmodia Evangelica

LIFT UP YOUR HEADS, O YE GATES see Leighton,
Kenneth

LIFT UP YOUR HEADS, O YE GATES see Michael,
Tobias

LIFT UP YOUR HEADS, O YE GATES see Schutz, Heinrich

LIFT UP YOUR HEADS, YE GATES see Adams, Thomas

LIFT UP YOUR HEADS, YE GATES OF BRASS *anthem (Leupold, Ulrich) SAB (easy) oct AUGSBURG 1462 $.22 contains also: Prepare The Way, O Zion (L1145)

LIFT UP YOUR HEADS YE GATES OF BRASS see Williams, P.

LIFT UP YOUR HEADS, YE MIGHTY GATES see Leisring, Volkmar

LIFT UP YOUR HEADS, YE MIGHTY GATES see Lundquist, Matthew Nathanael

LIFT UP YOUR HEADS, YE MIGHTY GATES see Powell, Robert J.

LIFT UP YOUR HEADS, YE MIGHTY GATES see Walker, Alan

LIFT UP YOUR HEADS, YE MIGHTY GATES see Warner, Richard

LIFT UP YOUR HEADS, YE MIGHTY GATES see Willan, Healey

LIFT UP YOUR HEART see Thiman, Eric Harding

LIFT UP YOUR HEARTS *CC12L (Bunjes, P.) mix cor CONCORDIA 97-6219 $1.25 contains works by: Bunjes, Paul G.; Bach, J.S.; Jeep, Joh.; Walter, Joh.; Lossius, Wienhorst, Richard; Luther; Wolff, S. Drummond; Handel, G.F.; Bourgeois, Louis; Goudimel, Claude; Boyce, Wm. (L1146)

LIFT UP YOUR HEARTS see Elgar, Edward, Sursum Corda

LIFT UP YOUR HEARTS see Heath, G.

LIFT UP YOUR HEARTS see Roff, Joseph

LIFT UP YOUR HEARTS see Smith, Sursum Corda

LIFT UP YOUR HEARTS, BOOK 1 see Grant

LIFT UP YOUR HEARTS, BOOK 2 see Grant

LIFT UP YOUR HEARTS, SING YE see Gretchaninov, Alexander Tikhonovitch

LIFT UP YOUR HEARTS, YE PEOPLE see Butler

LIFT UP YOUR HEARTS, YE PEOPLE see Darst, S. Glen

LIFT UP YOUR OFFERINGS see Saint-Saens, Camille

LIFT UP YOUR SONGS OF PRAISE see Saint-Saens, Camille

LIFT UP YOUR VOICES NOW! see Kennedy, John Brodbin

LIFT YOUR GLAD VOICES see Jackson

LIFT YOUR GLAD VOICES see Pike, Harry Hale

LIFT YOUR HEADS see Bach, Johann Sebastian

LIFT YOUR HEARTS YE SONS AND DAUGHTERS see Hutson, Wihla

LIFT YOUR VOICES see Obenshain, Kathryn G.

LIFT YOUR VOICES TO JEHOVAH see Scarlatti, Alessandro, Exultate Deo

LIFTED see Lister, Mosie

LIGETI, GYORGY (1923-   )
Lux Aeterna
[Lat] 16pt mix cor,acap PETERS 5934 $2.00 (L1147)

Requiem *Req
dbl cor,SMez soli,orch sc PETERS 4841 $30.00, voc sc PETERS 8152 (L1148)

LIGHT DIVINE see Mascagni, Pietro

LIGHT ETERNAL, THE see Petrie

LIGHT EVERLASTING see Christiansen, Olaf Christian

LIGHT EVERLASTING see Young

LIGHT IN DARKNESS see Jenkins, Cyril

LIGHT IN THE WILDERNESS, THE see Brubeck

LIGHT INVISIBLE, THE see Leighton, Kenneth

LIGHT, LIGHT THE CANDLE see Fisher

LIGHT LOOKED DOWN see Beveridge, Thomas G.

LIGHT OF BETHLEHEM *Xmas/Pageant
LORENZ $.75 (L1149)

LIGHT OF BETHLEHEM, THE *Xmas,folk,Slav (Mueller, Carl F.) 2pt jr cor&4pt mix cor oct SCHIRM.G 7800 $.25 (L1150)

LIGHT OF CHRISTMAS, THE see Thorpe, Frank

LIGHT OF HEAVEN, THE see Davis, Katherine K.

LIGHT OF LIFE, THE see Elgar, Edward, Lux Christi

LIGHT OF MAN, THE see Rogers, B.

LIGHT OF THE CHURCH see Illing

LIGHT OF THE WORLD
(Agate, E.) cor oct HART s.p. (L1151)

LIGHT OF THE WORLD see Blake, G.

LIGHT OF THE WORLD see Roff, Joseph

LIGHT OF THE WORLD, THE see Ellis

LIGHT OF THE WORLD, THE see Englert, Eugene

LIGHT OF THE WORLD, THE see McCormick

LIGHT OF THE WORLD, THE see Pasquet, Jean

LIGHT OF THE WORLD, THE see Sjolund, Paul

LIGHT OF THE WORLD, WE KNOW THY PRAISE see Elgar, Edward

LIGHT OF THY TRUTH see Pasquet, Jean

LIGHT SHINES FORTH, A see Clokey, Joseph Waddell

LIGHT SHONE DOWN *Xmas
(song and story) LORENZ $.75 (L1152)

LIGHT SO TENDER see Tcherepnin, Alexander

LIGHT, THE LOVE, THE see Artman

LIGHTEN MINE EYES see Ferris, W.

LIGHTEN OUR DARKNESS see Le Fleming, Christopher (Kaye)

LIGHTS ARE BRIGHT AT CHRISTMAS, THE *Xmas (Follett) SSA,opt fl/inst oct PRO ART 2743 $.30 (L1153)

LIGHT'S GLITTERING MORN see Parker, Horatio William

LIGHTS OF EASTER see Gaul, Alfred Robert

LIGHTS WE HAVE KINDLED, THE see Adler, Hugo Ch., Haneros Halolu

LIGHTSHINE see Red, Buryl

LIGTHART, B.J.
O Salutaris
mix cor voc sc ALSBACH&D s.p. (L1154)

LIJESTRAND
God Himself Comes Down From Heaven
SATB FLAMMER A 5593 $.30 (L1155)

LIJSEN, A.
Kerstverhaal
3pt jr cor,pno/org ALSBACH&D sc s.p., cor pts s.p. (L1156)

Kerstverhall *cant
3pt wom cor,Mez solo,pno/org ALSBACH&D sc s.p., cor pts s.p. (L1157)

LIK PETRUS JAG PA VILLANS STIG see Thyrestam, Gunnar

LIKE A CHOIR OF HOLY ANGELS see Nyquist

LIKE A FLOWER see Stanton, [Walter Kendall]

LIKE A MIGHTY RIVER see Allen

LIKE A MIGHTY RIVER see Allen, Lanny

LIKE A RIVER GLORIOUS see Mountain

LIKE A ROOT see Gilliam

LIKE A SHEPHERD see Johnson, Sidney

LIKE AS A FATHER see Cherubini, Luigi

LIKE AS A FATHER see Jerome, Frederick

LIKE AS A FATHER see Kay

LIKE AS A FATHER DOTH PITY HIS CHILDREN see Geisler, Johan C.

LIKE AS A HART DESIRETH THE WATERBROOKS see Novello, Vincent, In Manus Tuas

LIKE AS THE HART see Greene, Maurice

LIKE AS THE HART see Howells, Herbert Norman

LIKE AS THE HART see Hutton

LIKE AS THE HART see Novello

LIKE AS THE HART see Novello, Vincent, In Manus Tuas

LIKE AS THE HART see Palestrina, Giovanni, Sicut Cervus

LIKE AS THE HART see Palestrina, Giovanni, Sicut Cervus Desiderat

LIKE AS THE HART see Willan, Healey

LIKE AS THE HART DESIRETH see Novello, Vincent

LIKE AS THE HART DESIRETH THE WATER-BROOKS see Harker, F. Flaxington

LIKE AS THE HART DESIRETH THE WATER-BROOKS see Macfarlane, William Charles

LIKE AS THE HART DESIRETH THE WATERBROOKS see Howells, Herbert Norman

LIKE AS WE DO PUT OUR TRUST IN THEE see Wesley, Charles

LIKE SILVER LAMPS IN A DISTANT SHRINE see Bender, Jan

LIL OL' TRAIN see Bachman

LILIEN UND AKELEIEN *CCU,liturg (Wagner, Hermann) mix cor MOSELER s.p. (L1158)

LILIES see Mumma, [Gordon]

LILIES WHITE AND FAIR see Christiansen, Paul

LILIUS, FRANCISZEK
Iubilate Deo Omnis Terra *mot,Pol (Szweykowski, Z.M.) SSATB,cont,inst POLSKIE WDMP40 s.p. (L1159)

LILJESTRAND, PAUL
Amidst Us *Easter,cant
SATB voc sc WORD CS-405 $.75 (L1160)

Armour Of God, The
SATB,brass oct AGAPE F 940 $.30 (L1161)

If Ye Be Merry
4pt mix cor,acap oct SCHIRM.G 11776 $.30 (L1162)

Three Canticles For Treble Voices *CC3U
SSAA oct AGAPE SP 711 $.30 (L1163)

LILLE JULEKANTATE see Sennels, Richard

LILLENAS, HALDOR
Calvary Road, The *Easter
(Whitman) SATB oct LILLENAS AN-2305 $.30 (L1164)

First Easter, The (composed with Joy, Virginia) *Easter,cant
mix cor,pno/org voc sc LILLENAS ME-201 $.60 (L1165)

He Shall Reign *anthem
(Whitman) SATB oct LILLENAS AN-2232 $.30 (L1166)

I Know A Name
(Skillings) SSATB oct LILLENAS AT-1076 $.25 (L1167)

Immanuel Forever (composed with Green, Rachel K.) *Xmas,cant/gospel
cor (easy) voc sc LILLENAS MC-215 $.60 (L1168)

Living Redeemer, The (composed with Green, Rachel K.) *Easter,cant
mix cor,opt narrator,soli voc sc LILLENAS ME-205 $1.00 (L1169)

My Wonderful Lord
(Williams) SATB oct LILLENAS AN-1126 $.30 (L1170)

No Room In The Inn
(Clark) SSATB oct LILLENAS AN-1608 $.30 (L1171)

Prince Of Life, The *Easter,cant
mix cor,opt narrator voc sc LILLENAS ME-208 $.60 (L1172)

Soldiers Of Immanuel
(Schubert) SATB oct LILLENAS AN-1628 $.30 (L1173)

Touch Of God, The
(Whitman) SATB oct LILLENAS AN-1166 .00 (L1174)

Victorious Christ, The (composed with Lynn, Lori) *Easter,cant
mix cor,narrator,soli voc sc LILLENAS ME-214 $.60 (L1175)

While Shepherds Watched (composed with Wagner, Viola) *Xmas,Bibl/cant
cor,narrator,ABarT soli voc sc LILLENAS MC-231 $.60 (L1176)

Wonderful *Xmas,Bibl/cant
mix cor voc sc LILLENAS MC-232 $.60 (L1177)
(Whitsett) SATB oct LILLENAS AN-1619 $.30 (L1178)

Wonderful Peace
(Ferrin) SATB oct LILLENAS AN-1643 $.30 (L1179)

LILLIUM REGIS see Creston, Paul

LILY OF THE VALLEY, THE *Eng
(Collins) SATB oct LILLENAS AT-1023 $.30 (L1180)

LIND, JOSHUA
Hayom Teamtzenu *Heb
(Kaplan) [Heb] SATB,acap oct LAWSON 51553 $.35 (L1181)

LINDBERG, OSKAR [FREDRIK] (1887-1955)
Ett Ord Av Gud
mix cor NORDISKA 4971 s.p. (L1182)

Julkantat
unis,pno s.p. voc sc NORDISKA 3675, cor pts NORDISKA 1842 (L1183)

Kyrkokantat Nr. 2
voc sc NORDISKA s.p. (L1184)

Loven Herren (from Kyrkokantat Nr. 1)
mix cor,brass voc sc NORDISKA s.p. (L1185)

Lovsang (from Kyrkokantat Nr. 2)
cor pts NORDISKA 2667 s.p., voc sc NORDISKA s.p., ipa (L1186)

Pingst
mix cor NORDISKA 435 s.p. (L1187)

Requiem *Req
voc sc MUSIKAL. s.p. (L1188)

LINDBLAD, A.F.
Not Alone For Mighty Empire
(Lundquist) SATB,acap (med) oct WILLIS 8470 $.20 (L1189)

LINDE, GERHARD
Also Hat Gott Die Welt Geliebt
SAATTB HANSSLER 25.001 s.p. (L1190)

LINDEGREN, JOHAN
Laudamus
"Vi Prisa Dig" mix cor NORDISKA 1883 s.p. (L1191)

Vi Prisa Dig *see Laudamus

LINDEMAN
Alleluia, Jesus Lives *anthem
(Leupold) SAB (easy) oct AUGSBURG 1485 $.20 (L1192)

Built On A Rock *anthem
(Brandon) SAB (easy) oct AUGSBURG 1416 $.30 (L1193)

Built On The Rock
(Lundquist) SATB,acap oct FOX PS11 $.22 (L1194)

Come, Ye Faithful, Raise The Strain *anthem
(Sateren) SA&SATB (med) oct AUGSBURG 1132 $.22 (L1195)
(Sateren) SATB&jr cor (med) oct AUGSBURG

LINDEMAN (cont'd.)

1132 $.22 (L1196)

Hallelujah, Jesus Lives!
(Hastings) SATB oct BOURNE HA11 $.30 (L1197)

LINDEMAN, LUDVIG MATHIAS (1812-1887)
Built On A Rock *anthem
(Barthelson) SATB oct LAWSON 51030 $.25 (L1198)
(Christiansen) SSAATTBB,B solo (med) oct AUGSBURG 0104 $.25 (L1199)
(Hokanson) SATB FLAMMER A 5072 $.30 (L1200)
(Lorenz) SAB oct LORENZ 7363 $.25 (L1201)

Kirken Den Er Et Gammelt Hus
mix cor MUSIKK 59 s.p. (L1202)

Long Hast Thou Stood, O Church Of God
(Davis, K.) SATB&desc,pno SCHIRM.EC 1769 $.30, ipr (L1203)
(Davis, K.) unis&desc,pno SCHIRM.EC 1765 $.25 (L1204)
(Davis, K.) SSA&desc,pno SCHIRM.EC 1869 ipr (L1205)
(Davis, K.) TTBB,acap SCHIRM.EC 570 $.22, ipr (L1206)

No Livnar Det I Lundar
(Gjendem, J.J.) [Norw] cor,inst LYCHE 22 s.p. (L1207)

LINDEN, CORNELIS VAN DER
see VAN DER LINDEN, CORNELIUS

LINDEN, N. V.D.
Ave Maria Stella
men cor ALSBACH&D sc s.p., cor pts s.p. (L1208)
Kyrie
men cor,org ALSBACH&D sc s.p., cor pts s.p. (L1209)
Lente
mix cor ALSBACH&D sc s.p., cor pts s.p. (L1210)

LINDEN TREE CAROL, THE *carol
(Copley, I.A.) SAB LENGNICK s.p. (L1211)

LINDER
Sleep, Little Jesus *Xmas
SA ALFRED 6145 $.30 (L1212)

LINDH
If Thou But Suffer God To Guide Thee
SATB (med easy) SOUTHERN $.40 (L1213)

LINDH, JODY W.
If Thou But Suffer God To Guide Thee *Gen
SATB,kbd (med diff) oct CONCORDIA 98-2081 $.40 (L1214)

LINDHJELM, NILS
A Fikk Jeg Kun Vaere Den Minste Kvist
(Baldershade, Bernt) wom cor MUSIKK 37 s.p. (L1215)

LINDQUIST, M.
Christ Is Arisen *Easter
SATB oct PRESSER MC231 $.30 (L1216)

LINDROFF
Glory Of Jehovah Is Risen Upon Thee, The
SATB,TB soli oct PRO ART 1700 $.20 (L1217)

LINDROTH, HENRY
Gud Fader Bor I Himlen
unis jr cor/3pt jr cor/unis wom cor/3pt wom cor NORDISKA 4209 s.p. (L1218)

Hostpsalm *Psalm
mix cor NORDISKA 1257 s.p. (L1219)

Julmorgon
wom cor/jr cor,org NORDISKA 4801 s.p. (L1220)

LINDSTROM
Blessed Mary, Faithful Joseph
SA/TB FLAMMER E5082 $.25 (L1221)

Six Introits For Advent And Christmas *CC6U, Adv/Xmas
SATB FLAMMER A 5235 $.25 (L1222)

LINDUSKY, EUGENE
From The Depths
SATB oct WALTON 2952 $.35 (L1223)

Psalm 148 *see Sing To The Lord!

Send Forth Your Light
SATB oct WALTON 2953 $.35 (L1224)

Sing To The Lord! (Psalm 148)
SATB oct SUMMY M 2848 $.65 (L1225)

LINEK, JIRI IGNATZ (1725-1791)
Christ, Der Herr, Kommt In Die Welt *Boh
(Hellmann, Diethard) 4pt mix cor,cont,2vln, opt glockenspiel or triangle s.p. sc BREITKOPF-W PB-4843, cor pts BREITKOPF-W CHB-3566 (L1226)

LINKE, NORBERT (1933-)
Gelobt Sei Gott Im Hochsten Thron
SS/TT,treb inst/bass inst HANSSLER 14.079 s.p. contains also: Wenzel, Eberhard, Erschienen Ist Der Herrlich Tag (SA,treb inst/bass inst) (L1227)

Kommt Und Lasst Uns Christum Ehren
see Kukuck, Felicitas, Ich Steh An Deiner Krippen Hier

Markus-Passion
SAB,solo,narrator HANSSLER 7.095 s.p. (L1228)

O Susser Herre Jesu Christ
see Poos, Heinrich, O Susser Herre Jesu Christ

LINKENBACH, KLAUS (1932-)
Es Ist Ein Ros' Entsprugen
see Praetorius, Michael, Es Ist Ein Ros' Entsprungen

Ich Ruf Zu Dir, Herr Jesu Christ
SATB/SB/SAB HANSSLER 8.024 s.p. (L1229)

LINN, ROBERT (1925-)
Anthem Of Wisdom *anthem
SATB,orch/2pno oct LAWSON 51207 $.40, ipr (L1230)

Olympic Hymn *hymn
(Samara, S.) SATB (easy) PRESSER G-4011 $.35 (L1231)

LION AND THE LAMB, THE see Kalmanoff, [Martin]

LIPKIN, MALCOLM (1932-)
O Praise The Lord, All Ye Nations *Thanks, anthem
mix cor,acap oct NOVELLO 40.1522.03 s.p. (L1232)

LIPPAI, WAKE UP! *Xmas
(Warner) 4pt mix cor oct SCHIRM.G 11211 $.25 (L1233)

LIPSCOMB
Legend Of The Lilies *Easter/Lent
SAB oct PRO ART 2306 $.25 (L1234)

LIPSCOMB, EDNA
I've Got A Glory (composed with Lipscomb, Helen)
SATB oct SHAPIRO SK 2098 $.25 (L1235)

LIPSCOMB, HELEN
Ancient Prayer
SABar,org/pno oct SCHIRM.G 10990 $.30 (L1236)

Behtlehem Town *Xmas
2pt wom cor,org/pno oct SCHIRM.G 11037 $.20 (L1237)

I Sing The Mighty Power Of God
3pt mix cor oct SCHIRM.G 10656 $.30 (L1238)

I've Got A Glory *see Lipscomb, Edna

Jesu, Jesu, Why Did You Die?
3pt mix cor (easy) oct SCHIRM.G 11000 $.25 (L1239)

O Come And Mourn *Easter
3pt mix cor,org/pno oct SCHIRM.G 11036 $.20 (L1240)

O Holy Spirit Sent From Heaven
2pt boy cor/2pt wom cor/jr cor oct SCHIRM.G 10906 $.20 (L1241)

Pastoral Prayer, A
3pt mix cor oct SCHIRM.G 11154 $.30 (L1242)

Song Or Praise
2pt wom cor oct SCHIRM.G 10657 $.25 (L1243)

We Have Seen His Star In The East *Xmas
3pt mix cor,SA soli,org/pno oct SCHIRM.G 11042 $.25 (L1244)

We Praise Thee, O God
2pt wom cor oct SCHIRM.G 10724 $.25 (L1245)

LIRE BOULIRE, LIRE BOULA see Rontgen, [Julius]

LIRUM, LIRUM see Morley, Thomas

LISKEN, GERD
Das Ist Ein Kostlich Ding *mot
4pt mix cor (contains also: Trostet Mein Volk) MOSELER s.p. see also Funf Geistliche Motetten (L1246)

Funf Geistliche Motetten *see Das Ist Ein Kostlich Ding; Gott Sei Mir Gnadig; O Herr, Mach Mich Zum Werkzeug (L1247)

Gott Sei Mir Gnadig *mot
4-6pt mix cor MOSELER s.p. see also Funf Geistliche Motetten (L1248)

Lobe Den Herrn, Meine Seele *Psalm
4pt mix cor,ob,bsn,vln,vcl MOSELER sc s.p., cor pts s.p., ipa, voc pt s.p. (L1249)

O Herr, Mach Mich Zum Werkzeug *mot
4-6pt mix cor (contains also: Wie Der Hirsch Schreit) MOSELER s.p. see also Funf Geistliche Motetten (L1250)

LISSMANN, KURT (1902-)
Aus Der Tiefe Rufe Ich (Psalm 130)
mix cor,acap TONGER s.p. (L1251)

Das Leben Ist Nur Ein Kommen Und Gehn
see Vom Leben

Es Kommt Ein Schiff Geladen *Xmas
men cor&opt treb cor TONGER s.p. (L1252)

Feiger Gedanken *hymn
men cor,winds voc sc TONGER s.p., ipa (L1253)

Gott, Ich Atme Deine Kraft
men cor,winds,timp voc sc TONGER s.p., ipa (L1254)

Gross Ist Der Herr
see Vom Leben

In Dulci Jubilo *Xmas
men cor&opt treb cor TONGER s.p. (L1255)

Jauchzet Dem Herren (Psalm 100)
mix cor,acap TONGER s.p. (L1256)

Kommet, Ihr Hirten *Xmas
men cor&opt treb cor TONGER s.p. (L1257)

Lobe Den Herren (Psalm 103)
mix cor,acap TONGER s.p. (L1258)

O Heiland, Reiss Die Himmel Auf *Xmas
mix cor TONGER s.p. (L1259)

Psalm 100 *see Jauchzet Dem Herren

Psalm 103 *see Lobe Den Herren

Psalm 130 *see Aus Der Tiefe Rufe Ich

Rausche, Machtiger Psalm *Psalm
men cor,winds voc sc TONGER s.p., ipa (L1260)

Unendlich Meer
see Vom Leben

Vom Himmel Hoch, Da Komm Ich Her *Xmas
men cor&opt treb cor TONGER s.p. (L1261)

LISSMANN, KURT (cont'd.)

Vom Leben
mix cor,acap TONGER s.p.
contains: Das Leben Ist Nur Ein Kommen Und Gehn; Gross Ist Der Herr; Unendlich Meer (L1262)

Zum Sehen Geboren
men cor,winds/orch cor pts TONGER s.p., ipa (L1263)

Zwischen Ochs Und Eselein *Xmas
wom cor&jr cor TONGER s.p. (L1264)

LIST! THE CHERUBIC HOST see Gaul, Alfred Robert

LIST TO THE LARK see Dickinson, Clarence

LISTEN! see Feltmate

LISTEN see Skillings, Otis

LISTEN, LORD see Ward, William R.

LISTEN LORDLINGS, UNTO ME *Xmas
(Stone) SAB oct PRO ART 1548 $.18 (L1265)

LISTEN, LORDLINGS, UNTO ME see Ehret, Walter

LISTEN MY HEART see Dovenspike, William

LISTEN, O COASTLANDS see Boyd

LISTEN TO DE LAMBS *spir
(Roberton) mix cor ROBERTON 61404 s.p. (L1266)

LISTEN TO ME see Pinkham, Daniel

LISTEN TO THE ANGELS *spir
(Johnson, A.H.) SATB,ABar soli,acap FISCHER,J 10079 $.30 (L1267)
(Papale, Henry) SATB,T solo,acap oct WORLD ESE-1166-8 $.45 (L1268)
(Papale, Henry; Track, Gerhard) TTBB,B solo, acap oct WESTWOOD ESE-1870-4 $.45 (L1269)

LISTEN TO THE ANGELS SHOUTIN' *spir
(Follett) SATB oct PRO ART 2058 $.22 (L1270)

LISTEN TO THE ANGELS SHOUTING see Work

LISTEN TO THE LAMBS *anthem/spir
(Dett) mix cor,STB soli,acap oct SCHIRM.G 5956 $.25 (L1271)
(Dett) 4pt mix cor,S solo,acap oct SCHIRM.G 8010 $.35 (L1272)
(Dett) 4pt men cor,T solo,acap oct SCHIRM.G 7405 $.35 (L1273)
(Dett; Harris) 3pt wom cor/4pt men cor,S solo,acap oct SCHIRM.G 7028 $.25 (L1274)
(Dett; Nash) SAB oct SCHIRM.G 7337 $.30 (L1275)
(Ehret) SA MARKS 4067 $.30 (L1276)
(Ehret) SSA MARKS 4171 $.30 (L1277)
(Ehret) SAB MARKS 4172 $.30 (L1278)
(Kinsman) SSAATTBB oct SPRATT 139 $.30 (L1279)
(Tolmage) SATB oct STAFF 320 $.25 (L1280)

LISTEN TO THE LAMBS see Dett, Robert Nathaniel

LISTER, MOSIE
At The Crossing
(Mercer) SATB oct LILLENAS AL-1030 $.30 (L1281)

At The Journey's End
SATB oct LILLENAS AL-1010 $.25 (L1282)

Come To The Water
SATB oct LILLENAS AL-1003 $.30 (L1283)

Come Unto Me
SATB oct LILLENAS AL-1002 $.30 (L1284)

Day Of Miracles, The
SATB oct LILLENAS AL-1026 $.30 (L1285)

Evangelistic Choir *CC9UL
mix cor (easy) cmplt ed LILLENAS MB-045 $1.50 (L1286)

Fall On Us
SATB oct LILLENAS AL-1027 $.30 (L1287)

Gentle Stranger, The
SATB oct LILLENAS AL-1015 $.35 (L1288)

Give God A Chance
SATB oct LILLENAS AL-1024 $.35 (L1289)

Great And Mighty Are Thy Works, Oh, Lord
SATB oct LILLENAS AL-1001 $.30 (L1290)

He Has Surely Borne Our Sorrow *anthem
SATB oct LILLENAS AL-1009 $.30 (L1291)

He'll Open The Windows Of Heaven *anthem
SATB oct LILLENAS AL-1023 $.30 (L1292)

He's Only A Prayer Away
SATB oct LILLENAS AL-1022 $.30 (L1293)

Highest Hill, The
(Collins) SATB oct LILLENAS AN-1638 $.30 (L1294)

His Grace Is Sufficient For Me
SATB oct LILLENAS AL-1020 $.30 (L1295)

How Long Has It Been?
SATB oct LILLENAS AL-1004 $.30 (L1296)

If To Gain The World
SATB oct LILLENAS AL-1013 $.30 (L1297)

I'm Depending On Jesus
(Mercer) SATB oct LILLENAS AL-1032 $.30 (L1298)

I'm Feeling Fine
(Turner) SATB oct LILLENAS AL-1008 $.30 (L1299)

In That Hour
SATB oct LILLENAS AL-1012 $.25 (L1300)

I've Been Changed
(Turner) SATB oct LILLENAS AL-1017 $.30 (L1301)

Led By The Master's Hand
SATB oct LILLENAS AL-1011 $.30 (L1302)

LISTER, MOSIE (cont'd.)

Lifted
SATB oct LILLENAS AL-1016 $.30   (L1303)

O Builder Of The Stars
SATB oct LILLENAS AL-1018 $.30   (L1304)

O Lord Of The Universe
SATB oct LILLENAS AL-1025 $.30   (L1305)

Price Was Paid, The
(Mercer) SATB oct LILLENAS AL-1029 $.30
(L1306)

Psalm 1
SATB oct LILLENAS AL-1014 $.30   (L1307)

Tender Shepherd, The
SATB oct LILLENAS AL-1019 $.30   (L1308)

Then I Met The Master
(Turner) SATB oct LILLENAS AL-1007 $.30 (L1309)

There Go I
(Mercer) SATB oct LILLENAS AL-1028 $.30
(L1310)

These Drops Of Blood
SATB oct LILLENAS AL-1005 $.30   (L1311)

This Love Is Mine
SATB oct LILLENAS AL-1033 $.30   (L1312)

'Til The Storm Passes By
SATB oct LILLENAS AL-1006 $.30   (L1313)

Until I Found The Lord
(Mercer) SATB oct LILLENAS AL-1031 $.30
(L1314)

Where No One Stands Alone
(Turner) SATB oct LILLENAS AL-1021 $.30 (L1315)

LISTER'S GOSPEL CHOIR *CC16UL,gospel
(Lister, Mosie) cor,pno (easy) cmplt ed
LILLENAS MB-107 $1.50   (L1316)

LISZNEIWSKI, KAROL
Old Polish Christmas Carol *Xmas,carol
SATB oct HUNTZINGER 4049 $.20   (L1317)

LISZT, FRANZ (1811-1886)
A Munka Himnusza
(Bardos, L.) (Weiner, L.) [Hung] TTBB,orch
(diff) BUDAPEST 1090 s.p., ipa   (L1318)
(Bardos, L.) (Rossa, E.) [Hung] SATB,B solo
(diff) BUDAPEST 1409 s.p.   (L1319)
(Bardos, L.) [Hung] 3pt (diff) BUDAPEST
1408 s.p.   (L1320)
(Bardos, L.) [Hung] TTBB (diff) BUDAPEST
1707 s.p.   (L1321)
(Kossa, E.; Bardos, L.) [Hung] SATB,B solo
(diff) BUDAPEST 1409A s.p.   (L1322)

All My Heart And Soul
(Red, Virginia) SATB,acap WORD CRS-24 $.35
(L1323)

Ave Verum
(James) SATB oct GRAY GCMR 1876 $.30   (L1324)

Ave Verum Corpus
(Clough-Leighter, H.) "Blessed Lord, All
Love Excelling" SATB,org SCHIRM.EC 2621
$.30   (L1325)

Blessed Lord, All Love Excelling *see Ave
Verum Corpus

But I Have Trusted In Thy Mercy
(Hines) 3pt mix cor oct SCHIRM.G 11662 $.25
(L1326)

Christus *Xmas,ora
cor,orch sc KALMUS $50.00, ipa   (L1327)

Come Unto Me
SATB oct LORENZ 9056 $.30   (L1328)

Coronation Mass *Mass
[Lat] voc sc PETERS GM1 $4.50, ipr, min sc
PETERS E941 $10.00, ipr   (L1329)

Der Herr Bewahret Die Seelen Seiner Heiligen
(Frank) "Rejoice, Ye Who Love The Lord"
SATB oct FOX MM22 $.25   (L1330)

Der Kreuzweg *see Via Crucis

Die Toten *Req
men cor,2fl,2ob,2clar,2bsn,2trp,4horn,
3trom,tuba,strings,perc,timp,harp,opt org
BREITKOPF-L rental   (L1331)

Graner Festmesse *Mass
"Missa Solemnis" [Lat] voc sc PETERS GM6
$4.50, ipr, min sc PETERS E942 $10.00,
ipr   (L1332)

Graner Mass *see Missa Solemnis

Jesu, Word Of God Incarnate
(Ehret) mix cor CHAPPELL 0023440-358 $.40
(L1333)

Les Preludes
(Reibold) "Preludes To Eternity" SSAATTBB
oct SUMMY B 1442 $1.00   (L1334)

Liebestraume No. 3
"Love Divine" SATB ALLANS 117 s.p.   (L1335)

Lord How Long (Psalm 13) cant
BELWIN $1.00   (L1336)

Lord, How Long Wilt Thou Forget Me? (Psalm
13)
see Psalms
mix cor,T solo,orch voc sc SCHIRM.G $1.25
(L1337)
cor voc sc KALMUS 6282 $1.25   (L1338)

Love Divine *see Liebestraume No. 3

Mass For Male Voices *Mass/Req
(Busoni; Bartok; Raabe; da Motta; and
others) men cor (stiftung edition v.3)
GREGG ISBN 0:576 28732 6 s.p. contains
also: Missa Choralis (cor); Requiem (cor)
(L1339)

Missa C-Moll *Mass
4pt men cor,org (C min) sc BREITKOPF-W
PB-892 s.p., cor pts BREITKOPF-W CHB-3528
s.p.   (L1340)

LISZT, FRANZ (cont'd.)

Missa Choralis *Mass
see Liszt, Franz, Mass For Male Voices
cor voc sc KALMUS 6281 $1.75   (L1341)

Missa Solemnis *Mass
"Graner Mass" cor voc sc KALMUS 6284 $2.50
(L1342)

Missa Solemnis *see Graner Festmesse

Missa Solemnis
cor GREGG ISBN 0:576 28233 2 s.p.   (L1343)

O Lord Above, Whose Sacrifice *see O
Salutaris Hostia

O Salutaris Hostia *Easter/Lent
(Marshall, Charles) "O Lord Above, Whose
Sacrifice" SATB FRANK F-549 $.30   (L1344)

Oremus Pro Pontifice *Gen,mot
(Brun, L'abbe) [Lat] 4pt mix cor/2 eq
voices oct DURAND s.p.   (L1345)
(Brun, L'abbe F.) [Lat] 4pt mix cor/2 eq
voices,acap oct DURAND   (L1346)

Our Father, Who Art In Heaven *see Pater
Noster

Pater Noster (from Christus)
(Van Camp, L.) "Our Father, Who Art In
Heaven" 8pt mix cor,acap CONCORDIA
97-4885 $.85   (L1347)

Preludes To Eternity *see Les Preludes

Psalm 13 *see Lord, How Long Wilt Thou
Forget Me?

Psalm 18
see Psalms

Psalm 116
see Psalms

Psalm 129
see Psalms

Psalm 137
see Psalms

Psalms
GREGG ISBN 0:576 28230 8 s.p. also contains
solo work
contains: Psalm 13 (cor,T solo,orch)
Psalm 18 (men cor,orch); Psalm 116 (men
cor,pno); Psalm 129 (men cor,Bar solo,
org); Psalm 137 (wom cor,S solo,org,
vln,harp)   (L1348)

Rejoice, Ye Who Love The Lord *see Der Herr
Bewahret Die Seelen Seiner Heiligen

Requiem
see Liszt, Franz, Mass For Male Voices

Via Crucis *Psntd
mix cor,SATB soli,org/pno sc BREITKOPF-L
rental   (L1349)
cor voc sc KALMUS 6283 $1.75   (L1350)
"Der Kreuzweg" mix cor,SATB soli,org/pno,
2trp,2horn,2trom,strings BREITKOPF-L
rental   (L1351)

Ye Sons And Daughters Of The King (from
Christus)
[Lat/Eng] SSA SCHIRM.EC 1884   (L1352)

LITANEI "RUH'N IN FRIEDEN ALLE SEELEN" see
Schubert, Franz (Peter)

LITANEIEN see Mozart, Wolfgang Amadeus

LITANEIEN, MOTETTEN, UND PSALMEN-BAND XXVI see
Palestrina, Giovanni

LITANI see Geitvik, S.H.

LITANI see Jeppesen, Knud

LITANI see Laub, Thomas

LITANIA see Kox, Hans

LITANIA see Mozart, Wolfgang Amadeus, Litaniae
De Venerabili Altaris Sacramento

LITANIA see Mozart, Wolfgang Amadeus, Litanie
De Venerabili Altaris Sacramento

LITANIA CURSORIA see Szarzynski, Stanislaw
Silwester

LITANIA see Mozart, Wolfgang Amadeus, Litaniae
De Venerabili Altaris Sacramento

LITANIAE DE B.M.V. IN C-DUR see Haydn, (Franz)
Joseph

LITANIAE DE BEATA VIRGINE see Mozart, Wolfgang
Amadeus

LITANIAE DE BEATA VIRGINE MARIA see Palestrina,
Giovanni

LITANIAE DE S. JOSEPH see Volpi, Edoardo

LITANIAE DE VENERABILI ALTARIS SACRAMENTO see
Mozart, Wolfgang Amadeus

LITANIAE DE VENERABILI ALTARIS SACRAMENTO see
Mozart, Wolfgang Amadeus

LITANIAE DE VENERABILI ALTARIS SACRAMENTO see
Mozart, Wolfgang Amadeus

LITANIAE DEIPARAE VIRGINIS I see Palestrina,
Giovanni

LITANIAE DEIPARAE VIRGINIS II see Palestrina,
Giovanni

LITANIAE LAURETANAE see Mozart, Wolfgang
Amadeus

LITANIAE LAURETANAE B.M.V. see Mozart, Wolfgang
Amadeus

LITANIAE LAURETANAE see Mozart, Wolfgang
Amadeus

LITANIAE SS. CORDIS JESU see Volpi, Edoardo

LITANIAE see Mozart, Wolfgang Amadeus, Litaniae
De Venerabili Altaris Sacramento

LITANIE DE VENERABILI ALTARIS SACRAMENTO see
Mozart, Wolfgang Amadeus

LITANIE DEL S. CUORE DI GESU see Bottazzo,
Luigi

LITANIE LAURETANE see Visona', Gino

LITANIE, THE see Johnston, Jack

LITANIES A LA VIERGE NOIRE (NOTRE-DAME DE ROC-
AMADOUR) see Poulenc, Francis

LITANIES DE LA SAINTE VIERGE see Anonymous

LITANY see Peloquin, C. Alexander

LITANY see Pfautsch, Lloyd

LITANY see Schubert, Franz (Peter)

LITANY, A see Pinkham, Daniel

LITANY, A see Walton, William

LITANY AND PRAYER see Kubik, Gail

LITANY FOR A PENITENT see Cappadonia, Anthony

LITANY FOR ALL SOUL'S DAY see Schubert, Franz
(Peter)

LITANY FOR AMERICA see Lovelace, Austin C.

LITANY FOR EASTER see Young

LITANY FOR EASTER see Young, Gordon

LITANY IN B FLAT see Mozart, Wolfgang Amadeus

LITANY OF PRAISE see Hooper

LITANY OF THANKSGIVING see Beck, John Ness

LITANY OF THANKSGIVING, A see Schroth, Gerhard

LITANY TO THE HOLY SPIRIT see Hurford, Peter

LITANY TO THE HOLY SPIRIT, A see Milford, Robin

LITANY WITH THE LATER SUFFRAGES, THE (FERIAL)
see Tallis, Thomas

LITEN JULKANTATE see Hansen, Carl Willum

LITEN MASSA see Norman, Rudolf

LITEN MASSA see Thyrestam, Gunnar

LIT'L BOY CHILE *spir
(Dawson) SATB KJOS T120 $.30   (L1353)

LITLE FUGLEN see Geitvik, S.H.

LITTANY GLORY, PRAISE AND POWER see Mozart,
Wolfgang Amadeus, Litanie De Venerabili
Altaris Sacramento

LITTEN, JACK
Christ Is Born Today! *Xmas
SATB oct SHAPIRO SK 2041 $.25   (L1354)

Hosanna To The Living Lord!
SATB oct SHAPIRO SK 2076 $.30   (L1355)

Lord Reigneth, The
SATB oct SHAPIRO SK 2079 $.30   (L1356)

O God, Thou Art My God
SATB oct SHAPIRO SK 2058 $.25   (L1357)

O Lord, Purify Our Hearts
SAB oct SHAPIRO SK 5008 $.25   (L1358)

Prayer Of Supplication
SATB oct SHAPIRO SK 2045 $.25   (L1359)

Resignation
SATB oct SHAPIRO SK 2059 $.25   (L1360)

Ride On In Majesty!
SATB oct SHAPIRO SK 2076 $.30   (L1361)

Sing Ye Praise To The New Born King *Xmas
2pt oct SHAPIRO SK 4016 $.25   (L1362)
SSA oct SHAPIRO SK 3019 $.30   (L1363)

Sing Ye Praises To The New Born King *Xmas
SATB oct SHAPIRO SK 2065 $.25   (L1364)

Sleep, Little Child *Xmas
SATB oct SHAPIRO SK 2068 $.25   (L1365)

LITTLE ADVENT MUSIC, A see Distler, Hugo

LITTLE ANTHEM BOOK FOR CHILDREN, THE see Licht

LITTLE BABE IN A MANGER IS BORN, A see Bragg

LITTLE BABY BOY see Avery

LITTLE BABY JESUS see Johnson, Elwood

LITTLE BOOK OF HOURS see Klein, Lothar

LITTLE BOY JESUS AND I see Fenwick

LITTLE BOY JESUS, THE see Lekberg, Sven

LITTLE BROTHER JESUS see Niles, John Jacob

LITTLE CAROL, A see Rodgers

LITTLE CHILD, A *Xmas,carol,Dut
(Gordon, P.) SATB,opt pno AMP A240 $.20
(L1366)

LITTLE CHILD IS BORN see Grundman

LITTLE CHILD OF MARY *spir
(Burleigh) SSA RICORDI-ENG LD461 s.p.   (L1367)

LITTLE CHILD OF MARY see Burleigh, Henry Thacker

LITTLE CHILD ON EARTH HAS BEEN BORN see Powell

LITTLE CHILD ON EARTH HAS BEEN BORN, A see Powell, Robert J.

LITTLE CHILD ON THE EARTH *Xmas,carol
uns/SATB (very easy) OXFORD 08.074 $.15
(L1368)

LITTLE CHILD SO LOVELY, A see Praetorius, Michael, Ein Kindelein So Lobelich

LITTLE CHILD SO LOWLY, A see Ehret, Walter

LITTLE CHILD THERE IS YBORN see Joubert, John

LITTLE CHILD THERE IS YBORN, A see Copley, I.A.

LITTLE CHILD THERE IS YBORN, A see Rimmer, Frederick

LITTLE CHILDREN see Youse, Glad [Robinson]

LITTLE CHILDREN ALL see Ropartz, Joseph Guy

LITTLE CHILDREN, COME TO JESUS see Prichard, [Rowland Hugh]

LITTLE CHILDREN LISTEN see Di Julio, [Max]

LITTLE CHILDREN, PRAISE THE SAVIOUR
see Three More General Choruses

LITTLE CHILD'S PRAYER, A see Farrar, H.M.

LITTLE CHILLUN, DON'T YOU CRY see Kazze, L.

LITTLE CHRIST CHILD, SWEET AND HOLY see Williams

LITTLE CHRISTMAS CANTATA see Charpentier, Marc-Antoine

LITTLE CHRISTMAS CANTATA, A see Serly, Tibor

LITTLE CHRISTMAS CANTATA ACCORDING TO THE EVANGELIST ST. LUKE, A see Dietrich, Fritz

LITTLE CHRISTMAS CONCERT ON "FROM HEAVEN ABOVE", A see Beck, Theodore

LITTLE CHURCH CHOIR BOOK, THE *CC30U
(Lundquist, M.) uns,org SCHIRM.EC 1984 $1.75
(L1369)

LITTLE CHURCH YEAR, A see Lynn, George

LITTLE CRADLE ROCKS TONIGHT IN GLORY, THE see Walker, David S.

LITTLE CROCUS see Grime, William

LITTLE DAVID *spir
(Geller) SATB MARKS 4212 $.25 (L1370)

LITTLE DAVID PLAY *spir,US
(Aubanel, Georges) "Petit David Joue" [Eng/Fr] 3 eq voices OUVRIERES s.p. (L1371)
(Aubanel, Georges) "Petit David Joue" [Eng/Fr] 4pt mix cor OUVRIERES s.p. (L1372)
(Aubanel, Georges) "Petit David Joue De La Harpe" [Eng/Fr] 3 eq voices OUVRIERES s.p.
(L1373)

LITTLE DAVID PLAY ON YO' HARP *spir
see Negro Spirituals
(Widdicombe) 2pt jr cor/2pt wom cor CURWEN 72559 s.p. (L1374)
(Wilson) SAB SCHMITT 5005 $.35 (L1375)

LITTLE DAVID PLAY ON YOUR HARP *spir
(Burleigh) SSA RICORDI-ENG LD460 s.p. (L1376)
(Burleigh) SATB RICORDI-ENG LD454 s.p. (L1377)
(Christiansen, P.) SATB KJOS 53 $.30 (L1378)
(Durian, Tim) 4pt men cor,acap BREITKOPF-W Z-43 s.p. see also Dreizehn Negro-Spirituals (L1379)
(Malin, D.) SATB KJOS 5063 $.30 (L1380)
(Pasfield, W.R.) 2pt ASHDOWN E.A.306 s.p. (L1381)
(Roberton) 3pt jr cor/3pt wom cor ROBERTON 72101 s.p. (L1382)
(Schubert) SATB oct LILLENAS AN-3835 $.25 (L1383)

LITTLE DAVID, PLAY ON YOUR HARP see Hughes

LITTLE DAVID, PLAY ON YOUR HARP see Hughes, Robert J.

LITTLE FAMILY, THE see Ahrold, Frank

LITTLE FAMILY, THE see Niles, John Jacob

LITTLE FOLK MASS OF SAINT PHILIP, THE see Williams, Arthur

LITTLE HOLY JESUS see Norden

LITTLE HYMN TO MARY, A see Searle, Humphrey

LITTLE INFANT KING see Glover, R.F.

LITTLE INFANT, SWEET AND HOLY *Xmas,It
(Ehret) SSA MARKS 4353 $.30 (L1384)

LITTLE INNOCENT LAMB *spir
(Bartholomew) 4pt men cor,acap oct SCHIRM.G 9907 $.35 (L1385)
(Bartholomew) 4pt mix cor,acap oct SCHIRM.G 10049 $.40 (L1386)

LITTLE JESU OF BRAGA, THE see Gaul, Harvey Bartlet

LITTLE JESUS
see Three Polish Carols

LITTLE JESUS CAME TO TOWN see Rinehart

LITTLE JESUS, SWEETLY SLEEP *Xmas,carol
SATB (very easy) OXFORD 08.087 $.15 (L1387)

LITTLE JESUS SWEETLY SLEEP see Glarum, L. Stanley

LITTLE KING OF HEAVEN, THE see Rosa, M.

LITTLE KING OF THE WORLD, THE see Mealy

LITTLE LAMB
(De Cormier) SATB,acap oct LAWSON 51426 $.40
(L1388)

LITTLE LAMB see Artman

LITTLE LAMB see Demarest, A.

LITTLE LAMB see Rhea, Raymond

LITTLE LAMB, THE see Caldwell

LITTLE LAMB, WHO MADE THEE see Forest

LITTLE LAMB WHO MADE THEE? see Jones

LITTLE LAMB, WHO MADE THEE? see Kennedy

LITTLE LAMB, WHO MADE THEE see Pedrette

LITTLE, LEONARD
Thee Will I Love, O Lord
4pt men cor oct SCHIRM.G 10536 $.25 (L1389)

LITTLE LYKING, THE see Corbeil, Pierre de

LITTLE NEW-BORN BABY *Xmas
(Dunsmore) SATB SCHMITT 926 $.40 (L1390)

LITTLE NEWBORN JESUS CHILD, THE see Buxtehude, Dietrich, Das Neugeborne Kindelein

LITTLE ONES AT CHRISTMAS *Xmas
oct LORENZ $.40 (L1391)

LITTLE PINE TREE, THE see De Noon

LITTLE PINE TREE, THE see Maxwell

LITTLE PRAYER, A
2pt CHAPPELL 0018143-352 $.40 (L1392)
SSA CHAPPELL 0018143-354 $.40 (L1393)
SATB CHAPPELL 0018143-358 $.40 (L1394)

LITTLE PRAYER, BE ON YOUR WAY see McWhertor

LITTLE ROAD TO BETHLEHEM see Head, Michael
(Dewar)

LITTLE ROOM, THE
(Pitfield) uns/cong&SATB (med easy) OXFORD 84.143 $.35 (L1395)

LITTLE SAVIOUR, SLEEP see France

LITTLE SAVIOUR, THE see Ager, Laurence

LITTLE SHEEP OF BETHLEHEM see Warren

LITTLE SHEPHERD *Xmas/Pageant
LORENZ $.75 (L1396)

LITTLE SHEPHERD, THE see Gillette

LITTLE SHEPHERDS CAROL, THE see Ringwald, [Roy]

LITTLE STAR OF BETHLEHEM *Xmas/Pageant
LORENZ $.75 (L1397)

LITTLE STAR ON THE CHRISTMAS TREE see Thygerson

LITTLE STRANGER *Xmas
SATB BIG3 $.30 (L1398)

LITTLE TALK WITH JESUS, A
(Stevens) SATB oct PRO ART 1841 $.20 (L1399)

LITTLE TOWN see McAfee, Don

LITTLE WHITE DOVE see Grieb, Herbert [C.]

LITTLETON
Bless The Lord, O My Soul
SATB oct FISCHER,C R-6137 $.30 (L1400)

LITURGHIA SF. JOAN CHRISTOMUL see Popesco

LITURGIA DOMESTICA see Gretchaninov, Alexander Tikhonovitch

LITURGICAL CANTATA see Ben-Haim, Paul

LITURGICAL MOTETS see Willan, Healey

LITURGICAL RESPONSE see Lundquist, Matthew Nathanael

LITURGICAL RESPONSES AND ANTHEMS see Rogers

LITURGICAL SATZE *see Kyrie Minus Summum 1612
(L1401)

LITURGICAL SUITE see Zaninelli, Luigi

LITURGISCHE SATZE *Op.13, CCU
(Distler, Hugo) [Ger] 2-7 eq voices/2-8pt mix cor,acap (easy/med/diff) cloth BAREN. BA 884 $9.75
see also: Dreimaliges Kyrie Martin Luthers 1526; Dreimaliges Kyrie Nurnberg 1525; Dreimaliges Kyrie Strassburg 1525; Dreimaliges Kyrie Strassburg 1525 Und Nurnberg 1525; Neunmaliges Kyrie Cunctipotens "O Milder Gott"; Neunmaliges Kyrie Magnae Deus Potentiae; Nurnberger Grosses Gloria 1525; Spangenbergs Grosses Gloria 1545; Strassburger Grosses Gloria 1525
(L1402)

LITURGISCHE STUCKE ZUM GOTTESDIENST see Schwartz, Gerhard von

LITURGISCHES CHORBUCH, BAND 1 *CC9U,Allelu/Introit/liturg
(Brodde, Otto) [Ger] 3pt mix cor cloth BAREN. EM 351 s.p. (L1403)

LITURGISCHES CHORBUCH, BAND 2 *CCU,liturg/Psalm
(Brodde, Otto) [Ger] 3pt mix cor pap BAREN. EM 352 s.p. and songs of praise (L1404)

LITURGISK MUSIC see Laub, Thomas

LITURGISK MUSIK see Laub, Thomas

LIUZZI, FERNANDO (1884-1940)
La Passione Nelle Intonazioni Del "Laudario 97"
cor,pno SANTIS 996 rental (L1405)

LIVE A-HUMBLE *spir
(Noble) SATB oct SPRATT 133 $.25 (L1406)

LIVE IT LIVE see Wade

LIVE YOUR LIFE FOR HIM see Bach

LIVE YOUR LIFE FOR HIM see Bach, Johann Sebastian

LIVE YOUR LIFE FOR HIM ALWAYS see Bach, Johann Sebastian

LIVELY ONES, THE *CC8UL
(Baker, David) SATB voc sc WORD 30074 $1.95
(L1407)

LIVES ONCE AGAIN OUR GLORIOUS KING see Ehret, Walter

LIVIERI, C.
Ipsi Sum Desponsata
see PRO VESTITIONE MONIALIUM

O Sacrum Convivium
see SEI MOTTETTI EUCARISTICI

LIVING CHRIST see McWhertor

LIVING CHRIST, THE see Elmore, Robert [Hall]

LIVING FLAME OF LOVE see Surinach, Carlos, Llama De Amor Viva

LIVING FOR JESUS
(Jones) SATB oct WORD CS-2059 $.30 (L1408)

LIVING FOR JESUS see Lowden

LIVING GOD *Neth
SATB (easy) ALLANS 346 s.p. (L1409)

LIVING GOD, THE see O'Hara, Geoffrey

LIVING GOD, THE see O'Hara, Geoffrey

LIVING LIGHT see Thompson

LIVING LIGHT, THE see Abt, Franz

LIVING REDEEMER, THE see Lillenas, Haldor

LIVING SOUND, THE *CCU
(Dalton, Larry) jr cor voc sc WORD 37555 $1.95 (L1410)

LIVING SPIRIT see Toolan, S. Suzanne

LIVING SPIRIT see Toolan, S. Suzanne

LIVING WATERS see Toolan, S. Suzanne

LIVING WORD, THE see Lovelace, Austin C.

LIVINGSTONE
Peter, May I Please Come In *spir
(Wolf) SATB oct BOURNE DW2 $.25 (L1411)

Softly The Dawn Awakens *Easter
(Wolf) SATB oct BOURNE 746 $.25 (L1412)

That Blessed Night *Xmas
(Wolf) SATB oct BOURNE 739 $.25 (L1413)

When Christ Was Born *Xmas
(Wolf) SATB oct BOURNE 770 $.25 (L1414)

LJOSET see Beck, Thomas [Ludvigsen]

LJUSET UPPGAR see Olson, Daniel

LLAMA DE AMOR VIVA see Surinach, Carlos

LLANFAIR see Goemanne, Noel

LLEGA NAVIDAD see Martini

LLEGO! LLEGO! see Santa Cruz, Domingo

LLIEBSTER JESU
"Father, Thou That Hearest Prayer" see Two Wedding Hymns

LLOYD
Come Unto Me, Ye Weary
(Ehret) SATB,org/pno BOSTON 12753 $.40
(L1415)

Long, Long Ago *Xmas
SA BOOSEY-CAN s.p. (L1416)

LLOYD, CHARLES HARFORD (1849-1919)
Benedicite (Shortened Form)
SATB (B flat maj) oct NOVELLO 44.1148.10 s.p. (L1417)

Grieve Not The Holy Spirit *Gen,anthem
(Ascherberg) SS,opt pno oct ROYAL s.p. see also ANTHEMS FOR UNISON OR TWO PART SINGING (L1418)

LLOYD, RICHARD H.
All So Still
see FOUR CHRISTMAS CAROLS

Now Sing A Saviour's Birth *Xmas,anthem
mix cor oct NOVELLO 40.1364.06 s.p. (L1419)

Prayer, A *prayer
treb cor LENGNICK s.p. (L1420)

View Me, Lord *anthem
mix cor,acap oct NOVELLO 50.0338.05 s.p.
(L1421)

LO! A BRIGHTER STAR see Bolz

LO A ROSE see Praetorius, Michael, Es Ist Ein Ros Entsprungen

LO, A VOICE TO HEAVEN SOUNDING see Bortniansky, Dimitri Stepanovitch

LO, BEHOLD, WE COME TO ADORE HIM see Nivers, Guillaume Gabriel

LO, GOD IS HERE see Grieg, Edvard Hagerup

LO, GOD IS HERE see Lovelace, Austin C.

LO, GOD IS HERE! see Mueller, Carl F.

LO, GOD IS HERE see Shaw, Diccon

LO, GOD IS HERE see Webber, Lloyd

LO' HE COMES see Holler, John

LO, HE COMES see Johnson, Davis

LO' HE COMES see Williams, David H.

LO! HE COMES WITH CLOUDS ASCENDING see Neander, Joachim

LO, HE COMES WITH CLOUDS DESCENDING see Wade

LO! HE COMES WITH CLOUDS DESCENDING see Willan, Healey

LO, HEAVEN AND EARTH see Korner, D.

LO, HOW A ROSE see Praetorius, Michael, Es Ist Ein Ros Entsprungen

LO, HOW A ROSE E'ER BLOOMING *Xmas,Ger,16th cent
(Niles) SAB,acap oct FISCHER,C CM-6729 $.25
(L1422)
(Van Koert, Han) SA&SATB,org oct WORLD AC-593-8 $.45
(L1423)

LO, HOW A ROSE E'ER BLOOMING see Caldwell

LO, HOW A ROSE E'ER BLOOMING see Hahn, Harvey

LO, HOW A ROSE E'ER BLOOMING see Krapf, Gerhard

LO, HOW A ROSE E'ER BLOOMING see Lynn, George

LO! HOW A ROSE E'ER BLOOMING see Niles, John Jacob

LO, HOW A ROSE E'ER BLOOMING see Praetorius, Michael, Es Ist Ein Ros' Entsprungen

LO, HOW A ROSE E'ER BLOOMING see Suderburg, R.

LO, HOW A ROSE ERE BLOOMING see Praetorius, Michael

LO, I AM THE VOICE OF ONE CRYING IN THE WILDERNESS see Schutz, Heinrich, Ich Bin Eine Rufende Stimme In Der Wusten

LO, I AM WITH YOU see Moe, Daniel

LO, I AM WITH YOU ALWAYS see Hutson, Wihla

LO, I AM WITH YOU ALWAYS see Peek, Richard

LO I BRING TIDINGS see Vierdanck, Johann

LO, I REVEAL UNTO THEE see Gallus, Jacobus

LO, I TELL YOU A MYSTERY see McAfee, D.

LO, IN THE TIME APPOINTED see Harris, Jerry Weseley

LO, IN THE TIME APPOINTED see Willan, Healey

LO MY SHEPHERD see Haydn, (Franz) Joseph

LO, MY SHEPHERD IS DIVINE see Haydn, (Franz) Joseph

LO, MY SHEPHERD'S HAND DIVINE see Haydn, (Franz) Joseph

LO, MY TRANSGRESSION AND MY SIN see Goudimel, Claude, Du Mal In Le Meschant Vouloir

LO! NEW BORN JESUS see Forsblad

LO! NOW A ROSE IS BLOOMING see Praetorius, Michael

LO NOW, SO IS THE DEATH OF THE JUST MAN see Gallus, Jacobus, Ecce, Quomodo Moritur

LO OUR FATHER'S TENDER CARE see Durst, Sidney C.

LO, ROUND THE THRONE (from Trier Gesangbuch)
hymn
cor oct ST.MARTIN SMP644 s.p.
(L1424)

LO, ROUND THE THRONE see Herman

LO, ROUND THE THRONE A GLORIOUS BAND *ASD, anthem
(Ley, Henry G.) SATB,opt inst (easy) oct OXFORD $.30, ipr
(L1425)

LO, ROUND THE THRONE A GLORIOUS BAND see Powell, Robert J.

LO! STAR-LED CHIEFS see Crotch, William

LO! THE ANGEL HOST REJOICES see Martin

LO, THE ANGEL SAID TO THE SHEPHERDS see Gabrieli, Andrea, Der Engel Sprach Zu Den Hirten

LO, THE ANGEL SAID TO THE SHEPHERDS see Scheidt, Samuel

LO, THE ANGEL SAID TO THE SHEPHERDS see Schutz, Heinrich, Der Engle Sprach Zu Den Hirten

LO, THE CHILD see Fuller, [Esther Mary]

LO, THE EARTH see Longfellow

LO, THE EARTH IS RISEN AGAIN see Blake, G.

LO THE EARTH IS RISEN AGAIN see Mueller, Carl F.

LO, THE EARTH IS RIS'N AGAIN *Easter
(Lehmeier) SATB SCHMITT 8049 $.30
(L1426)

LO, THE EARTH IS RIS'N AGAIN see Longfellow

LO! THE EARTH IS RIS'N AGAIN see Williams

LO, THE FAIR BEAUTY OF THE EARTH see Meek, Kenneth

LO, THE FULL, FINAL SACRIFICE see Finzi, Gerald

LO, THE GOOD SHEPHERD RISETH see Coloma, Surrexit Paston Bonus

LO, THE MESSIAH see Castelnuovo-Tedesco, Mario

LO, THE MORNING BREAKS see Leonard, S.W.

LO, THE MUSIC OF THE ANGELS *Xmas,carol,Slav
(Ehret) SAB,opt vln oct FOX CC4 $.25 (L1427)
(Ehret, W.) SAB,opt vln PROWSE CC4 s.p.
(L1428)

LO, THE SCEPTER FROM JUDAH see Schutz, Heinrich

LO, THE STAR WHICH THEY SAW see Willan, Healey

LO! THE TOMB IS EMPTY see Broome, Ed

LO, THERE IS NONE see Bach, Johann Sebastian

LO, THEY HAVE BORNE AWAY JESUS see Palestrina, Giovanni, Alleluia! Tulerunt Dominum

LO, THOU ART NEAR see Safsten, Mary R. Decker

LO, WE GO UP TO JERUSALEM see Back, Sven-Erick, Ecce Ascendimus Jerosolymam

LO, WHO ARE THESE, A DAZZLING BAND see Prussing, Stephen

LOB AUS DER STILLE see Vogel, Heinrich

LOB DER MUSIK "FANGT AN UND SINGT" see Strohbach, Siegfried

LOB DES JESUSKINDES see Roeseling, Kaspar

LOB, EHR SEI GOTT see Staden, Johann

LOB, EHR SEI GOTT, DEM VATER see Distler, Hugo

LOB, EHR UND PREIS SEI GOTT see Bach, Johann Sebastian

LOB, EHR UND PREIS SEI GOTT DEM VATER see Bach, Johann Sebastian

LOB GOTT, DU WERTE CHRISTENHEIT see Wolleb, Johann Jakob

LOB GOTT GETROST MIT SINGEN see Bossler, Kurt

LOB GOTT GETROST MIT SINGEN see Gumpeltzhaimer, A.

LOB GOTT GETROST MIT SINGEN see Gumpeltzhaimer, Adam

LOB GOTT GETROST MIT SINGEN see Kubler, Emil

LOB GOTT GETROST MIT SINGEN see Schein, Johann Hermann

LOB GOTT GETROST MIT SINGEN see Stern, Hermann

LOB GOTT GETROST MIT SINGEN see Zipp, Friedrich

LOB GOTTES see Bach, Karl Philipp Emanuel

LOB GOTTES see Othegraven, August J. von

LOB, PREIS UND DANK SEI DIR see Anonymous

LOB SEI DEM ALLMACHTIGEN GOTT see Kaufmann, Diethelm

LOB UND DANK *Gen/Thanks
SATB,acap cmplt ed DOBLINGER s.p.
contains & see also: Ammon, Blasius, Confitemini Domino; Burck, Joachim, Nun Lasst Uns Gott Dem Herren Dank Sagen; Gesius, Bartholomaus, Christum Wir Sollen Loben Schon; Gumpeltzhaimer, Adam, Lobt Gott Getrost Mit Singen; Gumpeltzhaimer, Adam, Wir Danken Dir, Herr Gott Vater; Hagius, Carl, Ihr Kreatur Im Himmel Oben; Hagius, Carl, Nun Lobet Gott Im Hohen Thron; Hassler, Hans Leo, Cantate Domino; Lassus, Roland de (Orlandus), Jubilate Deo; Lassus, Roland de (Orlandus), Tibi Laus; Lechner, Leonhard, Danket Dem Herrn; Praetorius, Michael, Lobet Den Herren; Schutz, Heinrich, Dank Sagen Wir Alle Gott; Schutz, Heinrich, Danket Dem Herren; Schutz, Heinrich, Ich Danke Dem Herren; Schutz, Heinrich, Jauchzet Dem Herrn Alle Welt; Schutz, Heinrich, Kommt Herzu, Lasst Uns Frolichsein; Viadana, Lodovico Grossi da, Exsultate Iusti
(L1429)

LOB UND DANK see Bornefeld, Helmut

LOB UND DANK see Stolzel, Gottfried Heinrich

LOB UND EHR SEI GOTT see Baumann, Max

LOB UND EHRE UND WEISHEIT UND DANK see Bach, Johann Sebastian

LOB UND EHRE UND WIESHEIT see Telemann, Georg Philipp

LOB UND PREIS see Rohwer, Jens

LOB UND PREIS SEI GOTT see Schutz, Heinrich

LOB UND PREIS SEI GOTT see Zagatti, Francesco, Gloria Patri

LOB UND PREIS SEI GOTT DEM VATER see Bach, Johann Sebastian

LOB UND PREIS SEI GOTT, DEM VATER see Schutz, Heinrich

LOBE DEN HERREN see Borris, Siegfried

LOBE DEN HERREN see Coleman, Henry

LOBE DEN HERREN see Hebble

LOBE DEN HERREN see Lissmann, Kurt

LOBE DEN HERREN see Muller, Paul

LOBE DEN HERREN see Newbury, Kent A.

LOBE DEN HERREN! see Schmid, Walter

LOBE DEN HERREN see Toolan, S. Suzanne

LOBE DEN HERREN see Verdanck, Johann

LOBE DEN HERREN see Vierdanck, Johann

LOBE DEN HERREN, DEN MACHTGEN KONIG see Gwinner, Volker

LOBE DEN HERREN, DEN MACHITGEN KONIG see Stern, Hermann

LOBE DEN HERREN, DEN MACHITGEN KONIG see Neander, Joachim

LOBE DEN HERREN DEN MACHTIGEN see Berger, Hans Ludwig

LOBE DEN HERREN, DEN MACHTIGEN KONIG see Fischbach, K.

LOBE DEN HERREN, DEN MACHTIGEN KONIG see Oertzen, Rudolf von

LOBE DEN HERREN, DEN MACHTIGEN KONIG see Proske, Erwin

LOBE DEN HERREN, DEN MACHTIGEN KONIG see Trubel, Gerhard

LOBE DEN HERREN, DEN MACHTIGEN KONIG see Weber, Karl-Heinz

LOBE DEN HERREN, DEN MACHTIGEN KONIG DER EHREN see Bach, Johann Sebastian

LOBE DEN HERREN, DEN MACHTIGEN KONIG DER EHREN see Distler, Hugo

LOBE DEN HERREN, DEN MACHTIGEN KONIG DER EHREN see Kubizek, Augustinian

LOBE DEN HERREN, DEN MACHTIGEN KONIG DER EHREN see Pepping, Ernst

LOBE DEN HERREN, DEN MACHTIGEN KONIG DER EHREN [CHORALE] see Bach, Johann Sebastian

LOBE DEN HERREN, MEINE SEELE see Schutz, Heinrich

LOBE DEN HERREN, O MEINE see Wiemer, Wolfgang

LOBE DEN HERREN, O MEINE SEELE
see Cruger, Johann, Nun Danket Alle Gott

LOBE DEN HERREN, O MEINE SEELE see Kubler, Emil

LOBE DEN HERREN, O MEINE SEELE see Wagner, Alexander

LOBE DEN HERREN, O MEINE SEELE see Wenzel, Eberhard

LOBE DEN HERRN
"Praise To The Lord, The Almighty" mix cor, pno/org oct LAWSON 51328 $.35 (L1430)

LOBE DEN HERRN see Bach, Johann Sebastian, Lobe Den Herrn, Meine Seele

LOBE DEN HERRN see Borris, Siegfried

LOBE DEN HERRN see Cabena, Barrie

LOBE DEN HERRN see Dressler, John

LOBE DEN HERRN see Fryxell, Regina Holmen

LOBE DEN HERRN see Graap, Lothar

LOBE DEN HERRN see Hastings, Ross

LOBE DEN HERRN see Kratochwill, Heinrich

LOBE DEN HERRN see Vierdanck, Johann

LOBE DEN HERRN, MEINE SEELE see Anonymous

LOBE DEN HERRN, MEINE SEELE see Bach, Johann Sebastian

LOBE DEN HERRN, MEINE SEELE see Blarr, Oskar Gottlieb

LOBE DEN HERRN MEINE SEELE see Brunner, Adolf

LOBE DEN HERRN, MEINE SEELE see Eglin, Arthur

LOBE DEN HERRN, MEINE SEELE see Erlebach, Philipp Heinrich

LOBE DEN HERRN, MEINE SEELE see Lisken, Gerd

LOBE DEN HERRN, MEINE SEELE see Raphael, Gunther

LOBE DEN HERRN, MEINE SEELE see Schelle, Johann Hermann

LOBE DEN HERRN, MEINE SEELE see Schutz, Heinrich

LOBE DEN HERRN, MEINE SEELE see Schweizer, Rolf

LOBE DEN HERRN see Bach, Johann Sebastian, Lobe Den Herrn, Meine Seele

LOBE DENN HERRN, MEINE SELLE see Schwarz, Jochen

LOBET ALL UND SINGET see Rohwer, Jens

LOBET, CHRISTEN, EUREN HEILAND see Buxtehude, Dietrich

LOBET DEN HERREN
(Bamer, Alfred) wom cor,acap oct DOBLINGER s.p. see also Sechs Geistliche Chore

LOBET DEN HERREN see Kraft, Karl   (L1431)

LOBET DEN HERREN see Kukuck, Felicitas

LOBET DEN HERREN see Lassus, Roland de
(Orlandus)

LOBET DEN HERREN see Praetorius, Michael

LOBET DEN HERREN, ALLE DIE IHN EHREN see
Bornefeld, Helmut

LOBET DEN HERREN, ALLE, DIE IHN EHREN see
Cruger, Johann

LOBET DEN HERREN ALLE, DIE IHN EHREN see Horbe,
Ernst

LOBET DEN HERREN, ALLE, DIE IHN EHREN see
Kurig, Hans-Hermann

LOBET DEN HERREN, ALLE HEIDEN see Franck,
Melchior

LOBET DEN HERREN, ALLE HEIDEN see Hartmann,
Heinrich

LOBET DEN HERREN, ALLE HEIDEN see Marks,
Gunther

LOBET DEN HERREN, ALLE HEIDEN see Praetorius,
Michael

LOBET DEN HERREN ALLE HEIDEN see Staden, Johann

LOBET DEN HERREN AUF ERDEN see Scheidt, Samuel

LOBET DEN HERREN, DENN DER IST see Scheidt,
Samuel

LOBET DEN HERREN, DENN ER IST SEHR FREUNDLICH
see Poser, Hans

LOBET DEN HERREN, DENN ER IST SEHR FREUNDLICH
see Stern, Hermann

LOBET DEN HERREN, IHR SEINE ENGEL see Wehnert,
Wolfram

LOBET DEN HERREN IN SEINEM HEILIGTUM see
Meiland, Jacob

LOBET DEN HERREN IN SEINEM HEILIGTUM see
Scheidt, Samuel

LOBET DEN HERRN see Bach, Johann Sebastian,
Lobe Den Herren, Den Machtigen Konig Der
Ehren

LOBET DEN HERRN see Baumann, Max

LOBET DEN HERRN see Calvisius, Sethus

LOBET DEN HERRN see Hirzel, Erich

LOBET DEN HERRN see Luhn

LOBET DEN HERRN see Marckhl, Erich

LOBET DEN HERRN see Peter, Herbert

LOBET DEN HERRN, ALLE HEIDEN see Anonymous

LOBET DEN HERRN, ALLE HEIDEN see Bach, Johann
Sebastian

LOBET DEN HERRN, ALLE HEIDEN see Telemann,
Georg Philipp

LOBET DEN HERRN, ALLE HEIDEN see Zipp,
Friedrich

LOBET DEN HERRN, DENN WAS ER TUT see
Mareschall, Samuel

LOBET DEN HERRN, IHR HEIDEN see Vulpius,
Melchior

LOBET DEN HERRN IN SEINEM HEILIGTUM see Schein,
Johann Hermann

LOBET DEN HERRN UND DANKT IHM see Micheelsen,
Hans Friedrich

LOBET DIE TAGE see Bresgen, Cesar

LOBET GOTT see Bach, Johann Sebastian, Lobet
Gott In Seinen Reichen

LOBET GOTT IM HIMMELREICH see Mareschall,
Samuel

LOBET GOTT IN SEINEM HEILIGTUM see Albert,
Heinrich

LOBET GOTT IN SEINEN REICHEN see Bach, Johann
Sebastian

LOBET GOTT IN SEINEN RICHEN see Bach, Johann
Sebastian

LOBET GOTT MIT FROHEM MUND see Weismann,
Wilhelm

LOBET GOTT MIT FROHLICHEM MUND see Trubel,
Gerhard

LOBET GOTT, UNSERN HERREN, IN SEINEM HEILIGTUM
see Praetorius, Michael

LOBET GOTT, UNSERN HERRN see Gumpeltzhaimer,
Adam

LOBET GOTT, UNSERN HERRN see Praetorius,
Michael

LOBET GOTT, USERN HERREN see Gumpeltzhaimer,
Adam

LOBET IHR HIMMEL DEN HERREN see Scheidt, Samuel

LOBET, IHR KNECHTE DES HERREN see Hartmann,
Heinrich

LOBET, IHR KNECHTE DES HERRN see Zimmermann,
Heinz Werner

LOBET IM HIMMEL DEN HERREN see Scheidt, Samuel

LOBET IM HIMMEL DEN HERRN see Burkhard Willy

LOBGESANG see Hogner, Friedrich

LOBGESANG see Mendelssohn-Bartholdy, Felix

LOBGESANG see Ritter

LOBGESANG see Sternberg, E.W.

LOBGESANG AUS DER GROSSEN STADT see Schweizer,
Rolf

LOBGESANG AUS DER WUSTE see Ben-Haim, Paul

LOBGESANG DER MARIA see Micheelsen, Hans
Friedrich, Magnificat

LOBGESANG DES SIMEON see Micheelsen, Hans
Friedrich, Herr, Nun Lassest Du Deinen
Diener

LOBGESANG MARIA *BVM,17th cent
(Dawidowicz, Anton) wom cor,acap oct
DOBLINGER s.p. see also Acht Marienleider
(L1432)

LOBLIED AM MORGEN see Muller, Paul

LOBPREISE DEN HERRN see Doebler, Curt

LOBSINGET GOTT, DEM HERRN see Buxtehude,
Dietrich

LOBSINGET GOTT IN SEINEM HEILIGTUM see
Schweizer, Rolf

LOBSINGET UNSERM GOTT see Strohbach, Siegfried,
Cantate Domino Canticum Novum

LOBSINGT, IHR VOLKER ALLZUGLEICH see Goudimel,
Claude

LOBT DEN HERRN, DENN WAS ER TUT see Goudimel,
Claude

LOBT DEN HERRN, DENN WAS ER TUT see Hindermann,
Walter Felix

LOBT DEN HERRN, DENN WAS ER TUT see Pfiffner,
Ernst

LOBT GODT MITT SCHALL see Morales, Cristobal de

LOBT GOTT DEN HERRN see Micheelsen, Hans
Friedrich

LOBT GOTT, DEN HERRN DER HERRLICHKEIT see Marx,
Karl

LOBT GOTT, DEN HERRN DER HERRLICHKEIT see
Schutz, Heinrich

LOBT GOTT DEN HERRN, IHR HEIDEN ALL see Gadsch,
Herbert

LOBT GOTT DEN HERRN, IHR HEIDEN ALL see
Hufschmidt, Wolfgang

LOBT GOTT DEN HERRN, IHR HEIDEN ALL see Stern,
Hermann

LOBT GOTT DEN HERRN, IHR HEIDEN ALL see Werner,
Fritz

LOBT GOTT GETROST MIT SINGEN see Bruder, Bohm

LOBT GOTT GETROST MIT SINGEN see
Gumpeltzhaimer, Adam

LOBT GOTT GETROST MIT SINGEN see Kubler, Emil

LOBT GOTT IHR CHRISTEN see Berger, Hans Ludwig

LOBT GOTT, IHR CHRISTEN see Bach, Johann
Sebastian

LOBT GOTT, IHR CHRISTEN see Marx, Karl

LOBT GOTT, IHR CHRISTEN see Mendelssohn, Arnold

LOBT GOTT, IHR CHRISTEN see Praetorius, Michael

LOBT GOTT, IHR CHRISTEN see Schein, Johann
Hermann

LOBT GOTT, IHR CHRISTEN see Schroter, Leonhard

LOBT GOTT, IHR CHRISTEN see Weiss, Ewald

LOBT GOTT, IHR CHRISTEN ALLE GLEICH see Bender,
Jan

LOBT GOTT, IHR CHRISTEN ALLE GLEICH see
Gottschovius, Nikolaus

LOBT GOTT, IHR CHRISTEN ALLE GLEICH see Herman,
N.

LOBT GOTT, IHR CHRISTEN, ALLE GLEICH see
Kammerer, Imanuel Johannes

LOBT GOTT IHR CHRISTEN ALLE GLEICH see Oertzen,
Rudolf von

LOBT GOTT, IHR CHRISTEN ALLE GLEICH see
Schroter, Leonhard

LOBT GOTT, IHR CHRISTEN ALLE GLEICH see
Suthoff-Gross, Rudolf

LOBT GOTT, IHR CHRISTEN ALLE GLEICH see Trubel,
Gerhard

LOBT GOTT, IHR CHRISTEN ALLEGLEICH see
Schroter, Leonhard

LOBT GOTT, IHR CHRISTEN ALLZUGLEICH see Bach,
Johann Sebastian

LOBT GOTT, IHR CHRISTEN, ALLZUGLEICH see
Burkhart, Franz

LOBT GOTT, IHR CHRISTEN ALLZUGLEICH see
Distler, Hugo

LOBT GOTT IHR CHRISTEN ALLZUGLEICH see
Kappesser, Karl

LOBT GOTT, IHR CHRISTEN, ALLZUGLEICH see
Praetorius, Michael

LOBT GOTT, IHR CHRISTEN, ALLZUGLEICH see
Raphael, Gunther

LOBT GOTT, IHR CHRISTEN ALLZUGLEICH see Schein,
Johann Hermann

LOBT GOTT, IHR CHRISTEN ALLZUGLEICH see Stern,
Hermann

LOBT GOTT, IHR CHRISTEN ALLZUGLEICH see
Telemann, Georg Philipp

LOBT GOTT, IHR CHRISTEN [CHORALE] see Bach,
Johann Sebastian

LOBT GOTT, IHR FROMMEN CHRISTEN see Bender, Jan

LOBT GOTT, IHR FROMMEN CHRISTEN see Gadsch,
Herbert

LOBT GOTT, IHR FROMMEN CHRISTEN see Kukuck,
Felicitas

LOBT GOTT, IHR FROMMEN CHRISTEN see Kurig,
Hans-Hermann

LOBT GOTT, IHR FROMMEN CHRISTEN see Stern,
Hermann

LOBT GOTT IN ALLEN LANDEN see Berger, Hans
Ludwig

LOBT GOTT IN SEINEM HEILIGTUM see Schutz,
Heinrich

LOBT GOTT IN SEINEM HEILIGTUM see Stier, Alfred

LOBT GOTT MIT FROHEM MUND *CCU
[Ger] jr cor BAREN. EM 759 s.p.   (L1433)

LOBT GOTT MIT SCHALL see Schutz, Heinrich

LOBT GOTT MIT SCHALL, IHR HEIDEN ALL see
Schutz, Heinrich

LOBT GOTT VON HERZENSGRUNDE see Schutz,
Heinrich

LOBT, IHR HIMMEL, GOTT DEN HERRN see Schutz,
Heinrich

LOBT UND PREISET GOTT, DEN HERRN see Haydn,
(Johann) Michael, Confitemi Domino

LOCKE, MATTHEW (1630-1677)
Lord, Let Me Know Mine End
SATB oct MCA   (L1434)

Psalm 51 *see Turn Thy Face From My Sins

Turn Thy Face From My Sins (Psalm 51) Gen/
Lent
SSATB (med easy) oct OXFORD   (L1435)

When The Son Of Man Shall Come *Adv
SSAATB,B solo (diff) oct OXFORD 42.031 $.40
(L1436)

LOCKWOOD
Our Father, Who Art In Heaven
SATB oct GALAXY 1.0889.1 $.35   (L1437)

Psalm 114
see Lockwood, Psalm 137

Psalm 137
SATB KJOS 18 $.30 contains also: Psalm 114
(L1438)

LOCKWOOD, NORMAND (1906-   )
All My Heart Rejoices
SATB AMP A236 $.20   (L1439)

Alleluia *Easter,Allelu
SATB oct SOUTHERN $.25   (L1440)

Alleluia, Christ Is Risen *Easter
SATB,acap RONGWEN $.50   (L1441)

As A Hart
SATB oct SOUTHERN $.25   (L1442)

Babe Lies In The Cradle, A
SATB AMP A235 $.25   (L1443)

Birth Of Moses, The
SSA,fl oct PRESSER MC140 $.50   (L1444)

By'm By
SATB,acap oct PRESSER 312-40073 $.30
(L1445)

Closing Doxology, The (Psalm 150) Doxol
mix cor,band voc sc BROUDE BR. $2.00, ipr
(L1446)

Hail To Thee, Glad Day *Easter
SATB,opt soli oct SOUTHERN $.35   (L1447)

Hosanna *Easter
[Lat] 4pt mix cor,acap oct SCHIRM.G A391
$.35   (L1448)

Hymn Of Paradise *hymn
SATB SHAWNEE A 586 $.25   (L1449)

I Will Give Thanks With All My Heart *anthem
SATB (med diff) oct AUGSBURG 0622 $.35
(L1450)

Jesus, O Precious Name
SATB oct SOUTHERN $.25   (L1451)

Joseph, Dearest Joseph
SATB AMP A233 $.30   (L1452)

Joyful, Joyful We Adore Thee
SATB oct PRESSER MC248 $.30   (L1453)

King Shall Come, The *Xmas
SATB oct PRESSER MC249 $.30   (L1454)

Let Nothing Disturb Thee
SATB oct SOUTHERN $.25   (L1455)

Letter To Mother
SATB oct SOUTHERN $.25   (L1456)

LOCKWOOD, NORMAND (cont'd.)

Lord Is My Shepherd, The
2pt mix cor oct PRESSER MC279 $.35   (L1457)

O Lord, The Measure Of Our Prayers
SATB,acap SHAWNEE A 188 $.25   (L1458)

Open My Eyes, That I May See
SATB,acap SHAWNEE A 318 $.30   (L1459)

Praise To The Lord *mot
SATB,opt org/pno PETERS 6064 $.50   (L1460)

Psalm 123
SATB,acap AMP A278 $.20   (L1461)

Psalm 150 *see Closing Doxology, The

Rejoice In The Lord *Bibl
SATB,2horn,2trom,timp WORLD ESA-1916-8 voc
sc $.60, sc s.p., ipa   (L1462)

Remember Now Thy Creator *anthem
SATB (med diff) oct AUGSBURG 1433 $.25
                                        (L1463)

Shout For Joy
SATB,acap SHAWNEE A 196 $.30   (L1464)

Sing Unto The Lord A New Song
SATB,acap SHAWNEE A 184 $.25   (L1465)

Soe Wee May Sing
SATB,acap SHAWNEE A 197 $.25   (L1466)

Thou Hallowed Chosen Morn *Easter
SATB,acap oct PRESSER MC247 $.25   (L1467)

We Plow The Fields *Thanks
SATB oct SOUTHERN $.25   (L1468)

While Shepherds Watched *Xmas
SATB oct SOUTHERN $.25   (L1469)

LOCUS ESTE A DEO FACTUS EST see Bruckner, Anton

LOCUS ISTE see Aiblinger, Johann Kaspar

LOCUS ISTE see Bruckner, Anton

LODATE IL SIGNORE see Goi, M.

LODATE MARIA see Visona', Gino

LOEFFLER, CHARLES MARTIN (1861-1935)
By The Rivers Of Babylon (Psalm 137)
SSAA,org,2fl,vcl,harp voc sc SCHIRM.G $.50
                                        (L1470)

Psalm 137 *see By The Rivers Of Babylon

LOEILLET
God Be Merciful
(Stone) SAB,pno BOSTON 13715 $.35   (L1471)

LOES, [HARRY DIXON] (1892-1965)
God's Pattern
SATB oct WORD CS-2308 $.35   (L1472)

LOEWE, C.
Grant Us Thy Blessing *see Salvum Fac Regem

Salvum Fac Regem
"Grant Us Thy Blessing" [Lat/Eng] SATB,pno/
org BROUDE,A. 126 $.35   (L1473)

LOEWE, ERNEST
Star Eternal, The *Xmas,anthem
SATB LEONARD-ENG 27 s.p.   (L1474)

LOF GODS see Rontgen, [Julius]

LOF ZIJ DEN HEER *17th cent
mix cor sc ALSBACH&D s.p.   (L1475)
(Kuxhaven, D.) mix cor sc ALSBACH&D s.p.
                                        (L1476)

LOF ZIJ DEN HEER see Sohren, P.

LOFLIED (DEN HOGEN GOD ALLEEN ZIJ EER) see
Bach, Johann Sebastian

LOFPSALM see Bordewijk-Roepman, Johanna

LOFPSALM (LOOFT, LOOFT NU ALLER HEEREN HEER)
see Bach, Johann Sebastian

LOFT TROENS SKJOLD see Hovland, Egil

LOFZANG see Bonset, Jac.

LOFZANG VAN MARIA see Verhey, A.B.B.,
Magnificat

LOFZEGGING (LOF ZIJ DEN HEER) see Bach, Johann
Sebastian

LOGE
Dear Savior Bless Us *Gen
(Knorr) SATB SCHMITT 879 $.20   (L1477)

LOHR
First Christmas, The *Xmas
SATB SCHMITT 1751 $.25   (L1478)

LOHR, AL
Christmas Season *Xmas
(Kent, Dick) SATB,pno PEER $.35   (L1479)

He Is Everywhere (God Is Love)
(Youdin, Morris) SATB,pno PEER $.35   (L1480)

My Love For The Lord
(Kent, Dick) SATB,pno PEER $.35   (L1481)

Our Star Of Faith
(Kent, Dick) SATB,pno PEER $.35   (L1482)

Why Not Try Pray'r
(Youdin, Morris) SATB,pno PEER $.35   (L1483)

LOHR-EYLE
Kreuzfidel
men cor,acap ERDMANN 61 s.p.   (L1484)

LOHR, INA (1903-)
Der Tag Ist Seiner Hohe Nah
unis LAUDINELLA LR 7 s.p. contains also: Er
Weckt Mich Alle Morgen (SAT); Ich Liege,
Herr, In Deiner Hut (unis,2treb inst); In
Jeder Nacht, Die Mich Bedroht (unis)

LOHR, INA (cont'd.)
                                        (L1485)
Des Menschen Sohn Ist Gekommen Zu Suchen
SA,2treb inst,bass inst LAUDINELLA LR 113
s.p. contains also: Wer Nun Weiss, Gutes
Zu Tun (SA,treb inst); Einer Trage Des
Andern Last (unis,2treb inst);
Unser Keiner Lebet Ihm Selber (unis,2treb
inst)   (L1486)

Die Geburt Unseres Herrn Jesus Christus Nach
Dem Evangelisten Lukas *Xmas,Bibl
[Ger] men cor&3pt jr cor,SA soli,3vln,vla
(med easy) sc BAREN. BA 2168 $3.50   (L1487)

Einer Trage Des Andern Last
see Lohr, Ina, Des Menschen Sohn Ist
Gekommen Zu Suchen

Er Weckt Mich Alle Morgen
see Lohr, Ina, Der Tag Ist Seiner Hohe Nah

Erforsche Mich, Gott
unis,bass inst LAUDINELLA LR 87 s.p.
contains also: Ich Will Den Herrn Preisen
Allezeit (unis,treb inst); Was Betrubst
Du Dich, Meine Seele (unis,bass inst)
                                        (L1488)

Es Kommt Ein Schiff, Geladen
unis LAUDINELLA LR 22 s.p. contains also:
Mit Gott, So Wollen Wir Loben Und Ehrn;
Nun Komm, Der Heiden Heiland; Uns Ist
Geboren Ein Auserkoren; Vom Himmel Kam
Der Engel Schar   (L1489)

Ich Liege, Herr, In Deiner Hut
see Lohr, Ina, Der Tag Ist Seiner Hohe Nah

Ich Will Den Herrn Preisen Allezeit
see Lohr, Ina, Erforsche Mich, Gott

In Jeder Nacht, Die Mich Bedroht
see Lohr, Ina, Der Tag Ist Seiner Hohe Nah

Mein Gott Ich Will Von Hinnen Gehen
see Lohr, Ina, Nun Ruht Doch Alle Welt

Mit Gott, So Wollen Wir Loben Und Ehrn
see Lohr, Ina, Es Kommt Ein Schiff, Geladen

Nun Komm, Der Heiden Heiland
see Lohr, Ina, Es Kommt Ein Schiff, Geladen

Nun Ruht Doch Alle Welt *Xmas
unis/SAT/SAB,opt treb inst LAUDINELLA LR 57
s.p. contains also: Trostlied Am Abend
"In Jeder Nacht, Die Mich Bedroht" (unis,
treb inst); Mein Gott Ich Will Von Hinnen
Gehen (3pt); Sieh Nicht An, Was Du Selber
Bist (SAT/SAB) (CC)   (L1490)

Sieh Nicht An, Was Du Selber Bist
see Lohr, Ina, Nun Ruht Doch Alle Welt

Trostlied Am Abend "In Jeder Nacht, Die Mich
Bedroht"
see Lohr, Ina, Nun Ruht Doch Alle Welt

Uns Ist Geboren Ein Auserkoren
see Lohr, Ina, Es Kommt Ein Schiff, Geladen

Unser Keiner Lebet Ihm Selber
see Lohr, Ina, Des Menschen Sohn Ist
Gekommen Zu Suchen

Vom Himmel Kam Der Engel Schar
see Lohr, Ina, Es Kommt Ein Schiff, Geladen

Was Betrubst Du Dich, Meine Seele
see Lohr, Ina, Erforsche Mich, Gott

Wer Nun Weiss, Gutes Zu Tun
see Lohr, Ina, Des Menschen Sohn Ist
Gekommen Zu Suchen

L'OISEAU VIGILANT NOUS REVEILLE *Morn,hymn
(Racine, C.; Geveart, F.-A.) [Lat/Fr] 3pt wom
cor,acap (med easy) cor pts LEMOINE s.p.
see from Collection De Choeurs, premiere
Facsimile   (L1491)

LOKEY
Supplication
SATB oct LORENZ C276 $.30   (L1492)

Walk With Us, Lord
SATB oct LORENZ A432 $.25   (L1493)

LOMAKIN
Cherubim Hymn
(Ehret) SATB,acap MARKS 4145 $.25   (L1494)

LOMBARDO
As The Hart (Psalm 42)
SATB,acap oct PRO ART 2304 $.25   (L1495)

Psalm 42 *see As The Hart

LOMBARDO, ROBERT
As The Hart Panteth (Psalm 42) mot
SATB,acap PETERS 6455 $.25   (L1496)

Psalm 42 *see As The Hart Panteth

LONDON, EDWIN
Day Of Desolation
mix cor,acap,bells oct BOONIN 131 $1.25 (L1497)

Four Proverbs *CC4U
[Heb/Eng] SSAA,S solo,bsn,2trp BROUDE,A.
223 $.50   (L1498)

Osanna
[Lat] SSAA,pno SCHIRM.EC 2588   (L1499)

Third Day, The
mix cor,acap NEW VALLEY $.25   (L1500)

Three Settings Of The Twenty Third Psalm
*Psalm
[Heb/Lat/Eng] SATB&wom cor&men cor,acap/pno
cmplt MJQ $6.50   (L1501)

LONE, WILD BIRD, THE *anthem/folk,US
see Four Folksongs And Spirituals
see Ah, Jesus Lord, Thy Love To Me
(Johnson, David N.) SATB,org (easy) oct
AUGSBURG 0513 $.25   (L1502)

(Johnson, David N.) SATB,pno (easy) oct
AUGSBURG 0522 $.25   (L1503)
(Johnson, David N.) SAB,org,opt fl (easy) oct
AUGSBURG 0524 $.25   (L1504)
(Johnson, David N) SSA (easy) oct AUGSBURG
0516 $.25   (L1505)
(Johnson, David N.) TTBB (easy) oct AUGSBURG
0525 $.20 contains also: Ah, Jesus Lord,
Thy Love To Me   (L1506)

LONELY ROAD! UP CALVARY'S WAY see Mercer, M.

LONELY SHEPHERD BOY, THE see Besig

LONELY SHEPHERD, THE see Bartock

LONELY VOICES see Hanks, Voces Tristes

LONESOME VALLEY *spir
(Blaine, Gordon) SATB oct WALTON 2079 $.30
                                        (L1507)
(Frederick) SATB oct SHAPIRO SK 2024 $.25
                                        (L1508)
(Heller) SATB SCHMITT 1173 $.30   (L1509)
(Schubert) SB oct LILLENAS AN-3807 $.30
                                        (L1510)

LONESOME VALLEY see Cumming

LONESOME VALLEY see Hebble

LONESOME VALLEY see Lynn, George

LONESOME VALLEY see Wilson

LONG
Jesus Is The Sweetest Name I Know
(Schubert) SAB oct LILLENAS AN-1626 $.30
                                        (L1511)
Sing Glory Hallelujah *Xmas
SATB oct LORENZ B177 $.25   (L1512)

LONG AGO A PROPHET SANG see Grieb, Herbert [C.]

LONG AGO, AND FAR AWAY see Graham

LONG, AGO AND FAR AWAY see Melby, James

LONG AGO IN BETHLEHEM see De Vito

LONG AGO IN BETHLEHEM see Graham

LONG AGO IN BETHLEHEM see Thygerson

LONG HAST THOU STOOD, O CHURCH OF GOD see
Lindeman, Ludvig Mathias

LONG HAVE I LIFTED UP see Hanford, George

LONG, K.
Fight The Good Fight *Gen,anthem
unis,opt pno oct ROYAL 240 s.p. see also
ANTHEMS FOR UNISON OR TWO PART SINGING (L1513)

LONG, LONG AGO see Anderson, [William H.]

LONG, LONG AGO see Lloyd

LONG, LONG AGO see Rasley

LONG, LONG AGO see Tgettis, Nicholas

LONG, LONG TIME AGO, A see N'ia Gaire Que Auvit

LONG TIME AGO see Denton

LONG TIME AGO see Sleeth

LONG YEARS AGO see Ford, Virgil T.

LONGFELLOW
I Heard The Bells On Christmas Day *see
Palmer

Life That Maketh All Things New
(Rhea) SATB oct PLYMOUTH UIL-103 $.25
                                        (L1514)
Lo, The Earth (composed with Wilkes, R.W.)
(Kay) SATB,org oct MCA   (L1515)
Lo, The Earth Is Ris'n Again
(Williams; Rhea) SAB oct BOURNE 3014 $.25
                                        (L1516)

LONGMAN
Boy Who Wanted Two Drumsticks, The (composed
with Maltzman) *Xmas,cant
2pt jr cor (easy) PRO ART 598 $.85 (L1517)

No Room At The Inn *see Maltzman

LONGMIRE
Sing Praise To God
SATB,S solo,org FRANCIS s.p.   (L1518)

LONGMIRE, JOHN
O Life That Makest All Things New
unis&desc oct CURWEN 10224 $.20   (L1519)

Psalm 23
unis BOSWORTH s.p.   (L1520)

Sing A Merry Carol *Xmas,carol
SSATB,org/pno oct CURWEN 11475 $.30 (L1521)
mix cor CURWEN 61563 s.p.   (L1522)

Sing Lullabye *Xmas
SS CRAMER 180 s.p.   (L1523)
cor&desc CRAMER 180 s.p.   (L1524)

LONGTHORNE, BRIAN
O Be Joyful In The Lord (Psalm 100) Gen/
Thanks
SATB (easy) oct OXFORD 42.329 $.35 (L1525)

Psalm 100 *see O Be Joyful In The Lord

LOOF DEN HEERE (Psalm 117)
(Verwoerd, A.) wom cor sc ALSBACH&D s.p.
                                        (L1526)
LOOF NU DEN HEERE, MIJNE ZIELE *17th cent
mix cor sc ALSBACH&D s.p.   (L1527)

LOOFT GOD, LOOFT ZIJN NAAM see Maitre Pierre

LOOFT HEM see Zanen, P.

LOOK AND LIVE see Ogden

LOOK DOWN FROM HEAVEN, O GOD see Russell, Velma A.

LOOK DOWN, O HOLY DOVE see Bach, Johann Sebastian

LOOK DOWN, O LORD see Byrd, William

LOOK DOWN, O LORD see Jannequin, Clement

LOOK INSIDE *CCUL
(Floria, Cam) SATB voc sc WORD 37536 $1.95
(L1528)

LOOK ON HIM, MAN OF SORROWS see Byrd, William

LOOK ON THE FIELDS see Macpherson, Charles

LOOK SOFTLY, LORD see Eliot

LOOK TO HIM AND BE RADIANT see James, Allen

LOOK TO THIS DAY see Luboff, Norman

LOOK TOWARD THE SEA see Hovhaness, Alan

LOOK UP, SWEET BABE see Berkeley, Lennox

LOOK UPWARD see Reinecke, Carl

LOOK WITH MERCY, LORD see Milano, R.

LOOK YE SAINTS, THE SIGHT IS GLORIOUS see Rickard, Jeffrey

LOOK, YE SAINTS, THE SIGHT IS GLORIOUS see Wetzler, Robert

LOOKE DOWNE, O LORD see Byrd, William

LOOKING UPWARDS see Wolf, Hugo, Aufblick

LOOLA, JESUS *Xmas
(Kozinski, D.) SATB,acap oct PRESSER 312-40206 $.30   (L1529)

LOOREN DE JONG, E.D.
Te Deum Laudamus
wom cor ALSBACH&D sc s.p., cor pts s.p.
(L1530)

LOOSEMORE, HENRY (? -1670)
O Lord, Increase Our Faith *anthem
(Shaw, Watkins) mix cor oct NOVELLO 88.0007.03 s.p.   (L1531)
(Wulstan, D.) SATB CHESTER s.p.   (L1532)

Why Art Thou So Heavy *anthem
mix cor oct OXFORD 43.459 $.30   (L1533)

LOOTS, PH.
Kerstlied
3pt wom cor,acap ALSBACH&D sc s.p., cor pts s.p.   (L1534)
3pt wom cor,S solo,pno/org ALSBACH&D sc s.p., cor pts s.p.   (L1535)

LOPEZ
Magnificat No. 1 *Magnif,mot,Mex
(Barwick, S.; Hines, R.S.) SATB,acap PEER $.70   (L1536)

LOPEZ, ALMAGRO
Cuatro Villancicos *Xmas,carol
[Span] 2pt UNION ESP. 14588 s.p.
contains & see also: El Establo; El Viaje De Los Reyes Magos; En El Portal De Belen; Gloria A Dios   (L1537)

El Establo *Xmas,carol
[Span] 2pt UNION ESP. 14588-2 s.p. see also Cuatro Villancicos   (L1538)

El Viaje De Los Reyes Magos *Xmas,carol
[Span] 2pt UNION ESP. 14588-3 s.p. see also Cuatro Villancicos   (L1539)

En El Portal De Belen *Xmas,carol
[Span] 2pt UNION ESP. 14588-4 s.p. see also Cuatro Villancicos   (L1540)

Gloria A Dios *Xmas,carol
[Span] 2pt UNION ESP. 14588-1 s.p. see also Cuatro Villancicos   (L1541)

LO PRESTI
Alleluia! Christus Natus Est
SATB oct FISCHER,C CM-7443 $.35   (L1542)

Bell Song
SSAA oct FISCHER,C CM-7476 $.30   (L1543)

LOQUEBANTUR see Palestrina, Giovanni

LOQUEBANTUR (LYDT FORKYNDTE) see Palestrina, Giovanni

LOQUEBANTUR VARIIS LINGUIS see Palestrina, Giovanni

LOQUEBANTUS VARIIS LINGUIS see Marenzio, Luca

LORA
Lord Shall Bless His People With Peace
SATB,STB soli oct BOOSEY 5562 $.40   (L1544)

L'ORAISON DOMINICALE see Pater Noster

LORD, A-ROCK-A MY SOUL see Wetzler, Robert

LORD ABOVE, THE see Skillings, Otis

LORD, ABOVE ALL OTHER see Bach

LORD ABOVE, ENLIVEN THOU ME see Scarlatti, Domenico

LORD, ACCEPT THE GIFTS WE OFFER
see Offertory Hymns

LORD ALL GLORIOUS, LORD VICTORIOUS see Davis, Katherine K.

LORD, ALMIGHTY GOD see Van Hulse

LORD ALMIGHTY IS MY LIGHT see Hopkins

LORD AND SAVIOR, TRUE AND KIND see Bach

LORD, AS THAT HART WHICH WATER WANTS see Hopkins, Anthony

LORD, AS THOU WILT, DEAL THOU WITH ME see Othmayr, Kaspar

LORD ASCENDETH, THE see Philips, Peter, Ascendit Deus

LORD ASCENDETH UP ON HIGH see Powell

LORD ASCENDETH UP ON HIGH see Sowerby, Leo

LORD, AT ALL TIMES see Mendelssohn-Bartholdy, Felix

LORD AT FIRST DID ADAM
SATB (very easy) OXFORD 08.001 $.15   (L1545)

LORD AT FIRST DID ADAM MAKE, THE see Kirby, L.M. Jr.

LORD AT FIRST DID ADAM MAKE, THE see Williams, P.

LORD AT FIRST, THE *carol
TTB,acap (easy, contains also: Coventry Carol) OXFORD 41.907 $.25   (L1546)

LORD, BE THY WORD MY RULE see Wood, John

LORD BLESS AND KEEP YOU, THE see Lutkin, Peter Christian

LORD BLESS AND KEEP YOU, THE see Lutkin, Peter Christian

LORD BLESS THEE see Sateren, Leland Bernhard

LORD BLESS THEE AND KEEP THEE, THE see Smith, Gregg

LORD BLESS THEE, AND KEEP THEE, THE see Willan, Healey

LORD BLESS THEE , THE see Robertson, Leroy

LORD BLESS US, THE see Whyte, Robert

LORD BLESS YOU AND KEEP YOU see Lutkin, Peter Christian

LORD BLESS YOU AND KEEP YOU see Schroth

LORD BLESS YOU AND KEEP YOU, THE
(Wilson, Harry R.) SATB oct WALTON 2042 $.25
(L1547)

LORD BLESS YOU AND KEEP YOU, THE see Kimes

LORD BLESS YOU AND KEEP YOU, THE see Lutkin, Peter Christian

LORD BLESS YOU AND KEEP YOU, THE see Mueller, Carl F.

LORD BLESS YOU, THE see Bach, Johann Sebastian

LORD BLESS YOU, THE see Nyquist

LORD BROUGHT FORTH MOSES, THE see Pinkham, Daniel

LORD, BY WHOSE BREATH see Howells, Herbert Norman

LORD, BY WHOSE BREATH see Nystedt, Knut

LORD CHRIST, WHEN FIRST THOU CAM'ST TO MEN *Easter
(Shaw; Parker) mix cor,acap oct SCHIRM.G 9957 $.25   (L1548)

LORD CHRIST, WHEN FIRST THOU CAM'ST TO MEN see Howells, Herbert Norman

LORD CHRIST, WHEN FIRST THOU CAM'ST TO MEN see Johnson, David N.

LORD, DAVIS
Prayer For Peace *anthem
mix cor oct OXFORD 43.470 $.30   (L1549)

LORD DESCENDED, THE see Lyon, J.

LORD, DISMISS US WITH THY BLESSING see Bissell, Keith

LORD, DISMISS US WITH THY BLESSING see Ford, Virgil T.

LORD DISMISS US WITH THY BLESSING see Smith

LORD, DO NOT CRUSH US WITH THY WRATH see Byrd, William, Ne Irascaris Domine

LORD, DO THOU HAVE MERCY see Victoria, Tomas Luis de

LORD DOTH REIGN, THE see Lynn, George

LORD, ENTER NOT INTO WRATH see Bach, Johann Sebastian, Herr, Gehe Nicht Ins Gericht [Chorale]

LORD ETERNAL, ALMIGHTY see Traver

LORD, EVER BRIDLE MY DESIRES see Peerson, Martin

LORD, EVERY NATION see Peloquin, C. Alexander

LORD EXALTED AARON, THE see Pinkham, Daniel

LORD, FLOOD MY SOUL see Buck

LORD, FOR THY TENDER MERCIES see Rogers, J.H.

LORD, FOR THY TENDER MERCIES' SAKE
(Farrant, Richard) SA,org/pno SCHIRM.EC 1013 $.20   (L1550)
(Farrant, Richard; Whitford, H.) SSA,acap SCHIRM.EC 1890 $.25   (L1551)

LORD FOR THY TENDER MERCIES' SAKE see Farmer, [Henry George]

LORD FOR THY TENDER MERCIES SAKE see Farrant, Richard

LORD, FOR THY TENDER MERCIES' SAKE see Hilton, John (The Elder)

LORD FOR THY TENDER MERCY'S SAKE see Farrant, Richard

LORD, GIVE EAR see Gabrieli, Giovanni

LORD GIVE ME STRENGTH TO WALK THY WAY see Wells

LORD GIVE NEW TUNES see Wetzler

LORD GIVE US FAITH see Walton

LORD GIVETH, THE see Brooks

LORD GOD ALMIGHTY see Byrd, William

LORD GOD ALMIGHTY see Vivaldi, Antonio, Domine Deus

LORD GOD ANSWERED JOB see Posegate

LORD GOD, GREAT MASTER OF CREATION see Bach, Johann Sebastian

LORD GOD, HEAR MY PRAYER see Tartini, Giuseppe

LORD GOD, HEAR OUR PRAYER see Etler, Alvin [Derald]

LORD, GOD I AM WEARY see Brahms, Johannes, Ich Aber Bin Eland

LORD GOD MADE THEM ALL, THE see Rawls, Kathryn H.

LORD GOD OF ABRAHAM see Mendelssohn-Bartholdy, Felix

LORD GOD OF HEAVEN see Franck, Cesar, Panis Angelicus

LORD GOD OF HEAVEN see Palestrina, Giovanni, Panis Angelicus

LORD, GOD OF HOSTS see Durant, C.

LORD GOD OF HOSTS see Edmunds, John

LORD GOD OF HOSTS see Moore

LORD GOD OF HOSTS see Rogers, B.

LORD GOD OF HOSTS, HOW LOVELY see Sateren, Leland Bernhard

LORD, GOD OF MY FATHERS see Rolle

LORD, GOD OF OUR FATHERS see Armbruster

LORD GOD OF OUR FATHERS see Mendelssohn-Bartholdy, Felix

LORD GOD OF SABAOTH see Davis, Katherine K.

LORD GOD OF SABOATH see Cherubini, Luigi

LORD GOD REIGNETH, THE see Pachelbel, Johann, Der Herr Ist Konig

LORD GOD, THY PRAISE WE SING see Bach

LORD GOD, WE ALL TO THEE GIVE PRAISE see Schein, Johann Hermann

LORD, GOD WE PRAISE THEE see Mozart, Wolfgang Amadeus, Laudate Dominum

LORD GOD WE PRAISE THEE see Peeters, Flor, Te Deum

LORD GOD, WE PRAISE THY GOODNESS see Franck, Melchior, Herr Gott, Nun Sei Gepreiset

LORD GOD, WE WORSHIP THEE see Fritsch, [Magda von]

LORD GRANT GRACE, WE HUMBLY BESEECH THEE see Gibbons, Orlando

LORD, GRANT THY SERVANTS see Bortniansky, Dimitri Stepanovitch

LORD, GRANT US PEACE see Bach

LORD, GRANT US WHAT THOU WILT see Roff, Joseph

LORD, GUARD AND GUIDE THE MEN WHO FLY see Baker

LORD HAS A CHILD, THE see Schuman

LORD HAS A CHILD, THE see Schumann, William Howard

LORD HAS CHOSEN HIM, THE see Theophane, Sister M. (Hytrek), Elegit Eum Dominus

LORD HAS RISEN see van Berchem, J., Surrexit Dominus Vere

LORD HAS RISEN INDEED, THE see Strickland

LORD HAS SWORN, THE see Roff, Joseph

LORD HATH BEEN MINDFUL OF US, THE see Wesley, Samuel Sebastian Jr.

LORD HATH BROUGHT AGAIN ZION, THE see Robertson, Leroy

LORD HATH HELPED ME HITHERTO, THE see Bach, Johann Sebastian

LORD HATH SWORN, THE see Crone, R.

LORD, HAVE MERCY see Christiansen, P.

LORD, HAVE MERCY see Durante, Francesco, Kyrie

LORD, HAVE MERCY see Lotti, Antonio

LORD, HAVE MERCY see Lvovsky, F.V., Hospodi Pomilui

LORD HAVE MERCY see Pergolesi, Giovanni Battista, Kyrie

LORD, HAVE MERCY ON US see Lotti, Antonio, Kyrie Eleison

LORD HAVE MERCY ON US see Lvovsky, S., Hospodi Pomilui

LORD HAVE MERCY ON US see Zachau

LORD HAVE MERCY UPON ME see Lotti, Antonio, Miserere Mei Deus

LORD, HAVE MERCY UPON US see Beethoven, Ludwig van

LORD HAVE MERCY UPON US see Breydert, F.M., Kyrie Eleison

LORD HAVE MERCY UPON US see Buxtehude, Dietrich, Kyrie Eleison

LORD HAVE MERCY UPON US see Durante, Kyrie Eleison

LORD, HAVE MERCY UPON US see Lalande, Michel Richard de

LORD, HAVE MERCY UPON US see Lotti, Antonio, Kyrie Eleison

LORD HAVE MERCY UPON US see Mendelssohn-Bartholdy, Felix

LORD, HAVE MERCY UPON US see Mozart, Wolfgang Amadeus, Kyrie Eleison

LORD, HAVE MERCY UPON US see Palestrina, Giovanni, Kyrie Eleison

LORD, HAVE MERCY UPON US see Walter, Samuel

LORD, HEAR ME IN MY DISTRESS see Hopkins

LORD, HEAR MY CRY see Newbury

LORD, HEAR MY CRY see Vecchi, Orazio

LORD, HEAR MY PRAYER see Byrd, William

LORD, HEAR MY PRAYER see Lassus, Roland de (Orlandus)

LORD, HEAR MY VOICE see Wilson, James R.

LORD, HEAR OUR PRAYER see Shelley

LORD, HEAR THOU OUR PRAYER see Lassus, Roland de (Orlandus), Domini Exaudi Orationem Meum

LORD, HEARKEN AND PITY see Young, Gordon

LORD HELP US see Cechvala, Al

LORD HOLD MY HAND A LITTLE TIGHTER see McWhertor

LORD HOSANNA IN THE HIGHEST see Glarum, L. Stanley

LORD, HOW EXCELLENT THY NAME see Medler, Malcolm

LORD HOW LONG see Liszt, Franz

LORD HOW LONG see Mendelssohn-Bartholdy, Felix

LORD, HOW LONG WILT THOU BE ANGRY see Greene, Maurice

LORD, HOW LONG WILT THOU BE ANGRY see Purcell, Henry

LORD, HOW LONG WILT THOU FORGET ME? (Morris, W.) SATB LEONARD-US 08038400 $.25 (L1552)

LORD, HOW LONG WILT THOU FORGET ME see Brahms, Johannes, Herr, Wie Lange Willst Du Mein Gar Vergessen

LORD! HOW LONG WILT THOU FORGET ME see Brahms, Johannes, Herr, Wie Lange Willst Du Mein So Ganz Vergessen?

LORD, HOW LONG WILT THOU FORGET ME? see Liszt, Franz

LORD, I AM NOT HIGH MINDED see Amner, John

LORD I AM NOT WORTHY see Hillert, Richard

LORD, I CAN SUFFER see Purcell, Henry

LORD, I CAN'T TURN BACK see Williams

LORD, I CRY UNTO THEE see Diercks, John H.

LORD, I FLEE TO THEE see Mendelssohn-Bartholdy, Felix

LORD, I HAVE LOVED THE HABITATION OF THY HOUSE see Matthews, H.

LORD, I HAVE LOVED THE HABITATION OF THY HOUSE see Torrance, George William

LORD, I LONG FOR THEE ONLY see Schutz, Heinrich, Musikalische Exequien-Teil 2: Herr, Wenn Ich Nur Dich Liebe

LORD, I LOOKED DOWN THE ROAD see Still, William Grant

LORD, I LOVE THE HABITATION OF THY HOUSE see Graun, Karl Heinrich

LORD, I LOVE THE PLACE see Graun, Karl Heinrich

LORD, I LOVE THE PLACE WHERE THOU DWELLEST see Graun, K. Heinrich

LORD, I TRUST THEE see Handel, George Frideric

LORD, I WAN' TO BE MORE LOVIN' (Kemmer) SATB oct FISCHER,J 1264 $.25 (L1553)

LORD, I WANT TO BE see Wille

LORD, I WANT TO BE A CHRISTIAN *spir (Johnson) SSATTBB,S solo,acap oct SCHIRM.G 9561 $.35 (L1554)

LORD, I WANT TO BE A CHRISTIAN see Gerhold, Norbert

LORD, I WANT TO BE A CHRISTIAN see Martin, Warren

LORD, IF I BUT THEE MAY HAVE see Schutz, Heinrich, Herr, Wenn Ich Nur Dich Habe

LORD, IF I DECEIVE MYSELF see Redman, Reginald

LORD, I'M LOST see Johnson, Sidney

LORD, I'M OUT HERE ON YOUR WORD see Work

LORD, IN THE MORNING see Chapin, Amzi

LORD, IN THEE HAVE I TRUSTED see Klein

LORD, IN THEE I DO TRUST see Schutz, Heinrich

LORD, IN THIS, THY MERCY'S DAY see Cruger, Johann

LORD IN THY PRESENCE see Gregor

LORD IN THY PRESENCE LEAD US see Huerter, [Charles]

LORD IN THY RAGE see Byrd, William

LORD, IN THY RESURRECTION see Gallus, Jacobus

LORD, IN THY TENDER MERCY see Gluck, Christoph Willibald Ritter von

LORD INTO HIS GARDEN COMES, THE see Billings, William

LORD IS A LIGHT, THE see Greene, Maurice

LORD IS A MIGHTY GOD see Christiansen, Olaf Christian

LORD IS A MIGHTY GOD, THE see Hastings

LORD IS A MIGHTY GOD, THE see Mendelssohn-Bartholdy, Felix

LORD IS A SUN, THE see Bach, Johann Sebastian, Gott, Der Herr, Ist Sonn' Und Schild

LORD IS A SUN AND A SHIELD, THE *Fest BELWIN $1.00 (L1555)

LORD IS A SUN AND SHIELD, THE see Bach, Johann Sebastian, Gott Der Herr Ist Sonn' Und Schild

LORD IS COME, THE see Belt, T.

LORD IS COME, THE see Kirk, Theron W.

LORD IS EXALTED, THE see West, John Ebenezer

LORD IS GOD, THE see Davis, Katherine K.

LORD IS GOOD see Tye, Christopher

LORD IS GOOD, THE see Butler

LORD IS GOOD, THE see Kirk, Theron W.

LORD IS GOOD, THE see Lynn, George

LORD IS GOOD, THE see Tye, Christopher

LORD IS GOOD TO ALL, THE see Holden, [Oliver]

LORD IS GRACIOUS see Hamblen

LORD IS GRACIOUS, THE see Roff, Joseph

LORD IS GREAT IN ZION see Kountz

LORD IS GREAT, THE see Mendelssohn-Bartholdy, Felix

LORD IS GREAT, THE see Righini, Vincenzo

LORD IS HE WHOSE STRENGTH DOTH MAKE ME STRONG, THE see Davie, Cedric Thorpe

LORD IS HIS NAME, THE see King, Harold C.

LORD IS IN HIS HOLY TEMPLE, THE see Worship Responses

LORD IS IN HIS HOLY TEMPLE, THE see Anderson, [William H.]

LORD IS IN HIS HOLY TEMPLE, THE see Bell

LORD IS IN HIS HOLY TEMPLE, THE see Mechem, Kirke

LORD IS IN HIS HOLY TEMPLE, THE see Rhodes

LORD IS JUST, THE see Roff, Joseph

LORD IS KING, THE see Severson, Roland

LORD IS KING! LIFT UP THY VOICE, THE see Wolff, S. Drummond

LORD IS KING, THE *anthem (George, Graham) SA (easy) oct AUGSBURG 1543 $.25 (L1556)

LORD IS KING, THE see Binkerd, [Gordon]

LORD IS KING, THE see Boyce, William

LORD IS KING, THE see Kelley

LORD IS KING, THE see Lynn, George

LORD IS KING, THE see Purcell, Henry

LORD IS KING, THE see Sanborn, Jan

LORD IS LOVING, THE see Garrett, G.M.

LORD IS LOVING UNTO EVERY MAN, THE see Garrett, George Mursell

LORD IS MERCIFUL, THE see Bach, Johann Sebastian, Suscepit Israel

LORD IS MERCIFUL, THE see Kortkamp

LORD IS MY CAPTAIN, THE see O'Hara, Geoffrey

LORD IS MY LIGHT see Allitsen

LORD IS MY LIGHT see Allitsen, Frances

LORD IS MY LIGHT see Fletcher, Percy [E.]

LORD IS MY LIGHT see Wheeler, Alfred

LORD IS MY LIGHT AND MY SALVATION, THE see Bender, Jan

LORD IS MY LIGHT, THE see Allitsen

LORD IS MY LIGHT, THE see Allitsen, Frances

LORD IS MY LIGHT, THE see Carmichael, P.L.

LORD IS MY LIGHT, THE see Dean, T.W.

LORD IS MY LIGHT, THE see Edwards, Clara

LORD IS MY LIGHT, THE see Goldman, Maurice

LORD IS MY LIGHT, THE see Handel, George Frideric

LORD IS MY LIGHT, THE see James

LORD IS MY LIGHT, THE see MacDonald

LORD IS MY LIGHT, THE see Parker, Horatio William

LORD IS MY LIGHT, THE see Percy, Vince H.

LORD IS MY LIGHT, THE see Pfautsch, Lloyd

LORD IS MY LIGHT, THE see Protheroe

LORD IS MY LIGHT, THE see Speaks, [Oley]

LORD IS MY LIGHT, THE see Stoughton, R.

LORD IS MY LIGHT, THE see Zimmermann, Heinz Werner

LORD IS MY PORTION, THE see Roff, Joseph

LORD IS MY ROCK, THE see Woodman, Raymond Huntington

LORD IS MY SALVATION see Newbury, Kent A.

LORD IS MY SALVATION, THE see Marth, Helen Jun

LORD IS MY SHEPHERD (Rodby) SSA KJOS 6075 $.30 (L1557)

LORD IS MY SHEPHERD see Cain, Noble

LORD IS MY SHEPHERD see Clokey, Joseph Waddell

LORD IS MY SHEPHERD see Craston, E.S.

LORD IS MY SHEPHERD see Koschat

LORD IS MY SHEPHERD see Lekberg, Sven

LORD IS MY SHEPHERD see Leslie, H.T.

LORD IS MY SHEPHERD see Liddle, [Samuel]

LORD IS MY SHEPHERD see Lovelace, Austin C.

LORD IS MY SHEPHERD see Schubert, Franz (Peter)

LORD IS MY SHEPHERD, THE see Greene, Maurice

LORD IS MY SHEPHERD, THE see Smart, Henry Thomas

LORD IS MY SHEPHERD, THE (Psalm 23) (Follett) SATB oct PRO ART 2037 $.25 (L1558) (Pfautsch) unis/SA oct SUMMY 5025 $.25 (L1559)

LORD IS MY SHEPHERD, THE see Bach, Johann Sebastian, Der Herr Ist Mein Getreuer Hirt

LORD IS MY SHEPHERD, THE see Berger, Jean

LORD IS MY SHEPHERD, THE see Cain, Noble

LORD IS MY SHEPHERD, THE see Crook, A.T.

LORD IS MY SHEPHERD, THE see De Leone, [Francesco B.]

LORD IS MY SHEPHERD, THE see Dvorak, Antonin

LORD IS MY SHEPHERD, THE see Erhardt

LORD IS MY SHEPHERD, THE see Gardiner

LORD IS MY SHEPHERD, THE see Gardner, Maurice

LORD IS MY SHEPHERD, THE see Gover

LORD IS MY SHEPHERD, THE see Grant, David

LORD IS MY SHEPHERD, THE see Hoffrichter, B.

LORD IS MY SHEPHERD, THE see Hovhaness, Alan

LORD IS MY SHEPHERD, THE see Hughes

LORD IS MY SHEPHERD, THE see Humphreys, Don

LORD IS MY SHEPHERD, THE see Kent, Richard

LORD IS MY SHEPHERD, THE see Klein

LORD IS MY SHEPHERD, THE see Koschat

LORD IS MY SHEPHERD, THE see Le Fleming, Christopher (Kaye)

LORD IS MY SHEPHERD, THE see Lockwood, Normand

LORD IS MY SHEPHERD, THE see Lovelace, Austin C.

LORD IS MY SHEPHERD, THE see Mac Farren

LORD IS MY SHEPHERD, THE see Mac Farren, George Alexander

LORD IS MY SHEPHERD, THE see Milner, Arthur

LORD IS MY SHEPHERD, THE see Moschetti, [Giuseppe]

LORD IS MY SHEPHERD, THE see Owens, Jimmy

LORD IS MY SHEPHERD, THE see Palmer, William J.

LORD IS MY SHEPHERD, THE see Porter

LORD IS MY SHEPHERD, THE see Sacco

LORD IS MY SHEPHERD, THE see Schack, David

LORD IS MY SHEPHERD, THE see Schubert, Franz (Peter)

LORD IS MY SHEPHERD, THE see Schutz, Heinrich, Der Herr Ist Mein Hirt

LORD IS MY SHEPHERD, THE see Smart

LORD IS MY SHEPHERD, THE see Smart, Henry Thomas

LORD IS MY SHEPHERD, THE see Stanford, Charles Villiers

LORD IS MY SHEPHERD, THE see Thompson, Randall

LORD IS MY SHEPHERD, THE see Vermulst, Jan

LORD IS MY SHEPHERD, THE see Wesley, Samuel Sebastian Jr.

LORD IS MY SHEPHERD, THE see Wilson, Roger [C.]

LORD IS MY SHEPHERD, THE see Young

LORD IS MY STRENGH AND MY SONG, THE see Schroth

LORD IS MY STRENGTH, THE see Daniels

LORD IS MY STRENGTH AND MY SONG, THE see Newbury, Kent A.

LORD IS MY STRENGTH AND SONG, THE see Morgan

LORD IS MY STRENGTH, THE see Coleridge-Taylor, Samuel

LORD IS MY STRENGTH, THE see Demarest, A.

LORD IS MY STRENGTH, THE see Moe, Daniel

LORD IS MY STRENGTH, THE see Penn, Bennett

LORD IS MY STRENGTH, THE see Roff, Joseph

LORD IS MY STRENGTH, THE see Titcomb

LORD IS MY TRUE SHEPHERD, THE see Wollen, Russell

LORD IS NIGH, THE see Bircsak

LORD IS NIGH, THE see McAfee

LORD IS NIGH, THE see Sullivan, Sir Arthur Seymour

LORD IS NIGH, THE see Thompson

LORD IS NIGH UNTO US ALL see Roff, Joseph

LORD IS OUR FORTRESS, THE see Brahms, Johannes

LORD IS OVER ALL THE EARTH, THE see Harris, Jerry Weseley, Misericordia Domini

LORD IS RICH AND MERCIFUL, THE see Lovelace, Austin C.

LORD IS RIGHTEOUS, THE see Schalk, Carl

LORD IS RISEN INDEED, THE see Blake, G.

LORD IS RISEN INDEED, THE see Strickland, Lily Teresa

LORD IS RISEN, THE see Aichinger, Gregor

LORD IS RISEN, THE see Billings, William

LORD IS RISEN, THE see Dlugos

LORD IS RISEN, THE see Gallus, Jacobus, Surrexit Dominus

LORD IS RISEN TODAY, THE see Vail

LORD IS RIS'N INDEED, THE see Billings, William

LORD IS RULER see Geisler, Johan C.

LORD IS RULER OVER ALL see Schutz, Heinrich

LORD IS RULER OVER ALL, THE see Schutz, Heinrich

LORD IS, THE
    SACRED $1.75   (L1560)

LORD IS THE LORD *spir
    (Norman) SATB oct STAFF 561 $.30   (L1561)

LORD IS THY KEEPER, THE see Sateren, Leland Bernhard

LORD IS WITH US, THE see Kirk

LORD, IT BELONGS NOT TO MY CARE see Davies, Henry Walford

LORD JEHOVAH REIGNS, THE see Goss, John

LORD JEHOVAH REIGNS, THE see Wilson, John F.

LORD JESUS BY THY PASSION see Christiansen, Paul

LORD JESUS CHRIST see Gounod, Charles Francois

LORD JESUS CHRIST, IN THEE ALONE see Franck, Melchior, Allein Zu Dir Herr Jesu Christ

LORD JESUS CHRIST IS RIS'N see Scheidt, Samuel, Surrexit Christus

LORD JESUS CHRIST, MY SAVIOR BLEST see Schalk, Carl

LORD JESUS CHRIST, THE SON OF GOD see Le Maistre, Mattheus

LORD JESUS CHRIST, THOU PRINCE OF PEACE see Bach, Johann Sebastian

LORD JESUS CHRIST, WE HUMBLY PRAY see Martin, G.

LORD JESUS CHRIST, WITH US ABIDE see Krapf, Gerhard

LORD JESUS, GENTLE SAVIOR see Pelz, Walter L.

LORD JESUS HATH A GARDEN *carol
    see Six Traditional Carols, Set II
    SATB (very easy) OXFORD 08.105 $.15   (L1562)

LORD JESUS ON THE CROSS WAS HUNG see Schutz, Heinrich

LORD JESUS, THE INFANT HOLY *Xmas,carol,Dan
    (Ehret, Walter) SA FRANK F-613 $.35   (L1563)

LORD JESUS, THINK OF ME see Gibbons, Orlando

LORD JESUS, THINK ON ME (from Hymn Tune: St. Bride)
    (Grieb) jr cor&sr cor oct SCHIRM.G 10841 $.25
                                         (L1564)

LORD JESUS THINK ON ME see Elmore, Robert [Hall]

LORD JESUS, THINK ON ME see Freestone, G.S.

LORD JESUS, THINK ON ME see Hafso

LORD JESUS, THINK ON ME see Hamill

LORD JESUS, THINK ON ME see Hughes

LORD, JESUS, THINK ON ME see Lewis, John Leo

LORD, JESUS, THINK ON ME see Lovelace, Austin C.

LORD JESUS, THINK ON ME see Pedretti, Edward

LORD JESUS THINK ON ME see Talmadge, Charles L.

LORD JESUS, THINK ON ME see Thiman, Eric Harding

LORD JESUS THY DEAR ANGEL SEND see Bach, Johann Sebastian

LORD JESUS , WE GIVE THANKS TO THEE see Johnson, David N.

LORD JESUS, WE GIVE THANKS TO THEE see Praetorius, Michael

LORD JESUS WE STAND AFAR see York, D.

LORD JESUS, WHO DIDST REDEEM see Rolle

LORD, KEEP US STEADFAST see Frost

LORD, KEEP US STEADFAST see Luther, Martin

LORD KEEP US STEADFAST see Pasquet, Jean

LORD KEEP US STEADFAST see Pooler, Frank

LORD, KEEP US STEADFAST see Walter

LORD, KEEP US STEADFAST IN THY WORD see Buxtehude, Dietrich, Erhalt Uns, Herr, Bei Deinem Wort

LORD KEEP US STEADFAST IN THY WORD see Near, Gerald

LORD, KEEP US STEADFAST IN THY WORD see Praetorius, Michael

LORD KEEPETH THEE see Geisler, Johan C.

LORD, LEAD US STILL see Brahms, Johannes

LORD, LET AT LAST THINE ANGELS COME see Hassler, Hans Leo

LORD, LET ME KNOW MINE END see Greene, Maurice

LORD, LET ME KNOW MINE END see Locke, Matthew

LORD, LET ME LISTEN see Nason, Doug

LORD, LET ME LIVE TODAY see Moore, F.

LORD LIVETH, THE see Glarum, L. Stanley

LORD, LORD see Brubeck

LORD, LORD HAVE MERCY see Mendelssohn-Bartholdy, Felix

LORD, LORD, I'VE GOT SOME SINGIN' TO DO see Schmertz

LORD, LORD, LORD *spir
    (Higgins) SATB oct LILLENAS AN-3833 $.30
                                         (L1565)

LORD, LORD, LORD see Stone, L.

LORD, LORD, OPEN TO US see Bender, Jan

LORD LOVETH, THE see Novello, Vincent

LORD MAKE ME AN INSTRUMENT see Cassey

LORD, MAKE ME AN INSTRUMENT OF THY PEACE see Frank, Marcel [Gustave]

LORD, MAKE ME AN INSTRUMENT OF THY PEACE see McAfee, Don

LORD, MAKE ME AN INSTRUMENT OF THY PEACE see Mainville

LORD, MAKE ME AN INSTRUMENT OF THY PEACE see Wetzler, Robert

LORD, MAKE ME AN INSTRUMENT OF THY PEACE see Zaninelli, Luigi

LORD MAKE ME AN INSTRUMENT OF YOUR PEACE see Roff, Joseph

LORD MAKE ME THINE INSTRUMENT see York, D.

LORD, MAKE ME TO KNOW see Brahms, Johannes

LORD, MAKE ME TO KNOW MINE END see Pinkham, Daniel

LORD MAKE THY WORD A LANTERN see Pasquet, Jean

LORD, MAKE US INSTRUMENTS OF THY PEACE see Evans

LORD, MAKE US INSTRUMENTS OF THY PEACE see Shaw, Martin

LORD MOST HIGH see Marshall, Jane M.

LORD, MOST HIGH, MIGHTY ARE THY WONDERS see Hammerschmidt, Andreas

LORD MOST HOLY see Davis, Katherine K.

LORD MOST HOLY AND RIGHTEOUS see Arkhangelsky, G.

LORD MOST MIGHTY see Parker

LORD MY FAITHFUL SHEPHERD IS, THE see Bach, Johann Sebastian

LORD, MY GOD, ASSIST ME NOW see Martini, Padre, Domine, Ad Adjuvandum Me Festina

LORD, MY GOD, BE PRAISED, THE see Wolff, S. Drummond

LORD, MY GOD, SHOW MERCY UNTO ME see Guglielmi

LORD MY GUIDE, THE [CHORALE] see Bach, Johann Sebastian, Der Herr Ist Mein Getreuer Hirt' [Chorale]

LORD MY GUIDE WILL SURELY BE, THE see Decius, Nicolaus

LORD MY PASTURE SHALL PREPARE, THE see Harris, William Henry

LORD MY PASTURE SHALL PREPARE, THE see Nyquist

LORD MY PASTURE SHALL PREPARE, THE see Shaw

LORD MY PASTURE SHALL PREPARE, THE see Young

LORD, MY SAVIOR, MY SALVATION see Schubert, Franz (Peter)

LORD MY SHEPHERD E'ER SHALL BE, THE see Bach, Johann Sebastian, Allein Gott In Der Hoh' Sei Ehr'

LORD MY SHEPHERD IS, THE see Handel, George Frideric

LORD MY SHEPHERD IS, THE see Lovelace, Austin C.

LORD MY SHEPHERD IS, THE see Powell

LORD NELSON MASS see Haydn, (Franz) Joseph, Nelson-Missa

LORD, NO LETTEST THOU see Mendelssohn-Bartholdy, Felix

LORD, NOW LETTEST THOU see Purcell, Henry

LORD NOW LETTEST THOU SERVANT see Schutz, Heinrich, Herr, Nun Lassest Du Deinen Diener

LORD, NOW LETTEST THOU THY SERVANT see Brauer, James

LORD, NOW LETTEST THOU THY SERVANT see Schutz, Heinrich, Herr, Nun Lassest Du Deinen Diener

LORD, NOW LETTEST THOU THY SERVANT see Schutz, Heinrich, Herr, Nun Lassest Du Deinen Diener

LORD NOW LETTEST THOU THY SERVANT DEPART IN PEACE see Byrd, William

LORD, NOW LETTEST THOU THY SERVANT DEPART IN PEACE see McGehee, Nunc Dimittis

LORD, NOW VICTORIOUS, THE see Mascagni, Pietro

LORD OF ALL see Gillam, R.L.

LORD OF ALL BEING see Andrews, Mark

LORD OF ALL BEING see Butler

LORD OF ALL BEING see Hegenbart, Alex F.

LORD OF ALL BEING see Moore

LORD OF ALL BEING see Newton

LORD OF ALL BEING see Thompson

LORD OF ALL BEING see Young

LORD OF ALL BEING, THRONED AFAR
    (Kinsman) SAB oct PRO ART 2437 $.25   (L1566)

LORD OF ALL BEING, THRONED AFAR see Bristol, L.

LORD OF ALL HOPEFULNESS see Marshall, Jane M.

LORD OF ALL HOPEFULNESS see Willan, Healey

LORD OF ALL KINDNESS see Deering, Richard, Jesu, Summa Benignitas

LORD OF ALL NATIONS, GRANT ME GRACE see
Harding, Julius Dayle

LORD OF ALL POWER see Mason

LORD OF ALL POWER see Wesley, Samuel Sebastian
Jr.

LORD OF ALL POWER AND MIGHT see Lewis, J.

LORD OF ALL POWER AND MIGHT see Shaw, Geoffrey
[Turton]

LORD OF ALL POWER AND MIGHT see Tait, John

LORD OF ALL POWER AND MIGHT see Talmadge,
Charles L.

LORD OF ALL, THE see Gottlieb, J., Adon Olam

LORD OF ALL, TO THEE WE PRAY see Grieg, Edvard
Hagerup

LORD OF GLORY CAME TO EARTH, THE see Coggin

LORD OF GLORY, WHO HAST BROUGHT US
(Miller) SATB oct PRO ART 2412 $.30   (L1567)

LORD OF HEAVEN see Lassus, Roland de (Orlandus)

LORD OF HOSTS see Wennerberg, Gunnar

LORD OF HOSTS MOST HIGH, THE see Rogers, Sharon
Elery

LORD OF LIFE see Bach

LORD OF LIFE see Whitman, Don

LORD OF LIFE IS RISEN INDEED, THE see Cashmore,
Donald

LORD OF LIGHT, THE see Christiansen, Larry A.

LORD OF LIGHT, THE see Gerhardt

LORD OF LORDS see Graham, M.E.

LORD OF LOVE, TO THEE I FLEE see Cornelius,
Peter, Liebe Dir Ergeb' Ich Mich!

LORD OF LYFE see Lenel, Ludwig

LORD OF MERCY see Morley, Thomas

LORD OF MY LIFE WHOSE TENDER CARE see Geijer

LORD OF MY LIFE, WHOSE TENDER CARE see Pacius

LORD OF OUR BEING see Handel, George Frideric,
Sorge Nel Petto

LORD OF OUR HIGHEST LOVE *Gen
(Brandon) SATB SCHMITT 8053 $.35   (L1568)

LORD OF OUR LIFE see Barnby

LORD OF OUR LIFE see Bateman, Ronald

LORD OF OUR LIFE see Fleming

LORD OF OUR LIFE see Ford, Virgil T.

LORD OF OUR LIFE see Hoffman, M.

LORD OF OUR LIFE see Thiman, Eric Harding

LORD OF OUR LIFE see Wolff, S. Drummond

LORD OF SPIRITS see Christiansen, Larry A.

LORD OF SPIRITS see Reissiger

LORD OF THE BRAVE see Palmer, Peggy Spenser

LORD OF THE EARTH AND SKY see Lekberg, Sven

LORD OF THE HARVEST see Osborne, Hayward

LORD OF THE NATIONS see Handel, George
Frideric, Lascia Chio Pianga

LORD OF THE STARS see Weyse, Christoph Ernst
Friedrich

LORD OF THE WINDS see Clothier, Louita

LORD OF THE WORLDS ABOVE see Blake, Leonard

LORD OF THE WORLDS ABOVE see Harris, William
Henry

LORD OF THE WORLDS ABOVE see Young

LORD OF THE YEARS see Charles, Ernest

LORD OMNIPOTENT IS KING see Scull

LORD ONCE MORE IS COME, THE see Chashoudian,
Marshall G.

LORD, OPEN THOU MY HEART see Dressler, John

LORD, OPEN THOU OUR EYES see Sullivan, Sir
Arthur Seymour

LORD, OUR CREATOR see Cain, Noble

LORD, OUR CREATOR see Mendelssohn-Bartholdy,
Felix

LORD OUR GOD see Bortniansky, Dimitri
Stepanovitch

LORD OUR GOD see Dencke

LORD, OUR GOD, HAVE MERCY see Kranz, Albert,
Kyrie Eleison

LORD OUR GOD IS CLOTHED IN MIGHT, THE see
Peninger, David

LORD, OUR GOD IS FULL OF MIGHT, THE see
Purcell, Henry

LORD OUR GOD IS KING OF KINGS, THE see Leaf,
Robert

LORD, OUR LORD see Ford, Virgil T.

LORD, OUR LORD, IN POWER DIVINE see Handel,
George Frideric

LORD OUR REDEEMER see Bach, Johann Sebastian

LORD, RALLY THE RIGHTEOUS see Johnston

LORD, REDEEMER OF ALL WHO KNOW THEE see Schutz,
Heinrich

LORD REIGNETH, THE see Craston, E.S.

LORD REIGNETH, THE see Walter, Samuel

LORD REIGNETH, THE
SATB CHAPPELL 0015891-358 $.40   (L1569)

LORD REIGNETH, THE see Adler, Samuel

LORD REIGNETH, THE see Butler, Eugene

LORD REIGNETH, THE see Clare, Edwyn A.

LORD REIGNETH, THE see Cooper

LORD REIGNETH, THE see Litten, Jack

LORD REIGNETH, THE see Mc Kinney, J.

LORD REIGNETH, THE see Manz, Paul

LORD REIGNS, THE see Butler

LORD REIGNS, THE see Wapen, Francis A.

LORD, REMEMBER ME see Gesualdo, Don Carlo,
Reminiscere

LORD, REMEMBER NOT see Mendelssohn-Bartholdy,
Felix

LORD, REMEMBER US see Wetzler

LORD, REMEMBER US see Wetzler, Robert

LORD, REMEMBER US (GOD, HURRAH!) see Wetzler

LORD REMEMBERS US, THE see Frauenholtz, Johann
Christoph, Der Herr Gedenkt An Uns

LORD SAID TO ME, THE see Ferris, W.

LORD, SANCTIFY ME WHOLLY see Powell, Robert J.

LORD, SEE THE PROOF OUR LOVE IS TRUE *hymn
SATB oct ST.MARTIN CMA601AX s.p.   (L1570)

LORD, SEND OUT YOUR SPIRIT see Peloquin, C.
Alexander

LORD, SEND THY HOLY SPIRIT see Young, G.

LORD SHALL BE UNTO THEE, THE see Thompson,
Randall

LORD SHALL BLESS HIS PEOPLE WITH PEACE see Lora

LORD SHALL GIVE THEE REST, THE see Starer,
Robert

LORD SHALL GIVE YOU A SIGN, THE see Johnson

LORD SHALL INCREASE YOU see Peter

LORD SHALL PRESERVE THEE FROM ALL EVIL, THE see
Hovhaness, Alan

LORD SHALL RAISE ME UP, THE see Nelhybel,
Vaclav

LORD SHALL REIGN FOREVER, THE see Handel,
George Frideric

LORD SHINE see Moore, Michael

LORD, SPEAK TO ME see Cain, Noble

LORD, SPEAK TO ME THAT I MAY SPEAK see Bristol,
Lee H., Jr.

LORD, SURROUND US WITH HOLY SYMBOLS see Wetzler

LORD, SURROUND US WITH HOLY SYMBOLS see
Wetzler, Robert

LORD, TAKE ME HOME *spir
(Cain) SATB oct FOX R211 $.30   (L1571)

LORD, TAKE MY HEART see Hovdesven, E.A.

LORD, TAKE OUR PROMISES see Grime, William

LORD, TEACH ME HOW TO PRAY see Reske

LORD, TEACH US HOW TO PRAY see Darst, W. Glenn

LORD, TEACH US HOW TO PRAY see Roff, Joseph

LORD, TEACH US HOW TO PRAY ARIGHT see Tallis,
Thomas

LORD, TEACH US TO PRAY see Wheeler, Alfred

LORD TENDS ME WELL, THE see Schutz, Heinrich,
Der Herr Ist Mein Hirt

LORD THEE I LOVE WITH ALL MY HEART *Gen
(Schroth) SATB SCHMITT 1201 $.30   (L1572)

LORD, THEE I LOVE WITH ALL MY HEART see Bach,
Johann Sebastian

LORD, THERE IS NONE LIKE THEE see Perti,
Giacomo Antonio

LORD, THIS DAY THY CHILDREN MEET see Lenel,
Ludwig

LORD THIS NIGHT IS COME TO EARTH, THE *Xmas
(Ehret, W.) SSA,pno,opt fl FISCHER,J 10089
$.35   (L1573)

LORD, THOU ALONE ART GOD see Mendelssohn-
Bartholdy, Felix

LORD, THOU ART HOLY see Franck, Cesar

LORD, THOU ART MIGHTY see Valinoff

LORD, THOU ART OUR GOD
(Peninger) SATB oct PRO ART 2602 $.30 (L1574)

LORD, THOU GAV'ST US CHRIST TO SAVE US see
Vittoria, Ludovico, Nobis Datus

LORD, THOU HAS BEEN OUR DWELLING PLACE see
Monaco, Richard A.

LORD, THOU HAS BEEN OUR DWELLING PLACE see
Mueller, Carl F.

LORD, THOU HAS BEEN OUR REFUGE see Vaughan
Williams, Ralph

LORD, THOU HAST BEEN A REFUGE SURE see Gibbs,
[Cecil] Armstrong

LORD, THOU HAST BEEN OUR DWELLING PLACE see
Arnatt, Ronald

LORD, THOU HAST BEEN OUR DWELLING PLACE see
Fraser

LORD, THOU HAST BEEN OUR DWELLING PLACE see
Fraser, Shena

LORD, THOU HAST BEEN OUR DWELLING PLACE see
Lekberg

LORD, THOU HAST BEEN OUR REFUGE see Cooke,
Arnold

LORD, THOU HAST BEEN OUR REFUGE see Joubert,
John

LORD, THOU HAST BEEN OUR REFUGE see Kirk

LORD THOU HAST BEEN OUR REFUGE see Smart, Henry
Thomas

LORD, THOU HAST BEEN OUR REFUGE see Vaughan
Williams, Ralph

LORD, THOU HAST BEEN OUR REFUGE see Willan,
Healey

LORD, THOU HAST PUT GLADNESS see Pinkham,
Daniel

LORD, THOU HAST SEARCHED ME
(Anderson) SATB,Bar solo,acap oct LAWSON
51137 $.25   (L1575)

LORD, THOU HAST SEARCHED ME see Posegate

LORD THOU HAST SEARCHED ME OUT see Willan,
Healey

LORD, THOU KNOWEST ALL OUR BEING see
Hammerschmidt, Andreas, Herr, Du Weissest
Alle Dinge

LORD, THOU LIGHT OF ALL MY BEING see Bach,
Johann Sebastian

LORD, THY SERVANTS PRAISE THEE see Mozart,
Wolfgang Amadeus

LORD, THY WORD ABIDETH *hymn
(Ravenshaw) SATB oct ST.MARTIN s.p.   (L1576)

LORD, THY WORD ABIDETH see Marryott, Ralph E.

LORD, THY WORD ABIDETH see Westbrook, Francis
B.

LORD, TO THEE I MAKE MY MOAN see Weelkes

LORD TO THEE I MAKE MY MOAN see Weelkes, Thomas

LORD TO THEE OUR HEARTS ARE RAISED see Glinka,
Mikhail Ivanovitch

LORD, TO THEE OUR SONG see Milano, R.

LORD, TO THEE WE TURN see Lassus, Roland de
(Orlandus), Inimici Autem

LORD, TO WHOM SHALL WE GO? see Mudde, Willem

LORD TRIUMPHANT see Mascagni, Pietro

LORD UNTO THEE see Bestor, C.

LORD, WALK WITH ME see Artman

LORD, WE BESEECH THEE see Batten, Adrian

LORD, WE BESEECH THEE see Batten, Adrian

LORD, WE COME BEFORE THEE NOW see Gottschalk

LORD, WE CRY TO THEE see Zwingli

LORD WE GIVE THANKS TO THEE see Moore

LORD, WE IMPLORE THEE see Franck, Cesar

LORD, WE LOVE THE PLACE see Graun, Karl
Heinrich, Herr, Ich Habe Lieb De Statte

LORD, WE PRAISE YOU FOR THE RHYTHM see Wetzler,
Robert

LORD WE PRAY see Gounod, Charles Francois

LORD, WE PRAY, IN MERCY LEAD US see Sibelius,
Jean

LORD, WE PRAY THEE see Mozart, Wolfgang Amadeus

LORD WE PRAY THEE see Ryley

LORD, WE PRAY TO THEE see Mozart, Wolfgang
Amadeus

LORD, WE THANK THEE FOR THY GRACE see Franck,
Cesar

LORD, WHAT HAST THOU DONE? see Schutz, Heinrich

LORD, WHAT IS MAN *hymn
(Parker) SATB,acap oct LAWSON 51321 $.25
     (L1577)

LORD, WHAT IS MAN? see Fawcett, J.

LORD, WHEN I THINK see Weelkes, Thomas

LORD, WHEN THE SENSE OF THY SWEET GRACE see Berkeley, Lennox

LORD, WHEN THE WISE MEN CAME FROM FAR see Spedding, Frank

LORD, WHEN TO THEE I CRY see Pezel, Johann Christoph, Wenn Ich Zu Dir Empor

LORD, WHILE FOR ALL MANKIND WE PRAY see Thiman, Eric Harding

LORD, WHILE FOR ALL MANKIND WE PRAY see Wreford

LORD, WHO HAST MADE US see Holst, Gustav

LORD, WHO HAST MADE US FOR THINE OWN see Holst, Gustav

LORD, WHO IS MY GUIDE BUT THEE? see Schutz, Heinrich

LORD, WHO ORDAINEST see Lundquist, Matthew Nathanael, Mother's Hymn, The

LORD, WHO ORDAINETH see Lundquist, Matthew Nathanael, Mother's Hymn, The

LORD, WHO REIGNEST NOW ON HIGH see Mozart, Wolfgang Amadeus, Herr, Der Du Thronest

LORD WHO SHALL ABIDE see Darst, W. Glenn

LORD, WHO SHALL ABIDE IN THY TABERNACLE? see Bliss, Sir Arthur

LORD, WHO SHALL DWELL IN THY TABERNACLE? see Bevin, Elway

LORD, WHO SHALL DWELL IN THY TABERNACLE see Rogers, Benjamin

LORD, WHO THROUGHOUT THESE FORTY DAYS (Hemmer, Eugene) SATB,org oct WORLD $.30 (L1578)

LORD WILL BE GLORIFIED see Newbury

LORD WILL COME AND NOT BE SLOW, THE see Choral Hymn, A

LORD WILL COME, THE see Tye, Christopher

LORD WILL COME, THE see Vree

LORD WILL COMFORT ZION, THE (Cornwall, J.S.) SATB PIONEER 5060 $.20 (L1579)

LORD WILL NOT SUFFER see Bach

LORD WILL NOT SUFFER, THE see Bach, Johann Sebastian

LORD, WITH WHAT CARE see Rubbra, Edmund

LORD, YOU HAVE THE WORDS see Peloquin, C. Alexander

LORD'S DAY see Brandon

LORD'S DAY, THE see Brandon, George

LORD'S DAY, THE see Wetherill

LORD'S MY SHEPHERD see Hutcheson

LORD'S MY SHEPHERD see Mueller, Carl F.

LORD'S MY SHEPHERD, THE see Titcomb, Everett

LORD'S MY SHEPHERD, THE *Gen (Cornwall, J.S.) SATB PIONEER 5065 $.25 (L1580)
(Janes, Oliver) SATB WEINBERGER s.p. (L1581)
(Johnson) SATB SCHMITT 914 $.25 (L1582)
(Luboff, Norman) SATB oct WALTON 3023 $.30 (L1583)

LORD'S MY SHEPHERD, THE see Beck, Theodore

LORD'S MY SHEPHERD, THE see Gardiner

LORD'S MY SHEPHERD, THE see Grant, David

LORD'S MY SHEPHERD, THE see Hustad, Donald P.

LORD'S MY SHEPHERD, THE see Jolley

LORD'S MY SHEPHERD, THE see Landahl, [Carl Wilfred]

LORD'S MY SHEPHERD, THE see Mueller, Carl F.

LORD'S MY SHEPHERD, THE see Nops, Marjory

LORD'S MY SHEPHERD, THE see Van Dyke

LORD'S MY SHEPHERD, THE see Young

LORD'S OWN DAY, THE see Larson

LORD'S PRAYER *folk,Carib see Sursum Corda
(Saunders) SATB oct BOOSEY 1915 $.30 (L1584)
(Saunders) TTBB oct BOOSEY 1913 $.30 (L1585)

LORD'S PRAYER see Camilieri, L.

LORD'S PRAYER see Hilty

LORD'S PRAYER see Pont

LORD'S PRAYER see Solomin

LORD'S PRAYER see Zaumeyer

LORD'S PRAYER, THE *Bibl/folk/prayer (Dunaway) SATB oct LILLENAS AN-5027 $.30 (L1586)

LORD'S PRAYER, THE see Cory, George

LORD'S PRAYER, THE see Johnson

LORD'S PRAYER, THE see Nordman, Chester

LORD'S PRAYER, THE see Ratcliffe, Desmond

LORD'S PRAYER, THE see Stones, Robert

LORD'S PRAYER, THE see Thiman, Eric Harding

LORD'S PRAYER, THE *Bibl/prayer (Davis, K.K.) unis oct FISCHER,C CM-7728 $.25 (L1587)
(Hamblen) 2pt CHAPPELL 0018150-352 $.40 (L1588)
(Hamblen) SSA CHAPPELL 0018150-354 $.40 (L1589)
(Hamblen) SAB CHAPPELL 0018150-356 $.40 (L1590)
(Hamblen) SATB CHAPPELL 0018150-358 $.40 (L1591)

LORD'S PRAYER, THE see Anderson, R.

LORD'S PRAYER, THE see Bach

LORD'S PRAYER, THE see Beethoven, Ludwig van

LORD'S PRAYER, THE see Bock, F.

LORD'S PRAYER, THE see Bortniansky, Dimitri Stepanovitch

LORD'S PRAYER, THE see Brown, Frank Edwin

LORD'S PRAYER, THE see Cadzow, D.

LORD'S PRAYER, THE see Christiansen, Paul

LORD'S PRAYER, THE see Clements, John

LORD'S PRAYER, THE see Curwin, Clifford

LORD'S PRAYER, THE see Davies, Peter Maxwell

LORD'S PRAYER, THE see Dawney, Michael

LORD'S PRAYER, THE see Elgar, Edward

LORD'S PRAYER, THE see Fargo

LORD'S PRAYER, THE see Farmer, John

LORD'S PRAYER, THE see Farmer, John

LORD'S PRAYER, THE see Farrar, H.M.

LORD'S PRAYER, THE see Forsyth, [Josephine]

LORD'S PRAYER, THE see Fre, Hugo

LORD'S PRAYER, THE see Frederick

LORD'S PRAYER, THE see Gerschefski, Edwin

LORD'S PRAYER, THE see Gevaert, Francois Auguste, Pater Noster

LORD'S PRAYER, THE see Gretchaninov, Alexander Tikhonovitch

LORD'S PRAYER, THE see Handel, George Frideric

LORD'S PRAYER, THE see Helfer

LORD'S PRAYER, THE see Hovhaness, Alan

LORD'S PRAYER, THE see Kennerly

LORD'S PRAYER, THE see La Mure, [Pierre]

LORD'S PRAYER, THE see Langdon, R.

LORD'S PRAYER, THE see Malotte

LORD'S PRAYER, THE see Malotte, Albert Hay, Pater Noster

LORD'S PRAYER, THE see Morgan

LORD'S PRAYER, THE see Mueller, Carl F.

LORD'S PRAYER, THE see Pallma

LORD'S PRAYER, THE see Peeters, Flor

LORD'S PRAYER, THE see Peloquin, C. Alexander

LORD'S PRAYER, THE see Perera, Ronald

LORD'S PRAYER, THE see Pitfield, Thomas Baron

LORD'S PRAYER, THE see Raymond, Joseph

LORD'S PRAYER, THE see Robertson

LORD'S PRAYER, THE see Salathiel, Lyndon

LORD'S PRAYER, THE see Shepherd, John

LORD'S PRAYER, THE see Spieckerman, H.

LORD'S PRAYER, THE see Villa-Lobos, Heitor

LORD'S PRAYER, THE see Williamson, Inez McCune

LORD'S PRAYER, THE see Zimmermann, Heinz Werner

LORD'S SUPPER see Young

LORD'S SUPPER, THE see Lapin

LORD'S SUPPER, THE see Billson

LORD'S SUPPER, THE see Lapin

LORD'S SUPPER, THE see Young, Carlton R.

LORD'S TEMPLE see Gregor

LOREGIAN, SANDRO
Messa B. Vergine Della Salute *Mass
[It] unis sc ZANIBON 5048 s.p., cor pts ZANIBON 5049 s.p. (L1592)

Messa Nostra Signora Di Fatima *Mass
[It] ATB sc ZANIBON 5050 s.p., cor pts ZANIBON 5051 s.p. (L1593)

LORENTZEN, BENT
This Morning
mix cor HANSEN-DEN 29133 s.p. (L1594)

LORENZ
All Creatures Of Our God And King
2pt oct LORENZ 5721 $.30 (L1595)

Carols Of Christmas *Xmas,cant
SSA oct LORENZ $1.75 (L1596)
SA oct LORENZ $1.75 (L1597)
SAB oct LORENZ $1.75 (L1598)
SATB oct LORENZ $1.95 (L1599)

Christmas Invitation, The *Xmas
SATB oct LORENZ B86 $.30 (L1600)

Church's One Foundation, The
SATB oct LORENZ C11 $.30 (L1601)

Come, All Ye Faithful *Xmas
SATB oct LORENZ A418 $.25 (L1602)

Consecration
SATB oct LORENZ 9445 $.30 (L1603)

Easter Hallelujah, The *Easter
SATB oct LORENZ 9118 $.30 (L1604)

Echo Of Christmas, The *Xmas,cant
SATB oct LORENZ $1.95 (L1605)

Echoes Of Christmas Eve *Xmas
SATB oct LORENZ 9286 $.30 (L1606)
SAB oct LORENZ 7397 $.30 (L1607)

Festal Alleluia, A *Easter
SATB oct LORENZ E21 $.35 (L1608)

First Nowell, The *Xmas
SATB oct LORENZ B8 $.30 (L1609)

Gloria In Excelsis Deo *Gloria
SATB oct LORENZ C56 $.30 (L1610)

Good Christian Men, Rejoice *Xmas
unis oct LORENZ 8594 $.30 (L1611)

Gospel Song Of Christmas, The *Xmas,cant
SATB oct LORENZ $1.95 (L1612)

Gospel Song Of Easter, The *Easter,cant
SA/SAB LORENZ $1.75 (L1613)
SATB LORENZ $1.95 (L1614)

Great Is Thy Faithfulness
SATB oct LORENZ B62 $.30 (L1615)

Greatest Of These Is Love, The
SATB oct LORENZ C145 $.30 (L1616)

Hark! The Herald Angels Sing *Xmas
SATB oct LORENZ 9497 $.35 (L1617)

Have Thine Own Way, Lord
SATB oct LORENZ C161 $.30 (L1618)

He Lives! *Easter
SATB oct LORENZ A361 $.25 (L1619)

How Beautiful Upon The Mountains
SAB oct LORENZ 7063 $.30 (L1620)

I Love Thy Church, O God
SATB oct LORENZ 9480 $.30 (L1621)

In His Holy Temple
2pt oct LORENZ 5734 $.30 (L1622)

In The Quietness
SATB oct LORENZ C189 $.30 (L1623)

Jesus Is All The World To Me
SATB oct LORENZ A415 $.30 (L1624)

Joy Dawned On Easter Day *Easter
SAB oct LORENZ 7359 $.30 (L1625)

Joy, Joy, Joy
SATB oct LORENZ 9278 $.30 (L1626)

Joy Of Christmas, The *Xmas,cant
two-melody oct LORENZ $1.75 (L1627)

Memories Of Easter Morn *Easter,cant
SATB LORENZ $1.95 (L1628)
SA LORENZ $1.75 (L1629)
SSA LORENZ $1.75 (L1630)
SAB LORENZ $1.75 (L1631)

Mighty Triumph, The
SATB oct LORENZ 4483 $.30 (L1632)

Open My Eyes
SATB oct LORENZ 4441 $.30 (L1633)

Our Hymn Of Grateful Praise
SATB oct LORENZ 9790 $.30 (L1634)

Praises To The Giver
SATB oct LORENZ A302 $.25 (L1635)

Resurrection *Easter
SATB oct LORENZ B76 $.30 (L1636)

Silent Night, Holy Night *Xmas
SATB oct LORENZ 9105 $.30 (L1637)

Song In The Air, The *Xmas
SATB oct LORENZ B63 $.30 (L1638)

Stand In Awe
SATB oct LORENZ 9881 $.30 (L1639)

Story Of Easter Acc'd To St. Matt. *Easter, cant
SATB LORENZ $1.95 (L1640)

Sunrise On A Hill *Easter
SA oct LORENZ 5354 $.30 (L1641)
SATB oct LORENZ A277 $.30 (L1642)

Take It To The Lord In Prayer
SATB oct LORENZ B14 $.30 (L1643)

We Worship Thee
SATB oct LORENZ C267 $.30 (L1644)

Wondrous Cross, The *Easter
SATB oct LORENZ C196 $.30 (L1645)

LORENZ, ELLEN JANE (1907-)
Elect Of God
4pt mix cor oct SCHIRM.G 10281 $.20 (L1646)

Immortal, Invisible
SATB (easy) ABINGDON APM-222 $.25 (L1647)

Seven Sayings From The Cross *Gd.Fri.
cor,soli LORENZ $1.50 (L1648)

LORING
Cradle Song *Xmas
(Davis) SSA oct GALAXY 1.2193.1 $.20 (L1649)

O Love, Thy Grateful Beauty Shines
(Davis) SSA oct GALAXY 1.2194.1 $.25 (L1650)

L'ORPHEON DE LA JEUNESSE, PREMIERE VOLUME see Bordese

L'ORPHEON DE LA JEUNESSE, DEUXIEME VOLUME *sac/sec,CC25L
[Fr] 2-3pt jr cor,acap oct CHOUDENS s.p. contains sacred works by: Gounod And Semet (L1651)

L'ORPHEON DE LA JEUNESSE, QUATRIEME VOLUME *sac/sec,CC25L
[Fr/Lat] 2-3pt jr cor,acap oct CHOUDENS s.p. contains sacred works by: Audran; Paladilhe; Bizet (L1652)

L'ORPHEON MODERNE *sac/sec,CC96L
TTBB/SSTTBB,acap CHOUDENS s.p. contains sacred works by: Gounod; Mendelssohn; Bizet; and others (L1653)

LOS ANGELES Y LOS PASTORES see Benedito

LOS CINCUENTA Y DOS MOTETES CUADERNO I see Victoria, Tomas Luis de

LOS CINCUENTA Y DOS MOTETES CUADERNO II see Victoria, Tomas Luis de

LOS CINCUENTA Y DOS MOTETES CUADERNO III see Victoria, Tomas Luis de

LOS CINCUENTA Y DOS MOTETES CUADERNO IV see Victoria, Tomas Luis de

LOS, LOS, MEIN WOLFERL *Xmas,Aus
(Schemitsch, Hans) [Ger] mix cor,acap oct DOBLINGER s.p. see also Zehn Osterrichische Weihnachtsleider (L1654)

LOSER, J.H.
Kerstlied
men cor ALSBACH&D sc s.p., cor pts s.p. (L1655)

LOSS, LUIGI
Messa In Onore Della Madonna Di Loreto *Mass
[Lat] ATTB,org sc ZANIBON 4681 s.p., voc pt ZANIBON s.p. (L1656)

Tantum Ergo *Commun
[Lat] 3pt sc ZANIBON 4702 s.p., cor pts ZANIBON 4703 s.p. (L1657)

LOSSIUS, LUKAS (1508-1582)
Ehre Sei Gott In Der Hohe
see Stobaeus, Johann, Ich Hab Ein Herzlich Freud

LOST CAROL *Xmas,cant
oct LORENZ $1.00 (L1658)

LOST CHILD, THE see Nin-Culmell, Joaquin

LOST CHORD, THE see Sullivan, Sir Arthur Seymour

LOST IN THE NIGHT *anthem/folk,Finn
(Christiansen, F.M.) SSAA (med) oct AUGSBURG 0261 $.20 (L1659)

LOST IN THE NIGHT see Christiansen, F. Melius

LOST IN WONDER, LOVE, AND PRAISE see Ford, Virgil T.

LOTTI, ANTONIO (1667-1740)
Adoramus Te *Easter/Lent
"We Adore Thee" SATB oct WALTON 2130 $.25 (L1660)
(Ehret) "We Adore Thee" mix cor CHAPPELL 0023507-358 $.40 (L1661)

Agnus Dei (from Mass In D Minor) Agnus
"Lamb Of God" SSAA,acap SCHIRM.EC 1949 $.25 (L1662)
(Ehret) mix cor SOUTHERN $.20 (L1663)
(Ehret) [Eng/Lat] SATB,acap MARKS 4365 $.25 (L1664)

Benedictus (from Mass In D Minor)
see Lotti, Antonio, Sanctus

Bless The Lord, O My Soul (Psalm 103)
(Ehret) SAB LUDWIG L-9138 $.35 (L1665)

Blessed Is He *see Regina Caeli

Bow Our Hearts
(Harris) SAB oct ELKAN-V 362-1287 $.25 (L1666)

Christ Is Arisen (composed with Cozens, J.)
(Cozens) SATB THOMP.G G-533 s.p. (L1667)

Crucified *see Crucifixus

Crucifixus *Easter/Gd.Fri./Lent
(Davison, A.) [Lat] TTBB,acap SCHIRM.EC 42 $.30 (L1668)
(Knight, Gerald) SATB,acap oct FISCHER,C CM-7501 $.25 (L1669)
(Martens, Mason) "Loving Saviour, To The Cross Nailed" SSATTB oct WALTON 6022 $.30 (L1670)

Crucifixus
mix cor SOUTHERN $.30 (L1671)

Crucifixus
mix cor SOUTHERN $.30 (L1672)
[Lat/Eng] SSATTB,acap oct SCHIRM.G 11608 $.30 (L1673)
(Baldwin) mix cor oct SCHIRM.G 11915 $.30 (L1674)

Crucifixus *Easter/Gd.Fri./Lent/Psntd,mot
SSAATTBB,acap SCHIRM.EC 1192 $.35 (L1675)
dbl cor,acap oct SCHIRM.G 6396 $.30 (L1676)

LOTTI, ANTONIO (cont'd.)

"Crucified" SSAATTBB oct WALTON 6006 $.30 (L1677)
(Graulich) [Lat] SSAATTBB,cont HANSSLER 1.532 $.90 (L1678)

Dies Irae *ora
(Piccioli, G.) cor,SATB soli,org,ob,trp, strings CARISH rental (L1679)

Ecce Panis Angelorum
"Now With Hands To God Uplifted" SATB,acap SCHIRM.EC 1696 $.20 (L1680)

Gaude Maria *mot
[Lat] SATB,acap oct GIA G564 $.25 (L1681)

Gloria (from Mass In D Minor) Gloria
(Ehret) [Lat] SATB MARKS 4366 $.25 (L1682)
(Ehret) mix cor SOUTHERN $.25 (L1683)

Gloria In Excelsis *Gloria
(Williams) SATB oct FOX PS100 $.30 (L1684)

Hail, Queen Of Heaven
see TWO MOTETS IN HONOR OF THE BLESSED VIRGIN

Hail Queen Of Mercy *see Salve Regina

He Bears Our Burdens *see Vere Languores Nostros

Holy, Holy, Holy *see Sanctus

Joy Fills The Morning *Easter
(Dickinson) SATB oct GRAY GC 172 $.30 (L1685)

Kyrie (from Mass VII) Kyrie
[Lat] LYCHE 28 s.p. (L1686)
(Talmadge, A.) [Ger/Eng] SSAA,acap SCHIRM.EC 1904 $.25 (L1687)

Kyrie Eleison *Easter/Lent,Kyrie
mix cor SOUTHERN $.30 (L1688)
"Mighty Lord, Thy Faithfulness Abideth Ever" SAB/SAT,acap SCHIRM.EC 1716 $.30 (L1689)
(Kjelson) "Lord, Have Mercy Upon Us" SATB oct BELWIN 2204 $.30 (L1690)
(Richardson) "Lord, Have Mercy On Us" SATB oct SPRATT 2014 $.25 (L1691)

Lamb Of God *see Agnus Dei

Lord, Have Mercy
(Pfautsch) TBB oct AGAPE A 402 $.25 (L1692)

Lord, Have Mercy On Us *see Kyrie Eleison

Lord, Have Mercy Upon Me *see Miserere Mei Deus

Lord, Have Mercy Upon Us *see Kyrie Eleison

Loving Saviour, To The Cross Nailed *see Crucifixus

Mass
[Lat] SSA,acap (B flat maj) SCHIRM.EC 1845 $1.00 (L1693)
[Lat] TTB,acap (B flat maj) SCHIRM.EC 566 $1.00 (L1694)

Mass In C *Mass
"Student's Mass" cor voc sc KALMUS 6285 $1.25, ipa (L1695)
"Students' Mass" [Lat] boy cor,TB soli,org, 2vln sc UNIVER. 4957 $4.25, cor pts UNIVER. 4958 $2.55 (L1696)

Mass VII In The Doric Mode *Commun
[Lat/Eng] SATB,acap SCHIRM.EC 1264 $.75 (L1697)

Mighty Lord, Thy Faithfulness Abideth Ever *see Kyrie Eleison

Miserere
mix cor NORDISKA 1011 s.p. (L1698)

Miserere Mei
SATB oct WALTON 2178 $.30 (L1699)
(Ehret) [Lat/Eng] TTBB,acap oct BOOSEY 5521 $.30 (L1700)
(Ehret; Wilson) mix cor SOUTHERN $.30 (L1701)
(Wilson; Ehret) [Lat/Eng] SSA,acap oct BOOSEY 5232 $.30 (L1702)
(Wilson; Ehret) [Lat/Eng] SATB,acap oct BOOSEY 5590 $.30 (L1703)
(Wilson; Ehret) [Lat/Eng] SATB,acap oct BOOSEY 1938 $.30 (L1704)

Miserere Mei Deus *Adv/Lent
"Lord, Have Mercy Upon Me" SATB,acap SCHIRM.EC 1231 $.12 (L1705)

Missa *Mass
(Bauerle, Hermann) SATB,acap cor pts BREITKOPF-L PB-3140 s.p., voc pt BREITKOPF-L CHB-2550 s.p. (L1706)

Missa In A *Mass
(Bauerle, Hermann) SATB,acap cor pts BREITKOPF-L PB-3472 s.p., voc pt BREITKOPF-L CHB-2863 s.p. (L1707)

Missa In C *Mass
(Bauerle, Hermann) SATB,acap voc pt BREITKOPF-L CHB-2549 s.p. (L1708)

Missa In F *Mass
(Bauerle, Hermann) SATB,acap cor pts BREITKOPF-L PB-3471 s.p., voc pt BREITKOPF-L CHB-2862 s.p. (L1709)

Missa Octavi Toni *Mass
(Bauerle, Hermann) SATB,acap cor pts BREITKOPF-L PB-3447 s.p., voc pt BREITKOPF-L CHB-2824 s.p. (L1710)

Missa Pro Defunctis *Mass/Req
(Bauerle, Hermann) SATB,acap cor pts BREITKOPF-L PB-3473 s.p., voc pt BREITKOPF-L CHB-2864 s.p. (L1711)

LOTTI, ANTONIO (cont'd.)

Missa Sexti Toni *Mass
(Bauerle, Hermann) SATB,acap cor pts BREITKOPF-L PB-3470 s.p., voc pt BREITKOPF-L CHB-2861 s.p. (L1712)

Now With Hands To God Uplifted *see Ecce Panis Angelorum

O Queen Of Heaven Be Joyful *see Regina Coeli

Psalm 103 *see Bless The Lord, O My Soul

Queen Of Heaven *see Regina Coeli

Regina Caeli
"Blessed Is He" SATB,acap SCHIRM.EC 1232 $.12 (L1713)

Regina Coeli *Easter/Lent,anthem
see LA SCHOLA PALESTRINIENNE DEUXIEME CAHIER
mix cor ALSBACH&D sc s.p., cor pts s.p. (L1714)
(Klein, M.) "Queen Of Heaven" [Eng/Lat] SATB (easy) oct GIA G1527 F 25 $.30 (L1715)
(Marshall, Charles) "O Queen Of Heaven Be Joyful" SATB FRANK F-546 $.30 (L1716)

Salve Regina *mot
SATB,acap SCHIRM.EC $.25 (L1717)
[Lat] SATB RICORDI-ENG SY119 s.p. (L1718)
SATB,acap RICORDI-ENG SY119 s.p. (L1719)
(Collins, H.B.) [Lat] SATB CHESTER s.p. (L1720)
(Payson, A.) "Hail Queen Of Mercy" SATB, acap FRANK F-573 $.30 (L1721)

Sanctus (from Mass In D Minor) Sanctus
"Holy, Holy, Holy" SATB,acap SCHIRM.EC 2216 $.25 (L1722)
(Bement) girl cor SOUTHERN $.30 (L1723)
(Ehret) [Eng/Lat] SATB MARKS 4367 $.25 contains also: Benedictus (Bene) (L1724)
(Richardson) "Holy, Holy, Holy" SATB oct SPRATT 2000 $.30 (L1725)

Sanctus Dominus Deus
(Lavater, H.) [Lat] wom cor,acap (med diff) HUG s.p. (L1726)

Sing, Joyous Christians *Asc/Easter
SATB,kbd (med easy) oct CONCORDIA 98-1456 $.25 (L1727)
mix cor SOUTHERN $.25 (L1728)
(Buszin) SATB oct SOUTHERN $.25 (L1729)

Student's Mass *see Mass In C

Surely He Has Borne Our Griefs
(Stroud, Ray) SAT&SAB,acap FOSTER MF401 $.25 (L1730)

Surely He Hath Borne Our Griefs *see Vere Languores Nostros

Surely He Hath Bourne Our Griefs *see Vere Languores Nostros

Szivunkre Szall Ma
(Nadas, K.) [Hung] SATB (easy) BUDAPEST see also NASZDALOK VEGYESKARRA (L1731)

There Is One God And One Saviour
(Nolte) mix cor SOUTHERN $.40 (L1732)

Vere Languores Nostros *Easter/Lent
wom cor sc ALSBACH&D s.p. (L1733)
[Lat] TTB,acap SCHIRM.EC 70 $.25 (L1734)
3pt men cor,acap RICORDI-ENG SY130 s.p. (L1735)
"Surely He Hath Borne Our Griefs" SAB/ATB, acap SCHIRM.EC 1124 $.30 (L1736)
(Greyson) girl cor SOUTHERN $.25 (L1737)
(Greyson) "He Bears Our Burdens" SSA oct BOURNE ES22 $.25 (L1738)
(Hunter) "Surely He Hath Borne Our Griefs" [Eng/Lat] SSA,acap MARKS 4457 $.25 (L1739)
(Hunter) "Surely He Hath Borne Our Griefs" [Eng/Lat] TTB,acap MARKS 4458 $.30 (L1740)
(Woodworth, G.) "Surely He Hath Borne Our Griefs" SSA,acap SCHIRM.EC 1509 $.25 (L1741)
(Woodworth, G.) "Surely He Hath Bourne Our Griefs" SSA,acap SCHIRM.EC 1509 $.25 (L1742)

We Adore Thee *see Adoramus Te

Ye Who Pass By *Renais
(Ehret, Walter) SATB,acap PEER $.40 (L1743)

LOTZ, HANS-GEORG (1934-)
Es Ist Einer Fur Uns Gestorben
see Ruppel, Paul Ernst, Gott Liebt Den Menschen

Weise Mir, Herr, Deinen Weg
see Ruppel, Paul Ernst, Gott Liebt Den Menschen

LOUCKS
God's House
2pt oct LORENZ A245 $.30 (L1744)
2pt oct LORENZ 5706 $.30 (L1745)

My Redeemer Liveth
SATB oct LORENZ 4404 $.30 (L1746)

Thanks To God For My Mother
SATB oct LORENZ A306 $.30 (L1747)

LOUD ROAR OF THE ROCKET see Wilson, John F.

LOUEZ LE SEIGNEUR see Debussy, Claude

LOURDES-MESSE see Doebler, Curt

LOURDES PILGRIM HYMN
(Donath, J.) SSA oct PRESSER 312-40403 $.25 (L1748)
(Donath, J.) SATB oct PRESSER 312-40402 $.25 (L1749)

LOV HERREN see Rodseth, Johs.

LOV, PRIS OCH ARA VARE DIG, O GUD see Berg,
Gottfrid

LOV PRIS OG TAK GUD FADER see Distler, Hugo,
Lob, Ehr Sei Gott, Dem Vater

LOV VARE DIG, O JESU KRIST see Berg, Gottfrid

LOV VARE DIG, O JESU KRIST see Bjarnegard,
Gustaf

LOV VARE DIG, O JESU KRIST see Runback, Albert

LOV VARE DIG, O JESU KRIST see Schein, Johann
Hermann

LOV VARE DIG, O JESU KRIST see Walther, Johann
Gottfreid

LOVA HERREN see Vierdanck, Johann, Lobe Den
Herren

LOVA HERREN MIN SJAL
  (Soderholm, Valdemar) 3pt wom cor/3pt jr cor,
  acap NORDISKA 5266 s.p.   (L1750)

LOVA HERREN, MIN SJAL see Carlstedt, Gunnemer

LOVAD VARE HERREN see Bond, Anders

LOVAD VARE HERREN see Salonen, Sulo

LOVATO, ZENO
  Assumpta Est Maria *BVM
  [Lat] STB,org sc ZANIBON 4326 s.p.   (L1751)

LOVE see Eidsvoog

LOVE AND BLESSED BE THOU, KING see Pasquet,
Jean

LOVE CAME DOWN see Simeone

LOVE CAME DOWN see Vandre, Carl W.

LOVE CAME DOWN AT CHRISTMAS *anthem,Ir
  (Preus, Carol) SAB (easy) oct AUGSBURG 1432
  $.25   (L1752)

LOVE CAME DOWN AT CHRISTMAS see Bullock, Ernest

LOVE CAME DOWN AT CHRISTMAS see Copland, Aaron

LOVE CAME DOWN AT CHRISTMAS see Floyd, Alfred
E.

LOVE CAME DOWN AT CHRISTMAS see Freestone, G.S.

LOVE CAME DOWN AT CHRISTMAS see Goodman, Joseph

LOVE CAME DOWN AT CHRISTMAS see Hesford, Brian

LOVE CAME DOWN AT CHRISTMAS see Lovelace,
Austin C.

LOVE CAME DOWN AT CHRISTMAS see Morris,
Reginald Owen

LOVE CAME DOWN AT CHRISTMAS see Morse, [Charles
Henry]

LOVE CAME DOWN AT CHRISTMAS see Mueller, Carl
F.

LOVE CAME DOWN AT CHRISTMAS see Rosetti,
Francesco Antionio

LOVE CAME DOWN AT CHRISTMAS see Smith, Eric

LOVE CAME DOWN AT CHRISTMAS see Swaffield,
Ronald

LOVE CAME DOWN AT CHRISTMAS see Thiman, Eric
Harding

LOVE CAME DOWN AT CHRISTMAS see Thomas

LOVE CAME DOWN AT CHRISTMAS see Trant, Brian

LOVE CAME DOWN AT CHRISTMAS see Van Dyke

LOVE CAME DOWN AT CHRISTMAS see Wilson, R.

LOVE CAME DOWN AT CHRISTMAS see Young

LOVE CAME DOWN AT CHRISTMASTIDE see Steele

LOVE DEN HERREN, MEINE SEELE see Schutz,
Heinrich

LOVE DIVINE see Angell, Warren M.

LOVE DIVINE see Beethoven, Ludwig van

LOVE DIVINE see Belt, T.

LOVE DIVINE see Greener

LOVE DIVINE see Liszt, Franz, Liebestraume No.
3

LOVE DIVINE see Prichard, [Rowland Hugh]

LOVE DIVINE see Van Der Hoeck

LOVE DIVINE see Zundel, [John]

LOVE DIVINE! ALL LOVE EXCELLING see Stainer,
John

LOVE DIVINE, ALL LOVE EXCELLING see Zundel,
[John]

LOVE DIVINE, ALL LOVES EXCELLING see Bach,
Johann Sebastian

LOVE DIVINE, ALL LOVES EXCELLING see Nicholson,
S.H.

LOVE DIVINE, ALL LOVES EXCELLING see Prichard,
[Rowland Hugh]

LOVE DIVINE, ALL LOVES EXCELLING see Rorem, Ned

LOVE DIVINE, ALL LOVES EXCELLING see Rowlands,
W.P., Blaenwern

LOVE DIVINE, ALL LOVES EXCELLING see Stainer,
John

LOVE DIVINE, ALL LOVES EXCELLING see Thiman,
Eric Harding

LOVE DIVINE, ALL LOVES EXCELLING see Webber,
Lloyd

LOVE FAILETH NEVER see Evans

LOVE GIFT, THE see Martin

LOVE IN GRIEF see Christiansen, F. Melius

LOVE IS... *CCUL
  (Carmichael, Ralph) SATB voc sc WORD 37526
  $1.95   (L1753)

LOVE IS COME AGAIN *Easter/Lent,carol,Fr
  unis/SATB (easy) OXFORD 08.149 $.15 (L1754)
  (Scott) TTBB,acap oct FISCHER,C CM-6529 $.25
                                       (L1755)
  (Shaw; Parker) 4pt mix cor,acap oct SCHIRM.G
  9959 $.25   (L1756)

LOVE IS COME AGAIN see Brubaker, Gwen

LOVE IS COME AGAIN see Kerr

LOVE IS COME AGAIN see Kugelmann

LOVE IS EVERLASTING see Peloquin, C. Alexander

LOVE IS SURRENDER see Carmichael, Ralph

LOVE IS WHY see Ellis

LOVE KNOWS NO SEASON see Belt, T.

LOVE LED THE WAY see Mc Pherson, Aimee Semple

LOVE LIFTED ME see Rowe, J.

LOVE, LOVE, LOVE see Brokering, Lois

LOVE MUST RULE IN MAN'S HEART see Williams

LOVE NEVER FAILETH
  SATB CHAPPELL 0022491-358 $.40   (L1757)

LOVE NOT THE WORLD see Gaul, Alfred Robert

LOVE OF GOD see Hayes

LOVE OF GOD see James

LOVE OF GOD, THE see Lehman, Evangeline

LOVE OF GOD, THE
  see Great Choral Series
  SATB BIG3 $.25   (L1758)

LOVE OF GOD, THE see Rasley, [John M.]

LOVE OF GOD, THE see Wikehart, Lewis E.

LOVE OF GOD, THE see Woodman, Raymond
Huntington

LOVE OF JESUS, ALL DIVINE see Blake, George
[M.]

LOVE OF THE FATHER see Bancroft, H. Hugh

LOVE OF THE FATHER see Wolff, S. Drummond

LOVE OF THE FATHER, THE see Candlyn, T.
Frederick H.

LOVE ONE ANOTHER see Cacavas, [John]

LOVE ONE ANOTHER see Dean

LOVE ONE ANOTHER see Elliott

LOVE ONE ANOTHER see Marvin, J.H.

LOVE ONE ANOTHER see Wesley, Samuel Sebastian
Jr.

LOVE SONG, A see Mechem, Kirke

LOVE SONG, A see Peloquin, C. Alexander

LOVE SONGS FOR SABBATH see Gottlieb, J.

LOVE THAT IS HOARDED see Lovelace, Austin C.

LOVE THAT WILT NOT LET ME GO see Peace

LOVE THOU ART see Mc Call, Harlo

LOVE TRIUMPHANT see Wheeler, Alfred

LOVE WALKS THE WORLD IN FLESH see Sateren,
Leland Bernhard

LOVE WE IN ONE CONSENTING see Amner, John

LOVELACE, AUSTIN C.
  All Lands And Peoples
    2pt mix cor (easy) oct AUGSBURG 1397 $.25
                                       (L1759)

  All My Heart This Night Rejoices
    SAB oct AGAPE CH650 $.30   (L1760)

  American Folk Hymns For Junior Choir *CCU,
    folk,US
    jr cor FISCHER,C CM 7311 $.35   (L1761)

  Anthems For Junior Choristers *CCU,anthem
    unis&SA SUMMY $1.00   (L1762)

  Apple Tree Carol, The *carol
    unis oct KERBY 6902C $.35   (L1763)
    unis,kbd oct KERBY 6902 $.35   (L1764)

  Be Known To Us
    SATB,acap oct FISCHER,C CM-6408 $.25
                                       (L1765)

  Beauty Of The Lord, The
    SATB oct FISCHER,J 8921 $.30   (L1766)

  Behold, The Savior Of Mankind
    SATB KJOS 5355 $.30   (L1767)

LOVELACE, AUSTIN C. (cont'd.)

  Behold The Saviour Of Mankind *Lent
    SATB oct SOUTHERN $.25   (L1768)

  Beneath The Forms Of Outward Rite *Commun
    SATB (med) ABINGDON APM-940 $.20   (L1769)

  Bless Thou The Lord, O My Soul
    SATB oct KERBY 6011 $.40   (L1770)
    SATB,acap oct KERBY 6011C $.40   (L1771)

  Blessed Art Thou
    4pt jr cor/SATB (easy) FISCHER,C CM 6999
    $.25   (L1772)
    SATB oct FISCHER,C CM-6999 $.25   (L1773)

  Blessed Man Whom God Doth Aid
    jr cor oct FISCHER,J 9059 $.30   (L1774)

  Bread Of The World
    SATB,acap oct KERBY 6704C $.35   (L1775)
    SATB oct KERBY 6704 $.35   (L1776)

  Breaking Of The Bread
    SATB oct AGAPE A 430 $.30   (L1777)

  Breathe, On Me, Breath Of God
    4pt jr cor/SATB (very easy) FISCHER,C
    CM 7287 $.25   (L1778)

  Brothers
    SA oct KERBY 7001C $.35   (L1779)
    unis oct KERBY 90373 $.35   (L1780)
    unis/SSA,kbd oct KERBY 903 $.35   (L1781)

  Built On The Rock
    SATB FLAMMER A 5128 $.35   (L1782)

  By Christ Redeemed
    SATB oct GRAY GCMR 3021 $.30   (L1783)

  Calls To Praise And Prayer *prayer
    SATB oct FISCHER,C CM-7522 $.30   (L1784)

  Carol For Two Seasons, A *Xmas/Easter,carol
    2pt oct KERBY 90273 $.35   (L1785)
    2pt,pno/org oct KERBY 902 $.35   (L1786)

  Christ Is Risen! *Easter
    SAB oct SACRED S-7391 $.35   (L1787)

  Christ Is The World's Redeemer
    SAB oct SACRED S-7393 $.35   (L1788)

  Christ Whose Glory Fills The Skies *Easter
    SAB (med) ABINGDON APM-791 $.25   (L1789)

  Christmas Comes In The Morning
    unis FLAMMER F5003 $.30   (L1790)

  Christmas Darkness *Xmas
    jr cor oct FISCHER,J 10002 $.30   (L1791)

  Christmas Gloria *Xmas,Gloria
    SAB oct AGAPE CF 159 $.30   (L1792)

  Christmas Night *Xmas
    TTBB oct FISCHER,J 9927 $.30   (L1793)

  Christmas Song Of Peace *Xmas
    unis,pno oct KERBY 6253 $.30   (L1794)
    unis oct KERBY 6253C $.30   (L1795)

  Clothing Of My Mind, The
    SA/TB FLAMMER E5030 $.25   (L1796)

  Collection For Soprano, Alto And Tenor
    oct KERBY 6450C $1.50
      contains: Hymn Of Nations (SAT); I Would
      Be True (SAT) (hymn,US); Kura Kwa Kwa
      (SAT); O Shepherds, Come (carol,
      Fr); Praise The Lord, Ye Heavens Adore
      Him (SAT); Shalom Chaverim (SAT)
      (round,Heb); What Shall I Render To My
      God (SAT) (hymn,US)   (L1797)

  Come, Thou Long Expected Jesus *Xmas
    SATB (med easy) ABINGDON APM-411 $.30
                                       (L1798)

  Come To The Tomb *Easter
    SATB,acap (med) ABINGDON APM-141 $.24
                                       (L1799)

  Cradled In A Manger *Xmas
    SATB oct AGAPE A 404 $.30   (L1800)

  Cross Of Jesus, Cross Of Sorrow
    SATB FLAMMER A 5409 $.25   (L1801)

  Darkness Now Has Taken Flight, The
    SA/unis (easy) ABINGDON APM-302 $.18
                                       (L1802)

  Dear Lord And Father Of Mankind
    SATB (easy) ABINGDON APM-140 $.24 (L1803)

  Down To Earth
    unis oct AGAPE AD 1977 $.30   (L1804)

  Easter Carol, An *Easter,carol
    SATB oct AGAPE A 446 $.25   (L1805)

  Easter Day Carol *Easter,carol
    unis oct KERBY 6351C $.35   (L1806)
    unis,pno/org oct KERBY 6351 $.35   (L1807)

  Eternity Today
    SATB oct FISCHER,J 10001 $.30   (L1808)

  Every Stone Shall Cry
    SAB oct AGAPE CH 660 $.30   (L1809)

  Eyes Of Faith, The
    SAB oct KERBY 6201C $.35   (L1810)
    SAB,kbd oct KERBY 6201 $.35   (L1811)

  Festival Introits [1] *CCU,Easter/Fest/Lent,
    Introit
    SATB oct FISCHER,C CM-7380 $.25   (L1812)

  Festival Introits [2] *CCU,Xmas,Introit
    SATB oct FISCHER,C CM-7384 $.25   (L1813)

  Foolishness Carol, The *carol
    SATB oct AGAPE CE 4326 $.30   (L1814)

  From East To West *Xmas
    SAB oct SACRED S-7387 $.35   (L1815)

LOVELACE, AUSTIN C. (cont'd.)

Give Thanks *Thanks
  4pt jr cor/SATB (very easy) FISCHER,C
  CM 7652 $.25   (L1816)

Giver Of All, We Thank Thee
  unis/SA oct SACRED S-8626 $.30   (L1817)

Gladsome Hymn Of Praise, A
  SAB FLAMMER D5001 $.30   (L1818)
  (Lowden) SATB FLAMMER A 5114 $.25   (L1819)

Glory Be To God On High *Xmas
  SATB (easy) ABINGDON APM-268 $.25   (L1820)

God Is In His Holy Temple
  SAB oct SACRED S-7394 $.30   (L1821)

God Is My Strong Salvation
  SATB oct KERBY 90478 $.35   (L1822)
  SATB,org oct KERBY 904 $.35   (L1823)
  (Scott, W.) SATB,band oct KERBY 631 $.35,
  ipa   (L1824)

God Is Working His Purpose Out
  SATB (med) ABINGDON APM-833 $.45   (L1825)
  SATB (med) ABINGDON APM-833 $.45   (L1826)

God Make My Life A Shining Light
  SA/TB FLAMMER E5005 $.30   (L1827)

God Of Grace And God Of Glory
  SATB oct KERBY 90178 $.35   (L1828)
  SATB,kbd oct KERBY 901 $.35   (L1829)

Good Christian Men, Rejoice And Sing *Xmas
  SATB oct VOLKWEIN VB160 $.25   (L1830)

Hail To The Lord's Anointed
  SAB oct SACRED S-7388 $.35   (L1831)

Hark! Angel Carols *anthem/carol
  unis treb cor (easy) oct AUGSBURG 1592 $.25
                                        (L1832)

House In Which I Dwell, The
  jr cor oct FISCHER,J 9580 $.30   (L1833)

House Of God, The
  SATB oct AGAPE A 445 $.25   (L1834)

How Lovely Is The House Of God
  jr cor oct FISCHER,J 9841 $.30   (L1835)

How Wonderful This World
  unis jr cor oct AGAPE A 425 $.25   (L1836)

Hymn Of Nations *hymn
  see Collection For Soprano, Alto And Tenor
  SAB,kbd oct KERBY 5701 $.30   (L1837)
  SAB oct KERBY 5701C $.30   (L1838)

I Bind My Heart
  unis,kbd oct KERBY 7006 $.30   (L1839)
  unis oct KERBY 7006C $.30   (L1840)

I Sing Th'Almighty Power Of God
  SATB,kbd oct KERBY 906 $.35   (L1841)
  SATB oct KERBY 90678 $.35   (L1842)

I Sought The Lord
  SATB oct FISCHER,J 9832 $.30   (L1843)

I Worship Him
  SA/TB FLAMMER E5154 $.30   (L1844)

I Would Be True
  see Collection For Soprano, Alto And Tenor

I Would Sing, Sing, Sing
  SA/TB FLAMMER E5143 $.30   (L1845)

In The Lonely Midnight
  SATB oct VOLKWEIN VB187 $.25   (L1846)

In The Original Tongue *CC11U
  [Eng] 2pt jr cor oct KERBY 7009C $1.35
                                        (L1847)

Indian Hymn Of Praise
  SA/TB FLAMMER E5001 $.30   (L1848)

I've Found A Friend
  SATB oct AGAPE CH 655 $.30   (L1849)

Joyful, Joyful We Adore Thee
  2pt,kbd,bvl,drums oct KERBY 7101 $.40
                                        (L1850)
  2pt,opt bvl&perc oct KERBY 7101C $.40
                                        (L1851)

King Shall Come When Morning Dawns, The
  SAB oct SACRED S-7386 $.35   (L1852)

Kura Kwa Kwa
  see Collection For Soprano, Alto And Tenor

Let This Mind Be In You
  SATB oct FISCHER,J 8458 $.30   (L1853)

Lift High The Triumph Song
  2pt oct AGAPE A 453 $.30   (L1854)

Litany For America
  cor&cong,narrator,trp oct AGAPE SP 715 $.40
                                        (L1855)

Living Word, The *Gen
  SAB SCHMITT 5543 $.35   (L1856)

Lo, God Is Here *anthem
  SATB oct AUGSBURG 1166 $.20   (L1857)

Lord Is My Shepherd *Psalm
  SA SOUTHERN $.30   (L1858)

Lord Is My Shepherd, The
  SA oct SACRED S-5388 $.35   (L1859)

Lord Is Rich And Merciful, The
  SATB/SA/TB,kbd oct KERBY 6002 $.35   (L1860)
  SA oct KERBY 90972 $.35   (L1861)
  SA/TB/SATB,kbd oct KERBY 6002 $.35   (L1862)
  SATB oct KERBY 90972 $.35   (L1863)

Lord Jesus, Think On Me
  4pt jr cor/SATB (very easy) FISCHER,C
  CM 7124 $.25   (L1864)

Lord My Shepherd Is, The *anthem
  unis treb cor (easy) oct AUGSBURG 1284 $.25
                                        (L1865)

LOVELACE, AUSTIN C. (cont'd.)

  unis (easy) oct AUGSBURG 1284 $.25   (L1866)

Love Came Down At Christmas *Xmas
  SAB oct SACRED S-7419 $.35   (L1867)

Love That Is Hoarded
  SATB,acap oct KERBY 7978 $.40   (L1868)

Mercy, Pity, Peace And Love
  SATB oct KERBY 6003 $.30   (L1869)
  SATB oct KERBY 6003C $.30   (L1870)

More S.A.B. Anthems For The Church Year
  *CCU,anthem
  3pt jr cor/3pt sr cor SACRED $1.75   (L1871)

None Other Lamb
  SAB oct SACRED S-7415 $.35   (L1872)

Now The Green Blade Riseth
  SATB oct AGAPE A 398 $.30   (L1873)

O Darkest Woe! *Lent
  SATB,pno oct KERBY 67 $.30   (L1874)
  SATB oct KERBY 6778 $.30   (L1875)

O Dearest Lord *Lent
  SATB (med) ABINGDON APM-493 $.25   (L1876)

O God My Strength
  SATB oct FISCHER,J 9200 $.30   (L1877)

O Lord Of Stars And Sunlight
  SATB oct AGAPE A 435 $.30   (L1878)

O Love That Casts Out Fear
  SATB,kbd oct KERBY 907 $.35   (L1879)
  SATB oct KERBY 90778 $.35   (L1880)

O Shepherds, Come
  see Collection For Soprano, Alto And Tenor

O Thou Eternal Christ, Ride On! *Palm
  SATB (very easy) ABINGDON APM-105 $.30
                                        (L1881)

Oh, I Would Sing Of Mary's Child *anthem
  unis (very easy) oct AUGSBURG 1247 $.20
                                        (L1882)
  unis treb cor (very easy) oct AUGSBURG 1247
  $.20   (L1883)

Only-Begotten, Word Of God Eternal *anthem
  unis sr cor (med) oct AUGSBURG 1182 $.25
                                        (L1884)

Palm Sunday Welcome *Palm
  SATB FLAMMER A5004 $.30   (L1885)
  SAB FLAMMER D5205 $.30   (L1886)

Peace I Leave With You
  SATB oct KERBY 5312 $.35   (L1887)
  SATB oct KERBY 5312C $.35   (L1888)

Praise The Lord Who Reigns Above
  SATB,acap (med) ABINGDON $.25   (L1889)

Praise The Lord, Ye Heavens Adore Him
  see Collection For Soprano, Alto And Tenor

Praises Of A King, The *anthem
  2pt mix cor (easy) oct AUGSBURG 1545 $.30
                                        (L1890)

Prayer For Families, A *prayer
  SATB (easy) ABINGDON APM-267 $.22   (L1891)

Psalm 34
  SATB,pno/org oct KERBY 6210 $.35   (L1892)
  SATB oct KERBY 6210C $.35   (L1893)

Psalm That Swings, The *Psalm
  unis oct AGAPE CF 146 $.30   (L1894)

Rejoice And Be Merry *Xmas
  SA oct FISCHER,C CM-7726 $.25   (L1895)

Ride On, Ride On In Majesty
  SAB oct SACRED S-7390 $.35   (L1896)
  SATB/SA oct SACRED S-90 $.35   (L1897)

S.A.B. Anthems For The Church Year *CCU,
  anthem
  SAB SACRED $1.75   (L1898)

Sacred Feast, The
  SATB,acap FLAMMER A 5610 $.30   (L1899)

Shalom Chaverim
  see Collection For Soprano, Alto And Tenor

Sharing Carol, The *carol
  2pt,pno oct KERBY 71 $.40   (L1900)
  2pt oct KERBY 7172 $.40   (L1901)

Shepherd Lad's Gift
  SA/TB FLAMMER E5004 $.30   (L1902)

So Lowly Doth The Saviour Ride *Palm
  jr cor&sr cor (easy) FISCHER,C CM 7195 $.25
                                        (L1903)

Song Of Christ, A *Xmas
  unis,pno/org oct KERBY 6507 $.35   (L1904)
  unis oct KERBY 90871 $.35   (L1905)

Spirit Divine, Attend Our Prayers
  SATB oct VOLKWEIN VB705 $.30   (L1906)

Star In The East *Xmas
  SATB oct GALAXY 1.2408.1 $.30   (L1907)

Strengthen For Service, Lord
  unis,kbd oct KERBY 6905 $.30   (L1908)
  unis oct KERBY 6905C $.30   (L1909)

Sun Is On The Land And Sea, The
  unis mix cor GRAY GCMR 3268 $.30   (L1910)

Take Up Thy Cross *Easter/Lent
  SATB oct FISCHER,C CM-7097 $.25   (L1911)

Talk With Us, Lord
  SATB oct SUMMY 1545 $.35   (L1912)

Thanks To God Whose Word Was Spoken
  SATB oct FISCHER,J 9887 $.35   (L1913)

There's A Voice In The Wilderness *Adv,
  anthem
  SAB oct SACRED S-7418 $.35   (L1914)

LOVELACE, AUSTIN C. (cont'd.)

Thou Shepherd Of My Soul
  SATB KJOS 5312 $.30   (L1915)

Thought Of God, The
  SAB,kbd oct KERBY 6901 $.35   (L1916)
  SAB oct KERBY 6901C $.35   (L1917)

To Bless The Earth
  SAB oct SACRED S-7408 $.35   (L1918)

To Face The World
  SATB oct KERBY 9178 $.35   (L1919)

Tomorrow Christ Is Coming
  SATB (med easy) SOUTHERN $.35   (L1920)

Tree Springs To Life, The
  SAB oct AGAPE A 440 $.30   (L1921)

Universal Lord, The
  SAB oct SACRED S-7392 $.30   (L1922)

We Thank Thee, Lord, For Grace Of Home
  SSA KJOS 6107 $.30   (L1923)

What Shall I Render To My God
  see Collection For Soprano, Alto And Tenor
  SATB,org oct KERBY 905 $.35   (L1924)
  SATB oct KERBY 90578 $.35   (L1925)

When I Survey The Wondrous Cross
  SAB oct SACRED S-7389 $.35   (L1926)

LOVELESS
  Since Jesus Took All My Sins Away
  see TEMPO CHORAL PACKAGE NO. 2

LOVELOCK, WILLIAM
  Christmas *Xmas,carol
  SA ALLANS 416 s.p. contains also: Gabriel,
  Christmas Lullaby   (L1927)

  Christmas Lullaby *Xmas,carol,Austral
  SA ALLANS 332 s.p.   (L1928)

  Harvest Anthem, A *Harv,anthem,Austral
  SAB/unis ALLANS 417 s.p.   (L1929)

  O Praise God In His Holiness (Psalm 150) Gen/
  Thanks
  SATB (easy) oct OXFORD 42.837 $.25   (L1930)

  Psalm 150 *see O Praise God In His Holiness

LOVELY APPEAR see Gounod, Charles Francois

LOVELY APPEAR see Roberts

LOVELY CHILD, HOLY CHILD *anthem/folk,US
  (Johnson, David N.) SATB (easy) oct AUGSBURG
  0519 $.25   (L1931)
  (Johnson, David N) SAA (easy) oct AUGSBURG
  0526 $.25   (L1932)
  (Johnson, David N.) SAB (easy) oct AUGSBURG
  0534 $.25   (L1933)

LOVELY GARDEN, THE see Grieb, Herbert [C.]

LOVELY ONE IS HE, A *Xmas
  (Parrish, C.) SSA,acap oct PRESSER MC161 $.30
                                        (L1934)
  (Parrish, C.) SSAA,acap oct PRESSER MC161
  $.30   (L1935)

LOVELY PEACE see Handel, George Frideric

LOVELY ROSE IS SPRUNG, A see Hancock

LOVELY STAR see Hutson, Wihla

LOVEN GUD I HANS HELGEDOM see Noren, Yngve

LOVEN HERREN see Lindberg, Oskar [Fredrik]

LOVEN HERREN, I HANS ANGLAR see Soderholm,
  Valdemar

LOVEN HERRENS NAMN see Bjarnegard, Gustaf

LOVER GUD I HANS HELGEDOM see Wennerberg,
  Gunnar

LOVER GUD I HIMMELKOR see Hovland, Egil

LOVER GUD I HIMMELSHOJD see Thyrestam, Gunnar

LOVER HERREN see Jeppesen, Knud

LOVE'S AWAKENING! see Hughes

LOVE'S HOPE see Gastoldi, Speme Amorosa

LOVE'S REDEEMING WORK IS DONE see Thiman, Eric
  Harding

LOVET VAERE DU, JESUS KRIST see Laub, Thomas

LOVET VAERE HERREN see Jeppesen, Knud

LOVING LORD see Farina

LOVING SAVIOUR see Holler, John

LOVING SAVIOUR, TO THE CROSS NAILED see Lotti,
  Antonio, Crucifixus

LOVING SHEPHERD, LEAD ME see Wheeler, Alfred

LOVING SHEPHERD OF THE SHEEP see Lenel, Ludwig

LOVING SHEPHERD OF THY SHEEP *anthem
  (Pooler) SA (easy) oct AUGSBURG 1484 $.25
                                        (L1936)

LOVING SHEPHERD OF THY SHEEP see Cabena, Barrie

LOVING SHEPHERD OF THY SHEEP see Cooke, Arnold

LOVING SHEPHERD OF THY SHEEP see Pasfield, W.R.

LOVING SHEPHERD OF THY SHEEP see Williams, R.

LOVSANG
  (Sorass, Lars) mix cor MUSIKK 98 s.p. (L1937)

LOVSANG see Lindberg, Oskar [Fredrik]

LOVSJUNGEN HERREN see Bengtsson, [Gustav Adolf Tiburt]

LOVSJUNGEN HERREN see Norman, Rudolf

LOVSJUNGEN HERREN see Olson, Daniel

LOVSJUNGEN HERREN see Thyrestam, Gunnar

LOW, HOW A ROSÉ E'ER BLOOMING see Praetorius, Michael

LOW IN THE GRAVE HE LAY see Lowry

LOW, LEO
Bialik
"Eulogy" [Heb] SATB TRANSCON. TCL 225 $.45
(L1938)

Eulogy *see Bialik

Mogen Ovos
SATB HATIKVAH HCL 41 $.35   (L1939)

Rosh Hashanah L Ianot *cant
"Tree's Ne' Year's, The" [Eng/Heb/Jew] SATB
TRANSCON. TCL 203 $1.25   (L1940)

Tree's New Year's, The *see Rosh Hashanah
L'ilanot

V'shomru
SATB HATIKVAH HCL 26 $.35   (L1941)

LOWDEN
Living For Jesus
(Wilson) SATB oct LORENZ A364 $.25 (L1942)

What Child Is This? *Xmas
SATB FLAMMER A 5317 $.30   (L1943)
SSA FLAMMER B 5051 $.30   (L1944)
SAB FLAMMER D5109 $.30   (L1945)
SA/TB FLAMMER E5067 $.30   (L1946)

While By My Sheep *Xmas
SSA FLAMMER B 5121 $.30   (L1947)

LOWE
Be Still *Commun
(Simon) SATB,acap oct FISCHER,C CM-7272
$.25   (L1948)

God, My King, Thy Might Confessing
(Coggin) SAB,org BOSTON 13321 $.30 (L1949)

LOWE, ALBERT
Earth Is The Lord's, The *Harv,anthem
mix cor oct NOVELLO 28.1100.06 s.p. (L1950)

LOWELL
Come Into My Heart, Lord Jesus
(Wilson) SSA oct BOURNE 208 $.25   (L1951)

Easter In Heaven *Easter
(Wilson) SSA oct BOURNE 147 $.25   (L1952)
(Wilson) SATB oct BOURNE 669 $.25 (L1953)
(Wilson) SA oct BOURNE 2010 $.25   (L1954)

I Know The Touch Of His Hand
(Wilson) SATB oct BOURNE 778 $.40 (L1955)
(Wilson) SSA oct BOURNE 207 $.25   (L1956)

I Need Thee Heavenly Father
(Wilson) SATB oct BOURNE 680 $.25 (L1957)
(Wilson) SSA oct BOURNE 167 $.25   (L1958)

Psalm 62 *see Thanks Be To God

Thanks Be To God (Psalm 62)
(Wilson) SATB oct BOURNE 786 $.25 (L1959)

LOWELL, GENE
A L'eglise
TTBB oct STAFF 131 $.25   (L1960)

LOWENSTERN, MATTHAUS APPELLES VON (1594-1648)
Christe, Du Beistand Deiner Kreuzgemeinde
see Lassus, Roland de (Orlandus), Wer Gott
Vertrauen Tut, Den

Ich Hab Von Ferne, Herr, Deinen Thron
TTBB HANSSLER 6.2334 s.p. contains also:
Sunderreiter, G., Mein Schonste Zier Und
Kleinod Bist; Hintze, Jakob, Gib Dich
Zufrieden Und Sei Stille   (L1961)

Nun Preiset Alle Gottes Barmherzigkett
see Bach, Johann Sebastian, Liebster Herr
Jesu, Wo Bleibst

LOWLY OF HEART see Pasquet, Jean

LOWRY
Low In The Grave He Lay *Easter/Lent
(Follett) SATB,opt 3trp oct PRO ART 2314
$.35   (L1962)

LOWRY, [ROBERT] (1826-1899)
Beautiful River
(Martin, C.) SATB,acap oct PRESSER
312-40103 $.30   (L1963)

Follow On
(Graf) jr cor oct LILLENAS AN-4025 $.25
(L1964)

LOWRY, ROBERT (1826-1899)
I Need Thee Every Hour
(Parker) TTBB,acap oct LAWSON 51356 $.25
(L1965)

LOWRY, [ROBERT] (1826-1899)
Nothing But The Blood
see TEMPO CHORAL PACKAGE NO. 1

LOWRY, [ROBERT] (1826-1899)
Shall We Gather At The River
(Parker) TTBB,pno/gtr oct LAWSON 51295 $.30
(L1966)

LOWRY, [ROBERT] (1826-1899)
We're Marching To Zion
(Ferrin) SATB oct LILLENAS AN-2356 $.30
(L1967)

LU LULLA LAY see Veitch, William.

LUALDI
In Festivitate Sanctae Trinitatis *ora
dbl cor,soli,orch RICORDI-ENG 129825 s.p.
(L1968)

LUBECK, VINCENTIUS (1654-1740)
Gott, Wie Dein Name *cant/Psalm
(Stein) [Ger] ATB/TTB,bsn,3trp,vcl BAREN.
EM 909 sc s.p., cor pts s.p., ipa (L1969)

Velkommen, Herre Jesul il *see Wilkommen,
Susser Brautigam

Welcome Thou King Of Glory *see Willkommen,
Susser Brautigam

Wilkomen, Susser Brautigam *Xmas,cant
[Eng/Ger] SS/SSB,org,2vln,vcl HANSSLER sc
$2.50, cor pts $1.00, ipa   (L1970)

Willkommen, Susser Brautigam *Xmas,cant
(Videro, Finn) "Velkommen, Herre Jesulil"
[Ger/Dan] SS,org,2vln,vcl HANSEN-DEN
26848 s.p., ipa   (L1971)

Willkommen, Susser Brautigam *Xmas,cant
"Welcome Thou King Of Glory" [Eng/Ger] SS/
SA,opt low solo,2vln,cont sc CONCORDIA
97-6379 $1.50, cor pts CONCORDIA 97-6385
$.40, ipa   (L1972)
(Weiss) 3pt mix cor,cont,2vln MOSELER sc
s.p., cor pts s.p., ipa   (L1973)

LUBIN, ERNEST (1916-   )
May The Words
SATB,S solo,pno/org oct LAWSON 51353 $.25
(L1974)

LUBOFF, NORMAN (1917-   )
African Mass, The *Xmas,Mass
mix cor,soli,perc voc sc WALTON M 110
$2.50, ipa   (L1975)

Christmas Eve *Xmas
SSATTBB oct WALTON 3019 $.25   (L1976)

Gloria Patri
SATB oct WALTON 3058 $.30   (L1977)

Kyrie (from African Mass) Kyrie
SATB,perc oct WALTON 3033 $.40   (L1978)

Look To This Day
cor,med solo,pno,bvl,drums,gtr voc sc
WALTON M 118 $1.25, ipa   (L1979)

Psalm 150
SATB oct WALTON 3026 $.30   (L1980)

Sanctus (from African Mass) Sanctus
SATB,perc oct WALTON 3056 $.35   (L1981)

LUCAS, LEIGHTON (1903-   )
Every Wind That Blows
mix cor,acap oct CURWEN 8838 $.25 (L1982)

Mass In G Minor *Mass
unis voc sc WEINBERGER s.p.   (L1983)
SATB cor pts WEINBERGER s.p.   (L1984)
SSA/SSAA cor pts WEINBERGER s.p.   (L1985)
cong cor pts WEINBERGER s.p.   (L1986)

Parish Mass, A *Mass
unis voc sc WEINBERGER s.p.   (L1987)
SATB cor pts WEINBERGER s.p.   (L1988)
SSA/SSAA cor pts WEINBERGER s.p.   (L1989)
cong cor pts WEINBERGER s.p.   (L1990)

Proper Of Easter Day *Easter,Mass
unis voc sc WEINBERGER s.p.   (L1991)
SATB cor pts WEINBERGER s.p.   (L1992)
SSA/SSAA cor pts WEINBERGER s.p.   (L1993)
cong/unis cor pts WEINBERGER s.p.   (L1994)

LUCE DIVINA RUTIL. see Ravanello, Oreste

LUCIA see Torlind

LUCIS CREATOR OPTIME see Ingegneri, Marco
Antonio

LUCIS CREATOR OPTIME see Nystedt, Knut

LUCIS CREATOR OPTIME see Washington, Henry

LUCK
My Shepherd Will Supply My Need
SATB oct PRO ART 2194 $.30   (L1995)

LUDERS, RUDIGER (1936-   )
Gib Uns Frieden Jeden Tag *Gen
[Ger] unis,acap (easy) BOSSE BE 256 s.p.
(L1996)

LUDFORD, NICOLAS (ca. 1485-ca. 1557)
Collected Works vol. I *CC7L
(Bergsagel, John D.) cor AM.INST.MUS.
$21.00 Seven Lady Masses   (L1997)

LUDLOW
Cry Out And Shout
SATB FLAMMER A 5628 $.30   (L1998)

Easter Alleluia *Easter
SATB FLAMMER A 5619 $.30   (L1999)

Gospel According To Judas, The
SATB FLAMMER A 5620 $.35   (L2000)

Have You Heard
SATB SHAWNEE A 1215 $.30   (L2001)

Words Of Ruth, The
SATB,pno/org AMP A576 $.25   (L2002)

LUDUSKY
Hospodi Pomilui
(Hardwicke) SSA ALFRED 6209 $.35 (L2003)

LUEBECK
Hilf Deinem Volk, Herr Jesu Christ
[Ger] voc sc PETERS HU1660 $2.00, ipr
(L2004)

Willkommen, Suesser Braeutigam *Xmas,cant
[Ger] voc sc PETERS HU1773 $1.50, ipr
(L2005)

LUENING, OTTO (1900-   )
Alleluia *Easter/Gen
SATB oct PRESSER 312-40061 $.30 (L2006)

Psalm 146
SATB,opt org/pno PETERS 66349 $.80 (L2007)

LUHN
Lobet Den Herrn
see Luhn, O Gott, Du Mein Gott

Miserere (Psalm 50) meditation
mix cor HANSSLER 7.164 s.p.   (L2008)

O Gott, Du Mein Gott
mix cor HANSSLER 7.160 s.p. contains also:
Lobet Den Herrn   (L2009)

Psalm 50 *see Miserere

LUKAS-PASSION see Bach, Johann Sebastian

LUKAS-PASSION see Schutz, Heinrich

LUKAS-PASSION see Spar, Otto

LUKAS PASSION, 1728 see Telemann, Georg Philipp

LUKASPASSION see Bach, Johann Sebastian

LUKASPASSION see Schutz, Heinrich

LUKASPASSION see Telemann, Georg Philipp

LUKE
Song Of Simeon *anthem
(Wilkinson) SATB oct FISCHER,C CM-7673 $.25
(L2010)

LUKKIEN, H.G.
Bethlehems Kinderen *Xmas
4pt wom cor ALSBACH&D sc s.p., cor pts s.p.
(L2011)

LULAJZE JEZUNI *carol,Pol
(Bement, G.S.) "Sleep, Thou, My Jewel" SATB,
acap SCHIRM.EC 1788 $.25   (L2012)

LULLABY see Davis, Carl

LULLABY see Durrant

LULLABY see Grundman

LULLABY see Keel

LULLABY see Mattson

LULLABY see Thompson, Randall

LULLABY, A see Blyton, Carey

LULLABY AT CHRISTMAS see Lapo, Cecil E.

LULLABY FOR CHRISTMAS EVE *Xmas
(Henninger) SATB SCHMITT 1635 $.25 (L2013)

LULLABY FOR CHRISTMAS NIGHT see Track

LULLABY FOR CHRISTMAS NIGHT see Track, Gerhard

LULLABY FOR JESUS *Xmas,cradle
(Ehret; Walton) SATB oct FISCHER,C CM-7043
$.25   (L2014)
(Ehret; Walton) SSA oct FISCHER,C CM-6913
$.25   (L2015)

LULLABY FOR JESUS see Ehret, Walter

LULLABY FOR JESUS see Peloquin, C. Alexander

LULLABY FOR MARY'S SON see Andersen, Karl

LULLABY FOR THE CHRIST CHILD see Strimer

LULLABY FOR THE HOLY CHILD see Jacobsen,
Katherine

LULLABY, JESU *Xmas,carol,Pol
(Gordon, P.) SATB oct PRESSER 312-40232 $.30
(L2016)
(Kirk) SATB oct SHAPIRO SK 2070 $.25 (L2017)
(Kirk) SAB oct SHAPIRO SK 5018 $.25 (L2018)
(Kirk) 2pt oct SHAPIRO SK 4020 $.25 (L2019)
(Kirk) SSA oct SHAPIRO SK3024 $.25 (L2020)

LULLABY JESUS
see Two Polish Carols

LULLABY, JESUS CHILD see Nelson, Ronald A.

LULLABY, JESUS DEAR *Xmas,carol,Pol
(Salama) 4pt mix cor oct SCHIRM.G 7440 $.20
(L2021)

LULLABY, JESUS DEAR see Salama, A.

LULLABY, LITTLE BABE *Xmas,carol,Ger
(Barthelson) SSA,opt 2treb inst oct SHAPIRO
SK 3010 $.25, ipa   (L2022)
(Barthelson) 2pt,opt 2treb inst oct SHAPIRO
SK 4025 $.25, ipa   (L2023)
(Barthelson) SAB,opt 2treb inst oct SHAPIRO
SK 5018 $.25, ipa   (L2024)
(Barthelson) SATB,opt 2treb inst oct SHAPIRO
SK 2038 $.25, ipa   (L2025)

LULLABY, LULLABY, LU see Hopkins

LULLABY, MY SWEET LITTLE BABY-PARTS 1 & 2 see
Byrd, William

LULLABY, O LOVELY BABY see O Bel Bambino

LULLABY OF MARY AND THE ANGELS *Xmas,carol,Dut
(Ehret) 3pt mix cor oct LAWSON 51004 $.25
(L2026)
(Ehret) SA oct LAWSON 51005 $.25 (L2027)
(Ehret) SATB oct LAWSON 51228 $.25 (L2028)
(Ehret) 3pt men cor oct LAWSON 51229 $.25
(L2029)

LULLABY OF THE CHILDREN see Emig, Lois

LULLABY OF THE CHRIST-CHILD *carol,Ger
(Phelps, R.) SATB,org SCHIRM.EC 2267 $.30
(L2030)

LULLABY OF THE CHRIST CHILD see Christy

LULLABY OF THE CHRIST CHILD see Scott

LULLABY OF THE LITTLE ANGELS see Anderson

LULLABY OF THE LITTLE ANGELS see Anderson,
[William H.]

LULLABY OF THE SHEPHERD *Xmas,folk,Span
(Luboff, Norman) SATB oct WALTON 3008 $.30
(L2031)

LULLABY ON CHRISTMAS EVE see Christiansen

LULLABY ON CHRISTMAS EVE see Christiansen, F. Melius

LULLABY ON CHRISTMAS MORNING see Gretchaninov, Alexander Tikhonovitch

LULLABYE *Xmas
(Larson) SSA SCHMITT 352 $.30   (L2032)

LULLAY LAY, LAY see Wishart

LULLAY, MY JESUS see Young, G.

LULLAY MY LIKING
see Blake, William, Cradle Song

LULLAY, MY LIKING see Anderson, [William H.]

LULLAY MY LIKING see Holst, Gustav

LULLAY MYN LYKNG see Green, Ray

LULLAY, MYN LYKYING see Monelle, Raymond

LULLAY, MYN LYKYNG see Monelle, Raymond

LULLAY, THOU LITTLE CHILD see Gubby, Roy

LULLAY, THOU LITTLE TINY CHILD *Xmas,cradle
(Bishop) SATB,acap oct FISCHER,C CM-7070 $.25
(L2033)
(Davis, K.) SA,pno SCHIRM.EC 1566   (L2034)

LULLY (LULLI), JEAN-BAPTISTE (1632-1740)
Omnes Gentes *mot
[Lat] TTB/TBB oct GIA G676 $.25   (L2035)

Restore Unto Me *anthem
(Nelson) SS,2vln (med) oct AUGSBURG 0307
$.30   (L2036)

Te Deum *Te Deum
(Stanton) [Lat] dbl cor,SSATTB soli,orch
voc sc SCHOTT 10453 s.p., ipr   (L2037)

Venerabilis Barba Capucinorum
(Chailley) [Lat] SAATB oct SALABERT-US $.65
(L2038)

LULLY, LULLA *carol
ATB&SATB (very easy) OXFORD 08.020 $.15   (L2039)

LULLY LULLA see Nelhybel, Vaclav

LULLY, LULLAY see Kay, Ulysses Simpson

LULLY, THOU LITTLE TINY CHILD see Croo, R.

L'ULTIMO SELVAGGIO see Menotti, Gian Carlo

LUMSDEN, DAVID
Preces And Responses
boy cor/men cor,acap (med easy) oct OXFORD
41.022 $.25   (L2040)

LUND, SUNDT
Gluck Auf! Guds Fred! (composed with Eugen, Karl)
[Norw] mix cor LYCHE 102 s.p.   (L2041)

LUNDBORG, GOSTA
Credo *Credo
mix cor,org,opt 3bsn&3trp cor pts NORDISKA
3947 s.p.   (L2042)

Kom, Helge Ande, Herre God
mix cor NORDISKA 884 s.p.   (L2043)

LUNDE
Go To Dark Gethsemane
SATB KJOS PC773 $.30   (L2044)

My Hope Is Built On Nothing Less
SATB KJOS PC774 $.30   (L2045)

LUNDE, LAWSON
Beatitudes, The *Bibl
SATB,org BROUDE,A. 226 $.30   (L2046)

Psalm 120 *Op.22
SATB BROUDE,A. 711 $.30   (L2047)

LUNDGREN, PER
Uppstanden Ar Var Herre Krist
mix cor NORDISKA 4809 s.p.   (L2048)

LUNDQUIST
Children Of The Heavenly Father
SATB,acap oct FOX PS69 $.25   (L2049)

Come, Christians, Join To Sing
SATB oct ELKAN-V 362-1165 $.25   (L2050)

Come, Thou Quickening Spirit *Gen
SATB SCHMITT 8021 $.20   (L2051)

Come, Ye Faithful, Raise The Strain
SATB,acap (med) oct WILLIS 8471 $.25   (L2052)

Eternal Spring Of The Spirit
SATB oct VOLKWEIN VB145 $.25   (L2053)

From All That Dwell Below Skies
SAB oct VOLKWEIN VB151 $.25   (L2054)

Gentle Mary And Her Child *Xmas
SATB oct ELKAN-V 362-1152 $.30   (L2055)

Gracious Spirit *Gen
SATB SCHMITT 882 $.22   (L2056)

Grant Me, Lord, Thy Holy Spirit
SATB oct VOLKWEIN VB162 $.25   (L2057)

Haste Thee, O God
SATB,acap oct FOX PS40 $.25   (L2058)

Holy, Holy, Hosanna In The Highest *Gen
SATB SCHMITT 1789 $.22   (L2059)

King Of Love My Shepherd Is, The
SATB,acap (med) oct WILLIS 8473 $.20   (L2060)

Lead On, O King Eternal *mot
SATB oct VOLKWEIN VB204 $.25   (L2061)

LUNDQUIST (cont'd.)
Lift Up Your Heads *Adv,mot
SATB,opt org SCHIRM.EC 2605   (L2062)

Motet (Based On Swedish Gospel Song)
SATB,acap (med) oct WILLIS 5575 $.40
(L2063)

Now Let Every Tongue Adore Thee *Gen
SATB SCHMITT 1628 $.25   (L2064)

Once In Royal David's City *Xmas
SSA oct ELKAN-V 362-3079 $.25   (L2065)

Songs Of Praise The Angeles Sing
SATB,acap (med) oct WILLIS 8472 $.20
(L2066)

When In The Hour Of Utmost Need *Gen
SATB SCHMITT 1655 $.18   (L2067)

LUNDQUIST, MATTHEW NATHANAEL (1884-1964)
All Glory Be To God On High *chorale/mot
SATB,acap SCHIRM.EC 2274 $.30   (L2068)

Alleluia, Song Of Gladness *chorale/mot
SATB,acap SCHIRM.EC 2275 $.24   (L2069)

At The Cross *Lent
SATB,acap (easy) oct CONCORDIA 98-1204 $.25
(L2070)

Dear Christians One And All *mot
SATB,acap SCHIRM.EC 2276 $.30   (L2071)

Easter Cantata *Easter
SATB PRESSER $1.25   (L2072)

God Is Our Refuge (Psalm 46) chorale/mot
SATB,acap SCHIRM.EC 2225 $.16   (L2073)

I Know In Whom I Trust *chorale/mot
SATB,acap SCHIRM.EC 2277 $.30   (L2074)

Lift Up Your Heads, Ye Mighty Gates
*chorale/mot
SATB,acap (first setting) SCHIRM.EC 2226
$.18   (L2075)

Liturgical Response *CC26U
SATB,acap SCHIRM.EC 2279 $1.50   (L2076)

Lord, Who Ordainest *see Mother's Hymn, The

Lord, Who Ordaineth *see Mother's Hymn, The

Mother's Hymn, The *anthem
SATB,acap SCHIRM.EC 2422 $.35   (L2077)
"Lord, Who Ordainest" TTBB,acap SCHIRM.EC
2190   (L2078)
"Lord, Who Ordaineth" SSA,acap SCHIRM.EC
2557 $.35   (L2079)

Praise The Father, Son And Spirit *chorale/
mot
SATB,acap SCHIRM.EC 2278 $.35   (L2080)

Psalm 46 *see God Is Our Refuge

Who Trusts In God, A Strong Abode *chorale/
mot
SATB,acap SCHIRM.EC 2402 $.45   (L2081)

With Grateful Heart My Thanks I Bring
SATB,org SCHIRM.EC 2224 $.25   (L2082)

LUNDRIK, HILDOR
Vi Tillbedja Dig, Kriste
mix cor NORDISKA 4249 s.p.   (L2083)

LUNN
Ring Out The Heavens
SATB FLAMMER A 5566 $.30   (L2084)

LUPI II, DIDIER (ca. 1548?)
Chantez A Dieu Chanson Nouvelle (Psalm 149)
16th cent
(Honegger, Marc; Pidoux, Pierre) [Fr] SATB
OUVRIERES EO499 s.p.   (L2085)

O L'homme Heureux Qui A De Dieu La Crainte
(Psalm 112) 16th cent
(Honegger, Marc; Pidoux, Pierre) [Fr] SATB
OUVRIERES EO502 s.p.   (L2086)

Or Sus, Mon Ame, En Ce Bas Territoire (Psalm
146) 16th cent
(Honegger, Marc; Pidoux, Pierre) [Fr] SATB
OUVRIERES EO498 s.p.   (L2087)

Psalm 112 *see O L'homme Heureux Qui A De
Dieu La Crainte

Psalm 124 *see Qu'Israel Die Et Confesse En
Effet

Psalm 135 *see Sus, Sus, Qu'on Se Dispose De
Louer Le Seigneur

Psalm 146 *see Or Sus, Mon Ame, En Ce Bas
Territoire

Psalm 149 *see Chantez A Dieu Chanson
Nouvelle

Puisqu'en Toi Git Perfection *16th cent
(Honegger, Marc; Pidoux, Pierre) [Fr] SATB
OUVRIERES EO505 s.p.   (L2088)

Qu'Israel Die Et Confesse En Effet (Psalm
124) 16th cent
(Honegger, Marc; Pidoux, Pierre) [Fr] SATB
OUVRIERES EO503 s.p.   (L2089)

Sus, Sus, Qu'on Se Dispose De Louer Le
Seigneur (Psalm 135) 16th cent
(Honegger, Marc; Pidoux, Pierre) [Fr] SATB
OUVRIERES EO504 s.p.   (L2090)

LUPI, ROBERTO (1908-1971)
Nativitas (from Sacra Sinfonia)
cor,soli,orch sc SANTIS 803 s.p., ipr   (L2091)

cor,pno voc sc SANTIS 804 s.p.   (L2092)

Psalm 150 (from Sacra Sinfonia)
cor,T solo,orch sc SANTIS 800 s.p., ipr
(L2093)
cor,pno voc sc SANTIS 801 s.p.   (L2094)

LUPI, ROBERTO (cont'd.)
Stabat Mater (from Sacra Sinfonia)
wom cor,soli,strings sc SANTIS 708 s.p.,
ipr   (L2095)
wom cor,pno voc sc SANTIS 709 s.p.   (L2096)

LUPO, THOMAS (? -1628)
Have Mercy Upon Me, O Lord *see Miserere Mei
Domine

Hear My Prayer, O Lord (Psalm 143) Gen
SSATB,opt inst (med) oct OXFORD 43.383 $.30
(L2097)

Miserere Mei Domine *Gen
"Have Mercy Upon Me, O Lord" SSATB,acap
(med easy) oct OXFORD 43.363 $.25 (L2098)

O Lord, Give Ear *Gen
SATB,acap (med easy) oct OXFORD 43.366 $.25
(L2099)
(Greenberg) SATB,acap AMP N3 $.30   (L2100)

Out Of The Deep (Psalm 130) Gen/Lent
SSATB/SAATB,opt inst (med) oct OXFORD
43.384 $.35   (L2101)

Psalm 130 *see Out Of The Deep

Psalm 143 *see Hear My Prayer, O Lord

Salva Nos, Domine *Gen
"Save Us, Lord" SSATB,acap (med easy) oct
OXFORD 43.362 $.35   (L2102)

Save Us, Lord *see Salva Nos, Domine

LUPTIN, H.J.
Bells Are Ringing, The *Xmas
SATB&desc oct LESLIE 4058   (L2103)

On This Day The Lord Was Born *Xmas
SATB oct LESLIE 4098   (L2104)

Stars Look'd Down, The *Xmas
SATB oct LESLIE 4097   (L2105)

LUSH, RON
Ron Lush Choruses No. 1 *CC13UL
jr cor cmplt ed LILLENAS MB-161 $.50   (L2106)

Ron Lush Choruses No. 2 *CCU
jr cor,gtr cmplt ed LILLENAS MB-162 $.50
(L2107)

LUSKIN, SAMUEL
Feast Of Lights *Hanakkah
[Eng/Jew] SATB TRANSCON. TCL 227 $.35   (L2108)

LUTE-BOOK LULLABY
see Three Nativity Carols

LUTE BOOK LULLABY see Friedell, Harold W.

LUTE BOOK LULLABY see Kihlken, Henry

LUTE BOOK LULLABY see Means, Claude

LUTE CAROL, A see Caldwell, Mary [Elizabeth]

LUTHER
Sanctus, The
(Dickinson) SATB&jr cor oct GRAY GSC 235
$.25   (L2109)

LUTHER, MARTIN (1483-1546)
Av Djupets Nod, O Gud, Till Dig
mix cor NORDISKA 3275 s.p.   (L2110)

Away In A Manger *Xmas,carol
2pt ASHDOWN E.A.255 s.p.   (L2111)
(Ehret) SSA,opt vcl oct PRO ART 2512 $.30
(L2112)
(Ehret; Mueller) SATB oct SPRATT 518 $.25
(L2113)
(Ehret; Mueller) SSA oct SPRATT 531 $.30
(L2114)
(Ehret; Mueller) SAB oct SPRATT 626 $.30
(L2115)
(Ehret; Mueller) SA oct SPRATT 613 $.25
(L2116)
(Stone) 2pt oct PRO ART 1708 $.15   (L2117)
(Swift) SATB,acap oct PRO ART 1177 $.20
(L2118)

Away In The Manger *Xmas
(Kunz) SATB,acap oct KENDOR $.25   (L2119)

Christmas Chorale *Xmas,chorale
(Bach, J.S.; Parry) SATB oct PLYMOUTH
XM-100 $.25   (L2120)

In Death's Strong Grasp
(Lundquist) SATB,acap (med) oct WILLIS 8401
$.18   (L2121)

Isaiah Mighty Seer, In Days Of Old
(Lundquist) SATB,acap (med) oct WILLIS 6631
$.18   (L2122)

Isiah's Vision
(Hughes) SATB oct BOURNE 831 $.25   (L2123)

Lord, Keep Us Steadfast *anthem
(Distler) SAB (easy) oct AUGSBURG 1448 $.20
(L2124)
(Jennings, Kenneth) (med) oct AUGSBURG 1401
$.20   (L2125)
(Johns) SAB (easy) oct AUGSBURG 1394 $.30
(L2126)

Mighty Fortress Is Our God, A *Gen,anthem/
hymn
SAB oct BELWIN 952 $.30   (L2127)
SATB,band oct STAFF 268 $.30, ipa   (L2128)
(Alderfer) SATB,opt trp oct SPRATT 546 $.25
(L2129)
(Cailliet) SATB,band oct BOOSEY 1781 $.30,
ipa   (L2130)
(Cain) SATB SCHMITT 1599 $.30   (L2131)
(Duey) TTBB,acap BOSTON 13137 $.35   (L2132)
(Gerig) SATB oct LILLENAS AN-2293 $.35
(L2133)
(Hegedus, Arpad) SATB,opt 2trp oct WORLD
ESA-966-8 $.60   (L2134)
(Johnson, David N.) cor&cong,org,opt trp
(easy) oct AUGSBURG 1441 $.35   (L2135)
(Johnson, David N.) SSAA (med) oct AUGSBURG
1427 $.25   (L2136)
(Johnson, David N.) TTBB (med) oct AUGSBURG
1435 $.30   (L2137)
(Mueller) 8pt mix cor,S solo,acap oct

LUTHER, MARTIN (cont'd.)

SCHIRM.G 8179 $.35 (L2138)
(Mueller) 4pt mix cor oct SCHIRM.G 9371
$.35 (L2139)
(Mueller) 3pt mix cor oct SCHIRM.G 10689
$.25 (L2140)
(Mueller) jr cor&sr cor oct SCHIRM.G 10735
$.35 (L2141)
(Mueller) 4pt men cor oct SCHIRM.G 10058
$.30 (L2142)
(Mueller) 3pt wom cor oct SCHIRM.G 10346
$.35 (L2143)
(Mueller) 4pt wom cor,acap oct SCHIRM.G
9372 $.25 (L2144)
(Olds) SATB&dbl cor SCHMITT 1513 $.35 (L2145)
(Olds) SATB SCHMITT 1858 $.20 (L2146)
(Olds) TTBB SCHMITT 3501 $.25 (L2147)
(Rasley) SATB oct LORENZ C208 $.30 (L2148)
(Shaw; Parker) SATB oct LAWSON 770 $.30 (L2149)
(Simeone) SATB SHAWNEE A 349 $.35 (L2150)
(Stone) SATB oct PRO ART 1188 $.25 (L2151)
(Williams) SATB FLAMMER A 5400 $.30 (L2152)

Simeons Lovsang
mix cor NORDISKA 1705 s.p. (L2153)

LUTHERCHORALKANTATE see Micheelsen, Hans
Friedrich

LUTHER'S CAROL FOR HIS SON see Cowell, Henry
Dixon

LUTHER'S CRADLE HYMN see Bach, Johann Sebastian

LUTHERS KIRCHENLIEDER IN TONSATZEN SEINER ZEIT,
HEFT 2: DER OSTERFESTKREIS *CC19U,Easter,
chorale
(Ameln, Konrad) [Ger] 2-5pt mix cor,acap
BAREN. BA 727 $2.00 (L2154)

LUTHERS KIRCHENLIEDER IN TONSATZEN SEINER ZEIT,
HEFT I: DER WEIHNACHTSKREIS *CC15U,Xmas
(Ameln, Konrad) [Ger] 2-6pt mix cor,acap (med
easy) BAREN. BA 726 $2.00 (L2155)

LUTKIN, PETER CHRISTIAN (1858-1931)
Into The Woods My Master Went *Easter
SA oct LORENZ 5377 $.25 (L2156)
(Lynn, G.) SATB,acap oct PRESSER 312-40279
$.30 (L2157)

Lord Bless And Keep You, The
(Palmer) SATB ALFRED 6368 $.25 (L2158)

Lord Bless And Keep You, The
SSA oct STAFF 352 $.20 (L2159)

Lord Bless You And Keep You *cor-resp
SATB,acap oct FISCHER,C CM-6919 $.25
(L2160)
Lord Bless You And Keep You, The *Gen/
Marriage
SATB FLAMMER A 5299 $.30 (L2161)
SATB oct STAFF 339 $.30 (L2162)
SATB oct LILLENAS AN-2259 $.25 (L2163)
SATB,acap (sevenfold and ninefold amens)
oct PRESSER 312-40420 $.30 (L2164)
SATB oct SUMMY 1089 $.25 (L2165)
SATB,opt org BOSTON 12155 $.30 (L2166)
SATB oct LORENZ 9859 $.25 (L2167)
(Craig) SATB oct PLYMOUTH DC-106 $.25 (L2168)
(Craig, Don) SATB ALLANS 331 s.p. (L2169)
(Ehret) 2pt,acap oct PRO ART 1804 $.20 (L2170)
(Ehret) SSA,acap oct PRO ART 1797 $.25 (L2171)
(Ehret) SAB,acap oct PRO ART 1805 $.30 (L2172)
(Ehret) SATB,acap oct PRO ART 1796 $.30 (L2173)
(Hallagan, R.) SATB oct PRESSER 312-40436
$.25 (L2174)
(Hallagan, R.) SSA,acap oct PRESSER
312-40914 $.25 (L2175)
(Heller) SATB SCHMITT 1754 $.30 (L2176)
(Howorth, Wayne) SATB oct BELWIN 1718 $.30 (L2177)
(Howorth, Wayne) SAB oct BELWIN 1717 $.25 (L2178)
(Howorth, Wayne) SA/TB oct BELWIN 1715 $.25 (L2179)
(Jamison) SAB,org/pno BOSTON 12214 $.30 (L2180)
(Jamison) SSA,org/pno BOSTON 2976 $.30 (L2181)
(Martin) SATB oct SPRATT 550 $.22 (L2182)
(Pitcher, Gladys) 3pt mix cor,pno (med) oct
WILLIS 8485 $.25 (L2183)
(Simon) 3pt jr cor/SSA (very easy) FISCHER,
C CM 6921 $.25 (L2184)
(Simon) 3pt jr cor/SAB (very easy) FISCHER,
C CM 6920 $.25 (L2185)
(Simon) 2pt jr cor FISCHER,C CM 6922 $.25 (L2186)
(Stickles) SA&2pt jr cor,org/pno BOSTON
12271 $.30 (L2187)
(Stickles) 3pt mix cor oct SCHIRM.G 10933
$.25 (L2188)
(Stickles) 4pt mix cor,opt org/pno oct
SCHIRM.G 10476 $.25 (L2189)
(Stickles) 3pt wom cor oct SCHIRM.G 11032
$.25 (L2190)

LUVAAS
All Blessing, Honor, Thanks, And Praise
boy cor SOUTHERN $.30 (L2191)

Blessed Is He That Cometh
SATB KJOS $20.20 (L2192)

Christ Has Arisen *Easter
SATB KJOS 2010 $.30 (L2193)

Christmas Cradle Song *Xmas,cradle
SATB KJOS 2062 $.30 (L2194)

For The Beauty Of The Earth
SATB KJOS 2054 $.30 (L2195)

Hymn Of Praise
SATB KJOS 2009 $.30 (L2196)

I Sing To Thee
SATB KJOS 2022 $.30 (L2197)

LUVAAS (cont'd.)

In Thee Is Gladness
SATB KJOS 2039 $.35 (L2198)

O Come, O Come Emmanuel
SATB KJOS 2006 $.30 (L2199)

O, Rejoice, Ye Christians Loudly
SATB KJOS 5097 $.30 (L2200)

On Christmas Night *Xmas
SATB KJOS 2038 $.30 (L2201)
SSA KJOS 3014 $.30 (L2202)

Praise We Sing To Thee
SATB KJOS 2015 $.30 (L2203)

Rise, Arise
SSA KJOS 3016 $.30 (L2204)

Song Of Adoration
SATB KJOS 2037 $.30 (L2205)
SSA KJOS 3013 $.30 (L2206)

Two Chorals *CC2U,chorale
boy cor SOUTHERN $.20 (L2207)

While Stars Their Vigil Keep
SSATB oct SUMMY B 343 $.25 (L2208)

LUVASS
Shepherds' Christmas, The *Xmas,cant
SATB oct SUMMY $1.50 (L2209)

LUX AETERNA see Jommelli, Niccolo

LUX AETERNA see Ligeti, Gyorgy

LUX CHRISTI see Elgar, Edward

LUX ILLUXIT LETABUNDA see Reiss, Georg

LUX PERPETUA see Graves

LUZZI, LUIGI (1828-1876)
Ave Maria *BVM
[Lat] S/Mez ZANIBON 3612 s.p. (L2210)
(Harris) "I Hail Thee, Mary" [It/Eng] SSA
oct COLOMBO 1767 $.25 (L2211)

I Hail Thee, Mary *see Ave Maria

LVOFF, A. [VON]
O Holy Jesu
(Grant) 4pt mix cor,acap oct SCHIRM.G 4506
$.25 (L2212)

LVOV
Hospodi Pomilui
(Wilhousky) SATB,acap oct FISCHER,C CM-6580
$.30 (L2213)

LVOV, ALEXEY FEODOROVITCH (1798-1870)
O Praise The Name Of The Lord
(Lovelace) SAB oct SACRED S-7395 $.35
(L2214)
Of The Mystical Supper
SATB oct FISCHER,J 4549 $.30 (L2215)
(McKinney) SAB oct FISCHER,J 9765 $.30
(L2216)

Praise Ye The Name Of The Lord
(Tellep, L.) SATB,acap oct PRESSER
312-40114 $.25 (L2217)

Rest Eternal Grant Unto Them
see Lvov, Alexey Feodorovitch, Then Holy
Joseph Of Arimathaea

Then Holy Joseph Of Arimathaea *Gd.Fri.
SATB,acap (Holy Saturday) SCHIRM.EC 1233
$.16 contains also: Rest Eternal Grant
Unto Them (SSATTB,acap) (ASD,funeral)
(L2218)

LVOVSKY
Hospodi Pomilui
SATB KJOS 7010 $.30 (L2219)
(McKinney) SATB oct FISCHER,J 5999 $.30
(L2220)

LVOVSKY, F.V. (1830-1894)
Hospodi Pomilui
[Russ/Eng] SATB,acap SCHIRM.EC 2231 $.35
(L2221)
(Glaser, V.) "Lord, Have Mercy" [Russ/Eng]
TTBB,acap SCHIRM.EC 2180 $.16 (L2222)

Lord, Have Mercy *see Hospodi Pomilui

LVOVSKY, S.
Have Mercy O Lord *see Hospodi Pomilui

Hospodi Pomilui
(Churchill; Ehret) "Lord Have Mercy On Us"
SATB oct BOURNE BL2536 $.25 (L2223)
(Krone) "Have Mercy O Lord" SATB,acap
WARNER W2635 $.30 (L2224)

Lord Have Mercy On Us *see Hospodi Pomilui

Mercy On Us, O Lord *Gen
(Cain) SATB SCHMITT 1601 $.25 (L2225)

LWOFF
God Ever Glorious
(Wilson) TTBB oct BOOSEY 5046 $.30 (L2226)
(Wilson) boy cor SOUTHERN $.30 (L2227)

God The Omnipotent
(Ohl) SATB oct PLYMOUTH FO-101 $.25 (L2228)

LYBBERT, DONALD
Austro Terris Influente
SSAA oct PRESSER MC416 $1.00 (L2229)

LYDT FORKYNDTE see Palestrina, Giovanni,
Loquebantur

LYKKSALIG, LYKKSALIG see Karlsen, Rolf

LYMAN, ED.
I Evermore Shall Sing
SATB oct WORD CS-2525 $.30 (L2230)

LYNN
I Will Make A New Convenant
SAB KJOS PC740 $.30 (L2231)

LYNN (cont'd.)

Psalm 133
SATB KJOS PC767 $.30 (L2232)

LYNN, GEORGE (1915-   )
All Glory On High *Xmas
SATB,acap oct PRESSER 312-40086 $.30
(L2233)

All Were There *Xmas
SATB,acap oct PRESSER 332-40083 $.25
(L2234)

Alleluia
SAB,acap oct PRESSER MC281 $.30 (L2235)

Amazing Grace
SATB (easy) ABINGDON APM-185 $.35 (L2236)

And Can It Be?
SATB (med) ABINGDON APM-182 $.26 (L2237)

Candle In The Window *Xmas
SATB,acap oct PRESSER 332-40085 $.30
(L2238)

Clap Your Hands
SATB,acap oct PRESSER 312-40745 $.50
(L2239)

Come, Let Us Use The Grace Divine
SATB (easy) ABINGDON APM-139 $.22 (L2240)

Crucifixion *Easter
SATB,acap oct PRESSER 312-40218 $.30
(L2241)

Easter *Easter
SATB oct PRESSER 312-40635 $.30 (L2242)

Easter Hymn *Easter
mix cor&jr cor oct PRESSER MC186 $.30
(L2243)

Father, Forgive Them
SATB oct SOUTHERN $.25 (L2244)

Four Gospel Hymn Anthems *CC4U,anthem/
gospel/hymn
SATB (easy) ABINGDON APM-298 $.45 (L2245)

God Rest You Merry, Gentlemen *Xmas
SATB&jr cor,acap oct PRESSER 312-40094 $.30
(L2246)

I Got A Home In That Rock
SATB,acap oct PRESSER 312-40353 $.30 (L2247)

I Know I Have Another Building
SATB,acap oct PRESSER 312-40236 $.30
(L2248)

I Know That My Redeemer Lives
SATB,acap oct PRESSER MC185 $.30 (L2249)

I Need Thee Ev'ry Hour
SATB (easy) ABINGDON APM-151 $.22 (L2250)

I Want Jesus To Walk With Me
SATB,acap oct PRESSER 312-40113 $.30
(L2251)

Jesus Born *Xmas
2pt mix cor oct PRESSER MC250 $.30 (L2252)

Junior Choir Christmas Collection *see
McKasson, M.

Life Giver In The Light Realms *Easter
SATB,acap oct PRESSER 312-40638 $.25
(L2253)

Lift Up Your Heads *Easter
2pt mix cor oct PRESSER MC220 $.30 (L2254)

Little Church Year, A *CCU
SA oct PRESSER $.75 (L2255)

Lo, How A Rose E'er Blooming
2pt mix cor oct PRESSER MC219 $.25 (L2256)

Lonesome Valley
SATB,acap oct PRESSER 312-40062 $.30
(L2257)

Lord Doth Reign, The
SATB,opt acap (easy) ABINGDON $.18 (L2258)

Lord Is Good, The
SATB,acap oct PRESSER 312-40746 $.50
(L2259)

Lord Is King, The
SATB oct PRESSER 312-40548 $.30 (L2260)

Must Jesus Bear The Cross Alone? *Lent
SATB (easy) ABINGDON APM-270 $.20 (L2261)

My Faith, It Is An Oaken Staff
SATB (med) ABINGDON APM-896 $.35 (L2262)

Near The Inn In Bethlehem *Xmas
SAB,acap oct PRESSER 312-40251 $.25 (L2263)
SATB oct PRESSER 312-40251 $.30 (L2264)

New Year Carol *Xmas
SSA oct PRESSER 312-40330 $.30 (L2265)
SATB,acap oct PRESSER 312-40058 $.30
(L2266)

Now With The New Year Starting
SATB oct SOUTHERN $.25 (L2267)

O Come, Immanuel
2pt mix cor oct PRESSER MC217 $.30 (L2268)

Peter On The Sea
SATB,acap oct PRESSER 312-40350 $.30
(L2269)

Praise The Lord
SSAATTBB,acap oct PRESSER 312-40747 $.75
(L2270)

Rock Of Ages
SAB (easy) ABINGDON APM-271 $.18 (L2271)

Sinner, Please Don't Let This Harvest Pass
SATB,acap oct PRESSER 312-40210 $.30
(L2272)

Sleep My Little One *Xmas
SATB oct SOUTHERN $.25 (L2273)

Song Of An Indian Child *Xmas
SATB,acap oct PRESSER 332-40084 $.30
(L2274)

Suffer The Little Children
SATB oct PRESSER MC270 $.30 (L2275)

There Is A River
SATB (med) PRESSER 312-41013 $.35 (L2276)

LYNN, GEORGE (cont'd.)

To Our Fathers And Thee
SATB oct SOUTHERN $.25   (L2277)

True-Hearted, Whole-Hearted
SATB&jr cor (easy) ABINGDON APM-183 $.28
(L2278)

Who Shall Separate Us From The Love Of Christ
SATB oct SOUTHERN $.25   (L2279)

Why Thus Cradled Here? *Xmas
SATB (med) ABINGDON APM-138 $.25   (L2280)

Wise May Bring Their Learning *Xmas
SATB oct PRESSER 312-40237 $.30   (L2281)

Wondrous Love
2pt mix cor oct SOUTHERN $.25   (L2282)

LYNN, LORI
Victorious Christ, The *see Lillenas, Haldor

LYON
Praise Ye, Jehovah
SATB oct LORENZ 258 $.30   (L2283)

LYON, J.
Lord Descended, The
(Young, R.; Weinandt, E.) SATB oct FISCHER,
J 10004 $.35   (L2284)

Shepherd Boy's Song, The *Xmas
2pt ASHDOWN E.A.88 s.p.   (L2285)

LYRIC MASS ON THE HANDEL THEME "WHERE E'ER YOU
WALK", A see Handel, George Frideric

LYRISCHE KANTATE see Beck, Conrad

LYRISCHE SUITE see Roos, Robert de

LYTE
Let All The Nations Shout And Sing
(Kirk) SATB oct FISCHER,C CM-7715 $.25
(L2286)

M

MA CURLY HEADED BABY see Clutsam, G.H.

MA SO BEN, SIGNOR MIO see Palestrina, Giovanni

MA TOVU see Ben-Haim, Paul

MAASALO, ARMAS
Psalm 107 *Op.2
mix cor,org/pno cor pts NORDISKA 3602 s.p.
(M1)

MAASZ, GERHARD (1906-   )
Adventskantate *Adv,cant
4pt mix cor,inst MOSELER sc s.p., cor pts
s.p., ipa   (M2)

Ein Helles Licht Ist Uns Entbrannt *Xmas
men cor TONGER s.p.   (M3)
mix cor TONGER s.p.   (M4)
wom cor&jr cor TONGER s.p.   (M5)

O Jesulein Suss *Xmas
[Ger] 4pt men cor,acap (med) NAGELS NCH 207
s.p.   (M6)

Stille Nacht, Heilige Nacht *Xmas
[Ger] 4pt men cor,acap NAGELS NCH 208 s.p.
(M7)

MABRY
And Peace Shall Reign Again
SATB oct LORENZ C321 $.30   (M8)

MCAFEE
Earth Is The Lord's, The
SATB oct SACRED S-46 $.35   (M9)

Fourteen Choral Responses *CC14U,cor-resp
SATB oct SACRED S-78 $.40   (M10)

Go Ye Therefore
SATB oct SACRED S-63 $.35   (M11)

Heart Of God, The
SATB oct LORENZ 4406 $.30   (M12)

Holy Infant Of Bethlehem *Xmas
SATB oct SACRED E91 $.35   (M13)

How Excellent Is Thy Name
SATB oct SACRED S-43 $.35   (M14)

Hymn Of Trust, A
SA/TB FLAMMER E5051 $.30   (M15)

Let The People Praise Thee
SATB oct SACRED S-97 $.40   (M16)

Lord Is Nigh, The
SATB oct SACRED S-26 $.35   (M17)

Near To The Heart Of God *hymn
SATB ALLANS 365 s.p.   (M18)
SA ALLANS 366 s.p.   (M19)
(McLellan) SATB oct LILLENAS AT-1069 $.25
(M20)

O Clap Your Hands
SATB oct SACRED S-49 $.35   (M21)

Psalm 91
SATB oct SACRED E76 $.35   (M22)

Ride On, Ride On In Majesty *Palm
SATB oct SACRED S-4 $.35   (M23)
SATB oct SOUTHERN $.30   (M24)

Sing Unto The Lord A New Song
SATB oct SACRED S-12 $.35   (M25)

Through All The World Below
SATB (southern harmony) oct BOURNE 853 $.25
(M26)

MCAFEE, D.
Christ Is Risen *Easter
SATB,opt brass oct KERBY 6102C $.35   (M27)
SATB,org,brass oct KERBY 6102 $.35   (M28)

In Heavenly Love Abiding
unis oct KERBY 6601C $.30   (M29)
unis,kbd oct KERBY 6601 $.30   (M30)

Lo, I Tell You A Mystery
SATB oct KERBY 6302C $.35   (M31)
SATB,org oct KERBY 6302 $.35   (M32)

Psalm 8 *see Hymn In Praise Of God And Man,
A

Psalm 120 *see Hymn Of Praise, A

Psalm 121 *see Hymn Of Aspiration, A

Redemption Carol *carol
SATB oct KERBY 6211 $.25   (M33)
SATB,acap oct KERBY 6211C $.25   (M34)

MCAFEE, DON
Almighty God, Unto Whom All Hearts Are Open
*Commun
SATB (med) ABINGDON APM-394 $.30   (M35)

Amazing Grace
see Hansen's Jr. Choral Series

Beatitudes, The
SATB oct WALTON 2159 $.35   (M36)

Built On The Rocks
SATB (easy) ABINGDON APM-272 $.25   (M37)

Canticle Of Praise
SATB&desc&cong,org,opt brass&perc voc sc
BOURNE $.75, ipa   (M38)

Carol Of The New Year *Xmas,carol
SATB GENERAL CH222 $.40 see from
Contemporary Christmas Carols   (M39)

Choral Psalmist, The *see Butler, Eugene

Choric Psalm, A *Psalm
SATB,perc GENERAL CH234 $.40   (M40)

MCAFEE, DON (cont'd.)

Contemporary Christmas Carols *see Carol Of
The New Year; Little Town; Midnight
Carol; Minute Carol, The; Peace Carol,
The   (M41)

Everything Is Beautiful
see Hansen's Jr. Choral Series

Gates Of Jerusalem, The *Palm,anthem
SATB&unis jr cor&cong/SATB&3pt jr cor&cong,
org (easy) MCAFEE M1003 $.40   (M42)

Good Samaritan, The *Bibl
SATB GENERAL CH237 $.40 see from Two
Parables   (M43)

Hansen's Jr. Choral Series
SA HANSEN-US C551 $.40
contains: Amazing Grace; Everything Is
Beautiful   (M44)

Hymn Of Supplication
SATB oct GRAY GCMR 3033 $.30   (M45)

In The Bleak Midwinter
SATB oct AGAPE A 413 $.25   (M46)

Let All The World In Every Corner Sing
SATB oct AGAPE CH 643 $.30   (M47)

Little Town *Xmas,carol
SATB GENERAL CH224 $.40 see from
Contemporary Christmas Carols   (M48)

Lord, Make Me An Instrument Of Thy Peace
SATB oct WALTON 2061 $.30   (M49)

Midnight Carol *Xmas,carol
SATB GENERAL CH229 $.35 see from
Contemporary Christmas Carols   (M50)

Minute Carol, The *Xmas,carol
SATB GENERAL CH220 $.30 see from
Contemporary Christmas Carols   (M51)

Parable Of The Sower
SATB GENERAL CH236 $.40 see from Two
Parables   (M52)

Peace Carol, The *Xmas,carol
SATB GENERAL CH221 $.40 see from
Contemporary Christmas Carols   (M53)

Psalm 92
SATB oct WALTON 2084 $.25   (M54)

Psalm 150
SATB,pno/org PEER $.45   (M55)

Psalm For Today, A *Psalm
unis/2pt oct AGAPE CF 112 $.30   (M56)

Psalm Of Praise *Psalm
SATB oct WALTON 2158 $.25   (M57)

Sermon On The Mount, The *cant
mix cor BELWIN $1.50   (M58)

Song In The Air, A
SATB GENERAL CH230 $.40   (M59)

Song Of The Shepherds *Xmas,cant
unis BELWIN $1.25   (M60)

Two Christmas Carols *CC2U,Xmas,carol
SATB (easy) ABINGDON APM-297 $.18   (M61)

Two Parables *see Good Samaritan, The;
Parable Of The Sower   (M62)

Wake Up, World! *Easter,anthem
jr cor,pno/org,opt bvl&gtr&drums 2pt (med
easy) MCAFEE M1001 $.30   (M63)
jr cor,pno/org,opt bvl&gtr&drums SATB (med
easy) MCAFEE M1002 $.30   (M64)

Watchman, Tell Us *Adv
SATB/unis oct GRAY GCMR 3026 $.30   (M65)

Winter Carol, A *carol
TB,pno/org PEER $.40   (M66)
SA,pno/org PEER $.40   (M67)

MACAULAY
Christmas Vision *Xmas
(Whitman, Donald) SA oct AGAPE A 369 $.30
(M68)

MC BRADD
In The Inn
SATB FLAMMER A 5234 $.30   (M69)
(Lowden) SAB FLAMMER D5038 $.30   (M70)
(Lowden) SSA FLAMMER B 5054 $.25   (M71)

MC CABE
Coventry Carol *carol
SATB,S solo (med) OXFORD 84.114 $.25   (M72)

MC CABE, JOHN (1939-   )
Canticles For Salisbury (1966)
SATB BELWIN AP28 $.50   (M73)

Great Lord Of Lords *anthem
mix cor,orch oct NOVELLO 28.1466.08 s.p.,
ipr   (M74)

Hymne To God The Father, A *anthem
mix cor,acap oct NOVELLO 40.1483.09 s.p.
(M75)

Magnificat And Nunc Dimittis *Magnif/Nunc
SATB oct NOVELLO 86.0031.07 s.p.   (M76)
SATB oct NOVELLO 44.1433.00 s.p.   (M77)

Mary Laid Her Child
4pt mix cor,acap oct SCHIRM.G 11372 $.25
(M78)

Morning Watch, The *anthem
mix cor oct NOVELLO 86.0017.01 s.p.   (M79)

To Us In Bethlem City *Xmas,carol
SATB,acap NOVELLO AP225 $.30   (M80)

MC CAIN, LARRY
Rejoice, Man!
unis oct AGAPE CF 122 $.25   (M81)

MC CALL, HARLO
Be A Child Again!
  SATB BIG3 $.35   (M82)

Christ Must Live In Me
  SATB BIG3 $.35   (M83)

Christ Who Set Me Free, The
  SATB BIG3 $.35   (M84)

He's The One
  SATB BIG3 $.35   (M85)

I'm Not Afraid
  SATB BIG3 $.35   (M86)

Kind Of Man I Am! , The
  SATB BIG3 $.35   (M87)

Let's See What Happens Today
  SATB BIG3 $.35   (M88)

Love Thou Art
  SATB BIG3 $.35   (M89)

One Day At A Time
  SATB BIG3 $.35   (M90)

Our Prayer
  SATB BIG3 $.35   (M91)

Rest Of My Life!, The
  SATB BIG3 $.35   (M92)

MC CANDLESS, ROBERT
Father I'm Coming Home *see Freeman, Charles

I Found Jesus *see Freeman, Charles

We'll Kneel At Jesus' Feet *see Freeman,
  Charles

MACCARTHY
Psalm 23
  SATB oct COLOMBO 2380 $.35   (M93)

MC CLINTOCK, DONALD
We Have Seen His Star *Xmas,cant
  oct AGAPE $1.50   (M94)

MCCLURE
Hosanna In The Highest! *Easter
  SATB oct LORENZ C233 $.30   (M95)

MCCLUSKEY
Christmas Choral Festival No. 1 *CCU,Xmas
  SATB oct LORENZ $1.50   (M96)

Come, Ye Sinners, Poor And Needy
  SATB oct LORENZ B140 $.25   (M97)

Solid Rock, The
  SATB oct LORENZ C322 $.30   (M98)

Though Your Sins Be As Scarlet
  SATB oct LORENZ B166 $.30   (M99)

When I Stood At Calvary *Easter
  SATB oct LORENZ C305 $.30   (M100)

MCCOLLIN, FRANCES (1892-1960)
Welcome, Happy Morning *Easter
  SATB,org oct LAWSON 51303 $.30   (M101)

MCCORMICK
Anthems From Scripture *CCU
  SATB SHAWNEE GA34 $1.50   (M102)

As Smoke Is Driven Away
  SATB,acap SHAWNEE A 222 $.25   (M103)

Be Still And Know
  SATB SHAWNEE A 528 $.25   (M104)

Behold! I Stand At The Door
  SATB SHAWNEE A 471 $.30   (M105)

Behold, We Go Up To Jerusalem
  SATB,acap SHAWNEE A 1035 $.30   (M106)

By The Waters Of Babylon
  SATB,acap SHAWNEE A 224 $.25   (M107)

Celestial City, The
  SATB SHAWNEE A 522 $.25   (M108)

Christmas Bells *Xmas,cant
  SATB SHAWNEE A590 $1.00   (M109)

Consider The Lilies Of The Field
  SATB,acap SHAWNEE A 399 $.30   (M110)

Early In The Morning *Easter
  SATB,acap SHAWNEE A 307 $.30   (M111)
  SATB oct SOUTHERN $.25   (M112)

Earth Is The Lord's, The
  SATB SHAWNEE A 208 $.30   (M113)

Go Ye Into All The World
  SATB,acap SHAWNEE A 230 $.30   (M114)

God Is A Spirit
  SATB SHAWNEE A 400 $.30   (M115)

He Shall Come Down Like Rain
  SATB,acap SHAWNEE A 285 $.30   (M116)

If I Go Not Away
  SATB,acap SHAWNEE A 548 $.30   (M117)

If We Walk In The Light
  SATB,acap SHAWNEE A 581 $.30   (M118)

In Him Is Life
  SATB SHAWNEE A 1007 $.30   (M119)

It Is A Good Thing To Give Thanks
  SATB,acap SHAWNEE A 284 $.25   (M120)

Lenten Anthem *Lent
  SATB SHAWNEE A 472 $.30   (M121)

Light Of The World, The
  SATB SHAWNEE A 1038 $.30   (M122)

More Things Are Wrought By Prayer
  SATB,acap SHAWNEE A 748 $.30   (M123)

MCCORMICK (cont'd.)
On The Morning Of Christ's Nativity
  SATB SHAWNEE A808 $.50   (M124)

Song Of Deliverance *Easter
  SATB oct SOUTHERN $.25   (M125)

Song Of Deliverance, A *Easter
  SATB oct SACRED S-38 $.30   (M126)

Then Did Jesus Pray
  SATB SHAWNEE A 470 $.25   (M127)

Three Christmas Scenes *CC3U,Xmas
  SATB,acap SHAWNEE A 233 $.35   (M128)

Trust In The Lord
  SATB SHAWNEE A 549 $.25   (M129)

You Are Not Far From The Kingdom Of God
  SATB,acap SHAWNEE A 582 $.30   (M130)

You Must Be Born Again
  SATB,acap SHAWNEE A 1005 $.25   (M131)

MCCOWEN
Alleluia *Allelu
  SSAATTBB oct SUMMY 5350 $.40   (M132)

Fanfare For A Christmas Festival *Xmas
  SATB KJOS 5405 $.30   (M133)

Gloria In Excelsis Deo
  SATB KJOS 5359 $.30   (M134)

Introit-Response-Kyrie-Amen
  SATB KJOS 5406 $.30   (M135)

We Praise Thee, O Lord
  SATB KJOS 5371 $.30   (M136)

MCCOY
We All Need God
  SA oct LORENZ 5395 $.40   (M137)

MC CRAY, JAMES
Introit For Christmas *Xmas,Introit
  SATB&SSA,Bar solo,pno/org oct FOX UM124
  $.30   (M138)

O Magnum Mysterium
  SATB,acap (med diff/diff) SOUTHERN $.30
                                              (M139)
  SATB,opt pno/org oct FOX UM131 $.30   (M140)

Prophecy, The
  SATB,opt pno oct FOX UM130 $.35   (M141)

MCCULLEN, A.
Over The Hills *Xmas
  SSA oct PRESSER 312-40703 $.25   (M142)

MCCULLOUGH
Plead My Cause, O Lord (Psalm 35)
  SATB,acap,opt pno oct PRO ART 2643 $.30
                                              (M143)

Psalm 35 *see Plead My Cause, O Lord

MACDONALD
As Pants The Hart For Cooling Streams
  SATB oct LORENZ E26 $.35   (M144)

Hymn Of Dedication, A *Ded,hymn
  SATB oct LORENZ C279 $.25   (M145)

MC DONALD
Lord Is My Light, The
  SATB ALLANS 368 $.30   (M146)
  SATB oct LORENZ 36 $.30   (M147)

MACDONALD
One Step *see Hoffman

Tabernacle Of God, The
  SATB oct LORENZ E2 $.35   (M148)

MCDOUGAL, CAROL
O Jesus, I Have Promised *see Norman, Gus

Shall We Gather At The River
  cor HIGHLAND 2003 $.25   (M149)

MAC DOUGALL
Yuletide Carol *Xmas,carol
  SATB oct BELWIN 64141 $.30   (M150)

MCFARLAND
Holy Easter Morning *Easter
  unis oct LORENZ 8597 $.30   (M151)

MACFARLANE, WILLIAM CHARLES (1870-1945)
Christ Our Passover *Easter
  SATB oct PRESSER 322-35139 $.35   (M152)

God Is Our Refuge *Bibl
  4pt mix cor,B solo oct SCHIRM.G 3944 $.25
                                              (M153)

Ho, Every One That Thirsteth *Bibl
  4pt mix cor,high solo oct SCHIRM.G 4808
  $.35   (M154)
  (Downing) 3pt wom cor,S solo oct SCHIRM.G
  8941 $.25   (M155)

Jesus Call Us
  4pt mix cor,Bar solo oct SCHIRM.G 8404 $.30
                                              (M156)

Like As The Hart Desireth The Water-Brooks
  *Bibl
  4pt mix cor oct SCHIRM.G 8643 $.25   (M157)

O Rest In The Lord *Bibl
  4pt mix cor oct SCHIRM.G 8925 $.25   (M158)

Open Our Eyes
  (Deis) SAB oct SCHIRM.G 9535 $.30   (M159)
  (Deis) mix cor,acap oct SCHIRM.G 7273 $.35
                                              (M160)
  (Deis) 4pt men cor,acap oct SCHIRM.G 7872
  $.35   (M161)
  (Deis) 3pt wom cor oct SCHIRM.G 7383 $.30
                                              (M162)

Saviour, Like A Shepherd Lead Us
  (Mueller) SABar,Bar solo oct SCHIRM.G 8697
  $.30   (M163)

Thine, O Lord *anthem/Bibl
  4pt mix cor,org oct SCHIRM.G 4240 $.25   (M164)

MAC FARREN
Lord Is My Shepherd, The *Lent/Rembrnc
  SATB (easy) ALLANS 39 s.p.   (M165)

MAC FARREN, GEORGE ALEXANDER (1813-1887)
Day In Thy Courts, A *anthem
  mix cor oct NOVELLO 40.0444.02 s.p.   (M166)

Lord Is My Shepherd, The *anthem/Bibl
  4pt mix cor oct SCHIRM.G 5097 $.20   (M167)
  SATB oct LESLIE 4063   (M168)
  mix cor oct NOVELLO 40.0318.07 s.p.   (M169)

MACFARREN, WALTER [CECIL] (1826-1905)
Praise Ye The Lord *anthem
  SATB,org CRAMER C 0 s.p.   (M170)

MCGEHEE
Lord, Now Lettest Thou Thy Servant Depart In
  Peace *see Nunc Dimittis

Nunc Dimittis
  "Lord, Now Lettest Thou Thy Servant Depart
  In Peace" [Eng/Lat] SATB oct PRO ART 1219
  $.16   (M171)

MACGIMSEY, [ROBERT] (1938-   )
Sweet Little Jesus Boy *Xmas
  SATB PATERSON 1692 s.p.   (M172)
  SSA oct FISCHER,C CM-5216 $.25   (M173)
  (Andrews) 3pt jr cor/SSA (easy) FISCHER,C
  CM 5216 $.25   (M174)
  (Andrews) TTBB oct FISCHER,C CM-2194 $.25
                                              (M175)
  (Filkins) SATB,acap oct FISCHER,C CM-6779
  $.25   (M176)
  (Hinshaw) SA oct FISCHER,C CM-7770 $.25
                                              (M177)
  (Lee) 4pt jr cor/SATB (med) FISCHER,C
  CM 4638 $.25   (M178)
  (Lee) SATB oct FISCHER,C CM-4638 $.25
                                              (M179)

MC GRANAHAN
Halleluia! Christ Is Risen *Easter/Lent
  (Ehret) SAB oct SPRATT 641 $.35   (M180)

I Know Whom I Have Believed
  (Ferrin) SATB oct LILLENAS AN-1635 $.30   (M181)

I Will Sing Of My Redeemer *hymn
  (Whitman) SSATTBB oct LILLENAS AN-2222 $.30
                                              (M182)

O My Father *see Snow

MC GRATH
Mass Of The Blessed Sacrament *Mass
  unis/cong&SATB sc SUMMY M 2574 $1.00   (M183)

MC GRATH, JOSEPH J.
Earth Feared, The *Easter,anthem/Offer
  SATB (med) oct GIA G1195 $.30   (M184)

MC GRATH, MALCOLM
Song For The Nation, A *Thanks,anthem
  SATB,org oct HARRIS HC4041 $.45   (M185)

MC GRAW
Three French Noels *CC3U,Fr
  SATB SHAWNEE A 369 $.50   (M186)

MCGRAW, CAMERON (1919-   )
Devon Carol
  SATB oct JUSKO 244 $.25   (M187)

Psalm 130
  SATB oct JUSKO 243 $.20   (M188)

Ye Angels In The Heavens
  SATB oct JUSKO 242 $.20   (M189)

MC GUIRE, FELIX
Blessed Art Thou
  SATB oct GRAY GCMR 2879 $.35   (M190)

MACH DICH AUF see Steal Away

MACH DICH AUF, WERDE LICHT see Reger, Max

MACH DICH AUF, WERDE LICHT see Schein, Johann
  Hermann

MC HARRIS, W.
Praise (Psalm 117) Bibl
  4pt mix cor oct SCHIRM.G 10505 $.25   (M191)

Psalm 117 *see Praise

MACHAUT, GUILLAUME DE (ca. 1300-1377)
La Messe De Nostre Dame *Mass
  (Hubsch, Hanns) [Fr] SABB/SATBB,acap (med
  diff) cor pts MULLER SM 614 s.p.   (M192)

Messe De Nostre Dame
  [Lat] SATB,acap voc sc PETERS WM41 $3.50
                                              (M193)

Messe De Notre Dame And Lais *Mass
  mix cor min sc KALMUS 700 $1.30   (M194)

Notre Dame *BVM,Mass
  (Chailley) [Lat] TTBB oct SALABERT-US $5.00
                                              (M195)

MACHE DICH see Bach, Johann Sebastian, Mache
  Dich, Mein Geist, Bereit

MACHE DICH AUF, HERR, UND VERSTOSSE see
  Metzger, Hans-Arnold

MACHE DICH AUF, WERDE LICHT see Becker-Foss,
  Jurgen

MACHE DICH AUF, WERDE LICHT see Doernberg,
  Martin

MACHE DICH AUF, WERDE LICHT see Doppelbauer,
  Josef Friedrich

MACHE DICH AUF, WERDE LICHT see Franck,
  Melchior

MACHE DICH AUF, WERDE LICHT see Micheelsen,
  Hans Friedrich

MACHE DICH AUF, WERDE LICHT see Thomas, Kurt

MACHE DICH, MEIN GEIST, BEREIT see Bach, Johann
  Sebastian

MACHET DIE TORE WEIT see Bach, Johann Sebastian

MACHET DIE TORE WEIT see Becker-Foss, Jurgen

MACHET DIE TORE WEIT see Boxberg, Christian Ludwig

MACHET DIE TORE WEIT see Brunner, Adolf

MACHET DIE TORE WEIT see Grimm, Heinrich

MACHET DIE TORE WEIT see Hammerschmidt, Andreas

MACHET DIE TORE WEIT see Reda, Siegfried

MACHET DIE TORE WEIT see Schmid, Walter

MACHET DIE TORE WEIT see Schutz, Heinrich

MACHET DIE TORE WEIT see Selle, Thomas

MACHET DIE TORE WEIT see Telemann, Georg Philipp

MACHET DIE TORE WEIT see Thomas, Kurt

MACHET DIE TORE WEIT see Zipp, Friedrich

MACH'S MIT MIR, GOTT, NACH DEINER GUT' see Bach, Johann Sebastian

MACHT AUF DIE TOR see Schutz, Heinrich

MACHT HOCH DIE TUR *Adv,18th cent
   (Bauernfeind, Hans) mix cor,acap oct
   DOBLINGER s.p. see from Vier Adventlieder
                                                  (M196)

MACHT HOCH DIE TUR see Bauernfeind, Hans

MACHT HOCH DIE TUR see Distler, Hugo

MACHT HOCH DIE TUR see Gast

MACHT HOCH DIE TUR see Lang, Hans

MACHT HOCH DIE TUR see Rein, Walter

MACHT HOCH DIE TUR see Strohbach, Siegfried

MACHT HOCH DIE TUR see Studer, Hans

MACHT HOCH DIE TUR see Wagner, Alexander

MACHT VOCH DIE TUR, DIE TOR see Freylinghausen, Johann A.

MACHT HOCH DIE TUR, DIE TOR MACHT WEIT see Stern, Hermann

MACHT NOCH DIE TUR see Fegers, Karl

MACHTVOLL IN DER ZEITEN WUNDE see Stier, Alfred

MACIRONE, C.A.
   Break, Break, Break
   2pt ASHDOWN E.A.22 s.p.   (M197)

MCKASSON, M.
   Junior Choir Christmas Collection (composed
      with Lynn, George) *CCU,Xmas
      jr cor oct PRESSER 332-40082 $.35   (M198)

   With Sweetest Songs Of Joy
      (Lynn, G.) unis oct PRESSER 332-40082 $.35
                                                  (M199)

MCKAY
   Get Into Heav'n
      SATB oct SUMMY 5953 $.60   (M200)

   Morning Prayer, A *Gen
      SATB SCHMITT 1571 $.18   (M201)

   On The Morning Of Christ's Nativity *Xmas
      SATB SCHMITT 1749 $.22   (M202)

   People Called Christians, A
      SSA KJOS PC656 $.30   (M203)

   Prince Of Peace
      SATB FLAMMER A 5575 $.25   (M204)

MC KAY, DAVID PHARES
   Colonial Requiem, A *Req,US
      4pt mix cor/jr cor,S solo,pno voc sc SCHIRM.G
      $1.00   (M205)

MC KAY, G.
   Song Of The Creatures
      SATB,org/pno BOSTON 13687 $.35   (M206)

MCKAY, GEORGE FREDERICK (1899-1970)
   Prayer For This House
      SATB,acap oct LAWSON 51163 $.25   (M207)

MCKIE, WILLIAM
   Psalm 48 *see We Wait For Thy Loving
      Kindness

   Psalm 121 *see Psalm 121 And Wedding
      Responses

   Psalm 121 And Wedding Responses (Psalm 121)
      Gen
      SATB,acap (easy) oct OXFORD 43.338 $.25
                                                  (M208)
   We Wait For Thy Loving Kindness (Psalm 48)
      Ded/Gen/Thanks
      SATB,T solo (med easy) oct OXFORD 42.081
      $.25   (M209)
      (Hugh-Jones, Enid) SSAA,S solo (med) oct
      OXFORD $.25   (M210)

   Wedding Psalm: Put Thou Thy Trust In The Lord
      *Gen/Marriage,Psalm
      (Hugh-Jones, Enid) SATB,acap (easy) oct
      OXFORD 43.359 $.20   (M211)

MCKINNEY
   God, Give Us Christian Homes
      SATB oct LORENZ A522 $.25   (M212)

   Veni Emmanuel *Adv
      SATB oct BELWIN 64142 $.30   (M213)

   Wherever He Leads I'll Go
      (Wilson) SATB oct LORENZ B100 $.30   (M214)

MCKINNEY, HOWARD D. (1890-   )
   Easter Service *Easter,cant
      mix cor BELWIN $1.50   (M215)

   Mystery For Christmas, A *Xmas,cant
      SA BELWIN $1.25   (M216)
      mix cor BELWIN $1.25   (M217)

   O Babe Divine *see Tu Scendi Dalle Stelle

   Tu Scendi Dalle Stelle
      "O Babe Divine" SA oct FISCHER,J 8990 $.30
                                                  (M218)
MC KINNEY, J.
   Lord Reigneth, The (Psalm 99)
      SATB oct SOUTHERN $.25   (M219)

   Psalm 99 *see Lord Reigneth, The

MAC KINNON, H.A.
   Sleeps Judea Fair *Xmas
      SATB oct GRAY GCMR 754 $.30   (M220)
      SSA oct GRAY GCMR 2898 $.25   (M221)

MCLAUGHLIN, MARIAN
   Band Of Children, The *Epiph
      SATB&jr cor FISCHER,J 10088 $.30   (M222)

   Come Where The Christ Child Is Sleeping
      *Xmas
      SSA,acap oct PRESSER 312-40338 $.25   (M223)

   O Give Thanks Unto The Lord *Bibl
      SATB,acap oct LAWSON 873 $.25   (M224)

   Song Of The Ship
      SA,opt hndbl oct FISCHER,J 10040 $.25
                                                  (M225)
MC LELLAN
   Abundant Life *medley
      SATB oct LILLENAS AT-1036 $.30   (M226)

MAC LELLAN
   Put Your Hand In The Hand
      SATB oct HERITAGE H84 $.35   (M227)
      (Simeone) SA/TB SHAWNEE E121 $.40   (M228)

MCLIN
   All The Earth Sing Unto The Lord
      SATB KJOS 5459 $.30   (M229)

   Cert'nly Lord, Cert'nly Lord
      SATB KJOS 5458 $.35   (M230)

   Done Made My Vow To The Lord *spir
      SATB KJOS 5872 $.30   (M231)

   Earth Is The Lord's, The (Psalm 24)
      SATB oct PRO ART 2531 $.25   (M232)

   Eucharist Of The Soul
      SATB KJOS GC41 $.60   (M233)

   For Jesus Christ Is Born *Xmas
      SATB KJOS 5856 $.30   (M234)

   Glory, Glory, Hallelujah
      SATB KJOS 5430 $.30   (M235)

   In This World *CCU
      SATB KJOS $1.25   (M236)

   Let The People Sing Praise
      SSA KJOS GC48 $.35   (M237)

   My God Is So High
      SATB KJOS 5881 $.30   (M238)

   Psalm 24 *see Earth Is The Lord's, The

   Psalm 100
      SATB,acap,opt pno oct PRO ART 2603 $.30
                                                  (M239)
   Psalm 117
      SATB oct PRO ART 2604 $.30   (M240)

   Sanctus And Benedictus
      SATB KJOS GC34 $.30   (M241)

   Torch Has Been Passed, The
      SATB KJOS GC20 $.35   (M242)

MC LIN, LENA
   New Born King *Xmas
      SATB KJOS GC23 $.30   (M243)

MC LOUGHLIN
   My Hope Is Built *hymn
      SATB oct LILLENAS AN-2373 $.30   (M244)

MAC MAHON
   Feast Of Christmas, The *Xmas
      SATB MARKS $1.50   (M245)

MACMILLAN, [ERNEST] (1893-   )
   Song Of Deliverance
      SATB (med) OXFORD 42.974 $.25   (M246)

MACMURROUGH, DERMOT
   Meeting Of The Waters, The
      2pt ASHDOWN E.A.203 s.p.   (M247)

   Shepherdess, The
      TTBB ENOCH EC54 s.p.   (M248)

MAC NEIL
   Worship For Today
      (Moe) cor&cong sc FISCHER,C O-4817 $2.50,
      cor pts FISCHER,C O-4817A $.40   (M249)

MAC NUTT, WALTER
   Missa Brevis In D Major
      SATB,acap oct BERANDOL 910M4AG $.35   (M250)

   Three Songs Of The Crib *CC3U
      SATB THOMP.G G-572 s.p.   (M251)

MACONCHY, ELIZABETH (1907-   )
   Christmas Morning Carol Cantata *Xmas,cant
      wom cor/jr cor WESTWOOD voc sc s.p., cor
      pts s.p.   (M252)

   I Sing Of A Maiden *BVM/Xmas,carol
      3pt mix cor,S solo,acap oct FABER 11746
      $.30   (M253)
      SAT,S solo oct FABER 11746 $.30   (M254)

MACONCHY, ELIZABETH (cont'd.)
   Propheta Mendax
      cor FABER F0084 s.p.   (M255)

   This Day *Xmas,carol
      SA,S solo oct FABER 11745 $.25   (M256)
      2pt wom cor,S solo,acap oct SCHIRM.G 11745
      $.25   (M257)

MCPHAIL
   Teach Me To Pray
      SATB oct LORENZ A458 $.30   (M258)

MC PHERSON, AIMEE SEMPLE
   Love Led The Way *CC10UL
      (Owens, Jimmy) SATB voc sc WORD 37606 $1.95
                                                  (M259)

MACPHERSON, CHARLES (1870-1927)
   Awake, My Soul
      2pt oct NOVELLO 33.0051.10 s.p.   (M260)

   Look On The Fields *Harv,anthem
      mix cor oct NOVELLO 28.0711.04 s.p.   (M261)

   Thou, O God, Art Praised In Sion
      2pt oct NOVELLO 33.0126.05 s.p.   (M262)

MC RAE
   Shepherds, Shake Off Your Drowsy Sleep
      SATB oct BELWIN 60804 $.35   (M263)

MC RAE, WILLIAM
   Noel Des Musiciens *Xmas
      SATB oct WALTON 2191 $.40   (M264)

   Psalm 96 *Gen
      SATB SCHMITT 867 $.45   (M265)

MAC ROBERTS
   Before Us, Lord, The Sacrament
      SATB oct LORENZ C174 $.25   (M266)

   Great Peace Have They
      SATB oct LORENZ C293 $.30   (M267)

   I Surrender All
      SATB oct LORENZ A424 $.25   (M268)

MCWHERTOR
   Born To Be King *Xmas
      SA/unis oct VOLKWEIN VB691 $.25   (M269)

   Christmas Eve *Xmas
      SA/unis oct VOLKWEIN VB129 $.25   (M270)

   Dear Little Baby Jesus *Xmas
      SA/unis oct VOLKWEIN VB141 $.25   (M271)

   Jesus Dear Shepherd
      SA/unis oct VOLKWEIN VB195 $.25   (M272)

   Little Prayer, Be On Your Way *prayer
      SA/unis oct VOLKWEIN VB207 $.25   (M273)

   Living Christ
      SA/unis oct VOLKWEIN VB208 $.25   (M274)

   Lord Hold My Hand A Little Tighter
      SA/unis oct VOLKWEIN VB703 $.25   (M275)

   Wasted On Me
      SA/unis oct VOLKWEIN VB275 $.25   (M276)

   Who Is This Man Of Galilee?
      SA/unis oct VOLKWEIN VB280 $.25   (M277)

MACY, J.C.
   Jerusalem *see Parker, Horatio William

MADDEN
   Our Eternal King
      SATB oct FISCHER,C CM-7725 $.25   (M278)

MADE WE MERRY see Wishart

MADER, CLARENCE
   Fifth Mystery Cantata, The *cant
      mix cor,soli,narrator,org (med diff) oct
      WESTERN WIM33 $2.00   (M279)

MADER, RUD (1859-1935)
   Psalm 92
      [Ger] mix cor,Mez solo,org HUG s.p.   (M280)

   Zum Bettag
      [Ger] mix cor,acap (easy) HUG   (M281)

MADONNA see Haubiel, Charles

MADONNA AND CHILD see Donato

MADRE, A LA PUERTA HAY UN NINO see Martin
   Pompey

MADRIGALE-BAND XXVIII see Palestrina, Giovanni

MADRIGALE-BAND XXIX see Palestrina, Giovanni

MADRIGALE FUR FRAUENCHOR see Borris, Siegfried

MADRIGALOK ES KANONOK *sac/sec,CC43L,madrigal
   (Paulovits, G.) [Hung] SATB (med diff)
   BUDAPEST contains sacred work by:
   Palestrina, Giovanni   (M282)

MADSDEN
   Go Ye Forth With My Word
      SSA WARNER W3596 $.35   (M283)

MADSEN, FLORENCE JEFFERSON
   Come, Come Ye Saints
      SSA oct BELWIN 2123 $.25   (M284)

   Come Ye Blessed Of My Father
      SSA oct BELWIN 1816 $.35   (M285)

   O Home Beloved, Where'er I Wander
      SSA/SSAA PIONEER 1007 $.25   (M286)

   Still, Still With Thee
      3pt wom cor,org/pno oct FABER 10381 $.35
                                                  (M287)

MAEKELBERGHE, AUGUST [R.] (1909-   )
   On December Twenty-Fifth *Xmas,cant
      SATB,pno,fl,drums,fing.cym. voc sc WORLD
      AC-1873-8 $1.25   (M288)

MAELAND, LARS
Min Sjel Lovherren *mot
[Norw] cor,org,opt strings LYCHE 40 s.p.
(M289)

MAESSEN, ANTOON (1919-)
Hymnus Caelestis Urbs Jerusalem *hymn
[Lat] mix cor,S solo,pno,4brass DONEMUS min
sc s.p., cor pts s.p., ipa (M290)

Te Saeculorum Principem *hymn
[Lat] mix cor,S solo,2clar,2bsn,2trp,3trom,
strings,timp DONEMUS min sc s.p., cor pts
s.p., voc sc s.p. (M291)

MAGALDI, VINCENZO
Messa Gesu Redentore
2 eq voices,org sc SANTIS 142 s.p., cor pts
SANTIS 143 s.p. (M292)

MAGANINI, QUINTO (1897-)
Cathedral At Sens, The
SSAATTBBB,vcl,orch oct MUSICUS 1035 $.60,
ipa (M293)

MAGDALEN, CEASE FROM SOBS see Hurford, Peter

MAGDALENA see Brahms, Johannes

MAGDALENE see Warren, George William

MAGGIO, GIUSEPPE
Lauda Sion
see Quattro Canti Eucaristici

Pange Lingua *Mass
see Quattro Canti Eucaristici
[Lat] unis sc ZANIBON 495 s.p., cor pts
ZANIBON 496 s.p. (M294)

Quattro Canti Eucaristici *Commun/Proces
[Lat] ATB&unis,org sc ZANIBON 439 s.p., cor
pts ZANIBON s.p.
contains: Lauda Sion; Pange Lingua;
Sacris Solemnis; Verbum Supernum (M295)

Sacris Solemnis
see Quattro Canti Eucaristici

Verbum Supernum
see Quattro Canti Eucaristici

MAGIC MORNING, THE see White, Michael

MAGIC OF CHRISTMAS, THE see Church, Darrell G.

MAGIC OF CHRISTMAS, THE see Wilson

MAGIN, CHARLES
Ave Verum Corpus
"Jesu, Word Of God Incarnate" [Lat/Eng]
SAB,org SCHIRM.EC 2283 $.16 (M296)

Jesu, Word Of God Incarnate *see Ave Verum
Corpus

MAGNE MARTYR ADRIANE see Willaert, Adrian

MAGNE, MICHEL
Halleluyah *spir,US
[Eng] SATB,acap HEUGEL s.p. (M297)

Sky, The *spir,US
[Eng] SATB,acap HEUGEL s.p. (M298)

MAGNIFICAT *BVM
(Geveart, F.-A.) "Cantique De La Sainte
Vierge" [Lat/Fr] 4pt mix cor,acap (easy)
cor pts LEMOINE s.p. see from Collection De
Choeurs, troisieme Fascicule (M299)

MAGNIFICAT see Albinoni, Tomaso

MAGNIFICAT see Andriessen, Hendrik

MAGNIFICAT see Andriessen, Juriaan

MAGNIFICAT see Anonymous

MAGNIFICAT see Bach, J.C.

MAGNIFICAT see Bach, Johann Sebastian

MAGNIFICAT see Bach, Karl Philipp Emanuel

MAGNIFICAT see Barbe, Helmut

MAGNIFICAT see Berger, Jean

MAGNIFICAT see Berkeley, Lennox

MAGNIFICAT see Brixi, Simon

MAGNIFICAT see Busser, [Henri-Paul]

MAGNIFICAT see Buxtehude, Dietrich

MAGNIFICAT see Carissimi, Giacomo

MAGNIFICAT see Castellazzi, Giuseppe

MAGNIFICAT see Cavalli, Francesco

MAGNIFICAT see Certon, [Pierre]

MAGNIFICAT see Charpentier, Marc-Antoine

MAGNIFICAT see Chihara, Paul

MAGNIFICAT see Comes, Juan Bautista

MAGNIFICAT see Crawford, John

MAGNIFICAT see Cruft, Adrian

MAGNIFICAT see Descarries, Auguste

MAGNIFICAT see Diener, Theodor

MAGNIFICAT see Duke

MAGNIFICAT see Durante

MAGNIFICAT see Durante, Francesco

MAGNIFICAT see Erbach, Christian

MAGNIFICAT see Fayrfax, Robert

MAGNIFICAT see Gabrieli, Andrea

MAGNIFICAT see Galuppi, Baldassare

MAGNIFICAT see Garbelotto, Antonio

MAGNIFICAT see Gardner, John [Linton]

MAGNIFICAT see Giorgi, Piero

MAGNIFICAT see Gipps, Ruth

MAGNIFICAT see Glarum, L. Stanley

MAGNIFICAT see Gletle, Johann Melchoir

MAGNIFICAT see Hankey, Mark

MAGNIFICAT see Haydn, (Franz) Joseph

MAGNIFICAT see Haydn, (Johann) Michael

MAGNIFICAT see Hofer, A.

MAGNIFICAT see Hovhaness, Alan

MAGNIFICAT see Johns

MAGNIFICAT see Krol, Bernhard

MAGNIFICAT see Lajtha, Laszlo

MAGNIFICAT see Langdon, Jonn

MAGNIFICAT see Leoncini, Lorenzo

MAGNIFICAT see Mariani, Eligio

MAGNIFICAT see Micheelsen, Hans Friedrich

MAGNIFICAT see Monnikendam, Marius

MAGNIFICAT see Monteverdi, Claudio

MAGNIFICAT see Mozart, Wolfgang Amadeus

MAGNIFICAT see Osterc, S.

MAGNIFICAT see Paccagnella, Erminegildo

MAGNIFICAT see Pachelbel

MAGNIFICAT see Pachelbel, Carl Theodorus

MAGNIFICAT see Pachelbel, Johann

MAGNIFICAT see Palestrina, Giovanni

MAGNIFICAT see Parsley, Osbert

MAGNIFICAT see Pearson

MAGNIFICAT see Peeters, Flor

MAGNIFICAT see Pergolesi, Giovanni Battista

MAGNIFICAT see Petrassi, Goffredo

MAGNIFICAT see Pinkham, Daniel

MAGNIFICAT see Porpora, Nicola Antonio

MAGNIFICAT see Purvis, Richard

MAGNIFICAT see Radomski, Mikolaj

MAGNIFICAT see Reichel, Bernard

MAGNIFICAT see Roe, Betty

MAGNIFICAT see Rohlig, Harald

MAGNIFICAT see Rozycki, (Jacek) Hyacinthus

MAGNIFICAT see Runback, Albert

MAGNIFICAT see Sammartini

MAGNIFICAT see Sammartini, Giovanni Battista

MAGNIFICAT see Saunders, Niel

MAGNIFICAT see Schmitt, Florent

MAGNIFICAT see Schubert, Franz (Peter)

MAGNIFICAT see Schutz, Heinrich

MAGNIFICAT see Schwartz, Gerhard von

MAGNIFICAT see Shaw, Gerald

MAGNIFICAT see Sigurbjornsson, Thorkell

MAGNIFICAT see Stevens, Halsey

MAGNIFICAT see Taverner, John

MAGNIFICAT see Vaughan Williams, Ralph

MAGNIFICAT see Verhey, A.B.B.

MAGNIFICAT see Vivaldi, Antonio

MAGNIFICAT see White, Robert

MAGNIFICAT see Winchester, E.C.

MAGNIFICAT see Wyton, Alec

MAGNIFICAT see Zacher, Gerd

MAGNIFICAT see Zebrowski, Marcin Jozf

MAGNIFICAT see Runback, Albert

MAGNIFICAT A SEI VOCI see Monteverdi, Claudio

MAGNIFICAT AND "ALL PRAISE TO JESUS' HALLOWED
NAME" see Bunjes, Paul G.

MAGNIFICAT AND NUNC DIMITIS see Kelley, B.

MAGNIFICAT AND NUNC DIMITIS see Winter, John

MAGNIFICAT AND NUNC DIMITTIS see Vaughan
Williams, Ralph

MAGNIFICAT AND NUNC DIMITTIS see Amner, John

MAGNIFICAT AND NUNC DIMITTIS see Andreas,
Carolus

MAGNIFICAT AND NUNC DIMITTIS see Arnold

MAGNIFICAT AND NUNC DIMITTIS see Arnold, Samuel

MAGNIFICAT AND NUNC DIMITTIS see Barr, J.

MAGNIFICAT AND NUNC DIMITTIS see Bernard, James

MAGNIFICAT AND NUNC DIMITTIS see Blow, John

MAGNIFICAT AND NUNC DIMITTIS see Brewer, Sir
Alfred Herbert

MAGNIFICAT AND NUNC DIMITTIS see Bunnett,
Edward

MAGNIFICAT AND NUNC DIMITTIS see Bush, Geoffrey

MAGNIFICAT AND NUNC DIMITTIS see Byrd, William

MAGNIFICAT AND NUNC DIMITTIS see Causton,
Thomas

MAGNIFICAT AND NUNC DIMITTIS see Chappell,
Herbert

MAGNIFICAT AND NUNC DIMITTIS see Cook, E.T.

MAGNIFICAT AND NUNC DIMITTIS see Cooke, Arnold

MAGNIFICAT AND NUNC DIMITTIS see Cooke,
[Benjamin]

MAGNIFICAT AND NUNC DIMITTIS see Davies, Henry
Walford

MAGNIFICAT AND NUNC DIMITTIS see Dickinson,
Peter

MAGNIFICAT AND NUNC DIMITTIS see Drakeford,
Richard

MAGNIFICAT AND NUNC DIMITTIS see Dyson, George

MAGNIFICAT AND NUNC DIMITTIS see Farrant,
Richard

MAGNIFICAT AND NUNC DIMITTIS see Gibbons,
Orlando

MAGNIFICAT AND NUNC DIMITTIS see Gibbs, Alan

MAGNIFICAT AND NUNC DIMITTIS see Harker,
Clifford

MAGNIFICAT AND NUNC DIMITTIS see Harris,
William Henry

MAGNIFICAT AND NUNC DIMITTIS see Harwood, Basil

MAGNIFICAT AND NUNC DIMITTIS see Holman, Derek

MAGNIFICAT AND NUNC DIMITTIS see Holmes, John

MAGNIFICAT AND NUNC DIMITTIS see Hopkins,
Anthony

MAGNIFICAT AND NUNC DIMITTIS see Howells,
Herbert Norman

MAGNIFICAT AND NUNC DIMITTIS see Hunt, J.E.

MAGNIFICAT AND NUNC DIMITTIS see Hurford, Peter

MAGNIFICAT AND NUNC DIMITTIS see Hyslop

MAGNIFICAT AND NUNC DIMITTIS see Ireland, John

MAGNIFICAT AND NUNC DIMITTIS see Jackson,
Francis

MAGNIFICAT AND NUNC DIMITTIS see Joubert, John

MAGNIFICAT AND NUNC DIMITTIS see Kelly, Bryan

MAGNIFICAT AND NUNC DIMITTIS see Keys, Ivor

MAGNIFICAT AND NUNC DIMITTIS see Kitson,
Charles Herbert

MAGNIFICAT AND NUNC DIMITTIS see Lang, C.S.

MAGNIFICAT AND NUNC DIMITTIS see Leighton,
Kenneth

MAGNIFICAT AND NUNC DIMITTIS see Mc Cabe, John

MAGNIFICAT AND NUNC DIMITTIS see Maunder, J.H.

MAGNIFICAT AND NUNC DIMITTIS see Morley, Thomas

MAGNIFICAT AND NUNC DIMITTIS see Murrill,
Herbert

MAGNIFICAT AND NUNC DIMITTIS see Naylor,
Bernard

MAGNIFICAT AND NUNC DIMITTIS see Nicholson,
S.H.

MAGNIFICAT AND NUNC DIMITTIS see Orr, Robin

MAGNIFICAT AND NUNC DIMITTIS see Parry, Charles
Hubert Hastings

MAGNIFICAT AND NUNC DIMITTIS see Patrick,
Nathaniel

MAGNIFICAT AND NUNC DIMITTIS see Purcell,
Daniel

MAGNIFICAT AND NUNC DIMITTIS see Purcell, Henry

MAGNIFICAT AND NUNC DIMITTIS see Robinson,
Christopher

MAGNIFICAT AND NUNC DIMITTIS see Rogers,
Benjamin

MAGNIFICAT AND NUNC DIMITTIS see Rose, Bernard

MAGNIFICAT AND NUNC DIMITTIS see Rubbra, Edmund

MAGNIFICAT AND NUNC DIMITTIS see Shaw, Geoffrey [Turton]

MAGNIFICAT AND NUNC DIMITTIS see Shaw, Martin

MAGNIFICAT AND NUNC DIMITTIS see Shepherd, John

MAGNIFICAT AND NUNC DIMITTIS see Sowerby, Leo

MAGNIFICAT AND NUNC DIMITTIS see Stanford, Charles Villiers

MAGNIFICAT AND NUNC DIMITTIS see Sumsion, Herbert

MAGNIFICAT AND NUNC DIMITTIS see Tallis, Thomas

MAGNIFICAT AND NUNC DIMITTIS see Thiman, Eric Harding

MAGNIFICAT AND NUNC DIMITTIS see Tippett, Michael

MAGNIFICAT AND NUNC DIMITTIS see Titcomb, Thomas

MAGNIFICAT AND NUNC DIMITTIS see Tomkins, Thomas

MAGNIFICAT AND NUNC DIMITTIS see Walmisley, Thomas Attwood

MAGNIFICAT AND NUNC DIMITTIS see Warren, Raymond

MAGNIFICAT AND NUNC DIMITTIS see Weelkes, Thomas

MAGNIFICAT AND NUNC DIMITTIS see Whettam, Graham

MAGNIFICAT AND NUNC DIMITTIS see Wills, Arthur

MAGNIFICAT AND NUNC DIMITTIS see Wise, Michael

MAGNIFICAT AND NUNC DIMITTIS see Wood, Charles

MAGNIFICAT AND NUNC DIMITTIS see Wood, John

MAGNIFICAT AND NUNC DIMITTIS (FERIAL) see Davies, Henry Walford

MAGNIFICAT AND NUNC DIMITTIS (FESTAL) see Davies, Henry Walford

MAGNIFICAT AND NUNC DIMITTIS IN A see Harris, William Henry

MAGNIFICAT AND NUNC DIMITTIS IN A see Sumsion, Herbert

MAGNIFICAT AND NUNC DIMITTIS IN A MINOR see Darke, Harold [Edwin]

MAGNIFICAT AND NUNC DIMITTIS IN C see Greene, Maurice

MAGNIFICAT AND NUNC DIMITTIS IN C see Jackson, Francis

MAGNIFICAT AND NUNC DIMITTIS IN D see Byrt, John C.

MAGNIFICAT AND NUNC DIMITTIS IN E see Hand, Colin

MAGNIFICAT AND NUNC DIMITTIS IN E FLAT see Willan, Healey

MAGNIFICAT AND NUNC DIMITTIS IN E MINOR see Statham, Heathcote (Dicken)

MAGNIFICAT AND NUNC DIMITTIS IN E MINOR see Vann, Stanley

MAGNIFICAT AND NUNC DIMITTIS IN F MINOR see Holman, Derek

MAGNIFICAT AND NUNC DIMITTIS MINOR see Ashfield, Robert

MAGNIFICAT AND NUNC DIMITTIS MINOR see Cockshott, Gerald Wilfred

MAGNIFICAT AND NUNC DIMITTIS see Tomkins, Thomas

MAGNIFICAT AND NUNC DIMITTIS see Tomkins, Thomas

MAGNIFICAT AND NUNC DIMITTIS see Tomkins, Thomas

MAGNIFICAT ANIMA MEA see Buxtehude, Dietrich

MAGNIFICAT ANIMA MEA see Pachelbel, Johann

MAGNIFICAT ANIMA MEA see Vene, Ruggero

MAGNIFICAT ANIMA MEA DOMINUM see Pergolesi, Giovanni Battista

MAGNIFICAT ANIMA MEA DOMINUM see Schutz, Heinrich

MAGNIFICAT C-DUR see Caldara, Antonio

MAGNIFICAT D-DUR see Bach, Johann Sebastian

MAGNIFICAT ES-DUR see Bach, Johann Sebastian

MAGNIFICAT I see Monteverdi, Claudio

MAGNIFICAT IN C see Sharpe, Evelyn

MAGNIFICAT IN C MAJOR see Thalben-Ball, George [Thomas]

MAGNIFICAT IN D see Bach, Johann Sebastian

MAGNIFICAT IN G see Charpentier, Marc-Antoine

MAGNIFICAT IN THE 8TH MODE see Dufay, Guillaume

MAGNIFICAT IN THE FOURTH MODE see Palestrina, Giovanni, Magnificat Nel Quatro Tono

MAGNIFICAT NEL QUATRO TONO see Palestrina, Giovanni

MAGNIFICAT NO. 1 see Lopez

MAGNIFICAT OCTAVI TONI see Lassus, Roland de (Orlandus)

MAGNIFICAT ON CHRISTMAS CAROLS *Xmas,carol/ Magnif
(Rubsamen) [Eng/Lat] SATB,acap oct LAWSON 51567 $.50   (M300)

MAGNIFICAT PEREGRINI TONI see Reda, Siegfried

MAGNIFICAT PRIMI TONI see Lassus, Roland de (Orlandus)

MAGNIFICAT PRIMI TONI see Lechner, Leonhard

MAGNIFICAT PRIMI TONI see Victoria, Tomas Luis de

MAGNIFICAT QUARTI TONI see Des Prez, Josquin

MAGNIFICAT QUARTI TONI see Lassus, Roland de (Orlandus)

MAGNIFICAT QUINTI TONI see La Rue, Pierre de

MAGNIFICAT QUINTI TONI see Lechner, Leonhard

MAGNIFICAT SEPTIMI TONI see Casciolini, Claudio

MAGNIFICAT SOLENNE see Arnaldi, Antonio

MAGNIFICAT SOLENNE see Volpi, Edoardo

MAGNIFICAT SUPER CHORALE MELOS GERMANICUM see Praetorius, Michael

MAGNIFICAT, THE see Bouman, Paul

MAGNIFICAT, THE see Brauer, James

MAGNIFICAT, THE see Bunjes, Paul G.

MAGNIFICAT, THE see Diemer, Emma Lou

MAGNIFICAT, THE see Grieb, Herbert [C.]

MAGNIFICAT, THE see Hillert, Richard

MAGNIFICAT, THE see Wienhorst, Richard

MAGNIFICAT (TONE 1, NO. 7) see Ripolles, Vincente

MAGNIFICAT (TONE 2, NO. 2) see Ripolles, Vincente

MAGNIFICAT (TONE 4, NO. 1) see Ripolles, Vincente

MAGNIFICAT (TONE 5, NO. 1) see Ripolles, Vincente

MAGNIFICAT (TONE 6) see Torres, Eduardo

MAGNIFICAT (TONE 7, NO. 5) see Torres, Eduardo

MAGNIFICAT UND NUNC DIMITTIS see Purcell, Henry

MAGNIFICAT VIII TONO see Visona', Gino

MAGNIFICAT see Runback, Albert

MAGNIFICATION OF THE NATIVITY see Michaelides, P.

MAGNIFICEMUS IN CANTICO, CONCERTO DE SANCTIS see Rozycki, (Jacek) Hyacinthus

MAGNIFY, GLORIFY see Root, G.F.

MAGNIFY HIM see Schutz, Heinrich, Meine Seele Erhebt Den Herren

MAGNIFY HIM see Schutz, Heinrich, Meine Seele Erhebt Den Herren

MAGNIFY THE LORD see Grieb, Herbert [C.], Magnificat, The

MAGNIFY THE LORD see Haydn, (Johann) Michael, Magnificat

MAGNIFY THE LORD see Tee

MAGNIFY THE LORD WITH ME see Mueller, Carl F.

MAGNUM NOMEN DOMINI see Dangel, Arthur

MAGNUM NOMEN DOMINI see Campbell

MAGNUM NOMEN DOMINI see Dangel, Arthur

MAGNUM NOMEN DOMINI see Pekiel, Bertlomiej

MAGNUM NOMEN DOMINI see Picchi, Luigi

MAGRI, PIETRO
A S. Giuseppe *CC2U,ASD
[Lat] cor,S solo,org ZANIBON 2719 s.p.
                                                    (M301)

Angelus Pastoribus
see Tre Canti Pel Natale

Ave Verum
see Due Mottetti Eucaristici

Benedictus
see In Triduo Sacro Maioris Hebdomadae

Christus Factus Est
see In Triduo Sacro Maioris Hebdomadae

Credo *Op.192 (from Missa Angelorum) Credo
[Lat] 1-2pt,org sc ZANIBON 2663 s.p. (M302)

Dies Irae Ac Libera *Op.36
see Magri, Pietro, Missa Defunctorum

Dixit Dominus *Op.194
[Lat] 3 eq voices,org ZANIBON 2644 s.p.
                                                    (M303)

Domine Ad Adjuvandum *Op.176
[Lat] 3pt mix cor,org ZANIBON 2711 s.p.
                                                    (M304)

Due Laudi A Gesu Sacr. *see Branchina, Pietro

MAGRI, PIETRO (cont'd.)

Due Mottetti Eucaristici *Commun
[Lat] 3 eq voices,acap ZANIBON 2776 s.p.
contains: Ave Verum; O Esca Viatorum
                                                    (M305)

Flos Carmeli
see QUATTRO CANTI ALLA MADONNA DEL CARMINE

I Pastori Alla Capanna *Op.50, Xmas
3-4pt mix cor,S solo ZANIBON 2669 s.p. (M306)

In Triduo Sacro Maioris Hebdomadae *Op.115, Easter/Holywk,mot
[Lat] 3-4 eq voices,acap ZANIBON 2946 s.p.
contains: Benedictus; Christus Factus Est; Miserere I; Miserere II (M307)

La Pastorella Del Popolo
see Tre Canti Pel Natale

La Sacra Famiglia Cantiamo *Op.232
[Lat] unis/2 eq voices,solo ZANIBON 2954 s.p.   (M308)

Le Tre Ore Di Agonia Di N.S.G.C. *Op.135, CC8U,Gd.Fri./Holywk
[Lat] eq voices&mix cor,soli sc ZANIBON 2587 s.p., cor pts ZANIBON 2587A s.p.
                                                    (M309)

Miserere *Op.27, Holywk
[Lat] ATB,org ZANIBON 2586 s.p.   (M310)

Miserere I
see In Triduo Sacro Maioris Hebdomadae

Miserere II
see In Triduo Sacro Maioris Hebdomadae

Missa Defunctorum *Op.36, Mass/Req
[Lat] MezBar,org sc ZANIBON 1650 s.p., voc pt ZANIBON 1650A-B s.p. contains also: Dies Irae Ac Libera (M311)

Missa Pro Defunctis *Op.112, Mass/Req
[Lat] 3pt/4pt sc ZANIBON 2636 s.p.   (M312)

O Esca Viatorum
see Due Mottetti Eucaristici

Responsoria In Matutinis Tridui Sacri
*Op.155, CCU,Easter
[Lat] 3-4 eq voices,acap ZANIBON 2670 s.p.
                                                    (M313)

Responsoria In Matutinis Tridui Sacri
*Op.156, CCU,Easter
[Lat] 3-4 eq voices,acap ZANIBON 2671 s.p.
                                                    (M314)

Salve Jesu Parvule
see Tre Canti Pel Natale

Salve Regina *Op.5, BVM
[Lat] unis mix cor,org ZANIBON 2650 s.p.
                                                    (M315)

Stabat Mater *Op.119, BVM
see QUATTRO STABAT MATER
[Lat] 2pt/3pt,org sc ZANIBON 2588 s.p.   (M316)

Strofette Per La Funzione Della Coroncina
Solenne Del Pr. Sangue *Op.127
[Lat] unis/2 eq voices,org ZANIBON 2618 s.p.   (M317)

Tre Canti Al SS. Cuore Di Gesu *Op.141, CC3U
[Lat] 2 eq voices,org ZANIBON 2649 s.p.
                                                    (M318)

Tre Canti Pel Natale *Xmas
ZANIBON 2672 s.p.
contains: Angelus Pastoribus (unis&3 eq voices); La Pastorella Del Popolo (unis&3 eq voices); Salve Jesu Parvule (4pt mix cor) (M319)

Veritas Mea *Op.125, ASD,Offer
[Lat] unis,org ZANIBON 2778 s.p.   (M320)

MAH TOVU see Gottlieb, J.

MAH TOVU see Roskin

MAH YOKOR CHASDECHO see Lewandowski, Louis

MAHLER, GUSTAV (1860-1911)
Thou Spirit Of Love Divine
(Chapman) jr cor/wom cor CURWEN 72686 s.p.
                                                    (M321)
(Chapman) mix cor CURWEN 61577 s.p. (M322)
(Chapman) unis jr cor/unis wom cor CURWEN 72686 s.p.   (M323)

MAHU, STEPHEN
Ein Feste Burg Ist Unser Gott *Fest
[Ger] SATBB,acap (med easy) MULLER K 1 s.p.
                                                    (M324)

MAIDEN, MOTHER OF OUR SAVIOR see Philips, Peter, Alma Redemptoris Mater

MAIER
Oh, Rejoice Ye Christians Loudly *Xmas
SATB SCHMITT 1752 $.30   (M325)

MAILLARD, JEAN
Helas, Mon Dieu, Ton Ire S'est Tournee *16th cent
(Honegger, Marc; Pidoux, Pierre) [Fr] SATB OUVRIERES EO 600 s.p.   (M326)

MAILLARD-VERGER, P.
Allons Ouir Sur Nos Tetes *Xmas
[Fr] 5pt mix cor,acap cor pts LEMOINE s.p.
                                                    (M327)
[Fr] 4pt mix cor LEMOINE s.p.   (M328)

Jacotin *Xmas
[Fr] cor LEMOINE s.p.   (M329)

Les Anges Dans Nos Campagnes *Xmas
[Fr] cor LEMOINE s.p.   (M330)
[Fr] mix cor,acap cor pts LEMOINE s.p.
                                                    (M331)

MAILMAN, [MARTIN] (1932-   )
Alleluia
SAB oct BELWIN 60296 $.30   (M332)

Concord Hymn *hymn
SATB oct BELWIN 60838 $.30   (M333)

MAINVILLE
Christmas Triptych, A
SSA FLAMMER B5146 $2.00   (M334)

Lord, Make Me An Instrument Of Thy Peace
SSA FLAMMER B 5015 $.30   (M335)
SATB FLAMMER A 5129 $.30   (M336)
SA/TB FLAMMER E5061 $.30   (M337)
(Gilbert) SAB FLAMMER D5076 $.25   (M338)

Welcome Song, A
SSAA,acap (med) oct WILLIS 5830 $.10 (M339)

MAITLAND, JOHN ALEXANDER FULLER
Green Grow The Rushes *carol
unis CRAMER 41 s.p.   (M340)

MAITRE PIERRE
Halleluja, Looft Den Heer
(Lucas, Jan) men cor sc ALSBACH&D s.p.
                                           (M341)
Looft God, Looft Zijn Naam (Psalm 150)
(Lucas, Jan) men cor sc ALSBACH&D s.p.
                                           (M342)
Psalm 150 *see Looft God, Looft Zijn Naam

MAJESTY see Billings, William

MAJOR, DOUGLAS
Two Songs For The Christ Child
unis,pno oct BERANDOL 910M7AA $.35   (M343)

MAKAROV
An Angel Said To Mary
(Williams, W.) SSATB,acap SCHIRM.EC 1203
$.25   (M344)

Angel Said To Mary, An
SSAA,acap SCHIRM.EC 1204 $.20   (M345)

MAKE A CHEERFUL NOISE UNTO GOD see Deering,
Richard, Jubilate Deo

MAKE A JOYFUL NOISE see Drischner, Max

MAKE A JOYFUL NOISE see Ehret, Walter

MAKE A JOYFUL NOISE see Zettervall, Howard

MAKE A JOYFUL NOISE
SSA,brass KJOS BR6099 $.50   (M346)

MAKE A JOYFUL NOISE see Bach, Johann Sebastian

MAKE A JOYFUL NOISE see Cain, Noble

MAKE A JOYFUL NOISE see Donato

MAKE A JOYFUL NOISE see Fetler, Paul

MAKE A JOYFUL NOISE see Ford, Virgil T.

MAKE A JOYFUL NOISE see Frackenpohl, Arthur

MAKE A JOYFUL NOISE see Freed, Isadore

MAKE A JOYFUL NOISE see Hopson

MAKE A JOYFUL NOISE see Hovhaness, Alan

MAKE A JOYFUL NOISE see Marshall

MAKE A JOYFUL NOISE see Muus

MAKE A JOYFUL NOISE see Orr, Robin

MAKE A JOYFUL NOISE see Simeone

MAKE A JOYFUL NOISE see Simper, Caleb

MAKE A JOYFUL NOISE see Smith

MAKE A JOYFUL NOISE see Thygerson

MAKE A JOYFUL NOISE see Watson, Merla

MAKE A JOYFUL NOISE see Young, Gordon

MAKE A JOYFUL NOISE UNTO GOD see Glarum, L.
Stanley

MAKE A JOYFUL NOISE UNTO GOD see Handel, George
Frideric

MAKE A JOYFUL NOISE UNTO GOD see Mead

MAKE A JOYFUL NOISE UNTO THE LORD see Couperin,
Francois

MAKE A JOYFUL NOISE UNTO THE LORD see De
Coursey

MAKE A JOYFUL NOISE UNTO THE LORD see Gaus

MAKE A JOYFUL NOISE UNTO THE LORD see
Gumpeltzhaimer, Adam

MAKE A JOYFUL NOISE UNTO THE LORD see Iversen

MAKE A JOYFUL NOISE UNTO THE LORD see Lekberg,
Sven

MAKE A JOYFUL NOISE UNTO THE LORD see Mathias,
William

MAKE A JOYFUL NOISE UNTO THE LORD see Mechem,
Kirke

MAKE A JOYFUL NOISE UNTO THE LORD see Myers,
Fheldon

MAKE A JOYFUL NOISE UNTO THE LORD see Roff,
Joseph

MAKE A JOYFUL NOISE UNTO THE LORD see Smart,
David

MAKE A JOYFUL NOISE UNTO THE LORD see Wyatt

MAKE A JOYFUL SOUND see Prentice, Fred

MAKE A JOYFUL SOUND! see Ramsfield

MAKE BROAD THE PATH see Roff, Joseph

MAKE HASTE see Hovhaness, Alan

MAKE HASTE, O GOD see Fritschel, James

MAKE HASTE, O GOD, TO DELIVER ME see Sacco

MAKE HASTE, O GOD, TO DELIVER ME see Wienhorst,
Richard

MAKE HIS PRAISE GLORIOUS see Hovhaness, Alan

MAKE IN ME A CLEAN HEART see Brahms, Johannes

MAKE IN ME, O LORD, A PURE HEART see Brahms,
Johannes

MAKE ME A BLESSING see Schuler

MAKE ME A CAPTIVE, O LORD see Butler

MAKE ME, O LORD see Brahms, Johannes

MAKE MY STEPS STEADFAST see Asola, Giovanni
Matteo

MAKE SOME SORT OF JOYFUL NOISE see Butler,
Eugene

MAKE THOU IN ME, GOD see Brahms, Johannes,
Schaffe In Mir, Gott

MAKE US HOLY THINE see York

MAKE US ONE see Christiansen, Paul

MAKE US TO KNOW AND UNDERSTAND see Morgan,
Haydn

MAKE WE JOY
see Musica Britannica Vol. 4: Set 5
see Three Early Christmas Carols

MAKE WE JOY see Cugley

MAKE WE JOY see Tamblyn, William

MAKE WE JOY IN THIS FEST see Ierley, Merritt

MAKE WE JOY NOW see Brown

MAKE WE JOY NOW IN THIS FEAST see Emery, John

MAKE WE JOY NOW IN THIS FEST *carol
unis/SATB (easy) OXFORD 08.019 $.15   (M347)

MAKE WE JOY NOW IN THIS FEST see Tamblyn,
William

MAKE WE JOY NOW IN THIS FEST see Walton

MAKE WE JOYE NOWE IN THIS FEST see Kubik, Gail

MAKE WE NOW JOY IN THIS FEST see Schalk, Carl

MAKE YE A JOYFUL NOISE (Psalm 100) Bibl
(Brandon, George) SAB,org oct WORLD
ESA-1859-7 $.45   (M348)

MAKE YE A JOYFUL NOISE UNTO GOD see Scheidt,
Samuel

MAKE YE MERRY FOR HIM THAT IS COME see
Musgrave, Thea

MAKE YE MERRY FOR HIM THAT IS COME see Van
Wormer, G.

MAKER
Awake, Thou That Sleepest *Easter/Lent
SATB oct FISCHER,C CM-280 $.25   (M349)

Beneath The Cross Of Jesus
(Whitman) SATB oct LILLENAS AN-2211 $.25
                                           (M350)
Christ Is Risen! Alleluia! *anthem
(Wetzler) SATB&jr cor,opt trp (easy) oct
AUGSBURG 1305 $.30   (M351)

Dear Lord And Father Of Mankind
(Larson) SATB oct PRO ART 1139 $.25   (M352)

Mothers Everywhere
SA/SAB oct LORENZ 7828 $.25   (M353)

MAKER, [FREDERICK CHARLES] (1884-1927)
Arise, Shine *Xmas,Bibl
4pt mix cor,T solo oct SCHIRM.G 3926 $.30
                                           (M354)
Awake Thou That Sleepest *Easter,Bibl
SATB oct PRESSER 312-06022 $.35   (M355)
4pt mix cor,SB soli oct SCHIRM.G 3952 $.25
                                           (M356)
Christ Is Risen! Alleluia! *anthem
(Wetzler) unis treb cor&SATB,opt trp (easy)
oct AUGSBURG 1305 $.30   (M357)

Dear Lord And Father Of Mankind *Gen,anthem/
hymn
(Kiser, Max) SATB FOSTER MF105 $.20   (M358)
(Noble) SATB oct SPRATT 562 $.25   (M359)
(Olds) SATB SCHMITT 1870 $.30   (M360)
(Peery, R.) SAB oct PRESSER 312-40427 $.25
                                           (M361)
MAKER OF ALL THE EARTH see Kechley, [Gerald]

MAKI
How We Long For Christmas *Xmas
(Woolf) SSA ALFRED 6210 $.30   (M362)

MALAN
Take My Life And Let It Be *hymn
(Moore) SSATTB oct LILLENAS AN-2370 $.30
                                           (M363)

MALEINGREAU, PAUL DE (1887-1956)
Mass For Four Mixed Voices *Commun
SATB,acap SCHIRM.EC 1265   (M364)

Mass For Three Mixed Voices *Commun
SAB SCHIRM.EC 1266   (M365)

MALIN
Carol Of The Birds *Xmas,carol
SATB oct GALAXY 1.1458.1 $.30   (M366)
SSAA oct GALAXY 1.0922.1 $.30   (M367)

Let The Song Be Begun *see Piae Cantiones

Piae Cantiones
"Let The Song Be Begun" SATB,org,3trp MARKS
4432 $.30, ipa   (M368)
"Let The Song Be Begun" SSA,3trp MARKS 4497

MALIN (cont'd.)
$.30, ipa   (M369)

Psalm 100 *see Ye Servants Of God

To God With Heart And Voice
SATB oct BELWIN 64237 $.30   (M370)

Ye Servants Of God (Psalm 100)
SATB&treb cor oct BELWIN 64234 $.25   (M371)

MALIN, DON (1896-)
At The Name Of Jesus
SAB oct BELWIN 64313 $.30   (M372)

Babe Is Born, A *Xmas
SATB WARNER R3474 $.30   (M373)

Children Sang Their Praises, The
SATB&treb cor oct BELWIN 64282 $.25   (M374)

Come And Adore *Xmas
SATB,acap WARNER W2873 $.30   (M375)

Voices Of Worship
jr cor BELWIN $1.25   (M376)

MALIPIERO, GIAN FRANCESCO (1882-1973)
I Sette Peccati Mortali
mix cor,orgi voc sc ZERBONI 4129 s.p. (M377)

Missa Pro Mortuis *Mass
mix cor,Bar solo,orch voc sc ZERBONI 3605
s.p., ipr   (M378)
Santa Eufrosina
mix cor,SBarBar soli,orch voc sc ZERBONI
4054 s.p., ipr   (M379)

MALIPIERO, RICCARDO (1914-)
Cantata Di Natale *Xmas,cant
mix cor,S solo,orch voc sc ZERBONI 5662
s.p., ipr   (M380)

Cantata Sacra *cant
[Lat] SATB,S solo,orch sc SCHOTT AV83 s.p.,
ipr   (M381)

MALLOCH, J. DAVID
Christmas Chimes *Xmas
SATB (med) ABINGDON APM-739 $.30   (M382)

MALMFORS, AKE
Ordet Vordet Kott
"Verbum Caro Factum Est" [Lat/Swed] SATB,
acap GEHRMANS KRB 255   (M383)

Te Deum *Bibl/Psalm
mix cor,org voc sc NORDISKA s.p., cor pts
NORDISKA 3508 s.p.   (M384)

Verbum Caro Factum Est *see Ordet Vordet
Kott

MALMIN, DOROTHY
Songs And Hymns For Treble Voices (composed
with Malmin, Gunnar) *CC36U,hymn
2-3pt jr cor,acap,pno oct AUGSBURG 11-9426
$1.00   (M385)

Songs Of Devotion (composed with Malmin,
Gunnar) *CC22L,anthem
SA,opt pno (easy) oct AUGSBURG 11-9447
$1.50   (M386)

MALMIN, GUNNAR
Songs And Hymns For Treble Voices *see
Malmin, Dorothy

Songs Of Devotion *see Malmin, Dorothy

Thy Praises Sing
SSA,opt inst (easy) oct AUGSBURG
11-9496 $1.00   (M387)

MALOTTE
Lord's Prayer, The *Bibl/prayer
SATB ALLANS 170 s.p.   (M388)
(Dies, Carl) TB ALLANS 171 s.p.   (M389)
(Dies, Carl) SA ALLANS 340 s.p.   (M390)

MALOTTE, ALBERT HAY (1895-)
And Have Not Charity *Bibl
3pt wom cor,high solo/low solo&narrator oct
SCHIRM.G 10283 $.25   (M391)

Beatitudes, The *Bibl
(Treharne) 4pt mix cor oct SCHIRM.G 8400
$.25   (M392)

Faith
3pt men cor oct SCHIRM.G 10895 $.20   (M393)
4pt mix cor oct SCHIRM.G 10887 $.20   (M394)

Lord's Prayer, The *see Pater Noster

Pater Noster *Bibl
"Lord's Prayer, The" 4pt wom cor,acap oct
SCHIRM.G 8968 $.30   (M395)
(Deis) "Lord's Prayer, The" 4pt mix cor oct
SCHIRM.G 10626 $.25   (M396)
(Deis) "Lord's Prayer, The" 4pt mix cor,org
oct SCHIRM.G 7943 $.30   (M397)
(Deis) "Lord's Prayer, The" 4pt mix cor oct
SCHIRM.G 7988 $.25   (M398)
(Deis) "Lord's Prayer, The" 4pt mix cor,
high solo,acap oct SCHIRM.G 8685 $.25
                                           (M399)
(Deis) "Lord's Prayer, The" 3pt wom cor oct
SCHIRM.G 7987 $.25   (M400)
(Deis) "Lord's Prayer, The" 3pt wom cor,S
solo oct SCHIRM.G 9634 $.25   (M401)
(Deis) "Lord's Prayer, The" 2pt,org/pno oct
SCHIRM.G 10094 $.30   (M402)
(Deis) "Lord's Prayer, The" jr cor&sr cor,
org/pno oct SCHIRM.G 9896 $.25   (M403)
(Deis) "Lord's Prayer, The" 4pt mix cor oct
SCHIRM.G 9762 $.20   (M404)
(Downing) "Lord's Prayer, The" 2pt wom cor
oct SCHIRM.G 8743 $.30   (M405)
(Downing) "Lord's Prayer, The" 3pt mix cor
oct SCHIRM.G 9264 $.30   (M406)
(Ducrest; Weinrich) "Lord's Prayer, The"
[Lat] 4pt mix cor,T solo,org oct SCHIRM.G
8647 $.25   (M407)
(Duro) "Lord's Prayer, The" SSATB oct
SCHIRM.G 10223 $.25   (M408)
(Pfeiffer) "Lord's Prayer, The" 4pt mix

MALOTTE, ALBERT HAY (cont'd.)

    cor,acap (easy) oct SCHIRM.G 10518 $.30
    (M409)

    (Stickles) "Lord's Prayer, The" 4pt mix
    cor,org oct SCHIRM.G 10734 $.30   (M410)

    Psalm 23 *Bibl
    mix cor,Bar solo oct SCHIRM.G 8696 $.35
    (M411)
    (Downing) 4pt men cor oct SCHIRM.G 9612
    $.30   (M412)
    (Downing) 3pt wom cor oct SCHIRM.G 9471
    $.35   (M413)
    (Downing) 2pt wom cor oct SCHIRM.G 9470
    $.30   (M414)
    (Gilbert) mix cor,Mez solo oct SCHIRM.G
    8325 $.30   (M415)

MALTZEFF, A.
    Praise The Name Of The Lord
    SATB oct PRESSER 332-40048 $.30   (M416)

    This Day Is The Day Which The Lord Hath Made
    *Easter
    SATB,acap oct PRESSER 312-40287 $.30 (M417)

MALTZMAN
    Boy Who Wanted Two Drumsticks, The *see
    Longman

    No Room At The Inn (composed with Longman)
    SAB oct PRO ART 2074 $.25   (M418)

MAN ALIVE see Wilson, John F.

MAN AND HIS WORLD see Hughes

MAN, BE FROM GOD REBORN see Silesius, Angelus,
    Mensch, Werd Aus Gott Geborn

MAN BETET, HERR, IN ZIONS STILLE see
    Mareschall, Samuel

MAN BORN OF A WOMAN, A see Bach, Johann
    Christoph

MAN BORN TO TOIL see Holst, Gustav

MAN DREAM NO MORE see Peerson, Martin

MAN OF GALILEE see Procter

MAN OF LIFE, THE see Goehr, Alexander

MAN OF LIFE UPRIGHT, A see Hunt, Reginald

MAN OF NAZARETH, THE see Rogers, J.H.

MAN OF SORROWS see Pooler, Frank

MAN OF SORROWS see Thompson

MAN ON THE CROSS, THE see Martin

MAN SHALL NOT LIVE BY BREAD ALONE see Gardner

MAN SINGET MIT FREUDEN see Bach, Johann
    Sebastian

MAN SINGET MIT FREUDEN see Bach, Johann
    Sebastian, Man Singet Mit Freuden Vom Sieg

MAN SINGET MIT FREUDEN VOM SIEG see Bach,
    Johann Sebastian

MAN SINGET MIT FREUDEN VOM SIEG see Buxtehude,
    Dietrich

MAN SINGT MIT FREUDEN see Neubert, Gottfried

MAN SINGT MIT FREUDEN VOM SIEG see Kraft,
    Walter

MAN SINGT MIT FREUDEN VOM SIEG see Weinreich,
    Waltraut

MAN THAT IS BORN OF A WOMAN see Boyd, Jack

MAN THAT IS BORN OF WOMAN see Purcell, Henry

MAN, THE see Carmichael, Ralph

MANCHE MEINEN, DU HAST DICH ZUR RUHE GESETZT
    see Kameke, Ernst-Ulrich von

MANCHICOURT, PIERRE DE (1510-1586)
    Collected Works Vol. I *CCU
    (Wicks, John D.) cor AM.INST.MUS. $28.50
    The Attaingnant Motets   (M419)

    Thesauri Musici, Heft 9: Missa "Deus In
    Adiutorium" *Mass,Renais
    (Pass, Walter) 4pt mix cor cmplt ed
    DOBLINGER s.p.   (M420)

MANCHMAL see Bossler, Kurt

MANCHMAL see Kukuck, Felicitas

MANCHMAL DENK ICH: ES GIBT KEINE WEIHNACHT FUR
    MICH see Schneider, Martin Gotthard

MANCHMAL KENNEN WIR GOTTES WILLEN see
    Schweizer, Rolf

MANCINELLI, A.
    Isaias *ora
    (Vecchi, Prof. Giuseppe) [Lat] cor oct
    FORNI 285 s.p.   (M421)

MANCINI, VINCENZO
    Alleluia!
    see Mancini, Vincenzo, "Quid Retribuam"

    Pianto Di Maria Vergine
    cor,S solo,pno SANTIS 1011 s.p.   (M422)

    "Quid Retribuam"
    4-5pt mix cor SANTIS 879 s.p. contains
    also: Alleluia!   (M423)

    Salve Regina
    cor,T solo,org SANTIS 907 s.p.   (M424)

    San Francesco D'Assisi Nel Suo Felice
    Transito
    4-5pt mix cor,org SANTIS 1027 s.p.   (M425)

MANCINI, VINCENZO (cont'd.)

    Via Crucis E Adoremus Te Christi
    cor,soli,org SANTIS 819 s.p.   (M426)

MANCINUS, THOMAS (1550-1612)
    Celler Passion 1637 Nach Dem Evangelisten
    Matthaus *Psntd,evang
    (Schmidt, Fritz) [Ger] SATB,soli,acap (med)
    BAREN. BA 266 sc $3.50, cor pts $.65 (M427)

MANDATUM NOVUM see Foss, Julius

MANGER, THE see Jarret, Jack M.

MANGER CAROL *Xmas,carol
    (Sowerbry, Leo) unis oct GRAY GCMR 2419 $.25
    (M428)

MANGER CAROL see Kinsman

MANGER CAROL, A see Burnham

MANGER CAROL, A see Burnham, Cardon

MANGER CAROL, A see Jewell, Kenneth W.

MANGER CAROL, A see Purvis, Richard

MANGER CRIB, THE see Noble, Thomas Tertius

MANGER HOLDS AN INFANT PURE, A *Xmas
    SATB oct PRO ART 1979 $.22   (M429)
    SSA oct PRO ART 2106 $.25   (M430)

MANGER KING, THE see Johnston

MANGER LULLABY A see Brown, J.

MANGER PRINCE see Stairs, L.

MANGER SONG see Frederickson, Carl

MANGER SONG see Hannahs, R.C., Dormi Jesu

MANGER STORY, THE see Bock, Fred

MANGINOT BETH EL see Kaufman, H.H.

MANGINOT SHABBAT see Bugatch, Samuel

MANGON, JOHANNES
    Ave Maria
    (Richardson) SATB oct WORD CS-688 $.25
    (M431)

MANGONE, GIOACCHINO
    Ave Maria
    see CINQUE AVE MARIA
    ST,org CURCI 3865 s.p.   (M432)

    Cor Jesu
    see TRIA COR JESU

    Inno A S. Cecilia *ASD,hymn
    [Lat] 2 eq voices,org ZANIBON 2772 s.p.
    (M433)
    Le Tre Ore Di Agonia Di N. S. Gesu' Cristo
    2 eq voices,org CURCI 3877 s.p.   (M434)

    Messa In Onore Del SS. Cuore Di Gesu *Mass
    SAB/STB,org CURCI 3876 s.p.   (M435)

    Missa In Honorem S. Caeciliae *Mass
    2 eq voices,org CURCI 2922 s.p.   (M436)

    Missa Pro Defunctis *Mass
    cor,med solo,org CURCI 3872 s.p.   (M437)

    Sei Composizioni Sacre *CC6U
    2 eq voices,org CURCI 3864 s.p.   (M438)

MANHIRE, WILSON
    Christmas Song, A *Xmas,carol
    unis CRAMER 38 s.p.   (M439)

    O'er Bethlehem Manger *carol
    unis CRAMER 37 s.p.   (M440)

MANICKE, DIETRICH (1923-   )
    Cantate Domino Canticum Novum (Psalm 98) cant
    [Ger] 4pt mix cor,acap cor pts BAREN.
    EM 467 s.p.   (M441)

    Dic Nobis Maria, Quid Vidisti In Via?
    *Easter
    [Lat] 4pt mix cor,acap (sequentia
    paschalis) cor pts BAREN. EM 466 s.p.
    (M442)
    Domine, Non Secundum Peccata Nostra *Psntd
    [Lat] 4pt mix cor,acap (tract for ash
    wednesday) cor pts BAREN. EM 465 s.p.
    (M443)
    Jesu Einzug In Jerusalem *Psntd,Bibl/evang/
    mot
    [Ger] 4-5pt mix cor,acap cor pts BAREN.
    EM 213 s.p.   (M444)

    Psalm 98 *see Cantate Domino Canticum Novum

MANIFESTATIO CHRISTI see Beyer, Frank Michael

MANN, [ARTHUR HENRY] (1850-1929)
    O Jesus, I Have Promised *hymn
    (Smith) SATB oct LILLENAS AN-2354 $.30
    (M445)

    O Saviour, Precious Saviour
    (Kinsman) SATB oct PRO ART 2439 $.25 (M446)

MANNEY, CHARLES FONTEYN (1872-1951)
    Resurrection
    SATB PRESSER $1.25   (M447)

MANNING
    Christmas Is A Birthday *Xmas
    (Deutsch) SSA oct PLYMOUTH PCS-215 $.35
    (M448)
    (Deutsch) 2pt oct PLYMOUTH PCS-529 $.35
    (M449)
    (Deutsch) SATB oct PLYMOUTH PCS-74 $.35
    (M450)

MANNINO, F.
    Domenica Di Pentecoste *Pent
    cor,org CURCI 9492 s.p.   (M451)

    La Stirpe Di Davide
    mix cor,soli,orch CURCI 7655 s.p.   (M452)

MAN'S PRAISE see Sanders, Robert L.

MAN'S REDEMPTION see Headington, Christopher

MANSFIELD, PURCELL JAMES (1889-1968)
    Gospel Train, The *spir
    unis ASHDOWN U.55 s.p.   (M453)

MANSION OVER THE HILLTOP
    see Great Choral Series
    SATB/TTBB BIG3 $.25   (M454)

MANTON, ROBERT W.
    Earth Has Grown Old, The
    SATB,acap oct LAWSON 51369 $.30   (M455)

MANY HUNDRED YEARS AGO *Xmas,carol,Fr
    (Ehret, W.) SSA,2clar (med easy) oct
    CONCORDIA 98-1910 $.35   (M456)

MANY MOODS OF CHRISTMAS, THE, SUITE ONE *Xmas,
    carol
    (Shaw, Robert; Bennett, Robert) mix cor,orch/
    pno oct LAWSON $1.00
    contains: Good Christian Men Rejoice; O
    Come, All Ye Faithful; Patapan; Silent
    Night   (M457)

MANY MOODS OF CHRISTMAS, THE, SUITE TWO *Xmas,
    carol
    (Shaw, Robert; Bennett, Robert) mix cor,orch/
    pno oct LAWSON $1.00
    contains: Away In A Manger; Fum, Fum, Fum;
    Joy To The World; March Of The Kings; O
    Sanctissima   (M458)

MANY MOODS OF CHRISTMAS, THE, SUITE THREE
    *Xmas,carol
    (Shaw, Robert; Bennett, Robert) mix cor,orch/
    pno oct LAWSON $1.00
    contains: Angels We Have Heard On High;
    Bring A Torch, Jeanette Isabella;
    Hark! The Herald Angels Sing; What Child
    Is This?   (M459)

MANY MOODS OF CHRISTMAS, THE, SUITE FOUR
    *Xmas,carol
    (Shaw, Robert; Bennett, Robert) mix cor,orch/
    pno oct LAWSON $1.00
    contains: Break Forth, O Beauteous Heavenly
    Light; Deck The Halls With Boughs Of
    Holly; First Nowell, The; I Saw Three
    Ships; O Little Town Of Bethlehem   (M460)

MANY SHALL COME FROM THE EAST AND WEST see
    Bender, Jan

MANY SHALL COME FROM THE EAST AND WEST see
    Schutz, Heinrich, Viel Werden Kommen Von
    Morgen Und Von Abend

MANY YEARS AGO *Xmas,carol,Pol
    (Ehret, Walter) SA,opt ob FRANK F-609 $.35
    (M461)
    (Ehret, Walter) SSA,opt ob FRANK F-678 $.35
    (M462)
    (Ehret, Walter) SAB,opt ob FRANK F-677 $.35
    (M463)

MANY YEARS AGO see Sharpe, Evelyn

MANZ
    E'en So, Lord Jesus, Quickly Come
    mix cor SOUTHERN $.25   (M464)

MANZ, PAUL
    E'en So, Lord Jesus, Quickly Come *Adv/Gen
    SATB,kbd (med diff) oct CONCORDIA 98-1054
    $.25   (M465)
    SA,kbd (med diff) oct CONCORDIA 98-2037
    $.25   (M466)
    SSA,kbd (med diff) oct CONCORDIA 98-2036
    $.25   (M467)
    TTBB (med diff) oct CONCORDIA 98-2038 $.25
    (M468)

    I Caused Thy Grief *anthem
    SATB (med) oct AUGSBURG 1153 $.25   (M469)

    Lord Reigneth, The *anthem
    SATB (med) oct AUGSBURG 1372 $.25   (M470)

    Preserve Me, O Lord *anthem
    SATB (med diff) oct AUGSBURG 1228 $.20
    (M471)
    Psalm 130
    SATB oct SUMMY 1547 $.35   (M472)

MANZIARLY DE
    Adoration Of The Shepherds *see L'Adoration
    Des Bergers

    L'Adoration Des Bergers
    "Adoration Of The Shepherds" [Eng/Fr] SSA,
    pno oct SALABERT-US $.35   (M473)

MANZONI REQUIEM see Verdi, Giuseppe

MARANATHA, UNSER HERR KOMMT see Wunderlich,
    Heinz

MARANO
    Psalm 117
    SATB FLAMMER A 5598 $.30   (M474)

MARC, E.
    La Vie Et L'assomption De La Sainte- Vierge
    *BVM,ora
    mix cor,acap LEMOINE s.p.   (M475)

MARCELLO
    Father Of Glory
    SS oct SUMMY M 2897 $.30   (M476)

    Give Ear Unto Me
    girl cor SOUTHERN $.30   (M477)
    2pt ASHDOWN E.A.296 s.p.   (M478)
    (Ehret) SATB oct VOLKWEIN VB153 $.30 (M479)

    Give Ear Unto My Prayer
    (Novello) SS oct GRAY GCMR 1522 $.30 (M480)

    Heart's Adoration *anthem
    SA oct OXFORD 44.233 $.30   (M481)

    Heavens Declare, The *see I Cieli Immensi

    Heavens Declare The Glory Of God, The
    (McAfee) SATB oct BOURNE 835 $.35   (M482)

MARCELLO (cont'd.)

I Cieli Immensi (Psalm 18)
(Peloquin) "Heavens Declare, The" SATB,T
solo oct SUMMY M 2463 $.50   (M483)

Psalm 18   *see I Cieli Immensi

MARCELLO, BENEDETTO (1686-1739)
And With Songs I Will Celebrate *Gen
SA/TB,kbd (med easy) oct CONCORDIA 98-1047
$.30   (M484)

As The Hart Panteth
2pt oct NOVELLO 33.0045.05 s.p.   (M485)

As The Heart Panteth *Easter/Lent
SS oct GRAY GCMR 3091 $.25   (M486)

Give Ear Unto Me
2pt oct NOVELLO 48.0467.08 s.p.   (M487)

O Lord, Deliver Me *Gen
SA/TB,kbd (med easy) oct CONCORDIA 98-1044
$.25   (M488)

O Lord, Our Governor *Gen
unis,kbd (med easy) oct CONCORDIA 98-1045
$.30   (M489)

Oh, Hold Thou Me Up *Gen
SA/TB,kbd (med easy) oct CONCORDIA 98-1046
$.30   (M490)

Psalm 18   *see Salmo XVIII

Psalm 19
(Adler, H. Ch.) SATB TRANSCON. TCL 117
$.50, ipa   (M491)

Salmo XVIII (Psalm 18)
(Padovano) SATB,pno/org/cont s.p. sc
ZANIBON 5308, cor pts ZANIBON 5309, cor
pts ZANIBON 5310   (M492)

Thou, O Lord, Art My Shepherd *Easter/Gen
SA,kbd (easy) oct CONCORDIA 98-1851 s.p.
                  (M493)

MARCH AND CHORUS see Franck, Cesar, Marche Et
Choeur

MARCH OF THE KINGS *Xmas,carol,Fr
see Many Moods Of Christmas, The, Suite Two
(Cain) [Eng/Fr] 3pt mix cor oct SCHIRM.G
10943 $.30   (M494)
(Cain) [Eng/Fr] SATB oct SCHIRM.G 10769 $.30
                  (M495)
(Shaw; Parker) [Eng/Fr] 4pt men cor,acap oct
SCHIRM.G 10190 $.25   (M496)

MARCH OF THE KINGS see Cain, Noble, Marche Des
Rois

MARCH OF THE THREE KINGS *Xmas
(Ramsfield) SATB oct PRO ART 2667 $.30 (M497)

MARCH OF THE THREE KINGS see Bizet, Georges

MARCH OF THE THREE KINGS see Ramsfield

MARCH OF THE WISE MEN see Gaul, Harvey Bartlet

MARCH ON, O CHURCH TRIUMPHANT see Buck

MARCH ON, O SOUL, WITH STRENGTH see Darst, W.
Glenn

MARCH ON WITH CHRIST see Hughes

MARCH TO CALVARY, THE see Maunder, J.H.

MARCH TRIUMPHAL THUNDERS, THE see Elgar, Edward

MARCHANT, ARTHUR W.
Great Is The Lord *Harv,anthem
mix cor oct NOVELLO 28.0708.04 s.p.   (M498)

MARCHANT, STANLEY R. (1883-1949)
Judge Eternal *anthem
mix cor oct NOVELLO 28.1205.03 s.p.   (M499)

Te Deum *Te Deum
SATB (G maj) oct NOVELLO 44.1200.01 s.p.
                  (M500)

MARCHE DANS JERUSALEM see Walk In Jerusalem
Jus' Like John

MARCHE DES ROIS see Cain, Noble

MARCHE ET CHOEUR see Franck, Cesar

MARCHING FORWARD *CC24L,Xmas/Easter/Gen/Thanks
(Harris) unis jr cor/2pt jr cor PRO ART 346
$.85   (M501)

MARCHING SAINTS, THE see Thygerson

MARCKHL, ERICH
Lobet Den Herrn *mot
4pt mix cor MOSELER s.p.   (M502)

Requiem *Req
mix cor,4 soli,fl,2clar,2ob,2bsn,2trp,
2trom,vln,vla,vcl,bvl,perc MOSELER sc
rental, cor pts rental, ipr   (M503)

MARCUS, SISTER MARY
Crusader's Song
SATB,acap (easy) oct WILLIS 6598 $.20
                  (M504)
SA,pno (easy) oct WILLIS 6591 $.15   (M505)

MARENZIO, LUCA (1553-1599)
Aerens Konge God *see O Rex Gloriae

Born Today *Renais
(Ehret, Walter) SATB,acap PEER $.40 (M506)

Caecilliam Cantata *cant
mix cor,acap voc sc KALMUS 6296 $1.75 (M507)

Cantava La Piu Vaga Pastorella
[It/Eng] SSATB BROUDE,A. 180 $.35   (M508)

Cantibus Organis *Gen
[Ger] SATB,acap (med easy) MULLER MS 36
s.p.   (M509)

MARENZIO, LUCA (cont'd.)

Christ Is Born Today *see Hodie Christus
Natus Est

Conceptio Tua *Xmas/Fest,mot
[Lat] SATB,acap (med) MULLER M 45 s.p. (M510)
[Lat] mix cor,acap oct NOVELLO DM-45 s.p.
                  (M511)

Giovane Donna
(Arnold, Denis) SAATTB oct PENN STATE
0-271-73116-8 $4.25   (M512)

Hodie Christus Natus Est *Xmas
"Christ Is Born Today" SATB,acap (med diff)
oct CONCORDIA 98-1810 $.30   (M513)
"Today Is Born The King Of Heaven" SATB,
acap SCHIRM.EC 1267   (M514)
(David, H.) SATB/SAAB,acap oct PRESSER
352-00050 $.30   (M515)
(Thomas) mix cor SOUTHERN $.30   (M516)

Hodie Paulus Apostolus *Fest,mot
[Lat] SATB,acap (med) MULLER M 39 s.p. (M517)
[Lat] mix cor,acap oct NOVELLO DM-39 s.p.
                  (M518)

Io Piango
(Lynn, G.) SATB oct PRESSER 312-40369 $.30
                  (M519)

King All Glorious *see O Rex Gloriae

Loquebantus Variis Linguis *Whitsun,mot
[Lat] mix cor,acap oct NOVELLO DM-22 s.p.
                  (M520)

Non Fu Mai Cervo *Gen,madrigal
(Lipphardt, Walther) [It] SATTT,acap (med
diff) BAREN. BA 4390 $2.75   (M521)

O King, Glorious *see O Rex Gloriae

O King Of Glory *see O Rex Gloriae

O Quam Gloriosum *ASD/ECY,mot
[Ger] SATB,acap (med) MULLER M 43 s.p.
                  (M522)
SATB,acap SCHIRM.EC $.30   (M523)
[Lat] mix cor,acap oct NOVELLO DM-43 s.p.
                  (M524)
(Collins, H.B.) [Lat] SATB CHESTER s.p. (M525)

O Rex Gloriae *mot
(Bridge, Sir Fredk.) "O King Of Glory" SATB
BOSWORTH s.p.   (M526)
(Greyson) "O King, Glorious" SATB oct
BOURNE ES80 $.25   (M527)
(Martens, Mason) "King All Glorious" SATB
oct WALTON 2169 $.30   (M528)
(Sorenson, Soren) "Aerens Konge God" [Lat/
Dan] SATB,acap HANSEN-DEN 286 s.p. see
also MOTETTER OG LAUDER FRA DET 16.
ARHUNDREDE   (M529)
(Wyton) "O King Of Glory" SATB oct FISCHER,
C CM-7692 $.25   (M530)

O, Sacred Communion *see O, Sacrum Convivium

O, Sacrum Convivium
(Payson, A.) "O, Sacred Communion" SATB,
acap FRANK F-570 $.30   (M531)

O Sacrum Covivium
SATB,acap oct PRESSER 352-00077 $.35 (M532)

Quae Est Ista *BVM,mot
[Lat] mix cor,acap oct NOVELLO DM-47 s.p.
                  (M533)

Quam Pulchri Sunt *BVM,mot
[Lat] mix cor,acap oct NOVELLO DM-44 s.p.
                  (M534)

Quem Dicunt Homines *Fest,mot
[Lat] SATB,acap (med) MULLER M 38 s.p. (M535)
[Lat] mix cor,acap oct NOVELLO DM-38 s.p.
                  (M536)

Te Deum Patrem *Te Deum
(Martens, Mason) "Thee, God The Father"
SATB oct WALTON 6018 $.35   (M537)

Thee, God The Father *see Te Deum Patrem

Today Is Born The King Of Heaven *see Hodie
Christus Natus Est

Tribus Miraculis *Epiph,mot
[Lat] SATB,acap (med) MULLER M 9 s.p.
                  (M538)
[Lat] mix cor,acap oct NOVELLO DM-9 s.p.
                  (M539)

MARESCHALL, SAMUEL (1554-1640)
Auf, Seele Des Herren Lob Erklingen
SATB LAUDINELLA LR 60 s.p. contains also:
Ich Schau Nach Jenen Bergen Fern; Man
Betet, Herr, In Zions Stille; Vernimm, O
Gott, Mein Schreien   (M540)

Ich Schau Nach Jenen Bergen Fern
see Mareschall, Samuel, Auf, Seele Des
Herren Lob Erklingen

Konig Ist Der Herr
SATB LAUDINELLA LR 1 s.p. contains also:
Lobet Den Herrn, Denn Was Er Tut; Lobet
Gott Im Himmelreich; Mein Ganzes Herz
Erhebt Dich   (M541)

Lobet Den Herrn, Denn Was Er Tut
see Mareschall, Samuel, Konig Ist Der Herr

Lobet Gott Im Himmelreich
see Mareschall, Samuel, Konig Ist Der Herr

Man Betet, Herr, In Zions Stille
see Mareschall, Samuel, Auf, Seele Des
Herren Lob Erklingen

Mein Ganzes Herz Erhebt Dich
see Mareschall, Samuel, Konig Ist Der Herr

Vernimm, O Gott, Mein Schreien
see Mareschall, Samuel, Auf, Seele Des
Herren Lob Erklingen

MARESHALL, SAMUEL (1554-ca. 1640)
Der Lobgesang Des Simeon
see Goudimel, Claude, Der Lobgesang Des
Simeon

MARESHALL, SAMUEL (cont'd.)

Im Frieden Dein, O Herre Mein
SATB HANSSLER 6.002 s.p.   (M542)

MARGENBURG, ERICH
Ave Maria Zart *BVM
3 eq voices MOSELER M-59 s.p.   (M543)

MARGETSON, EDWARD
He Stooped To Bless
SATB oct FISCHER,J 7198 $.30   (M544)

MARGIOTTA, GIOVANNI
Dixit
[Lat] unis,org (easy) ZANIBON 2691 s.p.
                  (M545)

MARIA see Edlund, Lars

MARIA see Ryelandt, Joseph

MARIA AUFGENOMMEN IST see Callhoff, Herbert

MARIA DURCH DEN DORNWALD GING see David, Johann
Nepomuk

MARIA DURCH EIN' DORNEWALD GING see Kaminski,
Heinrich

MARIA DURCH EIN DORNWALD GING *Adv/BVM,folk,
Ger,19th cent
"Maria Walks Amid The Thorn" see Three Carols
For SAB
(Bauernfeind, Hans) mix cor,acap oct
DOBLINGER s.p. see from Vier Adventlieder
                  (M546)
(Dawidowicz, Anton) wom cor,acap oct
DOBLINGER s.p. see also Acht Marienlieder
                  (M547)
(Ehret) "Maria Walks Amid The Thorn" SSA oct
BOOSEY 5617 $.30   (M548)
(Ehret) "Maria Walks Amid The Thorn" SATB oct
BOOSEY 5427 $.30   (M549)
(Wasner) "Maria Walks Amid The Thorn" [Eng/
Ger] SAT,acap oct SCHIRM.G 8796 $.25 (M550)

MARIA DURCH EIN DORNWALD GING see Bauernfiend,
Hans

MARIA DURCH EIN DORNWALD GING see Distler, Hugo

MARIA DURCH EIN DORNWALD GING see Giefer, Willy

MARIA DURCH EIN DORNWALD GING see Gunsenheimer,
Gustav

MARIA DURCH EIN DORNWALD GING see Holscher,
Bernhard

MARIA DURCH EIN DORNWALD GING see Knab, Armin

MARIA DURCH EIN DORNWALD GING see Koch,
Johannes H.E.

MARIA DURCH EIN DORNWALD GING see Raphael,
Gunther

MARIA DURCH EIN DORNWALD GING see Stern, A

MARIA DURCH EIN DORNWALD GING see Wolters,
Gottfried

MARIA DURCH EIN DORWALD GING see Kropfreiter,
Augustinius Franz

MARIA DURCH EIN'M DORNWALD GING see Lehner,
F.X.

MARIA GAR OVER BJERGENE see Eccard, Johannes

MARIA GENNEM KRATSKOV GIK see Distler, Hugo,
Maria Durch Ein Dornwald Ging

MARIA, HIMMELSFREUD see Reger, Max

MARIA IM ADVENT see Woll, Erna

MARIA IN FRANKEN see Mockel, Franz

MARIA, JESU MODER see Skold, Yngve

MARIA JUNG UND ZART (from Psalteriolum 1642)
BVM
SATB,acap (contains also: O Quam Decora (from
Sirenes Symphoniacae)) voc pt DOBLINGER
s.p. see also Unsere Liebe Frau   (M551)

MARIA MAGDALENA see Brahms, Johannes

MARIA MAGDALENAE see Dulot, Francois

MARIA MAGDALENE see Gabrieli, Andrea

MARIA SEI GEGRUSSET see Lehner, F.X.

MARIA TERESIA see Haydn, (Franz) Joseph

MARIA THERESA MASS see Haydn, (Franz) Joseph,
Theresienmesse

MARIA UND DAS VOGELEIN see Keldorfer, Robert

MARIA UND ELIZABETH see Koch, Johannes H.E.

MARIA VERKUNDIGUNG see Kukuck, Felicitas

MARIA WALKS AMID THE THORN see Maria Durch Ein
Dornwald Ging

MARIA WALLT ZUM HEILIGTUM see Eccard, Johannes

MARIA WALLT ZUM HELIGTUM see Eccard, Johannes

MARIA WIEGENLIED see Reger, Max

MARIA WOLLT EINST WANDERN see Mockel, Franz

MARIA, WUNDER DER GNADE see Demerath, F.

MARIA ZART VON EDLER ART see Praetorius,
Michael

MARIACHI MASS *folk,Mex
[Eng] unis/2pt/SATB,opt trp,bvl,perc,gtr oct
PRO ART 1194 $1.25   (M552)

MARIACHI MASS see Avalos

MARIAE VERKUNDIGUNG see Kluge, Manfred

MARIANI, ELIGIO
In Me Gratia
see Fabiani, Angelo, In Me Gratia

Magnificat *Magnif
[Lat] 3pt mix cor,org ZANIBON 2584 s.p. (M553)

O Del Carmel Splendore!
see QUATTRO CANTI ALLA MADONNA DEL CARMINE

Otto Canti Per La S. Comunione *CC8U
unis,org RICORDI-ENG 129062 s.p. (M554)

Salve O Vergine Maria
see QUATTRO CANTI ALLA MADONNA DEL CARMINE

Tota Pulchra *BVM
[Lat] 2 eq voices,org ZANIBON 2750 s.p.
(M555)

MARIAS ERWAHLUNG see Raphael, Gunther

MARIAS KIRCHGANG see Brahms, Johannes

MARIAS LOB see Brahms, Johannes

MARIAS LOVSANG see Hovland, Egil

MARIAS WALLFAHRT see Brahms, Johannes

MARIAZELLER MASS see Haydn, (Franz) Joseph,
Missa Cellensis

MARIAZELLER MESSE see Haydn, (Franz) Joseph,
Missa Cellensis

MARIAZELLERMESSE see Haydn, (Franz) Joseph,
Missa Cellensis

MARIE, LEVEZ-VOUS *Xmas,carol,Fr
(Sheppard) "Mary, We Must Go" [Eng/Fr] 4pt
mix cor,acap oct SCHIRM.G 11430 $.25 (M556)

MARIEN-LITANEI II see Lang, Hans

MARIEN-MESSE see Jochum, Otto

MARIENFESTE see Tittel, Ernst

MARIENKLAGE see Mockel, Franz

MARIENLIED see Baumann, Max

MARIENLIED see Besch, Otto

MARIENLIED see Weismann, Wilhelm

MARIENLIEDER see Brahms, Johannes

MARIENLIEDER AND MOTETS see Brahms, Johannes

MARIENLIEDER see Brahms, Johannes

MARIENLOB UND MINNE see Raphael, Gunther

MARIENMESSE see Bamer, Alfred

MARIENPREIS "MAGET UND MUOTER" see David,
Johann Nepomuk

MARIENVESPER 1610 see Monteverdi, Claudio

MARIMESS see Beck, Thomas [Ludvigsen]

MARINER'S ANTHEM, THE see Billings, William

MARIONETTE DOUCE see Power, Lyonel

MARK see Dickinson, Peter

MARKEVITCH, IGOR (1912-)
Le Paradis Perdu *cant
[Fr] SATB,SST soli,orch SCHOTT rental
(M557)

MARKS
God So Loved The World *Lent
SATB oct SOUTHERN $.25 (M558)

MARKS, GUNTHER (1897-)
Aus Der Tiefe Rufe Ich, Herr
SAT/SAB HANSSLER 6.232 s.p. contains also:
Herr, Lass Ihn Doch Dies Jahr; Schmucket
Das Fest Mit Maien (M559)

Eden-Gethsemane *Psntd,ora
SATB,SATB soli,org HANSSLER 10.138 cor pts
s.p., voc sc s.p. (M560)

Geh Hin Nach Gottes Willen *prayer
SA/SAT/SAB HANSSLER 6.208 s.p. contains
also: Marks, Gunther, In Deine Hand Sind
Wir Gegeben (SA/SAT/SAB); Stier, Alfred,
O Herre Gott, Du Bleibst In Ewigkeit
(SATB) (M561)

Herr, Lass Ihn Doch Dies Jahr
see Marks, Gunther, Aus Der Tiefe Rufe Ich,
Herr

In Deine Hand Sind Wir Gegeben
see Marks, Gunther, Geh Hin Nach Gottes
Willen

Kleine Geburtstagskantate *cant
mix cor HANSSLER 6.206 s.p. (M562)

Kleine Kantate Fur Karfreitag *Gd.Fri.,cant
3pt mix cor,narrator HANSSLER 10.225 sc
s.p., cor pts s.p., voc sc s.p. (M563)

Lobet Den Herren, Alle Heiden (Psalm 117)
SATB&cong,brass HANSSLER 7.039 s.p. (M564)

O Herr, Mach Mich Zum Werkzeug Deines
Friedens *cant
SATB,SAT/SAB soli,org HANSSLER 10.148 cor
pts s.p., voc sc s.p. (M565)

O Traurigkeit, O Herzelied *mot
SAB HANSSLER 7.036 s.p. (M566)

Psalm 117 *see Lobet Den Herren, Alle Heiden

Schmucket Das Fest Mit Maien
see Marks, Gunther, Aus Der Tiefe Rufe Ich,
Herr

MARKS, GUNTHER (cont'd.)
Weihnachtskantate *Xmas,cant
mix cor,2trp,2vln,vcl HANSSLER 10.278 sc
s.p., cor pts s.p., ipa (M567)

MARKS, H.
Come, O Come Thou Quickening Spirit
SATB oct PRESSER 312-40363 $.30 (M568)

MARKS, J.
Day Is Past And Over *Eve
SA ALLANS 298 s.p. (M569)
SATB ALLANS 383 s.p. (M570)

God So Loved The World *Easter
SATB,acap oct PRESSER 312-10608 $.30 (M571)

Victory Divine *Easter
SSA PRESSER $1.00 (M572)

MARKT UND GASSEN see Gersbach, F.

MARKT UND STRASSEN see Barthel, Ursula

MARKT UND STRASSEN SIND VERLASSEN see Denhoff,
Joachim

MARKUS-PASSION see Driessler, Johannes

MARKUS-PASSION see Fiebig, Kurt

MARKUS-PASSION see Keiser, Reinhard

MARKUS-PASSION see Linke, Norbert

MARKUS-PASSION see Telemann, Georg Philipp

MARKUS PASSION see Thomas, Kurt

MARKUS-PASSION see Wenzel, Eberhard

MARKUSPASSION see Bach, Johann Sebastian

MARKUSPASSION see Beber, Ambrosius

MARKWORTH, HENRY (1900-1953)
All Glory, Laud, And Honor
see Three Hymn Arrangements

All Praise To God, Who Reigns Above
see Six Hymn Settings

Angels We Have Heard On High
see Six Hymn Settings

Christ The Lord Is Risen Today *Easter
SATB,acap (easy) oct CONCORDIA 98-1025 $.25
(M573)

Come, Holy Ghost, Creator Blest
see Six Hymn Settings

Great God, We Sing That Mighty Hand
see Three Hymn Arrangements

Hark! Ten Thousand Harps And Voices
see Three Hymn Arrangements

In Loud, Exalted Strains
see Three Hymn Arrangements

Let Us All With Gladsome Voice
see THREE CHRISTMAS HYMNS AND CAROLS

O Dearest Jesus, What Law
see Six Hymn Settings

O Holy Spirit, Enter In
see Three Hymn Arrangements

O Word Of God Incarnate
see Three Hymn Arrangements

Rise, Crowned With Light
see Six Hymn Settings

Six Hymn Settings *Gen
SSA,acap (med easy) oct CONCORDIA 98-1915
$.25
contains: All Praise To God, Who Reigns
Above; Angels We Have Heard On High;
Come, Holy Ghost, Creator Blest; O
Dearest Jesus, What Law; Rise, Crowned
With Light; When I Survey The Wondrous
Cross (M574)

Three Hymn Arrangements *Gen,hymn
SA,acap (easy) oct CONCORDIA 98-1440 $.25
contains: Great God, We Sing That Mighty
Hand; Hark! Ten Thousand Harps And
Voices; In Loud, Exalted Strains (M575)

Three Hymn Arrangements *Gen,hymn
SSA,kbd (med easy) oct CONCORDIA 98-1748
$.22
contains: All Glory, Laud, And Honor; O
Holy Spirit, Enter In; O Word Of God
Incarnate (M576)

When I Survey The Wondrous Cross
see Six Hymn Settings

MARLOW, RICHARD
O Lord God *anthem
mix cor,acap oct NOVELLO 29.0021.01 s.p.
(M577)

MAROT
Psalm 1 (composed with L'Estocart, Paschal
de)
(Seay) [Eng/Fr] SATB,acap oct MCA (M578)

MARRIAGE PRAYER, A see Kevan

MARRIAGE SERVICE see Barash, Morris

MARRIOTT, MICHAEL J.
O Holy Child Of Mary *Xmas
cor CRAMER 324 s.p. (M579)

MARRYOTT
Holiness Unto The Lord
TTBB,acap BOSTON 2894 $.30 (M580)

Praise Carol, The *Xmas
SATB SCHMITT 1560 $.30 (M581)
SAB&desc SCHMITT 5501 $.35 (M582)

MARRYOTT, RALPH E.
All In The Morning *Easter
SATB oct GRAY GCMR 1849 $.25 (M583)

Alleluia Of The Bells *Easter/Lent
SA/SAB oct GRAY GCMR 1904 $.35 (M584)

At The Name Of Jesus
SATB oct PRESSER 332-40023 $.30 (M585)

Gateway Carol *Easter
SATB oct GRAY GCMR 1970 $.30 (M586)

Holly Tree Carol, The *Xmas
SATB oct PRESSER 332-15091 $.35 (M587)

Holy Saviour, In Thy Keeping
SATB oct PRESSER 332-40003 $.30 (M588)

Hosanna, Blessed Is He *Easter/Gen
SSA oct PRESSER 332-15347 $.30 (M589)
SATB,acap oct PRESSER 332-15021 $.30 (M590)

I Worship Him
unis oct PRESSER 332-15290 $.25 (M591)

Immortal Love
SATB,acap oct PRESSER 332-15264 $.30 (M592)

Legend Of The Dogwood Tree *Easter
SATB,acap oct PRESSER 332-15176 $.30 (M593)

Lord, Thy Word Abideth
SATB oct PRESSER 332-40066 $.25 (M594)

Now The Holy Child *Xmas,Fr
SATB oct GRAY GCMR 1953 $.25 (M595)

One Early Easter Morning *Easter
SATB oct PRESSER 332-14814 $.25 (M596)

Searching Carol, The *Xmas,carol
SATB oct GRAY GCMR 1836 $.30 (M597)

This Is Easter Day *Easter,carol
SATB,acap oct PRESSER 332-15144 $.30 (M598)

MARSH
Behold The Lamb Of God
SATB SCHMITT 1673 $.20 (M599)

Benedictus Es, Domine *Gen
"Blessed Art Thou" SATB SCHMITT 1626 $.22
(M600)

Blessed Art Thou *see Benedictus Es, Domine

Born Again *see Avery

Choir Sings Hymns Hot And Carols Cool, The
*see Avery

Christ Is Made The Sure Foundation
SATB,Bar/B solo oct PRO ART 1301 $.20
(M601)

Christ The Lord Is Risen *see Avery

Come As A Child *see Avery

Doxology And Gloria Patri *see Avery

Here We Go A-Caroling *see Avery

Hey! Hey! Anybody Listening? *see Avery

I Was Glad *see Avery

I Wonder Why? *see Avery

If There Is A Holy Spirit *see Avery

Is It The Crowning Day
(Boersman) SATB oct WORD CS-2369 $.25
(M602)

Jesus, White Boy *see Avery

Join The Revolution *see Avery

Little Baby Boy *see Avery

Miracle Of Time, The *Easter/Lent
SATB oct PRO ART 1403 $.25 (M603)

O Let's Get On *see Avery

Possibly, Probably *see Avery

Praise The Lord, O My Soul *Gen
SATB SCHMITT 1631 $.25 (M604)

Put Down Your Guns *see Avery

Rebel, The *see Avery

Song Of Praise
(Stickles) SA,pno (med) oct WILLIS 7449
$.20 (M605)

Star Light, Star Bright *see Avery

Strife Is O'er, The *Gen
SATB SCHMITT 1644 $.25 (M606)

Take Time *see Avery

Taste The New Wine *see Avery

Thank You, Thank You *see Avery

We're Here To Be Happy And Go And Be Happy
*see Avery

What Makes The Wind Blow? *see Avery

When I'm Feeling Lonely *see Avery

Who's That Guy With The Beard *see Avery

MARSHALL
Alleluia
SAB oct SACRED S-7398 $.45 (M607)

Canticle For Communion *Commun
SATB,acap oct FISCHER,C CM-7434 $.25 (M608)

Drop, Drop Slow Tears
SATB,acap oct FISCHER,C CM-7093 $.30 (M609)

MARSHALL (cont'd.)

Eternal Gifts Of Christ The King
SATB oct FISCHER,C CM-7094 $.30   (M610)

Good News! *anthem
SATB oct FISCHER,C CM-7758 $.35   (M611)

He Comes To Us *anthem
SATB oct FISCHER,C CM-6996 $.30   (M612)

Instrument Of Thy Peace, An
SATB oct SACRED S-126 $.35   (M613)

Make A Joyful Noise
SA oct FISCHER,C CM-7322 $.25   (M614)

My Eternal King
SATB oct FISCHER,C CM-6752 $.30   (M615)
TTBB oct FISCHER,C CM-7718 $.30   (M616)

None Other Lamb
SATB oct FISCHER,C CM-6755 $.30   (M617)

Praise The Lord
SATB oct FISCHER,C CM-7722 $.30   (M618)

Prayers I Make, The
SATB oct SACRED E51 $.35   (M619)
SAB oct SACRED S-7396 $.35   (M620)

Tarry In The Garden
SATB oct LORENZ A496 $.30   (M621)

Unto The Hills *anthem
SATB oct FISCHER,C CM-6928 $.25   (M622)

We Come Unto Our Fathers' God *anthem
SATB oct FISCHER,C CM-7356 $.30   (M623)

We Would Offer Thee This Day
SATB oct SACRED E34 $.35   (M624)

MARSHALL, JANE M.

Awake, My Heart
SAB oct GRAY GCMR 2648 $.30   (M625)
SATB oct GRAY GCMR 2515 $.30   (M626)

Blessed Is The Man
SATB (med) ABINGDON APM-106 $.22   (M627)

Choral Ascription Of Praise, A
SATB (med) ABINGDON APM-273 $.25   (M628)

David's Song
SATB FLAMMER A 5601 $.30   (M629)

Fanfare For Easter *Easter/Lent
jr cor&SATB (med easy) FISCHER,C CM 7090
  $.30   (M630)
SATB,opt brass&timp oct FISCHER,C CM-7090
  $.30, ipa   (M631)
jr cor&sr cor,brass,timp FISCHER,C CM 7090A
                                          (M632)
jr cor&sr cor (med easy) FISCHER,C CM 7090
  $.50   (M633)
jr cor&SATB,brass,timp (med easy) FISCHER,C
  CM 7090A $.50   (M634)

Give To The Winds Thy Fears
SATB,opt acap (med) ABINGDON APM-331 $.25
                                          (M635)

Great King Of Glory, Come
SATB oct GRAY GCMR 2748 $.30   (M636)

Has Anybody Seen Christmas? *Xmas
SSA oct AGAPE CF 160 $.30   (M637)
SATB oct AGAPE CF 132 $.30   (M638)

He Who Would Valiant Be
SATB (med) ABINGDON APM-175 $.25   (M639)

Jesus
2pt jr cor/SA FISCHER,C CM 7126 $.25   (M640)

Jesus Was Born In Bethlehem *Xmas
2pt jr cor/SA FISCHER,C CM 6946 $.25   (M641)

Lord Most High
SATB,3trp&2trom/3trp&horn&trom (med,
  dedication of a new sanctuary) ABINGDON
  APM-435 $.35, ipa   (M642)

Lord Of All Hopefulness
SATB,pno/org oct FISCHER,C CM-7152 $.25
                                          (M643)
4pt jr cor/SATB (med easy) FISCHER,C
  CM 7152 $.25   (M644)

Sing Alleluia Forth
jr cor&sr cor,hndbl (med) FISCHER,C CM 7328
  $.30   (M645)

Sing! Sing!
2pt jr cor FISCHER,C CM 7125 $.25   (M646)

We Go To Church *CCU
(Montgomery) jr cor FISCHER,C O 4009 $.90
                                          (M647)

We Sing To Learn *CCU
(Montgomery) jr cor FISCHER,C O 4126 $.75
                                          (M648)

MARSHALL, PHILIP

Psalm 126 *see When The Lord Turned Again

When The Lord Turned Again (Psalm 126) Gen/
  Thanks
SATB (med) oct OXFORD 42.880 $.50   (M649)

MARSHALL, VIRGINIA

God Is So Wonderful
(Kaiser) SATB oct WORD CS-2542 $.25   (M650)

Spirit Of Life
SATB oct GRAY GCMR 2604 $.35   (M651)

MARTENS

Christ Is Risen *Easter
SA/SAB oct LORENZ 7818 $.25   (M652)

O Domine Jesu Christe
mix cor SOUTHERN $.25   (M653)

Prayer For Mothers, A
SATB oct LORENZ A494 $.25   (M654)

Star In The Night, A *Xmas
SATB oct LORENZ A393 $.25   (M655)

MARTH

Behold The King Cometh *Easter/Lent
SATB oct PRO ART 1272 $.30   (M656)

You Taught Me How To Pray
SATB HANSEN-US E9980 $.40   (M657)

MARTH, HELEN JUN

I Go To Prepare A Place For You *Commun/Lent
SATB oct BOURNE 801 $.25   (M658)

In The Stillness *Xmas
3pt wom cor oct SCHIRM.G 10767 $.25   (M659)

Lord Is My Salvation, The
SATB oct BELWIN 1313 $.35   (M660)

Sing, Oh Ye Heavens *Xmas,cant
mix cor,org/pno voc sc SCHIRM.G $1.00   (M661)

Triumph Of Christ, The *Easter,cant
mix cor,STBar soli,org/pno voc sc SCHIRM.G
  $1.00   (M662)

MARTIN

Amazing Grace!
2pt oct SACRED S-5760 $.35   (M663)

And The Sky Never Saw The Morning
SATB oct HERITAGE H92 $.35   (M664)

Arise, Shine *Xmas,cant
SATB oct LORENZ $1.95   (M665)

Awake, My Soul!
SATB oct LORENZ 9990 $.30   (M666)

Beatitudes, The
SATB oct LORENZ C176 $.30   (M667)

Christ's Entry *Easter
SATB oct GALAXY 1.2446.1 $.35   (M668)

Could This Be A Special Night? *Xmas
SATB oct HERITAGE H85 $.35   (M669)

Do What He Wants You Do
SATB oct LORENZ A521 $.30   (M670)

Easter Praise *Easter
SATB oct LORENZ 159 $.30   (M671)

Epiphany Prayer, An *Epiph
SATB oct SACRED S-146 $.35   (M672)

Fair Weather Today!
SATB oct HERITAGE H87 $.35   (M673)

Fight The Good Fight
SATB oct LORENZ C310 $.30   (M674)

Hark! The Herald Angels Sing *Xmas
SATB oct LORENZ B176 $.30   (M675)

Holy Child
(Cain) SATB oct BOOSEY 2521 $.30   (M676)

Holy Spirit, Come, O Come
SATB,acap oct PRO ART 1730 $.22   (M677)

Hush, Little Baby
SSA/SA/unis oct HERITAGE H6009 $.35   (M678)

I Think I Heard Him Say *Easter
SATB oct LORENZ B173 $.30   (M679)

Jesus Is Born *Xmas
SSA SCHMITT 2523 $.20   (M680)

Joseph Dearest, Joseph Mine
SA/SAB oct LORENZ 7835 $.30   (M681)

Joy To The World *Xmas
SATB oct LORENZ B163 $.30   (M682)

King Of Love My Shepherd Is, The
jr cor&sr cor (easy) FISCHER,C CM 583 $.20
                                          (M683)

Kum-Bah-Yah
SA/SAB oct LORENZ 7838 $.30   (M684)

Lo! The Angel Host Rejoices *Xmas
SSA oct SPRATT 637 $.30   (M685)
SA oct SPRATT 638 $.30   (M686)

Love Gift, The *Xmas
unis oct LORENZ 8871 $.25   (M687)

Man On The Cross, The
SATB oct SACRED S-36 $.35   (M688)

Melchoir, Caspar, Balthazar *Xmas
SATB oct HERITAGE H27 $.35   (M689)

My Redeemer
SATB oct LORENZ C318 $.30   (M690)

New Dimension, A
SATB oct HERITAGE H65 $.40   (M691)

No Golden Carriage, No Bright Toy *Xmas
SATB oct HERITAGE H46 $.35   (M692)
SA oct HERITAGE H5006 $.35   (M693)
SAB oct HERITAGE H7001 $.35   (M694)

O Freedom
SATB oct HERITAGE H20 $.40   (M695)

O Lord, Support Us
SATB oct SACRED S-142 $.30   (M696)

O Star Of Light
(Raymond) SATB oct PLYMOUTH JR-131 $.25
                                          (M697)

Poor Wayfarin' Stranger
SATB oct HERITAGE H69 $.35   (M698)

Praises For The Risen Christ
SATB,org,trp oct SACRED S-93 $.40   (M699)

Prayer Of Penitence, A
SATB oct LORENZ 9961 $.30   (M700)

Psalm 5
SSA oct PRO ART 1641 $.20   (M701)

Psalm Of Gratitude, A *Psalm
SATB oct LORENZ C309 $.30   (M702)

MARTIN (cont'd.)

Psalm Praises *Psalm
SATB oct LORENZ 9984 $.30   (M703)

Rejoice, For Christ Is Born! *Xmas
SATB oct LORENZ B97 $.25   (M704)

Rejoice, Rejoice, Believers *Xmas
SATB oct LORENZ B150 $.30   (M705)

Shall We Gather At The River?
SATB oct LORENZ C319 $.30   (M706)

Simple Gifts
SATB oct LORENZ B139 $.30   (M707)

Sing Praise To God
2pt oct LORENZ 5757 $.30   (M708)

Song For The New Year, A
SATB oct SACRED S-9960 $.35   (M709)

Thee We Adore
SSA oct PRO ART 1746 $.30   (M710)

This I Saw!
SATB oct LORENZ A461 $.30   (M711)

Three Good Citizens
SATB, 3 male soli oct HERITAGE H83 $.45
                                          (M712)

To See The Lord
SATB oct LORENZ B199 $.30   (M713)

Two Spirituals *CC2U,spir
boy cor SOUTHERN $.30   (M714)

With A Song
2pt oct LORENZ 5718 $.25   (M715)

Without Love, No Feeling
SAB oct LORENZ 7414 $.30   (M716)
unis/SA/SAB SOUTHERN $.30   (M717)

Wonder Of It All, The
SATB oct HERITAGE H64 $.40   (M718)

MARTIN, DOROTHY

Storke, The *Xmas
cor CRAMER 223 s.p.   (M719)

MARTIN, EASTHOPE

Holy Child, The *Xmas
2pt ENOCH T.P.106 s.p.   (M720)
SATB ENOCH EC53 s.p.   (M721)
TTBB ENOCH EC157 s.p.   (M722)
SSA ENOCH EC61 s.p.   (M723)

St. Nicholas Day In The Morning
2pt ENOCH T.P.134 s.p.   (M724)

MARTIN, F.

Mass For Double Chorus *Mass
dbl cor,acap oct BOONIN 150 $2.50   (M725)
SATB&SATB,acap oct KERBY B150 $3.00   (M726)

MARTIN, FRANK (1890-)

Golgotha
[Fr/Ger] voc sc UNIVER. 11949 $14.85, cor
  pts UNIVER. 11950A-D $1.15   (M727)

In Terra Pax
[Fr/Ger] voc sc UNIVER. 111984 $11.25, cor
  pts UNIVER. 11985 $1.60   (M728)

Psalms Of Geneva
[Fr/Ger] cor pts UNIVER. 13261 $7.20   (M729)

MARTIN, G.

Alas! And Did My Savior Bleed *Easter
SATB oct PRESSER 312-40682 $.30   (M730)

Go To Dark Gethsemane *Easter
SATB oct PRESSER 312-40681 $.25   (M731)

Lord Jesus Christ, We Humbly Pray
SATB,org GRAY GCMR 3290 $.30   (M732)

Psalm 67
SATB,acap oct PRESSER 312-40714 $.25   (M733)

When I Survey The Wondrous Cross *Easter
SATB oct PRESSER 312-40785 $.30   (M734)

MARTIN, GEORGE CLEMENT (1844-1916)

As It Began To Dawn *Easter,Bibl
4pt mix cor,high solo oct SCHIRM.G 3953
  $.30   (M735)

Great Day Of The Lord Is Near *Adv,Bibl
4pt mix cor oct SCHIRM.G 5150 $.25   (M736)

Hail, Gladdening Light *anthem
mix cor,orch oct NOVELLO 28.0545.06 s.p.,
  ipr   (M737)

Ho! Every One That Thrsteth *Bibl
4pt mix cor,B solo oct SCHIRM.G 3833 $.35
                                          (M738)

Preces And Responses (St. Paul's) (Ferial)
  *see Stainer, John

Preces And Responses With Litany (St. Paul's)
  (Ferial) *see Stainer, John

MARTIN, GILBERT M.

All By Ourselves *Gen,anthem
SA/SAB oct LORENZ 7841 $.30   (M739)

Holiday Bells! *Xmas,anthem
mix cor,acap HERITAGE H100 $.35   (M740)

O Lord, Shield Of Our Help *Gen/Refm,anthem
SATB (diff) oct LORENZ 9998 $.25   (M741)

Take It On Over *Gen,anthem
unis oct LORENZ 8873 $.30   (M742)

Then I Know *Gen,anthem
SATB (med easy) oct LORENZ B207 $.30   (M743)

Two Dwellings *Gen,anthem
SATB (med diff) oct LORENZ E95 $.30   (M744)

MARTIN, JAMES
Bless Thou The Lord *anthem
mix cor oct NOVELLO s.p.   (M745)

MARTIN, JOHN
Royal Child, A *carol
unis CRAMER 29 s.p.   (M746)

MARTIN OF TOURS see Dickinson, Peter

MARTIN POMPEY
A La Chiviribuela
see Seis Canciones De Navidad

A La Puerta De Tu Casa
see Schola Cantorum. Vol. IV

A Un Arroyo Me Baje
see Schola Cantorum. Vol II

Camino De Belen
see Seis Canciones De Navidad

Cantad, Pastorcitos
see Seis Canciones De Navidad

Del Cielo De Tus Ojus
see Schola Cantorum. Vol. IV

En Belen Tocan A Fuego
see Seis Canciones De Navidad

Fray Anton Tenia Una Bura
see Schola Cantorum. Vol II

Gitanillas En El Portal De Belen
see Seis Canciones De Navidad

Madre, A La Puerta Hay Un Nino
[Span] 4pt jr cor,acap UNION ESP. 18833
s.p.   (M747)

Nino Chiquirritito
see Schola Cantorum. Vol. IV

Pajarillo Amoroso
see Schola Cantorum. Vol. IV

Por Debajo Del Laurel
see Schola Cantorum. Vol II

Que Viva Aragon
see Schola Cantorum. Vol II

Schola Cantorum. Vol. I *CC7L
[Span] eq voices,acap UNION ESP. 18464 s.p.   (M748)

Schola Cantorum. Vol II
[Span] eq voices,acap UNION ESP. 18465 s.p.
contains: A Un Arroyo Me Baje; Fray Anton
Tenia Una Bura; Por Debajo Del Laurel;
Que Viva Aragon; Ya No Va La Nina   (M749)

Schola Cantorum. Vol. III *CC7L
[Span] mix cor,acap UNION ESP. 18768 $1.00   (M750)

Schola Cantorum. Vol. IV
[Span] mix cor,acap UNION ESP. 19320 $1.00
contains: A La Puerta De Tu Casa; Del
Cielo De Tus Ojus; Nino Chiquirritito;
Pajarillo Amoroso; Segaba La Nina; Viva
La Gala, Viva La Flor   (M751)

Segaba La Nina
see Schola Cantorum. Vol. IV

Seis Canciones De Navidad *Xmas
[Span] 3 eq voices,pno UNION ESP. 19416
s.p.
contains: A La Chiviribuela; Camino De
Belen; Cantad, Pastorcitos; En Belen
Tocan A Fuego; Gitanillas En El Portal
De Belen   (M752)

Viva La Gala, Viva La Flor
see Schola Cantorum. Vol. IV

Ya No Va La Nina
see Schola Cantorum. Vol II

MARTIN, R.P.E.
Noel Des Mages *carol
[Fr] 4pt mix cor CHAPPELL-FR s.p.   (M753)

MARTIN, REGINALD W.
Gethsemane *Gd.Fri./Holywk,cant
4pt mix cor,soli voc sc WILLIS $.75   (M754)

I Will Praise Thee
(Lynn, G.) SAB oct PRESSER MC290 $.30   (M755)

Praise Ye The Lord
SATB,pno (med) oct WILLIS 7295 $.25   (M756)

MARTIN, WARREN (1916-   )
Anthem Of Dedication
mix cor&mix cor oct PRESSER 312-40398 $.40   (M757)

Calvary *Easter
SATB,acap oct PRESSER 312-40215 $.30   (M758)

Great Day
SATB,acap oct PRESSER 312-40080 $.35   (M759)

Lord, I Want To Be A Christian
SATB,acap oct PRESSER 312-40082 $.30   (M760)

O Sons And Daughters
2pt mix cor oct PRESSER MC223 $.30   (M761)

Psalm 13
SATB,acap RONGWEN $.35   (M762)

Savior, Like A Shepherd Lead Us
SATB,acap oct PRESSER MC224 $.30   (M763)

Sun Of My Soul
dbl cor,acap oct PRESSER 312-40397 $.35   (M764)

MARTINI
Achallay El Nino
[Span] 3pt mix cor/3 eq voices,acap
RICORDI-ARG BA 12257 s.p.   (M765)

Drei Geistliche Gesange *CC3U
(Gerber) [Ger/Lat] 4pt mix cor MOSELER s.p.   (M766)

MARTINI (cont'd.)
Llega Navidad *Xmas
[Span] 3pt mix cor/3 eq voices,acap
RICORDI-ARG BA 12260 s.p.   (M767)

MARTINI, GIAMBATTISTA (1706-1784)
see MARTINI, PADRE

MARTINI, PADRE (1706-1784)
Adoramus Te
wom cor sc ALSBACH&D s.p.   (M768)

Behold And See *Lent
(Forester) SATB SCHMITT 886 $.35   (M769)

Blessed Are They Who Do Thy Will *see O
Salutaris

Christ The Lord Is Risen Today (composed with
Gehrke, Ralph)
see Three Lenten And Easter Hymns

Domine, Ad Adjuvandum Me Festina
(Castellini, J.) "Lord, My God, Assist Me
Now" [Lat/Eng] mix cor,soli,strings,org
voc sc CONCORDIA 97-6304 $1.00, ipr   (M770)

In Monte Oliveti (composed with Gehrke,
Ralph) *mot
"On The Mount Of Olives" see Three Lenten
And Easter Hymns
3pt men cor,acap RICORDI-ENG SY 113 s.p.   (M771)
[Lat] TTB RICORDI-ENG SY113 s.p.   (M772)
(Williams, W.) "On The Mount Of Olives"
SSA,acap SCHIRM.EC 1283 $.20   (M773)
(Williams, W.) "On The Mount Of Olives"
TTB,acap SCHIRM.EC 1234 $.20   (M774)

Lamb Of God (composed with Gehrke, Ralph)
see Three Lenten And Easter Hymns

Laudate Pueri
[Lat] SATB,acap voc sc PETERS HU1958 $1.00   (M775)

Lord, My God, Assist Me Now *see Domine, Ad
Adjuvandum Me Festina

O Salutaris
"Blessed Are They Who Do Thy Will" SSA,acap
SCHIRM.EC 1888 $.25   (M776)

O Vos Omnes *mot
[Lat] TTB,acap MUSICUS 1014 $.18   (M777)

On The Mount Of Olives *see In Monte Oliveti

Sei Mottetti Eucaristici *CC6U,Commun,mot
(Benetti, F.) [Lat] 2pt,org sc ZANIBON 4390
s.p., cor pts ZANIBON 4391 s.p.   (M778)

Three Lenten And Easter Hymns (composed with
Gehrke, Ralph) *Lent,hymn
SSA,acap (easy/med easy) oct CONCORDIA
98-1439 $.25
contains: Christ The Lord Is Risen Today;
Lamb Of God; On The Mount Of Olives   (M779)

Three Sacred Choruses *CC3U
mix cor,acap voc sc KALMUS 6297 $1.25   (M780)

Tristis Est Anima Mea *mot
[Lat] TTB RICORDI-ENG SY117 s.p.   (M781)
3pt men cor,acap RICORDI-ENG SY117 s.p.   (M782)
(Kuxhaven, D.) wom cor sc ALSBACH&D s.p.   (M783)

MARTINON, JEAN (1910-   )
Le Lis De Saron *ora,Heb
"Rose Of Sharon, The" SATB,soli,orch voc sc
ISRAELI 315 s.p.   (M784)

Rose Of Sharon, The *see Le Lis De Saron

MARTINU, BOHUSLAV (1890-   )
Birth Of Our Lord
SSA,vln oct BOOSEY 1945 $.30   (M785)

Die Weissagung Des Jesaja *cant,Heb
[Eng/Ger] men cor,SABar soli,pno,trp,vla,
timp voc sc HEINRICH. s.p.   (M786)
"Prophecy Of Isaiah, The" TTBB,SABar soli,
pno,trp,vla,perc sc ISRAELI 316 s.p.   (M787)

Prophecy Of Isaiah, The *see Die Weissagung
Des Jesaja

MARTINZ, ALFREDO
Ave Maria *BVM
[Lat] unis ZANIBON 2945 s.p.   (M788)

MARTORELL
Tota Pulchra
2 eq voices,org RICORDI-ENG 129136 s.p.   (M789)

MARTTI, HELA (1890-1965)
Negro Spirituals *CC12L,spir
[Eng] mix cor oct FAZER s.p.   (M790)

MARTYR, THE see Floyd, Carlisle

MARTYR OF GOD see Sowerby, Leo

MARTYR, THE see Diamond, David

MARTYRDOM OF SAINT STEPHEN, THE see Pinkham,
Daniel

MARVELOUS WORK, THE see Haydn, (Franz) Joseph

MARVIN, J.H.
Love One Another
SATB oct KERBY 7578 $.50   (M791)

MARV'LOUS WORK, THE see Haydn, (Franz) Joseph

MARX, KARL (1897-   )
Als Jesus Von Seiner Mutter Ging *Psntd,cant
SATB,SBar soli,fl,ob,2vln,vla,vcl HANSSLER
10.185 sc s.p., cor pts s.p., ipa   (M792)

Auferstanden Bin Ich
see VIER OSTERMOTETTEN

Christmas Cantata *Xmas,cant
[Ger] SAT/SAB,2vln,vcl voc sc PETERS 4866
$.90, ipa, cor pts PETERS 4866 $.40, ipa   (M793)

MARX, KARL (cont'd.)
Deutsche Liedmesse *Mass
[Ger] SAB,2vln,opt vcl BAREN. BA 1943 sc
$5.25, cor pts $1.50   (M794)

Die Heiligen Drei Konige *Op.28, Epiph,cant
[Ger] SATB,S solo,3fl,2vln,vla,vcl (med)
BAREN. BA 746 $1.50, cor pts $.55   (M795)

Funf Kleine Festmotetten *Gen,mot
[Ger] SA&men cor,opt 2fl&vln (med easy)
BA 2768 sc $2.50, cor pts $1.50, ipa
contains: Lobt Gott, Ihr Christen; Nun
Danket All Und Bringet Ehr; Nun Lasst
Uns Gehn Und Treten; Wir Wollen Alle
Frohlich Sein; Zeuch Ein Zu Deinen
Toren   (M796)

Gedenke An Deinen Schopfer *Op.51,No.3, Gen,
mot
[Ger] SATB,acap (med) BAREN. BA 3939 $2.25   (M797)

Gelobet Sei Der Herr
see Schutz, Heinrich, Ich Will Von Herzen
Danken Gott Dem Herrn
SATB HANSSLER 7.010 s.p. contains also:
Stern, Hermann, Ich Freu Mich In Dem
Herren (SAT/SAB)   (M798)

Gen Himmel Aufgefahren Ist
SAT/SAB,treb inst HANSSLER 14.092 s.p.
contains also: Werner, Fritz,
Siegesfurste, Ehrenkonig (SA,treb inst/
bass inst)   (M799)

Gott, Schweige, Doch Nicht Also (Psalm 83)
Op.51,No.1, Gen,mot
[Ger] 3pt wom cor&3pt men cor,acap (med
diff) BAREN. BA 2528 $2.25   (M800)

Halleluja, Der Herr Ist Auferstanden
see VIER OSTERMOTETTEN

Halleluja, Gott Der Ist Herr Sonne
see VIER PSALM-MOTETTEN

Herr, Du Hast Alles, Himmel
see DREI MOTETTEN

Herr, Hore Meine Stimme, Wenn Ich
see VIER PSALM-MOTETTEN

Jesu, Was Hast Du Verbrochen
see Schweppe, Joachim, Wir Danken Dir, Herr
Jesu Christ

Lobt Gott, Den Herrn Der Herrlichkeit *Gen
[Ger] SA&men cor,2vln (med) BAREN. BA 599
s.p.   (M801)

Lobt Gott, Ihr Christen
see Funf Kleine Festmotetten

Mein Schonste Zier Und Kleinod Bist *Gen,
cant
[Ger] SATB&cong,2trp,2trom (med) sc BAREN.
BA 2637 $1.75, cor pts $.40, ipa   (M802)

Mit Freuden Zart
SS/ST,treb inst HANSSLER 14.081 s.p.
contains also: Gottschick, Friedemann,
Wir Wollen Alle Frohlich Sein (SAT/SAB,
treb inst/bass inst)   (M803)

Nun Danket All Und Bringet Ehr *Trin
see Funf Kleine Festmotetten
[Ger] SA&men cor,opt 2trp (med easy) BAREN.
BA 3032 s.p. contains also: Wo Gott Der
Herr Nicht Bei Uns Halt   (M804)

Nun Freut Euch, Lieben Christen Gmein
*Easter/Pent,cant
[Ger] SATB&cong,3trp,2trom BAREN. BA 2636
sc $1.75, cor pts $.40, ipa   (M805)

Nun Lasst Uns Gehn Und Treten
see Funf Kleine Festmotetten

O Jesu Christe, Wahres Licht
see Schmeel, Dieter, Das Alte Jahr
Vergangen Ist

Psalm 83 *see Gott, Schweige, Doch Nicht
Also

Sei Lob Und Ehr Dem Hochsten Gut *Trin
[Ger] 3pt mix cor&8pt mix cor, opt 2trp&trom
BAREN. BA 3269 s.p.   (M806)

Siebzehn Geistliche Kanons *CC17U,Gen,Bibl/
canon
[Ger] 2-5 eq voices,acap (med easy) BAREN.
BA 2179 s.p.   (M807)

Wenn Mein Stundlein Vorhanden Ist *Op.51,
No.2, mot
[Ger] SATB,acap (med) BAREN. BA 2769 $1.75   (M808)

Wir Wollen Alle Frohlich Sein
see Funf Kleine Festmotetten

Wo Gott Der Herr Nicht Bei Uns Halt
see Marx, Karl, Nun Danket All Und Bringet
Ehr

Zeuch Ein Zu Deinen Toren
see Funf Kleine Festmotetten

MARX, W.B.
Pater Noster
[Lat] 2pt boy cor/TB,org AMP $.75   (M809)

MARY see Anderson, [William H.]

MARY AND-A MARTHA *spir
(Kent, Richard) SATB,acap oct WESTWOOD
ESA-1842 8 $.60   (M810)

MARY AND HER LITTLE BABY *Xmas,spir
(Schmutz) SATB,acap oct LAWSON 51070 $.35   (M811)

MARY AND MARTHA *spir
(Christiansen, P.) SATB SCHMITT 664 $.30   (M812)
(Kinsman) SAB oct BOOSEY 5479 $.30   (M813)

MARY AND MARTHA see Gardner, Maurice

MARY AND MARTHA see Wilson, Harry [Robert]

MARY AT THE CRIB see Daudet

MARY AT THE MANGER see Franck, Cesar

MARY, DEAR MOTHER OF JESUS see Harris, Jerry Weseley

MARY, FLOWER OF FLOWERS
see Three Carols

MARY GOES TO CHURCH see Brahms, Johannes

MARY HAD A BABY　*Xmas,spir
　　see Two Christmas Spirituals
　　men cor sc ALSBACH&D s.p.
　　(Johnson, Hall) mix cor oct SCHIRM.G 10359
　　　$.25　　　　　　　　　　　　　　　　　(M815)
　　(Jurey, E.) SSA oct PRESSER 312-40419 $.25
　　　　　　　　　　　　　　　　　　　　　(M816)
　　(Kinsman) SSA oct BOURNE 223 $.30　(M817)
　　(Kinsman) SA oct BOURNE 2037 $.30　(M818)
　　(Kinsman) SAB oct BOURNE 3032 $.30　(M819)
　　(Kirk) SATB,acap,opt pno oct PRO ART 1647
　　　$.25　　　　　　　　　　　　　　　　　(M820)
　　(Kirk) SAB oct PRO ART 2095 $.25　　(M821)
　　(Kirk) SSA oct PRO ART 1882 $.25　　(M822)
　　(Kirk) 2pt oct PRO ART 2100 $.20　　(M823)
　　(Reece) SSATB oct SUMMY 5316 $.35　(M824)
　　(Shaw; Parker) 4pt men cor,T solo,acap oct
　　　SCHIRM.G 1019 $.30　　　　　　　　　(M825)

MARY HAD A BABY see Angell

MARY HAD A BABY see Black

MARY HAD A BABY see Dawson

MARY HAD A BABY see Gardner, Maurice

MARY HAD A BABY see Kinsman

MARY HAD A BABY see Landon

MARY HAD A BABY see Schroth, G.

MARY HAD A BABY see Walker, David S.

MARY HAD A BABY BOY see Pickell

MARY HAD A BOY CHILD see Gilliam

MARY HAD A LITTLE BABY　*Xmas
　　(Dunsmore) SSA SCHMITT 338 $.30　　(M826)

MARY IS A LADY see Fricker, Peter Racine

MARY LAID HER CHILD see Mc Cabe, John

MARY MAGDALENE see Brahms, Johannes

MARY MAGDALENE see Eichorn, Hermene Warlick

MARY MAGDALENE see Gabrieli, Giovanni

MARY MAGDALENE see Steel, Christopher [Charles]

MARY, MAIDEN AND MOTHER see Scull

MARY, MARY see Pfautsch, Lloyd

MARY, MARY, MAIDEN
　　(Williams) S/SA OXFORD 50.106 $.25, ipa see
　　from Three Yugoslav Folksongs　　　(M827)

MARY MODYR, CUM AND SE see Whettam, Graham

MARY MOTHER　*Op.90, So Am
　　(Rubbra, E.) SSATB,acap LENGNICK s.p. (M828)

MARY, MOTHER see Rubbra, Edmund

MARY, MOTHER, COME AND SEE see Lenel, Ludwig

MARY, MOTHER SWEET AND MILD see Wetzler, Robert

MARY OF MAGDALA see Bliss, Sir Arthur

MARY ON THE MOUNTAIN　*Xmas,carol,Czech/Pol
　　(Ehret) SATB MARKS 875 $.25　　　　(M829)

MARY SANG TO HER BABY see Anderson, Marion

MARY SAT SPINNING　*Xmas,anthem/folk
　　(Christiansen, Paul) SATB,S solo (easy) oct
　　　AUGSBURG 1180 $.22　　　　　　　　　(M830)
　　(Kranz, A.) SATB,acap AMP A571 $.25 see from
　　　Christmas Choruses　　　　　　　　　(M831)

MARY SAW HER SON see Haines

MARY SINGS TO HER CHILD see Morgan, Haydn

MARY, STAR OF THE SEA see Castelnuovo-Tedesco, Mario

MARY THE ROSE see Niles, John Jacob

MARY, THE ROSE see Pehkonen

MARY THROUGH THE THORN-BUSH GOES　*Xmas
　　(Track) SSA oct PRO ART 2478 $.25　(M832)

MARY WAS WAITING FOR YOU see Grime, William

MARY, WE MUST GO see Marie, Levez-Vous

MARY WELCOMES THE SHEPHERDS see Sharpe, Evelyn

MARY WORE THREE LENGTHS OF CHAIN　*spir
　　(Hunter) unis,pno/org/strings oct LAWSON
　　　51497 $.30　　　　　　　　　　　　　(M833)

MARY WORE THREE LINKS OF CHAIN　*Xmas
　　(Lowe, J.) SATB,acap oct PRESSER 312-40720
　　　$.30　　　　　　　　　　　　　　　　　(M834)

MARY'S BABY see Cavalieri

MARY'S BABY see Ringwald, [Roy]

MARY'S BABY BOY see Walker

MARY'S BOY CHILD see Hairston, Jester

MARY'S CRADLE SONG　*folk,So Am
　　(Schimmerling, H.A.) SATB,acap AMP A238 $.20
　　　　　　　　　　　　　　　　　　　　　(M835)

MARY'S CRADLE SONG see Franck, Cesar

MARY'S CRADLE SONG see Grime, William

MARY'S JOURNEY see Thygerson, Robert

MARY'S JOURNEY TO CHURCH see Brahms, Johannes,
　　Marias Kirchgang

MARY'S LAMENT see Carlson, J. Bert

MARY'S LITTLE BABY see Davis, Elmer L.

MARY'S LULLABY see Collins

MARY'S LULLABY see Diemer, Emma Lou

MARY'S LULLABY see Hemmer, [Eugene]

MARY'S LULLABY see Lee, J.

MARY'S LULLABY see Plank, David L.

MARY'S LULLABY see Sharpe, Evelyn

MARY'S LULLABY see Winslow

MARY'S LULLABY TO THE INFANT KING　*Xmas
　　(Warner) SA/unis oct SUMMY B 1611 $.30 (M836)

MARY'S MANGER SONG see Salter, Sumner

MARY'S NOWELL see Thiman, Eric Harding

MARY'S PILGRIMAGE see Brahms, Johannes, Marias
　　Wallfahrt

MARY'S PRAYER
　　(Hall, Regnal) cor HIGHLAND 4123 $.30　(M837)

MARY'S SALUTATION see Eccard, Johannes

MARY'S SOLILOQUY see Effinger, Cecil

MARY'S WANDERING
　　unis/SATB (very easy) OXFORD 08.090 $.15
　　　　　　　　　　　　　　　　　　　　　(M838)

MARY'S WANDERING see Brahms, Johannes

MARY'S WANDERING see Williams, David H.

MARZO, EDUARDO (1852-1929)
　　Up To The Hills
　　　SA&unis/SA/unis oct HUNTZINGER 501 $.15
　　　　　　　　　　　　　　　　　　　　　(M839)

MASCAGNI, PIETRO (1863-1945)
　　Anthem For Spring
　　　(Simeone) SATB SHAWNEE A 478 $.40　(M840)

　　Ave Maria
　　　[Lat] unis HEUGEL s.p. see from CHANTS
　　　RELIGIEUX　　　　　　　　　　　　　(M841)

　　Hymn Of Praise (from Cavalleria Rusticana)
　　　SATB,pno (med) oct WILLIS 5139 $.15 (M842)

　　Jesus Is Risen
　　　(Trusler) SATB oct PLYMOUTH TR-109 $.30
　　　　　　　　　　　　　　　　　　　　　(M843)

　　Light Divine (from Cavalleria Rusticana)
　　　(Rix) SSAATTBB oct SCHIRM.G 5959 $.40
　　　　　　　　　　　　　　　　　　　　　(M844)

　　Lord, Now Victorious, The　*Easter
　　　SATB oct PRESSER 332-07777 $.50　　(M845)
　　　(Greely, P.) SATB oct PRESSER 312-20872
　　　　$.40　　　　　　　　　　　　　　　　(M846)

　　Lord Triumphant
　　　SATB KJOS 5363 $.40　　　　　　　　(M847)

　　Prayer　*Gen
　　　(Cain) SAB SCHMITT 5505 $.25　　　(M848)
　　　(Cain) SATB SCHMITT 1731 $.35　　(M849)

　　Quickly Come, Lord Jesus
　　　(Hawkins) SATB oct LILLENAS AN-2371 $.30
　　　　　　　　　　　　　　　　　　　　　(M850)

　　Regina Coeli (from Cavalleria Rusticana)
　　　[Eng/Lat] SSATTBB&SSATTB,SABar soli oct
　　　SCHIRM.G 2415 $.60　　　　　　　　　(M851)

MASCHOFF
　　Behold The Lamb Of God
　　　SATB SCHMITT 1715 $.30　　　　　　(M852)

　　Come Unto Him　*Xmas
　　　SATB SCHMITT 1780 $.20　　　　　　(M853)

MASLEN, BENJAMIN J.
　　Harvest Blessings, Richly Showered　*Harv,
　　　anthem
　　　mix cor oct NOVELLO 40.1312.03 s.p. (M854)

　　House Of God, The　*Ded/Gen,anthem
　　　mix cor oct NOVELLO 91.0009.01 s.p. (M855)

　　Rejoice, Rejoice! A Babe Is Born
　　　SATB,acap (med easy) OXFORD 84.072 $.20
　　　　　　　　　　　　　　　　　　　　　(M856)

MASON
　　Be Honor To God Eternal
　　　(McAfee) SATB oct BOURNE 841 $.35　(M857)

　　But In The Last Days
　　　(McAfee) SATB oct BOURNE 842 $.30　(M858)

　　Hark! Ten Thousand Harps And Voices
　　　(Ehret) SATB,org/pno BOSTON 13459 $.35
　　　　　　　　　　　　　　　　　　　　　(M859)

　　Joy To The World　*Xmas
　　　(Pens) SATB oct PRO ART 1179 $.20　(M860)

　　Lord Of All Power
　　　(Pisano) SATB,opt kbd oct PRO ART 2560 $.25
　　　　　　　　　　　　　　　　　　　　　(M861)

　　My Faith Looks Up To Thee　*Gen,hymn
　　　(Collins) SATB oct LILLENAS AT-1063 $.25
　　　　　　　　　　　　　　　　　　　　　(M862)
　　　(Gerig) SATB oct LILLENAS AN-2360 $.30
　　　　　　　　　　　　　　　　　　　　　(M863)
　　　(Olds) SATB SCHMITT 1868 $.20　　(M864)

　　Nearer My God To Thee
　　　(Wiley) SATB oct PRO ART 1362 $.20　(M865)

MASON (cont'd.)
　　O Sing To Jehovah
　　　(Pisano) SATB,acap,opt pno oct PRO ART 2520
　　　　$.25　　　　　　　　　　　　　　　　(M866)

　　When I Survey The Wondrous Cross　*Lent
　　　(Olds) SATB SCHMITT 1851 $.20　　(M867)

　　Wondrous Cross, The
　　　(Frederick) SATB oct SHAPIRO SK 2011 $.25
　　　　　　　　　　　　　　　　　　　　　(M868)

MASON, DANIEL GREGORY (1873-1953)
　　When I Survey The Wondrous Cross
　　　(Riegger) SAB FLAMMER $.25　　　　(M869)
　　　(Steckel) SATB FLAMMER A 5073 $.30 (M870)

MASON, ISABEL
　　Nunc Dimittis　*Nunc
　　　SATB WEINBERGER s.p.　　　　　　　(M871)
　　　SATB oct SHAPIRO SK 2029 $.25　　(M872)

MASON, L.
　　Naher Mein Gott Zu Dir
　　　[Ger] mix cor,acap (easy) HUG s.p. (M873)
　　　(Adams-Flower, S.) [Ger] wom cor,acap
　　　(easy) HUG s.p.　　　　　　　　　　(M874)

　　O Praise The Lord All Ye Nations
　　　(Young, R.; Weinandt, E.) SATB oct FISCHER,
　　　J 10010 $.30　　　　　　　　　　　　(M875)

MASON, LOWELL (1792-1872)
　　Jerusalem, My Glorious Home
　　　cor oct HART s.p.　　　　　　　　　(M876)
　　　SATB ALLANS 208 s.p.　　　　　　　(M877)

MASON, T.D.
　　Psalm 23　*Gen,anthem
　　　SSAATTBB (diff) oct GIA G1507 $.40 (M878)

　　When I Survey The Wondrous Cross　*Easter/
　　　Lent
　　　(Hastings) SATB oct BOURNE HA7 $.30 (M879)
　　　(Riegger) SAB oct SOUTHERN $.25　(M880)

MASONIC JOY see Mozart, Wolfgang Amadeus

MASQUE IN DIOCLESIAN see Purcell, Henry

MASS see Burrell

MASS see Charpentier, Marc-Antoine

MASS see Dello Joio, Norman

MASS see Dickinson, Peter

MASS see Faure, Gabriel-Urbain

MASS see Lotti, Antonio

MASS see Milner, Anthony

MASS see Monteverdi, Claudio

MASS see Noble, Harold

MASS see Persichetti, Vincent

MASS see Schumann, Robert (Alexander), Messe

MASS see Sessions, Roger

MASS see Stravinsky, Igor

MASS see Sveinsson, Gunnar Reynir

MASS see Tcherepnin, Alexander

MASS see Thompson

MASS see Thomson, Virgil

MASS see Mozart, Wolfgang Amadeus, Coronation
　　Mass

MASS see Mozart, Wolfgang Amadeus, Grosse Messe

MASS, B MINOR see Bach, Johann Sebastian

MASS DEDICATED TO FERDINAND KING OF SICILY AND
　　ARAGON see Tinctoris, Johannes

MASS FOR 4 VOICES see Saint-Saens, Camille,
　　Messe Solennelle

MASS FOR A SAINT'S DAY see Jackson

MASS FOR A SAINT'S DAY see Jackson, Nicholas

MASS FOR CHRISTIAN UNITY see Vermulst, Jan

MASS FOR CONGREGATIONS see Roff, Joseph

MASS FOR DOUBLE CHORUS see Martin, F.

MASS FOR FIVE VOICES see Berkeley, Lennox

MASS FOR FIVE VOICES see Byrd, William

MASS FOR FOUR MIXED VOICES see Maleingreau,
　　Paul de

MASS FOR FOUR VOICES see Byrd, William

MASS FOR FOUR VOICES see Tallis, Thomas

MASS FOR LIFE, A see Delius, Frederick

MASS FOR MALE VOICES see Liszt, Franz

MASS FOR PEACE see Miller

MASS FOR S.A.B. VOICES see Goemanne, Noel

MASS FOR ST. MICHAEL see Cruft, Adrian

MASS FOR THE FAMILY OF GOD, A see Hutson

MASS FOR THREE MIXED VOICES see Maleingreau,
　　Paul de

MASS FOR THREE VOICES see Byrd, William

MASS FOR TWO OR FOUR VOICES see Elaine, Sister
　　M. (Gentemann)

MASS FOR TWO VOICES see Roff, Joseph

MASS FOR YOUTH see Korte, Karl

MASS HYMN SUITES 1-15 *CCU,Gen/Reces,anthem/
  hymn/Mass/Offer
  (Hytrek,Sr. M. Theophane) unis/2pt,org (med
  easy) voc sc GIA G1502A $1.50, sc GIA
  G1412 & G1488 $6.00   (M881)

MASS II E MINOR see Bruckner, Anton

MASS III see Hassler, Hans Leo

MASS III see Monteverdi, Claudio

MASS III F MINOR see Bruckner, Anton

MASS IN A see Bach, Johann Sebastian, Messe A-
  Dur

MASS IN A FLAT see Schubert, Franz (Peter)

MASS IN A FLAT MAJOR see Schubert, Franz
  (Peter)

MASS IN B-FLAT see Haydn, (Franz) Joseph,
  Schoepfungsmesse

MASS IN B FLAT see Haydn, (Franz) Joseph,
  Theresienmesse

MASS IN B FLAT see Mozart, Wolfgang Amadeus

MASS IN B FLAT MAJOR see Schubert, Franz
  (Peter), Messe B-Dur

MASS IN B FLAT MAJOR see Schubert, Franz
  (Peter), Hymne An Den Unendlichen

MASS IN B-FLAT see Schubert, Franz (Peter),
  Messe B-Dur

MASS IN B MINOR see Bach, Johann Sebastian,
  Messe H-Moll

MASS IN C see Beethoven, Ludwig van, Messe C-
  Dur

MASS IN C see Boatwright, Howard

MASS IN C see Fuhrer, Robert

MASS IN C see Fux, Johann Joseph

MASS IN C see Gardner, John [Linton]

MASS IN C see Gounod, Charles Francois

MASS IN C see Harrison, Julius Allen Greenway

MASS IN C see Lotti, Antonio

MASS IN C see Mozart, Leopold

MASS IN C see Mozart, Wolfgang Amadeus,
  Coronation Mass

MASS IN C see Mozart, Wolfgang Amadeus, Missa

MASS IN C see Rheinberger, Josef, Messe Grosse

MASS IN C see Schubert, Franz (Peter), Messe C-
  Dur

MASS IN C MAJOR see Beethoven, Ludwig van,
  Messe C-Dur

MASS IN C MAJOR see Mozart, Wolfgang Amadeus,
  Coronation Mass

MASS IN C MAJOR see Schubert, Franz (Peter),
  Messe C-Dur

MASS IN C MINOR see Track, Gerhard

MASS IN C see Mozart, Wolfgang Amadeus, Missa
  In Honorem Sanctissimae Trinitas

MASS IN D see Beethoven, Ludwig van, Missa
  Solemnis

MASS IN D see Dvorak, Antonin

MASS IN D see Pergolesi, Giovanni Battista

MASS IN D see Wittmer, Eberhard Ludwig

MASS IN D MINOR see Bruckner, Anton, Messe D-
  Moll

MASS IN D MINOR see Mozart, Wolfgang Amadeus,
  Requiem

MASS IN E FLAT see Schubert, Franz (Peter)

MASS IN E FLAT see Sutermeister, Heinrich

MASS IN E FLAT MAJOR see Schubert, Franz
  (Peter)

MASS IN E MINOR see Bruckner, Anton, Messe E-
  Moll

MASS IN E MINOR see Jarvis, Caleb

MASS IN ENGLISH see James, Philip, Missa Brevis

MASS IN ENGLISH see Peloquin, C. Alexander

MASS IN F see Bach, Johann Sebastian, Messe F-
  Dur

MASS IN F see Leo, Leonardo

MASS IN F see Leonard, W.

MASS IN F see Schubert, Franz (Peter), Deutsche
  Messe

MASS IN F MAJOR see Schubert, Franz (Peter)

MASS IN F MINOR see Bruckner, Anton, Messe F-
  Moll

MASS IN F see Pergolesi, Giovanni Battista

MASS IN F see Pergolesi, Giovanni Battista

MASS IN FIVE MOVEMENTS see Steel, Christopher
  [Charles]

MASS IN G see Bach, Johann Sebastian, Messe G-
  Dur

MASS IN G see Mozart, Wolfgang Amadeus

MASS IN G see Schubert, Franz (Peter)

MASS IN G MAJOR see Schubert, Franz (Peter),
  Messe G-Dur

MASS IN G MAJOR see Weber, Carl Maria von

MASS IN G MINOR see Bach, Johann Sebastian,
  Messe G-Moll

MASS IN G MINOR see Lucas, Leighton

MASS IN G MINOR see Vaughan Williams, Ralph

MASS IN HONOR OF GOD THE HOLY SPIRIT see
  Schiavone, John

MASS IN HONOR OF MARY TOWER OF DAVID see
  Davida, Sister Mary

MASS IN HONOR OF OUR LADY, THE QUEEN OF THE
  ANGELS see Johnson

MASS IN HONOR OF POPE JOHN XXIII see Zaninelli,
  Luigi

MASS IN HONOR OF SAINT JOSEPH see Peeters, Flor

MASS IN HONOR OF SAINT SEBASTIAN see Villa-
  Lobos, Heitor

MASS IN HONOR OF ST. IGNATIUS see Boex, A.J.

MASS IN HONOR OF ST. JOSEPH see Roff, Joseph

MASS IN HONOR OF ST. LAWRENCE see Boex, A.J.

MASS IN HONOR OF ST. PAULINUS OF YORK see Dixon

MASS IN HONOR OF THE BLESSED VIRGIN MARY see
  Anonymous

MASS IN HONOR OF THE HOLY ROSARY see Schiffer,
  J.V.

MASS IN HONOR OF THE MOST BLESSED TRINITY see
  Cain, Noble

MASS IN HONOUR OF SAINT STEPHEN PROTOMARTYR see
  Roff, Joseph

MASS IN HONOUR OF ST. ANTHONY see Rush, John

MASS IN TIME OF WAR see Haydn, (Franz) Joseph,
  Missa In Tempore Belli

MASS NO. 2 IN G MAJOR see Gounod, Charles
  Francois

MASS NO. 3 IN D see Haydn, (Franz) Joseph,
  Nelson-Missa

MASS NO. 5 see Hassler, Hans Leo

MASS NO. 5 see Schubert, Franz (Peter), Messe
  B-Dur

MASS NO. 6 IN G MAJOR see Gounod, Charles
  Francois

MASS NO. 12 see Mozart, Wolfgang Amadeus

MASS OF FIVE MELODIES see Appleford, Rev.
  Patrick

MASS OF NATURE see La Montaine, John, Missa
  Naturae

MASS OF ONE ACCORD see Simpson, Reginald

MASS OF PRAISE see Pross, D.

MASS OF SAINT ANDREW see Williamson, Malcolm

MASS OF SAINT RICHARD see Slaney, Ivor

MASS OF SAINTS AND SINNERS see Lehr, Michael

MASS OF ST. ANDREW see Williamson, Malcolm

MASS OF ST. BUDEAX, THE see Beaumont, Rev.
  Gerard

MASS OF ST. TERESA see Willan, Healey

MASS OF ST. THOMAS OF CANTERBURY see Kendell,
  Iain

MASS OF TEXTURES, A see Ott, J.

MASS OF THE BELLS see Willson

MASS OF THE BLESSED SACRAMENT see Mc Grath

MASS OF THE GOOD SHEPHERD see Pinkham, Daniel

MASS OF THE HOLY CHILD: SLEEP, HOLY BABE see
  Andrews, C.T.

MASS OF THE HOLY EUCHARIST see Pinkham, Daniel

MASS OF THE HOLY RESSURECTION, THE see Purvis,
  Richard

MASS OF THE HOLY SPIRIT see Mildred, Sister M.

MASS OF THE HOLY SPIRIT see Thompson, Randall

MASS OF THE RECONCILIATION see Hewitt-Jones,
  Tony

MASS OF THE REDEEMER see Proulx, Richard

MASS OF THE SACRED HEART see Gounod, Charles
  Francois

MASS OF THE WORD OF GOD see Pinkham, Daniel

MASS SUS LE PONT D'AVIGNON see Certon, [Pierre]

MASS TE DEUM see Aston, Hugo

MASS TO ST. ANTHONY see Harrison, Lou

MASS (TWO-PART) see Thomson, Virgil

MASS VII IN THE DORIC MODE see Lotti, Antonio

MASS see Mozart, Wolfgang Amadeus, Missa

MASSA see Runback, Albert

MASSA see Soderholm, Valdemar

MASSA see Wideen, Ivar

MASSA see Wikander, David

MASSA FOR KRISTEN ENHET see Nilsson, Bo

MASSA VID MALAREN see Hemberg, Eskil

MASSAINO, TIBURTIUS
  Gabriel Angelus Locutus Est *cant
  SATB&SATB,4trp,4trom MOSELER sc s.p., cor
  pts s.p., ipa   (M882)

MASSANA, JOSE
  Seven Last Words Of Our Savior, The
  TTBB,S/T solo SCHIRM.EC 1268   (M883)

MASSENET, JULES (1842-1912)
  Ave Maria
  [Lat] unis HEUGEL s.p. see from CHANTS
  RELIGIEUX   (M884)

  Ave Maris Stella
  [Lat] 2pt,opt pno/org HEUGEL s.p.   (M885)

  Choeur Des Romains (from Herodiade)
  [Fr] TTBB,kbd HEUGEL voc sc s.p., voc pt
  s.p.   (M886)

  Choeur Des Servantes (from Marie-Magdeleine)
  [Fr] SSA,kbd HEUGEL voc sc s.p., voc pt
  s.p.   (M887)

  Grant Us Peace
  (Rogers) SATB oct STAFF 279 $.30   (M888)

  Noel *Xmas
  [Fr] SA,S solo,opt pno/org HEUGEL voc sc
  s.p., voc pt s.p.   (M889)

  O Salutaris
  [Lat] SATB,S solo,org,ob HEUGEL s.p.   (M890)

  Souvenez-Vous Vierge Marie
  [Fr] pt HEUGEL s.p. see from CHANTS
  RELIGIEUX   (M891)
  [Fr] SA,solo,opt pno/org HEUGEL voc sc
  s.p., voc pt s.p.   (M892)

  Vigil Of Christmas, The (The Vigil Of Little
  Jesus)
  SATB,pno BROUDE BR. $.45   (M893)

MASSENTIO, DOMENICO
  Sancta Maria
  (Klaes) [Lat] SS/SA,org SCHOTT voc sc s.p.,
  cor pts s.p.   (M894)

MASSES VOL. I see Gaforio, Franchino

MASSES VOL. II see Gaforio, Franchino

MASSES AND MOTETS see Finck, Heinrich

MASSOTTI LITTEL, M.
  Villancico Murciano *Xmas,carol
  [Span] 5pt mix cor UNION ESP. 19568 s.p.
                                             (M895)

MASTARE, VILKET AR DET YPPERSTA BUDET I LAGEN
  see Nilsson, Torsten

MASTER CHORUSES *CCU
  SATB PRESSER cmplt ed $5.00, voc pt $2.00
                                             (M896)

MASTER HATH CALLED US, THE see Hughes

MASTER LIVETH, THE *Easter/Pageant,cant
  2pt LORENZ $1.00   (M897)

MASTER OF EAGER YOUTH see Means, Claude

MASTER OF PEACE AND LOVE see Bach

MASTER, SHOW THY MERCY UNTO US see Hassler,
  Hans Leo

MASTER, SPEAK! THY SERVANT HEARETH see Glarum,
  L. Stanley

MASTER, SPEAK TO ME see Berggren

MASTER, WE TOILED ALL NIGHT see Krapf, Gerhard

MASTER, WHAT SHALL I DO? see Surovchak

MASTERS IN THE HALL *Xmas
  (Shaw; Parker) mix cor,SBar soli oct SCHIRM.G
  10192 $.40   (M898)

MASTERS IN THIS HALL *Xmas,anthem/carol,Fr
  see Three Early Christmas Carols
  see Three French Carols
  (Brown, W.H.) SAB,kbd (med easy) oct
  CONCORDIA 98-1907 $.40   (M899)
  (Candlyn) SATB oct FISCHER,C CM-374 $.35
                                             (M900)
  (Holst, G.) unis oct CURWEN 8469 $.25   (M901)
  (Oliver, R.) SATB LEONARD-US 08042240 $.25
                                             (M902)
  (Powell, Wilfred) SAB oct HARRIS HC3001 $.25
                                             (M903)
  (Wilson; Ehret) SSA oct BOOSEY 5585 $.30   (M904)
  (Wilson; Ehret) SAB oct BOOSEY 5006 $.30   (M905)
  (Ziemer, C.) SATB oct AGAPE AD 1971 $.30   (M906)

MASTERS IN THIS HALL see Currie, E.E.

MASTERS IN THIS HALL see Currie, E.R.

MASTERS IN THIS HALL see Spencer, W.

MATAI YAVO *folk,Isr
(Goldman) "When Will He Come" SATB,T/Bar solo
oct LAWSON 51269 $.35   (M907)

MATCHLESS MORN see Stairs, L.

MATELART, JOHANNES
Caro Mea *Fest
[Lat] SATB,acap (med) MULLER MS 66 s.p.
(M908)

MATER ADMIRABILIS CHAPEL, THE see Archer,
Violet

MATER CHRISTI see Taverner, John

MATER DIVINA GRATIAE see Gluck, Christoph
Willibald Ritter von

MATER DOLOROSO see Harris

MATER ORA FILIUM *Mediev
(Bell) SSA (med) OXFORD 44.014 $.50 see from
Four Medieval Songs   (M909)

MATER PATRIS ET FILIA see Brumel, Antoine

MATESKY
God Of Our Fathers
2pt treb cor KJOS 6102 $.30   (M910)

MATESKY, RALPH (1913-   )
Christmas Star, The *Xmas
SATB oct WALTON 2078 $.25   (M911)
SSA oct WALTON 5012 $.25   (M912)

MATESKY, T.
Holy, Holy, Holy *Xmas
SATB oct PRESSER MC422 $.30   (M913)
(Truitt, R.) SSA oct PRESSER MC445 $.30
(M914)

MATHESON
Carolers, The *Xmas
SSA SCHMITT 330 $.30   (M915)

MATHIAS, WILLIAM
All Thy Works Shall Praise Thee (Psalm 145)
Gen/Thanks
[Eng/Welsh] SATB (med) oct OXFORD 42.863
$.35   (M916)

Communion Service In C *Commun
mix cor&cong voc sc OXFORD 42.337 $1.75
(M917)

Festival Te Deum *Fest,Te Deum
SATB (med) oct OXFORD 42.891 $.65   (M918)

Make A Joyful Noise Unto The Lord (Psalm 100)
Gen/Thanks
SATB (med easy) oct OXFORD 42.889 $.30
(M919)

O Salutaris *anthem
TTBB oct OXFORD   (M920)

O Sing Unto The Lord *Fest/Gen
SATB (med easy) oct OXFORD 42.892 $.50
(M921)

Psalm 100 *see Make A Joyful Noise Unto The
Lord

Psalm 145 *see All Thy Works Shall Praise
Thee

Psalm 150 *anthem
mix cor oct OXFORD 46.159 $1.70   (M922)
mix cor oct OXFORD 46.159 $1.70   (M923)

Three Medieval Lyrics *CC3U
mix cor oct OXFORD 46.154 $4.10   (M924)

Wassail Carol *Xmas,carol
SATB (med diff) oct OXFORD 84.139 $.30 (M925)

MATINS see Raffman, Relly

MATONA, JUNGFRU KAR see Lassus, Roland de
(Orlandus)

MATONA, LOVELY MAIDEN see Lassus, Roland de
(Orlandus), Matona, Mia Cara

MATONA, MIA CARA see Lassus, Roland de
(Orlandus)

MATTERLING
All Creatures Of Our God And King
SATB KJOS 8012 $.30   (M926)

Amens And Responses
SSA KJOS 8251 $.30   (M927)

Emitte Spiritum Tuum
SATB KJOS 7017 $.30   (M928)

Misericordias Domini
SATB KJOS 7036 $.30   (M929)

Nunc Dimittis *Nunc
SATB KJOS 7039 $.30   (M930)

MATTHAUS-PASSION see Funcke

MATTHAUS-PASSION see Komma, Karl Michael

MATTHAUS-PASSION see Kuhnhausen

MATTHAUS-PASSION see Schutz, Heinrich

MATTHAUS-PASSION see Telemann, Georg Philipp

MATTHAUS-PASSION 1613 see Vulpius, Melchior

MATTHAUS PASSIONE see Bach, Johann Sebastian

MATTHAUSPASSION see Bach, Johann Sebastian

MATTHAUSPASSION see Schutz, Heinrich

MATTHES, RENE (1891-   )
Choral *chorale
[Ger] mix cor,acap (med easy) HUG s.p. (M931)

Der Herr Ist Konig
[Ger] men cor/wom cor,pno/org HUG s.p.
contains: Psalm 97; Psalm 99   (M932)

MATTHES, RENE (cont'd.)
Der Herr Ist Konig
[Ger] men cor,org HUG s.p.   (M933)

Derr Herr Ist Konig
[Ger] mix cor,org HUG s.p.   (M934)

Psalm 97
see Der Herr Ist Konig

Psalm 99
see Der Herr Ist Konig

Selig Sind Die Toten *Bibl
[Lat] wom cor,acap (med diff) HUG s.p. (M935)

Tripychon *CCU
[Ger] mix cor,acap (diff) HUG s.p.   (M936)

MATTHEW, MARK
see Six Traditional Carols, Set I

MATTHEW, MARK see Bergmann, Walter

MATTHEW, MARK, LUKE AND JOHN *folk,US
(Holst, G.) mix cor,acap oct CURWEN 8548 $.20
(M937)
(Holst, Gustav) mix cor CURWEN 61085 s.p.
(M938)
(Holst, Gustav) men cor CURWEN 50616 s.p.
(M939)

MATTHEW, MARK, LUKE, AND JOHN see Shaw, Martin

MATTHEWS
Christ Child, The *Xmas
SATB oct LILLENAS AN-3837 $.30   (M940)

Dear Name *Gen
SAB/SATB SCHMITT 665 $.30   (M941)

I Love To Hear The Story
SATB oct PRO ART 1673 $.20   (M942)

Jesus Lies Sleeping
SATB FLAMMER A 5207 $.25   (M943)

Nativity Service Of Nine Lessons And Carols
(composed with Detweiler) *Xmas
SSA/SAB BOOSEY $1.50   (M944)

O God, Thy Name Is Holy
SATB KJOS 5880 $.30   (M945)

Oh, Come To My Heart, Lord Jesus
(Rogers) SATB&2pt jr cor oct LILLENAS
AN-2344 $.30   (M946)

Praise Jehovah
SATB KJOS 5891 $.30   (M947)

When Jesus Was Born
SATB FLAMMER A 5257 $.25   (M948)

MATTHEWS, D.E.
Merry Christmas! *Xmas
SATB oct KERBY 7011 $.35   (M949)
SATB,acap oct KERBY 7011C $.35   (M950)

MATTHEWS, DAVID
Christ Is Born Of Maiden Fair *Xmas,carol
4pt mix cor,acap oct SCHIRM.G 11749 $.25
(M951)
SATB oct FABER 11749 $.25   (M952)

MATTHEWS, DONALD
Real Joy
SATB oct AGAPE CF 107 $.25   (M953)

MATTHEWS, H.
Benedictus Es, Domine *Easter/Gen
SATB oct PRESSER 332-40070 $.30   (M954)

Evening And Morning
SATB oct PRESSER 312-40491 $.30   (M955)

Lord, I Have Loved The Habitation Of Thy
House
SATB PRESSER $.85   (M956)

Thou Wilt Keep Him In Perfect Peace
SATB,acap oct PRESSER 312-20502 $.30 (M957)

Three Women Went Forth *Easter
SATB,acap oct PRESSER 332-13712 $.30 (M958)

Twelve Anthems For Young Singers *CC12U
SA oct PRESSER $1.25   (M959)

MATTHEWS, HARVEY ALEXANDER (1879-   )
Ballad Of Trees And The Master,
mix cor,acap oct SCHIRM.G 6909 $.30   (M960)

Blind And Alone (from Conversion, The) prayer
4pt mix cor,acap oct SCHIRM.G 5377 $.25
(M961)

City Of God, The *Fest/Gen
mix cor,soli,orch/org voc sc SCHIRM.G $1.50
(M962)

Eternal Light, The *Xmas,cant
BELWIN $1.75   (M963)

Eve Of Grace *Xmas,cant
BELWIN $2.00   (M964)

Eye Hath Not Seen
4pt mix cor,acap oct SCHIRM.G 10056 $.20
(M965)

Father, Once More Within Thy Holy Place
mix cor,acap oct SCHIRM.G 7076 $.30   (M966)

Father, We Praise Thee
4pt mix cor oct SCHIRM.G 10685 $.25   (M967)

Gethsemane To Golgotha *Holywk/Lent,cant
BELWIN $1.75   (M968)

Great Is The Lord
4pt mix cor oct SCHIRM.G 7779 $.25   (M969)

Immortal Love, For Ever Full
4pt mix cor oct SCHIRM.G 10310 $.30   (M970)

Life Everlasting, The *Op.29, Adv/Easter/
Gen,cant
cor,soli,org voc sc SCHIRM.G $1.25   (M971)

MATTHEWS, HARVEY ALEXANDER (cont'd.)
O Saviour Of The World *Lent,Bibl
4pt mix cor,S solo oct SCHIRM.G 6730 $.25
(M972)

Sleep, Holy Babe (from Story Of Christmas,
The) Xmas
4pt mix cor,A solo oct SCHIRM.G 8037 $.25
(M973)
unis oct SCHIRM.G 6462 $.25   (M974)

Story Of Christmas, The *Xmas/Epiph,cant
mix cor,4 soli,org voc sc SCHIRM.G $1.50
(M975)
4pt wom cor,SA/TB soli,org voc sc SCHIRM.G
$1.25   (M976)

Triumph Of The Cross, The *Lent,cant
cor,soli,org voc sc SCHIRM.G $1.50   (M977)

Voices Of The Sky (from Story Of Christmas,
The) Xmas
3pt wom cor oct SCHIRM.G 9519 $.25   (M978)

Welcome, Happy Morning *Easter
4pt mix cor oct SCHIRM.G 10644 $.30   (M979)

MATTHEWS, [TIMOTHY RICHARD] (1826-1910)
Dorian Anthem Of Praise, A *anthem
(Raymond) SATB oct PLYMOUTH JR-129 $.30
(M980)

I Am The Good Shepherd
2pt treb cor oct PRESSER MC460 $.25   (M981)

MATTONI, FILIPPO
Ave Maria *BVM
see CINQUE MOTECTA IN HON. B.V.M.
see DUE AVE MARIA
[Lat] 2 eq voices,org ZANIBON 2763 s.p.
contains also: Picchi, Luigi, Ave Maria
(M982)

MATTSON
Lullaby *Xmas
SSA SCHMITT 234 $.25   (M983)

One Little Tree
(Frank) SATB oct FOX $.35   (M984)
(Frank) 2pt oct FOX $.35   (M985)

MAUDUIT, JACQUES (1557-1627)
Eia Verba Dicite
(Expert) [Lat] SATB,acap oct SALABERT-US
$.65   (M986)

En Son Temple Sacre (Psalm 150)
"In His Holy Temple" [Fr/Eng] SSATB BROUDE
BR. $.40   (M987)

In His Holy Temple *see En Son Temple Sacre

Psalm 150 *see En Son Temple Sacre

Sus: Tous Ses Servantes, Benissez La Seigneur
(Expert) [Fr] SATB,acap oct SALABERT-US
$.65   (M988)

MAUERSBERGER, ERHARD
We Saw His Glory *Epiph/Gen/Trin
SA,kbd (med easy) oct CONCORDIA 98-1914
$.25   (M989)

MAUGERI, GIUSEPPE
Ave Verum
see Quattro Composizioni Sacre

Due Composizioni Sacre *BVM
[Lat] ZANIBON 194 s.p.
contains: Salve Regina (B,org); Salve
Regina (T,org)   (M990)

Quattro Composizioni Sacre *Commun
[Lat] sc ZANIBON 196 s.p.
contains: Ave Verum (A,org); Sit Nomen
Domini (2 eq voices,org); Tantum Ergo
(T,org); Tantum Ergo (A/B,org)   (M991)

Salve Regina
see Due Composizioni Sacre
see Due Composizioni Sacre

Sit Nomen Domini
see Quattro Composizioni Sacre

Tantum Ergo
see Quattro Composizioni Sacre
see Quattro Composizioni Sacre

MAUNDER, J.H.
Angels From The Realms Of Glory *Xmas,anthem
mix cor oct NOVELLO s.p.   (M992)

Bethlehem *Xmas,cant/hymn
SATB,STBarB soli,org voc sc NOVELLO s.p.,
ipr   (M993)

Blessed Be The Name Of The Lord *anthem
mix cor oct NOVELLO 28.1438.02 s.p.   (M994)

Calvary
SATB oct FISCHER,J 9427 $.30   (M995)

Christ Is Risen *Easter,anthem
mix cor oct NOVELLO 28.1410.02 s.p.   (M996)

Christians, Awake, Salute The Happy Morn
*Xmas,anthem
mix cor oct NOVELLO 28.1407.02 s.p.   (M997)

Complete Service *chant
SATB oct NOVELLO 02.0067.00 s.p.   (M998)

Conquering Kings Their Titles Take *anthem/
hymn
mix cor oct NOVELLO 28.1251.07 s.p.   (M999)

Droop Sacred Head (from Olivet To Calvary)
Easter/Gd.Fri.
(Hardwicke) SATB oct PRO ART 2397 $.25
(M1000)

Forever, O Lord
(Harris) SATB oct PRO ART 2746 $.35 (M1001)

Holy Communion *Commun
SATB (F maj) oct NOVELLO 44.0666.04 s.p.
(M1002)

It Is A Thing Most Wonderful
cor oct HART s.p.   (M1003)

MAUNDER, J.H. (cont'd.)

Just As I Am
(Schroeder) SATB&jr cor oct PRO ART 2555
$.30   (M1004)

Magnificat And Nunc Dimittis *chant/Magnif/
Nunc
SATB NOVELLO 02.0053.00 s.p.   (M1005)
SATB (G maj) oct NOVELLO 02.0052.02 s.p.
                                                   (M1006)
SATB (D maj) oct NOVELLO 02.0051.04 s.p.
                                                   (M1007)

March To Calvary, The
SATB oct FISCHER,J 9266 $.30   (M1008)

O Come, Let Us Sing (from Song Of
Thanksgiving)
(Wiley) SATB oct PRO ART 2619 $.35   (M1009)

O How Amiable Are Thy Dwellings *anthem
2pt oct NOVELLO 33.0025.00 s.p.   (M1010)
mix cor oct NOVELLO 28.0963.10 s.p.   (M1011)

O Worship The King *anthem/hymn
SATB oct PRESSER 332-12783 $.30   (M1012)
mix cor oct NOVELLO 28.1252.05 s.p.   (M1013)

Olivet To Calvary *Easter/Holywk/Lent/Psntd,
cant/hymn
mix cor,TB soli,pno voc sc SCHIRM.G $1.50
                                                   (M1014)
SATB LORENZ $1.95   (M1015)
SA/SAB LORENZ $1.75   (M1016)
BELWIN $1.50   (M1017)
SATB,TBar soli,org,fl,ob,2clar,bsn,2trp,
trom,strings,timp voc sc NOVELLO s.p.,
ipr   (M1018)
SATB,TBar soli,pno/org voc sc WILLIS $1.25
                                                   (M1019)

On The Way To Jerusalem (from Olivet To
Calvary) Easter/Palm
SATB FLAMMER A 5352 $.25   (M1020)
SATB oct LORENZ B127 $.30   (M1021)
4pt mix cor oct SCHIRM.G 10869 $.30   (M1022)
(Licht) SAB FLAMMER D5145 $.30   (M1023)

Penitence, Pardon, And Peace *Adv/Gen/Lent,
cant
BELWIN $1.00   (M1024)
SATB,SBar/STBar soli,org voc sc NOVELLO
s.p., ipr   (M1025)
(Deis) cor,SBar/TBar soli,pno voc sc
SCHIRM.G $1.25   (M1026)

Praise The Lord *Harv,anthem
mix cor,orch oct NOVELLO 28.0577.04 s.p.,
ipr   (M1027)

Praise The Lord, O Jerusalem *Easter/Gen/
Thanks
SATB oct LORENZ 9134 $.30   (M1028)
SATB (very easy) oct LORENZ 4359 $.30
                                                   (M1029)
SATB oct PRO ART 1042 $.30   (M1030)
SAB oct PRO ART 1165 $.30   (M1031)
SATB,org BOSTON 8572 $.40   (M1032)
SATB oct PRESSER 332-14421 $.35   (M1033)
SATB oct BELWIN 64069 $.35   (M1034)
SA oct BELWIN 64070 $.30   (M1035)
SATB oct GRAY GCMR 3178 $.35   (M1036)
(Peery, R.) SAB oct PRESSER 312-40533 $.30
                                                   (M1037)

Sing, O Heavens *Xmas,anthem
mix cor oct NOVELLO 40.0777.08 s.p.   (M1038)

Sing To The Lord Of Harvest *Harv/Thanks,
anthem
mix cor (also available in abridged
edition) oct NOVELLO 28.1404.08 s.p.
                                                   (M1039)

Song Of Thanksgiving *Fest/Gen/Harv/Thanks,
cant/hymn
SATB,STB/STA soli,fl,ob,2clar,bsn,2horn,
2trp,trom,strings,perc,timp voc sc
NOVELLO s.p., ipr   (M1040)
cor voc sc KALMUS 6286 $2.00   (M1041)

To Thee Our God *anthem
mix cor oct NOVELLO s.p.   (M1042)

'Twas Night O'er Lonely Olivet (from Olivet
To Calvary)
SATB oct FISCHER,J 9265 $.30   (M1043)

While The Earth Remaineth *Harv,anthem
mix cor oct NOVELLO 28.1401.03 s.p.   (M1044)

MAUREL, E. OLIVE
Sleep, My Jesu, Sleep *Xmas
3pt wom cor,pno (easy) oct WILLIS 5267 $.10
                                                   (M1045)

MAURICE, PIERRE (1868-1936)
La Fille De Jephte
[Fr] SATBarB,soli ENOCH voc sc s.p., voc pt
s.p.   (M1046)

MAW
Balulalow
SSAATBB,acap (med) OXFORD 84.158 $.30
                                                   (M1047)

MAWBY, C.
By The Waters Of Babylon *Gen,anthem
(Ascherberg) SS,opt pno oct ROYAL s.p. see
also ANTHEMS FOR UNISON OR TWO PART
SINGING   (M1048)

Four Psalm Settings *Gen,anthem/Psalm,
Contemp
2pt treb cor,org (med easy) cmplt ed GIA
G1098 $.50   (M1049)
contains: Psalm 95; Psalm 101; Psalm 137;
Psalm 148

Psalm 95
see Four Psalm Settings

Psalm 101
see Four Psalm Settings

Psalm 137
see Four Psalm Settings

Psalm 148
see Four Psalm Settings

MAXWELL
Little Pine Tree, The *Xmas
SAB oct SHAPIRO SK 5023 $.25   (M1050)

Peace I Leave With You
(Wirges; Hoggard) SATB SHAWNEE A 341 $.25
                                                   (M1051)

MAXWELL, J. GEDDES
O'er The Solemn Hush Of Midnight *Xmas
4pt mix cor,acap oct CURWEN 10327 $.25
                                                   (M1052)
mix cor CURWEN 61462 s.p.   (M1053)

MAY ALL THE ANGELS see Castellini, J., In
Paradisum

MAY CAROL, THE see Niles, John Jacob

MAY GOD BESTOW see Schutz, Heinrich

MAY GOD BESTOW ON US HIS GRACE
(Hadley) SATB oct PRO ART 2458 $.25   (M1054)

MAY GOD BESTOW ON US HIS GRACE see Hillert,
Richard

MAY GOD GRANT YOU PEACE see Bach, Johann
Sebastian

MAY GOD HAVE MERCY UPON US see Hoag, Charles K.

MAY GOD HAVE PITY ON US see Schoen, F.

MAY GOD SMILE ON YOU see Bach, Johann
Sebastian, Der Herr Segne Euch

MAY NO RASH INTRUDER see Handel, George
Frideric

MAY NO RASH INTRUDER DISTURB see Handel, George
Frideric

MAY NOW THY SPIRIT see Schuetky, Franz Joseph,
Emitte Spiritum Tuum

MAY PEACE ABIDE WITH YOU see Schubert, Franz
(Peter)

MAY THE GOD OF WIT INSPIRE see Purcell, Henry

MAY THE GRACE OF CHRIST see Davies, Ivor

MAY THE GRACE OF CHRIST see Eldridge, Guy H.

MAY THE GRACE OF CHRIST OUR SAVIOUR see Wolff

MAY THE HOLY GHOST see Colonna, Giovanni Paolo

MAY THE LORD BLESS YOU see Peeters, Flor

MAY THE WORDS see Altman, Ludwig

MAY THE WORDS see Berlinski, [Herman]

MAY THE WORDS see Donenfeld

MAY THE WORDS see Freed, Isadore

MAY THE WORDS see Lubin, Ernest

MAY THE WORDS see Starer, Robert

MAY THE WORDS see Weisgall, Hugo, Yih'uy
L'Rotzon

MAY THE WORDS see Zingg, Julius C.

MAY THE WORDS OF MY MOUTH see Levy

MAY THE WORDS OF MY MOUTH see Rogers, J.H.

MAY THE WORDS OF THE LORD see Amram, David
Werner

MAY THY SPIRIT REST UPON US see Gasparini,
Francesco

MAY WE BE WORTHY OF THY TRUST see Del Monte

MAY WE KNOW PEACE see Roe, Gloria [Ann]

MAY YOU BE STRENGTHENED see Newbury

MAYER
Festive Alleluia
SATB oct GALAXY 1.2384.1 $.50   (M1055)

MAYER, ELEANOR W.
I Will Lift Up Mine Eyes
SATB,S&A soli,pno (med) oct WILLIS 6124
$.16   (M1056)

MAYER, MARTIN (? -1671)
Christmas Gospel, The *Bibl
cor,opt kbd/inst&cont CONCORDIA 97-5100
$.50   (M1057)

MAZELLIER, J.
Ave Maria *BVM
[Lat] opt 2pt wom cor,ST soli,org,opt vln&
harp LEMOINE voc sc s.p., cor pts s.p.,
ipa   (M1058)

Cantique Nuptial *Marriage
opt 3pt wom cor,ST soli,org,vln,vcl,harp
LEMOINE sc s.p., cor pts s.p.   (M1059)

ME DICES QUE NO ME QUIERES see Benedito

ME HAVE BEREAVED see Morales, Cristobal de

MEAD
Beloved, Let Us Love One Another
SATB,acap BOSTON 13290 $.35   (M1060)

Benedictus Es, Domine
SATB oct GALAXY 1.0529.1 $.35   (M1061)

Christ, Whose Glory Fills The Skies
SATB oct FISCHER,C CM-7478 $.25   (M1062)

Dark The Night *Xmas
SATB oct GALAXY 1.1308.1 $.30   (M1063)
TTBB oct GALAXY 1.1229.1 $.30   (M1064)
SSA oct GALAXY 1.2134.1 $.30   (M1065)

In Thee, O Lord
SATB oct FISCHER,C CM-7634 $.25   (M1066)

MEAD (cont'd.)

Make A Joyful Noise Unto God
SATB oct SACRED E54 $.35   (M1067)

Once To Every Man And Nation
TTBB oct GALAXY 1.2264.1 $.35   (M1068)
SATB oct GALAXY 1.1531.1 $.35   (M1069)

With Gladness We Worship
SA,org BOSTON 12670 $.35   (M1070)

Ye Holy Angels Bright
3pt jr cor/SAB (med easy) FISCHER,C CM 7469
$.25   (M1071)

MEAD, E.G.
Starlight Over Bethlehem *Xmas,carol
SATB,acap (easy) oct WILLIS 6087 $.10
                                                   (M1072)
What Means This Glory Round Our Feet? *Xmas
SATB,acap (med) oct WILLIS 6222 $.10
                                                   (M1073)

MEAD, EDWARD G. (1892-   )
Blessed Art Thou
SATB,acap PEER $.40   (M1074)

Christmas Prayer *Xmas,prayer
SATB,acap PEER $.40   (M1075)

I Will Extol Thee
SATB,org PEER $.40   (M1076)

Praise Ye The Name Of The Lord
SATB oct BOURNE 865 $.35   (M1077)

MEALY
Little King Of The World, The *anthem
(Pooler) unis treb cor (easy) oct AUGSBURG
1558 $.18   (M1078)

MEANS, CLAUDE
Come Holy Ghost
SATB oct GRAY GCMR 3127 $.30   (M1079)

Day Of Resurrection, The *Easter
unis jr cor&desc FISCHER,C R 452 $.20
                                                   (M1080)
Gentle Mary *Xmas
SATB oct GRAY GCMR 2803 $.25   (M1081)

God Be Merciful Unto Us *Thanks,anthem
SATB oct GRAY GCMR 3218 $.35   (M1082)

Let Us With A Gladsome Mind
unis mix cor oct GRAY GCMR 2498 $.30   (M1083)

Lute Book Lullaby *Xmas
SATB oct GRAY GCMR 3210 $.30   (M1084)

Master Of Eager Youth
SATB/unis mix cor oct GRAY GCMR 3056 $.25 (M1085)

News Of Great Joy *Xmas,carol,Eng
SATB&opt jr cor oct GRAY GCMR 2145 $.30
                                                   (M1086)
Put Forth, O God, Thy Spirit's Might
SATB oct GRAY GCMR 3063 $.30   (M1087)

We Will Carol Joyfully *Easter/Lent
SA oct GRAY GCMR 2922 $.25   (M1088)

Ye Servants Of God
SATB oct SACRED E55 $.35   (M1089)

MECHEM, KIRKE (1925-   )
Canon Law For Newlyweds *Bibl/canon
3-6pt SCHIRM.EC 2725 $.45
contains: Hatred Stirreth Up Strife; Hear
Ye Children; Merry Heart, A; Who Can
Find A Virtuous Woman?; Who Hath Woe?;
Whoso Findeth A Wife   (M1090)

Canon Law For Newlyweds
3-6pt,acap SCHIRM.EC 2725   (M1091)

Forsake Me Not, O Lord *Op.23, mot
SATB,acap SCHIRM.EC 2733   (M1092)

Give Thanks Unto The Lord (Psalm 136)
SATB,acap PETERS 6213 $.25   (M1093)

Hatred Stirreth Up Strife
see Canon Law For Newlyweds

Hear Ye Children
see Canon Law For Newlyweds

Let All Mortal Flesh Kee Silence *Fr
SATB,acap SCHIRM.EC 2741 $.40   (M1094)

Lord Is In His Holy Temple, The *Op.7,No.1,
Introit
SATB,org/pno SCHIRM.EC 2734 $.30   (M1095)

Love Song, A *No.4 (from Songs Of Wisdom)
SATB,acap SCHIRM.EC 2738   (M1096)

Make A Joyful Noise Unto The Lord (Psalm 100)
SATB,acap SCHIRM.EC 2472 $.35   (M1097)

Merry Heart, A
see Canon Law For Newlyweds

O Oriens
[Lat/Eng] SSATBB,acap SCHIRM.EC 2724
                                                   (M1098)
Protest Of Job, The *No.6 (from Songs Of
Wisdom)
SATB,acap SCHIRM.EC 2739   (M1099)

Psalm 100 *see Make A Joyful Noise Unto The
Lord

Psalm 136 *see Give Thanks Unto The Lord

Seven Joys Of Christmas *Op.25b, sac/sec,
Xmas,carol/medley
SATB,opt pno SCHIRM.EC 2709 $1.25   (M1100)
SA&SSA,opt pno SCHIRM.EC 2583 $1.25   (M1101)
4 cor,opt pno SCHIRM.EC 2709 $1.25   (M1102)

Sing Unto The Lord A New Song
SSATB,org/trp cor pts FOSTER MF 403 $.40,
ipa   (M1103)

Song Of Comfort, A *No.8 (from Songs Of
Wisdom)
SATB,acap SCHIRM.EC 2740   (M1104)

MECHEM, KIRKE (cont'd.)

Song Of Moses, The *No.2 (from Songs Of
   Wisdom)
   SATB,acap SCHIRM.EC 2737   (M1105)

Song Of Praise, A *No.10 (from Songs Of
   Wisdom)
   SATB,acap SCHIRM.EC 2741   (M1106)

Songs Of Wisdom *Op.14, CC10L,cant
   SATB,acap SCHIRM.EC 2701 $2.00   (M1107)

Songs Of Wisdom *Op.14, cant
   4 cor,acap SCHIRM.EC 2701   (M1108)

Who Can Find A Virtuous Woman?
   see Canon Law For Newlyweds

Who Hath Woe?
   see Canon Law For Newlyweds

Whoso Findeth A Wife
   see Canon Law For Newlyweds

MED BON ME NO OSS VENDER see Heggen, Bodvar

MED ENGLAR SONG GUDS LOV
   see Det Hev Ei Rosa Sprunge

MED JESUS VIL EG FARA see Baden, Conrad

MED TACKSAM ROST OCH TACKSAM SJAL see Berg,
   Gottfrid

MEDIA VITA see Gombert, Nicolas

MEDIA VITA IN MORTE SUMUS see Philips, Peter

MEDITABOR see Biggs, John

MEDITABOR see Kaufmann, Ferdinand

MEDITASJON see Solberg Lief

MEDITATION see Hegenbart, Alex F.

MEDITATION AND SIMPLE REQUIEM see Takacs, Jeno

MEDITATION OF ST. THERESA, A see Wyton, Alex

MEDITATION ON "LYRA DAVIDICA" see Hastings

MEDITATION ON THE SYLLABLE "OM" see Nelson,
   Ronald A.

MEDITATION ON "WOODWORTH" see Wetzler, Robert

MEDITATIONEN ZUM KARSAMSTAG see Witte, Gerd

MEDLER, MALCOLM
   Lord, How Excellent Thy Name
   4pt mix cor,org/pno sc SCHIRM.G 10517 $.30
                                     (M1109)

MEDLEY OF PERFUME, A see Farjeon, Harry

MEDUSA - THE SHIP see Sindelar, Ronald

MEECE, DAVID
   One Small Child *Xmas
      unis oct WORD CS-2532 $.25   (M1110)
      unis/SA oct WORD   (M1111)

MEEK, KENNETH
   Lo, The Fair Beauty Of The Earth *Easter,
      carol
      SATB,acap oct BERANDOL 912M6AE $.35 see
         from Three Easter Carols   (M1112)

   Song Of The Fathers, The
      SATB oct LESLIE 4092   (M1113)

   Three Easter Carols *see Lo, The Fair Beauty
      Of The Earth; Wintertide Hath Passed
      Away; Ye Birds With Open Throat (M1114)

   Wintertide Hath Passed Away *Easter,carol
      SATB,acap oct BERANDOL 912M6AF $.35 see
         from Three Easter Carols   (M1115)

   Ye Birds With Open Throat *Easter,carol
      SATB,acap oct BERANDOL 912M6AD $.35 see
         from Three Easter Carols   (M1116)

MEERSTERN ICH DICH GRUSSE see Muller, A.M.

MEET AND RIGHT see Bradbury

MEETING IN THE AIR, THE see Roberts

MEETING OF THE WATERS
   (Wardale, Joseph) SSS CRAMER B65 s.p. (M1117)

MEETING OF THE WATERS, THE
   (Sharpe, E.) cor&desc CRAMER 36   (M1118)

MEETING OF THE WATERS, THE see Macmurrough,
   Dermot

MEETING PLACE, THE see Webber, Lloyd

MEHRSTIMMIGES GEMEINDESINGEN *CC60U
   (Siemoneit, Hans Rudolf) [Ger] 3pt mix cor
   BAREN. EM 320 s.p. settings of melodies
   from the Evangelisches Kirchengesangbuch
                                     (M1119)

MEHRSTIMMIGES GEMEINDESINGEN *CC80U
   (Siemoneit, Hans Rudolf) [Ger] 4pt mix cor
   BAREN. EM 320 s.p. settings of melodies
   from the Evangelisches Kirchengesangbuch
                                     (M1120)

MEHUL, H.
   Messe Solennelle *Mass
      4pt,org LEMOINE voc sc s.p., voc pt s.p.
                                     (M1121)

MEILAND, JACOB (1542-1577)
   Lobet Den Herren In Seinem Heiligtum *mot
      (Roller) SSATB HANSSLER 1.326 s.p. (M1122)

MEIM HERZEN IST'S EIN GROSSE FREUD see Schutz,
   Heinrich

MEIN FREUND, ICH TUE DIR NICHT see Vulpius,
   Melchior

MEIN FREUND, ICH TUE DIR NICHT UNRECHT see
   Driessler, Johannes

MEIN FREUND IST MEIN see Bohm, Georg

MEIN FREUND IST MEIN see Bohm, Joseph

MEIN GANZES HERZ ERHEBET DICH see Eglin, Arthur

MEIN GANZES HERZ ERHEBET DICH see Sweelinck,
   Jan Pieterszoon

MEIN GANZES HERZ ERHEBT DICH see Mareschall,
   Samuel

MEIN GOTT see Bach, Johann Sebastian, Mein
   Gott, Wie Lang', Ach Lange

MEIN GOTT ICH WILL VON HINNEN GEHEN see Lohr,
   Ina

MEIN GOTT, MEIN GOTT see Sweelinck, Jan
   Pieterszoon

MEIN GOTT, MEIN GOTT, WARUM HAST DU MICH
   VERLASSEN see Briegel, Wolfgang Carl

MEIN GOTT, NIMM MICH NICHT WEG INMITTEN MEINER
   TAGE see Reda, Siegfried

MEIN GOTT UND HERR, DU BIST MEIN HOCHSTES GUT
   see Sweelinck, Jan Pieterszoon

MEIN GOTT, WARUM see Mendelssohn-Bartholdy,
   Felix

MEIN GOTT, WARUM HAST DU MICH see Mendelssohn-
   Bartholdy, Felix

MEIN GOTT, WIE LANG see Bach, Johann Sebastian

MEIN GOTT, WIE LANG', ACH LANGE see Bach,
   Johann Sebastian

MEIN HEILAND, HERR UND MEISTER see Schubert,
   Franz (Peter)

MEIN HERZ DICHTET EIN LIED MIT FLEISS see
   Schutz, Heinrich

MEIN HERZ DICHTET EIN SCHONES LIED see
   Strohbach, Siegfried

MEIN HERZ ERHEBET GOTT, DEN HERRN see
   Mendelssohn-Bartholdy, Felix

MEIN HERZ IST BEREIT see Harrer

MEIN HERZ IST BEREIT see Vierdanck, Johann

MEIN HERZ UND HORT see Langius, G.

MEIN HERZ, WAS DIR BEGEGNEN see Zipp, Friedrich

MEIN HIRT, VERNAHMST DU see Katt, Leopold

MEIN HOFFNUNG, TROST UND ZUVERSICHT see Cruger,
   Johann

MEIN HOFFNUNG, TROST UND ZUVERSICHT see
   Gumpeltzhaimer, Adam

MEIN JESUS see Gerhold, Norbert, Nobody Knows

MEIN JUNGES LEBEN HAT EIN END see Sweelinck,
   Jan Pieterszoon

MEIN KONIG, DIR ZU SINGEN see Helder,
   Bartholomaeus

MEIN LEBEN IST EIN PILGRIMSTAND see Goudimel,
   Claude

MEIN LEBEN IST EIN PILGRIMSTAND see Goudimel,
   Claude

MEIN LIEBER HERR, ICH PREISE DICH see Schott,
   Johann Georg

MEIN LIEBSTER JESUS see Bach, Johann Sebastian,
   Mein Liebster Jesus Ist Verloren

MEIN LIEBSTER JESUS IST VERLOREN see Bach,
   Johann Sebastian

MEIN LIED SING AUF EWIG see Handel, George
   Frideric, My Song Shall Be Alway

MEIN ODEM IST SCHWACH see Reger, Max

MEIN SCHONSTE ZIER UND KLEINOD see Bornefeld,
   Helmut

MEIN SCHONSTE ZIER UND KLEINOD see Borris,
   Siegfried

MEIN SCHONSTE ZIER UND KLEINOD see Geisel,
   Gustav

MEIN SCHONSTE ZIER UND KLEINOD BIST see Marx,
   Karl

MEIN SCHONSTE ZIER UND KLEINOD BIST see
   Pepping, Ernst

MEIN SCHONSTE ZIER UND KLEINOD BIST see
   Sunderreiter, G.

MEIN SEEL' ERHEBT DEN HERREN see Bach, Johann
   Sebastian

MEIN SEEL ERHEBT DEN HERREN see Praetorius,
   Michael

MEIN SEEL ERHEBT DEN HERREN MEIN see Weismann,
   Wilhelm

MEIN SEEL ERHEBT DEN HERRN see Praetorius,
   Michael

MEIN SEEL ERHEBT ZU DIESER FRIST see
   Praetorius, Michael

MEIN SEEL IST STILL IN MEINEM GOTT see Schutz,
   Heinrich

MEIN SEEL, O HERR, MUSS LOBEN DICH see
   Bornefeld, Helmut

MEIN SEEL SOLL LOBEN GOTT, DEN HERRN see
   Schutz, Heinrich

MEIN SEELE ERHEBET DEN HERRN see Weyrauch,
   Johannes

MEIN SOHN, WARUM HAST DU UNS DAS see Vulpius,
   Melchior

MEIN SOHN, WARUM HAST DU UNS DAS GETAN? see
   Schutz, Heinrich

MEIN SUSSER TROST see Bach, Johann Sebastian

MEIN VOLK, WAS TAT ICH DIR see Lambertz, Johann
   Sebastian

MEINE AUGEN SEHEN STETS ZU DEM HERRN see
   Grunke, Friedrich

MEINE GEDANKEN see Callhoff, Herbert

MEINE SEEL' ERHEBT DEN HERREN see Bach, Johann
   Sebastian

MEINE SEEL ERHEBT DEN HERREN see Praetorius,
   Michael

MEINE SEEL' ERHEBT DEN HERREN [CHORALE] see
   Bach, Johann Sebastian

MEINE SEELE ERHEBET DEN HERREN see Selle,
   Thomas

MEINE SEELE ERHEBET DEN HERRN see Pepping,
   Ernst

MEINE SEELE ERHEBET DEN HERRN see Telemann,
   Georg Philipp

MEINE SEEL' ERHEBT DEN HERREN see Franck,
   Melchior

MEINE SEELE ERHEBT DEN HERREN see Schutz,
   Heinrich

MEINE SEELE ERHEBT DEN HERREN see Schutz,
   Heinrich

MEINE SEELE ERHEBT DEN HERREN see Schutz,
   Heinrich

MEINE SEELE ERHEBT DEN HERRN see Eccard,
   Johannes

MEINE SEELE ERHEBT DEN HERRN see Eglin, Arthur

MEINE SEELE ERHEBT DEN HERRN see Zimmermann,
   Heinz Werner

MEINE SEELE GOTT ERHEBT see Hammerschmidt,
   Andreas

MEINE SEELE HARRET AUF GOTT see Rosenmuller,
   Johann

MEINE SEELE IST see Kuhnau, Johann, Tristis Est
   Anima Mea

MEINE SEELE RUHMT see Bach, Johann Sebastian

MEINE SEUFZER see Bach, Johann Sebastian, Meine
   Seufzer, Meine Tranen

MEINE SEUFZER, MEINE TRANEN see Bach, Johann
   Sebastian

MEINE WORTE HORE see Schutz, Heinrich, Verba
   Mea Auribus Percipe

MEINEM GOTT GEHORT DIE WELT see Gadsch, Herbert

MEINEM JESU LASS ICH NICHT see Reger, Max

MEINEM JESUM LASS ICH NICHT see Bach, Johann
   Sebastian

MEINEN JESUM LASS ICH NICHT see Hammerschmidt,
   Andreas

MEINEN JESUM LASS ICH NICHT see Kurig, Hans-
   Hermann

MEINEN JESUM LASS ICH NICHT see Reger, Max

MEINEN JESUM LASS ICH NICHT see Bach, Johann
   Sebastian

MEISSNER, GEN. FRAUENLOB (1250-1318)
   Gott Ist Gewaltig
      mix cor,pno sc BREITKOPF-L PB-1115 s.p. see
      from Vier Geistlichen Minneliedern
                                     (M1123)
   Vier Geistlichen Minneliedern *see Gott Ist
      Gewaltig   (M1124)

MEISTER, G.
   Uberfahrt *Op.35,No.2
      men cor,acap ERDMANN 66 s.p.   (M1125)

MEISTER, WIR HABEN DIE GANZE NACHT see
   Raselius, Andreas

MEISTER, WIR HABEN DIE GANZE NACHT GEARBEITET
   see Schutz, Heinrich

MEISTER, WIR HABEN DIE GANZE NACHT GEARBEITET
   see Vulpius, Melchior

MEISTER, WIR WISSEN, DASS DU WAHRHAFTIG BIST
   see Schutz, Heinrich

MEISTERWERKE MITTELALTERLICHER MUSIK *Gen
   (Besseler, Heinrich) [Lat] (med) BAREN.
   BA 1711 $2.75
      contains: Des Prez, Josquin, In Pace (STB,
      acap); Dufay, Guillaume, Ave Regina
      Coelorum (STTB,acap); Dunstable, John,
      Quam Pulchra Es (ABB,acap); Finck,
      Sanctus (STB,acap); Obrecht, Jacob,
      Parce, Domine (STB,acap); Touront, O
      Gloriosa Regina (STB,acap)   (M1126)

MELBY, JAMES
   Long Ago And Far Away *anthem
      see Melby, James, Savior Of The Nations,
      Come
      unis treb cor (easy) oct AUGSBURG 1660 $.35
      contains also: Savior Of The Nations,
      Come   (M1127)

MELBY, JAMES (cont'd.)

Savior Of The Nations, Come *anthem
see Melby, James, Long, Ago And Far Away
unis treb cor (easy) oct AUGSBURG 1660 $.35
contains also: Long Ago And Far Away (M1128)

MELCHOIR, CASPAR, BALTHAZAR see Martin

MELLE, DE'
O Holy Jesus *see O Jesu Christe

O Jesu Christe
(Greyson) mix cor SOUTHERN $.25 (M1129)
(Greyson) "O Holy Jesus" SAB oct BOURNE
ES60C $.25 (M1130)
(Greyson) "O Holy Jesus" SATB oct BOURNE
ES60 $.25 (M1131)
(Kuxhaven, D.) mix cor ALSBACH&D s.p. (M1132)

MELLERS, WILFRED
Te Deum *Te Deum
SATB oct NOVELLO 07.0197.01 s.p. (M1133)

MELLERS, WILFRID HOWARD (1914-   )
Christmas Eve *Xmas,carol
SATB oct FABER FO109 $.35 (M1134)

City Not Forsaken, The
see Two Motets "In Diem Pacis"

City Of Desolation, The
see Two Motets "In Diem Pacis"

Four Carols *CC4U,carol
SSA, opt celesta LENGNICK s.p. (M1135)

Happy Meadow, The *cant
unis jr cor/2pt jr cor,narrator,vln,perc,
chimes,rec, glockenspiel, xylophone voc
sc NOVELLO 20.0008.03 s.p., ipa (M1136)

Te Deum Laudamus *Te Deum
[Eng/Lat] SATB,org voc sc NOVELLO s.p. (M1137)

Two Motets "In Diem Pacis" *Gen,Bibl
SATB,opt org/brass (diff) oct OXFORD rental
contains: City Not Forsaken, The; City Of
Desolation, The (M1138)

MELLNAS, ARNE (1933-   )
Dream
mix cor NORDISKA NMS-10.264 s.p. (M1139)

MELODEYEN-GESANGBUCH *see Vierstimmige Chorale
Nr. 1-12; Vierstimmige Chorale Nr. 13-23;
Vierstimmige Chorale Nr. 24-35 (M1140)

MELODIEHEFT ZU DEN 'BAUSTEINEN FUR DEN
GOTTESDIENST *CC76U
cong sc HANSSLER 19.701 s.p. (M1141)

MELODIES FOR POLISH PSALTER VOL. 1 see Gomolka,
Mikolaj

MELODIES FOR POLISH PSALTER VOL. 2 see Gomolka,
Mikolaj

MELODIES FOR POLISH PSALTER VOL. 3 see Gomolka,
Mikolaj

MELOY, ELIZABETH
Heaven And Earth And Sea And Air
SATB (med) ABINGDON APM-762 $.45 (M1142)

MEMBRA JESU NOSTRI see Buxtehude, Dietrich

MEMENTO CREATORIS see Musgrave, Thea

MEMENTO DOMINE DAVID see Willaert, Adrian

MEMENTO HOMO see Kubizek, Augustinian

MEMENTO NOSTRI, DOMINE see Soderholm, Valdemar

MEMOR ESTO see Palestrina, Giovanni

MEMORARE see Englert, Eugene

MEMORARE see Heiller, Anton

MEMORARE see Kronsteiner, Josef

MEMORARE see Mercenier, P.

MEMORIA JUDAEORUM see Dresden, Sem

MEMORIAL ACCLAMATIONS I-IV see Roff, Joseph

MEMORIAL PRAYER see Brenner, Walter

MEMORIAL SERVICE see Piket, Frederick

MEMORIES OF CHRISTMAS see Carleton

MEMORIES OF EASTER MORN see Lorenz

MEMORIES OF THE MANGER see Nolte

MEMPHIS CHOIR *CC10UL
(Ferrin, Paul) SATB,org,pno,bvl,drums,gtr voc
sc WORD 37510 $1.95 (M1143)

MEN AND ANGELS NOW ADORE THEE see Bach, Johann
Sebastian

MEN AND ANGELS SHARE see Taylor, P.

MEN AND ANGELS SING HALLELUJAH see Edward, J.

MEN FOR THE CRISIS HOUR see Smith, Lani

MEN OF OLD see Ford, Virgil T.

MENCER
Strangers In The Streets
(Chase) SATB SHAWNEE A 1086 $.30 (M1144)

MENDELSSOHN, ARNOLD (1855-1933)
Alles Ist An Gottes Segen
see Sechzehn Kirchliche Lieder Und
Motetten-Heft 1

Christus Lebet, Christus Sieget *Op.90,No.2,
Easter,mot
8pt mix cor,soli,acap cor pts BREITKOPF-L
PB-2679 s.p., voc pt BREITKOPF-L CHB-2442
s.p. (M1145)

MENDELSSOHN, ARNOLD (cont'd.)

Deutsche Messe *Op.89, Mass
SATB&SATB,acap cor pts BREITKOPF-W PB-2677
s.p. (M1146)

Erhalt Uns, Herr
see Sechzehn Kirchliche Lieder Und
Motetten-Heft 8

Frohlich Soll Mein Herze Springen
see Zwei Kleine Weihnachtsmotetten

Kommst Du, Licht Der Heiden?
see Sechzehn Kirchliche Lieder Und
Motetten-Heft 1

Lasst Uns Eilen, Lasst Uns Wallen
see Zwei Kleine Weihnachtsmotetten

Lobt Gott, Ihr Christen *Op.90,No.9, Xmas,
mot
SATB&SATB,acap cor pts BREITKOPF-W PB-3050
s.p. (M1147)

Motette Zum Pfingstfest *Op.90,No.4, Pent/
Whitsun,mot
8pt mix cor,acap cor pts BREITKOPF-L
PB-2696 s.p. (M1148)

O Welt, Ich Muss Dich Lassen
see Sechzehn Kirchliche Lieder Und
Motetten-Heft 8

Ostermorgenglockenklang
see Sechzehn Kirchliche Lieder Und
Motetten-Heft 5

Schmucke Dich
see Sechzehn Kirchliche Lieder Und
Motetten-Heft 4

Schmucket Das Fest Mit Maien *Op.90,No.4,
Pent/Whitsun,mot
8pt mix cor,acap cor pts BREITKOPF-W
PB-2696 s.p. (M1149)

Sechzehn Kirchliche Lieder Und Motetten-Heft
1 *Fest
3pt wom cor/3pt jr cor,acap cor pts
BREITKOPF-L CHB-2501 s.p.
contains: Alles Ist An Gottes Segen;
Kommst Du, Licht Der Heiden? (M1150)

Sechzehn Kirchliche Lieder Und Motetten-Heft
3 *see Wie Schon Leuchtet Der
Morgenstern (M1151)

Sechzehn Kirchliche Lieder Und Motetten-Heft
4 *Gd.Fri.
3pt wom cor/3pt jr cor,acap cor pts
BREITKOPF-L CHB-2504 s.p.
contains: Schmucke Dich; Wir Mochten Gern
Dein Kreuz (M1152)

Sechzehn Kirchliche Lieder Und Motetten-Heft
5 *Easter
3pt wom cor/3pt jr cor,acap cor pts
BREITKOPF-L CHB-2505 s.p.
contains: Ostermorgenglockenklang; Um
Dein Grab Sind Wir Gegangen (M1153)

Sechzehn Kirchliche Lieder Und Motetten-Heft
6 *see So Wisse Tun (M1154)

Sechzehn Kirchliche Lieder Und Motetten-Heft
8 *Refm,Req
3pt wom cor/3pt jr cor,acap cor pts
BREITKOPF-L CHB-2508 s.p.
contains: Erhalt Uns, Herr; O Welt, Ich
Muss Dich Lassen , (M1155)

So Wisse Tun *Easter
3pt wom cor/3pt jr cor,acap cor pts
BREITKOPF-L CHB-2506 s.p. see from
Sechzehn Kirchliche Lieder Und Motetten-
Heft 6 (M1156)

Traufelt Ihr Himmel Von Oben *Op.90,No.5,
Adv,mot
SATB&SATB,SATB soli,acap s.p. sc BREITKOPF-
W PB-2697, voc pt BREITKOPF-W CHB-2469 s.p. (M1157)

Um Dein Grab Sind Wir Gegangen
see Sechzehn Kirchliche Lieder Und
Motetten-Heft 5

Wir Mochten Gern Dein Kreuz
see Sechzehn Kirchliche Lieder Und
Motetten-Heft 4

Zwei Kleine Weihnachtsmotetten *Xmas,mot
3pt wom cor/3pt jr cor,acap cor pts
BREITKOPF-W CHB-2502 s.p.
contains: Frohlich Soll Mein Herze
Springen; Lasst Uns Eilen, Lasst Uns
Wallen (M1158)

Zwolf Altdeutsche Weihnachtslieder *CC12U,
Xmas,Ger
wom cor/jr cor,acap cor pts BREITKOPF-L
CHB-2782A-C s.p. (M1159)

MENDELSSOHN-BARTHOLDY, FELIX (1809-1847)
Above All Praise *Gen,anthem
mix cor oct OXFORD 43.458 $.45 (M1160)
SATB oct ROYAL 232 s.p. (M1161)

Adoro Te
see SIX MOTETS A L'UNISSON

Advent Chorale, The *Adv/Xmas
(Porter) SATB oct LORENZ 9979 $.25 (M1162)

All Men, All Things, Praise Thou The Lord
(from Hymn Of Praise) Thanks,anthem
SATB,S solo oct NOVELLO 34.0072.07 s.p. (M1163)

All That Has Life And Breath
see Mendelssohn-Bartholdy, Felix, Cast Thy
Burden
(Chambers) SATB oct BOOSEY 5335 $.40 (M1164)
(Hardwicke) SSA ALFRED 6239 $.35 (M1165)

All Ye That Cried Unto The Lord *see
Lobgesang

MENDELSSOHN-BARTHOLDY, FELIX (cont'd.)

And Then Shall The Light (from Elijah)
SATB ALLANS 312 s.p. (M1166)

And Then Shall Your Light (from Elijah)
4pt mix cor oct SCHIRM.G 7594 $.30 (M1167)
PARAGON 1022 $.20 (M1168)

And Then Shall Your Light Break Forth (from
Elijah)
SATB oct PRO ART 1381 $.25 (M1169)

As The Hart Longs
(Imig) SATB oct FOX R167 $.35 (M1170)

As The Hart Pants *see Wie Der Hirsch
Schreit

As The Heart (Psalm 42)
cor voc sc KALMUS 6305 $1.00 (M1171)

Au Pied Du Trone Celeste *see Periti Autem

Aus Tiefer Not Schrei Ich Zu Dir (Psalm 130)
Gen/Lent
(Nott, D.) "In Deep Despair I Call To Thee"
mix cor,S/T solo,kbd CONCORDIA 97-4857
$1.50 (M1172)

Ave Maria (from Loreley)
(Saar, L.) SSA,S solo,pno SCHIRM.EC 1090
$.16 (M1173)

Ave Verum *Commun,mot
(Kunc, P.) [Lat] 4pt mix cor oct DURAND
s.p. (M1174)

Be Not Afraid (from Elijah) anthem/Bibl
PARAGON 1020 $.22 (M1175)
4pt mix cor oct SCHIRM.G 6653 $.30 (M1176)
SATB ALLANS 51 s.p. (M1177)
SATB oct NOVELLO 34.0314.09 s.p. (M1178)
(Whitford, H.) SATB oct PRESSER 312-21615
$.30 (M1179)

Beati Mortui *Op.115,No.1, Gen,mot
[Lat] 4pt men cor,opt pno/org oct DURAND
s.p. (M1180)
"Heureux, Trois Fois Heureux" [Lat/Fr]
TTBBBarBar,acap oct DURAND s.p. (M1181)
(Hines) "Blessed Are The Dead" [Eng/Lat]
TTBB,acap oct LAWSON 51707 $.30 (M1182)

Beati Mortui *see Wie Selig Sind Die Toten

Behold A Star From Jacob Shining (from
Christus)
(Davison, A.) SATB,org SCHIRM.EC 1683 $.45 (M1183)

Behold God The Lord
SATB oct GRAY GCMR 3199 $.35 (M1184)

Blessed Are The Dead *see Beati Mortui

Blessed Are The Men Who Fear Him (from
Elijah) anthem
PARAGON 1019 $.22 (M1185)
SATB oct NOVELLO 34.6311.04 s.p. (M1186)

Blessed Lord, Wilt Thou Sustain Us *see
Geistliches Lied

Blessed Redeemer, At Thy Word
(Strickling) SAB oct PLYMOUTH PCS-207 $.25 (M1187)

But Our God Abideth In Heaven (from St. Paul)
ora
(Barker) 5pt mix cor,acap oct SCHIRM.G
11115 $.30 (M1188)

But The Lord Is Mindful Of His Own (from St.
Paul) Gen,anthem/Bibl
SATB (easy) oct AUGSBURG 0003 $.22 (M1189)
unis oct SCHIRM.G 5854 $.25 (M1190)
SATB,A solo ALLANS 204 s.p. (M1191)
unis SCHMITT 2578 $.25 (M1192)
unis,orch oct NOVELLO 48.0923.08 s.p., ipr (M1193)
4pt mix cor oct SCHIRM.G 4431 $.25 (M1194)
(Davis, K.) SSA,pno SCHIRM.EC 1856 $.25 (M1195)
(Deis) 2pt wom cor oct SCHIRM.G 9697 $.30 (M1196)
(Hines) 3pt mix cor,org/pno,acap oct
SCHIRM.G 11444 $.30 (M1197)
(Scarmolin) SATB oct PRO ART 1436 $.25 (M1198)
(Weaver) SSA oct GALAXY 1.0906.1 $.30 (M1199)
(Weaver) SAB oct GALAXY 1.1503.1 $.30 (M1200)

Cast Thy Burden (from Elijah) Lent/Rembrnc
SATB PATERSON 1622 s.p. contains also: All
That Has Life And Breath (M1201)
SATB ALLANS 316 s.p. (M1202)
(Wilson) SAB oct BOOSEY 5111 $.30 (M1203)

Cast Thy Burden Upon The Lord (from Elijah)
anthem
SATB KJOS 7003 $.30 (M1204)
SATB oct NOVELLO 34.0341.06 s.p. (M1205)
SATB oct FISCHER,C CM-6604 $.25 (M1206)
SATB oct PRESSER 332-00825 $.25 (M1207)
4pt mix cor oct SCHIRM.G 10015 $.25 (M1208)
(DeVito; Craig) SAB oct PLYMOUTH DC-203
$.25 (M1209)

Chorale Harmonizations *CC9L,chorale
mix cor CONCORDIA 98-1705 $.75 (M1210)

Christus *Op.97, cant/ora
see Mendelssohn-Bartholdy, Felix, Elijah
BELWIN $1.25 (M1211)
SATB,STBB soli,2fl,2ob,2clar,2bsn,2horn,
2trp,3trom,strings,timp voc sc NOVELLO
s.p., ipr (M1212)
mix cor,STBB soli,2fl,2ob,2clar,2bsn,2trp,
2horn,3trom,strings,timp BREITKOPF-L
rental (M1213)
cor,orch sc KALMUS $12.00, ipa (M1214)
cor voc sc KALMUS 6271 $1.25 (M1215)
cor,pno voc sc SCHIRM.G $1.00 (M1216)
(Ziemer; Rodby) "Christus" SATB KJOS V54
$2.00 (M1217)

Christus *see Christus

MENDELSSOHN-BARTHOLDY, FELIX (cont'd.)

Church Music
cor voc sc KALMUS 6307 $3.00
contains: Lauda Sion, Op.73; Tu Es Petrus, Op.97; Verleih Uns Frieden, Op.111 (M1218)

Collected Works :Miscellaneous Sacred Music *CCU
(Rietz, Julius) cor GREGG ISBN 0:576 28903 5 s.p. (M1219)

Collected Works : Psalms *CCU,Psalm
(Rietz, Julius) cor GREGG ISBN 0:576 28906 X s.p. (M1220)

Come, Let Us Sing *see Kommt, Lasst Uns Anbeten

Come Unto Him
SATB PATERSON 1623 s.p. contains also: He That Shall Endure (M1221)

Complete Works In 61 Volumes *CCU
cor min sc KALMUS $149.95 (M1222)

Courage, Brother (from Festegesang)
unis PATERSON 1625 s.p. (M1223)

Da Nobis Pacem *anthem/mot
[Lat] cor,B solo oct NOVELLO 40.0432.09 s.p. (M1224)
"Grant Us Thy Peace" mix cor,B solo oct NOVELLO 40.0432.09 s.p. (M1225)
"Grant Us Thy Peace" SATB oct GRAY GCMR 1663 $.25 (M1226)
"Grant Us Thy Peace" SATB KJOS 5082 $.30 (M1227)
(Barker) "Grant Us Thy Peace" SATB oct BELWIN 1952 $.30 (M1228)
(Ehret) "Grant Us Thy Peace" SATB oct BOOSEY 5236 $.30 (M1229)
(Hardwicke) "Grant Us Thy Peace" SSA ALFRED 6205 $.35 (M1230)
(Roach, Donald) "Grant Us Thy Peace" SATB oct BELWIN 2197 $.25 (M1231)

Daughters Of Zion
(Ehret) SATB oct BOOSEY 5228 $.35 (M1232)

Denn Er Hat Seinen Engeln Befohlen Uber Dir (Psalm 91) Bibl
SSAA&TTBB HANSSLER 25.013 s.p. (M1233)

Drei Motetten *see Herr, Nun Lassest Du Deinen Diener In Frieden Fahren, Op.69; Jauchzet Dem Herrn Alle Welt, Op.69; Mein Herz Erhebet Gott, Den Herrn, Op.69 (M1234)

Drei Psalmen *see Mein Gott, Warum (Psalm 22) Op.78; Richte Mich, Gott (Psalm 43) Op.78; Warum Toben Die Heiden (Psalm 2) Op.78 (M1235)

Du Omme Faderhjerte
mix cor MUSIKK 120 s.p. (M1236)

Earth Is Hushed In Silence, The
(Coggin) SAB oct PLYMOUTH PCS-210 $.25 (M1237)

Ecce Panis *Commun,mot
[Lat] 4pt mix cor,A/Bar solo oct DURAND s.p. (M1238)

Elias *Op.70, Bibl/ora
mix cor,SATB soli,org,2fl,2ob,2clar,2bsn, 2trp,4horn,3trom,tuba,strings,timp BREITKOPF-L rental (M1239)
"Elijah" cor SCHIRM.G voc sc $1.50, pap $1.50, bds $2.50, cloth $4.00, cor pts $1.25 (M1240)
"Elijah" [Eng/Ger] study sc UNIVER. PH. 29 $6.25 (M1241)
"Elijah" [Ger] SATB,SATB soli,org,orch voc sc PETERS 1749 $4.50, ipr, min sc PETERS E989 $12.00, ipr, min sc-cloth PETERS E989 $15.00, ipr (M1242)
"Elijah" cor cor pts KALMUS 6301 $1.25 (M1243)
"Elijah" SATB,SATB soli,org,2fl,2ob,2clar, 2ob,4horn,2trp,3trom,tuba,strings,timp bds,voc sc NOVELLO s.p., ipr (M1244)
"Elijah" cor,opt orch voc sc KALMUS 6300 $2.50, ipa (M1245)
"Elijah" cor min sc KALMUS 500 $8.00 (M1246)
"Elijah" cor sc KALMUS $35.00 (M1247)
"Elijah" cor KALMUS $7.00 (M1248)
"Elijah" cor,orch sc KALMUS $35.00, ipa (M1249)
(Stephens) "Elijah" cor,soli,org sc SCHIRM.G $7.50 (M1250)
(Werner) "Elijah" mix cor sc CHAPPELL 0024620-315 $4.50 (M1251)

Elijah *ora
(Rietz, Julius) cor GREGG ISBN 0:576 28902 7 s.p. contains also: Christus (M1252)

Elijah *see Elias

Es Strahlen Hell Die Gerechten
"Periti Autem" see Zwei Geistliche Chore

Favorite Anthems From Mendelssohn *CCU, anthem
SATB LORENZ $1.50 (M1253)

Festgesang *Fest
SATB,brass&brass,timp voc sc NOVELLO rental (M1254)

Festival Song Of Praise
(Wilson) SATB oct BOURNE 724 $.40 (M1255)

First Walpurgisnight
cor voc sc KALMUS 6304 $1.50 (M1256)

For He Shall Give His Angels (from Elijah)
8pt mix cor oct SCHIRM.G 7909 $.30 (M1257)

For My Soul Thirsteth For God *Gen
(Ehret) SATB SCHMITT 8001 $.30 (M1258)

For Our Offences *Psntd
(Trevor, C.H.) SSAA,acap oct NOVELLO 33.0128.01 s.p. (M1259)

MENDELSSOHN-BARTHOLDY, FELIX (cont'd.)

For So Hath The Lord (from St. Paul)
SA,pno (med) oct WILLIS 4372 $.12 (M1260)

Four Chorales (from St. Paul)
(Barker) 4pt mix cor oct SCHIRM.G 10915 $.40
contains: Sleepers, Wake, A Voice Is Calling; Thou, The True And Only Light; To God On High; To Thee, O Lord (M1261)

Geistliches Lied
"Blessed Lord, Wilt Thou Sustain Us" SATB,A solo,org SCHIRM.EC 2618 $.40 (M1262)

Give Us Peace
see Mendelssohn-Bartholdy, Felix, Tu Es Petrus

Gloria In Excelsis *Xmas,cant
SATB oct LORENZ $1.95 (M1263)

Grant Us Peace
(Gray) SAB oct PRO ART 1628 $.25 (M1264)

Grant Us Thy Peace *see Da Nobis Pacem

Hail The Heaven-Born Prince *Xmas,anthem
(Russell, Olive Nelson) SATB,org/pno oct WORLD CA-1945-8 $.60 (M1265)

Happy And Blest Are They (from St. Paul) Bibl
4pt mix cor oct SCHIRM.G 9443 $.30 (M1266)
SATB oct PRO ART 1384 $.30 (M1267)
SATB,org SCHIRM.EC 1133 $.35 (M1268)

Hark! The Herald Angels Sing *Xmas,carol
unis&desc oct NOVELLO 44.1319.09 s.p. (M1269)
(Shaw; Parker) SATB,acap oct LAWSON 728 $.30 (M1270)
(Swift) SATB oct PRO ART 1289 $.20 (M1271)

He Is The Tender Shepherd *see Surrexit Pastor Bonus

He That Shall Endure (from Elijah) anthem
see Mendelssohn-Bartholdy, Felix, Come Unto Him
SATB oct NOVELLO 34.0318.01 s.p. (M1272)
4pt mix cor oct SCHIRM.G 10713 $.25 (M1273)
(Palmer) SATB ALFRED 6348 $.25 (M1274)

He That Shall Endure To The End (from Elijah)
SATB oct PRESSER MC338 $.30 (M1275)
SATB oct PRESSER 332-00826 $.30 (M1276)
(Holmes) SSAA,acap oct PRO ART 1452 $.18 (M1277)

He, Watching Over All The World
(Hoggard) SATB SHAWNEE A 231 $.30 (M1278)

He Watching Over Israel *see Siehe, Der Huter Israels

Hear My Prayer *anthem/mot
cor oct HART s.p. (M1279)
SATB oct LESLIE 4044 (M1280)
cor voc sc KALMUS 6303 $.75 (M1281)
mix cor,S solo oct NOVELLO 28.0339.09 s.p. (M1282)
SATB oct PRESSER 312-10332 $.60 (M1283)
SATB ALLANS 125 s.p. (M1284)
SATB,S solo,pno/org oct HARRIS HC4024 $.50 (M1285)
cor,solo PATERSON 1627 s.p. (M1286)
cor,S solo voc sc SCHIRM.G $.75 (M1287)
cor,soli voc sc SCHIRM.G $.75 (M1288)

Hear Our Prayer, O Lord *see Veni Domine

Hebe Deine Augen Auf (from Elias)
3pt wom cor oct ALSBACH&D s.p. (M1289)
(Vogel, Moritz; Nagler, Franciscus) [Ger] wom cor&jr cor,org,opt strings HUG 25 s.p. (M1290)

Heilig
mix cor SOUTHERN $.30 (M1291)
"Holy" SATB&SATB oct WALTON 2163 $.30 (M1292)

Herr, Nun Lassest Du Deinen Diener In Frieden Fahren *Op.69, mot
4pt mix cor,soli,acap cor pts BREITKOPF-W CHB-3694 s.p. see from Drei Motetten (M1293)

Heureux, Trois Fois Heureux *Op.115
[Fr] 4pt men cor,opt pno/org oct DURAND (M1294)

Heureux, Trois Fois Heureux *see Beati Mortui

Holy *see Heilig

Holy, Holy, Holy *Gen
(Forrester) dbl cor SCHMITT 896 $.40 (M1295)

Holy Is God The Lord (from Elijah)
PARAGON 1021 $.20 (M1296)

Hope Thou In God *Gen
(Hines) SAB SCHMITT 5522 $.25 (M1297)

Hor Mein Bitten, Herr *hymn
mix cor cor pts ALSBACH&D s.p. (M1298)
4pt mix cor,S solo,org BREITKOPF-W voc pt s.p., voc sc s.p. (M1299)

How Lovely Are
SATB oct LESLIE 4027 (M1300)

How Lovely Are The Messengers (from St. Paul) Adv,anthem/Bibl
SAB oct LORENZ 7037 $.30 (M1301)
SATB oct LORENZ 484 $.30 (M1302)
SATB oct PRESSER 332-00927 $.30 (M1303)
3pt wom cor oct SCHIRM.G 4371 $.30 (M1304)
4pt mix cor oct SCHIRM.G 3741 $.30 (M1305)
SATB oct PRO ART 1323 $.30 (M1306)
2pt,orch oct NOVELLO 53.0292.07 s.p., ipr (M1307)
SATB oct NOVELLO 34.0173.01 s.p. contains also: Thus Saith The Lord (M1308)
SA,org SCHIRM.EC 1885 $.25 (M1309)
SATB,org SCHIRM.EC 1134 $.35 (M1310)
SATB oct FISCHER,C CM-620 $.25 (M1311)
(Bliss, P.) SSA oct PRESSER 312-20282 $.30 (M1312)
(Ehret, Walter) SATB oct BELWIN 1357 $.30

MENDELSSOHN-BARTHOLDY, FELIX (cont'd.)

(M1313)
(Gerhard) SATB oct SPRATT 509 $.30 (M1314)
(Riegger) SSA/TB FLAMMER E5110 $.30 (M1315)
(Riegger) SAB FLAMMER D5122 $.30 (M1316)
(Ryder, A.) SA oct PRESSER 332-13346 $.30 (M1317)
(Stickles) 3pt mix cor,3solo,org/pno oct SCHIRM.G 11539 $.30 (M1318)

How Lovely Are Thy Messengers (from St. Paul) Fest
SATB,A solo ALLANS 7 s.p. (M1319)

Hymn *Op.96
see Mendelssohn-Bartholdy, Felix, Tu Es Petrus

Hymn Of Praise *ora
(Rietz, Julius) cor GREGG ISBN 0:576 28913 2 s.p. (M1320)

Hymn Of Praise *see Lobgesang

I Heard The Voice Of Jesus *anthem
(Halloran) mix cor oct FOX R213 $.30 (M1321)

I Waited For The Lord (from Hymn Of Praise, The) anthem/Bibl
2pt ENOCH TP199 s.p. (M1322)
SA BOOSEY-CAN s.p. (M1323)
SA oct BOOSEY 862 $.30 (M1324)
SATB,S solo ALLANS 57 s.p. (M1325)
SA oct HARRIS HC2003 $.25 (M1326)
SATB,SS soli oct HARRIS HC4031 $.35 (M1327)
2pt,orch oct NOVELLO 53.0204.08 s.p., ipr (M1328)
SATB&SA oct NOVELLO 34.2169.04 s.p. (M1329)
SATB oct PRESSER 312-10269 $.30 (M1330)
4pt wom cor,SSA soli oct SCHIRM.G 14 $.25 (M1331)
4pt mix cor,S solo oct SCHIRM.G 3439 $.30 (M1332)
(Cain) SSA oct BOOSEY 1553 $.30 (M1333)
(Norman) SSA,org/pno BOSTON 2130 $.30 (M1334)
(Stickles) 2pt wom cor oct SCHIRM.G 10630 $.30 (M1335)
(Stickles) 3pt wom cor oct SCHIRM.G 10631 $.35 (M1336)
(Swift) SAB oct PRO ART 1160 $.25 (M1337)
(Swift) SATB oct PRO ART 1033 $.30 (M1338)
(Tudor, Frank) SA ALLANS 393 s.p. (M1339)
(Whitford, H.) SATB,acap oct PRESSER 312-21435 $.30 (M1340)

I Will Sing Of Thy Great Mercies (from St. Paul) Bibl
unis,orch oct NOVELLO 48.0922.10 s.p., ipr (M1341)
(Hines) 3pt mix cor,org/pno oct SCHIRM.G 11433 $.25 (M1342)
(Scarmolin) SATB oct PRO ART 1499 $.22 (M1343)

If With All Your Hearts (from Elijah) anthem
SA/TB oct BELWIN 1581 $.25 (M1344)
unis oct SCHIRM.G 5896 $.25 (M1345)
SATB (very easy) oct AUGSBURG 0007 $.25 (M1346)
SATB oct LORENZ 9212 $.25 (M1347)
(Baumbach, A.) SATB oct PRESSER 332-03737 $.25 (M1348)
(Christiansen, P.) SATB KJOS 80 $.30 (M1349)
(Davis, K.) SA,org SCHIRM.EC 1562 $.25 (M1350)
(Deis) 4pt mix cor oct SCHIRM.G 10019 $.30 (M1351)
(Ehret) SSA oct FOX R140 $.30 (M1352)
(Ehret, W.) SAB oct BELWIN 60522 $.30 (M1353)
(Ehret, W.) SATB oct BELWIN 60104 (M1354)
(Glaser, V.) SATB,pno SCHIRM.EC 2482 $.30 (M1355)
(Grant, Louise) SSA oct BELWIN 1773 $.30 (M1356)
(Peery, Rob Roy) SA oct BELWIN 1581 $.25 (M1357)
(Pitcher, Gladys) 3pt mix cor,pno (med) oct WILLIS 8492 $.20 (M1358)
(Stickles) 3pt mix cor,org/pno oct SCHIRM.G 11466 $.25 (M1359)
(Wilson) SATB,acap oct COLOMBO 1557 $.25 (M1360)

In Deep Despair I Call To Thee *see Aus Tiefer Not Schrei Ich Zu Dir

In Heavenly Love Abiding *anthem
(Barnes) SA BOSTON 1643 $.30 (M1361)
(Christiansen, F.M.) SATB (very easy) oct AUGSBURG 0166 $.18 (M1362)
(Coggin) SAB oct BELWIN 64303 $.30 (M1363)
(Wiley) SATB oct PRO ART 1765 $.25 (M1364)

In His Hand (Psalm 95) Bibl
2pt,orch oct NOVELLO 48.0886.10 s.p. (M1365)

Jauchzet Dem Herrn Alle Welt (Psalm 100) Op.69, Bibl/mot
4pt mix cor,soli,acap cor pts BREITKOPF-W CHB-3695 s.p. see from Drei Motetten (M1366)
SATB/SSAATTBB HANSSLER 25.022 $.50 (M1367)
8pt mix cor,acap cor pts BREITKOPF-W CHB-3607 s.p. (M1368)
(Ehret) mix cor CHAPPELL 0024257-358 $.40 (M1369)

Jerusalem (from St. Paul)
unis,orch oct NOVELLO 48.0854.01 s.p., ipr (M1370)

Judge Me, O God *anthem/Bibl
SSAATTBB,org oct HARRIS HC4029 $.35 (M1371)
SATB oct WALTON 2157 $.30 (M1372)
SATB oct PRESSER 312-10406 $.25 (M1373)
8pt mix cor oct SCHIRM.G 3613 $.25 (M1374)
(Salter) 4pt men cor oct SCHIRM.G 5169 $.25 (M1375)

Kommt, Lasst Uns Anbeten (Psalm 95) Op.46, Bibl/Psalm
mix cor,SST soli,2fl,2ob,2clar,2bsn,2horn, 2trp,3trom,strings,timp voc pt BREITKOPF-W CHB-484 s.p., ipr, sc BREITKOPF-W rental (M1376)
cor min sc KALMUS 1204 $1.30 (M1377)
cor voc sc KALMUS 6302 $1.25 (M1378)
"Come, Let Us Sing" SATB,SST soli,2fl,2ob, 2clar,2bsn,2horn,2trp,3trom,strings,timp voc sc NOVELLO s.p., ipr (M1379)

MENDELSSOHN-BARTHOLDY, FELIX (cont'd.)

"Come Let Us Sing" cor,soli,pno cmplt ed SCHIRM.G $1.50 (M1380)
"Come Let Us Sing" 4pt mix cor oct SCHIRM.G 2085 $.45 (M1381)
"Psalm" cor,orch sc KALMUS $15.00, ipa (M1382)

Kyrie *Kyrie
(Leavis, R.) mix cor,org/orch (med easy) voc sc OXFORD 46.136 $1.80, ipr (M1383)

Lauda Sion *Op.73, cant
see Church Music
cor min sc KALMUS 1206 $1.30 (M1384)
"Praise, Jehova" cor voc sc KALMUS 6289 $2.50 (M1385)
"Praise Jehovah" SATB,SATB soli,2fl,2ob, 2clar,2bsn,2horn,2trp,3trom,strings,timp voc sc NOVELLO s.p., ipr (M1386)

Laudate Pueri *Adv,Bibl
wom cor,pno sc ALSBACH&D s.p. (M1387)
"Praise Ye The Lord" girl cor SOUTHERN $.35 (M1388)
"Ye Sons Of Israel" [Eng/Lat] 3pt wom cor, 3solo oct SCHIRM.G 310 $.35 (M1389)
(Aks) "Praise Ye The Lord" [Eng/Lat] SSA MARKS 81 $.40 (M1390)

Laudate Pueri Dominum *Op.39,No.2
"Ye Sons Of Israel" SSA,pno SCHIRM.EC 1839 $.30 (M1391)

Let Our Hearts Be Joyful
(Cramer) SATB,acap MARKS 4295 $.25 (M1392)

Lift Thine Eyes (from Elijah) Gen,Bibl
girl cor SOUTHERN $.25 (M1393)
SSA oct LORENZ 6239 $.25 (M1394)
4pt,acap (staff notation only) oct NOVELLO 40.0388.08 s.p. (M1395)
4pt,acap (staff and tonic sol-fa notations) oct NOVELLO 47.0140.02 s.p. (M1396)
SSA,acap SCHIRM.EC 1017 $.30 (M1397)
SSA,acap oct FISCHER,C CM-618 $.25 (M1398)
SSA oct BELWIN 64123 $.30 (M1399)
SSA,acap oct PRESSER 332-00820 $.25 (M1400)
3pt wom cor oct SCHIRM.G 26 $.25 (M1401)
SSA ALLANS 172 s.p. (M1402)
SSA oct LESLIE 3011 (M1403)
SSA KJOS P766 $.30 (M1404)
SSA SCHMITT 2901 $.30 (M1405)
(Deis) 2pt boy cor/2pt wom cor,SS soli oct SCHIRM.G 10221 $.25 (M1406)
(Deis) 3pt mix cor oct SCHIRM.G 10256 $.25 (M1407)
(Ehret) SA BOOSEY-CAN s.p. (M1408)
(Ehret) SA oct BOOSEY 1920 $.30 (M1409)
(Grant) SA BOSTON 2355 $.30 (M1410)
(Logan; Baldwin) TTBB oct COLOMBO 851 $.25 (M1411)
(Logan; Baldwin) SSA oct COLOMBO 878 $.25 (M1412)
(Logan; Brower) SATB oct COLOMBO 909 $.25 (M1413)
(Long) SSA,opt kbd oct PRO ART 1141 $.30 (M1414)
(Pitcher, Gladys) 3pt mix cor,pno (med) oct WILLIS 8486 $.20 (M1415)
(Siegmeister; Ehret) SSA oct BOURNE 211 $.25 (M1416)
(Swift) SATB oct BELWIN 1757 $.30 (M1417)
(Swift, Frederic Fay) SATB oct BELWIN 1757 $.25 (M1418)
(Werner, Jack) 2pt (easy) oct OXFORD 44.205 $.30 (M1419)

Lift Thine Eyes To The Mountains (from Elijah)
3pt wom cor,acap (med) oct WILLIS 698 $.12 (M1420)

Lobgesang *Op.52 (from Hymn Of Praise) Bibl/ cant/hymn/ora
mix cor,SST soli,org,2fl,2ob,2clar,2bsn, 2trp,4horn,3trom,strings,timp BREITKOPF-L rental (M1421)
"All Ye That Cried Unto The Lord" SATB oct PRO ART 1685 $.30 (M1422)
"Hymn Of Praise" cor,pno voc sc SCHIRM.G $1.50 (M1423)
"Hymn Of Praise" BELWIN $1.50 (M1424)
"Hymn Of Praise" cor voc sc KALMUS 6299 $1.50 (M1425)
"Hymn Of Praise" cor min sc KALMUS 4856 $4.00 (M1426)
"Hymn Of Praise" cor,orch sc KALMUS $30.00, ipa (M1427)
"Hymn Of Praise" oct HART s.p. (M1428)
"Hymn Of Praise" SATB,SST soli,org,2fl,2ob, 2clar,2bsn,4horn,2trp,3trom,strings,timp voc sc NOVELLO s.p., ipr (M1429)
(Gray) "All Ye That Cried Unto The Lord" SSA oct PRO ART 1839 $.25 (M1430)
(Tillinghast) "All Ye That Cried Unto The Lord" SSA WARNER W3583 $.30 (M1431)

Lord, At All Times (from Lauda Sion)
unis oct NOVELLO 48.0798.07 s.p. (M1432)
SSA oct PRESSER G-3002 $.30 (M1433)

Lord God Of Abraham
(Willhoite) SATB SHAWNEE A 213 $.25 (M1434)

Lord God Of Our Fathers
SATB ALLANS 200 s.p. (M1435)

Lord Have Mercy Upon Us *Eve,Kyrie
SATB oct WALTON 6027 $.30 (M1436)

Lord How Long (Psalm 13) cant
BELWIN $.75 (M1437)

Lord, I Flee To Thee
(Ehret) SATB,A solo oct BOOSEY 5400 $.35 (M1438)

Lord Is A Mighty God, The
SATB FLAMMER A 5393 $.30 (M1439)

Lord Is Great, The
(Douglas) SATB oct PRO ART 1891 $.30 (M1440)

Lord, Lord Have Mercy
see Sacred A Capella Choruses

Lord, No Lettest Thou
see Sacred A Capella Choruses

Lord, Our Creator (from Elijah)
(Whitford) SATB,org BOSTON 13273 $.40 (M1441)

Lord, Remember Not
SSAATTBB oct WALTON 6010 $.30 (M1442)

Lord, Thou Alone Art God (from St. Paul) anthem
SATB oct NOVELLO 34.0176.06 s.p. (M1443)

Mein Gott, Warum (Psalm 22) Op.78
8pt mix cor,soli,acap cor pts BREITKOPF-W CHB-3570 s.p. see from Drei Psalmen (M1444)

Mein Gott, Warum Hast Du Mich (Psalm 22) Bibl
"My God, Wherefore Hast Thou Forsaken Me?" [Eng/Ger] SSAATTBB,SATB soli HANSSLER 25.002 $1.50 (M1445)

Mein Herz Erhebet Gott, Den Herrn *Op.69, mot
4pt mix cor,soli,acap cor pts BREITKOPF-W CHB-3696 s.p. see from Drei Motetten (M1446)

Motets, Hymn, Te Deum *CCU,hymn/mot/Te Deum
cor min sc KALMUS 1208 $1.30 (M1447)

My God, Wherefore Hast Thou Forsaken Me?
*see Mein Gott, Warum Hast Du Mich

My Son, Oh Be Joyful
see Sacred A Capella Choruses

My Soul Longeth For Thee *Bibl
(Pooler) 4pt mix cor,pno/org oct SCHIRM.G 11421 $.30 (M1448)

Night Is Departing, The (from Hymn Of Praise) anthem
SATB oct NOVELLO 34.0186.03 s.p. (M1449)

Not Unto Us, O Lord
(Samuel Adler) 4pt mix cor,STBar soli,pno voc sc SCHIRM.G $1.00 (M1450)

Now Thank We All Our God (from Hymn Of Praise)
(Tillinghast) SSAA WARNER W3584 $.30 (M1451)

O Come, Every One That Thirsteth (from Elijah)
PARAGON 1023 $.20 (M1452)

O Come, Let Us Worship (Psalm 95) (from Come, Let Us Sing) anthem/Bibl
4pt mix cor,T solo oct SCHIRM.G 2084 $.35 (M1453)
SATB oct NOVELLO 34.0250.09 s.p. (M1454)
(Ehret) SATB,T solo oct BOOSEY 5399 $.35 (M1455)

O For The Wings Of A Dove (from Hear My Prayer)
4pt mix cor,S solo,org/pno oct SCHIRM.G 2614 $.30 (M1456)
unis oct NOVELLO 47.0049.10 s.p. (M1457)
(Spiro) SSA oct PRO ART 1479 $.25 (M1458)
(West, John E.) 2pt oct NOVELLO 33.0066.08 s.p. (M1459)

O Great Is The Depth
SATB ALLANS 125 s.p. (M1460)

O Jesus, I Have Promised (from Italian Symphony)
unis,solo PATERSON 1632 s.p. (M1461)

O King Of Mercy
cor,solo PATERSON 1633 s.p. (M1462)

O Rest In The Lord (from Elijah) Gen
SATB oct LORENZ 9182 $.30 (M1463)
2pt ASHDOWN E.A.220 s.p. (M1464)
unis,orch oct NOVELLO 47.0201.08 s.p., ipr (M1465)
(Ehret) SATB oct BELWIN 1548 $.25 (M1466)
(Forest) cor HIGHLAND 5102 $.25 (M1467)
(Francis) SSA oct FOX PS46 $.25 (M1468)
(Glarum) SATB SCHMITT 1657 $.25 (M1469)
(Whipple, H.) SA,org SCHIRM.EC 1982 $.25 (M1470)

O Salutaris
[Lat] unis HEUGEL s.p. see from SAINTE-CECILE (M1471)

On Wings Of Song The Angels Came
(Habash) SSA/SATB/SAB/SA/TB BIG3 $.40 (M1472)

Paulus *Op.36, Bibl/ora
mix cor,SATBB soli,org,2fl,2ob,2clar,3bsn, 2trp,4horn,3trom,strings,timp, serpent BREITKOPF-L rental (M1473)
"Saint Paul" cor min sc KALMUS 491 $7.00 (M1474)
"Saint Paul" cor min sc KALMUS 1178 $1.30 (M1475)
"St. Paul" cor,soli,pno voc sc SCHIRM.G $2.50 (M1476)
"St. Paul" [Eng/Ger] SATB,STBB soli,orch voc sc PETERS 1748 $6.50, ipr (M1477)
"St. Paul" SATB,SATB soli,org,2fl,2ob, 2clar,3bsn,4horn,2trp,3trom,tuba,strings, timp voc sc NOVELLO s.p., ipr (M1478)
"St. Paul" [Ger/Eng] cor voc sc KALMUS 6298 $2.50 (M1479)
"St. Paul" cor,orch sc KALMUS $35.00, ipa (M1480)

Periti Autem *Op.112,No.2, Gen,mot
[Lat] 4pt men cor,opt pno/org oct DURAND s.p. (M1481)
"Au Pied Du Trone Celeste" [Fr] 4pt men cor,opt pno/org oct DURAND (M1482)
"Au Pied Du Trone Celeste" [Lat/Fr] TTBBBarBar,acap oct DURAND (M1483)

Periti Autem *see Es Strahlen Hell Die Gerechten

Pfingstlied *Pent,chorale
[Ger] mix cor,acap (easy) HUG (M1484)

Praise, Jehova *see Lauda Sion

Praise Jehovah *see Lauda Sion

Praise Ye The Lord *see Laudate Pueri

Prayer (from Hear My Prayer)
(Glaser, V.) SA,org SCHIRM.EC 2513 $.25 (M1485)

Prayer And Chorale *chorale
(Pfautsch) SATB oct LAWSON 849 $.40 (M1486)

Psalm *see Kommt, Lasst Uns Anbeten

Psalm 2 *see Warum Toben Die Heiden

Psalm 13 *see Lord How Long

Psalm 22 *see Mein Gott, Warum

Psalm 22 *see Mein Gott, Warum Hast Du Mich

Psalm 42 *see Wie Der Hirsch Schreit

Psalm 43 *see Richte Mich, Gott

Psalm 43 *see Richte Mich, Gott, Und Fuhre Meine Sache

Psalm 91 *see Denn Er Hat Seinen Engeln Befohlen Uber Dir

Psalm 95 *see Kommt, Lasst Uns Anbeten

Psalm 98 *Op.91
see Mendelssohn-Bartholdy, Felix, Psalm 114

Psalm 100 *see Jauchzet Dem Herrn, Alle Welt

Psalm 114 *Op.51
mix cor,2fl,2ob,2clar,2bsn,2trp,4horn, 3trom,strings,timp sc BREITKOPF-L rental (M1487)
cor min sc KALMUS 1205 $1.30 contains also: Psalm 98, Op.91 (M1488)

Psalm 115 *Op.31
cor min sc KALMUS 1202 $1.30 (M1489)

Psalm 130 *see Aus Tiefer Not Schrei Ich Zu Dir

Psalms, Motets, And Kyries *Op.78,Op.100, CCU,mot/Psalm/Te Deum
cor min sc KALMUS 1209 $1.30 (M1490)

Richte Mich, Gott (Psalm 43) Op.78, Psalm
8pt mix cor,soli,acap cor pts BREITKOPF-W CHB-3569 s.p. see from Drei Psalmen (M1491)
SATB,acap cor pts BREITKOPF-L rental (M1492)

Richte Mich, Gott, Und Fuhre Meine Sache (Psalm 43) Bibl
SSAA&TTBB HANSSLER 25.010 s.p. (M1493)

Sacred A Capella Choruses
[Ger/Eng] cor,acap voc sc KALMUS 6306 $1.25 contains: Lord, Lord Have Mercy; Lord, No Lettest Thou; My Son, Oh Be Joyful (M1494)

Sacred Choral Music A Cappela *CC13U
[Ger/Eng] SATB/SATB,SATB soli sc PETERS 1770B $7.50, voc pt PETERS 1770B $1.25 (M1495)

Sacred Choral Music With Organ *CC12U
[Ger/Lat/Eng] 3-8 cor,S,A,SATB soli,org PETERS 1770A $7.50, cor pts PETERS 1770A $1.25 (M1496)

Saint Paul *see Paulus

Say, Where Is He? (from Christus)
(Clough-Leighter, H.) ABB,org SCHIRM.EC 2609 $.30 (M1497)
(Clough-Leighter, H.) TBB,org SCHIRM.EC 2609 $.30 (M1498)

Say, Where Is He Born? (from Christus) Xmas, anthem
SSA oct PRO ART 1322 $.22 (M1499)
3pt wom cor oct SCHIRM.G 364 $.20 (M1500)
SATB oct GRAY GCMR 1695 $.30 contains also: There Shall A Star (M1501)
SATB,TBB soli oct NOVELLO 28.0085.03 s.p. contains also: There Shall A Star (SATB) (M1502)
(Walton) SATB oct SPRATT 589 $.25 (M1503)

Say, Where Is He That Is Born King Of Judah (from Christus)
(Clough-Leighter, H.) ABB/TBB,org SCHIRM.EC 2609 $.30 (M1504)
(Clough-Leighter, H.) TBB/ABB,org SCHIRM.EC 2609 $.30 (M1505)

Sechs Spruche *Op.79, CC6U,anthem
SSAATTBB,acap voc sc WALTON M-109 $1.25 (M1506)

See What Love *anthem
SATB (med) oct AUGSBURG 1281 $.22 (M1507)
(Kjelson) SATB oct BELWIN 2173 $.30 (M1508)

See What Love Hath The Father (from St. Paul) anthem
SATB oct NOVELLO 44.0044.07 s.p. (M1509)
(Barker) 4pt mix cor,acap oct SCHIRM.G 11116 $.25 (M1510)

Siehe, Der Huter Israels (from Elijah) anthem/Bibl
"He, Watching Over Israel" SATB PATERSON 1628 s.p. (M1511)
"He Watching Over Israel" SATB oct PRO ART 1124 $.30 (M1512)
"He, Watching Over Israel" 4pt,orch oct NOVELLO 51.0568.04 s.p., ipr (M1513)
"He Watching Over Israel" SATB oct NOVELLO 34.0315.07 s.p. (M1514)
"He Watching Over Israel" SSA,pno SCHIRM.EC 1073 $.30 (M1515)
"He, Watching Over Israel" SATB oct FISCHER,C CM-7245 $.25 (M1516)
"He Watching Over Israel" SATB oct BELWIN 766 $.25 (M1517)
"He, Watching Over Israel" SATB oct PRESSER 332-00827 $.30 (M1518)
"He, Watching Over Israel" 4pt mix cor oct SCHIRM.G 2498 $.30 (M1519)
"He, Watching Over Israel" SATB ALLANS 123 s.p. (M1520)
"He, Watching Over Israel" SATB oct HARRIS HC4016 $.30 (M1521)

MENDELSSOHN-BARTHOLDY, FELIX (cont'd.)

"He Watching Over Israel" SATB SCHIRM.EC
2786 $.35　　　　　　　　　　　　　(M1522)
(Campbell; Watson) "He Watching Over
Israel" SSA,acap WARNER W3547 $.30
　　　　　　　　　　　　　　　　　　(M1523)
(Carlton) "He, Watching Over Israel" SATB
oct BOOSEY 5177 $.40　　　　　　　(M1524)
(Deis) "He, Watching Over Israel" 3pt wom
cor oct SCHIRM.G 10086 $.35　　　(M1525)
(Ehret) "He Watching Over Israel" SSA
BOOSEY-CAN s.p.　　　　　　　　　(M1526)
(Glaser, V.) "He Watching Over Israel" SA
SCHIRM.EC 1979 $.30　　　　　　　(M1527)
(Milkey) "He, Watching Over Israel" 3pt mix
cor oct SCHIRM.G 11241 $.30　　　(M1528)
(Trusler) "He, Watching Over Israel" SATB
oct PLYMOUTH TR-119 $.30　　　　(M1529)
(Wallinger) "He, Watching Over Israel" SSA
oct FOX R135 $.30　　　　　　　　　(M1530)
(Wilson) "He, Watching Over Israel" SSA oct
BOOSEY 5121 $.35　　　　　　　　　(M1531)

Sing Ye Merrily *anthem
(Sateren) SSAATTBB (diff) oct AUGSBURG 1223
$.35　　　　　　　　　　　　　　　　(M1532)

Six Mendelssohn Anthems *CC6U,anthem
mix cor SCHMITT 7 $.50　　　　　　(M1533)

Sleeper's, Wake (from St. Paul)
see Mendelssohn-Bartholdy, Felix, To God On
High

Sleepers, Wake, A Voice Is Calling (from St.
Paul)
see Four Chorales

St. Paul *ora
(Rietz, Julius) cor GREGG
ISBN 0:576 28907 8 s.p.　　　　　(M1534)

St. Paul *see Paulus

St. Paul [Chorale] *chorale
SATB oct STAFF 643 $.25　　　　　(M1535)

Still With Thee
(Larson) SATB oct PRO ART 1316 $.20 (M1536)
(Larson) SSA oct PRO ART 1137 $.25 (M1537)

Sub Tuum *BVM,mot
[Lat] 3 eq voices oct DURAND s.p. (M1538)
[Lat] SS HEUGEL s.p. see from SAINTE-CECILE
　　　　　　　　　　　　　　　　　　(M1539)

Surrexit Pastor Bonus
girl cor SOUTHERN $.35　　　　　　(M1540)
[Lat/Eng] SSAA,pno/org BROUDE,A. 167 $.35
　　　　　　　　　　　　　　　　　　(M1541)
(Barrie) "He Is The Tender Shepherd" [Eng/
Lat] 3pt boy cor/SSA/SAA,pno/org oct
LAWSON 51699 $.30　　　　　　　　(M1542)

Tantum Ergo *Commun,mot
[Lat] SATBar oct DURAND s.p.　　(M1543)

Te Deum *Te Deum
[Lat] 4-8pt mix cor,cont sc DEUTSCHER
rental　　　　　　　　　　　　　　　(M1544)

Thanks Be To God (from Elijah) Thanks
SAB oct LORENZ 7365 $.25　　　　(M1545)
SATB oct PRO ART 1311 $.35　　　(M1546)
SATB WARNER W2534 $.30　　　　(M1547)
SATB ALLANS 43 s.p.　　　　　　　(M1548)
4pt mix cor oct SCHIRM.G 3742 $.35 (M1549)

Then Shall The Righteous Shine Forth (from
Elijah) anthem
SATB oct FISCHER,C CM-7101 $.25 (M1550)

There Shall A Star (from Christus) Xmas/Gen
see Mendelssohn-Bartholdy, Felix, Say Where
Is He Born
see Mendelssohn-Bartholdy, Felix, Say,
Where Is He Born
SATB oct GRAY GCMR 1695 $.30　(M1551)

There Shall A Star Come Out Of Jacob *Adv/
Xmas,Bibl
SATB oct PRO ART 1383 $.30　　　(M1552)
SATB SCHMITT 1903 $.45　　　　　(M1553)
(Buck) 4pt mix cor oct SCHIRM.G 3004 $.35
　　　　　　　　　　　　　　　　　　(M1554)

There Shall A Star From Jacob *anthem
SATB oct FISCHER,C CM-6228 $.30 (M1555)

Thou, Lord, Our Refuge
SATB oct PRESSER MC400 $.30　　(M1556)
SATB oct STAFF 427 $.25　　　　　(M1557)
(Davis) boy cor SOUTHERN $.30　(M1558)
(Hardwicke) SATB,acap oct PRO ART 2396 $.25
　　　　　　　　　　　　　　　　　　(M1559)

Thou, The True And Only Light (from St. Paul)
see Four Chorales

Three Motets For Chorus And Solo *Op.69,
CC3U,mot
cor,solo voc sc KALMUS 6288 $2.00　(M1560)

Thus Saith The Lord (from St. Paul)
see Mendelssohn-Bartholdy, Felix, How
Lovely Are The Messengers

To God On High (from St. Paul) anthem
see Four Chorales
SATB oct NOVELLO 40.0070.06 s.p. contains
also: Sleeper's, Wake; To Thee, O Lord
　　　　　　　　　　　　　　　　　　(M1561)

To Thee, O Lord (from St. Paul)
see Four Chorales
see Mendelssohn-Bartholdy, Felix, To God On
High

Trust Thou In God *Bibl
(Barker) 4pt mix cor oct SCHIRM.G 10916
$.25　　　　　　　　　　　　　　　　(M1562)
(Imig) [Ger/Eng] SATB,org oct MCA (M1563)

Tu Es Petrus *Gen,mot
see Church Music
[Lat] SBar oct DURAND s.p.　　　(M1564)

Tu Es Petrus *see Verleih Uns Frieden

Two Airs (from Elijah) CC2U
2pt ENOCH TP123 s.p.　　　　　　(M1565)

MENDELSSOHN-BARTHOLDY, FELIX (cont'd.)

Veni, Domine
girl cor SOUTHERN $.35　　　　　　(M1566)
[Lat/Eng] SSA,pno/org BROUDE,A. 166 $.35
　　　　　　　　　　　　　　　　　　(M1567)
(Aks) "Hear Our Prayer, O Lord" [Eng/Lat]
SSA MARKS 82 $.25　　　　　　　　(M1568)

Verleih Uns Frieden *Op.111, hymn/prayer
see Church Music
mix cor,2fl,2clar,2bsn,strings sc
BREITKOPF-L rental　　　　　　　　(M1569)
"Tu Es Petrus" cor min sc KALMUS 1207 $1.30
contains also: Give Us Peace; Hymn, Op.96
　　　　　　　　　　　　　　　　　　(M1570)

Wake, Awake (from St. Paul)
(Spiro) SATB oct PRO ART 1337 $.20 (M1571)

Warum Toben Die Heiden (Psalm 2) Op.78, Bibl
8pt mix cor,soli,acap cor pts BREITKOPF-W
CHB-3568 s.p. see from Drei Psalmen (M1572)
[Ger] dbl cor HANSSLER 25.009 $1.50 (M1573)

We Come Unto Our Father's God
(Kirk) SATB oct PRO ART 1588 $.25 (M1574)

Where Is He Born?
(Boyce) SATB FLAMMER A 5292 $.25 (M1575)

Wie Der Hirsch Schreit (Psalm 42) Op.42, Bibl
mix cor,STTBB soli,org,2fl,2ob,2clar,2bsn,
2trp,4horn,3trom,strings,timp BREITKOPF-L
rental　　　　　　　　　　　　　　　(M1576)
cor min sc KALMUS 1203 $1.30　　(M1577)
"As The Hart Pants" cor,S solo cmplt ed
SCHIRM.G $1.00　　　　　　　　　　(M1578)
"As The Hart Pants" SATB,S&TTBB soli,2fl,
2ob,2clar,2bsn,2horn,2trp,3trom,strings,
timp voc sc NOVELLO s.p., ipr　(M1579)
"As The Hart Pants" SATB ALLANS 210 s.p.
　　　　　　　　　　　　　　　　　　(M1580)
(Tillinghast) "As The Hart Pants" SSA
WARNER W3579 $.35　　　　　　　(M1581)

Wie Selig Sind Die Toten
"Beati Mortui" see Zwei Geistliche Chore

Ye Sons Of Israel *see Laudate Pueri

Ye Sons Of Israel *see Laudate Pueri Dominum

Zooals 'T Hert Dorst (Psalm 42)
[Neth] mix cor ALSBACH&D sc s.p., cor pts
s.p.　　　　　　　　　　　　　　　　(M1582)
[Ger] mix cor cor pts ALSBACH&D s.p.
　　　　　　　　　　　　　　　　　　(M1583)

Zwei Geistliche Chore *Op.115
4pt men cor,acap cor pts BREITKOPF-W
CHB-3548 s.p.
contains: Es Strahlen Hell Die Gerechten,
"Periti Autem"; Wie Selig Sind Die
Toten, "Beati Mortui"　　　　　(M1584)

MENDOZA, ANNE
A Festival Of Folk Carols (composed with
Rimmer, Joan) *Xmas
unis&2pt,pno,perc,rec,opt strings (may be
performed as Nativity play with mime) voc
sc NOVELLO 20.0107.01 s.p., ipa (M1585)

MENEGALI
Blessed Are The Merciful *see Jesu, Salvator
Mundi

Jesu, Our Holy Savior *see Jesu, Salvator
Mundi

Jesu, Salvator Mundi
"Jesu, Our Holy Savior" see RESPONSES FROM
THE WORKS OF OLD MASTERS
(Davis, K.) "Blessed Are The Merciful" SSA,
acap SCHIRM.EC 1888 $.25　　　　(M1586)

MENGELBERG, RUDOLF (1892-1959)
Antiphona De Morte
mix cor BROEKMANS 92 s.p.　　　(M1587)

Stabat Mater
[Lat] mix cor,pno,2fl,3ob,3clar,3bsn,3trp,
4horn,3trom,tuba,strings,perc,timp
DONEMUS min sc s.p., cor pts s.p., voc sc
s.p.　　　　　　　　　　　　　　　　(M1588)

Tantum Ergo
mix cor ALSBACH&D sc s.p., cor pts s.p.
　　　　　　　　　　　　　　　　　　(M1589)

Victimae Paschali Laudes
[Lat] mix cor,S solo,2fl,2ob,2clar,2bsn,
2trp,4horn,2trom,tuba,strings,perc,timp
DONEMUS min sc s.p., cor pts s.p., voc sc
s.p.　　　　　　　　　　　　　　　　(M1590)

MENNIN, PETER (MENNINI) (1923-   )
Christmas Story, The *Xmas,cant
SATB,opt strings&4brass&timp FISCHER,C
O 3700 $1.50, ipr　　　　　　　　　(M1591)

People That Walked In Darkness *Xmas
SSAA oct FISCHER,C CM-7044 $.25 (M1592)

MENOTTI, GIAN CARLO (1911-   )
Death Of The Bishop Of Brindisi, The
cor&jr cor,SB soli,orch SCHIRM.G voc sc
$3.50, cor pts $1.00, ipa　　　　　(M1593)

L'ultimo Selvaggio
[Fr/Eng] cor pts BELWIN $2.50　　(M1594)

Shepherd's Chorus, The (from Amahl And The
Night Visitors) Xmas
4pt mix cor oct SCHIRM.G 10801 $.40 (M1595)
3pt mix cor oct SCHIRM.G 10955 $.40 (M1596)

MEN'S GET-TOGETHER SONGS *CCU
men cor LORENZ $1.25　　　　　　(M1597)

MEN'S GOSPEL IN SONG *CCU
men cor LORENZ $1.25　　　　　　(M1598)

MENSCH, WERD AUS GOTT GEBORN see Silesius,
Angelus

MENSCH, WERDE WESENTLICH see Kratochwill,
Heinrich

MENSCH, WERDE WESENTLICH see Bauernfiend, Hans

MENSCH, WERDE WESENTLICH see Kratochwill,
Heinrich

MENTRE SPERAI DA TE see Monte, de

MER HAHN EN NEUE OBERKEET see Bach, Johann
Sebastian

MERBECKE *Commun
(Nicholson, Sydney H.) cor,pno/org sc ROYAL
s.p.　　　　　　　　　　　　　　　　(M1599)

MERBECKE, JOHN (1510-1585)
Communion Service *Commun
unis (adapted for Roman Catholic usage) oct
OXFORD 45.066 $1.00　　　　　　　(M1600)
(Arnold, J.H.) unis,org (very easy) oct
OXFORD 40.907 $.65　　　　　　　(M1601)

Holy Communion *Commun
(Harwood) SATB voc sc NOVELLO 44.0784.09
s.p., cor pts NOVELLO 44.2784.10 s.p.
　　　　　　　　　　　　　　　　　　(M1602)
(Shore, Royle) SATB NOVELLO voc sc s.p.,
cor pts s.p., ipa　　　　　　　　　(M1603)
(Stainer) SATB oct NOVELLO 44.0369.10 s.p.
　　　　　　　　　　　　　　　　　　(M1604)
(Stainer) SATB (contains complete Office of
Holy Communion from the Cathedral Prayer
Book) oct NOVELLO 02.0041.07 s.p. (M1605)
(Wyatt; Shore) SATB voc sc NOVELLO s.p.,
ipa　　　　　　　　　　　　　　　　(M1606)

Per Arma Justitiae *Mass
mix cor,acap voc sc KALMUS 6688 $1.35
　　　　　　　　　　　　　　　　　　(M1607)

Three Anthems *CC3U,anthem
mix cor,acap voc sc KALMUS 6689 $1.00
　　　　　　　　　　　　　　　　　　(M1608)

Three Sayings Of Jesus
(Davies, Walford) SATB oct NOVELLO s.p.
　　　　　　　　　　　　　　　　　　(M1609)

Virgin And Mother, A *Xmas,carol
SAB PETERS H1503 $.40　　　　　(M1610)
SAB,acap STAINER CC597 $.35　　(M1611)

MERCADANTE, G. SAVERIO (1795-1870)
Ave Verum *Commun,mot
[Lat] STBar oct DURAND s.p.　　　(M1612)

Sette Ultime Parole *ora
"Seven Last Words, The" [It/Eng] cor,soli,
orch voc sc SCHIRM.G $1.25　　　(M1613)

Seven Last Words, The *see Sette Ultime
Parole

MERCATALI, A.
Ave Verum Corpus
see SEI MOTTETTI EUCARISTICI

Elegi Abjectus Esse
see IN PRIMA MISSA CELEBRANDA

Gaudens Gaudebo
see IN SOLEMNI CLERICORUM VESTITIONE

Jesu Corona Virginum
see INNI DE COMUNE

MERCENIER, P.
Au Christ-Roi
[Lat] 3 eq voices,org LEMOINE voc sc s.p.,
cor pts s.p.　　　　　　　　　　　　(M1614)

Ave Rex Noster
[Lat] 3pt,acap LEMOINE s.p.　　　(M1615)

Fac Nos Domine
[Lat] 3 eq voices,org LEMOINE voc sc s.p.,
cor pts s.p.　　　　　　　　　　　　(M1616)

Invocations A Sainte-Therese De L'enfant
Jesus
3pt,solo,org LEMOINE voc sc s.p., cor pts
s.p.　　　　　　　　　　　　　　　　(M1617)

Memorare
2-3 eq voices,soli,org LEMOINE voc sc s.p.,
cor pts s.p.　　　　　　　　　　　　(M1618)

O Quam Suavis Est
[Lat] 3 eq voices,solo,org LEMOINE voc sc
s.p., cor pts s.p.　　　　　　　　　(M1619)

O Salutaris
[Lat] 4 eq voices,org LEMOINE voc sc s.p.,
cor pts s.p.　　　　　　　　　　　　(M1620)

Que Les Anges De Dieu
3pt,org LEMOINE voc sc s.p., cor pts s.p.
　　　　　　　　　　　　　　　　　　(M1621)

Salve Regina *BVM
[Lat] 3pt,solo,org LEMOINE voc sc s.p., cor
pts s.p.　　　　　　　　　　　　　　(M1622)

Sinite Parvulos
[Lat] 3pt,org LEMOINE voc sc s.p., cor pts
s.p.　　　　　　　　　　　　　　　　(M1623)

Therese Est Dans Les Cieux
3pt,org LEMOINE voc sc s.p., cor pts s.p.
　　　　　　　　　　　　　　　　　　(M1624)

MERCER, M.
Jesus Is His Name
(McLellan) SATB oct LILLENAS AT-1072 $.30
　　　　　　　　　　　　　　　　　　(M1625)

Lonely Road! Up Calvary's Way
(McLellan) SSATB oct LILLENAS AT-1052 $.30
　　　　　　　　　　　　　　　　　　(M1626)

Nobody But Jesus
(Schubert) SATB oct LILLENAS AN-1604 $.30
　　　　　　　　　　　　　　　　　　(M1627)

Prayer
2pt wom cor oct SCHIRM.G 10500 $.25 (M1628)

So Great Is His Love (composed with Benson)
(McLellan) SSATB oct LILLENAS AT-1053 $.25
　　　　　　　　　　　　　　　　　　(M1629)

Strangers In The Street
(Chase) SSA FLAMMER B 345 $.30　(M1630)

MERCHANTS' CAROL, THE see Frackenpohl, Arthur

MERCIFUL FATHER see Werbecke, G. Von, Virgo
Maria

MERCIFUL SAVIOUR
see Communion Hymns

MERCY AND TRUTH see Thompson, V.D.

MERCY, LORD, ON US see Gabrieli, Andrea, Kyrie

MERCY LORD, UPON US see Mozart, Wolfgang Amadeus, Kyrie

MERCY, O THOU SON OF DAVID see Clark, Keith

MERCY ON US, O LORD see Lvovsky, S.

MERCY, PITY, PEACE AND LOVE see Lovelace, Austin C.

MERIKANTO, [OSKAR] (1868-1924)
Sag Minnes Du Psalmen
men cor,T solo NORDISKA 1691 s.p. (M1631)
(Ahlen, David) mix cor,solo NORDISKA 679 s.p. (M1632)

MERKEL, GUSTAV A. (1827-1885)
This Is The Day Which The Lord Hath Made *Adv/Gen
(Lundquist) SATB,acap (med) oct WILLIS 5501 $.16 (M1633)

MERKT AUF DIE ZEIT see Weber, Bernhard

MERKX, C.J.E.
Ave Maria
men cor ALSBACH&D sc s.p., cor pts s.p. (M1634)

MERMAN
Greatest Is Love
SATB SHAWNEE A 1142 $.30 (M1635)

MERRICK, FRANK (1886-   )
Epiphany Carol *Epiph
SATB/unis,acap (very easy) oct OXFORD 84.163 $.15 (M1636)

MERRILY ON HIGH see Hadler

MERRITT, CHARLES
On Christmas Night *Xmas
SATB (med) ABINGDON APM-338 $.40 (M1637)

MERRY ARE THE BELLS see Barab

MERRY BELLS ARE RINGING see Praetorius, Michael

MERRY BELLS AT YULE, THE see Naylor, Edward Woodall

MERRY CHRISTMAS
see Four Songs For Christmas

MERRY CHRISTMAS see Matthews, D.E.

MERRY CHRISTMAS!, A see Vida

MERRY CHRISTMAS BELLS see Lawrence

MERRY CHRISTMAS BELLS, THE see Grime, William

MERRY CHRISTMAS, ONE AND ALL *Xmas,carol,Rum
(Luboff Norman) SATB/TTBB/2pt oct WALTON 3024 $.25 (M1638)

MERRY HEART, A see Mechem, Kirke

MERRY NOEL, A see Emig, Lois

MERRYMAN
Song Of Ruth *Bibl
SATB oct PRO ART 2157 $.30 (M1639)

MERULO, CLAUDIO (1533-1604)
Aspice Domine (With Crequillon's Chanson)
see Sacred Works vol. I

Benedicta Es Coelorum Regina
see Sacred Works vol. I

Oncques Amour
see Sacred Works vol. I

Sacred Works vol. I *Mass
(Bastian, James) cor AM.INST.MUS. $19.00
contains: Aspice Domine (With Crequillon's Chanson); Benedicta Es Coelorum Regina; Oncques Amour; Susanne Un Giour (M1640)

Sacred Works Vol. II *CCU,Mass
(Bastian, James) 8pt&12pt AM.INST.MUS. $22.00 (M1641)

Sacred Works Vol. III *CCU,mot
(Bastian, James) 5pt AM.INST.MUS. $19.00 (M1642)

Susanne Un Giour
see Sacred Works vol. I

MESSA see Hemberg-Eskil

MESSA see Monteverdi, Claudio

MESSA see Ramella

MESSA see Rodella, Sante

MESSA see Sonzogno, Giulio Cesare

MESSA A S. LUIGI see Schinelli, Achille

MESSA A TROIX VOIX see Franck, Cesar

MESSA ANTONIANA see Dalla Vecchia, Wolfango

MESSA B. VERGINE DELLA SALUTE see Loregian, Sandro

MESSA BREVE see Bottazzo, Luigi

MESSA BREVE E FACILE IN ON. DE S. MARTINO VESC. see Bottazzo, Luigi

MESSA BREVE E FACILE IN ONORE DI S LUIGI GONZAGA see Ravanello, Oreste

MESSA CONCERTATA see Casati

MESSA CONCERTATA see Cavalli, Francesco

MESSA CONCILIARE see Vianello, Gino

MESSA CORALE see Rancati, Ettore

MESSA DA REQUIEM see Paisiello, Giovanni

MESSA DA REQUIEN see Tommasini, Vincenzo

MESSA DEI POVERI see Farina, E.

MESSA DI GLORIA see Puccini, Giacomo

MESSA DI MADRID see Scarlatti, Domenico

MESSA DI REQUIEM see Perosi, (Dom) Lorenzo

MESSA DI REQUIEM see Pizzetti, [Ildebrando]

MESSA DI REQUIEM see Verdi, Giuseppe, Manzoni Requiem

MESSA DI SANTA CECILIA see Scarlatti, Alessandro

MESSA D'OGGI see Intra, E.

MESSA GESU REDENTORE see Magaldi, Vincenzo

MESSA GIUBILARE see Roussel, Mario

MESSA I A 6 VOCI see Monteverdi, Claudio

MESSA I IN ONORE DI S. TECLA see Paccagnella, Erminegildo

MESSA II A 4 VOCI see Monteverdi, Claudio

MESSA II IN ONORE DI S. PROSDOCIMO see Paccagnella, Erminegildo

MESSA IN C-DUR see Mozart, Wolfgang Amadeus

MESSA IN ON. DI MARIA BAMBINA see Bottazzo, Luigi

MESSA IN ON. DI S. CLARA V. see Bottazzo, Luigi

MESSA IN ON. DI S. ROMEDIO EREMITA E CONFESSORE see Tonetti, Ottone

MESSA IN ONORE DEL SS. CUORE DI GESU see Mangone, Gioacchino

MESSA IN ONORE DELLA B. MADDALENA DI CANOSSA see Giratto, Almerigo

MESSA IN ONORE DELLA MADONNA DI LORETO see Loss, Luigi

MESSA IN ONORE DI S. CATERINA DA SIENA see Ferrante

MESSA IN ONORE DI S. DOROTEA see Bottazzo, Luigi

MESSA IN ONORE DI S. ELIA, PROTETTORE DEGLI AVIATORI see Bottazzo, Luigi

MESSA IN ONORE DI S. GUGLIELMO AB. see Bottazzo, Luigi

MESSA IN ONORE DI S. NICOLAO DELLA FLUE see Picchi, Luigi

MESSA IN ONORE DI S. PIO X see Picchi, Luigi

MESSA IN ONORE DI S. TECLA see Bottazzo, Luigi

MESSA NOSTRA SIGNORA DI FATIMA see Loregian, Sandro

MESSA PASTORALE see Yon, Pietro Alessandro

MESSA PEI DEFUNTI see Bottazzo, Luigi

MESSA REQUIEM see Perosi, (Dom) Lorenzo

MESSA RITMATA see Passamonti, G.

MESSA S. FRANCESCO D'ASSISI see Serena, Bruno

MESSA SANCTA MARIA see Dalla Libera

MESSA SOLENNE see Arnaldi, Antonio, Lauda Sion

MESSA SOLENNE XX IN ONORE DI S. TIZANIO see Ravanello, Oreste

MESSA SOLENNE XXXV IN ONORE DI S. ANTONIO TAUMATURGO NEL VII CENTENARIO DELLA SUA MORTE see Ravanello, Oreste

MESSA SS. VITORRE E CORONA see Antoniol, Antonio

MESSA VERGINE E MADRE see Anonymous

MESSA VOTIVA PER IL GIORNO DI SABATO see Saraceni, Franco Maria

MESSA XVIII IN ONORE DI S. CECILIA see Ravanello, Oreste

MESSA XXII FACILISSIMA IN ON. DEL SS. NOME DI MARIA see Ravanello, Oreste

MESSA XXIII FUNEBRE FACILISSIMA see Ravanello, Oreste

MESSA XXVIII ALLA MADONNA DELLE VITTORIE see Ravanello, Oreste

MESSA XXXI IN ONORE DI S. DOMENICO see Ravanello, Oreste

MESSA XXXII IN ONORE DI S. CATERINA DA SIENA see Ravanello, Oreste

MESSAGE CAME TO A MAIDEN YOUNG, A see Held, Wilbur

MESSAGE OF THE CROSS, THE see Scott, J. Sheldon

MESSAGE, THE *carol
SATB (very easy) OXFORD 08.095 $.15 (M1643)

MESSAGER, ANDRE (1853-1929)
Le Credo De La Victoire *Credo
[Fr] 2pt ENOCH voc sc s.p., cor pts s.p. (M1644)

MESSAUS
O Blessed, Holy Bethlehem
see SIX SEVENTEENTH CENTURY CAROLS FROM THE NETHERLANDS

Sing We In Exultation
see SIX SEVENTEENTH CENTURY CAROLS FROM THE NETHERLANDS

MESSE see Aiblinger, Johann Kaspar

MESSE see Besozzi, L.D.

MESSE see Burkhard Willy

MESSE see Cherubini, Luigi

MESSE see Damase, Jean-Michel

MESSE see David, Johann Nepomuk

MESSE see Dubois, Theodore

MESSE see Durand, A.

MESSE see Faure, Gabriel-Urbain

MESSE see Franck, [Johann Wolfgang]

MESSE see Gehlen, Hermann

MESSE see Hindemith, Paul

MESSE see Hufschmidt, Wolfgang

MESSE see Petzold, Rudolf

MESSE see Philippart-Gonzalez, Renee

MESSE see Schmitt, Florent

MESSE see Schumann, Robert (Alexander)

MESSE see Yung, Alf.

MESSE see Rheinberger, Josef

MESSE see Rheinberger, Josef

MESSE see Rheinberger, Josef

MESSE A 4 VOCI see Monteverdi, Claudio

MESSE A-DUR see Bach, Johann Sebastian

MESSE A LA MEMOIRE DE JEANNE D'ARC see Gounod, Charles Francois

MESSE A NOTRE-DAME see Saint Jean Du Sacre Coeur, Soeur

MESSE A QUARTE VOIX see Pierne, Paul

MESSE A S.S. JEAN XXIII see Carrillo, Julian, Misa a S.S. Juan XXIII

MESSE AS-DUR see Schubert, Franz (Peter)

MESSE AUF DIE HEILIGEN DREIFALTIGKEIT see Pfiffner, Ernst

MESSE B-DUR see Schubert, Franz (Peter)

MESSE BASSE see Faure, Gabriel-Urbain

MESSE BREVE see Durand, A.

MESSE BREVE see La Tombelle, Fernand de

MESSE BREVE see Laurent, L.

MESSE BREVE see Yung, Alf.

MESSE BREVE DE ANGELIS see Chailley

MESSE BREVE EN L'HONNEUR DE SAINTE ANNE see Ropartz, Joseph Guy

MESSE BREVE IN C MAJOR NO. 7 see Gounod, Charles Francois

MESSE BREVE NO. 5, AUX SEMINAIRES see Gounod, Charles Francois

MESSE BREVE NO. 7, AUX CHAPELLES see Gounod, Charles Francois

MESSE C-DUR see Aiblinger, Johann Kaspar

MESSE C-DUR see Beethoven, Ludwig van

MESSE C-DUR see Mozart, Wolfgang Amadeus

MESSE C-DUR see Schubert, Franz (Peter)

MESSE C-MOLL see Schumann, Robert (Alexander)

MESSE CHORALE see Gounod, Charles Francois

MESSE D-DUR see Beethoven, Ludwig van

MESSE D-MOLL see Bruckner, Anton

MESSE D-MOLL see Haydn, (Franz) Joseph

MESSE D-MOLL see Haydn, (Franz) Joseph, Nelson-Missa

MESSE DA PACEM see Potiron, H.

MESSE DE DOMREMY A LA GLOIRE DE SAINTE JEANNE D'ARC see Busser, [Henri-Paul]

MESSE DE FERIA see Lassus, Roland de (Orlandus)

MESSE DE LA NATIVITE see Nicou-Charon

MESSE DE LA NATIVITE see Tomasi

MESSE DE LA VICTOIRE see Borne, Le

MESSE DE MINUIT see Charpentier, Marc-Antoine

MESSE DE MINUIT POUR NOEL see Charpentier, Marc-Antoine

MESSE DE MINUIT SUR DES AIRS DE NOEL see Charpentier, Marc-Antoine

MESSE DE NOEL see Busser, [Henri-Paul]

MESSE DE NOSTRE DAME see Machaut, Guillaume de

MESSE DE NOTRE DAME AND LAIS see Machaut, Guillaume de

MESSE DE NOTRE-DAME DE L'ASSOMPTION see Alix, Rene

MESSE DE PAQUES see Rousseau, Samuel-Alexandre

MESSE DE REQUIEM see Bozza, Eugene

MESSE DE REQUIEM see Delmas, M.

MESSE DE REQUIEM see Saint-Saens, Camille

MESSE DE REQUIEM see Verdi, Giuseppe

MESSE DE SA SAINTETE PIE XII see Bozza, Eugene

MESSE DE SAINT-BERTRAND DE COMMINGES see Busser, [Henri-Paul]

MESSE DE SAINT-JEAN see Gounod, Charles Francois

MESSE DE SAINTE-CECILE see Gounod, Charles Francois

MESSE DES ANGES GARDIENS see Gounod, Charles Francois

MESSE DES PAUVRES see Satie, Erik

MESSE DES PETITS DE SAINT-EUSTACHE-LA- FORET see Caplet, [Lucien]

MESSE DES ROIS MAGES see Pilot

MESSE DES ROIS MAGES, SUR DES NOELS ANCIENS see Pilot

MESSE DITE DE CLOVIS see Gounod, Charles Francois

MESSE, DITE "POUR LE JOUR DE LA PAIX" see Jolivet, Andre

MESSE DU CINQUIEME CENTENAIRE DE LA MORT DE JEANNE D'ARC see Paray, [Paul]

MESSE DU JUBILE see Lesur, Daniel

MESSE DU SACRE see Cherubini, Luigi

MESSE DU SACRE-COEUR DE JESUS see Gounod, Charles Francois

MESSE DU SACRE DE LOUIS XVI see Giroust, F., Gaudete In Domino Semper

MESSE E-MOLL see Bruckner, Anton

MESSE EN L'HONNEUR DE SAINT-ODILE see Weyer, J.

MESSE EN L'HONNEUR DE SAINTE ODILE see Ropartz, Joseph Guy

MESSE EN UT see Mozart, Wolfgang Amadeus

MESSE ES-DUR see Schubert, Franz (Peter)

MESSE F-DUR see Bach, Johann Sebastian

MESSE F-DUR see Schubert, Franz (Peter)

MESSE F-MOLL see Bruckner, Anton

MESSE FACILE see Franck, [Johann Wolfgang]

MESSE G-DUR see Bach, Johann Sebastian

MESSE G-DUR see Schubert, Franz (Peter)

MESSE G-MOLL see Bach, Johann Sebastian

MESSE GROSSE see Rheinberger, Josef

MESSE H-MOLL see Bach, Johann Sebastian

MESSE I A 6 VOCI see Monteverdi, Claudio

MESSE II A 4 VOCI see Monteverdi, Claudio

MESSE IN A see Thim, Gunther

MESSE IN A see Thomas, Kurt

MESSE IN A-MOLL see Schneider, Josef

MESSE IN DER LYDISCHEN TONART see Sechter, Simon

MESSE IN ES-DUR see Albrechtsberger, Johann Georg

MESSE IN F-DUR see Albrechtsberger, Johann Georg

MESSE IN F-MOLL see Wellesz, Egon

MESSE IN G MAJOR see Poulenc, Francis

MESSE MAIENZEIT see Kluge, Manfred

MESSE NO. 1, AUX ORPHEONISTES see Gounod, Charles Francois

MESSE NO. 2, AUX SOCIETES CHORALES see Gounod, Charles Francois

MESSE NO. 3 see Haydn, (Franz) Joseph, Nelson-Misse

MESSE NO. 3, AUX COMMUNAUTES RELIGIEUSES see Gounod, Charles Francois

MESSE NO. 4, A LA CONGREGATION DES DAMES AUXILIATRICES DE L'IMMACULEE -CONCEPTION see Gounod, Charles Francois

MESSE NO. 5 see Haydn, (Franz) Joseph, Missa Cellensis

MESSE NO. 6 see Haydn, (Franz) Joseph, Missa

MESSE NO. 6, AUX CATHEDRALES see Gounod, Charles Francois

MESSE NO. 7 see Haydn, (Franz) Joseph, Missa Sancti Nicolai

MESSE NOVALE see Grimbert, Jacques

MESSE PASTORALE see Lambiollotte, Louis

MESSE PASTORALE see Samuel-Rosseau, Marcel

MESSE POUR DEUX VOIX EGALES see Chaminade, Cecile

MESSE PRO DEFUNCTIS see Lassus, Roland de (Orlandus)

MESSE ROYALE PLAIN CHANT see Dumont, [Henri]

MESSE SOLENNE see Rossini, Gioacchino

MESSE SOLENNELLE see Durand, A.

MESSE SOLENNELLE see Gounod, Charles Francois

MESSE SOLENNELLE see Mehul, H.

MESSE SOLENNELLE see Saint-Saens, Camille

MESSE SOLENNELLE DE LA PENTECOTE see Paladilhe, [Emile]

MESSE SOLENNELLE DE SAINT-ETIENNE see Busser, [Henri-Paul]

MESSE SOLENNELLE DEST REMY see Dubois, Theodore

MESSE see Rheinberger, Josef

MESSEN-BAND X see Palestrina, Giovanni

MESSEN-BAND XI see Palestrina, Giovanni

MESSEN-BAND XII see Palestrina, Giovanni

MESSEN-BAND XIII see Palestrina, Giovanni

MESSEN-BAND XIV see Palestrina, Giovanni

MESSEN-BAND XV see Palestrina, Giovanni

MESSEN-BAND XVI see Palestrina, Giovanni

MESSEN-BAND XVII see Palestrina, Giovanni

MESSEN-BAND XVIII see Palestrina, Giovanni

MESSEN-BAND XIX see Palestrina, Giovanni

MESSEN-BAND XX see Palestrina, Giovanni

MESSEN-BAND XXI see Palestrina, Giovanni

MESSEN-BAND XXII see Palestrina, Giovanni

MESSEN-BAND XXIII see Palestrina, Giovanni

MESSEN-BAND XXIV see Palestrina, Giovanni

MESSIAEN, OLIVER (1908-   )
La Transfiguration De Notre Seigneur Jesus-Christ
mix cor,7inst,orch LEDUC rental, ipa
(M1645)

O Sacrum Convivium *Commun,mot
SATB oct ELKAN-V $.35   (M1646)
[Lat] 4pt mix cor,opt org oct DURAND s.p.
(M1647)

MESSIAH see Handel, George Frideric

MESSIAH A LA MOOG see Handel, George Frideric

MESSITER, ARTHUR HENRY (1834-1916)
Rejoice, Ye Pure In Heart *anthem
(Angell) SATB SHAWNEE A 308 $.25 (M1648)
(Cain) SATB,opt brass oct FOX R214 $.35
(M1649)
(Hadley) SATB oct PRO ART 1773 $.25 (M1650)
(Pankow) 2pt jr cor oct LILLENAS AN-4009
$.25   (M1651)
(Walton) SATB oct BOOSEY 5141 $.30 (M1652)

MESSNER, KARL
Sel in Sind Die Toten *Bibl
mix cor,acap oct DOBLINGER s.p.   (M1653)

Trauerchoral
mix cor,acap oct DOBLINGER s.p.   (M1654)

Zur Glockenweihe
mix cor,acap oct DOBLINGER s.p.   (M1655)

METER, C.
Prefaces *CC24U,Gen,Mass
unis voc sc GIA G1588 $2.00   (M1656)

METHINKS I HEAR THE FULL CELESTIAL CHOIR see Crotch, William

METHINKS I HEAR THE HEAVENS RESOUND see Bedell, [Robert Leech]

METHINKS I SEE AN HEAVENLY HOST
see Colonial Christmas Carols

METIS
Behold The Word
unis MARKS $1.00   (M1657)

METZGER, HANS-ARNOLD (1913-   )
Christ Lag In Todesbanden, Fur Unsre Sund
(from Matthaus-Passion) Holywk/Psntd
SAT/SAB HANSSLER 6.122 s.p. contains also:
Trubel, Gerhard, Wir Wollen Alle Frohlich
Sein (SATB)   (M1658)
SA/SAB/SATB HANSSLER 8.018 s.p.   (M1659)

Gott Tut Grosse Dinge, Die Nicht
see Metzger, Hans-Arnold, In Deiner Hand,
Herr, Steht

METZGER, HANS-ARNOLD (cont'd.)

Gott Vater, Sende Deinen Geist *mot
SAB HANSSLER 7.052 s.p.   (M1660)

Heiliger Geist, Du Troster Mein
SATB/SS/TT/SAB/unis,org/inst HANSSLER 8.021
s.p.   (M1661)

In Deiner Hand, Herr, Steht *mot
SATB HANSSLER 7.087 s.p. contains also:
Gott Tut Grosse Dinge, Die Nicht (M1662)

Jesus Ist Kommen, Grund Ewiger Freude
SS/SA/TB/SSB/SAB/SATB HANSSLER 8.040 s.p.
(M1663)

Kommt Her Zu Mir, Spricht Gottes Sohn
see Stern, Hermann, Kommt Her Zu Mir,
Spricht Gottes Sohn

Mache Dich Auf, Herr, Und Verstosse *Introit
SATB HANSSLER 7.070 s.p.   (M1664)

O Lebensbrunnlein Tief Und Gross
see Kurig, Hans-Hermann, Lobt Gott, Ihr
Frommen Christen
SATB/SS/SA/SAB HANSSLER 8.027 s.p. (M1665)

Siehe, Nun Kommt Der Herr, Der Herrscher
SAB HANSSLER 7.043 s.p.   (M1666)

Vater Unser Im Himmelreich
see Koch, Heinz, Jesus Christus, Unser
Heiland

METZLER, FRIEDRICH
Kreuzweg *Psntd
[Ger] mix cor,narrator&SB soli,fl,ob,clar,
bsn,2trom,2vcl (report and meditation in
14 stations) BAREN. EM 532 cor pts
rental, s.p.   (M1667)

O Dearest Jesus, What Law Hast Thou Broken
*Lent
SAB,acap (med easy) oct CONCORDIA 98-1146
$.20   (M1668)

MEWS, DOUGLAS
Hail, True Body
[Eng] 2 eq voices oct ST.MARTIN SMP652 s.p.
(M1669)

Praise The Lord, Ye Saints *see Sancti Et
Justi

Sancti Et Justi
"Praise The Lord, Ye Saints" [Eng/Lat]
SATB,acap oct ST.MARTIN SMP611 s.p.
(M1670)

MEXICAN CHRISTMAS PROCESSION *anthem/folk,Mex
(Christiansen, Paul) SATB (easy) oct AUGSBURG
0503 $.25   (M1671)

MEXICAN PSALM, A see Butler, Eugene

MEYER-JANSON, BURKHARD (1932-   )
Danket Dem Herrn (Psalm 118) Gen
[Ger] SSA&men cor,acap (med) BAREN. BA 4963
$.25   (M1672)

Der Herr Ist Mein Hirte (Psalm 23) Easter/
Pent
[Ger] unis jr cor,org (med) BAREN. BA 4964
$.40   (M1673)

Psalm 23 *see Der Herr Ist Mein Hirte

Psalm 84 *see Wie Lieblich Sind Deine
Wohnungen

Psalm 118 *see Danket Dem Herrn

Wer Kann Da Korn Anschauen *Gen
[Ger] STB,acap (med) BAREN. BA 4962 $.25
(M1674)

Wie Lieblich Sind Deine Wohnungen (Psalm 84)
Gen
[Ger] SATB,acap (med) BAREN. BA 4962 $.25
(M1675)

MEYEROWITZ, JAN (1913-   )
And He Never Said A Mumblin' Word *Lent
SATB oct SOUTHERN $.25   (M1676)

Ave Maria
[Lat/Eng] SATB,org BROUDE BR. $.30 (M1677)

Ave Maris Stella
"Hail, O Star Of Waters" [Lat/Eng] TTBB,
pno/org/winds RONGWEN $.40   (M1678)

Glory Around His Head, The *Easter,cant
SATB,orch voc sc RONGWEN $2.25, ipr (M1679)

Hail, O Star Of Waters *see Ave Maris Stella

How Godly Is The House Of God
SATB,org/brass/org&brass&timp RONGWEN $.70,
ipr   (M1680)

Music For Christmas *Xmas
SATB,orch voc sc BROUDE BR. $2.25, ipr
(M1681)

New Plymouth Cantata *cant
SATB,orch voc sc BROUDE BR. $2.25, ipr
(M1682)

On A Pallet Of Straw *Xmas,carol
SA,S solo,pno RONGWEN $.35   (M1683)

On The Land And On The Sea
SATB,opt org/pno BROUDE BR. $.30 (M1684)

Two Litanies *CC2U
SSA,pno/fl,2clar,harp,3vln,vla,vcl,bvl
BROUDE BR.   (M1685)

MEYERS, CARMEL
I'm Standing In The Sun
(Cleaveland) 4pt men cor,Bar solo,acap oct
SCHIRM.G 9359 $.20   (M1686)

MI CHAMOCHAH see Gottlieb, J.

MI CHOMOCHO see Roskin

MI SHEBERACH see Ancis, Solomon

MI-SHIREY BETH HA-KNESETH see Coopersmith,
Harry

MI Y'MALLEL *Hanakkah,madrigal
(Chajes, Julius) "Hanukkah Song" [Heb/Eng]
SATB TRANSCON. TCL 211 $.25 (M1687)
(Fromm, Herbert) "Hanukkah Madrigal" [Eng/
Heb] SATB TRANSCON. TCL 239 $.25 (M1688)

MI Y'MALLEL see Binder, Abraham Wolfe

MICAH - HOW SHALL I COME BEFORE THE LORD see
Demarest, A.

MICH JAMMERT DES VOLKS see Raselius, Andreas

MICH JAMMERT DES VOLKS see Vulpius, Melchior

MICHAEL
Hearken! Stay Close *Morav
(Dickinson) SATB oct GRAY GMCM 19 $.30
(M1689)

MICHAEL see Ross

MICHAEL see Whitecotton, Shirley

MICHAEL, ROGIER (ca. 1550-1619)
Die Geburt Unsers Herren Jesu Christi, Nach
Den Evangelisten Lukas Und Matthaus 1602
*Xmas,Bibl
(Osthoff, Helmuth) [Ger] SSATTB,T,soli,acap
(med) BAREN. BA 1207 sc $2.50, cor pts
$1.00 (M1690)

MICHAEL, ROW THE BOAT see Gardner

MICHAEL ROW THE BOAT see Gardner, John [Linton]

MICHAEL, ROW THE BOAT ASHORE *spir
(Papale, Henry) SATB&opt jr cor,opt SA soli,
acap oct WORLD ESE-771-8 $.45 (M1691)

MICHAEL, TOBIAS (1592-1657)
Lift Up Your Heads, O Ye Gates *Adv/Asc/Gen/
Palm
SSATB,T/Bar solo,5strings/5winds,cont
CONCORDIA 97-4815 $.75, ipa (M1692)

Unsre Trubsal, Die Zeitlich *mot
(Hellmann) SSATB HANSSLER 1.099 s.p.
(M1693)

MICHAELIDES, P.
Magnification Of The Nativity *Xmas
SATB oct PRESSER G-150 $.35 (M1694)

MICHAEL'S DAY CAROL FROM THE HEBRIDES see Gaul,
Alfred Robert

MICHEELSEN, HANS FRIEDRICH (1902-   )
Ach Gott Vom Himmel *Trin
[Ger] SA&men cor,acap (easy) MULLER
SM 2541, 13-15 s.p. (M1695)

Alle Gute Gabe *Easter/Pent,cant/mot
[Ger] 3 eq voices,acap (med) BAREN. BA 3188
$.25 see from Hamburger Motettenbuch,
Heft 4 (M1696)

Allein Zu Dir, Herr Jesu Christ *Trin,cant
[Ger] unis,3trp,3trom (med) BAREN. BA 2632
sc $1.75, cor pts $.55, ipa (M1697)

Als Unser Herr In Den Garten Ging *Psntd
[Ger] SSA,acap (med) BAREN. BA 1570 $.65
see from Hamburger Motettenbuch III
(M1698)

Amen, Gott Vater Und Sohne
[Ger] 3-5pt mix cor,acap (med easy) BAREN.
BA 172 s.p. contains also: Amen-Satze
(M1699)

Amen-Satze
see Micheelsen, Hans Friedrich, Amen, Gott
Vater Und Sohne

Aus Meines Herzens Grunde *Gen
[Ger] SA&men cor,acap (easy) MULLER
2541, 10-12 s.p. (M1700)

Befiehl Du Deine Wege *Gen
[Ger] SA&men cor,acap (easy) MULLER
SM 2541, 1-3 s.p. (M1701)

Bescher Uns, Herr, Das Taglich Brot *Gen
[Ger] SA&men cor,acap MULLER SM 2541, 16-18
s.p. (M1702)

Cantata 3 *see Da Jesus An Dem Kreuze Stund

Cantata 4 *see Mit Freuden Zart

Cantata 5 *see Nun Freut Euch, Lieben
Christen Gmein

Cantata 6 *see Nun Bitten Wir Den Heiligen
Geist

Choralmotetten *Gen,mot
[Ger] 3 eq voices,acap (med) BAREN. BA 1333
$1.75 see from Hamburger Motettenbuch III
(M1703)

Christ Ist Erstanden *Easter,cant
[Ger] SATB,3trp,3trom (med) BAREN. BA 3591
sc $3.25, cor pts $.55, ipa (M1704)

Christe, Du Lamm Gottes
[Ger] 3pt mix cor/4pt mix cor,acap (easy)
MULLER SM 2541:13-15 s.p. (M1705)

Da Jesus An Dem Kreuze Stund (Cantata 3)
Psntd
[Ger] SATB,opt inst (med) BAREN. BA 1798
$2.00 (M1706)

Das Ist Je Gewisslich Wahr *Trin
[Ger] 3 eq voices,acap (med) BAREN. BA 3195
$.25 see from Hamburger Motettenbuch 4
(M1707)

Das Jahr Des Herrn *CC10U,Gen
[Ger] 3-5pt mix cor,acap (med easy) BAREN.
BA 2410 $2.50 (M1708)

Den Aber, Der Eine Kleine Zeit *Gd.Fri./
Psntd,mot
[Ger] 3 eq voices,acap (med) BAREN. BA 3185
$.25 see from Hamburger Motettenbuch 4
(M1709)

Den Frieden Lasse Ich Euch *Pent
[Ger] SA&men cor,acap BAREN. BA 564
$.25 (M1710)

MICHEELSEN, HANS FRIEDRICH (cont'd.)

Denn Von Ihm Und Durch Ihn Sind Alle Dinge
*Trin
[Ger] 3 eq voices,acap (med) BAREN. BA 3190
$.25 see from Hamburger Motettenbuch 4
(M1711)

Der Geist Des Herrn Erfullt Den Erdkreis
*Pent
[Ger] SA&men cor,acap (med) BAREN. BA 3775
s.p. (M1712)

Der Herr Ist Konig *Gen
[Ger] 3pt mix cor,acap (med easy) BAREN.
BA 1321 s.p. (M1713)

Der Herr Ist Mein Hirte (Psalm 23) Easter/
Pent,canon
[Ger] SAATBB,acap (med diff) BAREN. BA 3688
$1.50 see from Hamburger Motettenbuch
(M1714)

[Ger] 3 eq voices,acap (med easy) BAREN.
BA 192 s.p. (M1715)

Der Morgenstern Ist Aufgedrungen *No.58,
Epiph
[Ger] SSATB,acap (med diff) BAREN. BA 2149
$2.50 (M1716)

Deutsche Liedmesse *Mass
[Ger] SSAB,acap (med) MULLER SM 2518 s.p.
(M1717)

Deutsche Messe *Mass
[Ger] SAATB,acap (med diff) BAREN. BA 1317
$2.00 (M1718)

Die Nacht Ist Vorgeruckt *Adv
[Ger] 3 eq voices,acap (med easy) BAREN. BA 3181
$.25 see from Hamburger Motettenbuch 4
(M1719)

Die Passion Jesu Christi Nach Dem
Evangelisten Johannes *Psntd
[Ger] SATB,acap (med diff) BAREN. BA 4358
rental (M1720)

Die Passion Jesu Christi Nach Dem
Evangelisten Markus *Psntd
[Ger] SSATBB,TB soli,soli,acap (med diff)
BAREN. BA 1320 sc $4.75, cor pts $1.50
(M1721)

Die Passion Jesu Christi Nach Dem
Evangelisten Matthaus *Psntd,evang
[Ger] 2-7pt mix cor,acap (med diff) BAREN.
BA 2169 $3.50 (M1722)

Drei Geistliche Gesange Fur Mannerchor *Gen
[Ger] (med easy) s.p.
contains: Herr, Schicke Was Du Willt
(TTB,acap); Ich Singe Dir (TTBB,acap);
In Ihm Seis Begonnen (TTBB,acap)
(M1723)

Dreistimmige Kirchenliedsatze *CC50U,Gen,
chorale
[Ger] SA&men cor,acap (med) BAREN. BA 3948
$5.25 (M1724)

Ehre Sei Dir, Christe
see Geistliche Chorsatze

Epistelspruche *Gen
[Ger] 3 eq voices,acap (med) BAREN. BA 3180
$3.00 see from Hamburger Motettenbuch IV
(M1725)

Es Ist Erschienen Die Heilsame Gnade *Xmas
[Ger] 3 eq voices,acap (med easy) BAREN. BA 3183
$.25 see from Hamburger Motettenbuch 4
(M1726)

Es Sungen Drei Engel *Gen,mot
[Ger] SSATBB,acap (med diff) BAREN. BA 2405
$1.75 (M1727)

Freuet Euch In Dem Herrn *Adv
[Ger] 3 eq voices,acap (med) BAREN. BA 3182
$.25 see from Hamburger Motettenbuch 4
(M1728)

Frohlich Wir Nun All Fangen An
[Ger] SA&men cor,acap (easy) MULLER
SM 2541:1-3 s.p. (M1729)

Furwahr, Er Trug Unsere Krankheit *Gd.Fri./
Psntd,mot
[Ger] 3 eq voices,acap (med) BAREN. BA 3168
$.25 see from Hamburger Motettenbuch 4
(M1730)

Gehet Hin In Alle Welt *Easter/Pent
[Ger] SAB,acap (med easy) BAREN. BA 790
$.25 (M1731)

Geistliche Chorsatze *Psntd
[Ger] SA&men cor,acap (easy) MULLER
SM 2541, 19:21 s.p.
contains: Ehre Sei Dir, Christe;
Herzliebster Jesu; Jesu, Deine Passion
(M1732)

Gott Aber Kann Machen, Dass Allerlei Gnade
*Fest,mot
[Ger] 3 eq voices,acap (med) BAREN. BA 3192
$.25 see from Hamburger Motettenbuch 4
(M1733)

Gott Ist Liebe *Trin
[Ger] 3 eq voices,acap (med) BAREN. BA 3191
s.p. see from Hamburger Motettenbuch 4
(M1734)

Hamburger Motettenbuch *see Der Herr Ist
Mein Hirte (Psalm 23) (M1735)

Hamburger Motettenbuch 4 *see Das Ist Je
Gewisslich Wahr; Den Aber, Der Eine
Kleine Zeit; Denn Von Ihm Und Durch Ihn
Sind Alle Dinge; Die Nacht Ist
Vorgeruckt; Es Ist Erschienen Die
Heilsame Gnade; Freuet Euch In Dem Herrn;
Furwahr, Er Trug Unsere Krankheit; Gott
Aber Kann Machen, Dass Allerlei Gnade;
Gott Ist Liebe; Lasset Das Wort Christi
Reichlich Unter Euch Wohnen; Lasset Uns
Rechtschaffen Sein; Leben Wir, So Leben
Wir Dem Herrn; Mache Dich Auf, Werde
Licht; Nun Aber Ist Christus
Auferstanden; Unser Wandel Ist Im Himmel
(M1736)

Hamburger Motettenbuch, Heft 4 *see Alle
Gute Gabe (M1737)

Hamburger Motettenbuch III *see Als Unser
Herr In Den Garten Ging; Choralmotetten;
Hinunter Ist Der Sonne Schein; Mit Fried
Und Freud (M1738)

MICHEELSEN, HANS FRIEDRICH (cont'd.)

Hamburger Motettenbuch IV *see
Epistelspruche (M1739)

Hamburger Motettenbuch Nr. 1:
Evangelienspruche *CCU,Gen,mot
[Ger] 2-4pt mix cor,acap (med) BAREN.
BA 1331 $1.75 (M1740)

Hamburger Motettenbuch Nr. 2: Psalmworte
*CCU,Gen,mot
[Ger] 3-4pt mix cor,acap (med) BAREN.
BA 1332 $2.00 (M1741)

Hamburger Motettenbuch Nr. 5 *see
Magnificat, "Lobgesang Der Maria" (M1742)

Hamburger Motettenbuch Nr. 6 *see Herr, Nun
Lassest Du Deinen Diener, "Lobgesang Des
Simeon" (M1743)

Hamburger Motettenbuch Nr. 7 *see Wohl Dem,
Der Nicht Wandelt Im Rat Der Gottlosen
(Psalm 1) (M1744)

Hamburger Motettenbuch Nr. 9 *see Wenn Der
Herr Die Gefangenen Zions Erlosen Wird
(Psalm 126) (M1745)

Hamburger Motettenbuch Nr. 10: Zeit Und
Ewigkeit *CCU,Gen
[Ger] 3-5pt mix cor,acap (med diff) BAREN.
BA 3690 $4.25 (M1746)

Herr Gott, Dich Loben Wir *Fest
[Ger] 5pt mix cor,acap (med) BAREN. BA 3041
s.p. (M1747)

Herr, Nun Lassest Du Deinen Diener
"Lobgesang Des Simeon" [Ger] SATB,acap (med
diff) BAREN. BA 3644 $1.50 see from
Hamburger Motettenbuch Nr. 6 (M1748)

Herr, Schicke Was Du Willt
see Drei Geistliche Gesange Fur Mannerchor

Herzliebster Jesu
see Geistliche Chorsatze

Hinunter Ist Der Sonne Schein *Gen,mot
[Ger] 3 eq voices,acap (med) BAREN. BA 1568
$.40 see from Hamburger Motettenbuch III
(M1749)

Hinunter Ist Der Sonnen Schein *Gen
[Ger] SA&men cor,acap (easy) MULLER
SM 2541, 7-9 s.p. (M1750)

Ich Ruf Zu Dir, Herr Jesu Christ *Trin
[Ger] SA&men cor,acap (easy) MULLER
SM 2541 , 4-6 s.p. (M1751)

Ich Singe Dir
see Drei Geistliche Gesange Fur Mannerchor

In Ihm Seis Begonnen
see Drei Geistliche Gesange Fur Mannerchor

Jesu, Deine Passion
see Geistliche Chorsatze

Kleines Psalmen-Chorbuch *CC9U,mot/Psalm
[Ger] 3pt mix cor BAREN. EM 780 s.p.
(M1752)

Komm, Du Herzlicher Troster *Pent
[Ger] SA&men cor,acap (easy) MULLER
SM 2541, 16-18 s.p. (M1753)

Kommt Und Lasst Uns Christum Ehren *Xmas
[Ger] SATB,T solo,fl,vln (med easy) BAREN.
BA 2163 sc $2.25, cor pts s.p., ipa
(M1754)

Kyrie *Kyrie
[Ger] SA&men cor,acap (easy) MULLER
SM 2541:13-15 s.p. (M1755)

Lasset Das Wort Christi Reichlich Unter Euch
Wohnen *Epiph
3 eq voices,acap (med) BAREN. BA 3194 $.25
see from Hamburger Motettenbuch 4 (M1756)

Lasset Uns Rechtschaffen Sein *Pent,mot
[Ger] 3 eq voices,acap (med) BAREN. BA 3189
$.25 see from Hamburger Motettenbuch 4
(M1757)

Leben Wir, So Leben Wir Dem Herrn *Trin
[Ger] 3 eq voices,acap (med) BAREN. BA 3191
$.25 see from Hamburger Motettenbuch 4
(M1758)

Lobet Den Herrn Und Dankt Ihm *Gen
[Ger] SA&men cor,acap (easy) MULLER
SM 2541, 16-18 s.p. (M1759)

Lobgesang Der Maria *see Magnificat

Lobgesang Des Simeon *see Herr, Nun Lassest
Du Deinen Diener

Lobt Gott Den Herrn *Gen
[Ger] SA&men cor,acap (easy) MULLER
SM 2541, 4-6 s.p. (M1760)

Lutherchoralkantate *Gen,cant
[Ger] SATB,strings,opt drums (med) BAREN.
BA 3164 sc $6.50, cor pts $1.00, ipa
(M1761)

Mache Dich Auf, Werde Licht *Epiph
3 eq voices,acap (med) BAREN. BA 3184 $.25
see from Hamburger Motettenbuch 4 (M1762)

Magnificat *Magnif
"Lobgesang Der Maria" [Ger] SAATBB,S solo,
acap (med diff) BAREN. BA 3643 $3.50 see
from Hamburger Motettenbuch Nr. 5 (M1763)

Mit Freuden Zart (Cantata 4) Easter
[Ger] SATB,org (med) sc BAREN. BA 1795 s.p.
(M1764)

Mit Fried Und Freud *funeral/mot
[Ger] 3 eq voices,acap BAREN. BA 1569 $.40
see from Hamburger Motettenbuch III
(M1765)

Nun Aber Ist Christus Auferstanden *Easter,
mot
[Ger] 3 eq voices,acap (med) BAREN. BA 3187
$.25 see from Hamburger Motettenbuch 4
(M1766)

MICHEELSEN, HANS FRIEDRICH (cont'd.)

Nun Bitten Wir Den Heiligen Geist (Cantata 6)
  Pent
  [Ger] SA&men cor,acap (med easy) BAREN.
    BA 1799 $.40   (M1767)
  [Ger] SAAB,acap (easy) MULLER SM 2541, 4-6
    s.p.   (M1768)

Nun Danket All Und Bringet Ehr *Gen
  [Ger] SA&men cor,acap (easy) MULLER
    SM 2541, 7-9 s.p.   (M1769)

Nun Freut Euch, Lieben Christen Gmein
  (Cantata 5) Easter/Pent
  [Ger] SAATB,opt soli,org,vln (med) sc
    BAREN. BA 1796 $2.00   (M1770)

O Christenheit Sei Hoch Erfreut *Gen
  [Ger] SATB&2pt mix cor,acap (med easy)
    BAREN. BA 3260 s.p.   (M1771)
  [Ger] 3pt mix cor,acap (med easy) BAREN.
    BA 590 s.p.   (M1772)
  [Ger] SSATTB,acap (med easy) BAREN. BA 3261
    s.p.   (M1773)

O Christenheit, Sei Hocherfreut *Gen,cant
  [Ger] SSATTB,horn,5trp,5trom (med) BAREN.
    BA 2484 rental   (M1774)

O Konig Jesu Christe *Trin
  [Ger] 3pt,acap (med easy) BAREN. BA 590
    s.p.   (M1775)

Psalm 1 *see Wohl Dem, Der Nicht Wandelt Im
  Rat Der Gottlosen

Psalm 23 *see Der Herr Ist Mein Hirte

Psalm 126 *see Wenn Der Herr Die Gefangenen
  Zions Erlosen Wird

Tod Und Leben *ECY,Req
  [Ger] SSATB,soli,acap (med diff) BAREN.
    BA 1363 $3.50   (M1776)

"Trostet, Trostet", Spricht Der Herr
  see Zillinger, Erwin, Dein Konig Kommt In
  Niedern Hullen

Uns Ist Ein Kind Geboren *Xmas
  [Ger] SA&men cor,acap (med) BAREN. BA 3391
    s.p.   (M1777)

Unser Wandel Ist Im Himmel *Trin
  [Ger] 3 eq voices,acap (med) BAREN. BA 3193
    $.25 see from Hamburger Motettenbuch 4
                                          (M1778)

Verleih Uns Frieden
  [Ger] SATB,acap (easy) MULLER SM 2541:10-12
    s.p.   (M1779)

Vom Morgen Bis Zum Abend *CC12U,Eve/Gen/
  Morn,Bibl/canon
  [Ger] 2 eq voices/3 eq voices,acap (med
    easy) BAREN. BA 2178 s.p.   (M1780)

Warum Sollt Ich Mich Denn Gramen *Gen
  [Ger] SAAB,acap (easy) MULLER SM 2541, 1-3
    s.p.   (M1781)

Was Gott Tut, Das Ist Wohlgetan *Gen
  [Ger] SA&men cor,acap (easy) MULLER
    SM 2541, 10-12 s.p.   (M1782)

Was Mein Gott Will *Trin
  [Ger] SA&men cor,acap (easy) MULLER
    SM 2541 7-9 s.p.   (M1783)

Wenn Der Herr Die Gefangenen Zions Erlosen
  Wird (Psalm 126) ECY,mot
  [Ger] SAATBB,acap (med diff) BAREN. BA 3689
    $1.50 see from Hamburger Motettenbuch Nr.
    9   (M1784)

Wir Wollen Alle Frohlich Sein *Easter,cant
  [Ger] 3-4pt mix cor,acap cor pts BAREN.
    EM 105 s.p.   (M1785)

With High Delight *Easter/Gen
  SATB&jr cor,kbd (med diff) oct CONCORDIA
    98-1942 $.30   (M1786)

Wohl Dem, Der Nicht Wandelt Im Rat Der
  Gottlosen (Psalm 1) Trin
  [Ger] SSATBB,acap (med diff) BAREN. BA 3687
    $2.25 see from Hamburger Motettenbuch Nr.
    7   (M1787)

MICHEL, JOSEP (1928-   )
Christus Ist Auferstanden
  see Michel, Josep, Credo, Das Ist, Ich
  Glaube, Herr

Credo, Das Ist, Ich Glaube, Herr *Easter
  [Ger] 4pt mix cor,opt 2-3trp BAREN. EM 81
    s.p. contains also: Christus Ist
    Auferstanden (3pt mix cor,org,opt winds)
                                          (M1788)

Der Du In Todesnachten *cant
  SATB/men cor,3trp,3trom sc HANSSLER 10.301
    s.p.   (M1789)

Es Wird Sein In Den Letzten Tagen
  see Schweizer, Rolf, Gott Ist Bei Uns, Und
  Wir Sind Sein Eigen

Herr Ruste Uns Von Neuem Aus
  unis,kbd sc HANSSLER 19.402 s.p. contains
    also: Michel, Josep, Sieh Nicht Deine
    Schwachheit An (SAT,gtr/bvl);
    Kretzschmar, Gunther, Gott Geht An Keinem
    Vorbei (SATB,narrator,2trp,trom/clar,
    bvl); Schweizer, Rolf, Wie Lange Noch,
    Herr (Psalm 13) (unis,kbd)   (M1790)

Herr, Sende Uns Botschaft
  see Ruppel, Paul Ernst, Gott Liebt Diese
  Welt

Ich Will Den Herren Loben *mot
  dbl cor&unis jr cor HANSSLER 7.126 s.p.
                                          (M1791)

Neue Lieder *CCU
  jr cor&cong HANSSLER 2.025 s.p.   (M1792)

Sieh Nicht Deine Schwachheit An
  see Michel, Josep, Herr Ruste Uns Von Neuem
  Aus

MICHEL, JOSEP (cont'd.)

Wir Wissen Nicht, Was Kommt
  see Bossler, Kurt, Fragst Du Nach Meiner
  Sunde

MICHELS, JOSEF
Ave Maria Gratia Plena
  mix cor,acap ERDMANN 528 s.p. contains
    also: Es Flog Ein Taublein Weisse (M1793)

Es Flog Ein Taublein Weisse
  see Michels, Josef, Ave Maria Gratia Plena

Freut Euch, Die Weihnachtszeit Bricht Nun
  Herein *Adv/Xmas
  mix cor,acap ERDMANN 537 s.p.   (M1794)
  men cor,acap ERDMANN 156 s.p.   (M1795)

MICHNA, ADAM VACLAV (ca. 1600-1676)
Missa S. Venceslai
  6pt,soli,org,2clar,2vln,2vla SUPRAPHON s.p.
                                          (M1796)

MICKELSON, PAUL
Young Sound, The *CCU
  SATB oct AGAPE $1.95   (M1797)

MIDDLETON
Sanctify, O Lord *Gen,anthem
  SS,opt pno oct ROYAL 246 s.p. see also
  ANTHEMS FOR UNISON OR TWO PART SINGING
                                          (M1798)

Saviour Like A Shepherd Lead Us
  SA BOOSEY-CAN s.p.   (M1799)
  SA oct BOOSEY 1763 $.30   (M1800)

MIDDLETON, J. ROLAND
Be Thou My Vision *anthem/hymn
  mix cor oct NOVELLO 28.1327.00 s.p. (M1801)

MIDNIGHT CAROL see McAfee, Don

MIDNIGHT MASS FOR CHRISTMAS see Charpentier,
  Marc-Antoine, Messe De Minuit

MIDNIGHT MASS FOR CHRISTMAS BASED ON FRENCH
  CAROLS see Charpentier, Marc-Antoine, Messe
  De Minuit Pour Noel

MIDNIGHT SERVICE see Piket, Frederick, S'lichos

MIDST THE DEEP SILENCE see Hunnicutt, Judy

MIDWINTER CAROL see Johnson, Alfred H.

MIELCZEWSKI, MARCIN
Benedictio Et Claritas *Pol
  (Szweykowski, Z.M.) cor,inst POLSKIE WDMP66
    s.p.   (M1802)

Veni Domine *Pol
  SSB,cont POLSKIE WDMP 38 s.p.   (M1803)

Vesperae Dominicales *Pol
  (Szweykowski, Z.M.) 4pt mix cor,solo,cont,
    inst POLSKIE WDMP42 s.p.   (M1804)

MIELENZ, H.
Kaschubisches Weihnachtslied *Xmas
  mix cor BIRNBACH s.p.   (M1805)

MIG GIVEN ALL MAKT see Nilsson, Torsten

MIGGL, ERWIN
Missa Brevis In Es-Dur *Mass
  mix cor,org (E flat maj) voc sc DOBLINGER
    s.p.   (M1806)

Proprium *Pent
  4pt mix cor,org cor pts DOBLINGER s.p.
                                          (M1807)

MIGHT I IN THY SIGHT APPEAR see Wesley, Samuel
  Sebastian Jr.

MIGHT IT BE TODAY?
  SATB BIG3 $.25   (M1808)

MIGHTY DAY see Gardner, Maurice

MIGHTY FORTRESS, A see Bunjes, Paul G.

MIGHTY FORTRESS, A see Hunter, Ein' Feste Burg

MIGHTY FORTRESS, A see Schalk, Carl

MIGHTY FORTRESS, A see Schein, Johann Hermann

MIGHTY FORTRESS, A see Slater

MIGHTY FORTRESS, A see Wilson

MIGHTY FORTRESS, A see Young, Gordon

MIGHTY FORTRESS, A see Zimmermann, Heinz Werner

MIGHTY FORTRESS IS OUR GOD see Hassler, Hans
  Leo

MIGHTY FORTRESS IS OUR GOD, A
  SAB oct STAFF 651 $.30   (M1809)

MIGHTY FORTRESS IS OUR GOD, A see Bach, Johann
  Sebastian

MIGHTY FORTRESS IS OUR GOD, A see Franck,
  Melchior, Ein Feste Burg Ist Unser Gott

MIGHTY FORTRESS IS OUR GOD, A see Gardner

MIGHTY FORTRESS IS OUR GOD, A see Hassler, Hans
  Leo

MIGHTY FORTRESS IS OUR GOD, A see Hughes

MIGHTY FORTRESS IS OUR GOD, A see Johnson,
  David N.

MIGHTY FORTRESS IS OUR GOD, A see Luther,
  Martin

MIGHTY FORTRESS IS OUR GOD, A see Schutz,
  Heinrich

MIGHTY GOD, WHILE ANGELS BLESS THEE see Selby,
  William

MIGHTY IS THE LORD see Hutson, Wihla

MIGHTY LORD, THY FAITHFULNESS ABIDETH EVER see
  Lotti, Antonio, Kyrie Eleison

MIGHTY ONE, THE see Newbury, Kent A.

MIGHTY ONE, THE see Whitcomb, R.

MIGHTY SPIRIT, ALL TRANSCENDING see Mozart,
  Wolfgang Amadeus, Ave Verum Corpus

MIGHTY TRIUMPH, THE see Lorenz

MIGLIAVACCA
Psallite Suaviter *mot
  unis,org RICORDI-ENG 127929 s.p.   (M1810)

MIGOT
Beati Qui (from Le Sermon Sur La Montagne)
  [Fr] SATB,SATB soli,org LEDUC BL736 voc sc
    s.p., cor pts s.p.   (M1811)

La Passion *ora
  [Fr] cor,soli,orch LEDUC sc rental, cor pts
    rental   (M1812)

Le Sermon Sur La Montagne *ora
  [Fr] cor,soli,org,5strings/orch fac ed
    LEDUC s.p.   (M1813)

Les Nativites
  [Fr] SATB,strings/opt pno voc sc LEDUC s.p.
                                          (M1814)

Noel *Xmas,Fr
  [Fr] SATB LEDUC sc s.p., cor pts s.p.
                                          (M1815)
  [Fr] STB/SAB cor pts LEDUC s.p.   (M1816)

Psalm 19
  [Eng/Fr] SATB,orch voc sc LEDUC s.p.
                                          (M1817)
  [Fr] SATB,orch cor pts LEDUC s.p.   (M1818)

Sainte-Germain D'Auxerre *ora
  [Fr] 3 cor,4 soli,acap cor LEDUC rental
                                          (M1819)

MIGOT, GEORGES (1891-   )
A La Venue De Noel *Xmas,carol
  [Fr] SATB OUVRIERES EO697 s.p.   (M1820)

Au Saint Nau *Xmas,carol
  [Fr] SATB OUVRIERES EO694 s.p.   (M1821)

Chantons, Je Vous En Prie *Xmas,carol
  [Fr] SATB OUVRIERES EO698 s.p.   (M1822)

Chantons Joyeusement *Xmas,carol
  [Fr] SATB OUVRIERES EO695 s.p.   (M1823)

Entre L'ane Et Le Bouvelet *Xmas,carol
  [Fr] SATB OUVRIERES EO699 s.p.   (M1824)

Est-Il Rien De Plus Charmant *Xmas,carol
  [Fr] SATB OUVRIERES EO701 s.p.   (M1825)

Kyrie Le Jour De Noel *Xmas,carol
  [Fr] SATB OUVRIERES EO700 s.p.   (M1826)

La Nativite De N.S. *Xmas
  [Fr] cor,soli,fl,bsn,4strings OUVRIERES
    rental   (M1827)

L'annonciation
  [Fr] 3pt wom cor,soli,5strings OUVRIERES
    rental   (M1828)

Noel Des Noels *Xmas,carol
  [Fr] SATB OUVRIERES EO702 s.p.   (M1829)

Noel, Noel, Iterumque Noel *Xmas,carol
  [Fr] SATB OUVRIERES EO693 s.p.   (M1830)

Psalm 118
  [Fr/Eng/Ger] mix cor,5winds,perc OUVRIERES
    rental   (M1831)

Que Tardez-Vous? *Xmas,carol
  [Fr] SATB OUVRIERES EO696 s.p.   (M1832)

Requiem A Cappella *Req
  [Lat] SATB OUVRIERES EO401 s.p.   (M1833)

MIHI AUTEM see Quack, Erhard

MIHI AUTEM NIMIS see Tallis, Thomas

MIJN HERT HEEFT see Obrecht, Jacob

MIJN ZOETE KONINGINNE see Noble, Felix de

MILANO, R.
He Who Hath Made Heaven *Xmas
  SATB oct WALTON 2192 $.35   (M1834)
  SATB oct WALTON 2192 $.35   (M1835)

Look With Mercy, Lord *Easter
  unis oct PRESSER MC451 $.30   (M1836)

Lord, To Thee Our Song *Thanks
  SATB/unis oct PRESSER MC449 $.25   (M1837)

Oh! Divine Community *Easter
  unis oct PRESSER MC453 $.30   (M1838)

Prayer For St. Ambrose, A *Easter/Gen
  1-2pt oct PRESSER MC505 $.30   (M1839)

Prayer For St. Augustine, A *Xmas/Easter
  1-2pt oct PRESSER MC504 $.30   (M1840)

Prayer For St. Francis *Xmas/Gen
  1-2pt oct PRESSER MC506 $.30   (M1841)

Prayer For St. Theodolph, A *Xmas/Easter
  unis/2pt oct PRESSER MC503 $.35   (M1842)

Prayer For Steadfastness, A *Easter/Gen
  unis oct PRESSER MC454 $.25   (M1843)

This Day Rejoice *Xmas
  unis oct PRESSER MC450 $.30   (M1844)

Whom Are You Seeking *Easter
  unis oct PRESSER MC452 $.30   (M1845)

MILD MOTHER, THE see Rorem, Ned

MILDE JESU see Sundberg, John

MILDE JESU, DEM LEDSAGA see Moren, John

MILDE JESU, HERRE GUD see Cherubini, Luigi

MILDE JESU, NADENS KALLA see Olson, Daniel

MILDE STJARNA, REN OCH KLAR see Ahlberg, Verner

MILDRED, SISTER M.
Mass Of The Holy Spirit
unis,org ALBERT s.p.   (M1846)

MILES
In The Garden
SATB oct WORD CS-2001 $.30   (M1847)
(Boersma) SAB oct WORD CS-2342 $.30   (M1848)
(Wilson) SATB oct LORENZ A315 $.30   (M1849)
(Wilson) SATB oct LORENZ C219 $.30   (M1850)
(Wilson) SATB oct LORENZ 4487 $.30   (M1851)

MILES COVERDALE'S CAROL see Paget, Michael

MILES, P. NADIER
Hymn Before Sunrise
mix cor,Bar solo,3fl,2ob,3clar,3bsn,2trp,
4horn,3trom,tuba,strings,harp,perc,timp
cmplt ed BOOSEY rental   (M1852)

MILFORD
Personent Hodie
SSA (very easy) OXFORD 44.041 $.20   (M1853)

Psalm 23
SSA (easy) OXFORD 44.703 $.35, ipr   (M1854)

MILFORD, ROBIN (1903-1959)
Laus Deo
[Lat] unis oct NOVELLO 40.1193.07 s.p.
                                        (M1855)

Litany To The Holy Spirit, A
SATB,acap LENGNICK s.p.   (M1856)

Psalm 121
SATB,acap LENGNICK s.p.   (M1857)

MILGROVE
Glory To God On High *anthem
(Harris) SATB,opt brass,org/pno BOSTON
12534 $.40   (M1858)
(Riedel) SAB (very easy) cor pts AUGSBURG
1197 $.25, ipa   (M1859)

MILHAUD, DARIUS (1892-   )
Cantata From Job
SATB,Bar solo,org PRESSER $2.00   (M1860)

Cantate De La Croix De Charite *cant
[Fr] 4pt mix cor,STB soli voc sc HEUGEL
s.p.   (M1861)

Cantate De L'Initiation *Bar mitzvah,liturg,
Heb
[Heb/Fr] mix cor,orch voc sc HEUGEL s.p.
                                        (M1862)

Cantate De Psaumes
voc sc UNIVER. 14253 $8.15   (M1863)

Invocation A L'ange Raphael
[Fr] 2pt jr cor,orch AMP $7.50   (M1864)

Pacem In Terris *cant
[Lat] cor,ABar soli,orch SALABERT-US voc sc
$20.00, cor pts $4.50   (M1865)

Sabbath Eve Service For Children *see
Service Pour La Vieille Du Sabbat A
L'usage Des Enfants

Service Pour La Veille Du Sabbat
[Heb/Fr/Eng] unis jr cor,org HEUGEL s.p.
                                        (M1866)

Service Pour La Vieille Du Sabbat A L'usage
Des Enfants *Sab-Eve,liturg,Jew
"Sabbath Eve Service For Children" SA oct
PRESSER MC309 $.75   (M1867)

Service Sacre Pour Le Samedi Matin *Sab-Morn
[Heb] cor,narrator,Bar solo,org/orch
SALABERT-US voc sc $17.50, cor pts $4.50
                                        (M1868)

Three Psalms Of David *CC3U,Psalm
[Lat] SATB,acap AMP $5.50   (M1869)

MILITIBUS IN TUENDA PATRIA GLORIOSA MORTE
PEREMPTIS see Bottazzo, Luigi

MILKEY, E.T.
Christmas Is Coming *Xmas
4pt men cor&opt unis treb cor,opt Mez solo
oct SCHIRM.G 9964 $.30   (M1870)
mix cor,S solo,acap oct SCHIRM.G 9518 $.30
                                        (M1871)
3pt wom cor oct SCHIRM.G 9965 $.25   (M1872)

MILLER
Gloria *Gloria
SSATBB oct FOX UM102 $.30   (M1873)

God Made Our Hands
(Ades) SATB SHAWNEE A 1017 $.35   (M1874)
(Ades) SSA SHAWNEE B 308 $.35   (M1875)
(Ades) TTBB SHAWNEE C215 $.35   (M1876)
(Ades) SAB SHAWNEE D116 $.35   (M1877)
(Ades) SA/TB SHAWNEE E71 $.35   (M1878)

God's Gift Of Love *Xmas,cant
SATB PRO ART 1103 $1.25   (M1879)

How Far Is It To Bethlehem *Xmas
unis BOOSEY-CAN s.p.   (M1880)

I Wanna Be Ready
SATB oct GALAXY 1.1370.1 $.35   (M1881)

Mass For Peace *Mass
cor voc sc KALMUS 6308 $2.50   (M1882)

O Gladsome Light
SATB BOOSEY-CAN s.p.   (M1883)

Sing, Sing For Christmas *Xmas
SATB oct LORENZ B188 $.30   (M1884)

Whole World Comes To Bethlehem, The *Xmas
SATB oct PRO ART 1894 $.25   (M1885)

MILLER, EDWARD
Seven Last Days, The
SATB,perc, 2 stereo systems, 16mm silent
color film (easy) SCHIRM.EC 2906 $.50,
ipa   (M1886)

Souls Of The Righteous, The *Rembrnc
SATB ALLANS 247 s.p.   (M1887)

MILLER, J.
Bring A Torch, Janette, Isabella *Xmas
SATB,acap oct PRESSER 312-40691 $.35   (M1888)

Gift Of Christmas Morn, The *Xmas
4pt mix cor,S solo oct SCHIRM.G 10261 $.25
                                        (M1889)

He Never Said A Mumblin' Word *Easter
SATB,acap oct PRESSER 312-40689 $.30
                                        (M1890)

MILLER, THOMAS A.
New Song, A *Bibl
SATB,pno,bvl oct WORLD CA-2066-8 $.45 (M1891)

MILLIGAN, H.V.
Hear My Cry
4pt mix cor oct SCHIRM.G 10020 $.25   (M1892)

MILLS, EDGAR
Chassidic Sabbath Eve Service *Sab-Eve
SATB TRANSCON. TCL 762 $3.00   (M1893)

Chassidic Sabbath Morning Service
SATB TRANSCON. TCL 871 $4.00   (M1894)

MILNER
Most Glorious Lord Of Life *anthem
mix cor oct OXFORD 42.352 $.35   (M1895)

MILNER, ANTHONY (1925-
Before Time, Beyond *Fest,anthem
mix cor oct NOVELLO 28.1381.05 s.p.   (M1896)

Chants For The Ordinary Of The Mass *CCU,
chant
cong oct NOVELLO 02.0072.07, 02.0073.05
s.p.   (M1897)

Form Of Compline, A
cong oct NOVELLO 02.0071.09 s.p.   (M1898)
mix cor oct NOVELLO 02.0070.00 s.p.   (M1899)

Form Of Sunday Vespers For Congregational
Use, A
mix cor oct NOVELLO 02.0081.06 s.p.   (M1900)
cong oct NOVELLO 02.0082.04 s.p.   (M1901)

Holy Communion *Commun
unis&cong,org s.p. sc NOVELLO 02.0083.02,
voc sc NOVELLO 02.0084.00   (M1902)

I Have Surely Built Thee A House To Dwell In
*anthem
mix cor oct NOVELLO 28.1373.04 s.p.   (M1903)

I Looked, And Behold! *ASD,anthem
mix cor oct NOVELLO 86.0026.00 s.p.   (M1904)

Mass *Op.3, Mass
mix cor,acap oct NOVELLO 44.1424.01 s.p.
                                        (M1905)

Praise The Lord Of Heaven *anthem
mix cor,ATB soli oct NOVELLO 40.1407.03
s.p.   (M1906)

Psalm 136
mix cor oct NOVELLO 44.1413.06 s.p.   (M1907)
cong oct NOVELLO 44.3413.07 s.p.   (M1908)

Salutatio Angelica
[Lat] voc sc UNIVER. 12736 $2.90   (M1909)

St. Francis *Op.8
SATB,T solo,3fl,2ob,2clar,2bsn,4horn,2trp,
3trom,tuba,strings,timp voc sc NOVELLO
s.p., ipr   (M1910)

Te Deum *Fest,Te Deum
SATB oct NOVELLO 44.1437.03 s.p.   (M1911)

Turbae For The Passion According To St. John
*anthem
mix cor,acap oct NOVELLO 03.0110.08 s.p.
                                        (M1912)

Turbae For The Passion According To St.
Matthew *anthem
mix cor,acap oct NOVELLO 03.0113.02 s.p.
                                        (M1913)

Water And The Fire, The *Op.16, ora
SATB,STBar soli,org,2fl,2ob,2clar,2bsn,
4horn,3trp,3trom,tuba,strings,2perc,timp,
2harp voc sc NOVELLO s.p., ipr   (M1914)

MILNER, ARTHUR
Hear My Prayer *prayer
SATB ENOCH EC330 s.p.   (M1915)

Lord Is My Shepherd, The
mix cor LENGNICK s.p.   (M1916)

O Be Joyful In God *anthem
mix cor oct NOVELLO 28.1426.09 s.p.   (M1917)

O Clap Your Hands *anthem
SAB oct NOVELLO 28.1443.09 s.p.   (M1918)

O Praise God In His Holiness *anthem
SAB oct NOVELLO 28.1363.07 s.p.   (M1919)

MILWID, ANTONI
Alla Polacca Sub Tuum Praesidium *Pol
(Dziewulska, M.; Ochlewski, T.) SB,fl&opt
bsn&2vln&vcl&org/hpsd POLSKIE FMA3 s.p.
                                        (M1920)

MIN GUD ER MED MIG see Buxtehude, Dietrich, Der
Herr Ist Mit Mir

MIN GUD OCH FADER KARE see Thyrestam, Gunnar

MIN GUD OCH OCH FADER KARE
(Berg, Gottfrid) 3pt mix cor NORDISKA 2187
s.p. see also Sacrae Cantiones   (M1921)

MIN SJAEL, LOV HERREN see Jeppesen, Knud

MIN SJAEL, LOV HERREN OG GLEM IKKE see
Jeppesen, Knud

MIN SJAEL NU LOVE HERREN see Pederson, Mogens

MIN SJAL DU MASTE NU GLOMMA *folk,Swed
(Salonen, Sulo) [Swed] SAB,acap GEHRMANS
TKS 45   (M1922)

MIN SJAL, DU MASTE NU GLOMMA see Berg, Gottfrid

MIN SJAL LANGTAR OCH TRANGTAR see Wennerberg,
Gunnar

MIN SJAL PRISAR STORLIGEN HERREN see
Bjarnegard, Gustaf

MIN SJEL, LOV HERREN see Karlsen, Rolf

MIN SJEL LOVHERREN see Maeland, Lars

MIN STJARNA OCH SVALORNA see Smetana, Bedrich

MINA KUNNIOITAN SINUA JUMILANI see Johansson,
Bengt

MINA LEFNADSTIMMAR STUPA see Gustaf

MINE EYES HAVE SEEN THE GLORY see Davies, Henry
Walford

MINE EYES I WILL LIFT UP see Morgan

MINE IS A RISEN SAVIOUR see Carmony, Bryan M.

MINI-MOTET FROM MICAH see Beversdorf, Thomas

MINOJA, AMBROSIO (1752-1825)
Parce Mihi Domine
[Lat] SATB,acap voc sc PETERS HU1617 $1.50,
ipr   (M1923)

MINTON, T.
Praise The Lord O My Soul
cor oct HART s.p.   (M1924)

MINUIT CHRETIEN, C'EST L'HEURE SOLENNELLE see
Adam, Adolphe-Charles

MINUTE CAROL, THE see McAfee, Don

MIOT, VITTORIO
In Paradisum *anti/Req
[Lat] 2 eq voices,org ZANIBON 1736 s.p.
                                        (M1925)

MIR NACH, SPRICHT CHRISTUS see Gesius,
Bartholomaus

MIR NACH, SPRICHT CHRISTUS, UNSER HELD see
Schein, Johann Hermann

MIRABILE MYSTERIUM see Gallus, Jacobus

MIRABILE MYSTERIUM see Wellesz, Egon

MIRABILE MYSTERIUM see Willaert, Adrian

MIRACLE OF BETHLEHEM see Rasley

MIRACLE OF CHRISTMAS, THE see Otteson

MIRACLE OF HANUKKAH, THE see Otteson

MIRACLE OF LOVE, THE see Moffatt

MIRACLE OF SAINT NICHOLAS
(Perle) SATB,acap oct BOOSEY 5225 $.40
                                        (M1926)

MIRACLE OF THE VIRGIN MARY, A see Schindler,
Kurt

MIRACLE OF TIME, THE see Marsh

MIRACLE, THE see Murray

MIRACLES OF CHRISTMAS see Rorem, Ned

MIRACULOUS see Roe, Gloria [Ann]

MIRACULOUS HARVEST, THE see Niles, John Jacob

MIRANDA, A.
Alleluia!
SATB PARAGON 1013 $.25   (M1927)

MIRIAMS SIEGESGESANG see Schubert, Franz
(Peter)

MIRIAM'S SONG OF TRIUMPH see Schubert, Franz
(Peter), Miriams Siegesgesang

MIRJAMS GESANG see Jacot, Andre

MIRJAM'S SIEGESGESANG see Schubert, Franz
(Peter), Miriams Siegesgesang

MIRON
Feed Thy People
SATB oct BELWIN 60822 $.35   (M1928)

MIRON, ISSACHAR
Golden Gates Of Joy *folk/ora
mix cor,opt orch BIG3 $4.95, ipr   (M1929)

MIS see Rontgen, [Julius]

MISA A S.S. JUAN XXIII see Carrillo, Julian

MISA DE PASTORELA see Busca

MISA DE REQUIEM see Guridi

MISA DE VILLANCICOS see Pardos Arrue

MISA DUCAL see Halffter, C.

MISA EN HONOR DE NTRA. SRA. DE LA ALMUNDENA see
Gonzalez Barron

MISA PASTORIL see Benito

MISA PASTORIL see Ferrer

MISA PASTORIL see Gomis

MISA POPULAR see Lee, J.

MISERE MEI, DEUS see Leo, Leonardo

MISEREMINI FIDELES ANIMARUM see Gines Perez,
Juan

MISEREMINI MEI see Steenman, J.

MISERERE see Allegri, Gregorio

MISERERE see Bachmann, F.

MISERERE see Beethoven, Ludwig van

MISERERE see Bottazzo, Luigi

MISERERE see Hammarstrom, Hugo

MISERERE see Hasse, Johann Adolph

MISERERE see Lassus, Roland de (Orlandus)

MISERERE see Lotti, Antonio

MISERERE see Luhn

MISERERE see Magri, Pietro

MISERERE see Muller, Giulio

MISERERE see Penderecki, Krzysztof

MISERERE see Pergolesi, Giovanni Battista

MISERERE see Volpi, Edoardo

MISERERE B-MOLL see Hoffmann, Ernst Theodor
   Amadeus

MISERERE I see Magri, Pietro

MISERERE II see Magri, Pietro

MISERERE MEI see Bunjes, Paul G.

MISERERE MEI see Johansson, Bengt

MISERERE MEI see Lotti, Antonio

MISERERE MEI see Pergolesi, Giovanni Battista

MISERERE MEI, DEUS see Allegri, Gregorio

MISERERE MEI DEUS see Des Prez, Josquin

MISERERE MEI, DEUS see Leo, Leonardo

MISERERE MEI DEUS see Lotti, Antonio

MISERERE MEI, DEUS see Ripolles, Vincente

MISERERE MEI, DEUS see Viero, Francesco

MISERERE MEI, DOMINE see Erbach, Christian

MISERERE MEI, DOMINE see Lassus, Roland de
   (Orlandus)

MISERERE MEI DOMINE see Lupo, Thomas

MISERERE MEI, DOMINE see Victoria, Tomas Luis
   de

MISERERE MIHI see Vries, Tom de

MISERERE NOSTRI see Palestrina, Giovanni

MISERERE NOSTRI see Volpi, Edoardo

MISERICORDE see Clemens, Jacobus

MISERICORDE A MOI POVRE AFFLIGE see Goudimel,
   Claude

MISERICORDIA see Kronsteiner, Josef

MISERICORDIA DOMINI see Harris, Jerry Weseley

MISERICORDIA DOMINI see Mozart, Wolfgang
   Amadeus

MISERICORDIA DOMINI see Mozart, Wolfgang
   Amadeus, Misericordia Domini

MISERICORDIA DOMINI see Pitoni, Giuseppe
   Ottavio

MISERICORDIA DOMINI see Waldbroel, Wilhelm

MISERICORDIAS DOMINI see Durante, Francesco

MISERICORDIAS DOMINI see Matterling

MISERICORDIAS DOMINI see Mozart, Wolfgang
   Amadeus

MISERICORS DEUS see Picchi, Luigi

MISEROCCA, SEBASTIAN (ca. 1600?)
   Im Namen Jesu Sollen Sich Beugen *mot
   (Hellmann) SS/SAT/SAB,cont HANSSLER 1.502
   s.p.   (M1930)

MISSA see Abril

MISSA see Aulen

MISSA see Baumann, Max

MISSA see Brunner, Adolf

MISSA see Callhoff, Herbert

MISSA see Diepenbrock, Alfons

MISSA see Haydn, (Franz) Joseph

MISSA see Kelterborn, Rudolf

MISSA see Kokkoven, Joonas

MISSA see Lajtha, Laszlo

MISSA see Lotti, Antonio

MISSA see Ryelandt, Joseph

MISSA see Salonen, Sulo

MISSA see Heilmann, Harald

MISSA A 3 see Rubbra, Edmund

MISSA A 5 VOCIBUS see Eccard, Johannes

MISSA A 15 see Pekiel, Bertlomiej

MISSA A LA SAMBA see Peloquin, C. Alexander

MISSA A L'OMBRE D'UNG BUISSONET see Brumel,
   Antoine

MISSA A LOMBRE DUNG BUISSONET see Genet, Elzear

MISSA A-MOLL see Canniciari, D. Pompeo

MISSA A QUATTRO VOCI see Johansson, Bengt

MISSA AD FUGAM IN PERPETUO CANONE see
   Palestrina, Giovanni

MISSA AD IMITATIONEM PATER NOSTER see Gallus,
   Jacobus

MISSA AD PLACITUM see Le Jeune, Claude

MISSA AEDIS CHRISTI see Howells, Herbert Norman

MISSA AETERNA see Palestrina, Giovanni

MISSA ALLELUIA see Mouton, Jean

MISSA ALLELUYA see Mouton, Jean

MISSA "ALLES REGRETS" see Compere, [Louis]

MISSA ALMA REDEMPTORIS MATER see Mouton, Jean

MISSA ANCHOR CHE COL PARTIRE see Jaquet Of
   Mantua

MISSA ANGELICA see Travaglia, Silvio

MISSA ANTONIANA XIX see Ravanello, Oreste

MISSA AVE REGINA CAELORUM see Arcadelt, Jacob

MISSA BEATAE VIRGINIS see Strohbach, Siegfried

MISSA BEATI LOANNIS see Joubert, John

MISSA BENEDICTUS DOMINUS DEUS see Mouton, Jean

MISSA BERZERETTE SAVOYENNE see Brumel, Antoine

MISSA BONTEMPS see Brumel, Antoine

MISSA BREVE see Torres, Eduardo

MISSA BREVIS see Pepping, Ernst

MISSA BREVIS
   (Barnard, P.) SSA,opt inst oct PRESSER
   352-00402 $.35   (M1931)

MISSA BREVIS see Ahrold, Frank

MISSA BREVIS see Andres

MISSA BREVIS see Anerio, Giovanni Francesco

MISSA BREVIS see Bach, Johann Sebastian

MISSA BREVIS see Barnes, Albert F.

MISSA BREVIS see Barrell, Bernard

MISSA BREVIS see Bernhard

MISSA BREVIS see Bloch, Waldemar

MISSA BREVIS see Britten, Benjamin

MISSA BREVIS see Brown, Christopher

MISSA BREVIS see Buxtehude, Dietrich

MISSA BREVIS see Callhoff, Herbert

MISSA BREVIS see Champagne, Claude

MISSA BREVIS see Cortes, Ramiro

MISSA BREVIS see Deegan, John

MISSA BREVIS see Ferneyhough, Brian

MISSA BREVIS see Gabrieli, Andrea

MISSA BREVIS see Gilbert, Anthony

MISSA BREVIS see Graap, Lothar

MISSA BREVIS see Hannahs, R.C.

MISSA BREVIS see Haydn, (Franz) Joseph

MISSA BREVIS see Holler, Karl

MISSA BREVIS see Hovhaness, Alan

MISSA BREVIS see Hurd, Michael

MISSA BREVIS see James, Philip

MISSA BREVIS see Kelly, Bryan

MISSA BREVIS see Kodaly, Zoltan

MISSA BREVIS see Kubizek, Augustinian

MISSA BREVIS see Leighton, Kenneth

MISSA BREVIS see Mozart, Wolfgang Amadeus

MISSA BREVIS see Pachelbel, Johann

MISSA BREVIS see Palester, Roman

MISSA BREVIS see Palestrina, Giovanni

MISSA BREVIS see Pavior

MISSA BREVIS see Pekiel, Bertlomiej

MISSA BREVIS see Pelegrini

MISSA BREVIS see Praetorius, Michael

MISSA BREVIS see Preston, Simon

MISSA BREVIS see Rubbra, Edmund

MISSA BREVIS see Runback, Albert

MISSA BREVIS see Salvesen, Th.

MISSA BREVIS see Saunders, Niel

MISSA BREVIS see Schilling, Hans Ludwig

MISSA BREVIS see Schubert, Heino

MISSA BREVIS see Seiber, Matyas

MISSA BREVIS see Smalley, R.

MISSA BREVIS see Soehner, L.

MISSA BREVIS see Thiele

MISSA BREVIS see Trant, Brian

MISSA BREVIS see Verkouteran, Adrian

MISSA BREVIS see Walker, Robin

MISSA BREVIS see Walton, William

MISSA BREVIS see Warner, Theodore

MISSA BREVIS see Watson, Frank Campbell

MISSA BREVIS see Westbrook, Francis B.

MISSA BREVIS see Whettam, Graham

MISSA BREVIS see Wienhorst, Richard

MISSA BREVIS see Wills, Arthur

MISSA BREVIS see Berkeley, Lennox

MISSA BREVIS see Berkeley, Lennox

MISSA BREVIS see Barbe, Helmut

MISSA BREVIS B-DUR see Mozart, Wolfgang Amadeus

MISSA BREVIS ET SIMPLEX see Hammarstrom, Hugo

MISSA BREVIS F-DUR see Mozart, Wolfgang Amadeus

MISSA BREVIS IN A MAJOR see Bach, Johann
   Sebastian

MISSA BREVIS IN C-DUR see Mozart, Wolfgang
   Amadeus

MISSA BREVIS IN D see Britten, Benjamin

MISSA BREVIS IN D MAJOR see Mac Nutt, Walter

MISSA BREVIS IN D-MOLL see Mozart, Wolfgang
   Amadeus

MISSA BREVIS IN ES-DUR see Miggl, Erwin

MISSA BREVIS IN F see Bruckner, Anton

MISSA BREVIS IN F MAJOR see Bach, Johann
   Sebastian

MISSA BREVIS IN F MAJOR see Mozart, Wolfgang
   Amadeus

MISSA BREVIS IN F MINOR see Drynan, Margaret

MISSA BREVIS IN FESTIS SOLEMNIBUS see Wikander,
   David

MISSA BREVIS IN G-DUR see Mozart, Wolfgang
   Amadeus

MISSA BREVIS IN G MAJOR see Bach, Johann
   Sebastian

MISSA BREVIS IN G MINOR see Bach, Johann
   Sebastian

MISSA BREVIS (K115), AND OTHERS see Mozart,
   Wolfgang Amadeus

MISSA BREVIS PRIMI TONI see Gaforio, Franchino

MISSA BREVIS SALISBURIENSIS see Bush, Geoffrey

MISSA BREVIS (SARISBURIENSIS) see Guest,
   Douglas

MISSA BREVIS SECUNDA see Alcock, Stanley

MISSA BREVIS ST. JOHANNIS DE DEO see Haydn,
   (Franz) Joseph

MISSA BREVIS SUPER: REGINA CAELI ET TANTUM ERGO
   see Willms, F.

MISSA BREVIS XIII see Willan, Healey

MISSA BREVIS XIV see Willan, Healey

MISSA BREVIS see Mozart, Wolfgang Amadeus

MISSA BREVIS see Mozart, Wolfgang Amadeus

MISSA BREVIS see Mozart, Wolfgang Amadeus

MISSA BREVIS see Mozart, Wolfgang Amadeus

MISSA BREVIS see Mozart, Wolfgang Amadeus

MISSA BREVIS see Mozart, Wolfgang Amadeus

MISSA BREVIS see Mozart, Wolfgang Amadeus

MISSA BREVIS see Mozart, Wolfgang Amadeus

MISSA BREVIS see Mozart, Wolfgang Amadeus

MISSA BREVIS see Mozart, Wolfgang Amadeus

MISSA BREVIS see Mozart, Wolfgang Amadeus

MISSA BREVIS see Mozart, Wolfgang Amadeus

MISSA C-DUR see Mozart, Wolfgang Amadeus

MISSA C-DUR see Mozart, Wolfgang Amadeus

MISSA C-MOLL see Liszt, Franz

MISSA C-MOLL see Mozart, Wolfgang Amadeus

MISSA C-MOLL see Mozart, Wolfgang Amadeus

MISSA CANTUARIENSIS see Rubbra, Edmund

MISSA CARMINIUM see Isaac, Heinrich

MISSA CARMINUM see Isaac

MISSA CARMINUM see Isaac, Heinrich

MISSA CARMINUM see Rener

MISSA CARMINUM AD HORAM MATUTINAM see Bloch, Waldemar

MISSA CELLENSIS see Haydn, (Franz) Joseph

MISSA CHIARE DOLCI E FRESCHE ACQUE see Jaquet Of Mantua

MISSA CHORALIS see Ahrens, Joseph

MISSA CHORALIS see David, Johann Nepomuk

MISSA CHORALIS see Gounod, Charles Francois

MISSA CHORALIS see Liszt, Franz

MISSA CHRISTMATIS see Rehmann, Theodor Bernhard

MISSA CONSOLATIONIS IN DEO see Jansen, Philipp

MISSA CORPORIS CHRISTI see Fux, Johann Joseph

MISSA COVENTRENSIS see Easdale, Brian

MISSA CRIOLLA see Ramirez, Ariel

MISSA CUM JUBILO see Creston, Paul

MISSA CUM JUBILO see Segarra, Dom Ireneu

MISSA CUM JUBILO see Tittel, Ernst

MISSA CUNCTIPOTENS see Serena, Bruno

MISSA D-DUR see Casini, Giovanni Maria

MISSA DA CAMERA see Naylor, Bernard

MISSA DA PACEM see Des Prez, Josquin

MISSA DE ANGELIS see Burgess, Francis

MISSA DE ANGELIS see Harwood, Basil

MISSA DE BEATA VIRGINE see Arcadelt, Jacob

MISSA DE BEATA VIRGINE see Brumel, Antoine

MISSA DE BEATA VIRGINE see Des Prez, Josquin

MISSA DE CARNEVALE see Gaforio, Franchino

MISSA DE CARNIVAL see Gaforio, Franchino

MISSA DE DOMINICA see Mozart, Wolfgang Amadeus

MISSA DE DRINGHS see Brumel, Antoine

MISSA DE FERIA see Pipelare, Mathaes

MISSA DE O CLARA LUCE see Gaforio, Franchino

MISSA DE SANCTA MARIA MAGDALENA see Willan, Healey

MISSA DE SANCTO ALBANO IN E FLAT see Willan, Healey

MISSA DE TOUS BIENS PLEINE see Gaforio, Franchino

MISSA DEFUNCTORUM see Clemens, Jacobus

MISSA DEFUNCTORUM see Magri, Pietro

MISSA DESCENDI IN HORTUM see Brumel, Antoine

MISSA DICIT DOMINUS: NIHIL TULERITS IN VIA see Pipelare, Mathaes

MISSA DICTES MOY TOUTES VOZ PENSEES (WITH COMPERE'S CHANSON) see Mouton, Jean

MISSA DODEKAPHONICA (1966) see Ahrens, Joseph

MISSA "DOMINA ANGELORUM" see Ferrari-Trecate, Luigi

MISSA DOMINICALIS see Brumel, Antoine

MISSA DOMINICALIS FACILIS see Volpi, Edoardo

MISSA DONA PACEM see Desderi, Ettore

MISSA DORICA see Ahrens, Joseph

MISSA DORICA see Schroeder, Hermann

MISSA DUODECANONICA see Rautavaara, Einojuhani

MISSA ECCE NUNC BENEDICITE see Lassus, Roland de (Orlandus)

MISSA ECCE QUAM BONUM see Mouton, Jean

MISSA, [EDMOND JEAN LOUIS] (1861-1910)
  Noel *Xmas,carol
    opt cor,solo,opt orch LEMOINE voc sc s.p.,
      cor pts s.p., ipa   (M1932)

  Noel D'enfant *Xmas
    (Darcieux) [Fr] 3 eq voices/3pt wom cor,
      acap LEMOINE s.p.   (M1933)
    (Darcieux) [Fr] 4pt mix cor,acap LEMOINE
      s.p.   (M1934)

MISSA ELEGIACA see Mortari, Virgilio

MISSA ELIENSIS see Wills, Arthur

MISSA ENCORE IRAY JE JOUER see Genet, Elzear

MISSA ET ECCE TERRAE MOTUS see Brumel, Antoine

MISSA EUCHARISTICA see Perosi, (Dom) Lorenzo

MISSA EXONIENSIS see Dakers, Lionel

MISSA EXULTATE see Young

MISSA FATIMA see Doebler, Curt

MISSA FAULT D'ARGENT see Mouton, Jean

MISSA FERIALIS *Mass,15th cent
  mix cor STAINER CS359 s.p. see from Early
    Church Music, Vol. 8   (M1935)

MISSA FERIALIS see Senfl, Ludwig

MISSA FESTIVA see Monnikendam, Marius

MISSA FESTIVA see Polzer, Odo

MISSA FESTIVA IN HON. S. CAROLI BORROMEI see Garbelotto, Antonio

MISSA FESTIVALIS E BREVIS see Werner

MISSA FESTIVO see Gretchaninov, Alexander Tikhonovitch

MISSA FI-FI see Dalby, Martin

MISSA FLORUIT EGREGIUS INFANS LIVANUS IN ACTIS see Pipelare, Mathaes

MISSA FORS SEULEMENT see Genet, Elzear

MISSA FORS SEULEMENT see Pipelare, Mathaes

MISSA G-DUR see Casali, Giovanni Battista

MISSA GAUDEAMUS see Victoria, Tomas Luis de

MISSA GOTICA see Gebhard, Hans

MISSA GREGORIANA see Eschmann, Hanns

MISSA GREGORIANA see Toepler, A.

MISSA HISPANICA see Haydn, (Franz) Joseph

MISSA HYMNICA see Ahrens, Joseph

MISSA ICH STUND see Gallus, Jacobus

MISSA IN A see Lotti, Antonio

MISSA IN ADVENTU CHRISTI see David, Thomas [Christian]

MISSA IN ANGUSTIIS see Haydn, (Franz) Joseph

MISSA IN ANGUSTIIS see Haydn, (Franz) Joseph, Nelson-Messe

MISSA IN B FLAT see Bottazzo, Aloysius

MISSA IN C see Galuppi, Baldassare

MISSA IN C see Lotti, Antonio

MISSA IN C see Mozart, Wolfgang Amadeus

MISSA IN D see Bernabei, Giuseppe Antonio

MISSA IN DIE TRIBULATIONIS see Jaquet Of Mantua

MISSA IN E IN HONOREM ST. MICHAELIS ARCHANGELI see Frommel, Gerhard

MISSA IN ES KL TERTS see Adriessen, Willem

MISSA IN ES KL. TERTS see Bijvanck, Henk

MISSA IN F see Carpani

MISSA IN F see Lotti, Antonio

MISSA IN G see Bernabei, Giuseppe Antonio

MISSA IN G see Caldara, Antonio

MISSA IN G see Casciolini, Claudio

MISSA IN HON. B. GREGORII CARD. BARBARICI see Bottazzo, Luigi

MISSA IN HON. B.M.V. A MONTE SANCTO see Toniutti, Vittorio

MISSA IN HON. B.M.V. IMMACULATAE see Giachetti, Enrico

MISSA IN HON. BEATI J.B. COTTOLENGO see Fino, Giocondo

MISSA IN HON. DIVI MARCI EV. see Pieressa, Luigi

MISSA IN HON. IMMAC. CONCEP. B.V.M. see Goicoechea, Vincente

MISSA IN HON. MARIAE ASSUMPTAE see Bottazzo, Luigi

MISSA IN HON. MARIAE SS. AUXILIATRICIS see Cossetti, Gio. Batta

MISSA IN HON. S. BENEDICITI AB. see Bottazzo, Luigi

MISSA IN HON. S. HILARII MARTYRIS CARNIAE PATRONI see Cossetti, Gio. Batta.

MISSA IN HON. S. JOANNIS BAPTISTAE see Bottazzo, Luigi

MISSA IN HON. S. JOSEPH UNIVERSALIS ECCLESIAE PATRONI see Refice, Licinio

MISSA IN HON. S. JUSTINAE M.V. see Gubinelli, Oderisio

MISSA IN HON. S. MARCELLINAE V see Bottazzo, Luigi

MISSA IN HON. S. MAURI ABBATIS see Bottigliero, Eduardo

MISSA IN HON. S. ROSAE VIR. LIMANAE see Bottazzo, Luigi

MISSA IN HON. SS. CORDIS JESU see Faccin, Gian Domenico

MISSA IN HON. VIRGINIS DEIPARAE see Bottazzo, Luigi

MISSA IN HONOREM ANGELORUM see Vocht, Lodewijk de

MISSA IN HONOREM B. BERNARDI DE OFFIDA see Haydn, (Franz) Joseph

MISSA IN HONOREM MARIAE see David, Thomas [Christian]

MISSA IN HONOREM S. CAECILIAE see Mangone, Gioacchino

MISSA IN HONOREM S. THEODULI see Moeschinger

MISSA IN HONOREM SANCTAE FRANCISCAE ROMANAE see Perosi, (Dom) Lorenzo

MISSA IN HONOREM SANCTAE MARIAE VISITATIONIS PAUPERUM see Somma, Bonaventura

MISSA IN HONOREM SANCTI DOMINICI see Rubbra, Edmund

MISSA IN HONOREM SANCTI HENRICI see Bergman, Erik

MISSA IN HONOREM SANCTI THOMAE MORI see Oldham, Arthur

MISSA IN HONOREM SANCTISSIMAE TRINITAS see Mozart, Wolfgang Amadeus

MISSA IN HONOREM SANCTISSIMAE TRINITATIS see Mozart, Wolfgang Amadeus

MISSA IN HONOREM SS. EUCHARISTICI CORDIS JESU see Garbelotto, Antonio

MISSA IN HONOREM VIRGINIS PERDOLENTIS see Refice, Licinio

MISSA IN MYNE ZYN see Agricola, Alexander

MISSA (IN NAT. D. N. J. C.) OMNIPOTENS GENITOR see Gaforio, Franchino

MISSA IN NOCTE see Heiller, Anton

MISSA IN PERPETUO CANONE see Strohbach, Siegfried

MISSA IN RESURRECTIONE DOMINI see Vecchi

MISSA IN SUMMIS see Finck

MISSA IN SUMMIS see Finck, Heinrich

MISSA IN TEMPORE BELLI see Haydn, (Franz) Joseph

MISSA IN TONO PHRYGIO see Lajtha, Laszlo

MISSA INTERNATIONALIS see Goemanne, Noel

MISSA IX CUM JUBILO see Bottazzo, Luigi

MISSA JE NAY DUEUL see Brumel, Antoine

MISSA JE NE DEMANDE see Agricola, Alexander

MISSA JOANNES CHRISTI CARE-ECCE PUER MEUS see Pipelare, Mathaes

MISSA LA SERVITEUR see Agricola, Alexander

MISSA LA-SOL-FA-RE-MI see Porta, Costanzo

MISSA LAUDA SION see Casajus, Vincente

MISSA LE CUEUR FUT MIEN- EN AMOUR NE SINON BIEN see Genet, Elzear

MISSA L'HOMME ARME see Brumel, Antoine

MISSA L'HOMME ARME see La Rue, Pierre de

MISSA L'HOMME ARME see Pipelare, Mathaes

MISSA L'HORA PASSA see Viadana, Lodovico Grossi da

MISSA LITURGICA see Harrison, Julius Allen Greenway

MISSA LO SERAI JE DIRE see Mouton, Jean

MISSA LONGA see Mozart, Wolfgang Amadeus, Messa In C-Dur

MISSA LUBA *Mass,Afr
  (Haazen, Guido) [Eng/Lat] mix cor,T solo,perc
    LAWSON $1.75   (M1936)

MISSA MALHEUR ME BAT see Agricola, Alexander

MISSA MARIA MADRE DELLA CHIESA see Serena, Bruno

MISSA MATER PATRIS see Des Prez, Josquin

MISSA MATER S. LAETITIAE see Klerk, Albert de

MISSA MEDIA VITA see Fiebig, Kurt

MISSA MI-MI see Ockeghem, Johannes

MISSA MI MI see Pipelare, Mathaes

MISSA MINUSCULA see Sigurbjornsson, Thorkell

MISSA MONODICA IN HONOREM ST. GREGORII MAGNI see Ghedini, Giorgio Federico

MISSA NATALIS see Kronsteiner, Josef

MISSA NATURAE see La Montaine, John

MISSA NOE NOE see Arcadelt, Jacob

MIT FREUDEN ZART ZU DIESER FAHRT see Horn, Paul

MIT FREUDEN ZART ZU DIESER FAHRT see Kubler, Emil

MIT FREUDEN ZART ZU DIESER FAHRT see Trubel, Gerhard

MIT FRIED' UND FREUD see Bach, Johann Sebastian, Mit Fried' Und Freud' Ich Fahr' Dahin

MIT FRIED UND FREUD see Micheelsen, Hans Friedrich

MIT FRIED UND FREUD FAHR ICH DAHIN see Gesius, Bartholomaus

MIT FRIED UND FREUD ICH FAHR DAHIN *CC15U, Rembrnc
    (Kurig) TTBB HANSSLER 2.011 s.p.   (M1940)

MIT FRIED UND FREUD ICH FAHR DAHIN see Agricola, Martin

MIT FRIED UND FREUD ICH FAHR DAHIN see Bach, Johann Sebastian

MIT FRIED UND FREUD ICH FAHR DAHIN see Buxtehude, Dietrich

MIT FRIED UND FREUD ICH FAHR DAHIN see Eccard, Johannes

MIT FRIED UND FREUD ICH FAHR DAHIN see Hellingk, Lupus

MIT FRIED UND FREUD ICH FAHR DAHIN see Praetorius, Michael

MIT FRIED UND FREUD ICH FAHR DAHIN see Schein, Johann Hermann

MIT FRIED UND FREUD ICH FAHR DAHIN see Schumann, Georg

MIT FRIED UND FREUD ICH FAHR DAHIN [CHORALE] see Bach, Johann Sebastian

MIT GOTT, SO WOLLEN WIR LOBEN UND EHRN see Lohr, Ina

MIT MEINEM GOTT GEH ICH ZUR RUH see Calvisius, Sethus

MIT SCHALL VON ZUNGEN see Lahusen, Christian

MIT SCHALL VON ZUNGEN see Schrenk, Johannes

MIT SCHALL VON ZUNGEN see Weismann, Wilhelm

MIT WEINEN HEBT SICHS AN see Bach, Johann Christoph

MITCHEL, WILLIAM
    Christmas Story *Xmas,carol
    unis CRAMER 35 s.p.   (M1941)

MITCHELL
    He Giveth More Grace *anthem
    (Mickelson) SATB oct LILLENAS AN-1155 $.25
                                                (M1942)

MITCHELL, L.
    Saint Mark's Easter Gospel *Easter,Bibl
    SATB,trp oct SOUTHERN $.35   (M1943)

    St. Mark's Easter Gospel *Easter
    SATB,trp oct PRESSER 312-40630 $.40, ipa
                                                (M1944)

    TTBB,3trp oct PRESSER 312-40631 $.35   (M1945)

MITCHELTREE, JOHN JR.
    Earth Is The Lord's, The (Psalm 24) anthem/
        folk/hymn
    SSA/unis treb cor,gtr (easy) oct AUGSBURG
        3005 $.10   (M1946)
    oct AUGSBURG 11-3005 $.10   (M1947)

    Psalm 24 *see Earth Is The Lord's, The

MITE BOX, THE see Grime, William

MITT ERNST, O MENSCHENKINDER see Koch, Heinz

MITT GOTT SO WOLLEN WIR LOBN UND EHRN see Spitta, Heinrich

MITT HJERTE ALLTID VANKER see Baden, Conrad

MITT HJERTE, NA MA DU GLEMME see Elgaroy, Jan

MITTEN IN DEM LEBEN see Schilling, Hans Ludwig

MITTEN WIR IM LEBEN see Bornefeld, Helmut

MITTEN WIR IM LEBEN see Raphael, Gunther

MITTEN WIR IM LEBEN SIND see Bruck, Arnold von

MITTEN WIR IM LEBEN SIND see Erythraus, Gotthard

MITTEN WIR IM LEBEN SIND see Gadsch, Herbert

MITTEN WIR IM LEBEN SIND see Nucius, Johannes

MITTEN WIR IM LEBEN SIND see Praetorius, Michael

MITTEN WIR IM LEBEN SIND see Resinarius, Balthasar

MITTEN WIR IM LEBEN SIND see Schein, Johann Hermann

MITTEN WIR IM LEBEN SIND see Walther, Johann Gottfried

MITTERGRADNEGGER, G.
    Heiligenbluter Krippenmesse (composed with
        Fhedoroff, Nikolaus) *Xmas,Mass
    mix cor,org DOBLINGER voc sc s.p., cor pts
        s.p.   (M1948)

MITTIT AD VIRGINEM see Des Prez, Josquin

MIZERNA CICHA *Pol
    (Mishkin, H.) "How Still And Tiny" [Pol/Eng]
    TTBB,acap SCHIRM.EC 2106 $.20   (M1949)

MIZMDR L'TODAH see Rosenberg, Emanuel

MIZ'MOR SHIRU LADONAI see Richards, Stephen

M'NUCHON V'SIMCHOH see Ancis, Solomon

MO MARIA see Jillett, David

MO MARIA YOU ARE NEAR see Jillett, David, Mo Maria

MOATS
    Gentle Jesus *Xmas
    SATB oct LORENZ A480 $.30   (M1950)

MOBACH, E.
    Ere Zij God
    mix cor ALSBACH&D sc s.p., cor pts s.p.
                                                (M1951)

    Pasch-Hymne
    mix cor,pno/org ALSBACH&D sc s.p., cor pts
        s.p.   (M1952)

    Psalm 33
    see Three Psalms

    Psalm 100
    mix cor ALSBACH&D sc s.p., cor pts s.p.
                                                (M1953)

    Psalm 103
    see Three Psalms
    mix cor,soli,pno/org ALSBACH&D sc s.p., cor
        pts s.p.   (M1954)

    Psalm 146
    see Three Psalms
    mix cor,pno/org ALSBACH&D sc s.p., cor pts
        s.p.   (M1955)

    Three Psalms
    mix cor ALSBACH&D s.p.
        contains: Psalm 33; Psalm 103; Psalm 146
                                                (M1956)

MOCKEL, FRANZ
    Ein Lied Auf Ostern *Easter
    [Ger] mix cor (easy) oct SIRIUS 15 s.p.
                                                (M1957)

    Maria In Franken *CC7L,BVM
    [Ger] mix cor,ob,harp voc sc SIRIUS s.p.,
        ipa   (M1958)

    Maria Wollt Einst Wandern
    see Zwei Passionslieder Aus Franken

    Marienklage
    see Mockel, Franz, Was Auch Kommen Mag

    Seht Nur An Die Zwei Herzen
    see Zwei Passionslieder Aus Franken

    Was Auch Kommen Mag
    [Ger] mix cor (easy) oct SIRIUS 20 s.p.
        contains also: Marienklage   (M1959)

    Zwei Passionslieder Aus Franken *Psntd
    [Ger] mix cor (easy) oct SIRIUS 16 s.p.
        contains: Maria Wollt Einst Wandern; Seht
        Nur An Die Zwei Herzen   (M1960)

MODAL SETTING OF THE COMMUNION SERVICE, A see Shaw, Martin

MODERN TE DEUM, A see Swann, Donald

MOE, DANIEL
    As Joseph Was A Walking
    SATB oct FISCHER,J 8778 $.30   (M1961)

    Babe Is Born, A
    SATB,acap oct PRESSER 312-40254 $.30   (M1962)

    Cantata Of Peace *cant
    SATB,trp ABINGDON APM-942 $1.35, ipa
                                                (M1963)

    Easter Canticle *Easter
    SATB oct FISCHER,J 9312 $.30   (M1964)

    Fall Softly, Snow *anthem
    SATB,S solo (med diff) oct AUGSBURG 0510
        $.35   (M1965)

    Fanfare And Choral Procession *Commun/
        Easter/Gen
    SATB,org,2trp,2trom (med easy) sc AUGSBURG
        11-9166 $.55, ipa   (M1966)

    Four Contemporary Hymns, Set II *hymn,
        Contemp
    oct AUGSBURG 11-9188 $.12
        contains: God Be Merciful; I Lift Up Mine
        Eyes; Let Us With A Gladsome Mind;
        Nativity Hymn   (M1967)

    God Be Merciful *anthem
    see Four Contemporary Hymns, Set II
    SATB (med) oct AUGSBURG 1176 $.30   (M1968)

    Hosanna The Son Of David *Xmas/Easter
    (Lynn, G.) SATB oct PRESSER 352-00212 $.40
                                                (M1969)

    Hosanna To The Son Of David *Palm
    SATB oct SOUTHERN $.40   (M1970)

    How Beautiful Upon The Mountains *Xmas/Gen
    SATB,acap oct PRESSER 312-40230 $.30
                                                (M1971)

    I Am The Alpha And The Omega *anthem
    SATB (med) oct AUGSBURG 1483 $.35   (M1972)

    I Lift Up Mine Eyes
    see Four Contemporary Hymns, Set II

    I Lift Up My Eyes
    (Lynn, G.) SATB oct PRESSER MC246 $.30
                                                (M1973)

    I Will Extol Thee *anthem
    TTBB (med diff) oct AUGSBURG 0623 $.40
                                                (M1974)

    Let Us With A Gladsome Mind
    see Four Contemporary Hymns, Set II

    Lo, I Am With You *anthem
    SATB (med diff) oct AUGSBURG 1270 $.22
                                                (M1975)

    Lord Is My Strength, The
    SATB oct SACRED S-27 $.35   (M1976)

MOE, DANIEL (cont'd.)

    Nativity Hymn
    see Four Contemporary Hymns, Set II

    Nunc Dimittis *Nunc
    unis&cong oct AGAPE AG 7113 $.30   (M1977)

    O Jesus Christ, To Thee May Hymns Be Rising
        *anthem/hymn
    see FOUR CONTEMPORARY HYMNS, SET I
    SATB (med) oct AUGSBURG 1193 $.30   (M1978)

    O Praise The Lord
    SATB oct FISCHER,J 8699 $.30   (M1979)

    Psalm 47 *anthem
    SATB,bvl,4brass (med) AUGSBURG 0634 $.40,
        ipa see also Psalm Concertato   (M1980)

    Psalm 103 *anthem
    SATB,bvl,4brass (med) AUGSBURG 0633 $.25
        see also Psalm Concertato   (M1981)

    Psalm 150 *anthem
    SATB,bvl,4brass (med) AUGSBURG 0632 $.40
        see also Psalm Concertato   (M1982)

    Psalm Concertato *anthem
    SATB,bvl,4brass (med) oct AUGSBURG ipa
        contains & see also: Psalm 47; Psalm 103;
        Psalm 150   (M1983)

    Rejoice In The Lord Always
    SATB (med) ABINGDON APM-131 $.35   (M1984)

    Rejoice, Ye People *anthem
    SATB,org,2trp,2trom (med diff) oct AUGSBURG
        1458 $.35, ipa   (M1985)

    Stranger, Share Our Fire *anthem/hymn
    oct AUGSBURG 11-9486 $.05   (M1986)
    SATB (med easy) oct AUGSBURG 0529 $.25   (M1987)

MOERAN
    Christmas Day In The Morning *Xmas
    unis (easy) OXFORD 45.707 $.25   (M1988)

MOESCHINGER
    Missa In Honorem S. Theoduli *Mass
    4pt mix cor,org s.p. sc RICORDI-ENG SY93,
        cor pts RICORDI-ENG SY94-95   (M1989)

MOEVS
    Brief Mass, A *Mass
    SATB MARKS $1.25   (M1990)

MOEVS, ROBERT W. (1921-   )
    Et Nunc, Reges
    [Lat] SSA,pno/fl,clar, bass clarinet
        SCHIRM.EC 2569 $.55, ipr   (M1991)

MOFFAT
    In The Beginning Was The Word
    SAB,Bar solo,acap WARNER W3595 $.35   (M1992)

MOFFATT
    All For Jesus
    SATB oct LORENZ A493 $.25   (M1993)

    Alone *Easter
    SATB oct LORENZ B129 $.30   (M1994)

    As It Began To Dawn *Easter/Lent,cant
    SATB FISCHER,C R-8017 $.35   (M1995)

    Beyond The Cross *Easter,cant
    SATB/SA LORENZ $1.50   (M1996)

    Call His Name Jesus *Xmas,cant
    SATB oct LORENZ $1.50   (M1997)

    Come Unto Me
    SATB oct LORENZ A450 $.25   (M1998)

    Miracle Of Love, The *Xmas,cant
    SATB/SA oct LORENZ $1.50   (M1999)

    O Come, All Ye Faithful *Xmas
    SATB oct LORENZ B112 $.30   (M2000)
    2pt oct LORENZ 5759 $.30   (M2001)

    O Praise The Lord *Gen
    SATB SCHMITT 1779 $.22   (M2002)

    Ring Out, Wild Bells
    SATB oct LORENZ B134 $.30   (M2003)

    Who At My Door Is Standing?
    SATB oct LORENZ B120 $.30   (M2004)

MOFFATT, JAMES
    I Know Where I'm Going *Gen,anthem/folk
    SATB (med easy) oct LORENZ B203 $.30
                                                (M2005)

    I Will Sing Of My Redeemer *Gen,anthem/spir
    SATB (med easy) oct LORENZ B202 $.30   (M2006)

    O Divine Master *Gen
    SATB (prayer of st. francis) SCHMITT 1765
        $.30   (M2007)

    There's No Hidin' Place Down Here *spir
    SATB oct BOURNE 812 $.25   (M2008)

MOGEN OVOS see Low, Leo

MOGEN OVOS see Rabinowitch

MOHR, T.W.
    Ein Haus Voll Glorie Schauet
    men cor,acap ERDMANN 340 s.p.   (M2009)

MOHRING, JOHN
    Lehr Mich *Gen
    [Ger] unis,acap (easy) BOSSE BE 266 s.p.
        contains also: O Herr, Hore   (M2010)

    O Herr, Hore
    see Mohring, John, Lehr Mich

MOI, J'Y AI DROIT see You Got A Right

MOINEAU, G.
    D'ou Viens-Tu, Bergere? *Xmas
    [Fr] 4pt mix cor,acap LEMOINE s.p.   (M2011)

MOINEAU, G. (cont'd.)

Ou Courez-Vous? *Xmas
   [Fr] 4pt mix cor,acap LEMOINE s.p. (M2012)

MOIOLI, ROMANO
   Accorri A Betlemme *Xmas
   unis,org (easy) ZANIBON 2661 s.p. (M2013)

   Annuntio Vobis *Xmas,mot
   2 eq voices,solo,org ZANIBON 2660 s.p.
                                          (M2014)

   Canzone A S. Francesco *ASD
   [Lat] unis/2 eq voices ZANIBON 2623 s.p. (M2015)

   Cor Jesu
   see TRIA COR JESU

   Haec Dies *Easter,mot
   [Lat] 2pt,org ZANIBON 2662 s.p. (M2016)

   Laudate Dominum De Coelis
   see PER LA SANTA PASQUA

   O Luigi *ASD
   [Lat] unis/2 eq voices,org ZANIBON 2659
   s.p.   (M2017)

   Sette Pastorali A Gesu Bambino *CC7U,Xmas
   unis,org ZANIBON 2581 s.p. (M2018)

   Stabat Mater
   see QUATTRO STABAT MATER

   Tantum Ergo
   see SEI MOTTETTI EUCARISTICI

   Tota Pulchra *BVM
   [Lat] 2 eq voices,org ZANIBON 2630 s.p.
                                          (M2019)

MOIR, F.L.
   I Will Thank Thee, O Lord (Psalm 86) Bibl
   (Deis) 4pt mix cor oct SCHIRM.G 8397 $.25
                                          (M2020)
   (Deis; Downing) 3pt wom cor oct SCHIRM.G
   8942 $.25   (M2021)
   (Dies) 3pt mix cor oct SCHIRM.G 9724 $.30
                                          (M2022)

   Psalm 86 *see I Will Thank Thee, O Lord

MOISE see Lacome, Paul

MOLFINO, L.
   Lieti Cantiamo *CCU
   1-3pt CURCI 6377 s.p.; 1-3pt,pno CURCI 6529
   s.p.   (M2023)

MOLITOR, J.B.
   Give To The World Thy Peace
   (Grant, Louise) SATB oct BELWIN 1713 $.30
                                          (M2024)

   Praise Ye The Lord
   SATB oct FISCHER,J 1181 $.30 (M2025)

MOLLER, FRIEDRICH
   Carol Of The Shepherds *Xmas,carol
   (Hoist) SATB WARNER G1661 $.30 (M2026)
   (Hoist) SSA WARNER G1838 $.30 (M2027)

MOLLER, SVEND-OVE (1903-1949)
   "Gak Under Jesu Kors At Sta" *Op.40, Psntd,
   cant
   [Dan] cor,soli,org,inst sc FOG III, 122
   s.p.   (M2028)
   "Gak Under Jesu Kors At Sta" [Dan] sc
   SAMFUNDET s.p.   (M2029)

   Gak Under Jesu Kors At Sta *see "Gak Under
   Jesu Kors At Sta"

MOLLICONE, H.
   Our Prayer Of Thanks
   SATB oct ELKAN-V 362-1229 $.30 (M2030)

MOMENT BY MOMENT see Smith

MON AME EN DIEU TANT SEULEMENT see Goudimel,
   Claude

MON BEAU SAPIN *Xmas,carol,Ger
   (Canteloube, J.) [Fr] 4pt mix cor,acap oct
   DURAND   (M2031)

MON BEAU SAPIN see Roesgen-Champion, Marquerie

MON BEAU SAPIN DE NOEL see Roesgen-Champion,
   Marquerie

MON BEAU SAPIN DES NOEL see Roesgen-Champion,
   Marquerie

MON DIEU ME PAIST SOUS SA PUISSANCE HAUTE see
   Goudimel, Claude

MON DIEU VEUILLE MA VOIX OUIR see Caulery, Jean

MONACO, RICHARD A.
   All Flesh Is Grass
   4pt mix cor oct SCHIRM.G 11274 $.25 (M2032)

   Blessed Be The Lord *cant
   mix cor,S solo BELWIN $1.75 (M2033)

   Lord, Thou Has Been Our Dwelling Place
   4pt mix cor,S solo,org oct SCHIRM.G 11228
   $.25   (M2034)

   Somerset Carol
   SSA oct FISCHER,J 9925 $.30 (M2035)

   This Is The Day
   SA oct FISCHER,J 9880 $.30 (M2036)

   We Praise Thee, Lord *Gen
   SATB SCHMITT 8019 $.25 (M2037)

MONACO, ROBERT A.
   Christ Is Risen *Easter
   jr cor,org,bells,tamb (easy) PRESSER
   362-01328 $.35   (M2038)

MONDO, MICHELE
   Quattro Litanie Della B.V. Maria *CC4U,BVM
   [Lat] 2 eq voices,org ZANIBON 997 s.p.
                                          (M2039)

MONE, F.J.
   Hymn I Latini Medii Aevi Vol. 3 *CCU
   (Vecchi, Prof. Giuseppe) cor oct FORNI 327
   s.p.   (M2040)

   Hymni Latini Medii Aevi Vol. 1 *CCU
   (Vecchi, Prof. Giuseppe) cor oct FORNI 327
   s.p.   (M2041)

   Hymni Latini Medii Aevi Vol.2 2 *CCU
   (Vecchi, Prof. Giuseppe) cor oct FORNI 327
   s.p.   (M2042)

MONELLE, RAYMOND
   Lullay, Myn Lyking *Xmas
   mix cor ROBERTON s.p. (M2043)

   Lullay, Myn Lykyng
   SATB,acap ROBERTON (M2044)

MONHARDT
   Let The People Praise Thee
   mix cor SOUTHERN $.25 (M2045)

MONHARDT, MAURICE
   Let The People Praise Thee *anthem
   SATB (med diff) oct AUGSBURG 0610 $.25 (M2046)

   Song On Christmas Night, A *Xmas,anthem
   SATB (med) oct AUGSBURG 0511 $.30 (M2047)

MONK
   Abide With Me
   (Kirk) SATB oct PRO ART 1297 $.22 (M2048)
   (Wilson) SATB oct LORENZ 4429 $.30 (M2049)

   Hark! A Thrilling Voice Is Sounding *Adv
   (Follett) SATB oct PRO ART 2311 $.25
                                          (M2050)

   Hark! The Sound Of Holy Voices
   (Stevens) SATB&desc oct PRO ART 1679 $.20
                                          (M2051)

   If Ye Love Me, Keep My Commandments
   (Ehret) SATB oct SPRATT 569 $.25 (M2052)

   Sing, My Soul, His Wondrous Love
   (Coggin) SATB oct PRO ART 2482 $.25 (M2053)

   We Love The Place, O God
   unis BOOSEY-CAN s.p. (M2054)

MONK, M.J.
   Except The Lord Build The House
   2pt oct NOVELLO 48.0466.10 s.p. (M2055)

MONK, WILLIAM HENRY (1823-1889)
   Blijf Bij Mij, Heer (Houd Hoog Uw Kruis)
   men cor&opt wom cor sc ALSBACH&D s.p.
                                          (M2056)

   Blijf Met Mij, Heer
   men cor sc ALSBACH&D s.p. see also Vier
   Geestelijke Liederen   (M2057)

   Hail The Day *Easter
   (Marth) 3pt mix cor,org/pno oct SCHIRM.G
   11601 $.25   (M2058)

   Vier Geestelijke Liederen *see Blijf Met
   Mij, Heer   (M2059)

MONKS
   Hail The King Of Glory
   SATB FLAMMER A 5275 $.25 (M2060)

MONNIKENDAM, MARIUS (1896-   )
   Apocalyps
   [Dut] mix cor,narrator,org sc DONEMUS s.p.
                                          (M2061)
   [Dut] men cor,narrator,org sc DONEMUS s.p.
                                          (M2062)

   Boetpsalmen *Psalm
   [Dut] mix cor,pno,2fl,3ob,3clar,3bsn,3trp,
   4horn,3trom,tuba,strings,perc,timp min sc
   DONEMUS s.p.   (M2063)

   Carmen Finale "Alleluia" *Allelu
   [Dut] mix cor,2fl,2ob,2clar,2bsn,2trp,
   4horn,2trom,tuba,strings,timp,harp min sc
   DONEMUS s.p., cor pts ROSSUM s.p., voc sc
   ROSSUM s.p.   (M2064)

   Hymne *hymn
   [Dut] men cor,A solo,pno,2fl,2ob,2clar,
   2bsn,3trp,4horn,3trom,tuba,2bvl,perc,
   timp,opt org, xylophone DONEMUS min sc
   s.p., cor pts s.p., voc sc s.p.   (M2065)

   Magnificat *Magnif
   [Lat] mix cor,S solo,pno,3fl,2ob,2clar,
   2bsn,3trp,4horn,3trom,strings,perc,timp,
   harp, vibraphone DONEMUS min sc s.p., cor
   pts s.p.   (M2066)
   [Lat] mix cor,S solo,pno,3fl,2ob,2clar,
   3bsn,3trp,4horn,3trom,tuba,2bvl,perc,
   timp,harp,celeste, xylophone DONEMUS min
   sc s.p., voc sc s.p.   (M2067)
   [Lat] mix cor,S solo,2pno min sc DONEMUS
   s.p., ipr   (M2068)
   [Lat] mix cor,S solo,2pno min sc DONEMUS
   s.p., ipr   (M2069)

   Missa Festiva *Fest,Mass
   [Lat] mix cor,2fl,2ob,2clar,2bsn,2trp,
   4horn,2trom,tuba,strings,perc,timp,harp
   min sc DONEMUS s.p., cor pts ROSSUM s.p., voc
   sc ROSSUM   (M2070)

   Pro Defunctis *Mass
   [Lat] men cor,A solo,org DONEMUS min sc
   s.p., cor pts s.p., ipa   (M2071)

   Sinfonia Sacra
   [Lat] men cor,3fl,3ob,3clar,3bsn,3trp,
   4horn,3trom,tuba,strings,perc,timp,harp
   DONEMUS min sc s.p., cor pts s.p., voc sc
   s.p.   (M2072)

   Sinfonia Sacra (II) "Domine Salvum Fac"
   [Lat] men cor&jr cor,3fl,3ob,2clar,2bsn,
   3trp,3trom,tuba,strings,perc DONEMUS min
   sc s.p., cor pts s.p., voc sc s.p.   (M2073)

   Te Deum *Te Deum
   [Lat] men cor,pno,2fl,2ob,2clar,2bsn,3trp,
   4horn,3trom,tuba,strings,perc,timp
   DONEMUS min sc s.p., cor pts s.p., voc sc
   s.p.   (M2074)
   [Lat] mix cor,pno,2fl,ob,clar,bsn,3trp,
   2horn,3trom,tuba,strings,perc,timp

MONNIKENDAM, MARIUS (cont'd.)

   DONEMUS min sc s.p., cor pts s.p., voc sc
   s.p.   (M2075)
   [Lat] men cor,org DONEMUS sc s.p., cor pts
   s.p.   (M2076)

   Veni Creator
   [Lat] men cor,opt S/A solo,org,opt trom
   DONEMUS sc s.p., cor pts s.p.   (M2077)
   [Lat] mix cor,org,opt trom DONEMUS sc s.p.,
   cor pts s.p.   (M2078)
   [Lat] men cor,opt S/A solo,org,opt trom
   DONEMUS min sc s.p., cor pts s.p., ipa
                                          (M2079)
   [Lat] mix cor,org,opt trom min sc DONEMUS
   s.p.   (M2080)

   Veni, Sancte Spiritus
   [Lat] mix cor,org DONEMUS sc s.p., cor pts
   s.p.   (M2081)

   Via Sacra
   [Lat/Eng] SATB&boy cor,narrator,org,2perc
   sc PETERS D528 $15.00, ipa, cor pts
   PETERS D528 $1.25, ipa   (M2082)

MONSELL
   Sing To The Lord Of The Harvest
   (Hallett) SATB oct WORD CS-2251 $.25
                                          (M2083)

MONSON
   Praise
   boy cor SOUTHERN $.25 (M2084)

MONSON, HELEN C.
   Song Of The Righteous, The *see Beck, Audrey

MONSTRA TE ESSE MATREM see Del Castillo

MONTAGUE
   Joshua Fit De Battle Ob Jericho *spir
   SATB,A/Bar solo,acap WARNER W2811 $.30
                                          (M2085)

   Let Us Break Bread Together *Commun,spir
   SATB,acap WARNER W3408 $.30 (M2086)

MONTANI, NICOLA A. (1880-1948)
   Missa Solemnis In E Flat *see Te Deum
   Laudamus

   Te Deum Laudamus *Mass
   "Missa Solemnis In E Flat" [Lat] 4pt mix
   cor,SATB soli voc sc SCHIRM.G $.60 (M2087)

MONTE, DE
   Che Poich'a Mortal Rischio
   (Malin) "Now, Past The Deadly Peril"
   SSAATB,acap MARKS 4415 $.25 (M2088)

   L'apparir Del Sol
   (Malin) "Rising Of The Sun, The" [Eng/It]
   SSAATB,acap MARKS 4419 $.25 (M2089)

   Mentre Sperai Da Te
   (Malin) "Once I Had Hoped For Thee" [Eng/
   It] SSATBB,acap MARKS 4427 $.35 (M2090)

   New Is The Triumph *see Nuovo Trionfo

   Now, Past The Deadly Peril *see Che Poich'a
   Mortal Rischio

   Nuovo Trionfo
   (Malin) "New Is The Triumph" [Eng/It]
   SSAATB,acap MARKS 4436 $.25 (M2091)

   Once I Had Hoped For Thee *see Mentre Sperai
   Da Te

   Rising Of The Sun, The *see L'apparir Del
   Sol

MONTER, JOSEF
   Geistliche Adventmusik *Adv
   mix cor,S solo,strings,rec ERDMANN 544 s.p.
                                          (M2092)

MONTEVERDI, CLAUDIO (ca. 1567-1643)
   Adoramus Te
   see Two Motets

   Adoramus Te, Christe *mot
   (Arnold) SATB OXFORD see from Two Motets
                                          (M2093)

   Angel Hosts Declare, The *see Angelus Ad
   Pastores Ait

   Angelus Ad Pastores Ait *Xmas
   see Sacrae Cantiunculae
   girl cor SOUTHERN $.35 (M2094)
   (Fellerer) [Lat] SAT SCHOTT 10918 s.p. (M2095)
   (Field) SSA/TTB,acap oct BOOSEY 5545 $.30
                                          (M2096)
   (Klein) "Angel Hosts Declare, The" [Eng/
   Lat] 3pt boy cor/3pt wom cor/3pt men cor,
   acap oct SCHIRM.G 11785 $.30   (M2097)

   Ave Maris Stella *hymn
   (Washington, Henry) [Lat] SATB,org CHESTER
   s.p.   (M2098)

   Baroque To The Great Classics, The Vol. 3-
   1550 To 1700 *sac/sec,CCUL
   mix cor min sc KALMUS 883 $1.30 (M2099)

   Be Joyful *see Laetatus Sum

   Beatus Vir (from Selva Morale Et Spirituale)
   (Steele, John) [Lat] SSATTB,org,strings,opt
   3trom voc sc NOVELLO s.p., ipr   (M2100)

   Before Day Came Again *see Non Havea Febo
   Ancora

   Cantate Domino *mot
   see Two Motets
   (Arnold) SATB OXFORD see from Two Motets
                                          (M2101)

   Christ We Adore Thy Name
   mix cor SOUTHERN $.25 (M2102)

   Christe, Adoramus Te *mot
   "Saviour, We Adore And Bless Thy Holy Name"
   [Eng/Lat] SSATB oct NOVELLO 40.1491.10
   s.p.   (M2103)

MONTEVERDI, CLAUDIO (cont'd.)

Come, Thou Faithful Servant *see Veni Sponsa Christi

Crucified *see Crucifixus

Crucifixus *Easter/Lent
(Marshall, Charles) "Crucified" SATB FRANK F-579 $.30 (M2104)

Deus In Adjutorium *BVM
(Wolters) 6pt mix cor MOSELER s.p. see from Vesperae Beatae Mariae Virginis 1610 (M2105)

Deus Tuorum Militum
TTBB sc OXFORD 41.028 $.25, ipa (M2106)

Dixit Dominus (Psalm 109) BVM
(Wolters) 6pt mix cor,cont,opt inst MOSELER s.p. see from Vesperae Beatae Mariae Virginis 1610 (M2107)

Gloria Concertata
(Steele, John) SSATTBB,cont,4trom,2vln oct PENN STATE 0-271-09118-5 $5.75 (M2108)

Hodie Christus Natus Est *Xmas
see Sacrae Cantiunculae
(Field) [Lat/Eng] SSA/TTB,acap oct BOOSEY 5544 $.30 (M2109)
(Klein) "On This Day Christ Is Born" [Eng/Lat] 3pt boy cor/3pt wom cor/3pt men cor, acap oct SCHIRM.G 11784 $.30 (M2110)
(Vene) "On This Day Christ Is Born" [Lat/Eng] TTB/SSA oct COLOMBO 2041 $.25 (M2111)

In Illa Temport *see Messa I A 6 Voci

In Illo Tempora *see Messe I A 6 Voci

Laetatus Sum (Psalm 121) BVM,Psalm
(Casella, Alfredo) 6pt,org,orch sc SANTIS s.p., ipr (M2112)
(McKelvy, James) "Be Joyful" SATB,soli,inst voc sc FOSTER MF109 $1.50, ipa, cor pts FOSTER 109A $.35, voc pt FOSTER 109X $.45 (M2113)
(Wolters) 6pt mix cor,cont MOSELER s.p. see from Vesperae Beatae Mariae Virginis 1610 (M2114)

Lamb Of God *Renais
(Ehret, Walter) SATB,acap PEER $.40 (M2115)

Lauda Jerusalem (Psalm 147) BVM
(Wolters) 3pt mix cor&3pt mix cor,cont MOSELER s.p. see from Vesperae Beatae Mariae Virginis 1610 (M2116)

Lauda Sion Salvatorem
(Vene) "Praise The King Of Heaven" [Lat/Eng] TTB/SSA,acap oct COLOMBO 2031 $.25 (M2117)

Laudate Dominum (Psalm 117)
[Lat] min sc PETERS E1069 $2.00, ipa (M2118)
8pt mix cor,2vln,cont cor pts NORDISKA 4458 s.p., sc NORDISKA s.p. (M2119)

Laudate Pueri (Psalm 112) BVM
(Wolters) 8pt mix cor,cont MOSELER s.p. see from Vesperae Beatae Mariae Virginis 1610 (M2120)

Magnificat (from Selva Morale) Magnif/mot
SATB HANSSLER 1.542 s.p. (M2121)
[Lat] SSATTB min sc PETERS E1071 $3.00 (M2122)
(Ghedini, G.F.) 7pt mix cor,orch voc sc ZERBONI 4663 s.p., ipr (M2123)
(Goehr, W.) [Lat] voc sc UNIVER. 12320, cor pts UNIVER. 12321 $2.70 (M2124)
(Matthaei, Karl) [Ger] SSATTB,org (med) BAREN. BA 1867 sc $4.00, cor pts $1.75 (M2125)
(Stevens, Denis; Steele, John) dbl cor, soli,org,4trom,strings voc sc NOVELLO s.p., ipr (M2126)

Magnificat A Sei Voci (from Sanctissimi Virginis Missa) Magnif
6pt,org voc sc KALMUS 6309 $1.25 (M2127)
(Smithers, Don) 6pt mix cor,org/inst LAWSON $1.75 (M2128)

Magnificat I *Magnif
(Wagner, Roger) mix cor,org/strings LAWSON $1.75 (M2129)

Marienvesper 1610 *BVM
mix cor,cont,inst MOSELER sc s.p., cor pts s.p., ipa (M2130)

Mass *Mass
[Lat] SATB,acap HINRICHSEN SM9 voc pt s.p., voc sc s.p. (M2131)

Mass III *Mass
(Redlich) SATB,opt org (G min) SCHOTT s.p. (M2132)

Messa *Mass
(Somma, B.) 4pt,acap sc SANTIS 716 s.p., cor pts SANTIS 717A-B s.p. (M2133)

Messa I A 6 Voci
"In Illa Temport" [Lat] 1-6pt,acap min sc PETERS E991 $2.50 (M2134)

Messa II A 4 Voci
[Lat] 4pt,acap min sc PETERS E990 $2.00 (M2135)

Messe A 4 Voci *Mass
[Lat] SATB,acap min sc PETERS E982 $2.00 (M2136)

Messe I A 6 Voci *Mass
(Redlich) "In Illo Tempora" SSATTB,opt org (C maj) SCHOTT s.p. (M2137)

Messe II A 4 Voci *Mass
(Arnold) SATB,opt org (F maj) SCHOTT s.p. (M2138)

Musica Religiosa I, Vol. 14-2 *CCU
(Malipiero, G.F.) cmplt ed UNIVER. 9609B $19.70 (M2139)

Musica Religiosa II, Vol. 15-1 *CCU
(Malipiero, G.P.) cmplt ed UNIVER. 9610A $21.25 (M2140)

MONTEVERDI, CLAUDIO (cont'd.)

Musica Religiosa II, Vol. 15-2 *CCU
(Malipiero, G.P.) cmplt ed UNIVER. 9610B $27.75 (M2141)

Musica Religiosa II, Vol. 15-3 *CCU
(Malipiero, G.P.) cmplt ed UNIVER. 9610C $31.50 (M2142)

Musica Religiosa III, Vol. 16-1 *CCU
(Malipiero, G.P.) cmplt ed UNIVER. 9611A $28.80 (M2143)

Musica Religiosa III, Vol. 16-2 *CCU
(Malipiero, G.P.) cmplt ed UNIVER. 9611B $28.80 (M2144)

Nisi Dominus (Psalm 126) BVM
(Wolters) 5pt mix cor&5pt mix cor,cont MOSELER s.p. see from Vesperae Beatae Mariae Virginis 1610 (M2145)

Non Havea Febo Ancora
"Before Day Came Again" SATB oct WALTON 7021 $.35 (M2146)

O Beatae Viae
(Goehr, W.) [Lat] sc UNIVER. 12323 $1.65, cor pts UNIVER. 12324 $1.20 (M2147)

O Bone Jesu *mot
[Lat] STB,acap MUSICUS 1016 $.15 (M2148)

On This Day Christ Is Born *see Hodie Christus Natus Est

Praise The King Of Heaven *see Lauda Sion Salvatorem

Psalm 109 *see Dixit Dominus

Psalm 112 *see Laudate Pueri

Psalm 117 *see Laudate Dominum

Psalm 121 *see Laetatus Sum

Psalm 126 *see Nisi Dominus

Psalm 147 *see Lauda Jerusalem

Sacrae Cantiuncluae, Sanctissimae Virgini Missa Senis Vocibus, Vol. 14-1
(Malipiero, G.F.) cmplt ed UNIVER. 9609A $21.25 (M2149)

Sacrae Cantiunculae
(Boepple) 3 eq voices,acap oct PRESSER 352-00024 $.35
contains: Angelus Ad Pastores Ait; Hodie Christus Natus Est (M2150)

Salmo
[Lat] SSTTB,SSTTBB soli,orch,org sc HINRICHSEN SM6 s.p. (M2151)

Salve Regina
(d'Indy, V.) [Lat] SA,org SCHIRM.EC 1006 $.20 (M2152)

Saviour, We Adore And Bless Thy Holy Name *see Christe, Adoramus Te

Sicut Erat In Principio *BVM
(Wolters) 7pt mix cor/8pt mix cor,cont MOSELER s.p. see from Vesperae Beatae Mariae Virginis (M2153)

Truly I Must Perish
SSATB MUSICUS 024 $.25 (M2154)

Two Motets *Gen,mot
(Sargent) SATB (med easy) oct OXFORD 43.345 $.15
contains: Adoramus Te; Cantate Domino (M2155)

Two Motets *see Adoramus Te, Christe; Cantate Domino (M2156)

Veni Sponsa Christi
(Vene) "Come, Thou Faithful Servant" [Lat/Eng] TTB/SSA,acap oct COLOMBO 2032 $.25 (M2157)

Vesperae Beatae Mariae Virginis *see Sicut Erat In Principio (M2158)

Vesperae Beatae Mariae Virginis 1610 *see Deus In Adjutorium; Dixit Dominus (Psalm 109); Laetatus Sum (Psalm 121); Lauda Jerusalem (Psalm 147); Laudate Pueri (Psalm 112); Nisi Dominus (Psalm 126) (M2159)

Vespers *Eve
(Stevens, Denis) [Lat] dbl cor,solo,org, 2fl,3ob,2bsn,2trom,strings,2rec voc sc NOVELLO s.p., ipr (M2160)

Vespro Della Beata Vergine *BVM
(Ghedini, G.F.) mix cor,SSMezABar soli,orch voc sc ZERBONI 4662 s.p., ipr (M2161)
(Goehr, Walter) [Lat] cmplt ed UNIVER. 12452 $17.50, cor pts UNIVER. 12454 $3.40 (M2162)

MONTGOMERY
Angels From The Realms Of Glory *Xmas
(Follett) SAB oct PRO ART 2389 $.25 (M2163)

Resting
SATB oct WORD CS-687 $.10 (M2164)

MONTGOMERY, BRUCE (1927-)
Christ's Birthday *CCU,Xmas,carol
SATB,opt pno,strings voc sc NOVELLO s.p., ipr (M2165)

My Joy, My Life, My Crown! *Gen
SATB (med) oct OXFORD 42.068 $.30 (M2166)

On The Resurrection Of Christ *Easter
SATB,2fl,2ob,2clar,2bsn,4horn,3trp,3trom, tuba,strings,2perc,timp,2harp voc sc NOVELLO s.p., ipr (M2167)

Oxford Requiem, An *Req
SATB,2fl,2ob,2clar,2bsn,4horn,3trp,3trom, tuba,strings,2perc,timp,2harp voc sc NOVELLO s.p., ipr (M2168)

MONUMENTI VATICANI DI PALEOGRAFIA MUSICALE LATINA *CCU
(Bannister, Henry Marriot) cor GREGG ISBN 0:576 28949 3 s.p. (M2169)

MONUMENTS OF RENAISSANCE MUSIC SERIES VOL. II MEDICI CODEX *CCU,mot,Renais
(Lowinsky) cor cloth UNIV.CH ISBN: 0-226-49481-0 $37.50 (M2170)

MONUMENTS OF RENAISSANCE MUSIC SERIES VOL. III MEDICI CODEX *CCU,mot,Renais
(Lowinsky) cor cloth UNIV.CH ISBN: 0-226-49482-9 $22.75 (M2171)

MONUMENTS OF RENAISSANCE MUSIC SERIES VOL. IV MUSICA NOVA *CCU,Renais
(Slim) 4pt cloth UNIV.CH ISBN: 0-226-76269-6 $15.00 contains works by: Benoit; Cavazzoni; Colin; Parabosco; Segni; Willaert (M2172)

MONUMENTS OF RENAISSANCE MUSIC SERIES VOL. V CANTI NOVA B: NUMERO CINQUANTA *sac/sec, CCU,Renais
(Petrucci) cor cloth UNIV.CH ISBN: 0-226-33209-8 $32.50 contains works by: Compere; Des Prez; Le Petit; Obrecht (M2173)

MOODIE, JAMES
Except The Lord Build The House
SATB oct LESLIE 4042 (M2174)

MOON AND STARS OF CHRISTMAS see Schroth

MOON SHINES BRIGHT
see Six Traditional Carols, Set IV

MOON SHINES BRIGHT, THE *Easter/Lent
(Stone) SATB,opt S solo oct PRO ART 1405 $.20 (M2175)

MOON SHINES BRIGHT, THE see Wilson

MOONLESS DARKNESS STANDS BETWEEN see Beattie, Herbert

MOORE
Come Before His Presence
SATB oct BELWIN 60223 $.25 (M2176)

Dear Lord To Thee
SAB BOSTON 13218 $.40 (M2177)
SATB BOSTON 13217 $.40 (M2178)

Four Canticles For The Christmas Season *CC4U,Xmas
SATB,acap oct SACRED S-139 $.35 (M2179)

Go, Lovely Rose!
TTBB oct HERITAGE H2872 $.30 (M2180)

Hand In Hand With God
SATB oct LORENZ C78 $.30 (M2181)

Haven Of Rest, The *anthem
(McLellan) SATB oct LILLENAS AT-1070 $.25 (M2182)

Hear My Cry
SATB oct HERITAGE H77 $.35 (M2183)

Hills Of Bethlehem
men cor KJOS P1526 $.30 (M2184)

I Knew That God Was There
SAB,org/pno BOSTON 13256 $.35 (M2185)

I Will Lift Up Mine Eyes
SATB,org BOSTON 12806 $.40 (M2186)

Let Jesus Fill Your Heart
SATB,org/pno BOSTON 13463 $.35 (M2187)
SAB,org/pno BOSTON 13401 $.35 (M2188)

Lord God Of Hosts *Gen
SATB SCHMITT 1662 $.22 (M2189)

Lord Of All Being
SATB THOMP.G E.A.1 s.p. (M2190)

Lord We Give Thanks To Thee
SATB,acap WARNER WB-299 (M2191)

Now Is The Caroling Season *Xmas
SATB oct HERITAGE H58 $.35 (M2192)

People Of God *folk/hymn
cor,gtr ALBERT s.p. (M2193)

Proud Music
SATB oct HERITAGE H89 $.40 (M2194)

Psalm Of Life
SATB oct HERITAGE H57 $.40 (M2195)

Twenty-Eight Sacred Choruses For Treble Voices *CC28U
(Parks) SSA KJOS $1.25 (M2196)

When I Met The Man Of Calvary
(Schubert) SATB oct LILLENAS AN-1639 $.30 (M2197)

Whom All Men Adore *Xmas
unis jr cor&desc FISCHER,C R 254 $.15 (M2198)

MOORE, DOUGLAS STUART (1893-1969)
O Lovely Son Of God
4pt mix cor,S solo oct SCHIRM.G 10512 $.25 (M2199)

MOORE, F.
Lord, Let Me Live Today *Easter
(Simonton, D.) SATB oct PRESSER 312-21605 $.30 (M2200)

MOORE, HAROLD
Darkest Hour, The *Lent,cant/hymn
SATB,STBarB soli,org,2fl,2ob,2clar,2bsn, 4horn,2trp,3trom,tuba,strings,perc,timp voc sc NOVELLO s.p., ipr (M2201)

God So Loved The World (from Darkest Hour The) Lent,anthem
mix cor,T solo,orch oct NOVELLO 28.0969.09 s.p., ipr (M2202)
SATB oct NOVELLO 28.0969.09 s.p. (M2203)

O Saviour Of The World (from Darkest Hour) Lent,anthem
SATB oct NOVELLO 28.0970.02 s.p. (M2204)
mix cor,orch oct NOVELLO 28.0970.02 s.p.,

MOORE, HAROLD (cont'd.)

    ipr   (M2205)

MOORE, MARIAN
  Invocation
    SATB KJOS P963 $.30   (M2206)

MOORE, MICHAEL
  Lord Shine
    SSA FOSTER MF 904 $.25   (M2207)

MOORE, P.J.
  Whoso Dwelleth
    SATB,org GRAY GCMR 3278 $.30   (M2208)

MOORE-RICHMAN
  Praise Him, All Ye Little Children
    2pt jr cor BOSTON 3085 $.30   (M2209)

MOORE, ROBERT
  Thou God Of All
    SATB,pno/org oct LAWSON 899 $.30   (M2210)

MORALES
  Holy Child Is Born, A *see Puer Natus Est

  Missus Est Gabriel
    girl cor SOUTHERN $.30   (M2211)

  Puer Natus Est *Xmas
    (Greyson) "Holy Child Is Born, A" SSA oct
    BOURNE ES73 $.30   (M2212)

MORALES, CRISTOBAL DE (ca. 1500-1553)
  Agnus Dei
    (Kraft, L.) SSA/TTB,acap oct PRESSER MC359
    $.25   (M2213)
    (Kraft, L.) SSA/TTB,acap oct PRESSER MC359
    $.25   (M2214)

  All Ye Who Pass By *see O Vos Omnes

  Annunciation, The *see Missas Est Gabriel

  Ecce Virgo Concipiet *Span
    (Goodale) [Lat] 4pt mix cor,acap oct
    SCHIRM.G 11233 $.30   (M2215)

  Enmendemus In Melius
    see Polifonia Espanola. Vol. I

  Lamentabatur Jacob
    see Polifonia Espanola. Vol. I

  Lobt Godt Mitt Schall
    "Praise God With Sound" [Ger/Eng] SATB,kbd
    BROUDE BR. $.40   (M2216)

  Me Ye Have Bereaved
    SSATB,acap SCHIRM.EC 1650 $.20   (M2217)

  Missas Est Gabriel *Xmas,Span
    (Goodale) "Annunciation, The" [Lat] 4pt wom
    cor,acap oct SCHIRM.G 11147 $.25 (M2218)

  O Cross! Thou Only Hope *see O Crux Ave,
    Spes Unica

  O Crux, Ave Spes Unica
    see Polifonia Espanola. Vol. I
    "O Cross! Thou Only Hope" [Lat/Eng] SATTB
    BROUDE BR. $.40   (M2219)

  O Magnum Mysterium *Xmas,Span
    (Goodale) [Lat] 4pt wom cor,acap oct
    SCHIRM.G 11077 $.25   (M2220)

  O Shepherds, Tell Us Now *see Pastores,
    Dicite, Quidnam Vidistis?

  O Vos Omnes *Easter/Lent
    (Marshall, Charles) "All Ye Who Pass By"
    SATB FRANK F-544 $.35   (M2221)

  Pastores, Dicite, Quidnam Vidistis? *Xmas,
    Span
    (Goodale) "O Shepherds, Tell Us Now" [Eng/
    Lat] 4pt mix cor oct SCHIRM.G 11367 $.30
        (M2222)

  Polifonia Espanola. Vol. I *mot
    [Lat] cor,acap UNION ESP. 18762 s.p.
    contains: Enmendemus In Melius;
    Lamentabatur Jacob; O Crux, Ave Spes
    Unica; Verbun Inquim   (M2223)

  Praise God With Sound *see Lobt Godt Mitt
    Schall

  Verbun Inquim
    see Polifonia Espanola. Vol. I

MORASSUTTI, DINO
  Ave Maria *BVM
    [Lat] unis,org ZANIBON 3692 s.p. (M2224)

MORAWETZ
  Crucifixion
    SATB oct MCA $.75   (M2225)

MORE 20TH CENTURY HYMN TUNES *CC30U,hymn
  cong,pno/org WEINBERGER $1.85   (M2226)

MORE CHORAL GEMS FROM THE MASTERS see Grant

MORE HOLINESS GIVE ME see Wilson

MORE HYMNS AND SPIRITUAL SONGS *CCU,canon/
  hymn/round
  cor/cong,inst voc sc WALTON $6.95 (M2227)

MORE LIKE JESUS see Landon

MORE LIKE THE MASTER
  (Bock) SATB oct WORD CS-2391 $.30 (M2228)

MORE LIKE THE MASTER see Hughes

MORE LOVE O CHRIST, TO THEE see Holzworth, A.

MORE LOVE TO THEE see Doane, [William Howard]

MORE LOVE TO THEE see Thompson

MORE LOVE TO THEE see Wolcott, J.

MORE LOVE TO THEE, O CHRIST see Speaks, [Oley]

MORE S.A.B. ANTHEMS FOR THE CHURCH YEAR see
  Lovelace, Austin C.

MORE SONGS AND CAROLS FOR CHILDREN see Grime,
  William

MORE STANDARD CHRISTMAS CAROLS *CC7L,Xmas,
  carol
  SATB ALLANS 290 s.p.   (M2229)

MORE THINGS ARE WROUGHT BY PRAYER see McCormick

MORE THINGS ARE WROUGHT BY PRAYER see Roff,
  Joseph

MOREN, JOHN
  Ave Crux *hymn
    "O Kors, Var Halsat" [Lat/Swed] mix cor
    NORDISKA 995 s.p. see from Tre Latinska
    Hymner   (M2230)

  Ave Verum Corpus *hymn
    "Hell Dig, Hell Dig, Sanna Kropp" [Lat/
    Swed] mix cor NORDISKA 993 s.p. see from
    Tre Latinska Hymner   (M2231)

  Dig Klad I Helighetens Skrud
    mix cor NORDISKA 2938 s.p.   (M2232)

  Fordenskull Jesu Led Du Mig
    mix cor NORDISKA 819 s.p.   (M2233)

  Hell Dig, Hell Dig, Sanna Kropp *see Ave
    Verum Corpus

  Herre, Ga Ej Till Doms
    mix cor NORDISKA 820 s.p.   (M2234)

  Herre Hor Min Rost
    mix cor NORDISKA 712 s.p.   (M2235)

  Herre, Jesu Herde God
    mix cor NORDISKA 822 s.p.   (M2236)

  Herre, Til Dig Upplyfter Jag Min Sjal
    mix cor NORDISKA 702 s.p.   (M2237)

  Herren Ar Min Herde (Psalm 23)
    mix cor NORDISKA 824 s.p.   (M2238)

  Jesus, Du Sankt Dig Djupt I Noden
    jr cor,org NORDISKA 4014 s.p.   (M2239)
    mix cor NORDISKA 4010 s.p.   (M2240)

  Kantat Vid Kyrkoinvigning
    mix cor&jr cor,org cor pts NORDISKA 813
    s.p., voc sc NORDISKA s.p.   (M2241)

  Krist Segerrike
    unis wom cor/3pt wom cor/unis jr cor/3pt jr
    cor,org NORDISKA 4228 s.p.   (M2242)

  Land, Hor Herrens Ord
    mix cor NORDISKA 711 s.p.   (M2243)

  Milde Jesu, Dem Ledsaga
    unis wom cor/3pt wom cor/unis jr cor/3pt jr
    cor,org NORDISKA 3944 s.p.   (M2244)

  O Du Helge Ande, Kom Till Oss In! *see Veni,
    Sancte Spiritus

  O Herre Gud, Oandelig
    mix cor NORDISKA 3501 s.p.   (M2245)

  O Herre Gud, Var Mild Och God
    mix cor NORDISKA 707 s.p.   (M2246)

  O, Hur Salla Aro Ej De Fromma
    mix cor,org cor pts NORDISKA 818 s.p.
        (M2247)

  O Jesu, Du Guds Rena Lamm
    mix cor NORDISKA 815 s.p.   (M2248)

  O Kors, Var Halsat *see Ave Crux

  Psalm 23 *see Herren Ar Min Herde

  Salig, Salig Den Som Kande
    mix cor NORDISKA 3509 s.p.   (M2249)

  Saliga De Som Hora Guds Ord
    mix cor NORDISKA 3018 s.p.   (M2250)

  Se Guds Lamm
    wom cor/jr cor,org NORDISKA 3280 s.p.
        (M2251)

  Se, Vi Ga Upp Till Jerusalem
    mix cor NORDISKA 3573 s.p.   (M2252)

  Sig Frojde Nu Var Kristen Man
    3pt mix cor NORDISKA 4230 s.p. (M2253)
    3pt mix cor/unis wom cor/unis jr cor,org
    NORDISKA 4230 s.p.   (M2254)

  Tre Latinska Hymner *see Ave Crux, "O Kors,
    Var Halsat"; Ave Verum Corpus, "Hell Dig,
    Hell Dig, Sanna Kropp"; Veni, Sancte
    Spiritus, "O Du Helge Ande, Kom Till Oss
    In!"   (M2255)

  Vart Hus, O Herre, Fardigt Star
    mix cor NORDISKA 823 s.p.   (M2256)

  Veni, Sancte Spiritus *hymn
    "O Du Helge Ande, Kom Till Oss In!" [Lat/
    Swed] mix cor NORDISKA 994 s.p. see from
    Tre Latinska Hymner   (M2257)

MORETON, H.
  Preces And Responses
    SATB oct NOVELLO s.p.   (M2258)

MORGAN
  Alleluia
    SATB KJOS 5171 $.30   (M2259)

  Arise, O God, And Show Thy Might
    SSATBB,acap WARNER R3170 $.30 (M2260)

  At The Cry Of The First Bird *Easter/Lent/
    Palm
    SATB oct FISCHER,C CM-7131 $.25 (M2261)

  Awake, Awake Good People All *Xmas
    SSATB SCHMITT 1697 $.22   (M2262)

MORGAN (cont'd.)

  Be Still And Know That I Am God
    SATB oct FISCHER,C CM-7327 $.25 (M2263)

  Be Thou Near Me Lord
    men cor KJOS 5536 $.30   (M2264)

  Be Thou Not Still, Oh Lord
    SATB,acap WARNER R3149 $.30 (M2265)

  Blessed Are They
    SATB oct FISCHER,C CM-7660 $.25 (M2266)

  Draw Near And Hear My Prayer
    SATB KJOS 5428 $.30   (M2267)

  Fret Not Thyself
    SATB (med diff/diff) SOUTHERN $.30 (M2268)

  Go Not Far From Me, O Lord
    SATB,acap WARNER G1629 $.30 (M2269)

  Grant Us Thy Holy Peace
    SATB KJOS 5066 $.30   (M2270)

  Guide Me, O Thou Great Jehovah
    SATB KJOS 5367 $.30   (M2271)

  Hear Us, Lord
    SATB oct LORENZ C50 $.30   (M2272)

  Hide Not Thy Face *anthem
    SATB,acap oct FISCHER,C CM-6296 $.25
        (M2273)

  Holy Birth, The *Xmas,cant
    (Johnson) SATB,4 soli,pno WARNER G1743
    $1.25   (M2274)

  How Excellent Is Thy Name
    SATB (med diff/diff) SOUTHERN $.30 (M2275)

  How Lovely Is This Place
    SATB KJOS 5817 $.30   (M2276)

  I Am The Good Shepherd
    SATB KJOS 5853 $.30   (M2277)

  I Am The Vine
    SATB oct SACRED E45 $.35   (M2278)

  Into The Hand Of God
    SATB KJOS 5288 $.30   (M2279)

  Lift Thyself Up O God
    SATB KJOS 5859 $.30   (M2280)

  Lord Is My Strength And Song, The
    men cor KJOS 5558 $.30   (M2281)

  Lord's Prayer, The
    SSA,acap oct PRO ART 1515 $.25 (M2282)

  Mine Eyes I Will Lift Up
    SATB oct FISCHER,C CM-7738 $.25 (M2283)

  My Lord What A Mornin'
    men cor KJOS 5551 $.30   (M2284)

  My Shepherd Is The Lord Most High
    SATB,acap WARNER R3324 $.30 (M2285)

  Night Journey Of The Wise Men *Xmas
    SATB,acap WARNER R3253 $.30 (M2286)

  None Other Lamb
    SSA WARNER R3462 $.30   (M2287)
    SATB WARNER R3459 $.30   (M2288)

  None Shall Separate Us From The Love Of God
    SATB oct LORENZ 9912 $.30   (M2289)

  Oh Hear These, Our Words
    SATB,acap,opt pno oct PRO ART 1069 $.25
        (M2290)
    SSA,acap,opt pno oct PRO ART 1134 $.22
        (M2291)
    TTBB,acap,opt pno oct PRO ART 1135 $.20
        (M2292)

  Oh Ye That Loveth The Lord *Gen
    SATB SCHMITT 1637 $.35   (M2293)

  Praise The Lord, Ye Heavens
    SATB KJOS 5854 $.30   (M2294)

  Prepare My Mind And Heart For Prayer
    SATB oct LORENZ 9918 $.30   (M2295)

  Rejoice And Be Merry
    SSA KJOS 6087 $.30   (M2296)

  Sing, O Sing, Blessed Morn *Xmas
    SSA,acap WARNER R3271 $.30 (M2297)

  Sing Praises To Our King *Xmas
    SATB oct LORENZ C315 $.30   (M2298)

  Sounding Joy
    (Lowens) SATB,acap MARKS 100 $.30 (M2299)

  They Who Considereth The Door Shall Be Blest
    SATB WARNER WB-163 $.30   (M2300)

  Think, Thou, On Me, O Lord
    SATB KJOS 5474 $.30   (M2301)

  Thy Word Is A Light *anthem
    SATB,acap oct FISCHER,C CM-6239 $.25
        (M2302)

  Trilogy For Holy Week, A *Easter,cant
    SATB LORENZ $1.95   (M2303)

  We Ask Thee, O Lord
    SATB KJOS 5137 $.30   (M2304)

  Wilt Thou Walk Beside Me, Lord
    SATB oct GALAXY 1.2023.1 $.30 (M2305)

MORGAN, HAYDN (1898-   )
  Be Thou My Judge O Lord
    SATB oct FISCHER,J 9048 $.30 (M2306)

  Be Thou Near Me, Lord
    SATB KJOS 5114 $.30   (M2307)

  Blessed Are They Who Fear The Lord
    SATB oct FISCHER,J 10027 $.25 (M2308)

MORGAN, HAYDN (cont'd.)

Bow Down Thine Ear, O Lord
SSAA,acap oct BELWIN 64209 $.25   (M2309)
SATB,acap oct BELWIN 64136 $.30   (M2310)

Fullness Of Joy
4pt jr cor/SATB (med easy) FISCHER,C
CM 7446 $.25   (M2311)

Hear What The Lord Sayeth
SATB oct FISCHER,J 9687 $.30   (M2312)

In David's Royal City *cant
jr cor&SA BELWIN $1.50   (M2313)

Incline Thy Spirit
SATB KJOS 5389 $.30   (M2314)

Instrument Of Thy Peace, An
SATB,acap oct BELWIN 64245 $.30   (M2315)
TTBB,acap oct BELWIN 64261 $.25   (M2316)

Lament And Alleluia *cant
mix cor BELWIN $1.50   (M2317)

Let Us Sing A Joyful Song
SATB FLAMMER A 5221 $.25   (M2318)

Make Us To Know And Understand
SATB oct BELWIN 64308 $.25   (M2319)

Mary Sings To Her Child
SATB FLAMMER A 5125 $.30   (M2320)

Rejoice And Be Merry
SATB KJOS 5281 $.30   (M2321)

Support Us O God
SATB oct FISCHER,J 9279 $.30   (M2322)

This Is My Commandment
SATB FLAMMER A 5075 $.25   (M2323)
SAB FLAMMER D5116 $.25   (M2324)

Turn Thou To Me
SATB oct FISCHER,J 8620 $.30   (M2325)

MORGEN UND ABEND *CCU,liturg
(Wagner, Hermann) mix cor MOSELER s.p.
(M2326)

MORGENGEBED see Bach, Johann Sebastian

MORGENGESANG see Bach, Karl Philipp Emanuel

MORGENGLANZ DER EWIGKEIT see Ahle, Johann Georg

MORGENGLANZ DER EWIGKEIT see Stier, Alfred

MORGENGLANZ DER EWIGKEIT see Trubel, Gerhard

MORGENHYMNE see Wolf

MORGENLIED see Weismann, Wilhelm

MORGENLIED (HOE GLANSRIJK ALLER HEEMLEN HEER)
see Bach, Johann Sebastian

MORGENLIED ZU JESU
see Eine Grosse Freud

MORGENPSALM see Jacot, Andre

MORGON-MOD see Nystedt, Knut

MORGONPSALM *Bibl/Psalm
(Carlstedt, Jan) [Swed] SATB,acap GEHRMANS
KRB 383   (M2327)

MORGONSTJERNA see Praetorius, Michael

MORLEY
Agnus Dei
(Christiansen, O.) SATB KJOS 21 $.30
(M2328)

Domine Fac Mecum
(Knight, Gerald) SATB,acap oct FISCHER,C
CM-7583 $.25   (M2329)

Nolo Mortem Peccatoris *mot
(Graetzer) [Eng/Lat] SATB,acap RICORDI-ARG
BA 9834 s.p.   (M2330)

O Lamb Of God *Lent
(Terry) SATB oct GRAY GCMR 1814 $.30
(M2331)

MORLEY, THOMAS (1557-1602)
Agnus Dei *Easter/Lent,Agnus/anthem/mot
SATB STAINER CC603 s.p.   (M2332)
"Lamb Of God" SATB,acap SCHIRM.EC 1771 $.30
(M2333)
(Christiansen, O.C.) mix cor SOUTHERN $.30
(M2334)
(Greyson) mix cor SOUTHERN $.25   (M2335)
(Greyson) "Lamb Of God" SATB oct BOURNE
ES36 $.25   (M2336)
(Terry, R.R.) [Lat] mix cor oct NOVELLO
52.0002.04 s.p.   (M2337)
(Terry, R.R.) "Lamb Of God" mix cor oct
NOVELLO 52.0002.04 s.p.   (M2338)

Alas!They Have Taken Jesus *see Eheu!
Sustulerunt Dominum

De Profundis Clamavi *Lent,anthem
SSAATB,acap (diff) oct OXFORD 43.332 $.50
(M2339)
"Out Of The Deep" SAATBB,T solo,acap (med
easy) oct OXFORD 42.677 $.30   (M2340)
(Le Huray, P.) "Out Of The Deep" SAATB,org
BROUDE,A. 708 $.30   (M2341)
(Palmer William) "Out Of The Deep" mix cor,
A solo oct NOVELLO 28.1365.03 s.p.
(M2342)

Deal With Me, Thy Servant *anthem
(Terry, R.R.) mix cor oct NOVELLO
52.0013.10 s.p.   (M2343)

Domine Fac Mecum *anthem
(Terry, R.R.) [Lat] mix cor oct NOVELLO
52.0013.10 s.p.   (M2344)

Eheu! Sustulerunt Dominum *Easter/Lent
(Marshall) "Alas! They Have Taken Jesus"
mix cor SOUTHERN $.30   (M2345)
(Marshall, Charles) "Alas!They Have Taken
Jesus" SATB FRANK F-552 $.30   (M2346)

MORLEY, THOMAS (cont'd.)

Father, We Thank Thee *Thanks
(Castleton) SA BOOSEY-CAN s.p.   (M2347)

Laboravi In Gemitu Meo *Gen/Lent
SSAATB,acap (diff) oct OXFORD 43.333 $.50
(M2348)

Lamb Of God *see Agnus Dei

Lirum, Lirum *Xmas
SSATB,acap GALAXY 2403 $.25   (M2349)
SSATB oct GALAXY 1.2403.1 $.25   (M2350)

Lord Of Mercy
(Eperson) 5pt mix cor,acap oct CURWEN 10629
$.25   (M2351)

Magnificat And Nunc Dimittis (from First
Service, The) Magnif/Nunc
oct ROYAL 104 $.35   (M2352)
SAATB&SSAAATB/SATB&SSAAATTB (med) oct
OXFORD 42.076 $1.30   (M2353)
SATB oct NOVELLO 44.0891.08 s.p.   (M2354)

Motets *CCU,mot
4-5pt STAINER SB:000 s.p.   (M2355)

Nolo Mortem Peccatoris *Lent/Psntd
SATB,opt inst (med easy) oct OXFORD 42.234
$.30   (M2356)

Out Of The Deep *see De Profundis Clamavi

"Short" Evening Service *Eve
SATB,acap (med easy) oct OXFORD 43.326 $.35
(M2357)
Thou Knowest Lord, The Secrets Of Our Hearts
*Bibl
(Simkins) 4pt mix cor,acap oct SCHIRM.G
11213 $.25   (M2358)

Three Motets *CC3U,Easter/Gen,mot
SATB,acap oct PRESSER 352-00053 $.35
(M2359)

Through The Day *Eve,anthem
SB oct ROYAL 218 $.35   (M2360)

MORNEMENT, INA
Rosy Glow Of Approaching Day *Austral
SA ALLANS 140 s.p.   (M2361)

Seek Ye The Lord
SATB/SA ALLANS 106 s.p.   (M2362)

MORNING AND EVENING CANTICLES WITH VERSICLES
AND RESPONSES *CCU,Eve/Morn
oct ROYAL s.p.   (M2363)

MORNING BREAKS, THE see Wheelwright, Lorin F.

MORNING CANTICLES see Weelkes, Thomas

MORNING GRACE see Grieb, Herbert [C.]

MORNING HAS BROKEN see Stevens

MORNING HYMN
(Henschel, I.) TTBB,acap SCHIRM.EC 599 $.18
(M2364)

MORNING HYMN see Boatwright, Howard

MORNING HYMN see Emerson, John

MORNING HYMN see Henschel, Isadore George

MORNING HYMN see Pasquet, Jean

MORNING HYMN see Wolf, Morgenhymne

MORNING HYMN, A see France, William E.

MORNING INTERLUDE see Rhea

MORNING INVOCATION see Brumel, Antoine

MORNING OF CHRISTMAS see Smith, Paul

MORNING OF CHRIST'S NATIVITY see Boeringer,
James

MORNING OF THE DAY OF DAYS see Williamson,
Malcolm

MORNING OF THE DAY OF DAYS, THE see Williamson,
Malcolm

MORNING PRAYER see Caldwell

MORNING PRAYER see Kubik, Gail

MORNING PRAYER see Lenn, Jay

MORNING PRAYER see Tchaikovsky, Piotr Ilyitch

MORNING PRAYER see Thiman, Eric Harding

MORNING PRAYER, A see McKay

MORNING PRAYER, A see Sibelius, Jean

MORNING PRAYER, A see Thiman, Eric Harding

MORNING PRAYER AND AN EVENING PRAYER, A
*prayer
(Martindale, James A.G.) unis&opt A&opt desc
LESLIE 2047 s.p.   (M2365)

MORNING SERVICE FOR THE NEW YEAR see Binder,
Abraham Wolfe

MORNING SERVICE IN D MINOR see Vaughan
Williams, Ralph

MORNING SERVICE IN E FLAT see Hunt, Thomas W.

MORNING SONG see Reger, Max

MORNING-SONG FOR THE CHRIST CHILD see
Sculthorpe, Peter [Joshua]

MORNING-SONG OF PRAISE see Bruch, Max

MORNING STAR *Adv,Morav
(Curry, W. Lawrence) SATB oct GRAY GCMR 2566
$.35   (M2366)

MORNING STAR see Cooper, Rose Marie

MORNING STAR see Dvorak, Antonin

MORNING STAR see Hagen

MORNING STAR, THE see Thomson, Virgil

MORNING STAR CHOIR BOOK, THE *CC28L
(Thomas, P.) jr cor/treb cor CONCORDIA
97-6287 $1.50 contains works by: Marcello;
Lenel; Pachelbel; Vaughan Williams; Greene;
Bender; Tunder; Handel; Buxtehude; Wolff;
Vierdanck; Bach; Willan; Schop; Bouman;
Franck; Mozart; Gumpeltzhaimer; Brahms
(M2367)

MORNING STAR ON HIGH IS GLOWING, THE see
Pepping, Ernst

MORNING STAR ON HIGH, THE see Praetorius,
Michael

MORNING STAR, THE see Praetorius, Michael

MORNING STAR, THE see Sjolund, Paul

MORNING STAR UPON US GLEAMS, THE see Nicolai,
Philipp, Wie Schon Leucht' Uns Die
Morgenstern

MORNING STARS see Wohlberg, Max, Kochve Voker

MORNING STARS SANG TOGETHER, THE see Steel,
Christopher [Charles]

MORNING TRUMPET
(Shaw; Parker) mix cor,Bar solo,acap oct
LAWSON 906 $.35   (M2368)

MORNING TRUMPET, THE (from Sacred Harp, The)
(Cram) 4pt mix cor,T solo,acap oct SCHIRM.G
11917 $.35   (M2369)

MORNING WATCH AND THE EVENING WATCH, THE see
Naylor, Bernard

MORNING WATCH, THE see Mc Cabe, John

MORN'S ROSEATE HUES see Emerson, John

MORPHEUS AND PARIS see Billings, William

MORRILL
Lay Not Up Treasures
SATB oct SACRED S-85 $.35   (M2370)

MORRIS
Stranger Of Galilee, The
(Richardson) SAB,org/pno BOSTON 2763 $.40
(M2371)
(Treharne) TTBB,acap BOSTON 1594 $.35
(M2372)
(Treharne) SATB,org/pno BOSTON 7346 $.45
(M2373)
(Treharne) SSA BOSTON 1596 $.35
(M2374)

'Tis Marvelous And Wonderful
SATB oct LILLENAS AN-1106 $.20   (M2375)

MORRIS, C.H.
Stranger Of Galilee, The
SATB ENOCH EC317 s.p.   (M2376)
2pt ENOCH TP229 s.p.   (M2377)

MORRIS, REGINALD OWEN (1886-1948)
Love Came Down At Christmas
see FOUR CHRISTMAS CAROLS

MORRISON, C.P.
Appear Thou Light Divine
SATB oct HUNTZINGER 7048 $.25   (M2378)

O Shepherd Of Israel
(Deis) 4pt mix cor oct SCHIRM.G 7400 $.25
(M2379)

MORRISON, KENNETH L.
When Christ Was Born Of Mary Free *Xmas
unis oct AGAPE CF 143 $.30   (M2380)

MORRISON, R.
King Of Glory *Easter
SATB PRESSER $.85   (M2381)

New Born King, The *Xmas
SATB oct PRESSER 312-10747 $.35   (M2382)

MORSE, [CHARLES HENRY] (1853-1927)
Love Came Down At Christmas *Xmas
(Oxley) SATB,acap (med easy) OXFORD 84.118
$.35   (M2383)

Short And Easy Anthems *CCU
SATB oct PRESSER $1.50   (M2384)

MORTARI, VIRGILIO (1902-   )
Missa Elegiaca *Mass
mix cor,org RICORDI-ENG 130982 s.p.   (M2385)

Requiem *Req
[Lat] voc sc UNIVER. 13213 $9.00   (M2386)

MORTUIS SEPULCRUM see Roeseling, Kaspar

MOSCHETTI, [GIUSEPPE] (1908-   )
Bells Of Christmas, The
unis oct PRESSER 312-40116 $.30   (M2387)

Christ, The Lord, Is Risen Again *Easter
SATB oct PRESSER 312-40293 $.30   (M2388)

Eight Sentences For The Seven Seasons Of The
Christian Church *CC8U
SATB,acap oct PRESSER 312-40132 $.35
(M2389)

Hosanna Now Through Advent *Xmas
jr cor oct PRESSER 312-40258 $.25   (M2390)

In This Night Christ Was Born *Xmas
SATB,acap oct PRESSER 332-40089 $.25
(M2391)

Joyous Easter Song, A *Easter
SATB oct PRESSER 312-40256 $.25   (M2392)

Let Music Break On This Blest Morn *Xmas
SATB,acap oct PRESSER 332-40118 $.25
(M2393)

Lord Is My Shepherd, The (Psalm 23)
SATB PRESSER $1.00   (M2394)

MOSCHETTI, [GIUSEPPE] (cont'd.)

O Praise The Lord
SATB,acap oct PRESSER 312-40124 $.30
(M2395)

O Worship The Lord
SA oct PRESSER 312-40259 $.25 (M2396)

Psalm 23 *see Lord Is My Shepherd, The

Unto Us A Child Is Born *Xmas
SATB oct PRESSER 332-40111 $.30 (M2397)

What Fragrance This *Xmas
SATB oct PRESSER 332-40117 $.30 (M2398)

MOSER, HANS JOACHIM (1889-1967)
Gott Ist Gewaltig
(Schaefers, Anton) [Ger] jr cor&men cor&wom
cor,opt winds BOTE sc s.p., voc sc s.p.,
ipa (M2399)

MOSER, RUDOLF
That Your Joy May Be Full *Gen
SATB,kbd (med diff) oct CONCORDIA 98-1354
$.20 (M2400)

MOSES see Gerhold, Norbert, Go Down, Moses

MOSS, L.
Rock The Baby Jesus *Xmas
SATB oct PLYMOUTH JCM-203 $.35 (M2401)

Song Of Solomon, A
SSA oct PRESSER MC284 $.30 (M2402)

MOST BELOVED SPIRITUALS *CCU,spir
SATB CHAPPELL 0013441-374 $2.00 (M2403)

MOST GLORIOUS LORD OF LIFE see Harris, William
Henry

MOST GLORIOUS LORD OF LIFE see Lenel, Ludwig

MOST GLORIOUS LORD OF LIFE see Milner

MOST GLORIOUS LORD OF LIFE see Webber, Lloyd

MOST HOLY TRINITY see Williams

MOST LOVING SAVIOUR see Tallis, Thomas,
Salvator Mundi

MOST MERCIFUL GOD see Ripolles, Vincente, Il
Est Ne

MOST MIGHTLY AND ALL-KNOWING LORD see Weelkes,
Thomas

MOTECTAE SACRAE, QUATUOR, QUINQUE ET SEX VOCUM
1575 see Lechner, Leonhard

MOTET see Brahms, Johannes, Schaffe In Mir,
Gott

MOTET see Chance, Nancy

MOTET see de la Rue, Pierre

MOTET see Leichtling, Alan

MOTET see Sveinsson, Gunnar Reynir

MOTET A SAINT JEAN L'EVANGELISTE see Gounod,
Charles Francois

MOTET (BASED ON SWEDISH GOSPEL SONG) see
Lundquist

MOTET FOR THE CIRCUMCISION see Naylor, Bernard

MOTETS see Bach, Johann Sebastian

MOTETS see Gallus, Jacobus

MOTETS see Morley, Thomas

MOTETS see Palestrina, Giovanni

MOTETS see Victoria, Tomas Luis de

MOTETS A QUATRE VOIX MIXTES see Sermisy, Claude
de

MOTETS AND CHORALE "SEI LOB UND PREIS" see
Bach, Johann Sebastian

MOTETS AND CHORALES FOR TREBLE CHOIRS *CCU
treb cor SCHMITT 32 $.50 (M2404)

MOTETS AND CHORALES FOR TREBLE CHOIRS see
Buszin

MOTETS FROM THE 16TH CENTURY *CC8L,mot,16th
cent
(Sorenson, Soren) [Lat] SATB HANSEN-DEN s.p.
contains works by: Palestrina; Marenzio;
Baldasar; and others (M2405)

MOTETS FROM THE SEVENTEENTH AND EIGHTEENTH
CENTURIES *CC9L,Gen,mot,17th cent/18th
cent
(Rider) [Lat] SATB PRO ART 929 $1.00 (M2406)

MOTETS, HYMN, TE DEUM see Mendelssohn-
Bartholdy, Felix

MOTETS OF OLD MASTERS *CC32U,mot
(Grote) [Ger] SATB,acap PETERS EM325 $5.00
contains works by: Bach, J.S.; Dressler,
M.; Franck; Gesius; Hassler; Lassus;
Lechner; Luther, M.; Palestrina;
Praetorius; Schuetz; Stader; Sweelinck;
Vulpius (M2407)

MOTETS OF THE MANUSCRIPTS CHANTILLY, THE *CCU,
mot,14th cent
(Gunther, Ursula) cor AM.INST.MUS. $27.00
(M2408)

MOTETT see Alfven, Hugo

MOTETT PA HELIGA TREFALDIGHETS DAG see Edlund,
Lars

MOTETTE see Aeschbacher, Walther

MOTETTE see Nageli, Hans George

MOTETTE ZUM PFINGSTFEST see Mendelssohn, Arnold

MOTETTEN see Bach, Johann Christoph

MOTETTEN see Fischer-Dieskau, Klaus

MOTETTEN AUS DEM NACHLASS-BAND VII see
Palestrina, Giovanni

MOTETTEN-BAND I see Palestrina, Giovanni

MOTETTEN-BAND II see Palestrina, Giovanni

MOTETTEN-BAND III see Palestrina, Giovanni

MOTETTEN-BAND IV see Palestrina, Giovanni

MOTETTEN-BAND V see Palestrina, Giovanni

MOTETTEN-BAND VI see Palestrina, Giovanni

MOTETTEN ZUR LITURGIE DER KARWOCHE UND DES
OSTERTAGES, HEFT I: PALMSONNTAG see
Palestrina, Giovanni

MOTETTEN ZUR LITURGIE DER KARWOCHE UND DES
OSTERTAGES, HEFT II: TRIDUUM SACRUM see
Palestrina, Giovanni

MOTETTEN ZUR LITURGIE DER KARWOCHE UND DES
OSTERTAGES, HEFT III: GRUNDONNERSTAG see
Palestrina, Giovanni

MOTETTEN ZUR LITURGIE DER KARWOCHE UND DES
OSTERTAGES, HEFT V: OSTERNACHT see
Palestrina, Giovanni

MOTETTEN ZUR LITURGIE DER KARWOCHE UND DES
OSTERTAGES, HEFT VI: OSTERSONNTAG see
Palestrina, Giovanni

MOTETTENBUCH *CC42U,Gen,mot
(Holliger, Hans) [Ger] 3-5pt mix cor,acap
(med) BAREN. BA 3451 $6.50 (M2409)

MOTETTER OG KORSANGE see Jeppesen, Knud

MOTETTER OG LAUDER FRA DET 16. ARHHUNDREDE see
Victoria, Tomas Luis de

MOTETTER OG LAUDER FRA DET 16. ARHUNDREDE
(Sorensen, Soren) [Lat/Dan] SATB,acap cmplt
ed HANSEN-DEN 26882 s.p. contains works by:
Palestrina; Marenzio: Philippo; Baldasar;
and others
contains & see also: Baldasar, O Jesu
Dolce, "O Jesus Blide"; de la Rue,
Pierre, O Salutaris Hostia, "O Jesus, Pa
Din Alterfod"; Lassus, Roland de
(Orlandus), Jubilate Deo, "Jord Og Himmel
Lover"; Marenzio, Luca, O Rex Gloriae,
"Aerens Konge God"; Palestrina, Giovanni,
Loquebantur, "Lydt Forkyndte";
Palestrina, Giovanni, Loquebantur (Lydt
Forkyndte); Palestrina, Giovanni, Sicut
Cervus Desiderat, "Ret Som Hjorten";
Palestrina, Giovanni, Sicut Cervus (Ret
Som Hjorten); Phillipo, Salve, Sacrata,
"Hil Dag, Du Hoje" (M2410)

MOTETTISCHER SATZ see Hollfelder, Waldram

MOTETUS MICHAELIS see Seitz, Rudiger

MOTHER, AT YOUR FEET IS KNEELING
SSA CHAPPELL 0018465-354 $.40 (M2411)

MOTHER, I DIDN'T BRING HOME THE FISH see Lewis

MOTHER LOVE ABIDETH *Aus
SATB oct LORENZ 9309 $.25 (M2412)

MOTHER MARY, THE *Xmas,carol,Fr
(Holloway) SATB oct SPRATT 612 $.30 (M2413)

MOTHER OF ALL see Ave Maria

MOTHER REJOICES, THE see Tal, Joseph, Die
Mutter Jubeit

MOTHER, WHITE AS LILY FLOWER see Greaves,
Terence

MOTHERLESS CHILD *spir
(Roberts) SATB,acap,opt perc oct LAWSON 51559
$.30 (M2414)

MOTHER'S CHRISTMAS SONG, A see Hemmer, [Eugene]

MOTHER'S DAY ANTHEM see Ohanian

MOTHER'S DAY CAROL see Ferguson

MOTHER'S DAY HYMN see Barnes, [Edward Shippen]

MOTHERS EVERYWHERE see Maker

MOTHER'S HYMN, THE see Lundquist, Matthew
Nathanael

MOTHER'S HYMNS see Jacobus

MOTHER'S LOVE (from Ben-Hur)
SSA BIG3 $.30 (M2415)

MOTHER'S LOVE, A see Kammerer, C.

MOTHERS NAME WAS MARY *Xmas
SATB CHARTER $.40 (M2416)

MOTHER'S PRAYER, A see Wilson

MOTHER'S PRAYER, A see Wilson, Ira B.

MOTHER'S PRAYERS HAVE FOLLOWED ME see Ackley

MOTHER'S TASK see Ashford

MOTT
Thunder Of The Lord
(Goodman) SATB oct STAFF 417 $.25 (M2417)

MOTTE, DIETHER DE LA (1928-   )
Es Wartet Alles Auf Dich (Psalm 104) Fest
SSATB,org,clar,trp,vln,vcl,perc (diff)
BAREN. BA 4126 sc s.p., cor pts s.p., ipa
(M2418)

MOTTE, DIETHER DE LA (cont'd.)

Psalm 104 *see Es Wartet Alles Auf Dich

Psalmen-Motette *Gen,mot/Psalm
[Ger] SATB,acap (diff) BAREN. BA 3934 $2.50
(M2419)

MOTTETEN ZUR LITURGIE DER KARWOCHE UND DES
OSTERTAGES, HEFT IV: KARFREITAG see
Palestrina, Giovanni

MOTTETTI E RICERCARI see Vinci, Pietro

MOTTETTI PER LA PASSIONE see Petrassi, Goffredo

MOULINE, ETIENNE
Missa Pro Defunctis *Mass
[Lat] 5pt mix cor HEUGEL s.p. (M2420)

MOULTON, JEAN
see MOUTON, JEAN

MOUNT CALVARY see Wright

MOUNT OF OLIVES see Beethoven, Ludwig van

MOUNT OF OLIVES, THE see Beethoven, Ludwig van,
Christus Am Olberge

MOUNTAIN
Like A River Glorious
(Bock) SATB oct WORD CS-2442 $.35 (M2421)
(Bock) SATB oct PRO ART 1982 $.25 (M2422)

MOUNTAIN CAROL, A see Kranz

MOUNTAIN OF THE LORD, THE see Griffin, Jack

MOUNTAINS OF GOD, THE see Pooler, Frank

MOURN, MOURN, YE SAINTS see Hovhaness, Alan

MOURNFUL DAY see Kprivsak, Lacrymosa

MOUTON, JEAN (ca. 1470-1522)
Ave Maria
see LA SCHOLA PALESTRINIENNE DEUXIEME
CAHIER
SATB,acap oct PRESSER 352-00040 $.30
(M2423)
(Ehret) 4pt mix cor,acap oct SCHIRM.G 11942
$.25 (M2424)

Funf Motetten *CC5U,mot
(Kast) [Ger/Lat] 4pt mix cor MOSELER s.p.
(M2425)

Gloria *Gloria
(Expert) [Lat] SATB,acap oct SALABERT-US
$.65 (M2426)
(Knight, Gerald) SATB,acap oct FISCHER,C
CM-7586 $.35 (M2427)

Iocundare Ierusalem *Xmas
SATB,acap oct PRESSER 352-00091 $.30
(M2428)

Missa Alleluia
see OPERA OMNIA VOL. I

Missa Alleluya *Mass
(Kast) 2-5pt mix cor MOSELER s.p. (M2429)

Missa Alma Redemptoris Mater
see OPERA OMNIA VOL. I

Missa Benedictus Dominus Deus
see OPERA OMNIA VOL. I

Missa Dictes Moy Toutes Voz Pensees (With
Compere's Chanson)
see Opera Omnia vol. II

Missa Ecce Quam Bonum
see Opera Omnia vol. II

Missa Fault D'argent
see Opera Omnia vol. II

Missa Lo Serai Je Dire
see Opera Omnia vol. III

Missa Quem Dicunt Homines
see Opera Omnia vol. III

Missa Regina Mearum
see Opera Omnia vol. III

Missa Sans Condence
see Opera Omnia vol. III

Noe, Noe, Noe Psallite *Xmas
(Swing, Peter Gram) SATB,acap (med) PRESSER
$.45 (M2430)

Noe, Noe, Psalite Noe *Xmas
(Gagnepain, Bernard) [Lat] SATB,acap
OUVRIERES LEO $.25 (M2431)

Noe, Noe, Psallite *Xmas,16th cent
(Cartier, Anita; Carol, Henri; Gagnepain,
Bernard) [Lat] SATB OUVRIERES EO667 s.p.
(M2432)

Opera Omnia vol. II
(Minor, Andrew) cor AM.INST.MUS. $19.50
contains: Missa Dictes Moy Toutes Voz
Pensees (With Compere's Chanson); Missa
Ecce Quam Bonum; Missa Fault D'argent
(M2433)

Opera Omnia vol. III *Mass
(Minor, Andrew) cor AM.INST.MUS. $20.00
contains: Missa Lo Serai Je Dire; Missa
Quem Dicunt Homines; Missa Regina
Mearum; Missa Sans Condence (M2434)

Puer Natus Est Nobis *Xmas
(Swing, Peter Gram) [Lat] SATB,acap (med)
PRESSER $.60 (M2435)

Quaeramus Cum Pastoribus *Xmas,mot
(Swing, Peter Gram) [Lat] SATB,acap (med)
PRESSER $.50 (M2436)

Reges Terrae Congregati Sunt *Epiph,16th
cent
(Cartier, Anita; Carol, Henri; Gagnepain,
Bernard) [Lat] SATB OUVRIERES EO 666 s.p.
(M2437)

MOVE! LET ME SHINE! *spir
(Jessye) SATB oct SHAPIRO SK 2093 $.25
(M2438)

MOYER, J. EDWARD
Surely The Lord Is In This Place
TTBB (easy) ABINGDON APM-307 $.25 (M2439)
SATB (easy) ABINGDON APM-296 $.25 (M2440)

MOYST WITH ONE DROP OF THY BLOOD see Young,
Gordon

MOYZES, ALEXANDER (1906-)
Wenn Die Orgeln Spielen *Gen
[Ger] 3 cor&SSAA,acap (med) ARTIA AP 1513
s.p. (M2441)

MOZART, LEOPOLD
Mass In C *Mass
(Townsend, D.) mix cor,solo oct FOX $3.00,
ipr (M2442)

MOZART, WOLFGANG AMADEUS (1756-1791)
Adoramus Te
4pt mix cor,acap oct SCHIRM.G 11942 $.25
(M2443)
Adoramus Te Christe
SATB oct PRESSER 332-14445 $.25 (M2444)
SATB,org SCHIRM.EC 1649 $.30 (M2445)
"Humbly Kneel We Before Thee" SATB,org
SCHIRM.EC 2619 $.30 (M2446)
(Marting, E.) "We Worship Thee, O Christ"
SSAA,org SCHIRM.EC 1818 $.20 (M2447)
(Marting, E.) "We Worship Thee, O Christ"
TTBB,org SCHIRM.EC 563 $.15 (M2448)
(Siegmeister; Ehret) [Lat] SATB,acap oct
PRO ART 1702 $.20 (M2449)
Aeterna Pax (from Te Deum)
(Rodby) "Eternal Peace" SATB oct VOLKWEIN
VB690 $.50 (M2450)
Agnus Dei (from Mass In G) Agnus/Allelu
[Lat] unis/2pt CHOUDENS s.p. (M2451)
(Ehret) SSA MARKS 4598 $.30 (M2452)
(Ehret) "Lamb Of God" [Eng/Lat] SATB WARNER
WB-126 $.30 (M2453)
(Harris) 3pt boy cor/SSA/SAA oct LAWSON
51305 $.35 (M2454)
(Wilson) "Lamb Of God" oct AGAPE A 441 $.30
(M2455)
Aleluya
(Martini) [Span] 2 eq voices,pno RICORDI-
ARG BA 8405 s.p. (M2456)
Alleluia (from Exsultate, Jubilate) Xmas/
Easter/Lent,Allelu/canon/mot
SA oct LORENZ 5316 $.30 (M2457)
unis oct LORENZ 8551 $.30 (M2458)
[Lat] SSSS,acap MUSICUS 1018 $.15 (M2459)
"Alleluja" SATB ENOCH EC122 s.p. (M2460)
"Alleluja" 2pt ENOCH TP133 s.p. (M2461)
(Aslanoff) SSA,orch oct FISCHER,C CM-536
$.25, ipr (M2462)
(Canavati) SATB oct PRO ART 1662 $.25
(M2463)
(Macrum) SATB,Mez solo oct COLOMBO 555 $.35
(M2464)
(Palmer) SATB ALFRED 6307 $.40 (M2465)
(Palmer) "Alleluja" SATB ALFRED 6307 $.40
(M2466)
(Riegger) SATB FLAMMER A5020 $.40 (M2467)
(Riegger) SSA FLAMMER B 5002 $.35 (M2468)
(Riegger) SA/TB FLAMMER E5015 $.35 (M2469)
(Riegger) SAB FLAMMER D5011 $.30 (M2470)
(Rosenberg) SATB oct FISCHER,C CM-541 $.30
(M2471)
(Stickles) "Alleluja" [Lat] 4pt mix cor oct
SCHIRM.G 10294 $.40 (M2472)
(Stickles) "Alleluja" [Lat] 3pt wom cor oct
SCHIRM.G 10293 $.30 (M2473)
(Treharne) SA BOSTON 10594 $.35 (M2474)

Alleluja *see Alleluia

Alma Dei Creatoria *K.277
cor voc sc KALMUS 6343 $1.25 (M2475)

Alma Dei Creatoris *K.277, BVM,mot/Offer
cor,orch sc KALMUS $4.00, ipa (M2476)
mix cor,SAT soli,org,strings BREITKOPF-L
rental (M2477)
mix cor,org,2vln,vcl,bvl WEINBERGER s.p.,
ipa voc sc, cor pts (M2478)
[Lat] voc sc PETERS HU 1663 $1.50, ipr
(M2479)
Auf Der Andacht Heil'gen Flugeln
mix cor,acap ERDMANN 557 s.p. contains
also: Haydn, (Franz) Joseph, Hier Liegt
Vor Deiner Majestat (M2480)
Ave Maria *BVM/Fest,canon/mot
[Lat] 2 eq voices oct DURAND s.p. (M2481)
[Lat] 4pt,acap (med easy) NAGELS NCH 206
s.p. (M2482)
(Brun, L'abbe, F.) [Lat] 4pt mix cor,2 soli
oct DURAND s.p. (M2483)
(Lannom) SATB oct PLYMOUTH AL-100 $.25
(M2484)
Ave Verum *Commun/Ded/Easter/Gen/Lent,
anthem/hymn/mot
see THREE WEDDING MOTETS
2pt ASHDOWN E.A.236 s.p. (M2485)
[Lat] SATB oct DURAND s.p. (M2486)
[Lat] 2 voices oct DURAND s.p. (M2487)
[Lat] A/Bar ZANIBON 3614 s.p. (M2488)
[Lat] S/T ZANIBON 3613 s.p. (M2489)
SATB,B solo ALLANS 207 s.p. (M2490)
[Lat] TTBB oct GIA G595 $.25 (M2491)
SATB,acap RICORDI-ENG SY133 s.p. (M2492)
[Lat] TTBB RICORDI-ENG SY133 s.p. (M2493)
"Hymn Of Praise" SSA oct STAFF 288 $.25
(M2494)
"Hymn Of Praise" SATB oct STAFF 207 $.25
(M2495)
"Hymn Of Praise" SATB/SSA,band oct STAFF
207 $.25, ipa (M2496)
"Jesu, Word Of God Incarnate" [Lat/Eng] 4pt
mix cor oct SCHIRM.G 6813 $.25 (M2497)
"Jesu, Word Of God Incarnate" mix cor,orch
oct NOVELLO 40.0190.07 s.p., ipr (M2498)
"Jesu, Word Of God Incarnate" SATB oct
BELWIN 64058 $.30 (M2499)
"Jesu, Word Of God Incarnate" 3pt mix cor
mix cor,org/pno oct SCHIRM.G 11238 $.25
(M2500)
"Jesu, Word Of God Incarnate" SATB oct GRAY
GCMR 3147 $.25 (M2501)
"Jesu, Word Of God Incarnate" SATB oct
PRESSER 312-21199 $.25 (M2502)
"Jesu, Word Of God Incarnate" SATB oct
LORENZ 9936 $.25 (M2503)
"Jesus Calls Us" SA oct GRAY GCMR 1592 $.30

MOZART, WOLFGANG AMADEUS (cont'd.)
(M2504)
(Ehret) SA oct BOURNE WE1 $.25 (M2505)
(Ehret) TB oct BOURNE WE1 $.25 (M2506)
(Ehret) SAB oct BOURNE WE2 $.30 (M2507)
(Elgar, E.) "Jesu, Word Of God Incarnate"
SATB oct GRAY GCMR 39 $.30 (M2508)
(Ley, Henry G.) "Jesu, Word Of God
Incarnate" 2pt (easy) oct OXFORD 44.204
$.25 (M2509)
(Page, N.) "Jesu, Word Of God Incarnate"
SSA oct PRESSER 332-11796 $.35 (M2510)
(Palmer) "Jesu, Word Of God Incarnate" SATB
ALFRED 6361 $.25 (M2511)
(Pitcher, Gladys) "Jesu, Word Of God
Incarnate" 3pt mix cor,pno (med) oct
WILLIS 8496 $.20 (M2512)
(Swift) "Jesu, Word Of God Incarnate" SATB
oct BELWIN 717 $.25 (M2513)
(Swift) "Jesu Word Of God Incarnate" SATB
oct BELWIN 717 $.30 (M2514)
(Trant, B.) oct NOVELLO 51.0601.10 s.p.
(M2515)
(Trant, B.) [Lat] SSA oct NOVELLO
51.0601.10 s.p. (M2516)
(Trusler) SAB WARNER W3676 $.30 (M2517)
(Younger) "Jesu, Word Of God Incarnate"
SATB oct SPRATT 507 $.25 (M2518)
Ave Verum Corpus *K.618, Xmas/Commun/Easter/
Lent,anthem/Gradual/mot
[Lat] mix cor HEUGEL s.p. see from LA
MAITRISE (M2519)
study sc UNIVER. PH. 54 $.80 contains also:
Gradule Ad Festum B.M.V., K.273 (M2520)
[Lat] TTBB SCHOTT s.p. (M2521)
[Lat/Ger] SATB SCHOTT s.p. (M2522)
cor voc sc KALMUS 6350 $.75 (M2523)
mix cor,org,4strings voc sc BREITKOPF-L
PB-1756 s.p., sc BREITKOPF-L EB-3705
s.p., cor pts BREITKOPF-L CHB-2839 s.p.,
ipa (M2524)
mem cor NORDISKA 3034 s.p. (M2525)
mix cor,org NORDISKA 1345 s.p. (M2526)
mix cor ALSBACH&D s.p. (M2527)
[Ger] mix cor,acap (med easy) HUG s.p.
(M2528)
mix cor,org,strings WEINBERGER s.p., ipa
voc sc, cor pts (M2529)
[Lat/Eng] SATB,pno/org/strings BROUDE BR.
$.30, ipa (M2530)
4pt mix cor,4strings/org MOSELER LB-77 s.p.
(M2531)
4pt mix cor,acap/org&4strings sc BREITKOPF-
W PB-4912 s.p., cor pts BREITKOPF-W
CHB-2839 s.p., ipa (M2532)
cor,orch sc KALMUS $10.00, ipa (M2533)
cor KALMUS $.75 (M2534)
"Jesu, Word Of God Incarnate" [Eng/Lat]
SATB oct HARRIS HC4014 $.25 (M2535)
"Jesu, Word Of God Incarnate" SATB oct PRO
ART 1449 $.25 (M2536)
"Jesu, Word Of God Incarnate" SATB,org
SCHIRM.EC 1170 $.25, ipr (M2537)
"Jesus, Word Of God Incarnate" SATB oct
PRESSER 312-21199 $.30 (M2538)
"Mighty Spirit, All Transcending" SATB,org
SCHIRM.EC 1695 $.25 (M2539)
"Tarry With Me" SA,pno SCHIRM.EC 484 $.25,
ipr (M2540)
(Davis, K.) "Jesu, Holy Spirit" SSAA,org
SCHIRM.EC 1064 $.25 (M2541)
(Davis, K.) "Jesu, Holy Spirit" SA,pno
SCHIRM.EC 1564 (M2542)
(Davis, K.) "Jesu, Holy Spirit" SSA,org/pno
SCHIRM.EC 1866 $.25 (M2543)
(Ehret) SSA oct FOX PS72 $.30 (M2544)
(Federhofer, Hellmut) [Ger] SATB,org,
strings voc sc BAREN. BA 4946 $.40
(M2545)
(Glaser, V.) "Jesus, Word Of God Incarnate"
[Lat/Eng] SSA,org SCHIRM.EC 2552 (M2546)
(Glaser, V.) "Mighty Spirit All
Transcending" SAB,org SCHIRM.EC 2244 $.20
(M2547)
(Gray) "Jesu, Word Of God Incarnate" 2pt
oct PRO ART 1929 $.30 (M2548)
(Gray) "Jesu, Word Of God Incarnate" SAB
oct PRO ART 1914 $.30 (M2549)
(Gray) "Jesu, Word Of God Incarnate" SSA
oct PRO ART 1634 $.25 (M2550)
(Muller; Montani) "Savior, Source Of Every
Blessing" [Lat/Eng] 4pt mix cor oct
SCHIRM.G 5471 $.25 (M2551)
(Norrman, J.) [Lat] wom cor MUSIKK 25 s.p.
(M2552)
(Oakey) [Lat/Eng] 2pt jr cor/2pt wom cor
CURWEN 70279 s.p. (M2553)
(Politti, E.) [Lat] wom cor,acap (med) HUG
s.p. (M2554)
(Quinn) SAB oct PLYMOUTH NBC-204 $.35
(M2555)
(Quinn) SATB oct PLYMOUTH NBC-103 $.35
(M2556)
(Reibold) SATB oct FOX C1500 $.30 (M2557)
(Saar, L.) "Jesu, Jesu, God, Incarnate"
TTBB,org SCHIRM.EC 547 $.25, ipr (M2558)

Ave Verum Corpus, And Other Works *CCUL
cor min sc KALMUS 933 $1.30 (M2559)

Ave Verum *K.618
"Jesu, Work Of God" SA ALLANS 274 s.p.
(M2560)

Be Gracious Unto Me
(Suchoff) SAB MARKS 4162 $.25 (M2561)

Benedictus Sit Deus *see Offertorium Pro
Omni Tempore

Betulia Liberata *K.118, Gen,cant/ora
"Betulia Liberata" cor min sc KALMUS 935
$1.30 (M2562)
(Tagliavini, Ferdinando) [Lat] SATB,SSSATB
soli,orch (med diff) sc BAREN. BA 4521
$26.00 (M2563)

Betulia Liberata *see Betulia Liberata

Bless The Lord For Ever And Ever
(Hilton, Arthur) SATB (med) PRESSER
352-00459 $.40 (M2564)

Bow Down Thine Ear
(Suchoff) SAB ALFRED 6503 $.30 (M2565)

MOZART, WOLFGANG AMADEUS (cont'd.)
Caecilien-Ode *Gen
(Holschneider, Andreas) [Ger] SATB,STB
soli,orch (diff) sc BAREN. BA 4556 s.p.
(M2566)
Canons
see Mozart, Wolfgang Amadeus, Cantata Dir
Selle Des Weltalls
Cantata Dir Selle Des Weltalls
cor min sc KALMUS 995 $1.30 contains also:
Canons; Concert Arias (M2567)
Christmas Lullaby
(Row) 3pt jr cor/SSA (very easy) FISCHER,C
R 241 $.18 (M2568)
Come, All Ye Children To Bethlehem Stall
*Xmas
(Ehret) SA SCHMITT 217 $.30 (M2569)
Concert Arias
see Mozart, Wolfgang Amadeus, Cantata Dir
Selle Des Weltalls
Contentment
(Davis) [Eng/Ger] SATB oct LAWSON 937 $.25
(M2570)
Coronation Mass *K.317, Mass
see Mozart, Wolfgang Amadeus, Missa
Solemnis
cor,orch sc KALMUS $5.00, ipa (M2571)
cor,opt orch voc sc KALMUS 6344 $1.50, ipa
(M2572)
"Coronation Mass" cor KALMUS $1.75 (M2573)
"Mass In C" [Eng/Lat] SATB,SATB soli,2ob,
2bsn,2horn,2trp,3trom,strings,timp voc sc
NOVELLO s.p., ipr (M2574)
"Mass In C Major" study sc UNIVER. PH. 53
$5.70 (M2575)
"Missa Solemnis" [Lat] 4pt mix cor,ATB soli
voc sc SCHIRM.G $1.50 (M2576)
(Moelich) "Mass " [Lat] min sc PETERS E971
$7.50, min sc-cloth PETERS E971 $10.00,
voc sc PETERS 8115 $3.00 (M2577)
Coronation Mass *see Coronation Mass
Credo Messe *see Messa In C-Dur
Credo-Messe *see Messe C-Dur
Crux Fidelis
[Lat] unis HEUGEL s.p. see from SAINTE-
CECILE (M2578)
Davidde Penitente *K.469, cant
[Eng/Ger/It] SATB,orch voc sc BROUDE BR.
$3.00, ipr (M2579)
cor,orch sc KALMUS $25.00, ipa (M2580)
cor min sc KALMUS 936 $1.30 (M2581)
[Eng/It/Ger] cor voc sc KALMUS 6349 $3.00
(M2582)
mix cor,SST soli,org,fl,2ob,clar,2bsn,2trp,
2horn,4trom,strings,timp sc BREITKOPF-L
PB-688 s.p., voc pt BREITKOPF-L
CHB-114A-C s.p., voc sc BREITKOPF-L
EB-2034 s.p., ipr (M2583)
Day Of Mourning *see Lacrymosa
Day Of Sadness *see Lacrymosa
De Profundis (Psalm 130) K.93, Bibl
[Lat] voc sc PETERS HU1638 $1.00 (M2584)
cor voc sc KALMUS 6327 $.60 (M2585)
cor voc sc KALMUS 6327 $.60 (M2586)
"Out Of The Deep" SATB,org SCHIRM.EC 2587
$.30 (M2587)
(Cramer) "From The Depths" [Eng/Lat] SATB
MARKS 4251 $.25 (M2588)
(Cramer) "From The Depths" [Eng/Lat] SSA
MARKS 4597 $.35 (M2589)
(Ohl) SATB oct SUMMY 5372 $.40 (M2590)
(Smithers) [Lat] 4pt mix cor,org/pno oct
SCHIRM.G 11322 $.30 (M2591)
(Smithers) mix cor SOUTHERN $.30 (M2592)
(Talmadge, A.) "Out Of The Deep" SSA,org
SCHIRM.EC 1972 $.20 (M2593)
Die Ersten Chore *Kyrie/mot
(Jode) mix cor MOSELER s.p.
contains: God Is Our Refuge, K.20; Kyrie,
K.33f (M2594)
Dies Irae (from Requiem)
[Lat] 4pt mix cor oct SCHIRM.G 10016 $.30
(M2595)
mix cor ALSBACH&D s.p. (M2596)
(Greene, E.) SSA,pno SCHIRM.EC 1594 $.25
(M2597)
Dir, Seele Des Weltalls
(Frank) "Hymn To The Sun" SATB oct FOX MM17
$.35 (M2598)
Dixit Dominus (Psalm 110) K.193, Bibl
see Mozart, Wolfgang Amadeus, Litaniae
mix cor SOUTHERN $.45 (M2599)
[Eng/Lat] SATB oct LAWSON 51164 $.45
(M2600)
Dixit Dominus And Magnificat *K.193
(Klein, Maynard) 4pt mix cor,pno voc sc
SCHIRM.G $1.50 (M2601)
Dominicus Messe *see Messa In C-Dur
Earth Rejoices
(Kurth) SA oct LESLIE 2036 (M2602)
Ehre Sei Gott
"Glory To God" SATB oct WALTON 6008 $.30
(M2603)
Et Incarnatus (from Grand Mass)
cor,orch sc KALMUS $4.00, ipa (M2604)
Eternal Peace *see Aeterna Pax
Exsulte, Jubilate
cor KALMUS $3.50 (M2605)
Exultate, Jubilate *K.165, mot
[Lat/Eng] cor min sc INTERNAT. $1.50
(M2606)
First Christmas Morn, The *Xmas
(Lipscomb) 2pt boy cor/2pt wom cor,pno/org
oct SCHIRM.G 11040 $.20 (M2607)

MOZART, WOLFGANG AMADEUS (cont'd.)

First Mass In C　*see Missa Brevis

Five Cannons　*CC5U,canon
(Trotter, Robert M.) [Eng/Ger] eq voices,
pno voc sc SCHIRM.G $.75　　　　　(M2608)

Four Canons　*CC4U,canon
[Ger/Lat] SSA SCHOTT s.p.　　　　(M2609)

Freut Euch, Freut Euch!　*hymn
"O Be Ye Joyful" mix cor SOUTHERN $.25
　　　　　　　　　　　　　　　　　(M2610)
(Frank) "O Be Ye Joyful" SATB oct FOX MM9
$.30　　　　　　　　　　　　　　(M2611)

From The Depths　*see De Profundis

Gloria (from Twelfth Mass) Easter/Fest,Gloria
SATB oct LORENZ 482 $.30　　　　(M2612)
SATB ALLANS 3 s.p.　　　　　　　(M2613)
cor oct HART s.p.　　　　　　　　(M2614)
[Lat] mix cor oct NOVELLO 34.0190.07 s.p.
　　　　　　　　　　　　　　　　　(M2615)
SATB oct BELWIN 765 $.25　　　　(M2616)
[Eng/Lat] SATB oct BELWIN 64125 $.35
　　　　　　　　　　　　　　　　　(M2617)
(Ehret) SATB oct BOURNE WE6 $.30　(M2618)
(Fletcher) 4pt men cor,org oct CURWEN 10705
$.25　　　　　　　　　　　　　　(M2619)
(Fletcher) men cor CURWEN 50538 s.p.
　　　　　　　　　　　　　　　　　(M2620)
(Woodruff) SATB oct SPRATT 542 $.30　(M2621)

Gloria In Excelsis (from Twelfth Mass) Xmas/
Fest/Gen,anthem/Bibl/Gloria
cor oct HART s.p.　　　　　　　　(M2622)
SATB oct LESLIE 4055　　　　　　(M2623)
[Eng/Lat] SATB,pno (med) oct WILLIS 697
$.20　　　　　　　　　　　　　　(M2624)
SATB oct FISCHER,C CM-255 $.25　(M2625)
SATB oct PRESSER 332-00152 $.40　(M2626)
SATB oct PRESSER 312-00039 $.30　(M2627)
[Lat/Eng] 4pt mix cor SCHIRM.G 3515
$.40　　　　　　　　　　　　　　(M2628)
SATB,org oct HARRIS HC4034 $.45　(M2629)
"Glorious Is Thy Name" SATB oct GRAY
GCMR 3196 $.35　　　　　　　　　(M2630)
"Glorious Is Thy Name" SATB oct NOVELLO
34.0198.07 s.p.　　　　　　　　(M2631)
(Brooks) SATB oct PLYMOUTH CC-9 $.25
　　　　　　　　　　　　　　　　　(M2632)
(Byrd) SATB oct PRO ART 1140 $.30　(M2633)
(Cramer) [Lat/Eng] SATB MARKS 4553 $.40
　　　　　　　　　　　　　　　　　(M2634)
(Ehret) SSA oct FOX PS77 $.30　(M2635)
(Manney) SSA oct PRESSER 332-14214 $.35
　　　　　　　　　　　　　　　　　(M2636)
(Milkey) [Lat/Eng] 3pt mix cor,acap oct
SCHIRM.G 11239 $.35　　　　　　(M2637)
(Owst) [Lat/Eng] 3pt wom cor oct SCHIRM.G
7212 $.40　　　　　　　　　　　(M2638)
(Robinson, C.) TTBB oct PRESSER 312-10458
$.35　　　　　　　　　　　　　　(M2639)

Gloria In Excelsis Deo　*Gloria
(Scott) SATB oct FOX R115 $.35　(M2640)

Glorious Is Thy Name　*see Gloria In Excelsis

Glory, Praise And Power　*see Litanie De
Venerabili Altaris Sacramento

Glory, Praise And Power　*see Litany In B
Flat

Glory To God　*see Ehre Sei Gott

God Is Our Refuge　*K.20, mot
see Die Ersten Chore
4pt mix cor,acap cor pts BREITKOPF-W s.p.
　　　　　　　　　　　　　　　　　(M2641)
"God Is Our Refuge" SATB BROUDE,A. 129 $.30
　　　　　　　　　　　　　　　　　(M2642)
(Kirk) "God Is Our Refuge" SAB oct PRO ART
2641 $.30　　　　　　　　　　　(M2643)

God Is Our Refuge　*see God Is Our Refuge

God Leads, God Helps　*see Justum Deduxit
Dominus

Gottheit! Dir Sei Preis Und Ehre　*K.123
(from Konig Thamos) hymn
mix cor,SATB soli,2fl,2ob,2bsn,2trp,2horn,
3trom,strings,timp BREITKOPF-L rental
　　　　　　　　　　　　　　　　　(M2644)
"Hymn Gottheit" cor,orch sc KALMUS $8.00,
ipa　　　　　　　　　　　　　　(M2645)

Grabmusik　*K.42, Psntd,cant
4pt mix cor,SB soli,2ob,2bsn,2horn,strings
BREITKOPF-W rental　　　　　　　(M2646)
"Passion Cantata" cor min sc KALMUS 934
$1.30　　　　　　　　　　　　　(M2647)

Gracious Lord, Have Mercy
(Suchoff) SATB oct FOX RM3 $.35　(M2648)

Gradual Ad Festum B.V.M.　*K.273
"Sancta Maria" [Lat] voc sc PETERS HU1356
$1.00, ipr　　　　　　　　　　(M2649)

Gradule Ad Festum B.M.V.　*K.273
see Mozart, Wolfgang Amadeus, Ave Verum
Corpus

Grand Mass　*see Grosse Messe

Grand Mass In C Minor　*see Grosse Messe

Grosse Messe　*K.427, Mass
"Grand Mass" cor voc sc KALMUS 6348 $2.50
　　　　　　　　　　　　　　　　　(M2650)
"Grand Mass" cor (C maj) min sc KALMUS 994
$1.30　　　　　　　　　　　　　(M2651)
"Grand Mass" cor,orch sc KALMUS $24.00, ipa
　　　　　　　　　　　　　　　　　(M2652)
"Grand Mass In C Minor" [Lat] dbl cor voc
sc SCHIRM.G $2.50　　　　　　　(M2653)
(Landon) "Mass " [Lat] SATB&SATB,SSTB soli,
orch,org voc sc PETERS 4856 $3.50, sc
PETERS 4856A $25.00, ipa, cor pts PETERS
4856 $3.50, sc PETERS 4856A $25.00, ipa,
voc pt PETERS 4856A $1.50, min sc PETERS
E983 $9.00, min sc-cloth PETERS E983
$12.50　　　　　　　　　　　　(M2654)
(Schmitt, Alois) SATB&SATB,SATB soli,org,

2fl,2ob,2clar,2bsn,2horn,2trp,4trom,
strings,timp sc BREITKOPF-W PB-4935 s.p.,
ipa　　　　　　　　　　　　　　(M2655)

Grosse Messe　*see Missa C-Moll

Halleluja (from Exulatate)
(Wild) SATB,S solo,org AMP A93 $.20　(M2656)

Hear Our Supplication
(Hilton, A.) SATB oct PRESSER 352-00378
$.30　　　　　　　　　　　　　(M2657)
(Hilton, Arthur) SSA (med easy) PRESSER
352-00463 $.35　　　　　　　　(M2658)
(Noble) SATB oct SPRATT 647 $.35　(M2659)

Hear Us Lord　*see Kyrie In D Minor

Heil Dem Tag, Dem Die Nacht Erlag
see Vulpius, Melchior, Die Helle Sonn
Leucht Jetzt Herfur

Herr, Der Du Thronest (from Davidde
Penitente)
"Lord, Who Reignest Now On High" SSAA,pno
SCHIRM.EC 1942 $.35　　　　　　(M2660)

Holy, Holy　*see Sanctus

Holy, Holy, Almighty God　*Xmas
(Coggin) SATB oct AGAPE A 395 $.25　(M2661)

Holy, Holy, Holy　*see Sanctus

Holy Lamb Of God (from Requiem) Agnus
(Coggin) SATB WARNER W7-1018 $.35　(M2662)

Hosanna (from Coronation Mass)
see Mozart, Wolfgang Amadeus, Sanctus

Humbly Kneel We Before Thee　*see Adoramus
Te, Christe

Hymn Gottheit　*see Gottheit! Dir Sei Preis
Und Ehre

Hymn Of Praise　*see Ave Verum

Hymn To The Sun　*see Dir, Seele Des Weltalls

Hymne
see Mozart, Wolfgang Amadeus, Weihe Des
Gesangs

I Will Call Upon The Lord
SAB oct PRO ART 2610 $.30　　　(M2663)
(Hilton, A.) SATB oct PRESSER MC372 $.30
　　　　　　　　　　　　　　　　　(M2664)

In Te, Domine　*K.14 (from Te Deum)
(Martens, Mason) SATB oct WALTON 2188 $.35
　　　　　　　　　　　　　　　　　(M2665)
(Rodby) "In Thee, Holy Lord" SATB oct
VOLKWEIN VB694 $.50　　　　　　(M2666)

In Thee, Holy Lord　*see In Te, Domine

Invocation (from Magic Flute, The)
(Craig) SATB oct PLYMOUTH SC-119 $.25
　　　　　　　　　　　　　　　　　(M2667)

Jesu, Holy Spirit　*see Ave Verum Corpus

Jesu, Jesu, God, Incarnate　*see Ave Verum
Corpus

Jesu, Son Of God　*Easter
(Martin) SAB SCHMITT 5502 $.30　(M2668)

Jesu, Word Of God Incarnate　*see Ave Verum

Jesu, Word Of God Incarnate　*see Ave Verum
Corpus

Jesu, Work Of God　*see Ave Verum

Jesus Calls Us　*see Ave Verum

Jesus, I My Cross Have Taken　*Gen
(Olds) SATB SCHMITT 1854 $.25　(M2669)

Jesus, Word Of God Incarnate　*see Ave Verum
Corpus

Jubilate Deo　*Jubil
"Let The Earth Sing" SATB oct SUMMY M 2802
$.25　　　　　　　　　　　　　(M2670)
(Noble) SATB oct BELWIN 05785 $.75　(M2671)
(Ronaldson) "O Be Joyful" [Lat/Eng] 2pt oct
PRO ART 1047 $.30　　　　　　　(M2672)
(Ronaldson) "O Be Joyful" [Lat/Eng] SSA,opt
kbd oct PRO ART 1028 $.25　　　(M2673)
(Ronaldson) "O Be Joyful" [Lat/Eng] SATB,
opt kbd oct PRO ART 1007 $.30　(M2674)
(Ronaldson) "O Be Joyful" [Lat/Eng] SAB,opt
kbd oct PRO ART 1063 $.25　　　(M2675)
(Scholin) SSA oct BELWIN 1193 $.30　(M2676)

Jubilate Deo　*see Offertorium Pro Omni
Tempore

Justum Deduxit Dominus　*K.326, hymn
4pt mix cor,cont cor pts BREITKOPF-W
CHB-3625 s.p.　　　　　　　　　(M2677)
(Richter) "God Leads, God Helps" [Eng/Lat]
SATB,acap AMP A420 $.35　　　　(M2678)
(Smithers) 4pt mix cor,pno/org oct SCHIRM.G
11321 $.30　　　　　　　　　　(M2679)

Kanonjai　*CC9L,canon
[Hung] 3-5pt (easy) BUDAPEST 2549 s.p.
　　　　　　　　　　　　　　　　　(M2680)

Kronungsmesse　*see Messe C-Dur

Kronungsmesse　*see Missa C-Dur

Kyrie (from Missa Brevis) Kyrie
see Die Ersten Chore
(Ehret) SATB oct HERITAGE H68 $.35　(M2681)
(Ehret) [Lat] SATB MARKS 4313 $.25　(M2682)
(Ehret) "Mercy Lord, Upon Us" SATB WARNER
WB-128 $.30　　　　　　　　　　(M2683)

Kyrie A Cinque Con Diversi Canoni　*K.89,
Kyrie
5 eq voices MOSELER LB-162 s.p.　(M2684)

MOZART, WOLFGANG AMADEUS (cont'd.)

Kyrie D-Moll　*K.341, Kyrie
mix cor,org,2fl,2ob,2clar,2bsn,2trp,4horn,
strings,timp (D min) sc BREITKOPF-L
rental　　　　　　　　　　　　(M2685)

Kyrie Eleison　*K.33 (from Missa Brevis In C
) Gen,Bibl/Kyrie
mix cor,strings sc BREITKOPF-L rental
　　　　　　　　　　　　　　　　　(M2686)
"Lord Have Mercy Upon Us" SATB oct WALTON
6024 $.30　　　　　　　　　　　(M2687)
(Cramer) [Eng/Lat] SATB MARKS 4554 $.25
　　　　　　　　　　　　　　　　　(M2688)
(Ehret) "Lord Have Mercy Upon Us" SATB
SCHMITT 1432 $.30　　　　　　　(M2689)
(Trusler) "Lord, Have Mercy Upon Us" SATB,
acap oct LAWSON 51123 $.30　　　(M2690)

Kyrie In D Minor　*K.341, Kyrie
(Herrmann) "Hear Us Lord" 4pt wom cor,org
oct SCHIRM.G 10867 $.30　　　　(M2691)
(Herrmann) "Hear Us Lord" 4pt mix cor,org
oct SCHIRM.G 10868 $.40　　　　(M2692)
(Senn, Walter) [Ger] SATB,org,orch (med
diff) BA 4702 sc $4.50, cor pts
$.55, ipr　　　　　　　　　　　(M2693)

Kyries　*CCUL
cor min sc KALMUS 931 $1.30　　(M2694)

Lacrymosa　*K.21 (from Requiem) Gen
mix cor,pno sc BREITKOPF-L PB-1543 s.p.
　　　　　　　　　　　　　　　　　(M2695)
SATB oct FISCHER,C CM-589 $.25　(M2696)
(Deis) "Day Of Sadness" [Lat] 3pt wom cor
oct SCHIRM.G 10065 $.25　　　　(M2697)
(Ehret) [Lat] SATB oct PRO ART 1493 $.30
　　　　　　　　　　　　　　　　　(M2698)
(Greene, E.) [Lat] SSA,pno SCHIRM.EC 1595
$.25　　　　　　　　　　　　　(M2699)
(Hoggard) SA/TB SHAWNEE E4 $.30　(M2700)
(Hoggard) SSAA SHAWNEE B 86 $.30　(M2701)
(Hoggard) SATB SHAWNEE A 109 $.30　(M2702)
(Mattfeld, V.) "Day Of Sadness" [Lat/Eng]
SATB,pno SCHIRM.EC 2414 $.35　(M2703)
(Mishkin, H.) [Lat/Eng] TTBB,pno SCHIRM.EC
2110 $.25　　　　　　　　　　　(M2704)
(Pierce, R.) [Lat/Eng] SSAA,pno SCHIRM.EC
891 $.20　　　　　　　　　　　(M2705)
(Strickling) SATB SCHMITT 1592 $.20　(M2706)
(Trusler) "Day Of Mourning" SATB oct
PLYMOUTH TR-113 $.25　　　　　　(M2707)

Lamb Of God　*see Agnus Dei

Laudate Dominum (Psalm 117) K.339 (from
Vesperae Solemnes De Confessore C-Dur)
anthem/Bibl
[Eng/Lat] SATB,S solo oct LAWSON 51165 $.35
　　　　　　　　　　　　　　　　　(M2708)
mix cor,S solo,orch voc pt BREITKOPF-L
CHB-954 s.p., voc sc BREITKOPF-L EB-5738
s.p.　　　　　　　　　　　　　(M2709)
wom cor,S solo ALSBACH&D sc s.p., cor pts
s.p.　　　　　　　　　　　　　(M2710)
mix cor,S solo ALSBACH&D s.p.　(M2711)
SSA oct OXFORD 83.090 $.45　　　(M2712)
4pt mix cor,S solo,org,bsn,3trom,strings sc
BREITKOPF-W PB-3766 s.p., cor pts
BREITKOPF-W CHB-3433 s.p., ipa see from
Vesperae Solennes
"O Praise Jehovah" [Lat/Eng] SATB,S solo,
org PLYMOUTH EC 2280 $.35, ipr　(M2714)
(Davis, K.) "Lord, God We Praise Thee"
[Lat/Eng] SATB WARNER R3350 $.35　(M2715)
(Glaser, V.) "O Praise Jehovah" SSA,S solo,
org/pno SCHIRM.EC 1988 $.30, ipr　(M2716)
(Lethbridge) SSA SOUTHERN $.45　(M2717)
(Phillips, John C.) [Lat] SSA,S solo,pno/
org oct NOVELLO 33.0129.10 s.p.　(M2718)
(Quinn) SATB oct PLYMOUTH NBC-102 $.35
　　　　　　　　　　　　　　　　　(M2719)
(Quinn) SAB oct PLYMOUTH NBC-203 $.35
　　　　　　　　　　　　　　　　　(M2720)
(Talmadge, A.) "O Praise Jehovah" SAAA,A
solo,org/pno SCHIRM.EC 1958 $.30, ipr
　　　　　　　　　　　　　　　　　(M2721)

Laudate Dominum In F　*mot
mix cor,S solo,org,strings,opt bsn
WEINBERGER s.p., ipa voc sc, cor pts
　　　　　　　　　　　　　　　　　(M2722)

Laudate Pueri (Psalm 113) Bibl
mix cor SOUTHERN $.35　　　　　(M2723)
[Eng/Lat] SATB oct LAWSON 51166 $.40
　　　　　　　　　　　　　　　　　(M2724)

Let The Earth Sing　*see Jubilate Deo

Litaneien　*see Litaniae De Venerabili
Altaris Sacramento, K.125; Litaniae
Lauretanae B.M.V., K.195　　　　(M2725)

Litania　*see Litaniae De Venerabili Altaris
Sacramento

Litania　*see Litanie De Venerabili Altaris
Sacramento

Litania　*see Litaniae De Venerabili Altaris
Sacramento

Litaniae De Beata Virgine　*K.109, BVM
cor,orch sc KALMUS $5.00, ipa　(M2726)
cor min sc KALMUS 928 $1.30 contains also:
Litaniae Lauretanae, K.195; Litanie De
Venerabili Altaris Sacramento, "Litania",
K.125　　　　　　　　　　　　　(M2727)
mix cor,SATB soli,org,strings BREITKOPF-L
rental　　　　　　　　　　　　(M2728)
(Steffen, Erich) [Ger] mix cor,SBar soli,
cont,2vln,vcl,bvl,opt vla SIRIUS sc s.p.,
cor pts s.p., ipa　　　　　　　(M2729)

Litaniae De Venerabili Altaris Sacramento
*K.243
(Federhofer, Hellmut; Federhofer, Renate)
[Lat] SATB,SATB soli,org,orch (medien) sc
BAREN. BA 4765 s.p. see from Litaneien
　　　　　　　　　　　　　　　　　(M2730)
(Federhofer, Hellmut; Federhofer, Renate)
[Lat] SATB,SATB soli,org,orch (med) sc
BAREN. BA 4763 s.p. see from Litaneien
　　　　　　　　　　　　　　　　　(M2731)

Litaniae De Venerabili Altaris Sacramento
*K.125
mix cor,ST soli,orch (B flat maj)
BREITKOPF-L rental　　　　　　　(M2732)

MOZART, WOLFGANG AMADEUS (cont'd.)

Litaniae De Venerabili Altaris Sacramento *K.243
mix cor,SATB soli,org,2fl,2ob,2bsn,2horn, 3trom,strings (E flat maj) BREITKOPF-L rental (M2733)
"Litania" cor,orch sc KALMUS $12.00, ipa (M2734)
"Litania" cor voc sc KALMUS 6337 $2.00 (M2735)
"Litaniae" cor min sc KALMUS 929 $1.30 contains also: Dixit Dominus, K.193 (M2736)

Litaniae Lauretanae *K.195
4pt mix cor,SATB soli,org,2ob,2horn,strings cor pts BREITKOPF-W CHB-3606 s.p., ipr, sc BREITKOPF-W rental (M2737)

Litaniae Lauretanae B.M.V. *K.195
(Federhofer, Hellmut; Federhofer, Renate) [Lat] SATB,SATB soli,org,orch (med) sc BAREN. BA 4764 s.p. see from Litaneien (M2738)
(Federhofer, Hellmut; Federhofer, Renate) [Lat] SATB,SATB soli,org,orch (med) sc BAREN. BA 4762 s.p. see from Litaneien (M2739)

Litaniae Lauretanae *K.195
see Mozart, Wolfgang Amadeus, Litaniae De Beata Virgine
cor voc sc KALMUS 6334 $2.00 (M2740)
cor,orch sc KALMUS $12.00, ipa (M2741)
mix cor,SATB soli,org,2ob,2horn,strings (D maj) voc sc BREITKOPF-L EB-540 s.p. (M2742)

Litaniae *see Litaniae De Venerabili Altaris Sacramento

Litanie De Venerabili Altaris Sacramento *K.125
"Litania" see Mozart, Wolfgang Amadeus, Litaniae De Beata Virgine
"Glory, Praise And Power" SATB oct STAFF 672 $.30 (M2743)
"Glory, Praise And Power" cor,orch sc KALMUS $12.00, ipa (M2744)
"Littany Glory, Praise And Power" cor voc sc KALMUS 6330 $1.50 (M2745)

Litany In B Flat *K.125, cant
"Glory, Praise And Power" BELWIN $1.25 (M2746)

Littany Glory, Praise And Power *see Litanie De Venerabili Altaris Sacramento

Lord, God We Praise Thee *see Laudate Dominum

Lord, Have Mercy Upon Us *see Kyrie Eleison

Lord, Thy Servants Praise Thee
(Ehret) SATB SHAWNEE A 1061 $.30 (M2747)

Lord, We Pray Thee
(Ehret) SAB ALFRED 6514 $.25 (M2748)
(Ehret) SATB oct SPRATT 574 $.25 (M2749)

Lord, We Pray To Thee
(Avalos) SATB oct PRO ART 1849 $.30 (M2750)

Lord, Who Reignest Now On High *see Herr, Der Du Thronest

Magnificat
(Davison, Nigel) SATB BOSWORTH s.p. (M2751)

Masonic Joy *K.471, cant
cor min sc KALMUS 934 $1.30 contains also: Short Masonic Cantata, A, K.623 (M2752)

Mass *see Coronation Mass

Mass *see Grosse Messe

Mass In B Flat *Mass
BELWIN $1.50 (M2753)

Mass In C *see Coronation Mass

Mass In C *see Missa

Mass In C Major *see Coronation Mass

Mass In C *see Missa In Honorem Sanctissimae Trinitas

Mass In D Minor *see Requiem

Mass In G *K.232, Mass
[Eng/Lat] SATB,SATB soli,2ob,2bsn,2horn, 2trp,strings,timp voc sc NOVELLO s.p., ipr (M2754)

Mass No. 12 *Mass
[Eng] cor voc sc KALMUS 6352 $2.50 (M2755)

Mass *see Missa

Mercy Lord, Upon Us *see Kyrie

Messa In C-Dur *K.262, Mass
(Pfannhauser, K.) "Missa Longa" 4pt mix cor,org,2ob,2horn,2trp,timp,strings (C maj) DOBLINGER voc sc s.p., cor pts s.p., ipa see from OSTERREICHISCHE KIRCHENMUSIK (M2756)
(Strassl, A.) "Credo Messe" 4pt mix cor, org,2ob,2trp,timp,strings (C maj) DOBLINGER voc sc s.p., cor pts s.p., ipa (M2757)
(Strassl, A.) "Dominicus Messe" 4pt mix cor,org,2trp,timp,strings (C maj) DOBLINGER voc sc s.p., cor pts s.p., ipa (M2758)

Messe C-Dur *K.257, Mass
"Credo-Messe" 4pt mix cor,SATB soli,org, 2ob,2trp,3trom,strings,timp (C maj) BREITKOPF-W rental (M2759)
"Kronungsmesse" 4pt mix cor,SATB soli,org, 2ob,bsn,2horn,2trp,3trom,strings,timp (C maj) sc BREITKOPF-W PB-4453 s.p., ipa (M2760)

Messe En Ut *Mass
[Fr] 3 eq voices,soli,orch (C maj) oct DURAND s.p. (M2761)

MOZART, WOLFGANG AMADEUS (cont'd.)

Mighty Spirit All Transcending *see Ave Verum Corpus

Misericordia Domini *K.222
cor voc sc KALMUS 6336 $.75 (M2762)
"Misericordia Domini" cor,orch sc KALMUS $6.00, ipa (M2763)

Misericordia Domini *see Misericordia Domini

Misericordias Domini *K.222
[Lat] SATB,org,2vln HINRICHSEN D841 voc pt s.p., voc sc s.p. (M2764)
SATB,inst sc FOSTER MF137 $1.50, ipa, cor pts FOSTER MF137A $.70 (M2765)

Missa Brevis *K.194, Mass
4pt mix cor,S solo,org,strings (D maj) sc BREITKOPF-W PB-4452 s.p., cor pts BREITKOPF-W CHB-3699 s.p., ipa, voc sc BREITKOPF-W EB-5739 s.p. (M2766)
(Senn, Walter) [Lat] SATB,SATB soli,org, 2vln,vcl/bvl (med) sc BAREN. BA 4736 $9.75, ipr, cor pts $.55 (M2767)

Missa Brevis B-Dur *K.275, Mass
4pt mix cor,S solo,org,strings (B maj) voc sc BREITKOPF-W EB-6564 s.p., cor pts BREITKOPF-W CHB-3693 s.p., sc BREITKOPF-W PB-4852 s.p. (M2768)
(Strobach, Siegfried) 4pt wom cor,3 soli, org,2vln,vcl (B flat maj) cor pts BREITKOPF-W CHB-3560 s.p., ipr, sc BREITKOPF-W rental (M2769)

Missa Brevis F-Dur *K.192, Mass
4pt mix cor,org,2vln,bvl (F maj) sc BREITKOPF-W PB-4853 s.p., cor pts BREITKOPF-W CHB-3579 s.p., voc sc BREITKOPF-W EB-6624 s.p. (M2770)

Missa Brevis In C-Dur *K.258, Mass
(Schabasser, J.) "Piccolomini-Messe" 4pt mix cor,org,2trp,timp,strings DOBLINGER voc sc s.p., cor pts s.p., ipa (M2771)

Missa Brevis In D-Moll *K.65, Mass
(Schabasser, J.) 4pt mix cor,org,2vln,bvl (D min) DOBLINGER voc sc s.p., cor pts s.p., ipa (M2772)

Missa Brevis In F Major
[Lat] 4pt mix cor,4 soli voc sc SCHIRM.G $1.25 (M2773)

Missa Brevis In G-Dur *K.49, Mass
(Strassl, A.) 4pt mix cor,org,strings (G maj) DOBLINGER voc sc s.p., cor pts s.p., ipa (M2774)

Missa Brevis (K115), And Others *CCUL,Mass
cor min sc KALMUS 995 $1.30 (M2775)

Missa Brevis *K.49, Mass
mix cor,SATB soli,org,strings (G maj) BREITKOPF-L rental (M2776)
cor min sc KALMUS 923 $1.30 contains also: Missa Brevis, K.65; Missa Brevis, K.66 (M2777)

Missa Brevis *K.65, Mass
see Mozart, Wolfgang Amadeus, Missa Brevis
mix cor,SATB soli,org,strings (D min) BREITKOPF-L rental (M2778)

Missa Brevis *K.66, Mass
see Mozart, Wolfgang Amadeus, Missa Brevis
"First Mass In C" BELWIN $1.25 (M2779)

Missa Brevis *K.91, Mass
[Lat] SATB,orch MARKS $1.85, ipr (M2780)

Missa Brevis *K.192, Mass
cor voc sc KALMUS 6324 $1.25 (M2781)
cor,orch sc KALMUS $10.00, ipa (M2782)
cor min sc KALMUS 925 $1.30 contains also: Missa, K.257; Missa, K.258 (M2783)

Missa Brevis *K.194, Mass
cor min sc KALMUS 92 $1.30 contains also: Missa Brevis, K.220 (M2784)
cor voc sc KALMUS 6333 $1.00 (M2785)
cor,orch sc KALMUS $4.50, ipa (M2786)
(Trexler, G.) mix cor,SATB soli,org,strings (D maj) sc BREITKOPF-L PB-650 s.p., voc pt BREITKOPF-L CHB-47A+B s.p., voc sc BREITKOPF-L EB-5739 s.p. (M2787)

Missa Brevis *K.220, Mass
see Mozart, Wolfgang Amadeus, Missa Brevis
cor voc sc KALMUS 6335 $1.50 (M2788)
cor,orch sc KALMUS $5.00, ipa (M2789)
"Spatzen-Messe" 4pt mix cor,S solo,org, 2trp,strings,timp (C maj) sc BREITKOPF-W PB-4758 s.p., ipa, cor pts BREITKOPF-W CHB-3538 s.p., voc sc BREITKOPF-W EB-6580 s.p. (M2790)
"Spatzenmesse" [Lat] min sc PETERS E988 $3.00 (M2791)
"Spatzenmesse" mix cor,SATB soli,org,2trp, strings,timp (C maj) voc pt BREITKOPF-L CHB-353 s.p., ipr (M2792)

Missa Brevis *K.275, Mass
cor,orch sc KALMUS $10.00, ipa (M2793)

Missa Brevis *K.258, Mass
mix cor,SATB soli,org,2trp,strings,timp (C maj) BREITKOPF-L rental (M2794)

Missa Brevis *K.259, Mass
mix cor,SATB soli,org,2trp,strings,timp BREITKOPF-L rental (M2795)
cor,orch sc KALMUS $10.00, ipa (M2796)
cor min sc KALMUS 927 $1.30 contains also: Missa, K.262; Missa, K.275 (M2797)
cor voc sc KALMUS 6339 $1.50 (M2798)

Missa Brevis *K.275, Mass
mix cor,SATB soli,org,strings (B flat maj) BREITKOPF-L rental (M2799)
cor voc sc KALMUS 6341 $3.00 (M2800)

Missa C-Dur *K.66, Mass
mix cor,SATB soli,org,2ob,4trp,strings,timp (C maj) voc pt BREITKOPF-L CHB-43 s.p., ipr (M2801)

MOZART, WOLFGANG AMADEUS (cont'd.)

Missa C-Dur *K.317, Mass
(Taubmann, O.) "Kronungsmesse" mix cor,SATB soli,org,2ob,bsn,2trp,2horn,3trom, strings,timp (C maj) sc BREITKOPF-L PB-657 s.p., voc pt BREITKOPF-L CHB-358A-D s.p., voc sc BREITKOPF-L EB-2256 s.p., ipa (M2802)

Missa C-Moll *K.139, Mass
mix cor,SATB soli,org,2ob,4trp,3trom, strings,timp (C min) voc pt BREITKOPF-L CHB-44 s.p., ipr (M2803)

Missa C-Moll *K.427, Mass
(Schmitt, A.) "Grosse Messe" mix cor,SMezTB soli,org,2fl,2ob,2clar,2bsn,2trp,2horn, 4trom,strings,timp (C min) voc pt BREITKOPF-L CHB-1434A-F s.p., voc sc BREITKOPF-L EB-1867 s.p., ipr (M2804)

Missa De Dominica *K.321, Mass
cor voc sc KALMUS 6345 $3.00 (M2805)

Missa In C *K.115, Mass
(Paumgartner, B.) sc UNIVER. HMP 1 $4.35, cor pts UNIVER. HMP 2A-D $.55 (M2806)

Missa In Honorem Sanctissimae Trinitas *K.167, Mass
4pt mix cor,org,2ob,4trp,strings,timp (C maj) BREITKOPF-W rental (M2807)
"Mass In C" cor,orch sc KALMUS $6.50, ipa (M2808)

Missa In Honorem Sanctissimae Trinitatis *K.167, Trin,Mass
mix cor,org,2ob,4trp,strings,timp (C maj) cor pts BREITKOPF-L CHB-45 s.p., ipr (M2809)

Missa Longa *see Messa In C-Dur

Missa Pro Defunctis *K.626, Mass/Req
"Requiem" cor KALMUS $1.25 (M2810)
"Requiem" cor sc KALMUS $7.00 (M2811)
"Requiem" [Lat] cor voc sc PETERS 76 $1.25 (M2812)
"Requiem" [Lat] 4pt mix cor,4 soli voc sc SCHIRM.G $1.40 (M2813)
"Requiem D-Moll" 4pt mix cor,SATB soli,org, 2clar,2bsn,2horn,2trp,3trom,strings,timp (D min) sc BREITKOPF-W PB-4454 s.p., voc pt BREITKOPF-W CHB-4454 s.p., ipa (M2814)
"Requiem In D Minor" [Lat] SATB,SATB soli, 2bsn,2trp,strings,timp, basset horn HUG s.p., ipr (M2815)
"Requiem Mass" [Lat] cor,opt orch voc sc KALMUS 6351 $1.25, ipa (M2816)
"Requiem Mass" cor min sc KALMUS 179 $5.00 (M2817)
(Beyer, Franz) "Requiem" [Lat] cor cloth PETERS 10039 $45.00, ipa (M2818)
(Beyer, Franz) "Requiem" [Lat] cor sc PETERS 10039 $30.00, ipa (M2819)
(Suessmayr) "Requiem" [Lat] cor sc PETERS 1873 $15.00, ipa (M2820)
(Suessmayr) "Requiem" [Lat] cor min sc PETERS E954 $5.50 (M2821)
(Suessmayr) "Requiem" [Lat] cor min sc-cloth PETERS E954 $9.00 (M2822)

Missa Solemnis *K.337, Mass
cor min sc KALMUS 926 $1.30 contains also: Coronation Mass, K.317 (M2823)
cor,orch sc KALMUS $12.00, ipa (M2824)
cor voc sc KALMUS 6346 $1.50 (M2825)

Missa Solemnis *see Coronation Mass

Missa *K.139, Mass
cor min sc KALMUS 924 $1.30 contains also: Missa, K.167 (M2826)

Missa *K.167
see Mozart, Wolfgang Amadeus, Missa

Missa *K.257
see Mozart, Wolfgang Amadeus, Missa Brevis

Missa *K.258, Mass
see Mozart, Wolfgang Amadeus, Missa Brevis
"Mass In C" cor voc sc KALMUS 6338 $1.00 (M2827)
"Mass" cor,orch sc KALMUS $8.00, ipa (M2828)

Missa *K.262
see Mozart, Wolfgang Amadeus, Missa Brevis

Missa *K.275
see Mozart, Wolfgang Amadeus, Missa Brevis

O Be Joyful *see Jubilate Deo

O Be Joyful In God
(Davies, L.H.) SATB ENOCH EC322 s.p. (M2829)

O Be Joyful In The Lord
(Scholin) SSA oct BELWIN 1193 $.25 (M2830)

O Be Ye Joyful *see Freut Euch, Freut Euch!

O God! O God!
(Suchoff) SATB oct FOX PS119 $.30 (M2831)

O Lord Most High, With All My Heart *Gen, anthem
(Track, G.) SAB (med easy) oct GIA G1751 $.35 (M2832)

O Praise Jehovah *see Laudate Dominum

O Praise The Lord
(Ehret, W.) SATB oct PRESSER MC264 $.35 (M2833)

O Praise Ye The Lord *anthem/mot
mix cor,S solo oct NOVELLO 40.0347.00 s.p. (M2834)

O Salutaris
[Lat] unis/2pt CHOUDENS s.p. (M2835)
[Lat] 4pt mix cor,T solo HEUGEL s.p. see from SAINTE-CECILE (M2836)

Offertories Vol. 1 *CCUL,Offer
cor min sc KALMUS 932 $1.30 (M2837)

Offertories Vol. 2 *CCUL,Offer
cor min sc KALMUS 933 $1.30 (M2838)

MOZART, WOLFGANG AMADEUS (cont'd.)

Offertorium Pro Festo Sancti Joannes
Baptistae *K.72, Offer
cor,orch sc KALMUS $5.00, ipa   (M2839)

Offertorium Pro Festo Sancti Joannis
Baptistae *K.72
4pt mix cor,org,strings BREITKOPF-W rental
(M2840)

Offertorium Pro Festo Sancti Joannis
Baptistae Inter Natos *K.72, Offer
mix cor,org,strings sc BREITKOPF-L rental
(M2841)

Offertorium Pro Omni Tempore *K.117, Jubil
"Benedictus Sit Deus" cor,orch sc KALMUS
$5.00, ipa   (M2842)
"Benedictus Sit Deus" cor voc sc KALMUS
6328 $1.00   (M2843)
"Jubilate Deo" [Lat] voc sc PETERS HU1600
$1.00, ipa   (M2844)

Out Of The Deep *see De Profundis

Passion Cantata *see Grabmusik

Piccolomini-Messe *see Missa Brevis In C-Dur

Pirkadat *canon
[Hung] 4pt (med diff) BUDAPEST 343 s.p.
(M2845)

Plead Thou My Cause
SATB,B solo ALLANS 212 s.p.   (M2846)

Praise God! (from Solemn Vespers)
(Kirk) SATB,orch oct PRO ART 2273 $.35, ipr
(M2847)

Praise The Lord For He Is Gracious *Easter/
Gen,anthem
SATB oct LORENZ 7417 $.30   (M2848)
(Ehret, Walter) SATB oct LORENZ 7417 $.25
(M2849)

Praise The Lord, Ye People
(Coggin) SAB FLAMMER D5020 $.30   (M2850)

Praise Ye The Lord
(Lynn, G.) SATB oct PRESSER 312-40059 $.30
(M2851)

Preis Dir, Gottheit! *K.121 (from Konig
Thamos) hymn
mix cor,SATB soli,2fl,2ob,2bsn,2trp,2horn,
3trom,strings,timp BREITKOPF-L rental
(M2852)
(Vogel, Moritz; Nagler, Franciscus) [Ger]
wom cor&jr cor,org,opt strings HUG 5 s.p.
(M2853)

Psalm 110 *see Dixit Dominus

Psalm 113 *see Laudate Pueri

Psalm 117 *see Laudate Dominum

Psalm 130 *see De Profundis

Regina Coeli *K.276
[Eng/Lat] 4pt mix cor,4 soli voc sc
SCHIRM.G $.85   (M2854)
mix cor,SATB soli,org,2ob,2trp,strings,timp
sc BREITKOPF-L PB-597 s.p., voc pt
BREITKOPF-L CHB-671 s.p., voc sc
BREITKOPF-L EB-5222 s.p., ipa   (M2855)
cor voc sc KALMUS 6342 $.75   (M2856)
cor sc KALMUS $3.50   (M2857)
cor,orch sc KALMUS $3.50, ipa   (M2858)
4pt mix cor,org,2ob,2trp,strings,timp (C
maj) sc BREITKOPF-W PB-4788 s.p., cor pts
BREITKOPF-W CHB-3430 s.p.   (M2859)

Requiem *K.626, ECY,Req
study sc UNIVER. PH. 59 $4.50   (M2860)
[Lat] cor,SATB soli,orch cor pts SALABERT-
US $1.25   (M2861)
cor,orch/org sc KALMUS $7.50, ipa   (M2862)
"Mass In D Minor" [Eng/Lat] SATB,SATB soli,
org,2clar,2bsn,2trp,3trom,strings,timp, 2
basset horn voc sc NOVELLO s.p., ipr
(M2863)
"Requiem Mass" [Lat] cor BELWIN $1.00
(M2864)
"Requiem Mass" [Eng] cor BELWIN $1.00
(M2865)
(Nowak, Leopold) [Lat] SATB,SATB soli,org,
2vln,vla,vcl,bvl (med diff, T.J. Boonin
sole distributor in U.S.A.) sc BAREN.
BA 4538 $20.50, cor pts BAREN. BA 4538
$4.00, voc pt BAREN. BA 4538A $3.75, min
sc BAREN. TP 152 $6.00, ipa   (M2866)
(Raphael, G.) mix cor,SATB soli,org,2clar,
2bsn,2trp,3trom,strings,timp (D min) sc
BREITKOPF-L PB-643 s.p., voc pt
BREITKOPF-L CHB-40A-C s.p., voc sc
BREITKOPF-L EB-210 s.p., ipa   (M2867)

Requiem *see Missa Pro Defunctis

Requiem D-Moll *see Missa Pro Defunctis

Requiem In D Minor *see Missa Pro Defunctis

Requiem Mass *see Missa Pro Defunctis

Requiem Mass *see Requiem

Sancta Maria *K.273, Gen,Gradual,mot
cor,orch sc KALMUS $5.00, ipa   (M2868)
"Sancta Maria" [Lat/Eng] SATB,pno/org/
strings BROUDE BR. $.45, ipa   (M2869)
(Federhofer, Hellmut) "Sancta Maria, Mater
Dei" [Lat] SATB,org,2vln,vla,vcl (med)
BAREN. BA 4751 sc $2.75, cor pts $.55,
ipa   (M2870)
(Smithers) "Sancta Maria Mater Dei" 4pt mix
cor,org/pno oct SCHIRM.G 11323 $.30
(M2871)

Sancta Maria *see Gradual Ad Festum B.V.M.

Sancta Maria *see Sancta Maria

Sancta Maria Mater Dei *K.273
cor voc sc KALMUS 6340 $1.00   (M2872)

Sancta Maria Mater Dei *see Sancta Maria

Sanctus (from Coronation Mass) Sanctus
4pt mix cor oct SCHIRM.G 11542 $.25
(M2873)
contains also: Hosanna
"Holy, Holy, Holy" SATB oct WALTON 6026
$.30   (M2874)
(Cramer) mix cor SOUTHERN $.30   (M2875)

MOZART, WOLFGANG AMADEUS (cont'd.)

(Ehret) SATB oct BOOSEY 5086 $.30   (M2876)
(Ehret) [Lat/Eng] SATB MARKS 4555 $.30
(M2877)
(Ehret) "Holy, Holy" SATB SHAWNEE A 1060
$.30   (M2878)
(Ehret) "Holy, Holy, Holy" SSA SHAWNEE A
2609 $.30   (M2879)
(Ehret) "Holy, Holy, Holy" [Lat/Eng] 4pt
mix cor,org/pno oct SCHIRM.G 11907 $.30
(M2880)
(Ehret) "Holy, Holy, Holy," SATB WARNER
WB-127 $.30   (M2881)

Sanctus And Hosanna (from Requiem) Sanctus
(Ehret) SATB SHAWNEE A 5569 $.30   (M2882)
(Ehret) SATB oct BOOSEY 1922 $.30   (M2883)
(Randolph) SATB oct PLYMOUTH SC-1 $.25
(M2884)
(Thompson) SATB oct BOURNE D3 $.30   (M2885)

Savior, Source Of Every Blessing *see Ave
Verum Corpus

Saviour Source Of Every Blessing (from Ave
Verum Corpus)
SATB oct FISCHER,C CM-6291 $.25   (M2886)

Short Masonic Cantata, A *K.623
see Mozart, Wolfgang Amadeus, Masonic Joy

Sing Praise To The Father *see Te Deum
Laudamus

Song Of Brotherhood
(Warren) SAB LUDWIG L-9146 $.40   (M2887)

Song Of Loyal Brotherhood
(Wasner) [Eng/Ger] 4pt mix cor,acap oct
SCHIRM.G 8651 $.25   (M2888)

Spatzen-Messe *see Missa Brevis

Spatzenmesse *see Missa Brevis

Sub Tuum Praesidium *mot
SS,org,strings WEINBERGER s.p., ipa voc sc,
cor pts   (M2889)

Take My Life And Let It Be
(Thompson) SAB LEONARD-US 08064160 $.25
(M2890)

Tantum Ergo
see SIX MOTETS A L'UNISSON

Tantum Ergo *K.142, Gen,mot
cor,orch sc KALMUS $6.00, ipa   (M2891)
"Tantum Ergo" mix cor,org,2vln,vla,vcl,bvl,
opt 2trp WEINBERGER s.p., ipa voc sc, cor
pts contains also: Tantum Ergo, K.197
(M2892)
(Federhofer, Hellmut) [Lat] SATB,S solo,
org,2trp,2vln,vla,vcl (med diff) sc
BAREN. BA 4752 $2.50, cor pts $.55, ipa
(M2893)

Tantum Ergo *see Tantum Ergo

Tantum Ergo *K.197, Gen
"Tantum Ergo" see Mozart, Wolfgang Amadeus,
Tantum Ergo
cor,orch sc KALMUS $6.00, ipa   (M2894)
(Federhofer, Hellmut) [Lat] SATB,org,2trp,
2vln,vla,vcl,drums (med diff) BAREN.
BA 4753 $2.50, cor pts $.40, ipa   (M2895)

Tantum Ergo *see Tantum Ergo

Tarry With Me *see Ave Verum Corpus

Te Deum *K.141, Te Deum
[Lat] SATB,org/orch voc sc PETERS HU1381
$2.00, ipr   (M2896)
[Lat] SATB,org/pno,strings BROUDE BR. $.75,
ipr   (M2897)
[Lat] SATB,orch voc sc BROUDE BR. $.75, ipr
(M2898)
mix cor,org,strings sc BREITKOPF-L rental
(M2899)
(Martens, Mason) SATB,orch voc sc WALTON
M 107 $1.50, ipr   (M2900)
(Rasmussen, Henning Bro) [Lat] SATB,org,
strings HANSEN-DEN 28303 s.p., ipa
(M2901)
(Rodby) mix cor SOUTHERN $1.80   (M2902)
(Rodby) SATB sc VOLKWEIN VB69A $1.80   (M2903)

Te Deum In C *K.141, Te Deum
[Lat] SATB,orch/org voc sc HINRICHSEN D838
s.p.   (M2904)

Te Deum Laudamus (from Te Deum)
(Martens, Mason) SATB oct WALTON 2182 $.40
(M2905)
(Rodby) "Sing Praise To The Father" SATB
oct VOLKWEIN VB699 $.80   (M2906)

Te Deum *K.141, Te Deum
cor voc sc KALMUS 6331 $1.00   (M2907)
cor,orch sc KALMUS $3.50, ipa   (M2908)
4pt mix cor,org,strings (C maj) sc
BREITKOPF-W PB-4796 s.p., ipa, cor pts
BREITKOPF-W CHB-3633 s.p., voc sc
BREITKOPF-W EB-6546 s.p.   (M2909)
(Martens, Mason) SATB,org,4trp,strings voc
sc WALTON M 107 $1.25, cmplt ed WALTON
rental   (M2910)

Teli Hangulat *canon
(Jankovich, F.) [Hung] 3pt (med diff)
BUDAPEST 343 s.p.   (M2911)

To Thee Be Glory
(Gillam) SATB oct PLYMOUTH PCS-65 $.25
(M2912)

Tu Virginum Corona
2pt ENOCH TP235 s.p.   (M2913)

Twelfth Mass *Mass/ora
oct HART s.p.   (M2914)

Veni Sancte Spiritus *K.47
cor,orch sc KALMUS $5.00, ipa   (M2915)

Veni Sanctus Spiritus *K.47
cor voc sc KALMUS 6326 $.75   (M2916)

MOZART, WOLFGANG AMADEUS (cont'd.)

Vesperae De Dominica *K.321
SATB,orch sc SCHIRM.EC 2796 $3.50
(M2917)
cor min sc KALMUS 930 $1.30 contains also:
Vesperae Solemnes De Confessore, K.339
(M2918)
cor KALMUS $1.25   (M2919)
cor,orch sc KALMUS $10.00, ipa   (M2920)
4pt mix cor,2vln,2trp,timp sc BREITKOPF-W
PB-4825 s.p., cor pts BREITKOPF-W
CHB-3605 s.p., voc sc BREITKOPF-W EB-6610
s.p., ipa   (M2921)

Vesperae Solemnes De Confessore *K.339, Mass
see Mozart, Wolfgang Amadeus, Vesperae De
Dominica
mix cor,SATB soli,org,bsn,2trp,3trom,
strings,timp (C maj) sc BREITKOPF-L
PB-603 s.p., voc pt BREITKOPF-L
CHB-1641A-C s.p., voc sc BREITKOPF-L
EB-1533 s.p., ipa   (M2922)
cor,orch sc KALMUS $5.00, ipa   (M2923)

Vesperae Solemnes Del Confessore *K.339,
Mass
cor voc sc KALMUS 6347 $2.00   (M2924)

Vesperae Solennes *see Laudate Dominum
(M2925)

Vesperae Solennes De Confessore *K.339
4pt mix cor,S solo,org,bsn,2trp,3trom,
strings,timp sc BREITKOPF-W PB-4455 s.p.,
voc pt BREITKOPF-W CHB-1641 s.p., voc sc
BREITKOPF-W EB-1533 s.p., ipa   (M2926)

Vesperare Solennes De Confessore *K.339
mix cor SOUTHERN $1.50   (M2927)

We Worship Thee, O Christ *see Adoramus Te,
Christe

Weihe Des Gesangs
mix cor,acap ERDMANN 555 s.p. contains
also: Hymne   (M2928)
men cor,acap ERDMANN 206 s.p. contains
also: Silcher, Sanctus (Sanctus)   (M2929)

Wiegenlied
mix cor,pno cor pts NORDISKA 3188 s.p., ipa
(M2930)

MSA GLAGSKAJA see Janacek, Leos

MUCH HAVE THEY OPPRESSED ME FROM MY YOUTH see
Felciano, Richard

MUCKE, F.
Gott Grusse Dich
men cor BIRNBACH s.p.   (M2931)

MUCZYNSKI, ROBERT (1929-   )
Alleluia
4pt mix cor,acap oct SCHIRM.G 11002 $.25
(M2932)

MUDD, THOMAS (ca. 1560-1632)
God Which Has Prepared *Gen,17th cent
SATB,opt inst (easy) oct OXFORD 43.392 $.30
(M2933)
God, Which Hast Prepared *Gen,anthem
(Morehen, J.) SATB oct ROYAL 235 s.p.
(M2934)
Let Thy Merciful Ears *anthem
mix cor oct OXFORD 43.076 $.25   (M2935)
Let Thy Merciful Ears, O Lord *Bibl
(Collins) SATB,acap oct LAWSON 895 $.25
(M2936)

MUDDE, WILLEM
At The Lamb's High Feast We Sing *Easter/Gen
SA,kbd (med easy) oct CONCORDIA 98-1829
$.25   (M2937)
Lord, To Whom Shall We Go? *anthem
SSATTB (med) oct AUGSBURG 1569 $.30   (M2938)
O Dearest Jesus, What Law Hast Thou Broken
*Lent
SATB,S solo,kbd (med diff) oct CONCORDIA
98-1799 $.30   (M2939)
Praise God The Lord, Ye Sons Of Men *Xmas
SATB,acap (med diff) oct CONCORDIA 98-1438
$.30   (M2940)

MUDE BIN ICH, GEH ZUR RUH see Trubel, Gerhard

MUELAS
O Holy Jesus
(Ehret) SATB,acap oct COLOMBO 2385 $.25
(M2941)

MUELLER, CARL F. (1892-   )
All Hail The Power *anthem
4pt mix cor,org oct SCHIRM.G 11605 $.35
(M2942)
All My Heart This Night Rejoices *Xmas,Bibl
4pt mix cor,AT&4 soli,acap oct SCHIRM.G
8435 $.35   (M2943)
4pt wom cor,opt 4 soli,acap oct SCHIRM.G
9367 $.30   (M2944)
All Praise To Thee
4pt mix cor,org oct SCHIRM.G 11163 $.25
(M2945)
Alleluia! Christ Has Triumphed *Easter/Lent
3pt jr cor/SAB (easy) FISCHER,C CM 7199
$.25   (M2946)
SATB,org oct FISCHER,C CM-6969 $.25   (M2947)
Alleluia! Morn Of Beauty
4pt mix cor,acap oct SCHIRM.G 8811 $.25
(M2948)
Antiphons *CCU,anti
SATB,acap FISCHER,C O-4589 $1.25   (M2949)
Be Ye Reconciled To God
TTBB oct FISCHER,C CM-7717 $.30   (M2950)
SATB oct FISCHER,C CM-7705 $.30   (M2951)
Beatitudes, The
SAB FLAMMER D5119 $.30   (M2952)
Beautiful Saviour
2pt jr cor FISCHER,C CM 6345 $.25   (M2953)
Beloved, Let Us Love One Another
SATB oct PRESSER 312-40395 $.30   (M2954)

MUELLER, CARL F. (cont'd.)

Blessing And Honor
SATB oct FISCHER,C CM-7420 $.25 (M2955)

Bow Down Thine Ear
SATB oct FISCHER,C CM-6561 $.25 (M2956)
2pt jr cor/SA FISCHER,C CM 6958 $.25 (M2957)

Children Who Have Said Their Prayers
2pt jr cor FISCHER,C CM 6620 $.20 (M2958)

Choral Introits For The Church Year *CCU, Introit
SATB oct FISCHER,C CM-7572 $.40 (M2959)

Christ Of The Upward Way
SATB FLAMMER A 5108 $.30 (M2960)
SAB FLAMMER D5085 $.25 (M2961)
TTBB FLAMMER C5054 $.30 (M2962)

Come Christians Join To Sing
jr cor&sr cor (easy) FISCHER,C CM 7470 $.25 (M2963)
3pt jr cor/SAB (easy) FISCHER,C CM 7086 $.25 (M2964)
4pt jr cor/SATB (easy) FISCHER,C CM 6820 $.25 (M2965)
2pt jr cor FISCHER,C CM 6326 $.25 (M2966)

Come Let Us Sing
SATB oct FISCHER,C CM-6640 $.25 (M2967)

Come, See The Place
SATB oct FISCHER,C CM-7649 $.25 (M2968)

Create In Me A Clean Heart, O God *Bibl
3pt wom cor oct SCHIRM.G 9301 $.30 (M2969)
3pt mix cor oct SCHIRM.G 9707 $.30 (M2970)
SATB oct SCHIRM.G 8682 $.30 (M2971)
4pt men cor oct SCHIRM.G 10059 $.30 (M2972)

Dawn Of Christmas, The *Xmas
4pt mix cor&opt 2pt jr cor,opt SA soli oct SCHIRM.G 9366 $.25 (M2973)

Day Of Resurrection, The *Easter
jr cor&sr cor (med easy) FISCHER,C CM 6214 $.25 (M2974)

Glory Be To God On High
SATB oct FISCHER,C CM-7419 $.25 (M2975)

Glory To God In The Highest *Xmas
jr cor&sr cor/SATB (easy) FISCHER,C CM 6515 $.25 (M2976)

God Bless Our Native Land
SAB oct SCHIRM.G 8998 $.20 (M2977)
4pt mix cor oct SCHIRM.G 8994 $.25 (M2978)

God Is In His Holy Temple
4pt mix cor,acap oct SCHIRM.G 7687 $.25 (M2979)

God Is Our Refuge And Strength *Bibl
4pt mix cor oct SCHIRM.G 9533 $.25 (M2980)

God Is Present Everywhere
SATB oct FISCHER,C CM-7050 $.25 (M2981)

God Of Abraham Praise, The
2pt jr cor FISCHER,C CM 6303 $.20 (M2982)

God Of Light
unis jr cor&sr cor oct SCHIRM.G 9324 $.25 (M2983)

God Of Our Salvation
see Mueller, Carl F., Great God

God Who Touchest Earth With Beauty
2pt jr cor FISCHER,C CM 7331 $.25 (M2984)

Good Christian Men Rejoice *Xmas
2pt jr cor FISCHER,C CM 6304 $.25 (M2985)

Great God
4pt jr cor/SATB (easy) FISCHER,C CM 6666 $.20 contains also: God Of Our Salvation (M2986)

Great God And God Of Our Salvation *anthem
3pt jr cor/SAB (easy) FISCHER,C CM 7087 $.25 (M2987)
SATB oct FISCHER,C CM-6666 $.25 (M2988)

Greater Love Hath No Man *anthem
SSA oct FISCHER,C CM-7663 $.25 (M2989)
SATB oct FISCHER,C CM-6522 $.25 (M2990)

Guide Me, O Thou Great Jehovah
SATB&jr cor oct GALAXY 1.2063.1 $.30 (M2991)
SATB oct GALAXY 1.1243.1 $.30 (M2992)
SAB oct GALAXY 1.1379.1 $.30 (M2993)
TTBB oct GALAXY 1.1510.1 $.30 (M2994)
SSA oct GALAXY 1.1428.1 $.30 (M2995)

Hark! What Mean Those Holy Voices *Xmas
SATB oct FISCHER,C CM-7236 $.25 (M2996)

Hast Thou Not Known? *Bibl
4pt mix cor,acap oct SCHIRM.G 8438 $.30 (M2997)

He Is Risen *Easter
2pt jr cor&sr cor oct SCHIRM.G 9435 $.25 (M2998)

I Say To All Men Far And Near *Easter/Lent
SATB oct FISCHER,C CM-7216 $.25 (M2999)

I Will Lift Up Mine Eyes (Psalm 121) Bibl
4pt mix cor,org oct SCHIRM.G 10360 $.25 (M3000)

In Praise Of God
SATB FISCHER,C O-4590 $1.50 (M3001)

Jesus Makes My Heart Rejoice
2pt jr cor FISCHER,C CM 7357 $.25 (M3002)

Joyful Psalmody
SA/SATB oct SACRED S-102 $.40 (M3003)

Judge Me, O God *Lent,Bibl
8pt mix cor,S solo,acap oct SCHIRM.G 8364 $.30 (M3004)

Junior Chorister, The, Vol. 2 *CCU
SA FLAMMER GE5020 $1.00 (M3005)

MUELLER, CARL F. (cont'd.)

Laudamus Te
SAB,org oct SCHIRM.G 10691 $.25 (M3006)
"We Praise Thee" [Eng] 4pt wom cor,acap oct SCHIRM.G 9355 $.35 (M3007)
"We Praise Thee" [Eng] 4pt mix cor oct SCHIRM.G 9233 $.25 (M3008)
"We Praise Thee" [Eng] 8pt mix cor,acap oct SCHIRM.G 8333 $.30 (M3009)
"We Praise Thee" [Eng] 4pt men cor,acap oct SCHIRM.G 8514 $.25 (M3010)
"We Praise Thee" [Eng] jr cor&sr cor,org oct SCHIRM.G 10458 $.25 (M3011)

Let Not Your Heart Be Troubled
SATB oct FISCHER,C CM-6521 $.25 (M3012)

Let This Mind Be In You
SATB oct FISCHER,C CM-6713 $.25 (M3013)

Lo, God Is Here!
4pt mix cor oct SCHIRM.G 8132 $.30 (M3014)
8pt mix cor,acap oct SCHIRM.G 7627 $.30 (M3015)
4pt men cor,acap oct SCHIRM.G 7864 $.25 (M3016)

Lo The Earth Is Risen Again *Easter/Lent
3pt jr cor/SSA (med easy) FISCHER,C CM 7198 $.25 (M3017)
SATB oct FISCHER,C CM-7141 $.25 (M3018)
3pt jr cor/SAB (med easy) FISCHER,C CM 7197 $.25 (M3019)

Lord Bless You And Keep You, The *Bene/Bibl
3pt wom cor oct SCHIRM.G 9821 $.25 (M3020)
4pt mix cor,opt T solo,acap oct SCHIRM.G 8069 $.25 (M3021)

Lord, Thou Has Been Our Dwelling Place *Bibl
4pt mix cor,org/pno oct SCHIRM.G 10563 $.30 (M3022)
4pt mix cor,acap oct SCHIRM.G 8172 $.30 (M3023)

Lord's My Shepherd (from Crimond) Bibl
SAB oct FISCHER,C CM-7719 $.25 (M3024)
SA oct FISCHER,C CM-6673 $.25 (M3025)

Lord's My Shepherd, The (Psalm 23) Bibl
2pt jr cor FISCHER,C CM 6673 $.25 (M3026)
4pt jr cor/SATB (easy) FISCHER,C CM 6616 $.25 (M3027)
SATB,pno/org oct FISCHER,C CM-6616 $.25 (M3028)

Lord's Prayer, The *Bibl
4pt mix cor oct SCHIRM.G 10528 $.20 (M3029)

Love Came Down At Christmas
SA/TB FLAMMER E5109 $.30 (M3030)

Magnify The Lord With Me
SAB oct FISCHER,C CM-6964 $.25 (M3031)
SAB oct FISCHER,C CM-6684 $.25 (M3032)

My Music Is A Prayer *prayer
2pt jr cor/SA FISCHER,C CM 7319 $.25 (M3033)
SATB oct FISCHER,C CM-7320 $.25 (M3034)

Now Thank We All Our God
jr cor&sr cor,org/pno oct SCHIRM.G 10473 $.25 (M3035)
8pt mix cor,acap oct SCHIRM.G 7745 $.30 (M3036)
4pt wom cor,S solo,acap oct SCHIRM.G 9373 $.30 (M3037)
3pt wom cor,S solo oct SCHIRM.G 9302 $.25 (M3038)
3pt mix cor oct SCHIRM.G 10690 $.35 (M3039)

O Come Let Us Sing
jr cor&sr cor (med) FISCHER,C CM 6640 $.25 (M3040)

O God, Our Help In Ages Past
SATB FLAMMER A 5191 $.30 (M3041)
SSAATTBB FLAMMER A 5444 $.30 (M3042)
TTBB FLAMMER C5061 $.30 (M3043)

O Sing Unto The Lord
3pt jr cor/SAB (med easy) FISCHER,C CM 6961 $.25 (M3044)

Once To Every Man And Nation
4pt mix cor,org oct SCHIRM.G 11618 $.30 (M3045)

One Hundredth Psalm, The (Psalm 100)
SATB FLAMMER A 5042 $.30 (M3046)
SAB FLAMMER D5005 $.30 (M3047)
SA/TB FLAMMER E5016 $.25 (M3048)

Over Bethlehem's Town *Xmas
SATB FLAMMER A 5355 $.25 (M3049)

Praise To The Living God
SATB,org oct SCHIRM.G 10409 $.25 (M3050)

Praise To The Lord The Almighty
2pt jr cor FISCHER,C CM 6327 $.20 (M3051)

Praise Ye The Lord, The Almighty
SATB oct FISCHER,C CM-6765 $.25 (M3052)

Prayer Of St. Francis *prayer
SATB oct FISCHER,C CM-7062 $.30 (M3053)

Psalm 23 *see Lord's My Shepherd, The

Psalm 100 *see One Hundredth Psalm, The

Psalm 121 *see I Will Lift Up Mine Eyes

Reading With Responses *CCU,cor-resp
SATB FISCHER,C O-4639 $1.25 (M3054)

Responses *CCU,cor-resp
SATB HANSEN-US E9935 $.40 (M3055)

Ring, O Ring Ye Christmas Bells *Xmas
4pt jr cor/SATB (med) FISCHER,C CM 7637 $.30 (M3056)

Saviour, Blessed Saviour
3pt jr cor/SAB (med easy) FISCHER,C CM 7088 $.25 (M3057)

Search Me, O God *Bibl
4pt mix cor,acap oct SCHIRM.G 7933 $.25 (M3058)

MUELLER, CARL F. (cont'd.)

Show Me Thy Ways
SA oct FISCHER,C CM-6686 $.25 (M3059)
SAB oct FISCHER,C CM-6963 $.25 (M3060)

Sing And Worship, Vol. 1 *CCU
2pt jr cor/SA,pno/org FISCHER,C O 4194 $1.00 (M3061)

Sing And Worship, Vol. 2 *CCU
2pt jr cor/SA,pno/org FISCHER,C O 4182 $1.00 (M3062)

Sing O Heavens
SAB oct FISCHER,C CM-7768 $.30 (M3063)

Singing With Grace In Your Heart *anthem
SATB oct FISCHER,C CM-6710 $.30 (M3064)

Snow Lay All Around, The *Xmas
3pt jr cor/SAB (med easy) FISCHER,C CM 7283 $.25 (M3065)

Softly The Night Is Sleeping *Xmas
SATB oct FISCHER,C CM-7315 $.30 (M3066)

Song Of Bethlehem *Xmas
SATB oct FISCHER,C CM-7235 $.30 (M3067)

Surely The Lord Is In This Place *anthem
3pt jr cor/SAB (med easy) FISCHER,C CM 7636 $.25 (M3068)
SATB oct FISCHER,C CM-6697 $.30 (M3069)

That They All May Be One *Bibl
4pt mix cor,org oct SCHIRM.G 11594 $.30 (M3070)
3pt mix cor,org oct SCHIRM.G 11656 $.30 (M3071)

Think On These Things *anthem
SATB oct FISCHER,C CM-6711 $.30 (M3072)

Thou Art The Way *Easter
SATB oct GALAXY 1.1405.1 $.30 (M3073)
SSAATTBB oct GALAXY 1.1164.1 $.30 (M3074)

Three Part Anthem Book *CC12U,Adv/Xmas/Commun/Easter/Fest/Gen/Lent/Palm
jr cor/SABar FISCHER,C O 3684 $1.00 (M3075)

Today The Prince Of Peace Is Born *Xmas
3pt jr cor/SAB (med easy) FISCHER,C CM 7306 $.25 (M3076)
SATB oct FISCHER,C CM-7133 $.25 (M3077)

Triumph-Song, The
4pt mix cor oct SCHIRM.G 8324 $.25 (M3078)

Truly My Soul Waiteth Upon The Lord
3pt jr cor/SAB (easy) FISCHER,C CM 6962 $.25 (M3079)

Twelve Choral Responses *CC12U,cor-resp
SATB HANSEN-US E9303 $.40 (M3080)

Two-Part Anthem Book *CCU,anthem
jr cor FISCHER,C O 3425 $1.25 (M3081)

Wake, Awake For Night Is Flying *Adv
jr cor&sr cor (easy) FISCHER,C CM 7640 $.30 (M3082)

Walk In The Light *anthem
SATB oct FISCHER,C CM-7376 $.25 (M3083)

We All Believe In One True God *anthem
SATB oct FISCHER,C CM-6293 $.25 (M3084)

We Come Unto Our Fathers' God *anthem
SATB oct FISCHER,C CM-7084 $.25 (M3085)
SATB,acap oct FISCHER,C CM-6238 $.25 (M3086)

We Praise Thee *see Laudamus Te

We Will Walk In The Name Of The Lord *anthem
SATB oct FISCHER,C CM-6644 $.30 (M3087)

When Thou Prayest *anthem
SATB oct FISCHER,C CM-6523 $.25 (M3088)
SSA oct FISCHER,C CM-7664 $.25 (M3089)

When Wilt Thou Save The People?
3pt mix cor oct SCHIRM.G 9375 $.25 (M3090)

Whither Shall I Go From Thy Spirit *anthem
SATB oct FISCHER,C CM-6272 $.25 (M3091)
SA oct FISCHER,C CM-6957 $.25 (M3092)

Who Shall Ascend Into The Hill Of The Lord *anthem
SA oct FISCHER,C CM-6688 $.25 (M3093)

Who Shall Ascend Into The Hills Of The Lord?
3pt jr cor/SAB (easy) FISCHER,C CM 6959 $.25 (M3094)

Wise May Bring Their Learning, The
2pt jr cor FISCHER,C CM 6302 $.25 (M3095)

Worship Christ, The Newborn King *Xmas
SATB oct FISCHER,C CM-7496 $.25 (M3096)

MUELLER, LUISE
Come, Holy Spirit
SATB (easy) ABINGDON APM-196 $.25 (M3097)

Depth Of Mercy *Commun
SATB (med) ABINGDON APM-398 $.30 (M3098)

O Praise The Lord
SATB (med) ABINGDON APM-223 $.40 (M3099)

MUHLENBERG
Sing The Glad Tidings *Xmas
(Whitney) SATB oct BOURNE 797 $.25 (M3100)

MUL, JAN (1911-)
Stabat Mater
[Lat] mix cor,fl,ob,clar,bsn,trp,horn, strings,perc,timp,harp min sc DONEMUS s.p. (M3101)

Te Deum Laudamus *Te Deum
[Lat] mix cor,2fl,2ob,2clar,2bsn,2trp, 3horn,3trom,strings,timp min sc DONEMUS s.p., cor pts BANK, voc sc DONEMUS s.p. (M3102)

MULDER, ERNEST W. (1898-1959)
Ars Contrapunctica
see Mulder, Ernest W., De Profundis

De Profundis (Psalm 130) mot/Psalm
[Dut] mix cor,SATB soli,org cor pts DONEMUS
s.p. contains also: Ars Contrapunctica
(M3103)

Pro Defunctis *Mass/Req
[Lat] mix cor&jr cor,SATB soli,3fl,2ob,
2clar,2bsn,2trp,4horn,3trom,strings,timp
sc DONEMUS s.p. (M3104)

Psalm 130 *see De Profundis

Stabat Mater Dolorosa
[Lat] mix cor,SATBar soli,2fl,2ob,2clar,
2bsn,2trp,3horn,3trom,strings,timp
DONEMUS sc s.p., cor pts s.p. (M3105)

MULDER, HERMAN (1894-)
Psalm 47
[Dut] mix cor,pno sc DONEMUS s.p. (M3106)

MULLER, A.M.
Ave Maria
see Muller, A.M., Ave Maria, Dich Lobt
Musica

Ave Maria, Dich Lobt Musica
mix cor,acap ERDMANN 518 s.p. contains
also: Ave Maria (M3107)

Es Bluht Der Blume Eine
see Zwei Marienlieder

Meerstern Ich Dich Grusse
see Zwei Marienlieder

Sagt An, Wer Ist Doch Diese
see Zwei Marienlieder

Terra Tremuit *mot
4-7pt&mix cor ERDMANN 538 s.p. (M3108)

Wunderschone Prachtige
see Zwei Marienlieder

Zwei Marienlieder
mix cor,acap ERDMANN 542 s.p.
contains: Es Bluht Der Blume Eine;
Wunderschone Prachtige (M3109)

Zwei Marienlieder
mix cor,acap ERDMANN 502 s.p.
contains: Meerstern Ich Dich Grusse; Sagt
An, Wer Ist Doch Diese (M3110)

MULLER, J.
Crux Ave
see PER LA SETTIMANA SANTA

Pange Lingua
see SEI MOTTETTI EUCARISTICI

Tantum Ergo
see SEI MOTTETTI EUCARISTICI

Tota Pulchra
see CINQUE MOTECTA IN HON. B.V.M.

Vexilla Regis
see IN HEBDOMADA SANCTA

MULLER, J.I.
Warum Hast Du Mich Geschlagen, Gott?
(Laubscher, K.A.) [Ger] wom cor,acap (med
easy) HUG s.p. (M3111)

MULLER, MANFRED (1926-)
Paul-Gerhardt-Kantate *cant
SATB,SATB soli,cont,org,fl,ob,bsn,2vln,vla,
vcl,bvl HANSSLER 10.048 sc s.p., cor pts
s.p., ipa (M3112)

Tut Mir Auf Die Schone Pforte *cant
SATB,SATB soli,2fl,2ob,2bsn,3trp,2vln,vla,
vcl,bvl,timp sc HANSSLER 10.065 rental
(M3113)

MULLER, P.
O Domine Deus Speravi In Te
[Lat] wom cor,acap (med easy) HUG s.p.
(M3114)

MULLER, PAUL (1898-)
Ich Wollt, Dass Ich Daheime War
[Ger] mix cor,acap (med diff) HUG s.p.
(M3115)

Lobe Den Herren (Psalm 57)
[Ger] mix cor,S/T solo,orch HUG s.p., ipr
(M3116)

Loblied Am Morgen (from Lob Des Jahres)
[Ger] mix cor,acap (med easy) HUG s.p.
(M3117)

Psalm 42 *see Wie Der Hirsch Schreit Nach
Frischem Wasser

Psalm 57 *see Lobe Den Herren

Wer Nur Den Lieben Gott Lasst Walten
see Zwei Chorale

Wie Der Hirsch Schreit Nach Frischem Wasser
(Psalm 42)
[Ger] wom cor,org HUG s.p. (M3118)

Wie Schon Leucht Uns Der Morgenstern
see Zwei Chorale

Zwei Chorale *chorale
[Ger] wom cor,opt org HUG s.p.
contains: Wer Nur Den Lieben Gott Lasst
Walten; Wie Schon Leucht Uns Der
Morgenstern (M3119)

Zwei Gesange Von Gott *CC2U
[Ger] HUG mix cor,2fl,2ob,2clar,2bsn,2horn,
2trp,trom,strings,timp s.p.; wom cor,opt
org s.p. (M3120)

MULLER, PETER (1791-1877)
O Salutaris Hostia
"O Saving Victim" SATB,org SCHIRM.EC 2291
$.18 (M3121)

O Saving Victim *see O Salutaris Hostia

MULLER, DON
Singing Joy
SSA HANSEN-US C625 $.75 (M3122)

MULLER, GIULIO
Benedic Anima Mea
see Sei Mottetti Eucaristici

Benedicam Domino
see Sei Mottetti Eucaristici

Cibavit Eos
see Sei Mottetti Eucaristici

Dixit *Greg
[Lat] 1-2pt,org ZANIBON 2694 s.p. (M3123)

Duo Motecta *Op.50, Commun,mot
[Lat] 2 eq voices,org ZANIBON 2687 s.p.
contains: O Salutaris; Tantum Ergo
(M3124)

In Te Speravi
see Sei Mottetti Eucaristici

Miserere *Op.172, Holywk
[Lat] 2 eq voices,org ZANIBON 2616 s.p.
(M3125)

O Cor Amore Saucium
see Sei Mottetti Eucaristici

O Salutaris
see Duo Motecta

Sei Mottetti Eucaristici *Op.170, Commun,mot
[Lat] 2 eq voices,org ZANIBON 2624 s.p.
contains: Benedic Anima Mea; Benedicam
Domino; Cibavit Eos; In Te Speravi; O
Cor Amore Saucium; Te Ergo Quaesumus
(M3126)

Tantum Ergo
see Duo Motecta

Te Ergo Quaesumus
see Sei Mottetti Eucaristici

MULLER, H.
Brotherhood Of Praise, The
SATB oct PRESSER MC539 $.40 (M3127)

By The Waters Of Babylon
SATB oct PRESSER MC418 $.40 (M3128)

Hymn Of Praise
SATB oct PRESSER MC538 $.35 (M3129)

MULLER-OLM, HORST
Heilger Geist, Du Troster Mein
SA/SAT/SAB,treb inst HANSSLER 14.101 s.p.
contains also: Herbert, Peter, Komm, O
Komm, Du Geist Des Lebens (SAT/SAB,treb
inst) (M3130)

MULLER-OTT, G.
Befiehl Du Deine Wege *cant
SATB,org,brass HANSSLER 10.233 sc s.p., cor
pts s.p. (M3131)

MULLER VON KULM, WALTER (1899-)
Bruder Kommt
[Ger] mix cor,acap (easy) HUG s.p. (M3132)

Das Lied Vom Kreuz
[Ger] men cor&jr cor/men cor&wom cor,winds
HUG s.p., ipr (M3133)

Heilig Wort
[Ger] mix cor,acap (easy) HUG s.p. (M3134)

Psalm 10
[Ger] men cor,winds HUG rental (M3135)

Vater Unser *ora
[Ger] mix cor,AB soli,org,2fl,2ob,2clar,
2bsn,2horn,2trp,trom,strings,timp HUG
rental, ipr (M3136)

MULLINS
Bold And Free
SATB oct WORD CS-2485 $.30 (M3137)

Reason To Be, A
(Shepard) SATB oct WORD CS-375 $.30 (M3138)

MULTER
Psalm 93
TTBB FLAMMER C5041 $.30 (M3139)

MULTI-USE ANTHEMS *CCU,anthem
treb cor/men cor/treb cor&men cor LORENZ
$1.50 (M3140)

MUMFORD
Prayer
(Fote) SATB oct KENDOR $.25 (M3141)

MUMMA, [GORDON] (1935-)
Lilies *Easter
unis oct LORENZ 8854 $.25 (M3142)

MUMMERS' CAROL *carol
see Two Christmas Carols
(Vaughan Williams) TTBB,acap (easy, contains
also: As Joseph Was A-Walking) OXFORD
41.901 $.30 see from Nine Carols (M3143)

MUMMERS, THE see Shaw, Martin

MUNDY
Latin Antiphons And Psalms *CCU,anti/Psalm,
Eng
[Lat] cor STAINER 3.8202.8 $12.00 (M3144)

MUNDY, JOHN (? -1630)
Sing Joyfully *Ded/Fest/Gen
SAATB,B solo (med) oct OXFORD 42.234 $.50,
ipr (M3145)

MUNDY, WILLIAM (ca. 1529-1591)
O Lord, Maker Of All Things *see Rerum,
Creator

O Lord, The Maker Of Al Thing *anthem
(Terry, R.R.) mix cor oct NOVELLO
52.0014.08 s.p. (M3146)

O Lord, The Maker Of All Things *Eve
SATB,acap (easy) oct OXFORD 43.250 $.30
(M3147)

MUNDY, WILLIAM (cont'd.)
Rerum, Creator
(McCarthy) "O Lord, Maker Of All Things"
SATB oct BOURNE 904 $.40 (M3148)

Rerum Creator Omnium *anthem
(Terry, R.R.) [Lat] mix cor oct NOVELLO
52.0014.08 s.p. (M3149)

MUNNINCKX
O Gentle Night
see SIX SEVENTEENTH CENTURY CAROLS FROM THE
NETHERLANDS

MUNSON
Christmas *Xmas
(Lowens) 4pt mix cor,acap oct SCHIRM.G
10325 $.20 (M3150)

MURPHY, J.A.
Behold A Great Priest *anthem
SATB/unis (easy) oct GIA G1284 $.30 (M3151)

Divine Praises, The *Gen,anthem
SSA&cong/TTB&cong (easy) oct GIA G1128 $.30
(M3152)

MURRAY
Four Short Introits *Introit
SATB THOMP.G G-580 s.p. (M3153)

Miracle, The *Xmas,ora
SATB,org,brass,perc,harp voc sc MCA (M3154)

Old Ark's A-Movering Along *spir
(Alexander) SATB oct BOOSEY 1733 $.40
(M3155)

Peace Comes To Me
SSA oct BOOSEY 1726 $.30 (M3156)
SATB oct BOOSEY 1725 $.30 (M3157)

Waken Happy People *Gen
SA SCHMITT 248 $.35 (M3158)

Walk With Me *Gen
unis,fl SCHMITT 251 $.35 (M3159)

MURRAY, ALAN
Shepherd Of Souls
SATB PROWSE s.p. (M3160)

MURRAY, BAIN
Sleep Now On Thy Natal Day *see Corwin

Winds Of Truth
SATB,acap oct LAWSON 51290 $.25 (M3161)

MURRAY, LYN (1909-)
Do Lord
SATB oct STAFF 271 $.30 (M3162)
SA/TB oct STAFF 289 $.30 (M3163)
SSA oct STAFF 283 $.30 (M3164)
TTBB oct STAFF 293 $.30 (M3165)
SAB oct STAFF 296 $.30 (M3166)

Jacob's Ladder
SAB oct STAFF 297 $.25 (M3167)
SATB oct STAFF 269 $.25 (M3168)
SSA oct STAFF 284 $.25 (M3169)
SA/TB oct STAFF 290 $.30 (M3170)
TTBB oct STAFF 294 $.25 (M3171)

Let His Name Be Sung *Fest
mix cor&jr cor/treb cor,org/pno oct WORD
CS-402 $.40 (M3172)

That Old Time Religion
SA/TB oct STAFF 291 $.25 (M3173)
SATB oct STAFF 270 $.25 (M3174)
SAB oct STAFF 298 $.30 (M3175)
SSA oct STAFF 285 $.25 (M3176)

MURRILL, HERBERT
Magnificat And Nunc Dimittis *Magnif/Nunc
SATB (med easy) oct OXFORD 42.190 $.50
(M3177)

MURSCHHAUSER, FRANZ XAVER ANTON (1663-1738)
Lasst Uns Das Kindlein Wiegen
see Werner, Gregor Joseph, Der Tag, Der Ist
So Freudenreich

MURTON, T.
Thanks Be To God
oct HART (M3178)

MUSETTE *Xmas,carol,18th cent
(Geveart, F.-A.) [Fr] 4pt mix cor,acap (med
easy) cor pts LEMOINE s.p. see from
Collection De Choeurs, septieme Fascicule
(M3179)

MUSGRAVE, THEA (1928-)
Carol For The Watchers
see Two Christmas Carols In Traditional
Style

Make Me Merry For Him That Is Come *Xmas,
15th cent
[Eng/Lat] SSSAAA&jr cor,SS soli,opt org
CHESTER s.p. (M3180)

Memento Creatoris *anthem
"Remember Thy Creator" [Eng/Lat] SATB,ST
soli,org CHESTER s.p. (M3181)

Remember Thy Creator *see Memento Creatoris

Two Christmas Carols In Traditional Style
*Xmas,carol
SATB/SA,S solo,ob/clar/vln,strings voc sc
CHESTER s.p.
contains: Carol For The Watchers; Wise
Men's Carol (M3182)

Wise Men's Carol
see Two Christmas Carols In Traditional
Style

MUSIC FOR CHRISTMAS see Meyerowitz, Jan

MUSIC FOR COURSES BOOK 1 *CCU,Commun/Psalm
ROYAL s.p. (M3183)

MUSIC FOR COURSES BOOK 2 *CC28U,hymn
ROYAL s.p. (M3184)

MUSIC FOR COURSES BOOK 3 *CC29U,hymn
ROYAL s.p. (M3185)

MUSIC FOR EVENSONG, SET C *CCUL,Eve,hymn/Psalm
oct ROYAL 323 s.p.   (M3186)

MUSIC FOR EVENSONG, SET D *CCUL,Eve,hymn/Psalm
oct ROYAL 324 s.p.   (M3187)

MUSIC FOR EVENSONG, SET E *CCUL,Eve,hymn/Psalm
oct ROYAL 327 s.p.   (M3188)

MUSIC FOR EVENSONG SET F *CCUL,Eve,hymn/Psalm
oct ROYAL 338 s.p.   (M3189)

MUSIC FOR EVENSONG, SET G *CCUL,Eve,hymn/Psalm
oct ROYAL 336 s.p.   (M3190)

MUSIC FOR EVENSONG SET H *CCUL,Eve,hymn/Psalm
(Gelineau) oct ROYAL 337 s.p.   (M3191)

MUSIC FOR LAUDS FOR THE VIGIL OF EASTER *CCU,
Easter
(Diemente) SATB,org oct LAWSON 51522 $.40
                                           (M3192)

MUSIC FOR LAUDS FOR THE VIGIL OF EASTER see
Diemente, Edward

MUSIC FOR MEN'S CHORUS see Schubert, Franz
(Peter)

MUSIC FOR MEN'S CHORUS see Schubert, Franz
(Peter)

MUSIC FOR PALM SUNDAY *Lent/Palm,anthem
(Diemente, E.) SATB/SA (easy) oct GIA G1313
$.60
contains: Diemente, Edward, Hosanna To The
Son Of David; Schubert, Franz (Peter),
Children Of The Hebrews; The; Schubert,
Franz (Peter), When The Lord Entered;
Teschner, All Glory, Laud And Honor
                                           (M3193)

MUSIC FOR RECEPTION CEREMONIES see Elaine,
Sister M. (Gentemann)

MUSIC FOR THE CONTEMPORARY CHOIR, BOOK 1
*CC12L,Contemp
1-2pt (med easy) oct AUGSBURG 11-9288 $1.50
contains works by: Leaf, Robert; Anders,
Charles; Johnson, David N.; and others
                                           (M3194)

MUSIC FOR THE CONTEMPORARY CHOIR, BOOK 2
*CC12L,Adv/Xmas/Commun/Gen/Thanks,Contemp
1-2pt (med easy) oct AUGSBURG 11-9285 $1.50
contains works by: Pooler, Marie; Lovelace,
Austin; Nelson, Ronald; and others
                                           (M3195)

MUSIC FOR THE DEDICATION OF A SYNAGOGUE see
Gallichi, Volunio, Musique Pour
L'Inauguration D'une Synagogue

MUSIC FOR THE EUCHARISTIC PRAYER ACCLAMATIONS
see Hughes, S.M. Howard

MUSIC FOR THE EUCHARISTIC PRAYER ACCLAMATIONS-2
see Hughes, S.M. Howard

MUSIC FOR THE HOLY COMMUNION *CC22U,mot
ROYAL s.p.   (M3196)

MUSIC FOR THE HOLY COMMUNION *CCU,Commun,hymn
ROYAL s.p.   (M3197)

MUSIC FOR THE HOLY COMMUNION *see Coventry
Mass, The; Beck, John Ness, Short Communion
Service In D; Gibbs, Alan, Octave Communion
Service   (M3198)

MUSIC FOR THE HOLY COMMUNION see Beck, John
Ness

MUSIC FOR THE HOLY COMMUNION see Gibbs, Alan

MUSIC FOR THE LORD'S SUPPER see Dean, T.W.

MUSIC FOR THE ORDINARY OF THE MASS see Carroll,
J.R.

MUSIC FOR THE YOUNG CHURCH *CC10L
SATB voc sc WORD 37614 $1.95   (M3199)

MUSIC FOR WEDDING SERVICES see Carroll, J.R.

MUSIC FOR WEDDINGS see Dooner, A.

MUSIC FOR WOMEN'S CHORUS see Schubert, Franz
(Peter)

MUSIC FOR YOUNG VOICES AND INSTRUMENTS see
Smart, David

MUSIC FROM SEMELE see Handel, George Frideric

MUSIC OF BETHLEHEM, THE see Holton

MUSIC OF CHRISTMAS, THE *sac/sec,CC8L,Xmas
(Kirk) SATB PRO ART 85 $.85   (M3200)

MUSIC OF CHRISTMAS, THE see Wilson, Ira B.

MUSIC OF CHRISTMAS, THE see Wilson, Irene

MUSIC OF EARLY LUTHERANISM, THE
(Albrecht, H.) cor CONCORDIA
contains & see also: Dietrich, Sixtus,
Novum Ac Insigne Opus Musicum 36
Antiphonarum, 1541; Resinarius,
Balthasar, Responsoriorum Numero
Octoginta, Band I; Resinarius, Balthasar,
Responsoriorum Numero Octoginta, Band II;
Rhaw, Georg, Postremum Vespertini Officii
Opus; Rhaw, Georg, Symphoniae Jucundae,
1538; Rhaw, Georg, Vesperarum Precum
Officia, 1540   (M3201)

MUSIC OF THE FLORENTINE RENAISSANCE VOL. I see
Pisano, Bernardo

MUSIC OF THE FLORENTINE RENAISSANCE VOL. II
*CCU
(D'Accone, Frank) cor AM.INST.MUS. $22.00
contains works by: Corpini, Alessandro;
Organi, Bartolomeo Degli; Seragli,
Giovanni; and others   (M3202)

MUSIC OF THE FLORENTINE RENAISSANCE VOL. V
*CCU,mot
(D'accone, Frank) cor AM.INST.MUS.   (M3203)

MUSIC OF THE FLORENTINE RENAISSANCE VOL. VI
*CCU,Mass/Psalm
(D'Accone, Frank) cor AM.INST.MUS. $46.00
                                           (M3204)

MUSIC, SPREAD THY VOICE AROUND see Handel,
George Frideric

MUSICA BRITANNICA VOL. 4: SET 1 *Xmas,carol,
Mediev
mix cor STAINER MB4-1 s.p.
contains: Alma Redemptoris Mater; Hail
Mary, Full Of Grace, "Nowell, Nowell"; In
Bethlem   (M3205)

MUSICA BRITANNICA VOL. 4: SET 2 *Xmas,carol,
Mediev
mix cor STAINER MB4-2 s.p.
contains: Agincourt Song, The; To Many A
Well   (M3206)

MUSICA BRITANNICA VOL. 4: SET 5 *Xmas,carol,
Mediev
mix cor STAINER MB4:5 s.p.
contains: Make We Joy; Nowell, Nowell
                                           (M3207)

MUSICA BRITANNICA VOL. 4: SET 7 *Xmas,carol,
Mediev
mix cor STAINER MB4-7 s.p.
contains: Nova, Nova; Nowell Sing We; What
Tidings Bringest Thou?   (M3208)

MUSICA BRITANNICA VOL. 4: SET 8 *Xmas,carol,
Mediev
mix cor STAINER MB4-8 s.p.
contains: Nowell, Nowell; Nowell Sing We; Saint Thomas
Honour We; Tidings True   (M3209)

MUSICA DEO SACRA 1 see Tomkins, Thomas

MUSICA DEO SACRA 2 see Tomkins, Thomas

MUSICA DIVINAS LAUDES see Hindemith, Paul

MUSICA, DONUM DEI OPTIMI see Lassus, Roland de
(Orlandus)

MUSICA ECCLESIAE *CCU
(Lundquist, M.) SATB oct PRESSER $1.00
                                           (M3210)

MUSICA ECCLESIASTICA *CCU,18th cent
(Dite, Prof. Louis) WEINBERGER s.p.   (M3211)

MUSICA, HIMMLISCH GUT see Werner, Hans

MUSICA RELIGIOSA I, VOL. 14-2 see Monteverdi,
Claudio

MUSICA RELIGIOSA II, VOL. 15-1 see Monteverdi,
Claudio

MUSICA RELIGIOSA II, VOL. 15-2 see Monteverdi,
Claudio

MUSICA RELIGIOSA II, VOL. 15-3 see Monteverdi,
Claudio

MUSICA RELIGIOSA III, VOL. 16-1 see Monteverdi,
Claudio

MUSICA RELIGIOSA III, VOL. 16-2 see Monteverdi,
Claudio

MUSICA RESERVATA, BAND 1 *Gen,16-17th cent
(Muller-Blattau, Joseph) [Ger] BAREN. BA 2641
$2.75
contains: Lassus, Roland de (Orlandus), In
Hora Ultima (SSATTB,acap); Lassus, Roland
de (Orlandus), In Me Transierunt (SATTB,
acap); Senfl, Ludwig, Non Moriar (SATB,
acap); Stobaeus, Johann, Laudent Deum
(SATB,acap)   (M3212)

MUSICA RESERVATA, BAND 2 *Gen,16th cent/17th
cent
(Muller-Blattau, Joseph) [Lat] (med diff)
BAREN. BA 2642 $2.75
contains: Des Prez, Josquin, Ave Maria
(SATB,acap); Lassus, Roland de
(Orlandus), Musica, Donum Dei Optimi
(SSATBB,acap); Senfl, Ludwig, O Herre
Gott, Begnade Mich (SATB,acap)   (M3213)

MUSICA SPEI see Kelterborn, Rudolf

MUSICA VOCALE ESEQUITA IN OCCASIONE
DELL'APERTURA DELLA NUOVO SCUOLA DI SIENA,
1786 see Gallichi, Volunio

MUSICESCU, GAVRIIL (1847-1903)
Cherubic Hymn *hymn
(Ehret) SSA oct BOOSEY 5026 $.30   (M3214)

MUSICKS EMPIRE see Pfautsch, Lloyd

MUSIK KRING JULEVANGELIST see Norman, Rudolf

MUSIK UBER EINEN CHORAL see Schafer, Karl

MUSIKALISCHE EXEQUIEN-TEIL 1 see Schutz,
Heinrich

MUSIKALISCHE EXEQUIEN-TEIL 2: HERR, WENN ICH
NUR DICH LIEBE see Schutz, Heinrich

MUSIKALISCHE EXEQUIEN-TEIL 3 see Schutz,
Heinrich

MUSIKALISCHE UBUNG, TEIL 1 see Burkhard Willy

MUSIKALISCHE UBUNG, TEIL 2 see Burkhard Willy

MUSIKALISCHE UBUNG, TEIL 3 see Burkhard Willy

MUSIKALISCHE UBUNG UBER DEN ZWOLFSTEN PSALM see
Burkhard Willy

MUSIKEN KLANG, LIEBLICHER G'SANG see Calvisius,
Sethus

MUSIQUE POUR L'INAUGURATION D'UNE SYNAGOGUE see
Gallichi, Volunio

MUSIQUE SACREE *see Boellmann, Leon, Tantum
Ergo (from Lyra Sacra); Busser, [Henri-
Paul], Laudate Dominum; Gounod, Charles
Francois, Laudate Dominum; Gounod, Charles
Francois, Sanctus (from Messe De Sainte-
Cecile)   (M3215)

MUSIQUE SACREE see Boellmann, Leon

MUSIQUE SACREE see Busser, [Henri-Paul]

MUSIQUE SACREE see Gounod, Charles Francois

MUSS NICHT DER MENSCH AUF DIESER ERDEN see
Bruhns, Nicholaus

MUSSORGSKY, MODEST (1839-1881)
Gates Of Jerusalem, The *Easter
SATB oct LORENZ B190 $.30   (M3216)

Gloire A Dieu (from Boris Godounov)
(Brun, L'abbe F.) [Fr] 4pt mix cor,org oct
DURAND s.p.   (M3217)

Joshua
mix cor,MezB soli,orch BOOSEY voc sc $1.50,
sc rental, ipr   (M3218)

Josua
SAATTB,2fl,2ob,2clar,2bsn,4horn,2trp,3trom,
strings,perc,timp BREITKOPF-W rental
                                           (M3219)

Prayer From "Boris Godunov" (from Boris
Godunov)
(Roepper) SSA BOSTON 1120 $.30   (M3220)

MUST JESUS BEAR ANOTHER CROSS? see O'Hara,
Geoffrey

MUST JESUS BEAR THE CROSS ALONE? see Lynn,
George

MUTIMA see Deutsch, Herbert

MUTTER
Psalm 121
SATB FLAMMER A 5277 $.30   (M3221)

MUTTER see Kopelent, Marek

MUTTER DER VIEL SCHONEN MINNE see Demerath, F.

MUTTER MARIA see Raphael, Gunther

MUTTERSPRACHE see Jones, Elsa Loaker

MUUS
Make A Joyful Noise (Psalm 100) Gen
SATB SCHMITT 7036 $.30   (M3222)

Psalm 100 *see Make A Joyful Noise

MUZICHESKI
Cherubim Song
(Tkach) SATB KJOS 6500 $.30   (M3223)

MY BELOVED SPAKE see Purcell, Henry

MY BELOVED SPAKE UNTO ME see Tomkins, Thomas

MY BLOOD, SO RED see Davies, Henry Walford

MY BREATH IS CORRUPT see Reger, Max, Mein Odem
Ist Schwach

MY CHILD see Bishop, Janice G.

MY CHOSEN KING see Bach, Johann Sebastian

MY CHRISTMAS PRAYER see Carleton

MY CHURCH IS A HOLY PLACE see Dunlap, Fern

MY CONSTANT JOY see Caldwell

MY COUNTRY 'TIS OF THEE see Johnson, Elwood

MY CUP OF JOY see Lehenbauer, Ruth B.

MY DANCING DAY *Eng
(Shaw; Parker) SATB,acap oct LAWSON 731 $.35
                                           (M3224)

MY DAYS ARE GONE LIKE A SHADOW see Blow, John

MY DELIGHT IS IN THE LORD see Powell

MY DESIRE
see Great Choral Series
SATB/TTBB BIG3 $.25   (M3225)

MY ETERNAL KING see Marshall

MY EYES FOR BEAUTY PINE see Howells, Herbert
Norman

MY EYES GROW MISTY FROM WEEPING see Ingegneri,
Marco Antonio, Caligaverunt Oculi Mei

MY FAINTING SOUL, AWAKEN NOW see Bach, Johann
Sebastian, Ermuntre Dich, Mein Schwacher
Geist

MY FAITH see Leaf, Robert

MY FAITH CLINGS TO HIM *Gen/Lent
(Ferguson) SATB,org/fl oct LAWSON 51259 $.25
                                           (M3226)

MY FAITH HATH FOUND A RESTING PLACE see
Kirkpatrick

MY FAITH IS AN OAKEN STAFF
(Coggin) SATB oct PRO ART 2441 $.25   (M3227)
(Vigeland, Hans) unis oct GRAY GCMR 2698 $.30
                                           (M3228)

MY FAITH IS STILL SECURE see Bach, Johann
Sebastian

MY FAITH, IT IS AN OAKEN STAFF see Lynn, George

MY FAITH LOOKS UP TO THEE see Conley, D.

MY FAITH LOOKS UP TO THEE see Mason

MY FAITH LOOKS UP TO THEE see Price, R.W.

MY FAITH LOOKS UP TO THEE see Ringwald, [Roy]

MY FAITH LOOKS UP TO THEE see Schnecker, P.

MY FATHER WALKS BESIDE ME see Emig, Lois

MY FATHER'S CARE *Norw
unis oct LORENZ 8862 $.25   (M3229)

MY FATHER'S HOUSE see Lewis

MY FLESH IS MEAT see Gabrieli, Andrea, Caro Mea

MY FRIEND OF CALVARY see Faure

MY GOD, ACCEPT MY HEART see Sheppard

MY GOD, ACCEPT MY HEART see Vick, Beryl, Jr.

MY GOD, ACCEPT MY HEART THIS DAY see Gibbons,
Orlando

MY GOD, ACCEPT MY HEART TODAY see Roff, Joseph

MY GOD AND I
(Martin) SATB oct SACRED S-109 $.45   (M3230)

MY GOD, AND IS THY TABLE SPREAD see Thiman,
Eric Harding

MY GOD, AND IS THY TABLE SPREAD see Van Der
Hoeck

MY GOD AND KING see Candlyn

MY GOD AND KING see Holman, Derek

MY GOD, HOW WONDERFUL *anthem,Scot
(Overby, Oscar) SATB,S solo (easy) oct
AUGSBURG 1097 $.25   (M3231)

MY GOD, HOW WONDERFUL THOU ART *Gen
(Riedel) SATB (Scottish Psalter) SCHMITT 1799
$.22   (M3232)

MY GOD, HOW WONDERFUL THOU ART see
Christiansen, F. Melius

MY GOD I THANK THEE see Ford

MY GOD, I THANK THEE see Powell, Robert J.

MY GOD, I THANK THEE see Roff, Joseph

MY GOD IS A ROCK *spir
(Shaw; Parker) mix cor,Bar solo,acap oct
LAWSON 51107 $.45   (M3233)

MY GOD IS REAL *anthem
SATB/SAB/SA/TB BIG3 $.25   (M3234)

MY GOD IS SO HIGH see McLin

MY GOD, MY FATHER see Abel, J.T.

MY GOD, MY GOD see Peloquin, C. Alexander

MY GOD, MY GOD, LOOK UPON ME see Blow

MY GOD, MY GOD, LOOK UPON ME see Blow, John

MY GOD, MY GOD, WHY HAST THOU FORSAKEN ME? see
Near, Gerald

MY GOD, MY GOD, WHY HAST THOU FORSAKEN ME? see
Swenson

MY GOD, MY KING, THY PRAISE I SING see Young,
Gordon

MY GOD SHALL RAISE ME UP see Noble, Harold

MY GOD, WHEREFORE HAST THOU FORSAKEN ME? see
Mendelssohn-Bartholdy, Felix, Mein Gott,
Warum Hast Du Mich

MY GOD'S A MIGHTY MAKER see Whitman

MY GRACE IS SUFFICIENT FOR YOU see Roe, Gloria
[Ann]

MY GRACIOUS LORD AND MASTER see Schubert, Franz
(Peter), Mein Heiland, Herr Und Meister

MY GRACIOUS LORD, I OWN THY RIGHT see Clements,
Fred

MY HEAR IS INDITING see Handel, George Frideric

MY HEART EVER FAITHFUL see Bach, Johann
Sebastian

MY HEART FOR JOY IS BOUNDING see Hassler, Hans
Leo

MY HEART IS A MANGER see Hovdesven, E.A.

MY HEART IS FULL TODAY see Proulx, Richard

MY HEART IS INDITING see Handel, George
Frideric

MY HEART IS LONGING TO PRAISE MY SAVIOR
*anthem/folk,Norw
(Sateren, Leland) SATB (easy) oct AUGSBURG
1211 $.20   (M3235)

MY HEART IS READY see Warren, Elinor Remick

MY HEART IS READY, O GOD see Lekberg, Sven

MY HEART IS STEADFAST, O GOD see Butler, Eugene

MY HEART IT SEEMED, WAS DYING see Palestrina,
Giovanni

MY HEART LOOKS IN FAITH *Chin
2pt oct LORENZ 5730 $.25   (M3236)

MY HEART REJOICETH IN THE LORD see Roff, Joseph

MY HEART SINGS TO THEE see Harrer, Mein Herz
Ist Bereit

MY HEART SINGS WITH JOY see Harrer

MY HEART THIS NIGHT REJOICES see Track, Gerhard

MY HEARTS TREASURE see Buxtehude, Dietrich

MY HELP COMES FROM THE LORD see Hovhaness, Alan

MY HELP COMETH FROM THE LORD see Royse

MY HOPE IS BUILT see Mc Loughlin

MY HOPE IS BUILT ON NOTHING LESS see Lunde

MY HOUSE SHALL BE CALLED OF ALL NATIONS see
Titcomb

MY JESUS see Bach

MY JESUS AS THOU WILT! see Larson

MY JESUS, AS THOU WILT see Weber, von

MY JESUS I LOVE THEE
(Carlton, Young) SATB (easy) ALLANS 442 s.p.
(M3237)

MY JESUS, I LOVE THEE see Benner

MY JESUS, I LOVE THEE see Gordon

MY JESUS, I LOVE THEE see Gordon, A.

MY JESUS, I LOVE THEE see Young, Carlton R.

MY JESUS IS MY LASTING JOY see Buxtehude,
Dietrich

MY JESUS LORD, I THEE ADORE see Dykes, John
Bacchus

MY JESUS WHO LOVES ME see Janes, Oliver

MY JOURNEY TO THE SKY
SATB BIG3 $.25   (M3238)

MY JOY, MY LIFE, MY CROWN! see Montgomery,
Bruce

MY LIFE IS LIKE A WEAVING
SSA BIG3 $.25   (M3239)

MY LIPS SHALL SPEAK OF THY PRAISE see Greene,
Maurice

MY LITTLE LAMB see Lewis, John Leo

MY LORD CALLS OUT TO ME see Hutson, Wihla

MY LORD DELIVERED DANIEL *spir
(Whitman) SATB oct LILLENAS AN-3804 $.25
(M3240)
(Whitman) SAB oct LILLENAS AN-3810 $.25
(M3241)

MY LORD HAS SET ME FREE see Grieg, Edvard
Hagerup

MY LORD, HOW BRIGHTLY SHINES THY GLORY see Bach

MY LORD IS LIKE A SHEPHERD see Smith, Lani

MY LORD IS WAITING IN THE GARDEN see Gruber,
Franz Xaver

MY LORD, MY LOVE see Tallis, Thomas

MY LORD, MY LOVE, IS CRUCIFIED! see Burroughs,
Bob

MY LORD, MY MASTER, AT THY FEET ADORING see
France, William E.

MY LORD SPEAKS PEACE TO ME see Roe, Gloria
[Ann]

MY LORD WHAT A MORNIN'
(Ehret; Siegmeister) SATB,opt kbd oct PRO ART
1857 $.30   (M3242)
(Ehret; Siegmeister) SSA,opt kbd oct PRO ART
2211 $.25   (M3243)
(Turner, E.) SSAA,acap oct PRESSER 312-40544
$.25   (M3244)
(Work, J.) SATB,acap oct PRESSER 312-40622
$.25   (M3245)

MY LORD WHAT A MORNIN' see Morgan

MY LORD, WHAT A MORNING *spir
see Four Negro Spirituals
(Barthelson) SATB MARKS 4011 $.25   (M3246)
(Gilliam) 4pt men cor,acap oct SCHIRM.G 10159
$.25   (M3247)
(Wilson) SA oct SPRATT 221 $.25   (M3248)
(Wilson) SSA oct SPRATT 179 $.25   (M3249)
(Wilson) SATB oct SPRATT 219 $.30   (M3250)

MY LORD, WHAT A MORNING see Owens

MY LORD, WHAT A MORNING see Wilson

MY LORD, WHAT A MOURNING *spir
(Papale, Henry) SATB&opt jr cor,SB soli,acap
oct WORLD ESE-1324-8 $.45   (M3251)

MY LORD'S A-WRITIN' ALL THE TIME *spir
(De Cormier) SATB,T solo,acap oct LAWSON
51226 $.30   (M3252)

MY LORD'S GOIN' TO RAIN DOWN FIRE *spir
(Kirk) SATB KJOS 5825 $.30   (M3253)

MY LOVE FOR THE LORD see Lohr, Al

MY MASTER see Carmichael, Ralph

MY MASTER HATH A GARDEN see Green, J.R.

MY MASTER HATH A GARDEN see Roff, Joseph

MY MASTER HATH A GARDEN see Thomson, Virgil

MY MASTER WAS SO VERY POOR see Barker

MY MASTER WAS SO VERY POOR see Graham

MY MASTER WAS SO VERY POOR see Nelson

MY MASTER WAS SO VERY POOR see Young

MY MASTERS, BE MERRY!
(Ehret, Walter) SATB oct AGAPE AD 1978 $.30
(M3254)

MY MUSIC IS A PRAYER see Mueller, Carl F.

MY PEACE I GIVE see Pooler, Frank

MY PEACE I GIVE UNTO YOU see Chevalier, Harold

MY PEOPLE SHALL BE SATISFIED see Sateren,
Leland Bernhard

MY PRAYER see Crow

MY PRAYER see Humphreys, Don

MY PRAYER see Hunt

MY PRAYER see Pearson, Edith

MY PRAYER see Shure, R. Deane

MY PRAYER FOR TODAY see Van Alstyne

MY PRAYER IS UNTO THEE see Roff, Joseph

MY REDEEMER see Billings, William

MY REDEEMER see Martin

MY REDEEMER LIVETH see Handel, George Frideric

MY REDEEMER LIVETH see Loucks

MY REFUGE IS THE GOD OF LOVE see Walker

MY ROCK AND MY CASTLE see Bowie, [William]

MY SAVIOUR DEAR, WHAT WOE OF SOUL see Bach,
Johann Sebastian

MY SHEEP HEAR MY VOICE see Trued, Clarence

MY SHEPHERD see Bach, Johann Sebastian

MY SHEPHERD see Hamill, Paul

MY SHEPHERD IS THE LIVING LORD see Tomkins,
Thomas

MY SHEPHERD IS THE LORD see Gelineau, [Joseph]

MY SHEPHERD IS THE LORD MOST HIGH see Haydn,
(Franz) Joseph

MY SHEPHERD IS THE LORD MOST HIGH see Morgan

MY SHEPHERD WILL SUPPLY MY NEED *anthem/folk,
US
(Pooler, Marie) unis treb cor/SA (easy) oct
AUGSBURG 0609 $.30   (M3255)
(Thomson, Virgil) SA oct GRAY GCMR 2562 $.30
(M3256)
(Thomson, Virgil) SSA oct GRAY GCMR 2558 $.30
(M3257)
(Thomson, Virgil) SAB oct GRAY GCMR 2571 $.30
(M3258)
(Thomson, Virgil) TTBB oct GRAY GCMR 2108
$.25   (M3259)
(Thomson, Virgil) SSAA oct GRAY GCMR 2294
$.25   (M3260)
(Thomson, Virgil) SATB oct GRAY GCMR 2046
$.30   (M3261)

MY SHEPHERD WILL SUPPLY MY NEED see Goemanne,
Noel

MY SHEPHERD WILL SUPPLY MY NEED see Hardwicke

MY SHEPHERD WILL SUPPLY MY NEED see Hutcheson

MY SHEPHERD WILL SUPPLY MY NEED see Luck

MY SHEPHERD WILL SUPPLY MY NEED see Wilson

MY SON FORGET NOT MY LAW see Fischer, Clare

MY SON, OH BE JOYFUL see Mendelssohn-Bartholdy,
Felix

MY SON, WHEREFORE HAST THOU DONE THIS TO US?
see Schutz, Heinrich, Mein Sohn, Warum Hast
Du Uns Das Getan?

MY SON, WHY HAST THOU SO DEALT WITH US? see
Schutz, Heinrich, Mein Sohn, Warum Hast Du
Uns Das Getan?

MY SONG see Peterson, John W.

MY SONG FOREVER SHALL RECORD see Frackenpohl

MY SONG FOREVER SHALL RECORD see Praetorius,
Michael

MY SONG IN THE NIGHT *Gen
(Christiansen, P.) SATB SCHMITT 8036 $.35
(M3262)

MY SONG IS LOVE UNKNOWN see Krapf, Gerhard

MY SONG IS LOVE UNKNOWN see Peninger

MY SONG IS LOVE UNKNOWN see Piggott, H.E.

MY SONG IS LOVE UNKNOWN see Younger, John B.

MY SONG SHALL BE ALWAY see Handel, George
Frideric

MY SONG SHALL BE ALWAY see Handel, George
Frideric, My Song Shall Be Alway

MY SONG SHALL BE ALWAYS OF THE LOVING-KINDNESS
see Sampson, Godfrey

MY SOUL AWAKE AND RENDER see Bach, Johann
Sebastian

MY SOUL DOTH MAGNIFY see Blumenschein, William
Leonard

MY SOUL DOTH MAGNIFY THE LORD see Bach, Johann
Sebastian, Mein Seel' Erhebt Den Herren

MY SOUL DOTH MAGNIFY THE LORD see Bach, Johann
Sebastian, Meine Seel' Erhebt Den Herren
[Chorale]

MY SOUL DOTH MAGNIFY THE LORD see Baksa, R.

MY SOUL DOTH MAGNIFY THE LORD see Cain, Noble

MY SOUL DOTH MAGNIFY THE LORD see Pergolesi,
Giovanni Battista, Magnificat Anima Mea
Dominum

MY SOUL DOTH MAGNIFY THE LORD see Pittman

MY SOUL DOTH MAGNIFY THE LORD see Prentice, Fred

MY SOUL DOTH MAGNIFY THE LORD see Purcell, Henry

MY SOUL DOTH MAGNIFY THE LORD see Saint-Saens, Camille, Tecum Principium

MY SOUL DOTH MAGNIFY THE LORD see Schutz, Heinrich, Deutsches Magnificat

MY SOUL DOTH MAGNIFY THE LORD see Sullivan, Sir Arthur Seymour

MY SOUL DOTH REST IN THEE see Sateren, Leland Bernhard

MY SOUL DOTH WAIT ON GOD see Glarum, L. Stanley

MY SOUL, INSPIRED see Beethoven, Ludwig van

MY SOUL IS A WITNESS see Cheatham

MY SOUL IS A WITNESS FOR MY LORD
    (Kinsman) SATB oct PRO ART 1976 $.22   (M3263)

MY SOUL IS ATHIRST see Palestrina, Giovanni, Sitivit Anima Mea

MY SOUL IS ATHIRST FOR GOD see Stickles, William

MY SOUL IS EXCEEDING SORROWFUL see Neff, James

MY SOUL LONGETH FOR THEE see Mendelssohn-Bartholdy, Felix

MY SOUL, NOW BLESS THY MAKER see Babst

MY SOUL, NOW BLESS THY MAKER see Kugelmann

MY SOUL, NOW BLESS THY MAKER see Schein, Johann Hermann

MY SOUL, PRAISE THE LORD see Vaughan Williams, Ralph

MY SOUL REJOICES see Bach, Johann Sebastian, Et Exultavit

MY SOUL SHALL BE JOYFUL see Keegan

MY SOUL SHALL CRY TO YOU see Haydn, (Franz) Joseph

MY SOUL SHALL EVER GLORIFY THE LORD see Lassus, Roland de (Orlandus), Lauda Anima Mea Dominum

MY SOUL, THERE IS A COUNTRY see Bach, Johann Sebastian, Der Leib Zwar In Der Erden

MY SOUL THERE IS A COUNTRY see Thiman, Eric Harding

MY SOUL THIRSTETH FOR GOD see James

MY SOUL THIRSTS FOR GOD see Schipp, C.M.

MY SOUL TRULY WAITETH STILL UPON GOD see Wood, John

MY SOUL WAIT THOU ONLY UPON GOD see Roff, Joseph

MY SOUL WAITETH IN SILENCE see Hooper

MY SOUL WILL EXULT see Pasquet, Jean

MY SOUL'S BEEN ANCHORED *spir
    (Shaw; Parker) SATB,T solo,acap oct LAWSON
    51111 $.30   (M3264)

MY SOUL'S BEEN ANCHORED IN DE LORD see Howorth, Wayne

MY SOUL'S GONNA RISE AGAIN see Hall, Dickson

MY SPIRIT see Bach, Johann Sebastian, Ich Hatte Viel Bekummernis

MY SPIRIT, BE JOYFUL see Bach, Johann Sebastian, Wie Will Ich Mich Freuen

MY SPIRIT FOR THEE see Hebble, R.

MY SPIRIT LONGS FOR THEE see Sanborn, Jan

MY SPIRIT SANG ALL DAY see Finzi

MY SPIRIT SANG ALL DAY see Finzi, Gerald

MY SPIRIT WAS IN HEAVINESS see Bach, Johann Sebastian, Ich Hatte Viel Bekummernis

MY STRENGTH AND MY SONG see Fitch

MY TASK see Ashford

MY TIME IS COME see Bach, Johann Christoph

MY TIMES ARE IN THY HAND see Roff, Joseph

MY VOICE SHALT THOU HEAR see Corfe, Joseph

MY WAY'S CLOUDY
    SATB CHAPPELL 0022616-358 $.40   (M3265)

MY WONDERFUL LORD see Lillenas, Haldor

MYEROV, JOSEPH
    Simchat Shabbat *Sab-Eve
    SATB TRANSCON. TCL 262 $4.00   (M3266)

MYERS, FHELDON
    Make A Joyful Noise Unto The Lord (Psalm 100)
    Bibl
    SATB,org/pno oct WORLD ESA-1524-8 $.45
                                        (M3267)
    Psalm 100 *see Make A Joyful Noise Unto The
    Lord

MYERS, G.
    Let Us Break Bread Together *Commun/Gen
    SATB (easy) ABINGDON APM-401 $.30   (M3268)

    Two With God
    SATB oct BOURNE 698 $.25   (M3269)

    Why Art Thou So Heavy, O My Soul?
    (Jenkins) SATB oct BOURNE 879 $.35   (M3270)

MYERS, J.C.
    Cradled In A Manger *Xmas
    4pt jr cor/SATB (easy) FISCHER,C CM 6691
    $.25   (M3271)

MYN LYKING see Terry, Richard Runciman

MYROW, JERRY
    Be Good, Be Gentle, And Believe
    SATB oct AGAPE WR 1011 $.40   (M3272)

MYSTERY FOR CHRISTMAS, A see McKinney, Howard D.

MYSTERY OF BETHLEHEM see Willan, Healey

MYSTERY OF THE HOLY INNOCENTS, THE see Barraud, Henry, Le Mystere Des Saints Innocents

MYSTIC STAR, THE
    2pt CHAPPELL 0018176-352 $.40   (M3273)

MYTYCH, J.F.
    Daily, Daily Sing To Mary *ASD/BVM, anthem
    SATB (easy) oct GIA G857 $.25   (M3274)

    God Father, Be Thou Praised *Gen, anthem
    SATB (easy) oct GIA G855 $.30   (M3275)

    Hail, Holy Queen Enthroned Above *ASD/BVM,
    anthem
    SATB (easy) oct GIA G851 $.25   (M3276)

    Holy God, We Praise Thy Name *Gen, anthem
    SATB (easy) oct GIA G858 $.25   (M3277)

    O Christ, Eternal King *Gen, anthem
    SATB (easy) oct GIA G853 $.25   (M3278)

N

N-N, J.
    Ene I Gud
    (Sorass, Lars) mix cor MUSIKK 160 s.p. see
    from RELIGIOSE KORSANGER   (N1)

NACH DEM DIE SONN BESCHLOSSEN see Eccard, Johannes

NACH DIR see Bach, Johann Sebastian, Nach Dir, Herr, Verlanget Mich

NACH DIR, HERR, VERLANGET MICH see Bach, Johann Sebastian

NACH DIR, NACH DIR, HERR see Jacot, Andre

NACH DIR, O HERR, VERLANGT MICH see Ruppel, Paul Ernst

NACH GRUNER FARB MEIN HERZ VERLANGT see Praetorius, Michael

NACHLAT ISRAEL see Adler, Hugo Ch.

NADVERSALME see Hassler, Hans Leo

NAEMERE DIG, MIN GUD see Carey, Lewis

NAERMERE DIG, MIN GUD see Carey, Lewis

NAERMERE DIG, MIN GUD see Karlsen, Rolf

NAGEL
    Psalm 44 *see We Have Heard The Words

    Triptych
    SATB,pno/org,opt brass MARKS 4595 $.35, ipa
                                        (N2)

    We Have Heard The Words (Psalm 44) Psalm
    (Aks) [Eng/Fr] SATB,acap MARKS 86 $.30 (N3)

NAGELI, HANS GEORGE
    Motette *mot
    men cor,acap ERDMANN 171 s.p.   (N4)

NAGELI, JOHANN (HANS) GEORG (1773-1836)
    Der Mensch Lebt Und Bestehet *mot
    [Ger] mix cor,acap (med) HUG s.p.   (N5)

    Faithful Shepherd Is My Lord, A *Gen
    (Buszin) SSAA SCHMITT 2548 $.30   (N6)
    (Stein) SATB SCHMITT 1543 $.30   (N7)

    Nun Danket Alle Gott *mot
    [Ger] mix cor,acap (med) HUG s.p.   (N8)

NAGELS MANNERCHORBUCH, AUSWAHLBAND *CCU,Gen
    (Weitemeyer, Herbert) [Ger] men cor (easy/
    med/diff) pap NAGELS EN 1205 $2.75   (N9)

NAGELS MANNERCHORBUCH TEIL 1 *CCU,Gen
    (Weitemeyer, Herbert) [Ger] men cor (med
    easy) cloth NAGELS EN 1200 $3.00   (N10)

NAGELS MANNERCHORBUCH, TEIL 2 *CCU,Gen
    (Weitemeyer, Herbert) [Ger] men cor (med
    easy) cloth NAGELS EN 1201 $3.00   (N11)

NAGELS MANNERCHORBUCH, TEIL 3 *CCU,Gen
    (Weitemeyer, Herbert) [Ger] men cor (med
    easy) cloth NAGELS EN 1202 $3.00   (N12)

NAGELS MANNERCHORBUCH, TEIL 4 *CCU,Gen
    (Weitemeyer, Herbert) [Ger] men cor (med
    diff) cloth NAGELS EN 1203 $3.00   (N13)

NAGELS MANNERCHORBUCH, TEIL1-3 *CCU,Gen
    (Weitemeyer, Herbert) [Ger] men cor (med
    easy) cloth NAGELS EN 1204 $13.25   (N14)

NAGLE, W.
    Behold, A Simple, Tender Babe *Xmas
    SATB oct PRESSER 332-40043 $.30   (N15)

    Festgesang
    [Ger] men cor,acap (med) HUG s.p.   (N16)

NAGLER, F.
    Beim Scheiden Eines Geistlichen Oder Lehrers
    [Ger] mix cor,acap (easy) HUG   (N17)

    Der Furst Des Lebens
    [Ger] mix cor,acap (easy) HUG   (N18)

    Hosianna, Gelobt Sei, De Da Kommt
    [Ger] mix cor,acap (med) HUG s.p.   (N19)

    Komm, Heiliger Geist
    [Ger] mix cor,acap (easy) HUG   (N20)

    Zum Jubilaum Eines Geistlichen Oder Lehrers
    [Ger] mix cor,acap (easy) HUG   (N21)

    Zur Einweisung Eines Geistlichen Oder Lehrers
    [Ger] mix cor,acap (easy) HUG   (N22)

NAHER, MEIN GOTT, ZU DIR! see Mason, L.

NAJERA, EDMUND
    Ad Flumina Babylonis
    [Lat] dbl cor,acap oct SCHIRM.G 11873 $.40
                                        (N23)

    Agnus Dei
    see Najera, Edmund, Sanctus

    Come Holy Spirit
    SATB (med diff) oct BRIGHT STAR BMP 27 $.15
    contains also: O Sacred Head Now Wounded
                                        (N24)

    O Sacred Head Now Wounded
    see Najera, Edmund, Come Holy Spirit

    Salve Regina
    SATB,pno (med diff) oct BRIGHT STAR BMP 28
    $.25   (N25)

    Sanctus *Agnus/Sanctus
    SATB (med diff) oct BRIGHT STAR BMP 26 $.20
    contains also: Agnus Dei   (N26)

NAME I HIGHLY TREASURE, A see Eliason

NAME IS JESUS, THE see Cain, Noble

NAME OF WONDROUS LOVE see Bass

NANINI
Diffusa Est Gratia
(Knight, Gerald) SATB,acap oct FISCHER,C
CM-7582 $.25   (N27)

NANINI (NANINO), GIOVANNI BERNARDINO
(ca. 1550-1623)
Hodie Nobis Caelorum Rex *Xmas
(Martens, Mason) "On This Day" SATB oct
WALTON 2073 $.25   (N28)

Hodie Nobis Coelorum Rex *Xmas
"This Glad Day To Us The King Of Heaven"
SATB,acap SCHIRM.EC $.30   (N29)

On This Day *see Hodie Nobis Caelorum Rex

Over Dig Ar Herrens Nad
mix cor NORDISKA 3278 s.p.   (N30)

Stabat Mater
(Ruiz) [Lat] SATB,acap RICORDI-ARG BA 10486
s.p.   (N31)

This Glad Day To Us The King Of Heaven *see
Hodie Nobis Coelorum Rex

NANINI (NANINO), GIOVANNI MARIA (ca. 1545-1607)
Christ Is Born Today *see Hodie Christus
Natus Est

Diffusa Est Gratia *mot
SATB,acap RICORDI-ENG SY152 s.p.   (N32)
mix cor ALSBACH&D s.p.   (N33)
[Lat] SATB,acap oct GIA G554 $.25   (N34)
"Grant Unto Us Thy Blessing" SATB,acap
SCHIRM.EC 1711 $.25   (N35)
"Great Is The Grace" [Eng/Fr] SATB,acap
BROUDE BR. $.35   (N36)
(Davison, A.) [Lat] TTBB,acap SCHIRM.EC 949
$.20   (N37)

Father In Heaven
(Suchoff) SAB MARKS 4163 $.30   (N38)

Feria V. In Coena Domini *mot
[Lat] 4pt men cor RICORDI-ENG SY124 s.p.
see from Five Lamentations   (N39)

Feria VI. In Parasceve *mot
[Lat] 4pt men cor RICORDI-ENG SY125 s.p.
see from Five Lamentations   (N40)

Five Lamentations *see Feria V. In Coena
Domini; Feria VI. In Parasceve; Sabbato
Sancto (Lectio Prima); Sabbato Sancto
(Lectio Secunda); Sabbato Sancto (Lectio
Tertia)   (N41)

Grant Unto Us Thy Blessing *see Diffusa Est
Gratia

Great Is The Grace *see Diffusa Est Gratia

Heute Christus Geboren Ist *see Hodie
Christus Natus Est

Hodie Christus Natus Est *Xmas,mot
(Hellmann) "Heute Christus Geboren Ist"
[Lat/Ger] SSAT/SSAB HANSSLER 1.509 s.p.
(N42)
(Sister Ida) SSA FLAMMER B 5041 $.30   (N43)
(Talmadge, A.) "Christ Is Born Today" [Lat/
Eng] SSAA,acap SCHIRM.EC 2545   (N44)
(Ziemer; Rodby) SATB oct PLYMOUTH WR-107
$.25   (N45)

Sabbato Sancto (Lectio Prima) *mot
[Lat] 4pt men cor RICORDI-ENG SY126 s.p.
see from Five Lamentations   (N46)

Sabbato Sancto (Lectio Secunda) *mot
[Lat] 4pt men cor RICORDI-ENG SY127 s.p.
see from Five Lamentations   (N47)

Sabbato Sancto (Lectio Tertia) *mot
[Lat] 4pt men cor RICORDI-ENG SY128 s.p.
see from Five Lamentations   (N48)

NAPIERSKY, H.
Liebliche Weihnacht *Xmas
mix cor TONGER s.p.   (N49)

NAR GUD ANDAS see Bjarnegard, Gustaf

NAR HERREN ATER UPPRATTADE SION see Robertson,
Karl-Olof

NAR JULDAGSMORGEN GLIMMAR see Soderholm,
Valdemar

NAR JULDAGSMORGON GLIMMAR *Xmas,anthem/carol,
Ger
(Barthelson) "Christmas Morn Is Dawning" SATB
oct LAWSON 822 $.25   (N50)
(Grams, W.P.) "When Christmas Morn Is
Dawning" SATB,kbd (med easy) oct CONCORDIA
98-1890 $.25   (N51)
(Luvaas) "When Christmas Morn Is Dawning"
SATB,S solo (easy) oct AUGSBURG 0909 $.30   (N52)
(Luvass, Morton) "Christmas Morn Is Dawning"
SA (easy) oct AUGSBURG 0910 $.22   (N53)
(Luvass, Morton) "Christmas Morn Is Dawning"
SSA (easy) oct AUGSBURG 0911 $.22   (N54)

NAR MIN TID OG STUND ER FOR HAND see Pederson,
Mogens

NAR MIT LEGEM DODEN MODER see Hartmann, Johan
Peder Emilius, Quando Corpus Morietur

NAR TILL JORDAN VAR HERRE DROG see Runback,
Albert

NAR VI I HOGSTA NODEN STA see Erseus, Torsten

NARAYGE see Ghiselin-Verbonnet, Johannes

NARES, JAMES (1715-1783)
By The Waters Of Babylon
(Holman) 2pt boy cor/2pt wom cor oct
SCHIRM.G 10931 $.25   (N55)

In The Sight Of The Unwise *Gen,anthem
unis,opt pno (contains also: Gentiles Shall
Come By, The by Greene, M.) oct ROYAL 237
s.p. see also ANTHEMS FOR UNISON OR TWO
PART SINGING   (N56)

Rejoice In The Lord *Gen,anthem
unis oct ROYAL 220 s.p.   (N57)

Try Me, O God *anthem
(Shaw, Watkins) SATB,org/pno NOVELLO AP222
$.30   (N58)
(Shaw, Watkins) mix cor oct NOVELLO
88.0019.07 s.p.   (N59)
(Watkins; Shaw) SATB SOUTHERN $.30   (N60)

Voice Of Joy, The
(Shaw, Watkins) unis oct NOVELLO 88.0016.02
s.p.   (N61)

NARUM, JEANNE
Even So, Lord Jesus, Quickly Come (composed
with Preus, Carol) *Adv
unis&cong/SAB&cong/SSA&cong,org (easy) sc
AUGSBURG 11-9152 $1.75, cor pts AUGSBURG
11-9153 $.70   (N62)

NARVIK
Evening Song *Eve
SATB KJOS 5112 $.30   (N63)

Now God We Praise
SATB KJOS 5136 $.30   (N64)

NASCE LA GIOIA MIA see Palestrina, Giovanni

NASCO
O Salutaris
(Ruiz) [Lat] 4pt men cor,acap RICORDI-ARG
BA 10487 s.p.   (N65)

Sorrowful Is My Soul *see Tristis Est Anima
Mea

Tristis Est Anima Mea *Easter/Lent
(Greyson) "Sorrowful Is My Soul" SATB oct
BOURNE ES94 $.25   (N66)

NASON, DOUG
Lord, Let Me Listen
SAB oct WORD CS-2531 $.30   (N67)

NASZDALOK VEGYESKARRA
(Matyas, J.) [Hung] SATB (easy) BUDAPEST 5823
s.p.
contains & see also: Lassus, Roland de
(Orlandus), Oly Szep Ma Minden; Lotti,
Antonio, Szivunkre Szall Ma; Palestrina,
Giovanni, Koszonto Enek; Schumann, Robert
(Alexander), Im Utnak Indul   (N68)

NATALE see Tesoriero

NATALE IN FAMIGLIA *CC7L,Xmas
(Travaglia, S.) [Lat/It] cor,pno ZANIBON 1760
s.p.   (N69)

NATIONAL HYMN OF VICTORY see Niles, John Jacob

NATION'S PRAYER see Franck, Cesar, Panis
Angelicus

NATIVE LAND, GOD KEEP THEE FREE see Haydn,
(Franz)

NATIVITAS see Lupi, Roberto

NATIVITAS EST HODIE see Binkerd, [Gordon]

NATIVITIE see Leighton

NATIVITY see Curwin, Clifford

NATIVITY see Neundorf

NATIVITY, THE see Barney, Margaret Higginson

NATIVITY, THE see Dirksen, Richard W.

NATIVITY, THE see Thiman, Eric Harding

NATIVITY ACCORDING TO SAINT LUKE, THE see
Thompson, Randall

NATIVITY ACCORDING TO ST. LUKE, THE see
Thompson, Randall

NATIVITY AS SUNG BY THE SHEPHERDS, THE see
Thomson, Virgil

NATIVITY AT NIGHT, THE see Teed, Roy

NATIVITY CAROL see Graf, Franz

NATIVITY CAROL see Pfautsch, Lloyd

NATIVITY CAROL see Rutter

NATIVITY CRADLE SONG see Roberton, Hugh S.

NATIVITY HYMN see Moe, Daniel

NATIVITY PLAY see Tcherepnin, Alexander

NATIVITY SERVICE OF NINE LESSONS AND CAROLS see
Matthews

NATIVITY SONG, A see Jones

NATIVITY, THE (from King Of Kings)
SATB BIG3 $.35   (N70)
(Lynn, G.) SA oct PRESSER 312-40202 $.25   (N71)

NATIVITY, THE see Dasher, James

NATIVITY, THE see Niles, John Jacob

NATIVITY, THE see Wilson

NATTEN AR FRAMSKRIDEN see Karkoff, Maurice
Ingvar

NATTEVAKTEN see Geitvik, S.H.

NATTLIG MADONNA see Boldemann, Laci

NATTLIG MADONNA see Berg, Gottfrid

NATTLIG MADONNA see Boldemann, Laci

NATUM MARIA VIRGINE see Rubbra, Edmund

NATURAL HIGH see Kaiser, Kurt

NATURE'S ANTHEM OF PRAISE see Sullivan, Sir
Arthur Seymour

NATURE'S HYMN OF PRAISE see Butler, Eugene

NATURE'S PRAISE OF GOD see Beethoven, Ludwig
van

NATUS IN CURAS see Sibelius, Jean

NAUMANN, JOHANN GOTTLIEB (1741-1801)
Dear Lord Jesus, Keep Us *Morav
(Dickinson) SATB oct GRAY GMCM 21 $.35
(N72)
Holy Is The Lord *see Sanctus Et Osanna

Praise Jehovah, All Creation
(Bennett) SATB oct FOX PS113 $.25   (N73)

Ruhig Ist Des Todes Schlummer
(Spangenberg, A.G.; Hauk, G.) [Lat] wom
cor,acap (easy) HUG s.p.   (N74)

Sanctus Et Osanna *Sanctus
mix cor SOUTHERN $.35   (N75)
(Suchoff) "Holy Is The Lord" [Eng/Lat] SATB
MARKS 4511 $.35   (N76)

NAUMBOURG
Praise Jehovah, Hallelujah!
(Suchoff, Benjamin) SATB oct BELWIN 2085
$.25   (N77)

S'u Sheorim
(Roskin) SATB HATIKVAH HCL 8 $.25   (N78)

NAVARRO
Lauda Jerusalem *Psalm,16th cent
[Lat] 4pt mix cor,acap UNION ESP. 19177
s.p.   (N79)

NAVIDAD, COLECCION DE VILLANCICOS POPULARES see
Benedito

NAVIDAD CRIOLLA see Irigaray

NAVIDAD NUESTRA see Ramirez, Ariel

NAYLOR
Shepherds In The Field Abiding *Xmas
unis&SATB (med) OXFORD 84.128 $.50   (N80)

NAYLOR, BERNARD
Arise, Shine *Epiph,anthem
mix cor oct NOVELLO 28.1395.05 s.p. see
also Nine Motets   (N81)

Armour Of Light, The *Adv,cant
SATB,S solo,pno,org voc sc NOVELLO s.p.   (N82)

Ascension, The *see In Ascensione Domine

Awake, Awake, Put On Thy Strength *Easter,
anthem
mix cor oct NOVELLO 28.1398.10 s.p. see
also Nine Motets   (N83)

Behold, My Servant Shall Deal Prudently
*Gd.Fri.,anthem
mix cor oct NOVELLO 28.1397.01. s.p. see
also Nine Motets   (N84)

Childing Slept, A *Xmas
4pt mix cor,SBar soli oct CURWEN 10822 $.25
(N85)
Come Holy Ghost, Eternal God
SATB,org ROBERTON   (N86)

Crown Of Thorns *see De Corona Spinea

De Corona Spinea
"Crown Of Thorns" SATB oct LESLIE 4070
(N87)
Does The Day-Star Rise? *ASD,anthem
mix cor oct NOVELLO 28.1442.00 s.p.   (N88)

Dull Soul Aspire *anthem/mot
dbl cor,acap oct NOVELLO 28.1440.04 s.p.   (N89)

Easter Sequence *see Sequentia Paschalis

Exultet Mundus Gaudio *cant
SSAATTBB&2pt treb cor,SATB soli ROBERTON
(N90)
dbl cor&treb cor ROBERTON s.p.   (N91)
8pt mix cor&treb cor,SATB soli ROBERTON
s.p.   (N92)

I Saw In The Night Visions *Asc,anthem
mix cor oct NOVELLO 28.1399.08 s.p. see
also Nine Motets   (N93)

I Will Pour Out My Spirit *Whitsun,anthem
mix cor oct NOVELLO 28.1400.05 s.p. see
also Nine Motets   (N94)

In Ascensione Domine *Asc
"Ascension, The" SATB oct LESLIE 4072   (N95)

In The Year That King Uzziah Died *Trin,
anthem
mix cor oct NOVELLO 28.1402.01 s.p. see
also Nine Motets   (N96)

Invitation To Music *anthem
mix cor ROBERTON s.p.   (N97)
SATB,org ROBERTON   (N98)

King Solomon's Prayer
[Eng/Ger] voc sc UNIVER. 12280 $1.80   (N99)

Magnificat And Nunc Dimittis *Magnif/Nunc
SATB,acap oct NOVELLO 44.1416.00 s.p.
(N100)
Missa Da Camera *Mass
SATB,4 soli/SATB soli,ob,2clar,2bsn,horn,
strings voc sc NOVELLO s.p., ipr   (N101)

NAYLOR, BERNARD (cont'd.)

Missa Sine Credo *Mass
SATB,acap ROBERTON (N102)

Morning Watch And The Evening Watch, The
SATB,acap ROBERTON (N103)

Motet For The Circumcision *Circum,anthem/mot
SSATB,acap oct NOVELLO 28.1439.00 s.p. (N104)

Nine Motets *CC9UL,anthem
mix cor oct NOVELLO
see also: Arise, Shine; Awake, Awake, Put On Thy Strength; Behold, My Servant Shall Deal Prudently; I Saw In The Night Visions; I Will Pour Out My Spirit; In The Year That King Uzziah Died; People That Walked In Darkness, The (N105)

O Be Joyful In The Lord *anthem
mix cor oct NOVELLO 28.1462.05 s.p. (N106)

Of One That Is So Fair And Bright
3pt wom cor,S solo,acap oct SCHIRM.G 11385 $.25 (N107)

People That Walked In Darkness, The *Xmas, anthem
mix cor oct NOVELLO 28.1394.07 s.p. see also Nine Motets (N108)

Resurrection, The *Easter,cant
SATB,SBarB soli,pno&strings&orch&timp&perc/pno&strings&winds/pno&strings voc sc NOVELLO s.p., ipr (N109)

Sequentia Paschalis *Easter
"Easter Sequence" SATB oct LESLIE 4071 (N110)

Service And Strength *ASD,anthem
4pt mix cor,org oct SCHIRM.G 11361 $.25 (N111)
mix cor oct NOVELLO 28.1444.07 s.p. (N112)

Six Poems From Miserere *CC6U
mix cor ROBERTON s.p. (N113)

Six Poems From Miserere *cant
dbl cor,SS soli ROBERTON (N114)
2pt mix cor,SS soli ROBERTON s.p. (N115)

Sonnet To The Trinity *Trin,anthem
mix cor oct NOVELLO 28.1468.04 s.p. (N116)

Stabat Mater
wom cor&wom cor,orch voc sc NOVELLO 07.0228.05 s.p. (N117)

NAYLOR, EDWARD WOODALL (1867-1934)
Benedicite In G
mix cor CURWEN 80545 s.p. (N118)

Cantate Domino *anthem
SA oct OXFORD 44.235 $.60 (N119)

Deus Misereatur *anthem
SA oct OXFORD 44.234 $.50 (N120)

Final Responses At Morning And Evening Prayer *Eve/Morn
SATB,acap (very easy) oct OXFORD 43.371 $.15 (N121)

Merry Bells At Yule, The *Xmas
mix cor ROBERTON 63001 s.p. (N122)

Vox Dicentis: Clama
mix cor CURWEN 80581 s.p. (N123)

NAYLOR, PETER
Come, Dearest Lord *anthem
mix cor oct NOVELLO 86.0033.03 s.p. (N124)

His Name Is John *anthem
mix cor oct NOVELLO 28.1450.01 s.p. (N125)

Now The Green Blade Riseth *Easter
SATB,acap (med easy) oct OXFORD 84.126 $.25 (N126)

O Sing Unto The Lord *anthem
mix cor oct NOVELLO 86.0027.09 s.p. (N127)

NAZARAEUS VOCABITUR see Willaert, Adrian

NAZARETH see Gounod, Charles Francois

NAZAREUS VOCABITUR see Willaert, Adrian

NE CRAINS PAS, JE SUIS TOUT PRES DE TOI see Bach, Johann Sebastian

NE IRASCARIS see Byrd, William

NE IRASCARIS DOMINE see Byrd, William

NE TIMEAS MARIA see Victoria, Tomas Luis de

NE VEUILLE PAS, O SIRE see Jannequin, Clement

NEALE
All Glory, Laud And Honor
(Rhea) TTBB oct PLYMOUTH UIL-106 $.25 (N128)

O Come, Emmanuel
(Kay) SATB oct MCA (N129)

NEANDER, JOACHIM (1650-1680)
God Is In His Temple
(Davis) girl cor SOUTHERN $.30 (N130)
(Davis, K.K.) SSA,acap WARNER R3299 $.30 (N131)
(Davis, K.K.) SAB,acap WARNER R3483 $.30 (N132)

Gott Ist Gegenwartig, Lasset Uns
TTBB HANSSLER 6.2330 s.p. contains also: Anonymous, Herr Jesu Christ, Dich Zu Uns Wend; Singet Hocherfreut, Gross Sind Gottes (N133)

Lo! He Comes With Clouds Ascending *Adv
(Barthelson) SAB oct PRO ART 2496 $.25 (N134)

Lobe Den Herren, Den Machitigen Konig
TTBB HANSSLER 6.2328 s.p. contains also: Kugelmann, Johann, Nun Lob, Mein Seel, Den Herren (N135)

NEANDER, JOACHIM (cont'd.)

Weicht, Ihr Berge, Fallt, Ihr Hugel
(Berger, H.L.) TTBB HANSSLER 6.5092 s.p. (N136)

NEAR, GERALD
Arise, My Love, My Fair One *anthem
SATB (med diff) oct AUGSBURG 0521 $.25 (N137)

Behold The Great Creator *Xmas
SATB,acap GRAY GCMR 3282 $.30 (N138)

Christ Hath A Garden
SATB,org GRAY GCMR 3271 $.30 (N139)

Come, Risen Lord *anthem
SATB (diff) oct AUGSBURG 1593 $.25 (N140)

Come, Thou Long Expected Jesus *anthem
SATB (diff) oct AUGSBURG 1588 $.30 (N141)

Drop, Drop, Slow Tears *Lent
SATB oct GRAY GCMR 3082 $.25 (N142)

Easter Processional, An *Easter/Proces
2pt mix cor GRAY GCMR 3285 $.30 (N143)

Four Selections From The Mass *CC4U,anthem
SATB (diff) oct AUGSBURG 1573 $.50 (N144)

I Sat Down Under His Shadow *anthem
SATB (med) oct AUGSBURG 0527 $.25 (N145)

Lord Keep Us Steadfast In Thy Word *anthem
SAB (med) oct AUGSBURG 1557 $.25 (N146)

My God, My God, Why Hast Thou Forsaken Me? (Psalm 22)
SATB oct GRAY GCMR 3208 $.35 (N147)

O Word That Goest Forth On High *Adv
SATB,org GRAY GCMR 3281 $.30 (N148)

Psalm 22 *see My God, My God, Why Hast Thou Forsaken Me?

Set Me As A Seal Upon Thine Heart *anthem
SATB (med) oct AUGSBURG 0528 $.30 (N149)

Sing, Men And Angels, Sing *anthem
SATB/unis (easy) oct AUGSBURG 1555 $.20 (N150)
unis treb cor (easy) oct AUGSBURG 1555 $.20 (N151)

This Is The Day The Lord Hath Made *anthem
SAB (med diff) oct AUGSBURG 1620 $.30 (N152)

NEAR THE INN IN BETHLEHEM see Lynn, George

NEAR TO THE HEART OF GOD
(Carmichael) SATB oct WORD CS-308 $.30 (N153)

NEAR TO THE HEART OF GOD see McAfee

NEARER, MY GOD, TO THEE *hymn
(Gardner) SSA (med easy) OXFORD 44.223 $.25, ipr see from Five Hymns In Popular Style (N154)

NEARER, MY GOD, TO THEE see Gardner, John [Linton]

NEARER MY GOD TO THEE see Handel, George Frideric

NEARER MY GOD TO THEE see Mason

NEARER, MY GOD, TO THEE see Wehr

NEARER THE CROSS see Doane, [William Howard]

NEC TU NATE DEI see Wenzel, Eberhard

NEEDHAM, LUCIEN
Christmas Gradual *Xmas
SATB,acap oct BERANDOL 911N3AA $.35 (N155)

NEEM, HERR, MIJN BEIDE HANDE see Silcher, Friedrich

NEES, STAF
Alleluia
3 eq voices,org/pno oct WORLD J-644 $.45 (N156)
SATB,org/pno oct WORLD $.45 (N157)

NEES, VIC
European Stabat Mater
4pt mix cor,AT soli MOSELER sc s.p., cor pts s.p. (N158)

Funf Geistliche Motetten *CC5U,mot
[Lat] 4-5pt mix cor MOSELER s.p. (N159)

NEFF, JAMES
Before The Paling Of The Stars *Xmas
SATB SCHMITT SD6204 $.25 (N160)

Crown Of Life
SATB,acap oct PRESSER MC337 $.25 (N161)

Drop Down Ye Heavens *anthem
SATB (med) oct AUGSBURG 1466 $.25 (N162)

Jesus, Thou Joy Of Loving Hearts *anthem
2 eq voices,opt fl/opt rec (easy) oct AUGSBURG 1477 $.25 (N163)

Lay Up Treasures In Heaven *Gen
SATB SCHMITT SD6210 $.20 (N164)

My Soul Is Exceeding Sorrowful *anthem
2pt mix cor (easy) oct AUGSBURG 1396 $.25 (N165)

O Lord, Thou Hast Searched Me *anthem
SATB (med) oct AUGSBURG 0601 $.25 (N166)

Praise The Lord, All Nations *anthem
SATB (med easy) oct AUGSBURG 0644 $.25 (N167)

Remember Now Thy Creator
SATB oct PRESSER MC426 $.45 (N168)

Star, The *Xmas
SATB,acap oct PRESSER MC305 $.30 (N169)

NEGEN OUD-NED. LIEDEREN see Rontgen, [Julius]

NEGRO BELL CAROL see James

NEGRO SPIRITUALS *CCU,spir
(Engstrom, Sune W.) men cor,pno cor pts NORDISKA s.p., ipa (N170)

NEGRO SPIRITUALS see Martti, Hela

NEGRO SPIRITUALS *CCU,spir
(Putz; Rosenstengel) mix cor/eq voices,pno, bvl,gtr voc sc GERIG 412 s.p. (N171)

NEGRO SPIRITUALS *spir
(Kristoffersen, Dag) [Eng] mix cor,Bar solo, pno LYCHE LY221 s.p.
contains: Cruicified, The; Dre's No Hidin' Place; Go Down, Moses; Heab'n; Little David Play On Yo' Harp; Oh Vait Till Put On My Crown; Steal Away (N172)

NEGRO SPIRITUALS *CCU
(Bayco, F.) TTBB CRAMER s.p. (N173)

NEGRO SPIRITUALS see Nieland, H.

NEGROSPIRITUALS DEEL I see Noble, Felix de

NEGROSPIRITUALS DEEL II see Noble, Felix de

NEGROSPIRITUALS DEEL III see Noble, Felix de

NEGROSPIRTUALS DEEL IV see Noble, Felix de

NEHMET EINHANDER AN see Kurig, Hans-Hermann

NEHMET HIN DEN HEILIGEN GEIST see Franck, Melchior

NEHMET HIN DEN HEILIGEN GEIST see Raselius, Andreas

NEHMT UND ESST, DAS IST MEIN LEIB see Arp, Klaus-Michael

NEHMT WAHR DAS LICHT see Haller, Hans Peter

NEHMT WAHR DAS LICHT see Zipp, Friedrich

NEIDLINGER
Birthday Of A King *Xmas
SATB oct PRO ART 1205 $.30 (N174)
SATB oct VOLKWEIN VB114 $.25 (N175)
SSA oct VOLKWEIN VB115 $.25 (N176)
(Dawson) SAB oct PRO ART 1473 $.30 (N177)
(Dawson) 2pt oct PRO ART 1451 $.25 (N178)
(Dawson) SSA oct PRO ART 1324 $.30 (N179)
(Holmes) TTBB oct PRO ART 2022 $.25 (N180)

Birthday Of A King, The *Xmas
(Hardwicke) SSA ALFRED 6171 $.25 (N181)

NEIDLINGER, P.
Birthday Of A King *Xmas
SATB (easy) ALLANS 351 s.p. (N182)
SA (easy) ALLANS 350 s.p. (N183)
(Dale, Phillip) SA ALLANS 350 s.p. (N184)

NEIDLINGER, WILLIAM HAROLD (1863-1924)
Birthday Of A King, The *Xmas
SATB oct LORENZ 4329 $.25 (N185)
SATB oct FISCHER,C CM-6421 $.25 (N186)
4pt mix cor,Bar solo oct SCHIRM.G 3576 $.30 (N187)
(Breck) 3pt jr cor/SSA (easy) FISCHER,C CM 6423 $.25 (N188)
(Breck) 2pt jr cor FISCHER,C CM 6422 $.25 (N189)
(Deis) 4pt mix cor,S/T solo,pno/org oct SCHIRM.G 9884 $.35 (N190)
(Deis) 4pt men cor oct SCHIRM.G 9739 $.35 (N191)
(Deis) 2pt wom cor oct SCHIRM.G 7246 $.30 (N192)
(Downing) 3pt mix cor,SABar soli oct SCHIRM.G 9536 $.25 (N193)
(Downing) 3pt wom cor oct SCHIRM.G 8878 $.25 (N194)
(Hallett) SAB&SATB,solo oct WORD CS-2225 $.30 (N195)
(Howorth) SAB oct BELWIN 1457 $.25 (N196)
(McKinney) SATB oct FISCHER,J 8413 $.30 (N197)
(McKinney) SSA oct FISCHER,J 8337 $.30 (N198)
(McKinney) SA oct FISCHER,J 8412 $.30 (N199)
(Whitman) SATB oct LILLENAS AN-3830 $.30 (N200)

Followers Of The Star *Xmas,cant
(Deis, Carl; 4pt mix cor,opt SMez soli,pno/org voc sc SCHIRM.G $1.00 (N201)

Judge Me, O God
SATB oct PRESSER 312-10634 $.35 (N202)

O Little Town Of Bethlehem *Xmas,Bibl
4pt mix cor,acap oct SCHIRM.G 3750 $.25 (N203)

Silent Sea, The
4pt mix cor,S solo oct SCHIRM.G 5196 $.25 (N204)
(Deis) 3pt mix cor,S solo oct SCHIRM.G 10033 $.25 (N205)
(Marzo) 3pt wom cor oct SCHIRM.G 7185 $.25 (N206)

Spirit Of God
(Greely, P.) SATB oct PRESSER 332-14498 $.30 (N207)
(Peery, R.) SSA oct PRESSER 332-15183 $.30 (N208)

NEIDT, F.E.
In Mirth And In Gladness
SATB,acap oct SCHIRM.G 7540 $.35 (N209)

NEIGHBOR, ARDEAN
Shout For Joy *Bibl
4pt mix cor oct SCHIRM.G 10904 $.30 (N210)

NEILSEN, LUDVIG
Benedicamus
[Lat] cor,org LYCHE 16 s.p. (N211)

Dig, Gud Lover Vi *see Te Deum

Exultate Deo Adjutori Nostro *see Pris Gud Var Hjelper

NEILSEN, LUDVIG (cont'd.)

Guds Rike *cant
mix cor,org MUSIKK 79 cor pts s.p., voc sc
s.p.   (N212)

Herre Var Herre *mot
8pt MUSIKK 45 s.p.   (N213)

Inrata Gotica
[Norw] men cor/mix cor,org s.p. cor pts
LYCHE 32, voc sc LYCHE LY256A   (N214)

Intrata Solemnis
[Norw] men cor/mix cor,org s.p. cor pts
LYCHE 30, voc sc LYCHE LY427   (N215)

Kling No, Klokka *cant
[Norw] mix cor,inst,org LYCHE 50 s.p.   (N216)

Pris Gud Var Hjelper *fugue
"Exultate Deo Adjutori Nostro" [Lat/Norw]
6pt MUSIKK 28 s.p.   (N217)

Se, Vi Gar Opp Til Jerusalem
[Norw] 3pt mix cor LYCHE 60 s.p.   (N218)

Te Deum *Te Deum
"Dig, Gud Lover Vi" [Lat/Norw] mix cor,
orch/org cor pts MUSIKK 84 s.p., ipr   (N219)

NELHYBEL, VACLAV (1919-   )
Birthday Of A King, The *Xmas
SAB oct LORENZ 7338 $.25   (N220)

Cantata Pacis *cant
SATB, soli BELWIN $3.00   (N221)

Celebrons *Xmas,carol
SSATTBB GENERAL CH373 $.30 see also Seven
Ancient Carols (Caroli Antiqui Varii)   (N222)

Dies Ultima *Bibl/liturg
[Lat/Eng] SATB&speak cor,narrator,STBar
soli,band,orch voc sc KERBY $4.00   (N223)

Es Kommt Ein Schiff *Xmas,carol
SSATTBB GENERAL CH375 $.30 see also Seven
Ancient Carols (Caroli Antiqui Varii)   (N224)

Five Short Anthems Or Responses *CC5U,anthem
SATB oct KERBY 9378 $.45   (N225)

Hymn Of Hope *hymn
cor,orch/band KERBY 17 sc $4.50, ipa, cor
pts $.30   (N226)

Let My People Go
SATB,soli,acap oct KERBY 878 $.55   (N227)
SATB,SATB soli oct KERBY 87 $.55   (N228)

Lord Shall Raise Me Up, The
SATB,acap oct KERBY 2878 $.40   (N229)
SATB oct KERBY 28 $.40   (N230)

Lully Lulla *Xmas,carol
SSATTBB GENERAL CH371 $.30 see also Seven
Ancient Carols (Caroli Antiqui Varii)   (N231)

O Jesu Christ *Xmas,carol
SSATTBB GENERAL CH374 $.30 see also Seven
Ancient Carols (Caroli Antiqui Varii)   (N232)

Puer Natus In Bethlehem *Xmas,carol
SSATTBB GENERAL CH376 $.40 see also Seven
Ancient Carols (Caroli Antiqui Varii)   (N233)

Que Creavit Caelum *Xmas,carol
SSATTBB GENERAL CH372 $.25 see also Seven
Ancient Carols (Caroli Antiqui Varii)   (N234)

Quem Vidistis *Xmas,carol
SSATTBB GENERAL CH370 $.30 see also Seven
Ancient Carols (Caroli Antiqui Varii)   (N235)

Seven Ancient Carols (Caroli Antiqui Varii)
*Xmas,carol
SSATTBB GENERAL
contains & see also: Celebrons; Es Kommt
Ein Schiff; Lully Lulla; O Jesu Christ;
Puer Natus In Bethlehem; Que Creavit
Caelum; Quem Vidistis   (N236)

NELSON
Hosanna To The Son Of David *Palm
SAB oct SOUTHERN $.25   (N237)

My Master Was So Very Poor *Xmas
SATB SCHMITT SD6227 $.30   (N238)

Slumber Now Beloved Child
girl cor SOUTHERN $.30   (N239)

To God All Praise And Glory
SATB SHAWNEE A 488 $.30   (N240)

Tree Of Life, The
SA BOOSEY-CAN s.p.   (N241)

NELSON, HAVELOCK
I See His Blood Upon The Rose
SSA LENGNICK s.p.   (N242)

NELSON, JERRY
All We Like Sheep
SATB oct LILLENAS AN-1647 $.30   (N243)

God Of Miracles
(Owens) SATB oct LILLENAS AN-1648 $.30   (N244)

It All Depends
(Kirk) SATB oct LILLENAS AT-1083 $.35   (N245)

On Love Alone *Xmas,Bibl/cant,Contemp
mix cor,narrator,opt ob,trp,trom,vln,harp,
perc voc sc LILLENAS MC-17, MC-17A $1.25   (N246)

NELSON MASS see Haydn, (Franz) Joseph, Messe D-
Moll

NELSON MASS see Haydn, (Franz) Joseph, Nelson-
Missa

NELSON-MESSE see Haydn, (Franz) Joseph

NELSON-MISSA see Haydn, (Franz) Joseph

NELSON-MISSE see Haydn, (Franz) Joseph

NELSON, MYRA HEDGES
I Thank Thee, O Lord
SSA oct JUSKO 200 $.25   (N247)

NELSON, PAUL (1929-   )
For Theirs Is The Kingdom Of Heaven *Bibl
3pt wom cor,acap oct SCHIRM.G 10506 $.20   (N248)

In Bethlehem, That Noble Place
SATB,acap oct BROWN 5476 $.50   (N249)

Thy Will Be Done
men cor,6brass,perc cor pts BROWN $1.50,
ipr   (N250)

NELSON, R. WAYNE
Blessed Be The Lord Alleluia
cor HIGHLAND 4118 $.30   (N251)

Bow Down Thine Ear
cor HIGHLAND 4102 $.25   (N252)

Praise Ye The Lord
cor HIGHLAND 4101 $.25   (N253)

NELSON, RONALD A.
All Praise To Music
SATB oct BOOSEY 5388 $.30 contains also:
Fanfare For A Festival   (N254)

Amazing Was The Sight
see Five Carols For Now

Angels Sang It Then
see Five Carols For Now

Behold Man!
TTBB,acap oct BROWN 5403 $.30   (N255)

Blessed Be The Lord *anthem
SAB (med diff) oct AUGSBURG 1245 $.25   (N256)

Cause Us, O Lord
see Four Anthems For Young Choirs

Cherry-Tree Carol *Xmas,carol
SA,S solo,opt fl oct BOOSEY 5792 $.30   (N257)

Choral Fanfare For Christmas *Xmas
SATB/TTBB oct BOOSEY 5337 $.30   (N258)

Christmas Story, The *Xmas
mix cor,narrator&Bar solo,org,brass,timp
BOOSEY voc sc $2.50, ipa, cor pts $.60   (N259)

Coming Of God To Man, The
see Five Carols For Now

Fanfare For A Festival
see Nelson, Ronald A., All Praise To Music

Five Carols For Now *carol,Asian/Braz/Chin/
Russ/Span
unis treb cor oct AUGSBURG 11-9171 $.40
contains: Amazing Was The Sight; Angels
Sang It Then; Coming Of God To Man,
The; Jesus Came For All Men; What Did
He Mean To Tell Us?   (N260)

For Your Light Has Come *anthem
SATB,org,2trp,opt timp (easy) oct AUGSBURG
1641 $.25   (N261)

Four Anthems For Young Choirs *anthem
unis/unis jr cor,org oct BOOSEY 5576 $.40
contains: Cause Us, O Lord; Hear, O
People; I Will Not Leave You
Comfortless; Let Thy Work Appear   (N262)

Glory To God (The Christmas Story) *Xmas
[Eng/Ger] SATB,org oct BOOSEY 5321 $.40   (N263)

God, Bring Thy Sword
SATB,org,opt perc oct BOOSEY 5661 $.40   (N264)

He Came Here For Me
SSAA,harp/pno oct BOOSEY 5371 $.30   (N265)
SATB,pno/harp/org,opt chimes oct BOOSEY
5370 $.30   (N266)

Hear, O Israel
SATB,org oct BOOSEY 5440 $.30   (N267)

Hear, O People
see Four Anthems For Young Choirs

Hosanna *anthem
SAB&SAB (med) oct AUGSBURG 1510 $.30   (N268)

Hosanna! O Blessed Is He *anthem
unis treb cor (easy) oct AUGSBURG 1521 $.25   (N269)

Hosanna To The Son Of David *anthem
SAB (easy) oct AUGSBURG 1258 $.25   (N270)

How Far Is It To Bethlehem? *cant
mix cor&opt jr cor,org/pno,opt orch (easy)
sc AUGSBURG 11-9210 $1.35   (N271)

I Am The Resurrection And The Life *anthem
SATB (med) oct AUGSBURG 1511 $.25   (N272)

I Will Not Leave You Comfortless
see Four Anthems For Young Choirs

In The Name Of The Lord *anthem
SS (med) oct AUGSBURG 1329 $.25   (N273)

Introit For Easter *Easter,Introit
SATB (med) oct ABINGDON APM-599 $.45   (N274)

Introits For Lent And Easter *CCU,Easter/
Lent,Introit
SAB (med) oct ABINGDON APM-598 $.25   (N275)

Jesus Came For All Men
see Five Carols For Now

Joy To The World (Psalm 98) anthem
SA&desc&cong,org (med) oct AUGSBURG 1634
$.30   (N276)

Let Thy Work Appear
see Four Anthems For Young Choirs

NELSON, RONALD A. (cont'd.)

Lift Up Your Heads (Psalm 24) anthem
SATB&cong,org,opt inst (med) oct AUGSBURG
1635 $.25   (N277)

Lullaby, Jesus Child *anthem
SA (easy) oct AUGSBURG 1316 $.18   (N278)

Meditation On The Syllable "Om"
TTBB oct BOOSEY 5809 $.30   (N279)

O Lord, How Can We Know Thee?
SATB,org oct BOOSEY 5439 $.35   (N280)

Passion According To Saint Mark, The
mix cor&cong,solo,narrator,pno/org,opt orch
(easy) voc sc AUGSBURG 11-9338 $1.35, ipa   (N281)

Present Tense, The *anthem/canon
2pt treb cor,kbd,opt bells (med) oct
AUGSBURG 1623 $.30   (N282)

Psalm 24 *see Lift Up Your Heads

Psalm 98 *see Joy To The World

Rise Up, O Men Of God
SATB (med) ABINGDON APM-597 $.35   (N283)

Sleep Little One
SSA oct BROWN 5262 $.30   (N284)
SATB,acap oct BROWN 5261 $.30   (N285)
TTBB,acap oct BROWN 5263 $.30   (N286)

Slumber Now Beloved Child (from Christmas
Story, The)
SSA,pno, or celesta oct BOOSEY 5542 $.30   (N287)

They That Wait Upon The Lord
SATB (med easy) ABINGDON APM-596 $.20   (N288)

Triumphal Te Deum *Te Deum
[Lat/Eng] mix cor,brass,perc voc sc BOOSEY
$.50, ipa   (N289)

Under The Eastern Sky *anthem
unis treb cor,org,opt clar (med) oct
AUGSBURG 0308 $.25   (N290)

What Did He Mean To Tell Us?
see Five Carols For Now

What Is Man?
[Lat] mix cor,narrator,SBar soli,inst/orch
BOOSEY voc sc $4.75, cor pts $1.50 (N291)

Whoever Would Be Great Among You *anthem
SAB,kbd/gtr (easy) oct AUGSBURG 1638 $.25   (N292)

NEMEC
Why Hast Thou Forsaken
(Henderson) SATB,org/pno BOSTON 13486 $.50   (N293)

NESCIENS MATER see Wright, Thomas

NESCIENS MATER VIRGO see Wright, Thomas

NESSE, SIGURD
Den Tyngste Sorg
(Steenberg, P.) mix cor MUSIKK s.p. (N294)

Hymne
(Steenberg, P.) mix cor MUSIKK 50 s.p.
                                              (N295)

So Takkar Mi Sjel *Psalm
(Steenberg, P.) mix cor MUSIKK 53 s.p.
                                              (N296)

NESSEN, HUGO VON (1921-   )
Singe, O Singe Dich, Seele
mix cor,acap TONGER s.p.   (N297)

NEUBERT, GOTTFRIED (1926-   )
Auf, Auf, Mein Herz
see Geisel, Gustav, Der Tod Ist
Verschlungen

Gott Des Himmels Und Der Erden
see Schlenker, Manfred, Die Guldne Sonne

Komm, Heiliger Geist, Herre Gott *No.98,
Asc/Pent,cant
[Ger] 5-6pt mix cor&cong,3trp,2trom BAREN.
EM 150 sc s.p., cor pts s.p., ipa see
from EVANGELISCHES KIRCHENGESANGBUCH   (N298)

Man Singt Mit Freuden
see Geisel, Gustav, Der Tod Ist
Verschlungen

O Komm, Du Geist Der Wahrheit
see Kretzschmar, Gunther, Pfingstruf

Steht Auf, Ihr Lieben Kinderlein
see Schlenker, Manfred, Die Guldne Sonne

Wir Wollen Alle Frolich Sein *cant
SAB&cong,org,2trp HANSSLER 10.178 sc s.p.,
cor pts s.p., ipa   (N299)

NEUE GEISTLICHE LIEDER *CC54U,Gen
(Blarr, Oskar Gottlieb; Heuser, Christine;
Seidel, Uwe) [Ger] unis,acap (med easy)
BOSSE BE 285 s.p.   (N300)

NEUE GEISTLICHE LIEDER *CC43U
SAT/SAB/SATB sc HANSSLER 19.509 s.p.   (N301)

NEUE LIEDER see Michel, Josep

NEUE WEIHNACHTSLIEDER *CC34U,Xmas
[Ger] (med easy) 3 eq voices,acap BAREN.
BA1372 $2.25; 3pt mix cor/4pt mix cor,acap
BAREN. BA 1373 $2.25   (N302)

NEUE WEINACHTS-LEIDLEIN see Schroter, Leonhard

NEUE WEINACHTS-LIEDLEIN see Schroter, Leonhard

NEUE WEINACHTSLEIDLEIN see Schroter, Leonhard

NEUE WIEHNACHTSLIEDLEIN 1587 see Schroter,
Leonhard

NEUES CHORALBUCH see Pepping, Ernst

NEUES CHORBUCH *CC129U,Gen
(Steinbach, Erika) [Ger] 2 eq voices/3 eq
voices,acap (med easy) BAREN. BA 1700 $3.25

NEUES CHORBUCH FUR GEMISCHTE STIMMEN *CCU,Trin
(Haag; Henny; Trotschel) [Ger] 4pt mix cor
BAREN. EM 355 s.p. (N304)

NEUES CHOREGESANGBUCH *CCU,Gen
(Stern; Weismann) mix cor HANSSLER 2.014 s.p.
(N305)

NEUJAHRSLIED see Stern, A

NEUKOMM, SIGISMUND RITTERVON (1778-1858)
Holy Is The Almighty
(Suchoff) SATB oct FOX RM6 $.30 (N306)

NEUMAN
Kiddush
(Weintraub; Roskin) SATB HATIKVAH HCL 4
$.30 (N307)

NEUMANN, ALFRED
Truly We Shall Be In Paradise With Him
4pt mix cor,org,opt brass&timp oct SCHIRM.G
11688 $.35 (N308)

NEUMANN, M.
Gebet *Op.67,No.1
(Arndt, E.M.) men cor (easy) cor pts
LEUCKART 5A s.p. (N309)

NEUMANN, RICHARD J.
Torah Service *Sab-Morn
SATB,cantor,T/Bar solo TRANSCON. TCL 870
$2.25 (N310)

NEUMARK, GEORG (1621-1681)
Wer Nur Den Lieben Gott
(Berger, H.L.) TTBB HANSSLER 6.5144 s.p.
(N311)

Wer Nur Den Lieben Gott Lasst Walten
SATB,acap DOBLINGER s.p. see also BITTE UND
VERTRAUEN (N312)

NEUMEYER, FRITZ (1900-   )
Als Ich Bei Meinen Schafen Wacht *Xmas
[Ger] SATB,Bar solo,acap (easy) BAREN.
BCH 26 s.p. contains also: Still, Still,
Still (SATB,acap) (N313)

Still, Still, Still
see Neumeyer, Fritz, Als Ich Bei Meinen
Schafen Wacht

NEUN ALTE WEIHNACHTSGESANGE *CC9U,Xmas
(Johner) [Ger] SATB/unis,opt kbd HUG s.p.
(N314)

NEUN GEISTLICHE LIEDER see Cruger, Johann

NEUN KANTATEN see Buxtehude, Dietrich

NEUNDORF
Nativity *Xmas
unis oct SUMMY 5843 $.20 (N315)

NEUNMALIGES KYRIE CUNCTIPOTENS "O MILDER GOTT"
*Kyrie
(Distler, Hugo) [Ger] cor&SATB,acap (med)
BAREN. BA 1049 $.40 see also Liturgische
Satze (N316)

NEUNMALIGES KYRIE MAGNAE DEUS POTENTIE *Kyrie
(Distler, Hugo) [Ger] SATB&SATB,acap (med
diff) BAREN. BA 1047 $.65 see also
Liturgische Satze (N317)

NEUNMALIGES KYRIE MAGNAE DEUS POTENTIAE 1531
*Gen,Kyrie,16th cent
(Distler, Hugo) [Lat] SATB&SATB,acap (med
diff) BAREN. BA 1047 $.65 (N318)

NEVENS, DAVID
Three Canticles Of Thomas a Kempis *CC3U
dbl cor,acap voc sc NOVELLO s.p. (N319)

NEVER A CHILD AS HE see Niblock

NEVER ALONE see Anonymous

NEVER DO BELLS SOUND MORE SWEETLY *Xmas,carol,
Ger
(Ehret, Walter) SA,opt bells FRANK F-612 $.35
(N320)
(Ehret, Walter) SSA,opt bells FRANK F-676
$.35 (N321)
(Ehret, Walter) SAB,opt bells FRANK F-675
$.35 (N322)

NEVER GROW TIRED OF PRAYING
SATB BIG3 $.25 (N323)

NEVER WAS A CHILD SO LOVELY *Xmas,carol/folk
(Parsons; Niles) 4pt mix cor,acap oct
SCHIRM.G 9534 $.30 (N324)
(Parsons; Niles) 3pt wom cor,acap oct
SCHIRM.G 9794 $.25 (N325)

NEVER WAS A CHILD SO LOVELY see Niles, John
Jacob

NEVER WEATHER-BEATEN SAIL see Armstrong, Thomas

NEVIN
Holy Hour, The
(Heartz) SSA BOSTON 593 $.30 (N326)

Rosary, The
(Churchill) SATB oct PLYMOUTH CH-104 $.25
(N327)

NEVIN, E.
Rosary, The
(Richardson, A.) SSAATB oct PRESSER
312-40280 $.30 (N328)

NEVIN, GEORGE [BALCH] (1859-1933)
Into The Woods My Master Went *Easter
SATB oct PRESSER 332-13935 $.30 (N329)

Jesus, My Saviour, Look On Me *Bibl
4pt mix cor,S solo SCHIRM.G 4027 $.25
(N330)

4pt men cor,T solo oct SCHIRM.G 7664 $.25
(N331)

NEVIN, GORDON BALCH (1892-1943)
Crucified *Easter
SATB PRESSER $.85 (N332)

Easy Anthems For Intermediate Choirs, Book 1
*CCU,anthem
SAB/SSA BELWIN $1.25 (N333)

NEVIN, GORDON BALCH (cont'd.)
Easy Anthems For Intermediate Choirs, Book 2
*CCU,anthem
SAB BELWIN $1.25 (N334)

Easy Anthems For Intermediate Choirs, Book 3
*CCU,anthem
SAB BELWIN $1.25 (N335)

NEW
Advent *Adv
(Kurtz) 2pt oct PRO ART 1169 $.16 (N336)

NEW BORN AGAIN see Ehret, Walter

NEW BORN AGAIN see Kuykendall, F.

NEW-BORN BABE, THE see Bach, Johann Sebastian,
Das Neugebor'ne Kindelein

NEW BORN KING see Mc Lin, Lena

NEW BORN KING, THE see Morrison, R.

NEW CHRISTMAS CAROL, A see Johnson, David N.

NEW CHRISTMAS SONGS see Schroeter

NEW COMMANDMENT, A see Burroughs, Bob

NEW COVENANT, THE see York, D.

NEW COVENTRY *Xmas,carol,16th cent
(Little) 4pt mix cor,S/T solo oct SCHIRM.G
10515 $.25 (N337)

NEW CREATION, A see Ball, Eric

NEW CREATURE, A see Wilson, John F.

NEW DAY, A see Thygerson

NEW DIMENSION, A see Martin

NEW HALLELUJAH, THE
(Carmichael) SATB,org,2fl,2ob,2clar,4trp,
horn,4trom,5vln,2vla,3vcl,3bvl,drums,timp,
gtr oct WORD CS-2432 $.75, ipa (N338)

NEW HEART WILL I GIVE YOU, A see Beck, John
Ness

NEW HEAVEN AND A NEW EARTH, A see Gaul, Alfred
Robert

NEW IS OLD, THE see Pfautsch, Lloyd

NEW IS THE TRIUMPH see Monte, de, Nuovo Trionfo

NEW KING, THE see Cain, Noble

NEW LIGHT, THE see Van Vactor, David

NEW LOOK AT THE PSALMS, A *folk
(Bevan, Bowles) cong&cor (easy) cmplt ed
WEINBERGER s.p.
contains: Psalm 14; Psalm 15; Psalm 95;
Psalm 100; Psalm 121 (N339)

NEW MASS FOR CONGREGATIONS, A see Andrews, C.T.

NEW MEANING FOR OUR AGE see Bitgood, Roberta

NEW MIND, A see Carmichael, Ralph

NEW MUSIC FOR WORSHIP *CCU
SATB FISCHER,C O-4846 $1.50 (N340)

NEW NAME IN GLORY, A
(Boersma) SAB oct WORD CS-2344 $.30 (N341)

NEW NOEL, A see Whitney

NEW OLD CAROL see Pitfield, Thomas Baron

NEW PLYMOUTH CANTATA see Meyerowitz, Jan

NEW PRINCE, NEW ROMP see Rand, Geffrey

NEW PROPHETS, THE *CC14U,Gen,folk/hymn/Psalm
unis,gtr (easy) cmplt ed GIA G1499 $1.00
(N342)

NEW PSALM, A see Alexander, Josef

NEW SETTINGS OF TWENTY WELL-KNOWN HYMNTUNES see
Wood, Dale

NEW SONG, A see Copes, V. Earle

NEW SONG, A *CC13U,hymn
cor,org CONCORDIA 3-1079 $.10 (N343)

NEW SONG, A see Kay

NEW SONG, A see Burroughs, B.

NEW SONG, A see Burroughs, Bob

NEW SONG, A see Hustad, Donald P.

NEW SONG, A see Kraft, Leo

NEW SONG, A see Miller, Thomas A.

NEW SONG, A see Richman, V.

NEW SONGS AND CAROLS FOR CHILDREN see Grime,
William

NEW SONGS FOR THE CHURCH BOOK 1 see Barrett-
Ayres, Reginald

NEW SONGS FOR THE CHURCH BOOK 2 *CCU
unis,kbd GALLIARD 2.9054.1 $1.75 (N344)

NEW SONGS FOR THE JUNIOR CHOIR see Bristol, Lee
H., Jr.

NEW TWENTY-THIRD, THE see Carmichael, Ralph

NEW VIBRATIONS see Smith, Tedd

NEW WINE see Carmichael, Ralph

NEW YEAR CAROL see Lynn, George

NEW YEAR CAROL, A see Stevens, Halsey

NEW YEAR CAROL, A see Britten, Benjamin

NEW YEAR COMES FLYING *Xmas
(Kozinski, D.) SATB,acap oct PRESSER
312-40253 $.30 (N345)

NEW YEAR'S DAY see Coates, Eric

NEW YEAR'S PRAYER see Fromm, Herbert

NEWBOLD, DAVID
Ode, Or Psalme, To God, An *anthem
mix cor,acap oct NOVELLO 40.1551.07 s.p.
(N346)

Susanni *Xmas,carol
SATB,org/pno NOVELLO AP231 $.35 (N347)

NEWBORN BABE, THE see Buxtehude, Dietrich, Das
Neugeborne Kindelein

NEWBORN BABY see Van Horn

NEWBORN KING, THE see Jacob, Gordon

NEWBURY
Awake, Thou That Sleepest
SATB oct SACRED S-72 $.35 (N348)

Christ Is Born *Xmas
SATB oct HERITAGE H28 $.40 (N349)

Follow Me
SATB oct HERITAGE H2147 $.35 (N350)

Give Praise To God
SATB,acap WARNER W7-1052 $.35 (N351)

God Is Our Refuge And Strength
SATB oct SACRED S-8 $.35 (N352)

Great And Wonderful Are Thy Deeds
SATB oct SACRED S-83 $.35 (N353)

Hear, O Lord
SATB KJOS 5804 $.30 (N354)
SSA KJOS 6112 $.30 (N355)

His Name Is Exalted
SATB,acap oct PRO ART 2325 $.30 (N356)

I Long For Thy Salvation
SATB,acap SOUTHERN $.30 (N357)

Let The Word Of Christ
SATB,acap (med diff/diff) SOUTHERN $.30
(N358)
SATB SOUTHERN $.30 (N359)

Lord, Hear My Cry *Gen
SATB SCHMITT 8031 $.30 (N360)

Lord Will Be Glorified
SATB KJOS 5419 $.30 (N361)

May You Be Strengthened
SATB,acap WARNER W7-1020 $.30 (N362)

Now We Are Singing Once Again *Xmas
SATB oct HERITAGE H61 $.35 (N363)

Praise The Lord *Gen
SATB SCHMITT 8061 $.35 (N364)

Psalm 117
SATB STANDARD A17MX3 $.50 (N365)

Rejoice In The Lord
SATB,acap WARNER W7-1022 (N366)
SSA,acap WARNER W7-1021 $.35 (N367)

Sing For Joy, O Heavens
SATB,acap WARNER W7-1051 $.30 (N368)

Sing Praises To The Lord *Contemp
SATB ALFRED 6571 $.35 (N369)

Sing To Him
SATB oct HERITAGE H24 $.35 (N370)

There Is No Other God
SATB KJOS 5420 $.30 (N371)

NEWBURY, KENT A.
And They Fell Down And Worshipped Him
SATB FLAMMER A 5592 $.30 (N372)

Be Exalted, O Lord
SATB SHAWNEE A 1039 $.30 (N373)

Beatitudes, The
SSA oct AGAPE SP 704 $.30 (N374)

Behold I Stand At The Door *Bibl
4pt mix cor,acap oct SCHIRM.G 11812 $.30
(N375)

Behold, Your God Will Come *Adv,Bibl
4pt mix cor,acap oct SCHIRM.G 11650 $.25
(N376)

Blessed Are Those Who Believe *Easter,Bibl
4pt mix cor,acap oct SCHIRM.G 11655 $.30 (N377)

Break Forth Into Joy *Fest
4pt mix cor,org/pno oct SCHIRM.G 11904 $.35
(N378)

Christ Is Made The Sure Foundation *Easter
SATB oct AGAPE A 443 $.30 (N379)

Christ Is Risen, Alleluia (Christ Is Born,
Alleluia) *Xmas/Easter
SATB,acap oct LAWSON 51502 $.30 (N380)

Christmas Symbol, The *Xmas,anthem
unis,2treb inst,pno,opt bvl&gtr (easy) oct
MCAFEE M1014 $.35 (N381)

Cliche Suite
SATB oct AGAPE WR 1007 $.30 (N382)

Egotist And Poets, The
treb cor oct AGAPE SP 707 $.30 (N383)

For We Have Seen His Star *Epiph,Bibl
4pt mix cor,acap oct SCHIRM.G 11533 $.25
(N384)

For You Shall Go Out In Joy *Xmas/Gen,Bibl
3pt wom cor oct SCHIRM.G 11653 $.25 (N385)
4pt mix cor oct SCHIRM.G 11615 $.30 (N386)

NEWBURY, KENT A. (cont'd.)

2pt wom cor oct SCHIRM.G 11654 $.25 (N387)

Give Ear To My Words *anthem/Bibl
4pt mix cor,acap oct SCHIRM.G 11931 $.25
                                         (N388)

Gloria *Xmas
4pt mix cor,org/pno oct SCHIRM.G 11902 $.30
                                         (N389)

Go Ye Forth, America
SATB oct AGAPE SP 693 $.35 (N390)

God Reigns Over The Nations
SATB,acap FLAMMER A 5557 $.30 (N391)

Great Is The Lord *Bibl
4pt mix cor,org/pno oct SCHIRM.G 11813 $.30
                                         (N392)

Hallelujah
SATB LEONARD-US 08021440 $.35 (N393)

Hear My Prayer, O Lord *Bibl
4pt mix cor,acap oct SCHIRM.G 11578 $.30
                                         (N394)

Hosanna *Easter
4pt mix cor,org oct SCHIRM.G 11350 $.30
                                         (N395)

How Lovely Is Thy Dwelling Place *Bibl
4pt mix cor,acap oct SCHIRM.G 11903 $.30
                                         (N396)

I Am *Gen,cant
oct AGAPE $1.50 (N397)

I Bring You Good News
SATB SHAWNEE A 1178 $.30 (N398)

I Long For Thy Salvation *anthem/Bibl
4pt mix cor,acap oct SCHIRM.G 11943 $.30 (N399)

I Will Praise God With A Song
SATB oct AGAPE A 420 $.30 (N400)

I Will Sing And Give Praise
SATB,acap SHAWNEE A 816 $.30 (N401)

Jacob's Ladder
SATB SHAWNEE A 814 $.35 (N402)
SSA SHAWNEE B 241 $.30 (N403)

Jesus Is Born In Bethlehem *Xmas
SATB LEONARD-US 08032320 $.30 (N404)
SSA LEONARD-US 08032480 $.30 (N405)

Keep His Commandments *Bibl
4pt mix cor,acap oct SCHIRM.G 11778 $.25
                                         (N406)

Late Autumn
SSA oct AGAPE CE 4327 $.30 (N407)

Let Earth Rejoice
SATB oct AGAPE 4323 $.30 (N408)

Let My Cry Come Before Thee *Bibl
3pt mix cor,acap oct SCHIRM.G 11392 $.25
                                         (N409)
3pt wom cor,acap oct SCHIRM.G 11387 $.25
                                         (N410)

Let The Word Of Christ
4pt mix cor oct SCHIRM.G 11938 $.30
                                         (N411)

Let Them Ever Sing For Joy *Bibl
4pt mix cor,acap oct SCHIRM.G 11666 $.30 (N412)

Lift Up Your Heads
SSATBB LEONARD-US 08036960 $.25 (N413)

Lobe Den Herren *anthem/hymn
"Praise To The Lord" 4pt mix cor,org/pno
oct SCHIRM.G 11944 $.30 (N414)

Lord Is My Salvation *Gen/Thanks,anthem
SATB oct BELWIN 2211 $.30 (N415)

Lord Is My Strength And My Song, The
SATB FLAMMER A 5603 $.30 (N416)

Mighty One, The (from Psalm 50)
unis,pno,opt bvl,gtr (easy) oct MCAFEE
M1031 $.35 (N417)

Now Sing Praise To The Lord
SATB FLAMMER A 5585 $.30 (N418)

Now Songs For Church Year *CCU
FLAMMER GE5025 $1.00 (N419)

O Come Let Us Sing Unto The Lord
SSA/SAA oct LAWSON 51199 $.35 (N420)

O Give Thanks To The Lord
SATB SHAWNEE A 928 $.30 (N421)

O Lamb Of God
4pt mix cor,acap oct SCHIRM.G 11557 $.25
                                         (N422)

On Them Hath Light Shined
SATB oct AGAPE A 434 $.25 (N423)

Palm Sunday Procession *Palm
4pt mix cor,org oct SCHIRM.G 11946 $.35 (N424)

Praise To The Lord *see Lobe Den Herren

Prepare The Way Of The Lord *Adv,Bibl
4pt mix cor,org/pno oct SCHIRM.G 11709 $.30
                                         (N425)

Psalm 150
SATB,acap oct LAWSON 638 $.35 (N426)
SSAA,acap oct LAWSON 51204 $.30 (N427)

Responses For The Church Service *CC22U
SATB,acap oct SCHIRM.G 11420 $.30 (N428)

Ring Out, Wild Bells
4pt mix cor oct SCHIRM.G 11815 $.45 (N429)

Save Us, O Lord *Bibl
4pt mix cor,acap oct SCHIRM.G 11699 $.30
                                         (N430)

Sing His Praises, Alleluia
TTBB oct AGAPE MM 9001 $.30 (N431)

Sing To His Name
SATB oct AGAPE A 452 $.30 (N432)

Sing To The Lord A New Song
SATB,acap SHAWNEE A 1032 $.35 (N433)

NEWBURY, KENT A. (cont'd.)

This Is The Day Which The Lord Hath Made
SATB oct AGAPE A 429 $.30 (N434)

Three Seasons
SSA oct AGAPE SP 702 $.40 (N435)

Three Short Holy Week Anthems *CC3U,Easter,
anthem/Bibl
4pt mix cor,acap oct SCHIRM.G 11349 $.30
                                         (N436)

We've Only Begun
SATB oct AGAPE SP 700 $.25 (N437)

Wisdom And Understanding
SSA oct AGAPE SP 692 $.30 (N438)

With A Voice Of Singing
SATB oct WORD CS-2496 $.30 (N439)

Ye Servants Of God *Gen/Thanks,anthem
SATB,pno,opt bvl&gtr (med easy) oct MCAFEE
M1015 $.40 (N440)

You Are The Light Of The World *Bibl
4pt mix cor,org/pno oct SCHIRM.G 11777 $.25
                                         (N441)

NEWE TEUTSCHE LIEDER 1577 see Lechner, Leonhard

NEWMAN

This Is My Prayer
(Stickles) 2pt jr cor,org/pno BOSTON 2897
$.30 (N442)
(Stickles) SSA,org/pno BOSTON 11895 $.35
                                         (N443)
(Stickles) SATB,org/pno BOSTON 2342 $.30
                                         (N444)

NEWS OF GREAT JOY see Means, Claude

NEWTON

Angels Roll The Rock Away
see SIX EASTER CAROLS

Christ Is Risen *Easter
(Bagnall) unis jr cor oct FISCHER,J 9667
$.30 (N445)

Easter Carol *Easter,carol
(Bliss; Brandon) SATB oct BOURNE 862 $.30
                                         (N446)

Every Morning Mercies New
SA,pno (easy) oct WILLIS 2821 $.12 (N447)

Far From My Heavenly Home
3pt wom cor,opt pno (easy) oct WILLIS 2860
$.12 (N448)

Jesus, The Very Thought Of Thee
3pt wom cor,opt acap (easy) oct WILLIS 2862
$.10 (N449)

Lead Us, O Father
SSAA,opt acap (easy) oct WILLIS 2955 $.12
                                         (N450)

Lord Of All Being
SA,pno (easy) oct WILLIS 2822 $.12 (N451)

Sing Praises To Our God
(Davis) SATB oct PLYMOUTH DC-113 $.25
                                         (N452)

NEWTON, ERNEST

First Christmas Morn
SATB LEONARD-ENG 43 s.p. (N453)

God, Who Madest Earth And Heaven
SATB LEONARD-ENG 35 s.p. (N454)

O Blest Redeemer!
2pt ENOCH TP28 s.p. (N455)

NI SALMETONER, HEFTE I see Geitvik, S.H.

NI SALMETONER, HEFTE II see Geitvik, S.H.

N'IA GAIRE QUE AUVIT *Xmas,carol,Fr
(Smith; Gregg) "Long, Long Time Ago, A" [Eng/
Fr] 4pt mix cor,2 high soli,acap oct
SCHIRM.G 11760 $.35 (N456)

NIBLOCK

Never A Child As He
SA/TB SHAWNEE E37 $.30 (N457)

NICENE CREED see Purcell, Henry

NICENE CREED, THE see Purcell, Henry

NICHEL, EKKEHART

God Calling Yet *anthem
unis,hpsd,rec/org (easy) oct AUGSBURG 0313
$.35 (N458)

NICHOL

Kingdom Of Love And Light, The
(Landon) SATB oct LORENZ B28 $.30 (N459)

We've A Story To Tell To The Nations
(Schubert) SATB oct LILLENAS AN-1192 $.35
                                         (N460)

NICHOL, H. ERNEST

We've A Story To Tell To The Nation
(Parker) SSAA,pno/gtr oct LAWSON 51357 $.30 (N461)

NICHOLS

O Come And Sing Unto The Lord
SATB (easy) ALLANS 440 s.p. (N462)

Son Of Man
SATB FLAMMER A 5578 $.30 (N463)

There Was Christ With God
SATB FLAMMER A 5577 $.30 (N464)

Walking With God
unis oct LILLENAS AN-1147 $.30 (N465)

NICHOLS, ANNA MAE

O Come And Sing Unto The Lord
SATB oct AGAPE CH 606 $.30 (N466)

O Sons And Daughters, Let Us Sing
SATB oct AGAPE A 341 $.25 (N467)

Sing Praise To God *CCU
SAB oct AGAPE $1.75 (N468)

NICHOLS, ANNA MAE (cont'd.)

Spirit Divine, Come Dwell Within
SATB oct AGAPE A 392 $.25 (N469)

NICHOLS, T.

Praise Ye Him
SATB FLAMMER A 5579 $.30 (N470)

Reach Out *Easter
SATB oct PRESSER G-130 $.35 (N471)

NICHOLS, TED

His Love *Xmas
SATB oct AGAPE A 351 $.25 (N472)

Opus For Contemporary Decision *Gen,cant
oct AGAPE $.90 (N473)

There Comes A Time
mix cor oct AGAPE CF 147 $.30 (N474)

NICHOLSON

Winter Birth, A *Xmas
SSAA MARKS 4480 $.30 (N475)
SATB MARKS 4521 $.30 (N476)

NICHOLSON, RALPH

Winter Birth, A *Xmas
SATB,pno WEINBERGER s.p. (N477)
SA,pno WEINBERGER s.p. (N478)

NICHOLSON, RICHARD (1570?-1639?)

O Pray For The Peace Of Jerusalem (Psalm 122)
Ded/Gen
SAATB,opt inst (med easy) oct OXFORD 43.369
$.35 (N479)

Psalm 122 *see O Pray For The Peace Of
Jerusalem

NICHOLSON, S.H.

Anthem For Christmastide *Xmas,anthem
SATB,org CRAMER A4 s.p. (N480)

Anthem For Easter And Other Festivals
 *Easter,anthem
SATB,org CRAMER A 6 s.p. (N481)

Anthem For Penetential Seasons
SATB,org CRAMER A 18 s.p. (N482)

Be Strong In The Lord *Gen,anthem
2pt jr cor/2pt wom cor CURWEN 71528 s.p.
                                         (N483)
(Curwen) SS,opt pno oct ROYAL s.p. see also
ANTHEMS FOR UNISON OR TWO PART SINGING
                                         (N484)

Children Of The Chapel
SATB/boy cor sc ROYAL 315 s.p., cor pts
ROYAL 316 s.p., voc sc ROYAL 317 s.p.
                                         (N485)

Come Let Us Join *Easter,anthem
SATB,org CRAMER A 6 s.p. (N486)

Let Us With A Gladsome Mind *Harv,anthem
SATB oct ROYAL 243 s.p. (N487)

Love Divine, All Loves Excelling *Gen,anthem
SATB oct ROYAL 212 s.p. (N488)

Magnificat And Nunc Dimittis *Magnif/Nunc
SATB (D flat maj) oct NOVELLO s.p. (N489)

Ode On The Birth Of Our Saviour, An
see Holman, Derek, Sweet Was The Song The
Virgin Sang

Teach Us, Good Lord *Gen,anthem
SS oct ROYAL 205 s.p. (N490)

NICHT ALSO STRENG see Weber, Bernhard

NICHT SO TRAURIG see Bach, Johann Sebastian

NICHT SO VIEL SCHEIDEN VON DER LIEBE GOTTES
see Buxtehude, Dietrich

NICHT UNS, HERR see Graap, Lothar

NICHT UNS, HERR, SONDERN DEINEM NAMEN see
Schutz, Heinrich

NICHT UNS, O HERR, GIB EHRE see Haydn, (Franz)
Joseph

NICHTS SOLL UNS SCHEIDEN VON DER LIEBE GOTTES
see Buxtehude, Dietrich

NICKEL, ECKEHARDT

Es Kommt Ein Schiff
jr cor,inst HANSSLER 12.211 sc s.p., voc sc
s.p. contains also: Gast, Macht Hoch Die
Tur (jr cor,inst) (N491)

Herr Christe, Treuer Heiland Wert
unis jr cor,org,S rec,A rec sc HANSSLER
12.209 s.p. contains also: Prautzsch,
Ludwig, Siehe, Ich Habe Dir Geboten (unis
jr cor&cor,rec,inst) (N492)

NICOLAI

Now Let All The Earth Adore Thee
(Bach; Lowden) SAB FLAMMER D5027 $.30
                                         (N493)
(Bach; Lowden) SA/TB FLAMMER E5087 $.30
                                         (N494)

Now Let Every Tongue Adore Thee
(Bach; Cain) SAB FLAMMER D5110 $.25 (N495)

O Holy Spirit, Enter In *anthem
(Moe) SSA (med) oct AUGSBURG 1402 $.20
                                         (N496)

Wake, Awake, For Night Is Flying *Xmas
(Bach) SATB BAR SCHMITT 1923 $.25 (N497)

NICOLAI, OTTO (1810-1849)

Der Herr Ist Konig (Psalm 97)
[Ger] SATB voc sc BOTE s.p. (N498)

Ehre Sei Gott In Der Hohe (Psalm 30)
[Ger] 8pt mix cor voc sc BOTE s.p. (N499)

Herr, Auf Dich Traue Ich (Psalm 31)
[Ger] 8pt mix cor voc sc BOTE s.p. (N500)

Psalm 30 *see Ehre Sei Gott In Der Hohe

NICOLAI, OTTO (cont'd.)

Psalm 31 *see Herr, Auf Dich Traue Ich

Psalm 97 *see Der Herr Ist Konig

Te Deum *Te Deum
(Schliepe, Ernst) [Lat] mix cor,soli,orch
BOTE s.p. (N501)

NICOLAI, PHILIPP (1556-1608)
Gloria Sei Dir Gesungen (from Wachet Auf)
Xmas,chorale
"Now Let Every Tongue Adore Thee" SATB,pno
SCHIRM.EC 354 $.30, ipr (N502)
(Bach; Ehret) "Now Let Every Tongue Adore
Thee" SAB oct SPRATT 597 $.25 (N503)
(Bach, J.S.; Davison, A.) "Now Let Every
Tongue Adore Thee" TTBB,pno SCHIRM.EC 30
$.30, ipr (N504)
(Bach, J.S.; Davison, A.) "Now Let Every
Tongue Adore Thee" SSA,pno SCHIRM.EC 1510
$.30 (N505)
(Glaser, V.) "Now Let Every Tongue Adore
Thee" SAB,pno SCHIRM.EC 2403 $.25 (N506)

Hear Thy Praise
(Lundquist) SSATTB,acap (diff) oct WILLIS
5730 $.12 (N507)

How Bright Appears The Morning Star *see Wie
Schon Leucht' Uns Der Morgenstern

How Brightly Beams The Morning Star *Xmas
(Paget) mix cor CURWEN 80903 s.p. (N508)

How Brightly Shines The Morning Star *see
Wie Schon Leucht' Uns Der Morgenstern

How Brightly Shines Yon Morning Star *see
Wie Schon Leuchtet Der Morgenstern
[Chorale]

How Lovely The Morning Star *see Wie Schon
Leucht' Uns Die Morgenstern

Morning Star Upon Us Gleams, The *see Wie
Schon Leucht' Uns Die Morgenstern

Now Let Every Tongue Adore Thee *see Gloria
Sei Dir Gesungen

Oh Holy Spirit, Enter In
(Bach, J.S.; Stuart) SATB oct PRO ART 1444
$.20 (N509)

Three Kings From Persian Lands *see
Cornelius, Peter

Wachet Auf, Ruft Uns Die Stimme *anthem
(Bach) "Wake, Awake" SATB (easy) oct
AUGSBURG 1320 $.22 (N510)
(Christiansen, F.M.) "Wake, Awake" SSAATTBB
(diff) oct AUGSBURG 0102 $.15 (N511)

Wake, Awake *see Wachet Auf, Ruft Uns Die
Stimme

Wie Schon Leucht' Uns Der Morgenstern *Xmas
"How Brightly Shines The Morning Star"
SATB,brass oct FISCHER,C CM-612 $.25, ipa
(N512)
(Bach; Coggin) "How Bright Appears The
Morning Star" SAB FLAMMER D5175 $.25 (N513)

Wie Schon Leucht' Uns Die Morgenstern *Xmas,
anthem
(Christiansen, Paul) "Morning Star Upon Us
Gleams, The" SATB (easy) oct AUGSBURG
1159 $.25 (N514)
(Spiro) "How Lovely The Morning Star" SATB
oct PRO ART 1340 $.20 (N515)

Wie Schon Leuchtet Der Morgenstern [Chorale]
*chorale
(Bach, J.S.) "How Brightly Shines Yon
Morning Star" mix cor,acap SCHIRM.EC 1781
$.30 (N516)

NICOLAU, [ANTONIO] (1858-1933)
At Montserrat
(Williamson) SATTBB oct SCHIRM.G 7503 $.20
(N517)

NICOLOSI, SALVATORE
Ave Regina
see QUATTRO ANTIFONE MARIANE

Cor Jesu Flagrans
see TRE CANTICI AL S. CUORE DI GESU

Dopo La Consacrazione
see Due Canti Eucaristici

Due Canti Eucaristici *Commun
[Lat] unis,org ZANIBON 174 s.p.
contains: Dopo La Consacrazione; Prima La
Consacrazione (N518)

Inno Popolare A S. Vincenzo De' Paoli *ASD,
hymn
[Lat] unis ZANIBON 176 s.p. (N519)

Iste Confessor
see INNI DE COMUNE

O Esca Viatorum
see SEI MOTTETTI EUCARISTICI

O Quot Undis *hymn
[Lat] unis/4pt mix cor ZANIBON 177 s.p.
(N520)

Prima La Consacrazione
see Due Canti Eucaristici

Stabat Mater *BVM
[Lat] SA/TB,org sc ZANIBON 416 s.p., cor
pts ZANIBON 416BIS s.p. (N521)

Tantum Ergo
see RACCOLTA DI SEI INNI

NICOLSON, R.
Cantate Domino Canticum Novum
(Simkins) [Lat] SSATB AMP 24 $.30 (N522)

O Pray For The Peace Of Jerusalem
(Simkins) SAATB AMP 23 $.30 (N523)

NICOU-CHARON
Messe De La Nativite *Xmas,Mass
[Lat] SSS,opt vln&vla&vcl&bvl&org HEUGEL
s.p. (N524)

NIE ZU STILLEN IST DIE SEHNSUCHT see Lehman,
Siegfried

NIEDERMANN, G.
Der Tod Jesu
[Ger] mix cor,acap (easy) HUG (N525)

Herr, Mein Gott, Verlass Mich Nicht! "Da Die
Tage So Voll Not"
(Schuler, G.) [Ger] wom cor,acap (med) HUG
s.p. (N526)

NIEDERMEYER, LOUIS (1802-1861)
Ave Maria
[Lat] cor,S/B solo,opt pno/org (F maj)
HEUGEL s.p. (N527)
[Lat] cor,S/T solo,opt pno/org (C maj)
HEUGEL s.p. (N528)

Deuxieme Messe Breve *Mass
[Lat] 4pt mix cor (G maj) HEUGEL voc sc
s.p., voc pt s.p. (N529)

Pater Noster *Gen,mot
[Lat] cor HEUGEL s.p. see from CHANTS
RELIGIEUX (N530)
[Lat] opt cor,Mez/Bar/S/T solo,org oct
DURAND s.p. (N531)
[Lat] SATB,solo,opt pno/org HEUGEL voc sc
s.p., voc pt s.p. (N532)

Pie Jesu
[Lat] SATB,med solo HEUGEL s.p. see from LA
MAITRISE (N533)

NIEHAUS, LENNIE
His Steadfast Love Endures Forever
SATB oct WORD CS-2559 $.45 (N534)

Let Us Sing To The Lord
SATB oct WORD CS-2558 $.40 (N535)

NIEHAUS, MANFRED (1933-)
Proprien-Messe *Mass
mix cor sc GERIG 880 s.p. (N536)

NIELAND, H.
Negro Spirituals *CCU,spir
2-3pt wom cor BROEKMANS 785 s.p. (N537)

Singet Frisch Und Wohlgemut *Xmas
4pt mix cor BROEKMANS 907 s.p. (N538)

NIELAND, JAN
Prayer Of Saint Francis *prayer
2 eq voices,org oct WORLD ESA-512-2 $.30
(N539)
3 eq voices,org oct WORLD ESA-513-3 $.30
(N540)
SATB,org oct WORLD ESA-514-8 $.30 (N541)

NIELSEN, CARL (1865-1931)
Affictus Sum
see Three Motets For A Capella

Benedictus Dominus
see Three Motets For A Capella

Dominus Regit Me
see Three Motets For A Capella

Three Motets For A Capella *mot
[Lat] cor,acap SKAND. SMF4414 s.p.
contains: Affictus Sum; Benedictus
Dominus; Dominus Regit Me (N542)

NIELSEN, RICCARDO (1908-)
Psalm 69 *see Psalmus In Confessione

Psalmus In Confessione (Psalm 69)
mix cor,2pno ZERBONI 4025 rental (N543)

NIEMAN, ALFRED
Sir Christemas *Xmas
SA/TB,pno/harp GALAXY CCL677 $.40 (N544)

NIEMAND HAT GROSSERE LIEBE see Thomas, Kurt

NIEMAND HAT GROSSERE LIEBE see Weismann,
Wilhelm

NIEMAND KANN JESUS EINEN HERRN NENNEN see Reda,
Siegfried

NIEUWENHOVEN, H. V.
Exaudi Deus Deprecationem Meam (Psalm 60)
mix cor ALSBACH&D sc s.p., cor pts s.p.
(N545)

Gloria
men cor ALSBACH&D sc s.p., cor pts s.p.
(N546)

Hymne Aan De Vrede
men cor ALSBACH&D sc s.p., cor pts s.p.
(N547)

Psalm 60 *see Exaudi Deus Deprecationem Meam

Salve Regina
mix cor ALSBACH&D sc s.p., cor pts s.p.
(N548)

NIGGLI, F.
Beresinalied
[Ger] mix cor,acap (easy) HUG (N549)

Wieder Raunt In Allen Gassen *Xmas
(Hagni, R.) [Ger] wom cor,acap (med easy)
HUG s.p. (N550)

NIGHT AFTER CHRISTMAS, THE see Grime, William

NIGHT, COLD AND SOMBER see Lassus, Roland de
(Orlandus), La Nuit Froide Et Sombre

NIGHT HYMN see Butler

NIGHT IS CALLING see Brown, Mary Helen

NIGHT IS DEPARTING, THE see Mendelssohn-
Bartholdy, Felix

NIGHT IS FAR SPENT, THE see Nystedt, Knut

NIGHT JOURNEY OF THE WISE MEN see Morgan

NIGHT OF FEAR IS OVER, THE see Hart, Fritz

NIGHT OF HOLY MEMORIES see Wilson, Ira B.

NIGHT OF NIGHTS see Jacobus, Dale Asher

NIGHT OF THE STAR see Carleton

NIGHT OF WONDER see Bach, Johann Christoph
Friedrich

NIGHT OF WONDER see Hulse, Camil Van

NIGHT OF WONDER see Kirk, Theron W.

NIGHT WINDS see Rozell

NIGHTINGALE CAROL see Hovdesven, E.A.

NIGHTINGALE, MAE [WHEELER] (1898-)
Young Singers' Choir Book *CC34U
SATB/jr cor FISCHER,C O-3921 $1.50 (N551)

NIGHTLY PRAYER see Di Ianni

NIGRA SUM see Palestrina, Giovanni

NIKOLSKY
Dear Lord And Master
mix cor SOUTHERN $.25 (N552)

NIKOLSKY, A.
Earth Is The Lord's, The
SATB oct FISCHER,J 4469 $.30 (N553)

O Taste And See
SATB oct FISCHER,J 4171 $.30 (N554)
(McKinney) SSA oct FISCHER,J 9386 $.30 (N555)

NIKOLSKY, ANTON
Dear Lord And Master
SATB oct BOURNE BL3037 $.25 (N556)

N'ILAH SERVICE see Binder, Abraham Wolfe

NILES, DAVID
Cantata On Appalachian Christmas Carols
(composed with Holden, [Oliver]) *Xmas,
cant,US
wom cor,Mez/Bar solo,pno/org voc sc
SCHIRM.G $1.00 (N557)

NILES, JOHN JACOB (1892-)
Bells Of Heaven, The *Xmas
4pt mix cor,acap SCHIRM.G 10493 $.20 (N558)

Blessed Bird, The *Xmas
4pt mix cor SCHIRM.G 11330 $.30 (N559)
3pt wom cor,S solo SCHIRM.G 11331 $.30 (N560)

Boundless Mercy
(Horton) 4pt mix cor,AT soli,acap SCHIRM.G
9935 $.25 (N561)

Carol Of The Angels, The *Xmas
3pt wom cor,S solo,acap SCHIRM.G 9674 $.25
(N562)
4pt mix cor,S solo,acap SCHIRM.G 9299 $.25
(N563)

Carol Of The Birds, The *Xmas
(Horton) 2pt wom cor,S solo,acap SCHIRM.G
8987 $.25 (N564)
(Horton) 3pt wom cor,S solo,acap SCHIRM.G
8986 $.25 (N565)
(Horton) mix cor,S solo,acap SCHIRM.G 8988
$.30 (N566)

Down In Yon Forest *Xmas,folk,US
(Niles; Brant) 4pt mix cor,acap SCHIRM.G
8024 $.20 (N567)

Flower Of Jesse *Xmas
3pt wom cor,S solo,acap SCHIRM.G 11592 $.25
(N568)

Gabriel's Message *Xmas
4pt mix cor SCHIRM.G 10760 $.25 (N569)

Garden Hymn
SATB,acap oct SCHIRM.G 10240 $.25 (N570)

God Send Us Peace In Good Time *Xmas
SATB,acap FOSTER MF509 $.35 (N571)

Hebrew Children
3pt wom cor,acap oct SCHIRM.G 9916 $.30
(N572)
(Niles; Horton; Jackson) 4pt mix cor,acap
oct SCHIRM.G 9901 $.20 (N573)

How Firm A Foundation
(Niles) 4pt mix cor,org/pno oct SCHIRM.G
11313 $.30 (N574)
(Niles; Shepherd) 3pt boy cor/3pt wom cor
oct SCHIRM.G 10899 $.25 (N575)

I Wonder As I Wander *Xmas
SSA ALLANS 282 s.p. (N576)
SATB (easy) ALLANS 287 s.p. (N577)
(Horton) 2pt boy cor/2pt wom cor,med solo
oct SCHIRM.G 9787 $.25 (N578)
(Horton) 4pt wom cor,S solo,acap oct
SCHIRM.G 8305 $.30 (N579)
(Horton) 3pt mix cor,med solo oct SCHIRM.G
9497 $.30 (N580)
(Horton) 2pt wom cor,med solo oct SCHIRM.G
9498 $.30 (N581)
(Horton) 3pt wom cor oct SCHIRM.G 9360 $.30
(N582)
(Horton) 4pt men cor,med solo,acap oct
SCHIRM.G 9292 $.25 (N583)
(Horton) 2pt men cor,med solo oct SCHIRM.G
9788 $.30 (N584)
(Niles; Horton) 4pt mix cor,high solo,acap
oct SCHIRM.G 8708 $.30 (N585)

In Bethlehem That Fair City *Xmas
3pt wom cor,S solo oct SCHIRM.G 11440 $.25
(N586)
4pt mix cor,S solo,acap oct SCHIRM.G 1439
$.25 (N587)

In That Lovely Far-Off City *Xmas
3pt wom cor,S solo,acap oct SCHIRM.G 10315
$.20 (N588)

Jesus, Jesus Rest Your Head *Xmas,carol,US
(Bement) 3pt wom cor,S solo,acap oct
SCHIRM.G 9456 $.30 (N589)
(Fischer) 4pt men cor,T solo,acap oct

NILES, JOHN JACOB (cont'd.)

SCHIRM.G 10622 $.25   (N590)
(Niles; Deis) 2pt wom cor oct SCHIRM.G
10306 $.30   (N591)
(Niles; Warrell) 4pt mix cor,acap oct
SCHIRM.G 8302 $.30   (N592)

Jesus The Christ Is Born *Xmas,folk
(Niles) 4pt mix cor,acap oct SCHIRM.G 8304
$.30   (N593)
(Talmadge) 4pt wom cor,acap oct SCHIRM.G
9454 $.25   (N594)
(Warrell) 4pt mix cor,acap oct SCHIRM.G
8301 $.30   (N595)

Kedron *Xmas
(Niles; Sheppard) SABar oct SCHIRM.G 10970
$.25   (N596)
(Niles; Sheppard) 4pt mix cor oct SCHIRM.G
10712 $.25   (N597)
(Niles; Sheppard) 3pt wom cor oct SCHIRM.G
10708 $.25   (N598)

King Shall Come When Morning Dawns, The
*Xmas,hymn
mix cor,acap oct SCHIRM.G 9269 $.20   (N599)

Little Brother Jesus *Xmas
3pt wom cor,S solo,acap oct SCHIRM.G 11691
$.30   (N600)
4pt mix cor,S solo,acap oct SCHIRM.G 11690
$.30   (N601)

Little Family, The *Easter
4pt mix cor,S solo oct SCHIRM.G 11073 $.25   (N602)
3pt mix cor,S solo oct SCHIRM.G 11089   (N603)
$.25

Lo! How A Rose E'er Blooming *Adv
3pt jr cor/SAB (very easy) FISCHER,C
CM 6729 $.20   (N604)

Mary The Rose *Xmas
mix cor voc sc SCHIRM.G $1.25   (N605)

May Carol, The *Easter/Gen,carol
4pt mix cor,S/T solo oct SCHIRM.G 10238   (N606)
$.25

Miraculous Harvest, The
4pt mix cor,S/T solo,acap oct SCHIRM.G
10498 $.25   (N607)

National Hymn Of Victory *hymn
(Horton) 2pt mix cor/2pt wom cor/2pt men
cor oct SCHIRM.G 8857 $.25   (N608)

Nativity, The *Xmas
4pt mix cor,S solo oct SCHIRM.G 11590 $.25   (N609)
3pt wom cor,S solo oct SCHIRM.G 11591 $.25   (N610)

Never Was A Child So Lovely *Xmas,folk
(Parsons) 4pt mix cor,acap oct SCHIRM.G
9534 $.30   (N611)
(Parsons) 3pt wom cor,acap oct SCHIRM.G
9794 $.25   (N612)

O Come Emmanuel *Adv
3pt jr cor/SAB,acap (med easy) FISCHER,C
CM 6751 $.25   (N613)

Once A Fair Maiden *Xmas
4pt mix cor oct SCHIRM.G 10761 $.25   (N614)

Our Lovely Lady Singing *Xmas
3pt jr cor/SSA (med) FISCHER,C CM 6827 $.30 (N615)

Primrose *Easter
3pt wom cor oct SCHIRM.G 10439 $.20   (N616)

Robin And The Thorn, The *Easter,folk
3pt wom cor,acap oct SCHIRM.G 9511 $.25   (N617)
unis oct SCHIRM.G 9326 $.25   (N618)

See Jesus The Saviour *Xmas,carol,US
4pt mix cor,acap oct SCHIRM.G 8303 $.25   (N619)

Shepherd On The Hill, The
4pt mix cor,Bar solo oct SCHIRM.G 10923   (N620)
$.30

Shepherd's Carol, The *Xmas,carol
SATB,acap FOSTER MF508 $.35   (N621)

Silent Stars *Xmas
SATB,acap oct FISCHER,C CM-6446 $.30   (N622)

Sing We Tne Virgin Mary *Xmas,carol
(Horton) 4pt mix cor,acap oct SCHIRM.G 8884
$.30   (N623)

Star In The East
(Niles; Sheppard) 3pt boy cor/3pt wom cor
oct SCHIRM.G 10897 $.25   (N624)

Sweet Little Boy Jesus *Xmas
(Parsons) 4pt mix cor,acap oct SCHIRM.G
9604 $.25   (N625)
(Parsons) 3pt wom cor,acap oct SCHIRM.G
9599 $.25   (N626)

Sweet Marie And Her Baby *Xmas
3pt wom cor oct SCHIRM.G 9666 $.25   (N627)
2pt wom cor oct SCHIRM.G 9675 $.25   (N628)

Waken, Little Shepherd
4pt mix cor,S solo,acap oct SCHIRM.G 9677
$.25   (N629)

Warrenton
(Niles; Sheppard) 3pt wom cor oct SCHIRM.G
10709 $.25   (N630)
(Niles; Sheppard) 4pt mix cor oct SCHIRM.G
10973 $.25   (N631)

Wayfaring Stranger
mix cor,T solo,acap oct SCHIRM.G 10040 $.35 (N632)

What Songs Were Sung *Xmas
4pt mix cor,acap oct SCHIRM.G 11245 $.25   (N633)
3pt wom cor,S solo,acap oct SCHIRM.G 11246   (N634)
$.25

NILES, JOHN JACOB (cont'd.)

When Jesus Lived In Galilee *Xmas,carol/folk
4pt mix cor&opt unis jr cor,opt S solo,acap
oct SCHIRM.G 9388 $.25   (N635)
3pt wom cor&unis jr cor,S solo,acap oct
SCHIRM.G 9268 $.25   (N636)

Wonder Thing, The *Xmas
SSA,acap FOSTER MF903 $.35   (N637)

Wondrous Love *Xmas
(Niles; Sheppard) 4pt mix cor oct SCHIRM.G
10972 $.25   (N638)
(Niles; Sheppard) 3pt mix cor oct SCHIRM.G
10971 $.25   (N639)
(Niles; Sheppard) 3pt wom cor oct SCHIRM.G
10710 $.25   (N640)

Ye Holy Angels Bright
3pt jr cor/SSA (med) FISCHER,C CM 6789 $.25 (N641)

You Got To Cross That Lonesome Valley *Xmas,
folk,US
3pt wom cor oct SCHIRM.G 9934 $.25   (N642)

N'ILHH KADDISH see Binder, Abraham Wolfe

NILSEN, ING. FREDERIK
Den Apostoliske Trosbekjennelse
[Norw] *mix cor LYCHE 98 s.p.   (N643)

Sanctus *Sanctus
[Lat] mix cor LYCHE 33 s.p.   (N644)

NILSSON, BO (1937-)
Massa For Kristen Enhet
mix cor,org,3fl,bsn,horn sc NORDISKA 10113
s.p., ipa   (N645)

NILSSON, CHRISTIAN
Given At Herren
mix cor NORDISKA 3647 s.p.   (N646)

O Herre Jesu
mix cor NORDISKA 3649 s.p.   (N647)

Snart Ibland De Helga Slakter
mix cor NORDISKA 3648 s.p.   (N648)

Underbar En Stjarna Blid
mix cor NORDISKA 1513 s.p.   (N649)

NILSSON, OLLE
Bar Jesu Minne I Ditt Brost
mix cor NORDISKA 5389 s.p.   (N650)

NILSSON, TORSTEN (1920-)
Blinda Fa Sin Syn *Adv,mot
3pt mix cor NORDISKA 5414 s.p.   (N651)

Bliv Kvar Hos Oss *mot
mix cor NORDISKA 5883 s.p.   (N652)

Da Nu Manniskorna Hade Sett Det Tecken *mot
3pt mix cor NORDISKA 5792 s.p.   (N653)

Den Sten Som Byggnigsmannen Forkastade *mot
3pt mix cor NORDISKA 5787 s.p.   (N654)

Detta Slakte Skall Icke Forgas *Adv,mot
3pt mix cor NORDISKA 5413 s.p.   (N655)

Fader, Forlat Dem *mot
mix cor NORDISKA 5882 s.p.   (N656)

Frid Vare Med Eder *mot
mix cor NORDISKA 5881 s.p.   (N657)

Gladjens Med Mig *mot
3pt mix cor NORDISKA 5409 s.p.   (N658)

Herre, Davids Son, Forbarma Dig *mot
mix cor NORDISKA 5551 s.p.   (N659)

Hosianna, Davids Son *Adv,mot
3pt mix cor NORDISKA 5411 s.p.   (N660)

Jag Ar Den Gode Herden *mot
mix cor NORDISKA 5790 s.p.   (N661)

Jag Ar Rosten Av En Som Ropar *Adv,mot
3pt mix cor NORDISKA 5415 s.p.   (N662)

Jesus Frestas I Oknen *mot
3pt mix cor NORDISKA 5794 s.p.   (N663)

Kommen Till Mig *Refm,mot
mix cor NORDISKA 5804 s.p.   (N664)

Kommen, Ty Nu Ar Allt Redo *mot
mix cor NORDISKA 5804 s.p.   (N665)

Mastare, Vilket Ar Det Yppersta Budet I Lagen
*mot
3pt mix cor NORDISKA 5789 s.p.   (N666)

Mig Given All Makt *mot
mix cor NORDISKA 5386 s.p.   (N667)

O Att Du I Dag Hade Insett *mot
3pt mix cor NORDISKA 5399 s.p.   (N668)

Och Da Skall Man Fa Se *Adv,mot
3pt mix cor NORDISKA 5412 s.p.   (N669)

Om En Manniska Icke Bliver Fodd Pa Nytt *mot
3pt mix cor NORDISKA 5970 s.p.   (N670)

Ordinarium Missae *Mass
[Lat] SATB,acap (diff) BAREN. BA 5409 $3.00 (N671)

Sagen Till Dottern Sion *Adv,mot
3pt mix cor NORDISKA 5410 s.p.   (N672)

Saligt Ar Det Modersskote Som Har Burit Dig
*mot
3pt mix cor NORDISKA 5791 s.p.   (N673)

Se, Vi Ga Upp Till Jerusalem *mot
3pt mix cor NORDISKA 5793 s.p.   (N674)

Valsignad Vare Han *mot
mix cor NORDISKA 5387 s.p.   (N675)

Varen Icke Forskrackta *mot
mix cor NORDISKA 5398 s.p.   (N676)

NILSSON, TORSTEN (cont'd.)

Ve Dig, Korasin *mot
mix cor NORDISKA 5384 s.p.   (N677)

NIMM VON UNS see Bach, Johann Sebastian, Nimm
Von Uns, Herr, Du Treuer Gott

NIMM VON UNS, HERR, DU TREUER GOTT see Bach,
Johann Sebastian

NIMM VON UNS, HERR, DU TREUER GOTT see
Buxtehude, Dietrich

NIMM VON UNS, HERR, DU TREUER GOTT see Poos,
Heinrich

NIMM WAS see Bach, Johann Sebastian, Nimm, Was
Dein Ist, Und Gehe Hin

NIMM, WAS DEIN IST see Bach, Johann Sebastian,
Nimm, Was Dein Ist, Und Gehe Hin

NIMM, WAS DEIN IST, UND GEHE HIN see Bach,
Johann Sebastian

NIN-CULMELL, JOAQUIN (1908-)
Fum, Fum, Fum *Xmas
[Eng/Span] SATB,tamb RONGWEN $.30   (N678)

La Virgen Lava Panales
SATB,tamb RONGWEN $.35   (N679)

Lost Child, The (from Three Traditional Cuban
Songs)
[Eng/Span] SATB,acap RONGWEN $.30   (N680)

NINE ANTHEMS see White, Robert

NINE CAROLS *see As Joseph Was A-Walking;
Coventry Carol; Dives And Lazarus; God Rest
You Merry; I Saw Three Ships; Mummer's
Carol; Virgin Most Pure, A   (N681)

NINE CAROLS *CC9L,Xmas,carol
(Murrill) SSA/SSAA,acap (easy) OXFORD 44.990
$.50
see also: First Nowell, The   (N682)

NINE CHOIR RESPONSES see Williams

NINE EASY CANNONS *CC9U,anthem/canon
(Riedel) SA/SSA/SSAA (easy) oct AUGSBURG 1333
$.25   (N683)

NINE-FOLD KYRIE see Darke, Harold [Edwin]

NINE INTROITS see Goode, Jack C.

NINE MOTETS AND ANTHEMS *CC9L,Gen,anthem/mot
(Lee, J.) SATB (med easy) cmplt ed GIA G1516
$1.25 contains works by: Bach; Casciolini;
Farrent; Lee; Remondi   (N684)

NINE MOTETS see Naylor, Bernard

NINE MUSICAL PACKAGES *CC9L,medley
(Carmichael, Ralph) SATB voc sc WORD 37548
$1.95   (N685)

NINE NEGRO SPRITUALS *CC9U,spir
(Heading, Noel) SSA,pno,gtr ALBERT s.p.   (N686)

NINE SHORT RESPONSES FOR GENERAL SERVICES see
Webb

NINE TENEBRAE MOTETS: FIRST NOCTURN see Rubbra,
Edmund

NINE TENEBRAE MOTETS: SECOND NOCTURN see
Rubbra, Edmund

NINE TENEBRAE MOTETS: THIRD NOCTURN see Rubbra,
Edmund

NINEFOLD KYRIE see Guilmant, Alexandre, Kyrie
Eleison, Alla Palestrina

NINETEEN ANTHEMS VOL. 1 see Tallis, Thomas

NINETEEN ANTHEMS VOL. 2 see Tallis, Thomas

NINETEEN ANTHEMS VOL. 3 see Tallis, Thomas

NINETEEN ANTHEMS VOL. 4 see Tallis, Thomas

NINETEEN CHORAL RESPONSES *CC19U,cor-resp
SATB LORENZ C182 $.30   (N687)

NINETEEN LITURGICAL ROUNDS see Tortolano, W.

NINETEEN RESPONSES AND AMENS see Walton

NINETY AND NINE, THE see Sankey, I.

NINETY AND NINE, THE see Calvisius, Sethus

NINETY AND NINE, THE see Protheroe, Daniel

NINETY AND NINE, THE see Sankey, I.

NINETY-NINE CAROLS *CC99U,Xmas,carol
oct HART s.p.   (N688)

NINNA-NANNA see Picchi, Luigi

NINNA NONNA see Tesoriero

NINO CHIQUIRRITITO see Martin Pompey

NISI DOMINUS see Monteverdi, Claudio

NISI DOMINUS see Tebaldini, Giovanni

NITSCHE, PAUL (1909-)
In Dulci Jubilo
see Zwei Weihnachtslieder

Nun Sei Uns Willkommen
see Zwei Weihnachtslieder

Zwei Weihnachtslieder *Xmas
mix cor TONGER s.p.
contains: In Dulci Jubilo; Nun Sei Uns
Willkommen   (N689)

NOEL, ALL GOOD PEOPLE *Fr
(Ehret) SSA MARKS 4354 $.30   (N775)

NOEL ANCIENS see Clouzot

NOEL BLESOIS AVEC NOEL D'ORLEANS see Tartarin,
A.

NOEL CAROL, THE *Xmas,carol,Fr
(Caldwell, Mary E.) SSA oct GRAY GCMR 2988
$.30   (N776)
(Caldwell, Mary E.) SAB oct GRAY GCMR 2767
$.25   (N777)
(Caldwell, Mary E.) SATB oct GRAY GCMR 2484
$.30   (N778)
(Caldwell, Mary E.) unis oct GRAY GCMR 2991
$.30   (N779)

NOEL CHORUS see Cain, Noble

NOEL, CHRIST IS BORN see Strickland

NOEL (D'ANDICHON) see Vuillermoz, [Jean]

NOEL D'APRES L'ADESTE FIDELES see Borne, Le

NOEL DE FRANCE see Dupre, Marcel

NOEL DE LA MARCHE DES ROIS see Aubanel, Georges

NOEL D'ENFANT see Croze

NOEL D'ENFANT see Darcieux, [F.]

NOEL D'ENFANT see Missa, [Edmond Jean Louis]

NOEL DES ANGES see Agostini, F.

NOEL DES MAGES see Martin, R.P.E.

NOEL DES MUSICIENS see Mc Rae, William

NOEL DES NOELS see Migot, Georges

NOEL DES SABOTS see Agostini, F.

NOEL D'HOLMES see Darcieux, [F.]

NOEL DIALOGUE see Darcieux, [F.]

NOEL DIALOGUE see Parozai, Gui

NOEL EN L'HONNEUR DE LA SAINTE-VIERGE *Xmas,
carol,16th cent
(Dauly, G.) [Fr] 2pt wom cor (med easy)
LEMOINE s.p.   (N780)

NOEL EN L'HONNEUR DE LA SAINTE VIERGE see
Dauly, G.

NOEL FANTASY see Stoneman

NOEL GREGORIEN see Brun, Abbe F., Puer Natus

NOEL IN A FORGOTTEN FARMYARD see Elsmith, Berta

NOEL NANTAIS *Xmas,carol,18th cent
(Du Bois, L.) [Fr] 4pt mix cor,acap (med
easy) cor pts LEMOINE s.p. see from
Collection De Choeurs, dixieme Fascicule
(N781)

NOEL NO. 4 see Adam, Adolphe-Charles

NOEL NO. 5 see Adam, Adolphe-Charles

NOEL, NOEL
(Grayson) men cor KJOS 5513 $.30   (N782)

NOEL! NOEL! see Cain, Noble

NOEL, NOEL see Chenoweth, Wilbur

NOEL, NOEL! see Gounod, Charles Francois

NOEL! NOEL! see Grieb, Herbert [C.]

NOEL! NOEL! A SAVIOUR IS BORN see Chaplin,
[Marian Wood]

NOEL! NOEL! BELLS ARE RINGING see Chenoweth,
Wilbur

NOEL NOEL, C'EST JOUR DE FETE see Parozai, Gui

NOEL, NOEL, ITERUMQUE NOEL see Migot, Georges

NOEL, NOEL, LET US SING MERRY CHRISTMAS see
Rodby

NOEL! NOEL! NOEL! see Allaire, G.

NOEL, NOEL, NOEL see Haupt, David

NOEL, NOEL, NOEL, LET YOUR VOICES RING see
Rotermund, Melvin

NOEL NOUVELET *Xmas,anthem/carol,Fr
(Hurford) SATB (easy) OXFORD 84.097 $.25
(N783)
(Terri) "Sing We Now Of Christmas" SATB,acap,
opt inst/pno oct LAWSON 51013 $.30   (N784)
(Terri) "Sing We Now Of Christmas" SATB
ALLANS 460 s.p.   (N785)
(Zgodava, Richard) "Sing We Now Of Christmas"
SATB (easy) oct AUGSBURG 0520 $.25   (N786)

NOEL NOUVELET see Bonnal, Ermend

NOEL NOUVELET see Bragg

NOEL NOUVELET see Peloquin, C. Alexander

NOEL NOUVELET see Roques, L.

NOEL, NOUVELET, NOEL PROVENCAL see Ketterer,
Laura

NOEL OF THE BAGPIPES see Hughes, Canten Nouve
Sus La Museto

NOEL OF THE FLOOD see Hughes, L'estrange Deluge

NOEL PROVENCAL DE SABOLY see Clouzot

NOEL, RIBON, RIBAINE see Darcieux, [F.]

NOEL RIBON RIBAINE see Parozai, Gui

NOEL SING WE NOW OF CHRISTMAS see Slates,
Philip M.

NOEL STAR, THE *Xmas,carol,Aus,17th cent
(Grant, Louise) SSA oct BELWIN 1701 $.25
(N787)
(Grant, Louise) SATB oct BELWIN 1710 $.25
(N788)

NOEL: SUS, DEBOUT, GENTILZ PASTEURS see
Costeley

NOEL! THE SAVIOR IS BORN see Wetzler, Robert

NOEL, UN ENFANT DU CIEL NOUS EST NE see Du
Caurroy, Francoise-Eustache

NOEL WALLON *Xmas,carol
(Du Bois, L.) [Fr] 4pt mix cor,acap (med) cor
pts LEMOINE s.p. see from Collection De
Choeurs, dixieme Fascicule   (N789)

NOEL WE SING see D'aquin, Louis-Claude

NOELS ANCIENS, LIVRE NO. 1 *CC14L,Xmas,Fr
[Fr] 2-3pt,acap voc sc LEDUC s.p. contains
works by: Dautremer,A.M.; Dautremer, M.
(N790)

NOELS ANCIENS, LIVRE NO. 3 *CC8U,Xmas,carol
[Fr] SATB/SMezTB,acap voc sc LEDUC s.p.
contains works by: Dautremer,A.M.;
Dautremer, M.   (N791)

NOELS DE LA PAIX see Romans, A.

NOELS D'EUROPE see Canteloube de Malaret,
Marie-Joseph

NOELS D'EUROPE *CC8L,Xmas,carol,Czech/It/Pol/
Span
(Canteloube) [Fr] unis/SAT/4pt mix cor oct
DURAND s.p.   (N792)

NOELS OLD AND NEW *CCU
mix cor SCHMITT 39 $.50   (N793)

NOELS PITTORESQUES DE FRANCE (VOL. 1A) see
Aubanel, Georges

NOELS POUR LES JEUNES *CC122U,Xmas,carol,Fr
(Villatte, J.) [Fr] 1-3 eq voices LEMOINE
s.p.   (N794)

NOELS WITH DESCANTS *CCU,Xmas
mix cor SCHMITT 9080 $.75   (N795)

NOGAREDE, C.J.
Spiritus Sancti Gratia
wom cor sc ALSBACH&D s.p.   (N796)

NOISE OF A MULTITUDE, THE see Thompson, Randall

NOLE EST VENU see Inghelbrecht, Desire Emile

NOLO MORTEM PECCATORIS see Morley

NOLO MORTEM PECCATORIS see Morley, Thomas

NOLTE
Dawn Of Christmas, The *Xmas,cant
SATB oct LORENZ $1.95   (N797)
SSA oct LORENZ $1.75   (N798)

Easter Dawn *Easter
SA oct LORENZ 5312 $.25   (N799)

Hosanna *Easter,cant
SATB LORENZ $1.95   (N800)

Just As I Am
SATB oct LORENZ A449 $.30   (N801)

King All-Glorious *Xmas,cant
SATB oct LORENZ $1.95   (N802)

Memories Of The Manger *Xmas,cant
SATB oct LORENZ $1.95   (N803)

Sing "Alleluia" *Xmas
SATB SCHMITT 1589 $.25   (N804)

Star Of The Silent Night *Xmas,cant
SATB oct LORENZ $1.95   (N805)

NOLTE, EDWALD VALENTIN (1909-   )
King Of Love My Shepherd Is, The *Gen
SATB,acap (med easy) oct CONCORDIA 98-1415
$.30   (N806)

NOMINE JESU see Taverner, John

NON E LASSO MARTIRE see Lechner, Leonhard

NON FU MAI CERVO see Lechner, Leonhard

NON FU MAI CERVO see Marenzio, Luca

NON HAVEA FEBO ANCORA see Monteverdi, Claudio

NON MORIAR see Senfl, Ludwig

NON NOBIS see Flanagan

NON NOBIS DOMINE see Byrd, William

NON NOBIS, DOMINE see Haydn, (Franz) Joseph

NON NOBIS, DOMINE see Quilter, Roger

NON NOBIS, DOMINE see Soderholm, Valdemar

NON PAPA, JACOBUS CLEMENS
see CLEMENS, JACOBUS

NON VOS RELINQUAM see Byrd, William

NON VOS RELINQUAM ORPHANOS see Byrd, William

NONE OTHER LAMB see Bayley, Robert Charlton

NONE OTHER LAMB see Burroughs, Bob

NONE OTHER LAMB see Edmundson, Garth

NONE OTHER LAMB see Lovelace, Austin C.

NONE OTHER LAMB see Marshall

NONE OTHER LAMB see Morgan

NONE OTHER LAMB see Phelps

NONE OTHER LAMB see Roff, Joseph

NONE OTHER LAMB see Sellew, Donald E.

NONE SHALL SEPARATE US FROM THE LOVE OF GOD see
Morgan

NONES see Klein, Lothar

NONNA see Orlando

NONNE HIC EST see Schutz, Heinrich

NOONA, WALTER
Children's Story Of Christmas, A *Xmas
BELWIN $1.00   (N807)

NOPS, MARJORY
Lord's My Shepherd, The *anthem/carol
SS CRAMER B73 s.p.   (N808)
SATB,org CRAMER B 70 s.p.   (N809)
unis CRAMER 49 s.p.   (N810)

NORA ELOHIM see Lidarti, C.G.

NORDEEN, LA JUANA
Walkin' In God's Country (composed with
Nordeen, Lynn) *CC10UL,folk
TTBB,pno,bvl,gtr voc sc WORD 30064
$1.95   (N811)

NORDEEN, LYNN
Walkin' In God's Country *see Nordeen, La
Juana

NORDEN
How Many Tears?
(Walton) SATB oct BOURNE 735 $.25   (N812)

Little Holy Jesus *Xmas
(Deacon) SA oct BOURNE 2024 $.25   (N813)

Our God
(Frank) SAB oct FISCHER,C CM-7624 $.25
(N814)

NORDEN, HUGO
Enlightenment Is From The Lord
SATB ALLANS 341 s.p.   (N815)
SAB ALLANS 234 s.p.   (N816)

Let God Lead The Way
(Frank) 2pt jr cor oct FOX R150 $.22 (N817)

O Satisfy Us Early With Thy Mercy
TTBB,acap (med) ABINGDON APM-406 $.25
(N818)

Sanctus
SATB FLAMMER A 5067 $.25   (N819)

Thou Art My Life
(Walton) SATB oct BOURNE 745 $.25   (N820)

NORDHOLM, H.
Christmas Story, The *Xmas
BELWIN $.50   (N821)

NORDMAN
Search Me, O Lord
SATB oct LORENZ C83 $.30   (N822)

NORDMAN, CHESTER
Behold What Manner Of Love
SATB,pno/org (med) oct WILLIS 6255 $.20
(N823)

I Hear The Words Of Jesus
SATB oct BELWIN 2005 $.25   (N824)

Lord's Prayer, The *Bibl/prayer
SSA HANSEN-US C249A $.40   (N825)

'Tis So Sweet To Trust In Jesus
SATB oct WORD CS-2312 $.30   (N826)

When Children Pray
SSA HANSEN-US C303A $.40   (N827)
SA HANSEN-US C303D $.40   (N828)
SAB HANSEN-US C303B $.40   (N829)
SATB HANSEN-US C303C $.40   (N830)

NORDOFF, PAUL (1909-   )
Psalm 23 *see Twenty-Third Psalm, The

Story Of Artaban, The Other Wise Man, The
(composed with Robbins, C.) *Xmas/Easter
SATB PRESSER $1.50   (N831)

Twenty-Third Psalm, The (Psalm 23)
SA&speak cor,bells,pno oct PRESSER
312-40789 $.35   (N832)
SATB,narrator,pno,bells oct PRESSER
312-40789 $.30   (N833)

NORDQVIST, GUSTAF
Ack, Saliga, Saliga
mix cor NORDISKA 2698 s.p.   (N834)
wom cor/jr cor NORDISKA 3279 s.p.   (N835)
men cor NORDISKA 2699 s.p.   (N836)

Bisp Thomas' Frihetssang
men cor NORDISKA 2006 s.p.   (N837)

Davids 23dje Psalm (Psalm 23)
[Swed] mix cor,pno LUNDQUIST 55 s.p. (N838)
[Swed] mix cor LUNDQUIST 55 s.p.   (N839)

Ditt Ord, O Jesu, Bliva Ma
mix cor NORDISKA 3117 s.p.   (N840)

I Juletid
mix cor NORDISKA 371 s.p.   (N841)

Jul, Jul, Stralande Jul
[Swed] mix cor LUNDQUIST 2 s.p.   (N842)
[Swed] 3pt wom cor LUNDQUIST 59 s.p. (N843)

Kommen Till En Fader
[Swed] mix cor LUNDQUIST 42 s.p.   (N844)

Psalm 23 *see Davids 23dje Psalm

Psalm 100
mix cor,org/pno cor pts NORDISKA 3119 s.p.
(N845)

NORDSTROM, CARL-ELOW
Kristallen Den Fina *folk
3pt mix cor NORDISKA 4291 s.p. (N846)

NOREN, YNGVE
Loven Gud I Hans Helgedom (Psalm 150)
mix cor,org cor pts NORDISKA 3861 s.p. (N847)

Psalm 150 *see Loven Gud I Hans Helgedom

NORHOLM, IB
Kenotafium *Op.23
cor,S solo,orch SAMFUNDET sc s.p., ipa, cor
pts s.p. (N848)

NORMAN
Christ Walked This Way Before
SATB oct LORENZ B1 $.30 (N849)

Come, Blessed Peace
SSA oct STAFF 322 $.25 (N850)
SATB oct STAFF 321 $.25 (N851)

Cross Of Redemption *Easter,cant
SATB LORENZ $1.95 (N852)

I Wish We'd All Been Ready
(Wilson) SAB oct AGAPE CF 162 $.35 (N853)

Rise, Arise'
SATB KJOS 5106 $.30 (N854)

Sweet Sweet Song Of Salvation
(Wilson) SATB oct AGAPE GC 807 $.35 (N855)

Twelve French Christmas Carols *CC12U,Xmas,
carol,Fr
[Fr/Eng] BOSTON 9479 $.45 (N856)

Victory Divine *Easter,cant
SATB LORENZ $1.95 (N857)

Walk Together Children
SATB oct STAFF 412 $.25 (N858)

NORMAN, GUS
O Jesus, I Have Promised (composed with
McDougal, Carol)
cor HIGHLAND 2005 $.25 (N859)

Shelter In The Time Of Storm, A
cor HIGHLAND 2002 $.25 (N860)

NORMAN, L.
I Wish We'd All Been Ready
(Gassman, C.) SATB oct PRESSER G-164 $.35 (N861)

NORMAN, ROBERT
I Know The Lord
SATB oct STAFF 491 $.25 (N862)

NORMAN, RUDOLF
Det Ar En Ros Utsprungen
3pt mix cor,A rec cor pts NORDISKA 4893
s.p., ipa (N863)

En Liten Julkantat
mix cor,fl cor pts NORDISKA 4323 s.p. (N864)

Eukaristi
mix cor NORDISKA 4940 s.p. (N865)

Kyrie *Kyrie
wom cor/jr cor NORDISKA 1804 s.p. (N866)

Liten Massa
mix cor,pno/org/2vln&vla&vcl/2vln&vla&bvl
cor pts NORDISKA 4208 s.p., ipa (N867)

Lovsjungen Herren
mix cor NORDISKA 4886 s.p. (N868)

Musik Kring Julevangelist
mix cor,soli,narrator voc sc NORDISKA 4423
s.p., ipa, cor pts NORDISKA 4422 s.p. (N869)

Passionkantat
mix cor,soli,narrator,org,2vln,vcl cor pts
NORDISKA 5130 s.p., sc NORDISKA s.p. (N870)

Se Bruggummen Kommer *mot
3pt mix cor NORDISKA 5981 s.p. (N871)

Uppfaren Ar Var Herre Krist
mix cor NORDISKA 5382 s.p. (N872)

NORRMAN, JOHN
Guds Lov *Bibl
[Swed] SAB,org GEHRMANS TKS 2 (N873)
[Swed] SATB,org/pno GEHRMANS KRB 58 (N874)

NORSK SALME see Kjeldaas, Arnljot

NORSK SALME see Nystedt, Knut

NORTH
Sing On Your Heavenly Way
SATB,acap oct PRO ART 1304 $.18 (N875)

NORTHFIELD see Ingalls

NORTON, HANCOCK
With God Thy Guide
2pt ASHDOWN E.A.297 s.p. (N876)

NORWEGIAN CHRISTMAS CAROL, A *Xmas
(Wilson) SATB oct LORENZ B34 $.30 (N877)

NOS AUTEM GLORIARI APORTET see Palestrina,
Giovanni

NOS GALAN *Xmas,carol,Welsh
(Brown) "Carol Of Praise, A" SATB,acap
SCHIRM.EC 2700 (N878)

NOS GALAN see Brown, Rex P.

NOS QUI SUMUS IN HOC MUNDO see Lassus, Roland
de (Orlandus)

NOSSE
Antiphone Of Praise
SATB oct VOLKWEIN VB106 $.30 (N879)
SAB oct VOLKWEIN VB106 $.30 (N880)

Christian's Prayer *prayer
SATB oct VOLKWEIN VB128 $.25 (N881)

NOSSE (cont'd.)
Know Ye Not?
SATB oct FOX R196 $.30 (N882)

O Thou Immortal Deity
SATB oct FOX R215 $.30 (N883)

Praise And Alleluia
SATB oct VOLKWEIN VB245 $.25 (N884)

Shepherd's Meditation *meditation
SATB oct VOLKWEIN VB255 $.25 (N885)

Steady Jesus Listening
SATB oct VOLKWEIN VB260 $.25 (N886)

Teach Me Thy Paths
SATB oct VOLKWEIN VB261 $.25 (N887)

NOT ALONE FOR MIGHTY EMPIRE see Frackenpohl

NOT ALONE FOR MIGHTY EMPIRE see Hoffelt, Robert
O.

NOT ALONE FOR MIGHTY EMPIRE see Lindblad, A.F.

NOT BUILT WITH HANDS see Twohig

NOT EVERYONE see Hutson

NOT EVERYONE WHO SAYS TO ME, "LORD, LORD" see
Hillert, Richard

NOT FOR OURSELVES O LORD see Dressler, John

NOT JERUSALEM see Johnson, Alfred H.

NOT ONLY UNTO ME see Roy, Klaus George

NOT SO IN HASTE, MY HEART see Young

NOT UNTO US, O LORD see Byrd, William, Non
Nobis Domine

NOT UNTO US, O LORD see Mendelssohn-Bartholdy,
Felix

NOT UNTO US, O LORD see Walmisley, Thomas
Attwood

NOT WITH A SWORD see Carmichael, Ralph

NOTE WELL, MY HEART see Hammerschmidt, Andreas

NOTHER, WILLI (1912-   )
Wir Danken, Herr, Fur Brot Und Kleid
SATB HANSSLER 6.300 s.p. contains also:
Trust, Heinz-Ewald, Im Anfang War's Auf
Erden (N888)

NOTHING BETWEEN see Tindley

NOTHING BUT MIRACLES see Hughes

NOTHING BUT THE BLOOD see Lowry, [Robert]

NOTHING IS HERE FOR TEARS see Pearson

NOTRE DAME see Machaut, Guillaume de

NOTRE-DAME DE FRANCE see Gounod, Charles
Francois

NOTRE-DAME DES PETITS ENFANTS see Gounod,
Charles Francois

NOTRE DIEU EST ROI see Wise, Judah L.

NOTRE DIEU SEUL EST LE MAITRE ETERNEL see Bach,
Johann Sebastian, Nun Ist Das Heil Und Die
Kraft

NOTRE PERE see Faure, Jean-Baptist

NOTTE DOLOROSA see Dall'Adria, Giovanni

NOURSE, JOHN
Holy Communion *Commun
SATB (E min) oct NOVELLO 44.1389.10 s.p. (N889)

unis (E min, series 2) oct NOVELLO
44.1462.04 s.p. (N890)

Jubilate (Psalm 100) Gen/Thanks
"O Be Joyful In The Lord" mix cor oct
OXFORD (N891)

O Be Joyful In The Lord *see Jubilate

Psalm 100 *see Jubilate

Te Deum *Te Deum
mix cor oct OXFORD 42.358 $.65 (N892)

We're All For Thee, Lord *hymn
cong,pno/org WEINBERGER s.p. (N893)

NOUS ALLONS, MA MIE see Roques, L.

NOUS ETIONS TROIS PASTOURELLES *Xmas,carol,
17th cent
(Dauly, G.) [Fr] 2pt wom cor (med easy)
LEMOINE s.p. (N894)

NOUS ETIONS TROIS PASTOURELLES see Dauly, G.

NOUS VOICI DANS LA VILLE *Xmas,carol,Fr
(Sheppard) "At Last We're In The Town" [Eng/
Fr] 4pt mix cor,acap oct SCHIRM.G 11427
$.25 (N895)

NOUS VOICI DANS LA VILLE see Hughes

NOVA, NOVA (from Anthology Of Carols, An)
see Musica Britannica Vol. 4: Set 7
see Verbum Patris

NOVA, NOVA see Biggs, John

NOVA SCOTIA NOEL, A see Gaul, Alfred Robert

NOVAE DE INFINITE LAUDES see Henze, Hans Werner

NOVE INNI D'USO PIU COMMUNE see Bottazzo, Luigi

NOVELLO
Like As The Hart (Psalm 42)
(Spiro) SATB,solo oct PRO ART 1509 $.18 (N896)

Psalm 42 *see Like As The Hart

NOVELLO ANTHEM BOOK, THE *CC50L,Gen,anthem
mix cor cloth NOVELLO 03.0094.02 s.p., cloth
NOVELLO 03.2094.03 %T TONIC SOLFA ED. s.p. (N897)

NOVELLO, VINCENT (1781-1861)
Adeste Fideles *Xmas,anthem
SATB oct FISCHER,J 570 $.30 (N898)
"Come All Ye Faithful" SATB oct GRAY
GCMR 3145 $.30 (N899)
"O Come All Ye Faithful" [Eng/Lat] mix cor,
orch oct NOVELLO 40.0166.04 s.p. (N900)
(Barlow) "O Come All Ye Faithful" TTBB,acap
oct FISCHER,J 5184 $.30 (N901)

Come All Ye Faithful *see Adeste Fideles

In Manus Tuas *anthem
(Baird) "Like As A Hart Desireth The
Waterbrooks" [Eng/Lat] 2pt boy cor/2pt
men cor,org/pno oct SCHIRM.G 10438 $.25 (N902)
(Button, Elliot H.) "Like As The Hart"
[Eng/Lat] mix cor oct NOVELLO 50.0219.02
s.p. (N903)
(Knight) "Like As The Hart" [Eng/Lat] 3pt
mix cor oct CURWEN 11201 $.20 (N904)

Like As A Hart Desireth The Waterbrooks *see
In Manus Tuas

Like As The Hart *see In Manus Tuas

Like As The Hart Desireth
SATB ALLANS 389 s.p. (N905)

Lord Loveth, The
SATB ALLANS 60 s.p. (N906)

O Come All Ye Faithful *see Adeste, Fideles

NOVUM AC INSIGNE OPUS MUSICUM 36 ANTIPHONARUM,
1541 see Dietrich, Sixtus

NOW A LOVELY CHILD IS BORN see Puer Nobis

NOW ABIDETH FAITH, HOPE, AND LOVE see Shelley,
[Harry Rowe]

NOW ALIEN TONGUES see Wehr, David A.

NOW ALL BELLS ARE RINGING
see Three Easter Hymns

NOW ALL GOOD FOLKS REJOICE *carol,Neth
(Davis, K.K.) mix cor SCHIRM.EC 1160 $.25 (N907)

NOW ALL MY WOES ARE OVER see Bach, Johann
Michael

NOW ALL THE WOODS ARE SLEEPING see Isaac,
Heinrich, Nun Ruhen Alle Walder

NOW AMEND WE OUR SINFUL LIVES see Byrd, William

NOW APRIL HAS COME *Easter,carol,Welsh
(Shaw; Parker) 4pt mix cor,acap oct SCHIRM.G
9955 $.25 (N908)

NOW, ARISE YE SHEPHERD'S MILD see Costeley,
Guillaume, Sus, Debout Gentilz Pasteurs

NOW AT THY FEET CREATION LIES see Bach

NOW BLESSED BE THOU, CHRIST JESU see Lenel,
Ludwig

NOW BLESSED BE THOU, CHRIST JESU see Schein,
Johann Hermann, Gelobet Seist Du, Jesu
Christ

NOW, BRIGHT AND STILL see Williams

NOW BROTHERS, LIFT YOUR VOICES *carol
SATB (easy) OXFORD 08.106 $.15 (N909)

NOW CHRIST LIVETH see Hutson, Wihla

NOW CHRIST OUR LORD IS RISEN AGAIN see
Bodenschatz, Erhard, Surrexit Christus
Hodie

NOW COME, LET US HASTEN see Bach, Johann
Sebastian

NOW COME, THE WORLD'S SALVATION see Bach,
Johann Sebastian, Nun Komm, Der Heiden
Heiland

NOW COME, THOU SAVIOR OF MEN see Schein, Johann
Hermann, Nun Komm, Der Heiden Heiland

NOW DEATH IS DEVOURED see Hammerschmidt,
Andreas, Der Tod Ist Verschlungen

NOW DECK THYSELF WITH MAJESTY see Bright,
Houston

NOW DO WE BEHOLD HIM see Palestrina, Giovanni

NOW EVERY CHILD see Reid, Robert A.

NOW EVERY STAR see Prentice, Fred

NOW FROM EVERY CHRISTIAN STEEPLE see Chapman,
Edward T.

NOW GLAD BE THE HEART OF EVERYONE see
Praetorius, Michael

NOW GLAD OF HEART *Ger,16th cent
(Bielawa, Herbert) SAB,acap oct WORLD
CA-1932-7 $.60 (N910)

NOW GLAD OF HEART see Parker, Alice

NOW GLAD OF HEART see Powell, Robert J.

NOW GLAD OF HEART BE EVERY ONE see Peek,
Richard

NOW GLAD OF HEART BE EVERYONE see Garlick,
Anthony

NOW GOD BE PRAISED IN HEAV'N ABOVE see Vulpius, Melchior, Gelobt Sei Gott

NOW GOD WE PRAISE see Narvik

NOW HE IS BORN see Hourdeaux

NOW HEAR THIS *CC10UL
(Carmichael, Ralph) SATB voc sc WORD 30063
$1.95   (N911)

NOW HYMNS FOR YOUNG PEOPLE see Draesel, Lederhouse

NOW I BELONG TO JESUS see Clayton

NOW I KNOW THAT THOU ART LOVING see Bach, Johann Sebastian, Nun, Ich Weiss, Du Wirst Mir Stillen

NOW I LAY ME DOWN TO SLEEP see Thompson, Randall

NOW I LAY ME DOWN TO SLEEP see Winans

NOW IF CHRIST BE PREACHED see Rogers, J.H.

NOW IS BORN A SAVIOUR *Xmas,carol,Pol
(Barrie) 2pt jr cor oct KENDOR $.25   (N912)

NOW IS BORN EMMANUEL see Christiansen, Olaf Christian

NOW IS CHRIST RISEN see Clare, Edwyn A.

NOW IS CHRIST RISEN see Frank

NOW IS CHRIST RISEN see Nystedt, Knut

NOW IS CHRIST RISEN FROM THE DEAD see Zaninelli, Luigi

NOW IS COME OUR SALVATION see Dagues

NOW IS THE CAROLING SEASON see Moore

NOW IS THE HOUR see Burck, Joachim

NOW IS THE HOUR OF DARKNESS PAST see Pyle, Francis [Johnson]

NOW IS THE OLD YEAR PASSED AWAY see Praetorius, Michael

NOW IS THE TIME OF HARVEST HOME see Shaw, Diccon

NOW ISRAEL MAY SAY
(Roberton H.S.) TTBB PATERSON 1652 s.p.
                                                        (N913)

NOW IT IS CHRISTMAS TIME see Nu Ar Det Jul Igen

NOW IT IS YULE AGAIN see Nu Ar Det Jul Igen

NOW LET ALL LOUDLY SING PRAISE see Chemin-Petit, Hans

NOW LET ALL LOUDLY SING PRAISE TO GOD see Bender, Jan

NOW LET ALL MEN THANK THEE see Danksagen Wir Alle Gott

NOW LET ALL THE EARTH ADORE THEE see Nicolai

NOW LET ALL THE HEAVENS ADORE THEE see Bach, Johann Sebastian

NOW LET EVERY TONGUE ADORE see Darst, W. Glenn

NOW LET EVERY TONGUE ADORE THEE
SATB oct STAFF 344 $.20   (N914)

NOW LET EVERY TONGUE ADORE THEE see Bach, Johann Sebastian

NOW LET EVERY TONGUE ADORE THEE see Lundquist

NOW LET EVERY TONGUE ADORE THEE see Nicolai

NOW LET EVERY TONGUE ADORE THEE see Nicolai, Philipp, Gloria Sei Dir Gesungen

NOW LET HEAVEN AND EARTH ADORE THEE see Bach, Johann Sebastian

NOW LET ME FLY see Rhea, A.

NOW LET THE EARTH WITH JOY RESOUND see Dicie

NOW LET THE HEAVENS BE JOYFUL *Easter/Gen, carol,Fr
(Chambers) SATB oct BOOSEY 5433 $.30   (N915)
(Chambers) SSA,org oct BOOSEY 5695 $.30
                                                        (N916)
(Chambers) SAB oct BOOSEY 5616 $.30   (N917)
(Halter) SAB SCHMITT 1663 $.35   (N918)
(Hustad, Donald) SATB oct AGAPE HA 120 $.30
                                                        (N919)
(Willan, H.) unis&desc (med easy) oct
CONCORDIA 98-1767 $.20   (N920)

NOW LET THE HEAVENS BE JOYFUL see Chambers, H.A.

NOW LET THE VAULT OF HEAVEN RESOUND *anthem
(Cassler, G. Winston) SATB,opt brass/orch
(easy) sc AUGSBURG 1240 $.30, ipa, ipr
                                                        (N921)

NOW LET US ALL GIVE THANKS see Schutz, Heinrich

NOW LET US ALL PRAISE GOD AND SING see Young

NOW LET US ALL WITH ONE ACCORD see Wolff, S. Drummond

NOW LET US HEAR WHAT ISRAEL HATH SAID see Goudimel, Claude

NOW LET US LIFT OUR YOUTHFUL VOICES see Hassler, Hans Leo

NOW LET US SING *Xmas,carol,Fr
(Wilson) SATB oct SPRATT 609 $.30   (N922)

NOW LET US SING see Rogers, Sharon Elery

NOW MAY THE LORD OF PEACE see Jones

NOW (MORE NEAR OUSELVES THAN WE) see Fuller, J.W.

NOW, MY TONGUE, THE MYSTERY TELLING see Aichinger, Gregor, Pange Lingua

NOW, MY TONGUE THE MYSTERY TELLING see Charpentier, Marc-Antoine

NOW NOEL HAS COME AGAIN see Darcieux, [F.]

NOW O LORD, I LAY ME DOWN see Purcell, Henry, Ego Cubui Et Dormivi

NOW ON HIGH O'ER ALL NATIONS see Pergolesi, Giovanni Battista, Excelsus Super Omnes Gentes Dominus

NOW ON LAND AND SEA DESCENDING see Handel, George Frideric

NOW ONCE AGAIN OUR HEARTS WE RAISE see Fletcher, Percy [E.]

NOW, PAST THE DEADLY PERIL see Monte, de, Che Poich'a Mortal Rischio

NOW PRAISE THE LORD see Sweelinck, Jan Pieterszoon, Or Soit Loue L'Eternel

NOW PRAISE WE see Rodby

NOW PRAISE WE CHRIST *5th cent
(Lundquist, M.) SATB,acap (plain song)
SCHIRM.EC 2436 $.18   (N923)

NOW PRAISE WE CHRIST, THE HOLY ONE see Enchitidion

NOW PRAISE WE CHRIST, THE HOLY ONE see Hooper, William L.

NOW PRAISE WE GREAT AND FAMOUS MEN see Bach, Johann Sebastian, Ach Gott Und Herr

NOW PRAISE WE GREAT AND FAMOUS MEN see Young

NOW REST IN PEACE see Bach, Johann Sebastian

NOW SHALL MY HEAD BE LIFTED HIGH *Gen,anthem
(Colvin, Herbert) SATB,acap WORD CRS-29 $.25
                                                        (N924)

NOW SHALL THE GRACE see Bach, Johann Sebastian, Nun Ist Das Heil

NOW SING A SAVIOUR'S BIRTH see Lloyd, Richard H.

NOW SING PRAISE TO THE LORD see Newbury, Kent A.

NOW SING WE ALL HIS PRAISE see Bright

NOW SING WE ALL NOEL see Young

NOW SING WE ALL THIS DAY see Hassler, Hans Leo

NOW SING WE JOYFULLY UNTO GOD see Young

NOW SING WE NOW, REJOICE *Xmas/Epiph,carol,Ger
(Pfust) SAB SCHMITT 5532 $.25   (N925)
(Schroeder, H.) SATB,inst (med easy) oct
CONCORDIA 98-2062 $.40   (N926)
(Wienhorst, R.) SATB,acap (med easy) oct
CONCORDIA 98-1345 $.25   (N927)
(Wienhorst, R.) SAB,acap (med easy) oct
CONCORDIA 98-1475 $.20   (N928)
(Wolff, S.D.) SAB,kbd (med easy) oct
CONCORDIA 98-1584 $.30   (N929)

NOW SING WE, NOW REJOICE see Buxtehude, Dietrich, In Dulci Jubilo

NOW SING WE, NOW REJOICE see Calvisius, Sethus

NOW SING WE, NOW REJOICE see Praetorius, Michael, In Dulci Jubilo

NOW SING WE, NOW REJOICE see Walter (Walther), Johann

NOW SING YE TO THE LORD see Pitoni, Giuseppe Ottavio, Cantate Domino

NOW SONGS FOR CHURCH YEAR see Newbury, Kent A.

NOW TELL US, GENTLE MARY see Fargo

NOW TELL US, GENTLE MARY see Hunnicutt, Judy

NOW THANK WE see Rodby

NOW THANK WE ALL OUR GOD *Thanks,17th cent
(Mueller, Carl F.) 4pt mix cor oct SCHIRM.G
8551 $.30   (N930)
(Parker) cor/cong,brass,perc cmplt ed
FISCHER,C 0-4868 $2.00, cor pts FISCHER,C
0-4868A $.15   (N931)

NOW THANK WE ALL OUR GOD see Bach, Johann Sebastian, Nun Danket Alle Gott

NOW THANK WE ALL OUR GOD see Burroughs, Bob

NOW THANK WE ALL OUR GOD see Cassler, G. Winston

NOW THANK WE ALL OUR GOD see Chambers, H.A.

NOW THANK WE ALL OUR GOD see Cruger, Johann

NOW THANK WE ALL OUR GOD see Kaufmann

NOW THANK WE ALL OUR GOD see Krone

NOW THANK WE ALL OUR GOD see Mendelssohn-Bartholdy, Felix

NOW THANK WE ALL OUR GOD see Mueller, Carl F.

NOW THANK WE ALL OUR GOD see Pachelbel, Johann, Nun Danket Alle Gott

NOW THANK WE ALL OUR GOD see Palmer

NOW THANK WE ALL OUR GOD see Rohlig, Harald

NOW THANK WE ALL OUR GOD see Willan, Healey, Nun Danket Alle Gott

NOW THANK WE ALL OUR GOD see Wolff, S. Drummond

NOW THAT THE DAYLIGHT FILLS THE SKY see Elmore, Robert [Hall]

NOW THAT THE SUN see Purcell, Henry

NOW THE DAY IS OVER see Bach, Johann Sebastian

NOW THE DAY IS OVER see Barnby

NOW THE DAY IS OVER see Barnby, Sir Joseph

NOW THE GREEN BLADE RISETH *Easter
(Strickler, David) SATB,opt inst (med) oct
OXFORD 94.320 $.30   (N932)

NOW THE GREEN BLADE RISETH see Lovelace, Austin C.

NOW THE GREEN BLADE RISETH see Naylor, Peter

NOW THE GREEN BLADE RISETH see Saxton

NOW THE HOLY CHILD see Marryott, Ralph E.

NOW THE HOLY CHILD IS BORN see Il Est Ne, Le Divin Enfant

NOW THE PRINCE OF PEACE IS COME see Caldwell, Mary [Elizabeth]

NOW THE RAREST DAY see Svatou Dobu Jiz Tu Mame

NOW THERE LIGHTENS UPON US see Sowerby, Leo

NOW THRICE WELCOME CHRISTMAS see Wishart

NOW TO THE LORD A NOBLE SONG see Vick

NOW TO THIS BABE SO TENDER *Xmas,carol,Ger
(Schroeder, H.) SATB,inst (med easy) oct
CONCORDIA 98-2070 $.30   (N933)

NOW UNTO HIM see Nyquist

NOW UNTO HIM THAT IS ABLE see Bender, Jan

NOW UNTO THEE see Tschesnokoff, P.I.

NOW WALK WITH GOD see Skillings, Otis

NOW WE ARE SINGING ONCE AGAIN see Newbury

NOW WE BESEECH THE HOLY GHOST see David, Johann Nepomuk, Nun Bitten Wir Den Heiligen Geist

NOW WE MAKE MERRY see Childs, Barney

NOW WE PRAISE THEE see Hassler, Hans Leo

NOW WE SING see Praetorius, Michael, Psallite

NOW WE SING A JOYFUL SONG see Grieg, Edvard Hagerup

NOW WE SING NOEL see Fitzgerald, B.

NOW WE SING NOEL see Yahres

NOW WE SING OF CHRISTMAS see Grundman

NOW WELL MAY WE MIRTHES MAKE see Brown

NOW WHEN THE DAY see Palestrina, Giovanni, Dum Complerentur

NOW WHEN THE DAY see Victoria, Tomas Luis de, Dum Complerentur Dies Pentecostes

NOW WITH HANDS TO GOD UPLIFTED see Lotti, Antonio, Ecce Panis Angelorum

NOW WITH ONE ACCORD see Constantini, Alessandro, Confitemini Domino

NOW WITH THE CHERUBIM see Russell

NOW WITH THE NEW YEAR STARTING see Lynn, George

NOWAK, LIONEL (1911-   )
Wisdom Exalteth Her Children
SSMezAeZAA BROUDE,A. 210 $.30   (N934)
TBB&TBB BROUDE,A. 216 $.30   (N935)

NOWAKOWSKY
V'shomru No 2
(Roskin) SATB HATIKVAH HCL 20 $.30   (N936)

NOWEL see Thompson, Randall

NOWELL see Brett

NOWELL see Davies, Peter Maxwell

NOWELL see Hannahs, R.C.

NOWELL see Joubert, John

NOWELL see Strilko, Anthony

NOWELL see Talmadge, Charles L.

NOWELL see Titcomb

NOWELL, NOWELL
see Musica Britannica Vol. 4: Set 5

NOWELL, NOWELL see Hail Mary, Full Of Grace

NOWELL, NOWELL, OUT OF YOUR SLEEP see Spencer, W.

NOWELL SING WE
see Musica Britannica Vol. 4: Set 7
see Six Traditional Carols, Set IV

NOWELL SING WE see Dirksen, Richard W.

NOWELLE see Smert, Richard

NOWELLE, NOWELLE
(Nieman, Alfred) S&T/A,acap oct BERANDOL
893N4AA $.35   (N937)

NOWHERE TO LAY HIS HEAD see Hairston, Jester

NOWLAN
    Rejoice, For Christ Is Born *see Foster

NOW'S THE TIME see Owens, Jimmy

NOW'S THE TIME FOR MIRTH AND PLAY see Oldham, Arthur

NOX PRAECESSIT see Back, Sven-Erick

NOYES, CHARLES F.
    And There Were Shepherds *Xmas
        SATB,SA,Bar soli,pno (easy) oct WILLIS 6305 $.12   (N938)

NOYES, E.P.
    By The Rivers Of Babylon
        cor oct HART s.p.   (N939)

NOYE'S FLUDDE see Britten, Benjamin

NU AR DET JUL IGEN *Xmas,anthem/folk,Swed
    (Pooler, Marie) "Now It Is Christmas Time"
        SATB (easy) oct AUGSBURG 0913 $.30   (N940)
    (Pooler, Marie) "Now It Is Christmas Time"
        SSA (easy) oct AUGSBURG 0917 $.20   (N941)
    (Smith, Gregg) "Now It Is Yule Again" [Eng/Swed] SATB,acap oct LAWSON 966 $.25 (N942)

NU AR DET SOMMAR BLID see Bach, Johann Sebastian

NU FRYDE SIG HVER KRISTEN MAND see Laub, Thomas

NU GLAD DIG, MIN ANDE, I HERRAN
    (Solonen, Sulo) [Swed] SAB,acap GEHRMANS TKS 46   (N943)

NU GLAD DIG MIN ANDE, I HERRAN see Runback, Albert

NU GRONSKAR DET see Bach, Johann Sebastian

NU HAVER DENNA DAG see Bond, Anders

NU HERREN AR UPPSTANDEN see Thyrestam, Gunnar

NU JUBLA HIMLAR OCH VARLDEN ALL see Sandberg, Folke

NU KOM VAR FRALSNINGS HERRE see Bach, Johann Sebastian, Nun Komm, Der Heiden Heiland

NU KOMMEN AR VAR PASKAFROJD see Bjarnegard, Gustaf

NU LA OSS TAKKE GUD see Compere, [Louis]

NU LASST UNS DEN LEIB BEGRABEN see Stahl, Johannes

NU LIGGER SATAN UNDER see Bach, Johann Michael, Nun Hab Ich Uberwunden

NU LOOFT DEN HEER see Franck, Melchior

NU MED SANG see Wikander, David

NU PRISEN ALLE GUD see Praetorius, Michael

NU RINDER SOLEN OP see Jeppesen, Knud

NU SJUNGA VI MED GLADJE STOR see Bjarnegard, Gustaf

NU SOLEN GAR NED
    (Olsen, Sparre) mix cor MUSIKK s.p.   (N944)

NU STIGE JUBLETS TON see Alvin, Erik

NU STIGE JUBLETS TON see In Dulci Jubilo

NU STIGE JUBLETS TON see Wideen, Ivar, In Dulci Jubilo

NU TACKAR GUD, ALLT FOLK see Bach, Johann Sebastian

NU TAKKER VI ALLE GUD see Schutz, Heinrich

NU VAER OS, GUD, MISKUNDELIG see Bach, Johann Sebastian, Es Woll Uns Gott Genadig Sein

NU VILANS DAG FORFLUTIT see Berg, Gottfrid

NU VILAR HELA JORDEN see Berg, Gottfrid

NUCIUS, JOHANNES (ca. 1556-1620)
    Mitten Wir Im Leben Sind
        SSATB HANSSLER 6.2038 s.p.   (N945)

    Tenebrae Factae Sunt *mot
        (Berger) SATTB HANSSLER 1.033 s.p.   (N946)

    Vier Motetten *CC4U,mot
        (Kindermann) [Ger/Lat] 5-6pt mix cor MOSELER s.p.   (N947)

NUIT D'AZUR see Beethoven, Ludwig van

NUIT DE FELICITE see Aubanel, Georges

NUL NE CONNAIT LES ENNUIS see Nobody Knows De Trouble I See

NULLA VITA SINE MUSICA see Bresgen, Cesar

NUMBER OUR DAYS see Fitch

NUN ABER IST CHRISTUS AUFERSTANDEN see Micheelsen, Hans Friedrich

NUN BITTEN WIR DEN HEIL'GEN GEIST see Weismann, Wilhelm

NUN BITTEN WIR DEN HEILIGEN GEIST *13th cent
    (Wasner) "To Thee, The Holy Ghost, We Now Pray" [Eng/Ger] 4pt mix cor,acap oct SCHIRM.G 9273 $.20   (N948)

NUN BITTEN WIR DEN HEILIGEN GEIST see Ahrens, Joseph

NUN BITTEN WIR DEN HEILIGEN GEIST see Barbe, Helmut

NUN BITTEN WIR DEN HEILIGEN GEIST see Bauernfiend, Hans

NUN BITTEN WIR DEN HEILIGEN GEIST see Bender, Jan

NUN BITTEN WIR DEN HEILIGEN GEIST see Callhoff, Herbert

NUN BITTEN WIR DEN HEILIGEN GEIST see Collum, Herbert

NUN BITTEN WIR DEN HEILIGEN GEIST see David, Johann Nepomuk

NUN BITTEN WIR DEN HEILIGEN GEIST see Eccard, Johannes

NUN BITTEN WIR DEN HEILIGEN GEIST see Fischer-Dieskau, Klaus

NUN BITTEN WIR DEN HEILIGEN GEIST see Fronmuller, Frieda

NUN BITTEN WIR DEN HEILIGEN GEIST see Gerhardt, Carl

NUN BITTEN WIR DEN HEILIGEN GEIST see Hassler, Hans Leo

NUN BITTEN WIR DEN HEILIGEN GEIST see Hellmann, Diethard

NUN BITTEN WIR DEN HEILIGEN GEIST see Kretzschmar, Gunther

NUN BITTEN WIR DEN HEILIGEN GEIST see Kurig, Hans-Hermann

NUN BITTEN WIR DEN HEILIGEN GEIST see Micheelsen, Hans Friedrich

NUN BITTEN WIR DEN HEILIGEN GEIST see Praetorius, Michael

NUN BITTEN WIR DEN HEILIGEN GEIST see Raphael, Gunther

NUN BITTEN WIR DEN HEILIGEN GEIST see Rohwer, Jens

NUN BITTEN WIR DEN HEILIGEN GEIST see Sartorius, Eramus

NUN BITTEN WIR DEN HEILIGEN GEIST see Selle, Thomas

NUN BITTEN WIR DEN HEILIGEN GEIST see Sendt, Willy

NUN BITTEN WIR DEN HEILIGEN GEIST see Stern, Hermann

NUN BITTEN WIR DEN HEILIGEN GEIST see Sultzberger, Johann Ulrich

NUN BITTEN WIR DEN HEILIGEN GEIST see Trubel, Gerhard

NUN BRINGEN WIR DEN LEIB ZUR RUH see Hollfelder, Waldram

NUN DANKET ALL see Blarr, Oskar Gottlieb

NUN DANKET ALL see Cruger, Johann

NUN DANKET ALL see Poos, Heinrich

NUN DANKET ALL UND BRINGET EHR' see Bauernfiend, Hans

NUN DANKET ALL UND BRINGET EHR see Distler, Hugo

NUN DANKET ALL UND BRINGET EHR see Hohlfeld, Christoph

NUN DANKET ALL UND BRINGET EHR see Horn, Paul

NUN DANKET ALL UND BRINGET EHR see Kretzschmar, Gunther

NUN DANKET ALL UND BRINGET EHR see Marx, Karl

NUN DANKET ALL UND BRINGET EHR see Micheelsen, Hans Friedrich

NUN DANKET ALL UND BRINGET EHR see Oertzen, Rudolf von

NUN DANKET ALL UND BRINGET EHR see Reda, Siegfried

NUN DANKET ALL UND BRINGET EHR see Rohwer, Jens

NUN DANKET ALLE GOTT see Altnikol, Johann Christoph

NUN DANKET ALLE GOTT see Bach, Johann Sebastian

NUN DANKET ALLE GOTT see Buxtehude, Dietrich

NUN DANKET ALLE GOTT see Cruger, Johann

NUN DANKET ALLE GOTT see Nageli, Johann (Hans) Georg

NUN DANKET ALLE GOTT see Pachelbel, Johann

NUN DANKET ALLE GOTT see Poos, Heinrich

NUN DANKET ALLE GOTT see Rolle

NUN DANKET ALLE GOTT see Scheidt, Samuel

NUN DANKET ALLE GOTT see Schein, Johann Hermann

NUN DANKET ALLE GOTT see Schutz, Heinrich

NUN DANKET ALLE GOTT see Stern, Hermann

NUN DANKET ALLE GOTT see Stobaeus, Johann

NUN DANKET ALLE GOTT see Waldbroel, Wilhelm

NUN DANKET ALLE GOTT see Willan, Healey

NUN DANKET ALLE GOTT, DER DA see Praetorius, Michael

NUN DANKET GOTT, ERHEBT UND PREISET see Goudimel, Claude

NUN DANKET GOTT, ERHEBT UND PREISET see Pfiffner, Ernst

NUN DIESER TAG IST VERGANGEN see Weber, Hanns Joachim

NUN ENTLASSEST DU see Etti, Karl

NUN FREUET EUCH, IHR ARM UND REICH see Gumpeltzhaimer, Adam

NUN FREUET EUCH IN GOTT, IHR FROMMEN see Le Jeune, Claude

NUN FREUT EUCH, GOTTES KINDER ALL see Cruger, Johann

NUN FREUT EUCH, GOTTES KINDER ALL see Franck, Melchior

NUN FREUT EUCH, GOTTES KINDER ALL see Praetorius, Michael

NUN FREUT EUCH, IHR ARM' UND REICH' see Gumpeltzhaimer, Adam

NUN FREUT EUCH, LEIBEN CHRISTEN GEMEIN see Praetorius, Michael

NUN FREUT EUCH, LIEBE CHRISTEN see Thomas, Kurt

NUN FREUT EUCH, LIEBEN CHRISTEN see Praetorius, Michael

NUN FREUT EUCH, LIEBEN CHRISTEN GEMEIN see Rohwer, Jens

NUN FREUT EUCH, LIEBEN CHRISTEN GMEIN *16th cent
    (Berger, H.L.) TTBB HANSSLER 6.5073 s.p. contains also: Gelobet Seist Du, Jesu Christ   (N949)

NUN FREUT EUCH, LIEBEN CHRISTEN GMEIN see Chemin-Petit, Hans

NUN FREUT EUCH, LIEBEN CHRISTEN GMEIN see Distler, Hugo

NUN FREUT EUCH, LIEBEN CHRISTEN G'MEIN see Ducis, Benedictus

NUN FREUT EUCH, LIEBEN CHRISTEN GMEIN see Eccard, Johannes

NUN FREUT EUCH, LIEBEN CHRISTEN GMEIN see Hassler, Hans Leo

NUN FREUT EUCH, LIEBEN CHRISTEN GMEIN see Marx, Karl

NUN FREUT EUCH, LIEBEN CHRISTEN GMEIN see Micheelsen, Hans Friedrich

NUN FREUT EUCH, LIEBEN CHRISTEN GMEIN see Praetorius, Michael

NUN FREUT EUCH, LIEBEN CHRISTEN GMEIN see Schein, Johann Hermann

NUN FREUT EUCH, LIEBEN CHRISTEN GMEIN see Schwartz, Gerhard von

NUN FREUT EUCH, LIEBEN CHRISTEN G'MEIN see Stern, Hermann

NUN FREUT EUCH, LIEBEN CHRISTEN GMEIN see Trubel, Gerhard

NUN FREUT EUCH, LIEBEN CHRISTEN GMEIN see Wenzel, Eberhard

NUN HAB ICH UBERWUNDEN see Bach, Johann Michael

NUN, ICH WEISS, DU WIRST MIR STILLEN see Bach, Johann Sebastian

NUN IST see Bach, Johann Sebastian, Nun Ist Das Heil Und Die Kraft

NUN IST DAS HEIL see Bach, Johann Sebastian

NUN IST DAS HEIL UND DIE KRAFT see Bach, Johann Sebastian

NUN IST DER HIMMEL AUFGETAN see Wenzel, Eberhard

NUN IST ES ZEIT ZU SINGEN see Burck, Joachim

NUN IST VORBEI DIE FINSTRE NACHT see Burkhard Willy

NUN JAUCHZ' DEM HERREN ALLE WELT see Franck, Melchior

NUN JAUCHZET ALL IHR FROMMEN see Bornefeld, Helmut

NUN JAUCHZET ALL, IHR FROMMEN see Cruger, Johann

NUN JAUCHZET, ALL IHR FROMMEN see Gesius, Bartholomaus

NUN JAUCHZET ALL IHR FROMMEN see Hufschmidt, Wolfgang

NUN JAUCHZET, ALL IHR FROMMEN see Lehman, Siegfried

NUN JAUCHZET, ALL IHR FROMMEN see Trubel, Gerhard

NUN JAUCHZET, ALL IHR FROMMEN see Wiemer, Wolfgang

NUN JAUCHZET MIT HELLEM TON see Schein, Johann Hermann

NUN JAUCHZT DEM HERREN ALLE WELT see Doppelbauer, Josef Friedrich

NUN JAUCHZT DEM HERREN, ALLE WELT see Horn, Paul

NUN JAUCHZT DEM HERREN ALLE WELT see Kurig, Hans-Hermann

NUN JAUCHZT DEM HERREN, ALLE WELT see Oertzen, Rudolf von

NUN JAUCHZT DEM HERREN, ALLE WELT see Reda, Siegfried

NUN JAUCHZT DEM HERREN, ALLE WELT see Siemoneit, Hans Rudolf

NUN JAUCHZT DEM HERREN, ALLE WELT see Stern, Hermann

NUN JUBILIERT DER MORGEN see Erdlen, Hermann

NUN JUBLE LAUT, ALL KREATOR see Koch, Johannes H.E.

NUN JUBLE LAUT, ALL KREATUR see Schwartz, Gerhard von

NUN KOMM see Bach, Johann Sebastian, Nun Komm, Der Heiden Heiland

NUN KOMM, DER HEIDEN HEILAND see Anonymous

NUN KOMM', DER HEIDEN HEILAND see Bach, Johann Sebastian

NUN KOMM, DER HEIDEN HEILAND see Cruger, Johann

NUN KOMM, DER HEIDEN HEILAND see Dangel, Arthur

NUN KOMM, DER HEIDEN HEILAND see David, Johann Nepomuk

NUN KOMM, DER HEIDEN HEILAND see Distler, Hugo

NUN KOMM, DER HEIDEN HEILAND see Eccard, Johannes

NUN KOMM, DER HEIDEN HEILAND see Hindermann, Walter Felix

NUN KOMM, DER HEIDEN HEILAND see Lohr, Ina

NUN KOMM, DER HEIDEN HEILAND see Praetorius, Michael

NUN KOMM, DER HEIDEN HEILAND see Raphael, Gunther

NUN KOMM, DER HEIDEN HEILAND see Scheidt, Samuel

NUN KOMM DER HEIDEN HEILAND see Schein, Johann Hermann

NUN KOMM, DER HEIDEN HEILAND see Spitta, Heinrich

NUN KOMM, DER HEIDEN HEILAND see Stern, Hermann

NUN KOMM, DER HEIDEN HEILAND see Strohbach, Siegfried

NUN KOMM DER HEIDEN HEILAND see Studer, Hans

NUN KOMM, DER HEIDEN HEILAND see Trubel, Gerhard

NUN KOMM, DER HEIDEN HEILAND see Weiss, Ewald

NUN KOMM, DER HEIDEN HEILAND see Wiemer, Wolfgang

NUN KOMM DER HEIDEN HEILAND see Borris, Siegfried

NUN KOMM DER HEIDEN HEILAND see Borris, Siegfried

NUN KOMM, DER HEIDEN HEILAND [CHORALE] see Bach, Johann Sebastian

"NUN KOMM DER HEIDEN HEILAND" FIVE SETTINGS OF THE CHRISTMAS CHORALE see Rikko

NUN KOMM, DER HEIDEN HEILAND see Bach, Johann Sebastian

NUN KOMM, DER HEIDEN HEILAND see Bach, Johann Sebastian

NUN KOMM see Bach, Johann Sebastian, Nun Komm, Der Heiden Heiland

NUN KOMM see Bach, Johann Sebastian, Nun Komm, Der Heiden Heiland

NUN KOMMST DU HERGEGANGEN see Schafer, Karl

NUN KOMMT FUR UNS DIE SCHONE ZEIT see Wolters, Gottfried

NUN LASSET UNS DEN LEIB BEGRABN see Kraft, Walter

NUN LASST UNS DEN LEIB BEGRABEN *CC14U,funeral (Brodde, Otto) [Ger] (easy/med easy) 3pt mix cor/4pt mix cor,acap BAREN. BA 2707 $1.50; 3 eq voices,acap BAREN. BA 2708 $2.50 (N950)

NUN LASST UNS DEN LEIB BEGRABEN see Brahms, Johannes

NUN LASST UNS GEHEN UND TRETEN see Kaminski, Heinrich

NUN LASST UNS GEHN UND TRETEN see Bach, Johann Sebastian

NUN LASST UNS GEHN UND TRETEN see Cruger, Johann

NUN LASST UNS GEHN UND TRETEN see Marx, Karl

NUN LASST UNS GEHN UND TRETEN see Praetorius, Michael

NUN LASST UNS GOTT see Gruschwitz, Gunther

NUN LASST UNS GOTT, DEM HERREN see Bach, Johann Sebastian

NUN LASST UNS GOTT DEM HERREN see Burck, Joachim

NUN LASST UNS GOTT DEM HERREN see Cruger, Johann

NUN LASST UNS GOTT DEM HERREN see Le Maistre, Mattheus

NUN LASST UNS GOTT DEM HERREN see Selnecker, N.A.

NUN LASST UNS GOTT DEM HERREN DANK SAGEN see Burck, Joachim

NUN LASST UNS GOTT, DEM HERREN, DANK SAGEN see Buxtehude, Dietrich

NUN LASST UNS MIT DEN ENGELEIN AUCH see Stobaeus, Johann

NUN LAST UNS GOTT, DEM HERREN see Bach, Johann Sebastian

NUN LAUFET, IHR HIRTEN see Haus, Karl

NUN LIEBE SEEL [CHORALE] see Bach, Johann Sebastian

NUN LIEBEN CHRISTEN FREUET EUCH see Kindermann, Johann Erasmus

NUN LOB, MEIN SEEL see Bach, Johann Sebastian

NUN LOB, MEIN SEEL see Wagner, Alexander

NUN LOB, MEIN SEEL, DEN HERREN see Bach, Johann Sebastian

NUN LOB, MEIN SEEL, DEN HERREN see Cruger, Johann

NUN LOB, MEIN SEEL, DEN HERREN see Hassler, Hans Leo

NUN LOB, MEIN SEEL, DEN HERREN see Horn, Paul

NUN LOB, MEIN SEEL, DEN HERREN see Kugelmann, Johann

NUN LOB, MEIN SEEL, DEN HERREN see Praetorius, Michael

NUN LOB, MEIN SEEL, DEN HERREN see Reda, Siegfried

NUN LOB, MEIN SEEL, DEN HERREN see Schein, Johann Hermann

NUN LOB, MEIN SEEL, DEN HERREN see Schutz, Heinrich

NUN LOB MEIN SEEL DEN HERRN see Praetorius, Michael

NUN LOB, MEIN SEEL, DEN HERRN see Schutz, Heinrich

NUN LOBET GOTT IM HOHEN THRON see Bauernfiend, Hans

NUN LOBET GOTT IM HOHEN THRON see Hagius, Carl

NUN LOBET GOTT IM HOHEN THRON see Lambertz, Johann Sebastian

NUN NIMMT DER TAG see Stier, Alfred

NUN PREISET ALLE GOTTES BARMHERZIGKEIT see Hufschmidt, Wolfgang

NUN PREISET ALLE GOTTES BARMHERZIGKEIT see Schmidt-Mannheim, Hans

NUN PREISET ALLE GOTTES BARMHERZIGKETT see Lowenstern, Matthaus Appelles von

NUN RUHE IN FRIEDEN see Casimir, Heinrich

NUN RUHEN ALLE WALDER see Bach, Johann Sebastian

NUN RUHEN ALLE WALDER see Isaac, Heinrich

NUN RUHEN ALLE WALDER see Schlicht, Johann Gottfried

NUN RUHEN ALLE WALDER, VIEH, MENSCHEN see Bach, Johann Sebastian

NUN RUHT DOCH ALLE WELT see Lohr, Ina

NUN RUSTE DICH, CHRISTENHEIT see Schrader, Oswald

NUN SCHEIN, DU GLANZ DER HERRLICHKEIT see Lechner, Leonhard

NUN SCHEIN, DU GLANZ DER HERRLICHKEIT see Staden, Johann

NUN SCHLAFET MAN see Kubler, Emil

NUN SCHWEBT AUF ENGELSFLUGELN see Hoffmann, Ernst Theodor Amadeus

NUN SEGNE DICH GOTT see Pfannenstiel, Ekkehart

NUN SEI DEM VATER DANK see Schutz, Heinrich

NUN SEI UNS WILLKOMMEN see Nitsche, Paul

NUN SEI UNS WILLKOMMEN, HERRE CHRIST see Stier, Alfred

NUN SEI UNS WILLKOMMEN, HERRE CHRIST see Werner, Fritz

NUN SICH DER TAG GEENDAT HAT see Schlicht, Johann Gottfried

NUN SICH DER TAG GEENDET HAT see Kriger, Adam

NUN SINGEN UND SEID FROH see Hindermann, Walter Felix

NUN SINGET see Praetorius, Michael, In Dulci Jubilo!

NUN SINGET UND SEID FROH *CC14U,Xmas (Meyer, Hermann; Votterle, Karl) [Ger] 2-5pt mix cor,acap (easy) BAREN. BA 2713 s.p. (N951)

NUN SINGET UND SEID FROH see Bach, Johann Sebastian

NUN SINGET UND SEID FROH see Eccard, Johannes

NUN SINGET UND SEID FROH see Henking, Bernhard

NUN SINGET UND SEID FROH see Raphael, Gunther

NUN SINGET UND SEID FROH see Ruppel, Paul Ernst

NUN SINGET UND SEID FROH see Stern, Hermann

NUN SINGET UND SEID FROH see Suthoff-Gross, Rudolf

NUN TAKES THE VEIL, A see Barber, Samuel

NUN WIR SIND GERECHT GEWORDEN see Reda, Siegfried

NUN WOLLEN WIR SINGEN DAS ABENDLIED see Kukuck, Felicitas

NUNC DIMITIS (Geveart, F.-A.) "Cantique De Simeon" [Lat/Fr] 4pt mix cor,acap (easy) cor pts LEMOINE s.p. see from Collection De Choeurs, troisieme Fascicule (N952)

NUNC DIMITTIS see Arkhangelsky

NUNC DIMITTIS see Cruft, Adrian

NUNC DIMITTIS see Dentice, Fabrizio

NUNC DIMITTIS see Gabrieli, Giovanni

NUNC DIMITTIS see Gretchaninov, Alexander Tikhonovitch

NUNC DIMITTIS see Hankey, Mark

NUNC DIMITTIS see Holt, Evelyn

NUNC DIMITTIS see McGehee

NUNC DIMITTIS see Mason, Isabel

NUNC DIMITTIS see Matterling

NUNC DIMITTIS see Moe, Daniel

NUNC DIMITTIS see Nystedt, Knut

NUNC DIMITTIS see Runback, Albert

NUNC DIMITTIS see Stevens, Halsey

NUNC DIMITTIS see Taylor, Clifford

NUNC DIMITTIS see Vaughan Williams, Ralph

NUNC DIMITTIS see Winchester, E.C.

NUNC DIMITTIS (TONE 2, NO. 1) see Torres, Eduardo

NUNC DIMITTIS (TONE 4, NO. 1, WITH FAUXBOURDONS) see Ripolles, Vincente

NUNC DIMITTIS (TONE 5, NO. 1) see Ripolles, Vincente

NUNC DIMITTIS (TONE 5, NO. 3 WITH FAUXBOURDONS) see Ripolles, Vincente

NUNC DIMITTIS (TONE 7, NO. 5) see Torres, Eduardo

NUNC DIMITTIS (TONUS PEREGRINUS) see Ripolles, Vincente

NUNC DIMITTUS see Gipps, Ruth

NUNC DIMITTUS see Roe, Betty

NUNC DIMITTUS see Shaw, Gerald

NUNC SANCTE NOBIS see Sargent, David

NUNC SANCTE NOBIS SPIRITUS see Boatwright, Howard

NUNC SCIO VERE see Quack, Erhard

NUOVE TANTUM ERGO *CC9U,Commun [Lat] unis,org ZANIBON 2681 s.p. contains works by: Bottazzo; Bottigliero; Crispo; Mangone; Margiotta; Muller; Volpi (N953)

NUOVO TRIONFO see Monte, de

NUR EINEN WUNSCH, NUR EIN VERLANGEN HAT UNSER see Berger, Hans Ludwig

NUR JEDEM DAS SEINE see Bach, Johann Sebastian

NUR WENN UNS CHRISTUS FREI MACHT see Schweizer, Rolf

NURNBERGER GROSSES GLORIA 1525 *Gloria (Distler, Hugo) [Ger] SATB,S solo,acap (med diff) BAREN. BA 1051 $.40 see also Liturgische Satze (N954)

NUTCRACKER SUITE see Tchaikovsky, Piotr Ilyitch

NYARSDAGEN see Bach, Johann Sebastian

NYARSHYMN see Alvin, Erik

NYARSHYMN, GIV, O JESU, FROJD OCH LYCKA *Bibl (Hallnas, Hilding) [Swed] SATB,acap GEHRMANS KRB 160 (N955)

NYBOER, MARTHA
I Can Believe *Gen,anthem cor,gtr, high and low voices oct LORENZ 5766 $.25 (N956)

NYBOER, MARTHA (cont'd.)

I Found Him In My Heart
SATB oct LORENZ 1686 $.30   (N957)

NYHUS, ROLF
Gud Er Var Tilflukt
[Norw] LYCHE 14 s.p.   (N958)

NYLANDER, GUNNAR
O, Jesu Krist, Sann Gud Och Man
mix cor NORDISKA 1877 s.p.   (N959)

NYQUIST
Bells Of Paradise *Xmas
SATB oct PRO ART 1613 $.18   (N960)

Bring To Us Thy Peace And Calm
see Introit And Benediction

Good Christian Men, Rejoice! *Xmas
SATB/dbl cor/2pt oct PRO ART 1350 $.22   (N961)

Hallelujah! Christ Is Risen! *Easter/Lent
SATB,acap oct PRO ART 1611 $.22   (N962)

Here, O My Lord
SATB,acap oct PRO ART 1609 $.20   (N963)

In Thee, O Lord, Do I Put My Trust (Psalm 31)
SATB,acap oct PRO ART 1511 $.22   (N964)

Into The Woods My Master Went *Easter/Lent
SATB,acap oct PRO ART 1352 $.22   (N965)

Introit And Benediction
SATB oct PRO ART 1732 $.22
    contains: Bring To Us Thy Peace And Calm;
    Lord Bless You, The   (N966)

Lead Us, O Father
SATB oct PRO ART 1610 $.18   (N967)

Life Of Ages
SATB oct PRO ART 1608 $.18   (N968)

Like A Choir Of Holy Angels
SATB,acap oct PRO ART 1495 $.18   (N969)

Lord Bless You, The
see Introit And Benediction

Lord My Pasture Shall Prepare, The
SATB,opt kbd oct PRO ART 1653 $.20   (N970)

Now Unto Him
SATB,opt kbd oct PRO ART 1539 $.15   (N971)

On Christmas Day *Xmas
SATB oct PRO ART 1378 $.25   (N972)

Psalm 31 *see In Thee, O Lord, Do I Put My
Trust

Spirit Blest
SATB,acap oct PRO ART 1348 $.15   (N973)

NYST MUNDE DET REGNA
(Sorass, Lars) mix cor MUSIKK 103 s.p. (N974)

NYSTEDT, KNUT (1915-   )
A Kom, Livsens Brod
[Norw] mix cor,org LYCHE 5 s.p.   (N975)

A Kristi, Som I Bryllaup Gjesta *mot
[Norw] mix cor LYCHE 97 s.p.   (N976)

A La La Deg Tirilill
mix cor MUSIKK s.p.   (N977)

Before Him *Adv/ECY/Gen
unis,kbd (med easy) oct CONCORDIA 98-1804
$.25   (N978)

Benediction, The
SATB,acap AMP A500 $.25   (N979)

Bon Karlek Och Tro
men cor MUSIKK 175 s.p.   (N980)

Built On A Rock The Church Doth Stand
    *anthem
SATB&opt cong (med) oct AUGSBURG 1322 $.25
                                                  (N981)

Cry And Shout
TTBB oct SUMMY 5577 $.50   (N982)
SSATTB oct SUMMY 1574 $.30   (N983)

De Profundis *Op.54
[Lat] SATB,acap AMP A499 $.40   (N984)

Den, Seg Selv Opphoyer, Skal Fornedres *mot
[Norw] mix cor LYCHE 100 s.p.   (N985)

Dominus Regnat (Psalm 93)
[Lat] SATB,acap PETERS 6540 $.40   (N986)

Fader Jeg Vil *mot
[Norw] mix cor LYCHE 48 s.p.   (N987)

Good Christian Men, Rejoice
SATB&cong,org,2vln sc AUGSBURG 11-9196
$.50, ipa   (N988)

Gud, I En Tid
[Norw] mix cor,org,trp cor pts LYCHE
ED.L.616 s.p., ipa   (N989)

Han Er Oppstanden *mot
[Norw] mix cor LYCHE 49 s.p.   (N990)

Himlenes Rike *mot
[Norw] mix cor LYCHE 61 s.p.   (N991)

Hosanna! Blessed Is He *anthem
SAB (easy) oct AUGSBURG 1410 $.20   (N992)

Hymnus *hymn
mix cor MUSIKK 153 s.p.   (N993)

I Will Be As The Dew *anthem
SATB (med diff) oct AUGSBURG 1266 $.30
                                                  (N994)

I Will Praise Thee, O Lord *anthem/mot
SATB (med) oct AUGSBURG 1217 $.30 see from
Three Motets   (N995)

NYSTEDT, KNUT (cont'd.)

Jesus, Din Sote Forening A Smake
[Norw] men cor LYCHE 40 s.p.   (N996)
[Norw] mix cor LYCHE 78 s.p.   (N997)

Jesus Sju Ord Pa Korset
[Norw] mix cor LYCHE 76 s.p.   (N998)

Kommer Vel Lyset Inn *mot
[Norw] mix cor LYCHE 53 s.p.   (N999)

Koral *chorale
mix cor MUSIKK 34 s.p.   (N1000)

Landet Har Gitt Sin Grode *mot
[Norw] mix cor LYCHE 44 s.p.   (N1001)

Lord, By Whose Breath *anthem/hymn
oct AUGSBURG 11-1585 $.05   (N1002)
SATB&cong,org,trp sc AUGSBURG 11-1584 $.35
                                                  (N1003)
SATB,org,trp (med) oct AUGSBURG 1584 $.35
                                                  (N1004)

Lucis Creator Optime *Op.58
[Lat/Eng/Norw] SATB,SBar soli AMP A645
$1.25   (N1005)

Morgon-Mod
wom cor MUSIKK 11 s.p.   (N1006)
mix cor MUSIKK 18 s.p.   (N1007)

Night Is Far Spent, The *anthem
SATB (med) oct AUGSBURG 1463 $.30   (N1008)

Norsk Salme *Psalm
mix cor MUSIKK 22 s.p.   (N1009)

Now Is Christ Risen *anthem
SATB,org,trp/fl,bells/chimes (med) oct
AUGSBURG 1453 $.30   (N1010)

Nunc Dimittis *anthem/Nunc
SAB (easy) oct AUGSBURG 1409 $.20   (N1011)

O Come, All Ye Faithful
SATB&cong,org,trp sc AUGSBURG 11-9301 $.50,
ipa   (N1012)

Path Of The Just, The *anthem
SSAATTBB (diff) oct AUGSBURG 9333 $.50
                                                  (N1013)

Peace Be Unto You *anthem
SATB (med) oct AUGSBURG 1455 $.25   (N1014)

Peace I Leave With You *anthem/mot
SATB (med) oct AUGSBURG 1216 $.25 see from
Three Motets   (N1015)

Praise To God
SATB,acap AMP A597 $.35   (N1016)

Psalm 93 *see Dominus Regnat

Psalm 96 *see Syng For Herren

Rop Ut Med Fryd
mix cor MUSIKK 198 s.p.   (N1017)
men cor MUSIKK 213 s.p.   (N1018)

Sanctus *Op.2,No.2
[Lat] SSATBB NORSK s.p.   (N1019)

Sangen
mix cor MUSIKK 93 s.p.   (N1020)

Se Hvor Nu Jesus Treder
[Norw] mix cor,org LYCHE 35 s.p.   (N1021)

Seven Words From The Cross, The *anthem
SATB (easy) oct AUGSBURG 1287 $.40 (N1022)

Sinn
mix cor MUSIKK 144 s.p.   (N1023)

Spirit Of Truth, The *Asc/Gen
SAB,kbd (med diff) oct CONCORDIA 98-1806
$.25   (N1024)

Syng For Herren (Psalm 96)
[Norw] men cor LYCHE 46 s.p.   (N1025)

This Is My Beloved Son *Gen/Trin
SAB,kbd (med easy) oct CONCORDIA 98-1805
$.25   (N1026)

Thou O Lord
SATB oct WALTON 2900 $.35   (N1027)

Three Motets *see I Will Praise Thee, O
Lord; Peace I Leave With You; Thus Saith
The Lord   (N1028)

Thus Saith The Lord *anthem/mot
SATB (med) oct AUGSBURG 1215 $.25 see from
Three Motets   (N1029)

Troens Triumf
mix cor MUSIKK s.p.   (N1030)

Trust In The Lord *anthem
SSAATTBB (diff) oct AUGSBURG 9502 $.35
                                                  (N1031)

Vaer Ikke Bekymret *mot
[Norw] mix cor LYCHE 50 s.p.   (N1032)

Velsignet Vaere Ham *mot
[Norw] mix cor LYCHE 45 s.p.   (N1033)

Yet A Little While
SSATBB oct SUMMY 5350 $.40   (N1034)

NYTESTAMENTLIGA LOVSANGER see Runback, Albert

NYVALL, DAVID JR.
Allelujah Festival Anthem *Easter/Gen,anthem
SATB,Bar solo,pno (med) oct WILLIS 6304
$.15   (N1035)

NYVALL, JACOB
Credo-Psalm Enligt Apostolicum
mix cor NORDISKA 2106 s.p.   (N1036)

Helig, Helig, Helig
mix cor NORDISKA 1158 s.p.   (N1037)

Herre, Till Vem Skulle Vi Ga
mix cor NORDISKA 3353 s.p.   (N1038)

NYVALL, JACOB (cont'd.)

Hymn Pa Tacksagelsedagen
3pt mix cor NORDISKA 2010 s.p.   (N1039)

O, Gud Allsmaktige
(Svedlund, Karl-Erik) mix cor,fl,clar,trp,
trom,vcl/bvl cor pts NORDISKA 3187 s.p.,
voc sc NORDISKA 2059 s.p., ipa   (N1040)

O

O ABGRUND, NOT, O HERZELIED see Stier, Alfred

O ADMIRABILE COMMERCIUM see Constantini, Fabio

O ADMIRABILE COMMERCIUM see Gallus, Jacobus

O ADMIRABILE COMMERCIUM see Palestrina, Giovanni

O ADMIRABILE COMMERCIUM see Stoltzer, Thomas

O, ALL YE NATIONS see Schutz, Heinrich

O ALL YE PEOPLE, CLAP YOUR HANDS see Purcell, Henry

O ALL YE THAT PASS BY see Deering, Richard

O ALL YE THAT PASS BY see Victoria, Tomas Luis de, O Vos Omnes

O ALL YE THAT PASS BY see Victoria, Tomas Luis de, O Vos Omnes, Qui Transitis Per Viam

O ALL YE WORKS OF THE LAND see Fetler, Paul

O ALLES LICHTES QUELL see Handel, George Frideric, Oh First Created Beam

O ALTITUDE DIVITIARUM see Castillo

O ATT DU I DAG HADE INSETT see Nilsson, Torsten

O BABE DIVINE *Xmas
    2pt CHAPPELL 0022665-352 $.40   (O1)
    SSA CHAPPELL 0022665-354 $.40   (O2)
    SATB CHAPPELL 0022665-358 $.40   (O3)

O BABE DIVINE see McKinney, Howard D., Tu Scendi Dalle Stelle

O BAMBINO see Capra

O BAPTISTA see Aston, Hugo

O BARMHERZIGER VATER see Hammerschmidt, Andreas

O BARMHERZIGER VATER, ICH ARMER see Hammerschmidt, Andreas

O BE JOYFUL see Aichinger, Gregor, Regina Coeli

O BE JOYFUL see Angell, Warren M.

O BE JOYFUL see Browne, H.M.

O BE JOYFUL see Christiansen, P.

O BE JOYFUL see Ellsworth, Eugene

O, BE JOYFUL see Harding, Harvey

O BE JOYFUL see Hoag, Charles K.

O BE JOYFUL see Humfrey, Pelham, Jubilate Deo

O BE JOYFUL see Le Fleming, Christopher (Kaye)

O BE JOYFUL see Mozart, Wolfgang Amadeus, Jubilate Deo

O BE JOYFUL see Ramsfield

O BE JOYFUL see Schubert, Franz (Peter)

O BE JOYFUL, ALL YE LANDS see Christiansen, Olaf Christian

O BE JOYFUL IN GOD see Kirk, T.

O BE JOYFUL IN GOD see Milner, Arthur

O BE JOYFUL IN GOD see Mozart, Wolfgang Amadeus

O BE JOYFUL IN GOD see Willan, Healey

O BE JOYFUL IN THE LORD see Blake

O BE JOYFUL IN THE LORD see Boyce, William, Jubilate

O BE JOYFUL IN THE LORD see Clark, Henry A., Jubilate Deo

O, BE JOYFUL IN THE LORD see Cox, A.

O BE JOYFUL IN THE LORD see Droste, Doreen, Jubilate Deo

O BE JOYFUL IN THE LORD see Gretchaninov, Alexander Tikhonovitch

O BE JOYFUL IN THE LORD see Handel, George Frideric

O BE JOYFUL IN THE LORD see Jacob, Gordon

O BE JOYFUL IN THE LORD see Jones, Bradwin

O BE JOYFUL IN THE LORD see Kelly, Bryan

O BE JOYFUL IN THE LORD see Lacey, David T., Jubilate Deo

O BE JOYFUL IN THE LORD see Leighton, Kenneth

O BE JOYFUL IN THE LORD see Ley, Henry George

O BE JOYFUL IN THE LORD see Longthorne, Brian

O BE JOYFUL IN THE LORD see Mozart, Wolfgang Amadeus

O BE JOYFUL IN THE LORD see Naylor, Bernard

O BE JOYFUL IN THE LORD see Nourse, John, Jubilate

O BE JOYFUL IN THE LORD see Powell

O BE JOYFUL IN THE LORD see Pritchard, Arthur J.

O BE JOYFUL IN THE LORD see Purcell, Henry

O BE JOYFUL IN THE LORD see Rogers

O BE JOYFUL IN THE LORD see Selby, William

O BE JOYFUL IN THE LORD see Shaw, G.

O BE JOYFUL IN THE LORD see Shaw, Geoffrey [Turton]

O BE JOYFUL IN THE LORD see Thalben-Ball, George [Thomas]

O BE JOYFUL IN THE LORD see Titcomb

O BE JOYFUL IN THE LORD see Tours, Berthold, Jubilate Deo

O BE JOYFUL IN THE LORD see Vaughan Williams, Ralph

O BE JOYFUL IN THE LORD see Willan, Healey

O BE JOYFUL IN THE LORD S-95 see Lee

O BE YE JOYFUL see Mozart, Wolfgang Amadeus, Freut Euch, Freut Euch!

O BEATA see Palestrina, Giovanni

O BEATA ET GLORIOSA see Palestrina, Giovanni

O BEATA ET GLORIOSA TRINITAS see Palestrina, Giovanni

O BEATAE VIAE see Monteverdi, Claudio

O BEATUM ET SACROSANCTUM DIEM see Philips, Peter

O BEL BAMBINO *carol,It
    (Peloquin) "Lullaby, O Lovely Baby" SATB oct
    SUMMY M 2503 $.25   (O4)

O BELLS IN THE STEEPLE see Bampton, R.

O BELOVED SHEPHERDS see Hammerschmidt, Andreas, O Ihr Lieben Hirten

O BERGERS, DANS LA MONTAGNE *Xmas,carol,Fr
    (Tomasi) [Fr] SMezA LEDUC s.p. see also Douze Noels De Saboly   (O5)

O BETHLEHEM *Xmas,carol,Span
    (Dickinson, C.) SATB oct GRAY GSC 121 $.30
                                               (O6)
    (Linstead) TTBB FRANCIS s.p.   (O7)
    (Poston, Elizabeth) 2pt jr cor/2pt wom cor
    CURWEN 72392 s.p.   (O8)

O BIONDO PICCINO! see Arnaldi, Antonio

O BLESS OUR GOD, YE PEOPLE see Schroth

O BLESS THE LORD see Leyden

O BLESS THE LORD, MY SOUL see Blake

O BLESS THE LORD, MY SOUL see Frederick

O BLESS THE LORD, MY SOUL see Schwartz, Stephen

O BLESS THE LORD, MY SOUL! see Watts

O BLESS THE LORD O MY SOUL see Brandon

O BLESSED AND EVER GRACIOUS LORD see Tchaikovsky, Piotr Ilyitch

O BLESSED DAY OF MOTHERHOOD see Vick

O BLESSED, HOLY BETHLEHEM see Messaus

O BLESSED JESU
    see Three Chorales

O BLESSED JESU see Palestrina, Giovanni

O BLESSED JESUS see Agostini, O Bone Jesu

O BLESSED JESUS see Anerio, Felice, O Bone Jesu

O BLESSED JESUS see De Lattre, [Roland], O Bone Jesu

O BLESSED JESUS see Palestrina, Giovanni, O Bone Jesu

O BLESSED JESUS see Pierluigi

O BLESSED LORD see Crosse, Gordon

O BLESSED LORD see Tchaikovsky, Piotr Ilyitch

O BLESSED LORD OUR GOD see Schutz, Heinrich, O Lieber Herre Gott, Wecke Uns Aub

O BLESSED NATIVITY see Byrd, William, O Magnum Mysterium

O BLESSED NATIVITY see Victoria, Tomas Luis de, O Magnum Mysterium

O BLESSED NATIVITY see Willaert, Adrian, O Magnum Mysterium

O BLESSED PEOPLE see Victoria, Tomas Luis de, Popule Meus

O BLESSED SACRAMENT see Bernabei, Giuseppe Antonio, O Sacrum Convivium

O BLEST IS THE WORK *Easter
    (Johnson) SATB SCHMITT 6003 $.25   (O9)

O BLEST REDEEMER! see Newton, Ernest

O BLICKE MIT ERBARMEN see Rossini, Gioacchino

O BONE see Schutz, Heinrich

O BONE JESU
    (Palestrina, G.) "O Holy Father" SSAA,acap
    SCHIRM.EC 1812 $.20   (O10)
    (Palestrina, G.) "O Holy Father" [Lat] TTBB,

acap SCHIRM.EC 527 $.20   (O11)

O BONE JESU see Agostini

O BONE JESU see Anerio, Felice

O BONE JESU see Anonymous

O BONE JESU see Brahms, Johannes

O BONE JESU see Carver, Robert

O BONE JESU see Child, Simon

O BONE JESU see Compere, [Louis]

O BONE JESU see Cossetti, Gio. Batta.

O BONE JESU see Deering, Richard

O BONE JESU see De Lattre, [Roland]

O BONE JESU see Fayrfax, Robert

O BONE JESU see Ingegneri, Marco Antonio

O BONE JESU see Lambert

O BONE JESU see Lewkovitch, Bernhard

O BONE JESU see Monteverdi, Claudio

O BONE JESU see Palestrina, Giovanni

O BONE JESU, FILI MARIAE see Schutz, Heinrich

O BONE JESUS see Palestrina, Giovanni

O BONE, O DULCIS see Schutz, Heinrich

O BORN OF LIGHT see Tallis, Thomas, O Nata Lux De Lumine

O BOUNDLESS GOODNESS see Cruger, Johann

O BREAD OF LIFE see Isaac, Heinrich

O BREAD OF MAN'S DELIGHT see Titcomb

O BREATH FROM OUT TH'ETERNAL SILENCE see Grant

O BROTHER MAN
    (Scott; Gatty; Litten) SATB oct SHAPIRO
    SK 2044 $.25   (O12)

O, BROTHER MAN see Anderson, [William H.]

O BROTHER MAN see Christiansen, Olaf Christian

O BROTHER MAN see Curry

O BROTHER MAN see Richolson

O BROTHER MAN! see Ringwald, [Roy]

O BROTHER MAN see Rogers

O BROTHER MAN see Russell, Leslie

O BROTHER, MAN see Vandre, Carl W.

O BROTHER MAN see Whittier

O BROTHER MAN see Wilson

O BROTHER MAN, FOLD TO THY HEART THY BROTHER see Whitier

O BROTHERS, LIFT YOUR VOICES see Smart, Henry Thomas

O BUILDER OF THE STARS see Lister, Mosie

O, CALL ON THE LORD see Lewis, J.

O CAST ME NOT AWAY see Brahms, Johannes

O CAST THY BURDEN see Crampton, T.

O CHE SPLENDOR see Palestrina, Giovanni

O CHILD OF LOWLY BIRTH see Richolson

O CHRIST CHILD, NOW I COME TO THEE see Bach, Johann Sebastian, Ich Steh' An Deiner Krippen Hier

O CHRIST, ETERNAL KING see Mytych, J.F.

O CHRIST, I LOOK TO THEE see Burroughs

O CHRIST JESUS see Taverner, John, Christe Jesu

O CHRIST JESUS, LOVING SHEPHERD see Taverner, John, Christe Jesu, Pastor Bone

O CHRIST, MY ALL IN LIVING see Bach, Johann Sebastian, Christus Der Ist Mein Leben

O CHRIST, OUR HOPE see Hermann, [Nikolaus]

O CHRIST, OUR TRUE AND ONLY LIGHT
    (Hadley) SATB oct PRO ART 2457 $.25   (O13)

O CHRIST, OUR TRUE AND ONLY LIGHT see Strube, Adolf

O CHRIST, SON OF OUR GOD see Des Prez, Josquin

O CHRIST THE HEAVENS see Bach

O CHRIST, THE HEAVENS' ETERNAL KING see Thiman, Eric Harding

O CHRIST, THOU LAMB OF GOD see Willan, Healey

O CHRIST WHO ART see Byrd, William, Christe, Qui Lux Es

O CHRIST, WHO ART THE LIGHT AND DAY see Byrd, William, Christe Qui Lux

O CHRIST, WHO ART THE LIGHT AND DAY see Byrd, William, Christe, Qui Lux Es Et Dies

O CHRIST, WHO ART THE LIGHT AND DAY see Whyte, Robert, Christe, Qui Lux Es Et Dies

O CHRIST WHO HOLDS THE OPEN GATE see Shaw, Martin

O CHRIST, WIR DANKEN DEINER GUT see Praetorius, Michael

O CHRISTE, MORGENSTERN see Gesius, Bartholomaus

O CHRISTE, SCHOPFER ALLER WELT see Schein, Johann Hermann

O CHRISTENHEIT SEI HOCH ERFREUT see Micheelsen, Hans Friedrich

O CHRISTENHEIT, SEI HOCHERFREUT see Micheelsen, Hans Friedrich

O CLAP YOUR HANDS see Christiansen

O CLAP YOUR HANDS see Couperin, Francois

O, CLAP YOUR HANDS see Gardner, John [Linton]

O CLAP YOUR HANDS see Gibbons, Orlando

O CLAP YOUR HANDS see Griffiths, Vernon

O CLAP YOUR HANDS see Hopson

O CLAP YOUR HANDS see Kirk, Theron W.

O CLAP YOUR HANDS see McAfee

O CLAP YOUR HANDS see Milner, Arthur

O CLAP' YOUR HANDS see Porter

O CLAP YOUR HANDS see Rohlig, Harald

O CLAP YOUR HANDS see Schutz, Heinrich

O CLAP YOUR HANDS see Shaw, Martin

O CLAP YOUR HANDS see Trued, Clarence

O CLAP YOUR HANDS see Turner, Edmund (Edmond)

O CLAP YOUR HANDS see Vaughan Williams, Ralph

O CLAP YOUR HANDS see Young

O CLAP YOUR HANDS, ALL YE PEOPLE see King, Alvin

O CLAP YOUR HANDS TOGETHER see Batten, Adrian

O CLAP YOUR HANDS TOGETHER see Hewitt-Jones, Tony

O CLAP YOUR HANDS TOGETHER see Steel

O CLAP YOUR HANDS TOGETHER see Steel, Christopher [Charles]

O COMBIEN EST PLAISANT ET SOUHAITABLE see Goudimel, Claude

O COME, ALL YE CHILDREN see Schutz, Heinrich

O COME, ALL YE FAITHFUL see Adams, Carrie, Adeste Fideles

O COME, ALL YE FAITHFUL see Adeste Fideles

O COME, ALL YE FAITHFUL see Adeste Fidelis

O COME, ALL YE FAITHFUL see Anonymous, Adeste Fideles

O COME, ALL YE FAITHFUL see Boughton, Rutland

O COME, ALL YE FAITHFUL see Hughes

O COME ALL YE FAITHFUL see Kinyon

O COME, ALL YE FAITHFUL see Krones

O COME, ALL YE FAITHFUL see Moffatt

O COME ALL YE FAITHFUL see Novello, Vincent, Adeste, Fideles

O COME, ALL YE FAITHFUL see Nystedt, Knut

O COME, ALL YE FAITHFUL see Reading, J., Adeste Fideles

O COME, ALL YE FAITHFUL see Smith

O COME ALL YE FAITHFUL see Titcomb, Everett, Adeste Fidelis

O COME, ALL YE FAITHFUL see Wade

O COME, AND DWELL IN ME see Ford, Virgil T.

O COME AND MOURN *Lent
(Johnson) SATB SCHMITT 8060 $.35   (O14)

O COME AND MOURN see Bingham

O COME AND MOURN see Bodycombe, [Aneurin]

O COME AND MOURN see Lipscomb, Helen

O COME AND MOURN see Smith, H.

O COME AND MOURN see Williams, David H.

O COME AND MOURN WITH ME see Burroughs

O COME AND MOURN WITH ME see Rogers, Sharon Elery

O COME AND MOURN WITH ME see Young

O COME AND MOURN WITH ME AWHILE see Dykes

O COME AND MOURN WITH ME AWHILE see Emig, Lois

O COME AND MOURN WITH ME AWHILE see Pergolesi, Giovanni Battista

O COME AND MOURN WITH ME AWHILE see Wood

O COME AND PRAISE THE LIVING GOD see Lawhon

O COME AND SING UNTO THE LORD see Nichols

O COME AND SING UNTO THE LORD see Nichols, Anna Mae

O COME AWAY YE SHEPHERDS *Xmas,carol,Fr
(Ehret, Walter) SATB,opt inst oct WALTON 2525 $.25   (O15)
(Ehret, Walter) SSA,opt inst oct WALTON 2534 $.30   (O16)

O COME CREATOR SPIRIT see Eichhorn

O COME, CREATOR SPIRIT, COME see Brandon, George

O COME, CREATOR SPIRIT, COME see Charpentier, Marc-Antoine

O COME, EMANUEL *Xmas,carol
(Terri) SATB ALLANS 463 s.p.   (O17)

O COME, EMMANUEL see Harris

O COME EMMANUEL see Hilty

O COME, EMMANUEL see Neale

O COME EMMANUEL see Niles, John Jacob

O COME EMMANUEL see Veni Emmanuel

O COME, EMMANUEL see Williams, David H.

O COME, EVERY ONE THAT THIRSTETH see Mendelssohn-Bartholdy, Felix

O COME HITHER, AND HEARKEN see Amner, John

O COME, HOLY SPIRIT see Bach

O COME, HOLY SPIRIT see Telemann, Georg Philipp

O COME, IMMANUEL see Lynn, George

O COME LET US PRAISE THE LORD see Graun, Karl Heinrich

O COME, LET US SING *sac/sec,CC17L,Xmas,carol
(Stone) SSA PRO ART 80 $.85   (O18)

O, COME LET US SING!
SATB CHAPPELL 0016220-358 $.40   (O19)

O COME LET US SING see Black

O COME, LET US SING see Brumbelow, Roy

O COME, LET US SING see Butler

O COME LET US SING see Couperin, Francois

O COME, LET US SING see Fischer

O, COME LET US SING see Francis, J.

O COME, LET US SING see Harries

O COME, LET US SING see Kirk, Theron W.

O COME LET US SING see Krul

O COME, LET US SING see Maunder, J.H.

O COME, LET US SING see Mueller, Carl F.

O COME LET US SING see Young, Gordon

O COME LET US SING GOOD TIDINGS see Tours, Berthold

O COME, LET US SING TO THE LORD see Track, Gerhard

O COME LET US SING UNTO THE LORD see Berger, Jean

O COME, LET US SING UNTO THE LORD see Byrd, William, Venite

O COME, LET US SING UNTO THE LORD see Douglas

O COME LET US SING UNTO THE LORD see Handel, George Frideric

O COME, LET US SING UNTO THE LORD see Hurd, Michael

O COME LET US SING UNTO THE LORD see Newbury, Kent A.

O COME, LET US SING UNTO THE LORD see Ramsey, Robert

O COME, LET US SING UNTO THE LORD see Steel, Christopher [Charles]

O COME LET US SING UNTO THE LORD see Swann, Donald, Venite

O COME LET US WORSHIP see Coggin

O COME, LET US WORSHIP see Mendelssohn-Bartholdy, Felix

O COME, LET US WORSHIP see Palestrina, Giovanni, Adoramus Te, Christe

O COME LET US WORSHIP see Thomas, T.A.

O COME LITTLE CHILDREN see Carissimi, Giacomo, O Felix Anima

O COME, LITTLE CHILDREN see Ehret, Walter

O COME, LITTLE CHILDREN see Glarum, L. Stanley

O COME LITTLE CHILDREN see Ihr Kinderlein Kommet

O COME LITTLE CHILDREN see Schulz, Joh. Abraham Peter, Ihr Kinderlein, Kommet

O COME, LOUD ANTHEMS LET US SING
(Coggin) SATB oct BELWIN 60821 $.30   (O20)

O COME, LOUD ANTHEMS LET US SING see Blake

O COME, LOUD ANTHEMS LET US SING see Hinebaugh

O COME LOUD ANTHEMS LET US SING see Kirk

O COME LOUD ANTHEMS LET US SING see Kirk, Theron W.

O COME NOW AND GATHER *Gen
(Track) SA SCHMITT 227 $.35   (O21)

O COME, O COME EMANUEL
(Shaw; Parker) SATB,acap oct LAWSON 727 $.30   (O22)

O COME, O COME, EMMANUEL *Xmas,anthem/carol
(Christian, Paul) SATB (easy) oct AUGSBURG 1085 $.20   (O23)
(Felciano) SSA,acap MARKS 4319 $.30   (O24)
(Johns, Donald) SAB (easy) oct AUGSBURG 1395 $.30   (O25)
(Kirk) SSA oct PRO ART 1880 $.25   (O26)
(Kirk) 2pt oct PRO ART 1540 $.30   (O27)
(Kirk) TTBB oct PRO ART 2066 $.25   (O28)
(Kirk) SATB oct PRO ART 1645 $.30   (O29)
(Kirk) SAB oct PRO ART 2065 $.30   (O30)

O COME, O COME EMMANUEL see Creston, Paul

O COME, O COME, EMMANUEL see Felciano, Richard

O COME, O COME, EMMANUEL see Goodwin

O COME, O COME, EMMANUEL see Hilty

O COME, O COME EMMANUEL see Kinsman

O COME, O COME EMMANUEL see Luvaas

O COME, O COME, EMMANUEL see Tkach

O COME, O COME, IMMANUEL see Butler, Eugene

O COME, SING UNTO THE LORD see Kimball

O COME, THOU SAVIOR OF OUR RACE *Xmas
(Johnson) SATB,opt bells SCHMITT 15005 $.30   (O31)

O COME THOU SPIRIT DIVINEST see Amner, John

O COME TO BETHLEHEM see Freed

O COME TO MY HEART, LORD JESUS see Ambrose, [Paul]

O COME TO THE MANGER see Davies

O COME TO THE MANGER see Schulz, Joh. Abraham Peter

O COME YE SERVANTS OF THE LORD see Tye, Christopher, Laudate Dominum Domini

O COME YE SERVANTS OF THE LORD see Tye, Christopher, Laudate Nomen Domini

O COME YE TO THE CROSS see Carissimi, Giacomo

O COME YE UNTO ME see Charpentier, Marc-Antoine, Venite Ad Me

O COME YOU NOW TO BETHLEHEM see Bratt, C. Griffith

O COR AMORE SAUCIUM see Muller, Giulio

O CROIX JE T'ACCEPTE AVEC JOIE! see Bach, Johann Sebastian, Ich Will Den Kreuzstab Gerne Tragen

O CROSS! THOU ONLY HOPE see Morales, Cristobal de, O Crux Ave, Spes Unica

O CROSS WE GREET THEE see Palestrina, Giovanni

O CROSS WE HAIL! see Palestrina, Giovanni, Crux Ave

O CRUCIS VICTORIA see Angerri

O CRUX AVE see Palestrina, Giovanni

O CRUX AVE see Siegl

O CRUX AVE, SPES UNICA see Morales, Cristobal de

O CRUX BENEDICTA see Ascenso, Antonio

O CRUX BENEDICTA see Bianchini, Carlo

O CRUX BENEDICTUS see Anonymous

O CRUX SPLENDIDIOR see Philips, Peter

O DANIEL! see Caldwell, Mary [Elizabeth]

O DARKEST WOE *Easter/Lent,anthem,Ger
(Cassler, G. Winston) unis (very easy) oct AUGSBURG 1232   (O32)
(Cassler, G. Winston) unis treb cor (very easy) oct AUGSBURG 1232 $.20   (O33)
(Ehret, Walter) SATB oct WALTON 2017 $.25   (O34)

O DARKEST WOE! see Lovelace, Austin C.

O DASS DOCH BALD DEIN FEUER BRENNTE see Kurig, Hans-Hermann

O DASS ICH TAUSEN ZUNGEN HATTE see Kramer, Gottfried

O DASS ICH TAUSEND ZUNGEN HATTE see Konig, Johann Balthasar

O DASS ICH TAUSEND ZUNGEN HATTE see Reda, Siegfried

O DASS ICH TAUSEND ZUNGEN HATTE see Stern, Hermann

O DAY FULL OF GRACE see Weyse, Christoph Ernst Friedrich

O DAY OF CONSECRATION see Palestrina, Giovanni, Dies Sanctificatus

O DAY OF GOD, DRAW NIGH see Butler

O DAY OF LIGHT AND LIFE AND GRACE see How

O DAY OF REST AND GLADNESS
(Stuart) SATB oct PRO ART 1657 $.20   (O35)

O, DAY OF REST AND GLADNESS see Adam, J.

O DAY OF REST AND GLADNESS AND ALL HAIL THE
POWER OF JESUS'NAME see Ringwald, [Roy]

O DAY OF RESURRECTION see Angell, Warren M.

O DEAR, O FRIENDLY, O KIND AND GENTLE SAVIOR
see Schutz, Heinrich

O DEAREST DAY, THOU'RT WELCOME see Bach, Johann
Michael, Sei Lieber Tag Willkommen

O DEAREST JESUS see Haydn, (Franz) Joseph

O DEAREST JESUS see Schack, David

O DEAREST JESUS, WHAT LAW see Markworth, Henry

O DEAREST JESUS, WHAT LAW HAST THOU BROKEN see
Metzler, Friedrich

O DEAREST JESUS, WHAT LAW HAST THOU BROKEN see
Mudde, Willem

O DEAREST LORD see Lovelace, Austin C.

O DEAREST LORD GOD see Schutz, Heinrich, O
Lieber Herre Gott

O DEAREST LORD, THY SACRED HEAD *anthem/folk,
US
(Johnson, David N.) SATB,opt fl (easy) oct
AUGSBURG 1607 $.30   (O36)

O DEATH, HOW BITTER see Reger, Max, O Tod, Wie
Bitter Bist Du

O DEATH NONE COULD CONQUER THEE see Bach,
Johann Sebastian

O DEATH ROCK ME ASLEEP see Berger, Jean

O DEEPEST WOE see Peninger

O DEL CARMEL SPLENDORE! see Mariani, Eligio

O DEUE D POB CRISTION *Xmas,carol,Welsh
(Brown) "Carol Of Humility, A" SATB,acap
SCHIRM.EC 2699   (O37)

O DEUE D POB CRISTION see Brown, Rex P.

O DIEU DE CLEMENCE
(Kite, H.) "God Who Watchest O'er Us" [Fr]
SA,pno SCHIRM.EC 1850 $.16   (O38)

O DIEU DES ARMEES see Goudimel, Claude

O DIEU, LA GLORIE QUI T'EST DEUE see Goudimel,
Claude

O DIEU, O DIEU *Xmas,carol,Aus
(Canteloube, J.) [Fr] 4pt mix cor,acap oct
DURAND   (O39)

O DIEU, OU MON ESPOIR J'AI MIS see Goudimel,
Claude

O DIEU! QUE N'ETAIS-JE EN VIE *Xmas,carol,18th
cent
(Geveart, F.-A.) [Fr] 4pt mix cor,acap (med
easy) cor pts LEMOINE s.p. see from
Collection De Choeurs, deuxieme Fascicule
                                         (O40)

O DIVINE MASTER see Moffatt, James

O DIVINE REDEEMER see Gounod, Charles Francois,
Repentir

O DIVINE REDEEMER see Parks, J.A.

O DOMINE see Victoria, Tomas Luis de

O DOMINE DEUS see Jeffries, George

O DOMINE DEUS SPERAVI IN TE see Muller, P.

O DOMINE JESU CHRISTE *Gen/Lent
(Martens) "O Gracious Lord God" SATB,kbd (med
easy) oct CONCORDIA 98-1743 $.25   (O41)

O DOMINE JESU CHRISTE see Collum, Herbert

O DOMINE JESU CHRISTE see Des Prez, Josquin

O DOMINE JESU CHRISTE see Hammerschmidt,
Andreas

O DOMINE JESU CHRISTE see Martens

O DOMINE JESU CHRISTE see Palestrina, Giovanni

O, DOMINE JESU CHRISTE see Scheidt, Samuel

O DOMINE JESU CHRISTE see Schein, Johann
Hermann

O DOMINE JESU CHRISTE see Scheit, Samuel

O DOMINE JESU CHRISTE see Willaert, Adrian

O DOMINE JESU CHRISTE ADORO TE see Gabrieli,
Giovanni

O DOMINE JESU CHRISTI see Gabrieli, Giovanni

O' DOVE OF PEACE see Pickell

O DU FROHLICHE
see Vier Weihnachtslieder

O DU FROHLICHE see Beethoven, Ludwig van, O
Sanctissima

O DU FROHLICHE see Schwartz, J.

O DU FROHLICHE see Trader, Willi

O DU FROHLICHE, O DU SELIGE see Schwartz, J.

O DU GUDS LAM see Scheidt, Samuel

O, DU HARLIGA *Xmas,hymn
(Lundvik, Hildor) men cor NORDISKA 1171 s.p.
see from Julhymner   (O42)
(Wikander, David) mix cor NORDISKA 944 s.p.
                                         (O43)

O DU HELGE ANDE, KOM TILL OSS IN! see Moren,
John, Veni, Sancte Spiritus

O DU LAMM GOTTES, JESU CHRIST see Staden,
Johann

O DU LIEBE MEINER LIEBE see Bach, Johann
Sebastian

O DU MAUER DER TOCHTER ZION see Bach, Johann
Ernst

O DU MEIN TROST see Trunk, [Richard]

O DU MIN ADLA SKATT
(Bjarnegard, Gustaf) [Swed] SAB,acap GEHRMANS
TKS 28   (O44)

O DU MIN IMMANUEL see Soraas, Lars

O DU SALIGA
see Frojda Dig O Kristenhet

O DU STILLE ZEIT see Wolters, Gottfried

O DU, VAR HERRE JESU KRIST see Thyrestam,
Gunnar

O DU VAR HERRE JESUS KRIST see Le Maistre,
Mattheus

O DULCIS see Schutz, Heinrich

O DULCIS JESU see Vecchi

O DURCHBRECHER ALLER BANDE see Horn, Paul

O EARTH, COVER NOT MY BLOOD see Boyd, Jack

O ESCA VIATORUM see Cervi, Luigi

O ESCA VIATORUM see Magri, Pietro

O ESCA VIATORUM see Nicolosi, Salvatore

O ESCA VIATORUM see Ravanello, Oreste

O ESCA VIATORUM see Volpi, Edoardo

O ETERNAL LORD see Gasparini, Quirino

O EWIGES FEUER see Bach, Johann Sebastian, O
Ewiges Feuer, O Ursprung Der Liebe

O EWIGES FEUER [CHORALE] see Bach, Johann
Sebastian

O EWIGES FEUER, O URSPRUNG DER LIEBE see Bach,
Johann Sebastian

O EWIGKEIT, DU DONNERWORT see Bach, Johann
Sebastian

O EWIGKEIT, DU DONNERWORT see Bach, Johann
Sebastian

O EWIGKEIT, DU DONNERWORT see Bach, Johann
Sebastian

O FADER VAR, BARMHARTIG, GOD *Bibl
(Olson, Daniel) [Swed] SATB,acap GEHRMANS
KRB 87   (O45)

O FADER VAR I HEMMERIK see Hassler, Hans Leo

O FADER VAR I HIMMERIK see Gumpeltzhaimer, Adam

O FADER VAR I HIMMERIK see Praetorius, Michael

O FAIR ZION see Verdi, Giuseppe

O FAITHFUL CROSS see Predmore, G.V.

O FAITHFUL CROSS see Roff, Joseph

O FAITHFUL LORD see Roff, Joseph

O FATHER OF LIFE see Grieg, Edvard Hagerup

O FATHER OF THE FAITHFUL see Hammerschmidt,
Andreas, O Vater Aller Frommen

O FATHER, WHOSE ALMIGHTY POWER see Handel,
George Frideric

O FEAR THE LORD see Haydn, (Johann) Michael,
Timete Dominum

O FEAR THE LORD, YE HIS SAINTS see Wood, Dale

O FEAR THEE NOT see Dressler, John

O FELIX ANIMA see Carissimi, Giacomo

O FILII ET FILIAE
(Racine, C.; Geveart, F.-A.) "Prose De La
Fete De Paques" [Lat/Fr] 3pt wom cor,acap
(med easy) cor pts LEMOINE s.p. see from
Collection De Choeurs, premiere Facsimile
                                         (O46)

O FILII ET FILIAE see Davies, Henry Walford

O FILII ET FILIAE see Gevaert, Francois Auguste

O FILII ET FILIAE see Leisring, Volkmar

O FLOS FLAGRANS see Brasart, J.

O FOOD OF MEN WAYFARING see Ouchterlony, David

O FOR A CLOSER WALK WITH GOD see Anderson,
[William H.]

O FOR A CLOSER WALK WITH GOD see Cowper

O! FOR A CLOSER WALK WITH GOD see Foster

O FOR A CLOSER WALK WITH GOD see Foster, Myles
Birket

O FOR A CLOSER WALK WITH GOD see Titcomb,
Everett

O FOR A CLOSER WALK WITH GOD see Webber, Lloyd

O FOR A CLOSER WALK WITH GOD see Williams

O FOR A CLOSER WALK WITH GOD see Young, Gordon

O FOR A HEART TO PRAISE MY GOD
(Ehret) SATB oct WORD CS-682 $.25   (O47)

O FOR A HEART TO PRAISE MY GOD see Darst, W.
Glenn

O FOR A HEART TO PRAISE MY GOD see Gibbons,
Orlando

O FOR A HEART TO PRAISE MY GOD! see Powell

O FOR A HEART TO PRAISE MY GOD see Webbe,
Samuel

O FOR A SHOUT OF SACRED JOY see Hovhaness, Alan

O FOR A THOUSAND TONGUES see Glaser

O FOR A THOUSAND TONGUES see Glazer, Carl

O FOR A THOUSAND TONGUES see Thompson

O, FOR A THOUSAND TONGUES TO SING
(Carmichael) SATB oct WORD CS-305 $.30   (O48)

O FOR A THOUSAND TONGUES TO SING see Denton

O FOR A THOUSAND TONGUES TO SING see Hughes,
Robert J.

O, FOR A THOUSAND TONGUES TO SING see Webb

O FOR A THOUSAND TONGUES TO SING see Williams,
David

O FOR A THOUSAND TONGUES TO SING see Wright, B.

O FOR THE WINGS OF A DOVE see Mendelssohn-
Bartholdy, Felix

O FOUNT OF LIFE see Larson

O FOUNT OF WISDOM see Ramsey, Robert, O
Sapientia

O FREEDOM! see Steiner, Luis

O FREEDOM see Martin

O FREUDE UBER FREUD see Eccard, Johannes

O FREUDE UBER FREUDE see Burkhart, Franz

O FREUDE UBER FREUDE see Eccard, Johannes

O FREUDENREICHER TAG see Werner, St.

O FROHLICHE STUNDEN, O HERRLICHE ZEIT see
Buxtehude, Dietrich

O FROHLOCKE IN DEM HERRN see Handel, George
Frideric

O FROHLOCKE IN DEM HERRN see Handel, George
Frideric, O Be Joyful In The Lord

O GATE OF HEAVEN see Grandi, Alessandro

O GAY IS THE DAY WE SING *Xmas,carol
(Whitehead, Alfred) SATB oct LESLIE 4008 see
from Three Christmas Carols, Set 2   (O49)

O GEMMA CLARISSIMA see Willaert, Adrian

O GENTLE JESU see Roff, Joseph

O GENTLE NIGHT see Munninckx

O GENTLE SAVIOR see Wheeler, Alfred

O GIJ MIJN TROOST see Zwart, Jan

O GIVE THANKS see Ford

O GIVE THANKS see Gardner

O GIVE THANKS see Hicks, Mary

O GIVE THANKS see Korte, Karl

O GIVE THANKS see Lehmeier, J.F.

O GIVE THANKS see Powell

O GIVE THANKS see Purcell, Henry

O GIVE THANKS see Smith

O GIVE THANKS TO THE LORD see Diemer, Emma Lou

O GIVE THANKS TO THE LORD see Frey, R.

O GIVE THANKS TO THE LORD see Newbury, Kent A.

O GIVE THANKS UNTO THE LORD see Berger

O GIVE THANKS UNTO THE LORD see Bliss, Sir
Arthur

O GIVE THANKS UNTO THE LORD see Bortniansky,
Dimitri Stepanovitch

O GIVE THANKS UNTO THE LORD see Clark

O GIVE THANKS UNTO THE LORD see Croft

O GIVE THANKS UNTO THE LORD see Croft, William

O GIVE THANKS UNTO THE LORD see Elvey, George
Job

O GIVE THANKS UNTO THE LORD see Gardner, John
[Linton]

O GIVE THANKS UNTO THE LORD see McLaughlin,
Marian

O GIVE THANKS UNTO THE LORD see Purcell, Henry

O GIVE THANKS UNTO THE LORD see Rogers,
Benjamin

O GIVE THANKS UNTO THE LORD see Smart, Roland

O GIVE THANKS UNTO THE LORD see Titcomb

O GIVE THANKS UNTO THE LORD see Tomkins, Thomas

O GIVE THANKS UNTO THE LORD see Williams

O GIVE THANKS UNTO THE LORD see Wood, John

O GIVE THE LORD, YOU SONS OF GOD see Grail

O GLADSOME LIGHT see Arkhangelsky

O GLADSOME LIGHT see Gretchaninov, Alexander Tikhonovitch

O GLADSOME LIGHT see Miller

O GLADSOME LIGHT see Sullivan, Sir Arthur Seymour

O GLADSOME LIGHT see Thiman, Eric Harding

O GLADSOME LIGHT see Wolff, S. Drummond

O GLAUBIG HERZ *CCU
(Strube, Adolf) [Ger] 2-3pt wom cor/2-3pt jr cor cloth BAREN. EM 343 s.p.   (050)

O GLAUBIG HERZ, GEBENEDEI see Bornefeld, Helmut

O GLAUBIG HERZ, GEBENEDEI see Praetorius, Michael

O GLAUBIG HERZ, GEBENEDEI UND GIB see Stern, Hermann

O GLORIOSA REGINA see Touront

O GLORIOSA VIRGINUM see Rodella, Sante

O GLORIOUS NIGHT see Andrews, C.T., Von Himmel Hoch

O, GO YOUR WAY INTO HIS GATES see Handel, George Frideric

O GO YOUR WAY INTO HIS GATES WITH THANKSGIVING see Handel, George Frideric

O GOD, ALMIGHTY FATHER
see Recessional Hymns

O GOD, AUTHOR OF ETERNAL LIGHT see Pasquet, Jean

O GOD BE MERCIFUL see Tye, Christopher

O GOD BENEATH THY GUIDING HAND see Hatton

O GOD, BENEATH THY GUIDING HAND see Hatton, John [Liptrot]

O GOD, CREATION'S SECRET FORCE see Harris, D.S.

O GOD, CREATOR OF MANKIND *folk,Ger
(Brahms, Johannes) SATB,acap SCHIRM.EC 1717 $.30   (051)

O GOD, ENFOLD ME IN THE SUN see Leighton, Kenneth

O GOD, ENLIGHTEN MY MIND see Whitford

O GOD, FATHER OF MERCY
SSA BIG3 $.25   (052)

O GOD, HOW GRIEVOUS IS THE WOE see Bach, Johann Sebastian, Ach Gott, Wie Manches Herzeleid [Chorale]

O GOD, HOW WONDERFUL THOU ART see Brown, Leon F.

O GOD, I OFFER THANKS TO THEE see Beethoven, Ludwig van

O GOD, I THANK THEE see Schumann, Robert (Alexander)

O GOD, I THANK THEE HEARTILY see Bouman, Paul

O GOD MOST HOLY see Schulthes

O GOD MY HEART IS READY see Wood, John

O GOD MY STRENGTH see Lovelace, Austin C.

O GOD! O GOD! see Mozart, Wolfgang Amadeus

O GOD, O LORD OF HEAVEN AND EARTH see Bender, Jan

O GOD OF ALL ABOVE, BELOW see Butler, Eugene

O GOD OF ALL BEAUTY see Roff, Joseph

O GOD OF ALL CREATION see Brown, Frank Edwin

O GOD OF BEAUTY see Sateren, Leland Bernhard

O GOD OF BETHEL see Tye, Christopher

O GOD OF BETHEL! see Younger, John B.

O GOD OF EARTH see Hill, Eugene

O GOD OF EARTH AND ALTAR *hymn
unis oct ST.MARTIN s.p.   (053)

O GOD OF EARTH AND ALTAR see Gibbs, [Cecil] Armstrong

O GOD OF EVERY RACE AND CREED see Grieb, Herbert [C.]

O GOD OF GRACE AND GOODNESS see Bach, Johann Sebastian

O GOD OF JACOB, BY WHOSE HAND see Tye, Christopher

O GOD OF LIFE see Franck, Cesar, Panis Angelicus

O GOD OF LIFE ABOVE see Werbecke, G. Von, Panis Angelicus

O GOD OF LOVE see Bizet, Georges, Agnus Dei

O GOD OF LOVE see Darst, W. Glenn

O GOD OF LOVE see Pasquet, Jean

O GOD OF LOVE see Thiman, Eric Harding

O GOD OF LOVE see Trued, Clarence

O GOD OF LOVE see York, D.

O GOD OF MERCY see Barnby

O GOD OF PEACE see Dieterich, M.

O GOD OF PEACE see James

O GOD OF PEACE see Wehr, David A.

O GOD OF THE QUIET SPIRIT see Hughes

O GOD OF WONDROUS GRACE see Pasquet, Jean

O GOD OF YOUTH see Darst, W. Glenn

O GOD OF YOUTH see Schroth, G.

O GOD OUR FATHER see Knight, Vincent

O GOD OUR FATHER IN HEAVEN see Phillips, Montague Fawcett

O, GOD OUR HELP see Croft, W.

O GOD, OUR HELP see Whitney, Maurice C.

O GOD, OUR HELP IN AGES PAST *hymn,Eng
(Cain) SATB,trp oct BOOSEY 5442 $.30   (054)
(Davis) SSA,org/pno BOSTON 2841 $.35   (055)
(Davis) SATB,org/pno BOSTON 9768 $.35   (056)
(Davis) TTBB,org/pno BOSTON 2268 $.35   (057)

O GOD, OUR HELP IN AGES PAST see Cassler, G. Winston

O GOD, OUR HELP IN AGES PAST see Croft, W.

O GOD, OUR HELP IN AGES PAST see Croft, William

O GOD OUR HELP IN AGES PAST see Hopkins

O GOD OUR HELP IN AGES PAST see Hovhaness, Alan

O GOD OUR HELP IN AGES PAST see Lamont

O GOD, OUR HELP IN AGES PAST see Mueller, Carl F.

O GOD, OUR HELP IN AGES PAST see Pike, Harry Hale

O GOD, OUR HELP IN AGES PAST see Price

O GOD, OUR HELP IN AGES PAST see Schipp, C.M.

O GOD OUR HELP IN AGES PAST see Sowerby, Leo

O GOD, OUR HELP IN AGES PAST see Thompson

O GOD, OUR HELP IN AGES PAST see Titcomb

O GOD, OUR HELP IN AGES PAST see Young

O GOD OUR STRENGTH AND REFUGE SURE see Butler, Eugene

O GOD, PRESERVE THE WORK see Wiltberger, Confirma Hoc Deus

O GOD, SEARCH ME see Geist

O GOD, THAT NO TIME DOEST DESPISE see Peerson, Martin

O GOD, THE AUTHOR OF PEACE see Roff, Joseph

O GOD, THE FATHER, ETERNAL ONE see Praetorius, Heironymous

O GOD, THE JOY OF OUR LIFE see Van Wyatt

O GOD THE KING OF GLORY see Cashmore, Donald

O GOD THE KING OF GLORY see Gibbons, Orlando

O GOD THE KING OF GLORY see Purcell, Henry

O GOD, THE PROTECTOR see Harris, William Henry

O GOD, THE PROTECTOR see Lewis, John Leo

O GOD, THE PROUD ROSE 'GAINST ME see Berger, Jean

O GOD THE REFUGE OF OUR FEARS see Stevens, Halsey

O GOD, THE ROCK OF AGES see Fearis, J.S.

O GOD, THE ROCK OF AGES see Sateren, Leland Bernhard

O GOD, THOU ART MY GOD see Bortniansky, Dimitri Stepanovitch

O GOD, THOU ART MY GOD see Lekberg, Sven

O GOD, THOU ART MY GOD see Litten, Jack

O GOD THOU ART MY GOD see Purcell, Henry

O GOD, THOU ART MY GOD see Rhea, Raymond

O GOD, THOU FAITHFUL GOD see Bach, Johann Sebastian

O GOD, THOU FAITHFUL GOD see Brahms, Johannes

O GOD, THY CHURCH ETERNAL see Powell

O GOD, THY GOODNESS REACHETH FAR see Beethoven, Ludwig van

O GOD, THY HANDS THE HEAVENS MADE see Wilson

O GOD, THY NAME IS HOLY see Matthews

O GOD, THY WORLD IS SWEET WITH PRAYER see Greener, Joseph H.

O GOD TO ME BE MERCIFUL see Brandon, G.

O GOD, TO US SHOW MERCY see Lassus, Roland de (Orlandus)

O GOD, UNSEEN YET EVER NEAR see Coleman, Henry

O GOD VAN HEMEL, ZEE EN AARD'
(Kuxhaven, J.) mix cor sc ALSBACH&D s.p.   (058)

O GOD, WE LAUD AND PRAISE THEE see Fink, Michael, Te Deum

O GOD, WE PRAISE THEE see Te Deum

O GOD, WE PRAY see Arensky, Anton Stepanovitch

O GOD, WHEN THOU WENT'ST see Peerson, Martin

O GOD, WHEREFORE ART THOU ABSENT FROM US see Child, William

O GOD, WHO ART THE AUTHOR OF PEACE see Pedrette

O GOD, WHO BY THE LEADING OF A STAR see Attwood, Thomas

O GOD WHO BY THE LEADING OF A STAR see Aubert, Pierre Francois Oliver

O GOD WHO HAST PREPARED see Hastings

O GOD, WHO HAST PREPARED see Pasquet, Jean

O GOD, WHO IN THY HEAVENLY HAND see Handel, George Frideric

O GOD, WHO IN THY HEAV'NLY HAND see Handel, George Frideric

O GOD WHOSE MIGHTY WORKS OF OLD see Darke, Harold [Edwin]

O GOD WHOSE VAST DOMAIN see Kirby

O GOD, WONDERFUL ART THOU see Tomkins, Thomas

O GODE JESU see Thyrestam, Gunnar

O GOEDE JEZUS ONTFERM U ONZER see Ingegneri, Marco Antonio, O Bone Jesu

O GOOD JESUS see Deering, Richard, O Bone Jesu

O GOOD LORD JESU see Palestrina, Giovanni

O GOOD MORNING, MY FAIR ONE! see Brahms, Johannes, Vergebliches Standchen

O GOTT DU FROMMER GOTT *17th cent
(Berger, H.L.) TTBB HANSSLER 6.5075 s.p.   (059)

O GOTT, DU FROMMER GOTT see Bach, Johann Sebastian

O GOTT, DU FROMMER GOTT see Stern, Hermann

O GOTT, DU MEIN GOTT see Luhn

O GOTT, NUN LASST UNS HEBEN DIE HAND see Roeseling, Kaspar

O GOTT WIR DANKEN DEINER GUT see Buxtehude, Dietrich

O GOTT, WIR DANKEN DEINER GUT see Praetorius, Michael

O GRACIOUS GOD see Goehr, Alexander

O GRACIOUS GOD, PARDON MY GREAT OFFENCE see Owen, H.

O GRACIOUS JESU see Brahms, Johannes, O Bone Jesu

O GRACIOUS JESUS see Palestrina, Giovanni, O Bone Jesu

O GRACIOUS KING see Thompson

O GRACIOUS LORD, CAST DOWN THINE EYES see Gaul, Alfred Robert

O GRACIOUS LORD GOD see O Domine Jesu Christe

O GRACIOUS LORD JESUS CHRIST see Sweelinck, Jan Pieterszoon

O GRACIOUS LORD, OUR GOD see Schutz, Heinrich

O GRANT US GRACE see Gesualdo, Don Carlo, Dignare Me

O GREAT IS THE DEPTH see Mendelssohn-Bartholdy, Felix

O GREAT IS THE LORD see Brahms, Johannes

O GROSSER GOTT see Schweizer, Rolf

O GROUND OF FAITH see Christiansen, P.

O, GUD ALLSMAKTIGE see Nyvall, Jacob

O GUD, AV DIN BARMHARTIGHET see Bach, Johann Sebastian

O GUD, DET AR EN HJARTANS TROST see Soderholm, Valdemar

O, GUD, DET AR MIN GLADJE see Sodersten, Gunno

O GUD, GIV OSS DIN ANDES NAD see Skold, Yngve

O GUD, JAG AR EJ VARDIG see Sandberg, Folke

O GUD, SOM AVEN RACKT DIN HAND see Praetorius, Michael

O GUD, SOM HORER ALLAS ROST see Thyrestam, Gunnar

O, GUDS LAMM see Ahlen, Waldemar

O GUDS LAMM see Frylof, [Harald Leonard]

O, GUDS LAMM see Palestrina, Giovanni, Agnus
     Dei

O, GUDS LAMM see Praetorius, Michael, O Lamm
     Gottes, Unschuding

O GUTER, O LIEBER see Schutz, Heinrich, O Bone,
     O Dulcis

O HAD I WINGS OF A DOVE see Clark, Keith

O HANUKKAH O HANUKKAH *folk,Heb
     (Johnson, Roy E.) SATB (easy) oct AGAPE
     WR 1002 $.30
     (Johnson, Roy E.) SAB (easy) oct AGAPE   (O60)
     WR 1003 $.30   (O61)

O HAPPINESS, O GLADNESS *Xmas
     (Kranz, A.) SATB,acap AMP A574 $.25 see from
     Christmas Choruses   (O62)

O HAPPY BAND OF PILGRIMS see Hankey, Mark

O HAPPY DAY see Hawkins, Ed.

O HAPPY HE WHOM THOU PROTECT'ST see Weelkes,
     Thomas

O HAPPY HOME see Rasley

O HAPPY MAN see Purcell, Henry

O HAPPY SOULS
     (Parker) SATB,acap oct LAWSON 51310 $.30
                                                     (O63)

O HARK TO THE BELL'S GLAD SONG see Sheppard

O HAUPT VOLL BLUT UND WUNDEN see Bach, Johann
     Sebastian

O HAUPT VOLL BLUT UND WUNDEN see Bloch,
     Waldemar

O HAUPT VOLL BLUT UND WUNDEN see Bornefeld,
     Helmut

O HAUPT VOLL BLUT UND WUNDEN see Borris,
     Siegfried

O HAUPT VOLL BLUT UND WUNDEN see Dietrich,
     Fritz

O HAUPT VOLL BLUT UND WUNDEN see Hassler, Hans
     Leo

O HAUPT VOLL BLUT UND WUNDEN see Reger, Max

O, HAVE MERCY ON US see Palestrina, Giovanni

O HEAR ME, LORD see Schutz, Heinrich

O HEAR ME WHEN I CALL ON THEE see Schubert,
     Franz (Peter), Sei Mutter Der
     Barmherzigkeit

O HEAR THE NEWS see Guerrero, Francisco, Oyd,
     Oyd Una Cosa

O HEARKEN YE see Burt, Alfred

O HEART SUBDUED WITH GRIEVING see Brahms,
     Johannes, Lass Dich Nur Nichts Dauren

O HEER DIE DAAR DES HEMELS TENTEN see Gallarde,
     Suit Margriet

O HEIL, DAS WIR ERKOREN see Stier, Alfred

O HEILAND, REISS DIE HIMMEL AUF *Adv,17th cent
     (Bauernfeind, Hans) mix cor,acap oct
     DOBLINGER s.p. see from Vier Adventlieder
                                                     (O64)

O HEILAND, REISS DIE HIMMEL AUF see
     Bauernfeind, Hans

O HEILAND, REISS DIE HIMMEL AUF see Berger,
     Hans Ludwig

O HEILAND REISS DIE HIMMEL AUF see Beuerle,
     Herbert

O HEILAND, REISS DIE HIMMEL AUF see Bornefeld,
     Helmut

O HEILAND, REISS DIE HIMMEL AUF see Brahms,
     Johannes

O HEILAND, REISS DIE HIMMEL AUF see Burkhart,
     Franz

O HEILAND, REISS DIE HIMMEL AUF see David,
     Johann Nepomuk

O HEILAND, REISS DIE HIMMEL AUF see Distler,
     Hugo

O HEILAND, REISS DIE HIMMEL AUF see Dittmann,
     Thomas

O HEILAND REISS DIE HIMMEL AUF see Friedrichs,
     Karl

O HEILAND, REISS DIE HIMMEL AUF see Giefer,
     Willy

O HEILAND, REISS DIE HIMMEL AUF see Graap,
     Lothar

O HEILAND, REISS DIE HIMMEL AUF see Hindermann,
     Walter Felix

O HEILAND, REISS DIE HIMMEL AUF see Hufschmidt,
     Wolfgang

O HEILAND, REISS DIE HIMMEL AUF see Kappesser,
     Karl

O HEILAND, REISS DIE HIMMEL AUF see Lau, Heinz

O HEILAND, REISS DIE HIMMEL AUF see Lissmann,
     Kurt

O HEILAND, REISS DIE HIMMEL AUF see Poser, Hans

O HEILAND, REISS DIE HIMMEL AUF see Raphael,
     Gunther

O HEILAND, REISS DIE HIMMEL AUF see Spitta,
     Heinrich

O HEILAND, REISS DIE HIMMEL AUF see Strohbach,
     Siegfried

O HEILAND, REISS DIE HIMMEL AUF see Studer,
     Hans

O HEILAND, REISS DIE HIMMEL AUF see Suthoff-
     Gross, Rudolf

O HEILAND, REISS DIE HIMMEL AUF see Teuscher,
     Hans

O HEILAND, REISS DIE HIMMEL AUF see Weber,
     Karl-Heinz

O HEILAND, REISS DIE HIMMEL AUF see Weiss,
     Ewald

O, HEILAND, TROUWE HEER
     (Kuxhaven, J.) mix cor sc ALSBACH&D s.p.
                                                     (O65)

O HEIL'GE SEELENSPEISE see Bach, Johann
     Sebastian

O HEIL'GE SEELENSPEISE see Isaac, Heinrich

O HEIL'GES GEIST- UND WASSERBAD see Bach,
     Johann Sebastian

O HEILIG KIND see Cadow, Paul

O HEILIGER GEIST see Bach, Johann Sebastian, O
     Heil'ges Geist- Und Wasserbad

O HEILIGER GEIST, DU GOTTLICH FEUR see Vulpius,
     Melchior

O HEILIGER GEIST, O HEILIGER GOTT see
     Hufschmidt, Wolfgang

O HEILIGER GEIST, O HEILIGER GOTT see Koch,
     Johannes H.E.

O HEILIGER GEIST, O HEILIGER GOTT see Kubler,
     Emil

O HEIMAT, SIEH DES MORGENS HELLE SCHWINGEN see
     Sibelius, Jean

O HELLIGE TREENIGHET see Vulpius, Melchior

O HERE GOTT, DEIN GOTTLICH WORT see Wiemer,
     Wolfgang

O HERR, AUF DICH STEHT MEIN HOFFEN see Handel,
     George Frideric

O HERR, DEINE GUTE see Kubizek, Augustinian

O HERR, DER DU DIE SONNE SENDEST see Siegl,
     Otto

O HERR, DU WARST UNSRE ZUFLUCHT see Schweizer,
     Rolf

O HERR, HILF, O HERR, LASS WOHL GELINGEN see
     Schutz, Heinrich

O HERR, HILF, O HERR, LASS WOHL GELINGEN see
     Schutz, Heinrich

O HERR, HORE see Mohring, John

O HERR, HORE MICH AN see Gruschwitz, Gunther

O HERR, ICH BIN DEIN KNECHT see Schein, Johann
     Hermann

O HERR JESU CHRISTE see Gumpeltzhaimer, Adam

O HERR JESU CHRISTE see Schein, Johann Hermann

O HERR JESU CHRISTE, DER DU BIST see
     Hammerschmidt, Andreas

O HERR JESU, DEINE LEUTE see Weber, Hans

O HERR, MACH MICH ZUM WERKZEUG see Lisken, Gerd

O HERR, MACH MICH ZUM WERKZEUG DEINES FRIEDENS
     see Marks, Gunther

O HERR, MACHE MICH ZUM WERKZEUG DEINES FRIEDENS
     see Thiele, Siegfried

O HERRE, FRELS MIG, DOM MIN SAG see Pederson,
     Mogens

O HERRE GOTT see Gallus, Jacobus

O HERRE GOTT, BEGNADE MICH see Senfl, Ludwig

O HERRE GOTT, DEIN GOTTLICH WORT see
     Hufschmidt, Wolfgang

O HERRE GOTT, DEIN GOTTLICH WORT see
     Praetorius, Heironymous

O HERRE GOTT, DEIN GOTTLICH WORT see Raphael,
     Gunther

O HERRE GOTT, DU BLEIBST IN EWIGKEIT see Stier,
     Alfred

O HERRE GUD, GOR NAD MED MIG see Thyrestam,
     Gunnar

O, HERRE GUD, GOR NAD MEG MIG see Berg,
     Gottfrid

O HERRE GUD, OANDELIG see Berg, Gottfrid

O HERRE GUD, OANDELIG see Moren, John

O, HERRE GUD, OSS NADIG VAR see Runback, Albert

O HERRE GUD, VAR MILD OCH GOD see Moren, John

O HERRE GUD, VI BEDJA DIG see Berg, Gottfrid

O HERRE GUD, VI BEDJA DIG see Thyrestam, Gunnar

O HERRE JESU see Nilsson, Christian

O HERRE KRIST, DEG TIL OSS VEN
     (Baden, Conrad) [Norw] LYCHE 9 s.p.   (O66)

O HERRLICHER TAG, O FROHLICHE ZEIT see Bach,
     Johann Sebastian

O HILF, CHRISTE, GOTTES SOHN see Praetorius,
     Michael

O HILF, CHRISTE, GOTTES SOHN see Schutz,
     Heinrich

O HOCHSTER, DEINE GUTIGKEIT see Cruger, Johann

O HOCHSTER, DEINE GUTIGKEIT see Goudimel,
     Claude, Anbetung, Ehre, Dank Und Ruhm Sei
     Unserm

O, HOGE KONUNG see Thyrestam, Gunnar

O HOHERPRIESTER JESU CHRIST see Peter, Herbert

O HOLY AND GLORIOUS TRINITY see Palestrina,
     Giovanni

O HOLY AND HEAVENLY FEAST see Byrd, William

O HOLY BANQUET see Theophane, Sister M.
     (Hytrek)

O HOLY, BLESSED FEAST DIVINE see Pergolesi,
     Giovanni Battista, O Sacrum Convivium

O HOLY BLESSED TRINITY *Trin
     (Wiley) SATB oct PRO ART 2088 $.22   (O67)

O HOLY CHILD *anthem/folk,Ger
     (Grauer, Frederick) 2pt treb cor (easy) oct
     AUGSBURG 1612 $.30   (O68)

O, HOLY CHILD see Pergolesi, Giovanni Battista

O HOLY CHILD OF MARY see Marriott, Michael J.

O HOLY CHILD, WE WELCOME THEE *Xmas,carol,Boh
     (Halter, C.) SATB,kbd (easy) oct CONCORDIA
     98-1236 $.25   (O69)

O HOLY CITY see Bach, Johann Sebastian

O HOLY CITY see Howells, Herbert Norman

O HOLY CITY, SEEN OF JOHN see Bach, Johann
     Sebastian, O Mensch, Schau' Jesum Christum
     An

O HOLY CITY SEEN OF JOHN see Butler

O HOLY FATHER see Lapo, Cecil E.

O HOLY FATHER see O Bone Jesu

O HOLY FATHER see Palestrina, Giovanni, O Bone
     Jesu

O HOLY GHOST see Krenek, Ernst

O HOLY, HOLY LORD see Ware

O HOLY JESU see Lvoff, A. [von]

O HOLY JESU see Palestrina, Giovanni, O Bone
     Jesu

O HOLY JESUS see Melle, De', O Jesu Christe

O HOLY JESUS see Muelas

O HOLY JESUS see Palestrina, Giovanni, O Bone
     Jesu

O HOLY JESUS see Rohlig, Harald

O HOLY LORD see Dett, Robert Nathaniel

O HOLY LORD see Tchaikovsky, Piotr Ilyitch

O HOLY NIGHT see Adam, Adolphe-Charles,
     Cantique De Noel

O HOLY NIGHT OF WONDER see Kirk, Theron W.

O HOLY ONE see Buck, [Carlton C.]

O HOLY SAVIOR
     (Bodycombe) SATB oct VOLKWEIN VB224 $.25
                                               (O70)

O HOLY SAVIOR see Soderstrom

O HOLY SAVIOR see Young

O HOLY SAVIOUR see Young

O HOLY SPIRIT, ENTER IN see Markworth, Henry

O HOLY SPIRIT, ENTER IN see Nicolai

O HOLY SPIRIT, LORD OF GRACE see Eaton, Richard
     S.

O HOLY SPIRIT, LORD OF GRACE see Tye,
     Christopher

O HOLY SPIRIT, LORD OF GRACE see Webber, Lloyd

O HOLY SPIRIT SENT FROM HEAVEN see Lipscomb,
     Helen

O HOME BELOVED, WHERE'ER I WANDER see Madsen,
     Florence Jefferson

O HOOFD BEDEKT MET WONDEN see Bach, Johann
     Sebastian

O HOR, MEIN FLEH'N! see Handel, George
     Frideric, Return, Oh God!

O HOVED, HOJT FORHANET see Bach, Johann
     Sebastian, O Haupt Voll Blut Und Wunden

O HOW AMIABLE see Barnby, Sir Joseph

O HOW AMIABLE see Faning, Eaton

O HOW AMIABLE see Leighton, Kenneth, Quam
     Dilecta!

O HOW AMIABLE see Perdue-Davis, Vernon

O HOW AMIABLE see Tomkins, Thomas

O HOW AMIABLE see Vaughan Williams, Ralph

O HOW AMIABLE see Weelkes, Thomas

O, HOW AMIABLE see West, John Ebenezer

O HOW AMIABLE ARE THY DWELLINGS see Barnby, Sir Joseph

O HOW AMIABLE ARE THY DWELLINGS see Cashmore, Donald

O HOW AMIABLE ARE THY DWELLINGS see Gardner, John [Linton]

O HOW AMIABLE ARE THY DWELLINGS see Maunder, J.H.

O HOW AMIABLE ARE THY DWELLINGS see Swaffield, Ronald

O HOW AMIABLE ARE THY DWELLINGS see Wesley, Samuel Sr.

O HOW AMIABLE ARE THY DWELLINGS see Wolff

O HOW BEAUTIFUL see O Sanctissima

O HOW BEAUTIFUL THE SKY *anthem/folk,Dan
(Pooler, Marie) unis treb cor/SA (easy) oct
AUGSBURG 0918 $.25   (O71)

O HOW BLESSED see Bruckner, Anton

O HOW BLESSED see Geisler, Johan C.

O HOW BLESSED IS THIS PLACE see Leaf, Robert

O HOW FULL OF GLORY see Victoria, Tomas Luis de, O Quam Gloriosum Est Regnum

O HOW GLORIOUS see Esquivel, Juan Barahona de, O Quam Gloriosum

O HOW GLORIOUS Vaet, Jacobus, O Quam Gloriosum

O HOW GLORIOUS see Victoria, Tomas Luis de, O Quam Gloriosum

O HOW GLORIOUS see Willan, Healey

O HOW GLORIOUS see Williams, David H.

O HOW GLORIOUS ART THOU see White, Robert

O HOW GREAT AND GLORIOUS see Vaet, Jacobus, O Quam Gloriosum

O HOW GREAT IS THE LORD OF ALL see Weldon

O HOW GREAT IS THY COMPASSION see Flittner

O HOW JOYFULLY *Xmas,Lat
(Ehret, Walter) SAB (easy) PRESSER
$.35   (O72)

O HOW LOVELY, O HOW SWEET see Richolson

O HOW MY HEART see Obrecht, Jacob, Mijn Hert Heeft

O HOW PLENTIFUL IS THY GOODNESS see Flagler, [Robert S.]

O HOW PLENTIFUL IS THY GOODNESS see Harwood, Basil

O HOW SWEET, O LORD see Ripolles, Vincente, O Quam Suavis

O HOW SWEET, O LORD see Willan, Healey

O HUBUD, BLODIGT, SARAT see Bjarnegard, Gustaf

O, HUR SALLA ARO EJ DE FROMMA see Moren, John

O, HUR SALLA ARO EJ DE FROMMA see Thyrestam, Gunnar

O HURU LJUVLIG AR DIN BONING, HERRE KAR see Soderholm, Valdemar

O, HURU SALLA ARO EJ DE FROMMA see Ahlberg, Verner

O HUVUD, BLODIGT, SARAT see Bach, Johann Sebastian

O HUVUD, BLODIGT SARAT see Berg, Gottfrid

O, I CRY UNTO THEE see Gluck, Christoph Willibald Ritter von, De Profundis

O I HAVE SEEN A KING'S NEW BABY *Xmas,carol
SATB (easy) OXFORD 08.104 $.15   (O73)

O IHR CHRISTEN, TEUER ERKAUFT see Pepping, Ernst

O IHR LIEBEN HIRTEN see Hammerschmidt, Andreas

O, I'M SICK OF LIFE see Purcell, Henry

O INFANT SWEET, O INFANT KIND *Xmas,carol,Ger
(Ehret, Walter) SA,opt vcl FRANK F-610 $.35
                                               (O74)

O INFANT SWEET, O INFANT MILD see Bach, Johann Sebastian

O, JERUSALEM see Ehret, Walter

O JERUSALEM see Williamson, Malcolm

O JESU, ALL MEIN LEBEN see Heiller, Anton

O JESU, ALL MEIN LEBEN BIST DU see Krams, Peter

O JESU BLESSED LORD, TO THEE see Byrd, William

O JESU CHRIST see Bach, Johann Sebastian, O Jesu Christ, Mein's Lebens Licht

O JESU CHRIST see Nelhybel, Vaclav

O JESU CHRIST see Staden, Johann

O JESU CHRIST, DEIN KRIPPLEIN see Telemann, Georg Philipp

O JESU CHRIST, DEIN KRIPPLEIN IST see Cruger, Johann

O, JESU CHRIST, DEIN NAM DER IST GEWALTIGLICH see Schein, Johann Hermann

O JESU CHRIST, MEINS LEBENS LICHT
(Berger, H.L.) TTBB HANSSLER 6.5141 s.p.
contains also: Decius, Nicolaus, Allein
Gott In Der Hoh Sei Ehr   (O75)

O JESU CHRIST, MEIN'S LEBENS LICHT see Bach, Johann Sebastian

O JESU CHRIST, MEINS LEBENS LICHT see Graap, Lothar

O JESU CHRISTE
(Lundquist) SATB,acap (diff) oct WILLIS 7479
$.20   (O76)

O JESU CHRISTE see Berchem, Jachet

O JESU CHRISTE see Melle, De'

O JESU CHRISTE see van Berchem, J.

O JESU CHRISTE, WAHRES LICHT see Bauernfeind, Hans

O JESU CHRISTE, WAHRES LICHT see Hufschmidt, Wolfgang

O JESU CHRISTE, WAHRES LICHT see Marx, Karl

O JESU, DIR SEI EWIG DANK see Bach, Johann Sebastian

O JESU DOLCE see Baldasar

O JESU DOLCE see Palestrina, Giovanni

O JESU, DU GUDS RENA LAMM see Moren, John

O JESU, FILI DAVID see Des Prez, Josquin

O JESU GOD, O JESU KAR see Bach, Johann Sebastian

O JESU KAR, VAD HAR VAL DU FORBRUTIT
wom cor/jr cor NORDISKA 1871 s.p.   (O77)

O JESU KRIST DIG TILL OSS VAND see Olson, Daniel

O JESU KRIST, DIG TILL OSS VAND see Thyrestam, Gunnar

O JESU KRIST, DU NADENS BRUNN see Olson, Daniel

O, JESU KRIST, SANN GUD OCH MAN see Nylander, Gunnar

O JESU, LOOK see Kirby, George

O JESU MEEK see Ravenscroft, Thomas

O JESU MI DULCISSIME see Anerio, Giovanni Francesco

O JESU MI DULCISSIME see Gabrieli, Giovanni

O JESU MI DULCISSIME see Rodella, Sante

O JESU MOST KIND see Bach, Johann Sebastian

O JESU, NAME MOST SWEET see Anerio, Giovanni Francesco, O Jesu Mi Dulcissime

O JESU, NAR JAG HADAN SKALL
see Fem Folkliga Koraler I Sattningar
(Berg, Gottfrid) mix cor NORDISKA 2245 s.p.
see also Sacrae Cantiones   (O78)

O, JESU, NAR JAG HADAN SKALL see Sjoblom, Heimer

O JESU SO DEAR see Bach, Johann Sebastian

O JESU SO SWEET *Xmas
(Track) SA SCHMITT 232 $.25   (O79)

O JESU SO SWEET see Bach, Johann Sebastian, O Jesulein Suss

O JESU SO SWEET, O JESU SO MILD see Gordon, P.

O JESU SOET see Rontgen, [Julius]

O JESU, SON OF GOD see Bach, Johann Christoph, Dir, Jesu, Gottes Sohn

O JESU SWEET *Xmas
(Mattson) SATB SCHMITT 8067 $.35   (O80)

O JESU SWEET see Bach, Johann Sebastian

O JESULEIN see Selle, Thomas

O JESULEIN see Spitta, Heinrich

O JESULEIN, MEIN JESULEIN see Schein, Johann Hermann

O JESULEIN SUSS see Bach, Johann Sebastian

O JESULEIN SUSS see Krause, Chr.

O JESULEIN SUSS see Maasz, Gerhard

O JESULEIN SUSS see Raphael, Gunther

O JESULEIN SUSS, O JESULEIN MILD see Bach, Johann Sebastian

O JESULEIN ZART see Holscher, Bernhard

O JESULEIN ZART see Kropfreiter, Augustinius Franz

O JESULEIN ZART see Scheidt, Samuel

O JESUS BLIDE see Baldasar, O Jesu Dolce

O JESUS CHRIST, MY LIFE AND LIGHT see Bach, Johann Sebastian, O Jesu Christ, Mein's Lebens Licht

O JESUS CHRIST, TO THEE MAY HYMNS BE RISING see Moe, Daniel

O JESUS, CROWNED WITH ALL RENOWN see Oberle, Grover

O JESUS, CRUCIFIED FOR MAN see Graham, Robert [V.]

O JESUS, CRUCIFIED FOR MAN see Peninger, David

O JESUS, CRUCIFIED FOR MAN see Young

O JESUS, GRANT ME HOPE AND COMFORT see Franck, Cesar

O, JESUS! GUDS UDKARNE see Eccard, Johannes

O JESUS, I HAVE PROMISED see Casner, Myron D.

O JESUS, I HAVE PROMISED see Mann, [Arthur Henry]

O JESUS, I HAVE PROMISED see Mendelssohn-Bartholdy, Felix

O JESUS I HAVE PROMISED see Norman, Gus

O JESUS I HAVE PROMISED see Wehr, David A.

O JESUS, KING MOST WONDERFUL see Tye, Christopher

O JESUS, KING MOST WONDERFUL see Wetzler, Robert

O JESUS, KING OF GENTLENESS see Ford, Virgil T.

O JESUS KRIST, DIG TILL OSS VAND see Carlstedt, Gunnemer

O JESUS, LORD, MY LIGHT AND LIFE see Bach, Johann Sebastian

O JESUS, LORD OF LIFE AND BREATH see Praetorius, Michael

O JESUS, MY LIGHT AND LIFE see Bach, Johann Sebastian, O Jesu Christ, Mein's Lebens Licht

O JESUS, PA DIN ALTERFOD see de la Rue, Pierre, O Salutaris Hostia

O JESUS, PRINCE OF PEACE see Hopson

O JESUS, SHOW THY GREAT COMPASSION see Grimm, Heinrich

O JESUS SO SWEET see Wolff, S. Drummond

O JESUS, TENDER SHEPHERD, HEAR see Ach Lieber Herre Jesu Christ

O JESUS TENDER SHEPHERD HEAR see Brahms, Johannes

O JESUS, THOU ARE STANDING see Emerson, John

O JESUS, THOU ARE STANDING see Shepard, T.G.

O JESUS THOU ART STANDING
(Kinsman) SATB oct VOLKWEIN VB225 $.25   (O81)

O JESUS, THOU ART STANDING see Ambrose, [Paul]

O JESUS, THOU ART STANDING see Hughes

O JESUS, THOU ART STANDING see Knecht

O JESUS, THOU ART STANDING see Speaks, [Oley]

O JESUS, WE ADORE THEE
see Communion Hymns

O JONATHAN see Weelkes, Thomas

O JOY ABOVE ALL JOY see Eccard, Johannes, O Freude Uber Freud'

O JOYFUL DAY! see Haydn, (Johann) Michael

O JOYFULLY SING *CCU
(Cheyette) unis/SA/SAB,opt band oct PRO ART
33, IPA $1.00   (O82)

O JUBEL, O FREUD *Xmas,Aus
(Schemitsch, Hans) [Ger] mix cor,acap oct
DOBLINGER s.p. see also Zehn Osterrichische
Weihnachtslieder   (O83)

O KIND CREATOR see Kingsbury, L.

O KIND, O WAHRER GOTTESSOHN see Raphael, Gunther

O, KINDEKEN KLEIN see Bach, Johann Sebastian

O KINDLY JESUS see Palestrina, Giovanni, O Jesu Dolce

O KING ALL GLORIOUS see Willan, Healey

O KING ENTHRONED ON HIGH see Goodman, Joseph

O KING, GLORIOUS see Marenzio, Luca, O Rex Gloriae

O KING MOST HIGH see Spence, Horace

O KING OF GLORY see Marenzio, Luca, O Rex Gloriae

O KING OF GLORY see Palestrina, Giovanni, O Rex Gloriae

O KING OF GLORY see Willan, Healey

O KING OF HEAVEN see Vittoria, Ludovico, O Regem Coeli

O KING OF KINGS see Thompson

O KING OF MERCY see Mendelssohn-Bartholdy, Felix

O KING OF MIGHT AND SPLENDOR see Offertory Hymns

O KIRCHE GOTTES see Stier, Alfred

O, KOM DU SKONA DAG see Bach, Johann Sebastian

O, KOM, GUDS ANDE GOD see Arcadelt, Jacob

O KOMM, DU GEIST DER WAHRHEIT see Neubert, Gottfried

O KONIG ALLER EHREN see Rohwer, Jens

O KONIG ALLER EHREN see Stern, Hermann

O KONIG JESU CHRISTE see Micheelsen, Hans Friedrich

O KONIGIN, GNADIGSTE FRAU (from Psalteriolum 1642) BVM
SATB,acap voc pt DOBLINGER s.p. see also Unsere Liebe Frau   (O84)

O KORS, VAR HALSAT see Moren, John, Ave Crux

O KRISTE, DU SOM LJUSET AR see Berg, Gottfrid

O KRISTE, OSS BENADA see Bjarnegard, Gustaf

O KRISTE, OSS BENADA see Eccard, Johannes

O LAMB OF GOD
see Ah, Holy Jesus

O LAMB OF GOD see Eccard, Johannes

O LAMB OF GOD see Kalinnikov, Vassili Sergeievitch

O LAMB OF GOD see Morley

O LAMB OF GOD see Newbury, Kent A.

O LAMB OF GOD see Robson, R. Walker

O LAMB OF GOD see Stainer, John

O LAMB OF GOD see Thompson, Randall, Agnus Dei

O LAMB OF GOD see Van Iderstine, A.P.

O LAMB OF GOD see Walter, Samuel

O LAMB OF GOD see Wichmann

O LAMB OF GOD see Young, Carlton R.

O LAMB OF GOD, I COME see Blair, F.

O LAMB OF GOD MOST HOLY see Eccard, Johannes, O Lamm Gottes Unschuldig

O LAMB OF GOD MOST HOLY see Gottschovius, Nikolaus

O LAMB OF GOD MOST HOLY see Schein, Johann Hermann

O LAMB OF GOD MOST LOWLY see Young

O LAMM GOTTES see Praetorius, Michael

O LAMM GOTTES, UNSCHULDIG see Bach, Johann Sebastian

O LAMM GOTTES UNSCHULDIG see Bloch, Waldemar

O LAMM GOTTES, UNSCHULDIG see Bobel, Karl

O LAMM GOTTES UNSCHULDIG see Eccard, Johannes

O LAMM GOTTES, UNSCHULDIG see Jeep, Johann

O LAMM GOTTES, UNSCHULDIG see Praetorius, Michael

O LAMM GOTTES, UNSCHULDIG see Reimerdes, Friedrich

O LAMM GOTTES, UNSCHULDIG see Scheidt, Samuel

O LAMM GOTTES, UNSCHULDIG see Schein, Johann Hermann

O LAMM GOTTES, UNSCHULDIG, AM STAMM see Eccard, Johannes

O LAMM GOTTES, UNSCHULDING see Praetorius, Michael

O LAND DER VATER see Dobler, W.

O LAUFET, IHR HIRTEN see Denhoff, Joachim

O LAWD HEAR MY PRAYER (A NEGRO'S LAMENT) see Taylor, M.T.

O LEAVE YOUR SHEEP *Xmas,carol,Fr
(Fuller) SAB oct PRO ART 1236 $.20   (O85)
(Grimes, T.) unis,inst (easy) oct CONCORDIA 98-3004 $.40   (O86)
(West) SSA SCHMITT 2581 $.25   (O87)

O LEAVE YOUR SHEEP see Jenkins, [Joseph Willcox], Quitez Pasteurs

O LEBENSBRUNNLEIN GROSS UND TIEF see Kurig, Hans-Hermann

O LEBENSBRUNNLEIN TIEF UND GROSS see Beck, Conrad

O LEBENSBRUNNLEIN TIEF UND GROSS see Kretzschmar, Gunther

O LEBENSBRUNNLEIN TIEF UND GROSS see Metzger, Hans-Arnold

O LET ME AT THY FOOT- STOOL FALL see Peerson, Martin

O, LET ME FLY *spir
(Wadsworth) SATB,acap oct LAWSON 51248 $.25   (O88)

O LET ME FLY see Eliot

O LET ME FLY see Elliot, Dennis

O LET ME TREAD IN THE RIGHT PATH see Ward, John

O LET MY WISH BE CROWNED see Lang, C.S.

O LET THE LIGHT, THE TRUTH see Young

O LET US ALL BE GLAD TODAY see Pritchard, Arthur J.

O LET'S GET ON see Avery

O L'HOMME HEUREUX QUI A DE DIEU LA CRAINTE see Lupi II, Didier

O LIEBER GOTT IM HOCHSTEN THRON see Gumpeltzhaimer, Adam

O LIEBER HERRE GOTT see Schutz, Heinrich

O LIEBER HERRE GOTT, WECKE UNS AUB see Schutz, Heinrich

O LIEBER HERRE GOTT, WECKE UNS AUF see Schutz, Heinrich

O LIFE THAT MAKEST ALL THINGS NEW see Longmire, John

O LIGHT DIVINE see Arkhangelsky, Alexander

O LIGHT DIVINE see Tschesnokoff, P.I.

O LIGHT EVERLASTING see Bach, Johann Sebastian, O Ewiges Feuer [Chorale]

O LIGHT FROM AGE TO AGE THE SAME see Shaw, Martin

O LIGHT MOST BLESSED see Walther, Johann Gottfreid, O Lux Beata

O LIGHT, O WAY, O TRUTH, O LIFE see Pergolesi, Giovanni Battista

O LIGHT OF LIFE see Roberton, Hugh S.

O LIGHT OF LIFE see Scheidt, Samuel

O LIGHT OF LIFE, O SAVIOUR DEAR see Bach, Johann Sebastian

O LIGHT OF LIGHT see Tallis, Thomas, O Nata Lux

O LIGHT OF LIGHT see Tallis, Thomas, O Nata Lux De Lumine

O LIGHT, WHOSE BEAMS ILLUMINE ALL see Bortniansky, Dimitri Stepanovitch

O LINGUA BENEDICTA see Bottazzo, Luigi

O LINGUA BENEDICTA see Ravanello, Oreste

O LISTEN TO THE ANGELS' SONG see Ringwald, [Roy]

O LITTLE BABY JESUS see Pens

O LITTLE CHRIST SWEET *Xmas,carol
(Whitehead, Alfred) SATB oct LESLIE 4008 see from Three Christmas Carols, Set 2   (O89)

O LITTLE JESUS CHILD *Xmas,carol,US
(Ehret, Walter) SA,opt vln FRANK F-619 $.35   (O90)
(Ehret, Walter) SSA,opt vln FRANK F-682 $.35   (O91)
(Ehret, Walter) SAB,opt vln FRANK F-681 $.35   (O92)

O LITTLE ONE
see Six Christmas Carols, Set III
see Six Two-Part Carols

O LITTLE ONE see Darst, W. Glenn

O LITTLE ONE SWEET *Xmas,carol
desc (very easy) OXFORD 54.603 $.25   (O93)
(Vine) SATB (very easy) OXFORD 08.109 $.15, ipr   (O94)

O LITTLE ONE SWEET see Dressler, John

O LITTLE ONE SWEET! see Durston, D.

O LITTLE ONE SWEET see Edwards, P.M.H.

O LITTLE ONE SWEET see Leist, Warren C.

O LITTLE STAR see Boland, Kathleen

O LITTLE STARS SHINE OUT see Chrysostom-Koppes, Sister M.

O LITTLE TOWN
see Six Traditional Carols, Set II

O LITTLE TOWN OF BETHLEHEM *Xmas,carol,Eng
see Glory To The Newborn King
see Many Moods Of Christmas, The, Suite Four
SATB (easy) OXFORD 08.136 $.15   (O95)
(Davis, K.) unis&SSA SCHIRM.EC 1830 $.18   (O96)
(Davis, K.) TTB,acap SCHIRM.EC 2101 $.25   (O97)
(Davis, K.K.) SATB,acap SCHIRM.EC 1793 $.25   (O98)
(Fearis, J.S.) SA,pno (easy) oct WILLIS 6460 $.12   (O99)
(Hinrichs, E.C.) SA,kbd (med easy) oct CONCORDIA 98-1528 $.25   (O100)
(Stubbs, H.) SATB,acap CRAMER B27 s.p.   (O101)
(Todd, M.F.) 3pt wom cor,SA soli,pno/org (med) oct WILLIS 6088 $.15   (O102)
(Worthing, R.) SATB,S solo,pno (easy) oct WILLIS 2789 $.15   (O103)

O LITTLE TOWN OF BETHLEHEM see Anonymous

O LITTLE TOWN OF BETHLEHEM see Burroughs, Bob

O LITTLE TOWN OF BETHLEHEM see Dinn, Freda

O LITTLE TOWN OF BETHLEHEM see Gounod, Charles Francois

O LITTLE TOWN OF BETHLEHEM see Neidlinger, William Harold

O LITTLE TOWN OF BETHLEHEM see Pasquet, Jean

O LITTLE TOWN OF BETHLEHEM see Redner, Lewis [Henry]

O LITTLE TOWN OF BETHLEHEM see Smith

O LITTLE TOWN OF BETHLEHEM see Suderburg, R.

O LIVING BREAD see Kihlken, Henry

O LIVING BREAD, WHO ONCE DIDST DIE see Whitlock, Percy

O, LOFTY MOUNTAINS
(Cornwall, J.S.) SATB PIONEER 5056 $.20   (O104)

O LORD, A STRANGE EVENT *Fr
(Van Christy) SATB oct BELWIN 2191 $.30   (O105)

O LORD ABOVE, WHOSE SACRIFICE see Liszt, Franz, O Salutaris Hostia

O LORD ARISE INTO THY RESTING PLACE see Weelkes, Thomas

O LORD, AS THOU ART KIND see Wright, Norman Soreng

O LORD, BE MERCIFUL see Potter

O LORD CORRECT ME see Handel, George Frideric

O LORD, CREATOR OF ALL THING see Schutz, Heinrich, Ach Herr, Du Schopfer Aller Ding

O LORD, DELIVER ME see Marcello, Benedetto

O LORD ETERNAL see Schubert, Franz (Peter), Salve Regina

O LORD FROM WHOM see Bales, [Richard]

O LORD, GIVE EAR see Beethoven, Ludwig van

O LORD GIVE EAR see Lupo, Thomas

O LORD, GIVE EAR TO ME see Haydn, (Franz) Joseph

O LORD GIVE ME THE GRACE see Filas, T.

O LORD, GIVE THY HOLY SPIRIT see Tallis, Thomas

O LORD, GIVE THY HOLY SPIRIT INTO OUR HEARTS see Tallis, Thomas

O LORD, GIVE US ALL see Lewis, J.L.

O LORD GOD see Buck, Sir Percy Carter

O LORD GOD see Harker, Clifford

O LORD GOD see Marlow, Richard

O LORD GOD see Tchesnokov, Pavel Grigorievitch

O LORD GOD ALMIGHTY see Weelkes, Thomas

O LORD, GOD, FORGIVE MY SINS see Lassus, Roland de (Orlandus), Domine Convertere

O LORD GOD, HOW MANY ARE MY OPPRESSORS see Purcell, Henry, Jehovah, Quam Multi

O LORD, GOD OF HOSTS see Hovhaness, Alan

O LORD GOD OF HOSTS see Purcell, Henry

O LORD GOD OF MY SALVATION see Blow, John

O LORD GOD OF MY SALVATION see Schubert, Franz (Peter)

O LORD GOD, THOU STRENGTH OF MY HEALTH see Brewer, Sir Alfred Herbert

O LORD GOD, THY GREAT RENOWN see Goudimel, Claude

O LORD GOD TO THEE BE PRAISE see Sweelinck, Jan Pieterszoon, O Seigneur Loue Sera

O LORD GOD TO WHOM VENGEANCE BELONGETH see Pinkham, Daniel

O LORD GOD, UNTO WHOM see Baker, Robert

O LORD GRANT THE KING A LONG LIFE see Weelkes, Thomas

O LORD, GREAT CREATOR see Byrd, William, Ave Verum Corpus

O LORD , HAVE MERCY see Palestrina, Giovanni, Kyrie Eleison

O LORD, HAVE MERCY see Stradella, Alessandro

O LORD HAVE MERCY see Williams

O LORD, HAVE MERCY ON ME
(Johnson) SSSAATTBB,S solo oct SCHIRM.G 9558 $.30   (O106)

O LORD HAVE MERCY ON ME see Burleigh, Henry Thacker

O LORD, HAVE THOU RESPECT see Jones, Daniel

O LORD, HEAR MY VOICE see Williams

O LORD, HOW CAN WE KNOW THEE? see Nelson, Ronald A.

O LORD HOW DO MY WOES INCREASE see Gibbons, Orlando

O LORD, HOW EXCELLENT IS THY NAME see Bortniansky, Dimitri Stepanovitch

O LORD, HOW EXCELLENT IS THY NAME see Ehret, Walter

O LORD HOW EXCELLENT THY NAME
SAB KJOS 5727 $.30   (O107)

O LORD, HOW GLORIOUS IS THY NAME see Kalmanoff

O LORD, HOW LONG see Pfautsch, Lloyd

O LORD, HOW MAJESTIC IS THY NAME see Wilson, John F.

O LORD, HOW MANIFOLD see Barnby, Sir Joseph

O LORD, HOW MANIFOLD ARE THY WORKS see Barnby, Sir Joseph

O LORD HOW MANIFOLD ARE THY WORKS see Piggott, H.E.

O LORD, HOW MANIFOLD ARE THY WORKS see Wills, Arthur

O LORD, HOW MANIFOLD THY WORKS see Shaw, Martin

O LORD, HOW SHALL I MEET THEE see Cruger, Johann

O LORD, HOW SHALL I MEET THEE? see Schreck

O LORD, HOW SHALL I MEET THEE? see Teschner

O LORD, I AM NOT WORTHY see Franck, Melchior

O LORD, I CRY TO THEE see Arcadelt, Jacob

O LORD, I HAVE LOVED see Gretchaninov, Alexander Tikhonovitch

O LORD, I HAVE LOVED see Tomkins, Thomas

O LORD, I HAVE TRUSTED IN THEE see Walker, Linda H.

O LORD I LIFT MY HEART TO THEE see Gibbons, Orlando

O LORD, I MEDITATE ON THEE see Gibbons, Orlando

O LORD, I WILL PRAISE THEE see Jacob, Gordon

O LORD, I WILL PRAISE THEE see Krapf, Gerhard, Confitebor Tibi

O LORD, I WILL PRAISE THEE see Pritchard, Arthur J.

O LORD I'M TIRED   *spir
(Kinsman) SSA oct PRO ART 2187 $.30   (O108)
(Kinsman) SATB oct PRO ART 1951 $.35   (O109)
(Kinsman) SAB oct PRO ART 2186 $.30   (O110)

O LORD, IN THEE DO I PUT MY TRUST see Palestrina, Giovanni

O LORD, IN THEE HAVE I TRUSTED see Handel, George Frideric

O LORD, IN THEE HAVE I TRUSTED see Klein

O LORD IN THY WRATH see Gibbons, Orlando

O LORD, INCREASE MY FAITH see Avalos

O LORD, INCREASE MY FAITH see Gibbons, Orlando

O LORD, INCREASE MY FAITH see Gibbs, [Cecil] Armstrong

O LORD, INCREASE OUR FAITH see Loosemore, Henry

O LORD, JESUS CHRIST see Berchem, Jacobus de

O LORD, KING OF THE ANGELS see Festa, Costanza, Regem Archangelorum

O LORD, LOOK DOWN FROM HEAVEN see Battishill, Jonathan

O LORD, LOOK DOWN FROM HEAVEN see Schein, Johann Hermann

O LORD, MAKE THY SERVANT, ELIZABETH see Byrd, William

O LORD, MAKER OF ALL THINGS see Mundy, William, Rerum, Creator

O LORD, MOST GLORIOUS see Rhea, A.

O LORD MOST HIGH see Palestrina, Giovanni

O LORD MOST HIGH, WITH ALL MY HEART see Mozart, Wolfgang Amadeus

O LORD MOST HOLY see Abt, Franz, Ave Maria

O LORD MOST HOLY see Bruckner, Anton

O LORD MOST HOLY see Cain, Noble

O LORD MOST HOLY see Franck, Cesar, Panis Angelicus

O LORD MOST HOLY see Frank, J.L.

O LORD MOST HOLY see Harker, F. Flaxington

O LORD MOST HOLY see Kjelson, Panis Angelicus

O LORD MOST MERCIFUL see Concone, Giuseppe

O LORD, MOST MERCIFUL see Franck, Cesar, Panis Angelicus

O LORD, MY FAITH IS IN THEE see Pevernage, Andries, Seigneur, Jai Confiance

O LORD MY GOD see Humfrey, Pelham

O LORD MY GOD see Palestrina, Giovanni

O LORD MY GOD see Rush, John

O LORD, MY GOD see Theron

O LORD MY GOD see Wesley, Samuel Sebastian Jr.

O LORD, MY GOD see Wesley, Samuel Sr.

O LORD, MY GOD, FORGIVE THOU ME see Bach, Johann Sebastian

O LORD, MY GOD, GIVE EAR UNTO MY PRAYER see Young

O LORD, MY GOD (SOLOMON'S PRAYER) see Wesley, Samuel Sebastian Jr.

O LORD MY TRUST IS IN THY MERCY see Hall, King

O LORD OF ALL see Hadley

O LORD OF ALL see Handel, George Frideric

O LORD OF HEAVEN see Lassus, Roland de (Orlandus)

O LORD OF HEAVEN AND EARTH see Rhea, Raymond

O LORD OF HEAV'N see Lassus, Roland de (Orlandus)

O LORD OF HOSTS see Aichinger, Gregor

O, LORD OF HOSTS see Hunter

O LORD OF HOSTS, JESUS, THE CHRIST see Gabrieli, Giovanni, O Domine Jesu Christi

O LORD OF LIFE   *Eng
SA oct LORENZ 5368 $.25   (O111)

O LORD OF LIFE see Blake, George [M.]

O LORD OF LIFE see Burroughs

O LORD OF LIFE see Cabena, Barrie

O LORD OF LIFE see Green

O LORD OF STARS AND SUNLIGHT see Lovelace, Austin C.

O LORD OF THE UNIVERSE see Lister, Mosie

O LORD, OPEN THOU MY LIPS see Adler, Samuel

O LORD OUR GOD see Byrd, William

O LORD OUR GOD see Schechtman

O LORD, OUR GOD see Schmutz, Albert C.

O LORD OUR GOD see Schvedov

O LORD, OUR GOD see Victoria, Tomas Luis de

O LORD, OUR GOVERNOR see Gadsby, [Henry Robert]

O' LORD, OUR GOVERNOR see Marcello, Benedetto

O LORD OUR GOVERNOR see Purcell, Henry

O LORD OUR GOVERNOR see Stevens, Halsey

O LORD OUR GOVERNOR see Willan, Healey

O LORD, OUR HEAVENLY FATHER see Weatherseed, J.J.

O LORD OUR LORD see Joubert, John

O LORD OUR LORD see Orgad, Ben-Zion

O LORD, OUR LORD see Tchaikovsky, Piotr Ilyitch

O LORD, OUR LORD see Thompson

O LORD, OUR LORD, MAJESTIC IS THY NAME see Hopson

O LORD, PURIFY OUR HEARTS see Litten, Jack

O LORD, RAISE UP THY POWER see Ford

O, LORD, REBUKE ME NOT see Beebe, Edward J.

O LORD, REBUKE ME NOT see Hovhaness, Alan

O LORD, RELENT, I PRAY THEE see Bach, Johann Sebastian, Ach Herr, Mich Armen Sunder [Chorale]

O LORD, RULER OF ALL NATIONS see Tchaikovsky, Piotr Ilyitch

O LORD, SEEK US see Jolley, Florence [W.]

O LORD, SHIELD OF OUR HELP see Martin, Gilbert M.

O LORD, SUPPORT US see Anders, Charles

O LORD, SUPPORT US see Bristol, Lee H., Jr.

O LORD, SUPPORT US see Elmore, Robert [Hall]

O LORD, SUPPORT US see Martin

O LORD SUPPORT US ALL THE DAY LONG see Young, Gordon

O LORD, THE HOPE OF ISRAEL see Lewis, John Leo

O LORD, THE MAKER OF AL THING see Mundy, William

O LORD, THE MAKER OF ALL THING see Anonymous

O LORD, THE MAKER OF ALL THINGS   *Harv
(Wienandt) SATB,acap,opt pno oct PRO ART 2360
$.25   (O112)

O LORD, THE MAKER OF ALL THINGS see Joubert, John

O LORD, THE MAKER OF ALL THINGS see Mundy, William

O LORD, THE MAKER OF ALL THINGS see Webber

O LORD, THE MEASURE OF OUR PRAYERS see Lockwood, Normand

O LORD, THINE ENEMIES ROAR see Wienhorst, Richard

O LORD, THIS GRIEVING SPIRIT see Bach, Johann Sebastian, Ach Herr, Mich Armen Sunder

O LORD, THOU ART MY GOD see Roff, Joseph

O LORD, THOU ART MY GOD AND KING   *anthem,Scot
(Sateren, Leland) SATB (easy) oct AUGSBURG
0619 $.30   (O113)

O LORD THOU ART MY GOD AND KING see Osborne

O LORD, THOU HAST FORMED MY EVERY PART see Bach, Johann Sebastian

O LORD, THOU HAST SEARCHED ME see Burroughs, B.

O LORD, THOU HAST SEARCHED ME see Neff, James

O LORD, THOU HAST SEARCHED ME AND KNOWN ME see Slater, Richard W.

O LORD, THOU HAST SEARCHED ME OUT see Batten, Adrian

O LORD, THY HEAVENLY GRACE IMPART see Vick

O LORD, THY MERCY see Beethoven, Ludwig van

O LORD THY WORD ENDURETH see Tye, Christopher

O LORD, TO THEE WE PRAY see Harris, Jerry Weseley

O LORD, TURN THY WRATH see Byrd, William, Ne Irascaris

O LORD, WE ADORE THEE see Chopin, Frederic

O LORD, WE BELIEVE see Kreutz, Robert E.

O LORD, WE BESEECH THEE see Bock, Fred

O LORD, WE BESEECH THEE see Garlick, Anthony

O LORD, WE BESEECH THEE see Langlois, H.G.

O LORD, WE BESEECH THEE see Ritchie, John

O LORD, WE BESEECH THEE see Roberts, Myron

O LORD, WE BRING TO THEE see Evans, Aubrey

O LORD WE PRAISE THEE see Praetorius, Michael, Gott Sei Gelobet

O LORD, WE PRAY see Drozdoff, I.

O LORD, WE TRUST see Handel, George Frideric

O LORD, WE TRUST ALONE IN THEE see Handel, George Frideric

O' LORD, WHAT IS LOVE?   *CCU
mix cor SCHMITT 9070 $1.25   (O114)

O LORD, WHERE NOW IS BETHLEHEM see Williams, David H.

O LORD WHO DIDST IN OLDEN TIME see Langlois, H.G.

O LORD, WHO HAS TAUGHT US see Roff, Joseph

O LORD, WHO NEVER FAILEST see Roff, Joseph

O LORD, WHOSE BOUNTEOUS HAND AGAIN
(Lundquist) SATB,acap (diff) oct WILLIS 7478
$.20   (O115)

O LORD, WHOSE MERCIES see Handel, George Frideric

O LORD, WITH HANDS SO HOLY see Gabrieli, Giovanni, Signor, Le Tue Man Sante

O LORD, WITH WONDROUS MYSTERY see Andriessen, Hendrik

O LORD, YOU HAVE BEEN OUR REFUGE see Sowerby, Leo

O LORD, YOU MADE THE RAINBOW see Pallock

O LORDE, THE MAKER OF AL THING see Joubert, John

O LOVE DIVINE   *hymn,US
(Ferguson) 3pt mix cor,opt S solo oct LAWSON
51174 $.25   (O116)

O LOVE DIVINE see Greenhill, Harold

O LOVE DIVINE see Handel, George Frideric

O LOVE DIVINE see James

O LOVE DIVINE see Wyatt

O LOVE DIVINE, HOW SWEET see Crook, A.T.

O LOVE, HOW DEEP see Bush, Geoffrey

O LOVE, HOW DEEP see Hamill

O LOVE, HOW DEEP see Rogers

O LOVE, HOW DEEP see Smith, Lani

O LOVE HOW DEEP see Thiman, Eric Harding

O LOVE HOW DEEP see Titcomb, Everett

O LOVE, HOW DEEP see Warner, Richard

O LOVE, HOW DEEP see Young

O LOVE, HOW DEEP, HOW BROAD, HOW HIGH see Dietterich, Philip R.

O LOVE HOW DEEP, HOW BROAD, HOW HIGH see Powell, R.

O LOVE, HOW DEEP, HOW BROAD, HOW HIGH see Powell, Robert J.

O LOVE, HOW DEEP, HOW BROAD, HOW HIGH see
  Schalk, Carl

O LOVE MOST PERFECT see Victoria, Tomas Luis de

O LOVE OF GOD see Thiman, Eric Harding

O LOVE OF GOD see Thompson

O LOVE OF GOD MOST FULL see Young

O LOVE THAT CASTS OUT FEAR see Lovelace, Austin
  C.

O LOVE THAT TRIUMPHS OVER LOSS see Dietterich,
  Philip R.

O LOVE THAT WILL NOT LET ME GO see Ambrose,
  [Paul]

O LOVE THAT WILL NOT LET ME GO see Janes,
  Oliver

O LOVE THAT WILL NOT LET ME GO see Pfeil

O LOVE THAT WILL NOT LET ME GO see Grieb,
  Herbert [C.]

O LOVE THAT WILT NOT LET ME GO see Peace

O LOVE THE LORD see Sullivan, Sir Arthur
  Seymour

O LOVE, THY GRATEFUL BEAUTY SHINES see Loring

O LOVELY BABE see Rowley, Alec

O LOVELY CHILD see Schein, Johann Hermann, O
  Schonestes Kindelein

O LOVELY CHRISTMAS ROSE see Caldwell

O LOVELY DAY see Webber, W.S. Lloyd

O LOVELY HOUR see Chopin, Frederic

O LOVELY IS HE TO BEHOLD   *Xmas,carol,Span
  (Ehret, Walter) SA FRANK F-620 $.35   (O117)

O LOVELY PEACE see Handel, George Frideric

O LOVELY PEACE, WITH PLENTY CROWN'D see Handel,
  George Frideric

O LOVELY SON OF GOD see Moore, Douglas Stuart

O LOVELY SPLENDOR see Palestrina, Giovanni, O
  Che Splendor

O LOVELY WORLD OF MINE see Walton

O LOVING FATHER
  SSA CHAPPELL 4227500-354 $.40   (O118)
  SATB CHAPPELL 4227500-358 $.40   (O119)

O LOVING FATHER, HEAR MY PRAYER see Hedges

O LOVING JESUS see Palestrina, Giovanni, O Bone
  Jesu

O LOVING SAVIOR see Auber, Daniel-Francois-
  Esprit

O LOVING SAVIOUR see Clement

O LUIGI see Moioli, Romano

O LUX BEATA see Walther, Johann Gottfried

O LUX BEATA TRINITAS see Strohbach, Siegfried

O LUX BEATA TRINITAS see Victoria, Tomas Luis
  de

O MAGNIFY AND HONOUR THE LORD see Goudimel,
  Claude

O MAGNIFY THE LORD see Berger, Jean

O MAGNIFY THE LORD see Saint-Saens, Camille

O MAGNIFY THE LORD WITH ME
  (Lynn, G.) SATB oct PRESSER 312-40056 $.35
                                          (O120)

O MAGNUM MYSTERIUM see Davies, Peter Maxwell

O MAGNUM MYSTERIUM see Byrd, William

O MAGNUM MYSTERIUM see Christiansen

O MAGNUM MYSTERIUM see Christiansen, Larry A.

O MAGNUM MYSTERIUM see Davies, Peter Maxwell

O MAGNUM MYSTERIUM see Gabrieli, Giovanni

O MAGNUM MYSTERIUM see Jean-Baptiste, L.

O MAGNUM MYSTERIUM see Mc Cray, James

O MAGNUM MYSTERIUM see Morales, Cristobal de

O MAGNUM MYSTERIUM see Palestrina, Giovanni

O MAGNUM MYSTERIUM see Poulenc, Francis

O MAGNUM MYSTERIUM see Scarlatti, Domenico

O MAGNUM MYSTERIUM see Victoria, Tomas Luis de

O MAGNUM MYSTERIUM see Willaert, Adrian

O MAGNUM MYSTERIUM see Palestrina, Giovanni

O MAKE A JOYFUL NOISE see Fissinger, Edwin

O MAKE ME LOVE THEE see Abel, J.T.

O MAKE OUR HEARTS TO BLOSSOM see Clokey

O MAN, BEWAIL THY SIN SO GREAT see Greitter,
  Mattheus, O Mensch Bewein' Dein' Sunde
  Gross

O MAN, LIST' TO HIS SIGHING see Isaac

O MAN, REJOICE see Burns, William K.

O MAN, THY GRIEF AND SIN BEMOAN see Williams

O MARIA, DIANA STELLA
  see Three Christmas Laude

O MARIA MATER GRATIAE see Crivelli, Giovanni
  Battista

O MARIA, SEI GEGRUSST
  (Strobl, Otto) mix cor,acap oct DOBLINGER
  s.p.   (O121)

O MARIA, VERNANS ROSA see Clemens, Jacobus

O MARIA, VIRGO PIA see Torra

O MARY, DON'T YOU WEEP
  SSA BIG3 $.25   (O122)

O MARY, OF ALL WOMEN
  see Two Hymns In The Dorian Mode

O MARY, WHERE IS YOUR BABY?   *Xmas,spir
  (Ehret) SATB MARKS 4322 $.25   (O123)

O MARY, WHERE IS YOUR BABY? see Frackenpohl,
  Arthur

O MARY, WHERE IS YOUR BABY? see Walker, David
  S.

O MASTER, LET ME WALK WITH THEE see Bodycombe,
  [Aneurin]

O MASTER, LET ME WALK WITH THEE see Hughes

O MASTER, LET ME WALK WITH THEE see Johnston

O MASTER LET ME WALK WITH THEE see Schroeder,
  John

O MASTER, LET ME WALK WITH THEE see Smith

O MASTER, LET ME WALK WITH THEE see Speaks,
  [Oley]

O MASTER, LET ME WALK WITH THEE see Swift, B.

O MASTER, LET ME WALK WITH THEE see Young

O MAY MY SOUL COMMUNE WITH THEE see Robertson,
  Leroy

O MAY MY SOUL COMMUNE WITH THEE see
  Wheelwright, Lorin F.

O MAY THE EYES OF ALL see Schutz, Heinrich,
  Oculi Omnium In Te Sperant, Domine

O MEINE HOFFNUNG, JESUS see Schutz, Heinrich,
  Spes Mea, Christe Deus

O MEINE SEEL, DU SOLLST DEN HERREN PREISEN see
  Cruger, Johann

O MEMORIALE see Sevim, Giuseppe

O MEN FROM THE FIELDS see Cooke

O MEN OF GOD see Wheelwright, Lorin F.

O MEN OF GOD ARISE see Butler

O MEN OF GOD, BE STRONG! S-76 see Butler

O MEN OF GOD, FIGHT ON! see Young, Gordon

O MENSCH, BETRACHT DEINER SEELE see Hagius,
  Conrad

O MENSCH, BEWEIN DEIN STUNDE GROSS see
  Goudimel, Claude, Jauchz, Erd Und Himmel,
  Juble Hell

O MENSCH, BEWEIN DEIN STUNDE GROSS see Stern,
  Hermann

O MENSCH, BEWEIN DEIN SUNDE GROSS see Franck,
  Melchior

O MENSCH BEWEIN' DEIN' SUNDE GROSS see
  Greitter, Matthaeus

O MENSCH, BEWEIN DEIN SUNDE GROSS see Hassler,
  Hans Leo

O MENSCH, BEWEIN DEIN SUNDE GROSS see Othmayr,
  Kaspar

O MENSCH, BEWEIN DEIN SUNDE GROSS see
  Praetorius, Michael

O MENSCH BEWEIN DEIN SUNDE GROSS see Raphael,
  Gunther

O MENSCH, BEWEIN DEIN SUNDE GROSS see
  Reimerdes, Friedrich

O MENSCH, BEWEIN DEIN SUNDE GROSS see Trubel,
  Gerhard

O MENSCH, SCHAU' JESUM CHRISTUM AN see Bach,
  Johann Sebastian

O MENSCH, SIEH, WIE HIER AUF ERDREICH see
  Pepping, Ernst

O MERCIFUL GOD see Helfman, Max

O MICHAELI see Taverner, John

O MIGHTY GOD, OUR LORD see Schutz, Heinrich, O
  Lieber Herre Gott, Wecke Uns Auf

O MIGHTY GOD, SET US AFLAME
  (Coggin) SATB oct PRO ART 2681 $.30   (O124)

O, MIN JESU, DIT DU GATT see Berg, Gottfrid

O MON AME see Berlioz, Hector

O MORN OF BEAUTY see Sibelius, Jean

O MORNING STAR, HOW FAIR AND BRIGHT see
  Praetorius, Michael

O MORNING STAR, SO PURE, SO BRIGHT see Lenel,
  Ludwig

O MORTAL MAN see Berger, Jean

O MORTAL MAN see Weelkes, Thomas

O MORTAL MAN see Young

O MOST BLESSED SPIRIT see Smith, Frank H., Ave
  Regina Caelorum

O MOST HIGH AND HOLY GOD see Sweelinck, Jan
  Pieterszoon

O MOST HOLY ONE AND ONLY see Goemanne, Noel

O MOST LOVING FATHER see Walter, Samuel

O MOST MERCIFUL see Bullock, Ernest

O MOST MERCIFUL REDEEMER see Dobie

O MOST PRECIOUS SAVIOR see Tkach

O MOTHER DEAR, JERUSALEM   *carol
  SATB (easy) OXFORD 08.132 $.15   (O125)

O MY DEAR HEART see Jacob, Gordon

O MY DEAR HEART see Williams, David H.

O MY DEAREST JESUS see Rogers, S.E.

O MY FATHER see Snow

O MY GOD I AM NOT WORTHY see Victoria, Tomas
  Luis de

O MY GOD, I CRY TO THEE see Tcherepnin,
  Alexander

O MY LOVELIEST ONE see Chiquirriquitin

O MY PEOPLE AND FAITHFUL CROSS see Victoria,
  Tomas Luis de

O MY SAVIOUR see Young, Carlton R.

O MY SOUL, BE NOT DISMAYED see Bach, Johann
  Sebastian

O MY SOUL, BLESS GOD THE FATHER
  (Simes) SATB&treb cor oct BELWIN 64171 $.30
                                          (O126)

O MY SOUL, BLESS GOD THE FATHER see Ehret,
  Walter

O MY SOUL, JEHOVAH BLESS see Brandon, George

O MY SOUL, ON WINGS ASCENDING see Pasquet, Jean

O NACHT, DU BIST BESIEGT see Woll, Erna

O NATA LUX see Tallis, Thomas

O NATA LUX DE LUMINE see Tallis, Thomas

O NEWBORN CHILD see Powell, Robert J.

O NIGHT OF HOLY MEMORY see Wilson, Ira B.

O NIGHTINGALE   *Xmas
  (Stanton, R.) SAB,acap oct PRESSER 312-40439
  $.30   (O127)

O NIMM AN MEIN TAGLICH KLAGEN see Schutz,
  Heinrich, Quoniam Ad Te Clamabo

O NOSTRE DIEU ET SEIGNEUR AMIABLE see Goudimel,
  Claude

O NOT TO US, GOOD LORD see Telemann, Georg
  Philipp

O NUIT, HEUREUSE NUIT
  (Geveart, F.-A.) [Fr] 4pt mix cor,acap (easy)
  cor pts LEMOINE s.p. see from Collection De
  Choeurs, quatrieme Fascicule   (O128)

O ONE WITH GOD, THE FATHER
  (Goggin) 2pt wom cor,org/pno oct SCHIRM.G
  11328 $.25   (O129)

O ORIENS see Mechem, Kirke

O PANE CELESTE see Arnaldi, Antonio

O PARADISE see Barnby

O PASSI SPARSI see Gabrieli, Andrea

O PATER EXCELSE NO. 2 REQUIEM MASS   *Gen
  (Christiansen, P.) SATB SCHMITT 1426 $.20
                                          (O130)

O PEOPLE OF SYON see Titcomb, Everett

O PERFECT LIFE OF LOVE see Wolff, S. Drummond

O PERFECT LIFE OF LOVE see Wood

O PERFECT LOVE see Barnby, Sir Joseph

O PORTA CAELI see Grandi, Alessandro

O PRAISE AND GLORIFY THE LORD see Pergolesi,
  Giovanni Battista, Laudate Pueri, Laudate
  Nomen Domini

O PRAISE GOD see Crampton, T.

O PRAISE GOD see Gilbert, Norman

O PRAISE GOD see La Forge, Benedicite Gentes

O PRAISE GOD! see Laudate Dominum

O PRAISE GOD see Purvis, Richard, Laudate
  Dominum

O PRAISE GOD see Weldon, John

O PRAISE GOD see Whyte, Psalm For A Coronation
  Year

O PRAISE GOD IN HIS HOLINESS see Gibbs, [Cecil]
  Armstrong

O PRAISE GOD IN HIS HOLINESS see Hewitt-Jones,
  Tony

O PRAISE GOD IN HIS HOLINESS see Joubert, John

O PRAISE GOD IN HIS HOLINESS see Le Fleming, Christopher (Kaye)

O PRAISE GOD IN HIS HOLINESS see Lovelock, William

O PRAISE GOD IN HIS HOLINESS see Milner, Arthur

O PRAISE GOD IN HIS HOLINESS see Paul, Leslie

O PRAISE GOD IN HIS HOLINESS see Pritchard, Arthur J.

O PRAISE GOD IN HIS HOLINESS see Weldon, John

O PRAISE GOD IN HIS HOLINESS see White, Matthew

O PRAISE GOD IN HIS HOLINESS see White, Robert

O PRAISE GOD IN HIS HOLINESS see Whyte, Robert

O PRAISE GOD IN HIS HOLINESS see Wills, Arthur

O PRAISE GOD IN HIS HOLINESS see Wolff

O PRAISE HIM see Kreutz, Robert E., Laudate Dominum

O PRAISE HIM ALLELUIA see Williams, R.

O PRAISE JEHOVAH see Mozart, Wolfgang Amadeus, Laudate Dominum

O PRAISE OUR GREAT AND GRACIOUS LORD see Elliot

O PRAISE THE KING OF GLORY see Kirk

O PRAISE THE LORD
(Simpson, Kenneth) SAB&unis LENGNICK s.p.
                                              (O131)

O PRAISE THE LORD see Bach, Johann Sebastian

O PRAISE THE LORD see Batten, Adrian

O PRAISE THE LORD see Beebe, Edward J.

O PRAISE THE LORD see Boyce, William

O PRAISE THE LORD see Corbitt

O PRAISE THE LORD see Goss, John

O PRAISE THE LORD see Graun, Karl Heinrich

O PRAISE THE LORD see Greene

O PRAISE THE LORD see Greene, Maurice

O PRAISE THE LORD see Grime, William

O PRAISE THE LORD see Handel, George Frideric

O PRAISE THE LORD see Heisinger, Brent

O PRAISE THE LORD see Kay

O PRAISE THE LORD see Moe, Daniel

O PRAISE THE LORD see Moffatt

O PRAISE THE LORD see Moschetti, [Giuseppe]

O PRAISE THE LORD see Mozart, Wolfgang Amadeus

O PRAISE THE LORD see Mueller, Luise

O PRAISE THE LORD see Perrin, Ronald

O PRAISE THE LORD see Pitoni, Giuseppe Ottavio, Laudate Dominum

O PRAISE THE LORD see Schwadron

O PRAISE THE LORD see Tchaikovsky, Piotr Ilyich

O PRAISE THE LORD see Tomkins, Thomas

O PRAISE THE LORD see Van Iderstine, A.P.

O PRAISE THE LORD see Weldon, John

O PRAISE THE LORD see Willan, Healey

O PRAISE THE LORD see Wills, Arthur

O PRAISE THE LORD, ALL NATIONS see Hahn

O PRAISE THE LORD, ALL NATIONS see Hahn, Harvey

O PRAISE THE LORD, ALL YE HEATHEN see Croft, W.

O PRAISE THE LORD ALL YE HEATHEN see Tomkins, Thomas

O PRAISE THE LORD, ALL YE NATIONS see Aldrich

O PRAISE THE LORD, ALL YE NATIONS see Bach, Johann Sebastian, Lobet Den Herrn, Alle Heiden

O PRAISE THE LORD, ALL YE NATIONS see Berger, Jean

O PRAISE THE LORD, ALL YE NATIONS see Fissinger, Edwin

O PRAISE THE LORD, ALL YE NATIONS see Johns, Donald

O PRAISE THE LORD, ALL YE NATIONS see Kozinski, [David B.]

O PRAISE THE LORD, ALL YE NATIONS see Lipkin, Malcolm

O PRAISE THE LORD ALL YE NATIONS see Mason, L.

O PRAISE THE LORD, ALL YE NATIONS see Petrich, Roger

O PRAISE THE LORD, ALL YE NATIONS see Scarlatti, Alessandro, Laudate Dominum Omnes Gentes

O PRAISE THE LORD, ALL YE NATIONS see Telemann, Georg Philipp, Laudate Jehovam, Omnes Gentes

O PRAISE THE LORD FOR ALL HIS MERCIES see Bach, Johann Sebastian, Gottlob! Nun Geht Das Jahr Zu Ende

O PRAISE THE LORD FOR ALL HIS MERCIES see Bach, Johann Sebastian, Gottlob! Nun Geht Das Jahr Zu Ende [Chorale]

O PRAISE THE LORD FROM THE HEAVENS see Hannahs, Roger

O PRAISE THE LORD IN JOYFUL SONG see Day

O PRAISE THE LORD, LAUD YE THE NAME see Goss, John

O PRAISE THE LORD, MY SOUL see Ippolitov-Ivanov, Mikhail Mikhailovitch

O PRAISE THE LORD OF HARVEST *anthem
(Johnson, David N.) SAB (easy) oct AUGSBURG
1505 $.25   (O132)

O PRAISE THE LORD OF HEAVEN see Steel, Christopher [Charles]

O PRAISE THE LORD OF HEAVEN see Vaughan Williams, Ralph

O PRAISE THE LORD OF HEAVEN see Wills, Arthur

O PRAISE THE LORD ON HIGH see Tallis, Thomas, Laudate Dominum

O PRAISE THE LORD WITH ONE CONSENT see Handel, George Frideric

O PRAISE THE LORD, YE ANGELS OF HIS see Handel, George Frideric

O PRAISE THE LORD, YE NATIONS see Knoche, Keith

O PRAISE THE LORD, YE PEOPLE ALL see Schutz, Heinrich, Cantate Domino

O PRAISE THE LORDS FROM THE HEAVENS see Arnatt, Ronald

O PRAISE THE NAME see Tchaikovsky, Piotr Ilyich

O PRAISE THE NAME OF CHRIST, THE LORD see Tye, Christopher

O PRAISE THE NAME OF THE LORD see Lvov, Alexey Feodorovitch

O PRAISE YE GOD see Tchaikovsky, Piotr Ilyitch

O PRAISE YE THE LORD see Franck, Cesar

O PRAISE YE THE LORD see Mozart, Wolfgang Amadeus

O PRAISE YE THE LORD see Parry, Charles Hubert Hastings

O PRAISE YE THE LORD see Pitoni, Giuseppe Ottavio

O PRAISE YE THE LORD see Scull

O PRAISE YE THE LORD see Thiman, Eric Harding

O PRAISE YE THE LORD see Wolff, S. Drummond

O PRAISE YE THE LORD see Wood

O PRAY FOR THE PEACE see Howells, Herbert Norman

O PRAY FOR THE PEACE OF JERUSALEM see Blow, John

O PRAY FOR THE PEACE OF JERUSALEM see Howells, Herbert Norman

O PRAY FOR THE PEACE OF JERUSALEM see Nicholson, Richard

O PRAY FOR THE PEACE OF JERUSALEM see Nicolson, R.

O PRAY FOR THE PEACE OF JERUSALEM see Tomkins, Thomas

O PREIST DEN HERRN MIT EINEM MUND see Handel, George Frideric, O Praise The Lord With One Consent

O PRIEST AND BISHOP see Crone, R.

O QUAM DECORA (from Sirenes Symphoniacae) BVM
SATB,acap (contains also: Maria Jung Und Zart
(from Psalteriolum 1642)) voc pt DOBLINGER
s.p. see also Unsere Liebe Frau   (O133)

O QUAM DULCIS EST DEUS NOSTER see Carissimi, Giacomo

O QUAM GLORIFICA see Fayrfax, Robert

O QUAM GLORIOSUM see Byrd, William

O QUAM GLORIOSUM see Esquivel, Juan Barahona de

O QUAM GLORIOSUM see Marenzio, Luca

O QUAM GLORIOSUM see Powell

O QUAM GLORIOSUM see Vaet, Jacobus

O QUAM GLORIOSUM see Victoria, Tomas Luis de

O QUAM GLORIOSUM see Wills, Arthur

O QUAM GLORIOSUM EST REGNUM see Victoria, Tomas Luis de

O QUAM METUENDUS see Victoria, Tomas Luis de

O QUAM METUENDUS EST see Victoria, Tomas Luis de

O QUAM SUAVIS see Bottazzo, Luigi

O QUAM SUAVIS see Byrd, William

O QUAM SUAVIS see Dubois, Theodore

O QUAM SUAVIS see Heidet, Le R. P.

O QUAM SUAVIS see Ripolles, Vincente

O QUAM SUAVIS see Rodella, Sante

O QUAM SUAVIS EST see Alix, Rene

O QUAM SUAVIS EST see Mercenier, P.

O QUAM SUAVIS EST, DOMINE see Byrd, William

O QUAM TRISTIS ET AFFLICTA see Pergolesi, Giovanni Battista

O QUANTA IN COELIS see Buchner, Philipp Friedrich

O QUANTUS LUCTUS see Palestrina, Giovanni

O QUEEN OF HEAVEN see Erbach, Christian, Regina Caeli

O QUEEN OF HEAVEN see Palestrina, Giovanni, Regina Coeli

O QUEEN OF HEAVEN see Viadana, Lodovico Grossi da, Regina Caeli

O QUEEN OF HEAVEN BE JOYFUL see Lotti, Antonio, Regina Coeli

O QUEEN OF HEAVEN WE PRAISE THEE see Aston, Peter, Regina Coeli, Laetare

O QUEEN OF VIRTUES see Oldham, Arthur

O QUI VIENT DONC DE SI LOIN see Who Dat A-Comin' Ovah Yondah

QU'IL EST DOUX (Psalm 132)
(Geveart, F.-A.) [Fr] 4pt mix cor,acap (easy)
cor pts LEMOINE s.p. see from Collection De
Choeurs, troisieme Fascicule   (O134)

O QUIT YOUR PASTURES *Xmas,carol/folk,Fr
(Strong) SATB/TTBB SCHMITT 1563 $.25   (O135)

O QUOT UNDIS see Nicolosi, Salvatore

O REGEM COELI see Palestrina, Giovanni

O REGEM COELI see Vittoria, Ludovico

O REGINA COELI see Wiesehahn, W.

O REGINA REGNI DEI see Philipp, Franz

O REJOICE, YE CHRISTIANS, LOUDLY see Bach, Johann Sebastian

O REJOICE YE CHRISTIANS LOUDLY see Hammerschmidt, Andreas

O, REJOICE, YE CHRISTIANS LOUDLY see Luvaas

O REST IN THE LORD see Macfarlane, William Charles

O REST IN THE LORD see Mendelssohn-Bartholdy, Felix

O REST IN THE LORD see Richolson

O REX GENTIUM see Heiller, Anton

O REX GLORIA see Byrd, William

O REX GLORIAE see Byrd, William

O REX GLORIAE see Marenzio, Luca

O REX GLORIAE see Palestrina, Giovanni

O RISEN LORD! O CONQUERING KING! see Schutz, Heinrich

O ROSA BELLA see Power, Lyonel

O ROSE OF SHARON see Schubert, Franz (Peter), Ave Maria

O SACRA CONVIVIUM see Carissimi, Giacomo

O SACRED AND HOLY FEAST see Bernabei, (Giuseppe) Ercole, O Sacrum Convivium

O SACRED AND HOLY FEAST see Palestrina, Giovanni, O Sacrum Convivium

O, SACRED COMMUNION see Marenzio, Luca, O, Sacrum Convivium

O SACRED FEAST see Willan, Healey

O SACRED HEAD see Bach, Johann Sebastian

O SACRED HEAD see Brown, R.

O SACRED HEAD see Hassler, Hans Leo

O SACRED HEAD, NOW WOUNDED see Bach, Johann Sebastian

O SACRED HEAD, NOW WOUNDED see Cruger, Johann

O SACRED HEAD, NOW WOUNDED see Hassler, Hans Leo

O SACRED HEAD NOW WOUNDED see Najera, Edmund

O SACRED HEAD, NOW WOUNDED see Pike, Harry Hale

O SACRED HEAD, NOW WOUNDED see Sjolund, Paul

O SACRED HEAD, SORE WOUNDED see Boatwright, Howard

O SACRED HEAD SURROUNDED see Hassler, Hans Leo

O SACRO CONVIVIUM see Oltrassi, Giuseppe

O SACRUM see Heidet, Le R. P.

O SACRUM CONVIVIUM see Bernabei, (Giuseppe) Ercole

O SACRUM CONVIVIUM see Bernabei, Giuseppe Antonio

O SACRUM CONVIVIUM see Byrd, William

O SACRUM CONVIVIUM see Croce, Giovanni

O SACRUM CONVIVIUM see Joly, Camille

O SACRUM CONVIVIUM see Livieri, C.

O, SACRUM CONVIVIUM see Marenzio, Luca

O SACRUM CONVIVIUM see Messiaen, Oliver

O SACRUM CONVIVIUM see Palestrina, Giovanni

O SACRUM CONVIVIUM see Pasini, Crescenzio

O SACRUM CONVIVIUM see Pergolesi, Giovanni Battista

O SACRUM CONVIVIUM see Porta

O SACRUM CONVIVIUM see Tallis, Thomas

O SACRUM CONVIVIUM see Viadana, Lodovico Grossi da

O SACRUM CONVIVIUM see Viadana, Th. L.A.

O SACRUM CONVIVIUM see Victoria

O SACRUM CONVIVIUM see Victoria, Tomas Luis de

O SACRUM CONVIVIUM see Volpi, Edoardo

O SACRUM CONVIVIUM see Zaccaria, Vittore

O SACRUM COVIVIUM see Marenzio, Luca

O SAINT AUTEL see Saint-Saens, Camille

O SALUTARI see Bottigliero, Eduardo

O SALUTARI HOSTIA see Rodella, Sante

O SALUTARIS see Anonymous

O SALUTARIS see Ascenso, Antonio

O SALUTARIS see Aubanel, Georges

O SALUTARIS see Aubert, [Louis-Francois-Marie]

O SALUTARIS see Bach, Johann Sebastian

O SALUTARIS see Beethoven, Ludwig van

O SALUTARIS see Bock, H.

O SALUTARIS see Bondeville, [Emmanuel de]

O SALUTARIS see Bonnel, L.

O SALUTARIS see Breville, Pierre-Onfroy de

O SALUTARIS see Brun, G.

O SALUTARIS see Busser, [Henri-Paul]

O SALUTARIS see Cardelus, F.-L. de

O SALUTARIS see Chaminade, Cecile

O SALUTARIS see Choisnel, G.

O SALUTARIS see Delannoy, Marcel

O SALUTARIS see Durand, A.

O SALUTARIS see Faure, Jean-Baptist

O SALUTARIS see Ferro, Stefano

O SALUTARIS see Franck, Cesar

O SALUTARIS see Handel, George Frideric

O SALUTARIS see Heidet, Le R. P.

O SALUTARIS see Indy, Vincent d'

O SALUTARIS see Lambiollotte, Louis

O SALUTARIS see Lefebure-Wely, Louis James Alfred

O SALUTARIS see Leoncini, Lorenzo

O SALUTARIS see Ligthart, B.J.

O SALUTARIS see Martini, Padre

O SALUTARIS see Massenet, Jules

O SALUTARIS see Mathias, William

O SALUTARIS see Mendelssohn-Bartholdy, Felix

O SALUTARIS see Mercenier, P.

O SALUTARIS see Mozart, Wolfgang Amadeus

O SALUTARIS see Muller, Giulio

O SALUTARIS see Nasco

O SALUTARIS see Paladilhe, [Emile]

O SALUTARIS see Pickaert, R.

O SALUTARIS see Ravanello, Oreste

O SALUTARIS see Rossini, Gioacchino

O SALUTARIS see Saint-Saens, Camille

O SALUTARIS see Schumann

O SALUTARIS see Schumann, Robert (Alexander)

O SALUTARIS see Volpi, Edoardo

O SALUTARIS see Yung, Alf.

O SALUTARIS HOSTIA see Anerio, Felice

O SALUTARIS HOSTIA see Bottazzo, Luigi

O SALUTARIS HOSTIA see Bush, Geoffrey

O SALUTARIS HOSTIA see Cherubini, Luigi

O SALUTARIS HOSTIA see de la Rue, Pierre

O SALUTARIS HOSTIA see Escovada, R.

O SALUTARIS HOSTIA see Gallus, Jacobus

O SALUTARIS HOSTIA see Gounod, Charles Francois

O SALUTARIS HOSTIA see Grassi, Ciro

O SALUTARIS HOSTIA see d'harcourt, [Eugene]

O SALUTARIS HOSTIA see La Rue, Pierre de

O SALUTARIS HOSTIA see Lenepveu, [Charles (Ferdinand)]

O SALUTARIS HOSTIA see Liszt, Franz

O SALUTARIS HOSTIA see Muller, Peter

O SALUTARIS HOSTIA see Oltrassi, Giuseppe

O SALUTARIS HOSTIA see Palestrina, Giovanni

O SALUTARIS HOSTIA see Pisari, [Pasquale]

O SALUTARIS HOSTIA see Rossini, Gioacchino

O SALUTARIS HOSTIA see Tallis, Thomas

O SALUTARIS HOSTIA see Zaccaria, Vittore

O SANCTISSIMA   *Xmas,carol,It
see Many Moods Of Christmas, The, Suite Two (Beck, Thomas) mix cor MUSIKK 95F s.p. (O136) (Shaw; Parker) [Eng/Lat] 4pt mix cor,acap oct SCHIRM.G 10194 $.30   (O137) (Smith, Gregg) "O How Beautiful" SATB oct WALTON 2006 $.25   (O138)

O SANCTISSIMA see Beethoven, Ludwig van

O SANCTISSIMA see Gardner, Maurice

O SANCTISSIMA see Hoffmann, Ernst Theodor Amadeus

O SANCTISSIMA see Perosi, (Dom) Lorenzo

O SANCTISSIMA see Williamson, Malcolm

O SAPIENTA! see Noble, Thomas Tertius

O SAPIENTA see Ramsey

O SAPIENTIA see Ramsey, Robert

O SATISFY US EARLY WITH THY MERCY see Norden, Hugo

O SAVE US, LORD see Schutz, Heinrich, O Herr, Hilf, O Herr, Lass Wohl Gelingen

O SAVE US, LORD see Schutz, Heinrich, O Herr, Hilf, O Herr, Lass Wohl Gelingen

O SAVING VICTIM see Gounod, Charles Francois, O Salutaris Hostia

O SAVING VICTIM see Harwood, Basil

O SAVING VICTIM see Hurd, Michael

O SAVING VICTIM see Kihlken, Henry

O SAVING VICTIM see La Rue, Pierre de, O Salutaris Hostia

O SAVING VICTIM see Muller, Peter, O Salutaris Hostia

O SAVING VICTIM see Pasquet, Jean

O SAVING VICTIM see Ratcliffe, Desmond

O SAVING VICTIM see Rowley, Alec

O SAVING VICTIM see Schein, Johann Hermann

O SAVING VICTIM see Schumann

O SAVIOR, FRIEND AND LOVING GUIDE see Handel, George Frideric

O SAVIOR OF THE WORLD see Goss, John

O SAVIOR, OUR REFUGE see Eberlin, Johann Ernst, Audiutor In Opportunitatibus

O SAVIOR, REND THE HEAVENS WIDE see Bauernfiend, Hans, O Heiland, Reiss Die Himmel Auf

O SAVIOR, REND THE HEAV'N ON HIGH see Brahms, Johannes, O Heiland, Reiss Die Himmel Auf

O SAVIOR SO SWEET see Scheidt, Samuel

O SAVIOR SWEET see Bach

O SAVIOR SWEET see Bach, Johann Sebastian, O Jesulein Suss

O SAVIOR SWEET see Scheidt, Samuel

O SAVIOR, THROW THE HEAVENS WIDE see Brahms, Johannes, O Heiland, Reiss Die Himmel Auf

O SAVIOUR, BLESS US ERE WE GO see Bach, Johann

O SAVIOUR BLEST see Hutson, Wihla

O SAVIOUR, HEAR ME see Gluck

O SAVIOUR HEAR ME see Gluck, Christoph Willibald Ritter von

O SAVIOUR MINE, WHAT AGONY see Bach, Johann Sebastian

O SAVIOUR OF THE WORLD see Goss, John

O SAVIOUR OF THE WORLD see Matthews, Harvey Alexander

O SAVIOUR OF THE WORLD see Moore, Harold

O SAVIOUR OF THE WORLD see Palestrina, Giovanni

O SAVIOUR OF THE WORLD see Pears, James R.

O SAVIOUR OF THE WORLD see Tallis, Thomas, Salvator Mundi Domine

O SAVIOUR OF THE WORLD see Wills, Arthur

O SAVIOUR OF THE WORLD (O LORD OF ALL MANKIND) see Goss, John

O SAVIOUR, PRECIOUS SAVIOUR see Mann, [Arthur Henry]

O SAVIOUR, PRECIOUS SAVIOUR see Smith, H.

O SAVIOUR SWEET see Bach, Johann Sebastian

O SAVIOUR, WITH PROTECTING CARE see Davies, Henry Walford

O SCHAR, BEI GOTT GEBORGEN see Stier, Alfred

O SCHONESTES KINDELEIN see Schein, Johann Hermann

O SEE MY DARK EYES see Victoria, Tomas Luis de, Caligaverunt Oculi Mei

O SEEL, SO TUE DYS TURLI UF! see Hess, W.

O SEIGNEUR DIEU, TA LOI PARFAITE ET SAINTE see Gardane, Antonie

O SEIGNEUR, J'ESPARS see Le Jeune, Claude

O SEIGNEUR, LOUE SERA see Sweelinck, Jan Pieterszoon

O SELIG, DEM DER TREUE GOTT see Lassus, Roland de (Orlandus)

O SELIG HAUS, WO MAN DICH see Schmidt, Wolfgang

O SELIGE NACHT see Ammann, Benno

O SEND OUT THY LIGHT see Chubb, F.

O SEND THY LIGHT see Balakirev, Mily Alexeyevitch

O SEND THY LIGHT FORTH see Balakirev, Mily Alexeyevitch

O SEND US THY LIGHT, O LORD
SATB BIG3 $.35   (O139)

O SHEPHERD OF ISRAEL see Morrison, C.P.

O SHEPHERDS see Beuerle, Herbert, Ihr Hirten

O SHEPHERDS, COME see Lovelace, Austin C.

O SHEPHERDS, TELL US NOW see Morales, Cristobal de, Pastores, Dicite, Quidnam Vidistis?

O SHINING LIGHT see Tallis, Thomas, O Nata Lux De Lumine

O SIEH, WIE DER GERECHTE STIRBT see Reger, Max

O SING A NEW SONG see Angell, Warren M.

O SING A NEW SONG see Black

O SING A NEW SONG see Hartley, Walter [S.]

O SING ALL YE LANDS see Berger, Jean

O SING, ALL YE LANDS see Darst, W. Glenn

O SING, AS THRUSHES see Holst, Gustav

O SING JOYFULLY see Batten, Adrian

O SING JOYFULLY see Palestrina, Giovanni, Gaude Barbara

O SING NOEL see Emig, Lois

O SING PRAISES see Kirk

O SING THE GLORIES OF OUR LORD see Andrews, H.K.

O SING THE GLORIES OF OUR LORD see Thiman, Eric Harding

O SING TO GOD see Christiansen, Paul

O SING TO GOD see Tchaikovsky, Piotr Ilyitch

O SING TO JEHOVAH see Mason

O SING TO THE LORD see Berger

O SING TO THE LORD A NEW SONG see Prentice, Fred

O SING UNTO THE LORD see Alexander, Josef

O SING UNTO THE LORD see Amner, John

O SING UNTO THE LORD see Anerio, Giovanni Francesco, Cantate Domino

O SING UNTO THE LORD see Banchieri, Adriano, Cantate Domino

O SING UNTO THE LORD see Cooke, Arnold

O SING UNTO THE LORD see Croce, Giovanni, Cantate Domino

O SING UNTO THE LORD see Deering, Richard, Cantate Domino

O SING UNTO THE LORD see Handel, George Frideric

O SING UNTO THE LORD see Hassler, Hans Leo, Cantate Domino

O SING UNTO THE LORD see Hill

O SING UNTO THE LORD see Mathias, William

O SING UNTO THE LORD see Mueller, Carl F.

O SING UNTO THE LORD see Naylor, Peter

O SING UNTO THE LORD see Purcell, Henry, O Syng Nu Hojt For Gud

O SING UNTO THE LORD see Rogers, G.

O SING UNTO THE LORD see Rohlig, Harald

O SING UNTO THE LORD see Sjostrand

O SING UNTO THE LORD A NEW SONG see Bender, Jan

O SING UNTO THE LORD A NEW SONG see Boyce, William

O SING UNTO THE LORD A NEW SONG see Burroughs, B.

O SING UNTO THE LORD A NEW SONG see Croce, Giovanni

O SING UNTO THE LORD A NEW SONG see Duke, John

O SING UNTO THE LORD A NEW SONG see Glarum, L. Stanley

O SING UNTO THE LORD A NEW SONG see Piston, Walter

O, SING UNTO THE LORD A NEW SONG see Russell, Velma A.

O SING UNTO THE LORD A NEW SONG see Smith

O SING UNTO THE LORD A NEW SONG see Tomkins, Thomas

O SING UNTO THE LORD A NEW SONG see Willan, Healey

O SING UNTO THE LORD WITH THANKSGIVING see Harris, William Henry

O SING WITH FULL VOICE see Sweelinck, Jan Pieterszoon

O SING YE TO THE LORD see Croce, Giovanni, Cantate Domino

O SING YE TO THE LORD see Pitoni, Giuseppe Ottavio, Cantate Domino

O SING YE TO THE LORD see Schutz, Heinrich, Cantate Domino

O SING YE TO THE LORD see Sweelinck, Jan Pieterszoon, Cantate Domino

O SING YE TO THE LORD see Vulpius, Melchior

O SING YE TO THE LORD A NEW SONG see Phelps, John R.

O SING YE UNTO THE LAMB see Schutz, Heinrich, Cantate Domino

O SING YE UNTO THE LORD see Schutz, Heinrich, Cantate Domino

O SING YOUR SONGS see Cain, Noble

O SINGET UNSERM GOTT see Handel, George Frideric, O Sing Unto The Lord

O SION'S DAUGHTER, WHERE ART THOU? *carol SATB (easy) OXFORD 08.087 $.15   (O140)

O SISTERS TOO (COVENTRY CAROL) *carol cor/cong oct MOWBRAY 65057 3 s.p. see also English Carol Book, The   (O141)

O SLEEP, MY FAIREST ONE see Wilson

O SOHN DES HOCHSTEN see Schutz, Heinrich, Quo, Nate Dei

O SOLIS ORTUS CARDINE see Binchois, Gilles

O SON OF GOD *Easter (Rogers, E.) SATB oct PRESSER 312-40375 $.25   (O142)

O SON OF GOD see Bach, Johann Sebastian

O SONS AND DAUGHTERS *Easter,Fr (Henninger) SATB SCHMITT 1638 $.25   (O143) (Shaw; Parker) 4pt mix cor,acap oct SCHIRM.G 9950 $.25   (O144)

O SONS AND DAUGHTERS see Barthelson, Joyce

O SONS AND DAUGHTERS see Davies, Henry Walford, O Filii Et Filiae

O SONS AND DAUGHTERS see Gevaert, Francois Auguste, O Filii Et Filiae

O SONS AND DAUGHTERS see Kirk, Theron W.

O SONS AND DAUGHTERS see Martin, Warren

O SONS AND DAUGHTERS LET US SING *anthem,Fr, 15th cent SAB oct LORENZ 7376 $.30   (O145) (Nelson, Ronald A.) SA,vln/fl,opt 2clar (easy) oct AUGSBURG 1459 $.30   (O146)

O SONS AND DAUGHTERS, LET US SING! see Gillette

O SONS AND DAUGHTERS LET US SING see Howorth, Wayne

O SONS AND DAUGHTERS, LET US SING see Nichols, Anna Mae

O SORROW DEEP see Brahms, Johannes

O SORROW DEEP see Young, Gordon

O SOUVERAIN PASTEUR ET MAITRE see L'Estocart, Paschal de

O SPIRIT OF THE LIVING GOD see Butler

O SPIRIT, WHO FROM JESUS CAME see Havey, Marguerite

O SPLENDOR OF GOD'S GLORY BRIGHT see Jolley, Florence [W.]

O SPLENDOR OF GOD'S GLORY BRIGHT see Rhea, Raymond

O SPOTLESS LAMB see Bach, Johann Sebastian

O STAR O'ER BETHLEHEM SHINING *Xmas,carol,Pol (Ehret, Walter) SATB,opt inst oct WALTON 2519 $.30   (O147)

O STAR OF LIGHT see Martin

O STARRY NIGHT see Bissell, Keith

O STORE GUD VI LOVER DEG see Houge

O STORE GUD, VI LOVER DEG see Hovland, Egil

O STORE KONGE, DAVIDS SON see Valen, Fartein

O STRENGTH AND STAY see Thiman, Eric Harding

O STRENGTH AND STAY see Willan, Healey

O STRONG YOUNG CHRIST see Brook

O STRONG YOUNG CHRIST see Brook, Harry

O SUCH HOLINESS see Victoria, Tomas Luis de, O Quam Metuendus Est

O SUSSER HERRE JESU CHRIST see Linke, Norbert

O SUSSER HERRE JESU CHRIST see Poos, Heinrich

O SUSSER HERRE JESU CHRIST see Schlenker, Manfred

O SUSSER JESU CHRIST see Schutz, Heinrich

O SUSSER JESU CHRIST see Schutz, Heinrich

O SUSSER JESU CHRIST see Schutz, Heinrich

O SUSSER, O FREUNDLICHER, O GUTIGER see Hammerschmidt, Andreas

O SYNG NU HOJT FOR GUD see Purcell, Henry

O TAKE MY HAND, LORD see Koller

O TANNENBAUM *Xmas,carol,Ger (Shaw; Parker) [Eng/Ger] 4pt men cor,T solo, acap oct SCHIRM.G 10195 $.30   (O148)

O TANNENBAUM see Harris

O TAPFRER FURST see Handel, George Frideric

O TASTE AND SEE see Bortniansky, Dimitri Stepanovitch

O TASTE AND SEE see Ferris, W.

O TASTE AND SEE see Goss, John

O TASTE AND SEE see Nikolsky, A.

O TASTE AND SEE see Rogers, J.H.

O TASTE AND SEE see Van Vliet, J.R.

O TASTE AND SEE see Vaughan Williams, Ralph

O TASTE AND SEE see Williams

O TASTE, AND SEE, HOW GRACIOUS THE LORD IS see Goss, John

O TASTE AND SEE HOW GRACIOUS THE LORD IS see Sullivan, Sir Arthur Seymour

O TEACH ME, LORD, MY DAYS TO NUMBER see Bach, Johann Sebastian, Wer Weiss, Wie Nahe Mir Mein Ende

O THAT HEAVENLY MUSIC see Bach, Johann Sebastian

O THAT I HAD A THOUSAND VOICES see Darst, W. Glenn

O THAT I HAD A THOUSAND VOICES see Lamb

O THAT MEN WOULD PRAISE THE LORD SATB KJOS 5818 $.30   (O149)

O THAT MEN WOULD PRAISE THE LORD see Thiman, Eric Harding

O THAT MY HEAD WERE WATERS see Clark, Keith

O THAT SALVATION FOR ISRAEL WOULD COME see Geisler, Johan C.

O THE BEAUTIFUL TREASURE *US (Aks) SATB,acap MARKS 4044 $.30 see from Three Shaker Songs   (O150)

O THE BLESSEDNESS IS GREAT see Bechler

O THOU DIVINER MYSTERY see Young, Carlton R.

O THOU ETERNAL CHRIST see James, Allen

O THOU ETERNAL CHRIST, RIDE ON! see Lovelace, Austin C.

O THOU, EVERLASTING VIRTUE see Bach, Johann Sebastian, O Du Liebe Meiner Liebe

O THOU FORTRESS OF ZION'S DAUGHTER see Bach, Johann Ernst, O Du Mauer Der Tochter Zion

O THOU, FROM WHOM ALL BLESSINGS COME see Tchaikovsky, Piotr Ilyitch

O THOU, FROM WHOM ALL GOODNESS FLOWS see Lewis, John Leo

O THOU FROM WHOM ALL GOODNESS FLOWS see Rossini, Gioacchino

O THOU GOD OF MY SALVATION see Towner, Daniel B.

O THOU HOLY SPIRIT see Hutson, Wihla

O THOU IMMORTAL DEITY see Nosse

O THOU IN ALL THY MIGHT SO FAR see Walter

O THOU IN WHOSE PRESENCE (Shaw; Parker) SATB,acap oct LAWSON 917 $.30   (O151)

O, THOU IN WHOSE PRESENCE see Lewis

O THOU, IN WHOSE PRESENCE see Lewis, Freeman

O THOU IN WHOSE PRESENCE MY SOUL TAKES DELIGHT see Peninger, David

O THOU JOY OF LOVING HEARTS see Victoria, Tomas Luis de, Jesu Dulcis Memoria

O THOU LAMB OF GOD see Frylof, [Harald Leonard]

O THOU MERCIFUL FATHER see Hammerschmidt, Andreas, O Barmherziger Vater

O THOU MOST HIGH see Christiansen, Paul

O THOU NOT MADE WITH HANDS see Bancroft, H. Hugh

O THOU NOT MADE WITH HANDS see Skeat

O THOU NOT MADE WITH HANDS see Stanton

O THOU OUR JOY see Geisler, Johan C.

O THOU THAT ART THE LIGHT ETERNAL see Webber, Lloyd

O THOU THAT HEAREST PRAYER see Anderson, [William H.]

O THOU THAT HEAREST PRAYER see Davies, Henry Walford

O THOU THAT TELLEST see Handel, George Frideric

O THOU THAT TELLEST see Krone

O THOU THAT TELLEST GOOD TIDINGS see Handel, George Frideric

O THOU THAT TELLEST GOOD TIDINGS TO ZION see Handel, George Frideric

O THOU, THE CENTRAL ORB see Gibbons, Orlando

O THOU, TO WHOM IN ANCIENT TIME see Thiman, Eric Harding

O THOU TO WHOSE ALL SEARCHING SIGHT see Porter, Walter

O THOU TO WHOSE ALL-SEARCHING SIGHT see Powell, Robert J.

O THOU WHO ART ALL LOVING see Gade, Niels [W.]

O THOU, WHO AT THY EUCHARIST DIDST PRAY *hymn SATB oct ST.MARTIN SMP656A s.p.   (O152)

O THOU, WHO BY A STAR DIDST GUIDE see Fink, Christian

O THOU WHO CAMEST FROM ABOVE see Wesley

O THOU WHO HEAREST EVERY HEARTFELT PRAYER see Walton

O THOU WHO HEAREST OUR PRAYERS see Young

O THOU WHO THROUGH THIS HOLY WEEK see Purcell, Henry

O THOU WHOSE GLORY SHONE LIKE FIRE see Bodycombe, [Aneurin]

O THOU WHOSE POW'R see Fast, Willard S.

O TIDINGS GREAT AND WONDROUS see Barnard

O TO PRAISE GOD AGAIN see Diemer, Emma Lou

O TOD, WIE BITTER BIST DU see Reger, Max

O TOD, WO IST DEIN STACHEL NUN see Zipp, Friedrich

O TRANQUIL LIGHT see Kastalsky, Alexander Dmitrievitch

O TRAURIGKEIT see Kubizek, Augustinian

O TRAURIGKEIT, O HERZELEID see Bloch, Waldemar

O TRAURIGKEIT, O HERZELEID see Bornefeld, Helmut

O TRAURIGKEIT, O HERZELEID see Grabner, Hermann

O TRAURIGKEIT, O HERZELEID see Zillinger, Erwin

O TRAURIGKEIT, O HERZELIED see Bach, Johann Sebastian

O TRAURIGKEIT, O HERZELIED see Marks, Gunther

O TRAURIGKEIT, O HERZELIED see Schop, Johann

O TRAURIGKEIT, O HERZELIED see Wagner, Alexander

O TREUER GOTT, WIR DANKEN DIR see Schmidt-Mannheim, Hans

O TRINITY, MOST BLESSED LIGHT see Turner, C. Kenneth

O TRINITY, MOST BLESSED LIGHT see Wienhorst, Richard

O TRINITY OF BLESSED LIGHT see Cassler, G. Winston

O TRINITY OF BLESSED LIGHT see Clark

O TRINITY OF BLESSED LIGHT see Goodman, Joseph

O TRINITY OF BLESSED LIGHT see Powell, Robert J.

O TRINITY OF BLESSED LIGHT see Willan, Healey

O TRIUMPH, ALL YE RANSOM'D see Beethoven, Ludwig van

O TURN AWAY MINE EYES see Boyce, William

O UP! AS-TU ENTENDU see Aubanel, Georges

O VATER ALLER FROMMEN see Hammerschmidt, Andreas

O VERY GOD OF VERY GOD see Warner

O VIRGIN MOTHER MARY MILD see Harrhy, Edith

O VIRGO INTEMERATA see Hummel, Johann Nepomuk

O VIRUM MIRABILEM see Philips, Peter

O VOS OMNES see Berchem, Jacobus de

O VOS OMNES see Burkhart, Franz

O VOS OMNES see Casals, Pablo

O VOS OMNES see Chailley

O VOS OMNES see Cimbro, A.

O VOS OMNES see Compere, [Louis]

O VOS OMNES see Correa, Carlos

O VOS OMNES see Croce, Giovanni

O VOS OMNES see Deering, Richard

O VOS OMNES see Duron

O VOS OMNES see Esquivel, Juan Barahona de

O VOS OMNES see Gesualdo, Don Carlo

O VOS OMNES see Martini, Padre

O VOS OMNES see Morales, Cristobal de

O VOS OMNES see Palestrina, Giovanni

O VOS OMNES see Perti, Giacomo Antonio

O, VOS OMNES see Praetorius, Michael

O VOS OMNES see Serra, Louis Maria

O VOS OMNES see van Berchem, J.

O VOS OMNES see Vaughan Williams, Ralph

O VOS OMNES see Victoria, Tomas Luis de

O VOS OMNES see Vittoria, Ludovico

O VOS OMNES see Volpi, Edoardo

O VOS OMNES see Weitz, Guy

O VOS OMNES see Wickens, Dennis [John]

O VOS OMNES, QUI TRANSITIS PER VIAM see Victoria, Tomas Luis de

O VOSO GALO, COMADRE see Benedito

O WAKE AND SING, GOOD CHRISTIANS *Xmas,carol, Czech
(Ehret) SAB,opt fl/inst oct FOX CC11 $.25
(O153)
(Ehret, W.) SAB,opt 2fl PROWSE CC11 s.p.
(O154)

O WAS-N'T DAT A WIDE RIVER *spir,US
(Aubanel, Georges) "Oh Que C'etait Un Large Fleuve" [Eng/Fr] 3 eq voices OUVRIERES s.p.
(O155)

O WASN'T THAT A WIDE RIVER *spir
(Ehret) men cor oct SPRATT 198 $.30
(O156)

O, WE BELIEVE IN ONE TRUE GOD see Peninger

O WEEP, YE DAUGHTERS OF ISRAEL see Carissimi, Giacomo

O WEH DES SCHMERZEN see Sendt, Willy

O WEH MIR, HERR, MEIN GOTT see Schutz, Heinrich, Heu Mihe, Domine

O, WELCH EINE TIEFE see Reda, Siegfried

O WELCHE FREUDE see Buchner, Philipp Friedrich

O WELCOME THE SAVIOR *Xmas
(Ehret, W.) SATB oct PRESSER 312-40768 $.35
(O157)

O WELT, ICH MUSS DICH LASSEN see Gesius, Bartholomaus

O WELT, ICH MUSS DICH LASSEN see Isaac, Heinrich

O WELT, ICH MUSS DICH LASSEN see Kraft, Walter

O WELT, ICH MUSS DICH LASSEN see Lechner, Leonhard

O WELT, ICH MUSS DICH LASSEN see Mendelssohn, Arnold

O WELT, ICH MUSS DICH LASSEN see Praetorius, Michael

O WELT, SIEH HIER DEIN LEBEN see Gesius, Bartholomaus, O Welt, Ich Muss Dich Lassen

O WELT, SIEH HIER DEIN LEBEN see Isaac, Heinrich

O WELT, SIEH HIER DEIN LEBEN see Lechner, Leonhard

O WELT, SIEH HIER DEIN LEBEN see Poser, Hans

O, WER KANN DIES WUNDER FASSEN see Ammann, Benno

O WERTER HEIL'GER GEIST see Bruhns, Nicholaus

O WHAT THEIR GLORY MUST BE see Hadley

O WHAT THEIR JOY AND THEIR GLORY see Brown

O WHAT THEIR JOY AND THEIR GLORY MUST BE see Harris, William Henry

O WHAT THEIR JOY AND THEIR GLORY MUST BE see Willan, Healey

O WHAT THEIR JOY AND THEIR GLORY MUST BE see Wolff, S. Drummond

O WHERE ARE KINGS AND EMPIRES NOW see Strickler, David

O WHERE SHALL WISDOM see Boyce, William

O WHEREFORE DO THE NATIONS RAGE see Hopkins

O, WHO LIKE THEE see Oliver, Henry Kemble

O WIE HERBE IST DAS SCHEIDEN see Silcher, Friedrich

O WIE SELIG SEID IHR DOCH, IHR FROMMEN see Reger, Max

O, WIE WONNIG see Handel, George Frideric

O WIR ARMEN SUNDER see Kukuck, Felicitas

O WISDOM! see Noble, Thomas Tertius, O Sapienta!

O WISDOM FROM ON HIGH see Ramsey, O Sapienta

O WONDER OF THIS CHRISTMAS NIGHT see Lekberg, Sven

O WONDROUS CHILD see Palmer

O WONDROUS MYSTERY see Gabrieli, Giovanni, O Magnum Mysterium

O WONDROUS NATIVITY see Victoria, Tomas Luis de, O Magnum Mysterium

O WONDROUS NIGHT *Xmas
2pt CHAPPELL 0018184-352 $.40
(O158)

O WONDROUS NIGHT see Hokanson, M.

O WORD OF GOD INCARNATE see Markworth, Henry

O WORD OF GOD INCARNATE see Stevens

O WORD THAT GOEST FORTH ON HIGH see Near, Gerald

O WORLD, I MUST BE PARTING see Isaac, Heinrich, O Welt, Ich Muss Dich Lassen

O WORSHIP THE KING
(Cornwall, J.S.) SATB PIONEER 5057 $.20
(O159)

O WORSHIP THE KING see Barnes, [Edward Shippen]

O WORSHIP THE KING see Bullock, Ernest

O WORSHIP THE KING see Carter, Charles

O WORSHIP THE KING see Croft, W.

O WORSHIP THE KING see Darst, W. Glenn

O WORSHIP THE KING see Haydn, (Franz) Joseph

O WORSHIP THE KING see Haydn, (Johann) Michael

O WORSHIP THE KING see Johnson, N.F. Byng

O WORSHIP THE KING see Kay

O WORSHIP THE KING see Maunder, J.H.

O WORSHIP THE KING see Ringwald, [Roy]

O WORSHIP THE KING see Sellew, Donald E.

O WORSHIP THE KING see Stevens, Halsey

O WORSHIP THE KING see Vree

O WORSHIP THE KING see Wright

O WORSHIP THE LORD
(Follett) SATB oct PRO ART 2126 $.25   (O160)

O WORSHIP THE LORD see Fischer

O WORSHIP THE LORD see Hollins, Alfred

O WORSHIP THE LORD see Moschetti, [Giuseppe]

O WORSHIP THE LORD see Purcell, Henry

O WORSHIP THE LORD see Travers, John

O WORSHIP THE LORD see Wesley

O WUNDER UBER WUNDER *Xmas,folk
(Schollum, Robert) mix cor,soli,orch DOBLINGER voc sc s.p., cor pts s.p., ipa
(O161)

O YE LITTLE FLOCK see Amner

O YE MIGHTY see Willaert, Adrian, Magne Martyr Adriane

O YE PEOPLE see Duron, O Vos Omnes

O YE PEOPLE see Esquivel, Juan Barahona de, O Vos Omnes

O YE PEOPLE see Haydn, (Johann) Michael

O YE PEOPLE see Perti, Giacomo Antonio, O Vos Omnes

O YE PEOPLE see Victoria, Tomas Luis de, O Vos Omnes

O YE PEOPLE WHO PASS ME BY see Praetorius, Michael, O, Vos Omnes

O YE STARS AND HIGHEST HEAVENS see Bach, Johann Sebastian, Ihr Gestirn', Ihr Hohen Lufte

O YE THAT LOVE THE LORD see Coleridge-Taylor, Samuel

O YE WHO BEAR CHRIST'S HOLY NAME see Sampson, Godfrey

O YOU THAT PASS THIS WAY see Kreutz, Robert E.

O ZION, HASTE see Walch

O ZION, THAT BRINGETH GOOD TIDINGS see Stainer, John

O ZION THAT BRINGETH GOOD TIDINGS see Tours, Berthold

OAK AND THE ASH, THE
(Gibbs) SSA (med easy) OXFORD 83.041 $.30
(O162)
(Jacob) SSA,acap OXFORD 54.228 $.35
(O163)

OAKELEY
Evening And Morning *Rembrnc
(Chambers, H.A.) SA ALLANS 272 s.p.   (O164)
(Curnow, Leslie) SATB (easy) ALLANS 199 s.p.
(O165)

OAKELEY, HERBERT STANLEY (1830-1903)
Evening And Morning *Eve/Morn,anthem
mix cor oct NOVELLO 28.1008.05 s.p.   (O166)
SATB oct LESLIE 4029   (O167)

OB ALLE WELT see Lahusen, Christian

OB BEI UNS IS DER SUNDEN VIEL see Bach, Johann Sebastian

OBENSHAIN, KATHRYN G.
Lift Your Voices *CCU
SA FLAMMER GE5022 $1.00   (O168)

Shepherds In The Field *Xmas,anthem
SATB/SA (easy) oct LORENZ A529 $.30   (O169)

OBERLE, GROVER
O Jesus, Crowned With All Renown *Thanks
SATB oct GRAY GCMR 3071 $.30   (O170)

OBRAS CORALES DE AUTORES ANTIGUOS *sac/sec, CC18L
(Castellazzi) [Span/It/Lat] 2-4 eq voices, acap RICORDI-ARG BA 11536 s.p. contains works by: Lasso; Mozart; Palestrina; De Victoria; and others   (O171)

OBRAS CORALES *CC36L,So Am
(Lasala) 2 eq voices,pno sc RICORDI-ARG BA 10418 s.p., cor pts RICORDI-ARG BA 10497 contains works by: Arcadelt; Des Pres; Handel; and others   (O172)

OBRAS CORALES *sac/sec,CC29L,So Am
(Lasala) 3 eq voices,pno sc RICORDI-ARG BA 10419 s.p., cor pts RICORDI-ARG BA 10498 s.p. contains works by: Palestrina; Verdi; and others   (O173)

OBRECHT, JACOB (ca. 1430-1505)
Collected Works In Seven Volumes *CCU,Mass/ mot
(Wolf, Johannes) cor GREGG
ISBN 0:576 289663 s.p. and other works   (O174)

Collected Works Vol. 3: Masses *CCU,Mass
(Wolf, Johannes) cor GREGG
ISBN 0:576 28969 8 s.p. including Si Dedero   (O175)

Collected Works Vol. 1: Masses *CCU,Mass
(Wolf, Johannes) cor GREGG
ISBN 0:576 28967 1 s.p. including Fortuna Desperata   (O176)

Collected Works Vol. 2:Masses *CCU,Mass
(Wolf, Johannes) cor GREGG
ISBN 0:576 28968 X s.p. including De Sancto Martino   (O177)

Collected Works Vol. 4: Masses *CCU,Mass
(Wolf, Johannes) cor GREGG
ISBN 0:576 28970 1 s.p. including Adieu Mes Amours   (O178)

Collected Works Vol. 5: Masses *CCU,Mass
(Wolf, Johannes) cor GREGG
ISBN 0:576 28971 X s.p. including Beata Vicerea   (O179)

Collected Works Vol. 6: Motets *CCU,mot
(Wolf, Johannes) cor GREGG
ISBN 0:576 28972 8 s.p.   (O180)

Collected Works Vol. 7: St. Matthew Passion And Miscellaneous Works *CCU
(Wolf, Johannes) cor GREGG
ISBN 0:576 28973 6 s.p.   (O181)

Fuga A 4 (Alleluja) *Allelu
4pt mix cor MOSELER LB-365 s.p.   (O182)

Mijn Hert Heeft
"O How My Heart" SATB oct WALTON 7011 $.25
(O183)

O How My Heart *see Mijn Hert Heeft

Parce, Domine
see MEISTERWERKE MITTELALTERLICHER MUSIK

OBSECRO DOMINE see Gallus, Jacobus

OBSERVO DOMINE see Gallus, Jacobus

OCCASIONAL ORATORIO see Handel, George Frideric

OCCULI OMNIUM see Wood, Charles

OCH DA SKALL MAN FA SE see Nilsson, Torsten

OCH DU BETLEHEM see Carlstedt, Gunnemer

OCH DU BETLEHEM see Karkoff, Maurice Ingvar

OCH GOTT OL KOM see Smedeby, Sune

OCHS, VOLKER
Frohlich Wir Nun All Fangen An
see Kretzschmar, Gunther, Jauchzet Dem
Herrn

OCKEGHEM, JOHANNES (ca. 1430-1495)
Alma Redemptoris Mater
see ALTNIEDERLANDISCHE MOTETTEN

Collected Works: Vol. 1 *CCU,Eng
cor GALAXY 9.AMS.8 $16.50   (O184)

Collected Works: Vol. 2 *CCU,Eng
cor GALAXY 9.AMS.8 $16.50   (O185)

Kyrie (from Requiem)
[Lat] SATB,acap BROUDE BR. $.40   (O186)

Missa Mi-Mi *Mass
mix cor,acap voc sc KALMUS 6357 $1.50
                                   (O187)
(Besseler) 4pt mix cor MOSELER s.p. (O188)

Rex Gloriae (from Requiem)
[Eng/Lat] SATB,kbd BROUDE BR. $.35 (O189)

O'CONNOR
Blessed Christmas Morn *Xmas
SATB SCHMITT 1729 $.25   (O190)

Christ Is Born *Xmas
SATB SCHMITT 1728 $.25   (O191)

Jesus Christ Is Risen Today *Easter
(Roff) SATB oct SHAPIRO SCE 2503 $.30 (O192)

OCTAVE COMMUNION SERVICE see Gibbs, Alan

OCTAVE DAY OF CHRISTMAS see Binkerd, [Gordon]

OCTAVI TONI see Palestrina, Giovanni

OCTO MOTECTA NATALICIA *CC8L,Xmas,mot
[Lat] unis/2 eq voices/3pt mix cor,org
ZANIBON 2675 s.p. contains works by: Ferro,
S.; Ascenso, A.; Maggio, R.; Moioli, R.;
Negri, A.; Oltrasi, C.; Oltrasi, G. (O193)

OCULI MEI SEMPER AD DOMINUM see Krenek, Ernst

OCULI OMNIUM see Schutz, Heinrich

OCULI OMNIUM IN TE SPERANT, DOMINE see Schutz,
Heinrich

ODE AN GOTT see Tobler, J.H.

ODE FOR ST. CECILIA'S DAY see Handel, George
Frideric

ODE OF THANKSGIVING see Yahres

ODE ON ST. CECILIA'S DAY see Cooke

ODE ON ST. CECILIA'S DAY see Handel, George
Frideric

ODE ON THE BIRTH OF OUR SAVIOUR, AN see
Nicholson, S.H.

ODE, OR PSALME, TO GOD, AN see Newbold, David

ODE ST. CECILIA'S DAY see Purcell, Henry

ODE TO IMMORTALITY see Wheelwright, Lorin F.

ODE TO MUSIC see Butler, Eugene

ODE TO ST. CECILIA see Handel, George Frideric

ODE TO THE BIRTH OF OUR SAVIOR see Stanton,
[Walter Kendall]

ODE TO THE MUSIC MAKERS, AN see Kodaly, Zoltan

OECHSLER, ELIAS
Wach Auf, Meins Herzens Schone
see Burdett, E.S., Du Lieber Herre Jesu
Christ

OELWEIHE-MESSE see Rehmann, Theodor Bernhard,
Missa Christmatis

O'ER ALL NATIONS GOD ALONE see Wilkes

O'ER BETHLEHEM A STAR IS SHINING *Xmas
(Follett) 2pt,opt fl, triangle oct PRO ART
2738 $.30   (O194)

O'ER BETHLEHEM CITY *Xmas
SATB CHAPPELL 0018192-358 $.40   (O195)

O'ER BETHLEHEM MANGER see Manhire, Wilson

O'ER JUDEA'S PLAINS see Ogden

O'ER PEACEFUL JUDEA *Xmas,Eng
(Black, Charles) SATB&opt jr cor oct GRAY
GCMR 2616 $.25   (O196)

O'ER THE DISTANT MOUNTAINS see Bliss, Paul

O'ER THE SOLEMN HUSH OF MIDNIGHT see Maxwell,
J. Geddes

O'ER US BUT ONE GOD see Cohen, D., En Kelohenu

OERTZEN, RUDOLF VON (1910-   )
Dir, Dir Jehova
SATB,treb inst,kbd,bvl,perc HANSSLER 19.603
s.p. contains also: Lobe Den Herren, Den
Machtigen Konig   (O197)

OERTZEN, RUDOLF VON (cont'd.)
Du Meine Seele, Singe
mix cor HANSSLER 19.601 s.p. contains also:
Such, Wer Da Will   (O198)

In Dir Ist Freude
mix cor HANSSLER 19.602 s.p. contains also:
Nun Jauchzt Dem Herren, Alle Welt (O199)

Ist Gott Fur Mich
see Oertzen, Rudolf von, Warum Sollt Ich
Mich Denn Gramen

Jesu, Deine Passion Will Ich Jetzt Bedenken
SAT/SAB,bass inst HANSSLER 14.067 s.p.
                                   (O200)

Lobe Den Herren, Den Machtigen Konig
see Oertzen, Rudolf von, Dir, Dir Jehova

Lobt Gott Ihr Christen Alle Gleich
see Bender, Jan, Lobt Gott, Ihr Christen
Alle Gleich

Nun Danket All Und Bringet Ehr
see Oertzen, Rudolf von, Wunderbarer Konig

Nun Jauchzt Dem Herren, Alle Welt
see Oertzen, Rudolf von, In Dir Ist Freude

Such, Wer Da Will
see Oertzen, Rudolf von, Du Meine Seele,
Singe

Warum Sollt Ich Mich Denn Gramen
SATB,treb inst,kbd,bvl,perc HANSSLER 19.604
s.p. contains also: Ist Gott Fur Mich
                                   (O201)

Wunderbarer Konig
SATB,treb inst,kbd,bvl,perc HANSSLER 19.605
s.p. contains also: Nun Danket All Und
Bringet Ehr   (O202)

OEUVERS CHRETIENNES see Gounod, Charles
Francois

OEUVRES COMPLETES see Adam de la hale

OEUVRES DU REPERTOIRE DE LA COMMUNAUTE
PORTUGAISE D'AMSTERDAM (from Repertoire Of
The Portuguese Jewish Community Of
Amsterdam) Heb
(Adler, I.) SATB,acap ISRAELI 704-709 s.p.
                                   (O203)

OEUVRES RELIGIEUSES *CC20L
[Lat] unis,pno/org oct CHOUDENS s.p. contains
works by: Bach; Beethoven; Handel; Mozart;
and others   (O204)

OF A ROSE SING WE see Brown

OF A SHEPHERD AND A LAMB see Brydson

OF CHRIST WE SING see Hafso

OF CHRISTES BIRTH see Williams, David H.

OF MY SOUL THOU DELIGHT see Giovanelli,
[Ruggero], Tu, Mentis Delectatio

OF ONE THAT IS SO FAIR AND BRIGHT see Holst,
Gustav

OF ONE THAT IS SO FAIR AND BRIGHT see Naylor,
Bernard

OF SUCH IS THE KINGDOM see Paul

OF THE FATHER'S HEART BEGOTTEN
(Willcocks) SATB (easy) OXFORD 42.856 $.30
                                   (O205)

OF THE FATHER'S LOVE BEGOTTEN *Xmas
(Chenoweth) 3pt mix cor,pno/org oct LAWSON
51498 $.35   (O206)
(Lundquist) SATB,acap (med) oct WILLIS 6623
$.16   (O207)
(Young, Robert) SATB oct WORD CS-2449 $.30
                                   (O208)

OF THE FATHER'S LOVE BEGOTTEN see Anonymous

OF THE FATHER'S LOVE BEGOTTEN see Ashfield,
Robert, Divinum Mysterium

OF THE FATHER'S LOVE BEGOTTEN see Chenoweth,
Wilbur

OF THE FATHER'S LOVE BEGOTTEN see Couper

OF THE FATHER'S LOVE BEGOTTEN see Pasquet, Jean

OF THE FATHER'S LOVE BEGOTTEN see Powell,
Robert J.

OF THE FATHER'S LOVE BEGOTTEN see Rodgers, John

OF THE FATHER'S LOVE BEGOTTEN see Thiman, Eric
Harding, Corde Natus

OF THE GLORIOUS BODY TELLING see Victoria,
Tomas Luis de

OF THE KINDNESS OF THE LORD see Proulx, Richard

OF THE MYSTICAL SUPPER see Lvov, Alexey
Feodorovitch

OF THE NATIVITIE OF CHRIST see Cole, Hugo

OF THE NEW YEAR see Hoddinott, Alun

OF WISDOM AND FOLLY see Berger, Jean

OFF TO BETHLEHEM see Grime, William

OFFENBACH, JACQUES (1819-1880)
Barcarolle (from Tales Of Hoffman) anthem
SA oct HARRIS HC2004 $.25   (O209)

OFFER
Songs Of Bethlehem
(Grimes) unis BOOSEY $1.25   (O210)

OFFER, CHARLES K.
Desert Shall Rejoice, The
(Rapley) unis jr cor/unis wom cor&opt desc
CURWEN 72672 s.p.   (O211)

OFFER, CHARLES K. (cont'd.)
Sweet Bells Of Bethlehem *Xmas
(Rapley) 1-2pt jr cor/1-2pt wom cor CURWEN
72613 s.p.   (O212)

OFFER UNTO GOD see Christiansen, F. Melius

OFFER UNTO GOD THANKSGIVING see Glarum, L.
Stanley

OFFERING see Anderson, [William H.]

OFFERING, THE see Hoiby, Lee

OFFERING OF PRAISE, AN see Warner, Richard

OFFERINGS see Rodgers

OFFERTOIRE see Saint-Saens, Camille, Justorum
Animae

OFFERTORIEN-BAND IX see Palestrina, Giovanni

OFFERTORIES FOR THE SUNDAYS OF ADVENT see
Campbell-Watson, Frank

OFFERTORIES VOL. 1 see Mozart, Wolfgang Amadeus

OFFERTORIES VOL. 2 see Mozart, Wolfgang Amadeus

OFFERTORIO see Grassi, Ciro

OFFERTORIO PER LA FESTA DI S. LUIGI see
Bottazzo, Luigi

OFFERTORIUM see Bruckner, Anton

OFFERTORIUM see Palestrina, Giovanni

OFFERTORIUM see Ravanello, Oreste

OFFERTORIUM see Schubert, Franz (Peter)

OFFERTORIUM PRO FESTO SANCTI JOANNES BAPTISTAE
see Mozart, Wolfgang Amadeus

OFFERTORIUM PRO FESTO SANCTI JOANNIS BAPTISTAE
see Mozart, Wolfgang Amadeus

OFFERTORIUM PRO FESTO SANCTI JOANNIS BAPTISTAE
INTER NATOS see Mozart, Wolfgang Amadeus

OFFERTORIUM PRO OMNI TEMPORE see Mozart,
Wolfgang Amadeus

OFFERTORIUM ZU EHREN DES HL. LUDGERUS see
Baumann, Max

OFFERTORY see Schubert, Franz (Peter), Intende
Voci Orationis Meae

OFFERTORY HYMNS
LITURGICAL $.50
contains: Accept, Almighty Father; Lord,
Accept The Gifts We Offer; O King Of
Might And Splendor   (O213)

OFFERTORY RESPONSE see Grant

OFFICE OF THE HOLY COMMUNION see Graham, George

OFFICE OF THE HOLY COMMUNION, THE see Rowley,
Alec

OFFICIUM DE CORPORE CHRISTI see Isaac, Heinrich

OFFICIUM DE RESURRECTIONE CHRISTI see Isaac,
Heinrich

OFFICIUM EPIPHANIAE DOMINI see Isaac, Heinrich

OFFICIUM ET MISSA IN FESTO S. ANTONII PAT. see
Gorlatto, Giacomo

OFFICIUM NATIVITATIS DOMINI see Isaac, Heinrich

OFRENDA see Benedito

OFT I THINK WHEN I READ THAT SWEET STORY OF OLD
see Soderman

OG HAN FRONEDRET SEG see Roberton, K.O.

OG ORDET BLEV KJOD see Hovland, Egil

OGDEN
How Beautiful Upon The Mountains
SATB oct LORENZ 277 $.30   (O214)

Look And Live
(Ferrin) SATB oct LILLENAS AN-1634 $.30
                                   (O215)

O'er Judea's Plains *Xmas
(Brandon) SAB oct SHAPIRO SCE 5506 $.30 (O216)

OGDEN, W.A.
Consider The Lilies
cor oct HART s.p.   (O217)

OH, BE JOYFUL IN THE LORD see Handel, George
Frideric

OH BE JOYFUL IN THE LORD see Pinkham, Daniel,
Jubilate Deo

OH, BE NOT FAR FROM HELPING ME see Wienhorst,
Richard

OH BETHLEHEM see Ehret, Walter

OH, BLEST THE HOUSE, WHATE'ER BEFALL see
Praetorius, Michael

OH, BY AN' BY *spir
(Roberton) 3pt jr cor/3pt wom cor ROBERTON
72102 s.p.   (O218)

OH, COME, ALL YE FAITHFUL see Adeste Fideles

OH COME, AND DWELL IN ME
(Stuart) SATB oct PRO ART 1457 $.22 (O219)

OH, COME AND MOURN WITH US see Faber

OH COME LET US SING see Brubeck

OH COME, LITTLE CHILDREN *Xmas
  (Fargo) SSA oct KENDOR $.25   (O220)
  (Fargo) 2pt jr cor oct KENDOR $.25   (O221)

OH, COME, LITTLE CHILDREN see Rotermund, Melvin

OH, COME, OH, COME, EMMANUEL see Lenel, Ludwig

OH, COME TO MY HEART, LORD JESUS see Ambrose,
  [Paul]

OH, COME TO MY HEART, LORD JESUS see Matthews

OH COME, YE SERVANTS OF THE LORD see Tye,
  Christopher

OH! DIVINE COMMUNITY see Milano, R.

OH FATHER, WHOSE ALMIGHTY POW'R see Handel,
  George Frideric

OH FIRST CREATED BEAM see Handel, George
  Frideric

OH, FOR A CLOSER WALK WITH GOD see Foster,
  Myles Birket

OH, FOR A THOUSAND TONGUES see Glazer, Carl

OH, FREEDOM!
  (Johnson) 5pt mix cor oct SCHIRM.G 10520 $.35
                                                 (O222)

OH, GIVE THANKS UNTO THE LORD see Forsblad

OH GOD, IT MUST BE YOU see Grime, William

OH GOD OF LOVE see Zaninelli, Luigi

OH GOD, OUR HELP IN AGES PAST
  (Cornwall, J.S.) SATB PIONEER 5064 $.20
                                                 (O223)

OH GOD, OUR HELP IN AGES PAST see Croft,
  William

OH! GOD! THY BOUNTY REACHETH WIDE see
  Beethoven, Ludwig van

OH GOD, YOUR WORLD IS WONDERFUL see Van
  Iderstine, A.P.

OH, HAD I JUBAL'S LYRE see Handel, George
  Frideric

OH, HAPPY DAY see Skillings, Otis

OH, HEAR ME WHEN I CRY TO THEE see Schutz,
  Heinrich

OH HEAR THESE, OUR WORDS see Morgan

OH, HERE'S A DAY FOR JOYFUL SINGING see Dvorak,
  Antonin

OH, HOLD THOU ME UP see Marcello, Benedetto

OH, HOLY LORD *spir
  (Johnson) SATTBB,acap oct SCHIRM.G 10449 $.35
                                                 (O224)
  (Johnson) SATTBB,acap oct SCHIRM.G 10449 $.35
                                                 (O225)

OH, HOLY NIGHT! see Adam, Adolphe-Charles

OH HOLY SPIRIT, ENTER IN see Nicolai, Philipp

OH, HOW BEAUTIFUL THE SKY see Deilig Er Den
  Himmel Blaa

OH, HOW BLESSED see Buxtehude, Dietrich

OH HOW GREAT THE MYSTERY see Poulenc, Francis,
  O Magnum Mysterium

OH, HOW JOYFULLY! *Xmas
  (Noyes) SATB (Sicilian hymn) SCHMITT 1769
  $.35   (O226)

OH, HOW JOYFULLY see Rotermund, Melvin

OH, HOW JOYFULLY, OH, HOW MERRILY *Xmas
  (Miller) SATB oct PRO ART 2422 $.25   (O227)

OH, HOW MY HEART REJOICES see Praetorius,
  Michael, Herzlich Tut Mich Erfreuen

OH, I WOULD SING OF MARY'S CHILD see Lovelace,
  Austin C.

OH, IT'S WONDERFUL see Basham, Robert A.

OH JOHN *spir
  (Reynolds) mix cor,A solo,acap oct SCHIRM.G
  9531 $.25   (O228)

OH LAMB OF GOD see Handel, George Frideric

OH, LET THE MERRY BELLS RING ROUND see Handel,
  George Frideric

OH, LITTLE CHILD OF BETHLEHEM see White,
  Michael

OH, LITTLE CHILDREN LEAD US *Xmas,carol
  (Anderson, W.H.) SATB oct LESLIE 4017 see
  from Two Christmas Carols Set 3   (O229)

OH LORD AND FATHER OF US ALL see Craig

OH LORD DIVINE see Handel, George Frideric

OH LORD! HOW EXCELLENT THY NAME see Benford

OH LORD OF HEAVEN AND EARTH AND SEA see Larson

OH LORD, REBUKE ME NOT see Freestone, G.S.

OH, LORD SPREAD THY WINGS O'ER ME see Webber,
  W.S. Lloyd

OH! LORD SPREAD THY WINGS OVER ME see Webber,
  W.S. Lloyd

OH, MARY DON'T YOU WEEP *spir
  (Genuchi) TTBB LUDWIG SS-013 $.30   (O230)
  (Kelly) SATB oct PRO ART 2010 $.25   (O231)

OH, MAY GOD BLESS THEE see Lechner, Leonhard

OH, MY SPIRIT see Berlioz, Hector

OH, NIGHTINGALE, AWAKE! *Xmas
  (Brott) SATB SCHMITT 1748 $.20   (O232)

OH, NOW BE JOYFUL ALL see Taffs, J.

OH, PETER GO RING A DEM BELLS *spir
  (Clements, J.) SATB PROWSE s.p.   (O233)

OH, PETER, GO RING DEM BELLS *spir
  (Roberton) 3pt jr cor/3pt wom cor ROBERTON
  72095 s.p.   (O234)

OH, PO' LITTLE JESUS *spir
  (de Paur) TTBB,acap oct LAWSON 710 $.30   (O235)

  (James) 4pt mix cor,S solo,acap oct SCHIRM.G
  8170 $.25   (O236)

OH, PRAISE THE LORD see Handel, George
  Frideric, Oh Praise The Lord With One
  Consent

OH, PRAISE THE LORD WITH JOYFUL NOISE see
  Schein, Johann Hermann

OH PRAISE THE LORD WITH ONE CONSENT see Handel,
  George Frideric

OH, PRAISE THE LORD, YE NATIONS ALL see Franck,
  Cesar

OH QUE C'ETAIT UN LARGE FLEUVE see O Was-n't
  Dat A Wide River

OH, REJOICE, YE CHRISTIANS, LOUDLY see Bach,
  Johann Sebastian

OH, REJOICE YE CHRISTIANS LOUDLY see Maier

OH, REJOICE, YE CHRISTIANS LOUDLY, ALLELUIA!
  see Hammerschmidt, Andreas

OH, RELIGION IS A FORTUNE *spir
  (Genuchi) TTBB LUDWIG SS-022 $.35   (O237)
  (Genuchi) SATB LUDWIG SS-023 $.30   (O238)

OH REMEMBER NOT see Battishill, Jonathan

OH SAVIOUR LET THE SKIES BE RIV'N see Brahms,
  Johannes, O Heiland, Reiss Die Himmel Auf

OH! SAY, BUT I'M GLAD see Sullivan, Sir Arthur
  Seymour

OH SENORA see Franco

OH, SHEPHERDS, WHISPER SOFTLY
  see Belgian Christmas Songs, Set 2

OH, SING OF HIS MIGHTY LOVE see Bradbury,
  William Batchelder

OH, SING TO GOD, THE LORD see Gabrieli,
  Giovanni, Cantate Domino

OH SING UNTO THE LORD see Hassler, Hans Leo,
  Cantate Domino

OH, SLEEP, BABY JESUS *Xmas,folk,Braz
  (Ream) SATB SCHMITT 1623 $.22   (O239)

OH SLEEP, FAIR CHILD *Xmas
  (Christiansen, P.) SATB SCHMITT 911 $.30
                                                (O240)

OH, THAT I HAD A THOUSAND VOICES see Konig

OH, THOU, FROM WHOM ALL BLESSINGS COME see
  Tchaikovsky, Piotr Ilyitch

OH THOU, WHO CAMEST FROM ABOVE see Dunn

OH VAIT TILL PUT ON MY CROWN
  see Negro Spirituals

OH WEIHNACHT, DU SELIGE, FROHLICHE ZEIT *Norw
  (Korda, Viktor) 2pt wom cor,acap oct s.p.
    contains also: Frohliche Weihnacht Uberall
  (Eng) (CC)   (O241)

OH, WHAT A BEAUTIFUL CITY *spir
  (Boatner) mix cor,acap oct SCHIRM.G 8843 $.25
                                                (O242)
  (Ehret) SSA oct FISCHER,C CM-7614 $.25   (O243)

OH, WHAT A BEAUTIFUL CITY see Dawson

OH, WHAT A BEAUTIFUL CITY! see Oliver

OH, WHAT A DAY see Schuler

OH, WHAT A WONDER see Eilers

OH, WHAT CAN I GIVE TO THE HOLY CHILD? see
  Whitaker

OH, WHAT CAN I GIVE TO THE HOLY CHILD? see
  Whittaker, Howard

OH, WHAT PRAISES SHALL WE RENDER see Young

OH! WHAT SORROW! see d'Astorga, Emanuelle

OH, WORSHIP THE KING *hymn
  (Wolff) SATB&unis/SATB&cong,opt org&trp oct
  LAWSON 51379 $.30   (O244)

OH, WORSHIP THE KING see Haydn, (Franz) Joseph

OH, WORSHIP THE LORD see Purcell, Henry

OH YE THAT LOVETH THE LORD see Morgan

OH, YES!
  see Eight Negro Spirituals: Book Ii

OHANIAN
  Mother's Day Anthem
  SA/TB FLAMMER E5073 $.25   (O245)

  Sing Thanksgiving
  SA/TB FLAMMER E5037 $.25   (O246)

O'HARA, F.
  Sing Noel *Xmas
  SA oct PRESSER 312-40027 $.25   (O247)

O'HARA, GEOFFREY (1882-1967)
  Art Thou The Christ
  (Deis) 4pt mix cor,T solo oct SCHIRM.G 9741
  $.30   (O248)

  Come To The Stable With Jesus *Xmas
  jr cor&sr cor oct SCHIRM.G 10388 $.25
                                                (O249)
  4pt men cor,opt acap oct SCHIRM.G 10154
  $.25   (O250)
  (Deis) 4pt mix cor,pno/org oct SCHIRM.G
  10038 $.25   (O251)
  (Deis) 3pt wom cor,pno/org oct SCHIRM.G
  10039 $.25   (O252)
  (Deis) 2pt wom cor,pno/org oct SCHIRM.G
  10047 $.25   (O253)
  (Deis) 4pt mix cor,acap oct SCHIRM.G
  9931 $.25   (O254)
  (Deis) 4pt men cor,pno/org oct SCHIRM.G
  10048 $.25   (O255)

  Count Your Blessings
  (Deis) 4pt mix cor oct SCHIRM.G 10021 $.25
                                                (O256)

  Fool Hath Said "There Is No God", The
  SATB ALLANS 174 s.p.   (O257)

  Forward To Christ
  SAB WARNER H3075 $.30   (O258)
  SATB WARNER H2933 $.40   (O259)

  God Lives In My Heart
  (Deis) 4pt mix cor,ST soli oct SCHIRM.G
  9914 $.30   (O260)

  He Smiled On Me
  (Deis) 2pt wom cor oct SCHIRM.G 9848 $.25
                                                (O261)
  (Downing) 4pt mix cor oct SCHIRM.G 8519
  $.30   (O262)
  (Downing) 3pt wom cor oct SCHIRM.G 9549
  $.35   (O263)
  (Stickles) jr cor&sr cor oct SCHIRM.G 10397
  $.25   (O264)

  I Am Going To Sunday School
  SA&unis/SA/unis oct HUNTZINGER 7055 $.20   (O265)

  I Sing A Song Of The Saints Of God
  SATB oct VOLKWEIN VB188 $.25   (O266)

  I Walked Today Where Jesus Walked
  SSA ALLANS 302 s.p.   (O267)
  SA ALLANS 301 s.p.   (O268)
  SATB (easy) ALLANS 300 s.p.   (O269)
  (Deis) SATB&2pt jr cor oct SCHIRM.G 9867
  $.35   (O270)
  (Downing) 4pt mix cor oct SCHIRM.G 8401
  $.35   (O271)
  (Downing) 2pt wom cor oct SCHIRM.G 8933
  $.25   (O272)
  (Downing) 3pt mix cor oct SCHIRM.G 9615
  $.35   (O273)
  (Downing) 4pt men cor oct SCHIRM.G 9699
  $.30   (O274)
  (Downing) 3pt wom cor oct SCHIRM.G 8723
  $.35   (O275)
  (Downing, K.) SAB (easy) ALLANS 302 s.p.   (O276)

  I Was The Tree
  TTBB oct HUNTZINGER 3034 $.20   (O277)

  If Christ Came Back
  (Richardson, A.) SSA oct PRESSER 332-40110
  $.30   (O278)

  King Of Kings
  (Angell) SATB SHAWNEE A 325 $.30   (O279)

  Let Us Walk In The Light Of The Lord
  (Wilson) SATB oct COLOMBO 1338 $.30   (O280)

  Living God, The
  SA ALLANS 347 s.p.   (O281)

  Living God, The
  TTBB oct HUNTZINGER 3015 $.20   (O282)
  SATB oct HUNTZINGER 4024 $.20   (O283)
  SATB oct HUNTZINGER 4055 $.25   (O284)

  Lord Is My Captain, The
  SATB oct HUNTZINGER 7001 $.25   (O285)

  Must Jesus Bear Another Cross?
  (Deis) 4pt mix cor oct SCHIRM.G 10162 $.25
                                                (O286)

  Prayer For Peace *see Wolfe

  Soft Were Your Hands, Dear Jesus
  SSA oct HUNTZINGER 506 $.22   (O287)
  SATB oct HUNTZINGER 4042 $.25   (O288)

  Star Road, The *Xmas
  (Deis) 4pt mix cor oct SCHIRM.G 11041 $.25
                                                (O289)

  This Is The Story Of Jesus
  SATB BOSTON 11834 $.40   (O290)

  Waters Of Thy Love, The
  SATB oct HUNTZINGER 4051 $.20   (O291)

  We Call To Thee
  SATB oct VOLKWEIN VB276 $.25   (O292)

OHL, [JEREMIAH FRANKLIN] (1850-1941)
  How Firm A Foundation
  SATB oct PLYMOUTH FO-105 $.25   (O293)

  Once To Every Man And Nation
  SATB oct PLYMOUTH FO-100 $.25   (O294)

  Sweeter The Bells Never Ring *Xmas
  2pt oct PLYMOUTH FO-500 $.25   (O295)

OHLSON
  Vigils Of Mary, The *Xmas/Easter
  4pt mix cor,S solo,acap oct SCHIRM.G 9880
                                                (O296)

OHN ALLE SCHULD see Schutz, Heinrich, Nonne Hic
  Est

OHSE, REINHARD
  Pharisaer Und Zollner *Trin,Bibl/mot
  [Ger] SATB,acap (med diff) DEUTSCHER
  DV 7626 s.p.   (O297)
  [Ger] mix cor oct DEUTSCHER 7626 $1.25
                                                (O298)

OI BETLEEM see Donostia, [Jose Antonio de]

OKEOVER, JOHN (? -1663?)
Grant, We Beseech Thee, Merciful Lord *Gen/
Lent
SATB,kbd (med easy) oct CONCORDIA 98-1902
$.35   (O299)

OKOLO, A.
Rejoice, Our Lord Is Born *Xmas
(Kulaks) SATB oct LORENZ E20 $.35   (O300)

OL' ARK'S A-MOVERIN', THE *spir
(Ehret; Siegmeister) SAB oct PRO ART 1669
$.25   (O301)
(Schubert) SB oct LILLENAS AN-3817 $.35
(O302)

OL' GREY ROBE *spir
(Huntley) 4pt men cor,acap oct SCHIRM.G 7142
$.30   (O303)

OLD AMERICAN SONGS *see At The River; Simple
Gifts   (O304)

OLD ARK'S A-MOVERIN' *spir
see Steal Away
(Bartholomew) mix cor,acap oct SCHIRM.G 10078
$.20   (O305)
(Bartholomew) 4pt mix cor,acap oct SCHIRM.G
7756 $.30 contains also: Steal Away   (O306)

OLD ARK'S A-MOVERIN', THE *spir
(Williamson, W.) SA LEONARD-US 08047120 $.25
(O307)

OLD ARK'S A-MOVERING ALONG see Murray

OLD CAROLS FOR YOUNG MEN *CCU,Xmas,carol
(Lefebvre) TBB GALAXY 1.1520.1 $.75   (O308)

OLD CHRISTMAS see Shaw, Martin

OLD CRUSADER'S HYMN
(Griffith, Allen) SAB oct BELWIN 959 $.25
(O309)

OLD ENGLISH CHRISTMAS, AN see Van Etten,
Eleanor

OLD FRENCH CHRISTMAS CAROL see Krone

OLD GAELIC BLESSING, AN see Grant

OLD GEMS-NEW SETTINGS *CC9L,medley
(Carmichael, Ralph) SATB voc sc WORD 30071
$1.95   (O310)

OLD HUNDRETH PSALM TUNE, THE see Vaughan
Williams, Ralph

OLD LATIN HYMN see Kyrie Eleison

OLD MASTERS IN SETTINGS BY J.S. BACH, VOL. I
see Bach, Johann Sebastian

OLD MASTERS IN SETTINGS BY J.S. BACH, VOL. II
see Bach, Johann Sebastian

OLD NETHERLANDS MOTETS *CCU,mot,Neth
mix cor,acap voc sc KALMUS 6364 $1.25
contains works by: Compere; Des Prez,
Josquin; Ockeghem   (O311)

OLD POLISH CHRISTMAS CAROL see Liszneiwski,
Karol

OLD POLISH PASTORALS *CCU,Xmas,Pol
[Pol/Lat] POLSKIE ZHMP12 s.p.   (O312)

OLD RUGGED CROSS *CC5L
(Burroughs, Bob; Brown, Charles F.) SATB voc
sc WORD 37617 $1.00   (O313)

OLD RUGGED CROSS
SATB/SA BIG3 $.30   (O314)

OLD RUGGED CROSS see Benguerel, Xavier

OLD RUGGED CROSS, THE see Bennard, George

OLD RUGGED CROSS, THE see Bennard, George

OLD SHIP OF ZION
(Douglas) SATB oct PRO ART 2067 $.22   (O315)

OLD SHIP OF ZION see Scott

OLD TESTAMENT, THE see Harker, Jeanne

OLD TESTAMENT, THE see Harker, Jeanne

OLD-TIME POWER see Tillman

OLD WOMAN, THE see Wilson, H.

OLDENBURG, BOB
Real *cant
(Allen, Lanny) SATB voc sc WORD 37542 $2.95
(O316)

OLDHAM, ARTHUR (1926-   )
Experience Does Me So Inspire
see Oldham, Arthur, O Queen Of Virtues

Hymns For The Amusement Of Children *CCU,
hymn
mix cor,S solo,org/orch (med) voc sc OXFORD
46.133 $1.80, ipr   (O317)

Missa In Honorem Sancti Thomae Mori *Mass
[Lat] SATB CHESTER s.p.   (O318)

Now's The Time For Mirth And Play *hymn
SATB oct NOVELLO 44.1448.09 s.p.   (O319)

O Queen Of Virtues *hymn
SATB oct NOVELLO 44.1447.00 s.p. contains
also: Experience Does Me So Inspire   (O320)

Sacerdos Et Pontifex *Proces,anthem
[Lat] SATB,org FABER F0085 $.35   (O321)
cor FABER F0085 s.p.   (O322)

OLDROYD, GEORGE (1886-1951)
Communion Service: The "Mass Of The Quiet
Hour" *Commun,Agnus/Bene/Credo/Gloria/
Kyrie/Sanctus
SATB,acap oct OXFORD 42.316 $.65   (O323)

Heart That's Broken And Contrite, An *Gen/
Lent
SATB (med easy) oct OXFORD 42.080 $.25

OLDROYD, GEORGE (cont'd.)
(O324)

Jhesu Christ Saint Mary's Sone
"Spiritual Rhapsody, A" SATB,T solo,hpsd,
2fl,2ob,2clar,2bsn,4horn,2trp,3trom,tuba,
strings,perc,timp,harp voc sc NOVELLO
s.p., ipr   (O325)

Paean Of Remembrance *ASD/Rembrnc,Bibl
SATB (diff) oct OXFORD 40.300 $.65, ipr   (O326)

Prayer To Jesus *Lent
SATB (easy) oct OXFORD 43.037 $.25   (O327)

Song Of The Passion *Gen/Psntd
SATB,acap (med easy) oct OXFORD 43.705 $.25
(O328)

Spiritual Rhapsody, A *see Jhesu Christ
Saint Mary's Sone

OLDS
St. Francis Prayer *prayer
SATB HANSEN-US C272B $.40   (O329)

Sunrise On Easter Morning *Easter/Lent
SATB,opt 3trp oct FISCHER,C CM-473 $.25   (O330)

OLDS, [WILLIAM BENJAMIN] (1874-1948)
Let Us Praise God *Gen
SATB&speak cor SCHMITT 1649 $.35   (O331)
SAB&speak cor SCHMITT 5512 $.30   (O332)
SSA&speak cor SCHMITT 2547 $.25   (O333)

Sing, All Ye Christian People *Gen
SATB SCHMITT 1606 $.30   (O334)

W.B. Olds Choruses For Mixed Voices-No. 1
*CCU
mix cor SCHMITT 27 $.50   (O335)

W.B. Olds Choruses For Mixed Voices-No. 2
*CCU
mix cor SCHMITT 28 $.50   (O336)

W.B. Olds Male Choruses-No. 1 *CCU
men cor SCHMITT 25 $.50   (O337)

W.B. Olds Male Choruses-No. 2 *CCU
men cor SCHMITT 26 $.50   (O338)

W.B. Olds Treble Choruses-No. 1 *CCU
treb cor SCHMITT 23 $.50   (O339)

Welcome, Happy Morning *Easter
SATB SCHMITT 1607 $.30   (O340)

OLIVE TREE LULLABY see Hovdesven, E.A.

OLIVE TREES see Atzey Zeydim Omdim

OLIVE TREES ARE STANDING see Schwadron

OLIVER
Gooding Carol *Xmas,carol
SAB oct PLYMOUTH PCS-401 $.25   (O341)

Oh, What A Beautiful City!
SATB oct PLYMOUTH FO-108 $.25   (O342)

Praise To The Living God (Yigdal)
2pt oct PLYMOUTH PCS-514 $.25   (O343)

OLIVER, F.
Noel
[Eng/Fr/Ger] voc sc UNIVER. 12405 $3.15,
cor pts UNIVER. 12406 $.90   (O344)

OLIVER, HENRY KEMBLE (1800-1885)
O, Who Like Thee
(Davis, Katherine K.) SATB,S solo,pno/org
oct FISCHER,C CM-7135 $.25   (O345)

OLIVER, HERBERT
God Bless The Morning
2pt ASHDOWN E.A.245 s.p.   (O346)

Spreading The News
2pt ASHDOWN E.A.209 s.p.   (O347)

OLIVET TO CALVARY see Dasher, James

OLIVET TO CALVARY see Maunder, J.H.

OLLONE, MAX D' (1875-1959)
Elevation
[Fr] SMez,pno/harp,opt org ENOCH voc sc
s.p., cor pts s.p.   (O348)

Jeanne D'arc A Domremy
[Fr] SATB,org,orch ENOCH voc sc s.p., voc
pt s.p., ipr   (O349)

OLMAN, ISR, J.
De Heer Regeerde *see Dominus Regnavit

Divis Orte Bonis
men cor ALSBACH&D sc s.p., cor pts s.p.
(O350)

Dominus Regnavit
"De Heer Regeerde" men cor ALSBACH&D sc
s.p., cor pts s.p.   (O351)

Jerusalem
[Neth/Ger] men cor ALSBACH&D sc s.p., cor
pts s.p.   (O352)

Jom Kipoer (Dag Van Verzoening) *Yom Kippur
men cor ALSBACH&D sc s.p., cor pts s.p.
(O353)

Kerstmis
mix cor ALSBACH&D sc s.p., cor pts s.p.
(O354)

Lente
men cor ALSBACH&D sc s.p., cor pts s.p.
(O355)

Lentelicht
men cor ALSBACH&D sc s.p., cor pts s.p.
(O356)

Populus Sion
"Volk Van Sion" men cor ALSBACH&D sc s.p.,
cor pts s.p.   (O357)

Psalm 47
mix cor ALSBACH&D sc s.p., cor pts s.p.
(O358)

Volk Van Sion *see Populus Sion

OLSEN, DANIEL
Honom Tillhor Aran *Bibl
[Swed] SATB,acap GEHRMANS KRB 152   (O359)

OLSEN, SPARRE (1903-   )
A Leva
wom cor MUSIKK 26 s.p.   (O360)
men cor MUSIKK 61 s.p.   (O361)
mix cor MUSIKK 221 s.p.   (O362)

Di Makt
men cor MUSIKK 215 s.p.   (O363)

Gud, Nar Du Til Oppbrudd Kaller
mix cor MUSIKK 253 s.p.   (O364)

Heilag Var *see Ver Sanctum

Paskehymne
men cor MUSIKK 137 s.p.   (O365)
wom cor MUSIKK 22 s.p.   (O366)

Salme *Psalm
mix cor MUSIKK 67 s.p.   (O367)

Sjung Hjerte, Sjung En Aftensang
mix cor MUSIKK 203 s.p.   (O368)

Vagen
mix cor MUSIKK 249 s.p.   (O369)

Velsignet Vaere Jesu Navn
wom cor MUSIKK 23 s.p.   (O370)

Velsignet Vare Jesu Navn
men cor MUSIKK 159 s.p.   (O371)

Ver Sanctum
"Heilag Var" [Lat/Norw] mix cor,orch/pno
MUSIKK 44 s.p. sc, voc sc, cor pts   (O372)

OLSON
Alleluia, Glorious Is Thy Name
SATB oct SUMMY B 1575 $.40   (O373)

Eternal Song
SATB,acap oct BOOSEY 5551 $.30   (O374)

Two Carols For Christmas *CC2U,Xmas,carol
SATB FLAMMER A 5606 $.30   (O375)

OLSON, DANIEL
Adventskantat
mix cor,solo,org voc sc NORDISKA 2059 s.p.,
ipa   (O376)

Allenast Hos Gud
wom cor/jr cor NORDISKA 1886 s.p.   (O377)

Av Himlens Hojd *Xmas,cant
[Swed] SATB&eq voices,org GEHRMANS KRB 85
s.p.   (O378)

Herre, Till Vem Skulle Vi Ga?
3pt mix cor,org NORDISKA 2186 s.p.   (O379)
wom cor/jr cor,org NORDISKA 2186 s.p.   (O380)

Ljuset Uppgar *Bibl
[Swed] SATB,acap GEHRMANS KRB 309   (O381)

Lovsjungen Herren
[Swed] SATB,acap GEHRMANS KRB 90   (O382)

Milde Jesu, Nadens Kalla
mix-cor NORDISKA 3438 s.p.   (O383)

O Jesu Krist Dig Till Oss Vand
wom cor/jr cor,org NORDISKA 2234 s.p.   (O384)

O Jesu Krist, Du Nadens Brunn
mix cor NORDISKA 1696 s.p.   (O385)

Passionskoral *Psntd,Bibl/cant
[Swed] SATB,acap GEHRMANS KRB 89   (O386)

Psalm 84
4-6pt mix cor,soli,opt fl,2vla,vla,vcl cor
pts NORDISKA 4502 s.p., voc sc NORDISKA
s.p., ipa   (O387)

Saliga Aro De Doda
[Swed] SAB&eq voices,org GEHRMANS KRB 181
(O388)

Sen Till *Bibl
[Swed] SAB,acap GEHRMANS TKS 30   (O389)

Sommarnattspalm
mix cor NORDISKA 1088 s.p.   (O390)

Stora Och Underbara *Bibl
[Swed] SATB,acap GEHRMANS KRB 88   (O391)

Trygghet Hos Gud
3pt wom cor/3pt jr cor,acap NORDISKA 4259
s.p.   (O392)

Uppfaren Ar Var Herre Krist
mix cor NORDISKA 5798 s.p.   (O393)

Ur Djupet Ropar Jag *Bibl
[Swed] SATB,acap GEHRMANS KRB 310   (O394)

OLSON, ROBERT G. (1913-   )
Christmas Haiku *Xmas
SATB oct LAWSON 51687 $.30   (O395)

OLSSON, OTTO EMMANUEL (1879-1964)
Ave Maris Stella *Op.40, hymn
7pt mix cor NORDISKA 4485 4490 s.p. see
from Sex Latinska Hymner   (O396)

Canticum Simeonis *Op.40, hymn
5pt mix cor,Bar solo NORDISKA 4485 4487
s.p. see from Sex Latinska Hymner   (O397)

Jesu Dulcis Memoria *Op.40, hymn
5pt mix cor,Bar solo NORDISKA 4485 4489
s.p. see from Sex Latinska Hymner   (O398)

Psalm 110 *see Rex Gloriose Martyrium

Psalm 120 *see Rex Gloriose Martyrium

Rex Gloriose Martyrium (Psalm 110) Op.40,
hymn
8pt mix cor NORDISKA 4485 4488 s.p. see
from Sex Latinska Hymner   (O399)
4pt mix cor NORDISKA 4485 4486 s.p. see
from Sex Latinska Hymner   (O400)

OLSSON, OTTO EMMANUEL (cont'd.)

6pt mix cor NORDISKA 4485 4491 s.p. see
from Sex Latinska Hymner   (O401)

Sex Latinska Hymner *see Ave Maris Stella,
Op.40; Canticum Simeonis, Op.40; Jesu
Dulcis Memoria, Op.40; Psalm 110, Op.40;
Psalm 120, Op.40; Rex Gloriose Martyrium,
Op.40   (O402)

OLTRASSI, GIUSEPPE
Assumpta Est *BVM
[Lat] 2 eq voices,org ZANIBON 2757 s.p.
        (O403)

Ave Maria
see CINQUE AVE MARIA

In Festo S. Ceciliae *ASD,Offer
[Lat] 2 eq voices,org ZANIBON 2668 s.p.
        (O404)

Ipsi Sum Desponsata
see Pro Vestitione

Laudate Dominum
[Lat] 2 eq voices,org ZANIBON 2716 s.p.
        (O405)

O Sacro Convivium
see Tre Mottetti Eucaristici

O Salutaris Hostia
see Tre Mottetti Eucaristici

Pro Vestitione *mot
[Lat] 2 eq voices,org ZANIBON 2735 s.p.
contains: Ipsi Sum Desponsata; Regnum
Mundi   (O406)

Quasi Stella *ASD,mot
[Lat] TB,org ZANIBON 2620 s.p.   (O407)

Regnum Mundi
see Pro Vestitione

Salve Regina
see CINQUE MOTECTA IN HON. B.V.M.
see CINQUE MOTECTA IN HON. B.V.M.

Tantum Ergo
see Tre Mottetti Eucaristici

Tre Mottetti Eucaristici *Commun,mot
[Lat] ZANIBON 2679 s.p.
contains: O Sacro Convivium (2 eq voices,
org); O Salutaris Hostia (2 eq voices);
Tantum Ergo (unis)   (O408)

OLY SZEP MA MINDEN see Lassus, Roland de
(Orlandus)

OLYMPIC HYMN see Linn, Robert

OM EN MANNISKA ICKE BLIVER FODD PA NYTT see
Nilsson, Torsten

OM GUDS ORD see Sorenson, Torsten

OM HIMMERIGES RIGE SA VILLE VI TALE see
Pederson, Mogens

OM I AREN UPPSTANDNA MED KRISTUS see Wikander,
David

OM KRISTI FODSEL see Eccard, Johannes, In Dulci
Jubilo

OMKRING DITT KORS, O JESUS KAR see Bach, Johann
Sebastian

OMNES ADORATE DOMINUM see Carissimi, Giacomo

OMNES AMICI MEI DERELIQUERUNT ME see Haydn,
(Johann) Michael

OMNES DE SABA see Gallus, Jacobus

OMNES DE SABA VENIENT see Gallus, Jacobus

OMNES GENERATIONES see Hovhaness, Alan

OMNES GENTES see Binkerd, [Gordon]

OMNES GENTES see Gabrieli, Giovanni

OMNES GENTES see Lully (Lulli), Jean-Baptiste

OMNES GENTES see Stein, Josef

OMNES GENTES PLAUDITE (from Anthology Of
Carols, An)
see Ave Maris Stella

OMNES GENTES PLAUDITE see Casini, Giovanni
Maria

OMNES GENTES, PLAUDITE see White

OMNES GENTES PLAUDITE MANIBUS see Tye,
Christopher

OMNIA VINCIT AMOR see Gallus, Jacobus

OMNIPOTENCE see Schubert, Franz (Peter)

OMNIPOTENCE, THE see Schubert, Franz (Peter)

OMNIPRESENCE see James, Allen

OMNIS PULCHRITUDO DOMINI see Palestrina,
Giovanni

ON A FAR AWAY HILL *Psntd
(Kirk) SATB oct PRO ART 2363 $.25   (O409)

ON A MORN ALL CRISP AND COLD *Xmas
(Johnson) SATB SCHMITT 7044 $.40   (O410)

ON A MORNING LONG AGO *Xmas,carol,Span
(Davis) 2pt wom cor oct SCHIRM.G 7355 $.25
        (O411)

ON A PALLET OF STRAW see Meyerowitz, Jan

ON BETHLEHEM HILL see Rowley, Alec

ON BETHLEHEM'S HILL *Xmas,carol,Aus
(Ehret, Walter) SA FRANK F-615 $.35   (O412)

ON CALVARY'S CROSS see Gillette

ON CALVARY'S HILL see Kvamme

ON CALVARY'S HILL see Wetzler, Robert

ON CHRIST THE SOLID ROCK I STAND see Hustad,
Donald P.

ON CHRISTMAS DAY *Xmas
(Sargent) SSAATTBB,acap (med) OXFORD 43.093
$.30   (O413)

ON CHRISTMAS DAY see Davenport, G.

ON CHRISTMAS DAY see Larson, Earl R.

ON CHRISTMAS DAY see Nyquist

ON CHRISTMAS DAY see Strickland, Lily Teresa

ON CHRISTMAS DAY see Veitch, William.

ON CHRISTMAS EVE see Osborne

ON CHRISTMAS EVE see Pfust

ON CHRISTMAS MORN THE CHRIST WAS BORN *Xmas,It
(Ehret) SSA MARKS 4355 $.25   (O414)

ON CHRISTMAS NIGHT *Xmas,cant/carol/folk/pop,
Eng
(Ehret) SAB oct VOLKWEIN VB230 $.25   (O415)
(Ehret) SA/SSA/unis oct VOLKWEIN VB231 $.25
        (O416)
(Grams, W.P.) SATB,kbd (med easy) oct
CONCORDIA 98-1760 $.25   (O417)
(Stone) SATB oct PRO ART 1345 $.25   (O418)
(Stone) SSA oct PRO ART 1787 $.30   (O419)
(Vaughn Williams, Ralph) SATB/unis,pno GALAXY
s.p. see also Eight Traditional Carols
        (O420)
(Wiley) unis/2pt/SATB,opt bvl,perc,gtr oct
PRO ART 1159, IPA $1.00   (O421)

ON CHRISTMAS NIGHT see Arnatt, Ronald

ON CHRISTMAS NIGHT see Ehret, Walter

ON CHRISTMAS NIGHT see Hutton

ON CHRISTMAS NIGHT see Luvaas

ON CHRISTMAS NIGHT see Merritt, Charles

ON CHRISTMAS NIGHT see Vaughan Williams, Ralph

ON CHRISTMAS NIGHT see Wiley

ON CHRISTMAS NIGHT ALL CHRISTIANS SING *Xmas,
carol,Eng
(Powell, R.J.) unis,fl (easy) oct CONCORDIA
98-2106 $.30   (O422)

ON CHRISTMAS NIGHT ALL CHRISTIANS SING see
Powell

ON DECEMBER TWENTY-FIFTH see Maekelberghe,
August [R.]

ON EAGLES' WINGS
2pt CHAPPELL 0022699-352 $.40   (O423)

ON EASTER MORN see Perrine, R.

ON EASTER MORN, ERE BREAK OF DAY (from Piae
Cantiones)
see Four Easter Carols

ON EASTERN MORN *Easter,Scot
(Shaw; Parker) 4pt mix cor,acap oct SCHIRM.G
9958 $.25   (O424)

ON GOD, AND NOT ON HUMAN TRUST see Pachelbel

ON GOD, AND NOT ON HUMAN TRUST see Pachelbel,
Johann

ON GREAT LONE HILLS see Sibelius, Jean

ON HIS MIGHT see Goode, Jack C.

ON HOLY NIGHT see Adam, Adolphe-Charles,
Cantique De Noel

ON JESUS ALL MY LOVE IS CAST see Bach, Johann
Sebastian, Wie Bin Ich Doch So Herzlich
Froh

ON JORDAN'S BANKS see Willing

ON JORDAN'S STORMY BANKS I STAND see Williams

ON LIFE'S HIGHWAY see Brown

ON LOVE ALONE see Nelson, Jerry

ON MARY'S HEART HER BABY LAY see Durston, D.

ON MY JOURNEY HOME see Siegmeister, Elie

ON MY WAY TO THE HILL see Friend

ON THAT CHRISTMASTIDE IN THE LONG AGO see
Reinecke, Carl

ON THAT FIRST BRIGHT EASTER DAY see Lang, C.
Tilghman

ON THAT FIRST CHRISTMAS MORNING see Brown, Mary
Helen

ON THAT HOLY CHRISTMAS NIGHT see Karvonen

ON THAT HOLY MIDNIGHT see Pablo, Juan

ON THAT SABBATH MORN see Dett

ON THE BANKS OF JORDAN *spir
(Ehret) SATB oct SPRATT 132 $.30   (O425)

ON THE BIRTHDAY OF OUR LORD see Praetorius,
Michael, In Natali Domini

ON THE BIRTHDAY OF THE LORD *Xmas,carol
oct HART s.p.   (O426)

ON THE BIRTHDAY OF THE LORD see Peek, Richard

ON THE CHRISTMAS MORNING see Ford, Virgil T.

ON THE CROSS OF CALVARY see Gerig

ON THE DAY WHEN GOD WAS BORN
see Two Polish Carols

ON THE FIRST DAY OF THE WEEK see Gillette

ON THE FIRST THANKSGIVING DAY
see Three Thanksgiving Hymns

ON THE GALLOWS TREE see Engel, [A. Lehman]

ON THE HILL DIED CHRIST THE SAVIOUR see
Sanjuan, Pedro, En El Monte Murio Christo

ON THE LAND AND ON THE SEA see Meyerowitz, Jan

ON THE MORNING OF CHRIST'S NATIVITY see
McCormick

ON THE MORNING OF CHRIST'S NATIVITY see McKay

ON THE MOUNT OF OLIVE GROVES see Hourdeaux

ON THE MOUNT OF OLIVES see Bruckner, Anton, In
Monte Oliveti

ON THE MOUNT OF OLIVES see Leo, Leonardo, In
Monte Oliveti

ON THE MOUNT OF OLIVES see Martini, Padre, In
Monte Oliveti

ON THE MOUNTAINSIDE *anthem/carol,Aus
(Christiansen, Paul) SATB (easy) oct AUGSBURG
0412 $.20   (O427)

ON THE OTHER SIDE OF TIME see Johnston

ON THE PASSION OF CHRIST see Williams, David H.

ON THE RESURRECTION see Williams, David H.

ON THE RESURRECTION OF CHRIST see Montgomery,
Bruce

ON THE VERY FIRST CHRISTMAS MORNING *carol,US
(Ehret) SA,opt ob MARKS 4410 $.25   (O428)
(Ehret) SSA,opt ob MARKS 4356 $.30   (O429)
(Ehret) SAB,opt ob MARKS 4456 $.25   (O430)
(Ehret) SATB,opt ob MARKS 4525 $.25   (O431)

ON THE WAY TO BETHLEHEM see Beck

ON THE WAY TO JERUSALEM see Maunder, J.H.

ON THE WOOD HIS ARMS ARE STRETCHED see
Gumpeltzhaimer, Adam

ON THE WOOD HIS ARMS ARE STRETCHED see Vulpius,
Melchior

ON THEE MORTAL EYES WAIT, LORD see Bach, Johann
Sebastian, Aller Augen Warten, Herr

ON THEM HATH LIGHT SHINED see Newbury, Kent A.

ON THIS CHRISTMAS MORNING *Xmas
(Kinsman, F.) SSA oct PRESSER MC467 $.30
        (O432)

ON THIS DAY see Byrd, William, Hodie Beata
Virgo

ON THIS DAY see Nanini (Nanino), Giovanni
Bernardino, Hodie Nobis Caelorum Rex

ON THIS DAY see Pitfield, Thomas Baron

ON THIS DAY CHRIST IS BORN see Clerambault,
Louis Nicolas, Hodie Christus Natus Est

ON THIS DAY CHRIST IS BORN see Monteverdi,
Claudio, Hodie Christus Natus Est

ON THIS DAY CHRIST WAS BORN see Skolnik, Walter

ON THIS DAY EARTH SHALL RING see Johnson,
Marlowe

ON THIS DAY, EARTH SHALL RING see Stewart

ON THIS DAY EARTH SHALL SING see Petri, T.

ON THIS DAY, SAINT JOSEPH BROUGHT US see
Guerrero, Francisco, Hoy, Jose, Se Os Da En
El Suelo

ON THIS DAY THE CHRIST APPEARS see Lassus,
Roland de (Orlandus), Hodie Apparuit

ON THIS DAY THE LORD WAS BORN see Luptin, H.J.

ON THIS EVE IN COLD DECEMBER *Xmas,carol,Fr
(Ehret, Walter) SA FRANK F-621 $.35   (O433)

ON THIS FAIR, HOLY MORN see Richardson, John

ON THIS GOOD CHRISTMAS MORN see Cain, Noble

ON THIS HAPPY CHRISTMAS DAY *Xmas
(Kozinski, D.) 2pt treb cor oct PRESSER
312-40381 $.25   (O434)

ON THIS HOLY NIGHT see Cavalieri

ON TOP OF THE HILL see Bizet, Georges

ON TOUR WITH THE KOREAN ORPHAN CHOIR *CCU
2pt jr cor voc sc WORD 15018 $1.25   (O435)

ON WINGS OF LIVING RADIANCE see Schutz,
Heinrich

ON WINGS OF SONG THE ANGELS CAME see
Mendelssohn-Bartholdy, Felix

ONCE A FAIR MAIDEN see Niles, John Jacob

ONCE AGAIN THE BELLS ARE RINGING
SATB CHAPPELL 0018200-358 $.40   (O436)

ONCE FOR US A BOY WAS BORN *Xmas
(Ellsworth) SATB SCHMITT SD6219 $.35   (O437)

ONCE FOR US A CHILD see Curry, L.

ONCE HE CAME IN BLESSING see Strube, Adolf

ONCE HE CAME IN BLESSING see Wienhorst, Richard

ONCE I HAD HOPED FOR THEE see Monte, de, Mentre Sperai Da Te

ONCE I SANG see Sateren, Leland Bernhard

ONCE IN A MANGER LOWLY see Noe, J.T.

ONCE IN BETHLEHEM OF JUDAH *Xmas,carol
oct HART s.p.   (O438)

ONCE: IN MEMORIAM MARTIN LUTHER KING, JR. see Beveridge, Thomas G.

ONCE IN ROYAL DAVID'S CITY *Xmas
(Fraser) SATB,acap oct FOX PS152 $.25   (O439)
(Grieb) jr cor&sr cor oct SCHIRM.G 10827 $.30
                                          (O440)

ONCE IN ROYAL DAVID'S CITY see Alexander, Johann

ONCE IN ROYAL DAVID'S CITY see Cooper

ONCE IN ROYAL DAVID'S CITY see Gauntlett, [Henry John]

ONCE IN ROYAL DAVID'S CITY see Hughes

ONCE IN ROYAL DAVID'S CITY see Lewis, J.

ONCE IN ROYAL DAVID'S CITY see Lundquist

ONCE IN ROYAL DAVID'S CITY see Warner, Richard

ONCE MARY WOULD GO WANDERING *carol
SATB (med) oct OXFORD 08.090 $.15   (O441)

ONCE MORE, MY SOUL see Elkins

ONCE THERE CAME TO EARTH see Dobbs, J.P.B.

ONCE THROUGH A WOODLAND MARY WALKED see Bauernfiend, Hans, Maria Durch Ein Dornwald Ging

ONCE TO EVERY MAN AND NATION see Hornibrook

ONCE TO EVERY MAN AND NATION see Kjelson

ONCE TO EVERY MAN AND NATION see Mead

ONCE TO EVERY MAN AND NATION see Mueller, Carl F.

ONCE TO EVERY MAN AND NATION see Ohl, [Jeremiah Franklin]

ONCE TO EVERY MAN AND NATION see Williams

ONCE TO EVERY MAN AND NATION see York, D.

ONCE TO EV'RY MAN AND NATION see Perdue-Davis, Vernon

ONCE TO JERUSALEM JESUS DID COME see Grime, William

ONCE UPON A STARLIT NIGHT see Brown, E. Bouldin

ONCQUES AMOUR see Merulo, Claudio

ONDERDONK
How Wondrous And Great
(Haydn-Colyar) SATB oct BELWIN 60812 $.40
                                          (O442)

ONE ABOVE ALL OTHERS
(Brandon) SAB,org oct SCHIRM.G 11447 $.25
                                          (O443)

ONE CHRISTMAS NIGHT *Xmas,carol,Eng
(Vaughn Williams, Ralph) SSAA,acap GALAXY
s.p.   (O444)

ONE DAY AT A TIME see Mc Call, Harlo

ONE EARLY EASTER MORNING see Marryott, Ralph E.

ONE FELLOWSHIP see James

ONE FOLD AND ONE SHEPHERD see Redmond

ONE FOLD, ONE SHEPHERD see Wollen, Russell

ONE GENERATION PASSETH see Thomas, Mansel

ONE GOD see Johnston

ONE GOD see Wilson

ONE HOLY CHURCH *Gen
(Butler) SATB SCHMITT 8038 $.30   (O445)

ONE HOLY CHURCH see Christiansen, Paul, Una Sancta

ONE HOLY NIGHT see Gilbert, J.R.

ONE HOLY NIGHT see Gilbert, Norman

ONE HUNDRED EIGHTY-FIVE FOUR PART CHORALES see Bach, Johann Sebastian

ONE HUNDRED ONE CHORALES HARMONIZED BY J.S. BACH see Bach, Johann Sebastian

ONE HUNDRED SIXTY-FIVE KANON *sac/sec,CC165L, canon
(Peter, J.) [Hung] 3pt (med diff) BUDAPEST
1052 s.p. contains sacred works by: Bardos,
L.; Schubert, Franz   (O446)

ONE HUNDREDTH PSALM, THE see Beverst

ONE HUNDREDTH PSALM, THE see Mueller, Carl F.

ONE IN CHRIST see Atkinson, Condit R.

ONE IN GOD see Hutson, Wihla

ONE IS FOR THE CHRIST CHILD see Eaton, John

ONE IS HOLY see Becker

ONE LIFE TO LIVE see Owens, Jimmy

ONE LITTLE TREE see Mattson

ONE MIDNIGHT LONG AGO see Kinsman

ONE MORE RIVER *spir
(Dexter, Harry) 2pt ENOCH TP269 s.p.   (O447)

ONE NATION, UNDER GOD see Kuykendall, F.

ONE NIGHT see Brown, Charles F.

ONE NIGHT IN BETHLEHEM see Goldsworthy, William Arthur

ONE NIGHT IN BETHLEHEM see Schroth

ONE SMALL CHILD see Meece, David

ONE SOLITARY LIFE see Bock, Fred

ONE STAR see Weaver

ONE STEP see Hoffman

ONE SWEETLY SOLEMN THOUGHT see Ambrose

ONE SWEETLY SOLEMN THOUGHT see Ambrose, R.S.

ONE THERE IS ABOVE ALL OTHERS see Berrggren

ONE THING HAVE I DESIRED see Howells, Herbert Norman

ONE THING HAVE I DESIRED see Schutz, Heinrich

ONE VIEW, LORD JESUS, OF THY PASSION see Gambold

ONE WAY see Hughes

ONE WINTER NIGHT see Austin

ONE WINT'RY NIGHT see Clark, K.

ONLY A MANGER see Jordan

ONLY A MANGER BED *Xmas,carol,Pol
(Ehret, Walter) SATB,opt inst oct WALTON 2529
$.30   (O448)

ONLY BEGOTTEN WORD OF GOD see Brown, A.G.Y.

ONLY-BEGOTTEN, WORD OF GOD see Casner, Myron D.

ONLY-BEGOTTEN, WORD OF GOD ETERNAL see Lovelace, Austin C.

ONLY BEGOTTEN WORD OF GOD ETERNAL see Wolff

ONLY-BEGOTTEN WORD OF GOD ETERNAL see Wood, James H.

ONLY BELIEVE see Rader

ONLY FOLLOW HIM see Roff, Joseph

ONLY JESUS see Latham, [William P.]

ONLY SON FROM HEAVEN, THE see Bach, Johann Sebastian

ONLY SON FROM HEAVEN, THE see Cruger, Johann

ONLY SON, THE see Grainger, Percy Aldridge

ONS IS GHEBOREN EEN KINDEKIJN see Badings, Henk

ONVERGANKLIJK LEVENSLICHT see Bach, Johann Sebastian

ONWARD CHRISTIAN SOLDIERS see Dressler, John

ONWARD, CHRISTIAN SOLDIERS see Hughes

ONWARD, CHRISTIAN SOLDIERS see Rasley

ONWARD CHRISTIAN SOLDIERS see Sullivan, Sir Arthur Seymour

ONWARD, CHRISTIAN SOLDIERS see Thompson

ONWARD FOR GOD AND MY COUNTRY see Williams

ONWARD WITH CHRIST see Felts

ONWARD YE SAINTS see Wetzler, Robert

ONZE VADER see Geraedts, Jaap

OOMES, P.J.
Benedictus
men cor sc ALSBACH&D s.p.   (O449)

OORT, H.C.V.
Christuskind
wom cor ALSBACH&D sc s.p., cor pts s.p. (O450)
Drie Kerstliederen
4pt wom cor,pno sc ALSBACH&D s.p. score and
choral parts separately published
contains: Kerstlied; Kerstnacht;
Kerstnacht   (O451)

Kerstlied
see Drie Kerstliederen
wom cor ALSBACH&D sc s.p., cor pts s.p. (O452)

Kerstnacht
see Drie Kerstliederen
see Drie Kerstliederen

Wie Op God Betrouwt
men cor ALSBACH&D sc s.p., cor pts s.p. (O453)

OOSTERZEE, CORNELIUS VAN (1863-1943)
Te Bethlehem
mix cor ALSBACH&D sc s.p., cor pts s.p. (O454)

OP MIN SJAEL! EN MORGEN KLAR see Bach, Johann Sebastian, Auf Mein Herz! Des Herren Tag

OPELLA NOVA (V, VI, VII) see Schein, Johann Hermann

OPELLA NOVA-PART 1 see Schein, Johann Hermann

OPEN MY EYES see Lorenz

OPEN MY EYES see Scott

OPEN MY EYES, THAT I MAY SEE see Hughes

OPEN MY EYES, THAT I MAY SEE see Lockwood, Normand

OPEN MY EYES, THAT I MAY SEE see Scott

OPEN MY HEART see Bach, Johann Sebastian

OPEN NOW THY GATES OF BEAUTY see Bach, Johann Sebastian

OPEN NOW THY GATES OF BEAUTY see Peninger

OPEN OUR EYES see Macfarlane, William Charles

OPEN OUR EYES see Pasquet, Jean

OPEN OUR EYES, O LORD
2pt CHAPPELL 0016287-352 $.40   (O455)
SSA CHAPPELL 0016287-354 $.40   (O456)
SATB CHAPPELL 0016287-358 $.40   (O457)

OPEN THE GATES OF THE TEMPLE see Knapp, Lavater

OPEN THOU MY LIPS see Ramseth, Ann

OPEN THY GATES see Harrison, Julius Allen Greenway

OPEN TO ME GATES OF JUSTICE see Buxtehude, Dietrich, Aperite Mihi Portas

OPEN TO ME THE GATES OF RIGHTEOUSNESS see Pinkham, Daniel

OPEN UP YOUR HEART see Belt, T.

OPEN WIDE, OH YE GATES see Howorth, Wayne

OPEN WIDE THE STABLE DOOR see Grime, William

OPEN YE THE GATES see Hughes, J.W.

OPENING LITANY AND 2ND ANTIPHON see Tchaikovsky, Piotr Ilyitch

OPENING SENTENCES, RESPONSES AND AMENS see Cronham

OPENING SENTENCES, RESPONSES AND AMENS, SET 1 see Kurth, Burton

OPENING SENTENCES, RESPONSES AND AMENS, SET 2 see Kurth, Burton

OPERA OMNIA VOL. I see Agricola, Alexander

OPERA OMNIA VOL. II see Agricola, Alexander

OPERA OMNIA VOL. III see Agricola, Alexander

OPERA OMNIA VOL. IV see Agricola, Alexander

OPERA OMNIA VOL. I see Arcadelt, Jacob

OPERA OMNIA VOL. X see Arcadelt, Jacob

OPERA OMNIA see Barbireau, Maitre Jacques

OPERA OMNIA VOL. I see Brassart, Johannes

OPERA OMNIA VOL. II see Brassart, Johannes

OPERA OMNIA VOL. I see Brumel, Antoine

OPERA OMNIA VOL. II see Brumel, Antoine

OPERA OMNIA VOL. III see Brumel, Antoine

OPERA OMNIA VOL. IV see Brumel, Antoine

OPERA OMNIA VOL. V see Brumel, Antoine

OPERA OMNIA VOL. VI see Brumel, Antoine

OPERA OMNIA VOL. I see Clemens, Jacobus

OPERA OMNIA VOL. II see Clemens, Jacobus

OPERA OMNIA VOL. III see Clemens, Jacobus

OPERA OMNIA VOL. IV see Clemens, Jacobus

OPERA OMNIA VOL. V see Clemens, Jacobus

OPERA OMNIA VOL. VI see Clemens, Jacobus

OPERA OMNIA VOL. VII see Clemens, Jacobus

OPERA OMNIA VOL. VIII see Clemens, Jacobus

OPERA OMNIA VOL. IX see Clemens, Jacobus

OPERA OMNIA VOL. XII see Clemens, Jacobus

OPERA OMNIA VOL. XIII see Clemens, Jacobus

OPERA OMNIA VOL. XIV see Clemens, Jacobus

OPERA OMNIA VOL. XV see Clemens, Jacobus

OPERA OMNIA VOL. XVI see Clemens, Jacobus

OPERA OMNIA VOL. XVII see Clemens, Jacobus

OPERA OMNIA VOL. XVIII see Clemens, Jacobus

OPERA OMNIA VOL. XIX see Clemens, Jacobus

OPERA OMNIA VOL. XX see Clemens, Jacobus

OPERA OMNIA VOL. I see Compere, [Louis]

OPERA OMNIA VOL. II see Compere, [Louis]

OPERA OMNIA VOL. III see Compere, [Louis]

OPERA OMNIA VOL. IV see Compere, [Louis]

OPERA OMNIA VOL. V see Compere, [Louis]

OPERA OMNIA VOL. I see De Silva, Andreas

OPERA OMNIA VOL. II see De Silva, Andreas

OPERA OMNIA TOM. I see Dufay, Guillaume

OPERA OMNIA TOM. II see Dufay, Guillaume

OPERA OMNIA TOM. III see Dufay, Guillaume

OPERA OMNIA TOM. IV see Dufay, Guillaume

OPERA OMNIA VOL. I see Festa, Costanza

OPERA OMNIA VOL. II see Festa, Costanza

OPERA OMNIA see Frye, Walter

OPERA OMNIA VOL. I see Gabrieli, Giovanni

OPERA OMNIA VOL. II see Gabrieli, Giovanni

OPERA OMNIA VOL. III see Gabrieli, Giovanni

OPERA OMNIA VOL. IV see Gabrieli, Giovanni

OPERA OMNIA VOL. V see Gabrieli, Giovanni

OPERA OMNIA VOL. II see Ghiselin-Verbonnet,
Johannes

OPERA OMNIA VOL. III see Ghiselin-Verbonnet,
Johannes

OPERA OMNIA VOL. IV see Ghiselin-Verbonnet,
Johannes

OPERA OMNIA VOL. I see Gombert, Nicolas

OPERA OMNIA VOL. II see Gombert, Nicolas

OPERA OMNIA VOL. III see Gombert, Nicolas

OPERA OMNIA VOL. IV see Gombert, Nicolas

OPERA OMNIA VOL. V see Gombert, Nicolas

OPERA OMNIA VOL. VI see Gombert, Nicolas

OPERA OMNIA VOL. VII see Gombert, Nicolas

OPERA OMNIA VOL. VIII see Gombert, Nicolas

OPERA OMNIA VOL. I *Mass/mot
(Minor, Andrew) cor AM.INST.MUS. $19.50
contains: Fevin, Antoine de, Benedictus
Dominus Deus; Mouton, Jean, Missa
Alleluia; Mouton, Jean, Missa Alma
Redemptoris Mater; Mouton, Jean, Missa
Benedictus Dominus Deus   (O458)

OPERA OMNIA VOL. II see Mouton, Jean

OPERA OMNIA VOL. III see Mouton, Jean

OPERA OMNIA VOL. I see Phinot, Dominique

OPERA OMNIA VOL. I see Pipelare, Mathaeus

OPERA OMNIA VOL. II see Pipelare, Mathaeus

OPERA OMNIA VOL. III see Pipelare, Mathaeus

OPERA OMNIA VOL. V see Regnart, Jacob

OPERA OMNIA VOL. I see Di Rore, Cipriano

OPERA OMNIA VOL. II see Di Rore, Cipriano

OPERA OMNIA VOL. VII see Di Rore, Cipriano

OPERA OMNIA VOL. I see Sermisy, Claude de

OPERA OMNIA VOL. II *see Gabrieli, Andrea,
Benedicam Dominum; Sermisy, Claude de,
Beatae Mariae Virginis; Sermisy, Claude de,
Benedicam Dominum; Sermisy, Claude de, Cara
La Vita Mia   (O459)

OPERA OMNIA VOL. II see Gabrieli, Andrea

OPERA OMNIA VOL. II see Sermisy, Claude de

OPERA OMNIA VOL. I see Verdelot, Phillippe

OPERA OMNIA VOL. II see Verdelot, Phillippe

OPERA OMNIA VOL. XI see Wert, Giaches de

OPERA OMNIA VOL. XIII; SECOND BOOK OF MOTETS
(1581) see Wert, Giaches de

OPERA OMNIA VOL. XVI see Wert, Giaches de

OPERA OMNIA VOL. I see Willaert, Adrian

OPERA OMNIA VOL. II see Willaert, Adrian

OPERA OMNIA VOL. III see Willaert, Adrian

OPERA OMNIA VOL. IV see Willaert, Adrian

OPERA OMNIA VOL. V see Willaert, Adrian

OPERA OMNIA VOL. VII see Willaert, Adrian

OPERA OMNIA VOL. VIII see Willaert, Adrian

OPERA OMNIA IV: PSALMI, ANTIPHOANE MARIANE,
ETC. see Victoria, Tomas Luis de

OPERA OMNIA I: MOTECTA, MISSARUM LIBER PRIMUS
see Victoria, Tomas Luis de

OPERA OMNIA II: CANTICA BVM VULGO MAGNIFICAT,
CANTICUM SEIMEONIS, MISSARUM LIBER SECUNDUS
see Victoria, Tomas Luis de

OPERA OMNIA III: HYMNI, OFFICIUM HEBDOMADAE
SANCTAE, MISSARUM LIBER TERTIUS see
Victoria, Tomas Luis de

OPERA OMNIA: LA MUSICA RELIGIOSA VOL. 4A see
Pergolesi, Giovanni Battista

OPERA OMNIA: LA MUSICA RELIGIOSA VOL. 4B see
Pergolesi, Giovanni Battista

OPERA OMNIA VOL. I see Ghiselin-Verbonnet,
Johannes

OPERA OMNIA VOL. I see Tinctoris, Johannes

OPIE, M.P.
Communion Hymn *Commun
4pt mix cor,acap oct SCHIRM.G 7370 $.25
(O460)

OPITZ
Awake, The Joyous Day Is Here (composed with
Bach)
(Gordon) SAB oct BELWIN 60531 $.30   (O461)
(Gordon) SATB oct BELWIN 60609   (O462)
(Gordon) SATB oct BELWIN 60609 $.30   (O463)
(Gordon) SAB oct BELWIN 60531 $.30   (O464)

OPLOFT DIG, DOR see Distler, Hugo, Macht Hoch
Die Tur

OPPSTANDEN ER VAR FRELSERMANN see Vulpius,
Melchior

OPRUNDET ER DEN SKONNE DAG see Bach, Johann
Sebastian, Erschienen Ist Der Herrlich Tag

OPUS FOR CONTEMPORARY DECISION see Nichols, Ted

OR COMBIEN EST see Clemens, Jacobus

OR PEUT BIEN DIRE ISRAEL MAINTENANT see
Goudimel, Claude

OR SOIT LOUE L'ETERNEL see Sweelinck, Jan
Pieterszoon

OR SUS, LOUEZ DIEU TOUT LE MONDE see Goudimel,
Claude

OR SUS, MON AME, EN CE BAS TERRITOIRE see Lupi
II, Didier

OR SUS, SERVITEURS see Sweelinck, Jan
Pieterszoon

OR SUS, SERVITEURS DU SEIGNEUR see Champion,
Thomas

OR SUS, SORTEZ BERGERS *Xmas,carol,16th cent
(Geveart, F.-A.) [Fr] 4pt mix cor,acap (med
easy) cor pts LEMOINE s.p. see from
Collection De Choeurs, dixieme Fascicule
(O465)

ORA PRO NOBIS see Isaac, Heinrich

ORA PRO NOBIS see Raphael, Gunther

ORAISON DOMENICALE see Caplet, Adrien

ORAISON DOMINICALE see Clergue, J.

ORAL ROBERTS PRESENTS *CC11L
(Carmichael, Ralph) SATB voc sc WORD 30035
$1.95   (O466)

ORATE FRATRES see Berthier, P.

ORATIO NOCTURNA see Strohbach, Siegfried

ORATIO SANCTI AUGUSTINI "SPIRA IN ME" see
Beckerath, Alfred von

ORATORIO see Aperghis, Georges

ORATORIO DE NOEL see Bach, Johann Sebastian,
Weihnachtsoratorium

ORATORIO DE NOEL see Le Sueur, [Jean Francois]

ORATORIO DE NOEL see Saint-Saens, Camille

ORATORIO DELLA PASSIONE see Perti, Giacomo
Antonio

ORATORIO DI NATALE see Bach, Johann Sebastian

ORATORIUM FESTO PASCHALI see Bach, Johann
Sebastian, Osteroratorium

ORD, B.
Adam Lay Ybounden
SATB BELWIN AP 160 $.25   (O467)

ORDERING OF MOSES, THE see Dett, Robert
Nathaniel

ORDET VORDET KOTT see Malmfors, Ake

ORDINARIUM MISSAE see Nilsson, Torsten

ORDNUNG EINER CHRISTVESPER see Franck, Melchior

OREMUS PRO ANTISTITE see Baroni, Giovanni

OREMUS PRO ANTISTITE see Bottazzo, Luigi

OREMUS PRO PONTIFICE see Liszt, Franz

OREMUS PRO PONTIFICE see Ravanello, Oreste

OREMUS PRO PONTIFICE see Schmitt, Florent

OREMUS PRO PONTIFICI see Fabiani, Angelo

ORES QUE JE SUIS DISPOS see Lassus, Roland de
(Orlandus)

ORFF, CARL (1895-   )
Cantatas On Texts By Franz Werfel *see Der
Gute Mensch, "Noble Man, The"; Fremde
Sind Wir, "Strangers Are We"; Veni
Creator Spiritus   (O468)

Cantus-Firmus-Satze *CC10L
[Ger/Lat] 2-4pt SCHOTT 4454 s.p. (O469)

Concenti Di Voci *sac/sec
[Lat] SCHOTT s.p.
contains: Laudes Creaturarum (SSSATTTB);
Sirmio, Tria Catulli Carmina (SATB);
Sunt Lacrimae Rerum (men cor)   (O470)

Der Gute Mensch *cant
"Noble Man, The" [Ger/Eng] SSAATTBB,2-3pno,
perc voc sc SCHOTT 6021 s.p., ipa see
from Cantatas On Texts By Franz Werfel
(O471)

Die Sanger Der Vorwelt *hymn
[Ger] 6pt,bvl,harp,perc,2pno sc SCHOTT 4699
s.p., ipa, voc sc SCHOTT 4367 s.p., ipa,
cor pts SCHOTT 4367 s.p., ipa   (O472)

ORFF, CARL (cont'd.)
Fremde Sind Wir *cant
"Strangers Are We" [Ger/Eng] SATB,2pno voc
sc SCHOTT 6022 s.p., ipa see from
Cantatas On Texts By Franz Werfel (O473)

Laudes Creaturarum
see Concenti Di Voci

Noble Man, The *see Der Gute Mensch

Sirmio, Tria Catulli Carmina
see Concenti Di Voci

Sonnengesang Des Heiligen Franziskus:
Incipiunt Laudes Creaturarum
[Lat] SSSA SCHOTT s.p.   (O474)
[Lat] TTTB SCHOTT s.p.   (O475)

Strangers Are We *see Fremde Sind Wir

Sunt Lacrimae Rerum
see Concenti Di Voci
[Lat] TTBBBB,TBB soli SCHOTT s.p. (O476)

Veni Creator Spiritus *cant
[Ger/Eng] mix cor,3pno,perc voc sc SCHOTT
6020 s.p., ipa see from Cantatas On Texts
By Franz Werfel   (O477)

Vom Fruhjahr, Oltank Und Vom Fliegen *cant
[Ger/Eng] mix cor,3pno,perc sc SCHOTT 6023
s.p., ipa, cor pts SCHOTT 6023 s.p., ipa
(O478)

ORGAD, BEN-ZION
Cantata 2 *see Isaiah's Vision

Isaiah's Vision (Cantata 2) Bibl/liturg,Jew
SATB oct PRESSER MC216 $1.50   (O479)

O Lord Our Lord (Psalm 8) mot,Heb
[Eng/Heb] TTB,acap cor pts HEINRICH. s.p.
(O480)
TTB,acap ISRAELI 304 s.p.   (O481)

Psalm 8 *see O Lord Our Lord

Story Of The Spies *liturg,Heb
SATB oct PRESSER MC188 $2.00   (O482)

ORGAN SCORE ANTHEMS [VOL. 1] see Sweney, J.

ORGAN SCORE ANTHEMS [VOL. 2] see Sweney, J.

ORHEIM, OLAV
Halleluja Og Koral
[Norw] mix cor LYCHE 36 s.p.   (O483)

ORIETUR STELLA see Gallus, Jacobus

ORJALA
God Is In Every Tomorrow
(Whitman) SATB oct LILLENAS AN-2322 $.30
(O484)

ORLAND, HENRY
Christmas Candlelight Procession, A *Xmas
SATB,orch sc SEESAW $16.00   (O485)

Christmas Legend *Xmas
SATB,orch sc SEESAW $12.00   (O486)

ORLANDO
Nonna
see Orlando, Pastorale

Pastorale
2pt,pno RICORDI-ENG 97203 s.p. contains
also: Nonna; Te Deum   (O487)

Te Deum
see Orlando, Pastorale

ORLEANS, ILO
Within Thy Light (composed with Gordon)
SATB WARNER WB-169 $.35   (O488)

Woman Of Valor, A (composed with Goldman,
Maurice)
SATB CRITERION $.50   (O489)

ORR, ROBIN (1909-   )
Come And Let Yourselves Be Built *Ded,Bibl
SATB (med diff) oct OXFORD 42.859 $.50
(O490)

I Was Glad *mot
SATB,acap PETERS H537 $.40   (O491)

Magnificat And Nunc Dimittis *Magnif/Nunc
SATB (easy) oct OXFORD   (O492)

Make A Joyful Noise *anthem
SA oct OXFORD 44.080 $.45   (O493)

Psalm 125 *see They That Put Their Trust In
The Lord

Sing Aloud Unto God *anthem
mix cor oct OXFORD 42.347 $.50   (O494)

They That Put Their Trust In The Lord (Psalm
125) ASD/Gen
SATB,acap (med) oct OXFORD 43.297 $.30
(O495)

ORTIZ
Pereat Dies *mot,16th cent
[Lat] 5pt mix cor,acap UNION ESP. 19348
s.p.   (O496)

ORTIZ, DIEGO (ca. 1525- ?)
Siehe, Erschienen Ist Der Herr *mot
(Heilmann) SATB HANSSLER 1.111 s.p. (O497)

ORTLIP, STEPHEN
At Pentecost *Gen/Whitsun
4pt mix cor,org oct SCHIRM.G 10580 $.25
(O498)

ORTON, IRV
Just One Day At A Time
(Stickles) 4pt mix cor,ST soli oct SCHIRM.G
10546 $.30   (O499)
(Stickles) 2pt boy cor/2pt wom cor/2pt men
cor/2pt mix cor oct SCHIRM.G 10549 (O500)
(Stickles) 3pt wom cor,S solo oct SCHIRM.G
10548 $.20   (O501)
(Stickles) 4pt men cor,ST soli oct SCHIRM.G
10547 $.20   (O502)

ORY, DAVID
  Yerushalayim *Heb
    SATB,A solo,orch voc sc ISRAELI 333 s.p.
                                                    (O503)

OS IUSTI MEDITABITUR see Gorczycki, Gregor
  Gervasius

OS JUSTI see Bruckner, Anton

OS JUSTI MEDITABITUR SAPIENTIAM see Bruckner,
  Anton

OSANNA see Beck, John Ness

OSANNA see London, Edwin

OSANNA O SIGNORE see Arnaldi, Antonio

OSBORNE
  Early One Morning *Xmas
    SATB,acap PETERS 6241 $.25   (O504)

  O Lord Thou Art My God And King
    SAB THOMP.G G-564 s.p.   (O505)

  On Christmas Eve *Xmas
    SATB,acap PETERS 6242 $.25   (O506)

OSBORNE, HAYWARD
  Father, Forgive Them *CC7U,folk
    cmplt ed WEINBERGER s.p.   (O507)

  Lord Of The Harvest *CC5U,Harv/Thanks,hymn
    cong,pno/org cmplt ed WEINBERGER s.p.
                                                    (O508)

OSBORNE, W.
  Come, O Come, My Life's Delight
    SATB,acap oct PRESSER 312-40241 $.30 (O509)

OSCARSON, GUN *Agnus
  Agnus Dei *Agnus
    [Swed] SATB,acap GEHRMANS KRB 280 see from
    LAT   (O510)

OSCULETUR ME see Palestrina, Giovanni

OSER, H.
  Hymne
    [Ger] mix cor,acap (easy) HUG s.p.   (O511)

OSIANDER, LUCAS (1534-1604)
  Come O Holy Ghost, God And Lord *see Komm,
    Heiliger Geist, Herre Gott

  Gott Der Vater Wohn Uns Bei
    see Brassicanus, Johannes, Gott Vater,
    Herr, Wir Danken Dir

  Herr, Wie Du Willst, So Schicks Mit Mir
    see Eccard, Johannes, Herr, Wie Du Willst,
    So Schicks Mit Mir

  Komm, Heiliger Geist, Herre Gott
    "Come O Holy Ghost, God And Lord" see
    Schutz, Heinrich, Psalm 121

OSS AR FODD IMMANUEL see Thyrestam, Gunnar

OSSEWAARDE, JACK
  Carol Of The Stork *Xmas,carol
    SATB,S solo oct GRAY GCMR 3211 $.35 (O512)

  Draw Us In The Spirit's Tether
    SATB oct GRAY GCMR 2476 $.30   (O513)

  Paean Of Praise
    SATB oct GRAY GCMR 2886 $.30   (O514)

OSTENDE NOBIS see Radulescu, Michael

OSTER-DIALOG see Schindler, Walter

OSTER-ORATORIUM see Constantinescu, Paul

OSTER-ORATORIUM see Schindler, Walter

OSTERC, S.
  Magnificat *Magnif
    [Lat] voc sc UNIVER. 10510 $5.10   (O515)

OSTERCHORE see Weinreich, Waltraut

OSTERGESANG see Eccard, Johannes

OSTERGESANG see Franck, [Johann Wolfgang]

OSTERGESCHICHTE see Barbe, Helmut

OSTERHALLELUJA (DER HERR IST WAHRHAFTIG) see
  Berchem, Jachet

OSTERHYMNE see Kranz, Albert

OSTERHYMNE see Pestalozza, Heinrich

OSTERKANTATE see Kukuck, Felicitas

OSTERKANTATE NACH WORTEN VON K. MULLER-OSTEN
  see Schwartz, Gerhard von

OSTERLIED see Feyhl, J.

OSTERLIED see Liebleitner, K.

OSTERMESSE see Galliculus, Johann

OSTERMESSE see Genzmer, Harald

OSTERMESSE see Stoltzer, Thomas

OSTERMORGEN see Hoffmann, Ernst Theodor Amadeus

OSTERMORGENGLOCKENKLANG see Mendelssohn, Arnold

OSTERMOTETTE see Reger, Max

OSTERMOTETTE see Wenzel, Eberhard

OSTERMUSIK see Leu, Ferd. Oscar

OSTERN see Bruckner, Anton

OSTERN see Tittel, Ernst

OSTERORATORIUM see Bach, Johann Sebastian

OSTERORATORIUM see Degen, Helmut

OSTERPSALM see Fehrmann, Paul

OSTERREICHISCHE KIRCHENMUSIK *see Tantum Ergo,
    Teil 1 Und 2; Tantum Ergo, Teil 3;
    Albrechtsberger, Johann Georg, Messe In Es-
    Dur; Albrechtsberger, Johann Georg, Messe
    In F-Dur; Eybler, Joseph, Dies
    Sanctificatus, Tui Sunt Coeli; Haydn,
    (Johann) Michael, Missa Sanctae Crucis In
    A-Moll, "Kreuzmesse"; Haydn, (Johann)
    Michael, Te Deum; Herbeck, Johann Franz
    von, Pueri Concinite; Herbeck, Johann Franz
    von, Redemptor Nobis; Mozart, Wolfgang
    Amadeus, Messa In C-Dur, "Missa Longa",
    K.262   (O516)

OSTERREICHISCHE KIRCHENMUSIK see
  Albrechtsberger, Johann Georg

OSTERREICHISCHE KIRCHENMUSIK see Eybler, Joseph

OSTERREICHISCHE KIRCHENMUSIK see Haydn,
  (Johann) Michael

OSTERREICHISCHE KIRCHENMUSIK see Herbeck,
  Johann Franz von

OSTERREICHISCHE KIRCHENMUSIK see Mozart,
  Wolfgang Amadeus

OSTERRUF see Schindler, Walter

OSTERSEQUENZ see Weismann, Wilhelm

OSTLING
  Hela Varlden Frojdes Herran
    [Swed] LUNDQUIST 37 s.p.   (O517)

OSTROW
  Angelus, The *see Kammenoi

OT EVSZAZDA KORUSA *sac/sec,CC118L
    (Forrai, M.) [Hung] SSTB (med diff) BUDAPEST
    1075 s.p. contains sacred works by: Haydn,
    F.J.; Handel, G.F.; Schein, Heinrich (O518)

OTHEGRAVEN, AUGUST J. VON (1864-1946)
  Advent *Op.70, Adv,cant/folk
    men cor,S solo,org,opt 2trp&3trom&timp (med
    diff) LEUCKART s.p., ipr   (O519)

  Lob Gottes *Op.43,No.3
    men cor,org/orch (med) LEUCKART s.p., ipr
                                                    (O520)

OTHER NIGHT, THE *Xmas,carol,Eng
    SSA ALLANS 344 s.p.   (O521)
    SATB ALLANS 329 s.p.   (O522)

OTHER NIGHT, THE see Hunt, Reginald

OTHER NIGHT, THE see This Enders Nyzgt

OTHERS see Shields, Mc Edward

OTHMAYR, KASPAR (1515-1553)
  Erbe Deutscher Musik: Vol. 16 *CCU
    (Albrecht, Hans) cor,org cloth,fac ed
    PETERS $20.00   (O523)

  Erbe Deutscher Musik: Vol. 26 *CCU
    (Albrecht, Hans) cor,org cloth,fac ed
    PETERS $20.00   (O524)

  Es Steht Ein Lind In Jenem Tal
    SATB HANSSLER 6.2181 s.p. contains also:
    Lassus, Roland de (Orlandus); Am Morgen
                                                    (O525)

  Fra Himlen Hojt Kom Bucskab Her *Xmas,17th
    cent
    (Larsen, Jens Peter) [Dan] SATB (contains
    also: Hassler, Hans Leo, Fra Himlen Hojt
    Kom Budskab Her; Gumpeltzhaimer, Adam,
    Fra Himlen Hojt Kom Budskab Her) HANSEN-
    DEN 207 s.p. see also JULESANGE   (O526)

  Geistliche Lieder *CC7L,Gen
    (Ameln, Konrad) [Ger] SATB,acap (med easy)
    BAREN. BA 834 sc s.p., cor pts s.p.   (O527)

  Geistliche Zwiegesange, 32 Bicinien *CC32U,
    Gen
    (Lipphardt, Walther) [Ger] 2 eq voices/2pt
    mix cor,acap (med) BAREN. BA 1933 $2.25
                                                    (O528)

  Lord, As Thou Wilt, Deal Thou With Me
    *Easter
    SATB,acap oct PRESSER 312-40159 $.30 (O529)

  O Mensch, Bewein Dein Sunde Gross (from
    Matthaus-Passion)
    SATB HANSSLER 6.117 s.p.   (O530)

  Verleih Uns Frieden Gnadiglich *mot
    (Roller) SATB HANSSLER 1.325 s.p.   (O531)

  Wer In Dem Schutz Des Hochsten Ist *mot
    (Roller) SATB HANSSLER 1.324 s.p.   (O532)

OTIS
  Alleluia, Christ Is Risen! *Easter
    SATB SCHMITT 1768 $.25   (O533)

OTT, J.
  Mass Of Textures, A *Mass
    SATB BOURNE rental   (O534)

  Sanctus (from Mass Of Textures, A) Sanctus
    SATB oct BOURNE 938 $.40   (O535)

OTTE KORALUDSAETTELSER see Bach, Johann
  Sebastian

OTTE KORALUDSAETTELSER see Bach, Johann
  Sebastian

OTTE SALMER OG SANGE see Aagaard, Thomas

OTTESEN, [MILTON F.]
  Christmas Eve *Xmas
    SAB oct PRO ART 2394 $.30   (O536)
    SATB oct PRO ART 2406 $.25   (O537)

OTTESON
  Miracle Of Christmas, The *Xmas,cant
    SATB,narrator PRO ART 1135 $1.00   (O538)

  Miracle Of Hanukkah, The *Hanakkah
    SAB,opt narrator oct PRO ART 2503 $.25
                                                    (O539)

OTTO CANONI ANTICHI see Tocchi, [Gian-Luca]

OTTO CANTI AL S. CUOR DI GESU *CC8U
    [Lat] 1-2 eq voices,org ZANIBON 2770 s.p.
    contains works by: Ascenso, A.; Geri, G.;
    Chiesa, F.; Magri, P.; Moioli, R.;
    Vittadini, F.; Volpi, E.   (O540)

OTTO CANTI MARIANI *CC8U,BVM
    [Lat] unis&2 eq voices&4pt mix cor,org
    ZANIBON 2756 s.p. contains works by:
    Bottigliero; Amatucci; Bottazzo; Coronaro;
    Fabiani; Mauri; Zavarise   (O541)

OTTO CANTI PER LA S. COMUNIONE see Mariani,
  Eligio

OTTO CANTICA EUCARISTICA see Bottazzo, Luigi

OTTO INNI *CC8L,Greg/hymn
    [Lat] unis,org ZANIBON 1889 s.p. contains
    works by: Bottazzo, L.; Ravanello, O.
                                                    (O542)

OTTO TANTUM ERGO see Bottazzo, Luigi

OU COUREZ-VOUS? see Moineau, G.

OU S'EN VONT CES GAIS BERGERS
  see Five French Noels

OUCHTERLONY, DAVID
  God Is Our Refuge And Strength (Psalm 46)
    anthem/Bibl
    unis&cong oct HARRIS HC1001   (O543)

  Let Them That Say They Love The Lord *anthem
    SATB,org oct HARRIS HC4036 $.35   (O544)

  O Food Of Men Wayfaring *Commun,anthem
    SATB,acap oct HARRIS HC4035 $.35   (O545)

  Praise God! *anthem/Bibl
    SATB,org/orch oct HARRIS HC4023 $.60   (O546)

  Psalm 46 *see God Is Our Refuge And Strength

  There Came A Star *Xmas,anthem
    SATB,S solo,drums oct HARRIS HC4025 $.40
                                                    (O547)
    SA,S solo,drums oct HARRIS HC2005 $.30
                                                    (O548)

  Trust In The Lord And Do Good
    SATB THOMP.G G-562 s.p.   (O549)

OUD KERSTLIED see Pothast, Ed.

OUD KERSTLIEDEKE see Santen, B. Th.

OUR ASSURANCE IS IN HEAVEN see Franck,
  Melchior, Unser Wandel Ist Im Himmel

OUR BLESSED SAVIOR see Emig, Lois

OUR BLESSED SAVIOR SEVEN TIMES SPOKE see
  Schein, Johann Hermann

OUR BLEST REDEEMER see Fraser

OUR BLEST REDEEMER see Wadely, F.W.

OUR BLEST REDEEMER ERE HE BREATHED see White,
  John

OUR CHRIST HAS RISEN *Easter
    SATB/SAB BIG3 $.25   (O550)

OUR COAL AND OIL SONG see Grime, William

OUR DAILY BREAD see Grime, William

OUR DAILY BREAD see Johnson

OUR DAILY BREAD see Lewis

OUR DAY OF PRAISE IS DONE see Anderson,
  [William H.]

OUR DAYS ARE AS A SHADOW see Bach, Johann
  (Hans)

OUR DEDICATION PRAYER see Harris

OUR ETERNAL KING see Madden

OUR FATHER see Bortniansky, Dimitri
  Stepanovitch, Pater Noster

OUR FATHER see Diemente, Edward

OUR FATHER see Dinerstein, N.

OUR FATHER see Elaine, Sister M. (Gentemann)

OUR FATHER see Gallus, Jacobus, Pater Noster

OUR FATHER see Gretchaninov, Alexander
  Tikhonovitch

OUR FATHER see Henderson, Ruth Watson, Pater
  Noster

OUR FATHER see Jillett, David

OUR FATHER see Levy, Marvin David

OUR FATHER see Peeters, Flor, Pater Noster

OUR FATHER see Rohlig, Harald

OUR FATHER see Santucci, Pellegrino, Padre
  Nostro

OUR FATHER see Schutz, Heinrich, Das Vaterunser

OUR FATHER see Tchaikovsky, Piotr Ilyitch,
  Pater Noster

OUR FATHER BY WHOSE NAME see Becker, J.

OUR FATHER, BY WHOSE SERVANTS *Ded/Gen
    (Coleman, Henry) SATB (easy) oct OXFORD $.30
                                                    (O551)

OUR FATHER, BY WHOSE SERVANTS see Bristol, L.

OUR FATHER, HELP US see Hastings

OUR FATHER, THOU IN HEAVEN ABOVE *anthem
    (Distler, Hugo) SSA (easy) oct AUGSBURG 1449
    $.20   (O552)

OUR FATHER, THOU IN HEAVEN ABOVE see Bach, Johann Sebastian

OUR FATHER, THOU IN HEAVEN ABOVE see Franck, Melchior, Vater Unser In Himmelreich

OUR FATHER, THOU IN HEAVEN ABOVE see Telemann, Georg Philipp

OUR FATHER, THOU IN HEAV'N ABOVE see Lassus, Roland de (Orlandus)

OUR FATHER THRONED IN HEAVEN HIGH see Praetorius, Michael, Vater Unser In Himmelreich

OUR FATHER WHICH ART IN HEAVEN see Schutz, Heinrich, Vater Unser, Der Du Bist Im Himmel

OUR FATHER WHO ART IN HEAVEN see Cain, Noble

OUR FATHER WHO ART IN HEAVEN see Glarum, L. Stanley

OUR FATHER, WHO ART IN HEAVEN see Liszt, Franz, Pater Noster

OUR FATHER, WHO ART IN HEAVEN see Lockwood

OUR FATHER'S CARE see Ball, Eric

OUR FATHERS' GOD IN YEARS LONG GONE see Gresens, Walter

OUR FATHER'S HOME see Wheeler, Alfred

OUR FATHER'S HOME ETERNAL (TUNE OF ERFREUT EUCH)
    see Two Processional Hymns

OUR FATHERS HOPED IN THEE see Brahms, Johannes

OUR FRONT PORCH *CCUL
    (Carmichael, Ralph) jr cor voc sc WORD 37521
    $1.95   (O553)

OUR GOD see Frank

OUR GOD see Norden

OUR GOD AND FATHER *Easter/Lent
    (Canavati) SATB oct PRO ART 1875 $.25   (O554)

OUR GOD AND OUR FATHER see Brahms, Johannes

OUR GOD ASCENDED see Schutz, Heinrich

OUR GOD IS A ROCK see Davis, Katherine K.

OUR GOD IS GREAT *Swed
    SATB oct LORENZ B56 $.30   (O555)
    SA/SAB oct LORENZ 7819 $.30   (O556)

OUR GOD IS KING see Wise, Judah L., Notre Dieu Est Roi

OUR GOD IS LOVE see Knight, Vincent

OUR GOD IS ONE GOD see Angell, Warren M.

OUR GOD, OUR HELP IN AGES PAST see Croft, William

OUR GOD OUR HELP IN AGES PAST see Koehler

OUR GOD, TO WHOM WE TURN see Bach

OUR HEARTS SHALL REJOICE see Baines, W.

OUR HYMN OF GRATEFUL PRAISE see Lorenz

OUR ISRAEL MAY SAY (Psalm 124) Bibl
    (Shaw; Parker) SATB,acap oct LAWSON 583 $.30
                                             (O557)

OUR KING IS BORN see Gallus, Jacobus, Regem Natum

OUR LADY AND QUEEN OF HEAVEN see Brahms, Johannes, Regina Coeli

OUR LADY IN THE STABLE see Swaffield, Ronald

OUR LADY'S SONG see Amicus

OUR LADY'S VISION see Reger, Max

OUR LIVING LORD see Wilson, Ira B.

OUR LORD AND CHRIST AROSE TODAY see Vulpius, Melchior

OUR LORD AND COMFORTER see Crocker

OUR LORD DID SUFFER DEATH see Schutz, Heinrich

OUR LORD IS BORN THIS NIGHT *Xmas
    (Ehret) SSA SCHMITT 243 $.30   (O558)

OUR LORD IS RISEN see Arensky, Anton Stepanovitch

OUR LORD IS RISEN see Darst, W. Glenn

OUR LORD IS RISEN see Hastings

OUR LORD IS RISEN see Powell

OUR LORD IS RISEN FROM THE DEAD see Wolff, S. Drummond

OUR LORD, WHO CHOSEN BLESSINGS SHED see Handel, George Frideric

OUR LORD'S NATIVITY see Raasted, Niels Otto, Kristi Fodsel

OUR LOVELY LADY SINGING see Niles, John Jacob

OUR MASTER HAS A GARDEN see Grundman

OUR MASTER HATH A GARDEN
    (Malin) SA oct BELWIN 64257 $.30   (O559)
    (Malin) SSA oct BELWIN 64264 $.30   (O560)
    (Malin) SATB oct BELWIN 64292 $.30   (O561)

OUR MASTER HATH A GARDEN see Crimp, Herbert E.

OUR MIGHTY LORD see Boalt

OUR PARISH PRAYS AND SINGS *hymn
    cong,org cloth LITURGICAL OPS71 $.95, ipa
                                             (O562)

OUR PASCHAL JOY see Yon, Pietro Alessandro

OUR PRAYER see Mc Call, Harlo

OUR PRAYER OF THANKS see Mollicone, H.

OUR SAVIOR'S PASSION see Ford

OUR SONG OF PRAISE see Wetherill

OUR SONGS OF PRAISE *CC147U,hymn
    (Klammer, E.) jr cor,kbd voc sc CONCORDIA
    3-1060 $4.50, cor pts CONCORDIA 3-1054
    $2.50 contains harmonizations by: Bunjes,
    P.   (O563)

OUR SOUL WAITS FOR THE LORD see Heussenstamm, George

OUR STAR OF FAITH see Lohr, Al

OUR THANKS TO THEE see Ager

OUR TROUBLES WAS HARD see Hairston, Jester

OUSELEY, FREDERICK ARTHUR GORE (1825-1889)
    From The Rising Of The Sun *Epiph,anthem
    SATB ALLANS 320 s.p.   (O564)
    mix cor oct NOVELLO 40.0370.05 s.p.   (O565)
    (Knight) 3pt mix cor oct CURWEN 11282 $.25
                                             (O566)
    How Goodly Are Thy Tents *anthem
    mix cor oct NOVELLO 40.0247.04 s.p.   (O567)

OUT IN THE FIELDS WITH GOD see Rhea, Raymond

OUT OF DARKNESS see Gounod, Charles Francois

OUT OF MY SORROW see Sjolund, Paul

OUT OF SIGHT (THE ASCENSION THAT NOBODY SAW)
    see Felciano, Richard

OUT OF THE DEEP see Batten, Adrian

OUT OF THE DEEP see Giles, Nathaniel

OUT OF THE DEEP see Gluck, Christoph Willibald Ritter von, De Profundis

OUT OF THE DEEP see Jones, G.

OUT OF THE DEEP see Kelly, Bryan

OUT OF THE DEEP see Lupo, Thomas

OUT OF THE DEEP see Morley, Thomas, De Profundis Clamavi

OUT OF THE DEEP see Mozart, Wolfgang Amadeus, De Profundis

OUT OF THE DEEP see Thomson, Virgil, De Profundis

OUT OF THE DEEP see Tomkins, Thomas

OUT OF THE DEEP HAVE I CRIED UNTO THEE see Schmutzler, T.

OUT OF THE DEPTHS see Beadell, Robert M.

OUT OF THE DEPTHS see Butler

OUT OF THE DEPTHS see Charpentier, Marc-Antoine

OUT OF THE DEPTHS see Chorbajian, John, De Profundis

OUT OF THE DEPTHS see Clokey, Joseph Waddell

OUT OF THE DEPTHS see Dawney, Michael

OUT OF THE DEPTHS see Englert, Eugene

OUT OF THE DEPTHS see Fichthorn, [Claude L.]

OUT OF THE DEPTHS see Graun, Karl Heinrich

OUT OF THE DEPTHS see Hovhaness, Alan

OUT OF THE DEPTHS see Purvis, Richard, De Profundis

OUT OF THE DEPTHS see Scott, John Prindle

OUT OF THE DEPTHS see Silver, Frederick

OUT OF THE DEPTHS see Thomson, Virgil, De Profundis

OUT OF THE DEPTHS see Todd, M. Flora

OUT OF THE DEPTHS see Vierra

OUT OF THE DEPTHS see Wienhorst, Richard

OUT OF THE DEPTHS I CRY see Piket, Frederick

OUT OF THE DEPTHS I CRY TO THEE see Bach, Johann Sebastian, Aus Tiefer Not Schrei'ich Zu Dir [Chorale]

OUT OF THE DEPTHS I CRY TO THEE see Franck, Melchior, Aus Tiefer Not Not Schrei Ich Zu Dir

OUT OF THE DEPTHS I CRY TO THEE see James, Will

OUT OF THE DEPTHS, O LORD, WE CRY see Kiekbusch

OUT OF THE DEPTHS WE CRY, LORD see Schutz, Heinrich

OUT OF THE EAST see Noble, Thomas Tertius

OUT OF THE ORIENT
    (Waring) SAB oct SUMMY M 2877 $.45   (O568)

OUT OF THE ORIENT see Byrd, William

OUT OF THE ORIENT CRYSTAL SKIES *carol
    SATB (easy) oct OXFORD 08.121 $.15   (O569)

OUT OF THE ORIENT CRYSTAL SKIES see Hubicki

OUT OF THE SILENCE see Galbraith, J.

OUT OF YOUR SLEEP ARISE AND WAKE see Beckhard

OUT OF YOUR SLEEP ARISE AND WAKE see Davis, Katherine K.

OUT OF YOUR SLEEP ARISE AND WAKE see Holst, Imogen

OUT ON THE WATERS see Caldicott, Alfred James

OUTBURST FOR EASTER, AN see Young

OUTBURST OF PRAISE see Diemer, Emma Lou

OUTGOING OF THE BOATS, THE see Roberton, Hugh S.

OVER BETHLEHEM'S TOWN see Mueller, Carl F.

OVER DIG AR HERRENS NAD see Nanini (Nanino), Giovanni Bernardino

OVER IN BETHLEHEM see Carmichael

OVER SLUMB'RING BETHL'EM TOWN see Vorse, R.

OVER THE HILLS see Blosdale, Don

OVER THE HILLS see McCullen, A.

OVER THE HILLS AND MIDNIGHT AIR *carol,Fr
    (Strimer, Joseph) SATB ALLANS 270 s.p.   (O570)

OVER THE HILLS AND MIDNIGHT AIR see Stimer

OVER THE HILLS MARIA WENT see Eccard, Johannes, Uber's Gebirg Maria Geht

OVERHOLT
    Ten Thousand Angels *Easter
    SATB oct LORENZ A453 $.30   (O571)
    SATB oct LILLENAS AN-1122 $.25   (O572)
    (Mickelson) SATB oct LILLENAS AN-1178 $.25
                                             (O573)
    (Skillings) SATB oct LILLENAS AT-1078 $.30
                                             (O574)

OVERMADE FULL AV NADE see Rosemuller, J.

OVERTON, HALL (1920-   )
    Fifteen Original Amens, Sevenfold Amen
    (composed with Stainer, John) *CC15U
    SATB FLAMMER A 5430 $.25   (O575)

OVERTURE FOR EASTER see Knighton

OWEN
    Easter Song *Easter
    SATB oct FOX UM107 $.30   (O576)
    SATB oct SOUTHERN $.30   (O577)

    Laudamus
    (Protheroe) SATB BOSTON 8770 $.35   (O578)
    (Protheroe) TTBB BOSTON 1766 $.35   (O579)
    (Protheroe; Watson) SSA BOSTON 3126 $.35
                                             (O580)

OWEN, BLYTHE
    Harken Unto Me
    SATB,org SEESAW $1.50   (O581)

OWEN, H.
    O Gracious God, Pardon My Great Offence
    SATB,acap oct PRESSER 312-40657 $.30   (O582)

OWENS
    Jubilate Deo *Gen
    SATB SCHMITT 8012 $.25   (O583)

    My Lord, What A Morning
    SATB KJOS P1807 $.30   (O584)

    Walk In Jerusalem *spir
    SATB SCHMITT 15015 $.35   (O585)

OWENS, BARBARA
    Three Early American Christmas Carols *CC3U,
    Xmas,carol,US
    SATB (med) ABINGDON APM-676 $.65   (O586)

OWENS, CAROL
    Come Together (composed with Owens, Jimmy)
    SATB&audience,soli voc sc WORD 37560 $2.95
                                             (O587)
    He Wants You To Fly (composed with Owens,
    Jimmy) *CCU
    jr cor voc sc WORD 32031 $1.95   (O588)

OWENS, DEWLEY
    Christ Is Made The Sure Foundation
    4pt mix cor,org oct SCHIRM.G 11715 $.35
                                             (O589)

OWENS, JIMMY
    Come Together *see Owens, Carol

    Discovery
    SATB oct LILLENAS AN-5020 $.30   (O590)

    Friendship With Jesus
    SATB oct LILLENAS AT-1045 $.25   (O591)

    He Cares For Me *anthem
    SATB oct LILLENAS AN-5018 $.30   (O592)

    He Wants You To Fly *see Owens, Carol

    Is It Any Wonder?
    SATB oct LILLENAS AN-5024 $.30   (O593)

    It's A Wonderful Day
    (Collins) SATB oct LILLENAS AT-1041 $.30
                                             (O594)
    Lord Is My Shepherd, The
    (Brown) SAB oct WORD CS-2549 $.30   (O595)

    Nobody Cared
    SATB oct LILLENAS AN-5012 $.35   (O596)

    Now's The Time
    SATB oct LILLENAS AN-5022 $.35   (O597)

    One Life To Live *CC8UL
    cor,pno,bvl,gtr cmplt ed LILLENAS MB-240
    $1.95   (O598)

OWENS, JIMMY (cont'd.)

Roll, Jordan, Roll
  SATB oct LILLENAS AN-3838 $.30   (O599)

Somebody Tell Me
  SATB oct LILLENAS AN-5028 $.40   (O600)

Sunday Afternoon
  SATB oct LILLENAS AN-5029 $.40   (O601)

There's A Reason For It All
  SATB oct LILLENAS AN-5014 $.35   (O602)

We Shall Walk Through The Valley
  SATB oct LILLENAS AN-3839 $.35   (O603)

Where Has He Gone?
  SATB oct LILLENAS AN-5013 $.35   (O604)

OX AND ASS HE DOES NOT SHUN! see Eccard,
  Johannes, Entre Le Beouf Et L'ane Gris

OX AND THE DONKEY'S CAROL, THE see Wallace,
  William

OXEN, THE see Britten, Benjamin

OXEN, THE see Constantino

OXFORD BOOK OF CAROLS *see Praise To God In
  The Highest   (O605)

OXFORD BOOK OF CAROLS, THE *CCU,carol
  (Vaughan Williams; Dearmer; Shaw) unis/SATB
  (easy) cmplt ed OXFORD $5.00   (O606)

OXFORD EASY ANTHEM BOOK *CC50U
  (easy) OXFORD pap $1.95, cloth $5.00   (O607)

OXFORD EASY ANTHEM BOOK, THE *CCU,anthem
  all voices (easy) OXFORD bds $3.00, pap $1.95
                                          (O608)

OXFORD EASY ANTHEM BOOK, THE *CC50U,anthem
  OXFORD bds $3.00, pap $1.95   (O609)

OXFORD REQUIEM, AN see Montgomery, Bruce

OXFORD SAB SONG BOOK: BOOK 2 *sac/sec,CCU,
  canon/carol/folk/hymn/round
  (Jacques) SAB oct OXFORD 58.602 $1.40 (O610)

OXLEY, HARRISON
  Be Strong And Of A Good Courage *Ded/Gen,
    Bibl
    SATB (med easy) oct OXFORD 42.854 $.35 (O611)

OXTOBY, CHARLES
  Time To Be Glad, A *Xmas,carol
    unis,pno,opt rec,opt bells/chimes SCHOTT
    CHR6 s.p.   (O612)

OYD, OYD UNA COSA see Guerrero, Francisco

OZOLINS, V.
  Angel Of Tears
    SATB,S solo oct PRESSER 312-40942 $.35
                                          (O613)

P

PA GRAVBAKKEN VART DETTE SONGI see Johansen,
  David Monrad

PA GUD OCH EJ PA EGET RAD see Bach, Johann
  Sebastian

PA GUD OCH EJ PA EGET RAD see Runback, Albert

PA GUD OCH JE PA EGET RAD see Berg, Gottfrid

PA KRISTI FODSELSDAG (KYRIE, GUD FADER AF
  HIMMERIG) see Pederson, Mogens

PA KRUBBANS STRA see Wideen, Ivar

PA MARIE BEBADELSEDAG see Hammarstrom, Hugo

PA PINSEDAG (KYRIE GUD FADER ALLERSOMHOJESTE
  TROST) see Pederson, Mogens

PA SCT. MICHAELS DAG (HVOR LADER GUD SIN
  KRISTENHED) see Eccard, Johannes

PABLO, JUAN
  Hasten Shepherds On *Xmas,carol,Carib
    [Eng/Span] 2pt,org/pno,opt perc&gtr SIFLER
    see from Three Puerto Rican Carols   (P1)

  On That Holy Midnight *Xmas,carol,Carib
    [Eng/Span] 2pt,org/pno,opt perc&gtr SIFLER
    see from Three Puerto Rican Carols   (P2)

  Three Holy Kings, The *Xmas,carol,Carib
    [Eng/Span] 2pt,org/pno,opt perc&gtr SIFLER
    see from Three Puerto Rican Carols   (P3)

  Three Puerto Rican Carols *see Hasten
    Shepherds On; On That Holy Midnight;
    Three Holy Kings, The   (P4)

PACCAGNELLA, ERMINEGILDO
  Magnificat *Magnif
    [Lat] 2 eq voices,org ZANIBON 494 s.p. (P5)

  Messa I In Onore Di S. Tecla *Mass
    [Lat] TB,org sc ZANIBON 1 s.p., voc pt
    ZANIBON 1A-B s.p.   (P6)

  Messa II In Onore Di S. Prosdocimo *Mass
    [Lat] unis,org sc ZANIBON 8 s.p., cor pts
    ZANIBON 8A s.p.   (P7)

PACE, ROBERT
  Happy Jubilee, The *anthem
    (McLellan) SSATB oct LILLENAS AN-1138 $.25
                                          (P8)

PACEM IN TERRIS see Milhaud, Darius

PACHELBEL
  Deus In Adjutorium
    (Woodward) [Eng/Lat] SSATB,orch MARKS
    $1.00, ipr   (P9)

  Give Thanks Unto Our God *Thanks
    mix cor SOUTHERN $.35   (P10)

  Magnificat *cant/Magnif
    (Woodward) SSATB (C maj) sc SUMMY $2.00,
    ipa   (P11)

  On God, And Not On Human Trust
    mix cor SOUTHERN $.30   (P12)

PACHELBEL, CARL THEODORUS (1690-1750)
  Magnificat *Magnif
    [Lat] SATB&SATB,org/pno voc sc PETERS 6087
    $.80   (P13)

PACHELBEL, JOHANN (1653-1706)
  Christ Lag In Todes Banden *Easter,cant
    (Eggebrecht, Hans Heinrich) [Eng/Ger] SATB,
    SATB soli,cont,bsn,3vln,3vla/3vln,3vla,
    2vcl,bvl (med) BAREN. BA 2875 sc s.p.,
    cor pts s.p.   (P14)

  Christ Lag In Todesbanden *Easter,cant
    "Christ Lay In Grim Death's Prison" [Ger/
    Eng] mix cor,soli,strings,bsn sc
    CONCORDIA 97-6211 $3.00, cor pts
    CONCORDIA 97-6218 $.75, ipa   (P15)

  Christ Lay In Grim Death's Prison *see
    Christ Lag In Todesbanden

  Das Vokalwerk *see Der Herr Ist Konig; Gott
    Ist Unser Zuversicht; Jauchzet Dem Herrn;
    Nun Danket Alle Gott   (P16)

  Der Herr Ist Konig (Psalm 99) mot
    "Lord God Reigneth, The" dbl cor,cont
    CONCORDIA 97-7568 $2.00   (P17)
    (Eggebrecht, Hans Heinrich) [Eng/Ger] SATB&
    SATB,cont (med diff) sc BAREN. BA 2871
    s.p., ipa see from Das Vokalwerk   (P18)

  Der Herr Ist Konig *mot
    (Kruger) dbl cor,cont HANSSLER 1.132 s.p.
                                          (P19)
  Der Herr Ist Konig *mot
    (Kruger) dbl cor,cont HANSSLER 1.135 s.p.
                                          (P20)
  Der Herr Ist Konig *mot
    (Kruger) SSATB HANSSLER 1.137 s.p.   (P21)

  Exsurgat Deus *mot
    (Kruger) [Lat] dbl cor,cont HANSSLER 1.134
    s.p.   (P22)

  Give Thanks Unto Our God *see Nun Danket
    Alle Gott

  God Is Our Refuge And Strength *see Gott Ist
    Unser Zuversicht

  Gott Ist Unser Zuversicht (Psalm 46) mot
    "God Is Our Refuge And Strength" dbl cor,
    cont CONCORDIA 97-6244 $1.80   (P23)
    (Eggebrecht, Hans Heinrich) [Eng/Ger] SATB&
    SATB,cont (med diff) sc BAREN. BA 2872
    s.p., ipa see from Das Vokalwerk   (P24)

PACHELBEL, JOHANN (cont'd.)

  Gott Ist Unsere Zuversicht *mot
    (Kruger) dbl cor,cont HANSSLER 1.133 s.p.
                                          (P25)

  Jauchzet Dem Herrn (Psalm 100) mot
    "Shout To The Lord" dbl cor,cont CONCORDIA
    97-7570 $2.15   (P26)
    (Eggebrecht, Hans Heinrich) [Eng/Ger] SATB&
    SATB,cont (med diff) sc BAREN. BA 2874
    s.p. see from Das Vokalwerk   (P27)

  Jauchzet Dem Herrn, Alle Welt *cant
    (Kruger) SSATB,SATB soli,cont,2ob,3vln,
    2vla,vcl HANSSLER 10.157 sc s.p., voc sc
    s.p., ipa   (P28)

  Lord God Reigneth, The *see Der Herr Ist
    Konig

  Magnificat
    SATB,cont CONCORDIA 97-7612 $1.65, ipa
                                          (P29)
  Magnificat Anima Mea *Magnif/mot
    (Eggebrecht, Hans Heinrich) [Lat] SATB,
    cont/vcl (med) sc BAREN. BA 2877 $2.75,
    ipa   (P30)
  Missa Brevis *Mass
    [Lat] SATB,acap voc sc PETERS HU1601 $2.00
                                          (P31)

  Now Thank We All Our God *see Nun Danket
    Alle Gott

  Nun Danket Alle Gott *Ded/Gen/Thanks/Trin,
    mot
    "Now Thank We All Our God" SATB,kbd (med
    easy) oct CONCORDIA 98-1944 $.30   (P32)
    "Now Thank We All Our God" dbl cor,cont
    CONCORDIA 97-7569 $1.75, ipa   (P33)
    (Eggebrecht, Hans Heinrich) [Eng/Ger] SATB&
    SATB,cont (med diff) sc BAREN. BA 2873
    s.p., ipa see from Das Vokalwerk   (P34)
    (Ehret) "Now Thank We All Our God" SATB oct
    ELKAN-V 362-1290 $.35   (P35)
    (Granville) "Give Thanks Unto Our God"
    SATB&SATB oct FOX CM13 $.40   (P36)
    (Harris) "Now Thank We All Our God" SSA&SSA
    oct LAWSON 51664 $.45   (P37)
    (Kruger) dbl cor,cont HANSSLER 1.131 s.p.
                                          (P38)

  On God, And Not On Human Trust *Gen
    SATB,acap (diff) oct CONCORDIA 98-1006 $.30
                                          (P39)

  Psalm 46 *see Gott Ist Unser Zuversicht

  Psalm 98 *see Singet Dem Herrn Ein Neues
    Lied

  Psalm 99 *see Der Herr Ist Konig

  Psalm 100 *see Jauchzet Dem Herrn

  Send, O Lord, Thy Holy Spirit *Gen
    SATB,kbd (med easy) oct CONCORDIA 98-1560
    $.30 contains also: What God Ordains Is
    Always Good   (P40)

  Shout To The Lord *see Jauchzet Dem Herrn

  Singet Dem Herrn Ein Neues Lied (Psalm 98)
    Gen,mot
    [Ger] SATB&SATB,acap (med) MULLER K 21 s.p.
                                          (P41)
    (Berger) dbl cor HANSSLER 1.008 $.40 (P42)

  Synger For Gud
    (Elgaroy, Jan) [Norw] mix cor LYCHE 33 s.p.
                                          (P43)

  Troste, Troste Uns Gott *Gen,mot
    (Hermann) dbl cor HANSSLER 1.002 s.p. (P44)
    (Trotschel, Heinrich Richard) [Ger] SATB&
    SATB,cont (med) MULLER K 34 s.p.   (P45)

  Was Gott Tut, Das Ist Wohlgetan *Gen,cant
    "What God Ordains Is Always Good" see
    Pachelbel, Johann, Send, O Lord, Thy Holy
    Spirit
    [Ger/Dut] voc sc PETERS HU1313 $2.00, ipr
                                          (P46)
    "What God Ordains Is Always Good" [Ger/Eng]
    mix cor,soli,strings,bsn sc CONCORDIA
    97-6230 $3.00, cor pts CONCORDIA 97-6231
    $.90, ipa   (P47)
    (Eggebrecht, Hans Heinrich) [Eng/Ger] SATB,
    cont,2vln,2vla,bsn (med) BAREN. BA 2876
    sc s.p., cor pts s.p., ipa   (P48)

  What God Ordains Is Always Good *see Was
    Gott Tut, Das Ist Wohlgetan

  Whate'er My God Ordains Is Right
    SATB oct SACRED E69 $.40   (P49)

PACIUS
  Lord Of My Life, Whose Tender Care
    (Lundquist) SATB,acap (med) oct WILLIS 8475
    $.25   (P50)

PADERBORN GESANGBUCH *see Rejoice In His Word
                                          (P51)

PADILLA
  Dominica In Ramis *mot,Mex
    (Barwick, S.; Hines, R.S.) "Passion
    According To Saint Matthew" SATB,acap
    PEER $.50   (P52)

  Passion According To Saint Matthew *see
    Dominica In Ramis

PADRE NOSTRO see Chiappani, Carlo

PADRE NOSTRO see Santucci, Pellegrino

PADRE NOSTRO see Tortorella, Luigi

PADRE NOSTRO see Travaglia, Silvio

PADRE NOSTRO see Vianello, Piero

PAEAN see Coker, [Wilson]

PAEAN OF BROTHERHOOD see Butler, Eugene

PAEAN OF PRAISE see Ossewaarde, Jack

PAEAN OF PRAISE see Purvis, Richard

PAEAN OF PRAISE, A see Handel, George Frideric

PAEAN OF REMEMBRANCE see Oldroyd, George

PAGE, ARTHUR
  From Egypt's Bondage Come
    4pt mix cor oct SCHIRM.G 3945 $.25   (P53)

PAGE, R.
  Angel Band, The *Xmas,spir
    SA AMP A373 $.25 see from Three Christmas
    Spirituals   (P54)

  Blessing Of Mary, The *Xmas,spir
    SSA AMP A371 $.25 see from Three Christmas
    Spirituals   (P55)

  Do You Know The One *Xmas
    SSAA,acap AMP A339 $.20   (P56)

  Good Night, Little Jesus
    SSA AMP A427 $.20   (P57)

  It Was Poor Little Jesus *Xmas,spir
    SSAA,A solo AMP A372 $.25 see from Three
    Christmas Spirituals   (P58)

  Prayer Of Peter Marshall, The
    SATB,acap oct PRESSER 312-40347 $.30   (P59)

  Three Christmas Spirituals *see Angel Band,
    The; Blessing Of Mary, The; It Was Poor
    Little Jesus   (P60)

PAGE, ROBERT E.
  Joy, Joy, Joy
    SSA&TTB&SATB STANDARD A3MX3 $.50   (P61)

  There's A City Called Heaven
    SATB,acap oct PRESSER 312-40211 $.30   (P62)

PAGEANT OF CAROLS see Suchoff, B.

PAGEANT OF CHRISTMAS see Jason

PAGEANT OF THE HOLY NATIVITY see Williams, D.M.

PAGELLA, G.
  Trionfa O Sole! *hymn
    TTBB sc ZANIBON 450 s.p., voc pt ZANIBON
    450A-B-C-D s.p.   (P63)

PAGE'S ROAD SONG, A see Byles, B. D.

PAGET, KATE
  Christmas Carol Pageant, A *see Diller,
    Angela

PAGET, MICHAEL
  God's Eternal Son
    SATB,acap LENGNICK s.p.   (P64)

  In Excelsis Gloria
    SATB,acap LENGNICK s.p.   (P65)

  Miles Coverdale's Carol *Xmas
    4pt mix cor,acap oct SCHIRM.G 11215 $.25   (P66)

PAHISSA, [JAIME] (1880-1969)
  Quomodo Sedet Sola
    see DOS MOTETES

PAHLITZSCH, WOLFGANG (1909-)
  Allein Zu Dir, Herr Jesu Christ
    SA/SAB/SATB,brass HANSSLER 8.033 s.p. (P67)

  Gottes Sohn Ist Kommen
    see Gumpeltzhaimer, Adam, Nun Freuet Euch,
    Ihr Arm Und Reich

  Was Mein Gott Will, Das Gscheh Allzeit
    SB/SAB/SATB,org HANSSLER 8.037 s.p.   (P68)

PAISIELLO, GIOVANNI (1740-1816)
  Ave Maria *BVM,mot
    [Lat] 2 eq voices oct DURAND s.p.   (P69)

  Messa Da Requiem *Mass/Req
    dbl cor,soli,orch CURCI 7048 s.p.   (P70)

PAIX DU CIEL see Bach, Johann Sebastian

PAJARILLO AMOROSO see Martin Pompey

PALADILHE, [EMILE] (1844-1926)
  Benedictus
    (Christiansen, O.) SATB KJOS 15 $.30 (P71)

  Choeur Des Olivettes
    [Fr] SSTTBB HEUGEL voc sc s.p., voc pt s.p.
        (P72)

  Deux Motets A La Tres Sainte-Vierge *CC2U,
    BVM,mot
    cor,acap LEMOINE   (P73)

  Les Saintes-Marie De La Mer *Fr
    [Fr] mix cor,soli,orch LEDUC sc rental, cor
    pts rental   (P74)

  Messe Solennelle De La Pentecote *Mass
    [Fr] SATB,SATB soli,orch/ob&vln&harp (vocal
    parts available separately) voc sc LEDUC
    BL454 s.p., ipr   (P75)
    (Samuel-Rousseau, Marcel) [Fr] LEDUC BL454
    ipr   (P76)

  O Salutaris
    [Lat] 2-3pt CHOUDENS s.p. see also CHOEURS
    POUR DISTRIBUTIONS DE PRIX OU POUR
    ENFANTS   (P77)

  Tu Es Petrus *mot
    [Lat] 4pt mix cor,solo,org,opt 5strings
    LEMOINE voc sc s.p., cor pts s.p., ipa
        (P78)

PALATINES DAUGHTER, THE see Hughes, H.

PALESTER, ROMAN (1907-)
  Missa Brevis *Mass
    [Lat] SATB,acap PEER $.85   (P79)

PALESTRINA, GIOVANNI (1525-1594)
  A Reggel *canon
    (Nadasdy, K.) [Hung] 3pt (easy) BUDAPEST
    1973 s.p.   (P80)
    (Nadasdy, K.) [Hung] TBarB (easy) BUDAPEST
    1973 s.p.   (P81)

PALESTRINA, GIOVANNI (cont'd.)
  Ad Coenam Agni
    see Complete Editions Vol. 3

  Ad Fugam
    see Complete Editions Vol. 9

  Ad Te Levavi Oculos Meos *Adv/Lent
    "Unto Thee Lift I Up Mine Eyes" SATB,acap
    SCHIRM.EC 1272 $.30   (P82)

  Ad Te Levavi Oculos Meos; Misere Nostri,
    Domine
    see Four Motets

  Adoramus Te *Commun/Easter/Gen/Lent/Psntd,
    anthem/mot
    [Lat] SSTBar oct DURAND s.p.   (P83)
    SATB,acap (easy) oct OXFORD 43.345 $.15
        (P84)
    4pt wom cor sc ALSBACH&D s.p.   (P85)
    [Lat] SMezTBar oct DURAND s.p.   (P86)
    (Cramer) [Eng/Lat] SATB,acap MARKS 4299
    $.25   (P87)
    (Davison, A.) [Lat] anti cor,acap SCHIRM.EC
    44 $.25   (P88)
    (Ehret, Walter) "We Adore Thee" SA/TB oct
    BELWIN 1649 $.30   (P89)
    (Gibb) TTBB,acap BOSTON 9381 $.30   (P90)
    (Greyson) "We Adore Thee" TTBB oct BOURNE
    ES16 $.30   (P91)
    (Holler) "We Adore Thee" SATB oct GRAY
    GCMR 1585 $.30   (P92)
    (Stewart, C. Hylton) "We Adore Thee, Lord
    Jesu" [Eng/Lat] mix cor,acap oct NOVELLO
    50.0333.04 s.p.   (P93)
    (Swift) "We Adore Thee" SSA oct BELWIN 1655
    $.30   (P94)
    (Swift) "We Adore Thee" SATB oct BELWIN 769
    $.30   (P95)
    (Swift) "We Adore Thee" SAB oct BELWIN 1660
    $.30   (P96)

  Adoramus Te Christe *Xmas/Easter/Gen/Lent
    see Palestrina, Giovanni, O Bone Jesu
    SATB,acap oct PRESSER 332-03069 $.25   (P97)
    [Lat] TTBB,acap SCHIRM.EC 950 $.22   (P98)
    SATB,acap SCHIRM.EC 1760 $.25   (P99)
    SATB,acap RICORDI-ENG SY199 s.p.   (P100)
    [Lat] SSAT,acap oct SCHIRM.G 6216 $.25
        (P101)
    "Alleluia, Lord God" anti cor,acap
    SCHIRM.EC 307 $.25   (P102)
    "Here We Worship Thee" SATB oct LESLIE 4041
        (P103)
    "O Come, Let Us Worship" SATB,acap
    SCHIRM.EC 1136 $.25   (P104)
    (Cain) SATB SCHMITT 1598 $.20   (P105)
    (Christiansen, O.) SATB KJOS 32 $.30 (P106)
    (Damrosch) [Lat/Eng] 4pt mix cor,acap oct
    SCHIRM.G 6091 $.25   (P107)
    (Gerhard) "We Adore Thee" SATB oct SPRATT
    501 $.25   (P108)
    (Glaser, V.) "Alleluia, Lord God" SAB,acap
    SCHIRM.EC 2239 $.20   (P109)
    (Glaser, V.) "Alleluia, Lord God" [Lat/Eng]
    SSA,acap SCHIRM.EC 2510 $.25   (P110)
    (Krone) [Lat] SATB,acap WARNER W2849 $.30
        (P111)
    (Long) "We Adore Thee" [Lat/Eng] SATB,acap
    oct PRO ART 1146 $.30   (P112)
    (Long) "We Adore Thee" [Lat/Eng] SAB oct
    PRO ART 1145 $.30   (P113)
    (Morgan) "We Adore Thee" SSAA SCHMITT 2529
    $.30   (P114)
    (Townsend) "We Adore Thee" [Lat/Eng] SSA
    oct PRO ART 1712 $.30   (P115)
    (Wilhousky) SATB,acap FISCHER,C CM-6578
    $.25   (P116)
    (Wilson; Ehret) [Lat] SSA,acap oct BOOSEY
    5214 $.30   (P117)

  Adoremus *see Adoramus Te Christe

  Adoremus Te Christe
    "Adoremus" [Lat] 4pt mix cor HEUGEL s.p.
    see from LA MAITRISE   (P118)
    (Lundquist) "We Do Worship Thee" SATB,acap
    (med) oct WILLIS 5502 $.10   (P119)

  Aeterna Christi Munera *Mass
    mix cor SOUTHERN $.80   (P120)
    (Ewerhart) [Lat] SATB,acap AMP A527 $.50
        (P121)
    (Somma, B.) 4pt sc SANTIS 1037 s.p., cor
    pts SANTIS 1038A-B s.p.   (P122)
    (Washington, Henry) [Lat] SATB CHESTER s.p.
        (P123)

  Aeterna Munera Christi *Commun/Mass
    see Complete Editions Vol. 39
    SATB oct NOVELLO s.p.   (P124)
    mix cor,acap voc sc KALMUS 6370 $1.25
        (P125)
    (Bauerle, Hermann) SATB,acap cor pts
    BREITKOPF-L PB-1855 s.p., voc pt
    BREITKOPF-L CHB-1661 s.p.   (P126)
    (Ewerhart, Rudolf) 4pt mix cor,acap cor pts
    BREITKOPF-W CHB-3062   (P127)

  Agnus Dei (from Veni Sponsa Christi) Agnus
    SATB oct PLYMOUTH K-2 $.25   (P128)
    "O, Guds Lamm" mix cor NORDISKA 1332 s.p.
        (P129)
    (Ehret, W.) "Lamb Of God" SATB,acap oct
    PRESSER 312-40616 $.30   (P130)
    (Pfautsch) SATB,acap oct LAWSON 884 $.25
        (P131)

  Agnus Dei No. 2
    mix cor ALSBACH&D sc s.p., cor pts s.p.
        (P132)

  All Ye People *see O Vos Omnes

  Alleluia *Easter,hymn
    see ALLELUIA AND VERSE
    (Nieland, Jan) SATB&boy cor,S solo,org oct
    WORLD $.45   (P133)

  Alleluia And Hymn *Allelu/hymn
    (Forsblad; Livingston) SAB,opt orch oct PRO
    ART 2564 $.30   (P134)
    (Forsblad; Livingston) SATB,opt orch oct
    PRO ART 2385 $.30   (P135)
    (Forsblad; Livingston) 2pt,opt orch oct PRO
    ART 2673 $.30   (P136)
    (Forsblad; Livingston) SSA,opt orch oct PRO
    ART 2387 $.30   (P137)

PALESTRINA, GIOVANNI (cont'd.)
  Alleluia, Lord God *see Adoramus Te, Christe

  Alleluia! The Strife Is O'er *Easter,hymn
    (Jewell, Kenneth W.) SATB,org oct WORLD
    CA-1935-8 $.60   (P138)
    (Nieland, Jan) SSA,org oct WORLD $.45
        (P139)

  Alleluia The Strife Is Over
    (Wright) SATB&jr cor&jr cor FLAMMER A 5350
    $.30   (P140)
    (Wright) SATB&jr cor FLAMMER A 5117 $.30
        (P141)

  Alleluia! Tulerunt Dominum *Easter,Bibl
    "Lo, They Have Borne Away Jesus" [Lat/Eng]
    SATTB,acap oct SCHIRM.G 7663 $.30   (P142)

  Alma Redemptoris Mater *anti/Bibl/mot
    see Complete Editions Vol. 67
    see LA SCHOLA PALESTRINIENNE DEUXIEME
    CAHIER
    mix cor SOUTHERN $.30   (P143)
    SATB oct SUMMY M 921 $.30   (P144)
    SATB,acap SCHIRM.EC $.25   (P145)
    mix cor ALSBACH&D sc s.p., cor pts s.p.
        (P146)
    [Lat] SATB RICORDI-ENG SY193 s.p.   (P147)
    "Bow Down Thine Ear" [Lat/Eng] 4pt mix cor,
    acap oct SCHIRM.G 7729 $.30   (P148)
    (Collins, H.B.) [Lat] SATB CHESTER s.p.
        (P149)

  Antiphon I *BVM
    SSSA/SSST/SATB PETERS WM58 $1.50 see also
    ANTIPHONS IN HONOR OF THE BLESSED VIRGIN
        (P150)

  Ars Nova To Rennaisance Vol. 6-1200 To About
    1500 *sac/sec,Mass
    mix cor min sc KALMUS 706 $1.30
    contains: My Heart It Seemed, Was Dying;
    Papae Marcelli; Sooner The Heavens;
    Time As He Flies; Tu Es Petrus   (P151)

  As The Hart Pants *see Sicut Cervus

  Ascendit Deus *Asc,Offer
    (Ewerhart, Rudolf) SATTB,acap cor pts
    BREITKOPF-W CHB-3507 s.p.   (P152)
    (Runkel, K.) [Lat] SSAA,acap SCHIRM.EC 1962
    $.22   (P153)

  Ascendo Ad Patrem
    see Complete Editions Vol. 69

  Aspice Domine
    see Complete Editions Vol. 9

  Assumpta Est Maria *Mass/mot
    see Complete Editions Vol. 61
    mix cor,acap voc sc KALMUS 6369 $1.25
        (P154)
    (Boepple, P.) TTB,strings oct PRESSER
    352-00001 $.45   (P155)
    (Boepple, P.) SSA,strings oct PRESSER
    352-00001 $.45   (P156)
    (Ewerhart) [Lat] SSATTB,acap AMP A532 $1.00
        (P157)
    (Ewerhart) [Lat] SSATTB,acap AMP 544 $.40
        (P158)
    (Ewerhart, Rudolf) 6pt mix cor,acap cor pts
    BREITKOPF-W CHB-3067   (P159)
    (Ewerhart, Rudolf) 6pt mix cor,acap cor pts
    BREITKOPF-W CHB-3149 s.p.   (P160)
    (Haberl, Fr.X.) 6pt mix cor,acap voc pt
    BREITKOPF-L CHB-1391 s.p.   (P161)
    (Petti, Anthony G.) [Lat] SSATTB CHESTER
    s.p.   (P162)
    (Washington, Henry) [Lat] SSATTB CHESTER
    s.p.   (P163)

  Ave Maria *mot
    see Drei Motetten
    [Lat] 3 eq voices,acap oct GIA G582 $.25
        (P164)
    (Damrosch, F.) [Lat] SSSA,acap oct SCHIRM.G
    6251 $.25   (P165)

  Ave Maria Gratia Plena *BVM
    SATB,acap voc pt DOBLINGER s.p. see also
    UNSERE LIEBE FRAU   (P166)

  Ave Maria
    see Complete Editions Vol. 53
    see Complete Editions Vol. 51

  Ave Maris Stella *mot
    [Lat] SATB,acap oct GIA G563 $.25   (P167)

  Ave Regina Coelorum *Mass
    see Complete Editions Vol. 59
    (Bauerle, Hermann) SATB,acap cor pts
    BREITKOPF-L PB-1874 s.p., voc pt
    BREITKOPF-L CHB-1716 s.p.   (P168)

  Ave Regina Coelorum; Gaude Virgo Gloriosa
    see Four Motets

  Beatus Laurentius
    see Complete Editions Vol. 58

  Benedicta Sit Sancta Trinitatis
    see Drei Motetten

  Benedictus (from Missa Papae Marcelli) Bene/
    Bene
    mix cor ALSBACH&D sc s.p., cor pts s.p.
        (P169)
    girl cor SOUTHERN $.30   (P170)
    TTB,acap oct PRESSER 352-00346 $.30 (P171)
    (Castellazzi) [Lat] SATB,acap RICORDI-ARG
    BA 9889 s.p.   (P172)
    (Kraft, L.) SSA/TTB,acap oct PRESSER
    352-00346 $.30   (P173)
    (Vene) "He Is Blessed" [Lat/Eng] TTB/SSA,
    acap oct COLOMBO 2185 $.25   (P174)
    (Woodworth) [Eng] 4pt mix cor,acap oct
    SCHIRM.G 9814 $.30   (P175)

  Benedictus Sit Deus *Trin,Offer
    (Ewerhart, Rudolf) SATTB,acap cor pts
    BREITKOPF-W CHB-3503 s.p.   (P176)

  Bonum Est Confiteri *Bibl
    (Williamson) "It Is A Good Thing To Give
    Thanks" [Lat/Eng] SATBarB,acap oct
    SCHIRM.G 9391 $.25   (P177)

PALESTRINA, GIOVANNI (cont'd.)

Bow Down Thine Ear *see Alma Redemptoris
Mater

Brevis *Mass
see Complete Editions Vol. 15
(Ewerhart, Rudolf) 4pt mix cor,acap cor pts
BREITKOPF-W CHB-3063 (P178)

By The Waters Of Babylon *anthem
(Bennett, G.J.) mix cor,acap oct NOVELLO
28.1074.03 s.p. (P179)

By What Master Hand *see Da Cosi Dotta Man

Canite Tuba In Sion *mot
(Petti, Anthony G.) [Lat] SSATB CHESTER
s.p. (P180)

Christ Our Savior *see Crucifixus

Christus Factus Est *Easter/Lent
(Richardson) "Jesus Christ, Our Lord Was
Crucified" SATB oct SPRATT 2002 $.25
(P181)

Citta Di Dio *madrigal
(Malin) "City Of God" [Eng/It] SSATB,acap
MARKS 4420 $.30 (P182)

City Of God *see Citta Di Dio

Collected Works Vol. 1: Motets *CCU,mot
(Commer; Espange; Haberl; Rauch; de Witt)
cor GREGG ISBN 0:567 28651 6 s.p. (P183)

Collected Works Vol. 2: Motets *CCU,mot
(Commer; Espange; Haberl; Rauch; de Witt)
cor GREGG ISBN 0:576 28652 4 s.p. (P184)

Collected Works Vol. 3: Motets *CCU,mot
(Commer; Espange; Haberl; Rauch; de Witt)
cor GREGG ISBN 0:576 28653 2 s.p. (P185)

Collected Works Vol. 4: Motets *CCU,mot
(Commer; Espange; Haberl; Rauch; de Witt)
cor GREGG ISBN 0:576 28654 0 s.p. (P186)

Collected Works Vol. 5: Motets *CCU,mot
(Commer; Espange; Haberl; Rauch; de Witt)
cor GREGG ISBN 0:576 28655 9 s.p. (P187)

Collected Works Vol. 6: Motets *CCU,mot
(Commer; Espange; Haberl; Rauch; de Witt)
cor GREGG ISBN 0:576 28656 7 s.p. (P188)

Collected Works Vol. 7: Motets *CCU,mot
(Commer; Espange; Haberl; Rauch; de Witt)
cor GREGG ISBN 0:576 28657 5 s.p. (P189)

Collected Works Vol. 8: Hymns *CCU,hymn
(Commer; Espange; Haberl; Rauch; de Witt)
cor GREGG ISBN 0:576 28658 3 s.p. (P190)

Collected Works Vol. 9: Masses *CCU,Mass
(Commer; Espange; Haberl; Rauch; de Witt)
cor GREGG ISBN 0:576 28659 1 s.p. (P191)

Collected Works Vol. 10: Masses *CCU,Mass
(Commer; Espange; Haberl; Rauch; de Witt)
cor GREGG ISBN 0:576 28660 5 s.p. (P192)

Collected Works Vol. 11: Masses *CCU,Mass
(Commer; Espange; Haberl; Rauch; de Witt)
cor GREGG ISBN 0:576 28661 3 s.p. (P193)

Collected Works Vol. 12: Masses *CCU,Mass
(Commer; Espange; Haberl; Rauch; de Witt)
cor GREGG ISBN 0:576 28662 1 s.p. (P194)

Collected Works Vol. 13: Masses *CCU,Mass
(Commer; Espange; Haberl; Rauch; de Witt)
cor GREGG ISBN 0:576 28663 X s.p. (P195)

Collected Works Vol. 14: Masses *CCU,Mass
(Comer; Espagne; Haberl; Rauch; de Witt)
cor GREGG ISBN 0:576 28664 8 s.p. (P196)

Collected Works Vol. 15: Masses *CCU,Mass
(Comer; Espagne; Haberl; Rauch; de Witt)
cor GREGG ISBN 0:576 28665 6 s.p. (P197)

Collected Works Vol. 16: Masses *CCU,Mass
(Comer; Espagne; Haberl; Rauch; de Witt)
cor GREGG ISBN 0:576 28666 4 s.p. (P198)

Collected Works Vol. 17: Masses *CCU,Mass
(Comer; Espagne; Haberl; Rauch; de Witt)
cor GREGG ISBN 0:576 28667 2 s.p. (P199)

Collected Works Vol. 18: Masses *CCU,Mass
(Comer; Espagne; Haberl; Rauch; de Witt)
cor GREGG ISBN 0:576 28668 0 s.p. (P200)

Collected Works Vol. 19: Masses *CCU,Mass
(Comer; Espagne; Haberl; Rauch; de Witt)
cor GREGG ISBN 0:576 28669 9 s.p. (P201)

Collected Works Vol. 20: Masses *CCU,Mass
(Comer; Espagne; Haberl; Rauch; de Witt)
cor GREGG ISBN 0:576 18670 2 s.p. (P202)

Collected Works Vol. 21: Masses *CCU,Mass
(Comer; Espagne; Haberl; Rauch; de Witt)
cor GREGG ISBN 0:576 18671 0 s.p. (P203)

Collected Works Vol. 22: Masses *CCU,Mass
(Comer; Espagne; Haberl; Rauch; de Witt)
cor GREGG ISBN 0:576 28672 9 s.p. (P204)

Collected Works Vol. 23: Masses *CCU,Mass
(Comer; Espagne; Haberl; Rauch; de Witt)
cor GREGG ISBN 0:576 28673 7 s.p. (P205)

Collected Works Vol. 24: Masses *CCU,Mass
(Comer; Espagne; Haberl; Rauch; de Witt)
cor GREGG ISBN 0:576 28674 5 s.p. (P206)

Collected Works Vol. 25: Lamentation Of
Jeremiah *CCU,Bibl
(Comer; Espagne; Haberl; Rauch; de Witt)
cor GREGG ISBN 0:576 28675 3 s.p. (P207)

Collected Works Vol. 26: Litanies, Motets,
Psalms *CCU,mot/Psalm
(Comer; Espagne; Haberl; Rauch; de Witt)
cor GREGG ISBN 0:576 28676 1 s.p. (P208)

PALESTRINA, GIOVANNI (cont'd.)

Collected Works Vol. 27: Magnificats *CC35U,
Magnif
(Comer; Espagne; Haberl; Rauch; de Witt)
cor GREGG ISBN 0:576 28677 X s.p. (P209)

Come, Holy Ghost *anthem/Bibl
mix cor,acap oct NOVELLO 28.0829.03 s.p.
(P210)
(Roberts) 4pt mix cor,acap oct SCHIRM.G
5309 $.25 (P211)

Come, Let Us Worship *anthem
mix cor oct NOVELLO 50.0059.09 s.p. (P212)
(Carlton) SATB,acap oct BOOSEY 5226 $.30 (P213)

Come, Then, O Holy Breath Of God *see Dunque
Divin Spiracolo

Come, Thou Holy Spirit, Come *see Veni
Sancte Spiritus

Complete Editions Vol. 1 *Mass
4pt,acap oct KALMUS $1.75
contains: Ecce Sacerdos Magnus (4pt,
acap); O Regem Coeli (P214)

Complete Editions Vol. 2 *Mass
oct KALMUS $1.75
contains: Gabrile Archanglus (4pt,acap);
Virtute Magna (4pt,acap) (P215)

Complete Editions Vol. 3 *Mass
oct KALMUS $1.75
contains: Ad Coenam Agni (5pt,acap); Pro
Defunctis (5pt,acap); Sine Domine (5pt,
acap) (P216)

Complete Editions Vol. 6: Thirty-Six Motets
*CCU,mot
mix cor,acap oct KALMUS $1.75 (P217)

Complete Editions Vol. 7: Thirty-Six Motets
*CCU,mot
mix cor,acap oct KALMUS $1.75 (P218)

Complete Editions Vol. 8 *Mass
oct KALMUS $1.75
contains: De Beata Virgine (4pt,acap);
Inviolata (4pt,acap); Sine Nomine II
(4pt,acap) (P219)

Complete Editions Vol. 9 *Mass
oct KALMUS $1.75
contains: Ad Fugam (4pt,acap); Aspice
Domine (5pt,acap); Salvum Me Fac (5pt,
acap) (P220)

Complete Editions Vol. 10 (from De Beata
Virgine) Mass
6pt,acap oct $1.75
contains: Gloria; Papae Marcelli (6pt,
acap) (P221)

Complete Editions Vol. 11: Forty-Three Motets
*CCU,mot
5-7pt,acap oct KALMUS $1.75 (P222)

Complete Editions Vol. 12: Forty-Three Motets
*CCU,mot
5-7pt,acap oct KALMUS $1.75 (P223)

Complete Editions Vol. 13: Forty-Three Motets
*CCU,mot
5-7pt,acap oct KALMUS $1.75 (P224)

Complete Editions Vol. 14 *Mass
oct $1.75
contains: Primi Toni (4pt,acap); Spem In
Alium (4pt,acap) (P225)

Complete Editions Vol. 15 *Mass
oct KALMUS $1.75
contains: Brevis (4pt,acap); De Feria
(4pt,acap); L'Homme Arme (5pt,acap) (P226)

Complete Editions Vol. 16 *Mass
oct KALMUS $1.75
contains: De Beata Virgine (6pt,acap);
Repleatur Os Meus (5pt,acap); Ut Re Mi
(6pt,acap) (P227)

Complete Editions Vol. 17: Eighty-Eight
Motets *CCU,mot
5pt/6pt/8pt,acap oct KALMUS $1.75 (P228)

Complete Editions Vol. 18: Eighty- Eight
Motets *CCU,mot
5pt/6pt/8pt,acap oct KALMUS $1.75 (P229)

Complete Editions Vol. 19: Eighty-Eight
Motets *CCU,mot
5pt/6pt/8pt,acap oct KALMUS $1.75 (P230)

Complete Editions Vol. 20: Eighty-Eight
Motets *CCU,mot
5pt/6pt/8pt,acap oct KALMUS $1.75 (P231)

Complete Editions Vol. 21: Eighty-Eight
Motets *CCU,mot
5pt/6pt/8pt,acap oct KALMUS $1.75 (P232)

Complete Editions Vol. 22: Eighty-Eight
Motets *CCU,mot
5pt/6pt/8pt,acap oct KALMUS $1.75 (P233)

Complete Editions Vol. 23: Thirty-Nine
Secular And Sacred Madrigals *sac/sec,
CCU,Mass
mix cor,acap oct KALMUS $1.75 (P234)

Complete Editions Vol. 24: Thirty-Nine
Secular And Sacred Madrigals *sac/sec,
CCU,Mass
oct KALMUS $1.75 (P235)

Complete Editions Vol. 25 *Mass
oct KALMUS $1.75
contains: Jesu, Nostra Redemptio (4pt,
acap); Lauda Sion (4pt,acap); L'homme
Arme (4pt,acap); Primi Toni (4pt,acap) (P236)

Complete Editions Vol. 26 *Mass
oct KALMUS $1.75
contains: Eripe Me Do Inimicie (4pt,
acap); O Magnum Mysterium (5pt,acap);
Primi Toni (5pt,acap) (P237)

PALESTRINA, GIOVANNI (cont'd.)

Complete Editions Vol. 27: Twenty-Nine Motets
*CCU,mot
3pt/5pt,acap oct KALMUS $1.75 (P238)

Complete Editions Vol. 28: Twenty-Nine Motets
*CCU,mot
3pt/5pt,acap oct KALMUS $1.75 (P239)

Complete Editions Vol. 29: Twenty-Nine Motets
*CCU,mot
3pt/5pt,acap oct KALMUS $1.75 (P240)

Complete Editions Vol. 30: Twenty-Eight
Motets *mot
cor oct KALMUS $1.75 (P241)

Complete Editions Vol. 31: Twenty-Eight
Motets *CCU,mot
cor oct KALMUS $1.75 (P242)

Complete Editions Vol. 32: Lamentationes
*CCU,Mass
oct KALMUS $1.75 (P243)

Complete Editions Vol. 33: Lamentationes
*CCU,Mass
oct KALMUS $1.75 (P244)

Complete Editions Vol. 34: Lamentationes
*CCU,Mass
oct KALMUS $1.75 (P245)

Complete Editions Vol. 35: Lamentationes
*CCU,Mass
oct KALMUS $1.75 (P246)

Complete Editions Vol. 36: Forty-Five Hymns
*CCU,hymn
oct KALMUS $1.75 (P247)

Complete Editions Vol. 37: Forty-Five Hymns
*CCU,hymn
oct KALMUS $1.75 (P248)

Complete Editions Vol. 38: Forty-Five Hymns
*CCU,hymn
oct KALMUS $1.75 (P249)

Complete Editions Vol. 39 *Mass
oct KALMUS $1.75
contains: Aeterna Munera Christi (4pt,
acap); Iste Confessor (4pt,acap); Jam
Christus Astra Ascenderat (4pt,acap);
Panis Quem Ergo Dabo (4pt,acap) (P250)

Complete Editions Vol. 40 *Mass
oct KALMUS $1.75
contains: Nasce La Gioia Mia (6pt,acap);
Sine Nomine (6pt,acap) (P251)

Complete Editions Vol. 41: Thirty-Five
Magnificats *CCU,Magnif
4-6pt,acap oct KALMUS $1.75 (P252)

Complete Editions Vol. 42: Thirty-Five
Magnificats *CCU,Magnif
4-6pt,acap oct KALMUS $1.75 (P253)

Complete Editions Vol. 43: Thirty-Five
Magnificats *CCU,Magnif
4-6pt,acap oct KALMUS $1.75 (P254)

Complete Editions Vol. 44: Thirty-Five
Magnificats *CCU,Magnif
4-6pt,acap oct KALMUS $1.75 (P255)

Complete Editions Vol. 45: Sixty-Eight
Offertories *CCU,Offer
cor oct KALMUS $1.75 (P256)

Complete Editions Vol. 46: Sixty-Eight
Offertories *CCU,Offer
cor oct KALMUS $1.75 (P257)

Complete Editions Vol. 47: Sixty-Eight
Offertories *CCU,Offer
cor oct KALMUS $1.75 (P258)

Complete Editions Vol. 48 *Mass
oct KALMUS $1.75
contains: Litaniae Deiparae Virginis I;
Litaniae Deiparae Virginis II (P259)

Complete Editions Vol. 49 *Mass
oct KALMUS $1.75
contains: Litaniae De Beata Virgine
Maria; [Three] Litaniae Domini; [Two]
Litaniae Sacrosanctae Eucharistiae (P260)

Complete Editions Vol. 50 *Mass
oct KALMUS $1.75
contains: Dies Sanctificatus (4pt,acap);
In Te Domine Speravi (4pt,acap); Sine
Nomine (4pt,acap) (P261)

Complete Editions Vol. 51 *Mass
oct KALMUS $1.75
contains: Ave Maria (4pt,acap); Dilexi
Quoniam (4pt,acap); Quam Pulchra Est
(4pt,acap) (P262)

Complete Editions Vol. 52: Thirty Sacred
Madrigals *CC30U
mix cor oct KALMUS $1.75 (P263)

Complete Editions Vol. 53 *Mass
oct KALMUS $1.75
contains: Ave Maria (4pt,acap); Emendemus
(4pt,acap); Sanctorum Meritis (4pt,
acap) (P264)

Complete Editions Vol. 55 *Mass
oct KALMUS $1.75
contains: In Majoribus Duplicibus (4pt,
acap); In Minoribus Dublicibis (4pt,
acap) (P265)

Complete Editions Vol. 56 *Mass
oct KALMUS $1.75
contains: Dum Esset Summus Pontifex (4pt,
acap); O Admirabile Commercium (4pt,
acap); Quem Dicunt Homines (4pt,acap) (P266)

Complete Editions Vol. 57 *Mass
oct KALMUS $1.75
contains: Dum Complerentur (6pt,acap);
Memor Esto (5pt,acap) (P267)

PALESTRINA, GIOVANNI (cont'd.)

Complete Editions Vol. 58 *Mass
oct KALMUS $1.75
contains: Beatus Laurentius (5pt,acap); O Sacrum Convivium (5pt,acap); Sacerdotes Domini (6pt,acap) (P268)

Complete Editions Vol. 59 *Mass
oct KALMUS $1.75
contains: Ave Regina Coelorum (4pt,acap); Veni Sponsa Christi (4pt,acap); Vestiva I Colli (5pt,acap) (P269)

Complete Editions Vol. 61 *Mass
oct KALMUS $1.75
contains: Assumpta Est Maria (6pt,acap); Te Deum Laudamus (6pt,acap); Veni Creator Spiritus (6pt,acap) (P270)

Complete Editions Vol. 63 *Mass
oct KALMUS $1.75
contains: Gia Fu Chi' M' Ebbe Cara (4pt, acap); In Illo Tempore (4pt,acap); Petra Sancta (5pt,acap) (P271)

Complete Editions Vol. 64 *Mass
oct KALMUS $1.75
contains: Illumina Oculos Meos, "Quinti Toni" (6pt,acap); Virgo Simul Et Mater (5pt,acap) (P272)

Complete Editions Vol. 65 *Mass
oct $1.75
contains: Panem Nostrum (5pt,acap); Pater Noster (4pt,acap) (P273)

Complete Editions Vol. 66 *Mass
oct KALMUS $1.75
contains: Descendit Angelus Domini (4pt, acap); Quando Lieta Sperai (4pt,acap); Regina Coeli (5pt,acap) (P274)

Complete Editions Vol. 67 *Mass
oct KALMUS $1.75
contains: Alma Redemptoris Mater (6pt, acap); Octavi Toni (6pt,acap); Salve Regina (5pt,acap) (P275)

Complete Editions Vol. 68 *Mass
oct KALMUS $1.75
contains: In Te Domine Speravi (6pt, acap); Sine Nomine (5pt,acap) (P276)

Complete Editions Vol. 69 *Mass
oct KALMUS $1.75
contains: Ascendo Ad Patrem (5pt,acap); O Rex Gloriae (4pt,acap); Regina Coeli (4pt,acap) (P277)

Complete Editions Vol. 70 *Mass
oct $1.75
contains: Qual E Il Piu Grande Amor (5pt, acap); Tu Es Petrus (6pt,acap) (P278)

Complete Editions Vol. 71 *Mass
oct KALMUS $1.75
contains: Ecce Ego Joannes (4pt,acap); Viri Galialei (6pt,acap) (P279)

Complete Editions Vol. 72 *Mass
oct KALMUS $1.75
contains: Hodie Christus Natus Est (8pt, acap); Laudate Dominum (8pt,acap) (P280)

Complete Editions Vol. 73 *Mass
oct KALMUS $1.75
contains: Confitebor Tibi Domine (8pt, acap); Fratres Ego Enim Accepi (8pt, acap) (P281)

Confirma Hoc *Pent/Whitsun,Offer
(Ewerhart, Rudolf) SATTB cor pts BREITKOPF-W CHB-3508 s.p. (P282)

Confitebor Tibi Domine *Mass
see Complete Editions Vol. 73
(Bauerle, Hermann) 8pt mix cor,acap cor pts BREITKOPF-L PB-3141 s.p. (P283)

Confitemini Domino
(Ruiz) [Lat] 4pt men cor,acap RICORDI-ARG BA 10488 s.p. (P284)

Corporis Mysterium *mot
[Lat] SATB RICORDI-ENG SY194 s.p. (P285)
(Zanon; Vene) "Sacrament Of Priceless Worth" [Lat/Eng] SATB,acap oct COLOMBO 1852 $.25 (P286)

Credo (from Missa Papae Marcelli) Xmas,Credo
(Rubio) [Lat] SATTBB,acap UNION ESP. 19696-3 $1.25 (P287)

Credo And Gloria (from Missa Quarta) Credo/Gloria
SATB,acap oct OXFORD 43.329 $.70 (P288)

Creed (from Missa Aeterna)
mix cor oct OXFORD 43.467 $.35 (P289)

Crown Eternal, The *see Veni Sponsa Christi

Crucem Sanctam Subiit *mot
SSATB,acap SCHIRM.EC $.25 (P290)
(Steele, Jonathan) SSATB CHESTER s.p. (P291)

Crucifixus *Bibl
"Christ Our Savior" [Eng/Lat] 4pt wom cor, acap oct SCHIRM.G 258 $.25 (P292)

Crux Ave
(Greyson) "O Cross We Hail!" SATB oct BOURNE ES109 $.30 (P293)

Da Cosi Dotta Man
(Vene) "By What Master Hand" SAT,acap oct COLOMBO 1915 $.20 (P294)

Das Hohe Lied Salomonis *see Ecce Tu Pulchra Es; Fasciculus Myrrae; Nigra Sum; Osculetur Me; Pulchra Sunt Genae Tuae; Si Ignoras Te; Tota Pulchra Es; Trahe Me; Vineam Meam; Vulnerasti Cor Meum (P295)

De Beata Virgine *Mass
(Bauerle, Hermann) SATB,acap cor pts BREITKOPF-L PB-1872 s.p., voc pt BREITKOPF-L CHB-1714 s.p. (P296)

PALESTRINA, GIOVANNI (cont'd.)

(Ewerhart) [Lat] SATB,acap AMP A536 $.75 (P297)
(Ewerhart, Rudolf) 4pt mix cor,acap cor pts BREITKOPF-W CHB-3141 (P298)

De Beata Virgine
see Complete Editions Vol. 8

De Beata Virgine
see Complete Editions Vol. 16

De Feria *Mass
see Complete Editions Vol. 15
(Bauerle, Hermann) SATB,acap cor pts BREITKOPF-L PB-1865 s.p., voc pt BREITKOPF-L CHB-1707 s.p. (P299)

De Profundis *Offer
SATTB,acap SCHIRM.EC $.25 (P300)

De Profundis Clamavi *mot
(Steele, Jonathan) SATTB CHESTER s.p. (P301)

Dei Mater Alma
"Holy, Loving Father" SATB,acap SCHIRM.EC 1712 $.18 (P302)

Descend, Thou Heav'nly Dove *see Salvete Flores Martyrum

Descendit Angelus Domini
see Complete Editions Vol. 66

Dextera Domini *mot
(Washington, Henry) [Lat] SATTB CHESTER s.p. (P303)

Dies Sanctificatus *Xmas,Mass/mot
see Complete Editions Vol. 50
[Lat] SATB,acap oct GIA G571 $.25 (P304)
[Lat] SATB RICORDI-ENG SY180 s.p. (P305)
(Bauerle, Hermann) SATB,acap voc pt BREITKOPF-L CHB-1663 s.p. (P306)
(Ewerhart) [Lat] SATB,acap AMP A538 $.30 (P307)
(Ewerhart) [Lat] SATB,acap AMP A534 $.75 (P308)
(Ewerhart, Rudolf) 4pt mix cor,acap cor pts BREITKOPF-W CHB-3143 s.p. (P309)
(Ewerhart, Rudolf) 4pt mix cor,acap cor pts BREITKOPF-W CHB-3069 s.p. (P310)
(Greyson) "O Day Of Consecration" SATB oct BOURNE ES47 $.30 (P311)
(Haberl, Fr.X.) SATB,acap cor pts BREITKOPF-L PB-2787 s.p., voc pt BREITKOPF-L CHB-442 s.p. (P312)
(Haberl, Fr.X.) SATB,acap cor pts BREITKOPF-L PB-2786 s.p., voc pt BREITKOPF-L CHB-716 s.p. (P313)
(Montani) [Lat] 4pt mix cor,acap oct SCHIRM.G 6443 $.30 (P314)

Dies Santificatus
SATB,acap oct PRESSER MC342 $.35 (P315)

Dilexi Quoniam
see Complete Editions Vol. 51

Drei Motetten *Gen,mot
(Fellerer, Karl Gustav) SATB,acap (med) MULLER SM 936 s.p.
contains: Ave Maria; Benedicta Sit Sancta Trinitatis; Pulchra Es Amica Mea (P316)

Dritter Nachtrag Zur Gesamtausgabe-Band XXXII (from Samtliche Werke) CCU
(De Witt; Rausch; Espagne; Commer; Haberl) BREITKOPF-W s.p. (P317)

Dum Complerentur *Pent,mot
see Complete Editions Vol. 57
SAATTB,acap SCHIRM.EC $.30 (P318)
(Petti, Anthony G.) "Now When The Day" [Eng/Lat] SAATTB CHESTER s.p. (P319)

Dum Ergo Essent *mot
(Petti, Anthony G.) "When All Disciples" [Eng/Lat] SAATTB CHESTER s.p. (P320)

Dum Esset Summus Pontifex
see Complete Editions Vol. 56

Dunque Divin Spiracolo *madrigal
(Malin) "Come, Then, O Holy Breath Of God" [Eng/It] SATB,acap MARKS 4414 $.25 (P321)

Ecce Ego Joannes *Mass
see Complete Editions Vol. 71
(Ewerhart) [Lat] SATTBarB AMP A542 $.75 (P322)
(Ewerhart, Rudolf) 6pt mix cor,acap cor pts BREITKOPF-W CHB-3147 s.p. (P323)

Ecce, Quomodo Moritur
(Davison, A.) [Lat] TTBB,acap SCHIRM.EC 45 $.25 (P324)
(Woodworth, G.) [Lat] SSAA,acap SCHIRM.EC 826 $.25 (P325)

Ecce Quomodo Moritur Justus *mot
[Lat] SATB RICORDI-ENG SY136 s.p. (P326)
(Veneziani) SATB,acap cor pts RICORDI-ENG 121645-46 s.p. (P327)

Ecce Sacerdos Magnus
see Complete Editions Vol. 1

Ecce Tu Pulchra Es *Gen,Bibl
(Hubsch, Hanns) [Lat] SATTB,acap (med) MULLER SM 758 s.p. see from Das Hohe Lied Salomonis (P328)

Ecce Vidimus Eum
see Tria Responsoria
mix cor SOUTHERN $.25 (P329)

Ego Sum Panis Vivus *mot
[Lat] SATB,acap oct GIA G570 $.25 (P330)

Elegerunt Apostoli *Fest,Offer
(Ewerhart, Rudolf) SATTB,acap cor pts BREITKOPF-W CHB-3506 s.p. (P331)

Emendemus
see Complete Editions Vol. 53

PALESTRINA, GIOVANNI (cont'd.)

Eripe Me Do Inimicie
see Complete Editions Vol. 26

Erster Nachtrag Zur Gesamtausgabe-Band XXX (from Samtliche Werke) CCU
(De Witt; Rausch; Espagne; Commer; Haberl) BREITKOPF-W s.p. (P332)

Esurientes
(Ruiz) [Lat] 3pt men cor,acap RICORDI-ARG BA 10489 s.p. (P333)

Et Resurrexit
SATB,acap RICORDI-ENG SY186 s.p. (P334)

Exaltabo Te, Domine *Bibl/mot/Offer
"Thee Will I Extol" [Lat/Eng] SATTB,acap oct SCHIRM.G 7620 $.30 (P335)
(Collins, H.B.) [Lat] SATTB CHESTER s.p. (P336)
(Ewerhart, Rudolf) mix cor cor pts BREITKOPF-W CHB-3509 (P337)

Exsultate Deo *mot
(Washington, Henri) [Lat] SAATB CHESTER s.p. (P338)

Exultate Deo *Gen,Bibl/mot
[Lat] SAATB,acap oct GIA G558 $.25 (P339)
SAATB,acap SCHIRM.EC 322 $.35 (P340)
[Ger] SAATB (med) MULLER MS 43 s.p. (P341)
"Sing And Praise Jehovah" [Lat/Eng] SAATB, acap oct SCHIRM.G 7672 $.25 (P342)
(Payson, A.) "Praise The Lord, Jehovah" SSATB FRANK F-571 $.35 (P343)

Fasciculus Myrrae *Gen,Bibl
(Hubsch, Hanns) [Lat] SATTB,acap (med) MULLER SM 757 s.p. see from Das Hohe Lied Salomonis (P344)

Feria VI. In Parasceve *see Lamentation Des Karfreitags (P345)

Finsternis Ward Uber Das Land *Holywk/Psntd
SATB HANSSLER 6.2540 s.p. contains also: Burck, Joachim, Schwer Gehet Uber Mein Haupt (P346)

Four Motets *mot
(Hamburger, P.) [Lat] oct MUSIKHOJ 2 $4.00
contains: Ad Te Levavi Oculos Meos; Misere Nostri, Domine (SATB); Ave Regina Coelorum; Gaude Virgo Gloriosa (SSSA); Isti Sunt (SATB); Quae Est Ista (SSATB) (P347)

Four Motets *mot
[Lat] voc sc HINRICHSEN D2411 s.p.
contains: Motet 1 (SATB,acap); Motet 2 (SATB,acap); Motet 3 (SSSA,acap); Motet 4 (SSATB,acap) (P348)

Fratres Ego Enim Accepi
see Complete Editions Vol. 73

Fuit Homo *mot
(Bauerle, Hermann) SATB,acap voc pt BREITKOPF-L CHB-1693 s.p. (P349)

Funfunddreissig Magnificat-Band XXVII (from Samtliche Werke) CCU,Magnif
(De Witt; Rausch; Espagne; Commer; Haberl) BREITKOPF-W s.p. (P350)

Gabrile Archanglus
see Complete Editions Vol. 2

Gaude Barbara
(Vene) "O Sing Joyfully" [Lat/Eng] SSAA, acap oct COLOMBO 1877 $.30 (P351)

Gia Fu Chi' M' Ebbe Cara
see Complete Editions Vol. 63

Gloria (from De Beata Virgine) Gloria
see Complete Editions Vol. 10
SATB,acap RICORDI-ENG SY201 s.p. (P352)
(Colacicchi, L.) 4pt SANTIS 959 s.p. (P353)
(Somma, B.) 4pt mix cor SANTIS 995 s.p. (P354)

Gloria Patri
"Praise To The Father" see RESPONSES FROM THE WORKS OF OLD MASTERS
SATB KJOS $.30 (P355)
mix cor SOUTHERN $.30 (P356)
(Damrosch) [Lat/Eng] 8pt mix cor,acap oct SCHIRM.G 11566 $.30 (P357)
(Davis, K.) "Glory To God" SSA SCHIRM.EC 1860 (P358)
(Davis, K.) "Glory To God" SA SCHIRM.EC 1556 (P359)
(Greyson) "Glory To God" SSA oct BOURNE ES46A $.25 (P360)
(Greyson) "Glory To God" SATB oct BOURNE ES46 $.25 (P361)
(Howorth) boy cor SOUTHERN $.30 (P362)
(Howorth) [Eng/Lat] SATB,acap WARNER G1704 $.30 (P363)
(Howorth) [Eng/Lat] TTBB,acap WARNER G1482 $.30 (P364)

Glory To God *see Gloria Patri

Great Woe Hath Touched This Holy Man *see O Quantus Luctus

Haec Dies *Easter/Lent/Psntd,anthem/mot
SSATTB,acap voc pt DOBLINGER s.p. see also PASSION UND OSTERN (P365)
(Bauerle, Hermann) dbl cor,acap cor pts BREITKOPF-L PB-2404 s.p., voc pt BREITKOPF-L CHB-1229 s.p. (P366)
(Marshall, Charles) "This Glad Day" SSATBB FRANK F-585 $.30 (P367)
(Row) "This Day" SSATTB oct FISCHER,C R-277 $.25 (P368)

Haec Dies Quam Fecit *Easter
(Geiringer) "Jehovah Did Make This Holy Day" [Lat/Eng] SSATT,acap oct SCHIRM.G 8336 $.25 (P369)

Haec Dies Quam Fecit Dominus *Easter,mot
(Bridge, Sir Fredk.) "This Is The Day" SSATTB BOSWORTH s.p. see from Motets (P370)

PALESTRINA, GIOVANNI (cont'd.)

Haec Dies Quem Fecit *Gen
[Ger] SATB,acap (med) MULLER MS 41 s.p.
(P371)

Have Mercy Upon Us *see Miserere Nostri

He Is Blessed *see Benedictus

Here We Worship Thee *see Adoramus Te,
Christe

Hodie Christus Natus Est *Xmas,mot
see Complete Editions Vol. 72
girl cor SOUTHERN $.30   (P372)
men cor sc ALSBACH&D s.p.   (P373)
[Lat/Eng] SSAA BROUDE BR. $.35   (P374)
(Damrosch, F.) [Lat/Eng] SSSAATBB,acap oct
SCHIRM.G 11607 $.40   (P375)
(Ewerhart) [Lat] SSAATTBB,acap AMP A529
$.30   (P376)
(Ewerhart, Rudolf) 8pt mix cor,acap cor pts
BREITKOPF-W CHB-3064 s.p.   (P377)
(Gronquist, R.) [Lat/Eng] SSAA BROUDE,A.
170 $.30   (P378)

Holy, Holy, Holy (from Aeterna Munera
Christi) Sanctus
SATB oct FISCHER,J 6354 $.30   (P379)
mix cor SOUTHERN $.30   (P380)
(Zanon; Vene) [Lat/Eng] SATB,acap oct
COLOMBO 2001 $.30   (P381)

Holy, Loving Father *see Dei Mater Alma

Hosanna In The Highest
(Davies) mix cor CURWEN 80884 s.p.   (P382)

Hymnen-Band VIII (from Samtliche Werke) CCU,
hymn
(De Witt; Rausch; Espagne; Commer; Haberl)
BREITKOPF-W s.p.   (P383)

Iam Christus Astra Ascenderat *Mass
(Bauerle, Hermann) SATB,acap s.p. cor pts
BREITKOPF-L PB-1869, voc pt BREITKOPF-L
CHB-1711   (P384)

Illumina Oculos Meos
"Quinti Toni" see Complete Editions Vol. 64

Improperia
anti cor,acap (abridged) SCHIRM.EC 1191
$.25   (P385)
(Davison, A.) [Lat] anti cor,acap SCHIRM.EC
46 $.18   (P386)

Improperium Expectavit *Psntd,Offer
(Ewerhart, Rudolf) SSATB,acap cor pts
BREITKOPF-W CHB-3505 s.p.   (P387)

In Divers Tongues Spake The Apostles
*Whitsun,anthem/mot
(West, John E.) mix cor oct NOVELLO
28.0913.03 s.p.   (P388)

In Gethsemane *see Tristis Est Anima Mea

In Illo Tempore
see Complete Editions Vol. 63

In Majoribus Duplicibus
see Complete Editions Vol. 55

In Minoribus Dublicibis
see Complete Editions Vol. 55

In Monte Oliveti *Easter/Lent
see Tria Responsoria
(Richardson) "Upon The Mount Of Olives"
SATB oct SPRATT 2007 $.25   (P389)

In Te Domine Speravi
see Complete Editions Vol. 50

In Te Domine Speravi
see Complete Editions Vol. 68

Innocentes Pro Christo
[Lat] 4pt wom cor,acap oct SCHIRM.G 5605
$.25   (P390)

Introduxit Me Rex
mix cor SOUTHERN $.20   (P391)

Inviolata
see Complete Editions Vol. 8

Is It Nothing, All Of You Who Pass By *see O
Vos Omnes

Iste Confessor *Mass
see Complete Editions Vol. 39
[Lat] SATB MARKS $1.00   (P392)
(Ewerhart) [Lat] SATB,acap AMP A537 $.50
(P393)
(Ewerhart, Rudolf) 4pt mix cor,acap cor pts
BREITKOPF-W CHB-3142 s.p.   (P394)

Isti Sunt
see Four Motets

It Is A Good Thing To Give Thanks *see Bonum
Est Confiteri

Jam Christus Astra Ascenderat
see Complete Editions Vol. 39

Jehovah Did Make This Holy Day *see Haec
Dies Quam Fecit

Jerusalem Remembered *see Recordata

Jesu, Nostra Redemptio
see Complete Editions Vol. 25
(Schabasser, Josef) mix cor,acap oct
DOBLINGER s.p. see also CHRISTUS, DER
HERR   (P395)

Jesu Nostra Redemptis *Mass
(Bauerle, Hermann) SATB,acap voc pt
BREITKOPF-L CHB-1665 s.p.   (P396)

Jesu! Rex Admirabilis
"Jesu, Transcendent, Glorious King" SSA,
acap SCHIRM.EC 1074 $.20   (P397)
"Thou All-Transcendent Deity" SAB/SAT,acap
SCHIRM.EC 1697 $.25   (P398)

PALESTRINA, GIOVANNI (cont'd.)

Jesu, Transcendent, Glorious King *see Jesu!
Rex Admirabilis

Jesus Christ, Our Lord Was Crucified *see
Christus Factus Est

Joy So Delights My Heart
mix cor SOUTHERN $.40   (P399)

Jubilate Deo *mot
(Bauerle, Hermann) dbl cor,acap cor pts
BREITKOPF-L PB-2403 s.p., voc pt
BREITKOPF-L CHB-1228 s.p.   (P400)
(Bauerle, Hermann) 8pt mix cor,acap cor pts
BREITKOPF-W PB-2403 s.p.   (P401)

Jubilate Deo *see Lassus, Roland de
(Orlandus)

Justorum Animae *Offer
(Ewerhart, Rudolf) mix cor cor pts
BREITKOPF-W CHB-3510   (P402)

Komm, Heiliger Geist *see Veni, Creator,
Spiritus

Koszonto Enek
(Rajcs, I.) [Hung] SAT (easy) BUDAPEST see
also NASZDALOK VEGYESKARRA   (P403)

Kyrie (from Missa Brevis) Kyrie
mix cor NORDISKA 5175 s.p.   (P404)
SATB oct WALTON 2126 $.25   (P405)
SATB,acap RICORDI-ENG SY185 s.p.   (P406)

Kyrie Eleison *Easter/Lent,Kyrie
(Marshall, Charles) "O Lord , Have Mercy"
SATB FRANK F-597 $.30   (P407)
(Tolmage) SATB oct STAFF 562 $.25   (P408)

Kyrie Eleison Sanctus, Benedictus, And Agnus
Dei (from Missa Quarta) Agnus/Bene/Kyrie/
Sanctus
SATB,acap oct OXFORD 43.330 $.65   (P409)

Kyrie Eleison (from Missa Emendemus) Kyrie
(Douglas) "Lord Have Mercy Upon Us" [Eng/
Lat] SATB,opt kbd oct PRO ART 2317 $.30   (P410)

Lamb Of God *see Agnus Dei

Lamentation Des Karfreitags *Gd.Fri.
(Filke, M.) SATB,acap voc pt BREITKOPF-L
CHB-1389 s.p. see from Feria VI. In
Parasceve   (P411)

Lamentationen Band XXV (from Samtliche Werke)
CCU
(De Witt; Rausch; Espagne; Commer; Haberl)
BREITKOPF-W s.p.   (P412)

Lat Oss Med Jesus Vandra
mix cor NORDISKA 2538 s.p.   (P413)

Lauda Sion *Mass
see Complete Editions Vol. 25
(Bauerle, Hermann) SATB,acap voc pt
BREITKOPF-L CHB-1667 s.p.   (P414)
(Ewerhart) [Lat] SATB,acap AMP A533 $.60
(P415)

Lauda Sion Salvatorem *Pent/Whitsun,Mass/mot
SATB,acap voc pt DOBLINGER s.p. see also
PFINGSTEN UND EUCHARISTIE   (P416)
(Ewerhart) [Lat] SATB,acap AMP A539 $.30
(P417)
(Ewerhart, Rudolf) 4pt mix cor,acap cor pts
BREITKOPF-W CHB-3068 s.p.   (P418)
(Ewerhart, Rudolf) 4pt mix cor,acap cor pts
BREITKOPF-W CHB-3144 s.p.   (P419)

Laudate Dominum
see Complete Editions Vol. 72
"We Adore You, O Christ" see Palestrina,
Giovanni, O Bone Jesu

Laudate Dominum, Heft VIII, Part 1: Die
Marianischen Antiphone *CC4U,BVM/Fest
(Hubsch, Hanns) [Ger] 4pt mix cor,acap
(med) MULLER SM 1514A s.p.   (P420)

Laudate Dominum, Heft VIII, Part 2: Die
Marianischen Antiphone *CC4U,BVM/Fest
(Hubsch, Hanns) [Ger] 5pt mix cor,acap
(med) MULLER SM 1514B s.p.   (P421)

Leichte Chorsatze *CC13L,anthem
SATB,acap cor pts BREITKOPF-L EB-1350 s.p.
(P422)

Leichte Chorsatze *CC18L
wom cor/jr cor,acap cor pts BREITKOPF-L
EB-1352 s.p.   (P423)

L'homme Arme
see Complete Editions Vol. 25

L'Homme Arme
see Complete Editions Vol. 15

Like As The Hart *see Sicut Cervus

Like As The Hart *see Sicut Cervus Desiderat

Litaneien, Motetten, Und Psalmen-Band XXVI
(from Samtliche Werke) CCU,mot/Psalm
(De Witt; Rausch; Espagne; Commer; Haberl)
BREITKOPF-W s.p.   (P424)

Litania De Beata Virgine Maria
see Complete Editions Vol. 49

Litaniae Deiparae Virginis I
see Complete Editions Vol. 48

Litaniae Deiparae Virginis II
see Complete Editions Vol. 48

Lo, They Have Borne Away Jesus *see
Alleluia! Tulerunt Dominum

Loquebantur
(Sorensen, Soren) "Lydt Forkyndte" [Lat/
Dan] SATB,acap HANSEN-DEN 283 s.p. see
also MOTETTER OG LAUDER FRA DET 16.
ARHUNDREDE   (P425)

PALESTRINA, GIOVANNI (cont'd.)

Loquebantur (Lydt Forkyndte)
(Sorenson, Soren) [Lat/Dan] SATB,acap
HANSEN-DEN 283 s.p. see also MOTETTER OG
LAUDER FRA DET 16. ARHUNDREDE   (P426)

Loquebantur Variis Linguis *Pent
[Lat] SATB,acap (med) MULLER M 22 s.p.
(P427)

Lord God Of Heaven *see Panis Angelicus

Lord Have Mercy Upon Us *see Kyrie Eleison

Lydt Forkyndet *see Loquebantur

Ma So Ben, Signor Mio *madrigal
(Malin) "Well Do I Know, My Lord" [Eng/It]
SSATB,acap MARKS 4466 $.25   (P428)

Madrigale-Band XXVIII (from Samtliche Werke)
CCU,madrigal
(De Witt; Rausch; Espagne; Commer; Haberl)
BREITKOPF-W s.p.   (P429)

Madrigale-Band XXIX (from Samtliche Werke)
CCU,madrigal
(De Witt; Rausch; Espagne; Commer; Haberl)
BREITKOPF-W s.p.   (P430)

Magnificat *Magnif
girl cor SOUTHERN $.35   (P431)

Magnificat In The Fourth Mode *see
Magnificat Nel Quatro Tono

Magnificat Nel Quatro Tono
(Boepple, P.) "Magnificat In The Fourth
Mode" SSAA,acap oct PRESSER 352-00012
$.35   (P432)

Memor Esto
see Complete Editions Vol. 57

Messen-Band X (from Samtliche Werke) CCU,Mass
(De Witt; Rausch; Espagne; Commer; Haberl)
BREITKOPF-W s.p.   (P433)

Messen-Band XI (from Samtliche Werke) CCU,
Mass
(De Witt; Rausch; Espagne; Commer; Haberl)
BREITKOPF-W s.p.   (P434)

Messen-Band XII (from Samtliche Werke) CCU,
Mass
(De Witt; Rausch; Espagne; Commer; Haberl)
BREITKOPF-W s.p.   (P435)

Messen-Band XIII (from Samtliche Werke) CCU,
Mass
(De Witt; Rausch; Espagne; Commer; Haberl)
BREITKOPF-W s.p.   (P436)

Messen-Band XIV (from Samtliche Werke) CCU,
Mass
(De Witt; Rausch; Espagne; Commer; Haberl)
BREITKOPF-W s.p.   (P437)

Messen-Band XV (from Samtliche Werke) CCU,
Mass
(De Witt; Rausch; Espagne; Commer; Haberl)
BREITKOPF-W s.p.   (P438)

Messen-Band XVI (from Samtliche Werke) CCU,
Mass
(De Witt; Rausch; Espagne; Commer; Haberl)
BREITKOPF-W s.p.   (P439)

Messen-Band XVII (from Samtliche Werke) CCU,
Mass
(De Witt; Rausch; Espagne; Commer; Haberl)
BREITKOPF-W s.p.   (P440)

Messen-Band XVIII (from Samtliche Werke) CCU,
Mass
(De Witt; Rausch; Espagne; Commer; Haberl)
BREITKOPF-W s.p.   (P441)

Messen-Band XIX (from Samtliche Werke) CCU,
Mass
(De Witt; Rausch; Espagne; Commer; Haberl)
BREITKOPF-W s.p.   (P442)

Messen-Band XX (from Samtliche Werke) CCU,
Mass
(De Witt; Rausch; Espagne; Commer; Haberl)
BREITKOPF-W s.p.   (P443)

Messen-Band XXI (from Samtliche Werke) CCU,
Mass
(De Witt; Rausch; Espagne; Commer; Haberl)
BREITKOPF-W s.p.   (P444)

Messen-Band XXII (from Samtliche Werke) CCU,
Mass
(De Witt; Rausch; Espagne; Commer; Haberl)
BREITKOPF-W s.p.   (P445)

Messen-Band XXIII (from Samtliche Werke) CCU,
Mass
(De Witt; Rausch; Espagne; Commer; Haberl)
BREITKOPF-W s.p.   (P446)

Messen-Band XXIV (from Samtliche Werke) CCU,
Mass
(De Witt; Rausch; Espagne; Commer; Haberl)
BREITKOPF-W s.p.   (P447)

Miserere Nostri *Lent
"Have Mercy Upon Us" SATB,acap SCHIRM.EC
1269 $.20   (P448)

Missa Ad Fugam In Perpetuo Canone *Mass
(Jode) 2pt mix cor MOSELER s.p.   (P449)

Missa Aeterna *Mass
mix cor oct OXFORD 43.466 $.65   (P450)

Missa Brevis *Mass
cor voc sc KALMUS 6372 $1.00   (P451)
[Lat] S/A&T/B,acap voc sc HINRICHSEN SP6
s.p.   (P452)
SATB,acap SCHIRM.EC $1.50   (P453)
(Bauerle, Hermann) SATB,acap cor pts
BREITKOPF-L PB-1856 s.p., voc pt
BREITKOPF-L CHB-1662 s.p.   (P454)
(Damrosch, Frank) [Lat] mix cor,acap voc sc
SCHIRM.G $1.00   (P455)
(Ewerhart) [Lat] SATB,acap AMP A528 $.60

PALESTRINA, GIOVANNI (cont'd.)

(Somma, B.) 4pt sc SANTIS 703 s.p.,
     (P456)
SANTIS 704-705 s.p.
     (P457)
(Washington, Henry) [Lat] SATB CHESTER s.p.
     (P458)

Missa Papae Marcelli *Mass
mix cor,acap voc sc KALMUS 6365 $1.50
     (P459)
[Lat] SATTBB,acap min sc PETERS E963 $2.00
     (P460)
(Deis, Carl) [Eng/Lat] cor,acap voc sc
SCHIRM.G $1.50
     (P461)
(Schering) [Lat] SATTBB,acap min sc SCHOTT
EUL963 s.p.
     (P462)

Missa Sine Nomine *Mass
cor pts BELWIN $1.50
     (P463)

Missa Sine Nomine II *Mass
(Bauerle, Hermann) SATB,acap voc pt
BREITKOPF-L CHB-1669 s.p.
     (P464)

Motet 1
see Four Motets

Motet 2
see Four Motets

Motet 3
see Four Motets

Motet 4
see Four Motets

Motets *see Haec Dies Quam Fecit Dominus,
"This Is The Day"; Ssattb; Tu Es Petrus,
"Thou Art Peter"; With Other Tongues
Spake The Apostles
     (P465)

Motetten Aus Dem Nachlass-Band VII (from
Samtliche Werke) CCU,mot
(De Witt; Rausch; Espagne; Commer; Haberl)
BREITKOPF-W s.p.
     (P466)

Motetten-Band I (from Samtliche Werke) CCU,
mot
(De Witt; Rausch; Espagne; Commer; Haberl)
BREITKOPF-W s.p.
     (P467)

Motetten-Band II (from Samtliche Werke) CCU,
mot
(De Witt; Rausch; Espagne; Commer; Haberl)
BREITKOPF-W s.p.
     (P468)

Motetten-Band III (from Samtliche Werke) CCU,
mot
(De Witt; Rausch; Espagne; Commer; Haberl)
BREITKOPF-W s.p.
     (P469)

Motetten-Band IV (from Samtliche Werke) CCU,
mot
(De Witt; Rausch; Espagne; Commer; Haberl)
BREITKOPF-W s.p.
     (P470)

Motetten-Band V (from Samtliche Werke) CCU,
mot
(De Witt; Rausch; Espagne; Commer; Haberl)
BREITKOPF-W s.p.
     (P471)

Motetten-Band VI (from Samtliche Werke) CCU,
mot
(De Witt; Rausch; Espagne; Commer; Haberl)
BREITKOPF-W s.p.
     (P472)

Motetten Zur Liturgie Der Karwoche Und Des
Ostertages, Heft I: Palmsonntag *CCU,
Palm/Psntd,mot
(Hahn, Albert; Hahn, Wilhelm) [Ger] SATB,
acap (med) MULLER SM 1830, 31 s.p. (P473)

Motetten Zur Liturgie Der Karwoche Und Des
Ostertages, Heft II: Triduum Sacrum
*CCU,Psntd,mot
(Hahn, Albert; Hahn, Wilhelm) [Ger] SATB,
acap (med) MULLER SM 1830, 32 s.p. (P474)

Motetten Zur Liturgie Der Karwoche Und Des
Ostertages, Heft III: Grundonnerstag
*CCU,Psntd,mot
(Hahn, Albert; Hahn, Wilhelm) [Ger] SATB,
acap (med) MULLER SM 1380, 33 s.p. (P475)

Motetten Zur Liturgie Der Karwoche Und Des
Ostertages, Heft V: Osternacht *CCU,
Easter,liturg/mot
(Hahn, Albert; Hahn, Wilhelm) [Ger] SATB,
acap (med) MULLER SM 1830, 35 s.p. (P476)

Motetten Zur Liturgie Der Karwoche Und Des
Ostertages, Heft VI: Ostersonntag *CCU,
Easter,liturg/mot
(Hahn, Albert; Hahn, Wilhelm) [Ger] SATB,
acap (med) MULLER SM 1830, 36 s.p. (P477)

Motteten Zur Liturgie Der Karwoche Und Des
Ostertages, Heft IV: Karfreitag *CCU,
Gd.Fri./Psntd,mot
(Hahn, Albert; Hahn, Wilhelm) [Ger] SATB,
acap (med) MULLER SM 1830, 34 s.p. (P478)

My Heart It Seemed, Was Dying
see Ars Nova To Rennaissance Vol. 6-1200 To
About 1500

My Soul Is Athirst *see Sitivit Anima Mea

Nasce La Gioia Mia
see Complete Editions Vol. 40

Nigra Sum *Gen,Bibl
(Hubsch, Hanns) [Lat] SATTB,acap (med)
MULLER SM 753 s.p. see from Das Hohe Lied
Salomonis
     (P479)

Nos Autem Gloriari Aportet *mot
(Bauerle, Hermann) SATB,acap voc pt
BREITKOPF-L CHB-1678 s.p.
     (P480)

Now Do We Behold Him *Xmas,anthem
(Richardson) SAB oct WORD CS-2446 $.30
     (P481)
(Richardson, John A.) unis/SA WORD CS-325
$.30
     (P482)

Now When The Day *see Dum Complerentur

PALESTRINA, GIOVANNI (cont'd.)

O Admirabile Commercium *Xmas/Gen,Mass
see Complete Editions Vol. 56
mix cor,acap voc sc KALMUS 6367 $1.25
     (P483)
SSATB,acap (med) oct OXFORD 43.370 $.35
     (P484)
(Bauerle, Hermann) 5pt mix cor,acap voc pt
BREITKOPF-L CHB-1885 s.p.
     (P485)

O Beata *mot
mix cor,acap voc sc KALMUS 6371 $1.25
     (P486)

O Beata Et Gloriosa *mot
(Haberl, Fr.X.) 5pt mix cor,acap cor pts
BREITKOPF-L PB-2800 s.p., voc pt
BREITKOPF-L CHB-1721 s.p.
     (P487)

O Beata Et Gloriosa Trinitas
see O Holy And Glorious Trinity

O Blessed Jesu *anthem
(Galloway, G.) mix cor oct NOVELLO
50.0273.07 s.p.
     (P488)

O Blessed Jesus *see O Bone Jesu

O Bone Jesu *Easter/Gen/Lent,anthem/mot
see LA SCHOLA PALESTRINIENNE PREMIERE
CAHIER
[Lat] 4pt mix cor HEUGEL s.p. see from LA
MAITRISE
     (P489)
[Lat/Ger] SATB SCHOTT s.p.
     (P490)
SATB oct FISCHER,C CM-198 $.25 contains
also: Adoramus Te Christe
     (P491)
SATB KJOS 7018 $.30
     (P492)
[Lat] SATB,acap SCHIRM.EC 1166 $.25
     (P493)
"O Blessed Jesus" [Lat/Eng] 4pt mix cor,
acap oct SCHIRM.G 10022 $.25
     (P494)
"O Gracious Jesus" SATB oct FISCHER,J 9705
$.30
     (P495)
"O Holy Father" SATB,acap SCHIRM.EC 1137
$.25
     (P496)
(Castellazzi) [Lat] SATB,acap RICORDI-ARG
BA 10368 s.p.
     (P497)
(Davis, K.) "O Holy Jesu" SSA,acap
SCHIRM.EC 1871 $.20
     (P498)
(Ehret) SAB,acap oct PRO ART 1714 $.30
     (P499)
(Ehret) SATB,opt kbd oct PRO ART 1432 $.30
     (P500)
(Ehret) SSA oct PRO ART 2206 $.30
     (P501)
(Greyson) "O Holy Jesus" TTBB oct BOURNE
ES45 $.25
     (P502)
(Harthan, H.) SATB,acap oct PRESSER
332-03070 $.25
     (P503)
(Lee, J.) "O Loving Jesus" [Lat/Eng] SATB
(easy) oct GIA G1384 $.30 contains also:
Laudate Dominum, "We Adore You, O Christ"
     (P504)
(Pisano) SAB oct PLYMOUTH SC-402 $.25
     (P505)
(Saar, L.) SSA oct PRESSER 332-14207 $.25
     (P506)
(Schinelli, A.) [It/Eng/Ger] 4pt mix cor
CURCI 6082 s.p. see from COLLANA DI
COMPOSIZIONI POLIFONICHE VOCALE SACRE E
PROFANE, VOL. 1
     (P507)
(Scott) "O Blessed Jesus" SATB oct SPRATT
534 $.25
     (P508)

O Bone Jesus *mot
(Zanon) SATB,acap RICORDI-ENG SY155 s.p.
     (P509)

O Che Splendor
"O Lovely Splendor" SATB oct WALTON 7013
$.30
     (P510)

O Come, Let Us Worship *see Adoramus Te,
Christe

O Cross We Greet Thee
(Lundquist) SATB,acap (diff) oct WILLIS
8422 $.22
     (P511)

O Cross We Hail! *see Crux Ave

O Crux Ave *Easter/Psntd
mix cor sc ALSBACH&D s.p.
     (P512)
[Lat] SATB,acap (med) MULLER MS 18 s.p.
     (P513)
SATB,acap voc pt DOBLINGER s.p. see also
PASSION UND OSTERN
     (P514)

O Day Of Consecration *see Dies
Sanctificatus

O Domine Jesu Christe
men cor sc ALSBACH&D s.p.
     (P515)
[Lat] SATB,acap (med) oct WILLIS 909 $.10
     (P516)
SATB,acap SCHIRM.EC 1734 $.20
     (P517)
(Harris) SAB FLAMMER D5146 $.30
     (P518)
(Harris) SSA FLAMMER B 5071 $.30
     (P519)
(Knight, Gerald) SATB,acap oct FISCHER,C
CM-7590 $.25
     (P520)
(Ruiz) [Lat] 4pt men cor,acap RICORDI-ARG
BA 10084 s.p.
     (P521)

O Good Lord Jesu
(Currie) [Lat/Eng] SATB oct JUSKO 232 $.20
     (P522)

O Gracious Jesus *see O Bone Jesu

O, Guds Lamm *see Agnus Dei

O, Have Mercy On Us
(Kingsbury, John) SSATB ALFRED 6402 $.30
     (P523)

O Holy And Glorious Trinity *Trin
SSATB,acap (diff) oct OXFORD 43.924 $.65
contains: O Beata Et Gloriosa Trinitas; O
Salutaris Hostia
     (P524)

O Holy Father *see O Bone Jesu

O Holy Jesu *see O Bone Jesu

O Holy Jesus *see O Bone Jesu

O Jesu Dolce *madrigal
(Malin) "O Kindly Jesus" [Eng/It] SATTB,
acap MARKS 4418 $.25
     (P525)

O Kindly Jesus *see O Jesu Dolce

PALESTRINA, GIOVANNI (cont'd.)

O King Of Glory *see O Rex Gloriae

O Lord, Have Mercy *see Kyrie Eleison

O Lord, In Thee Do I Put My Trust (from
Aeterna Christi Munera)
(Trusler) SATB oct PLYMOUTH TR-116 $.25
     (P526)

O Lord Most High
(Lundquist) SSA oct ELKAN-V 362-3095 $.25
     (P527)

O Lord, My God *anthem
mix cor oct NOVELLO 40.0125.07 s.p. (P528)

O Lovely Splendor *see O Che Splendor

O Loving Jesus *see O Bone Jesu

O Magnum Mysterium *mot
see Complete Editions Vol. 26
(Ewerhart, Rudolf) 6pt mix cor,acap cor pts
BREITKOPF-W CHB-3061 s.p.
     (P529)

O Magnum Mysterium *mot
(Ewerhart) [Lat] SSAATB,acap AMP A526 $.35
     (P530)

O Quantus Luctus
(Ewerhart) "Great Woe Hath Touched This
Holy Man" [Lat/Eng] SATB,acap AMP A408
$.25
     (P531)

O Queen Of Heaven *see Regina Coeli

O Regem Coeli
see Complete Editions Vol. 1

O Rex Gloriae *Asc
see Complete Editions Vol. 69
"O King Of Glory" SATB,acap SCHIRM.EC 1271
$.35
     (P532)

O Sacred And Holy Feast *see O Sacrum
Convivium

O Sacrum Convivium *Mass
see Complete Editions Vol. 58
(Bauerle, Hermann) 5pt mix cor,acap cor pts
BREITKOPF-L PB-2033 s.p., voc pt
BREITKOPF-L CHB-1886 s.p.
     (P533)
(Greyson) "O Sacred And Holy Feast" SATB
oct BOURNE ES106 $.30
     (P534)

O Salutaris Hostia
see O Holy And Glorious Trinity

O Saviour Of The World *anthem
mix cor oct NOVELLO 50.0308.03 s.p. (P535)

O Sing Joyfully *see Gaude Barbara

O Vos Omnes
(Greyson) "All Ye People" SATB oct BOURNE
ES108 $.30
     (P536)
(Klein) "Is It Nothing, All Of You Who Pass
By" [Lat/Eng] 4pt mix cor,acap oct
SCHIRM.G 11417 $.30
     (P537)

Octavi Toni
see Complete Editions Vol. 67

Offertorien-Band IX (from Samtliche Werke)
CCU,Offer
(De Witt; Rausch; Espagne; Commer; Haberl)
BREITKOPF-W s.p.
     (P538)

Offertorium (from Super Flumina Babylonis)
Pent,Offer
(Haberl, Fr.X.) 5pt mix cor,acap cor pts
BREITKOPF-L PB-2798 s.p., voc pt
BREITKOPF-L CHB-1636 s.p.
     (P539)

Omnis Pulchritudo Domini
[Lat] SSAT&ATTB,acap cor pts HINRICHSEN
D235 s.p.
     (P540)
(Maselli, G.F.) dbl cor sc SANTIS 799 s.p.
     (P541)

Osculetur Me *Gen,Bibl
(Hubsch, Hanns) [Lat] SATTB,acap (med)
MULLER SM 751 s.p. see from Das Hohe Lied
Salomonis
     (P542)

Panem Nostrum
see Complete Editions Vol. 65

Panis Angelicus
"Lord God Of Heaven" SATB oct FISCHER,J
3369 $.30
     (P543)
(Ruiz) [Lat] 4pt men cor,acap RICORDI-ARG
BA 10092 s.p.
     (P544)

Panis Quem Ergo Dabo
see Complete Editions Vol. 39

Papae Marcelli (from De Beata Virgine) Xmas,
Mass
see Complete Editions Vol. 10
see Ars Nova To Rennaissance Vol. 6-1200 To
About 1500
mix cor BELWIN $1.25
     (P545)
[Lat] SATTBB,acap cor pts HINRICHSEN SP3
s.p.
     (P546)
(Ewerhart) [Lat] SATTBB,acap AMP A530 $1.00
     (P547)
(Goldschmidt, Otto) [Lat] SSATB,acap voc
sc NOVELLO s.p.
     (P548)
(Haberl, Fr.X.) 6pt mix cor,acap voc pt
BREITKOPF-L PB-894 s.p., voc pt
BREITKOPF-L CHB-3065 s.p.
     (P549)
(Rubio) [Lat] SATTBB,acap UNION ESP. 19696
$4.00
     (P550)
(Somma, B.) 6pt sc SANTIS 609 s.p., cor pts
SANTIS 609A-B s.p.
     (P551)
(Washington, Henry) [Lat] SATTBB CHESTER
s.p.
     (P552)

Pars Mea Dominus
girl cor SOUTHERN $.30
     (P553)
(Vene) "Thou Are My Soul's Delight" [Lat/
Eng] SSA,acap oct COLOMBO 2186 $.20 (P554)

Pater Noster *Mass
see Complete Editions Vol. 65
(Bauerle, Hermann) SATB,acap cor pts
BREITKOPF-L PB-1870 s.p.,
BREITKOPF-L CHB-1712 s.p.
     (P555)
(Ewerhart) [Lat] SATB,acap AMP A540 $.60
     (P556)

PALESTRINA, GIOVANNI (cont'd.)

(Ewerhart, Rudolf) 4pt mix cor,acap cor pts
BREITKOPF-W CHB-3145 s.p.   (P557)

Patres Nostri Peccaverunt
(Rossini) "So Must We Bear Guilt" wom cor
oct FISCHER,J 9671 $.30   (P558)

Petra Sancta
see Complete Editions Vol. 63

Pleni Sunt Coeli
[Lat] TTBB HEUGEL s.p. see from LA MAITRISE
(P559)
(Werle, H.) [Lat] men cor,acap (med) HUG
s.p.   (P560)

Popule Meus *anti
[Lat] dbl cor,acap oct SCHIRM.G 6400 $.25
(P561)
SATB,acap RICORDI-ENG SY139 s.p.   (P562)

Praise Be To Thee
(Pisano) SAB oct PLYMOUTH SC-403 $.25   (P563)

Praise Be To Thee (Holy Trinity)
(Lundquist) SATB,acap (diff) oct WILLIS
5678 $.16   (P564)

Praise The Lord, Jehovah *see Exultate Deo

Praise To The Father *see Gloria Patri

Preis Und Ehre, Herr Jesu, Lob
see Herzog, Johann Georg, Freut Euch, Freut
Euch In Dieser Zeit

Primi Toni
see Complete Editions Vol. 14
see Complete Editions Vol. 25
see Complete Editions Vol. 26

Pris Vaere Deg
mix cor MUSIKK 107 s.p.   (P565)

Pro Defunctis *Mass
see Complete Editions Vol. 3
(Bauerle, Hermann) 5pt mix cor,acap cor pts
BREITKOPF-L PB-2035 s.p., voc pt
BREITKOPF-L CHB-1888 s.p.   (P566)

Pueri Hebraeorum *16th cent
(Cartier, Anita; Carol, Henri; Gagnepain,
Bernard) [Lat] SSAB OUVRIERES EO606 s.p. (P567)

Pulchra Es Amica Mea
see Drei Motetten

Pulchra Sunt Genae Tuae *Gen,Bibl
(Hubsch, Hanns) [Lat] SATTB,acap (med)
MULLER SM 756 s.p. see from Das Hohe Lied
Salomonis   (P568)

Quae Est Ista *Fest,mot
see Four Motets
[Lat] SATB,acap (med) MULLER M 47 s.p.   (P569)
(Collins, H.B.) [Lat] SSATB CHESTER s.p. (P570)

Quae Vox
[Lat] 4pt mix cor HEUGEL s.p. see from LA
MAITRISE   (P571)

Qual E Il Piu Grand' Amor *Mass
(Fink, J.) 5pt mix cor,acap DOBLINGER sc
s.p., cor pts s.p.   (P572)

Qual E Il Piu Grande Amor
see Complete Editions Vol. 70

Quam Pulchra Est
see Complete Editions Vol. 51

Quam Pulchri Sunt *Fest
[Lat] SATB,acap (med) MULLER M 44 s.p.   (P573)

Quando Lieta Sperai
see Complete Editions Vol. 66

Quem Dicunt Homines
see Complete Editions Vol. 56

Quinti Toni *see Illumina Oculos Meos

Quodcumque Ligaveris *mot
(Steele, Jonathan) [Lat] SSATBB CHESTER
s.p.   (P574)

Recordata
girl cor SOUTHERN $.25   (P575)
(Castellazi; Vene) "Jerusalem Remembered"
[Lat/Eng] TTB/SSA,acap oct COLOMBO 2033
$.25   (P576)
(Schinelli, A.) [It/Eng/Ger] 3pt CURCI 6299
s.p. see from COLLANA DI COMPOSIZIONI
POLIFONICHE VOCALE SACRE E PROFANE, VOL.
1   (P577)

Reges Tharsis *Offer
(Ewerhart, Rudolf) SATTB,acap cor pts
BREITKOPF-W CHB-3501 s.p.   (P578)

Regina Coeli *anti/Mass
(Dower, C.) "O Queen Of Heaven" [Lat/Eng]
SATB BROUDE,A. 721 $.35   (P579)
(Ewerhart) [Lat] SATB,acap AMP A543 $.75 (P580)
(Ewerhart) 4pt mix cor,acap cor pts
BREITKOPF-W CHB-3148 s.p.   (P581)

Regina Coeli
see Complete Editions Vol. 69

Regina Coeli
see Complete Editions Vol. 66

Repleatur Os Meus
see Complete Editions Vol. 16

Response No. 3
SATB KJOS 7028 $.30   (P582)
(Cain) SATB FLAMMER A 5291 $.30   (P583)

Ret Som Hjorten *see Sicut Cervus Desiderat

Rorate Caeli Desuper *Adv
SSATB,acap SCHIRM.EC $.25   (P584)

PALESTRINA, GIOVANNI (cont'd.)

Rorate Coeli De Super *mot
(Petti, Anthony G.) [Lat] SSATB CHESTER
s.p.   (P585)

Royal Banners Forward Go, The *see Vexilla
Regis Prodeunt

Sacerdos Et Pontifex *Mass
(Bauerle, Hermann) 5pt mix cor,acap voc pt
BREITKOPF-L CHB-1890 s.p.   (P586)

Sacerdotes Domini *Offer
see Complete Editions Vol. 58
(Ewerhart, Rudolf) SAATB,acap cor pts
BREITKOPF-W CHB-3521 s.p.   (P587)

Sacrament Of Priceless Worth *see Corporis
Mysterium

Sad Is My Soul Unto Death *see Tristis Est
Anima Mea

Salvator Mundi *Fest
TTBB,opt pno oct PRO ART 2454 $.30   (P588)
[Lat] SATB,acap (med) MULLER M 40 s.p.   (P589)

Salve Regina *anti
see Complete Editions Vol. 67
(Collins, H.B.) [Lat] SATB&SATB CHESTER
s.p.   (P590)

Salvete Flores Martyrum
SATB,acap RICORDI-ENG SY187 s.p.   (P591)
(Zanon; Vene) "Descend, Thou Heav'nly Dove"
[Lat/Eng] SATB,acap oct COLOMBO 1866 $.25 (P592)

Salvum Me Fac
see Complete Editions Vol. 9

Samtliche Werke *CCU
(De Witt; Rausch; Espagne; Commer; Haberl)
BREITKOPF-W s.p.   (P593)

Sanctorum Meritis *Mass
see Complete Editions Vol. 53
mix cor,acap voc sc KALMUS 6368 $1.25   (P594)
(Bauerle, Hermann) SATB,acap voc pt
BREITKOPF-L CHB-1715 s.p.   (P595)

Sanctus (from Missa Aeterna Christi Munera)
Sanctus
mix cor ALSBACH&D sc s.p., cor pts s.p.   (P596)
SATB,acap RICORDI-ENG SY188 s.p.   (P597)
(Herrmann) [Lat] 4pt wom cor,acap oct
SCHIRM.G 11587 $.30   (P598)

Sasom Hjorten Trangtar *see Sicut Cervus
Desiderat

Selected Compositions Of Palestrina *CCU
mix cor SCHMITT 49 $.50   (P599)

Si Ignoras Te *Gen,Bibl
(Hubsch, Hanns) [Lat] SATTB,acap (med)
MULLER SM 755 s.p. see from Das Hohe Lied
Salomonis   (P600)

Sicut Cervus *anthem/Bibl/mot
SATB,acap oct PRESSER 352-00075 $.30   (P601)
"Like As The Hart" SATB,acap SCHIRM.EC 1135
$.25   (P602)
(Graetzer) [Lat] SATB,acap RICORDI-ARG
BA 9835 s.p.   (P603)
(Messiter) "Like As The Hart" 4pt mix cor
oct SCHIRM.G 3509 $.25   (P604)
(Montani) [Lat] 4pt mix cor,acap oct
SCHIRM.G 6444 $.30   (P605)
(Parkinson, John A.) "As The Hart Pants"
[Eng/Lat] mix cor oct NOVELLO 28.1312.02
s.p.   (P606)

Sicut Cervus Desiderat *mot
mix cor sc ALSBACH&D s.p.   (P607)
"Sasom Hjorten Trangtar" mix cor NORDISKA
5173 s.p.   (P608)
(Scott) "Like As The Hart" SATB oct FOX
R102 $.25   (P609)
(Sorensen, Soren) "Ret Som Hjorten" [Lat/
Dan] SATB,acap HANSEN-DEN s.p. see
also MOTETTER OG LAUDER FRA DET 16.
ARHUNDREDE   (P610)
(Steele, Jonathan) [Lat] SATB CHESTER s.p.
(P611)
(Williams, W.) "Like As The Hart" [Lat/Eng]
SATB,acap SCHIRM.EC 1270 $.50 contains
also: Sitivit Anima Mea, "My Soul Is
Athirst"   (P612)

Sicut Cervus (Ret Som Hjorten)
(Sorenson, Soren) [Lat/Dan] SATB,acap
HANSEN-DEN 282 s.p. see also MOTETTER OG
LAUDER FRA DET 16. ARHUNDREDE   (P613)

Sicut Lilium Inter Spinas *Mass
(Bauerle, Hermann) 5pt mix cor,acap voc pt
BREITKOPF-L CHB-1891 s.p.   (P614)

Sine Domine
see Complete Editions Vol. 3

Sine Nomine II
see Complete Editions Vol. 8

Sine Nomine
see Complete Editions Vol. 50

Sine Nomine
see Complete Editions Vol. 68

Sine Nomine
see Complete Editions Vol. 40

Sing And Praise Jehovah *see Exultate Deo

Sitivit Anima Mea *mot
"My Soul Is Athirst" see Palestrina,
Giovanni, Sicut Cervus Desiderat
(Steele, Jonathan) [Lat] SATB CHESTER s.p.
(P615)

So Must We Bear Guilt *see Patres Nostri
Peccaverunt

Soave Fia Il Morir
(Ehret) "Sweet Is That Dying" [Eng/It]
SAATB,acap oct LAWSON 51383 $.30   (P616)

PALESTRINA, GIOVANNI (cont'd.)

Sooner The Heavens
see Ars Nova To Rennaissance Vol. 6-1200 To
About 1500

Sooner The Heavens *see Vedrassi Prima

Spem In Alium
see Complete Editions Vol. 14

Ssattb *mot
(Bridge, Sir Fredk.) BOSWORTH s.p. see from
Motets   (P617)

Stabat Mater *cant/mot
study sc UNIVER. PH. 90 $1.00   (P618)
[Lat] SATB&SATB min sc PETERS E966 $2.00 (P619)
[Lat] BELWIN $.75   (P620)
(Bauerle, Hermann) dbl cor,acap voc pt
BREITKOPF-L CHB-1225 s.p.   (P621)
(Ewerhart) [Lat] SSAATTBB,acap AMP A541
$.50   (P622)
(Squire Barclay, W.) [Lat] dbl cor,acap voc
sc NOVELLO s.p.   (P623)
(Wagner, Richard) [Lat] dbl cor,acap voc sc
SCHIRM.G $.75   (P624)
(Woodworth, Wallace) [Lat] dbl cor,acap voc
sc SCHIRM.G $.85   (P625)

Stabat Mater Dolorosa *Easter/Psntd,mot
SATB,acap voc pt DOBLINGER s.p. see also
PASSION UND OSTERN   (P626)
(Ewerhart, Rudolf) 8pt mix cor cor pts
BREITKOPF-W CHB-3146 s.p.   (P627)
(Schering) [Lat] SSAATTBB min sc EULENBURG
EUL966 s.p.   (P628)

Strife Is O'er *Easter
mix cor SOUTHERN $.25   (P629)
(Lynn, G.) 2pt mix cor oct PRESSER MC218
$.30   (P630)
(Shaw; Parker) SATB oct SOUTHERN $.25   (P631)

Strife Is O'er, The *Easter
(Shaw; Parker) 4pt mix cor,acap oct
SCHIRM.G 9943 $.25   (P632)

Super Flumina Babylonis *mot/Offer
SATB oct FISCHER,J 7259 $.30   (P633)
(Bauerle, Hermann) SATB,acap voc pt
BREITKOPF-L CHB-1697 s.p.   (P634)
(Ewerhart, Rudolf) mix cor cor pts
BREITKOPF-W CHB-3522   (P635)
(Parratt, W.) SATB,acap LEONARD-ENG 75 s.p. (P636)
(Steele, Jonathan) [Lat] SATB CHESTER s.p. (P637)
(Track) TTBB,acap oct PRO ART 2453 $.30   (P638)
(Track) boy cor SOUTHERN $.30   (P639)

Supplications
(Woodworth) [Lat] 4pt men cor,acap oct
SCHIRM.G 9798 $.35   (P640)

Surge, Illuminare *Epiph
dbl cor,acap SCHIRM.EC $.30   (P641)

Surge Illuminare Hierusalem *mot
(Collins, H.B.) "Surge, Illuminare
Jerusalem" [Lat] SATB&SATB CHESTER s.p.   (P642)

Surge, Illuminare Jerusalem *see Surge
Illuminare Hierusalem

Sweet Is That Dying *see Soave Fia Il Morir

Take My Yoke *see Tollite Jugum Meum

Te Deum Laudamus
see Complete Editions Vol. 61

Ten Four-Part Motets For The Church's Year
*CC10U,mot
(Harman, Alec) [Eng/Lat] SATB (med) oct
OXFORD $3.85   (P643)

Tenebrae Factae Sunt *Easter/Gd.Fri.,mot
SATB,acap oct PRESSER 332-14705 $.30   (P644)
SATB,acap SCHIRM.EC 36 1 $.30   (P645)
SATB,acap (diff) oct WILLIS 908 $.12   (P646)
[Lat] SATB RICORDI-ENG SY189 s.p.   (P647)
(Andersen) SATB SCHMITT 1515 $.30   (P648)
(Clough-Leighter) SATB,acap BOSTON 537 $.30
(P649)
(Davison, A.) [Lat] TTBB,acap SCHIRM.EC 72
$.25   (P650)
(Veneziani) SATB,acap cor pts RICORDI-ENG
121657-58 s.p.   (P651)
(Woodworth, G.) [Lat] SSAA,acap SCHIRM.EC
827 $.22   (P652)

Terra Tremuit *Easter,Offer
(Ewerhart, Rudolf) SATTB,acap cor pts
BREITKOPF-W CHB-3502 s.p.   (P653)

Thee We Adore
SATB oct STAFF 682 $.30   (P654)

Thee Will I Extol *see Exaltabo Te, Domine

This Day *see Haec Dies

This Glad Day *see Haec Dies

This Is The Day *see Haec Dies Quam Fecit
Dominus

Thou All-Transcendent Deity *see Jesu, Rex
Admirabilis

Thou Are My Soul's Delight *see Pars Mea
Dominus

Thou Art Peter *see Tu Es Petrus

[Three] Litaniae Domini
see Complete Editions Vol. 49

Time As He Flies
see Ars Nova To Rennaissance Vol. 6-1200 To
About 1500

Tollite Jugum Meum
"Take My Yoke" [Lat/Eng] 4pt mix cor,acap
oct SCHIRM.G 9702 $.25   (P655)

PALESTRINA, GIOVANNI (cont'd.)

Tota Pulchra Es *Gen,Bibl
(Hubsch, Hanns) [Lat] SATTB,acap (med)
MULLER SM 759 s.p. see from Das Hohe Lied
Salomonis   (P656)

Trahe Me *Gen,Bibl
(Hubsch, Hanns) [Lat] SATTB,acap (med)
MULLER SM 752 s.p. see from Das Hohe Lied
Salomonis   (P657)

Tria Responsoria
(Damrosch) [Lat] 4pt mix cor,SSA&med solo,
acap oct SCHIRM.G 11587 $.30
contains: Ecce Vidimus Eum; In Monte
Oliveti; Tristis Est Anima Mea   (P658)

Tristis Est Anima Mea
see Tria Responsoria
SATB,acap RICORDI-ENG SY190 s.p.   (P659)
(Ehret) "Sad Is My Soul Unto Death" SATB,
acap,opt pno oct PRO ART 2281 $.25 (P660)
(Zanon; Vene) "In Gethsemane" [Lat/Eng]
SATB,acap oct COLOMBO 1883 $.25   (P661)

Tu Es Petrus *Fest,anthem/Mass/mot
see Complete Editions Vol. 70
see Ars Nova To Rennaisance Vol. 6-1200 To
About 1500
mix cor SOUTHERN $.35   (P662)
[Lat/Eng] SSAATB,acap oct SCHIRM.G 11567
$.35   (P663)
[Lat] SSAATB,acap (med) MULLER MS 10 s.p. (P664)
SSAATB,acap SCHIRM.EC 1156 $.30   (P665)
[Lat] SSAATB,acap oct NOVELLO MS-10 s.p. (P666)
mix cor,acap voc sc KALMUS 6306 $1.25 (P667)
(Bridge, Sir Fredk.) "Thou Art Peter"
BOSWORTH see from Motets   (P668)
(Ewerhart) [Lat] SSATBarB AMP A531 $.50 (P669)
(Ewerhart) [Lat] SSATBarB,acap AMP A535
$.75   (P670)
(Ewerhart, Rudolf) 6pt mix cor,acap cor pts
BREITKOPF-W CHB-3066 s.p.   (P671)
(Ewerhart, Rudolf) 6pt mix cor,acap cor pts
BREITKOPF-W CHB-3070 s.p.   (P672)
(Quadflieg, J.) 6pt mix cor,acap cor pts
BREITKOPF-L PB-2807 s.p., voc pt
BREITKOPF-L CHB-1964 s.p.   (P673)
(Quadflieg, J.) 6pt mix cor,acap cor pts
BREITKOPF-L PB-2806 s.p., voc pt
BREITKOPF-L CHB-1896 s.p.   (P674)
(Steele, Jonathan) [Lat] SSATBB CHESTER
s.p.   (P675)

Tui Sunt Coeli *Xmas,Offer
(Ewerhart, Rudolf) SATTB,acap cor pts
BREITKOPF-W CHB-3504 s.p.   (P676)

[Two] Litaniae Sacrosanctae Eucharistiae
see Complete Editions Vol. 49

Unto Thee Lift I Up Mine Eyes *see Ad Te
Levavi Oculos Meos

Upon The Mount Of Olives *see In Monte
Oliveti

Ut Re Mi
see Complete Editions Vol. 16

Vedrassi Prima
(Bement, G.) "Sooner The Heavens" [It/Eng]
TTBB,acap (canzonetta) SCHIRM.EC 2192
    (P677)
(Mattfeld, V.) "Sooner The Heavens" [It/
Eng] SATB,acap SCHIRM.EC 2645   (P678)

Veni Creator Spiritus *hymn
see Complete Editions Vol. 61
(Hellmann) "Komm, Heiliger Geist" [Lat/Ger]
SATB HANSSLER 1.096 $.80   (P679)

Veni Sancte Spiritus *Whitsun
"Come, Thou Holy Spirit, Come" SSAATBB,
acap (med) oct OXFORD 43.084 $.25 (P680)
"Come, Thou Holy Spirit, Come" [Lat/Eng]
SATB&SATB PETERS H1525   (P681)

Veni Sponsa Christi
see Complete Editions Vol. 59
(Zanon) [Lat] SATB,pno RICORDI-ENG SY146
s.p.   (P682)
(Zanon; Vene) "Crown Eternal, The" [Lat/
Eng] SATB,acap oct COLOMBO 1882 $.30 (P683)

Verbum Caro *Xmas
see LA SCHOLA PALESTRINIENNE PREMIERE
CAHIER
(Greyson) "Word Of True Flesh" SATB oct
BOURNE ES95 $.25   (P684)

Vergine Chiara *madrigal
(Schinelli, A.) 5pt mix cor CURCI 6299 s.p.
see from COLLANA DI COMPOSIZIONI
POLIFONICHE VOCALE SACRE E PROFANE, VOL.
1   (P685)

Vestiva I Colli
see Complete Editions Vol. 59

Vexilla Regis Prodeunt
"Royal Banners Forward Go, The" [Lat/Eng]
SATB,acap PETERS H1524 $.75   (P686)

Videntes Stellam *Epiph
SSAATTBB,acap (med) oct OXFORD 43.396 $.35
    (P687)

Vierter Nachtrag Zur Gesamtausgabe-Band
XXXIII (from Samtliche Werke) CCU
(De Witt; Rausch; Espagne; Commer; Haberl)
BREITKOPF-W s.p.   (P688)

Vineam Meam *Gen,Bibl
(Hubsch, Hanns) [Lat] SATTB,acap (med)
MULLER SM 754 s.p. see from Das Hohe Lied
Salomonis   (P689)

Virgo Simul Et Mater
see Complete Editions Vol. 64

Viri Galialei
see Complete Editions Vol. 71

PALESTRINA, GIOVANNI (cont'd.)

Virtute Magna
see Complete Editions Vol. 2

Vulnerasti Cor Meum *Gen,Bibl
(Hubsch, Hanns) [Lat] SATTB,acap (med)
MULLER SM 760 s.p. see from Das Hohe Lied
Salomonis   (P690)

Was Habe Ich Dir Getan, Mein Volk
see Erk, Ludwig, Wahrlich, All Unsre Qualen

We Adore Thee *see Adoramus Te

We Adore Thee *see Adoramus Te, Christe

We Adore Thee, Lord Jesu *see Adoramus Te

We Adore You, O Christ *see Laudate Dominum

We Do Worship Thee *see Adoremus Te, Christe

We Give Thanks To Thee, O Lord *Lent
(Dietterich, Philip R.) SATB (easy)
ABINGDON APM-613 $.18   (P691)

We Pray To Thee
(Morgan) men cor KJOS 5540 $.30   (P692)

Well Do I Know, My Lord *see Ma So Ben,
Signor Mio

When All Disciples *see Dum Ergo Essent

With Other Tongues Spake The Apostles
*Whitsun,mot
(Bridge, Sir Fredk.) BOSWORTH s.p. see from
Motets   (P693)

Word Of True Flesh *see Verbum Caro

Zweiter Nachtrag Zur Gesamtausgabe-Band XXXI
(from Samtliche Werke) CCU
(De Witt; Rausch; Espagne; Commer; Haberl)
BREITKOPF-W s.p.   (P694)

PALLMA

Come, Blessed Master
SAB KJOS PC1005 $.30   (P695)

Lead Us, Dear Lord
SAB KJOS PC1006 $.30   (P696)

Lord's Prayer, The
SA KJOS PC516 $.30   (P697)

PALLOCK

Come Home To God
SATB oct LORENZ A524 $.30   (P698)

O Lord, You Made The Rainbow
unis oct LORENZ 8614 $.25   (P699)
SATB oct LORENZ B157 $.30   (P700)

Someone, Somewhere
SATB oct LORENZ A472 $.25   (P701)

PALM BRANCHES see Faure, Gabriel-Urbain

PALM BRANCHES see Faure, Jean-Baptist

PALM SUNDAY see Kountz

PALM SUNDAY see Whitney, Maurice C.

PALM SUNDAY ANTHEM see Johnson

PALM SUNDAY ANTHEM, A see Hancock, E.W.

PALM SUNDAY PROCESSION see Newbury, Kent A.

PALM SUNDAY WELCOME see Lovelace, Austin C.

PALM TREES, THE see Faure, Jean-Baptist, Les
Rameaux

PALMA

Gloria
(Lasala) [Lat] 3 eq voices,pno/org RICORDI-
ARG BA 11280 s.p.   (P702)

PALMER

Behold! A Star *Xmas
SSA ALFRED 6169 $.25   (P703)

Christmas! Christmas! *Xmas
SATB ALFRED 6324 $.30   (P704)

I Heard The Bells On Christmas Day (composed
with Longfellow) *Xmas
SATB ALFRED 6354 $.35   (P705)

Now Thank We All Our God *Thanks
SSATB ALFRED 6379 $.30   (P706)

O Wondrous Child *Xmas
SATB ALFRED 6411 $.30   (P707)

Peace, Be Still
SATB oct LORENZ B13 $.30   (P708)

Silent Night *Xmas
SATB ALFRED 6428 $.35   (P709)

Sing A Round For Christmas *Xmas
SATB ALFRED 6429 $.35   (P710)

Yield Not To Temptation *hymn
(Gerig) SAB oct LILLENAS AN-1617 $.30 (P711)

PALMER, ANTHONY

Christmas Pastoral *Xmas
SATB oct BELWIN 2127 $.25   (P712)

PALMER, C.

Psalm 92
(Soraas, Lars) mix cor MUSIKK 181 s.p.
    (P713)

Troster Mitt Folk
(Sorass, Lars) mix cor MUSIKK 157 s.p. see
from RELIGIOSE KORSANGER   (P714)

PALMER, H.

Father, O Hear Us
SATB oct PRESSER 312-20280 $.35   (P715)

PALMER, JANE

Praise Our Lord *CC5U,hymn
jr cor cmplt ed WEINBERGER s.p.   (P716)

Three Hymns In Modern Style *CC5U,hymn
SATB oct PAXTON P85386 s.p.   (P717)

PALMER, PEGGY SPENSER

Except The Lord Build The House *anthem
SSAA/SSAT,acap CRAMER B 67 s.p.   (P718)

God With Us *Xmas,carol
unis CRAMER 3   (P719)
SATB CRAMER B81 s.p.   (P720)

Lord Of The Brave
unis&opt 2pt/3pt CRAMER 300 s.p.   (P721)

PALMER, T.

Suffer The Little Children *Bibl
oct HART   (P722)

PALMER, WILLIAM J. (1890-)

Lord Is My Shepherd, The
cor HIGHLAND 4115 $.25   (P723)

See The Star (composed with Hardy)
cor HIGHLAND 4122 $.30   (P724)

PALMS see Faure, Jean-Baptist

PALMS, THE see Faure, Les Rameaux

PALMS, THE see Faure, Jean-Baptist, Les Rameaux

PALMS, THE see Faure

PALMS, THE see Faure, Jean-Baptist, Les Rameaux

PALSSON, PALL P. (1928-)

Requiem *Req
mix cor ICELAND s.p.   (P725)

PALUMBO, GUIDO

Preghiera Ai Genitori
3 eq voices ZANIBON 99 s.p.   (P726)

PAMINGER, LEONHARD

Christmas Motet *Xmas,mot
(Pizarro) [Eng/Ger/Lat] SATTB,acap oct
SCHIRM.G 11065 $.25   (P727)

Exiit Edictum *Xmas,mot
(Zirnbauer, Heinz) [Lat] SSATB,acap (med)
BAREN. BA 1084 $2.25   (P728)

PANEM COELESTEM see Volpi, Edoardo

PANEM NOSTRUM see Palestrina, Giovanni

PANGE LINGUA see Aichinger, Gregor

PANGE LINGUA see Asola, Giovanni Matteo

PANGE LINGUA see Baden, Conrad

PANGE LINGUA see Barraud, Henry

PANGE LINGUA see Bezzi, Enrico

PANGE LINGUA see Bottazzo, Luigi

PANGE LINGUA see Bruckner, Anton

PANGE LINGUA see Des Prez, Josquin

PANGE LINGUA see Grassi, Ciro

PANGE LINGUA see Grazioli, Giovanni

PANGE LINGUA see Kodaly, Zoltan

PANGE LINGUA see Maggio, Giuseppe

PANGE LINGUA see Muller, J.

PANGE LINGUA see Ravanello, Oreste

PANGE LINGUA see Renzi, Angelo

PANGE LINGUA see Rodella, Sante

PANGE LINGUA see Sacchetto, Guido

PANGE LINGUA see Tebaldini, Giovanni

PANGE LINGUA see Victoria, Tomas Luis de

PANGE LINGUA GLORIOSI see Buxtehude, Dietrich

PANGE LINGUA - TANTUM ERGO
(Bamer, Alfred) wom cor,acap oct DOBLINGER
s.p. see also Sechs Geistliche Chore (P729)

PANIS ANGELICUS see Baroni, Giovanni

PANIS ANGELICUS see Caplet, [Lucien]

PANIS ANGELICUS see Casciolini, Claudio

PANIS ANGELICUS see Claussmann, A.

PANIS ANGELICUS see Dubois, Theodore

PANIS ANGELICUS see Dumont, [Henri]

PANIS ANGELICUS see Fauchey, Paul

PANIS ANGELICUS see Faure, Jean-Baptist

PANIS ANGELICUS see Favero, Gino

PANIS ANGELICUS see Franck, Cesar

PANIS ANGELICUS see Grassi, Ciro

PANIS ANGELICUS see Kjelson

PANIS ANGELICUS see Palestrina, Giovanni

PANIS ANGELICUS see Philipp, Franz

PANIS ANGELICUS see Pierne, Paul

PANIS ANGELICUS see Roumefort, R. de

PANIS ANGELICUS see Saint-Saens, Camille

PANIS ANGELICUS see Samuel-Rosseau, Marcel

PANIS ANGELICUS see Verhaalen, B.

PANIS ANGELICUS see Werbecke, G. Von

PANIS ANGELICUS HOSTIA see Franck, Cesar

PANIS QUEM EGO DABO see Clemens, Jacobus

PANIS, QUEM EGO DEDERO see Vranken, Alph.

PANIS QUEM ERGO DABO see Palestrina, Giovanni

PANIS VITAE see Dixon

PAPAE MARCELLI see Palestrina, Giovanni

PAPER REEDS see Christiansen, Larry A.

PAPER REEDS BY THE BROOK, THE see Thompson, Randall

PAPERINI, PIETRO
Inno Alla Beata Maddalena Di Canossa *ASD, hymn
[Lat] unis,org/pno ZANIBON 3509 s.p. (P730)

PAPINEAU-COUTURE, JEAN (1916-)
Psalm 150 *see Psaume CL

Psaume CL (Psalm 150)
SATB,acap oct BERANDOL 910P5AK $.50 (P731)

PAPP, AKOS G.
Good Lord, Shall I Ever Be The One
SAB,acap (med) ABINGDON APM-371 $.18 (P732)

PAQUES see Lacome, Paul

PARABLE OF THE SOWER see McAfee, Don

PARABLES see Kay

PARABLES, THE see Thiman, Eric Harding

PARADISE (from Sacred Harp, The)
(Cram) 4pt mix cor,T solo,acap oct SCHIRM.G 11917 $.35 (P733)

PARAFRAS OVER O KRISTE, DU SOM LJUSET AR see Wideen, Ivar

PARAISSEZ MONARQUE AIMABLE *Adv/Gen,carol,Fr
(Sheppard) "Come, Beloved Monarch" [Eng/Fr] 3pt wom cor,acap oct SCHIRM.G 11432 $.25 (P734)
(Sheppard) "Come, Beloved Monarch" [Eng/Fr] 4pt mix cor,acap oct SCHIRM.G 11425 $.30 (P735)

PARAISSEZ, MONARQUE AIMABLE see Roques, L.

PARAY, [PAUL] (1886-)
Messe Du Cinquieme Centenaire De La Mort De Jeanne D'arc *Mass
cor,soli,orch voc sc LEMOINE s.p., ipr (P736)

PARCE DOMINE see Bottigliero, Eduardo

PARCE, DOMINE see Obrecht, Jacob

PARCE MIHI, DOMINE see Gines Perez, Juan

PARCE MIHI DOMINE see Minoja, Ambrosio

PARCE MIHI DOMINI see Franco

PARDOS ARRUE
Misa De Villancicos *Xmas,carol/Mass
[Span] unis/2pt UNION ESP. 18857 s.p. (P737)

PARENTE, SISTER ELIZABETH
Ave Maria
[Lat] 3pt wom cor oct SCHIRM.G 10615 $.25 (P738)

PARIS
Again And Again
(McLellan) SATB oct LILLENAS AT-1073 $.30 (P739)

Behold, A Greater
(McLellan) SATB oct LILLENAS AT-1037 $.25 (P740)

Glad That I'm A Christian
(McLellan) SATB oct LILLENAS AT-1038 $.25 (P741)

I Have A Peace In My Heart
(McLellan) SATB oct LILLENAS AT-1050 $.25 (P742)

I Shall Live
(McLellan) SATB oct LILLENAS AT-1074 $.30 (P743)

Please Stop Running Away From God
(McLellan) SATB oct LILLENAS AT-1071 $.30 (P744)

Somebody Died For You
(Collins) SATB oct LILLENAS AT-1067 $.30 (P745)

PARISH CHOIR BOOK NO. 2 *CCU,Xmas/Epiph,hymn/Psalm
[Eng] oct ST.MARTIN SMP6412A s.p. (P746)

PARISH CHOIR BOOK NO. 3 *CCU,Lent/Septua,hymn/Psalm
[Eng] oct ST.MARTIN SMP651A s.p. (P747)

PARISH CHOIR BOOK NO. 4, THE *CCU,Holywk,hymn/Psalm
cong&opt cor,cantor oct ST.MARTIN SMP689 s.p. contains works by: Baxter, Timothy; Bevenot, Laurence; Laloux, Fernand; Washington, Henry (P748)

PARISH CHOIR BOOK NO. 4A *CCU,Psntd,hymn/Psalm
cor oct ST.MARTIN SMP654A s.p. (P749)

PARISH CHOIR BOOK NO. 5 *CCU,Easter,hymn/Psalm
cor oct ST.MARTIN SMP655A s.p. (P750)

PARISH CHOIR BOOK NO. 5A, THE *CCU,Easter
cong&opt cor,cantor oct ST.MARTIN SMP6810 s.p. contains works by: Baxter, Timothy; Bevenot, Laurence; Laloux, Fernand; Washington, Henry (P751)

PARISH CHOIR BOOK NO. 6 *CCU,Adv/Whitsun,hymn/Psalm
cor oct ST.MARTIN SMP656A s.p. (P752)

PARISH CHOIR BOOK NO. 11, THE see Tamblyn, William

PARISH CHOIR BOOK NO. 12, THE see Baxter, T.

PARISH CHOIR BOOK NO. 22, THE *CCU,Xmas/Epiph, Allelu/Gradual
cong&opt cor,cantor oct ST.MARTIN SMP6713 s.p. contains works by: Baxter, T.; Lord, David; Rush, John (P753)

PARISH CHOIR BOOK NO. 32, THE *CCU,Lent,Bibl/Gradual
cong&opt cor,cantor oct ST.MARTIN SMP681 s.p. contains works by: Baxter, Timothy; Bevenot, Laurence; Laloux, Fernand (P754)

PARISH CHOIR BOOK NO. 52, THE see Senator, Ronald

PARISH CHOIR BOOK NO. 62, THE *CCU,Pent, Allelu/Gradual
cong&opt cor,cantor oct ST.MARTIN s.p. contains works by: Laloux, F.; Tamblyn, W. (P755)

PARISH CHOIR BOOK NO. 101, THE *CCUL,Mass
cong&opt cor,cantor oct ST.MARTIN SMP682A s.p. contains works by: rush, john; tamblyn, william (P756)

PARISH CHOIR BOOK, THE *CC22L
(Thomas, P.) mix cor CONCORDIA 97-7574 $1.50 contains works by: Tye; Wolff; Sateren; Willan; Schroeter; Von Burck; Halter; Praetorius; Scheidt; Gumpeltzhaimer; Bach; Franck; Gesius; Markworth; Helder; Palestrina; Bunjes; Vulpius; Willan; Farrant; Hilton; Brahms; Attwood (P757)

PARISH MASS, A see Lucas, Leighton

PARKE
Bethlehem
unis THOMP.G G-148 s.p. (P758)

PARKE, DOROTHY
Bethlehem *Xmas
unis LENGNICK s.p. (P759)

Evensong (A Child's Prayer) *prayer
jr cor LEONARD-ENG 47 s.p. (P760)

PARKER
Feat Of Ingathering
SATB oct FISCHER,C O-4882 $2.00 (P761)

Jerusalem *Easter/Lent/Palm
SATB oct FISCHER,C CM-6261 $.25 (P762)
(Holmes) SATB,S/Bar solo oct PRO ART 1344 $.30 (P763)

Lord Most Mighty
(Wiley) SATB oct PRO ART 2693 $.30 (P764)
(Wiley) SATB (med diff/diff) SOUTHERN $.30 (P765)

PARKER, ALICE (1925-)
Blessings *Bibl
SATB,acap oct LAWSON 51592 $.30 (P766)

Now Glad Of Heart *Easter
SATB,B solo,opt orch oct LAWSON 885 $.30 (P767)

Praise To The Lord
unis,org,brass,perc oct LAWSON 51605 $.50 (P768)

Prayer
8pt mix cor/SATB,acap/org/4inst oct LAWSON 51737 $.40 (P769)

Psalm 136
SATB,Bar solo,acap oct LAWSON 51250 $.30 (P770)

Psalms Of Praise *CCU,Bibl/Psalm
TB,perc oct LAWSON 51385 $.35 (P771)

PARKER, HENRY
Jerusalem *Easter
SATB oct LORENZ 1040 $.30 (P772)
unis oct LORENZ 8577 $.25 (P773)
unis oct SCHIRM.G 9420 $.30 (P774)
SAB oct LORENZ 7370 $.25 (P775)
SATB&jr cor oct LORENZ B24 $.25 (P776)
SATB oct LORENZ C75 $.30 (P777)
(Deis) SABar,ABar soli oct SCHIRM.G 10084 $.25 (P778)
(Rees) 4pt mix cor,AT soli oct SCHIRM.G 3210 $.30 (P779)
(Stickles) jr cor&sr cor,AT soli,org/pno oct SCHIRM.G 10469 $.35 (P780)

PARKER, HORATIO WILLIAM (1863-1919)
Bow Down Thine Ear *Bibl
4pt mix cor oct SCHIRM.G 3551 $.25 (P781)

Holy Child, The *Xmas,cant
cor,pno voc sc SCHIRM.G $1.25 (P782)

Hora Novissima *Op.30, cant
dbl cor,4 soli,org,orch cloth DA CAPO LC-75-169652 $18.50 (P783)
BELWIN $2.75 (P784)

Jerusalem (composed with Macy, J.C.) *Easter
SATB oct PRESSER 332-08818 $.30 (P785)
SATB oct PRESSER 312-15623 $.30 (P786)

Light's Glittering Morn *Easter
4pt mix cor,B solo oct SCHIRM.G 3725 $.30 (P787)

Lord Is My Light, The *Bibl
4pt mix cor oct SCHIRM.G 3552 $.30 (P788)
(McKinney) SAB oct FISCHER,J 9766 $.30 (P789)

PARKS
King Of Glory
SSA KJOS P1776 $.30 (P790)

King Of Glory, The
SATB oct LORENZ 208 $.30 (P791)

Silent Night! Holy Night! *Xmas
SATB KJOS P1384 $.30 (P792)

PARKS, J.A.
O Divine Redeemer
SATB KJOS P1324 $.30 (P793)

PARKYN, W.
Hark! 'Tis The Watchman's Cry
SATB PATERSON 1649 s.p. (P794)

PARODI, LORENZO
Ave Maria *BVM
[Lat] unis/2pt,org ZANIBON 1513 s.p. (P795)

Three Canzoncine *CC3U
jr cor,pno RICORDI-ENG 128532 s.p. (P796)

PAROZAI, GUI
A La Nativite *Xmas,carol,18th cent
(Darcieux) [Fr] 4pt mix cor,acap LEMOINE s.p. see from Six Noels Anciens (P797)

J'entends Par Notre Rue *Xmas,carol,18th cent
(Darcieux) [Fr] 3pt,acap LEMOINE s.p. see from Six Noels Anciens (P798)

Noel Dialogue *Xmas,carol,18th cent
(Darcieux) [Fr] 2pt,acap LEMOINE s.p. see from Six Noels Anciens (P799)

Noel Noel, C'est Jour De Fete *Xmas,carol, 18th cent
(Darcieux) [Fr] 3pt,acap LEMOINE s.p. see from Six Noels Anciens (P800)

Noel Ribon Ribaine *Xmas,carol,18th cent
(Darcieux) [Fr] 2pt,acap LEMOINE s.p. see from Six Noels Anciens (P801)

Six Noels Anciens *see A La Nativite; J'entends Par Notre Rue; Noel Dialogue; Noel Noel, C'est Jour De Fete; Noel Ribon Ribaine; Voici Le Saint Temps Mes Freres (P802)

Voici Le Saint Temps Mes Freres *Xmas,carol, 18th cent
(Darcieux) [Fr] 4pt mix cor,acap LEMOINE s.p. see from Six Noels Anciens (P803)

PARR, ANDY
He Came To Give Life
(Ehret) SATB oct WORD CS-2553 $.30 (P804)

PARRIS, HERMAN M. (1903-)
Glory To God The Creator
SATB PARAGON 1033 $.30 (P805)

PARROTT, IAN (1916-)
Psalm 91
SATB,B solo,orch, semi chorus LENGNICK s.p., ipa (P806)

PARRY, CHARLES HUBERT HASTINGS (1848-1918)
Dear Lord And Father *hymn
SATB oct NOVELLO 44.1121.08 s.p. (P807)

Dear Lord And Father Of Mankind (from Judith) anthem
(Chambers, H.A.) mix cor oct NOVELLO 40.1175.09 s.p. (P808)

He Delivered The Poor *Gen,anthem
unis oct ROYAL 239 s.p. see also ANTHEMS FOR UNISON OR TWO PART SINGING (P809)

Hymn For Christmas Day *Xmas,hymn
SATB,acap (med easy) OXFORD 84.032 $.35 (P810)

I Was Glad
SATB oct GRAY GCMR 2404 $.35 (P811)

I Was Glad When They Said Unto Me *anthem
mix cor,orch oct NOVELLO 28.0743.02 s.p., ipr (P812)

Jerusalem
unis oct CURWEN 8110 $.25 (P813)
unis jr cor/unis wom cor ROBERTON 40009 s.p. (P814)
(Jacobson) 4pt men cor oct CURWEN 10488 $.20 (P815)
(Jacobson) 3pt wom cor oct CURWEN 10963 $.20 (P816)
(Jacobson) 4pt mix cor oct CURWEN 10489 $.25 (P817)
(Jacobson) mix cor CURWEN 61648 s.p. (P818)
(Jacobson) unis jr cor/unis wom cor CURWEN 40061 s.p. (P819)

Job *Bibl/ora
SATB,STBarB soli,org,2fl,2ob,2clar,3bsn, 4horn,2trp,3trom,tuba,strings,timp voc sc NOVELLO s.p., ipr (P820)

Magnificat And Nunc Dimittis *Magnif/Nunc
SATB (D maj) oct NOVELLO 44.1131.05 s.p. (P821)
unis (D maj) oct NOVELLO 22.0054.09 s.p. (P822)

O Praise Ye The Lord *Thanks,anthem/hymn
SATB oct NOVELLO 28.1282.07 s.p. (P823)
(Havergal, Henry) mix cor oct NOVELLO 28.1282.07 s.p. (P824)

Te Deum *Te Deum
SATB (D maj) oct NOVELLO 44.1128.05 s.p. (P825)

Voces Clamantium *mot
SATB,SB soli,org,2fl,2ob,3clar,3bsn,4horn, 2trp,3trom,tuba,strings,timp,harp voc sc NOVELLO s.p., ipr (P826)

Wine And Water
SAB/SATB (easy) OXFORD 86.007 $.30 (P827)

PARRY, JOSEPH (1841-1903)
Jesus, Lover Of My Soul
(Janes, Oliver) SATB WEINBERGER s.p. (P828)

PARRY, W.H.
I Will Magnify Thee
2pt LENGNICK s.p. (P829)

Sacred Morn, The
SAB ASHDOWN V.T.58 s.p. (P830)

PARS MEA DOMINUS see Palestrina, Giovanni

PARSIFAL, GRANDE SCENE RELIGIEUSE, FINAL DU PREMIER ACTE see Wagner, Richard

PARSLEY, OSBERT (1511-1585)
Conserva Me
    mix cor,acap voc sc KALMUS 6690 $.80
    contains also: Lamentationes   (P831)

Lamentationes
    see Parsley, Osbert, Conserva Me

Magnificat
    see Parsley, Osbert, Te Deum

Te Deum *Magnif/Te Deum
    mix cor,acap voc sc KALMUS 6691 $1.35
    contains also: Te Deum; Magnificat (P832)

Te Deum
    see Parsley, Osbert, Te Deum

PARSONS, ROBERT
Deliver Me From Mine Enemies *anthem/mot
    SSAATB,org oct NOVELLO 28.1297.05 s.p.
                                              (P833)

PARTHUN, PAUL
Adoramus Te Christe
    "We Adore Thee" SATB (easy) oct AUGSBURG
    1560 $.25   (P834)

Ave Verum Corpus
    [Eng/Lat] S/AA/TB,org AMP A570 $.25 (P835)

We Adore Thee *see Adoramus Te Christe

PARTI VARIABLI O SEQUENZA DELLA MESSA DI PASQUA
    see Bottazzo, Luigi

PARTING FROM YOU see Des Prez, Josquin

PARTON, K.
We Praise Thee O God
    SATB,org GRAY GCMR 3295 $.35   (P836)

PARVULUS FILIUS see Clemens, Jacobus

PASCH-HYMNE see Mobach, E.

PASCHA NOSTRUM see Ferro, Stefano

PASCHAL PAEAN see Lewis, J.

PASFIELD, W.R.
Child's Song Of Christmas, A *Xmas
    unis LENGNICK s.p.   (P837)

Drop, Drop, Slow Tears
    SS,org FRANCIS s.p.   (P838)

Grieve Not The Holy Spirit Of God
    SATB ENOCH EC336 s.p.   (P839)

Loving Shepherd Of Thy Sheep
    unis ASHDOWN U.90 s.p.   (P840)

Praise The Lord
    SATB ENOCH EC334 s.p.   (P841)

This Winter's Night *Xmas,carol
    unis PROWSE s.p.   (P842)

Thou Whose Birth On Earth *Xmas
    2pt ASHDOWN E.A.365 s.p.   (P843)

PASINI, CRESCENZIO
Ecce Sacerdos Magnus
    [Lat] ATB,org ZANIBON 3799 s.p.   (P844)

O Sacrum Convivium *Mass
    [Lat] AT/2 eq voices,org (easy) sc ZANIBON
    3802 s.p., cor pts ZANIBON 3803 s.p.
                                            (P845)

Protector Noster *mot
    [Lat] ATB,org ZANIBON 1115 s.p.   (P846)

Quem Vidistis *Xmas,mot
    3 eq voices,soli,org ZANIBON 3801 s.p. (P847)

Sacerdos Et Pontifex
    [Lat] 2 eq voices,org ZANIBON 3800 s.p. (P848)

Scendi Dal Cielo *Xmas
    2pt jr cor,org/pno ZANIBON 1707 s.p. (P849)

Tu Es Sacerdos
    [Lat] ATB,org ZANIBON 1114 s.p.   (P850)

Veni Sponsa Christi In Hon. Beatae Mariae
    Bertillae Boscardon *Mass
    .Lat] TTB,org sc ZANIBON 3925 s.p.   (P851)

Vox Domini *mot
    [Lat] 3pt mix cor ZANIBON 1113 s.p.   (P852)

PASKDIALOG see Schutz, Heinrich

PASKEHYMNE see Bach, Johann Sebastian

PASKEHYMNE see Olsen, Sparre

PASKEMOTETT see Stockhausen, Karlheinz

PASKENS OFFERLAM TIL AERE see Pederson, Mogens,
    Victimae Paschali Laudes

PASKHYMN see Ahlen, Waldemar

PASKHYMN see Thyrestam, Gunnar

PASQUET, JEAN (1896-   )
Acquaint Thyself With God *anthem/Bibl
    4pt jr cor/SATB (easy) FISCHER,C CM 7364
    $.20   (P853)
    SATB,acap oct FISCHER,C CM-7364 $.20 (P854)

Alleluia! Hearts And Voices
    4pt mix cor oct SCHIRM.G 11498 $.25   (P855)

Almighty God In Trinity
    SATB oct JUSKO 284 $.25   (P856)

Angels' Song, The *anthem
    SA (easy) oct AUGSBURG 1360 $.22   (P857)

Away In A Manger *Xmas
    SA,pno (very easy) PRESSER $.35   (P858)

Bless Thou The Lord *anthem
    SAB (med) oct AUGSBURG 0602 $.25   (P859)

PASQUET, JEAN (cont'd.)
Blessed Are They
    SATB oct BELWIN 64256 $.25   (P860)

Blessed Art Thou
    SATB oct ELKAN-V 362-1167 $.25   (P861)

Blessing Of The Trinity *Gen/Trin
    4pt mix cor,org oct SCHIRM.G 11574 $.30 (P862)

Chorale Anthems Based On Chorale Preludes,
    Vol. II *CC13L,Asc/Easter/Gen/Lent/Pent/
    Trin
    unis/4pt,org oct AUGSBURG 11-9144 $1.75 (P863)

Come, Holy Ghost
    SATB oct FISCHER,C CM-7274 $.25   (P864)

Come Thou To Dwell Within Us
    SATB oct BELWIN 64324 $.30   (P865)

Create In Me A Clean Heart *anthem
    SAB (easy) oct AUGSBURG 0627 $.25   (P866)

Day By Day I Seek Thee
    SATB oct ELKAN-V 362-1183 $.25   (P867)

Entrance Into Jerusalem
    SATB oct ELKAN-V 362-1291 $.30   (P868)

Father Of Truth, The
    SATB oct ELKAN-V 362-1308 $.30   (P869)

Father, We Thank Thee
    SA oct FISCHER,C CM-7412 $.25   (P870)

Fret Not Thyself
    SATB oct ELKAN-V 362-1188 $.25   (P871)

From Heaven Above To Earth I Come *Xmas
    SA,pno (easy) PRESSER $.30   (P872)

Give Ear To Our Prayers
    SATB,acap WARNER W3711 $.30   (P873)

Glory To Thy Holy Name
    4pt mix cor,org oct SCHIRM.G 11407 $.25
                                            (P874)
God Be In My Head
    SATB oct GRAY GCMR 3222 $.30   (P875)

God Of Our Life
    SA oct ELKAN-V 362-526 $.30   (P876)

Grace Unto Us
    SATB oct ELKAN-V 362-1249 $.25   (P877)

Great And Mighty Wonder, A *Xmas
    SATB oct ELKAN-V 362-1259 $.25   (P878)

How Goodly Are Thy Tents
    4pt mix cor,org/pno oct SCHIRM.G 11711 $.30
                                            (P879)
Hymn Of Praise *hymn
    SATB (med diff/diff) SOUTHERN $.30   (P880)

Hymn Of The Initiants
    4pt mix cor,S/T solo oct SCHIRM.G 11229
    $.30   (P881)

I Will Show Forth Thy Glory
    SATB WARNER W3709 $.30   (P882)

I Will Wait On Thy Mercy
    4pt jr cor/SATB (easy) FISCHER,C CM 7600
    $.30   (P883)

In All Things I Sought Rest
    SATB oct JUSKO 285 $.25   (P884)

In My Father's House
    4pt mix cor,acap oct SCHIRM.G 11451 $.25
                                            (P885)
In The Beginning
    SATB KJOS 5331 $.30   (P886)

Jesu, Grant Me Grace
    SATB oct JUSKO 286 $.25   (P887)

Joyful Hosanna
    SATB KJOS 5263 $.30   (P888)

Lenten Meditation *Lent
    SATB oct GRAY GCMR 2052 $.30   (P889)

Let Heaven And Earth Exult *Xmas
    SATB oct ELKAN-V 362-1234 $.25   (P890)

Let My Mouth Be Filled
    SATB oct GRAY GCMR 2981 $.25   (P891)

Let Us Pray *prayer
    SA oct FISCHER,C CM-7599 $.25   (P892)

Lift Up Your Hands
    SATB oct ELKAN-V 362-1282 $.30   (P893)

Light Of The World, The *cant
    SATB BELWIN $1.00   (P894)
    SATB GRAY $1.00   (P895)

Light Of Thy Truth
    SATB oct ELKAN-V 362-1311 $.30   (P896)

Lord Keep Us Steadfast
    SA oct ELKAN-V 362-525 $.25   (P897)

Lord Make Thy Word A Lantern
    SATB oct GRAY GCMR 3086 $.25   (P898)

Love And Blessed Be Thou, King
    4pt mix cor,org oct SCHIRM.G 11327 $.25
                                            (P899)
Lowly Of Heart
    SA oct ELKAN-V 362-514 $.25   (P900)

Morning Hymn *Morn,hymn
    SATB oct FISCHER,C CM-7532 $.25   (P901)

My Soul Will Exult
    SAB oct ELKAN-V 362-1214 $.30   (P902)

O God, Author Of Eternal Light
    SATB oct BELWIN 60802 $.35   (P903)

O God Of Love
    SATB oct BELWIN 64271 $.30   (P904)

PASQUET, JEAN (cont'd.)
O God Of Wondrous Grace *prayer
    SATB,S solo,pno/org oct FISCHER,C CM-7338
    $.25   (P905)

O God, Who Hast Prepared
    SATB oct ELKAN-V 362-1213 $.25   (P906)

O Little Town Of Bethlehem *Xmas,carol
    SAB oct GRAY GCMR 2985 $.25   (P907)

O My Soul, On Wings Ascending *anthem
    unis/SATB (easy) oct AUGSBURG 1430 $.25
                                            (P908)
O Saving Victim *anthem
    SAB (easy) oct AUGSBURG 1367 $.25   (P909)

Of The Father's Love Begotten
    oct ELKAN-V 362-517 $.30   (P910)

Open Our Eyes
    SATB oct PRESSER 362-01324 $.30   (P911)
    SATB oct ELKAN-V 362-1324 $.25   (P912)

Prayer Of Trust *Lent
    SA oct SOUTHERN $.25   (P913)

Psalm 116 *see Return Unto Thy Rest

Psalm 117
    SATB oct BELWIN 64297 $.25   (P914)

Psalm Of Worship, A
    SATB oct BELWIN 64288 $.30   (P915)

Rejoice And Be Merry
    SA SOUTHERN $.30   (P916)

Return Unto Thy Rest (Psalm 116)
    SATB oct PRESSER 362-01322 $.30   (P917)
    SATB oct ELKAN-V 362-1322 $.30   (P918)

Seven Short Introits Or Orisons *CC7U,
    Introit
    SATB oct JUSKO 256 $.25   (P919)

Shepherd Of Sheep
    SA oct ELKAN-V 362-515 $.25   (P920)

Shepherds Saw A Star, The *Xmas
    2pt wom cor,org/pno oct SCHIRM.G 11758 $.25
                                            (P921)
Sleep, Thou Holy Child *Xmas
    SA/SAB oct BELWIN 64356 $.30   (P922)
    SATB oct BELWIN 64269 $.30   (P923)

Snow Lay On The Ground, The *Xmas
    SATB oct ELKAN-V 362-1156 $.25   (P924)

Songs Of Praise The Angels Sang *anthem
    SAB (easy) oct AUGSBURG 1384 $.30   (P925)

Thanked Be Thou, Jesu, My King
    SATB oct JUSKO 257 $.25   (P926)

That Wondrous Night *Xmas
    SA oct ELKAN-V 362-522 $.25   (P927)

Thee Adore
    SA oct ELKAN-V 362-524 $.25   (P928)

Thee Will I Love
    SATB oct GRAY GCM 2810 $.25   (P929)

Then Shall The King Say Unto Them *Bibl
    4pt mix cor,org/pno oct SCHIRM.G 11408 $.25
                                            (P930)
They That Seek Thy Truth
    SATB oct ELKAN-V 362-1189 $.25   (P931)

Thou Art He *anthem
    SATB oct FISCHER,C CM-7602 $.30   (P932)

Thou Who Art Peace Eternal
    SATB oct ELKAN-V 362-1228 $.25   (P933)

Thou Who Hast Taught Us
    SATB,acap WARNER W3734 $.30   (P934)

Thy Law Is An Evergreen
    SATB oct BELWIN 64360 $.30   (P935)

Thy Word Is A Lamp
    SAB MARKS 4442 $.25   (P936)

To The God Of Peace
    3pt jr cor/SAB (very easy) FISCHER,C
    CM 7448 $.25   (P937)

Vision Of The Shepherds, The *Xmas
    SATB oct ELKAN-V 362-1201 $.30   (P938)

We Praise Thee
    SATB oct GRAY GCMR 3090 $.30   (P939)

Why Seek Ye The Living?
    SATB oct ELKAN-V 362-1316 $.30   (P940)

Worship We The Father
    SATB oct ELKAN-V 362-1250 $.25   (P941)

PASS IT ON see Kaiser, Kurt

PASS ME NOT see Doane, [William Howard]

PASS ME NOT, O GENTLE SAVIOR see Rasley

PASSAMONTI, G.
Italian Mass *see Messa Ritmata

Messa Ritmata *Mass,It
    "Italian Mass" cor&cong,org oct BERBEN
    EB 1293 $2.40   (P942)

PASSANI, EMILE
Sept Noels Provencaux De Saboly *CC7U,Xmas,
    carol,Fr
    [Fr] 3 eq voices,opt pno/org HEUGEL s.p.
                                            (P943)

PASSIO DOMINI see Bloch, Waldemar

PASSIO ET MORS DOMINI NOSTRI JESU CHRISTI
    SECUNDUM LUCAM see Penderecki, Krzysztof

PASSIO JESU CHRISTI see Burck, Joachim

PASSION see Baumann, Max

PASSION see Bruckner, Anton

PASSION see Handel, George Frideric

PASSION, THE see Handel, George Frideric

PASSION, THE see Haydn, (Franz) Joseph, Die Sieben Worte Des Erlosers Am Kreuze

PASSION, THE see Warren, Raymond

PASSION ACCORDING TO SAINT LUKE, THE see Thompson, Randall

PASSION ACCORDING TO SAINT MARK, THE see Nelson, Ronald A.

PASSION ACCORDING TO SAINT MATTHEW see Padilla, Dominica In Ramis

PASSION ACCORDING TO SAINT MATTHEW, THE see Boatwright, Howard

PASSION ACCORDING TO ST. JOHN see Handel, George Frideric

PASSION ACCORDING TO ST. JOHN, THE see Bach, Johann Sebastian, La Passione Di N.S. Gesu Cristo Secondo Giovanni

PASSION ACCORDING TO ST. JOHN, THE see Byrd, William

PASSION ACCORDING TO ST. JOHN, THE see Schutz, Heinrich, Johannespassion

PASSION ACCORDING TO ST. LUKE *Psntd,15th cent mix cor STAINER CS358 s.p. see from Early Chruch Music, Vol. 8   (P944)

PASSION ACCORDING TO ST. LUKE, THE see Schutz, Heinrich, Lukaspassion

PASSION ACCORDING TO ST. MATTHEW, THE see Schutz, Heinrich, Matthauspassion

PASSION ACCORDING TO ST. MATTHEW, THE see Victoria, Tomas Luis de

PASSION CANTATA see Mozart, Wolfgang Amadeus, Grabmusik

PASSION CHORALE see Bach, Johann Sebastian

PASSION CHORALE see Bach, Johann Sebastian

PASSION MOTET, A see Frylof, [Harald Leonard]

PASSION MOTETS see Haydn, (Johann) Michael

PASSION MUSIC see Handel, George Frideric

PASSION MUSIC ON THE SEVEN WORDS OF JESUS CHRIST ON THE CROSS see Pfleger, Augustin

PASSION NACH B.H. BROCKES see Handel, George Frideric, Der Fur Die Sunden Der Welt Gemarterte Und Sterbende Jesus

PASSION NACH DEM EVANGELISTEN JOHANNES see Ahrens, Joseph

PASSION NACH DEM EVANGELISTEN JOHANNES see Handel, George Frideric

PASSION NACH DEM EVANGELISTEN MATTHAUS see Ahrens, Joseph

PASSION NACH DEM EVANGELIUM DES JOHANNES see Weyrauch, Johannes

PASSION NACH JOHANNES see Gallus, Jacobus

PASSION OF CHRIST see Van Dyke

PASSION OF CHRIST, THE see Fletcher, Percy [E.]

PASSION OF CHRIST, THE see Handel, George Frideric

PASSION OF CHRIST, THE see Somervell, Arthur

PASSION OF MARY, THE see Redman, Reginald

PASSION OF OUR LORD see Graun, Karl Heinrich

PASSION OF OUR LORD, ACCORDING TO ST. MATTHEW see Bach, Johann Sebastian, La Passione Di N.S. Gesu Cristo Secondo Matteo

PASSION OF OUR LORD JESUS CHRIST, THE see Schutz, Heinrich

PASSION OF ST. JOHN, THE see Schutz, Heinrich, Johannespassion

PASSION OF ST. LUKE, THE see Schutz, Heinrich, Lukaspassion

PASSION OF ST. MATTHEW, THE see Schutz, Heinrich, Matthauspassion

PASSION-OSTERN *CCU,Easter/Psntd (Wagner, Hermann) mix cor MOSELER s.p. (P945)

PASSION SELON SAINT MATHIEU see Bach, Johann Sebastian, Matthauspassion

PASSION SONG see Bach, Johann Sebastian

PASSION, THE see Schutz, Heinrich

PASSION UND OSTERN *Easter/Psntd mix cor,acap cmplt ed DOBLINGER s.p. contains & see also: Die Ganze Welt (from Sirenes Symphoniacae); Aichinger, Gregor, Regina Coeli; Anerio, Giovanni Francesco, Christus Factus Est; Bach, Johann Sebastian, Herzliebster Jesu; Bach, Johann Sebastian, O Haupt Voll Blut Und Wunden; Eccard, Johannes, Im Garten Leidet Christus Not; Eccard, Johannes, O Lamm Gottes Unschuldig; Eccard, Johannes, Zu Dieser Osterlichen Zeit; Franck, Melchior, Furwahr, Er Trug Unsre Krankheit; Gallus, Jacobus, Ecce, Quomodo Moritur; Hassler, Hans Leo, Christ Ist

Erstanden; Ingegneri, Marco Antonio, O Bone Jesu; Palestrina, Giovanni, Haec Dies; Palestrina, Giovanni, O Crux, Ave; Palestrina, Giovanni, Stabat Mater Dolorosa; Praetorius, Michael, Wohlauf, Ihr Christen; Schutz, Heinrich, Ehre Sei Dir, Christe; Schutz, Heinrich, Wer Gottes Marter In Ehren Hat; Vittoria, Ludovico, O Vos Omnes; Vittoria, Ludovico, Popule Meus   (P946)

PASSIONE see Haydn, (Franz) Joseph

PASSIONKANTAT see Norman, Rudolf

PASSIONSBERICHT DES MATTHAUS see Pepping, Ernst

PASSIONSKORAL see Olson, Daniel

PASSIONSMOTETTE see Barbe, Helmut

PASSIONSMUSIK see Pfleger, Augustin

PASSIONSMUSIK see Raasted, Niels Otto

PASSIONSMUSIK NACH DEM EVANGELISTEN MARKUS see Thomas, Kurt

PASSIONSORATORIUM see Bach, Johann Ernst

PASSIONTIDE CAROL see Anderson, Ruth

PASSIONTIDE CAROL, A see Tans'ur, William

PASSMORE, C.M.
    Daylight Is Fading *Eve
        SATB ALLANS 249 s.p.   (P947)

PASSOVER TO FREEDOM see Binder, Abraham Wolfe

PAST IS DARK, THE
    4pt mix cor,org oct SCHIRM.G 11669 $.35
                                         (P948)

PAST THREE O'CLOCK *Xmas,carol
    (Steele) SATB ALLANS 266 s.p.   (P949)

PAST THREE O'CLOCK see Dinn, Freda

PASTERZE MILI *carol,Pol
    (Mishkin, H.) "Tell Me, Shepherds Dear" [Pol/ Eng] TTBB,acap SCHIRM.EC 2105 $.18   (P950)

PASTORAL MASS see Yon, Pietro Alessandro, Messa Pastorale

PASTORAL MASS IN F see Diabelli, Anton

PASTORAL PRAYER, A see Lipscomb, Helen

PASTORAL SYMPHONY see Bach, Johann Sebastian

PASTORALE *Xmas,folk,It
    (Pisano) 2pt oct PLYMOUTH PCS-511 $.25 (P951)

PASTORALE see Gilbert, J.R.

PASTORALE see Orlando

PASTORALE see Santucci, Pellegrino

PASTORALE POUR NOEL see Dallier, H.

PASTORCITO QUE TE VAS see Benedito

PASTORES A BELEN *Xmas,carol,Span
    (Smith) 4pt mix cor,S solo oct SCHIRM.G 10945 $.25   (P952)

PASTORES, DICITE, QUIDNAM VIDISTIS? see Morales, Cristobal de

PASTORES ERANT VIGILANTES see Lambiollotte, Louis

PASTORES LOQUEBANTUR see Brixi, Franz Xaver

PASTORES QUIDNAM VIDISTIS see Clemens, Jacobus

PASTRE, PASTRESSO see Saboly, Nicholas

PAT-A-PAN *Xmas,carol,Fr
    (Charles, G.) SAB LEONARD-US 08050720 $.30
                                         (P953)
    (Charles, G.) SSA LEONARD-US 08050760 $.25
                                         (P954)
    (Davis, K.) [Fr/Eng] SATB,pno,opt inst SCHIRM.EC 1616 $.30   (P955)
    (Davis, K.) [Fr/Eng] SSA,opt pno SCHIRM.EC 1052 $.25   (P956)
    (Davis, K.) [Fr/Eng] TTBB,opt pno SCHIRM.EC 2100 $.30   (P957)
    (De Vito) SATB oct SPRATT 621 $.30   (P958)
    (Glaser, V.) [Fr/Eng] SAB,pno,opt inst SCHIRM.EC 2297 $.35   (P959)
    (Glaser, V.) [Fr/Eng] SA,pno/opt fl,pic/rec, opt drums SCHIRM.EC 2527 $.30 (P960)
    (Wilson) SA oct SPRATT 602 $.30   (P961)

PAT-A-PAN see Krones

PATAPAN *Xmas,anthem/carol,Fr
    see Many Moods Of Christmas, The, Suite One
        SATB (easy) oct OXFORD 08.082 $.15 (P962)
    (Christiansen, Paul) SATB (med) oct AUGSBURG 0502 $.30   (P963)
    (Collins) SATB,acap oct PRO ART 1680 $.25
                                         (P964)
    (De Cormier) SATB,pno/org oct LAWSON 51484 $.35   (P965)
    (Hand) SSA (very easy) OXFORD 83.057 $.50, ipa   (P966)
    (Jacques) SA (very easy) oct OXFORD 82.086 $.25, ipa   (P967)
    (Seiber) unis&SSAA (easy) sc OXFORD 44.068 $1.50, ipa   (P968)
    (Seiber) unis&SSAA voc pt OXFORD 44.069 $.25
                                         (P969)

PATAPAN see Rhea

PATER see Cartan

PATER DE CAELIS see de la Rue, Pierre

PATER NOSTER
    (Geveart, F.-A.) "L'oraison Dominicale" [Lat/ Fr] 4pt mix cor,acap (easy) cor pts LEMOINE s.p. see from Collection De Choeurs, troisieme Fascicule   (P970)
    (Racine, C.; Geveart, F.-A.) "L'oraison

Dominicale" [Lat/Fr] 3pt wom cor,acap (med easy) cor pts LEMOINE s.p. see from Collection De Choeurs, premiere Facsimile
                                         (P971)

PATER NOSTER see Bazin, [Francois-Emanuel- Joseph]

PATER NOSTER see Bortniansky, Dimitri Stepanovitch

PATER NOSTER see Bottazzo, Luigi

PATER NOSTER see Dubois, Theodore

PATER NOSTER see Egaddi

PATER NOSTER see Gallus, Jacobus

PATER NOSTER see Gevaert, Francois Auguste

PATER NOSTER see Henderson, Ruth Watson

PATER NOSTER see Johansson, Bengt

PATER NOSTER see Kent, James

PATER NOSTER see Liszt, Franz

PATER NOSTER see Malotte, Albert Hay

PATER NOSTER see Marx, W.B.

PATER NOSTER see Niedermeyer, Louis

PATER NOSTER see Palestrina, Giovanni

PATER NOSTER see Peeters, Flor

PATER NOSTER see Roeske, F.J.

PATER NOSTER see Schubert, Franz (Peter)

PATER NOSTER see Schutz, Heinrich

PATER NOSTER see Stravinsky, Igor

PATER NOSTER see Tchaikovsky, Piotr Ilyitch

PATER NOSTER see Travaglia, Silvio

PATER NOSTER see Verdi, Giuseppe

PATH OF THE JUST, THE see Berger, Jean

PATH OF THE JUST, THE see Nystedt, Knut

PATH OF THE JUST, THE see Rogers, J.H.

PATRES, BERGERS see Saboly, Nicholas, Pastre, Pastresso

PATRES DES MONTAGNES see Tomasi

PATRES NOSTRI PECCAVERUNT see Palestrina, Giovanni

PATRICK, NATHANIEL
    Magnificat And Nunc Dimittis (from Service In G Minor) Magnif/Nunc
        SATB (A min,med) oct OXFORD 42.857 $.65
                                         (P972)

PATTERSON
    Follow The Road
        SATB oct LORENZ A386 $.25   (P973)

    That I May Too Arise *Easter
        SATB oct LORENZ A465 $.25   (P974)

PATTERSON, A.E.
    Hail, The King *Easter
        (O'Hare) 3pt wom cor,pno/org (easy) oct WILLIS 6077 $.15   (P975)

PATTISON, LEE (1890-1966)
    Christ Is Risen From The Dead *Easter
        SATB oct LAWSON 744 $.25   (P976)

    Mistletoe *Xmas
        SATB,acap oct LAWSON 743 $.25   (P977)

PAUKENMESSE see Haydn, (Franz) Joseph, Missa In Tempore Belli

PAUL
    Altar Of Christmas, The *see Fuller, [Esther Mary]

    Christmas Bells *Xmas
        (Fuller) SATB oct PRO ART 1909 $.25 (P978)

    Let's Sing To God *see Fuller, [Esther Mary]

    Of Such Is The Kingdom (composed with Fuller, [Esther Mary])
        unis jr cor,narrator PRO ART 258 $.50
                                         (P979)

    Peace *see Fuller, [Esther Mary]

    Remember Thy Creator *see Fuller, [Esther Mary]

    Seasonal Songs For Children (composed with Fuller, [Esther Mary]) *CC16L,Adv/Xmas/ Easter/Gen/Palm/Thanks
        unis jr cor PRO ART 345 $.75   (P980)

    Thirty-Eight Introits And Responses *see Fuller, [Esther Mary]

    Thou Art My Lamp (composed with Fuller, [Esther Mary])
        SATB oct PRO ART 1170 $.20   (P981)

    Thou Shalt Rejoice In The Lord
        (Fuller; Raymond) SATB oct PLYMOUTH JR-128 $.30   (P982)

PAUL-GERHARDT-KANTATE see Muller, Manfred

PAUL JOHNSON AND THE SURE FOUNDATION *CCU
    (Johnson, P.) SATB voc sc WORD 37533 $1.95
                                         (P983)

PAUL, LESLIE
    O Praise God In His Holiness (Psalm 150) Fest/Gen/Thanks
        (med easy) oct OXFORD 42.897 $.30 (P984)

PAUL, LESLIE (cont'd.)

Psalm 150 *see O Praise God In His Holiness

PAUL OF TARSUS see Effinger, Cecil

PAUL TO THE PHILIPPIANS see Huston, Scott

PAUL'S FAREWELL TO THE CHURCH AT EPHESUS see
Ferguson, Edwin Earle

PAULSEN, HELMUT (1909-1943)
Sing Und Jubiliere, Weihnachtsnachtigall
*Xmas,cant
2pt,strings cor pts TONGER s.p., ipa (P985)

PAULSSON, CARL
Kristallen Den Fina *folk
mix cor NORDISKA 2668 s.p.   (P986)

PAULUS see Mendelssohn-Bartholdy, Felix

PAVIOR
Evening Service *Eve
SATB/unis,org ALBERT s.p.   (P987)

Missa Brevis
[Eng] unis/SATB,org ALBERT s.p. (P988)

PAX see Dandelot, [Georges]

PAX DEI see Troman, Thomas

PAX VOBISCUM see Schubert, Franz (Peter)

PAXSON, THEODORE
He Was Alone
(Stickles) 4pt mix cor,pno/org oct SCHIRM.G
10669 $.25   (P989)

PEACE
Love That Wilt Not Let Me Go
(Lorenz) SATB oct LORENZ B27 $.30 (P990)

O Love That Wilt Not Let Me Go
(Ehret) SATB oct VOLKWEIN (VB227) $.25 (P991)

PEACE see Denton, James

PEACE see Fuller, [Esther Mary]

PEACE see Kesnar

PEACE see Schubert, Franz (Peter), Pax Vobiscum

PEACE AND BROTHERHOOD THROUGH MUSIC see
Kessler, Minuetta

PEACE BE ON EARTH see Billings, William

PEACE, BE STILL see Palmer

PEACE BE UNTO ISRAEL! see Bach, Johann
Sebastian, Friede Uber Israel!

PEACE BE UNTO YOU see Etler, Alvin [Derald]

PEACE BE UNTO YOU see Nystedt, Knut

PEACE BE UNTO YOU see Van Dyke

PEACE BE UNTO YOU see Walter, Samuel

PEACE BE UNTO YOU see Wise, Judah L.

PEACE CAROL, THE see McAfee, Don

PEACE COMES TO ME see Murray

PEACE, F.W.
How Sweet The Name
cor oct HART s.p.   (P992)

PEACE, GENTLE PEACE see Goodhart

PEACE HYMN see Toolan, S. Suzanne

PEACE I LEAVE WITH YOU see Clare, Edwyn A.

PEACE I LEAVE WITH YOU see Dungan

PEACE I LEAVE WITH YOU see Glarum, L. Stanley

PEACE I LEAVE WITH YOU see Iams

PEACE I LEAVE WITH YOU see Landgrave, Phillip

PEACE I LEAVE WITH YOU see Lovelace, Austin C.

PEACE I LEAVE WITH YOU see Maxwell

PEACE I LEAVE WITH YOU see Nystedt, Knut

PEACE I LEAVE WITH YOU see Pelz, Walter L.

PEACE I LEAVE WITH YOU see Roberts, J.

PEACE I LEAVE WITH YOU see Roberts, J. Varley

PEACE I LEAVE WITH YOU see Wilhelm

PEACE I LEAVE WITH YOU see York, D.

PEACE LIKE A RIVER
(Kirby, Charles) SATB oct AGAPE HO 1800 $.30
(P993)

PEACE MAKER see De Jong, Conrad

PEACE O LORD see Slates, Philip M.

PEACE OF GOD, THE see York, D.

PEACE ON EARTH *Xmas/Pageant
LORENZ $.75   (P994)

PEACE ON EARTH see Lehmeier, J.F.

PEACE ON EARTH see Reeker

PEACE ON EARTH see Rhea, A.

PEACE ON EARTH see Schoenberg, Arnold, Friede
Auf Erden

PEACE ON EARTH see Strommen

PEACE ON EARTH see Vivaldi, Antonio, Et In
Terra Pax Hominibus

PEACE ON EARTH see Wild, W.

PEACE, PEACE see Powell, Rich

PEACE PRAYER OF ST. FRANCIS OF ASSISI
(Van Christy) SATB oct BELWIN 2178 $.30
(P995)

PEACE TO EVERY NEIGHBOR see Diplock, Cyril

PEACE TO MANKIND see Bruckner, Anton

PEACE TO THIS HOUSE see Roff, Joseph

PEACE WITH OUR FELLOW MEN see Arensky, Anton
Stepanovitch

PEACE WITHIN THY WALLS see Young

PEACEABLE KINGDOM, THE see Thompson, Randall

PEACH
Let Praise Devote Thy Work
SATB PATERSON 1691 s.p.   (P996)

PEARCE
When He Shall Come
(Hustad) SATB oct AGAPE HA 119 $.25 (P997)
(Hustad) TTBB oct AGAPE HA 115 $.25 (P998)
(Hustad) SSATTBB oct AGAPE HA 509 $.30
(P999)

PEARS, JAMES R.
Almighty God, Unto Whom All Hearts Be Open
SATB FLAMMER A 5305 $.30   (P1000)

Behold How Good And Joyful A Thing It Is
SATB oct HUNTZINGER 4027 $.20   (P1001)

Bread Of The World *Commun
SATB BOOSEY-CAN s.p.   (P1002)

Come Unto Me All Ye That Labour
SATB oct HUNTZINGER 4028 $.20   (P1003)

God Is Our Hope And Strength *Gen
SATB SCHMITT 1691 $.25   (P1004)

O Saviour Of The World
SATB FLAMMER A 5246 $.30   (P1005)
(Riegger) SSA FLAMMER B 5138 $.30 (P1006)

PEARSALL, ROBERT LUCAS DE (1795-1856)
In Dulci Jubilo *Xmas,carol,Ger
(Davies, L.H.) 2pt ASHDOWN E.A.315 s.p.
(P1007)
(Ramsey, Basil) [Lat] SSA oct NOVELLO
51.0655.09 s.p.   (P1008)
(Westbrook, W.) [Lat] SATB ALLANS 377 s.p.
(P1009)

PEARSON
Be Thou My Vision
SATB FLAMMER A 5370 $.30   (P1010)

Behold Now, Praise The Lord (Psalm 134)
see Pearson, Nothing Is Here For Tears

Magnificat *Magnif
unis wom cor,pno PETERS H454 $.30 (P1011)

Nothing Is Here For Tears *mot
SATB,acap PETERS H344 $.40 contains also:
Behold Now, Praise The Lord (Psalm 134)
(P1012)
Psalm 134 *see Behold Now, Praise The Lord

Seven-Fold Amen
SSAA,acap PETERS H539 $.30   (P1013)

Sweet Was The Song The Virgin Sang *Xmas
SSA,pno PETERS H58 $.30   (P1014)

Te Deum Laudamus *Te Deum
[Lat] unis wom cor/unis men cor,org PETERS
H804 $.40   (P1015)

Then Sing We All, Nowell
SS (easy) OXFORD 45.026 $.30   (P1016)

PEARSON, EDITH
Easter Tide *Easter
2pt ENOCH TP273 s.p.   (P1017)

Let Us Rejoice
2pt ASHDOWN E.A.303 s.p.   (P1018)

My Prayer *prayer
3pt ASHDOWN V.T.59 s.p.   (P1019)
2pt ENOCH TP225 s.p.   (P1020)

Star That Shone, A
2pt ENOCH TP272 s.p.   (P1021)

They Called Him Jesus
2pt ENOCH TP242 s.p.   (P1022)

PECCAVIMUS CUM PATRIBUS NOSTRIS see Tye,
Christopher

PEDERSON, MOGENS (1580-1623)
En Bornesang (Behold Os, Herre, Ved Dit Ord)
(from Pratum Spirituale)
(Hatting, Carsten) SATTB HANSEN-DEN 434
s.p. see also Femten Fem-Seks-Stemmige
Satser   (P1023)

Femten Fem-Seks-Stemmige Satser (from Pratum
Spirituale)
(Hatting, Carsten) SATTB/SSATTB cmplt ed
HANSEN-DEN 28604 s.p.
contains & see also: En Bornesang (Behold
Os, Herre, Ved Dit Ord) (from Pratum
Spirituale); Grates Nunc Omnes Reddamus
(from Pratum Spirituale); Jeg Raber Til
Dig, O Herre Krist (Psalm 18) (from
Pratum Spirituale); Jesus Kristus
Sejren Vandt (from Pratum Spirituale);
Jesus Kristus Vandt Os Freden (from
Pratum Spirituale); Min Sjael Nu Love
Herren (Psalm 103) (from Pratum
Spirituale); Nar Min Tid Og Stund Er
For Hand (from Pratum Spirituale); O
Herre, Frels Mig, Dom Min Sag (Psalm
63) (from Pratum Spirituale); Om
Himmeriges Rige Sa Ville Vi Tale (from
Pratum Spirituale); Pa Kristi
Fodselsdag (Kyrie, Gud Fader Af
Himmerig) (from Pratum Spirituale); Pa
Pinsedag (Kyrie Gud Fader
Allersomhojeste Trost) (from Pratum
Spirituale); Sjunge Vi Af Hjertens

PEDERSON, MOGENS (cont'd.)
Grund (from Pratum Spirituale); Vi Tro
Allesammen Pa En Gud (from Pratum
Spirituale); Victimae Paschali Laudes,
"Paskens Offerlam Til Aere" (from
Pratum Spirituale); Vor Gud Han Er Sa
Fast En Borg (Psalm 66) (from Pratum
Spirituale)

Grates Nunc Omnes Reddamus (from Pratum
Spirituale)
(Hatting, Carsten) SATTB HANSEN-DEN 423
s.p. see also Femten Fem-Seks-Stemmige
Satser   (P1025)

Jeg Raber Til Dig, O Herre Krist (Psalm 18)
(from Pratum Spirituale)
(Hatting, Carsten) SATTB HANSEN-DEN 429
s.p. see also Femten Fem-Seks-Stemmige
Satser   (P1026)

Jesus Kristus Sejren Vandt (from Pratum
Spirituale)
(Hatting, Carsten) SATTB HANSEN-DEN 427
s.p. see also Femten Fem-Seks-Stemmige
Satser   (P1027)

Jesus Kristus Vandt Os Freden (from Pratum
Spirituale)
(Hatting, Carsten) SATTB HANSEN-DEN 433
s.p. see also Femten Fem-Seks-Stemmige
Satser   (P1028)

Min Sjael Nu Love Herren (Psalm 103) (from
Pratum Spirituale)
(Hatting, Carsten) SATTB HANSEN-DEN 428
s.p. see also Femten Fem-Seks-Stemmige
Satser   (P1029)

Nar Min Tid Og Stund Er For Hand (from Pratum
Spirituale)
(Hatting, Carsten) SATTB HANSEN-DEN 436
s.p. see also Femten Fem-Seks-Stemmige
Satser   (P1030)

O Herre, Frels Mig, Dom Min Sag (Psalm 63)
(from Pratum Spirituale)
(Hatting, Carsten) SATTB HANSEN-DEN 431
s.p. see also Femten Fem-Seks-Stemmige
Satser   (P1031)

Om Himmeriges Rige Sa Ville Vi Tale (from
Pratum Spirituale)
(Hatting, Carsten) SATTB HANSEN-DEN 432
s.p. see also Femten Fem-Seks-Stemmige
Satser   (P1032)

Pa Kristi Fodselsdag (Kyrie, Gud Fader Af
Himmerig) (from Pratum Spirituale)
(Hatting, Carsten) SATTB HANSEN-DEN 422
s.p. see also Femten Fem-Seks-Stemmige
Satser   (P1033)

Pa Pinsedag (Kyrie Gud Fader Allersomhojeste
Trost) (from Pratum Spirituale)
(Hatting, Carsten) SATTB HANSEN-DEN 424
s.p. see also Femten Fem-Seks-Stemmige
Satser   (P1034)

Paskens Offerlam Til Aere *see Victimae
Paschali Laudes

Psalm 18 *see Jeg Raber Til Dig, O Herre
Krist

Psalm 63 *see O Herre, Frels Mig, Dom Min
Sag

Psalm 66 *see Vor Gud Han Er Sa Fast En Borg

Psalm 103 *see Min Sjael Nu Love Herren

Sjunge Vi Af Hjertens Grund (from Pratum
Spirituale)
(Hatting, Carsten) SATTB HANSEN-DEN 435
s.p. see also Femten Fem-Seks-Stemmige
Satser   (P1035)

Tolv Fem-Stemmige Satser (from Pratum
Spirituale) CC12L
(Jeppesen, Knud) [Dan] SATTB,acap HANSEN-
DEN 24385 s.p.   (P1036)

Vi Tro Allesammen Pa En Gud (from Pratum
Spirituale)
(Hatting, Carsten) SATTB HANSEN-DEN 426
s.p. see also Femten Fem-Seks-Stemmige
Satser   (P1037)

Victimae Paschali Laudes (from Pratum
Spirituale)
[Lat] 3-6pt mix cor,acap sc SKAND. SMF5367
s.p.   (P1038)
(Hatting, Carsten) "Paskens Offerlam Til
Aere" SSATTB HANSEN-DEN 425 s.p. see also
Femten Fem-Seks-Stemmige Satser (P1039)

Vor Gud Han Er Sa Fast En Borg (Psalm 66)
(from Pratum Spirituale)
(Hatting, Carsten) SATTB HANSEN-DEN 430
s.p. see also Femten Fem-Seks-Stemmige
Satser   (P1040)

PEDRETTE
Almighty God *Bibl
4pt mix cor,org/pno oct SCHIRM.G 11816 $.25
(P1041)

Breathe On Me, Breath Of God
SATB oct VOLKWEIN VB120 $.25   (P1042)

Dear Lord And Father Of Mankind
SATB oct PRO ART 1351 $.20   (P1043)

Father Of Mercies
SATB oct VOLKWEIN VB147 $.25   (P1044)

Grant, We Beseech Thee
SATB,org/pno BOSTON 13237 $.30   (P1045)

Is It Nothing To You
4pt mix cor,acap,org/pno oct SCHIRM.G 11926
$.25   (P1046)

Little Lamb, Who Made Thee *Xmas
SATB SCHMITT 8005 $.30   1047)

PEDRETTE (cont'd.)

O God, Who Art The Author Of Peace
SATB,org BOSTON 13642 $.35   (P1048)

Thy Kingdom Come
SATB,S/T solo oct PRO ART 1500 $.16   (P1049)

PEDRETTI, EDWARD
Lord Jesus, Think On Me
SATB oct HUNTZINGER 7009 $.20   (P1050)

PEEK
Be Joyful In The Lord
SATB oct FISCHER,C CM-7472 $.25   (P1051)

I Would Be True
SA/SAB oct LORENZ 7803 $.25   (P1052)

PEEK, RICHARD
Christ Whose Glory Fills The Skies *Adv/Gen
4pt jr cor/SATB (med easy) FISCHER,C
CM 7226 $.25   (P1053)
SATB,acap oct FISCHER,C CM-7226 $.25
                                   (P1054)

Come, Faithful People, Come Away *Palm
SA/TB oct SOUTHERN $.25   (P1055)
SATB ABINGDON APM-494 $.35   (P1056)

Come, Thou Fount Of Every Blessing
SATB (med) ABINGDON APM-506 $.35   (P1057)

God Of Love My Shepherd Is, The
2pt oct KERBY 5602C $.30   (P1058)
SATB oct KERBY 5602C $.30   (P1059)
SATB/SA/TB,org oct KERBY 5602 $.30 (P1060)

It Is Good To Sing Thy Praises
SATB,org oct KERBY 6508 $.35   (P1061)
SATB oct KERBY 81978 $.35   (P1062)

Lo, I Am With You Always
SATB (med) ABINGDON APM-755 $.30   (P1063)

Now Glad Of Heart Be Every One
SATB oct KERBY 80278 $.25   (P1064)
SATB,org oct KERBY 802 $.25   (P1065)

On The Birthday Of The Lord *14th cent
SATB oct ELKAN-V 362-1245 $.25   (P1066)

Praise The Lord Ye Servants
unis mix cor GRAY GCMR 3289 $.30   (P1067)

Psalm 130
SATB (med) ABINGDON APM-477 $.25   (P1068)

Righteous Joseph *Xmas
SATB,org oct KERBY 5209 $.25   (P1069)
SATB oct KERBY 82078 $.25   (P1070)

Royal Banners Forward Go, The *Palm
SATB ABINGDON APM-246 $.25   (P1071)

Unto The Hills I Lift Mine Eyes
SATB oct KERBY 6204 $.30   (P1072)
SATB,acap oct KERBY 6204C $.30   (P1073)

Winter Carol *Xmas,carol
SATB,opt hndbl oct KERBY 5901 $.35 (P1074)
SATB,opt hndbl oct KERBY 82178 $.35 (P1075)

PEERSON, MARTIN (1580?-1650?)
Blow Out The Trumpet
(Wailes) SSATB,org/strings SCHOTT 10604
s.p.   (P1076)

Lord, Ever Bridle My Desires
(Wailes) SSATB SCHOTT 10286 s.p.   (P1077)

Man Dream No More
(Wailes) SSATB,opt org SCHOTT 10291 s.p.
                                   (P1078)

O God, That No Time Doest Despise
(Wailes) SATB SCHOTT 10283 s.p.   (P1079)

O God, When Thou Went'st
(Wailes) SSATB,SSATB soli,org/strings
SCHOTT 10292 s.p.   (P1080)

O Let Me At Thy Foot- Stool Fall
(Wailes) SSATB SCHOTT 10285 s.p.   (P1081)

Upon My Lap My Soveraigne Sits *Renais
(Ehret, Walter) SATB,acap PEER $.40 (P1082)

Upon My Lap My Sovereign Sits *Xmas
SATB,opt pno SCHIRM.EC 1608 $.25   (P1083)

PEERY
Beautiful Savior
SATB oct LORENZ C175 $.30   (P1084)

Behold The Star! *Xmas,cant
SATB oct LORENZ $1.95   (P1085)

Christ Arose *Easter
SATB oct LORENZ A293 $.30   (P1086)

Christ Is Risen! *Easter
SATB oct LORENZ C112 $.30   (P1087)

For Spacious Skies
SATB oct LORENZ B149 $.30   (P1088)

I Would Be True
SATB oct LORENZ 4423 $.30   (P1089)

In The Stillness Of The Night *Xmas
SA oct LORENZ 5350 $.30   (P1090)
SATB oct HORENZ 4416 $.30   (P1091)

Jesus Is A Rock
SATB oct LORENZ E3 $.30   (P1092)

Just As I Am
SATB oct LORENZ C135 $.30   (P1093)

Last Words Of Jesus, The *Easter,cant
SATB LORENZ $1.95   (P1094)

This Be My Song
SATB oct LORENZ C345 $.30   (P1095)

Thou Wilt Keep Him
SATB oct LORENZ 9791 $.30   (P1096)

PEERY (cont'd.)

Ye, Who Seek The Truth
oct GALAXY 1.1901.1 $.30   (P1097)

Your SSA Choir *CCU
SSA FLAMMER GB5003 $1.25   (P1098)

PEERY, [ROB ROY] (1900-   )
Altar Choir Book *CCU
SATB BELWIN $1.00   (P1099)

Carols Old And New *CCU,Xmas,carol
multiple choirs BOSTON 13490 $.50 (P1100)

Chancel Choir Book *CCU
SA BELWIN $1.25   (P1101)

Give Me This Day
SAB oct PRESSER 312-40462 $.30   (P1102)

Joyous Easter Hymn *Easter
SAB oct PRESSER 312-40245 $.30   (P1103)

Praise The Lord
SA oct PRESSER 312-40931 $.30   (P1104)

Sanctuary Choir Book *CCU
SAB BELWIN $1.25   (P1105)

Strife Is O'er *Easter
SAB oct SOUTHERN $.25   (P1106)

This Be My Song *Gen,anthem
SATB (med diff) oct LORENZ C345 $.30 (P1107)

PEERY, ROBERT ROY (1903-   )
Chapel Choir Book *CCU
SAB oct PRESSER $1.25   (P1108)

Ride On, O Lord And King! *Easter
SATB,acap oct PRESSER 312-40610 $.30 (P1109)

Singing Children Of The Church *CCU
SA oct PRESSER $1.00   (P1110)

Young People's Choir Book *CCU
SAB oct PRESSER $1.00   (P1111)

PEETERS, FLOR
All My Heart Today Rejoices *Xmas,hymn
SATB,org/pno PETERS 6347 $.35   (P1112)

Ave Maria
girl cor SOUTHERN $.20   (P1113)
SSA oct SUMMY M 1845 $.35   (P1114)
"Hail Mary" [Lat/Eng] SATB,org/pno PETERS
6344 $.20   (P1115)
"Hail Mary" [Lat/Eng] SA/TB,org/pno PETERS
6343 $.20   (P1116)

Canticum Gaudii (Psalm 91) Op.118
SATB,org,2trp,2trom sc PETERS 66426, voc sc
PETERS 66426A   (P1117)

Entrata Festiva *Proces/Reces
[Eng/Lat] unis,2trp,2trom,org,opt timp sc
PETERS 6159 $3.50
contains: Processional; Recessional
                                   (P1118)

Flor, Missa In Hon. St. Josephi *Op.21, Mass
cor voc sc KALMUS 6359 $1.00   (P1119)

Four Flemish Christmas Carols
[Eng/Belg] SATB,org,2ob/2rec,2bsn,2trp,
3trom, English horn PETERS 66160 $.60,
ipa   (P1120)

Hail Mary *see Ave Maria

I Know That My Redeemer Liveth *anthem/hymn
SATB,org/pno PETERS 6346 $.25   (P1121)

In Excelsis Gloria *anthem
SATB (very easy) oct AUGSBURG 1196 $.25
                                   (P1122)

Jubilate Deo Omnis Terra (Psalm 99)
"Sing To God With Gladness" SATB,inst oct
SUMMY M 2096 $.75, ipa   (P1123)

Jubilee Mass In Honour Of St. Nicholas
*Op.92, Mass
SATB,org voc sc PETERS 66289 $2.00 (P1124)

Lord God We Praise Thee *see Te Deum

Lord's Prayer, The *Bibl/prayer
SATB,org/pno PETERS 6200 $.20   (P1125)
SA,org/pno PETERS 6202 $.20   (P1126)

Magnificat *Magnif
SATB,inst oct SUMMY M-2346 $1.00, ipa
                                   (P1127)

Mass In Honor Of Saint Joseph *Mass
[Lat] SATB sc SUMMY M 1562 $1.00   (P1128)

May The Lord Bless You
SA,org,drums/maracas,gtr oct SUMMY M 2863
$.35   (P1129)

Our Father *see Pater Noster

Pater Noster
"Our Father" [Eng/Lat] SATB,org/pno PETERS
6340 $.20   (P1130)
"Our Father" [Lat/Eng] SA/TB,org/pno PETERS
6341 $.20   (P1131)

Prayer On Christmas Eve *anthem
SATB (med) oct AUGSBURG 1174 $.20 (P1132)

Processional
see Entrata Festiva

Psalm 91 *see Canticum Gaudii

Psalm 99 *see Jubilate Deo Omnis Terra

Recessional
see Entrata Festiva

Sing To God With Gladness *see Jubilate Deo
Omnis Terra

Te Deum *Te Deum
"Lord God We Praise Thee" SATB,orch/inst
oct SUMMY M 1483 $1.20   (P1133)

PEETERS, FLOR (cont'd.)

This Is The Day Which The Lord Hath Made
*anthem
SATB (med diff) oct AUGSBURG 1260 $.20
                                   (P1134)

PEHKONEN
Boy Is Born
SATB,org oct BOOSEY 5738 $.40   (P1135)

Mary, The Rose
SATB,acap OXFORD   (P1136)

PEI DEFUNTI see Volpi, Edoardo

PEI NOSTRI SOLDATI see Cossetti, Gio. Batta.

PEKIEL, BERTLOMIEJ (? -ca. 1670)
Audite Mortales *Pol
(Szweykowski, Z.M.) SSAATB,cont,strings
POLSKIE WDMP4 s.p.   (P1137)

Magnum Nomen Domini *Pol
(Feicht, H.) mix cor,acap POLSKIE WDMP19
s.p. contains also: Resonet In Laudibus
                                   (P1138)

Missa A 15 *Pol
(Szweykowski, Z.M.; Mrowiec, K.) dbl cor,
cont,2vln,3vla POLSKIE WDMP69 s.p. (P1139)

Missa Brevis *Pol
(Feicht, H.) mix cor,acap POLSKIE WDMP62
s.p.   (P1140)

Missa Paschalis *Pol
(Feicht, H.) mix cor,acap POLSKIE WDMP58
s.p.   (P1141)

Missa Pulcherrima Ad Instar Praenestini *Pol
(Feicht, H.) mix cor,acap POLSKIE WDMP17
s.p.   (P1142)

Resonet In Laudibus
see Pekiel, Bertlomiej, Magnum Nomen Domini

Two Patrem For Christmas *CC2U,Pol
(Feicht, H.) mix cor/men cor POLSKIE WDMP52
s.p.   (P1143)

PEL MESE MARIANO see Volpi, Edoardo

PEL S. NATALE E L'EPIFANIA see Ascenso, Antonio

PEL TEMPO PASQUALE *Easter
[Lat] ZANIBON 2951 s.p.
contains: Fabiani, Angelo, In Dominica
Palmarum (3pt mix cor); Gerli, Giovanni,
Regina Coeli (unis); Gerli, Giovanni,
Regina Coeli (2 eq voices); Volpi,
Edoardo, Haec Dies (2 eq voices) (P1144)

PELEGRINI
Missa Brevis *Mass
mix cor,acap voc sc KALMUS 6373 $1.00
                                   (P1145)

PELOQUIN, C. ALEXANDER
All The Ends Of The Earth (Psalm 98) Xmas/
Gen,anthem
SATB/cong (med) oct GIA G1655 $.45 (P1146)

Beat The Drum *Xmas,anthem/carol,Pol
(Trzaska, J.R.) SATB (med) oct GIA G1309
$.30   (P1147)

Behold How Good It Is (Psalm 132) Gen,anthem
SA&cong/TB&cong/SB&cong,cantor,acap (easy)
oct GIA G1141 $.25   (P1148)

Bread Is One, The *Commun,anthem/prayer
SATB (med easy) oct GIA G1396 $.30 see also
Four Prayers For Christian Unity (P1149)

Christ Is King
boy cor SOUTHERN $.20   (P1150)

Christ, The Light Of The Nations *Gen,anthem
SA&cong/TB&cong/SB&cong,brass,bvl,perc (med
easy) voc sc GIA G1486 $1.50, ipa, ipr
                                   (P1151)

Come Nearer *ASD/BVM,anthem
(Patenaude, A.A.) SATB/cong (med easy) oct
GIA G1704 $.50   (P1152)

Earthquake *Gen,anthem
SATB,Bar solo (med diff) voc sc GIA G1521
$.60 see also Four Freedom Songs   (P1153)

Four Freedom Songs *CC4U,Gen,anthem
SATB,Bar solo,opt orch (med diff) voc sc
GIA G1492 $1.95, ipr
see also: Earthquake   (P1154)

Four Prayers For Christian Unity *anthem
SATB,3trp,3trom,timp (med) cmplt ed GIA
G1301 $1.50, ipr
contains & see also: Bread Is One, The;
In Christ The Lord; Prayer For Peace;
Psalm For Unity   (P1155)

Give Praise To The Lord *see Laudate Dominum

Gloria (from Missa A La Samba) Gen,Mass
2 eq voices/3 eq voices,opt inst (med) cor
pts GIA G1567 $.50, ipa   (P1156)
SATB,opt inst (med) voc sc GIA G1565 $.60,
ipa   (P1157)

Gloria Of The Bells *Gen,Gloria/Mass
opt SATB&cong,cantor,org (med easy) voc sc
GIA G1785 $.40   (P1158)

God Mounts His Throne (Psalm 46) Asc/Gen,
anthem
SATB&cong,opt cantor (med diff) oct GIA
G1661 $.45   (P1159)

Have Mercy On Me (Psalm 50) Lent,anthem
cong&opt SATB,cantor (easy) oct GIA G1657
$.35   (P1160)

How Lovely Is Your Dwelling Place (Psalm 83)
Gen,anthem
SSA&cong/TTB&cong,cantor (med easy) oct GIA
G1140 $.50   (P1161)

How Still And Tiny *Xmas,anthem/carol,Pol
(Trzaska, J.R.) SATB (med) oct GIA G1308
$.30   (P1162)

PELOQUIN, C. ALEXANDER (cont'd.)

I Believe That My Redeemer Lives *Easter,
anthem
SATB (med easy) oct GIA G1635 $.35   (P1163)

In Christ The Lord *Gen,anthem/prayer
SATB (med) oct GIA G1456 $.60 see also Four
Prayers For Christian Unity   (P1164)

Laudate Dominum (Psalm 117) Gen,anthem
"Give Praise To The Lord" SATB (med easy)
oct GIA G835 $.50   (P1165)

Litany *Gen,anthem
SATB (easy) oct GIA G1092 $.30   (P1166)
SA/TB (easy) oct GIA G1172 $.25   (P1167)

Lord, Every Nation (Psalm 72) Epiph,anthem
SATB&cong (med) oct GIA G1656 $.45   (P1168)

Lord, Send Out Your Spirit (Psalm 104) Pent,
anthem
SATB/cong (med) oct GIA G1662 $.40   (P1169)

Lord, You Have The Words (Psalm 19) Gen,
anthem
SATB&cong (easy) oct GIA G1663 $.35   (P1170)

Lord's Prayer, The *Gen,anthem/Doxol
SATB (med) oct GIA G977 $.60   (P1171)

Love Is Everlasting *Gen,anthem/Bibl
SATB&cong/SSA&cong/TTB&cong,cantor,org,opt
inst (med) voc sc GIA G1457 $1.50, cor
pts GIA G1475A $.75   (P1172)

Love Song, A (from Common Mass Of The Blessed
Virgin Mary) BVM,Introit
SSA&cong oct SUMMY M 2701 $.50   (P1173)

Lullaby For Jesus *Xmas,anthem/carol,Pol
(Trzaska,J.R.) SATB (med) oct GIA G1310
$.25   (P1174)

Mass In English *Mass
unis/cong&SATB,inst sc SUMMY M 2511 $1.50,
ipa   (P1175)
unis/cong&SATB,inst voc sc SUMMY M 2511A
$.80, ipa   (P1176)

Missa A La Samba *Gen,Mass,Contemp
SATB,inst (med) voc sc GIA G1582 $1.25, ipa
(P1177)
2 eq voices/3 eq voices,inst (med) voc sc
GIA G1581 $1.25, ipa   (P1178)
unis,inst (med) cor pts GIA G1580 $1.25,
ipa   (P1179)

My God, My God (Psalm 22) Holywk/Lent,anthem
opt SATB&cong,cantor (easy) oct GIA G1658
$.35   (P1180)

Noel Nouvelet
SATB FLAMMER A 5410 $.30   (P1181)

Prayer For Peace *Gen,anthem/prayer
SATB&cong (med) oct GIA G1340 $.60 see also
Four Prayers For Christian Unity   (P1182)

Psalm 9 *see Why, O Lord, Do You Stand
Aloof?

Psalm 19 *see Lord, You Have The Words

Psalm 22 *see My God, My God

Psalm 24 *see To You, O Lord

Psalm 34 *see Taste And See

Psalm 46 *see God Mounts His Throne

Psalm 50 *see Have Mercy On Me

Psalm 72 *see Lord, Every Nation

Psalm 83 *see How Lovely Is Your Dwelling
Place

Psalm 98 *see Shout For Joy

Psalm 100 *see We Are His People

Psalm 104 *see Lord, Send Out Your Spirit

Psalm 117 *see Laudate Dominum

Psalm 118 *see This Is The Day

Psalm 132 *see Behold How Good It Is

Psalm 136 *see Resurrection Psalm

Psalm For Unity *Gen,anthem/prayer
SATB (med) oct GIA G1455 $.60 see also Four
Prayers For Christian Unity   (P1183)

Rejoice In Hope *Gen,anthem
SATB&cong,cantor,brass,timp (med easy) oct
GIA G1735 $.60, ipr   (P1184)

Resurrection Psalm (Psalm 136) Easter,anthem
SATB&cong,cantor (med) oct GIA G1659 $.35
(P1185)

Shout For Joy (Psalm 98) Gen,anthem
SATB&cong,cantor (med) oct GIA G1624 $1.50
(P1186)

Song Of Daniel *Gen,anthem
SATB&opt cong,cantor,org,2trp,2trom,timp
(med easy) voc sc GIA G1185 $1.00   (P1187)
TTBB&opt cong,cantor,org,2trp,2trom,timp
(med easy) voc sc GIA G1158 $1.00   (P1188)

Song Of Zachary *Gen,anthem
SATB (med easy) oct GIA G1188 $.60   (P1189)

Songs Of Israel *CC12L,Adv/Asc/Xmas/Easter/
Epiph/Gen/Holywk/Lent,Bibl/Mass/Psalm
opt SATB&cong,cantor (med easy) voc sc GIA
G1666 $3.50   (P1190)

Taste And See (Psalm 34) Gen,anthem
SATB&cong (easy) oct GIA G1664 $.40   (P1191)

This Is The Day (Psalm 118) Easter,anthem
SATB&cong,cantor (med easy) oct GIA G1660
$.40   (P1192)

PELOQUIN, C. ALEXANDER (cont'd.)

To The Town Of Bethlehem *Xmas,anthem/carol,
Pol
(Trzaska,J.R.) SATB (med) oct GIA G1311
$.40   (P1193)

To You, O Lord (Psalm 24) Adv,anthem
SATB (easy) oct GIA G1654 $.40   (P1194)

Triple Amen, The *CC5U
SATB/SSA/TTB&cong oct SUMMY M 2567 $.25 (P1195)

We Are His People (Psalm 100) Gen,anthem
SATB&cong (easy) oct GIA G1665 $.35 (P1196)

When The Lord Was Born *Xmas,anthem/carol,
Pol
(Trzaska,J.R.) SATB (med easy) oct GIA
G1307 $.30   (P1197)

Why, O Lord, Do You Stand Aloof? (Psalm 9)
Gen,anthem
SATB (med easy) oct GIA G1087 $.75   (P1198)

PELZ, WALTER L.
Arise, O God, And Shine *Epiph/Gen
SATB,kbd (med easy) oct CONCORDIA 98-1718
$.30   (P1199)

Christ The Lord Is Risen *anthem
SATB (easy) oct AUGSBURG 1478 $.25   (P1200)

Come Let Us Join *Gen
SATB SCHMITT 8042 $.35   (P1201)

Crown Him With Many Crowns
SATB&cong,org,3trp sc AUGSBURG 11-9093 $.35
(P1202)

Day Of Rejoicing *anthem
SATB,trp (med) oct AUGSBURG 1561 $.30
(P1203)

He Is Risen *anthem
unis treb cor&opt desc (easy) oct AUGSBURG
1358 $.25   (P1204)

He's Risen, Christ Jesus, The Lord *anthem
SATB,opt org,opt trp (easy) oct AUGSBURG
1368 $.30   (P1205)

Holy God, We Praise Thy Name
SATB&cong,org,3trp sc AUGSBURG 11-9202
$.35, ipa   (P1206)

I Pray Thee, Dear Lord Jesus *Gen
SATB SCHMITT 8016 $.35   (P1207)

Jesus Christ Is Risen Today
SATB&cong,org,2trp sc AUGSBURG 11-1451 $.30
(P1208)

Lord Jesus, Gentle Savior *Gen
SATB SCHMITT 504 $.35   (P1209)

Peace I Leave With You *anthem
SATB (easy) oct AUGSBURG 1364 $.25   (P1210)

Psalm 25 *see Show Me Thy Ways

Psalm Of Joy, A *Gen
SATB,opt inst SCHMITT 913 $.45, ipa   (P1211)

Rejoice And Be Merry *anthem
SATB,org,ob (easy) oct AUGSBURG 1605 $.35
(P1212)

Show Me Thy Ways (Psalm 25) anthem
SATB,ob,gtr (easy) oct AUGSBURG 0642 $.30
(P1213)

Who Are These That Earnest Knock *Xmas
SATB,kbd (med easy) oct CONCORDIA 98-1588
$.25   (P1214)

Who Shall Abide *anthem
SAB,fl,gtr (med) oct AUGSBURG 0617 $.25
(P1215)

PENALOSA, FRANCISCO (1470-1535)
Sancta Mater *mot
[Lat] 4pt mix cor,acap UNION ESP. 19181
$.75   (P1216)

PENDERECKI, KRZYSZTOF (1933-   )
Dies Irae *ora
mix cor,SBarB soli,harmonium,pno,4fl,3ob,
4bsn,6horn,4trp,4trom,2tuba,strings,perc,
3 saxophones sc MOECK s.p.   (P1217)

From The Psalms Of David *Bibl
[Lat] mix cor,2pno,4bvl,perc,harp,celesta
sc MOECK s.p.   (P1218)

In Pulverem Mortis
see Two Choruses From The Passion According
To St. Luke

Miserere
see Two Choruses From The Passion According
To St. Luke

Passio Et Mors Domini Nostri Jesu Christi
Secundum Lucam *Psntd
3pt mix cor&jr cor,SBarB&narrator,
harmonium,org,pno,4fl,clar,bsn,6horn,
4trp,4trom,tuba,strings,perc,harp, 2
saxophones sc MOECK s.p.   (P1219)

Stabat Mater *Pol
3 cor BELWIN $2.50   (P1220)
3 cor/16pt POLSKIE s.p.   (P1221)

Two Choruses From The Passion According To
St. Luke
[Lat] sc MOECK s.p.
contains: In Pulverem Mortis (3pt mix
cor,acap); Miserere (3pt mix cor&opt jr
cor,acap)   (P1222)

PENDLETON
Come, Come Away *carol,Fr
2pt jr cor FISCHER,C R 448 $.18   (P1223)

PENINGER
Easter Fanfare *Easter
SSATBB oct SACRED S-117 $.40   (P1224)

I Sing The Mighty Power Of God
SATB oct SACRED S-121 $.35   (P1225)

Jesus, Gentle Shepherd
SATB oct PRO ART 2569 $.25   (P1226)

PENINGER (cont'd.)

My Song Is Love Unknown
SATB oct SACRED S-131 $.35   (P1227)

O Deepest Woe
SATB oct SACRED S-92 $.35   (P1228)

O, We Believe In One True God
SATB oct PRO ART 2568 $.25   (P1229)

Open Now Thy Gates Of Beauty
SATB oct SACRED S-79 $.35   (P1230)

Praise Ye The Sovereign Lord
SATB oct PRO ART 2601 $.30   (P1231)

Sing We All Now Alleluia
SATB (med diff/diff) SOUTHERN $.30   (P1232)

These Things Shall Be
SATB oct PRO ART 2634 $.35   (P1233)

PENINGER, DAVID
All Men Sing Noel! *Xmas
SATB WORD CS-2472 $.25   (P1234)

All Praise To Our Redeeming Lord
4pt mix cor,org/pno oct SCHIRM.G 11737 $.30
(P1235)

Canticle For Easter, A *Easter
jr cor&sr cor oct FISCHER,J 9700 $.35   (P1236)

God Eternal Is My Refuge *anthem/hymn,US
4pt mix cor,org oct SCHIRM.G 11550 $.30
(P1237)

God Is Our Strength And Song
4pt mix cor,org/pno oct SCHIRM.G 11532 $.25
(P1238)

In Every Hand Begin The Song
SATB oct FISCHER,J 10015 $.30   (P1239)

Jesus, Our Strength, Our Hope
4pt mix cor,org/pno oct SCHIRM.G 11738 $.25
(P1240)

Jesus, Thou Joy Of Loving Hearts
4pt mix cor,org/pno oct SCHIRM.G 11739 $.30
(P1241)

Lord Our God Is Clothed In Might, The *Fest
SATB,brass oct WORD CS-2470 $.40   (P1242)

O Jesus, Crucified For Man
SATB SHAWNEE A 5296 $.30   (P1243)

O Thou In Whose Presence My Soul Takes
Delight
SATB,org/pno FISCHER,J 10080 $.30   (P1244)

Praise! Praise! *CCU,cant
SATB voc sc WORD 20051 $1.50   (P1245)

Sing Joyfully, Joyfully, Christmas Is Come
*CCU,Xmas
unis treb cor FISCHER,J $1.00   (P1246)

Thou Art The Way
SATB oct FISCHER,J 10014 $.30   (P1247)

PENITENCE, PARDON AND PEACE see Maunder, J.H.

PENITENT, THE see Van De Water, B.

PENITENTIAL PSALMS VOL. I: DOMINE see Lassus,
Roland de (Orlandus)

PENITENTIAL PSALMS VOL. VI: DE PROFUNDIS see
Lassus, Roland de (Orlandus)

PENITENTIAL PSALMS VOL. VII: DOMINI EXAUDI see
Lassus, Roland de (Orlandus)

PENITENTIAL TEARS OF ST. PETER VOL. 1 see
Lassus, Roland de (Orlandus)

PENITENTIAL TEARS OF ST. PETER VOL. 2 see
Lassus, Roland de (Orlandus)

PENITENTIAL TEARS OF ST. PETER VOL. 3 see
Lassus, Roland de (Orlandus)

PENN, BENNETT
Lord Is My Strength, The
SATB TRANSCON. TCL 622 $.25   (P1248)

PENN, WILLIAM
Humana Sine Nomine
TTBB/SATB/SSAA,narrator,pno,perc oct
HERITAGE H105 $.90   (P1249)

PENNARTZ, P.
Aan Bethlehems Sterre *Xmas
mix cor ALSBACH&D sc s.p., cor pts s.p.
(P1250)

PENNELL
Angel's Carol, The *Xmas,carol
SATB oct LILLENAS AN-3831 $.30   (P1251)

PENS
O Little Baby Jesus *Xmas
SATB,acap oct PRO ART 1128 $.22   (P1252)

PENTATONIC SONGBOOK *CCU
(Brocklehurst, Brian) voc sc SCHOTT 10909
s.p., cor pts SCHOTT 1090A s.p.   (P1253)

PENTECOSTAL FIRE IS FALLING see Bennard, George

PENTECOSTAL MEDLEY see Collins

PEOPLE CALLED CHRISTIANS, A see McKay

PEOPLE, LOOK EAST see Warner, Richard

PEOPLE OF GOD see Moore

PEOPLE THAT IN DARKNESS see Herbst

PEOPLE THAT WALKED IN DARKNESS see Mennin,
Peter (Mennini)

PEOPLE THAT WALKED IN DARKNESS, THE see Naylor,
Bernard

PEOPLE THAT WALKED IN DARNESS, THE see Bright,
Houston

PEOPLE'S EUCHARIST, A see Wyton, Alec

PEOPLE'S MASS see Roff, Joseph

PEOPLE'S PARISH COMMUNION SERVICE BOOK *CCU
ROYAL s.p. (P1254)

PEPPING, ERNST (1901-)
Ach Wie Gross Ist Gottes Gut Und Wohltat
*Psntd,mot
[Ger] SSATBB,acap (med diff) BAREN. BA 2521
$2.50 see from LIEDMOTETTEN NACH WEISEN
DER BOHMISCHEN BRUDER (P1255)

Auf Meinen Lieben Gott *Trin
[Ger] 2-3pt&5pt mix cor,acap (med) BAREN.
BA 782 s.p. (P1256)

Aus Hartem Weh Die Menschheit Klagt *Adv,mot
[Ger] SATB,acap (med diff) BAREN. BA 3931
$1.75 (P1257)

Barmherziger, Ewiger Gott *Gen,mot
[Ger] SATB,acap (med diff) BAREN. BA 2519
$1.75 see from Liedmotetten Nach Weisen
Der Bohmischen Bruder (P1258)

Bicinien, Heft 1: 34 Chorale *CC34U,Gen,
chorale
[Ger] 2 eq voices,acap (med) BAREN. BA 2759
$4.00 (P1259)

Bicinien, Heft 2: 12 Psalmen *CC12U,Gen,
Psalm
[Ger] 2 eq voices,acap (med) BAREN. BA 2746
$4.25 (P1260)

Bicinien, Heft 3: 9 Evangelien Und Episteln
*CC9U,Gen,evang
[Ger] 2 eq voices,acap (med) BAREN. BA 3217
$3.25 (P1261)

Das Weltgericht *ECY,evang/mot
[Ger] SATB,acap (med diff) BAREN. BA 3218
$2.50 (P1262)

Deines Lichtes Glanz *Gen,mot
[Ger] SSATBB,acap (med) BAREN. BA 3520
$3.50 (P1263)

Denk, Mensch, Wie Dein Heiland Dich Liebet
*Psntd,mot
[Ger] SSATBB,acap (med diff) BAREN. BA 2514
$2.25 see from LIEDMOTETTEN NACH WEISEN
DER BOHMISCHEN BRUDER (P1264)

Der Herr Ist Mein Hirte (Psalm 23) Easter/
Pent
[Ger] SATB,acap (med) BAREN. BA 4360 $2.25
(P1265)

Der Morgenstern Ist Aufgedrungen *Adv
[Ger] 3 eq voices/SATB,acap (med) BAREN.
BA 2277 s.p. (P1266)

Die Nacht Ist Kommen *Gen,mot
[Ger] SSATBB,acap (med diff) BAREN. BA 2516
$1.75 see from Liedmotetten Nach Weisen
Der Bohmischen Bruder (P1267)

Die Weihnachtsgeschichte Des Lukas *Xmas,
Bibl
[Ger] 4-7pt mix cor,acap (med diff) BAREN.
BA 3947 $8.75 (P1268)

Dona Nobis Pacem *Gen,Mass
[Ger] SATB&SATB,acap (diff) BAREN. BA 2262
$5.25 (P1269)

Ein Kind Ist Uns Geboren Heut *Xmas,mot
[Ger] SSATBB,acap (med diff) BAREN. BA 2756
$1.50 (P1270)

Erhalt Uns, Herr, Bei Deinem Wort *Fest
[Ger] 2-4pt men cor,acap (med) BAREN.
BCH 153 s.p. (P1271)

Freud Und Wollust Dieser Welt *Gen,mot
[Ger] SATB/SSATBB,acap (med diff) BAREN.
BA 2757 $2.25 see from Liedmotetten Nach
Weisen Der Bohmischen Bruder (P1272)

Frohlockt Und Ruhmt Mit Herz Und Mund *Gen,
mot
[Ger] SSATB,acap (med diff) BAREN. BA 2512
$2.25 see from Liedmotetten Nach Weisen
Der Bohmischen Bruder (P1273)

Gesange Der Bohmischen Bruder In Variationen,
Heft 2 *CC9L,Gen
[Ger] SATB,acap (med diff) BAREN. BA 4342
$3.75 (P1274)

Gesange Der Bohmischen Bruder In Variationen,
Heft I *CC9L,Xmas
[Ger] SATB,acap (med diff) BAREN. BA 4341
$3.75 (P1275)

Glaubige Seel, Schau, Dein Herr Und Konig
Will Kommen *Adv,mot
[Ger] SATB,acap (med diff) BAREN. BA 2518
$1.75 (P1276)

Gloria
see Missa Brevis

Gloria In Excelsis
see Kleine Messe

Herr, Du Erforschest Mich (Psalm 139) Gen
[Ger] SATB,A solo,orch sc BAREN. BA 4179
rental, ipr, voc sc BAREN. TP 129 s.p.
(P1277)

Herr, Neige Deine Ohren *Gen
[Ger] SATB,acap BA 1129 s.p. see also Sechs
Kleine Motetten (P1278)

Herr, Unser Herrscher (Psalm 8) Trin
[Ger] SATB,acap (med) BAREN. BA 4359 $2.25
(P1279)

Heut Singt Die Liebe Christenheit *Fest
[Ger] 3pt men cor,acap (med) BAREN. BCH 149
s.p. (P1280)

I Am The Lord *Asc/Cnfrm/Ded/Gen
SATB,kbd (med diff) oct CONCORDIA 98-2044
$.40 (P1281)

Ich Bin Der Herr *Gen
[Ger] SATB,acap (med diff) BAREN. BA 1127
s.p.
[Ger] SATB,acap BA 1127 s.p. see also Sechs
(P1282)

PEPPING, ERNST (cont'd.)
Kleine Motetten (P1283)

Ich Habe Alles Dinges Ein Ende Gesehen *Gen
[Ger] SATB,acap BA 1122 $1.75 see also
Sechs Kleine Motetten (P1284)

Jauchzt, Alle Lande, Gott Zu Ehren *Gen
[Ger] 3pt men cor,acap (med) BAREN. BCH 151
s.p. (P1285)

Johannes Der Taufer (Ecce Mitto Angelum Meum)
*Gen
[Ger] 4-6pt mix cor,acap (med diff) BAREN.
BA 4357 $6.50 (P1286)

Kleine Messe *Gloria/Kyrie/Mass/Sanctus
[Lat] SAB,acap (med diff) BAREN. BA 2260
$2.25
contains: Gloria In Excelsis; Kyrie;
Sanctus (P1287)

Komm, Gott Troster, Heiliger Geist *Pent,mot
[Ger] SATB,acap (med diff) BAREN. BA 2511
$1.75 (P1288)

Kommt, Und Lasst Uns Christum Ehren (from Die
Weihnachtsgeschichte Des Lukas) Xmas
[Ger] SATB,acap (med diff) BAREN. BA 3999
$1.50 (P1289)

Kyrie
see Kleine Messe
see Missa Brevis

Laud Him
(Christiansen, O.C.) SATB KJOS 30 $.30
(P1290)

Liedmotetten Nach Weisen Der Bohmischen
Bruder *see Barmherziger, Ewiger Gott;
Die Nacht Ist Kommen; Freud Und Wollust
Dieser Welt; Frohlockt Und Ruhmt Mit Herz
Und Mund; O Mensch, Sieh, Wie Hier Auf
Erdreich; Schau, Wie Lieblich Und Gut
Ists Allen Brudern; Wohlauf, Die Ihr
Hungrig Seid (P1291)

Lobe Den Herren, Den Machtigen Konig Der
Ehren *Gen
[Ger] 2-4pt men cor,acap (med) BAREN.
BCH 148 s.p. (P1292)

Mein Schonste Zier Und Kleinod Bist *Gen
[Ger] 3pt men cor,acap (med) BAREN. BCH 152
s.p. (P1293)

Meine Seele Erhebet Den Herrn (from Die
Weihnachtsgeschichte Des Lukas) Xmas,
Magnif
[Ger] SSATBB,acap (med diff) BAREN. BA 3997
$1.50 (P1294)

Missa Brevis *Gloria/Kyrie/Mass
[Lat] SAB,acap BAREN. BA 2272 $3.00
contains: Gloria; Kyrie (P1295)

Morning Star On High Is Glowing, The *Adv/
Epiph
SSA,acap/kbd (med easy) oct CONCORDIA
98-1909 $.30 (P1296)

Neues Choralbuch *CC75U,Gen,chorale
[Ger] 3pt mix cor/4pt mix cor,acap (med
diff) BAREN. BA 3219 $8.75 (P1297)

O Ihr Christen, Teuer Erkauft *Psntd,mot
[Ger] SATB,acap (med diff) BAREN. BA 2513
$1.50 see from LIEDMOTETTEN NACH WEISEN
DER BOHMISCHEN BRUDER (P1298)

O Mensch, Sieh, Wie Hier Auf Erdreich *Gen,
mot
[Ger] SATB,acap (med diff) BAREN. BA 2517
$1.75 see from Liedmotetten Nach Weisen
Der Bohmischen Bruder (P1299)

Passionsbericht Des Matthaus *Psntd
[Ger] SATBB&SSATB,acap (diff) cor pts
BAREN. BA 2276 $14.25 (P1300)

Psalm 8 *see Herr, Unser Herrscher

Psalm 23 *see Der Herr Ist Mein Hirte

Psalm 139 *see Herr, Du Erforschest Mich

Sanctus
see Kleine Messe

Schau, Wie Lieblich Und Gut Ists Allen
Brudern *Gen,mot
[Ger] SATB,acap (med diff) BAREN. BA 2510
$2.25 see from Liedmotetten Nach Weisen
Der Bohmischen Bruder (P1301)

Sechs Kleine Motetten *CC6UL,Gen,mot
[Ger] SATB,acap (med diff) BAREN. BA 1199 s.p.
see also: Herr, Neige Deine Ohren; Ich
Bin Der Herr; Ich Habe Alles Dinges Ein
Ende Gesehen (P1302)

Te Deum Laudamus *Te Deum
[Lat] SATB,SBar soli,orch (diff) sc BAREN.
BA 2790 rental, voc sc BAREN. BA 2970A
$17.50, min sc BAREN. TP 28 $8.25 (P1303)

Ten Chorale Settings *CC10L,chorale
3-4pt mix cor CONCORDIA 97-6313 $1.00
(P1304)

Und Es Wird Ein Reis Aufgehen (from Die
Weihnachtsgeschichte Des Lukas) Xmas
[Ger] SSATB,acap (med diff) BAREN. BA 3998
$.90 (P1305)

Verleih Uns Frieden Gnadiglich
[Ger] 3pt men cor,acap (med) BAREN. BCH 150
s.p. (P1306)

Wohlauf, Die Ihr Hungrig Seid *Gen,mot
[Ger] SSATBB,acap (med diff) BAREN. BA 2520
$1.75 see from Liedmotetten Nach Weisen
Der Bohmischen Bruder (P1307)

Wunderlich Ding Hat Sich Ergangen *Psntd,mot
[Ger] SATB,acap (med diff) BAREN. BA 2515
$1.75 see from LIEDMOTETTEN NACH WEISEN
DER BOHMISCHEN BRUDER (P1308)

PEPPING, ERNST (cont'd.)
Zu Bethlehem Geboren *Xmas,mot
[Ger] SATB&SA&men cor,acap (med) BAREN.
BA 4938 s.p. (P1309)

PER ARMA JUSTITIAE see Merbecke, John

PER IL MESE MARIANO see Visona', Gino

PER LA FESTA DEL PAPA see Arnaldi, Antonio

PER LA FESTA DELL'IMMACOLATA CONCEZIONE see
Grassi, Ciro

PER LA NOTTE DEL SANTO NATALE see Bottazzo,
Luigi

PER LA S. COMUNIONE see Accordi, Carlo

PER LA SANTA PASQUA *Easter,mot
[Lat] 2 eq voices ZANIBON 2952 s.p.
contains: Fabiani, Angelo, Haec Dies;
Moioli, Romano, Laudate Dominum De
Coelis; Volpi, Edoardo, Resurrexi In
Epiphanietate Paschali (P1310)

PER LA SETTIMANA SANTA *Holywk,mot
[Lat] 2 eq voices,kbd&acap ZANIBON 2950 s.p.
contains: Ascenso, Antonio, O Crux
Benedicta; Brambilla, E., Improperium;
Cucchi, Colleoni G., Foderunt Manus Meas;
Fabiani, Angelo, Vexilla Regis; Muller,
J., Crux Ave; Sevim, Giuseppe, Adoremus
Te Christe (P1311)

PER LA SETTIMANA SANTA see Volpi, Edoardo

PER LA VIA CRUCIS SOLENNE DEL VENERDI SANTO see
Volpi, Edoardo

PER LA VISITA PASTORALE see Bottazzo, Luigi

PER L'INGRESSO DEL PARROCO see Colle, Giuseppe

PER L'INGRESSO PARROCCHIALE see Bottazzo, Luigi

PER L'ORA DI ADORAZIONE see Bottazzo, Luigi

PER L'ORA SANTA see Bottigliero, Eduardo

PER NOUN LANGUI see Saboly, Nicholas

PERAGALLO, MARIO (1910-)
Corale E Aria
voc sc UNIVER. 12516 $3.60, cor pts UNIVER.
12517 $1.90
contains: Corale E Aria [Lat]; Corale E
Aria [It/Ger] (P1312)

Corale E Aria
see Corale E Aria

Corale E Aria
see Corale E Aria

PERCEVAL, JULIO (1903-1963)
Salve, Virilis Pectoris Virgo, Patrona
Galliae
[Lat] SSATBB oct BOOSEY BAR $.35 (P1313)

PERCY, VINCE H.
Lord Is My Light, The
SATB oct HUNTZINGER 4023 $.20 (P1314)

PERDUE-DAVIS, VERNON (1919-)
O How Amiable
see Cook, Claude Karon, Hallelujah For
Christmas, A

Once To Ev'ry Man And Nation
SA&TB,pno SCHIRM.EC 1969 $.35 (P1315)

Psalm 150
SATB SCHIRM.EC 11 $.35 (P1316)

PERE DE NOUS see L'Estocart, Paschal de

PERE DE NOUS QUI ES LA-HAUT see Caulery, Jean

PERE ETERNEL QUI NOUS ORDONNES see L'Estocart,
Paschal de

PEREAT DIES see Ortiz

PEREGRINUS *Easter,12th cent
(Smoldon, W.L.) [Eng/Lat] SATB,4 soli,opt
org&chimes&harp (med easy) sc OXFORD 46.146
$4.00, ipr, rental (P1317)

PERERA, RONALD (1941-)
Garden Hymn, The *folk/hymn,US
SATB,acap SCHIRM.EC 2715 (P1318)

Lord's Prayer, The
SATB,acap SCHIRM.EC 2716 (P1319)

PEREZ
see GINES PEREZ, JUAN

PERFECT THROUGH SUFFERING see Bingham

PERGAMENT, MOSES (1893-)
Julgranslius *Xmas
3pt wom cor/3pt jr cor,pno/inst NORDISKA
5565 s.p. (P1320)

PERGOLESI, GIOVANNI BATTISTA (1710-1736)
Abroad The Regal Banners Fly *Easter
(Agey, C. Buell) SATB (med) ABINGDON
APM-405 $.18 (P1321)

Agnus Dei *Agnus
SATB oct PRESSER MC147 $.30 (P1322)
mix cor SOUTHERN $.30 (P1323)

Alleluia *Allelu
(Agey, C. Buell) SSATB,acap (diff) ABINGDON
APM-374 $.26 (P1324)

Alleluia, Alleluia (from Motet: Domine Ad
Adiuvandum) Allelu
mix cor SOUTHERN $.30 (P1325)
(Agey) [Lat] SSATB,org/pno SCHIRM.G
11676 $.30 (P1326)

Amen *Easter/Gen
(Hilton, A.) SATB oct PRESSER 352-00379
$.30 (P1327)

PERGOLESI, GIOVANNI BATTISTA (cont'd.)

(Hilton, Arthur) SSA (med) PRESSER
352-00461 $.35   (P1328)
(Kingsbury, John) SATB ALFRED 6309 $.30
(P1329)

Be Not Silent Unto Us
(Forester) SATB SCHMITT 1421 $.25   (P1330)

Beatus Vir
see Psalms

Blessed Jesu *see Stabat Mater

Confitebor
see Psalms

Dies Irae
see Pergolesi, Giovanni Battista, Stabat
Mater
[Lat] SATB,SA soli,orch,org voc sc
HINRICHSEN D576 s.p. contains also:
Stabat Mater   (P1331)

Dixit Dominus
see Psalms

Domine, Ad Adiuvandum
see Six Motets

Eleven Motets *CC11U,mot
[Lat] SATB/S/A/B,acap/orch/org/strings voc
sc HINRICHSEN D567A s.p.   (P1332)

Excelsus Super Omnes Gentes Dominus
(Agey) "Now On High O'er All Nations" [Eng/
Lat] 4pt mix cor,SA soli,org oct SCHIRM.G
11456 $.30   (P1333)

Fac, Ut Ardeat Cor Meum (from Stabat Mater)
[Lat] SA,pno SCHIRM.EC 1526 $.30, ipr (P1334)

Gloria Patri *Xmas,Bibl
"Glory To God In The Highest" SAB oct
LORENZ 7380 $.30   (P1335)
"Glory To God In The Highest" SATB oct
LORENZ 9658 $.30   (P1336)
"Glory To God In The Highest" SATB oct PRO
ART 1201 $.35   (P1337)
"Glory To God In The Highest" SATB oct
PRESSER 332-14507 $.35   (P1338)
"Glory To God In The Highest" SATB oct
BELWIN 761 $.30   (P1339)
"Glory To God In The Highest" SATB oct
BELWIN 64046 $.35   (P1340)
"Glory To God In The Highest" SATB oct
FISCHER,C CM-551 $.30   (P1341)
(Agey) "Glorify The Lord" 5pt mix cor,org/
pno oct SCHIRM.G 11673 $.40   (P1342)
(Agey) "Glory To The Father" [Eng/Lat] 4pt
mix cor,org oct SCHIRM.G 11409 $.25
(P1343)
(Clough-Leighter, H.) "Glory To God In The
Highest" SATB,pno/org SCHIRM.EC 370 $.35,
ipr   (P1344)
(Davison, A.) "Glory To God In The Highest"
TTBB,pno/org SCHIRM.EC 47 $.35, ipr
(P1345)
(Mueller) "Glory To God In The Highest" 2pt
jr cor FISCHER,C CM 6896 $.25   (P1346)
(Novello) "Glory To God In The Highest" 4pt
mix cor oct SCHIRM.G 4424 $.30   (P1347)
(Novello-Coggin) "Glory To God In The
Highest" SATB oct FISCHER,J 9452 $.30
(P1348)
(Riegger) "Glory To God In The Highest!"
SATB FLAMMER A 5457 $.30   (P1349)
(Riegger) "Glory To God In The Highest!"
SAB FLAMMER D5158 $.30   (P1350)
(Riegger) "Glory To God In The Highest" SSA
FLAMMER B 5042 $.30   (P1351)
(Wilson) "Glory To God In The Highest" SATB
ALFRED 6339 $.35   (P1352)
(Woodworth, G.) "Glory To God In The
Highest" SSA,soli,pno/org SCHIRM.EC 839
$.30, ipr   (P1353)
(Younger) "Glory To God In The Highest"
SATB oct SPRATT 502 $.25   (P1354)
(Younger) "Glory To God In The Highest" SSA
oct SPRATT 514 $.30   (P1355)

Glorify The Lord *see Gloria Patri

Glory Be To Thee
(Suchoff) SATB oct PLYMOUTH BS-100 $.25
(P1356)

Glory To God In The Highest *see Gloria
Patri

Glory To God In The Highest *see Hosanna In
Excelsis

Glory To The Father *see Gloria Patri

Glory To The Newborn King *Xmas
(Gordon, Philip) SA/TB oct BELWIN 2195 $.25
(P1357)
(Gordon, Philip) SAB oct BELWIN 2194 $.30
(P1358)
(Gordon, Philip) SSA oct BELWIN 2078 $.30
(P1359)
(Gordon, Philip) SATB oct BELWIN 2082 $.25
(P1360)

Grant Thy Grace To Me, O God
(Lundquist) SATB FLAMMER A 5308 $.25
(P1361)

Grant To Us Thy Mercy, O Lord *see Miserere
Mei

Grant Us Thy Grace *see Miserere Mei

Grant Us Thy Great Mercy *see Miserere Mei

Hallelujah Amen *Xmas/Gen
(Ehret, W.) SATB oct PRESSER 312-40755 $.40
(P1362)

Have Mercy Upon Us
(Suchoff) SATB oct FOX RM4 $.40   (P1363)

Hear My Prayers, O Lord
(Richardson) SATB oct WORD CS-313 $.30
(P1364)

Holy And All Glorious *see Sanctum Et
Terrible Nomen Ejus

Hosanna In Excelsis *Easter/Lent
(Marshall, Charles) "Glory To God In The
Highest" SATB,pno/org FRANK F-606 $.30
(P1365)

PERGOLESI, GIOVANNI BATTISTA (cont'd.)

How Wondrous The Sacrament *see O Sacrum
Convivium

I Will Be Glad And Rejoice In Thee
(Kinsman) SATB,org/pno BOSTON 13427 $.40
(P1366)

In Hac Die
see Six Motets

Ista Sicut Flamma
see Two Motets

Kyrie *Easter
"Lord, Have Mercy" SATB oct PRESSER
352-00396 $.30   (P1367)
(Agey) "Lord Have Mercy" [Eng/Lat] 5pt mix
cor,org/pno oct SCHIRM.G 11457 $.35
(P1368)

Kyrie And Gloria *Gloria/Kyrie
(Caffarelli, Filippo) 5pt (D maj) voc sc
AMICI s.p.   (P1369)
(Caffarelli, Filippo) dbl cor (F maj) voc
sc AMICI s.p.   (P1370)
(Caffarelli, Filippo) 5pt (F maj) voc sc
AMICI s.p.   (P1371)

Laudate Pueri
see Psalms
[Lat] voc sc PETERS HU1181 $2.00, ipr (P1372)

Laudate Pueri, Laudate Nomen Domini
(Agey) "O Praise And Glorify The Lord"
[Eng/Lat] 4pt mix cor,S solo,org/pno oct
SCHIRM.G 11675 $.35   (P1373)

Lord Have Mercy *see Kyrie

Magnificat *Magnif
see Six Motets
SATB,cont,strings voc sc WALTON M 102
$1.75, ipr, sc WALTON rental   (P1374)
cor voc sc KALMUS 6376 $1.50   (P1375)
SATB,soli,orch,cont,strings voc sc WALTON
M102 $1.75, ipr, sc WALTON rental (P1376)
cor,orch/kbd sc KALMUS $9.00, ipa (P1377)

Magnificat Anima Mea Dominum
(Agey) "My Soul Doth Magnify The Lord"
[Eng/Lat] 4pt mix cor,kbd oct SCHIRM.G
11674 $.35   (P1378)

Mass In D *Mass
[Lat] SSATB,orch,org voc sc HINRICHSEN D565
s.p.   (P1379)

Mass In F *Mass
[Lat] SSATB&SSATB,strings,2org voc sc
HINRICHSEN D568 s.p.   (P1380)

Mass In F *Mass
[Lat] SSATB,orch,org voc sc HINRICHSEN D556
s.p.   (P1381)

Miserere
(Caffarelli, Filippo) 4pt (C min) voc sc
AMICI s.p.   (P1382)

Miserere Mei *Easter/Lent
"Grant Us Thy Great Mercy" SATB oct WALTON
6011 $.25   (P1383)
"Grant Us Thy Great Mercy" SATB oct WALTON
6011 $.30   (P1384)
(Richardson) "Grant To Us Thy Mercy, O
Lord" SATB oct SPRATT 2017 $.30   (P1385)
(Trusler) "Grant Us Thy Grace" SATB oct
PLYMOUTH TR-111 $.25   (P1386)

Missa Solemnis *Mass
(Caffarelli, Filippo) 4pt (C maj) voc sc
AMICI s.p.   (P1387)

My Soul Doth Magnify The Lord *see
Magnifical Anima Mea Dominum

Now On High O'er All Nations *see Excelsus
Super Omnes Gentes Dominus

O Come And Mourn With Me Awhile *anthem
(Riedel) SATB (very easy) oct AUGSBURG 1327
$.20   (P1388)

O Holy, Blessed Feast Divine *see O Sacrum
Convivium

O, Holy Child *Xmas
(Barrie) SATB,acap oct LAWSON 928 $.25
(P1389)

O Light, O Way, O Truth, O Life
(Hardwicke) SATB,acap,opt pno oct PRO ART
2627 $.30   (P1390)

O Praise And Glorify The Lord *see Laudate
Pueri, Laudate Nomen Domini

O Quam Tristis Et Afflicta (from Stabat
Mater)
(Ehret) SATB oct BOOSEY 1923 $.30 (P1391)

O Sacrum Convivium *Easter/Lent
see Six Motets
"How Wondrous The Sacrament" SATB oct
WALTON 2133 $.30   (P1392)
(Agey) "O Holy, Blessed Feast Divine" [Eng/
Lat] 4pt mix cor,acap oct SCHIRM.G 11280
$.35   (P1393)

Opera Omnia: La Musica Religiosa Vol. 4a
*CCUL,Mass/ora/Req
(Caffarelli, Filippo) cmplt ed AMICI s.p.
(P1394)

Opera Omnia: La Musica Religiosa Vol. 4b
*CCUL,canon/mot/Psalm
(Caffarelli, Filippo) cmplt ed AMICI s.p.
(P1395)

Psalm 51 *see Stabat Mater

Psalm 109
see Psalms

Psalm 110
see Psalms

Psalm 111
see Psalms

PERGOLESI, GIOVANNI BATTISTA (cont'd.)

Psalm 112
see Psalms

Psalms *Psalm
(Caffarelli, Filippo) AMICI s.p.
contains: Beatus Vir (4pt); Confitebor
(5pt); Dixit Dominus (5pt); Laudate
Pueri (4pt,S solo); Sanctum Et
Terrible (5pt)   (P1396)

Psalms
[Lat] voc sc HINRICHSEN D558 s.p. contains
also solo work
contains: Psalm 109 (5pt/6pt/10pt,org,
strings); Psalm 110 (SSATB,S solo,orch,
org); Psalm 111 (SATB,org,strings);
Psalm 112 (SSATB,S solo,org,orch) (P1397)

Quando Corpus Morietur (from Stabat Mater)
[Lat] SA,pno SCHIRM.EC 1527 $.22, ipr (P1398)

Regina Coeli
see Two Motets

Requiem *Req
[Lat] SATB,org,2horn,strings voc sc
HINRICHSEN D577 s.p.   (P1399)
(Caffarelli, Filippo) 4pt (B flat maj) voc
sc AMICI s.p.   (P1400)

Salve Regina
[Lat] S/SB/SS/S,cembalo,strings voc sc
HINRICHSEN D566 s.p.   (P1401)

Sanctum Et Terribile
see Psalms

Sanctum Et Terrible Nomen Ejus
(Agey) "Holy And All Glorious" [Eng/Lat]
5pt mix cor,kbd oct SCHIRM.G 11412 $.35
(P1402)

Seven Cantatas *CC7U,cant
[It] S/ST,strings voc sc HINRICHSEN D560
s.p.   (P1403)

Sing Unto The Lord Most High
(Chambers) SATB,acap oct BOOSEY 5478 $.30
(P1404)

Six Motets *see Super Flumina Babylonis
(P1405)

Six Motets *mot
(Caffarelli, Filippo) AMICI s.p.
contains: Domine, Ad Adiuvandum (5pt); In
Hac Die (5pt); Magnificat (4pt); O
Sacrum Convivium (4pt,acap); Super
Flumina Babylonis (4pt); Vexilla Regis
(4pt)   (P1406)

Stabat Mater (Psalm 51) Easter/Lent,Commun
see Pergolesi, Giovanni Battista, Dies Irae
[Lat] SA,SA soli,orch voc sc NOVELLO
07.0244.07 s.p., ipr   (P1407)
cor voc sc KALMUS 6375 $1.25   (P1408)
cor sc KALMUS $6.50   (P1409)
cor,orch/org sc KALMUS $6.50, ipa (P1410)
2pt wom cor,SA soli,org,strings sc
BREITKOPF-W PB-4927 s.p.   (P1411)
[Lat] 2pt wom cor,pno RICORDI-ARG BA 11881
s.p.   (P1412)
[Lat] cor,SA soli voc sc SCHIRM.G $1.50
(P1413)
[Lat] voc sc UNIVER. 695 $1.95   (P1414)
[Lat] SA,SA soli,org voc sc PETERS 774
$3.50, min sc PETERS E973 $2.50   (P1415)
girl cor SOUTHERN $1.50   (P1416)
[Lat] 2 eq voices oct DURAND s.p. (P1417)
[Eng] SA,SA soli,orch voc sc NOVELLO
07.0243.09 s.p.   (P1418)
(Bach, Johann Sebastian) [Ger] 2pt,cont,
2vln,via HANSSLER 10.151 sc $6.00, cor
pts $1.25, ipa   (P1419)
(Hadley) "Blessed Jesu" SATB oct PRO ART
2294 $.25   (P1420)
(Howorth) SATB BELWIN $1.50   (P1421)
(Mohler) [Lat/Ger] SA,SA soli,strings,kbd
sc SCHOTT 4526 s.p., ipa, cor pts SCHOTT
4526 s.p., ipa   (P1422)
(Schreck, G.) 2pt wom cor,SA soli,org,
strings sc BREITKOPF-L PB-2116 s.p., voc
pt BREITKOPF-L CHB-1219A+B s.p., voc sc
BREITKOPF-L EB-60 s.p.   (P1423)
(Scott, C. Kennedy) 2pt wom cor,strings
(med) OXFORD 46.100 voc sc $2.00, ipr,
cor pts $1.00   (P1424)
(Somma) [Lat] SA,SA soli,org voc sc
HINRICHSEN D576 s.p., voc sc HINRICHSEN
SM7 s.p., voc pt HINRICHSEN SM7 s.p.
contains also: Dies Irae   (P1425)
(Somma, B.) cor,SA soli,org,strings sc
SANTIS 686 s.p., ipa   (P1426)
(Somma, B.) cor,SA soli,org,strings cor pts
SANTIS 687 s.p., ipa   (P1427)
(Somma, B.) cor,pno voc sc SANTIS 681 s.p.
(P1428)
(Zanon) [Lat] 2pt wom cor,strings,org voc
sc RICORDI-ENG 123718 s.p.   (P1429)

Super Flumina *mot
[Lat] SATB,SS soli,orch,org voc sc
HINRICHSEN D567B s.p.   (P1430)

Super Flumina Babylonis *mot
see Six Motets
(Caffarelli, Filippo) 4pt AMICI s.p. see
from Six Motets   (P1431)

Two Masses And Fragments (from Messa Solenne)
*CC8UL,Mass
[Lat] SATB,SATB soli,orch,org voc sc
HINRICHSEN D573 s.p.   (P1432)

Two Miserere *CC2U
[Lat] SATB,SATB soli,strings,org voc sc
HINRICHSEN D563 s.p.   (P1433)

Two Motets *mot
(Berger) [Lat] SATB,opt org oct LAWSON
51560 $.35
contains: Ista Sicut Flamma; Regina Coeli
(P1434)

Vexilla Regis
see Six Motets
mix cor SOUTHERN $.25   (P1435)
(Kaplan, A.) [Lat/Eng] SATTB BROUDE,A. 108
$.30   (P1436)

PERGOLESI, GIOVANNI BATTISTA (cont'd.)

Wash Me, O Lord God
(Hines, Robert S.) SA (med) PRESSER
362-03146 $.35   (P1437)

Worthy Art Thou, O Lord
(Ehret) 5pt mix cor,pno/org oct LAWSON
51499 $.35   (P1438)

PERI, JACOPO (1561-1633)
Praise God In All His Glory
(Barrett; Craig) SATB oct PLYMOUTH DC-101
$.25   (P1439)
(Barrett; Craig) TTBB oct PLYMOUTH DC-300
$.25   (P1440)

PERITI AUTEM see Mendelssohn-Bartholdy, Felix

PERITI AUTEM see Mendelssohn-Bartholdy, Felix,
Es Strahlen Hell Die Gerechten

PERKINS, PHIL
Celebrate
SATB oct WORD CS-2538 $.35   (P1441)

Greatest Gift, The
SATB oct WORD CS-2537 $.30   (P1442)

PEROSI, (DOM) LORENZO (1872-1956)
Benedicamus Domino *Mass
SATB,org s.p. sc RICORDI-ENG 103407, cor
pts RICORDI-ENG 127503-06   (P1443)

Cerviana *Mass
TTB,org (D min) s.p. sc RICORDI-ENG 101741,
cor pts RICORDI-ENG 127526-28   (P1444)

Il Natale Del Redentore *ora
cor,soli,orch voc sc RICORDI-ENG 102772
s.p.   (P1445)

In Transitu Sancti Patris Nostri Francisci
SATTBB sc SANTIS 674 s.p., cor pts SANTIS
675A-C s.p.   (P1446)

La Passione Di Cristo Secondo Marco *Psntd
cor,soli,orch voc sc RICORDI-ENG 101642
s.p.   (P1447)

La Resurrezione Di Cristo *ora
cor,soli,orch voc sc RICORDI-ENG 102440
s.p.   (P1448)

Messa Di Requiem *Mass/Req
TTB,org s.p. voc sc RICORDI-ENG 101742, sc
RICORDI-ENG 127529-31   (P1449)

Messa Requiem *Mass/Req
2 eq voices sc SANTIS 836 s.p., cor pts
SANTIS 837 s.p.   (P1450)

Missa Eucharistica *Mass
ATTB,org s.p. sc RICORDI-ENG 103456,
cor pts RICORDI-ENG 12515-18   (P1451)

Missa In Honorem Sanctae Franciscae Romanae
*Mass
3 eq voices/7pt,opt org sc SANTIS 796 s.p.,
cor pts SANTIS 797 s.p.   (P1452)

Missa Pio XII Pontifici Maximo *Mass
SATB,org cor pts RICORDI-ENG 125622-25 s.p.
(P1453)
SATB,org sc RICORDI-ENG 125621 s.p.   (P1454)
ATB,org cor pts RICORDI-ENG 125648-50 s.p.
(P1455)
ATB,org sc RICORDI-ENG 125647 s.p.   (P1456)

Missa Pontificalis *Mass
[Lat] 3pt mix cor,org sc RICORDI-ARG
BA 10939 s.p., cor pts RICORDI-ARG
BA 8292 s.p.   (P1457)
STBar,org s.p. sc RICORDI-ENG 102378, cor
pts RICORDI-ENG 127507-09   (P1458)

Missa Secunda In Honorem Beati Caroli *Mass
SATTB,org s.p. voc sc RICORDI-ENG 125591,
cor pts RICORDI-ENG 125592-93 ; 125670-72
(P1459)

Missa Secunda Pontificalis
ATB,org s.p. sc RICORDI-ENG 111228, cor pts
RICORDI-ENG 111299A-C   (P1460)

O Sanctissima *Mass
eq voices,org sc SANTIS 729 s.p., cor pts
SANTIS 730 s.p.   (P1461)

Te Deum Laudamus *Mass
TB,org s.p. voc sc RICORDI-ENG 102299, cor
pts RICORDI-ENG 127519-20   (P1462)
[Lat] 2pt men cor,org s.p. sc RICORDI-ARG
BA 8264, cor pts RICORDI-ARG BA 8291
(P1463)

Transitus Animae *ora
cor,Mez solo,orch voc sc RICORDI-ENG 112178
s.p.   (P1464)

PEROTIN
Viderunt Omnes Sederunt
cor min sc KALMUS 1241 $1.30   (P1465)

Works With Performance Directions *CCU
mix cor,acap voc sc KALMUS 6378 $12.50
(P1466)

PERPETUA see Rohwer, Jens

PERRIN
Jesus Walked
unis oct LORENZ 8867 $.25   (P1467)

PERRIN, RONALD
O Praise The Lord *Gen/Thanks
SATB (med diff) oct OXFORD 42.864 $.65
(P1468)

PERRIN, SUSAN F.
Hymn Of Trust, A: "Iona" *Gen
(Branson, David) SATB (easy) oct OXFORD
42.155 $.30   (P1469)
(Branson, David) unis&desc (easy) oct
OXFORD 40.302 $.35, ipa   (P1470)

PERRINE, R.
On Easter Morn *Easter
(Bedell, R.) SA oct PRESSER 312-40168 $.25
(P1471)

PERRY
Carillon Heigh-Ho *Xmas
SATB,acap oct FISCHER,C CM-6318 $.25
(P1472)

Song Of Our Saviour
SATB oct GALAXY 1.1946.1 $.30   (P1473)

PERRY, JULIA
Frammenti Dalle Lettere De Santa Caterina
[It] mix cor,S solo,orch PEER rental
(P1474)

PERRY, R.
Give Me This Day
SATB oct PRESSER 312-40009 $.25   (P1475)

PERSICHETTI, VINCENT (1915-   )
Agnus Dei *Agnus
SATB oct ELKAN-V 362-1173 $.30   (P1476)
mix cor SOUTHERN $.30   (P1477)

Gloria (from Mass) Gloria
SATB oct ELKAN-V 362-1172 $.35   (P1478)

Hymns And Responses For The Church Year *CCU
cor&cong oct ELKAN-V $1.10   (P1479)

Mass *Mass
SATB,acap oct ELKAN-V $1.75   (P1480)

Proverb
SATB oct ELKAN-V 362-1102 $.30   (P1481)

Seek The Highest
SAB oct ELKAN-V 362-505 $.30   (P1482)

Stabat Mater
SATB voc sc ELKAN-V $2.25   (P1483)

Te Deum *Te Deum
SATB oct ELKAN-V 362-1196 $1.80   (P1484)

This Is The Garden *anthem
SSA,acap oct FISCHER,C CM-6652 $.30   (P1485)

PERSONENT HODIE see Milford

PERSONET HODIE (from Anthology Of Carols, An)
Xmas,carol/folk
(Holst) "Christmas Song" unis jr cor/unis wom
cor CURWEN 71655 s.p.   (P1486)
(Holst, Gustav) "Christmas Song" unis oct
CURWEN 8119 $.25   (P1487)
(Roseberry) "Boys' Carol, The" [Eng/Lat] unis
oct SCHIRM.G 11629 $.25   (P1488)
(Roseberry, Eric) "Boy's Carol, The" unis,pno
oct FABER 11629 $.25   (P1489)
(Wulstan, David) SATB CHESTER s.p. contains
also: Shepherd's Carol (STB)   (P1490)

PERTI, GIACOMO ANTONIO (1661-1756)
Adoramus Te, Christe *Easter/Gen/Lent,anthem
(Klein, M.) "We Adore You" [Eng/Lat] SATB
(med) oct GIA G1523 $.25   (P1491)
(Richardson) "We Adore Thee" SATB oct
SPRATT 2008 $.25   (P1492)

Ave Regina
(Berger) [Lat] 5pt mix cor,opt org oct
LAWSON 51597 $.35   (P1493)

Come, Ye People *see O Vos Omnes

Lord, There Is None Like Thee
(Richardson) SATB oct WORD CS-317 $.30   (P1494)

O Vos Omnes *Easter/Lent
(Beveridge) "Come, Ye People" [Eng/Lat] 4pt
mix cor,acap oct SCHIRM.G 8351 $.25   (P1495)
(Richardson) "O Ye People" SATB oct SPRATT
2012 $.25   (P1496)

O Ye People *see O Vos Omnes

Oratorio Della Passione *ora
(Vecchi, Prof. Giuseppe) cor oct FORNI 353
s.p.   (P1497)

Praise And Honor Be Unto Thee
(Richardson) SAB oct WORD CS-2402 $.25   (P1498)
(Richardson) SATB oct WORD CS-680 $.25   (P1499)

Preis Und Ehre, Herr Jesu
see Hassler, Hans Leo, Nun Lob, Mein Seel,
Den Herren

Three "Adoramus Te" Settings *CC3U
(Berger) [Lat] SATB,opt org oct LAWSON
51609 $.35   (P1500)

We Adore Thee *see Adoramus Te, Christe

We Adore You *see Adoramus Te, Christe

PERTI, J.
Adoramus Te
mix cor sc ALSBACH&D s.p.   (P1501)

PESKO, ZOLTAN (1937-   )
Ritratto Di Una Santa
jr cor,S solo,15inst ZERBONI 6964 rental
(P1502)

PESTALOZZA, HEINRICH (1873-1949)
Osterhymne *Easter
[Ger] mix cor,acap (med easy) HUG   (P1503)

Pfingstgesang *Pent
[Ger] mix cor,acap (easy) HUG   (P1504)

Weihelied
[Ger] mix cor,acap (med easy) HUG   (P1505)

PETER
Good Lord Willed It So, The *spir
SSATTB SCHMITT 1168 $.20   (P1506)

I Will Freely Sacrifice To Thee
(Stilwell; Nolte) [Eng/Ger] SSTB/SATB,org
oct MORAVIAN 5787 $.40   (P1507)

Lord Shall Increase You
(Stilwell; Nolte) [Eng/Ger] SSAB/SATB,org
oct MORAVIAN 5788 $.35   (P1508)

PETER, GO RING THEM BELLS see Gardner

PETER, HERBERT (1926-   )
Bewahre Mich, Gott, Denn Ich Trau (Psalm 16)
SSAA HANSSLER 7.114 s.p.   (P1509)

Christum Wir Sollen Loben Schon *cant
SATB,org,2vln,opt vcl HANSSLER
10.158 sc s.p., voc sc s.p., ipa   (P1510)

Christus, Der Uns Selig Macht
SAT/SAB,treb inst HANSSLER 14.056 s.p.   (P1511)

Das Magnificat *Magnif
SAB HANSSLER 7.062 s.p.   (P1512)

Der Verlorene Sohn *Gen,ora
[Ger] SATB&SATB,org (diff) BAREN. BA 2027
s.p.   (P1513)

Die Auferstandene Und Der Unglaubige Thomas
*Psntd
SAT/SAB,cantor HANSSLER 14.609 s.p.   (P1514)

Die Auferstehung Jesu *Psntd
SAT/SAB,cantor HANSSLER 14.607 s.p.   (P1515)

Die Seligpreisungen *cant
SATB,SB soli,org,2fl,2trp,2trom,2vln,vla,
vcl,bvl,timp HANSSLER 10.137 rental   (P1516)

Du Meine Seele, Singe
SA/SAT/SAB HANSSLER 14.197 s.p.   (P1517)

Du Pfingstlich Hoher Geist Der Gnaden *mot
SATB HANSSLER 7.080 s.p.   (P1518)

Es Ist Dir Gesagt, Mensch, Was Gut Ist *Trin
[Ger] 2pt/3pt,opt inst (med) BAREN. BA 4953
$.40   (P1519)

Es Wird Gesaet Verweslich Und Wird
Auferstehen *mot
SSATBB HANSSLER 7.096 s.p.   (P1520)

Gottes Sohn Ist Kommen
SAT/SAB,treb inst HANSSLER 14.002 s.p.
contains also: Stegen, Wilfried, Ihr
Lieben Christen, Freut Euch Nun (SAT/SAB,
treb inst)   (P1521)

Im Anfang War Das Wort *Bibl
4-6pt mix cor,acap HANSSLER 7.115 s.p.   (P1522)

Lobet Den Herrn (Psalm 147) cant
[Ger] 3-4pt mix cor,acap BAREN. EM 85 s.p.
(P1523)

O Hoherpriester Jesu Christ *mot
SAB HANSSLER 7.047 s.p.   (P1524)

Psalm 16 *see Bewahre Mich, Gott, Denn Ich
Trau

Psalm 147 *see Lobet Den Herrn

Zwei Tag Hat Er Gelegen *cant
SAB/unis wom cor,S/T solo,org,vln HANSSLER
10.153 sc s.p., voc sc s.p., ipa   (P1525)

PETER, JOHANN FRIEDRICH (1746-1813)
Blessed Are They
(Dickinson) SATB oct GRAY GMCM 4 $.35
(P1526)

Golden Gates Are Lifted
(Dickinson) SATB oct GRAY GMCM 3 $.25
(P1527)

He Who Soweth Weeping
[Eng/Ger] SATB,org/pno,fl,bsn,2vln,vla,vcl,
opt bvl voc sc PETERS 6086 $.80, ipa
(P1528)

I Will Sing To The Lord
(Dickinson) SATB oct GRAY GMCM 22 $.30
(P1529)

It Is A Precious Thing
(Dickinson) SATB oct GRAY GMCM 2 $.30
(P1530)

PETER, MAY I PLEASE COME IN see Livingstone

PETER ON THE SEA see Lynn, George

PETER, PETER HEAR ME see Hourdeaux

PETER, SIMON (1743-1819)
Behold A Sight *Gen/Lent,Morav
(Dickinson) SATB oct GRAY GMCM 9 $.30
(P1531)

PETERS, J.V.
Ye Watchers And Ye Holy Ones *ASD,anthem
SATB oct ROYAL 225 s.p.   (P1532)

PETERS, SIDNEY
Atonement, The *Easter,cant
cor,org/pno voc sc SCHIRM.G $1.25   (P1533)

PETERS, W.C.
Kyrie (from Mass In C Major) Kyrie
(Boyd, J.) SATB,pno oct BOONIN 144   (P1534)

PETERSEN, GUNNAR
Herre, Ar Det Du, Som Nalkas
mix cor,solo,pno/org cor pts NORDISKA 1035
s.p.   (P1535)

PETERSEN, T.
Psalm 150
SATB oct JUSKO 172 $.28   (P1536)

PETERSON-BERGER
Himlars Rymd *hymn
[Swed] mix cor LUNDQUIST 8 s.p.   (P1537)

PETERSON, JOHN W.
Heaven Came Down *Xmas
(Hustad) SATB oct AGAPE GC 804 $.40 (P1538)

Heaven Came Down (And Glory Filled My Soul)
(Collins) SATB oct LILLENAS AT-1039 $.30
(P1539)

I Believe In Miracles *Gen,anthem
SATB/SA,opt med solo (easy) oct LORENZ A530
$.30   (P1540)
SATB oct LORENZ A530 $.30   (P1541)

I Can Believe
SATB oct LORENZ 5766 $.25   (P1542)

It Took A Miracle
(Sanborn) SATB oct WORD CS-322 $.30 (P1543)

PETERSON, JOHN W. (cont'd.)

My Song
(McLellan) SATB oct LILLENAS AT-1058 $.25
(P1544)

No One Understands
(LaRowe) SATB oct WORD CS-2338 $.35
contains also: Nobody Knows (P1545)

No One Understands Like Jesus
SATB oct LORENZ A468 $.30 (P1546)
(Felts) SSA WORD CS-2204 $.30 (P1547)

Nobody Knows
see Peterson, John W., No One Understands

Surely Goodness And Mercy
(Hustad) SATB oct AGAPE HA 121 $.40 (P1548)

PETERSON, WAYNE
Psalm 56 *Bibl
SATB,acap oct LAWSON 818 $.25 (P1549)

PETIT DAVID JOUE see Little David Play

PETIT DAVID JOUE DE LA HARPE see Little David
Play

PETIT NOEL *Xmas,cant
mix cor CHAPPELL 0016303-3691 $.75 (P1550)
treb cor CHAPPELL 0016303-3692 $.75 (P1551)

PETIT VILLAGE see Danhieux, G.

PETITE MESSE PASTORALE see Sauguet, Henri

PETITE NOEL AVEC MYSTERE see Audran, Edmond

PETITES HIRONDELLES see Danhieux, G.

PETITION CAROL see Waters, Charles F.

PETITIONS FOR HELP see Hoffman, Richard

PETRA SANCTA see Palestrina, Giovanni

PETRASSI, GOFFREDO (1904-   )
Magnificat *Magnif
cor,S solo,orch voc sc RICORDI-ENG 124988
s.p. (P1552)

Mottetti Per La Passione *CCU,Psntd,mot
mix cor,acap oct ZERBONI 6533 s.p. (P1553)

Salmo IX
cor,orch voc sc RICORDI-ENG 123983 s.p. (P1554)

PETRI, T.
On This Day Earth Shall Sing *Xmas
(Vree, Marion) SATB,acap (med easy) PRESSER
$.35 (P1555)

PETRICH, ROGER
Choral Variations On "Ah, Holy Jesus" *see
Herzliebster Jesu

Herzliebster Jesu *Psntd
"Choral Variations On "Ah, Holy Jesus""
SATB,acap (med easy) oct OXFORD 94.317
$.50 (P1556)

Introits And Graduals For The Paschal Season,
The *CCU,Gradual/Introit/liturg
mix cor CONCORDIA 97-4722 $1.00 (P1557)

O Praise The Lord, All Ye Nations *anthem
SAB (med) oct AUGSBURG 0615 $.22 (P1558)

PETRIE
Life Everlasting *Easter,cant
SATB LORENZ $1.95 (P1559)

Light Eternal, The *Xmas,cant
SATB LORENZ $1.95 (P1560)

PETZOLD, JOHANNES
see PEZEL, JOHANN CHRISTOPHER

PETZOLD, RUDOLF (1908-   )
Consolatio *Op.44
mix cor,S solo,org GERIG 774 sc s.p., cor
pts s.p. (P1561)

Komm, Heiliger Geist, Du Schopferisch *cant
(Werfel, F.) mix cor,soli,orch voc sc GERIG
287 s.p. (P1562)

Messe *Op.30, Mass
mix cor,acap GERIG 1025 sc s.p., cor pts
s.p. (P1563)

PEUPLES, CHANTEZ (Psalm 97)
(Geveart, F.-A.) [Fr] 4pt mix cor,acap (easy)
cor pts LEMOINE s.p. see from Collection De
Choeurs, quatrieme Fascicule (P1564)

PEVERNAGE, ANDRIES (1543-1591)
Christmas Gloria *see Gloria In Excelsis Deo

Gloria In Excelsis Deo *Xmas,Gloria/mot
(Hellmann) "Christmas Gloria" [Lat]
SSSAAATBB HANSSLER 1.119 $.60 (P1565)

I Would, O Lord *see Je Veux, Seigneur

Je Veux, Seigneur
(Malin) "I Would, O Lord" [Eng/Fr] SSATB,
acap MARKS 4424 $.30 (P1566)

O Lord, My Faith Is In Thee *see Seigneur,
Jai Confiance

Seigneur, Jai Confiance
(Malin) "O Lord, My Faith Is In Thee" [Eng/
Fr] SSATB,acap MARKS 4421 $.25 (P1567)

PEZEL, JOHANN CHRISTOPH (1639-1694)
And Lo, The Star *anthem
SA,pno/org,inst (easy) oct AUGSBURG 0305
$.25 (P1568)

Christmas Story, The *Xmas,cant
SAB,org,opt fl/rec/ob/vln CONCORDIA 97-6221
$.65, ipa (P1569)

Der Herr Ward Aufgehoben Gen Himmel *mot
SATB HANSSLER 7.075 s.p. (P1570)

PEZEL, JOHANN CHRISTOPH (cont'd.)

Der Herr Ward Gehorsam Bis Zum Tode *mot
see DREI MOTETTEN
SATB HANSSLER 7.072 s.p. (P1571)

Die Nacht Ist Vorgedrungen *Adv
[Ger] SA&men cor,acap (med easy) BAREN.
BA 3009 s.p. (P1572)

God The Father, Be Our Stay *Gen/Trin
SAB,acap (easy) oct CONCORDIA 98-1149 $.25
(P1573)

Lord, When To Thee I Cry *see Wenn Ich Zu
Dir Empor

Rejoice Greatly *anthem
unis treb cor (med) oct AUGSBURG 1651 $.30
(P1574)

Wenn Ich Zu Dir Empor
(Frank) "Lord, When To Thee I Cry" SATB oct
FOX MM2 $.25 (P1575)

PEZZATI, MAURO (1939-   )
Dixitque Fiat
mix cor,acap oct ZERBONI 7619 s.p. (P1576)

Frammenti Biblici *CCU,Bibl
mix cor,orch ZERBONI 7223 rental (P1577)

Psalm 43
8pt mix cor/cor oct ZERBONI 7327 s.p.
(P1578)

Viditque Quod Esset Bonum
mix cor,acap oct ZERBONI 7618 s.p. (P1579)

PFANNENSTIEL, EKKEHART
Frolich Soll Mein Herze Springen *Xmas,mot
4pt mix cor MOSELER LB-328 s.p. (P1580)

Hoch Am Himmel Fliegt Ein Falke
4pt mix cor MOSELER LB-253 s.p. (P1581)

Im Himmel Ist Freude Viel
4pt mix cor MOSELER LB-254 s.p. (P1582)

Nun Segne Dich Gott
4pt mix cor MOSELER LB-256 s.p. contains
also: Wo Des Sees Wellen Gehn (P1583)

Wo Des Sees Wellen Gehn
see Pfannenstiel, Ekkehart, Nun Segne Dich
Gott

PFATTEICHER, KARL FRIEDRICH (1882-1957)
Christian Church Year In Chorals, The *CCU,
chorale
jr cor FISCHER,C O 3656 $1.25 (P1584)

PFAUTSCH, LLOYD (1921-   )
Abraham And Isaac
SATB (med) ABINGDON APM-143 $.25 (P1585)

Advent Carol *Adv,carol
TTBB,acap oct LAWSON 51014 $.30 (P1586)
boy cor SOUTHERN $.30 (P1587)

Annunciation
SSAA oct LAWSON 51627 $.35 (P1588)

Beatitude Of John, The *cant
SATB FLAMMER A5542 $1.50 (P1589)

Beatitudes, The
SATB FLAMMER A 5137 $.30 (P1590)

Canticle Of Commemoration, A *ASD
TTBB,acap (med) ABINGDON APM-225 $.25
(P1591)
SATB,acap (med) ABINGDON APM-224 $.25
(P1592)

Canticle Of Thanksgiving, A *Thanks
SATB,opt brass (easy) ABINGDON APM-424
$.25, ipa (P1593)

Carol For Children *carol
SATB SOUTHERN $.30 (P1594)

Carol For Children, A *Xmas,carol
(Nash) SATB oct HERITAGE H88 $.35 (P1595)

Christ: Foundation, Head And Cornerstone
SATB,opt brass oct LAWSON 959 $.30 (P1596)

Christ Is Arisen! *Easter
SATB (easy) ABINGDON APM-274 $.25 (P1597)

Christian! Dost Thou See Them
SATB,inst ABINGDON APM-226 $.25, ipa
(P1598)

Christmas In The Straw *Xmas
SATB,vln oct LAWSON 51587 $.35 (P1599)

Commitment *anthem
SATB,fl (easy) cor pts AUGSBURG 1596 $.25,
ipa (P1600)

Coverdale's Carol *Xmas,carol
TBB (easy) ABINGDON APM-421 $.30 (P1601)

Easter Bell Carol *Easter,carol
SATB (easy) ABINGDON APM-168 $.22 (P1602)

Easter Fanfare *Easter
SATB WARNER W3508 $.30 (P1603)

Fanfare For Christmas *Xmas
SATB FLAMMER A 5003 $.25 (P1604)
SSA FLAMMER B 5016 $.30 (P1605)

Fanfare For Easter *Easter
SATB FLAMMER A 5030 $.30 (P1606)
SATB&SATB,4brass oct SOUTHERN $.25 (P1607)

Gloria *Gloria
mix cor,A solo,pno/3trp,perc oct LAWSON
$1.75 (P1608)

Go And Tell John
SAB oct AGAPE CY 3342 $.30 (P1609)
SATB oct AGAPE CY 3334 $.35 (P1610)
TTBB oct AGAPE MM 9007 $.30 (P1611)

God Is My Strong Salvation
TTBB,acap (med) ABINGDON APM-423 $.25
(P1612)

God Of Might, We Praise Thy Name
SATB (med) ABINGDON APM-109 $.30 (P1613)

PFAUTSCH, LLOYD (cont'd.)

God So Loved The World *Lent
SATB FLAMMER A 5541 $.30 (P1614)
SATB oct SOUTHERN $.25 (P1615)

God With Us *Xmas,cant
cor,opt brass (easy) ABINGDON APM-236 $1.25
(P1616)

Guiding Christ Our Shepherd, The
SATB,opt inst (med) ABINGDON APM-856 $.60,
ipa (P1617)

He Rose! Allelujah! *Xmas/Easter
SATB,trp oct AGAPE F 945 $.30 (P1618)

How Far Is It To Bethlehem?
SATB,acap SHAWNEE A 367 $.30 (P1619)

I Thank You God
SATB,acap oct LAWSON 51215 $.25 (P1620)

I Want A Principle Within
SATB,opt 2trp&2trom (easy) ABINGDON APM-399
$.30, ipa (P1621)

I Will Lift Up Mine Eyes
SATB (med) ABINGDON APM-400 $.30 (P1622)

I'll Praise My Maker
SATB,opt brass (med) ABINGDON APM-110 $.25,
ipa (P1623)

In Terra Pax *Bibl
SATB,acap oct LAWSON 51618 $.35 (P1624)

Jerusalem, My Happy Home
SATB oct FISCHER,J 9410 $.30 (P1625)

Join To Rejoice
cor&cong oct AGAPE CY 3340 $.40 (P1626)

Joseph Dearest, Joseph Mine
SATB oct SACRED S-30 $.35 (P1627)

Jubilate Deo *Jubil
SATB,org,brass oct LAWSON 51624 $.40 (P1628)

Knight Without A Sword
SATB (med) ABINGDON APM-694 $.30 (P1629)

Litany
SATB&jr cor (med) ABINGDON APM-420 $.25
(P1630)

Lord Is My Light, The
SATB oct SACRED S-24 $.35 (P1631)

Mary, Mary *Xmas
SATB (easy) ABINGDON APM-892 $.35 (P1632)

Musicks Empire (from Triptych)
SATB,acap oct LAWSON 51418 $.35 (P1633)

Nativity Carol *Xmas,carol
SATB&TTBB oct AGAPE F 927 $.30 (P1634)

New Is Old, The
SATB (med) ABINGDON APM-855 $.40 (P1635)

O Lord, How Long
SATB oct FISCHER,C R-488 $.25 (P1636)

Praise The Lord Who Reigns Above
SATB oct FISCHER,C CM-7797 $.30 (P1637)

Psalm 150
SATB FLAMMER A 5143 $.25 (P1638)

Puer Nobis *Xmas
SATB (med) ABINGDON APM-422 $.35 (P1639)

Reconciliation
SATB&speak cor,trp (diff) ABINGDON APM-345
$.35 (P1640)

Seven Words Of Love *Gd.Fri.,ora
SATB&speak cor cor pts ABINGDON APM-356
$.50, sc ABINGDON APM-362 $2.00 (P1641)

Sing In Excelsis Gloria!
SATB,Bar solo oct SUMMY B 392 $.35 (P1642)

Sing Praise To God
SATB oct SUMMY 5315 $.40 (P1643)

Sing Praises
SATB,acap oct LAWSON 51367 $.35 (P1644)

Temptation Of Christ, The *Lent
SATB,acap (diff) ABINGDON APM-142 $.25
(P1645)

Virgin's Slumber Song, The *Xmas
SATB,A solo,acap oct LAWSON 51298 $.25
(P1646)

Watchman, Tell Us Of The Night
SATB FLAMMER A 5122 $.25 (P1647)

PFEIL
O Love That Will Not Let Me Go *Lent/Rembrnc
(Tudor, G.) SATB (easy) ALLANS 291 s.p.
(P1648)
(Tudor, George) SA ALLANS 292 s.p. (P1649)

PFIFFNER, ERNST (1910-   )
Cogitationes Cordis Ejus *Fest/Gen
[Lat] 2-4pt mix cor,acap (med) MULLER
SM 718 s.p. (P1650)

Der Hochste Herrscht In Majestat Und Pracht
SATB LAUDINELLA LR 93 s.p. contains also:
Lobt Den Herrn, Denn Was Er Tut (SATB/
SAT/SAB,opt 3treb inst&bass inst); Singt
Mit Froher Stimm (SATB) (P1651)

Lobt Den Herrn, Denn Was Er Tut
see Pfiffner, Ernst, Der Hochste Herrscht
In Majestat Und Pracht

Messe Auf Die Heiligen Dreifaltigkeit *Mass
SATB,org HANSSLER 10.230 sc s.p., cor pts
s.p. (P1652)

Nun Danket Gott, Erhebt Und Preiset
SSATB LAUDINELLA LR 71 s.p. contains also:
Wie Der Hirsch Nach Frischer Quelle
(SATB) (P1653)

PFIFFNER, ERNST (cont'd.)

Singt Mit Froher Stimm
see Pfiffner, Ernst, Der Hochste Herrscht
In Majestat Und Pracht

Wie Der Hirsch Nach Frischer Quelle
see Pfiffner, Ernst, Nun Danket Gott,
Erhebt Und Preiset

PFINGST-CHOR see Bach, Johann Sebastian

PFINGSTEN see Bruckner, Anton

PFINGSTEN see Buchtger, Fritz

PFINGSTEN see Tittel, Ernst

PFINGSTEN UND EUCHARISTIE *Pent
mix cor,acap cmplt ed DOBLINGER s.p.
contains & see also: Allegri, Gregorio,
Veni Sancte Spiritus; Bach, Johann
Sebastian, Komm, Heiliger Geist; Bach,
Johann Sebastian, O Heil'ge Seelenspeise;
Bach, Johann Sebastian, O Jesu, Dir Sei
Ewig Dank; Brant, Johann von, Gott Sei
Gelobt; Christenius, Johann, Kommet Her
Zu Mir Alle; Croce, Giovanni, O Sacrum
Convivium; Franck, Melchior, Jesu, Dein'
Seel; Gallus, Jacobus, O Salutaris
Hostia; Isaac, Heinrich, O Heil'ge
Seelenspeise; Palestrina, Giovanni, Lauda
Sion Salvatorem; Praetorius, Michael, Nun
Bitten Wir Den Heiligen Geist;
Praetorius, Michael, Veni Creator
Spiritus; Resinarius, Balthasar, Komm,
Gott Schopfer, Heiliger Geist; Schutz,
Heinrich, Aller Augen Warten Auf Dich,
Herre; Schutz, Heinrich, Den Heil'gen
Geistes Gnade Gross; Senfl, Ludwig,
Erfreut Euch, Liebe Seelen; Stobaeus,
Johann, Der Heilige Geist Vom Himmel Kam;
Victoria, Tomas Luis de, Pange Lingua;
Vulpius, Melchior, Spiritus Sancti Gratia
(P1654)

PFINGSTGESANG see Pestalozza, Heinrich

PFINGSTKANTATE see Feckers, Adolf

PFINGSTLIED see Mendelssohn-Bartholdy, Felix

PFINGSTMONTAG see Schieri, Fritz

PFINGSTRUF see Kretzschmar, Gunther

PFINGSTSONNTAG see Schieri, Fritz

PFIRSTINGER, F.
Auf Pfingsten
[Ger] mix cor,acap (med) HUG s.p. (P1655)

PFLEGER
Passionsmusik (from Sieben Worte Jesu Christi
Am Kreuz) Psntd
(Stein) 4pt mix cor,strings MOSELER s.p.,
ipa (P1656)

PFLEGER, AUGUSTIN (ca. 1670)
Passion Music On The Seven Words Of Jesus
Christ On The Cross
[Ger/Eng] 4pt mix cor,soli,inst SCHIRM.EC
2721 ipa (P1657)
(Pinkham, D.) .Ger/Eng] SATB,soli,inst,cont
SCHIRM.EC 2721 ipa (P1658)

PFLUEGER, CARL
Consider And Hear Me *anthem
SATB BOSWORTH s.p. (P1659)
(Stanbridge, C.) SATB (easy) ALLANS 150
s.p. (P1660)

How Long Wilt Thou Forget Me?
SATB oct LORENZ 9457 $.30 (P1661)
SATB HANSEN-US E9859 $.40 (P1662)
SA&unis/SA/unis oct HUNTZINGER 7007 $.20
(P1663)
SSA oct HUNTZINGER 7006 $.20 (P1664)
(Pitcher) SATB oct HUNTZINGER 7005 $.20
(P1665)

PFOHL
Antiphonal Psalm
SATB FLAMMER A 5018 $.30 (P1666)

Exhortation To Faith
SATB FLAMMER A 5454 $.25 (P1667)

In God Is My Salvation
TTBB FLAMMER C5022 $.25 (P1668)

Know That The Lord Is God
SATB FLAMMER A 5267 $.25 (P1669)

Prayer For A Right Spirit
SATB FLAMMER A 5186 $.30 (P1670)

PFUST
On Christmas Eve *Xmas
SA SOUTHERN $.35 (P1671)
SA SCHMITT 246 $.35 (P1672)

When Christmas Morn Is Dawning *Xmas
SSA SCHMITT 2576 $.25 (P1673)
SAB SCHMITT 5524 $.25 (P1674)

PHARAOH'S NUMBER TWO see Webber, Andrew

PHARISAEER UND ZOELLNER see Schutz, Heinrich

PHARISAER UND ZOLLNER see Ohse, Reinhard

PHARISEE AND THE PUBLICAN see Schutz, Heinrich

PHARISEE AND THE PUBLICAN, THE see Schutz,
Heinrich

PHARISEE AND THE PUBLICAN, THE see Schutz,
Heinrich, Es Gingen Zweene Menschen

PHARISEE ONE DAY, THE see Grime, William

PHELPS
Bread Of The World
SATB,acap BOSTON 12459 $.30 (P1675)

None Other Lamb
SATB oct VOLKWEIN VB217 $.25 (P1676)

PHELPS, JOHN R.
O Sing Ye To The Lord A New Song
cor HIGHLAND 4116 $.25 (P1677)

PHILADOR, ANNE (1681-1728)
see DANICAN-PHILIDOR, ANNE

PHILIPP, FRANZ (1890-
Aus Den Tiefen Schreie Ich Zu Dir, O Herr
*see Friedensmesse

Ave Maria *Fest
[Lat] SATB,acap (med) MULLER MS 27 s.p.
(P1678)

Friedensmesse *Op.12, Mass
"Aus Den Tiefen Schreie Ich Zu Dir, O Herr"
[Ger] SATB,S solo,org,orch (med diff) sc
MULLER SM 380 s.p., cor pts MULLER SM 380
s.p., voc sc MULLER SM 380A s.p. (P1679)

O Regina Regni Dei *Fest
[Lat] SATB,acap (med) MULLER MS 28 s.p.
(P1680)

Panis Angelicus *Fest
[Lat] SATB,acap (med) MULLER MS 28 s.p.
(P1681)

St. Martinus-Lied *Op.19,No.2, Fest
[Ger] SSAATTBB,acap (med) MULLER SM 378 sc
s.p., cor pts s.p. (P1682)

Tantum Ergo *Op.19, Gen
[Ger] SSAATTBB,acap (med) MULLER SM378 sc
s.p., cor pts s.p. (P1683)

PHILIPPART-GONZALEZ, RENEE
Messe *Mass
[Fr] 4pt mix cor,org/4inst DURAND sc s.p.,
cor pts s.p. (P1684)

Salve Regina *BVM,mot
[Lat] 4pt mix cor oct DURAND s.p. (P1685)

PHILIPS, PETER (1561-1628)
see PHILLIPS, PETER

Alma Redemptoris Mater *mot
SSATB,acap SCHIRM.EC $.50 (P1686)
(Collins, H.B.) [Lat] SSATB CHESTER s.p.
(P1687)
(McCarthy) "Maiden, Mother Of Our Savior"
SSATB oct BOURNE 900 $.50 (P1688)

Ascendit Deus *Asc
"Lord Ascendeth, The" SSATB,acap (med) oct
OXFORD 43.452 $.50 (P1689)

Ave Regina *mot
SSATB,acap SCHIRM.EC $.30 (P1690)
(Collins, H.B.) [Lat] SSATB CHESTER s.p.
(P1691)

Cantantibus Organis *anthem
(Terry, R.R.) [Lat] SSATB oct NOVELLO
52.0011.03 s.p. (P1692)

Elegi Abjectus Esse *mot
SSATB,acap SCHIRM.EC $.25 (P1693)
(Collins, H.B.) [Lat] SSATB CHESTER s.p.
(P1694)

He Is Risen *see Surgens Jesus

Lord Ascendeth, The *see Ascendit Deus

Maiden, Mother Of Our Savior *see Alma
Redemptoris Mater

Media Vita In Morte Sumus *mot
(Petti, Anthony G.) [Lat] SATTB CHESTER
s.p. (P1695)

O Beatum Et Sacrosanctum Diem *mot
(Petti, Anthony G.) [Lat] SSATB CHESTER
s.p. (P1696)

O Crux Splendidior *mot
(Turner) [Lat] SSATB SCHOTT s.p. (P1697)

O Virum Mirabilem *mot
SSATB,acap SCHIRM.EC $.30 (P1698)
(Collins, H.B.) [Lat] SSATB CHESTER s.p.
(P1699)

Praise To Thee *see Tibi Laus, Tibi Gloria

Psalm 15
SATB oct BOURNE 872 $.30 (P1700)

Queen Of Heaven *see Regina Coeli

Regina Coeli
(Greyson) "Queen Of Heaven" SATB oct BOURNE
ES93 $.30 (P1701)

Surgens Jesus *Easter,anthem
"He Is Risen" SATB oct GRAY GCMR 3023 $.25
(P1702)
(Terry, R.R.) [Lat] SSATB oct NOVELLO
52.0021.00 s.p. (P1703)
(Terry, R.R.) "He Is Risen" SSATB oct
NOVELLO 52.0021.00 s.p. (P1704)

Tibi Laus, Tibi Gloria *mot
(McCarthy) "Praise To Thee" SSATB oct
BOURNE 906 $.40 (P1705)
(Petti, Anthony G.) [Lat] SSATB CHESTER
s.p. (P1706)

While Organs Made Harmony *anthem
(Terry, R.R.) SSATB oct NOVELLO 52.0011.03
s.p. (P1707)

PHILLIPO
Hil Dag, Du Hoje *see Salve, Sacrata

Salve, Sacrata
(Sorensen, Soren) "Hil Dag, Du Hoje" [Lat/
Dan] SATB,acap HANSEN-DEN 287 s.p. see
also MOTETTER OG LAUDER FRA DET 16.
ARHUNDREDE (P1708)

PHILLIPS
Caecilia Virgo
(McCarthy) "Cecilia, Virgin" SATB&SATB oct
BOURNE 901 $1.00 (P1709)

Cecilia, Virgin *see Caecilia Virgo

Festival Anthem *Fest,anthem/Bibl
SATB&desc,S solo,org oct SUMMY M 2620 $.65
(P1710)

PHILLIPS (cont'd.)
You Got To Live! *anthem/pop
SATB,opt perc oct PRO ART 2683 $.30 (P1711)

PHILLIPS, C. HENRY
To God The Mighty Lord
SATB (very easy) oct OXFORD 42.131 $.30
(P1712)

PHILLIPS, MONTAGUE FAWCETT (1885-1969)
O God Our Father In Heaven *anthem
mix cor oct NOVELLO 40.1430.08 s.p. (P1713)

PHINOT, DOMINIQUE
Opera Omnia vol. I *CCU,mot
(Hofler, Janez) cor AM.INST.MUS. $28.00
(P1714)

PIAE CANTIONES *see Klemetti, Heikki, Scribere
Proposui; Wikander, David, Nu Med Sang
(P1715)

PIAE CANTIONES see Klemetti, Heikki

PIAE CANTIONES see Wikander, David

PIAE CANTIONES see Malin

PIAE CANTIONES, DIE MEHRSTIMMIGEN LIEDER *CCU,
16th cent
(Andersen; Makinen) [Finn/Lat] mix cor cmplt
ed FAZER s.p. (P1716)

PIAE CANTIONES ECCLESIASTICAE ET SCHOLASTICAE
VETERUM EPISCOPORUM *CCU,16th cent
[Finn/Lat] mix cor FAZER pap s.p., cloth s.p.
(P1717)

PIAE CANTIONES *CCU,16th cent
(Andersen; Makinen) [Swed/Lat] mix cor FAZER
cmplt ed s.p., cmplt ed s.p. (P1718)

PIAE CANTIONES *CCU,16th cent
(Andersen; Makinen) [Finn/Lat] mix cor cmplt
ed FAZER s.p. (P1719)

PIANTO DI MARIA VERGINE see Mancini, Vincenzo

PICCHI, LUIGI
Alleluja, Christo E Risorto
see Cinque Canti Pasquali

Ave Maria
see DUE AVE MARIA
see Mattoni, Filippo, Ave Maria

Cinque Canti Pasquali
RICORDI-ENG 128666 s.p.
contains: Alleluja, Christo E Risorto
(3pt mix cor,org); Regina Coeli (3 eq
voices,opt solo,org); Regina Coeli
Jubila (3 eq voices/4 eq voices,org);
Resurrexi (3 eq voices/3pt mix cor,
org); Squillate, Campane (2-4pt mix
cor,org) (P1720)

Magnum Nomen Domini
SA,org s.p. voc sc RICORDI-ENG 127678, cor
pts RICORDI-ENG 127679-80 see also Sei
Canti Natalizi (P1721)

Messa In Onore Di S. Nicolao Della Flue
*Mass
TTB s.p. sc RICORDI-ENG 127578, cor pts
RICORDI-ENG 12579-81 (P1722)

Messa In Onore Di S. Pio X *Mass
2 eq voices,org s.p. sc RICORDI-ENG 128656,
cor pts RICORDI-ENG 128759 (P1723)

Misericors Deus *Mass
2 eq voices/3 eq voices,org s.p. sc
RICORDI-ENG 128072, cor pts RICORDI-ENG
128073-79 (P1724)
ATB,org s.p. sc RICORDI-ENG 128030, cor pts
RICORDI-ENG 128031-33 (P1725)

Ninna-Nanna
unis,org s.p. voc sc RICORDI-ENG 127676,
cor pts RICORDI-ENG 127677 see also Sei
Canti Natalizi (P1726)

Puer Natus Est Nobis
SA,org s.p. voc sc RICORDI-ENG 127681, cor
pts RICORDI-ENG 127682-83 see also Sei
Canti Natalizi (P1727)

Puer Nobis Nascitur
SATB,org s.p. voc sc RICORDI-ENG 127687,
cor pts RICORDI-ENG 127688-91 see also
Sei Canti Natalizi (P1728)

Regina Coeli
see Cinque Canti Pasquali

Regina Coeli Jubila
see Cinque Canti Pasquali

Resurrexi
see Cinque Canti Pasquali

Sei Canti Natalizi
RICORDI-ENG
contains & see also: Magnum Nomen Domini;
Ninna-Nanna; Puer Natus Est Nobis; Puer
Nobis Nascitur; Tu Scendi Dalle Stelle;
Tui Sunt Coeli (P1729)

Squillate, Campane
see Cinque Canti Pasquali

Tu Scendi Dalle Stelle
4 eq voices/3 eq voices/ATB/SATB s.p. voc
sc RICORDI-ENG 128467, cor pts RICORDI-
ENG 128468-70 see also Sei Canti Natalizi
(P1730)

Tui Sunt Coeli
SA,org s.p. voc sc RICORDI-ENG 127684, cor
pts RICORDI-ENG 127685-86 see also Sei
Canti Natalizi (P1731)

Veni Sponsa Christi
[It] unis,org ZANIBON 2732 s.p. (P1732)

PICCOLA SINFONIA CORALE see Giorgi, Piero

PICCOLO
Sleep, Baby Jesus *Xmas
SATB,acap,opt pno oct PRO ART 2612 $.30
(P1733)

PICCOLO REPERTORIO PER LE FIGLIE DI MARIA see
  Visona', Gino

PICCOLOMINI-MESSE see Mozart, Wolfgang Amadeus,
  Missa Brevis In C-Dur

PICKAERT, R.
  O Salutaris
    [Lat] opt cor,solo/Mez solo,org,vln,harp
    LEMOINE cor pts s.p., voc sc s.p. (P1734)

PICKELL
  Christmas Is A Comin' *Xmas,spir,Contemp
    SATB oct PRO ART 2650 $.30   (P1735)

  It's The Time Of The Year *Xmas
    SSA oct PRO ART 2724 $.30   (P1736)
    SATB oct PRO ART 2721 $.30   (P1737)

  Mary Had A Baby Boy *Xmas,carol
    SATB oct PRO ART 2733 $.30   (P1738)

  O' Dove Of Peace
    SATB oct PRO ART 2730 $.30   (P1739)

PIE JESU see Bazin, [Francois-Emanuel-Joseph]

PIE JESU see Caplet, [Lucien]

PIE JESU see Charpentier, Marc-Antoine

PIE JESU see Cherubini, Luigi

PIE JESU see Faure

PIE JESU see Franck, Cesar

PIE JESU see Gounod, Charles Francois

PIE JESU see Haumesser, A.

PIE JESU see Niedermeyer, Louis

PIE JESU see Volpi, Edoardo

PIE JESU, NO. 2 see Saint-Saens, Camille

PIECHLER, ARTHUR
  Hymn
    [Lat] men cor,fl,ob,2clar,bsn,2trp,2horn,
    2trom,tuba,strings,perc,timp cmplt ed
    BOOSEY rental   (P1740)

  Sursum Corda
    [Lat/Eng] mix cor&boy cor,soli,org,fl,2ob,
    clar,2bsn,2trp,2horn,2trom,strings,harp,
    perc,timp cmplt ed BOOSEY rental (P1741)

PIED BEAUTY see Widdoes, Lawrence

PIEDAD SENOR! see Stradella, Alessandro

PIERCE, ANNE E.
  Prince Of Peace *Xmas,cant
    jr cor voc sc WILLIS $.80   (P1742)

  Prince Of Peace, The *Bibl
    jr cor,pno (easy) voc sc WILLIS $.75
                                       (P1743)

PIERCE, BRENT
  How Still He Rests *Xmas
    SATB,ob,chimes oct WALTON 2951 $.35 (P1744)

  Rising Sun, The *see Pooler, Frank

PIERCE, T.C.
  Christmas Hymn *Xmas,hymn
    SAB,pno/org/harp oct KERBY 5902 $.25
                                       (P1745)
    SAB,opt harp oct KERBY 5902C $.25 (P1746)

PIERESSA, LUIGI
  Missa In Hon. Divi Marci Ev. *Mass
    [Lat] TTB,org sc ZANIBON 4639 s.p., voc pt
    ZANIBON s.p.   (P1747)

PIERLUIGI
  O Blessed Jesus *Renais
    (Ehret, Walter) SATB,acap PEER $.40 (P1748)

PIERNE, GABRIEL (1863-1937)
  Children's Crusade, The *Xmas
    cor voc sc SCHIRM.G $1.25   (P1749)

  La Route (from La Croisade Des Enfants)
    [Fr] cor,S solo,opt pno/org voc sc HEUGEL voc sc
    s.p., voc pt s.p.   (P1750)

  Psalm 24
    [Fr] cor,Bar solo,org,orch voc sc SALABERT-
    US $7.00   (P1751)

  Song Of Praise, A
    (Reibold; Jurey) SSA,orch oct BELWIN 64326
    $.30, ipa   (P1752)
    (Reibold; Jurey) SAB,orch oct BELWIN 64325
    $.25, ipa   (P1753)
    (Reibold; Jurey) SATB,orch oct BELWIN 64206
    $.30, ipa   (P1754)

PIERNE, PAUL (1874-1950)
  Messe A Quarte Voix *Mass
    4pt,soli,org,harp,vln,vcl LEMOINE voc sc
    s.p., cor pts s.p., ipa   (P1755)

  Panis Angelicus
    [Lat] unis/unis,org,vln CHOUDENS s.p.
                                       (P1756)

PIEROBON, GIUSEPPE
  Ave Maria
    see Gloriosa Virginum

  Beata Es Virgo
    see Gloriosa Virginum

  Gloriosa Virginum *BVM
    [Lat] 2 eq voices,org ZANIBON 633 s.p.
    contains: Ave Maria; Beata Es Virgo;
    Salve Regina   (P1757)

  Salve Regina
    see Gloriosa Virginum

PIERPONT, J.
  For The Beauty Of The Earth
    (Kinyon; Kocher) SA ALFRED 6131 $.25
                                       (P1758)

PIETA (from King Of Kings)
  SSA BIG3 $.35   (P1759)
  SATB BIG3 $.30   (P1760)

PIETA, SIGNORE! see Stradella, Alessandro

PIGANI, GIOVANNI
  Te Deum *Te Deum
    [Lat] 3pt mix cor/4pt mix cor sc ZANIBON
    4446 s.p., cor pts ZANIBON 4447 s.p.
                                       (P1761)

PIGGOTT, H.E.
  Babe Lies In A Manger, A *Xmas
    unis (easy) OXFORD 81.026 $.25   (P1762)

  Come All You Children, Join And Sing
    unis (very easy) OXFORD 81.025 $.25 (P1763)

  Come, My Way, My Truth, My Life *Ded/Gen/
    Thanks
    unis (easy) oct OXFORD 45.704 $.25 (P1764)

  Communion Service *Commun,Agnus/Bene/Credo/
    Gloria/Kyrie/Sanctus
    unis&opt SATB (easy) oct OXFORD 40.311 $.50
                                       (P1765)

  My Song Is Love Unknown *Gen/Psntd
    unis (med) oct OXFORD 55.011 $.30 (P1766)

  O Lord How Manifold Are Thy Works
    SATB oct LESLIE 4100   (P1767)

PIKE, HARRY HALE
  Come Unto Me, Ye Weary
    SATB,org (med) oct WILLIS 1081 $.15 (P1768)

  Father, What E'er Of Earthly Bliss
    SATB,S solo,pno (easy) oct WILLIS 754 $.12
                                       (P1769)

  Hear My Prayer, O Lord
    SATB,S/T solo,pno (easy) oct WILLIS 641
    $.12   (P1770)

  Jesus, My Saviour, Look On Me
    SATB,Bar solo,pno (easy) oct WILLIS 1069
    $.12   (P1771)

  Lift Your Glad Voices *Easter
    SATB,S solo,pno (easy) oct WILLIS 940 $.25
                                       (P1772)

  O God, Our Help In Ages Past
    SATB,SA soli,pno (easy) oct WILLIS 6315
    $.12   (P1773)

  O Sacred Head, Now Wounded *Gd.Fri.
    (Parmelee) SATB,opt acap (med) oct WILLIS
    203 $.15   (P1774)

  Praise, My Soul The King Of Heaven
    SATB,pno (easy) oct WILLIS 6329 $.12
                                       (P1775)

PIKET, FREDERICK (1903-   )
  Count Down Or Covenant *Fest
    [Eng] SATB TRANSCON. TCL 338 $2.00 (P1776)

  Kavod La-Torah *Sab-Eve
    SATB TRANSCON. TCL 839 $1.50   (P1777)

  Memorial Service
    SATB,cantor,T/Bar solo TRANSCON. TCL 872
    $2.50   (P1778)
    SATB,cantor,T/Bar solo TRANSCON. TCL 872
    $2.50   (P1779)

  Midnight Service *see S'lichos

  Out Of The Depths I Cry (Psalm 130)
    [Eng] SATB TRANSCON. TCL 616 $.40 (P1780)

  Psalm 130 *see Out Of The Depths I Cry

  Seventh Day Friday Eve Service *Sab-Eve
    SATB TRANSCON. TCL 840 $3.50   (P1781)

  Six High Holiday Selections *CC6U
    SATB,cantor TRANSCON. TCL 874 $2.00 (P1782)

  S'lichos
    "Midnight Service" SATB,cantor,T/Bar solo
    TRANSCON. TCL 873 $2.50   (P1783)

PILGRIM CARAVAN, THE see Arnold

PILGRIM HYMN see Bacon, Ernst

PILGRIM PSALMS see Finney

PILGRIM SONG see Gibbs, [Cecil] Armstrong

PILGRIM SONG see Roberts, Mervyn

PILGRIM WAY, THE see Chapman, M.B.

PILGRIM'S CHORUS see Christiansen, P.

PILGRIM'S CHORUS see Dawson

PILGRIM'S CHORUS see Wagner, Richard

PILGRIMS' HYMN see Leuning, O.

PILGRIM'S JOURNEY see Vaughan Williams, Ralph

PILGRIM'S SONG OF THANKSGIVING see Angell

PILGRIM'S SONG, THE see Coates, Henry

PILGRIMS TO BETHLEHEM see Thiman, Eric Harding

PILKINGTON, FRANCIS (ca. 1562-1638)
  Hidden, O Lord
    (Greenberg) [Eng] SATB,acap AMP N6 $.30
                                       (P1784)
  Sovereign Of My Delight
    (Ehret) SSA/SAA oct LAWSON 51602 $.30 (P1785)

PILLIN, BORIS
  So Gehst Du Nun *cant
    mix cor,soli,org (diff) oct WESTERN WIM 34
    $1.75   (P1786)

PILOT
  Messe Des Rois Mages *Xmas,Mass
    [Fr] TTB/SSTTB,orch LEDUC BL442 voc sc
    s.p., voc pt s.p.   (P1787)

  Messe Des Rois Mages, Sur Des Noels Anciens
    *Xmas,Mass
    [Fr] 2 eq voices,soli,orch LEDUC BL428 voc

PILOT (cont'd.)
    sc s.p., voc pt s.p.   (P1788)

PINGST see Lindberg, Oskar [Fredrik]

PINGSTHYMN see Rogberg, Carl

PINGSTHYMN see Soderholm, Valdemar

PINKHAM, DANIEL (1923-   )
  All Flesh Is Grass
    see Songs Of Peaceful Departure

  Ave Maria *BVM
    [Lat] SA,acap AMP A367 $.25   (P1789)

  Behold, How Good And How Pleasant (Psalm 133)
    *mot
    SATB,opt org/pno PETERS 66038 $.25 (P1790)

  Call Of Isaiah, The
    mix cor/SA/TB,org,opt perc,electronic tape
    (med easy) SCHIRM.EC 2911 $.35, ipa (P1791)

  Canticle Of Praise
    SATB,S solo,pno/brass&perc SCHIRM.EC 2694
    $1.50, ipr   (P1792)
    SATB,S solo,pno,brass,perc SCHIRM.EC 2694
    $1.75, ipr   (P1793)

  Christmas Eve (The Snow Lies Crisp) *Xmas
    SATB,acap SCHIRM.EC 2653 $.30   (P1794)

  David Played With Lions *mot
    SA,opt inst SCHIRM.EC 2586 see from Let Us
    Now Praise Famous Men   (P1795)

  Easter Cantata *Easter,cant
    SATB,2horn,4trp,3trom,2perc,timp,opt tuba,
    Celesta voc sc PETERS 6393 $1.25, ipr
                                       (P1796)

  Elegy (Now Time Has Gathered To Itself)
    SATB,acap SCHIRM.EC 2655 $.30   (P1797)

  Festival Magnificat And Nunc Dimittis
    *Magnif/Nunc
    SATB,org/pno,opt horn/trom&opt 2trp&opt
    trom,opt acap PETERS 6555 $.50, ipa
                                       (P1798)

  Glory Be To God *Xmas,mot
    dbl cor,opt org SCHIRM.EC 2696 $.75 (P1799)
    dbl cor,acap SCHIRM.EC 2696 $.75   (P1800)

  God Is A Spirit
    SATB,org SCHIRM.EC 2692 $.45   (P1801)
    SATB,org SCHIRM.EC 2692 $.45   (P1802)

  Grace Is Poured Abroad *mot/Psalm
    SATB,opt org/pno PETERS 66297 $.30 (P1803)
    mix cor SOUTHERN $.30   (P1804)

  Here Repose, O Broken Body *Easter
    SATB oct HIGHLAND 7.0010.1 $.30   (P1805)

  How Precious Is Thy Lovingkindness *mot/
    Psalm
    SATB,opt org/pno PETERS 66100 $.25 (P1806)

  If Ye Love Me
    SSA,org SCHIRM.EC 2568 $.30   (P1807)

  In The Beginning Of Creation
    SATB,electronic tape (very easy) SCHIRM.EC
    2902 $.35, ipa   (P1808)

  Jonah *cant
    SATB,soli,orch SCHIRM.EC 2731 $1.75, ipr
                                       (P1809)
    4 cor,soli,orch SCHIRM.EC 2731 $1.50, ipr
                                       (P1810)

  Jubilate Deo (Psalm 100)
    SATB/SSAA&opt unis treb cor,org SCHIRM.EC
    2687 $1.50, ipa   (P1811)
    "Oh Be Joyful In The Lord" SATB&SSA&opt
    unis treb cor,org SCHIRM.EC 2687 $1.25
                                       (P1812)

  Lamentations Of Jeremiah
    voc sc PETERS 66036 $1.50, ipr   (P1813)

  Let Us Now Praise Famous Men *see David
    Played With Lions; Lord Brought Forth
    Moses, The; Lord Exalted Aaron, The;
    Prophet Elijah Arose, The; Solomon
    Reigned In Days Of Peace   (P1814)

  Listen To Me *CC5U,mot
    SA,opt inst SCHIRM.EC 2581 $.35   (P1815)

  Litany, A
    SS,pno/org AMP A483 $.25   (P1816)

  Lord Brought Forth Moses, The *mot
    SA,opt inst SCHIRM.EC 2586 see from Let Us
    Now Praise Famous Men   (P1817)

  Lord Exalted Aaron, The *mot
    SA,opt inst SCHIRM.EC 2586 see from Let Us
    Now Praise Famous Men   (P1818)

  Lord, Make Me To Know Mine End
    see Songs Of Peaceful Departure

  Lord, Thou Hast Put Gladness
    see Songs Of Peaceful Departure

  Magnificat *Magnif
    [Eng/Lat] SSA,S solo,pno voc sc PETERS
    66180 $.90, ipr   (P1819)

  Martyrdom Of Saint Stephen, The
    SATB,gtr/pno SCHIRM.EC 2736 ipa   (P1820)

  Mass Of The Good Shepherd
    unis&cong,org SCHIRM.EC 2713 $.40, ipa
                                       (P1821)
    unis&cong,org SCHIRM.EC 2713 $.40 (P1822)

  Mass Of The Holy Eucharist *Commun
    unis&cong,org SCHIRM.EC 2710   (P1823)
    unis&cong,org SCHIRM.EC 2710   (P1824)

  Mass Of The Word Of God
    4 cor/unis&cong,org SCHIRM.EC 2708 $1.00 (P1825)
    SATB&cong/SATB&unis,org SCHIRM.EC 2708
    $1.00   (P1826)

PINKHAM, DANIEL (cont'd.)

O Lord God To Whom Vengeance Belongeth (Psalm 4) mot
SATB,opt org/pno PETERS 6355 $.25 see from Three Psalm Motets (P1827)

Oh Be Joyful In The Lord *see Jubilate Deo

Open To Me The Gates Of Righteousness (Psalm 4) mot/Psalm
SATB,opt org/pno PETERS 66037 $.90 (P1828)

Prelude Adagio And Chorale
opt unis cor,2trp,horn,trom,tuba PETERS 66294 $3.50, ipa (P1829)

Prophet Elijah Arose, The *mot
SA,opt inst SCHIRM.EC 2586 see from Let Us Now Praise Famous Men (P1830)

Psalm 4 *see Open To Me The Gates Of Righteousness

Psalm 42 *see Why Art Thou So Cast Down O My Soul

Psalm 45 *see Thou Hast Loved Righteousness

Psalm 100 *see Jubilate Deo

Psalm 133 *see Behold, How Good And How Pleasant

Psalm Set *CCU,Psalm
SATB,org/pno voc sc PETERS 66295 $1.25, ipa (P1831)

Requiem *Req
[Lat] voc sc PETERS 6650 $1.50, ipr (P1832)

Seven Last Words Of Christ, The *cant
SATB,T,Bar/B soli,org,electronic tape (med diff) SCHIRM.EC 2907 $.60, ipa (P1833)

Solomon Reigned In Days Of Peace *mot
SA,opt inst SCHIRM.EC 2586 see from Let Us Now Praise Famous Men (P1834)

Song Of Jephthah's Daughter, The *cant
voc sc PETERS 6835 $1.50 (P1835)
SSA,SBar soli,pno PETERS 6835 $1.50 (P1836)

Songs Of Peaceful Departure
SATB,gtr/pno SCHIRM.EC 2735 $.35, ipa
contains: All Flesh Is Grass; Lord, Make Me To Know Mine End; Lord, Thou Hast Put Gladness (P1837)

Songs Of Peaceful Departure
4 cor,gtr/pno SCHIRM.EC 2735 $.35 (P1838)

St. Mark Passion
voc sc PETERS 6900 $2.50, ipr (P1839)

Stabat Mater
[Lat] voc sc PETERS 6855 $2.00 (P1840)

Star-Tree Carol *Xmas
SATB oct FISCHER,C R-419 $.25 (P1841)

Thou Hast Loved Righteousness (Psalm 45) mot
SATB,opt org/pno PETERS 6841 $.30 see from Three Psalm Motets (P1842)

Three Lenten Poems Of Richard Crashaw *Lent
SATB,pno/4strings/orch/hndbl/harp, or celesta SCHIRM.EC 2693 $.50, ipa (P1843)
SATB,pno,4strings/orch,hndbl SCHIRM.EC 2693 $.75, ipa (P1844)
SSA,pno/4strings&opt orch&harp SCHIRM.EC 2572 $.50, ipa (P1845)

Three Psalm Motets *see O Lord God To Whom Vengeance Belongeth (Psalm 4); Thou Hast Loved Righteousness (Psalm 45); Why Art Thou So Cast Down O My Soul (Psalm 42) (P1846)

Thy Statutes Have Been My Songs
SAB,org SCHIRM.EC 2705 $.30 (P1847)

Wedding Cantata *Marriage,cant
voc sc PETERS 66039 $1.50 (P1848)

Why Art Thou So Cast Down O My Soul (Psalm 42) mot
SATB,opt org/pno PETERS 6366 $.25 see from Three Psalm Motets (P1849)

PINKSTERLIED see Franck, [Johann Wolfgang]

PINSUTI, CIRO (1829-1888)
Psalm Of Life, A
2pt ASHDOWN E.A.63 s.p. (P1850)

PIONNIER
Quem Dicunt Homines
see Richafort, Quem Dicunt Homines

PIPELARE, MATHAES (ca. 1450-ca. 1512)
Credo De Sancta Johannes Evangelista
see Opera Omnia vol. II

Missa De Feria
see Opera Omnia vol. II

Missa Dicit Dominus: Nihil Tulerits In Via
see Opera Omnia vol. II

Missa Floruit Egregius Infans Livanus In Actis
see Opera Omnia vol. II

Missa Fors Seulement
see Opera Omnia vol. II

Missa Joannes Christi Care-Ecce Puer Meus
see Opera Omnia vol. III

Missa L'homme Arme
see Opera Omnia vol. III

Missa Mi Mi
see Opera Omnia vol. III

Missa Sine Nomine (Segovia-Jena)
see Opera Omnia vol. III

PIPELARE, MATHAES (cont'd.)

Missa Sine Nomine (Vienna)
see Opera Omnia vol. III

Opera Omnia vol. I *sac/sec,CCU,mot
(Cross, Ronald) cor AM.INST.MUS. $12.00 (P1851)

Opera Omnia vol. II
(Cross, Ronald) cor AM.INST.MUS. $19.00
contains: Credo De Sancta Johannes Evangelista; Missa De Feria; Missa Dicit Dominus: Nihil Tulerits In Via; Missa Floruit Egregius Infans Livanus In Actis; Missa Fors Seulement (P1852)

Opera Omnia vol. III *Mass
(Cross, Ronald) cor AM.INST.MUS. $20.00
contains: Missa Joannes Christi Care-Ecce Puer Meus; Missa L'homme Arme; Missa Mi Mi; Missa Sine Nomine (Segovia-Jena); Missa Sine Nomine (Vienna) (P1853)

PIPERS' CAROL see Johnson

PIRCHAY SHIR KODESH see Steinberg, Ben

PIRIOU, A.
La Nativite De La Tres Sainte Vierge *BVM, ora
SATB,acap LEMOINE (P1854)

PIRKADAT see Mozart, Wolfgang Amadeus

PIS-CHU LI see Ancis, Solomon

PISANO
I Want Jesus To Walk With Me
SATB oct PLYMOUTH PCS-48 $.25 (P1855)

PISANO, BERNARDO (? -1548)
Music Of The Florentine Renaissance Vol. I *CCU
(D'Accone, Frank) cor AM.INST.MUS. $22.00 (P1856)

PISARI, [PASQUALE] (1725-1778)
O Salutaris Hostia
wom cor sc ALSBACH&D s.p. (P1857)

PISK, PAUL AMADEUS (1893-)
Psalm 30
TTBB,acap PEER $.40 (P1858)

Psalm 54
SATB,acap oct PRESSER MC310 $.35 (P1859)

PISTON, WALTER (1894-)
Bow Down Thine Ear, O Lord
[Eng] SATB,7inst AMP A641 $.35 (P1860)

O Sing Unto The Lord A New Song
SATB,7inst AMP A640 $.35 (P1861)

Psalm And Prayer Of David
[Eng] SATB,inst AMP A304 $.80, ipa (P1862)

PITCHER, GLADYS
All Praise To Thee *see Tallis Canon

Day Of Gladness *Xmas,Bibl/cant/carol
SATB oct WILLIS $1.50 (P1863)

Tallis Canon *canon
"All Praise To Thee" SAB WARNER 3555 $.30 (P1864)

PITFIELD, THOMAS BARON (1903-)
Anthem
see Short Community Service, A

Born Is He
see Three Festive Carols

Citizens Of Chatres
see Three Festive Carols

Everyman's Prayer
4pt mix cor oct CURWEN 10104 $.25 (P1865)

For Evening *Eve
oct HART see from Two Short Litanies (P1866)

Hills, The (Psalm 121)
SATB&opt boy cor,org PETERS H654A $1.50 (P1867)

Hills, The *hymn
audience/cong voc sc HINRICHSEN H654D s.p. (P1868)

Hymn Of Penitence
see Short Community Service, A

Hymn Of Trust
see Short Community Service, A

If God Build Not The House (Psalm 127)
see Two Metrical Psalms
SSA,pno PETERS H556 $.30 (P1869)

Lord's Prayer, The
see Short Community Service, A

New Old Carol *carol
unis CRAMER 26 s.p. (P1870)

On This Day *Xmas
SATB oct FOX PS147 $.35 (P1871)

Psalm 23
see Two Metrical Psalms

Psalm 121 *see Hills, The

Psalm 127 *see If God Build Not The House

Short Community Service, A *hymn
SATB,org cor pts PETERS H789A $.40, ipa
contains: Anthem; Hymn Of Penitence; Hymn Of Trust; Lord's Prayer, The (P1872)

Sing Noel
see Three Festive Carols

Sweet Spirit Comfort Me
oct HART see from Two Short Litanies (P1873)

Three Festive Carols *Xmas,carol
SSA,pno,opt winds&perc voc sc NOVELLO 07.0354.00 s.p., ipa
contains: Born Is He; Citizens Of Chatres; Sing Noel (P1874)

PITFIELD, THOMAS BARON (cont'd.)

Two Angel Songs *Xmas
SSA CRAMER 321 s.p. (P1875)

Two Metrical Psalms
unis wom cor/unis men cor,org/pno PETERS H556B $.30
contains: Psalm 23; Psalm 127 (P1876)

Two Short Litanies *see For Evening; Sweet Spirit Comfort Me (P1877)

PITONI, GIUSEPPE OTTAVIO (1657-1743)
Adoramus Te
(Ehret) [Lat] SATB,acap oct PRO ART 2181 $.25 (P1878)

Adoramus Te, Christe
(Krone) [Lat] SATB,acap WARNER W2629 $.30 (P1879)

Cantate Domino
mix cor sc ALSBACH&D s.p. (P1880)
(Greyson) mix cor SOUTHERN $.30 (P1881)
(Greyson) "O Sing Ye To The Lord" SSA oct BOURNE ES5A $.30 (P1882)
(Greyson) "O Sing Ye To The Lord" SAB oct BOURNE ES5C $.30 (P1883)
(Greyson) "O Sing Ye To The Lord" SATB oct BOURNE ES5 $.30 (P1884)
(Greyson) "O Sing Ye To The Lord" TTBB oct BOURNE ES5B $.30 (P1885)
(Hadley) "Now Sing Ye To The Lord" SATB oct PRO ART 2293 $.25 (P1886)
(Harris) SATB FLAMMER A 5175 $.25 (P1887)
(Harris) SSA FLAMMER B 5057 $.30 (P1888)
(Pruett) "Sing To The Lord, Our God" 4pt mix cor,acap oct SCHIRM.G 11396 $.30 (P1889)
(Row) "Sing To The Lord" SATB oct FISCHER,C R-293 $.25 (P1890)

Christus Factus Est *Easter/Lent
"Jesus Christ, Our Lord" SATB oct WALTON 6005 $.30 (P1891)

Christus Factus Est Pro Nobis *mot
(Hellman) "Christus Ward Fur Uns Gehorsam" [Lat/Ger] SATB HANSSLER 1.138 s.p. (P1892)

Christus Ward Fur Uns Gehorsam *see Christus Factus Est Pro Nobis

Ex Altari Tuo *mot
[Lat] mix cor,acap oct NOVELLO DM-29 s.p. (P1893)

Ex Altari Tuo, Domine
[Lat] SATB,acap (med) MULLER M 29 s.p. (P1894)

Hymn Pa Adventsundagen *Adv,hymn
mix cor NORDISKA 948 s.p. (P1895)

In Voce Exsulationis
[Lat] SATB,acap (med) MULLER M 28 s.p. (P1896)

In Voce Exultationies *Commun,mot
[Lat] mix cor,acap oct NOVELLO DM-30 s.p. (P1897)

Jesus Christ, Our Lord *see Christus Factus Est

Laudate Dominum *Gen,anthem/mot
[Ger] SATB,acap (easy) MULLER MS 30 s.p. (P1898)
[Lat] mix cor,acap oct NOVELLO MS-30 s.p. (P1899)
(Davies) "Praise Ye The Lord" [Lat/Eng] mix cor CURWEN 80867 s.p. (P1900)
(Martens, Mason) "O Praise The Lord" SATB oct WALTON 2092 $.25 (P1901)
(Steele, Jonathan) [Lat] SATB CHESTER s.p. (P1902)

Misericordia Domini
(Harris) [Lat] SATB,opt kbd oct PRO ART 2308 $.25 (P1903)

Now Sing Ye To The Lord *see Cantate Domino

O Praise The Lord *see Laudate Dominum

O Praise Ye The Lord *Easter/Gen
SATB,kbd (med easy) oct CONCORDIA 98-1739 $.25 (P1904)
mix cor SOUTHERN $.25 (P1905)

O Sing Ye To The Lord *see Cantate Domino

Praise Ye The Lord *see Laudate Dominum

Praise Ye The Lord Of Heaven
(Richardson) SAB oct WORD CS-2448 $.30 (P1906)
(Richardson) SATB oct WORD CS-312 $.30 (P1907)

Qui Manducat *Commun,mot
[Lat] SATB,acap (med) MULLER M 30 s.p. (P1908)
[Lat] mix cor,acap oct NOVELLO DM-28 s.p. (P1909)

Sing To The Lord *see Cantate Domino

Sing To The Lord, Our God *see Cantate Domino

Tantum Ergo *Commun/Gen,anthem
[Lat] SATB,acap (med easy) MULLER MS 49 s.p. (P1910)
[Lat] mix cor,acap oct NOVELLO MS-49 s.p. (P1911)

We Do Worship Thee
(Lundquist) SATB oct ELKAN-V 362-1164 $.25 (P1912)

PITTMAN
My Soul Doth Magnify The Lord
SATB ALLANS 137 s.p. (P1913)

PITTS
Church In The Wildwood, The
(Benson) SATB oct LORENZ A272 $.25 (P1914)

PIZZETTI, [ILDEBRANDO] (1880-1968)
De Profundis
SSATTBB cor pts RICORDI-ENG 124102-04 s.p. (P1915)

Filiae Jerusalem, Adjuro Vos *cant
[Lat] wom cor,S solo,orch voc sc RICORDI-ENG s.p. (P1916)

PIZZETTI, [ILDEBRANDO] (cont'd.)

Messa Di Requiem *Mass/Req
SATB,acap s.p. voc sc RICORDI-ENG 119490,
cor pts RICORDI-ENG 119491-92   (P1917)

Requiem Mass *Req
[Lat] SATB voc sc RICORDI-ENG s.p. (P1918)

PLAINSONG PRIMER, A
SCHIRM.EC 20 $2.00   (P1919)

PLAINTIVE CAROL, A see Kindig

PLAN OF GOD, THE see Kaiser, Kurt

PLANCTUS see Ham

PLANCTUS MARIAE *Psntd,14th cent
(Smoldon, W.L.) [Eng/Lat] SATB,SSAT soli,opt
org&chimes (med easy) sc OXFORD 46.147
$3.15, ipr, rental   (P1920)

PLANETS, STARS AND AIRS OF SPACE see Bach,
Johann Sebastian

PLANGE QUASI see Ingegneri, Marco Antonio

PLANK, DAVID L.
Christmas Legend, A *Xmas
SATB,acap SHAWNEE A 869 $.25   (P1921)

Easter Morn *Easter
SATB SHAWNEE A 527 $.25   (P1922)

For Thy Church We Thank Thee
SATB LUDWIG L-1128 $.30   (P1923)

Mary's Lullaby *Xmas
SATB oct LORENZ C170 $.25   (P1924)

Sing Noel *Xmas
SATB,acap SHAWNEE A 710 $.30   (P1925)

PLANYAVSKY, PETER
Deutsches Ordinarium
mix cor&cong,cantor,org DOBLINGER voc sc
s.p., cor pts s.p.   (P1926)

Deutsches Proprium Der Ersten Weihnachtsmesse
*Xmas,Mass
4pt mix cor,org DOBLINGER voc sc s.p., cor
pts s.p.   (P1927)

PLANZER, EMANUEL (1939-)
Gott Ist Der Herr *Gen
[Ger] 3pt mix cor,acap (med easy) BOSSE
BE 227 s.p.   (P1928)
[Ger] unis,acap (easy) BOSSE BE 253 s.p.
(P1929)

Psalm 25 *see Wende Dich Zu Mir

Wende Dich Zu Mir (Psalm 25)
see Schweizer, Rolf, Denn Dein Ist Das
Reich

PLAUDITE see Gabrieli, Giovanni

PLAUDITE OMNIS TERRA see Gabrieli, Giovanni

PLAUTZ, GABRIEL
Ave Mundi Spes Maria *Fest,anthem
[Lat] mix cor oct NOVELLO MS-2 s.p. (P1930)
(Gottron, Adam) [Lat] SATB,opt soli,cont
(med) MULLER MS 2 s.p.   (P1931)

Dix Maria Quid Vidisti *Psntd
(Gottron, Adam) [Ger] SATB,cont (med)
MULLER LS 17 s.p.   (P1932)

PLAY OF DANIEL, THE *13th cent
(Greenberg, Noah) mix cor,
SSSSTTTBarBarBarBarBB soli,orch (med easy)
sc OXFORD 94.600 $3.95, rental   (P1933)

PLAY OF HEROD *12th cent
(Greenberg, Noah; Smoldon, W.L.) mix cor,
soli,inst (med easy) sc OXFORD 94.602
$4.00, rental   (P1934)

PLAY YOUR HARPS see Santa Cruz, Domingo, Toquen
Arpas Y Guitarras

PLAYFORD
Sing Ye With Praise
(Ehret) SATB oct PRO ART 2510 $.25 (P1935)

PLAYFORD, JOHN (1623-1686)
We Sing To Thee
(Couper, A.) SATB oct PRESSER 352-00444
$.30   (P1936)
(Couper, A.) SA oct PRESSER 352-00444 $.30
(P1937)

PLAYFUL SHEPHERD, THE see Serly, Tibor

PLAYN SONG see Taverner, John

PLEAD MY CAUSE, O LORD see McCullough

PLEAD THOU MY CAUSE see Mozart, Wolfgang
Amadeus

PLEASE PORRIDGE HOT see Simpson, Kenneth

PLEASE STOP RUNNING AWAY FROM GOD see Paris

PLEASURE IT IS see Cope, Cecil

PLEASURE IT IS TO HEAR see Forbes, Sebastian

PLEBS ANGELICA see Tippett, Michael

PLEGARIA A LA VIRGEN see Alvarez

PLEGARIA A LA VIRGEN see Franco

PLEGARIA A LA VIRGEN &E MONTSERRAT see Alvarez

PLEGARIA A LA VIRGIN see Franco

PLENI SUNT COELI see Des Prez, Josquin

PLENI SUNT COELI see Palestrina, Giovanni

PLENTY GOOD ROOM *spir
(Charles, G.) SSA LEONARD-US 08051920 $.25
(P1938)
(Hardwicke) SA ALFRED 6542 $.30 (P1939)
(Hardwicke) SAB ALFRED 6520 $.30 (P1940)

PLETTNER, A.
Away In A Manger *Xmas,carol
SATB,org AMP A191 $.25   (P1941)
SSA,org AMP A313 $.20   (P1942)

Fanfare For Christmas Day *Xmas
SATB,org AMP A305 $.30   (P1943)

PLEYEL, IGNAZ JOSEPH (1757-1831)
Children Of The Heavenly King *Gen
(Walton) SA SCHMITT 2565 $.30   (P1944)

Gentle Jesus, Meek And Mild
(Roff) SA/TB SHAWNEE E21 $.25   (P1945)

PLORANS PLORAVIT see Correa, Carlos

PLORATE, FILII ISRAEL see Carissimi, Giacomo

PLUISTER, SIMON (1913-)
De Emmausgangers *Bibl
[Dut] men cor&jr cor,TTBarB soli,hpsd,fl,
ob,clar,bsn,trp,horn,trom,strings,perc,
celeste min sc DONEMUS s.p.   (P1946)

Jesaja IX: 1-6 *Bibl
[Dut] men cor,orch DONEMUS min sc s.p., cor
pts s.p.   (P1947)

Psalm 137
[Ger] mix cor,SATBarB soli,4fl,3ob,3clar,
3bsn,3trp,4horn,3trom,tuba,strings,perc,
timp,2harp, celeste min sc DONEMUS s.p.
(P1948)

Psalm 138
[Dut] mix cor,SATB soli,3fl,3ob,3clar,3bsn,
3trp,4horn,3trom,tuba,strings,perc,timp,
2harp, celeste min sc DONEMUS s.p.
(P1949)

PLUM, P.-J.-M.
Crux Fidelis *Mass
3 eq voices,org LEMOINE voc sc s.p., cor
pts s.p.   (P1950)

PLUMPTRE
Rejoice, Ye Pure In Heart
(Vandre) SAB oct BELWIN 60524 $.30 (P1951)

PLUNG'D IN THE CONFINES OF DESPAIR see Purcell,
Henry

PLUS NE SUIS CE QUE J'AI ETE see Crawford, John

PO' MO'NER GOT A HOME AT LAS' see Johnson, Hall

POCH, GAIL (1936-)
Alleluia
SATB STANDARD B301MX1 $.45   (P1952)

POEM AND ALLELUIA FOR THE CHRIST CHILD see
Lehr, M.

POHLE, DAVID (1624-1695)
Herr, Wenn Ich Nur Dich Habe
(Moser, H.J.) SSB,cont,bsn,2vln,vcl,bvl
HANSSLER 10.198 sc s.p., voc sc s.p., ipa
(P1953)

POHLMANN, HELEN FRYFOGLE
Sing Noel! *Xmas
SATB,acap (med) oct WILLIS 7031 $.18 (P1954)

POLIFONIA ESPANOLA. VOL. I see Morales,
Cristobal de

POLIFONIA ESPANOLA. VOL. I *CC40L,BVM/Xmas
(Rubio) [Span] 3-5pt,acap UNION ESP. 19015
$6.50 contains works by: Encina; Baena;
Escobar; Alonso; Guerrero; Cabezon; Comes;
and anonymous works   (P1955)

POLIFONIA ESPANOLA. VOL. II *CC39L
(Rubio) [Span] 3-5pt UNION ESP. 19026 $8.00
contains works by: Guerrero; Torre; Comes;
Tafalla; Ponce; Langa; Troya; Vargas;
Baena; Encina; Morata, and anonymous works
(P1956)

POLIFONISTI VENETI *sac/sec,CC24U
(Pasut, Bruno) 3-4pt ZANIBON 4598 s.p.
contains works by: Pera, G.; Croce, G.;
Donato, B.; Nasco, G.; Ruffo, V.; Gabrieli,
A.; Bell'Haver, V.   (P1957)

POLIFRONE, J.J.
Canticles For Christmas *Xmas,cant
SATB FLAMMER A5276 $1.25   (P1958)

POLISH EASTER CAROL *Easter,Pol
(Caldwell, Mary E.) SATB&desc oct GRAY
GCMR 2778 $.40   (P1959)
(Caldwell, Mary E.) SA oct GRAY GCMR 2740
$.35   (P1960)

POLISH EASTER CAROL see Caldwell

POLISH LAMENTATIONS *CCU,Lent,Pol,17th cent/
18th cent
(Mrowiec, K.) cor,inst POLSKIE ZHMP15 s.p.
(P1961)

POLISH TUNE,
see Hark To The Angels

POLLERI, GIO. BATTA.
Sacerdotes Domini *Commun
[Lat] unis ZANIBON 2775 s.p.   (P1962)

POLZER, ODO
Es Hat Sich Eroffnet Das Himmlische Tor
*Gen,cradle,Aus
[Ger] SATB&SSA,narrator,SATB soli,orch
(med) MULLER SM 886 voc sc s.p., cor pts
s.p.   (P1963)

Heilig-Jahr-Messe *folk/Mass
(Beer, N.) unis,pno/org (easy) cor pts
LEUCKART s.p.   (P1964)

Missa Festiva *Mass
mix cor,acap/org/2trp&2horn&2trom
WEINBERGER s.p., ipa sc, voc sc, cor pts
s.p.   (P1965)

Sacerdotes Ejus *Gradual
mix cor,acap WEINBERGER s.p., ipa sc, cor
pts contains also: Veritas Mea (Offer)
(P1966)

Veritas Mea
see Polzer, Odo, Sacerdotes Ejus

POMMER, HELMUT
Christkindl-Wiegenlied
[Ger] mix cor,acap KRENN 93 s.p. (P1967)

Uns Ist Gebor'n Ein Kindelein *Xmas
[Ger] mix cor,acap KRENN 88 s.p. (P1968)

POMPER, A.
Het Gebed Des Heeren
mix cor ALSBACH&D sc s.p., cor pts s.p.
(P1969)

POND, S.B.
Be Joyful In God *Bibl
(Brandon, George) SA&desc,org oct WORLD
CA-1937-2 $.45   (P1970)

PONDER MY WORDS see Walmisley, Thomas Attwood

PONDER MY WORDS, O LORD see Kelly, Bryan

PONDER MY WORDS, O LORD see Schutz, Heinrich

PONSONBY, NOEL
Go Not Far From Me, O God *anthem
SATB,acap CRAMER A 1 s.p.   (P1971)

Service In D *Commun
SATB CRAMER A10 s.p.   (P1972)

PONT
Lord's Prayer *anthem
unis sc OXFORD 40.019 $2.50, ipa, cor pts
OXFORD 40.020 $.35, ipa   (P1973)

PONZILACQUA
Regina Coeli
see QUATTRO ANTIFONE MARIANE

POOL, K.
God Is My Strong Salvation
SATB oct WORD CS-671 $.25   (P1974)

God So Loved The World
SATB oct WORD CS-2372 $.35   (P1975)

POOLE-CONNOR, DAVID
If Ye Then Be Risen *Easter,anthem
mix cor oct NOVELLO 40.1237.02 s.p. (P1976)

POOLER
If I Take The Wings Of The Morning (Psalm
139)
SATB,acap oct PRO ART 2418 $.25 (P1977)

Psalm 139 *see If I Take The Wings Of The
Morning

So Far To Bethlehem
SA FLAMMER E5011 $1.10   (P1978)

Thanks Be To God *Gen
SATB&unis SCHMITT 15017 $.35   (P1979)

Wondrous Love *Lent
unis oct SOUTHERN $.25   (P1980)

POOLER, FRANK
Christmas Lullaby
see TWO CHRISTMAS SONGS FOR UNISON CHOIR

Gethsemane *anthem
SATB (med) oct AUGSBURG 1225 $.20 (P1981)

Gird Yourself With Lamentations
TTBB oct AGAPE MM 9009 $.30   (P1982)

Gud Regjerer
men cor MUSIKK 184 s.p.   (P1983)

Lord Keep Us Steadfast *Gen/Refm
SA&SATB,kbd (med easy) oct CONCORDIA
98-1161 $.25   (P1984)

Man Of Sorrows *anthem
unis treb cor&TB (easy) oct AUGSBURG 1082
$.25   (P1985)

Mountains Of God, The *Gen
SATB SCHMITT 852 $.20   (P1986)

My Peace I Give *Gen
SATB SCHMITT 866 $.30   (P1987)

Praise Him With Trumpets
SATB oct WALTON 2907 $.30   (P1988)

Ride On In Majesty *see Pooler, Marie

Rising Sun, The (composed with Pierce, Brent)
SATB oct AGAPE CE 4328 $.75   (P1989)

Thou Art Worthy *anthem
SATB (med) oct AUGSBURG 1187 $.30 (P1990)

We Will Rock You *Xmas
SATB,opt kbd oct KERBY 6603 $.30 (P1991)
SATB,acap oct KERBY 6603C $.30   (P1992)

POOLER, MARIE
Carol For The King *Xmas,carol
SATB oct WALTON 2172 $.35   (P1993)

Children Of The Heavenly Father
SATB FLAMMER A 5123 $.30   (P1994)
SA (easy) ABINGDON APM-705 $.20 (P1995)

Children's Choir Book *CC9L
unis (easy) oct AUGSBURG 11-9125 $1.00
(P1996)

December Song
see TWO CHRISTMAS SONGS FOR UNISON CHOIR

Everlasting Light
SATB oct WALTON 2173 $.35   (P1997)

Festival Hymns With Descants *CC7L,Fest,hymn
cor&cong,org (easy) oct AUGSBURG 11-9181
$1.00   (P1998)

Good Shepherd, The *Lent,cant
jr cor (easy) ABINGDON APM-553 $.65 (P1999)

Hosanna *anthem
SA (easy) oct AUGSBURG 1405 $.25 (P2000)

Hosanna Now Through Advent *anthem
SA (easy) oct AUGSBURG 1439 $.25 (P2001)

POOLER, MARIE (cont'd.)

Praise The Lord
SATB oct GRAY GCMR 2644 $.30 (P2002)

Prepare The Way, O Zion
SAB oct KERBY 6051C $.35 (P2003)

Ride On In Majesty (composed with Pooler, Frank) *anthem
SATB&jr cor (easy) oct AUGSBURG 1151 $.25 (P2004)

Unison And Two-Part Anthems *CC18L,anthem
unis jr cor&opt 2pt jr cor (easy) oct
AUGSBURG 11-9517 $1.35 (P2005)

Unison Hymns With Descants *CC10L,anthem/hymn
jr cor/sr cor oct AUGSBURG 11-9518 $1.00 (P2006)

POOR AND NEEDY, THE see Sateren, Leland Bernhard

POOR LI'L JESUS *Xmas
(Ehret, W.) SATB oct PRESSER 312-40541 $.30 (P2007)

POOR LITTLE JESUS *spir
(Ehret) SSA MARKS 4357 $.25 (P2008)

POOR MARY see Davis, Katherine K.

POOR MOURNER *spir
(Shaw; Parker) mix cor,T solo,acap oct LAWSON 51102 $.25 (P2009)

POOR WAYFARIN' STRANGER
(Terri, Salli) SATB,SA soli,acap oct LAWSON 831 $.30 (P2010)

POOR WAYFARIN' STRANGER see Martin

POOR WAYFARIN' STRANGER see Schroth

POOR WAYFARING STRANGER *spir
(Lynn, G.) SATB,acap oct PRESSER 312-40111 $.30 (P2011)
(Williamson, W.) SA LEONARD-US 08052000 $.25 (P2012)
(Williamson, W.) SSA LEONARD-US 08052160 $.25 (P2013)

POOS, HEINRICH (1928-)
Christe Du Bist Der Helle Tag *Gen
[Ger] SATB,opt org&ob (med) BAREN. BA 3268 s.p. (P2014)

Christus In Die Welt
see Poos, Heinrich, So Nicht War Gekommen

Das Vater Unser
4pt,org HANSSLER 7.097 s.p. (P2015)

Der Tag, Der Ist So Freudenreich
SAT/SAB,2treb inst,kbd HANSSLER 14.018 s.p.
contains also: Ein Kindelein So Lobelich (P2016)

Deutsche Messe *Mass
mix cor sc HANSSLER 15.102 s.p. (P2017)

Ein Kindelein So Lobelich
see Poos, Heinrich, Der Tag, Der Ist So Freudenreich

Heilger Geist, Du Troster Mein *No.101,Asc/Pent,mot
[Ger] 3pt mix cor,org BAREN. EM 450 sc s.p., cor pts s.p. see from EVANGELISCHES KIRCHENGESANGBUCH (P2018)

Herr Christ, Der Einig Gotts Sohn *cant
unis/S,org,fl HANSSLER 10.121 sc s.p., voc sc s.p., ipa (P2019)

Herr, Dein Wort Ist Meines Fusses Leuchte *Gen
[Ger] 2 eq voices&opt men cor,acap BAREN. BA 4968 s.p. (P2020)

Herr, Du Hast Worte Des Ewigen Lebens *Gen
[Ger] SA&men cor,acap (med) BAREN. BA 4942 s.p. (P2021)

Ich Bin Der Weg Und Die Wahrheit Und Das Leben *Gen
[Ger] 2 eq voices,opt inst (easy) BAREN. BA 4967 s.p. (P2022)

Komm, Heiliger Geist *mot
[Ger] SA&men cor&unis/SA&men cor,inst (med) BAREN. BA 3270 s.p. (P2023)

Nimm Von Uns, Herr, Du Treuer Gott *cant
SAB,org HANSSLER 10.099 sc s.p., voc sc s.p. (P2024)

Nun Danket All
mix cor HANSSLER 14.231 s.p. (P2025)

Nun Danket Alle Gott *mot
SSATTB,acap TONGER s.p. (P2026)

O Susser Herre Jesu Christ
S/SA/SAT/SAB,treb inst&kbd/2treb inst HANSSLER 14.047 contains also: Linke, Norbert, O Susser Herre Jesu Christ (SA/men cor,treb inst/bass inst) (P2027)

Schmuckt Das Fest Mit Maien
SA/SAT,treb inst HANSSLER 14.107 s.p. (P2028)
ST/SB,kbd/2treb inst HANSSLER 14.107 s.p. (P2029)

So Nicht War Gekommen *Psntd,mot
[Ger] 1-5pt mix cor,acap cor pts BAREN. EM 462 s.p. contains also: Christus In Die Welt (P2030)

Uns Ist Ein Kind Geboren
SAT/SAB HANSSLER 14.601 s.p. contains also: Poser, Hans, Siehe, Dein Heil Kommt (P2031)

Wir Glauben Gott Im Hochsten Thorn *mot
(Schroeder, R.A.) SATB sc HANSSLER 15.101 s.p. (P2032)

Wir Wollen Alle Frohlich Sein *No.82, Easter
[Ger] 4pt mix cor,org,fl,ob (choral partita) BAREN. EM 232 s.p. see from EVANGELISCHES KIRCHENGESANGBUCH (P2033)

POOS, HEINRICH (cont'd.)

Wo Willst Du Hin, Weils Abend Ist *Easter/Eve
[Ger] 4pt mix cor&3 cor/4pt mix cor,3 soli, org,2vln,vla,vcl,bvl BAREN. EM 154 sc s.p., cor pts s.p., ipa (P2034)

POPESCO
Liturghia Sf. Joan Christomul
[Rum] SATB,acap oct SALABERT-US $16.00 (P2035)

POPS WITH A PURPOSE see Blake, Rev. Canon, E.C.

POPULAR PSALM SETTINGS see Wills, Arthur

POPULARSERIE NR. 2 *sac/sec,CC7L
(Kristoffersen, Dag) 3pt,pno NORDISKA s.p. contains works by: Arne; Winkler; Hill; and others (P2036)

POPULARSERIE NR. 3 *sac/sec,CC7L
(Kristoffersen, Dag) 3pt,pno NORDISKA s.p. contains works by: Morley; Adam De La Hale; Bizet; and others (P2037)

POPULARSERIE NR. 4 *sac/sec,CC8L
(Kristoffersen, Dag) 3pt,pno NORDISKA s.p. contains works by: Buxtehude; Mozart; Brahms; and others (P2038)

POPULARSERIE NR. 6 *sac/sec,CC7L
(Kristoffersen, Dag) 3pt,pno NORDISKA s.p. contains works by: Hassler; Bach; Martini; and others (P2039)

POPULE MEUS see Bianchini, Carlo

POPULE MEUS see Bottazzo, Luigi

POPULE MEUS see Corradini, Vasco Lodovico

POPULE MEUS see Palestrina, Giovanni

POPULE MEUS see Serra, Louis Maria

POPULE MEUS see Strickling

POPULE MEUS see Victoria, Tomas Luis de

POPULE MEUS see Vittoria, Ludovico

POPULUS SION see Olman, Isr, J.

POR DEBAJO DEL LAUREL see Martin Pompey

PORENA, BORIS (1927-)
Der Gott Und Die Bajadere
mix cor,SBar soli,orch voc sc ZERBONI 6471 s.p., ipr (P2040)

Ueber Aller Dieser Deiner Trauer *cant
mix cor,SB soli,orch voc sc ZERBONI 6618 rental (P2041)

PORPORA, NICOLA ANTONIO (1686-1768)
Credidi *mot
(Hyde, D.E.) [Lat] SSAA,org,strings voc sc NOVELLO 20.1042.10 s.p. (P2042)

Laetatus Sum
(David) [Lat] SSAA,orch MARKS $1.50, ipr (P2043)

Lauda Jerusalem
(Hunter) [Lat] SSAA,orch MARKS $1.25, ipr (P2044)

Magnificat
(Hunter) [Lat] SSAA,orch MARKS $1.25 (P2045)

PORTA
O Sacrum Convivium
(Ruiz) [Lat] 4pt men cor,acap RICORDI-ARG BA 10490 s.p. (P2046)

Regina Caeli
(Ruiz) [Lat] 4pt men cor,acap RICORDI-ARG BA 10491 s.p. (P2047)

PORTA, COSTANZO (1529-1601)
Conceptio Tua *Fest,mot
[Lat] SATB,acap (med) MULLER M 46 s.p. (P2048)
[Lat] mix cor,acap oct NOVELLO DM-46 s.p. (P2049)

Hodie Nobis De Caelo *Xmas,mot
[Lat] SATB,acap (med) MULLER M 5 s.p. (P2050)
[Lat] mix cor,acap oct NOVELLO DM-5 s.p. (P2051)

Missa La-Sol-Fa-Re-Mi *Mass
(Mischiati) 6pt mix cor MOSELER s.p. (P2052)

Vidi Turbam Magnam *ASD/ECY,mot
[Lat] SATB,acap (med) MULLER M 42 s.p. (P2053)
[Lat] mix cor oct NOVELLO DM-42 s.p. (P2054)

PORTER
Alleluia! Christ Is Born *Xmas
SSA oct SPRATT 302 $.20 (P2055)
SATB oct SPRATT 309 $.25 (P2056)

Blessed Are The Meek *Gen,Bibl
SATB oct SPRATT 308 $.25 (P2057)

Christmas Lullaby, A *Xmas
SATB oct SPRATT 307 $.30 (P2058)

Lord Is My Shepherd, The *Gen
SATB oct SPRATT 303 $.25 (P2059)

O Clap' Your Hands *Gen
SATB SCHMITT 662 $.35 (P2060)

Praise Ye The Lord *Gen
SATB oct SPRATT 306 $.25 (P2061)

Silence Of God, The
SATB oct LORENZ 9930 $.30 (P2062)

Tidings Of Comfort And Joy *Xmas,cant
SATB oct LORENZ 9934 (P2063)

Whence Comes This Rush Of Wings Afar?
SATB FLAMMER A5327 $.30 (P2064)

PORTER, STEVEN
Creation, The *see Bobrowitz, David

PORTER, WALTER (ca. 1595-1659)
O Thou To Whose All Searching Sight *Gen
SAB,2vln (med easy) oct CONCORDIA 98-1946 $.25 (P2065)

PORTRATET see Boldemann, Laci

POSCHIO, ISAAC (ca. 1623?)
Auf Dich, Herr, Steht Mein Vertrauen
(Horn) unis,cont HANSSLER 5.124 s.p. (P2066)

POSCHL, A.
Dreikonigslied *CC3U
[Ger] 3pt men cor/3pt wom cor KRENN 109 s.p. (P2067)

POSEGATE
Accursed Tree, The
SATB SHAWNEE A 657 $.30 (P2068)

Came The Wise Men *Xmas
SATB KJOS 5323 $.30 (P2069)

Christmas Glory *Xmas
SATB SHAWNEE A 871 $.30 (P2070)

Consider The Lilies
SATB oct VOLKWEIN VB138 $.30 (P2071)

Dost Thou In A Manger Lie *Xmas
SATB oct VOLKWEIN VB143 $.25 (P2072)

Empty Tomb, The
SATB SHAWNEE A 658 $.30 (P2073)

Farefare For Thanksgiving *Thanks
SATB FLAMMER A 5052 $.30 (P2074)

Gift Of Love, The
SATB SHAWNEE A 713 $.30 (P2075)
SSA SHAWNEE B 234 $.30 (P2076)

God Is With Us
SATB FLAMMER A 5581 $.30 (P2077)

Hosanna *Easter
SATB oct VOLKWEIN VB171 $.25 (P2078)

How Excellent Is Thy Name
SATB oct VOLKWEIN VB172 $.25 (P2079)

I'm A Pilgrim
SATB SHAWNEE A 785 $.25 (P2080)

In A Manger *Xmas
SATB oct VOLKWEIN VB183 $.25 (P2081)

Lord God Answered Job
SATB oct VOLKWEIN VB723 $.25 (P2082)

Lord, Thou Hast Searched Me
SATB oct VOLKWEIN VB212 $.25 (P2083)

Procession To Jerusalem, The
SATB SHAWNEE A 656 $.30 (P2084)

Still Prayer Of Devotion, The
SATB,acap SHAWNEE A 959 $.30 (P2085)

Thou Shalt Call His Name Jesus
SATB oct VOLKWEIN VB706 $.30 (P2086)

To The Holy Child
SATB SHAWNEE A 1087 $.30 (P2087)

Woodland Hymn *hymn
SATB oct VOLKWEIN VB281 $.25 (P2088)

POSEGATE, MAXCINE W.
God Of The Universe
SATB oct AGAPE CH 656 $.30 (P2089)

Holy, Lord Of Hosts *Xmas
SATB oct AGAPE A 832 $.30 (P2090)

Lead On Softly, Lord
SATB oct AGAPE HO 1802 $.30 (P2091)

Spanish Lullaby *Span
SA oct AGAPE SP 683 $.30 (P2092)

POSER, HANS (1917-1970)
Ach Bleib Bei Uns
see Wagner, Alexander, Herr, Fur Dein Wort

Christe, Du Schopfer Aller Welt
SST/SSB,bass inst HANSSLER 14.072 s.p. contains also: Zillinger, Erwin, O Traurigkeit, O Herzeleid (SST/SSB,bass inst) (P2093)

Da Jesus An Dem Kreuze Stund *Psntd,mot
[Ger] 3 eq voices&3pt mix cor,acap (med easy) BAREN. BA 2276 s.p. contains also: O Welt, Sieh Hier Dein Leben (3pt mix cor) (P2094)

Die Ostergeschichte *Easter
[Ger] 2pt jr cor,2fl,vcl,opt org&vla (easy) BAREN. BA 2895 sc $3.00, cor pts $1.25, ipa (P2095)

Komm, Heiliger Geist, Herre Gott
SAT/SAB HANSSLER 14.098 s.p. contains also: Barbe, Helmut, Nun Bitten Wir Den Heiligen Geist (SS/ST,treb inst) (P2096)

Lobet Den Herren, Denn Er Ist Sehr Freundlich *Gen
[Ger] 2-5pt mix cor,acap (med) BAREN. BA 4956 $.40 (P2097)

O Heiland, Reiss Die Himmel Auf *mot
5pt mix cor MOSELER s.p. (P2098)

O Welt, Sieh Hier Dein Leben
see Poser, Hans, Da Jesus An Dem Kreuze Stund

Requiem *Req
4-12pt mix cor MOSELER s.p. (P2099)

Siehe, Dein Heil Kommt
see Poos, Heinrich, Uns Ist Ein Kind Geboren

POSER, HANS (cont'd.)

Singt, Singt Dem Herren Neue Lieder *Easter/
Pent
[Ger] 3pt mix cor&jr cor,acap (med) BAREN.
BA 4956 $.40   (P2100)

Wenn Meine Sund Mich Kranken
see Gadsch, Herbert, Wenn Meine Sund Mich
Kranken

Wie Soll Ich Dich Empfangen
SA/men cor,treb inst HANSSLER 14.010 s.p.
contains also: Fiebig, Kurt, Gott Sei
Dank Durch Alle Welt (SAT/SAB,bass inst)
(P2101)

POSSIBLY, PROBABLY see Avery

POST NATIVITATEM DOMINI see Byrd, William

POST PASCHA see Byrd, William

POST SEPTUAGESIMA see Byrd, William

POSTEL, C.M.
I Hold The Kingdom *Gen,anthem
SSA (easy) oct GIA G1381 $.25   (P2102)

POSTHUMA, D.
Lenteavond
mix cor ALSBACH&D sc s.p., cor pts s.p.
(P2103)

POSTON, ELIZABETH (1905-   )
Happy Are Thy Men *Gen,Bibl
SATB/unis (easy) oct OXFORD 40.915 $.25
(P2104)

Sing Unto The Lord *Gen,Bibl
SATB (med) oct OXFORD 42.826 $.35   (P2105)

POSTQUAM CALIX BABILONIS see Reiss, Georg

POSTREMUM VESPERTINI OFFICII OPUS see Rhaw,
Georg

POSTULA A ME see Pressmann, W.

POTHAST, ED.
Oud Kerstlied
mix cor ALSBACH&D sc s.p., cor pts s.p.
(P2106)

POTIRON, H.
Messe Da Pacem *Mass
[Lat] 4pt mix cor,org voc sc DURAND s.p.
(P2107)

POTTER
O Lord, Be Merciful *Gen
SATB SCHMITT 1782 $.20   (P2108)

Supplication *Gen
SATB SCHMITT 1725 $.20   (P2109)

POULENC, FRANCIS (1899-1963)
Ave Maria *BVM
SSA BELWIN AP 51 $.30   (P2110)

Ave Verum Corpus
[Lat] SSA oct SALABERT-US $.65   (P2111)

Beholding The Star *see Videntes Stella

Born Today Is Christ *see Hodie Natus
Christus Est

Darkness Fell Upon The Earth *see Tenebrae
Factae Sunt

Exultate Deo
[Lat] SATB,acap oct SALABERT-US $.75
(P2112)

Gloria *cant/Gloria
[Eng/Lat] cor,S solo,orch SALABERT-US voc
sc $14.25, cor pts $2.25   (P2113)

Great Fear And Trembling Have Taken Hold Of
Me *see Timor Et Tremor Venerunt Super
Me

Hodie Christus Natus Est *Xmas
mix cor SOUTHERN $.50   (P2114)

Hodie Natus Christus Est *Xmas,mot
"Born Today Is Christ" [Eng/Lat] SATB,acap
oct SALABERT-US $.65 see from Quatre
Motets Pour Un Temps De Noel   (P2115)

Laudes De St. Antoine De Padoue *Morn
[Lat] TBB oct SALABERT-US $.75   (P2116)

Litanies A La Vierge Noire (Notre-Dame De
Roc-Amadour) *CCU,BVM,hymn
[Fr] wom cor/jr cor,orch oct DURAND s.p.,
ipr   (P2117)

Messe In G Major *Mass
[Lat] SATB,acap oct SALABERT-US $2.25
(P2118)

O Magnum Mysterium *Xmas,mot
"Oh How Great The Mystery" [Eng/Lat] SATB,
acap oct SALABERT-US $.65 see from Quatre
Motets Pour Un Temps De Noel   (P2119)

Oh How Great The Mystery *see O Magnum
Mysterium

Quatre Motets Pour Un Temps De Noel *see
Hodie Natus Christus Est, "Born Today Is
Christ"; O Magnum Mysterium, "Oh How
Great The Mystery"; Quem Vidistis
Pastores Dicite, "Whom Have You Seen,
Shepherds?"; Videntes Stellam, "Beholding
The Star"   (P2120)

Quatre Motets Pour Un Temps De Penitence
*see Tenebrae Factae Sunt, "Darkness Fell
Upon The Earth"; Timor Et Tremor Venerunt
Super Me, "Great Fear And Trembling Have
Taken Hold Of Me"; Tristis Est Animae
Mea, "Sad Is My Soul"; Vinea Mea Electa,
"Vine That I Have Chosen As My Own"   (P2121)

Quem Vidistis Pastores Dicite *Xmas,mot
"Whom Have You Seen, Shepherds?" [Eng/Lat]
SATB,acap oct SALABERT-US $.65 see from
Quatre Motets Pour Un Temps De Noel
(P2122)

Sad Is My Soul *see Tristis Est Animae Mea

POULENC, FRANCIS (cont'd.)

Salve Regina
[Lat] SATB,acap oct SALABERT-US $.75   (P2123)

Sept Repons De Tenebres *CC7U
[Lat] boy cor&men cor,S solo,orch SALABERT-
US voc sc $14.25, cor pts $2.25   (P2124)

Stabat Mater
[Lat] SATBB,S solo,orch SALABERT-US voc sc
$15.50, cor pts $2.25   (P2125)

Tenebrae Factae Sunt *Lent,mot
"Darkness Fell Upon The Earth" [Eng/Lat]
SAATB oct SALABERT-US $.65 see from
Quatre Motets Pour Un Temps De Penitence
(P2126)

Timor Et Tremor Venerunt Super Me *Lent,mot
"Great Fear And Trembling Have Taken Hold
Of Me" [Eng/Lat] SATB,acap oct SALABERT-
US $.65 see from Quatre Motets Pour Un
Temps De Penitence   (P2127)

Tristis Est Animae Mea *Lent,mot
"Sad Is My Soul" [Eng/Lat] SATB,S solo oct
SALABERT-US $.65 see from Quatre Motets
Pour Un Temps De Penitence   (P2128)

Videntes Stellam *Xmas,mot
"Beholding The Star" [Eng/Lat] SATB,acap
oct SALABERT-US $.65 see from Quatre
Motets Pour Un Temps De Noel   (P2129)

Vine That I Have Chosen As My Own *see Vinea
Mea Electa

Vinea Mea Electa *Lent,mot
"Vine That I Have Chosen As My Own" [Eng/
Lat] SAATBB oct SALABERT-US $.65 see from
Quatre Motets Pour Un Temps De Penitence
(P2130)

Whom Have You Seen, Shepherds? *see Quem
Vidistis Pastores Dicite

POUR FORTH THY SPIRIT see Tallis, Thomas

POUR INTO OUR HEARTS see Roff, Joseph

POUR LA FETE DE LA PENTECOTE see Veni Creator

POUR LA FETE DES VOEUX D'UNE SOEUR DE CHARITE
see Gigout, [Eugene]

POUR LA FETE DU SAINT NOM DE JESUS see Jesu
Dulcis

POUR LE JOUR DE NOEL see Puer Natus In Bethleem

POUR LE JOUR DE PACQUES see Surexit Christus
Hodie

POUR LE TEMPS DE L'AVENT see Veni Redemptor
Gentium

POUR NE LANGUIR see Saboly, Nicholas, Per Noun
Langui

POUR RESTER HUMBLE see Cant You Live Humble

POUR VOUS BENIR, SEIGNEUR see Saint-Saens,
Camille

POVERTY see Suitor, M. Lee

POWELL
All Praise To Thee *Gen
SATB oct SPRATT 577 $.25   (P2131)

All They From Saba Shall Come
mix cor SOUTHERN $.30   (P2132)

Ancient Of Days
SAB/SATB SCHMITT 8007 $.25   (P2133)

As Pants The Hart *Gen
SATB oct SPRATT 579 $.25   (P2134)

Blessed Lord Of Heaven Above *Gen
SA SCHMITT 2570 $.25   (P2135)

Drop, Drop Slow Tears *Easter
SATB oct SACRED S-133 $.35   (P2136)

Hark! The Glad Sound
SA/TB FLAMMER E5155 $.25   (P2137)

I Call With My Whole Heart
SATB,acap WARNER WB-157 $.30   (P2138)

I Will Sing Of The Mercies Of The Lord
SATB oct SACRED S-45 $.35   (P2139)

Jesus, My Lord, My God, My All
SATB oct SACRED S-77 $.35   (P2140)

Joyfully Sing *CCU
2pt FISCHER,C O-4850 $1.25   (P2141)

Let Thy Love Flow Down
SAB oct SACRED S-7403 $.35   (P2142)

Little Child On Earth Has Been Born *Xmas
unis,fl SOUTHERN $.30   (P2143)

Lord Ascendeth Up On High
SAB KJOS 5726 $.30   (P2144)

Lord My Shepherd Is, The
see Two Unison Anthems

My Delight Is In The Lord
SAB oct BELWIN 64306 $.30   (P2145)

O Be Joyful In The Lord
SATB (med diff/diff) SOUTHERN $.30   (P2146)

O For A Heart To Praise My God! *Gen
SATB SCHMITT SD6209 $.25   (P2147)

O Give Thanks
SATB oct SACRED S-48 $.35   (P2148)

O God, Thy Church Eternal
SATB KJOS 5842 $.30   (P2149)

O Quam Gloriosum *Gen
SATB SCHMITT SD6203 $.20   (P2150)

POWELL (cont'd.)

On Christmas Night All Christians Sing *Xmas
unis,fl SOUTHERN $.30   (P2151)

Our Lord Is Risen *Easter
SATB oct SACRED S-119 $.40   (P2152)

Praise The Lord, All Ye Nations
SAB oct BELWIN 64310 $.30   (P2153)

Psalm 13
SATB oct SACRED E83 $.35   (P2154)

Savior Of The Nations
SATB KJOS 5843 $.30   (P2155)

See The Conqueror
SAB KJOS 5714 $.30   (P2156)

Sing We *canon
unis&desc/2pt&desc WARNER WB-167 $.30 (P2157)

Soon May The Last Glad Song Arise
SAB oct BELWIN 64311 $.30   (P2158)

Surely The Lord Is In This Place
SATB oct SACRED E71 $.35   (P2159)

They That Know Thy Name *Gen
SAB/SATB SCHMITT 8011 $.35   (P2160)

To Worship, Work And Witness
SATB KJOS 5844 $.35   (P2161)

Twelve Folk Hymns *CC12U,folk/hymn
(Buchanan) BELWIN $1.25   (P2162)

Two Unison Anthems *Gen
unis SCHMITT 218 $.30
contains: Lord My Shepherd Is, The; We
Love The Place, O God   (P2163)

We Love The Place, O God
see Two Unison Anthems

POWELL, C.T.
Benedicite (Shortened Form)
SATB (F maj) oct NOVELLO s.p.   (P2164)

While The Earth Remaineth *Harv,anthem
mix cor oct NOVELLO s.p.   (P2165)

POWELL, R.
Can You Count The Stars
unis,pno/org oct KERBY 6352 $.30   (P2166)

Creator Of The Stars Of Night *Adv
SATB oct GRAY GCMR 3103 $.35   (P2167)

O Love How Deep, How Broad, How High
SAB,opt kbd oct KERBY 6408 $.35   (P2168)

POWELL, RICH
Peace, Peace (composed with Powell, Sylvia)
*Xmas
(Bock, Fred) 3pt (easy) PRESSER $.35 (P2169)

POWELL, ROBERT J.
Can You Count The Stars?
unis oct KERBY 6352C $.30   (P2170)

Choral Psalmist, The *see Butler, Eugene

Choral Thanksgiving, A *Thanks
SATB oct BOURNE 838 $.35   (P2171)

Christ Is Our Cornerstone *anthem
SATB (med) oct AUGSBURG 1377 $.25   (P2172)

Christ Is The World's True Light
SATB oct GRAY GCMR 3223 $.25   (P2173)

Christ The Lord, Is Risen Again *Easter
4pt mix cor,acap oct SCHIRM.G 11085 $.25
(P2174)

Comprehending The Other Person
SAB oct AGAPE SP 695 $.30   (P2175)

Eternal Ruler Of The Ceaseless Round *Gen/
Pent
SATB,acap (med diff) oct CONCORDIA 98-1667
$.30   (P2176)

Festival Anthems For SAB *CCU,Fest,anthem
SAB (med) oct ABINGDON APM-535 $1.50 (P2177)

Five Narrative Carols *CC5U,carol
SSA,inst oct SUMMY B 1616 $1.00   (P2178)

From The Rising Of The Sun *Xmas
SATB (easy) ABINGDON APM-116 $.22   (P2179)

God Be Merciful Unto Us *Gen/Lent
SATB,acap (med easy) oct CONCORDIA 98-1670
$.25   (P2180)

God Is My Strong Salvation *anthem
SAB (med) oct AUGSBURG 1378 $.25   (P2181)

Hear Us, Holy Jesus
SA oct BELWIN 64305 $.30   (P2182)

If Ye Then Be Risen *Easter
SSATB,opt acap (med) ABINGDON APM-275 $.25
(P2183)

Jesus! Name Of Wondrous Love
SATB (med) ABINGDON APM-120 $.35   (P2184)

Let All The People Praise Thee *Ded/Gen
SA,kbd (easy) oct CONCORDIA 98-1973 $.25
(P2185)

Let Saints On Earth *ASD
SATB (easy) ABINGDON APM-112 $.22   (P2186)

Let Thy Merciful Ears
SATB oct FISCHER,J 10034 $.25   (P2187)

Lift Up Your Heads, Ye Mighty Gates *anthem
SATB (easy) oct AUGSBURG 1418 $.30   (P2188)

Little Child On Earth Has Been Born, A *Xmas
unis,fl (easy) oct CONCORDIA 98-2107 $.30
(P2189)

Lo, Round The Throne A Glorious Band
4pt mix cor,org oct SCHIRM.G 11088 $.25
(P2190)

POWELL, ROBERT J. (cont'd.)

Lord, Sanctify Me Wholly *anthem
SATB (easy) oct AUGSBURG 1331 $.25 (P2191)

My God, I Thank Thee
SAB oct AGAPE CH 629 $.30 (P2192)

Now Glad Of Heart
SATB,org/pno oct SCHIRM.G 11086 $.25 (P2193)

O Love, How Deep, How Broad, How High
SAB,acap oct KERBY 6408C $.35 (P2194)

O Newborn Child *Xmas
SATB,acap (med) ABINGDON APM-181 $.24 (P2195)

O Thou To Whose All-Searching Sight *Lent
SATB (med) ABINGDON APM-200 $.24 (P2196)

O Trinity Of Blessed Light
SATB (med) ABINGDON APM-146 $.25 (P2197)

Of The Father's Love Begotten *Xmas,cant
mix cor,ST/Bar soli,2fl,org CONCORDIA
97-6411 $.85, ipa (P2198)

See The Destined Day Arise *Easter/Lent
SATB oct WALTON 2083 $.25 (P2199)

Seven Words From The Cross *Lent,ora
SATB,strings sc ABINGDON APM-715 $3.25, voc
sc ABINGDON APM-716 $1.25, ipa (P2200)

Sing A Song Of Joy *anthem
2pt mix cor (easy) oct AUGSBURG 1374 $.30 (P2201)

Sing Praise To God *anthem
SA (easy) oct AUGSBURG 1417 $.25 (P2202)

Three Christmas Anthems For SA Voices *CC3U,
Xmas,anthem
SA (med) ABINGDON APM-446 $.40 (P2203)

Three Treble Choir Anthems *CC3U,anthem
SA (easy) ABINGDON APM-198 $.30 (P2204)

Today In Bethlehem *Xmas
SATB (med) ABINGDON APM-511 (P2205)

Trumpeters And Singers Were As One, The
SATB,opt brass (med) ABINGDON APM-346 $.40,
ipa (P2206)

Unfold, Unfold! Take In His Light
4pt mix cor,acap oct SCHIRM.G 11085 $.25 (P2207)

When Jesus Left His Father's Throne *Xmas
unis,kbd (med easy) oct CONCORDIA 98-2161
$.25 (P2208)

Wilt Thou Not Turn Again? *Gen/Lent
SATB,acap (med diff) oct CONCORDIA 98-1671
$.30 (P2209)

POWELL, SYLVIA
Peace, Peace *see Powell, Rich

POWER AND THE GLORY, THE see Leonard, Harry

POWER, LYONEL (? -1445)
Ave Regina Caelorum
(Stevens, D.) [Lat] ATB BROUDE,A. 220 $.30 (P2210)

Collected Works vol.I *CCU,mot
(Hamm, Charles) cor AM.INST.MUS. $13.50 (P2211)

English Gothic Music *see Sanctus (P2212)

English Gothic Music *Eng
(Hughes, Dom Anselm; Grainger, Percy)
SCHOTT s.p.
contains: Marionette Douce [Lat/Eng]
(SATB); O Rosa Bella [It/Eng] (SATTBB);
Sanctus [Lat/Eng] (ATB) (P2213)

Marionette Douce
see English Gothic Music

O Rosa Bella
see English Gothic Music

Sanctus
see English Gothic Music
(Hughes, Dom Anselm; Grainger, Percy) 3pt
men cor/3pt mix cor oct SCHIRM.G 9873
$.20 see from English Gothic Music (P2214)

POWER OF PRAYER, THE see Bottenberg, [Wolfgang]

POWER TO CHOOSE, THE see Skillings, Otis

POZZA, ETTORE
Combatti I Nemici Di Dio
unis mix cor ZANIBON 1706 s.p. (P2215)

PRACTICAL POLOPHONY *anthem,16th cent
(White, E.) (easy) oct PRESSER 352-00072 $.40
contains: Arcadelt, Jacob, Ave Maria (SATB,
acap); Lassus, Roland de (Orlandus),
Adoramus Te (SSA,acap); Lassus, Roland de
(Orlandus), Adoramus Te (SSAT,acap);
Roselli, Adoramus Te (SATB,acap); Ruffo,
[Vincenzo], Adoramus Te (SATB,acap) (P2216)

PRAEPARATE CORDA VESTRA see Sermisy, Claude de

PRAESEPE see Chiesa, Cesare

PRAETER RERUM SERIEM see Calvisius, Sethus

PRAETORIUS, HEIRONYMOUS (1560-1629)
Also Hat Gott Die Welt Geliebt *Bibl/mot
(Muller) 6pt mix cor MOSELER s.p. (P2217)

Gaudete Omnes *mot
[Lat] SSATTB CHESTER s.p. (P2218)

O God, The Father, Eternal One *mot
(Gable, Fredrick K.) dbl cor/mix cor,4inst,
opt org (med) oct AUGSBURG 11-9308 $.75 (P2219)

O Herre Gott, Dein Gottlich Wort
SATB HANSSLER 6.2543 s.p. contains also:
Altenburg, Michael, Verzage Nicht, Du
Hauflein Klein (P2220)

PRAETORIUS, JAKOB (1586-1651)
In Peace And Joy I Now Depart
SATB,acap oct PRESSER 312-40142 $.25 (P2221)

Vom Himmel Hoch, Da Komm
see Bach, Johann Sebastian, Lobt Gott Ihr
Christen

PRAETORIUS, MICHAEL (1571-1621)
Ach Gott, Vom Himmel Sieh Darein
see Praetorius, Michael, Der Herr Ist Mein
Getreuer Hirt
SAB/SSB HANSSLER 6.066 s.p. (P2222)

Ach Gott, Vom Himmelreiche
SATB HANSSLER 6.2530 s.p. contains also:
Bach, Johann Sebastian, Es Wolle Gott Uns
Gnadig Sein, S.311 (P2223)

Ach Herr, Du Allerhochster Hort
4pt mix cor MOSELER LB-343 s.p. (P2224)

All Glory Be To God On High
(Schalk) dbl cor/mix cor&cong (med) oct
AUGSBURG 1609 $.30 (P2225)

Allein Gott In Der Hoh Sei Ehr *mot
see Praetorius, Michael, Der Tag, Der Ist
So Freudenreich
4pt mix cor&4pt mix cor&4pt mix cor MOSELER
s.p. (P2226)
3 cor HANSSLER 1.542 s.p. (P2227)
(Trubel) SSATTB HANSSLER 1.425 s.p. (P2228)

Allein Zu Dir, Herr Jesu Christ
see Praetorius, Michael, Von Himmel Kam Der
Engel Schar
SATB HANSSLER 6.215 s.p. contains also:
Herr, Fur Dein Wort Sei Hochgepreiset (P2229)

Als Der Gutige Gott *BVM
SATB,acap voc pt DOBLINGER s.p. see also
UNSERE LIEBE FRAU (P2230)

Alt Morgenstjernen Er Oprunden *Xmas,17th
cent
[Dan] SATB HANSEN-DEN 211 s.p. see also
JULESANGE (P2231)

Angels From The Realm Of Glory
see Three Christmas Carols

At The Sweet Birth Of Our Lord *see In
Natali Domini

Aus Meines Herzens Grunde Sag Ich Dir
see Goudimel, Claude, Es Geht Daher Des
Tages Schein

Aus Tiefer Not Schrei Ich Zu Dir
see Praetorius, Michael, Vater Unser Im
Himmelreich
see Praetorius, Michael, Komm, Heiliger
Geist, Herre Gott
4pt mix cor&4pt mix cor MOSELER s.p. (P2232)

3 eq voices MOSELER M-26 s.p. (P2233)

Av Hjartat Vill Jag Prisa
mix cor NORDISKA 3779 s.p. (P2234)

Babe Is Born
see Three Christmas Carols

Benedicamus *Easter
[Ger] mix cor,acap (easy) HUG s.p. see also
ZWEI OSTERLICHE ZWIEGESANGE (P2235)
(Stern, A.) [Lat] men cor,acap (easy) HUG
s.p. (P2236)

Benedicamus Domino
see ZWEI OSTERLICHE ZWIEGESANGE

Benedicamus In Adventu Domini *Adv
"Gelobt Sei, Der Da Kommt" [Ger/Lat] 2pt,
acap (easy) BAREN. BA 1174 s.p. (P2237)

Bide With Us, Lord *Gen
(Buszin) SATB SCHMITT 1550 $.30 (P2238)

Born Is The Lord Emanuel *see En Natus Est
Emanuel

Child Is Born, A
(Upshur) SA/TB FLAMMER E5126 $.25 (P2239)

Child Is Born In Bethlehem, A *Xmas/Epiph
SATB,acap (med easy) oct CONCORDIA 98-1392
$.25 (P2240)

Choralmotetten *CCU,mot
3pt men cor MOSELER s.p. (P2241)

Choralsatze-Heft 1 *CC19U,Adv/Pent
(Nitsche) 3pt mix cor HANSSLER 4.003 s.p. (P2242)

Choralsatze-Heft 2 *CC24U,Trin
(Nitsche) 3pt mix cor HANSSLER 4.004 s.p. (P2243)

Christ Ist Erstanden *Easter/Psntd
4pt mix cor MOSELER LB-85 s.p. contains
also: Christ Lag In Todesbanden (P2244)

Christ Lag In Todesbanden *Easter/Gd.Fri./
Holywk,anthem/Bibl/mot
see Praetorius, Michael, Christ Ist
Erstanden
STT/STB/SAT/SAB HANSSLER 6.055 s.p.
contains also: Durch Adams Fall Ist Ganz
Verderbt (SAB/SAT) (P2245)
[Ger] SATB,acap (easy) BAREN. BA 848 s.p. (P2246)
(Schalk) "Christ, Our Lord, Who Died To
Save Us" 4 cor,acap/mix cor,opt inst (med) oct
AUGSBURG 1608 $.25 (P2247)
(Trubel) SSATTB HANSSLER 1.436 s.p. (P2248)

Christ, Our Lord, Who Died To Save Us *see
Christ Lag In Todesbanden

Christ Unser Herr Zum Jordan Kam *Bibl
STB/SAB HANSSLER 6.072 s.p. (P2249)

Christe, Der Du Bist Tag Und Licht
SAT/SAB HANSSLER 6.076 s.p. (P2250)

Christmas Song, A *Xmas
(Gardner) SATB,acap (very easy) OXFORD
84.150 $.25 (P2251)

PRAETORIUS, MICHAEL (cont'd.)

Christus, Der Uns Selig Macht
4pt mix cor&4pt mix cor MOSELER s.p.
contains also: O Hilf, Christe, Gottes
Sohn (P2252)
4pt mix cor MOSELER LB-81 s.p. contains
also: Zeuner, Martin, Jesu, Deine Passion
(4pt mix cor) (P2253)

Clouds Of Night Are Passed Away *Easter
(Wienhorst) SAB oct SOUTHERN $.25 (P2254)

Clouds Of Night Are Passed Away, The (from
Musae Sioniae) Easter
see Six Settings From "Musae Sioniae,"
1609
SAB,acap (med easy) oct CONCORDIA 98-1985
$.25 (P2255)

Come, Thou Redeemer Of The Earth
(Paget) mix cor CURWEN 80904 s.p. (P2256)

Da Jesus An Dem Kreuze Stund *Gd.Fri.
SST/SSB/SSB HANSSLER 6.054 s.p. contains
also: Jesus Christus Unser Heiland (SSB) (P2257)

Dank Sagen Wir Alle
see Praetorius, Michael, Gelobet Seist Du,
Jesu Christ

Das Alte Jahr Ist Nun Dahin *Xmas/ECY/Thanks
see Trubel, Gerhard, Freut Euch, Ihr Lieben
Christen
SATB HANSSLER 6.105 s.p. contains also:
Bach, Johann Sebastian, Das Neugebor'ne
Kindelein, Das Herzensliebe; Gesius,
Bartholomaus, Freut Euch, Ihr Lieben
Christen All (P2258)
SATB HANSSLER 6.2528 s.p. contains also:
Jesus Ist Ein Susser Nam' (P2259)

Das Deutsche Te Deum *mot/Te Deum
3 cor,cont HANSSLER 1.540 s.p. (P2260)

Dear Christians, One And All, Rejoice (from
Musae Sioniae)
see Six Settings From "Musae Sioniae,"
1609

Dem Neugebornen Kindelein
see Praetorius, Michael, Ein Kind Geborn Zu
Bethlehem

Den Die Hirten Lobeten Sehre *Xmas
[Ger] SATB,acap (easy) BAREN. BA 1027 s.p.
contains also: Heut Sein Die Lieben
Engelein (Der Quempas) (P2261)

Der Du Bist Drey *anthem
"Thou Who Art Three" SAT/SAB,acap oct
NOVELLO 40.1546.00 s.p. (P2262)

Der Engel Sprach Zu Den Hirten *Xmas
4pt mix cor MOSELER LB-247 s.p. (P2263)
[Ger] SATB,acap (easy) BAREN. BA 1324 s.p.
contains also: Geborn Ist Der Emanuel (P2264)

Der Herr Ist Mein Getreuer Hirt *Bibl
SATB HANSSLER 6.213 s.p. contains also: Ach
Gott, Vom Himmel Sieh Darein (P2265)
SAB HANSSLER 6.057 s.p. contains also: Nun
Bitten Wir Den Heiligen Geist (P2266)

Der Morgenstern Ist Aufgedrungen
4pt mix cor MOSELER LB-48 s.p. contains
also: Der Tag Vertreibt Die Finstre Nacht (P2267)
SATB HANSSLER 6.200 s.p. contains also:
Schein, Johann Hermann, Mir Nach, Spricht
Christus, Unser Held (SSATB); Hassler,
Hans Leo, Wo Gott Zum Haus Nicht Gibt
Sein Gunst (SATB); Franck, Melchior, Wo
Gott Der Herr Nicht Bei Uns Halt (SATTB) (P2268)

Der Morgenstern Ist Aufgegangen
see Drei Weihnachtliche Liedsatze

Der Spiegel Der Dreifaltigkeit
4pt mix cor MOSELER LB-298 s.p. contains
also: Anonymous, Lasst Uns Das Kindelein
Wiegen (P2269)

Der Tag, Der Ist So Freudenreich
SAB/SA,inst HANSSLER 6.045 s.p. contains
also: Allein Gott In Der Hoh Sei Ehr
(SAB) (P2270)

Der Tag Vertreibt Die Finstre Nacht *Gen
see Praetorius, Michael, Der Morgenstern
Ist Aufgedrungen
[Ger] SATB,acap (easy) BAREN. BCH 45 s.p. (P2271)
(Stone, Kurt) [Ger/Eng] SATB,opt org oct
BOONIN 135 $.25 (P2272)

Despair Not Heart
(Hines) SSATB,acap MARKS 4443 $.25 (P2273)

Det Ar En Ros Utsprungen *see Es Ist Ros'
Entsprungen

Det Lille Barn I Krybben Trang *Xmas,17th
cent
[Dan] SATB HANSEN-DEN 213 s.p. see also
JULESANGE (P2274)

Deutsches Magnificat *Magnif
4pt mix cor&4pt mix cor MOSELER s.p. (P2275)

Deutsches Te Deum *Te Deum
4pt mix cor&4pt mix cor&4pt mix cor MOSELER
s.p. (P2276)

Dies Sind Die Heilgen Zehn Gebot *Bibl
SST/SAT HANSSLER 6.073 s.p. (P2277)

Drei Weihnachtliche Liedsatze *Xmas
cor pts BREITKOPF-W CHB-3492 s.p.
contains: Der Morgenstern Ist Aufgegangen
(2pt wom cor/2pt jr cor,acap); Nun
Komm, Der Heiden Heiland (3pt wom cor/
3pt jr cor,acap); Preis Sei Gott In Der
Hohe (3pt wom cor/3pt jr cor,acap) (P2278)

Dreistimmige Osterlieger *CCU,Easter
3pt mix cor MOSELER s.p. (P2279)

PRAETORIUS, MICHAEL (cont'd.)

Durch Adams Fall Ist Ganz Verderbt
see Franck, Melchior, Durch Adams Fall Ist Ganz Verderbt
see Praetorius, Michael, Christ Lag In Todesbanden

Ein Engel Schon Aus Gottes Thron *BVM
SATB,acap voc pt DOBLINGER s.p. see also UNSERE LIEBE FRAU (P2280)

Ein Feste Burg Ist Unser Gott
see Franck, Melchior, Ein Feste Burg Ist Unser Gott
SAT/SAB HANSSLER 6.068 s.p. (P2281)

Ein Kind Geborn Zu Bethlehem *Xmas,mot,17th cent
see Gesius, Bartholomaus, Ein Kind Geborn Zu Bethlehem
see Schroter, Leonhard, Ein Kind Geborn Zu Bethlehem
see Trubel, Gerhard, Freut Euch, Ihr Lieben Christen
[Ger] 3pt mix cor,acap (easy) BAREN. BCH 178 s.p. contains also: Vom Himmel Hoch, Da Komm Ich Her (P2282)
[Ger] SATB,acap (easy) BAREN. BA 1028, 1029 s.p. contains also: Dem Neugebornen Kindelein (P2283)
2-4 eq voices MOSELER LB-129 s.p. (P2284)
"Et Lille Barn I Davids Stad" [Dan] SATB HANSEN-DEN 212 s.p. see also JULESANGE (P2285)
"Ett Barn Ar Fott I Betlehem" 2-3pt wom cor/2-3pt jr cor NORDISKA 1693 s.p. (P2286)
(Berger) 2-6pt/SSATTB HANSSLER 1.032 s.p. (P2287)

Ein Kind Geborn Zu Bethlehem
see Praetorius, Michael, Lobt Gott, Ihr Christen Allzugleich

Ein Kindelein, So Lobelich *Xmas/Gen,mot
(Grusnick, Bruno) [Ger] SATB&SATB,acap (med diff) BAREN. BA 2903 sc $2.75, cor pts $1.30 (P2288)
(Iseler) SATB,brass THOMP.G E.I.2003 s.p., ipa (P2289)
(Iseler) "Little Child So Lovely, A" [Eng/Ger] SATB&SATB/SATB,opt brass THOMP.G s.p., ipa (P2290)
(Trubel) SSATB HANSSLER 1.433 s.p. (P2291)

En Natus Est Emanuel
"Born Is The Lord Emanuel" SATB,acap SCHIRM.EC 2612 $.30 (P2292)
"Born Is The Lord Emanuel" SATB,acap SCHIRM.EC 2298 $.30 (P2293)

En Natus Est Emmanuel *Xmas
SATB,acap oct PRESSER MC190 $.30 (P2294)

Enatus Est Emmanuel *Xmas/Epiph
"To Us Is Born Emmanuel" SATB,acap (med easy) oct CONCORDIA 98-1868 $.25 (P2295)

Er Is Een Roos Ontsprongen *see Es Ist Ein Ros' Entsprungen

Erhalt Uns Herr, Bei Deinem Wort
4 cor/16-20pt mix cor MOSELER s.p. (P2296)
3 eq voices MOSELER M-25 s.p. (P2297)

Erhalt Uns Herr Bei Deinen Wort
see Praetorius, Michael, Gott Der Vater Wohn Bei Uns

Erhalt Uns Herr Bei Dienem Wort *mot
(Trubel) dbl cor HANSSLER 1.488 s.p. contains also: Verleih Uns Frieden Gnadiglich (P2298)

Erschienen Ist Der Herrlich Tag *Easter
4pt mix cor MOSELER LB-96 s.p. contains also: Heut Triumphiert Gottes Sohn (P2299)

Erstanden Ist Der Heilig Christ *No.78, Easter,mot
see Lechner, Leonhard, O Welt, Sieh Hier Dein Leben
SAB HANSSLER 6.056 s.p. (P2300)
(Berger) SSAATTB HANSSLER 1.031 $.40 (P2301)
(Grote, Gottfried) [Ger] 2-7pt mix cor,acap BAREN. EM 22 s.p. see from EVANGELISCHES KIRCHENGESANGBUCH (P2302)

Erweckt Hat Mir Das Herz Zu Dir
see Stobaeus, Johann, Such, Wer Da Will, Ein Ander Ziel
SATB HANSSLER 6.159 s.p. contains also: Bach, Johann Sebastian, Du Herzog Meiner Seligkeit, Herr Jesu (from Halt' Im Gedachtnis Jesum Christ) (Easter) (P2303)

Es Ist Das Heil Uns Kommen Her
SAB HANSSLER 6.051 s.p. (P2304)

Es Ist Ein Ros' Entsprungen *Adv/Xmas, anthem/carol/cor-resp/chorale/mot
see CHORE ZUR WEIHNACHT
see VIER WEIHNACHTSLIEDER
[Ger] SATB,acap (easy) BAREN. BA 997 s.p. (P2305)
4pt mix cor MOSELER LB-60 s.p. contains also: Scheidt, Samuel, O Jesulein Zart (P2306)
SATB HANSSLER 6.011 s.p. contains also: Linkenbach, Klaus, Es Ist Ein Ros' Entsprugen (STB/SSB/SB,inst) (P2307)
[Ger/Lat] SATB,acap (easy) MULLER MS 60 s.p. contains also: In Dulci Jubilo; Geborn Ist Der Emanuel (P2308)
SATB,acap (contains also: Schutz, Heinrich, Macht Auf Die Tor) voc pt DOBLINGER s.p. see also ADVENT UND WEIHNACHT, HEFT 1 (P2309)
"Er Is Een Roos Ontsprongen" men cor sc ALSBACH&D s.p. (P2310)
"Lo, How A Rose E'er Blooming" SATB,acap SCHIRM.EC 380 $.25 (P2311)
"Lo, How A Rose E'er Blooming" SATB,kbd (med easy, with cannon by Vulpius) oct CONCORDIA 98-1519 $.25 (P2312)
"Lo, How A Rose E'er Blooming" 4pt mix cor, acap oct SCHIRM.G 2484 $.25 (P2313)
"Lo, How A Rose E'er Blooming" 4pt men cor, acap oct SCHIRM.G 1542 $.25 (P2314)
"Lo, How A Rose E'er Blooming" SSA,acap SCHIRM.EC 497 $.30 contains also: While Shepherds Watched Their Flocks By Night (P2315)
"Lo, How A Rose E'er Blooming" SATB,acap oct BELWIN 64051 $.30 (P2316)
(Berger, H.L.) TTBB HANSSLER 6.5045 s.p. (P2317)
(Christiansen, F.M.) "Lo, How A Rose" SATB (med) oct AUGSBURG 0181 $.22 (P2318)
(Davison, A.) "Lo, How A Rose E'er Blooming" TTBB,acap SCHIRM.EC 24 $.20 (P2319)
(Deis) "Lo, How A Rose E'er Blooming" 2pt boy cor,SS soli,org/pno oct SCHIRM.G 10216 $.25 (P2320)
(Deis) "Lo, How A Rose E'er Blooming" 3pt mix cor,acap oct SCHIRM.G 9826 $.25 (P2321)
(Distler, H.) "Lo! How A Rose E'er Blooming" SATB,acap (diff) oct CONCORDIA 97-4849 $.50 (P2322)
(Distler, H.) "Lo! How A Rose E'er Blooming" SATB,acap (med easy) oct CONCORDIA 98-1925 $.25 (P2323)
(Gaul) "Lo, How A Rose E'er Blooming" 4pt men cor,acap oct SCHIRM.G 5109 $.25 (P2324)
(Gray) "Lo, How A Rose" SATB,acap,opt pno oct PRO ART 1259 $.20 (P2325)
(Gray) "Lo, How A Rose" SAB,acap,opt pno oct PRO ART 1799 $.20 (P2326)
(Gray) "Lo, How A Rose" TTBB,acap,opt pno oct PRO ART 2149 $.20 (P2327)
(Gray) "Lo, How A Rose" SSA,acap,opt pno oct PRO ART 1474 $.20 (P2328)
(Gray) "Lo, How A Rose" 2pt oct PRO ART 1803 $.20 (P2329)
(Griffith, Allen) "Lo, How A Rose E'er Blooming" SSA oct BELWIN 1278 $.30 (P2330)
(Griffith, Allen) "Lo, How A Rose E'er Blooming" SAB oct BELWIN 2072 $.25 (P2331)
(Kingsbury, John) "Lo, How A Rose" SATB ALFRED 6367 $.25 (P2332)
(Lundquist, M.) "Lo, How A Rose E'er Blooming" SAB,acap SCHIRM.EC 2484 $.16 (P2333)
(Manney, C.) "Lo A Rose" SSA oct PRESSER 332-12557 $.25 (P2334)
(Overby) "Lo, How A Rose E'er Blooming" SATB (med) oct AUGSBURG 1036 $.30 (P2335)
(Pasquet, Jean) "Lo, How A Rose" SATB oct GRAY GCMR 3069 $.25 (P2336)
(Shand) "Lo, How A Rose E'er Blooming" 3pt wom cor,acap oct SCHIRM.G 8954 $.25 (P2337)
(Shaw; Parker) "Lo, How A Rose E'er Blooming" SATB,acap oct LAWSON 730 $.30 (P2338)
(Street) "Lo, How A Rose" SSA oct GRAY GCMR 1005 $.30 (P2339)
(Van Christy) "Lo, How A Rose E'er Blooming" SATB oct BELWIN 2177 $.30 (P2340)
(Wagner; Terri) "Lo, How A Rose E'er Blooming" SATB,acap oct LAWSON 667 $.30 (P2341)
(Weitemeyer, Herbert) [Ger] 4pt men cor, acap (easy) NAGELS NCH 11 s.p. contains also: In Dulci Jubilo (P2342)
(Wilson) "Lo, How A Rose E'er Blooming" SAB oct SPRATT 607 $.25 (P2343)

Es Ist Gewisslich An Der Zeit
SAT/SAB HANSSLER 6.067 s.p. (P2344)

Es Ist Ros' Entsprungen
"Det Ar En Ros Utsprungen" mix cor NORDISKA 3661 s.p. (P2345)
(Moren, John) "Det Ar En Ros Utsprungen" 3pt wom cor/3pt jr cor NORDISKA 2706 s.p. (P2346)

Es Kam Ein Engel, Hell Und Klar *Xmas
SATB HANSSLER 6.2666 s.p. contains also: Stobaeus, Johann, Nun Lasst Uns Mit Den Engelein Auch (SSATB) (P2347)

Es War Des Ewigen Vaters Rat
SATB HANSSLER 6.134 s.p. contains also: Schroter, Leonhard, Allein Gott In Der Hoh Sei Ehr (P2348)

Es Wolle Gott Uns Gnadig Sein
see Praetorius, Michael, Wo Gott Der Herr Nicht Bei Uns Halt
SSA/SAB HANSSLER 6.074 s.p. (P2349)

Et Lille Barn I Davids Stad *see Ein Kind Geborn Zu Bethlehem

Ett Barn Ar Fott I Betlehem *see Ein Kind Geborn Zu Bethlehem

Four Chorale Harmonizations *Adv/Xmas/Commun/Gen,chorale
SATB,kbd (easy) oct CONCORDIA 98-3000 $.35 contains: From God Shall Naught Divide Me; From Heav'n Above To Earth I Come; Jesus Christ, Our Blessed Savior; Savior Of The Nations, Come (P2350)

Four Christmas Chorales *CC4U,Xmas,chorale
(Rikko) SATB,acap FRANK F-624 $.35 (P2351)

Four Christmas Songs *CC4U,Xmas
(Simkins, C.F.) mix cor CURWEN s.p. (P2352)

Four Christmas Songs *CC4U,Xmas
(Simkins, C.F.) SATB,acap ROBERTON (P2353)

Freu Dich, Du Himmelskonigin *BVM
SATB,acap voc pt DOBLINGER s.p. see also UNSERE LIEBE FRAU (P2354)

From God Shall Naught Divide Me
see Four Chorale Harmonizations

From Heaven Above To Earth I Come (from Musae Sioniae)
see Six Settings From "Musae Sioniae," 1609

PRAETORIUS, MICHAEL (cont'd.)

From Heaven On High *see Vom Himmel Kommt

From Heav'n Above To Earth I Come
see Four Chorale Harmonizations

From Heav'n On High
mix cor SOUTHERN $.25 (P2355)

Geboren Ist Immanuel, Der Herr Christ *Xmas
SATB HANSSLER 6.1957 s.p. contains also: Anonymous, Seligkeiten, Freudenzeiten Kamen Fur Uns (P2356)
SATB HANSSLER 6.2659 s.p. contains also: Herzog, Johann Georg, Der Morgenstern Ist Aufgedrungen; Gesius, Bartholomaus, Frohlock, Du Tochter Zion, Sehr Und Jauchz (P2357)

Geborn Ist Der Emanuel *Xmas
see Praetorius, Michael, Der Engel Sprach Zu Den Hirten
see Praetorius, Michael, Es Ist Ein Ros Entsprungen
[Ger] SATB,acap (easy) MULLER MS 45 s.p. (P2358)

Geborn Ist Gottes Sohnelein *Xmas
4pt mix cor MOSELER LB-299 s.p. (P2359)

Geborn Ist Gottes Sohnlein *Xmas
"God's Infant Son" mix cor SOUTHERN $.25 (P2360)
(Beveridge) "God's Infant Son" 4pt mix cor, acap oct SCHIRM.G 9640 $.30 (P2361)

Geborn Ist Uns Emanuel *Adv/Xmas
4pt mix cor MOSELER LB-59 s.p. (P2362)
SATB,acap voc pt DOBLINGER s.p. see also ADVENT UND WEIHNACHT, HEFT 1 (P2363)

Gelobet Seist Du, Jesu Christ *Xmas,mot
see Gumpeltzhaimer, Adam, Gelobet Seist Du, Jesu Christ
SSB HANSSLER 6.046 s.p. contains also: Wo Gott Zum Haus Nicht Gibt Sein Gunst (SAT/SAB) (P2364)
[Ger] SATB&SSB,acap (med easy) BAREN. BA 175 s.p. contains also: Dank Sagen Wir Alle (SATB,acap) (P2365)
(Trubel) SSATB HANSSLER 1.432 s.p. (P2366)

Gelobt Sei, Der Da Kommt *see Benedicamus In Adventu Domini

German Agnus *Agnus
[Ger] SSATTB PETERS EM522 $1.25 contains also: German Sanctus (SSATBB) (Sanctus) (P2367)

German Sanctus
see Praetorius, Michael, German Agnus

God's Blessed Son Today Is Born *Xmas
(Knight, Gerald) SATB,acap oct FISCHER,C CM-7503 $.25 (P2368)

God's Infant Son *see Geborn Ist Gottes Sohnlein

Gott Dem Vater Im Hochsten Thron
see DEUTSCHES SANCTUS UND PSALM 111
SATB HANSSLER 6.2665 s.p. contains also: Victoria, Tomas Luis de, Gott, Dem Vater Und Dem Sohne; Praetorius, Michael, Lobet Den Herren, Alle Heiden; Franck, Melchior, Gen Himmel Aufgefahren Ist, Halleluja (P2369)

Gott Der Vater Wohn Bei Uns
SSB HANSSLER 6.052 s.p. contains also: Erhalt Uns Herr Bei Deinen Wort (SAB) (P2370)

Gott Der Vater Wohn Uns Bei *mot
4pt mix cor&4pt mix cor MOSELER s.p. (P2371)
(Kubler) dbl cor HANSSLER 1.024 s.p. (P2372)
(Trubel) SATTB HANSSLER 1.439 s.p. (P2373)

Gott Sei Gelobet *Commun
(Schalk, C.) "O Lord We Praise Thee" SATB, SSB soli,strings,winds,brass CONCORDIA 97-5095 $.50, ipa (P2374)

Gottes Sohn, Unser Lieber Herr *see Veni, Redemptor Gentium

Gud Trefaldig Statt Oss Bi
mix cor NORDISKA 1649 s.p. (P2375)

Guds Kirkes Grunnvoll Ene
(Nielsen, Ludvig) [Norw] LYCHE 63 s.p. (P2376)

Hail To The Lords Annointed *Xmas
SATB oct PRESSER MC366 $.30 (P2377)

Halleluja Ist Ein Frohlich Gesang *Easter
SATB HANSSLER 6.0830 s.p. contains also: Burck, Joachim, Ich Weiss, Dass Mein Erloser Lebt (P2378)
TTBB HANSSLER 6.1267 s.p. contains also: Vulpius, Melchior, Gelobt Sei Gott Im Hochsten Thron (P2379)

Herr Christ, Der Einig Gotts Sohn
see Praetorius, Michael, O Mensch, Bewein Dein Sunde Gross
SST/SSB HANSSLER 6.050 s.p. (P2380)

Herr, Fur Dein Wort Sei Hoch Gepreist *Thanks
SSB/SAB HANSSLER 6.071 s.p. (P2381)

Herr, Fur Dein Wort Sei Hochgepreiset
see Praetorius, Michael, Allein Zu Dir, Herr Jesu Christ

Herr Jesu Christ, Dieweil Du Bist
SATB HANSSLER 6.2597 s.p. (P2382)

Herr Jesu Christe, Gottes Sohn
SATB HANSSLER 6.171 s.p. contains also: Bach, Johann Sebastian, Kommt Her Zu Mir, Spricht Gottes Sohn (P2383)
(Schabasser, Josef) mix cor,acap oct DOBLINGER s.p. see also CHRISTUS, DER HERR (P2384)

PRAETORIUS, MICHAEL (cont'd.)

Herr, Kehre Dich Wieder Zu Mir
(Horn) unis,cont HANSSLER 5.125 s.p.
(P2385)

Herr, Nun Lasst Du Deinen Diener *mot
(Trubel) SSA&TTBB HANSSLER 1.434 s.p.
(P2386)

Herre, Nun Lassest Du Deinen Diener *Gd.Fri.
SATB,acap voc pt DOBLINGER s.p. see also
TOD UND VERGANGLICHKEIT
(P2387)

Herzlich Tut Mich Arfreuen
see Franck, Cesar, Kommt, Ihr G'spielen
"Oh, How My Heart Rejoices" SATB oct WALTON
7012 $.25
(P2388)
(Mason) "Oh, How My Heart Rejoices" mix cor
SOUTHERN $.25
(P2389)

Herzlich Tut Mich Erfreuen Die Liebe
HANSSLER 6.2507 s.p. contains also: Lobet
Gott, Unsern Herren, In Seinem Heiligtum
(P2390)

Heut Sein Die Lieben Engelein (Der Quempas)
see Praetorius, Michael, Den Die Hirten
Lobeten Sehre

Heut Triumphieret Gottes Sohn
SATB HANSSLER 6.253 s.p. contains also:
Jesus Christus Unser Heiland
(P2391)

Heut Triumphiert Gottes Sohn
see Praetorius, Michael, Erschienen Ist Der
Herrlich Tag

Hogtlovad Vare Davids Son
mix cor NORDISKA 4524 s.p.
(P2392)

Honor, Praise And Glory
(Gordon) SATB oct SHAPIRO SK 2074 $.25
(P2393)

Hort Zu, Ihr Lieben Leute *BVM
SSATB,acap voc pt DOBLINGER s.p. see also
UNSERE LIEBE FRAU
(P2394)

Hosanna To The Son Of David *see Hosianna In
Der Hohe Dem Sohne Davids

Hosianna In Der Hohe Dem Sohne Davids
*Easter/Palm,Bibl/mot
"Hosanna To The Son Of David!" SATB BOOSEY-
CAN s.p.
(P2395)
"Hosanna To The Son Of David" mix cor
SOUTHERN $.30
(P2396)
(Buszin) "Hosanna To The Son Of David"
SSATB SCHMITT 1516 $.30
(P2397)
(Field) "Hosanna To The Son Of David"
SSATB,acap oct BOOSEY 5528 $.30
(P2398)
(Field) "Hosanna To The Son Of David" SATB
oct SOUTHERN $.30
(P2399)
(Prentiss) "Hosanna To The Son Of David"
SATB oct SUMMY M 2843 $.25
(P2400)
(Trubel) SSATTB HANSSLER 1.431 s.p.
(P2401)

How Bright And Fair The Morning Star *see
Wie Schon Leuchtet Der Morgenstern

How Brightly Beams The Morning Star *CC4U
(Berger, Jean) SATB,org oct LAWSON 51200
$.50
(P2402)

How Brightly Shines The Morning Star *see
Wie Schon Leuchtet Der Morgenstern

How Long, O God, In My Great Need *see Wie
Lang, O Gott

How Lovely Shines The Morning Star
SATB,acap oct PRESSER 312-40184 $.30
(P2403)
(Carlton) SSATB,acap oct BOOSEY 5532 $.30
(P2404)

Hymn Pa Kyndelsmassodagen
mix cor NORDISKA 1463 s.p.
(P2405)

I Dodens Band Lag Herren Krist
mix cor NORDISKA 1197 s.p.
(P2406)

Ich Dank Dir Schon Durch Deinen Sohn
SATB HANSSLER 6.083 s.p. contains also:
Trubel, Gerhard, Der Tag Geht Mud Von
Hinnen; Calvisius, Sethus, Mit Meinem
Gott Geh Ich Zur Ruh
(P2407)

Ich Ruf Zu Dir, Herr Jesu Christ
see Franck, Melchior, Ich Ruf Zu Dir, Herr
Jesu Christ
SAB/SAT HANSSLER 6.064 s.p.
(P2408)

In Dich Hab Ich Gehoffet
see Franck, Melchior, Vater Unser Im
Himmelreich

In Dulci Jubilo *Adv/Xmas,anthem/mot
see Praetorius, Michael, Es Ist Ein Ros
Entsprungen
see Praetorius, Michael, Es Ist Ein Ros
Entsprungen
4pt wom cor sc ALSBACH&D s.p.
(P2409)
SAT HANSSLER 6.103 s.p.
(P2410)
4pt mix cor MOSELER LB-61 s.p. contains
also: Walter, In Dulci Jubilo
(P2411)
3 eq voices MOSELER LB-121 s.p.
(P2412)
SSAT,acap voc pt DOBLINGER s.p. see also
ADVENT UND WEIHNACHT, HEFT 1
(P2413)
SAT,acap voc pt DOBLINGER s.p. see also
ADVENT UND WEIHNACHT, HEFT 1
(P2414)
ST,acap voc pt DOBLINGER s.p. see also
ADVENT UND WEIHNACHT, HEFT 1
(P2415)
(Bliss) "Now Sing We, Now Rejoice" SS
(easy) oct AUGSBURG 1350 $.25
(P2416)
(Douglas) "Now Sing We, Now Rejoice" 2pt
oct PRO ART 2282 $.30
(P2417)
(Douglas) "Now Sing We, Now Rejoice" girl
cor SOUTHERN $.30
(P2418)
(Hellmann) "Nun Singet" SA/SSA/SATB
HANSSLER 1.511 s.p.
(P2419)

In Dulci Jubilo, Nun Singet *Thanks
mix cor NORDISKA 5086 s.p.
(P2420)
SATB HANSSLER 6.104 s.p. contains also:
Seid Frohlich Und Jubilieret Jesu (P2421)

In Natali Domini *Xmas
mix cor NORDISKA 1152 s.p.
(P2422)
"At The Sweet Birth Of Our Lord" SATB,acap
SCHIRM.EC 2610 $.30
(P2423)
(Cramer) "On The Birthday Of Our Lord"
[Eng/Lat] SATB,acap MARKS 4289 $.25

PRAETORIUS, MICHAEL (cont'd.)

(P2424)
(Glaser, V.) "At The Sweet Birth Of Our
Lord" [Lat/Eng] SSA,acap SCHIRM.EC 1993
$.25
(P2425)
(Rider) SSA,acap,opt pno oct PRO ART 2345
$.25
(P2427)
(Rider) SATB,acap,opt pno oct PRO ART 2142
$.25

In Peace And Joy *Gen
TBB,acap (med diff) oct CONCORDIA 98-1715
$.30
(P2428)

Jesu, Deine Passion Will Ich Jetzt Bedenken
(from Matthaus-Passion) Psntd
SATB HANSSLER 6.116 s.p. contains also:
Gesius, Bartholomaus, Wenn Meine Sund'
Mich Kranken
(P2429)

Jesus Christ, Our Blessed Savior
see Four Chorale Harmonizations

Jesus Christ Our Lord Is Born *Xmas
(King) SATB oct PLYMOUTH PCS-10 $.25
(P2430)

Jesus Christ Today Is Born *Xmas
(Trusler) SATB oct PLYMOUTH TR-104 $.25
(P2431)

Jesus Christus Unser Heiland
see Praetorius, Michael, Heut Triumphieret
Gottes Sohn
see Praetorius, Michael, Da Jesus An Dem
Kreuze Stund

Jesus Ist Ein Susser Nam'
see Praetorius, Michael, Das Alte Jahr Ist
Nun Dahin

Jesus, Unto Thee Be Praise
see Three Chorales For Lent And Holy Week

Joy Dawned Again On Easter Day *Easter/Lent
(Stevens) SATB oct PRO ART 1752 $.25
(P2432)
(Stevens) SS oct PRO ART 2043 $.25
(P2433)

Joyous News To You I'm Bringing *Xmas
SATB PROWSE s.p.
(P2434)
(Granville) SATB oct FOX R148 $.25
(P2435)

Kom Hit Og Hor De Ti Budord
[Norw] LYCHE 52 s.p.
(P2436)

Komm, Heiliger Geist, Herre Gott *No.98,
Asc/Pent,mot
[Ger] 4pt mix cor,acap BAREN. EM 85 s.p.
see from EVANGELISCHES KIRCHENGESANGBUCH
(P2437)
STT/STB/SAB HANSSLER 6.061 s.p. contains
also: Aus Tiefer Not Schrei Ich Zu Dir
(SAT/SAB)
(P2438)
(Trubel) SATB HANSSLER 1.437 s.p. (P2439)

Kommt Her Zu Mir, Spricht Gottes Sohn
SAB/SAT HANSSLER 6.063 s.p.
(P2440)

Kommt Und Lasst Uns Christum *Xmas
SATB HANSSLER 6.256 s.p. contains also:
Hassler, Hans Leo, Ein Kindelein So
Lobelich
(P2441)

Kyrie, Fader I Evighet *Kyrie
[Norw] LYCHE 42 s.p.
(P2442)

Little Child So Lovely, A *see Ein Kindelein
So Lobelich

Lo A Rose *see Es Ist Ein Ros Entsprungen

Lo, How A Rose *see Es Ist Ein Ros
Entsprungen

Lo, How A Rose E'er Blooming *see Es Ist Ein
Ros Entsprungen

Lo, How A Rose Ere Blooming
(Lundquist) SATB,acap (med) oct WILLIS 8404
$.16
(P2443)

Lo! Now A Rose Is Blooming *Xmas
(Wheeler, A.) SATB (easy) ALLANS 222 s.p.
(P2444)

Lobet Den Herren *Gen/Thanks
SATB,acap voc pt DOBLINGER s.p. see also
LOB UND DANK
(P2445)
"Praise The Lord" mix cor SOUTHERN $.30
(P2446)
(Beveridge) "Praise The Lord" [Eng/Ger]
SATB,acap oct SCHIRM.G 9817 $.30 (P2447)
(Rosewall) "Praise The Lord" TTBB oct SUMMY
5838 $.30
(P2448)

Lobet Den Herren, Alle Heiden
see Schutz, Heinrich, Meim Herzen Ist's Ein
Grosse Freud
see Praetorius, Michael, Gott, Dem Vater Im
Hochsten Thron

Lobet Gott, Unsern Herren, In Seinem
Heiligtum
see Praetorius, Michael, Herzlich Tut Mich
Erfreuen Die Liebe

Lobet Gott, Unsern Herrn *Psalm
SATB,acap DOBLINGER s.p. see from
PSALMLIEDER
(P2449)

Lobt Gott, Ihr Christen *Adv/Xmas
4pt mix cor MOSELER LB-300 s.p. (P2450)
SATB,acap voc pt DOBLINGER s.p. see also
ADVENT UND WEIHNACHT, HEFT 1
(P2451)
"Praise God, Ye Christians" mix cor
SOUTHERN $.25
(P2452)
(Beveridge) "Praise God, Ye Christians"
[Eng/Lat] 4pt mix cor,acap oct SCHIRM.G
9818 $.35
(P2453)

Lobt Gott, Ihr Christen Allzugleich
SATB LAUDINELLA LR 45 s.p. contains also:
Ein Kind Geborn Zu Bethlehem (SATB&SATB)
(P2454)
SATB HANSSLER 6.231 s.p. contains also:
Bach, Johann Sebastian, Vom Himmel Hoch,
Da Komm Ich Her (from Weihnachts-
Oratorium) (Xmas)
(P2455)

PRAETORIUS, MICHAEL (cont'd.)

Lord Jesus, We Give Thanks To Thee
see Three Chorales For Lent And Holy Week

Lord, Keep Us Steadfast In Thy Word (from
Musae Sioniae)
see Six Settings From "Musae Sioniae, "
1609

Low, How A Rose E'er Blooming
see Three Christmas Carols

Magnificat Super Chorale Melos Germanicum
*Magnif
4pt mix cor&4pt mix cor MOSELER s.p.
(P2456)

Maria Zart Von Edler Art *BVM
SATB,acap voc pt DOBLINGER s.p. see also
UNSERE LIEBE FRAU
(P2457)

Mein Seel Erhebt Den Herren *Magnif
(Gurlitt) dbl cor,5 soli,inst sc MOSELER
s.p.
(P2458)

Mein Seel Erhebt Den Herrn
4pt mix cor&4pt mix cor&4pt mix
cor MOSELER s.p.
(P2459)

Mein Seel Erhebt Zu Dieser Frist
SATB HANSSLER 6.003 s.p.
(P2460)

Meine Seel Erhebt Den Herren *mot
(Witte) 3 cor HANSSLER 1.321 s.p. (P2461)

Merry Bells Are Ringing
(Manney, C.) SA oct PRESSER 332-14215 $.30
(P2462)

Missa Brevis *Mass
(Trubel) [Lat] SSATTB HANSSLER 1.493 s.p.
(P2463)

Missa Sine Nomine *Mass
(Blume) mix cor,acap MOSELER s.p. contains
also: Salve Regina
(P2464)
(Trubel) [Lat] SATB HANSSLER 1.492 s.p.
(P2465)

Mit Fried Und Freud Ich Fahr Dahin
STB/SAB HANSSLER 6.069 s.p.
(P2466)

Mitten Wir Im Leben Sind
4pt mix cor&4pt mix cor MOSELER s.p.
(P2467)

Morgonstjerna
mix cor MUSIKK 223 s.p.
(P2468)

Morning Star On High, The
(Beveridge, L.) TTBB,acap SCHIRM.EC 2193
$.30
(P2469)

Morning Star, The *Xmas
4pt mix cor,acap oct SCHIRM.G 2554 $.25
(P2470)
(Shand) 3pt wom cor,acap oct SCHIRM.G 8953
$.25
(P2471)

My Song Forever Shall Record
(Lundquist) SATB,acap (med) oct WILLIS 6625
$.16
(P2472)
(Lundquist) SATB,acap (med) oct WILLIS 6625
$.16
(P2473)

Nach Gruner Farb Mein Herz Verlangt
4pt mix cor MOSELER LB-370 s.p. (P2474)

Now Glad Be The Heart Of Everyone *Xmas
SATB,acap oct PRESSER 312-40088 $.30
(P2475)

Now Is The Old Year Passed Away
4pt mix cor,acap oct SCHIRM.G 7541 $.25
(P2476)

Now Sing We, Now Rejoice *see In Dulci
Jubilo

Now We Sing *see Psallite

Nu Prisen Alle Gud
mix cor NORDISKA 1648 s.p.
(P2477)

Nun Bitten Wir Den Heiligen Geist *No.99,
Asc/Pent/Whitsun,mot
see Praetorius, Michael, Der Herr Ist Mein
Getreuer Hirt
[Ger] 3pt mix cor,acap BAREN. EM 39 s.p.
see from EVANGELISCHES KIRCHENGESANGBUCH
(P2478)
SATB,acap voc pt DOBLINGER s.p. see also
PFINGSTEN UND EUCHARISTIE
(P2479)
4pt mix cor MOSELER LB-90 s.p. (P2480)
(Trubel) SSATTB HANSSLER 1.438 s.p. (P2481)

Nun Danket Alle Gott, Der Da
see Schutz, Heinrich, Danket Dem Herren,
Gebt Ihm Ehr

Nun Freut Euch, Gottes Kinder All
see Gesius, Bartholomaus, Wir Danken Dir,
Herr Jesu Christ

Nun Freut Euch, Leiben Christen Gemein
4pt mix cor&4pt mix cor MOSELER s.p.
(P2482)

Nun Freut Euch, Lieben Christen *mot
(Dubler) dbl cor HANSSLER 1.026 s.p.
(P2483)

Nun Freut Euch, Lieben Christen Gmein
SAB HANSSLER 6.058 s.p.
(P2484)

Nun Komm, Der Heiden Heiland *mot
see Drei Weihnachtliche Liedsatze
SAT/SAB/SA,inst HANSSLER 6.044 s.p. (P2485)
(Trubel) SSATTB HANSSLER 1.430 s.p. (P2486)

Nun Lasst Uns Gehn Und Treten
SSB HANSSLER 6.048 s.p.
(P2487)

Nun Lob, Mein Seel, Den Herren *Gen/Trin,mot
see Schutz, Heinrich, Jauchzet Dem Herren
Alle Welt
[Ger] 3 eq voices/3pt mix cor,acap (easy)
BAREN. BA 3029 s.p.
(P2488)
(Brodde, Otto) [Ger] SATB&SATB,acap (med
diff) BAREN. BA 2911 sc $3.00, cor pts
$2.00
(P2489)
(Hausberg) 4 cor HANSSLER 1.423 s.p.
(P2490)
(Kubler) dbl cor HANSSLER 1.025 s.p.
(P2491)
(Nitsche) SAT HANSSLER 1.082 s.p. (P2492)

PRAETORIUS, MICHAEL (cont'd.)

Nun Lob Mein Seel Den Herrn
4pt mix cor&4pt mix cor MOSELER s.p.
(P2493)

Nun Singet *see In Dulci Jubilo!

O Christ, Wir Danken Deiner Gut (from
Matthaus-Passion)
see Bach, Johann Sebastian, Sei Gegrusset,
Jesu Gutig, Uber Alle Mass

O Fader Var I Himmerik
see Gumpeltzhaimer, Adam, O Fader Var I
Himmerik

O Glaubig Herz Gebenedei
see Schein, Johann Hermann, Auf Meinen
Lieben Gott, Trau Ich

O Gott, Wir Danken Deiner Gut *mot
SATB HANSSLER 6.191 s.p. contains also:
Cruger, Johann, Nun Lasst Uns Gott Dem
Herren
(Hellmann) SAB HANSSLER 1.251 s.p. (P2495)
(P2494)

O Gud, Som Aven Rackt Din Hand
mix cor NORDISKA 1803 s.p.
(P2496)

O, Guds Lamm *see O Lamm Gottes, Unschulding

O Hilf, Christe, Gottes Sohn
see Praetorius, Michael, Christus, Der Uns
Selig Macht

O Jesus, Lord Of Life And Breath (from Musae
Sioniae)
see Six Settings From "Musae Sioniae, "
1609

O Lamm Gottes
see Hassler, Hans Leo, O Mensch, Bewein
Dein Sunde Gross

O Lamm Gottes, Unschuldig *Bibl/mot
(Trubel) SSAATTB HANSSLER 1.435 s.p. (P2497)

O Lamm Gottes, Unschuldig
"O, Guds Lamm" mix cor NORDISKA 1029 s.p.
(P2498)

O Lord We Praise Thee *see Gott Sei Gelobet

O Mensch, Bewein Dein Sunde Gross
SATB HANSSLER 6.216 s.p. contains also:
Herr Christ, Der Einig Gotts Sohn (P2499)

O Morning Star, How Fair And Bright *Adv/
Epiph/Gen
SSATB,kbd (med easy) oct CONCORDIA 98-2096
$.25
(P2500)

O, Vos Omnes *Easter/Lent
(Marshall, Charles) "O Ye People Who Pass
Me By" SATTB FRANK F-603 $.30 (P2501)

O Welt, Ich Muss Dich Lassen *Gd.Fri.
SATB,acap voc pt DOBLINGER s.p. see also
TOD UND VERGANGLICHKEIT (P2502)

O Ye People Who Pass Me By *see O, Vos Omnes

Oh, Blest The House, Whate'er Befall (from
Musae Sioniae)
see Six Settings From "Musae Sioniae, "
1609

Oh, How My Heart Rejoices *see Herzlich Tut
Mich Erfreuen

On The Birthday Of Our Lord *see In Natali
Domini

Our Father Throned In Heaven High *see Vater
Unser In Himmelreich

Praise God, The Lord
(Ehret) SATB,acap MARKS 4138 $.30 (P2503)

Praise God, Ye Christians *see Lobt Gott,
Ihr Christen

Praise The Lord *see Lobet Den Herren

Preis Sei Gott In Der Hohe
see Drei Weihnachtliche Liedsatze

Psallite *Xmas
SATB,acap oct PRESSER MC167 $.30 (P2504)
(Greyson) mix cor SOUTHERN $.25 (P2505)
(Greyson) "Now We Sing" SATB,band oct
BOURNE ES21 $.25 (P2506)
(Greyson) "Now We Sing" SSA oct BOURNE
ES21A $.25 (P2507)
(Trusler) SAB oct PLYMOUTH TR-400 $.25
(P2508)

Psallite, Singt Und Klingt
(Stone, Kurt) [Lat/Ger/Eng] SATB,/jr cor oct
BOONIN 133 $.35 (P2509)

Quem Pastores Laudavere *Adv/Xmas
SATB,acap voc pt DOBLINGER s.p. see also
ADVENT UND WEIHNACHT, HEFT 1 (P2510)

Rejoice, Rejoice, Ye Nations *Xmas,carol
(Gordon, Philp) SATB oct BELWIN 1969 $.25
(P2511)
(Gordon, Philp) SA/TB oct BELWIN 1968 $.25
(P2512)
(Gordon, Philp) SAB oct BELWIN 2077 $.25
(P2513)

Rejoice, Ye Christian Brethern
(Ehret) SATB,acap oct BOOSEY 5243 $.30
(P2514)

Rejoice, Ye Christian Brethren
4pt mix cor,acap oct SCHIRM.G 2483 $.25
(P2515)

Rejoice, Ye Christian Men, Rejoice
SSA,acap SCHIRM.EC 1505 $.18 (P2516)

Rejoice Ye Christians
(Holle) SATB,acap AMP A290 $.20 (P2517)

Resonet In Laudibus
7pt mix cor MOSELER s.p. (P2518)

Road To Bethlehem, The *CC13L,carol
cor CONCORDIA 97-6358 $1.25 lessons (P2519)

PRAETORIUS, MICHAEL (cont'd.)

Salve Regina
see Praetorius, Michael, Missa Sine Nomine

Savior Of The Nations, Come
see Four Chorale Harmonizations

Seid Frohlich Und Jubilieret Jesu
see Praetorius, Michael, In Dulci Jubilo,
Nun Singet

Seid Frohlich Und Jubiliert
see Trubel, Gerhard, Freut Euch, Ihr Lieben
Christen

Shepherd Band, A *Xmas
(Ehret) SATB oct WORD CS-658 $.30 (P2520)

Sie Ist Mir Lieb *BVM
SATB,acap voc pt DOBLINGER s.p. see also
UNSERE LIEBE FRAU (P2521)

Sie Ist Mir Lieb, Die Werte Magd *Fest
[Ger] SATB,acap (med easy) BAREN. BA 4955
$.40 (P2522)
SATB HANSSLER 6.2536 s.p. contains also:
Zwingli, Huldreich, Herr, Nun Selbst Den
Wagen Halt (P2523)

Siehe, Das Ist Gottes Lamm
mix cor sc ALSBACH&D s.p. (P2524)

Sing, Beloved Christians *see Singt, Ihr
Lieben Christen All!

Sing The Birth *Xmas,anthem
(Parkinson, J.A.) SATB oct ROYAL 248 s.p.
(P2525)

Sing We All Now With One Accord
4pt mix cor,acap oct SCHIRM.G 7543 $.25
(P2526)

Sing We Triumphant Hymns
SATB WEINBERGER s.p. (P2527)

Sing With Joy, Glad Voices Raise *Xmas
SSATB&SS/SSATB&SA,opt inst (med diff)
CONCORDIA 97-4883 $.50 (P2528)

Sing Your Psalms To The Holy Child *Xmas
SATB,acap (med easy) oct CONCORDIA 98-1869
$.25 (P2529)

Singen Wir Aus Herzensgrund *Thanks
see Gumpeltzhaimer, Adam, Lobet Gott, Usern
Herren
SAB HANSSLER 6.075 s.p. (P2530)

Singt, Ihr Lieben Christen All! *mot
(Hunter) "Sing, Beloved Christians" [Eng/
Ger] SATB&treb cor MARKS 4446 $.35
(P2531)
(Trubel) SSAATTB HANSSLER 1.426 s.p. (P2532)

Singt Und Klingt *Adv/Xmas
4pt mix cor MOSELER LB-48 s.p. (P2533)
SATB,acap voc pt DOBLINGER s.p. see also
ADVENT UND WEIHNACHT, HEFT 1 (P2534)

Six Settings From "Musae Sioniae, " 1609
(from Musae Sioniae)
SAB CONCORDIA 97-7571 $.75
contains: Clouds Of Night Are Passed
Away, The; Dear Christians, One And
All, Rejoice; From Heaven Above To
Earth I Come; Lord, Keep Us Steadfast
In Thy Word; O Jesus, Lord Of Life And
Breath; Oh, Blest The House, Whate'er
Befall (P2535)

They Slumber Not, Nor Sleep
(Hadley) SATB oct PRO ART 2135 $.25 (P2536)
(Hadley) SSA oct PRO ART 2329 $.25 (P2537)

Thou Who Art Three *see Der Du Bist Drey

Three Choral Songs For Christmas *CC3U,Xmas
(Rikko, F.) SATB,acap oct PRESSER MC244
$.40 (P2538)

Three Chorales For Lent And Holy Week
*Holywk/Lent,chorale
SATB,acap (easy) oct CONCORDIA 98-1486 $.20
contains: Jesus, Unto Thee Be Praise;
Lord Jesus, We Give Thanks To Thee; We
Sing The Praise Of Him Who Died (P2539)

Three Christmas Carols *Xmas,carol
(Ehret) SATB,acap oct BOOSEY 5128 $.30
contains: Angels From The Realm Of Glory;
Babe Is Born; Low, How A Rose E'er
Blooming (P2540)

Till Dig Allena, Jesu Krist
3pt mix cor NORDISKA 1346 s.p. (P2541)

To Us Is Born *Xmas
(Dietterich, Philip R.) SAB,org/hndbl
(easy) ABINGDON APM-486 $.18 (P2542)

To Us Is Born A Little Child *Xmas
SATB PROWSE s.p. (P2543)
(Granville) SATB oct FOX R149 $.25 (P2544)

To Us Is Born Emmanuel *see Enatus Est
Emmanuel

To Us Is Born Immanuel *Xmas,carol
4pt mix cor,acap (first setting) oct
SCHIRM.G 2481 $.30 (P2545)
4pt mix cor,acap (second setting) oct
SCHIRM.G 2482 $.25 (P2546)
(Buszin) SATB SCHMITT 1562 $.35 (P2547)
(Cramer) SAB MARKS 4478 $.25 (P2548)
(Cramer) SATB,acap MARKS 4005 $.25 (P2549)
(Pfautsch) TTBB FLAMMER C5005 $.25 (P2550)
(Trusler) SABar/TBarBar WARNER W3749 $.30
(P2551)

Today Arose Christ From The Grave *Easter
SATB,acap (easy) oct CONCORDIA 98-1173 $.30
contains also: We All Rejoice On This
Glad Day (P2552)

Today Is Born A Child On Earth *Xmas
(Gardner) SATB,acap OXFORD s.p. (P2553)

Today Is Born Emmanuel *Xmas
(Vree, M.) SATB FOSTER MF510 $.25 (P2554)

PRAETORIUS, MICHAEL (cont'd.)

Twelve Christmas Hymns *CC12U,Xmas,hymn
SATB STAINER CH129 s.p. (P2555)

Twelve Christmas Hymns *CC12UL,Xmas,hymn
SATB,acap STAINER CH129 $.75 (P2556)

Uppfaren Ar Var Herre Krist
mix cor NORDISKA 3589 s.p. (P2557)

Vad Min Gud Vill, Det Alltid Sker
mix cor NORDISKA 1805 s.p. (P2558)

Vater Unser Im Himmelreich *Bibl/mot/prayer
STB/SAB HANSSLER 6.059 s.p. (P2559)
SATB HANSSLER 6.212 s.p. contains also: Aus
Tiefer Not Schrei Ich Zu Dir (P2560)
(Hausberg) dbl cor HANSSLER 1.422 s.p.
(P2561)

Vater Unser In Himmelreich
"Our Father Throned In Heaven High" SA,acap
SCHIRM.EC 1967 $.18 (P2562)

Veni Creator Spiritus *Pent/Whitsun
SATB,acap voc pt DOBLINGER s.p. see also
PFINGSTEN UND EUCHARISTIE (P2563)

Veni, Redemptor Gentium *mot
(Hellmann) "Gottes Sohn, Unser Lieber Herr"
[Lat/Ger] SATTB HANSSLER 1.510 s.p.
(P2564)

Verleih Uns Frieden Gnadiglich
see Praetorius, Michael, Erhalt Uns Herr
Bei Dienem Wort
SAT/SAB HANSSLER 6.070 s.p. (P2565)

Vier Weihnachtslieder *CC4U,Xmas
4-5pt mix cor MOSELER s.p. (P2566)

Vom Himmel Hoch, Da Komm Ich Her *mot
see Praetorius, Michael, Ein Kind Geborn Zu
Bethlehem
see Gumpeltzhaimer, Adam, Vom Himmel Hoch
Da Komm Ich Her
3 eq voices MOSELER LB-128 s.p. (P2567)
(Trubel) SSATTB HANSSLER 1.424 s.p. (P2568)

Vom Himmel Kommt *Xmas
(Beveridge) "From Heaven On High" [Eng/Ger]
4pt mix cor,acap oct SCHIRM.G 9641 $.25
(P2569)

Von Himmel Kam Der Engel Schar *Xmas
SSB HANSSLER 6.047 s.p. contains also:
Allein Zu Dir, Herr Jesu Christ (SAT/SAB)
(P2570)

Wachet Auf Ihr Christen Alle
mix cor ALSBACH&D s.p. (P2571)

Wachet Auf, Ruft Uns Die Stimme *CC4U,ECY
(Goebel, Georg) [Ger] 2-7pt mix cor,opt
inst (med) MULLER SM 1840 s.p. (P2572)

Wachet Auf, Ruft Uns Die Stimme *mot
(Nitsche) SST HANSSLER 1.065 s.p. (P2573)
(Trubel) SAT&STTB HANSSLER 1.427 s.p.
(P2574)

Wacht Auf Ihr Christen Alle
SATB,acap DOBLINGER s.p. see also BITTE UND
VERTRAUEN (P2575)

Wake, Awake, For Night Is Flying
SATB oct PRESSER 312-40150 $.30 (P2576)

War Gott Nicht Mit Uns Diese Zeit
see Franck, Melchior, War Gott Nicht Mit
Uns Diese Zeit
SAB HANSSLER 6.060 s.p. (P2577)

We All Rejoice On This Glad Day
see Praetorius, Michael, Today Arose Christ
From The Grave

We Sing The Praise Of Him Who Died
see Three Chorales For Lent And Holy Week

We Turn Our Eyes To Thee
(Inglis) SATB,acap (med diff/diff) SOUTHERN
$.30 (P2578)

Wenn Mein Stundlein Vorhanden Ist
see Franck, Melchior, Wenn Mein Stundlein
Vorhanden Ist
SATB HANSSLER 6.2529 s.p. contains also:
Bach, Johann Sebastian, Es Ist Genug,
Herr, Wenn Es Dir (from O Ewigkeit, Du
Donnerswort) (Trin) (P2579)

Wenn Wir In Hochsten Noten Sein
see TROSTGESANG UND STERBELIED
TTB/SSB HANSSLER 6.053 s.p. (P2580)
(Stern, A.) [Ger] men cor,acap (easy) HUG
s.p. (P2581)

Wer In Dem Schutz Des Hochsten Sitzt
4pt mix cor&4pt mix cor MOSELER s.p.
(P2582)

What Star Is This *Xmas
(Owens) SATB SCHMITT 887 $.30 (P2583)

While Shepherds Watched Their Flocks *Xmas,
Bibl
(Salter) 4pt mix cor,acap oct SCHIRM.G 6446
$.25 (P2584)

While Shepherds Watched Their Flocks By Night
see Praetorius, Michael, Lo, How A Rose
E'er Blooming

Wie Lang, O Gott
(Hunter) "How Long, O God, In My Great
Need" [Eng/Ger] SSATB,acap MARKS 4509
$.30 (P2585)

Wie Schon Leuchtet Der Morgenstern *CC6U,
Epiph
(Goebel, Georg) [Ger] 2-5pt mix cor,opt
inst (med) MULLER SM 1841 s.p. (P2586)

Wie Schon Leuchtet Der Morgenstern
SAB HANSSLER 6.049 s.p. (P2587)
"How Brightly Shines The Morning Star"
[Ger/Eng] SATB,SSTTB soli,opt acap/opt
org&brass&strings min sc PETERS E1045
$2.00, ipa (P2588)
"How Brightly Shines The Morning Star"
[Ger] SATB or 9, 10, or 14pt dbl cor min
sc PETERS 4806 $1.25 (P2589)
(Blume) mix cor MOSELER s.p. (P2590)

PRAETORIUS, MICHAEL (cont'd.)

(Redlich) "How Bright And Fair The Morning Star" [Ger/Eng] SATB,SSTTB soli,orch min sc EULENBURG EUL1045 s.p., ipa (P2591)

Will Of God Is Always Best SATB,acap oct PRESSER 312-40151 $.25 (P2592)

Wir Glauben All An Einen Gott *Bibl SAB/SA HANSSLER 6.062 s.p. (P2593)

Wir Wollen Alle Frohlich Sein SATB HANSSLER 6.261 s.p. contains also: Bach, Johann Sebastian, Es Fahret Heute Gottes Sohn (P2594)

Wo Gott Der Herr Nicht Bei Uns Halt SSB/SST HANSSLER 6.065 s.p. (P2595) SATB HANSSLER 6.214 s.p. contains also: Es Wolle Gott Uns Gnadig Sein (P2596)

Wo Gott Zum Haus Nicht Gibt Sein Gunst see Franck, Melchior, Wo Gott Zum Haus Nicht Gibt Sein Gunst see Praetorius, Michael, Gelobet Seist Du, Jesu Christ

Wohlauf, Ihr Christen *Easter/Psntd SATB,acap voc pt DOBLINGER s.p. see also PASSION UND OSTERN (P2597)

Wohlauf, Ihr Christen, Freuet Euch SATB HANSSLER 6.126 s.p. contains also: Bodenschatz, Erhard, Jesus Christus, Unser Heiland, Der Den Tod (P2598)

Zu Dir Ich Mein Herz Erhebe 4pt mix cor&4pt mix cor MOSELER s.p. (P2599)

Zwiegesange, Heft 1: Der Jahreskreis *CC21U, Gen (Schwarz, Gerhard) [Ger] 2pt,acap (med easy) BAREN. BA 1929 $3.00 choralbicinien (P2600)

Zwiegesange, Heft 2; Der Tages Kreis *CC29U, Gen (Schwarz, Gerhard) [Ger] 2pt,acap (med easy) BAREN. BA 1930 $4.25 choralbicinien (P2601)

PRAGER see Caldara, Antonio, Te Deum

PRAIE THE LORD: YOU HEAVENS ADORE HIM see Recessional Hymns

PRAISE see Bergsma, William Laurence

PRAISE see Dyson, George

PRAISE! see Kirk, Theron W.

PRAISE see Mc Harris, W.

PRAISE see Monson

PRAISE see Rowley, Alec

PRAISE see Young, Gordon

PRAISE AND ALLELUIA see Nosse

PRAISE AND GIVE THANKS see Adair

PRAISE AND GLORY see Davis, Katherine K.

PRAISE AND HONOR BE THINE see Lassus, Roland de (Orlandus)

PRAISE AND HONOR BE UNTO THEE see Perti, Giacomo Antonio

PRAISE AND JUBILEE see Draesel, Lederhouse

PRAISE AND PRAYER see Anonymous

PRAISE AND REJOICE *CC12L,Xmas/Easter/Gen (Gray) SSA PRO ART 388 $1.25 (P2602)

PRAISE AND RENOWN TO GOD see Bach, Johann Sebastian, Lob, Ehr Und Preis Sei Gott

PRAISE AND SING see Davies

PRAISE AND SING see Butler, Eugene

PRAISE AND SUPPLICATION see Couper, Alinda B.

PRAISE AND THANKS see Bach, Johann Sebastian

PRAISE AND THANKS GIVING see Kirk

PRAISE AND THANKS TO GOD see Schutz, Heinrich, Lob Und Preis Sei Gott

PRAISE AND THANKSGIVING see Graham, R.W.

PRAISE BE TO THEE see Handel, George Frideric

PRAISE BE TO THEE see Palestrina, Giovanni

PRAISE BE TO THEE see Schutz, Heinrich

PRAISE BE TO THEE (HOLY TRINITY) see Palestrina, Giovanni

PRAISE BE UNTO GOD see Weisgall, Hugo

PRAISE BE UNTO THE FATHER see Tallis, Thomas

PRAISE CAROL, THE see Marryott

PRAISE CHORALE, THE see Banks, Robert

PRAISE CHRIST, ALLELUIA see Butler

PRAISE FOR THE YEAR see Hoffmann

PRAISE GOD! see Bock

PRAISE GOD! see Mozart, Wolfgang Amadeus

PRAISE GOD! see Ouchterlony, David

PRAISE GOD AND SING *CC13U (Bock, Fred) SATB (med easy) PRESSER $1.95 (P2603)

PRAISE GOD FOR HE IS KIND see Webber

PRAISE GOD IN ALL HIS GLORY see Peri, Jacopo

PRAISE GOD IN HIS HOLINESS see Shaw, Geoffrey [Turton]

PRAISE GOD IN HIS HOLINESS see Thompson

PRAISE GOD IN HIS HOLY PLACE (Psalm 150) SSA,acap oct WORLD ESA-972-3 $.30 (P2604)

PRAISE GOD IN HIS SANCTUARY see Thygerson

PRAISE GOD, THE LORD see Praetorius, Michael

PRAISE GOD, THE LORD, YE PEOPLE ALL see Schutz, Heinrich

PRAISE GOD THE LORD, YE SONS OF MEN see Distler, Hugo

PRAISE GOD THE LORD, YE SONS OF MEN see Freundt, Cornelius

PRAISE GOD THE LORD, YE SONS OF MEN see Hermann, [Nikolaus]

PRAISE GOD THE LORD, YE SONS OF MEN see Mudde, Willem

PRAISE GOD WITH SOUND see Morales, Cristobal de, Lobt Godt Mitt Schall

PRAISE GOD, YE CHRISTIANS see Praetorius, Michael, Lobt Gott, Ihr Christen

PRAISE GOD YE CHRISTIANS ALL ALIKE see Harter, [Harry]

PRAISE GOD, YE LANDS see Schutz, Heinrich

PRAISE HIM see Smith, Tedd

PRAISE HIM! (Parker) TTBB oct LAWSON 51296 $.30 (P2605)

PRAISE HIM! see Allen, Chester G.

PRAISE HIM see Bach

PRAISE HIM see Bach, Johann Sebastian

PRAISE HIM see Tchesnokov, Pavel Grigorievitch

PRAISE HIM, ALL YE LITTLE CHILDREN see Moore-Richman

PRAISE HIM EVERMORE see Brandon, G.

PRAISE HIM EVERMORE see Flint

PRAISE HIM IN GLADNESS see Christiansen, Olaf Christian

PRAISE HIM, NO. 1 see Ringwald, [Roy]

PRAISE HIM, NO. 2 see Ringwald, [Roy]

PRAISE HIM, PRAISE YE THE LORD see Caldara, Antonio

PRAISE HIM WITH TRUMPETS see Pooler, Frank

PRAISE HIM, YE PEOPLE see Coggin

PRAISE HIS NAME see Kirk

PRAISE HIS NAME FOREVER see Rosenmuller, Johann

PRAISE IN SONG see Ehret, Walter

PRAISE, JEHOVA see Mendelssohn-Bartholdy, Felix, Lauda Sion

PRAISE JEHOVAH see Frylof, [Harald Leonard]

PRAISE JEHOVAH see Matthews

PRAISE JEHOVAH see Mendelssohn-Bartholdy, Felix, Lauda Sion

PRAISE JEHOVAH, ALL CREATION see Naumann, Johann Gottlieb

PRAISE JEHOVAH, ALL YE NATIONS see James, Philip

PRAISE JEHOVAH, HALLELUJAH! see Naumbourg

PRAISE, LORD, FOR THEE IN ZION WAITS see Thiman, Eric Harding

PRAISE, MY SOUL see Andrews, Mark, Lauda Anima

PRAISE, MY SOUL, THE KING see Darst, W. Glenn

PRAISE, MY SOUL, THE KING see Hallett, John C.

PRAISE, MY SOUL, THE KING OF HEAVEN see Clokey

PRAISE, MY SOUL, THE KING OF HEAVEN see Duncan

PRAISE MY SOUL THE KING OF HEAVEN see Fischer, H.

PRAISE MY SOUL THE KING OF HEAVEN see Fryxell, Regina Holmen

PRAISE, MY SOUL, THE KING OF HEAVEN see Gilbert, Norman

PRAISE, MY SOUL, THE KING OF HEAVEN see Goss, John

PRAISE, MY SOUL, THE KING OF HEAVEN see Larson

PRAISE, MY SOUL THE KING OF HEAVEN see Pike, Harry Hale

PRAISE, MY SOUL, THE KING OF HEAVEN see Welsh

PRAISE MY SOUL THE KING OF HEAVEN see Williams, David H.

PRAISE, MY SOUL, THE KING OF HEAVEN see Wilson, John F.

PRAISE, MY SOUL, THE KING OF HEAVEN see York, D.

PRAISE, MY SOUL, THE KING OF HEAVEN see Young

PRAISE, O PRAISE OUR GOD AND KING see Barnby, Sir Joseph

PRAISE, O PRAISE OUR GOD AND KING see Frackenpohl, Arthur

PRAISE, O PRAISE OUR GOD AND KING see Hall, E. Vine

PRAISE, O PRAISE OUR GOD AND KING see Jewell

PRAISE, O PRAISE OUR GOD AND KING! see Wilkes

PRAISE, O PRAISE THE LORD OF HARVEST see Thiman, Eric Harding

PRAISE OF CREATED THINGS see Diemer, Emma Lou

PRAISE OF MARY see Brahms, Johannes, Marias Lob

PRAISE, OH, PRAISE OUR GOD AND KING see Wolff, S. Drummond

PRAISE ON HIGH *CC12L,Gen (Stevens) 2pt jr cor PRO ART 310 $.85 (P2606)

PRAISE OUR GOD see Denton

PRAISE OUR GOD ABOVE *Harv,anthem (Hilty, Everett Jay) 2 eq voices,pno/org,opt hndbl oct WORLD CA-2140-2 $.30 (P2607)

PRAISE OUR GOD IN ALL HIS SPLENDOR see Bach, Johann Sebastian, Lobet Gott In Seinen Richen

PRAISE OUR GOD WHO REIGNS IN HEAVEN see Bach, Johann Sebastian, Lobet Gott In Seinen Reichen

PRAISE OUR GOD, YE SONS OF MEN see Lautner, L.

PRAISE OUR LORD see Palmer, Jane

PRAISE OUR LORD ALL YE GENTILES see Byrd, William

PRAISE! PRAISE! see Peninger, David

PRAISE, PRAISE YE THE LORD see Kirk

PRAISE SHALL BE THINE 2pt oct LORENZ 5724 $.25 (P2608)

PRAISE SONG see Williams

PRAISE, THANKSGIVING, GLORY see Bechler

PRAISE THE ALMIGHTY, MY SOUL, ADORE HIM see Zipp, Friedrich

PRAISE THE FATHER, SON AND SPIRIT see Lundquist, Matthew Nathanael

PRAISE THE GOD OF OUR SALVATION see Haydn, (Franz) Joseph

PRAISE THE GOD OF OUR SALVATION see Pritchard

PRAISE THE GOD, WHOSE GREAT SALVATION see Coggin

PRAISE THE KING OF GLORY see Englert, Eugene

PRAISE THE KING OF HEAVEN see Monteverdi, Claudio, Lauda Sion Salvatorem

PRAISE THE LORD see Silver, Mark

PRAISE THE LORD see Adler, Samuel

PRAISE THE LORD see Bach, Johann Sebastian

PRAISE THE LORD see Baines, W.

PRAISE THE LORD see Cramer

PRAISE THE LORD see Creston, Paul

PRAISE THE LORD see Diemer, Emma Lou

PRAISE THE LORD see Elvey, George Job

PRAISE THE LORD see Franck, Cesar

PRAISE THE LORD see Goemanne, Noel

PRAISE THE LORD see Goi, M., Lodate Il Signore

PRAISE THE LORD see Gordon, P.

PRAISE THE LORD see Gounod, Charles Francois, Judex

PRAISE THE LORD see Hadler

PRAISE THE LORD see Hafso

PRAISE THE LORD see Hall, Regnal L.

PRAISE THE LORD see Hassler, Hans Leo, Laudate Dominum

PRAISE THE LORD see Haydn, (Franz) Joseph

PRAISE THE LORD! see Hopson, Hal H.

PRAISE THE LORD see Hutchinson, W.

PRAISE THE LORD see Johnston

PRAISE THE LORD see Jolley

PRAISE THE LORD see Kirk

PRAISE THE LORD see Krone, Max

PRAISE THE LORD see Lynn, George

PRAISE THE LORD see Marshall

PRAISE THE LORD see Maunder, J.H.

PRAISE THE LORD see Newbury

PRAISE THE LORD see Pasfield, W.R.

PRAISE THE LORD see Peery, [Rob Roy]

PRAISE THE LORD see Pooler, Marie

PRAISE THE LORD see Praetorius, Michael, Lobet
Den Herren

PRAISE THE LORD see Pritchard

PRAISE THE LORD see Purcell, Henry

PRAISE THE LORD see Rachmaninoff, Sergey
Vassilievitch

PRAISE THE LORD see Randegger

PRAISE THE LORD see Randegger, Alberto

PRAISE THE LORD see Stark, Richard

PRAISE THE LORD see Tomkins, Thomas

PRAISE THE LORD see Washburn, Robert

PRAISE THE LORD see Wetzler, Robert

PRAISE THE LORD see Zimmermann, Heinz Werner

PRAISE THE LORD, ALL NATIONS see Neff, James

PRAISE THE LORD, ALL YE NATIONS see Bach,
Johann Sebastian, Lobet Den Herrn, Alle
Heiden

PRAISE THE LORD, ALL YE NATIONS see Goemanne,
Noel

PRAISE THE LORD, ALL YE NATIONS see Jommelli,
Niccolo

PRAISE THE LORD, ALL YE NATIONS see Powell

PRAISE THE LORD, ALL YE NATIONS see Randegger,
Alberto

PRAISE THE LORD AMONG HIS HOLY ONES see Byrd,
William

PRAISE THE LORD AND CALL UPON HIS NAME see
Darnton, C.

PRAISE THE LORD AND CALL UPON HIS NAME see
Elvey, George Job

PRAISE THE LORD FOR HE IS GOD see Joly,
Camille, O Sacrum Convivium

PRAISE THE LORD FOR HE IS GRACIOUS see Mozart,
Wolfgang Amadeus

PRAISE THE LORD FOR HIS GOODNESS see Rogers

PRAISE THE LORD FROM THE HEAVENS see Wollen, P.

PRAISE THE LORD HIS GLORIES SHOW see Burroughs

PRAISE THE LORD, HIS GLORIES SHOW see
Burroughs, Bob

PRAISE THE LORD, HIS GLORIES SHOW see Greener

PRAISE THE LORD, HIS GLORIES SHOW see Sateren,
Leland Bernhard

PRAISE THE LORD, HIS GLORIES SHOW see Thiman,
Eric Harding

PRAISE THE LORD, HIS GLORIES SHOW see Williams,
R.

PRAISE THE LORD IN HEAV'N ABOVE see Schumann,
Robert (Alexander)

PRAISE THE LORD, JEHOVAH see Gabrieli,
Giovanni, Jubilate Deo

PRAISE THE LORD, JEHOVAH see Palestrina,
Giovanni, Exultate Deo

PRAISE THE LORD JEHOVAH see Scarlatti,
Domenico, Exsultate Deo

PRAISE THE LORD, O JERUSALEM see Clare, Edwyn
A.

PRAISE THE LORD, O JERUSALEM see Duncan, C.

PRAISE THE LORD, O JERUSALEM see Hall, E. Vine

PRAISE THE LORD, O JERUSALEM see Maunder, J.H.

PRAISE THE LORD, O JERUSALEM see Purcell, Henry

PRAISE THE LORD, O MY HEART see Handel, George
Frideric

PRAISE THE LORD, O MY SOUL
(Pisano) SATB,acap,opt pno oct PRO ART 2517
$.35
(P2609)

PRAISE THE LORD, O MY SOUL see Bush, Geoffrey

PRAISE THE LORD, O MY SOUL see Child

PRAISE THE LORD, O MY SOUL see Child, William

PRAISE THE LORD, O MY SOUL see Clarke, Jeremiah

PRAISE THE LORD, O MY SOUL see Ferris, W.

PRAISE THE LORD, O MY SOUL see Harris, William
Henry

PRAISE THE LORD, O MY SOUL see 'Laud, Mr.'
William

PRAISE THE LORD, O MY SOUL see Marsh

PRAISE THE LORD O MY SOUL see Minton, T.

PRAISE THE LORD, O MY SOUL see Scarmolin,
(Anthony) Louis

PRAISE THE LORD, O MY SOUL see Smart, Roland

PRAISE THE LORD, O MY SOUL see Tomkins, Thomas

PRAISE THE LORD, O MY SOUL see Watson, M.

PRAISE THE LORD, O MY SOUL see Yeaman, W.
Holliday

PRAISE THE LORD OF HEAVEN see Darst, S. Glen

PRAISE THE LORD OF HEAVEN see Milner, Anthony

PRAISE THE LORD OF HEAVEN see Thiman, Eric
Harding

PRAISE THE LORD OF HEAVEN see Thompson

PRAISE THE LORD OF HEAVEN see Wolff, S.
Drummond

PRAISE THE LORD OH MY SOUL
(Cornwall, J.S.) SAB PIONEER 4002 $.20
(P2610)

PRAISE THE LORD OUR KING see Traver

PRAISE THE LORD, WE PRAISE THEE see Arensky,
Anton Stepanovitch

PRAISE THE LORD WHO REIGNS ABOVE see Lovelace,
Austin C.

PRAISE THE LORD WHO REIGNS ABOVE see Pfautsch,
Lloyd

PRAISE THE LORD WHO REIGNS ABOVE see Stevens,
Halsey

PRAISE THE LORD WHO REIGNS ABOVE see Williams

PRAISE THE LORD WITH GLADNESS see Hassler, Hans
Leo

PRAISE THE LORD WITH JOYFUL SONG see
Christiansen, Larry A.

PRAISE THE LORD WITH PSALTERY see Hovhaness,
Alan

PRAISE THE LORD WITH SONG see Barthelson, Joyce

PRAISE THE LORD WITH SOUNDING CYMBALS see
Stanton

PRAISE THE LORD, YE HEAVENS see Morgan

PRAISE THE LORD, YE HEAVENS see Prichard, Hugh

PRAISE THE LORD! YE HEAVENS see Pritchard

PRAISE THE LORD, YE HEAVENS see Thiman, Eric
Harding

PRAISE THE LORD, YE HEAVENS see Turner, Edmund
(Edmond)

PRAISE THE LORD YE HEAVENS, ADORE HIM
(Peek) SATB oct FISCHER,C CM-7113 $.25
(P2611)

PRAISE THE LORD! YE HEAVENS ADORE HIM see
Haydn, (Franz) Joseph

PRAISE THE LORD, YE HEAVENS ADORE HIM see
Lovelace, Austin C.

PRAISE THE LORD, YE HEAVENS ADORE HIM see
Prichard, [Rowland Hugh]

PRAISE THE LORD, YE HEAVENS ADORE HIM see
Thiman, Eric Harding

PRAISE THE LORD, YE HEAVENS ADORE HIM see
Williams

PRAISE THE LORD, YE PEOPLE see Mozart, Wolfgang
Amadeus

PRAISE THE LORD, YE SAINTS see Mews, Douglas,
Sancti Et Justi

PRAISE THE LORD, YE SERVANTS see Blow, John

PRAISE THE LORD YE SERVANTS see Peek, Richard

PRAISE THE NAME OF THE LORD see Archangelsky

PRAISE THE NAME OF THE LORD see Ivanoff, P.

PRAISE THE NAME OF THE LORD see Maltzeff, A.

PRAISE THE SAVIOR see Cassler, G. Winston

PRAISE THE SAVIOR, NOW AND FOREVER see Proulx,
Richard

PRAISE THE SAVIOUR see Darst, S. Glen

PRAISE THEE, LORD see Kirk

PRAISE THEE, O GOD see Rhodes, Phillip

PRAISE THOU THE LORD see Darst, W. Glenn

PRAISE THOU THE LORD see Statham, Heathcote
(Dicken)

PRAISE THOU THE LORD, JERUSALEM see Bach,
Johann Sebastian, Preise, Jerusalem, Den
Herrn

PRAISE THY GOD, JEHOVAH, ALL YE NATIONS see
Lassus, Roland de (Orlandus), Jubilate Deo
Omnis Terra

PRAISE TO GOD see Kirk, Theron W.

PRAISE TO GOD see Nystedt, Knut

PRAISE TO GOD see Rheinberger, Josef, Laus Deo

PRAISE TO GOD! ALLELUIA see Saint-Saens,
Camille

PRAISE TO GOD IMMORTAL PRAISE see Clarke, Henry
Leland

PRAISE TO GOD, IMMORTAL PRAISE see Darst, W.
Glenn

PRAISE TO GOD IMMORTAL PRAISE see Ratcliffe,
Desmond

PRAISE TO GOD, IMMORTAL PRAISE see Warner

PRAISE TO GOD, IMMORTAL PRAISE see Williams

PRAISE TO GOD IN THE HIGHEST *Fest/Gen
(Campbell, S.S.) SATB (easy) oct OXFORD
44.008 $.35 see from Oxford Book Of Carols
(P2612)

PRAISE TO GOD WHO GIVES US BEAUTY see
Schimmerling, H.A.

PRAISE TO GOD, WHO RULES THE EARTH see Handel,
George Frideric, Dio Si Lode Cielo, In
Terra

PRAISE TO HIM, ALLELUIA see Glarum, L. Stanley

PRAISE TO JESUS, OUR SALVATION *Xmas,carol,
Czech
(Ehret, Walter) SATB,opt inst oct WALTON 2509
$.30
(P2613)

PRAISE TO MARY see Brahms, Johannes

PRAISE TO THE FATHER see Palestrina, Giovanni,
Gloria Patri

PRAISE TO THE HOLIEST IN THE HEIGHT *hymn
(Billing) SATB oct ST.MARTIN s.p.
(P2614)

PRAISE TO THE LIVING GOD
(Brandon) SAB,org/pno BOSTON 13327 $.35
(P2615)

PRAISE TO THE LIVING GOD see Mueller, Carl F.

PRAISE TO THE LIVING GOD see Vree

PRAISE TO THE LIVING GOD (YIGDAL) see Oliver

PRAISE TO THE LORD (from Stralsund Gesangbuch)
Fest/Thanks,hymn,17th cent
see Entrance Hymns
(Davis, K.) SA&desc,pno/org SCHIRM.EC 1572
$.30
(P2616)
(Gray) SATB oct PRO ART 1856 $.25   (P2617)
(Gray) SSA oct PRO ART 2287 $.25   (P2618)
(Parker) unis oct LAWSON 51605 $.50 (P2619)
(Phillips) SATB&cong&desc,org,opt trp oct
SUMMY M 2559 $.60, ipa   (P2620)
(Sanders, H.) SATB oct PRESSER 332-14827 $.30
(P2621)
(Shaw) mix cor,org oct SCHIRM.G 10098 $.25
(P2622)
(Van Koert, Han) SA&SATB,S solo,org oct WORLD
$.45   (P2623)

PRAISE TO THE LORD see Bach, Johann Sebastian

PRAISE TO THE LORD see Cabena, Barrie, Lobe Den
Herrn

PRAISE TO THE LORD see Cassler, G. Winston

PRAISE TO THE LORD see Christiansen, F. Melius

PRAISE TO THE LORD see Coleman, Henry, Lobe Den
Herren

PRAISE TO THE LORD see Den Herren

PRAISE TO THE LORD see Dressler, John, Lobe Den
Herrn

PRAISE TO THE LORD see Fryxell, Regina Holmen,
Lobe Den Herrn

PRAISE TO THE LORD see Gilbert, Norman

PRAISE TO THE LORD see Greenhill, Harold

PRAISE TO THE LORD see Groom, Lester H.

PRAISE TO THE LORD see Hastings, Ross, Lobe Den
Herrn

PRAISE TO THE LORD see Karam, Frederick

PRAISE TO THE LORD see Lockwood, Normand

PRAISE TO THE LORD see Newbury, Kent A., Lobe
Den Herren

PRAISE TO THE LORD see Parker, Alice

PRAISE TO THE LORD see Rohlig, Harald

PRAISE TO THE LORD see Smart, David

PRAISE TO THE LORD see Stralsund

PRAISE TO THE LORD see Toolan, S. Suzanne, Lobe
Den Herren

PRAISE TO THE LORD see Willan, Healey

PRAISE TO THE LORD THE ALMIGHTY see Angell

PRAISE TO THE LORD, THE ALMIGHTY see Bunjes,
Paul G.

PRAISE TO THE LORD, THE ALMIGHTY see Hebble,
Lobe Den Herren

PRAISE TO THE LORD THE ALMIGHTY see Howorth,
Wayne

PRAISE TO THE LORD, THE ALMIGHTY see Hughes

PRAISE TO THE LORD, THE ALMIGHTY see Krapf,
Gerhard

PRAISE TO THE LORD, THE ALMIGHTY see Lobe Den
Herrn

PRAISE TO THE LORD THE ALMIGHTY see Mueller,
Carl F.

PRAISE TO THE LORD, THE ALMIGHTY see Spar, Otto

PRAISE TO THE LORD, THE ALMIGHTY see Stralsund

PRAISE TO THE LORD, THE ALMIGHTY see Thompson

PRAISE TO THE LORD, THE ALMIGHTY see Van Dyke

PRAISE TO THE LORD, THE ALMIGHTY see Wilson

PRAISE TO THE LORD WHO LIVES ON HIGH see
Vulpius, Melchior

PRAISE TO THE RISEN LORD see White, L.J.

PRAISE TO THE SPIRIT see Shaw, Martin

PRAISE TO THEE see Philips, Peter, Tibi Laus,
Tibi Gloria

PRAISE TO THEE, LORD JESUS see Schutz, Heinrich

PRAISE TO YOU, FATHER see Roff, Joseph

PRAISE UNTO HIM *CC10L,Gen
    SATB PRO ART 136 $1.25   (P2624)

PRAISE WAITETH FOR THEE see Ambrose, [Paul]

PRAISE WE GOD THE FATHER'S NAME see Sateren,
Leland Bernhard

PRAISE WE HIS NAME see Bach

PRAISE WE OUR GOD see Vulpius, Melchior, Gelobt
Sei Gott

PRAISE WE, PRAISE WE, GOD THE LORD see Shave,
E.

PRAISE WE SING TO THEE see Haydn, (Franz)
Joseph

PRAISE WE SING TO THEE see Luvaas

PRAISE WE THE LORD *carol
    SATB (easy) OXFORD 08.164 $.15   (P2625)

PRAISE WE THE LORD see Elliot, Robert

PRAISE WE THE LORD see Hanson

PRAISE WE THE LORD see Haselton, Robert

PRAISE WE THE LORD IN HIGHEST HEAVEN see
Vulpius, Melchior

PRAISE WE THE NAME OF GOD see Bach

PRAISE WE THE NAME OF THE LORD see Bach, Johann
Sebastian

PRAISE YE see Christiansen, Paul

PRAISE YE see Lekberg, Sven

PRAISE YE see Sternberg, E.W., Lobgesang

PRAISE YE FOREVER see Glarum, L. Stanley

PRAISE YE HIM see Nichols, T.

PRAISE YE HIM, ALL HIS ANGELS see Hovhaness,
Alan

PRAISE YE JEHOVAH see Agey, C. Buell

PRAISE YE, JEHOVAH see Lyon

PRAISE YE, O PRAISE THE LORD see Hassler, Hans
Leo, Laudate Dominum, Omnes Gentes

PRAISE YE THE FATHER see Christe Sanctorem

PRAISE YE THE FATHER see Darst, S. Glen

PRAISE YE THE FATHER see Gounod, Charles
Francois

PRAISE YE THE LORD
    (Sargent) SATB,acap (med) OXFORD 84.084 $.25
                                                   (P2626)

PRAISE YE THE LORD see Aston, Peter

PRAISE YE THE LORD see Bach, Johann Sebastian

PRAISE YE THE LORD see Bantock, Granville

PRAISE YE THE LORD see Bernardi, Steffano,
Laudate Dominium

PRAISE YE THE LORD see Boccard, C.C.

PRAISE YE THE LORD see Brubeck

PRAISE YE THE LORD see Bruckner, Anton

PRAISE YE THE LORD see Butler, Eugene

PRAISE YE THE LORD see Cherubini, Luigi

PRAISE YE THE LORD see Diemer, Emma Lou

PRAISE YE THE LORD see Fearing, John

PRAISE YE THE LORD see Fetler, Paul

PRAISE YE THE LORD see Franck, Cesar

PRAISE YE THE LORD see Geisler, Johan C.

PRAISE YE THE LORD see Glarum, L. Stanley

PRAISE YE THE LORD see Guenther

PRAISE YE THE LORD see Hagemann, P.

PRAISE YE THE LORD see Harris

PRAISE YE THE LORD see Hawkey

PRAISE YE THE LORD see Henderson

PRAISE YE THE LORD see Hovhaness, Alan

PRAISE YE THE LORD see Humphreys, Don

PRAISE YE THE LORD see Hurd, Michael

PRAISE YE THE LORD see Karg-Elert, Sigfrid

PRAISE YE THE LORD see Koch, Frederick

PRAISE YE THE LORD see Lauridsen, Morten

PRAISE YE THE LORD see Lehmeier, J.F.

PRAISE YE THE LORD see Lekberg, Sven

PRAISE YE THE LORD see MacFarren, Walter
[Cecil]

PRAISE YE THE LORD see Martin, Reginald W.

PRAISE YE THE LORD see Mendelssohn-Bartholdy,
Felix, Laudate Pueri

PRAISE YE THE LORD see Molitor, J.B.

PRAISE YE THE LORD see Mozart, Wolfgang Amadeus

PRAISE YE THE LORD see Nelson, R. Wayne

PRAISE YE THE LORD see Pitoni, Giuseppe
Ottavio, Laudate Dominum

PRAISE YE THE LORD see Porter

PRAISE YE THE LORD see Randegger, Alberto

PRAISE YE THE LORD see Redman, Reginald

PRAISE YE THE LORD see Rutter

PRAISE YE THE LORD see Saint-Saens, Camille

PRAISE YE THE LORD see Staden

PRAISE YE THE LORD see Stevens, Halsey

PRAISE YE THE LORD see Sweelinck, Jan
Pieterszoon

PRAISE YE THE LORD see Tchaikovsky, Piotr
Ilyitch

PRAISE YE THE LORD see Track, Gerhard

PRAISE YE THE LORD see Vulpius, Melchior

PRAISE.YE THE LORD see Walton, Kenneth

PRAISE YE THE LORD see Weed, Maurice

PRAISE YE THE LORD see Wienhorst, Richard

PRAISE YE THE LORD see Williams

PRAISE YE THE LORD see Young

PRAISE YE THE LORD see Younger, John B.

PRAISE YE THE LORD, ALLELUIA see Stroh,
Virginia

PRAISE YE THE LORD IN HEAVEN see Arensky, Anton
Stepanovitch

PRAISE YE THE LORD, MY SOUL, ADORE HIM see
Rameau, Jean-Philippe

PRAISE YE THE LORD OF HEAVEN see Bortniansky,
Dimitri Stepanovitch

PRAISE YE THE LORD OF HEAVEN see Pitoni,
Giuseppe Ottavio

PRAISE YE THE LORD OF HOSTS see Arkhangelsky,
G.

PRAISE YE THE LORD OF HOSTS see Gallus, Jacobus

PRAISE YE THE LORD OF HOSTS see Saint-Saens,
Camille, Oratorio De Noel

PRAISE YE THE LORD, THE ALMIGHTY (from
Stralsund Gesungbuch)
    (Rogers) 2pt jr cor/3pt jr cor oct LILLENAS
    AN-4007 $.25   (P2627)

PRAISE YE THE LORD, THE ALMIGHTY see Gesangbuch

PRAISE YE THE LORD, THE ALMIGHTY see Hanson,
Wesley

PRAISE YE THE LORD, THE ALMIGHTY see Mueller,
Carl F.

PRAISE YE THE LORD WITH SINGING see
Gumpeltzhaimer, Adam, Lob Gott Getrost Mit
Singen

PRAISE YE THE LORD, YE CHILDREN see Tye,
Christopher

PRAISE YE THE NAME OF THE LORD
    SATB oct STAFF 330 $.25   (P2628)

PRAISE YE THE NAME OF THE LORD see
Arkhangelsky, Alexander

PRAISE YE THE NAME OF THE LORD see Lvov, Alexey
Feodorovitch

PRAISE YE THE NAME OF THE LORD see Mead, Edward
G.

PRAISE YE THE NAME OF THE LORD see
Rachmaninoff, Sergey Vassilievitch

PRAISE YE THE NAME OF THE LORD see Tchaikovsky,
Piotr Ilyitch

PRAISE YE THE NAME OF THE LORD see Tcherepnin,
Nikolay Nikolayevitch

PRAISE YE THE NAME OF THE LORD see Tellep, Leo
M.

PRAISE YE THE NAME OF THE LORD see Young,
Gordon

PRAISE THE SOVEREIGN LORD see Peninger

PRAISE THE TRIUNE GOD see Hanson, Wesley

PRAISE YE, WITH ME, THE LORD OUR GOD see
Carissimi, Giacomo, Cantata Mecum Domino

PRAISED BE MY LORD see Thompson

PRAISED BE THE LORD
    (Wienandt) SATB,acap oct LAWSON 51507 $.35
                                                   (P2629)

PRAISED BE THE LORD see Garlick, Anthony

PRAISED BE THE LORD see Greene, Maurice

PRAISED BE THE LORD BY DAY see Adler, Samuel

PRAISED BE THOU, O LORD see Berger, Jean

PRAISES FOR THE RISEN CHRIST see Martin

PRAISES FROM THE CORNERS OF THE EARTH see
Avshalomov, Jacob

PRAISES OF A KING, THE see Lovelace, Austin C.

PRAISES OF THE TRINITY, THE see Wills, Arthur

PRAISES TO OUR GOD see Bach, Johann Sebastian

PRAISES TO THE GIVER see Lorenz

PRAISES TO THE VIRGIN MARY see Verdi, Giuseppe

PRAISEYE THE LORD see Donato

PRAISIN' THE LORD see Hathaway, C.

PRAISING SONG see Brooks

PRAUTZSCH, LUDWIG (1926-   )
    Siehe, Ich Habe Dir Geboten
        see Nickel, Eckehardt, Herr Christe, Treuer
        Heiland Wert

PRAY FOR HONOR see Kodaly, Zoltan

PRAY FOR LOVE see Johnson, Sidney

PRAYER see Agustsson, Herbert H.

PRAYER see Andrews, C.T.

PRAYER see Beebe

PRAYER see Beethoven, Ludwig van

PRAYER see Brahms, Johannes

PRAYER see Britain, [Radie]

PRAYER see Diercks, L.H.

PRAYER see Faure, Gabriel-Urbain, En Priere

PRAYER see Gardner, Maurice

PRAYER see Geibel

PRAYER see Gluck, Christoph Willibald Ritter
von

PRAYER see Grant

PRAYER see Guion, David Wendall Fentress

PRAYER see Humperdinck, Engelbert

PRAYER see Kountz, Richard

PRAYER see Krider, Dale

PRAYER see Krul

PRAYER see Levy

PRAYER see Mascagni, Pietro

PRAYER see Mendelssohn-Bartholdy, Felix

PRAYER see Mercer, M.

PRAYER see Mumford

PRAYER see Parker, Alice

PRAYER see Scarmolin, (Anthony) Louis

PRAYER see Untermeyer

PRAYER see Wagner, Richard

PRAYER see York, D.

PRAYER, A see Harrhy, Edith

PRAYER, A see Brown, William [H., Jr.]

PRAYER, A see Evans

PRAYER, A see Lloyd, Richard H.

PRAYER, A see Reske

PRAYER, A see Stewart

PRAYER AND CHORALE see Mendelssohn-Bartholdy,
Felix

PRAYER AND PRAISE *CCU,anthem
    SATB/SA LORENZ $1.75   (P2630)

PRAYER AND PRAISE see Wilson, Harry [Robert]

PRAYER AT SEA see Reinecke, Carl

PRAYER BEFORE SINGING see Hustad, Donald P.

PRAYER FOR A RIGHT SPIRIT see Pfohl

PRAYER FOR ALL NATIONS see Evans

PRAYER FOR AN OCCASION *Xmas/Gen
    SATB CHAPPELL 0016360-358 $.40   (P2631)

PRAYER FOR BROTHERHOOD, A see Franck, Cesar

PRAYER FOR BROTHERHOOD, A see Franck, Cesar

PRAYER FOR COMMUNION, A see Bitgood, Roberta

PRAYER FOR EPIPHANY, A see Cashmore, Donald

PRAYER FOR FAMILIES, A see Lovelace, Austin C.

PRAYER FOR GOD'S BLESSING see Van Dyke

PRAYER FOR GUIDANCE see Kountz

PRAYER FOR LIGHT, A see Darst, W. Glenn

PRAYER FOR MAN AND HIS WORLD see Buckner

PRAYER FOR MOTHERS, A see Martens

PRAYER FOR OUR CHILDREN see Hemmer, [Eugene]

PRAYER FOR OUR COUNTRY, A see Rogers

PRAYER FOR OUR NATION'S HOMES, A see Hutson

PRAYER FOR OUR NATIVE LAND, A see Kilpatrick, Jack F.

PRAYER FOR OUR TIME see Hopson

PRAYER FOR PEACE see Freed, Isadore

PRAYER FOR PEACE
    see Folio Of Sacred Music (Volume 3)
    SATB CHAPPELL 0022798-358 $.40   (P2632)

PRAYER FOR PEACE see Day, R.E.

PRAYER FOR PEACE see Diamond, David

PRAYER FOR PEACE see Fetler, Paul

PRAYER FOR PEACE see Freed, Isadore

PRAYER FOR PEACE see Goemanne, Noel

PRAYER FOR PEACE see Leonard

PRAYER FOR PEACE see Lord, Davis

PRAYER FOR PEACE see Peloquin, C. Alexander

PRAYER FOR PEACE see Wolfe

PRAYER FOR PEACE OF ST. FRANCIS see Goemanne, Noel

PRAYER FOR PENTECOSTAL FIRE see Keys, Ivor

PRAYER FOR REJOICING, A see Chandler, Mary

PRAYER FOR SONG see Branscombe, [Gina]

PRAYER FOR ST. AMBROSE, A see Milano, R.

PRAYER FOR ST. AUGUSTINE, A see Milano, R.

PRAYER FOR ST. FRANCIS see Milano, R.

PRAYER FOR ST. THEODOLPH, A see Milano, R.

PRAYER FOR STEADFASTNESS, A see Milano, R.

PRAYER FOR STRENGTH see Graham

PRAYER FOR STRENGTH AND LIGHT see Bohlen, D.

PRAYER FOR THE QUEEN, A see Dyson, George

PRAYER FOR THE UNITED NATIONS see Hastings

PRAYER FOR THIS HOUSE see Fast, Willard S.

PRAYER FOR THIS HOUSE see McKay, George Frederick

PRAYER FOR TODAY, A see Hoffmann

PRAYER FOR TODAY, A see Rosenmuller, Johann

PRAYER FROM "BORIS GODUNOV" see Mussorgsky, Modest

PRAYER FROM OUTER SPACE see Roff, Joseph

PRAYER IN WINTER see Jordan

PRAYER IS THE SOUL'S SINCERE DESIRE
    (Walton) SATB oct BOOSEY 5142 $.30   (P2633)

PRAYER IS THE SOUL'S SINCERE DESIRE see Bitgood, Roberta

PRAYER IS THE SOUL'S SINCERE DESIRE see Jordan, A.

PRAYER MODES see Glantz, Yehuda Leib

PRAYER OF DEDICATION, A see Frederick, Donald R.

PRAYER OF HUMBLE ACCESS, A see Wetherill

PRAYER OF INNOCENCE see Richman

PRAYER OF KING CHARLES see Ley, Henry George, Evening Hymn

PRAYER OF KING HENRY VI, A see Ley, Henry George

PRAYER OF MANASSEH, THE see Berger, Jean

PRAYER OF MOSES' MOTHER see Gordon, P.

PRAYER OF OUR LORD (from King Of Kings)
    SSA/SATB BIG3 $.35   (P2634)

PRAYER OF PATRIOTISM see Strong

PRAYER OF PEACE see Schubert, Franz (Peter)

PRAYER OF PENITENCE, A see Martin

PRAYER OF PETER MARSHALL, THE see Page, R.

PRAYER OF SAINT FRANCIS see Nieland, Jan

PRAYER OF SAINT FRANCIS, A see Prinz, Leonhard

PRAYER OF SAINT PATRICK see Hastings, Ross

PRAYER OF ST. CHRYSOSTOM see Butler

PRAYER OF ST. FRANCIS see Hastings, E.

PRAYER OF ST. FRANCIS see Kalmanoff, [Martin]

PRAYER OF ST. FRANCIS see Mueller, Carl F.

PRAYER OF ST. FRANCIS see Woolen, R.

PRAYER OF ST. FRANCIS see Wright

PRAYER OF ST. FRANCIS, A see Hunter

PRAYER OF ST. FRANCIS OF ASSISI see Foltz

PRAYER OF ST. FRANCIS OF ASSISI see White, Louie

PRAYER OF ST. PATRICK see Hastings, Ross

PRAYER OF ST. RICHARD OF CHICHESTER, A see White, L.J.

PRAYER OF SUPPLICATION see Litten, Jack

PRAYER OF THANKSGIVING *Gen/Thanks,folk/
    prayer,Dut/Neth
    see Thanksgiving Songs
    (Anderson, W.H.) SATB oct LESLIE 4036 (P2635)
    (Anderson, W.H.) unis oct LESLIE 1038 (P2636)
    (Anderson, W.H.) SA oct LESLIE 1038   (P2637)
    (Dawson) SATB oct PRO ART 1402 $.30   (P2638)
    (Dawson) SAB oct PRO ART 1533 $.30   (P2639)
    (Dawson) 2pt oct PRO ART 1802 $.22   (P2640)
    (Holmes) TTBB oct PRO ART 1964 $.20   (P2641)
    (Kremser) 4pt mix cor oct SCHIRM.G 4345 $.30
                                          (P2642)
    (Kremser) 4pt men cor oct SCHIRM.G 4947 $.30
                                          (P2643)
    (Kremser) 3pt wom cor oct SCHIRM.G 6812 $.25
                                          (P2644)
    (Kremser) SATB oct BELWIN 64124 $.30 (P2645)
    (Kremser) SATB SCHMITT 1918 $.35   (P2646)
    (Kremser; Deis) 3pt mix cor oct SCHIRM.G 9904
    $.30   (P2647)
    (Kremser, E.) SATB oct PRESSER 332-12606 $.30
                                          (P2648)
    (Kremser; Owning) 2pt boy cor/2pt wom cor oct
    SCHIRM.G 7950 $.30   (P2649)
    (Newbury) mix cor,org,opt brass oct SCHIRM.G
    11761 $.35   (P2650)
    (Shaw) mix cor oct LAWSON 772 $.30   (P2651)

PRAYER OF THANKSGIVING see Kremser

PRAYER OF THANKSGIVING see Krones

PRAYER OF THANKSGIVING see Valerius

PRAYER OF THE CHRISTMAS ANIMALS see Hopson

PRAYER OF THE NORWEGIAN CHILD see Kountz, Richard

PRAYER OF THE PROPHET see Geisler, Johan C.

PRAYER OF THE PUBLICAN, THE see Blakley, D. Duane

PRAYER OF TRUST see Pasquet, Jean

PRAYER ON CHRISTMAS EVE see Peeters, Flor

PRAYER PERFECT see Speaks, [Oley]

PRAYER PERFECT, THE see Speaks, [Oley]

PRAYER PERFECT, THE see Stenson, E.J.

PRAYER TO JESUS see Church

PRAYER TO JESUS see Oldroyd, George

PRAYER TO MARY see Brahms, Johannes

PRAYER TO THE FATHER OF HEAVEN see Vaughan Williams, Ralph

PRAYER TO THE HOLY SPIRIT see Brigitta, St.

PRAYER TO THE HOLY SPIRIT see Tcherepnin, Alexander

PRAYER TO THE INFANT JESUS, A see Bliss, Sir Arthur

PRAYER WITH PSALM see Songer

PRAYERS see Hugh-Jones, Llifon

PRAYERS AND RESPONSES see Rorem, Ned

PRAYERS I MAKE, THE see Marshall

PRAYERS OF CARDINAL NEWMAN see Dello Joio, Norman

PRAYERS OF KIERKEGAARD see Barber, Samuel

PRAYERS OF STEEL see Christiansen, Paul

PRECAMUR SANCTE DOMINE see White, Robert

PRECEPTS OF ANGELUS SILESIUS see Bacon, Ernst

PRECES see Gibbons, Orlando

PRECES AND RESPONSES see Winchester, E.C.

PRECES AND RESPONSES see Ayleward, Richard

PRECES AND RESPONSES see Bullock, Ernest

PRECES AND RESPONSES see Gardner, John [Linton]

PRECES AND RESPONSES see Greiner, Allen

PRECES AND RESPONSES see Leighton, Kenneth

PRECES AND RESPONSES see Lumsden, David

PRECES AND RESPONSES see Moreton, H.

PRECES AND RESPONSES see Rose, Bernard

PRECES AND RESPONSES see Tallis, Thomas

PRECES AND RESPONSES see Wills, Arthur

PRECES AND RESPONSES ACCORDING TO TALLIS
    (FESTAL) see Barnby, Sir Joseph

PRECES AND RESPONSES (CANTERBURY) see Campbell, Sydney S.

PRECES AND RESPONSES (CANTERBURY) see Howells, Herbert Norman

PRECES AND RESPONSES (FERIAL) see Tallis, Thomas

PRECES AND RESPONSES (FESTAL) see Westoby, C.F.

PRECES AND RESPONSES FOR EVENING PRAYER see Rutter

PRECES AND RESPONSES (ST. PAUL'S) (FERIAL) see Stainer, John

PRECES AND RESPONSES, THE see Ayleward, Richard

PRECES AND RESPONSES, THE see Clucas, Humphrey

PRECES AND RESPONSES (WINDSOR) see Campbell, Sydney S.

PRECES AND RESPONSES WITH HARMONIZED CONFESSION
    (ELY) see Barnby, Sir Joseph

PRECES AND RESPONSES WITH LITANY (FERIAL) see Barnby, Sir Joseph

PRECES AND RESPONSES WITH LITANY (ST. PAUL'S)
    (FERIAL) see Stainer, John

PRECIOUS CHILD SO SWEETLY SLEEPING see Trued

PRECIOUS JESUS, (BURDEN BEARER) see Iden, Raymond

PRECIOUS LORD, TAKE MY HAND see Allan

PRECIOUS LORD, TAKE MY HAND see Allen

PREDMORE, G.V.
    O Faithful Cross *Lent,anthem
    SATB (easy) oct GIA G1721 $.30   (P2652)
    2 eq voices (easy) oct GIA G1722 $.25
                                      (P2653)

PREFACE AND SANCTUS see Fouser, C.E.

PREFACES see Meter, C.

PREGHIERA see Veneziani, Vittore

PREGHIERA AI GENITORI see Palumbo, Guido

PREGHIERA ALLA VIRGINE see Zandonai, Riccardo

PREGHIERA DEI BIMBI D'ITALIA see Cossetti, Gio. Batta.

PREGON PARA UNA PASCUA POBRE see Halffter, Rodolfo

PREHL-SCHMALZRIED
    Geistlicher Liederschatz *CC130U,mot
    2-3pt wom cor/2-3pt jr cor cloth LEUCKART
    s.p.   (P2654)

PREIBISCH, HILDE
    Introitus-Psalmen-Heft 1 *CCU,Adv/Lent,
    Introit/Psalm
    4pt mix cor MOSELER s.p.   (P2655)

    Introitus-Psalmen-Heft 2 *CCU,Easter/ECY,
    Introit/Psalm
    4pt mix cor MOSELER s.p.   (P2656)

PREIS, DANK, LOB, EHR UND HERRLICHKEIT see Gallus, Jacobus

PREIS DEN HERRN ALLE ZEITEN see Reger, Max

PREIS DIR, GOTTHEIT see Mozart, Wolfgang Amadeus

PREIS DIR O TON see Weber

PREIS, LOB UND DANK SEI GOTT DEM HERREN see Goudimel, Claude

PREIS, LOB UND DANK SEI GOTT DEM HERREN see Kubler, Emil

PREIS, LOB UND DANK SEI GOTT, DEM HERREN see Schmidt-Mannheim, Hans

PREIS SEI GOTT IN DER HOHE see Praetorius, Michael

PREIS UND ANBETUNG see Rinck, Johann Christian Hein.

PREIS UND EHRE, HERR JESU see Perti, Giacomo Antonio

PREIS UND EHRE, HERR JESU, LOB see Palestrina, Giovanni

PREIS UND EHRE SEI DIR, O GOTT see Lassus, Roland de (Orlandus)

PREISE, JERUSALEM see Bach, Johann Sebastian, Preise, Jerusalem, Den Herrn

PREISE, JERUSALEM, DEN HERRN see Bach, Johann Sebastian

PRELUDE see Gounod, Charles Francois

PRELUDE A JERUSALEM see Sadai, Yizhak

PRELUDE ADAGIO AND CHORALE see Pinkham, Daniel

PRELUDE, ANUNCIATION AND ALLELUIA see Giasson

PRELUDE, ARIA AND CHORALE see Karg-Elert, Sigfrid

PRELUDE NO. 9 see Bach, Johann Sebastian

PRELUDE NO. 11 see Bach, Johann Sebastian

PRELUDE NO. 23 see Bach, Johann Sebastian

PRELUDE ON PSALMS see Bach, Johann Sebastian

PRELUDE TO A SOLEMN MUSIC see Harris, William Henry

PRELUDE TO CHRISTMAS see Christiansen, Olaf Christian

PRELUDES TO ETERNITY see Liszt, Franz, Les
   Preludes

PREMIER JOUR DE NOEL *Xmas,carol,Eng
   (Canteloube, J.) 4pt mix cor,acap oct DURAND
                                              (P2657)

PREMIER SALUT see Heidet, Le R. P.

PREMIERE MESSE see Battmann

PREMIERE MESSE BREVE see Boissiere

PREMIERE IESSE DE STE CECILE see Cherubini,
   Luigi

PREMIERE MESSE SOLENNELLE see Fauchey, Paul

PREMIERE MESSE SOLENNELLE see Franck, Cesar

PRENNER, GEORG (1517- ?)
   Assumpta Est Maria *Fest
   [Lat] SSATB,acap (med) MULLER MS 64 s.p.
                                              (P2658)

PRENTICE, CHARLES
   Sing We Merrily Unto God Our Strength
      *anthem
   SATB WEINBERGER s.p.   (P2659)

PRENTICE, FRED
   All Poor Men *Xmas
   SATB WORD CS-346 $.30   (P2660)

   Day Of Resurrection *Easter,cant
   SATB&cong,2 narrators,brass,perc,chimes voc
      sc WORD 20027 $1.50, ipa   (P2661)

   Glory In The Church
   SATB oct PRESSER G-132 $.35   (P2662)

   Glory To God *Xmas
   SATB oct WORD CS-2427 $.40   (P2663)

   Great God Of Our Salvation
   SA oct WORD CS-692 $.25   (P2664)

   Jesus Walked This Lonesome Valley
   SATB oct WORD CS-331 $.30   (P2665)

   Let Love Be Genuine
   SATB,org,bells,chimes,gtr oct WORD CS-2398
      $.50   (P2666)

   Make A Joyful Sound
   SATB oct WORD CS-329 $.30   (P2667)
   SSA WORD CS-352 $.30   (P2668)

   My Soul Doth Magnify The Lord
   SSAATTBB,acap (med) PRESSER G-211 $.50   (P2669)

   Now Every Star
   SATB oct WORD CS-115 $.35   (P2670)

   O Sing To The Lord A New Song (from Day Of
      Resurrection) Easter/Lent
   SATB,brass,perc oct WORD CS-404 $.40, ipa
                                              (P2671)
   Spirit Of God
   SATB oct WORD CS-2404 $.35   (P2672)

   Sweet Dreams *Xmas
   SATB oct WORD CS-697 $.25   (P2673)

   We've Got One Hour, Lord
   SATB oct WORD CS-330 $.30   (P2674)

PREPARE HIM ROOM see Hadler

PREPARE MY MIND AND HEART FOR PRAYER see Morgan

PREPARE THE HYMN see Handel, George Frideric

PREPARE THE WAY *Easter
   (Luvaas M.) SATB oct PRESSER 332-14449 $.30
                                              (P2675)
PREPARE THE WAY, O ZION
   see Lift Up Your Heads, Ye Gates Of Brass
   (Pooler, M.) SAB,pno/org oct KERBY 6051 $.35
                                              (P2676)
PREPARE THE WAY, O ZION see Pooler, Marie

PREPARE THE WAY, O ZION see Willan, Healey

PREPARE THE WAY OF THE LORD see Newbury, Kent
   A.

PREPARE THYSELF ZION see Bach, Johann
   Sebastian, Bereite Dich, Zion

PREPARE YE THE WAY OF THE LORD see Benner

PREPARE YE THE WAY OF THE LORD see Garrett,
   G.M.

PREPARE YE THE WAY OF THE LORD see Leyden

PREPARE YE THE WAY OF THE LORD see Wise,
   Michael

PRES DU FLEUVE ETRANGER see Gounod, Charles
   Francois

PRESENCE, THE see Schoenfeld, William C.

PRESENT TENSE, THE see Nelson, Ronald A.

PRESENTATION OF CHRIST see Eccard, Johannes

PRESENTATION OF CHRIST IN THE TEMPLE see
   Eccard, Johannes

PRESERVE ME, O GOD see Berger, Jean

PRESERVE ME, O GOD see Goodman, Joseph

PRESERVE ME, O GOD see Schuff

PRESERVE ME, O LORD see Manz, Paul

PRESERVE US, O LORD see Hastings

PRESERVE US, O LORD see Willan, Healey

PRESIDENT'S MESSAGE, THE see Heifetz, Vladimir

PRESSER CHORAL COLLECTION NO. 2 *sac/sec,CCU
   2-4pt treb cor oct PRESSER $2.75 (P2677)

PRESSER CHORAL COLLECTION NO. 3 *sac/sec,CCU
   SATB oct PRESSER $2.50   (P2678)

PRESSMANN, W.
   Postula A Me *Offer
   mix cor,acap ERDMANN 541 s.p.   (P2679)

PRESSO IL FIUME STRANIER see Gounod, Charles
   Francois

PRESTON
   Blessed Are The Poor In Spirit
   SATB FLAMMER A 5615 $.30   (P2680)

PRESTON, SIMON
   God Is Our Hope And Strength (Psalm 46) Gen/
      Thanks
   SSAATTBB,acap (med) oct OXFORD 43.948 $.65
                                      (P2681)
   Jubilate Deo
   SATB (med diff) oct OXFORD 42.866 $.35
                                      (P2682)
   Missa Brevis *Mass
   mix cor oct OXFORD 42.355 $1.00   (P2683)

   Psalm 46 *see God Is Our Hope And Strength

PREUS, CAROL
   Even So, Lord Jesus, Quickly Come *see
      Narum, Jeanne

PREUS, SOLVEIG D.
   Haste Not! Rest Not!
   SSAA,Bar/Mez solo,pno/chimes SCHIRM.EC 2571
      $.55   (P2684)

PREVENT US, O LORD see Byrd, William

PREVENT US, O LORD see Holman, Derek

PREVENT US, O LORD see Le Fleming, Christopher
   (Kaye)

PREVENT US O LORD, IN ALL OUR DOINGS see Byrd,
   William

PRICE
   Alleluia
   SATB oct LORENZ C169 $.30   (P2685)

   Breathe On Me, Breath Of God
   SATB oct LORENZ A495 $.25   (P2686)

   Garden Hymn, T
   SATB oct LORENZ B135 $.30   (P2687)

   God Of Grace And God Of Glory
   SATB oct LORENZ C247 $.30   (P2688)

   I Sing Of God
   2pt oct LORENZ 5749 $.30   (P2689)

   I Sing The Mighty Power Of God
   SATB oct LORENZ A523 $.30   (P2690)

   I Will Extol Thee
   SATB oct LORENZ C202 $.30   (P2691)

   King Is Riding By, The *Easter
   SATB oct LORENZ A519 $.30   (P2692)

   O God, Our Help In Ages Past
   SATB oct LORENZ 9909 $.30   (P2693)

   Show Me The Way
   SA/SAB oct LORENZ 7827 $.25   (P2694)

   Surely God Is In This Place
   SATB oct LORENZ B68 $.30   (P2695)

   'Tis So Sweet To Trust In Jesus
   SATB oct LORENZ A486 $.30   (P2696)

   We Thank Thee, O Lord
   SATB oct LORENZ B132 $.30   (P2697)

PRICE, BENTON
   Soldiers Of Christ, Arise *Gen,anthem
   SATB/SA (easy) oct LORENZ A531 $.30 (P2698)

   'Twas On One Sunday Morning *Easter
   SATB oct LORENZ A501 $.30   (P2699)
   2pt oct LORENZ 5719 $.25   (P2700)

PRICE, FLO
   Back Home *CCUL
   (Carmichael, Ralph) SATB voc sc WORD 37552
      $1.95   (P2701)

PRICE, MILBURN
   Unto The Least Of These
   SATB oct WORD CS-2486 $.30   (P2702)

PRICE OF PEACE, THE
   SATB BIG3 $.40   (P2703)

PRICE, PAUL
   All The Rest Is Up To You
   SA oct WORD CS-2330 $.30   (P2704)

PRICE, R.W.
   My Faith Looks Up To Thee
   SATB,SSA soli,pno (easy) oct WILLIS 4429
      $.20   (P2705)

PRICE WAS PAID, THE see Lister, Mosie

PRICHARD, HUGH
   Praise The Lord, Ye Heavens *Bibl
   (De Sutter, Guido) SATB,org,opt 2trp&2trom
      oct WORLD ESA-1066-8 $.60   (P2706)

PRICHARD, [ROWLAND HUGH] (1811-1887)
   Little Children, Come To Jesus *anthem
   (Pooler) unis (easy) oct AUGSBURG 1527 $.20
                                      (P2707)
   Love Divine *chorale,Welsh
   (Jones) [Eng/Welsh] mix cor,SABar soli,acap
      oct SCHIRM.G 8064 $.30   (P2708)
   Love Divine, All Loves Excelling *anthem
   (Cassler) TTBB (easy) oct AUGSBURG 1389
      $.20   (P2709)
   Praise The Lord, Ye Heavens Adore Him
   (Malin) SA&SATB oct SUMMY B 1476 $.40
                                      (P2710)
   (Malin) SSAB oct SUMMY B 1475 $.40 (P2711)

PRIERE see Gounod, Charles Francois

PRIERE A SAINTE THERESE DU CARMEL see Roesgen-
   Champion, Marguerite

PRIERE AU REDEMPTEUR see Busser, [Henri-Paul]

PRIERE DES ALBIGEOIS *Xmas,carol,13th cent
   (Geveart, F.-A.) [Fr] 4pt mix cor,acap (med
   easy) cor pts LEMOINE s.p. see from
   Collection De Choeurs, dixieme Fascicule
                                      (P2712)
PRIESING
   Carol Of The Children
   unis SHAWNEE E30 $.25   (P2713)

PRIEST, A
   Surely God Is In This Place *Bibl
   4pt mix cor,high solo oct SCHIRM.G 7432
      $.25   (P2714)

PRIEST AND BISHOP see Roff, Joseph

PRIESTY BLESSING, THE see Jablonsky, Stephan,
   Birkat Kohanim-Ssim Shalom

PRIMA DELLA COMMUNIONE see Bottazzo, Luigi

PRIMA DELLA COMMUNIONE see Corradini, Vasco
   Lodovico

PRIMA LA CONSACRAZIONE see Nicolosi, Salvatore

PRIMAVERA see Benedito

PRIME see Klein, Lothar

PRIMI TONI see Palestrina, Giovanni

PRIMO LIBRO see Bottazzi, B.

PRIMROSE
   (Niles) 3pt wom cor oct SCHIRM.G 10439 $.20
                                      (P2715)

PRIMROSE see Niles, John Jacob

PRINCE IS BORN, A see Tate, Toby

PRINCE OF LIFE, THE see Lillenas, Haldor

PRINCE OF LIGHT, THE see Schiavone, John

PRINCE OF PEACE *Xmas,carol
   (Bancroft, H.H.) SATB oct LESLIE 4014 see
   from Two Christmas Carols, Set 1   (P2716)

PRINCE OF PEACE see McKay

PRINCE OF PEACE see Pierce, Anne E.

PRINCE OF PEACE see Simon

PRINCE OF PEACE see Williams, Ralph E.

PRINCE OF PEACE see Young

PRINCE OF PEACE IS BORN TODAY see Auerbach, N.

PRINCE OF PEACE IS COME! THE see Grieb, Herbert
   [C.]

PRINCE OF PEACE, THE see Clare, Edwyn A.

PRINCE OF PEACE, THE see Halloran, Ella Rose

PRINCE OF PEACE, THE see Holton

PRINCE OF PEACE, THE see Hughes, Robert J.

PRINCE OF PEACE, THE see Kirby

PRINCE OF PEACE, THE see Pierce, Anne E.

PRINCE OF PEACE, THE see Wilson, Harry [Robert]

PRINE
   This Is Life
   (Graf) SATB oct LILLENAS AN-1644 $.30
                                      (P2717)

PRINT THINE IMAGE see Sellew, Donald E.

PRINZ, LEONHARD
   Prayer Of Saint Francis, A *prayer
   SATB ENOCH EC314 s.p.   (P2718)

PRIOLI, GIOVANNI
   Salvum Me Fac Deus *mot,It
   cor FABER F0063 s.p.   (P2719)
   (Roche, Jerome) [Lat] SATTBarBB FABER F0063
      $2.00   (P2720)

PRIS DIG, O HERRE see Bach, Johann Sebastian

PRIS GUD VAR HJELPER see Neilsen, Ludvig

PRIS HERREN see Sundberg, Ove Kr.

PRIS VAERE DEG see Palestrina, Giovanni

PRIS VARE GUD see Waldis, B.

PRIS VARE GUD see Wikander, David

PRITCHARD
   Alleluia! Sing To Jesus!
   (Ehret) SATB oct PLYMOUTH HA-8 $.25 (P2721)

   Christmas Sequence
   SATB THOMP.G s.p.   (P2722)

   Come, Thou Long-Expected Jesus
   (Whitman) SATB oct LILLENAS AN-2330 $.30
                                      (P2723)
   Praise The God Of Our Salvation
   (Rogers) 2pt jr cor/3pt jr cor oct LILLENAS
      AN-4016 $.25   (P2724)
   Praise The Lord
   (Kirk) SAB oct BELWIN 1449 $.25   (P2725)

   Praise The Lord! Ye Heavens
   (Angell) SATB oct PLYMOUTH HA-5 $.25
                                      (P2726)

PRITCHARD, ARTHUR J.
   In Heavenly Love *anthem
   mix cor oct NOVELLO 40.1309.03 s.p. (P2727)

PHITCHARD, ARTHUR J. (cont'd.)

O Be Joyful In The Lord
SATB,org GRAY GCMR 3276 $.30   (P2728)

O Let Us All Be Glad Today *Xmas,anthem
SAT/SAB oct NOVELLO 28.1376.09 s.p.   (P2729)

O Lord, I Will Praise Thee *anthem
mix cor oct NOVELLO 28.1389.00 s.p.   (P2730)

O Praise God In His Holiness *anthem
mix cor oct NOVELLO 40.1321.02 s.p.   (P2731)

Teach Me, My God And King
unis oct NOVELLO 28.1361.00 s.p.   (P2732)

We Thank Thee Lord
cor CRAMER 231 s.p.   (P2733)
unis jr cor CRAMER 231 s.p.   (P2734)

With A Voice Of Singing *anthem
mix cor oct NOVELLO 28.1425.00 s.p.   (P2735)

PRO ADVENTU see Byrd, William

PRO DEFUNCTIS see Monnikendam, Marius

PRO DEFUNCTIS see Mulder, Ernest W.

PRO DEFUNCTIS see Palestrina, Giovanni

PRO HOC DOMINE NON EST see Schutz, Heinrich

PRO HOC MAGNO MYSTERIO see Schutz, Heinrich

PRO NOBIS PUER NATUS EST see Jones

PRO PACE see Casella, Alfredo

PRO PACE ET GLORIA see Bottazzo, Luigi

PRO SUMMO PONTIFICE see Ravanello, Oreste

PRO VESTITIONE see Oltrassi, Giuseppe

PRO VESTITIONE MONIALIUM *mot
[Lat] 2pt wom cor,org sc ZANIBON 771 s.p.,
cor pts ZANIBON 772 s.p.
contains: Bottazzo, Luigi, Veni Sponsa
Christi; Livieri, C., Ipsi Sum
Desponsata; Rodella, Sante, Jesu Corona
Virginum   (P2736)

PROBA ME DEUS oee Lassus, Roland de (Orlandus)

PROCESSION OF PALMS see Williamson, Malcolm

PROCESSION OF THE MAGI see Shields, A. McC.

PROCESSION TO JERUSALEM, THE see Posegate

PROCESSIONAL see Peeters, Flor

PROCESSIONAL AND ALLELUIA see Rockwood, Gay
Hylander

PROCESSIONAL AND RECESSIONAL HYMNS *CC7U,Gen/
Proces/Reces,anthem/hymn
(Jurgens, W.A.; Andolsen, A.A.) unis/SA/TB
(easy) sc GIA G1364 $1.00, voc sc GIA
G1364A $.40   (P2737)

PROCESSIONAL CAROL FOR CHRISTMAS, A see Schalk,
Carl

PROCESSIONAL HYMN see Work

PROCESSIONAL HYMNS *CC20U,Gen/Proces,anthem/
hymn
(Roff, J.) [Eng/Lat] (easy) cmplt ed SA/TB
GIA G988 $1.00; TTBB GIA G989 $1.00; SATB
GIA 987 $1.00   (P2738)

PROCESSIONAL PSALMS (PLAINSONG WITH
FAUXBOURDONS) *Greg/Psalm
(Nicholson, Sydney H.) oct ROYAL 331 s.p.
contains: Psalm 121; Psalm122   (P2739)

PROCESSIONAL SERVICE, A see Black, Charles

PROCESSIONAL SONG see Proulx, Richard

PROCHE DE CETTE ETABLE see Saboly, Nicholas,
Aupres D'aquel Estable

PROCLAIM LIBERTY! see Williams

PROCTER
Man Of Galilee (composed with Kirk) *CC7L,
Easter,So Am
SATB PRO ART 44 $1.00   (P2740)

PROCTER, A.
Quiet Hillside, The *Xmas
SATB oct ELKAN-V 362-1294 $.30   (P2741)

Silently Came The Three Shepherds *Xmas
SATB oct ELKAN-V 362-1325 $.30   (P2742)

PROCTER, LELAND
Tiny Bells Rang, The *Xmas
SATB oct ELKAN-V 362-1293 $.30   (P2743)

PROCTOR, CHARLES
Holy Communion
SATB,org LENGNICK s.p.   (P2744)

Te Deum Laudamus *Te Deum
SATB,org LENGNICK s.p.   (P2745)

Veni, Creator Spiritus
SATB LENGNICK s.p.   (P2746)

PRODIGAL JAZZ, THE see Chappell, Herbert

PRODIGAL SON, THE see Sullivan, Sir Arthur
Seymour

PROFETIE, JESAJA 25, 26 see Braal, Andreas de

PROGRAM OF SIX CHORALES, A see Bach, Johann
Sebastian

PROKOFIEV, SERGE (1891-1953)
Bells Of Christmas, The *Xmas
(Allen) SSAATTBB oct GALLEON GCS1021
                                   (P2747)

PROME NOVAS, HYMENAEE see Verdonck, Cornelius

PROMISE see Sateren, Leland Bernhard

PROMISE, THE see Dunford, Benjamin

PROMISE WHICH WAS MADE, THE see Bairstow,
Edward Cuthbert

PROMISED LAND, THE see Burleigh, Henry Thacker

PROMISED LAND, THE
SATB,band oct STAFF 433 $.25, ipa   (P2748)

PROMISED LAND, THE see Chajes, Julius

PROMISED LAND, THE see Tolmage, Gerald

PROMISED ONE, THE see Sydow

PROPE EST DOMINUS see Haydn, (Johann) Michael

PROPER FOR THE VOTIVE MASS OF THE HOLY SPIRIT
see Rorem, Ned

PROPER OF EASTER DAY see Lucas, Leighton

PROPER OFFERTORIES OF THE SUNDAYS IN ADVENT see
Hegedus, A.

PROPHECIES OF EASTER EVEN, THE
SCHIRM.EC 9 $2.00   (P2749)

PROPHECY see Avshalomov, Jacob

PROPHECY AND ANNUNCIATION see Ringwald, [Roy]

PROPHECY FULFILLED, THE see Upshur

PROPHECY OF ISAIAH, THE see Martinu, Bohuslav,
Die Weissagung Des Jesaja

PROPHECY OF JOEL see Butler

PROPHECY, THE see Mc Cray, James

PROPHESY OF JOEL see Butler

PROPHET ELIJAH AROSE, THE see Pinkham, Daniel

PROPHET ISAIAH, THE see Tansman, Alexander

PROPHET UNWILLING see Wehr, David A.

PROPHETA MENDAX see Maconchy, Elizabeth

PROPHETIAE SIBYLLARUM see Lassus, Roland de
(Orlandus)

PROPHETS, THE see Sheppard, [Joseph] Stanley

PROPITIUS ESTO, DOMINE see Boon, C.

PROPRIEN-MESSE see Niehaus, Manfred

PROPRIUM see Miggl, Erwin

PROPRIUM DER DRITTEN WEIHNACHTSMESSE see
Lassus, Roland de (Orlandus)

PROPRIUM FUR DAS DREIFALTIGKEITSFEST see
Krenek, Ernst

PROPRIUM FUR DEN ACHTZEHNTEN SONNTAG NACH
PFINGSTEN see Bauernfiend, Hans

PROPRIUM MISSAE see Bottazzo, Luigi

PROPRIUM MISSAE see Bottazzo, Luigi

PROPRIUM MISSAE IN FESTO S. BENEDICTI ABATIS
see Corradini, Vasco Lodovico

PROPRIUM MISSAE IN FESTO ST. BARTHOLOMAEI
APOSTOLI see Strohbach, Siegfried

PROPRIUM MISSARUM IN FESTO SACRATISSIMI CORDIS
JESU see Bottazzo, Luigi

PROPRIUM MISSARUM IN FESTO SS. CORPUS CHRISTI
see Bottazzo, Luigi

PROPRIUM MISSARUM IN FESTO SS. TRINITATIS see
Bottazzo, Luigi

PROPRIUM VON 1 ADVENTSSONNTAG see Senfl, Ludwig

PROPRIUM VON FRONLEICHNAM see Lassus, Roland de
(Orlandus)

PROPRIUM VON KIRCHWEIHFEST see Aichinger,
Gregor

PROPRIUM VON OSTERN see Lassus, Roland de
(Orlandus)

PROPRIUM VON PFINGSTEN see Lassus, Roland de
(Orlandus)

PROPRIUM ZU JUBILATE see Suthoff-Gross, Rudolf

PROPRIUM ZUM ERSTEN ADVENTSONNTAG see Schiff,
Helmut

PROPRIUM ZUM FRONLEICHNAMSFEST see Heiller,
Anton

PROPRIUM ZUM GRUNDONNERSTAG see Heilmann,
Harald

PROS ROMAIOUS see Dijk, Jan van

PROSE DE LA FETE DE PAQUES see O Filii Et
Filiae

PROSE DE LA FETE DES SEPT DOULEURS see Stabat
Mater Dolorosa

PROSKE, ERWIN
Lobe Den Herren, Den Machtigen Konig *cant
unis&4pt mix cor,2-6brass HANSSLER 10.266
sc s.p., cor pts s.p.   (P2750)

Wachet Auf Ruft Uns Die Stimme *cant
unis men cor/unis mix cor,3-6brass HANSSLER
10.206 s.p., cor pts s.p.   (P2751)

PROSS, D.
Gospel Acclamations And Verses *Gen,liturg/
Mass
SATB,acap/kbd (med easy) voc sc GIA G1652
$3.00, ipa   (P2752)

Mass Of Praise *Gen,Mass
SATB/2 eq voices (med) voc sc GIA G1634
$1.00   (P2753)

PROTECTOR NOSTER see Pasini, Crescenzio

PROTEST OF JOB, THE see Mechem, Kirke

PROTHEROE
Lord Is My Light, The (Psalm 27)
(Coggin) SAB oct PRO ART 2268 $.25 (P2754)

Psalm 27 *see Lord Is My Light, The

PROTHEROE, DANIEL (1866-1934)
Eastertide *cant
cor,4 soli,org voc sc SCHIRM.G $1.00
                                   (P2755)
(Treharne, Bryceson) 3pt wom cor,SA soli,
org/pno voc sc SCHIRM.G $1.00   (P2756)

Father, In Thy Mysterious Presence
SATB ALLANS 162 s.p.   (P2757)

For He Shall Give His Angels Charge
SA&jr cor,org (easy) oct WILLIS 5237 $.12
                                   (P2758)

Ninety And Nine, The
SATB oct PRESSER 332-13528 $.35   (P2759)

Sing Unto The Lord
SA&jr cor,org (easy) oct WILLIS 5244 $.15
                                   (P2760)

Thy House Forever
SA&jr cor,org (easy) oct WILLIS 5243 $.12
                                   (P2761)

PROUD MUSIC see Moore

PROUDLY SOUNDS THE TAMBOURINE *Xmas,carol,Span
(Ehret, Walter) SA,opt tamb,bells FRANK F-622
$.35   (P2762)
(Ehret, Walter) SSA,opt tamb,bells FRANK
F-680 $.35   (P2763)
(Ehret, Walter) SAB,opt tamb,bells FRANK
F-679 $.35   (P2764)

PROUIX
Jesu, The Very Thought Of Thee *Gen
SATB SCHMITT 6006 $.35   (P2765)

PROULX, RICHARD
Advent Anthem *Adv,anthem
SATB (med diff) oct AUGSBURG 1559 $.35
                                   (P2766)

And The Best Is Love *anthem
unis treb cor (med) oct AUGSBURG 1639 $.25
                                   (P2767)

Behold, Now, The House Of God *anthem
SATB (med) oct AUGSBURG 1572 $.40 (P2768)

Christ The Lord Is Risen Again *Easter,
anthem
SATB,org,4brass,timp (med) oct GIA G1709
$.50   (P2769)

Christmas Processional *Xmas/Proces,anthem
2pt,cantor,4hndbl (easy) oct GIA G1708 $.25
                                   (P2770)

Community Mass, A *Gen,Mass
SATB&cong&desc,opt 2trp,2trom,timp (med
easy) voc sc GIA G1605 $1.00, ipa (P2771)

Festival Anthem On "Crown Him With Many
Crowns" *Fest,anthem
SATB&cong,org,3trp,3trom (med) sc AUGSBURG
11-9167 $2.00, ipa, cor pts AUGSBURG
11-9168 $.50   (P2772)

Happy The Man Who Fears The Lord *anthem
SS,fl,ob (med) oct AUGSBURG 0312 $.30
                                   (P2773)

How Lovely Are Thy Dwellings Fair (Psalm 84)
Gen,anthem
SATB (easy) oct GIA G1706 $.40   (P2774)

Jesus, Lead The Way *Gen,anthem
SATB (easy) oct GIA G1707 $.40   (P2775)

Just Man Shall Flourish, The *anthem
unis treb cor,org,fl,ob (med) oct AUGSBURG
0637 $.30   (P2776)

Mass Of The Redeemer *Gen,Mass
SAB&cong,cantor (easy) voc sc GIA G1749
$1.00   (P2777)

My Heart Is Full Today *anthem
mix cor,kbd,perc,bells (med) oct AUGSBURG
0645 $.35   (P2778)

Of The Kindness Of The Lord *anthem
unis treb cor/SA (med) oct AUGSBURG 1539
$.25   (P2779)

Praise The Savior, Now And Forever *Easter
SATB SCHMITT SD6225 $.30   (P2780)

Processional Song *Gen/Proces,anthem
2pt&cong,cantor,4hndbl (easy) oct GIA G1750
$.30   (P2781)

Psalm 81 *see Sing We Merrily

Psalm 84 *see How Lovely Are Thy Dwellings
Fair

Sing We Merrily (Psalm 81)
mix cor,org,2trp,2trom (med diff) sc
AUGSBURG 11-9392 $.85, ipa   (P2782)

This Is The Day The Lord Has Made *anthem
SSA (med) oct AUGSBURG 1513 $.25   (P2783)

PROUT, [EBENEZER] (1835-1909)
Glory To God On High
(Coggin) SATB oct PRO ART 2621 $.30 (P2784)

PROVERB see Persichetti, Vincent

PROVERB OF SOLOMON, A see Franco

PSALM 23 see Acheson, Mark

PSALM 23 see Aschaffenburg, [Walter], Twenty-Third Psalme, The

PSALM 23 see Beeson, Jack Hamilton

PSALM 23 see Berger, Jean, Lord Is My Shepherd, The

PSALM 23 see Billings, William

PSALM 23 see Binkerd, [Gordon]

PSALM 23 see Bodycombe, [Aneurin]

PSALM 23 see Braal, Andreas de, Psalm 23, Een Psalm Van David

PSALM 23 see Brooks, Nigel

PSALM 23 see Brown, William [H., Jr.]

PSALM 23 see Christiansen, Paul, Kyrie

PSALM 23 see Christiansen, Paul, Twenty-Third Psalm, The

PSALM 23 see Comer

PSALM 23 see Creston, Paul

PSALM 23 see Davis, Katherine K.

PSALM 23 see Filkins

PSALM 23 see Fromm, Herbert

PSALM 23 see Goudimel, Claude, Mon Dieu Me Paist Sous Sa Puissance Haute

PSALM 23 see Graves, Richard, In Pastures Green

PSALM 23 see Greene, Maurice, Lord Is My Shepherd, The

PSALM 23 see Hammarstrom, Hugo, Herren Ar Min Herde

PSALM 23 see Harter, [Harry], Twenty-Third Psalm

PSALM 23 see Hennagin, Michael

PSALM 23 see Hopkinson, [Francis]

PSALM 23 see Hovhaness, Alan, Lord Is My Shepherd, The

PSALM 23 see Jacob, Gordon, Twenty-Third Psalm, The

PSALM 23 see Kent, Richard, Lord Is My Shepherd, The

PSALM 23 see Kjelson

PSALM 23 see Klein, Bernhard, Der Herr Ist Mein Hirte

PSALM 23 see Klein, Richard Rudolf, Der Herr Ist Mein Hirt

PSALM 23 see Krieg, H.

PSALM 23 see Lavater, H., Der Herr Ist Mein Hirte

PSALM 23 see Le Fleming, Christopher (Kaye), Lord Is My Shepherd, The

PSALM 23 see London, Edwin

PSALM 23 see Longmire, John

PSALM 23 see MacCarthy

PSALM 23 see Malotte, Albert Hay

PSALM 23 see Mason, T.D.

PSALM 23 see Meyer-Janson, Burkhard, Der Herr Ist Mein Hirte

PSALM 23 see Micheelsen, Hans Friedrich, Der Herr Ist Mein Hirte

PSALM 23 see Milford

PSALM 23 see Moren, John, Herren Ar Min Herde

PSALM 23 see Moschetti, [Giuseppe], Lord Is My Shepherd, The

PSALM 23 see Mueller, Carl F., Lord's My Shepherd, The

PSALM 23 see Nordoff, Paul, Twenty-Third Psalm, The

PSALM 23 see Nordqvist, Gustaf, Davids 23dje Psalm

PSALM 23 see Pepping, Ernst, Der Herr Ist Mein Hirte

PSALM 23 see Pitfield, Thomas Baron

PSALM 23 see Rasely

PSALM 23 see Reda, Siegfried, Der Herr Ist Iein Getreuer Hirt

PSALM 23 see Rochberg, George

PSALM 23 see Schubert, Franz (Peter), Gott Ist Mein Hirt

PSALM 23 see Schubert, Franz (Peter), Gott Ist Mein Hirte

PSALM 23 see Schubert, Franz (Peter), Gott Meine Zuversicht

PSALM 23 see Schubert, Franz (Peter), Lord Is My Shepherd, The

PSALM 23 see Schutz, Heinrich, Der Herr Ist Mein Getreuer Hirt

PSALM 23 see Schutz, Heinrich, Der Herr Ist Mein Hirt

PSALM 23 see Smart, Lord Is My Shepherd, The

PSALM 23 see Smart, Henry Thomas, Lord Is My Shepherd, The

PSALM 23 see Steinke, Greg

PSALM 23 see Stern, Hermann, Der Herr Ist Mein Hirte

PSALM 23 see Sweelinck, Jan Pieterszoon, Der Herr Ist Mein Hirt

PSALM 23 see Thompson, Randall, Lord Is My Shepherd, The

PSALM 23 see Van Dyke, Lord's My Shepherd, The

PSALM 23 see Vaughan Williams, Ralph, Twenty-Third Psalm, The

PSALM 23 see Vermulst, Jan, Lord Is My Shepherd, The

PSALM 23 see Warner, Richard, God Of Love My Shepherd Is, The

PSALM 23 see Weismann, Wilhelm, Der Herr Ist Mein Hirte

PSALM 23 see Williamson, Malcolm, King Of Love, The

PSALM 23 see Wilson, Harry [Robert]

PSALM 23 see Wright, Norman Soreng

PSALM 23 see Zemlinsky, [Alexander von]

PSALM 23 see Zimmermann, Heinz Werner

PSALM 23, EEN PSALM VAN DAVID see Braal, Andreas de

PSALM 24 see Adler, Samuel

PSALM 24 see Angell, Earth Is The Lord's, The

PSALM 24 see Bach, Johann Sebastian, Machet Die Tore Weit

PSALM 24 see Bevans, William

PSALM 24 see Boulanger, Lili, Psaume 24

PSALM 24 see Bush, Geoffrey, Earth Is The Lord's, The

PSALM 24 see Canavati

PSALM 24 see Coleridge, Lift Up Your Heads

PSALM 24 see Gibbons, Orlando, Lift Up Your Heads

PSALM 24 see Ives, Charles

PSALM 24 see Kullnes, Ake

PSALM 24 see McLin, Earth Is The Lord's, The

PSALM 24 see Mitcheltree, John Jr., Earth Is The Lord's, The

PSALM 24 see Nelson, Ronald A., Lift Up Your Heads

PSALM 24 see Peloquin, C. Alexander, To You, O Lord

PSALM 24 see Pierne, Gabriel

PSALM 24 see Reda, Siegfried, Machet Die Tore Weit

PSALM 24 see Schmid, Walter, Machet Die Tore Weit

PSALM 24 see Schutz, Heinrich, Domini Est Terra

PSALM 24 see Sweelinck, Jan Pieterszoon, Ihr Pforten, Hebt Das Haupt Empor

PSALM 24 see Wennerberg, Gunnar, Goren Portarna Hoga

PSALM 24 see Williamson, Malcolm, Who Is The King Of Glory

PSALM 24 see Wills, Arthur

PSALM 25 see Boyce, William, Sorrows Of My Heart, The

PSALM 25 see Cruger, Johann, Ich Erhebe Mein Gemute

PSALM 25 see Goudimel, Claude, A Toi, Mon Dieu, Mon Coeur Monte

PSALM 25 see Hilton, John (The Elder), Call To Remembrance

PSALM 25 see Holtz, J.

PSALM 25 see Jacot, Andre, Nach Dir, Nach Dir, Herr

PSALM 25 see Jambe

PSALM 25 see Jannequin, Clement, A Toi, Mon Dieu, Mon Coeur Monte

PSALM 25 see Kirk

PSALM 25 see Lassus, Roland de (Orlandus)

PSALM 25 see Pelz, Walter L., Show Me Thy Ways

PSALM 25 see Planzer, Emanuel, Wende Dich Zu Mir

PSALM 25 see Ruppel, Paul Ernst, Nach Dir, O Herr, Verlangt Mich

PSALM 25 see Sweelinck, Jan Pieterszoon, Ich Erhebe Mein Gemute

PSALM 25 see Zaumeyer

PSALM 26 see Reda, Siegfried, Herr, Ich Habe Lieb Die Statte Deines Hauses

PSALM 26 see Tomkins, Thomas, O Lord, I Have Loved

PSALM 27 see Algazi, Leon

PSALM 27 see Edwards, Clara, Lord Is My Light, The

PSALM 27 see Handel, George Frideric, Der Herr Ist Mein Licht

PSALM 27 see Kammerer, Imanuel Johannes

PSALM 27 see Protheroe, Lord Is My Light, The

PSALM 27 see Raphael, Gunther, Der Herr Ist Mein Licht Und Mein Heil

PSALM 27 see Schwarz-Schilling, Reinhard, Ich Tret Hinzu

PSALM 28 see Hovhaness, Alan, Unto Thee Will I Cry

PSALM 28 see Rocherolle, Give To The Lord

PSALM 29 see Elgar, Edward, Give Unto The Lord

PSALM 29 see Ford, All Cry Glory

PSALM 29 see Kersters, Willem

PSALM 29 see Schutz, Heinrich

PSALM 29 see Weisgall, Hugo

PSALM 30 see Amner, John, Hear, O Lord

PSALM 30 see Berlinski, Herman

PSALM 30 see Goudimel, Claude, Seigneur, Puis Que M'as Retire

PSALM 30 see Nicolai, Otto, Ehre Sei Gott In Der Hohe

PSALM 30 see Pisk, Paul Amadeus

PSALM 30 see Schwartz, Gerhard von, Magnificat

PSALM 30 see Sharvit, Uri

PSALM 31 see Gaburo, Kenneth

PSALM 31 see Glarum, L. Stanley, In Thee Lord

PSALM 31 see Gumpeltzhaimer, Adam, Mein Hoffnung, Trost Und Zuversicht

PSALM 31 see Kirk, In Thee, O Lord, I Put My Trust

PSALM 31 see Kretzschmar, Gunther, Herr, Auf Dich Traue Ich

PSALM 31 see Kukuck, Felicitas, Herr Auf Dich Traue Ich

PSALM 31 see Nicolai, Otto, Herr, Auf Dich Traue Ich

PSALM 31 see Nyquist, In Thee, O Lord, Do I Put My Trust

PSALM 31 see Reda, Siegfried, In Dich Hab Ich Gehoffet, Herr

PSALM 31 see Roder, E., Karfreitag (Totenfest)

PSALM 31 see Stevens, In Te, Domini Speravi

PSALM 32
(Klerk, Cor De) mix cor sc ALSBACH&D s.p.
(P2792)

PSALM 32 see Head, Michael (Dewar), Blessed Is He

PSALM 32 see Roff, Joseph, Let Thy Mercy, O Lord, Be Upon Us

PSALM 32 see Wagener, Gregor, Wohl Dem, Dem Die Ubertretung

PSALM 33 see Baumann, Herbert

PSALM 33 see Graap, Lothar, Des Herren Wort

PSALM 33 see Jaeggi, Oswald

PSALM 33 see Mobach, E.

PSALM 33 see Schmid, Walter, Dankt Dem Herrn!

PSALM 33 see Vaughan Williams, Ralph, Choral Flourish, A

PSALM 33 see Vautaz, R.

PSALM 33 see Wagener, Gregor, Freuet Euch Des Herren

PSALM 34
(Kirk) SATB oct PRO ART 1424 $.25   (P2793)

PSALM 34 see Berger, Jean, Glorify The Lord With Me

PSALM 34 see Eibl, Th.

PSALM 34 see Faignient, Noel, Jamais Ne Cesserai De Magnifier Le Seigneur

PSALM 34 see Glarum, L. Stanley, Behold, Bless Ye The Lord

PSALM 34 see Hughes, Rita Mea, Through All The Changing Scenes Of Life

PSALM 34 see Lovelace, Austin C.

PSALM 34 see Peloquin, C. Alexander, Taste And See

PSALM 34 see Reda, Siegfried, Schmecket Und Sehet, Wie Freundlich Der Herr Ist

PSALM 34 see Schmid, Walter, Ich Will Den Herren Loben

PSALM 34 see Schweizer, Rolf, Ich Will Den Herrn Loben Allezeit

PSALM 34 see Schweizer, Rolf, Schmecket Und Sehet, Wie Freundlich Der Herr Ist

PSALM 34 see Strohbach, Siegfried, Kommt Her, Ihr Kinder

PSALM 34 see Vaughan Williams, Ralph, O Taste And See

PSALM 35 see McCullough, Plead My Cause, O Lord

PSALM 36 see Adler, Samuel, How Precious Is Thy Lovingkindness

PSALM 36 see Cruger, Johann, O Hochster, Deine Gutigkeit

PSALM 36 see Goudimel, Claude, Du Mal In Le Meschant Vouloir

PSALM 36 see Goudimel, Claude, Du Malin Le Meschant Vouloir

PSALM 36 see Kubizek, Augustinian, O Herr, Deine Gute

PSALM 36 see Lassus, Roland de (Orlandus), Herr, Deine Gut Und Wahrheit Steht

PSALM 36 see Lewandowski, Louis, Mah Yokor Chasdecho

PSALM 36 see Reda, Siegfried, Herr, Deine Gute Reicht So Weit Die Wolken Gehen

PSALM 36 see Schweizer, Rolf, Herr, Deine Gute Reicht So Weit Der Himmel Ist

PSALM 37 see Heiller, Anton

PSALM 37 see Reda, Siegfried, Befiehl Dem Herrn Deine Wege

PSALM 37 see Roman, Johan Helmich

PSALM 37 see Schauss-Flake, Magdalene, Befiehl &em Herrn &eine Wege

PSALM 37 see Schmid, Walter, Befiehl Dem Herrn Deine Wege

PSALM 37 see Stoltzer, Thomas, Erzune Dich Nicht

PSALM 37 see Toebosch, Louis

PSALM 37 see Wagener, Gregor, Erzurne Dich Nicht Uber Die

PSALM 38 see Blow, John, Put Me Not To Rebuke

PSALM 38 see Bourgeois, Loys (Louis)

PSALM 38 see Sweelinck, Jan Pieterszoon, Straf Mich Nicht In Deinem Grimme

PSALM 38 see Wagener, Gregor, Ach Herr, Strafe Mich Nicht

PSALM 38 see Weis, Flemming, Liber Psalmorum

PSALM 39 see Goudimel, C.W.

PSALM 39 see Greene, Maurice, Lord, Let Me Know Mine End

PSALM 39 see Reda, Siegfried, Herr, Lehre Doch Mich, Dass Es Ein Ende Mit Mir Haben Muss

PSALM 39 see Wagener, Gregor, Ich Habe Mir Vorgesetzt

PSALM 40 see Adler, Samuel

PSALM 40 see Jacot, Andre, Ich Harrete Des Herrn

PSALM 40 see Reda, Siegfried, Es Mussen Sich Freuen Und Frohlich Sein

PSALM 42 see Bohlen, D., Prayer For Strength And Light

PSALM 42 see Bonset, Jac.

PSALM 42 see Goudimel, Claude, Ainsi Qu'on Oit Le Cerf Bruire

PSALM 42 see Handel, George Frideric, As Pants The Hart

PSALM 42 see Handel, George Frideric, As Pants The Heart

PSALM 42 see Handel, George Frideric, Gern Wallt' Ich Mit Dem Volke Hin

PSALM 42 see Hawkins, Gordon, As The Hart Panteth

PSALM 42 see Hopkins, Anthony, Lord, As That Hart Which Water Wants

PSALM 42 see Imbrie, Andrew Welsh, As The Hart Panteth

PSALM 42 see Lassus, Roland de (Orlandus), Sicut Cervus

PSALM 42 see Le Jeune, Claude, Ainsi Qu'on Oit Le Cerf Bruire

PSALM 42 see Lombardo, As The Hart

PSALM 42 see Lombardo, Robert, As The Hart Panteth

PSALM 42 see Mendelssohn-Bartholdy, Felix, As The Heart

PSALM 42 see Mendelssohn-Bartholdy, Felix, Wie Der Hirsch Schreit

PSALM 42 see Mendelssohn-Bartholdy, Felix, Zooals 'T Hert Dorst

PSALM 42 see Muller, Paul, Wie Der Hirsch Schreit Nach Frischem Wasser

PSALM 42 see Novello, Like As The Hart

PSALM 42 see Pinkham, Daniel, Why Art Thou So Cast Down O My Soul

PSALM 42 see Reda, Siegfried, Wie Der Hirsch Schreit Nach Frischem Wasser

PSALM 42 see Schilling, Hans Ludwig, Du Bist Der Gott Meiner Zuflucht

PSALM 42 see Schipp, C.M., My Soul Thirsts For God

PSALM 42 see Schutz, Heinrich, Was Betrubst Du Dich, Meine Seele

PSALM 42 see Schweizer, Rolf, Wie Ein Hirsch Schreit Nach Frischem Wasser

PSALM 42 see Spohr

PSALM 42 see Zaumeyer

PSALM 43 see Barbee, N., Judge Me, O God

PSALM 43 see Beclard d'Harcourt, M.

PSALM 43 see Lassus, Roland de (Orlandus)

PSALM 43 see Mendelssohn-Bartholdy, Felix, Richte Mich, Gott

PSALM 43 see Mendelssohn-Bartholdy, Felix, Richte Mich, Gott, Und Fuhre Meine Sache

PSALM 43 see Pezzati, Mauro

PSALM 43 see Purvis, Richard, Judica Me, Deus

PSALM 43 see Rochberg, George

PSALM 43 see Zaumeyer

PSALM 44 see Byrd, William, Exsurge, Domine

PSALM 44 see Nagel, We Have Heard The Words

PSALM 45 see Horst, Anthon van der, Choros III, Psalmus 45

PSALM 45 see Jackson, Francis, Audi Filia

PSALM 45 see Pinkham, Daniel, Thou Hast Loved Righteousness

PSALM 45 see Strohbach, Siegfried, Mein Herz Dichtet Ein Schones Lied

PSALM 46 see Anders, Charles, God Is For Us A Refuge And Strength

PSALM 46 see Boatwright, Howard, God Is Our Refuge

PSALM 46 see Gardner, John [Linton]

PSALM 46 see Glarum, L. Stanley, Be Still And Know

PSALM 46 see Goode, J.

PSALM 46 see Goode, Jack C.

PSALM 46 see Hopson, God Is Our Refuge, God Is Our Strength

PSALM 46 see Klein, Richard Rudolf, Gott Ist Unsre Zuversicht

PSALM 46 see Lundquist, Matthew Nathanael, God Is Our Refuge

PSALM 46 see Ouchterlony, David, God Is Our Refuge And Strength

PSALM 46 see Pachelbel, Johann, Gott Ist Unser Zuversicht

PSALM 46 see Peloquin, C. Alexander, God Mounts His Throne

PSALM 46 see Preston, Simon, God Is Our Hope And Strength

PSALM 46 see Roff, Joseph, All You Peoples Clap Your Hands

PSALM 46 see Roman, Johan Helmich, God Is Our Refuge

PSALM 46 see Schutz, Heinrich, Mighty Fortress Is Our God, A

PSALM 46 see Zimmermann, Heinz Werner, Gott Ist Unsre Zuversicht

PSALM 46 see Zutphen, Th. v.

PSALM 47 see Altman, Ludwig

PSALM 47 see Beeson, Jack Hamilton

PSALM 47 see Blarr, Oskar Gottlieb, Frolocket Mit Handen

PSALM 47 see Gardner, John [Linton], O, Clap Your Hands

PSALM 47 see Gibbons, Orlando, O Clap Your Hands

PSALM 47 see Gomolka, Mikolaj, Let Us Clap Our Hands

PSALM 47 see Henking, Bernhard, Singt Mit Froher Stimm

PSALM 47 see King, Alvin, O Clap Your Hands, All Ye People

PSALM 47 see Kirk, Theron W., O Clap Your Hands

PSALM 47 see Moe, Daniel

PSALM 47 see Mulder, Herman

PSALM 47 see Olman, Isr, J.

PSALM 47 see Schmitt

PSALM 47 see Whear, Paul William, Psalms Of Celebration Part IV

PSALM 47 see Wieruszowski, Lili, Singt Mit Froher Stimm

PSALM 48 see Elgar, Edward, Great Is The Lord

PSALM 48 see McKie, William, We Wait For Thy Loving Kindness

PSALM 50 see Allegri, Gregorio, Miserere Mei Deus

PSALM 50 see Callhoff, Herbert

PSALM 50 see Christiansen, F. Melius, Offer Unto God

PSALM 50 see Des Prez, Josquin, Miserere Mei Deus

PSALM 50 see Leo, Leonardo, Misere Mei, Deus

PSALM 50 see Leo, Leonardo, Miserere Mei, Deus

PSALM 50 see Luhn, Miserere

PSALM 50 see Peloquin, C. Alexander, Have Mercy On Me

PSALM 50 see Reda, Siegfried, Gott, Der Herr, Der Machtige, Ruft Der Welt

PSALM 50 see Whitcomb, R., Mighty One, The

PSALM 51 see Allegri, Gregorio, Miserere Mei, Deus

PSALM 51 see Bunjes, Paul G., Miserere Mei

PSALM 51 see Giannini, Vincenzo, Abbi Pieta Di Me, O Dio!

PSALM 51 see Glarum, L. Stanley, Create In Me A Clean Heart, O God

PSALM 51 see Hasse, Johann Adolph, Miserere

PSALM 51 see Henderson

PSALM 51 see Johansson, Bengt, Miserere Mei

PSALM 51 see Lasso, Rudolph de, Gott, Sei Mir Gnadig Dieser Zeit

PSALM 51 see Latrobe

PSALM 51 see Le Jeune, Claude

PSALM 51 see Locke, Matthew, Turn Thy Face From My Sins

PSALM 51 see Pergolesi, Giovanni Battista, Stabat Mater

PSALM 51 see Reda, Siegfried, Herr, Tue Meine Lippen Auf

PSALM 51 see Schein, Johann Hermann, Gott Sei Mir Gnadig

PSALM 51 see Suitor

PSALM 51 see Wagener, Gregor, Gott Sei Mir Gnadig

PSALM 51 see Wesley, Samuel Sebastian Jr., Wash Me Throughly

PSALM 54 see Ives, Charles

PSALM 54 see Lewis, John Leo, Save Me, O God, By Thy Name

PSALM 54 see Pisk, Paul Amadeus

PSALM 55 see Bond, Anders, Ar Halsad Skona Morgonstund

PSALM 56 see Goudimel, Claude, Misericorde A Moi Povre Afflige

PSALM 56 see Peterson, Wayne

PSALM 57 see Baumann, Herbert

PSALM 57 see Berger, Jean

PSALM 57 see Brandon, G., O God To Me Be Merciful

PSALM 57 see Butler, Eugene, My Heart Is Steadfast, O God

PSALM 57 see L'Estocart, Paschal de

PSALM 57 see Muller, Paul, Lobe Den Herren

PSALM 57 see Schmid, Walter, Lobe Den Herren!

PSALM 60 see Nieuwenhoven, H. v., Exaudi Deus Deprecationem Meam

PSALM 61 see Boatwright, Howard, Hear My Cry, O God

PSALM 61 see Hovhaness, Alan, From The End Of The Earth

PSALM 61 see Trued, Clarence, Hear Me, O Lord

PSALM 61 see Weldon, John, Hear My Crying

PSALM 61 see Zentner, Johannes, Hore Gott, Mein Schreien

PSALM 62 see Galuppi, Baldassare, Beatus Vir

PSALM 62 see Goudimel, Claude, Mon Ame En Dieu Tant Seulement

PSALM 62 see Kubizek, Augustinian, Sei Stille Zu Gott, Meine Seele

PSALM 62 see Lowell, Thanks Be To God

PSALM 63 see Pederson, Mogens, O Herre, Frels Mig, Dom Min Sag

PSALM 63 see Ramberg, Paul, Davids Psalm 63

PSALM 63 see Russell, Velma A., In The Shadow Of Thy Wings

PSALM 64 see Bassett, Leslie, Hear My Prayer, O Lord

PSALM 65 see Corfe, Joseph, Thou, O God, Art Praised In Sion

PSALM 65 see Goemanne, Noel, Song Of Praise

PSALM 65 see Goudimel, Claude, O Dieu, La Glorie Qui T'est Deue

PSALM 65 see Waters, Charles F., Thou Visitest The Earth

PSALM 66 see Goudimel, Claude, Or Sus, Louez Dieu Tout Le Monde

PSALM 66 see Gumpeltzhaimer, Adam, Make A Joyful Noise Unto The Lord

PSALM 66 see Hassler, Hans Leo, Praise The Lord With Gladness

PSALM 66 see Pederson, Mogens, Vor Gud Han Er Sa Fast En Borg

PSALM 66 see Rohwer, Jens, Jauchzet Gott, Alle Lande

PSALM 66 see Schmid, Walter, Jauchzet Gott

PSALM 66 see Wyatt, Make A Joyful Noise Unto The Lord

PSALM 67 see Alexander, God Be Merciful

PSALM 67 see Altman, Ludwig

PSALM 67 see Fehres, Wilhelm, Gott Sei Uns Gnadig

PSALM 67 see Fryxell, Regina Holmen

PSALM 67 see Gordon, P., Sixty-Seventh Psalm, The

PSALM 67 see Harris

PSALM 67 see Hillert, Richard, May God Bestow On Us His Grace

PSALM 67 see Ives, Charles, God Be Merciful Unto Us

PSALM 67 see Kline, Spirit Of The Lord, The

PSALM 67 see Martin, G.

PSALM 67 see Reda, Siegfried, Es Wolle Gott Uns Gnadig Sein

PSALM 67 see Schmid, Walter, Gott, Sei Uns Gnadig

PSALM 67 see Schoen, F., May God Have Pity On Us

PSALM 67 see Smyth, William

PSALM 67 see Waring, Peter, God Be Merciful Unto Us

PSALM 67 see Wills, Arthur

PSALM 68 see Gore, Richard T., Let God Arise

PSALM 68 see Goudimel, Claude, Que Dieu Se Monstre Seulement

PSALM 68 see Handel, George Frideric, Let God Arise

PSALM 69 see Blow, John, I Will Praise The Name Of God

PSALM 69 see Goudimel, Claude, Helas, Seigneur, Je Te Pri' Sauve Moi

PSALM 69 see Le Jeune, Claude, Helas, Seigneur!

PSALM 69 see Nielsen, Riccardo, Psalmus In Confessione

PSALM 70 see Burkhard Willy, Eile, Gott, Mich Zu Erretten

PSALM 70 see Fritschel, James, Make Haste, O God

PSALM 70 see Goudimel, Claude, O Dieu, Ou Mon Espoir J'ai Mis

PSALM 70 see Hovhaness, Alan, Make Haste

PSALM 70 see Le Jeune, Claude

PSALM 70 see Sowerby, Leo

PSALM 70 see Wangenheim, [Volker], Eile, Gott, Mich Zu Eretten

PSALM 70 see Zimmermann, Heinz Werner, Eile Gott, Mich Zu Erretten

PSALM 71 see Schutz, Heinrich, Auf Dich, Herr, Trau Ich Allezeit

PSALM 71 see Weismann, Wilhelm

PSALM 72 see Peloquin, C. Alexander, Lord, Every Nation

PSALM 73 see Goudimel, Claude, Si Est-Ce Que Dieu Est Tres Doux

PSALM 73 see Reda, Siegfried, Dennoch Bleibe Ich Stets An Dir

PSALM 73 see Roff, Joseph, Thou Shalt Guide Me

PSALM 75 see Kline, Confirm, O God

PSALM 75 see Sweelinck, Jan Pieterszoon, O Seigneur, Loue Sera

PSALM 75 see Wagner, Voice Of The Lord, The

PSALM 76 see Strategier, Herman

PSALM 76 see Weismann, Wilhelm

PSALM 80 see Jaeggi, Oswald

PSALM 80 see Rossi, Salomone

PSALM 80 see Schieri, Fritz, Alleluja-Psalm I

PSALM 80 see Schoenberg, Arnold, De Profundis

PSALM 81 see Batten, Adrian, O Sing Joyfully

PSALM 81 see Hovhaness, Alan, Sing Aloud

PSALM 81 see Proulx, Richard, Sing We Merrily

PSALM 81 see Sweelinck, Jan Pieterszoon

PSALM 83 see Eder, Helmut, Gott, Hulle Dich Nicht In Schweigen

PSALM 83 see Marx, Karl, Gott, Schweige, Doch Nicht Also

PSALM 83 see Peloquin, C. Alexander, How Lovely Is Your Dwelling Place

PSALM 83 see Ritter, Christian, Wie Lieblich Sind Deine Wohnungen

PSALM 83 see Vermulst, Jan, How Lovely Is Your Dwelling Place

PSALM 84 see Andriessen, N.H.

PSALM 84 see Burkhard Willy, Wie Lieblich Sind Deine Wohnungen

PSALM 84 see Dieterich

PSALM 84 see Gardner, John [Linton], O How Amiable Are Thy Dwellings

PSALM 84 see Goudimel, Claude, O Dieu Des Armees

PSALM 84 see Meyer-Janson, Burkhard, Wie Lieblich Sind Deine Wohnungen

PSALM 84 see Olson, Daniel

PSALM 84 see Proulx, Richard, How Lovely Are Thy Dwellings Fair

PSALM 84 see Reda, Siegfried, Gott Der Herr Ist Sonn Und Schild

PSALM 84 see Schutz, Heinrich, Wie Lieblich Sind Deine Wohnungen

PSALM 84 see Somary, J., How Lovely Is Thy Dwelling Place

PSALM 84 see Tomkins, Thomas, O How Amiable

PSALM 84 see Toolan, S. Suzanne

PSALM 84 see Weelkes, Thomas, O How Amiable

PSALM 84 see Wennerberg, Gunnar, Min Sjal Langtar Och Trangtar

PSALM 84 see Wenzel, Eberhard, Wie Lieblich Sind Deine

PSALM 85 see Schutz, Heinrich, Herr, Der Du Vormals Gnadig Warst

PSALM 85 see Smith

PSALM 86 see Blow, John, Bow Down Thine Ear, O Lord

PSALM 86 see Blow, John, In The Time Of Trouble

PSALM 86 see Holst, Gustav, To My Humble Supplication, Lord

PSALM 86 see Moir, F.L., I Will Thank Thee, O Lord

PSALM 88 see Le Jeune, Claude, O Seigneur, J'Espars

PSALM 89 see Goudimel, Claude, Du Seigneur Les Bontez Sans Fin

PSALM 89 see Handel, George Frideric, My Song Shall Be Alway

PSALM 90 see Barbe, Helmut, Herr Gott, Du Bist Unsre Zuflucht

PSALM 90 see Chemin-Petit, Hans

PSALM 90 see Chihara, Paul

PSALM 90 see Driessler, Johannes, Herr Gott, Du Bist Unsre Zuflucht

PSALM 90 see Garlick, Anthony

PSALM 90 see Ives, Charles

PSALM 90 see Kirk, Lord, Thou Hast Been Our Refuge

PSALM 90 see Schmid, Walter, Herr Gott, Du Bist Unsere Zuflucht!

PSALM 90 see Schweizer, Rolf, O Herr, Du Warst Unsre Zuflucht

PSALM 90 see Strobl, Otto

PSALM 90 see Sweelinck, Jan Pieterszoon

PSALM 91 see Blarr, Oskar Gottlieb, Wer Wohnt Unterm Schirm Des Hochsten

PSALM 91 see Evans

PSALM 91 see Goodenough, F., Who So Dwelleth

PSALM 91 see McAfee

PSALM 91 see Mendelssohn-Bartholdy, Felix, Denn Er Hat Seinen Engeln Befohlen Uber Dir

PSALM 91 see Parrott, Ian

PSALM 91 see Peeters, Flor, Canticum Gaudii

PSALM 91 see Reda, Siegfried, Wer In Dem Schutz Des Hochsten Ist

PSALM 91 see Richter, M.

PSALM 91 see Scandrett, Robert

PSALM 91 see Scarmolin, (Anthony) Louis, He That Dwelleth In The Secret Place

PSALM 91 see Schein, Johann Hermann, Wer Unter Dem Schirm Des Hochsten

PSALM 91 see Whittredge

PSALM 92 see Arbatsky, [Yury]

PSALM 92 see Christiansen, Paul

PSALM 92 see Fehrmann, Paul

PSALM 92 see Gwinner, Volker

PSALM 92 see Kukuck, Felicitas, Das Ist Ein Kostlich Ding

PSALM 92 see McAfee, Don

PSALM 92 see Mader, Rud

PSALM 92 see Palmer, C.

PSALM 92 see Reda, Siegfried, Das Ist Ein Kostlich Ding

PSALM 92 see Roskin, Tzadik Katomor

PSALM 92 see Schroth, G.

PSALM 92 see Schubert, Franz (Peter)

PSALM 92 see Whear, Paul William, Psalms Of Celebration Part II

PSALM 92 see Zeisl, Eric, Requiem Ebraico

PSALM 92 see Zentner, Johannes

PSALM 93 see Binkerd, [Gordon], Lord Is King, The

PSALM 93 see Cooper, Lord Reigneth, The

PSALM 93 see Cruger, Johann, Der Hochste Herrscht In Majestat Und Pracht

PSALM 93 see Kaufmann, Otto, Der Herr Ist Konig

PSALM 93 see Multer

PSALM 93 see Nystedt, Knut, Dominus Regnat

PSALM 93 see Sweelinck, Jan Pieterszoon, Der Herr Ist Konig

PSALM 94 see Wapen, Francis A., Come Let Us Bow Down

PSALM 95
see New Look At The Psalms, A

PSALM 95 see Buxtehude, Dietrich, Afferte Domino

PSALM 95 see Couperin, Francois, O Come Let Us Sing

PSALM 95 see Goudimel, Claude, Sus, Esgaions Au Seigneur

PSALM 95 see Jaeggi, Oswald

PSALM 95 see Kirk

PSALM 95 see Krul, O Come Let Us Sing

PSALM 95 see Le Jeune, Claude

PSALM 95 see Mawby, C.

PSALM 95 see Mendelssohn-Bartholdy, Felix, In His Hand

PSALM 95 see Mendelssohn-Bartholdy, Felix, Kommt, Lasst Uns Anbeten

PSALM 95 see Mendelssohn-Bartholdy, Felix, O Come, Let Us Worship

PSALM 95 see Track, Gerhard, O Come, Let Us Sing To The Lord

PSALM 96 see Adler, Samuel

PSALM 96 see Burkhard Willy, Singet Dem Herrn Ein Neues Lied

PSALM 122
see Four Modern Psalm Tunes

PSALM 122 see Durst, Sidney C., I Was Glad

PSALM 122 see Gibbs, Laetatus Sum

PSALM 122 see Graap, Lothar, Ich Freute Mich

PSALM 122 see Halevy, [Jacques-Francois-Fromental-Elie], Somachti Beomrim

PSALM 122 see Nicholson, Richard, O Pray For The Peace Of Jerusalem

PSALM 122 see Schollom, Robert

PSALM 122 see Schutz, Heinrich, Ich Freu Mich Des, Das Mir Geredt Ist

PSALM 122 see Slack, Roy, I Was Glad

PSALM 122 see Sowerby, Leo, I Was Glad

PSALM 122 see Vivaldi, Antonio, Laetatus

PSALM 122 see Williamson, Malcolm, O Jerusalem

PSALM 123 see Lockwood, Normand

PSALM 123 see Ruppel, Paul Ernst, Ich Hebe Meine Augen Auf Zu Dir

PSALM 123 see Wangenheim, [Volker], Ich Hebe Meine Augen Auf

PSALM 124 see Benary, Peter

PSALM 124 see Driessler, Johannes, Wo Der Herr Nicht Bei Uns Ware

PSALM 124 see Goudimel, Claude, Or Peut Bien Dire Israel Maintenant

PSALM 124 see Lupi II, Didier, Qu'Israel Die Et Confesse En Effet

PSALM 124 see Reda, Siegfried, War Gott Nicht Mit Uns Diese Zeit

PSALM 124 see Reda, Siegfried, Wo Gott Der Herr Nicht Bei Uns Halt

PSALM 124 see Sowerby, Leo

PSALM 125
(Vaal, O. De) mix cor sc ALSBACH&D s.p.
(P2795)

PSALM 125 see Orr, Robin, They That Put Their Trust In The Lord

PSALM 126 see Hartmann, Heinrich, Wenn Der Herr Die Gefangenen Zions

PSALM 126 see Krenek, Ernst

PSALM 126 see Kubizek, Augustinian

PSALM 126 see Marshall, Philip, When The Lord Turned Again

PSALM 126 see Micheelsen, Hans Friedrich, Wenn Der Herr Die Gefangenen Zions Erlosen Wird

PSALM 126 see Monteverdi, Claudio, Nisi Dominus

PSALM 126 see Raphael, Gunther, Wenn Der Herr Die Gefangenen Zions

PSALM 126 see Reda, Siegfried, Wenn Der Herr Die Gefangenen Zions Erlosen Wird

PSALM 126 see Romanovsky, Erich, Wenn Der Herr Das Haus Nicht Baut

PSALM 126 see Schutz, Heinrich, Die Mit Tranen Saen

PSALM 126 see Silver, Frederick

PSALM 126 see Tebaldini, Giovanni, Nisi Dominus

PSALM 126 see Toebosch, Louis

PSALM 126 see Wikander, David, Psalm 126 I Psaltaren

PSALM 126 I PSALTAREN see Wikander, David

PSALM 127 see Callhoff, Herbert

PSALM 127 see Dinn, Freda, Except The Lord Build The House

PSALM 127 see Pitfield, Thomas Baron, If God Build Not The House

PSALM 127 see Reda, Siegfried, Wo Gott Zum Haus Nicht Gibt Sein Gunst

PSALM 127 see Schneider, Willy

PSALM 127 see Schutz, Heinrich, Wo Der Herr Nicht Das Haus Bauet

PSALM 128 see Berger, Jean, Blessed Is Every One

PSALM 128 see Brown, Thomas, Blessed Are All They

PSALM 128 see Callhoff, Herbert

PSALM 129 see Dawney, Michael, Out Of The Depths

PSALM 129 see Espla, De Profundis

PSALM 129 see Gattermayer, Heinrich, Aus Der Tiefe

PSALM 129 see Lassus, Roland de (Orlandus), De Profundis Clamavi

PSALM 129 see Liszt, Franz

PSALM 129 see Romanovsky, Erich, Aus Der Tiefe

PSALM 129 see Ropartz, Joseph Guy, De Profundis

PSALM 130 see Allanbrook

PSALM 130 see Charpentier, Marc-Antoine, Out Of The Depths

PSALM 130 see Dowland, John

PSALM 130 see Flanagan, William

PSALM 130 see Giles, Nathaniel, Out Of The Deep

PSALM 130 see Gluck, Christoph Willibald Ritter von, De Profundis

PSALM 130 see Goudimel, Claude, Du Fons De Ma Pensee

PSALM 130 see Gounod, Charles Francois, De Profundis

PSALM 130 see Gounod, Charles Francois, Out Of Darkness

PSALM 130 see Hovhaness, Alan, Out Of The Depths

PSALM 130 see Klein, Richard Rudolf, Aus Der Tiefe Rufe Ich

PSALM 130 see Kullnes, Ake, Utur Djupen Ropar Jag

PSALM 130 see Lissmann, Kurt, Aus Der Tiefe Rufe Ich

PSALM 130 see Lupo, Thomas, Out Of The Deep

PSALM 130 see McGraw, Cameron

PSALM 130 see Manz, Paul

PSALM 130 see Mendelssohn-Bartholdy, Felix, Aus Tiefer Not Schrei Ich Zu Dir

PSALM 130 see Mozart, Wolfgang Amadeus, De Profundis

PSALM 130 see Mulder, Ernest W., De Profundis

PSALM 130 see Peek, Richard

PSALM 130 see Piket, Frederick, Out Of The Depths I Cry

PSALM 130 see Purvis, Richard, De Profundis

PSALM 130 see Reda, Siegfried, Aus Tiefer Not Schrei Ich Zu Dir

PSALM 130 see Schoenberg, Arnold, De Profundis

PSALM 130 see Schutz, Heinrich, Aus Der Tiefe Rufe Ich

PSALM 130 see Schutz, Heinrich, Aus Tiefer Not Schrei Ich Zu Dir

PSALM 130 see Schutz, Heinrich, From Depths Of Woe I Cry To Thee

PSALM 130 see Silver, Frederick, Out Of The Depths

PSALM 130 see Stier, Alfred, Aus Meines Jammers Tiefe

PSALM 130 see Thomson, Virgil, De Profundis

PSALM 131 see Allanbrook

PSALM 131 see Beeson, Jack Hamilton

PSALM 131 see Burkhard Willy, Herr, Mein Herz Ist Nicht Hoffartig

PSALM 131 see Escovada, R.

PSALM 131 see Goudimel, Claude, Seigneur, Je Ne Point Le Coeur Fier

PSALM 131 see Toebosch, Louis

PSALM 131 see Willaert, Adrian, Memento Domine David

PSALM 131 see Zentner, Johannes

PSALM 132 see Gattermayer, Heinrich, Siehe, Wie Gut Ist's

PSALM 132 see Peloquin, C. Alexander, Behold How Good It Is

PSALM 133 see Goudimel, Claude, O Combien Est Plaisant Et Souhaitable

PSALM 133 see Lynn

PSALM 133 see Pinkham, Daniel, Behold, How Good And How Pleasant

PSALM 133 see Whear, Paul William

PSALM 133 see Williamson, Malcolm, Together In Unity

PSALM 134 see Buxtehude, Dietrich, Siehe, Lobet Den Herrn

PSALM 134 see Champion, Thomas, Or Sus, Serviteurs Du Seigneur

PSALM 134 see Le Jeune, Claude

PSALM 134 see Pearson, Behold Now, Praise The Lord

PSALM 134 see Rorem, Ned

PSALM 134 see Sweelinck, Jan Pieterszoon, Or Sus, Serviteurs

PSALM 134 see Sweeny, Jack

PSALM 135 see Borris, Siegfried

PSALM 135 see Goemanne, Noel

PSALM 135 see Handel, George Frideric, O Praise The Lord With One Consent

PSALM 135 see Handel, George Frideric, Oh Praise The Lord With One Consent

PSALM 135 see Hutchinson, W., Praise The Lord

PSALM 135 see Lupi II, Didier, Sus, Sus, Qu'on Se Dispose De Louer Le Seigneur

PSALM 135 see Walton, Kenneth, Praise Ye The Lord

PSALM 136
(Parker) SATB,Bar solo,acap oct LAWSON 51250
$.30   (P2796)

PSALM 136 see Bordewijk-Roepman, Johanna, Lofpsalm

PSALM 136 see Gounod, Charles Francois, Pres Du Fleuve Etranger

PSALM 136 see Hammerschmidt, Andreas, Danket Dem Herrn, Denn Er Ist

PSALM 136 see Mechem, Kirke, Give Thanks Unto The Lord

PSALM 136 see Milner, Anthony

PSALM 136 see Parker, Alice

PSALM 136 see Peloquin, C. Alexander, Resurrection Psalm

PSALM 136 see Schutz, Heinrich, Danket Dem Herren, Denn Er Ist Freundlich

PSALM 136 see Staden, Johann, Danket Dem Herren

PSALM 136 see Van Lier, Bertus

PSALM 137 see Braal, Andreas de

PSALM 137 see Gomolka, Mikolaj, Siedzac Po Niskich Brzegach Babilonskiej Wody

PSALM 137 see Goudimel, Claude, Estans Assis Aux Rives Aquatiques

PSALM 137 see Hopkins, By Babel's Stream We Sat And Wept

PSALM 137 see Humfrey, Pelham, By The Waters Of Babylon

PSALM 137 see Liszt, Franz

PSALM 137 see Lockwood

PSALM 137 see Loeffler, Charles Martin, By The Rivers Of Babylon

PSALM 137 see Mawby, C.

PSALM 137 see Pluister, Simon

PSALM 137 see Roeske, F.J.

PSALM 137 see Schutz, Heinrich, An Den Wasserflussen Zu Babel Sassen Wir Und Weineten

PSALM 137 see Thomas, Kurt, An Den Wassern Zu Babel

PSALM 137 see Vaal, O. de, Aan De Stromen Babylon

PSALM 138 see Goemanne, Noel

PSALM 138 see Pluister, Simon

PSALM 138 see Schutz, Heinrich, Aus Meines Herzens Grunde

PSALM 138 see Sweelinck, Jan Pieterszoon, Mein Ganzes Herz Erhebet Dich

PSALM 138 see Whear, Paul William, Psalms Of Celebration part I

PSALM 138 see Wienhorst, Richard, I Will Praise Thee With My Whole Heart

PSALM 139 see David, Johann Nepomuk, Herr, Du Erforschest Mich

PSALM 139 see Geist, O God, Search Me

PSALM 139 see Pepping, Ernst, Herr, Du Erforschest Mich

PSALM 139 see Pooler, If I Take The Wings Of The Morning

PSALM 139 see Reda, Siegfried, Herr, Du Erforschest Mich

PSALM 139 see Toolan, S. Suzanne, Stilled And Quiet Is My Soul

PSALM 139 see Wennerberg, Gunnar

PSALM 139 see Young, Carlton R.

PSALM 140 see Berger, Jean

PSALM 141 see Track, Gerhard, To The Lord I Cry

PSALM 142 see Chajes, Julius

PSALM 142 see Rab, Valentin, Ich Schreie Zum Herren

PSALM 142 see Vecchi, Orazio, Lord, Hear My Cry

PSALM 143 see Holst, Gustav, Lord, Who Hast Made Us For Thine Own

PSALM 143 see Hovhaness, Alan, Hear My Prayer, O Lord

PSALM OF PRAISE see Brown, Leon F.

PSALM OF PRAISE see Cho-Tung Tang, Jordan

PSALM OF PRAISE see Darst, W. Glenn

PSALM OF PRAISE see Dvorak, Antonin

PSALM OF PRAISE see Hedges, H.

PSALM OF PRAISE see McAfee, Don

PSALM OF PRAISE see Wagner, Doug

PSALM OF PRAISE, A see Cacavas, [John]

PSALM OF PRAISE, A see Davis, Allan

PSALM OF PRAISE, A see Hopson, Hal H.

PSALM OF PRAISE, A see Jones, R.W.

PSALM OF PRAISE, A see Reed, Herbert Owen

PSALM OF PRAISE, A see Travers, John

PSALM OF PRAISE, A see Williamson, Malcolm

PSALM OF PRAYER AND PRAISE, A see Weiner

PSALM OF REDEMPTION see Elmore, Robert [Hall]

PSALM OF SION *carol/Psalm
   SATB (easy) OXFORD 08.132 $.15   (P2798)

PSALM OF THANKSGIVING, A see Darke, Harold
   [Edwin]

PSALM OF THANKSGIVING, A see Thompson

PSALM OF THE SEA (THAT THEY GO DOWN IN SHIPS)
   see Epstein, June

PSALM OF TRUST see Haydn, (Franz) Joseph

PSALM OF WORSHIP, A see Pasquet, Jean

PSALM PRAISES see Martin

PSALM SET see Pinkham, Daniel

PSALM THAT SWINGS, THE see Lovelace, Austin C.

PSALM- UND EVANGELIENMOTETTEN see Rohwer, Jens

PSALM122
   see Processional Psalms (Plainsong With
   Fauxbourdons)

PSALMEN see Bornefeld, Helmut

PSALMEN MIT ANTIPHONEN, MAGNIFICAT UND
   SELIGPREISUNGEN see Schwartz, Gerhard von

PSALMEN-MOTETTE see Motte, Diether de la

PSALMEN-TRYPTICHON see Baumann, Herbert

PSALMEN UND CHRISTLICHE GESANG FUGWEISS, ERSTE
   FOLGE see Hassler, Hans Leo

PSALMEN UND CHRISTLICHE GESANG FUGWEISS, ZWEITE
   FOLGE see Hassler, Hans Leo

PSALMEN UND CHRISTLICHE GESANGE FUGWEISS see
   Hassler, Hans Leo

PSALMEN UND GEISTLICHE LIEDER DER CHRISTENHEIT
   (Vischer, Wilhelm) [Ger] mix cor,acap HUG
   s.p.
      contains: Der Bund; Der Osterkreis; Der
      Weihnachtskreis; Die Predigt; Die Psalmen
      ; Die Psalmen; Die Psalmen; Tages- Und
      Lebenslauf   (P2799)

PSALMENKANTATE see Burkhard Willy

PSALMENKANTATE see Avidom, Menachem

PSALMENKANTATE see Heiller, Anton

PSALMENKANTATE see Lechner, Konrad

PSALMENSYMPHONIE see Badings, Henk

PSALMENTRIPTYCHON see Callhoff, Herbert

PSALMI see Baumann, Max

PSALMI VESPERTINI see Volpi, Edoardo

PSALMKOMMENTARE see Schollom, Robert

PSALMKONZERT see Wenzel, Eberhard

PSALMKONZERT see Zimmermann, Heinz Werner

PSALMLIEDER *see Bach, Johann Sebastian, Nun
   Lob, Mein Seel; Bach, Johann Sebastian, War
   Gott Nicht Mit Uns; Hagius, Conrad, Ihr
   Kreatur Im Himmel Oben; Hagius, Conrad, Wer
   Heimlich Seine Wohnesatt; Hassler, Hans
   Leo, Singet Ein Neues Lied; Lassus, Roland
   de (Orlandus), Gott Ists, Auf Den Wir Immer
   Hoffen; Lassus, Roland de (Orlandus), Gross
   Ist Der Herr; Lassus, Roland de (Orlandus),
   Herr, Der Du Meine Starke Bist; Lassus,
   Roland de (Orlandus), Lobet Den Herren;
   Praetorius, Michael, Lobet Gott, Unsern
   Herrn; Schutz, Heinrich, Danket Dem Herren;
   Schutz, Heinrich, Danket Dem Herrn; Schutz,
   Heinrich, Der Herr Ist Konig Uberall;
   Schutz, Heinrich, Der Herr Ist Konig Und
   Regiert; Schutz, Heinrich, Die Himmel,
   Herr, Preisen Sehr; Schutz, Heinrich, Ich
   Heb Mein Augen; Schutz, Heinrich, Ich Ruf
   Zu Dir; Schutz, Heinrich, Jauchzet Dem
   Herren Alle Welt; Schutz, Heinrich, Wie
   Ists So Lieblich; Schutz, Heinrich, Wohl
   Denen, Die Da Wandeln   (P2800)

PSALMLIEDER see Bach, Johann Sebastian

PSALMLIEDER see Hagius, Conrad

PSALMLIEDER see Hassler, Hans Leo

PSALMLIEDER see Lassus, Roland de (Orlandus)

PSALMLIEDER see Praetorius, Michael

PSALMLIEDER see Schutz, Heinrich

PSALMO BRASILEIRO see Berger, Jean

PSALMODIA EVANGELICA *Gen,anthem
   (Andersen, C. Wesley) "Lift Up Your Heads"
   SATB (easy) oct AUGSBURG 1109 $.25   (P2801)
   (Christiansen, O.) "Lift Up Your Heads" SATB
   SCHMITT 8048 $.35   (P2802)
   (Hadley) "Behold The King" SATB oct PRO ART
   1659 $.25   (P2803)
   (Hadley) "Behold The King" SSA oct PRO ART
   2214 $.25   (P2804)

PSALMODIA EVANGELICA see Hastings, Paul

PSALMS see Foss, Lukas

PSALMS see Grieg, Edvard Hagerup

PSALMS see Thordarson, Sigurdur

PSALMS AND HYMNS FOR USE IN THE LITURY OF HOLY
   WEEK *CCU,Holywk,hymn/Psalm
   (Milner, Paulinus) mix cor oct NOVELLO
   02.0074.03 s.p.   (P2805)

PSALMS AND HYMNS OF EARLY AMERICA PART I: TWO
   TUNES FROM THE AINSWORTH PSALTER *CC2U,
   hymn/Psalm,US
   (Noss, L.) TBarB,acap AMP A225 $.35 (P2806)

PSALMS AND HYMNS OF EARLY AMERICA PART II:
   THREE TUNES FROM THE BAY PSALM BOOK *CC3U,
   hymn/Psalm,US
   (Noss, L.) TBarB,acap AMP A226 $.50 (P2807)

PSALMS AND HYMNS OF EARLY AMERICA PART PART
   III: TWO TUNES FROM THE MISSOURI HARMONY
   *CC2U,hymn/Psalm,US
   (Noss, L.) TBarB,acap AMP A227 $.35 (P2808)

PSALMS, MOTETS, AND KYRIES see Mendelssohn-
   Bartholdy, Felix

PSALMS OF CELEBRATION PART I see Whear, Paul
   William

PSALMS OF CELEBRATION PART IV see Whear, Paul
   William

PSALMS OF CELEBRATION see Whear, Paul William

PSALMS OF CELEBRATION PART II see Whear, Paul
   William

PSALMS OF GENEVA see Martin, Frank

PSALMS OF PENITENCE see Berger, Jean

PSALMS OF PRAISE see Parker, Alice

PSALMS OF REJOICING see Steinman, W.

PSALMS see Liszt, Franz

PSALMS see Pergolesi, Giovanni Battista

PSALMS see Pergolesi, Giovanni Battista

PSALMUS see Cockshott, Gerald Wilfred

PSALMUS see Straesser, Joep

PSALMUS HUNGARICUS see Kodaly, Zoltan

PSALMUS IN CONFESSIONE see Nielsen, Riccardo

PSAUME see Boulanger, Lili

PSAUME 24 see Boulanger, Lili

PSAUME CL see Franck, Cesar

PSAUME CL see Papineau-Couture, Jean

PSAUME CXII see Schmitt, Florent

PSAUME CXXIX see Ropartz, Joseph Guy, De
   Profundis

PSAUME CXXX see Gounod, Charles Francois, De
   Profundis

PSAUME DU SERVITEUR see Reveyron, Joseph

PSAUME VIII see Schmitt, Florent, Domine,
   Dominus Noster

PSAUME XVIII see Saint-Saens, Camille, Coeli
   Enarrant

PSAUMES see Bozza, Eugene

PUBLICAN, THE see Van De Water, B.

PUCCINI, GIACOMO (1858-1924)
   Messa Di Gloria *Mass
   SATB,TBarB soli BELWIN $4.00   (P2809)

PUELLARE GREMIUM
   see English Gothic Music

PUER NATUS *Xmas,carol,Ger
   "Boy Was Born, A" see Dormi Jesu
   SATB OXFORD 08.080 $.15   (P2810)
   (med) OXFORD 08.080 $.15   (P2811)
   (Barrow, R.) "Child Was Born In Bethlehem, A"
   TTBB,org SCHIRM.EC 2156 $.22   (P2812)
   (Barrow, R.) "Child Was Born In Bethlehem, A"
   TTBB,org SCHIRM.EC 2156 $.30   (P2813)
   (Gilbert) unis&SSAA (easy) OXFORD 40.015 $.30
                                        (P2814)

PUER NATUS see Brun, Abbe F.

PUER NATUS see Scheidt, Samuel

PUER NATUS see Wilkinson

PUER NATUS see Williams, David H.

PUER NATUS EST see Ammann, Benno

PUER NATUS EST see Morales

PUER NATUS EST see Regnart, Jacob

PUER NATUS EST see Scheierling, Konrad

PUER NATUS EST see Schroeder, Hermann

PUER NATUS EST see Trexler, Georg

PUER NATUS EST NOBIS see Gevaert, Francois
   Auguste

PUER NATUS EST NOBIS see Mouton, Jean

PUER NATUS EST NOBIS see Picchi, Luigi

PUER NATUS IN BETHLEEM *Xmas
   (Gevaert, F.-A.) "Pour Le Jour De Noel" [Lat/
   Fr] 4pt mix cor,acap (easy) cor pts LEMOINE
   s.p. see from Collection De Choeurs,
   troisieme Fascicule   (P2815)

PUER NATUS IN BETHLEHEM see Bach, Johann
   Sebastian

PUER NATUS IN BETHLEHEM see Nelhybel, Vaclav

PUER NATUS IN BETHLEHEM see Scheidt, Samuel

PUER NATUS IN BETHLEHEM see Werner, Gregor
   Joseph

PUER NOBIS *Xmas,carol
   unis (very easy) OXFORD 08.029 $.20 (P2816)
   "Now A Lovely Child Is Born" TTBB oct GRAY
   GCMR 3214 $.30   (P2817)
   "Unto Us A Boy Is Born" unis (easy) OXFORD
   08.029 $.20   (P2818)
   (Roseberry) "Unto Us A Boy Is Born" 4pt mix
   cor oct SCHIRM.G 11626 $.30   (P2819)
   (Roseberry, Eric) "Unto Us A Boy Is Born"
   SATB,pno oct FABER 11626 $.30   (P2820)

PUER NOBIS see Pfautsch, Lloyd

PUER NOBIS NASCITUR see Picchi, Luigi

PUERI CANTORES *CCU
   mix cor sc HANSSLER 25.025 s.p.   (P2821)

PUERI CANTORES see Kropfreiter, Augustinius
   Franz

PUERI CONCINITE see Gallus, Jacobus

PUERI CONCINITE see Herbeck, Johann Franz von

PUERI HEBRAEORIUM see Thompson

PUERI HEBRAEORUM see Palestrina, Giovanni

PUERI HEBRAEORUM see Thompson, Randall

PUERI HEBRAEORUM see Victoria, Tomas Luis de

PUERI HEBRAEORUM see Zorita, Nicosia

PUGATCHOV, E.
   Draw Ye Waters Joyfully *see Ush'avtem Mayim

   Ush'avtem Mayim *Fest,Bibl,Heb
   (Coopersmith, H.) "Draw Ye Waters Joyfully"
   SATB TRANSCON. TCL 714 $.30   (P2822)

PUGH
   Shepherds' Carol, The *Xmas,carol
   SATB oct LORENZ E12 $.25   (P2823)

PUGHE-EVANS, D.
   Lead, Kindly Light *anthem
   (West, John E.) mix cor,S solo,orch oct
   NOVELLO 28.0589.08 s.p., ipr   (P2824)

PUISQU'EN TOI GIT PERFECTION see Lupi II,
   Didier

PULCHRA ES AMICA MEA see Palestrina, Giovanni

PULCHRA SUNT GENAE TUAE see Palestrina,
   Giovanni

PULL, PULL, THE YULE LOG see Grime, William

PULLEN, ALICE M.
   Holiday Thanksgiving Song *Thanks,carol
   unis CRAMER 9   (P2825)

PULS, HANS (1914-   )
   Hilf, Herr Meines Lebens *Gen
   [Ger] unis,acap (easy) BOSSE BE 267 s.p.
                                        (P2826)

   Wir Leben Nicht Allein Vom Brot *Gen
   [Ger] unis (easy) BOSSE BE272 s.p.   (P2827)
   (Blarr, Oskar Gottlieb) [Ger] 5pt mix cor,
   bvl (med easy) BOSSE BE 239 s.p.   (P2828)

PURCELL, DANIEL (ca. 1660-1717)
   Magnificat And Nunc Dimittis *Magnif/Nunc
   (Dearnley, Christopher) SATB (F min) oct
   NOVELLO 88.0022.07 s.p.   (P2829)

PURCELL, HENRY (ca. 1659-1695)
   Allelujah *Easter/Gen
   (Hilton, A.) SATB oct PRESSER 352-00380
   $.30   (P2830)

   Beati Omnes *Gen
   "How Blest Are They" SSATB oct OXFORD
                                        (P2831)

   Beati Omnes Qui Timent Dominum
   SATB SCHIRM.G A 878 $.40   (P2832)

   Behold, I Bring You Glad Tidings *Xmas,
   anthem
   SATB,ATB soli,org PETERS H1527   (P2833)
   (Just) SATB,TTB/SSB soli,strings,kbd sc
   SCHOTT 4547 s.p., cor pts SCHOTT 4547
   s.p.   (P2834)

   Benedicite
   SATB&SSA (med) oct OXFORD 43.306 $.90
                                        (P2835)

   Blessed Be The Lord
   (Whitford) SAB oct FISCHER,J 9475 $.30
                                        (P2836)

   Blessed Is He *anthem
   SSATTB oct NOVELLO 28.1261.04 s.p.   (P2837)

PURCELL, HENRY (cont'd.)

Blow, Blow The Clarion Trumpet *Gen
(Barthelson) SATB oct SPRATT 594 $.30
(P2838)

Blow Up The Trumpet In Sion *anthem
SSSAATTTBB oct NOVELLO 46.0017.07 s.p.
(P2839)

Briton's Sing!
2pt,opt orch ASHDOWN E.A.200 s.p., ipr
(P2840)

Christ Is Made The Sure Foundation
*Marriage,hymn
SATB (easy) ALLANS 328 s.p.
(P2841)

Consider And Hear Me
(Roberts, Jason) SATB (med) PRESSER G-193
$.35
(P2842)

Declare His Honor
SATB oct STAFF 484 $.25
(P2843)

Early, O Lord, My Fainting Soul *anthem
SATB/SSAB,org oct NOVELLO 46.0008.08 s.p.
(P2844)
(Lewis; Fortune; Goldsbrough) SATB/SSAB,
org/hpsd oct SCHIRM.G 11462 $.30 (P2845)

Ego Cubui Et Dormivi
(Davies) "Now O Lord, I Lay Me Down" [Eng/
Lat] 4pt mix cor,acap oct CURWEN 11378
$.25
(P2846)
(Davies) "Now O Lord, I Lay Me Down" mix
cor CURWEN 80894 s.p.
(P2847)

Evening Hymn *Eve,hymn
(Grace) unis (med) OXFORD 45.410 $.35, ipr
(P2848)
(Grace, Harvey) SATB (med easy) oct OXFORD
42.204 $.65
(P2849)
(Whittaker, W.G.) unis (med easy) oct
OXFORD 45.410 $.35
(P2850)

Evening Hymn, An *Eve
unis oct NOVELLO 33.0122.02 s.p.
(P2851)

Evening Service *see Magnificat Und Nunc
Dimittis

Evening Service In G Minor
SATB (A min,med easy) oct OXFORD 42.824
$.65
(P2852)

Five Sacred Choruses *CC5U
mix cor,acap voc sc KALMUS 6385 $1.75
(P2853)

Funeral Sentences *anthem
mix cor oct NOVELLO 46.0006.01 s.p. (P2854)

Funf Geistliche Chore *CC5U
(Blume) [Eng/Ger] 4-6pt mix cor MOSELER
s.p.
(P2855)

Gedenke Nicht, Herr *see Remember Not, Lord,
Our Offences

Gloria Patri
(Greyson) "Glory To God" SATB oct BOURNE
ES57 $.25
(P2856)

Glory And Worship Are Before Him
SATB,org (abridged) SCHIRM.EC 1108 $.30
(P2857)
(Bement, G.) TTBB,org (abridged) SCHIRM.EC
2124 $.22
(P2858)
(Bement, G.) SSAA,org SCHIRM.EC 1945 $.20
(P2859)
(Davis, K.) SA,pno SCHIRM.EC 1555 (P2860)

Glory To God *see Gloria Patri

Hail, Bright Cecilia (from Ode For St.
Cecilia's Day)
(Tippett; Bergmann) SATB,SAATBB soli,orch
sc SCHOTT 10296 s.p., cor pts SCHOTT
10452 s.p.
(P2861)

Hear Me, O Lord, The Great Support *anthem/
ATB/TTB,org oct NOVELLO 46.0009.06 s.p.
(P2862)
(Lewis; Fortune; Goldsbrough) ATB/TTB,org/
hpsd oct NOVELLO 11459 $.30 (P2863)

Hear My Prayer, O Lord *anthem/prayer
mix cor SOUTHERN $.35
(P2864)
8pt BELWIN AP29 $.35
(P2865)
(Davies) mix cor CURWEN 80907 s.p. (P2866)
(Davies) 1-2pt jr cor/1-2pt wom cor CURWEN
72693 s.p.
(P2867)
(Dearnley, C.) SSAATTBB BROUDE,A. 221 $.35
(P2868)
(Hilton, Arthur) SSAATTBB (med easy)
PRESSER 352-00463 $.35
(P2869)
(Shaw, Watkins) SSAATTBB oct NOVELLO
88.0009.10 s.p.
(P2870)
(West, John E.) mix cor oct NOVELLO
28.1001.08 s.p.
(P2871)

Hear The Prayer We Raise
(Stroud, Ray) SATB,org FOSTER MF101 $.20
(P2872)

How Blest Are They *see Beati Omnes

Hymn For Ascensiontide *Asc,hymn
SATB (easy) oct OXFORD 42.843 $.25 (P2873)

In The Midst Of Life
(Boepple, P.) SATB oct PRESSER 352-00034
$.30
(P2874)

Jehova Quam Multi Sunt *see Jehovah, Quam
Multi

Jehovah, How Many Are They *see Jehovah,
Quam Multi

Jehovah, Quam Multi (Psalm 3) anthem/Psalm
"Jehova Quam Multi Sunt" SATB oct GRAY
GCMR 3064 $.35
(P2875)
"Jehovah, How Many Are They" SSATB oct
NOVELLO 03.0124.08 s.p.
(P2876)
(Pinkham, D.) "O Lord God, How Many Are My
Oppressors" [Lat/Eng] SSATB,TB soli,org
SCHIRM.EC 2717 $.50
(P2877)

Jubilate (from Ode For St. Cecilia's Day
1694) Jubil
see Purcell, Henry, Te Deum

PURCELL, HENRY (cont'd.)

(Shaw, Watkins) SATB (D maj) oct NOVELLO
44.1338.05 s.p.
(P2878)

Jubilate Deo
see Purcell, Henry, Te Deum Laudamus

Let Mine Eyes Run Down With Tears *anthem
(Lewis; Fortune; Nigel) SSATB,org,
cont oct NOVELLO 46.0003.07 s.p. (P2879)

Let My Prayer Come Up *anthem/Offer
SATB oct GRAY GCMR 1527 $.30
(P2880)
SSSATB oct BELWIN 64088 $.30
(P2881)
(Bridge, Frederick) mix cor oct NOVELLO
50.0118.08 s.p.
(P2882)
(Davies, L.H.) 2pt ASHDOWN E.A.300 s.p.
(P2883)
(Hilton, A.) SSATB oct PRESSER 352-00440
$.25
(P2884)

Let My Prayer Come Up Into Thy Presence
(Bridge, F.) SSATB,org (abridged) SCHIRM.EC
1109 $.20
(P2885)

Lord, How Long Wilt Thou Be Angry *anthem
SSATB oct NOVELLO 28.1262.02 s.p. (P2886)
(Boepple, P.) SSATB oct PRESSER 352-00035
$.40
(P2887)

Lord, I Can Suffer *anthem
SATB/SSAB,org oct NOVELLO 46.0010.10 s.p.
(P2888)
(Lewis; Fortune; Goldsbrough) SATB/SSAB,org/hpsd
oct NOVELLO 11463 $.30 (P2889)

Lord Is King, The *anthem
(Finney, T.M.) mix cor,S solo,org oct
NOVELLO 28.1409.09 s.p.
(P2890)

Lord, Now Lettest Thou
mix cor SOUTHERN $.25
(P2891)
(Aks) SATB MARKS 85 $.25
(P2892)

Lord, Our God Is Full Of Might, The
(Coggin) SAB oct PRO ART 2269 $.30 (P2893)

Magnificat And Nunc Dimittis (from Service In
B Flat, The) Magnif/Nunc
SATB (G min) oct NOVELLO 44.0852.07 s.p.
(P2894)
SATB,opt org/pno PETERS 66266 $.50 (P2895)
SATB (C maj,med easy) oct OXFORD 42.850
$.80
(P2896)

Magnificat Und Nunc Dimittis *Magnif/Nunc
(Just, Herbert) "Evening Service" [Eng/Ger]
SATB&opt jr cor,SATB soli,acap (med easy)
BAREN. BA 2923 $2.25
(P2897)

Man That Is Born Of Woman *anthem/funeral
SATB,org STAINER D31 s.p.
(P2898)

Masque In Dioclesian *cant
BELWIN $1.25
(P2899)

May The God Of Wit Inspire
mix cor SOUTHERN $.20
(P2900)

My Beloved Spake *anthem
(Dent, E.J.) mix cor oct NOVELLO 28.1280.00
s.p.
(P2901)

My Soul Doth Magnify The Lord
(Aks) SATB MARKS 84 $.40
(P2902)
(Knight, Gerald) SATB,acap oct FISCHER,C
CM-7508 $.25
(P2903)

Nicene Creed *Credo
SATB (med easy) oct OXFORD 43.342 $.65
(P2904)

Nicene Creed, The
(Whitworth) SATB (med) OXFORD 43.342 $.65
(P2905)

Now O Lord, I Lay Me Down *see Ego Cubui Et
Dormivi

Now That The Sun *Eve,anthem/hymn
(Chambers, H.A.) mix cor oct NOVELLO
28.1259.02 s.p.
(P2906)

O All Ye People, Clap Your Hands *anthem/
Psalm
SSTB,org oct NOVELLO 46.0011.08 s.p.
(P2907)

O Be Joyful In The Lord
(Mason) SATB oct WORD CS-358 $.30 (P2908)

O Give Thanks
SAB oct LORENZ 7406 $.25
(P2909)

O Give Thanks Unto The Lord *Thanks,anthem/
Bibl
(Davson, A.) SATB,org (abridged) SCHIRM.EC
1700 $.40
(P2910)
(Lewis, Anthony; Fortune, Nigel) mix cor,
SATB soli,org,strings oct NOVELLO
46.0018.05 s.p., ipr
(P2911)

O God The King Of Glory *anthem
(Lewis, Anthony; Fortune, Nigel) mix cor
oct NOVELLO 46.0007.10 s.p.
(P2912)
(Lynn) SATB,org oct SCHIRM.G 11438 $.25
(P2913)

O God Thou Art My God *anthem
(Lewis, Anthony; Fortune, Nigel) SATB,org,
cont oct NOVELLO 46.0005.03 s.p. (P2914)

O Happy Man *anthem/Psalm
SATB/SSAB,org oct NOVELLO 46.0012.06 s.p.
(P2915)
(Lewis; Fortune; Goldsbrough) SATB/SSAB oct
NOVELLO 11464 $.25
(P2916)

O, I'm Sick Of Life *anthem
TTB,org oct NOVELLO 46.0013.04 s.p. (P2917)

O Lord God, How Many Are My Oppressors *see
Jehovah, Quam Multi

O Lord God Of Hosts *anthem
(Lewis, Anthony; Fortune, Nigel) SSAATTBB,
org oct NOVELLO 46.0002.09 s.p. (P2918)

O Lord Our Governor *anthem
SSAB/SSTB,org oct NOVELLO 46.0014.02 s.p.
(P2919)

PURCELL, HENRY (cont'd.)

O Sing Unto The Lord *see O Syng Nu Hojt For
Gud

O Syng Nu Hojt For Gud *anthem
"O Sing Unto The Lord" [Eng/Ger] SATB,SATB
soli,strings,org min sc PETERS E1063
$2.00, ipa
(P2920)
"O Sing Unto The Lord" [Ger/Eng] SATB,
strings,org min sc EULENBURG EUL1063
s.p., ipa
(P2921)
"O Sing Unto The Lord" cor,orch sc KALMUS
$7.00, ipa
(P2922)
"O Sing Unto The Lord" SATB,org (abridged)
SCHIRM.EC 1103 $.30
(P2923)
"O Sing Unto The Lord" SATB,orch oct
NOVELLO 28.0142.06 s.p., ipr (P2924)
(Rasmussen, Henning Bro) "O Sing Unto The
Lord" SATB,soli,org,strings HANSEN-DEN
27957 s.p., ipa
(P2925)
(Shaw, Watkins) "O Sing Unto The Lord"
SATB,org,strings oct NOVELLO 28.1325.04
s.p., ipr
(P2926)

O Thou Who Through This Holy Week *Easter/
Lent
(Follett) SATB oct PRO ART 2313 $.25
(P2927)

O Worship The Lord
(Hilton, A.) SATB,acap oct PRESSER MC392
$.25
(P2928)

Ode St. Cecilia's Day
cor voc sc KALMUS 6382 $1.75
(P2929)

Oh, Worship The Lord
SATB,org (abridged) SCHIRM.EC 2633 $.30
(P2930)

Plung'd In The Confines Of Despair *anthem
TTB,org oct NOVELLO 46.0015.00 s.p. (P2931)

Praise The Lord
(Anderson) SSA oct LESLIE 3014 (P2932)
(Anderson) SSA oct BELWIN 60397 $.25 (P2933)

Praise The Lord, O Jerusalem *anthem
mix cor,orch oct NOVELLO 28.0510.03 s.p.,
ipr
(P2934)

Psalm 3 *see Jehovah, Quam Multi

Psalm 150 *Psalm
unis oct LORENZ 8601 $.25
(P2935)

Rejoice In The Lord Alway *Adv/Gen,anthem/
Bibl
SATB,kbd (med diff) oct CONCORDIA 98-6344
$.50
(P2936)
SATB,opt acap (med) OXFORD 43.243 $.35
(P2937)
SATB,org,strings (med easy) oct OXFORD
42.325 $1.15
(P2938)
SATB,org STAINER D32 $.30 (P2939)
SATB (bell anthem) oct BELWIN 64145 $.30
(P2940)
SATB oct FISCHER,C CM-6308 $.30 (P2941)
SATB,org (abridged) SCHIRM.EC 1101 $.30
(P2942)
(Davis, K.) SSA,pno/org SCHIRM.EC 1875 $.30
(P2943)
(Dent, E.J.) ATB,org,strings oct NOVELLO
28.1352.01 s.p., ipr
(P2944)
(Dent, E.J.) ATB,orch (abridged version)
oct NOVELLO 28.0145.00 s.p., ipr (P2945)
(Gieschen, T.) mix cor,ATB soli,strings,
cont (verse anthem) sc CONCORDIA 97-4472
$4.00, cor pts CONCORDIA 97-6344 $.50,
ipa
(P2946)
(Glaser, V.) SAB,org SCHIRM.EC 2488 (P2947)

Rejoice In The Lord Always
(Greyson) SATB oct BOURNE ES81 $.30 (P2948)

Remember Not, Lord, Our Offences *Lent,
anthem
SSATB,opt org SCHIRM.EC 1689 $.25 (P2949)
SSATB oct NOVELLO 50.0322.09 s.p. (P2950)
SATB oct WALTON 6013 $.30 (P2951)
"Gedenke Nicht, Herr" [Eng/Ger] 5pt mix cor
MOSELER LB-728 s.p.
(P2952)

Remember Not, Lord, Our Offenses
SSATB,acap PETERS H1526 $.40 (P2953)

Since God So Tender A Regard *Gen
(Goldsbrough, Arnold) SSA,pno/org/hpsd (med
easy) oct OXFORD 44.214 $.35 (P2954)

Sing, Oh Sing To The Lord
cor voc sc KALMUS 6392 $1.25 (P2955)

Sing To The Lord *canon
(Kirk) SATB,acap,opt pno oct PRO ART 2473
$.25
(P2956)

Sing Unto The Lord *anthem
[Eng/Dan] mix cor,soli,org,strings cor pts
HANSEN-DEN s.p., ipa
(P2957)
SATB,org (abridged) SCHIRM.EC 2626 $.30
(P2958)

Singt, O Singt Dem Herrn *Gen,anthem
(Just, Herbert) [Eng/Ger] SATB,SATB soli,
2vln,vla,vcl,bvl (med) BAREN. BA 2901 sc
$3.50, cor pts $1.50, ipa (P2959)

Sound The Trumpet
(Ehret, Walter) SATB (med) PRESSER
362-03141 $.40
(P2960)
(Whittaker) SS/TT (med) OXFORD 54.604 $.30
(P2961)

Te Deum (from Ode For St. Cecilia's Day 1694)
Te Deum
[Eng/Ger] SATB,SATB soli,cembalo,org,
strings min sc PETERS E1064 $2.00, ipa
contains also: Jubilate (Jubil) (P2962)
(Baylis, Philip L.) SSA (D maj) oct NOVELLO
33.0092.07 s.p.
(P2963)

Te Deum And Jubilate (from Ode For St.
Cecilia's Day 1694)
(Arnold) [Ger/Eng] SATB,SSAATB soli,2trp,
strings,cont min sc EULENBURG EUL1064
s.p., ipr
(P2964)

Te Deum In D
cor voc sc KALMUS 6381 $1.25 (P2965)

PURCELL, HENRY (cont'd.)

Te Deum Laudamus *Te Deum
(Baylis, Philip L.) SSA (D maj) NOVELLO
33.0092.07 s.p.   (P2966)
(Bridge, J.F.; Terry, R.R.) [Eng/Lat]
SSATB,SSAATB soli,2trp,strings,timp (D
maj) voc sc NOVELLO s.p., ipr (P2967)
(Seidmann, B.) [Ger] mix cor,acap (diff)
HUG s.p.   (P2968)
(Smithers, Don) cor voc sc SCHIRM.G $1.50
contains also: Jubilate Deo (Jubil)
(P2969)

Thanks To These Lonesome Vales
(Mason, Vito) SATB oct WORD CS-2480 $.30
(P2970)

Thou Knowest, Lord *see Thou Knowest, Lord,
The Secrets Of Our Hearts

Thou Knowest, Lord The Secrets Of My Heart
mix cor SOUTHERN $.30   (P2971)

Thou Knowest, Lord, The Secrets Of Our Hearts
(from Book Of Common Prayer) Easter/Gen/
Lent,anthem,17th cent
SATB,acap oct BELWIN 64006 $.30   (P2972)
TTBB,acap oct BELWIN 64071 $.25   (P2973)
SATB oct FISCHER,C CM-6340 $.25   (P2974)
SATB,org SCHIRM.EC 376 $.30   (P2975)
"Thou Knowest, Lord" SATB oct GRAY
GCMR 1665 $.30   (P2976)
(Christiansen, O.) SATB KJOS 4 $.30   (P2977)
(Davis, K.) SSA SCHIRM.EC 1878 $.20   (P2978)
(Davis, K.) SSAA,acap SCHIRM.EC 1541 $.18
(P2979)
(Dearnley, C.) SATB,org BROUDE,A. 704 $.30 (P2980)
(Gordon) "Thou Knowest, Lord" SATB oct
SHAPIRO SK 2120 $.30   (P2981)
(Gordon) "Thou Knowest, Lord" SSA oct
SHAPIRO SK 3029 $.25   (P2982)
(Hines) "Thou Knowest Lord" SAB SCHMITT
5527 $.25   (P2983)
(Knight) "Thou Knowest, Lord" 3pt mix cor
oct CURWEN 11197 $.25   (P2984)
(Knight) "Thou Knowest, Lord" SAB CURWEN
80871 s.p.   (P2985)
(Lynn) SAB oct SPRATT 630 $.25   (P2986)
(Lynn) SSA oct SPRATT 629 $.25   (P2987)
(Lynn) SATB oct SPRATT 511 $.25   (P2988)
(Shaw, Watkins) "Thou Knowest, Lord" mix
cor oct NOVELLO 28.1339.04 s.p.   (P2989)

Thy Spirit Ascending
(Rodby) 2pt oct PLYMOUTH WR-501 $.25   (P2990)

Thy Word Is A Lantern *anthem/Bibl
SATB oct BELWIN 64066 $.35   (P2991)
(Shaw, Watkins) ATB,org oct NOVELLO
28.1338.06 s.p.   (P2992)

Welcome To All The Pleasures (from Ode For
St. Cecilia's Day 1683)
(Bergmann) [Ger/Eng] SATB,SSATB soli,
strings,cont min sc EULENBURG EUL1062
s.p., ipa   (P2993)
(Collings, Geoffrey) SSAA,orch voc sc
NOVELLO 20.0053.09 s.p., ipr   (P2994)

When On My Sick Bed I Languish *anthem
TTB,org oct NOVELLO 46.0016.09 s.p.   (P2995)

PURDY, HUNTER
Donkey, The *Palm
4pt mix cor,acap oct SCHIRM.G 10987 $.25
(P2996)

PURER IN HEART, O GOD see Greener

PURER IN HEART, O GOD see Greener, Joseph H.

PURER IN HEART, O GOD see Landon

PURGE ME, O LORD see Haydn, (Johann) Michael,
Asperges Me

PURGE ME, O LORD see Tallis, Thomas

PURGE OUT THEREFORE THE OLD LEAVEN see Schutz,
Heinrich

PURIM HYMN see Shoshanas Yaakov

PURSWELL, PATRICK
No One Who Waits For You Shall Be Put To
Shame *Adv,Gradual
TB,T solo,acap oct WORLD EMP-1314-3 $.45
contains also: Show Us, O Lord, Your
Kindness (Allelu)   (P2997)

Show Us, O Lord, Your Kindness
see Purswell, Patrick, No One Who Waits For
You Shall Be Put To Shame

PURVIS, RICHARD
Advent Carol *Adv,carol
unis FLAMMER E5142 $.30   (P2998)

All Glory, Laud, And Honor
SATB,org oct MCA $1.25   (P2999)
SATB,org,brass,timp oct MCA $2.50   (P3000)

Ballad Of Judas Iscariot
SATB,org,vln,2harp, celesta voc sc ELKAN-V
$2.00, ipa   (P3001)

Canticle For God's Kingdom On Earth, A *cant
SA,org oct WORD CS-2465 $.40   (P3002)

Canticle Of Brotherhood, A *cant
unis oct WORD CS-2467 $.35   (P3003)

Canticle Of Joy, A
SA oct WORD CS-2468 $.40   (P3004)

Canticle Of Light, A
SATB FLAMMER A 5076 $.30   (P3005)

Canticle Of Praise
SA oct WORD CS-2464 $.50   (P3006)

Carol For The Unity Of All Mankind, A
SA/TB FLAMMER E5144 $.30   (P3007)

Carol Of The Bamboo Flute
jr cor oct FISCHER,J 9626 $.30   (P3008)

Christians Awake
SA oct WORD CS-332 $.30   (P3009)

PURVIS, RICHARD (cont'd.)

Cradle Carol, A *carol
SATB&jr cor oct FISCHER,J 9627 $.25 (P3010)

De Profundis (Psalm 130)
"Out Of The Depths" SATB,org,opt trp oct
MCA   (P3011)

Easter Alleluia, An
SA/TB FLAMMER E5146 $.30   (P3012)

Forth In Thy Name, O Lord
SA/TB FLAMMER E5101 $.25   (P3013)

Joyous Psalm Of Praise, A *Fest
SATB,org,perc oct WORD CS-2426 $.50 (P3014)

Jubilate Deo
[Lat] unis,org oct MCA   (P3015)

Judica Me, Deus (Psalm 43)
SATB,org,opt trp oct MCA   (P3016)

Laudate Dominum
"O Praise God" SATB,org,timp,fing.cym.,
cymbals oct WORD CS-501 $.50   (P3017)

Lenten Carol, A *Lent
SATB FLAMMER A 5100 $.30   (P3018)

Lenten Motet, A *Lent,mot
SATB oct WORD CS-695 $.25   (P3019)

Magnificat
mix cor,Bar solo oct SCHIRM.G 8707 $.30
(P3020)

Manger Carol, A
SA/TB FLAMMER E5141 $.30   (P3021)

Mass Of The Holy Ressurrection, The *Mass
SATB FLAMMER A5408 $1.00   (P3022)

O Praise God *see Laudate Dominum

Out Of The Depths *see De Profundis

Paean Of Praise *cant
mix cor BELWIN $1.50   (P3023)

Psalm 43 *see Judica Me, Deus

Psalm 130 *see De Profundis

Psalm Of Ascent, A *Psalm
SATB,org,opt trp oct MCA   (P3024)

Resurrection Canticle, A *cant
SA oct WORD CS-2466 $.30   (P3025)

Uns Ist Ein Kind Geboren
"Unto Us A Child Is Born" SATB,org,opt trp
oct MCA   (P3026)

Unto Us A Child Is Born *see Uns Ist Ein
Kind Geboren

Winter Passes Over
SSA/SSAA,acap oct MCA   (P3027)
SATB,acap oct MCA   (P3028)

PUT BACK THE STAR OF BETHLEHEM INTO OUR
NATION'S FLAG see Graff

PUT DOWN THAT HORN GABRIEL *spir
(Touchette) TTBB oct FISCHER,C CM-7631 $.30
(P3029)

PUT DOWN YOUR GUNS see Avery

PUT FORTH, O GOD, THY SPIRIT'S MIGHT see Means,
Claude

PUT FORTH, O GOD, THY SPIRIT'S MIGHT see Wehr,
David A.

PUT IN YOUR HAND see Sterne, Colin

PUT ME NOT TO REBUKE see Blow, John

PUT ON THE WHOLE ARMOUR OF GOD see Curry, R.D.

PUT THOU THY TRUST IN GOD see Tomblings, Philip

PUT THOU THY TRUST IN THE LORD see Bliss, Sir
Arthur

PUT YE ON THE LORD JESUS see Roff, Joseph

PUT YO' TRUST IN DE LAWD see Himebaugh, H.A.

PUT YOUR HAND IN THE HAND see Mac Lellan

PUTNEY HYMN see Imig

PUTTEN, P. V.D.
Tota Pulchra Es Maria
mix cor ALSBACH&D sc s.p., cor pts s.p.
(P3030)

PUTTERILL, JACK
Thaxted Mass *Mass
3pt mix cor,opt acap ST.GREG. s.p. (P3031)

PYLE, FRANCIS [JOHNSON] (1901-   )
Angels High And Holy
SATB,acap oct WILLIS 6958 $.22   (P3032)

Father, We Praise Thee
SATB,acap SEESAW $1.00   (P3033)

Full Stature
SATB (diff) ABINGDON APM-801 $.50   (P3034)

I Hear No Voice
SATB,acap (med) oct WILLIS 7061 $.20   (P3035)

Now Is The Hour Of Darkness Past
SATB,pno (diff) oct WILLIS 6959 $.18   (P3036)

Winds Through The Olive Trees
3pt wom cor,acap (easy) oct WILLIS 6956
$.16   (P3037)

Q

QUACK, ERHARD (1904-   )
Dominus Illuminatio Mea *Trin
[Lat] SATB,acap (med) MULLER SM 927 s.p.
(Q1)

Gaudeamus Omnes In Domino *ASD/ECY
[Lat] SATB,acap (med) MULLER SM 1639 s.p.
(Q2)

Karfreitag Die Liturgische Chorgesange
*Gd.Fri./Psntd
[Ger] 3pt mix cor/4pt mix cor,acap (med)
MULLER SM 785 s.p.   (Q3)

Leidensgeschichte *Psntd
[Ger] SATB,acap (easy) MULLER SM 786 s.p.
(Q4)

Mihi Autem *Fest
[Lat] SATB,acap (med) MULLER SM 921 s.p.
(Q5)

Nunc Scio Vere *Fest
[Lat] SATB,acap (med, appropriate for
festivals of apostles peter and paul)
MULLER SM 719 s.p.   (Q6)

Respice, Domine *Trin
[Lat] SATB,acap (med) MULLER SM 920 s.p.
(Q7)

Resurrexi *Easter
[Lat] SATB,acap (med easy) MULLER SM 708
s.p.   (Q8)

Salve Sancta Parens *Fest
[Lat] SATB,acap (med, appropriate for birth
and visitation of mary) MULLER SM 926
s.p.   (Q9)

Suscepimus *Trin
[Lat] SATB,acap (med) MULLER SM 924 s.p.
(Q10)

QUAE EST ISTA see Marenzio, Luca

QUAE EST ISTA see Palestrina, Giovanni

QUAE VOX see Palestrina, Giovanni

QUAERAMUS CUM PASTORIBUS see Mouton, Jean

QUAERITE PRIMUM, REGNUM see Scheidt, Samuel

QUAERITE PRIMUM REGNUM DEI see Calvisius,
Sethus

QUAL E IL PIU GRAND' AMOR see Palestrina,
Giovanni

QUAL E IL PIU GRANDE AMOR see Palestrina,
Giovanni

QUAL TUST OYCI? see Canteloube de Malaret,
Marie-Joseph

QUAM AMABILIA see Volpi, Edoardo

QUAM DILECTA see Ascenso, Antonio

QUAM DILECTA! see Leighton, Kenneth

QUAM DILECTA see Rameau, Jean-Philippe

QUAM DILECTA see Saint-Saens, Camille

QUAM DILECTA TABERNACULA TUA! see Gounod,
Charles Francois

QUAM MAGNA see Sevim, Giuseppe

QUAM PULCHRA ES see Clemens, Jacobus

QUAM PULCHRA ES see Dunstable, John

QUAM PULCHRA ES ET QUAM DECORA see Gombert,
Nicolas

QUAM PULCHRA EST see Palestrina, Giovanni

QUAM PULCHRI SUNT see Marenzio, Luca

QUAM PULCHRI SUNT see Palestrina, Giovanni

QUAM VIDISTIS PASTORES see Deering, Richard

QUAND DIEU NAQUIT A NOEL *Fr
(Geer, E.) "When At Christmas" [Fr/Eng] SSAA,
acap SCHIRM.EC 899 $.18   (Q11)

QUAND DIEU NAQUIT A NOEL see Canteloube de
Malaret, Marie-Joseph

QUAND IO PENS see Lassus, Roland de (Orlandus)

QUAND IO PENS OTHER MASSES AND MADRIGALS see
Lassus, Roland de (Orlandus)

QUAND JE T'INVOQUE, HELAS, ESCOUTE see
Goudimel, Claude

QUAND LA MINUIT SONNAIT *Xmas,carol,Fr
(Tomasi) [Fr] SMezA LEDUC s.p. see also Douze
Noels De Saboly   (Q12)

QUAND MON MARI SE FACHERA see Aubanel, Georges

QUAND MON MARY VIENT DE DEHORS see Lassus,
Roland de (Orlandus)

QUANDO CORPUS see Rossini, Gioacchino

QUANDO CORPUS MORIETUR see Hartmann, Johan
Peder Emilius

QUANDO CORPUS MORIETUR see Pergolesi, Giovanni
Battista

QUANDO LIETA SPERAI see Palestrina, Giovanni

QUARANTA FALSIBORDONI see Ravanello, Oreste

QUARANTE NOELS ANCIENS see Anonymous

QUARE FREMUERUNT GENTES see Lalande, Michel
Richard de

QUARTET AND CHORUS OF MAGI see Berlioz, Hector

QUARTIERO
    Quem Vidistis Pastores
        (Krumscheid) [Ger/Lat] 5pt mix cor MOSELER
        s.p.   (Q13)

QUASI OLIVA see Giorgi, Piero

QUASI ROSA PLANTATA see Ravanello, Oreste

QUASI STELLA see Oltrassi, Giuseppe

QUATORDICI CANZONCINE CATECHISTICHE see
    Bottazzo, Luigi

QUATRE CHOERS POUR VOIX DE FEMMES see Schubert,
    Franz (Peter)

QUATRE MOTETS see Ammann, Benno

QUATRE MOTETS see Durufle, Maurice

QUATRE MOTETS POUR UN TEMPS DE NOEL see
    Poulenc, Francis

QUATRE MOTETS POUR UN TEMPS DE PENITENCE see
    Poulenc, Francis

QUATRE MOTETS SUR DES THEMES GREGORIENS see
    Durufle, Maurice

QUATRE NOELS see Aubanel, Georges

QUATRIEME MESSE BREVE see Fauchey, Paul

QUATRIEME MESSE SOLENNELLE see Cherubini, Luigi

QUATRO FACILES HYMNI see Sacchetto, Guido

QUATTRO ANTIFONE DELLA B.V. see Ravanello,
    Oreste

QUATTRO ANTIFONE MARIANE *BVM,anti
    [Lat] 2pt,org ZANIBON 424 s.p.
    contains: Bottazzo, Luigi, Salve Regina;
        Nicolosi, Salvatore, Ave Regina;
        Ponzilacqua, Regina Coeli; Thermignon,
        Alma Redemptoris   (Q14)

QUATTRO CANTI ALLA MADONNA DEL CARMINE *BVM
    [It] unis,org ZANIBON 2739 s.p.
    contains: Bottigliero, Eduardo, Flos
        Carmeli; Magri, Pietro, Flos Carmeli;
        Mariani, Eligio, O Del Carmel Splendore!;
        Mariani, Eligio, Salve O Vergine Maria
                                                    (Q15)

QUATTRO CANTI EUCARISTICI see Maggio, Giuseppe

QUATTRO CANTI EUCARISTICI see Bottigliero,
    Eduardo

QUATTRO CANTI EUCARISTICI see Grassi, Ciro

QUATTRO CANZONCINE MARIANE see Bottazzo, Luigi

QUATTRO COMPOSITIONI SACRE see Bottazzo, Luigi

QUATTRO COMPOSIZIONI SACRE see Maugeri,
    Giuseppe

QUATTRO DEE CHE'L MONDO ONORA see Donato,
    Baldassare

QUATTRO INNI DEL COMUNE DEI SANTI see Arnaldi,
    Antonio

QUATTRO INNI PER LA FESTE PRINCIPALI DELL'ANNO
    see Arnaldi, Antonio

QUATTRO INNI PROCESSIONALI see Rodella, Sante

QUATTRO LITANIE DELLA B.V. MARIA see Mondo,
    Michele

QUATTRO LITANIE LAURETANE see Bottazzo, Luigi

QUATTRO MOTTETTI EUCARISTICI *Commun,mot
    [Lat] 3pt mix cor,org ZANIBON 2685 s.p.
    contains: Baroni, Giovanni, Tantum Ergo;
        Bernasconi, Luigi, Tantum Ergo; Bottazzo,
        Luigi, Tantum Ergo; Tebaldini, Giovanni,
        Pange Lingua   (Q16)

QUATTRO MOTTETTI EUCARISTICI see Bottigliero,
    Eduardo

QUATTRO MOTTETTI SACRI see Faccin, Gian
    Domenico

QUATTRO PANGE LINGUA see Bottazzo, Luigi

QUATTRO PASTORALI PER IL SANTO NATALE see
    Garbelotto, Antonio

QUATTRO PEZZI SACRI see Verdi, Giuseppe

QUATTRO STABAT MATER *BVM
    [Lat] ZANIBON 2748 s.p.
    contains: Magri, Pietro, Stabat Mater
        (unis,org); Moioli, Romano, Stabat Mater
        (unis,org); Volpi, Edoardo, Stabat Mater
        (2 eq voices,org); Volpi, Edoardo, Stabat
        Mater (3 eq voices,org)   (Q17)

QUATUOR PANGE LINGUA see Zimarino, Settimio

QUE CREAVIT CAELUM see Nelhybel, Vaclav

QUE DIEU SE MONSTRE SEULEMENT see Goudimel,
    Claude

QUE DIEU SE MONTRE SEULEMENT (Psalm 67)
    (Geveart, F.-A.) [Fr] 4pt mix cor,acap (easy)
    cor pts LEMOINE s.p. see from Collection De
    Choeurs, quatrieme Fascicule   (Q18)

QUE LES ANGES DE DIEU see Mercenier, P.

QUE PEUT AU FOL RICHESSE PROFITER see
    Faignient, Noel

QUE TARDEZ-VOUS? see Migot, Georges

QUE VIVA ARAGON see Martin Pompey

QUEEN OF HEAVEN see Lotti, Antonio, Regina
    Coeli

QUEEN OF HEAVEN see Philips, Peter, Regina
    Coeli

QUEEN OF HEAVEN see Rimmer, Frederick

QUEEN OF THE HEAVENS, WE HAIL THEE see Torres,
    Eduardo, Ave Regina Caelorum

QUELLE EST CETTE ODEUR AGREABLE? *Xmas,carol,
    Fr
    (Ramseyer) "Whence Comes This Fragrance?"
        [Eng/Fr] 3pt wom cor,acap oct SCHIRM.G 9596
        $.25   (Q19)
    (Sheppard) "What Is The Pleasant Fragrance?"
        [Eng/Fr] 3pt wom cor,acap oct SCHIRM.G
        11434 $.30   (Q20)
    (Sheppard) "What Is The Pleasant Fragrance?"
        [Eng/Fr] 4pt mix cor,acap oct SCHIRM.G
        11426 $.35   (Q21)

QUEM AD MODUM see Hemel, Oscar van

QUEM DICUNT HOMINES see Gombert, Nicolas

QUEM DICUNT HOMINES see Marenzio, Luca

QUEM DICUNT HOMINES see Palestrina, Giovanni

QUEM DICUNT HOMINES see Pionnier

QUEM DICUNT HOMINES see Richafort

QUEM PASTORES (from Anthology Of Carols, An)
    Xmas,carol
    see Six Traditional Carols, Set IV
    (Wulstan, David) SATB CHESTER s.p. contains
        also: Coverdale's Carol   (Q22)

QUEM PASTORES see Jaeckel, Daniel

QUEM PASTORES LAUDAVERE *Xmas
    unis/SATB (easy) OXFORD 08.077 $.15   (Q23)

QUEM PASTORES LAUDAVERE see Praetorius, Michael

QUEM VIDISTIS see Nelhybel, Vaclav

QUEM VIDISTIS see Pasini, Crescenzio

QUEM VIDISTIS, PASTORES? see Deering, Richard

QUEM VIDISTIS PASTORES see Felis

QUEM VIDISTIS, PASTORES? see Gabrieli, Andrea,
    Wen Denn Sahet Ihr, Hirten?

QUEM VIDISTIS, PASTORES? see Gabrieli, Giovanni

QUEM VIDISTIS, PASTORES? see Gallus, Jacobus

QUEM VIDISTIS PASTORES see Quartiero

QUEM VIDISTIS PASTORES see Santucci, Pellegrino

QUEM VIDISTIS PASTORES DICITE see Poulenc,
    Francis

QUEM VIDISTIS, PASTORES, DICITE see Roger-
    Ducasse, Jean-Jules Aimable

QUEMPAS CAROL, THE *Xmas,carol
    (Praetorius, M.) SATB&unis,kbd (med easy) oct
        CONCORDIA 98-1518 $.25   (Q24)
    (Strube, A.) SAB,kbd (med easy) oct CONCORDIA
        98-1747 $.20   (Q25)
    (Wienhorst, R.) unis&SATB (med easy) sc
        CONCORDIA 97-4597 $1.25, cor pts CONCORDIA
        98-1653 $.30   (Q26)

QUEMPAS CAROL, THE see Wienhorst, Richard

QUEST FOR GOD see Rhea, Raymond

QUEST FOR THE VICTORIOUS LIFE see Gesangbuch,
    S.

QUEST, THE *carol
    SATB (med easy) OXFORD 08.179 $.15   (Q27)

QUI CREAVIT COELUM *Xmas
    unis/SATB (med) OXFORD 08.067 $.20   (Q28)

QUI CREAVIT COELUM see Cook, E.T.

QUI FRAPPE ICI? see Canteloube de Malaret,
    Marie-Joseph, Qual Tust Oyci?

QUI HABITAT see Andriessen, Hendrik

QUI MANDUCAT see Pitoni, Giuseppe Ottavio

QUI MANDUCAT CARNEM MEAM see Lassus, Roland de
    (Orlandus)

QUI POURRA, SEIGNEUR, EN BONNE PAIS see Le
    Jeune, Claude

QUI SEDES DOMINE see Haydn, (Johann) Michael

QUI SEQUITUR ME see Lassus, Roland de
    (Orlandus)

QUICK CHOIR, THE *CC12UL
    (Schubert, Myra) 2pt mix cor (easy) cmplt ed
        LILLENAS MB-156 $1.50   (Q29)

QUICKLY COME, LORD JESUS see Mascagni, Pietro

QUICKLY RAN THE SHEPHERDS see Richards

QUID COMMISISTI see Schutz, Heinrich

QUID DETUR TIBI see Schutz, Heinrich

"QUID RETRIBUAM" see Mancini, Vincenzo

QUIESCAT VOX TUA see Wert, Giaches de

QUIET CAROL, THE *Xmas
    2pt oct LORENZ 5732 $.25   (Q30)

QUIET CAROL, THE see Hadler

QUIET CHAMBER, A *Xmas,carol
    (Anderson, W.H.) SATB oct LESLIE 4015 see
        from Two Christmas Carols, Set 1   (Q31)

QUIET CHRISTMAS see Grundman

QUIET HILLSIDE, THE see Procter, A.

QUIET LORD, MY FROWARD HEART see Bach, Johann
    Sebastian

QUIET MY HEART see Hanks, Sybil A.

QUIET PLACE, A *CCUL
    (Shepard, Bob) SATB voc sc WORD 30030 $1.95
                                                    (Q32)

QUIGNARD, R.
    For Unto Us Is Born Today *Xmas
        SA oct PRESSER 312-40197 $.30   (Q33)

QUILICI, ABBE F.
    Ave Verum Corpus
        "Jesu, Word Of God Incarnate" [Lat/Eng]
        SATB,org SCHIRM.EC 2285 $.18   (Q34)

    Jesu, Word Of God Incarnate *see Ave Verum
        Corpus

QUILTER, ROGER (1877-1953)
    Cradle In Bethlehem *Xmas
        2pt jr cor/2pt wom cor CURWEN 72221 s.p.
                                                    (Q35)
        unis jr cor/unis wom cor CURWEN 72597 s.p.
                                                    (Q36)
    Non Nobis Domine
        [Lat/Eng] unis oct BOOSEY 69 $.30   (Q37)
        [Lat/Eng] SATB,band/strings oct BOOSEY 461
        $.30   (Q38)
        [Lat/Eng] SSA oct BOOSEY 1876 $.30   (Q39)
        [Lat/Eng] TTB,band/strings oct BOOSEY 348
        $.30   (Q40)
        [Eng/Lat] mix cor,2fl,2ob,2clar,2bsn,2trp,
        4horn,3trp,strings,harp,perc,timp cmplt
        ed BOOSEY rental   (Q41)

QUINDICI LITANAE LAURETANE see Gorlatto,
    Giacomo

QUINQUE CANTUS AD BENEDICTIONEM SANTISSIMI
    SACRAMENTI see Schmitt, Florent

QUINTI TONI see Palestrina, Giovanni, Illumina
    Oculos Meos

QUIS MULTA GRACILIS see Thompson, Randall

QU'ISRAEL DIE ET CONFESSE EN EFFET see Lupi II,
    Didier

QUITEZ PASTEURS see Jenkins, [Joseph Willcox]

QUITTEZ PASTEURS *Xmas,carol,Fr
    see Silent Night
    (Wasner) "Lay Down Your Staffs, O Shepherds"
        4pt mix cor,acap oct SCHIRM.G 8789 $.30
                                                    (Q42)

QUITTEZ PASTEURS see Gronquist, R.

QUITTEZ, PASTEURS, VOS BREBIS see Roques, L.

QUO, NATE DEI see Schutz, Heinrich

QUOD CHORUS VATUM see Tallis, Thomas

QUODCUMQUE LIGAVERIS see Palestrina, Giovanni

QUODLIBET see Katz, E.

QUOMODO SEDET SOLA see Pahissa, [Jaime]

QUONIAM AD TE see Schutz, Heinrich

QUONIAM AD TE CLAMABO see Schutz, Heinrich

QUONIAM NON EST IN MORTE see Schutz, Heinrich

QUOTH AN ANGEL see Angelus Ad Virginem

R

RAASTED, NIELS OTTO (1888-1966)
Kristi Fodsel *Op.67, Xmas
  "Our Lord's Nativity" [Dan] cor,soli,org,
    orch FOG III, 51 voc sc s.p., cor pts
    s.p., ipa   (R1)
  "Our Lord's Nativity" cor,orch SAMFUNDET
    voc sc s.p., cor pts s.p., ipa   (R2)

Our Lord's Nativity *see Kristi Fodsel

Passionsmusik *Op.86, Psntd,Bibl
  cor,orch SAMFUNDET voc sc s.p., cor pts
    s.p., ipa   (R3)
  [Dan] cor,soli,org,strings FOG III, 115 voc
    sc s.p., cor pts s.p., ipa   (R4)

RAB, VALENTIN (ca. 1548?)
Ich Schreie Zum Herren (Psalm 142) Bibl/mot
  (Dehnhard) SATB HANSSLER 1.518 s.p.   (R5)

Psalm 142 *see Ich Schreie Zum Herren

RABAUD, H.
Ave Verum *Commun
  [Lat] 4pt mix cor,org (contains also solo
    work) LEMOINE s.p. see also BREVIAIRE DE
    PIERRE L'ERMITE   (R6)
  [Lat] 4pt mix cor,org LEMOINE voc sc s.p.,
    cor pts s.p. see from LE BREVIAIRE DE
    PIERRE L'ERMITE   (R7)

Job *Op.9, ora
  [Fr] SATB,soli,orch ENOCH voc sc s.p., voc
    pt s.p., ipr   (R8)

Psalm 4 *Op.4
  [Fr] SATB,soli,orch ENOCH voc sc s.p., voc
    pt s.p., ipr   (R9)

RABINOWITCH
Hashkivenu
  (Roskin) SATB HATIKVAH HCL 2 $.35   (R10)

Hashkivenu No. 2
  (Roskin) SATB HATIKVAH HCL 12 $.35   (R11)

Hogen Ovos
  (Roskin) SATB HATIKVAH HCL 13 $.25   (R12)

RABSCH, EDGAR
Gelobet Seist Du, Jesu Christ *cant
  SAB,org,2inst sc HANSSLER 10.003 s.p., ipa
                                                (R13)
Jauchzet Gott, Alle Lande
  see Kretzschmar, Gunther, Pfingstruf

Von Der Mutter Und Dem Kind *Xmas,cant
  cor,opt org,opt pno,vln,vla,vcl,bvl,perc
  MOSELER voc sc s.p., cor pts s.p., ipa   (R14)

RACCOLTA DI 32 LITANIE LAURETANE see Gubinelli,
  Oderisio

RACCOLTA DI CANZONCINE POPULARI SACRE *CC8L
  (Nicolosi, S.) .Lat] cor,org sc ZANIBON 398
  s.p.   (R15)

RACCOLTA DI SEI INNI *hymn
  [Lat] 2 eq voices,org 2 eq voices,org sc
    ZANIBON 441 s.p.
    contains: Bortolan, C., Vexilla Regis;
      Bottazzo, Luigi, Ave Maris Stella;
      Grassi, Ciro, Celestis Urbs; Nicolosi,
      Salvatore, Tantum Ergo; Ravanello,
      Oreste, Veni Creator; Rodella, Sante, O
      Gloriosa Virginum   (R16)

RACCOLTA DI SEI MOTTETTI EUCARISTICI see Volpi,
  Edoardo

RACE THAT LONG IN DARKNESS PINED see Staton

RACHMANINOFF, SERGEY VASSILIEVITCH (1873-1943)
Ave Maria
  SATB,acap oct PRESSER 332-14564 $.25   (R17)
  (Cramer) [Eng/Lat] SATB,acap MARKS 4246
    $.25   (R18)
  (Douglas) SATB oct GRAY G.RACH. 6 $.25   (R19)

Blessed Is The Man
  (Douglas) SATB oct GRAY G. RACH. 3 $.30   (R20)

Blessing And Glory
  (Ehret) SATB oct BOURNE BL2542 $.30   (R21)
  (Ehret) SSA oct BOURNE BL3046 $.30   (R22)
  (Ehret) SAB oct BOURNE BL3045 $.30   (R23)
  (Markaroff, R.) SATB oct PRESSER 332-13675
    $.30   (R24)

Cherubic Hymn
  SATB,acap oct PRESSER 332-14712 $.25   (R25)

Cherubim Hymn *hymn
  SSAATTBB oct WALTON 6004 $.30   (R26)

Dear Lord, We Praise Thee
  (Harris) SSA,acap,opt kbd oct PRO ART 2505
    $.30   (R27)

Glorious Forever
  SA BOSTON 3317 $.30   (R28)
  (Harling) TTBB BOSTON 4469 $.30   (R29)
  (Shepherd) SATB BOSTON 1080 $.35   (R30)

Glory And Honor
  SATB KJOS 7059 $.30   (R31)
  (Jurey) SATB,orch BELWIN 64034 $.30,
    ipa   (R32)
  (Jurey) SAB,orch oct BELWIN 64035 $.25, ipa
                                                (R33)
  (Jurey) SSA,orch oct BELWIN 64309 $.30, ipa
                                                (R34)

Glory Be To God
  (Douglas) SATB oct GRAY G. RACH. 7 $.30
                                                (R35)

Glory To God *Xmas
  (Douglas) SATB oct GRAY G. RACH. 5 $.25
                                                (R36)

Humming Prayer *prayer
  (Wilhousky) SATB oct FISCHER,C CM-7735 $.25
                                                (R37)

RACHMANINOFF, SERGEY VASSILIEVITCH (cont'd.)
I Will Extol Thee, O God
  SATB oct WALTON 2057 $.25   (R38)

In The Silent Night
  (Sears) SATB WARNER R3396 $.30   (R39)

Praise The Lord
  (Norden) SATB oct FISCHER,J 4127 $.30   (R40)

Praise Ye The Name Of The Lord
  (Ehret) SATB LUDWIG L-1123   (R41)

Thy Will, Not Mine
  (Ehret) SATB oct PRO ART 2184 $.20   (R42)
  (Ehret) SAB&camb oct PRO ART 2182 $.25   (R43)

To Thee O Lord
  SATB oct FISCHER,J 4175 $.30   (R44)

Triumph! Thanksgiving *Thanks
  (Clough-Leighter, H.) SATB,org SCHIRM.EC
    309 $.25, ipr   (R45)
  (Clough-Leighter, H.) SA,org SCHIRM.EC 1012
    $.20, ipr   (R46)
  (Davis, K.) SA,pno SCHIRM.EC 1578 ipr   (R47)
  (Manton, R.) TTBB,org SCHIRM.EC 541 $.22,
    ipr   (R48)

We Praise Thee
  SATB oct FISCHER,J 4483 $.30   (R49)

·RADER
Only Believe
  (Roe) SATB oct WORD CS-2884 $.30   (R50)

RADIANT CHRIST, THE see Cain, Noble

RADIANT MORN HATH PASSED AWAY see Woodward,
  H.H.

RADIANT MORN HATH PASSED AWAY, THE see Woodward

RADIANT MORN HATH PASSED AWAY, THE see
  Woodward, H.H.

RADIANT SUN SHINES IN THE SKIES, THE see
  Vulpius, Melchior

RADIX JESSE see Gallus, Jacobus

RADOMSKI, MIKOLAJ
Magnificat *Pol
  (Chominski, J.) mix cor,A solo,4vcl,4trom
  POLSKIE FMA18 s.p.   (R51)

RADS EJ BEKANNA KRISTI NAMN
  (Soderholm, Valdemar) 3pt wom cor/3pt jr cor,
  acap NORDISKA s.p.   (R52)

RADS EJ BEKANNA KRISTI NAMN see Berg, Gottfrid

RADULESCU, MICHAEL
Beati Immaculati *mot
  wom cor,acap oct DOBLINGER s.p. see from
  Drei Motetten   (R53)

Deutsche Zwolftonmesse *Mass
  dbl cor,perc DOBLINGER sc s.p., ipr, cor
  pts s.p.   (R54)

Drei Motetten *see Beati Immaculati; Laudate
  Pueri; Ostende Nobis   (R55)

Laudate Pueri *mot
  wom cor,acap oct DOBLINGER s.p. see from
  Drei Motetten   (R56)

Ostende Nobis *mot
  wom cor,acap oct DOBLINGER s.p. see from
  Drei Motetten   (R57)

RAE, KENNETH
Evening Pastoral
  2pt ASHDOWN E.A.133 s.p.   (R58)

RAFFMAN, RELLY
God The Lord Is Gracious *see Jubilate Deo

I Cannot Ope Mine Eyes *see Matins

In The Beginning
  SAATB oct PRESSER MC374 $.40   (R59)

Jubilate Deo
  "God The Lord Is Gracious" [Lat/Eng] SATB,
  org,brass SCHIRM.EC 2691 $.45, ipr   (R60)

Matins
  "I Cannot Ope Mine Eyes" SSATB,acap
  SCHIRM.EC 2682 $.30   (R61)

Sweet Was The Song *Xmas,carol
  SSA,pno SCHIRM.EC 2574 $.30   (R62)

RAHNER, HUGO (1875-1953)
Es Bluhn Drei Rosen Auf Einem Zweig *Adv
  [Ger] TTBB,acap (med easy) MULLER SM 438 sc
  s.p., cor pts s.p.   (R63)

Lied Der Hirten "Als Ich Bei Meinen Schafen
  Wacht" *Gen
  [Ger] TTBB&TTBB,acap (med) MULLER SM 437 sc
  s.p., cor pts s.p.   (R64)

RAIMUND, BALTHASAR
Jesus Ist Mein Starker Held
  (Berger, H.L.) TTBB HANSSLER 6.5123 s.p.   (R65)

RAIN see Lehenbauer, Ruth B.

RAIN OF PEACE see Red, Buryl

RAINS, DOROTHY
Father, At Thy Throne We Bow
  2 eq voices oct AGAPE A 339 $.25   (R66)

RAINY DAYS see Larson, Leroy

RAISE HIGH THE DOOR see Bauernfeind, Hans,
  Macht Hoch Die Tur

RAISE THE CROSS see Appleford, Rev. Patrick

RAISE YOUR VOICES AND REJOICE see Kozinski,
  [David B.]

RAISING OF LAZARUS, THE see Willaert, Adrian,
  Videns Dominus

RALPH, ALAN
Christmas Night
  4pt mix cor,pno,opt trp,horn,gtr,drums,bvl
  oct SCHIRM.G 11945 $.25   (R67)

RALPH CARMICHAEL CHOIR #1, THE see Carmichael,
  Ralph

RALPH CARMICHAEL CHORAL ARRANGEMENTS FOR
  EVERYONE *CC15UL
  SATB/jr cor/wom cor/men cor voc sc WORD 30034
  $1.95   (R68)

RAMBERG, PAUL
Davids Psalm 63 (Psalm 63)
  [Swed] SATB,org,vln GEHRMANS KRB 145 $.25   (R69)

Psalm 63 *see Davids Psalm 63

RAMEAU, JEAN-PHILIPPE (1683-1764)
Come, Thou Long Expected Jesus *anthem
  (Nelson) unis treb cor,vln (easy/med) oct
  AUGSBURG 0301 $.25   (R70)

En Ce Doux Asile (from Castor Et Pollux)
  (Gounod) [Fr] 3pt,orch cor pts LEDUC s.p.
                                              (R71)
  (Gounod-Drouin) [Fr] 2pt,orch cor pts LEDUC
  s.p.   (R72)

In Convertendo *mot
  [Lat] mix cor,STB soli,pno/org oct DURAND
  s.p., ipa   (R73)

Laboravi (from Des Oeuvres Completes Tome V)
  Gen,mot
  [Lat] SSTTB,org oct DURAND s.p.   (R74)

Laboravi Clamans
  (Pinkham) [Lat] SSATB,org PETERS 66276
                                              (R75)
Praise Ye The Lord, My Soul, Adore Him *Gen/
  Trin
  unis,vln,vcl (med easy) oct CONCORDIA
  98-2121 $.25, ipa   (R76)

Quam Dilecta *mot
  [Lat] mix cor,SSTBarB soli,pno/org oct
  DURAND s.p., ipr   (R77)

Wake, O Shepherds *anthem
  (Nelson) unis treb cor,vln (med) oct
  AUGSBURG 0300 $.25   (R78)

RAMELLA
Ave Maria
  unis,org RICORDI-ENG 127925 s.p.   (R79)

Ecce Annuntio Vobis
  2 eq voices/3 eq voices,org cor pts
  RICORDI-ENG 129758 s.p.   (R80)

Gaudeamus Omnes Fideles
  2 eq voices,org RICORDI-ENG 127924 s.p.
                                              (R81)
Messa *Mass
  2 eq voices,org s.p. voc sc RICORDI-ENG
  127555, cor pts RICORDI-ENG 127556-57   (R82)

Tre Canti Eucaristici *CC3U
  unis/2 eq voices,org RICORDI-ENG 129757
  s.p.   (R83)

RAMIN, GUNTHER (1898-1956)
Alta Trinita Beata *Trin,15th cent
  4pt mix cor,acap cor pts BREITKOPF-W
  CHB-2833 s.p.   (R84)

RAMIREZ
Gloria *Gloria
  (Segade) mix cor SOUTHERN $.40   (R85)

RAMIREZ, ARIEL
Gloria (from Missa Criolla) Gloria
  (Segade) [Eng/Span] SATB,SA soli,pno/hpsd,
  perc oct LAWSON 51596 $.40   (R86)

Missa Criolla *folk/Mass,So Am
  [Eng/Span] mix cor,soli,pno/hpsd,perc,gtr
  oct LAWSON $1.75   (R87)

Navidad Nuestra *folk,So Am
  [Eng/Span] mix cor,soli,pno/hpsd,perc,gtr
  oct LAWSON $2.50   (R88)

RAMSETH, ANN
Come, Sing And Ring *CC12L,Xmas,folk
  jr cor,perc oct AUGSBURG 11-9132 $1.25
                                              (R89)
Open Thou My Lips *CC12U,anthem/canon
  jr cor oct AUGSBURG 11-9324 $.50   (R90)

That I May Speak
  speak cor,inst oct AUGSBURG 11-9490 $1.00
                                              (R91)

RAMSEY
Blessing Of Aaron, The
  (Rodby) SATB oct PLYMOUTH WR-106 $.25   (R92)
  (Rodby) SAB oct PLYMOUTH WR-200 $.25   (R93)
  (Rodby) SAB oct PLYMOUTH WR-500 $.25   (R94)

Bone Pastor
  (Pisano) SATB oct PLYMOUTH SC-27 $.25   (R95)

O Sapienta
  (Ehret) "O Wisdom From On High" [Lat/Eng]
  SATB,acap oct COLOMBO 2389 $.25   (R96)

O Wisdom From On High *see O Sapienta

RAMSEY, ROBERT (ca. 1595- ?)
Almighty And Everlasting God
  (Thompson) SSATB SCHOTT 10837 s.p.   (R97)

English Sacred Music *CCU,Eng
  cor STAINER 3.8207.8 $11.00   (R98)

God, Who As Upon This Day
  (Thompson) SSATB SCHOTT 10836 s.p.   (R99)

O Come Let Us Sing Unto The Lord
  (Thompson) SATTB SCHOTT 10848 s.p.   (R100)

O Fount Of Wisdom *see O Sapientia

RAMSEY, ROBERT (cont'd.)

O Sapientia
"O Fount Of Wisdom" [Lat/Eng] SSATB,acap
PETERS H1505 $.40   (R101)

When David Heard That Absalom Was Slain
(Thompson) SSATBB SCHOTT s.p.   (R102)

RAMSFIELD
Blest Day Of God
SATB oct PRO ART 2082 $.30   (R103)

Make A Joyful Sound
TTBB SHAWNEE C174 $.35   (R104)
SATB FLAMMER A 5559 $.30   (R105)

March Of The Three Kings *Xmas
SATB (med easy) SOUTHERN $.30   (R106)

O Be Joyful
SATB FLAMMER A 5558 $.30   (R107)
TTBB FLAMMER C5006 $.30   (R108)

RANCATI, ETTORE
Messa Corale *Mass
[Lat] 2pt men cor,org sc ZANIBON 2574 s.p.,
voc pt ZANIBON s.p.   (R109)

RAND, GEFFREY
New Prince, New Romp *Xmas
SATB oct WALTON 2075 $.25   (R110)

RANDALL
Come, Christians, Join To Sing
SATB KJOS 5328 $.30   (R111)

RANDALL, BRUCE
Sing Hosanna
SATB KJOS 5397 $.30   (R112)

RANDEGGER
Praise The Lord *Thanks
(Cain) SATB oct PRO ART 1481 $.30   (R113)

RANDEGGER, ALBERTO (1832-1911)
Praise The Lord (Psalm 150) Fest/Gen,Bibl
4pt mix cor oct SCHIRM.G 3763 $.25   (R114)
SATB ALLANS 411 $.30   (R115)
cor oct HART s.p.   (R116)
SATB,pno (diff) oct WILLIS 257 $.15   (R117)
SATB oct PRESSER 312-10214 $.30   (R118)

Praise The Lord, All Ye Nations (Psalm 150)
Gen
SATB SCHMITT 1917 $.18   (R119)

Praise Ye The Lord (Psalm 150) Bibl
4pt mix cor,S solo oct SCHIRM.G 3401 $.35   (R120)

Psalm 150 *see Praise Ye The Lord

RANGSTROM, TURE (1884-1947)
Jungfru Mariae Vaggvisa *BVM
wom cor/jr cor,pno NORDISKA 3325 s.p.   (R121)

RANKIN, W.S.
I Heard The Voice Of Jesus Say
3pt wom cor,opt pno (easy) oct WILLIS 3730
$.12   (R122)

RAPHAEL, GUNTHER (1903-1960)
Das Glaubensbekenntnis *Op.64
dbl cor,acap (chorus i in Ger, chorus II in
Lat) sc BREITKOPF-L rental   (R123)

Denn Siehe, Bei Dir Wohnen Will Unser Herr
Und Gott
see Funf Marienlieder

Denn Unser Keiner Lebt Sich Selber *Bibl
SSA HANSSLER 7.118 s.p.   (R124)

Der Herr Ist Mein Licht Und Mein Heil (Psalm
27) mot
SATB HANSSLER 7.011 s.p.   (R125)

Der Mond Ist Aufgegangen *Op.55,No.3, Gen,
mot
[Ger] 3 eq voices,fl (med easy) MULLER
SM 1637 s.p.   (R126)

Der Tag, Der Ist So Freudenreich *Gen
[Ger] SATB&SATB,acap (med easy)
HEIDELBERGER HC 2 s.p.   (R127)

Die Auferstehung Jesu *Op.63,No.4, Easter
4pt mix cor,acap cor pts BREITKOPF-W
CHB-3013 s.p.   (R128)

Die Gute Des Herrn *Op.56,No.2, Gen
[Ger] SATB,acap (med diff) MULLER SM 1642
s.p.   (R129)

Die Versuchung Jesu *Op.35
4-8pt,acap voc pt BREITKOPF-L CHB-2792 s.p. (R130)

Dies Irae *Op.73
SATB&SATB,acap cor pts BREITKOPF-W PB-3710
s.p.   (R131)

Ein Kindlein Zart *Op.39,No.1, Xmas,mot
SATB,acap voc pt BREITKOPF-L CHB-2821 s.p. (R132)

Einen Anderen Grund Kann Zwar Niemand Legen
*mot
SAABB HANSSLER 7.034 s.p.   (R133)

Erhalt Uns Herr, Bei Deinem Wort *Op.30,
No.2, mot
5pt mix cor,acap cor pts BREITKOPF-L
PB-3421 s.p.   (R134)

Es Ist Ein Ros Entsprungen *Xmas
[Ger] SATB,acap (easy) HEIDELBERGER HC 5
s.p.   (R135)

Es Ist Ein Schnitter, Heisst Der Tod
SAT&SAT HANSSLER 7.113 s.p.   (R136)

Es Kommt Ein Schiff Geladen *Adv
[Ger] SATB,acap (med easy) HEIDELBERGER
s.p.   (R137)

Frohlich Soll Mein Herze Springen *Op.55,
Xmas,mot
[Ger] SATB,acap (med easy) HEIDELBERGER
HC 3 s.p.   (R138)
[Ger] 2 eq voices,fl (easy) MULLER SM 1635

RAPHAEL, GUNTHER (cont'd.)

s.p.   (R139)

Funf Marienlieder *Op.13, BVM
cor pts BREITKOPF-W s.p.
contains: Denn Siehe, Bei Dir Wohnen Will
Unser Herr Und Gott; Marias Erwahlung;
Marienlob Und Minne; Mutter Maria; Ora
Pro Nobis   (R140)

Gehet Hin In Alle Welt *mot
SSAATTBB,T solo HANSSLER 7.006 s.p.   (R141)

Gelobet Seist Du, Jesu Christ *Xmas/Easter
[Ger] SATB,acap HEIDELBERGER HC 6 s.p.   (R142)

Gott Sei Dank Durch Alle Welt *Adv
[Ger] SSATB,acap (med easy) HEIDELBERGER
s.p.   (R143)

Heil'ger Geist, Du Troster Mein *Op.39,No.3,
Pent/Whitsun
SATB,acap voc pt BREITKOPF-L CHB-2823 s.p. (R144)

Herr Christ, Hilf Uns In Dieser Zeit
SA,org,2rec HANSSLER 5.029 s.p.   (R145)

Herr, Du Bist Wurdig Zu Nehmen Preis *mot
SATB HANSSLER 7.004 s.p.   (R146)

Herr Gott, Dich Loben Alle Wir *Op.84, cant
4pt mix cor,ABar soli,org,ob,vla,vcl sc
BREITKOPF-W PB-3847 s.p., cor pts
BREITKOPF-W CHB-2956 s.p., ipr   (R147)

Herr, Verherrliche Deinen Namen *mot
SAB HANSSLER 7.055 s.p.   (R148)

Ich Hab Mein Sach Gott Heimgestellt *Op.55,
No.5, ECY,mot
[Ger] 4pt mix cor/SAAB,acap (med easy)
MULLER SM 1639 s.p.   (R149)

Ich Rede Von Deinen Zeugnissen *mot
see VIER PSALM-MOTETTEN
SAB HANSSLER 7.058 s.p.   (R150)

Ich Singe Dir Mit Herz Und Mund *Op.55,No.2,
Gen,cant
[Ger] 3pt mix cor,fl (easy) MULLER SM 1636
s.p.   (R151)

Ich Steh An Deiner Krippen Hier *Xmas
[Ger] SATB,acap (med easy) HEIDELBERGER
HC 7 s.p.   (R152)

In Bethlehem Ein Kindelein *Xmas
[Ger] SATB,acap (med) HEIDELBERGER HC 9
s.p.   (R153)

In Dem Herren Freuet Euch
SA,org,2rec HANSSLER 5.039 s.p.   (R154)

Jesus Christus Unser Heiland *Op.39,No.2,
Easter,mot
SATB,acap voc pt BREITKOPF-L CHB-2822 s.p. (R155)

Joseph, Leiber Joseph Mein *Xmas
[Ger] SSATBB,acap (med easy) HEIDELBERGER
HC 9 s.p.   (R156)

Komm, Heiliger Geist, Erfulle Die Herzen
3pt wom cor/3pt jr cor,acap cor pts
BREITKOPF-W CHB-3135 s.p.   (R157)

Kommt Und Lasst Uns Christum Ehren *Xmas
[Ger] SSATB,acap (easy) HEIDELBERGER HC 4
s.p.   (R158)

Lobe Den Herrn, Meine Seele (Psalm 104) Op.29
12pt mix cor,acap cor pts BREITKOPF-L
PB-3406 s.p., voc pt BREITKOPF-L CHB-2698
s.p.   (R159)

Lobt Gott, Ihr Christen, Allzugleich *Xmas
[Ger] SATBB,acap (med easy) HEIDELBERGER
HC 6 s.p.   (R160)

Maria Durch Ein Dornwald Ging *Adv
[Ger] SATBB,acap (med) HEIDELBERGER s.p.   (R161)

Marias Erwahlung
see Funf Marienlieder

Marienlob Und Minne
see Funf Marienlieder

Mitten Wir Im Leben *Trin
[Ger] SATB,org (med diff, choralpartita)
BAREN. BA 2669 sc $2.50, cor pts $.65   (R162)

Mutter Maria
see Funf Marienlieder

Nun Bitten Wir Den Heiligen Geist
mix cor,S solo,org/pno (choralpartita) sc
BREITKOPF-L PB-3548 s.p.   (R163)

Nun Komm Der Heiden Heiland *Adv,mot
SATB HANSSLER 7.121 s.p.   (R164)
[Ger] SATB,acap (med easy) HEIDELBERGER
s.p.   (R165)

Nun Singet Und Seid Froh *Xmas
[Ger] SATBB,acap (med easy) HEIDELBERGER
HC 11 s.p.   (R166)

O Heiland, Reiss Die Himmel Auf *Adv
[Ger] SATB,acap (med easy) HEIDELBERGER
s.p.   (R167)

O Herre Gott, Dein Gottlich Wort *mot
SATB HANSSLER 7.012 s.p.   (R168)

O Jesulein Suss *Xmas
[Ger] SATB,acap (easy) HEIDELBERGER HC 5
s.p.   (R169)

O Kind, O Wahrer Gottessohn *Xmas
[Ger] SATB,acap (med easy) HEIDELBERGER
HC 12 s.p.   (R170)

O Mensch Bewein Dein Sunde Gross *cant
SAATBB&boy cor,Bar solo,2fl,2ob,2bsn,3horn,
2trp,2trom,tuba,2vln,vla,vcl,bvl,timp,
harp sc HANSSLER 10.066 rental   (R171)

RAPHAEL, GUNTHER (cont'd.)

Ora Pro Nobis
see Funf Marienlieder

Psalm 27 *see Der Herr Ist Mein Licht Und
Mein Heil

Psalm 98 *see Singet Dem Herren

Psalm 104 *see Lobe Den Herrn, Meine Seele

Psalm 119 *see Wohl Denen, Die Ohne Tadel
Leben

Psalm 126 *see Wenn Der Herr Die Gefangenen
Zions

Requiem *Op.20, Req
mix cor,SATB soli,org,3fl,3ob,3clar,3bsn,
3trp,4horn,3trom,tuba,strings,perc,timp,
harp (G maj) BREITKOPF-L rental   (R172)

Schmucket Das Fest Mit Maien *Fest
SA,org,2rec HANSSLER 5.055 s.p.   (R173)

Sechs Choralmotetten *Op.55, CC6U,Gen,mot
[Ger] 2-4 eq voices/2-4pt mix cor,fl (med)
MULLER SM 1635-40 s.p.   (R174)

Sei Mir Ein Starker Fels *mot
SAB HANSSLER 7.044 s.p.   (R175)

Singet Dem Herren (Psalm 98) mot
SATB HANSSLER 7.005 s.p.   (R176)

So Seid Ihr Nun Nicht Mehr Gaste Und
Fremdlinge *mot
SATBB HANSSLER 7.013 s.p.   (R177)

Te Deum *Op.26, Te Deum
8pt mix cor,SAB soli,org,4ob,3bsn,4trp,
strings,timp BREITKOPF-L rental   (R178)

Triptychon Zu Worten Des St. Thomas *Gen
[Ger] 2-6pt mix cor,acap (diff) BAREN.
BA 3987 $3.00   (R179)

Vater Unser *Op.58, cant
[Ger] SATB,org,orch (med diff) MULLER
SM 1646 sc s.p., cor pts s.p.   (R180)

Verleih Uns Frieden Gnadiglich
[Ger] SAB,org (med diff, choralpartita)
BAREN. BA 2667 sc $1.50, cor pts $.25   (R181)

Verzage Nicht, Du Hauflein Klein *Op.55,
No.4, Gen
[Ger] 3pt mix cor,acap (med) MULLER SM 1638
s.p.   (R182)

Vom Himmel Hoch, O Englein Kommt *Xmas
[Ger] SSATBB,acap (med easy) HEIDELBERGER
HC 13 s.p.   (R183)

Vom Jungsten Gericht *Op.30,No.1
4-8pt,acap voc pt BREITKOPF-L CHB-2766 s.p. (R184)

Was Mein Gott Will *Op.55,No.6, Trin,mot
[Ger] SATB,fl (med) MULLER SM 1640 s.p.   (R185)

Was Mein Gott Will, Das Gscheh Allzeit *Gen
[Ger] SATB,org (med diff, choralpartita)
BAREN. BA 2668 sc $2.50, cor pts $.65   (R186)

Wenn Aber Jener, Der Geist Der Wahrheit *mot
AABB/SATB HANSSLER 7.007 s.p.   (R187)

Wenn Der Herr Die Gefangenen Zions (Psalm
126) Op.56,No.1, ECY
[Ger] SATB,acap (med diff) MULLER SM 1641
s.p.   (R188)

Wenn Wir In Hochsten Noten Sein
SAT&SAT HANSSLER 7.112 s.p.   (R189)

Wer Sich Selbst Erhohet, Der Wird Erniedrigt
SATB HANSSLER 7.124 s.p.   (R190)

Wohl Denen, Die Ohne Tadel Leben (Psalm 119)
SATB HANSSLER 7.117 s.p.   (R191)

Zu Bethlehem Geboren *Xmas
[Ger] SSATBB,acap (med easy) HEIDELBERGER
HC 8 s.p.   (R192)

Zwolf Spruchmotetten *CC12U,Gen,mot
[Ger] SATB,acap (med) MULLER SM 1081 s.p.   (R193)

RAPLEY
Angel-Voices Ever Singing
SATB,org oct BOOSEY 5567 $.35   (R194)

If The Lord Himself Had Not Been On Our Side
SATB,org FRANCIS s.p.   (R195)

Though I Speak With The Tongues Of Men And Of
Angels
SATB,B solo,org oct BOOSEY 5421 $.30   (R196)

RARE CHORAL MASTERPIECES *CCU
mix cor SCHMITT 9066 $2.00   (R197)

RASELIUS, ANDREAS (ca. 1563-1602)
Also Auch Sage Ich Euch, Wird Freude Sein
*mot
(Stern; Nitsche) SSATB HANSSLER 1.398 s.p. (R198)

Also Hat Gott Die Welt Geliebt *Bibl/mot
(Schwammlein) dbl cor HANSSLER 1.533 $.90   (R199)

Also Werden Die Letzten Die Ersten Sein
*Bibl/mot
(Stern; Nitsche) SAATB HANSSLER 1.379 s.p. (R200)

Also Wird Euch Mein Himmlischer Vater *Bibl/
mot
(Stern; Nitsche) SATTB HANSSLER 1.417 s.p. (R201)

Da Nun Die Menschen Das Zeichen Sahen *mot
(Stern; Nitsche) SAATB HANSSLER 1.385 s.p. (R202)

Darum Seid Barmherzig *mot
(Stern; Nitsche) SSATB HANSSLER 1.399 s.p. (R203)

Das Aber Auf Dem Guten Land *mot
(Stern; Nitsche) SSATB HANSSLER 1.380 s.p. (R204)

RASELIUS, ANDREAS (cont'd.)

Denn Gleich Wie Der Blitz Ausgeht *mot
(Stern; Nitsche) SSATB HANSSLER 1.419 s.p.
(R205)

Denn Wer Sich Selbst Erhohet *mot
(Stern; Nitsche) SSATB HANSSLER 1.406 s.p.
(R206)

Der Herr Hat Gesagt Zu Meinem Herren *Bibl/
mot
(Stern; Nitsche) SSATB HANSSLER 1.413 s.p.
(R207)

Deutsche Sonntagliche Evangelienspruche
*CC53U,mot,Ger
(Stern; Nitsche) 5pt cloth HANSSLER 4.008
$12.00
(R208)

Die Hochzeit Ist Zwar Bereit *mot
(Stern; Nitsche) SSAATB HANSSLER 1.415 s.p.
(R209)

Du Sollst Gott, Deinen Herren, Lieben *Bibl/
mot
(Stern; Nitsche) SSATB HANSSLER 1.408 s.p.
(R210)

Ar Hat Alles Wohlgemacht *Bibl/mot
(Stern; Nitsche) SSATB HANSSLER 1.407 s.p.
(R211)

Erstanden Ist Der Heilig Christ *Easter,mot
(Stern; Nitsche) SSATB HANSSLER 1.387 s.p.
(R212)

Es Ist Ein Grosser Prophet *Bibl/mot
(Stern; Nitsche) SSATB HANSSLER 1.411 s.p.
(R213)

Es Werden Nicht Alle, Die Zu Mir Sagen *mot
(Stern; Nitsche) SSATB HANSSLER 1.403 s.p.
(R214)

Furchtet Euch Nicht, Siehe, Ich Verkundig
*mot
(Stern; Nitsche) SSATB HANSSLER 1.371 s.p.
(R215)

Geh Aus Auf Die Landstrassen *mot
(Stern; Nitsche) SATTB HANSSLER 1.397 s.p.
(R216)

Geht Hin Und Saget Johannes *Bibl/mot
(Stern; Nitsche) SSATB HANSSLER 1.369 s.p.
(R217)

Heb Dich Von Mir, Satan *mot
(Stern; Nitsche) SSATB HANSSLER 1.382 s.p.
(R218)

Herr, Hilf Uns, Wir Verderben *mot/prayer
(Stern; Nitsche) SAATB HANSSLER 1.377 s.p.
(R219)

Herr, Komm Hinab, Ehe Denn Mein Kind *mot
(Stern; Nitsche) SSAATB HANSSLER 1.416 s.p.
(R220)

Hosianna, Dem Sohne Davids *Bibl/mot
(Stern; Nitsche) SAATB HANSSLER 1.367 s.p.
(R221)

Ich Bin Der Gute Hirte *Bibl/mot
(Stern; Nitsche) SSATB HANSSLER 1.389 s.p.
(R222)

Ich Habe Euch Noch Viel Zu Sagen *mot
(Stern; Nitsche) SSATB HANSSLER 1.391 s.p.
(R223)

Ich Sage Euch: Viel Werden Kommen *mot
(Stern; Nitsche) SSATB HANSSLER 1.376 s.p.
(R224)

Ich Taufe Mit Wasser *mot
(Stern; Nitsche) SSATB HANSSLER 1.370 s.p.
(R225)

Ihr Werdet Weinen Und Heulen *mot
(Stern; Nitsche) SSATB HANSSLER 1.390 s.p.
(R226)

Jedermann Gibt Zuerst Den Guten Wein *mot
(Stern; Nitsche) SSATB HANSSLER 1.375 s.p.
(R227)

Jesus Christus, Unser Heiland, Der Von Uns
Den Gotteszorn
SSATB HANSSLER 6.173 s.p.
(R228)

Meister, Wir Haben Die Ganze Nacht *mot
(Stern; Nitsche) SATTB HANSSLER 1.400 s.p.
(R229)

Mich Jammert Des Volks *mot
(Stern; Nitsche) SATTB HANSSLER 1.402 s.p.
(R230)

Nehmet Hin Den Heiligen Geist *mot
(Stern; Nitsche) SSATB HANSSLER 1.388 s.p.
(R231)

Sammelt Zuvor Das Unkraut *mot
(Stern; Nitsche) SAATB HANSSLER 1.378 s.p.
(R232)

Sehet, Wir Gehen Hinauf Nach Jerusalem
*Bibl/mot
(Stern; Nitsche) SSATB HANSSLER 1.381 s.p.
(R233)

Sei Willfahrig Deinem Widersacher Bald *mot
(Stern; Nitsche) SAATB HANSSLER 1.401 s.p.
(R234)

Selig Ist Der Leib, Der Dich *mot
(Stern; Nitsche) SSATB HANSSLER 1.384 s.p.
(R235)

Siehe, Dieser Wird Gesetzt Zu Einem Fall
*mot
(Stern; Nitsche) SSATB HANSSLER 1.372 s.p.
(R236)

Sind Ihr' Nicht Zehn Rein Geworden *mot
(Stern; Nitsche) SSATB HANSSLER 1.409 s.p.
(R237)

So Steht Geschrieben: Mein Haus Ist Ein
Bethus *Bibl/mot
(Stern; Nitsche) SSATB HANSSLER 1.405 s.p.
(R238)

Solches Hab Ich Zu Euch Geredt *mot
(Stern; Nitsche) SAATB HANSSLER 1.393 s.p.
(R239)

Steh Auf, Nimm Das Kindlein Und Seine Mutter
*Xmas,mot
(Stern; Nitsche) SSATB HANSSLER 1.373 s.p.
(R240)

Trachtet Am Ersten Nach Dem Reich Gottes
*Bibl/mot
(Stern; Nitsche) SSATB HANSSLER 1.410 s.p.
(R241)

Und Es Begab Sich Nach Dreien Tagen *mot
(Stern; Nitsche) SSATB HANSSLER 1.374 s.p.
(R242)

Und Ich Sage Euch Auch: Machet Euch Freunde
*mot
(Stern; Nitsche) SSATB HANSSLER 1.404 s.p.
(R243)

Und Siehe, Ein Kananaisch Weib *Bibl/mot
(Stern; Nitsche) SATTB HANSSLER 1.383 s.p.
(R244)

Und Wie Mose In Der Wuste *Bibl/mot
(Stern; Nitsche) SSATB HANSSLER 1.395 s.p.
(R245)

RASELIUS, ANDREAS (cont'd.)

Vater Abraham, Erbarm Dich Mein *Bibl/mot
(Stern; Nitsche) SSATB HANSSLER 1.396 s.p.
(R246)

Wahrlich, Ich Sage Euch, Dies Geschlecht
*mot
(Stern; Nitsche) SSATB HANSSLER 1.368 s.p.
(R247)

Wahrlich, Ich Sage Euch, So Jemand Mein Wort
*Bibl/mot
(Stern; Nitsche) SSATB HANSSLER 1.386 s.p.
(R248)

Wahrlich, Ich Sage Euch: Wenn Ihr Den Vater
Etwas Bitten *mot
(Stern; Nitsche) SAATB HANSSLER 1.392 s.p.
(R249)

Warum Denket Ihr So Arges In Euren *mot
(Stern; Nitsche) SATTB HANSSLER 1.414 s.p.
(R250)

Wenn Du Geladen Wirst, So Gehe Hin *Bibl/mot
(Stern; Nitsche) SSATB HANSSLER 1.412 s.p.
(R251)

Wer Mich Liebet, Der Wird Mein Wort *Bibl/
mot
(Stern; Nitsche) SSATB HANSSLER 1.394 s.p.
(R252)

Wes Ist Das Bild Und Die Uberschrift *mot
(Stern; Nitsche) SSATB HANSSLER 1.418 s.p.
(R253)

Wohl Dem Menschen, Der Wandelt
SATB HANSSLER 6.174 s.p. contains also:
Schutz, Heinrich, Mit Dank Wir Sollen
Loben, SWV 104
(R254)

RASELY

Bread Of Heaven
SATB ALLANS 369 s.p.
(R255)

Church's One Foundation, The
(Raymond) SATB oct PLYMOUTH JR-103 $.25
(R256)

Lamb, The
SATB oct PLYMOUTH JR-147 $.25
(R257)

Psalm 23
(Raymond) SATB oct PLYMOUTH JR-116 $.25
(R258)

Surely God Is In This Place
SATB (easy) ALLANS 448 s.p.
(R259)

RASLEY

Beneath The Cross Of Jesus
SATB oct LORENZ C173 $.30
(R260)

Bread Of Heaven
SATB oct LORENZ E17 $.30
(R261)

Canticle Of Praise, A
SATB oct LORENZ E28 $.30
(R262)

Carol For Eastertide, A *Easter
SATB oct LORENZ C284 $.25
(R263)

Carol For The Christ-Child, A *Xmas
SATB oct LORENZ 9846 $.25
(R264)

Children's Hymn Of Praise, The
SA oct LORENZ 5369 $.25
(R265)

Choral Fanfare On "Holy, Holy, Holy"
SATB oct LORENZ B137 $.30
(R266)

Come And Adore Him *Xmas
SATB oct LORENZ C262 $.30
(R267)

Come, Ye Children, Sweetly Singing
unis oct LORENZ 8586 $.25
(R268)

Crown Him Lord Of All!
SATB oct LORENZ B113 $.30
(R269)

Easter Carol, An *Easter
SATB oct LORENZ A477 $.30
(R270)

Hand In Hand With God
SATB oct LORENZ B26 $.30
(R271)

He's My Friend
SATB oct LORENZ B99 $.30
(R272)

Holy, Holy, Holy
SATB oct LORENZ C257 $.30
(R273)

I Am The Resurrection And The Life
SATB oct LORENZ C300 $.30
(R274)

Jesus, I Come
SATB oct LORENZ A440 $.25
(R275)

Lead On, O King Eternal
SATB oct LORENZ B59 $.30
(R276)

Long, Long Ago *Xmas
SATB oct LORENZ C203 $.25
(R277)

Miracle Of Bethlehem *Xmas,cant
SATB oct LORENZ $1.95
(R278)

O Happy Home
SATB oct LORENZ A483 $.25
(R279)

Onward, Christian Soldiers
SATB oct LORENZ B33 $.30
(R280)

Pass Me Not, O Gentle Savior
SATB oct LORENZ B81 $.30
(R281)

Song Of Easter *Easter
SATB oct LORENZ C160 $.30
(R282)

Song Of God, The
SATB oct LORENZ C255 $.30
(R283)

Surely God Is In This Place
SATB oct LORENZ C15 $.30
(R284)

Tell Me, Shepherds *Xmas
SATB oct LORENZ C193 $.30
(R285)

What A Friend
SATB oct LORENZ A417 $.25
(R286)

Who Will Light My Lamp?
SATB oct LORENZ C213 $.30
(R287)

RASLEY, [JOHN M.] (1913-   )

Love Of God, The
SATB,acap oct PRESSER 312-40475 $.30 (R288)

Shepherds In The Field *Xmas
SATB oct LORENZ B50 $.30
(R289)

Trust In Him
SATB,S,A,T soli,pno (diff) oct WILLIS 7008
$.22
(R290)

What Can I Give Him? *Xmas,anthem
SATB,S solo (med diff) oct LORENZ C349 $.30
(R291)

When His Salvation Bringing
unis/2pt oct PRESSER 332-40045 $.30 (R292)

RATCLIFFE, DESMOND

As Jesus Went To Calvary *Lent,anthem
unis/mix cor oct NOVELLO 40.1488.10 s.p.
(R293)

At The Lamb's High Feast We Sing *Easter,
anthem
SAT/SAB oct NOVELLO 40.1415.04 s.p. (R294)

Bethlehem's Babe *Xmas,Bibl/carol
SATB,narrator,org voc sc NOVELLO s.p.
(R295)

Communion Trilogy, A *Commun
unis oct NOVELLO 44.1410.01 s.p.
contains: Hail, True Body, Born Of Mary!;
O Saving Victim; Therefore We, Before
Him Bending
(R296)

Creator Of The Earth And Sky *anthem
mix cor oct NOVELLO 91.0005.09 s.p. (R297)

From Darkness To Light *Easter/Holywk,Bibl
SATB,org voc sc NOVELLO s.p. (R298)

Give Us The Wings Of Faith
unis oct NOVELLO 33.0110.09 s.p. (R299)

God's Seasons *Harv
SATB,narrator,org voc sc NOVELLO s.p.
(R300)

Good News
SATB HANSEN-US C221A $.40 (R301)

Great Shepherd Of Thy People, Hear *anthem
mix cor,acap oct NOVELLO 40.1554.01 s.p.
(R302)

Hail, True Body, Born Of Mary!
see Communion Trilogy, A

Hark! Hark! What News The Angels Bring
SATB THOMP.G G-557 s.p. (R303)

Holy Communion *Commun
unis&cong,org (D maj) s.p. sc NOVELLO
44.1421.07, voc sc NOVELLO 44.3421.08
(R304)

How Long Wilt Thou Forget Me? *anthem
mix cor oct NOVELLO 28.1472.02 s.p. (R305)

Lord's Prayer, The *Bibl/prayer
unis oct NOVELLO 44.1388.01 s.p. (R306)

O Saving Victim
see Communion Trilogy, A

Praise To God Immortal Praise
SATB THOMP.G G-548 s.p. (R307)

Risen Christ, The
SATB THOMP.G G-538 s.p. (R308)

Therefore We, Before Him Bending
see Communion Trilogy, A

This Joyful Eastertide *Easter
4pt,acap oct NOVELLO 51.0652.04 s.p. (R309)

Three Carols For Christmas *CC3U,Xmas,carol
SATB THOMP.G G-553 s.p. (R310)

To Thee, O Lord, Our Hearts We Raise *anthem
unis oct NOVELLO 28.1473.00 s.p. (R311)
mix cor oct NOVELLO 28.1473.00 s.p. (R312)

RATHAUS, KAROL (1895-1954)

Requiem *Req
SATB oct BOOSEY 1674 $.30 (R313)

RATHBONE, GEORGE

Christians, Awake *Xmas,anthem
mix cor oct NOVELLO 28.1191.10 s.p. (R314)

God Sends The Night *anthem
2pt oct NOVELLO 48.1291.03 s.p. (R315)
mix cor oct NOVELLO 40.1016.07 s.p. (П316)

Rejoice In The Lord Alway *anthem
mix cor oct NOVELLO 28.1169.03 s.p. (Я317)

Strife Is O'er, The *Easter,anthem
mix cor oct NOVELLO 28.1084. 00 s.p. (R318)

RATHBUN, F.

I Heard The Voice Of Jesus Say
(Bliss, P.) SA oct PRESSER 312-20234 $.30
(R319)

(Mauro, M.; Cottone) SATB oct PRESSER
312-15580 $.30 (R320)

RATHGEBER

Singer's Creed *anthem
TTBB oct OXFORD 85.017 $.30 (R321)

RATHOM, A.

Adon Olam
see Lidarti, C.G., Befi Yesharim

RAUCH, JOSEPH (1904-   )

Antoniusgesange *Fest
[Ger] TTBB,Bar solo,pno (med diff) MULLER
SM 2361 sc s.p., cor pts s.p. (R322)

Ein Deutscher Psalter *Op.16
7pt&mix cor (diff) LEUCKART rental (R323)

RAUSCH, JORDAN, RAUSCH see Roll, Jordan, Roll

RAUSCHE, MACHTIGER PSALM see Lissmann, Kurt

RAUTAVAARA, EINOJUHANI (1928-)
Missa Duodecanonica *Op.19, Agnus/Kyrie/
Sanctus
[Lat] 3pt wom cor oct FAZER s.p.   (R324)

RAVAGNAN, BICE
Ave Maria *BVM
[Lat] 3 eq voices ZANIBON 2453 s.p.   (R325)

RAVANELLO, ORESTE (1871-1938)
A S. Teresa Del Bambino Gesu *ASD
[Lat] 3 eq voices,org ZANIBON 1807 s.p.
contains: Luce Divina Rutil. (hymn);
Quasi Rosa Plantata (mot)   (R326)

Ad Recipiendum Solemniter Episcopum *anti
[It] 2pt men cor,org sc ZANIBON 1579 s.p.,
cor pts ZANIBON 1580 s.p.
contains: Ecce Sacerdos Magnus; Sacerdos
Et Pontifex; Tu Es Sacerdos   (R327)

Alma Redemptoris
see Quattro Antifone Della B.V.

Ave Maria *BVM
[Lat] 2pt ZANIBON 2608 s.p.   (R328)

Ave Regina Coelorum
see Quattro Antifone Della B.V.

Cantica In Hon. S. Antonii Taumat *ASD
[Lat] ZANIBON 515 s.p.
contains: Engratulemur (3 eq voices); O
Lingua Benedicta (3 eq voices); Si
Quaeris (2 eq voices)   (R329)

Cantus Sacri In Hon. D. Antonii Pat.
Collectio I *ASD
[Lat] ZANIBON 2283 s.p.
contains: Engratulemur (unis,org); O
Lingua Benedicta (2 eq voices,org); Si
Quaeris (3 eq voices,org); Transitus S. Antonii
(unis,org)   (R330)

Cantus Sacri In Hon. D. Antonii Pat.
Collectio II *ASD
[Lat] ZANIBON 2284 s.p.
contains: Engratulemur (3pt mix cor,org);
O Lingua Benedicta (4pt mix cor,org);
Si Quaeris (4 eq voices,org); Si Quaeris
(3 eq voices,org); Veritas Mea (4pt mix
cor,org)   (R331)

Communio
see Domenica Di Pasqua

Domenica Di Pasqua *Easter
[Lat] TTBB,org sc ZANIBON 4008 s.p.
contains: Communio (Commun); Graduale
(Gradual); Offertorium (Offer);
Sequentia   (R332)

Due Tota Pulchra *Op.114, BVM
[Lat] sc ZANIBON 968 s.p., cor pts ZANIBON
969 s.p.
contains: Tota Pulchra (unis/2pt); Tota
Pulchra (3-4pt mix cor)   (R333)

Ecce Sacerdos Magnus
see Ad Recipiendum Solemniter Episcopum
[It] 3 eq voices,org sc ZANIBON 1326 s.p.,
voc pt ZANIBON 1327-29 s.p.   (R334)

Engratulemur
see Cantica In Hon. S. Antonii Taumat
see Cantus Sacri In Hon. D. Antonii Pat.
Collectio II
see Cantus Sacri In Hon. D. Antonii Pat.
Collectio I

Eucaristica *Commun,hymn
[Lat] ATB,org ZANIBON 3261 s.p.
contains: O Esca Viatorum; O Salutaris;
Pange Lingua; Tantum Ergo   (R335)

Graduale
see Domenica Di Pasqua

In Ascensione Domini
[Lat] 4 eq voices sc ZANIBON 3983 s.p., cor
pts ZANIBON 3984 s.p.   (R336)

In Festo S. Francisci *ASD,Commun/Gloria/
Offer
[Lat] 2 eq voices,org sc ZANIBON 1721 s.p.,
cor pts ZANIBON 1722 s.p.   (R337)

In Nativitate Domini *Xmas,Offer
ZANIBON 1717 s.p.
contains: In Nocte Nativitatis (4 eq
voices,org); In Tertia Missa
Nativitatis (4 eq voices,acap)   (R338)

In Nocte Nativitatis
see In Nativitate Domini

In Tertia Missa Nativitatis
see In Nativitate Domini

Luce Divina Rutil.
see A S. Teresa Del Bambino Gesu

Messa Breve E Facile In Onore Di S Luigi
Gonzaga *Op.75, Mass
2 eq voices,org s.p. sc RICORDI-ENG 110742,
voc pt RICORDI-ENG 115398-99   (R339)

Messa Solenne XX In Onore Di S. Tizanio
*Op.97, Mass
[Lat] ATTB sc ZANIBON 3410 s.p., voc pt
ZANIBON s.p.   (R340)

Messa Solenne XXXV In Onore Di S. Antonio
Taumaturgo Nel VII Centenario Della Sua
Morte *Mass
[Lat] SATTBB,org,opt strings sc ZANIBON
3231 s.p., voc pt ZANIBON 3232-7 s.p.,
ipr   (R341)

Messa XVIII In Onore Di S. Cecilia *Op.87,
Mass
[Lat] SATTBB,org sc ZANIBON 3783 s.p., voc
pt ZANIBON 3784-5-6 s.p.   (R342)

Messa XXII Facilissima In On. Del Ss. Nome Di
Maria *Op.100, Mass
[Lat] AT/ABar (very easy) sc ZANIBON 428

RAVANELLO, ORESTE (cont'd.)

s.p., voc pt ZANIBON 428A-B s.p.   (R343)

Messa XXIII Funebre Facilissima *Op.101,
Mass/Req
[Lat] unis,org (very easy) sc ZANIBON 141
s.p., cor pts ZANIBON 144 s.p.   (R344)

Messa XXVIII Alla Madonna Delle Vittorie
*Mass
unis,org/strings sc ZANIBON 901 s.p., cor
pts ZANIBON 902 s.p., ipr   (R345)

Messa XXXI In Onore Di S. Domenico *Op.127,
Mass
[Lat] TTBB,org,opt strings sc ZANIBON 1731
s.p., voc pt ZANIBON 1806 s.p., ipr (R346)

Messa XXXII In Onore Di S. Caterina Da Siena
*Op.130, Mass
[Lat] 2 eq voices,org,opt strings sc
ZANIBON 1500 s.p., voc pt ZANIBON s.p.,
ipr   (R347)

Missa Antoniana XIX *Op.91, Mass
[Lat] SATB,org sc ZANIBON 3774 s.p., voc pt
ZANIBON s.p.   (R348)

Missa XXIX Pacis *Op.120, Mass
[Lat] TTB,strings (easy) sc ZANIBON 1081
s.p., ipr   (R349)
(Garbeiotto, A.) [Lat] TTB,org (easy) sc
ZANIBON 3642 s.p.   (R350)

Missa XXVI Pro Defunctis *Op.107, Mass/Req
[Lat] SATB,org sc ZANIBON 3360 s.p., voc pt
ZANIBON s.p.   (R351)

Missa XXXIII In Hon. Linguae S. Antonii
*Op.131, Mass
[Lat] ATB,org sc ZANIBON 1525 s.p., voc pt
ZANIBON s.p.   (R352)
"Missa XXXIII In Hon. Linguae S. Antonii"
[Lat] unis/3pt ZANIBON 1525 s.p., cor
pts ZANIBON 1526 s.p.   (R353)

Missa XXXIII In Hon. Linguae S. Antonii *see
Missa XXXIII In Hon. Linguae S. Antonii

O Esca Viatorum
see Eucaristica

O Lingua Benedicta
see Cantica In Hon. S. Antonii Taumat
see Cantus Sacri In Hon. D. Antonii Pat.
Collectio I
see Cantus Sacri In Hon. D. Antonii Pat.
Collectio II

O Salutaris
see Eucaristica

Offertorium
see Domenica Di Pasqua

Oremus Pro Pontifice
see Pro Summo Pontifice

Pange Lingua
see Eucaristica

Pro Summo Pontifice *mot
[It] TTBB,org sc ZANIBON 3182 s.p., voc pt
ZANIBON 3183-84 s.p.
contains: Oremus Pro Pontifice; Tu Es
Petrus   (R354)

Psallite Domino Parti I-IV *Op.124, CC64U,
BVM/Easter/Eve/Gen,hymn/Psalm
[Lat] unis/3pt mix cor,org sc ZANIBON 1193
s.p., cor pts ZANIBON 1806 s.p.   (R355)

Quaranta Falsibordoni *Op.134, CC40U,Eve
[Lat] 1-4 eq voices&mix cor,org ZANIBON
1014 s.p.   (R356)

Quasi Rosa Plantata
see A S. Teresa Del Bambino Gesu

Quattro Antifone Della B.V. *Op.113, BVM
[Lat] cor pts ZANIBON 967 s.p., sc ZANIBON
966 s.p.
contains: Alma Redemptoris (unis); Ave
Regina Coelorum (unis); Regina Coeli
(2pt); Salve Regina (2pt)   (R357)

Regina Coeli
see Quattro Antifone Della B.V.

Sacerdos Et Pontifex
see Ad Recipiendum Solemniter Episcopum

Salve Regina
see Quattro Antifone Della B.V.

Salve Sancte Pater *ASD,anti
[Lat] TB,org sc ZANIBON 1318 s.p., cor pts
ZANIBON 1319 s.p.   (R358)

Sequentia
see Domenica Di Pasqua

Si Quaeris
see Cantica In Hon. S. Antonii Taumat
see Cantus Sacri In Hon. D. Antonii Pat.
Collectio II
see Cantus Sacri In Hon. D. Antonii Pat.
Collectio II
see Cantus Sacri In Hon. D. Antonii Pat.
Collectio II
see Cantus Sacri In Hon. D. Antonii Pat.
Collectio I
see Cantus Sacri In Hon. D. Antonii Pat.
Collectio I

Tantum Ergo
see Eucaristica

Tota Pulchra
see Due Tota Pulchra
see Due Tota Pulchra

Transitus S. Antonii
see Cantus Sacri In Hon. D. Antonii Pat.
Collectio I

RAVANELLO, ORESTE (cont'd.)

Tu Che Nell'etere Vivi Beato *ASD,hymn
[Lat] unis,org sc ZANIBON 333 s.p., cor pts
ZANIBON 334 s.p.   (R359)

Tu Es Petrus
see Pro Summo Pontifice

Tu Es Sacerdos
see Ad Recipiendum Solemniter Episcopum

Veni Creator
see RACCOLTA DI SEI INNI

Veritas Mea
see Cantus Sacri In Hon. D. Antonii Pat.
Collectio II

RAVENSCROFT, THOMAS (1593-1635)
O Jesu Meek
SSA,org SCHIRM.EC 892 $.20   (R360)

Remember, O Thou Man *Xmas
(Stone) SATB,acap/inst oct WORD CRS-12 $.30
(R361)

Two Sacred Pieces *CC2U,anthem
mix cor oct OXFORD 42.360 $.65   (R362)

RAWLS
God Of Harvest Praise, The
SA/TB FLAMMER E5041 $.25   (R363)

Hosanna Be The Children's Song *Palm
unis/SA oct SACRED S-8613 $.35   (R364)

RAWLS, KATHRYN H.
Christmas Is A Beautiful Word *Xmas
unis/SA ABINGDON APM-732 $.25   (R365)

Christmas Symbol, The *Xmas
unis jr cor oct FISCHER,J 9715 $.30 (R366)

Hearken All, What Holy Singing
jr cor oct FISCHER,J 9474 $.30   (R367)

Hymn Of Glory Let Us Sing, A
SA oct FISCHER,J 9881 $.30   (R368)

I Love Thy Kingdon Lord
unis jr cor oct FISCHER,J 9035 $.30 (R369)

Lord God Made Them All, The
SA oct FISCHER,J 9795 $.30   (R370)

Shepherd Of Thy Little Flock
unis oct FISCHER,J 10026 $.30   (R371)

RAWSTHORNE
Canticle Of Man, A *cant
SSAATTBB (med diff) OXFORD 56.806 $.75, ipr
(R372)

RAWSTHORNE, ALAN (1905-1971)
Carmen Vitale
SATB,S solo (diff) OXFORD 46.139 $7.70, ipr
(R373)

RAY, CHARLES
Ezekial Saw De Wheel
SSA oct STAFF 220 $.30   (R374)
SA/TB oct STAFF 217 $.30   (R375)
SAB oct STAFF 229 $.25   (R376)
TTBB oct STAFF 173 $.25   (R377)

RAY, DON [BRANDON] (1926-   )
Let Joy Resound
SATB,Bar solo,acap oct LAWSON 51139 $.25
(R378)

RAYE
I Know What God Is (composed with Bowen,
Caylor; Freeman)
(Naylor) SAB oct MCA   (R379)
(Naylor) SSA/SSAA oct MCA   (R380)
(Naylor) SATB oct MCA   (R381)
(Naylor) TTBB oct MCA   (R382)

RAYE, DON (1909-   )
I Know What God Is
mix cor ALSBACH&D sc s.p., cor pts s.p.
(R383)

RAYMOND, JOSEPH
Friendly Beasts, The
(Hutson) SATB oct PLYMOUTH JR-154 $.30
(R384)

Great Is Thy Reward *Bibl
4pt mix cor oct SCHIRM.G 10840 $.25 (R385)

Lord's Prayer, The
TTBB oct PLYMOUTH LC-300 $.25   (R386)
SSA oct PLYMOUTH LC-200 $.25   (R387)

Son Of Mary *Xmas
(Ades) SATB SHAWNEE A 987 $.25   (R388)
(Ades) SSA SHAWNEE B 303 $.25   (R389)

RAZZI, FAUSTO (1932-   )
Tre Pezzi Sacri *CC3U
mix cor,acap oct ZERBONI 6678 s.p. (R390)

RAZZI, SERAFINO
Libro Primo Delle Laudi Spirituali *CCU
(Vecchi, Prof. Giuseppe) cor oct FORNI 378
s.p.   (R391)

REACH OUT see Nichols, T.

REACH OUT AND TOUCH see Brown, Charles F.

REACH OUT TO YOUR NEIGHBOR see Copland, Aaron

REACHING OUT *CCUL
(Carmichael, Ralph) cor,soli voc sc WORD
37541 $1.95   (R392)

READ, DANIEL (1757-1836)
Broad Is The Road
(Shaw; Parker) SATB,acap oct LAWSON 910
$.25   (R393)

Sherburne
(Lowens) 4pt mix cor,acap oct SCHIRM.G
10324 $.30   (R394)

READ, GARDNER (1913-   )
Though I Speak With The Tongues Of Men
SSAATBB (diff) ABINGDON APM-386 $.75 (R395)

Unknown God, The *Op.23,No.2a
SSA AMP A134 $.20   (R396)

READ, GARDNER (cont'd.)
Vital Spark Of Heav'nly Flame
SATB,acap (med) ABINGDON APM-276 $.32
(R397)

READING, J.
Adeste Fideles *Xmas,carol
[Lat] 3 eq voices,pno UNION ESP. 18722 s.p.
(R398)
[Lat] 4pt mix cor,acap UNION ESP. 18772
s.p. (R399)
"O Come, All Ye Faithful" SATB ALLANS 12
s.p. (R400)
(Cain) "O Come, All Ye Faithful" SAB
FLAMMER D5082 $.30 (R401)
(Cain) "O Come All Ye Faithful" SATB
FLAMMER A 5368 $.35 (R402)
(Dello Joio) "O Come All Ye Faithful"
2pno MARKS 4570 $.50 (R403)
(Novello, V.) "O Come, All Ye Faithful"
SATB oct PRESSER 332-00016 $.40 (R404)
(Ryder, A.) "O Come, All Ye Faithful" TTBB,
T solo oct PRESSER 332-12704 $.35 (R405)

O Come, All Ye Faithful *see Adeste Fideles

READING WITH RESPONSES see Mueller, Carl F.

READY
(Hicks, L'roy E.) TTBB oct AGAPE TB 203 $.30
(R406)

READY BE, MY SOUL, ALWAY see Bach, Johann
Sebastian, Mache Dich, Mein Geist, Bereit

READY WHEN HE COMES
see Bones, Come a-Knittin'

REAL see Oldenburg, Bob

REAL JOY see Matthews, Donald

REAM
Day Of Dawning Brotherhood
SATB oct SACRED S-129 $.35 (R407)
God's Wisdom
SSATBB oct HERITAGE H86 $.35 (R408)
Lambs Also Love Thee, The *Xmas
SATB oct HERITAGE H44 $.35 (R409)
So Lowly Doth The Savior Ride
SATB oct SACRED S-99 $.35 (R410)
Ye Weary And Burdened *Gen
SATB SCHMITT SD6216 $.25 (R411)
You Shall Love The Lord *Gen
SATB SCHMITT 1932 $.35 (R412)

REAM, ALBERT
Fanfare For Easter *Easter
SATB,org&trp SCHMITT 4006 $.25 (R413)
Holy Stillness, A
SATB (easy) ABINGDON APM-194 $.25 (R414)
Uttermost Dawn, The *Xmas
SATB oct PRESSER 312-40791 $.30 (R415)
Ye Folk Afar *Xmas
SATB (med) ABINGDON APM-600 $.35 (R416)

REAPER, THE see Webber, W.S. Lloyd

REASON TO BE, A see Mullins

REASONS FOR SINGING see Kent, Richard

REASONS TO SING *CCUL
jr cor cmplt ed LILLENAS MB-241 $1.00 (R417)

REBAY, FERD. (1889-)
Weihnachtskantate *Xmas,cant
[Ger] mix cor,SBar soli,vln HUG s.p. (R418)

REBEL, THE see Avery

RECEIVE NOW THE BODY OF CHRIST see Carroll,
J.R.

RECEIVE THE HOLY SPIRIT see Hillert, Richard

RECEIVE YE THE BODY OF CHRIST see Roff, Joseph

RECESSIONAL see De Koven, [Henry Louis
Reginald]

RECESSIONAL see Gounod, Charles Francois

RECESSIONAL see Peeters, Flor

RECESSIONAL see Schaffer, Robert J.

RECESSIONAL see Young

RECESSIONAL AND POSTLUDE see Suderburg, R.

RECESSIONAL HYMNS
LITURGICAL $.50
contains: O God, Almighty Father; Praie The
Lord: You Heavens Adore Him; To Jesus
Christ, Our Sovereign King (R419)

RECESSIT PASTOR NOSTER see Victoria, Tomas Luis
de

RECHSTEINER
Deutsche Messe *Mass
cor sc HANSSLER 27.006 s.p. (R420)

RECONCILIATION see Pfautsch, Lloyd

RECORDARE see Volpi, Edoardo

RECORDARE, VIRGO MATER see Casals, Pablo

RECORDATA see Palestrina, Giovanni

RECUEIL DE MOTETS *CC35L,mot
[Lat/Fr] 1-6pt,pno/org oct CHOUDENS s.p.
contains works by: Beethoven; Mozart;
Gounod; and others (R421)

RECUEIL DE SIX CANTIQUES see Gounod, Charles
Francois

RECUERDO see House, M.

RED, BURYL
Answer, The
SATB WORD CS-2565 $.30 (R422)
Get It Together *Xmas
SATB oct WORD CS-2566 $.30 (R423)
Good Life, The
SATB oct WORD CS-2567 $.30 (R424)
He Felt The Whip
SATB oct WORD CS-2568 $.30 (R425)
Inherit The Earth
SATB oct WORD CS-2569 $.30 (R426)
Lightshine (composed with Hawthorne, G.)
*folk
SATB,narrator voc sc WORD 37601 $1.95
(R427)
Rain Of Peace
SATB oct WORD CS-2564 $.30 (R428)
Weep No More
SATB oct WORD CS-2570 $.40 (R429)
Would You
SATB oct WORD CS-2551 $.35 (R430)

RED SEA JAZZ, THE see Chappell, Herbert

REDA, SIEGFRIED (1916-1968)
Ach Gott, Vom Himmel Sieh Darein (Psalm 12)
Trin
[Ger] SSAATBB/AAT,acap/4inst (med diff)
BAREN. BA 2383 $1.50 see also Das
Psalmbuch (R431)
Ach Herr, Straf Mich Nicht In Deinem Zorn
(Psalm 6) Gen
[Ger] SSA/SAA&men cor,acap (contains also:
Aus Tiefer Not) BAREN. BA 2382 $.40 see
also Das Psalmbuch (R432)
Aller Augen Warten Auf Dich (Psalm 145) Fest
[Ger] SATB,acap (contains also: Befiehl Dem
Herrn Deine Wege) BAREN. BA 2387 $.25 see
also Das Psalmbuch (R433)
Armor Dei *ECY
[Ger] SATB,S solo,org (med diff) BAREN.
BA 4453 sc s.p., cor pts s.p. (R434)
Aus Tiefer Not Schrei Ich Zu Dir (Psalm 130)
ECY
[Ger] SSATB/SAATB,acap (contains also: Ach
Herr, Straf Mich Nicht In Deinem Zorn)
BAREN. BA 2382 $.40 see also Das
Psalmbuch (R435)
Befiehl Dem Herrn Deine Wege (Psalm 37) Gen
[Ger] SA&men cor/2 eq voices,acap (contains
also: Aller Augen Warten Auf Dich) BAREN.
BA 2387 $.25 see also Das Psalmbuch (R436)
Christus Ist Gekommen *Psntd
[Ger] SSA,acap (med diff) BAREN. BA 2326
$.25 see from Epistellesungen, Teil II (R437)
Danket Dem Herrn, Denn Er Ist Freundlich
(Psalm 106) Gen
[Ger] unis BAREN. BA 2387 $.25 see also Das
Psalmbuch (R438)
Danksaget Dem Vater
[Ger] SSA/SAA&men cor,acap (med diff)
BAREN. BA 2355 $.25 see from Die Alten
Epistellesungen, Teil IV: Trinitatiszeit
(R439)
Das Evangelium Auf Den 4. Advent *Adv,evang
[Ger] SATBB,acap (med diff) BAREN. BA 2361
$1.25 (R440)
Das Gottliche Spiel, Teil II; DIE HEIMSUCHUNG
*Gen
[Ger] SSAATTBB,SS soli,acap (med diff,
choir-trilogy on the Revelation of St.
John) BAREN. BA 2771 $2.50 (R441)
Das Graduallied, Teil I: Advent Bis Pfingsten
*CC39U,Gen
[Ger] 3-8pt mix cor,S/SS soli BAREN.
BA 3060 s.p. Advent to Whitsuntide (R442)
Das Ist Ein Kostlich Ding (Psalm 92) Gen
[Ger] SA&men cor,acap BAREN. BA 2384 $1.25
see also Das Psalmbuch (R443)
Das Psalmbuch *CCU,Gen,Psalm
[Ger] 2-8pt mix cor,acap (med diff) BAREN.
BA 2418 s.p.
see also: Ach Gott, Vom Himmel Sieh
Darein (Psalm 12); Ach Herr, Straf Mich
Nicht In Deinem Zorn (Psalm 6); Aller
Augen Warten Auf Dich (Psalm 145); Aus
Tiefer Not Schrei Ich Zu Dir (Psalm
130); Befiehl Dem Herrn Deine Wege
(Psalm 37); Danket Dem Herrn, Denn Er
Ist Freundlich (Psalm 106); Das Ist Ein
Kostlich Ding (Psalm 92); Das Verlangen
Der Elenden Horst Du, Herr (Psalm 10);
Dennoch Bleibe Ich Stets An Dir (Psalm
73); Der Herr Ist Gott, Der Uns
Erleuchtet (Psalm 118); Der Herr Ist
Mein Getreuer Hirt (Psalm 23); Die
Elenden Sollen Essen (Psalm 22); Die
Furcht Des Herren Ist Der Weisheit
Anfang (Psalm 111); Die Toren Sprechen
In Ihren Herzen (Psalm 14); Du Wirst
Meine Seele Nicht Dem Tode Lassen
(Psalm 16); Ein Mensch Ist In Seinem
Leben Wie Gras; Es Mussen Sich Freuen
Und Frohlich Sein (Psalm 40); Es Wolle
Gott Uns Gnadig Sein (Psalm 67); Gott,
Der Herr, Der Machtige, Ruft Der Welt
(Psalm 50); Gott Der Herr Ist Sonn Und
Schild (Psalm 84); Herr, Deine Gute
Reicht So Weit Die Wolken Gehen (Psalm
36); Herr, Du Erforschest Mich (Psalm
139); Herr, Ich Habe Lieb Die Statte
Deines Hauses (Psalm 26); Herr, Lehre
Doch Mich, Dass Es Ein Ende Mit Mir
Haben Muss (Psalm 39); Herr, Tue Meine
Lippen Auf (Psalm 51); Herr, Wer Wird
Wohnen In Deiner Hutte (Psalm 15);
Herr, Wie Sind Deine Werke So Gross Und
Viel (Psalm 104); Ich Hebe Meine Augen

REDA, SIEGFRIED (cont'd.)
Auf Zu Den Bergen (Psalm 121); Ich
Liege Und Schlafe Ganz In Frieden
(Psalm 4); In Dich Hab Ich Gehoffet,
Herr (Psalm 31); Jesus Christus, Unser
Heiland, Der Den Tod Uberwand; Machet
Die Tore Weit (Psalm 24); Mein Gott,
Nimm Mich Nicht Weg Inmitten Meiner
Tage (Psalm 102); Nun Jauchzt Dem
Herren, Alle Welt (Psalm 100); Nun Lob,
Mein Seel, Den Herren (Psalm 103);
Schmecket Und Sehet, Wie Freundlich Der
Herr Ist (Psalm 34); Vor Dir Ist Freude
Die Fulle; War Gott Nicht Mit Uns Diese
Zeit (Psalm 124); Wenn Der Herr Die
Gefangenen Zions Erlosen Wird (Psalm
126); Wie Der Hirsch Schreit
Nach Frischem Wasser (Psalm 42); Wo
Gott Zum Haus Nicht Gibt Sein Gunst
(Psalm 127); Wohl Dem, Der Nicht
Wandelt Im Rat Der Gottlosen (Psalm 1)
(R444)
Das Verlangen Der Elenden Horst Du, Herr
(Psalm 10) Gen
[Ger] SA&men cor,acap (contains also: Die
Elenden Sollen Essen) BAREN. BA 2392 s.p.
see also Das Psalmbuch (R445)
De Paasgeschiedenis *see Die Ostergeschichte
Denn Es Ist Hier Kein Unterschied
[Ger] SATB,acap (med diff) BAREN. BA 2344
$.40 see from Die Alten Epistellesungen,
Teil IV: Trinitatiszeit (R446)
Denn Ich Halte Es Dafur, Dass Dieser Welt
Leiden
[Ger] SATB,acap (med diff) BAREN. BA 2335
$.25 see from Die Alten Epistellesungen,
Teil IV: Trinitatiszeit (R447)
Dennoch Bleibe Ich Stets An Dir (Psalm 73)
Gen
[Ger] SA&men cor,acap BAREN. BA 2394 $.65
see also Das Psalmbuch (R448)
Der Herr Ist Der Armen Schutz (Psalm 9) Gen
[Ger] 2pt,acap (contains also: Du Wirst
Meine Seele Nicht Dem Tode Lassen) BAREN.
BA 2393 $.40 (R449)
Der Herr Ist Gott, Der Uns Erleuchtet (Psalm
118) Pent,canon
[Ger] 3pt,acap BAREN. BA 2397 $1.50 see
also Das Psalmbuch (R450)
Der Herr Ist Mein Getreuer Hirt (Psalm 23)
Easter/Pent
[Ger] SSA/SAA&men cor,acap (med) BAREN.
BA 2389 $1.25 see also Das Psalmbuch
(R451)
Der Tod Ist Der Sunde Sold
[Ger] SATB,acap (med diff) BAREN. BA 2338
$.40 see from Die Alten Epistellesungen,
Teil IV: Trinitatiszeit (R452)
Die Alten Epistellesungen *see Von Gottes
Gnade Bin Ich; Wenn Ich Mit Menschen -
Und Mit Engelszungen Redete (R453)
Die Alten Epistellesungen, Teil I: Advent Bis
Epiphanias *see Es Ist Erschienen Die
Heilsame Gnade Gottes; Ihr Seid Alle
Gottes Kinder (R454)
Die Alten Epistellesungen, Teil II:
Vorfasten, Passion *see Ein Jeglicher
Sei Gesinnt; Lass Dir An Meiner Gnade
Genugen; Nun Wir Sind Gerecht Geworden;
Ringet Darnach, Dass Ihr Stille Seid; So
Oft Ihr Von Diesem Brot Esset; Wandelt In
Der Liebe; Wir Ermahnen Euch Aber; Wir
Gingen Alle In Der Irre; Wisset Ihr Nicht
(R455)
Die Alten Epistellesungen, Teil IV:
Trinitatiszeit *see Danksaget Dem Vater;
Denn Es Ist Hier Kein Unterschied; Denn
Ich Halte Es Dafur, Dass Dieser Welt
Leiden; Der Tod Ist Der Sunde Sold; Ein
Solch Vertrauen Haben Wir; Einer Trage
Des Andern Last; Erkennet, Dass Christus
Liebhaben; Erneuert Euch Im Geist; Es
Wird Aber Des Herren Tag Kommen; Euch
Aber, Die Ihr Trubsal Leidet; Gott Ist
Liebe; Gott Widerstehet Den Hoffartigen;
Ich Danke Meinem Gott; Niemand Kann Jesus
Einen Herrn Nennen; O, Welch Eine Tiefe;
So Sehet Nun Zu, Wie Ihr Vorsichtig
Wandelt; Unser Wandel Ist Im Himmel;
Vertraget Einander In Der Liebe;
Verwundert Euch Nicht, Wenn Euch Die Welt
Hasst; Wandelt Im Geist; Welche Der Geist
Gottes Treibt; Wer Sich Lasst Dunken,
Dass Er Fest Stehe; Wir Wollen Euch Aber,
Lieben Bruder, Nicht Verhalten Von Denen,
Die Da Schlafen; Wisset, Dass Ihr Dazu
Berufen Seid; Wisset Ihr Nicht, Dass
Alle, Die Wir In Jesum Christum Getauft
Sind; Zuletzt, Meine Bruder, Seid Stark
In Dem Herrn (R456)
Die Beiden Schacher *Gd.Fri./Gen,evang
[Ger] SAATTB&SATB,T solo,acap (diff) BAREN.
BA 2330 $1.25 (R457)
Die Elenden Sollen Essen (Psalm 22) Psntd
[Ger] SATB,acap (contains also: Das
Verlangen Der Elenden Horst Du, Herr)
BAREN. BA 2392 $.40 see also Das
Psalmbuch (R458)
Die Furcht Des Herren Ist Der Weisheit Anfang
(Psalm 111) Psntd
[Ger] SSAB/SAAB,acap BAREN. BA 2394 s.p.
see also Das Psalmbuch (R459)
Die Ostergeschichte *Easter
[Ger] SATB,SS soli,acap BAREN. BA 2318
$2.75 (R460)
"De Paasgeschiedenis" [Dut] SATB,SS soli,
acap BAREN. BA 2318 $2.75 (R461)
Die Toren Sprechen In Ihren Herzen (Psalm 14)
Gen
[Ger] SSA&men cor,acap (contains also: Wie
Der Hirsch Schreiet) BAREN. BA 2381 $.40
see also Das Psalmbuch (R462)

REDA, SIEGFRIED (cont'd.)

Die Weihnachtsgeschichte *Xmas
[Ger] SSATB,narrator,T solo,acap (med diff)
BAREN. BA 2379 $1.25   (R463)

Dies Ist Der Tag, Den Der Herr Macht (Psalm
118) Pent
[Ger] SATBB,acap BAREN. BA 2385 $.90 see
also Das Psalmbuch   (R464)

Du Wirst Meine Seele Nicht Dem Tode Lassen
(Psalm 16) Easter
[Ger] SSA,acap (contains also: Der Herr Ist
Der Armen Schutz) BAREN. BA 2393 $.40 see
also Das Psalmbuch   (R465)

Ecce Homo (Psalm 22) Psntd,mot
.[Ger] SATB,acap (med diff) BAREN. BA 2527
$2.25   (R466)

Ein Jeglicher Sei Gesinnt *Palm/Psntd
[Ger] SSATB/SAATB,acap (med diff) BAREN.
BA 2327 $.55 see from Die Alten
Epistellesungen, Teil II: Vorfasten,
Passion   (R467)

Ein Mensch Ist In Seinem Leben Wie Gras
*Trin
[Ger] SATB,acap (med diff) BAREN. BA 2384
$1.25 see also Das Psalmbuch   (R468)

Ein Solch Vertrauen Haben Wir
[Ger] SATB,acap (med diff) BAREN. BA 2343
$.40 see from Die Alten Epistellesungen,
Teil IV: Trinitatiszeit   (R469)

Einer Trage Des Andern Last
[Ger] SATB,acap (med diff) BAREN. BA 2346
$.40 see from Die Alten Epistellesungen,
Teil IV: Trinitatiszeit   (R470)

Epistellesungen, Teil II *see Christus Ist
Gekommen   (R471)

Erkennet, Dass Christus Liebhaben
[Ger] wom cor&TB,acap (med diff) BAREN.
BA 2347 $.25 see from Die Alten
Epistellesungen, Teil IV: Trinitatiszeit (R472)

Erneuert Euch Im Geist
[Ger] SATB,acap (med diff) BAREN. BA 2350
$.40 see from Die Alten Epistellesungen,
Teil IV: Trinitatiszeit   (R473)

Es Ist Erschienen Die Heilsame Gnade Gottes
*Xmas
[Ger] SATB,acap (med) BAREN. BA 2371 $.40
see from Die Alten Epistellesungen, Teil
I: Advent Bis Epiphanias   (R474)

Es Mussen Sich Freuen Und Frohlich Sein
(Psalm 40) Gen
[Ger] SA&men cor,acap BAREN. BA 2384 $1.25
see also Das Psalmbuch   (R475)

Es Wird Aber Des Herren Tag Kommen *Trin
[Ger] SAATTB,acap BAREN. BA 2358 $.55 see
from Die Alten Epistellesungen, Teil IV:
Trinitatiszeit   (R476)

Es Wolle Gott Uns Gnadig Sein (Psalm 67) Gen,
Psalm
[Ger] 2 eq voices/3 eq voices,acap BAREN.
BA 3114 $.40 see also Das Psalmbuch   (R477)

[Ger] SATB,acap BAREN. BA 2385 $.90 see
also Das Psalmbuch   (R478)

Euch Aber, Die Ihr Trubsal Leidet *Trin
[Ger] SATB,acap BAREN. BA 2357 $.25 see
from Die Alten Epistellesungen, Teil IV:
Trinitatiszeit   (R479)

Frohlich Soll Mein Herze Springen *Xmas
[Ger] 4pt mix cor,T solo,org (med) BAREN.
BA 2412 s.p.   (R480)

Gott, Der Herr, Der Machtige, Ruft Der Welt
(Psalm 50) ECY
[Ger] SA&men cor,T solo,acap BAREN. BA 2386
$.90 see also Das Psalmbuch   (R481)

Gott Der Herr Ist Sonn Und Schild (Psalm 84)
Trin
[Ger] 3 eq voices,acap (med diff) BAREN.
BA 2394 $.65 see also Das Psalmbuch   (R482)

Gott Ist Liebe
[Ger] SATB,acap (med diff) BAREN. BA 2332
$.25 see from Die Alten Epistellesungen,
Teil IV: Trinitatiszeit   (R483)

Gott Widerstehet Den Hoffartigen
[Ger] SATB,acap (med diff) BAREN. BA 2334
$.40 see from Die Alten Epistellesungen,
Teil IV: Trinitatiszeit   (R484)

Herr, Deine Gute Reicht So Weit Die Wolken
Gehen (Psalm 36) Pent
[Ger] SSA/SAA&men cor,acap BAREN. BA 2388
$1.25 see also Das Psalmbuch   (R485)

Herr, Du Erforschest Mich (Psalm 139) Gen
[Ger] SATB&unis wom cor,acap (contains
also: Ich Hebe Meine Augen Auf Zu Den
Bergen) BAREN. BA 2388 $1.25 see also Das
Psalmbuch   (R486)

Herr, Ich Habe Lieb Die Statte Deines Hauses
(Psalm 26) Gen
[Ger] 2pt,acap (contains also: Herr, Wer
Wird Wohnen In Deiner Hutte) BAREN.
BA 2396 $.40 see from Das Psalmbuch   (R487)

Herr Jesu Christ, Du Hochstes Gut *Gen
[Ger] 3pt mix cor,acap (med easy) BAREN.
BA179 s.p. contains also: Im Frieden Dein
(3-4pt mix cor,acap)   (R488)

Herr, Lehre Doch Mich, Dass Es Ein Ende Mit
Mir Haben Muss (Psalm 39) Gen
[Ger] STB&SATB,acap (med diff) BAREN.
BA 2383 $1.50 see from Das Psalmbuch   (R489)

Herr, Tue Meine Lippen Auf (Psalm 51) Gen
[Ger] SATB/jr cor,T solo,acap (contains
also: Wohldem, Der Nicht Wandelt) BAREN.
BA 2395 $.65 see from Das Psalmbuch

REDA, SIEGFRIED (cont'd.)

Herr, Unser Herrscher (Psalm 8) Trin   (R490)
[Ger] SATB,SBar soli,org (med diff) BAREN.
BA 4455 s.p.   (R491)

Herr, Wer Wird Wohnen In Deiner Hutte (Psalm
15) Gen
[Ger] SATB,acap (contains also: Herr, Ich
Habe Lieb Die Statte Deines Hauses)
BAREN. BA 2396 $.40 see from Das
Psalmbuch   (R492)

Herr, Wie Sind Deine Werke So Gross Und Viel
(Psalm 104) Gen
[Ger] 2pt mix cor,acap BAREN. BA 2384 $1.25
see from Das Psalmbuch   (R493)

Ich Danke Meinem Gott *Trin
[Ger] SATB,acap (med diff) BAREN. BA 2349
$.25 see from Die Alten Epistellesungen,
Teil IV: Trinitatiszeit   (R494)

Ich Hebe Meine Augen Auf Zu Den Bergen (Psalm
121) Gen
[Ger] SSB&ATB,acap (med diff, contains
also: Herr, Du Erforschest Mich) BAREN.
BA 2388 $1.25 see from Das Psalmbuch   (R495)

Ich Liege Und Schlafe Ganz In Frieden (Psalm
4) Gen
[Ger] SATB/jr cor,S solo,acap BAREN.
BA 2390 $.40 see from Das Psalmbuch   (R496)

Ich Ruf Zu Dir, Herr Jesu Christ *Trin
[Ger] treb cor&opt unis,org (med easy)
BAREN. BA 167 s.p.   (R497)

Ihr Seid Alle Gottes Kinder *ECY
[Ger] SATB,acap (med) BAREN. BA 2372 $.40
see from Die Alten Epistellesungen, Teil
I: Advent Bis Epiphanias   (R498)

Im Frieden Dein
see Reda, Siegfried, Herr Jesu Christ, Du
Hochstes Gut

In Dich Hab Ich Gehoffet, Herr (Psalm 31)
Trin
[Ger] SSA&men cor,acap (med diff) BAREN.
BA 2391 $.65 see from Das Psalmbuch   (R499)

Jesus Christus, Unser Heiland, Der Den Tod
Uberwand *Easter/Pent
[Ger] SSA,acap (easy) BAREN. BA 2393 $.40
see from Das Psalmbuch   (R500)

Lass Dir An Meiner Gnade Genugen *Psntd/Sexa
[Ger] SATB,acap (med diff) BAREN. BA 2321
$.25 see from Die Alten Epistellesungen,
Teil II: Vorfasten, Passion   (R501)

Leidensverkundigung Und Heilung Eines Blinden
*Psntd,evang
[Ger] SATB,acap (med diff, estomihi sunday)
BAREN. BA 2378 $1.50   (R502)

Machet Die Tore Weit (Psalm 24) Adv
[Ger] SSA&men cor/SAA&men cor,T solo,acap
BAREN. BA 2385 $.90 see from Das
Psalmbuch   (R503)

Magnificat Peregrini Toni *Magnif
[Ger] SATB&treb cor,org (med diff) BAREN.
BA 2411 $2.25   (R504)

Mein Gott, Nimm Mich Nicht Weg Inmitten
Meiner Tage (Psalm 102) Psntd
[Ger] STBB/SABB,acap BAREN. BA 2383 $1.50
see from Das Psalmbuch   (R505)

Niemand Kann Jesus Einen Herrn Nennen *Trin
[Ger] SATB,acap (med diff) BAREN. BA 2341
$.25 see from Die Alten Epistellesungen,
Teil IV: Trinitatiszeit   (R506)

Nun Danket All Und Bringet Ehr *Gen,anti
[Ger] SATB,org (med diff) BAREN. BA 3972 sc
$4.25, cor pts $.40   (R507)

Nun Jauchzt Dem Herren, Alle Welt (Psalm 100)
Epiph
[Ger] SA&men cor,opt S solo,acap/inst
BAREN. BA 2384 $1.25 see from Das
Psalmbuch   (R508)

Nun Lob, Mein Seel, Den Herren (Psalm 103)
Trin
[Ger] SAAB/SATB,acap (med diff) BAREN.
BA 2384 $1.25 see from Das Psalmbuch   (R509)

Nun Wir Sind Gerecht Geworden *Psntd
[Ger] SSATB/SAATB,acap (med diff, latare)
BAREN. BA 2325 $.40 see from Die Alten
Epistellesungen, Teil II: Vorfasten,
Passion   (R510)

O Dass Ich Tausend Zungen Hatte *Gen
[Ger] 4pt mix cor,opt inst (med easy)
BAREN. BA 4945 s.p.   (R511)

O, Welch Eine Tiefe *Trin
[Ger] SATB,acap (med diff) BAREN. BA 2331
$.40 see from Die Alten Epistellesungen,
Teil IV: Trinitatiszeit   (R512)

Psalm 1 *see Wohl Dem, Der Nicht Wandelt Im
Rat Der Gottlosen

Psalm 4 *see Ich Liege Und Schlafe Ganz In
Frieden

Psalm 6 *see Ach Herr, Straf Mich Nicht In
Deinem Zorn

Psalm 8 *see Herr, Unser Herrscher

Psalm 9 *see Der Herr Ist Der Armen Schutz

Psalm 10 *see Das Verlangen Der Elenden
Horst Du, Herr

Psalm 12 *see Ach Gott, Vom Himmel Sieh
Darein

Psalm 14 *see Die Toren Sprechen In Ihren
Herzen

REDA, SIEGFRIED (cont'd.)

Psalm 15 *see Herr, Wer Wird Wohnen In
Deiner Hutte

Psalm 16 *see Du Wirst Meine Seele Nicht Dem
Tode Lassen

Psalm 22 *see Die Elenden Sollen Essen

Psalm 23 *see Der Herr Ist Mein Getreuer
Hirt

Psalm 24 *see Machet Die Tore Weit

Psalm 26 *see Herr, Ich Habe Lieb Die Statte
Deines Hauses

Psalm 31 *see In Dich Hab Ich Gehoffet, Herr

Psalm 34 *see Schmecket Und Sehet, Wie
Freundlich Der Herr Ist

Psalm 36 *see Herr, Deine Gute Reicht So
Weit Die Wolken Gehen

Psalm 37 *see Befiehl Dem Herrn Deine Wege

Psalm 39 *see Herr, Lehre Doch Mich, Dass Es
Ein Ende Mit Mir Haben Muss

Psalm 40 *see Es Mussen Sich Freuen Und
Frohlich Sein

Psalm 42 *see Wie Der Hirsch Schreit Nach
Frischem Wasser

Psalm 50 *see Gott, Der Herr, Der Machtige,
Ruft Der Welt

Psalm 51 *see Herr, Tue Meine Lippen Auf

Psalm 67 *see Es Wolle Gott Uns Gnadig Sein

Psalm 73 *see Dennoch Bleibe Ich Stets An
Dir

Psalm 84 *see Gott Der Herr Ist Sonn Und
Schild

Psalm 91 *see Wer In Dem Schutz Des Hochsten
Ist

Psalm 92 *see Das Ist Ein Kostlich Ding

Psalm 100 *see Nun Jauchzt Dem Herren, Alle
Welt

Psalm 102 *see Mein Gott, Nimm Mich Nicht
Weg Inmitten Meiner Tage

Psalm 103 *see Nun Lob, Mein Seel, Den
Herren

Psalm 104 *see Herr, Wie Sind Deine Werke So
Gross Und Viel

Psalm 106 *see Danket Dem Herrn, Denn Er Ist
Freundlich

Psalm 111 *see Die Furcht Des Herren Ist Der
Weisheit Anfang

Psalm 118 *see Dies Ist Der Tag, Den Der
Herr Macht

Psalm 121 *see Ich Hebe Meine Augen Auf Zu
Den Bergen

Psalm 124 *see Wo Gott Der Herr Nicht Bei
Uns Halt

Psalm 126 *see Wenn Der Herr Die Gefangenen
Zions Erlosen Wird

Psalm 127 *see Wo Gott Zum Haus Nicht Gibt
Sein Gunst

Psalm 130 *see Aus Tiefer Not Schrei Ich Zu
Dir

Psalm 139 *see Herr, Du Erforschest Mich

Psalm 145 *see Aller Augen Warten Auf Dich

Requiem, Vel Vivorum Consolatio *ECY
[Lat] SATB,SBar soli,orch (diff) BAREN.
BA 3513 rental   (R513)

Ringet Darnach, Dass Ihr Stille Seid *Psntd
[Ger] SSSTB,acap (med diff, reminiscere)
BAREN. BA2323 $.25 see from Die Al†n
Epistellesungen, Teil II: Vorfasten,
Passion   (R514)

Schmecket Und Sehet, Wie Freundlich Der Herr
Ist (Psalm 34) Trin
[Ger] SATB,acap (med diff) BAREN. BA 2397
$1.50 see from Das Psalmbuch   (R515)

So Oft Ihr Von Diesem Brot Esset *Psntd
[Ger] TTB&treb cor,acap (med diff, Maundy
Thursday) BAREN. BA 2328 $.25 see from
Die Alten Epistellesungen, Teil II:
Vorfasten, Passion   (R516)

So Sehet Nun Zu, Wie Ihr Vorsichtig Wandelt
*Trin
[Ger] SATB,acap (med diff) BAREN. BA 2351
$.40 see from Die Alten Epistellesungen,
Teil IV: Trinitatiszeit   (R517)

Te Deum Laudamus *Gen
[Lat] SATB&SATB,3trp,3trom,tuba (med diff)
BAREN. BA 2485 sc $6.50, cor pts $1.75,
ipr   (R518)

Und Ich Sah Einen Engel *Gen
[Ger] SATB,acap (med easy) BAREN. BA 3039
s.p.   (R519)

Unser Wandel Ist Im Himmel *Trin
[Ger] SSATBB,acap (med diff) BAREN. BA 2354
$.40 see from Die Alten Epistellesungen,
Teil IV: Trinitatiszeit   (R520)

Verbum Supernum Prodiens *Gen,hymn
[Ger] SATB,S solo,org,2vln,vcl (diff)
BAREN. BA 3623 rental   (R521)

REDA, SIEGFRIED (cont'd.)

Verkundigung Der Geburt Unseres Heilandes *Adv
[Ger] unis,solo,2fl,2vln (med) sc BAREN. BA 2159 $2.25 (R522)

Vertraget Einander In Der Liebe *Trin
[Ger] SATB,acap (med diff) BAREN. BA 2348 $.40 see from Die Alten Epistellesungen, Teil IV: Trinitatiszeit (R523)

Verwundert Euch Nicht, Wenn Euch Die Welt Hasst *Trin
[Ger] SATB,acap (med diff) BAREN. BA 2333 $.40 see from Die Alten Epistellesungen, Teil IV: Trinitatiszeit (R524)

Von Gottes Gnade Bin Ich *Gen
[Ger] 3pt&SATB,acap (med diff) BAREN. BA 2342 $.40 see from Die Alten Epistellesungen (R525)

Vor Dir Ist Freude Die Fulle *Easter,canon
[Ger] SSS,acap BAREN. BA 2393 $.50 see from Das Psalmbuch (R526)

Wandelt Im Geist *Trin
[Ger] SATB,acap (med diff) BAREN. BA 2345 $.40 see from Die Alten Epistellesungen, Teil IV: Trinitatiszeit (R527)

Wandelt In Der Liebe *Psntd
[Ger] SAATTB,acap (med diff, oculi) BAREN. BA 2324 s.p. see from Die Alten Epistellesungen, Teil II: Vorfasten, Passion (R528)

War Gott Nicht Mit Uns Diese Zeit (Psalm 124) Easter/Pent
[Ger] SATB,acap (med) BAREN. BA 2389 $1.25 see from Das Psalmbuch (R529)

Was Ist Fur Neue Freud *Xmas,cradle
[Ger] SATB,solo,pno,2fl,2vln (med easy) sc BAREN. BA 2414 $2.25, ipa (R530)

Weihnachtskyrie *Xmas,Kyrie
[Ger] SSA,S solo,org,2vln,vcl (med diff) BAREN. BA 3621 rental (R531)

Welche Der Geist Gottes Treibt *Trin
[Ger] SATB,acap (med diff) BAREN. BA 2339 $.25 see from Die Alten Epistellesungen, Teil IV: Trinitatiszeit (R532)

Wenn Der Herr Die Gefangenen Zions Erlosen Wird (Psalm 126) Gen
[Ger] SST&ABB,acap (med diff) BAREN. BA 2397 $1.50 see from Das Psalmbuch (R533)

Wenn Ich Mit Menschen - Und Mit Engelszungen Redete *Gen
[Ger] SSAA&TTBB,acap (med diff) BAREN. BA 2319 $1.50 see from Die Alten Epistellesungen (R534)

Wer In Dem Schutz Des Hochsten Ist (Psalm 91) Psntd
[Ger] SSATB,acap BAREN. BA 2389 $1.25 see from Das Psalmbuch (R535)

Wer Sich Lasst Dunken, Dass Er Fest Stehe *Trin
[Ger] SATB,acap (med diff) BAREN. BA 2340 $.25 see from Die Alten Epistellesungen, Teil IV: Trinitatiszeit (R536)

Wie Der Hirsch Schreit Nach Frischem Wasser (Psalm 42) Easter/Pent
[Ger] 2 eq voices/3 eq voices,acap (contains also: Die Toren Sprechen In Ihren Herzen) BAREN. BA 2381 $.40 see from Das Psalmbuch (R537)

Wir Ermahnen Euch Aber *Psntd
[Ger] SATB,acap (med diff, invocation) BAREN. BA 2322 $.25 see from Die Alten Epistellesungen, Teil II: Vorfasten, Passion (R538)

Wir Gingen Alle In Der Irre *Gd.Fri./Psntd
[Ger] SSATBB,acap (med diff) BAREN. BA 2329 $.25 see from Die Alten Epistellesungen, Teil II: Vorfasten, Passion (R539)

Wir Grussen Dich, Herr Jesu Christ *Xmas
[Ger] SATB,acap (med easy) BAREN. BA 3206 s.p. (R540)

Wir Wollen Euch Aber, Lieben Bruder, Nicht Verhalten Von Denen, Die Da Schlafen *Trin
[Ger] SATB,acap BAREN. BA 2356 $.40 see from Die Alten Epistellesungen, Teil IV: Trinitatiszeit (R541)

Wisset, Dass Ihr Dazu Berufen Seid *Trin
[Ger] SATB,acap (med diff) BAREN. BA 2336 $.40 see from Die Alten Epistellesungen, Teil IV: Trinitatiszeit (R542)

Wisset Ihr Nicht *Psntd/Septua,Bibl
[Ger] SATB,T solo,acap (med diff) BAREN. BA 2320 $.25 see from Die Alten Epistellesungen, Teil II: Vorfasten, Passion (R543)

Wisset Ihr Nicht, Dass Alle, Die Wir In Jesum Christum Getauft Sind *Trin
[Ger] SATB,acap (med diff) BAREN. BA 2337 $.25 see from Die Alten Epistellesungen, Teil IV: Trinitatiszeit (R544)

Wo Gott Der Herr Nicht Bei Uns Halt (Psalm 124) Trin
[Ger] SSA/SSA&men cor,acap (med diff) BAREN. BA 2389 $1.25 see from Das Psalmbuch (R545)

Wo Gott Zum Haus Nicht Gibt Sein Gunst (Psalm 127) Gen
[Ger] SATB&SATB,acap (med diff) BAREN. BA 2389 $1.25 see from Das Psalmbuch (R546)

Wohl Dem, Der Nicht Wandelt Im Rat Der Gottlosen (Psalm 1) Gen
[Ger] 3pt wom cor&SATB,acap (med diff, contains also: Herr, Tue Meine Lippen

REDA, SIEGFRIED (cont'd.)

Auf) BAREN. BA 2395 $.65 see from Das Psalmbuch (R547)

Zuletzt, Meine Bruder, Seid Stark In Dem Herrn *Trin
[Ger] SATB,acap (med diff) BAREN. BA 2532 $.25 see from Die Alten Epistellesungen, Teil IV: Trinitatiszeit (R548)

Zwolf Kanonische Chorale *CC12U,Gen,canon/chorale
[Ger] 2 eq voices,acap BA 1789 s.p. (R549)

REDEEMER, COME see Wilson, John F.

REDEEMING LOVE *CC25L
(Wismar, W.) mix cor CONCORDIA 97-7547 $1.00 contains works by: Bach; Gomolka; Vulpius; Tallis; Purcell; Da Palestrina; Jeep; Gippenbusch; Hirsch; Naegeli-Stein; Ingegneri; Gumpeltzhaimer; Eccard; Isaac; Schumacher; Homilius; Cruger; Schutz; Lotti; Praetorius (R550)

REDEMPTION see Franck, Cesar

REDEMPTION see Gounod, Charles Francois

REDEMPTION CAROL see McAfee, D.

REDEMPTION, THE see Gounod, Charles Francois

REDEMPTION'S SONG see Holton

REDEMPTOR NOBIS see Herbeck, Johann Franz von

REDFORD, JOHN (? -1547)
Rejoice In The Lord *Adv,anthem
(Mckie, W.) SSTB oct NOVELLO 28.0258.09 s.p. (R551)

Rejoice In The Lord Alway
SATB,acap PETERS H1528 (R552)

REDHEAD
Gracious Spirit Dwell With Me
(Mueller) 2pt jr cor FISCHER,C CM 6429 $.20 (R553)

REDHEAD, ALFRED
Story Of The Cross, The *Psntd
SATB oct NOVELLO 44.1401.02 s.p. (R554)

REDHEAD, [RICHARD] (1820-1901)
Holy Offerings Rich And Rare *Offer
cor oct HART s.p. (R555)

REDMAN, REGINALD
Lord, If I Deceive Myself
SATB,acap LENGNICK s.p. (R556)

Passion Of Mary, The
SATB,orch LENGNICK s.p., ipa (R557)

Praise Ye The Lord (Psalm 150)
mix cor CURWEN 72646 s.p. (R558)
2pt jr cor/2pt wom cor CURWEN 72646 s.p. (R559)

Psalm 150 *see Praise Ye The Lord

Song Of Angels, A *Easter
4pt oct NOVELLO 40.1461.06 s.p. (R560)

Song Of Angels, A *Easter,anthem
SSATB,pno oct NOVELLO 40.1462.06 s.p. (R561)

Thou Wilt Keep Him In Perfect Peace *anthem
mix cor oct NOVELLO 40.1261.05 s.p. (R562)

When The Herds Were Watching *Xmas
4pt mix cor oct CURWEN 11820 $.30 (R563)
mix cor CURWEN 61573 s.p. (R564)

REDMOND
God Made Everything Good
SA MARKS 4541 $.30 (R565)

One Fold And One Shepherd
(Frank) SATB oct MCA (R566)

REDNER, LEWIS [HENRY] (1831-1908)
Everywhere, Everywhere, Christmas Tonight *Xmas
(McKelvy, J.) SATB,acap FOSTER MF504 $.20 (R567)

O Little Town Of Bethlehem *Xmas,carol
(Shaw; Parker) mix cor,acap oct LAWSON 739 $.25 (R568)

REDUC, DOMINE DEUS MEUS see Schutz, Heinrich

REE, KNUT
I Himmelen, I Himmelen
men cor MUSIKK 205 s.p. (R569)

REED
Baby Jesus Stirred In Sleep
SA HANSEN-US C202 $.40 (R570)

Battle Hymn Of The Republic (from Sacred Suite, A)
SATB,band MARKS 4249 $.30, ipa (R571)

Forgiveness Divine
(McLellan) SATB oct LILLENAS AT-1068 $.25 (R572)

Let All The World In Every Corner Sing
SATB oct FISCHER,C CM-7538 $.25 (R573)

Saints Of God, The
unis jr cor FISCHER,C CW 7019 $.25 (R574)
2pt jr cor FISCHER,C CM 7258 $.25 (R575)
3pt jr cor/SSA (easy) FISCHER,C CM 7529 $.25 (R576)
SATB oct FISCHER,C CM-7257 $.25 (R577)

Seek Ye First The Kingdom Of God
SATB,acap MARKS 4258 $.30 (R578)

REED, ELMORE M.G.
Carol Of The Wind *carol
SATB oct FISCHER,J 7881 $.30 (R579)

REED, HERBERT OWEN (1910-)
Psalm Of Praise, A *Psalm
SSAATB oct FOX R151 $.25 (R580)

REED, ROBERT B. (1900-)
Easter Story, The *Easter,cant
mix cor BELWIN $1.50 (R581)

Rise Up O Men Of God
SAB oct FISCHER,J 9247 $.30 (R582)
SATB oct FISCHER,J 8004 $.30 (R583)
(Culver) TTBB oct FISCHER,J 8377 $.30 (R584)

Upon The Rock Of Faith
SATB oct GRAY GCMR 2731 $.20 (R585)

REED, W.
Te Deum Laudamus In A Flat
SATB oct PRESSER 332-12202 $.30 (R586)

REEKER
Peace On Earth *Gen
SATB SCHMITT 7042 $.35 (R587)

REES
Breathe On Me, Breath Of God
(Morgan) boy cor SOUTHERN $.30 (R588)
(Morgan) SATB,acap WARNER R3336 $.30 (R589)

Supplication
(Davis; Craig) SATB oct PLYMOUTH DC-114 $.25 (R590)

Winds Through The Olive Trees *Xmas
SATB oct LORENZ B49 $.30 (R591)
SAB oct LORENZ 7399 $.25 (R592)
unis oct LORENZ 8606 $.25 (R593)

REES-DAVIES, IEUAN
Close Thine Eyes *see Cyn Cau Llygaid

Cyn Cau Llygaid
"Close Thine Eyes" [Welsh/Eng] mix cor CURWEN 61382 s.p. (R594)

REESE
Welsh Choral
(Jones) SATB,S/T solo,acap WARNER W3343 $.30 (R595)

REFICE, LICINIO (1883-1954)
Missa In Hon. S. Joseph Universalis Ecclesiae Patroni *Mass
[Lat] STB,org,opt strings sc ZANIBON 4096 s.p., voc pt ZANIBON s.p., cor pts ZANIBON 4100 s.p., ipr (R596)

Missa In Honorem Virginis Perdolentis
SATB,org s.p. voc sc RICORDI-ENG 124757, cor pts RICORDI-ENG 124758-59 (R597)

REFLECTION see Salsbury, Sonny

REFLECTIONS ON CHRISTMAS see Gross

REFORMATION ANTIPHON, A see Dressler, John

REFORMATION DAY see Fetler, Paul

REFORMATIONSKANTATE see Weyse, Christoph Ernst Friedrich

REGEM ARCHANGELORUM see Festa, Costanza

REGEM NATUM see Gallus, Jacobus

REGENERATION see Christiansen, F. Melius

RE'GENERATION SONGS *CC12UL
(Johnson, Derric) cor,pno,bvl,gtr cmplt ed LILLENAS MB-242 $1.95 (R598)

REGER, MAX (1873-1916)
Ach, Herr, Strafe Mich Nicht *Op.110, mot
[Ger] 5pt mix cor voc sc BOTE s.p. see from Drei Motetten (R599)

Acht Geistliche Gesaenge *Op.138, anthem
[Ger] 4-8pt,acap PETERS 3984 $3.00 (R600)

Acht Geistliche Gesange *see Agnus Dei, Op.138,No.6; All Men Live And Thrive Briefly, Op.138,No.1; Crusader's Hymn, Op.138,No.5; Evening Hymn, An, Op.138, No.3; God Guide Us Hence, Op.138,No.7; Morning Song, Op.138,No.2; Our Lady's Vision, Op.138,No.4; We All Believe In One God, Op.138,No.8 (R601)

Agnus Dei *Op.138,No.6, Agnus
SATB,acap (contains also: Evening Hymn, An; God Guide Us Hence) PETERS 6601C $.40 see from Acht Geistliche Gesange (R602)

Agnus Dei, The
see Three Anthems

All Men Live And Thrive Briefly *Op.138,No.1
SATB&SATB,acap PETERS 6601A $.30 see from Acht Geistliche Gesange (R603)

Auferstanden, Auferstanden *cant
(Haas) [Ger] SATB,A solo,org sc PETERS 3567 $4.00, voc sc PETERS 3567 $.60 (R604)

Choral Cantata No. 4 *see Meinem Jesu Lass Ich Nicht

Christ, Von Den Toten Erweckt
see Zwanzig Responsorien-Heft 2

Crusader's Hymn *Op.138,No.5, hymn
see Two Anthems
SSATB,acap (contains also: We All Believe In One God) PETERS 6601E $.30 see from Acht Geistliche Gesange (R605)

Das Wort Ward Fleisch
see Zwanzig Responsorien-Heft 1

Dein, O Herr, Ist Die Kraft
see Zwanzig Responsorien-Heft 3
mix cor,acap cor pts BREITKOPF-W CHB-4928 s.p. (R606)

Dein Wort, O Herr, Wohnt Weit Und Ewig
see Zwanzig Responsorien-Heft 3
mix cor,acap cor pts BREITKOPF-W CHB-4939 s.p. (R607)

Denn So Wir Glauben, Dass Jesus Gestorben Und Auferstanden Ist
see Zwanzig Responsorien-Heft 5

REGER, MAX (cont'd.)

Drei Motetten *see Ach, Herr, Strafe Mich
  Nicht, Op.110; Mein Odem Ist Schwach, "My
  Breath Is Corrupt", Op.110; O Tod, Wie
  Bitter Bist Du, "O Death, How Bitter",
  Op.110   (R608)

Er Ward Gefuhrt Wie Ein Lamm Zur Schlachtbank
  see Zwanzig Responsorien-Heft 1

Es Kommt Die Zeit, So Spricht Der Herr
  see Zwanzig Responsorien-Heft 1

Evening Hymn, An *Op.138,No.3, hymn
  see Three Anthems
  SATB,acap (contains also: Agnus Dei; God
    Guide Us Hence) PETERS 6601C $.40 see
    from Acht Geistliche Gesange   (R609)

Furchte Gott Und Halte Seine Gebote
  see Zwanzig Responsorien-Heft 3

Gehet Hin In Alle Welt
  see Zwanzig Responsorien-Heft 2

God Guide Us Hence *Op.138,No.7
  SATB,acap (contains also: Evening Hymn, An;
    Agnus Dei) PETERS 6601C $.40 see from
    Acht Geistliche Gesange   (R610)

God Guide Us Hence, Our Guardian Be
  see Three Anthems

Haben Wir Gutes Empfangen Von Gott
  see Zwanzig Responsorien-Heft 4

Herr, Fuhre Mich Auf Dem Pfad Deiner Gebote
  see Zwanzig Responsorien-Heft 4

Ich Weiss, Dass Mein Erloser Lebt *funeral
  4pt mix cor,acap cor pts BREITKOPF-W
  CHB-3573 s.p. see also Zwanzig
  Responsorien-Heft 5   (R611)

Ich Will In Frieden Mich Niederlegen Zum
  Schlaf
  see Zwanzig Responsorien-Heft 5

Lasset Uns Den Herren Preisen *Easter,mot
  SSATB,acap cor pts BREITKOPF-W PB-3262 s.p.
                                            (R612)

Mach Dich Auf, Werde Licht
  see Zwanzig Responsorien-Heft 1

Maria, Himmelsfreud *BVM
  4pt mix cor,acap cor pts BREITKOPF-W
  PB-3728 s.p.   (R613)

Maria Wiegenlied *Op.76,No.52
  "Virgin's Slumber Song, The" :Eng/Ger] SSA,
    opt kbd AMP A91 $.30   (R614)
  "Virgin's Slumber Song, The" [Eng/Ger] SA
    AMP A94 $.25   (R615)
  "Virgin's Slumber Song, The" [Eng/Ger] TTBB
    AMP A90 $.30   (R616)
  (Mack) "Virgin's Slumber-Song, The" [Eng/
    Ger] SATB,acap AMP A92 $.30   (R617)

Mein Odem Ist Schwach *Op.110, mot
  "My Breath Is Corrupt" [Eng/Ger] 5pt mix
  cor voc sc BOTE s.p. see from Drei
  Motetten   (R618)

Meinem Jesu Lass Ich Nicht *cant
  "Choral Cantata No. 4" [Ger] SATB,S solo,
  org,vln,vla voc sc PETERS HU1972 $2.50   (R619)

Meinen Jesum Lass Ich Nicht
  [Ger] mix cor,S solo,org,vln,vla BOTE sc
  s.p., cor pts s.p., ipa   (R620)

Morning Song *Op.138,No.2
  SSATB,acap PETERS 6601B $.30 see from Acht
  Geistliche Gesange   (R621)

My Breath Is Corrupt *see Mein Odem Ist
  Schwach

O Death, How Bitter *see O Tod, Wie Bitter
  Bist Du

O Haupt Voll Blut Und Wunden *Gd.Fri.
  [Ger] mix cor,SA/AT soli,org,vln,ob BOTE
  voc sc s.p., cor pts s.p., ipa   (R622)

O Sieh, Wie Der Gerechte Stirbt
  see Zwanzig Responsorien-Heft 5

O Tod, Wie Bitter Bist Du *Op.110, mot
  "O Death, How Bitter" [Eng/Ger] 5pt mix cor
  voc sc BOTE s.p. see from Drei Motetten
                                            (R623)

O Wie Selig Seid Ihr Doch, Ihr Frommen *Req
  [Ger] mix cor&cong,S solo,org,5strings BOTE
  voc sc s.p., cor pts s.p., ipa   (R624)

Ostermotette *Easter,mot
  5pt mix cor,acap voc pt BREITKOPF-L
  CHB-2588 s.p.   (R625)

Our Lady's Vision *Op.138,No.4
  SATB,acap PETERS 6601D $.25 see from Acht
  Geistliche Gesange   (R626)

Preis Den Herrn Alle Zeiten
  see Zwanzig Responsorien-Heft 4

Psalm 100 *Op.106
  (Paul Hindemith) [Eng/Ger] SATB,orch cor
    pts PETERS 3218A $.50, ipr   (R627)
  (Paul Hindemith) [Ger] SATB,orch min sc
    PETERS 3819A $6.50, ipr   (R628)
  (Paul Hindemith) [Ger] SATB,orch voc sc
    PETERS 3218AA $2.00, ipr   (R629)

Requiem *Op.144b, Req
  [Ger] SATB,Bar solo,2pno voc sc PETERS
    3996A $7.50   (R630)
  [Ger] SATB,Bar solo,orch voc sc PETERS
    3996 $5.00, ipr   (R631)

Requiem-Satz *Op.145a, Req
  4pt mix cor,SATB soli,org,3fl,2ob,2clar,
  3bsn,4horn,3trp,3trom,tuba,strings,perc,
  timp,English horn voc sc BREITKOPF-W
  EB-5698 s.p., ipr, voc pt BREITKOPF-W
  CHB-2873 s.p., sc BREITKOPF-W rental
                                            (R632)

REGER, MAX (cont'd.)

Sieh Drein, O Herr, Aus Deinem Heiligtum
  see Zwanzig Responsorien-Heft 4

Tantum Ergo Sacramentum
  5pt mix cor,acap cor pts BREITKOPF-L
  CHB-2921 s.p.   (R633)

Three Anthems *anthem
  SATBB PETERS 6601C $.40
    contains: Agnus Dei, The, Op.138,No.6;
    Evening Hymn, An, Op.138,No.3; God
    Guide Us Hence, Our Guardian Be,
    Op.138,No.7   (R634)

Totenfeier *Op.145a, Req
  mix cor,SATB soli,org,3fl,3ob,2clar,3bsn,
  3trp,4horn,3trom,tuba,strings,perc,timp
  BREITKOPF-L rental   (R635)

Two Anthems *anthem/hymn
  SSATB PETERS 6601E $.30
    contains: Crusader's Hymn, Op.138,No.5;
    We All Belive In One God, Op.138,No.8   (R636)

Und Es Erschienen Den Aposteln Zungen
  see Zwanzig Responsorien-Heft 2

Vater Unser
  (Stein, Fritz) SATB&SATB&SATB,acap sc
  BREITKOPF-W PB-3789 s.p., cor pts
  BREITKOPF-W CHB-3045, CHB-3046, CHB-3047
  s.p.   (R637)

Virgin's Slumber-Song, The *see Maria
  Wiegenlied

Von Himmel Hoch, Da Komm Ich Her *Xmas
  [Ger] cong&jr cor,SATB soli,org,2vln BOTE
  voc sc s.p., cor pts s.p., ipa   (R638)

We All Belive In One God *Op.138,No.8
  SSATB,acap (contains also: Crusader's Hymn)
  PETERS 6601E $.30 see from Acht
  Geistliche Gesange   (R639)

We All Belive In One God
  see Two Anthems

Wir Kennen Keinen Andern Gott
  see Zwanzig Responsorien-Heft 3

Wir Loben Den Vater Und Den Sohn
  see Zwanzig Responsorien-Heft 2

Zwanzig Responsorien-Heft 1 *cor-resp
  (Schreiber, Ottmar) 4pt mix cor,acap cor
  pts BREITKOPF-W CHB-3422A s.p.
    contains: Das Wort Ward Fleisch (Xmas);
    Er Ward Gefuhrt Wie Ein Lamm Zur
    Schlachtbank (Psntd); Es Kommt Die
    Zeit, So Spricht Der Herr (Adv); Mach
    Dich Auf, Werde Licht (Epiph)   (R640)

Zwanzig Responsorien-Heft 2 *cor-resp
  (Schreiber, Ottmar) 4pt mix cor,acap cor
  pts BREITKOPF-W CHB-3422B s.p.
    contains: Christ, Von Den Toten Erweckt
    (Easter); Gehet Hin In Alle Welt (Asc);
    Und Es Erschienen Den Aposteln Zungen
    (Pent); Wir Loben Den Vater Und Den
    Sohn (Trin)   (R641)

Zwanzig Responsorien-Heft 3 *cor-resp
  (Schreiber, Ottmar) 4pt mix cor,acap cor
  pts BREITKOPF-W CHB-3422C s.p.
    contains: Dein, O Herr, Ist Die Kraft
    (Gen); Dein Wort, O Herr, Wohnt Weit
    Und Ewig (Gen); Furchte Gott Und Halte
    Seine Gebote (Gen); Wir Kennen Keinen
    Andern Gott (Gen)   (R642)

Zwanzig Responsorien-Heft 4 *cor-resp
  (Schreiber, Ottmar) 4pt mix cor,acap cor
  pts BREITKOPF-W CHB-3422D s.p.
    contains: Haben Wir Gutes Empfangen Von
    Gott (funeral); Herr, Fuhre Mich Auf
    Dem Pfad Deiner Gebote (Gen); Preis Den
    Herrn Alle Zeiten (Gen); Sieh Drein, O
    Herr, Aus Deinem Heiligtum (Gen)   (R643)

Zwanzig Responsorien-Heft 5 *cor-resp
  (Schreiber, Ottmar) 4pt mix cor,acap cor
  pts BREITKOPF-W CHB-3422E s.p.
    contains: Denn So Wir Glauben, Dass Jesus
    Gestorben Und Auferstanden Ist
    (funeral); Ich Weiss, Dass Mein Erloser
    Lebt (funeral); Ich Will In Frieden
    Mich Niederlegen Zum Schlaf (funeral);
    O Sieh, Wie Der Gerechte Stirbt
    (funeral)
  see also: Ich Weiss, Dass Mein Erloser
    Lebt   (R644)

REGES TERRAE CONGREGATI SUNT see Mouton, Jean

REGES THARSIS see Palestrina, Giovanni

REGINA CAELI see Anonymous

REGINA CAELI see Erbach, Christian

REGINA CAELI see Lotti, Antonio

REGINA CAELI see Porta

REGINA CAELI see Suriano, Francesco

REGINA CAELI see Viadana, Lodovico Grossi da

REGINA CAELI LAETARE see Aichinger, Gregor

REGINA CAELI LAETARE see Suriano, Francesco

REGINA CELI LETARE see Des Prez, Josquin

REGINA COELI see Aichinger, Gregor

REGINA COELI see Andrews, C.T.

REGINA COELI see Anonymous

REGINA COELI see Arnaldi, Antonio

REGINA COELI see Bedell, [Robert Leech]

REGINA COELI see Bottazzo, Luigi

REGINA COELI see Boulay, J.

REGINA COELI see Brahms, Johannes

REGINA COELI see Busser, [Henri-Paul]

REGINA COELI see Caldara, Antonio

REGINA COELI see Cardelus, F.-L. de

REGINA COELI see Dubois, Theodore

REGINA COELI see Gerli, Giovanni

REGINA COELI see Halffter, C.

REGINA COELI see Herold, Louis-Joseph-Ferdinand

REGINA COELI see Lalande, Michel Richard de

REGINA COELI see Lotti, Antonio

REGINA COELI see Mascagni, Pietro

REGINA COELI see Mozart, Wolfgang Amadeus

REGINA COELI see Palestrina, Giovanni

REGINA COELI see Pergolesi, Giovanni Battista

REGINA COELI see Philips, Peter

REGINA COELI see Picchi, Luigi

REGINA COELI see Ponzilacqua

REGINA COELI see Ravanello, Oreste

REGINA COELI see Roques, L.

REGINA COELI JUBILA see Picchi, Luigi

REGINA COELI, LAETARE see Aston, Peter

REGINA COELI LAETARE see Roger-Ducasse, Jean-
  Jules Aimable

REGINA COELI see Palestrina, Giovanni

REGINA COELI see Palestrina, Giovanni

REGNALI see Fayrfax, Robert

REGNART
  Deutsche Liedlein *see Sayve

  When I Recall The Hour *madrigal
    (Kirk) SAB oct PRO ART 2445 $.22   (R645)

REGNART, JACOB (ca. 1540-1599)
  Auf Meinen Lieben Gott Trau Ich
    see Bach, Johann Sebastian, Der Lieben
    Sonne Licht Und Pracht

  Born Unto Us *see Puer Natus Est

  Opera Omnia vol. V *CCU
    (Pass, Walter) cor AM.INST.MUS. $20.00
    Motets, 1577   (R646)

  Puer Natus Est *Xmas
    (Rubsamen, Walter) "Born Unto Us" 6pt mix
    cor,acap oct LAWSON $.75   (R647)

  Thesauri Musici, Heft 4: Litania Deiparae
    Virginis Mariae *Renais
    (Pass, Walter) 6pt mix cor,acap cmplt ed
    DOBLINGER s.p.   (R648)

REGNEY
  Do You Hear What I Hear?
    (Shayne; Simeone) TTBB SHAWNEE C194 $.35
                                            (R649)
    (Shayne; Simeone) SA/TB SHAWNEE E47 $.35
                                            (R650)
    (Shayne; Simeone) SAB SHAWNEE D60 $.35
                                            (R651)
    (Shayne; Simeone) SSA SHAWNEE B218 $.35
                                            (R652)

REGNUM MUNDI see Gallus, Jacobus

REGNUM MUNDI see Oltrassi, Giuseppe

REGUM MUNDI see Gallus, Jacobus

REHFELD
  Tov L'hodos
    (Roskin) SATB HATIKVAH HCL 18 $.40   (R653)

REHMANN, THEODOR BERNHARD (1895-   )
  Abendmahl-Messe *see Coena Domini

  Coena Domini *Eve/Psntd,Mass
    "Abendmahl-Messe" [Ger] SATB,acap (med
    easy, Maundy Thursday) MULLER SM 731 s.p. (R654)

  Missa Christmatis *Psntd,Mass
    "Oelweihe-Messe" [Lat] SATB,acap (med easy,
    Maundy Thursday) MULLER SM 730 s.p.   (R655)

  Oelweihe-Messe *see Missa Christmatis

REIBOLD, BRUNO
  Spirit Of Christmas *Xmas
    SATB oct FOX $.75   (R656)

REICH, PHILLIP (1909-   )
  Der Chorvers, Heft 1 *CCU,Bibl/mot
    [Ger] 3pt mix cor/4pt mix cor BAREN. EM 782
    s.p.   (R657)

  Der Chorvers, Heft 2 *CCU,Bibl/mot
    [Ger] 3pt mix cor/4pt mix cor BAREN. EM 783
    s.p.   (R658)

REICH UND ARM SOLL FROHLICH SEIN see Ammann,
  Benno

REICHARDT, JOHANN FRIEDRICH (1752-1814)
  Heilige Nacht
    (Franken, P.) wom cor sc ALSBACH&D s.p.
                                            (R659)

REICHEL, BERNARD (1901-   )
  Magnificat *Gen
    [Ger] SATB&SATB,acap (med diff) BAREN.
    BA 3645 $2.75   (R660)

REICHNER
  If You Know The Lord
    SATB oct FOX $.30   (R661)
    SSA oct FOX $.30   (R662)

REID, ROBERT A.
  Now Every Child *Xmas
    SATB oct WORD CS-2524 $.35   (R663)

  Who Am I? *Gen,anthem
    SAB oct WORD CS-2504 $.35   (R664)

REIFF
  From The Cross *Lent,cant
    SATB FISCHER,C O-2019 $.75   (R665)

REIGN OVER ME, LORD JESUS see Roff, Joseph

REIFF, S.T.
  Wonder Child, The *Xmas,cant
    mix cor,SATB soli,org (med) oct WILLIS $.75
                                               (R666)

REIMANN, [JOHANN BALTHASAR] (1702-1749)
  By Early Morning Light *Easter
    (Dickinson) SATB oct GRAY GSC 57 $.30   (R667)

  Shepherd's Christmas Song *Xmas,Aus
    (Dickinson) SSA oct GRAY GSC 106 $.25
                                               (R668)
    (Dickinson) SATB oct GRAY GSC 7 $.25   (R669)

REIMERDES, FRIEDRICH
  Auf, Auf, Mein Herz, Mit Freuden *No.86,
      Easter
    [Ger] 4pt mix cor,acap BAREN. EM 65 s.p.
      see from EVANGELISCHES KIRCHENGESANGBUCH
                                               (R670)

  Evangelisches Kirchengesangbuch *Psntd
    [Ger] 4pt mix cor,acap BAREN. EM 64 s.p.
      contains: O Lamm Gottes, Unschuldig,
      No.55; O Mensch, Bewein Dein Sunde
      Gross, No.54   (R671)

  O Lamm Gottes, Unschuldig
    see Evangelisches Kirchengesangbuch

  O Mensch, Bewein Dein Sunde Gross
    see Evangelisches Kirchengesangbuch

REIN, WALTER (1893-1955)
  Auf, Haltet Euer Herz Bereit *Xmas,cant
    see CHORE ZUR WEIHNACHT
    wom cor&jr cor TONGER s.p.   (R672)
    mix cor TONGER s.p.   (R673)
    SATB,S solo,pno,brass,strings cor pts
      TONGER s.p., ipa   (R674)
    men cor TONGER s.p.   (R675)

  Bemesst Den Schritt, Bemesst Den Schwung
    see Erntefeier

  Das Feld Ist Weiss
    see Erntefeier

  Dem Dunklen Schoss Der Heilgen Erde
    see Erntefeier

  Deutsche Lieder Vergangener Jahrhunderte-Heft
      2 *CCU
    3 eq voices&3pt mix cor MOSELER s.p. (R676)

  Die Ernt' Ist Nun Zu Ende
    see Erntefeier

  Dies Ist Der Tag, Den Der Herr Macht (Psalm
      118) Easter,cant
    [Ger] 4pt mix cor,brass BAREN. EM 131 s.p.
                                               (R677)
    (Zoll, Paul) [Ger] 4pt men cor,brass BAREN.
      EM 132 sc s.p., ipa, cor pts s.p.   (R678)
    (Zoll, Paul) [Ger] 4pt men cor,strings
      BAREN. EM 132A sc s.p., ipa, cor pts s.p.
                                               (R679)

  Du Meine Seele, Singe *Gen,cant
    [Ger] SATB&cong,2trp,2trom (med easy)
      BAREN. BA 2631 sc $2.75, cor pts $.55,
      ipa   (R680)

  Er Ist Erschienen *Xmas
    [Ger] SATB,acap (med) MULLER MS 7 s.p.
                                               (R681)

  Erntefeier *cant
    mix cor,orch cor pts TONGER s.p., ipa
      contains: Bemesst Den Schritt, Bemesst
      Den Schwung; Das Feld Ist Weiss; Dem
      Dunklen Schoss Der Heilgen Erde; Die
      Ernt' Ist Nun Zu Ende; Wir Danken, Herr
                                               (R682)

  Es Kommt Ein Schiff Geladen *Adv,cant
    4pt mix cor,org/inst MOSELER sc s.p., cor
      pts s.p., ipa   (R683)

  Glockenkantate *Gen,cant
    [Ger] SATB,cantor,org,2vln (easy) BAREN.
      BA 2192 sc $2.75, cor pts $.40, ipa
                                               (R684)

  Liebliche Weihnacht *Xmas
    men cor TONGER s.p.   (R685)

  Macht Hoch Die Tur *Adv,cant
    [Ger] SATB&cong,2trp,2trom BAREN. BA 2638
      sc $2.75, cor pts $.55, ipa   (R686)

  Psalm 118 *see Dies Ist Der Tag, Den Der
      Herr Macht

  Wir Danken, Herr
    see Erntefeier

  Wo Find Ich Deines Vaters Haus
    4pt mix cor MOSELER LB-243 s.p.   (R687)

  Zu Bethlehem Geboren *Xmas,cant/cradle
    [Ger] SATB,solo,pno,2fl,2vln (med easy) sc
      BAREN. BA 2414 $2.25, ipa   (R688)
    [Ger] SATB,ob&2vln&vla&vcl/fl&2vln&vla/
      clar&2vln&vla&vcl/3vln&vla&vcl (med easy)
      BAREN. BA 2524 $2.50, cor pts $.40,
      ipa   (R689)

REINAGLE, [ALEXANDER ROBERT] (1799-1877)
  Festival Hallelujah *Fest,Allelu
    (Pisano) SATB,acap,opt pno oct PRO ART 2515
      $.25   (R690)

REINE DES CIEUX, O DIVINE MARIE see Saint-
    Saens, Camille

REINECKE, CARL (1824-1910)
  Look Upward *canon
    SS,pno SCHIRM.EC 1937 $.20   (R691)

  On That Christmastide In The Long Ago
    2pt oct GALAXY 1.0898.1 $.30   (R692)

  Prayer At Sea *prayer
    (Bement) SSA oct GALAXY 1.1368.1 $.25
                                               (R693)
    (Bement) SA oct GALAXY 1.1000.1 $.25 (R694)

REINHART
  Alle, Alleluia
    SATB FLAMMER A 5627 $.30   (R695)

REISS, GEORG
  Lux Illuxit Letabunda
    see Sekvenser (Lovsange)

  Postquam Calix Babilonis
    see Sekvenser (Lovsange)

  Sekvenser (Lovsange)
    [Lat/Norw] SATB NORSK s.p.
      contains: Lux Illuxit Letabunda; Postquam
      Calix Babilonis   (R696)

REISSIGER
  Lord Of Spirits *anthem
    (Christiansen, F.M.) SATB,S solo (med) oct
      AUGSBURG 0123 $.30   (R697)

  Thy Guiding Hand *Morav
    (Dickinson) SATB oct GRAY GMCM 13 $.30
                                               (R698)

REISSIGER, F.A.
  En Sangers Bonn
    mix cor MUSIKK 122 s.p.   (R699)

REITER, A.
  Kommet, Ihr Hirten
    [Ger] mix cor,acap oct DOBLINGER s.p.
                                               (R700)

REIZENSTEIN, FRANZ (1911-   )
  Genesis
    SATB,SBar soli,orch LENGNICK s.p., ipa
                                               (R701)

REJOICE *CCU
  SAB FLAMMER GD5007 $1.35   (R702)

REJOICE! see Berger, Jean

REJOICE see Darwall

REJOICE see Draesel, Lederhouse

REJOICE! see Kirk

REJOICE, ALL YE BELIEVERS see Hokanson, M.

REJOICE, ALL YE BELIEVERS see Karvonen, Paul

REJOICE AND BE GLAD
  (Track, Gerhard) TTBB oct AGAPE MM 9006 $.30
                                               (R703)

REJOICE AND BE GLAD see Track

REJOICE AND BE MERRY *Xmas,carol/round
  see Six Christmas Carols, Set III
  SATB oct OXFORD 08.019 $.30, ipr   (R704)
  (easy) oct OXFORD 08.019 $.30, ipr   (R705)
  (easy) oct OXFORD 40.918 $.35   (R706)
  (Hinton) SSSS,opt acap oct OXFORD 40.918 $.35
                                               (R707)

REJOICE AND BE MERRY see Cashmore, Donald

REJOICE AND BE MERRY see Davie, Cedric Thorpe

REJOICE AND BE MERRY see Lovelace, Austin C.

REJOICE AND BE MERRY see Morgan

REJOICE AND BE MERRY see Morgan, Haydn

REJOICE AND BE MERRY see Pasquet, Jean

REJOICE AND BE MERRY see Pelz, Walter L.

REJOICE AND GIVE THANKS see Williams

REJOICE AND SING *CCU,anthem
  SATB/SA LORENZ $1.75   (R708)

REJOICE AND SING see Bach

REJOICE AND SING see Bach, Johann Sebastian,
    Freut Euch Und Jubilirt

REJOICE AND SING see Darst, W. Glenn

REJOICE AND SING see Ehret, Walter

REJOICE, BELOVED CHRISTIANS see Buxtehude,
    Dietrich

REJOICE BELOVED CHRISTIANS see Klein

REJOICE, EARTH AND HEAVEN see Buxtehude,
    Dietrich

REJOICE EMMANUEL SHALL COME see White

REJOICE EXULTANTLY see Calvisius, Sethus, Freut
    Euch Und Jubiliert

REJOICE, FOR CHRIST IS BORN see Foster

REJOICE, FOR CHRIST IS BORN! see Martin

REJOICE GREATLY see Pezel, Johann Christoph

REJOICE GREATLY see Woodward

REJOICE GREATLY see Woodward, H.H.

REJOICE GREATLY, O DAUGHTER OF ZION see Willan,
    Healey

REJOICE IN GOD, OH YE RIGHTEOUS see Bach,
    Johann Sebastian

REJOICE IN HIS WORD
  (Coggin) SAB oct PRO ART 2723 $.30 see from
    Paderborn Gesangbuch   (R709)

REJOICE IN HOPE see Peloquin, C. Alexander

REJOICE IN LIFE see Dexter, Harry

REJOICE IN THE LAMB see Britten, Benjamin

REJOICE IN THE LORD see Leupold, Ulrich
    Siegfried

REJOICE IN THE LORD see Bowen, Caylor

REJOICE IN THE LORD see Elvey, George Job

REJOICE IN THE LORD see Glarum, L. Stanley

REJOICE IN THE LORD see Guzman

REJOICE IN THE LORD see Harper, M.

REJOICE IN THE LORD see Hollins, Alfred

REJOICE IN THE LORD see Humfrey, Pelham

REJOICE IN THE LORD see Huston, Scott

REJOICE IN THE LORD see Kirk

REJOICE IN THE LORD see Lenel, Ludwig

REJOICE IN THE LORD see Lockwood, Normand

REJOICE IN THE LORD see Nares, James

REJOICE IN THE LORD see Newbury

REJOICE IN THE LORD see Redford, John

REJOICE IN THE LORD see Rickard

REJOICE IN THE LORD see Rickard, Jeffrey

REJOICE IN THE LORD see Ultan, L.

REJOICE IN THE LORD see Wheeler, Alfred

REJOICE IN THE LORD ALWAY see Anonymous

REJOICE IN THE LORD ALWAY see Caustun, Thomas

REJOICE IN THE LORD ALWAY see Lang, C.S.

REJOICE IN THE LORD ALWAY see Ley, Henry George

REJOICE IN THE LORD ALWAY see Purcell, Henry

REJOICE IN THE LORD ALWAY see Rathbone, George

REJOICE IN THE LORD ALWAY see Redford, John

REJOICE IN THE LORD ALWAY see Willan, Healey

REJOICE IN THE LORD ALWAYS see Beck

REJOICE IN THE LORD ALWAYS see Benson, Warren

REJOICE IN THE LORD ALWAYS see Kirk

REJOICE IN THE LORD ALWAYS see Moe, Daniel

REJOICE IN THE LORD ALWAYS see Purcell, Henry

REJOICE IN THE LORD, O YE RIGHTEOUS see Titcomb

REJOICE IN THE LORD, O YOU RIGHTEOUS see Couper

REJOICE, IT IS CHRISTMAS see Reske

REJOICE, MAN! see Mc Cain, Larry

REJOICE, O HEAVEN AND EARTH *Xmas,carol,Dut
  (Blaine, G.Gordon) SATB oct WALTON 2069 $.25
                                               (R710)

REJOICE, O JERUSALEM, BEHOLD THY KING COMETH
    see Willan, Healey

REJOICE, O LAND see Willan, Healey

REJOICE, O MY SPIRIT see Bach, Johann Sebastian

REJOICE, O QUEEN OF HEAVEN see Andrews, C.T.,
    Regina Coeli

REJOICE, O ZION, SHOUT AND SING! see Trued,
    Clarence

REJOICE, OH JUDAH! HALLELUJAH, AMEN! see
    Handel, George Frideric

REJOICE, OUR LORD IS BORN see Okolo, A.

REJOICE, PEOPLE OF GOD see Roff, Joseph

REJOICE, QUEEN OF HEAVEN see Elaine, Sister M.
    (Gentemann)

REJOICE, REJOICE! A BABE IS BORN see Maslen,
    Benjamin J.

REJOICE, REJOICE, BELIEVERS see Gumpeltzhaimer,
    Adam

REJOICE, REJOICE, BELIEVERS see Martin

REJOICE! REJOICE! CHRISTMAS see Byrd, William

REJOICE, REJOICE, FOR GOD IS KING see Hutson

REJOICE, REJOICE, THIS GLAD EASTER DAY see
    Leaf, Robert

REJOICE, REJOICE, YE CHRISTIANS
  (Ehret) SSA oct VOLKWEIN VB249 $.25   (R711)

REJOICE, REJOICE, YE CHRISTIANS see Ehret,
    Walter

REJOICE, REJOICE, YE CHRISTIANS see Schroeter

REJOICE, REJOICE, YE CHRISTIANS see Schroeter,
    Leonhardt

REJOICE, REJOICE YE CHRISTIANS see Schroter

REJOICE, REJOICE, YE CHRISTIANS see Schroter,
    L.

REJOICE, REJOICE, YE NATIONS see Praetorius,
    Michael

REJOICE, THE LORD IS KING! see Darwall

REJOICE, THE LORD IS KING see Darwell

REJOICE THE LORD IS KING see Ehret, Walter

REJOICE! THE LORD IS KING see Gilbert, Norman

REJOICE, THE LORD IS KING see Goemanne, Noel

REJOICE, THE LORD IS KING see Jordan

REJOICE THE LORD IS KING! see Kelly, Bryan

REJOICE, THE LORD IS KING see Killgrove

REJOICE, THE LORD IS KING see Saint-Saens, Camille

REJOICE, THE LORD IS KING see Spence, Horace

REJOICE THE LORD IS KING see Thiman, Eric Harding

REJOICE, THE LORD IS KING see Wilson, Roger [C.]

REJOICE, THE LORD IS KING see Wolff, S. Drummond

REJOICE, THEN, CHRIST IS BORN *Xmas
(Dunsmore) SATB SCHMITT 894 $.25   (R712)

REJOICE THIS HAPPY MORN see Darst, W. Glenn

REJOICE THIS NIGHT see Ebeling

REJOICE TO WELCOME OUR SAVIOUR ON EARTH *Xmas
(Follett) SATB oct PRO ART 2011 $.22   (R713)

REJOICE TODAY see Darst, W. Glenn

REJOICE TODAY WITH ONE ACCORD see Lawson, Gordon

REJOICE UNTO THE LORD see Goemanne, Noel, Entrata

REJOICE WITH HEART AND VOICE see Byrd, William

REJOICE WITH ME, FOR I HAVE FOUND MY SHEEP see Krapf, Gerhard

REJOICE, YE CHRISTIAN BRETHERN see Praetorius, Michael

REJOICE, YE CHRISTIAN BRETHREN see Praetorius, Michael

REJOICE, YE CHRISTIAN MEN, REJOICE see Praetorius, Michael

REJOICE YE CHRISTIANS see Praetorius, Michael

REJOICE YE CHRISTIANS LOUDLY see Bach, Johann Sebastian

REJOICE, YE HEARTS, BE GLAD AND SING see Butler

REJOICE, YE HEAVENS see Hassler, Hans Leo

REJOICE, YE PEOPLE see Moe, Daniel

REJOICE YE PURE IN HEART
see Three General Hymns

REJOICE YE PURE IN HEART see Churchill

REJOICE, YE PURE IN HEART see Darst, W. Glenn

REJOICE, YE PURE IN HEART see Messiter, Arthur Henry

REJOICE, YE PURE IN HEART see Plumptre

REJOICE, YE PURE IN HEART see Willan, Healey

REJOICE YE PURE IN HEART see Wilson

REJOICE, YE SHINING WORLD'S ON HIGH *Xmas
(Reynolds) SATB oct FISCHER,C CM-7711 $.25
(R714)

REJOICE, YE WHO LOVE THE LORD see Liszt, Franz,
Der Herr Bewahret Die Seelen Seiner
Heiligen

RELAXA FACINORA see Eccher

RELEVANT see Skillings, Otis

RELIGION IS A FORTUNE
(Stone) SAB oct PRO ART 1784 $.20   (R715)

RELIGIOSE FOLKETONER, VOL. I see Baden, Conrad

RELIGIOSE FOLKTONER, VOL. II see Baden, Conrad

RELIGIOSE KORSANGER *see Jeg Lofter Opp Til
Gud Min Sang; Conradi, J.G.; Solnedgang;
Gaudimel, Claude, Hold Oppe, Gud; N-N, J.,
Ene I Gud; Palmer, C., Troster Mitt Folk
(R716)

RELIGIOSE KORSANGER see Conradi, J.G.

RELIGIOSE KORSANGER see Gaudimel, Claude

RELIGIOSE KORSANGER see N-N, J.

RELIGIOSE KORSANGER see Palmer, C.

RELIGIOSE KORSNAGER see Stenhammar, [Per Ulrik]

RELIGIOUS AND LITURGICAL CHORAL WORKS see
Kraft, Walter

RELIGIOUS FOLK SONGS see Brahms, Johannes

RELIGIOUS MUSIC see Faure, Gabriel-Urbain

RELIGISE KORSANGER *see Vaer Meg Naer   (R717)

REMEMBER ALL THE PEOPLE see Baumgartner, H.
Leroy

REMEMBER ALSO THY CREATOR see Trued, Clarence

REMEMBER FOR GOOD, O FATHER see Jackson,
Francis

REMEMBER GOD'S GOODNESSE *Xmas
(Deale) SATB,acap (med easy) OXFORD 84.015
$.35 see from Four Old Carols   (R718)
(Deale) SATB,acap (med easy) OXFORD 84.015
$.35 see from Four Old Carols   (R719)

REMEMBER NOT, LORD see Arcadelt, Jacob, Ave
Maria

REMEMBER NOT, LORD, OUR OFFENCES see Purcell,
Henry

REMEMBER NOT, LORD, OUR OFFENSES see Purcell,
Henry

REMEMBER NOW THY CREATOR
SATB BIG3 $.25   (R720)

REMEMBER NOW THY CREATOR see Adams, Stephen

REMEMBER NOW THY CREATOR see Binkerd, [Gordon]

REMEMBER NOW THY CREATOR see Lockwood, Normand

REMEMBER NOW THY CREATOR see Neff, James

REMEMBER NOW THY CREATOR see Steggall, Charles

REMEMBER, O LORD see Schalk, Carl

REMEMBER, O LORD see Wolff

REMEMBER O MOST GRACIOUS VIRGIN see Englert,
Eugene, Memorare

REMEMBER, O THOU MAN *carol
SATB (easy) OXFORD 08.041 $.15   (R721)

REMEMBER, O THOU MAN see Ravenscroft, Thomas

REMEMBER, O THOU MAN see Sheppard

REMEMBER, O THOU MAN see Sheppard, [Joseph]
Stanley

REMEMBER OUR SAVIOR see Eberlin

REMEMBER OUR SAVIOUR see Eberlin

REMEMBER THY CREATOR see Fuller, [Esther Mary]

REMEMBER THY CREATOR see Musgrave, Thea,
Memento Creatoris

REMEMBRANCE see Bassett, Leslie

REMINISCERE see Gesualdo, Don Carlo

REMONDI, R.
We Adore You, O Lord Jesus Christ *Lent,
anthem
(Lee, J.) SATB oct GIA G1553 $.25   (R722)

RENAISSANCE CHORAL MUSIC *CCU,Renais
(Malin) SATB MARKS $3.00 original texts and
English   (R723)

RENAISSANCE MOTETS FOR LENT AND PASSIONTIDE see
Viadana, Lodovico Grossi da

RENAISSANCE MOTETS IN ENGLISH *CCU,mot,Renais
(Linduskey) boy cor SOUTHERN $2.00   (R724)

RENAISSANCE TO BAROQUE, VOL. 1 *CCU,Renais/
Baroq
(Engel) mix cor SOUTHERN $2.50   (R725)

RENAISSANCE TO BAROQUE, VOL. 2 *CCU,Renais/
Baroq
(Engel) mix cor SOUTHERN $2.50   (R726)

RENAISSANCE TO BAROQUE, VOL. 3 *CCU,Renais/
Baroq
(Engel) mix cor SOUTHERN $2.50   (R727)

RENAISSANCE TO BAROQUE, VOL. 4 *CCU,Renais/
Baroq
(Engel) mix cor SOUTHERN $2.50   (R728)

RENAISSANCE TO BAROQUE, VOL. 5 *CCU,Renais/
Baroq
(Engel) mix cor SOUTHERN $2.50   (R729)

RENAUD, E.
Au Christ-Roi Dans La Sainte Eucharistie
(Simonetti, M) unis,org/pno LEMOINE voc sc
s.p., cor pts s.p.   (R730)

RENDALL, HONOR
First London Carol, The *carol
unis CRAMER 50 s.p.   (R731)

Second London Carol, The *carol
unis CRAMER 51 s.p.   (R732)

RENER
Missa Carminum *Mass
(Kindermann) 4pt mix cor MOSELER s.p.
(R733)

RENEW A RIGHT SPIRIT WITHIN ME see Davis,
Katherine K.

RENNES, CATH. V.
Avondrust
see Lente-Leven

Goeden Nacht
see Lente-Leven

Het Angelus
see Lente-Leven

Het Angelus Klept In De Verte
mix cor ALSBACH&D sc s.p., cor pts s.p.
(R734)

Lente
see Lente-Leven

Lente-Leven *Op.5
2pt wom cor,pno sc ALSBACH&D s.p. score and
choral parts separately published
contains: Avondrust; Goeden Nacht; Het
Angelus; Lente; 'T Viooltje   (R735)

T Viooltje
see Lente-Leven

RENOLDS
God Be With You *Gen
SSA oct SPRATT 516 $.25   (R736)
SATB oct SPRATT 515 $.25   (R737)

RENZI, ANGELO
Ave Maria *BVM
[Lat] SATB,T solo,org ZANIBON 1730 s.p.
(R738)

Missa Tertia Divo Antonio Dicata *Mass
[Lat] ABar,org sc ZANIBON 1556 s.p., voc pt
ZANIBON s.p.   (R739)

Pange Lingua
see Tre Inni Eucaristici

Responsoria Trium Nocturnorum *Xmas
ABar,org sc ZANIBON 3200 s.p., cor pts
ZANIBON 3201 s.p.   (R740)

Tantum Ergo
see Tre Inni Eucaristici
see Tre Inni Eucaristici

Te Deum *Greg/Te Deum
[Lat] 3 eq voices&unis,opt org voc pt
ZANIBON 3197A-B-C s.p., sc ZANIBON 3197
s.p.   (R741)

Tre Inni Eucaristici *Commun,hymn
[Lat] ZANIBON 3198 s.p.
contains: Pange Lingua (3 eq voices);
Tantum Ergo (3pt mix cor,acap); Tantum
Ergo (3pt mix cor)   (R742)

Tu Es Petrus *mot
[It] ABar ZANIBON 3199 s.p.   (R743)

RENZI, ARMANDO
Cantico Di Mose
5pt mix cor ZANIBON 4172 s.p.   (R744)

REPENTIR see Gounod, Charles Francois

REPERTOIRE DES CHORALES D'HOMMES *CC14L
(Brun, L'abbe F.) [Lat] 3-4pt men cor oct
DURAND s.p. contains works by: Lassus;
Liszt; Palestrina; D'Indy; Saint-Saens
(R745)

REPLEATUR OS MEUS see Palestrina, Giovanni

REPLETI SUNT see Gallus, Jacobus

REPLETI SUNT OMNES see Gallus, Jacobus

REQUIEM see Thompson, Randall

REQUIEM *Gen,Greg
(Christiansen, P.) SATB SCHMITT 1425 $.20
(R746)

REQUIEM see Beck, Conrad

REQUIEM see Berlioz, Hector

REQUIEM see Blacher, Boris

REQUIEM see Bossi, Marco Enrico

REQUIEM see Brahms, Johannes, Ein Deutsches
Requiem

REQUIEM see Bresgen, Cesar

REQUIEM see Bruckner, Anton

REQUIEM see Buchtger, Fritz

REQUIEM see Cherubini, Luigi, Missa Pro
Defunctis

REQUIEM see de la Rue, Pierre

REQUIEM see Delius, Frederick

REQUIEM see Durufle, Maurice

REQUIEM see Dvorak, Antonin

REQUIEM see Dvorak, Antonin, Requiem

REQUIEM see Erpf, Hermann

REQUIEM see Faure, Gabriel-Urbain

REQUIEM see Giannini, V.

REQUIEM see Gounod, Charles Francois

REQUIEM see Inghelbrecht, Desire Emile

REQUIEM see Josephson, Jacob Axel

REQUIEM see Kaun, [Hugo]

REQUIEM see Koch, Karl

REQUIEM see La Rue, Pierre de

REQUIEM see Ligeti, Gyorgy

REQUIEM see Lindberg, Oskar [Fredrik]

REQUIEM see Liszt, Franz

REQUIEM see Marckhl, Erich

REQUIEM see Mortari, Virgilio

REQUIEM see Mozart, Wolfgang Amadeus

REQUIEM see Mozart, Wolfgang Amadeus, Missa Pro
Defunctis

REQUIEM see Palsson, Pall P.

REQUIEM see Pergolesi, Giovanni Battista

REQUIEM see Pinkham, Daniel

REQUIEM see Poser, Hans

REQUIEM see Raphael, Gunther

REQUIEM see Rathaus, Karol

REQUIEM see Reger, Max

REQUIEM see Roeske, F.J.

REQUIEM see Ropartz, Joseph Guy

REQUIEM see Schumann, Robert (Alexander), Requiem Des-Dur

REQUIEM see Verdi, Giuseppe

REQUIEM see Verdi, Giuseppe, Manzoni Requiem

REQUIEM see Vogt, Hans

REQUIEM see Warren, Elinor Remick

REQUIEM see Wideen, Ivar

REQUIEM see Zwierzchowski, Mateusz

REQUIEM see Barbe, Helmut

REQUIEM A CAPPELLA see Migot, Georges

REQUIEM AETERNAM see Cherubini, Luigi

REQUIEM AETERNAM see Cornelius, Peter

REQUIEM AETERNAM see Roumefort, R. de

REQUIEM AETERNAM see Volpi, Edoardo

REQUIEM AETERNUM see Verdi, Giuseppe

REQUIEM C-MOLL see Cherubini, Luigi

REQUIEM C-MOLL see Cherubini, Luigi, Missa Pro Defunctis

REQUIEM C-MOLL see Haydn, (Franz) Joseph

REQUIEM C-MOLL see Haydn, (Johann) Michael

REQUIEM CANTICLES see Stravinsky, Igor

REQUIEM CHORALE see David, Johann Nepomuk

REQUIEM D-MOLL see Bruckner, Anton

REQUIEM D-MOLL see Cherubini, Luigi, Requiem

REQUIEM D-MOLL see Mozart, Wolfgang Amadeus, Missa Pro Defunctis

REQUIEM DES-DUR see Schumann, Robert (Alexander)

REQUIEM DI MADRID see Fellegara, Vittorio

REQUIEM EBRAICO see Zeisl, Eric

REQUIEM FOR A FRIEND see Bobrowitz, David

REQUIEM FOR A NOBODY see Smith, Tedd

REQUIEM FOR THE LIVING see Swann, Donald

REQUIEM FUER MIGNON see Schumann, Robert (Alexander)

REQUIEM FUR MIGNON see Schumann, Robert (Alexander)

REQUIEM IN C MINOR see Cherubini, Luigi

REQUIEM IN D MINOR see Cherubini, Luigi, Requiem

REQUIEM IN D MINOR see Mozart, Wolfgang Amadeus, Missa Pro Defunctis

REQUIEM IN F MAJOR see Stadler, Maximillian (Abbe)

REQUIEM IN G-MOLL see Werner, Gregor Joseph

REQUIEM: IN MEMORIAM MATRIS ET FRATRIS see Strategier, Herman

REQUIEM IN MEMORIAM UXORIS see Landre, Willem

REQUIEM MASS see Harrison, Julius Allen Greenway

REQUIEM MASS see Hunt, J.E.

REQUIEM MASS see Mozart, Wolfgang Amadeus, Missa Pro Defunctis

REQUIEM MASS see Mozart, Wolfgang Amadeus, Requiem

REQUIEM MASS see Pizzetti, [Ildebrando]

REQUIEM MASS see Victoria, Tomas Luis de, Missa Pro Defunctus

REQUIEM MASS IN C MINOR see Cherubini, Luigi, Missa Pro Defunctis

REQUIEM MESSA E ASSOLUZIONE see Eccher

REQUIEM MOTER see de la Rue, Pierre

REQUIEM PER LA MORTE DI UN POVERO see Davico, Vincenzo

REQUIEM-SATZ see Reger, Max

REQUIEM SOLEMNE see Haydn, (Johann) Michael, Requiem C-Moll

REQUIEM, VEL VIVORUM CONSOLATIO see Reda, Siegfried

REQUIEM-YIZKOR see Binder, Abraham Wolfe

REQUIEM see Cherubini, Luigi, Missa Pro Defunctis

REQUIEM see Cherubini, Luigi

REQUIEM see Cherubini, Luigi, Requiem

RERUM, CREATOR see Mundy, William

RERUM CREATOR OMNIUM see Mundy, William

RES' MY SHOES see Wilson, Harry [Robert]

RESCIA
Behold, Bless Ye The Lord
SA,org/pno BOSTON 13297 $.35 (R747)

RESCUE ME FROM MY ENEMIES, O LORD see Felciano, Richard

RESIGNATION see Litten, Jack

RESIGNATION see Wolf, Hugo

RESIGNATION see Wolf, Hugo, Resignation

RESIGNATION: KOMM, TROST DER WELT, DU STILLE NACHT see Wolf, Hugo

RESINARIUS, BALTHASAR (ca. 1480-1546)
Aus Tiefer Not *ECY
[Ger] SATB,acap (med easy) MULLER K30 s.p.
(R748)

Christum Wir Sollen Loben Schon *Xmas
[Ger] SATB,acap (med) MULLER K 10 s.p.
contains also: Gelobet Seist Du, Jesu
Christ (R749)

Come, Holy Ghost, Creator Blest *Cnfrm/Gen/
Pent
SATB,kbd (med easy) oct CONCORDIA 98-2048
$.25 (R750)

Das Vater Unser
[Ger] SATB,acap (med) MULLER K 2 s.p. (R751)

Erhalt Uns Herr Bei Deinem Wort
see Goudimel, Claude, Es Geht Daher Des
Tages Schein

Gelobet Seist Du, Jesu Christ
see Resinarius, Balthasar, Christum Wir
Sollen Loben Schon

Johannes-Passion *Psntd
(Blume; Schulze) [Ger/Lat] 4pt mix cor
MOSELER s.p. (R752)

Komm, Gott Schopfer, Heiliger Geist *Pent/
Whitsun
SATB,acap voc pt DOBLINGER s.p. see also
PFINGSTEN UND EUCHARISTIE (R753)

Komm, Heiliger Geist, Herre Gott *Pent
[Ger] SATB,acap (med easy) MULLER K 6 s.p.
(R754)

Mitten Wir Im Leben Sind *ECY
[Ger] SATB,acap (med) MULLER K 18 s.p.
(R755)

Responsoriorum Numero Octoginta, Band I
(Albrecht, H.) cor CONCORDIA 97-2013 $8.50
see also MUSIC OF EARLY LUTHERANISM, THE
(R756)

Responsoriorum Numero Octoginta, Band II
(Albrecht, H.) cor CONCORDIA 97-2016 $8.50
see also MUSIC OF EARLY LUTHERANISM, THE
(R757)

St. John's Passion
mix cor,acap voc sc KALMUS 6222 $1.25
(R758)

Verleih Uns Frieden Gnadiglich
SATB,acap DOBLINGER s.p. see also BITTE UND
VERTRAUEN (R759)

RESKE
Dedication
SATB oct LORENZ C286 $.30 (R760)

Easter Carol *Easter/Lent,carol
SATB,acap oct FISCHER,C CM-6975 $.25 (R761)

Lamb Of Calvary
SATB oct SACRED E52 $.35 (R762)

Let Our Gladness Have No End *Xmas
SSA oct FISCHER,C CM-7632 $.25 (R763)
SATB,acap oct FISCHER,C CM-6667 $.25 (R764)

Lord, Teach Me How To Pray
SATB oct FISCHER,C CM-7210 $.25 (R765)

Prayer, A
SA/SAB oct LORENZ 7831 $.25 (R766)

Rejoice, It Is Christmas *Xmas
SATB,acap oct FISCHER,C CM-7352 $.25 (R767)

RESONET IN LAUDIBUS *Xmas,hymn
"Who Is He In Yonder Stall" cor oct ST.MARTIN
SMP648 s.p. (R768)
(Wood) SAB/unis SCHMITT SD6004 $.30 (R769)

RESONET IN LAUDIBUS see Anonymous

RESONET IN LAUDIBUS see Bottazzo, Luigi

RESONET IN LAUDIBUS see Eccard, Johannes

RESONET IN LAUDIBUS see Gallus, Jacobus

RESONET IN LAUDIBUS see Pekiel, Bertlomiej

RESONET IN LAUDIBUS see Praetorius, Michael

RESONET IN LAUDIBUS see Rodella, Sante

RESONET IN LAUDIBUS see Strutius, Thomas,
Singet Frisch Und Wohlgemut

RESPICE, DOMINE see Quack, Erhard

RESPICE STELLAM *CC39U,BVM
(Garbelotto) [Lat] 1-3pt,org ZANIBON 3773
s.p. (R770)

RESPICE STELLAM *CCU,BVM
[Lat] 1-3pt,org ZANIBON 3773 s.p. (R771)

RESPIGHI, OTTORINO (1879-1936)
Laud To The Nativity *Xmas
mix cor,soli,inst BELWIN $1.75 (R772)

RESPONSARIES FOR THE OFFICES OF TENEBRAE see
Willan, Healey

RESPONSE AFTER BENEDICTION see Grant

RESPONSE AFTER PRAYER see Grant

RESPONSE NO. 3 see Palestrina, Giovanni

RESPONSES
see Sursum Corda

RESPONSES see Barnard, John

RESPONSES AND AMENS *CCU,cor-resp
(Whear; Warren) LUDWIG SATB $.10; SAB $.10
(R773)

RESPONSES AND AMENS see Wichmann

RESPONSES FOR MIXED CHOIR see Troxell

RESPONSES FOR THE CHURCH SERVICE see Newbury,
Kent A.

RESPONSES FOR TREBLE VOICES see Darke, Harold
[Edwin]

RESPONSES FOR TREBLE VOICES see Rose, Bernard

RESPONSES FOR WORSHIP, SET 1 see Sjolund, Paul

RESPONSES FOR WORSHIP, SET 2 see Sjolund, Paul

RESPONSES FOR WORSHIP, SET 3 see Sjolund, Paul

RESPONSES FROM THE WORKS OF OLD MASTERS
[Lat/Eng] SSA&SSAA,acap SCHIRM.EC 869 $.30
contains: Byrd, William, Non Nobis Domine,
"Not Unto Us, O Lord"; Gallus, Jacobus,
Christus Factus Est, "Jesus Christ Became
For Our Sins, Obedient"; Menegali, Jesu,
Salvator Mundi, "Jesu, Our Holy Savior";
Palestrina, Giovanni, Gloria Patri,
"Praise To The Father" (R774)

RESPONSES see Mueller, Carl F.

RESPONSES see Rhodes

RESPONSORIA see Gesualdo, Don Carlo

RESPONSORIA IN MATUTINIS TRIDUI SACRI see
Magri, Pietro

RESPONSORIA IN MATUTINIS TRIDUI SACRI see
Magri, Pietro

RESPONSORIA TRIUM NOCTURNORUM see Renzi, Angelo

RESPONSORIEN FUR GRUNDONNERSTAG-HEFT I see
Ingegneri, Marco Antonio

RESPONSORIEN FUR GRUNDONNERSTAG-HEFT II see
Ingegneri, Marco Antonio

RESPONSORIEN FUR GRUNDONNERSTAG-HEFT III see
Ingegneri, Marco Antonio

RESPONSORIES FOR TENEBRAE see Victoria, Tomas
Luis de

RESPONSORIES FOR THE CHURCH YEAR, THE see
Willan, Healey

RESPONSORIO see Grassi, Ciro

RESPONSORIORUM NUMERO OCTOGINTA, BAND I see
Resinarius, Balthasar

RESPONSORIORUM NUMERO OCTOGINTA, BAND II see
Resinarius, Balthasar

RESPONSORIUM (ALLELUJA) see Schutz, Heinrich

RESPONSORIUM IN HON. S. DOMINICI see Fino,
Giocondo

RESPONSORY FOR PASSIONTIDE, THE see Willan,
Healey

REST AND JOY see Ancis, Solomon, M'nuchon
V'simchoh

REST ETERNAL GRANT UNTO THEM see Lvov, Alexey
Feodorovitch

REST HERE IN PEACE see Bach, Johann Sebastian

REST IN PEACE see Stainer, John

REST IN THE LORD see Ashford, E.L.

REST IN THE LORD see Stickles, William

REST OF MY LIFE!, THE see Mc Call, Harlo

REST OF THE WEARY see Handel, George Frideric

REST THOU MY CHILD *Czech
(Ehret) SA MARKS 4411 $.25 (R775)
(Ehret) SSA MARKS 4358 $.25 (R776)

REST WELL see Bach, Johann Sebastian

RESTING see Montgomery

RESTLESS ONES, THE see Carmichael, Ralph

RESTORE OUR FORTUNES, O GOD see Clark, Keith

RESTORE UNTO ME see Lully (Lulli), Jean-
Baptiste

RESURRECTION see Billings, William

RESURRECTION see Christiansen, Olaf Christian

RESURRECTION see Jillett, David

RESURRECTION see Koshetz

RESURRECTION see Lorenz

RESURRECTION see Manney, Charles Fonteyn

RESURRECTION see Sateren, Leland Bernhard

RESURRECTION see Sourire, Souer

RESURRECTION, THE see Naylor, Bernard

RESURRECTION ACCORDING TO NICODEMUS, THE see
Gillette

RESURRECTION ACCORDING TO ST. MATTHEW , THE see
Keel, Richard

RESURRECTION AND ASCENSION OF JESUS see Bach,
Johann Sebastian

RESURRECTION CANTICLE, A see Purvis, Richard

RESURRECTION CAROL *Easter
(Roberts, J.) SATB,acap oct PRESSER G-124
$.30   (R777)

RESURRECTION HISTORY see Schutz, Heinrich

RESURRECTION MORN see Filkins

RESURRECTION MORN see Keating, L.

RESURRECTION MORN see Van Woert

RESURRECTION MORN, THE see Rodney, Paul

RESURRECTION ORATORIO see Schutz, Heinrich,
Historia Der Geburt Jesu Christi

RESURRECTION PSALM see Peloquin, C. Alexander

RESURRECTION SONG, THE see Dressler, John

RESURRECTION SONG, THE see Cain, Noble

RESURRECTION, THE see Curran, Pearl
Gildersleeve

RESURRECTION, THE see Dasher, James

RESURRECTION, THE see Rubbra, Edmund, Sinfonia
Sacra

RESURRECTION, THE see Shelley, [Harry Rowe]

RESURRECTION, THE see Young, Gordon

RESURRECTION TIDINGS see Ferguson

RESURREXI see Ferro, Stefano

RESURREXI see Picchi, Luigi

RESURREXI see Quack, Erhard

RESURREXI IN EPIPHANIETATE PASCHALI see Volpi,
Edoardo

RESURREXIT see Berlioz, Hector

RET SOM HJORTEN see Palestrina, Giovanni, Sicut
Cervus Desiderat

RETSAY ADONA'I see Steinberg, Ben

RETURN see Sateren, Leland Bernhard

RETURN, O MAN see Smith, Don

RETURN, O MY SOUL see Vene, Ruggero, Convertere
Anima Mea

RETURN, OH GOD! see Handel, George Frideric

RETURN UNTO THY REST see Pasquet, Jean

REUCHSEL, L.
Ecce Panis
[Lat] 4pt,acap LEMOINE s.p.   (R778)

REULAND, JACQUES (1918-   )
Hymni Mediaevales *hymn
[Dut] mix cor,AT soli,fl,ob,bsn,trp,horn
DONEMUS min sc s.p., cor pts s.p.   (R779)

REVELATION, A see James, [Marion]

REVELATION MOTET see Franck, Cesar

REVELATION MOTET see Franck, Melchior

REVELATION OF SAINT JOHN THE DIVINE see
Argento, Dominick

REVEYRON, JOSEPH
La Cantate Des Commencements *Heb
cor,soli,narrator,org ISRAELI 338 s.p.
                                        (R780)
Psalm 18 *see Psaume Du Serviteur

Psaume Du Serviteur (Psalm 18) Heb
SATB,acap ISRAELI 331 s.p.   (R781)

REVICKI
Alleluia
see Songs Of Praise

Dominus Illuminatio Mea
see Songs Of Praise

Songs Of Praise
SA/TB,acap,opt perc oct BROWN 5597 $.30
contains: Alleluia; Dominus Illuminatio
Mea   (R782)

REVIL, H.
A La Saint-Medard
(Bereau, J.S.) [Fr] 3pt mix cor HEUGEL PJ59
s.p.   (R783)

REVIVE US AGAIN see Husband, [Edward]

REX AUTEM DAVID see Ribera

REX CHRISTE, FACTOR OMNIUM see Schein, Johann
Hermann

REX GLORIAE see Ockeghem, Johannes

REX GLORIOSE MARTYRIUM see Olsson, Otto
Emmanuel

REX PACIFICUS see Jaeggi, Oswald

REX PACIFICUS see Romanovsky, Erich

REYNOLDS, GORDON
Alleluia! God Is Gone Up With A Merry Noise
*Asc
4pt,acap oct NOVELLO 33.0127.03 s.p. (R784)

REYNOLDS, ROGER
Come, Thou Fount Of Ev'ry Blessing
SATB FLAMMER A 5413 $.30   (R785)

God Be Merciful
SATB oct MCA   (R786)

REZNICEK, EMIL NIKOLAUS VON (1860-1945)
In Memoriam
[Ger] voc sc UNIVER. 5640, cor pts UNIVER.
5641A-D $1.65   (R787)

RHAU, JOHANNES (1520-1600)
Der Mai Tritt Ein Mit Freuden
see Rhau, Johannes, Erfreu Sich Alles, Was
Da Lebt

Erfreu Sich Alles, Was Da Lebt
TB LAUDINELLA LR 68 s.p. contains also: Der
Mai Tritt Ein Mit Freuden; Herzlich Tut
Mich Erfreuen   (R788)

Herzlich Tut Mich Erfreuen
see Rhau, Johannes, Erfreu Sich Alles, Was
Da Lebt

Wetterer Gesangbuch *CC18U,Gen
(Wenckelbach, Karl; Schwarz, Rosemarie)
[Ger] SATB,acap (med easy) BAREN. BA 3893
$1.50   (R789)

RHAW, GEORG (1488-1548)
Postremum Vespertini Officii Opus
(Albrecht, H.) cor (contains also:
Magnificat Octo Tonorum, 1544) CONCORDIA
97-2022 $27.50 see also MUSIC OF EARLY
LUTHERANISM, THE   (R790)

Symphoniae Jucundae, 1538
(Albrecht, H.) cor CONCORDIA 97-2018 $9.50
see also MUSIC OF EARLY LUTHERANISM, THE
                                      (R791)

Vesperarum Precum Officia, 1540
(Albrecht, H.) cor CONCORDIA 97-2020 $9.75
see also MUSIC OF EARLY LUTHERANISM, THE
                                      (R792)

RHEA
Baloo, Lammy *Xmas
SA/TB oct HERITAGE H5001 $.35   (R793)

De Angel Roll De Stone Away *Lent,spir
SATB oct BOURNE RSS2 $.25   (R794)

Do Don't Toucha My Garment *Lent,spir
SATB oct BOURNE RSS3 $.25   (R795)

Done Found My Lost Sheep *spir
SATB oct BOURNE RSS4 $.25   (R796)

Easy Anthems With Descants *CCU
SATB&desc FLAMMER GA5009 $1.25   (R797)

God Is Alive *Xmas
SATB ALFRED 6342 $.30   (R798)

Gonna Ride Up In The Chariot *spir
SAB oct BOURNE 3013 $.25   (R799)

Gwine Up *spir
SA oct BOURNE 2027 $.25   (R800)

Heav'n Bound Soldier *spir
SATB oct BOURNE RSS5 $.30   (R801)

Let My Soul Rise In Song
SSAATTBB oct SUMMY B 1503 $.30   (R802)

Morning Interlude
SSA oct HERITAGE H6001 $.35   (R803)

Patapan *Xmas
"Willie Bring Your Little Drum" SA oct
BOURNE 2021 $.25   (R804)

Wait 'Til I Get On My Robe *spir
TB oct BOURNE SB4 $.25   (R805)

Wait 'Til I Git On My Robe
SB/TB oct BOURNE SBY $.25   (R806)

Walk Together, Children *spir
SA oct BOURNE 2029 $.25   (R807)

Willie Bring Your Little Drum *see Patapan

RHEA, A.
Echo Noel *Xmas
SATB oct PLYMOUTH RR-102 $.25   (R808)

Everlasting Mercies Of Our Lord, The
SSAATTBB oct FOX R123 $.25   (R809)

God All Over
SATB oct PLYMOUTH RR-112 $.25   (R810)

God Of The Earth
SATB oct PLYMOUTH RR-111 $.25   (R811)

Hail, Our Redeemer
SATB FLAMMER A 5294 $.25   (R812)

He Came So Still *Xmas
SATB oct PLYMOUTH RR-110 $.25   (R813)

Hear My Cry, O God
SATB oct PLYMOUTH RR-115 $.25   (R814)

Hear Us, Our Father
SATB oct PLYMOUTH UIL-102 $.25   (R815)

I Hear Children Singing *Xmas
SATB&jr cor SCHMITT 846 $.25   (R816)

I Heard The Bells On Christmas Day
SAB oct FOX PS164 $.30   (R817)

Now Let Me Fly *spir
SATB oct BOURNE RSS6 $.25   (R818)

O Lord, Most Glorious
SATB FLAMMER A 5478 $.25   (R819)

Peace On Earth *anthem
SATB oct FOX R204 $.25   (R820)

Voices Of God
SATB oct PLYMOUTH RR-114 $.25   (R821)

RHEA, A. (cont'd.)
Where Is The Child Today *Xmas
SSA oct PLYMOUTH RR-104 $.25   (R822)

RHEA, RAYMOND (1910-   )
Did You In A Manger Lie?
cor HIGHLAND 4124 $.30   (R823)

From Out The Earth
SATB LUDWIG L-1125 $.35   (R824)

Hymn To The Night *hymn
SATB oct WALTON 2065 $.35   (R825)

I Am The Good Shepherd
SATB oct SHAPIRO SK 2007 $.25   (R826)

Let Music Live
SATB LUDWIG L-1101 $.30   (R827)

Little Lamb
SATB LEONARD-US 08037440 $.25   (R828)

O God, Thou Art My God
SATB oct SOUTHERN $.25   (R829)

O Lord Of Heaven And Earth
SATB oct ELKAN-V 362-1185 $.25   (R830)

O Splendor Of God's Glory Bright
SAB oct ELKAN-V 362-511 $.25   (R831)

Out In The Fields With God
SATB oct BOURNE 689 $.25   (R832)

Psalm 100
SATB LUDWIG L-1115 $.30   (R833)
TTBB LUDWIG L-5100 $.30   (R834)

Psalm 117
cor HIGHLAND 4127 $.25   (R835)

Quest For God
SATB LUDWIG L-1102 $.30   (R836)

Sing, Soul Of Mine *Easter
SATB oct BOURNE 684 $.25   (R837)

RHEENEN, H. V.
Lente
mix cor ALSBACH&D sc s.p., cor pts s.p.
                                      (R838)

RHEINBERGER, JOSEF (1839-1901)
Ad Te Levavi *Adv,mot
mix cor (med easy) oct LEUCKART 651 s.p.
see from Advent-Mottetten   (R839)

Advent-Mottetten *see Ad Te Levavi; Ave
Maria; Benedixisti; Ex Sion   (R840)

Ave Maria *Adv,mot
mix cor (med easy) oct LEUCKART 597 s.p.
see from Advent-Mottetten   (R841)

Benedixisti *Adv,mot
mix cor (med easy) oct LEUCKART 653 s.p.
see from Advent-Mottetten   (R842)

Ex Sion *Adv,mot
mix cor (med easy) oct LEUCKART 652 s.p.
see from Advent-Mottetten   (R843)

Laus Deo
"Praise To God" SATB oct PLYMOUTH RR-1001
$.75   (R844)

Mass In C *see Messe Grosse

Messe *Op.126, Mass
mix cor,org (A maj,med) cor pts LEUCKART
s.p.   (R845)

Messe *Op.151, Mass
mix cor (G maj,med) cor pts LEUCKART s.p.
                                      (R846)

Messe *Op.172, Mass
mix cor,org (A flat maj,med easy) cor pts
LEUCKART s.p.   (R847)

Messe Grosse *Op.169, Mass
mix cor,SATB soli,orch/org&strings (C maj,
med) cor pts LEUCKART s.p.   (R848)
"Mass In C" cor voc sc KALMUS 6414 $1.50
                                      (R849)

Messe *Op.159, Mass
mix cor,org (F min,med easy) cor pts
LEUCKART s.p.   (R850)

Praise To God *see Laus Deo

Stabat Mater *cant
(Biedermann) mix cor BELWIN $1.25   (R851)
(Campbell; Watson) SSA BELWIN $1.25   (R852)

Star Of Bethlehem *Op.164
cor voc sc KALMUS 6395 $1.50   (R853)

Star Of Bethlehem, The *Op.164, Xmas
[Ger/Eng] voc sc PETERS F110 $6.00, ipr
                                      (R854)

Way Is Long And Dreary
(Emerson, I.) SATB,acap oct PRESSER
332-00609 $.30   (R855)

RHENE-BATON (1879-1940)
Espoir En Dieu
[Fr] cor oct DURAND   (R856)

RHODA, H.
C'est Noel *Xmas
3pt wom cor BROEKMANS 114 s.p.   (R857)

RHODEN, D.C.
Hosanna *anti
SSAA,acap oct LAWSON 51610 $.35   (R858)

RHODES
God Be With You
see Responses

Hear Our Prayer, O Lord
see Responses

Kyrie *Kyrie
[Lat] SSA,acap PETERS 66171 $.30   (R859)

RHODES (cont'd.)

Legend Of The Bells *Xmas
SATB,S solo,opt chimes WARNER G1190 $.30
(R860)

Lord Is In His Holy Temple, The
see Responses

Responses
SATB WARNER WB-272 $.35
contains: God Be With You; Hear Our
Prayer, O Lord; Lord Is In His Holy
Temple, The   (R861)

They Shall See The Glory Of The Lord!
TTBB WARNER WB-166 $.35   (R862)

RHODES, HAROLD
Fight The Good Fight *Gen
SATB (very easy) oct OXFORD 42.701 $.30
(R863)

RHODES, PHILLIP
Praise Thee, O God
SATB FLAMMER A 5336 $.30   (R864)

RHYTHM IN RELIGION *CC8U,pop
cmplt ed WEINBERGER s.p.   (R865)

RIBERA
Rex Autem David *mot,16th cent
[Lat] 5pt mix cor,acap UNION ESP. 19352
s.p.   (R866)

RICE, TIM
Any Dream Will Do *see Webber, Andrew

Close Every Door To Me *see Webber, Andrew

Joseph And The Amazing Technicolor Dreamcoat
*see Webber, Andrew

Joseph's Coat *see Webber, Andrew

Pharaoh's Number Two *see Webber, Andrew

Song Of The King *see Webber, Andrew

RICHAFORT
Quem Dicunt Homines *mot
(Lockwodd) [Ger/Lat] 4-6pt mix cor MOSELER
s.p. contains also: Pionnier, Quem Dicunt
Homines; Gombert, Nicolas, Quem Dicunt
Homines   (R867)

RICHAR, ELSA
Ja, Griass Die God
[Ger] 3pt men cor/3pt wom cor KRENN 116
s.p.   (R868)

RICHARD DE CASTRE'S PRAYER TO JESUS see Terry

RICHARD DE CASTRE'S PRAYER TO JESUS see Terry,
Richard Runciman

RICHARDS
Quickly Ran The Shepherds
SA/TB oct BELWIN 2252 $.30   (R869)

RICHARDS, STEPHEN
Ki Lekach Tov *Sab-Morn
opt unis,solo oct TRANSCON. TCL 396 $2.50
(R870)

Miz'mor Shiru Ladonai (Psalm 98)
[Heb] SATB TRANSCON. TCL 670 $.40   (R871)

Psalm 98 *see Miz'mor Shiru Ladonai

RICHARDSON
Behold That Star *Xmas
SSA ALFRED 6170 $.30   (R872)
SA ALFRED 6120 $.25   (R873)

Crown Him Lord Of All
SAB&desc oct PRO ART 2319 $.30   (R874)

Thou Art The Way
(Cain) SATB oct PRO ART 1520 $.20   (R875)

RICHARDSON, D.
Behold Thy Son Beloved
SATB oct KENDOR $.35   (R876)

RICHARDSON, JOHN (1816-1879)
On This Fair, Holy Morn *Xmas
SATB oct WORD CS-2492 $.30   (R877)

RICHMAN
Prayer Of Innocence
SSA BOSTON 13225 $.35   (R878)

RICHMAN, V.
New Song, A
SSA oct PRESSER MC255 $.30   (R879)

RICHOLSON
Christ Is Born *Xmas
SATB oct LORENZ B143 $.30   (R880)

Gloria In Excelsis Deo *Gloria
SATB oct LORENZ C159 $.30   (R881)

God Be In By Head
SATB oct PRO ART 1595 $.18   (R882)

Het Not Your Heart Be Troubled
SATB oct LORENZ C66 $.30   (R883)

O Brother Man *spir
SATB,S/T solo oct PRO ART 1501 $.16 (R884)

O Child Of Lowly Birth
SATB oct PRO ART 1594 $.18   (R885)

O How Lovely, O How Sweet
SATB,solo oct PRO ART 1562 $.18   (R886)

O Rest In The Lord
SATB oct PRO ART 1389 $.18   (R887)

Something For Thee
SATB oct PRO ART 1823 $.22   (R888)

Song Of Thanksgiving, A
SATB oct LORENZ C69 $.30   (R889)

RICHTE MICH, GOTT see Mendelssohn-Bartholdy,
Felix

RICHTE MICH, GOTT, UND FUHRE see Scheidt,
Samuel

RICHTE MICH, GOTT, UND FUHRE MEINE SACHE see
Mendelssohn-Bartholdy, Felix

RICHTER
Birth Of Christ, The
SAB FLAMMER D5191 $.40   (R890)
SATB FLAMMER A5325 $.40   (R891)

Creation, The
SATB FLAMMER A 5001 $.30   (R892)
TTBB FLAMMER C5003 $.30   (R893)
SSA FLAMMER B 5068 $.30   (R894)

RICHTER, GOTTHOLD LUDWIG (1903-   )
Johannes-Passion *Psntd
[Ger] 3pt mix cor,acap cor pts BAREN.
EM 495 s.p.   (R895)

RICHTER, M.
Psalm 91
SATB oct ELKAN-V 362-1209 $.25   (R896)

RICHTER, WILLY
Be Thou Faithful Unto Death *Bibl
4pt mix cor,SB soli oct SCHIRM.G 9215 $.25
(R897)

RICKARD
Carol Of The Stork *Xmas,carol
SATB oct FISCHER,C CM-7795 $.30   (R898)

Let Thy Blood In Mercy Poured
SATB,acap oct FISCHER,C CM-7447 $.25 (R899)

Rejoice In The Lord
SATB,acap (med diff/diff) SOUTHERN $.30
(R900)

RICKARD, JEFFREY
Gloria
mix cor,acap (diff) oct AUGSBURG 11-9191
$.60   (R901)

Look Ye Saints, The Sight Is Glorious
SATB oct WORD CS-353 $.30   (R902)

Rejoice In The Lord *anthem
dbl cor (med) oct AUGSBURG 1631 $.30 (R903)

RIDE ON see Belt, T.

RIDE ON, CONQUERING KING see Gerhold, Norbert

RIDE ON, ETERNAL KING see Leaf, Robert

RIDE ON IN MAJESTY *anthem
(Pooler, Frank; Pooler, Marie) SA&SATB (easy)
oct AUGSBURG 1151 $.25   (R904)

RIDE ON IN MAJESTY! see Litten, Jack

RIDE ON IN MAJESTY see Pooler, Marie

RIDE ON, JESUS! *spir
(Johnson) SATTBB,acap oct SCHIRM.G 10483 $.35
(R905)

RIDE ON KING JESUS *spir
(Cain) SATB oct PRO ART 1466 $.20   (R906)
(De Cormier) SATB,T solo,acap oct LAWSON
51402 $.25   (R907)
(Forbes, E.) TTBB,acap SCHIRM.EC 2306 $.25
(R908)
(Johnson) SATB oct FISCHER,C CM-6702 $.30
(R909)
(Shaw; Parker) mix cor,acap oct LAWSON 51106
$.25   (R910)

RIDE ON, KING JESUS see Burleigh, Henry Thacker

RIDE ON, KING JESUS! see Southbridge

RIDE ON, O KING! see Dressler, John

RIDE ON, O LORD AND KING! see Peery, Robert Roy

RIDE ON, RIDE ON see Candlyn, T. Frederick H.

RIDE ON, RIDE ON see Darst, W. Glenn

RIDE ON, RIDE ON see George, Graham

RIDE ON! RIDE ON! see Scott

RIDE ON, RIDE ON see Thompson, V.D.

RIDE ON, RIDE ON IN MAJESTY *Fr,17th cent
(Nevin) 4pt mix cor,acap oct SCHIRM.G 7673
$.25   (R911)

RIDE ON, RIDE ON IN MAJESTY see Butler, Eugene

RIDE ON, RIDE ON IN MAJESTY see Candlyn, T.
Frederick H.

RIDE ON! RIDE ON IN MAJESTY see Darst, W. Glenn

RIDE ON! RIDE ON IN MAJESTY see Droste, Doreen

RIDE ON! RIDE ON IN MAJESTY see Ehret, Walter

RIDE ON, RIDE ON IN MAJESTY see Hughes

RIDE ON, RIDE ON IN MAJESTY see Johnson, David
N.

RIDE ON, RIDE ON IN MAJESTY see Lovelace,
Austin C.

RIDE ON, RIDE ON IN MAJESTY see McAfee

RIDE ON, RIDE ON IN MAJESTY see Titcomb

RIDE ON RIDE ON IN MAJESTY see Young

RIDE THE CHARIOT
(Krones) SSA KJOS 1234 $.30   (R912)
(Smith) men cor KJOS 1102 $.30   (R913)

RIDE THE CHARIOT see Smith

RIDGEWAY
Christ The Lord Is Risen Today *Easter
SATB FLAMMER A 5562 $.25   (R914)

Holy Infant Rest Your Head *Xmas
SATB oct PRO ART 2647 $.30   (R915)

RIDGEWAY (cont'd.)

Joy To The Earth *Xmas
SATB oct PRO ART 2648 $.30   (R916)

RIDOUT
Ave Maria
SSA THOMP.G G-312 s.p.   (R917)

Communion
mix cor&cong voc sc OXFORD 40.018 $1.00
(R918)

General Invitation To Praise God, A
SATB THOMP.G G-576 s.p.   (R919)

RIEGGER ANTHEM BOOK see Riegger, Wallingford

RIEGGER, WALLINGFORD (1885-   )
Beautiful Saviour
SA/TB FLAMMER E5063 $.30   (R920)
SSA FLAMMER B 5027 $.30   (R921)
SAB FLAMMER D5006 $.25   (R922)
TTB FLAMMER C5033 $.30   (R923)
TTBB FLAMMER C5010 $.25   (R924)
SATB&jr cor&jr cor FLAMMER A 5385 $.30
(R925)
SATB FLAMMER A 5127 $.30   (R926)

Children Of The Heavenly Father
SAB FLAMMER D5105 $.30   (R927)

Coventry Carol, The *carol
SSA FLAMMER B 5141 $.30   (R928)

Easter Passacaglia *Easter
SATB FLAMMER A 5139 $.30   (R929)
SAB FLAMMER D5168 $.25   (R930)

Evil Shall Not Prevail
SSA&SSA BROUDE,A. 211 $.30   (R931)
TBB&TBB BROUDE,A. 211 $.30   (R932)

Riegger Anthem Book *CCU
SAB FLAMMER GD5011 $1.25   (R933)

RIEGO, TERESA DEL
Way, The Life, The
2pt ENOCH TP100 s.p.   (R934)

RIENECKER
Die Weihnachtsgeschichte *Xmas,cant
SSATB&cong,5 cantors,org sc HANSSLER 10.294
s.p.   (R935)

RIETZ, JOHANNES (1905-   )
Te Deum *Te Deum
dbl cor,acap GERIG 571 s.p.   (R936)

RIGHINI, VINCENZO (1756-1812)
Blessed Are The People
(Suchoff) SATB oct FOX RM1 $.35   (R937)

He Is Blessed
(Suchoff) SATB oct FOX RM5 $.30   (R938)

Lord Is Great, The
SATB oct PRO ART 1724 $.30   (R939)

RIGHT HAND OF THE LORD see Lassus, Roland de
(Orlandus), Dextera Domini

RIGHT ON WITH NUMBER ONE! see Thygerson

RIGHTEOUS JOSEPH *carol
SATB (easy) OXFORD 08.041 $.15   (R940)

RIGHTEOUS JOSEPH see Peek, Richard

RIGHTEOUS LIVE FOR EVERMORE, THE see Sowerby,
Leo

RIGHTEOUS PERISHETH, THE see Gallus, Jacobus

RIGHTEOUS, THE see Bach, Johann Christoph, Der
Gerechte

RIKKO
"Nun Komm Der Heiden Heiland" Five Settings
Of The Christmas Chorale *Xmas,chorale
SATB,acap FRANK F-625 $.30   (R941)

RILEY
Let My Heart Find Peace
SATB oct GALAXY 1.2106.1 $.30   (R942)

RILEY, DENNIS
Beata Viscera *Xmas,mot
SATB THOMP.G E.I.1011 s.p.   (R943)
SATB THOMP.G s.p.   (R944)

Blessed Be The Lord *Bibl
SATB,org,opt trp oct LAWSON 51125 $.30
(R945)

Cantata II
SATB,acap oct BERANDOL 914R5AA $.75 (R946)

RILEY, TERRY
La Messe Des Morts A Is *Op.71, Mass
[Fr] mix cor,acap CBDM s.p.   (R947)

RIMANOCZY, F.E.
Behold The Risen King *Easter
SATB,pno (easy) oct WILLIS 1452 $.12 (R948)

RIMMER
Christus Natus Est, Alleluia *Xmas
SATB oct FISCHER,C CM-7713 $.40   (R949)

RIMMER, FREDERICK
As I Out Rode This Enders Night *Xmas,carol
SATB,acap PETERS H647A $.30 see from Three
Carols Of The Nativity   (R950)

In Bethlehem, That Noble Place *Xmas,carol
SATB,org/pno PETERS H647C $.40 see from
Three Carols Of The Nativity   (R951)

Little Child There Is Yborn, A *Xmas,carol
SATB,acap PETERS H647B $.30 see from Three
Carols Of The Nativity   (R952)

Queen Of Heaven
SATB,acap PETERS H847D   (R953)

Sing We Merrily *anthem
mix cor oct NOVELLO 40.1443.10 s.p. (R954)

RIMMER, FREDERICK (cont'd.)

Three Carols Of The Nativity *see As I Out
Rode This Enders Night; In Bethlehem,
That Noble Place; Little Child There Is
Yborn, A   (R955)

RIMMER, JOAN
A Festival Of Folk Carols *see Mendoza, Anne

RIMSKY-KORSAKOV, NIKOLAI (1844-1908)
Choral Suite (from Christmas Night)
mix cor,soli,3fl,2ob,3clar,2bsn,3trp,4horn,
3trom,tuba,strings,harp,perc,timp cmplt
ed BOOSEY rental   (R956)

Christ The King Now Is Born *Xmas
(Kirk) SATB,acap oct PRO ART 2350 $.25
                                             (R957)

Glory *see Slaua

Slaua *Easter/Fest,anthem
(Amend) "Glory" SATB WARNER W3799 $.40
                                             (R958)
(Pascal, Stone) "Glory" SATB,opt orch
WARNER 3790 $.40   (R959)

RINCK, JOHANN CHRISTIAN HEIN. (1770-1846)
Jesus Is Lord Of The World
(Borucchia; Prentiss) SATB oct SUMMY M 2904
$.30   (R960)

Preis Und Anbetung
(Dobler, J.) [Ger] mix cor,org/winds HUG
s.p., ipr   (R961)

Tantum Argo *Commun,mot
see SIX MOTETS A L'UNISSON
(Kunc, P.) [Lat] 4pt/4pt mix cor oct DURAND
s.p.   (R962)

RINEHARD
Alleluia
SATB KJOS 5395 $.30   (R963)

Bless The Lord, O My Soul
SATB oct KENDOR $.25   (R964)

I Believe In One God
(Ohl) SATB oct PLYMOUTH FO-111 $.35   (R965)

Little Jesus Came To Town *Xmas
SATB SCHMITT 1747 $.22   (R966)

Send Out Thy Truth
SATB KJOS 5462 $.30   (R967)

To Make His Coming Sweet
(Thorley) SSA FLAMMER B 5154 $.30   (R968)

Why Do Bells On Christmas Ring? *Xmas
unis oct BELWIN 64287 $.30   (R969)

Wind Through The Olive Trees *Xmas
SA/TB oct BELWIN 2018 $.30   (R970)

RINEHARTS
Sacred Songs Of Praise *CCU
2pt treb cor KJOS $1.25   (R971)

RING, CHRISTMAS BELLS see Jordan, Alice

RING CHRISTMAS BELLS see Roesch

RING IN NOEL see Caldwell, Mary [Elizabeth]

RING, LITTLE BELLS *Xmas,carol,Ger
(Ehret, Walter) SATB,opt inst oct WALTON 2508
$.30   (R972)
(Ehret, Walter) SSA,opt inst oct WALTON 2533
$.30   (R973)

RING MERRY BELLS see Bliss, Paul

RING MORE BRIGHTLY see Cromie, M.

RING, O RING, YE CHRISTMAS BELLS see Ham

RING, O RING YE CHRISTMAS BELLS see Mueller,
Carl F.

RING ON, SWEET ANGELS see Adam, Adolphe-Charles

RING OUT, O BELLS OF GLADNESS see Blake, G.

RING OUT THE BELLS see Williams, Becket

RING OUT THE HEAVENS see Lunn

RING OUT, WILD BELLS see Atkinson, Condit R.

RING OUT, WILD BELLS see Fletcher, Percy [E.]

RING OUT, WILD BELLS see Gounod, Charles
Francois

RING OUT, WILD BELLS see Moffatt

RING OUT, WILD BELLS see Newbury, Kent A.

RING OUT, WILD BELLS see Sacco

RING OUT WILD BELLS see Sanders, Robert L.

RING OUT WILD BELLS see Tregaskis

RING OUT YE BELLS, IN EXULTATION *Xmas,carol,
It
(Ehret, W.) SATB WARNER WB-137 $.35   (R974)

RING OUT, YE BELLS OF CHRISTMAS see Harris,
Jerry Weseley

RING OUT YE CRYSTAL SPHEARS see Willan, Healey

RING OUT, YE CRYSTAL SPHERES see Shaw, Geoffrey
[Turton]

RING, RING, RING YE BELLS see Langstroth, Ivan
Shed

RING THE BELLS see Bollback

RING THE BELLS see Cooper, Irvin

RING THE JOY-BELLS see Blake, G.

RING YE GLAD VOICES see Day

RING YE GLAD VOICES see Day, R.E.

RINGET DARNACH, DASS IHR STILLE SEID see Reda,
Siegfried

RINGING AND SINGING see Brown, J.

RINGWALD, [ROY] (1910-   )
Amen
SATB SHAWNEE A 1082 $.30   (R975)

Antiphonal Hosanna
SATB SHAWNEE A 923 $.30   (R976)

Blest Be The Tie That Binds
SATB SHAWNEE F 5 $.30 contains also: Son Of
God Goes Forth, The   (R977)

Celebration Of Easter, A *Easter,cant
SATB SHAWNEE A597 $1.25   (R978)

Christmas Crib, The
SAB SHAWNEE D16 $.75   (R979)

Christmas Hymns, Set 1 *CCU,Xmas
(Shaw) SATB,acap SHAWNEE A 50 $.35   (R980)

Christmas Hymns, Set 2 *CCU,Xmas
(Shaw) SATB,acap SHAWNEE A 51 $.40   (R981)

Christmas Hymns, Set 3 *CCU,Xmas
(Shaw) SATB,acap SHAWNEE A 52 $.40   (R982)

Christmas Hymns, Set 4 (composed with Shaw)
*CCU,Xmas
SATB,acap SHAWNEE A 53 $.30   (R983)

Come, Thou Almighty King
see Ringwald, [Roy], My Faith Looks Up To
Thee

Gloria "From The Mass"
SATB,acap SHAWNEE A 676 $.30   (R984)

God's Trombones *cant
SATB SHAWNEE A353 $1.00   (R985)

He's Got The Whole World In His Hands
SATB SHAWNEE A 398 $.35   (R986)
SAB SHAWNEE D43 $.30   (R987)

How Firm A Foundation
SATB SHAWNEE F 1 $.35 contains also: Jesus
Lover Of My Soul   (R988)

In Bethlehem
SSA,acap SHAWNEE B261 $.30   (R989)

Jesus Christ Is Born Today
SATB SHAWNEE A 1168 $.30   (R990)
SA/TB SHAWNEE E119 $.30   (R991)
SAB SHAWNEE D162 $.30   (R992)
TTBB SHAWNEE C229 $.30   (R993)
SSA FLAMMER B 367 $.30   (R994)

Jesus Lover Of My Soul
see Ringwald, [Roy], How Firm A Foundation

Lesson For Lent *Lent
SATB SHAWNEE A 908 $.25   (R995)

Let Us Break Bread Together
SSA SHAWNEE B 259 $.25   (R996)
SATB SHAWNEE A 726 $.30   (R997)

Let Us Go To Bethlehem *Xmas
SAB SHAWNEE D138 $.30   (R998)
SA/TB SHAWNEE E97 $.30   (R999)
SSA SHAWNEE B 346 $.30   (R1000)

Little Shepherds Carol, The
SSA SHAWNEE B 369 $.35   (R1001)
SA/TB SHAWNEE E113 $.35   (R1002)
SAB SHAWNEE D163 $.35   (R1003)

Mary's Baby
SSA SHAWNEE B 296 $.25   (R1004)
SATB SHAWNEE A 872 $.30   (R1005)

My Faith Looks Up To Thee
SATB SHAWNEE F 4 $.30 contains also: Come,
Thou Almighty King   (R1006)

O Brother Man!
SATB SHAWNEE A 401 $.30   (R1007)
TTBB SHAWNEE C164 $.30   (R1008)

O Day Of Rest And Gladness And All Hail The
Power Of Jesus'name
SATB SHAWNEE F 2 $.35   (R1009)

O Listen To The Angels' Song
SA/TB SHAWNEE E46 $.30   (R1010)
SAB SHAWNEE D155 $.35   (R1011)
SSA SHAWNEE B 357 $.35   (R1012)
SATB SHAWNEE A 873 $.35   (R1013)

O Worship The King
see Ringwald, [Roy], When I Survey The
Wondrous Cross

Praise Him, No. 1 *CCU
SAB SHAWNEE GD15 $2.25   (R1014)

Praise Him, No. 2 *CCU
SATB SHAWNEE GA54 $2.25   (R1015)

Prophecy And Annunciation
SATB,acap SHAWNEE A 396 $.30   (R1016)

Rise Up Shepherd An' Foller
SATB,acap SHAWNEE A 40 $.25   (R1017)

Son Of God Goes Forth, The
see Ringwald, [Roy], Blest Be The Tie That
Binds

Song Of Christmas, The *sac/sec
SATB SHAWNEE A134 $1.00   (R1018)
SSA SHAWNEE B179 $1.00   (R1019)

Song Of Easter, The *sac/sec
SATB SHAWNEE A143 $1.00   (R1020)

Swing Low, Sweet Chariot *spir
SATB,acap SHAWNEE A 54 $.30   (R1021)

RINGWALD, [ROY] (cont'd.)
This Is My Father's World
SATB,acap SHAWNEE A 118 $.30   (R1022)
TTBB SHAWNEE C77 $.25   (R1023)
SSAA,acap SHAWNEE B 61 $.25   (R1024)
SAB SHAWNEE D35 $.25   (R1025)
SA/TB SHAWNEE E16 $.25   (R1026)

Were You There When They Crucified My Lord?
SATB,acap SHAWNEE A 32 $.30   (R1027)
SSAA,acap SHAWNEE B 39 $.30   (R1028)
TTBB,acap SHAWNEE C38 $.25   (R1029)

When I Survey The Wondrous Cross
SATB SHAWNEE F 3 $.30 contains also: O
Worship The King   (R1030)

RIODA, UMBERTO
Domine, Salvum Fac Pastorem Nostrum
see Tre Mottetti Per Visita Pastorale Ed
Ingresso Parrocchiale

Ecce Sacerdos Magnus
see Tre Mottetti Per Visita Pastorale Ed
Ingresso Parrocchiale

Tre Mottetti Per Visita Pastorale Ed Ingresso
Parrocchiale *mot
[It] 3 eq voices,org sc ZANIBON 3110 s.p.,
voc pt ZANIBON 3111-13 s.p.
contains: Domine, Salvum Fac Pastorem
Nostrum; Ecce Sacerdos Magnus; Tu Es
Sacerdos   (R1031)

Tu Es Sacerdos
see Tre Mottetti Per Visita Pastorale Ed
Ingresso Parrocchiale

RIPOLLES, VINCENTE (1867-   )
Christ Was Made Obedient *see Christus
Factus Est

Christus Factus Est *Commun/Holywk
"Christ Was Made Obedient" SATB,acap
SCHIRM.EC 1273   (R1032)

Communion Service In C Major *see Missa
Sacratissimi Cordis Jesu

Have Mercy Upon Me, O Lord *see Miserere
Mei, Deus

Il Est Ne *carol/hymn
"Most Merciful God" SCHIRM.EC 4 $.25
                                             (R1033)

Magnificat (Tone 1, No. 7) (composed with
Torres, Eduardo)
(Williams, Walter) SATB SCHIRM.EC 1206 $.18
contains also: Nunc Dimittis (Tone 4, No.
1, With Fauxbourdons)   (R1034)

Magnificat (Tone 2, No. 2) (composed with
Torres, Eduardo)
(Williams, Walter) SATB SCHIRM.EC 1207 $.18
contains also: Nunc Dimittis (Tone 5, No.
3 With Fauxbourdons)   (R1035)

Magnificat (Tone 4, No. 1) (composed with
Torres, Eduardo)
(Williams, Walter) SATB SCHIRM.EC 1214 $.18
contains also: Nunc Dimittis (Tone 5, No.
1)   (R1036)

Magnificat (Tone 5, No. 1) (composed with
Torres, Eduardo)
(Williams, Walter) SATB SCHIRM.EC 1213 $.18
contains also: Nunc Dimittis (Tonus
Peregrinus)   (R1037)

Magnificat (Tone 6) *see Torres, Eduardo

Magnificat (Tone 7, No. 5) *see Torres,
Eduardo

Miserere Mei, Deus *Adv/Lent
"Have Mercy Upon Me, O Lord" SSATTBB,acap
SCHIRM.EC 1236 $.60   (R1038)

Missa Sacratissimi Cordis Jesu *Commun
unis,org (C maj) SCHIRM.EC 1212 $.55
                                             (R1039)
"Communion Service In C Major" unis,org
SCHIRM.EC 1212 $.55   (R1040)
(Williams, W.) "Communion Service In C
Major" [Lat/Eng] unis,org SCHIRM.EC 1212
$.55   (R1041)
(Williams, W.) "Communion Service In C
Major" [Lat/Eng] unis,org SCHIRM.EC 1212
$.55   (R1042)

Most Merciful God *see Il Est Ne

Nunc Dimittis (Tone 2, No. 1) *see Torres,
Eduardo

Nunc Dimittis (Tone 4, No. 1, With
Fauxbourdons) (composed with Torres,
Eduardo)
see Ripolles, Vincente, Magnificat (Tone 1,
No. 7)

Nunc Dimittis (Tone 5, No. 1) (composed with
Torres, Eduardo)
see Ripolles, Vincente, Magnificat (Tone 4,
No. 1)

Nunc Dimittis (Tone 5, No. 3 With
Fauxbourdons) (composed with Torres,
Eduardo)
see Ripolles, Vincente, Magnificat (Tone 2,
No. 2)

Nunc Dimittis (Tone 7, No. 5) *see Torres,
Eduardo

Nunc Dimittis (Tonus Peregrinus) (composed
with Torres, Eduardo)
see Ripolles, Vincente, Magnificat (Tone 5,
No. 1)

O How Sweet, O Lord *see O Quam Suavis

O Quam Suavis
"O How Sweet, O Lord" SATB,acap SCHIRM.EC
1274   (R1043)

RISE, ARISE see Luvaas

RISE, ARISE' see Norman

RISE, CROWNED WITH LIGHT see Markworth, Henry

RISE, CROWNED WITH LIGHT see Willan, Healey

RISE, GOD! JUDGE THOU THE EARTH IN MIGHT see
    Tallis, Thomas

RISE HEART, THY LORD IS RISEN see Cummins, R.

RISE, MY SOUL see Butler

RISE, MY SOUL, ADORE THY MAKER see Bach, Johann
    Sebastian

RISE, MY SOUL, AND PRAISE GOD'S KINDNESS see
    Albert, Heinrich

RISE, MY SOUL, AND STRETCH THY WINGS
    (Coggin, E.) SAB oct PRESSER 312-40753 $.25
                                              (R1044)

RISE, MY SOUL, AND STRETCH THY WINGS see
    Kennedy

RISE, O LORD see Burroughs, Bob

RISE, O SOUL, THIS HAPPY MORNING see Bach,
    Johann Sebastian, Schmucke Dich, O Liebe
    Seele

RISE, TAKE THE CHILD AND HIS MOTHER see
    Hillert, Richard

RISE UP BELOVED BRETHREN
    SATB,acap,opt pno oct PRO ART 2138 $.25
                                              (R1045)

RISE UP EARLY see Kountz

RISE UP, MY LOVE see Bruckner, Anton

RISE UP, MY LOVE see Fletcher

RISE UP, MY LOVE see Willan, Healey

RISE UP, O CHURCH *medley
    (Skillings) SATB oct LILLENAS AT-1080 $.35
                                              (R1046)

RISE UP, O MEN OF GOD see Brydson

RISE UP, O MEN OF GOD see Cain, Noble

RISE UP, O MEN OF GOD see Church

RISE UP, O MEN OF GOD! see Gumma, Victor L.

RISE UP, O MEN OF GOD see Hutson, Wihla

RISE UP, O MEN OF GOD see Jones

RISE UP, O MEN OF GOD see Kinsman

RISE UP, O MEN OF GOD see Landgrave, Phillip

RISE UP, O MEN OF GOD see Nelson, Ronald A.

RISE UP O MEN OF GOD see Reed, Robert B.

RISE UP, O MEN OF GOD see Scull, Harold
    [Thomas]

RISE UP O MEN OF GOD see Thiman, Eric Harding

RISE UP O MEN OF GOD see Wallace

RISE UP, O MEN OF GOD see Walter

RISE UP, O MEN OF GOD see Walter, William Henry

RISE UP, O MEN OF GOD see Wolff

RISE UP, O MEN OF GOD see York, D.

RISE UP, O MEN OF GOD see Young

RISE UP O YOUTH OF GOD see Kirby

RISE UP, SHEPARD, AND FOLLOW see Averre, R.

RISE UP, SHEPHERD
    see Eight Negro Spirituals: Book I
    (Brown) 2pt (easy) OXFORD 82.063 $.25 (R1047)

RISE UP, SHEPHERD, AN' FOLLER *spir
    (Wilson) SSA oct BOOSEY 5034 $.30   (R1048)

RISE UP, SHEPHERD AN' FOLLER see Besch

RISE UP SHEPHERD AN' FOLLER see Ringwald, [Roy]

RISE UP SHEPHERD, AND FOLLER *Xmas,spir
    (Parker) SATB,acap oct LAWSON 749 $.25
                                              (R1049)

RISE UP SHEPHERD AND FOLLOW
    SSA CHAPPELL 0016428-354 $.40   (R1050)

RISE UP, SHEPHERD, AND FOLLOW see Hughes

RISE UP SHEPHERD AND FOLLOW see Simon

RISE UP, SHEPHERD, AND FOLLOW see Spencer, W.

RISE UP, SHEPHERD, AND FOLLOW see Walker, David
    S.

RISE UP SHEPHERDS AND FOLLER *Xmas
    (Cheyette) SAB/SA/unis oct PRO ART 1193 $.30
                                              (R1051)

RISE UP SHEPHERDS AND FOLLOW see Dett

RISEN CHRIST! see Caldwell

RISEN CHRIST see Holler, John

RISEN CHRIST see Stairs, L.

RISEN CHRIST, THE see Holler, John

RISEN CHRIST, THE see Ratcliffe, Desmond

RISEN CHRIST, THE see Smith

RISEN JESUS *Easter,cant
    (Lorenz) 2pt LORENZ $1.75   (R1052)

RISEN KING see Carleton

RISEN KING see Schnecker, P.

RISEN LORD, THE see Tarner, Evelyn F.

RISEN WITH CHRIST *Easter
    cor&cong ROYAL 85402 010 1 s.p.   (R1053)

RISING OF THE SUN, THE see Monte, de, L'apparir
    Del Sol

RISING SUN, THE see Pooler, Frank

RITCHIE, JOHN
    O Lord, We Beseech Thee *anthem
    mix cor,acap oct NOVELLO 40.1544.04 s.p.
                                              (R1054)

RITE OF LOW MASS, THE *CC3U,Mass
    [Lat/Eng] oct ST.MARTIN SMP668 s.p. contains
    works by: Baxter, T.; Bevenot, L.;
    Vermulst, J.   (R1055)

RITRATTO DI UNA SANTA see Pesko, Zoltan

RITTER
    Lobgesang
    (Buck) men cor BIRNBACH s.p.   (R1056)

    Seven Last Words, The *Easter
    SATB oct LORENZ A157 $.60   (R1057)

RITTER, CHRISTIAN (ca. 1640-ca. 1720)
    Gott Hat Jesum Erwecket *Easter,cant
    [Ger] cor,soli,org,cembalo,bsn,strings
    KISTNER sc s.p., cor pts s.p., ipa   (R1058)

    (Bunjes, P.) "We Sing With Rejoicing" mix
    cor,soli,org/strings CONCORDIA 97-6296
    $.75, ipa   (R1059)

    Psalm 83 *see Wie Lieblich Sind Deine
    Wohnungen

    We Sing With Rejoicing *see Gott Hat Jesum
    Erwecket

    Wie Lieblich Sind Deine Wohnungen (Psalm 83)
    Gen
    (Selen, Ebbe) [Ger] SSATB,SATB soli,cont,
    2clar,2vln,2vla (med) BAREN. BA 3464 sc
    $4.75, cor pts $1.50, ipa   (R1060)

RIU, RIU, CHIU *Xmas,carol,Span,16th cent
    (Greenberg, N.) [Span/Eng] SATB,opt Bar/B
    solo,opt perc AMP N10 $.30 see from Three
    Spanish Christmas Carols   (R1061)

ROAD IS RUGGED BUT I MUST GO see Gerhold,
    Norbert

ROAD LEADS INTO TOMMOROW, THE see Cowell, Henry
    Dixon

ROAD TO BETHLEHEM, THE see Praetorius, Michael

ROAD TO CALVARY see Westbrook, Francis B.

ROAD TO CALVARY, THE see Bach, Johann Sebastian

ROAD TO GALILEE see Davis, Katherine K.

ROAD TO THE LAMB, THE see Candlyn

ROAD TO THE STABLE see Keys, Ball-Ivor

ROADWAY, THE see Hutson

ROBB, JOHN
    We Love The Place, O God
    SATB,acap oct BERANDOL 915R8AA $.35 (R1062)

ROBBINS
    His Love
    (Skiles) SAB oct LILLENAS AN-1630 $.30
                                              (R1063)

ROBBINS, C.
    Story Of Artaban, The Other Wise Man, The
    *see Nordoff, Paul

ROBBINS CHORAL COLLECTION OF NEGRO SPIRITUALS
    *CC12UL,spir
    SATB BIG3 $1.25   (R1064)

ROBBINS CHORAL COLLECTION OF SACRED SONGS
    *CCUL
    SATB BIG3 $1.25   (R1065)

ROBE OF CALVARY
    SATB/TTBB BIG3 $.25   (R1066)

ROBERT, PIERRE
    Deux Motets Pour La Chapelle Du Roy (from Le
    Pupitre) CCU,mot
    [Fr] cor,orch HEUGEL s.p., ipr   (R1067)

ROBERT, W.
    Psalm 8
    mix cor ALSBACH&D sc s.p., cor pts s.p.
                                              (R1068)

ROBERTON, HUGH S. (1874-1952)
    All In The April Evening *Easter/Lent
    4pt mix cor,acap oct CURWEN 8100 $.25
                                              (R1069)

    4pt men cor,acap oct CURWEN 8356 $.25
                                              (R1070)

    SATB oct SOUTHERN $.25   (R1071)
    3pt mix cor,acap oct CURWEN 9988 $.30
                                              (R1072)

    2pt wom cor oct CURWEN 8837 $.25   (R1073)
    3pt wom cor oct CURWEN 9564 $.30
                                              (R1074)

    SAB ROBERTON 61427 s.p.   (R1075)
    mix cor ROBERTON 60976 s.p.   (R1076)

    Cloths Of Heaven, The
    2pt men cor ROBERTON 50794 s.p.   (R1077)

    Dedication
    mix cor ROBERTON 80708 s.p.   (R1078)

    For Tonight A King Is Born In Bethlehem
    *Xmas
    SSATB,acap oct CURWEN 10964 $.25   (R1079)

    He Came All So Still *Xmas
    mix cor ROBERTON 61359 s.p.   (R1080)

ROBERTON, HUGH S. (cont'd.)

    Herrick's Litanie
    mix cor ROBERTON 61447 s.p.   (R1081)

    Hymn To Peace *hymn
    mix cor ROBERTON 61392 s.p.   (R1082)

    I See His Blood Upon The Rose
    men cor ROBERTON 50803 s.p.   (R1083)
    mix cor ROBERTON 61335 s.p.   (R1084)
    5pt mix cor,acap oct CURWEN 8597 $.25
                                              (R1085)

    Jesus, Thou Joy Of Loving Hearts
    mix cor ROBERTON 61444 s.p.   (R1086)

    Let All The World In Every Corner Sing *Gen/
    Thanks
    4pt mix cor,acap oct SCHIRM.G 8721 $.25
                                              (R1087)

    (Stickles) 3pt mix cor oct SCHIRM.G 11136
    $.25   (R1088)

    Let Us Homage Bring
    mix cor ROBERTON 61372 s.p.   (R1089)

    Nativity Cradle Song *Xmas
    mix cor ROBERTON 61390 s.p.   (R1090)

    O Light Of Life
    TBB PATERSON 1512 s.p.   (R1091)

    Outgoing Of The Boats, The *hymn,Ir
    mix cor,acap oct CURWEN 8104 $.25   (R1092)
    4pt mix cor,acap oct CURWEN 8234 $.30
                                              (R1093)

    There Is A Green Hill Far Away
    mix cor,Mez solo ROBERTON 61378 s.p.
                                              (R1094)

    4pt men cor ROBERTON 50761 s.p.   (R1095)

    Yno Yn Hwyrddydd Ebrill
    [Welsh] mix cor ROBERTON 60976 s.p. (R1096)

ROBERTON, K.O.
    Og Han Fronedret Seg
    [Norw] mix cor,org LYCHE 12 s.p.   (R1097)

ROBERTS
    Jesus Is The Name Exalted *Gen
    (Coggin) SATB SCHMITT SD6220 $.35   (R1098)

    Lovely Appear
    (Mueller) 3pt jr cor/SAB (very easy)
    FISCHER,C CM 7335 $.25   (R1099)

    Meeting In The Air, The
    (Mickelson) SATB oct LILLENAS AN-1181 $.25
                                              (R1100)

    Seek Ye The Lord *anthem
    SATB,T solo (easy) oct AUGSBURG 1030 $.22
                                              (R1101)
    SATB,T solo WARNER G1719 $.30   (R1102)
    SATB oct BELWIN 64074 $.30   (R1103)
    SATB oct FISCHER,C CM-143 $.25   (R1104)
    SA oct FISCHER,C CM-6347 $.25   (R1105)
    SATB KJOS 8009 $.30   (R1106)
    (Byrd) SATB oct PRO ART 1150 $.25   (R1107)
    (Howorth, Wayne) SAB oct BELWIN 1987 $.25
                                              (R1108)

    Unto Us A Child Is Born *Xmas
    SATB FLAMMER A 5565 $.35   (R1109)

ROBERTS, J.
    Angels From The Realms Of Glory *Xmas
    (Montgomery, J.) SATB oct PRESSER G-103
    $.35   (R1110)

    Peace I Leave With You *Easter
    SATB oct PRESSER 332-07756 $.30   (R1111)

    Seek Ye The Lord
    SAB oct LORENZ 7061 $.30   (R1112)
    SATB oct PRESSER 312-06245 $.30   (R1113)
    SATB oct LORENZ 466 $.30   (R1114)
    2pt oct LORENZ 5710 $.25   (R1115)

ROBERTS, J.D.
    I Heard A Voice
    SATB PATERSON 1693 s.p.   (R1116)

ROBERTS, J. VARLEY
    Grant We Beseech Thee
    (Howorth, Wayne) SATB oct BELWIN 1781 $.25
                                              (R1117)

    Jesu, Priceless Treasure *anthem
    mix cor,SS soli oct NOVELLO 40.0617.08 s.p.
                                              (R1118)

    Peace I Leave With You *Commun/Lent,Bibl
    4pt mix cor oct SCHIRM.G 4471 $.30 (R1119)
    (Deis) 2pt wom cor oct SCHIRM.G 9696 $.25
                                              (R1120)
    (Mueller) SABar oct SCHIRM.G 9746 $.25
                                              (R1121)
    (Spicker) 3pt wom cor oct SCHIRM.G 5065
    $.25   (R1122)

    Seek Ye The Lord *anthem/Bibl
    4pt mix cor,T solo oct SCHIRM.G 3731 $.30
                                              (R1123)
    mix cor,T solo oct NOVELLO 28.0189.02 s.p.
                                              (R1124)
    SSAA,S solo,org (easy) oct WILLIS 1104 $.12
                                              (R1125)
    SATB,T solo,org (med) oct WILLIS 791 $.10
                                              (R1126)
    (Downing) 3pt wom cor,S solo oct SCHIRM.G
    8938 $.25   (R1127)
    (Salter) 4pt men cor,T solo oct SCHIRM.G
    5702 $.25   (R1128)

ROBERTS, MERVYN
    Pilgrim Song
    2pt oct NOVELLO 48.1858.10 s.p.   (R1129)

ROBERTS, MYRON
    O Lord, We Beseech Thee *Gen/Lent
    SATB oct GRAY GCMR 2901 $.30   (R1130)

ROBERTS, N.
    Father, O Forgive Thou Me
    SATB oct WORD CS-2461 $.35   (R1131)

ROBERTSON
    All Creatures Of Our God And King
    SSAATTBB oct GALAXY 1.1882.1 $.35   (R1132)

ROBERTSON (cont'd.)

Come, Come Ye Saints
SATB oct GALAXY 1.2181.1 $.50   (R1133)

Hymns From The Crossroads *CCU,hymn
SATB/TTBB/SSA,org cor pts FISCHER,C O-4516E
$1.25, sc FISCHER,C O-4516 $2.00   (R1134)

Lord's Prayer, The *prayer
SSA oct GALAXY 1.2208.1 $.30   (R1135)
SATB oct GALAXY 1.1199.1 $.30   (R1136)

ROBERTSON, KARL-OLOF
Nar Herren Ater Upprattade Sion
mix cor NORDISKA 5024 s.p.   (R1137)

ROBERTSON, LEROY (1896-   )
Blessed The Bread And Water
see Hymns Of Faith

Hymns Of Faith
SATB PIONEER 6003 $.25
contains: Blessed The Bread And Water;
Lord Bless Thee , The; O May My Soul
Commune With Thee; Temple, The (R1138)

Lord Bless Thee , The
see Hymns Of Faith

Lord Hath Brought Again Zion, The
SATB PIONEER 6006 $.45   (R1139)

O May My Soul Commune With Thee
see Hymns Of Faith

Song Of Praise
SATB PIONEER 6005 $.40   (R1140)

Song Of Prayer
SATB PIONEER 6004 $.25   (R1141)

Temple, The
see Hymns Of Faith

ROBIN AND THE THORN, THE *Easter,carol
(Niles) unis oct SCHIRM.G 9326 $.25 (R1142)
(Parsons; Niles) 3pt wom cor,acap oct
SCHIRM.G 9511 $.25   (R1143)

ROBIN AND THE THORN, THE see Niles, John Jacob

ROBINSON, CHRISTOPHER
Let All On Earth Their Voices Raise
4pt mix cor,B solo oct SCHIRM.G 7114 $.25
(R1144)
Magnificat And Nunc Dimittis *Magnif/Nunc
treb cor (med) oct OXFORD 44.220 $.35
(R1145)

ROBINSON, G.W.
Very
erry Christmas, A *Xmas
3pt wom cor oct SCHIRM.G 10044 $.30 (R1146)
2pt mix cor oct SCHIRM.G 10295 $.25 (R1147)
4pt mix cor oct SCHIRM.G 10258 $.20 (R1148)
SAB oct SCHIRM.G 10259 $.20   (R1149)

ROBSON, R. WALKER
Awakening, An *anthem
mix cor oct NOVELLO 40.1171.06 s.p. (R1150)
unis oct NOVELLO 48.1837.07 s.p.   (R1151)

Gate Of The Year, The
SATB PATERSON 1620 s.p.   (R1152)

God Be In My Head
unis oct NOVELLO 48.1714.01 s.p.   (R1153)

Hark!The Song Of Jubilee *anthem
mix cor,acap oct NOVELLO s.p.   (R1154)

Heaven Is There *anthem
mix cor oct NOVELLO 40.1199.06 s.p. (R1155)

Holy Spirit, Truth Divine *Gen/Whitsun
SATB,org oct FISCHER,C PT-1646 $.20 (R1156)
SATB PATERSON 1646 s.p.   (R1157)

O Lamb Of God *anthem
mix cor oct NOVELLO s.p.   (R1158)

Sweet Is The Work *anthem/hymn
mix cor oct NOVELLO 50.0252.04 s.p. (R1159)

Thou Hast A Work For Me To Do *anthem
mix cor,acap oct NOVELLO 40.1123.06 s.p.
(R1160)

ROCHBERG, GEORGE (1918-   )
Psalm 23
SATB,acap oct PRESSER 312-40297 $.35
(R1161)
mix cor SOUTHERN $.30   (R1162)

Psalm 43
SATB,acap oct PRESSER 312-40298 $.35
(R1163)

Psalm 150 *liturg,Heb
SATB,acap oct PRESSER 312-40299 $.50
(R1164)

ROCHEROLLE
All You Peoples Clap Your Hands
SATB WARNER W7-1015 $.35   (R1165)

And So It Was *Xmas
SATB WARNER WB-210 $.40   (R1166)

Baby Boy *Xmas
WARNER WB-161 $.40   (R1167)

Give To The Lord (Psalm 28)
SATB WARNER WB-129 $.30   (R1168)

Joyful Song, A
SATB WARNER WB-158 $.35   (R1169)

Joyous Alleluia
SATB,acap oct WARNER W3777 $.30   (R1170)
mix cor SOUTHERN $.30   (R1171)

Psalm 28 *see Give To The Lord

See The Pretty Baby
unis/2pt/SAB WARNER WB-111 $.35   (R1172)

ROCK-A-MA SOUL
(Christiansen, P.) SATB KJOS 52 $.30 (R1173)

ROCK-A-MY SOUL *spir
SATB oct LILLENAS AN-3816 $.30   (R1174)
(Barthelson) SATB oct LAWSON 618 $.30 (R1175)

(Barthelson) 3pt boy cor/SSA/SAA oct LAWSON
51387 $.35   (R1176)
(Ganschow, T.) SATB,acap oct PRESSER
312-40149 $.30   (R1177)
(Gilliam) 4pt men cor oct SCHIRM.G 10161 $.20
(R1178)
(Heaton, W.) SATB,acap oct PRESSER 312-40566
$.30   (R1179)
(Kirk) TTBB oct PRO ART 2379 $.30 (R1180)
(Kirk) SATB,acap,opt pno oct PRO ART 1364
$.30   (R1181)
(Kirk) SAB oct PRO ART 1878 $.30 (R1182)
(Kirk) SSA oct PRO ART 1738 $.30 (R1183)
(Kirk) 2pt oct PRO ART 2331 $.30 (R1184)
(Papale, Henry) SATB,clar, chinese temple
blocks oct WORLD CE-2186-8 $.45   (R1185)
(Tepper) SATB oct BOOSEY 1972 $.35 (R1186)
(Wilson) SA oct SPRATT 177 $.25   (R1187)

ROCK-A MY SOUL see De Vaux, Joseph

ROCK-A MY SOUL see Drewes, Capt. Barry

ROCK-A MY SOUL see Williamson, Warren

ROCK-A MY SOUL see Wilson

ROCK-A MY SOUL IN THE BOSOM OF ABRAHAM
(Page, R.) SATB,acap oct PRESSER 312-40204
$.30   (R1188)

ROCK HIM GENTLY see Davies, Lawrence H.

ROCK, MOUNT SINAI see Work

ROCK, MOUNT ZION *spir
(Clark) SATB,acap oct LAWSON 51490 $.35
(R1189)

ROCK MT. SINAI! *spir
(Jessye) SATB oct SHAPIRO SK 2095 $.25 (R1190)

ROCK OF AGES
(Adler, Samuel) SATB TRANSCON. TCL 134 $.25,
ipa   (R1191)
(Suchoff) SA oct BOOSEY 5324 $.30 (R1192)
(Suchoff) SAB oct BOOSEY 5501 $.30 (R1193)

ROCK OF AGES see Buck, Dudley

ROCK OF AGES see Hastings

ROCK OF AGES see Hoffman

ROCK OF AGES see Humperdinck, Engelbert

ROCK OF AGES see Lynn, George

ROCK THE BABY JESUS see Moss, L.

ROCK THE CRADLE FOR A KING see Durrant,

Frederick

ROCKA MY SOUL! see Cain, Noble

ROCKIN' JERUSALEM
(Work, J.) SATB,acap oct PRESSER 312-21427
$.35   (R1194)

ROCKIN' JERUSALEM see Gardner

ROCKING *Xmas,carol,Czech
see Six Two-Part Carols
see Three Christmas Carols
SATB (easy) OXFORD 08.087 $.15, ipr (R1195)
(Cashmore) SSAATTBB,acap (easy) OXFORD 84.033
$.25   (R1196)
(Churchill, Stuart) SATB oct BELWIN 1465 $.25
(R1197)
(Churchill, Stuart) SSA oct BELWIN 1425 $.25
(R1198)
(Felciano) SA,acap MARKS 4512 $.30 (R1199)
(Felciano) SSA,acap MARKS 4259 $.30 (R1200)
(Felciano) SATB,acap MARKS 4513 $.30 (R1201)
(Ossewaarde, Jack) SATB oct GRAY GCMR 2843
$.30   (R1202)
(Trant) SSA (easy) OXFORD 83.069 $.25
contains also: Silent Night   (R1203)
(Woodgate) unis (very easy) OXFORD 81.015
$.20 see from Four Carols   (R1204)
(Woodgate) unis (very easy) OXFORD 81.015
$.20 see from Four Carols   (R1205)
(Woodgate) SATB,acap (easy) OXFORD 84.024
$.30 see from Four Carols   (R1206)
(Woodgate) SATB,acap (easy) OXFORD 84.024
$.30 see from Four Carols   (R1207)

ROCKING CAROL *Xmas,Czech
(Graham, R.) SATB,acap oct PRESSER 312-40554
$.30   (R1208)
(Graham, R.) SSA,acap oct PRESSER 312-40553
$.30   (R1209)

ROCKING CAROL see Graham, Robert [V.]

ROCKING HYMN, THE see Wither

ROCKWOOD, GAY HYLANDER
Christ Was Born Today
SATB,acap (diff) oct WILLIS 7104 $.25
(R1210)
Glory, Laud, Honor *Palm
jr cor&sr cor (med) FISCHER,C CM 7372 $.30
(R1211)
Processional And Alleluia *Xmas/Easter
[Lat] SATB,acap (very easy) oct OXFORD
94.321 $.25   (R1212)

ROD OF JESSE HATH BLOSSOMED, THE see Bruckner,
Anton, Virga Jesse

RODBY
All Earth Be Glad
SATB KJOS 5380 $.30   (R1213)
SSA KJOS 6113 $.30   (R1214)

Noel, Noel, Let Us Sing Merry Christmas
*Xmas
(Roff) SATB SCHMITT 7032 $.35   (R1215)

Now Praise We *CCU
(Roff) SATB KJOS $1.25   (R1216)

Now Thank We (composed with Roff, Joseph)
*CCU
SAB KJOS $1.25   (R1217)

Sing We All At Christmastide *Xmas
(Roff) SATB SCHMITT 8039 $.30   (R1218)

RODBY, JOHN
Chorale *chorale
SATB oct AGAPE CE 4325 $.40   (R1219)

RODBY, WALTER (1917-   )
I Got The Spirit
SATB oct AGAPE WR 1008 $.30   (R1220)
SSA oct AGAPE WR 1015 $.30   (R1221)

In Praise Of Friday
SSA oct AGAPE WR 1014 $.30   (R1222)
SATB oct AGAPE WR 1013 $.30   (R1223)

Waltz For Two Left Feet, A
SAB oct AGAPE WR 1010 $.35   (R1224)
SATB oct AGAPE WR 1006 $.35   (R1225)

RODELLA, SANTE
Ave Verum Corpus
see Hora Eucaristica

Dominus Pars
see IN SOLEMNI CLERICORUM VESTITIONE

Gloria Laus
see Quattro Inni Processionali

Hora Eucaristica *Commun,mot
[Lat] unis,org sc ZANIBON 643 s.p., cor pts
ZANIBON s.p.
contains: Ave Verum Corpus; O Jesu Mi
Dulcissime; O Quam Suavis; O Salutari
Hostia; Pange Lingua; Tantum Ergo
(R1226)

Jesu Corona Virginum
see PRO VESTITIONE MONIALIUM

Jesu Redemptor Omnium
see Tre Inni E Cantici

Laetabundus Exultet Fidelis
see Tre Inni E Cantici

Messa *Mass
[Lat] ATB,org sc ZANIBON 142 s.p., voc pt
ZANIBON s.p.   (R1227)

O Gloriosa Virginum
see RACCOLTA DI SEI INNI

O Jesu Mi Dulcissime
see Hora Eucaristica

O Quam Suavis
see Hora Eucaristica

O Salutari Hostia
see Hora Eucaristica

Pange Lingua

see Hora Eucaristica
see Quattro Inni Processionali
see Tre Inni Eucaristici
see Tre Inni Eucaristici

Quattro Inni Processionali *Proces
[Lat] unis/4pt mix cor sc ZANIBON 1194 s.p.
contains: Gloria Laus; Pange Lingua;
Stabat Mater; Vexilla Regis   (R1228)

Resonet In Laudibus
see Tre Inni E Cantici

Sette Litanie Lauretane *CC7U
[Lat] 2 eq voices,org ZANIBON 1378 s.p.
(R1229)

Stabat Mater
see Quattro Inni Processionali

Tantum Ergo
see Hora Eucaristica
see Tre Inni Eucaristici

Tre Inni E Cantici *Xmas,hymn
[Lat] unis/ATB,opt org ZANIBON 1384 s.p.
contains: Jesu Redemptor Omnium;
Laetabundus Exultet Fidelis; Resonet In
Laudibus   (R1230)

Tre Inni Eucaristici *Commun,hymn
[Lat] sc ZANIBON 331 s.p.
contains: Pange Lingua (2 eq voices,org)
(G maj); Pange Lingua (2 eq voices,org)
(in modo III); Tantum Ergo (3 eq
voices,org)   (R1231)

Tu Es Petrus *mot
[It] SATB,acap ZANIBON 1514 s.p. (R1232)

Vexilla Regis
see Quattro Inni Processionali

RODER, E.
Karfreitag (Totenfest) (Psalm 31)
[Ger] mix cor,acap (easy) HUG s.p. (R1233)

Psalm 31 *see Karfreitag (Totenfest)

RODGERS
Little Carol, A *Xmas,carol,Fr
SATB oct GALLEON GCS1019   (R1234)

Offerings *Xmas
jr cor oct GALLEON GCS1017   (R1235)
unis jr cor oct FISCHER,C GCS 1017 $.20 (R1236)

Sky Can Still Remember, The *Xmas
SATB oct GALLEON GCS1013   (R1237)

RODGERS, IRENE
Christmas Lullaby, A *Xmas
SA,pno (easy) oct WILLIS 5715 $.12 (R1238)

That First, Best Christmas Night *Xmas
SATB,S solo,acap (med) oct WILLIS 6091 $.12
(R1239)

RODGERS, JOHN (1917-   )
Annunciation Carol *Xmas,carol
SATB oct GRAY GCMR 2697 $.30   (R1240)

Of The Father's Love Begotten *Xmas
SATB oct GRAY GCMR 2427 $.25   (R1241)

RODNEY
Calvary *Easter/Lent
(Townsend) SATB oct PRO ART 1454 $.30
(R1242)

(Townsend) SAB oct PRO ART 1913 $.30
(R1243)

RODNEY (cont'd.)

(Townsend) SSA oct PRO ART 1813 $.22
(R1244)
(Whitman) SATB oct LILLENAS AN-2263 $.35
(R1245)

RODNEY, PAUL
Calvary *Easter
4pt mix cor oct SCHIRM.G 3299 $.35 (R1246)
SATB ENOCH EC1 s.p.   (R1247)
2pt ENOCH TP8 s.p.   (R1248)
2pt LORENZ 5715 $.25   (R1249)
SAB oct LORENZ 7068 $.30   (R1250)
SSA oct LORENZ 6070 $.30   (R1251)
SATB oct LORENZ 986 $.30   (R1252)
(Ehret) SATB oct BELWIN 1416 $.25   (R1253)

Resurrection Morn, The *Easter
cor,A/Bar solo ENOCH s.p.   (R1254)

RODRIGO
Ave Maria *BVM/Xmas
[Lat] SSATB,acap UNION ESP. 19896 $.75
(R1255)

Jo Tinc Un Burro
[Lat] 4pt mix cor,acap UNION ESP. 19897
s.p.   (R1256)

Triste Estaba El Rey David
[Lat] mix cor,acap UNION ESP. s.p. (R1257)

RODSETH, JOHS.
Forlat Oss, Krist
[Norw] wom cor/jr cor/eq voices LYCHE 15
s.p.   (R1258)

Lov Herren (Psalm 106)
[Norw] wom cor/jr cor/eq voices LYCHE 17
s.p.   (R1259)

Psalm 106 *see Lov Herren

ROE
Unworthy
(Collins) SATB oct LILLENAS AT-1065 $.25
(R1260)

ROE, BETTY
Christus Victor *cant
SATB&speak cor,narrator,ABar soli,ob,2clar,
horn,trp,strings,timp,perc,gtr (with
mime) voc sc NOVELLO s.p., ipr (R1261)

Jubilate Deo
see Roe, Betty, Venite Exultemus Domino

Magnificat *Bibl/Magnif
unis voc sc WEINBERGER s.p. contains also:
Nunc Dimittus (Nunc)   (R1262)

Nunc Dimittus
see Roe, Betty, Magnificat

Venite Exultemus Domino *Bibl/Venite
unis,org voc sc WEINBERGER s.p. contains
also: Jubilate Deo (Jubil)   (R1263)

ROE, CHRISTOPHER
Welcome Our Messias
LENGNICK s.p.   (R1264)
unis LENGNICK s.p.   (R1265)

ROE, GLORIA [ANN] (1935-   )
&oes It Make Any Difference To You
SATB oct WORD CS-2231 $.30   (R1266)

He Is The One *Xmas
SATB oct WORD CS-2215 $.30   (R1267)

May We Know Peace
SATB oct WORD CS-2386 $.30   (R1268)

Miraculous
SATB oct WORD CS-2299 $.30   (R1269)

My Grace Is Sufficient For You
SATB oct WORD CS-2365 $.30   (R1270)

My Lord Speaks Peace To Me
SATB oct WORD CS-2304 $.25   (R1271)

Safe In His Hands
SATB oct WORD CS-2235 $.30   (R1272)

So Great Salvation *Xmas
SATB oct WORD CS-2216 $.30   (R1273)

Surrender
SATB oct WORD CS-2323 $.30   (R1274)

Unworthy
SATB oct WORD CS-2212 $.25   (R1275)

ROE, N. CLAYTON
We Shall See His Lovely Face
SATB oct WORD CS-2301 $.30   (R1276)

ROECKEL, J.L.
Cast Thy Bread On The Waters
cor,S/T solo ENOCH EC6 s.p.   (R1277)

Coming Of The King, The *Adv
2pt ENOCH TP50 s.p.   (R1278)

ROESCH
Gotts True
SSA FLAMMER B 5156 $.30   (R1279)

Ring Christmas Bells *Xmas
SATB FLAMMER A 5591 $.30   (R1280)

ROESELING, KASPAR (1894-1961)
Lob Des Jesuskindes *Xmas,ora
SATB,narrator,orch voc sc TONGER s.p., ipa
(R1281)

Mortuis Sepulcrum
4-8pt mix cor MOSELER s.p.   (R1282)

O Gott, Nun Lasst Uns Heben Die Hand
mix cor,acap TONGER s.p.   (R1283)

ROESGEN-CHAMPION, MARGUERITE (1894-   )
Deux Chants De Noel *Xmas
[Fr] LEMOINE s.p.
contains: La Creche De Noel (4pt mix cor,
acap); Mon Beau Sapin De Noel (4pt mix
cor,acap)
see also: La Creche De Noel; Mon Beau
Sapin   (R1284)

ROESGEN-CHAMPION, MARGUERITE (cont'd.)

La Creche De Noel *Xmas
[Fr] 2pt jr cor,acap LEMOINE s.p. see from
Deux Chants De Noel   (R1285)
[Fr] mix cor (easy) cmplt ed LEMOINE s.p.
contains also: Mon Beau Sapin De Noel
(R1286)
[Fr] mix cor cor pts LEMOINE s.p. (R1287)

La Visitation
unis/cor,pno/org LEMOINE s.p.   (R1288)
4pt mix cor,acap LEMOINE s.p.   (R1289)

L'annonciation
cor,pno/org LEMOINE voc sc s.p., cor pts
s.p.   (R1290)

Mon Beau Sapin *Xmas
[Fr] 2pt jr cor,acap LEMOINE s.p. see from
Deux Chants De Noel   (R1291)

Mon Beau Sapin De Noel
see Deux Chants De Noel
see Roesgen-Champion, Marguerite, La Creche
De Noel

Mon Beau Sapin Des Noel *Xmas
[Fr] mix cor cor pts LEMOINE s.p. (R1292)

Priere A Sainte Therese Du Carmel *prayer
cor LEMOINE s.p.   (R1293)

Sur La Naissance De Notre Seigneur *Xmas
cor LEMOINE s.p.   (R1294)

ROESKE, F.J.
Gebed Voor De Tempel
[Neth/Ger] men cor ALSBACH&D sc s.p., cor
pts s.p.   (R1295)

Groot Is De Heer
men bor ALSBACH&D sc s.p., bor pts s.p.
(R1296)

Pater Noster
mix cor ALSBACH&D sc s.p., cor pts s.p.
(R1297)

Psalm 137
men cor ALSBACH&D sc s.p., cor pts s.p.
(R1298)

Requiem *Req
men cor ALSBACH&D sc s.p., cor pts s.p.
(R1299)

ROFF, JOSEPH
All My Heart This Night Rejoices *Xmas,
anthem
SATB (easy) oct GIA G1489 $.30   (R1300)
SA/TB (easy) oct GIA G1586 $.30   (R1301)

All You Peoples Clap Your Hands (Psalm 46)
*Gen,anthem
unis (easy) oct GIA G1618 $.25   (R1302)

Almighty And Everlasting God *ASD/BVM,anthem
SATB,2trp (med easy) oct GIA G1610 $.35
(R1303)
SATB oct FISCHER,C R-434 $.25   (R1304)
SA (easy) oct GIA G1616 $.35   (R1305)
SA/TB,org,opt 2trp (med easy) oct GIA G1616
$.35   (R1306)

And There Shall Come Forth A Rod
SATB oct VOLKWEIN VB701 $.30   (R1307)

Angel Of The Lord, The
SATB oct BOURNE JR1 $.25   (R1308)

Angels Of The Crown
SATB WARNER WB-290 $.40   (R1309)

Anima Christi *Lent,anthem
"Soul Of My Savior" [Eng/Lat] SATB (easy)
oct GIA G1592 $.35   (R1310)
"Soul Of My Savior" SA/TB (easy) oct GIA
G1593 $.30   (R1311)

Art Thou A King, Then? *Xmas
SATB oct SHAPIRO SK 2107 $.30   (R1312)

At The Name Of Jesus
SATB SHAWNEE A 899 $.25   (R1313)

Be Glad Then And Rejoice
SATB oct LORENZ 9970 $.30   (R1314)

Be Merciful To Me
SATB AMP A388 $.20   (R1315)

Be Thou Exalted, O God
SATB oct PRESSER MC491 $.30   (R1316)

Be With Me Lord
SATB oct VOLKWEIN VB113 $.25   (R1317)

Before The Paling Of The Stars *Xmas
SATB oct GRAY GCMR 3108 $.30   (R1318)

Blessed Be The Name Of God
SATB oct SHAPIRO SK 2057 $.30   (R1319)

Blessed Is The Nation
SATB oct VOLKWEIN VB118 $.25   (R1320)

But The Lord Is Faithful
SATB,acap oct BOOSEY 5477 $.30   (R1321)

Child's Prayer, A *prayer
SA LEONARD-US 08006880 $.25   (R1322)

Christ, Our Paschal Lamb *Easter,anthem
SA/TB (easy) oct GIA G1595 $.25   (R1323)
SATB (med easy) oct GIA G1594 $.30 (R1324)

Christ Was Born On Christmas Day *Xmas,
anthem
SA/TB (easy) oct GIA G1487 $.25   (R1325)

Christmas Star, The *Xmas
SATB oct JUSKO 231 $.20   (R1326)

Come And Hear
SATB oct VOLKWEIN VB133 $.30   (R1327)

Come, My Way, My Truth, My Life *Easter/Lent
SATB oct WORD CS-2359 $.30   (R1328)

Come To Me, All Ye That Labour
SAB SHAWNEE D32 $.30   (R1329)
SATB SHAWNEE A 288 $.30   (R1330)

ROFF, JOSEPH (cont'd.)

Dear Lord, Remember Me
SATB oct VOLKWEIN VB142 $.25   (R1331)

Earth Feared And Was Silent, The *Easter,
anthem
SATB (med easy) oct GIA G1186 $.30 (R1332)
SA/TB (easy) oct GIA G1187 $.25   (R1333)

Earth Shall Be Filled, The *Adv/Xmas/Gen,
anthem
SATB (easy) oct GIA G 1597 $.30   (R1334)
SA/TB (easy) oct GIA G1598 $.25   (R1335)
SATB (easy) oct GIA G1597 $.30   (R1336)
SA/TB (easy) oct GIA G1598 $.25   (R1337)

Easter Anthem
SATB,S/T solo,pno oct BERANDOL 916R2AB $.35
(R1338)

Easter On Earth *Easter
SSA/SAA oct LAWSON 871 $.25   (R1339)

End Of The Road, The
SATB oct JUSKO 183 $.25   (R1340)
SSA oct JUSKO 184 $.25   (R1341)

Father We Thank Thee
SATB oct HIGHLAND 7.0015.1 $.30   (R1342)

Give Thanks To The Lord *Gen,anthem
SSA (easy) oct GIA G1444 $.25   (R1343)
SATB (easy) oct GIA G1417 $.25   (R1344)

God Be Merciful Unto Us
SATB ALFRED 6341 $.40   (R1345)

God Is Love
SATB oct BOURNE JR2 $.25   (R1346)

God Is Not Dead
SATB oct SACRED E90 $.40   (R1347)

God's Plan
2pt oct SACRED S-5748 $.35   (R1348)

God's Sunshine
SATB oct COLOMBO 1827 $.25   (R1349)

Grace Of Thy Consolation
SATB ALLANS 367 s.p.   (R1350)

Grant Us Strength And Protection
SATB,acap BOSTON 13655 $.35   (R1351)

Hail Mary *ASD/BVM,anthem
SATB (easy) oct GIA G1344 $.25   (R1352)
SA/TB (easy) oct GIA G1346 $.25   (R1353)
SAB (easy) oct GIA G1345 $.25   (R1354)

Hail, True Virginity *Gen,anthem
SSA (easy) oct GIA G1453 $.25   (R1355)

Hasten Thy Kingdom
SATB,acap SHAWNEE A585 $.30   (R1356)

He Careth For Me
SA/TB/SSA SHAWNEE E23 $.25   (R1357)

He Who Follows Me *Gen,anthem
SATB (easy) oct GIA G416 $.25   (R1358)
SSA (easy) oct GIA G1433 $.25   (R1359)

He Will Receive The Blessing Of The Lord
*Gen,anthem/mot
SATB (easy) oct GIA G1423 $.25   (R1360)
SSA (easy) oct GIA G1450 $.25   (R1361)

Here Is A Great Priest *anthem
SATB (easy) oct GIA G1420 $.25   (R1362)
SSA (easy) oct GIA G1447 $.25   (R1363)

Holy Spirit, Hear Us
2pt LORENZ 5722 $.30   (R1364)

How Can We Thank You, Lord
SATB oct ELKAN-V 362-1267 $.25   (R1365)

How Lovely Are The Words Of Jesus
SA/TB SHAWNEE E13 $.25   (R1366)

I Am The Bread Of Life
SATB oct SACRED E41 $.35   (R1367)

I Do Not Ask, O Lord
SATB MARKS 4305 $.25   (R1368)

I Have Trusted In Thee
SATB SHAWNEE A 731 $.25   (R1369)

I Love My God
SATB oct ELKAN-V 362-1306 $.30   (R1370)

I Sing Of A Maiden
SSA SHAWNEE B 270 $.25   (R1371)
SATB SHAWNEE A 918 $.25   (R1372)

I Thank You, Lord
SATB (med diff) THOMP. C010 $.30   (R1373)

I Will Extol Thee
SATB,acap AMP A360 $.25   (R1374)

I Will Feed My Flock
SATB oct KERBY 6502C $.35   (R1375)
SATB,pno/org oct KERBY 6502 $.35   (R1376)

I Will Praise The Lord *anthem
SATB/jr cor oct FOX PS91 $.30   (R1377)

I Will Walk Before The Lord (Psalm 116)
SATB oct SHAPIRO SCE 2505 $.30   (R1378)

If A Man Love Me *Gen
SATB SCHMITT 15006 $.30   (R1379)

If Anyone Wishes To Come After Me *Gen,
anthem
SSA (easy) oct GIA G1429 $.25   (R1380)
SATB (easy) oct GIA G1415 $.25   (R1381)

If Ye Love Me
SATB LEONARD-US 08031760 $.25   (R1382)

If Ye Then Be Risen With Christ
SATB oct SHAPIRO SK 2056 $.25   (R1383)

ROFF, JOSEPH (cont'd.)

In A Manger *Xmas
  SA ALFRED 6135 $.25   (R1384)

Inspire Us, Almighty God
  SATB oct VOLKWEIN VB185 $.25   (R1385)

It Is You, O Lord *Gen,anthem/mot
  SSA (easy) oct GIA G1449 $.25   (R1386)
  SATB (easy) oct GIA G1422 $.25   (R1387)

Just A Little
  SAB oct VOLKWEIN VB199 $.25   (R1388)

Lead Us, Heavenly Father
  SATB SHAWNEE A 484 $.25   (R1389)

Lead Us Unto All Truth
  SAB FLAMMER D5131 $.25   (R1390)

Let All The Saints *Easter/Lent
  SAB oct PRO ART 2167 $.25   (R1391)

Het Me Be With Thee (from On Jordan's Bank
    The Baptist's Cry)
  SATB oct BOURNE JR3 $.25   (R1392)

Let The Heavens Be Glad *Xmas,anthem
  SATB (med easy) oct GIA G1149 $.30   (R1393)
  SA/TB (easy) oct GIA G1151 $.25   (R1394)

Let The Light Of Thy Countenance (Psalm 4)
    Gen,Allelu/anthem
  SATB (easy) oct GIA G1038 $.35   (R1395)

Let Them Trust In Thee
  SATB BOOSEY-CAN s.p.   (R1396)

Let Thy Mercy, O Lord, Be Upon Us (Psalm 32)
    Gen,Allelu/anthem
  SATB (med) oct GIA G1041 $.30   (R1397)

Lift Up Your Hearts
  SATB oct VOLKWEIN VB206 $.25   (R1398)

Light Of The World
  SATB MARKS 4042 $.25   (R1399)

Lord, Grant Us What Thou Wilt
  SATB,acap SHAWNEE A 733 $.30   (R1400)

Lord Has Sworn, The *Gen,anthem
  SSA (easy) oct GIA G1428 $.25   (R1401)
  SATB (easy) oct GIA G1414 $.25   (R1402)

Lord Is Gracious, The *anthem
  SATB (easy) oct AUGSBURG 0612 $.30   (R1403)

Lord Is Just, The
  SATB oct PRESSER 312-40366 $.30   (R1404)

Lord Is My Portion, The *Gen,anthem
  SSA (easy) oct GIA G1452 $.25   (R1405)

Lord Is My Strength, The
  SATB FLAMMER A 5120 $.30   (R1406)

Lord Is Nigh Unto Us All
  SATB oct VOLKWEIN VB210 $.30   (R1407)

Lord Make Me An Instrument Of Your Peace
    *prayer
  SATB oct VOLKWEIN VB211 $.30   (R1408)

Lord, Teach Us How To Pray
  SATB oct STAFF 362 $.25   (R1409)

Make A Joyful Noise Unto The Lord
  SATB,acap oct PRESSER 312-40492 $.35   (R1410)

Make Broad The Path
  SATB FLAMMER A 5040 $.30   (R1411)

Mass For Congregations *Gen,Mass
  unis (easy) voc sc GIA G1611 $1.25   (R1412)

Mass For Two Voices *Gen,Mass
  2pt (easy) voc sc GIA G1603 $1.00   (R1413)

Mass In Honor Of St. Joseph *Gen,Mass
  SATB (easy) voc sc GIA G1545 $1.00   (R1414)

Mass In Honour Of Saint Stephen Protomartyr
    *Mass
  2pt oct SHAPIRO SK 4013 $.50   (R1415)

Memorial Acclamations I-IV *CC4U,Gen,Mass
  SATB&cong voc sc GIA G1546 $.35   (R1416)

More Things Are Wrought By Prayer
  SATB PROWSE s.p.   (R1417)

My God, Accept My Heart Today
  SATB BOOSEY-CAN s.p.   (R1418)

My God, I Thank Thee
  SATB WARNER W3610 $.30   (R1419)

My Heart Rejoiceth In The Lord
  SATB,org BOSTON 13654 $.35   (R1420)

My Master Hath A Garden
  3pt jr cor/SSA (med easy) FISCHER,C CM 7526
    $.25   (R1421)

My Prayer Is Unto Thee
  SATB,S/T solo,pno/org AMP A480 $.25   (R1422)

My Soul Wait Thou Only Upon God
  SATB (easy) ABINGDON APM-432 $.35   (R1423)

My Times Are In Thy Hand
  SATB oct BOOSEY 5066 $.30   (R1424)

No Longer Will I Call You Servants *Gen,
    anthem
  SATB (easy) oct GIA G1427 $.25   (R1425)
  SSA (easy) oct GIA G1451 $.25   (R1426)

None Other Lamb
  SATB oct KERBY 5408 $.30   (R1427)
  SATB,acap oct KERBY 5408C $.30   (R1428)

Now Thank We *see Rodby

O Faithful Cross *Lent
  SATB oct GRAY GCMR 3083 $.30   (R1429)

ROFF, JOSEPH (cont'd.)

O Faithful Lord
  SATB oct VOLKWEIN VB222 $.25   (R1430)

O Gentle Jesu
  SATB oct PRESSER 332-40062 $.25   (R1431)

O God Of All Beauty
  SATB (easy) ABINGDON APM-133 $.24   (R1432)

O God, The Author Of Peace
  SATB,acap WARNER W3735 $.30   (R1433)

O Lord, Thou Art My God *Gen
  SATB,kbd (med easy) oct CONCORDIA 98-1857
    $.30   (R1434)

O Lord, Who Has Taught Us
  SATB,acap oct PRESSER 312-40504 $.30   (R1435)

O Lord, Who Never Failest
  SATB oct ELKAN-V 362-1239 $.25   (R1436)

Only Follow Him
  SATB oct BOOSEY 5379 $.30   (R1437)

Peace To This House
  SATB MARKS 4187 $.25   (R1438)

People's Mass *Gen,Mass
  unis,opt kbd (easy) voc sc GIA G1557 $1.25 (R1439)

Pour Into Our Hearts
  SATB,acap oct BOOSEY 1995 $.30   (R1440)

Praise To You, Father *prayer
  SATB (med diff) THOMP. CO09 $.30   (R1441)

Prayer From Outer Space *prayer
  SATB WARNER WB-105 $.35   (R1442)

Priest And Bishop *anthem
  SATB (med easy) oct GIA G1419 $.25   (R1443)
  SSA (med easy) oct GIA G1446 $.25   (R1444)

Psalm 4 *see Let The Light Of Thy
    Countenance

Psalm 32 *see Let Thy Mercy, O Lord, Be Upon
    Us

Psalm 46 *see All You Peoples Clap Your
    Hands

Psalm 73 *see Thou Shalt Guide Me

Psalm 100 *see Sing Joyfully To The Lord

Psalm 116 *see I Will Walk Before The Lord

Put Ye On The Lord Jesus
  SATB,acap oct COLOMBO 2356 $.25   (R1445)

Receive Ye The Body Of Christ *Commun,anthem
  (Bobak, J.) SATB (easy) oct GIA G1042 $.35 (R1446)

Reign Over Me, Lord Jesus
  SA/TB SHAWNEE E27 $.25   (R1447)

Rejoice, People Of God
  SATB LEONARD-US 08054500 $.25   (R1448)

Saviour Of The Nations Come
  SATB oct VOLKWEIN VB254 $.25   (R1449)

Seasonal Responsorial Psalms *CC13U,Gen,
    Mass/Psalm
  opt SATB&cong,cantor (easy) voc sc GIA
    G1744 $2.00   (R1450)

See That You Love One Another
  SATB oct GRAY GCMR 3224 $.30   (R1451)

Seek Ye The Lord
  SATB oct WORD CS-2317 $.30   (R1452)

Simon The Cyrenean Speaks
  SATB oct SACRED S-37 $.35   (R1453)

Sing For Joy, O Heavens
  SATB,opt Bar solo AMP A417 $.25   (R1454)

Sing Joyfully To The Lord (Psalm 100) Gen,
    anthem
  unis (easy) oct GIA G1617 $.25   (R1455)

Sing To The Lord *Gen
  SATB SCHMITT 1738 $.25   (R1456)

So Precious In The Sight Of The Lord *Gen
  SATB SCHMITT 1770 $.20   (R1457)

Song Of Thanksgiving, A *Gen/Thanks
  SATB,kbd (med easy) oct CONCORDIA 98-1433
    $.30   (R1458)

Soul Of My Savior *see Anima Christi

Strengthen, O God *Gen,anthem/mot
  SSA (easy) oct GIA G1448 $.25   (R1459)

Surely He Hath Borne Our Griefs
  SATB oct SACRED S-68 $.35   (R1460)

Tantum Ergo
  "Therefore We" SATB oct LESLIE 4073 (R1461)

Teach Us, Good Lord
  SATB,acap AMP A336 $.25   (R1462)

Thanks Be To Thee
  SATB,acap SHAWNEE A 520 $.30   (R1463)

That They All May Be One
  SATB,acap SHAWNEE A 892 $.25   (R1464)

Thee Will I Cherish
  SAB oct ELKAN-V 362-508 $.25   (R1465)

Therefore We *see Tantum Ergo

Thine Forever, God Of Love *Gen
  SATB,kbd (easy) oct CONCORDIA 98-1376 $.25 (R1466)

This Is The Day *Easter/Lent
  SAB oct PRO ART 2154 $.25   (R1467)

ROFF, JOSEPH (cont'd.)

This Little Babe *Xmas
  SATB oct GALLEON GCS1007   (R1468)

Thou Art My God *Gen
  SATB oct SPRATT 595 $.25   (R1469)

Thou Art The Way
  SATB MARKS 4041 $.25   (R1470)

Thou Hast Made Us For Thyself
  SATB oct SHAPIRO SK 2108 $.30   (R1471)

Thou Shalt Guide Me (Psalm 73)
  SATB oct SHAPIRO SCE 2508 $.30   (R1472)

Thou Shalt Love The Lord Thy God
  SATB KJOS PC769 $.30   (R1473)

Three Prayers For Today *CC3U,prayer
  SATB oct VOLKWEIN VB720 $.30   (R1474)

Thy Love Declare
  SAB oct ELKAN-V 362-503 $.25   (R1475)

Tidings Of Peace
  SATB oct AGAPE CF 130 $.30   (R1476)

'Tis Christmas *Xmas
  jr cor LILLENAS AN-4024 $.25   (R1477)

Virgin Mother *ASD/BVM,anthem,Russ
  (Bobak, J.) SATB (easy) oct GIA G1021 $.25 (R1478)

Walk As Children Of Light
  SATB,opt Bar solo,pno/org AMP A603 $.30   (R1479)

Way, The Truth, And The Life, The *Gen
  SATB SCHMITT 8004 $.22   (R1480)

We Have Waited For Him *Xmas,Bibl
  SATB oct SHAPIRO SCE 2509 $.30   (R1481)

What Return Shall I Make To The Lord *Gen,
    anthem
  SATB (easy) oct GIA G1418 $.25   (R1482)
  SSA (easy) oct GIA G1445 $.25   (R1483)

Whatsoever Ye Shall Ask *anthem/hymn
  SATB oct SPRATT 619 $.30   (R1484)

Who Was Born *Xmas
  SSA oct ELKAN-V 362-3098 $.25   (R1485)

Whole Bright World Rejoices, The *Easter
  SATB oct GRAY GCMR 2847 $.25   (R1486)

Why Do Bells For Christmas Ring? *Xmas
  2pt oct SHAPIRO SK 4014 $.25   (R1487)

With An Everlasting Love *Gen,anthem
  SSA (easy) oct GIA G1454 $.25   (R1488)

With Him For All Eternity
  SATB oct SHAPIRO SK 2043 $.25   (R1489)

Yours Are The Heavens *Xmas,anthem
  SATB (easy) oct GIA G1153 $.30   (R1490)
  SA/TB (easy) oct GIA G1154 $.25   (R1491)

ROGATION CAROL see Swaffield, Ronald

ROGBERG, CARL
  Pingsthymn
  mix cor NORDISKA 889 s.p.   (R1492)

ROGER
  Holy Child Sleeps *Xmas
  SATB oct GALAXY 1.2288.1 $.30   (R1493)

ROGER-DUCASSE, JEAN-JULES AIMABLE (1873-1954)
  Alma Redemptoris Mater *BVM,mot
  [Lat] 4pt mix cor,S solo oct DURAND s.p.   (R1494)

  Chant De La Nativite *Xmas/Gen,mot
  [Fr] SA oct DURAND s.p.   (R1495)

  Crux Fidelis *Gen,mot
  [Lat] 4pt mix cor,S solo oct DURAND s.p.   (R1496)

  Ego Sum Panis Vivus *Commun,anti/mot
  [Lat] opt wom cor,S solo oct DURAND s.p.   (R1497)
  [Lat] 3pt jr cor&wom cor,org oct DURAND
    s.p.   (R1498)

  Quem Vidistis, Pastores, Dicite *Gen,mot
  [Lat] cor,org oct DURAND s.p.   (R1499)

  Regina Coeli Laetare *BVM,mot
  [Lat] 4pt mix cor,S solo oct DURAND s.p.   (R1500)

ROGERS
  All Nature's Works His Praise Declare
  SATB oct GALAXY 1.2223.1 $.30   (R1501)

  Amazing Grace *Gen
  SATB,S solo GALLEON GCS3003   (R1502)

  Balm In Gilead
  SATB oct LORENZ 9686 $.30   (R1503)

  Benedictus, Es Domine
  SA/TB FLAMMER E5066 $.25   (R1504)

  Born In A Manger
  (Ades) SATB FLAMMER A 5587 $.30   (R1505)

  Carol Of The Bells *Xmas,cant
  SATB oct LORENZ $1.95   (R1506)

  Chant Of Glory And Praise
  SSA FLAMMER B 5087 $.40   (R1507)

  Christ The Lord Is Risen Today *Easter
  SATB oct LORENZ 9986 $.30   (R1508)

  Christ Was Born Today *see Christus Natus
    Hodie

  Christus Natus Hodie *Xmas
  "Christ Was Born Today" SATB FLAMMER A 5089
    $.25   (R1509)

  Contemporary Noel, A
  SATB FLAMMER A 5166 $.35   (R1510)

ROGERS (cont'd.)

Earth Is The Lord's, The
SAB,org/pno BOSTON 13223 $.40   (R1511)

Easter Triumph *Easter
SATB FLAMMER A 5209 $.30   (R1512)

For In My House Are Many Mansions
SATB oct GALAXY 1.2224.1 $.30   (R1513)

Give Thanks And Praise
(Lundquist) SATB,acap oct FOX PS31 $.22 (R1514)

Gladness Of Easter, The *Easter
2pt jr cor/3pt jr cor oct LILLENAS AN-4005
$.25   (R1515)

Glory To God *Xmas
SAB oct LORENZ 7312 $.30   (R1516)
SATB oct LORENZ 4151 $.35   (R1517)

God Is Near
2pt jr cor oct LILLENAS AN-4002 $.25   (R1518)

Hear The Sound Of The Shepherds Piping
SATB&jr cor,opt fl oct BOURNE 929 $.50 (R1519)

Hear Us, O Lord *Gen
SATB SCHMITT 1622 $.35   (R1520)

Hosanna! Hosanna! *Easter
SATB oct LORENZ 9579 $.30   (R1521)

Jerusalem My Happy Home
SATB oct GALAXY 1.2216.1 $.30   (R1522)

Jesu, Lord Of Heavenly Grace
SATB oct GALAXY 1.2225.1 $.30   (R1523)

Joy Dawned Again On Easter Day *Easter
SATB oct SACRED S-5382 $.35   (R1524)

Jubilate Deo
SATB FLAMMER A 5301 $.35   (R1525)

Liturgical Responses And Anthems *CCU
SA FLAMMER GE5012 $1.10   (R1526)

O Be Joyful In The Lord
SATB FLAMMER A 5326 $.25   (R1527)

O Brother Man
SATB FLAMMER A 5174 $.30   (R1528)

O Love, How Deep
SATB oct SACRED S-9963 $.35   (R1529)

Praise The Lord For His Goodness
SATB,org BOSTON 13424 $.35   (R1530)

Prayer For Our Country, A
SA oct LORENZ 5384 $.30   (R1531)

Savior, Like A Shepherd Lead Us
2pt oct SACRED S-5751 $.35   (R1532)

Shepherds Had An Angel
SA/TB FLAMMER E5092 $.30   (R1533)

Song Of Triumph, The
SATB FLAMMER A 5214 $.30   (R1534)

Teach Me, O Lord
(Payson, A.) SATB,acap FRANK F-443 $.30
                                       (R1535)
(Wienandt) SATB,acap FLAMMER A 5552 $.25 (R1536)

That Child So Dear
SATB FLAMMER A 5199 $.30   (R1537)

ROGERS, B.
Light Of Man, The
SATB oct PRESSER 312-40608 $.60   (R1538)

Lord God Of Hosts
SATB oct PRESSER 312-40601 $.45   (R1539)

ROGERS, BENJAMIN (1614-1698)
Behold, Now Praise The Lord *17th cent
(Wienandt) SATB,acap oct LAWSON 51400 $.30
                                       (R1540)
Evening Service In "A Re" *Magnif/Nunc
SATB,opt inst (med easy) oct OXFORD 43.395
$.30   (R1541)

Lord, Who Shall Dwell In Thy Tabernacle
SATB,acap PETERS H1520 $.40   (R1542)

Magnificat And Nunc Dimittis (from Sharp
Service, The) Magnif/Nunc
(Rose, Bernard) SATB,acap oct NOVELLO
44.1443.08 s.p.   (R1543)

O Give Thanks Unto The Lord
SATB,acap PETERS H1518   (R1544)

Teach Me, O Lord
SATB,acap PETERS H1519   (R1545)

ROGERS, BERNARD (1893-1968)
Hear My Prayer, O God
SATB oct PRESSER 312-40250 $.40   (R1546)

Psalm 18
TTBB oct PRESSER 312-40600 $.40   (R1547)

Psalm 114
SATB oct PRESSER 312-40717 $.35   (R1548)

ROGERS, DAVID
By The Manger *Xmas
SATB,acap SEESAW $.50   (R1549)

ROGERS, E.
From The Psalms
SATB,acap oct PRESSER MC322 $.40   (R1550)

I Will Extol Thee *CCU
SATB PRESSER $1.00   (R1551)

Jesus, Bread Of Life Divine
SATB,acap oct PRESSER 312-40487 $.30   (R1552)

Let Us Sing To The Lord *CCU
SATB oct PRESSER $1.25   (R1553)

ROGERS, E. (cont'd.)

Spring Carol
2pt mix cor oct PRESSER MC272 $.30   (R1554)

Winds At Bethlehem, The *Xmas
SATB,acap oct PRESSER MC409 $.35   (R1555)

ROGERS, ETHEL TRENCH
Behold The Empty Tomb *Easter/Gd.Fri.,cant
SAB voc sc LILLENAS ME-219 $1.00   (R1556)

Day To Rejoice, A *Easter,Bibl/cant
unis&2pt jr cor&opt 3pt jr cor voc
sc LILLENAS ME-218 $1.00   (R1557)

Jesus Is Born *Xmas,cant
unis&2pt&opt 3pt voc sc LILLENAS MC-233
$1.00   (R1558)

ROGERS, G.
O Sing Unto The Lord
SAB oct FISCHER,J 9490 $.30   (R1559)

ROGERS, J.
Seek Him That Maketh The Seven Stars
*Easter/Gen
SATB oct PRESSER 332-12733 $.30   (R1560)

ROGERS, J.H.
Be Ye Therefore Followers Of God *Bibl
4pt mix cor,T solo oct SCHIRM.G 5026 $.20 (R1561)

Doth Not Wisdom Cry *Bibl
4pt mix cor,B solo oct SCHIRM.G 5199 $.25 (R1562)

Fear Not, O Land *Thanks,Bibl
4pt mix cor oct SCHIRM.G 4064 $.25   (R1563)

Great Peace Have They *Bibl
(Deis) 4pt mix cor oct SCHIRM.G 7238 $.25 (R1564)

I Will Lift Up Mine Eyes *Bibl
4pt mix cor,S solo oct SCHIRM.G 5813 $.30 (R1565)

I Will Magnify Thee *Bibl
4pt mix cor,SB soli oct SCHIRM.G 5442 $.25 (R1566)

Lord, For Thy Tender Mercies *Bibl
4pt mix cor,S solo oct SCHIRM.G 5588 $.20 (R1567)

Man Of Nazareth, The
cor,STBar soli,org voc sc SCHIRM.G $1.00 (R1568)

May The Words Of My Mouth (Psalm 19) Bibl
4pt mix cor oct SCHIRM.G 8405 $.20   (R1569)

Now If Christ Be Preached *Easter,Bibl
4pt mix cor,ST soli oct SCHIRM.G 5136 $.25 (R1570)

O Taste And See *Bibl
4pt mix cor,T solo oct SCHIRM.G 4644 $.25 (R1571)

Path Of The Just, The
SATB oct HUNTZINGER 4006 $.16   (R1572)

Psalm 19 *see May The Words Of My Mouth

Thus Saith The Lord Of Hosts *Bibl
4pt mix cor,STB soli oct SCHIRM.G 7258 $.35 (R1573)

ROGERS, S.E.
Babe Of Bethlehem, The
SATB&opt jr cor,opt hndbl oct BOURNE 832
$.25   (R1574)

O My Dearest Jesus *Easter,cant
SA LORENZ $1.75   (R1575)

ROGERS, SHARON ELERY
Bells On Easter Morn, The *Easter
SA,opt hndbl oct BOURNE 2035 $.30   (R1576)

Jesus Is Born On This Happy New Day *Xmas
2pt,opt hndbl oct AGAPE F 934 $.35   (R1577)

Lord Of Hosts Most High, The
SATB,org/pno oct WORLD ESA-1868-8 $.45 (R1578)

Now Let Us Sing
2pt oct AGAPE CF 152 $.30   (R1579)

O Come And Mourn With Me
SATB oct AGAPE A 406 $.25   (R1580)

ROGERS, VIVIENNE R.
Thanks Be To God *Xmas,Bibl/cant
unis jr cor&2pt jr cor,narrator, woodblock,
resonator bells, autoharp voc sc LILLENAS
MC-19 $1.00   (R1581)

ROGERS, WILLIAM KEITH
Two Christmas Carols *CC2U
SSAA,acap oct BERANDOL 846R6AC $.35   (R1582)

ROHACZEWSKI, ANDRIEJ
Crucifixus Surrexit *mot,Pol
(Sutkowski, A.) 9pt mix cor POLSKIE WDMP46
s.p.   (R1583)

ROHLFING, RICHARD T.
Christmas Cantata *Xmas,cant
unis&SA,org (revised edition) sc CONCORDIA
97-5110 $2.25, cor pts CONCORDIA 98-2150
$.25   (R1584)

ROHLIG, HARALD (1914-   )
Arise, O Lord
mix cor oct AGAPE A 427 $.30   (R1585)

Behold, A Branch Is Growing *Xmas,cant
mix cor,T solo,2fl,org CONCORDIA 97-6391
$.50, ipa   (R1586)

Christ Is Arisen *Easter
unis,pno,trp,perc oct AGAPE F 943 $.35 (R1587)

Hodie Christus Natus Est *Xmas,cant
mix cor,T solo,org,3trp CONCORDIA 97-6354
$.90   (R1588)

How Lovely Shines The Morning Star *Adv/
Epiph/Gen
SATB&cong/SATB&jr cor,org,trp (med easy)
CONCORDIA 97-4687 $1.50, cor pts
CONCORDIA 98-1795 $.30, ipa   (R1589)

ROHLIG, HARALD (cont'd.)

Magnificat
mix cor,2fl,2trp,org CONCORDIA 97-6436
$1.25, ipa   (R1590)

Now Thank We All Our God *Thanks,cant
BELWIN $1.50   (R1591)
mix cor&cong,3trp,org sc CONCORDIA 97-6381
$1.00, cor pts CONCORDIA 98-1638 $.30,
ipa   (R1592)

O Clap Your Hands *anthem
SATB (med) oct AUGSBURG 0607 $.25   (R1593)

O Holy Jesus *Psntd,cant
mix cor,fl,org CONCORDIA 97-6311 $.75, ipa (R1594)

O Sing Unto The Lord
mix cor oct AGAPE A 431 $.30   (R1595)

Our Father
unis oct AGAPE CF 140 $.30   (R1596)

Praise To The Lord *Gen
SATB&cong/SATB&jr cor,org,trp,fl (med easy)
sc CONCORDIA 97-4423 $1.80, cor pts
CONCORDIA 98-1448 $.25, ipa   (R1597)

Sing Unto The Lord A New Song
SATB,acap oct ABINGDON APM-277 $.25   (R1598)

Wake, Awake, For Night Is Flying *Adv/ECY
SATB&cong/SATB&jr cor,org,trp (med easy) sc
CONCORDIA 97-4670 $1.50, cor pts
CONCORDIA 98-1782 $.30, ipa   (R1599)

We Come Unto Our Father's God *ASD
unis (easy) ABINGDON APM-412 $.25   (R1600)

ROHRER
Collect
SSA (for club women) oct VOLKWEIN VB132
$.25   (R1601)

ROHWER, JENS (1914-   )
Ach Bleib Bei Uns, Herr Jesu Christ
3pt mix cor MOSELER LB-277 s.p.   (R1602)

Ach Gott, Vom Himmel Sieh Darein
3pt mix cor MOSELER LB-229 s.p. contains
also: Die Helle Sonn Leucht Jetzt Herfur (R1603)

Als Jesus Von Seiner Mutter Ging
men cor,acap TONGER s.p.   (R1604)

Aus Tiefer Not
3pt mix cor MOSELER LB-202 s.p.   (R1605)

Bedenk Mensch *canon
3pt mix cor MOSELER LB-70 s.p. contains
also: Senke Den Lichten Schein (3pt mix
cor); Werft Euer Herz In Die Flamme (4pt
mix cor)   (R1606)

Christus Triumphator *CC3U,Bibl/mot
mix cor,SAT soli,acap cor pts MOSELER s.p. (R1607)

Da Christus Geboren War
SA/men cor,treb inst&bass inst/kbd HANSSLER
14.019 s.p.   (R1608)

Denk Ich Der Walder
4pt mix cor MOSELER LB-277 s.p. contains
also: Herr Gott, Dein Wille   (R1609)

Der Herr Sendet Eine Erlosung *evang/mot
"Psalm 111" 4pt mix cor,acap cor pts
BREITKOPF-W CHB-3100 s.p. see also Psalm-
Und Evangelienmotetten   (R1610)

Der Mond Ist Aufgegangen *mot
6pt mix cor&cong,S solo MOSELER sc s.p.,
cor pts s.p.   (R1611)

Die Helle Sonn Leucht Jetzt Herfur
see Rohwer, Jens, Ach Gott, Vom Himmel Sieh
Darein

Ein Feste Burg
3pt mix cor MOSELER LB-230 s.p.   (R1612)

Gebete Der Deutschen *prayer
4pt mix cor MOSELER s.p.   (R1613)

Gib, Dass Ein Licht Uns Wieder Schein *mot
3 gem voices,opt clar/vla, or English horn
MOSELER cor pts s.p., sc s.p., ipa   (R1614)

Gott Im Himmel
3pt mix cor MOSELER LB-41 s.p.   (R1615)

Herr, Erhore Mein Gebet (Psalm 143) evang/mot
4pt mix cor,acap cor pts BREITKOPF-W
CHB-3101 s.p. see also Psalm- Und
Evangelienmotetten   (R1616)

Herr Gott, Dein Wille
see Rohwer, Jens, Denk Ich Der Walder

Hore, Herr, Hore Meine Worte (Psalm 5)
mix cor,4 narrators MOSELER s.p.   (R1617)

Ich Danke Dem Herrn *evang/mot
"Psalm 111" 4pt mix cor,acap cor pts
BREITKOPF-W CHB-3099 s.p. see also Psalm-
Und Evangelienmotetten   (R1618)

Ihr Volker, Bringet Her Dem Herrn (Psalm 96)
evang/mot
4pt mix cor,acap BREITKOPF-W CHB-3098 s.p.
see also Psalm- Und Evangelienmotetten (R1619)

Jauchzet Gott, Alle Lande (Psalm 66) evang/
mot
4pt mix cor,acap cor pts BREITKOPF-W
CHB-3097 s.p. see also Psalm- Und
Evangelienmotetten   (R1620)

Jesu Leiden Unsere Seligkeit *mot
4pt mix cor,med solo,acap cor pts
BREITKOPF-W CHB-3183 s.p.   (R1621)

Komm, Troster Geist *cant
4-6pt mix cor,3vln,3rec, glockenspiel
MOSELER sc s.p., cor pts s.p., ipa   (R1622)

ROHWER, JENS (cont'd.)

Lob Und Preis *CCU
(Wagner, Hermann) mix cor MOSELER s.p.
(R1623)

Lobet All Und Singet *mot
4pt mix cor MOSELER s.p.   (R1624)

Nun Bitten Wir Den Heiligen Geist *mot
4pt mix cor MOSELER LB-212 s.p.   (R1625)
5pt mix cor&cong,S solo MOSELER sc s.p.,
cor pts s.p.   (R1626)

Nun Danket All Und Bringet Ehr
3pt mix cor MOSELER LB-203 s.p.   (R1627)

Nun Freut Euch, Lieben Christen Gemein
3pt mix cor MOSELER LB-233 s.p.   (R1628)

O Konig Aller Ehren
SAT/SAB HANSSLER 14.049   (R1629)

Perpetua *CCU
mix cor MOSELER s.p.   (R1630)

Psalm 5 *see Hore, Herr, Hore Meine Worte

Psalm 66 *see Jauchzet Gott, Alle Lande

Psalm 96 *see Ihr Volker, Bringet Her Dem
Herrn

Psalm 111 *see Der Herr Sendet Eine Erlosung

Psalm 111 *see Ich Danke Dem Herrn

Psalm 143 *see Herr, Erhore Mein Gebet

Psalm- Und Evangelienmotetten *evang/mot
4pt mix cor,acap BREITKOPF-W
contains & see also: Der Herr Sendet Eine
Erlosung, "Psalm 111"; Herr, Erhore
Mein Gebet (Psalm 143); Ihr Volker,
Bringet Her Dem Herrn (Psalm 96);
Jauchzet Gott, Alle Lande (Psalm 66);
Uber Ein Kleines, So Werdet Ihr Mich
Nicht Sehen; Wenn Des Menschen Sohn
Kommen Wird   (R1631)

Senke Den Lichten Schein
see Rohwer, Jens, Bendenk Mensch

Singenden Jahr *see Wir Loben Noch Und
Singen   (R1632)

Uber Ein Kleines, So Werdet Ihr Mich Nicht
Sehen *Bibl/evang/mot
4pt mix cor,acap cor pts BREITKOPF-W
CHB-3103 s.p. see also Psalm- Und
Evangelienmotetten   (R1633)

Vater Im Himmel, Sieh Darein *prayer
3pt mix cor MOSELER LB-228 s.p.   (R1634)

Vater, Vergib Uns *prayer
1-3 eq voices/1-3pt mix cor,inst MOSELER
LB-158 s.p.   (R1635)

Von Gott Will Ich Nicht Lassen
3pt mix cor MOSELER LB-231 s.p.   (R1636)

Wach Auf, Wach Auf, 's Ist Hochste Zeit
4pt mix cor,strings BREITKOPF-W sc s.p.,
cor pts s.p., ipa   (R1637)

War Gott Nicht Mit Uns
3pt mix cor MOSELER LB-232 s.p.   (R1638)

Wen Der Tod Trifft *Bibl/ora
mix cor&mix cor&cong,STB soli,orch MOSELER
rental   (R1639)

Wenn Des Menschen Sohn Kommen Wird *Bibl/
evang/mot
4pt mix cor,acap cor pts BREITKOPF-W
CHB-3102 s.p. see also Psalm- Und
Evangelienmotetten   (R1640)

Werft Euer Herz In Die Flamme
see Rohwer, Jens, Bendenk Mensch

Wir Loben Noch Und Singen
4 eq voices/4pt mix cor MOSELER LB-531 s.p.
see from Singenden Jahr   (R1641)

Zeuch Ein Zu Deinen Toren
SA/SAT,treb inst HANSSLER 14.105 s.p.   (R1642)

ROIS ET BERGERS see Vasseur, Henry

ROLFE
Closer Still With Thee
(MacLean) SAB WARNER W3455 $.30   (R1643)

ROLL DE OL' CHARIOT *spir
SATB CHAPPELL 0022830-358 $.40   (R1644)

ROLL DE OL'CHARIOT ALONG *spir,US
(Aubanel, Georges) "Roule Le Vieux Chariot"
[Eng/Fr] 4pt mix cor OUVRIERES s.p.   (R1645)

ROLL, JORDAN *spir
(Durian, Tim) 4pt men cor,opt solo,acap
BREITKOPF-W Z-56 s.p. see also Dreizehn
Negro-Spirituals   (R1646)

ROLL, JORDAN, ROLL *spir
"Rausch, Jordan, Rausch" see Funf Negro-
Spirituals
(Caddo) dbl cor oct PRO ART 1332 $.16 (R1647)
(Gillum, Ruth) SATB oct FISCHER,J 8390 $.30
(R1648)
(Kemmer) SATB,acap oct COLOMBO 1287 $.30
(R1649)

ROLL, JORDAN, ROLL see Joosen, B.

ROLL, JORDAN, ROLL see Owens, Jimmy

ROLL, JORDON, ROLL
see Bones, Come a-Knittin'

ROLL THE CHARIOT *spir
SATB oct STAFF 487 $.25   (R1650)
(Gardner) SA/TB oct STAFF 568 $.30   (R1651)
(Gardner) SAB oct STAFF 567 $.30   (R1652)
(Gardner) SSA oct STAFF 566 $.30   (R1653)

ROLLE
Let All Give Thanks To God *see Nun Danket
Alle Gott

Lord God Of My Fathers
(Suchoff) SATB oct FOX RM8 $.30   (R1654)

Lord Jesus, Who Didst Redeem *Morav
(Dickinson) SATB oct GRAY GMCM 18 $.30   (R1655)

Nun Danket Alle Gott *mot
(Frank) "Let All Give Thanks To God" SATB
oct FOX MM4 $.30   (R1656)

ROLLED AWAY *medley
(Ferrin) SATB oct LILLENAS AN-1191 $.30   (R1657)

ROMAN, JOHAN HELMICH (1694-1758)
Beati Omnes
cor,soli,org,strings cor pts NORDISKA 1655
s.p., voc sc NORDISKA s.p.   (R1658)

Befall Din Vag At Herren
[Norw] 3pt mix cor,org LYCHE 57 s.p.   (R1659)

Besinner Dock *Bibl
(Soderholm, Valdemar) [Swed] SATB,org,
strings GEHRMANS sc s.p., cor pts s.p.,
ipa   (R1660)

God Is Our Refuge (Psalm 46)
SATB,2ob,2vln,vla,vcl,bvl voc sc PETERS
66122 $.40, ipa   (R1661)
(Hans Keuning) SATB,S solo,org/2ob,2vln,
vla,vcl,bvl PETERS 66122 $.40, ipa   (R1662)

Gud Ar Var Tillflykt *cant
mix cor,org,2ob,5strings sc NORDISKA 2060
s.p., ipa, cor pts NORDISKA 2012 s.p.   (R1663)

Hjalp, Herre De Heliga *Bibl
(Soderholm, Valdemar) [Swed] SATB,org,
strings sc GEHRMANS s.p., cor pts
GEHRMANS KRB 220 ipa   (R1664)

Joyful Be To God *see Jubilate Deo

Jubilate Deo
(Wolff, S.D.) "Joyful Be To God" SATB,SB
soli,orch voc sc CONCORDIA 97-5025 $2.00,
ipa, sc CONCORDIA 97-5121 s.p.   (R1665)

Psalm 37
(Soderholm, Valdemar) 3pt mix cor,2vln,vla,
vcl cor pts NORDISKA 1636 s.p., sc
NORDISKA 1621 s.p.   (R1666)

Psalm 46 *see God Is Our Refuge

ROMANCE DEL NARANJEL see Benedito

ROMANOVSKY, ERICH
Aus Der Tiefe (Psalm 129)
[Ger] mix cor,acap oct DOBLINGER s.p. see
from Zwei Deutsche Psalmen   (R1667)

Deutsche Messe In C *Mass
"Doblinger Messe" 4pt mix cor,acap voc sc
DOBLINGER s.p.   (R1668)

Deutsches Ordinarium
unis/unis&mix cor,org DOBLINGER voc sc
s.p., cor pts s.p.   (R1669)

Doblinger Messe *see Deutsche Messe In C

Psalm 126 *see Wenn Der Herr Das Haus Nicht
Baut

Psalm 129 *see Aus Der Tiefe

Rex Pacificus *Mass
4pt mix cor,acap sc DOBLINGER s.p.   (R1670)

Wenn Der Herr Das Haus Nicht Baut (Psalm 126)
[Ger] mix cor,acap oct DOBLINGER s.p. see
from Zwei Deutsche Psalmen   (R1671)

Zwei Deutsche Psalmen *see Aus Der Tiefe
(Psalm 129); Wenn Der Herr Das Haus Nicht
Baut (Psalm 126)   (R1672)

ROMANS, A.
Noel De La Paix
[Fr] 4pt mix cor CHAPPELL-FR s.p.   (R1673)

ROMERO, GARY (1912-)
My Soul's Gonna Rise Again *see Hall,
Dickson

ROMME, DONALD R.
Cross Of Christ, The *cant
mix cor BELWIN $1.50   (R1674)

ROMMEL, KURT (1926-)
Herr, Unser Herrscher *Gen
[Ger] unis,acap (easy) BOSSE BE 256 s.p. (R1675)

RON LUSH CHORUSES NO. 1 see Lush, Ron

RON LUSH CHORUSES NO. 2 see Lush, Ron

RONDO FOR CHILDREN see Goemanne, Noel

RONTGEN, [JULIUS] (1855-1932)
Den Dag En Wil Niet Verborghen Sijn
see Zes Oud-Ned. Liederen

Een Kind Is Ons Gheboren
see Zes Oud-Ned. Liederen

Ick Wil Mi Gaen Vertroosten
see Zes Oud-Ned. Liederen

Kerstliedeje
see Zes Vrouwenkoren

Lire Boulire, Lire Boula
see Zes Vrouwenkoren

Lof Gods
see Zes Vrouwenkoren

Mis
3pt wom cor BROEKMANS 88 s.p.   (R1676)

Negen Oud-Ned. Liederen *CC9L
mix cor ALSBACH&D sc s.p., cor pts s.p.
(R1677)

RONTGEN, [JULIUS] (cont'd.)
O Jesu Soet
see Zes Oud-Ned. Liederen

Schoonheid
see Zes Vrouwenkoren

Sijt Vrolic, Groot En Cleijne
see Zes Oud-Ned. Liederen

Van Liefden Comt Groot Liden
see Zes Oud-Ned. Liederen

Wat De Sneeuwvlokken Zingen
see Zes Vrouwenkoren

Zes Oud-Ned. Liederen
mix cor sc ALSBACH&D s.p. score and choral
parts separately published
contains: Den Dag En Wil Niet Verborghen
Sijn; Een Kind Is Ons Gheboren; Ick Wil
Mi Gaen Vertroosten; O Jesu Soet; Sijt
Vrolic, Groot En Cleijne; Van Liefden
Comt Groot Liden   (R1678)

Zes Vrouwenkoren *Op.84, sac/sec
3-4pt wom cor,pno sc ALSBACH&D s.p. score
and choral parts separately published
contains: Kerstliedeje; Lire Boulire,
Lire Boula; Lof Gods; Schoonheid; Wat
De Sneeuwvlokken Zingen; Zondag   (R1679)

Zondag
see Zes Vrouwenkoren

ROOS, ROBERT DE (1907-)
Lyrische Suite *Bibl
[Dut] mix cor,fl,clar,trom,strings,perc,
timp, alto saxophone min sc DONEMUS s.p.
(R1680)

ROOT
Blessed Is The Nation
(Karlin) SATB,acap oct MCA   (R1681)

Come To The Saviour, Make No Delay *Gen
(Lynn) SATB,S/A solo oct SOUTHERN $.25
(R1682)

God Of The World! Thy Glories Shine
(Coggin) 2pt jr cor FISCHER,C CM 7518 $.25
(R1683)

He Is The King Of Glory *Bibl
(Wiley) SATB oct PRO ART 2546 $.25   (R1684)

ROOT, G.F.
Magnify, Glorify
cor oct HART s.p.   (R1685)

Saviour, Breathe An Evening Blessing *Eve
oct HART contains also: Soft Floating On
The Evening Air   (R1686)

Soft Floating On The Evening Air
see Root, G.F., Saviour, Breathe An Evening
Blessing

ROP UT MED FRYD see Nystedt, Knut

ROPARTZ, JOSEPH GUY (1864-1955)
Antienne A Sainte Jeanne D'arc *anthem
[Fr] 3 eq voices,acap oct DURAND   (R1687)

Ave Verum *Commun,mot
[Lat] oct DURAND s.p.   (R1688)

De Profundis (Psalm 129)
"Psaume CXXIX" [Lat] mix cor,B solo,orch,
opt org voc sc DURAND s.p., ipr   (R1689)

Little Children All
(Davis) SSAA oct GALAXY 1.1332.1 $.30
(R1690)

Messe Breve En L'honneur De Sainte Anne
*Mass
[Fr] 3 eq voices oct DURAND s.p.   (R1691)

Messe En L'honneur De Sainte Odile *Mass
[Fr] 3pt men cor&unis jr cor oct DURAND
s.p.   (R1692)

Psalm 129 *see De Profundis

Psaume CXXIX *see De Profundis

Requiem *Mass/Req
[Fr] cor,soli,orch voc sc DURAND s.p.
(R1693)

ROQUES, L.
Le Fils Du Roi De Gloire *Xmas,carol
[Fr] 2 eq voices,pno oct DURAND s.p. see
from Six Noels Anciens   (R1694)

Les Anges Dans Nos Campagnes *Xmas,carol
[Fr] 2 eq voices,pno oct DURAND s.p. see
from Six Noels Anciens   (R1695)

Noel Nouvelet *Xmas,carol
[Fr] 2 eq voices,pno oct DURAND s.p. see
from Six Noels Anciens   (R1696)

Nous Allons, Ma Mie *Xmas,carol
[Fr] 2 eq voices,pno oct DURAND s.p. see
from Six Noels Anciens   (R1697)

Paraissez, Monarque Aimable *Xmas,carol
[Fr] 2 eq voices,pno oct DURAND s.p. see
from Six Noels Anciens   (R1698)

Quittez, Pasteurs, Vos Brebis *Xmas,carol
[Fr] 2 eq voices,pno oct DURAND s.p. see
from Six Noels Anciens   (R1699)

Regina Coeli *BVM,mot
(Kunc, P.) [Lat] mix cor oct DURAND s.p.
(R1700)

Six Noels Anciens *see Le Fils Du Roi De
Gloire; Les Anges Dans Nos Campagnes;
Noel Nouvelet; Nous Allons, Ma Mie;
Paraissez, Monarque Aimable; Quittez,
Pasteurs, Vos Brebis   (R1701)

RORATE see Haydn, (Franz) Joseph

RORATE CAELI see Schroeder, Hermann

RORATE CAELI DESUPER see Palestrina, Giovanni

RORATE COELI see Byrd, William

RORATE COELI see Tye, Christopher

RORATE COELI DE SUPER see Palestrina, Giovanni

ROREM, NED (1923-   )
All Glorious God *anthem/hymn
  SATB,acap PETERS 6389 $.25   (R1702)

Behold, How Good And How Pleasant It Is
  see Two Psalms And A Proverb

Canticle Of The Lamp *cant
  SATB,acap oct BOOSEY 5843 $.30   (R1703)

Canticles, Set I *CCU,cant
  SATB,acap oct BOOSEY 5843 $.30   (R1704)

Canticles, Set II *CCU,cant
  SATB,acap oct BOOSEY 5841 $.45   (R1705)

Christ The Lord Is Ris'n Today *Easter,
  anthem/hymn
  SATB,acap PETERS 6390 $.25   (R1706)

Corinthians, The
  SATB,org PETERS 6193 $.60   (R1707)

Five Prayers For The Young *CC5U
  SSA,acap oct PRESSER 312-40307 $.40 (R1708)

Gentle Visitation
  SSA,acap oct ELKAN-V 362-3086 $.45 (R1709)

He Shall Rule From Sea To Sea
  SATB,org oct BOOSEY 5651 $.35   (R1710)

How Long Wilt Thou Forget Me, O Lord?
  see Two Psalms And A Proverb

Jesu, Christ's Mild Mother Stood *see Mild
  Mother, The

Lift Up Your Heads *Asc
  mix cor,kbd/brass/winds voc sc BOOSEY
  $1.00, ipa, ipr   (R1711)

Love Divine, All Loves Excelling
  SATB,acap oct BOOSEY 5650 $.30   (R1712)

Mild Mother, The
  "Jesu, Christ's Mild Mother Stood" unis wom
  cor,pno SCHIRM.EC 2584 $.30   (R1713)

Miracles Of Christmas *Xmas
  mix cor,org/pno voc sc BOOSEY $2.50 (R1714)

Prayers And Responses *CCU
  SATB,acap oct BOOSEY 5697 $.30   (R1715)

Prayers And Responses *CCU,prayer
  SA BOOSEY-CAN s.p.   (R1716)

Proper For The Votive Mass Of The Holy Spirit
  unis,org oct BOOSEY 5618 $.60   (R1717)

Psalm 134
  see Two Holy Songs

Psalm 150
  see Two Holy Songs

Sermon On Miracles, A
  unis,solo,strings/kbd voc sc BOOSEY $.75,
  ipr   (R1718)

Sing, My Soul, His Wondrous Love *anthem/
  hymn
  SATB,acap PETERS 6386 $.25   (R1719)
  mix cor SOUTHERN $.25   (R1720)

Two Holy Songs
  SATB,org/pno PEER $.40
  contains: Psalm 134; Psalm 150   (R1721)

Two Psalms And A Proverb
  SATB,5strings SCHIRM.EC 2674 $1.00, ipa
  contains: Behold, How Good And How
    Pleasant It Is; How Long Wilt Thou
    Forget Me, O Lord?; Wounds Without
    Cause   (R1722)

Two Psalms And A Proverb
  4 cor,4strings SCHIRM.EC 2674 $1.00, ipa
                                     (R1723)

Wounds Without Cause
  see Two Psalms And A Proverb

ROSA, M.
Little King Of Heaven, The *Xmas
  SA oct PRESSER 312-40394 $.25   (R1724)

ROSA MYSTICA see Bitgod, Rob.

ROSARY, THE see Nevin

ROSARY, THE see Nevin, E.

ROSE
According To His Promise
  SSAA BOOSEY-CAN s.p.   (R1725)

Babe Is Born, A *Xmas
  SATB/unis (med) OXFORD 84.142 $.35 (R1726)

I Shall Make Of My Spirit A Cradle *Xmas
  (Barrett; Craig) SSA oct PLYMOUTH DC-202
  $.25   (R1727)

ROSE, BERNARD
Magnificat And Nunc Dimittis *Magnif/Nunc
  SATB,acap (C min) oct NOVELLO 44.1397.00
  s.p.   (R1728)
  SATB (C min) oct NOVELLO 86.0018.10
  s.p.   (R1729)

Preces And Responses
  ATB,acap oct NOVELLO 44.1460.08 s.p.
                                     (R1730)
  SATB oct NOVELLO 44.1436.05 s.p.   (R1731)

Responses For Treble Voices
  treb cor,acap (easy) oct OXFORD 44.226 $.25
                                     (R1732)

Te Deum, Jubilate, And Benedictus *Bene/
  Jubil/Te Deum
  boy cor (med) oct OXFORD 44.201 $.75
                                     (R1733)

ROSE, BERNARD (cont'd.)
Versicles And Responses
  SATB oct NOVELLO 44.1395.04 s.p.   (R1734)

ROSE, MICHAEL
Christ, Who Knows All His Sheep *anthem
  mix cor,acap oct NOVELLO 86.0023.06 s.p.
                                     (R1735)

Jubilate Deo *Jubil
  SATB (med) oct OXFORD 42.326 $.35 (R1736)

Sing To The Lord A Joyful Song
  SATB (med) oct OXFORD 42.328 $.35 (R1737)

ROSE OF CHRISTMAS, THE see Thompson

ROSE OF SHARON, THE see Martinon, Jean, Le Lis
  De Saron

ROSE, THE see Caldwell

ROSE TOUCHED BY THE SUN'S WARM RAYS, A see
  Berger, Jean

ROSEINGRAVE, THOMAS
Arise, Shine
  (Young, Percy) mix cor,soli,cont,2ob,opt
  bsn,2trp,strings,opt timp cmplt ed BOOSEY
  rental   (R1738)

ROSELLI
Adoramus Te
  see PRACTICAL POLOPHONY
  (Imig) SATB,acap oct FOX PS 148 $.25
                                     (R1739)

Adoramus Te, Christe
  (Ehret) [Lat] SAB,acap oct PRO ART 2201
  $.20   (R1740)
  (Ehret) [Lat] SATB,acap oct PRO ART 1490
  $.20   (R1741)
  (Ehret) [Lat] SSA oct PRO ART 1980 $.20
                                     (R1742)

ROSEMULLER, J.
Overmade Full Av Nade
  (Elvestrand, Magne) [Norw] LYCHE 7 s.p.
                                     (R1743)

ROSEN see Boldemann, Laci

ROSENBERG, EMANUEL
Mizmdr L'todah *Sab-Eve
  unis oct TRANSCON. TCL 395 $2.50   (R1744)

Shabbat Nusach S'fard *Sab-Eve
  SATB TRANSCON. TCL 866 $3.50   (R1745)

ROSENBERG, HILDING (1892-   )
Den Heliga Natten *Xmas,ora
  mix cor,solo,orch/strings&org cor pts
  NORDISKA 2565 s.p., voc sc NORDISKA 2621
  s.p.   (R1746)

Herre, Jag Vill Tacka Dig Bland Folken
  mix cor NORDISKA 3583 s.p.   (R1747)

Herren, Min Gud, Gor Mitt Morker Ljust
  mix cor NORDISKA 3582 s.p.   (R1748)

Se Gud Ar Min Fralsnig
  mix cor NORDISKA 3581 s.p.   (R1749)

ROSENMUELLER
Blessing Of Our Lord, The *see Die Gnade
  Unsers Herrn

Die Gnade Unsers Herrn
  (Ehret) "Blessing Of Our Lord, The" [Ger/
  Eng] SATB oct COLOMBO 2426 $.30   (R1750)

ROSENMULLER, JOHANN (ca. 1620-1684)
All Men Living Are But Mortal
  SATB,acap oct PRESSER 312-40145 $.30
                                     (R1751)

Also Hat Gott Die Welt Geliebet *Bibl/cant
  (Tunger) SSATB,cont&2vln&2vla&bvl/cont&
  2vln&3trom HANSSLER 10.064 sc s.p., cor
  pts s.p., ipa   (R1752)

Danket Dem Herrn *cant
  (Kruger) AT,cont,2vln HANSSLER 10.041 sc
  s.p., cor pts s.p., ipa   (R1753)

Danksaget Dem Vater *cant
  (Kruger) SSATB,cont,2vln HANSSLER 10.021
  cor pts s.p., voc sc s.p., ipa   (R1754)

Daran Ist Erschienen Die Liebe Gottes *cant
  (Kruger) SSATB,cont,2vln HANSSLER 10.024
  cor pts s.p., voc sc s.p., ipa   (R1755)

Das Ist Das Ewige Leben *cant
  (Kruger; Hellmann) 3pt mix cor,cont
  HANSSLER 10.023 cor pts s.p., voc sc
  s.p., ipa   (R1756)

Das Ist Ein Kostlich Ding, Dem Herren Danken
  *cant
  (Kruger) ST,cont,2vln,2vla HANSSLER 10.044
  sc s.p., cor pts s.p., ipa   (R1757)

Die Augen Des Herrn *cant
  (Schmid, E.F.) [Ger] mix cor,cont,2vln,opt
  vcl/bvl VIEWEG voc sc s.p., cor pts s.p.,
  ipa   (R1758)

Die Augen Des Herrn Sehen Auf Die Gerechten
  *cant
  (Kruger) SATB,cont,2vln HANSSLER 10.022 cor
  pts s.p., voc sc s.p., ipa   (R1759)

Die Gnade Unseres Herren Jesu *mot
  (Tunger) SATB,cont HANSSLER 1.128 s.p.
                                     (R1760)

Ein Tag In Deinen Vorhofen *cant
  (Kruger) STB,cont,2vln HANSSLER 10.109 sc
  s.p., cor pts s.p., ipa   (R1761)

Hebet Eure Augen Auf *cant
  (Kruger) ST,cont,2vln HANSSLER 10.038 sc
  s.p., cor pts s.p., ipa   (R1762)

Herr, Mein Gott, Ich Danke Dir *cant
  (Tunger) TTB,cont,2vln HANSSLER 10.164 sc
  s.p., voc sc s.p., ipa   (R1763)

Ich Bin Das Brot Des Lebens *cant
  (Tunger) ATB/AAB,cont,2vln HANSSLER 10.163
  sc s.p., voc sc s.p., ipa   (R1764)

ROSENMULLER, JOHANN (cont'd.)
Ich Hielte Mich Nicht Dafur *mot
  (Tunger) SATB,cont HANSSLER 1.184 s.p.
                                     (R1765)

Ich Will Dich, Mein Gott, Erhohen *Thanks
  SSATB HANSSLER 6.193 s.p. contains also:
  Kubler, Emil, Lob Gott Getrost Mit Singen
  (SAT/SAB)   (R1766)

Kundlich Gross Ist Das Gottselige Geheimnis
  *mot
  (Hellmann) SAB,cont HANSSLER 1.089 s.p.
                                     (R1767)
  (Tunger) ATB/TTB,cont HANSSLER 1.185 s.p.
                                     (R1768)

Meine Seele Harret Auf Gott *cant
  (Kruger) ATB,cont,2vln HANSSLER 10.040 sc
  s.p., cor pts s.p., ipa   (R1769)

Praise His Name Forever *Xmas
  (Davis, K.) 2pt WARNER R3481 $.30 (R1770)

Prayer For Today, A *chorale
  (Klein) SSATB,org/pno oct SCHIRM.G 11772
  $.25   (R1771)

Siehe, Des Herren Auge Siehet Auf Die *cant
  (Tunger) STB,cont,2vln HANSSLER 10.162 sc
  s.p., voc sc s.p., ipa   (R1772)

Since This World Is Only Passing *ECY/Gen
  unis,kbd (med easy) oct CONCORDIA 98-1820
  $.25   (R1773)

Wahrlich, Wahrlich, Ich Sage Euch *cant
  (Tunger) 4pt mix cor,cont,2vln HANSSLER
  10.074 sc s.p., voc sc s.p., ipa   (R1774)

Weil Wir Wissen, Dass Der Mensch *cant
  (Tunger) ATB/AAB,cont,2vln HANSSLER 10.161
  sc s.p., voc sc s.p., ipa   (R1775)

Welt Ade! *Gd.Fri.
  SSATB,acap voc pt DOBLINGER s.p. see also
  TOD UND VERGANGLICHKEIT   (R1776)

Welt Ade, Ich Bin Dein Mude
  see Franck, Melchior, Die Erloseten Des
  Herren Werden Wiederkommen
  TTBB HANSSLER 6.0495 s.p. contains also:
  Bach, Johann Sebastian, Wenn Ich Einmal
  Soll Scheiden (TTBB)   (R1777)

ROSENQUIST, CARL E.
Dig Helge Ande, Bedja Vi
  SABar,org,2vln cor pts NORDISKA 2818 s.p.,
  voc sc NORDISKA 2062 s.p.   (R1778)

Hosianna
  (Ahlen, Waldemar) 2pt wom cor/2pt jr cor,
  acap NORDISKA 4818 s.p.   (R1779)

ROSENTHAL, MANUEL (1904-   )
Cantate Pour Le Temps De La Nativite *Xmas,
  cant
  cor,S solo,2fl,ob,2clar,2bsn,horn,timp,
  perc,strings JOBERT sc s.p., voc sc s.p.,
  ipr   (R1780)

Saint Francois D'Assise *ora
  mix cor,narrator,3fl,3ob,3clar,3bsn,4horn,
  4trp,3trom,tuba,2harp,8perc,strings sc
  JOBERT s.p., ipr   (R1781)

Trois Pieces Liturgiques *CC3U,BVM,liturg/
  prayer
  cor,2fl,ob,2clar,2bsn,horn,timp,2perc,
  strings JOBERT sc s.p., voc sc s.p., ipr
                                     (R1782)

ROSETTI, FRANCESCO ANTIONIO (1746-1792)
Love Came Down At Christmas *Xmas
  (Latimer) SATB,acap oct MCA   (R1783)

ROSEWALL, RICHARD B.
Surely He Hath Borne Our Griefs *Bibl
  SATB,acap oct WORLD CA-2183-8 $.30 (R1784)

ROSEWIG, A.
First Mass In F *Op.327,No.2
  [Lat] SATB PRESSER $1.50   (R1785)

ROSH HASHANAH L'ILANOT see Low, Leo

ROSKIN
Bor' Chu
  SATB HATIKVAH HCL 1 $.35 contains also: Sh'
  Ma   (R1786)

Humming
  SATB HATIKVAH HCL 14 $.20   (R1787)

Kol Nidre
  SATB HATIKVAH HCL 16 $.35   (R1788)

Mah Tovu
  SATB HATIKVAH HCL 17 $.25   (R1789)

Mi Chomocho
  SATB HATIKVAH HCL 19 $.25   (R1790)

Psalm 92 *see Tzadik Katomor

Sh' Ma
  see Roskin, Bor' Chu

Tzadik Katomor (Psalm 92)
  men cor HATIKVAH HCL 11 $.25   (R1791)

ROSS
At The Gate Of The Year
  SATB,Bar solo,org/pno PETERS 6217 $.25
                                     (R1792)

Lamb, The
  SSA oct GALAXY 1.1868.1 $.25   (R1793)

Michael
  SSA HANSEN-US C259A $.40   (R1794)

ROSS, TONI
Five Songs For Five To Ten *see Hankey, Mark

ROSSEL, DENTON
All Glory, Laud And Honor
  6pt mix cor&sr cor&jr cor,pno/org (med) oct
  WILLIS 7512 $.22   (R1795)

ROSSEL, DENTON (cont'd.)

Christ, Our Captain
SA,pno (easy) oct WILLIS 7508 $.20   (R1796)

ROSSEL, W.
Wom Himmel Hoch Herab *Xmas
[Ger] wom cor,acap (easy) HUG s.p.   (R1797)

ROSSELLI, FRANCESCO
Adoramus Te *Commun
"We Worship Thee, O Christ" SATB,acap
SCHIRM.EC 1205 $.22   (R1798)

We Worship Thee, O Christ *see Adoramus Te

ROSSELLO
Adoramus Te *Lent
(Beveridge) "We Adore Thee, O Christ" [Eng/
Lat] 4pt mix cor,acap oct SCHIRM.G 8377
$.35   (R1799)

We Adore Thee, O Christ *see Adoramus Te

ROSSI, SALOMONE (ca. 1570-ca. 1630)
Adon-Olam *Sab-Eve/Sab-Morn
[Heb] SATB,acap oct SALABERT-US $.65 see
from Cinq Choeurs Religieux   (R1800)

Barekhu *Sab-Morn
[Heb] SATB,acap oct SALABERT-US $.65 see
from Cinq Choeurs Religieux   (R1801)

Cinq Choeurs Religieux *see Adon-Olam;
Barekhu; Keduscha; Psalm 80; Psalm 146
(R1802)

Keduscha
[Heb] SATB,acap oct SALABERT-US $.65 see
from Cinq Choeurs Religieux   (R1803)

Psalm 80
[Heb] SATB,acap oct SALABERT-US $.65 see
from Cinq Choeurs Religieux   (R1804)

Psalm 146
[Heb] SATB,acap oct SALABERT-US $.65 see
from Cinq Choeurs Religieux   (R1805)

Sacred Service *Sab-Eve
(Freed, I.) SATB TRANSCON. TCL 774 $5.50,
ipa   (R1806)

ROSSINI, GIOACCHINO (1792-1868)
Benedictus (from Missa Solemnis)
see Rossini, Gioacchino, Sanctus

Dolcissima Maria
[It/Eng] SSA,S solo oct KERBY 7480 $.55
(R1807)

Hear Us As We Pray
(Harris) SATB oct PRO ART 2689 $.30 (R1808)

Hear Us, Lord
(Carlton) SATB oct BOOSEY 5406 $.30 (R1809)

I Will Give Thanks Unto Thee, O Lord
(Fitzhugh) SATB FLAMMER A 5046 $.35 (R1810)

Inflammatus (from Stabat Mater)
SATB oct FISCHER,C CM-6175 $.30   (R1811)
"When Thou Comest" SATB,S solo oct PRO ART
1308 $.25   (R1812)
"When Thou Comest" 4pt mix cor,S solo oct
SCHIRM.G 2041 $.40   (R1813)
"When Thou Comest" SATB oct PRESSER
312-10313 $.35   (R1814)

Inflammatus Et Accensus (from Stabat Mater)
SATB oct BELWIN 1159 $.25   (R1815)
(Howorth) "When Thou Comest To The
Judgment" SATB oct BELWIN 1159 $.25
(R1816)
(Platt) TTBB oct PLYMOUTH DC-303 $.40
(R1817)

Kyrie (from Messe Solennelle) Kyrie
SATB oct STAFF 688 $.30   (R1818)

La Carita
see Tre Cori

La Fede
see Tre Cori

La Speranza
see Tre Cori

Messe Solenne *Mass
SATB,soli,pno RICORDI-ENG 41310 s.p.
(R1819)

O Blicke Mit Erbarmen *prayer
SATB,acap voc pt BREITKOPF-L CHB-2012 s.p.
(R1820)

O Salutaris
[Lat] 4pt mix cor HEUGEL s.p. see from LA
MAITRISE   (R1821)

O Salutaris Hostia
"Thou Whose Redeeming Sacrifice" [Lat/Eng]
SATB,acap BROUDE BR. $.35   (R1822)

O Thou From Whom All Goodness Flows *anthem/
hymn
(Kinsman) SATB oct SPRATT 585 $.25 (R1823)

Quando Corpus (from Stabat Mater)
SATB,acap RICORDI-ENG SY121 s.p. (R1824)

Salve O Vergine Maria
"Save Us, O Holy Virgin" [Eng/It] SATB AMP
A411 $.20   (R1825)

Sanctus (from Missa Solemnis) Sanctus
SATB,acap RICORDI-ENG SY123 s.p. contains
also: Benedictus (Bene)   (R1826)

Save Us, O Holy Virgin *see Salve O Vergine
Maria

Stabat Mater *ora
[Eng/Lat] cor,SSTB soli voc sc SCHIRM.G
$1.25   (R1827)
[Lat/Ger] SATB,SSTB soli,orch voc sc SCHOTT
1067 s.p., ipr   (R1828)
[Eng/Lat] SATB,SATB soli,2fl,2ob,2clar,
2bsn,4horn,3trp,3trom,strings,timp voc sc
NOVELLO s.p., ipr   (R1829)
SATB,soli,orch voc sc RICORDI-ENG 49182
s.p.   (R1830)
cor,opt orch voc sc KALMUS 6398 $1.50, ipa

ROSSINI, GIOACCHINO (cont'd.)

cor sc KALMUS $18.00   (R1831)
cor KALMUS $2.25   (R1832)
cor KALMUS $18.00   (R1833)
cor,orch sc KALMUS $18.00, ipa   (R1834)

Thou Whose Redeeming Sacrifice *see O
Salutaris Hostia

Toast For The New Year
SATB,acap oct KERBY 9078 $.75   (R1835)

Tre Cori
[It/Fr] 3pt wom cor,pno RICORDI-ENG s.p.
contains: La Carita; La Fede; La Speranza
(R1836)

When Thou Comest *see Inflammatus

When Thou Comest To The Judgment *see
Inflammatus Et Accensus

ROSSO, R.
Christus
see IN HEBDOMADA SANCTA

ROSY GLOW OF APPROACHING DAY see Mornement, Ina

ROTERMUND, DONALD
I Will Greatly Rejoice *Gen/Refm
SATB,acap (med diff) oct CONCORDIA 98-1877
$.25   (R1837)

Lamb Of God, Pure And Holy *Lent
SATB,acap (med diff) oct CONCORDIA 98-1871
$.25   (R1838)

ROTERMUND, MELVIN
From All Thy Saints In Warfare *Gen
SATB,kbd (easy) oct CONCORDIA 98-2092 $.25
(R1839)
Gospel Shows The Father's Grace, The *Gen
SA,inst (med easy) oct CONCORDIA 98-1941
$.25   (R1840)
Noel, Noel, Noel, Let Your Voices Ring *Xmas
SA,kbd oct CONCORDIA 98-1888 $.25   (R1841)
Oh, Come, Little Children
SATB&jr cor oct AGAPE F 942 $.30   (R1842)
Oh, How Joyfully *Xmas
SATB/unis,opt inst (easy) oct CONCORDIA
98-1997 $.30   (R1843)

ROTGOLDENE SONNENGLUT see Kern, Matthais

ROTH
In My Heart There Rings A Melody
(Haag) SSATB oct LILLENAS AT-1005 $.35
(R1844)
(Hustad, Don) SATB ALLANS 406 s.p.   (R1845)
(Landon) SATB oct LORENZ A387 $.25   (R1846)

ROTH, J.
In Bethlehem Of Judah *Xmas
SATB oct PRESSER 312-40708 $.30   (R1847)

ROTH, N.
Summer In Winter
SATB oct KERBY 5903 $.30   (R1848)

ROTH, R.N.
Christ Our Passover *Easter
unis,org oct KERBY 6101 $.40   (R1849)
unis,org oct KERBY 6101C $.40   (R1850)
Jubilate Deo (Psalm 100)
unis,kbd oct KERBY 5801 $.30   (R1851)
unis oct KERBY 81071 $.30   (R1852)
Psalm 100 *see Jubilate Deo
Summer In Winter *Xmas,carol
SATB,acap oct KERBY 81580 $.30   (R1853)

ROTHENBERG
Alles Ist Eitel
see Bach, Johann Sebastian, Und Wollte
Alles Wanken

ROTHENBERG, FRIEDRICH SAMUEL
Das Junge Chorlied (composed with Rothenberg,
Theophil) *CC120U
[Ger] 4pt mix cor cloth BAREN. EM 360 s.p.
(R1854)
Kinderlob (composed with Rothenberg,
Theophil) *sac/sec,CCU
[Ger] jr cor BAREN. EM 777 s.p.   (R1855)

ROTHENBERG, THEOPHIL
Das Junge Chorlied *see Rothenberg,
Friedrich Samuel
Kinderlob *see Rothenberg, Friedrich Samuel

ROTHER, CORBINIAN (1900-1966)
Johannes-Passion *Op.62, Psntd
4pt mix cor,3 cantors,acap cor pts
BREITKOPF-W CHB-3138 s.p.   (R1856)

ROTHSCHUH, F.
Es Sungen Drei Engel *mot
mix cor (med easy) oct LEUCKART 559 s.p.
(R1857)
Freu Dich, Erd' Und Sternenzelt
see Zwei Weihnachtslieder
Salzburger Weihnachtslied
see Zwei Weihnachtslieder
Weihnachts-Hymnus *Xmas,14th cent
mix cor (med easy) oct LEUCKART 562 s.p.
(R1858)
Zwei Weihnachtslieder *Xmas
mix cor (easy) oct LEUCKART 583 s.p.
contains: Freu Dich, Erd' Und
Sternenzelt; Salzburger Weihnachtslied
(R1859)

ROTHSTEIN, ARNOLD
Village Fiddler, The
1-2pt jr cor TRANSCON. TCL 727 $1.50
(R1860)

ROTOLI
Jesus Only
SATB,org/pno BOSTON 667 $.35   (R1861)

ROUHER, M.
Ave Maria
TB/SMez (D flat maj) LEMOINE s.p.   (R1862)

ROULE LE VIEUX CHARIOT see Roll De Ol'chariot
Along

ROUMEFORT, R. DE
Panis Angelicus
[Lat] unis,org,opt vln&vcl LEMOINE s.p.
(R1863)
Requiem Aeternam *Req
[Lat] cor,opt solo,opt org LEMOINE cor pts
s.p., voc sc s.p.   (R1864)

ROUN' DE GLORY MANGER
(James) SATTBB,high solo,acap oct SCHIRM.G
8169 $.30   (R1865)

'ROUND AND 'ROUND *spir
(Gardner) SATB oct STAFF 610 $.30   (R1866)

ROUND FOR CHRISTMAS, A see Emig, Lois

ROUND ME FALLS THE NIGHT see Thiman, Eric
Harding

ROUND THE LORD IN GLORY SEATED *Easter/Lent
(Couper) unis oct FISCHER,C CM-7661 $.30
(R1867)

ROUNDS FOR CHRISTMAS see Jaffe

ROUNDS FOR THE CHRISTIAN YEAR see Krapf,
Gerhard

ROUNDS OF ISRAEL *round,Isr
(De Cormier) [Heb] SATB,pno oct LAWSON 51542
$.40
contains: A Kum Bachur Atsel; Hiney Matov;
Shalom Chaverim   (R1868)

ROUSE YE, SHEPHERDS *Xmas,carol,Swiss
(Ehret, Walter) SA,opt bells FRANK F-614 $.35
(R1869)

ROUSSEAU, MARCEL-SAMUEL (1882-1955)
In Paradisium *mot
unis,org CHOUDENS s.p.   (R1870)

ROUSSEAU, SAMUEL-ALEXANDRE (1853-1904)
Hodie Christus Natus Est *mot
[Lat] STB,S/T&Mez/Bar soli,orch LEDUC voc
sc s.p., voc pt s.p.   (R1871)
Messe De Paques *Easter,Mass
[Fr] 2 eq voices,soli,pno LEDUC BL429 voc
sc s.p., voc pt s.p.   (R1872)

ROUSSEL, MARIO
Messa Giubilare *Mass
[Lat] TTB,org sc ZANIBON 3041 s.p., voc pt
ZANIBON s.p.   (R1873)
Missa Solemnis *see Sancte Dei Genitrix
Sancte Dei Genitrix *Mass
"Missa Solemnis" [Lat] ATB,org,opt strings
sc ZANIBON 3077 s.p., voc pt ZANIBON
s.p., ipr   (R1874)

ROUTH, FRANCIS
Babe Is Born, A *Xmas
SATB,acap (med) OXFORD 84.110 $.35 (R1875)
In The Year That King Ussiah Died *Trin,
anthem
mix cor,S solo oct NOVELLO 28.1423.04 s.p.
(R1876)

ROUTLEY
Eternal Light *CCU,hymn
unis FISCHER,C O-4877 $1.50   (R1877)

ROUX, ABBE M.
Hail To Thee, Lord God *see Salve Regina
Salve Regina
"Hail To Thee, Lord God" SATB,org SCHIRM.EC
2284 $.18   (R1878)

ROVENSTRUNCK, BERNHARD
Das Wunder Des Heiligen Jakobus *see El
Miracle De Sant Jaume
El Miracle De Sant Jaume
"Das Wunder Des Heiligen Jakobus" [Ger/
Span] 4pt mix cor MOSELER LB-716 s.p.
(R1879)
L'Antonia
[Ger/Span] 4pt mix cor MOSELER LB-715 s.p.
(R1880)

ROVETTA, GIOVANNI
Laudate Dominum (from Salmi Concertati)
(Steele, John) SSTTB/SATTB/SAATB,org,2vln,
cont voc sc NOVELLO s.p., ipr   (R1881)

ROWE, F.
Love Lifted Me (composed with Smith, H.)
(Elrich, D.) SATB (med) PRESSER G-206 $.40
(R1882)

ROWLANDS
Works Of God, The *Harv,Austral
SATB,SAB soli ALLANS 61 s.p.   (R1883)

ROWLANDS, W.P.
Blaenwern
"Love Divine, All Loves Excelling" SATB
WEINBERGER s.p.   (R1884)
Love Divine, All Loves Excelling *see
Blaenwern

ROWLEY
Divine Intercession, A
SATB,acap,opt kbd oct PRO ART 1755 $.25
(R1885)
Thou Visitest The Earth
SA oct BOOSEY 1912 $.30   (R1886)

ROWLEY, ALEC (1892-1958)
Be Strong
unis oct NOVELLO 40.1048.05 s.p.   (R1887)
Benediction, A *Bene
SATB,acap oct LAWSON 676 $.25   (R1888)
Christ The Lord Is Risen Today *Easter
unis oct NOVELLO 40.1210.00 s.p.   (R1889)

ROWLEY, ALEC (cont'd.)

Garden And The Cross *Easter/Lent,cant
BELWIN $1.50   (R1890)

God Is The Beauty Of The World
SATB oct FISCHER,J 8923 $.30   (R1891)

I Will Give You Rain In Due Season
SATB THOMP.G G-540 s.p.   (R1892)

Into The Woods My Master Went
SATB oct LAWSON 677 $.30   (R1893)

Let All The World In Every Corner Sing
*Fest/Gen
SATB (med) oct OXFORD 42.168 $.35   (R1894)

O Lovely Babe *Xmas,anthem
mix cor oct NOVELLO 40.1338.07 s.p.   (R1895)

O Saving Victim *anthem
mix cor oct NOVELLO 40.1300.10 s.p.   (R1896)

Office Of The Holy Communion, The
SATB (A min) ENOCH s.p.   (R1897)

On Bethlehem Hill
unis,narrator,soli,pno voc sc BOOSEY $1.50
                                           (R1898)

Praise *Fest/Gen
SSA (very easy) oct OXFORD 44.018 $.35   (R1899)

SATB (easy) oct OXFORD 42.013 $.35   (R1900)
SATB (easy) OXFORD 42.013 $.35   (R1901)
SSA (easy) OXFORD 44.018 $.35, ipr   (R1902)

Service
unis,orch oct NOVELLO 40.1117.01 s.p., ipr
                                           (R1903)

Service Of Holy Communion In D Major *Commun
SATB,opt org CRAMER A14 s.p.   (R1904)

Sing To The Lord *Harv
unis oct NOVELLO 40.1217.08 s.p.   (R1905)

ROY, KLAUS GEORGE (1924-   )
Not Only Unto Me
mix cor,acap oct LAWSON 546 $.25 see from
Three Songs Of Praise   (R1906)

Three Songs Of Praise *see Not Only Unto Me
                                           (R1907)

ROYAL BANNERS FORWARD GO see Bruckner, Anton

ROYAL BANNERS FORWARD GO, THE see Boatwright,
Howard

ROYAL BANNERS FORWARD GO, THE see Bruckner,
Anton

ROYAL BANNERS FORWARD GO, THE see Cashmore,
Donald

ROYAL BANNERS FORWARD GO, THE see Palestrina,
Giovanni, Vexilla Regis Prodeunt

ROYAL BANNERS FORWARD GO, THE see Peek, Richard

ROYAL BANNERS, THE *Lent
(Fischer, R.H.) unis,kbd (med easy) oct
CONCORDIA 98-1947 $.25   (R1908)

ROYAL CHILD, A see Martin, John

ROYAL PROCLAMATION, THE see Beadell, Robert M.

ROYAL PROCLAMATION, THE see Brandon, G.

ROYCE THORNAL CRUSADE CHOIR *CC10L
(Brown, C.; Kaiser, K.; Perkins, P.) SATB voc
sc WORD 37603 $1.50   (R1909)

ROYSE
Hear My Prayer, O Lord
SATB oct PRESSER MC447 $.35   (R1910)

My Help Cometh From The Lord
SATB oct PRESSER 352-00454 $.30   (R1911)

Snowbound Mountains *Xmas
SATB oct PRESSER MC466 $.30   (R1912)

ROZELL
Night Winds
SSAA oct HERITAGE H3501 $.35   (R1913)

We Behold Our Dying Saviour *Gd.Fri./Lent,
chorale
SATB oct SOUTHERN $.25   (R1914)
SATB,acap SHAWNEE A 1010 $.30   (R1915)
SSA,acap SHAWNEE B 248 $.30   (R1916)

ROZYCKI, (JACEK) HYACINTHUS
Confitebor *Pol
(Szweykowski) cor,soli,cont,2vln POLSKIE
WDMP60 s.p.   (R1917)

Exsultemus Omnes *Pol
(Szweykowski) SSB,cont POLSKIE WDMP44 s.p.
                                           (R1918)

Hymni Ecclesiastici *Pol
(Chybinski, A.) mix cor,acap POLSKIE WDMP 3
s.p.   (R1919)

Magnificat *Pol
(Szweykowski) cor,soli,cont,2vln POLSKIE
WDMP54 s.p.   (R1920)

Magnificemus In Cantico, Concerto De Sanctis
*Pol
(Chybinski, A.) SSB,cont POLSKIE WDMP16
s.p.   (R1921)

RSCM CAROL BOOK, THE *CC10U,Xmas,carol
oct ROYAL s.p.   (R1922)

RUBBEN, HERMANNJOSEF (1928-   )
Spielheft Zur Weihnacht *CC10L,Xmas
2pt jr cor,inst cor pts BREITKOPF-W MSP-24
s.p.   (R1923)

RUBBRA, EDMUND (1901-   )
Amicus Meus
see Nine Tenebrae Motets: Second Nocturn

And When The Builders *Op.125
SATB,org LENGNICK s.p.   (R1924)

RUBBRA, EDMUND (cont'd.)

Beatitudes, The *Op.109
SSA,acap LENGNICK s.p.   (R1925)

Benedictus (from Missa Cantuariensis)
see Rubbra, Edmund, Sanctus

Cantata, In Honorem Mariae Matris Dei *see
In Honorem Mariae Matris Dei

Creature-Songs To Heaven
SSA LENGNICK s.p.   (R1926)

Crucifixus Pro Nobis *Op.111
mix cor,T solo,org,fl,vln,vcl,harp (Cantata
Di Camera) LENGNICK s.p.   (R1927)

Ecce Vidimus Eum
see Nine Tenebrae Motets: First Nocturn

Entrez-Y Tous En Surete *Op.93
"Let Us Securely Enter" [Fr/Eng] SATB,acap
LENGNICK s.p.   (R1928)

Eram Quasi Agnus Innocens
see Nine Tenebrae Motets: Third Nocturn

Except The Lord Build The House
see Three Motets

Festival Gloria *Op.94, Fest
SSAATTBB,SBar soli,acap LENGNICK s.p.   (R1929)

Festival Te Deum *Op.71, Fest
SATB,S solo,org,2fl,2ob,2clar,4horn,3trp,
3trom,strings,perc,harp, celeste LENGNICK
s.p.   (R1930)

Haec Est Domus Domini *Op.95, Ded,mot
"This Is Truly The House Of God" [Lat/Eng]
SATB,acap LENGNICK s.p.   (R1931)

Holy Communion Service In A *see Missa In
Honorem Sancti Dominici

In Honorem Mariae Matris Dei *Op.97, Bibl
SATB&jr cor,SA soli,org/2fl&2ob&2clar&2bsn&
2horn&trp&strings&timp&harp LENGNICK s.p.
                                           (R1932)
"Cantata, In Honorem Mariae Matris Dei"
SATB&jr cor,org/orch LENGNICK s.p., ipa
                                           (R1933)

In Monte Oliveti
see Nine Tenebrae Motets: First Nocturn

Infant Holy
SATB,acap oct BELWIN 60647 $.25   (R1934)

Judas Mercator Pessimus
see Nine Tenebrae Motets: Second Nocturn

Lauda Sion *Op.110
SSAATTBB,SB soli,acap LENGNICK s.p. (R1935)

Let Us Now Praise Famous Men
see Three Motets

Let Us Securely Enter *see Entrez-Y Tous En
Surete

Lord, With What Care *Op.107
SATB,acap LENGNICK s.p.   (R1936)

Magnificat And Nunc Dimittis *Op.65, Magnif/
Nunc
SATB,org LENGNICK s.p.   (R1937)

Mary, Mother *Op.90
SSATB oct BELWIN 05172 $.25   (R1938)

Missa A 3 *Op.98, Agnus/Bene/Gloria/Kyrie/
Mass/Sanctus
SAB/STB,acap LENGNICK s.p.   (R1939)

Missa Brevis *Mass
treb cor,org LENGNICK s.p.   (R1940)

Missa Cantuariensis *Op.59, Mass
SSAATTBB,acap&org LENGNICK s.p.   (R1941)

Missa In Honorem Sancti Dominici *Op.66,
Agnus/Bene/Credo/Gloria/Kyrie/Sanctus
SATB LENGNICK s.p.   (R1942)
"Holy Communion Service In A" SATB,acap
LENGNICK s.p.   (R1943)

Natum Maria Virgine *Op.136, Adv,Bibl/cant
SATB,Bar solo,2fl,2ob,2clar,2bsn,2horn,
strings,bells,harp LENGNICK s.p.   (R1944)

Nine Tenebrae Motets: First Nocturn *Op.72,
No.1, mot
SATB LENGNICK s.p.
contains: Ecce Vidimus Eum; In Monte
Oliveti; Tristis Est Anima Mea   (R1945)

Nine Tenebrae Motets: Second Nocturn *Op.72,
No.2, mot
SATB LENGNICK s.p.
contains: Amicus Meus; Judas Mercator
Pessimus; Unus Ec Discipulis   (R1946)

Nine Tenebrae Motets: Third Nocturn *Op.72,
No.3, mot
SATB LENGNICK s.p.
contains: Eram Quasi Agnus Innocens;
Seniores Populi; Una Hora Non Potuistis (R1947)

Psalm 104 *see Up, O My Soul

Resurrection, The *see Sinfonia Sacra

Sanctus (from Missa Cantuariensis)
SSAATTBB LENGNICK s.p. contains also:
Benedictus   (R1948)

Seniores Populi
see Nine Tenebrae Motets: Third Nocturn

Sinfonia Sacra
"Resurrection, The" mix cor,SABar soli
LENGNICK s.p.   (R1949)

Song Of The Soul *Op.78, Bibl
SSATBB,strings,timp,harp LENGNICK s.p.
                                           (R1950)

RUBBRA, EDMUND (cont'd.)

Star Of The Mystic East *Op.81
SATB LENGNICK s.p.   (R1951)

Te Deum *Op.115, Te Deum
SSAATTBB,acap LENGNICK s.p.   (R1952)

There Is A Spirit
see Three Motets

This Is Truly The House Of God *see Haec Est
Domus Domini

Three Motets *Op.76, mot
SATB,acap LENGNICK s.p.
contains: Except The Lord Build The
House; Let Us Now Praise Famous Men;
There Is A Spirit   (R1953)

To Him We Sing
unis LENGNICK s.p.   (R1954)

Tristis Est Anima Mea
see Nine Tenebrae Motets: First Nocturn

Una Hora Non Potuistis
see Nine Tenebrae Motets: Third Nocturn

Unus Ec Discipulis
see Nine Tenebrae Motets: Second Nocturn

Up, O My Soul (Psalm 104) Op.108
SATB,acap LENGNICK s.p.   (R1955)

Veni Creator Spiritus *Op.130
SATB,org/brass LENGNICK s.p.   (R1956)

Virgin's Cradle Hymn *BVM/Xmas,carol/cradle/
hymn
SATB,acap (med) OXFORD 43.302 $.20   (R1957)
SSA,acap OXFORD 83.024 $.20   (R1958)
mix cor SOUTHERN $.20   (R1959)

RUBINSTEIN, ANTON (1829-1894)
Angel, The *see Engel, Der

Engel, Der
(Imig) "Angel, The" SA oct FOX R182 $.30
                                           (R1960)

Hear Our Prayer
SATB oct LORENZ 9003 $.30   (R1961)

Just As I Am
(Fischer) SAATB,SA soli,pno (F maj,med) oct
WILLIS 4426 $.15   (R1962)

Seraphic Song *Xmas
(Gaines, S.) SATB oct PRESSER 332-13980
$.50   (R1963)
(Gaines, S.) SSAA,A solo,vln oct PRESSER
332-13981 $.50   (R1964)

Vesper Bells
(Hallet, K.; Hanna, J.) SATB oct PRESSER
312-20880 $.35   (R1965)

RUBUM QUEM VIDERAT MOYSES see Tye, Christopher

RUDNICK, WILHELM (1850-1927)
Der Verlorene Sohn *Op.100, ora
mix cor,TBarB soli,org,2fl,3ob,2clar,2bsn,
2trp,2horn,3trom,strings,timp BREITKOPF-L
rental   (R1966)

RUEGGER, F.
Das Licht Bricht Durch
[Ger] mix cor,acap (med diff) HUG s.p.
                                           (R1967)

RUF ZUR MARIA see Brahms, Johannes

RUFE MICH AN IN DER NOT see Schweizer, Rolf

RUFET NICHT DIE WEISHEIT see Krieger, Johann
Philipp

RUFFI, V.
Missae 3.a Missae Quatuor Concinatae Ad Ritum
Concilii Mediolani *CC3U
3-4pt mix cor quarto FORNI 396 s.p. (R1968)

RUFFO, [VINCENZO] (1510-1587)
Adoramus Te
see PRACTICAL POLOPHONY
(Hufstader, R.) TTBB,acap oct PRESSER
352-00078 $.30   (R1969)

Adoramus Te, Christe *Adv/Commun/Lent
"We Adore Thee, O Christ" TTBB,acap
SCHIRM.EC 1238 $.22   (R1970)

We Adore Thee, O Christ *see Adoramus Te,
Christe

RUH
Easter Psalm *Easter,mot/Psalm
SATB oct LILLENAS AN-2376 $.30   (R1971)

RUHE SANFT see Flemming, F.

RUHIG IST DES TODES SCHLUMMER see Naumann,
Johann Gottlieb

RUHL, HERBERT
Alle Menschen Sind Nun Aufgewacht
see Ruhl, Herbert, Lasst Uns Alle Frohlich
Singen

Lasst Uns Alle Frohlich Singen
4pt mix cor MOSELER LB-245 s.p. contains
also: Alle Menschen Sind Nun Aufgewacht
(3pt mix cor) (canon)   (R1972)

RUMORS ARE A-FLYING see Gloria In Excelsis

RUN, RUN TO THE STABLE see Staley

RUN, SHEPHERDS, RUN see Burke, John

RUN TO JESUS see Gardner, Maurice

RUN TO MY LORD see Shaw, R.

RUN, YE SHEPHERDS, TO THE LIGHT see Haydn,
(Johann) Michael, Lauft, Ihr Hirten,
Allzugleich

RUNBACK, ALBERT
Adventsbon *Adv
3pt mix cor NORDISKA 3040 s.p.   (R1973)

Anglarna Och Herdarna
(Ahlen, Waldemar) 2pt wom cor/2pt jr cor,
acap NORDISKA 4252 s.p.   (R1974)
(Ahlen, Waldemar) 2pt wom cor/2pt jr cor,
pno,inst NORDISKA 4251 s.p.   (R1975)

Av Himlens Hojd
wom cor NORDISKA 3660 s.p.   (R1976)

Benedictus *Bene
3pt mix cor NORDISKA 2711 s.p.   (R1977)

Bliv Kvar Hos Mig *cant
unis,solo,org cor pts NORDISKA 3959 s.p.
                                        (R1978)

De Heliga Martyrena
mix cor,org cor pts NORDISKA 5416 s.p.
                                        (R1979)

De Heliga Martyrerna
unis,org NORDISKA 5416 s.p.   (R1980)
mix bor NORDISKA 5416 s.p.   (R1981)

Dette Er Den Dag Som Herren Har Gjort
[Norw] mix cor,org LYCHE 31 s.p.   (R1982)

Dig, Helge Ande, Bedja Vi
mix cor NORDISKA 4821 s.p.   (R1983)

Domssondagen Samt Nattvardgudstjanster
*Easter,Introit
mix cor,acap NORDISKA 2942 s.p. see from
Introitus   (R1984)

En Salig Frojd Den Dag Beskar
3pt mix cor NORDISKA 1697 s.p.   (R1985)

Fosterlandsk Hymn
mix cor NORDISKA 2675 s.p.   (R1986)

Gloria
3pt mix cor NORDISKA 3041 s.p.   (R1987)

Glud Har Uppvaxt Kristus Jesus
3pt mix cor NORDISKA 2107 s.p.   (R1988)

Hellig, Hellig Er Herren Gud
[Norw] mix cor,org LYCHE 32 s.p.   (R1989)

Herre, Du Har Varit Var Tillflykt
mix cor,org cor pts NORDISKA 1870 s.p.
                                        (R1990)

Herre, Sand Ditt Ljus
mix cor NORDISKA 1027 s.p.   (R1991)

Herren Skall Utgjuta Sin Ande
mix cor NORDISKA 2109 s.p.   (R1992)

Hur Ljuv, O Gud Hurr Sall Den Lott
3pt mix cor,org cor pts NORDISKA 5128 s.p.,
ipa   (R1993)

I Dodens Band Lag Herren Krist
3pt mix cor NORDISKA 1698 s.p.   (R1994)

I Pingsten Blev Guds Ande Sand
3pt mix cor NORDISKA 4366 s.p.   (R1995)

Introitus *see Domssondagen Samt
Nattvardgudstjanster; Landfredagen
                                        (R1996)

Introitus *CCU,Introit
unis,org NORDISKA 3588 s.p., ipa   (R1997)

Introitus. Del 1 *CCU,Adv
mix cor NORDISKA 2705 s.p.   (R1998)

Introitus. Del 2 *CCU,Easter
mix cor NORDISKA 2942 s.p.   (R1999)

Jag Vill Lova Herren
mix cor NORDISKA 3854 s.p.   (R2000)

Jesus Hav I Standigt Minne
men cor NORDISKA 1873 s.p.   (R2001)

Julbon
3pt mix cor NORDISKA 3043 s.p.   (R2002)

Kantat Pa Den Helige Mikaels Dag *cant
mix cor,org cor pts NORDISKA 1801 s.p.
                                        (R2003)

Koltrasten
(Ahlen, Waldemar) wom cor/jr cor,pno,inst
NORDISKA 4318 s.p.   (R2004)
(Ahlen, Waldemar) wom cor/jr cor,acap
NORDISKA 4319 s.p.   (R2005)

Korsang Vid Skorde-Vesper
mix cor NORDISKA 3853 s.p.   (R2006)

Landfredagen *Adv,Introit
mix cor,acap NORDISKA 2705 s.p. see from
Introitus   (R2007)

Lov Vare Dig, O Jesu Krist
3pt mix cor NORDISKA 1656 s.p.   (R2008)

Magnificat *Magnif
3pt mix cor NORDISKA 2712 s.p.   (R2009)

Magnificat
see Nytestamentliga Lovsanger

Magnificat
see Nytestamentliga Lovsanger

Massa
mix cor NORDISKA 2240 s.p.   (R2010)

Missa Brevis *Mass
3pt mix cor NORDISKA 3042 s.p.   (R2011)

Nar Till Jordan Var Herre Drog
3pt mix cor NORDISKA 1511 s.p.   (R2012)

Nu Glad Dig Min Ande, I Herran
mix cor NORDISKA 5586 s.p.   (R2013)

Nunc Dimittis
see Nytestamentliga Lovsanger

Nytestamentliga Lovsanger
mix cor NORDISKA 6115 s.p.
contains: Magnificat ; Magnificat ; Nunc
Dimittis   (R2014)

RUNBACK, ALBERT (cont'd.)
O, Herre Gud, Oss Nadig Var
3pt mix cor NORDISKA 1699 s.p.   (R2015)

Pa Gud Och Ej Pa Eget Rad
wom cor/jr cor NORDISKA 4013 s.p.   (R2016)

Sa Gar En Dag An Fran Var Tid *cant
mix cor,solo,org cor pts NORDISKA 3709 s.p.
                                        (R2017)

Sang Och Psalm *CCU,hymn
wom cor/jr cor NORDISKA 5050 s.p.   (R2018)

Si Natten Flyr For Dagens Frojd *cant
mix cor,org cor pts NORDISKA 2178 s.p.
                                        (R2019)

Valsignad Gud
3pt mix cor NORDISKA 1189 s.p.   (R2020)

Var Kristtrogen Frojde Sig
3pt mix cor NORDISKA 1784 s.p.   (R2021)

Vid Min Jesu Sida
3pt mix cor NORDISKA 1510 s.p.   (R2022)

RUNNING, ARNOLD
Come, Holy Ghost, In Love *Cnfrm/Gen/Pent
SATB,kbd (med easy) oct CONCORDIA 98-1777
$.30   (R2023)

RUNOLFSSON, KARL OTTO (1900-1970)
Christmas Cantata *Xmas,cant
SATB,soli,2fl,ob,2clar,bsn,2horn,2trp,trom,
strings,perc,timp ICELAND s.p.   (R2024)

RUNYAN
Great Is Thy Faithfulness
(Bock) TTBB oct AGAPE TB 201 $.25   (R2025)
(Hustad) SATB oct AGAPE HA 113 $.25   (R2026)
(Landon) SATB oct LORENZ A447 $.30   (R2027)

RUPPEL, PAUL ERNST (1913-   )
Auf Diesen Tag Bedenken Wir
see Evangelisches Kirchengesangbuch

Christus-Hymnus
see Schweizer, Rolf, Gebet Des Franz Von
Assisi

Cruzifixion *Psntd,cant
SATB,narrator,cantor,trom,bvl HANSSLER
10.097 sc s.p., voc sc s.p., ipa   (R2028)

Da Pacem, Domine
2pt,kbd sc HANSSLER 19.304 s.p. contains
also: Kretzschmar, Gunther, Wie Sich Ein
Vater Erbarmt (SSAT/SSAB,org/4winds);
Kretzschmar, Gunther, Gott, Gib Fried
Unserm Lande (3pt mix cor/3 eq voices,
org/4winds)   (R2029)

Dankt Dem Herrn Und Predigt Seinen Namen
(Psalm 105)
see Schwarz, Jochen, Seihe, Es Ist Alles
Neu Geworden

Der Herr Denkt An Uns
see Schweizer, Rolf, Denn Dein Ist Das
Reich

Der Herr Ist Mein Hirte *Bibl
jr cor,org sc HANSSLER 12.220 s.p.   (R2030)

Die Ernste Ist Gross, Aber Wenige Sind
see Stier, Alfred, Gottes Stimme Lasst Uns
Sein

Die Stillung Des Seesturms *cant
SATB,narrator,3trp,2trom HANSSLER 10.092 sc
s.p., cor pts s.p., ipa   (R2031)

Dienet Einander
see Ruppel, Paul Ernst, Gott, Zu Dir Rufe
Ich

Du Sollst Gott, Deinen Herrn
see Schweizer, Rolf, Denn Dein Ist Das
Reich

Es Soll Nicht Durch Heer Oder Kraft Geschehen
see Blarr, Oskar Gottlieb, Frolocket Mit
Handen

Es Sprach Zu Mir
see Ruppel, Paul Ernst, Glaube Ist Ein Baum

Evangelisches Kirchengesangbuch *Asc/Pent
[Ger] 3pt mix cor,acap BAREN. EM 20 s.p.
contains: Auf Diesen Tag Bedenken Wir,
No.91; Gen Himmel Aufgefahren Ist,
No.92; Ihr Manner Von Galilaa   (R2032)

Fahret Auf Die Hohe Und Werfet Euer Netz Aus
see Ruppel, Paul Ernst, Gelobt Sei Der Herr
Taglich

Fragst Du Nach Meiner Sunde
see Schweizer, Rolf, Friede Den Brudern,
"Dein Reich Ist Nicht Unsre Kirche"

Gelobt Sei Der Herr Taglich
unis/2pt,kbd sc HANSSLER 19.303 s.p.
contains also: Blarr, Oskar Gottlieb,
Hilf, Herr Meines Lebens (SATB&cong,kbd);
Ruppel, Paul Ernst, Fahret Auf Die Hohe
Und Werfet Euer Netz Aus (unis,kbd)
                                        (R2033)

Gen Himmel Aufgefahren Ist
see Evangelisches Kirchengesangbuch

Glaube Ist Ein Baum
4pt mix cor/5pt mix cor MOSELER LB-331 s.p.
contains also: Es Sprach Zu Mir; Zu Den
Fussen Jesu   (R2034)

Gleich Wie Mich Mein Vater Gesandt Hat *Gen
[Ger] SATB&cong,kbd,fl,bvl,perc (med easy)
BOSSE BE 241 s.p.   (R2035)

Gott Liebt Den Menschen
unis,kbd HANSSLER 19.201 s.p. contains
also: Ruppel, Paul Ernst, Herr Gott, Wann
Offenbarst Du Deine Sohne (unis,narrator,
opt kbd); Lotz, Hans-Georg, Weise Mir,
Herr, Deinen Weg (SAT); Lotz, Hans-Georg,
Es Ist Einer Fur Uns Gestorben (SATB)
                                        (R2036)

RUPPEL, PAUL ERNST (cont'd.)
Gott Liebt Die Welt Mit Ihrer Schuld
see Schweizer, Rolf, Friede Den Brudern,
"Dein Reich Ist Nicht Unsre Kirche"

Gott Liebt Diese Welt *Bibl
SATB,org sc HANSSLER 19.401 s.p. contains
also: Schweizer, Rolf, Singet Dem Herrn
Ein Neues Lied (Psalm 98) (unis,kbd,treb
inst); Michel, Josep, Herr, Sende Uns
Botschaft (unis,kbd/winds)   (R2037)

Gott Schenkt Freiheit
see Schweizer, Rolf, Singt Ein Lied Vom
Licht Der Worte

Gott, Zu Dir Rufe Ich
unis,org sc HANSSLER 19.206 s.p. contains
also: Ruppel, Paul Ernst, Dienet Einander
(SSA,kbd); Schweizer, Rolf, Bei Dir,
Herr, Bin Ich Geborgen (SATB)   (R2038)

Halt Im Gedachtnis Jesum Christ *mot
SATB HANSSLER 7.002 s.p.   (R2039)

Herr, Deine Welt Ist Zum Staunen
see Schweizer, Rolf, Herr, Wohin Sollen Wir
Gehen?

Herr Gott, Wann Offenbarst Du Deine Sohne
see Ruppel, Paul Ernst, Gott Liebt Den
Menschen

Herr, Tue Meine Lippen Auf
see Jeep, Johann, Allein Auf Gottes Wort

Herr, Unser Herrscher *cant
unis cor,4-5brass HANSSLER 10.173 sc s.p.,
cor pts s.p., ipa   (R2040)

Ich Hebe Meine Augen Auf Zu Dir (Psalm 123)
see Wehnert, Wolfram, Lobet Den Herren, Ihr
Seine Engel

Ich Will Dir Danken, Herr (Psalm 108)
see Schwarz, Jochen, Seihe, Es Ist Alles
Neu Geworden

Ich Wollt Ein Baumlein Steign
SAB HANSSLER 6.1896 s.p.   (R2041)

Ihr Manner Von Galilaa
see Evangelisches Kirchengesangbuch

...Ist Nichts Zu Gross Und Nichts Zu Klein
*Gen
[Ger] SAB/SATB,acap BAREN. BA 6307 s.p.
                                        (R2042)

Jesus Ist Kommen, Grund Ewiger Freude
SAT/SAB,treb inst,bass inst HANSSLER 14.053
                                        (R2043)

Kommet Her! Horet *mot
SSATB HANSSLER 7.008 s.p.   (R2044)

Lasset Uns Aber Wahrhaftig Sein
SATB,org,opt brass sc HANSSLER 19.203 s.p.
contains also: Lasset Uns Ablegen Die
Sunde (unis,cantor,kbd); Nach Dir, O
Herr, Verlangt Mich (Psalm 25) (unis,kbd)
                                        (R2045)

Lasset Uns Ablegen Die Sunde
see Ruppel, Paul Ernst, Lasset Uns Aber
Wahrhaftig Sein

Nach Dir, O Herr, Verlangt Mich (Psalm 25)
see Ruppel, Paul Ernst, Lasset Uns Aber
Wahrhaftig Sein

Nun Singet Und Seid Froh
SA,treb inst/bass inst HANSSLER 14.026 s.p.
                                        (R2046)

Psalm 25 *see Nach Dir, O Herr, Verlangt
Mich

Psalm 105 *see Dankt Dem Herrn Und Predigt
Seinen Namen

Psalm 108 *see Ich Will Dir Danken, Herr

Psalm 123 *see Ich Hebe Meine Augen Auf Zu
Dir

Psalm 145 *see Unser Herr Ist Gross Und Von
Grosser Kraft

Suchet Den Herrn
see Bach, Johann Sebastian, Ich Liebe Jesum
Alle Stund

Unser Herr Ist Gross Und Von Grosser Kraft
(Psalm 145)
see Wehnert, Wolfram, Lobet Den Herren, Ihr
Seine Engel

Vater Alles Lebens *cant
SSATB,A/B solo,org,fl,vln sc HANSSLER
10.299 s.p., ipa   (R2047)

Vater Unser Im Himmelreich
see Schweizer, Rolf, Vater, Der In Den
Himmeln Ist

Werdet Tater Aus Dem Wort *Gen
[Ger] SAB,acap (med) BAREN. BA 6307 s.p.
                                        (R2048)

Wir Glauben Gott
mix cor HANSSLER 14.133 s.p.   (R2049)

Wohlan, Alle, Die Ihr Durstig Seid, Kommet
Her
see Bach, Johann Sebastian, O Gott, Du
Frommer Gott

Zu Den Fussen Jesu
see Ruppel, Paul Ernst, Glaube Ist Ein Baum

Zu Gottes Ehre Mein Saitenspiel
see Schweizer, Rolf, Manchmal Kennen Wir
Gottes Willen

RUSH, JOHN
Mass In Honour Of St. Anthony *ASD,Mass
mix cor oct NOVELLO 02.0077.08 s.p.   (R2050)
cong oct NOVELLO 02.0078.06   (R2051)

O Lord My God
4pt mix cor oct SCHIRM.G 11611 $.30 (R2052)

RUSSEL, ELEANOR
  Commit Your Way Unto The Lord *Marriage
    (Zilch, Margot) cor,opt gtr LESLIE 4202
    s.p.   (R2053)

  Don't Look At Me, Look At Jesus
    (Zilch, Margot) cor,opt gtr LESLIE 4204
    s.p.   (R2054)

  God's Limitless Love
    (Zilch, Margot) SATB,opt gtr LESLIE 4200
    s.p.   (R2055)

  I'm Praising The Lord
    (Zilch, Margot) cor,opt gtr LESLIE 4201
    s.p.   (R2056)

  Let God Plan For You
    (Zilch, Margot) cor,opt gtr LESLIE 4203
    s.p.   (R2057)

RUSSELL
  American Folk Hymns For Christmas *CCU,Xmas,
    folk/hymn,US
    unis oct FISCHER,C CM-7707 $.40   (R2058)

  Bread Of Life
    SATB oct LORENZ B43 $.25   (R2059)

  Christmas All Year 'Round *Xmas
    (Maxwell) SATB oct SHAPIRO SK 2106 $.25
                                       (R2060)

  Come All You Faithful Christians
    SATB,acap (easy) OXFORD 84.146 $.20 (R2061)

  Now With The Cherubim *Xmas
    SATB,acap oct FISCHER,C CM-7297 $.25
                                       (R2062)

  Seven Introits For The Morning Service
    *CC7U,Morn,Introit
    unis SOUTHERN $.35   (R2063)

  Stabat Mater
    men cor,org/pno voc sc MCA   (R2064)

  Standing At The Door
    SATB,acap (med easy) oct OXFORD 84.145 $.25
                                       (R2065)

RUSSELL, KENNEDY
  Saint Christopher
    2pt ASHDOWN E.A.213 s.p.   (R2066)

RUSSELL, LESLIE
  O Brother Man *Fest/Gen
    SS (very easy) oct OXFORD 54.145 $.15, ipr
                                       (R2067)

RUSSELL, VELMA A.
  In The Shadow Of Thy Wings (Psalm 63)
    SATB,S solo,pno/org (easy) oct WILLIS 6140
    $.15   (R2068)

  Look Down From Heaven, O God *prayer
    SATB,pno (easy) oct WILLIS 6280 $.15
                                       (R2069)

  O, Sing Unto The Lord A New Song
    3pt wom cor,pno (easy) oct WILLIS 6577 $.18
                                       (R2070)

  Psalm 63 *see In The Shadow Of Thy Wings

  Unto The Sky
    SATB,Mez solo,pno (med) oct WILLIS 7459
    $.25   (R2071)

RUSSIAN CHRISTMAS HYMN see Ippolitov-Ivanov,
  Mikhail Mikhailovitch

RUSSIAN CREDO see Stravinsky, Igor

RUSSIAN EASTER ALLELUIA see Gaul, Harvey
  Bartlet

RUSSIAN EASTER CAROL OF THE TREES see Gaul,
  Harvey Bartlet

RUTH see Gaul, Alfred Robert

RUTH AND NAOMI see Kosakoff, Reuven

RUTH ET NOEMIE see Lacome, Paul

RUTHENBERG, OTTO (1936-   )
  Bei Stiller Nacht *Psntd,mot
    4pt men cor,BarBar soli TONGER s.p. (R2072)

RUTTER
  Christ The Lord Is Risen *anthem
    mix cor oct OXFORD 42.362 $.45   (R2073)

  God Be In My Head *anthem
    mix cor oct OXFORD 94.326 $.20   (R2074)

  Nativity Carol *Xmas,carol
    SSA SOUTHERN $.25   (R2075)

  Praise Ye The Lord *anthem
    mix cor oct OXFORD 42.357 $.35   (R2076)

  Preces And Responses For Evening Prayer
    TTBB oct OXFORD 41.027 $.30   (R2077)

RYDER, NOAH F. (1914-1964)
  See That Babe In The Lowly Manger *Xmas,spir
    4pt mix cor,acap oct SCHIRM.G 9550 $.35
                                       (R2078)
  What You Gonna Call Yo' Pretty Little Baby?
    *Xmas,spir
    4pt mix cor,acap oct SCHIRM.G 9501 $.30
                                       (R2079)

RYDER, THOMAS PHILANDER (1836-1887)
  Hear Our Prayer
    SATB,acap oct PRESSER 332-01677 $.30
                                       (R2080)

RYELANDT, JOSEPH
  Christus Rex *Op.79, ora
    [Fr/It] cor,soli,orch voc sc CBDM s.p.
                                       (R2081)
  Le Bon Pasteur *Op.54, cant
    [Dut/Fr/Ger] cor,soli,orch voc sc CBDM s.p.
                                       (R2082)
  Maria *Op.48, ora
    [Dut/Fr/Ger] cor,soli,orch voc sc CBDM s.p.
                                       (R2083)
  Missa *Op.111, Mass
    6pt mix cor,acap CBDM s.p.   (R2084)

  Te Deum *Te Deum
    [Lat] mix cor,org voc sc CBDM s.p. (R2085)

RYLEY
  Fierce Raged The Tempest
    SATB ALLANS 196 s.p.   (R2086)

  Lord We Pray Thee
    SATB ALLANS 420 s.p.   (R2087)

S

S.A. AND B ANTHEMS *CCU,anthem
  SA/SAB LORENZ $1.75   (S1)

S.A.B. ANTHEMS FOR THE CHURCH YEAR see
  Lovelace, Austin C.

S.A.B. CAROLS FOR CHRISTMAS *CCU,Xmas
  SAB SCHMITT 9081 $1.00   (S2)

S.A.B. CHOIR NO. 1 *CCU,anthem
  SAB LORENZ $1.75   (S3)

S.A.B. CHOIR NO. 2 *CCU,anthem
  SAB LORENZ $1.75   (S4)

S.A.B. CHOIR NO. 3 *CCU,anthem
  SAB LORENZ $1.75   (S5)

S.A.B. CHOIR NO. 4 *CCU,anthem
  SAB LORENZ $1.75   (S6)

S.A.B. CHOIR NO. 5 *CCU,anthem
  SAB LORENZ $1.75   (S7)

S.A.B. CHOIR NO. 6 *CCU,anthem
  SAB LORENZ $1.75   (S8)

S.A.B. CHOIR NO. 7 *CCU,anthem
  SAB LORENZ $1.75   (S9)

S.A.B. CHOIR RESPONSES *CCU,cor-resp
  SAB LORENZ 7347 $.30   (S10)

S.A.B. CHORISTER *CCU
  SAB SCHMITT 9180 $1.25   (S11)

S.A.B. CHORISTER, THE *CCU
  (Trusler, Ivan) SAB WARNER $1.50   (S12)

S.A.B. CHORUS COLLECTION *sac/sec,CC18L
  (Fearis, J.S.) SAB (easy) voc sc WILLIS $.75
                                       (S13)

S.A.B. CHORUSES *CCU
  SAB SCHMITT 20 $.50   (S14)

S.A.B. GOSPEL SONG ANTHEMS NO. 1 *CCU,anthem
  SAB LORENZ $1.75   (S15)

S.A.B. GOSPEL SONG ANTHEMS NO. 2 *CCU,anthem
  SAB LORENZ $1.75   (S16)

S.A.B. STANDARD ANTHEMS *CCU,anthem
  SAB LORENZ $1.75   (S17)

S.A.B. VOICES (BOOK 1) *CC28UL,hymn
  SAB cmplt ed LILLENAS MB-163 $1.00   (S18)

S.A.B. VOICES (BOOK 2) *CC23UL,hymn
  SAB cmplt ed LILLENAS MB-164 $1.00   (S19)

S.A.B. VOICES (BOOK 3) *CC21UL
  (Whitman, Don; Rogers, Ethel T.) SAB cmplt ed
    LILLENAS MB-165 $1.00   (S20)

S.A.(T.)B. CHOIR *CCU,anthem
  SAB/SATB LORENZ $1.75   (S21)

S. ANTONIO DI PADOVA see Gorlatto, Giacomo

S.S.A.B. CHOIR BOOK *CCU
  SSAB SCHMITT 9165 $1.00   (S22)

S.S.A.B. CHORUSES *CCU
  SSAB SCHMITT 9166 $1.60   (S23)

S.S.A.B. SACRED COLLECTION see Ehret, Walter

S.S.A. CHOIR *CCU
  SSA SCHMITT 9171 $1.00   (S24)

S.S.A. CHOIR RESPONSES *CCU,cor-resp
  SSA LORENZ 6219 $.30   (S25)

S.S.A. STANDARD ANTHEMS *CCU,anthem
  SSA/SSAA LORENZ $1.75   (S26)

SA ALSKADE GUD VARLDEN
  see Sex Koraler I Folkton I Sattningar

SA ALSKADE GUD VARLDEN ALL *Bibl
  (Wallin, Bertil) [Swed] SAB,acap GEHRMANS
    TKS 22   (S27)

SA GAR EN DAG AN FRAN VAR TID see Runback,
  Albert

SA HAR GUD ELSKET VERDEN see Haaland, Ingebret

SAAR, LOUIS VICTOR (1868-1937)
  Almighty God, Our Heavenly Father *Op.131,
    No.1
    SATB,S solo,acap SCHIRM.EC 1161 $.16 (S28)

SAB CHORALE BOOK, THE *CC22L
  (Thomas, P.) SAB CONCORDIA 97-7575 $1.35
    contains works by: Spar; Rothenberg;
    Strube; Chemin-Petit; Lenel; Halter;
    Wenzel; Hennig; Metzler; Wolff; Vogel;
    Petzold; Zipp   (S29)

SAB SACRED COLLECTION, VOL. 3 *CCU
  SAB FLAMMER GD5001 $1.35   (S30)

SABBATH BELLS see Stainer, John

SABBATH EVE SERVICE see Starer, Robert

SABBATH EVE SERVICE see Starer, Robert

SABBATH EVE SERVICE see Weinberg, Jacob,
  Servizio Pentatonico

SABBATH EVE SERVICE FOR CHILDREN see Milhaud,
  Darius, Service Pour La Vielle Du Sabbat A
  L'usage Des Enfants

SABBATH EVENING SERVICE see Cohen, Joel I.

SABBATH EVENING SERVICE, A see Fink, Michael

SABBATH FOR ISRAEL see Binder, Abraham Wolfe

SABBATH MORNING SERVICE see Freed, Isadore

SABBATH MUSIC see Altman, Ludwig

SABBATH SERVICE FOR CONGREGATIONAL SINGING see
Weinberg, Jacob

SABBATO SANCTO (LECTIO PRIMA) see Nanini
(Nanino), Giovanni Maria

SABBATO SANCTO (LECTIO SECUNDA) see Nanini
(Nanino), Giovanni Maria

SABBATO SANCTO (LECTIO TERTIA) see Nanini
(Nanino), Giovanni Maria

SABESTON
No More Than A Manger　*Xmas
SATB BOOSEY-CAN s.p.　　　　　　(S31)

SABOLY, NICHOLAS
Aupres D'aquel Estable　*Xmas,carol,Fr
(Aubanel, G.) "Proche De Cette Etable" 1-
3pt (easy) LEMOINE voc sc s.p., cor pts
s.p. see also Douze Noels Provencaux
(S32)

Beaucoup De Gens　*see Li A Proun De Gent

Chut! Taisez-Vous　*see Chut! Teisas-Vous

Chut! Teisas-Vous　*Xmas,carol,Fr
(Aubanel, G.) "Chut! Taisez-Vous" 1-3pt
(easy) LEMOINE voc sc s.p., cor pts s.p.
see also Douze Noels Provencaux　(S33)

Dieu Vous Gard', Nostre Mestre　*Xmas,carol,
Fr
(Aubanel, G.) "Dieu Vous Gard', Notre
Maitre" 1-3pt (easy) LEMOINE voc sc s.p.,
cor pts s.p. see also Douze Noels
Provencaux　　　　　　　　　　(S34)

Dieu Vous Gard', Notre Maitre　*see Dieu Vous
Gard', Nostre Mestre

Douze Noels Provencaux　*Xmas,carol,Fr
(Aubanel, G.) [Fr] 1-3pt (easy) LEMOINE voc
sc s.p., cor pts s.p.
contains & see also: Aupres D'aquel
Estable, "Proche De Cette Etable";
Chut! Teisas-Vous, "Chut! Taisez-Vous";
Dieu Vous Gard', Nostre Mestre, "Dieu
Vous Gard', Notre Maitre"; Guihaume,
Toni, Peire, "Guillaume, Antoine,
Pierre"; Hou! De L'oustau, "He! La
Maison"; Lei Pastoureu, "Les
Pastoureaux"; Li A Proun De Gent,
"Beaucoup De Gens"; Pastre, Pastresso,
"Patres, Bergers"; Per Noun Langui,
"Pour Ne Languir"; Sortez D'ici, Race
Maudite; Touro-Louro-Louro, "Ture-Lure-
Lure"; Uno Estello, "Une Etoile" (S35)

Guihaume, Toni, Peire　*Xmas,carol,Fr
(Aubanel, G.) "Guillaume, Antoine, Pierre"
1-3pt (easy) LEMOINE voc sc s.p., cor pts
s.p. see also Douze Noels Provencaux
(S36)

Guillaume, Antoine, Pierre　*see Guihaume,
Toni, Peire

He! La Maison　*see Hou! De L'oustau

Hou! De L'oustau　*Xmas,carol,Fr
(Aubanel, G.) "He! La Maison" 1-3pt (easy)
LEMOINE voc sc s.p., cor pts s.p. see
also Douze Noels Provencaux　(S37)

Lei Pastoureu　*Xmas,carol,Fr
(Aubanel, G.) "Les Pastoureaux" 1-3pt
(easy) LEMOINE voc sc s.p., cor pts s.p.
see also Douze Noels Provencaux　(S38)

Les Pastoureaux　*see Lei Pastoureu

Li A Proun De Gent　*Xmas,carol,Fr
(Aubanel, G.) "Beaucoup De Gens" 1-3pt
(easy) LEMOINE voc sc s.p., cor pts s.p.
see also Douze Noels Provencaux　(S39)

Pastre, Pastresso　*Xmas,carol,Fr
(Aubanel, G.) "Patres, Bergers" 1-3pt
(easy) LEMOINE voc sc s.p., cor pts s.p.
see also Douze Noels Provencaux　(S40)

Patres, Bergers　*see Pastre, Pastresso

Per Noun Langui　*Xmas,carol,Fr
(Aubanel, G.) "Pour Ne Languir" 1-3pt
(easy) LEMOINE voc sc s.p., cor pts s.p.
see also Douze Noels Provencaux　(S41)

Pour Ne Languir　*see Per Noun Langui

Proche De Cette Etable　*see Aupres D'aquel
Estable

Sortez D'ici, Race Maudite　*Xmas,carol,Fr
(Aubanel, G.) 1-3pt (easy) LEMOINE voc sc
s.p., cor pts s.p. see also Douze Noels
Provencaux　　　　　　　　　　(S42)

Touro-Louro-Louro　*Xmas,carol,Fr
(Aubanel, G.) "Ture-Lure-Lure" 1-3pt (easy)
LEMOINE voc sc s.p., cor pts s.p. see
also Douze Noels Provencaux　(S43)
(Shaw; Parker) mix cor,acap oct SCHIRM.G
10167 $.30　　　　　　　　　　(S44)

Ture-Lure-Lure　*see Touro-Louro-Louro

Une Etoile　*see Uno Estello

Uno Estello　*Xmas,carol,Fr
(Aubanel, G.) "Une Etoile" 1-3pt (easy)
LEMOINE voc sc s.p., cor pts s.p. see
also Douze Noels Provencaux　(S45)

SACCHETTO, GUIDO
Pange Lingua
see Quatro Faciles Hymni
see Quatro Faciles Hymni

Quatro Faciles Hymni　*Commun,hymn
[Lat] (easy) ZANIBON 634 s.p.
contains: Pange Lingua (unis,org); Pange
Lingua (2 eq voices,org); Tantum Ergo

SACCHETTO, GUIDO (cont'd.)

(unis,org); Tantum Ergo (2 eq voices,
org)　　　　　　　　　　　　(S46)

Tantum Ergo
see Quatro Faciles Hymni
see Quatro Faciles Hymni

Transitus Div. Antonii Pat.　*ASD
[Lat] unis,org ZANIBON 3471 s.p.　(S47)

SACCHINI, A.
Salvum Fac Regem
wom cor sc ALSBACH&D s.p.　　(S48)

SACCO
Awake, O Shepherds
SATB (med diff) oct OSTARA OP114 $.30 (S49)

Lord Is My Shepherd, The
SSA (med diff) oct OSTARA OP121 $.55 (S50)
SATB (med diff) oct OSTARA OP120 $.55 (S51)
TTBB (med diff) oct OSTARA OP123 $.55 (S52)

Make Haste, O God, To Deliver Me
SATB FISCHER,C O-4527 $1.00　　(S53)

Ring Out Wild Bells
cor,pno,3trp,4horn,3trom,tuba,perc,timp
(med diff) OSTARA OP 100E sc $23.00, cor
pts $.75, ipa　　　　　　　　(S54)
SATB (med diff) oct OSTARA OP100 $.75 (S55)

Teach Me O Lord
SATB,narrator (med easy) oct OSTARA OP103
$.45　　　　　　　　　　　　(S56)

SACCO, JOHN [CHARLES] (1905-　　)
Bells Ring Out For Christmas, The
4pt mix cor,opt bells,chimes,vcl oct
SCHIRM.G 10698 $.25　　　　　(S57)
3pt wom cor,opt bells,chimes,vcl oct
SCHIRM.G 10821 $.25　　　　　(S58)
2pt wom cor,opt bells,chimes,vcl oct
SCHIRM.G 10820 $.30　　　　　(S59)
3pt mix cor,opt bells,chimes,vcl oct
SCHIRM.G 10773 $.25　　　　　(S60)

Spelling Of Christmas, The
4pt mix cor,opt bells&tamb oct SCHIRM.G
10947 $.30　　　　　　　　　(S61)
3pt mix cor,opt bells,tamb oct SCHIRM.G
10948 $.30　　　　　　　　　(S62)
2pt wom cor,opt bells,tamb oct SCHIRM.G
10949 $.30　　　　　　　　　(S63)
4pt men cor,opt bells,tamb oct SCHIRM.G
10950 $.30　　　　　　　　　(S64)
2pt wom cor,opt bells,tamb oct SCHIRM.G
11161 $.30　　　　　　　　　(S65)

SACCO, P.
Truly My Soul Waiteth Upon God
SATB,acap oct PRESSER FH-110 $.30　(S66)

SACERDOS ET PONTIFEX see Arnaldi, Antonio

SACERDOS ET PONTIFEX see Bottazzo, Luigi

SACERDOS ET PONTIFEX see Oldham, Arthur

SACERDOS ET PONTIFEX see Palestrina, Giovanni

SACERDOS ET PONTIFEX see Pasini, Crescenzio

SACERDOS ET PONTIFEX see Ravanello, Oreste

SACERDOTES DOMINI see Byrd, William

SACERDOTES DOMINI see Palestrina, Giovanni

SACERDOTES DOMINI see Polleri, Gio. Batta.

SACERDOTES EJUS see Polzer, Odo

SACRAE CANTIONES
(Berg, Gottfrid) mix cor NORDISKA 2704 s.p.
(S67)

SACRAE CANTIONES　*CCU,chorale/mot
(Berg, Gottfrid) cor NORDISKA 2704 s.p., ipa
see also: Din Spira, Jesu, Strackes Ut;
Forlan Oss, Gud, Den Helga Frid; Friden
Herrens Helgon Fingo; Gud Faders Son, O
Jesus Kar; Gud, Var Gud, For Varlden All;
Guds Nad Vi Skola Prisa; Jesus Kristus Ar
Var Halsa; Min Gud Och Och Fader Kare; O
Jesu, Nar Jag Hadan Skall; Skulle Jag Min
Gud Ej Lova; Vi Tro Pa En Allsmaktig Gud
(S68)

SACRAE CANTIONES VOL. I see Gesualdo, Don Carlo

SACRAE CANTIONES VOL. II see Gesualdo, Don
Carlo

SACRAE CANTIUNCLUAE, SANCTISSIMAE VIRGINI MISSA
SENIS VOCIBUS, VOL. 14-1 see Monteverdi,
Claudio

SACRAE CANTIUNCULAE see Monteverdi, Claudio

SACRAMENT OF PRICELESS WORTH see Palestrina,
Giovanni, Corporis Mysterium

SACRED A CAPELLA CHORUSES see Mendelssohn-
Bartholdy, Felix

SACRED CHOIR MUSIC, 1648 see Schutz, Heinrich

SACRED CHORAL FAVORITES, VOLUME 1　*CCU
SATB oct FOX $1.25　　　　　(S69)

SACRED CHORAL GEMS FROM THE MASTERS see Grant

SACRED CHORAL MUSIC A CAPPELA see Mendelssohn-
Bartholdy, Felix

SACRED CHORAL MUSIC WITH ORGAN see Mendelssohn-
Bartholdy, Felix

SACRED CHORISTER see Thompson, Ronald

SACRED CHORUS COLLECTIONS VOL. I　*CC20L
eq voices/mix cor voc sc KALMUS 6402 $1.75
contains works by: Palestrina; Lassus;
Gallus; and others　　　　　(S70)

SACRED CHORUS COLLECTIONS VOL. II　*CC24L
eq voices/mix cor voc sc KALMUS 6403 $1.75
contains works by: Vittoria; Lassus;

Palestrina; and others　　　　(S71)

SACRED CHORUS COLLECTIONS VOL. III　*CC24L
eq voices/mix cor voc sc KALMUS 6404 $1.75
contains works by: Palestrina; Pitoni; and
others　　　　　　　　　　　(S72)

SACRED CHORUS COLLECTIONS VOL. IV　*CC26L
eq voices/mix cor voc sc KALMUS $1.75
contains works by: Vittoria; Gallus;
Lassus; and others　　　　　(S73)

SACRED CHORUSES, CANONS, AND SONGS see Brahms,
Johannes

SACRED CHORUSES FOR MIXED VOICES　*CC12L,Gen
SATB PRO ART 111 $1.25　　　(S74)

SACRED CHORUSES see Brahms, Johannes

SACRED CHORUSES see Bruckner, Anton

SACRED CHORUSES see Bruckner, Anton

SACRED CHORUSES see Buxtehude, Dietrich

SACRED CONCERTO see Lechner, Leonhard

SACRED FEAST, THE see Lovelace, Austin C.

SACRED FLAME, THE
2pt CHAPPELL 0018218-352 $.40　(S75)
SSA CHAPPELL 0018218-354 $.40　(S76)

SACRED HARP, THE　*CCU
(Dunford, Benjamin) S/SA BELWIN $1.25　(S77)

SACRED HYMNS see Dufay, Guillaume

SACRED MORN, THE see Parry, W.H.

SACRED MUSIC FOR MALE CHORUS　*CC26L,Gen
(Holmes) TTBB PRO ART 102 $1.25　(S78)

SACRED MUSIC FOR MIXED VOICES see Kjelson

SACRED MUSIC FOR TREBLE VOICES see Kjelson

SACRED MUSIC OF THE XVI CENTURY　*CCU
(Tovey, D.) SSA pap SCHIRM.EC 832 $2.25 (S79)

SACRED SERVICE see Bloch, Ernest, Avodath
Hakodesh

SACRED SERVICE see Rossi, Salomone

SACRED SERVICE, A see Berman, Judith M.

SACRED SERVICE, A see Di Julio, [Max]

SACRED SERVICE, A see Hadley

SACRED SERVICE FOR SABBATH EVE see Freed,
Isadore

SACRED SERVICE FOR SABBATH MORNING see Freed,
Isadore

SACRED SERVICE SHABBAT SHALOM see Leichtling,
Alan

SACRED SINGER　*CC14L,Gen
(Barthelson) 2pt jr cor PRO ART 1105 $1.00
(S80)

SACRED SONGS see Hoffman, M.

SACRED SONGS FOR JUNIOR CHOIR see Hoffman, M.

SACRED SONGS OF PRAISE see Rineharts

SACRED TREBLE CHORUSES　*CCU
SSA SCHMITT 57 $.50　　　　　(S81)

SACRED TRIOS FOR WOMEN'S VOICES　*CCU
SSA&SAA oct PRESSER $2.00 sold only in USA
(S82)

SACRED TWO-PART CHORUSES FOR JUNIOR CHOIRS see
Bliss, Paul

SACRED WORKS VOL. I see Merulo, Claudio

SACRED WORKS VOL. II see Merulo, Claudio

SACRED WORKS VOL. III see Merulo, Claudio

SACRIFICE TRIUMPHANT see Harwood, Basil

SACRIFICIAL SONG see Beethoven, Ludwig van

SACRIS SOLEMNIS see Maggio, Giuseppe

SAD IS MY SOUL see Haydn, (Johann) Michael,
Tristis Est Anima Mea

SAD IS MY SOUL see Poulenc, Francis, Tristis
Est Animae Mea

SAD IS MY SOUL see Tristis Est Anima Mea

SAD IS MY SOUL UNTO DEATH see Haydn, (Johann)
Michael, Tristis Est Anima Mea

SAD IS MY SOUL UNTO DEATH see Palestrina,
Giovanni, Tristis Est Anima Mea

SADAI, YIZHAK
Prelude A Jerusalem　*Heb
SATB,3 narrators,orch ISRAELI 8006 s.p.
(S83)

SADLER, ARTHUR
Frohlich Soll Mein Herze Springen
3 eq voices MOSELER LB-1002 s.p.　(S84)

SAELE JOLEKVELD see Beck, Thomas [Ludvigsen]

SAETERJENTENS SONDAG　*Gen
(Christiansen, P.) "Chalet Girl's Sunday"
SATB SCHMITT 1190 $.25　　　(S85)

SAETERJENTENS SONDAG see Alfven, Hugo

SAFE IN HIS CARE see Gotterman, G.

SAFE IN HIS HANDS see Roe, Gloria [Ann]

SAFE IN THE ARMS OF JESUS see Burroughs

SAFSTEN, MARY R. DECKER
Lo, Thou Art Near (composed with Safsten, Ranghildl Linde)
SSA PIONEER 1009 $.40 (S86)

SAFSTEN, RANGHILDL LINDE
Lo, Thou Art Near *see Safsten, Mary R. Decker

SAG MIG DEN VAGEN, SOM DRAGER TILL LIVET
(Bond, Anders) [Swed] SATB,acap GEHRMANS KRB 248 (S87)

SAG MINNES DU PSALMEN see Merikanto, [Oskar]

SAG, WAS IST GESCHEHEN? see Watkinson, Gerd

SAGEN TILL DOTTERN SION see Nilsson, Torsten

SAGES OF SHEBA, THE see Bach, Johann Sebastian, Sie Werden Aus Saba Alle Kommen

SAGET DEN GASTEN see Schutz, Heinrich

SAGITTARIUS
see SCHUTZ, HEINRICH

SAGT AN, WER IST DOCH DIESE *BVM,17th cent
(Dawidowicz, Anton) wom cor,acap oct DOBLINGER s.p. see also Acht Marienleider (S88)

SAGT AN, WER IST DOCH DIESE see Muller, A.M.

SAILOR'S ALLELUIA see Bright

SAINT CHRISTOPHER see Russell, Kennedy

SAINT FRANCIS see Weigl, Vally

SAINT FRANCOIS D'ASSISE see Rosenthal, Manuel

SAINT GREGORY'S DAY see Kodaly, Zoltan

SAINT HELENA
Show Me The Way
SATB oct STAFF 679 $.30 (S89)

SAINT JEAN DU SACRE COEUR, SOEUR
Messe A Notre-Dame
SA,pno oct BERANDOL 786SOAB $.75 (S90)

SAINT JOHN PASSION see Schutz, Heinrich, Johannespassion

SAINT JOSEPH see Schimmerling, H.A.

SAINT JOSEPH AVEC MARIE see Favre, Georges

SAINT JOSEPH M'A DIT *Xmas,carol,Fr
(Tomasi) [Fr] SMezA LEDUC s.p. see also Douze Noels De Saboly (S91)

SAINT LUKE PASSION see Schutz, Heinrich, Lukaspassion

SAINT MARK PASSION, THE
SCHIRM.EC 5 $1.50 (S92)

SAINT MARK'S EASTER GOSPEL see Mitchell, L.

SAINT MARY GOES A-SEEKING *carol
SATB (med easy) OXFORD 08.179 $.15 (S93)

SAINT MATTHEW PASSION see Schutz, Heinrich, Matthauspassion

SAINT PATRICK'S PRAYER see Burke, John

SAINT PAUL see Mendelssohn-Bartholdy, Felix, Paulus

SAINT-SAENS, CAMILLE (1835-1921)
Alleluia (from Christmas Oratorio)
SATB oct STAFF 601 $.30 (S94)

Angel Bands *see Ave Verum Corpus

Ave Maria *BVM,mot
see SIX MOTETS A L'UNISSON
[Lat] 4pt mix cor oct DURAND s.p. (S95)
(Kunc, P.) [Lat] 4pt mix cor oct DURAND s.p. (S96)

Ave Maria, En La *BVM,mot
[Lat] 2 eq voices (A maj) oct DURAND s.p. (S97)

Ave Verum *Commun,mot
[Lat] SATBar (E flat maj) oct DURAND s.p. (S98)
[Lat] 2 eq voices (B min) oct DURAND s.p. (S99)
[Lat] 4pt wom cor,horn oct DURAND s.p. (S100)
[Lat] 4pt wom cor (D maj) oct DURAND s.p. (S101)
(Kunc, P.) [Lat] 4pt/4pt mix cor,org oct DURAND s.p. (S102)

Ave Verum Corpus
(Kaplan) "Hail, True Body" [Eng/Lat] SATB, acap oct LAWSON 51521 $.25 (S103)
(Montani) [Lat] 4pt mix cor oct SCHIRM.G 5507 $.20 (S104)
(White) "Angel Bands" [Lat/Eng] 4pt mix cor oct SCHIRM.G 3473 $.25 (S105)

Benedictus *Gen,Bene/mot
[Lat] SBar oct DURAND s.p. (S106)

Bring Costly Offerings *see Tollite Hostias

Choeur Triomphal (from Quoniam)
(Brun, L'abbe F.) [Fr] 4pt mix cor,org oct DURAND s.p. (S107)

Chorale (from Symphony No. 3) chorale
SAB oct STAFF 509 $.30 (S108)

Christmas Oratorio *see Oratorio De Noel

Coeli Enarrant (Psalm 18) Op.42, Gen,mot
[Lat] SATB,org,harp,5strings oct DURAND s.p., ipa (S109)
"Psaume XVIII" [Lat] cor,SMezT soli,orch, opt pno DURAND sc ipr, voc sc s.p. (S110)

Coeli Enarrant Introduction
[Lat] 4pt mix cor,org,5strings oct DURAND s.p., ipa (S111)

SAINT-SAENS, CAMILLE (cont'd.)

Coeli Enarrant No. 1 (Psalm 19)
cor voc sc KALMUS 6411 $1.00 (S112)

De Dugue (from La Messe) Commun,mot
[Lat] unis (D maj) oct DURAND s.p. (S113)

Deus Abraham *Gen,mot
[Lat/Fr] SATBar,Mez/Bar solo,org,harp oct DURAND s.p. (S114)
[Lat] SATB,opt harp oct DURAND s.p. (S115)

Give Praise All Earthly Men (from Christmas Oratorio, The)
(Hines) 3pt mix cor,org/pno oct SCHIRM.G 11572 $.25 (S116)
(Hines) 4pt mix cor,org/pno,opt 5brass oct SCHIRM.G 11573 $.30 (S117)

Gloria (from Christmas Oratorio) Xmas,Gloria
SATB oct STAFF 599 $.25 (S118)
(Hines) "Glory To The Father" 4pt mix cor, org/pno oct SCHIRM.G 11571 $.25 (S119)
(Hines) "Glory To The Father" 3pt mix cor, org/pno oct SCHIRM.G 11570 $.25 (S120)

Glory To God In Highest *Xmas,ora
(Williams) SATB oct GRAY GCMR 2987 $.30 (S121)

Glory To The Father *see Gloria

Grant Unto Me
(Lundquist) 4pt mix cor,acap oct SCHIRM.G 11377 $.25 (S122)

Gud, Vaere Meg Nadig
mix cor MUSIKK 110 s.p. (S123)

Hail, True Body *see Ave Verum Corpus

Hark To The Tiding
SATB oct FISCHER,J 1474 $.30 (S124)

Heureux Qui Du Coeur De Marie
unis oct DURAND s.p. (S125)

Jesu, Gentlest Saviour *see Sub Tuum

Jesu, Word Of God Incarnate *Easter/Lent
mix cor SOUTHERN $.25 (S126)
(Brooks) SATB oct SPRATT 549 $.25 (S127)

Justorum Animae *Gen,mot
"Offertoire" [Lat] 4pt mix cor,orch,opt vcl,bvl oct DURAND s.p., ipr (S128)

Laudate Dominum *Gen,mot
[Lat] 2 eq voices oct DURAND s.p. (S129)
(Kung, P.) [Lat] 4pt mix cor,org oct DURAND s.p. (S130)

Le Deluge *Op.45, Bibl
[Fr/Eng/Ger/It] mix cor,SATB soli,orch,opt pno DURAND sc s.p., ipa, voc sc s.p. (S131)

Lift Up Your Offerings
(Kaplan) SATB oct LAWSON 51717 $.30 (S132)

Lift Up Your Songs Of Praise
SATB oct LORENZ B144 $.30 (S133)

Mass For 4 Voices *see Messe Solennelle

Messe De Requiem *Op.54, Mass/Req
[Fr] SATB,T solo,orch,org/winds DURAND oct s.p., sc s.p., ipa (S134)

Messe Solennelle *Op.4, Mass
[Fr] SATB,orch/org voc sc DURAND s.p., ipr (S135)
"Mass For 4 Voices" cor,solo voc sc KALMUS 6412 $3.00 (S136)

My Soul Doth Magnify The Lord *see Tecum Principium

O Magnify The Lord
(Trusler) SAB WARNER W3718 $.30 (S137)

O Saint Autel *Commun,hymn
[Fr] 3 eq voices,soli oct DURAND s.p. (S138)

O Salutaris *Commun,mot
[Lat] TBar/SA (E maj) oct DURAND s.p. (S139)
[Lat] SABar (A flat maj) oct DURAND s.p. (S140)
[Lat] SABar (B flat maj) oct DURAND s.p. (S141)

Offertoire *see Justorum Animae

Oratorio De Noel *Op.12 (from Christmas Oratorio) Xmas,ora
[Fr] cor,TMez soli,orch,opt pno/org DURAND sc s.p., ipa, voc sc s.p. (S142)
"Christmas Oratorio" cor,orch sc KALMUS $12.00, ipa (S143)
"Christmas Oratorio" cor,opt inst voc sc KALMUS 6406 $1.50, ipa (S144)
"Christmas Oratorio" cor,strings,harp,org KALMUS $1.75, ipa (S145)
"Christmas Oratorio" [Eng/Lat] cor,soli voc sc SCHIRM.G $1.50 (S146)
"Praise Ye The Lord Of Hosts" SATB KJOS 704 $.30 (S147)
(Elwood) "Praise Ye The Lord Of Hosts" SATB oct PLYMOUTH SE-2 $.25 (S148)
(Fargo) "Praise Ye The Lord Of Hosts" SATB oct KENDOR $.30 (S149)
(Fargo) "Praise Ye The Lord Of Hosts" SA/jr cor oct KENDOR $.25 (S150)
(Fargo) "Praise Ye The Lord Of Hosts" SSA oct KENDOR $.25 (S151)
(Hadley) "Praise Ye The Lord Of Hosts" SATB oct PRO ART 2297 $.30 (S152)
(Hallett) "Praise Ye The Lord Of Hosts" SATB oct WORD CS-2318 $.25 (S153)
(Jury) "Praise Ye The Lord Of Hosts" SA oct BELWIN 60508 $.25 (S154)
(Jury) "Praise Ye The Lord Of Hosts" SSA oct BELWIN 60405 $.30 (S155)
(Jury) "Praise Ye The Lord Of Hosts" SATB oct BELWIN 60597 $.30 (S156)
(Jury) "Praise Ye The Lord Of Hosts" SAB oct BELWIN 60530 $.25 (S157)
(Stephens) "Christmas Oratorio" cor,soli, org sc SCHIRM.G $5.00 (S158)

SAINT-SAENS, CAMILLE (cont'd.)

Panis Angelicus *Commun,mot
(Kunc, P.) [Lat] 4pt/4pt mix cor oct DURAND s.p. (S159)

Pie Jesu, No. 2 *Gen,mot
[Lat] opt cor,T solo oct DURAND s.p. (S160)

Pour Vous Benir, Seigneur
[Fr] 3 eq voices,soli oct DURAND s.p. (S161)

Praise To God! Alleluia (from Christmas Oratorio) Xmas
(Barker) SATB,acap oct FISCHER,C CM-7222 $.25 (S162)

Praise Ye The Lord (from Christmas Oratorio) Bibl
4pt mix cor oct SCHIRM.G 10254 $.25 (S163)
(Ehret) SA&SATB oct BOOSEY 5129 $.30 (S164)
(Ehret) SA oct BOOSEY 5285 $.30 (S165)
(Ehret) SSAB oct BOOSEY 5050 $.30 (S166)
(Ehret) SSA oct BOOSEY 1911 $.30 (S167)
(Ehret) TTBB oct BOOSEY 1952 $.30 (S168)
(Gilbert) SATB FLAMMER A 5161 $.30 (S169)
(Gilbert) SAB FLAMMER D5060 $.30 (S170)
(Gilbert) SSA FLAMMER B 5118 $.25 (S171)
(Wilson; Ehret) SAB oct BOOSEY 1937 $.30 (S172)
(Wilson; Ehret) SATB oct BOOSEY 1951 $.30 (S173)

Praise Ye The Lord Of Hosts *see Oratorio De Noel

Psalm 18 *see Coeli Enarrant

Psalm 19 *see Coeli Enarrant No. 1

Psaume XVIII *see Coeli Enarrant

Quam Dilecta *Gen,mot
[Lat] mix cor,opt org&harp oct DURAND s.p. (S174)

Reine Des Cieux, O Divine Marie
unis oct DURAND s.p. (S175)

Rejoice, The Lord Is King
(Martin) SATB oct SPRATT 513 $.25 (S176)
(Martin) SAB oct SPRATT 575 $.25 (S177)
(Martin) SSA oct SPRATT 592 $.25 (S178)
(Martin) SA oct SPRATT 591 $.25 (S179)

Sub Tuum *BVM,mot
[Lat] SA (F min) oct DURAND s.p. (S180)
(White) "Jesu, Gentlest Saviour" [Eng/Lat] 2pt wom cor/2pt men cor oct SCHIRM.G 3470 $.25 (S181)

Tantum Ergo *Commun,mot
[Lat] SSAATTBarBar (E flat maj) oct DURAND s.p. (S182)
[Lat] 3 eq voices&opt unis (E flat maj) oct DURAND s.p. (S183)

Tecum Principium *Bibl
"My Soul Doth Magnify The Lord" [Lat/Eng] STB oct SCHIRM.G 5428 $.30 (S184)

Tecum Principum *Gen,mot
[Lat] STBar,opt org&harp oct DURAND s.p. (S185)

Tollite Hostias?
[Lat] cor oct DURAND s.p. (S186)
(Engel) "Bring Costly Offerings" [Eng/Lat] 4pt mix cor,acap oct SCHIRM.G 3397 $.25 (S187)

Tu Es Petrus *Gen,mot
[Lat] 4pt mix cor oct DURAND s.p. (S188)

Veni Creator, En Ut *Gen,mot
[Lat] TTBarBar (C maj) oct DURAND s.p. (S189)

Vingt Motets *CC20L,mot
[Lat] DURAND 2-3pt,soli s.p.; 2-3pt,soli s.p. (S190)

Wherefore Do The Heathen Clamor
(Dole; Trusler) SATB oct PLYMOUTH TR-110 $.25 (S191)

SAINT THOMAS (1835-1921)
I Love Thy Kingdom, Lord
(Cain) SATB FLAMMER A 5435 $.30 (S192)

SAINT THOMAS CHURCH DESCANT BOOK see Coke, Norman

SAINT THOMAS HONOUR WE
see Musica Britannica Vol. 4: Set 8

SAINTE-ANNE-LA-PALUD see Houdy

SAINTE-CECILE *see Bach, Johann Sebastian, Tantum Ergo; Beethoven, Ludwig van, Agnus Dei; Beethoven, Ludwig van, Sanctus; Bellini, Vincenzo, Tantum Ergo; Cherubini, Luigi, Adoremus; Gluck, Christoph Willibald Ritter von, Ave Maria; Gluck, Christoph Willibald Ritter von, Mater Divina Gratiae; Hummel, Johann Nepomuk, O Virgo Intemerata; Lefebure-Wely, Louis James Alfred, Ave Maria; Lefebure-Wely, Louis James Alfred, Tantum Ergo; Mendelssohn-Bartholdy, Felix, O Salutaris; Mendelssohn-Bartholdy, Felix, Sub Tuum; Mozart, Wolfgang Amadeus, Crux Fidelis; Mozart, Wolfgang Amadeus, O Salutaris; Schumann, O Salutaris (S193)

SAINTE-CECILE see Bach, Johann Sebastian

SAINTE-CECILE see Beethoven, Ludwig van

SAINTE-CECILE see Bellini, Vincenzo

SAINTE-CECILE see Cherubini, Luigi

SAINTE-CECILE see Gluck, Christoph Willibald Ritter von

SAINTE-CECILE see Hummel, Johann Nepomuk

SAINTE-CECILE see Lefebure-Wely, Louis James Alfred

SAINTE-CECILE see Mendelssohn-Bartholdy, Felix

SAINTE-CECILE see Mozart, Wolfgang Amadeus

SAINTE-CECILE see Schumann

SAINTE-CECILE see Gounod, Charles Francois,
    Messe Solennelle

SAINTE-GERMAIN D'AUXERRE see Migot

SAINTE MADELEINE see Chaminade, Cecile

SAINTE MARIE MAGDELEINE, CANTATE see Indy,
    Vincent d'

SAINTE NUIT see Haydn, (Franz) Joseph

SAINTS AND SINNERS see Young, Carlton R.

SAINTS BOUND FOR HEAVEN
    (Shaw; Parker) SATB,acap oct LAWSON 911 $.35
                                                    (S194)

SAINTS OF GOD, THE see Reed

SAKNAD see Heggen, Bodvar

SAKRAMENT see Bornefeld, Helmut

SAKRAMENTSHYMNE see Geitvik, S.H.

SALADIN, LOUIS
    Canticum Hebraicum *Heb
    (Adler, Israel) SATB,soli,cont,inst ISRAELI
    702 s.p.   (S195)

SALAMA, A.
    Jesus Christ Is Born *Xmas,carol,Rum
    4pt mix cor oct SCHIRM.G 7443 $.25   (S196)

    Lullaby, Jesus Dear *Xmas,carol,Pol
    4pt mix cor oct SCHIRM.G 7440 $.20   (S197)

    Wake, Ye Shepherds *Xmas,carol,Morav
    4pt mix cor oct SCHIRM.G 7438 $.25   (S198)

SALATHIEL, LYNDON
    Did Not Our Heart Burn Within Us
    4pt mix cor,B solo,org/pno oct SCHIRM.G
    10396 $.25   (S199)

    Lord's Prayer, The
    TTBB,pno/org (med) oct WILLIS 5947 $.12   (S200)

    Surely He Hath Borne Our Griefs
    4pt mix cor oct SCHIRM.G 10651 $.25   (S201)

    Twelve Prayer And Closing Responses *CC12U,
    Gen
    SATB SCHMITT 1612 $.25   (S202)

SALEM *Easter
    (Shaw;&arker) 4pt mix bor,acap oct SCHIRM.G
    9947 $.30   (S203)
    (Wood) SATB oct SUMMY 5828 $.30   (S204)

SALEYNU see Gorochov, Y.

SALIERI, ANTONIO (1750-1825)
    Confirma Hoc Deus
    see Two Inni Di Pentecoste

    Two Inni Di Pentecoste *Pent,hymn
    (Dite, L.) 4pt mix cor,pno RICORDI-ENG
    129844 s.p.
    contains: Confirma Hoc Deus (Offer); Veni
    Sancte Spiritus (Gradual)   (S205)

    Veni Sancte Spiritus
    see Two Inni Di Pentecoste

SALIG AR DEN STILLA STUNDEN see Bjarnegard,
    Gustaf

SALIG, SALIG DEN SOM KANDE see Cruger, Johann

SALIG, SALIG DEN SOM KANDE see Moren, John

SALIGA see Hammarstrom, Hugo

SALIGA ARO DE see Lassus, Roland de (Orlandus)

SALIGA ARO DE DODA see Olson, Daniel

SALIGA ARO DE DODA see Soderholm, Valdemar

SALIGA ARO DE RENHJARTADE see Carlstedt,
    Gunnemer

SALIGA ARO DE, SOM HORA GUDS ORD see Sandberg,
    Folke

SALIGA ARO DE, SOM HORA GUDS ORD see Thyrestam,
    Gunnar

SALIGA DE SOM HORA GUDS ORD see Moren, John

SALIGA DE, SOM IFRAN VARLDENS ODEN see
    Wikander, David

SALIGA HELIGA
    see Fem Korkoraler

SALIGE DE see Jeppesen, Knud

SALIGE ER DE SOM HORER GUDS ORD see Hovland,
    Egil

SALIGE ER DE SOM SORGER see Skauen, Guttorn

SALIGPRISNINGARNA see Edlund, Lars

SALIGT AR DET MODERSSKOTE SOM HAR BURIT DIG see
    Nilsson, Torsten

SALISBURY see Brownson

SALKOV, ABRAHAM
    El Hay'ladim B'yisrael *Sab-Eve
    2pt jr cor/3pt jr cor/2pt wom cor/3pt wom
    cor,cantor,pno/org,perc TRANSCON. TCL 342
    $2.50   (S206)

SALL DEN SOM HAVER JESUS KAR *Bibl
    (Bjarnegard, Gustaf) [Swed] SAB,acap GEHRMANS
    TKS 29   (S207)

SALME
    (Groven, Eivind) men cor MUSIKK 52 s.p.
                                                    (S208)

SALME see Olsen, Sparre

SALME OG FOLKEVISER see Laub, Thomas

SALMEMELODIER FRA REFORMATIONSTIDEN *Psalm,
    16th cent
    (Woldike, Mogens) [Dan] HANSEN-DEN 24570 s.p.
    contains works by: Praetorius; Melchior;
    and others
    contains & see also: Franck, Melchior, En
    Salme Om Vort Fald Og Forlosning;
    Hassler, Hans Leo, Nadversalme; Stobaeus,
    Johann, Jesus, Vor Gud Og Frelser;
    Walther, Johann Gottfried, En Salme Om
    Kristus; Walther, Johann Gottfreid,
    Herre, Nu Lader Du Din Tjener Fare (S209)

SALMER OG FOLKEVISER see Laub, Thomas

SALMI DELLA COMPIETE AND CANZONETTES see
    Gesualdo, Don Carlo

SALMO see Monteverdi, Claudio

SALMO DE ALEGRIA see Ficher, Jacobo

SALMO IX see Petrassi, Goffredo

SALMO VI see Caamano

SALMO XVIII see Marcello, Benedetto

SALONEN, SULO (1899-   )
    Adventsmusik *Adv
    [Swed] SATB,org cor pts GEHRMANS KRB 306
                                                    (S210)

    Aftonkantat *cant
    [Swed] SATB,org cor pts GEHRMANS KRB 224
    s.p.   (S211)

    De Profundis *Op.55
    [Lat] mix cor,acap oct FAZER s.p.   (S212)
    [Lat] mix cor,T solo,acap oct FAZER s.p.
                                                    (S213)

    Lar Mig Da Besinna
    mix cor NORDISKA NMS-6290 s.p.   (S214)

    Lovad Vare Herren *Bibl
    [Swed] SATB,acap GEHRMANS KRB 334   (S215)

    Missa *Op.27, Mass
    [Lat] 4-8pt,acap oct FAZER s.p.   (S216)

    Sasom Hjorten Trangtar *Bibl
    [Swed] SATB,acap GEHRMANS KRB 333   (S217)

    Sta Upp, Var Ljus *Bibl
    [Swed] SATB,acap GEHRMANS KRB 337   (S218)

SALSBURY, SONNY
    Communion Song
    SAB oct WORD CS-2540 $.30   (S219)

    Electric Church, The *CCUL,folk
    SAB voc sc WORD 30032 $1.95   (S220)

    Father Loves You, The
    SAB oct WORD CS-2456 $.30   (S221)

    Here Comes Jesus
    SAB oct WORD CS-2455 $.30   (S222)

    Psalm 19
    SAB oct WORD CS-2454 $.30   (S223)

    Reflection *CCUL
    (Gassman, Clark) SATB voc sc WORD 32030
    $1.95   (S224)

SALTER, SUMNER (1856-1944)
    Mary's Manger Song *Xmas
    (Stickles) 4pt mix cor,S/T solo,org/pno oct
    SCHIRM.G 10494 $.25   (S225)

SALUT AU SAINT-SACREMENT see Busser, [Henri-
    Paul]

SALUT SOLENNEL EN SOL see Delvincourt, Claude

SALUTATIO ANGELICA see Milner, Anthony

SALUTATION see Christiansen, Paul

SALUTATION ANGELIQUE see Caplet, Adrien

SALUTATION ANGELIQUE see Clergue, J.

SALUTATION CAROL *carol
    see Six Traditional Carols, Set IV
    SATB (med) OXFORD 08.035 $.15   (S226)
    (Gibbs) SATB,acap (med easy) OXFORD 84.067
    $.30   (S227)

SALUTATION OF THE DAWN see Tgettis, Nicholas

SALUTATION, THE (from Anthology Of Carols, An)
    see Verbum Patris

SALVA NOS, DOMINE see Lupo, Thomas

SALVA NOS-HEFT 3 see Isaac, Heinrich

SALVATION BELONGETH TO OUR GOD see Tchesnokov,
    Pavel Grigorievitch

SALVATION BELONGETH UNTO THE LORD see Copley,
    R. Evan

SALVATION BELONGETH UNTO THE LORD see Kent, J.

SALVATION IS CREATED see Tchesnokov, Pavel
    Grigorievitch

SALVATION IS CREATED see Tschesnokoff, P.I.

SALVATION IS FOR ALL see Ford

SALVATION IS NEARER see Ford, Virgil T.

SALVATION NOW TO US HAS COME see Schein, Johann
    Hermann

SALVATION TO OUR GOD see Horton

SALVATION UNTO US HAS COME see Bender, Jan

SALVATION UNTO US HAS COME see Distler, Hugo

SALVATION UNTO US HAS COME see Schalk, Carl

SALVATION'S AUTHOR see Ana, d', Sapientissimus
    Salutis Auctor

SALVATOR MUNDI see Blow, John

SALVATOR MUNDI see Palestrina, Giovanni

SALVATOR MUNDI see Tallis, Thomas

SALVATOR MUNDI DOMINE see Tallis, Thomas

SALVE see Franco

SALVE, ESTRELLA DE LOS MARES see Benedito

SALVE, FESTA DIES see Daniels, Mabel Wheeler

SALVE INTEMERATA see Tallis, Thomas

SALVE JESU PARVULE see Magri, Pietro

SALVE, JESU, PATRIS see Buxtehude, Dietrich

SALVE MATER SALVATORIS see de la Rue, Pierre

SALVE MONTSERRATINA see Casals, Pablo

SALVE MUNDI SALUTARE see Weismann, Wilhelm

SALVE O VERGINE MARIA see Mariani, Eligio

SALVE O VERGINE MARIA see Rossini, Gioacchino

SALVE REGINA see Aichinger, Gregor

SALVE REGINA see Arnaldi, Antonio

SALVE REGINA see Bauernfiend, Hans

SALVE REGINA see Baumann, Max

SALVE REGINA see Bellini, Vincenzo

SALVE REGINA see Berkeley, Lennox

SALVE REGINA see Bossi, Marco Enrico

SALVE REGINA see Bottazzo, Luigi

SALVE REGINA see Busser, [Henri-Paul]

SALVE REGINA see Byrd, William

SALVE REGINA see Cavalli, Francesco

SALVE REGINA see Cavalli, Pier Francesco

SALVE REGINA see Creston, Paul

SALVE REGINA see Des Prez, Josquin

SALVE REGINA see Fuser, Ireneo

SALVE REGINA see Gerli, Giovanni

SALVE, REGINA see Gletle, Johann Melchoir

SALVE REGINA see Hacomplaynt, Robert

SALVE REGINA see Haydn, (Franz) Joseph

SALVE REGINA see Heiller, Anton

SALVE REGINA see La Forge

SALVE REGINA see Lassus, Roland de (Orlandus)

SALVE REGINA see Lotti, Antonio

SALVE REGINA see Magri, Pietro

SALVE REGINA see Mancini, Vincenzo

SALVE REGINA see Maugeri, Giuseppe

SALVE REGINA see Mercenier, P.

SALVE REGINA see Monteverdi, Claudio

SALVE REGINA see Najera, Edmund

SALVE REGINA see Nieuwenhoven, H. v.

SALVE REGINA see Oltrassi, Giuseppe

SALVE REGINA see Palestrina, Giovanni

SALVE REGINA see Pergolesi, Giovanni Battista

SALVE REGINA see Philippart-Gonzalez, Renee

SALVE REGINA see Pierobon, Giuseppe

SALVE REGINA see Poulenc, Francis

SALVE REGINA see Praetorius, Michael

SALVE REGINA see Ravanello, Oreste

SALVE REGINA see Roux, Abbe M.

SALVE REGINA see Scarlatti, Alessandro

SALVE REGINA see Schubert, Franz (Peter)

SALVE REGINA see Trexler, Georg

SALVE REGINA see Victoria, Tomas Luis de

SALVE REGINA see Vivaldi, Antonio

SALVE REGINA see Volpi, Edoardo

SALVE REGINA see Vranken, Alph.

SALVE REGINA COELITUM see Ascenso, Antonio

SALVE REGINA see Haydn, (Franz) Joseph

SALVE S. PATER IN ONORE DI S. FRANCESCO see
    Arnaldi, Antonio

SALVE, SACRATA see Phillipo

SALVE SANCTA PARENS see Baroni, Giovanni

SALVE SANCTA PARENS see Byrd, William

SALVE SANCTA PARENS see Quack, Erhard

SALVE SANCTE PATER see Ravanello, Oreste

SALVE, VIRILIS PECTORIS VIRGO, PATRONA GALLIAE
see Perceval, Julio

SALVESEN, TH.
Missa Brevis *Mass
[Lat] mix cor,org MUSIKK s.p.   (S228)

SALVETE FLORES MARTYRUM see Palestrina,
Giovanni

SALVUM FAC REGEM see Loewe, C.

SALVUM FAC REGEM see Sacchini, A.

SALVUM ME FAC see Palestrina, Giovanni

SALVUM ME FAC DEUS see Prioli, Giovanni

SALZBURGER MESSE see Hasselbock, Hans

SALZBURGER WEIHNACHTSLIED see Rothschuh, F.

SAMANNS LIED see Weismann, Wilhelm

SAME TRAIN *spir,US
(Aubanel, Georges) "Ce Train" [Eng/Fr] 4pt
mix cor OUVRIERES s.p.   (S229)
(Shaw; Parker) SATB,acap oct LAWSON 51113
$.35   (S230)

SAMMARTINI
Magnificat *Magnif
[Lat] sc PETERS 10028 $6.00, ipa, voc sc
PETERS 10028 $1.50, ipa   (S231)

SAMMARTINI, GIOVANNI BATTISTA (1701-1775)
Magnificat *Magnif
(Miller, Michael R.) [Lat] 4pt mix cor,SATB
soli,pno voc sc SCHIRM.G $1.25   (S232)

SAMMELT ZUVOR DAS UNKRAUT see Driessler,
Johannes

SAMMELT ZUVOR DAS UNKRAUT see Raselius, Andreas

SAMMELT ZUVOR DAS UNKRAUT see Schutz, Heinrich

SAMMELT ZUVOR DAS UNKRAUT see Vulpius, Melchior

SAMOTHRAKE see Hellden, Daniel

SAMPSON see Handel, George Frideric

SAMPSON, GODFREY
Come, My Way, My Truth, My Life *anthem
mix cor oct NOVELLO 40.1149.10 s.p.   (S233)

My Song Shall Be Always Of The Loving-
Kindness *anthem/Introit
mix cor oct NOVELLO 40.1133.03 s.p.   (S234)
SATB BELWIN AP10 $.30   (S235)

O Ye Who Bear Christ's Holy Name
unis&desc oct NOVELLO 40.1173.02 s.p.
(S236)

SAMPSON, W.
Across The Bar *Rembrnc,Austral
SATB ALLANS 16 s.p.   (S237)

Guide Me, O Great Jehovah *Austral
SATB ALLANS 110 s.p.   (S238)

SAMSON see Handel, George Frideric

SAMTLICHE HYMNEN see Dufay, Guillaume

SAMTLICHE WERKE see Palestrina, Giovanni

SAMUEL-ROSSEAU, MARCEL
Libera Me
[Lat] SATTB,2 soli (B min) HEUGEL voc sc
s.p., voc pt s.p.   (S239)

Messe Pastorale *Mass
[Lat] STB,SMez soli HEUGEL voc sc s.p., voc
pt s.p.   (S240)

Noel *Xmas
[Fr] SATB,solo,opt pno/org&opt ob HEUGEL
voc sc s.p., voc pt s.p.   (S241)

Panis Angelicus
[Fr] opt cor,BB soli,vln,ob,bvl HEUGEL s.p.
(S242)

SAN FILIPPO NERI see Scarlatti, Alessandro

SAN FRANCESCO D'ASSISI NEL SUO FELICE TRANSITO
see Mancini, Vincenzo

SAN GIOVANNI LATTERANO see Clausetti

SANBORN, JAN
Christ Is Risen *Easter
SATB oct WORD CS-669 $.25   (S243)

Lord Is King, The
SATB oct WORD CS-656 $.25   (S244)

My Spirit Longs For Thee
SATB oct WORD CS-651 $.30   (S245)

SANCTA CIVITAS see Vaughan Williams, Ralph

SANCTA MARIA see Breville, Pierre-Onfroy de

SANCTA MARIA see Cooper, David S.

SANCTA MARIA see De Taeye

SANCTA MARIA see Faure, Jean-Baptist

SANCTA MARIA see Gombert, Nicolas

SANCTA MARIA see Handel, George Frideric

SANCTA MARIA see Massentio, Domenico

SANCTA MARIA see Mozart, Wolfgang Amadeus

SANCTA MARIA see Mozart, Wolfgang Amadeus,
Gradual Ad Festum B.V.M.

SANCTA MARIA see Mozart, Wolfgang Amadeus,
Sancta Maria

SANCTA MARIA see Sandberg, Folke

SANCTA MARIA MATER DEI see Mozart, Wolfgang
Amadeus

SANCTA MARIA, MATER DEI see Mozart, Wolfgang
Amadeus, Sancta Maria

SANCTA MATER see Crispo, E.

SANCTA MATER see Penalosa, Francisco

SANCTA TRINITAS see Ammann, Benno

SANCTA TRINITAS see Fevin, Antoine de

SANCTE DEI GENITRIX see Roussel, Mario

SANCTI ANTONI VIENNENSIS see Dufay, Guillaume

SANCTI AUGUSTINI PSALMUS see Veress, Sandor

SANCTI ET JUSTI see Mews, Douglas

SANCTI IACOBI see Dufay, Guillaume

SANCTI SPIRITUS see Gesualdo, Don Carlo

SANCTIFICABIS ANNUM QUINQUAGESIMUM see Bossi,
Marco Enrico

SANCTIFICATION see Bloch, Ernest

SANCTIFICATION OF THE SABBATH see Gottlieb, J.,
Kiddush

SANCTIFY, O LORD see Middleton

SANCTISSIMAE VIRGINIS MARIAE CANTICUM 1578 see
Lechner, Leonhard

SANCTORUM MERITIS see Grassi, Ciro

SANCTORUM MERITIS see Palestrina, Giovanni

SANCTUARY CHOIR BOOK see Peery, [Rob Roy]

SANCTUM ET TERRIBILE see Pergolesi, Giovanni
Battista

SANCTUM ET TERRIBILE NOMEN EJUS see Pergolesi,
Giovanni Battista

SANCTUS (from Missa Luba) Sanctus
(Haazen) SATB,2drums oct LAWSON 51504 $.30
(S246)

SANCTUS see Bach

SANCTUS see Bach, Johann Sebastian

SANCTUS see Baden, Conrad

SANCTUS see Beethoven, Ludwig van

SANCTUS see Bruckner, Anton

SANCTUS see Brunner, Adolf

SANCTUS see Byrd, William

SANCTUS see Caplet, [Lucien]

SANCTUS see Cherubini, Luigi

SANCTUS see Daun

SANCTUS see Des Prez, Josquin

SANCTUS see Dufay, Guillaume

SANCTUS see Dvorak, Antonin

SANCTUS see Faure, Gabriel-Urbain

SANCTUS see Finck

SANCTUS see Fink

SANCTUS see Flipse, E.

SANCTUS see Franck, Cesar

SANCTUS see Gounod, Charles Francois

SANCTUS see Handel, George Frideric

SANCTUS see Hassler, Hans Leo

SANCTUS see Haydn, (Franz) Joseph

SANCTUS see Haydn, (Johann) Michael

SANCTUS see Hoogerwerf, N.

SANCTUS see Larsson, Lars-Erik

SANCTUS see Lotti, Antonio

SANCTUS see Luboff, Norman

SANCTUS see Mozart, Wolfgang Amadeus

SANCTUS see Najera, Edmund

SANCTUS see Nilsen, Ing. Frederik

SANCTUS see Norden, Hugo

SANCTUS see Nystedt, Knut

SANCTUS see Ott, J.

SANCTUS see Palestrina, Giovanni

SANCTUS see Pepping, Ernst

SANCTUS see Power, Lyonel

SANCTUS see Rossini, Gioacchino

SANCTUS see Rubbra, Edmund

SANCTUS see Scarlatti, Alessandro

SANCTUS see Schubert, Franz (Peter)

SANCTUS see Silcher

SANCTUS see Soderholm, Valdemar

SANCTUS see Tchesnokov, Pavel Grigorievitch

SANCTUS see Thompson, Randall

SANCTUS see Verheul, W.P.

SANCTUS see Viadana, Lodovico Grossi da

SANCTUS see Victoria

SANCTUS see Victoria, Tomas Luis de

SANCTUS see Volpi, Edoardo

SANCTUS see Warren, Elinor Remick

SANCTUS, THE see Dietterich, Philip R.

SANCTUS, THE see Luther

SANCTUS AND AGNUS DEI *Greg
(Christiansen, P.) SATB SCHMITT 1427 $.20
(S247)

SANCTUS AND BENEDICTUS see Anonymous

SANCTUS AND BENEDICTUS see Gounod, Charles
Francois

SANCTUS AND BENEDICTUS see Hassler, Hans Leo

SANCTUS AND BENEDICTUS see McLin

SANCTUS AND BENEDICTUS see Victoria, Tomas Luis
de

SANCTUS AND HOSANNA see Gabrieli, Andrea

SANCTUS AND HOSANNA see Haydn, (Franz) Joseph

SANCTUS AND HOSANNA see Mozart, Wolfgang
Amadeus

SANCTUS AND HOSANNA see Schubert, Franz (Peter)

SANCTUS AND HOSANNA see Suriano, Francesco

SANCTUS & BENEDICTUS see Anonymous

SANCTUS-BENEDICTUS see Ceccherini

SANCTUS DOMINUS DEUS see Lotti, Antonio

SANCTUS, DOMINUS DEUS see Silcher, Friedrich

SANCTUS ET BENEDICTUS see Chaminade, Cecile

SANCTUS ET BENEDICTUS see Zuccoli, Gastone

SANCTUS ET OSANNA see Naumann, Johann Gottlieb

SANCTUS IN D see Bach, Johann Sebastian

SANCTUS IN D-DUR see Bach, Johann Sebastian

SANCTUS IN D-DUR see Bach, Johann Sebastian

SANCTUS NO. 4 see Gounod, Charles Francois

SANCTUS NO. 4 IN G see Bach, Johann Sebastian

SANCTUS, SANCTUS, SANCTUS see Clemens, Jacobus

SAND, HERRE, DINA ANGLAR UT see Bach, Johann
Sebastian

SAND-MAN'S SONG see Humperdinck, Engelbert

SAND UT DIN ANGEL, FADER KAR see Buxtehude,
Dietrich, Befiehl Dem Engel, Dass Er Komm

SANDBERG, FOLKE
Aftonpsalm
3pt mix cor NORDISKA 4978 s.p.   (S248)

Jesu, Lat Mig Hjartat Boja
jr cor,Bar solo NORDISKA 4243 s.p.   (S249)

Nu Jubla Himlar Och Varlden All *Xmas
wom cor&jr cor,Bar solo NORDISKA 3543 s.p.
(S250)

O Gud, Jag Ar Ej Vardig
3pt mix cor NORDISKA 4979 s.p.   (S251)

O, Guds Lamm
3pt mix cor NORDISKA 1479 s.p.   (S252)

Saliga Aro De, Som Hora Guds Ord
mix cor NORDISKA 1637 s.p.   (S253)

Sancta Maria
(Ahlen, Waldemar) 2pt wom cor/2pt jr cor,
acap NORDISKA 4204 s.p.   (S254)
(Ahlen, Waldemar) 2pt wom cor/2pt jr cor,
pno,inst NORDISKA 4203 s.p.   (S255)

SANDE
Faith Unlocks The Door *see Scott

SANDERS
Song Of The Spirit
SATB oct GALAXY 1.2069.1 $.30   (S256)

Truly My Soul Waiteth Upon God
SATB oct GALAXY 1.2015.1 $.30   (S257)

SANDERS, FAITH
Songs Of Worship *CCU
jr cor&SA BELWIN $1.25   (S258)

SANDERS, JOHN
Festival Te Deum *Te Deum
SATB (med) oct OXFORD 42.851 $.80   (S259)

SANDERS, ROBERT L. (1906-   )
Beautiful Valley, The
SATB,acap BROUDE BR. $.35   (S260)

Christ Became Obedient For Us Unto Death
*Eve/Holywk,Gradual
TBB,acap oct WORLD EMP-1127-3 $.30   (S261)

SANDERS, ROBERT L. (cont'd.)

Death Of Absalom, The
  SATB,acap BROUDE BR. $.35   (S262)

Fellowship
  SAB nct PRESSER LC358 $.35   (S263)

In My Distress I Called To The Lord *Pent,
  Gradual
  (Snow, Robert J.) TB,org oct WORLD
  EMP-1168-2 $.45   (S264)

Jesus Calls Us
  SATB,acap BROUDE BR. $.35   (S265)

Man's Praise
  SATB,acap BROUDE BR. $.35   (S266)

Psalm 117 *see This Is The Day The Lord Has
  Made

Ring Out Wild Bells
  unis jr cor FISCHER,C CM 598 $.20   (S267)

Spring
  SAB,acap oct PRESSER MC355 $.30   (S268)

This Is The Day The Lord Has Made (Psalm 117)
  Gradual
  (Snow, Robert L.) TTB,org oct WORLD
  EMP-1143-3 $.75   (S269)

Winter
  SAB,acap oct PRESSER MC354 $.30   (S270)

SANDERSON
  Green Pastures
  (Ehret) SAB oct BOOSEY 5307 $.30   (S271)
  (Samuelson) SATB oct BOOSEY 1454 $.30
                                               (S272)
  (Spencer) SSA oct BOOSEY 1691 $.30   (S273)

  Victory *Easter,cant
  wom cor&opt TB,pno/org (easy) voc sc WILLIS
  $.75   (S274)
  jr cor&opt TB,pno/org (easy) voc sc WILLIS
  $.75   (S275)
  cor/wom cor/jr cor&opt TB,org/pno (easy)
  oct WILLIS $.75   (S276)

SANDVOLD, ARILD
  Ego Clamavi
  see Fem Latinske Kirkekor

  Fem Latinske Kirkekor
  [Lat] SATB NORSK s.p.
  contains: Ego Clamavi; Jubilate Deo Omnis
  Terra; Lauda Anima Mea Dominum; Tantum
  Ergo Sacramentum; Venite, Filii   (S277)

  Jubilate Deo Omnis Terra
  see Fem Latinske Kirkekor

  Lauda Anima Mea Dominum
  see Fem Latinske Kirkekor

  Sjelefest
  [Norw] LYCHE 2 s.p.   (S278)

  Tantum Ergo Sacramentum
  see Fem Latinske Kirkekor

  Venite, Filii
  see Fem Latinske Kirkekor

SANFORD
  God Of Love My Shepherd Is, The
  SATB oct PRO ART 1678 $.22   (S279)

  Good News In The Kingdom
  SATB oct LORENZ A498 $.30   (S280)

  Hear The Lambs
  SATB oct LORENZ B187 $.25   (S281)

  Jesus, Son Of God
  SATB oct LORENZ C274 $.25   (S282)

SANFT UND STILL SCHLAFT UNSER FREUND see
  Schubert, Franz (Peter)

SANFT WIE DU LEBTEST see Beethoven, Ludwig van

SANG OCH PSALM see Runback, Albert

SANGEN oee Nystedt, Knut

SANJUAN, PEDRO (1886-   )
  En El Monte Murio Christo
  "On The Hill Died Christ The Saviour" [Eng/
  Span] SSAA,solo,acap AMP A129 $.20 (S283)

  On The Hill Died Christ The Saviour *see En
  El Monte Murio Christo

SANKEY, I.
  Ninety And Nine, The
  (Hustad, Don) SATB ALLANS 410 s.p.   (S284)
  (McLellan) SATB oct LILLENAS AN-1165 $.25
                                               (S285)
  Ninety And Nine, The
  (Lynn, G.) SATB,acap oct PRESSER 312-40485
  $.30   (S286)

  Shelter In The Time Of Storm, A
  (Schubert) SB oct LILLENAS AN-1189 $.30   (S287)

SANKT ANTONIUS see Brand, Th.

SANKT ANTONIUS see Dresden, Sem

SANKT CHRISTOPH see Brand, Th.

SANKT JUDAS THADDAUS see Brand, Th.

SANKT MICHAEL see Brand, Th.

SANS DAY CAROL (from Anthology Of Carols, An)
  Xmas,carol
  SATB (easy) OXFORD 08.035 $.15   (S288)
  (Gould, J.) SATB,S solo CHESTER s.p.   (S289)

SANS DAY CAROL see Gould, John

SANT JOSEP I LA MARE DEDEU see Civil

SANTA CHIARA, NOVA STELLA see Somma

SANTA CRUZ, DOMINGO
  Adoremos A Jesus *Xmas
  girl cor SOUTHERN $.20   (S290)
  "Let Us Adore Jesus" [Span/Lat/Eng] SSAA,
  acap PEER $.35 see from Cantares De
  Pascua   (S291)

  Alabanzas Del Adviento *CCU,Adv,hymn
  [Span/Eng] jr cor,org PEER $.50   (S292)

  Alleluia, A Holy Day *see Alleluia, Dies
  Sanctificatus

  Alleluia, Dies Sanctificatus *Xmas
  "Alleluia, A Holy Day" [Span/Lat/Eng]
  SMezA,acap PEER $.35 see from Cantares De
  Pascua   (S293)

  Cantares De Pascua *see Adoremos A Jesus,
  "Let Us Adore Jesus"; Alleluia, Dies
  Sanctificatus, "Alleluia, A Holy Day"; De
  Los Montes Y Los Valles, "From The Hills
  And From The Vales"; Del Cielo Salia
  Dios, "From Heaven The Lord Came Forth";
  Desde El Fondo De Mi Alma, "Deep Within
  My Soul's Recesses"; Dialogo De Reyes,
  "Dialogue Of The Kings"; El Nino Divino
  Nace, "Son Of God Has Been Born, The";
  Llego! Llego!, "He Comes! He Comes!";
  Toquen Arpas Y Guitarras, "Play Your
  Harps"   (S294)

  Cantares Di Pascua *see Hodie Christus Natus
  Est, "This Day Christ Is Born"   (S295)

  De Los Montes Y Los Valles *Xmas
  "From The Hills And From The Vales" [Span/
  Lat/Eng] SSAA,acap PEER $.40 see from
  Cantares De Pascua   (S296)

  Deep Within My Soul's Recesses *see Desde El
  Fondo De Mi Alma

  Del Cielo Salia Dios *Xmas
  girl cor SOUTHERN $.20   (S297)
  "From Heaven The Lord Came Forth" [Span/
  Lat/Eng] SA,acap PEER $.35 see from
  Cantares De Pascua   (S298)

  Desde El Fondo De Mi Alma *Xmas
  "Deep Within My Soul's Recesses" [Span/Lat/
  Eng] SMezA,acap PEER $.35 see from
  Cantares De Pascua   (S299)

  Dialogo De Reyes *Xmas
  "Dialogue Of The Kings" [Span/Lat/Eng]
  SMezA&SMezA,acap PEER $.45 see from
  Cantares De Pascua   (S300)

  Dialogue Of The Kings *see Dialogo De Reyes

  El Nino Divino Nace *Xmas
  "Son Of God Has Been Born, The" [Span/Eng/
  Lat] SMezA,acap PEER $.35 see from
  Cantares De Pascua   (S301)

  From Heaven The Lord Came Forth *see Del
  Cielo Salia Dios

  From The Hills And From The Vales *see De
  Los Montes Y Los Valles

  He Comes! He Comes! *see Llego! Llego!

  Hodie Christus Natus Est *Xmas
  "This Day Christ Is Born" [Span/Lat/Eng]
  SSAA,acap PEER $.40 see from Cantares Di
  Pascua   (S302)

  Let Us Adore Jesus *see Adoremos A Jesus

  Llego! Llego! *Xmas
  "He Comes! He Comes!" [Span/Eng/Lat] SA,
  acap PEER $.35 see from Cantares De
  Pascua   (S303)

  Play Your Harps *see Toquen Arpas Y
  Guitarras

  Son Of God Has Been Born, The *see El Nino
  Divino Nace

  This Day Christ Is Born *see Hodie Christus
  Natus Est

  Toquen Arpas Y Guitarras *Xmas
  "Play Your Harps" [Span/Lat/Eng] SMezA PEER
  $.35 see from Cantares De Pascua   (S304)

SANTA EUFROSINA see Malipiero, Gian Francesco

SANTA LUCIA see Anonymous

SANTA MADRE see Volpi, Edoardo

SANTA MADRE DEL CIEL see Ingegneri, Marco
  Antonio

SANTA MARIA
  Faberdon Del I Tono *16th cent
  [Lat] 4pt mix cor,acap UNION ESP. 19345
  s.p.   (S305)

SANTA MARIA, THOMAS DE (1510-1570)
  All Holy Lord *anthem
  mix cor oct NOVELLO s.p.   (S306)

SANTEN, B. TH.
  Oud Kerstliedeke
  mix cor,pno/org ALSBACH&D sc s.p., cor pts
  s.p.   (S307)

SANTINI, ALESSANDRO
  Concentus Eucharistici *CC8L,Commun
  .Lat] 2-4 eq voices,org ZANIBON 2452 s.p.
                                               (S308)

SANTUCCI, PELLEGRINO
  In Fraterna Carita
  SATB,org oct BERBEN EB 1277 $1.20   (S309)

  Inno *hymn
  SATB,pno/org oct BERBEN EB 1278 $1.20
                                               (S310)

  Our Father *see Padre Nostro

SANTUCCI, PELLEGRINO (cont'd.)

  Padre Nostro
  "Our Father" unis,org oct BERBEN EB 1279
  $.90   (S311)

  Pastorale
  SATB,org oct BERBEN EB 1276 $1.20   (S312)

  Quem Vidistis Pastores *Xmas
  4pt mix cor,med solo,org ZANIBON 4035 s.p.
                                               (S313)

SAPIENTIA IN CHRISTO see Kern, Matthais

SAPIENTISSIMUS NOSTRAE SALUTIS AUCTOR see
  D'Aana

SAPIENTISSIMUS SALUTIS AUCTOR see Ana, d'

SAPIENZA
  Joseph Was A Happy Man *Xmas,Ir
  (Roff) 2pt WARNER WB-159 $.30   (S314)

SARACENI, FRANCO MARIA
  Messa Votiva Per Il Giorno Di Sabato *Mass
  STB,org sc SANTIS 516 s.p.   (S315)

SARGENT, DAVID
  Nunc Sancte Nobis
  SATB sc MEDIA 4112 $3.50, study sc MEDIA
  4112A $.50   (S316)

SARIO, SEBASTIAN
  Benedictus
  SATB SCHIRM.EC 1275   (S317)

SARJEANT, DAVID
  Watchman! What Of The Night?
  (Field) SATB oct BOOSEY 1154 $.40   (S318)

SARTI
  Cherubic Hymn *hymn
  (Ehret) SATB,acap oct BOOSEY 5175 $.30
                                               (S319)

  Sing Unto The Lord A New Song
  (Williams) SAB oct FOX PS109 $.25   (S320)

SARTORI, BALDASARO
  Christus Factus Est *Lent
  (Beveridge) "For Us Christ Was Made
  Obedient" [Eng/Lat] 4pt mix cor,acap oct
  SCHIRM.G 8350 $.25   (S321)

  For Us Christ Was Made Obedient *see
  Christus Factus Est

SARTORIUS, ERAMUS (1577-1637)
  Nun Bitten Wir Den Heiligen Geist
  see Kurig, Hans-Hermann, Jauchzet, Alle
  Lande, Gott Zu Ehren

SASOM HJORTEN TRANGTAR see Palestrina,
  Giovanni, Sicut Cervus Desiderat

SASOM HJORTEN TRANGTAR see Salonen, Sulo

SASOM HJORTEN TRANGTAR TILL VATTUBACKER see
  Wikander, David

SATAN'S KINGDOM'S FALLEN DOWN *spir
  (Forsblad) SAB SCHMITT 5018 $.35   (S322)
  (Forsblad) SATB SCHMITT 1169 $.35   (S323)

SATEREN, LELAND BERNHARD (1913-   )
  Abiding Presence, The
  SATB SCHMITT SD6008 $.30   (S324)

  Accept My Heart
  dbl cor SCHMITT 832 $.25   (S325)

  As Men Of Old Their First Fruits Brought
  *anthem
  SATB (easy) oct AUGSBURG 1412 $.25   (S326)

  Ascension (from Redeemer, The) Easter
  SATB SCHMITT 1775 $.35   (S327)

  Ascription Of Praise, An
  SATB oct AGAPE A 444 $.35   (S328)

  Beside The Sepulchre *Easter
  SATB SCHMITT 1793 $.20   (S329)

  Birth (from Redeemer, The) Xmas
  SATB SCHMITT 1772 $.25   (S330)

  Breath Of God *anthem
  SATB (med) oct AUGSBURG 1050 $.25   (S331)

  Celebrate This Holy One *Xmas
  SATB SCHMITT SD6213 $.25   (S332)

  Christ Is The World's True Light *Gen
  SATB,2ob/2clar/2trp (med diff) oct
  CONCORDIA 98-1800 $.30, ipa   (S333)

  Come, Holy Ghost In Love *anthem
  SATB (easy) oct AUGSBURG 1283 $.25   (S334)

  Come, Thou Long Expected Jesus *anthem
  SATB (easy) oct AUGSBURG 1252 $.25   (S335)

  Cycle For Christmas *Xmas,anthem
  SATB (med diff) oct AUGSBURG 1371 $.30
                                               (S336)

  Dearest Lord And Savior *Gen
  SATB SCHMITT 851 $.20   (S337)

  Death (from Redeemer, The) Lent
  SATB SCHMITT 1773 $.25   (S338)

  Faith-Orbit *Gen
  SATB SCHMITT 8002 $.25   (S339)

  Faithful Cross *anthem
  SATB (easy) oct AUGSBURG 1475 $.20   (S340)

  Gift He Gave, The
  SATB,acap (easy) oct WILLIS 7002 $.20
                                               (S341)

  Go To Dark Gethsemane *Lent
  SATB SCHMITT 5905 $.25   (S342)
  SATB oct SOUTHERN $.25   (S343)

  God Is God *anthem
  see FOUR CONTEMPORARY HYMNS, SET I
  SATB (easy) oct AUGSBURG 1380 $.25   (S344)

SATEREN, LELAND BERNHARD (cont'd.)

God Walks Beside Thee *Gen
SATB SCHMITT 831 $.35 (S345)

Good Friday *Gd.Fri.
SATB,acap oct KERBY 6103C $.25 (S346)
SATB oct KERBY 6103 $.25 (S347)

Good Old Way, The *Gen
SATB SCHMITT 1794 $.18 (S348)

Great And Mighty Wonder, A *Xmas
mix cor,acap oct SCHIRM.G 9790 $.40 (S349)

Hail, Thou Once Despised Jesus *Gen
SATB SCHMITT SD6201 $.25 (S350)

He Is My Savior
SATB KJOS 5131 $.30 (S351)

Heart Of Prayer, A *Gen
SATB SCHMITT 845 $.20 (S352)

His Compassions Fail Not *Gen
SAATBB SCHMITT 878 $.35 (S353)

Hosanna, Son Of David *anthem
SATB (med) oct AUGSBURG 1071 $.25 (S354)

I Come, O Lord, Unto Thee
SATB oct SACRED E58 $.30 (S355)

I Have Called Thee *anthem
SATB (med) oct AUGSBURG 1336 $.25 (S356)

I Hear Thy Welcome Voice *Gen/Lent
SATB,pno (easy) oct WILLIS 7001 $.20 (S357)

I Love The Church *anthem
SATB (med) oct AUGSBURG 1354 $.25 (S358)

In Every Corner Sing *Gen
SATB SCHMITT 853 $.20 (S359)

In The Moon Of Wintertime *Xmas,carol,Ind
SATB,acap oct KERBY 81678 $.30 (S360)
SATB oct KERBY 6213 $.30 (S361)

In Thee I Trust
SATB KJOS 5111 $.30 (S362)

Jesus, Let Our Souls Be Fed *anthem
SATB (easy) oct AUGSBURG 1489 $.25 (S363)

Joyous Easter Dawning *Easter
SATB SCHMITT SD6218 $.25 (S364)

King Is Knocking, The
SSAATB oct KERBY 5702 $.40 (S365)
SSAATB,acap oct KERBY 5702C $.40 (S366)

Let All Mortal Flesh Keep Silence *Gen
SATB SCHMITT 8009 $.25 (S367)

Let Thy Lovingkindness Be Upon Us *anthem
SATB (easy) oct AUGSBURG 0625 $.25 (S368)

Lift High The Cross
SATB KJOS 5153 $.30 (S369)

Lift Up Thy Voice, My Heart, And Praise *Gen
SATB SCHMITT 854 $.15 (S370)

Lord Bless Thee
men cor KJOS 5532 $.30 (S371)

Lord God Of Hosts, How Lovely
SSAATTBB,acap WARNER G1734 $.30 (S372)

Lord Is Thy Keeper, The
SATB oct SACRED S-28 $.35 (S373)

Love Walks The World In Flesh *Xmas,anthem/carol
SATB (med) oct AUGSBURG 0535 $.25 (S374)

My People Shall Be Satisfied *Gen
SATB SCHMITT 859 $.22 (S375)

My Soul Doth Rest In Thee *Gen
SATB SCHMITT 827 $.25 (S376)

O God Of Beauty *Gen
SATB SCHMITT SD6207 $.25 (S377)

O God, The Rock Of Ages *anthem
SATB&opt cong,org (easy) oct AUGSBURG 1642
$.40 (S378)

Once I Sang
4pt mix cor,acap oct SCHIRM.G 10920 $.20
(S379)

Poor And Needy, The
mix cor,acap (med diff) oct AUGSBURG
11-9337 $.80 (S380)

Praise The Lord, His Glories Show *anthem
SATB (very easy) oct AUGSBURG 1210 $.20
(S381)

Praise We God The Father's Name *Gen
SATB,acap (easy) oct CONCORDIA 98-1073 $.25
(S382)

Promise (from Redeemer, The) Xmas
SATB SCHMITT 1771 $.30 (S383)

Resurrection (from Redeemer, The) Easter
SATB SCHMITT 1774 $.30 (S384)

Return (from Redeemer, The) Gen
SATB SCHMITT 1776 $.30 (S385)

Sorrowful Road, The *Lent
SATB (med) ABINGDON APM-650 $.30 (S386)

Thy Follow Me *anthem
SATB (easy) oct AUGSBURG 1335 $.20 (S387)

Thy Hand, O God, Has Guided
SATB KJOS 5245 $.30 (S388)

Thy Years Have No End *anthem
SATB,cont,org (easy) oct AUGSBURG 1642 $.40
(S389)

Turn Not Thy Face *anthem
SATB (easy) oct AUGSBURG 1173 $.20 (S390)
TTBB (easy) oct AUGSBURG 1403 $.20 (S391)

SATEREN, LELAND BERNHARD (cont'd.)

We Praise Thee, O God
SSA KJOS 6010 $.30 (S392)

Where Love Might Enter In *Gen
SATB SCHMITT 841 $.18 (S393)

Whom These Hands Hold *Gen
SATB SCHMITT 836 $.25 (S394)

SATIE, ERIK (1866-1925)
Messe Des Pauvres *Mass
[Lat] SB,org/orch voc sc SALABERT-US $4.25
(S395)

SAUGUET, HENRI (1901-)
Petite Messe Pastorale *Mass
[Lat] SS oct SALABERT-US $.50 (S396)

SAUL see Handel, George Frideric

SAUL see Hiller, Ferdinand

SAUL! see Hovland, Egil

SAUL see Schutz, Heinrich

SAUL, SAUL, WAS VERFOLGST DU MICH see Schutz,
Heinrich

SAUL, WAS VERFOLGST DU MICH? see Schutz,
Heinrich

SAUNDERS, NIEL (1918-)
Magnificat *Magnif
[Lat] SSATB CHESTER s.p. (S397)

Missa Brevis *Mass
[Lat] SATB CHESTER s.p. (S398)

SAVAGE
Fourteen Responses And Amens *CC14U
SATB SCHMITT 1582 $.20 (S399)

Twelve Short Responses And Amens *CC12U,Gen
SATB SCHMITT 1542 $.25 (S400)

SAVE ME, O GOD see Butler

SAVE ME, O GOD see Hovhaness, Alan

SAVE ME, O GOD see Strickler, David

SAVE ME, O GOD, BY THY NAME see Lalande, Michel
Richard de

SAVE ME, O GOD, BY THY NAME see Lewis, John Leo

SAVE ME, O LORD see Bock, Fred

SAVE ME, O LORD see Faure, Gabriel-Urbain,
Libera Me

SAVE ME, O LORD! see Trued, S. Clarence

SAVE US, LORD see Lupo, Thomas, Salva Nos,
Domine

SAVE US LORD see Scarlatti, Domenico

SAVE US, LORD JESUS see Bruckner, Anton

SAVE US, O HOLY VIRGIN see Rossini, Gioacchino,
Salve O Vergine Maria

SAVE US O LORD see Bairstow, Edward Cuthbert

SAVE US, O LORD see Newbury, Kent A.

SAVE US, O LORD, WAKING see Chambers, H.A.

SAVED ME see Skillings, Otis

SAVING HEALTH TO US BROUGHT, A see Brahms,
Johannes

SAVIOR, AGAIN TO THY DEAR NAME
(Aikenhead) SATB oct WORD CS-2433 $.30 (S401)

SAVIOR IS BORN, THE see Comino

SAVIOR IS WAITING, THE see Carmichael, Ralph

SAVIOR, LEAD ME see Hughes

SAVIOR, LIKE A SHEPHERD LEAD US see Bradbury,
William Batchelder

SAVIOR, LIKE A SHEPHERD LEAD US see Martin,
Warren

SAVIOR, LIKE A SHEPHERD LEAD US see Rogers

SAVIOR, LIKE A SHEPHERD LEAD US see Wolff, S.
Drummond

SAVIOR, MAKE MY HEART A TEMPLE see Buettell

SAVIOR MY HEART IS THINE see Stebbins, George
[Coles]

SAVIOR OF THE NATIONS see Powell

SAVIOR OF THE NATIONS, COME see Altenburg,
Michael

SAVIOR OF THE NATIONS COME see Cruger, Johann

SAVIOR OF THE NATIONS, COME see Krapf, Gerhard

SAVIOR OF THE NATIONS, COME see Melby, James

SAVIOR OF THE NATIONS, COME see Praetorius,
Michael

SAVIOR OF THE WORLD IS BORN, THE see Holst,
Gustav

SAVIOR OF THE WORLD IS HERE, THE see Darst, W.
Glenn

SAVIOR, SOURCE OF EVERY BLESSING see Mozart,
Wolfgang Amadeus, Ave Verum Corpus

SAVIOR'S EYES, THE see Gruber, Franz Xaver

SAVIOUR, THE see Webber, Lloyd

SAVIOUR, AGAIN TO THY DEAR NAME *hymn
(Gardner) SSA (med easy) OXFORD 44.222 $.25,
ipr see from Five Hymns In Popular Style
(S402)

SAVIOUR, AGAIN TO THY DEAR NAME WE RAISE see
Gardner, John [Linton]

SAVIOUR, BLESSED SAVIOUR
(Mueller) SA oct FISCHER,C CM-6328 $.25
(S403)
(Mueller) SAB oct FISCHER,C CM-7088 $.25
(S404)

SAVIOUR, BLESSED SAVIOUR see Mueller, Carl F.

SAVIOUR BORN, A see Gibbs

SAVIOUR, BREATHE AN EVENING BLESSING see Root,
G.F.

SAVIOUR BREATHE AN EVENING BLESSING see
Whitehead, Alfred

SAVIOUR, BREATHE FORGIVENESS see Haydn, (Franz)
Joseph, Ave Verum

SAVIOUR, CHRIST THE LORD, A see Clare, Edwyn A.

SAVIOUR HAS COME, THE see Basham, Robert A.

SAVIOUR HAS COME, THE see Tarner, Evelyn F.

SAVIOUR HAS COME TO EARTH, THE see Tarner,
Evelyn F.

SAVIOUR, HEAR US WHEN WE PRAY see Strickland,
Lily

SAVIOUR IS BORN, THE see Gray

SAVIOUR LIKE A SHEPHERD see Bixby, A.K.

SAVIOUR, LIKE A SHEPHERD LEAD US see Gluck,
Christoph Willibald Ritter von

SAVIOUR, LIKE A SHEPHERD LEAD US see
Macfarlane, William Charles

SAVIOUR, LIKE A SHEPHERD LEAD US see Middleton

SAVIOUR, LIKE A SHEPHERD LEAD US see Vincent,
Charles John

SAVIOUR, LIKE A SHEPHERD LEAD US see Wallis, C.

SAVIOUR, LORD, TO THEE WE PRAY see Wells

SAVIOUR OF MANKIND see Cechvala, Al

SAVIOUR OF THE NATIONS, COME see Eccard,
Johannes, Nun Komm Der Heiden Heiland

SAVIOUR OF THE NATIONS COME see Roff, Joseph

SAVIOUR OF THE WORLD see Goss, John

SAVIOUR SHEPHERD see Bach, Johann Sebastian

SAVIOUR SOURCE OF EVERY BLESSING see Mozart,
Wolfgang Amadeus

SAVIOUR, TEACH ME see Holler, John

SAVIOUR TEACH ME DAY BY DAY see Graham

SAVIOUR TEACH ME DAY BY DAY see Greener

SAVIOUR, THY CHILDREN KEEP *anthem
(Sullivan, Arthur) mix cor oct NOVELLO
28.0840.04 s.p. (S405)

SAVIOUR, WE ADORE AND BLESS THY HOLY NAME see
Monteverdi, Claudio, Christe, Adoramus Te

SAVIOUR, WHEN NIGHT INVOLVES THE SKIES see
Shelley, [Harry Rowe]

SAVIOUR WHILE MY HEART IS TENDER see Webber

SAVIOUR'S WORK, THE *carol
SATB (med) OXFORD 08.069 $.15 (S406)

SAVONAROLA
Lauda Del Crocifisso: Giesu Sommo Conforto
(Castellazzi) [It] 3pt mix cor,acap
RICORDI-ARG BA 10369 s.p. (S407)

SAW YE MY SAVIOR? *anthem/folk
(Johnson, David) SATB,opt fl (easy) oct
AUGSBURG 1531 $.30 (S408)

SAW YE MY SAVIOR? see Ehret, Walter

SAW YOU NEVER, IN THE TWILIGHT see Graham,
Robert [V.]

SAW YOU NEVER IN THE TWILIGHT see Held, Wilbur

SAXTON
Now The Green Blade Riseth *Easter
SATB oct GALAXY 1.1769.1 $.30 (S409)

SAY, O SHEPHERDS, WHOM SAW YE? see Deering,
Richard

SAY, WHERE IS HE see Mendelssohn-Bartholdy,
Felix

SAY, WHERE IS HE BORN see Mendelssohn-
Bartholdy, Felix

SAY, WHERE IS HE THAT IS BORN KING OF JUDAH see
Mendelssohn-Bartholdy, Felix

SAY YE TO THE RIGHTEOUS see Thompson, Randall

SAY! YE WOND'RING SHEPHERDS, SAY! *Xmas,carol,
Ger
(Caswell; Ehret) SSA oct SHAPIRO SK 3036 $.30
(S410)

SAYINGS OF JESUS (FIVE) see Davies, Henry
Walford

SAYINGS OF JESUS (THREE) see Davies, Henry
Walford

SAYINGS OF OUR LORD see Davies, Henry Walford

SAYLOR, B.
Jesu, Thou Joy Of Loving Hearts
SATB oct PRESSER 312-40758 $.30 (S411)

SAYVE
Deutsche Liedlein (composed with Regnart) *CCU
(Blume) 4pt mix cor MOSELER s.p. (S412)

Vier Motetten *CC4U,mot
(Rebscher) [Ger/Lat] 5-6pt mix cor&8-9pt mix cor MOSELER s.p. (S413)

SCANDALIZE MY NAME
(Johnson) mix cor,T solo oct SCHIRM.G 10608 $.40 (S414)

SCANDELLI, A.
Bongiorno Madonna
(Szabo, M.) [Hung] SATB (med diff) BUDAPEST 5538 s.p. (S415)

SCANDELLO
Alleluia (from Graduale To St. Cecilia)
(Ross) SSATB oct COLOMBO 783 $.35 (S416)

Bonzorno, Madonna *BVM
4pt mix cor MOSELER LB-732 s.p. (S417)

Gelobet Seist Du *mot
5pt mix cor MOSELER s.p. contains also: Vom Himmel Hoch (S418)

Johannespassion *Psntd
mix cor HANSSLER 2.031 s.p. (S419)

Missa Super Epithaphium Mauritii *Mass
(Hoffmann; Erbrecht) 6pt mix cor MOSELER s.p. (S420)

Spirit Most Holy *Gen
(Lundquist) SATB SCHMITT 1583 $.20 (S421)

Vom Himmel Hoch
see Scandello, Gelobet Seist Du

SCANDELLUS, ANTONIUS
Die Auferstehungshistorie *Asc
(Herrmann) 2-5pt/SSATB HANSSLER 2.008 s.p. (S422)

SCANDINAVIAN CHORALES *CCU
mix cor SCHMITT 53 $.50 (S423)

SCANDRETT, ROBERT
Adam Lay Y Bounden
jr cor oct FISCHER,J 9849 $.35 (S424)

Cause Us, O Lord
SATB,pno/org,bvl oct LAWSON 51628 $.35 (S425)

Psalm 91
SATB,opt org&2horn oct FISCHER,J 10018 $.25 (S426)

SCARBOROUGH FAIR
(Wilson, John F.) TBB/TTBB oct AGAPE MM 9004 $.30 (S427)

SCARCO DI DOGLIA see Lassus, Roland de (Orlandus)

SCARLATTI, ALESSANDRO (1660-1725)
Agnus Dei (from Messa Ottoboniana)
see Scarlatti, Alessandro, Kyrie
see Scarlatti, Alessandro, Sanctus

Audi Filia *Gradual
(Steele, John) "Gradual For St. Cecilia's Day" [Lat] SSATB,SSA soli,org,2ob,opt bsn,strings voc sc NOVELLO s.p., ipr (S428)

Caro Mea
(Castellini, J.) SATB oct PRESSER 312-40356 $.30 (S429)

Credo
mix cor,acap voc sc KALMUS 6410 $1.00 (S430)

Credo Concertato A Quattro Voci
(Napoli, J.) mix cor,orch sc CURCI 7006 s.p. (S431)

Exsultate Deo
(Rikko, Fritz) SATB WEINBERGER s.p. (S432)

Exultate Deo *Gen
SATB,acap oct PRESSER 352-00071 $.35 (S433)
SATB,acap oct PRESSER 312-40166 $.35 (S434)
[Ger] SATB,acap (med) MULLER MS 24 s.p. (S435)
(Agey) "Lift Your Voices To Jehovah" [Lat/Eng] 4pt mix cor,acap oct SCHIRM.G 11001 $.35 (S436)
(Bianchi, Lino) [Lat] SSAA,acap voc sc HINRICHSEN D1855 s.p. (S437)
(Lavater, H.) [Lat] wom cor,acap (med) HUG s.p. (S438)
(Track) [Lat] TTBB,acap,opt pno oct PRO ART 2600 $.35 (S439)

Gradual For St. Cecilia's Day *see Audi Filia

Holy, Holy, Holy *see Sanctus

How Long Wilt Thou Forget Me?
SATB oct WALTON 6025 $.30 (S440)

Il David-Davidis Pugna Et Victoria *ora
(Bianchi, Lino) cor,soli,cont SANTIS 1083 s.p., ipr (S441)

Il Primo Omicidio *ora
(Bianchi, Lino) 6pt,inst SANTIS 1071 s.p., ipr (S442)

Johannespassion *cant
(Defner) [Lat/Ger] SATB,ABar soli,cont, 2vln,vla,bvl HANSSLER 10.007 sc $7.50, voc sc $.80, ipa (S443)

Kyrie (from Messa Ottoboniana) Kyrie
4pt,org CURCI 7188 s.p. contains also: Agnus Dei (Agnus) (S444)

La Giuditta (Di Napoli) *ora
(Bianchi, Lino) cor,soli,inst,cont SANTIS 1029 s.p., ipr (S445)

SCARLATTI, ALESSANDRO (cont'd.)

Laudate Dominum Omnes Gentes (Psalm 117)
(Shaffer, J.) "O Praise The Lord, All Ye Nations" SATB,strings,cont CONCORDIA 97-4973 $2.00, ipa (S446)

Lift Your Voices To Jehovah *see Exultate Deo

Messa Di Santa Cecilia *Mass
(Steffin, Fritz) [Lat] mix cor,soli,cont, strings BOTE voc sc s.p., cor pts s.p. (S447)

O Praise The Lord, All Ye Nations *see Laudate Dominum Omnes Gentes

Psalm 117 *see Laudate Dominum Omnes Gentes

Salve Regina *Op.2,No.10
SATB,orch voc sc WALTON M 103 $1.00, ipr, sc WALTON rental (S448)
(Martens, Mason) SATB,cont,vln,vcl,bvl voc sc WALTON M 103 $1.25, ipa (S449)

San Filippo Neri *ora
mix cor,soli,orch CURCI 7079 s.p. (S450)

Sanctus (from Messa Clementina)
5pt,org CURCI 7189 s.p. contains also: Agnus Dei (S451)
(Ehret) "Holy, Holy, Holy" [Eng/Lat] SSATB, org/pno oct SCHIRM.G 11876 $.30 (S452)

Sedecia Re Di Gerusalemme *ora
(Guerrini, G.) mix cor,soli,orch CURCI 7681 s.p. (S453)

St. Cecilia Mass *Mass
(Steele, John) [Lat] SATB,SSATB soli,org, strings voc sc NOVELLO s.p., ipr (S454)

Stabat Mater
2pt wom cor BELWIN $2.00 (S455)

Te Deum Laudamus
(Castellini, J.) SATB PRESSER $1.00 (S456)

Tu Es Petrus
dbl cor,orch CURCI 7094 s.p. (S457)

SCARLATTI, DOMENICO (1685-1757)
Exsultate Deo
(Greyson) mix cor SOUTHERN $.35 (S458)
(Greyson) "Praise The Lord Jehovah" SATB oct BOURNE ES37 $.35 (S459)
(White) mix cor SOUTHERN $.30 (S460)

Exultate Deo
[Lat] SATB,acap MARKS 76 $.40 (S461)

Holy, Holy, Holy
(Ehret) mix cor CHAPPELL 0023424-358 $.40 (S462)

Laetatus Sum
mix cor SOUTHERN $.40 (S463)
(Martens) [Eng/Lat] SATB,acap oct MCA (S464)

Lord Above, Enliven Thou Me *Gen
(Brandvik) SATB SCHMITT 1434 $.30 (S465)

Messa Di Madrid *Mass
(Bianchi, Lino) SATB,acap HINRICHSEN D1685 voc sc s.p., voc pt s.p. (S466)

Missa Quatour Vocum *Mass
4pt s.p. sc SANTIS 1023, cor pts SANTIS 1024A-B (S467)

O Magnum Mysterium *Xmas
(Brandvik) dbl cor SCHMITT 1439 $.45 (S468)

Praise The Lord Jehovah *see Exsultate Deo

Save Us Lord *Gen
(Brandvik) SATB SCHMITT 1433 $.35 (S469)

Stabat Mater
[Lat] SSSAATTBB,org voc sc HINRICHSEN SM1 s.p. (S470)
(Somma, B.) 10pt mix cor,org sc SANTIS 573 rental (S471)

SCARMOLIN, (ANTHONY) LOUIS (1890-1969)
Be Merciful Unto Me, O God
SATB oct PRO ART 1302 $.18 (S472)

Blessed Are The Hearts *Xmas
SSA oct PRO ART 1670 $.20 (S473)

He That Dwelleth In The Secret Place (Psalm 91)
SATB oct PRO ART 1257 $.25 (S474)

Praise The Lord, O My Soul
SATB LUDWIG L-1105 $.30 (S475)

Prayer *prayer
SATB oct PRO ART 1571 $.18 (S476)

Psalm 91 *see He That Dwelleth In The Secret Place

SCATTER PALM BRANCHES see Tunder, Franz

SCATTERED SEED see Bixel, James W.

SCENDI DAL CIELO see Pasini, Crescenzio

SCENE OF THE WISE MEN, THE see Bach

SCENE ON EASTER MORNING see Bartow

SCENES FROM THE HOLY INFANCY (ACCORDING TO ST. MATTHEW) see Thomson, Virgil

SCHABASSER, JOSEPH
Zwolf Muttergotteslieder *CC12U,BVM
3pt wom cor,acap cmplt ed DOBLINGER s.p. (S477)

SCHACK, DAVID
Lord Is My Shepherd, The *Gen
unis,kbd (easy) oct CONCORDIA 98-2145 $.25 (S478)

O Dearest Jesus *Lent
unis,kbd (easy) oct CONCORDIA 98-2135 $.25 (S479)

SCHAEFER
Sing Hosanna To The King
SA/TB FLAMMER E5062 $.25 (S480)

SCHAEFER, CHRISTOPHER
Christmas Carol, A *Xmas,anthem/carol
2pt mix cor oct AUGSBURG 1579 $.35 (S481)

Christmas Is A Time For Singing
SAB oct ELKAN-V 362-1280 $.50 (S482)

Keep A Quiet Place Apart *anthem
SAB (easy/med) oct AUGSBURG 1594 $.40 (S483)

Sleep, Tiny Savior *Xmas
SATB oct ELKAN-V 362-1281 $.30 (S484)

Wave Him On *anthem
SAB (med) oct AUGSBURG 1610 $.30 (S485)

Wise Men, On Your Lonely Journey *anthem
SATB (med) oct AUGSBURG 1562 $.25 (S486)

SCHAEFERS, ANTON
Wo Ist Mein Gott, Der Hohe, Der Hehre *mot
[Ger] SATB voc sc BOTE s.p. (S487)

SCHAFE KONNEN SICHER WEIDEN see Bach, Johann Sebastian

SCHAFER, KARL (1899-)
Musik Uber Einen Choral *Gen
[Ger] men cor,S solo,org,2trp (med diff) MULLER SM 1663 sc s.p., cor pts s.p., ipa (S488)

Nun Kommst Du Hergegangen
see Schafer, Karl, Verweht Sind Weg Und Graben
see Schafer, Karl, Verweht Sind Weg Und Graben
see Schafer, Karl, Verweht Sind Weg Und Graben

Verweht Sind Weg Und Graben *Xmas
men cor TONGER s.p. contains also: Nun Kommst Du Hergegangen (S489)
wom cor&jr cor TONGER s.p. contains also: Nun Kommst Du Hergegangen (S490)
mix cor TONGER s.p. contains also: Nun Kommst Du Hergegangen (S491)

SCHAFER, WALTER
Geistliche Lieder *CC25U
(Stier) mix cor HANSSLER 2.018 s.p. (S492)

SCHAFF IN MIR, GOTT, EIN REINES HERZ see Krieger, Johann Philipp

SCHAFFE IN MIR, GOTT see Brahms, Johannes

SCHAFFE IN MIR, GOTT, EIN REINES HERZ see Hammerschmidt, Andreas

SCHAFFE IN MIR, GOTT, EIN REINES HERZ see Schutz, Heinrich

SCHAFFE IN MIR GOTT EIN REINES HERZE see Werner, Fritz

SCHAFFER, JEANNE E.
Show Me, O Lord *Commun
SATB,acap oct KERBY 6605C $.30 (S493)

Words From The Cross, The *Lent,cant
cor ABINGDON APM-658 $1.75 (S494)

SCHAFFER, ROBERT J.
Gloria *Gloria
SATB oct WORLD CC-2085-8 $.45 contains also: Recessional (Reces) (S495)

Recessional
see Schaffer, Robert J., Gloria

SCHAFSTALL, JOH.
Christus' Geboorte
mix cor ALSBACH&D sc s.p., cor pts s.p. (S496)

Gloria In Excelsis Deo
men cor ALSBACH&D sc s.p., cor pts s.p. (S497)

In Dulci Jubilo
mix cor ALSBACH&D sc s.p., cor pts s.p. (S498)

SCHALK
Four Choruses (from Lamentations Of Jeremiah) CC4U
mix cor SOUTHERN $.30 (S499)

Let All That Are To Mirth Inclined
mix cor SOUTHERN $.20 (S500)

SCHALK, CARL
Awake, Thou Spirit Bold And Daring *Gen
SATB,acap (easy) oct CONCORDIA 98-1537 $.25 contains also: God Is Our Sun And Shield; How Blest Are They (S501)

By The Name We Bow Before
see Canonic Litanies

By Thy Wounds And Thorncrowned Head
see Canonic Litanies

Canonic Litanies *Gen
SS/eq voices,kbd (med easy) oct CONCORDIA 98-1696 $.25
contains: By The Name We Bow Before; By Thy Wounds And Thorncrowned Head; From Refusing To Obey; God The Father, God The Son; Jesus Savior, Ever Mild (S502)

Christ The Lord Is Risen Again *Easter
2pt mix cor,kbd (easy) oct CONCORDIA 98-1984 $.25 (S503)

Crown Choir Book, The *CC13L,anthem
2pt mix cor CONCORDIA 97-7618 $1.25 (S504)

For The Sins Of Her Prophets (from Lamentations Of Jeremiah)
see Four Choruses From The Lamentations Of Jeremiah

Four Choruses From The Lamentations Of Jeremiah (from Lamentations Of Jeremiah) Gen/Lent
SATB,acap (med diff) oct CONCORDIA 98-1578 $.30

SCHALK, CARL (cont'd.)

contains: For The Sins Of Her Prophets;
From Above He Hath Sent Fire; Lord Is
Righteous, The; Remember, O Lord (S505)

From Above He Hath Sent Fire (from
Lamentations Of Jeremiah)
see Four Choruses From The Lamentations Of
Jeremiah

From Refusing To Obey
see Canonic Litanies

God Is Our Sun And Shield
see Schalk, Carl, Awake, Thou Spirit Bold
And Daring

God Of Mercy, God Of Grace *Gen
SATB,kbd (med easy) oct CONCORDIA 98-1526
$.22 (S506)

God The Father, God The Son
see Canonic Litanies

God The Father, Son, And Spirit *Gen/Trin
SATB,kbd (med easy) oct CONCORDIA 98-1531
$.30 (S507)

How Blest Are They
see Schalk, Carl, Awake, Thou Spirit Bold
And Daring

In Adam We Have All Been One *Gen
SATB,kbd (med easy) oct CONCORDIA 98-1666
$.25 (S508)

Jesus Savior, Ever Mild
see Canonic Litanies

Jesus Shall Reign Where'er The Sun *Epiph/
Gen
SATB,kbd (med easy) oct CONCORDIA 98-1797
$.25 (S509)

King Of Love My Shepherd Is, The *Gen
SATB,acap (easy) oct CONCORDIA 98-1523 $.20
(S510)

Let All That Are To Mirth Inclined *Xmas
SATB,acap (med easy) oct CONCORDIA 98-1695
$.20 (S511)

Lord Is Righteous, The (from Lamentations Of
Jeremiah)
see Four Choruses From The Lamentations Of
Jeremiah

Lord Jesus Christ, My Savior Blest *Gen
SATB,kbd (med easy) oct CONCORDIA 98-1524
$.25 contains also: O Love, How Deep, How
Broad, How High (S512)

Make We Now Joy In This Fest *carol
SAB,fl,ob/inst,opt gtr CONCORDIA 97-5014
$1.25 (S513)
SATB,fl,ob/inst,opt gtr CONCORDIA 97-5013
$1.25 (S514)

Mighty Fortress, A *Gen/Refm
SATB,kbd (med easy) oct CONCORDIA 98-1842
$.25 (S515)

O Love, How Deep, How Broad, How High
see Schalk, Carl, Lord Jesus Christ, My
Savior Blest

Processional Carol For Christmas, A *Xmas,
carol
unis,kbd (easy) oct CONCORDIA 98-1732 $.25
(S516)

Remember, O Lord (from Lamentations Of
Jeremiah)
see Four Choruses From The Lamentations Of
Jeremiah

Salvation Unto Us Has Come *Gen/Refm
unis,kbd (med easy) oct CONCORDIA 98-2144
$.40 (S517)

Second Crown Choir Book, A *CC11L,anthem
2pt mix cor&opt 4pt CONCORDIA 97-4882 $1.00
(S518)

Star Carol Book, A *CC9L,carol
mix cor,opt perc CONCORDIA 97-4858 $1.00
(S519)

Two-Part Canons On Classic Hymns And
Chorales, Set I *CC8L,canon
jr cor/treb cor CONCORDIA 98-1762 $.40
(S520)

Two-Part Canons On Classic Hymns And
Chorales, Set II *CC9L,canon
jr cor/treb cor CONCORDIA 98-1763 $.40
(S521)

Two-Part Canons On Classic Hymns And
Chorales, Set III *CC8L,canon
jr cor/treb cor CONCORDIA 98-1764 $.45
(S522)

When Morning Gilds The Skies *Gen
SATB,kbd (med easy) oct CONCORDIA 98-1789
$.25 (S523)

Ye Servants Of God, Your Master Proclaim
*Gen
SATB,trp (easy) oct CONCORDIA 98-1536 $.25
(S524)

SCHALLIBAUM, G.
Die Stunden, Die Tage, Und Jahre
[Lat] wom cor,acap HUG s.p. (S525)

SCHANDL, ERNST
Deutsches Proprium *Easter
4pt mix cor,org DOBLINGER voc sc s.p., cor
pts s.p. (S526)
4pt men cor,org DOBLINGER voc sc s.p., cor
pts s.p. (S527)

Segne, Du, Maria *BVM,cant
mix cor,soli,org,vln DOBLINGER voc sc s.p.,
cor pts s.p. (S528)

SCHAPER, HEINZ-CHRISTIAN (1927-   )
Der Herr Ist Auferstanden
see Zwei Oster-Motetten

Du Wirst Meine Seele Nicht Dem Tode Lassen
(Psalm 16) *mot
mix cor (med easy) oct LEUCKART 619 s.p.
(S529)

SCHAPER, HEINZ-CHRISTIAN (cont'd.)

Kommet Her Und Sehet Die Statte
see Zwei Oster-Motetten

Psalm 16 *see Du Wirst Meine Seele Nicht Dem
Tode Lassen

Zwei Oster-Motetten *Easter,mot
[Ger] 4pt mix cor,acap cor pts BAREN.
EM 469 s.p.
contains: Der Herr Ist Auferstanden;
Kommet Her Und Sehet Die Statte (S530)

SCHATTENBERG, THOMAS
Amor Jesu
see Schattenberg, Thomas, Jesu Dulcedo
Cordium

Jesu Dulcedo Cordium *hymn
4pt mix cor,acap sc SKAND. SMF5427 s.p.
contains also: Amor Jesu (S531)

SCHAU AUF, MEIN HERZ, IN EPHRATA see Anonymous

SCHAU, LIEBER GOTT see Bach, Johann Sebastian,
Schau, Lieber Gott, Wie Meine Feind'

SCHAU, LIEBER GOTT, WIE MEINE FEIND' see Bach,
Johann Sebastian

SCHAU, SCHAU, WIE SIE RENNEN
see Seht Das Kleine

SCHAU, SCHAU, WIE SIE RENNEN see Lehner, Walter

SCHAU, WIE LIEBLICH UND GUT ISTS ALLEN BRUDERN
see Pepping, Ernst

SCHAUE DOCH, VATER see Schutz, Heinrich,
Aspice, Pater

SCHAUET DOCH see Bach, Johann Sebastian,
Schauet Doch Und Sehet

SCHAUET DOCH UND SEHET see Bach, Johann
Sebastian

SCHAUSS-FLAKE, MAGDALENE (1921-   )
Befiehl Dem Herrn Deine Wege (Psalm 37)
see Schweizer, Rolf, Wie Ein Hirsch Schreit
Nach Frischem Wasser

Jauchzet Dem Herrn
mix cor,ob see HANSSLER 7.159 s.p., ipa
(S532)

Psalm 37 *see Befiehl Dem Herrn Deine Wege

SCHECHTMAN
O Lord Our God
SATB,acap oct MCA (S533)

SCHEDE, PAUL
Bewahr Mich, Herr, Und Sei Nicht Fern *mot
(Haberl) SATB HANSSLER 1.459 s.p. (S534)

SCHEIDEMANN, HEINRICH
Frisch Auf, Und Lasst Uns Singen
SSATB HANSSLER 6.2503 s.p. (S535)

SCHEIDT, SAMUEL (1587-1654)
Ach, Mein Herzliebes Jesulein *Xmas,mot
(Granville) "Ah! My Beloved Jesus Child"
SSATB oct FOX CM4 $.35 (S536)
(Herrmann) SSATB,cont HANSSLER 1.141 s.p.
(S537)

Ah! My Beloved Jesus Child *see Ach, Mein
Herzliebes Jesulein

Angelus Ad Pastores Ait *mot
(Herrmann) [Lat] dbl cor HANSSLER 1.155
$.80 (S538)

Ascendo Ad Patrem Meum *mot
(Herrmann) [Lat] dbl cor HANSSLER 1.151
$.80 (S539)

Av Himlens Hojd Oss Kommet Ar
see TVA JULKONSERTER

Boy Is Born, A *see Puer Natus

Child Is Born In Bethlehem, A *Xmas
(Kaplan) SATB oct LAWSON 51716 $.25 (S540)
(Willcocks) SSAATTBB,acap (easy) OXFORD
84.144 $.25 (S541)

Christ Lag In Todesbanden *Holywk,mot
(Herrmann) dbl cor HANSSLER 1.164 s.p.
(S542)
Christe, Der Du Bist Tag Und Licht *Gen/mot
(Herrmann) dbl cor HANSSLER 1.161 s.p.
(S543)
(Mahrenholz, Christhard) [Ger] SATB&SATB,
acap BAREN. BA 759 sc $2.75, cor pts
$2.00 (S544)

Christo, Dem Osterlammlein *Psntd,mot
(Herrmann) SATTB HANSSLER 1.313 s.p. (S545)

Cum Ergo Fleret, Cum *mot
(Herrmann) [Lat] dbl cor HANSSLER 1.163
$.80 (S546)

Das Alte Jahr Vergangen Ist *ECY,mot
(Herrmann) dbl cor HANSSLER 1.156 s.p.
(S547)

Duo Seraphim Clamabant *Gen,mot
(Herrmann) [Lat] SSAT&ATBB HANSSLER 1.152
$.80 (S548)
(Mahrenholz, Christhard) [Ger] SSAT&ATBB,
acap (med diff) sc BAREN. BA 2905 $2.00,
cor pts $1.10 (S549)

Ein Feste Burg Ist Unser Gott *Gen,mot
(Herrmann) dbl cor HANSSLER 1.158 s.p.
(S550)
(Mahrenholz, Christhard) [Ger] SATB&SATB,
acap (med diff) BAREN. BA 691 sc $2.50,
cor pts $1.10 (S551)

Ein Kindelein So Lobelich *Xmas,mot
(Herrmann) SATB,cont HANSSLER 1.323 s.p.
(S552)
Er Gebe Uns Ein Frohliches Herz *mot
(Herrmann) SSAT&ATBB HANSSLER 1.173 s.p.
(S553)

SCHEIDT, SAMUEL (cont'd.)

Gelobet Seist Du, Jesu Christ *mot
(Herrmann) dbl cor HANSSLER 1.153 s.p.
(S554)

Gib Uns Heut Unser Taglich Brot
see Staden, Johann, Danket Dem Herrn

Good Christians, Now Rejoice *anthem
(Nelson) SS,org,opt bsn,vcl (med) oct
AUGSBURG 0306 $.25 (S555)

Gott Der Vater Wohn Uns Bei *mot
(Herrmann) dbl cor HANSSLER 1.159 s.p.
(S556)

Herr, Unser Herrscher *mot
(Schmidt) dbl cor,soli,cont HANSSLER 1.182
s.p. (S557)

Herr, Wie Lang Willst Du Mein *mot
(Herrmann) SSAATT,2vla,2vcl HANSSLER 1.143
s.p. (S558)

Herzlich Lieb Hab Ich Dich *mot
(Herrmann) dbl cor HANSSLER 1.170 s.p.
(S559)

Hosanna To The Son Of David *see Hosianna
Filio David

Hosianna, Dem Sohne *see Hosianna, Filio
David

Hosianna Filio David *mot
(Granville) "Hosanna To The Son Of David"
SSATB oct FOX CM14 $.25 (S560)
(Herrmann) "Hosianna, Dem Sohne" [Lat]
SSATB,cont HANSSLER 1.139 $.90 (S561)

Ich Hebe Meine Augen Auf *mot
(Herrmann) SSAATT,2vla,2vcl HANSSLER 1.146
s.p. (S562)

Ich Hebe Meine Augen Auf Zu Den Bergen *Gen
(Mahrenholz, Christhard) [Ger] SSAA&TTBB,
acap (med diff) BAREN. BA 2904 sc $2.75,
cor pts $2.00 (S563)

Ich Hoffe Aber Darauf *mot
(Herrmann) SSAATT,2vla,2vcl HANSSLER 1.145
s.p. (S564)

In Dulci Jubilo *Gen,mot
[Ger] SSAT&ATBB,opt 2clar/2trp BAREN.
BA 692 sc $2.25, cor pts $.80, ipa (S565)
(Herrmann) [Lat] SSAT&ATBB,2vln HANSSLER
1.157 $.80 (S566)

Ist Nicht Ephraim Mein Teurer Sohn *Bibl/mot
(Herrmann) SSA&TTB,cont HANSSLER 1.315 s.p.
(S567)

Jauchzet Gott, Alle Land *mot
(Herrmann) SSATB,cont HANSSLER 1.142 s.p.
(S568)

Komm, Heiliger Geist *mot
(Herrmann) dbl cor HANSSLER 1.150 s.p.
(S569)

Komm, Heiliger Geist, Herre Gott *mot
(Herrmann) SS,2vcl HANSSLER 1.181 s.p.
(S570)

Lo, The Angel Said To The Shepherds *Xmas
dbl cor,acap oct PRESSER MC436 $.55 (S571)

Lobet Den Herren Auf Erden *Thanks,mot
(Herrmann) dbl cor HANSSLER 1.179 s.p.
(S572)

Lobet Den Herren, Denn Der Ist *mot
(Herrmann) SSAT&TBB HANSSLER 1.169 s.p.
(S573)

Lobet Den Herren In Seinem Heiligtum
*Thanks,mot
(Herrmann) dbl cor HANSSLER 1.180 s.p.
(S574)

Lobet Ihr Himmel Den Herren *Thanks,mot
(Herrmann) SSAT&ATBB HANSSLER 1.178 s.p.
(S575)

Lobet Im Himmel Den Herren (Psalm 148)
*Thanks,mot/Psalm
SSATTB,cont HANSSLER 1.183 s.p.
(S576)

Lord Jesus Christ Is Ris'n *see Surrexit
Christus

Make Ye A Joyful Noise Unto God *Easter/Gen
(Ehret, W.) SATB,opt 3trp&2trom oct PRESSER
312-40757 $.50 (S577)

Nun Danket Alle Gott *Thanks,mot
(Herrmann) SSAT&ATBB HANSSLER 1.172 s.p.
(S578)
(Schmidt) SSAT&SATB&TTBB,cont,bsn,3trp,
3trom,2vln,2vla HANSSLER 1.140 sc s.p.,
cor pts s.p., ipa (S579)

Nun Komm, Der Heiden Heiland *Gen,mot
(Herrmann) dbl cor HANSSLER 1.154 s.p.
(S580)
(Mahrenholz, Christhard) [Ger] SATB&SATB,
acap (med diff) BAREN. BA 2906 $2.00,
cor pts $.80 (S581)

O, Domine Jesu Christe *mot
(Herrmann) [Lat] SSAT&ATBB HANSSLER 1.148
$.50 (S582)

O Du Guds Lam
[Norw] SA/SATB/TB,org LYCHE 61 s.p. (S583)

O Jesulein Zart *Adv/Xmas
see Praetorius, Michael, Es Ist Ein Ros
Entsprungen
SATB,acap voc pt DOBLINGER s.p. see also
ADVENT UND WEIHNACHT, HEFT 1 (S584)

O Lamm Gottes, Unschuldig
(Herrmann) SS/TT,cont HANSSLER 5.073 s.p.
(S585)

O Light Of Life
(Chambers) SATB oct LESLIE 4060 (S586)

O Savior So Sweet
(Barrow, R.) TTBB,acap SCHIRM.EC 2172 $.22
(S587)

O Savior Sweet
(Ehret) SATB MARKS 4113 $.30 (S588)

Psalm 148 *see Lobet Im Himmel Den Herren

SCHEIDT, SAMUEL (cont'd.)

Puer Natus *Xmas/Easter
(Collins) "Boy Is Born, A" [Eng/Lat] 8pt mix cor,acap oct LAWSON 51142 $.25 contains also: Surrexit Christus, "Lord Jesus Christ Is Ris'n" (S589)

Puer Natus In Bethlehem *Xmas,mot
(Herrmann) [Lat] dbl cor HANSSLER 1.160 $.30 (S590)

Quaerite Primum, Regnum *mot
(Herrmann) [Lat] SSAT&ATBB HANSSLER 1.176 $.90 (S591)

Richte Mich, Gott, Und Fuhre *mot
(Herrmann) SSAT&ATBB HANSSLER 1.166 s.p. (S592)

Sende Dein Licht Und Deine Wahrheit *mot
(Herrmann) SSAT&ATTB HANSSLER 1.167 s.p. (S593)

Sic Deus Dilexit Mundum *mot
(Herrmann) [Lat] SSAT&TTBB HANSSLER 1.168 $.80 (S594)

Siehe, Der Huter Israels *mot
(Herrmann) SSAATT,2vla,2vcl HANSSLER 1.147 s.p. (S595)

Surrexit Christus
"Lord Jesus Christ Is Ris'n" see Scheidt, Samuel, Puer Natus

Surrexit Pastor Bonus *mot
(Herrmann) [Lat] SSAT,2vla,vcl,bvl HANSSLER 1.165 s.p. (S596)

Tulerunt Dominum Meum *mot
(Herrmann) [Lat] dbl cor HANSSLER 1.162 $.80 (S597)

Und Wenn Mir Gleich Mein Herz *mot
(Herrmann) dbl cor HANSSLER 1.171 s.p. (S598)

Vater Unser Im Himmelreich *mot
(Herrmann) dbl cor HANSSLER 1.174 s.p. (S599)

Veni, Sancte Spiritus *mot
(Herrmann) [Lat] dbl cor HANSSLER 1.149 $.80 (S600)

Wie Lang Soll Sich Mein Feind *mot
(Herrmann) SSAT,2vla,2vcl HANSSLER 1.144 s.p. (S601)

Zion Spricht: Der Herr Hat Mich *mot
(Herrmann) SSAT&ATBB HANSSLER 1.175 s.p. (S602)
(Herrmann) dbl cor HANSSLER 1.177 s.p. (S603)

Zion Spricht: Der Herr Hat Mich Verlassen *Gen
(Mahrenholz, Christhard) [Ger] SSAT&ATBB, acap (med diff) BAREN. BA 2909 sc $2.75, cor pts $1.30 (S604)

SCHEIERLING, KONRAD
Puer Natus Est
1-3pt mix cor MOSELER s.p. (S605)

SCHEIN
From Heaven Above *see Vom Himmel Hoch

Psalm 116
see Demantius, Christoph, Psalm 116

Sechs Deutsche Motetten *CC6U,mot
(Adrio) 5pt mix cor MOSELER s.p. (S606)

Vom Himmel Hoch
(Cramer) "From Heaven Above" [Eng/Ger] SATB,acap MARKS 4293 $.30 (S607)

We Thank Thee
(Kirk) SATB oct PRO ART 1866 $.25 (S608)

Ye Nations Bow In Sacred Joy
(Coggin) SATB oct PRO ART 2502 $.25 (S609)

SCHEIN, JOHANN HERMANN (1586-1630)
Ach Gott, Vom Himmel Sieh Darien
(Horn) SS,cont HANSSLER 5.110 s.p. (S610)

Ach Herr, Ach Meiner Schone *mot
(Adrio, Adam) SSATB,cont (med) BAREN. BA 2569 $.55 see also Israelsbrunnlein (S611)

Allein Gott In Der Hoh Sei Ehr (from Opella Nova)
(Kessler, Franz) 3pt mix cor,cont cor pts BREITKOPF-W CHB-3435 s.p., ipa (S612)

Amen Wir Frohlich Sprechen
[Ger] SATB,acap (med easy) BAREN. BA 6306 s.p. contains also: Unser Vater In Der Hohe (S613)

An Wasserflussen Babylon *Bibl
(Horn) SS,cont HANSSLER 5.115 s.p. (S614)

Auf Meinen Lieben Gott
SATB,acap DOBLINGER s.p. see also BITTE UND VERTRAUEN (S615)

Auf Meinen Lieben Gott, Trau Ich
SATB HANSSLER 6.156 s.p. contains also: Praetorius, Michael, O Glaubig Herz Gebenedei (S616)

Aus Tiefer Not Schrei Ich Zu Dir
(Horn) SS,cont HANSSLER 5.105 s.p. (S617)

Cantional Oder Gesangbuch Augsburgischer Konfession, Teil I *CC119U,Gen
(Adrio, Adam) [Ger] SATB/SSATB,acap/cont (med easy) BAREN. BA 5471 $8.00 (S618)

Cantional Oder Gesangbuch Augsburgischer Konfession, Teil II *CC126U,Gen
(Adrio, Adam) [Ger] SATB/5pt mix cor,acap (med diff) BAREN. BA 5472 $8.00 (S619)

Christ Lag In Todesbanden *Holywk/Psntd
boy cor SOUTHERN $.40 (S620)
[Ger/Eng] 3pt mix cor,kbd,opt bass inst BROUDE,A. 225 $.40 see from Two Sacred Concertos (S621)
(Horn) SST/SSB,cont HANSSLER 5.098 s.p. (S622)

SCHEIN, JOHANN HERMANN (cont'd.)

Christ Unser Herr Zum Jordan Kam *Bibl
(Horn) SSAT,cont,vln,vla HANSSLER 5.104 s.p. (S623)

Christe, Der Du Bist Tag Und Licht
see Sechs Choralkonzerte
(Horn) SST/SSB,cont HANSSLER 5.095 s.p. (S624)

Christmas Chorale *Xmas
(Boepple, P.) SAATB/SATTB oct PRESSER 352-00007 $.25 (S625)

Da Jakob Vollendet Hatte *mot
(Adrio, Adam) SSATB,cont (med) BAREN. BA 2560 $.65 see also Israelsbrunnlein (S626)

Da Jesus An Dem Kreuze Stund *Gd.Fri./Psntd
(Horn) SS,cont HANSSLER 5.096 s.p. (S627)

Dear Christians, One And All, Rejoice *Commun/Gen/Refm
SA/TB,kbd (med easy, or New Year) oct CONCORDIA 98-1863 $.25 (S628)

Dennoch Bleibe Ich Stets An Dir *Xmas,mot
[Ger] SSATB,cont (med) BAREN. BA 2555 $.55 see also Israelsbrunnlein (S629)

Der Herr Denket An Us *mot
(Adrio, Adam) SSATB,cont (med) BAREN. BA 2559 $.75 see also Israelsbrunnlein (S630)

Der Kuhle Maien
(Berger, H.L.) TTBB HANSSLER 6.5014 s.p. (S631)

Die Mit Tranen Saen *ECY/Gd.Fri.,mot
SSATB,acap voc pt DOBLINGER s.p. see also TOD UND VERGANGLICHKEIT (S632)
(Adrio, Adam) [Ger] SSATB,cont (med) BAREN. BA 2553 $.55 see also Israelsbrunnlein (S633)
(Greyson) "They Who Grieving Soweth" SSATB oct BOURNE ES61 $.35 (S634)

Die Nacht Ist Kommen *Gen
[Ger] SATB,acap (med easy) BAREN. BCH 44 s.p. (S635)

Die Nacht Ist Kommen, Drin Wir Ruhen
see Trubel, Gerhard, So Wunsch Ich Euch Ein Gute Nacht

Dies Sind Die Heiligen Zehn Gebot *Bibl
(Horn) SS,cont HANSSLER 5.102 s.p. (S636)

Drei Schone Dinge Sind *mot
(Adrio, Adam) SSATB,cont (med) BAREN. BA 2570 $.75 see also Israelsbrunnlein (S637)

Durch Adams Fall Ist Ganz Verderbt *Bibl
see Bach, Johann Sebastian, Durch Adams Fall Ist Ganz Verderbt
(Horn) SS,cont HANSSLER 5.117 s.p. (S638)

Eight Chorale Settings From Opella Nova (from Opella Nova) CC8L
SA,cont sc CONCORDIA 97-4713 $2.25 (S639)

Eight Chorale Settings From Opella Nova *CC8U,chorale
girl cor SOUTHERN $2.25 (S640)

Ein Feste Burg
see Sechs Choralkonzerte

Ein Feste Burg Ist Unser Gott
(Horn) SS,cont HANSSLER 5.112 s.p. (S641)

Ein Wahrer Glaube Gotts Zorn Stillt
see Eccard, Johannes, Verleih Uns Frieden Gnadiglich

Erbarm Dich Mein, O Herre Gott
(Horn) SS,cont HANSSLER 5.106 s.p. (S642)

Erschienen Ist Der Herrlich Tag (from Opella Nova)
2pt men cor,cont sc BREITKOPF-W CHB-3436 s.p., ipa (S643)
(Horn) SS/TT,cont&opt bsn/trom sc HANSSLER 5.023 s.p., ipa (S644)
(Kessler, Franz) 2pt mix cor,cont cor pts BREITKOPF-W CHB-3436 s.p., ipa (S645)

Erschienen Ist Der Herrliche Tag
see Sechs Choralkonzerte

Es Ist Das Heil Uns Kommen Her
see Bach, Johann Sebastian, Es Ist Das Heil Uns Kommen Her [Chorale]
2pt wom cor/2pt jr cor,cont cor pts BREITKOPF-W CHB-3493 s.p. (S646)
(Horn) SS,cont HANSSLER 5.118 s.p. (S647)

Es Ist Gewisslich An Der Zeit
SATB HANSSLER 6.140 s.p. contains also: Goudimel, Claude, Freu Dich Sehr, O Meine Seele, "Wie Nach Einer Wasserquelle" (S648)

Es Spricht Der Unweisen Mund
(Horn) SS,cont HANSSLER 5.111 s.p. (S649)

For Fred Och Overhet *Bibl
[Swed] SATB,acap GEHRMANS KRB 321 (S650)

Freu Dich Des Weibes *mot
(Adrio, Adam) [Ger] SSATB,cont (med) BAREN. BA 2552 $.55 see also Israelsbrunnlein (S651)

From Depths Of Woe I Cry To Thee *Gen
SA/TB,kbd (med diff, Ash Wednesday) oct CONCORDIA 98-1866 $.25 (S652)

From Heaven Above *see Vom Himmel Hoch

From Heaven High *Xmas
SAB,kbd,opt brass oct WORD CRS-17 $.40 (S653)

Gelobet Seist Du, Jesu Christ *Thanks
[Ger/Eng] 3pt mix cor,kbd,opt bass inst BROUDE,A. 224 $.30 see from Two Sacred Concertos (S654)
(Berger) SSB,cont HANSSLER 5.093 s.p. (S655)
(Horn) SST/SAB/SAT,cont HANSSLER 5.093 s.p. (S656)

SCHEIN, JOHANN HERMANN (cont'd.)

(Martens, J.) "Now Blessed Be Thou, Christ Jesu" SST/SAB,org SCHIRM.EC 2451 $.35 (S657)

Gott Der Vater Wohn Uns Bei
see Sechs Choralkonzerte
(Horn) SS,cont HANSSLER 5.101 s.p. (S658)

Gott Sei Gelobet Und Gebenedeiet *Thanks
(Horn) SST,cont&opt bsn/trom sc HANSSLER 5.024 s.p., ipa (S659)

Gott Sei Mir Gnadig (Psalm 51) (from Cymbalum Sionium) mot
(Hasse, K.) 6pt mix cor,acap cor pts BREITKOPF-L PB-3381 s.p. (S660)
(Metzger) 2-6pt/SSATB HANSSLER 1.066 s.p. (S661)

Hail Ye, Believers All *see Wohl Dir, Du Christenschar

Herr Christ, Der Einig Gottes Sohn
2pt wom cor/2pt jr cor cor pts BREITKOPF-W CHB-3489 s.p. (S662)

Herr Christ, Der Einig Gotts Sohn
(Horn) SS,cont HANSSLER 5.116 s.p. (S663)

Herr Gott, Dich Loben Alle Wir *Thanks
(Horn) SS,cont HANSSLER 5.119 s.p. (S664)

Herr Gott, Dich Loben Wir *Te Deum
[Ger] 4pt mix cor,acap (med easy) BAREN. BA 4961 $.40 (S665)

Herr, Lass Meine Klage *mot
(Adrio, Adam) SSATB,cont (med) BAREN. BA 2567 $.55 see also Israelsbrunnlein (S666)

Heut Triumphieret Gottes Sohn *Easter
SSATBB HANSSLER 6.124 s.p. (S667)

I Am The Root And The Branch Of David *Adv/Gen
SSATB,acap (med diff) oct CONCORDIA 98-1895 $.50 (S668)

Ich Bin Die Wurzel Des Geschlechtes David *ECY,mot
(Adrio, Adam) [Ger] SSATB,cont (med) BAREN. BA 2574 $.65 see also Israelsbrunnlein (S669)

Ich Bin Jung Gewesen *mot
(Adrio, Adam) SSATB,cont (med) BAREN. BA 2558 $.65 see also Israelsbrunnlein (S670)

Ich Bring Die Nicht Mit Silber, Gold
(Horn) SS,cont HANSSLER 5.132 s.p. (S671)

Ich Danke Gott Dem Herren Mein
see DEUTSCHES SANCTUS UND PSALM 111

Ich Freue Mich Im Herren *Epiph
[Ger] SSATB,cont (med) BAREN. BA 2564 $.55 see also Israelsbrunnlein (S672)

Ich Lasse Dich Nicht *Trin,mot
(Adrio, Adam) [Ger] SSATB,cont (med) BAREN. BA 2554 $.55 see also Israelsbrunnlein (S673)

Ich Ruf Zu Dir, Herr Jesu Christ
see Sechs Choralkonzerte
(Horn) SS,cont HANSSLER 5.107 s.p. (S674)

Ihr Heiligen, Lobsinget *mot
(Adrio, Adam) SSATB,cont (med) BAREN. BA 2566 $.65 see also Israelsbrunnlein (S675)

Israelsbrunnlein *CC26U,Gen,mot
(Adrio, Adam) [Ger] SSATB,cont (med) BAREN. BA 4491 $27.50
see also: Ach Herr, Ach Meiner Schone; Da Jakob Vollendet Hatte; Dennoch Bleibe Ich Stets An Dir; Der Herr Denket An Us; Die Mit Tranen Saen; Drei Schone Dinge Sind; Freu Dich Des Weibes; Herr, Lass Meine Klage; Ich Bin Die Wurzel Des Geschlechtes David; Ich Bin Jung Gewesen; Ich Freue Mich Im Herren; Ich Lasse Dich Nicht; Ihr Heiligen, Lobsinget; Ist Nicht Ephraim Mein Teurer Sohn; Lehre Uns Bedenken, Dass Wir Sterben Mussen; Lieblich Und Schone Sein Ist Nichts; Nun Danket Alle Gott; O Herr Jesu Christe; Siehe An Die Werk Gottes; Siehe, Nach Trost War Mir Sehr Bange; Unser Leben Wahret Siebnzig Jahr; Wem Ein Tugendsam Weib Bescheret Ist; Wende Dich, Herr, Wieder Zu Mir; Zion Spricht: Der Herr Hat Mich Verlassen (S676)

Ist Nicht Ephraim Mein Teurer Sohn *mot
(Adrio, Adam) SSATB,cont (med) BAREN. BA 2562 $.65 see also Israelsbrunnlein (S677)

Jesu, Wollst Uns Weisen *Gen
[Ger] SATB,acap (easy) BAREN. BA 4954 $.40 contains also: O, Jesu Christ, Dein Nam Der Ist Gewaltiglich; Rex Christe, Factor Omnium (S678)

Komm Heiliger Geist (from Opella Nova)
(Kessler, Franz) 3pt mix cor,cont cor pts BREITKOPF-W CHB-3159 s.p., ipa (S679)

Komm, Heiliger Geist, Herre Gott
(Horn) SST/SSB,cont HANSSLER 5.100 s.p. (S680)

Lasset Die Kindlein Zu Mir Kommen *Bibl/mot
(Metzger) SSATTB HANSSLER 1.063 s.p. (S681)

Lehre Uns Bedenken, Dass Wir Sterben Mussen *ECY,mot
(Adrio, Adam) [Ger] SSATB,cont (med) BAREN. BA 2575 $.65 see also Israelsbrunnlein (S682)

Lieblich Und Schone Sein Ist Nichts *mot
(Adrio, Adam) [Ger] SSATB,cont (med) BAREN. BA 2561 $.65 see also Israelsbrunnlein (S683)

Lob Gott Getrost Mit Singen *Gen
[Ger] SATB,acap (easy) BAREN. BA 4955 $.40 (S684)

Lobet Den Herrn In Seinem Heiligtum (Psalm 150) Gen,mot
[Ger] SSATB,acap (med) BAREN. BA 994, 995 s.p. (S685)

SCHEIN, JOHANN HERMANN (cont'd.)

(Metzger) SSATB HANSSLER 1.060 s.p. (S686)

Lobt Gott, Ihr Christen (from Opella Nova)
2pt men cor,cont cor pts BREITKOPF-W
CHB-3434 s.p., ipa (S687)

Lobt Gott, Ihr Christen Allzugleich (from
Opella Nova) Thanks
2pt wom cor/2pt jr cor,cont cor pts
BREITKOPF-W CHB-3434 s.p., ipa (S688)
(Horn) SS/TT,cont HANSSLER 5.127 s.p. (S689)
(Kessler, Franz) 2pt mix cor,cont cor pts
BREITKOPF-W CHB-3434 s.p., ipa (S690)

Lord God, We All To Thee Give Praise *Gen
SATB,acap (easy) oct CONCORDIA 98-1250 $.20
contains also: Oh, Praise The Lord With
Joyful Noise (S691)

Lov Vare Dig, O Jesu Krist
see TVA JULKONSERTER

Mach Dich Auf, Werde Licht
[Ger] voc sc PETERS HU1979 $2.50, ipr (S692)
(Horn) SSATB,ST soli,cont&fl&ob&2vln&opt
trom/2vla HANSSLER 5.133 sc s.p., cor pts
s.p., ipa (S693)

Mighty Fortress, A *Gen/Refm
SA/TB,kbd (med diff) oct CONCORDIA 98-1859
$.25 (S694)

Mir Nach, Spricht Christus, Unser Held
see Praetorius, Michael, Der Morgenstern
Ist Aufgedrungen

Mit Fried Und Freud Ich Fahr Dahin
(Horn) SS,cont HANSSLER 5.121 s.p. (S695)

Mitten Wir Im Leben Sind (from Opella Nova)
(Hasse, K.) 2pt wom cor,org sc BREITKOPF-L
PB-3383 s.p. (S696)
(Horn) SS,cont HANSSLER 5.120 s.p. (S697)

My Soul, Now Bless Thy Maker *Gen/Thanks
SA/TB,kbd (med diff) oct CONCORDIA 98-1865
$.25 (S698)

Now Blessed Be Thou, Christ Jesu *see
Gelobet Seist Du, Jesu Christ

Now Come, Thou Savior Of Men *see Nun Komm,
Der Heiden Heiland

Nun Danket Alle Gott *mot
(Adrio, Adam) SSATB,cont (med) BAREN.
BA 2576 $1.00 see also Israelsbrunnlein (S699)

Nun Freut Euch, Lieben Christen Gmein (from
Opella Nova)
2pt wom cor/2pt jr cor,cont cor pts
BREITKOPF-W CHB-3158 s.p., ipa (S700)
(Horn) SS,cont HANSSLER 5.099 s.p. (S701)
(Kessler, Franz) 2pt mix cor,cont cor pts
BREITKOPF-W CHB-3158 s.p., ipa (S702)

Nun Jauchzet Mit Hellem Ton *Easter
[Ger] 3pt mix cor,cont (easy) BAREN.
BA 3761 s.p. (S703)

Nun Komm Der Heiden Heiland
(Horn) SST/SSB,cont HANSSLER 5.092 s.p. (S704)
(Martens, J.) "Now Come, Thou Savior Of
Men" SST/SSB,org SCHIRM.EC 2450 $.35 (S705)

Nun Lob, Mein Seel, Den Herren *Thanks
(Horn) SS,cont HANSSLER 5.109 s.p. (S706)

O Christe, Schopfer Aller Welt
(Schabasser, Josef) mix cor,acap (contains
also: Gesius, Bartholomaus, Mir Nach,
Spricht Christus) oct DOBLINGER s.p. see
also CHRISTUS, DER HERR (S707)

O Domine Jesu Christe (from Cymbalum Sionium-
1615) Psntd,mot/prayer
SATTBB,acap cor pts BREITKOPF-W PB-2341
s.p., ipa (S708)
(Metzger) [Lat/Ger] SSATTB HANSSLER 1.062
$.80 (S709)

O Herr,..Ich Bin Dein Knecht (from
Israelsbrunnlein) Easter/Pent,mot
(Adrio, Adam) [Ger] SSATB,cont (med) BAREN.
BA 2551 $.55 (S710)

O Herr Jesu Christe *mot
(Adrio, Adam) SSATB,cont (med) BAREN.
BA 2573 $.55 see also Israelsbrunnlein (S711)

O, Jesu Christ, Dein Nam Der Ist Gewaltiglich
see Schein, Johann Hermann, Jesu, Wollst
Uns Weisen

O Jesulein, Mein Jesulein
(Horn) SS,cont HANSSLER 5.131 s.p. (S712)

O Lamb Of God Most Holy *Lent
SA/TB,kbd (med easy) oct CONCORDIA 98-1864
$.25 (S713)

O Lamm Gottes Unschuldig
(Horn) SS,cont HANSSLER 5.108 s.p. (S714)

O Lord, Look Down From Heaven *Gen/Refm
SA/TB,kbd (med diff) oct CONCORDIA 98-1860
$.25 (S715)

O Lovely Child *see O Schonestes Kindelein

O Saving Victim
see THREE MOTETS IN HONOR OF THE BLESSED
SACRAMENT

O Schonestes Kindelein *Xmas
"O Lovely Child" SSB,org SCHIRM.EC 2611
s.p. (S716)
(Glaser, V.) "O Lovely Child" SS,org
SCHIRM.EC 2519 $.25 (S717)

Oh, Praise The Lord With Joyful Noise
see Schein, Johann Hermann, Lord God, We
All To Thee Give Praise

SCHEIN, JOHANN HERMANN (cont'd.)

Opella Nova (V, VI, VII) *CCU
(Prufer Arthur) cor GREGG
ISBN 0:567 28166 2 s.p. Reprint From
Breitkopf & Hartel, 1901-23 (S718)

Opella Nova-Part 1 *CC30U
(Horn) [Ger] 3-5pt HANSSLER 4.012 $10.00 (S719)

Our Blessed Savior Seven Times Spoke *anthem
(Bliss) 2 eq voices,bass inst/org/hpsd
(med) oct AUGSBURG 1406 $.30 (S720)

Psalm 51 *see Gott Sei Mir Gnadig

Psalm 91 *see Wer Unter Dem Schirm Des
Hochsten

Psalm 150 *see Lobet Den Herrn In Seinem
Heiligtum

Rex Christe, Factor Omnium
see Schein, Johann Hermann, Jesu, Wollst
Uns Weisen

Salvation Now To Us Has Come *Gen/Refm
SA/TB,kbd (med diff) oct CONCORDIA 98-1861
$.25 (S721)

Sechs Choralkonzerte *Gen
(Doorman, Ludwig) [Ger] SA,cont (med) sc
BAREN. BA 1115 $2.50, cor pts $1.00
contains: Christe, Der Du Bist Tag Und
Licht; Ein Feste Burg; Erschienen Ist
Der Herrliche Tag; Gott Der Vater Wohn
Uns Bei; Ich Ruf Zu Dir, Herr Jesu
Christ; Vater Unser Im Himmelreich (S722)

Seligpreisungen
(Engelke, B.) 5pt mix cor,SSATB soli,org,
2trp,3trom,bvl BREITKOPF-L rental (S723)

Siehe An Die Werk Gottes *mot
(Adrio, Adam) SSATB,cont (med) BAREN.
BA 2563 $.65 see also Israelsbrunnlein (S724)

Siehe, Nach Trost War Mir Sehr Bange *Trin,
mot
(Adrio, Adam) [Ger] SSATB,cont (med) BAREN.
BA 2568 $.65 see also Israelsbrunnlein (S725)

Singet Frohlich Gotte (from Cymbalum Sionium)
mot
(Hasse, K.) 5pt mix cor,acap cor pts
BREITKOPF-L PB-3385 s.p. (S726)

They Who Grieving Soweth *see Die Mit Tranen
Saen

Truly Was The Word Made Flesh *see Verbum
Caro Factum Est

Two Sacred Concertos *see Christ Lag In
Todesbanden; Gelobet Seist Du, Jesu
Christ (S727)

Unser Leben Wahret Siebnzig Jahr *ECY,mot
(Adrio, Adam) [Ger] SSATB,cont (med) BAREN.
BA 2565 $.65 see also Israelsbrunnlein (S728)

Unser Vater In Der Hohe
see Schein, Johann Hermann, Amen Wir
Frohlich Sprechen

Vater Unser *prayer
(Engelke, B.) 5pt mix cor,TBar soli,org,
2fl,bsn,2trp,3trom,strings BREITKOPF-L
rental (S729)

Vater Unser, Der Du Bist
[Ger] SATB (med) BAREN. BA 4944 $.40 (S730)

Vater Unser Im Himmelreich *Bibl/prayer
see Sechs Choralkonzerte
(Horn) SS,cont HANSSLER 5.103 s.p. (S731)

Verbum Caro Factum Est *Xmas
(Granville) "Truly Was The Word Made Flesh"
SSATBB,acap oct FOX CM8 $.35 (S732)

Vom Himmel Hoch (from Opella Nova) anthem
"From Heaven Above" SST/SSB SCHIRM.EC 2722
$.35 (S733)
(Kessler, Franz) 3pt mix cor,cont cor pts
BREITKOPF-W CHB-3157 s.p., ipa (S734)
(Pinkham, D.) "From Heaven Above" [Ger/Eng]
SST/SSB,org SCHIRM.EC 2722 $.35 (S735)
(Riedel) "From Heaven Above" SSATB (med)
oct AUGSBURG 1471 $.30 (S736)

Von Himmel Hoch, Da Komm Ich Her
(Horn) SST/SSB,cont HANSSLER 5.094 s.p. (S737)

Was Betrubst Du Dich, Meine Seele (from
Israelsbrunnlein) Easter/Pent,mot
(Adrio, Adam) [Ger] SSATB,cont (med) BAREN.
BA 2571 $.55 (S738)

Wem Ein Tugendsam Weib Bescheret Ist *mot
(Adrio, Adam) [Ger] SSATB,cont (med) BAREN.
BA 2572 $.65 see also Israelsbrunnlein (S739)

Wende Dich, Herr, Wieder Zu Mir *Psntd,mot
[Ger] SSATB,cont (med) BAREN. BA 2556 $.65
see also Israelsbrunnlein (S740)

Wenn Wir In Hochsten Noten Sein
SATB,acap DOBLINGER s.p. see also BITTE UND
VERTRAUEN (S741)

Wer Unter Dem Schirm Des Hochsten (Psalm 91)
mot
(Metzger) 2-6pt/SSATTB HANSSLER 1.061 s.p. (S742)

Who With Grieving Soweth
SSATB,acap oct PRESSER 352-00019 $.40 (S743)

Why Art Thou Cast Down, My Spirit *Gen/Lent
SSATB,acap (med diff) oct CONCORDIA 98-1852
$.30 (S744)

Wo Gott Der Herr Nicht Bei Uns Halt
(Horn) SS,cont HANSSLER 5.113 s.p. (S745)

Wo Gott Zum Haus Nicht Gibt Sein Gunst
(Horn) SS,cont HANSSLER 5.114 s.p. (S746)

SCHEIN, JOHANN HERMANN (cont'd.)

Wohl Dir, Du Christenschar
(Glaser, V.) "Hail Ye, Believers All" SATB,
acap SCHIRM.EC 2623 $.30 (S747)
(Mattfeld, V.) "Hail, Ye Believers All!"
SS,org SCHIRM.EC 2520 $.18 (S748)

Zion Speaks *see Zion Spricht

Zion Speaks: I Am By God Forsaken *Gen
SSATB,acap (med diff) oct CONCORDIA 98-1894
$.60 (S749)

Zion Spricht
(Hayes) "Zion Speaks" [Eng/Ger] 6pt mix
cor,acap oct LAWSON 51585 $.40 (S750)

Zion Spricht: Der Herr Hat Mich Verlassen
*Trin,mot
(Adrio, Adam) [Ger] SSATB,cont (med) BAREN.
BA 2557 $.75 see also Israelsbrunnlein (S751)

SCHEIT, SAMUEL
O Domine Jesu Christe *mot
(Seiber, Matyas) [Lat] dbl cor oct NOVELLO
28.1318.01 s.p. (S752)

SCHELLE, JOHANN HERMANN (1648-1701)
Actus Musicus Auf Weihnachten *Xmas
(Baselt, Bernd) [Ger] SSATB,ST soli,orch
BAREN. BA 4444 rental (S753)

Alleluja, Man Singet Mit Freuden Vom Sieg
*cant
(Kruger) SSATB,cont,bsn,2trp,2vln,2vla
HANSSLER 10.039 sc s.p., cor pts s.p.,
ipa (S754)

Barmherzig Und Gnadig Ist Der Herr *cant
(Kruger) SSATB,cont,bsn,2vln,2vla HANSSLER
10.166 sc s.p., voc sc s.p., ipa (S755)

Christus Ist Des Gesetzes Ende *mot
"Jesus Christ From The Law Hath Freed Us"
dbl cor,cont CONCORDIA 97-6297 $1.50 (S756)

Ehre Sei Gott In Der Hohe *cant
(Kruger) SSATB,cont,bsn,2trp,2vln,timp,
2trom/vla HANSSLER 10.090 sc s.p., voc sc
s.p., ipa (S757)

Jesus Christ From The Law Hath Freed Us *see
Christus Ist Des Gesetzes Ende

Lobe Den Herrn, Meine Seele *cant
5pt mix cor,SSATB soli,org,bsn,4trom,
strings,timp, 2 cornettino BREITKOPF-L
rental (S758)

SCHELLING, J.
Bettagslied
[Ger] mix cor,acap (med easy) HUG s.p. (S759)

SCHERER, GEORGE
Gift, The
SATB oct AGAPE CE 4322 $.30 (S760)

SCHIAVONE, JOHN
Hear Us, O Jesus *Lent
SATB,kbd (med easy) oct CONCORDIA 98-2125
$.25 (S761)

Mass In Honor Of God The Holy Spirit *Gen,
Mass
SATB&cong,org (med) voc sc GIA G1764 $1.00 (S762)

Prince Of Light, The *Xmas
SATB,acap (med easy) oct CONCORDIA 98-2120
$.25 (S763)

Wilt Thou Forgive? *Gen/Lent
SATB,acap (med easy) oct CONCORDIA 98-2119
$.25 (S764)
SATB,acap (med diff/diff) SOUTHERN $.25 (S765)

SCHICHT, JOHANN GOTTFRIED (1753-1823)
Ascension Hymn *Asc,hymn
SATB oct NOVELLO 44.1077.07 s.p. (S766)

SCHICKELE, PETER (1935-   )
Birth Of Christ, The
SATB (York Mystery Play) oct ELKAN-V $1.75 (S767)

Last Supper, The
SSA oct ELKAN-V 362-3110 $.30 (S768)

Two Prayers
SATB oct ELKAN-V 362-1163 $.25 (S769)

SCHICKSALSLIED see Brahms, Johannes

SCHIEDEMANN
Frisch Auf Und Lasst Uns Singen *Easter
(Granville) "Wake Ye And Join The Singing"
SATB,acap oct FOX CM22 $.30 (S770)

Wake Ye And Join The Singing *see Frisch Auf
Und Lasst Uns Singen

SCHIEFERDECKER, JOHANN C. (1679-1732)
Heilig Ist Der Herr Zebaoth *Sanctus
(Grusnick, Bruno) [Ger] SATB,2vln,2vla,opt
cont,vcl (med) BAREN. BA 3365 sc $2.25,
cor pts $.55, ipa (S771)

SCHIERI, FRITZ (1922-   )
Abendlied *Eve
3pt mix cor MOSELER s.p. see also Achtzehn
Chorsatze Aus Dem Geistlichen Jahr Der
Annette Von Droste-Hulshoff (S772)

Achtzehn Chorsatze Aus Dem Geistlichen Jahr
Der Annette Von Droste-Hulshoff
4pt mix cor MOSELER s.p.
contains: Allerseelen; Fur Die Armen
Seelen
see also: Abendlied; Advent; Am Letzten
Tage Des Jahres; Am Weihnachtstage; Der
Jungling Zu Naim; Der Verdorrte
Feigenbaum; Die Heilung Der
Taubstummen; Gleichnis Vom Konig, Der
Rechnen Wollte; Gleichnis Vom Splitter
Und Balken; Gleichnis Vom Weinberg;
Grundonnerstag; Karsamstag;
Pfingstmontag; Pfingstsonntag; Von Der
Auferstehung Der Toten; Zum
Palmsonntag; Zum Passionssonntag (S773)

SCHIERI, FRITZ (cont'd.)

Advent *Adv
5pt mix cor MOSELER s.p. see also Achtzehn Chorsatze Aus Dem Geistlichen Jahr Der Annette Von Droste-Hulshoff (S774)

Alleluja-Psalm I (Psalm 80) Gen
[Ger] SATB,acap (easy) MULLER SM 166 s.p. (S775)

Alleluja-Psalm II (Psalm 148) Gen
[Ger] SSATB,acap (med easy) MULLER SM 167 s.p. (S776)

Allerseelen
see Achtzehn Chorsatze Aus Dem Geistlichen Jahr Der Annette Von Droste-Hulshoff

Am Letzten Tage Des Jahres
6pt mix cor MOSELER s.p. see also Achtzehn Chorsatze Aus Dem Geistlichen Jahr Der Annette Von Droste-Hulshoff (S777)

Am Weihnachtstage *Xmas
6pt mix cor MOSELER s.p. see also Achtzehn Chorsatze Aus Dem Geistlichen Jahr Der Annette Von Droste-Hulshoff (S778)

Christi Himmelfahrt *Easter/Pent,liturg
[Ger] 4pt mix cor/5pt mix cor,acap (med easy) MULLER SM 788 s.p. (S779)

Cibavit *Corpus/Fest,Mass
[Lat] 4-6pt mix cor,acap (med easy) MULLER SM 795 sc s.p., cor pts s.p. (S780)

Der Jungling Zu Naim
6pt mix cor MOSELER s.p. see also Achtzehn Chorsatze Aus Dem Geistlichen Jahr Der Annette Von Droste-Hulshoff (S781)

Der Verdorrte Feigenbaum
6pt mix cor MOSELER s.p. see also Achtzehn Chorsatze Aus Dem Geistlichen Jahr Der Annette Von Droste-Hulshoff (S782)

Dicit Dominus *Pent
[Lat] 5pt mix cor,acap (med) MULLER SM 734 s.p. (S783)

Die Heilung Der Taubstummen
5pt mix cor/4 eq voices MOSELER s.p. see also Achtzehn Chorsatze Aus Dem Geistlichen Jahr Der Annette Von Droste-Hulshoff (S784)

Fur Die Armen Seelen
see Achtzehn Chorsatze Aus Dem Geistlichen Jahr Der Annette Von Droste-Hulshoff

Gleichnis Vom Konig, Der Rechnen Wollte
6pt mix cor MOSELER s.p. see also Achtzehn Chorsatze Aus Dem Geistlichen Jahr Der Annette Von Droste-Hulshoff (S785)

Gleichnis Vom Splitter Und Balken
4pt mix cor MOSELER s.p. see also Achtzehn Chorsatze Aus Dem Geistlichen Jahr Der Annette Von Droste-Hulshoff (S786)

Gleichnis Vom Weinberg
5pt mix cor MOSELER s.p. see also Achtzehn Chorsatze Aus Dem Geistlichen Jahr Der Annette Von Droste-Hulshoff (S787)

Grundonnerstag *Holywk
6pt mix cor MOSELER s.p. see also Achtzehn Chorsatze Aus Dem Geistlichen Jahr Der Annette Von Droste-Hulshoff (S788)

Karsamstag *Gd.Fri.
7pt mix cor MOSELER s.p. see also Achtzehn Chorsatze Aus Dem Geistlichen Jahr Der Annette Von Droste-Hulshoff (S789)

Pfingstmontag *Pent/Whitsun
3 eq voices/3pt mix cor MOSELER s.p. see also Achtzehn Chorsatze Aus Dem Geistlichen Jahr Der Annette Von Droste-Hulshoff (S790)

Pfingstsonntag *Pent/Whitsun
7pt mix cor MOSELER s.p. see also Achtzehn Chorsatze Aus Dem Geistlichen Jahr Der Annette Von Droste-Hulshoff (S791)

Psalm 80 *see Alleluja-Psalm I

Psalm 148 *see Alleluja-Psalm II

Spiritus Domini *Pent
[Lat] 3-6pt mix cor,acap (med) MULLER SM 727 s.p. (S792)

Unruhig Ist Mein Herz *mot
4pt mix cor,3 soli MOSELER LB-235 s.p. (S793)

Von Der Auferstehung Der Toten *Asc
6pt mix cor MOSELER s.p. see also Achtzehn Chorsatze Aus Dem Geistlichen Jahr Der Annette Von Droste-Hulshoff (S794)

Weisser Sonntag *Easter/Pent
[Ger] 4pt mix cor/5pt mix cor,acap (med easy, low sunday) MULLER SM 787 s.p. (S795)

Zum Palmsonntag *Palm
4pt mix cor MOSELER s.p. see also Achtzehn Chorsatze Aus Dem Geistlichen Jahr Der Annette Von Droste-Hulshoff (S796)

Zum Passionssonntag *Psntd
6pt mix cor/4 eq voices MOSELER s.p. see also Achtzehn Chorsatze Aus Dem Geistlichen Jahr Der Annette Von Droste-Hulshoff (S797)

SCHIFF, HELMUT
Proprium Zum Ersten Adventsonntag *Adv
4pt mix cor,acap DOBLINGER sc s.p., cor pts s.p. (S798)

SCHIFFER, J.V.
Mass In Honor Of The Holy Rosary *Mass
2pt wom cor/2pt men cor,org (easy) voc sc WILLIS $.60 (S799)

SCHILLING, HANS LUDWIG (1927-)
Die Heiligen Drei Konige *Xmas
wom cor/jr cor cor pts BREITKOPF-W CHB-3440 s.p. (S800)
men cor cor pts BREITKOPF-W CHB-3440 s.p. (S801)

Du Bist Der Gott Meiner Zuflucht (Psalm 42)
unis&mix cor,org s.p. cor pts BREITKOPF-W CHB-3484, voc sc BREITKOPF-W EB-6465 (S802)

Ein Kind Geborn Zu Bethlehem *Xmas,cant
mix cor HANSSLER 10.279 sc s.p., cor pts s.p. (S803)

Es Kam Ein Engel Hell Und Klar *mot
4pt men cor,acap cor pts BREITKOPF-W CHB-3518 s.p. (S804)

Missa Brevis *Mass
4pt mix cor/unis mix cor,org voc sc BREITKOPF-W PB-3885 s.p., cor pts BREITKOPF-W CHB-3438 (S805)

Mitten In Dem Leben *mot
mix cor&mix cor cor pts BREITKOPF-W CHB-3683 (S806)

Psalm 42 *see Du Bist Der Gott Meiner Zuflucht

Singet Dem Herrn Ein Neues Lied
eq voices&cong,cantor,org,fl,vcl,perc,gtr HANSSLER 25.004 sc s.p., cor pts s.p., ipr (S807)

Singet, Preiset Gott Mit Freuden
unis,org HANSSLER 25.003 s.p. (S808)

Sonne Der Gerechtigkeit *cant
4pt mix cor,org voc sc BREITKOPF-W EB-6469 s.p., cor pts BREITKOPF-W CHB-3516 (S809)

SCHIMMERLING, H.A.
Praise To God Who Gives Us Beauty *folk,Slav
SATB,acap AMP A229 $.20 (S810)

Saint Joseph *folk,Slav
SATB,acap AMP A230 $.20 (S811)

SCHINDLER, KURT (1882-1935)
Miracle Of The Virgin Mary, A
8pt oct PRESSER 332-13313 $.50 (S812)

SCHINDLER, WALTER (1909-)
Fischpredigt Des Heiligen Antonius
4pt men cor,pno cor pts BREITKOPF-W CHB-3512A s.p. see from Funf Schwank- Und Spottlieder (S813)

Funf Schwank- Und Spottlieder *see Fischpredigt Des Heiligen Antonius (S814)

Oster-Dialog *Easter
[Ger] 3pt men cor,SBar soli,vln,2vla,2vcl, bvl,timp cor pts SIRIUS s.p., ipa (S815)

Oster-Oratorium *Easter,Bibl/ora
[Ger] mix cor,SATB soli,org,fl,2ob,bsn, 3trp,strings,perc,timp, english horn SIRIUS voc sc s.p., cor pts s.p., ipa (S816)

Osterruf *Easter
[Ger] SATB,acap cor pts SIRIUS s.p. (S817)

Tedeum *Te Deum
SSATB&unis boy cor,SB soli,pno,opt org,2fl, 2bsn,3trp,3trom,2vln,vla,opt vcl/bvl, perc,drums,2timp, English horn sc HANSSLER 10.136 rental (S818)

SCHINELLI, ACHILLE
Collana Di Composizioni Polifoniche Vocali Sacre E Profane, Vol. 1 *CC32U,hymn/ madrigal/mot,15th cent/16th cent/17th cent
[It/Eng/Ger] 2-5pt CURCI 6075 s.p. (S819)

La Preghiera Del Mattino
unis/2pt,pno RICORDI-ENG 128725 s.p. (S820)

Messa A S. Luigi *Mass
[Lat] 2 eq voices,org sc ZANIBON 2597 s.p., voc pt ZANIBON s.p. (S821)

SCHIPP, C.M.
My Soul Thirsts For God (Psalm 42)
SATB oct SOUTHERN $.25 (S822)

O God, Our Help In Ages Past
SATB oct SOUTHERN $.25 (S823)

Psalm 42 *see My Soul Thirsts For God

SCHIRMER, RUDOLPH [E.] (1919-)
Gift Of Christmas, The *Xmas
4pt mix cor oct SCHIRM.G 11437 $.25 (S824)

SCHIRMER'S FAVORITE A CAPELLA SELECTIONS *sac/sec,CC20L
SSA/SSAA SOUTHERN $1.25 contains works by: Bach; Aichinger; Moderati and others (S825)

SCHIRMER'S SSA CHORAL PROGRAM *sac/sec,CC28L
SSA SOUTHERN $2.50 contains works by: Bach; Glarum; Bernstein and others (S826)

SCHIRRMANN
I Am Not Worthy, Holy Lord *Gen
SAB oct SPRATT 578 $.25 (S827)

Let Thy Mercy, O Lord
SAB oct PRO ART 2168 $.25 (S828)

SCHISKE, KARL (1916-)
Cunctipotens Genitor Deus *Op.43, Mass
4pt mix cor,opt org DOBLINGER sc s.p., cor pts s.p. (S829)

Psalm 99 *Op.30
[Ger] 6pt mix cor,acap oct DOBLINGER s.p. (S830)

SCHLAF, MEIN KINDLEIN *Xmas
(Strobl, Otto) mix cor,acap oct DOBLINGER s.p. (S831)

SCHLAF, SCHLAF, HOLDSELIGES JESULEIN *Xmas,Aus
(Schemitsch, Hans) [Ger] mix cor,acap oct DOBLINGER s.p. see also Zehn Osterrichische Weihnachtsleider (S832)

SCHLAF WOHL, DU HIMMELSKNABE DU see Biebl, Franz

SCHLAFE, GOTTLICH KIND see Ammann, Benno

SCHLAFE MIT RUH
see Am Funfundzwanzigsten Dezember

SCHLAGE DOCH see Bach, Johann Sebastian

SCHLAGETER, WALTER (1907-)
Vom Himmel Hoch *CC12U,Xmas
[Ger] 3-6 eq voices,acap (med easy) sc MULLER SM 377 s.p. (S833)

SCHLAGT, KUNSTLER, DIE PAUKEN see Buxtehude, Dietrich

SCHLENKER, MANFRED
Allein Gott In Der Hoh Sei Ehr
unis jr cor,2rec, or xylophone or glockenspiel sc HANSSLER 12.202 s.p. contains also: Kretzschmar, Gunther, Erhalt Uns, Herr, Bei Deinem Wort (unis jr cor,bvl/timp, xylophones); Becker-Foss, Jurgen, Brunn Alles Heils (jr cor,S rec,A rec, or glockenspiel, xylophone); Kretzschmar, Gunther, All Morgen Ist Ganz Frisch Und Neu (unis jr cor, xylophone, glockenspiel); Suthoff-Gross, Rudolf, Ach Bleib Mit Deiner Gnade (2pt jr cor,A rec) (S834)

Aller Augen Warten Auf Das Brot Von Dir
see Schweizer, Rolf, Friede Den Brudern, "Dein Reich Ist Nicht Unsre Kirche"

Aus Meines Herzens Grunde
see Schlenker, Manfred, Die Guldne Sonne

Die Guldne Sonne
unis jr cor,timp,2rec, glockenspiel, xylophone sc HANSSLER 12.205 s.p. contains also: Schlenker, Manfred, Aus Meines Herzens Grunde (unis jr cor,timp, 1rec, glockenspiel, xylophone); Neubert, Gottfried, Steht Auf, Ihr Lieben Kinderlein (unis jr cor,fl, glockenspiel, xylophone); Neubert, Gottfried, Gott Des Himmels Und Der Erden (2pt jr cor/SS,2fl) (S835)

O Susser Herre Jesu Christ
see Koch, Johannes H.E., Herr Christ, Der Einig Gotts Sohn

Untitled Choral Collection *CC8L
unis jr cor/SSA,2-3inst sc HANSSLER 12.208 s.p. (S836)

Wer Unter Dem Schirm Des Hochsten
(Horn) unis,kbd,2vln/2rec HANSSLER 5.123 s.p. (S837)

SCHLICHT, JOHANN GOTTFRIED (1753-1823)
Ascension Hymn *Asc,anthem
mix cor oct NOVELLO 44.1077.07 s.p. (S838)

Das Walt Gott Vater Und Gott Sohn
SAAT LAUDINELLA LR 99 s.p. contains also: Es Geht Daher Des Tagen Schein; Herr Gott, Vater Im Himmelreich; Nun Ruhen Alle Walder; Nun Sich Der Tag Geendat Hat (S839)

Es Geht Daher Des Tagen Schein
see Schlicht, Johann Gottfried, Das Walt Gott Vater Und Gott Sohn

Herr Gott, Vater Im Himmelreich
see Schlicht, Johann Gottfried, Das Walt Gott Vater Und Gott Sohn

Nun Ruhen Alle Walder
see Schlicht, Johann Gottfried, Das Walt Gott Vater Und Gott Sohn

Nun Sich Der Tag Geendat Hat
see Schlicht, Johann Gottfried, Das Walt Gott Vater Und Gott Sohn

SCHLOEMANN, BURGHARD (1935-)
Das Gleichnis Vom Unkraut Unter Dem Weizen *Epiph
[Ger] SATB,Bar solo,2trp,2trom (med) BAREN. BA 5431 sc s.p., cor pts s.p., ipa (S840)

SCHMALZ, PAUL (1904-)
Harrgott, O Lueg, Es Volch Isch Da
[Ger] mix cor,acap (med) HUG s.p. (S841)

Jubelt Gott!
[Ger] mix cor,S solo,org,opt 2ob&2horn& 2trp&trom&strings&timp HUG s.p., ipr (S842)

SCHMECKET UND SEHET, WIE FREUNDLICH DER HERR IST see Reda, Siegfried

SCHMECKET UND SEHET, WIE FREUNDLICH DER HERR IST see Schweizer, Rolf

SCHMEEL, DIETER (1923-)
Das Alte Jahr Vergangen Ist
SAT/SAB,treb inst HANSSLER 14.038 contains also: Marx, Karl, O Jesu Christe, Wahres Licht (SA,treb inst) (S843)

SCHMERTZ
Lord, Lord, I've Got Some Singin' To Do
(Touchette) TTBB oct FISCHER,C CM-6887 $.25 (S844)
(Touchette) SATB oct FISCHER,C CM-7013 $.25 (S845)

SCHMID, E.
Bitte
[Ger] mix cor,acap (easy) HUG s.p. (S846)

Herr, Du Weisst Wie Arm Wir Wandern
[Ger] mix cor,acap (easy) HUG s.p. (S847)

SCHMID, H.
Heilge Nacht Der Ew'gen Liebe *Xmas
(Walcker, M.) [Ger] wom cor,acap (easy) HUG s.p. (S848)

SCHMID, WALTER (1906-)
Am Jahresende
[Ger] mix cor,org HUG s.p. (S849)

Befiehl Dem Herrn Deine Wege (Psalm 37)
[Ger] mix cor,org HUG s.p. (S850)

SCHMID, WALTER (cont'd.)

Dankt Dem Herrn! (Psalm 33)
[Ger] mix cor,acap (med) HUG s.p.   (S851)

Gang Zum Herrn
nee Zwei Kirchliche Lieder

Gebet
[Ger] mix cor,acap (easy) HUG s.p.   (S852)

Gott, Sei Uns Gnadig (Psalm 67)
see Zwei Psalmen

Herr, Dein Wort Bleibt Ewiglich (Psalm 119)
[Ger] men cor,org HUG s.p.   (S853)
[Ger] mix cor,org HUG s.p.   (S854)

Herr Gott, Du Bist Unsere Zuflucht! (Psalm 90)
[Ger] mix cor,org HUG s.p.   (S855)

Hoch Weht Das Kreuz
[Ger] men cor,acap (easy) HUG s.p.   (S856)

Ich Will Den Herren Loben (Psalm 34)
[Ger] mix cor,acap (easy) HUG s.p.   (S857)

Ich Will Dich Erheben (Psalm 145)
[Ger] mix cor,org HUG s.p.   (S858)

Jauchzet Dem Herrn (Psalm 100)
[Ger] mix cor,org HUG s.p.   (S859)

Jauchzet Dem Herrn Alle Welt (Psalm 100)
[Ger] men cor,pno/org HUG s.p.   (S860)

Jauchzet Gott (Psalm 66)
see Zwei Psalmen

Kleine Passions-Kantate
[Ger] mix cor,org/orch HUG s.p., ipr   (S861)

Kleine Weihnachts-Kantate *Xmas,cant
[Ger] mix cor,solo,org HUG s.p.   (S862)

Lobe Den Herren! (Psalm 57)
[Ger] mix cor,org HUG s.p.   (S863)

Machet Die Tore Weit (Psalm 24) Adv,cant
[Ger] mix cor,org HUG s.p.   (S864)

Psalm 24 *see Machet Die Tore Weit

Psalm 33 *see Dankt Dem Herrn!

Psalm 34 *see Ich Will Den Herren Loben

Psalm 37 *see Befiehl Dem Herrn Deine Wege

Psalm 57 *see Lobe Den Herren!

Psalm 66 *see Jauchzet Gott

Psalm 67 *see Gott, Sei Uns Gnadig

Psalm 90 *see Herr Gott, Du Bist Unsere
Zuflucht!

Psalm 100 *see Jauchzet Dem Herrn

Psalm 119 *see Herr, Dein Wort Bleibt
Ewiglich

Psalm 145 *see Ich Will Dich Erheben

Trost
see Zwei Kirchliche Lieder

Zur Konfirmation *Cnfrm
[Ger] mix cor,acap (easy) HUG s.p.   (S865)

Zwei Kirchliche Lieder
[Ger] mix cor,acap (easy) HUG s.p.
contains: Gang Zum Herrn; Trost   (S866)

Zwei Psalmen
[Ger] men cor,acap (easy) HUG s.p.
contains: Gott, Sei Uns Gnadig (Psalm
67); Jauchzet Gott (Psalm 66)   (S867)

SCHMIDLIN, J.
Dans La Nuit De Noel *Xmas
3pt wom cor BROEKMANS 123 s.p.   (S868)

Geh Aus, Mein Herz, Und Suche Freud
(Berger, H.L.) TTBB HANSSLER 6.5110 s.p.
(S869)

SCHMIDT
Behold, I Stand At The Door
SATB oct LORENZ B101 $.30   (S870)

Comfort Ye My People *Gen
SATB SCHMITT 1597 $.25   (S871)

In The Hollow Of Your Hand
SATB oct LORENZ A536 $.30   (S872)

SCHMIDT, MELVIN
In The Hollow Of Your Hand *Ded/Gen,anthem
SA/SATB,med solo (easy) oct LORENZ A536
$.30   (S873)

SCHMIDT, MINNIE ANNE
Shepherds Found Him *Xmas,Bibl/cant
jr cor,pno voc sc LILLENAS MC-14 $1.00
(S874)

SCHMIDT, WALTHER (1913-   )
Ihr Lieben Christen, Freut Euch Nun *Adv
[Ger] SATB,acap (med easy) BAREN. BA 3009
s.p.   (S875)

SCHMIDT, WOLFGANG (1929-   )
O Selig Haus, Wo Man Dich
2pt wom cor/3pt mix cor/SA/SAT/SAB,org
HANSSLER 6.249 s.p.   (S876)

Wer Nun Den Lieben Gott Lasst Walten *cant
SAB,SB soli,cont,2vln HANSSLER 10.102 sc
s.p., voc sc s.p., ipa   (S877)

SCHMIDT-GORG, JOSEPH (1897-   )
Das Musikwerk *see Die Messe   (S878)

Die Messe *Mass
(Fellerer, Karl Gustav) mix cor GERIG s.p.
see from Das Musikwerk   (S879)

SCHMIDT-MANNHEIM, HANS (1931-   )
Nun Preiset Alle Gottes Barmherzigkeit
see Schmidt-Mannheim, Hans, Wir Danken Gott
Fur Seine Gaben

O Treuer Gott, Wir Danken Dir
see Schmidt-Mannheim, Hans, Wir Danken Gott
Fur Seine Gaben

Preis, Lob Und Dank Sei Gott, Dem Herren
unis&SATB,kbd HANSSLER 6.307 s.p. contains
also: Wohl Denen, Die Da Wandeln   (S880)

Wir Danken Gott Fur Seine Gaben *Thanks
SAT/SAB HANSSLER 6.282 s.p. contains also:
O Treuer Gott, Wir Danken Dir (SATB); Nun
Preiset Alle Gottes Barmherzigkeit (SSA/
SAT/SAB)   (S881)

Wohl Denen, Die Da Wandeln
see Schmidt-Mannheim, Hans, Preis, Lob Und
Dank Sei Gott, Dem Herren

SCHMITT
Psalm 47
[Eng/Fr] cor,S solo,org,orch SALABERT-US
voc sc $22.00, cor pts $3.00   (S882)

SCHMITT, FLORENT (1870-1958)
Adjiciat Dominus
see Trois Liturgies Joyeuses

Ave Regina *BVM,mot
[Lat] 4pt mix cor oct DURAND s.p.   (S883)

Ave Verum *Op.121, Commun,mot
see Quinque Cantus Ad Benedictionem
Santissimi Sacramenti
[Lat] 4pt mix cor,opt org oct DURAND s.p.
(S884)

Benedictus Dominus
see Quinque Cantus Ad Benedictionem
Santissimi Sacramenti

Cantique De Simeon *Op.135
see Schmitt, Florent, Psaume CXII
see Schmitt, Florent, Psaume CXII

De Profundis *Gen,mot
[Lat] 4pt men cor oct DURAND s.p.   (S885)

Domine, Dominus Noster (Psalm 8) Op.119, Gen,
mot
"Psaume VIII" [Lat] 4pt mix cor,opt org sc
DURAND s.p.   (S886)

Hymne A Saint-Nicolas De Lorraine *Gen,hymn/
mot
[Fr] 4pt men cor oct DURAND s.p.   (S887)

Laudate Dominum *Gen,mot
[Lat] 4pt mix cor oct DURAND s.p.   (S888)

Laudate, Pueri Dominum *Op.126, Gen,mot
[Lat] 4pt mix cor,opt org sc DURAND s.p.
(S889)

Magnificat
see Trois Liturgies Joyeuses

Messe *Op.138, Mass
[Fr] 4pt mix cor,org voc sc DURAND s.p. (S890)

Oremus Pro Pontifice *Op.127, Gen,mot
[Lat] 4pt mix cor,opt org sc DURAND s.p. (S891)

Psalm 8 *see Domine, Dominus Noster

Psalm 112 *see Psaume CXII

Psaume CXII (Psalm 112) Op.135, hymn
[Fr] 4pt men cor,opt org sc DURAND s.p.
contains also: Cantique De Simeon;
Cantique De Simeon   (S892)

Psaume VIII *see Domine, Dominus Noster

Quinque Cantus Ad Benedictionem Santissimi
Sacramenti *Op.121, Gen,Bene/mot/Sanctus
[Lat] 4pt mix cor,opt org oct DURAND s.p.
contains: Ave Verum; Benedictus Dominus;
Sub Tuum; Tantum Ergo; Tu Es Petrus   (S893)

Sub Tuum *Op.121, BVM,mot
see Quinque Cantus Ad Benedictionem
Santissimi Sacramenti
[Lat] 4pt mix cor,opt org oct DURAND s.p.
(S894)

Tantum Ergo *Op.121, Commun,mot
see Quinque Cantus Ad Benedictionem
Santissimi Sacramenti
[Lat] 4pt mix cor,opt org oct DURAND s.p.
(S895)

Trois Liturgies Joyeuses *Op.116, Gen,mot
[Lat] 4pt mix cor,opt org sc DURAND s.p.
contains: Adjiciat Dominus; Magnificat;
Veni Creator   (S896)

Tu Es Petrus
see Quinque Cantus Ad Benedictionem
Santissimi Sacramenti

Veni Creator
see Trois Liturgies Joyeuses

Virgo Gloriosa *BVM,mot
[Lat] 4pt men cor oct DURAND s.p.   (S897)

SCHMUCKE DICH
"Bless, O God, This Glad Endeavor" see Two
Wedding Hymns

SCHMUCKE DICH see Mendelssohn, Arnold

SCHMUCKE DICH, O LIEBE SEELE see Bach, Johann
Sebastian

SCHMUCKE DICH, O LIEBE SEELE [CHORALE] see
Bach, Johann Sebastian

SCHMUCKET DAS FEST see Thomas, Kurt

SCHMUCKET DAS FEST MIT MAIEN see Hammerschmidt,
Andreas

SCHMUCKET DAS FEST MIT MAIEN see Marks, Gunther

SCHMUCKET DAS FEST MIT MAIEN see Mendelssohn,
Arnold

SCHMUCKET DAS FEST MIT MAIEN see Raphael,
Gunther

SCHMUCKT DAS FEST see Stier, Alfred

SCHMUCKT DAS FEST MIT MAIEN see Poos, Heinrich

SCHMUECKE DICH see Bach, Johann Sebastian,
Schmucke Dich, O Liebe Seele

SCHMUTZ, ALBERT C.
Bread Of The World *Commun
SATB (med) ABINGDON APM-635 $.20   (S898)

O Lord, Our God
SATB (med) ABINGDON APM-920 $.40   (S899)

SCHMUTZLER, T.
Out Of The Deep Have I Cried Unto Thee
*Easter
SATB oct PRESSER 312-40641 $.30   (S900)

SCHNABEL, J.J.
Herr Unser Gott
(Muller, A.M.) mix cor,acap ERDMANN 567
s.p.   (S901)

SCHNECKER, P.
Hope Of The World *Xmas
SA PRESSER $.75   (S902)
SATB PRESSER $.75   (S903)

My Faith Looks Up To Thee *Easter
SATB oct PRESSER 332-10322 $.35   (S904)
(Page, N.) SAB oct PRESSER 332-15213 $.35
(S905)

Risen King *Easter
SSA PRESSER $1.25   (S906)

Story Of Calvary *Easter
SATB PRESSER $.85   (S907)

SCHNEIDER, HERBERT
Es Kommt Der Herr Der Herrlichkeit *Xmas,
Bibl/cant
1-3pt wom cor/jr cor&unis men cor,2-3inst
HANSSLER 10.068 sc s.p., cor pts s.p.
(S908)

SCHNEIDER, JOSEF
Messe In A-Moll *Mass
mix cor (A min) VOLK 109 s.p.   (S909)

SCHNEIDER, KENT
All That Has Life Praise God
SATB,inst oct AGAPE F 946 $.35, ipa   (S910)

Church Within Us, The
(Hustad) SATB oct AGAPE CF 105 $.30   (S911)

Song Of Thankfulness
mix cor oct AGAPE CF 161 $.30   (S912)

SCHNEIDER, MARTIN GOTTHARD (1930-   )
Bleibe Bei Uns, Herr *Gen
[Ger] 3pt mix cor,opt bvl (med easy) BOSSE
BE 229 s.p.   (S913)
[Ger] unis,acap (easy) BOSSE BE 252 s.p.
(S914)
[Ger] 3pt men cor,acap (med easy) BOSSE
BE 281 s.p.   (S915)

Danke *Gen
[Ger] unis,acap (easy) BOSSE BE 251 s.p.
(S916)
[Ger] 3pt men cor,acap (med easy) BOSSE
BE 280 s.p.   (S917)
[Ger] SA&men cor,opt bvl (med easy) BOSSE
BE 225 s.p.   (S918)

Der Weg Der Barmherzigkeit *Gen
[Ger] unis,acap (easy) BOSSE BE 262 s.p.
(S919)

Diesen Tag, Herr *Gen
[Ger] unis,acap (easy) BOSSE BE 268 s.p.
(S920)
[Ger] SATB,fl,bvl (easy) BOSSE BE 244 s.p.
(S921)

Ein Kindlein Liegt In Dem Armen Stall *Xmas
[Ger] unis,acap (easy) BOSSE BE 258 s.p.
(S922)
[Ger] 3pt men cor,acap (med easy) BOSSE
BE 282 s.p.   (S923)
[Ger] 3pt mix cor,opt bvl BOSSE BE 231 s.p.
(S924)

Gott Meint Es Gut Mit Dir *Gen
[Ger] 3pt men cor,acap (med easy) BOSSE
BE 283 s.p.   (S925)

Manchmal Denk Ich: Es Gibt Keine Weihnacht
Fur Mich *Xmas
[Ger] 3pt mix cor,opt bvl (med easy) BOSSE
BE 230 s.p.   (S926)

SCHNEIDER, WILLY
Psalm 127 *cant
[Ger] 1-4 cor,ob,strings,opt org sc
HEINRICH. 48 s.p.   (S927)

Sieben Mannerchore Zur Weihnacht *CC7L,Xmas
[Ger] men cor,acap cor pts HEINRICH. 683
s.p.   (S928)

SCHNEIDT, H.-M.
Wenn Wir In Hochsten Noten Sein *mot
2-8pt&mix cor (diff) cor pts LEUCKART 13 C
s.p.   (S929)

SCHNIEDER
Children Of The Heavenly Father
SA/TB FLAMMER E5057 $.30   (S930)

SCHNITZLER, HEINRICH (1908-   )
Gott Ist Das Grosse Schweigen
see Zwei Abendlieder

Viel Sterne Gloriieren
see Zwei Abendlieder

Zwei Abendlieder
men cor,acap TONGER s.p.
contains: Gott Ist Das Grosse Schweigen;
Viel Sterne Gloriieren   (S931)

SCHNYDER, CH.
Gebet Fur Das Vaterland
[Ger] mix cor,acap (easy) HUG s.p.   (S932)

SCHOECK, OTHMAR (1886-1957)
Jauchzet Dem Herrn, Alle Welt (Psalm 100)
[Ger] wom cor,org/orch HUG s.p., ipr (S933)

Psalm 100 *see Jauchzet Dem Herrn, Alle Welt

SCHOEN, F.
May God Have Pity On Us (Psalm 67) Gen,anthem
cong,cantor (easy) oct GIA G1711 $.40   (S934)

Psalm 67 *see May God Have Pity On Us

SCHOENBERG, ARNOLD (1874-1951)
De Profundis (Psalm 80) Op.50b, Heb
[Heb] SSATBB,acap cor pts HEINRICH. s.p.
(S935)
SSATBB,acap ISRAELI 301 s.p.   (S936)

Friede Auf Erden *Op.13
"Peace On Earth" [Ger/Eng] SSAATTBB,acap/
orch voc sc SCHOTT s.p., ipr   (S937)

Peace On Earth *see Friede Auf Erden

Psalm 80 *see De Profundis

Psalm 130 *see De Profundis

SCHOENDLINGER, ANTON (1919-   )
Der Grimmig Tod Mit Seinem Pfeil *mot
SATB,acap cor pts BREITKOPF-L CHB-2923 s.p.
(S938)
Jauchzet Dem Herrn
mix cor HANSSLER 7.153 s.p.   (S939)

SCHOENFELD, WILLIAM C. (1893-   )
Presence, The *anthem
SATB,opt high solo&low solo (easy) ABINGDON
APM-310 $.25   (S940)

Secret, The
SATB (easy) ABINGDON APM-363 $.25 (S941)

Steward's Prayer, The
SATB (easy, Stewardship Sunday) ABINGDON
APM-359 $.25   (S942)

SCHOEPFUNGSMESSE see Haydn, (Franz) Joseph

SCHOFFER
Sing A Hymn Of Praise *see Zemer Lach

Zemer Lach
(Frank) "Sing A Hymn Of Praise" SATB oct
FOX $.40   (S943)

SCHOLA CANTORUM. VOL. I see Martin Pompey

SCHOLA CANTORUM. VOL II see Martin Pompey

SCHOLA CANTORUM. VOL. III see Martin Pompey

SCHOLA CANTORUM. VOL. IV see Martin Pompey

SCHOLIN
God Is A Spirit
SATB FLAMMER A 5053 $.30   (S944)
(Gore) SSA FLAMMER B 5089 $.25   (S945)

SCHOLIN, C. ALBERT (1896-1958)
Christmas Blessing *Xmas,cant
SSA BELWIN $1.00   (S946)
SATB BELWIN $1.00   (S947)

Christmas Spirit *Xmas,cant
SSA BELWIN $1.00   (S948)
SATB BELWIN $1.00   (S949)

Christmas Time *Xmas,cant
SATB BELWIN $1.00   (S950)

Easter Message *Easter,cant
SATB BELWIN $1.00   (S951)

Junior And Senior Choir Book *CCU
jr cor&sr cor BELWIN $1.00   (S952)

SCHOLL
Dreissig Kanon Und Andere Lieder *CC30U,
canon
mix cor HANSSLER 2.032 s.p.   (S953)

SCHOLLOM, ROBERT (1913-   )
Psalm 122 *Op.58b
mix cor,org/orch voc sc DOBLINGER s.p., ipr
(S954)
Psalmkommentare *Op.80
mix cor,2pno,perc cor pts DOBLINGER s.p.,
ipr   (S955)

SCHOLTES
They'll Know We Are Christians
(Wilson) SAB oct AGAPE AG 7101 $.35 (S956)

They'll Know We Are Christians By Our Love
(Wilson) SATB SOUTHERN $.35   (S957)

SCHOLTES, P.
They'll Know We Are Christians By Our Love
(Bock, F.) SATB oct PRESSER G-133 $.35
(S958)

SCHON IST DIE WELT see Benker, Heinz

SCHONBACH, [DIETER] (1931-   )
Canticum Psalmi Resurrectionis *cant
oct UNIVER. PH. 13061 $3.80   (S959)

SCHONSTER HERR JESU, HERRSCHER ALLER ENDEN see
Schreck, Gustav

SCHONSTER HERR JESUS see Heiller, Anton

SCHOONHEID see Rontgen, [Julius]

SCHOP
Dearest Jesus, Draw Thou Near Me
(Luvaas) boy cor SOUTHERN $.30   (S960)

I Will Sing My Maker's Praises
(Harris) SATB oct PRO ART 1960 $.25 (S961)

Jesus, Name All Names Above *anthem
(Bach; Pooler, M.) SA (easy) oct AUGSBURG
1319 $.20   (S962)

SCHOP, JOHANN (? -1665)
O Traurigkeit, O Herzelied
see Bach, Johann Sebastian, Brich Entzwei,

Vom Himmel Hoch, Da Komm Ich Her *Xmas
(Strube, Adolf) [Ger] STB,cont (med) NAGELS
NMA 69 sc $3.25, cor pts $1.00   (S963)

SCHOPFUNGSMESSE see Haydn, (Franz) Joseph,
Missa Solennis

SCHOTT, JOHANN GEORG (ca. 1600?)
Mein Lieber Herr, Ich Preise Dich
SATB HANSSLER 6.004 s.p.   (S964)

Singet Dem Herrn Ein Neues Lied Denn Er Tut
Grosse Wunder
SATB HANSSLER 6.296 s.p. contains also:
Kurig, Hans-Hermann, Singet Dem Herrn Ein
Neues Lied (SSA); Franck, Melchior, Nun
Freut Euch, Gottes Kinder All (SATB);
Franck, Melchior, Bleib Bei Mir, Herr
(mix cor); Franck, Melchior, Dienet
Einand (mix cor)   (S965)

SCHOTT'S CHORBUCH I *CCU
(Hanshang) [Ger] 4pt SCHOTT 4051 s.p. (S966)

SCHOTT'S CHORBUCH II *CCU
(Hanshang) [Ger] 4pt SCHOTT 4052 s.p. (S967)

SCHOTT'S CHORBUCH III *CCU
(Hanshang) [Ger] 3pt SCHOTT 4053 s.p. (S968)

SCHOTT'S CHORBUCH IV *CCU
(Hanshang) [Ger] 3pt SCHOTT 4054 s.p. (S969)

SCHRADER, OSWALD (1907-   )
All Ding Auf Erden
see Funf Spruchmotetten

Bei Dir Ist Die Quelle Des Lebens
see Funf Spruchmotetten

Dein Wort Ist Meines Herzens Freude
see Funf Spruchmotetten

Der Du Die Welt Geschaffen Hast
see Funf Spruchmotetten

Funf Spruchmotetten *mot
SSA HANSSLER 7.022 s.p.
contains: All Ding Auf Erden; Bei Dir Ist
Die Quelle Des Lebens; Dein Wort Ist
Meines Herzens Freude; Der Du Die Welt
Geschaffen Hast; Und Jesus Trat Zu
Ihnen   (S970)

Nun Ruste Dich, Christenheit *mot
SATB HANSSLER 7.023 s.p.   (S971)

Und Jesus Trat Zu Ihnen
see Funf Spruchmotetten

Werfet Euer Vertrauen Nicht Weg *mot
SSA HANSSLER 7.025 s.p.   (S972)
SSA HANSSLER 7.026 s.p.   (S973)

SCHRECK
Advent Motet 1st Mvt *Adv,mot
(Christiansen, O.) SATB KJOS 5083A $.30
(S974)
Advent Motet 2nd Mvt *Adv,mot
(Christiansen, O.) SATB KJOS 5083B $.30
(S975)
Advent Motet 3rd Mvt *Adv,mot
(Christiansen, O.) SATB KJOS 5083C $.30
(S976)
O Lord, How Shall I Meet Thee?
(Cramer) SATB&unis,acap MARKS 4303 $.30
(S977)
We Sing The Praise Of Him
men cor KJOS 5550 $.30   (S978)

We Sing The Praise Of Him Who Died
(Schroth, G.) SATB KJOS 5258 $.30 (S979)

SCHRECK, GUSTAV (1849-1918)
Schonster Herr Jesu, Herrscher Aller Enden
*17th cent
mix cor cor pts BREITKOPF-W PB-1945 s.p.
(S980)
Wie Soll Ich Dich Empfangen *Op.32, Adv
SATB,acap cor pts BREITKOPF-L PB-1435 s.p.
(S981)

SCHREINER, ALEXANDER (1901-   )
All Glory, Laud And Honor
TTBB oct FISCHER,J 9325 $.30   (S982)
SATB oct FISCHER,J 9008 $.30   (S983)

SCHRENK, JOHANNES
Mit Schall Von Zungen
see Zwei Lieder Zum Heiligen Christfest

Steht Auf Und Wacht
see Zwei Lieder Zum Heiligen Christfest

Zwei Lieder Zum Heiligen Christfest *Fest
unis,org,2vln,vcl HANSSLER 7.020A s.p.;
SATB,inst HANSSLER 7.020B s.p., ipa
contains: Mit Schall Von Zungen; Steht
Auf Und Wacht   (S984)

SCHREURS, J.
Sinte Cecilia
men cor BROEKMANS 134 s.p.   (S985)

SCHRIJVERS, J.
Domine Salvam Fac Regina Nostram
mix cor ALSBACH&D sc s.p., cor pts s.p.
(S986)

SCHROEDER
Bread Of The World
SATB,acap oct PRO ART 2484 $.25   (S987)

Easter Alleluia *Easter
SATB&jr cor oct SOUTHERN $.25   (S988)
SATB FLAMMER A 5554 $.30   (S989)

Service Suite For Junior Choir
unis/SA oct SACRED S-8629 $.35   (S990)

Shadows Are Falling
SATB,opt vln (med easy) SOUTHERN $.30
(S991)
Sing With Joy, Glad Voices Lift
SATB,fl,strings (med diff/diff) SOUTHERN
$.30   (S992)

SCHROEDER, HERMANN (1904-   )
Die Responsorien Der Karwoche *CCU,Gd.Fri./
Psntd
[Ger] SATB,acap (med) MULLER SM 1979 s.p.
(S993)
Hymni Ad Processionem In Festo Corporis
Christi
[Lat] SATB,org/brass SCHOTT sc s.p., ipa,
cor pts s.p., ipa   (S994)

Kein Meister Fallt Vom Himmel
men cor,acap TONGER s.p.   (S995)

Kyrie-Litanei *Kyrie
[Ger] SATB,org,opt winds (med easy) MULLER
SM 2477 sc s.p., cor pts s.p.   (S996)

Missa Dorica *Op.15, Mass
[Lat] SSATBB SCHOTT s.p.   (S997)

Puer Natus Est *Xmas
[Lat] SATB,acap (med, appropriate for third
christmas mass) MULLER SM 779 s.p. (S998)

Rorate Caeli *Adv
[Lat] SATB,acap (med easy) MULLER MS 47
s.p.   (S999)

Singe, O Singe Dich, Seele
men cor,acap TONGER s.p.   (S1000)

St. Paulus War Ein Medikus
men cor,acap TONGER s.p.   (S1001)

Tantum Ergo *Gen
[Lat] unis,org/brass SCHOTT voc sc s.p.,
cor pts s.p., ipa   (S1002)
[Lat] SATB,acap (easy) MULLER MS 48 s.p.
(S1003)
Te Deum *Op.16, Te Deum
[Lat] SSATBB,acap/org/brass SCHOTT sc s.p.,
ipa, cor pts s.p., ipa   (S1004)

SCHROEDER, JOHN
I Met The Master Face To Face *Xmas
SATB oct WORD CS-2536 $.30   (S1005)

O Master Let Me Walk With Thee
2pt oct AGAPE CF 113 $.30   (S1006)

SCHROETER
Hail To The Lord's Anointed
mix cor SOUTHERN $.25   (S1007)
(Ehret) SATB,acap MARKS 4107 $.30 (S1008)

New Christmas Songs *CC18U,Xmas
SATB/SSAA/SSATB/dbl cor/SSAT&ATBB PETERS
3468 $1.50   (S1009)

Rejoice, Rejoice, Ye Christians
(Malin) TTBB,acap oct BELWIN 64273 $.35
(S1010)
(Malin) SAB oct BELWIN 64252 $.30 (S1011)

SCHROEDER, LEONHARDT (1540-1602)
All Glory Be To God On High *Gen/Trin
SATB,acap (med easy) oct CONCORDIA 98-1248
$.25   (S1012)

Freut Euch Ihr Lieben Christen
see Bach, Johann Sebastian, Freuet Euch Ihr
Christen Alle

Hail To The Lord's Annointed *Adv/Epiph
SATB,acap (med easy) oct CONCORDIA 98-1049
$.25   (S1013)

Rejoice, Rejoice, Ye Christians *Xmas
SATB,acap (med easy) oct CONCORDIA 98-1917
$.25   (S1014)

SCHROTER
Rejoice, Rejoice Ye Christians *Xmas
(Lundquist) SATB SCHMITT 1505 $.20 (S1015)

SCHROTER, L.
All Glory Be To God On High
SATB,acap oct PRESSER 312-40158 $.30
(S1016)
Baby Boy, So Wonderful, A *see Ein Kindelein
So Lobelich

Ein Kindelein So Lobelich
(Payson, A.) "Baby Boy, So Wonderful, A"
SATB,acap FRANK F-541 $.30   (S1017)

Rejoice, Rejoice, Ye Christians
(Malin) boy cor SOUTHERN $.25   (S1018)

SCHROTER, LEONHARD (ca. 1540-1600)
Allein Gott In Der Hoh
see Trubel, Gerhard, Jauchz, Erd Und Himmel

Allein Gott In Der Hoh Sei Ehr *Xmas
see Praetorius, Michael, Es War Des Ewigen
Vaters Rat
4 eq voices/4pt mix cor MOSELER LB-354 s.p.
see from Neue Weinachtsliedlein   (S1019)
[Ger] TTTB,acap (easy) NAGELS NCH 44 s.p.
(S1020)
4 eq voices MOSELER M-32 s.p.   (S1021)
4 eq voices MOSELER LB-122 s.p.   (S1022)
4pt mix cor MOSELER LB-62 s.p.   (S1023)

Ein Kind Geborn Zu Bethlehem *Xmas
4pt mix cor&4pt mix cor/4 eq voices/8pt mix
cor MOSELER LB-353 s.p. see from Neue
Weinachts-Liedlein   (S1024)
4 eq voices MOSELER M-33 s.p. contains
also: Praetorius, Michael, Ein Kind
Geborn Zu Bethlehem   (S1025)

Ein Kindelein So Lobelich *Xmas
SATB HANSSLER 6.0821 s.p.   (S1026)
SATB HANSSLER 6.097 s.p.   (S1027)
(Wolters) 4pt mix cor (contains also: Gott,
Ihr Christen) MOSELER LB-357 s.p. see
from Neue Wiehnachtsliedlein 1587 (S1028)

Freut Euch, Ihr Lieben Christen *Xmas
TTBB HANSSLER 6.0321 s.p.   (S1029)
(Wolters) 4pt mix cor MOSELER LB-355 s.p.
see from Neue Wiehnachtsliedlein 1587
(S1030)
Freut Euch Von Herzen Sehr *CCU,Xmas
(Wagner, Hermann) mix cor MOSELER s.p.
(S1031)

SCHROTER, LEONHARD (cont'd.)

Helft Mir Gottes Gute Preisen *Xmas
(Wolters) 4pt mix cor (contains also: In Natali Dominio) MOSELER LB-352 s.p. see from Neue Wiehnachtsliedlein 1587 (S1032)

In Dulci Jubilo *Xmas/Gen
(Goebel, Georg) [Ger] SSAT&ATBB,acap (med) MULLER MS 9 s.p. (S1033)
(Wolters) 4pt mix cor&4pt mix cor MOSELER LB-360 s.p. see from Neue Wiehnachtsliedlein 1587 (S1034)

In Natali Domini *Xmas
(Wolters) 4pt mix cor (contains also: Helft Mir Gottes Gute Preisen) MOSELER LB-352 s.p. see from Neue Wiehnachtsliedlein 1587 (S1035)

Josef, Lieber Josef Mein *Xmas
4 eq voices/4pt mix cor MOSELER LB-358 s.p. see from Neue Weinachts-Leidlein (S1036)
4 eq voices MOSELER LB-165 s.p. (S1037)

Joseph Lieber, Joseph Mein *Xmas/Gen
(Douglas) "Joseph Tender, Joseph Mine" SATB,acap,opt pno oct PRO ART 2278 $.25 (S1038)
(Goebel, Georg) [Ger] SSAT&ATBB,acap (med) MULLER MS 8 s.p. (S1039)
(Wolters) 4pt mix cor&4pt mix cor MOSELER LB-359 s.p. see from Neue Wiehnachtsliedlein 1587 (S1040)

Joseph Tender, Joseph Mine *see Joseph Lieber, Joseph Mein

Lobt Gott Ihr Christen *Xmas
5pt mix cor MOSELER LB-53 s.p. (S1041)
(Wolters) 4pt mix cor (contains also: Ein Kindelein So Lobelich) MOSELER LB-357 s.p. see from Neue Wiehnachtsliedlein 1587 (S1042)

Lobt Gott, Ihr Christen Alle Gleich *Thanks
SSATB HANSSLER 6.233 s.p. (S1043)

Lobt Gott, Ihr Christen Allegleich *Thanks
SSATB HANSSLER 6.233 s.p. (S1044)

Neue Weinachts-Leidlein *see Josef, Lieber Josef Mein (S1045)

Neue Weinachts-Liedlein *see Ein Kind Geborn Zu Bethlehem (S1046)

Neue Weinachtsleidlein *see Allein Gott In Der Hoh Sei Ehr (S1047)

Neue Wiehnachtsliedlein 1587 *see Ein Kindelein So Lobelich; Freut Euch, Ihr Lieben Christen; Helft Mir Gottes Gute Preisen; In Dulci Jubilo; In Natali Domini; Joseph, Lieber Joseph Mein; Lobt Gott, Ihr Christen (S1048)

Von Gott Will Ich Nicht Lassen
SATB HANSSLER 6.165 s.p. contains also: Bach, Johann Sebastian, Was Gott Tut, Das Ist Wohlgetan [Chorale] (from Was Gott Tut, Das Ist Wohlgetan) (Trin) (S1049)

Wo Der Herr Nicht Das Haus Bauet *Gen,mot
(Hofmann, Gertrud) [Ger] SSAT&TTBB,acap (med) BAREN. BA 625 $2.00 (S1050)

SCHROTH

Anthems Of Praise *CCU,anthem
SAB KJOS $1.25 (S1051)

Arise, My Soul, Arise
SATB KJOS 5486 $.30 (S1052)

Beautiful Savior
SATB KJOS 5260 $.30 (S1053)

Bless The Lord
SATB KJOS 5314 $.35 (S1054)

Blessing, A
SATB KJOS 5887 $.30 (S1055)

Cantate Domino
SATB KJOS 5336 $.30 (S1056)

Come To The Manger *Xmas
SA KJOS 6096 $.30 (S1057)

Drawn To The Cross
SATB KJOS 5178 $.30 (S1058)

Early One Morning
SATB KJOS 5352 $.30 (S1059)

Evening Song, An
SATB KJOS 5488 $.30 (S1060)

Glory To God *CCU
SATB KJOS $1.25 (S1061)

God So Loved The World
SATB KJOS 7060 $.30 (S1062)

Good Christian Men, Rejoice
SATB KJOS 5318 $.30 (S1063)

Holy Night! *Xmas
SSAATBB oct SACRED S-87 $.35 (S1064)

If Thou But Suffer God To Guide Thee
SATB KJOS 5875 $.30 (S1065)

I'm Weary Lord
SSAATBB oct VOLKWEIN VB181 $.25 (S1066)

Jesus, Holy Child *Xmas
SATB KJOS 5184 $.30 (S1067)
SA KJOS 6070 $.30 (S1068)

Jesus, Jesus, Rest Your Head
SATB KJOS 5361 $.30 (S1069)

Jesus, Shepherd Of The Sheep
SATB KJOS 5211 $.30 (S1070)

Keeping Holy Vigil
SATB KJOS 5185 $.30 (S1071)

SCHROTH (cont'd.)

Lamb Of God
SAB KJOS 5731 $.30 (S1072)

Let Us Break Bread Together
SATB KJOS 5236 $.30 (S1073)

Lord Bless You And Keep You
SATB KJOS 5228 $.30 (S1074)

Lord Is My Strengh And My Song, The
SATB KJOS 5200 $.30 (S1075)

Moon And Stars Of Christmas
SATB,fl,fing.cym. oct VOLKWEIN VB704 $.30 (S1076)

O Bless Our God, Ye People
SATB KJOS 5303 $.30 (S1077)
SSA KJOS 6093 $.30 (S1078)

One Night In Bethlehem *Xmas
SATB KJOS 5472 $.30 (S1079)

Poor Wayfarin' Stranger
SATB KJOS 5808 $.30 (S1080)

Sing To The Lord
SATB KJOS 5338 $.35 (S1081)

Sing Together Hymns *CCU,hymn
SATB KJOS $1.25 (S1082)

Song Of Simeon
SSAA KJOS 6094 $.30 (S1083)

Spanish Easter Carol *Easter,carol,Span
SATB KJOS $.30 (S1084)

Te Deum *Te Deum
SATB oct VOLKWEIN VB262 $.25 (S1085)

Thou Wilt Keep Him
SATB KJOS 5264 $.30 (S1086)

When Children Sing Songs Of Praise *CCU
unis treb cor KJOS $.60 (S1087)

Wondrous Child
SATB KJOS 5471 $.30 (S1088)

Ye Sons And Daughters
SATB KJOS 5888 $.30 (S1089)

SCHROTH, ELIZABETH

Child Of Heaven
SATB KJOS 5830 $.30 (S1090)

SCHROTH, G.

Coventry Carol *carol
SATB KJOS 5313 $.30 (S1091)

From Heaven Above
SATB KJOS 5473 $.30 (S1092)

How Fair The Church
SATB KJOS 5874 $.30 (S1093)

Hymn To The Trinity
SATB KJOS 5337 $.30 (S1094)

If With All Your Hearts
SATB KJOS 5238 $.30 (S1095)

Mary Had A Baby *Xmas
SATB KJOS 5362 $.30 (S1096)

O God Of Youth
SATB KJOS 5179 $.30 (S1097)

Psalm 92
SATB KJOS 5812 $.30 (S1098)

Psalm 100
SATB KJOS 5813 $.30 (S1099)

SCHROTH, GERHARD

All From Saba Shall Come *Epiph,anthem
SA/TB/SB (med easy) oct GIA G1517 $.25 (S1100)

Come Down, O Love Divine *Pent,anthem
SATB (med) oct GIA G1519 $.25 (S1101)

For The People Of God *Gen,anthem
SATB&opt cong (med easy) oct GIA G1522 $.25 (S1102)

He Has Borne Our Woes *Lent,anthem
SATB (med easy) oct GIA G1520 $.25 (S1103)

He Shall Rule From Sea To Sea *Gen,anthem
SATB/SA/TB (med) oct GIA G1518 $.25 (S1104)
SA/TB/SATB (med) oct GIA G1518 $.25 (S1105)

Jesus The Christ Is Born *Xmas
SATB oct AGAPE A 436 $.30 (S1106)

Let Us Stand In Prayer *Gen,anthem/liturg/prayer
SA/TB/SB (easy) oct GIA G1547 $.25 (S1107)
2pt (easy) oct GIA G1547 $.25 (S1108)

Litany Of Thanksgiving, A *Gen/Thanks,anthem
3pt mix cor/2pt&cong (easy) oct GIA G1548 $.25 (S1109)
2pt&cong/3pt (easy) oct GIA G1548 $.25 (S1110)

Song Of Praise, A
SA oct AGAPE SP 709 $.30 (S1111)

This Is The Day *Easter,anthem
SSATB,org,opt fl,3trp,2trom,bvl (med) oct GIA G1604 $.45, ipr (S1112)

Yours Is Princely Power *Xmas,anthem
SATB (med) oct GIA G1549 $.25 (S1113)

SCHROTH, GODFREY

Who Are These That Earnest Knock *Xmas
SATB,acap (med easy, ballad) oct CONCORDIA 98-2110 $.40 (S1114)

SCHUBERT, FRANZ (PETER) (1797-1828)

Agnus Dei (from Mass In G Major) Agnus
(Ehret) [Lat] SATB MARKS 4191 $.25 (S1115)

Allerseelen
[Ger] mix cor,acap (med diff) HUG s.p. (S1116)

SCHUBERT, FRANZ (PETER) (cont'd.)

Almighty, The
(Ringwald) SATB SHAWNEE A 122 $.35 (S1117)

Ave Maria *Op.52,No.6, BVM/Commun
3pt ASHDOWN V.T.27 s.p. (S1118)
SA/TB FLAMMER E5094 $.30 (S1119)
SSA oct FISCHER,C CM-5053 $.25 (S1120)
[Lat] unis/2pt CHOUDENS s.p. (S1121)
SATB ENOCH EC253 s.p. (S1122)
2pt ASHDOWN E.A.195 s.p. (S1123)
(Downing) "O Rose Of Sharon" [Lat/Eng] 3pt wom cor oct SCHIRM.G 9570 $.30 (S1124)
(Downing) "O Rose Of Sharon" [Lat/Eng] SAB oct SCHIRM.G 9449 $.30 (S1125)
(Duey) TTBB,org/pno BOSTON 12074 $.40 (S1126)
(Hall) [Lat/Ger/Eng] TTBB,high solo oct SCHIRM.G 9542 $.30 (S1127)
(Jacobson) 3pt jr cor/3pt wom cor CURWEN 72592 s.p. (S1128)
(Mansfield, P.J.) SSA LEONARD-ENG 77 s.p. (S1129)
(Martini) [Lat] 3 eq voices,pno sc RICORDI-ARG BA 8947 s.p., sc RICORDI-ARG BA 8948 s.p. (S1130)
(McCarthy, J.) [Lat] SATB,opt S solo,pno/org CHESTER s.p. (S1131)
(Radford) "O Rose Of Sharon" [Lat/Eng] SATB,S solo oct SCHIRM.G 3474 $.30 (S1132)
(Riegger) SATB FLAMMER A 5110 $.35 (S1133)
(Riegger) SSA FLAMMER B 5049 $.30 (S1134)
(Riegger) SAB FLAMMER D5155 $.35 (S1135)
(Ringwald) SATB SHAWNEE A83 $.30 (S1136)
(Ringwald) SSA SHAWNEE B 59 $.30 (S1137)
(Siegmeister; Ehret) SSA oct BOURNE 204 $.30 (S1138)
(Treharne) SA,opt vln BOSTON 9704 $.35 (S1139)
(Vene) [Lat] TTBB,T solo,acap oct COLOMBO 1727 $.25 (S1140)
(Vogel, Moritz; Nagler, Franciscus) [Ger] wom cor&jr cor,org,opt strings HUG 52 s.p. (S1141)

Ave Verum *Commun,mot
see SIX MOTETS A L'UNISSON
(Kunc, P.) [Lat] 4pt/4pt mix cor oct DURAND s.p. (S1142)

Benedictus Es Domine *Op.150, Gradual
mix cor,org,2ob,2clar,2trp,3trom,strings, timp sc BREITKOPF-L PB-609 s.p. (S1143)

Blessed Savior, Now Before Us *Lent
(Hines) SAB SCHMITT 5533 $.30 (S1144)

Children Of The Hebrews, The
see MUSIC FOR PALM SUNDAY

Chorus Of Angels (Christ Is A-Risen) (from Goethe's "Faust")
[Eng/Lat] 4pt mix cor,acap oct SCHIRM.G 4282 $.30 (S1145)

Christ Has Risen (from Faust) Easter/Lent
(Stone) SATB,acap,opt pno oct PRO ART 1246 $.25 (S1146)
(Stone) SSA,acap,opt pno oct PRO ART 1707 $.20 (S1147)

Christ Is Arisen *see Christ Ist Erstanden

Christ Ist Erstanden (from Faust) Easter/Lent
mix cor SOUTHERN $.30 (S1148)
[Ger/Eng] SATB BROUDE,A. 113 $.30 (S1149)
SATB,acap cor pts BREITKOPF-L rental (S1150)
"Christ Is Arisen" TTBB,acap oct FISCHER,C CM-312 $.25 (S1151)
(Pinkham, D.) "Christ Is Arisen" [Ger/Eng] SATB,acap SCHIRM.EC 2686 $.25 (S1152)

Christmas Lullaby, A *Xmas
(Goldman) TTBB,S solo oct LAWSON 51635 $.30 (S1153)

Come, Let Us Sing Unto The Lord
(Brooks) SATB oct SPRATT 559 $.25 (S1154)

Come Unto Me
SATB oct LORENZ 470 $.30 (S1155)
(Wilson, Ira) SATB ALLANS 116 s.p. (S1156)

Communion Service In G *Commun
SATB,STB soli,org,2ob,2bsn,2trp,strings, timp voc sc NOVELLO s.p., ipr (S1157)

Cradle Song, Schubert's *Xmas
(Ganschow) dbl cor SCHMITT 1139 $.18 (S1158)

Credo (from Mass In A Flat)
(Davison, A.) [Lat] TTBB,pno SCHIRM.EC 933 $.60 (S1159)

Das Gebet Des Herrn (from Deutsche Messe)
see Schubert, Franz (Peter), Gesange Zur Feier Des Heiligen Opfers Der Messe

Das Grosse Hallelujah
"Hallelujah" [Ger/Eng] SSA,pno SCHIRM.EC 1041 $.30 (S1160)
(Imig) "Glory To God" SAA oct FOX R187 $.30 (S1161)

Der Geist Gottes
see Schubert, Franz (Peter), Ehre Sei Gott In Der Hohe

Deutsche Messe *Mass
4pt mix cor,org,2ob,2clar,2bsn,2horn,2trp, 3trom,timp sc BREITKOPF-W PB-4914 s.p., cor pts BREITKOPF-W CHB-3692 s.p., voc sc BREITKOPF-W s.p. (S1162)
"German Mass In F" cor,orch sc KALMUS $3.00, ipa (S1163)
(Dressler, John) "Mass In F" [Eng/Ger] mix cor,org/pno voc sc SCHIRM.G $.75 (S1164)
(Haas) [Ger] S/SA/SATB,acap/org/orch/strings/brass voc sc SCHOTT 3883 s.p., ipa, sc SCHOTT 3883 s.p., ipa (S1165)
(McChesney, Richard) "Mass In F" [Eng] SAB, org/pno voc sc SCHIRM.G $.75 (S1166)

Deutsche Messe F-Dur *Mass
4pt mix cor,opt org (F maj) cor pts BREITKOPF-W CHB-3692 s.p., voc sc BREITKOPF-W s.p. (S1167)

SCHUBERT, FRANZ (PETER) (cont'd.)

Die Allmacht
(Zollner, H.) [Ger] mix cor,3fl,2ob,2clar,
2bsn,4horn,3trp,3trom,tuba,strings,harp,
cymbal HUG s.p., ipr (S1168)

Dieu Dans La Nature
see Quatre Choers Pour Voix De Femmes

Dieu Est Mon Guide *see Gott Ist Mein Hirt

Drei Chore *Op.112, CC3U
mix cor,pno sc BREITKOPF-L PB-1050 s.p. (S1169)

Du Bist Die Ruh'
[Ger] mix cor,acap (med) HUG s.p. (S1170)

Ehre Sei Dem Hocherhabenen
mix cor,pno/strings cor pts TONGER s.p.,
ipa (S1171)
(Erdlen, Hermann) men cor/wom cor,pno/orch/
winds voc sc TONGER s.p., ipa (S1172)

Ehre Sei Gott In Der Hohe *Xmas
men cor,acap ERDMANN 179 s.p. contains
also: Der Geist Gottes (S1173)
(Steiger, G.; Politti, E.) [Ger] wom cor,
acap (easy) HUG s.p. (S1174)

Fem Sange For Mandskor *see Sanctus (S1175)

First Mass In F *Mass
cor voc sc KALMUS 6416 $1.75 (S1176)

First Offertorium *Offer
cor,orch sc KALMUS $5.00, ipa (S1177)

Fischerlied
see Schubert, Franz (Peter), Tantum Ergo

Franz Schubert Songs For Treble Voices *CCU
treb cor SCHMITT 46 $.50 (S1178)

German Mass In F *see Deutsche Messe

Gesange Zur Feier Des Heiligen Opfers Der
Messe (from Deutsche Messe)
mix cor,org,2ob,2clar,2bsn,2trp,2horn,3trp,
timp (F maj) sc BREITKOPF-L PB-668 s.p.,
voc sc BREITKOPF-L OB-2579 s.p., voc pt
BREITKOPF-L CHB-449 s.p. contains also:
Das Gebet Des Herrn (S1179)

Gloria (from German Mass) Gloria
(Craig) SAB oct PLYMOUTH DC-205 $.25 (S1180)
(Craig) SATB oct PLYMOUTH DC-111 $.25 (S1181)
(Ehret) [Lat] SSA MARKS 4445 $.35 (S1182)
(Ehret) [Lat] SATB MARKS 4190 $.25 (S1183)

Glory Be To God
(Rodby) SATB MARKS 4102 $.40 (S1184)
(Rodby) SSA MARKS 4101 $.25 (S1185)

Glory To God *see Das Grosse Hallelujah

Glory To God In The Highest
(Trusler) SAB WARNER W3720 $.30 (S1186)

God For Man Is Born *Xmas
(Ehret) SATB oct WORD CS-659 $.25 (S1187)

God In Nature *Op.133
SSAA,pno/org PETERS 6878 $.40 (S1188)

God In The Storm Cloud *see Gott Im
Ungewitter

God Is My Guide *Bibl
(Cornell) 4pt mix cor oct SCHIRM.G 3103
$.25 (S1189)

God Of Wisdom
(Rodby) SATB MARKS 4161 $.25 (S1190)

Gott Im Ungewitter
(Imig) "God In The Storm Cloud" SATB oct
FOX PS143 $.35 (S1191)

Gott Ist Mein Hirt (Psalm 23) Op.132, mot
see Quatre Choers Pour Voix De Femmes
wom cor,pno sc BREITKOPF-L PB-1657 s.p.,
voc pt BREITKOPF-L CHB-602 s.p. (S1192)
"Dieu Est Mon Guide" [Fr] 4pt wom cor oct
DURAND s.p. (S1193)
"Gud Er Min Hyrde" [Ger/Dan] SSAA,pno
HANSEN-DEN 28238 s.p. (S1194)
(Trusler) SSA MARKS 4186 $.35 (S1195)

Gott Ist Mein Hirte (Psalm 23)
(Vogel, Moritz; Nagler, Franciscus) [Ger]
wom cor&jr cor,org,vln,vcl HUG 59 s.p. (S1196)

Gott Meine Zuversicht (Psalm 23)
men cor,pno ALSBACH&D sc s.p., cor pts s.p. (S1197)
4pt wom cor,pno ALSBACH&D sc s.p., cor pts
s.p. (S1198)

Great Is Jehovah *anthem
TTBB oct NOVELLO 28.0223.06 s.p. (S1199)
SATB oct GRAY GCMR 1617 $.30 (S1200)
(Messiter) mix cor,ST soli oct SCHIRM.G
3503 $.30 (S1201)

Great Is Jehovah, The Lord
SATB oct PRESSER G-4014 $.40 (S1202)

Gud Ar Min Hyrde *see Gott Ist Iein Hirt

Hallelujah *see Das Grosse Hallelujah

Heavenly Father
(Thompson) SATB oct BOURNE D1 $.25 (S1203)

Heilig, Heilig (from Deutschen Messe)
(Neumann, J.P.) [Ger] mix cor,acap (easy)
HUG s.p. (S1204)

Heilig, Heilig, Heilig *Sanctus
"Holy, Holy, Holy" boy cor SOUTHERN $.25 (S1205)
(Ehret) "Holy, Holy, Holy" boy cor SOUTHERN
$.25 (S1206)
(Ehret) "Holy, Holy, Holy" TTBB,acap MARKS
4126 $.25 (S1207)
(Ehret) "Holy, Holy, Holy" SSA,acap MARKS
4124 $.30 (S1208)
(Ehret) "Holy, Holy, Holy" SA MARKS 4127
$.30 (S1209)
(Ehret) "Holy, Holy, Holy" SAB,acap MARKS
4125 $.30 (S1210)
(Ehret) "Holy, Holy, Holy" SATB,acap MARKS
4061 $.25 (S1211)
(Mattfeld, V.) "Holy, Holy, Holy" SATB,org
SCHIRM.EC 2427 $.25 (S1212)
(Morgan) "Holy, Holy, Holy" TTBB,acap
WARNER R3440 $.30 (S1213)
(Richardson) "Holy, Holy, Holy" SSA oct
SPRATT 646 $.35 (S1214)
(Talmadge, A.) "Holy, Holy, Holy," SSAA,
acap SCHIRM.EC 1977 $.25 (S1215)

Heilig Ist Der Herr (from Deutsche Messe)
see Schubert, Franz (Peter), Wohin Soll Ich
Mich Wenden

Helig, Helig, Helig (from Sanctus)
mix cor NORDISKA 2301 s.p. (S1216)
"Zum Sanctus" men cor NORDISKA 2300 s.p. (S1217)
"Zum Sanctus" mix cor sc ALSBACH&D s.p. (S1218)
"Zum Sanctus" men cor sc ALSBACH&D s.p. (S1219)

Herr, Du Hast Das Flehen Vernommen (from
Deutschen Messe)
[Ger] mix cor,acap (easy) HUG s.p. (S1220)

Herr Unser Gott *Op.154, hymn
(Schmidl, A.) men cor,TTBB soli,2ob,2clar,
2bsn,2trp,2horn,3trom BREITKOPF-L rental (S1221)

Holy Father
(Brandvik) SATB SHAWNEE A 1203 $.35 (S1222)

Holy, Holy, Holy *see Heilig, Heilig, Heilig

Holy, Holy, Holy *see Sanctus

Holy Is The Lord *see Sanctus

Hymne
men cor,acap ERDMANN 163 s.p. contains
also: Weihegesang (S1223)

Hymne A La Vierge *BVM,hymn
unis/2pt CHOUDENS s.p. (S1224)

Hymne An Den Unendlichen *No.3, hymn/Mass
mix cor,org voc pt BREITKOPF-L CHB-629 s.p. (S1225)
"Mass In B Flat Major" cor,orch sc KALMUS
$14.00, ipa (S1226)

In Monte Oliveti
SATB,acap RICORDI-ENG SY115 s.p. (S1227)

Intende Voci Orationis *Offer
mix cor,T solo,ob,2clar,2bsn,3trp,2horn,
strings sc BREITKOPF-L PB-980 s.p., ipa (S1228)

Intende Voci Orationis Meae
"Offertory" see Schubert, Franz (Peter),
Tantum Ergo
(Hermann, William) "Offertory" [Lat] 4pt
mix cor,T solo,org/pno voc sc SCHIRM.G
$1.25 (S1229)

Jesus Our Savior
(Habash) SATB oct BELWIN 60839 $.30 (S1230)

Jubilate Deo
(Buck) [Eng] 4pt mix cor,ST soli oct
SCHIRM.G 3045 $.30 (S1231)

King Of Glory Standeth, The
SATB oct WALTON 2015 $.25 (S1232)

Kyrie (from Mass In G) Kyrie
SATB,acap cor pts BREITKOPF-L PB-1574 s.p. (S1233)
(Ehret) [Lat] SAB MARKS 4520 $.30 (S1234)
(Ehret) [Lat] SATB MARKS 4189 $.25 (S1235)
(Ehret) [Lat] SSA MARKS 4329 $.25 (S1236)
(Herrmann) 4pt wom cor oct SCHIRM.G 11151
$.30 (S1237)

La Pastorella
boy cor SOUTHERN $.25 (S1238)

La Vie
see Quatre Choers Pour Voix De Femmes

Lamentation Sur La Mort D'un Jeune Heros
see Quatre Choers Pour Voix De Femmes

Lazarus *Bibl
mix cor,soli,2fl,2ob,2clar,2bsn,2horn,
3trom,strings BREITKOPF-L rental (S1239)
mix cor min sc KALMUS 1063 $1.30 (S1240)

Liebe Rauscht Der Silberbach
men cor,acap ERDMANN 130 s.p. contains
also: Sanctus (Sanctus) (S1241)

Litanei "Ruh'n In Frieden Alle Seelen"
mix cor sc ALSBACH&D s.p. (S1242)

Litany *Rembrnc
(Harris, William H.) SATB (easy) oct OXFORD
42.898 $.20 (S1243)

Litany For All Soul's Day
unis oct NOVELLO 48.2074.06 s.p. (S1244)

Lord Is My Shepherd
girl cor SOUTHERN $.25 (S1245)

Lord Is My Shepherd, The (Psalm 23) Gen/Lent/
Marriage,anthem/Bibl/prayer/Psalm
2pt,orch oct NOVELLO 53.0244.07 s.p., ipr (S1246)
SSAA oct GRAY GCMR 3207 $.25 (S1247)
4pt wom cor oct SCHIRM.G 5302 $.35 (S1248)
2pt ENOCH TP162 s.p. (S1249)
men cor CURWEN 50346 s.p. (S1250)
SATB,pno (med) oct WILLIS 614 $.10 (S1251)
SSAA,orch oct NOVELLO 28.0067.05 s.p., ipr (S1252)
(Deis) 4pt mix cor,org/pno oct SCHIRM.G
10130 $.40 (S1253)
(Higgs, Percy) SSAA (med easy) oct OXFORD
44.044 $.40 (S1254)
(Higgs, Percy) 2pt (med easy) oct OXFORD
44.032 $.50 (S1255)
(Stainer) SATB oct GRAY GCMR 1622 $.25 (S1256)
(Stainer, J.) SATB ALLANS 343 s.p. (S1257)
(Stainer, J.) SATB oct PRESSER 332-14660
$.35 (S1258)
(Stainer, John) mix cor oct NOVELLO
28.0594.04 s.p. (S1259)
(Tudor, Frank) SA ALLANS 342 s.p. (S1260)
(Whittaker) SSAA (med easy) OXFORD 44.044
$.40, ipr (S1261)

Lord, My Savior, My Salvation
(Klein, M.) SATB KJOS 5479 $.30 (S1262)

Magnificat *Magnif
mix cor min sc KALMUS 1050 $1.30 contains
also: [Two] Stabat Mater (S1263)
cor,orch sc KALMUS $6.00, ipa (S1264)

Mass In A Flat *Mass
[Lat] SATB,SATB soli,fl,2ob,2clar,2bsn,
2horn,2trp,3trom,strings,timp voc sc
NOVELLO s.p., ipr (S1265)

Mass In A Flat Major *Mass
cor min sc KALMUS 454 $4.00 (S1266)
cor voc sc KALMUS 6420 $2.50 (S1267)
cor,orch sc KALMUS $18.00, ipa (S1268)

Mass In B Flat Major *see Messe B-Dur

Mass In B Flat Major *see Hymne An Den
Unendlichen

Mass In B-Flat *see Messe B-Dur

Mass In C *see Messe C-Dur

Mass In C Major *see Messe C-Dur

Mass In E Flat *Mass
cor voc sc KALMUS 6521 $2.50 (S1269)

Mass In E Flat Major *No.6, Mass
cor,orch sc KALMUS $15.00, ipa (S1270)
cor min sc KALMUS 455 $4.00 (S1271)

Mass In F *see Deutsche Messe

Mass In F Major *Mass
cor min sc KALMUS 450 $3.00 (S1272)

Mass In G *Mass
[Lat] cor BELWIN $1.25 (S1273)
[Eng] cor BELWIN $1.25 (S1274)
cor KALMUS $.80 (S1275)
cor,opt orch voc sc KALMUS 6418 $1.50, ipa (S1276)
[Lat] SATB,orch MARKS $1.25, ipr (S1277)
[Lat] SATB,STB soli,org,2ob,2bsn,2trp,
strings,timp voc sc NOVELLO s.p., ipr (S1278)
cor,orch/org sc KALMUS $4.50, ipa (S1279)
cor sc KALMUS $4.50 (S1280)
(Parker, A.; Shaw, R.) [Lat] mix cor,STB
soli,org,strings voc sc SCHIRM.G $1.40 (S1281)
(Rush) [Lat] SA FISCHER,C PT-2735 $.60 (S1282)

Mass In G Major *see Messe G-Dur

Mass No. 5 *see Messe B-Dur

May Peace Abide With You
(Mueller) SAB oct FISCHER,C CM-7667 $.25 (S1283)

Mein Heiland, Herr Und Meister (from Deutsche
Messe) Agnus
(Malin) "My Gracious Lord And Master" [Eng/
Ger] SATB MARKS 4449 $.30 (S1284)
(Malin) "My Gracious Lord And Master" [Eng/
Ger] TTBB MARKS 4450 $.40 (S1285)
(Malin) "My Gracious Lord And Master" [Eng/
Ger] SSA MARKS 4447 $.35 (S1286)
(Malin) "My Gracious Lord And Master" [Eng/
Ger] SA MARKS 4452 $.30 (S1287)
(Malin) "My Gracious Lord And Master" [Eng/
Ger] SAB MARKS 4448 $.30 (S1288)
(Malin) "My Gracious Lord And Master" boy
cor SOUTHERN $.30 (S1289)

Messe As-Dur *Mass
SATB&SATB,SATB soli,org,fl,2ob,2clar,2bsn,
2horn,2trp,3trom,strings,timp (A flat
maj) sc BREITKOPF-W PB-4498 s.p., ipr (S1290)
(Spengel, J.) mix cor,SATB soli,org,fl,2ob,
2clar,2bsn,2trp,2horn,3trom,strings,timp
(A flat maj) cor pts BREITKOPF-L
CHB-362A-D s.p., voc sc BREITKOPF-L
EB-1629 s.p., ipr (S1291)

Messe B-Dur *Op.141, Mass
mix cor,SATB soli,org,2ob,2bsn,2trp,
strings,timp (B flat maj) sc BREITKOPF-L
PB-664 s.p., voc pt BREITKOPF-L
CHB-2817A+B s.p. (S1292)
"Mass In B Flat Major" cor voc sc KALMUS
6419 $1.50 (S1293)
"Mass In B Flat Major" cor min sc KALMUS
452 $2.00 (S1294)
"Mass In B-Flat" cor,orch sc KALMUS $12.00,
ipa (S1295)
"Mass No. 5" [Lat] SATB,SATTB soli,orch voc
sc PETERS 1052 $3.50, min sc PETERS E970
$9.00, min sc-cloth PETERS E970 $12.50 (S1296)

Messe C-Dur *Op.48, Mass
mix cor,SATB soli,org,2ob/2clar,2trp,
strings,timp (C maj) BREITKOPF-L rental (S1297)
4pt mix cor,SATB soli,org,strings,opt 2ob&
2clar&2trp&timp (C maj) sc BREITKOPF-W
PB-4866 s.p., cor pts BREITKOPF-W
CHB-3580 s.p., voc sc BREITKOPF-W EB-6668
s.p. (S1298)
"Mass In C" mix cor,org,2vln,bvl,opt 2ob&
2horn&2trp&timp WEINBERGER s.p., ipa voc
sc, cor pts (S1299)
"Mass In C Major" cor voc sc KALMUS 6422
$1.50 (S1300)
"Mass In C Major" cor min sc KALMUS 453
$2.50 contains also: Pater Noster (S1301)
"Mass In C Major" cor,orch sc KALMUS
$12.00, ipa (S1302)

SCHUBERT, FRANZ (PETER) (cont'd.)

(Ramsey, William) "Mass In C Major" [Lat] 4pt mix cor,pno voc sc SCHIRM.G $1.25 (S1303)

Messe Es-Dur *Mass
mix cor,SATB soli,2ob,2clar,2bsn,2trp, 2horn,3trom,strings,timp (E flat maj) sc BREITKOPF-L PB-667 s.p., voc pt BREITKOPF-L CHB-360A-E s.p., voc sc BREITKOPF-L EB-1626 s.p., ipa (S1304)

Messe F-Dur *Mass
mix cor,SATB soli,org,2ob,2clar,2bsn,2trp, 2horn,3trom,strings,timp (F maj) sc BREITKOPF-L PB-662 s.p., ipr (S1305)

Messe G-Dur *Mass
"Mass In G Major" mix cor,org,strings,opt 2timp WEINBERGER s.p., ipa voc sc, cor pts (S1306)
"Mass In G Major" cor min sc KALMUS 451 $2.00 (S1307)
"Mass In G Major" [Lat] SATB,orch voc sc BROUDE BR. $1.25, ipr (S1308)
(Spiro, F.) mix cor,STB soli,org,2ob,2bsn, 2trp,strings,timp (G maj) sc BREITKOPF-L PB-663 s.p., voc pt BREITKOPF-L CHB-718A-C s.p., voc sc BREITKOPF-L EB-1997 s.p., ipa (S1309)

Miriams Siegesgesang *Op.136, Bibl/cant
"Miriam's Song Of Triumph" cor voc sc KALMUS 6423 $1.25 (S1310)
"Miriam's Song Of Triumph" cor,S solo,pno voc sc SCHIRM.G $1.25 (S1311)
"Miriam's Song Of Triumph" cor,orch sc KALMUS $7.00, ipa (S1312)
"Mirjam's Siegesgesang" mix cor ALSBACH&D sc s.p., cor pts s.p. (S1313)
"Song Of Miriam, The" SATB,S solo,2fl,2ob, 2clar,2bsn,2horn,2trp,3trom,strings,timp voc sc NOVELLO s.p., ipr (S1314)
(Clough-Leighter, H.) "Strike The Cymbal, Bow The String" SATB,S solo,org SCHIRM.EC 2627 $.35 (S1315)

Miriam's Song Of Triumph *see Miriams Siegesgesang

Mirjam's Siegesgesang *see Miriams Siegesgesang

Music For Men's Chorus *sac/sec,CCU
men cor min sc KALMUS 1060 $1.30 op.136ab; op.154; op.167; op. 11, no.1-3; op.16, no.1-2 (S1316)

Music For Men's Chorus *sac/sec,CCU
men cor min sc KALMUS 1061 $1.30 op.28; op.52, no.3; op.51, no.3; op.105, no1; op.134-135; op.17, no.1-4; op.64, no.1-3; op.102; op.151; op.153; op.156 (S1317)

Music For Women's Chorus *sac/sec,CCU
wom cor min sc KALMUS $1.30 contains opus': 52-4, 132, 133, 135, etc. (S1318)

My Gracious Lord And Master *see Mein Heiland, Herr Und Meister

O Be Joyful
(Rodby) SATB oct AGAPE A 418 $.35 (S1319)
(Rodby) TTBB oct AGAPE MM 9002 $.30 (S1320)

O Hear Me When I Call On Thee *see Sei Mutter Der Barmherzigkeit

O Lord Eternal *see Salve Regina

O Lord God Of My Salvation *Bibl
4pt mix cor,org/pno oct SCHIRM.G 11707 $.25 (S1321)

O Rose Of Sharon *see Ave Maria

Offertorium *Mass
cor voc sc KALMUS 6417 $1.25 (S1322)

Offertory *see Intende Voci Orationis Meae

Omnipotence
(Mansfield, P.) SSA ALLANS 435 s.p. (S1323)

Omnipotence, The
(Deis) 4pt mix cor oct SCHIRM.G 10146 $.35 (S1324)
(Felton, W.) SATB oct PRESSER 312-20859 $.45 (S1325)
(Harris, V.) 3pt wom cor oct SCHIRM.G 7813 $.35 (S1326)
(Lambert) sr cor&jr cor BOSTON 10196 $.40 (S1327)
(Lizst) 4pt men cor,T solo oct SCHIRM.G 1228 $.40 (S1328)
(Sacco) 3pt mix cor,SA soli oct SCHIRM.G 10633 $.30 (S1329)
(Spicker) mix cor,S solo oct SCHIRM.G 4346 $.35 (S1330)

Pater Noster
see Schubert, Franz (Peter), Mass In C Major

Pax Vobiscum
"Peace" unis,pno SCHIRM.EC 1078 $.25 (S1331)

Peace *see Pax Vobiscum

Prayer Of Peace (from Stabat Mater)
4pt mix cor,acap oct SCHIRM.G 11617 $.30 (S1332)

Psalm 23 *see Gott Ist Mein Hirt

Psalm 92
(Meyerowitz, J.) [Heb/Eng] SATB,Bar solo BROUDE,A. 110 $.40 (S1333)

Quatre Choers Pour Voix De Femmes
CHOUDENS s.p.
contains: Dieu Dans La Nature (4pt wom cor,pno); La Vie (3pt wom cor,pno); Lamentation Sur La Mort D'un Jeune Heros (3pt wom cor,pno); Psalm 23 (4pt wom cor,pno) (S1334)

Salve Regina *Op.149
men cor,acap voc pt BREITKOPF-L rental (S1335)
(Pinkham, D.) "O Lord Eternal" [Lat/Eng]

SCHUBERT, FRANZ (PETER) (cont'd.)

SATB,opt strings SCHIRM.EC 2685 $.30, ipr (S1336)

Sanctus (from German Mass) Sanctus
see Schubert, Franz (Peter), Liebe Rauscht Der Silberbach
[Lat] mix cor MUSIKK 6 s.p. (S1337)
"Holy Is The Lord" SATB oct LORENZ C54 $.25 (S1338)
"Holy Is The Lord" SAB oct LORENZ 7375 $.25 (S1339)
(Brown, F.) [Eng/Ger] SATB ALLANS 430 s.p. (S1340)
(Craig) TTBB oct PLYMOUTH DC-302 $.25 (S1341)
(Craig) SATB oct PLYMOUTH DC-109 $.25 (S1342)
(Dash) "Holy Is The Lord" SATB oct SUMMY J 1 $.20 (S1343)
(Davis; Craig) TTBB oct PLYMOUTH DC-302 $.25 (S1344)
(Davis; Craig) SAB oct PLYMOUTH DC-400 $.25 (S1345)
(Davis; Craig) "Holy Is The Lord" SSA oct PLYMOUTH DC-201 $.25 (S1346)
(Ehret) "Holy, Holy, Holy" SSA oct PRO ART 2511 $.30 (S1347)
(Guenther, F.) "Holy Is The Lord" SATB oct PRESSER 312-21416 $.30 (S1348)
(Luvaas) SATB KJOS 2041 $.30 (S1349)
(Moller; Holst) "Holy, Holy, Holy" SAB,acap WARNER G1671 $.30 (S1350)
(Rachlew, Anders) [Ger/Dan] TTBB,acap HANSEN-DEN 24899 s.p. see from Fem Sange For Mandskor (S1351)
(Tolmage) SSA oct STAFF 446 $.25 (S1352)
(Tolmage) SATB oct STAFF 370 $.25 (S1353)
(Tolmage) SA/TB oct STAFF 476 $.25 (S1354)
(Tolmage) SAB oct STAFF 508 $.25 (S1355)

Sanctus And Hosanna (from Mass No. 2)
(Carlton) SATB oct BOOSEY 5130 $.30 (S1356)
(Carlton) SSA oct BOOSEY 5290 $.30 (S1357)

Sanft Und Still Schlaft Unser Freund (from Lazarus)
mix cor,2clar,2bsn,2horn,3trom,strings sc BREITKOPF-L rental (S1358)

Second Offertorium *Offer
cor,orch sc KALMUS $5.00, ipa (S1359)

Sei Mutter Der Barmherzigkeit
(Pinkham, D.) "O Hear Me When I Call On Thee" [Ger/Eng] SATB,org SCHIRM.EC 2684 $.30 (S1360)

Shepherd's Chorus (from Rosamunde)
(Berger) SATB oct FOX PS125 $.35 (S1361)

Song Of Miriam, The *see Miriams Siegesgesang

Song Of Praise
(Rossi) SATB,S solo oct MCA (S1362)

Songs, Cantatas, And Canons *CC38U
cor min sc KALMUS 1067 $1.30 (S1363)

Sound The Trumpet
(Harris) SSA oct PLYMOUTH SC-203 $.30 (S1364)
(Harris) SAB oct PLYMOUTH SC-405 $.30 (S1365)

Sound The Trumpet, Strike The Cymbal *Bibl
(Whitford) 4pt mix cor,org oct SCHIRM.G 11329 $.30 (S1366)

Stabat Mater
cor voc sc KALMUS 6424 $2.00 (S1367)
cor,orch sc KALMUS $4.00, ipa (S1368)
(Gohler, G.; Klopstock, F.G.) [Eng/Ger] mix cor,STB soli,2fl,2ob,3bsn,2horn,3trom, strings (F maj) voc pt BREITKOPF-L CHB-684A+B s.p., voc sc BREITKOPF-L EB-3342 s.p., ipr (S1369)
(Kjelson) "There The Mother Stands" SATB oct BELWIN 2164 $.25 (S1370)

Strike The Cymbal, Bow The String *see Miriams Siegesgesang

Tantum Ergo *Op.45
[Lat] SATB,SATB soli,orch voc sc PETERS 2510 $1.50, sc PETERS 2512 $4.00, ipa (S1371)
mix cor,org,2ob,2clar,2trp,strings,timp (C maj) sc BREITKOPF-L PB-622 s.p. (S1372)
mix cor,S solo,org,2ob,2trp,strings,timp (C maj) sc BREITKOPF-L PB-623 s.p. (S1373)
cor min sc KALMUS 1097 $1.30 contains also: Offertory; Fischerlied (S1374)

Tantum Ergo In E Flat *Bibl
(Herrmann) [Lat] 4pt mix cor,opt 4 soli,opt org/pno oct SCHIRM.G 11821 $.35 (S1375)

There The Mother Stands *see Stabat Mater

They Sang That Night In Bethlehem *Xmas
(Deis) [Eng] 4pt mix cor oct SCHIRM.G 8290 $.25 (S1376)
(Deis) [Eng] 3pt wom cor oct SCHIRM.G 8291 $.25 (S1377)

[Three] Offertories
mix cor min sc KALMUS 1049 $1.30 contains also: [Two] Salve Reginas; [Three] Tantum Ergo (S1378)

[Three] Tantum Ergo
see Schubert, Franz (Peter), [Three] Offertories

To God On High
(Imig) [Ger/Eng] SATB oct MCA (S1379)

Turn Your Thoughts To Those Who're Gone (from Lazarus) cant
SATB,pno/orch BROUDE BR. $.40, ipr (S1380)

[Two] Salve Reginas
see Schubert, Franz (Peter), [Three] Offertories

[Two] Stabat Mater
see Schubert, Franz (Peter), Magnificat

SCHUBERT, FRANZ (PETER) (cont'd.)

Upon The Mount Of Olives
(Granville, Heiberg) SATB oct FOX R153 $.30 (S1381)

Various Mixed And Mens' Choruses *CCU
men cor/mix cor min sc KALMUS 1051 $1.30 (S1382)

Weihegesang
see Schubert, Franz (Peter), Hymne

When The Lord Entered
see MUSIC FOR PALM SUNDAY

Where Thou Reignest *Asc/Easter
SATB oct GRAY GCMR 3092 $.25 (S1383)

Wohin Soll Ich Mich Wenden (from Deutsche Messe)
4pt mix cor,acap cor pts BREITKOPF-W CHB-4818 s.p. contains also: Heilig Ist Der Herr (S1384)
(Neumann, J.P.) [Ger] mix cor,acap (easy) HUG s.p. (S1385)
(Neumann, J.Ph.) [Ger] wom cor,acap (easy) HUG s.p. (S1386)

Zum Offertorium
men cor sc ALSBACH&D s.p. (S1387)

Zum Sanctus *see Helig, Helig, Helig

SCHUBERT, GUNTER
Allein Gott In Der Hoh Sei Ehr
see Schubert, Gunter, Strassburger Kyrie Und Gloria

Strassburger Kyrie Und Gloria *Gloria/Kyrie
mix cor HANSSLER 6.290 s.p. contains also: Allein Gott In Der Hoh Sei Ehr (S1388)

SCHUBERT, HEINO (1928-)
Ave Maria, Gratia Plena *Adv,cant
[Lat] SATB&cong,org,opt inst (med easy) MULLER SM 652 s.p. (S1389)

Dominus Fortitudo Plebii *Pent
[Lat] SATB,brass,opt org (med) MULLER SM 735 s.p. (S1390)

Gelobet Seist Du, Jesu Christ *Xmas,cant
[Ger] SATB&cong,org,opt inst (med) MULLER SM 655 s.p. (S1391)

Grosser Gott, Wir Loben Dich *Gen,cant
[Ger] SATB,org/brass (med easy) sc MULLER SM 2180 s.p., cor pts s.p. (S1392)

Jubilate Deo *Easter/Pent
[Lat] SATB,acap (med) MULLER SM 726 s.p. (S1393)

Keiner Weiss, Wie Arm Er Ist *Req
men cor,acap TONGER s.p. (S1394)

Konigin Im Himmelreich *Fest,cant
[Ger] SATB&cong,org (med easy) MULLER SM 666 sc s.p., cor pts s.p. (S1395)

Missa Brevis *Mass
mix cor,acap (E maj) VOLK 108 sc s.p., cor pts s.p. (S1396)
mix cor (E maj) cor pts VOLK 108 s.p. (S1397)

SCHUETKY, FRANZ JOSEPH
Emitte Spiritum Tuum *Gen/Pent/Whitsun
SATB oct FISCHER,J 3368 $.30 (S1398)
"May Now Thy Spirit" [Eng/Lat] 3pt wom cor, acap (diff) oct WILLIS 6241 $.12 (S1399)
"May Now Thy Spirit" SATB ALLANS 187 s.p. (S1400)
"Send Forth Thy Spirit" [Eng/Lat] SATB,acap WARNER G1705 $.30 (S1401)
"Send Forth Thy Spirit" [Eng/Lat] 4pt mix cor,acap oct SCHIRM.G 10870 $.30 (S1402)
"Send Forth Thy Spirit" [Eng/Lat] 3pt mix cor,acap oct SCHIRM.G 11505 $.30 (S1403)
"Send Forth Thy Spirit" SSAATTBB,acap oct PRESSER MC335 $.30 (S1404)
"Send Forth Thy Spirit" SSATTBB oct SUMMY B 150 $.45 (S1405)
"Send Out Thy Spirit" [Eng/Lat] SSATTB oct BELWIN 64050 $.30 (S1406)
(Davids, Dean) TTBB oct BELWIN 1621 $.25 (S1407)
(High) "May Now Thy Spirit" 3pt wom cor, acap (med) oct WILLIS 7071 $.20 (S1408)
(Holler) "Send Out Thy Spirit" [Eng/Lat] SATB oct GRAY GCMR 1483 $.30 (S1409)
(Hornish) "Send Forth Thy Spirit" SAB oct PRO ART 1017 $.25 (S1410)
(Mahlenbrock) "May Now Thy Spirit" [Eng/Lat] SA&jr cor,pno/org (med) oct WILLIS 6102 $.10 (S1411)
(Martin) "Send Forth Thy Spirit" SAB oct SPRATT 636 $.30 (S1412)
(Martin) "Send Forth Thy Spirit" SSA oct SPRATT 554 $.25 (S1413)
(McKinney) "Send Forth Thy Spirit" TTBB oct FISCHER,J 8171 $.30 (S1414)
(Swift) "Send Forth Thy Spirit" SATB oct PRO ART 1076 $.30 (S1415)
(Swift) "Send Forth Thy Spirit" SSA oct PRO ART 1075 $.30 (S1416)
(Treharne) "May Now Thy Spirit" [Eng/Lat] TTBB,acap (diff) oct WILLIS 5641 $.10 (S1417)
(Treharne) "May Now Thy Spirit" [Eng/Lat] SATB,opt pno (med) oct WILLIS 5874 $.10 (S1418)
(Warner) "Send Forth Thy Spirit" SATB oct PLYMOUTH SC-21 $.25 (S1419)

May Now Thy Spirit *see Emitte Spiritum Tuum

Send Forth Thy Spirit *see Emitte Spiritum Tuum

Send Out Thy Spirit *see Emitte Spiritum Tuum

Send Out Thy Sprirt *see Emitte Spiritum Tuum

SCHUETKY, JOSEPH
Baroque To The Great Classics, The Vol. 2a- 1550 To 1700 *CCU,Bibl/ora
mix cor min sc KALMUS 882 $3.00 (S1420)

SCHUETKY, JOSEPH (cont'd.)

Die Sieben Worte Jesu Am Kreuz *Gd.Fri./
Holywk
"Seven Last Words Of Christ, The" cor,orch
sc KALMUS $4.00, ipa　　　　　　(S1421)

Seven Last Words Of Christ, The *see Die
Sieben Worte Jesu Am Kreuz

SCHUETZ, H.
see SCHUTZ, HEINRICH

SCHUFF
Preserve Me, O God *Gen
SATB SCHMITT 1764 $.20　　　　　　(S1422)

SCHULER
Make Me A Blessing
(Boersma) SATB oct WORD CS-1988 $.30
(S1423)

Oh, What A Day
(Boersma) SATB oct WORD CS-2324 $.35
(S1424)

SCHULTHES
O God Most Holy
(Durick) SATB oct SUMMY M 2893 $.30 (S1425)

SCHULTZ, RALPH
Star Proclaims The King Is Here, The *Xmas/
Epiph
SATB,kbd (med easy) oct CONCORDIA 98-1959
$.30　　　　　　　　　　　　　　(S1426)

SCHULZ
Bright Angel Hosts Are Heard On High *Xmas
(Andersen) SSATBB SCHMITT 1720 $.25 (S1427)

Her Kommer Dine Arme Smaa *anthem
(Wetzler) "Thy Little Ones, Dear Lord, Are
We" unis treb cor,opt org,opt inst oct
AUGSBURG 0920 $.25　　　　　　　(S1428)

Thy Little Ones, Dear Lord, Are We *see Her
Kommer Dine Arme Smaa

SCHULZ, JOH. ABRAHAM PETER (1747-1800)
Christi Dod *see Death Of Christ, The

Death Of Christ, The *ora
(Barnekow, Chr.) "Christi Dod" [Dan] cor,
orch voc sc FOG I, 13 s.p.　　　　(S1429)

Der Mond Ist Aufgegangen
(Pfanner, A.) fr cor&men cor (easy) oct
LEUCKART 19 s.p.　　　　　　　　(S1430)

Drei Lieder Im Volkston
(Lehmann, Siegfried) [Ger] mix cor,fl,vln,
vla,vcl SIRIUS voc sc s.p., cor pts s.p.,
ipa
contains: Herr, Es Gescheh Dein Wille;
Seligste Der Lebensstunden; Singt,
Singt　　　　　　　　　　　　(S1431)

Herr, Es Gescheh Dein Wille
see Drei Lieder Im Volkston
(Lehmann, Siegfried) [Ger] mix cor (easy)
oct SIRIUS 5 s.p.　　　　　　　　(S1432)

Ihr Kinderlein, Kommet *Xmas,carol
"O Come, Little Children" SA/unis (easy)
oct WILLIS 5409 $.12　　　　　　(S1433)
(Van Koert, Han) "O Come Little Children" 2
eq voices,org oct WORLD AC-652-2 $.30
(S1434)
(Wasner) "O, Come, Little Children" [Eng/
Ger] SAT,2S rec oct SCHIRM.G 10612 $.25
(S1435)

O, Come, Little Children *see Ihr
Kinderlein, Kommet

O Come To The Manger *Xmas
unis ASHDOWN E.A.353 s.p.　　　　(S1436)
(Davies, L.H.) 2pt &SHDOWN E.A.353 s.p.
(S1437)

Seligste Der Lebensstunden
see Drei Lieder Im Volkston

Serenade (To Be Sung In The Woods)
(Stone) SSA/SA,pno/inst WORD CRS-23 $.40
(S1438)

Singt, Singt
see Drei Lieder Im Volkston

SCHULZ, PETER
Wir Pflugen Und Wir Streuen
(Berger, H.L.) TTBB HANSSLER 6.5070 s.p.
(S1439)

SCHULZ, RAIMUND
Dies Ist Der Tag, Den Der Herr Macht
see Kretzschmar, Gunther, Pfingstruf

SCHUMAN
Last Invocation, The (from Carols Of Death)
SATB,acap oct PRESSER 342-40011 $.30
(S1440)

Lord Has A Child, The
SATB oct PRESSER 342-40009 $.30 (S1441)

SCHUMANN
All Glory Be To God On High
(Harris) SATB oct PRO ART 1543 $.20 (S1442)

From Heaven Above *anthem
(Christiansen) SSAATTBB (diff) oct AUGSBURG
0101 $.35　　　　　　　　　　　(S1443)

How Fair The Church Of Christ Shall Stand
*anthem
(Christiansen, F.M.) SSAATBB (med diff) oct
AUGSBURG 0081 $.30　　　　　　　(S1444)

O Salutaris
[Lat] unis HEUGEL s.p. see from SAINTE-
CECILE　　　　　　　　　　　　(S1445)

O Saving Victim *Gen
(Hines) 2pt mix cor SCHMITT 922 $.30 (S1446)

Yea, Though I Wander *anthem
(Christiansen) SSAATTBB (diff) oct AUGSBURG
1063 $.30　　　　　　　　　　　(S1447)

SCHUMANN, GEORG (1886-1952)
How Great Are Thy Wonders *anthem
(Christiansen, P.) SATB (med diff) oct
AUGSBURG 1274 $.30　　　　　　　(S1448)

SCHUMANN, GEORG (cont'd.)

Jerusalem, Du Hochgebaute Stadt
see Three Choral-Motetten

Mit Fried Und Freud Ich Fahr Dahin
see Three Choral-Motetten

Sollt Ich Meinem Gott Nicht Singen
see Three Choral-Motetten

Three Choral-Motetten *Op.75, mot
LIENAU s.p.
contains: Jerusalem, Du Hochgebaute Stadt
(8pt mix cor); Mit Fried Und Freud Ich
Fahr Dahin (8pt mix cor,S solo,org,
3horn&3trom&tuba&timp); Sollt Ich
Meinem Gott Nicht Singen (8pt mix cor)
(S1449)

SCHUMANN, ROBERT (ALEXANDER) (1810-1856)
Advent Song *see Adventlied

Adventlied *Op.84, Adv
cor sc KALMUS 1124 $1.30　　　　(S1450)
cor voc sc KALMUS 1130 $1.30　　(S1451)
"Advent Song" [Ger] cor oct KALMUS 1130
$1.30 contains also: Beim Abschied Zu
Singe, Verzweifle Nicht, Op.93 (S1452)

Beim Abschied Zu Singe, Verzweifle Nicht
*Op.93
see Schumann, Robert (Alexander), Advent
Song

Csonakon
(Nadas, K.) [Hung] SATB,fl (med diff)
BUDAPEST 2034 s.p.　　　　　　　(S1453)

Dein Konig Kommt In Niedern Hullen *Op.71,
Adv
(Ruckert) SATTB,S solo,2fl,2ob,2clar,2bsn,
4horn,2trp,3trom,strings,timp BREITKOPF-W
rental　　　　　　　　　　　　(S1454)

Ecce Panis *Commun,mot
[Lat] 3S oct DURAND s.p.　　　　(S1455)

Freiheitslied
men cor sc ALSBACH&D s.p.　　　　(S1456)

I Think On Thee *see Ich Denke Dein

Ich Denke Dein
(Frank) "I Think On Thee" SATB,acap oct FOX
MM24 $.25　　　　　　　　　　　(S1457)

Im Utnak Indul
(Rajcs, I.) [Hung] SATB (easy) BUDAPEST see
also NASZDALOK VEGYESKARRA　　　(S1458)

Mass *see Messe

Messe *Op.147, Mass/Req
cor sc KALMUS 474 $1.30　　　　　(S1459)
cor voc sc KALMUS 1135 $1.30　　(S1460)
"Mass" [Ger] cor oct KALMUS 1136 $1.30
contains also: Requiem, Op.148　(S1461)

Messe C-Moll *Op.147, Mass
mix cor,STB soli,org,2fl,2ob,2clar,2bsn,
2trp,2horn,3trom,strings,timp (C min)
BREITKOPF-L rental　　　　　　　(S1462)

O God, I Thank Thee
(Lundquist) SATB,acap (med) oct WILLIS 8466
$.20　　　　　　　　　　　　　(S1463)

O Salutaris *Commun,mot
[Lat] SBar oct DURAND s.p.　　　(S1464)

Praise The Lord In Heav'n Above
(Craig) SATB oct PLYMOUTH DC-108 $.25
(S1465)

Requiem *see Requiem Des-Dur

Requiem Des-Dur *Op.148, Mass/Req
"Requiem" see Schumann, Robert (Alexander),
Mass
mix cor,SATB soli,2fl,2ob,2clar,2bsn,2trp,
2horn,3trom,strings,timp (D flat maj)
BREITKOPF-L rental　　　　　　　(S1466)
"Requiem" cor voc sc KALMUS 1136 $1.30
(S1467)
"Requiem" cor sc KALMUS 475 $2.50　(S1468)

Requiem Fuer Mignon *Op.98b, Req
cor $1.30 sc KALMUS 1126, voc sc KALMUS
1131　　　　　　　　　　　　　(S1469)

Requiem Fur Mignon *Op.98b, Req
SATTBB,SSAAB soli,2fl,2ob,2clar,2bsn,2horn,
2trp,3trom,strings,timp,opt harp voc pt
BREITKOPF-W CHB-99 s.p., ipr, sc
BREITKOPF-W rental　　　　　　　(S1470)

Tantum Ergo *Commun,mot
[Lat] SATBar oct DURAND s.p.　　(S1471)
(Kunc, P.) [Lat] mix cor,org oct DURAND
s.p.　　　　　　　　　　　　　(S1472)

SCHUMANN, WILLIAM HOWARD (1910-　　)
Deo Ac Veritati
TTB,acap oct PRESSER 342-40015 $.30 (S1473)

Lord Has A Child, The
SSA oct PRESSER 342-40008 $.30　(S1474)

Te Deum (from Coronation Scene Of
Shakespeare's "Henry VIII") Bibl
[Lat] 4pt mix cor,acap oct SCHIRM.G 9453
$.25　　　　　　　　　　　　　(S1475)

To All, To Each
SATB,acap oct PRESSER 342-40013 $.30
(S1476)

Unknown Region, The
SATB,acap oct PRESSER 342-40012 $.40 (S1477)

SCHUTZ, HEINRICH (1585-1672)
Ach Gott, Der Du Vor Dieser Zeit *SWV 157
see Goudimel, Claude, Singt Mit Froher
Stimm

Ach Herr, Du Schopfer Aller Ding *SWV 450,
Xmas,madrigal
"O Lord, Creator Of All Thing" SATTB,org,
vcl HANSSLER 20.450 sc $1.50, cor pts
$.50, ipa　　　　　　　　　　　(S1478)
(Bittinger, Werner) [Ger] SATTB,cont (med)

SCHUTZ, HEINRICH (cont'd.)

sc BAREN. BA 1723 $1.25, ipa　　(S1479)

Ach Herr, Du Sohn David
6pt mix cor,opt cont cor pts BREITKOPF-W
PB-3127 s.p.　　　　　　　　　　(S1480)

Ach Herr, Strafe Mich Nicht (Psalm 6) SWV 24,
Gen,mot
(Ehmann, Wilhelm) [Ger] SATB&SATB,org,cont/
vcl (med) BAREN. BA 1718 sc $4.00, cor
pts $1.30, ipa see also Die Psalmen
Davids　　　　　　　　　　　　(S1481)
(Kruger) dbl cor,cont HANSSLER 1.070 s.p.
(S1482)

Ach Herr, Verwirf Mich Nicht *see Et Ne
Despicias

Ach Herr, Wie Lang Willt Du Denn Noch (Psalm
13) SWV 109, Trin
[Ger] SATB,acap (med easy) BAREN. BA 843
$.25 see from Beckerscher Psalter (S1483)

Ad Dominum, Cum Tribularer
"Ich Rief Zum Herrn" see Cantiones Sacrae
1625 Band 1 [Nr. 19-20]

Adventshymn *Adv,hymn
mix cor NORDISKA 1267 s.p.　　　(S1484)

Aera Vere Faderen
mix cor MUSIKK 222 s.p.　　　　　(S1485)

All Ehr Und Lob Soll Gottes Sein *SWV 421
SATB,opt cont HANSSLER 20.421 sc s.p., cor
pts s.p., ipa see also Zwolf Geistliche
Gesange　　　　　　　　　　　　(S1486)
(Kessler, Franz) 4pt mix cor,opt org cor
pts BREITKOPF-W PB-3774B see also Zwolf
Geistliche Gesange-1657　　　　(S1487)

All Thanks Be To God *see Danksagen Wir Alle
Gott Christo, Der Uns Mit Seinem Wort

Allas Ogon Vanta Pa Dig, Herre
mix cor NORDISKA 5427 s.p.　　　(S1488)

Alle Vender Augo Sine Til Deg
mix cor MUSIKK 224 s.p.　　　　　(S1489)

Alleluia *Allelu
mix cor SOUTHERN $.25　　　　　　(S1490)
SATB,opt kbd BROUDE,A. 123 $.30　(S1491)

Aller Augen Warten Auf Dich
SATB HANSSLER 6.082 s.p. contains also:
Anonymous, Komm, Herr Jesu, Sei Du Unser
Gast (3pt) (canon); Trubel, Gerhard, Wir
Danken Dir, Herr Jesu Christ, Das Du
(SAB/SAT); Vulpius, Melchior, Hinunter
Ist Der Sonnen Schein (SATB)　　(S1492)

Aller Augen Warten Auf Dich, Herre (from Das
Benedicite Vor Dem Essen) Fest/Pent/
Whitsun
see Zwolf Geistliche Gesange
SATB,acap voc pt DOBLINGER s.p. see also
PFINGSTEN UND EUCHARISTIE　　　(S1493)
[Ger] SATB,acap (easy) BAREN. BCH 33 s.p.
(S1494)
4pt mix cor MOSELER LB-223 s.p. contains
also: Vater Unser　　　　　　　(S1495)

Alles Oyne Yokter Pa Deg
[Norw] LYCHE 44 s.p.　　　　　　(S1496)

Alles, Was Odem Hat, Lobe Den Herren *SWV
256
see Schutz, Heinrich, Lobt Gott Mit Schall,
Ihr Heiden All

Alles, Was Odem Hat, Lobe Den Herrn *SWV 256
see Schutz, Heinrich, Mein Seel Soll Loben
Gott, Den Herrn

Also Hat Gott Die Welt Geliebt *SWV 380,
Xmas/Gen/Lent/Pent/Whitsun,Bibl/mot
[Ger] SATTB,acap (med) BAREN. BA 512 $.25
see also Geistliche Chormusik 1648 (S1497)

5pt mix cor,acap cor pts BREITKOPF-L
PB-3362 s.p. see also Geistliche
Chormusik 1648 [BH]　　　　　　(S1498)
[Ger/Fr] SATTB,cont,orch sc HANSSLER
20.380F s.p.　　　　　　　　　　(S1499)
"For God So Loved The World" mix cor
SOUTHERN $.25　　　　　　　　　　(S1500)
"For God So Loved The World" SATTB/
SATTBarB,kbd (med diff) oct CONCORDIA
98-1472 $.30　　　　　　　　　　(S1501)
(Berger) "For God So Loved This Sinful
World" SATTB,cont,orch HANSSLER 20.380 sc
s.p., cor pts $.90, ipa　　　　(S1502)
(Granville) "For God So Loved The World"
SSATB,acap cor FOX CM7 $.25　　(S1503)
(Schabasser, Josef) mix cor,acap oct
DOBLINGER s.p. see also CHRISTUS, DER
HERR　　　　　　　　　　　　　(S1504)

An Den Wasserflussen Zu Babel Sassen Wir Und
Weineten (Psalm 137) Gen
(Breig, Werner) [Ger] SSB&T&opt TTTTB&4pt
treb cor,cont (med) BAREN. BA 5915 sc
s.p., cor pts s.p., ipa　　　　(S1505)

And Take Heed To Yourselves
(Stevens, Denis) SSATTB,org,2vln/2ob,vcl,
bvl/bsn voc sc PETERS 6595 $.40, ipa see
from Three Sacred Concertos　　(S1506)

Annuciation, The *cant
mix cor BELWIN $.80　　　　　　　(S1507)

Annunciation According To St. Luke, The *see
Lukaspassion

Ara Ske Dig Kristus
mix cor NORDISKA 1708 s.p.　　　(S1508)

Aspice, Pater
"Schaue Doch, Vater" see Cantiones Sacrae
1625 Band 2 [Nr. 21-23]

Auf Dein Wort Will Ich Trauen *SWV 243
SATB HANSSLER 6.020 s.p. contains also:
Freut Euch Des Herrn, Ihr Christen All,
SWV 130　　　　　　　　　　　　(S1509)

SCHUTZ, HEINRICH (cont'd.)

Auf Dem Gebirge Hat Man Ein Geschrei Gehoret *SWV 396, Xmas/Fest,mot
7pt mix cor,inst cor pts BREITKOPF-L PB-3378 s.p. see also Geistliche Chormusik 1648 [BH] (S1510)
(Kamlah, Wilhelm) [Ger] AA,2vla,3vcl (med) BAREN. BA 528 $.65 see also Geistliche Chormusik 1648 (S1511)

Auf Dem Gebirge Hat Man Ein Geschrei Gehort *SWV 396
SSAATBB,cont,7inst sc HANSSLER 20.396T s.p., ipa (S1512)

Auf Dich, Herr, Trau Ich Allezeit (Psalm 71) SWV 168 (from Der Psalter Nach Cornelius Beckers Dichtungen) Gen
[Ger] SATB,acap (med easy) BAREN. BA 844 $.25 (S1513)

Aus Der Tiefe Rufe Ich (Psalm 130) SWV 25, Gen,mot
(Ehmann, Wilhelm) [Ger] SATB&SATB,cont (med) sc BAREN. BA 1717 s.p. see also Die Psalmen Davids (S1514)
(Kruger) dbl cor,cont HANSSLER 20.025 sc s.p., ipa, cor pts s.p. (S1515)

Aus Meines Herzens Grunde (Psalm 138) SWV 243
[Ger] SATB,acap (med easy) BAREN. BA 931 $.25 see from Beckerscher Psalter (S1516)

Aus Meines Herzens Grunde *SWV 138
see Schutz, Heinrich, Wenn Gott Einmal Erlosen Wird

Aus Tiefer Not
see Schutz, Heinrich, Ich Harrete Des Herren
SATB,acap DOBLINGER s.p. see also BITTE UND VERTRAUEN (S1517)

Aus Tiefer Not Schrei Ich Zu Dir (Psalm 130) SWV 235, ECY
[Ger] SATB,acap (med easy) BAREN. BA 848 $.25 see from Beckerscher Psalter (S1518)

Ave Maria *SWV 334, Adv
(Ehmann, Wilhelm) [Ger] SSATB,ST soli,cont, 3vln,vla,vcl (med) BAREN. BA 3436 sc $2.25, cor pts $.40, ipa (S1519)

Ave Maria, Gratia Plena *SWV 333
"Sei Gegrusset, Maria" [Lat] SSATB,SA soli, org,3vln,2vla,vcl/bvl sc HANSSLER 30.334 $1.25, ipa (S1520)

Baroque To The Great Classics, The Vol. 2b- 1550 To 1700 *Psntd
mix cor min sc KALMUS 872 $2.00
contains: Passion Of St. John, The, SWV 481; Passion Of St. Luke, The, SWV 480; Passion Of St. Matthew, The, SWV 479 (S1521)

Be Ye Loving Even As Your Father Hath Loved You *see Seid Barmherzig, Wie Auch Euer Vater Barmherzig Ist

Beckerscher Psalter *see Ach Herr, Wie Lang Willt Du Denn Noch (Psalm 13) SWV 109; Aus Meines Herzens Grunde (Psalm 138) SWV 243; Aus Tiefer Not Schrei Ich Zu Dir (Psalm 130) SWV 235; Der Herr Ist Mein Getreuer Hirt (Psalm 23) SWV 120; Herr, Der Du Vormals Gnadig Warst (Psalm 85) SWV 182; Herr, Mein Gebet Erhor (Psalm 143) SWV 248; Singet Dem Herrn (Psalm 98) SWV 196; Wohl Denen, Die Da Wandeln (Psalm 119) SWV 217 (S1522)

Behold My Redeemer Is In Heaven
(Agey) SATB oct PRO ART 1998 $.25 (S1523)

Behold, There Appeared *see Siehe, Es Erschien Der Engel

Behold This Child Is Set For The Fall
(Stevens, Denis) SSATB,org,2vln/2ob,vcl, bvl/bsn voc sc PETERS 6594 $.40, ipa see from Three Sacred Concertos (S1524)

Benedicam Dominum *SWV 5, Gen,mot
(Engelbrecht, Christiane) [Ger] SATB&SATB, soli,cont (med diff) BAREN. BA 3427 sc $9.00, cor pts $3.00 (S1525)

Benedicite
(Graetzer) [Ger] SATB,acap RICORDI-ARG BA 9836 s.p. (S1526)

Blessed Are The Dead *see Selig Sind Die Toten

Blessed Are The Faithful *see Selig Sind Die Toten

Blessed Is He Who Walks Not In The Path Of The Wicked *Gen
SA,kbd (med diff) oct CONCORDIA 98-1920 $.25 (S1527)

Bringt Ehr Und Preis Dem Herren *SWV 126
SATB HANSSLER 6.024 s.p. contains also: Freut Euch Des Herrn, Ihr Christen All, SWV 130 (S1528)

Bringt Her Dem Herren
(Herrmann, W.) "Give To Jehovah" [Ger/Eng] unis wom cor,cont SCHIRM.EC 2538 $.30 (S1529)
(Ohl) "Give To Jehovah" unis oct SUMMY 5440 $.35 (S1530)

Calicem Salutaris
"Ich Will Den Kelch Des Heiles Annehmen" see Cantiones Sacrae 1625 Band 1 [Nr. 4-8]

Cantata Dominum
see Cantiones Sacrae [43]

Cantate Domine *cant
(Stone) mix cor CURWEN 80703 s.p. (S1531)

Cantate, Domini Canticum Novum
cor voc sc KALMUS 6439 $1.25 (S1532)

SCHUTZ, HEINRICH (cont'd.)

Cantate Domino *SWV 81, Ded/Easter/Gen/Pent, Bibl
mix cor SOUTHERN $.35 (S1533)
[Ger/Lat] dbl cor,vln,2vla,2vcl HANSSLER 20.463 sc $1.25, ipa, cor pts s.p. (S1534)
[Ger/Lat] SATB,org sc HANSSLER 20.081T $.80 (S1535)
"O Sing Ye To The Lord" SATB,kbd (med diff) oct CONCORDIA 98-1974 $.50 (S1536)
"Singet Ein Neues Lied" [Lat/Ger] SATB,cont (med) BAREN. BA 1969 $1.50 see from Cantiones Sacrae 1625 Band 2 [Nr. 29] (S1537)
(Beveridge) "O Sing Ye Unto The Lamb" [Eng/ Lat] 4pt mix cor,acap oct SCHIRM.G 8678 $.40 (S1538)
(Greyson) "O Sing Ye Unto The Lord" SATB oct BOURNE ES33 $.35 (S1539)
(Iseler) SATB,brass THOMP.G s.p., ipa (S1540)
(Iseler) SATB,opt brass THOMP.G s.p., ipa (S1541)
(Richardson) "O Praise The Lord, Ye People All" SATB oct WORD CS-324 $.30 (S1542)

Cantiones Sacrae [36]
cor voc sc KALMUS 6436 $1.25
contains: Heu Mihi Domine; In Te Domine (S1543)

Cantiones Sacrae [41]
mix cor,acap voc sc KALMUS 6441 $1.25
contains: Deus Misereatur; O Bone; O Dulcis; Quoniam Ad Te; Verba Mea (S1544)

Cantiones Sacrae [42]
mix cor,acap voc sc KALMUS 6442 $1.25
contains: Dulcissime Et Benignissime Christe; Heu Mihi; In Te Domine; Sicut Moses Serpentem In Deserto Exaltavit (S1545)

Cantiones Sacrae [43]
mix cor,acap voc sc KALMUS 6443 $1.25
contains: Cantata Dominum; Spes Mea, Christe, Deus; Turbabor (S1546)

Cantiones Sacrae [44]
mix cor,acap voc sc KALMUS 6444 $1.50
contains: Inter Bracchia; Pro Hoc Domine Non Est; Sin Non Humiliter Speret Israel; Supereminet Omnem Scientiam (S1547)

Cantiones Sacrae 1625, Band 1 *SWV 53-73, CC20U,Gen
(Grote, Gottfried) [Ger/Lat] SATB,cont (med diff) BAREN. BA 1950 $16.50 (S1548)

Cantiones Sacrae 1625 Band 1 [Nr. 1-3]
(Grote, Gottfried) [Ger/Lat] SATB,cont (med) BAREN. BA 1953 $.90
contains: Deus Misereatur Nostri, "Herr Gott, Hilf", SWV 55; Et Ne Despicias, "Ach Herr, Verwirf Mich Nicht", SWV 54; O Bone, O Dulcis, "O Guter, O Lieber", SWV 53 (S1549)

Cantiones Sacrae 1625 Band 1 [Nr. 4-8] *Psntd,mot
(Grote, Gottfried) [Ger/Lat] SATB,cont (med) BAREN. BA 1954 $3.50
contains: Calicem Salutaris, "Ich Will Den Kelch Des Heiles Annehmen", SWV 60; Ego Enim Inique Egi, "Ich, Nur Ich Bin Der Missetater", SWV 58; Ego Sum Tui Plaga Doloris, "Ich, O Ich Bin Die Qual Deiner Schmerzen", SWV 57; Quid Commisisti, "Was Hast Du Verwirket", SWV 56; Quo, Nate Dei, "O Sohn Des Hochsten", SWV 59 (S1550)

Cantiones Sacrae 1625 Band 1 [Nr. 9-10] *ECY
(Schoneich, Friedrich) [Lat/Ger] 6-8pt mix cor,cont (med diff) BAREN. BA 1959 $1.50
contains: Quoniam Ad Te Clamabo, "O Nimm An Mein Taglich Klagen", SWV 62; Verba Mea Auribus Percipe, "Meine Worte Hore", SWV 61 (S1551)

Cantiones Sacrae 1625 Band 1 [Nr. 11-12]
(Grote, Gottfried) [Ger/Lat] SATB,cont (med) BAREN. BA 1960 $1.50
contains: Ego Dormio, "Wenn Ich Schlafend Ruh", SWV 63; Vulnerasti Cor Meum, "Hast Verwundet Mein Herze", SWV 64 (S1552)

Cantiones Sacrae 1625 Band 1 [Nr. 13-14]
(Grote, Gottfried) [Ger/Lat] SATB,cont (med) BAREN. BA 1964 $1.50
contains: Heu Mihe, Domine, "O Weh Mir, Herr, Mein Gott", SWV 65; In Te, Domine, Speravi, "In Dich, Gott, Hab Ich Gehoffet", SWV 66 (S1553)

Cantiones Sacrae 1625 Band 1 [Nr. 15] *see Dulcissime Et Benignissime Christe, "Du Liebster Herr, Du Allergutigster, Christe", SWV 67 (S1554)

Cantiones Sacrae 1625 Band 1 [Nr. 17-18]
(Grote, Gottfried) [Ger/Lat] SATB,cont (med) BAREN. BA 1967 $1.50
contains: Spes Mea, Christe Deus, "O Meine Hoffnung, Jesus", SWV 69; Turbabor, Sed Non Pertubabor, "Furcht Storet, Doch Nichts Zerstoret Den Trost", SWV 70 (S1555)

Cantiones Sacrae 1625 Band 1 [Nr. 19-20]
(Grote, Gottfried) [Ger/Lat] SATB,cont (med) BAREN. BA 1961 $1.50
contains: Ad Dominum, Cum Tribularer, "Ich Rief Zum Herrn", SWV 71; Quid Detur Tibi, "Was Er Dir Geben Moge, Du Zunge Voll Falschheit", SWV 72 (S1556)

Cantiones Sacrae 1625, Band 2 *SWV 74-93, CC20U,Gen
(Grote, Gottfried) [Ger/Lat] SATB,cont (med diff) BAREN. BA 1955 $16.50 (S1557)

Cantiones Sacrae 1625 Band 2 [Nr. 16] *see Sicut Moses Serpentem In Deserto Exaltavit, "So Wie Moses Die Schlange", SWV 68 (S1558)

SCHUTZ, HEINRICH (cont'd.)

Cantiones Sacrae 1625 Band 2 [Nr. 21-23] *Psntd
(Grote, Gottfried) [Ger/Lat] SATB,cont (med) BAREN. BA 1958 $1.75
contains: Aspice, Pater, "Schaue Doch, Vater", SWV 73; Nonne Hic Est, "Ohn Alle Schuld", SWV 74; Reduc, Domine Deus Meus, "Wende, Du Unser Richter", SWV 75 (S1559)

Cantiones Sacrae 1625 Band 2 [Nr. 24-25] *Xmas
[Ger] SATB,cont (med) BAREN. BA 1968 $1.50
contains: Pro Hoc Magno Mysterio, "Fur Solch Grosses Mysterium", SWV 77; Supereminet Omnem Scientiam, "Uber Alle Erkenntnis Erhebet Sich", SWV 76 (S1560)

Cantiones Sacrae 1625 Band 2 [Nr. 26-28] *ECY
(Grote, Gottfried) [Lat/Ger] SATB,cont (med) BAREN. BA 1971 $1.50
contains: Domine, Non Est Exaltatum, "Herr, Mein Gott, Nicht Vermessen", SWV 78; Si Non Humiliter Sentiebam, "Demutig Will Ich Mich Dir Ergeben", SWV 79; Speret Israel, "Hoffe Israel", SWV 80 (S1561)

Cantiones Sacrae 1625 Band 2 [Nr. 29] *see Cantate Domino, "Singet Ein Neues Lied", SWV 81 (S1562)

Cantiones Sacrae 1625 Band 2 [Nr. 30] *see Inter Brachia Salvatoris Mei, "In Den Armen Des Heilandes Und Herren", SWV 82 (S1563)

Cantiones Sacrae 1625 Band 2 [Nr. 31] *see Veni, Rogo In Cor Meum, "Komm, Ich Bitt Dich, In Mein Herze", SWV 83 (S1564)

Cantiones Sacrae 1625 Band 2 [Nr. 32] *see Ecce Advocatus Meus, SWV 84 (S1565)

Cantiones Sacrae 1625 Band 2 [Nr. 33-35] *ECY
(Grote, Gottfried) [Lat/Ger] SATB,cont (med) BAREN. BA 1952 $2.25
contains: Discedite A Me, "Weichet Hinweg Von Mir", SWV 87; Domine, Ne In Furore Tuo, "Herr, Mein Gott, Ach, Nicht In Deinem Zorne", SWV 85; Quoniam Non Est In Morte, "Hore Mich, Herr, Bei Den Toten Gedenkt Man Deiner Nicht", SWV 86 (S1566)

Cantiones Sacrae 1625 Band 2 [Nr. 36-40]
[Lat] SATB,cont (med) BAREN. BA 1963 $1.50
contains: Confitemini Domino; Domine Deus, Pater Coelestis; Gratias Agimus Tibi; Oculi Omnium; Pater Noster (S1567)

Child To Us Is Born, A *see Ein Kind Ist Uns Geboren

Chorheft Zum Schutzjahr 1972 *CCU
mix cor HANSSLER 2.051 s.p. (S1568)

Chorus Of Angels (from The Christmas Story) Xmas
(Mendel) [Eng/Ger] 6pt mix cor oct SCHIRM.G 11165 $.25 (S1569)

Christ, Be Thine The Glory! *see Ehre Sei Dir Christe

Christ Is Arisen *Easter
(Gore) SSATB,kbd (med easy) oct CONCORDIA 98-1582 $.30 (S1570)

Christ, Our Blessed Savior *see Ehre Sei Dir, Christe

Christ, To Thee Be Glory (from St. Matthew Passion) Easter/Lent
SATB oct PRESSER MC375 $.30 (S1571)
TTBB,acap (med easy) oct CONCORDIA 98-1355 $.30 (S1572)
SATB KJOS 9000 $.30 (S1573)

Christe Eleison *SWV 458
(Engelbrecht, Christiane) [Ger] SSATTB/ SATTB,S solo,cont (med) sc BAREN. BA 3531 $4.75, ipa (S1574)

Christe, Fac Ut Sapiam *SWV 431 (from Das Deo Gratias Nach Dem Essen)
[Lat] SATB,cont,opt 4inst HANSSLER 20.431 sc s.p., voc sc s.p., ipa see also Zwolf Geistliche Gesange (S1575)
(Kessler, Franz) 4pt,opt org cor pts BREITKOPF-W PB-3774M s.p. see also Zwolf Geistliche Gesange-1657 (S1576)

Christmas History *see Weihnachtsgeschicte

Christmas Oratorio *see Weinachts-Oratorium

Christmas Story, The
(Mendel) [Eng/Ger] mix cor,STB soli,org, inst voc sc SCHIRM.G $2.00 (S1577)

Come, I Pray Thee, Dwell Within Me *see Veni, Rogo, In Cor Meum

Comfort Ye My People *see Troset Troset Mein Volk

Confitemini Domino
see Cantiones Sacrae 1625 Band 2 [Nr. 36-40]

Da Pacem, Domine, In Diebus Nostris
[Ger/Lat] SSATB&SATB,org,opt inst HANSSLER 20.465 sc $3.50, cor pts s.p., ipa (S1578)

Dank Sagen Wir Alle Gott *Gen/Thanks
SATB,acap voc pt DOBLINGER s.p. see also LOB UND DANK (S1579)
(Ehret) "Thanksgiving We Give To God" [Ger/ Eng] SATB oct COLOMBO 2427 $.25 (S1580)
(Ehret) "Thanksgiving We Give To God" mix cor SOUTHERN $.25 (S1581)
(Kessler, Franz) 4pt,opt org sc BREITKOPF-W PB-3774F s.p. see also Zwolf Geistliche Gesange-1657 (S1582)

SCHUTZ, HEINRICH (cont'd.)

Dank Sei Unserm Herrn (from St. Marks Passion) Easter/Lent
(Beveridge) "Thanks Be Unto Christ" [Eng/Ger] 4pt mix cor,acap oct SCHIRM.G 9658 $.25 (S1583)
(Marshall, Charles) "Thanks Be To Our Lord" SATB FRANK F-547 $.30 (S1584)

Dank Sei Unserm Herrn Jesu Christo
SATB HANSSLER 6.0731 s.p. contains also: Vulpius, Melchior, Des Heilgen Geistes Gnade Gross (S1585)

Danket Dem Herren *Gen/Thanks
SATB,acap voc pt DOBLINGER s.p. see also LOB UND DANK (S1586)

Danket Dem Herren, Denn Er Ist Freundlich (Psalm 136) SWV 45, Gen
(Ehmann, Wilhelm) [Ger] SSAT&AT&SSATB,3trp, 3trom,drums,opt cont&vcl (med) BAREN. BA 1710 sc $5.25, cor pts $1.50, ipa see also Die Psalmen Davids (S1587)

Danket Dem Herren, Denn Er Ist Sher Freundlich (from Das Deo Gratias Nach Dem Essen)
SATB sc HANSSLER 20.430-1 s.p. see also Zwolf Geistliche Gesange (S1588)

Danket Dem Herren, Gebt Ihm Ehr *Thanks
SATB HANSSLER 6.190 s.p. contains also: Praetorius, Michael, Nun Danket Alle Gott, Der Da (S1589)

Danket Dem Herren, Lobt Ihn Frei *SWV 203, Thanks
see Kurig, Hans-Hermann, Lasset Uns Wahrhaftig Sein In Der Liebe
SATB HANSSLER 6.181 s.p. contains also: Goudimel, Claude, Nun Danket Gott, Erhebt Und Preiset (S1590)

Danket Dem Herren *Psalm
SATB,acap (contains also: Wie Ists So Lieblich) DOBLINGER s.p. see from PSALMLIEDER (S1591)

Danket Dem Herrn
see Bach, Johann Sebastian, Der Herr Ist Mein Getreuer Hirt

Danket Dem Herrn Erzeigt Ihm Ehr
SATB HANSSLER 6.182 s.p. contains also: Kommt Herzu, Lasst Uns Frohlich Sein, SWV 193 (S1592)

Danket Dem Herrn *Psalm
SATB,acap DOBLINGER s.p. see from PSALMLIEDER (S1593)

Danksagen Wir Alle Gott (from Der Weihnachtshistorie) Xmas
[Ger] SATB,acap (easy) BAREN. BA 996 s.p. (S1594)
SATB,cont,bsn,2trom,2vln HANSSLER 20.435-2 s.p. (S1595)

Danksagen Wir Alle Gott Christo, Der Uns Mit Seinem Wort *SWV 425, mot
(Berger) "All Thanks Be To God" [Ger/Eng] SATB,org HANSSLER 20.425 sc $.75, cor pts $.50, ipa see also Zwolf Geistliche Gesange (S1596)

Das Benedicite Vor Dem Essen *SWV 429, Bene
SATB,cont,opt 4inst sc HANSSLER 20.429 s.p., ipa see also Zwolf Geistliche Gesange (S1597)

Das Benedicite Vor Dem Essen "Aller Augen Warten Auf Dich"
(Kessler, Franz) 4pt,opt org cor pts BREITKOPF-W PB-3774K s.p. see also Zwolf Geistliche Gesange-1657 (S1598)

Das Blut Jesu Christi Machet Uns Rein
(Berger) SAB,cont HANSSLER 5.001 s.p. (S1599)

Das Deo Gratias Nach Dem Essen *SWV 430
SATB,cont,opt 4inst HANSSLER 20.430 sc s.p., voc sc s.p., ipa see also Zwolf Geistliche Gesange (S1600)

Das Gratias Nach Dem Essen "Danket Dem Herren, Denn Er Ist Sehr Freundlich"
(Kessler, Franz) 4pt,opt org cor pts BREITKOPF-W PB-3774L s.p. see also Zwolf Geistliche Gesange-1657 (S1601)

Das Ist Je Gewisslich Wahr *SWV 388, Epiph/Trin,mot
6pt mix cor,acap cor pts BREITKOPF-L PB-3370 s.p. see also Geistliche Chormusik 1648 [BH] (S1602)
(Kamlah, Wilhelm) [Ger] SSATTB,acap (med) BAREN. BA 520 $.65 see also Geistliche Chormusik 1648 (S1603)
(Schrader) SSATTB,cont,inst HANSSLER 20.388 sc s.p., cor pts s.p., ipa (S1604)

Das Ist Mir Lieb *see Das Ist Mir Lieb, Dass Der Herr Mein Stimm Und Flehen Horet

Das Ist Mir Lieb, Dass Der Herr Mein Stimm Und Flehen Horet (Psalm 116) SWV 51, Easter/Pent,Bibl
"Das Ist Mir Lieb" SSATB sc HANSSLER 20.051 $2.50 (S1605)
(Holle, Rudolf) [Ger] SSATB,acap (med) BAREN. BA 485 $2.75 (S1606)

Das "Vater Unser" *see Vater Unser, Der Du Bist In Himmel

Das Vaterunser (from Deutschen Konzerten)
"Our Father" [Ger/Eng] SATTB,opt T solo, pno/org/orch BROUDE BR. $.75, ipa (S1607)
(Sporn, F.) dbl cor,org,strings,opt brass sc BREITKOPF-L rental (S1608)

Das Wort Ward Fleisch *see Das Wort Ward Fleisch Und Wohnet Unter Uns

Das Wort Ward Fleisch Und Wohnet Unter Uns *SWV 385, Xmas,mot
6pt mix cor,acap cor pts BREITKOPF-L PB-3367 s.p. see also Geistliche Chormusik 1648 [BH] (S1609)
"Das Wort Ward Fleisch" SSATTB,cont,inst sc HANSSLER 20.385 s.p., ipa (S1610)
(Ramlah, Wilhelm) [Ger] SSATTB,acap (med) BAREN. BA 517 $.55 see also Geistliche Chormusik 1648 (S1611)

Demutig Will Ich Mich Dir Ergeben *see Si Non Humiliter Sentiebam

Den Heil'gen Geistes Gnade Gross *Pent/Whitsun
SATB,acap voc pt DOBLINGER s.p. see also PFINGSTEN UND EUCHARISTIE (S1612)

Den Herren Lobt Mit Freuden *SWV 239
see Schutz, Heinrich, Wenn Gott Einmal Erlosen Wird

Den Kristi Pina Pa Hjartat Lagt
mix cor NORDISKA 5013 s.p. (S1613)

Den Tolvarige Jesus I Templet
(Ahlen, David) [Swed/Ger] mix cor,soli,org, 2vln,bvl NORDISKA 3332 s.p., ipa see from Tre Bibliska Scener (S1614)

Dennoch Hat Israel Zum Trost *SWV 170, Bibl
SATB HANSSLER 6.031 s.p. contains also: Herr, Der Du Vormals Gnadig Warst, SWV 182 (S1615)

Der Engel Sprach Zu Den Hirten *SWV 395, Xmas,mot
7pt mix cor,inst cor pts BREITKOPF-L PB-3377 s.p. see also Geistliche Chormusik 1648 [BH] (S1616)
SSAATBB,cont,7inst sc HANSSLER 20.395 s.p., ipa (S1617)
(Kamlah, Wilhelm) [Ger] 7pt mix cor/ST,vln, 2vla,2vcl (med) BAREN. BA 527 $.55 see also Geistliche Chormusik 1648 (S1618)
(Thomas, Kurt) STB,org,fl,ob,bsn,trp,trom, vln,vla,vcl sc BREITKOPF-W PB-3377 s.p. see also Geistliche Chormusik 1648 (S1619)

Der Engle Sprach Zu Den Hirten *Xmas
(Schutz; Agey) "Lo, The Angel Said To The Shepherds" [Eng/Ger] SATTTBB,opt org oct SCHIRM.G 10865 $.35 (S1620)

Der Herr Erhor Dich In Der Not
SAT HANSSLER 6.023 s.p. contains also: Die Erd Und Was Sich Auf Ihr Regt (S1621)

Der Herr Ist Gross
"Great Is The Lord" 2 eq voices SCHIRM.EC 2788 $.30 see from Three Little Sacred Concertos (S1622)
(Boepple, P.) "Great Is Our Lord" TB oct PRESSER 352-00017 $.30 (S1623)
(Boepple, P.) "Great Is Our Lord" SA/TB oct PRESSER 352-00017 $.30 (S1624)

Der Herr Ist Konig, Herrlich Schon *SWV 191
see Schutz, Heinrich, Ich Lieb Dich, Herr, Von Herzen Sehr

Der Herr Ist Konig Uberall (Psalm 97) SWV 195 (from Der Psalter Nach Cornelius Beckers Dichtungen) Gen,Psalm
SATB,acap DOBLINGER s.p. see from PSALMLIEDER (S1625)
[Ger] SATB,acap (med easy) BAREN. BA 844 $.25 (S1626)

Der Herr Ist Konig Und Regiert (Psalm 99) SWV 197 (from Der Psalter Nach Cornelius Beckers Dichtungen) Gen,Psalm
SATB,acap DOBLINGER s.p. see from PSALMLIEDER (S1627)
[Ger] SATB,acap (med easy) BAREN. BA 785 $.25 (S1628)

Der Herr Ist Mein Getreuer Hirt (Psalm 23) SWV 120, Easter/Pent
see Two Short Psalms
[Ger] SATB,acap (med easy) BAREN. BA 834 $.25 see from Beckerscher Psalter (S1629)

Der Herr Ist Mein Hirt (Psalm 23) Bibl/mot
SATB,acap DOBLINGER s.p. see also BITTE UND VERTRAUEN (S1630)
(Friedrichs) 3pt mix cor,org/pno,2vln cor pts MOSELER s.p., ipa (S1631)
(Grischkat) "Lord Tends Me Well, The" [Ger/Eng] dbl cor HANSSLER 20.033 $1.25 (S1632)
(Kubler) "Lord Is My Shepherd, The" [Eng/Ger] SAB&opt SATB,cont,2vln HANSSLER 20.398 sc $3.00, cor pts s.p., ipa see from Symphoniae Sacrae II (S1633)

Der Herr Schauet Vom Himmel (Psalm 14) Bibl
(Arfken) SB,cont HANSSLER 5.003 s.p. (S1634)

Der Herr Sprach Zu Meim Herren
see Schutz, Heinrich, Singet Dem Herrn Ein Neues Lied, All Welt Soll Frohlich Singen Mit

Der Psalter *SWV 97-256, CCU,Gen
(Blankenburg, Walter) [Ger] SATB,acap (med easy) BAREN. BA 984 $8.75 (S1635)

Der Zwolfjahrige Jesus *see Mein Sohn, Warum Hast Du Uns Das Getan?

Des Heilgen Geistes Gnade Gross *SWV 204
see Bach, Johann Sebastian, Der Herr Ist Mein Getreuer Hirt

Deus Misereatur
see Cantiones Sacrae [41]

Deus Misereatur Nostri
"Herr Gott, Hilf" see Cantiones Sacrae 1625 Band 1 [Nr. 1-3]

Deutsches Magnificat *Magnif
(Klein, Maynard) "My Soul Doth Magnify The Lord" [Eng/Ger] dbl cor,acap voc sc SCHIRM.G $1.25 (S1636)
(Steinitz, Paul) "German Magnificat" [Eng/Ger] dbl cor,org,opt inst (med) voc sc OXFORD 46.148 $3.70, ipr, rental (S1637)
(Straube, K.) dbl cor,acap cor pts BREITKOPF-L PB-2685 s.p., voc pt BREITKOPF-L CHB-2430 s.p. (S1638)

Deutsches Magnificat 1671 *SWV 494, Gen, Magnif
(Ameln, Konrad) [Ger] SATB&SATB,opt 2cont (med) sc BAREN. BA 2155 $2.50 (S1639)

Die Deutsche Litanei "Kyrie Eleison" *SWV 428, Kyrie
SATB,cont,opt 4inst HANSSLER 20.428 sc s.p., voc sc s.p., ipa see also Zwolf Geistliche Gesange (S1640)

Die Erd Und Was Sich Auf Ihr Regt
see Schutz, Heinrich, Der Herr Erhor Dich In Der Not

Die Furcht Des Herren Ist Der Weisheit Anfang *SWV 318
(Trubel) SS/TT,cont cor pts HANSSLER 20.318 s.p., cor pts HANSSLER 5.016 s.p. (S1641)

Die Himmel Erzahlen Die Ehre Gottes *Fest, mot
6pt mix cor,acap cor pts BREITKOPF-L PB-3368 s.p. see also Geistliche Chormusik 1648 [BH] (S1642)
(Agey) "Heavens Declare The Glory Of The Lord, The" [Eng/Ger] SSATTB,org/pno oct SCHIRM.G 11400 $.35 (S1643)

Die Himmel Erzahlen Die Ehre Gottes (Psalm 19) SWV 386, Gen,mot
(Kamlah, Wilhelm) [Ger] SSATTB,acap (med) BAREN. BA 518 $.55 see also Geistliche Chormusik 1648 (S1644)
(Schrader) SSATBB,cont,inst HANSSLER 20.386 sc s.p., cor pts s.p., voc pt s.p., ipa (S1645)

Die Himmel Erzahlen Die Ehre Gottes (Psalm 19) SWV 455, Bibl
SSATTB,acap/cont&6inst HANSSLER 20.455 sc s.p., cor pts s.p., ipa (S1646)

Die Himmel, Herr, Preisen Sehr *SWV 115, Psalm
see Schutz, Heinrich, Ich Lieb Dich, Herr, Von Herzen Sehr
SATB,acap (contains also: Ich Heb Mein Augen) DOBLINGER s.p. see from PSALMLIEDER (S1647)

Die Mit Tranen Saen (Psalm 126) SWV 378, ECY/Trin,Bibl/mot
5pt mix cor,acap cor pts BREITKOPF-L PB-3360 s.p. see also Geistliche Chormusik 1648 [BH] (S1648)
SSATB,cont,inst sc HANSSLER 20.378 s.p., ipa (S1649)
(Couraud) [Ger] SSATB oct SALABERT-US $2.25 (S1650)
(Kamlah, Wilhelm) [Ger] SSATB,acap BAREN. BA 510 $.40 see also Geistliche Chormusik 1648 (S1651)
(Kubler) SATBB&SATBB HANSSLER 1.022 s.p. (S1652)
(Shaw; Speer) "He Who With Weeping Soweth" [Eng/Ger] SSATB,opt org,acap oct SCHIRM.G 10115 $.45 see from Sacred Choir Music, 1648 (S1653)
(Spitta) 5pt mix cor&5pt mix cor MOSELER s.p. (S1654)

Die Psalmen Davids *CC35U,Psalm
(Kubler) [Ger] SATB HANSSLER 2.004 $2.00 see also: Ach Herr, Strafe Mich Nicht (Psalm 6) SWV 24; Aus Der Tiefe Rufe Ich (Psalm 130) SWV 25; Danket Dem Herren, Denn Er Ist Freundlich (Psalm 136) SWV 45; Herr, Unser Herrscher (Psalm 8) SWV 27; Ich Freu Mich Des, Das Mir Geredt Ist (Psalm 122) SWV 26; Ich Hebe Meine Augen Auf Zu Den Bergen (Psalm 121) SWV 31; Lobe Den Herrn, Meine Seele (Psalm 103) SWV 39; Warum Toben Die Heiden (Psalm 2) SWV 23; Wie Lieblich Sind Deine Wohnungen (Psalm 84) SWV 29 (S1655)

Die Sieben Worte Jesu Am Kreuz *SWV 478, Easter/Gd.Fri./Holywk/Psntd,ora
"Seven Last Words" [Ger] SATB,acap min sc PETERS E977 $2.50, ipa (S1656)
"Seven Last Words From The Cross, The" [Eng] mix cor,soli,org,strings (med easy) voc sc OXFORD 46.127 $1.40, ipr (S1657)
"Seven Last Words Of Christ, The" SATB SCHIRM.EC 2756 $.75, ipa (S1658)
"Seven Last Words, The" cor voc sc KALMUS 6434 $.75 (S1659)
"Seven Last Words, The" SATTB,SATTB soli, org,2vln,2vla,vcl HANSSLER 20.478 sc $3.50, cor pts s.p., ipa (S1660)
(Ghedini, G.F.) "Le Sette Parole Di Cristo Sulla Croce" [Lat] mix cor,SATTB soli, orch voc sc ZERBONI 6063 s.p., ipr (S1661)
(Gore, R.T.) "Seven Words Of Christ From The Cross, The" SSATB,soli,org,opt strings sc CONCORDIA 98-1621 $1.00, cor pts CONCORDIA 98-1627 $.40, ipa (S1662)
(Grusnick, Bruno) [Ger] SATTB,SATTB soli, cont,2vln,2vla,vcl,bvl (med) BAREN. BA 1577 sc $3.50, cor pts $.65, ipa (S1663)
(Jadassohn, S.) 5pt mix cor,SATTB soli,orch sc BREITKOPF-L EB-1770 s.p., voc pt BREITKOPF-L CHB-533A+B s.p., voc sc BREITKOPF-L EB-1420 s.p., ipa (S1664)
(Riedel, Carl) "Seven Last Words Of Our Dear Redeemer And Saviour, The Lord Jesus Christ, The" cor,5 soli,org,strings voc sc SCHIRM.G $.75 (S1665)
(Stein) "Seven Last Words Of Jesus Christ, The" [Ger] SATTB,SATTB soli,strings,kbd min sc EULENBURG EUL977 s.p., ipa (S1666)

Discedite A Me
"Weichet Hinweg Von Mir" see Cantiones Sacrae 1625 Band 2 [Nr. 33-35]

Ditt Namn, O Gud Jag Lova Vill
(Soderholm, V.) 3pt wom cor/3pt jr cor,acap NORDISKA 5036 s.p. (S1667)

SCHUTZ, HEINRICH (cont'd.)

Domine Deus, Deus Virtutum
cor,cont,inst HANSSLER 20.603 sc s.p., voc sc s.p., ipa (S1668)

Domine Deus, Pater Coelestis
see Cantiones Sacrae 1625 Band 2 [Nr. 36-40]

Domine, Ne In Furore Tuo
"Herr, Mein Gott, Ach, Nicht In Deinem Zorne" see Cantiones Sacrae 1625 Band 2 [Nr. 33-35]

Domine, Non Est Exaltatum
"Herr, Mein Gott, Nicht Vermessen" see Cantiones Sacrae 1625 Band 2 [Nr. 26-28]

Domine, Non Est Exaltatum Cor Meum
cor voc sc KALMUS 6438 $1.25 (S1669)

Domini Est Terra (Psalm 24)
SATB&SATB&SSATTB,cont,22inst HANSSLER 20.476 sc s.p., cor pts s.p., ipa (S1670)

Du Liebster Herr, Du Allergutigster, Christe
*see Dulcissime Et Benignissime Christe

Du Schalksknecht *SWV 397, Trin
SSATTBB,cont,7inst sc HANSSLER 20.397 s.p. (S1671)
(Kamlah, Wilhelm) [Ger] cor,T solo,5vcl& vla/5vcl&trom, or 6 viola da gamba (med) BAREN. BA 529 $.65 see also Geistliche Chormusik 1648 (S1672)

Du Schalksknecht, Alle Diese Schuld *Trin, mot
7pt mix cor,inst cor pts BREITKOPF-L PB-3379 s.p. see also Geistliche Chormusik 1648 [BH] (S1673)

Du Tust Viel Guts Beweisen *SWV 219
SATB HANSSLER 6.184 s.p. contains also: Goudimel, Claude, Ich Schau Nach Jenen Bergen Gern (S1674)

Dulcissime Et Benignissime Christe *SWV 67
see Cantiones Sacrae [42]
cor voc sc KALMUS 6437 $1.25 (S1675)
(Grote, Gottfried) "Du Liebster Herr, Du Allergutigster, Christe" [Ger/Lat] SATB, cont (med) BAREN. BA 1965 $.90 see from Cantiones Sacrae 1625 Band 1 [Nr. 15] (S1676)

Earth Is The Lord's, The
see Three Choral Psalms

Easter Dialogue *Easter
(Lamb) SATB oct BOURNE 863 $.35 (S1677)

Ecce Advocatus Meus *SWV 84
(Grote, Gottfried) [Ger/Lat] SATB,cont (med) BAREN. BA 1962 $.90 see from Cantiones Sacrae 1625 Band 2 [Nr. 32] (S1678)

Ego Dormio
"Wenn Ich Schlafend Ruh" see Cantiones Sacrae 1625 Band 1 [Nr. 11-12]

Ego Enim Inique Egi
"Ich, Nur Ich Bin Der Missetater" see Cantiones Sacrae 1625 Band 1 [Nr. 4-8]

Ego Sum Tui Plaga Doloris
"Ich, O Ich Bin Die Qual Deiner Schmerzen" see Cantiones Sacrae 1625 Band 1 [Nr. 4-4]
SATB,acap oct PRESSER 312-40368 $.30 (S1679)

Ehre Sei Dem Vater
[Ger] SATB,opt cont BAREN. BA 581 s.p. (S1680)
"Glory Be To The Father" SATB,acap oct PRESSER 312-40147 $.30 (S1681)
"Glory Be To The Father" mix cor SOUTHERN $.25 (S1682)
(Granville) "Glory Be To The Father" SATB, acap oct FOX CM16 $.30 (S1683)

Ehre Sei Dem Vater Und Dem Sohn (from Meine Seele Erhebt Den Herren) mot
(Hermann) SATB HANSSLER 20.426-1 s.p. see also Zwolf Geistliche Gesange (S1684)

Ehre Sei Dem Vater
cor,cont,inst HANSSLER 20.492-1 sc s.p., voc pt s.p., ipa (S1685)

Ehre Sei Dir, Christe (from Matthaus Passion) Easter/Lent/Psntd,Bibl
SATB,acap voc pt DOBLINGER s.p. see also PASSION UND OSTERN (S1686)
"Glory Be To Jesus" [Ger/Eng] SATB,org cor pts HANSSLER 20.479-1 $.50 (S1687)
(Beveridge) "Christ, Our Blessed Savior" [Eng/Ger] 4pt mix cor,acap oct SCHIRM.G 9657 $.30 (S1688)
(Shaw) "Christ, Be Thine The Glory!" [Eng/Ger] 4pt mix cor,acap oct SCHIRM.G 10123 $.30 (S1689)

Ehre Sei Gott In Der Hohe (from Der Weihnachtschistorie) Xmas
SSATTB,cont,bsn,2vln sc HANSSLER 20.435-1 s.p. (S1690)

Ein Kind Ist Uns Geboren *Xmas,mot
6pt mix cor,acap cor pts BREITKOPF-L PB-3366 s.p. see also Geistliche Chormusik 1648 [BH] (S1691)

Ein Kind Ist Uns Geboren *SWV 302, Xmas
(Agey) "Child To Us Is Born, A" [Eng/Ger] 4pt mix cor,org oct SCHIRM.G 10829 $.40 (S1692)
(Kubler) SATB,cont HANSSLER 20.302 sc s.p., cor pts s.p. (S1693)

Ein Kind Ist Uns Geboren *SWV 384, Xmas
SSATTB,cont,inst sc HANSSLER 20.384 s.p., ipa (S1694)
(Ramlah, Wilhelm) [Ger] SSATTB,acap (med) BAREN. BA 516 $.45 see also Geistliche Chormusik 1648 (S1695)

SCHUTZ, HEINRICH (cont'd.)

Er Wird Sein Kleid In Wein Waschen *SWV 370, Adv/Gen,mot
5pt mix cor,acap cor pts BREITKOPF-L PB-3352 s.p. see also Geistliche Chormusik 1648 [BH] (S1696)
SSATB,cont,opt inst sc HANSSLER 20.370 s.p., ipa (S1697)
(Kamlah, Wilhelm) [Ger] SATTB,acap (med) BAREN. BA 502 $.40 see also Geistliche Chormusik 1648 (S1698)

Erbarm Dich Mein, O Herre Gott *SWV 148
see Schutz, Heinrich, Gott Unser Herr, Machtig Durchs Wort
mix cor,cont,opt 4inst sc HANSSLER 20.447 s.p., ipa (S1699)

Erhoere Mich
(Boepple, P.) "Give Ear, O Lord" TB oct PRESSER 352-00013 $.30 (S1700)

Erhor Mich, Wenn Ich Ruf Zu Dir
SATB,acap DOBLINGER s.p. see also BITTE UND VERTRAUEN (S1701)

Erhore Mich
"Give Ear O Lord" boy cor SOUTHERN $.30 (S1702)
"Give Ear, O Lord" 2 eq voices SCHIRM.EC 2789 $.30 see from Three Little Sacred Concertos (S1703)

Es Erhub Sich Ein Streit, Michael *mot
(Horn) dbl cor,cont,ob,3bsn,3trp,2vln,2vla, vcl,bvl HANSSLER 1.260 sc s.p., cor pts s.p., ipa (S1704)

Es Ging Ein Samann Aus Zu Saen Seinen Samen *SWV 408, Psntd
"Sower In His Field His Seed Was Sowing, A" [Ger/Lat] SATB,soli,org,bsn,2vln,vcl sc HANSSLER 20.408 $4.00, ipa see from SYMPHONIAE SACRAE III (S1705)
(Hoffmann, Hans) "Es Ging Ein Samann Aus, Zu Saen Seinen Samen" [Ger] SATB,SATB soli,cont,bsn,2vln (med) BAREN. BA827 sc $4.75, cor pts $2.00, ipa see from SYMPHONIAE SACRAE III (S1706)

Es Ging Ein Samann Aus, Zu Saen Seinen Samen
*see Es Ging Ein Samann Aus Zu Saen Seinen Samen

Es Gingen Zweene Menschen *SWV 444, Bibl/mot
"Pharisee And The Publican, The" SATB,SSTB soli,pno/org MUSICUS 021 $.30 (S1707)
"Pharisee And The Publican, The" 4pt mix cor oct SCHIRM.G 7473 $.35 (S1708)
(Graulich) SSAB/SATB,cont HANSSLER 1.499 sc s.p., cor pts s.p. (S1709)

Es Ist Ein Freud Dem Herzen Mein *SWV 227
see Schutz, Heinrich, Ich Heb Mein Augen Sehnlich Auf

Es Ist Erschienen Die Heilsame Gnade Gottes *SWV 371, Xmas,mot
5pt mix cor,acap cor pts BREITKOPF-L PB-3353 s.p. see also Geistliche Chormusik 1648 [BH] (S1710)
SSATB,cont,inst HANSSLER 20.371 sc s.p., cor pts s.p., ipa (S1711)
(Ramlah, Wilhelm) [Ger] SSATB,acap (med) BAREN. BA 503 $.55 see also Geistliche Chormusik 1648 (S1712)

Es Steh Gott Auf, Dass Seine Feind *SWV 165
see Schutz, Heinrich, Jauchzet Gott, Alle Lande Sehr

Es Wird Das Szepter Von Juda Nicht Entwendet Werden *SWV 369
SSATB,cont,inst sc HANSSLER 20.369 s.p., ipa (S1713)

Es Wird Das Zepter Von Juda Nicht Entwendet Werden *SWV 369, Adv/Gen,mot
5pt mix cor,acap cor pts BREITKOPF-L PB-3351 s.p. see also Geistliche Chormusik 1648 [BH] (S1714)
(Kamlah, Wilhelm) [Ger] SATTB,acap (med) BAREN. BA 501 $.40 see also Geistliche Chormusik 1648 (S1715)

Et Ne Despicias
"Ach Herr, Verwirf Mich Nicht" see Cantiones Sacrae 1625 Band 1 [Nr. 1-3]

Fariseen Och, Publikanen
(Ahlen, David) [Swed/Ger] wom cor&mix cor, TB soli,org NORDISKA 3330 s.p. see from Tre Bibliska Scener (S1716)

Father Abraham, Have Mercy On Me *see Vater Abraham, Erbarme Dich Mein

Fear The Almighty *Gen/Refm
SA/TB,kbd (med diff) oct CONCORDIA 98-1854 $.25 (S1717)

Feget Den Alten Sauerteig Aus Und Lasst Uns Ostern Halten *Easter
(Kubler) SATB,cont,2vln HANSSLER 5.008 sc s.p., cor pts s.p., ipa (S1718)

Five Psalms From The "Becker Psalter" *Psalm
(Wunderlich, R.) men cor CONCORDIA 98-1954 $.30
contains: From Depths Of Woe I Cry To Thee (Psalm 130); I Lift My Longing Eyes With Love (Psalm 121); Mighty Fortress Is Our God, A (Psalm 46); Oh, Hear Me When I Cry To Thee (Psalm 4); Praise God, The Lord, Ye People All (Psalm 150) (S1719)

For God So Loved The World *see Also Hat Gott Die Welt Geliebt

For God So Loved This Sinful World *see Also Hat Gott Die Welt Geliebt

Four Psalms *CC4U,Psalm
SATB,acap oct PRESSER 352-00006 $.35 (S1720)

SCHUTZ, HEINRICH (cont'd.)

Freut Euch Des Herrn, Ihr Christen All *SWV 130
see Schutz, Heinrich, Bringt Ehr Und Preis Dem Herren
see Schutz, Heinrich, Auf Dein Wort Will Ich Trauen
see Fiebig, Kurt, Sollt Ich Meinem Gott Nicht Singen

Frohlockt Mit Freud', Ihr Volker All *SWV 144
see Schutz, Heinrich, Lobt Gott In Seinem Heiligtum
see Bach, Johann Sebastian, O Herrlicher Tag, O Frohliche Zeit
SATB HANSSLER 6.027 s.p. contains also: Gross Ist Der Herr Und Hoch Gepreist, SWV 145 (S1721)

From Depths Of Woe
(Ehret) SATB,acap MARKS 4115 $.30 (S1722)

From Depths Of Woe I Cry To Thee (Psalm 130)
see Five Psalms From The "Becker Psalter"

From God Shall Naught Divide Me *see Von Gott Will Ich Nicht Lassen

Fur Solch Grosses Mysterium *see Pro Hoc Magno Mysterio

Furcht Storet, Doch Nichts Zerstoret Den Trost *see Turbabor, Sed Non Pertubabor

Geistliche Chormusik 1648 *SWV 369-397, CCU, Gen
(Kamlah, Wilhelm) [Ger] 5-7pt mix cor,acap/inst (med) BAREN. BA 500 s.p.
see also: Also Hat Gott Die Welt Geliebt, SWV 380; Auf Dem Gebirge Hat Man Ein Geschrei Gehoret, SWV 396; Das Ist Je Gewisslich Wahr, SWV 388; Das Wort Ward Fleisch Und Wohnet Unter Uns, SWV 385; Der Engel Sprach Zu Den Hirten, SWV 395; Die Himmel Erzahlen Die Ehre Gottes, SWV 386; Die Mit Tranen Saen, SWV 378; Du Schalksknecht, SWV 397; Ein Kind Ist Uns Geboren, SWV 384; Er Wird Sein Kleid In Wein Waschen, SWV 370; Es Ist Erschienen Die Heilsame Gnade Gottes, SWV 371; Es Wird Das Zepter Von Juda Nicht Entwendet Werden, SWV 369; Gib Unsern Fursten Und Aller Obrigkeit, SWV 373; Herr, Auf Dich Traue Ich, SWV 377; Herzlich Lieb Hab Ich Dich, O Herr, SWV 387; Ich Bin Ein Rechter Weinstock, SWV 389; Ich Bin Eine Rufende Stimme, SWV 383; Ich Weiss, Dass Mein Erloser Lebt, SWV 393; O Lieber Herre Gott, Wecke Uns Auf, SWV 381; Sammelt Zuvor Das Unkraut, SWV 376; Sehet An Den Feigenbaum, SWV 394; Selig Sind Die Toten, SWV 391; So Fahr Ich Hin Zu Jesu Christ, SWV 379; Trostet, Trostet Mein Volk, SWV 382; Unser Keiner Lebet Ihm Selber, SWV 374; Unser Wandel Ist Im Himmel, SWV 390; Verleih Uns Frieden Gnadiglich, SWV 372; Viel Werden Kommen Von Morgen Und Von Abend, SWV 375; Was Mein Gott Will; Was Mein Gott Will, Das Gscheh Allzeit, SWV 392 (S1723)

Geistliche Chormusik 1648 [BH] *CC29U,mot
(Thomas, Kurt) 5pt mix cor,acap cmplt ed BREITKOPF-L PB-3954 s.p.
see also: Also Hat Gott Die Welt Geliebt; Auf Dem Gebirge Hat Man Ein Geschrei Gehoret; Das Ist Je Gewisslich Wahr; Das Wort Ward Fleisch Und Wohnet Unter Uns; Der Engel Sprach Zu Den Hirten; Die Himmel Erzahlen Die Ehre Gottes; Die Mit Tranen Saen; Du Schalksknecht, Alle Diese Schuld; Ein Kind Ist Uns Geboren; Er Wird Sein Kleid In Wein Waschen; Es Ist Erschienen Die Heilsame Gnade Gottes; Es Wird Das Zepter Von Juda Nicht Entwendet Werden; Gib Unsern Fursten Und Aller Obrigkeit; Herr, Auf Dich Traue Ich; Herzlich Lieb Hab Ich Dich, O Herr; Ich Bin Ein Rechter Weinstock; Ich Bin Eine Rufende Stimme; Ich Weiss, Dass Mein Erloser Lebt; O Lieber Herre Gott, Wecke Uns Auf; Sammelt Zuvor Das Unkraut; Sehet An Den Feigenbaum; Selig Sind Die Toten; So Fahr Ich Hin Zu Jesu Christ; Trostet, Trostet Mein Volk; Unser Keiner Lebet Ihm Selber; Unser Wandel Ist Im Himmel; Verleih Uns Frieden Gnadiglich; Viel Werden Kommen Von Morgen Und Von Akend; Was Mein Gott Will, Das Gscheh Allzeit (S1724)

German Magnificat *see Deutsches Magnificat

German Requiem, A *Req
(Mendel, Arthur) [Eng/Ger] mix cor,soli, org/bvl voc sc SCHIRM.G $1.50 (S1725)

Gesang Der Drei Manner Im Feurigen Ofen *mot
(Gottwald) SSATB&SSATB,cont/2trp&3trom& 2vln&2vla&opt vcl/bvl HANSSLER 1.456 sc s.p., ipr, cor pts s.p. (S1726)

Gib Unsern Fursten Und Aller Obrigkeit *SWV 373, Fest,mot
5pt mix cor,acap cor pts BREITKOPF-L PB-3355 s.p. see also Geistliche Chormusik 1648 [BH] (S1727)
SSATB,cont,inst sc HANSSLER 20.373 s.p., ipa (S1728)
(Kamlah, Wilhelm) [Ger] SSATB,acap (med) BAREN. BA 505 $.40 see also Geistliche Chormusik 1648 (S1729)

Give Ear, O Lord *see Erhoere Mich

Give Ear, O Lord *see Erhore Mich

Give Ear, Oh Lord
(Boepple, P.) SA/TB oct PRESSER 352-00013 $.30 (S1730)

Give To Jehovah *see Bringt Her Dem Herren

SCHUTZ, HEINRICH (cont'd.)

Give To Our Leaders And All Ruling Powers *Gen
SSATB,acap (med diff) oct CONCORDIA 98-1586 $.30 (S1731)
(Agey) mix cor SOUTHERN $.30 (S1732)

Give To Us Peace, Lord *Gen
(Coggin) SATB SCHMITT 1435 $.30 (S1733)

Glory Be To Jesus *see Ehre Sei Dir, Christe

Glory Be To The Father *see Ehre Sei Dem Vater

Glory To God *Xmas
(Ehert, Walter) SSATTB (med) ABINGDON APM-416 $.60 (S1734)

God So Loved The World *Xmas/Gen/Lent
SATTB/SATTBarB,kbd (med diff) oct CONCORDIA 98-1472 $.30 (S1735)

Gott Sei Dank, Der Uns Den Sieg Gegebem Hat (from Auferstehengs-Historie) Bibl
"Thanks Be To God" [Ger/Eng] dbl cor,T solo,org sc HANSSLER 20.050-1 $.80 (S1736)

Gott Unser Herr, Machtig Durchs Wort *SWV 147
SATB HANSSLER 6.028 s.p. contains also: Erbarm Dich Mein, O Herre Gott, SWV 148 (S1737)

Gratias Agimus Tibi
see Cantiones Sacrae 1625 Band 2 [Nr. 36-40]

Great Is Our Lord *see Der Herr Ist Gross

Great Is The Lord *see Der Herr Ist Gross

Gross Ist &er Herr Und Hoch Gepreist *SWV 145
see Schutz, Heinrich, Frohlockt Mit Freud', Ihr Volker All

Gutes Und Barmherzigkeit Werden Mir Folgen Mein Leben Lang *SWV 95, Gen,mot
(Moser, Hans Joachim) [Ger] SSATTB,cont (med) BAREN. BA 986 $1.25 (S1738)

Hail, O Hail To Thee, Mary *see Sei Gegrusset, Maria

Hast Verwundet Mein Herze *see Vulnerasti Cor Meum

He Who God's Suffering In Honor Holds *see Wer Gottes Marter In Ehren Hat

He Who With Weeping Soweth *see Die Mit Tranen Saen

Hear Us, Jesus, Son Of God *Easter
(Coggin) SATB SCHMITT 1423 $.25 (S1739)

Hearken Unto My Cry *see Verba Mea Auribus Percipe

Heavens Declare The Glory Of The Lord, The *see Die Himmel Erzahlen Die Ehre Gottes

Help Us, Jesus Christ, God's Son *Easter
SATB oct SACRED S-135 $.35 (S1740)

Herr, Auf Dich Traue Ich *SWV 377, Gen/Psntd,mot
[Ger] SSATB,acap (med) BAREN. BA 509 $.45 see also Geistliche Chormusik 1648 (S1741)
5pt mix cor,acap cor pts BREITKOPF-L PB-3359 s.p. see also Geistliche Chormusik 1648 [BH] (S1742)
SSATB,cont,inst sc HANSSLER 20.377 s.p., ipa (S1743)
(Kruger) SSATB,cont HANSSLER 20.377 s.p. (S1744)

Herr, Der Du Vormals Gnadig Warst (Psalm 85) SWV 182, Adv
see Schutz, Heinrich, Dennoch Hat Israel Zum Trost
[Ger] SATB,acap (med easy) BAREN. BA 879 $.25 see from Beckerscher Psalter (S1745)

Herr Gott, Erzeig Mir Hilf Und Gnad *SWV 148
SATB HANSSLER 6.029 s.p. contains also: Mein Seel Ist Still In Meinem Gott, SWV 159 (S1746)

Herr Gott, Hilf *see Deus Misereatur Nostri

Herr, Ich Hoffe Darauf
(Trubel) SS/TT,cont HANSSLER 20.312 s.p. (S1747)

Herr, Mein Gebet Erhor (Psalm 143) SWV 248, Trin
[Ger] SATB,acap (med easy) BAREN. BA 879 $.25 see from Beckerscher Psalter (S1748)

Herr, Mein Gebet Erhor In Gnad *SWV 248, prayer
SATB HANSSLER 6.036 s.p. contains also: Ich Will Sehr Hoch Erhohen Dich, SWV 250 (S1749)

Herr, Mein Gott, Ach, Nicht In Deinem Zorne *see Domine, Ne In Furore Tuo

Herr, Mein Gott, Nicht Vermessen *see Domine, Non Est Exaltatum

Herr, Nun Lassest Du Deinen Diener
mix cor,cont,inst HANSSLER 20.352 sc s.p., cor pts s.p., ipa (S1750)

Herr, Nun Lassest Du Deinen Diener
"Lord, Now Lettest Thou Thy Servant" see Musikalische Exequien-Teil 3

Herr, Nun Lassest Du Deinen Diener *SWV 432, Nunc
"Lord, Now Lettest Thou Thy Servant" [Ger/Eng] SSATTB,org,vcl HANSSLER 20.432 sc $1.50, voc pt $.40, ipa (S1751)

Herr, Nun Lassest Du Deinen Diener *SWV 433, Nunc
"Lord Now Lettest Thou Servant" [Ger/Eng] SSATTB,org,vcl HANSSLER 20.433 sc $1.50, voc pt $.50, ipa (S1752)

Herr, Unser Herrscher (Psalm 8) SWV 27, Gen
(Huber, Walter Simon) [Ger] SSAT&ATBB&opt SSATB,org/cont,3trp&2trom/3vln&vla&vcl (med) BAREN. BA 2399 sc $3.75, cor pts $1.20, ipa see also Die Psalmen Davids (S1753)

Herr, Wenn Ich Nur Dich Habe *mot
(Hermann) dbl cor,cont,inst HANSSLER 20.280 sc s.p., cor pts s.p., voc pt s.p., ipa (S1754)
(Mendel) "Lord, If I But Thee May Have" [Eng/Ger] dbl cor,acap,opt org oct SCHIRM.G 8771 $.45 (S1755)

Herre Gott, Himmlischer Vater, Wir Danken Dir (from Das Benedicite Vor Dem Essen)
SATB sc HANSSLER 20.429-3 s.p. see also Zwolf Geistliche Gesange (S1756)

Herzlich Lieb Hab Ich Dich, O Herr *SWV 387, Fest/Trin,mot
6pt mix cor,acap cor pts BREITKOPF-L PB-3369 s.p. see also Geistliche Chormusik 1648 [BH] (S1757)
SSATB,cont,inst sc HANSSLER 20.387 s.p. (S1758)
(Kamlah, Wilhelm) [Ger] SSATB,acap (med) BAREN. BA 519 $.65 see also Geistliche Chormusik 1648 (S1759)

Heu Mihe, Domine
"O Weh Mir, Herr, Mein Gott" see Cantiones Sacrae 1625 Band 1 [Nr. 13-14]

Heu Mihi
see Cantiones Sacrae [42]

Heu Mihi Domine
see Cantiones Sacrae [36]

Heut Ist Christus, Der Herr, Geboren *Xmas
4pt mix cor,strings MOSELER s.p. (S1760)

Heute Ist Christ, Der Herr, Geboren *SWV 439, Xmas
"This Happy Morning Was Christ The Lord Born" SSS/SSAB,org,3vln,vcl/bvl sc HANSSLER 20.439 $1.25, ipa (S1761)

Heute Ist Christus Der Herr Geboren *SWV 439, Xmas,cant
(Bittinger, Werner) [Ger] SSA/SSA&men cor, SSA soli,cont (med) BAREN. BA 3445 $2.25 (S1762)
(Wolters) eq voices/mix cor,cont,opt inst MOSELER sc s.p., cor pts s.p., ipa (S1763)

Historia Der Auferstehung Jesu Christi 1623 *SWV 50, Easter
(Huber, Walter Simon) [Ger] SATB&SATB,ATTB soli,3vln&2vla&vcl&bvl, or 4 viola da gamba (med) BAREN. BA 242 sc $7.75, cor pts $1.60, ipa (S1764)

Historia Der Geburt Jesu Christi *SWV 435, Xmas,ora
"Resurrection Oratorio" [Ger] SATB,acap min sc PETERS E980 $2.50 (S1765)
(Schoneich, Friedrich) [Ger] SSATTB,ST soli,soli,org,cont,2fl,2trp,2trom,bsn, 2vln,3vla,2vcl,bvl (med diff) sc BAREN. BA 1709 $7.75, cor pts BAREN. BA 1709 $2.00, min sc BAREN. TP 132 $2.50 (S1766)

Hodie Christus Natus Est *SWV 456, Xmas
[Ger/Lat] SSATTB,org,vcl HANSSLER 20.456 sc $3.00, voc pt $1.00 (S1767)
(Bittinger, Werner) [Ger] SSATTB,cont (med) sc BAREN. BA 3446 $2.75, ipa (S1768)

Hoffe Israel *see Speret Israel

Hore Mich, Herr, Bei Den Toten Gedenkt Man Deiner Nicht *see Quoniam Non Est In Morte

How Lovely Is Thy Dwelling Place *Ded/Gen
TTBB,acap (med easy) oct CONCORDIA 98-1681 $.25 contains also: Praise God, Ye Lands (S1769)

Hutet Euch, Dass Eure Herzen Nicht Beschweret Werden (from Symphoniae Sacrae III)
SSATTB,cont,2vln sc BREITKOPF-W PB-4740 s.p., cor pts BREITKOPF-W CHB-3546 s.p., ipa (S1770)
SSATTB,cont,strings sc BREITKOPF-W PB-4741 s.p., cor pts BREITKOPF-W CHB-3546 s.p., ipa (S1771)

I Am The Resurrection And The Life *mot
(Stevens, Denis) SSAATTBB,opt org/pno PETERS 6591 $.50 (S1772)

I Am The Resurrection And The True Life *Easter
dbl cor,acap oct PRESSER 312-40165 $.35 (S1773)

I Know That My Redeemer Lives *see Ich Weiss Dass Mein Erloser Lebt

I Lift My Longing Eyes With Love (Psalm 121)
see Five Psalms From The "Becker Psalter"

I Thank Thee, O Lord
(Ingle) [Eng/Ger] 4pt mix cor,acap oct SCHIRM.G 10368 $.30 (S1774)

I Waited For The Lord
SATB oct SOUTHERN $.25 (S1775)

I Will Praise The Lord *Bibl
4pt mix cor,acap oct SCHIRM.G 7556 $.40 (S1776)

Ich Bin Dein Rechter Weinstock *SWV 389
SSATTB,cont,inst sc HANSSLER 20.389 s.p., ipa (S1777)

Ich Bin Die Auferstehung
cor sc HANSSLER 20.464 s.p. (S1778)

Ich Bin Die Auferstehung Und Das Leben *mot
[Ger] dbl cor,acap HINRICHSEN P4177 s.p. (S1779)

SCHUTZ, HEINRICH (cont'd.)

Ich Bin Ein Rechter Weinstock *SWV 389, Gen/Trin,mot
6pt mix cor,acap cor pts BREITKOPF-L PB-3371 s.p. see also Geistliche Chormusik 1648 [BH] (S1780)
(Kamlah, Wilhelm) [Ger] SSATTB,acap (med) BAREN. BA 521 $.55 see also Geistliche Chormusik 1648 (S1781)

Ich Bin Eine Rufende Stimme *SWV 383, Adv, mot
6pt mix cor,acap cor pts BREITKOPF-L PB-3365 s.p. see also Geistliche Chormusik 1648 [BH] (S1782)
SSATTB,cont,inst sc HANSSLER 20.383 s.p., ipa (S1783)
(Kamlah, Wilhelm) [Ger] SSATTB,acap (med) BAREN. BA 515 $.55 see also Geistliche Chormusik 1648 (S1784)

Ich Bin Eine Rufende Stimme In Der Wusten *Xmas,Bibl/mot
"Lo, I Am The Voice Of One Crying In The Wilderness" SSATTB oct PRESSER MC437 $.40 (S1785)
(Shaw; Speer) "Lo, I Am The Voice Of One Crying In The Wilderness" SSATTB,Bar solo,acap,opt org oct SCHIRM.G 10116 $.40 see from Sacred Choir Music, 1648 (S1786)

Ich Bin Verstummet Ganz Und Still *SWV 136
SATB HANSSLER 6.026 s.p. contains also: Mein Herz Dichtet Ein Lied Mit Fleiss, SWV 142 (S1787)

Ich Danke Dem Herren *Gen/Thanks
SATB,acap voc pt DOBLINGER s.p. see also LOB UND DANK (S1788)

Ich Danke Dem Herrn Von Ganzem Herzen (Psalm 111) SWV 424
SATB,cont,opt 4inst HANSSLER 20.424 sc s.p., cor pts s.p., ipa see also Zwolf Geistliche Gesange (S1789)
(Kessler, Franz) 4pt mix cor,opt org cor pts BREITKOPF-W PB-3774E see also Zwolf Geistliche Gesange-1657 (S1790)

Ich Freu Mich Des, Das Mir Geredt Ist (Psalm 122) SWV 26, Gen
(Ehmann, Wilhelm) [Ger] SSAB&SSAB&SATB& SATB,cont/vcl (med) BAREN. BA 1715 sc $4.50, cor pts $2.20, ipa see also Die Psalmen Davids (S1791)

Ich Glaube An Einen Einigen Gott *SWV 422
SATB,opt cont,4inst HANSSLER 20.422 sc s.p., cor pts s.p., ipa see also Zwolf Geistliche Gesange (S1792)
(Kessler, Franz) 4pt mix cor,opt org cor pts BREITKOPF-W PB-3774C see also Zwolf Geistliche Gesange-1657 (S1793)

Ich Hab Mein Sach Gott Heimgestellt *SWV 305, ECY
(Ehmann, Wilhelm) [Ger] SSATB,SSATB soli, cont (med) BAREN. BA 1708 sc $3.50, cor pts $.55 (S1794)

Ich Harrete Des Herren *SWV 137
see Schutz, Heinrich, Ich Will Bei Meinen Leben Ruhmen
SATB HANSSLER 6.1926 s.p. contains also: Aus Tiefer Not (S1795)

Ich Heb Mein Augen (Psalm 121) SWV 226 (from Der Psalter Nach Cornelius Beckers Dichtungen) Gen,Psalm
SATB,acap (contains also: Die Himmel, Herr, Preisen Sehr) DOBLINGER s.p. see from PSALMLIEDER (S1796)
[Ger] SATB,acap (med easy) BAREN. BA 845 $.25 (S1797)

Ich Heb Mein Augen Sehnlich Auf *SWV 226
SATB,acap DOBLINGER s.p. see also BITTE UND VERTRAUEN (S1798)
SATB HANSSLER 6.034 s.p. contains also: Es Ist Ein Freud Dem Herzen Mein, SWV 227 (S1799)

Ich Hebe Meine Augen Auf Zu Den Bergen (Psalm 121) SWV 31, Gen,Bibl/mot
(Axenfeld) ATB&SATB,cont,2vln cor pts HANSSLER 5.005 s.p., ipa (S1800)
(Ehmann, Wilhelm) [Ger] SATB&SATB,SATB soli,cont/vcl (med) BAREN. BA 1713 sc $3.50, cor pts $1.30, ipa see also Die Psalmen Davids (S1801)
(Kruger) dbl cor,solo,cont sc HANSSLER 20.031 s.p., ipa (S1802)
(Lynn) [Eng/Ger] 4pt mix cor,opt pno oct SCHIRM.G 11900 $.30 contains also: Osiander, Lucas, Komm, Heiliger Geist, Herre Gott, "Come O Holy Ghost, God And Lord" (S1803)

Ich Lieb Dich, Herr, Von Herzen Sehr *SWV 114
SATB HANSSLER 6.175 s.p. contains also: Ich Will, Solang Ich Lebe, Ruhmen Den Herren Mein, SWV 131; In Dich Hab Ich Gehoffet, Herr, SWV 128 (S1804)
SATB HANSSLER 6.022 s.p. contains also: Die Himmel, Herr, Preisen Sehr, SWV 115; Der Herr Ist Konig, Herrlich Schon, SWV 191 (S1805)

Ich, Nur Ich Bin Der Missetater *see Ego Enim Inique Egi

Ich, O Ich Bin Die Qual Deiner Schmerzen *see Ego Sum Tui Plaga Doloris

Ich Rief Zum Herrn *see Ad Dominum, Cum Tribularer

Ich Ruf Zu Dir *Psalm
SATB,acap DOBLINGER s.p. see from PSALMLIEDER (S1806)

Ich Weiss, Dass Mein Erloser Lebet *SWV 457, ECY,mot
(Moser, Hans Joachim) [Ger] SSATTB,acap (med) BAREN. BA 985 $1.75 (S1807)

Ich Weiss, Dass Mein Erloser Lebet *SWV 457
mix cor sc HANSSLER 20.457 s.p. (S1808)

SCHUTZ, HEINRICH (cont'd.)

Ich Weiss, Dass Mein Erloser Lebt *SWV 393, Easter/ECY,mot
6pt mix cor,inst cor pts BREITKOPF-L PB-3375 s.p. see also Geistliche Chormusik 1648 [BH] (S1809)
(Agey) "I Know That My Redeemer Lives" SSAATBB,org/pno oct SCHIRM.G 11386 $.40 (S1810)
(Kamlah, Wilhelm) [Ger] SSAATBB,acap BAREN. BA 525 $.55 see also Geistliche Chormusik 1648 (S1811)

Ich Weiss, Dass Mein Erloser Lebt *SWV 393
SSATTBB,cont,7inst sc HANSSLER 20.393 s.p., ipa (S1812)

Ich Weiss, Woran Ich Glaube
see Kubler, Emil, Ich Weiss, Woran Ich Glaube

Ich Will Bei Meinen Leben Ruhmen *SWV 131
SATB HANSSLER 6.025 s.p. contains also: Ich Harrete Des Herren, SWV 137 (S1813)

Ich Will Den Kelch Des Heiles Annehmen *see Calicem Salutaris

Ich Will Sehr Hoch Erhohen Dich (Psalm 145) SWV 250 (from Der Psalter Nach Cornelius Beckers Dictungen) Gen
see Schutz, Heinrich, Herr, Mein Gebet Erhor In Gnad
[Ger] SATB,acap (med easy) BAREN. BA 845 $.25 (S1814)

Ich Will, Solang Ich Lebe, Ruhmen Den Herren Mein *SWV 131
see Schutz, Heinrich, Ich Lieb Dich, Herr, Von Herzen Sehr
see Stobaeus, Johann, Ich Hab Ein Herzlich Freud

Ich Will Von Herzen Danken Gott, Dem Herrn *SWV 209, Thanks
SATB HANSSLER 6.033 s.p. contains also: Lasst Uns Gott, Unserm Herren (S1815)
SATB HANSSLER 6.2616 s.p. contains also: Kubler, Emil, Sei Lob Und Ehr Dem Hochsten Gut; Marx, Karl, Gelobet Sei Der Herr (S1816)

If God Be For Us, Who Shall Be Against Us? *see Ist Gott Fur Uns, Wer Mag Wider Uns Sein?

Ihr Heiligen Lobsinget Dem Herrn *SWV 288
(Arfken) SA,cont HANSSLER 5.004 s.p. (S1817)

In Den Armen Des Heilandes Und Herren *see Inter Brachia Salvatoris Mei

In Dich, Gott, Hab Ich Gehoffet *see In Te, Domine, Speravi

In Dich Hab Ich Gehoffet, Herr *SWV 128
see Schutz, Heinrich, Ich Lieb Dich, Herr, Von Herzen Sehr
SATB,acap DOBLINGER s.p. see also BITTE UND VERTRAUEN (S1818)

In Te Domine
see Cantiones Sacrae [36]
see Cantiones Sacrae [42]

In Te, Domine, Speravi *mot
"In Dich, Gott, Hab Ich Gehoffet" see Cantiones Sacrae 1625 Band 1 [Nr. 13-14]
[Lat] SATB,acap oct GIA G572 $.25 (S1819)

In Thee, O Lord Do I Put My Trust
(Ehret) mix cor CHAPPELL 0023432-358 $.40 (S1820)

Inter Bracchia
see Cantiones Sacrae [44]

Inter Brachia Salvatoris Mei *SWV 82, Psntd
(Grote, Gottfried) "In Den Armen Des Heilandes Und Herren" [Ger] SATB,cont (med) BAREN. BA 1970 $1.50 see from Cantiones Sacrae 1625 Band 2 [Nr. 30] (S1821)

Ist Gott Fur Uns, Wer Mag Wider Uns Sein? *SWV 329, Bibl/mot
(Agey) "If God Be For Us, Who Shall Be Against Us?" [Eng/Ger] 4pt mix cor,org oct SCHIRM.G 10876 $.40 (S1822)
(Hermann) SATB HANSSLER 1.009 s.p. (S1823)

Ist Nicht Ephraim
mix cor voc sc OXFORD 46.170 $4.15, cor pts OXFORD 46.171 $.75 (S1824)

Ist Nicht Ephraim Mein Teurer Sohn? *Bibl/mot
(Schneider, M.) mix cor,org,2ob,3bsn,4horn, 4trom,strings sc BREITKOPF-L rental (S1825)
(Schneider, Max) 4pt mix cor,org,2ob,3bsn, 4horn,4trom,strings BREITKOPF-W rental (S1826)
(Stern; Nitsche) SATB&SATB&SSAB&ATTB,cont, 4trp,2trom,2vln,vla,opt vcl/bvl, English horn HANSSLER 1.473 sc s.p., ipa, cor pts s.p. (S1827)

Jag Vet, Att Herren Jesus Krist
wom cor/jr cor NORDISKA 2674 s.p. (S1828)

Jauchzet Dem Herren Alle Welt (Psalm 100) SWV 198 (from Der Psalter Nach Cornelius Beckers Dichtungen) Gen,mot/Psalm
SATB&SATB,acap DOBLINGER s.p. see from PSALMLIEDER (S1829)
SATB HANSSLER 6.180 s.p. contains also: Praetorius, Michael, Nun Lob, Mein Seel, Den Herren (S1830)
[Ger] SATB,acap (med easy) BAREN. BA 785 $.25 (S1831)
(Couraud) [Ger] SSSAAATTTBBB oct SALABERT-US $2.50 (S1832)
(Grischkat) SSATB&SSATB&ST&SSATB,orch HANSSLER 1.041 sc s.p., cor pts s.p., ipr (S1833)

Jauchzet Dem Herrn Alle Welt (Psalm 100) SWV 36, Gen/Thanks,mot
SATB,acap voc pt DOBLINGER s.p. see also LOB UND DANK (S1834)

SCHUTZ, HEINRICH (cont'd.)

(Breig, Werner) [Ger] SATB&SATB&SATB,cont (med) sc BAREN. BA 5914 s.p., ipa (S1835)
(Huber, Walter Simon) [Ger] SATB&SATB,acap sc BAREN. BA 480 $1.50 (S1836)
(Iseler) SATB,brass THOMP.G E.I.2002 s.p., ipa (S1837)
(Iseler) [Eng/Ger] SATB&SATB/SATB,opt brass THOMP.G s.p., ipa (S1838)
(Kubler) dbl cor HANSSLER 1.021 s.p. (S1839)
(Lynn, G.) dbl cor,acap oct PRESSER 312-40084 $.40 (S1840)

Jauchzet Gott, Alle Lande Sehr *SWV 163
SATB HANSSLER 6.030 s.p. contains also: Es Steh Gott Auf, Dass Seine Feind, SWV 165 (S1841)

Jesu, I Will Ponder Now *Lent
SATB,acap (med diff) oct CONCORDIA 98-1004 $.30 (S1842)

Jesu Kristi Sju Ord Pa Korset
(Sahlin, Ingvar) sc NORDISKA 1249 s.p., ipa, cor pts NORDISKA 1328 s.p. (S1843)

Jesu Kristi Syv Ord Pa Korset *ora
(Videro, Finn) [Dan] SATTB,soli,cont, strings HANSEN-DEN 26014 s.p., ipa (S1844)

Jesus, Our Lord And Savior *anthem
(Coggin) SATB (easy) oct AUGSBURG 1438 $.22 (S1845)

Jesus, Our Savior For Us Was Born *Xmas
SSA,kbd (diff) oct CONCORDIA 98-1570 $.40 (S1846)

Jesus, Our Saviour, For Us Was Born
(Gore) girl cor SOUTHERN $.40 (S1847)

Jesus, Son Of God
(Coggin) SATB,acap BOSTON 13323 $.30 (S1848)

Johannes-Passion *SWV 481, Psntd
(Kamlah, Wilhelm) [Ger] SATB,TB soli,soli, acap (med) BAREN. BA 960 sc $3.25, cor pts $1.50 (S1849)

Johannespassion *SWV 481, Psntd,Bibl
"Passion Of St. John, The" see Baroque To The Great Classics, The Vol. 2b-1550 To 1700
"St. John Passion" [Ger/Eng] SATB&opt ATTB, soli HANSSLER 20.481 sc $3.50, voc sc $1.50 (S1850)
(Holst, Imogen; Pears, Peter) "Passion According To St. John, The" [Eng] SATB, soli,acap (med) voc sc OXFORD $1.80 (S1851)
(Holst; Pears) "Saint John Passion" SATB,T solo,acap (med diff) voc sc OXFORD 46.131 $1.80 (S1852)
(Mendelssohn, A.) 4pt mix cor,STTBB soli, org/acap BREITKOPF-W rental (S1853)
(Mendelssohn, Arnold) mix cor,soli,org/pno sc BREITKOPF-L EB-1250 s.p., voc pt BREITKOPF-L CHB-336 s.p. (S1854)

Know All That God So Loved The World *Xmas/Easter
(Stone) SATTB/SAATB,acap oct WORD CRS-16 $.40 (S1855)

Komm Heiliger Geist *SWV 417 (from Deutschen Konzerten) Bibl/mot
dbl cor,cont,inst sc HANSSLER 1.675 s.p., cor pts HANSSLER 20.417 s.p.† ipa see from SYMPHONIAE SACRAE III (S1856)
(Sporn, F.) dbl cor,6 soli,org,strings sc BREITKOPF-L PB-3274 s.p., cor pts BREITKOPF-L CHB-2597 s.p. (S1857)

Komm, Ich Bitt Dich, In Mein Herze *see Veni, Rogo In Cor Meum

Kommt Her, Des Konigs Aufgebot *SWV 195
see Bach, Johann Sebastian, Komm, Gott Schopfer, Heiliger Geist
SATB HANSSLER 6.2564 s.p. contains also: Bach, Johann Sebastian, O Haupt Voll Blut Und Wunden (from Matthaus-Passion) (Easter) (S1858)

Kommt Herzu, Lasst Uns Frohlich Sein *SWV 193
see Schutz, Heinrich, Danket Dem Herrn Erzeigt Ihm Ehr

Kommt Herzu, Lasst Uns Frolichsein *Gen/Thanks
SATB,acap voc pt DOBLINGER s.p. see also LOB UND DANK (S1859)

Kyrie Eleison *Kyrie
cor,cont sc HANSSLER 20.602 $1.75 (S1860)

Kyrie Eleison, Christe Erhore Uns
(Kessler, Franz) 4pt,opt org cor pts BREITKOPF-W PB-3774J s.p. see also Zwolf Geistliche Gesange-1657 (S1861)

Kyrie, God Vater *see Kyrie, Gott Vater In Ewigkeit

Kyrie, Gott Vater In Ewigkeit *SWV 420, mot
(Kessler, Franz) 4pt mix cor,opt org cor pts BREITKOPF-W PB-3774A see also Zwolf Geistliche Gesange-1657 (S1862)
(Kubler) "Kyrie, God Vater" [Eng/Ger] SATB, cont,orch HANSSLER 20.420 sc $1.25, cor pts s.p., voc pt $.60, ipa see also Zwolf Geistliche Gesange (S1863)

Lamb Of God *Gen
(Riedel) SATB SCHMITT 1402 $.30 (S1864)

Lasset Uns Doch Den Herren, Unsern Gott, Loben *SWV 407
"Let Us Declare The Glory Of The Lord, Our God" [Ger/Eng] SSTB&opt SATB,soli,org, 2vln,vcl sc HANSSLER 20.407 $2.50, ipa see from SYMPHONIAE SACRAE III (S1865)

Lasst Uns Den Herren Loben *SWV 239, Thanks
SATB HANSSLER 6.1425 s.p. contains also: Anonymous, Wir Fahr'n Dahin, Wirf Helles Licht (S1866)
SATB HANSSLER 6.195 s.p. contains also: Stern, Hermann, Ich Freu Mich In Dem

SCHUTZ, HEINRICH (cont'd.)

Herren (SAT/SAB); Horn, Paul, Nun Danket All Und Bringet Ehr (SAT/SAB) (S1867)

Lasst Uns Gott, Unserm Herren
see Schutz, Heinrich, Ich Will Von Herzen Danken Gott, Dem Herrn

Le Sette Parole Di Cristo Sulla Croce *see Die Sieben Worte Jesu Am Kreuz

Let The People Give Thanks
(Lynn, G.) SATB oct PRESSER MC271 $.25 (S1868)

Let Us Declare The Glory Of The Lord, Our God *see Lasset Uns Doch Den Herren, Unsern Gott, Loben

Lift Up Your Heads, O Ye Gates *mot
(Stevens, Denis) SSAATTBB,opt org/pno PETERS 6592 $.90 (S1869)

Lo, I Am The Voice Of One Crying In The Wilderness *see Ich Bin Eine Rufende Stimme In Der Wusten

Lo, The Angel Said To The Shepherds *see Der Engle Sprach Zu Den Hirten

Lo, The Scepter From Judah *Adv/Gen
SATTB,kbd (med diff) oct CONCORDIA 98-1559 $.30 (S1870)

Lob Und Preis Sei Gott
(Martens, Mason) "Praise And Thanks To God" SATB oct WALTON 2094 $.25 (S1871)

Lob Und Preis Sei Gott, Dem Vater (from Ich Danke Dem Herrn Von Ganzem Herzen) mot
(Gerger) SATB HANSSLER 20.424-1 s.p. (S1872)

Lobe Den Herren, Meine Seele *mot
(Hermann) dbl cor HANSSLER 1.018 s.p. (S1873)
(Kubler) dbl cor,opt SATB soli,cont HANSSLER 1.040 s.p. (S1874)

Lobe Den Herrn, Meine Seele (Psalm 103) SWV 39, Gen
(Rabenschlag, Friedrich) [Ger] SATB&SATB, SATB soli,cont/vcl (med) sc BAREN. BA 1588 $2.50, ipa see also Die Psalmen Davids (S1875)

Lobt Gott, Den Herrn Der Herrlichkeit
see Franck, Melchior, Aus Tiefer Not Schrei Ich Zu Dir

Lobt Gott In Seinem Heiligtum *SWV 255
SATB HANSSLER 6.1927 s.p. contains also: Frohlockt Mit Freud', Ihr Volker All, SWV 144 (S1876)

Lobt Gott Mit Schall (Psalm 117)
[Ger/Eng] SATB,pno BROUDE BR. $.35 (S1877)
[Norw] LYCHE 19 s.p. (S1878)

Lobt Gott Mit Schall, Ihr Heiden All (Psalm 150) SWV 256SWV 215, cor-resp/mot
(Nitsche) SATB HANSSLER 20.215 s.p. contains also: Alles, Was Odem Hat, Lobe Den Herren (S1879)

Lobt Gott Von Herzensgrunde *Thanks
SATB HANSSLER 6.189 s.p. contains also: Goudimel, Claude, Lobt Den Herrn, Denn Was Er Tut (S1880)

Lobt, Ihr Himmel, Gott Den Herrn *SWV 253
see Schutz, Heinrich, Mein Seel Soll Loben Gott, Den Herrn

Lord, I Long For Thee Only *see Musikalische Exequien-Teil 2: Herr, Wenn Ich Nur Dich Liebe

Lord, If I But Thee May Have *see Herr, Wenn Ich Nur Dich Habe

Lord, In Thee I Do Trust *Gen/Lent
SSATB,kbd (med diff) oct CONCORDIA 98-1921 $.60 (S1881)

Lord Is My Shepherd, The *see Der Herr Ist Mein Hirt

Lord Is Ruler Over All
(Lenel) boy cor SOUTHERN $.25 (S1882)

Lord Is Ruler Over All, The *Gen
TTBB,kbd (med easy) oct CONCORDIA 98-1484 $.25 (S1883)

Lord Jesus On The Cross Was Hung (from Seven Last Words, The)
(Coggin) 4pt mix cor,acap oct SCHIRM.G 11552 $.30 (S1884)

Lord Now Lettest Thou Servant *see Herr, Nun Lassest Du Deinen Diener

Lord, Now Lettest Thou Thy Servant *see Herr, Nun Lassest Du Deinen Diener

Lord, Now Lettest Thou Thy Servant *see Herr, Nun Lassest Du Deinen Diener

Lord, Redeemer Of All Who Know Thee (from St. Matthew Passion)
(Coggin) 4pt mix cor,acap oct SCHIRM.G 11559 $.30 (S1885)

Lord Tends Me Well, The *see Der Herr Ist Mein Hirt

Lord, What Hast Thou Done? *Easter
(York, S.) SATB,acap oct PRESSER 312-40609 $.40 (S1886)

Lord, Who Is My Guide But Thee?
dbl cor,acap oct PRESSER 312-40173 $.35 (S1887)

Love Den Herren, Meine Seele
(Granville) "Sing, O My Soul, The Father's Praises" SATB&SATB,acap oct FOX CM28 $.35 (S1888)

SCHUTZ, HEINRICH (cont'd.)

Lukas-Passion *SWV 480, Psntd
(Kamlah, Wilhelm) [Ger] SATB,TB soli,acap (med) BAREN. BA 696 sc $3.75, cor pts $1.50 (S1889)

Lukaspassion *SWV 480, Psntd,Bibl
"Passion Of St. Luke, The" see Baroque To The Great Classics, The Vol. 2b-1550 To 1700
"St. John Passion" [Ger] SATB,acap min sc PETERS E979 $2.50 (S1890)
"St. Luke Passion" [Ger] SATB,acap min sc PETERS E978 $2.50 (S1891)
"St. Luke Passion" [Ger/Eng] SATB,soli HANSSLER 20.480 sc $3.50, voc sc $2.50 (S1892)
(Agey, C. Buell) "Annunciation According To St. Luke, The" [Eng/Ger] 5pt mix cor,SA soli,org/pno/inst voc sc SCHIRM.G $.75 (S1893)
(Mendelssohn, A.) 4pt mix cor,STTBB soli, org/acap s.p. cor pts BREITKOPF-W CHB-3466, voc sc BREITKOPF-W EB-5346 (S1894)
(Mendelssohn, Arnold) mix cor,TB soli,org/pno sc BREITKOPF-L EB-5346 s.p. (S1895)
(Steinitz) "Saint Luke Passion" SATB (med diff) voc sc OXFORD 46.120 $2.50 (S1896)
(Steinitz, Paul) "Passion According To St. Luke, The" [Eng] SATB,acap (med) voc sc OXFORD $2.50 (S1897)

Machet Die Tore Weit *Xmas,mot
[Ger] dbl cor voc sc HINRICHSEN P4176 s.p. (S1898)

Macht Auf Die Tor *Adv/Xmas
SATB,acap (contains also: Praetorius, Michael, Es Ist Ein Ros Entsprungen) voc pt DOBLINGER s.p. see also ADVENT UND WEIHNACHT, HEFT 1 (S1899)

Magnificat *SWV 468, Gen,Magnif
(Ehmann, Wilhelm) [Ger] 3 cor/dbl cor,SATB soli,org,cont,3trom,2vln,bvl,opt vcl (med diff) BAREN. BA 4334 sc $8.50, cor pts $1.30, ipa (S1900)
(Spitta, H.) mix cor,org,2fl,ob,2bsn,trp, 3trom,7strings cor pts BREITKOPF-L CHB-2566 s.p., sc BREITKOPF-L EB-5422 s.p., ipr (S1901)
(Spitta, Heinrich) SATB&SATB,org,ob,2bsn, trp,3trom,strings cor pts BREITKOPF-W CHB-3498 s.p., ipr, voc sc BREITKOPF-W EB-5422 s.p., sc BREITKOPF-W rental (S1902)

Magnificat Anima Mea Dominum *Magnif
"Uppsala-Magnificat" [Lat/Ger] SATB&SATB, SATB soli,org,3trom,2vln,vcl,bvl HANSSLER 20.468 sc $5.00, voc sc $1.75, cor pts $.90, ipa (S1903)

Magnify Him *see Meine Seele Erhebt Den Herren

Magnify Him *see Meine Seele Erhebt Den Herren

Many Shall Come From The East And West *see Viel Werden Kommen Von Morgen Und Von Abend

Matthaus-Passion *SWV 479, Psntd
(Schmidt, Fritz) [Ger] SATB,TB soli,acap (med) sc BAREN. BA 300 $3.50, cor pts BAREN. BA 390 $1.50 (S1904)

Matthauspassion *SWV 479, Psntd,Bibl
"Passion Of St. Matthew, The" see Baroque To The Great Classics, The Vol. 2b-1550 To 1700
cor HANSSLER 20.479 sc s.p., voc sc s.p. (S1905)
"St. Matthew Passion" [Ger] SATB,acap min sc PETERS E976 $2.50 (S1906)
(Gore, R.T.) "Passion According To St. Matthew, The" mix cor,soli sc CONCORDIA 97-7573 $2.25, cor pts CONCORDIA 97-6224 $1.00 (S1907)
(Holst, Imogen; Pears, Peter) "Passion According To St. Matthew, The" [Eng] SATB,soli,acap (med) voc sc OXFORD $2.30 (S1908)
(Holst; Pears) "Saint Matthew Passion" SATB (med) voc sc OXFORD 46.145 $2.30 (S1909)
(Mendelssohn, A.) 4pt mix cor,STTBB soli, org/acap voc pt BREITKOPF-W CHB-326 s.p., voc sc BREITKOPF-W EB-720 s.p. (S1910)
(Mendelssohn, Arnold) mix cor,soli,org/pno sc BREITKOPF-L EB-720 s.p., voc pt BREITKOPF-L CHB-326 s.p. (S1911)

May God Bestow
see Three Choral Psalms

Meim Herzen Ist's Ein Grosse Freud *SWV 214
SATB HANSSLER 6.183 s.p. contains also: Praetorius, Michael, Lobet Den Herren, Alle Heiden; Schutz, Heinrich, Wohl Denen, Die Da Wandeln (S1912)

Mein Herz Dichtet Ein Lied Mit Fleiss *SWV 142
see Schutz, Heinrich, Ich Bin Verstummet Ganz Und Still

Mein Seel Ist Still In Meinem Gott *SWV 159
see Schutz, Heinrich, Herr Gott, Erzeig Mir Hilf Und Gnad

Mein Seel Soll Loben Gott, Den Herrn *SWV 251, Thanks
SATB HANSSLER 6.037 s.p. contains also: Lobt, Ihr Himmel, Gott Den Herrn, SWV 253; Alles, Was Odem Hat, Lobe Den Herrn, SWV 256 (S1913)

Mein Sohn, Warum Hast Du Uns Das Getan? *SWV 401 (from Symphoniae Sacrae, III, No. 4) mot
mix cor,cont,inst cor pts HANSSLER 20.401 r.p., sc HANSSLER 1.659 s.p., ipa (S1914)
"Der Zwolfjahrige Jesus" [Ger] SATB,acap voc sc PETERS HU1354 $1.50, ipr (S1915)
(Gore, R.T.) "My Son, Wherefore Hast Thou Done This To Us?" [Ger/Eng] cor,SAB soli, strings,cont sc CONCORDIA 97-9347 $2.50, cor pts CONCORDIA 97-6393 $.25, ipa (S1916)
(Steinitz, Paul) "My Son, Why Hast Thou So Dealt With Us?" mix cor,SAB soli,2vln& cont&opt winds/org (med) sc OXFORD 46.129 $1.55, ipr (S1917)

Meine Seele Erhebt Den Herren *SWV 426
(Kessler, Franz) 4pt,opt org cor pts BREITKOPF-W PB-3774G s.p. see also Zwolf Geistliche Gesange-1657 (S1918)

Meine Seele Erhebt Den Herren *SWV 494, Magnif
"Magnify Him" dbl cor,org/vcl HANSSLER 20.494 sc $3.00, voc sc $1.00 (S1919)

Meine Seele Erhebt Den Herren *SWV 426, Magnif/mot
(Berger) "Magnify Him" [Ger/Eng] SATB,org, vcl HANSSLER 20.426 sc $1.50, cor pts $.60, ipa see also Zwolf Geistliche Gesange (S1920)

Meine Worte Hore *see Verba Mea Auribus Percipe

Meister, Wir Haben Die Ganze Nacht Gearbeitet *SWV 317
(Stern) SS/TT,cont HANSSLER 5.032 s.p. (S1921)

Meister, Wir Wissen, Dass Du Wahrhaftig Bist *SWV 414, Trin
(Holle, Rudolf) [Ger] SATB,SSATB soli,cont, bsn,2vln (med) BAREN. BA 1486 sc $3.00, cor pts $.80, ipa see from SYMPHONIAE SACRAE III (S1922)

Mighty Fortress Is Our God, A (Psalm 46)
see Five Psalms From The "Becker Psalter"

Mit Dank Wir Sollen Loben *SWV 104
see Raselius, Andreas, Wohl Dem Menschen, Der Wandelt

Musikalische Exequien-Teil 1 *SWV 279, CCU, funeral,Ger
[Ger/Eng] SSATTBB&opt SSATTB,org sc HANSSLER 20.279 $5.00 (S1923)

Musikalische Exequien-Teil 2: Herr, Wenn Ich Nur Dich Liebe *SWV 280
"Lord, I Long For Thee Only" sc HANSSLER 20.280 $1.25 (S1924)

Musikalische Exequien-Teil 3 *SWV 391, Nunc
[Ger/Eng] SATB&SSB&opt SSB&SSB,org sc HANSSLER 20.281 $1.25
contains: Herr, Nun Lassest Du Deinen Diener, "Lord, Now Lettest Thou Thy Servant"; Selig Sind Die Toten, "Blessed Are The Dead" (S1925)

My Son, Wherefore Hast Thou Done This To Us? *see Mein Sohn, Warum Hast Du Uns Das Getan?

My Son, Why Hast Thou So Dealt With Us? *see Mein Sohn, Warum Hast Du Uns Das Getan?

My Soul Doth Magnify The Lord *see Deutsches Magnificat

Nicht Uns, Herr, Sondern Deinem Namen *mot
(Grischkat) 3 cor,orch HANSSLER 1.043 voc sc s.p., ipr, sc s.p. (S1926)

Nonne Hic Est
"Ohn Alle Schuld" see Cantiones Sacrae 1625 Band 2 [Nr. 21-23]

Now Let Us All Give Thanks *cant
(Niven) mix cor BELWIN $1.00 (S1927)

Nu Takker Vi Alle Gud
[Norw] LYCHE 43 s.p. (S1928)

Nun Danket Alle Gott *Thanks
cor,6 soli,org,2horn,trp,trom,strings sc BREITKOPF-L rental (S1929)
(Horn) SSATB&SATB,cont,2vln HANSSLER 5.010 sc s.p., cor pts s.p., ipa (S1930)

Nun Lob, Mein Seel, Den Herren (Psalm 103) SWV 41, Gen,mot
(Ehmann, Wilhelm) [Ger] SATB&SATB&SSATB& SSATB/SATB&SATB,cont&org/vcl&bvl/3trp& 2trom&3vln&vla&vcl/2vcl&bvl/2bvl (med) BAREN. BA 3465 sc $9.50, cor pts $1.15, ipa see also Die Psalmen Davids (S1931)
(Grischkat) dbl cor,orch voc sc HANSSLER 1.044 s.p., ipr (S1932)

Nun Lob, Mein Seel, Den Herrn
(Spitta, H.) dbl cor,org,4trp,trom,strings sc BREITKOPF-L rental (S1933)

Nun Sei Dem Vater Dank (from Das Benedicite Vor Dem Essen)
see Zwolf Geistliche Gesange

O, All Ye Nations
SATB,acap oct PRESSER 332-13992 $.30 (S1934)

O Blessed Lord Our God *see O Lieber Herre Gott, Wecke Uns Aub

O Bone
see Cantiones Sacrae [41]

O Bone Jesu, Fili Mariae *SWV 471
SSAATB/SSAATTB,org,3vln,2vla,2vcl sc HANSSLER 20.471 $2.00, ipa (S1935)

O Bone, O Dulcis
"O Guter, O Lieber" see Cantiones Sacrae 1625 Band 1 [Nr. 1-3]

O Clap Your Hands
see Three Choral Psalms

O Come, All Ye Children *anthem
(Bender) unis treb cor,opt inst (easy) oct AUGSBURG 0405 $.20 (S1936)

O Dear, O Friendly, O Kind And Gentle Savior *Gen
unis,kbd (med easy) oct CONCORDIA 98-1585 $.25 (S1937)

O Dearest Lord God *see O Lieber Herre Gott

O Dulcis
see Cantiones Sacrae [41]

O Gracious Lord, Our God *Adv/Gen
SS,kbd (med easy) oct CONCORDIA 98-1558 $.30 (S1938)

O Guter, O Lieber *see O Bone, O Dulcis

O Hear Me, Lord *anthem
(Wunderlich) SS/SA (med) oct AUGSBURG 1512 $.25 (S1939)

O Herr, Hilf, O Herr, Lass Wohl Gelingen
"O Save Us, Lord" SST,org,vcl HANSSLER 20.297 sc $1.25, voc pt $.60 (S1940)
(Stern) SAB,cont HANSSLER 5.031 s.p. (S1941)

O Herr, Hilf, O Herr, Lass Wohl Gelingen *SWV 402
"O Save Us, Lord" [Ger/Eng] SST,org,2vln, vcl HANSSLER 20.402 sc $1.25, cor pts s.p., ipa see from SYMPHONIAE SACRAE III (S1942)

O Hilf, Christe, Gottes Sohn *SWV 342 (from Johannespassion)
SATB,opt cont cor pts HANSSLER 20.481-1 s.p. (S1943)
(Trubel) TT,cont HANSSLER 5.014 s.p. (S1944)

O Lieber Herre Gott *Adv
"O Dearest Lord God" SSATTB,acap (med diff) oct CONCORDIA 98-1884 $.65 (S1945)

O Lieber Herre Gott, Wecke Uns Aub
"O Blessed Lord Our God" 2 eq voices SCHIRM.EC 2787 $.30 see from Three Little Sacred Concertos (S1946)

O Lieber Herre Gott, Wecke Uns Auf *SWV 381, Adv,mot
6pt mix cor,acap cor pts BREITKOPF-L PB-3363 s.p. see also Geistliche Chormusik 1648 [BH] (S1947)
2pt wom cor/2pt jr cor,org/pno/cembalo cor pts BREITKOPF-W CHB-3488 s.p. (S1948)
SSATB,cont,inst sc HANSSLER 20.381 s.p., ipa (S1949)
"O Mighty God, Our Lord" boy cor/girl cor SOUTHERN $.25 (S1950)
(Boepple, P.) "O Mighty God, Our Lord" SA/TB oct PRESSER 352-00018 $.30 (S1951)
(Kamlah, Wilhelm) [Ger] SSATTB,acap (med) BAREN. BA 513 $.55 see also Geistliche Chormusik 1648 (S1952)
(Stern) SS/TT,cont HANSSLER 20.287 s.p. (S1953)

O Lord, Creator Of All Thing *see Ach Herr, Du Schopfer Aller Ding

O May The Eyes Of All *see Oculi Omnium In Te Sperant, Domine

O Meine Hoffnung, Jesus *see Spes Mea, Christe Deus

O Mighty God, Our Lord *see O Lieber Herre Gott, Wecke Uns Auf

O Nimm An Mein Taglich Klagen *see Quoniam Ad Te Clamabo

O Praise The Lord, Ye People All *see Cantate Domino

O Risen Lord! O Conquering King *Easter
see Three Chorales For Easter And Ascension
SATB,kbd (easy) oct CONCORDIA 98-1234 $.20 (S1954)

O Save Us, Lord *see O Herr, Hilf, O Herr, Lass Wohl Gelingen

O Save Us, Lord *see O Herr, Hilf, O Herr, Lass Wohl Gelingen

O Sing Ye To The Lord *see Cantate Domino

O Sing Ye Unto The Lamb *see Cantate Domino

O Sing Ye Unto The Lord *see Cantate Domino

O Sohn Des Hochsten *see Quo, Nate Dei

O Susser Jesu Christ
(Kessler, Franz) 4pt,opt org cor pts BREITKOPF-W PB-3774H s.p. see also Zwolf Geistliche Gesange-1657 (S1955)

O Susser Jesu Christ *SWV 405 (from Symphoniae Sacrae III) Gen
(Bittinger, Werner) [Ger] SATB,SSAT soli, opt cont&2vln (med) BAREN. BA 3369 sc $3.75, cor pts $1.00, ipa (S1956)

O Susser Jesu Christ *SWV 427, Bibl/mot
mix cor,cont,inst HANSSLER 20.427 sc s.p., voc pt s.p., ipa (S1957)

O Weh Mir, Herr, Mein Gott *see Heu Mihe, Domine

Oculi Omnium
see Cantiones Sacrae 1625 Band 2 [Nr. 36-40]

Oculi Omnium In Te Sperant, Domine *Gen
"To Thee We Turn Our Eyes" SATB,kbd (med easy) oct CONCORDIA 98-1885 $.25 (S1958)
(Payson, A.) "O May The Eyes Of All" SATB, acap FRANK F-572 $.30 (S1959)

Oh, Hear Me When I Cry To Thee (Psalm 4)
see Five Psalms From The "Becker Psalter"

Ohn Alle Schuld *see Nonne Hic Est

On Wings Of Living Radiance *Easter
see Three Chorales For Easter And Ascension
SATB,kbd (easy) oct CONCORDIA 98-1234 $.20 (S1960)

One Thing Have I Desired *Gen
SA/TB,kbd (med easy) oct CONCORDIA 98-1369 $.25 (S1961)

SCHUTZ, HEINRICH (cont'd.)

Our Father *see Das Vaterunser

Our Father Which Art In Heaven *see Vater
Unser, Der Du Bist Im Himmel

Our God Ascended *Easter
see Three Chorales For Easter And Ascension
SATB (easy) oct CONCORDIA 98-1234 $.20
(S1962)

Our Lord Did Suffer Death
(Ehret) SATB ct SACRED S-115 $.35 (S1963)

Out Of The Depths We Cry, Lord *anthem
(Coggin) mix cor SOUTHERN $.25 (S1964)
(Coggin) SATB (easy) oct AUGSBURG 1546 $.25
(S1965)

Paskdialog
(Ahlen, David) [Swed/Ger] cor,org NORDISKA
3331 s.p. see from Tre Bibliska Scener
(S1966)

Passion According To St. John, The *see
Johannespassion

Passion According To St. Luke, The *see
Lukaspassion

Passion According To St. Matthew, The *see
Matthauspassion

Passion Of Our Lord Jesus Christ, The
(Klein, Maynard) mix cor,acap voc sc BOOSEY
$1.50 (S1967)

Passion Of St. John, The *see
Johannespassion

Passion Of St. Luke, The *see Lukaspassion

Passion Of St. Matthew, The *see
Matthauspassion

Passion, The (from Four Passions) Lent/Psntd
SATB,ATB soli,org voc sc NOVELLO s.p.
(S1968)

Pater Noster
see Cantiones Sacrae 1625 Band 2 [Nr. 36-
40]

Pharisaeer Und Zoellner
[Ger] SATB,acap voc sc PETERS HU1353 $1.25
(S1969)

Pharisee And The Publican
(Dickinson) SATB oct GRAY GSC 139 $.25
(S1970)

Pharisee And The Publican, The
see Two Dialogues

Pharisee And The Publican, The *see Es
Gingen Zweene Menschen

Ponder My Words, O Lord (from Cantiones
Sacrae) mot
SATB,acap PETERS H111 $.40 (S1971)

Praise And Thanks To God *see Lob Und Preis
Sei Gott

Praise Be To Thee
(Lundquist) SATB,acap (diff) oct WILLIS
8406 $.18 (S1972)

Praise God, The Lord, Ye People All (Psalm
150)
see Five Psalms From The "Becker Psalter"

Praise God, Ye Lands
see Schutz, Heinrich, How Lovely Is Thy
Dwelling Place

Praise To Thee, Lord Jesus *Lent,anthem
(Harris, William, H.) mix cor oct NOVELLO
28.1202.09 s.p. (S1973)

Pro Hoc Domine Non Est
see Cantiones Sacrae [44]

Pro Hoc Magno Mysterio
see Schutz, Heinrich, Supereminet Omnem
Scientiam
"Fur Solch Grosses Mysterium" see Cantiones
Sacrae 1625 Band 2 [Nr. 24-25]

Psalm 1
mix cor SOUTHERN $.25 (S1974)
SATB oct PRESSER MC171 $.30 (S1975)

Psalm 2 *see Warum Toben Die Heiden

Psalm 4 *see Oh, Hear Me When I Cry To Thee

Psalm 6 &see Ach Herr, Strafe Mich Nicht

Psalm 8 *see Herr, Unser Herrscher

Psalm 13 *see Ach Herr, Wie Lang Willt Du
Denn Noch

Psalm 14 *see Der Herr Schauet Vom Himmel

Psalm 19 *see Die Himmel Erzahlen Die Ehre
Gottes

Psalm 19 *see Die Himmel Erzahlen Die Ehre
Gottes

Psalm 23 *see Der Herr Ist Mein Getreuer
Hirt

Psalm 23 *see Der Herr Ist Mein Hirt

Psalm 24 *see Domini Est Terra

Psalm 29
see Two Short Psalms
(Lynn, G.) SATB,acap oct PRESSER 312-40072
$.30 (S1976)

Psalm 42 *see Was Betrubst Du Dich, Meine
Seele

Psalm 46 *see Mighty Fortress Is Our God, A

Psalm 71 *see Auf Dich, Herr, Trau Ich
Allezeit

SCHUTZ, HEINRICH (cont'd.)

Psalm 84 *see Wie Lieblich Sind Deine
Wohnungen

Psalm 85 *see Herr, Der Du Vormals Gnadig
Warst

Psalm 96 *see Singet Dem Herrn Ein Neues
Lied, All Welt Soll Frohlich Singen Mit

Psalm 97 *see Der Herr Ist Konig Uberall

Psalm 98 *see Singet Dem Herrn Ein Neues
Lied

Psalm 98 *see Singet Dem Herrn Ein Neues
Lied, Denn Durch Ihn Gross Wunder
Geschieht

Psalm 98 *see Singet Dem Herrn

Psalm 99 *see Der Herr Ist Konig Und Regiert

Psalm 100 *see Jauchzet Dem Herren Alle Welt

Psalm 100 *see Jauchzet Dem Herrn, Alle Welt

Psalm 103 *see Lobe Den Herrn, Meine Seele

Psalm 103 *see Nun Lob, Mein Seel, Den
Herren

Psalm 111 *see Ich Danke Dem Herrn Von
Ganzem Herzen

Psalm 116 *see Das Ist Mir Lieb, Dass Der
Herr Mein Stimm Und Flehen Horet

Psalm 117 *see Lobt Gott Mit Schall

Psalm 119 *see Wohl Denen, Die Da Wandeln

Psalm 121 *see Ich Heb Mein Augen

Psalm 121 *see Ich Hebe Meine Augen Auf Zu
Den Bergen

Psalm 122 *see Ich Freu Mich Des, Das Mir
Geredt Ist

Psalm 126 *see Die Mit Tranen Saen

Psalm 127 *see Wo Der Herr Nicht Das Haus
Bauet

Psalm 130 *see Aus Der Tiefe Rufe Ich

Psalm 130 *see Aus Tiefer Not Schrei Ich Zu
Dir

Psalm 136 *see Danket Dem Herren, Denn Er
Ist Freundlich

Psalm 137 *see An Den Wasserflussen Zu Babel
Sassen Wir Und Weineten

Psalm 138 *see Aus Meines Herzens Grunde

Psalm 143 *see Herr, Mein Gebet Erhor

Psalm 145 *see Ich Will Sehr Hoch Erhohen
Dich

Psalm 150 *see Lobt Gott Mit Schall, Ihr
Heiden All

Purge Out Therefore The Old Leaven
(Stevens, Denis) SATB,org,2vln/2ob,vcl/
bsn voc sc PETERS 6593 $.40, ipa see from
Three Sacred Concertos (S1977)

Quid Commisisti
"Was Hast Du Verwirket" see Cantiones
Sacrae 1625 Band 1 [Nr. 4-8]

Quid Detur Tibi
"Was Er Dir Geben Moge, Du Zunge Voll
Falschheit" see Cantiones Sacrae 1625
Band 1 [Nr. 19-20]

Quo, Nate Dei
"O Sohn Des Hochsten" see Cantiones Sacrae
1625 Band 1 [Nr. 4-8]

Quoniam Ad Te
see Cantiones Sacrae [41]

Quoniam Ad Te Clamabo
"O Nimm An Mein Taglich Klagen" see
Cantiones Sacrae 1625 Band 1 [Nr. 9-10]

Quoniam Non Est In Morte
"Hore Mich, Herr, Bei Den Toten Gedenkt Man
Deiner Nicht" see Cantiones Sacrae 1625
Band 2 [Nr. 33-35]

Reduc, Domine Deus Meus
"Wende, Du Unser Richter" see Cantiones
Sacrae 1625 Band 2 [Nr. 21-23]

Responsorium (Alleluja)
(Agey) 4pt mix cor,org oct SCHIRM.G 11520
$.25 (S1978)

Resurrection History
[Ger] dbl cor,SATB soli,strings&opt org/
cembalo s.p. voc sc HINRICHSEN P4661,sc
HINRICHSEN P4661 (S1979)

Resurrection Oratorio *see Historia Der
Geburt Jesu Christi

Sacred Choir Music, 1648 *see Die Mit Tranen
Saen, "He Who With Weeping Soweth"; Ich
Bin Eine Rufende Stimme In Der Wusten,
"Lo, I Am The Voice Of One Crying In The
Wilderness"; Selig Sind Die Toten,
"Blessed Are The Faithful" (S1980)

Saget Den Gasten *SWV 459, mot
(Graulich) SATB,cont,bsn,2vln HANSSLER
20.459 sc $2.00, cor pts s.p., ipa
(S1981)

Saint John Passion *see Johannespassion

Saint Luke Passion *see Lukaspassion

SCHUTZ, HEINRICH (cont'd.)

Saint Matthew Passion *see Matthauspassion

Sammelt Zuvor Das Unkraut *SWV 376, Epiph,
mot
5pt mix cor,acap cor pts BREITKOPF-L
PB-3358 s.p. see also Geistliche
Chormusik 1648 [BH] (S1982)
SATTB,cont,inst sc HANSSLER 20.376 s.p.,
ipa (S1983)
(Kamlah, Wilhelm) SATTB,acap (med) BAREN.
BA 508 $.40 see also Geistliche Chormusik
1648 (S1984)

Saul
[Ger] dbl cor,SSATBB soli,2vln,cont sc
HINRICHSEN P4815 s.p. (S1985)
[Ger] 14pt,org/pno,opt 2vln PETERS 4815
$1.00, ipa (S1986)

Saul, Saul, Was Verfolgst Du Mich *SWV 415
(from Symphoniae Sacrae III) Gen,Bibl
SSTTBB,org,4horn,3trp,3trom,strings
BREITKOPF-W rental (S1987)
(Bittinger, Werner) [Ger] SATB&SATB, SSATBB
soli,cont&2vln/2vln&vcl (med) BAREN.
BA 3466 sc $2.75, cor pts $.80, ipa
(S1988)
(Horn) SSATBB&SATB&SATB,cont,2vln HANSSLER
20.415 sc s.p., cor pts s.p., ipa (S1989)

Saul, Was Verfolgst Du Mich? (from Symphonie
Sacrae III)
6pt mix cor,org,3trp,4horn,3trom,strings sc
BREITKOPF-L rental (S1990)

Schaffe In Mir, Gott, Ein Reines Herz
(Trubel) ST,cont HANSSLER 5.013 s.p.
(S1991)

Schaue Doch, Vater *see Aspice, Pater

See The Fig Tree
(Bowman) [Eng/Ger] 2pt mix cor oct LAWSON
806 $.25 (S1992)

Sehet An Den Feigenbaum *SWV 394, Adv,mot
7pt mix cor,inst cor pts BREITKOPF-L
PB-3376 s.p. see also Geistliche
Chormusik 1648 [BH] (S1993)
SSATTBB,cont,7inst sc HANSSLER 20.394 s.p.,
ipa (S1994)
(Kamlah, Wilhelm) [Ger] ST,vln,2vla,2vcl
(med) BAREN. BA 526 $.65 see also
Geistliche Chormusik 1648 (S1995)
(Thomas, Kurt) ST,org,fl,ob,bsn,trp,trom,
vcl sc BREITKOPF-W PB-3376 s.p. see also
Geistliche Chormusik 1648 (S1996)

Sei Gegrusset, Maria *SWV 333, Adv
[Ger] SSATB,ST soli,cont,3vln,vla,vcl (med)
BAREN. BA 3433 sc $2.50, cor pts $.40,
ipa (S1997)
"Hail, O Hail To Thee, Mary" [Eng/Ger]
SSATB,SA soli,org,3vln,2vla,vcl sc
HANSSLER 20.333 $1.25, ipa (S1998)

Sei Gegrusset, Maria *see Ave Maria, Gratia
Plena

Seid Barmherzig, Wie Auch Euer Vater
Barmherzig Ist *SWV 409, mot
"Be Ye Loving Even As Your Father Hath
Loved You" [Ger/Lat] SATB,org,bsn,2vln,
vcl sc HANSSLER 20.409 $2.50, ipa see
from SYMPHONIAE SACRAE III (S1999)
(Bittinger, Werner) [Ger] SATB,SATB soli,
cont,bsn,2vln,opt inst (med) BAREN.
BA 3370 sc $4.00, cor pts $1.50, ipa
(S2000)

Sein Zorn Auf Erden Hab Ein End *mot
(Hermann) SATB HANSSLER 1.010 s.p. (S2001)

Selig Sind, Die Da Geistlich Arm Sind *mot
(Kruger) SSATB,cont HANSSLER 1.064 s.p.
(S2002)

Selig Sind Die Toten *Ded/Gd.Fri./Rembrnc,
Bibl/mot
"Blessed Are The Dead" see Musikalische
Exequien-Teil 3
6pt mix cor,acap cor pts BREITKOPF-L
PB-3373 s.p. see also Geistliche
Chormusik 1648 [BH] (S2003)
SSATTB,acap voc pt DOBLINGER s.p. see also
TOD UND VERGANGLICHKEIT (S2004)
"Blessed Are The Faithful" mix cor SOUTHERN
$.40 (S2005)
(Shaw; Speer) "Blessed Are The Faithful"
[Eng/Ger] SSATT,Bar solo,acap,opt org oct
SCHIRM.G 10114 $.40 see from Sacred Choir
Music, 1648 (S2006)

Selig Sind Die Toten *SWV 391, ECY,mot
(Hermann) SSATTB,cont,6inst HANSSLER 20.391
s.p. (S2007)
(Kamlah, Wilhelm) [Ger] SSATTB,acap BAREN.
BA 523 $.45 see also Geistliche Chormusik
1648 (S2008)

Seven Last Words *see Die Sieben Worte Jesu
Am Kreuz

Seven Last Words From The Cross, The *see
Die Sieben Worte Jesu Am Kreuz

Seven Last Words Of Christ, The *see Die
Sieben Worte Jesu Am Kreuz

Seven Last Words Of Jesus Christ, The *see
Die Sieben Worte Jesu Am Kreuz

Seven Last Words Of Our Dear Redeemer And
Saviour, The Lord Jesus Christ, The *see
Die Sieben Worte Jesu Am Kreuz

Seven Last Words, The *see Die Sieben Worte
Jesu Am Kreuz

Seven Words Of Christ From The Cross, The
*see Die Sieben Worte Jesu Am Kreuz

Si Non Humiliter Sentiebam
"Demutig Will Ich Mich Dir Ergeben" see
Cantiones Sacrae 1625 Band 2 [Nr. 26-28]

Sicut Moses Serpentem
mix cor SOUTHERN $.25 (S2009)
"Thus As Moses" [Lat/Eng] SATB AMP A412
$.35 (S2010)

SCHUTZ, HEINRICH (cont'd.)

Sicut Moses Serpentem In Deserto Exaltavit
*SWV 68, Trin
see Cantiones Sacrae [42]
mix cor,acap voc sc KALMUS 6445 $1.25
(S2011)

"So Wie Moses Die Schlange" [Lat/Ger] SATB,
cont (med) BAREN. BA 1966 $.90 see from
Cantiones Sacrae 1625 Band 2 [Nr. 16]
(S2012)

Siehe, Dieser Wird Gesetzt Zu Einem Fall
(from Symphoniae Sacrae III)
SSATB,cont,strings sc BREITKOPF-W PB-4742
s.p., cor pts BREITKOPF-W CHB-3545 s.p.,
ipa
(S2013)

Siehe, Es Erschien Der Engel *SWV 403
"Behold, There Appeared" [Ger/Eng] STBB&
SATB,org,4vln,vla,opt vcl HANSSLER
20.403 $2.50, ipa see from SYMPHONIAE
SACRAE III
(S2014)

Siehe, Wie Fein Und Lieblich *mot
(Horn) SSATB,cont,bsn,2vln,bvl
HANSSLER 1.286 sc s.p., cor pts s.p., ipa
(S2015)

Sin Non Humiliter Speret Israel
see Cantiones Sacrae [44]

Since Christ His Head In Sorrow Bowed (from
Seven Last Words, The)
SATTB,acap SCHIRM.EC 1690 $.20
(S2016)

Since Christ Our Lord Was Crucified (from
Seven Last Words, The)
(Davison, A.) TTBB,acap SCHIRM.EC 88 $.25
ipr
(S2017)

Sing, O My Soul, The Father's Praises *see
Love Den Herren, Meine Seele

Sing Praise To Our Glorious Lord *Gen
TTBB,acap (med easy) oct CONCORDIA 98-1400
$.30
(S2018)
(Lenel) boy cor SOUTHERN $.30
(S2019)

Sing To The Lord *see Singet Dem Herrn, Ein
Neues Lied

Sing To The Lord A New Song
mix cor SOUTHERN $.45
(S2020)

Singet Dem Herrn, Ein Neues Lied (Psalm 98)
SWV 35, Gen,Bibl/mot
"Sing To The Lord" 8pt mix cor,acap oct
SCHIRM.G 5962 $.45
(S2021)
(Grischkat) "Sing To The Lord" [Ger/Eng]
dbl cor HANSSLER 20.035 sc $1.75, cor pts
s.p.
(S2022)
(Thate, Albert) [Ger] SATB&SATB,acap sc
BAREN. BA 2398 $2.50
(S2023)

Singet Dem Herrn Ein Neues Lied, All Welt
Soll Frohlich Singen Mit (Psalm 96) SWV
194, Bibl
SATB HANSSLER 6.032 s.p. contains also:
Singet Dem Herrn Ein Neues Lied, Denn
Durch Ihn Gross Wunder Geschieht (Psalm
98) SWV 196; Der Herr Sprach Zu Meim
Herren
(S2024)

Singet Dem Herrn Ein Neues Lied, Denn Durch
Ihn Gross Wunder Geschieht
see Kurig, Hans-Hermann, Wer In Mir Bleibet
Und Ich In Ihm

Singet Dem Herrn Ein Neues Lied, Denn Durch
Ihn Gross Wunder Geschieht (Psalm 98) SWV
196
see Schutz, Heinrich, Singet Dem Herrn Ein
Neues Lied, All Welt Soll Frohlich Singen
Mit
(Kaplan) SSAATTBB oct BELWIN 60829 $1.00
(S2025)

Singet Dem Herrn (Psalm 98) SWV 196, Easter/
Pent
[Ger] SATB,acap (med easy) BAREN. BA 785
$.25 see from Beckerscher Psalter (S2026)

Singet Ein Neues Lied *see Cantate Domino

So Fahr Ich Hin
(Schreck, G.) 6pt mix cor,acap voc pt
BREITKOPF-L CHB-2046 s.p.
(S2027)

So Fahr Ich Hin *see So Fahr Ich Hin Zu
Jesus Christ

So Fahr Ich Hin Zu Jesu Christ *SWV 379,
ECY/Trin,mot
5pt mix cor,acap cor pts BREITKOPF-L
PB-3361 s.p. see also Geistliche
Chormusik 1648 [BH]
(S2028)
(Kamlah, Wilhelm) [Ger] SSATB,acap BAREN.
BA 511 $.40 see also Geistliche Chormusik
1648
(S2029)

So Fahr Ich Hin Zu Jesus Christ *SWV 379,
Gd.Fri.
SSATB,cont,inst sc HANSSLER 20.379 s.p.,
ipa
(S2030)
"So Fahr Ich Hin" SSATB,acap voc pt
DOBLINGER s.p. see also TOD UND
VERGANGLICHKEIT
(S2031)

So Lehr Mich Doch *SWV 139a, Gd.Fri.
SATB,acap voc pt DOBLINGER s.p. see also
TOD UND VERGANGLICHKEIT
(S2032)

So Lehr Mich Doch, Du Treuer Gott *SWV 136a
SATB HANSSLER 6.1928 s.p. contains also:
Von Gott Will Ich Nicht Lassen, SWV 131
(S2033)

So Wie Moses Die Schlange *see Sicut Moses
Serpentem In Deserto Exaltavit

Song Of Praise *Bibl
8pt mix cor,acap oct SCHIRM.G 7648 $.35
(S2034)

Sower In His Field His Seed Was Sowing, A
*see Es Ging Ein Samann Aus Zu Saen
Seinen Samen

Speret Israel
"Hoffe Israel" see Cantiones Sacrae 1625
Band 2 [Nr. 26-28]

SCHUTZ, HEINRICH (cont'd.)

Spes Mea, Christe, Deus
see Cantiones Sacrae [43]
"O Meine Hoffnung, Jesus" see Cantiones
Sacrae 1625 Band 1 [Nr. 17-18]
cor voc sc KALMUS 6440 $1.25
(S2035)

St. John Passion *SWV 481, Psntd
(Stein) [Ger] SATB,soli min sc EULENBURG
EUL979 s.p.
(S2036)

St. John Passion *see Johannespassion

St. John Passion *see Lukaspassion

St. Luke Passion *SWV 480, Psntd
(Stein) [Ger] SATB,soli min sc EULENBURG
EUL978 s.p.
(S2037)

St. Luke Passion *see Lukaspassion

St. Matthew Passion *SWV 479, Psntd
(Stein) [Ger] SATB,soli min sc EULENBURG
EUL976 s.p.
(S2038)

St. Matthew Passion *see Matthauspassion

Sumite Psalmum *SWV 9, Gen,mot
(Engelbrecht, Christiane) [Lat] SSATB,cont&
3trom&2vln/cont&2vln&2vla/vcl (med)
BAREN. BA 3428 sc $6.50, cor pts $1.50,
ipa
(S2039)

Supereminet Omnem Scientiam
see Cantiones Sacrae [44]
"Uber Alle Erkenntnis Erhebet Sich" see
Cantiones Sacrae 1625 Band 2 [Nr. 24-25]
cor voc sc KALMUS 6433 $1.00 contains also:
Pro Hoc Magno Mysterio
(S2040)

Symphoniae Sacrae II *see Der Herr Ist Mein
Hirt, "Lord Is My Shepherd, The" (Psalm
23)
(S2041)

Ten More Psalms From The "Becker Psalter"
*CC10L,Psalm
mix cor CONCORDIA 97-4880 $.75
(S2042)

Ten Psalms From The "Becker Psalter" *CC10L,
Psalm
mix cor CONCORDIA 97-6303 $.60
(S2043)

Thanks Be To God *see Gott Sei Dank, Der Uns
Den Sieg Gegebem Hat

Thanks Be To Our Lord *see Dank Sei Unserm
Herrn

Thanks Be Unto Christ *see Dank Sei Unserm
Herrn

Thanksgiving We Give To God *see Dank Sagen
Wir Alle Gott

This Happy Morning Was Christ The Lord Born
*see Heute Ist Christ, Der Herr, Geboren

Thou Art Jesus, Savior And Lord *anthem
(Coggin) SATB (med) oct AUGSBURG 1469 $.25
(S2044)

Thou God And Father In Heaven Above *anthem
(Coggin) SATB,acap oct FISCHER,C CM-7370
$.25
(S2045)

Thou Wilt Keep Him In Perfect Peace
SATB oct WORD CS-311 $.30
(S2046)

Three Choral Psalms
(Riedel) SATB SCHMITT 1403 $.30
contains: Earth Is The Lord's, The; May
God Bestow; O Clap Your Hands (S2047)

Three Chorales For Easter And Ascension
*Asc/Easter,chorale
SATB,kbd (easy) oct CONCORDIA 98-1234 $.25
contains: O Risen Lord! O Conquering
King; On Wings Of Living Radiance; Our
God Ascended
(S2048)

Three Little Sacred Concertos *see Der Herr
Ist Gross, "Great Is The Lord"; Erhore
Mich, "Give Ear, O Lord"; O Lieber Herre
Gott, Wecke Uns Aub, "O Blessed Lord Our
God"
(S2049)

Three Sacred Concertos *see And Take Heed To
Yourselves; Behold This Child Is Set For
The Fall; Purge Out Therefore The Old
Leaven
(S2050)

Thus As Moses *see Sicut Moses Serpentem

Thy Little Ones, Dear Lord, Are We *Xmas
(Barthelson) SATB oct PRO ART 1962 $.22
(S2051)

To Thee We Turn Our Eyes *see Oculi Omnium
In Te Sperant, Domine

To Us A Child Is Born *Xmas
SATB,kbd (med diff) oct CONCORDIA 98-1494
$.25
(S2052)
SATB oct WALTON 2123 $.30
(S2053)

Tre Bibliska Scener *see Den Tolvarige Jesus
I Templet; Fariseen Och, Publikanen;
Paskdialog
(S2054)

Troset Troset Mein Volk
(Agey) "Comfort Ye My People" [Eng/Ger]
SSATB,org oct SCHIRM.G 11423 $.40
(S2055)

Trostet, Trostet Mein Volk *SWV 382, Adv,mot
6pt mix cor,acap cor pts BREITKOPF-L
PB-3364 s.p. see also Geistliche
Chormusik 1648 [BH]
(S2056)
SSATTB,cont,inst sc HANSSLER 20.382 s.p.,
ipa
(S2057)
(Kamlah, Wilhelm) [Ger] SSATTB,acap (med)
BAREN. BA 514 $.45 see also Geistliche
Chormusik 1648
(S2058)

Turbabor
see Cantiones Sacrae [43]

Turbabor, Sed Non Pertubabor
"Furcht Storet, Doch Nichts Zerstoret Den
Trost" see Cantiones Sacrae 1625 Band 1
[Nr. 17-18]

SCHUTZ, HEINRICH (cont'd.)

Two Dialogues
(Gal, Hans) mix cor CURWEN 61408 s.p.
contains: Pharisee And The Publican, The;
Woman Why Weepest Thou?
(S2059)

Two Men Betook Themselves To Pray In The
Temple *Gen
SATB,kbd (med easy) oct CONCORDIA 98-1569
$.40
(S2060)

Two Short Psalms
SATB,acap BROUDE BR. $.40
contains: Psalm 23; Psalm 29
(S2061)

Uber Alle Erkenntnis Erhebet Sich *see
Supereminet Omnem Scientiam

Unser Herr Jesus Christus *see Unser Herr
Jesus Christus, In Der Nacht, Da Er
Verraten Ward

Unser Herr Jesus Christus, In Der Nacht, Da
Er Verraten Ward *SWV 423, mot
SATB,cont,opt 4inst HANSSLER 20.423 sc
s.p., cor pts s.p., ipa see also Zwolf
Geistliche Gesange
(S2062)
(Kessler, Franz) "Unser Herr Jesus
Christus" 4pt mix cor,opt org cor pts
BREITKOPF-W PB -3774D see also Zwolf
Geistliche Gesange-1657
(S2063)
(Kubler) SATB,cont,inst HANSSLER 20.423 sc
s.p., cor pts s.p., voc pt s.p.
(S2064)

Unser Herr Jesus Christus, In Der Nacht, Da
Er Verraten Ward *SWV 495, Eve/Gen,mot
(Braun, Werner) [Ger] SATB&SATB,acap (med
easy) BAREN. BA 1722 $2.50
(S2065)

Unser Keiner Lebet Ihm Selber *SWV 374,
Fest/Trin,mot
5pt mix cor,acap cor pts BREITKOPF-L
PB-3356 s.p. see also Geistliche
Chormusik 1648 [BH]
(S2066)
SSATB,cont,inst sc HANSSLER 20.374 s.p.,
ipa
(S2067)
(Kamlah, Wilhelm) [Ger] SSATB,acap (med)
BAREN. BA 506 $.40 see also Geistliche
Chormusik 1648
(S2068)

Unser Wandel Ist Im Himmel *SWV 390, Trin,
mot
6pt mix cor,acap cor pts BREITKOPF-L
PB-3372 s.p. see also Geistliche
Chormusik 1648 [BH]
(S2069)
SSATTB,cont,6inst sc HANSSLER 20.390 s.p.,
ipa
(S2070)
(Kamlah, Wilhelm) [Ger] SSATTB,acap (med)
BAREN. BA 522 $.55 see also Geistliche
Chormusik 1648
(S2071)

Unser Wandel Ist In Himmel
(Agey) "Wondrous Is The Life In Heaven"
[Eng/Ger] SSATTB,org oct SCHIRM.G 10875
$.35
(S2072)

Uppsala-Magnificat *see Magnificat Anima Mea
Dominum

Vater Abraham, Erbarme Dich Mein *SWV 477,
Bibl/mot
"Father Abraham, Have Mercy On Me" SSATB,
org,2fl,2vln,vcl/bvl HANSSLER 20.477 sc
$3.00, ipa, cor pts s.p.
(S2073)
(Gore, R.T.) "Father Abraham, Have Mercy On
Me" [Ger/Eng] SSATB,2vln,2fl,cont sc
CONCORDIA 97-9348 $3.00, cor pts
CONCORDIA 97-6392 $.25, ipa
(S2074)
(Graulich) SSATB,cont,inst HANSSLER 20.477
sc s.p., cor pts s.p., ipa
(S2075)

Vater Unser *SWV 411
see Schutz, Heinrich, Aller Augen Warten
Auf Dich, Herre
(Bittinger, Werner) [Ger] SATB,SMezTTB
soli,2vln,cont,opt inst (med) BAREN.
BA 3426 sc $3.00, cor pts $.40, ipa
(S2076)

Vater Unser, Der Du Bist Im Himmel (from Das
Benedicite Vor Dem Essen) mot
(Granville) "Our Father Which Art In
Heaven" SATB oct FOX CM1 $.40
(S2077)
(Hermann) SATB HANSSLER 20.429-2 s.p. see
also Zwolf Geistliche Gesange
(S2078)

Vater Unser, Der Du Bist In Himmel *prayer
(Sporn, F.) "Das 'Vater Unser'" SATB&SATB,
org,strings BREITKOPF-W rental (S2079)

Veni, Rogo, In Cor Meum *SWV 83
(Geer) "Come, I Pray Thee, Dwell Within Me"
[Eng/Lat] 4pt wom cor,acap oct SCHIRM.G
8981 $.30
(S2080)
(Grote, Gottfried) "Komm, Ich Bitt Dich, In
Mein Herze" [Ger/Lat] SATB,cont (med)
BAREN. BA 1951 $.90 see from Cantiones
Sacrae 1625 Band 2 [Nr. 31]
(S2081)

Veni, Sancte Spiritus *SWV 475, mot
(Graulich) SSB&SSB&ATTBB&SSATB,cont,inst
HANSSLER 20.475 sc $2.50, cor pts s.p.,
ipa
(S2082)

Verba Mea
see Cantiones Sacrae [41]

Verba Mea Auribus Percipe
"Meine Worte Hore" see Cantiones Sacrae
1625 Band 1 [Nr. 9-10]
(Ehret, W.) "Hearken Unto My Cry" [Lat/Eng]
SATB,acap BROUDE,A. 715 $.35
(S2083)

Verleih Uns Frieden Gnadiglich *SWV 372,
Fest,mot
5pt mix cor,acap cor pts BREITKOPF-L
PB-3354 s.p. see also Geistliche
Chormusik 1648 [BH]
(S2084)
SSATB,cont,inst sc HANSSLER 20.372 s.p.,
ipa
(S2085)
(Kamlah, Wilhelm) [Ger] SSATB,acap (med)
BAREN. BA 504 $.40 see also Geistliche
Chormusik 1648
(S2086)

Vi Tacka Dig, Herre Gud
mix cor NORDISKA 5134 s.p.
(S2087)

SCHUTZ, HEINRICH (cont'd.)

Viel Werden Kommen Von Morgen Und Von Abend *SWV 375
SSATT,cont,inst sc HANSSLER 20.375 s.p., ipa (S2088)
(Agey) "Many Shall Come From The East And West" [Eng/Ger] SATTB,org oct SCHIRM.G 11521 $.30 (S2089)
(Kamlah, Wilhelm) SATTB,acap (med) BAREN. BA 507 $.40 see also Geistliche Chormusik 1648 (S2090)

Viel Werden Kommen Von Morgen Und Von Akend *Epiph,mot
5pt mix cor,acap cor pts BREITKOPF-L PB-3357 s.p. see also Geistliche Chormusik 1648 [BH] (S2091)

Vierstimmige Chorsaetze Zu Liedern Des Evangelischen Kirchen-Gesangbuches *CC20U
[Ger] SATB,acap PETERS EM326 $3.50 (S2092)

Vierstimmige Chorsatze Zu Liedern Des Evangelisches Kirchengesangbuch *CCU
[Ger] 4pt mix cor BAREN. EM 326 s.p. (S2093)

Voice Of The Lord Sounds Upon The Waters, The
(Agey, C.) SATB oct PRESSER MC407 $.45 (S2094)

Von Gott Will Ich Nicht Lassen *SWV 131
see Schutz, Heinrich, So Lehr Mich Doch, Du Treuer Gott
SATTB,acap DOBLINGER s.p. see also BITTE UND VERTRAUEN (S2095)
SATB HANSSLER 6.017 s.p. contains also: Kurig, Hans-Hermann, Auf Ihn Will Ich Vertrauen (SS); Walter (Walther), Johann, Wach Auf, Wach Auf, Du Deutsches Land (SATB); Kurig, Hans-Hermann, Wach Auf, Du Deutsches Land (SATB); Kurig, Hans-Hermann, Wach Auf, Du Deutsches Land (SS); Bach, Johann Sebastian, Unsere Saat, Die Wir Gesaet (SATB) (S2096)
"From God Shall Naught Divide Me" SATB,acap oct PRESSER 312-40146 $.25 (S2097)
(Gombosi, O.) "From God Shall Naught Divide Me" SSB,2vln,cont sc CONCORDIA 97-9330 $2.50, ipa (S2098)

Vulnerasti Cor Meum
"Hast Verwundet Mein Herze" see Cantiones Sacrae 1625 Band 1 [Nr. 11-12]

Walts Gott, Mein Werk Ich Lasse *Gen
[Ger] SATB,acap (easy) BAREN. BCH 44 s.p. (S2099)

Wann Unsre Augen Schlafen Ein
(Stern) SB,cont HANSSLER 5.030 s.p. (S2100)

Warum Toben Die Heiden (Psalm 2) SWV 23, Gen
(Ehmann, Wilhelm) [Ger] SATB&SATB&SATB&SATB,org,cont/vcl (med) BAREN. BA 1716 sc $4.50, cor pts $.95, ipa see also Die Psalmen Davids (S2101)

Was Betrubst Du Dich, Meine Seele (Psalm 42)
[Ger] 2pt men cor/2pt wom cor/2pt mix cor, 2vln,pno/org,opt vcl,bvl cor pts VIEWEG s.p., ipa (S2102)

Was Betruebst Du Dich, Meine Seele
(Boepple, P.) "Why Afflict Thyself, Oh My Spirit" TT oct PRESSER 352-00020 $.45 (S2103)

Was Er Dir Geben Moge, Du Zunge Voll Falschheit *see Quid Detur Tibi

Was Hast Du Verwirket *see Quid Commisisti

Was Mein Gott Will *Holywk/Psntd
(Thomas, Kurt) AT,org,bsn,trom,vla, English horn sc BREITKOPF-W PB-3374 s.p. see also Geistliche Chormusik 1648 (S2104)

Was Mein Gott Will, Das Gscheh Allzeit *SWV 392, Psntd/Trin,mot
6pt mix cor,inst cor pts BREITKOPF-L PB-3374 s.p. see also Geistliche Chormusik 1648 [BH] (S2105)
(Kamlah, Wilhelm) [Ger] cor,AT soli,2vla, 2vcl (med) BAREN. BA 524 $.45 see also Geistliche Chormusik 1648 (S2106)

Was Mein Gott Woll, Das Gscheh Allzeit *SWV 392
AATTBB,cont,6inst sc HANSSLER 20.392 s.p., ipa (S2107)

Weib, Was Weinest Du? *SWV 443, Easter,mot
"Woman Why Weepest Thou?" see Two Dialogues
(Gore, R.T.) "Woman, Why Weepest Thou?" [Eng/Ger] SATB,cont sc CONCORDIA 97-6369 $1.00, cor pts CONCORDIA 98-1582 $.30 (S2108)
(Graulich) SSAT/SSTT,cont HANSSLER 1.500 sc s.p., cor pts s.p. (S2109)

Weichet Hinweg Von Mir *see Discedite A Me

Weihnachts-Oratorium *Xmas,ora
(Mendelssohn, Arnold) mix cor,SATB soli, org/pno voc pt BREITKOPF-L CHB-1430 s.p. (S2110)
(Schering, A.; Taubmann, O.) mix cor,STB soli,org,2fl,bsn,2trp,2trom,strings sc BREITKOPF-L PB-2138 s.p., voc pt BREITKOPF-L CHB-1977A-C s.p., voc sc BREITKOPF-L EB-3131 s.p., ipa (S2111)

Weihnachtsgeschicte *Xmas
(Stein) "Christmas History" [Ger] SSATTB, soli,orch min sc SCHOTT EUL 981 s.p., ipa (S2112)

Weinachts-Oratorium *Xmas,ora
"Christmas Oratorio" cor,orch oc KALMUS $5.50, ipa (S2113)
"Christmas Oratorio" cor voc sc KALMUS 6435 $2.00 (S2114)
"Christmas Oratorio" [Ger] SATB,acap min sc PETERS E981 $2.50 (S2115)

Wende, Du Unser Richter *see Reduc, Domine Deus Meus

Wenn Gott Einmal Erlosen Wird *SWV 231
SATB HANSSLER 6.035 s.p. contains also: Den Herren Lobt Mit Freuden, SWV 239; Aus Meines Herzens Grunde, SWV 138 (S2116)

Wenn Ich Schlafend Ruh *see Ego Dormio

Wer Gottes Marter In Ehren Hat (from Lukaspassion) Easter/Psntd
SATB,acap voc pt DOBLINGER s.p. see also PASSION UND OSTERN (S2117)
SATB,opt cont cor pts HANSSLER 20.480-1 $.50 (S2118)
(Payson) "He Who God's Suffering In Honor Holds" mix cor SOUTHERN $.30 (S2119)
(Payson, A.) "He Who God's Suffering In Honor Holds" SATB,acap FRANK F-450 $.30 (S2120)

Wer Will Uns Scheiden Von Der Liebe Gottes? *SWV 330, Bibl
SATB,cont sc HANSSLER 20.330 s.p. (S2121)
(Agey) "Who Shall Separate Us From The Love Of God?" [Eng/Ger] 4pt mix cor,org oct SCHIRM.G 10874 $.25 (S2122)
(Kubler) SATB,cont sc HANSSLER 20.330 s.p. (S2123)

What God Ordains Is Always Good
(Lindquist, M.) SATB oct PRESSER MC235 $.25 (S2124)

What Pain Our Master Didst Endure *anthem
(Coggin) SATB (med) oct AUGSBURG 1508 $.30 (S2125)

Who Shall Separate Us From The Love Of God? *see Wer Will Uns Scheiden Von Der Liebe Gottes?

Why Afflict Thyself, Oh My Spirit *see Was Betruebst Du Dich, Meine Seele

Wie Ists So Lieblich *Psalm
SATB,acap (contains also: Danket Dem Herren) DOBLINGER s.p. see from PSALMLIEDER (S2126)

Wie Lieblich Sind Deine Wohnungen (Psalm 84) SWV 29, Gen,Bibl
SSABarTTBB,org,vcl HANSSLER 20.029 sc $3.00, voc pt $.75, ipa (S2127)
(Ehmann, Wilhelm) [Ger] SSAB&TTBB,cont/vcl (med) BAREN. BA 1714 sc $3.50, cor pts $1.20, ipa see also Die Psalmen Davids (S2128)
(Reese, William H.) [Eng/Ger] dbl cor,org voc sc SCHIRM.G $1.25 (S2129)

Wir Danken Dir, Herr Gott, Himmlischer Vater (from Das Deo Gratias Nach Dem Essen)
SATB sc HANSSLER 20.430-3 s.p. see also Zwolf Geistliche Gesange (S2130)

Wo Der Herr Nicht Das Haus Bauet (Psalm 127) SWV 400, Bibl
mix cor,inst voc sc HANSSLER 20.400 s.p., ipa see from SYMPHONIAE SACRAE III (S2131)

Wohl Denen, Die Da Wandeln *SWV 219, Psalm
see Schutz, Heinrich, Meim Herzen Ist's Ein Grosse Freud
see Bach, Johann Sebastian, Es Ist Vollbracht! Vergiss Ja Nicht Dies Wort
see Vulpius, Melchior, Der Tag Bricht An Und Zeiget Sich
SATB,acap DOBLINGER s.p. see from PSALMLIEDER (S2132)
TTBB HANSSLER 6.2381 s.p. contains also: Helder, Bartholomaeus, Mein Konig, Dir Zu Singen (S2133)

Wohl Denen, Die Da Wandeln (Psalm 119) SWV 217, Trin
[Ger] SATB,acap (med easy) BAREN. BA 931 $.25 see from Beckerscher Psalter (S2134)

Wohl Denen, Die Ohne Tadel Leben *SWV 482
cor,cont,inst HANSSLER 20.482 sc s.p., voc pt s.p., ipa (S2135)

Woman, Why Weepest Thou? *see Weib, Was Weinest Du?

Wondrous Is The Life In Heaven *see Unser Wandel Ist In Himmel

Zion Spricht: Der Herr Hat Mich Verlassen *Bibl/cant
(Schneider, M.) 3 cor,org,2fl,2ob,2clar, 3bsn,4horn,3trom,tuba,strings,timp sc BREITKOPF-L rental (S2136)

Zwolf Geistliche Gesange (from Das Benedicite Vor Dem Essen)
sc HANSSLER 20.429-1 s.p.
contains: Aller Augen Warten Auf Dich, Herre (SATB,opt cont); Nun Sei Dem Vater Dank (SATB)
see also: All Ehr Und Lob Soll Gottes Sein, SWV 421; Christe, Fac Ut Sapiam, SWV 431 (from Das Deo Gratias Nach Dem Essen); Danket Dem Herren, Denn Er Ist Sher Freundlich (from Das Deo Gratias Nach Dem Essen); Danksagen Wir Alle Gott Christo, Der Uns Mit Seinem Wort, "All Thanks Be To God", SWV 425; Das Benedicite Vor Dem Essen, SWV 429; Das Deo Gratias Nach Dem Essen, SWV 430; Die Deutsche Litanei "Kyrie Eleison", SWV 428; Ehre Sei Dem Vater Und Dem Sohn (from Meine Seele Erhebt Den Herren); Herre Gott, Himmlischer Vater, Wir Danken Dir (from Das Benedicite Vor Dem Essen); Ich Danke Dem Herrn Von Ganzem Herzen (Psalm 111) SWV 424; Ich Glaube An Einen Einigen Gott, SWV 422; Kyrie, Gott Vater In Ewigkeit, "Kyrie, God Vater", SWV 420; Meine Seele Erhebt Den Herren, "Magnify Him", SWV 426; Unser Herr Jesus Christus, In Der Nacht, Da Er Verraten Ward, SWV 423; Vater Unser, Der Du Bist Im Himmel (from Das Benedicite Vor Dem Essen); Wir Danken Dir, Herr Gott, Himmlischer Vater (from Das Deo Gratias Nach Dem Essen) (S2137)

Zwolf Geistliche Gesange-1657 *CC12L
(Kessler, Franz) 4pt,opt org BREITKOPF-W see also: All Ehr Und Lob Soll Gottes Sein, SWV 421; Christe, Fac Ut Sapiam; Dank Sagen Wir Alle Gott; Das Benedicite Vor Dem Essen "Aller Augen Warten Auf Dich"; Das Gratias Nach Dem Essen "Danket Dem Herren, Denn Er Ist Sehr Freundlich"; Ich Danke Dem Herrn Von Ganzem Herzen (Psalm 111); Ich Glaube An Einen Einigen Gott; Kyrie Eleison, Christe Erhore Uns; Kyrie, Gott Vater In Ewigkeit; Meine Seele Erhebt Den Herren, SWV 426; O Susser Jesu Christ; Unser Herr Jesus Christus, SWV 423 (S2138)

SCHUTZENGEL-MESSE see Baumann, Max

SCHVEDOV
O Lord Our God
(Wilson) SAB oct BOURNE T5 $.25 (S2139)
(Wilson) SATBB oct BOURNE BL3074 $.25 (S2140)
To Thee We Sing
(Krone) SATB,acap WARNER W2638 $.30 (S2141)

SCHVEDOV, CONSTANTINE (1889-)
With Joyful Song
SATB,acap SCHIRM.EC 1669 $.20 (S2142)

SCHWAAB, MAURICE
Berceuse De L'Enfant Jesus *Xmas
[Fr] SATB,acap HEUGEL s.p. (S2143)

SCHWADRON
Hear, O Israel *see Sh'ma Yisroeyl

Keep Not Thy Silence
SATB oct SACRED E93 $.35 (S2144)

Lamb, The (from Songs Of Innocence)
4pt mix cor,acap oct SCHIRM.G 11577 $.25 (S2145)

O Praise The Lord
SATB ALFRED 6406 $.30 (S2146)

Olive Trees Are Standing
SATB oct STAFF 578 $.30 (S2147)

Sh'ma Yisroeyl *Bibl
"Hear, O Israel" [Heb/Eng] 4pt mix cor,acap oct SCHIRM.G 11493 $.30 (S2148)

SCHWARTZ
Day By Day
(Hayward) SA/TB SHAWNEE E117 $.35 (S2149)
(Hayward) SATB SHAWNEE A 1187 $.35 (S2150)
(Hayward) SAB SHAWNEE D165 $.35 (S2151)

SCHWARTZ, GERHARD VON (1902-)
Also Liebt Gott Die Arge Welt
see Fiebig, Kurt, Jauchzet, Ihr Himmel, Frohlocket, Ihr Engel, In Choren

Befiehl Du Deine Wege *Gen
[Ger] 2 eq voices,opt inst (easy) BAREN. BA 791 s.p. contains also: Wer Kann Der Treu Vergessen (S2152)

Das Apostolische Glaubenbekenntnis
see Liturgische Stucke Zum Gottesdienst

Das Nizanische Glaubensbekenntnis
see Liturgische Stucke Zum Gottesdienst

Die Weihnachtsgeschichte *Xmas
[Ger] SATB/dbl cor,AT soli,opt orch (med diff) sc BAREN. BA 3946 $8.75, ipa (S2153)

Ein Kindlein Liegt In Dem Armen Stall *Xmas
[Ger] 3pt mix cor,acap (easy) BAREN. BA 1498 s.p. (S2154)

Erhalt Uns, Herr, Bei Deinem Wort *Fest
[Ger] 3pt,acap (easy) BAREN. BCH 82 s.p. contains also: Sonne Der Gerechtigkeit (2pt,acap) (S2155)

Geschichte Vom Verlorenen Sohn *Bibl/cant
SSATB,pno,fl,ob,bsn,timp,cembalo, vibraphon, xylophone sc HANSSLER 10.190 rental (S2156)

Gloria
see Liturgische Stucke Zum Gottesdienst

Halleluja
see Liturgische Stucke Zum Gottesdienst

Ihr Habt Nicht Einen Knechtischen Geist Empfangen *Gen
[Ger] S/T/unis,org (med easy) BAREN. BA 2136 $2.50 (S2157)

Introitus
see Liturgische Stucke Zum Gottesdienst

Kleine Weihnachtskantate Nach Worten Von K. Muller-Osten *Xmas
[Ger] SATB,3vln,vcl/3fl,vcl (easy) BAREN. BA 1653 sc $2.50, cor pts $.40, ipa (S2158)

Kyrie
see Liturgische Stucke Zum Gottesdienst

Liturgische Stucke Zum Gottesdienst *liturg
SAB/SAT HANSSLER 7.127 s.p.
contains: Das Apostolische Glaubenbekenntnis; Das Nizanische Glaubensbekenntnis; Gloria; Halleluja; Introitus; Kyrie (S2159)

Magnificat (Psalm 30) Magnif
[Ger] SSATBB,acap BAREN. BA 3273 $.40 (S2160)

Nun Freut Euch, Lieben Christen Gmein *Easter/Pent,cant
[Ger] SATB,org&2vln&vcl/2trp&2trom&2vln&vcl (med easy) BAREN. BA 1452 sc $2.50, cor pts $1.50 (S2161)

Nun Juble Laut, All Kreatur *Xmas
[Ger] unis/3pt mix cor/4pt mix cor/cong,org (easy) BAREN. BA 1602 s.p. (S2162)
[Ger] unis,acap (very easy) BAREN. BA 1357 s.p. (S2163)

Osterkantate Nach Worten Von K. Muller-Osten *Easter,cant
[Ger] SATB,solo,org,3fl&2trp/3fl&ob&clar (med easy) BAREN. BA 1660 sc $2.50, cor pts $1.75 (S2164)

SCHWARTZ, GERHARD VON (cont'd.)

Psalm 30 *see Magnificat

Psalmen Mit Antiphonen, Magnificat Und
Seligpreisungen *CCU,Gen,anti/Magnif
[Ger] 4-8pt mix cor,org,opt inst (med)
BAREN. BA 3950 $2.25   (S2165)

Sonne Der Gerechtigkeit
see Schwartz, Gerhard von, Erhalt Uns,
Herr, Bei Deinem Wort

Wer Kann Der Treu Vergessen
see Schwartz, Gerhard von, Befiehl Du Deine
Wege

Wir Galuben All An Einen Gott *cant
SATB&cong,4brass HANSSLER 10.192 sc s.p.,
cloth s.p.   (S2166)

SCHWARTZ, J.
O Du Frohliche *Xmas,It
men cor TONGER s.p.   (S2167)

O Du Frohliche, O Du Selige *Xmas
TTBB TONGER s.p. contains also: Stille
Nacht, Heilige Nacht   (S2168)

Stille Nacht, Heilige Nacht
see Schwartz, J., O Du Frohliche, O Du
Selige

Von All Den Tausend Klangen *Xmas
mix cor TONGER s.p.   (S2169)
men cor TONGER s.p.   (S2170)

SCHWARTZ, PAUL (1907-   )
It Is Good To Give Thanks
TTBB RONGWEN $.35   (S2171)

SCHWARTZ, STEPHEN
Choral Selections From "Godspell"
HANSEN-US SSA $1.50; SAB $1.50; SATB $1.50
                                        (S2172)

Day By Day (from Godspell)
SAB HANSEN-US $.40   (S2173)

O Bless The Lord, My Soul (from Godspell)
SATB HANSEN-US $.40   (S2174)

Turn Back, O Man (from Godspell)
SATB HANSEN-US $.40   (S2175)

SCHWARZ, HERMAN
Kol Emunah *Sab-Eve
"Voice Of Faith, The" SATB TRANSCON.
TCL 269 $2.50   (S2176)

Voice Of Faith, The *see Kol Emunah

SCHWARZ, JOCHEN (1930-   )
Lobe Denn Herrn, Meine Selle (Psalm 103)
see Schweizer, Rolf, Wie Ein Hirsch Schreit
Nach Frischem Wasser

Psalm 103 *see Lobe Denn Herrn, Meine Selle

Psalm 149 *see Seihe, Es Ist Alles Neu
Geworden

Seihe, Es Ist Alles Neu Geworden (Psalm 149)
Bibl
SSATBB/SAT/SAB sc HANSSLER 19.101 s.p.
contains also: Ruppel, Paul Ernst, Dankt
Dem Herrn Und Predigt Seinen Namen (Psalm
105) (unis,cantor,gtr/treb inst); Ruppel,
Paul Ernst, Ich Will Dir Danken, Herr
(Psalm 108) (unis,gtr/treb inst);
Schweizer, Rolf, O Herr, Du Warst Unsre
Zuflucht (Psalm 90) (SATB&cong,inst)
                                        (S2177)

Zu Dir Heb Ich Die Augen Auf
see Schweizer, Rolf, Friede Den Brudern,
"Dein Reich Ist Nicht Unsre Kirche"

SCHWARZ-SCHILLING, REINHARD (1904-   )
Ein Wenig Nur, Herr, Wende Dich Uns Zu *Gen
[Ger] SSAATB,acap (med) BAREN. BA 3179
$1.00   (S2178)

Ich Tret Hinzu (Psalm 27) Gen
[Ger] SSAATB,acap (med) BAREN. BA 3178 s.p.
                                        (S2179)

In Terra Pax *Mass
[Lat] 4-6pt mix cor,acap (med diff) BAREN.
BA 3169 $4.25   (S2180)

Laetare *Psntd,cant
[Ger] 5-6pt mix cor,2trp,strings BAREN.
EM 523 voc sc rental, cor pts s.p., s.p.,
ipr   (S2181)

Lass Mich In Treue Deine Wege Wandeln (Psalm
16) Gen
[Ger] SSATBB,acap (med) BAREN. BA 3177
$1.00   (S2182)

Psalm 16 *see Lass Mich In Treue Deine Wege
Wandeln

Psalm 27 *see Ich Tret Hinzu

SCHWEIGT GOTT EIN ZEIT SO MEINST DU see Cruger,
Johann

SCHWEIZER, ROLF (1936-   )
Bei Dir, Herr, Bin Ich Geborgen
see Ruppel, Paul Ernst, Gott, Zu Dir Rufe
Ich

Christe, Du Lamm Gottes
SATB&cong,kbd,fl,bvl, vibraphone sc
HANSSLER 19.209 s.p. contains also:
Schmecket Und Sehet, Wie Freundlich Der
Herr Ist (SAT/SAB,bvl) (S2183)

Danket Gott Und Lobet Ihn
see Schweizer, Rolf, Denn Dein Ist Das
Reich

Das Ist Ein Kostlich Ding
see Kretzschmar, Gunther, Komm, Heiliger
Geist

Denn Dein Ist Das Reich
unis,4trom sc HANSSLER 19.302 s.p. contains
also: Schweizer, Rolf, Danket Gott Und
Lobet Ihn (unis,kbd,bvl,treb inst);

SCHWEIZER, ROLF (cont'd.)

Schweizer, Rolf, Kyrie (unis,org,bvl,
6inst); Ruppel, Paul Ernst, Du Sollst
Gott, Deinen Herrn (3pt mix cor/3 eq
voices,org,trp,3-4trom); Ruppel, Paul
Ernst, Der Herr Denkt An Uns (SA);
Planzer, Emanuel, Wende Dich Zu Mir
(Psalm 25) (unis/pno/org/inst)   (S2184)

Der Herr Hat Uns Das Salz Genannt
see Schweizer, Rolf, Ihr Werdet Kraft
Empfangen

Deutsches Sanctus
SSATTBB,3trp,3trom,fl, vibraphone sc
HANSSLER 19.210 s.p. contains also: Arp,
Klaus-Michael, Nehmt Und Esst, Das Ist
Mein Leib (unis,kbd, vibraphone) (S2185)

Friede Den Brudern, "Dein Reich Ist Nicht
Unsre Kirche"
unis,inst sc HANSSLER 19.410 s.p. contains
also: Ruppel, Paul Ernst, Fragst Du Nach
Meiner Sunde (unis); Ruppel, Paul Ernst,
Gott Liebt Die Welt Mit Ihrer Schuld
(unis,kbd); Schwarz, Jochen, Zu Dir Heb
Ich Die Augen Auf (SAT/SAB); Schlenker,
Manfred, Aller Augen Warten Auf Das Brot
Von Dir (unis,kbd/winds)   (S2186)

Frieden Tragt Der Herr Uns An *Gen
[Ger] SATB,opt vcl/bvl (med) BAREN. BA 6307
s.p.   (S2187)

Furchtet Euch Nicht *Gen
[Ger] SATB,opt inst (med) BAREN. BA 6307
s.p.   (S2188)

Gebet Des Franz Von Assisi *prayer
unis,kbd,clar,trp,2trom,bvl sc HANSSLER
19.202 s.p. contains also: Ruppel, Paul
Ernst, Christus-Hymnus (SATB)   (S2189)

Gebet Des Nikolaus Von Der Flue "O Gott, Nimm
Von Mir"
unis,kbd,trp,bvl sc HANSSLER 19.211 s.p.
contains also: Ich Bitte Dich, Herr, Um
Die Grosse Kraft Fur Diesen Kleinen Tag
(unis,kbd,trp,bvl)   (S2190)

Gott Ist Bei Uns, Und Wir Sind Sein Eigen
SATB&cong,kbd,fl,bvl, vibraphone sc
HANSSLER 19.404 s.p. contains also:
Schweizer, Rolf, Lobgesang Aus Der
Grossen Stadt (unis,kbd); Michel, Josep,
Es Wird Sein In Den Letzten Tagen (SATB/
unis,winds,opt kbd)   (S2191)

Gott Ist Doch Herr In Deiser Welt
see Schweizer, Rolf, Sie Boten Gottes Sohne

Herr, Deine Gute Reicht So Weit Der Himmel
Ist (Psalm 36)
see Schweizer, Rolf, Lobe Den Herrn, Meine
Seele

Herr, Lass Uns In Deinem Lichte Wandeln
see Schweizer, Rolf, Ihr Seid Das Licht Der
Welt

Herr, Mein Nachster Ruft Mich
see Schweizer, Rolf, Ihr Werdet Kraft
Empfangen

Herr, Wohin Sollen Wir Gehen?
SATB,kbd,bvl sc HANSSLER 19.412 s.p.
contains also: Ruppel, Paul Ernst, Herr,
Deine Welt Ist Zum Staunen (SATB&cong,opt
inst)   (S2192)

Ich Bitte Dich, Herr, Um Die Grosse Kraft Fur
Diesen Kleinen Tag
see Schweizer, Rolf, Gebet Des Nikolaus Von
Der Flue "O Gott, Nimm Von Mir"

Ich Will Den Herrn Loben Allezeit (Psalm 34)
see Kretzschmar, Gunther, Erhore Mich, Wenn
Ich Rufe

Ihr Seid Das Licht Der Welt
unis,kbd,treb inst sc HANSSLER 19.407 s.p.
contains also: Tobender Sturm, Sinkendes
Schiff (SATB&cong,kbd,bvl); Herr, Lass
Uns In Deinem Lichte Wandeln (unis,kbd,
2treb inst)   (S2193)

Ihr Werdet Kraft Empfangen
1-2pt,kbd,bvl,treb inst sc HANSSLER 19.406
s.p. contains also: Herr, Mein Nachster
Ruft Mich (unis,kbd,treb inst); Der Herr
Hat Uns Das Salz Genannt (unis,kbd)
                                  (S2194)

Komm, Heiliger Geist, Und Wecke, Die Da
Schlafen
SATB&cong,opt inst HANSSLER 19.205 s.p.
                                  (S2195)

Kyrie
see Schweizer, Rolf, Denn Dein Ist Das
Reich

Lobe Den Herrn, Meine Seele (Psalm 103) Bibl
SATB&cong,kbd,bvl,treb inst sc HANSSLER
19.403 s.p. contains also: Herr, Deine
Gute Reicht So Weit Der Himmel Ist (Psalm
36) (unis,kbd,treb inst)   (S2196)

Lobgesang Aus Der Grossen Stadt
see Schweizer, Rolf, Gott Ist Bei Uns, Und
Wir Sind Sein Eigen

Lobsinget Gott In Seinem Heiligtum
see Schweizer, Rolf, Singt Ein Lied Vom
Licht Der Worte

Manchmal Kennen Wir Gottes Willen
SSA&cong,kbd oc HANSSLER 19.207 s.p.
contains also: Schweizer, Rolf, Verleih
Uns Frieden Gnadiglich (SATB&unis,trom,
opt bsn,vcl); Ruppel, Paul Ernst, Zu
Gottes Ehre Mein Saitenspiel (unis,kbd)
                                  (S2197)

Nur Wenn Uns Christus Frei Macht
SATB&cong,kbd,bvl HANSSLER 19.204 s.p.
                                  (S2198)

O Grosser Gott *Gen
[Ger] SATB,kbd,bvl (med easy) BOSSE BE 234
s.p.   (S2199)

SCHWEIZER, ROLF (cont'd.)

O Herr, Du Warst Unsre Zuflucht (Psalm 90)
see Schwarz, Jochen, Seihe, Es Ist Alles
Neu Geworden

Psalm 13 *see Wie Lange Noch, Herr

Psalm 34 *see Ich Will Den Herrn Loben
Allezeit

Psalm 34 *see Schmecket Und Sehet, Wie
Freundlich Der Herr Ist

Psalm 36 *see Herr, Deine Gute Reicht So
Weit Der Himmel Ist

Psalm 42 *see Wie Ein Hirsch Schreit Nach
Frischem Wasser

Psalm 90 *see O Herr, Du Warst Unsre
Zuflucht

Psalm 98 *see Singet Dem Herrn Ein Neues
Lied

Psalm 103 *see Lobe Den Herrn, Meine Seele

Rufe Mich An In Der Not *Gen
[Ger] SATB,kbd,bvl (med easy) BOSSE BE 235
s.p.   (S2200)

Schmecket Und Sehet, Wie Freundlich Der Herr
Ist (Psalm 34)
see Schweizer, Rolf, Christe, Du Lamm
Gottes

Sie Boten Gottes Sohne
unis,org/kbd/treb inst sc HANSSLER 19.408
s.p. contains also: Gott Ist Doch Herr In
Deiser Welt (SATB,kbd,treb inst) (S2201)

Singet Dem Herrn Ein Neues Lied (Psalm 98)
see Ruppel, Paul Ernst, Gott Liebt Diese
Welt

Singt Ein Lied Vom Licht Der Worte
unis,kbd sc HANSSLER 19.405 s.p. contains
also: Schweizer, Rolf, Lobsinget Gott In
Seinem Heiligtum (unis,kbd); Ruppel, Paul
Ernst, Gott Schenkt Freiheit (unis,org/
brass)   (S2202)

Tobender Sturm, Sinkendes Schiff
see Schweizer, Rolf, Ihr Seid Das Licht Der
Welt

Vater, Der In Den Himmeln Ist *prayer
unis,kbd,treb inst sc HANSSLER 19.212 s.p.
contains also: Ruppel, Paul Ernst, Vater
Unser Im Himmelreich (unis/SSA,kbd);
Schweizer, Rolf, Vater Unser (SATB&cong,
winds,bvl)   (S2203)

Vater Im Himmel, Wir Rufen Zu Dir *Gen
[Ger] unis,acap (easy) BOSSE BE 254 s.p.
                                  (S2204)

Vater Unser
see Schweizer, Rolf, Vater, Der In Den
Himmeln Ist

Verleih Uns Frieden Gnadiglich
see Schweizer, Rolf, Manchmal Kennen Wir
Gottes Willen

Wie Ein Hirsch Schreit Nach Frischem Wasser
(Psalm 42)
SATB&cong,inst sc HANSSLER 19.102 s.p.
contains also: Schwarz, Jochen, Lobe Den
Herrn, Meine Selle (Psalm 103) (SAAT/
SAAB); Schauss-Flake, Magdalene, Befiehl
Dem Herrn Deine Wege (Psalm 37) (SAT/SAB)
                                  (S2205)

Wie Lange Noch, Herr (Psalm 13)
see Michel, Josep, Herr Ruste Uns Von Neuem
Aus

SCHWEIZER WEIHEGESANG see Dobler, W.

SCHWEIZER WEIHNACHTSLIEDER see Ammann, Benno

SCHWEIZERGEBET see Hegar, Friedrich

SCHWEIZERGEBET see Hess, E.

SCHWEIZERHYMNE see Huber, Hans

SCHWEIZERPSALM see Zwyssig, [Alberich]

SCHWEPPE, JOACHIM (1926-   )
Gesang Des Abgeschiedenen *mot
5pt mix cor,acap cor pts BREITKOPF-W
CHB-3642 s.p.   (S2206)

Verleih Uns Frieden
see Barbe, Helmut, Christe, Du Lamm Gottes

Wir Danken Dir, Herr Jesu Christ
SS/SSA/SAT/SAB HANSSLER 14.059 s.p.
contains also: Marx, Karl, Jesu, Was Hast
Du Verbrochen (SA/TB,treb inst)   (S2207)

SCHWER GEHET UBER MEIN HAUPT see Burck, Joachim

SCHWINGET EUCH HIMMELAN, HERZEN UND SINNE see
Buxtehude, Dietrich

SCHWINGT FREUDIG see Bach, Johann Sebastian,
Schwingt Freudig Euch Empor

SCHWINGT FREUDIG EUCH EMPOR see Bach, Johann
Sebastian

SCIAMMARELLO
Tantum Ergo
[Lat] 2 eq voices,pno/org RICORDI-ARG
BA 6077 s.p.   (S2208)

SCIANT GENTES see Eberlin, Johann Ernst

SCIO ENIM QUOD REDEMPTOR see Lassus, Roland de
(Orlandus)

SCOTT
Coventry Carol, The *carol
TTBB,acap SHAWNEE C58 $.25   (S2209)
SSA,acap SHAWNEE B 33 $.35   (S2210)
SATB,acap SHAWNEE A 44 $.25   (S2211)

SCOTT (cont'd.)

Early One Morning
SATB SHAWNEE A 190 $.30 (S2212)
SSA SHAWNEE B 71 $.30 (S2213)

Ev'ry Time I Feel The Spirit
SATB FLAMMER A 5176 $.30 (S2214)

Faith Unlocks The Door (composed with Sande)
(Ehret) TTBB oct MCA (S2215)
(Ehret) SSA/SSAA oct MCA (S2216)
(Ehret) SATB oct MCA (S2217)

Holy God, We Praise Thy Name
SATB oct PRO ART 1681 $.22 (S2218)

Junior Anthem Album, The, Vol. 1 *CCU,anthem
jr cor FISCHER,C O 2698 $1.00 (S2219)

Lullaby Of The Christ Child
SATB,acap SHAWNEE A 81 $.30 (S2220)

Old Ship Of Zion
SATB FLAMMER A 5255 $.30 (S2221)

Open My Eyes
(Johnston) SATB oct LORENZ B60 $.30 (S2222)

Open My Eyes, That I May See *hymn
(Rogers) SATB oct LILLENAS AN-2341 $.30 (S2223)

Ride On! Ride On!
SATB FLAMMER A 5050 $.30 (S2224)
(Riegger) SAB FLAMMER D5181 $.30 (S2225)

Think On Me *anthem
(Fischer) SSA oct FISCHER,C R-624 $.25 (S2226)
(Wilson) SATB oct LORENZ C158 $.25 (S2227)

To The Name Of Our Salvation
SATB oct PRO ART 1771 $.22 (S2228)

SCOTT, J. SHELDON
Message Of The Cross, The *Gd.Fri./Lent,cant
SATB,SATBar soli,org (med) oct WILLIS $.60 (S2229)

SCOTT, HADY JOHN
Think On Me
2pt ASHDOWN E.A.285 s.p. (S2230)
(Perrenot) SA oct GALAXY 1.1707.1 $.25 (S2231)
(Perrenot) SSA oct GALAXY 1.1381.1 $.30 (S2232)
(Perrenot) SSAA oct GALAXY 1.0965.1 $.30 (S2233)
(Perrenot) TTBB oct GALAXY 1.0951.1 $.30 (S2234)
(Perrenot) SATB oct GALAXY 1.0964.1 $.30 (S2235)

SCOTT, JOHN PRINDLE
Angels, Roll The Rock Away
SATB oct HUNTZINGER 4025 $.20 (S2236)

Arise, Shine
SATB oct HUNTZINGER 4016 $.20 (S2237)

Come, Ye Blessed *Bibl
(Deis) 4pt mix cor,T solo oct SCHIRM.G 7464 $.35 (S2238)
(Deis) 2pt wom cor,org/pno oct SCHIRM.G 10175 $.30 (S2239)
(Deis) 3pt wom cor,org/pno oct SCHIRM.G 10176 $.30 (S2240)
(Deis) SABar oct SCHIRM.G 10174 $.30 (S2241)

Consider The Lilies *Easter/Gen.Bibl
4pt mix cor,T solo oct SCHIRM.G 9819 $.35 (S2242)

Out Of The Depths
SATB oct HUNTZINGER 4017 $.25 (S2243)

Voice In The Wilderness, The
SATB oct HUNTZINGER 4011 $.25 (S2244)
SSA oct HUNTZINGER 7037 $.25 (S2245)
SA&unis/SA/unis oct HUNTZINGER 7037 $.20 (S2246)

When I Consider The Heavens
SATB oct HUNTZINGER 4032 $.20 (S2247)

SCOTT, SARAH
Three Introits For Festival Worship *CC3U,
Xmas/Commun/Easter/Fest/Gen,Introit
SATB (diff) ABINGDON APM-404 $.45 (S2248)

SCOTT, T.
Creation, The
SATB,acap oct PRESSER 312-40077 $.40 (S2249)

Go Down Death
SATB,acap oct PRESSER 312-40085 $.45 (S2250)

Jesus Born In Bethlea *Xmas
SATB,acap oct PRESSER 312-40093 $.35 (S2251)

Story Of The Twelve, The
SATB,acap oct PRESSER 312-40054 $.40 (S2252)

SCRIBERE PROPOSUI see Klemetti, Heikki

SCT. HANS HYMNE see Henrichsen, Roger,
Johannisnacht Hymne

SCULL
Baby Jesus *Xmas
unis BOOSEY-CAN s.p. (S2253)

Lord Omnipotent Is King
SATB oct BOOSEY 5431 $.30 (S2254)

Mary, Maiden And Mother *Xmas
unis jr cor FISCHER,C PT 1760 $.20 (S2255)

O Praise Ye The Lord
unis WEINBERGER 4487 $.30 (S2256)

Snow Lay On The Ground
SATB,org FRANCIS s.p. (S2257)

SCULL, HAROLD [THOMAS] (1898-   )
Hosanna In The Highest
SATB PATERSON 1688 s.p. (S2258)

Judge Eternal, Throned In Splendor
unis oct NOVELLO 28.1340.08 s.p. (S2259)

SCULL, HAROLD [THOMAS] (cont'd.)

Rise Up, O Men Of God *anthem
unis,orch oct NOVELLO 40.1140.06 s.p., ipr (S2260)
unis oct NOVELLO 40.1140.06 s.p. (S2261)

SCULTHORPE, PETER [JOSHUA] (1929-   )
Morning-Song For The Christ Child *Xmas,
carol
4pt mix cor,acap oct SCHIRM.G 11632 $.25 (S2262)
SATB oct FABER 11632 $.25 (S2263)

SE BRUDGUMMEN KOMMER see Norman, Rudolf

SE DETTA AR DAGEN, SOM HERREN OSS GOR see
Wikander, David

SE, DETTA AR GUDS LAMM see Handel, George
Frideric

SE, DETTA AR GUDS LAMM see Thyrestam, Gunnar

SE DIN KONGE KOMMER see Hovland, Egil

SE GUD AR MIN FRALSNIG see Rosenberg, Hilding

SE GUDS LAMM see Moren, John

SE, GUDS SON TILL DODEN SKRIDER see Alvin, Erik

SE, GUDS SON TILL DODEN SKRIDER see Sorenson,
Torsten

SE, GUDS TID AR FOR OSS DEN BASTA see Bach,
Johann Sebastian, Gottes Zeit Ist Die
Allerbeste Zeit

SE HVOR NU JESUS TREDER see Nystedt, Knut

SE JEG STAR FOR DOREN see Baden, Conrad

SE LA FACE AY PALE see Dufay, Guillaume

SE SOLENS SKJONNE LYS OG PRAKT
(Baldershage, Bernt) wom cor MUSIKK 42 s.p. (S2264)

SE, VI GA NU UPP TILL JERUSALEM see Carlstedt,
Gunnemar

SE, VI GA UPP TILL JERUSALEM see Moren, John

SE, VI GA UPP TILL JERUSALEM see Nilsson,
Torsten

SE, VI GAR OPP TIL JERUSALEM see Neilsen,
Ludwig

SEA CHANGE see Warren, Raymond

SEARCH INTO ME see Bach, Karl Philipp Emanuel

SEARCH ME, O GOD see Blakley

SEARCH ME, O GOD see Emerson, John

SEARCH ME, O GOD see Fearis, J.S.

SEARCH ME, O GOD see Glarum, L. Stanley

SEARCH ME, O GOD see Lassus, Roland de
(Orlandus), Proba Me Deus

SEARCH ME, O GOD see Mueller, Carl F.

SEARCH ME, O GOD see Smith

SEARCH ME, O GOD see Young, Phillip

SEARCH ME, O GOD, AND KNOW MY HEART see Herbek

SEARCH ME, O LORD see Nordman

SEARCH MY HEART see White

SEARCH OF THE THREE KINGS see Gibb

SEARCHING CAROL, THE see Marryott, Ralph E.

SEARLE, HUMPHREY (1915-   )
Canticle Of The Rose
cor FABER F0056 s.p. (S2265)

Little Hymn To Mary, A *BVM/Xmas,carol
SATB oct FABER 11744 $.30 (S2266)
4pt mix cor,acap oct SCHIRM.G 11744 $.30 (S2267)

SEARS
Calm On The List'ning Ear Of Night
(Rhea) SAB oct PLYMOUTH UIL-101 $.25 (S2268)

SEASONAL ANTHEMS *CCU,Adv/Epiph,anthem
(Wyton) SATB FISCHER,C O-4811 $1.25 (S2269)

SEASONAL ANTHEMS see Davis, Katherine K.

SEASONAL INTROITS AND RESPONSES see Demming

SEASONAL RESPONSES FOR UNISON VOICES see
Hillert, Richard

SEASONAL RESPONSORIAL PSALMS see Roff, Joseph

SEASONAL SONGS FOR CHILDREN see Paul

SEASONAL THANKSGIVING, A see Thiman, Eric
Harding

SEASONS see Haydn, (Franz) Joseph

SEASON'S GREETINGS *sac/sec,CC23L,Xmas,carol
(Pease) SATB,opt band PRO ART 481 $.85, ipa (S2270)

SEASONS, THE see Haydn, (Franz) Joseph

SEASONS, THE, PART A-FALL THROUGH CHRISTMAS
*CC12L,Xmas/Gen,anthem
(Hadley) SAB PRO ART 920 $1.25 (S2271)

SEASONS, THE, PART B-WINTER THROUGH EASTER
*CC13L,Easter/Gen,anthem
(Hadley) SAB PRO ART 928 $1.25 (S2272)

SEAY, A.
Born To Us Is The Christ Child *Xmas
SATB,acap oct PRESSER 312-40371 $.50 (S2273)

SECCHI
Grant, Lord, Thy Joy Supernal
(Elkins) SATB,org BOSTON 13574 $.35 (S2274)

SECHS ALTE GEISTLICHE GESANGE *CC6U
(Henking, B.) [Ger] men cor,acap (easy) HUG
s.p. (S2275)

SECHS CHORALE see Bloch, Waldemar

SECHS CHORALKONZERTE see Schein, Johann Hermann

SECHS CHORALMOTETTEN see Raphael, Gunther

SECHS DEUTSCHE MOTETTEN see Schein

SECHS GEISTLICHE CHORE
(Bamer, Alfred) wom cor,acap cmplt ed
DOBLINGER s.p.
contains & see also: Ich Glaub' An Gott;
Lobet Den Herren; Pange Lingua - Tantum
Ergo; Sei Lob Und Ehr; Trauungsgesang;
Zum Jahresschluss (S2276)

SECHS GEISTLICHE KONZERTE see Selle, Thomas

SECHS GEISTLICHE LIEDER see Hessenberg, Kurt

SECHS GEISTLICHE LIEDER see Wolf, Hugo

SECHS HYMNEN see Victoria, Tomas Luis de

SECHS KLEINE CHORALMOTETTEN see Thomas, Kurt

SECHS KLEINE MOTETTEN see Pepping, Ernst

SECHS KLEINE PSALMENMOTTEN see Kubizek,
Augustinian

SECHS LATEINISCHE MOTETTEN see Ahrens, Joseph

SECHS MARIENMOTETTENLIEDER *see Strohbach,
Siegfried, Der Bankelsanger "Als Vater Noah
Die Arche Gemacht Hat"; Strohbach,
Siegfried, Die Nudeln "Bin Ein Armer
Kleiner Bube" (S2277)

SECHS MARIENMOTETTENLIEDER see Strohbach,
Siegfried

SECHS MOTETTEN see Werner, Fritz

SECHS MOTETTEN-HEFT 1 see Zipp, Friedrich

SECHS MOTETTEN-HEFT 2 see Zipp, Friedrich

SECHS MOTETTEN see Burkhart, Franz

SECHS MOTETTEN see Vaet, Jacobus

SECHS NEGRO SPIRITUALS, BLATT 1 *spir
(Holtz, Jos.) [Ger/Eng] men cor,acap HUG s.p.
contains: Good News, "Gluck Auf" (easy); I
Got A Robe, "Er Kronet Mich" (easy) (S2278)

SECHS NEGRO SPIRITUALS, BLATT 2 *spir
(Holst, Jos.) [Ger/Eng] men cor,acap HUG s.p.
contains: Go Down, Moses, "Auf, Auf, Moses"
(easy); Were You There, "Warst Du Dort"
(med) (S2279)

SECHS NEGRO SPIRITUALS, BLATT 3 *spir
(Holst, Jos.) [Ger/Eng] men cor,acap HUG s.p.
contains: Go Tell It On The Mountain, "Geh,
Ruf Es Vom Berg" (med); Swing Low, Sweet
Chariot, "Fahre Sanft, Schoner Wagen"
(easy) (S2280)

SECHS RESPONSORIEN see Sheppard

SECHS SPRUCHE see Mendelssohn-Bartholdy, Felix

SECHS UND ZWANZIG LITURGISCHE GESANGE *CC26U,
liturg
(Hogner, F.) SATB,acap cor pts BREITKOPF-L
PB-3551 s.p. (S2281)

SECHS VERSMOTETTEN see Seckinger, Konrad

SECHS WEIHNACHTSMOTETTEN *see Clemens,
Jacobus, Parvulus Filius; Senfl, Ludwig, Et
Filius Datus Est Nobis; Stoltzer, Thomas,
Dies Sanctificatus; Stoltzer, Thomas,
Grates Nunc Omnes; Verdelot, Phillippe,
Angelus Domini; Willaert, Adrian, Mirabile
Mysterium (S2282)

SECHS WEIHNACHTSMOTETTEN see Clemens, Jacobus

SECHS WEIHNACHTSMOTETTEN see Senfl, Ludwig

SECHS WEIHNACHTSMOTETTEN see Stoltzer, Thomas

SECHS WEIHNACHTSMOTETTEN see Verdelot,
Phillippe

SECHS WEIHNACHTSMOTETTEN see Willaert, Adrian

SECHSUNDDREISSIG GEISTLICHE SPRUCHKANONS see
Bornefeld, Helmut

SECHSUNDVIERZIG CHORALSATZE see Bach, Johann
Sebastian

SECHTER, SIMON (1788-1867)
Messe In Der Lydischen Tonart
(Dite, L.) 4pt mix cor,acap DOBLINGER sc
s.p., cor pts s.p. see from DER KLEINE
KIRCHENCHOR (S2283)

Tenuisti, Improperium, Graduale Und
Offertorium Fur Den Palmsonntag *Palm,
Gradual/Offer
(Dite, L.) 4pt mix cor,acap DOBLINGER sc
s.p., cor pts s.p. see from DER KLEINE
KIRCHENCHOR (S2284)

SECHZEHN CHORALE see Knab, Armin

SECHZEHN KIRCHLICHE LIEDER UND MOTETTEN-HEFT 1
see Mendelssohn, Arnold

SECHZEHN KIRCHLICHE LIEDER UND MOTETTEN-HEFT 3
see Mendelssohn, Arnold

SECHZEHN KIRCHLICHE LIEDER UND MOTETTEN-HEFT 4
see Mendelssohn, Arnold

SECHZEHN KIRCHLICHE LIEDER UND MOTETTEN-HEFT 5
see Mendelssohn, Arnold

SECHZEHN KIRCHLICHE LIEDER UND MOTETTEN-HEFT 6
see Mendelssohn, Arnold

SECHZEHN KIRCHLICHE LIEDER UND MOTETTEN-HEFT 8
see Mendelssohn, Arnold

SECHZEHN SPRUCHMOTETTEN see Brunner, Adolf

SECKINGER, KONRAD (1935-   )
Erde, Singe
cor,2fl,2ob,2clar,4horn,2trp,3trom,tuba,
timp HANSSLER 25.006 sc s.p., cor pts
s.p., ipa   (S2285)

Sechs Versmotetten *CC6U,Gen,mot
[Ger] SATB,acap (med diff) MULLER SM 2296
s.p.   (S2286)

Wir Sagen Dir Dank
[Ger] SABar,acap (med diff, small German
ordinary) MULLER SM 2297 s.p.   (S2287)

SECOND BEATITUDE, THE see Crandell, R.

SECOND BOOK OF BACH CHORALES see Bach, Johann
Sebastian

SECOND CHORAL SUITE see Kubik, Gail

SECOND CONCORD ANTHEM BOOK, THE *CC40U
(Davison, A.; Foote, H.) SATB SCHIRM.EC 1200
$3.50   (S2288)

SECOND CROWN CHOIR BOOK, A see Schalk, Carl

SECOND ENGLISH MASS see Bevenot, Laurence

SECOND JUNIOR CHOIR BOOK see Keating, L.

SECOND LONDON CAROL, THE see Rendall, Honor

SECOND MASS IN C see Haydn, (Franz) Joseph

SECOND MORNING STAR CHOIR BOOK, A *CC25L
(Thomas, P.) jr cor/treb cor CONCORDIA
97-4702 61.50 bontains works by: Bach;
Marcello; Dvorak; Neumark; Tunder; Vaughan
Williams; Buxtehude; Lenel; Schein; Holst;
Telemann; Mauersberger; Willan; Leo; Rhau;
Handel; Mudde; Distler; Charpentier;
Bender; Schutz; Gumpeltzhaimer   (S2289)

SECOND OFFERTORIUM see Schubert, Franz (Peter)

SECOND SERVICE see Byrd, William

SECOND SERVICE see Tomkins, Thomas

SECOND SERVICE, THE see Gibbons, Orlando

SECRET, THE see Schoenfeld, William C.

SEDEBIT DOMINUS see Lassus, Roland de
(Orlandus)

SEDECIA RE DI GERUSALEMME see Scarlatti,
Alessandro

SEDICI CANZONCINE A MARIA VERGINE see Bottazzo,
Luigi

SEDIT ANGELUS see Johnson, Robert Sherlaw

SEDULIUS, TR.
From The Lands That See The Sun Arise *Xmas
(Roff) SATB oct SHAPIRO SCE 2506 $.25
                                         (S2290)
SEE, AMID THE WINTER SNOW *Xmas,carol
oct HART s.p.   (S2291)

SEE, AMID THE WINTER'S SNOW *Xmas,carol
SATB (easy) OXFORD 08.190 $.20   (S2292)

SEE, AMID THE WINTER'S SNOW see Beckhard

SEE AMID THE WINTER'S SNOW see Goss, John

SEE AMID THE WINTER'S SNOW see Tchaikovsky,
Piotr Ilyitch

SEE AMID THE WINTER'S SNOW see West, John
Ebenezer

SEE HIM THERE see Simpson

SEE HOW THE RIGHTEOUS ONE DIETH see Haydn,
(Johann) Michael, Ecce! Quomodo Moritur
Justus

SEE JESUS THE SAVIOR *Xmas
(Niles) 4pt mix cor,acap oct SCHIRM.G 8303
$.25 see from Ten Christmas Carols From The
Southern Appalachian Mountains   (S2293)

SEE JESUS THE SAVIOUR see Niles, John Jacob

SEE NOW, HOW THE RIGHTEOUS MAN DIETH see
Ingegneri, Marco Antonio

SEE NOW, THAT THE RIGHTEOUS MAN DIETH see
Gallus, Jacobus, Ecce Quomodo Moritur

SEE THAT BABE IN THE LOWLY MANGER see Ryder,
Noah F.

SEE THAT YOU LOVE ONE ANOTHER see Roff, Joseph

SEE, HE CONQUERING HERO COMES oee Handel,
George Frideric

SEE THE CONQUEROR see Powell

SEE THE CONQUEROR MOUNTS IN TRIUMPH
see Three Easter Hymns

SEE THE CONQUEROR MOUNTS IN TRIUMPH see Smart

SEE THE CONQU'RING HERO COMES see Handel,
George Frideric

SEE THE DESTINED DAY ARISE see Powell, Robert
J.

SEE THE DESTINED DAY ARISE see Talmadge,
Charles L.

SEE THE FIG TREE see Schutz, Heinrich

SEE THE PRETTY BABY see Rocherolle

SEE THE RADIANT SKY ABOVE *Xmas,carol
(Cummings) SATB oct FOX S131 $.25   (S2294)
(Cummings) SSA oct FOX S152 $.25   (S2295)
(Cummings) SA oct FOX S143 $.25   (S2296)

SEE THE SHEPHERD'S DANCING see Goodale, R.L.

SEE THE STAR see Palmer, William J.

SEE THEN, HOW THE HOLY MAN DIETH see Ingegneri,
Marco Antonio, Ecce Quomodo Moritur

SEE WHAT LOVE see Mendelssohn-Bartholdy, Felix

SEE WHAT LOVE HATH THE FATHER see Mendelssohn-
Bartholdy, Felix

SEE WHAT LOVE HATH THE FATHER see Thiman, Eric
Harding

SEED IS THE WORD OF GOD, THE see Vulpius,
Melchior

SEEK AND YE SHALL FIND see Tarner

SEEK AND YE SHALL FIND see Wolff, S. Drummond

SEEK HIM THAT MAKETH THE SEVEN STARS see
Rogers, J.

SEEK THE HIGHEST see Persichetti, Vincent

SEEK THE LORD see Tomblings, Philip

SEEK THE LORD see Trued

SEEK YE FIRST HIS KINGDOM see Fargo

SEEK YE FIRST THE KINGDOM OF GOD see Bruckner,
Anton

SEEK YE FIRST THE KINGDOM OF GOD see Reed

SEEK YE THE LORD
(Cornwall, J.S.) SAB PIONEER 4003 $.20
                                         (S2297)
SEEK YE THE LORD see Berger, Jean

SEEK YE THE LORD see Burns, William K.

SEEK YE THE LORD see Burroughs

SEEK YE THE LORD see Butler, Eugene

SEEK YE THE LORD see Hedges, Anthony

SEEK YE THE LORD see Mornement, Ina

SEEK YE THE LORD see Roberts

SEEK YE THE LORD see Roberts, J.

SEEK YE THE LORD see Roberts, J. Varley

SEEK YE THE LORD see Roff, Joseph

SEEK YE THE LORD see Wetzler, Robert

SEEK YE THE LORD see Wyrtzen

SEEK YE THE LORD see Youse

SEEK YE THE MASTER see Townsend, John

SEEKING FOR A CITY
see Two Negro Spirituals

SEELE CHRISTI, HEILIGE MICH see Heiller, Anton

SEELE, VERGISS SIE NICHT see Cornelius, Peter

SEEN FIRST BY CANDLE-LIGHT see Grime, William

SEG JERUSALEM see Geitvik, S.H.

SEG TIL SIONS DATTER see Gjendem, J.J.

SEGABA LA NINA see Martin Pompey

SEGARRA, DOM IRENEU
Missa Cum Jubilo *Mass
[Lat] SSATTB,org voc sc NOVELLO s.p.
                                         (S2298)
Missa Paschalis *Mass
[Lat] SSAATTBB,org voc sc NOVELLO s.p.
                                         (S2299)

SEGNE, DU, MARIA see Schandl, Ernst

SEGNE VATER, UNSER ESSEN see Weber, Ludwig

SEGUIDILLAS MANCHEGAS see Benedito

SEHET see Bach, Johann Sebastian, Sehet, Welch
Eine Liebe

SEHET AN DEN FEIGENBAUM see Schutz, Heinrich

SEHET, DER TAG IST GEKOMMEN see Kubizek,
Augustinian

SEHET EUCH VOR VOR DEN FALSCHEN PROPHETEN see
Wenzel, Eberhard

SEHET, WELCH EIN LIEBE see Bach, Johann
Sebastian

SEHET, WELCH EINE LIEBE see Bach, Johann
Sebastian

SEHET, WELCH EINE LIEBE HAT UNS DER VATER
ERZEIGET see Bach, Johann Sebastian

SEHET, WIR GEHEN HINAUF see Bach, Johann
Sebastian, Sehet, Wir Gehn Hinauf Gen
Jerusalem

SEHET, WIR GEHEN HINAUF NACH JERUSALEM see
Raselius, Andreas

SEHET, WIR GEHN HINAUF GEN JERUSALEM see Bach,
Johann Sebastian

SEHLBACH, OSWALD ERICH (1898-   )
Wir Stehen Im Dasein Als Kampfer Des Lebens
*hymn
men cor,winds,drums cor pts TONGER s.p.
ipa   (S2300)

SEHT DAS KLEINE *Pol
(Korda, Viktor) 2pt wom cor,acap oct s.p.
contains also: Schau, Schau, Wie Sie Rennen
(Czech)   (S2301)

SEHT, ER KOMMT MIT PREIS GEKRONT see Handel,
George Frideric

SEHT NUR AN DIE ZWEI HERZEN see Mockel, Franz

SEI CANTI AL S. CUORE DI GESU *CC6U
[Lat] 2 eq voices,org ZANIBON 2769 s.p.
contains works by: Ascenso, A.; Bottazzo,
L.; Mangone, G.; Muller, J.; Volpi, E.
                                         (S2302)

SEI CANTI IN ONORE DI MARIA SANTISSIMA see
Tonetti, Ottone

SEI CANTI NATALIZI see Picchi, Luigi

SEI CANTI SACRI *CC6U
[Lat] unis,org sc ZANIBON 2789 s.p.   (S2303)

SEI CANZONI ALLA B.V. MARIA see Cicognani, Gino

SEI COMPOSIZIONI SACRE see Mangone, Gioacchino

SEI FROHLICH ALLE ZEIT see Eccard, Johannes

SEI GEGRUSSET, JESU GUTIG, UBER ALLE MASS see
Bach, Johann Sebastian

SEI GEGRUSSET, MARIA see Schutz, Heinrich

SEI GEGRUSSET, MARIA see Schutz, Heinrich, Ave
Maria, Gratia Plena

SEI GEPRIESEN see Buchtger, Fritz

SEI GETREU BIS AN DAS ENDE see Bloch, Waldemar

SEI GETREU BIS AN DEN TOD see Hufschmidt,
Wolfgang

SEI GETREU BIS IN DEN TOD see Bach, Johann
Christoph

SEI GETREU BIS IN DEN TOD see Brunner, Adolf

SEI GETROST, DEIN GLAUBE HAT DIR GEHOLFEN see
Driessler, Johannes

SEI GETROST, MEIN SOHN see Driessler, Johannes

SEI GNADIG MIR, O GOTT see Goudimel, Claude

SEI INNI ANTONIANI see Gorlatto, Giacomo

SEI LIEBER TAG WILLKOMMEN see Bach, Johann
Michael

SEI LITANIE LAURETANE see Bottazzo, Luigi

SEI LOB UND EHR *CC118U
(Hofmann, Friedrich; Weiss, Ewald) [Ger] 2pt
wom cor/2pt jr cor cloth BAREN. EM 346 s.p.
settings of songs from evangelisches
kirchengesangbuch   (S2304)

SEI LOB UND EHR
(Bamer, Alfred) wom cor,acap oct DOBLINGER
s.p. see also Sechs Geistliche Chore
                                         (S2305)
SEI LOB UND EHR see Bach, Johann Sebastian, Sei
Lob Und Ehr' Dem Hochsten Gut

SEI LOB UND EHR' DEM HOCHSTEN GUT see Bach,
Johann Sebastian

SEI LOB UND EHR DEM HOCHSTEN GUT see Cruger,
Johann

SEI LOB UND EHR DEM HOCHSTEN GUT see Gadsch,
Herbert

SEI LOB UND EHR DEM HOCHSTEN GUT see Kubler,
Emil

SEI LOB UND EHR DEM HOCHSTEN GUT see Marx, Karl

SEI LOB UND EHR DEM HOCHSTEN GUT see Spar, Otto

SEI LOB UND EHR DEM HOCHSTEN GUT see Stern,
Hermann

SEI LOB UND EHR DEM HOCHSTEN GUT see Trubel,
Gerhard

SEI LOB UND EHR DEM HOCHSTEN GUT see Zipp,
Friedrich

SEI LOB UND PREIS MIT EHREN see Bach, Johann
Sebastian

SEI LOB UND PREIS MIT EHREN see Erlebach,
Philipp Heinrich

SEI MIR EIN STARKER FELS see Raphael, Gunther

SEI MIR GNADIG see Selle, Thomas, Missa Super

SEI MOTTETTI EUCARISTICI *Commun,mot
[Lat] 2 eq voices,org ZANIBON 370 s.p.
contains: Bottazzo, Luigi, O Salutaris
Hostia; Corradini, Vasco Lodovico, Ecce
Panis; Favero, Gino, Panis Angelicus;
Livieri, C., O Sacrum Convivium;
Mercatali, A., Ave Verum Corpus;
Nicolosi, Salvatore, O Esca Viatorum
                                         (S2306)

SEI MOTTETTI EUCARISTICI *Commun,mot
[Lat] 3 eq voices,org ZANIBON 2680 s.p.
contains: Borsieri, C., Tantum Ergo;
Cerquetelli, Giuseppe, Tantum Ergo;
Muller, J., Pange Lingua; Muller, J.,
Tantum Ergo; Volpi, Edoardo, Caro Mea;
Volpi, Edoardo, Tantum Ergo   (S2307)

SEI MOTTETTI EUCARISTICI *Commun,mot
[Lat] unis,org ZANIBON 2678 s.p.
contains: Ascenso, Antonio, O Salutaris;
Ascenso, Antonio, Quam Dilecta; Baroni,
Giovanni, Panis Angelicus; Borsieri, C.,

Ego Dilecto Meo; Leoncini, Lorenzo, O
Salutaris; Moioli, Romano, Tantum Ergo
(S2308)

SEI MOTTETTI EUCARISTICI see Martini, Padre

SEI MOTTETTI EUCARISTICI see Muller, Giulio

SEI MUTTER DER BARMHERZIGKEIT see Schubert,
Franz (Peter)

SEI NUR STILLE ZU GOTT, MEINE SEELE see Zipp,
Friedrich

SEI RESPONSORI PER LA SETTIMANA SANTA see
Eccher

SEI STILLE ZU GOTT, MEINE SEELE see Kubizek,
Augustinian

SEI TANTUM ERGO *CC6U,Commun
[Lat] 2pt,org ZANIBON 2684 s.p. contains
works by: Bottazzo; Bottigliero; Jannazzi;
Malandra; Margiotta; Muller   (S2309)

SEI UNS WILLKOMMEN, HERRE CHRIST see Ahrens,
Joseph

SEI WILLFAHRIG DEINEM WIDERSACHER BALD see
Raselius, Andreas

SEI WILLFAHRIG DEINEM WIDERSACHER BALD see
Vulpius, Melchior

SEIBER, MATYAS (1905-   )
David's Lament
mix cor,SA soli CURWEN 61478 s.p. (S2310)

Missa Brevis *Mass
[Eng] 4pt mix cor,opt SA soli,acap oct
CURWEN 11610 $.25   (S2311)
mix cor CURWEN 80895 s.p.   (S2312)
[Lat] mix cor CURWEN 80792 s.p.   (S2313)

SEID BARMHERZIG, WIE AUCH EUER VATER BARMHERZIG
IST see Schutz, Heinrich

SEID FROH see Bach, Johann Sebastian

SEID FROH DIEWEIL [CHORALE] see Bach, Johann
Sebastian

SEID FROHLICH IN HOFFNUNG see Gwinner, Volker

SEID FROHLICH UND JUBILIERET JESU see
Praetorius, Michael

SEID FROHLICH UND JUBILIERT see Praetorius,
Michael

SEID IHR NUN MIT CHRISTO AUFERSTANDEN see
Hufschmidt, Wolfgang

SEID IHR NUN MIT CHRISTUS AUFERSTANDEN see
Brunner, Adolf

SEID NUN FROHLICH, JUBILIERET see Holscher,
Bernhard

SEIDEL
Christmas Lullaby *Xmas
SSA FLAMMER B 5030 $.25   (S2314)

SEIGNEUR, JAI CONFIANCE see Pevernage, Andries

SEIGNEUR, JE NE POINT LE COEUR FIER see
Goudimel, Claude

SEIGNEUR, PUIS QUE M'AS RETIRE see Goudimel,
Claude

SEIHE, DAS IST GOTTES LAMM see Telemann, Georg
Philipp

SEIHE, ES IST ALLES NEU GEWORDEN see Schwarz,
Jochen

SEIN ZORN AUF ERDEN HAB EIN END see Schutz,
Heinrich

SEIS CANCIONES DE NAVIDAD see Martin Pompey

SEITZ, RUDIGER (1927-   )
Christ Ist Erstanden *Easter,mot
mix cor,acap oct DOBLINGER s.p.   (S2315)

Motetus Michaelis *mot
mix cor,acap oct DOBLINGER s.p.   (S2316)

Vier Lieder Fur Kammerchor Und Moetus
Michaelis *CC5UL,mot
mix cor,acap cmplt ed DOBLINGER s.p.
(S2317)

SEKVENSER (LOVSANGE) see Reiss, Georg

SELBY, WILLIAM
Mighty God, While Angels Bless Thee
(Ehret) SATB,org/pno BOSTON 13449 $.35
(S2318)

O Be Joyful In The Lord
(McAfee) SATB oct BOURNE 851 $.35   (S2319)

Psalm 117
SATB oct FISCHER,J 9967 $.35   (S2320)

SELECT A CAPPELLA CHORUSES *CCU
mix cor,acap SCHMITT 1 $.50   (S2321)

SELECT ANTHEMS FOR JUNIOR CHOIR *CCU
2p* jr cor FLAMMER GE5002 $1.25   (S2322)

SELECT ANTHEMS FOR MIXED VOICES, VOL. I *CCU,
anthem
(Strickling, George F.) SATB (easy) ABINGDON
APM-278 $1.25   (S2323)

SELECT ANTHEMS FOR MIXED VOICES, VOL. II *CCU,
anthem
(Strickling, George F.) SATB (med) ABINGDON
APM-306 $2.25   (S2324)

SELECT CHORALES *CCU,chorale
mix cor SCHMITT 2 $.50   (S2325)

SELECT FAVORITE ANTHEMS *CCU
SATB FLAMMER GA5014 $1.25   (S2326)

SELECT UNISON ANTHEMS see Hoffmann

SELECTED CHORUSES see Handel, George Frideric

SELECTED CHORUSES FROM THE MESSIAH see Handel,
George Frideric

SELECTED COMPOSITIONS OF PALESTRINA see
Palestrina, Giovanni

SELECTED SONGS FOR MEN *CC53L
4pt men cor oct AUGSBURG 11-9377 $1.25
contains works by: Christiansen, F. Melius;
Wycisk, Kurt J.   (S2327)

SELECTED WORKS VOL. I see Stoltzer, Thomas

SELECTED WORKS VOL. II see Stoltzer, Thomas

SELECTIONS FROM DER JAHRKREIS see Distler, Hugo

SELECTIONS FROM ST. LUKE PASSION see Bach,
Johann Sebastian

SELF
Child Is Born, A *Xmas
SATB oct FISCHER,C HO-376 $.25   (S2328)

SELIG DIE TOTEN see Doebler, Curt

SELIG IST see Lassus, Roland de (Orlandus)

SELIG IST, DER AUF GOTT SEIN HOFFNUNG SETZET
see Lassus, Roland de (Orlandus)

SELIG IST DER LEIB see Driessler, Johannes

SELIG IST DER LEIB, DER DICH see Raselius,
Andreas

SELIG IST DER MANN see Bach, Johann Sebastian

SELIG SIND, DEI LEIDE TRAGEN see Albert,
Heinrich

SELIG SIND DIE AUGEN see Driessler, Johannes

SELIG SIND, DIE DA GEISTLICH ARM SIND see
Schutz, Heinrich

SELIG SIND DIE TOTEN see Distler, Hugo

SELIG SIND DIE TOTEN see Doernberg, Martin

SELIG SIND DIE TOTEN see Graap, Lothar

SELIG SIND DIE TOTEN see Matthes, Rene

SELIG SIND DIE TOTEN see Schutz, Heinrich

SELIG SIND DIE TOTEN see Schutz, Heinrich

SELIGKEITEN, FREUDENZEITEN KAMEN FUR UNS see
Anonymous

SELIGPREISUNGEN see Schein, Johann Hermann

SELIGSTE DER LEBENSSTUNDEN see Schulz, Joh.
Abraham Peter

SELIN SIND DIE TOTEN see Messner, Karl

SELLARS
Psalm 100
SATB oct FISCHER,C CM-7739 $.25   (S2329)

SELLE, THOMAS (1599-1663)
Aus Der Tiefe Ruf Ich, Herr, Zu Dir *mot
(Vetter) SSATB HANSSLER 1.339 s.p. (S2330)

Ausgewahlte Kirchenmusik *CC24U
(Vetter) 2-10pt HANSSLER 4.007 $10.00
s.p.   (S2331)

Benedicam Dominum In Omni Tempora *mot
(Vetter) [Lat] TTBB,cont HANSSLER 1.349
s.p.   (S2332)

Christ Ist Erstanden
(Egidi, A.) [Ger] 2pt,cont,vln/opt pno&vcl/
opt pno&bsn/opt org&vcl/opt org&bsn
VIEWEG s.p., ipa voc sc, cor pts see also
Sechs Geistliche Konzerte   (S2333)

Confitemini Domino Et Invocate Nomen Ejus
*mot
(Vetter) [Lat] TTBB,cont HANSSLER 1.348
$.90   (S2334)

Danket Dem Herrn
(Egidi, A.) [Ger] 2pt,cont VIEWEG voc sc
s.p., cor pts s.p., ipa see also Sechs
Geistliche Konzerte   (S2335)

Die Mit Tranen Saen *mot
(Vetter) SATTB&SATTB HANSSLER 1.350 $.90
(S2336)

Domine Exaudi Orationem Meam *mot/prayer
(Vetter) "Herr Erhore Mein Flehen" [Lat/
Ger] ATTB HANSSLER 1.346 $.30   (S2337)

Ehre Sei Gott In Der Hohe *mot
(Vetter) SSBB/SATB,cont HANSSLER 1.515 s.p.
(S2338)

Eine Deutsche Missa Brevis *Mass
(Vetter) [Ger] dbl cor,SSTT soli,3vln,cont
HANSSLER 1.351 s.p.   (S2339)

Erstanden Ist Der Herre Christ *Easter
(Vetter) SSB,cont,2vln HANSSLER 5.084 sc
s.p., cor pts s.p., ipa   (S2340)

Es Begab Sich Aber Zu Der Zeit *Xmas,cant
(Vetter) SSATB&SSATB,ST soli,cont,bsn,2trp,
3trom,2vln,opt 2fl HANSSLER 10.155 sc
s.p., voc sc s.p., ipa   (S2341)

Es Werden Nicht Alle, Die Zu Mir Sagen *mot
(Vetter) SSB&ATB,cont HANSSLER 1.343 s.p.
(S2342)

Gelobet Seist Du Jesu Christ *mot
(Vetter) SSSS/SASA/TBTB,cont HANSSLER 1.514
s.p.   (S2343)

Herr Erhore Mein Flehen *see Domine Exaudi
Orationem Meam

Herr, Nun Lassest Du Deinen *mot
(Vetter) SSSB,cont HANSSLER 1.519 s.p.
(S2344)

SELLE, THOMAS (cont'd.)

Hosianna, Dem Sohne Davids *Bibl/mot
(Vetter) SSATTTBB HANSSLER 1.345 s.p.
(S2345)

In Me Transierunt Irae Tuae *mot
(Vetter) [Lat] TTBB,org HANSSLER 1.342 $.90
(S2346)

Jesus Sprach Zu Seinen Jungern: Mich Jammert
Des Volks *Bibl/mot
(Vetter) SATB,cont HANSSLER 1.340 s.p. (S2347)

Johannes-Passion Mit Intermedien *Psntd
(Gerber) 6pt mix cor,6 soli,cont,2brass,
3strings MOSELER sc s.p., cor pts s.p.
(S2348)

Komm, Heiliger Geist, Herre Gott
(Vetter) SSSB&SATB,cont,2vln,vla,vcl
HANSSLER 5.085 sc s.p., cor pts s.p., ipa
(S2349)

Machet Die Tore Weit *mot
(Vetter) S&3pt men cor/STTB/SATB,cont/vln
sc HANSSLER 1.516 s.p., ipa   (S2350)

Meine Seele Erhebet Den Herren *Magnif
(Vetter) SSATB,2vln,2vla,2vcl HANSSLER
1.520 s.p.   (S2351)

Missa Super *Mass
(Vetter) "Sei Mir Gnadig" SATTB,org
HANSSLER 1.341 $1.50   (S2352)

Nun Bitten Wir Den Heiligen Geist
(Egidi, A.) [Ger] mix cor,cont&2vln/org/
pno,vcl/bsn,opt strings VIEWEG voc sc
s.p., cor pts s.p., ipa see also Sechs
Geistliche Konzerte   (S2353)

O Jesulein
(Egidi, A.) [Ger] 2pt,ST soli,cont VIEWEG
voc sc s.p., cor pts s.p., ipa see also
Sechs Geistliche Konzerte   (S2354)

Sechs Geistliche Konzerte
(Egidi, A.) [Ger] VIEWEG
contains & see also: Christ Ist
Erstanden; Danket Dem Herrn; Nun Bitten
Wir Den Heiligen Geist; O Jesulein;
Wenn Trubsal Da Ist; Wie Eine Rose
Unter Den Dornen   (S2355)

Sei Mir Gnadig *see Missa Super

Si Bona Suscepimus De Manu Domini *mot
(Vetter) [Lat] TTBB,cont HANSSLER 1.347
$.90   (S2356)

Und Als Der Sabbath Vergangen War *Easter,
cant
(Vetter) SSATB&SSATB,SSAT soli,cont,3trp,
2trom,2vln,2vla HANSSLER 10.156 sc s.p.,
voc sc s.p., ipa   (S2357)

Veni Sancte Spiritus Et Emitte Coelitus *mot
(Vetter) [Lat] SSAT&SATB&ATTB HANSSLER
1.344 $1.50   (S2358)

Wenn Trubsal Da Ist
(Egidi, A.) [Ger] SSAB,cont,opt pno/org,opt
vcl/bsn VIEWEG voc sc s.p., cor pts s.p.,
ipa see also Sechs Geistliche Konzerte (S2359)

Wie Eine Rose Unter Den Dornen
(Egidi, A.) [Ger] 2pt,cont VIEWEG voc sc
s.p., cor pts s.p., ipa see also Sechs
Geistliche Konzerte   (S2360)

Zwei Kurzmessen *CC2U,Mass
(Birke) 5pt mix cor/8pt mix cor,cont
MOSELER s.p.   (S2361)

SELLEW
This Little Pilgrim *Xmas
SATB SCHMITT 1643 $.22   (S2362)

When Christ Was Born Of Mary Free *Xmas
SATB SCHMITT 1642 $.25   (S2363)

SELLEW, DONALD E.
Ben Johnson's Carol *Xmas
SATB SCHMITT 1641 $.25   (S2364)

Hanukkah Candles *Hanakkah,folk
SATB SCHMITT 1179 $.25   (S2365)

Hanukkah Song *Hanakkah,folk
SATB SCHMITT 1178 $.25   (S2366)

Noel *Xmas,carol
SATB,Bar solo,acap (diff) oct WILLIS 6162
$.15   (S2367)

None Other Lamb *Lent
SATB SCHMITT 1688 $.22   (S2368)

O Worship The King
unis jr cor BELWIN $1.00   (S2369)

Print Thine Image *Gen
SATB SCHMITT 1193 $.30   (S2370)

SELNECKER, N.A.
Nun Lasst Uns Gott Dem Herren
(Berger, H.L.) TTBB HANSSLER 6.5076 s.p.
contains also: Cruger, Johann, Nun Danket
All   (S2371)

SELNER, J.
Favorite Christmas Carols *CC8U,Xmas,anthem/
carol
TB/TTB/TTBB (easy) oct GIA G643 $.60
(S2372)

SEMELE see Handel, George Frideric

SEMMLER
Christmas Day In The Morning *Xmas
SATB oct GALAXY 1.2129.1 $.30   (S2373)

SEN PA FAGLARNA see Bjarnegard, Gustaf

SEN TILL see Olson, Daniel

SENATOR, RONALD
Parish Choir Book No. 52, The *CCU,Easter,
Gradual
cong&opt cor,cantor oct ST.MARTIN SMP683
s.p.   (S2374)

SENATOR, RONALD (cont'd.)

Whitsun Mass *Whitsun,Mass
unis/2pt,org oct ST.MARTIN SMP678 s.p., ipa (S2375)

SEND DOWN THY TRUTH see Beadell, Robert M.

SEND DOWN THY TRUTH see Brandon, G.

SEND DOWN THY TRUTH O GOD see Young

SEND FORTH, O GOD see Brandon, George

SEND FORTH THY LIGHT see Balakirev, Mily Alexeyevitch

SEND FORTH THY LIGHT UPON US see Klein

SEND FORTH THY SPIRIT see Schuetky, Franz Joseph, Emitte Spiritum Tuum

SEND FORTH YOUR LIGHT see Lindusky, Eugene

SEND HID DIN ENGEL, HERRE FROM see Buxtehude, Dietrich, Befiehl Dem Engel, Dass Er Komm

SEND, O LORD, THY HOLY SPIRIT see Pachelbel, Johann

SEND OUT THY LIGHT
SATB CHAPPELL 0016584-358 $.40 (S2376)

SEND OUT THY LIGHT see Balakirev, Mily Alexeyevitch

SEND OUT THY LIGHT see Gounod, Charles Francois

SEND OUT THY LIGHT see Lamont

SEND OUT THY SPIRIT see Schuetky, Franz Joseph, Emitte Spiritum Tuum

SEND OUT THY SPRIRT see Schuetky, Franz Joseph, Emitte Spiritum Tuum

SEND OUT THY TRUTH see Rinehart

SEND SOME MESSAGE FROM THY WORD see Cherubini, Luigi

SEND THY PEACE see Burgstahler, Elton

SEND US THY HEAV'NLY LIGHT see Foltz

SENDE DEIN LICHT see Koch, Johannes H.E.

SENDE DEIN LICHT UND DEINE WAHRHEIT see Anonymous

SENDE DEIN LICHT UND DEINE WAHRHEIT see Eglin, Arthur

SENDE DEIN LICHT UND DEINE WAHRHEIT see Knupfer, Sebastian

SENDE DEIN LICHT UND DEINE WAHRHEIT see Scheidt, Samuel

SENDT, WILLY (1907-1952)

Aus Hartem Weh *Xmas
men cor TONGER s.p. (S2377)
mix cor TONGER s.p. (S2378)

Christ Ist Erstanden *Easter
mix cor,acap TONGER s.p. (S2379)

Gott In Der Hoh Sei Preis Und Ehr
mix cor,acap TONGER s.p. (S2380)

Ich Weiss, Dass Ohne Mich *mot
men cor,acap TONGER s.p. (S2381)

In Dulci Jubilo *Xmas
see CHORE ZUR WEIHNACHT
men cor TONGER s.p. (S2382)

In Stiller Nacht, Zur Ersten Wacht
see Zwei Ernste Gesange

Nun Bitten Wir Den Heiligen Geist
mix cor,acap TONGER s.p. (S2383)

O Weh Des Schmerzen
see Zwei Ernste Gesange

Unser Lieben Fraue Traum *Xmas
mix cor TONGER s.p. (S2384)

Zwei Ernste Gesange
men cor,acap TONGER s.p.
contains: In Stiller Nacht, Zur Ersten Wacht; O Weh Des Schmerzen (S2385)

SENECAUT, TH. J.L.

Lenteliedje
men cor ALSBACH&D sc s.p., cor pts s.p. (S2386)

SENEX PUERUM PORTABAT see Byrd, William

SENEX PUERUM PORTABAT see Victoria, Tomas Luis de

SENFL, LUDWIG (ca. 1490-1543)

Alleluja
see Proprium Von 1 Adventssonntag

Ave Domine Jesu Christe
(Schabasser, Josef) mix cor,acap oct DOBLINGER s.p. see also CHRISTUS, DER HERR (S2387)

Ave Maria, Gratia Plene *mot
(Greenberg) [Lat] SSATBarB,acap AMP N29 $.60 (S2388)

Bells At Speyer, The
(Glarum) 6pt mix cor,acap oct SCHIRM.G 11375 $.35 (S2389)

Communio
see Proprium Von 1 Adventssonntag

Arde Mese
(Lukin, L.) [Hung] SATB (easy) BUDAPEST (S2390)

Erfreut Euch, Liebe Seelen *Pent/Whitsun
SATB,acap voc pt DOBLINGER s.p. see also PFINGSTEN UND EUCHARISTIE (S2391)

SENFL, LUDWIG (cont'd.)

Et Filius Datus Est Nobis *Xmas,mot
[Eng/Lat/Ger] PETERS V115 $.75 see also CHRISTMAS MOTETS OF PRE-PALESTRINA DAYS (S2392)
[Eng/Lat/Ger] SATB,acap PETERS V115 $.75 (S2393)
(Egidi, A.) [Eng/Ger/Lat] mix cor cor pts VIEWEG s.p. see from SECHS WEIHNACHTSMOTETTEN (S2394)

Ewiger Gott *Gen
[Ger] SATB,acap (med easy) MULLER K 17 s.p. (S2395)

Fecit Potentiam (from Magnificat Primitoni)
(Guettler) SATB,acap WARNER WB-133 $.30 (S2396)

Gelobet Seist Du, Christe *Psntd
[Ger] SATTB,acap (med) MULLER K 3 s.p. (S2397)

Introitus
see Proprium Von 1 Adventssonntag

Missa Ferialis *Mass
(Fellerer) [Lat] STTBB/STTB SCHOTT s.p. (S2398)

Non Moriar
see MUSICA RESERVATA, BAND 1

O Herre Gott, Begnade Mich
see MUSICA RESERVATA, BAND 2

Proprium Von 1 Adventssonntag *Adv
mix cor sc VOLK 144 s.p.
contains: Alleluja; Communio; Introitus (S2399)

Zwei Marienmotetten *CC2U,BVM,mot
(Gerstenberg) [Ger/Lat] 5pt mix cor MOSELER s.p. (S2400)

SENGSTOCK

What Is Man
SATB KJOS 5404 $.30 (S2401)

SENIORES POPULI see Rubbra, Edmund

SENIORES POPULI see Victoria, Tomas Luis de

SENIORES POPULI CONSILIUM FECERUNT see Ingegneri, Marco Antonio

SENKE DEN LICHTEN SCHEIN see Rohwer, Jens

SENKE, O VATER, HERAB DEINEN GOTTLICHEN FRIEDEN see Bach, Johann Sebastian

SENNELS, RICHARD

Lille Julekantate *cant
[Norw] mix cor&jr cor,solo,2fl,vln,pno/org LYCHE cor pts s.p., ipa, voc sc s.p., ipa (S2402)

SENOB

In A Manger
SATB&SSA,S solo oct BELWIN 60050 $.25 (S2403)

SENOR ZAPATERITERO see Benedito

SENSE OF HIM, A see Jones, Marjorie

SENTENCES FOR THE SEASONS see Bender, Jan

SEPT NOELS PROVENCAUX DE SABOLY see Passani, Emile

SEPT REPONS DE TENEBRES see Poulenc, Francis

SEPTEM ANGELI see Fink, Michael

SEPULTO DOMINO see Victoria, Tomas Luis de

SEQUENCE FOR ST. MICHAEL, A see Howells, Herbert Norman

SEQUENCE OF CAROLS, A *Xmas,carol
(Hattey) SATB (easy) OXFORD 46.007 $.65, ipr (S2404)

SEQUENTIA see Ravanello, Oreste

SEQUENTIA PASCHALIS see Naylor, Bernard

SEQUENTIA PRO FESTO SANCTI AUGUSTINI see Lerperger, Kurt

SEQUENTIA VENI SANCTE SPIRITUS see Andriessen, Juriaan

SERAPHIC SONG see Rubinstein, Anton

SERAPHIM ON HIGH, THE see Geisler, Johan C.

SERENA, BRUNO

Iessa S. Francesco D'Assisi *Mass
[It] ATB sc ZANIBON 4704 s.p., cor pts ZANIBON 4705 s.p. (S2405)

Missa Cunctipotens *Mass
[Lat] SATB,org sc ZANIBON 4676 s.p., voc pt ZANIBON 4677-4678 s.p. (S2406)

Missa Maria Madre Della Chiesa *Mass
[It] unis sc ZANIBON 4693 s.p., cor pts ZANIBON 4694 s.p. (S2407)

SERENADE (TO BE SUNG IN THE WOODS) see Schulz, Joh. Abraham Peter

SERENE ALLELUIAS see Ferris, W.

SERLY, TIBOR (1900-)

Hymn Of Nativity *Xmas,hymn
TTBBB,acap PEER $.35 (S2408)

Little Christmas Cantata, A *Xmas,cant
audience,orch/pno oct SCHIRM.G 10614 $.35 (S2409)

Playful Shepherd, The
SATTBB,pno PEER $.45 (S2410)

SERMISY, CLAUDE DE (ca. 1490-1562)

Au Roi Des Rois, Immortel, Invisible *16th cent
(Honegger, Marc; Pidoux, Pierre) [Fr] SATB OUVRIERES E0568 s.p. (S2411)

Ave Maria
(Agnel, A.) [Lat] 3pt mix cor HEUGEL PJ186 s.p. (S2412)

SERMISY, CLAUDE DE (cont'd.)

Beatae Mariae Virginis *Mass/mot
(Allaire, Gaston) cor AM.INST.MUS. see from OPERA OMNIA VOL. II (S2413)

Benedicam Dominum *Mass/mot
(Allaire, Gaston) cor AM.INST.MUS. see from OPERA OMNIA VOL. II (S2414)

Cara La Vita Mia *Mass/mot
(Allaire, Gaston) cor AM.INST.MUS. see from OPERA OMNIA VOL. II (S2415)

Motets A Quatre Voix Mixtes *CCU,mot
(Dottin, G.) [Fr] 4pt mix cor HEUGEL s.p. (S2416)

Opera Omnia vol. I *CCU,Magnif
(Allaire, Gaston) cor AM.INST.MUS. $12.00 (S2417)

Praeparate Corda Vestra
(Expert) [Lat] SATB,acap oct SALABERT-US $.65 (S2418)

Thesauri Musici, Heft 7: Missa Da Requiem *Mass/Req,Renais
(Pass, Walter) 4pt mix cor cmplt ed DOBLINGER s.p. (S2419)

SERMON, A NARRATIVE, AND A PRAYER, A see Stravinsky, Igor

SERMON FOR OUR TIME, A see Berger, Jean

SERMON ON MIRACLES, A see Rorem, Ned

SERMON ON THE MOUNT (from King Of Kings)
SATB BIG3 $.30 (S2420)

SERMON ON THE MOUNT see Brown, William [H., Jr.]

SERMON ON THE MOUNT see Kalmanoff

SERMON ON THE MOUNT, THE see Brubeck

SERMON ON THE MOUNT, THE see Koch, Johannes H.E., Die Bergrede

SERMON ON THE MOUNT, THE see McAfee, Don

SERMONE BLANDO ANGELUS see Tallis, Thomas

SERRA, LOUIS MARIA

O Vos Omnes
[Lat] 3 cor,opt pno/org HEUGEL CPJ98 s.p. (S2421)

Popule Meus
[Lat] 3 cor,opt pno/org HEUGEL CPJ99 s.p. (S2422)

SERRANO

Valencia Canta *Xmas
[Span] mix cor UNION ESP. 15312 s.p. (S2423)

SERVANT UNTO THEE, A see Fromm, Herbert

SERVE BONE see Lassus, Roland de (Orlandus)

SERVE THE LORD WITH GLADNESS see Handel, George Frideric

SERVICE see Rowley, Alec

SERVICE AND STRENGTH see Naylor, Bernard

SERVICE BOOK NO. 1 *CCUL,Fest/Gen,anthem/hymn/Psalm
mix cor (easy) voc sc ROYAL s.p. contains works by: Kelway, T.; Goss, John; Nicholson, S.H. (S2424)

SERVICE BOOK NO. 2 *CCUL,Fest/Gen,anthem/hymn/Psalm
mix cor (easy) voc sc ROYAL s.p. contains works by: Hunt, J. Eric; Crotch, William (S2425)

SERVICE BOOK NO. 3 *CCUL,Fest/Gen,anthem/hymn/Psalm
mix cor (easy) voc sc ROYAL s.p. contains works by: Willan, Healy; Goss, John (S2426)

SERVICE BOOK NO. 4 *CCUL,Fest/Gen,anthem/hymn/Psalm
mix cor (easy) voc sc ROYAL s.p. contains works by: Jones, J.; Turner, W.; Tomblings, Ph. (S2427)

SERVICE BOOK NO. 5 *CCUL,Fest/Gen,anthem/hymn/Psalm
mix cor (easy) voc sc ROYAL s.p. contains works by: Nicholson, S.H.; Ouseley, F.A.G. (S2428)

SERVICE BOOK NO. 6 *CCUL,Fest/Gen,anthem/hymn/Psalm
mix cor (easy) voc sc ROYAL s.p. contains works by: Morley, T.; Attwood, T. (S2429)

SERVICE BOOK NO. 7 *CCUL,Fest/Gen,anthem/hymn/Psalm
mix cor (easy) voc sc ROYAL s.p. contains works by: Wesley, S.S.; Shaw, G. (S2430)

SERVICE BOOK NO. 8 *CCUL,Fest/Gen,anthem/hymn/Psalm
mix cor (easy) voc sc ROYAL s.p. contains works by: Ley, H.; Ouseley, F.A. G.; Lang, C.S. (S2431)

SERVICE BOOK NO. 9 *CCUL,Fest/Gen,anthem/hymn/Psalm
mix cor (easy) voc sc ROYAL s.p. contains works by: Smart, Henry; Gray, Alan; Novello, V. (S2432)

SERVICE BOOK NO. 10 *CCUL,Fest/Gen,anthem/hymn/Psalm
mix cor (easy) voc sc ROYAL 85402 043 8 s.p. contains works by: Morley, T.; Pitoni, G. (S2433)

SERVICE IN D see Ponsonby, Noel

SERVICE IN G see Smith, R.

SERVICE MUSIC see Christiansen, Paul

SERVICE MUSIC FOR SAB CHOIR see Kirby

SERVICE OF DARKNESS, A see Wood

SERVICE OF HOLY COMMUNION IN D MAJOR see
   Rowley, Alec

SERVICE OF NINE LESSONS AND CAROLS, A see
   Johnson, David N.

SERVICE OF SHADOWS, A see Smith, Lani

SERVICE POUR LA VEILLE DU SABBAT see Milhaud,
   Darius

SERVICE POUR LA VIELLE DU SABBAT A L'USAGE DES
   ENFANTS see Milhaud, Darius

SERVICE PROPERS NOTED, THE see Bunjes, Paul G.

SERVICE RESPONSES (SET 1) see Hopkins, Paul

SERVICE RESPONSES (SET 2) see Weiss, Donn

SERVICE SACRE see Algazi, Leon

SERVICE SACRE POUR LE SAMEDI MATIN see Milhaud,
   Darius

SERVICE SUITE FOR JUNIOR CHOIR see Schroeder

SERVIN, JEAN (ca. 1540-ca. 1596)
   Fais-Moi Ouir, Des Le Matin, Ta Misericorde
      (Psalm 143) 16th cent
      (Honegger, Marc; Pidoux, Pierre) [Fr] SATB
      OUVRIERES EO598 s.p.   (S2434)

   Psalm 143 *see Fais-Moi Ouir, Des Le Matin,
      Ta Misericorde

SERVING MAN IS SERVING THEE
   SATB CHAPPELL 0016600-358 $.40   (S2435)

SERVIZIO PENTATONICO see Weinberg, Jacob

SESSIONS, ROGER (1896-   )
   Mass *Mass
      unis,org MARKS $1.00   (S2436)

SET DOWN *spir
   (Morris) SATB,acap oct LAWSON 51529 $.45
                                                (S2437)

SET DOWN see Joosen, B.

SET DOWN, SERVANT *spir
   (Ehret, W.) SA ALFRED 6543 $.25   (S2438)
   (Ehret, W.) SAB ALFRED 6560 $.30   (S2439)
   (Ehret, W.) SSA ALFRED 6223 $.30   (S2440)
   (Hruby, Dolores) SA,pno oct WORLD ESE-1331-2
      $.45   (S2441)
   (Wiley) SATB oct PRO ART 1756 $.30   (S2442)
   (Wiley) SAB oct PRO ART 2376 $.35   (S2443)
   (Wiley) SSA oct PRO ART 2378 $.35   (S2444)

SET DOWN SERVANT see Shaw

SET ME AS A SEAL see Adler, Samuel

SET ME AS A SEAL see Grieb, Herbert [C.]

SET ME AS A SEAL see Johansson, Bengt

SET ME AS A SEAL see Smith, Gregg

SET ME AS A SEAL UPON TH1NE HEART see Near,
   Gerald

SET ME AS A SEAL UPON THINE HEART see Walton,
   William

SET OF THREE, A see Stevens, Halsey

SET THY LOVE see Bock, Fred

SETTE CANTI PASTORALI *CC7L,Xmas
   [It/Lat] unis/2pt ZANIBON 2676 s.p. contains
      works by: Bottazzo, L.; Ascenso, A.;
      Oltrasi, G.; Volpe, E.   (S2445)

SETTE INVOCAZIONI A MARIA see De Luca,
   Alessandro

SETTE LITANIE LAURETANE see Rodella, Sante

SETTE MOTECTA EUCHARISTICA *CC7L,Commun,mot
   [Lat] 2 eq voices,org ZANIBON 2688 s.p.
      contains works by: Bottazzo; Fabiani;
      Magri; Socal; Moioli; Volpi   (S2446)

SETTE MOTETTI EUCARISTICI *CC7L,Commun,mot
   [Lat] 2pt,org ZANIBON 2677 s.p. contains
      works by: Bottigliero; Ferro; Moiolio;
      Oltrasi; Volpi   (S2447)

SETTE MOTETTI EUCARISTICI see Bottazzo, Luigi

SETTE MOTETTI EUCARISTICI see Bottazzo, Luigi

SETTE PASTORALI A GESU BAMBINO see Moioli,
   Romano

SETTE ULTIME PAROLE see Mercadante, G. Saverio

SETTINGS OF CHORALES FOR TREBLE VOICES *CC28U
   1-3pt jr cor/1-3pt wom cor,acap,inst,rec,perc
      oct AUGSBURG 11-9382 $1.60   (S2448)

SEVEN AMENS BY MODERN COMPOSERS *CC7U
   SATB oct NOVELLO 44.1405.05 s.p.   (S2449)

SEVEN ANCIENT CAROLS (CAROLI ANTIGUI VARII) see
   Nelhybel, Vaclav

SEVEN ANGELS see Fink, Michael, Septem Angeli

SEVEN CANTATAS see Pergolesi, Giovanni Battista

SEVEN CHOIR RESPONSES FOR THE WORSHIP SERVICE
   see Wright

SEVEN CHORAL SERVICE SETTINGS see Fryxell,
   Regina Holmen

SEVEN CHRISTMAS CAROLS FOR JUNIORS see
   Greenfield, Marjorie H.

SEVEN CHRISTMAS CAROLS FOR LITTLE CHILDREN see
   Greenfield, Marjorie H.

SEVEN-FOLD AMEN see Pearson

SEVEN FRENCH NOELS *CC7L,Xmas,anthem/carol,Fr
   (Carroll, J.R.) (easy) oct SATB GIA G1745
      $1.00; SA/TB GIA G1746 $1.00   (S2450)

SEVEN GENERAL ANTHEMS FOR UNISON- TREBLE VOICES
   see Copley, R. Evan

SEVEN HYMN TUNES, PART I see Dowland, John

SEVEN HYMN TUNES, PART II see Dowland, John

SEVEN INTROITS FOR THE MORNING SERVICE see
   Russell

SEVEN JOYS OF CHRISTMAS see Mechem, Kirke

SEVEN JOYS OF MARY
   (Warren, B.) SSA,acap SCHIRM.EC 1939 $.18
                                                (S2451)

SEVEN JOYS OF MARY see Cain, Noble

SEVEN JOYS OF MARY, THE *Xmas
   (Johnston) SATB,org oct LAWSON 51355 $.40
                                                (S2452)
   (Kirk) SATB,acap,opt pno oct PRO ART 1953
      $.25   (S2453)

SEVEN JOYS OF MARY, THE see Taylor, H. Stanley

SEVEN LAST DAYS, THE see Miller, Edward

SEVEN LAST WORDS see Dubois, Theodore, Les Sept
   Paroles Du Christ

SEVEN LAST WORDS see Haydn, (Franz) Joseph, Die
   Sieben Worte Des Erlosers Am Kreuze

SEVEN LAST WORDS see Schutz, Heinrich, Die
   Sieben Worte Jesu Am Kreuz

SEVEN LAST WORDS FROM THE CROSS, THE see
   Schutz, Heinrich, Die Sieben Worte Jesu Am
   Kreuz

SEVEN LAST WORDS OF CHRIST, THE see Dubois,
   Theodore, Les Sept Paroles Du Christ

SEVEN LAST WORDS OF CHRIST, THE see Haydn,
   (Franz) Joseph, Die Sieben Worte Des
   Erlosers Am Kreuze

SEVEN LAST WORDS OF CHRIST, THE see Pinkham,
   Daniel

SEVEN LAST WORDS OF CHRIST, THE see Schuetky,
   Joseph, Die Sieben Worte Jesu Am Kreuz

SEVEN LAST WORDS OF CHRIST, THE see Schutz,
   Heinrich, Die Sieben Worte Jesu Am Kreuz

SEVEN LAST WORDS OF JESUS CHRIST, THE see
   Schutz, Heinrich, Die Sieben Worte Jesu Am
   Kreuz

SEVEN LAST WORDS OF OUR DEAR REDEEMER AND
   SAVIOUR, THE LORD JESUS CHRIST, THE see
   Schutz, Heinrich, Die Sieben Worte Jesu Am
   Kreuz

SEVEN LAST WORDS OF OUR LORD JESUS CHRIST, THE
   see Alfonso, Jose

SEVEN LAST WORDS OF OUR SAVIOR, THE see
   Massana, Jose

SEVEN LAST WORDS, THE see Dubois, Theodore, Les
   Sept Paroles Du Christ

SEVEN LAST WORDS, THE see Mercadante, G.
   Saverio, Sette Ultime Parole

SEVEN LAST WORDS, THE see Ritter

SEVEN LAST WORDS, THE see Schutz, Heinrich, Die
   Sieben Worte Jesu Am Kreuz

SEVEN LENTEN CHORALES see Bach, Johann
   Sebastian

SEVEN LONG DAYS WAS THE JOURNEY OF THE WISE MEN
   see Thygerson

SEVEN MORE CHRISTMAS CAROLS FOR LITTLE CHILDREN
   see Greenfield, Marjorie H.

SEVEN MORE MOTETS FOR OCCASIONAL USE *CC7L,
   Gen,anthem
   (Klein, M.) SATB (med easy) cmplt ed GIA
      G1495 $1.25 contains works by: Arcadelt;
      Bruckner; Hassler; Lassus; Lotti; Perti;
      Vittoria   (S2454)

SEVEN MOTETS see Victoria, Tomas Luis de

SEVEN MOTETS FOR OCCASIONAL USE *CC7L,Gen,
   anthem/mot
   (Klein, A.) SATB (med easy) cmplt ed GIA
      G1469 $1.25 contains works by: Brahms;
      Bruckner; Gasparini; Gumpeltzhaimer (S2455)

SEVEN SACRED HYMNS see Bruckner, Anton

SEVEN SACRED MOTETS see Lassus, Roland de
   (Orlandus)

SEVEN SAYINGS FROM THE CROSS see Lorenz, Ellen
   Jane

SEVEN SELECT ANTHEMS *CC7U
   mix cor SCHMITT 35 $.50   (S2456)

SEVEN SHORT INTROITS OR ORISONS see Pasquet,
   Jean

SEVEN SIMPLE SACRED SONGS see Fox, George

SEVEN SONGS FOR CHRISTMAS *CC7U,Xmas,carol
   cmplt ed WEINBERGER s.p.   (S2457)

SEVEN STARS OF THE ASSINIBOINE see Track,
   Gerhard

SEVEN TIMES HE SPAKE see Grieb, Herbert [C.]

SEVEN TRADITIONAL CAROLS see Hutchinson,
   Godfrey

SEVEN TREBLE CHOIR ANTHEMS FOR THE CHRISTIAN
   YEAR see Copley, R. Evan

SEVEN WORDS FROM THE CROSS see Powell, Robert
   J.

SEVEN WORDS FROM THE CROSS, THE see Nystedt,
   Knut

SEVEN WORDS OF CHRIST see Dubois, Theodore, Les
   Sept Paroles Du Christ

SEVEN WORDS OF CHRIST see Gounod, Charles
   Francois

SEVEN WORDS OF CHRIST see Haydn, (Franz)
   Joseph, Die Sieben Worte Des Erlosers Am
   Kreuze

SEVEN WORDS OF CHRIST FROM THE CROSS, THE see
   Schutz, Heinrich, Die Sieben Worte Jesu Am
   Kreuz

SEVEN WORDS OF CHRIST FROM THE CROSS, THE see
   Wienhorst, Richard

SEVEN WORDS OF CHRIST, THE see Busarow, Donald

SEVEN WORDS OF LOVE see Pfautsch, Lloyd

SEVENFOLD AMEN
   see Worship Responses

SEVENFOLD AMEN see Stainer, John

SEVENFOLD AND DRESDEN AMENS see Stainer, John

SEVENTEEN ANTHEMS see Taverner, John

SEVENTEEN PSALMS *CC17U,Psalm
   ROYAL s.p.   (S2458)

SEVENTEEN RESPONSES AND SENTENCES *CC17U,cor-
   resp
   SATB LORENZ 9050 $.30   (S2459)

SEVENTH DAY FRIDAY EVE SERVICE see Piket,
   Frederick

SEVERSON, ROLAND
   Lord Is King, The
      (Wetzler, Robert P.) SATB (med) ABINGDON
      APM-679 $.20   (S2460)

SEVIM, GIUSEPPE
   Adoremus Te Christe
      see PER LA SETTIMANA SANTA

   Beata Es Virgo
      see CINQUE MOTECTA IN HON. B.V.M.

   O Memoriale *Commun,mot
      [Lat] ABar ZANIBON 2963 s.p.   (S2461)

   Quam Magna *Commun,mot
      [Lat] 2 eq voices ZANIBON 2809 s.p. (S2462)

SEX KORALER I FOLKTON I SATTNINGAR
   (Nordstrom Carl-Elow) mix cor NORDISKA
      NMS-6415 s.p.
      contains: Den Ljusa Dag Framgangen Ar; Den
      Signade Dag; Det Ar En Ros Utsprungen; Du
      Som Harlig Stallde; I Hoppet Sig Min
      Fraista Sjal Fornojer; Sa Alskade Gud
      Varlden   (S2463)

SEX LATINSKA HYMNER see Olsson, Otto Emmanuel

SEXT see Klein, Lothar

SEYMOUR, H.
   Abide With Me
      (Monk, W.H.) TTBB,acap (easy) oct WILLIS
      1801 $.10   (S2464)

SH' MA see Roskin

SHABBAT BA-ARETS see Weinberg, Jacob

SHABBAT KODESH see Helfman, Max

SHABBAT NUSACH S'FARD see Rosenberg, Emanuel

SHABBAT SHALOM see Chajes, Julius

SHABBIT M'NUCHAH see Helfman, Max

SHADOWS ARE FALLING see Schroeder

SHADOWS ARE FALLING, THE *Xmas,carol,Ger
   (Schroeder, H.) SATB,inst (med easy) oct
      CONCORDIA 98-2064 $.30   (S2465)

SHADOWS OF EVENING see Baker, Dalton

SHADOWS OF THY WINGS see Andrews, Mark

SHAFFER, J.
   Show Me, O Lord
      SATB oct KERBY 6605 $.30   (S2466)

SHAFFER, SHERWOOD M.
   Ave Maria
      "Hail, Virgin Mary" [Lat/Eng] SATB,acap
      SCHIRM.EC 2421 $.35   (S2467)

   Hail, Virgin Mary *see Ave Maria

SHAKER WORSHIP SERVICE, A
   (Terri, Salli) SSA&TTB&2pt jr cor oct LAWSON
      51295 $.30   (S2468)

SHALL I COMPARE THEE TO A SUMMER'S DAY? see
   Butler, Eugene

SHALL I CRUCIFY HIM? see Ellis

SHALL I CRUCIFY MY SAVIOR? see Landon

SHALL I DIE FOR MANNIS' SAKE see Davies

SHALL I EMPTY-HANDED BE? see Hillis

SHALL I NOT TO GOD SING PRAISES see Bach,
   Johann Sebastian

SHALL WE GATHER AT THE RIVER
   (Parker) TTBB,pno/gtr oct LAWSON 51295 $.30
                                                (S2469)

SHALL WE GATHER AT THE RIVER see Boyd

SHALL WE GATHER AT THE RIVER see Lawry

SHALL WE GATHER AT THE RIVER see Lowry, Robert

SHALL WE GATHER AT THE RIVER see McDougal, Carol

SHALL WE GATHER AT THE RIVER? see Martin

SHALOM CHAVERIM
see Rounds Of Israel

SHALOM CHAVERIM see Lovelace, Austin C.

SHANKS
He Abides *anthem
(Ferrin) SATB oct LILLENAS AN-1629 $.30
(S2470)

SHAPERO, HAROLD (1920-)
Hebrew Cantata *cant,Heb
[Heb/Eng] mix cor,SATBar soli,org,fl,trp,
vln,harp sc PEER $1.60 (S2471)

SHARING CAROL, THE see Lovelace, Austin C.

SHARPE, EVELYN
Ash Grove, The
jr cor&desc LEONARD-ENG 64 s.p. (S2472)

Child Divine, A *Xmas
cor CRAMER 199 s.p. (S2473)

Child's Carol, A *Xmas
unis cor CRAMER 268 ipr (S2474)

Child's Hymn Of Praise *carol
unis cor CRAMER 34 s.p. (S2475)

Christ Child Sleeps, The
unis jr cor CRAMER 157 s.p. (S2476)

Crowded Inn, The *Xmas
unis jr cor CRAMER 156 s.p. (S2477)

Dream, Lovely Babe *Xmas
cor CRAMER 274 s.p. (S2478)

Easter Day *Easter
jr cor LEONARD-ENG 30 s.p. (S2479)

I Dreamt I Came To Nazareth
jr cor LEONARD-ENG 34 s.p. (S2480)

Magnificat In C *Magnif
SATB,acap LEONARD-ENG L0 s.p. (S2481)
SATB CRAMER L0 s.p. (S2482)

Many Years Ago *carol
jr cor LEONARD-ENG 27 s.p. (S2483)

Mary Welcomes The Shepherds
unis jr cor CRAMER 160 s.p. (S2484)

Mary's Lullaby *Xmas
unis jr cor CRAMER 244 s.p. (S2485)

Speedwell And Hyacinth *Xmas
cor CRAMER 234 s.p. (S2486)

Stars All Dotted Over The Sky
unis jr cor CRAMER 50 s.p. (S2487)

There Was A Little Baby King *Xmas
unis jr cor CRAMER 71 s.p. (S2488)
cor CRAMER s.p. (S2489)

Visit Of The Magi, The *Xmas
SS CRAMER 158 s.p. (S2490)
SS CRAMER 158 s.p. (S2491)

SHARVIT, URI
Psalm 30 *Heb
SATB,inst ISRAELI 326 s.p. (S2492)

SHAVE, E.
Praise We, Praise We, God The Lord
SATB,org/pno GRAY GCMR 3284 $.30 (S2493)

SHAW
Benediction
SATB SCHMITT SD6224 $.25 (S2494)

Christ The Lord Hath Risen *Easter
(Parker) boy cor SOUTHERN $.25 (S2495)

Christmas Hymns, Set 4 *see Ringwald, [Roy]

Lord My Pasture Shall Prepare, The
unis oct SUMMY B 1182 $.45 (S2496)

Set Down Servant *spir
SATB SHAWNEE A 29 $.30 (S2497)
8pt SHAWNEE A 69 $.30 (S2498)

Three Kings In Great Glory *Xmas
SA/SAB oct LORENZ 7816 $.30 (S2499)

Tis Finished *Holywk
(Parker) mix cor SOUTHERN $.25 (S2500)

SHAW, C.
Lamb
(Lynn, G.) SATB,acap oct PRESSER 332-40090
$.30 (S2501)

SHAW, DICCON
Lo, God Is Here *anthem
SAT/SAB oct NOVELLO 28.1362.09 s.p. (S2502)

Now Is The Time Of Harvest Home *Harv
unis&desc oct NOVELLO 28.1437.04 s.p.
(S2503)

SHAW, G.
O Be Joyful In The Lord
SATB BELWIN AP 24 $.35 (S2504)

Worship
SATB BELWIN AP3 $.35 (S2505)

SHAW, GEOFFREY [TURTON] (1879-1943)
Child's Prayer, A
unis oct CURWEN 10292 $.25 (S2506)

Glad That I Live Am I *Gen
(Barnes, A.F.) SATB,acap (easy) oct OXFORD
43.039 $.25 (S2507)

SHAW, GEOFFREY [TURTON] (cont'd.)
Hail, Gladdening Light *anthem
mix cor oct NOVELLO 40.0895.02 s.p. (S2508)

Happy Day, The
unis jr cor/unis wom cor CURWEN 71999 s.p.
(S2509)

Holy Communion *Commun
SATB (modal) oct NOVELLO 44.1182.10 s.p.
(S2510)

How Far Is It To Bethlehem? *Xmas,anthem
unis oct NOVELLO 48.1366.09 s.p. (S2511)
mix cor oct NOVELLO 50.0245.01 s.p. (S2512)
4pt oct NOVELLO 51.0499.08 s.p. (S2513)
TTBB oct NOVELLO 43.0652.10 s.p. (S2514)

In Peaceful Fields
unis jr cor/unis wom cor CURWEN 72118 s.p.
(S2515)

Lamb, The
unis jr cor/unis wom cor CURWEN 71368 s.p.
(S2516)

Let All The World *anthem
unis oct NOVELLO 40.1107.04 s.p. (S2517)

Let All The World In Every Corner Sing
*anthem
mix cor oct NOVELLO 28.1212.06 s.p. (S2518)

Lord Of All Power And Might *anthem
mix cor,acap oct NOVELLO 28.1198.07 s.p.
(S2519)

Magnificat And Nunc Dimittis *Magnif/Nunc
unis NOVELLO 44.1158.07 s.p. (S2520)

O Be Joyful In The Lord *anthem
mix cor oct NOVELLO 28.1193.06 s.p. (S2521)

Praise God In His Holiness
SAB CURWEN 80584 s.p. (S2522)
SAB/3pt boy cor/3pt men cor,org oct CURWEN
8574 $.25 (S2523)

Ring Out, Ye Crystal Spheres
SATB CRAMER C 34 s.p. (S2524)

Spring Bursts Today *Easter,anthem
2pt,orch oct NOVELLO 53.0270.07 s.p., ipr
(S2525)
mix cor,acap oct NOVELLO 40.0960.06 s.p.
(S2526)

Unto Us Is Born A Son *Xmas
cor/cong oct MOWBRAY 65056 5 s.p. see also
ENGLISH CAROL BOOK, THE (S2527)

Worship *anthem
mix cor,orch oct NOVELLO 28.1147.02 s.p.,
ipr (S2528)
unis,orch oct NOVELLO 40.0967.03 s.p., ipr
(S2529)

SHAW, GERALD
Magnificat
see Twentieth Century Evening Service, A

Nunc Dimittus
see Twentieth Century Evening Service, A

Twentieth Century Evening Service, A *Bibl
SATB,cantor voc sc WEINBERGER s.p.
contains: Magnificat (Magnif); Nunc
Dimittus (Nunc) (S2530)

Versicles And Responses *CCU,Bibl
SATB,cantor voc sc WEINBERGER s.p. (S2531)

SHAW, MARTIN (1875-1958)
Anglican Folk Mass *Commun,Mass
cor,pno/org sc ROYAL s.p. (S2532)

Anglican Folk Mass, An *Bibl/folk/Mass,Eng
mix cor voc sc CURWEN 80583 s.p. (S2533)
unis oct CURWEN 10229 $.25 (S2534)

Anglican Folk Mass, Series 3 *folk/Mass
SATB,org ROBERTON (S2535)

Arise In Us *anthem
mix cor oct NOVELLO 28.1178.02 s.p. (S2536)

Benedicite (Shortened Form)
SATB (F maj) oct NOVELLO 44.1220.06 s.p.
(S2537)

Blessed Art Thou, O Lord Of Our Fathers
*anthem
SATB BELWIN AP 20 $.35 (S2538)
mix cor oct NOVELLO 40.1181.03 s.p. (S2539)

Blessing, A
girl cor SOUTHERN $.25 (S2540)
mix cor CURWEN 80648 s.p. (S2541)
(Jacobson) 2pt boy cor/2pt wom cor oct
CURWEN 10958 $.25 (S2542)
(Jacobson) 3pt mix cor oct CURWEN 10959
$.25 (S2543)
(Jacobson) 3pt wom cor oct CURWEN 10960
$.25 (S2544)
(Jacobson) 3pt jr cor/3pt wom cor CURWEN
72510 s.p. (S2545)
(Jacobson) SATB/SA/TB CURWEN 61508 s.p.
(S2546)

Blessing, A (Go Forth Into The World In
Peace)
4pt mix cor,org oct CURWEN 8668 $.25
(S2547)

Break Forth Into Thanksgiving *anthem
mix cor,orch oct NOVELLO 45.1438.06 s.p.
(S2548)

Christ Is Our Corner-Stone *anthem
mix cor,S solo oct NOVELLO 28.1366.01 s.p.
(S2549)

Christmas Reading, A *Xmas,carol/hymn
SATB,org voc sc NOVELLO s.p. (S2550)

Christ's Flock
4pt mix cor,S solo oct CURWEN 10584 $.25
(S2551)

Crib, The *Xmas,cant
cor,pno voc sc CURWEN $1.00 (S2552)

Crib, The *Xmas
4pt mix cor,STB soli,acap oct CURWEN 10332
$.50 (S2553)

Easter Alleluia *Easter
4pt mix cor,ST soli,acap oct CURWEN 10052
$.25 (S2554)

SHAW, MARTIN (cont'd.)
Easter Anthems, The *Easter
SSAATTBB,2T (med easy) oct OXFORD 42.045
$.35, ipr (S2555)

Fanfare *see Gloria In Excelsis Deo

Fanfare For Christmas Day *see Gloria In
Excelsis Deo

For Courage
SA ALLANS 433 s.p. (S2556)

Glad Hearts Adventuring
unis boy cor CRAMER 20 ipr (S2557)

Gloria In Excelsis Deo *Xmas
"Fanfare" mix cor CURWEN 80596 s.p. (S2558)
(Jacobson) "Fanfare" unis jr cor/unis wom
cor CURWEN 72464 s.p. (S2559)
(Jacobson) "Fanfare For Christmas Day" 4pt
men cor CURWEN 10467 $.25 (S2560)
(Jacobson) "Fanfare For Christmas Day" 4pt
mix cor CURWEN 8745 $.25 (S2561)
(Jacobson) "Fanfare For Christmas Day" 3pt
wom cor CURWEN 10706 $.25 (S2562)

Go Forth Unto The World
SATB ALLANS 432 s.p. (S2563)
SAB ALLANS 381 s.p. (S2564)

Go Forth With God! *Gen
SATB (easy) oct OXFORD 42.901 $.50, ipr
(S2565)
unis&desc (easy) oct OXFORD 44.030 $.35,
ipr (S2566)

Grant, We Beseech Thee *anthem
mix cor oct NOVELLO 50.0269.09 s.p. (S2567)

Greater Light, The
mix cor,T solo,org oct CURWEN 11473 $.30
(S2568)
mix cor,T solo CURWEN 80896 s.p. (S2569)

Hills Of The North Rejoice
mix cor CURWEN 80634 s.p. (S2570)
(Cassler) mix cor CURWEN 61569 s.p. (S2571)

Holy Communion *Commun
SAT/SATB,acap (C min) oct NOVELLO
44.1449.07 s.p. (S2572)

Joyous Day, This *Gen/Marriage
4pt mix cor,org oct CURWEN 11025 $.20
(S2573)

Let All The People Praise Thee, O God *Harv,
anthem
SATB BELWIN AP 15 $.35 (S2574)
SAT/SAB oct NOVELLO 28.1267.03 s.p. (S2575)

Lord, Make Us Instruments Of Thy Peace
*anthem
SATB BELWIN AP 26 $.30 (S2576)
mix cor,acap oct NOVELLO 40.1377.08 s.p.
(S2577)

Magnificat And Nunc Dimittis *Magnif/Nunc
SATB (C min) oct NOVELLO 44.1403.09 s.p.
(S2578)
SAT/SAB (E flat maj) oct NOVELLO 44.1309.01
s.p. (S2579)

Matthew, Mark, Luke, And John
2pt jr cor/2pt wom cor CURWEN 72128 s.p.
(S2580)

Modal Setting Of The Communion Service, A
*Commun
mix cor voc sc CURWEN 80558 s.p. (S2581)

Mummers, The *Xmas
cor CRAMER 40 (S2582)

O Christ, Who Holds The Open Gate *Harv,
anthem
mix cor oct NOVELLO 28.1192.08 s.p. (S2583)
4pt mix cor,org oct SCHIRM.G 11359 $.25
(S2584)

O Clap Your Hands *anthem
mix cor oct NOVELLO 28.1237.01 s.p. (S2585)

O Light From Age To Age The Same *Fest/Gen
SATB (med easy) oct OXFORD 42.050 $.25
(S2586)

O Lord, How Manifold Thy Works *Thanks
unis oct NOVELLO 28.1310.06 s.p. (S2587)

Old Christmas *Xmas
unis oct CURWEN 10672 $.20 (S2588)

Praise To The Spirit *anthem
mix cor,S/T solo oct NOVELLO 28.1303.03
s.p. (S2589)

Sing We Merrily *anthem
dbl cor,acap (choral fanfare) oct NOVELLO
28.1181.02 s.p. (S2590)

Sing We Merrily Unto God Our Strength
dbl cor BELWIN AP 16 $.50 (S2591)

Song Of December *Xmas
SA CRAMER 47 (S2592)

St. Georges's Day *carol
unis CRAMER 1 (S2593)

Sursum Corda *cant
[Lat] SATB,T solo,3fl,3ob,2clar,2bsn,2horn,
2trp,3trom,strings,2perc,timp,harp voc sc
NOVELLO s.p., ipr (S2594)

Te Deum And Benedictus *Bene/Te Deum
SATB,org (G maj) CRAMER A11 s.p. (S2595)

This Joyous Day
mix cor CURWEN 80849 s.p. (S2596)

Through The Night Of Doubt And Sorrow
mix cor CURWEN 80631 s.p. (S2597)

With A Voice Of Singing
4pt mix cor oct CURWEN 8103 $.35 (S2598)
2pt wom cor oct CURWEN 10227 $.30 (S2599)
3pt wom cor oct CURWEN 10041 $.35 (S2600)
4pt mix cor oct CURWEN 10454 $.30 (S2601)
SA ALLANS 353 s.p. (S2602)
SATB ALLANS 352 s.p. (S2603)
mix cor CURWEN 80599 s.p. (S2604)

SHAW, MARTIN (cont'd.)
SAB CURWEN 61453 s.p.   (S2605)
3pt jr cor/3pt wom cor CURWEN 72222 s.p.
                                                  (S2606)
men cor CURWEN 50843 s.p.   (S2607)
2pt jr cor/2pt wom cor CURWEN 72276 s.p.
                                                  (S2608)
(Jacobson) unis 3pt mix cor oct CURWEN
  11765 10226 $.25 $.30   (S2609)
(Jacobson) jr cor/wom cor CURWEN 72417 s.p.
                                                  (S2610)

SHAW, R.
Run To My Lord
  SATB,acap oct PRESSER 332-40041 $.30   (S2611)

This Joyful Eastertide   *Easter
  (Parker) SATB oct SOUTHERN $.30   (S2612)

SHAW, WILFRED
Evening Pastorale, An
  4pt men cor CURWEN 50549 s.p.   (S2613)

SHEA
Alleluia, Sing To Jesus
  2pt oct LORENZ 5762 $.25   (S2614)

Where Have You Gone, My Lonely Lord?   *Easter
  SAB oct LORENZ 7409 $.30   (S2615)

Who Knows The Answer?
  SAB oct LORENZ 7411 $.30   (S2616)

SHEEBY
Christmas Story, The   *Xmas
  SATB oct LORENZ C217 $.30   (S2617)

SHEEP AND LAMBS see Homer, Sidney

SHEEP AND LAMBS MAY SAFELY GRAZE see Bach,
  Johann Sebastian

SHEEP LAY WHITE AROUND, THE see Shure, R. Deane

SHEEP MAY GRAZE IN PASTURES SAFELY see Bach,
  Johann Sebastian

SHEEP MAY SAFELY GRAZE see Bach, Johann
  Sebastian, Was Mir Behast, Ist Mur Die
  Muntre Jagd

SHEEPS LAMENT, THE see Brown, J.

SHELDON
Forty Days (from The Life Of Christ)
  (Cole) SATB,opt gtr (med easy) SOUTHERN
    $.40   (S2618)
  (Cole) SATB MARKS 4578 $.40   (S2619)

In The City Of David (from The Life Of
  Christ)
  (Frank) SATB,opt bvl&bells MARKS 4429 $.30
                                                  (S2620)

SHELLEY
Another Blessed Easter   *Easter/Lent
  (Martin) SA oct FISCHER,C CM-7098 $.25
                                                  (S2621)

Blessed Be The Lord God Of Israel
  SATB oct PRO ART 1206 $.15   (S2622)

Christian, The Morn Breaks Sweetly O'er Thee
  SATB oct PRO ART 1056 $.20   (S2623)
  (Watson) SAB/SSA oct PRO ART   (S2624)

God Is Love
  (Mueller) SAB oct FISCHER,C CM-6883 $.25
                                                  (S2625)

Holy Saviour Grant Thy Mercy
  SATB oct PRO ART 1204 $.22   (S2626)

King Of Love My Shepherd Is, The
  SATB,SAB soli oct PRO ART 1200 $.30 s.p.   (S2627)

Lord, Hear Our Prayer
  SATB oct PRO ART 1199 $.20   (S2628)

Still, Still With Thee
  SATB oct LORENZ 1901 $.30   (S2629)

SHELLEY, [HARRY ROWE] (1858-1947)
Breast The Wave, Christian   *Bibl
  4pt mix cor,SAB soli oct SCHIRM.G 4292 $.25
                                                  (S2630)

Christian, The Morn Breaks Sweetly O'er Thee
  *Gen
  SATB SCHMITT 1913 $.20   (S2631)
  4pt mix cor,SB soli oct SCHIRM.G 3149 $.25
                                                  (S2632)

Death And Life   *Easter,cant
  cor,soli,org voc sc SCHIRM.G $1.00   (S2633)

God Is Love
  4pt mix cor,B solo oct SCHIRM.G 3273 $.25
                                                  (S2634)
  3pt wom cor oct SCHIRM.G 4562 $.20   (S2635)
  (Pitcher, Gladys) 3pt mix cor,pno (med) oct
    WILLIS 8480 $.20   (S2636)

Hark!Hark, My Soul   *Bibl
  cor oct HART s.p.   (S2637)
  SATB oct LESLIE 4052   (S2638)
  SATB,A solo ALLANS 11 s.p.   (S2639)
  SSA oct SCHIRM.G 4878 $.25   (S2640)
  4pt mix cor,SA soli oct SCHIRM.G 3209 $.35
                                                  (S2641)
  (Deis) 3pt mix cor,SABar soli oct SCHIRM.G
    9740 $.30   (S2642)
  (Stickles) jr cor&sr cor oct SCHIRM.G 10390
    $.30   (S2643)

How Beautiful On The Mountains
  SATB ALLANS 60 s.p.   (S2644)

King Of Love My Shepherd Is, The   *Gen,Bibl/
  hymn
  SATB SCHMITT 1912 $.35   (S2645)
  SATB oct LILLENAS AN-2262 $.30   (S2646)
  SATB oct PRESSER 312-40023 $.30   (S2647)
  SATB ALLANS 33 s.p.   (S2648)
  3pt wom cor oct SCHIRM.G 7172 $.35   (S2649)
  4pt men cor,B solo oct SCHIRM.G 4266 $.25
                                                  (S2650)
  4pt mix cor,SAB soli oct SCHIRM.G 3125 $.30
                                                  (S2651)
  (Deis) SAB oct SCHIRM.G 9738 $.35   (S2652)

King Of Love, The   *Bibl
  (Stickles) jr cor&sr cor oct SCHIRM.G 10392
    $.30   (S2653)

SHELLEY, [HARRY ROWE] (cont'd.)
Now Abideth Faith, Hope, And Love
  SSA oct SCHIRM.G 4600 $.20   (S2654)

Resurrection, The   *Easter
  4pt mix cor,SATB soli oct SCHIRM.G 3293
    $.25   (S2655)

Saviour, When Night Involves The Skies   *Bibl
  SATB,org oct SCHIRM.G 3256 $.20   (S2656)

Star Of The Orient   *Xmas,Bibl
  4pt mix cor,S solo oct SCHIRM.G 4464 $.25
                                                  (S2657)

SHELTER IN THE TIME OF STORM, A see Norman, Gus

SHELTER IN THE TIME OF STORM, A see Sankey, I.

SHEMAR, N.
Jerusalem In Or
  [Fr] 4pt mix cor CHAPPELL-FR s.p.   (S2658)

SHEPARD, T.G.
O Jesus, Thou Are Standing   *Bibl
  4pt mix cor,ST soli oct SCHIRM.G 3710 $.25
                                                  (S2659)

SHEPHEDS, THE   *Mediev
  (Gundry) SATB&SSA,soli (med) voc sc OXFORD
    46.117 $1.75   (S2660)
  (Gundry) SSA (med) cor pts OXFORD 46.118 $.35
                                                  (S2661)

SHEPHERD see Goldsworthy, Broun

SHEPHERD see Kennedy

SHEPHERD, THE see Howells, Herbert Norman

SHEPHERD AND HIS LAMB, THE see Gillette

SHEPHERD AND HIS SHEEP, THE see Townsend, John

SHEPHERD AND THE ANGELS, THE see Bennett, F.
  Roy

SHEPHERD AND THE KING, THE see Gilbert, J.R.

SHEPHERD AND THE STONE, THE see Cain, Noble

SHEPHERD, [ARTHUR] (1880-1958)
Jolly Wat And Carol   *Xmas
  2 eq voices oct PRESSER 352-00106 $.35   (S2662)

SHEPHERD BAND, A see Praetorius, Michael

SHEPHERD, BLOW YOUR HORN see Grime, William

SHEPHERD BOY, THE see Jones

SHEPHERD BOY'S SONG, THE see Healey, D.

SHEPHERD BOY'S SONG, THE see Lyon, J.

SHEPHERD, HARK see Takacs, Jeno

SHEPHERD HAS ARISEN, THE see Lassus, Roland de
  (Orlandus), Surrexit Pastor Bonus

SHEPHERD, HEAR OUR CRY see Beethoven, Ludwig
  van

SHEPHERD, JOHN (ca. 1516-ca. 1562)
French Mass, The   *Mass
  mix cor,acap SCHIRM.EC $1.50   (S2663)
  (Collins, H.B.) [Lat] SATB CHESTER s.p.   (S2664)

Haec Dies, Quam Fecit   *mot
  (Collins, H.B.) [Lat] SATTBarB CHESTER s.p.
                                                  (S2665)

Haste Thee   *anthem
  mix cor oct OXFORD 43.256 $.35   (S2666)

I Give You A New Commandment   *Whitsun
  men cor (easy) oct OXFORD 41.301 $.25   (S2667)

Lord's Prayer, The   *prayer
  (Wulstan, D.) [Eng] SAATB CHESTER s.p.   (S2668)

Magnificat And Nunc Dimittis (from First
  Service, The) Magnif/Nunc
  men cor (med) oct OXFORD 40.102 $.65   (S2669)

Te Deum Laudamus   *Te Deum
  (Turner) [Lat] SATTBarB,acap AMP N26 $.35   (S2670)

SHEPHERD LAD'S GIFT see Lovelace, Austin C.

SHEPHERD LOUD THEIR PRAISES SINGING
  (Rowley) SATB (easy) OXFORD 42.071 $.35   (S2671)

SHEPHERD OF EAGER YOUTH see Walker, C.

SHEPHERD OF ISRAEL see Elmore, Robert [Hall]

SHEPHERD OF SHEEP see Pasquet, Jean

SHEPHERD OF SOULS see Blakley

SHEPHERD OF SOULS see Murray, Alan

SHEPHERD OF SOULS (SIGN OF THE CROSS) see
  Jones, Edward

SHEPHERD OF TENDER YOUTH see Darst, W. Glenn

SHEPHERD OF TENDER YOUTH see Hopkins

SHEPHERD OF TENDER YOUTH see Vick

SHEPHERD OF THY LITTLE FLOCK see Rawls, Kathryn
  H.

SHEPHERD ON THE HILL, THE see Niles, John Jacob

SHEPHERD, SHEPHERD   *spir
  see Folio Of Sacred Music (Volume 3)
  (Gardner) SATB oct STAFF 523 $.30   (S2672)
  (Gardner) SAB oct STAFF 619 $.35   (S2673)
  (Gardner) SSA oct STAFF 621 $.35   (S2674)
  (Gardner) TTBB oct STAFF 622 $.35   (S2675)

SHEPHERD, SHEPHERD see Gardner, Maurice

SHEPHERD SONG see Soule

SHEPHERD SONG, THE see Watters

SHEPHERD, THE
  SATB (easy) OXFORD 08.161 $.15   (S2676)

SHEPHERD, THE see Caldwell, Mary [Elizabeth]

SHEPHERD, THE see Ippolitov-Ivanov, Mikhail
  Mikhailovitch

SHEPHERDESS, THE see Macmurrough, Dermot

SHEPHERDS see Carrington, O.M.

SHEPHERDS AND THE ANGELS, THE see Artman

SHEPHERDS AND THE INN, THE   *Xmas
  (Gaul, H.) SATB oct PRESSER 332-14318 $.35
                                                  (S2677)

SHEPHERDS AND THE KINGS, THE see Hume

SHEPHERDS AND WISE MEN see Gillette

SHEPHERDS, AWAKE see Davis, Katherine K.

SHEPHERDS, AWAKE see Di Julio, [Max]

SHEPHERDS AWAKE see Hall

SHEPHERDS AWOKE TO THE HEAVENLY SOUNDS, THE
  *Xmas,carol,Pol
  (Ehret) SAB oct FOX CC15 $.25   (S2678)
  (Ehret, W.) SAB,opt ob/inst PROWSE CC15 s.p.
                                                  (S2679)

SHEPHERDS BRING CANDY AND MILK
  see Belgian Christmas Songs, Set 1

SHEPHERDS BY THE CRADLE   *Xmas
  (Hansen) SSA SCHMITT 340 $.25   (S2680)

SHEPHERDS BY THE MANGER see Dinn, Freda

SHEPHERDS CAME TO BETHLEHEM   *Xmas,carol,Pol
  (Ehret, Walter) SSA,opt inst oct WALTON 2539
    $.30   (S2681)
  (Ehret, Walter) SATB,opt inst oct WALTON 2518
    $.30   (S2682)

SHEPHERDS CAME TO BETHLEHEM see Davis,
  Katherine K.

SHEPHERD'S CAROL (from Anthology Of Carols, An)
  see Personet Hodie

SHEPHERD'S CAROL see Billings, William

SHEPHERD'S CAROL see Britten, Benjamin

SHEPHERD'S CAROL, THE see Niles, John Jacob

SHEPHERDS CAROL, A see Banyon, Arthur

SHEPHERD'S CAROL, THE see Billings, William

SHEPHERDS' CAROL, THE see Emig, Lois

SHEPHERD'S CAROL, THE see Jewell

SHEPHERDS' CAROL, THE see Pugh

SHEPHERD'S CHORUS see Kozinski, [David B.]

SHEPHERD'S CHORUS see Schubert, Franz (Peter)

SHEPHERD'S CHORUS, THE see Menotti, Gian Carlo

SHEPHERD'S CHRISTMAS SONG see Reimann, [Johann
  Balthasar]

SHEPHERD'S CHRISTMAS SONG, A see Hutson

SHEPHERD'S CHRISTMAS SONGS see Bartok, Bela

SHEPHERDS' CHRISTMAS, THE see Luvass

SHEPHERDS COME see Caldwell

SHEPHERDS COME AWAY see Costeley

SHEPHERDS, COME BEFORE HIM
  see Three Spanish Carols

SHEPHERDS COME, NOW LEAVE YOUR SHEEP see Green

SHEPHERDS CRADLE SONG see Somervell, Arthur

SHEPHERDS CRADLE SONG, THE   *Xmas
  (Macpherson, Charles) [Ger] mix cor CURWEN
    60992 s.p.   (S2683)

SHEPHERD'S FAREWELL see Berlioz, Hector

SHEPHERD'S FAREWELL, THE see Berlioz, Hector

SHEPHERD'S FAREWELL, THE see Berlioz, Hector

SHEPHERD'S FAREWELL TO THE HOLY FAMILY, THE see
  Berger, Jean

SHEPHERDS' FAREWELL TO THE HOLY FAMILY, THE see
  Berlioz, Hector

SHEPHERDS FOUND HIM see Schmidt, Minnie Anne

SHEPHERDS FROM THE FIELD
  (Harter) cor oct BELWIN 2103 $.25   (S2684)

SHEPHERDS GO TO THE MANGER, THE see Brook

SHEPHERDS HAD AN ANGEL, THE   *Xmas
  (Barker, D.W.) SATB,acap (med easy) oct
    CONCORDIA 98-1468 $.30   (S2685)
  (Wiley) 2pt oct PRO ART 1411 $.20   (S2686)

SHEPHERDS HAD AN ANGEL, THE see Besly, Maurice

SHEPHERDS HAD AN ANGEL, THE see Ehret, Walter

SHEPHERDS, HARK THE SONG see D'aquin, Louis-
  Claude

SHEPHERDS' HYMN, THE see Whitehead, Alfred

SHEPHERDS I CAN SEE YOU see Emig, Lois

SHEPHERDS IN JUDEA   *Xmas,carol,folk,US
  (Walker, D.S.) unis, orff inst (easy) oct
    CONCORDIA 98-2078 $.25   (S2687)

SHEPHERDS IN THE FIELD see Effinger, Cecil

SHEPHERDS IN THE FIELD see Obenshain, Kathryn G.

SHEPHERDS IN THE FIELD see Rasley, [John M.]

SHEPHERDS IN THE FIELD ABIDING *Xmas,carol
cor/cong oct MOWBRAY 65028 X s.p. see also
Cowley Carol Book, The   (S2688)

SHEPHERDS IN THE FIELD ABIDING see Naylor

SHEPHERDS IN THIS HALL see Young

SHEPHERDS KEEP THEIR FLOCKS, THE see Bach,
Johann Sebastian

SHEPHERDS KEEPING WATCH THAT NIGHT see Harris

SHEPHERDS LOUD THEIR PRAISES SINGING *Xmas
(Walton) SATB SCHMITT 868 $.30   (S2689)

SHEPHERD'S MEDITATION see Nosse

SHEPHERD'S NOEL, THE see Honey, Henry

SHEPHERD'S NOEL, THE see Honey, Henry

SHEPHERDS OF BETHLEHEM, THE see Demarest,
Clifford

SHEPHERDS OF TENDER YOUTH see Hopkins

SHEPHERDS ON THE MOUNTAIN STEEPS AFAR! see
Ehret, Walter

SHEPHERDS ON THIS HILL *Xmas,Greek
(Dickinson, C.) SATB oct GRAY GSC 180 $.30
          (S2690)

SHEPHERDS PSALM see Hastings, E.

SHEPHERDS QUAKED WHEN THE ANGEL TOLD THEM see
Hassler, Hans Leo, Angelus Ad Pastores Ait

SHEPHERDS REJOICE see Fuller, [Esther Mary]

SHEPHERDS, REJOICE see Wilson, John F.

SHEPHERDS, ROUSE YE QUICKLY *Xmas,carol,Fr
(Ehret, Walter) SA,opt ob FRANK F-608 $.35
          (S2691)

SHEPHERDS SANG IN JUBILATION see Bach, J.C.

SHEPHERDS SAW A STAR, THE see Pasquet, Jean

SHEPHERDS, SHAKE OFF YOUR DROWSY SLEEP see
Bergers, Secoue Ton Sommeil Profond

SHEPHERDS! SHAKE OFF YOUR DROWSY SLEEP see
Besancon

SHEPHERDS SHAKE OFF YOUR DROWSY SLEEP see Freed

SHEPHERDS, SHAKE OFF YOUR DROWSY SLEEP see
Hardwicke

SHEPHERDS, SHAKE OFF YOUR DROWSY SLEEP see Mc
Rae

SHEPHERD'S SONG *Xmas
(Krumnach) SATB SCHMITT 8027 $.25   (S2692)

SHEPHERD'S SONG see Giasson

SHEPHERDS' STORY, THE *Xmas
(Dickinson, C.) SSAA oct GRAY GSC 77 $.35
          (S2693)
(Dickinson, C.) SATB oct GRAY GSC 264 $.30
          (S2694)
(Dickinson, C.) SSAATTBB oct GRAY GSC 30 $.30
          (S2695)

SHEPHERD'S STORY, THE see Thiman, Eric Harding

SHEPHERDS' STORY, THE see Fisher

SHEPHERDS, THE *CCU,Xmas
mix cor cmplt ed SCHMITT 9156 $6.95, cor pts
SCHMITT 9156A $.40   (S2696)

SHEPHERDS, THE see Fjerstad

SHEPHERDS, UP! *Xmas
(Glover, R.F.) SS,org oct KERBY 6021 $.35
          (S2697)

SHEPHERDS, UP! see Glover, R.F.

SHEPHERD'S VIGIL, THE *anthem/folk,Dut
(Beurele, Herbert) unis treb cor,inst (easy)
oct AUGSBURG 0309 $.20   (S2698)

SHEPHERDS WAKE *Xmas
(Track) SSA SCHMITT 241 $.30   (S2699)

SHEPHERDS WATCHING LATE ONE NIGHT see Grime,
William

SHEPHERDS WENT THEIR HASTY WAY, THE *Xmas,
Carol
unis,brass oct SUMMY M 2917 $.40   (S2701)

Join, Every Tongue
SSAA,acap BOSTON 13620 $.35   (S2702)
TTBB,acap BOSTON 13621 $.35   (S2703)

King Of Glory, King Of Peace
TTBB,acap BOSTON 12275 $.35   (S2704)

My God, Accept My Heart
SA oct BELWIN 64293 $.30   (S2705)

SHOUT TO GOD see Gerig

SHOUT TO THE LORD see Berger, Jean

SHOUT TO THE LORD see Pachelbel, Johann,
Jauchzet Dem Herrn

SHOUT UNTO THE LORD see Donenfeld

SHOUT WITH JOY see Track, Gerhard, Jubilate Deo

SHOUT YE! see Young, Gordon

SHEPPARD (cont'd.)

Sechs Responsorien *CC6U,cor-resp
(Harrison) [Ger/Lat] 4pt mix cor&6pt mix
cor MOSELER s.p.   (S2708)

This Is My Father's World *hymn
(Rogers) SAB oct LILLENAS AN-2312 $.30
          (S2709)

SHEPPARD, [JOSEPH] STANLEY (1915-)
Benedicite, Omnia Opera Domini
[Eng] 4pt mix cor,org/pno oct SCHIRM.G
11693 $.35   (S2710)

Good News Is Here *carol,Fr
SAB oct ELKAN-V 362-1279 $.30   (S2711)

Prophets, The
SATB oct ELKAN-V 362-1272 $.40   (S2712)

Remember, O Thou Man *Xmas
4pt mix cor oct SCHIRM.G 11132 $.30 (S2713)

SHERBURNE see Read, Daniel

SHERILL, G.
Zaccheus
SATB,acap oct PRESSER MC462 $.30   (S2714)

SHERLAW-JOHNSON, ROBERT
Congregational Mass *Mass
cong,org FABER F0296 s.p.   (S2715)

Veni Sancte
cor FABER F0287 s.p.   (S2716)

SHERMAN
In God We Trust
(Simeone) SATB SHAWNEE A 925 $.35   (S2717)
(Simeone) SSA SHAWNEE B307 $.35   (S2718)

SHERWIN
Break Thou The Bread Of Life *Commun
(Lockwood) SATB oct SOUTHERN $.25   (S2719)

SHIELDS
Beside The Still Waters
SATB oct LORENZ B78 $.30   (S2720)

SHIELDS, A. MCC.
Procession Of The Magi *Xmas
2pt jr cor/2pt wom cor,rec,perc CURWEN
72501 s.p.   (S2721)

SHIELDS, MC EDWARD
Others
(MacLean) unis WARNER W3665 $.30   (S2722)
(MacLean) SSA WARNER W3664 $.30   (S2723)

SHIFRIN, SEYMOUR J. (1926-)
Give Ear, O Ye Heavens
SSAATTBB,org PETERS 6206 $.30   (S2724)

SHILLING, F.
Alleluia
TTBB SCHMITT 415 $.30   (S2725)

Jubilate In C *Bibl
SATB,SATB soli oct SCHIRM.G 3120 $.25
          (S2726)

SHIMMIRE
In Bethlehem *Xmas
2pt jr cor FISCHER,C ARD 625 $.20   (S2727)

SHINE see Jones, Marjorie

SHINE FORTH, O BEAUTEOUS MORNING LIGHT see
Bunjes, Paul G.

SHINE LOVELY CHRISTMAS STAR see Caldwell

SHINE ON OUR SOULS, ETERNAL GOD see Young

SHINE OUT, GREAT SUN see Handel, George
Frideric

SHINE, SHINE
see Eight Negro Spirituals: Book I

SHINES A STAR IN HIGHEST HEAVEN *Aus
(Ehret) SSA MARKS 4359 $.25   (S2728)

SHINN, G.
Captives Of Babylon *ora
oct HART s.p.   (S2729)

SHIP WITH CARGO PRECIOUS, A see Wunderlich,
Heinz

SHIR CHADASH see Adler, Samuel

SHIR L'EREV SHABBAT see Amram, David Werner

SHIR L'YOM HASHBOS see Weiner, Lazar

SHIR NAMAL *Fest
(Helfman, Max) "Song Of The Harbor" [Heb]
SATB TRANSCON. TCL 716 $.30   (S2730)

Very First Christmas, The *see Jenkins

SHIRU LADONAI see Gottlieb, J.

SHIRU LADONOY see Adler, Samuel

SHIVISI see Lewandowski, Louis

SH'MA KOLENU see Davidson, Charles

SH'MA YISRAEL see Gottlieb, J.

SI QUAERIS see Arnaldi, Antonio

SI QUAERIS see Bottazzo, Luigi

SI QUAERIS see Cerquetelli, Giuseppe

SI QUAERIS see Grassi, Ciro

SI QUAERIS see Ravanello, Oreste

SI QUAERIS see Volpi, Edoardo

SHOFAR SERVICE see Berlinski, [Herman]

SHOFAR SERVICE see Fromm, Herbert

SHORT AND EASY ANTHEMS see Morse, [Charles
Henry]

SHORT AND EASY ANTHEMS (SET 1) *CC15L,anthem
mix cor (easy) cmplt ed NOVELLO 03.0095.00
s.p.   (S2733)

SHORT AND EASY ANTHEMS (SET 2) *CC15L,anthem
mix cor (easy) cmplt ed NOVELLO 03.0096.09
s.p.   (S2734)

SHORT AND EASY COMMUNION SERVICE, A see
Stewart, C. Hylton

SHORT COMMUNION SERVICE see Arensky, Anton
Stepanovitch

SHORT COMMUNION SERVICE see Batten, Adrian

SHORT COMMUNION SERVICE see Bortniansky,
Dimitri Stepanovitch

SHORT COMMUNION SERVICE see Elmore, Robert
[Hall]

SHORT COMMUNION SERVICE see Hall, Alan

SHORT COMMUNION SERVICE see Sokolov, Nikolai
Alexandrovitch

SHORT COMMUNION SERVICE, A see Blake, Leonard

SHORT COMMUNION SERVICE, A see Gibbs, Alan

SHORT COMMUNION SERVICE, A see Westbrook,
Francis B., Missa Brevis

SHORT COMMUNION SERVICE IN C see Davison, John

SHORT COMMUNION SERVICE IN D see Beck, John
Ness

SHORT COMMUNION SERVICE IN D see Wright, S.

SHORT COMMUNITY SERVICE, A see Pitfield, Thomas
Baron

SHORT EVENING SERVICE see Ayleward, Richard

"SHORT" EVENING SERVICE see Morley, Thomas

"SHORT" EVENING SERVICE see Tallis, Thomas

"SHORT" EVENING SERVICE, THE see Hooper, Edmund

SHORT FESTIVAL TE DEUM see Holst, Gustav

SHORT MASONIC CANTATA, A see Mozart, Wolfgang
Amadeus

SHORT MASS see Lee, J.

SHORT MASS, A see Waters, Peter

SHORT, MICHAEL
Cantate Domino (Psalm 98) Gen/Thanks
SATB,acap (med) oct OXFORD 43.952 $.35
          (S2735)

Psalm 98 *see Cantate Domino

SHORT PASSION FROM ST. MATTHEW'S GOSPEL, A see
Bach, Johann Sebastian

SHORT PASSION STORY see Sigurbjornsson,
Thorkell

SHORT SERVICE see Byrd, William

SHORT SERVICE see Byrd, William

SHORT SERVICE see Gibbons, Orlando

SHORT SERVICE FOR MEN see Batten, Adrian

SHORT SERVICE, THE see Gibbons, Orlando

SHORT SETTING OF THE COMMUNION SERVICE see
DeTar

SHORT TE DEUM, A see Day, W.

SHORT'NIN' BREAD *spir
(Wilson) SSAA SCHMITT 2076 $.30   (S2736)

SHOSHANAS YAAKOV *Purim
(Feuer, Joseph) "Purim Hymn" [Heb] SATB
TRANSCON. TCL 235 $.40   (S2737)
(Fromm, Herbert) [Heb] SATB TRANSCON. TCL 797
$.50   (S2738)

SHOUT AMEN see Aloyse, Sr. M.

SHOUT FOR JOY *Xmas
(Ehret) SA SCHMITT 2586 $.35   (S2739)
(Ehret

SHOUT HOSANNA! see Dretke, L.N.

SHOUT IN JOY UNTO THE LORD see Graham

SHOUT JOYFULLY TO GOD see Englert, Eugene

SHOUT, O EARTH, IN JOYFUL CHORUS (from Piae
Cantiones, 1582) anthem/carol
(Whitehiad) 4pt mix cor,org oct CURWEN 10593
$.20   (S2743)

SICUT CERVUS see Lassus, Roland de (Orlandus)

SICUT CERVUS see Palestrina, Giovanni

SICUT CERVUS DESIDERAT see de la Rue, Pierre

SICUT CERVUS DESIDERAT see Palestrina, Giovanni

SICUT CERVUS (RET SOM HJORTEN) see Palestrina,
Giovanni

SHOUT THE GLAD TIDINGS oee Brackett, F.H.

SHOUT THE GLAD TIDINGS see Willcoxon, Larry

SHOUT THE GLAD TIDINGS see Williams, David H.

SHOUT TO GOD see Gerig

SHOUT TO THE LORD see Berger, Jean

SHOUT TO THE LORD see Pachelbel, Johann,
   Jauchzet Dem Herrn

SHOUT UNTO THE LORD see Donenfeld

SHOUT WITH JOY see Track, Gerhard, Jubilate Deo

SHOUT YE! see Young, Gordon

SHOW ANEW THY SALVATION see Strand

SHOW ME A WINDOW see Tarner

SHOW ME A WINDOW see Tarner, Evelyn F.

SHOW ME, O LORD see Schaffer, Jeanne E.

SHOW ME, O LORD see Shaffer, J.

SHOW ME THE WAY see Price

SHOW ME THE WAY see Saint Helena

SHOW ME THE WAY TO THEE see Ellsworth, Eugene

SHOW ME THY WAYS see Mueller, Carl F.

SHOW ME THY WAYS see Pelz, Walter L.

SHOW ME THY WAYS, O LORD
   SATB CHAPPELL 0016634-358 $.40   (S2744)

SHOW ME THY WAYS, O LORD see Greene, Maurice

SHOW PITY, LORD see Bach, Johann Sebastian

SHOW PITY, O LORD, FORGIVE
   (Reynolds) SATB oct FISCHER,C CM-7710 $.25
                                            (S2745)
SHOW US, O LORD, YOUR KINDNESS see Purswell,
   Patrick

SHOW US THY WAYS, O LORD see Kreter

SHOWALTER
   Leaning On The Everlasting Arms *hymn
   (Skiles) SAB oct LILLENAS AN-1160 $.30
                                            (S2746)
SHOWERS OF BLESSING *CC137U,gospel
   cong cmplt ed LILLENAS MB-185 $.60   (S2747)

SHRINE, THE see Latham

SHROETER
   Hail To The Lord's Anointed
   (Aufdemberge) SATB FLAMMER A 5464 $.30
                                            (S2748)
SHRUBSOLE
   All Hail The Power
   (Cartford) SATB (easy) oct AUGSBURG 1113
   $.25   (S2749)

   All Hail The Power Of Jesus' Name
   (Riegger) SAB FLAMMER D5128 $.30   (S2750)
   (Ward) SATB FLAMMER A 5011 $.40   (S2751)

SHUMAKER
   Christ Child, Divine *Xmas
   SSA SCHMITT 2552 $.25   (S2752)

SHUMM SHEI *Xmas
   (Backer) SATB (Silesian cradle song) SCHMITT
   837 $.30   (S2753)

SHUR, BONIA
   Three Songs For Hanukah *CC3U,Hanakkah
   2pt oct WALTON 5022 $.30   (S2754)

SHURE
   Star, A Shepherd, A Lamb, A *Xmas
   SATB oct LORENZ 9941 $.30   (S2755)

SHURE, D.
   Dark Cloud, Cover The Sea
   SATB,acap oct PRESSER 332-15022 $.40   (S2756)

SHURE, R. DEANE (1885-   )
   Folk Lore Christmas Cantata *Xmas,cant/folk
   SATB BELWIN $1.00   (S2757)

   Galilean Easter Carol *Easter,carol
   SATB oct BELWIN 879 $.25   (S2758)
   SSA oct BELWIN 878 $.25   (S2759)

   I Will Lift Up Mine Eyes
   SATB BELWIN 2286 $.35   (S2760)

   My Prayer
   SATB oct BELWIN 2214 $.25   (S2761)

   Sheep Lay White Around, The
   jr cor&sr cor oct FISCHER,J 7882 $.35
                                             (S2762)
   Watt's Nativity Carol *Xmas,carol
   SA oct BELWIN 1219 $.25   (S2763)
   SATB oct BELWIN 1035 $.30   (S2764)

SHVEDOF, C.
   Come Hither, All Ye Weary Souls
   SATB oct WALTON 2116 $.25   (S2765)

   Forever Is It Meet And Right
   (Rosewall) TTBB oct SUMMY 5839 $.30   (S2766)

SI BONA SUSCEPIMUS DE MANU DOMINI see Selle,
   Thomas

SI DIEU VIENT AU MONDE *Xmas
   (Geveart, F.-A.) [Fr] 4pt mix cor,acap (med)
   cor pts LEMOINE s.p. see from Collection De
   Choeurs, deuxieme Fascicule   (S2767)

SI DIGILIS E see Weiser, Willi

SI EST-CE QUE DIEU EST TRES DOUX see Goudimel,
   Claude

SI IGNORAS TE see Palestrina, Giovanni

SI NATTEN FLYR FOR DAGENS FROJD see Runback,
   Albert

SI NON HUMILITER SENTIEBAM see Schutz, Heinrich

SI QUAERIS see Arnaldi, Antonio

SI QUAERIS see Bottazzo, Luigi

SI QUAERIS see Cerquetelli, Giuseppe

SI QUAERIS see Grassi, Ciro

SI QUAERIS see Ravanello, Oreste

SI QUAERIS see Volpi, Edoardo

SIA GLORIA AL DIVIN PARGOLO! see Arnaldi,
   Antonio

SIBELIUS, JEAN (1865-1957)
   Accept Our Thanks (from Finlandia)
   (Hodson, W.) SAB oct PRESSER 312-21439 $.25
                                             (S2768)
   (Hodson, W.) SATB oct PRESSER 312-21252
   $.30   (S2769)

   Be Still My Soul (from Finlandia) Lent,hymn,
   18th cent
   SATB ALLANS 283 s.p.   (S2770)
   3pt wom cor/3pt jr cor,pno cor pts
   BREITKOPF-W s.p.   (S2771)
   SSA ALLANS 284 s.p.   (S2772)
   (Collins) SATB oct LILLENAS AN-2324 $.30
                                             (S2773)
   Be Thou Our Guide (from Finlandia)
   (Peery, Rob Roy) SA oct BELWIN 1042 $.30
                                             (S2774)
   (Peery, Rob Roy) SAB oct BELWIN 1043 $.30
                                             (S2775)
   Before The Dawn *Easter
   unis oct LORENZ 8558 $.25   (S2776)

   Carminalia *CCU,Lat,18th cent
   [Lat] mix cor cmplt ed FAZER s.p.   (S2777)

   Christmas Song *see Weihnachtslied

   Dark And Dawn
   SATB oct LORENZ 9827 $.35   (S2778)

   Festliche Hymne "O Heimat, Sieh Des Morgens
   Helle Schwingen" (from Finlandia) hymn
   4pt mix cor,acap cor pts BREITKOPF-W
   CHB-3630 s.p.   (S2779)

   Hymn Till Jorden (from Maan Virsi)
   cor pts NORDISKA 2870 s.p., voc sc NORDISKA
   2869 s.p., ipa   (S2780)

   Hymn To The Earth *Op.95
   [Eng/Swed/Ger] mix cor,orch voc sc PEER
   $.60, ipr   (S2781)

   Julpsalm
   see Two Christmas Songs

   Julvisa
   see Two Christmas Songs

   Lord, We Pray, In Mercy Lead Us (from
   Finlandia)
   (Sammond) SATB,S solo,org AMP A71 $.20
                                             (S2782)
   Morning Prayer, A
   (Carroll) 8pt mix cor,acap oct SCHIRM.G
   8016 $.25   (S2783)

   Natus In Curas *Op.21,No.2, hymn
   4pt men cor,acap cor pts BREITKOPF-W
   PB-2007 s.p.   (S2784)

   O Heimat, Sieh Des Morgens Helle Schwingen
   *Op.26,No.7, hymn
   4pt men cor,acap cor pts BREITKOPF-W
   CHB-2884 s.p.   (S2785)

   O, Morn Of Beauty *Easter/Gen
   (Matthews, H.) mix cor&mix cor,acap oct
   PRESSER 332-14489 $.30   (S2786)
   (Matthews, H.) SATB oct PRESSER 332-14714
   $.30   (S2787)
   (Matthews, H.) SAB oct PRESSER 332-15154
   $.30   (S2788)
   (Matthews, H.) TTBB oct PRESSER 312-14905
   $.30   (S2789)

   On Great Lone Hills (from Finlandia)
   (Matthews, H.) SATB,acap oct PRESSER
   332-14637 $.30   (S2790)
   (Matthews, H.; Havlovie, A.) SATB,acap oct
   PRESSER 332-14929 $.30   (S2791)

   Song Of Peace, A
   SSA oct LORENZ 6222 $.25   (S2792)
   SATB oct LORENZ 2094 $.30   (S2793)

   Trust (from Finlandia)
   (Stickles) 4pt mix cor,org/pno oct SCHIRM.G
   10418 $.30   (S2794)
   (Stickles) 3pt wom cor,org oct SCHIRM.G
   10419 $.25   (S2795)
   (Stickles) 2pt boy cor/2pt wom cor,org oct
   SCHIRM.G 10422 $.25   (S2796)
   (Stickles) 4pt men cor,org oct SCHIRM.G
   10420 $.25   (S2797)

   Two Christmas Songs *Xmas
   (Bryan) SATB (easy) OXFORD 42.984 $.35, ipr
   contains: Julpsalm; Julvisa   (S2798)

   Weihnachtslied *Xmas
   "Christmas Song" [Ger] wom cor oct FAZER
   s.p.   (S2799)

SIC DEUS DILEXIT MUNDUM see Scheidt, Samuel

SIC TRANSIT see Felciano, Richard

SICILIAN BAGPIPERS CAROL *Xmas,carol,It
   (Davis, K.K.) SSA WARNER R3479   (S2800)
   (Davis, K.K.) SATB,acap WARNER R3499 $.35
                                             (S2801)
   (Davis, K.K.) SAB WARNER R3498 $.35   (S2802)

SICILIAN HYMN *It
   (Cook, C.A.) SSA CRESCENDO $.20   (S2803)

SICUT CEDRUS see Anerio, Felice

SICUT CERVUS see Huble, M.R.

SICUT CERVUS see Lassus, Roland de (Orlandus)

SICUT CERVUS see Palestrina, Giovanni

SICUT CERVUS DESIDERAT see de la Rue, Pierre

SICUT CERVUS DESIDERAT see Palestrina, Giovanni

SICUT CERVUS (RET SOM HJORTEN) see Palestrina,
   Giovanni

SICUT ERAT IN PRINCIPIO see Monteverdi, Claudio

SICUT LILIUM see Brumel, Antoine

SICUT LILIUM INTER SPINAS see Palestrina,
   Giovanni

SICUT LOCUTUS EST see Bach, Johann Sebastian

SICUT MOSES SERPENTEM see Schutz, Heinrich

SICUT MOSES SERPENTEM IN DESERTO EXALTAVIT see
   Schutz, Heinrich

SICUT ROSA see Lassus, Roland de (Orlandus)

SICUT ROSE see Lassus, Roland de (Orlandus)

SICUT ROSE see Lassus, Roland de (Orlandus)

SICUT SERVUS see Gounod, Charles Francois

SIDE BY SIDE see Wood, Jeff

SIDERUM RECTOR see Byrd, William

SIE BOTEN GOTTES SOHNE see Schweizer, Rolf

SIE IST MIR LIEB see Praetorius, Michael

SIE IST MIR LIEB, DIE WERTE MAGD see Heller,
   Joachim

SIE IST MIR LIEB, DIE WERTE MAGD see
   Praetorius, Michael

SIE WERDEN see Bach, Johann Sebastian, Sie
   Werden Aus Saba Alle Kommen

SIE WERDEN AUS SABA ALLE KOMMEN see Bach,
   Johann Sebastian

SIE WERDEN EUCH see Bach, Johann Sebastian, Sie
   Werden Euch In Den Bann Tun

SIE WERDEN EUCH IN DEN BANN TUN see Bach,
   Johann Sebastian

SIEBEN BUSSPSALMEN see Lassus, Roland de
   (Orlandus)

SIEBEN CHORALSATZE see Bach, Johann Sebastian

SIEBEN CHROMATISCHE MOTETTEN DES BARROCK
   *CC7U,mot,Baroq
   [Ger/Lat] 4-6pt mix cor MOSELER s.p. contains
   works by: Lasso; Praetorius; Sweelinck;
   Hassler; Schein   (S2804)

SIEBEN MANNERCHORE ZUR WEIHNACHT see Schneider,
   Willy

SIEBEN MOTETTEN see Bruckner, Anton

SIEBEN NEUE MARIENLIEDER see Strohbach,
   Siegfried

SIEBEN SPIRITUALS see Kaufmann, Otto

SIEBEN SPIRITUALS see Kaufmann, Otto

SIEBEN SPRUCHMOTETTEN see Gottwald, Clytus

SIEBZEHN GEISTLICHE KANONS see Marx, Karl

SIEBZEHN GEISTLICHE KANONS see Thate, Albert

SIEDZAC PO NISKICH BRZEGACH BABILONSKIEJ WODY
   see Gomolka, Mikolaj

SIEGEL, BENJAMIN
   L'chu N'ran'noh *Sab-Eve
   SATB TRANSCON. TCL 761 $3.00   (S2805)

   T'filat Shel Y'ladim *Sab-Eve
   jr cor&cong,cantor TRANSCON. TCL 341 $2.50
                                             (S2806)
SIEGESFURSTE, EHRENKONIG see Werner, Fritz

SIEGL
   Cross Of Jesus *see O Crux Ave

   O Crux Ave *Easter
   "Cross Of Jesus" SATB SCHMITT 891 $.25
                                             (S2807)
SIEGL, OTTO (1896-   )
   Licht Muss Wieder Werden *hymn
   men cor,winds/pno/org TONGER s.p., ipa
                                             (S2808)
   O Herr, Der Du Die Sonne Sendest *prayer
   men cor,acap TONGER s.p.   (S2809)

SIEGMEISTER
   He Never Said A Mumbalin' Word *Easter,spir
   (Ehret) SSA oct BOURNE 202 $.25   (S2810)

SIEGMEISTER, ELIE (1909-   )
   Christmas Is Coming (composed with Wheeler,
   Rufus) *Xmas,cant
   mix cor,narrator,opt inst,pno LAWSON $1.50
                                             (S2811)
   On My Journey Home
   SATB,acap oct PRESSER 312-40186 $.30
                                             (S2812)
   You Can Dig My Grave
   (Read, G.) SATB oct PRESSER 312-40317 $.30
                                             (S2813)
SIEH DREIN, O HERR, AUS DEINEM HEILIGTUM see
   Reger, Max

SIEH, ICH KOMME IN TRANEN see Weismann, Wilhelm

SIEH MICH, O HERR see It's Me, O Lord

SIEH NICHT AN, WAS DU SELBER BIST see Lohr, Ina

SIEH NICHT DEINE SCHWACHHEIT AN see Michel, Josep

SIEH, WIE DER ABENDSTERN see Wolters, Gottfried

SIEHE AN DIE WERK GOTTES see Schein, Johann Hermann

SIEHE, DAS IST DER HERR, AUF DEN see Hartmann, Heinrich

SIEHE, DAS IST GOTTES LAMM see Holsten, Martin

SIEHE, DAS IST GOTTES LAMM see Praetorius, Michael

SIEHE, DAS IST GOTTES LAMM see Telemann, Georg Philipp

SIEHE, DAS IST GOTTES LAMM see Trust, Heinz-Ewald

SIEHE, DAS LAMM GOTTES, DAS DER WELT see Brunner, Adolf

SIEHE, DEIN HEIL KOMMT see Poser, Hans

SIEHE, DEIN KONIG see Kretzschmar, Gunther

SIEHE, DEIN KONIG KOMMT see Gallus, Jacobus, Acce Concipies

SIEHE! DER HERR KOMMT MIT VIEL TAUSEND see Buxtehude, Dietrich

SIEHE, DER HERR WIRD KOMMEN MIT FEUER see Weyrauch, Johannes

SIEHE, DER HUTER ISRAELS see Mendelssohn-Bartholdy, Felix

SIEHE, DER HUTER ISRAELS see Scheidt, Samuel

SIEHE, DER TAG DES HERRN IST NAHE see Studer, Hans

SIEHE, DES HERREN AUGE SIEHET AUF DIE see Rosenmuller, Johann

SIEHE, DIESER WIRD GESETZT see Driessler, Johannes

SIEHE, DIESER WIRD GESETZT ZU EINEM FALL see Franck, Melchior

SIEHE, DIESER WIRD GESETZT ZU EINEM FALL see Raselius, Andreas

SIEHE, DIESER WIRD GESETZT ZU EINEM FALL see Schutz, Heinrich

SIEHE, EIN WEIB, DAS ZWOLF JAHR see Vulpius, Melchior

SIEHE, EINE JUNGFRAU IST SCHWANGER see Franck, Melchior

SIEHE, ERSCHIENEN IST DER HERR see Ortiz, Diego

SIEHE, ES ERSCHIEN DER ENGEL see Schutz, Heinrich

SIEHE, ES KOMMT DIE ZEIT see Gieser, Walther

SIEHE! GEKOMMEN IST DER HERRSCHER see Ahrens, Joseph

SIEHE, ICH BIN BEI EUCH see Driessler, Johannes

SIEHE, ICH HABE DIR GEBOTEN see Prautzsch, Ludwig

SIEHE, ICH SENDE MEINEN ENGEL VOR DIR HER see Vulpius, Melchior

SIEHE, ICH STEHE VOR DER TUR see Gwinner, Volker

SIEHE, ICH VERKUNDIGE EUCH GROSSE FREUDE see Erlebach, Philipp Heinrich

SIEHE, ICH WILL see Bach, Johann Sebastian, Siehe, Ich Will Fur Fischer Aussenden

SIEHE, ICH WILL MEINEN ENGEL SENDEN see Bach, Johann Ludwig

SIEHE, ICH WILL VIEL FISCHER AUSSENDEN see Bach, Johann Sebastian

SIEHE LOBET DEN HERREN, ALLE KNECHTE see Hartmann, Heinrich

SIEHE, LOBET DEN HERRN see Buxtehude, Dietrich

SIEHE, NACH TROST WAR MIR SEHR BANGE see Schein, Johann Hermann

SIEHE, NUN KOMMT DER HERR, DER HERRSCHER see Metzger, Hans-Arnold

SIEHE, WIE FEIN UND LIEBLICH see Schutz, Heinrich

SIEHE, WIE FEIN UND LIEBLICH ISTS see Vierdanck, Johann

SIEHE, WIE GUT IST'S see Gattermayer, Heinrich

SIEHE, WIR ZIEHEN HINAUF GEN JERUSALEM see Zimmermann, Heinz Werner

SIEHE ZU see Bach, Johann Sebastian, Siehe Zu, Dass Deine Gottesfurcht

SIEHE ZU, DASS DEINE GOTTESFURCHT see Bach, Johann Sebastian

SIEHE ZU, DASS DEINE GOTTESFURCHT NICHT HEUCHELEI SEI see Bach, Johann Sebastian

---

SIEHE ZU, DASS DEINE GOTTESFURCHT NICHT HEUCHELEI SEI see Fasch, Johann Friedrich

SIEMONEIT, HANS RUDOLF (1927-   )
  Nun Jauchzt Dem Herren, Alle Welt *No.187, cant/mot
    [Ger] 1-5pt mix cor,acap BAREN. EM 70 s.p.
    see from EVANGELISCHES KIRCHENGESANGBUCH
                                              (S2814)

SIG FROJDE NU VAR KRISTEN MAN see Moren, John

SIG MANEN LANGSOMT HAEVER see Jeppesen, Knud

SIGNATURE OF GOD, THE see Coulthard, Jean

SIGNOR, LE TUE MAN SANTE see Gabrieli, Giovanni

SIGNPOSTS see Hemberg-Eskil

SIGNUM MAGNUM see Waldbroel, Wilhelm

SIGTENHORST-MEYER, [BERNHARD VAN DEN] (1888-1953)
  Canticum Fratis Solis
    mix cor ALSBACH&D sc s.p., cor pts s.p.
                                              (S2815)
  Vijf Geestelijke Liederen *CC5U
    wom cor,acap sc ALSBACH&D s.p.   (S2816)

SIGURBJORNSSON, THORKELL (1938-   )
  Gloria, Song Of Simeon (Psalm 150) (from Cinque Laudi)
    mix cor ICELAND s.p.   (S2817)

  Magnificat (from Cinque Laudi) Magnif
    wom cor ICELAND s.p.   (S2818)

  Missa Minuscula *Mass
    wom cor ICELAND s.p.   (S2819)

  Psalm 150 *see Gloria, Song Of Simeon

  Short Passion Story *Psntd
    jr cor,T solo,fl,vla,vcl ICELAND s.p.
                                              (S2820)
  Te Deum (from Cinque Laudi) Te Deum
    jr cor,harp ICELAND s.p.   (S2821)

SIJT VROLIC, GROOT EN CLEIJNE see Rontgen, [Julius]

SILCHER
  Glory To God On High
    (Pisano) SATB,acap oct PRO ART 2519 $.25
                                              (S2822)
  Sanctus
    see Mozart, Wolfgang Amadeus, Weihe Des Gesangs

SILCHER, FRIEDRICH (1789-1860)
  Neem, Herr, Mijn Beide Hande
    mix cor sc ALSBACH&D GEZ.232 s.p.   (S2823)

  O Wie Herbe Ist Das Scheiden
    [Ger] mix cor,acap (easy) HUG s.p.   (S2824)

  Sanctus, Dominus Deus
    [Lat/Ger] TTBB SCHOTT s.p.   (S2825)

  So Nimm Denn Meine Hande
    [Ger] mix cor,acap (easy) HUG s.p.   (S2826)

  Weinachts-Motette *Xmas,mot
    mix cor,acap ERDMANN 565 s.p.   (S2827)

SILENCE see Stimer

SILENCE OF GOD, THE see Porter

SILENCE PREVAILED IN HEAVEN see Deering, Richard

SILENT DEVOTION AND RESPONSE see Bloch, Ernest

SILENT MEDITATION (MAY THE WORDS...) see Gottlieb, J.

SILENT NIGHT *Xmas,carol
  see Five Christmas Carols
  see Many Moods Of Christmas, The. Suite One
  see Rocking
    (Dexter) SATB,S solo FRANCIS s.p.   (S2828)
    (Geehl, H.) 3pt ASHDOWN V.T.34 s.p.   (S2829)
    (Geehl, Henry) 2pt ENOCH TP137 s.p. contains
      also: Quittez Pasteurs; Bethlehem (carol, Span)
                                              (S2830)
    (Geehl, Henry) SATB ENOCH EC250 s.p.   (S2831)
    (Lefebvre) SATB oct GALAXY 1.0979.1 $.30
      contains also: Adeste Fideles   (S2832)
    (Lefebvre) TTBB oct GALAXY 1.0980.1 $.30
      contains also: Adeste Fideles   (S2833)
    (McConnell, J.W.) SATB LEONARD-US 08058080
      $.30   (S2834)
    (Noe, J.T.) jr cor,vln PARAGON 1010 $.25
                                              (S2835)
    (Sargent) SSAATTBB,acap (very easy) OXFORD
      43.057 $.25   (S2836)

SILENT NIGHT see Biggs, John

SILENT NIGHT see Gruber, Franz Xaver, Stille Nacht, Heilige Nacht

SILENT NIGHT see Palmer

SILENT NIGHT! HOLIEST NIGHT! see Gruber, Franz Xaver, Stille Nacht, Heil'ge Nacht

SILENT NIGHT, HOLY NIGHT *Xmas
  (Cotton, W.J.) TTBB,acap LEONARD-ENG 48 s.p.
                                              (S2837)
  (Page, Robert) SATB STANDARD A2MX3 $.45   (S2838)

SILENT NIGHT, HOLY NIGHT see Gruber, Franz Xaver, Stille Nacht, Heilige Nacht

SILENT NIGHT, HOLY NIGHT see Lorenz

SILENT NIGHT! HOLY NIGHT! see Parks

SILENT SEA, THE see Neidlinger, William Harold

SILENT STARS see Niles, John Jacob

SILENT STARS GO BY, THE see Wilson, D.

SILENT WORSHIP see Handel, George Frideric

SILENTLY CAME THE THREE SHEPHERDS see Procter, A.

SILENTLY THE WONDEROUS GIFT IS GIVEN see Greckel

SILESIAN LULLABY *folk,Russ
  (Meyerowitz) SATB,acap BROUDE BR. $.30
                                              (S2839)

SILESIUS, ANGELUS
  Bluh Auf, Gefrorner Christ (from Der Cherubinische Wandersmann)
    "Unfold, Thou Frozen Christ" see Drei Gemischte Chore

  Drei Gemischte Chore *Op.43 (from Der Cherubinische Wandersmann)
    (Wellesz, Egon) [Eng/Ger] SATB voc sc BOTE s.p.
      contains: Bluh Auf, Gefrorner Christ, "Unfold, Thou Frozen Christ"; Mensch, Werd Aus Gott Geborn, "Man, Be From God Reborn"; Wo Ist Mein Aufenthalt, "Where Is My Dwelling Place"   (S2840)

  Man, Be From God Reborn *see Mensch, Werd Aus Gott Geborn

  Mensch, Werd Aus Gott Geborn (from Der Cherubinische Wandersmann)
    "Man, Be From God Reborn" see Drei Gemischte Chore

  Unfold, Thou Frozen Christ *see Bluh Auf, Gefrorner Christ

  Where Is My Dwelling Place *see Wo Ist Mein Aufenthalt

  Wo Ist Mein Aufenthalt (from Der Cherubinische Wandersmann)
    "Where Is My Dwelling Place" see Drei Gemischte Chore

SILESIUS-MOTETTE see Ahrens, Joseph

SILK
  Sing And Rejoice *anthem
    mix cor oct OXFORD 42.361 $.60   (S2841)

SILVER BELLS, THE see White, Michael

SILVER, FREDERICK
  Child's Christmas Prayer, A *Xmas
    SATB oct BOURNE 857 $.30   (S2842)

  Out Of The Depths (Psalm 130) Gen/Lent
    SA/men cor&wom cor,pno (med) oct MCAFEE
      M1012 $.35   (S2843)

  Psalm 126
    SATB oct BOURNE 868 $.35   (S2844)

  Psalm 130 *see Out Of The Depths

  Time To Be Born, A
    SATB oct BOURNE 866 $.40   (S2845)

SILVER, MARK (1892-1965)
  Hallelujah
    see Praise The Lord

  Praise The Lord
    [Lat/Eng] SATB TRANSCON. TCL 223 $.60
      contains: Hallelujah; Psalm 117; Psalm 118   (S2846)

  Psalm 117
    see Praise The Lord

  Psalm 118
    see Praise The Lord

SIM SHOLOM see Weisgal, A.

SIMCHAT SHABBAT see Myerov, Joseph

SIMEON see Buchtger, Fritz

SIMEONE
  Beatitudes, The
    SATB SHAWNEE A 178 $.30   (S2847)

  Carol Of The Star *carol
    SAB SHAWNEE D151 $.30   (S2848)

  Carol Of The Star, The *carol
    SSA SHAWNEE B 302 $.30   (S2849)

  Go Tell It On The Mountain
    SATB SHAWNEE A 482 $.35   (S2850)
    SA/TB SHAWNEE E50 $.30   (S2851)
    TTBB SHAWNEE C201 $.30   (S2852)
    SSA SHAWNEE B 184 $.30   (S2853)

  Love Came Down
    SA/TB SHAWNEE E94 $.30   (S2854)

  Make A Joyful Noise
    SATB SHAWNEE A 179 $.30   (S2855)

  Sing We Now Of Christmas *sac/sec,CCU,Xmas
    SATB SHAWNEE A921 $1.75   (S2856)

  True And Living Way
    SAB SHAWNEE D142 $.30   (S2857)

SIMEONS LOVSANG see Luther, Martin

SIMON
  All Things Are Thine
    SATB oct FISCHER,C CM-7567 $.25   (S2858)

  Prince Of Peace
    SATB oct FISCHER,C CM-7408 $.25   (S2859)

  Rise Up Shepherd And Follow
    SATB oct FISCHER,C CM-7604 $.20   (S2860)

SIMON, PAUL
  Benedictus (composed with Garfunkel, Art)
    *Bene
    (Dahlen) SATB MARKS 4534 $.35   (S2861)

SIMON THE CYRENEAN SPEAKS see Roff, Joseph

SIMON, W.
Jesus Our Lord Is Crucified *Lent
  SATB,acap oct GRAY GCMR 3126 $.30   (S2862)

SIMPER, CALEB
And God Said, Let The Earth
  SATB oct PRESSER 312-05952 $.30   (S2863)

Behold I Bring You Good Tidings *Xmas
  SATB oct PRESSER 332-10164 $.30   (S2864)
  SATB,org (med) oct WILLIS 1188 $.15   (S2865)

Break Forth Into Joy *Xmas/Gen,Bibl
  SATB oct LORENZ 458 $.30   (S2866)
  SATB oct PRESSER 332-09920 $.35   (S2867)
  SATB oct PRO ART 1119 $.30   (S2868)
  (Baird) 4pt mix cor,S solo oct SCHIRM.G
    5010 $.30   (S2869)
  (Buckner) SAB FLAMMER D5117 $.30   (S2870)
  (Ehret, Walter) SAB oct BELWIN 1755 $.30
                                           (S2871)
  (Mueller) 3pt mix cor,S solo,org oct
    SCHIRM.G 10673 $.30   (S2872)
  (Townsend) SSA oct PRO ART 1812 $.22
                                           (S2873)

Hallelujah! Christ Is Risen *Easter
  SATB oct PRESSER 312-00091 $.30   (S2874)

He Is Risen *Easter
  SATB,S/TB soli,org (easy) oct WILLIS 1089
    $.15   (S2875)

He Shall Reign Forever *Xmas,Bibl
  4pt mix cor,S solo oct SCHIRM.G 5033 $.25
                                           (S2876)
  SATB oct LORENZ 1957 $.30   (S2877)

I Am He That Liveth *Easter
  SATB oct PRESSER 312-20661 $.35   (S2878)

I Will Feed My Flock *Gen/Thanks,Bibl
  SATB oct PRESSER 312-15546 $.30   (S2879)
  4pt mix cor oct SCHIRM.G 5238 $.25   (S2880)
  (Fearis) TTBB,med solo,pno (easy) oct
    WILLIS 6322 $.12   (S2881)

If Ye Love Me
  SATB oct PRESSER 312-00100 $.30   (S2882)

King Of Kings *Easter,Bibl
  SATB oct PRESSER 332-13717 $.30   (S2883)
  SATB oct LORENZ 9663 $.35   (S2884)
  SATB FLAMMER A 5197 $.25   (S2885)
  4pt mix cor,high solo,B solo oct SCHIRM.G
    7389 $.30   (S2886)
  (Deis) 3pt wom cor,S solo oct SCHIRM.G 7394
    $.30   (S2887)
  (Stickles) jr cor&sr cor,S/T solo,org oct
    SCHIRM.G 10462 $.30   (S2888)

King Of Love My Shepherd Is, The
  SAB oct LORENZ 7324 $.30   (S2889)
  SATB (very easy) oct LORENZ 4396 $.30
                                           (S2890)
  SSA oct LORENZ 6234 $.30   (S2891)
  SATB oct LORENZ 9339 $.30   (S2892)

Make A Joyful Noise
  SATB oct PRESSER 312-05953 $.30   (S2893)

Sing, O Heavens *Xmas,Bibl
  4pt mix cor,ST soli oct SCHIRM.G 5031 $.30
                                           (S2894)
  SATB oct PRESSER 312-05951 $.30   (S2895)
  SATB,S,T soli,org (easy) oct WILLIS 1033
    $.12   (S2896)

SIMPKINS
When God Speaks
  (Gerig) SATB oct LILLENAS AN-2254 $.30
                                           (S2897)

SIMPLE 3-PART EVENING CANTICLES see Arnold,
  J.H.

SIMPLE BIRTH, THE *Xmas,carol,Belg
  (Ehret, Walter) SATB,opt inst oct WALTON 2514
    $.30   (S2898)
  (Ehret, Walter) SSA,opt inst oct WALTON 2541
    $.30   (S2899)

SIMPLE COMMUNION SERVICE IN F see Burton, Peter

SIMPLE COMMUNION SERVICE IN F see Harris,
  William Henry

SIMPLE ENGLISH MASS, A see Bryden-Brook, Simon

SIMPLE GIFTS *hymn
  see Two Shaker Songs
  (Copland; Fine) SA/TB oct BOOSEY 1903 $.30
    see from Old American Songs   (S2900)
  (Friend) SAB oct FISCHER,C CM-7625 $.25
                                           (S2901)
  (Kirk) SSA oct PRO ART 2665 $.30   (S2902)
  (Kirk) SATB oct PRO ART 2659 $.30   (S2903)
  (Kirk) SAB oct PRO ART 2662 $.30   (S2904)
  (Stone, L.) SA/TB oct BELWIN 2155 $.30
                                           (S2905)
  (Stone, L.) SSA oct BELWIN 2200 $.25   (S2906)
  (Stone, L.) SAB oct BELWIN 2227 $.25   (S2907)
  (Stone, L.) SATB oct BELWIN 2002 $.30   (S2908)
  (Vance, M.) SATB oct BELWIN 2205 $.25   (S2909)

SIMPLE GIFTS see Martin

SIMPLIFIED STANDARD ANTHEMS NO. 1 *CCU,anthem
  SATB LORENZ $1.95   (S2910)

SIMPLIFIED STANDARD ANTHEMS NO. 2 *CCU,anthem
  SATB LORENZ $1.75   (S2911)

SIMPLIFIED STANDARD ANTHEMS NO. 3 *CCU,anthem
  SATB LORENZ $1.75   (S2912)

SIMPSON
Alleluia *Allelu
  SATB oct LILLENAS AN-6001 $.30   (S2913)

See Him There
  SATB oct SACRED S-70 $.40   (S2914)

Six Songs For Christmastide *CC6U,Xmas
  unis oct BELWIN 05244 $.60   (S2915)

SIMPSON, KENNETH
Blind Man
  see Six Songs For Younger Children

SIMPSON, KENNETH (cont'd.)
Christmas Is A-Coming
  see Six Songs For Younger Children

Gitty- Tiggy Touchwood
  see Six Songs For Younger Children

I Had A Little Hen
  see Six Songs For Younger Children

Please Porridge Hot
  see Six Songs For Younger Children

Six Songs For Christmastide *Xmas
  unis LENGNICK s.p.   (S2916)

Six Songs For Younger Children *sac/sec
  unis LENGNICK s.p.
    contains: Blind Man; Christmas Is A-
    Coming; Gitty- Tiggy Touchwood; I Had A
    Little Hen; Please Porridge Hot; Trir
    And Go   (S2917)

Trir And Go
  see Six Songs For Younger Children

SIMPSON, REGINALD
Mass Of One Accord *Commun,Mass
  SATB WEINBERGER s.p. voc sc, cor pts
                                           (S2918)

Three Hymn Tunes (Set 2) *CC3U,hymn,20th
  cent
  SATB oct PAXTON P85382 s.p.   (S2919)

Three Hymn Tunes (Set 3) *CC3U,hymn,20th
  cent
  SATB oct PAXTON P85383 s.p.   (S2920)

Twentieth Century Hymn Tunes For Young People
  *CC20U,hymn,20th cent
  SATB oct PAXTON P85384 s.p.   (S2921)

SIMSON see Handel, George Frideric

SIMSON, ALEC BUCKINGHAM
Sleep Holy Child *Xmas,carol
  SATB/SATB,acap (med easy) THOMP. C007 $.25
                                           (S2922)

SIN NON HUMILITER SPERET ISRAEL see Schutz,
  Heinrich

SINCE BY MAN CAME DEATH see Handel, George
  Frideric

SINCE CHRIST HIS HEAD IN SORROW BOWED see
  Schutz, Heinrich

SINCE CHRIST OUR LORD WAS CRUCIFIED see Schutz,
  Heinrich

SINCE FIRST I SAW YOUR FACE
  (Kirk, Theron) SATB oct AGAPE SP 703 $.30
                                           (S2923)

SINCE GOD SO TENDER A REGARD see Purcell, Henry

SINCE JESUS CAME INTO MY HEART see Allen, Lanny

SINCE JESUS TOOK ALL MY SINS AWAY see Loveless

SINCE THIS WORLD IS ONLY PASSING see
  Rosenmuller, Johann

SINCE THOU ART RISEN see Bach, Johann Sebastian

SIND IHR' NICHT ZEHN REIN GEWORDEN see
  Raselius, Andreas

SIND IHR' NICHT ZEHN REIN GEWORDEN see Vulpius,
  Melchior

SINDELAR, RONALD
Medusa - The Ship
  cor,perc,electronic tape voc sc WALTON 2912
    $1.00, ipa   (S2924)

SINE DOMINE see Palestrina, Giovanni

SINE MONINE see Dufay, Guillaume

SINE MUSICA NULLA DISCIPLINA see Hindemith,
  Paul

SINE NOMEN see Dufay, Guillaume

SINE NOMINE see Taverner, John

SINE NOMINE see Vaughan Williams, Ralph

SINE NOMINE II see Palestrina, Giovanni

SINE NOMINE see Palestrina, Giovanni

SINE NOMINE see Palestrina, Giovanni

SINE NOMINE see Palestrina, Giovanni

SINFONIA SACRA see Driessler, Johannes

SINFONIA SACRA see Monnikendam, Marius

SINFONIA SACRA see Rubbra, Edmund

SINFONIA SACRA see Veretti, Antonio

SINFONIA SACRA (II) "DOMINE SALVUM FAC" see
  Monnikendam, Marius

SING A CAROL see Kozinski, [David B.]

SING A HAPPY SONG *CC10L
  (Floria, Cam) jr cor voc sc WORD 20025 $1.50
                                           (S2925)

SING A HYMN OF PRAISE see Schoffer, Zemer Lach

SING A JOYFUL SONG see Knighton

SING A JOYFUL SONG IN PRAISE see Wood

SING A MERRY CAROL see Longmire, John

SING A NEW NOWELL! *Xmas
  (Waring) SATB oct SUMMY M 2839 $.45   (S2926)

SING A NEW SONG *CC10L,Gen
  (Mitchell, E.) SATB PRO ART 1200 $1.50
                                           (S2927)

SING A NEW SONG TO THE LORD see Wills, Arthur

SING A ROUND FOR CHRISTMAS see Palmer

SING A SONG OF GLADNESS see Elmore, Robert
  [Hall]

SING A SONG OF JOY see Harris, William Henry

SING A SONG OF JOY see Hurford, Peter

SING A SONG OF JOY see Jacob, Gordon

SING A SONG OF JOY see Powell, Robert J.

SING A SONG OF PRAISE see Harris, Cuthbert

SING A SONG OF PRAISE see West

SING, ALL GOOD PEOPLE GATHERED *carol
  SATB (easy) OXFORD 08.111 $.15   (S2928)

SING ALL YE CHRISTIAN PEOPLE see Blake, G.

SING, ALL YE CHRISTIAN PEOPLE see Olds,
  [William Benjamin]

SING ALL YE LANDS see Gretchaninov, Alexander
  Tikhonovitch

SING, ALL YE RIGHTEOUS see Graun, Karl Heinrich

SING ALLELUIA see Forsblad

SING ALLELUIA see Garlick, Anthony

SING ALLELUIA see Gretchaninov, Alexander
  Tikhonovitch

SING ALLELUIA! see Hughes

SING "ALLELUIA" see Nolte

SING ALLELUIA see Weaver, H.

SING ALLELUIA FOR YOUR SOUL see Friend

SING ALLELUIA FORTH see Bixby, A.K.

SING ALLELUIA FORTH see Brumel, Antoine

SING ALLELUIA FORTH see Buck, Dudley

SING ALLELUIA FORTH see Dagand, Abbe J., Adoro
  Te Supplex

SING ALLELUIA FORTH see Dickey, Mark

SING ALLELUIA FORTH see Lang, C.S.

SING ALLELUIA FORTH see Marshall, Jane M.

SING ALLELUIA FORTH see Talmadge, Charles L.

SING ALLELUIA FORTH see Thiman, Eric Harding

SING ALLELUIA FORTH see Waters, Charles F.

SING ALLELUIA FORTH see Williams, David H.

SING ALLELUIA FORTH see Wolff, S. Drummond

SING ALLELUIA NOW see Giasson

SING ALLELUJAH! CHRIST IS BORN see Dretke, L.N.

SING ALLELUYA FORTH IN DUTEOUS PRAISE see
  Willan, Healey

SING ALOUD see Hovhaness, Alan

SING ALOUD, ALL NATIONS see Coggin

SING ALOUD TO GOD see Erbach, Christian,
  Jubilate Deo

SING ALOUD TO GOD see Haydn, (Johann) Michael,
  Effunderunt Sanguinem

SING ALOUD TO GOD, OUR STRENGTH see Butler

SING ALOUD UNTO GOD see Glarum, L. Stanley

SING ALOUD UNTO GOD see Orr, Robin

SING AND BE GLAD see Hutson, Wihla

SING AND BE HAPPY SONGS FOR CHILDREN *CCU
  (Smith, Alfred B.) jr cor voc sc WORD 20046
    $1.95   (S2929)

SING AND BE JOYFUL see Graun, Karl Heinrich

SING AND GIVE PRAISE see Thompson

SING AND PRAISE JEHOVAH see Palestrina,
  Giovanni, Exultate Deo

SING AND PRAY AND KEEP HIS WAYS see Darst, W.
  Glenn

SING AND REJOICE! see Kirk, Theron W.

SING AND REJOICE see Silk

SING AND REJOICE see Stuart

SING AND REJOICE see Tagg, Lawrence E.

SING AND REJOICE see Thygerson

SING AND REJOICE, O ZION see Geisler, Johan C.

SING AND WORSHIP, VOL. 1 see Mueller, Carl F.

SING AND WORSHIP, VOL. 2 see Mueller, Carl F.

SING BALOO, SING BALOW see Gordon, Philip

SING, BELOVED CHRISTIANS see Praetorius,
  Michael, Singt, Ihr Lieben Christen All!

SING BOYS AND GIRLS NO. 1 *CC64U
  (Loes, Harry Dixon) jr cor cmplt ed LILLENAS
    MB-186 $.65   (S2930)

SING BOYS AND GIRLS NO. 2 *CC65U
  2pt jr cor cmplt ed LILLENAS MB-187 $.65
                                           (S2931)

SING, BOYS, SING see Cooper, Irvin

SING BROTHERS, SING see Ferguson

SING CHRISTMAS ALLELUIA see Davis, J.R.

SING, CHRISTMAS BELL see Beveridge, Thomas G.

SING FOR JOY *CC12L
  (Thomas, P.) SAB CONCORDIA 97-5046 $1.50
    contains works by: Couperin; Nystedt; Zipp;
    Weldon; Porter; Wolff; Bach; Handel; King;
    Kindermann; Willan; Buxtehude   (S2932)

SING FOR JOY see Kirk

SING FOR JOY see Tanner, Peter

SING FOR JOY! see Underwood

SING FOR JOY see Wood

SING FOR JOY, O HEAVENS see Newbury

SING FOR JOY, O HEAVENS see Roff, Joseph

SING FOR JOY, YE RANSOMED BAND see Bach, Johann
  Sebastian

SING FOR THE JOY OF EASTER see Carley, Isabel
  L.

SING FORTH HIS PRAISE see Alderfer

SING FORTH THE HONOR OF HIS NAME see Engel, [A.
  Lehman]

SING GLORIA see Davis, Katherine K.

SING GLORIA see Hunnicutt, Judy

SING GLORIAS! *CC24L,Xmas,carol/hymn
  (Thomas, P.) mix cor CONCORDIA 97-5029 $1.00
    contains works by: Cruger; Bach; Nicholson;
    Willan; Woodward; Hillert; Metzger; Beck;
    Marx, Karl; Bender; Barnes; Herman; Vaughan
    Williams; Shaw, Martin; Vulpius;
    Praetorius; Stainer, John; Bunjes;
    Osiander, Hukas; Wood, Charles; Bobel, Karl
                                            (S2933)

SING GLORY HALLELUJAH see Long

SING GOD'S PRAISE see Tkach, P.

SING HALLELU (SING NOEL) *Easter/Lent
  (Harris) SSA,acap,opt pno oct PRO ART 2227
  $.25   (S2934)

SING HALLELUJAH, PRAISE THE LORD *Easter
  (Mueller) 3pt mix cor oct SCHIRM.G 10753 $.25
                                            (S2935)
  (Mueller) 2pt wom cor oct SCHIRM.G 10754 $.25
                                            (S2936)
  (Mueller) 4pt mix cor oct SCHIRM.G 10888 $.30
                                            (S2937)
  (Mueller, Carl F.) 3pt mix cor oct SCHIRM.G
  10753 $.25   (S2938)
  (Mueller, Carl F.) 2pt wom cor oct SCHIRM.G
  10754 $.25   (S2939)
  (Mueller, Carl F.) SATB oct SCHIRM.G 10888
  $.30   (S2940)

SING, HAPPY CHILD see Le Fleming, Christopher
  (Kaye)

SING, HEAVEN IMPERIAL see Byrd, William, Rorate
  Coeli

SING HIS PRAISE see Vandre, Carl W.

SING HIS PRAISES see Bach, Johann Sebastian

SING HIS PRAISES, ALLELUIA see Newbury, Kent A.

SING HOSANNA see Armitage, Ellen M.

SING HOSANNA see Chaplin, N.W.

SING HOSANNA see Randall, Bruce

SING HOSANNA see Sullivan, Sir Arthur Seymour

SING HOSANNA TO THE KING see Schaefer

SING HOSANNAS! see De Coursey

SING HYMNS OF PRAISE TO THE HOST see Carissimi,
  Giacomo, Hymnus Cantemus Domino

SING, I WILL ALWAYS SING see Skillings, Otis

SING IN EXCELSIS GLORIA! see Pfautsch, Lloyd

SING IN EXULTATION, VOLUME 1 *CC20U,Gen,anthem
  (Pitcher, G.) SAB oct WILLIS $1.25   (S2941)

SING IN EXULTATION, VOLUME 2 *CC20U,Gen,anthem
  (Pitcher, G.) SAB oct WILLIS $1.25   (S2942)

SING IN JOY see Tkach, Hazel

SING JEHOVAH'S PRAISE see James, Allen

SING JESUS CHRIST IS BORN see Hallett, John C.

SING JOYFULLY see Berlinski, [Herman]

SING JOYFULLY see Byrd, William

SING JOYFULLY see Mundy, John

SING JOYFULLY see Wyton, Alec

SING JOYFULLY, JOYFULLY, CHRISTMAS IS COME see
  Peninger, David

SING JOYFULLY TO THE LORD see Roff, Joseph

SING JOYFULLY UNTO GOD see Byrd, William

SING, JOYOUS CHRISTIANS see Lotti, Antonio

SING LOB see Jacot, Andre

SING LULLABYE see Longmire, John

SING MARY'S LULLABYE see Kozinski, [David B.]

SING ME THE MEN see Holst, Gustav

SING, MEN AND ANGELS, SING see Butler

SING, MEN AND ANGELS, SING see Near, Gerald

SING, MEN, SING! *CCU
  TBB SCHMITT 48 $.50   (S2943)

SING MERRILY TO GOD see Thygerson

SING, MY SOUL, HIS WONDROUS LOVE see Monk

SING, MY SOUL, HIS WONDROUS LOVE see Rorem, Ned

SING MY TONGUE, THE GLORIOUS BATTLE see
  Boatwright, Howard

SING NACHTIGALL *CCU,Xmas
  (Wagner, Hermann) mix cor MOSELER s.p.
                                            (S2944)

SING NOEL *CCU,Xmas,carol/hymn
  jr cor&sr cor cmplt ed LILLENAS MC-226 $1.00
                                            (S2945)

SING NOEL *Xmas
  (Fisher, W.) SATB,acap oct PRESSER 332-14578
  $.30   (S2946)

SING NOEL see Bury

SING NOEL see Hyatt

SING NOEL see Lekberg, Sven

SING NOEL see O'Hara, F.

SING NOEL see Pitfield, Thomas Baron

SING NOEL see Plank, David L.

SING NOEL! see Pohlmann, Helen Fryfogle

SING NOEL see Snyder, J.

SING NOEL, MERRY NOEL see Stainer, John

SING NOEL, RING NOEL see Brown

SING NOEL (SING HALLELU) *Xmas
  (Harris) SSA,acap,opt pno oct PRO ART 2227
  $.25   (S2947)

SING NOW WITH GREAT REJOICING see Bach, Johann
  Sebastian

SING NOWELL see Greenfield, Marjorie H.

SING NOWELL, SING GLORIA! see Christiansen,
  Olaf Christian

SING, O HEAVENS see Amner, John

SING, O HEAVENS see Clare, Edwyn A.

SING, O HEAVENS see Maunder, J.H.

SING O HEAVENS see Mueller, Carl F.

SING, O HEAVENS see Simper, Caleb

SING, O HEAVENS see Tours

SING, O HEAVENS see Tours, Berthold

SING, O HEAVENS see Webber, Lloyd

SING, O MY LOVE see Hall

SING, O MY SOUL, THE FATHER'S PRAISES see
  Schutz, Heinrich, Love Den Herren, Meine
  Seele

SING, O SING see Hegenbart, Alex F.

SING, O SING, BLESSED MORN see Morgan

SING O SING THIS BLESSED MORN see Butler

SING, O SING THIS BLESSED MORN see Coggin

SING, O SING, THIS BLESSED MORN see Graham,
  Robert [V.]

SING, O SING THIS BLESSED MORN see Smart

SING, O SING THIS BLESSED MORN see Thiman, Eric
  Harding

SING, O SING, THIS BLESSED MORN see Titcomb

SING OF HIM see Brown, William [H., Jr.]

SING OF MARY, PURE AND LOWLY see Adam, Adolphe-
  Charles

SING, OH SING TO THE LORD see Purcell, Henry

SING, OH YE HEAVENS see Marth, Helen Jun

SING, OH YE HEAV'NS! see Handel, George
  Frideric

SING ON YOUR HEAVENLY WAY see North

SING ONE, SING TWO, SING TOGETHER *CC15L,Gen
  (Vandre) 2pt PRO ART 916 $1.00   (S2948)

SING OUT IN JOYFUL PRAISE see Stouffer

SING OUT THE NEWS see Langstroth, Ivan Shed

SING OUT WITH JOY see Clemens, Jacobus

SING OUT, YE VOICES, LOUD AND CLEAR see Bach,
  Johann Sebastian, Es Bringt Das Rechte
  Jubeljahr

SING! PEOPLE OF GOD, SING! see Temple, S.

SING PRAISE *CCU,anthem
  SATB/SA LORENZ $1.75   (S2949)

SING PRAISE see Brubaker, Gwen

SING PRAISE! see Fraser

SING PRAISE, PART I see Lenel, Ludwig

SING PRAISE, PART II see Lenel, Ludwig

SING PRAISE, SING PRAISE see Eisleben

SING PRAISE TO CHRIST see Bach

SING PRAISE TO CHRIST see Bach, Johann
  Sebastian

SING PRAISE TO GOD see Nichols, Anna Mae

SING PRAISE TO GOD see Sydow, Ralph Karl

SING PRAISE TO GOD *10th cent
  (Kelly) SATB oct PRO ART 1874 $.22   (S2950)
  (Olds) SATB SCHMITT 1687 $.25   (S2951)
  (Vree) SATB oct LAWSON 805 $.35   (S2952)

SING PRAISE TO GOD see Bach

SING PRAISE TO GOD see Bach, Johann Sebastian

SING PRAISE TO GOD see Curry, W. Lawrence

SING PRAISE TO GOD see Darst, W. Glenn

SING PRAISE TO GOD see Dressler, John

SING PRAISE TO GOD see Franck, Cesar,
  Halleluja! Lobt Gott

SING PRAISE TO GOD see Haydn, (Franz) Joseph

SING PRAISE TO GOD see Longmire

SING PRAISE TO GOD see Martin

SING PRAISE TO GOD see Pfautsch, Lloyd

SING PRAISE TO GOD see Powell, Robert J.

SING PRAISE TO GOD see Swift, F. F.

SING PRAISE TO GOD see Warner, Richard

SING PRAISE TO GOD see Weiner

SING PRAISE TO GOD THE FATHER
  (Prentiss) SA oct SUMMY M 2876 $.45   (S2953)

SING PRAISE TO GOD, THE LORD see Franck, Cesar,
  Halleluja! Lobt Gott

SING PRAISE TO GOD WHO REIGNS ABOVE *anthem,
  Ger,15th cent
  (Mudde, Willem) SAB (easy) oct AUGSBURG 1214
  $.20   (S2954)

SING PRAISE TO GOD WHO REIGNS ABOVE see Bach,
  Johann Sebastian

SING PRAISE TO GOD WHO REIGNS ABOVE see Brahms,
  Johannes

SING PRAISE TO GOD WHO REIGNS ABOVE see
  Whitlock, Percy

SING PRAISE TO GOD, WHO REIGNS ABOVE see Wolff,
  S. Drummond

SING PRAISE TO GOD, WHO SPOKE THROUGH MAN see
  Bristol, L.

SING PRAISE TO HIS NAME see Avalone

SING PRAISE TO OUR GLORIOUS LORD see Schutz,
  Heinrich

SING PRAISE TO THE FATHER see Mozart, Wolfgang
  Amadeus, Te Deum Laudamus

SING PRAISES *CC101U
  cong cmplt ed LILLENAS MB-188 $.60   (S2955)

SING PRAISES see Clare, Edwyn A.

SING PRAISES see Glarum, L. Stanley

SING PRAISES! see Harris

SING PRAISES see Pfautsch, Lloyd

SING PRAISES TO GOD see Henderson, R.

SING PRAISES TO GOD see Williams

SING PRAISES TO GOD THIS HOLY DAY see Byrd,
  William, Haec Dies

SING PRAISES TO OUR GOD see Kalinnikov, Vassili
  Sergeievitch

SING PRAISES TO OUR GOD see Newton

SING PRAISES TO OUR KING see Morgan

SING PRAISES TO OUR SAVIOR see Celebrons La
  Naissance

SING PRAISES TO THE LORD see Newbury

SING PRAISES, YE FAITHFUL see Bach, Johann
  Sebastian, Erschallet, Ihr Lieder [Chorale]

SING! REJOICE TOGETHER! see Doran

SING ROUND THE YEAR see Swann

SING! SING! see Marshall, Jane M.

SING! SING! EV'RYONE SING! see Wild, Eric

SING, SING FOR CHRISTMAS see Miller

SING SOFTLY see Hoag, Charles K.

SING, SOUL OF MINE see Rhea, Raymond

SING, SOUL OF MINE! THE LORD IS RISEN see
  Clothier, Louita

SING THANKSGIVING see Ohanian

SING THE BIRTH see Praetorius, Michael

SING THE GLAD TIDINGS see Muhlenberg

SING THE LIFE see Webber, Lloyd

SING, THIS BLESSED MORN see Van Dyke

SING THIS JOYOUS MORNING see Larson, Earl R.

SING TO GOD see Harris

SING TO GOD see Hokanson, Margrethe

SING TO GOD see Wagner, Richard

SING TO GOD see Wiltberger, Jubilate Deo

SING TO GOD THE LORD see Buxtehude, Dietrich, Cantate Domino

SING TO GOD WITH GLADNESS see Peeters, Flor, Jubilate Deo Omnis Terra

SING TO HIM see Newbury

SING TO HIS NAME see Newbury, Kent A.

SING PO OUR GOD IMMORTAL PRAISE see Young, Gordon

SING TO THE GREAT JEHOVAH'S PRAISE see Wesley

SING TO THE LORD! *CC18L,Gen
(Townsend) unis/SA/SAB PRO ART 70 $1.00
(S2956)

SING TO THE LORD *hymn
(Chambers) SAB BOOSEY $1.50   (S2957)
(Parker) SATB,acap oct LAWSON 51322 $.30
(S2958)

SING TO THE LORD see Aichinger, Gregor

SING TO THE LORD see Bach, Johann Sebastian, Singet Dem Herrn Ein Neues Lied

SING TO THE LORD see Darst, W. Glenn

SING TO THE LORD see Goode, Jack C.

SING TO THE LORD see Handel, George Frideric

SING TO THE LORD see Haydn, (Franz) Joseph, Gloria

SING TO THE LORD see Hopkins

SING TO THE LORD see Kirk, Theron W.

SING PO THE LORD! see Lindusky, Eugene

SING TO THE LORD see Pitoni, Giuseppe Ottavio, Cantate Domino

SING TO THE LORD see Purcell, Henry

SING TO THE LORD see Roff, Joseph

SING TO THE LORD see Rowley, Alec

SING TO THE LORD see Schroth

SING TO THE LORD see Schutz, Heinrich, Singet Dem Herrn, Ein Neues Lied

SING TO THE LORD see Tye, Christopher

SING PO PHE LORD see Vance, Margaret Shelley

SING TO THE LORD see Wheeler, Alfred

SING TO THE LORD A JOYFUL SONG see Hopson

SING TO THE LORD A JOYFUL SONG see Rose, Michael

SING TO THE LORD A MARVELOUS SONG see Butler, Eugene

SING TO THE LORD A NEW-MADE SONG see Geisler, Johan C.

SING TO THE LORD A NEW SONG see Bender, Jan

SING TO THE LORD A NEW SONG see Kirk

SING TO THE LORD A NEW SONG see Newbury, Kent A.

SING TO THE LORD A NEW SONG see Schutz, Heinrich

SING TO THE LORD A NEW SONG see Staden, Johann, Cantate Domino Canticum Novum

SING TO THE LORD A NEW SONG see Taylor, Clifford

SING TO THE LORD A NEW SONG see Track

SING TO THE LORD GOD see Dressler, John

SING TO THE LORD OF HARVEST see Blake, Leonard

SING TO THE LORD OF HARVEST see Maunder, J.H.

SING TO THE LORD OF HARVEST see Willan, Healey

SING TO THE LORD OF HARVEST see Wolff, S. Drummond

SING TO THE LORD OF HARVEST see Young

SING TO THE LORD OF HOSTS see Young

SING TO THE LORD OF THE HARVEST see Ehret, Walter

SING TO THE LORD OF THE HARVEST see Monsell

SING TO THE LORD, OUR GOD see Pitoni, Giuseppe Ottavio, Cantate Domino

SING TO THE LORD WITH CHEERFUL VOICE see Bach, Johann Sebastian

SING TO THE LORD WITH THANKSGIVING see Brandon, George

SING TO THE NEWBORN KING *Xmas,carol,Fr
(Pfautsch) SATB,pic,2trp,drums oct LAWSON
51421 $.35   (S2959)

SING TODAY WITH ONE ACCORD see Williams, David H.

SING TOGETHER *CC82U,folk/hymn/round/spir
(Latham, Joy) jr cor cmplt ed LILLENAS MB-189
$.75   (S2960)

SING TOGETHER HYMNS see Schroth

SING TRIUMPHANT HYMNS see Brown, Frank Edwin

SING UND JUBILIERE, WEIHNACHTSNACHTIGALL see Paulsen, Helmut

SING UND JUBILIERE, WEIHNACHTSNACHTIGALL see Wolters, Gottfried

SING UNTO GOD *CCU,anthem
SATB/SA LORENZ $1.75   (S2961)

SING UNTO GOD *CCU
mix cor SCHMITT 9067 $1.50   (S2962)

SING UNTO GOD see Brunetti, Domenico, Cantemus Domino

SING UNTO GOD see Clare, Edwyn A.

SING UNTO GOD see Fetler, Paul

SING UNTO GOD see Handel, George Frideric

SING UNTO GOD see Lewis

SING UNTO GOD see Tomkins, Thomas

SING UNTO GOD see Young

SING UNTO GOD see Young, G.

SING UNTO GOD-L.D.S. EDITION *CCU
mix cor SCHMITT 9068 $1.50   (S2963)

SING UNTO GOD LOUDLY see Young, G.

SING UNTO HIM *CC31L
mix cor BIG3 $1.50   (S2964)

SING UNTO HIS NAME see Wilson, John F.

SING UNTO THE LORD see Ashira Ladonai

SING UNTO THE LORD see Burroughs

SING UNTO THE LORD see Christiansen, P.

SING UNTO THE LORD see Clark, Keith

SING UNTO THE LORD see Croce, Giovanni

SING UNTO THE LORD see Kay

SING UNTO THE LORD see Kettering, Eunice Lea

SING UNTO THE LORD see Poston, Elizabeth

SING UNTO THE LORD see Protheroe, Daniel

SING UNTO THE LORD see Purcell, Henry

SING UNTO THE LORD see Thiman, Eric Harding

SING UNTO THE LORD see Tye, Christopher

SING UNTO THE LORD see Vecchi, Orazio, Cantate Domino

SING UNTO THE LORD see Williams, R.

SING UNTO THE LORD A NEW SONG see Couperin, Francois

SING UNTO THE LORD A NEW SONG see Lockwood, Normand

SING UNTO THE LORD A NEW SONG see McAfee

SING UNTO THE LORD A NEW SONG see Mechem, Kirke

SING UNTO THE LORD A NEW SONG see Rohlig, Harald

SING UNTO THE LORD A NEW SONG see Sarti

SING UNTO THE LORD A NEW SONG see Young

SING UNTO THE LORD MOST HIGH see Pergolesi, Giovanni Battista

SING UNTO THE LORD, O YE SAINTS see Blakley

SING UNTO THE LORD YE CHILDREN see Grime, William

SING WE see Powell

SING WE ALL
see Two Noels

SING WE ALL AT CHRISTMASTIDE see Rodby

SING WE ALL NOEL see Trusler

SING WE ALL NOW ALLELUIA *Easter/Lent
(Peninger) SATB oct PRO ART 2666 $.30 (S2965)

SING WE ALL NOW ALLELUIA see Peninger

SING WE ALL NOW WITH ONE ACCORD see Praetorius, Michael

SING WE IN EXULTATION see Messaus

SING WE MERRILY see Greene, Maurice

SING WE MERRILY see Proulx, Richard

SING WE MERRILY see Rimmer, Frederick

SING WE MERRILY see Shaw, Martin

SING WE MERRILY see Symons

SING WE MERRILY TO GOD see Freestone

SING WE MERRILY UNTO GOD see Batten, Adrian

SING WE MERRILY UNTO GOD see Kirk, Theron W.

SING WE MERRILY UNTO GOD see Thiman, Eric Harding

SING WE MERRILY UNTO GOD OUR STRENGTH see Campbell, Sydney S.

SING WE MERRILY UNTO GOD OUR STRENGTH see Hoag, Charles K.

SING WE MERRILY UNTO GOD OUR STRENGTH see King, Oliver A.

SING WE MERRILY UNTO GOD OUR STRENGTH see Prentice, Charles

SING WE MERRILY UNTO GOD OUR STRENGTH see Shaw, Martin

SING WE NOEL *sac/sec,CC19L,Xmas,carol
(Stone) unis/SA/SAB PRO ART $1.00   (S2966)

SING WE NOEL *Xmas,carol,Fr,16th cent
(Davis, K.) unis&desc,pno/org SCHIRM.EC 1574
$.25   (S2967)
(Davis, K.) SSA,acap SCHIRM.EC 1589 $.25
(S2968)
(Davis, K.K.) SAB,acap SCHIRM.EC 1738 $.30
(S2969)
(Gaul, H.) SATB oct PRESSER 332-11575 $.30
(S2970)
(Kinsman, F.) SA LEONARD-US 08059520 $.25
(S2971)
(Warner, Richard) unis/SA oct GRAY GCMR 2723
$.30   (S2972)
(Warner, Richard) SATB oct GRAY GCMR 2721
$.30   (S2973)

SING WE NOEL see Greene

SING WE NOEL see Van Dyke

SING WE NOEL see Wilhelm

SING WE NOEL see Young

SING WE NOEL, NOEL *Xmas
(Kirk) SATB,acap,opt pno oct PRO ART 2134
$.35   (S2974)
(Kirk) SAB,acap,opt pno oct PRO ART 2372 $.35
(S2975)
(Kirk) SSA,acap,opt pno oct PRO ART 2344 $.35
(S2976)
(Kirk) TTBB,acap,opt pno oct PRO ART 2374
$.35   (S2977)

SING WE NOEL ONCE MORE see Smith

SING WE NOW FOR CHRIST IS KING see Dretke, L.N.

SING WE NOW HASANNA see Graham

SING WE NOW HOSANNA see Graham

SING WE NOW OF CHRISTMAS see Simeone

SING WE NOW OF CHRISTMAS see Noel Nouvelet

SING WE NOW OF CHRISTMAS see Wilson

SING WE NOW THE SAVIOUR'S PRAISE *Czech
(Ehret) SA MARKS 4529 $.30   (S2978)
(Ehret) SSA MARKS 4360 $.25   (S2979)

SING WE NOW THY PRAISE see Tschesnokoff, P.I.

SING WE NOWELL see Talmadge, Charles L.

SING WE OF PASCHAL JOY see Freed

SING WE THE BIRTH see Bach, Johann Sebastian, Das Neugeborne Kindelein

SING WE THE BIRTH see Wadely, F.W.

SING WE THE PRAISE OF GOD see Bach, Johann Sebastian

SING WE THE VIRGIN MARY *Xmas,carol
(Niles; Horton) 4pt mix cor,acap oct SCHIRM.G
8884 $.30   (S2980)

SING WE THE VIRGIN MARY see Niles, John Jacob

SING WE TO CHRIST THE KING see Chaplin, [Marian Wood]

SING WE TO GOD see Ehret, Walter

SING WE TRIUMPHANT see Thiman, Eric Harding

SING WE TRIUMPHANT HYMNS see Helder, Bartholomaeus

SING WE TRIUMPHANT HYMNS see Praetorius, Michael

SING WE TRIUMPHANT SONGS see Willan, Healey

SING, WITH ALL THE SONS OF GLORY see Blake, G.

SING WITH JOY see Caldwell

SING WITH JOY see Van Dyke

SING WITH JOY AND GLADNESS see Haydn, (Franz) Joseph

SING WITH JOY, GLAD VOICES LIFT *Xmas,carol, Ger
(Schroeder, H.) SATB,inst (med easy) oct
CONCORDIA 98-2065 $.30   (S2981)

SING WITH JOY, GLAD VOICES LIFT see Distler, Hugo

SING WITH JOY, GLAD VOICES LIFT see Schroeder

SING WITH JOY, GLAD VOICES RAISE see Praetorius, Michael

SING WITH JOY THE SAVIOUR'S GLORY
see Communion Hymns

SING WITH ONE ACCORD see Kirby, Charles

SING WITH THE SPIRIT see Hall, Arthur

SING WITH WONDER AND DELIGHT see Graham

SING YE see Wienhorst, Richard

SING YE A JOYFUL SONG see Dvorak, Antonin

SING YE A JOYFUL SONG UNTO THE LORD see Dvorak, Antonin

SING, YE CHOIRS see Zaninelli, Luigi

SING YE CHOIRS see Gallus, Jacobus, Pueri Concinite

SING YE GLORY ALLELUIA see Hallstrom, Henry

SING YE JOYFULLY TO THE LORD see Young, Phillip

SING YE MERRILY see Mendelssohn-Bartholdy, Felix

SING YE PEOPLE see Brandt

SING YE PEOPLE, SING   *Xmas/Gen,carol,Fr
   (Spencer, W.) SATB,acap oct PRESSER MC339
   $.30   (S2982)

SING YE PRAISE TO THE NEW BORN KING see Litten, Jack

SING YE PRAISES TO THE NEW BORN KING see Litten, Jack

SING, YE RIGHTEOUS see Viadana, Lodovico Grossi da, Exultate Justi

SING YE SHEPHERDS see Beadell, Robert M.

SING YE TO THE INFANT KING see Hardwicke

SING YE TO THE LORD see Bach, Johann Sebastian, Singet Dem Herrn

SING YE TO THE LORD see Bach, Johann Sebastian, Singet Dem Herrn Ein Neues Lied

SING YE TO THE LORD! see Handel, George Frideric

SING YE TO THE LORD see Krapf, Gerhard

SING YE TO THE LORD see Tchaikovsky, Piotr Ilyitch

SING YE TO THE LORD see Titcomb

SING YE UNTO THE LORD see Viadana, Lodovico Grossi da, Cantata Domino

SING YE WITH PRAISE see Playford

SING YOUR PSALMS TO THE HOLY CHILD see Praetorius, Michael

SINGE, O SINGE DICH, SEELE see Nessen, Hugo von

SINGE, O SINGE DICH, SEELE see Schroeder, Hermann

SINGEN WIR AUS HERZENSGRUND see Praetorius, Michael

SINGENDEN JAHR see Rohwer, Jens

SINGER OF THE UNIVERSE see Butler, Eugene

SINGER'S CREED see Rathgeber

SINGERS, SING, AND TRUMPETS, PLAY *Easter,Ger,
   12th cent
   (Vermulst, Jan) 3 eq voices,opt org,opt 2trp
   oct WORLD LE-740-3 $.30   (S2983)

SINGET DEM HERREN see Raphael, Gunther

SINGET DEM HERRN see Bach, Johann Sebastian

SINGET DEM HERRN see Graf, Franz

SINGET DEM HERRN EIN NEUES LIED see Bach, Johann Sebastian

SINGET DEM HERRN EIN NEUES LIED see Becker-Foss, Jurgen

SINGET DEM HERRN EIN NEUES LIED see Bender, Jan

SINGET DEM HERRN EIN NEUES LIED see Blarr, Oskar Gottlieb

SINGET DEM HERRN EIN NEUES LIED see Briegel, Wolfgang Carl

SINGET DEM HERRN EIN NEUES LIED see Burkhard Willy

SINGET DEM HERRN EIN NEUES LIED see Calvisius, Sethus

SINGET DEM HERRN EIN NEUES LIED see Distler, Hugo

SINGET DEM HERRN EIN NEUES LIED see Hammerschmidt, Andreas

SINGET DEM HERRN EIN NEUES LIED see Hellmann, Diethard

SINGET DEM HERRN EIN NEUES LIED see Krieger, Johann Philipp

SINGET DEM HERRN EIN NEUES LIED see Kubler, Emil

SINGET DEM HERRN EIN NEUES LIED see Kurig, Hans-Hermann

SINGET DEM HERRN EIN NEUES LIED see Pachelbel, Johann

SINGET DEM HERRN EIN NEUES LIED see Schilling, Hans Ludwig

SINGET DEM HERRN, EIN NEUES LIED see Schutz, Heinrich

SINGET DEM HERRN EIN NEUES LIED see Schweizer, Rolf

SINGET DEM HERRN EIN NEUES LIED see Stockmeier, Wolfgang

SINGET DEM HERRN EIN NEUES LIED see Waldbroel, Wilhelm

SINGET DEM HERRN EIN NEUES LIED see Witte, Gerd

SINGET DEM HERRN EIN NEUES LIED, ALL WELT SOLL FROHLICH SINGEN MIT see Schutz, Heinrich

SINGET DEM HERRN EIN NEUES LIED, DENN DURCH IHN GROSS WUNDER GESCHIEHT see Schutz, Heinrich

SINGET DEM HERRN EIN NEUES LIED, DENN DURCH IHN GROSS WUNDER GESCHIEHT see Schutz, Heinrich

SINGET DEM HERRN EIN NEUES LIED DENN ER TUT GROSSE WUNDER see Schott, Johann Georg

SINGET DEM HERRN-HEFT 1 *CCU,Adv/Xmas
   (Schroder, Gerhard) 2-3pt wom cor&T/B
   HANSSLER 2.024 s.p.   (S2984)

SINGET DEM HERRN-HEFT 2 *CCU
   mix cor HANSSLER 2.035 s.p.   (S2985)

SINGET DEM HERRN-HEFT 3 *CCU
   mix cor HANSSLER 2.044 s.p.   (S2986)

SINGET DEM HERRN-HEFT 4 *CCU
   mix cor HANSSLER 2.045 s.p.   (S2987)

SINGET DEM HERRN-HEFT 5 *CCU
   mix cor HANSSLER 2.048 s.p.   (S2988)

SINGET DEM HERRN-HEFT 6 *CCU
   mix cor HANSSLER 2.050 s.p.   (S2989)

SINGET DEM HERRN see Bach, Johann Sebastian

SINGET DEM HERRN see Schutz, Heinrich

SINGET DEM KINDLEIN see Krause, Chr.

SINGET EIN NEUES LIED see Hassler, Hans Leo

SINGET EIN NEUES LIED see Schutz, Heinrich, Cantate Domino

SINGET EIN NEUES LIED see Staden, Johann

SINGET EIN NEUS LIED see Hassler, Hans Leo, Cantate Domino

SINGET FRISCH UND WOHLGEMUT see Brautigam, Helmut

SINGET FRISCH UND WOHLGEMUT see Distler, Hugo

SINGET FRISCH UND WOHLGEMUT see Nieland, H.

SINGET FRISCH UND WOHLGEMUT see Strutius, Thomas

SINGET FRISCH UND WOHLGEMUT see Wolleb, Johann Jakob

SINGET FRISCH UND WOHLGEMUT see Zipp, Friedrich

SINGET FROHLICH GOTTE see Schein, Johann Hermann

SINGET FROHLICH UNSERM GOTT see Jacot, Andre

SINGET HOCHERFREUT, GROSS SIND GOTTES
   see Neander, Joachim, Gott Ist Gegenwartig, Lasset Uns

SINGET, PREISET GOTT MIT FREUDEN see Schilling, Hans Ludwig

SINGET UNSEREM GOTT! see Handel, George Frideric, Sing Ye To The Lord!

SINGING ALLELUIA see Leaf, Robert

SINGING CATECHISM see Ylvisaker, John

SINGING CHILDREN OF THE CHURCH see Peery, Robert Roy

SINGING CHRISTIAN CHILDREN see Dressler, John

SINGING FAITH, A see Caldwell, Mary [Elizabeth]

SINGING FAITH, A see Caldwell, Mary [Elizabeth]

SINGING HILLS see Forsblad

SINGING I GO see Kirkpatrick

SINGING JOY see Muller, Don

SINGING ON THE MOUNTAIN see Gardner

SINGING WITH GRACE IN YOUR HEART see Mueller, Carl F.

SINGT DEM HERREN, ALLE STIMMEN! see Haydn, (Franz) Joseph

SINGT DEM HERRN EIN NEUES LIED see Glossner, Herbert

SINGT DEM HERRN EIN NEUES LIED see Horn, Paul

SINGT EIN LIED VOM LICHT DER WORTE see Schweizer, Rolf

SINGT, HIMMEL! see Handel, George Frideric, Sing, Oh Ye Heav'ns!

SINGT, IHR LIEBEN CHRISTEN ALL! see Praetorius, Michael

SINGT LIEBLICH UND LOBT DEN HERRN see Hartmann, Heinrich

SINGT MIT FROHER STIMM see Eglin, Arthur

SINGT MIT FROHER STIMM see Goudimel, Claude

SINGT MIT FROHER STIMM see Henking, Bernhard

SINGT MIT FROHER STIMM see Pfiffner, Ernst

SINGT MIT FROHER STIMM see Wieruszowski, Lili

SINGT, O SINGT DEM HERRN see Purcell, Henry

SINGT, SINGT see Schulz, Joh. Abraham Peter

SINGT, SINGT DEM HERREN NEUE LIEDER see Poser, Hans

SINGT, SINGT JEHOVA NEUE LIEDER see Chemin-Petit, Hans

SINGT, SINGT JEHOVA NEUE LIEDER see Kubler, Emil

SINGT UND KLINGT see Knab, Armin

SINGT UND KLINGT see Praetorius, Michael

SINGT UND KLINGT (PSALLITE) see Anonymous

SINGT UNSERM GOTT see Doebler, Curt

SINGT UNSERM GOTT, IHR REICHE ALLER WELT see Handel, George Frideric

SINITE PARVULOS see Mercenier, P.

SINN see Nystedt, Knut

SINNER, PLEASE DON'T LET THIS HARVEST PASS see Lynn, George

SINNER, PLEASE DON'T LET THIS HARVEST PASS see Work, John [Wesley]

SINNERS COME, THE SAVIOUR SEE see Ehret, Walter

SINNER'S SOUL, A see York

SINTE CECILIA see Schreurs, J.

SION'S DAUGHTER see Hill

SIONS DOTTRE see Aquilius, Jacobus

SIONS VEKTER HEVER ROSTEN see Tunder, Franz

SIR CHRISTEMAS see Bonta, Stephen

SIR CHRISTEMAS see Gilbert, J.R.

SIR CHRISTEMAS see Gilbert, Norman

SIR CHRISTEMAS see Nieman, Alfred

SIR CHRISTEMAS see Yeakle, Thomas

SIR, COME DOWN BEFORE MY CHILD DIES see Bender, Jan

SIRMIO, TRIA CATULLI CARMINA see Orff, Carl

SISTER ADELE see Sourire, Souer

SISTER AWAKE! CLOSE NOT YOUR EYES see Bridge

SISTER MARY HAD-A-BUT ONE CHILD see Ehret, Walter

SISTER OF MERCY see Gerald, Immaculata Conceptio

SISTINIUS, TRUID AAGESEN (ca. 1570-1620)
   Four Old Italian Cantiones *CC4U,It
   3pt mix cor,acap sc SKAND. SMF5316 s.p.
                                              (S2990)

SIT DOWN, LORD see Lamb

SIT NOMEN DOMINI see Maugeri, Giuseppe

SITIENTES, VENITE AD AQUAS see Victoria, Tomas Luis de

SITIVIT ANIMA MEA see Palestrina, Giovanni

SITT OGA JESUS OPPNAT HAR see Berg, Gottfrid

SITTING BY THE LOW BANKS OF THE WATERS OF BABYLON see Gomolka, Mikolaj, Siedzac Po Niskich Brzegach Babilonskiej Wody

SIX CHRISTMAS CAROLS, SET III *Xmas,carol
   (Holst) SSA,acap (very easy) OXFORD 44.019
   $.65
      contains: Coventry Carol; Es Ist Ein' Ros';
      In The Bleak Mid-Winter; O Little One;
      Rejoice And Be Merry; Wassail Song
                                              (S2991)

SIX CHRISTMAS SONGS see Williamson, Malcolm

SIX CHRISTMAS SONGS FOR THE YOUNG see Williamson, Malcolm

SIX CLOSING RESPONSES *CC6U
   (Russell, Wilbur F.) SATB/unis,acap (med
   easy) PRESSER 312-41003 $.50   (S2992)

SIX DUOS BIBLIQUES see Lacome, Paul

SIX EASTER CAROLS see Garlick, Anthony

SIX EASTER CAROLS see Garlick, Anthony

SIX EASTER CAROLS *Easter,carol
   (Bliss, Paul) (easy) oct WILLIS 2905 $.15
      contains: Bliss, Paul, Ring Merry Bells
      (unis); Emerson, He Is Risen (unis);
      Franke, Golden Harps Are Sounding (unis);
      Johns, Hail The Day That Sees Him Rise
      (SATB); Newton, Angels Roll The Rock Away
      (unis); Worthing, Richard, Hark! Ten
      Thousand Voices Sounding (SATB)   (S2993)

SIX ELIZABETHAN PASTORALES see Stanford

SIX EVENING HYMNS see Williamson, Malcolm

SIX EVENING HYMNS see Williamson, Malcolm

SIX HIGH HOLIDAY SELECTIONS see Piket, Frederick

SIX HYMN ANTHEMS *CC6U,anthem/hymn
   (Johnson, S.) SATB KJOS $1.25   (S2994)

SIX HYMN SETTINGS see Markworth, Henry

SIX HYMNS see Draesel, Lederhouse

SIX HYMNS FOR ALL SEASONS see Appleford, Rev.
Patrick

SIX HYMNS OF COURAGE AND PRAISE see Thiman,
Eric Harding

SIX INTROITS FOR ADVENT AND CHRISTMAS see
Lindstrom

SIX LITURGICAL CHANTS see Tcherepnin, Alexander

SIX MADRIGALS see Fromm, Herbert

SIX MENDELSSOHN ANTHEMS see Mendelssohn-
Bartholdy, Felix

SIX MODERNISTIC CAROLS see Gross

SIX MORE AFRO-AMERICAN CHRISTMAS CAROLS *CC6U,
Xmas,carol,Afr/US
(Clark) SATB MARKS 4600 $.40   (S2995)

SIX MOTETS see Pergolesi, Giovanni Battista

SIX MOTETS A L'UNISSON *mot
[Lat] unis cmplt ed DURAND s.p.
contains: Bach, Johann Sebastian, Ave aris
Stella; Mendelssohn-Bartholdy, Felix,
Adoro Te; Mozart, Wolfgang Amadeus,
Tantum Ergo; Rinck, Johann Christian
Hein., Tantum Ergo; Saint-Saens, Camille,
Ave Maria; Schubert, Franz (Peter), Ave
Verum   (S2996)

SIX MOTETS IN POLISH AND ENGLISH see Chojnacki,
J.

SIX MOTETS see Pergolesi, Giovanni Battista

SIX MOTETS see Bach, Johann Sebastian

SIX MOTETS see Vaet, Jacobus

SIX NEGRO SPIRITUALS *CC6U,spir
(Jacobson,Caurice) 4pt men bor CURWEN 50682
s.p.   (S2997)

SIX NEGRO SPIRITUALS *CC6U,spir
(Jacobson) 4pt mix cor CURWEN 61264 s.p.
                                      (S2998)

SIX NEW CAROLS *CC6U,Xmas,carol
unis/cong cmplt ed WEINBERGER s.p.   (S2999)

SIX NEW CAROLS *CC6U,Xmas,carol
unis MARKS $1.00   (S3000)

SIX NOELS ANCIENS see Roques, L.

SIX NOELS ANCIENS see Parozai, Gui

SIX OLD FRENCH CHRISTMAS CAROLS (2ND SET)
*CC6U,Xmas
(Manney, C.) SATB oct PRESSER 332-13692 $.35
                                      (S3001)

SIX POEMES EVANGELIQUES see Chaminade, Cecile

SIX POEMS FROM MISERERE see Naylor, Bernard

SIX POEMS FROM MISERERE see Naylor, Bernard

SIX POLYPHONIC MOTETS *CC6U,mot
[Lat] SSA/TTB cmplt ed GIA G 641 $1.00
contains works by: Lassus; Lotti;
Palestrina; Vittoria   (S3002)

SIX RESPONSES AND SANCTUS see Whitford

SIX RESPONSES FOR GENERAL USE see Grant

SIX SACRED ANTHEMS FOR MALE VOICES see Cassler,
G. Winston

SIX SACRED SONGS see Bach, Johann Sebastian

SIX SACRED SONGS see Gallus, Jacobus

SIX SACRED SONGS see Wolf, Hugo

SIX SCRIPTURAL ANTHEMS see Englert, Eugene

SIX SETTINGS FROM "MUSAE SIONIAE," 1609 see
Praetorius, Michael

SIX SEVENTEENTH CENTURY CAROLS FROM THE
NETHERLANDS *sac/sec,Xmas,carol,Neth,17th
cent
(Noske) SATB (easy) OXFORD 48.004 $1.40
contains: Bull, John, As Bountiful As May;
De Leeuw, To Us A Little Child Is Born;
Messaus, O Blessed, Holy Bethlehem;
Messaus, Sing We In Exultation;
Munninckx, O Gentle Night; Sweelinck, Jan
Pieterszoon, How Brightly Beams (S3003)

SIX SHORT ANTHEMS *see Come, Thou Holy Spirit,
Come; Herman, Lo, Round The Throne; Ley,
Henry George, Eternal Ruler; Ley, Henry
George, Evening Hymn, "Prayer Of King
Charles"   (S3004)

SIX SHORT ANTHEMS see Herman

SIX SHORT ANTHEMS see Ley, Henry George

SIX SONGS FOR CHRISTMASTIDE see Simpson

SIX SONGS FOR CHRISTMASTIDE see Simpson,
Kenneth

SIX SONGS FOR YOUNGER CHILDREN see Simpson,
Kenneth

SIX TANTUM ERGO see Bruckner, Anton

SIX TRADITIONAL CAROLS, SET I *Xmas,carol
(Holst) SSA,acap (very easy) OXFORD 44.118
$.65
contains: Bedfordshire May Day; Holly And
The Ivy; I Saw Three Ships; Joy Seven;
Matthew, Mark; Virgin Most Pure (S3005)

SIX TRADITIONAL CAROLS, SET II *Xmas,carol
(Holst) SSA,acap (very easy) OXFORD 44.042
$.65
contains: God Rest You Merry; In Dulci

Jubilo; Joseph Dearest; Lord Jesus Hath A
Garden; O Little Town; This Endris Night
                                      (S3006)

SIX TRADITIONAL CAROLS, SET IV *Xmas,carol
(Holst) SSA/SSAA,acap (very easy) OXFORD
44.064 $.65
contains: Boy Was Born In Bethlehem; Moon
Shines Bright; Nowell Sing We; Quem
Pastores; Salutation Carol; Unto Us Is
Born A Son   (S3007)

SIX TWO-PART CAROLS *Xmas,carol
(Woodgate) SS (easy) OXFORD 44.057 $.55
contains: First Nowell; Gloucestershire
Wassail; I Saw Three Ships; O Little One;
Rocking; Virgin Most Pure
see also: I Saw Three Ships   (S3008)

SIX VESPER HYMNS see Lang, C.S.

SIX WESLEY SONGS FOR THE YOUNG see Williamson,
Malcolm

SIXTEEN AMENS FROM THE ORATORIOS see Bitgood,
Roberta

SIXTEEN CANTIONES SACRAE (1575) VOL. 1 see
Tallis, Thomas

SIXTEEN CANTIONES SACRAE (1575) VOL. 2 see
Tallis, Thomas

SIXTEEN CHORAL RESPONSES see Dethier

SIXTEEN CHORALES see Bach, Johann Sebastian

SIXTEEN SENTENCES, RESPONSES, AMENS *CC16U
SATB KJOS 8024 $.30   (S3009)

SIXTEENTH-CENTURY ANTHEM BOOK, A *CC20U,
anthem,16th cent
SATB,acap (med) OXFORD $2.50   (S3010)

SIXTEENTH-CENTURY ANTHEM BOOK, A *CC20U,anthem
4pt oct OXFORD $2.50   (S3011)

SIXTEENTH MASS see Haydn, (Franz) Joseph,
Sanctus

SIXTY CAROLS OF ALL NATIONS see Anonymous

SIXTY CHORALES see Bach, Johann Sebastian

SIXTY-SEVENTH PSALM, THE see Gordon, P.

SJELEFEST see Sandvold, Arild

SJOBERG, SVEN-GOSTA
Helige Ande
mix cor NORDISKA 1071 s.p.   (S3012)

SJOBLOM, HEIMER
Jesu Ar Min Van Den Basta
mix cor NORDISKA 5781 s.p.   (S3013)

O, Jesu, Nar Jag Hadan Skall
mix cor NORDISKA 5782 s.p.   (S3014)

SJOGREN
Vise Konungars Tag
[Swed] unis LUNDQUIST 28 s.p.   (S3015)

SJOLUND, PAUL
All Glory, Laud And Honor
SA oct WORD CS-2417 $.30   (S3016)

Brightest And Best Of The Sons Of The Morning
*Xmas
unis/SA oct WORD CS-360 $.30   (S3017)

Carol Of The Incarnation *Xmas,carol
SATB oct WALTON 2119 $.25   (S3018)

Christ Is Risen *Easter/Lent
SATB oct WALTON 2160 $.30   (S3019)

Christmas Folk Song *Xmas,carol/folk
SATB ALLANS 457 s.p.   (S3020)

Christmas Folk Song, A *Xmas
SATB oct AGAPE A 313 $.30   (S3021)

Come To Me And Rest
SATB oct WALTON 2168 $.25   (S3022)

Four Chorales For Communion *CC4U,Commun,
chorale
SATB oct WORD CS-2395 $.30   (S3023)

Guide Me, O Thou Great Jehovah
SATB oct WORD CS-670 $.30   (S3024)

I Beeseech You To Look
unis oct WORD CS-2444 $.30   (S3025)

In The Beginning
SATB oct WORD CS-686 $.25   (S3026)

Infant Holy, Infant Lowly *Xmas
SATB oct WORD CS-2397 $.30   (S3027)

Light Of The World, The
SSATTBB oct WALTON 2166 $.25   (S3028)

Morning Star, The
SATB oct WORD CS-309 $.30   (S3029)

O Sacred Head, Now Wounded
SATB (choral variations) oct WORD CS-2399
$.40   (S3030)

Out Of My Sorrow
SATB oct WALTON 2167 $.25   (S3031)

Responses For Worship, Set 1
SATB oct WORD CS-665 $.30   (S3032)

Responses For Worship, Set 2 *Adv/Xmas
SATB oct WORD CS-679 $.30   (S3033)

Responses For Worship, Set 3
SATB oct WORD CS-2401 $.30   (S3034)

Throned Upon That Awful Tree *Easter/Lent
SATB oct WALTON 2132 $.30   (S3035)

Walk With Me
SA oct WORD CS-2523 $.25   (S3036)

SJOLUND, PAUL (cont'd.)
Ye Sons And Daughters Of The King *Easter/
Lent
unis&desc oct WORD CS-2405 $.30   (S3037)

SJOSTRAND
O Sing Unto The Lord
SATB FLAMMER A 5555 $.30   (S3038)

SJUNG AMERN see Baden, Conrad

SJUNG HJERTE, SJUNG EN AFTENSANG see Olsen,
Sparre

SJUNGE VI AF HJERTENS GRUND see Pederson,
Mogens

SJUNGEN NU ALLA *CCU
mix cor NORDISKA 3700 s.p., ipa   (S3039)

SKAGERBURG, EINAR
Ty Du Glader Mig, Herre *mot
mix cor NORDISKA 3116 s.p.   (S3040)

SKALD I KIRKJUGAROI see Sveinsson, Gunnar
Reynir

SKAUEN, GUTTORN
Han Kom Til Sitt Eget
[Norw] mix cor,org LYCHE 49 s.p.   (S3041)

Hvem Er Den Storste *mot
[Norw] mix cor LYCHE 105 s.p.   (S3042)

Salige Er De Som Sorger *mot
[Norw] LYCHE 68 s.p.   (S3043)

SKEAT
O Thou Not Made With Hands
SATB oct VOLKWEIN VB234 $.25   (S3044)

SKEAT, WLLIAM J.
Jesus, These Eyes Have Never Seen
SATB oct FISCHER,J 8667 $.30   (S3045)

Ye Fair Green Hills Of Galilee
SATB oct FISCHER,J 8787 $.30   (S3046)

SKETCHES FROM REVELATION see Christiansen, Paul

SKIES ARE CLEARER NOW, THE see Noe, J.T.

SKII
There Is No Other Comforter *see Kastal

SKILLINGS, OTIS
Answer, The
SATB oct LILLENAS AN-5009 $.30   (S3047)

Born Again
SATB oct LILLENAS AN-5019 $.30   (S3048)

Come Along With Me
SATB oct LILLENAS AN-5007 $.30   (S3049)

Everybody Sing
SATB oct LILLENAS AN-1652 $.30   (S3050)

God Is
SATB oct LILLENAS AN-5010 $.30   (S3051)

Great To Be Alive *CC10UL
SATB cmplt ed LILLENAS MB-238 $1.95   (S3052)

Great To Be Alive
SATB oct LILLENAS AN-5032 $.35   (S3053)

He Is The Way *anthem
SATB oct LILLENAS AN-5021 $.30   (S3054)

How About You?
SATB oct LILLENAS AN-5031 $.30   (S3055)

I've Got A Reason To Sing
SATB oct LILLENAS AN-5026 $.35   (S3056)

Listen
SATB oct LILLENAS AN-5004 $.25   (S3057)

Lord Above, The
SATB oct LILLENAS AN-5002 $.30   (S3058)

Now Walk With God
SATB oct LILLENAS AN-5005 $.30   (S3059)

Oh, Happy Day
SATB oct LILLENAS AN-5035 $.40   (S3060)

Power To Choose, The
SATB oct LILLENAS AN-5023 $.30   (S3061)

Relevant
SATB oct LILLENAS AN-5017 $.30   (S3062)

Saved Me
SATB oct LILLENAS AT-1081 $.25   (S3063)

Sing, I Will Always Sing
SATB oct LILLENAS AN-1651 $.30   (S3064)

World Without Love, A
SATB oct LILLENAS AN-5011 $.30   (S3065)

You Can Experience
SATB oct LILLENAS AN-5025 $.35   (S3066)

Young World *CC10UL
jr cor,pno,bvl,gtr cmplt ed LILLENAS MB-229
$1.95   (S3067)

SKJUL EI DITT ASYN see Farrant, Richard

SKOLD, BENGT-GORAN
Missa Nova *Mass
mix cor NORDISKA NMS 6395 s.p.   (S3068)

SKOLD, YNGVE
Maria, Jesu Moder
mix cor NORDISKA 5030 s.p.   (S3069)

O Gud, Giv Oss Din Andes Nad
mix cor NORDISKA 5028 s.p.   (S3070)

SKOLNIK, WALTER
On This Day Christ Was Born
SATB oct ELKAN-V 362-1257 $.25   (S3071)

SKOLNIK, WALTER (cont'd.)

Psalm 96
SATB oct ELKAN-V 362-1288 $.30   (S3072)

SKROUP, JAN NEPOMUK (1811-1892)
Graduale And Offertory *ASD
voc sc WEINBERGER s.p., ipa
contains: Justorem Animae (mix cor,B
solo,org,strings,opt 2ob&2trp&timp)
(Offer); Timete Dominum (mix cor,org,
strings,opt 2horn) (Gradual)   (S3073)

Justorem Animae
see Graduale And Offertory

Missa Pro Populo *Mass
mix cor,org WEINBERGER s.p. voc sc, cor pts
(S3074)

Timete Dominum
see Graduale And Offertory

SKULLE JAG MIN GUD EJ LOVA
(Berg, Gottfrid) mix cor NORDISKA 2231 s.p.
see also Sacrae Cantiones   (S3075)

SKY CAN STILL REMEMBER, THE see Rodgers

SKY, THE see Magne, Michel

SLACK, ROY
I Was Glad (Psalm 122) Fest/Gen/Thanks
SATB (easy) oct OXFORD 42.884 $.25 (S3076)

Psalm 122 *see I Was Glad

SLANEY, IVOR
Mass Of Saint Richard *Mass
unis voc sc WEINBERGER $1.25   (S3077)
cong cor pts WEINBERGER s.p.   (S3078)
SSA/SSAA cor pts WEINBERGER $.35   (S3079)
SATB cor pts WEINBERGER $.35   (S3080)

SLATER
Easter Introit, An *Easter,Introit
SATB oct SACRED S-39 $.35   (S3081)

Mighty Fortress, A
SATB oct SACRED S-88 $.45   (S3082)

With Broken Heart And Contrite Sigh
SATB oct SACRED S-91 $.35   (S3083)

SLATER, DAVID D.
Song Of Holiday, A
2pt SACRED E.A.152 s.p.   (S3084)

SLATER, RICHARD W.
Christ Hath Humbled Himself
SATB,acap AMP A653 $.35   (S3085)

Festival Antiphons *CCU,Adv/Asc/Xmas/Easter/
Epiph/Lent/Pent/Refm/Thanks/Trin
4pt mix cor,acap oct SCHIRM.G 11366 $.30
(S3086)
O Lord, Thou Hast Searched Me And Known Me
SATB (easy) ABINGDON APM-714 $.40 (S3087)

SLATES, PHILIP M.
I Wait For The Lord
SA/TB (easy) ABINGDON APM-497 $.30 (S3088)

Noel Sing We Now Of Christmas *Xmas
unis WARNER R3331 $.30   (S3089)

Peace O Lord *Xmas
SATB (med) ABINGDON APM-471 $.40 (S3090)

SLAUA see Rimsky-Korsakov, Nikolai

SLEEP, BABE DIVINE see Gevaert, Francois
Auguste, Le Somneil De L'enfant Jesus

SLEEP BABY JESU *Xmas,Braz
(Pfust) SA SCHMITT 2580 $.35   (S3091)
(Pfust) SATB SCHMITT 1192 $.30   (S3092)

SLEEP, BABY JESUS see Piccolo

SLEEP, BABY JESUS see Swisher, Charles

SLEEP, BABY, SLEEP see Bell

SLEEP, BABY, SLEEP see Chtic Aby Spal

SLEEP, BLESSED JESUS *Xmas,folk,Boh
(Olds) SSAA SCHMITT 2533 $.25   (S3093)

SLEEP CHILD SWEET AND MILD see Track

SLEEP, DEAR LITTLE CHILD *Xmas
(Wiley) SATB oct PRO ART 2526 $.25 (S3094)

SLEEP, DEAR SON OF HEAVEN *Xmas
(Carlson) SATB SCHMITT 5907 $.35 (S3095)

SLEEP, GENTLE JESUS *Xmas,Boh
(Lipscomb, Helen) SSA oct GRAY GCMR 2769 $.30
(S3096)
SLEEP, HOLY BABE *Xmas,carol
oct HART s.p.   (S3097)
(Dexter) SA FRANCIS s.p.   (S3098)
(Sharpe, E.) cor&desc CRAMER 52   (S3099)

SLEEP HOLY BABE see Caswell

SLEEP, HOLY BABE see Creston, Paul

SLEEP, HOLY BABE see Dykes

SLEEP, HOLY BABE see Dykes, John Bacchus

SLEEP, HOLY BABE see Matthews, Harvey Alexander

SLEEP, HOLY BABE see Thomas

SLEEP HOLY CHILD see Hovdesven, E.A.

SLEEP HOLY CHILD see Simson, Alec Buckingham

SLEEP, HOLY CHILD! see Young, C.

SLEEP IN PEACE, O HEAVENLY CHILD see Haydn,
(Johann) Michael

SLEEP, LITTLE CHILD see Litten, Jack

SLEEP LITTLE JESUS *Xmas
SATB HANSEN-US T9577 $.40   (S3100)
SSA HANSEN-US T9578 $.40   (S3101)
SA HANSEN-US T9652 $.40   (S3102)

SLEEP LITTLE JESUS see Anderson, [William H.]

SLEEP, LITTLE JESUS see Bartholemew

SLEEP, LITTLE JESUS see Blanchard

SLEEP, LITTLE JESUS see Carpenter, S.M.

SLEEP, LITTLE JESUS see Linder

SLEEP, LITTLE KING see Gibbs

SLEEP, LITTLE LORD see White, Michael

SLEEP LITTLE ONE see Nelson, Ronald A.

SLEEP, LITTLE TINY KING see Besig

SLEEP, MY BABY, LOVELY CHILD *Xmas,carol,It
(Halter, C.) SA/SAB/SATB,acap (easy) oct
CONCORDIA 98-1662 $.22   (S3103)

SLEEP, MY JESU, SLEEP see Maurel, E. Olive

SLEEP, MY JESUS *Xmas,Neth
(Dickinson, C.) SATB oct GRAY GSC 141 $.25
(S3104)
SLEEP, MY LITTLE JESUS see Bergman

SLEEP, MY LITTLE JESUS see Bergmann

SLEEP, MY LITTLE ONE *Xmas
(Allen) SATB&opt jr cor,opt S solo oct
GALLEON GCS1012   (S3105)

SLEEP MY LITTLE ONE see Lynn, George

SLEEP, MY SAVIOUR, SLEEP *Xmas
(Caldwell, Mary E.) SATB (easy) PRESSER G-221
$.35   (S3106)

SLEEP NOW ON THY NATAL DAY see Corwin

SLEEP, O HOLY CHILD OF HEAVEN *Xmas,carol,It
(Barrie) 2pt jr cor oct KENDOR $.30 (S3107)

SLEEP, O SLEEP, MY LOVELY CHILD *Xmas,carol,It
(Ehret, Walter) SATB,opt inst oct WALTON 2500
$.30   (S3108)
(Ehret, Walter) SSA,opt inst oct WALTON 2537
$.30   (S3109)

SLEEP OF THE CHILD JESUS *Xmas,Fr
(Crowell, M.) SSA oct PRESSER 312-40569 $.25
(S3110)
SLEEP OF THE CHILD JESUS see Crowell, M.

SLEEP OF THE CHILD JESUS see Gevaert, Francois
Auguste

SLEEP OF THE CHILD JESUS see Howell, Richard D.

SLEEP OF THE CHILD JESUS, THE see Gevaert,
Francois Auguste

SLEEP OF THE CHILD JESUS, THE *Xmas,carol,Fr
(Baggott) SSA ALLANS 467 s.p.   (S3111)
(Grimes, T.) unis,inst (easy) oct CONCORDIA
98-3005 $.25   (S3112)

SLEEP OF THE CHILD JESUS, THE see Gevaert,
Francois Auguste

SLEEP OF THE INFANT JESUS *Xmas,Fr
(Christy) SSATBB SCHMITT 1647 $.22 (S3113)
(Christy) SSA SCHMITT 2546 $.20   (S3114)
(Christy) SATB SCHMITT 1581 $.30   (S3115)

SLEEP, OH SLEEP see Kirk, T.

SLEEP ON THY NATAL DAY see Corwin

SLEEP, SLEEP, HOLY BABE see Van Dyke

SLEEP SOFTLY, SOFTLY, BEAUTIFUL JESUS *Xmas,
carol,Fr
(Schroeder, H.) SATB,inst (med easy) oct
CONCORDIA 98-2069 $.25   (S3116)

SLEEP, SWEET JESU see Aston, Peter, Dormi, Jesu

SLEEP, SWEET JESUS, SLEEP see Abbey, H.

SLEEP, THOU BLESSED CHILD *Xmas
(Gordon, P.) SATB oct PRESSER 312-40233 $.30
(S3117)
SLEEP, THOU HOLY CHILD see Pasquet, Jean

SLEEP, THOU, MY JEWEL see Lulajze Jezuni

SLEEP, TINY SAVIOR see Schaefer, Christopher

SLEEP WELL, DEAR HEAVENLY BOY *Xmas,carol,Ger
(Schroeder, H.) SATB,inst (med easy) oct
CONCORDIA 98-2067 $.25   (S3118)

SLEEP WELL, THOU CHILD OF HEAVEN
(Ehret, W.) SAB LEONARD-US 08060200 $.25
(S3119)
SLEEPERS AWAKE see Bach, Johann Sebastian,
Wachet Auf, Ruft Uns Die Stimme

SLEEPERS, WAKE! see Bach, Johann Sebastian,
Wachet Auf, Ruft Uns Die Stimme

SLEEPER'S, WAKE see Mendelssohn-Bartholdy,
Felix

SLEEPERS, WAKE, A VOICE IS CALLING see
Mendelssohn-Bartholdy, Felix

SLEEPS JUDEA FAIR see Mac Kinnon, H.A.

SLEETH
Feed My Lambs
unis,2fl SOUTHERN $.35   (S3120)

Long Time Ago *Xmas
2pt oct SACRED S-5396 $.35   (S3121)

SLEETH, NATALIE
Amen So Be It
2pt oct FISCHER,C CM-7807 $.35   (S3122)

Baby, What You Goin' To Be
SATB oct FISCHER,C CM-7790 $.35   (S3123)
2pt oct FISCHER,C CM-7791 $.30   (S3124)

Feed My Lambs
unis oct FISCHER,C CM-7777 $.35   (S3125)

Gaudeamus Hodie
3pt oct FISCHER,C CM-7776 $.35   (S3126)

God Of Great And God Of Small
unis oct FISCHER,C CM-7808 $.30   (S3127)

Hallelujah Day
SATB oct FISCHER,C CM-7767 $.35   (S3128)

Isn't It Reassuring
2pt oct FISCHER,C CM-7828 $.35   (S3129)

Jubilate Deo *Easter/Gen
SATB,brass (med) ABINGDON APM-885 $.55, ipa
(S3130)
SLETTEN, JACOB
Blomstre Som En Rosengard
(Ree, Knut) mix cor MUSIKK 219 s.p. (S3131)

Dyp Av Nade
(Nystedt, Knut) [Norw] mix cor,org LYCHE 17
s.p.   (S3132)

S'LICHOS see Piket, Frederick

SLOGEDAL, BJARNE
Adoramus The Christie
[Norw] mix cor LYCHE 86 s.p.   (S3133)

Antiphona De Morte *anti
SATB oct WALTON 2903 $.35   (S3134)

Cantate Domino *mot
[Lat] mix cor LYCHE 87 s.p.   (S3135)

Hosianna Til Sonn Av David
[Norw] mix cor LYCHE 57 s.p.   (S3136)

La De Sma Barn Komme Til Meg
[Norw] LYCHE 1 s.p.   (S3137)

Til Dig Herre, Tar Jeg Min Tilflukt
[Norw] mix cor LYCHE 65 s.p.   (S3138)

SLOWAKISCHES WEIHNACHTSLIED *Xmas
(Schmid, Reinhold) mix cor,acap oct DOBLINGER
s.p. see from Zwei Alte Weihnachtslieder
(S3139)
SLUKT ER DAGENS LYSE FLAMMER *folk
(Hovland, Egil) [Norw] 3pt mix cor LYCHE 38
s.p.   (S3140)

SLUMBER, BELOVED see Bach, Johann Sebastian

SLUMBER, INFANT DIVINE see Fisher, Herbert R.

SLUMBER JESU see Dormi Jesu

SLUMBER NOW BELOVED CHILD see Nelson

SLUMBER NOW BELOVED CHILD see Nelson, Ronald A.

SLUMBER, O HOLY JESU see Wood, Dale

SLUMBER OF THE INFANT JESUS see Gevaert,
Francois Auguste, Le Sommeil De L'Enfant
Jesus

SLUMBER OF THE INFANT JESUS, THE see Gevaert,
Francois Auguste, Le Sommeil De L'Enfant
Jesus

SLUMBER SOFTLY, JESUS HOLY see Bragg

SLUMBER SONG OF THE INFANT JESUS see Gevaert,
Francois Auguste

SLUMBER SONG OF THE MADONNA see Head, Michael
(Dewar)

SLVOVSKY
Hospodi Pomiloi
(Weaver, P.) TTBB,acap oct PRESSER
332-14373 $.30   (S3141)

SMALL DEVOTION see Taverner, John

SMALL SONG OF GRATITUDE see Yahres

SMALLEY, R.
Missa Brevis *Mass
cor FABER F0154 s.p.   (S3142)

SMART
Angels From The Realms Of Glory *Xmas,
anthem/carol
(Hastings) SATB oct BOURNE HA5 $.30 (S3143)
(Pooler) SA&SATB (easy) oct AUGSBURG 1224
$.25   (S3144)
(Pooler) SATB&jr cor (easy) oct AUGSBURG
1224 $.25   (S3145)
(Rogers) 2pt jr cor oct LILLENAS AN-4013
$.25   (S3146)
(Whitman) SATB oct LILLENAS AN-3805 $.30
(S3147)
God, The Lord, A King *anthem/hymn
(Angell;Cooper) SATB oct SPRATT 547 $.25
(S3148)
Holy Father, Great Creator
(Holmes) SATB oct PRO ART 1770 $.20 (S3149)

Lead On, O King Eternal *hymn
(Gerig) SATB oct LILLENAS AN-2292 $.30
(S3150)
(Rogers) 2pt jr cor/3pt jr cor oct LILLENAS
AN-4004 $.25   (S3151)

Lord Is My Shepherd, The (Psalm 23)
SATB oct PRO ART 1729 $.30   (S3152)

Psalm 23 *see Lord Is My Shepherd, The

See The Conqueror Mounts In Triumph *Easter/
Lent
(Townsend) SATB oct PRO ART 1762 $.25
(S3153)

SMART (cont'd.)

Sing, O Sing This Blessed Morn *Xmas
(Follett) SATB oct PRO ART 2080 $.25
(S3154)

SMART, DAVID
Alleluia! Jesus Lives! *Easter,anti/anthem
SA (easy) oct AGAPE A 383 $.25
(S3155)

Creation, The *Gen,cant
jr cor oct AGAPE $1.25
(S3156)

Echo
2pt treb cor oct AGAPE SP 699 $.25 (S3157)

Hark, The Glad Sound *Xmas,cant
jr cor oct AGAPE $1.25
(S3158)

I Lay My Sins On Jesus *anthem
2pt oct AGAPE A 310 $.30
(S3159)

In The Bleak Midwinter
jr cor oct AGAPE A 335 $.25
(S3160)

Make A Joyful Noise Unto The Lord *anthem
treb cor,perc oct AGAPE F 931 $.30 (S3161)

Music For Young Voices And Instruments *CCU
jr cor,inst oct AGAPE $1.50
(S3162)

Praise To The Lord
unis,2trp,drums oct AGAPE F 939 $.30
(S3163)

Three Seasonal Anthems For Junior Choir
*CC3U,anthem
jr cor oct AGAPE A 319 $.30
(S3164)

SMART, HENRY THOMAS (1813-1879)
Angels From The Realms Of Glory *Xmas,carol
(Hustad, Don) SATB/SAB ALLANS 450 s.p.
(S3165)

Holy Communion *Commun
unis (E flat maj) NOVELLO 44.1244.03 s.p.
(S3166)

How Lovely Are Thy Dwellings
SSA oct PRESSER 312-05984 $.30   (S3167)

Jubilate Deo *Jubil
SATB CRAMER C0 s.p.
(S3168)

Kyrie, Sursum Corda, Creed And Gloria
*Credo/Gloria/Kyrie
SATB CRAMER C0 s.p.
(S3169)

Lead On, O King Eternal
(Byles) 4pt mix cor oct SCHIRM.G 10855 $.25
(S3170)

Let Us Now Our Voices Raise
(Coggin, Elwood) SAB oct BELWIN 2040 $.25
(S3171)

Lord Is My Shepherd, The (Psalm 23)
2pt jr cor/2pt wom cor CURWEN 71279 s.p.
(S3172)

Lord Is My Shepherd, The *Bibl
2pt wom cor oct SCHIRM.G 4415 $.25 (S3173)
2pt oct NOVELLO 48.1074.01 s.p.   (S3174)
SA oct LESLIE 2008   (S3175)
(Bellairs) 4pt mix cor oct SCHIRM.G 4448
$.25   (S3176)
(Dexter, H.) 2pt ENOCH TP276 s.p.   (S3177)

Lord Thou Hast Been Our Refuge
cor oct HART s.p.
(S3178)

O Brothers, Lift Your Voices
(Simeone) SATB SHAWNEE A 784 $.30   (S3179)

Psalm 23 *see Lord Is My Shepherd, The

Star Of The East *Xmas
2pt ENOCH TP161 s.p.   (S3180)
3pt ASHDOWN V.T.29 s.p.   (S3181)

Te Deum *Te Deum
SATB (F maj) oct NOVELLO 44.0032.01 s.p.
(S3182)
unis (F maj) oct NOVELLO 02.0014.10 s.p.
(S3183)
(West, John E.) SS (F maj) oct NOVELLO
33.0065.10 s.p.   (S3184)

Te Deum Laudamus *Te Deum
(West, John E.) SS (F maj) NOVELLO
33.0065.10 s.p.   (S3185)

SMART, ROLAND
O Give Thanks Unto The Lord *Harv/Thanks,
anthem
mix cor oct NOVELLO 28.1248.07 s.p. (S3186)

Praise The Lord, O My Soul *Harv/Thanks,
anthem
mix cor oct NOVELLO 28.1249.05 s.p. (S3187)

SMEDEBY, SUNE
Och Gott Ol Kom
men oct NORDISKA NMS-6289 s.p.   (S3188)

SMERT, RICHARD
Nowelle *Xmas
(Simkins, C.F.) unis,2vln/2rec STAINER F18
$.25   (S3189)

SMETANA, BEDRICH (1824-1884)
Min Stjarna Och Svalorna
wom cor NORDISKA NSM 6377, NMS-6376 s.p.
(S3190)

SMILING DAWN OF HAPPY DAYS see Handel, George
Frideric

SMIT
Carol *carol
SSA,acap MARKS 10 $.25   (S3191)

SMIT, H.J.
Dreizehn Geestelijke Liederen
3pt mix cor BROEKMANS 790 s.p.   (S3192)

Psallite Deo
3pt wom cor BROEKMANS 841 s.p.   (S3193)

SMIT, JOHANNES
Christmas Eve *Xmas
SATB oct SHAPIRO SK 2086 $.25   (S3194)

No Joy But His
SATB oct SHAPIRO SK 2085 $.25   (S3195)

SMIT, LEO (1921-   )
Christmas Carol *Xmas,carol
2pt treb cor,acap PEER $.35   (S3196)

Psalm *Psalm
SATB,acap PEER $.35   (S3197)

SMIT SIBINGA, TH. H. (1899-1958)
Psalm 121
[Dut] mix cor,org DONEMUS sc s.p., cor pts
s.p.   (S3198)

SMITH
Ballad Of Easter *Easter
SATB oct LORENZ C206 $.30   (S3199)

Calm Is The Storm
SATB oct LILLENAS AN-2289 $.30   (S3200)

Cheer The Weary Traveller
SATB KJOS 1004 $.30   (S3201)

Child Of Hope, A *Xmas
SATB,pno oct HERITAGE H56 $.40   (S3202)
SATB,org oct LORENZ C325 $.30   (S3203)

Children Don't Get Weary
SATB KJOS 1007 $.30   (S3204)

Christ The Lord Is Risen Again *Easter
SATB,org FRANCIS s.p.   (S3205)

Come Let's Be Merry
SATB oct VOLKWEIN VB134 $.30   (S3206)

Come Unto Me Ye Weary
SATB WARNER W2572 $.30   (S3207)

Didn't My Lord Deliver Daniel?
SATB KJOS 1014 $.30   (S3208)

Emmaus Road *Easter
SB oct LORENZ 5763 $.30   (S3209)

Even For One *Easter
SATB oct LORENZ B161 $.30   (S3210)

Faith, Folk And Clarity *CCU
unis,gtr GALLIARD 2.9050.1 $1.75   (S3211)

Faith, Folk, And Festivity *CCU
unis,gtr GALLIARD 2.9051.1 $1.75   (S3212)

Faith, Folk, And Nativity *CCU,Xmas
unis,gtr GALLIARD 2.9052.1 $1.75   (S3213)

Father, We Praise Thee
SATB oct LORENZ C312 $.30   (S3214)

Go Tell It On The Mountains
SATB KJOS 1010 $.30   (S3215)

Goin' To Heaven Anyhow
SATB KJOS 1009 $.30   (S3216)

Good News
SATB KJOS 1005 $.30   (S3217)

Guide Me, O Thou Great Jehovah
SATB oct LORENZ C282 $.30   (S3218)

Happy Side Of Life, The *anthem
(Skillings) SATB oct LILLENAS AN-5030 $.30
(S3219)

He Never Said A Mumbalin' Word
SATB oct LORENZ A518 $.30   (S3220)

Hey, Manger Child *Xmas
SATB oct HERITAGE H81 $.35   (S3221)
SAB oct LORENZ 7412 $.30   (S3222)

Hosanna, Loud Hosanna *Easter
SATB oct LORENZ A488 $.30   (S3223)

How Beautiful Upon The Mountain
SATB ALLANS 60 s.p.   (S3224)

Hymn Of Praise *hymn
SATB oct LORENZ C291 $.30   (S3225)

I Sing Of The Glory Of The Lord
SAB oct LORENZ 7413 $.25   (S3226)
unis/SAB SOUTHERN $.25   (S3227)

I Stood By The River Of Jordan
SATB KJOS 5029 $.30   (S3228)

I Will Arise And Go To My Father
SATB FRANCIS s.p.   (S3229)

I Will Publish The Name Of The Lord
SATB oct PRO ART 2631 $.35   (S3230)

In Memoriam-Beryl Rubinstein
SATB oct HIGHLAND 7.0056.1 $.50   (S3231)

Is There Anybody Here?
SATB oct LORENZ B184 $.30   (S3232)

Just As I Am
SA/SAB oct LORENZ 7837 $.30   (S3233)
SATB oct LORENZ C329 $.30   (S3234)

King Of Glory, King Of Peace
SATB FRANCIS s.p.   (S3235)

Lift Up Your Hearts *see Sursum Corda

Lord Dismiss Us With Thy Blessing
(Pisano) SATB,opt kbd oct PRO ART 2561 $.25
(S3236)

Make A Joyful Noise
SATB oct LORENZ B175 $.30   (S3237)

Moment By Moment
SATB oct LORENZ A508 $.30   (S3238)

No Rose Of Such Vertu *Xmas
SSAA,acap (med) OXFORD 44.056 $.30 (S3239)

O Come, All Ye Faithful *Xmas
SATB oct LORENZ 9927 $.30   (S3240)

O Give Thanks
(Pisano) SATB,acap,opt pno oct PRO ART 2516
$.25   (S3241)

SMITH (cont'd.)

O Little Town Of Bethlehem *Xmas
SATB oct LORENZ A489 $.30   (S3242)

O Master, Let Me Walk With Thee *hymn
(Gerig) SATB oct LILLENAS AN-2339 $.30 (S3243)
(Wiley) SATB oct PRO ART 2476 $.30 (S3244)
(Winans) 2pt jr cor oct LILLENAS AN-4020
$.25   (S3245)

O Sing Unto The Lord A New Song
SATB oct LORENZ B169 $.30   (S3246)

Psalm 85 *anthem
mix cor oct OXFORD 42.350 $.65   (S3247)

Ride The Chariot
SATB KJOS 1015 $.30   (S3248)

Risen Christ, The *Easter
SATB oct LORENZ A500 $.30   (S3249)

Search Me, O God
SATB oct LORENZ B172 $.30   (S3250)

Sing We Noel Once More
SATB oct STAINER 3.2738.1 $.25   (S3251)
TTBB oct GALAXY 1.1581.1 $.25   (S3252)

Sursum Corda
(Darst) "Lift Up Your Hearts" [Lat/Eng]
SATB&desc oct PRO ART 1648 $.20   (S3253)

Take It To Jesus
SATB oct LORENZ A510 $.30   (S3254)

Take Time To Be Holy
SATB oct LORENZ B193 $.30   (S3255)

Under His Wings
SATB oct LORENZ B182 $.30   (S3256)

When I Need Him
(Skillings) SATB oct LILLENAS AN-1650 $.30
(S3257)

Worship The Lord In The Beauty Of Holiness
SATB oct LORENZ B198 $.30   (S3258)

Ye Gates Lift Up Your Heads
BOOSEY-CAN s.p.   (S3259)

Ye Servants Of God
SATB oct FISCHER,C CM-7355 $.25   (S3260)

SMITH, ALFRED M.
Blessed Jesus *anthem/Commun
(Darst, W.G.) SATB oct GRAY GCMR 3116 $.30
(S3261)

SMITH, BERNARD
Cradled In A Manger *Xmas
SA BOOSEY-CAN s.p.   (S3262)
SATB BOOSEY-CAN s.p.   (S3263)
SATB ENOCH EC327 s.p.   (S3264)
2pt ASHDOWN E.A.305 s.p.   (S3265)

SMITH, C.N.
Lamb
SSATB oct VOLKWEIN VB202 $.25   (S3266)

SMITH, DON
Let The Rafters Ring
SATB oct HERITAGE H54 $.45   (S3267)

Return, O Man
SATB oct SHAPIRO SK 2075 $.25   (S3268)

SMITH, ERIC
Love Came Down At Christmas
SA/TB oct BOOSEY 1889 $.30   (S3269)

SMITH, FRANK H. (1923-1958)
Ave Regina Caelorum
"O Most Blessed Spirit" [Lat/Eng] SSATB,
acap SCHIRM.EC 2430 $.40   (S3270)

Ego Ipse Consolabor Vos
"I Am He That Comforteth You" [Lat/Eng]
SATB,acap SCHIRM.EC 2448 $.35   (S3271)

I Am He That Comforteth You *see Ego Ipse
Consolabor Vos

O Most Blessed Spirit *see Ave Regina
Caelorum

SMITH, GREGG
Ave Maria
[Lat] 4pt mix cor&treb cor,bells,org/pno
oct SCHIRM.G 11817 $.50   (S3272)

Babel
4pt mix cor&5 speak cor,2pno oct SCHIRM.G
11793 $.60   (S3273)

Bible Songs For Young Voices *CCU,Bibl
1-3pt jr cor,pno voc sc SCHIRM.G $1.25
(S3274)

Lord Bless Thee And Keep Thee, The (from
Other Wiseman, The)
SA oct SCHIRM.G 11160 $.25   (S3275)

Set Me As A Seal
4pt mix cor,acap oct SCHIRM.G 11713 $.25
(S3276)

SMITH, H.
Love Lifted Me *see Rowe, J.

O Come And Mourn
SATB oct SOUTHERN $.30   (S3277)

O Saviour, Precious Saviour
SATB oct SOUTHERN $.30   (S3278)

Two Introits *CC2U,Introit
SATB oct SOUTHERN $.30   (S3279)

SMITH, H. HAMILTON
Easter Meditation Song *Easter,meditation
SATB,org,2trp oct WORLD CA-2136-8 $.60
(S3280)

SMITH, HENRY
Hear Us As We Pray *Bibl
4pt mix cor,acap oct SCHIRM.G 11004 $.30
(S3281)

SMITH, LANI
Day By Day *Gen,anthem
SATB (med easy) oct LORENZ B206 $.30
(S3282)

It's All About Love *folk
SATB,pno,opt bvl&drums&tamb&gtr LORENZ
$2.95
(S3283)

It's The Lord's Thing *Xmas,folk
cor,pno,gtr,opt bvl&drums voc sc LORENZ
$2.95
(S3284)

Jubilation *pop
SATB,4 soli,pno,opt gtr, opt rock inst
cmplt ed LORENZ $2.95
(S3285)

Men For The Crisis Hour *Gen/Refm,anthem
SATB (med easy) oct LORENZ B209 $.30
(S3286)

My Lord Is Like A Shepherd *Gen,anthem/folk
SATB oct LORENZ B204 $.30
(S3287)

O Love, How Deep *Gen,anthem
SATB (med diff) oct LORENZ C339 $.30
(S3288)

Service Of Shadows, A *Holywk
SATB SACRED $1.50
(S3289)

Spirit Of God *Gen/Pent,anthem
SATB (med easy) oct LORENZ B208 $.30
(S3290)

Vistor, The *Xmas/Gen,pop
SATB,pno,opt bvl&drums&gtr (med easy) voc
sc LORENZ $2.95
(S3291)

With All Who Love Thy Name, O Lord *Commun,
anthem
SATB/SA (easy) oct LORENZ A532 $.30 (S3292)

SMITH, NOEL (1923-   )
Great Mover Of All Hearts
mix cor LENGNICK s.p.
(S3293)

SMITH, NORMAN O.
Blessed Lord
SATB oct LESLIE 4048
(S3294)

SMITH, OLIVE [KENT] (1904-   )
Jesus In Bethlehem Is Born *Xmas,carol
unis CRAMER 11
(S3295)

SMITH, PAUL
Christ Is Born In Bethlehem *Xmas
SATB oct FISCHER,J 9717 $.30
(S3296)

Morning Of Christmas *Xmas
SATB oct STAFF 408 $.25
(S3297)

SMITH, PETER
When Christ Was Born
see FOUR CHRISTMAS CAROLS

SMITH, R.
Gloria
SATB,acap oct COLOMBO 2300 $.30
(S3298)

Service In G
SATB oct COLOMBO 2292 $.40
(S3299)

SMITH, R.A.
Earth Is The Lord's
cor oct HART s.p.
(S3300)

SMITH, TEDD
New Vibrations *folk
SATB,kbd,fl,2vln,vla,vcl,bvl,drums,2gtr voc
sc WORD 37508 $2.95, ipa
(S3301)

Praise Him *CCU
SATB oct AGAPE $1.50
(S3302)

Requiem For A Nobody *cant
SATB&jr cor,soli voc sc WORD 37537 $2.95
(S3303)

SMITH, WILLIAM
see SMYTH, WILLIAM

SMITH BOOK OF SPIRITUALS *CCU,spir
(Smith; Krones) SATB KJOS $1.25
(S3304)

SMOLANOFF, MICHAEL
Hear O Israel
SATB,B solo,pno/strings sc SEESAW $4.00
(S3305)

SMOLIN
Let's Say A Rosary Each Day *see Tanous

SMOLOVER, R.
Where The Rainbow Ends
(inter- faith rock ceremony) voc sc BELWIN
$2.00
(S3306)

SMYTH, WILLIAM (1603-1645)
Psalm 67 *Gen/Whitsun
SAATB,opt inst (med) oct OXFORD 43.398 $.50
(S3307)

Wedding Responses *Marriage
SAATB/SATB,acap (easy) oct OXFORD 43.386
$.20
(S3308)

SNART IBLAND DE HELGA SLAKTER see Nilsson,
Christian

SNOW
Blessed Are They
SATB oct BELWIN 64218 $.25
(S3309)

O My Father (composed with Mc Granahan)
(Gates) SATB oct MCA $.50
(S3310)

SNOW LAY ALL AROUND *Xmas
(Mueller) SATB oct FISCHER,C CM-6989 $.25
(S3311)

(Mueller) SSA oct FISCHER,C CM-6990 $.25
(S3312)

(Mueller) SAB oct FISCHER,C CM-7283 $.25
(S3313)

SNOW LAY ALL AROUND, THE see Mueller, Carl F.

SNOW LAY ON THE GROUND *Xmas
(Stone) SATB oct PRO ART 1758 $.35 (S3314)

SNOW LAY ON THE GROUND see Scull

SNOW LAY ON THE GROUND, THE see Ehret, Walter

SNOW LAY ON THE GROUND, THE see Gillam

SNOW LAY ON THE GROUND, THE see Hallstrom,
Henry

SNOW LAY ON THE GROUND, THE see Pasquet, Jean

SNOW LAY ON THE GROUND, THE see Venite Adoremus

SNOW LAY ON THE GROUND, THE see Young, Carlton
R.

SNOW, THE see Elgar, Edward

SNOWBOUND MOUNTAINS see Royse

SNOWFLAKES see Baber, Joseph

SNOWFLAKES see Barber, J.

SNOWY FLAKES ARE FALLING SOFTLY *Xmas,carol,
Pol
(Willan, H.) unis,kbd (easy) oct CONCORDIA
98-1090 $.25
(S3315)

SNYDER, J.
Bow Down Thine Ear
SATB,acap oct PRESSER 312-40214 $.30
(S3316)

Sing Noel *Xmas
SATB FLAMMER A 5237 $.30
(S3317)

This Christmastide *Xmas
SATB oct LORENZ A470 $.30
(S3318)

SO BLEST A SIGHT *Xmas,carol,Eng
(Shaw; Parker) 4pt mix cor,S solo oct
SCHIRM.G 10196 $.25
(S3319)

SO BLYSSID BE THE TYME see Terry, Richard
Runciman

SO DARK THE NIGHT see Emery, Dorothy R.

SO DU MIT DEINEM MUNDE see Dedekind,
Constantine Christian

SO FAHR ICH HIN see Schutz, Heinrich

SO FAHR ICH HIN see Schutz, Heinrich, So Fahr
Ich Hin Zu Jesus Christ

SO FAHR ICH HIN ZU JESU CHRIST see Schutz,
Heinrich

SO FAHR ICH HIN ZU JESUS CHRIST see Schutz,
Heinrich

SO FAR TO BETHLEHEM see Pooler

SO FEIERN WIR DAS HOHE FEST see Bach, Johann
Sebastian

SO GEHST DU NUN see Pillin, Boris

SO GIBST DU NUN, MEIN JESU, GUTE NACHT see
Bach, Johann Sebastian

SO GOD LOVED THE WORLD see Gibbons, Orlando

SO GREAT IS HIS LOVE see Mercer, M.

SO GREAT SALVATION see Roe, Gloria [Ann]

SO GREAT THE LIGHT see Beadell, Robert M.

SO HALTEN WIR NUN DAFUR see Hohlfeld, Christoph

SO IHR BLEIBEN WERDET see Stockmeier, Wolfgang

SO JEMAND MEIN WORT WIRD HALTEN see Vulpius,
Melchior

SO KEEP WE ALL THIS HOLY FEAST see Bach, Johann
Sebastian, So Feiern Wir Das Hohe Fest

SO KOMM DENN, HEILIGE NACHT see Gneist, Verner

SO LASSET UNS GEHEN IN SALEM see Bach, Johann
Sebastian

SO LEHR MICH DOCH see Schutz, Heinrich

SO LEHR MICH DOCH, DU TREUER GOTT see Schutz,
Heinrich

SO LET ME LIVE see Wyrtzen

SO LITTLE TIME see Benedict

SO LOWLY DOTH THE SAVIOR RIDE see Ream

SO LOWLY DOTH THE SAVIOUR RIDE see Lovelace,
Austin C.

SO MUST WE BEAR GUILT see Palestrina, Giovanni,
Patres Nostri Peccaverunt

SO MY HEART SEEKS EVER AFTER see Goudimel,
Claude, Ainsi Qu'on Oit Le Cerf Bruire

SO NEAR TO GOD AM I see Eville

SO NICHT WAR GEKOMMEN see Poos, Heinrich

SO NIMM DENN MEINE HANDE see Silcher, Friedrich

SO OFT IHR VON DIESEM BROT ESSET see Reda,
Siegfried

SO PRECIOUS IN THE SIGHT OF THE LORD see Roff,
Joseph

SO QUIETLY HE CAME see Dexter

SO REJOICE, GOOD CHRISTIAN PEOPLE! *carol,Ger
(Davies, L.H.) 2pt ASHDOWN E.A.311 s.p.
(S3320)

SO RUHEST DU, O IEINE RUH see Bach, Johann
Sebastian, O Traurigkeit, O Herzeleid

SO SEHET NUN ZU, WIE IHR VORSICHTIG WANDELT see
Reda, Siegfried

SO SEID IHR NUN NICHT MEHR GASTE UND FREMDLINGE
see Raphael, Gunther

SO SINGEN WIR ALL AMEN see Distler, Hugo

SO SINGEN WIR DEN WINTER AN see Bresgen, Cesar

SO SPAKE RABBI AKIBA see Weisgall, Hugo

SO SPRICHT DER HERR see Franz, Walter

SO SPRICHT GOTT DER HERR see Callhoff, Herbert

SO STARK DIE STURME WEHEN see Stier, Alfred

SO STEHT GESCHRIEBEN: MEIN HAUS IST EIN BETHUS
see Raselius, Andreas

SO TAKKAR MI SJEL see Nesse, Sigurd

SO VERY SMALL see Hallett, John C.

SO WAHR ICH LEB, SPRICHT GOTT DER HERR see
Cruger, Johann

SO WAHR ICH LEBE, SPRICHT DEIN see Anonymous

SO WIE DER HIRSCH see Handel, George Frideric,
As Pants The Hart

SO WIE DER HIRSCH NACH WASSER SCHREIT see
Handel, George Frideric, As Pants The Hart

SO WIE MOSES DIE SCHLANGE see Schutz, Heinrich,
Sicut Moses Serpentem In Deserto Exaltavit

SO WISSE TUN see Mendelssohn, Arnold

SO WUNSCH ICH EUCH EIN GUTE NACHT see Trubel,
Gerhard

SO ZIEHET NUN AN ALS DIE AUSERWAHLTEN see
Werner, Fritz

SOAVE FIA IL MORIR see Palestrina, Giovanni

SOCAL, PIETRO
Canticum Episcopale (Laudate Episcopum)
[It] unis,org ZANIBON 2705 s.p. (S3321)

SODERHOLM, VALDEMAR (1919-   )
Angelus Et Pastores Ait *mot
wom cor/jr cor,acap NORDISKA 4346 s.p.
(S3322)

Beati Qui Lugent
mix cor NORDISKA 3849 s.p.
(S3323)

Denne Jesus
mix cor NORDISKA 2564 s.p.
(S3324)

Domine, Ne In Furore Tuo Arguas Me
mix cor NORDISKA 3848 s.p.
(S3325)

Ett Har Jag Begart Av Herren
mix cor NORDISKA 3286 s.p.
(S3326)

Herre, Ga Ej Till Doms Med Din Tjanare
mix cor NORDISKA 3510 s.p.
(S3327)

I Nodtider
mix cor NORDISKA 4244 s.p.
(S3328)

Jesu, Lar Mig Ratt Betanka
mix cor NORDISKA 3360 s.p.
(S3329)

Jesu Namm Begynna Skall
(Ahlen, Waldemar) 3pt wom cor/3pt jr cor,
acap NORDISKA 4110 s.p.
(S3330)

Kyrkokantat Nr. 5
cor pts NORDISKA 4225 s.p., voc sc NORDISKA
s.p.
(S3331)

Lat Oss Nu Jesu Prisa
(Ahlen, Waldemar) 2pt wom cor/2pt jr cor,
acap NORDISKA 4065 s.p.
(S3332)
(Ahlen, Waldemar) 2pt wom cor/2pt jr cor,
pno,inst NORDISKA 4064 s.p.
(S3333)

Loven Herren, I Hans Anglar
mix cor NORDISKA 4036 s.p.
(S3334)

Massa
wom cor/jr cor NORDISKA 5192 s.p. (S3335)

Memento Nostri, Domine
mix cor NORDISKA 3850 s.p.
(S3336)

Nar Juldagsmorgen Glimmar
wom cor NORDISKA 3724 s.p.
(S3337)

Non Nobis, Domine
mix cor NORDISKA 3613 s.p.
(S3338)

O Gud, Det Ar En Hjartans Trost
mix cor NORDISKA 2093 s.p.
(S3339)

O Huru Ljuvlig Ar Din Boning, Herre Kar
mix cor NORDISKA 3864 s.p.
(S3340)

Pingsthymn
mix cor NORDISKA 4035 s.p.
(S3341)

Saliga Aro De Doda
mix cor NORDISKA 3441 s.p.
(S3342)

Sanctus
3pt wom cor/3pt jr cor,acap NORDISKA 4521
s.p.
(S3343)

SODERLUNDH, LILLE BROV
Herre, Lar Mig Betanka
3pt mix cor NORDISKA 5321 s.p. (S3344)

SODERMAN
Oft I Think When I Read That Sweet Story Of
Old
(Lundquist) SATB,acap (med) oct WILLIS 8474
$.20
(S3345)

SODERMAN, (JOHAN) AUGUST (1832-1876)
Benediction (from Prayers Of Innocence) Bene
(Johnson; Rodby) SATB,acap oct LAWSON 51535
$.30
(S3346)

Hosanna In Excelsis *Sanctus
"Hosanna In The Highest" SATB oct WALTON
2014 $.30
(S3347)

Hosanna In The Highest *see Hosanna In
Excelsis

SODERMAN, (JOHAN) AUGUST (cont'd.)

I Manans Skimmer
(Alfven, Hugo) [Swed] SATB,acap GEHRMANS
KRB 242A   (S3348)

Kyrie Eleison *Kyrie
SATB oct WALTON 2105 $.25   (S3349)

To The Blessed Virgin (from Prayers Of
Innocence)
(Johnson; Rodby) SATB,S solo,acap oct
LAWSON 51534 $.30   (S3350)

To The Father (from Prayers Of Innocence)
(Johnson; Rodby) SATB,acap oct LAWSON 51531
$.25   (S3351)

To The Holy Spirit (from Prayers Of
Innocence)
(Johnson; Rodby) SATB,acap oct LAWSON 51533
$.30   (S3352)

To The Son (from Prayers Of Innocence)
(Johnson; Rodby) SATB,acap oct LAWSON 51532
$.30   (S3353)

SODERSTEN, GUNNO
O, Gud, Det Ar Min Gladje
unis,org/pno/strings NORDISKA 5256 s.p.   (S3354)

SODERSTROM
O Holy Savior
SATB oct WORD CS-2348 $.25   (S3355)

SOE WEE MAY SING see Lockwood, Normand

SOECHTIG
Song That The Angels Sang, The *Xmas
SAB oct LORENZ 7304 $.30   (S3356)

SOEGIJO, PAUL GUTAMA
Deus, Deus Meus
[Lat] mix cor voc sc BOTE s.p.   (S3357)

SOEHNER, L.
Missa Brevis *Mass
[Lat] SA,org SCHOTT voc sc s.p., cor pts
s.p.   (S3358)

SOERENSEN
Blessed Are All They *Easter,Morav
(Dickinson) SATB oct GRAY GMCM 16 $.30   (S3359)

SOFT FLOATING ON THE EVENING AIR see Root, G.F.

SOFT WERE YOUR HANDS, DEAR JESUS see O'Hara,
Geoffrey

SOFTLY AND TENDERLY see Thompson, W.

SOFTLY AND TENDERLY see Thompson, Will
Lamaritne

SOFTLY SLEEP, JESUS
see Three Christmas Carols

SOFTLY, SOFTLY FELL THE SNOW see Anderson

SOFTLY THE DAWN AWAKENS see Livingstone

SOFTLY THE NIGHT *Xmas,carol,It
(Kirk, Theron) SATB oct AGAPE A 448 $.35   (S3360)

SOFTLY THE NIGHT IS SLEEPING see Mueller, Carl
F.

SOFTLY THE WINDS BLEW *Xmas
(Coggin) SAB oct PRO ART 2729 $.30   (S3361)

SOHR, PETER
Bis Hierher Hat Mich Gott Gebracht
(Berger, H.L.) TTBB HANSSLER 6.5064 s.p.
contains also: Gesius, Bartholomaus, Du
Friedefurst, Herr Jesu Christ   (S3362)

SOHREN, P.
Lof Zij Den Heer
wom cor sc ALSBACH&D s.p.   (S3363)

SOK FORST GUDS RIKE see Hovland, Egil

SOKOLOV, NIKOLAI ALEXANDROVITCH (1859-1922)
Short Communion Service
SSA,acap SCHIRM.EC 1276   (S3364)
TTB,acap SCHIRM.EC 1276   (S3365)

SOLBERG LIEF
Bonn
mix cor MUSIKK 31 s.p.   (S3366)

Kyrie Eleison *Kyrie
mix cor MUSIKK 68 s.p.   (S3367)

Meditasjon
cor,soli,orch cor pts MUSIKK 147 ipr   (S3368)

SOLCHES HABE ICH ZU EUCH GEREDT see Raselius,
Andreas

SOLCHES HABE ICH MIT EUCH GEREDET see Jacot,
Andre

SOLDIER OF CHRIST, ARISE! see Warner, Richard

SOLDIERS OF CHRIST, ARISE see Lewis, John Leo

SOLDIERS OF CHRIST, ARISE see Price, Benton

SOLDIERS OF CHRIST, ARISE! see Warner, Richard

SOLDIERS OF IMMANUEL see Lillenas, Haldor

SOLEIL COUCHANT see Bach, Johann Sebastian

SOLEM, EDVIN
Kyrie *Kyrie
mix cor NORDISKA 1798 s.p.   (S3369)

SOLEMN MASS see Franck, Cesar

SOLEMN MASS, A see Thordarson, Sigurdur

SOLEMN MASS, F MINOR see White, John

SOLEMN MASS IN A see Franck, Cesar

SOLID ROCK, THE see Bradbury, William
Batchelder

SOLID ROCK, THE see McCluskey

SOLITARY CITY, THE see Christiansen, Paul

SOLLT ICH MEINEM GOTT NICHT SINGEN see Bach,
Johann Sebastian

SOLLT ICH MEINEM GOTT NICHT SINGEN see Fiebig,
Kurt

SOLLT ICH MEINEM GOTT NICHT SINGEN see Kendel,
Adolf

SOLLT ICH MEINEM GOTT NICHT SINGEN see Koch,
Johannes H.E.

SOLLT ICH MEINEM GOTT NICHT SINGEN see
Schumann, Georg

SOLLT ICH MEINEM GOTT NICHT SINGEN see Woehl,
Waldemar

SOLLTE ABER GOTT NICHT AUCH RETTEN see Werner,
Fritz

SOLNEDGANG see Conradi, J.G.

SOLOMIN
Lord's Prayer
(Tellep) SATB,acap oct BOOSEY 5095 $.30   (S3370)

SOLOMON see Handel, George Frideric

SOLOMON REIGNED IN DAYS OF PEACE see Pinkham,
Daniel

SOLOMON'S GARDEN see Sowerby, Leo

SOLTER, HEINZ
Allein Zu Dir Herr Jesu Christ
see Tzschoppe, Eberhart, Ach, Wie Fluchtig,
Ach Wie Nichtig

Wenn Mein Stundlein Vorhanden Ist
see Tzschoppe, Eberhart, Ach, Wie Fluchtig,
Ach Wie Nichtig

SOLUS AD VICTIMAM see Joubert, John

SOLVEJG'S SONG see Grieg, Edvard Hagerup

SOM ET STILLE OFFERLAM see Foss, Julius

SOM SOL OM VAREN STIGER *Bibl
(Hallnas, Hilding) [Swed] SATB,acap GEHRMANS
KRB 197   (S3371)

SOMACHTI BEOMRIM see Halevy, [Jacques-Francois-
Fromental-Elie]

SOMARY, J.
How Lovely Is Thy Dwelling Place (Psalm 84)
Gen,anthem
SATB (med) oct GIA G1615 $.30   (S3372)

Let All Mortal Flesh Keep Silence *Gen,
anthem
SATB (med) oct GIA G1614 $.40   (S3373)

Psalm 84 *see How Lovely Is Thy Dwelling
Place

SOME CHILDREN SEE HIM see Burt, Alfred

SOME GLORIOUS WAY see Furman, James

SOME GOLDEN DAYBREAK see Blackmore

SOME OF THESE MORNIN'S *spir
(Stanton, R.) SAB oct PRESSER 312-40454 $.30
                                             (S3374)
SOME OF THESE MORNIN'S see Stanton, Royal [W.]

SOME TRUST IN CHARIOTS see Kirby

SOMEBODY BIGGER THAN YOU AND I *anthem
SSA/SATB/SAB/SA/TB/TTBB BIG3 $.25   (S3375)

SOMEBODY DIED FOR YOU see Paris

SOMEBODY TALKIN' 'BOUT JESUS
(Ehret) SSA oct AGAPE CF 116 $.35   (S3376)
(Ehret) SATB oct AGAPE CF 117 $.30   (S3377)

SOMEBODY TELL ME see Owens, Jimmy

SOMEBODY TOUCHED ME *folk/spir
(Johnson) SATB oct LILLENAS AN-5001 $.25   (S3378)
(Sutherland) SATB SCHMITT 921 $.35   (S3379)

SOMEBODY'S KNOCKIN' *spir
(Holloway) SA oct SPRATT 212 $.25   (S3380)

SOMEBODY'S KNOCKIN' AT YOUR DOOR *spir
(Barthelson) 3pt mix cor oct LAWSON 51727
$.30   (S3381)
(Barthelson) SATB oct LAWSON 51338 $.30   (S3382)
(Schubert) SB oct LILLENAS AN-3809 $.30   (S3383)

SOMEBODY'S KNOCKING *spir
see Eight Negro Spirituals: Book I
(Durian, Tim) 4pt men cor,acapl BREITKOPF-W
Z-44 s.p. see also Dreizehn Negro-
Spirituals   (S3384)

SOMEBODY'S KNOCKING AT YOUR DOOR see Wilson

SOMEDAY
see Great Choral Series

SOMEONE see Hughes

SOMEONE, SOMEWHERE see Pallock

SOMERS, HARRY STEWART (1925-   )
Gloria *Fest/Thanks
SATB,opt 2trp (med) oct OXFORD 42.881 $.40,
ipr   (S3385)

God The Master Of This Scene *Ded/Marriage
SATB (diff) oct OXFORD 43.381 $.30   (S3386)

SOMERS, HARRY STEWART (cont'd.)

Vexilla Regis
[Lat/Eng] SATB oct KERBY 7678 $.45   (S3387)

SOMERSET CAROL see Monaco, Richard A.

SOMERSET, H.
There Is A Green Hill *Psntd,anthem
mix cor oct NOVELLO 40.0445.00 s.p.   (S3388)

SOMERVELL, ARTHUR (1863-1937)
Passion Of Christ, The
mix cor,SATB soli,org/pno/strings BOOSEY
voc sc $2.00, cor pts $.75, sc rental,
ipr   (S3389)

Shepherd's Cradle Song *Xmas,cradle
3pt ASHDOWN V.T.30 s.p.   (S3390)
2pt ASHDOWN E.A.108 s.p.   (S3391)
SA BOOSEY-CAN s.p.   (S3392)

Te Deum *Te Deum
SATB (F maj) oct NOVELLO 44.0388.06 s.p.   (S3393)

SOMETHING FOR THEE see Richolson

SOMETIMES I CATCH SWEET GLIMPSES see Gounod,
Charles Francois, Cor Jesu

SOMETIMES I FEEL *spir
(Parker) TTBB,Bar solo,acap oct LAWSON 51629
$.35   (S3394)
(Shaw; Parker) SATB,A solo,acap oct LAWSON
51112 $.35   (S3395)

SOMETIMES I FEEL LIKE A MOTHERLESS CHILD *spir
SATB CHAPPELL 0022947-358 $.40   (S3396)
SATB oct STAFF 264 $.25   (S3397)
(De Cormier) SATB,SA soli oct LAWSON 51479
$.30   (S3398)
(De Cormier) 2pt boy cor/SA,S solo oct LAWSON
51480 $.30   (S3399)
(Ehret) SA oct SPRATT 163 $.25   (S3400)
(Ehret) SSA oct SPRATT 128 $.25   (S3401)
(Ehret) SAB oct SPRATT 162 $.25   (S3402)
(Ehret) SATB oct SPRATT 116 $.25   (S3403)
(Heath) 4pt men cor oct SCHIRM.G 10567 $.30 (S3404)
(Labach, P.) TTBB oct PRESSER MC176 $.30
                                             (S3405)
(Papale, Henry) SATB&opt SSA/3pt jr cor,T/S
solo,acap oct WORLD ESE-778-8 $.45   (S3406)
(Schroth) SATB KJOS 5375 $.30   (S3407)
(Smith) SATB KJOS 1013 $.30   (S3408)
(Smith) men cor KJOS 1113 $.30   (S3409)

SOMETIMES I FEEL LIKE A MOTHERLESS CHILD see
Brown, William [H., Jr.]

SOMETIMES I FEEL LIKE A MOTHERLESS CHILD see
Burnham

SOMETIMES I FEEL LIKE A MOTHERLESS CHILE *spir
(Swift) SATB oct PRO ART 1266 $.20   (S3410)

SOMEWHERE AROUND A THRONE
(Lynn, G.) SATB,acap oct PRESSER 312-40354
$.30   (S3411)

SOMMA
Due Canti Per Bambini
4 eq voices,acap RICORDI-ENG 128892 s.p.
contains: La Preghiera Dell' Anno
Mariano; L'Ave Maria   (S3412)

Due Cori Franescani *CC2U
4pt RICORDI-ENG 129743 s.p.   (S3413)

Fila, Fila Lunga
see Tre Canti Per Bambini

La Preghiera Dell' Anno Mariano
see Due Canti Per Bambini

L'Ave Maria
see Due Canti Per Bambini

Santa Chiara, Nova Stella
see Tre Canti Per Bambini

Tre Canti Per Bambini *sac/sec
4 eq voices,acap RICORDI-ENG 128893 s.p.
contains: Fila, Fila Lunga; Santa Chiara,
Nova Stella; Vieni, Vieni, Gesu Bambino   (S3414)

Vieni, Vieni, Gesu Bambino
see Tre Canti Per Bambini

SOMMA, BONAVENTURA
Cantico Del Sole
TTBarB,orch SANTIS 751 s.p., ipr   (S3415)
cor,pno voc sc SANTIS 752 $.20   (S3416)
TTBarB,orch cor pts SANTIS 753A-B s.p.   (S3417)

Missa In Honorem Sanctae Mariae Visitationis
Pauperum *Mass
3pt mix cor,opt org sc SANTIS 636 s.p., cor
pts SANTIS 637 s.p.   (S3418)

Missa Pro Defunctis Cum Sequentia *Mass
5pt&6pt&8pt sc SANTIS 608 s.p., cor pts
SANTIS 608A-B s.p.   (S3419)

SOMMAR I BERGEN see Boldemann, Laci

SOMMARNATTSPALM see Olson, Daniel

SOMMARPSALM (EN VANLIG GRONSKAS RIKA DRAKT) see
Gastorius, Severius

SOMMER, VLADIMIR (1921-   )
Herr, Unser Herrscher *mot
(Wagner, Hermann) 4pt mix cor&4pt mix cor&
4pt mix cor MOSELER s.p.   (S3420)

SOMMERLIED see Weismann, Wilhelm

SON IS BORN, A, FIVE CAROLS TO OLD ENGLISH
TEXTS see Edmunds, John

SON IS BORN OF MARY, A see Wetzler, Robert

SON OF A CARPENTER see White, Phil

SON OF DAVID see Elaine, Sister M. (Gentemann)

SON OF GOD see Cannon, Philip

SON OF GOD see Haydn, (Johann) Michael

SON OF GOD ARISEN TODAY see Fraser

SON OF GOD, ETERNAL SAVIOR see Blake

SON OF GOD, ETERNAL SAVIOUR
(Kirk) SATB, opt S solo oct PRO ART 1605 $.18
(S3421)

SON OF GOD GOES FORTH, THE see Ringwald, [Roy]

SON OF GOD GOES FORTH TO WAR, THE see Sullivan,
Sir Arthur Seymour

SON OF GOD HAS BEEN BORN, THE see Santa Cruz,
Domingo, El Nino Divino Nace

SON OF GOD IS COME TO EARTH, THE see Brahms,
Johannes, Es Ist Das Heil Uns Kommen Her

SON OF GOD, THE see Wilson, John F.

SON OF LAN nee Nichols

SON OF MAN, THE *cant
(McKinney, Howard D.) mix cor BELWIN $1.50
(S3422)

SON OF MARY see Raymond, Joseph

SON OF MARY, THE *Xmas,carol,Span
(Ehret, Walter) SATB, opt inst oct WALTON 2506
$.30
(S3423)

SON TRE MESI see Noble, Felix de

SON, WHY HAVE YOU TREATED US SO? see Bender,
Jan

SONDAG MORGEN FRA DE DODE see Laub, Thomas

SONG-A-LOG *CC70UL
(Fisher, Douglas R.) SATB voc sc WORD 15038
$1.25
(S3424)

SONG AGAINST BORES, A see Kraehenbuehl, D.

SONG AND A PRAYER, A see Carrington

SONG ANTHEMS see Cain, Noble

SONG FOR CHRISTMAS see Van Dyke, May

SONG FOR CHRISTMAS, A see Wilson

SONG FOR CHRISTMAS DAY, A see Gass, Irene

SONG FOR DANIEL, A see Davis, Allan

SONG FOR EASTER see Eichorn, Hermene Warlick

SONG FOR PEACE see Davis, Katherine K.

SONG FOR THE JUNIOR SCHOOL see Browne

SONG FOR THE NATION, A see Mc Grath, Malcolm

SONG FOR THE NEW YEAR, A see Martin

SONG FROM ST. MATTHEW see Kettering, Eunice Lea

SONG IN THE AIR, A see McAfee, Don

SONG IN THE AIR, THE see Lorenz

SONG IN THE NIGHT see Hawkins, Floyd W.

SONG IN THE SILENT NIGHT, A *medley
(Rogers) 2pt jr cor/3pt jr cor oct LILLENAS
AN-4017 $.30
(S3425)

SONG IS NOT A SONG, A see Landgrave, Phillip

SONG OF ADORATION see Luvaas

SONG OF AN INDIAN CHILD see Lynn, George

SONG OF ANGELS, A see Redman, Reginald

SONG OF ANGELS, A see Redman, Reginald

SONG OF BENEDICTION see Forcucci, S.L.

SONG OF BETHLEHEM see Bampton, R.

SONG OF BETHLEHEM see Mueller, Carl F.

SONG OF BETHLEHEM, A see Emig, Lois

SONG OF BROTHERHOOD see Mozart, Wolfgang
Amadeus

SONG OF CAPTIVITY see Alexander, Josef

SONG OF CHRIST, A see Lovelace, Austin C.

SONG OF CHRISTMAS see Fuller, [Esther Mary]

SONG OF CHRISTMAS, A see Grieg, Edvard Hagerup

SONG OF CHRISTMAS, THE see Ringwald, [Roy]

SONG OF COMFORT, A see Mechem, Kirke

SONG OF DANIEL see Butler

SONG OF DANIEL see Peloquin, C. Alexander

SONG OF DAVID see Guttman, Oskar

SONG OF DAVID see Yancey

SONG OF DAVID, THE *Bibl/cant
mix cor CHAPPELL 0016873-369 $1.00 (S3426)

SONG OF DAVID, THE see Guenther

SONG OF DAVID, THE see Yancey

SONG OF DEBORAH *Bibl/cant
mix cor, SBar soli CHAPPELL 0016881-369 $1.95
(S3427)

SONG OF DEBORAH AND BARAK see Greene, Maurice

SONG OF DECEMBER see Shaw, Martin

SONG OF DELIVERANCE see James

SONG OF DELIVERANCE see McCormick

SONG OF DELIVERANCE see MacMillan, [Ernest]

SONG OF DELIVERANCE, A see McCormick

SONG OF DESTINY see Brahms, Johannes

SONG OF DUTY
(Barnes, E.S.) 2pt wom cor (easy) oct WILLIS
6125 $.12
(S3428)

SONG OF EASTER see Rasley

SONG OF EASTER see Wilson

SONG OF EASTER, THE see Ringwald, [Roy]

SONG OF EXALTATION, A see Adler, Samuel

SONG OF EXHALTATION see Beck, John Ness

SONG OF FAITH see Kodaly, Zoltan

SONG OF FATE, THE see Brahms, Johannes,
Schicksalslied

SONG OF GOD, THE see Rasley

SONG OF GRATITUDE AND PRAISE see Hokanson,
Margrethe

SONG OF HANUKKAH, A see Adler, Samuel

SONG OF HOLIDAY, A see Slater, David D.

SONG OF HOPE see Goemanne, Noel

SONG OF HOPE see Krones

SONG OF JEPHTHAH'S DAUGHTER, THE see Pinkham,
Daniel

SONG OF JESUS see Williams

SONG OF JESUS, A see Vaughan Williams, Ralph

SONG OF JOY see Wolford, Julie L.

SONG OF JUDEA see Clark

SONG OF KOHELETH, THE see Harris, A.

SONG OF LOYAL BROTHERHOOD see Mozart, Wolfgang
Amadeus

SONG OF MARIA MAGDALENA see Lied Van Maria
Magdalena

SONG OF MARY see Beard

SONG OF MARY see Brandon, George

SONG OF MARY see Christiansen, F. Melius

SONG OF MARY see Friedell, Harold W.

SONG OF MARY, THE see Fisher

SONG OF MARY, THE see Fisher

SONG OF MARY, THE see Fisher, C.A.

SONG OF MARY, THE see Kern

SONG OF MIRIAM, THE see Schubert, Franz
(Peter), Miriams Siegesgesang

SONG OF MOSES, THE see Ettinger, Max, Das Lied
Von Moses

SONG OF MOSES, THE see Mechem, Kirke

SONG OF OUR SAVIOUR see Perry

SONG OF PEACE see Christiansen, Olaf Christian

SONG OF PEACE see Kalmanoff, [Martin]

SONG OF PEACE, A see Sibelius, Jean

SONG OF PEACE, A see Wood

SONG OF PENITENCE see Beethoven, Ludwig van

SONG OF PRAISE
see Two Songs Of Praise

SONG OF PRAISE see Arnold

SONG OF PRAISE see Caldwell, Mary [Elizabeth]

SONG OF PRAISE see Darst, W. Glenn

SONG OF PRAISE see Goemanne, Noel

SONG OF PRAISE see Johnston

SONG OF PRAISE see Marsh

SONG OF PRAISE see Robertson, Leroy

SONG OF PRAISE see Schubert, Franz (Peter)

SONG OF PRAISE see Schutz, Heinrich

SONG OF PRAISE see Williams, Donald O.

SONG OF PRAISE, A see Pierne, Gabriel

SONG OF PRAISE, A see Gulbins

SONG OF PRAISE, A see Jewell

SONG OF PRAISE, A see Mechem, Kirke

SONG OF PRAISE, A see Schroth, Gerhard

SONG OF PRAYER see Robertson, Leroy

SONG OF REJOICING, A see Candlyn, T. Frederick
H.

SONG OF REPENTANCE see Bach, Johann Sebastian

SONG OF RUTH see Merryman

SONG OF SIMEON see Arnold

SONG OF SIMEON see Christiansen, Olaf Christian

SONG OF SIMEON see Luke

SONG OF SIMEON see Schroth

SONG OF SIMEON, THE see Grime

SONG OF SIMEON, THE see Grime, G.

SONG OF SOLOMON, A see Moss, L.

SONG OF SONGS, THE see Van Lier, Bertus

SONG OF THANKFULNESS see Schneider, Kent

SONG OF THANKSGIVING see Allitsen

SONG OF THANKSGIVING see Maunder, J.H.

SONG OF THANKSGIVING, A see Richolson

SONG OF THANKSGIVING, A see Roff, Joseph

SONG OF THANKSGIVING, A see Vaughan Williams,
Ralph

SONG OF THANSGIVING see Vaughan Williams,
Ralph, Thanksgiving For Victory

SONG OF THE ANGEL
see Three Mennonite Christmas Hymns

SONG OF THE ANGELS see Denton

SONG OF THE ANGELS see Vidal, Paul, Chanson Des
Anges

SONG OF THE ANGELS, THE see Hughes

SONG OF THE ANGELS, THE see Thompson

SONG OF THE BIBLE
SSA/SATB BIG3 $.30 (S3429)

SONG OF THE BIRDS, THE *folk, Span
(Millet) 4pt men cor, high solo, acap oct
SCHIRM.G 7651 $.20 (S3430)
(Millet) 4pt men cor, high solo, acap oct
SCHIRM.G 7651 $.20 (S3431)

SONG OF THE BIRTH OF OUR LORD JESUS CHRIST see
Charpentier, Marc-Antoine, In Nativitatem
Domini Nostri Jesu Christi Canticum

SONG OF THE CREATURES see Dungan, O.

SONG OF THE CREATURES see Mc Kay, G.

SONG OF THE CRIB *Xmas, anthem/carol/folk, Ger
unis (easy) OXFORD 08.077 $.15 (S3432)
(Candlyn) SATB oct FISCHER,C CM-6748 $.25
(S3433)
(Christiansen, Paul) SATB (easy) oct AUGSBURG
1102 $.22 (S3434)

SONG OF THE CRIB see Candlyn, T. Frederick H.

SONG OF THE CRIB, THE see Hesford, Brian

SONG OF THE CRIB, THE see Hullah, John [Pyke]

SONG OF THE DOVE see Chappell

SONG OF THE DOVE see Chappell, Herbert

SONG OF THE FATHERS, THE see Meek, Kenneth

SONG OF THE GARO CHRISTIANS
(Cain) 4pt mix cor, B solo, acap oct SCHIRM.G
10891 $.30 (S3435)

SONG OF THE GARO CHRISTIANS see Cain, Noble

SONG OF THE GYPSY GIRLS see Verdi, Giuseppe

SONG OF THE HARBOR see Shir Namal

SONG OF THE HOLY NIGHT see Wilson

SONG OF THE KING see Webber, Andrew

SONG OF THE LAMB, THE see Horton

SONG OF THE LITTLE LAMB see Frank

SONG OF THE NUNS OF CHESTER (from Anthology Of
Carols, An)
see Immortal Babe

SONG OF THE PASSION see Oldroyd, George

SONG OF THE REAPERS see Kieserling, Richard

SONG OF THE RESURRECTION see Wilson

SONG OF THE RIGHTEOUS, THE see Beck, Audrey D.

SONG OF THE SHEPHERD BOY see Hughes

SONG OF THE SHEPHERDS see McAfee, Don

SONG OF THE SHIP see McLaughlin, Marian

SONG OF THE SOUL see Rubbra, Edmund

SONG OF THE SOUL SET FREE, THE see Ackley

SONG OF THE SPIRIT see Sanders

SONG OF THE TREE OF LIFE see Vaughan Williams,
Ralph

SONG OF THE VIRGIN
see Three Mennonite Christmas Hymns

SONG OF THE WISE, A see Kosakoff, Reuven

SONG OF THE WOMEN see Britten, Benjamin

SONG OF TRIUMPH see Bock, Fred

SONG OF TRIUMPH, A see Bitgood, Roberta

SONG OF TRIUMPH, THE see Rogers

SONG OF WORSHIP, A see Gibbs, [Cecil] Armstrong

SONG OF ZACHARY see Peloquin, C. Alexander

SONG ON CHRISTMAS NIGHT, A see Monhardt, Maurice

SONG OR PRAISE see Lipscomb, Helen

SONG OVER TH WORLD *Xmas/Pageant
LORENZ $.75 (S3436)

SONG THAT THE ANGELS SANG, THE see Soechtig

SONG TO SING, A see Biggs, John

SONG TO THE LAMB, A see Hancock, G.

SONGARBON see Aamodt, Valter

SONGER
Great Art Thou, O Lord
SSA FLAMMER B 5116 $.25 (S3437)

Prayer With Psalm *prayer/Psalm
girl cor SOUTHERN $.25 (S3438)

SONGS AND HYMNS FOR THE JUNIOR CHOIR *CC20L
(Ganschow, T.; Ganschow, L.L.) SA/SSA (easy)
voc sc WILLIS $.75 (S3439)

SONGS AND HYMNS FOR TREBLE VOICES see Malmin, Dorothy

SONGS AT THE STABLE
see Three Mennonite Christmas Hymns

SONGS, CANTATAS, AND CANONS see Schubert, Franz (Peter)

SONGS FOR CHILDREN'S WORSHIP *CCU
jr cor LORENZ $1.00 (S3440)

SONGS FOR FEMALE VOICES see Brahms, Johannes

SONGS FOR LITURGY *CCU,liturg
cor/cong,inst oct WALTON $6.95 (S3441)

SONGS FOR PRE-TEEN TIME see Cooper, Irvin

SONGS FOR THE ADVENT AND CHRISTMAS SEASONS see Bach, Johann Sebastian

SONGS FOR THE LENTEN AND EASTER SEASONS see Bach, Johann Sebastian

SONGS FOR TODAY *CC47U,folk/spir
(Ylvisaker, John) oct AUGSBURG 32-999 $.50 (S3442)

SONGS FROM LUKE see Bristol, L.

SONGS FROM LUKE see Bristol, Lee H., Jr.

SONGS FROM MATTHEW see Bristol, L.

SONGS FROM MATTHEW see Bristol, Lee H., Jr.

SONGS FROM THE BOOK OF REVELATION see Goemanne, Noel

SONGS OF BETHLEHEM see Offer

SONGS OF BROTHERHOOD see Kearney

SONGS OF CHRISTMAS *Xmas,medley
(Smith) SAB/SATB oct LILLENAS AT-C104 $.30 (S3443)

SONGS OF DEDICATION *CCU,Ded
SATB oct LILLENAS AT-1031 $.35 (S3444)

SONGS OF DELIVERANCE see Dvorak, R.

SONGS OF DEVOTION oee Malmin, Dorothy

SONGS OF FAITH *Gen,hymn/medley
(Scott, James, A.) SATB,band oct RUBANK
2179-PL $.20, oct (S3445)

SONGS OF GLADNESS see Grant, Louise

SONGS OF IMMORTAL PRAISE see Kirk, Theron W.

SONGS OF ISRAEL see Peloquin, C. Alexander

SONGS OF ISRAELI CHILDREN, PART ONE see Fleisher, Simi

SONGS OF ISRAELI CHILDREN, PART TWO see Fleisher, Simi

SONGS OF JESUS *Xmas
(Nelson) SATB SCHMITT 8057 $.35 (S3446)

SONGS OF JOY TO HEAVEN RAISE see Gallus, Jacobus, Resonet In Laudibus

SONGS OF LIVING FAITH see Ashton, Bob

SONGS OF LIVING HOPE see Ashton, Bob

SONGS OF PEACEFUL DEPARTURE see Pinkham, Daniel

SONGS OF PEACEFUL DEPARTURE see Pinkham, Daniel

SONGS OF PRAISE see Beveridge, Thomas G.

SONGS OF PRAISE THE ANGELES SING see Lundquist

SONGS OF PRAISE THE ANGELS SANG see Attwood, Thomas

SONGS OF PRAISE THE ANGELS SANG see Eldridge, Guy H.

SONGS OF PRAISE THE ANGELS SANG see Fiske, Milton

SONGS OF PRAISE THE ANGELS SANG see Pasquet, Jean

SONGS OF PRAISE THE ANGELS SANG see Thiman, Eric Harding

SONGS OF PRAISE THE ANGELS SANG see Wiley

SONGS OF PRAISE THE ANGELS SANG see Wolff

SONGS OF PRAISE, VOL. 1 see Ehret, Walter

SONGS OF PRAISE, VOL. 2 see Ehret, Walter

SONGS OF PRAISE see Dallin

SONGS OF PRAISE see Revicki

SONGS OF PRAISES see Hughes, John

SONGS OF SOLEMN JOY see Brandon, George

SONGS OF THE NATIVITY see La Montaine, John

SONGS OF THE SINGING NUN see Sourire, Souer

SONGS OF THE SOUL see Surinach, Carlos

SONGS OF WISDOM see Mechem, Kirke

SONGS OF WISDOM see Mechem, Kirke

SONGS OF WORSHIP *CC21L,Gen
(Fuller) unis/SA/SAB PRO ART 83 $.85 (S3447)

SONGS ON WORSHIP see Sanders, Faith

SONGS ON ENGLISH MEDIEVAL TEXTS see Sveinsson, Gunnar Reynir

SONGS TO LIVE BY *CCUL
(Carmichael, Ralph) SATB voc sc WORD 30057
$1.95 (S3448)

SONNE DER GERECHTIGKEIT see Berger, Hans Ludwig

SONNE DER GERECHTIGKEIT see Doppelbauer, Josef Friedrich

SONNE DER GERECHTIGKEIT see Horn, Paul

SONNE DER GERECHTIGKEIT see Kretzschmar, Gunther

SONNE DER GERECHTIGKEIT see Schilling, Hans Ludwig

SONNE DER GERECHTIGKEIT see Schwartz, Gerhard von

SONNE DER GERECHTIGKEIT, GEHE AUF see Berger, Hans Ludwig

SONNE DER GERECHTIGKEIT , GEHE AUF see Koch, Heinz

SONNE DER GERECHTIGKEIT, GEHE AUF see Trubel, Gerhard

SONNENGESANG DES HEILIGEN FRANZISKUS: INCIPIUNT LAUDES CREATURARUM see Orff, Carl

SONNET see Williamson, Malcolm

SONNET FOR CHRISTMAS, A see Noble, Whitney

SONNET (ON HEARING THE DIES IRAE SUNG IN THE SISTINE CHAPEL) see Williamson, Malcolm

SONNET TO THE TRINITY see Naylor, Bernard

SONNO DIVINO see Arnaldi, Antonio

SONNTAGLICHE EVANGELIENSPRUCHE FUR DAS KIRCHENJAHR see Vulpius, Melchior

SONNTAGMORGEN see Dechant, A.

SONS AND DAUGHTERS LET US SING *Easter/Lent
(Mueller) SA oct FISCHER,C CM-6379 $.25 (S3449)

SONS AND DAUGHTERS, LET US SING see Tallis, Thomas

SONS OF EVE, REWARD MY TIDINGS *Xmas,carol,
Span,16th cent
(Greenberg, N.) [Span/Eng] SATB,opt S solo,
acap AMP N9 $.30 see from Three Spanish
Christmas Carols (S3450)

SONS OF GOD, THE see Bitgood

SONT TROIS HOMMES FORT SAGES see Aubanel, Georges

SONZOGNO, GIULIO CESARE (1906-   )
Messa *Mass
mix cor,ST soli,orch voc sc ZERBONI 3645
s.p., ipr (S3451)

SOON-A WILL BE DONE *spir
(Howorth, Wayne) SATB oct BELWIN 1154 $.25 (S3452)
(Howorth, Wayne) SA/TB oct BELWIN 1417 $.30 (S3453)
(Howorth, Wayne) SSA oct BELWIN 1216 $.35 (S3454)
(Howorth, Wayne) SAB oct BELWIN 1418 $.30 (S3455)
(Kinsman) SATB oct SPRATT 137 $.30 (S3456)
(Schubert) SATB oct LILLENAS AN-3824 $.30 (S3457)

SOON-AH WILL BE DONE *spir
(Dawson) men cor KJOS T101A $.35 (S3458)

SOON AH WILL BE DONE see Joosen, B.

SOON I WILL BE DONE *spir
(Boatner) SATB,acap oct GRAY 1655 $.30 (S3459)
(Roberts) SATB oct LAWSON 51558 $.30 (S3460)

SOON MAY THE LAST GLAD SONG ARISE see Powell

SOON ONE MORNIN' *spir
(Gilliam) 4pt men cor,acap oct SCHIRM.G 10770
$.25 (S3461)

SOON ONE MORNIN' DEATH COMES CREEPIN' see Kubik, Gail

SOON ONE MORNING' DEATH COMES CREEPIN' *folk,
US
(Kubik) mix cor,Bar solo,acap oct SCHIRM.G
9855 $.35 (S3462)

SOONER THE HEAVENS see Palestrina, Giovanni

SOONER THE HEAVENS see Palestrina, Giovanni, Vedrassi Prima

SOPRANO-ALTO ANTHEMS *CCU
SA SCHMITT 9154 $1.25 (S3463)

SORAAS, LARS
Bon
mix cor MUSIKK 96 s.p. (S3464)

Gloria *Gloria
mix cor MUSIKK 163 s.p. (S3465)

Jesusnavnet
mix cor MUSIKK 126 s.p. (S3466)

Julaften *Xmas
mix cor MUSIKK 108 s.p. (S3467)

O Du Min Immanuel
(Runge, Chr.) mix cor MUSIKK 113 s.p. (S3468)

Uverdig Er Jeg, Herre
mix cor MUSIKK 109 s.p. (S3469)

SORCE
Turn Back O Man
SATB,pno STANDARD B310MX $.50 (S3470)
SATB,pno/org,2fl,3clar STANDARD B310FS
$3.00, ipa (S3471)

SORENSON, TORSTEN
Blott Du Mig, Jesu, Kan Lara
[Swed] SAB,acap GEHRMANS TKS 58 (S3472)

De Som Med Tarar Sa *Bibl
[Swed] SATB,acap GEHRMANS KRB 269 (S3473)

Lar Oss Betanka *Bibl
[Swed] SATB,acap GEHRMANS KRB 311 (S3474)

Om Guds Ord
mix cor NORDISKA 4883 s.p. (S3475)

Se, Guds Son Till Doden Skrider
[Swed] SAB,acap GEHRMANS TKS 59 (S3476)

Tacksagelshymn
mix cor NORDISKA 3713 s.p. (S3477)

SORGE, ERICH
Uns Ist Ein Kindlein Heut Geborn *Xmas,cant
girl cor/boy cor,ST soli,pno/org GERIG 390
sc s.p., voc pt s.p. (S3478)

SORGE NEL PETTO see Handel, George Frideric

SORIANO, FRANCESCO(ALSO SURIANO)
see SURIANO, FRANCESCO

SORROW DOTH VEX NOW MY SPIRIT see Kuhnau,
Johann, Tristis Est Anima Mea

SORROWFUL IS MY SOUL see Nasco, Tristis Est
Anima Mea

SORROWFUL NOW IS MY SOUL see Lassus, Roland de
(Orlandus)

SORROWFUL ROAD, THE see Sateren, Leland
Bernhard

SORROWS OF MARY, THE see Bennett, Richard
Rodney

SORROWS OF MY HEART ARE ENLARGED, THE see
Ferris, W.

SORROWS OF MY HEART, THE see Boyce, William

SORROWS THOU ART BEARING, THE
see Three Chorales

SORS DE TON LIT PARE see Du Caurroy, Francoise-
Eustache

SORTEZ D'ICI, RACE MAUDITE see Saboly, Nicholas

SOUGHT THE LORD see Glarum, L. Stanley

SOUL *CCUL
(Carmichael, Ralph; Floria, Cam) SATB voc sc
WORD 30062 $1.95 (S3479)

SOUL, ADORN THYSELF WITH GLADNESS see Handel,
George Frideric

SOUL, ADORN THYSELF WITH GLADNESS see Wolff, S.
Drummond

SOUL, ARRAY THYSELF see Handel, George Frideric

SOUL, BE STILL see Franck, [Johann Wolfgang]

SOUL LONGING TO SEE GOD, THE see Surinach,
Carlos, Delirio Del Alma Por Vera Dios

SOUL OF MY SAVIOR see Roff, Joseph, Anima
Christi

SOULE
Beside Thy Cradle
SATB,acap SHAWNEE A 865 $.25 (S3480)

Boy Was Born, A
SATB,acap SHAWNEE A 712 $.25 (S3481)

Shepherd Song
SATB SHAWNEE A 711 $.25 (S3482)

SOULFULLY see Crouch, Andrae

SOULS OF MEN *anthem
(Ratcliffe, Desmond) mix cor oct NOVELLO
50.0343.01 s.p. (S3483)

SOULS OF RIGHTEOUS MEN, THE see Lassus, Roland
de (Orlandus), Justorum Animae

SOULS OF THE RIGHTEOUS see Byrd, William

SOULS OF THE RIGHTEOUS see Elvey, George Job

SOULS OF THE RIGHTEOUS see Noble, Thomas
Tertius

SOULS OF THE RIGHTEOUS, THE see Bevan, Richard T.

SOULS OF THE RIGHTEOUS, THE see Boustead, William

SOULS OF THE RIGHTEOUS, THE see Byrd, William, Iustorum Animae

SOULS OF THE RIGHTEOUS, THE see Davies, Henry Walford

SOULS OF THE RIGHTEOUS, THE see Miller, Edward

SOULS OF THE RIGHTEOUS, THE see Noble, Thomas Tertius

SOULS OF THE RIGHTEOUS, THE see Thiman, Eric Harding

SOULS OF THE RIGHTEOUS, THE see Vaughan Williams, Ralph

SOUND AN ALARM see Handel, George Frideric

SOUND OF ANGELS, A see Tye, Christopher

SOUND OVER ALL WATERS see Butler, Eugene

SOUND THE TRUMPET see Purcell, Henry

SOUND THE TRUMPET see Schubert, Franz (Peter)

SOUND THE TRUMPET, STRIKE THE CYMBAL see Schubert, Franz (Peter)

SOUNDING JOY see Morgan

SOUNDING SKIES, THE (from Hymn-Tune: Condescension) Xmas
    (Brandon) 2pt mix cor,org/pno oct SCHIRM.G 11531 $.25   (S3484)

SOUNDING SKIES, THE see Brandon

SOUNDS FOR NOW see Ford, Virgil T.

SOUNDS OF A NEW GENERATION see Wilson, John F.

SOURCE ETERNAL OF JOYS DIVINE see Kalinnikov, Vassili Sergeievitch

SOURCE ETERNELLE DE LUMIERE *Eve,hymn
    (Racine, C.; Geveart, F.-A.) [Lat/Fr] 3pt wom cor,acap (med) cor pts LEMOINE s.p. see from Collection De Choeurs, premiere Facsimile   (S3485)

SOURIRE, SOUER
Hallelujah
    SATB GENERAL CH346 $.30 see from Songs Of The Singing Nun   (S3486)

I Found The Lord
    SATB GENERAL CH347 $.30 see from Songs Of The Singing Nun   (S3487)

Resurrection
    SATB GENERAL CH345 $.30 see from Songs Of The Singing Nun   (S3488)

Sister Adele
    SATB GENERAL CH338 $.30 see from Songs Of The Singing Nun   (S3489)

Songs Of The Singing Nun *see Hallelujah; I Found The Lord; Resurrection; Sister Adele   (S3490)

SOUTHALL, MITCHELL
In Silent Night
    SSA oct JUSKO 169 $.20   (S3491)
    SATB oct JUSKO 106 $.20   (S3492)

SOUTHBRIDGE
I Have Been To The Mountaintop
    2pt oct LORENZ 5761 $.30   (S3493)

Ride On, King Jesus! *Easter
    SAB oct LORENZ 7410 $.30   (S3494)

We Welcome Glad Easter *Easter
    unis oct LORENZ 8625 $.25   (S3495)

SOUVENEZ-VOUS VIERGE MARIE see Massenet, Jules

SOVEREIGN OF MY DELIGHT see Pilkington, Francis

SOWANDE
Heav'n Bells Are Ringing *spir
    SATB,A solo,acap COLOMBO 2095 $.30
                                          (S3496)

SOWER IN HIS FIELD HIS SEED WAS SOWING, A see Schutz, Heinrich, Es Ging Ein Samann Aus Zu Saen Seinen Samen

SOWER, THE
    SATB HANSEN-US C634 $.40   (S3497)

SOWER, THE see Darke, Harold [Edwin]

SOWERBY, LEO (1895-)
All Hail, Adored Trinity *Trin
    SAB/SATB (easy) oct OXFORD 42.833 $.30
                                          (S3498)

Beneath The Forms Of Outward Rite
    (Lovelace) SATB (med diff/diff) SOUTHERN $.20   (S3499)

Blessed Are All They That Fear
    SATB nct GRAY GCMR 1573 $.35   (S3500)

Christ Reborn *cant
    BELWIN $1.50   (S3501)

Come, Children, Hear Me *Pent,Gradual
    (Snow, Robert J.) 2pt mix cor,org oct WORLD EMP-1380-5 $.45   (S3502)

Come, Holy Ghost, Draw Near Us *Whitsun
    SAB (med easy) oct OXFORD 42.834 $.35
                                          (S3503)

Come, Risen Lord
    SATB oct GRAY GCMR 3059 $.30   (S3504)

Forsaken Of Man *Holywk/Lent,cant
    BELWIN cmplt ed $2.75, cor pts $1.00
                                          (S3505)

SOWERBY, LEO (cont'd.)

God Mounts His Throne *Asc
    (Snow, Robert J.) SBar,org oct WORLD EMP-1189-5 $.45   (S3506)

Great Is The Lord *cant
    BELWIN $1.00   (S3507)

Happy The Nation *Pent,Gradual
    (Snow, Robert J.) 2pt mix cor,org oct WORLD EMP-1500-5 $.45   (S3508)

I Sing A Song Of The Saints
    SATB oct GRAY GCMR 2608 $.30   (S3509)

I Was Glad (Psalm 122)
    SATB oct GRAY GCMR 1787 $.45   (S3510)

I Will Lift Up Mine Eyes
    SATB,org BOSTON 6350 $.35   (S3511)

Jesu, Bright And Morning Star *Epiph
    SAB (med easy) oct OXFORD 42.829 $.30
                                          (S3512)

Let Us Now Praise Famous Men *Rembrnc,anthem
    SATB oct ROYAL 223 s.p.   (S3513)

Lord Ascendeth Up On High *Asc
    2pt (med easy) oct OXFORD 42.832 $.30
                                          (S3514)

Magnificat And Nunc Dimittis *Magnif/Nunc
    SATB (E min) oct NOVELLO 44.1382.02 s.p.
                                          (S3515)

Martyr Of God *Gen
    SAB/SATB (med easy) oct OXFORD 42.835 $.30
                                          (S3516)

Now There Lightens Upon Us
    SATB oct GRAY GCMR 1307 $.45   (S3517)

O God Our Help In Ages Past
    SATB,org,brass,timp GRAY GCMR 3291 $.35
                                          (S3518)

O Lord, You Have Been Our Refuge *Pent, Gradual
    (Snow, Orbert J.) 2pt mix cor,org oct WORLD EMP-1642-5 $.45   (S3519)

Psalm 70
    TTBB oct GRAY GCMR 2995 $.25   (S3520)

Psalm 122 *see I Was Glad

Psalm 124
    TTBB oct GRAY GCMR 2986 $.25   (S3521)

Righteous Live For Evermore, The *ASD
    SAB/SATB (med) oct OXFORD 42.836 $.35
                                          (S3522)

Solomon's Garden *cant
    BELWIN $1.35   (S3523)

Throne Of God *cant
    BELWIN $2.00   (S3524)

SPACIOUS FIRMAMENT see Drayton

SPACIOUS FIRMAMENT, THE see Thiman, Eric Harding

SPACIOUS FIRMAMENT ON HIGH see Wagner

SPACIOUS FIRMAMENT ON HIGH, THE see Andrews, H.K.

SPACIOUS FIRMAMENT ON HIGH, THE see Broadhead, G.F.

SPACIOUS FIRMAMENT ON HIGH, THE see Graves, John

SPACIOUS FIRMAMENT ON HIGH, THE see Jacob, Gordon

SPACIOUS FIRMAMENT ON HIGH, THE see Thiman, Eric Harding

SPACIOUS FIRMAMENT, THE see Haydn, (Franz) Joseph

SPACIOUS FIRMAMENT, THE see Trant, Brian

SPAHR, A.
Am Traualtar
    [Ger] mix cor,acap (easy) HUG s.p.   (S3525)

SPALDER, FRITHJOF
Jubilate Deo Omnis Terra
    [Lat] mix cor,org s.p. cor pts LYCHE 37, voc sc LYCHE LY351   (S3526)

SPANGENBERGS GROSSES GLORIA 1545 *Gloria
    (Distler, Hugo) [Ger] SATB,acap (med diff) BAREN. BA 1055 $.40 see also Liturgische Satze   (S3527)

SPANISCHES HYMNAR UM 1500 *CCU,hymn,Span
    (Gerber) [Ger/Lat] 4pt mix cor MOSELER s.p.
                                          (S3528)

SPANISH CAROL *carol,Span
    see Two Folk Carols
    SATB (easy) OXFORD 08.111 $.15   (S3529)

SPANISH EASTER CAROL see Schroth

SPANISH EASTER PROCESSION *Easter
    (Gaul, H.) SATB oct PRESSER 332-14269 $.30
                                          (S3530)

SPANISH LULLABY see Campbell, Madge E.

SPANISH LULLABY see Posegate, Maxcine W.

SPAR, OTTO (1909-)
Jesu Kreuz, Leiden Und Pein
    see Zwei Passions-Motetten

Jesus Christus Erniedrigte Sich Selbst
    see Zwei Passions-Motetten

Lukas-Passion *Psntd
    [Ger] 1-4pt mix cor,cantor BAREN. EM 470 sc s.p., cor pts s.p.   (S3531)

Praise To The Lord, The Almighty *Gen
    SAB,acap (easy) oct CONCORDIA 98-1080 $.25
                                          (S3532)

Sei Lob Und Ehr Dem Hochsten Gut *No.233, cant
    [Ger] 4pt mix cor,acap BAREN. EM 41 s.p.

SPAR, OTTO (cont'd.)

    see from EVANGELISCHES KIRCHENGESANGBUCH
                                          (S3533)

Zwei Passions-Motetten *Psntd,mot
    [Ger] 3pt mix cor,3 soli cor pts BAREN. EM 470A s.p.
    contains: Jesu Kreuz, Leiden Und Pein; Jesus Christus Erniedrigte Sich Selbst
                                          (S3534)

SPARROW AND THE SWALLOW, THE see Bentz, Cecil

SPATZEN-MESSE see Mozart, Wolfgang Amadeus, Missa Brevis

SPATZENMESSE see Mozart, Wolfgang Amadeus, Missa Brevis

SPEAK, LORD TO ME see Chopin, Frederic

SPEAK LOW TO ME, MY SAVIOR see Ford

SPEAK TO ME, LORD JESUS CHRIST see Young

SPEAK TO ONE ANOTHER OF PSALMS see Berger, Jean

SPEAK WORDS OF PRAISE see Bengtson, F.

SPEAKS, [OLEY] (1874-1948)
Come, Spirit Of The Living God
    (Deis) SATB oct SCHIRM.G 7433 $.30   (S3535)

How Long Wilt Thou Forget Me *Bibl
    (Chaffin) 4pt mix cor,T solo oct SCHIRM.G 6605 $.25   (S3536)

I Lay My Sins On Jesus
    SATB oct PRESSER 322-35093 $.30   (S3537)

In Heavenly Love Abiding *Bibl
    (Deis) SATB oct SCHIRM.G 7309 $.25   (S3538)

In The End Of The Sabbath *Easter,Bibl
    (Chaffin) 4pt mix cor,A solo oct SCHIRM.G 6795 $.30   (S3539)
    (Deis) 3pt wom cor oct SCHIRM.G 9735 $.30
                                          (S3540)
    (Stickles) jr cor&sr cor,org/pno oct SCHIRM.G 10466 $.30   (S3541)

Jesus, Thou Art Standing
    SATB oct PRESSER 322-35070 $.30   (S3542)

Let Not Your Heart Be Troubled *Bibl
    (Chaffin) 4pt mix cor,S solo oct SCHIRM.G 6915 $.30   (S3543)

Lord Is My Light, The
    (Chaffin) 4pt mix cor,ST soli oct SCHIRM.G 6858 $.30   (S3544)

More Love To Thee, O Christ
    4pt mix cor,S solo oct SCHIRM.G 6591 $.20
                                          (S3545)

O Jesus, Thou Art Standing *Easter
    SATB oct PRESSER 322-35070 $.30   (S3546)

O Master, Let Me Walk With Thee *Bibl
    (Chaffin) 4pt mix cor,S solo oct SCHIRM.G 6966 $.25   (S3547)

Prayer Perfect *prayer
    SA ALLANS 339 s.p.   (S3548)
    (Deis, Care) SATB (easy) ALLANS 160 s.p.
                                          (S3549)

Prayer Perfect, The
    (Deis) 4pt mix cor oct SCHIRM.G 7522 $.25
                                          (S3550)
    (Stickles) 3pt mix cor,org/pno oct SCHIRM.G 10317 $.25   (S3551)
    (Treharne) 3pt wom cor oct SCHIRM.G 9571 $.25   (S3552)

Still, Still With Thee
    SATB ALLANS 201 s.p.   (S3553)

There's A Song In The Air
    (Deis) 4pt mix cor,A solo oct SCHIRM.G 9759 $.40   (S3554)
    (Deis) 3pt wom cor oct SCHIRM.G 9820 $.25
                                          (S3555)

Thou Wilt Keep Him In Perfect Peace *Bibl
    (Chaffin) 4pt mix cor,S solo oct SCHIRM.G 6604 $.30   (S3556)

Twilight And Dawn
    (Chaffin) 4pt mix cor,S solo oct SCHIRM.G 6755 $.25   (S3557)

SPECIAL STARLIGHT see Haslam, [Herbert]

SPEDDING, FRANK
Hosanna! Music Is Divine *Gen
    unis (easy) oct OXFORD $.25   (S3558)

Let All The World In Every Corner Sing *Gen/ Thanks
    unis (easy) oct OXFORD $.25   (S3559)

Lord, When The Wise Men Came From Far *Epiph
    SATB,acap (med easy) oct OXFORD 84.031 $.25
                                          (S3560)

SPEEDWELL AND HYACINTH see Sharpe, Evelyn

SPEEN BELTET OM LIVET see Hovland, Egil

SPELLING OF CHRISTMAS, THE see Sacco, John [Charles]

SPEM IN ALIUM see Palestrina, Giovanni

SPEM IN ALIUM NUNQUAM HABUI see Tallis, Thomas

SPEME AMOROSA see Gastoldi

SPENCE, HORACE
O King Most High *Asc,anthem
    SATB oct ROYAL 224 s.p.   (S3561)

Rejoice, The Lord Is King
    SATB ALLANS 72 s.p.   (S3562)
    (Chambers, H.A.) SA ALLANS 279 s.p.   (S3563)

SPENCER
In Excelsis Gloria
    SSA,acap SOUTHERN $.25   (S3564)

SPENCER, S. REID (1872-1945)
Festival Magnificat And Nunc Dimittis
dbl cor,SATB soli,pno/org (diff) oct WILLIS
2792 $.40   (S3565)

SPENCER, W.
Adam Lay Ybounden *Xmas,madrigal
SATB,acap AMP A652 $.30 see from Two
Christmas Madrigals   (S3566)

As I Rode Out This Enders Night *Xmas,
madrigal
SATB,acap AMP A299 $.25   (S3567)

As I Sat Under A Sycamore Tree *Xmas,
madrigal
SATB,acap AMP A300 $.25   (S3568)

At The Round Earth's Imagined Corners
SATB,acap SHAWNEE A 986 $.30   (S3569)

Babe Is Born, A *Xmas,madrigal
SATB,acap AMP A662 $.30   (S3570)

Cantate Domino
SATB,acap SHAWNEE A 1158 $.35   (S3571)

Masters In This Hall *Xmas
SATB,acap oct PRESSER MC331 $.30   (S3572)

Nowell, Nowell, Out Of Your Sleep *Xmas,
madrigal
SATB,acap AMP A651 $.30 see from Two
Christmas Madrigals   (S3573)

Rise Up Shepherd And Follow *Xmas
SATB,acap oct PRESSER MC329 $.30   (S3574)

There Is No Rose Of Such Virtue *Xmas
SATB,acap AMP A602 $.25 see from Two
Christmas Madrigals   (S3575)

Two Christmas Madrigals *see Adam Lay
Ybounden; Nowell, Nowell, Out Of Your
Sleep; There Is No Rose Of Such Virtue;
Welcome Yule   (S3576)

Wassail, Wassail, All Over The Town! *Xmas,
madrigal
SATB,acap AMP 663 $.30   (S3577)

Welcome Yule *Xmas
SATB,acap AMP A601 $.25 see from Two
Christmas Madrigals   (S3578)

SPENCER, WILLIAMETTA
Angelus Ad Virginem *Xmas
SSA FOSTER MF 905 $.30   (S3579)

SPERET ISRAEL see Schutz, Heinrich

SPES MEA, CHRISTE DEUS see Schutz, Heinrich

SPES SALUTIS see Clemens, Jacobus

SPICKER, M.
Fear Not, O Israel *Bibl
SATB,SATB soli oct SCHIRM.G 4004 $.25
                                            (S3580)

Holy, Holy, Holy *see Kedushah

Kedushah
"Holy, Holy, Holy" [Eng] SATB,Bar solo oct
SCHIRM.G 8571 $.35   (S3581)

SPIECKERMAN, H.
Lord's Prayer, The
3pt wom cor,pno (easy) oct WILLIS 7113 $.16
                                            (S3582)

SPIELE, KLEINE FLOTE see Trubel, Gerhard

SPIELHEFT ZUR WEIHNACHT see Rubben,
Hermannjosef

SPIES, CLAUDIO (1925-   )
In Paradisum
SSATB oct ELKAN-V 362-1208 $.30   (S3583)

Proverbs On Wisdom
TTBB oct ELKAN-V 362-131 $1.40   (S3584)

Verses From The Book Of Ruth *Bibl
SSAA oct PRESSER 312-40516 $1.00   (S3585)

SPIES, LEO
Anmut Sparet Nicht Noch Muhe *hymn
(Brecht) [Ger] unis jr cor/mix cor,pno/
strings sc HINRICHSEN L5296A s.p. (S3586)

SPILMAN
Away In A Manger *Xmas
SATB oct LORENZ A455 $.25   (S3587)

SPINNEY, W.
Ye That Stand In The House Of The Lord
SATB oct LORENZ 477 $.30   (S3588)
SATB oct PRESSER 312-05997 $.25   (S3589)

SPIRIT, ALL HOLY see Videro, Finn

SPIRIT ALSO HELPETH, THE see Bach, Johann
Sebastian

SPIRIT ALSO HELPETH US see Bach, Johann
Sebastian

SPIRIT ALSO HELPETH US, THE see Bach, Johann
Sebastian, Der Geist Hilft

SPIRIT ALSO HELPETH US, THE see Bach, Johann
Sebastian, Der Geist Hilft Unsrer
Schwachheit Auf

SPIRIT BLEST see Nyquist

SPIRIT DIVINE
2pt CHAPPELL 0018234-352 $.40   (S3590)
SSA CHAPPELL 0018234-354 $.40   (S3591)
SATB CHAPPELL 0018234-358 $.40   (S3592)

SPIRIT DIVINE see Darst, W. Glenn

SPIRIT DIVINE, ATTEND OUR PRAYERS see Lovelace,
Austin C.

SPIRIT DIVINE, ATTEND OUR PRAYERS see Wright

SPIRIT DIVINE, COME DWELL WITHIN see Nichols,
Anna Mae

SPIRIT MOST HOLY see Scandello

SPIRIT OF CHRISTMAS see Reibold, Bruno

SPIRIT OF GOD see Ford

SPIRIT OF GOD see Lewis, Jessie D.

SPIRIT OF GOD see Neidlinger, William Harold

SPIRIT OF GOD see Prentice, Fred

SPIRIT OF GOD see Smith, Lani

SPIRIT OF GOD see Tschesnokoff, P.I.

SPIRIT OF GOD see Underwood

SPIRIT OF GOD see Weaver

SPIRIT OF GOD DESCEND
(Gardner) SATB oct STAFF 516 $.25   (S3593)

SPIRIT OF GOD, THIS VERY HOUR see Blakley

SPIRIT OF LIFE see Dressler, John

SPIRIT OF LIFE see Marshall, Virginia

SPIRIT OF MERCY, TRUTH, AND LOVE see Chambers,
H.A.

SPIRIT OF MERCY, TRUTH AND LOVE see Lewis, J.

SPIRIT OF THE LORD, THE see Davye, John F.

SPIRIT OF THE LORD IS UPON ME, THE see Elgar,
Edward

SPIRIT OF THE LORD, THE see Ammon, Blasius

SPIRIT OF THE LORD, THE see Kline

SPIRIT OF THE LORD, THE see Titcomb, Everett

SPIRIT OF THE LORD, THE see Willan, Healey

SPIRIT OF THE LORD, THE see Wilson

SPIRIT OF TRUTH, THE see Nystedt, Knut

SPIRITED CHORUSES *CCU
SAB SCHMITT 18 $.50   (S3594)

SPIRIT'S YEARNING, THE see Christiansen, F.
Melius

SPIRITUAL QUODLIBET FOR CHRISTMAS, A see
Walker, David S.

SPIRITUAL RHAPSODY, A see Oldroyd, George,
Jhesu Christ Saint Mary's Sone

SPIRITUAL SONGS see Davies, Henry Walford

SPIRITUALS OF THE NEW TESTAMENT *CCU,spir
mix cor SCHMITT 9158 $.85   (S3595)

SPIRITUALS OF THE OLD TESTAMENT *CCU,spir
mix cor SCHMITT 9157 $.85   (S3596)

SPIRITUALS SONGS FOR UNISON AND S.A. CHOIRS
*CCU,spir
unis/SA SCHMITT 9155 $.85   (S3597)

SPIRITUALS see Stickles

SPIRITUALS see Stickles

SPIRITUALS see Stickles

SPIRITUALS see Stickles

SPIRITUS DOMINI see Schieri, Fritz

SPIRITUS SANCTI GRATIA see Nogarede, C.J.

SPIRITUS SANCTI GRATIA see Vulpius, Melchior

SPIRT OF GOD see Darst, W. Glenn

SPITE OF MICHAL, THE see Frank, Rene

SPITTA, HEINRICH
Alle Engel Zu Diesem Fest *Op.93, Xmas,cant
3pt mix cor,2vln,vcl,2A rec MOSELER s.p.
see also Leichte Weihnachtskantaten
                                            (S3598)

2 eq voices,inst MOSELER LB-161 s.p.
                                            (S3599)

Als Ich Bei Mein Schafen Wacht *Op.93, Xmas,
cant
3pt mix cor,A rec,vla&vcl, lute MOSELER
s.p. see also Leichte Weihnachtskantaten
                                            (S3600)

Christum Wir Wollen Loben *cant
3pt mix cor MOSELER s.p. see from Leichte
Liedkantaten   (S3601)

Da Jesus An Dem Kreuze Stund *Op.95, cant
4pt mix cor,ST soli,org,strings MOSELER sc
s.p., cor pts s.p.   (S3602)

Das Kindlein, Das Maria Halt *Op.93, Xmas,
cant
3pt mix cor,2vln,vcl MOSELER s.p. see also
Leichte Weihnachtskantaten   (S3603)

Der Tag, Der Ist So Freudenreich *cant
3pt mix cor MOSELER s.p. see from Leichte
Liedkantaten   (S3604)

Die Macht Des Gesanges *hymn
4pt mix cor,S/T solo,trp,strings MOSELER sc
s.p., cor pts s.p., ipa   (S3605)

Drei Konig Von Saba Kommen
see Leichte Weihnachtskantaten

Ei Was Grosses Wunder *Op.93, Xmas,cant
3pt mix cor,2A rec,vla&vcl, lute MOSELER
s.p. see also Leichte Weihnachtskantaten
                                            (S3606)

Ein Schones Kindlein *Op.93, Xmas,cant
3pt mix cor,3strings MOSELER s.p. see also
Leichte Weihnachtskantaten   (S3607)

SPITTA, HEINRICH (cont'd.)
Es Freuen Sich Die Engelein *Op.13, Xmas,
cant
mix cor,inst MOSELER s.p.   (S3608)

Es Kommt Ein Schiff, Geladen *Op.93, Xmas,
cant
3pt mix cor,2A rec/2vln MOSELER s.p. see
also Leichte Weihnachtskantaten   (S3609)

From Heaven Above, Ye Angels All *Xmas,cant
treb cor/men cor/mix cor,strings/winds,cont
CONCORDIA 97-7597 $.75, ipa   (S3610)

Geboren Ist Uns Ein Kindlein Klein *Op.93,
Xmas,cant
3pt mix cor,2vln,A rec MOSELER s.p. see
also Leichte Weihnachtskantaten   (S3611)

Herbergssuche Der Maria *Xmas
3pt mix cor,soli,kbd,inst MOSELER s.p.   (S3612)

Leichte Liedkantaten *see Christum Wir
Wollen Loben; Der Tag, Der Ist So
Freudenreich; Nun Komm, Der Heiden
Heiland; O Heiland, Reiss Die Himmel Auf
                                            (S3613)

Leichte Weihnachtskantaten *Op.93, Xmas,cant
3pt mix cor,2A rec/2vln MOSELER s.p.
contains: Drei Konig Von Saba Kommen;
Mitt Gott So Wollen Wir Lobn Und Ehrn
see also: Alle Engel Zu Diesem Fest,
Op.93; Als Ich Bei Mein Schafen Wacht,
Op.93; Das Kindlein, Das Maria Halt,
Op.93; Ei Was Grosses Wunder, Op.93;
Ein Schones Kindlein, Op.93; Es Kommt
Ein Schiff, Geladen, Op.93; Geboren Ist
Uns Ein Kindlein Klein, Op.93; O
Jesulein, Op.93   (S3614)

Mitt Gott So Wollen Wir Lobn Und Ehrn
see Leichte Weihnachtskantaten

Nun Komm, Der Heiden Heiland *cant
3pt mix cor MOSELER s.p. see from Leichte
Liedkantaten   (S3615)

O Heiland, Reiss Die Himmel Auf *cant
3pt mix cor MOSELER s.p. see from Leichte
Liedkantaten   (S3616)

O Jesulein *Op.93, Xmas,cant
3pt mix cor,2vln,vcl MOSELER s.p. see also
Leichte Weihnachtskantaten   (S3617)

Vom Himmel Hoch, Da Komm Ich Her *Xmas
2-4pt wom cor MOSELER s.p.   (S3618)

Weihnachtliche Liedkantate *Xmas,cant
3 eq voices/3pt mix cor,opt solo,inst
MOSELER sc s.p., cor pts s.p., ipa
                                            (S3619)

Winteraustreiben *Op.17, cant
[Ger] SATB,S solo,2vln,vcl/bvl PETERS 4803
voc sc $.80, cor pts $.50   (S3620)

SPOHR
Psalm 42
(Kirk) SATB oct PRO ART 1837 $.25   (S3621)
(Kirk) SAB oct PRO ART 2032 $.25   (S3622)
(Kirk) SA oct PRO ART 2036 $.18   (S3623)
(Kirk) SSA,acap oct PRO ART 1445 $.22
                                            (S3624)

SPOHR, LUDWIG (LOUIS) (1784-1859)
As Pants The Hart *anthem/Bibl
(Jamieson, Hugh) SATB ALLANS 205 s.p.
                                            (S3625)
(Stimpson) SAATB,S solo oct SCHIRM.G 4498
$.25   (S3626)
(Stimpson, James) SAATB,S solo,orch oct
NOVELLO 40.0175.03 s.p., ipr   (S3627)

In Seiner Todesnot
[Ger/Eng] SATB,pno BROUDE,A. 185 $.30
                                            (S3628)

Last Judgment, The *ora
SATB,SATB soli,2fl,2ob,2clar,2bsn,2horn,
2trp,3trom,tuba,strings,timp voc sc
NOVELLO s.p., ipr   (S3629)

SPONSUS AMAT SPONSAM see Fayrfax, Robert

SPORR, KARL
Bereden Vag For Herran
mix cor NORDISKA 3318 s.p.   (S3630)

SPRATTE, HERMANN
Der Feldjager
see Spratte, Hermann, Frisch Auf In Gottes
Namen

Frisch Auf In Gottes Namen *sac/sec
2-3pt mix cor,brass MOSELER sc s.p., cor
pts s.p., ipa contains also: Der
Feldjager   (S3631)

SPRAUGUE, RICHARD L.
Gloria In Excelsis Deo
[Lat] 4pt mix cor,acap oct SCHIRM.G 11889
$.30   (S3632)

SPREADING THE NEWS see Oliver, Herbert

SPRING see Sanders, Robert L.

SPRING BURSTS TODAY see Shaw, Geoffrey [Turton]

SPRING CAROL see Britten, Benjamin

SPRING CAROL see Dicie

SPRING CAROL see Rogers, E.

SPRING LEADS DEATH TO LIFE see Licht

SPRING PRAYER see Caldwell

SPRING RETURNS see Christiansen, F. Melius

SPRING SONG see Bach, Johann Sebastian, Mer
Hahn En Neue Oberkeet

SPRINGS IN THE DESERT see Jennings, Arthur B.

SPRINGTANZ see Csenki, I.

SPRUCH EINES FAHRENDEN see Hindemith, Paul

SPRUCHE NACH ANGELUS SILESIUS see Brunner, Adolf

SPRUCHKANONS see Graap, Lothar

SPRUYTE DAVIDS see Bonset, Jac.

SPURR
First Place
(Kirk) SATB oct LILLENAS AT-1061 $.30
(S3633)

SQUILLATE, CAMPANE see Picchi, Luigi

SSA CAROLS FOR CHRISTMAS see Strickling, George F.

SSA CHORALE BOOK, THE *CC34L,chorale
(Thomas, P.) SSA CONCORDIA 97-7592 $1.50
contains works by: Weber; Strube; Petzold;
Weber; Vogel; Hennig; Chemin-Petit;
Petzold; Strube; Otthmayr; Praetorius;
Vulpius; Metzler; Kindermann; Willan;
Abraham; Scheidt; Kugelmann
(S3634)

SSATTB see Palestrina, Giovanni

ST. ANTONI [CHORALE] see Haydn, (Franz) Joseph

ST. CECILIA see Gounod, Charles Francois, Messe Solennelle

ST. CECILIA ANTHEM BOOK see Holler, John

ST. CECILIA MASS see Gounod, Charles Francois, Messe Solennelle

ST. CECILIA MASS see Scarlatti, Alessandro

ST. FRANCIS see Milner, Anthony

ST. FRANCIS' HYMN *Gen
(Olds) SATB/SA/jr cor SCHMITT 1570 $.40
(S3635)
(Olds) SAB SCHMITT 5504 $.25
(S3636)

ST. FRANCIS' PRAYER see Beveridge, Thomas G.

ST. FRANCIS' PRAYER see Gilbert, J.R.

ST. FRANCIS PRAYER see Olds

ST. GEORGES'S DAY see Shaw, Martin

ST. JOHANNISNACHT see Huber, Hans

ST. JOHN PASSION see Handel, George Frideric

ST. JOHN PASSION see Schutz, Heinrich

ST. JOHN PASSION see Schutz, Heinrich, Johannespassion

ST. JOHN PASSION see Schutz, Heinrich, Lukaspassion

ST. JOHN PASSION, THE see Handel, George Frideric, Johannespassion

ST. JOHN, THE EVANGELIST see Hourdeaux

ST. JOHN'S PASSION see Bach, Johann Sebastian, Johannespassion

ST. JOHN'S PASSION see Bach, Johann Sebastian, La Passione Di N.S. Gesu Cristo Secondo Giovanni

ST. JOHN'S PASSION see Handel, George Frideric, Johannespassion

ST. JOHN'S PASSION see Resinarius, Balthasar

ST. LUKE CHRISTMAS STORY, THE see Effinger, Cecil

ST. LUKE PASSION see Schutz, Heinrich

ST. LUKE PASSION see Schutz, Heinrich, Hukaspassion

ST. LUKES' PASSION see Bach, Johann Sebastian, Lukas-Passion

ST. LUKE'S PASSION see Telemann, Georg Philipp, Lukaspassion

ST. MARK PASSION see Pinkham, Daniel

ST. MARK'S EASTER GOSPEL see Mitchell, L.

ST. MARK'S PASSION see Bach, Johann Sebastian, Markuspassion

ST. MARTIN [CHORALE] *chorale
(Gardner) SATB,band oct STAFF 553 $.30, ipa
(S3637)

ST. MARTIN [CHORALE] see Haydn, (Franz) Joseph

ST. MARTINUS-LIED see Philipp, Franz

ST. MATTHEW PASSION see Bach, Johann Sebastian, La Passione Di N.S. Gesu Cristo Secondo Matteo

ST. MATTHEW PASSION see Schutz, Heinrich

ST. MATTHEW PASSION see Schutz, Heinrich, Matthauspassion

ST. MATTHEW PASSION, PART I see Bach, Johann Sebastian, La Passione Di N.S. Gesu Cristo Secondo Matteo

ST. MATTHEW PASSION, PART II see Bach, Johann Sebastian, La Passione Di N.S. Gesu Cristo Secondo Matteo

ST. MATTHEW'S PASSION see Bach, Johann Sebastian, La Passione Di N.S. Gesu Cristo Secondo Matteo

ST. MATTHEW'S PASSION see Bach, Johann Sebastian, Matthauspassion

ST. NICHOLAS DAY IN THE MORNING see Martin, Easthope

ST. NICHOLAS MASS see Haydn, (Franz) Joseph, Missa Sancti Nicolai

ST. NICOLAS AT CHRISTMAS TIME see Crawford, T.J.

ST. NICOLAS CAROL BOOK, THE *CC12U,Xmas,carol
oct ROYAL 85402 045 4 s.p.
(S3638)

ST. OSWALD'S MUSIC FOR THE PARISH COMMUNION see Hutchings, Arthur

ST. PAUL see Mendelssohn-Bartholdy, Felix

ST. PAUL see Mendelssohn-Bartholdy, Felix, Paulus

ST. PAUL [CHORALE] see Mendelssohn-Bartholdy, Felix

ST. PAULUS WAR EIN MEDIKUS see Schroeder, Hermann

ST. PETER see Clemens, Jacobus, Tu Es Petrus

ST. PETER see Jones, Daniel

ST. THEODULPH'S HYMN see Teschner

STA UPP, VAR LJUS see Bjarnegard, Gustaf

STA UPP, VAR LJUS see Salonen, Sulo

STABAT MATER see d'Astorga, Emanuelle

STABAT MATER see Benson, Warren

STABAT MATER see Boccherini, Luigi

STABAT MATER see Browne, John [Lewis]

STABAT MATER see Caldara, Antonio

STABAT MATER see Casciolini, Claudio

STABAT MATER see Cornelius, Peter

STABAT MATER see David, Johann Nepomuk

STABAT MATER see Des Prez, Josquin

STABAT MATER see Devreese, Godefroid

STABAT MATER see Dohnanyi, Ernst von

STABAT MATER see Dvorak, Antonin

STABAT MATER see Ferradini, Antonio

STABAT MATER see Ferrari, Giovanni

STABAT MATER see Geiser, Walther

STABAT MATER see Hand, Colin

STABAT MATER see Haydn, (Franz) Joseph

STABAT MATER see Heiller, Anton

STABAT MATER see Hollingsworth, Stanley

STABAT MATER see Howells, Herbert Norman

STABAT MATER see Klebe, Giselher

STABAT MATER see Klerk, Albert de

STABAT MATER see Kubelik, Rafael

STABAT MATER see Lewkovitch, Bernhard

STABAT MATER see Lupi, Roberto

STABAT MATER see Magri, Pietro

STABAT MATER see Mengelberg, Rudolf

STABAT MATER see Moioli, Romano

STABAT MATER see Mul, Jan

STABAT MATER see Nanini (Nanino), Giovanni Bernardino

STABAT MATER see Naylor, Bernard

STABAT MATER see Nicolosi, Salvatore

STABAT MATER see Palestrina, Giovanni

STABAT MATER see Penderecki, Krzysztof

STABAT MATER see Pergolesi, Giovanni Battista

STABAT MATER see Persichetti, Vincent

STABAT MATER see Pinkham, Daniel

STABAT MATER see Poulenc, Francis

STABAT MATER see Rheinberger, Josef

STABAT MATER see Rodella, Sante

STABAT MATER see Rossini, Gioacchino

STABAT MATER see Russell

STABAT MATER see Scarlatti, Alessandro

STABAT MATER see Scarlatti, Domenico

STABAT MATER see Schubert, Franz (Peter)

STABAT MATER see Stanford, Charles Villiers

STABAT MATER see Steffani, Agostino

STABAT MATER see Strategier, Herman

STABAT MATER see Szmanowski

STABAT MATER see Testi

STABAT MATER see Tuma, Frantisek Ignaz Antonin

STABAT MATER see Verdi, Giuseppe

STABAT MATER see Visser, Dick

STABAT MATER see Vivaldi, Antonio

STABAT MATER see Volpi, Edoardo

STABAT MATER see Wangenheim

STABAT MATER see Wideen, Ivar

STABAT MATER DOLOROSA
(Racine, C.; Geveart, F.-A.) "Prose De La
Fete Des Sept Douleurs" [Lat/Fr] 3pt wom
cor,acap (med easy) cor pts LEMOINE s.p.
see from Collection De Choeurs, premiere
Facsimile
(S3639)

STABAT MATER DOLOROSA see Diepenbrock, Alfons

STABAT MATER DOLOROSA see Mulder, Ernest W.

STABAT MATER DOLOROSA see Palestrina, Giovanni

STABAT MATER SPECIOSA see Diepenbrock, Alfons

STABLE AT BETHLEHEM, THE *Xmas,cant
unis CHAPPELL 0016956-369 $1.00
(S3640)

STABLE COLD AND BARREN, A see Ehret, Walter

STABLE DOOR see Gibbs

STADEN
Die Gerechten
(Payson) "For The Righteous" mix cor
SOUTHERN $.30
(S3641)
(Payson, A.) "For The Righteous" SATB,acap
FRANK F-451 $.30
(S3642)

For The Righteous *see Die Gerechten

Herr, Unser Herrscher
3 eq voices MOSELER LB-160 s.p.
(S3643)

Praise Ye The Lord (Psalm 117)
(Guetter) SSA WARNER WB-136 $.30
(S3644)

Psalm 117 *see Praise Ye The Lord

Was Ist Das Menschenleben
see Bach, Johann Sebastian, Und Wollte
Alles Wanken

STADEN, JOHANN (1581-1634)
Ach Bleib Bei Uns, Herr Jesu Christ
see Anonymous, So Wahr Ich Lebe, Spricht
Dein

Ack, Bliv Hos Oss, O Jesu Krist
mix cor NORDISKA 5600 s.p.
(S3645)

Cantate Domino
[Lat] 3pt,2treb inst,cont HEUGEL CPJ70 s.p.
(S3646)
Cantate Domino *see Singet Ein Neues Lied

Cantate Domino Canticum Novum *Ded/Easter/
Gen
"Sing To The Lord A New Song" SAB,strings/
fl (med diff) oct CONCORDIA 98-1886 $.40
(S3647)

Danket Dem Herren (Psalm 136)
see Jeep, Johann, Allein Auf Gottes Wort

Danket Dem Herrn *Easter/Psntd
SAB HANSSLER 6.2189 s.p. contains also:
Scheidt, Samuel, Gib Uns Heut Unser
Taglich Brot (SST/SSA); Walter (Walther),
Johann, Jesus Chrstus, Unser Heiland, Der
Den Tod (SATB); Hassler, Hans Leo,
Erstanden Ist Der Heilige Christ (SATB)
(S3648)
Danket Dem Herrn Allezeit *Fest
[Ger] 3pt mix cor,acap (easy) BAREN.
BCH 166 s.p.
(S3649)

Dig, Helge Ande, Bedja Vi
3pt mix cor NORDISKA 1334 s.p.
(S3650)

Ein Jeder Mensch Bedenke Eben
see Gumpeltzhaimer, Adam, Wir Danken Dir,
Gott, Fur Und Fur

Erhalt Uns, Herr *Fest,mot
[Ger] 3-4pt mix cor,acap (med) MULLER K 31
s.p.
(S3651)

Es Ist Ein Kostlich Ding *Gen
[Ger] 3 eq voices,acap (easy) BAREN. BCH 60
s.p.
(S3652)

Es Ist Ein Kostlich Ding, Dem Herren
SSA/TTB HANSSLER 6.211 s.p. contains also:
Ducis, Benedictus, Herr Jesu Christ, Du
Hochstes Gut (SAB/SAT)
(S3653)

Fahr Hin, Du Liebste Seele Mein *see O Du
Lamm Gottes, Jesu Christ

Ich Hab Einen Guten Kampf Gekampfet *Gen
[Ger] SATB,acap (easy) MULLER K 23 s.p.
(S3654)

Lob, Ehr Sei Gott
2pt wom cor/2pt jr cor,org/pno/cembalo cor
pts BREITKOPF-W CHB-3491 s.p. (S3655)

Lobet Den Herren Alle Heiden (Psalm 117) Bibl
SAT HANSSLER 6.2207 s.p.
(S3656)

Nun Schein, Du Glanz Der Herrlichkeit
SAT HANSSLER 6.110 s.p.
(S3657)

O Du Lamm Gottes, Jesu Christ
"Fahr Hin, Du Liebste Seele Mein" see
Lechner, Leonhard, O Welt, Sieh Hier Dein
Leben

O Jesu Christ
(Schabasser, Josef) mix cor,acap oct
DOBLINGER s.p. see also CHRISTUS, DER
HERR
(S3658)

Psalm 117 *see Lobet Den Herren Alle Heiden

Psalm 136 *see Danket Dem Herren

Sing To The Lord A New Song *see Cantate
Domino Canticum Novum

STADEN, JOHANN (cont'd.)

Singet Ein Neues Lied *Gen
"Cantate Domino" [Lat/Ger] 3pt mix cor, cont&2vln/cont&fl (med) BAREN. BA 1689 s.p. (S3659)

Zion Spricht: Der Herr Hat Mich *mot
(Hellmann) SAB HANSSLER 1.242 s.p. (S3660)

STADLER, MAXIMILLIAN (ABBE) (1748-1833)
Behold The Great Priest *anthem
(Andrews, C.T.) SATB (easy) oct GIA G1480 $.30 (S3661)

Credidi Propter
(Pizarro) [Lat] oct SCHIRM.G 11436 $.30 (S3662)

Requiem In F Major *Req
mix cor,org,2vln,opt 2horn&bvl WEINBERGER s.p., ipa voc sc, cor pts (S3663)

STADLMAIR, HANS
Der Du Der Menschen Heiland Bist
see Funf Geistliche Liedsatze

Der Himmel Soll Sich Heute Freun
see Funf Geistliche Liedsatze

Erhabner Furst Der Ewigkeit
see Funf Geistliche Liedsatze

Funf Geistliche Liedsatze
4pt men cor,acap cor pts BREITKOPF-W CHB-3171 s.p.
contains: Der Du Der Menschen Heiland Bist; Der Himmel Soll Sich Heute Freun; Erhabner Furst Der Ewigkeit; Ich Glaub An Gott In Aller Not; Jener Tag, Der Tag Der Zahren (S3664)

Funf Marterln
4pt men cor,acap cor pts BREITKOPF-W CHB-3177 s.p.
contains: Hier Liegt Ein Armes Sundenaas; Hier Liegt Ein Junges Ochselein; Hier Ruhet Gottfried Sterkel; Hier Ruht Der Brauersepp; Hier Ruht Mein Weib, Gott Sei's Gedankt (S3665)

Hier Liegt Ein Armes Sundenaas
see Funf Marterln

Hier Liegt Ein Junges Ochselein
see Funf Marterln

Hier Ruhet Gottfried Sterkel
see Funf Marterln

Hier Ruht Der Brauersepp
see Funf Marterln

Hier Ruht Mein Weib, Gott Sei's Gedankt
see Funf Marterln

Ich Glaub An Gott In Aller Not
see Funf Geistliche Liedsatze

Jener Tag, Der Tag Der Zahren
see Funf Geistliche Liedsatze

STADLMAYR, JOHANN (1929-)
Conditor Alme Siderum *Adv/Xmas
SATB,acap voc pt DOBLINGER s.p. see also ADVENT UND WEIHNACHT, HEFT 2 (S3666)

Jesu Redemptor Omnium *Adv/Xmas
SATB,acap voc pt DOBLINGER s.p. see also ADVENT UND WEIHNACHT, HEFT 2 (S3667)

Vierstimmige Hymnen *CCU,hymn
(Quadflieg, J.) SATB,acap cor pts BREITKOPF-L PB-1996 s.p. (S3668)

STAEMPFLI, EDWARD (1908-)
Zions Klage Und Trostung *ora,Heb
"Zion's Lament And Consolation" SATB, narrator,SABar soli,orch voc sc ISRAELI 336 s.p. (S3669)

Zion's Lament And Consolation *see Zions Klage Und Trostung

STAFFAN VAR EN STALLEDRANG *Xmas,carol,Swed
(Blyton) "Stephen Was A Stable-Boy" [Eng] unis,pno&opt vcl/bass inst,rec/treb inst, bells&tamb/bells/tamb oct SCHIRM.G 11743 $.30 (S3670)
(Blyton, Carey) "Stephen Was A Stable Boy" unis,pno,opt strings&perc&rec (easy) oct FABER 11743 $.30 (S3671)

STAFFANSVISA see Berg, Gottfrid

STAFFANSVISA FOR SANG OCH SPEL
(Lunden, Lennart) cor,inst sc NORDISKA 4831 s.p. (S3672)

STAFFORD, DAVE
Thoughts On A Wonderous Event *Xmas
SATB,org/pno/hpsd,rec oct FOX R217 $.30 (S3673)

STAFFORD, F.J.
Hark The Glad Sound *Xmas
SATB,pno (easy) oct WILLIS 6316 $.10 (S3674)

Jesus, I My Cross Have Taken
SATB,Bar solo,pno (easy) oct WILLIS 6323 $.12 (S3675)

Just As I Am
SATB,S,A,T soli,pno (med) oct WILLIS 6451 $.12 (S3676)

STAHL, JOHANNES
Nu Lasst Uns Den Leib Begraben
[Ger] SATTB,acap (med easy) MULLER K 5 s.p. (S3677)

STAHMER, KLAUS
Furchte Dich Nicht
see Zwei Kleine Spruchmotetten

Surge Qui Dormis
see Zwei Kleine Spruchmotetten

Zwei Kleine Spruchmotetten *mot
4-5pt mix cor MOSELER LB-605 s.p.
contains: Furchte Dich Nicht; Surge Qui Dormis (S3678)

STAINER, JOHN (1840-1901)
Appeal Of The Crucified, The (from Crucifixion, The) Easter/Lent
oct SCHIRM.G 9834 $.25 (S3679)
SATB oct PRO ART 1325 $.30 (S3680)

Chorales From The Crucifixion (from Crucifixion, The) Easter/Lent
(Berglund) SATB SCHMITT 1928 $.35 (S3681)

Could Ye Not Watch? (from Crucifixion, The) Lent
SATB oct GRAY GCMR 2409 $.30 (S3682)
(Swift) SAB oct BELWIN 1727 $.25 (S3683)
(Swift) SA/TB oct BELWIN 1362 $.25 (S3684)
(Swift) SATB oct BELWIN 1235 $.25 (S3685)

Crucifixion, The *Psntd,cant/hymn/meditation
BELWIN $1.25 (S3686)
SATB,TB soli voc sc NOVELLO s.p., ipr (S3687)
(Horworth) SAB BELWIN $1.25 (S3688)

Crucifixion, The *Easter,cant
SATB PRESSER $1.00 (S3689)
SAB LORENZ $1.75 (S3690)
SATB LORENZ $1.95 (S3691)
cor&cong,TB soli,org voc sc SCHIRM.G $1.25 (S3692)
(Cain) SAB FLAMMER D5134 $1.35 (S3693)
(Stephens) cor,TB soli,org sc SCHIRM.G $5.00 (S3694)

Cruxifixion, The *Lent,cant
SATB FISCHER,C O-3784 $1.25 (S3695)

Daughter Of Jairus, The *Bibl/cant
cor,pno voc sc SCHIRM.G $1.25 (S3696)
SATB,STB soli,org,2fl,2ob,2clar,2bsn,4horn, 2trp,3trom,strings,perc,timp voc sc NOVELLO s.p., ipr (S3697)

Fifteen Original Amens, Sevenfold Amen *see Overton, Hall

Fling Wide The Gates (from Crucifixion, The) Easter/Lent/Palm,Bibl
oct SCHIRM.G 4537 $.35 (S3698)
(Page) SATB oct FISCHER,C CM-284 $.25 (S3699)

God So Loved The World (from Crucifixion, The) Commun/Easter/Gen/Lent/Psntd,anthem/ Bibl
4pt mix cor oct SCHIRM.G 3798 $.25 (S3700)
SATB (easy) oct AUGSBURG 1038 $.20 (S3701)
SATB oct LORENZ 461 $.25 (S3702)
SSA oct LORENZ 6243 $.30 (S3703)
SA oct LORENZ 5352 $.25 (S3704)
SATB (easy) oct LORENZ A420 $.25 (S3705)
SATB (very easy) oct LORENZ 4443 $.30 (S3706)
SAB oct LORENZ 7354 $.30 (S3707)
SATB oct NOVELLO 40.0588.00 s.p. (S3708)
SATB oct BELWIN 64151 $.30 (S3709)
SATB oct LILLENAS AN-2252 $.25 (S3710)
SATB oct PRESSER 332-08621 $.25 (S3711)
SATB (easy) ALLANS 268 s.p. (S3712)
SATB oct SOUTHERN $.25 (S3713)
(Byrd) SATB,acap oct PRO ART 1149 $.25 (S3714)
(Cain) SAB oct FOX R177 $.25 (S3715)
(Chambers, H.A.) TTBB oct NOVELLO 38.0135.07 s.p. (S3716)
(Deis) SABar,acap,opt org/pno oct SCHIRM.G 10085 $.30 (S3717)
(Ehret, Walter) SA oct BELWIN 1579 $.25 (S3718)
(Manten) SSA oct FOX R109 $.30 (S3719)
(Martin) SATB SCHMITT 5509 $.35 (S3720)
(Morrell) SATB oct SPRATT 503 $.25 (S3721)
(Mueller) SA oct FISCHER,C CM-6348 $.25 (S3722)
(Mueller) SAB oct FISCHER,C CM-7085 $.25 (S3723)
(Nevin, G.) TTBB,acap oct PRESSER 332-14356 $.30 (S3724)
(Page) SATB oct FISCHER,C CM-283 $.25 (S3725)
(Peery, R.) SAB oct PRESSER 312-21440 $.30 (S3726)
(Pitcher, Gladys) 3pt mix cor,pno (easy) oct WILLIS 8490 $.20 (S3727)
(Swift, Frederic Fay) SATB oct BELWIN 669 $.35 (S3728)
(Treharne) 3pt wom cor oct SCHIRM.G 7847 $.25 (S3729)
(Trevor, C.H.) SSAA oct NOVELLO 33.0124.09 s.p. (S3730)
(Wilson; Ehret) SAB oct BOOSEY 5110 $.30 (S3731)
(Wyatt) SSA oct PRO ART 2375 $.25 (S3732)
(Wyatt) SAB oct PRO ART 1579 $.30 (S3733)

Grieve Not The Holy Spirit
SATB ALLANS 262 s.p. (S3734)

Grieve Not The Holy Spirit Of God *Bibl
4pt mix cor,opt 4 soli oct SCHIRM.G 4383 $.25 (S3735)
SATB oct PRESSER 312-10755 $.30 (S3736)
SATB,acap oct PRO ART 1696 $.25 (S3737)
(Elwood) SATB oct SPRATT 541 $.25 (S3738)

How Beautiful Upon The Mountain
SATB ALLANS 414 s.p. (S3739)

How Beautiful Upon The Mountains *anthem
mix cor oct NOVELLO 50.0323.07 s.p. (S3740)

I Am Alpha And Omega *Easter/Gen/Trin, anthem/Bibl
4pt mix cor,high solo oct SCHIRM.G 3897 $.30 (S3741)
SATB oct PRESSER 312-06099 $.30 (S3742)
SATB ALLANS 310 s.p. (S3743)
mix cor,S/T solo oct NOVELLO 40.0423.10 s.p. (S3744)
SATB oct FISCHER,C CM-6253 $.25 (S3745)
(Lynn) SATB oct SPRATT 523 $.25 (S3746)

I Am The Bread Of Life
(Ehret) SATB oct BELWIN 1741 $.25 (S3747)
(Gray) SSA oct PRO ART 1625 $.18 (S3748)

I Saw The Lord *Trin,anthem
dbl cor oct NOVELLO 28.0171.10 s.p. (S3749)

STAINER, JOHN (cont'd.)

Jesus Said Unto The People *Bibl
oct SCHIRM.G 4909 $.25 (S3750)

Leave Us Not, Neither Forsake Us *Asc,anthem
mix cor oct NOVELLO 40.0410.08 s.p. (S3751)

Love Divine! All Love Excelling (from Daughter Of Jairus)
(Nevin) SATB,S,T,B soli,pno (easy) oct WILLIS 1121 $.15 (S3752)

Love Divine, All Loves Excelling *Lent/ Marriage
SA ALLANS 337 s.p. (S3753)

O Lamb Of God
(York) oct SCHIRM.G 7788 $.20 (S3754)

O Zion, That Bringeth Good Tidings *Xmas, anthem
SATB ALLANS s.p. (S3755)
mix cor oct NOVELLO 40.0381.00 s.p. (S3756)

Preces And Responses (St. Paul's) (Ferial) (composed with Martin, George Clement)
SATB oct NOVELLO 02.0005.00 s.p. (S3757)

Preces And Responses With Litany (St. Paul's) (Ferial) (composed with Martin, George Clement)
SATB oct NOVELLO 02.0006.09 s.p. (S3758)

Rest In Peace *Easter/Lent
GALLEON GCS2006 (S3759)

Sabbath Bells
SA/TB FLAMMER E5035 $.25 (S3760)
2pt oct LORENZ 5725 $.30 (S3761)
SATB oct LORENZ C183 $.30 (S3762)

Sevenfold Amen
see THREE AMENS

Sevenfold And Dresden Amens *CCU
SATB oct NOVELLO 44.0656.07 s.p. (S3763)

Sing Noel, Merry Noel *Xmas
(Anderson) 4pt mix cor,acap oct SCHIRM.G 10682 $.25 (S3764)

Story Of The Cross *Easter/Lent
SATB (easy) ALLANS 336 s.p. (S3765)

Story Of The Cross, The *Lent,anthem
mix cor oct NOVELLO 28.0452.02 s.p. (S3766)

They Have Taken Away My Lord *Easter,anthem/ Bibl
SATB oct SCHIRM.G 3882 $.30 (S3767)
SATB oct PRESSER 312-10826 $.30 (S3768)
SATB ALLANS 387 s.p. (S3769)
mix cor oct NOVELLO 40.0384.05 s.p. (S3770)

What Are These? *Rembrnc
SATB (easy) ALLANS 314 s.p. (S3771)

What Are These That Are Arrayed *ASD,anthem/ Bibl
SATB oct SCHIRM.G 3865 $.30 (S3772)
mix cor,orch oct NOVELLO 28.0057.08 s.p., ipr (S3773)

What Are These That Are Arrayed In White Robes? *Easter
SATB oct PRESSER 312-10097 $.30 (S3774)

Ye Shall Dwell In The Land *Harv/Thanks, anthem/Bibl
4pt mix cor,SB soli oct SCHIRM.G 4468 $.25 (S3775)
SATB ALLANS 309 s.p. (S3776)
mix cor,orch oct NOVELLO 40.0414.00 s.p. (S3777)
(Devito) SATB oct PRO ART 1672 $.20 (S3778)

STAIR, PATTY (1869-1926)
These Are They *Bibl
SATB,acap oct SCHIRM.G 4333 $.25 (S3779)

STAIRS, L.
Just For Today
SATB oct PRESSER 312-21583 $.30 (S3780)

King All Glorious *Easter
SATB PRESSER $1.25 (S3781)

Manger Prince *Xmas
SATB PRESSER $1.00 (S3782)

Matchless Morn *Easter
SATB PRESSER $1.25 (S3783)

Risen Christ *Easter
SATB PRESSER $1.25 (S3784)

Stars Over Bethlehem *Xmas
SATB PRESSER $.75 (S3785)

STALEY
Blessed Are They
SATB FLAMMER A 5164 $.35 (S3786)

Carol Of Wonder *carol
SATB FLAMMER A 5438 $.25 (S3787)

Christ, The Lord Is Born
SATB FLAMMER A 5098 $.25 (S3788)

Glorious Is The Son Of Mary
SATB FLAMMER A 5339 $.30 (S3789)

Go To Bethlehem, Shepherds
SATB FLAMMER A 5141 $.30 (S3790)

If You Keep Holy Night
SATB FLAMMER A 5244 $.30 (S3791)

Jesus Christ Triumphant
SATB FLAMMER A 5081 $.30 (S3792)

Run, Run To The Stable
SATB FLAMMER A 5024 $.30 (S3793)
SAB FLAMMER D5053 $.25 (S3794)

Star Was Like A Candle, The
SATB FLAMMER A 5288 $.30 (S3795)

STALEY (cont'd.)

Tan, Tan, They Saw A Star
SATB FLAMMER A 5367 $.25　　　　(S3796)
SSA FLAMMER B 5094 $.30　　　　(S3797)
SAB FLAMMER D5104 $.25　　　　(S3798)

What Can This Mean?
SATB FLAMMER A 5187 $.30　　　　(S3799)

STALEY, F. BROADUS
God Be Merciful Unto Us
SATB (med) ABINGDON APM-247 $.40　　(S3800)

STALIN, G.
Tu Es Petrus
[Lat] 4pt mix cor,org LEMOINE s.p.　(S3801)

STAND IN AWE see Lorenz

STAND IN THE GATE OF THE LORD'S HOUSE see Young

STAND STILL JORDAN
(Gardner) SATB oct STAFF 426 $.25　　(S3802)

STAND THE STORM see Billups, [W.]

STAND UP AND BLESS THE LORD see Bliss, Sir
Arthur

STAND UP, AND BLESS THE LORD see Coggin, Elwood

STAND UP, AND BLESS THE LORD see Darst, W.
Glenn

STAND UP AND BLESS THE LORD see George, Graham

STAND UP AND BLESS THE LORD see Thiman, Eric
Harding

STAND UP AND BLESS THE LORD see Turner, C.
Kenneth

STAND UP AND BLESS THE LORD see Wolff

STAND UP FOR JESUS see Hughes

STAND UP FOR JESUS see Thompson

STAND UP FOR JESUS see Webb

STAND UP FOR JESUS see Young

STAND UP! STAND UP FOR JESUS see Thiman, Eric
Harding

STAND UP, STAND UP FOR JESUS see Webb

STAND UP, STAND UP FOR JESUS see Young

STANDARD ANTHEMS, VOL. 1 see Dann, H.

STANDARD ANTHEMS, VOL. 2 see Dann, H.

STANDARD CHORAL RESPONSES　*CCU,cor-resp
SATB LORENZ C114 $.30　　　　(S3803)

STANDARD CHRISTMAS CAROLS　*CCU,Xmas,carol
SATB/unis LORENZ 1300 $.35　　　(S3804)

STANDARD CHRISTMAS CAROLS　*CCU,Xmas,carol
SATB/unis LORENZ A 1300 $.35 revised ed.
(S3805)

STANDARD CHRISTMAS CAROLS　*CCU,Xmas,carol
2pt&opt desc LORENZ 5322 $.30　　(S3806)

STANDARD CHRISTMAS CAROLS　*CCU,Xmas,carol
SSA LORENZ 6200 $.30　　　　(S3807)

STANDARD CHRISTMAS CAROLS　*CCU,Xmas,carol
SAB LORENZ 7308 $.30　　　　(S3808)

STANDARD CHRISTMAS CAROLS　*CCU,Xmas,carol
SSAA LORENZ 3545 $.30　　　　(S3809)

STANDARD CHRISTMAS CAROLS　*CCU,Xmas,carol
TTBB LORENZ 2811 $.35　　　　(S3810)

STANDIN' IN THE NEED O' PRAYER　*spir
(Bartholomew) 4pt men cor,acap oct SCHIRM.G
8050 $.25　　　　(S3811)

STANDIN' IN THE NEED OF PRAYER　*spir
(Ehret) SATB oct SPRATT 118 $.25　(S3812)

STANDIN' IN THE NEED OF PRAYER see Kjelson

STANDIN ON THE WALLS OF ZION
SSA oct STAFF 470 $.25　　　　(S3813)
SAB oct STAFF 468 $.25　　　　(S3814)
SATB oct STAFF 430 $.25　　　　(S3815)

STANDING AT THE DOOR see Russell

STANDING HERE WONDERING WHICH WAY TO GO
SATB BIG3 $.40　　　　(S3816)

STANDING IN THE NEED OF PRAYER
(Trant) SSAA,acap (med easy) oct OXFORD
83.047 $.25　　　　(S3817)

STANDING ON PROMISES see Blakley, D. Duane

STANFORD
And I Saw Another Angel　*ASD
SATB,T solo oct PRO ART 1698 $.20　(S3818)

Beati Quorum Via
[Lat] SSATBB,acap oct BOOSEY 5318 $.30
(S3819)

Coelos Ascendit Hodie (from Three Motets) mot
SATB BOOSEY-CAN s.p.　　　　(S3820)

Justorum Animae
[Lat] SATB,acap oct BOOSEY 5316 $.30
(S3821)

Six Elizabethan Pastorales　*CC6U
SATB BOOSEY-CAN s.p.　　　　(S3822)

STANFORD, CHARLES VILLIERS (1852-1924)
And I Saw Another Angel　*anthem
mix cor oct NOVELLO 50.0020.03 s.p. (S3823)

Benedicite (Shortened Form)
SATB oct NOVELLO 44.1183.08 s.p.　(S3824)

Benedictus　*Bene
unis (B flat maj) oct NOVELLO 02.0023.09
s.p.　　　　(S3825)

STANFORD, CHARLES VILLIERS (cont'd.)

SATB (B flat maj) oct NOVELLO 02.0022.00
s.p.　　　　(S3826)

Holy Communion　*Commun
SATB (B flat maj) oct NOVELLO 02.0042.05
s.p.　　　　(S3827)

How Beauteous Are Their Feet　*ASD,anthem
mix cor oct NOVELLO 40.0968.01 s.p. (S3828)

Jubilate　*Bibl/Jubil
SATB (B flat maj) oct NOVELLO 02.0030.01
s.p.　　　　(S3829)
[Eng] SATB oct SCHIRM.G 5259 $.25　(S3830)
unis (B flat maj) oct NOVELLO 02.0031.10
s.p.　　　　(S3831)

Lord Is My Shepherd, The　*anthem
mix cor,orch oct NOVELLO 28.0305.04 s.p.
ipr　　　　(S3832)

Magnificat And Nunc Dimittis　*Magnif/Nunc
SATB (B flat maj) oct NOVELLO 02.0057.03
s.p.　　　　(S3833)
SATB (A maj) oct NOVELLO 02.0056.05 s.p.
(S3834)
unis (B flat maj) oct NOVELLO 02.0058.01
s.p.　　　　(S3835)

Psalm 150
SATB oct NOVELLO 44.0864.00 s.p.　(S3836)

Stabat Mater
[Eng/Lat] mix cor,soli,org,3fl,3ob,3clar,
3bsn,3trp,4horn,3trom,tuba,strings,harp,
perc,timp cmplt ed BOOSEY rental (S3837)

Te Deum　*Bibl/Te Deum
[Eng] SATB oct SCHIRM.G 5261 $.35　(S3838)
SATB (B flat maj) oct NOVELLO 02.0016.06
s.p.　　　　(S3839)
unis (B flat maj) oct NOVELLO 02.0017.04
s.p.　　　　(S3840)

STANFORD, PATRIC
How Amiable Are Thy Dwellings
SATB BELWIN 19904 $1.00　　　　(S3841)

STANISLAUS
As Evening's Shadow Falls
(Nevin) SATB,S,T/Bar soli,pno (easy) oct
WILLIS 988 $.12　　　　(S3842)

STANLEY, JOHN (1713-1786)
Come, Let Us Join Our Cheerful Songs
(Coggin) SATB FLAMMER A 5371 $.25　(S3843)

STANPHILL
Follow Me
(Kirk) SATB oct LILLENAS AT-1059 $.35
(S3844)

I Know Who Holds Tomorrow
(Kirk) SATB oct LILLENAS AT-1049 $.35
(S3845)

Inside Those Pearly Gates
(Eleiott; Collins) SATB oct LILLENAS
AT-1004 $.35　　　　(S3846)

There's Room At The Cross For You　*Easter
SATB oct LORENZ B174 $.25　　　(S3847)

STANSELL
His Presence
SATB FLAMMER A 5528 $.25　　　　(S3848)

STANTON
All Men Are List'ning
SATB KJOS 5484 $.30　　　　(S3849)

Blest Are They
SATB,acap WARNER R3348 $.30　　　(S3850)

Cry Hosanna
SA/TB FLAMMER E5119 $.25　　　　(S3851)

O Thou Not Made With Hands
SATB,org oct BOOSEY 5148 $.30　　(S3852)

Praise The Lord With Sounding Cymbals
SATB WARNER R3306 $.30　　　　(S3853)

STANTON, R.
Glory! Hear The Song
SATB KJOS 5448 $.30　　　　(S3854)

STANTON, ROYAL [W.] (1916-　)
Behold And See　*Lent,mot
SATB oct WALTON 2024 $.30　　　(S3855)

Calm The Hillside　*Xmas
SATB oct WALTON 2011 $.30　　　(S3856)

God Is Here With Us
jr cor oct FISCHER,J 9208 $.30　　(S3857)

God's Son Is Born　*cant
mix cor BELWIN $1.75　　　　(S3858)

He Dies, The Friend Of Sinners Dies　*Easter/
Lent,mot
SATB oct WALTON 2025 $.30　　　(S3859)

He Was Despised　*Easter/Lent,mot
SATB oct WALTON 2023 $.25　　　(S3860)

I Will Lift Up Mine Eyes
3pt mix cor,acap oct LAWSON 51131 $.25
(S3861)

King Jesus Is A-Listenin'
SSA oct FISCHER,J 8553 $.30　　　(S3862)
TTBB oct FISCHER,J 8908 $.30　　　(S3863)
SATB oct FISCHER,J 9631 $.30　　　(S3864)
SAB oct FISCHER,J 9807 $.30　　　(S3865)

Lead Us, O Father
SATB FLAMMER A 5570 $.25　　　　(S3866)

Some Of These Mornin's
SATB oct PRESSER 312-40453 $.35　(S3867)

Steal Away And Pray
SATB oct PRESSER 312-40302 $.30　(S3868)

STANTON, [WALTER KENDALL] (1891-　)
Alleluia! Hearts To Heaven　*Easter
2pt (easy) oct OXFORD 45.018 $.30　(S3869)

Christ Is The World's True Light　*Gen
2pt (easy) oct OXFORD 40.007 $.30　(S3870)

Like A Flower　*carol
unis CRAMER 31 s.p.　　　　(S3871)

Ode To The Birth Of Our Savior　*carol
unis CRAMER 17　　　　(S3872)

When I Survey The Wondrous Cross　*Psntd
SATB (med easy) oct OXFORD 42.988 $.30
(S3873)

STANTON, [WALTER] KENDALL (1891-　)
With Happy Voices Ringing
unis ABINGDON APM-902 $.25　　　(S3874)

STAR
see Three Polish Carols

STAR, A see Track, Gerhard

STAR, A SHEPHERD, A LAMB, A see Shure

STAR AND THE STABLE, THE see Kountz, Richard

STAR AT CHRISTMAS see Davis, Katherine K.

STAR BRIGHT see Wheelwright, Lorin F.

STAR CANDLES see Head, Michael (Dewar)

STAR CAROL see Burt, Alfred

STAR CAROL see Carter

STAR CAROL, A (SAW YOU NEVER IN THE TWILIGHT)
see Couperin, Francois

STAR CAROL BOOK, THE see Schalk, Carl

STAR ETERNAL, THE see Loewe, Ernest

STAR IN THE EAST　*Xmas,folk/hymn,US
see Two Folk Carols
(Ehret) SATB LUDWIG L-1111 $.30　(S3875)
(Niles; Sheppard) 3pt boy cor/3pt wom cor oct
SCHIRM.G 10897 $.25　　　　(S3876)
(Stanton) SATB,med solo,acap oct LAWSON 807
$.25　　　　(S3877)

STAR IN THE EAST see Boatwright, Howard

STAR IN THE EAST see Lovelace, Austin C.

STAR IN THE EAST see Niles, John Jacob

STAR IN THE NIGHT, A see Martens

STAR IN THE SKY, A see Carleton

STAR IS MOVING, A　*carol,Mediev
(Lundquist, M.) SATB,acap SCHIRM.EC 2434 $.25
(S3878)

STAR-LED SHEPHERS, THE　*Xmas,Czech
(Jewell, Kenneth W.) SATB,opt pno oct WORLD
AC-1520-8 $.30　　　　(S3879)

STAR LIGHT, STAR BRIGHT see Avery

STAR MOVES BRIGHTLY THROUGH THE SKY, A　*Xmas
(Ehret) SATB oct PRO ART 2707 $.30　(S3880)

STAR OF BEATITUDE see Curtis, C.

STAR OF BETHLEHEM (from Ben-Hur)
SSA/SATB BIG3 $.35　　　　(S3881)

STAR OF BETHLEHEM see Ehret, Walter

STAR OF BETHLEHEM see Rheinberger, Josef

STAR OF BETHLEHEM, THE see Harker, F.
Flaxington

STAR OF BETHLEHEM, THE see Rheinberger, Josef

STAR OF JACOB see Gallus, Jacobus, Orietur
Stella

STAR OF THE EAST　*Epiph
SSA/SATB/SA BIG3 $.30　　　　(S3882)
(Warner, R.) unis/SA oct GRAY GCMR 3217 $.30
(S3883)

STAR OF THE EAST see Frackenpohl, Arthur

STAR OF THE EAST see Kennedy

STAR OF THE EAST see Smart, Henry Thomas

STAR OF THE MYSTIC EAST see Rubbra, Edmund

STAR OF THE ORIENT see Shelley, [Harry Rowe]

STAR OF THE SILENT NIGHT see Nolte

STAR ON THE CHRISTMAS TREE see Federer, R.

STAR OVER BETHLEHEM　*Xmas
(Ehret) SA SCHMITT 249 $.35　　　(S3884)

STAR OVER BETHLEHEM see Frederickson, Carl

STAR PROCLAIMS THE KING IS HERE, THE see
Schultz, Ralph

STAR PROCLAIMS THE KING IS HERE, THE see
Vulpius, Melchior

STAR PROCLAIMS THE KING, THE see Frank

STAR ROAD, THE see O'Hara, Geoffrey

STAR SHONE BRIGHT, A see Eilers

STAR SHONE OUT, A see Davis, Katherine K.

STAR SONG, THE see Forsblad

STAR SONG, THE see Kraehenbuehl, D.

STAR SPANGLED BANNER, THE see Key, F.S.

STAR-SWING IS HIGH see Hall

STAR THAT SHONE, A see Pearson, Edith

STAR, THE see Boatner, [Edward H.]

STAR, THE see Knighton

STAR, THE see Neff, James

STAR-TREE CAROL see Pinkham, Daniel

STAR WAS HIS CANDLE see Del Riego

STAR WAS HIS CANDLE, A see Del Riego

STAR WAS LIKE A CANDLE, THE see Staley

STARER
Joseph And His Brothers
SATB,narrator,STBarB soli,org/pno voc sc MCA $2.75, ipr (S3885)

STARER, ROBERT (1924-)
Ariel (Visions Of Isaiah)
SATB,SBar soli,pno/org voc sc MCA $2.75, ipr (S3886)

Ecelesiastes *see Kohelet

Give Thanks Unto The Lord
SATB oct GALAXY 1.2196.1 $.40 (S3887)

Kohelet
"Ecelesiastes" [Eng/Heb] SATB,SBar soli, pno/org/orch voc sc MCA $2.00, ipr (S3888)

Lord Shall Give Thee Rest, The
SATB,SATB soli,acap oct MCA (S3889)

May The Words
[Lat/Eng] mix cor,S solo,org oct MCA see from Sabbath Eve Service (S3890)

Psalm Of David, A
SATB oct PRESSER 312-40477 $.45 (S3891)

Sabbath Eve Service *see May The Words (S3892)

Sabbath Eve Service
SATB,TBar soli,org voc sc MCA $4.00 (S3893)

To Everything There Is A Season
SATB oct MCA (S3894)

Tune Me, O Lord
SATB oct MCA (S3895)

Vayechulu Hashamayim *liturg,Heb
cor,cantor oct PRESSER MC196 $.30 (S3896)

STARK, RICHARD
Praise The Lord
unis&4 cor,solo,org SCHIRM.EC 2425 $.35 (S3897)
unis&4pt,solo,org SCHIRM.EC 2425 $.35 (S3898)

STARKS
Christmas Introit *Xmas
SATB oct LORENZ C327 $.25 (S3899)

STARKS, HOWARD
God Wants A Man
TTBB oct AGAPE TB 200 $.30 (S3900)

STARLIGHT OVER BETHLEHEM see Mead, E.G.

STARLIT NIGHT see Brook, Harry

STARS ALL DOTTED OVER THE SKY see Sharpe, Evelyn

STARS ARE SHINING BRIGHT, THE *Xmas,carol
oct HART s.p. (S3901)

STARS LEAD US EVER ON *Xmas
(Gaul, H.) SATB oct PRESSER 332-14320 $.30 (S3902)

STARS LEAD US EVER ON see Gaul, Harvey Bartlet

STARS LOOK'D DOWN, THE see Luptin, H.J.

STARS OF ICE *Xmas,carol,Chin
(Berglund) SATB SCHMITT 915 $.35 (S3903)
(Walker, D.S.) unis, orff inst (easy) oct CONCORDIA 98-2079 $.30 (S3904)

STARS OVER BETHLEHEM see Stairs, L.

STARS SHED THEIR LIGHT see Gass, Irene

STARS SHONE BRIGHT, THE *Xmas,Norw
unis oct LORENZ 8861 $.25 (S3905)

STARS SHONE BRIGHT, THE see Williams

STATHAM, HEATHCOTE (DICKEN) (1889-)
Christmas Song, A *Xmas
SA (easy) OXFORD 82.073 $.25 (S3906)

Communion Service In D *Commun,Agnus/Bene/Gloria/Kyrie/Sanctus
SATB/unis,opt org (easy) oct OXFORD 43.296 $.50 (S3907)

Drop Down, Ye Heavens *BVM,Bibl
SS (very easy) oct OXFORD $.25 (S3908)

Magnificat And Nunc Dimittis In E Minor *Magnif/Nunc
oct ROYAL 113 s.p. (S3909)

Praise Thou The Lord *Thanks,anthem
mix cor oct NOVELLO 40.1345.10 s.p. (S3910)

There Were Shepherds *Xmas,anthem
mix cor oct NOVELLO 40.1388.03 s.p. (S3911)

Ie Know That The Lord Is Gracious *anthem
mix cor oct NOVELLO 28.1392.00 s.p. (S3912)

STATIONS, THE see Eager, Mary Anne

STATON
Race That Long In Darkness Pined
SAB KJOS 5736 $.30 (S3913)

STEADFAST IN FAITH see Clokey, Joseph Waddell

STEADY JESUS LISTENING see Nosse

STEAL AWAY *anthem/spir,US
see Negro Spirituals
see Old Ark's A-Moverin'
"Mach Dich Auf" see Funf Negro-Spirituals
SATB CHAPPELL 0023010-358 $.40 (S3914)
(Bartholomew) 4pt men cor,acap oct SCHIRM.G 7756 $.30 contains also: Old Ark's A-Moverin' (S3915)
(Burleigh) SSA RICORDI-ENG LD459 s.p. (S3916)
(Christiansen, P.) SATB SCHMITT 1803 $.35 (S3917)
(Clements, J.) SATB PROWSE s.p. (S3918)
(Genuchi) SATB LUDWIG SS-024 $.30 (S3919)
(Genuchi) TTBB LUDWIG SS-026 $.35 (S3920)
(Hall) SATB oct WORD CS-1945 $.30 (S3921)
(Johnson) SATB oct FISCHER,C CM-4581 $.25 (S3922)
(Johnson) SSA oct FISCHER,C CM-5214 $.25 (S3923)
(Johnson) TTBB oct FISCHER,C CM-2184 $.25 (S3924)
(Mittergradnegger, Gunther) [Ger] mix cor, acap oct &OBLINGER s.p. see also Funf Amerikanische Negro-Spirituals (S3925)
(Pens) SATB,acap oct PRO ART 1191 $.25 (S3926)
(Ritz, James) SA,pno oct WESTWOOD ESE-1444-2 $.30 (S3927)
(Roberts) SATB,acap,opt perc oct LAWSON 51554 $.30 (S3928)
(Shaw; Parker) SATB,T solo,acap oct LAWSON 51104 $.30 (S3929)
(Trant) SSA,acap (med easy) oct OXFORD 83.046 $.25 (S3930)
(Widen) TTBB oct LILLENAS AN-3832 $.25 (S3931)

STEAL AWAY AND PRAY
(Stanton, R.) SAB oct PRESSER 312-40438 $.30 (S3932)

STEAL AWAY AND PRAY see Stanton, Royal [W.]

STEAL AWAY TO JESUS *spir
(Jerome, F.) TB,pno (easy) oct WILLIS 6465 $.12 (S3933)
(Peery) SA/SAB oct LORENZ 7804 $.25 (S3934)
(Roberton) 3pt jr cor/3pt wom cor ROBERTON 72104 s.p. (S3935)
(Roberton) mix cor ROBERTON 61288 s.p. (S3936)
(White) 4pt mix cor,acap oct SCHIRM.G 11003 $.25 (S3937)

STEANE, BRUCE
Great Is The Lord *Harv/Thanks,anthem
mix cor oct NOVELLO 28.0481.06 s.p. (S3938)

STEARNS
Christmas Carol Pageant, A *see Diller, Angela

STEBBINS
In The Secret Of His Presence
(Whitman) SATB oct LILLENAS AN-2309 $.30 (S3939)

There Is A Green Hill *Psntd,hymn
(Rogers) 2pt jr cor/3pt jr cor oct LILLENAS AN-4011 $.25 (S3940)

STEBBINS, GEORGE [COLES] (1846-1945)
Have Thine Own Way, Lord
(Hustad) SATB oct AGAPE HA 116 $.30 (S3941)
(Landon) SATB oct LORENZ A375 $.25 (S3942)

Savior My Heart Is Thine *hymn
(Hustad, Don) SATB ALLANS 455 s.p. (S3943)

STECKEL
Favorite Hymn For Women's Voices *CCU
SSA FLAMMER GB5006 $.80 (S3944)

STEDFAST AND GOOD IS JEHOVAH see Goudimel, Claude

STEEL
O Clap Your Hands Together
SATB,opt brass SOUTHERN $.40 (S3945)

STEEL AWAY TO JESUS *spir
(Dexter, Harry) 2pt ENOCH TP270 s.p. (S3946)

STEEL, CHRISTOPHER [CHARLES] (1939-)
Gethsemane *Psntd,cant
SA,orch voc sc NOVELLO 20.0021.00 s.p., ipr, sc NOVELLO rental (S3947)

Mary Magdalene *cant
SSA,pno/orch voc sc NOVELLO 20.0119.05 s.p., ipr (S3948)

Mass In Five Movements *Op.17, Mass
[Lat] SATB,ST soli,pno,3fl,2ob,2clar,2bsn, 4horn,2trp,3trom,tuba,strings,perc,timp, harp, vibraphone, celesta voc sc NOVELLO s.p., ipr (S3949)

Morning Stars Sang Together, The *Xmas, anthem
mix cor oct NOVELLO 28.1469.02 s.p. (S3950)

O Clap Your Hands Together *anthem
SATB,org/pno,brass NOVELLO AP 223 $.40, ipr (S3951)
SATB,org/brass oct NOVELLO 29.0015.07 s.p., ipr (S3952)

O Come, Let Us Sing Unto The Lord *anthem
mix cor oct NOVELLO 28.1467.06 s.p. (S3953)

O Praise The Lord Of Heaven *Thanks,anthem
mix cor oct NOVELLO 28.1480.03 s.p. (S3954)

Thou Art The Way *anthem/hymn
mix cor,TBar/B soli oct NOVELLO 91.0003.02 s.p. (S3955)

Thou, O God, Art Praised In Zion *Gen/Harv, anthem/Bibl
4pt mix cor,org oct SCHIRM.G 11465 $.30 (S3956)
mix cor oct NOVELLO 40.1479.00 s.p. (S3957)

STEELE
How Firm A Foundation
(Iderstine) SATB oct FISCHER,C CM-7466 $.25 (S3958)

STEELE (cont'd.)

Love Came Down At Christmastide *Xmas,carol
SATB ALLANS 267 s.p. (S3959)

STEELE, J.A.
He, Remembering His Mercy *Austral
SATB ALLANS 197 s.p. (S3960)

STEENMAN, J.
Miseremini Mei
[Fr] opt STBB,solo,pno/org HEUGEL s.p. (S3961)

STEER, MICHAEL
Easter Song *Easter
unis oct NOVELLO 91.0011.03 s.p. (S3962)

STEFFANI, AGOSTINO (1654-1728)
Come, Ye Children, And Harken To Me *Gen
SA,kbd oct CONCORDIA 98-1593 $.25 (S3963)

Stabat Mater
(Sievers) 6pt mix cor,soli,cont,strings MOSELER sc rental, voc sc s.p., cor pts s.p., ipa (S3964)

STEFFANS
Amica Mea *mot
(Wagner, Hermann) 4pt mix cor&4pt mix cor MOSELER s.p. (S3965)

STEFFE, [WILLIAM]
Battle Hymn Of The Republic
(Duncan) sr cor&jr cor BOSTON 10693 $.30 (S3966)
(Ringwald) SATB SHAWNEE A 28 $.40 (S3967)
(Skiles) SAT oct LILLENAS AN-3801 $.30 (S3968)
(Wilhousky) 3pt jr cor/SSA (med easy) FISCHER,C CM 6777 $.30 (S3969)
(Wilhousky) SSA oct FISCHER,C CM-6777 $.30 (S3970)
(Wilhousky) SATB oct FISCHER,C CM-4743 $.30 (S3971)
(Wilhousky) TTBB oct FISCHER,C CM-6778 $.30 (S3972)
(Wilson) SAB oct LORENZ 7373 $.25 (S3973)

STEFFENS
Lasst Uns Zusammen
(Merrill) "Let Every Voice Raise" SSATB, acap (med) OXFORD 95.302 $.50 (S3974)

Let Every Voice Raise *see Lasst Uns Zusammen

Let Him Who Would Not *see Wer Leben Will

Wer Leben Will
(Merrill) "Let Him Who Would Not" SSATB, acap (med) OXFORD 95.304 $.35 (S3975)

STEGEN, WILFRIED (1938-)
Erstanden Ist Der Heilig Christ
see Hennig, Walter, Jesus Christus, Unser Heiland, Der Den Tod Uberwand

Ihr Lieben Christen, Freut Euch Nun
see Peter, Herbert, Gottes Sohn Ist Kommen

STEGGALL, CHARLES (1826-1905)
Remember Now Thy Creator *anthem
mix cor oct NOVELLO 28.0038.01 s.p. (S3976)

STEH AUF, HERR GOTT see Burkhard Willy

STEH AUF, NIMM DAS KINDLEIN UND SEINE MUTTER see Raselius, Andreas

STEHE AUF UND NIMM DAS KINDLEIN see Driessler, Johannes

STEHT AUF, IHR LIEBEN KINDERLEIN see Koch, Johannes H.E.

STEHT AUF, IHR LIEBEN KINDERLEIN see Neubert, Gottfried

STEHT AUF, IHR LIEBEN KINDERLEIN see Stern, Hermann

STEHT AUF UND WACHT see Schrenk, Johannes

STEIGLEDER, JOH. ULRICH (1593-1635)
Veni Sancte Spiritus *mot
(Gottwald) STTTBB HANSSLER 1.457 s.p. (S3977)

STEIN
Bless The Lord, O My Soul *Gen
(Wismar) TTBB SCHMITT 3513 $.25 (S3978)

STEIN, C.
Sursum Corda Vol. 1 *CCU
4pt men cor (easy) LEUCKART s.p. cloth, pap (S3979)

Sursum Corda Vol. 2 *CCU
4pt men cor (easy) LEUCKART s.p. cloth, pap (S3980)

Sursum Corda Vol. 4 *mot
mix cor (easy) cloth,pap LEUCKART s.p. (S3981)

Sursum Corda Vol. 5 *CCU
3pt men cor (easy) LEUCKART s.p. cloth, pap (S3982)

Sursum Corda Vol. 6 *mot
3pt jr cor/3pt wom cor/men cor (easy) cloth LEUCKART s.p. (S3983)

STEIN, JOSEF (1910-)
Omnes Gentes *Trin
[Lat] SATB,acap (med) MULLER SM 925 s.p. (S3984)

STEINBERG, BEN
And I Will Betroth You To Me *see V'erastich Li

Pirchay Shir Kodesh *Sab-Eve
SATB TRANSCON. TCL 860 $3.75 (S3985)

Retsay Adona'i *Heb
SATB,acap ISRAELI 330 s.p. (S3986)

V'erastich Li
"And I Will Betroth You To Me" [Eng/Heb] cor,solo TRANSCON. TCL 689 $.75 (S3987)

STEINEL
Great Peace Have They
SATB oct LORENZ 9400 $.30 (S3988)

STEINER, LUIS
O Freedom! *sac/sec,CC2U,spir
[Eng] 4pt mix cor MOSELER s.p. (S3989)

STEINKE, GREG
Psalm 23
mix cor,ob/harp&strings sc SEESAW $3.00 (S3990)

STEINMAN, W.
Psalms Of Rejoicing
SSAATTBB,acap oct PRESSER MC385 $.40 (S3991)

STEKKE, LEON
Chant De Paix *Op.27
[Fr] jr cor (easy) BROGNEAUX s.p. (S3992)

Inmemoriam *Op.14
sc BROGNEAUX s.p. (S3993)

L'Ame Des Forgerons
[Fr] 4pt men cor sc BROGNEAUX s.p. (S3994)

STELLARIO IN ONORE DI MARIA SS. see Bottazzo,
Luigi

STELLHORN, AUGUST W.
Come, Your Hearts And Voices Raising
see THREE CHRISTMAS HYMNS AND CAROLS

Hark, Now, O Shepherds
see THREE CHRISTMAS HYMNS AND CAROLS

STENHAMMAR, [PER ULRIK] (1829-1875)
Jeg Har Hort Hvor Sangen Gar
(Sorass, Lars) mix cor MUSIKK 139 s.p. see
from Religiose Korsnager (S3995)

Religiose Korsnager *see Jeg Har Hort Hvor
Sangen Gar (S3996)

STENSON, E.J.
Prayer Perfect, The
2pt PROWSE s.p. (S3997)

STEP BY STEP
SATB CHAPPELL 0017004-358 $.40 (S3998)

STEP INTO THE SUNSHINE *CCU
(Gassman, Clark) jr cor voc sc WORD 37547
$1.95 (S3999)

STEPHEN WAS A STABLE-BOY see Staffan Var En
Stalledrang

STEPHENS, EVAN
Let The Mountains Shout For Joy
(Scholin) SAB oct BELWIN 1475 $.25 (S4000)
(Scholin) SSA oct BELWIN 1240 $.30 (S4001)
(Scholin) SATB oct BELWIN 1119 $.25 (S4002)

STERBEMOTETTE *mot
(Burkhart, Franz) mix cor,acap DOBLINGER s.p.
see also In Seiner Handen (S4003)

STERN, A
Geistliche Zwiegesange Zum Morgen Und Abend
*CC2U
[Ger] mix cor,acap (med) HUG s.p. (S4004)

Maria Durch Ein Dornwald Ging *Xmas
[Ger] wom cor,acap (med easy) HUG s.p. (S4005)

Neujahrslied
[Ger] mix cor,acap (easy) HUG s.p. (S4006)

STERN, HERMANN (1912-   )
All Morgen Ist Ganz Frisch Und Neu
see Stern, Hermann, Der Tag Bricht An Und
Zeiget Sich

Aller Augen Warten Auf Dich, Herre
SAT/SAB,cont HANSSLER 7.059 s.p. (S4007)

Auf Meinen Lieben Gott Trau Ich
SATB HANSSLER 8.016 s.p. contains also:
Christ, Du Lamm Gottes (S4008)

Aus Meines Herzens Grunde
see Stern, Hermann, Die Helle Sonn Leucht'
Jetzt Herfur

Befiehl Du Deine Wege
see Stern, Hermann, Bis Hieher Hat Mich
Gott Gebracht

Bis Hieher Hat Mich Gott Gebracht
SAT/SAB,fl,vcl HANSSLER 8.051 s.p. contains
also: Befiehl Du Deine Wege (SAT/SAB,fl,
vln) (S4009)

Christ, Du Lamm Gottes
see Stern, Hermann, Auf Meinen Lieben Gott
Trau Ich

Christe, Du Bist Der Helle Tag
see Stern, Hermann, Himmel, Erde, Luft Und
Meer

Christus, Der Ist Mein Leben
see Stern, Hermann, Was Gott Tut, Das Ist
Wohlgetan

Das Alte Jahr Vergangen Ist *cant
SAB&cong,brass HANSSLER 10.061 sc s.p., cor
pts s.p. (S4010)

Der Herr Ist Mein Getreuer Hirt
SAT/SAB HANSSLER 8.047 s.p. contains also:
Nun Jauchzt Dem Herren, Alle Welt (SAT/
SAB,vln,2timp); Lobt Gott Den Herrn, Ihr
Heiden All (SAT/SAB,vln,2timp); Ein Feste
Burg Ist Unser Gott (SAT/SAB) (S4011)

Der Herr Ist Mein Hirte (Psalm 23) mot
2 eq voices,inst JEHLE EJ5 s.p. (S4012)

Der Tag Bricht An Und Zeiget Sich
SAT/SAB,fl HANSSLER 8.054 s.p. contains
also: All Morgen Ist Ganz Frisch Und Neu
(SAT/SAB,fl,bvl, xylophone or glock-
enspiel instead of flute); Steht Auf, Ihr
Lieben Kinderlein (SAT/SAB,vln) (S4013)

STERN, HERMANN (cont'd.)
Der Tag, Der Ist So Freudenreich
see Trubel, Gerhard, Lobt Gott, Ihr
Christen Alle Gleich

Die Helle Sonn Leucht' Jetzt Herfur
SAT/SAB,vln,bvl, xylophone HANSSLER 8.055
s.p. contains also: Aus Meines Herzens
Grunde (SAT/SAB) (S4014)

Dir, Dir, Jehova, Will Ich Singen
SAT/SAB,fl, xylophone HANSSLER 8.052 s.p.
contains also: O Dass Ich Tausend Zungen
Hatte (SAT/SAB,fl,vcl) (S4015)

Durchs Kirchenjahr *CC8U,chorale/mot
SAT/SAB,inst JEHLE EJ4 s.p. (S4016)

Ein Feste Burg Ist Unser Gott
see Stern, Hermann, Der Herr Ist Mein
Getreuer Hirt

Erschienen Ist Der Herrlich Tag *cant
SATB,4brass HANSSLER 10.076 sc s.p., cor
pts s.p. (S4017)

Es Ist Das Heil Uns Kommen Her *cant
SATB,TS soli,org,3trp,2trom,tuba,2timp
HANSSLER 10.017 sc s.p., voc sc s.p., ipa (S4018)

Es Ist Ein Ros Entsprungen
SAT/SAB,S rec,bvl, xylophone HANSSLER 8.042
s.p. contains also: Nun Singet Und Seid
Froh (SAT/SAB,fl,bvl, xylophone or
glockenspiel) (S4019)

Es Ist Gewisslich An Der Zeit
SA/ST,treb inst HANSSLER 14.120 s.p. (S4020)

Es Wandeln Sich Die Reiche
see Stier, Alfred, Gottes Stimme Lasst Uns
Sein

Freuet Euch, Ihr Christen Alle
SAT/SAB/SAT/SAB&cong,org/fl&vcl HANSSLER
8.043 s.p. contains also: Ich Steh An
Deiner Krippen Hier (SAT/SAB,fl) (S4021)

Freut Euch, Ihr Lieben Christen All
SAT/SAB,fl/vln, xylophone HANSSLER 8.044
s.p. contains also: Herr Christ, Der
Einig Gott's Sohn (SAT/SAB); Wie Schon
Leuchtet Der Morgenstern (SAT/SAB,fl,vcl) (S4022)

Frohlich Soll Mein Herze Springen *cant
SAB&cong,4brass HANSSLER 10.060 sc s.p.,
cor pts s.p. (S4023)

Geh Aus, Mein Herz, Und Suche Freud
SAT/SAB,vln,bvl HANSSLER 8.057 s.p.
contains also: Wer Wohlauf Ist Und Gesund
(SAT/SAB,bvl,rec, or xylophone) (S4024)

Gelobt Sei Gott Im Hochsten Thorn
SAT/SAB,fl,vcl, xylophone HANSSLER 8.046
s.p. contains also: Gen Himmel
Aufgefahren Ist (SAT/SAB,fl,vcl); Wachet
Auf, Ruft Uns Die Stimme (SAT/SAB,ob/trp/
vln) (S4025)

Gen Himmel Aufgefahren Ist
see Stern, Hermann, Gelobt Sei Gott Im
Hochsten Thorn

Gott Ruft Dich Heut Durch Jesum Christ
see Stier, Alfred, Gottes Stimme Lasst Uns
Sein

Gottes Sohn Ist Kommen
SAT/SAB,fl,bvl HANSSLER 8.041 s.p. contains
also: Macht Hoch Die Tur, Die Tor Macht
Weit (SAT/SAB,vcl,bvl, xylophone or
glockenspiel) (S4026)

Herr Christ, Der Einig Gott's Sohn
see Stern, Hermann, Freut Euch, Ihr Lieben
Christen All

Himmel, Erde, Luft Und Meer
SAT/SAB,2vln HANSSLER 8.056 s.p. contains
also: Christe, Du Bist Der Helle Tag
(SAT/SAB/AT/AB); Hinunter Ist Der Sonnen
Schein (SAT/SAB, xylophone and
glockenspiel) (S4027)

Hinunter Ist Der Sonnen Schein
see Stern, Hermann, Himmel, Erde, Luft Und
Meer
SA,org,2rec HANSSLER 5.061 s.p. (S4028)

Ich Freu Mich In Dem Herren
see Schutz, Heinrich, Lasst Uns Den Herren
Loben
see Marx, Karl, Gelobet Sei Der Herr
see Bach, Johann Sebastian, O Gott, Du
Frommer Gott

Ich Singe Dir Mit Herz Und Mund
SAT/SAB, xylophone HANSSLER 8.050 s.p.
contains also: Sei Lob Und Ehr Dem
Hochsten Gut (SAT/SAB,fl,2timp, or
xylophone) (S4029)

Ich Steh An Deiner Krippen Hier
see Stern, Hermann, Freuet Euch, Ihr
Christen Alle

Ihr Lieben Christen, Freut Euch Nun
SATB/SA/SAB HANSSLER 8.012 s.p. (S4030)
SATB/SAB HANSSLER 6.088 s.p. contains also:
Koch, Heinz, Mitt Ernst, O Menschenkinder (S4031)

Jesu Kreuz, Leiden Und Pein
see Stern, Hermann, O Konig Aller Ehren

Jungend-Kantate
see Stier, Alfred, Gottes Stimme Lasst Uns
Sein

Kirchenlied Im Kanon *CC42U
SAB,opt inst HANSSLER 2.019 s.p. (S4032)

Klingende Kette *CC130U,canon
[Ger] mix cor BAREN. EM 429 s.p. (S4033)

Kommt Her Zu Mir, Spricht Gottes Sohn
SS/TT/TB/STB,3brass HANSSLER 8.032 s.p.
contains also: Metzger, Hans-Arnold,

STERN, HERMANN (cont'd.)
Kommt Her Zu Mir, Spricht Gottes Sohn
(SATB) (S4034)

Lob Gott Getrost Mit Singen
see Stern, Hermann, Lobt Gott, Ihr Frommen
Christen

Lobe Den Herren, Den Machitgen Konig
see Stern, Hermann, Nun Danket Alle Gott

Lobet Den Herren, Denn Er Ist Sehr Freundlich
*cant
SAB,2fl/fl,ob,vcl/bsn,org HANSSLER 10.091
sc s.p., voc sc s.p., ipa (S4035)

Lobt Gott Den Herrn, Ihr Heiden All
see Stern, Hermann, Der Herr Ist Mein
Getreuer Hirt

Lobt Gott, Ihr Christen Allzugleich *Xmas,
cant
[Ger] 2pt mix cor&cong,3trp,2trom (med
easy) BAREN. BA 2639 sc $2.75, cor pts
$.40, ipa (S4036)

Lobt Gott, Ihr Frommen Christen *Thanks,
canon
SAT/SAB,trp/vln,2timp HANSSLER 8.048 s.p.
contains also: Lob Gott Getrost Mit
Singen (SAT/SAB,vln) (S4037)
SATB/SSATB HANSSLER 6.021 s.p. contains
also: Telemann, Georg Philipp, Ich Wis
Den Herren Loben Allezeit (3pt); Clemens,
Jacobus, Sanctus, Sanctus, Sanctus (5pt) (S4038)

Macht Hoch Die Tur, Die Tor Macht Weit
see Stern, Hermann, Gottes Sohn Ist Kommen

Mit Einem Mund *CCU
[Ger] unis BAREN. EM 390 s.p. (S4039)

Nun Bitten Wir Den Heiligen Geist *cant
SATB,5-6brass HANSSLER 10.095 sc s.p., cor
pts s.p. (S4040)

Nun Danket Alle Gott
SAT/SAB,trp,2timp, xylophone HANSSLER 8.049
s.p. contains also: Lobe Den Herren, Den
Machitgen Konig (SAT/SAB,fl,trp,2timp) (S4041)

Nun Freut Euch, Lieben Christen G'mein
see Ducis, Benedictus, Nun Freut Euch,
Lieben Christen G'mein

Nun Jauchzt Dem Herren, Alle Welt
see Stern, Hermann, Der Herr Ist Mein
Getreuer Hirt

Nun Komm, Der Heiden Heiland
SA/SAT/SATB HANSSLER 8.001 s.p. contains
also: Kubler, Emil, Mit Freuden Zart Zu
Dieser Fahrt (SS/ST/SATB/SAB,inst) (S4042)

Nun Singet Und Seid Froh
see Stern, Hermann, Es Ist Ein Ros
Entsprungen

O Dass Ich Tausend Zungen Hatte
see Stern, Hermann, Dir, Dir, Jehova, Will
Ich Singen

O Glaubig Herz, Gebenedei Und Gib
SATB/SA HANSSLER 8.014 s.p. (S4043)

O Gott, Du Frommer Gott
SAT/SAB,fl HANSSLER 8.058 s.p. contains
also: Wach Auf, Wach Auf, Du Deutsches
Land (SAT/SAB,vln/trp) (S4044)

O Konig Aller Ehren
SAT/SAB,fl,bvl HANSSLER 8.045 s.p. contains
also: Jesu Kreuz, Leiden Und Pein (SAT/
SAB,fl) (S4045)

O Mensch, Bewein Dein Stunde Gross
SA/TB,treb inst HANSSLER 14.054 (S4046)

Psalm 23 *see Der Herr Ist Mein Hirte

Sei Lob Und Ehr Dem Hochsten Gut
see Stern, Hermann, Ich Singe Dir Mit Herz
Und Mund

Steht Auf, Ihr Lieben Kinderlein
see Stern, Hermann, Der Tag Bricht An Und
Zeiget Sich
SATB/SAB/SA HANSSLER 8.031 s.p. (S4047)

Such, Wer Da Will, Ein Ander Ziel *cant
SATB&cong,narrator,5brass HANSSLER 10.094
sc s.p., cor pts s.p. (S4048)

Vater Unser Im Himmelreich
see Koch, Heinz, Jesus Christus, Unser
Heiland

Wach Auf, Wach Auf, Du Deutsches Land
see Stern, Hermann, O Gott, Du Frommer Gott

Wachet Auf, Ruft Uns Die Stimme
see Stern, Hermann, Gelobt Sei Gott Im
Hochsten Thorn

Walte, Walte Nah Und Fern
see Stier, Alfred, Gottes Stimme Lasst Uns
Sein

Was Gott Tut, Das Ist Wohlgetan
SAT/SAB,fl,vcl HANSSLER 8.053 s.p. contains
also: Christus, Der Ist Mein Leben (SAT/
SAB,vln); Wir Danken Gott Fur Seine Gaben
(SAT/SAB) (S4049)

Wer Wohlauf Ist Und Gesund
see Stern, Hermann, Geh Aus, Mein Herz, Und
Suche Freud

Wie Schon Leuchtet Der Morgenstern
see Bach, Johann Sebastian, Herr Christ,
Der Einig Gotts Sohn [Chorale]
see Stern, Hermann, Freut Euch, Ihr Lieben
Christen All

Wir Danken Gott Fur Seine Gaben
see Stern, Hermann, Was Gott Tut, Das Ist
Wohlgetan

STERN, PATRICIA
Beckoning Star, The *Xmas
SATB,acap oct WORLD AC-600-8 $.30 (S4050)

STERN UBER BETHLEHEM see Zoller, Alfred Hans

STERNBERG, E.W.
Lobgesang *Heb
"Praise Ye" SATB,Bar solo,acap ISRAELI 303
s.p. (S4051)

Praise Ye *see Lobgesang

STERNBURG, DANIEL
Be Merciful, Lord
SATB oct WORD CS-2571 $.30 (S4052)

Grant, We Beseech Thee
SATB oct WORD CS-2392 $.30 (S4053)

STERNE, COLIN
Angel Of The Lord, An
see Three Anthems For Easter

Crave As Newborn Babes
see Three Anthems For Easter

Put In Your Hand
see Three Anthems For Easter

Three Anthems For Easter *Bibl
oct WORLD EMP-1595 $.60
contains: Angel Of The Lord, An (TB&
cong); Crave As Newborn Babes (unis&
cong); Put In Your Hand (TB&cong)
(S4054)

STEUBING
Jesus The Christ Is Born
SATB,acap SHAWNEE A 443 $.35 (S4055)

STEURLEIN, JOHANN (1546-1613)
Wie Lieblich Ist Der Maien
(Berger,H.L.) TTBB HANSSLER 6.5085 s.p.
(S4056)

STEVENS
In Te, Domini Speravi (Psalm 31)
"In Thee, O Lord, Have I Put My Trust"
SATB,org/pno PETERS 6520 $.40 (S4057)

In Thee, O Lord, Have I Put My Trust *see In
Te, Domini Speravi

Morning Has Broken
(Simeone) SATB SHAWNEE A 1175 $.35 (S4058)
(Simeone) SAB SHAWNEE D156 $.35 (S4059)

O Word Of God Incarnate
SATB&desc oct PRO ART 1682 $.22 (S4060)

Psalm 31 *see In Te, Domini Speravi

STEVENS, HALSEY (1908-)
All This Night Shrill Chanticleer *sac/sec,
Xmas,carol
TBB,acap PEER $.35 see from Four Carols
(S4061)
As I Rode Out This Enderes Night *sac/sec,
Xmas,carol
TBB,acap PEER $.35 see from Four Carols
(S4062)
Beatus Vir (Psalm 1)
"Blessed Is The Man" SATB,acap FOSTER MF112
$.30 (S4063)

Blessed Be Thy Glorious Name
SATB FOSTER MF114 $.30 (S4064)

Blessed Is The Man *see Beatus Vir

Epitaph For Sara And Roland Cotton, An
SATB,acap FOSTER MF132 $.35 (S4065)

Four Carols *see All This Night Shrill
Chanticleer; As I Rode Out This Enderes
Night; Virgin Most Pure, A; What Sweeter
Music (S4066)

God Is My Strong Salvation
SATB FOSTER MF 118 $.25 (S4067)

Magnificat *Magnif
SATB,kbd&trp/trp&strings FOSTER MF108
$1.00, ipa, ipr (S4068)

New Year Carol, A *carol
SATB FOSTER EH $.20 (S4069)

Nunc Dimittis *Nunc
SATB,acap FOSTER MF 130 $.30 (S4070)

O God The Refuge Of Our Fears
SATB,acap FOSTER MF128 $.35 (S4071)

O Lord, Our Governor (Psalm 8)
SATB FOSTER $.35 (S4072)

O Worship The King
SATB,org FOSTER EH $.40 (S4073)

Praise The Lord Who Reigns Above *canon
SA/unis,kbd FOSTER EH $.35 (S4074)

Praise Ye The Lord (Psalm 148)
SATB,acap FOSTER EH $.35 (S4075)

Psalm 1 *see Beatus Vir

Psalm 8 *see O Lord, Our Governor

Psalm 98
SSA,pno PEER $.45 (S4076)

Psalm 148 *see Praise Ye The Lord

Set Of Three, A *CC3U,Xmas
TTBB FOSTER EH $.50 (S4077)

Te Deum *Te Deum
SATB,org,2trp,2horn,2trom,tuba,timp sc
FOSTER MF120 $3.50, ipa, cor pts FOSTER
MF120A $.65 (S4078)

Virgin Most Pure, A *sac/sec,Xmas,carol
TBB,acap PEER $.45 see from Four Carols
(S4079)

Way Of Jehovah, The *Adv
SATB,pno/org FOSTER MF 110 $.30 (S4080)

STEVENS, HALSEY (cont'd.)
What Sweeter Music *sac/sec,Xmas,carol
TBB,acap PEER $.40 see from Four Carols
(S4081)

STEVENSON
Hark! The Vesper Hymn Is Stealing
(Howorth) SAB oct PRO ART 1136 $.25 (S4082)
(Howorth) SATB oct PRO ART 1089 $.25
(S4083)
(Howorth) TTBB,acap oct PRO ART 1002 $.16
(S4084)
(Howorth) SSA oct PRO ART 1068 $.20 (S4085)

STEVENSON, D.
What Color Is God's Skin? *see Wilkes, T.

STEVENSON, F.
I Sought The Lord
SATB oct PRESSER 332-10100 $.25 (S4086)

To Come, O Lord, To Thee
4pt mix cor,S/T solo oct SCHIRM.G 10501
$.25 (S4087)

STEVENSON, RONALD (1928-)
No Coward Soul Is Mine
4pt oct NOVELLO 40.1512.06 s.p. (S4088)

STEWARD'S PRAYER, THE see Schoenfeld, William
C.

STEWART
All God's Chillun'
SATB SHAWNEE A 894 $.30 (S4089)

Glory To Our King
(Wiley) SATB oct PRO ART 1865 $.25 (S4090)

Hail The Victor *Easter,cant
SATB LORENZ $1.95 (S4091)

On This Day, Earth Shall Ring
SATB (med easy) oct OXFORD 42.238 $.25 (S4092)

Prayer, A *prayer
(Bown) SSA oct SOUTHERN $.25 (S4093)

STEWART, C. HYLTON
Christ Being Raised From The Dead *Easter
SATB (very easy) oct OXFORD 42.128 $.25 (S4094)

Evening Service In C *Eve,Magnif/Nunc
unis (very easy) oct OXFORD 45.302 $.30 (S4095)

God Will Answer Prayer (composed with
Stewart,[Herbert G.])
SATB oct LORENZ B44 $.25 (S4096)

Short And Easy Communion Service, A *Commun,
Agnus/Bene/Credo/Gloria/Kyrie/Sanctus
SATB (easy) oct OXFORD 42.315 $.65 (S4097)

To The Name Of Our Salvation *anthem
SATB,org CRAMER A 2 s.p. (S4098)

STEWART, H.C.
Veni Sancte Spiritus *Whitsun,anthem/mot
SSATB,acap oct NOVELLO 86.0003.01 s.p.
(S4099)

STEWART, [HERBERT G.] (1909-)
God Will Answer Prayer *see Stewart, C.
Hylton

STEWART, HUMPHREY JOHN (1856-1932)
Holy, Holy, Holy Lord God Almighty
4pt mix cor oct SCHIRM.G 4050 $.30 (S4100)

STEWART, KENSEY D.
Alleluia
SATB,acap oct LAWSON 51407 $.30 (S4101)

STIBBE, A.
Ave Maria
men cor ALSBACH&D sc s.p., cor pts s.p.
(S4102)

STICKLES
Easter Songs For Community Singing *CCU,
Easter
SATB HANSEN-US H274 $.40 (S4103)

God So Loved The World
SSA HANSEN-US C220 $.40 (S4104)

Spirituals *CCU,spir
SSA HANSEN-US H283 $.40 (S4105)

Spirituals *CCU,spir
SAB HANSEN-US H284 $.40 (S4106)

Spirituals *CCU,spir
SATB HANSEN-US H285 $.40 (S4107)

Spirituals *CCU,spir
TTBB HANSEN-US H286 $.40 (S4108)

STICKLES, WILLIAM
Angel's Song, The
SATB oct HUNTZINGER 4022 $.20 (S4109)

Faithful Shepherd, Guide Me
(Verrall) 4pt mix cor,high solo oct
SCHIRM.G 9710 $.30 (S4110)

Grant Me, Dear Lord, Deep Peace Of Mind
SATB oct HUNTZINGER 4044 $.16 (S4111)
SSA oct HUNTZINGER 508 $.25 (S4112)

My Soul Is Athirst For God
SATB AMP A362 $.20 (S4113)

Recessional *see De Koven, [Henry Louis
Reginald]

Rest In The Lord
SATB AMP A364 $.20 (S4114)

STIEFEL, M.V.
Gott, Der Da Hiess Das Licht
[Ger] mix cor,acap (diff) HUG s.p. (S4115)

Komm, Heil'ger Geist *chorale
[Ger] mix cor,acap (easy) HUG s.p. (S4116)

STIER, ALFRED (1880-1971)
Aus Meines Jammers Tiefe (Psalm 130)
see Stier, Alfred, Nun Sei Uns Willkommen,
Herre Christ

STIER, ALFRED (cont'd.)
Dass Ich Wieder Frohlich Preise
see Stier, Alfred, Heut Greift Nach Deinem
Herzen

Dass Wir Getroster
see Stier, Alfred, Kyrie Eleison, O
Erbarmen Gross

Des Sommers Will Ich Singen
see Stier, Alfred, Volk Will Leben, Herr
Gott, Hilf

Du Bist Der Herr, Ins Amt Gestellt
see Stier, Alfred, Machtvoll In Der Zeiten
Wunde

Ehre Sei Dir, Christe *No.57, Psntd
[Ger] 4pt mix cor,acap BAREN. EM 65 s.p.
see from Evangelisches Kirchengesangbuch
(S4117)

Ein Kleines Weihnachtsoratorium *Xmas,ora
1-3pt wom cor/1-3pt boy cor,SAT soli,org,
3fl,2vln HANSSLER 10.168 sc s.p., voc sc
s.p., ipa (S4118)

Ein Ruf Hat Uns Getroffen
SAB HANSSLER 6.224 s.p. contains also:
Herr, Aller Enden (S4119)

Eingeborner Gottessohn Wahrer Gott *Xmas
SATB HANSSLER 6.209 s.p. contains also:
Geht Nun Mud Der Tag (SATB); Hort, Eine
Helle Stimme Erklingt (SAB) (S4120)

Es Muss Ein Zeichen Sein
see Stier, Alfred, Volk Will Leben, Herr
Gott, Hilf

Evangelisches Kirchengesangbuch *see Ehre
Sei Dir, Christe, No.57 (S4121)

Frohlocke, Wem Vergeben
SAB HANSSLER 6.217 s.p. contains also: O
Heil, Das Wir Erkoren (SATB) (S4122)

Funfzig Geistliche Kanons *CC50U,canon
[Ger] 2-4pt BAREN. EM 432 s.p. (S4123)

Geht Nun Mud Der Tag
see Stier, Alfred, Eingeborner Gottessohn
Wahrer Gott

Gelobet Sei Der Herr Taglich
SATB HANSSLER 6.227 s.p. contains also:
Herr, Dem Zu Ehren In Himmelsheeren (SAB)
(S4124)

Gottes Stimme Lasst Uns Sein
4pt HANSSLER 6.234 s.p. contains also:
Stern, Hermann, Gott Ruft Dich Heut Durch
Jesum Christ (SAA); Stern, Hermann,
Jungend-Kantate (cor,narrator); Stern,
Hermann, Walte, Walte Nah Und Fern (SSA);
Ruppel, Paul Ernst, Die Ernste Ist Gross,
Aber Wenige Sind (SATB/SSAA/SSAB); Stern,
Hermann, Es Wandeln Sich Die Reiche
(SSA); Gruber, Erich, Herr, Wir Stehen
Hand In Hand (SAA/SSA) (S4125)

Herr, Aller Enden
see Stier, Alfred, Ein Ruf Hat Uns
Getroffen

Herr, Dem Zu Ehren In Himmelsheeren
see Stier, Alfred, Gelobet Sei Der Herr
Taglich

Herr Gott, An Dessen Thron
see Stier, Alfred, O Kirche Gottes

Herr, Lass Deine Wunder Sehen
see Stier, Alfred, Komm, O Jesus, Unser
Gast

Heut Greift Nach Deinem Herzen
SATB HANSSLER 6.223 s.p. contains also:
Dass Ich Wieder Frohlich Preise (S4126)

Hort, Eine Helle Stimme Erklingt
see Stier, Alfred, Eingeborner Gottessohn
Wahrer Gott

Ich Habe Nun Den Grund Gefunden *cant
[Ger] SATB,org,2trp,horn,trom,vln,opt drums
(med) BAREN. BA 1757 rental sc $2.00, cor
pts $.65 (S4127)

In Deinem Frieden Still
SATB HANSSLER 6.219 s.p. contains also: Nun
Nimmt Der Tag (SAB); So Stark Die Sturme
Wehen (TT/SA/SATB) (S4128)

Komm, O Jesus, Unser Gast
SATB HANSSLER 6.221 s.p. contains also:
Unser Keiner Lebt Sich; Herr, Lass Deine
Wunder Sehen (S4129)
-r

Kyrie Eleison, O Erbarmen Gross
SAB HANSSLER 6.225 s.p. contains also: Dass
Wir Getroster (S4130)

Lasst Uns Erfreuen Herzlich Sehr
see Stier, Alfred, Nun Sei Uns Willkommen,
Herre Christ

Lobt Gott In Seinem Heiligtum (Psalm 150)
see Stier, Alfred, Nun Sei Uns Willkommen,
Herre Christ

Machtvoll In Der Zeiten Wunde
SATB HANSSLER 6.222 s.p. contains also: Du
Bist Der Herr, Ins Amt Gestellt (SATB); O
Abgrund, Not, O Herzelied (SATB); Werft
Fort Den Stein (SAB) (S4131)

Mit Freuden Lasst Uns Singen
see Stier, Alfred, O Schar, Bei Gott
Geborgen

Morgenglanz Der Ewigkeit *cant
SATB,org,2trp,opt horn/trom,vln HANSSLER
10.167 sc s.p., voc sc s.p., ipa (S4132)

Nun Nimmt Der Tag
see Stier, Alfred, In Deinem Frieden Still

STIER, ALFRED (cont'd.)

Nun Sei Uns Willkommen, Herre Christ
SSA HANSSLER 6.210 s.p. contains also:
Lasst Uns Erfreuen Herzlich Sehr (SSA);
Schmuckt Das Fest (SSA); Lobt Gott In
Seinem Heiligtum (Psalm 150) (SSA); Aus
Meines Jammers Tiefe (Psalm 130) (SS/SA/
SSA) (S4133)

O Abgrund, Not, O Herzelied
see Stier, Alfred, Machtvoll In Der Zeiten
Wunde

O Heil, Das Wir Erkoren
see Stier, Alfred, Frohlocke, Wem Vergeben

O Herre Gott, Du Bleibst In Ewigkeit
see Marks, Gunther, Geh Hin Nach Gottes
Willen

O Kirche Gottes
SATB HANSSLER 6.218 s.p. contains also:
Herr Gott, An Dessen Thron (SAB) (S4134)

O Schar, Bei Gott Geborgen
SAB HANSSLER 6.226 s.p. contains also: Mit
Freuden Lasst Uns Singen (SATB) (S4135)

Psalm 130 *see Aus Meines Jammers Tiefe

Psalm 150 *see Lobt Gott In Seinem Heiligtum

Schmuckt Das Fest
see Stier, Alfred, Nun Sei Uns Willkommen,
Herre Christ

So Stark Die Sturme Wehen
see Stier, Alfred, In Deinem Frieden Still

Unser Keiner Lebt Sich
see Stier, Alfred, Komm, O Jesus, Unser
Gast

Volk Will Leben, Herr Gott, Hilf
SATB HANSSLER 6.220 s.p. contains also: Des
Sommers Will Ich Singen (SAB); Es Muss
Ein Zeichen Sein (SATB) (S4136)

Werft Fort Den Stein
see Stier, Alfred, Machtvoll In Der Zeiten
Wunde

STILL AND HUSHED see Gerhardt

STILL ARE THE HILLS *Xmas,carol,Ir
(Bouman, P.) SATB,opt vln (med easy) oct
CONCORDIA 98-2109 $.35 (S4137)

STILL GROWS THE EVENING *Xmas,Boh
(Dickinson, C.) SATB oct GRAY GSC 70 $.25 (S4138)

STILL, O ERDEN, STILL, O HIMMEL see Lehner,
Walter

STILL, O HIMMEL *Xmas,Aus
(Schemitsch, Hans) [Ger] mix cor,acap oct
DOBLINGER s.p. see also Zehn Osterrichische
Weihnachtslieder (S4139)

STILL PRAYER OF DEVOTION, THE see Posegate

STILL, SMALL VOICE, THE
2pt CHAPPELL 0023028-352 $.40 (S4140)
SSA CHAPPELL 0023028-354 $.40 (S4141)
SATB CHAPPELL 0023028-358 $.40 (S4142)

STILL, STILL see Track, Gerhard

STILL, STILL, STILL *Xmas,anthem/carol/folk,
Aus/Ger
(Kirk) SATB,acap,opt pno oct PRO ART 2692
$.30 (S4143)
(Luboff, Norman) SATB oct WALTON 3003 $.30 (S4144)
(Luboff, Norman) SSA oct WALTON 5021 $.30 (S4145)
(Rodgers, John) SATB oct GRAY GCMR 2722 $.35 (S4146)
(Rodgers, John) TTBB oct GRAY GCMR 2842 $.25 (S4147)
(Wetzler) SATB,opt fl (easy) oct AUGSBURG
0409 $.25 (S4148)
(Wetzler, Robert) unis treb cor (easy) oct
AUGSBURG 0401 $.25 (S4149)
(Wetzler, Robert) SSA,org,opt fl (easy) oct
AUGSBURG 0410 $.25 (S4150)

STILL, STILL, STILL see Brautigam, Helmut

STILL, STILL, STILL see Kirk

STILL, STILL, STILL see Neumeyer, Fritz

STILL, STILL, STILL see Young, C.

STILL, STILL WITH THEE see Madsen, Florence
Jefferson

STILL, STILL WITH THEE see Mendelssohn-
Bartholdy, Felix

STILL, STILL WITH THEE see Shelley

STILL, STILL WITH THEE see Speaks, [Oley]

STILL, WER GOTT ERKENNEN WILL see Wolters,
Gottfried

STILL, WILLIAM GRANT (1895-)
Hard Prails !spir
SATB oct BOURNE 808 $.30 (S4151)

Holy Spirit, Don't You Leave Me *spir
SATB,ST soli oct BOURNE 809 $.30 (S4152)

I Feel Like My Time Ain't Long
SATB,acap oct PRESSER 312-40304 $.30 (S4153)

Is There Anybody Here?
SATB oct PRESSER 312-40305 $.30 (S4154)

Hord, I Looked Down The Road !spir
SATB,ST soli oct BOURNE 807 $.30 (S4155)

Psalm For The Living, A *Psalm
SATB,opt orch oct BOURNE 825 $.40, ipr (S4156)

STILLA NATT *Xmas,hymn
see Frojda Dig O Kristenhet
(Lundvik, Hildor) men cor NORDISKA 1172 s.p.
see from Julhymner (S4157)

STILLA NATT see Gruber, Franz Xaver

STILLA NATT, GRUBER *Xmas,hymn
(Wikander, David) mix cor NORDISKA 946 s.p. (S4158)

STILLA NATT, HELIGA NATT see Gruber, Franz
Xaver

STILLE NACHT *Xmas
see Tanti Auguri
(Damrosch) "Christmas Night" [Eng/Ger] mix
cor,Bar solo oct SCHIRM.G 2526 $.20 (S4159)

STILLE NACHT see Gruber, Franz Xaver, Stille
Nacht, Heil'ge Nacht

STILLE NACHT, HEIL'GE NACHT see Gruber, Franz
Xaver

STILLE NACHT, HEILIGE NACHT see Gruber, Franz
Xaver

STILLE NACHT, HEILIGE NACHT see Maasz, Gerhard

STILLE NACHT, HEILIGE NACHT see Schwartz, J.

STILLE-NACHT-MESSE see Kronsteiner, Herman

STILLED AND QUIET IS MY SOUL see Toolan, S.
Suzanne

STILLING OF THE STORM, THE see Hillert, Richard

STILLING THE TEMPEST see Wilson, Ira B.

STIMER
Christmas Day *Xmas
(Strimer) 3pt wom cor,pno (easy) oct WILLIS
6853 $.16 (S4160)

Over The Hills And Midnight Air
(Strimer) SATB,pno (med) oct WILLIS 6974
$.22 (S4161)
(Strimer) 3pt wom cor,pno (med) oct WILLIS
6855 $.18 (S4162)

Silence
(Strimer) SATB,pno (med) oct WILLIS 6854
$.20 (S4163)

STIMMT AN DEN PSALM see Handel, George
Frideric, Prepare The Hymn

STIMMT AN DIE SAITEN see Haydn, (Franz) Joseph

STIMMT UNSERM GOTT EIN LOBLIED AN see Kickstat,
Paul

STITT, MARGARET MCCLURE
Choral Grace
SSA oct HUNTZINGER 510 $.16 (S4164)

STOBAEUS, JOHANN (1580-1646)
Der Heilige Geist Vom Himmel Kam *Pent/
Whitsun
SATB,acap voc pt DOBLINGER s.p. see also
PFINGSTEN UND EUCHARISTIE (S4165)

Ich Hab Ein Herzlich Freud
SSATB HANSSLER 6.146 s.p. contains also:
Bach, Johann Sebastian, Herr Jesu Christ,
Dich Zu Uns Wend, S.332 (SATB); Lossius,
Lukas, Ehre Sei Gott In Der Hohe (SATB) (S4166)
SSATB HANSSLER 6.278 s.p. contains also:
Schutz, Heinrich, Ich Will, Solang Ich
Lebe, Ruhmen Den Herren Mein, SWV 131
(SATB); Goudimel, Claude, Brunn Alles
Heils, Dich (SATB) (S4167)

Im Finstern Stall, O Wunder Gross
SSATB HANSSLER 6.101 s.p. (S4168)

Jesus, Vor Gud Og Frelser (composed with
Bohm, Brodre) *Psalm,16th cent
(Woldike, Mogens) [Dan] SSATB HANSEN-DEN 84
s.p. see also SALMEMELODIER FRA
REFORMATIONSTIDEN (S4169)

Laudent Deum
see MUSICA RESERVATA, BAND 1

Nun Danket Alle Gott *mot
(Hermann) SSATBB HANSSLER 1.001 s.p. (S4170)

Nun Lasst Uns Mit Den Engelein Auch
see Praetorius, Michael, Es Kam Ein Engel,
Hell Und Klar

Such, Wer Da Will, Ein Ander Ziel
SSATB HANSSLER 6.299 s.p. contains also:
Hanssler, Friedrich, Such, Wer Da Will
(SATB) (S4171)
SSATB HANSSLER 6.2505 s.p. contains also:
Praetorius, Michael, Erweckt Hat Mir Das
Herz Zu Dir (SATB) (S4172)

Uns Ist Ein Kind Geboren *Xmas,mot
(Berger) SSATTB HANSSLER 1.071 s.p. (S4173)

STOCK
Let The Song Go Round The Earth
(Coggin) SAB,org BOSTON 13319 $.35 (S4174)

STOCKBRIDGE see Billings, William

STOCKER, DAVID
Festival Response
SATB oct AGAPE SP 716 $.30 (S4175)
SSAA oct AGAPE SP 717 $.30 (S4176)

STOCKHAUSEN, KARLHEINZ (1928-)
Paskemotett *mot
[Norw] mix cor LYCHE 94 s.p. (S4177)

STOCKMEIER, WOLFGANG
Aus Der Tiefe Rufe Ich
4-8pt mix cor MOSELER s.p. see from Funf
Geistliche Stucke (S4178)

Die Versuchung Jesu *Bibl/mot
SAB,org MOSELER s.p. (S4179)

STOCKMEIER, WOLFGANG (cont'd.)

Funf Geistliche Stucke *see Aus Der Tiefe
Rufe Ich; In Der Welt Habt Ihr Angst; So
Ihr Bleiben Werdet; Und Ich Sah Einen
Neuen Himmel; Vater Unser (S4180)

Gott, Dem Ewigen Konige *Introit
4pt mix cor MOSELER s.p. (S4181)

Halleluja! Die Rechte Des Herrn Ist Erhoht
see Stockmeier, Wolfgang, Singet Dem Herrn
Ein Neues Lied

Halleluja! Ich Will Anbeten
see Stockmeier, Wolfgang, Wie Heilig Ist
Dies Statte

In Der Welt Habt Ihr Angst
4-8pt mix cor MOSELER s.p. see from Funf
Geistliche Stucke (S4182)

Jesu Kreuz, Leiden Und Pein *Psntd,mot
4pt mix cor MOSELER LB-371 s.p. (S4183)

Singet Dem Herrn Ein Neues Lied *Introit
4pt mix cor MOSELER s.p. contains also:
Halleluja! Die Rechte Des Herrn Ist
Erhoht (S4184)

So Ihr Bleiben Werdet
4-8pt mix cor MOSELER s.p. see from Funf
Geistliche Stucke (S4185)

Und Ich Sah Einen Neuen Himmel
4-8pt mix cor MOSELER s.p. see from Funf
Geistliche Stucke (S4186)

Vater Unser
4-8pt mix cor MOSELER s.p. see from Funf
Geistliche Stucke (S4187)

Wie Heilig Ist Dies Statte *Fest,Introit
4pt mix cor MOSELER s.p. contains also:
Halleluja! Ich Will Anbeten (S4188)

Zwei Psalmen *CC2U,Psalm
mix cor,org MOSELER s.p. (S4189)

Zwei Weihnachtsmotetten *CC2U,Xmas,mot
4pt mix cor MOSELER s.p. (S4190)

STOERL
Jesus Came, Alleluia *Adv
(Wyatt) SATB oct PRO ART 1958 $.22 (S4191)

STOKER
Gloria In Excelsis Deo
SATB oct MCA $.60 (S4192)

STOKES, ERIC
Doomsday Carol, A *carol
SATB,acap oct LAWSON 51242 $.30 (S4193)

STOLL, HELENE MARIANNE
Ein Feste Burg Ist Unser Gott *cant
SAB,org,2trp,timp HANSSLER 10.071 sc s.p.,
voc sc s.p., ipa (S4194)

Ich Singe Dir Mit Herz Und Mund *cant
SAB,fl,vln,vcl HANSSLER 10.103 sc s.p., cor
pts s.p., ipa (S4195)

STOLTZER, THOMAS (1475-1526)
Christmas Motets *see Dies Sanctificaus;
Grates Nunc Omnes; O Admirabile
Commercium (S4196)

Dies Sanctificatus *Xmas,mot
[Eng/Lat/Ger] PETERS V113 $.75 see also
CHRISTMAS MOTETS OF PRE-PALESTRINA DAYS (S4197)
(Egidi, A.) [Eng/Ger/Lat] mix cor cor pts
VIEWEG s.p. see from SECHS
WEIHNACHTSMOTETTEN (S4198)

Dies Sanctificaus *Xmas,mot
[Eng/Lat/Ger] SATB,acap PETERS V113 $.75
see from Christmas Motets (S4199)

Erzune Dich Nicht (Psalm 37) Bibl
(Gombosi) 6pt mix cor MOSELER s.p. (S4200)

Grates Nun Omnes *Xmas,mot
[Eng/Lat/Ger] PETERS 4114 $.75 see also
CHRISTMAS MOTETS OF PRE-PALESTRINA DAYS (S4201)

Grates Nunc Omnes *Xmas,mot
[Eng/Lat/Ger] SATB,acap PETERS V114 $.75
see from Christmas Motets (S4202)
(Egidi, A.) [Eng/Ger/Lat] mix cor cor pts
VIEWEG s.p. see from SECHS
WEIHNACHTSMOTETTEN (S4203)

Ich Bin Bei Gott In Gnaden
SATB HANSSLER 6.160 s.p. (S4204)

O Admirabile Commercium *Xmas,mot
[Lat/Ger] SSATB PETERS 4824 $.60 see from
Christmas Motets (S4205)

Ostermesse *Easter,Mass
(Hoffmann; Erbrecht) 4pt mix cor MOSELER
s.p. (S4206)

Psalm 37 *see Erzune Dich Nicht

Selected Works Vol. I *CC13U
(Albrecht, Hans) [Ger] 4-5pt,8inst sc
HINRICHSEN P7018 s.p. with facsimile
reproductions (S4207)

Selected Works Vol. II *CC19U,mot/Psalm
(Hoffman-Erbrecht, Lothar) [Ger] 3-7pt mix
cor sc HINRICHSEN P7019 s.p. (S4208)

STOLZEL, GOTTFRIED HEINRICH (1690-1749)
Kundlich Gross Ist Das Gottselige Geheimnis
*Xmas,cant
[Ger] cor,SA soli,org/cembalo,ob,strings
KISTNER sc s.p., cor pts s.p., ipa (S4209)

Lob Und Dank *chorale
[Ger] cor,T solo,org,ob,strings KISTNER sc
s.p., cor pts s.p., ipa (S4210)

STOLZER, THOMAS
see STOLTZER, THOMAS

STONARD, WILLIAM (? -1630)
Hearken, All Ye People *Gen
SAATB,kbd (med diff) oct CONCORDIA 98-1856
$.50 (S4211)

STONE IS ROLLED AWAY, THE see Davis, Katherine K.

STONE, L.
Coventry Carol *Xmas,carol
SAB oct BELWIN 1998 $.30 (S4212)
SSA oct BELWIN 2070 $.30 (S4213)
SA/TB oct BELWIN 2142 $.25 (S4214)
SATB oct BELWIN 2110 $.30 (S4215)

Lord, Lord, Lord
SATB oct BELWIN 2000 $.25 (S4216)
SAB oct BELWIN 2068 $.25 (S4217)
SA/TB oct BELWIN 2153 $.30 (S4218)

STONEMAN
Noel Fantasy
SATB FLAMMER A 5402 $.35 (S4219)

STONES CRY OUT, THE see Carmony, Bryan M.

STONES, ROBERT (1516-1613)
Lord's Prayer, The *Bibl/prayer
unis oct NOVELLO 44.1175.09 s.p. (S4220)
SATB oct NOVELLO 44.1175.07 s.p. (S4221)

STORA OCH UNDERBARA see Olson, Daniel

STORE UP YOUR RICHES IN HEAVEN see Buchanan, [Annabel Morris]

STORK CAROL, THE see Surplice, [Reginald] Alwyn

STORK SHE ROSE ON CHRISTMAS EVE, THE
see Five Dutch Carols

STORKE, THE see Jewell, Kenneth W.

STORKE, THE see Martin, Dorothy

STORY OF ARTABAN, THE OTHER WISE MAN, THE see Nordoff, Paul

STORY OF BETHLEHEM, THE see Willan, Healey

STORY OF CALVARY see Schnecker, P.

STORY OF CHRISTMAS see Jacobus

STORY OF CHRISTMAS, THE see Dale, A.J.

STORY OF CHRISTMAS, THE see Matthews, Harvey Alexander

STORY OF EASTER see Swift, F. F.

STORY OF EASTER ACC'D TO ST. MATT. see Lorenz

STORY OF JESUS, THE see Wilson

STORY OF LOVE, THE see Hughes

STORY OF THE CREATION, THE
SATB oct STAFF 275 $.25 (S4222)

STORY OF THE CREATION, THE see Gilkyson

STORY OF THE CROSS see Stainer, John

STORY OF THE CROSS see Woodward, H.H.

STORY OF THE CROSS, THE see Buck, Dudley

STORY OF THE CROSS, THE see Redhead, Alfred

STORY OF THE CROSS, THE see Stainer, John

STORY OF THE FIRST CHRISTMAS see Grand, L.

STORY OF THE SPIES see Orgad, Ben-Zion

STORY OF THE TWELVE, THE see Scott, T.

STOUFFER
Sing Out In Joyful Praise
SATB oct PRO ART 2164 $.30 (S4223)

STOUGHTON, R.
As It Began To Dawn *Easter
SATB oct PRESSER 332-15346 $.35 (S4224)

I Know A Beautiful Theme
SATB oct PRESSER 312-21620 $.35 (S4225)

Lord Is My Light, The
SATB oct PRESSER 312-21157 $.30 (S4226)
SAB oct PRESSER 312-21445 $.30 (S4227)

STOUT, ALAN (1932-   )
Creator Spirit
unis wom cor,pno PETERS 6990 $.30 (S4228)

Great Day Of The Lord, The *Op.28a
SATB,org/pno PETERS 6883 (S4229)

STRADELLA, ALESSANDRO (1642-1749)
Air D'Eglise
[Fr] unis (F maj) HEUGEL s.p. see from
CHANTS RELIGIEUX (S4230)

Almighty Father
(Elkins) SATB,org/pno BOSTON 13573 $.40 (S4231)

Father Almighty *see Pieta, Signore!

O Lord, Have Mercy
(Blakley) SATB oct FOX R203 $.25 (S4232)

Piedad Senor!
(Martini) 3 eq voices,pno sc
RICORDI-ARG BA 8380 s.p., cor pts
RICORDI-ARG BA 8381 s.p. (S4233)

Pieta, Signore! *17th cent
(Rodby; Roff) "Father Almighty" [Eng/It]
SSA/SAA oct LAWSON 51081 $.30 (S4234)

STRAESSER, JOEP (1934-   )
Psalmus *Psalm
[Dut] men cor,2fl,2clar,2trp,4horn,2trom,
tuba,perc,timp, 2 saxophones DONEMUS min
sc s.p., cor pts s.p. (S4235)

STRAF MICH NICHT IN DEINEM GRIMME see
Sweelinck, Jan Pieterszoon

STRAF MIR, HERR, NICHT IM EIFERMUT see Lassus,
Roland de (Orlandus)

STRAIN UPRAISE OF JOY AND PRAISE, THE see
Titcomb

STRALSUND
Praise To The Lord
(Anders) SA/TB FLAMMER E5079 $.30 (S4236)

Praise To The Lord, The Almighty
(Wohlfeil) SATB,pno (med) oct WILLIS 7049
$.20 (S4237)

STRAND
Show Anew Thy Salvation *anthem
(Sateren) SATB (very easy) oct AUGSBURG
1098 $.20 (S4238)

STRANGER OF GALILEE, THE see Morris

STRANGER OF GALILEE, THE see Morris, C.H.

STRANGER, SHARE OUR FIRE see Moe, Daniel

STRANGERS ARE WE see Orff, Carl, Fremde Sind
Wir

STRANGERS IN THE STREET see Mercer, M.

STRANGERS IN THE STREETS see Chase

STRANGERS IN THE STREETS see Mencer

STRANGERS SAY A KING IS BORN see Kuku, Kuku,
Chaso Zhuru

STRASSBURGER GROSSES GLORIA 1525 *Gloria
(Distler, Hugo) [Ger] cor&SATB/SATTB,acap
(med diff) BAREN. BA 1054 $1.00 see also
Liturgische Satze (S4239)

STRASSBURGER KYRIE UND GLORIA see Schubert,
Gunter

STRATEGIER, HERMAN (1912-   )
Psalm 76
[Dut] men cor,2fl,2ob,3clar,2bsn,3trp,
4horn,3trom,tuba,strings,perc,timp,harp
DONEMUS min sc s.p., cor pts s.p., voc sc
s.p. (S4240)

Requiem: In Memoriam Matris Et Fratris *Req
[Lat] mix cor,fl,ob,clar,bsn,horn,strings
DONEMUS min sc s.p., cor pts s.p., voc sc
s.p. (S4241)

Stabat Mater
[Lat] mix cor,2fl,2ob,2clar,2bsn,2trp,
2horn,strings min sc DONEMUS s.p. (S4242)

Te Deum
[Dut] mix cor,SA soli,2fl,2ob,2clar,2bsn,
3trp,4horn,3trom,strings,perc,timp,
celeste DONEMUS min sc s.p., cor pts
s.p., voc sc s.p. (S4243)

STRATTNER, G.
Father, Lead Me Day By Day
(York, D.) SATB oct PRESSER 312-40264 $.30 (S4244)

Herr, Wir Stehen Hand In Hand
TTBB HANSSLER 6.2335 s.p. contains also:
Freylinghausen, Johann A., Macht Hoch Die
Tur, Die Tor (S4245)

STRAUSS, RICHARD (1864-1949)
Devotion
(Trusler) SAB oct PLYMOUTH TR-200 $.25 (S4246)

German Motet *Op.62
[Eng/Ger] 16pt mix cor,soli,acap cmplt ed
BOOSEY rental (S4247)

STRAVINSKY, IGOR (1882-1972)
Ave Maria
mix cor SOUTHERN $.30 (S4248)
[Lat] SATB,acap oct BOOSEY 1832 $.30 (S4249)
[Russ/Lat] SATB,acap (Church Slavonic
version) oct BOOSEY 5702 $.30 (S4250)

Babel *cant
[Eng/Ger] TTBB,narrator,orch voc sc SCHOTT
4342 s.p., min sc SCHOTT 4412 s.p., cor
pts SCHOTT 4412 s.p. (S4251)

Credo *Credo
[Lat] SATB,acap oct BOOSEY 5187 $.30 (S4252)

Flood, The
mix cor,narrator,TBB soli,orch BOOSEY voc
sc $5.00, ipr, sc $10.00, min sc $4.00 (S4253)

Mass *Mass
[Lat] mix cor,10winds BOOSEY voc sc $1.50,
cor pts $.30, sc $7.50, ipr, min sc $3.00 (S4254)

Pater Noster
[Russ] SATB,acap (Church Slavonic version)
oct BOOSEY 5703 $.30 (S4255)
[Lat] SATB,acap oct BOOSEY 1833 $.30 (S4256)

Requiem Canticles *cant/Req
[Lat] mix cor,AB soli,orch BOOSEY voc sc
$3.75, cor pts $.40, sc $6.00, ipr, min
sc $3.00 (S4257)

Russian Credo *Credo
[Russ] SATB,acap oct BOOSEY 5639 $.35 (S4258)

Sermon, A Narrative, And A Prayer, A
mix cor,narrator,AT soli,orch BOOSEY voc sc
$3.00, sc $7.50 (S4259)

Symphony Of Psalms *Psalm
[Lat] mix cor,orch BOOSEY voc sc $1.50, sc
$12.50, min sc $3.50, ipr (S4260)
cor oct KALMUS 6467 $1.50 (S4261)

STRAVINSKY, IGOR (cont'd.)

Threni *Bibl
mix cor,SATTBB soli,orch BOOSEY voc sc
$6.00, sc $15.00, ipr, min sc $5.00 (S4262)

STRAW CAROL, THE see Friesen

STREAMS IN THE DESERT see Hanson

STREET CORNER SPIRITUALS *spir
(Parker) SATB,opt S solo,pno/gtr,trp,drums
oct LAWSON 51594 $.45
contains: Blow Yo' Gospel Trumpet; Can't
You Hear What My Lord Said; Come And Go
With Me; Glory, Hallelujah; Holy, Holy;
Let The Church Roll On (S4263)

STREETS OF GLORY see Tolmage, Gerald

STRENGTHEN FOR SERVICE, LORD see Lovelace,
Austin C.

STRENGTHEN FOR SERVICE, LORD, THE HANDS see
Willan, Healey

STRENGTHEN, O GOD see Roff, Joseph

STRENGTHEN US, O LORD see Handel, George
Frideric

STRENGTHEN YE THE WEAK HANDS see Harris,
William Henry

STRICKLAND
Lord Has Risen Indeed, The *Easter/Lent,cant
SATB FISCHER,C R-4001 $.75 (S4264)

Noel, Christ Is Born *Xmas
SA oct LORENZ 5370 $.25 (S4265)

What Child Is This? *Xmas
SA oct ALFRED 6156 $.30 (S4266)

STRICKLAND, LILY
Jesus, Tender Shepherd *Gen
SSA SCHMITT 2513 $.20 (S4267)

Saviour, Hear Us When We Pray *Bibl
4pt mix cor,acap oct SCHIRM.G 6963 $.20 (S4268)

STRICKLAND, LILY TERESA (1887-1958)
Christ Child, The *Xmas
SATB SCHMITT 1545 $.20 (S4269)

Lord Is Risen Indeed, The *Easter,cant
SATB,soli voc sc WILLIS $.75 (S4270)

On Christmas Day *Xmas
SATB oct PRESSER 332-40072 $.30 (S4271)

STRICKLER, DAVID
God Send Us Men
unis (easy) ABINGDON APM-683 $.20 (S4272)

Hymn Anthems *CCU,anthem/hymn
SATB (easy) ABINGDON APM-699 $.50 (S4273)

O Where Are Kings And Empires Now
SATB,trp (med) ABINGDON APM-415 $.20 (S4274)

Save Me, O God
SATB,acap SEESAW $1.00 (S4275)

STRICKLING
Hear, O My People *see Popule Meus

Popule Meus *Gen
"Hear, O My People" SATB SCHMITT 1519 $.30 (S4276)

STRICKLING, GEORGE F.
Father, O Hear Me *Lent
SATB (med) ABINGDON APM-311 $.45 (S4277)

SSA Carols For Christmas *CCU,Xmas,carol
SSA (easy) ABINGDON APM-485 $1.25 (S4278)

STRIFE IS O'ER see Palestrina, Giovanni

STRIFE IS O'ER see Peery, [Rob Roy]

STRIFE IS O'ER, THE see Cartford, Gerhard M.

STRIFE IS O'ER, THE see Cashmore, Donald

STRIFE IS O'ER, THE see Helder, Bartholomaeus

STRIFE IS O'ER, THE see Jolley, Florence [W.]

STRIFE IS O'ER, THE see Marsh

STRIFE IS O'ER, THE see Palestrina, Giovanni

STRIFE IS O'ER, THE see Rathbone, George

STRIFE IS O'ER, THE see Thiman, Eric Harding

STRIFE IS O'ER, THE see Vulpius, Melchior

STRIFE IS O'ER, THE see Wolff, S. Drummond

STRIFE IS O'ER, THE BATTLE DONE see Gesius,
Bartholomaus

STRIFE IS O'ER THE BATTLE DONE, THE see Bach,
Johann Sebastian

STRIFE O'ER, THE *Easter,anthem
(Ley, Henry G.) SATB,opt inst (easy) oct
OXFORD 42.219 $.25 (S4279)

STRIKE THE CYMBAL, BOW THE STRING see Schubert,
Franz (Peter), Miriams Siegesgesang

STRIKE THOU HOUR see Bach, Johann Sebastian

STRILKO, ANTHONY (1931-   )
Carol Of The Animals *Xmas,carol
SATB,acap oct LAWSON 51251 $.30 (S4280)

Nowell *Xmas
SATB,acap oct PRESSER MC401 $.30 (S4281)

STRIMER
Around The Manger *Xmas,carol
3pt wom cor,pno (easy) oct WILLIS 7382 $.20 (S4282)

STRIMER (cont'd.)

Lullaby For The Christ Child *Xmas
SA MARKS 2009 $.30 (S4283)

STRIMPLE, N.
To Him That Overcometh
SATB,org/pno FISCHER,J 10084 $.30 (S4284)

STROBL, K.
Konfirmationslied *Cnfrm,chorale
[Ger] mix cor,acap (easy) HUG s.p. (S4285)

STROBL, OTTO (1927-)
Deutsches Ordinarium
cor&cong,opt org/2clar&2horn&2trp&2trom&tuba&timp DOBLINGER voc sc s.p., oct s.p., ipa (S4286)

Herr, Ich Bin Dein Eigentum (Psalm 117)
mix cor,acap oct DOBLINGER s.p. (S4287)

Psalm 90
mix cor,acap oct DOBLINGER s.p. (S4288)

Psalm 117 *see Herr, Ich Bin Dein Eigentum

Weihelied
men cor,acap oct DOBLINGER s.p. contains also: Wir Sind Nur Gast Auf Erden (S4289)

Wir Sind Nur Gast Auf Erden
see Strobl, Otto, Weihelied

STROFETTE PER LA FUNZIONE DELLA CORONCINA SOLENNE DEL PR. SANGUE see Magri, Pietro

STROH, E.
Gebet *prayer
[Ger] mix cor,acap (easy) HUG s.p. (S4290)

STROH, VIRGINIA (1935-)
Praise Ye The Lord, Alleluia (Psalm 113)
SATB,acap BROUDE BR. $.35 (S4291)

Psalm 113 *see Praise Ye The Lord, Alleluia

STROHBACH, SIEGFRIED (1929-)
Alte Adventslieder In Neuen Satzen *Adv
cor pts BREITKOPF-W CHB-3039 s.p.
contains: Es Kommt Ein Schiff, Geladen (3pt men cor,acap); Macht Hoch Die Tur (4pt men cor,acap); Mit Ernst, O Menschenkinder (4pt men cor,acap); Nun Komm, Der Heiden Heiland (3pt men cor, acap); O Heiland, Reiss Die Himmel Auf (3pt men cor,acap) (S4292)

Cantate Domino Canticum Novum (Psalm 98)
"Lobsinget Unserm Gott" SSATB,acap cor pts BREITKOPF-W CHB-3432 s.p. (S4293)

Das Nonnchen "Als Mich Mein Mutterlein Zum Nonnchen Macht"
4pt mix cor,acap cor pts BREITKOPF-W CHB-2963 see from Sechs Marienmotettenlieder (S4294)

Das Nonnlein Und Der Teufel "Ging Das Nonnlein Und Sucht Im Garten"
4pt mix cor,acap cor pts BREITKOPF-W CHB-2963 see from Sechs Marienmotettenlieder (S4295)

Das Wort Und Die Musik "Ein Stilles Wort Mag Tief Und Weise Sein" *hymn
2pt wom cor&3pt men cor,Bar solo,pno/brass voc sc BREITKOPF-W EB-6335 s.p., cor pts BREITKOPF-W CHB-3161A, CHB-3161B s.p., ipr (S4296)

Denn Der Herr Ist Nahe *cant
4-6pt mix cor,SBar soli,3fl,2ob,3bsn,4horn, 3trp,3trom,strings,perc,timp,harp, celeste, English horn cor pts BREITKOPF-W CHB-3052 s.p., sc BREITKOPF-W rental (S4297)

Der Bankelsanger "Als Vater Noah Die Arche Gemacht Hat"
4pt mix cor,acap cor pts BREITKOPF-W CHB-2961 see from SECHS MARIENMOTETTENLIEDER (S4298)

Deutsches Te Deum *see Dich, Gott, Loben Wir

Dich, Gott, Loben Wir *Te Deum
"Deutsches Te Deum" 7pt mix cor,opt bvl cor pts BREITKOPF-W CHB-3140 s.p., ipa (S4299)

Die Liebste Als Schlangenkochin "Wo Bist Du Denn Gewesen?"
4pt mix cor,acap cor pts BREITKOPF-W CHB-2962 see from Sechs Marienmotettenlieder (S4300)

Die Nudeln "Bin Ein Armer Kleiner Bube"
4pt mix cor,acap cor pts BREITKOPF-W CHB-2964 see from SECHS MARIENMOTETTENLIEDER (S4301)

Drei Geistliche Konzerte
wom cor,Bar solo, metallophone sc BREITKOPF-W PB-4823 s.p.
contains & see also: Kommt Her, Ihr Kinder (Psalm 34); Mein Herz Dichtet Ein Schones Lied (Psalm 45); Verleih Uns Frieden Gnadiglich (S4302)

Es Kommt Ein Schiff, Geladen
see Alte Adventslieder In Neuen Satzen

Festliches Lied "Einmal Nur In Unserm Leben" *Fest
SSATBB,acap cor pts BREITKOPF-W CHB-2966 s.p. (S4303)

Freuen Sollen Sich Die Himmel *Adv,mot
6pt mix cor,acap cor pts BREITKOPF-W CHB-3139 s.p. (S4304)

Giannetta "Sag Mir, Giannetta, Willst Du Wirklich Frein?"
4pt mix cor,acap cor pts BREITKOPF-W CHB-2962 see from Sechs Marienmotettenlieder (S4305)

Kommt Her, Ihr Kinder (Psalm 34)
wom cor,Bar solo, metallophone cor pts BREITKOPF-W CHB-4813 s.p. see also Drei

STROHBACH, SIEGFRIED (cont'd.)

Geistliche Konzerte (S4306)

Laudate Dominum In Sanctis Ejus (Psalm 150)
canon
4pt mix cor&4pt mix cor,acap sc BREITKOPF-W PB-4499 s.p., cor pts BREITKOPF-W CHB-3475A, CHB-3475B (S4307)

Lob Der Musik "Fangt An Und Singt" *cant
4pt men cor&2pt boy cor,pno/8brass voc sc BREITKOPF-W EB-6443 s.p., cor pts BREITKOPF-W CHB-2983, CHB-2984 s.p., ipr (S4308)

Lobsinget Unserm Gott *see Cantate Domino Canticum Novum

Macht Hoch Die Tur
see Alte Adventslieder In Neuen Satzen

Mein Herz Dichtet Ein Schones Lied (Psalm 45)
wom cor,Bar solo, metallophone cor pts BREITKOPF-W CHB-4812 s.p. see also Drei Geistliche Konzerte (S4309)

Missa Beatae Virginis *Mass
3-4pt wom cor/3-4pt jr cor,org (D min) voc sc BREITKOPF-W EB-6526 s.p., cor pts BREITKOPF-W CHB-3534 s.p. (S4310)

Missa In Perpetuo Canone *Mass
4pt mix cor,acap cor pts BREITKOPF-W CHB-3130 s.p. (S4311)

Mit Ernst, O Menschenkinder
see Alte Adventslieder In Neuen Satzen

Nun Komm, Der Heiden Heiland
see Alte Adventslieder In Neuen Satzen

O Heiland, Reiss Die Himmel Auf
see Alte Adventslieder In Neuen Satzen

O Lux Beata Trinitas *hymn
4pt mix cor,solo,acap cor pts BREITKOPF-W CHB-2960 s.p. (S4312)

Oratio Nocturna
4-5pt mix cor MOSELER s.p. (S4313)

Proprium Missae In Festo St. Bartholomaei Apostoli
3pt men cor,org/3horn&3trp&2trom&tuba&timp voc sc BREITKOPF-W EB-6419 s.p., cor pts BREITKOPF-W CHB-3403 s.p., ipr (S4314)

Psalm 34 *see Kommt Her, Ihr Kinder

Psalm 45 *see Mein Herz Dichtet Ein Schones Lied

Psalm 98 *see Cantate Domino Canticum Novum

Psalm 150 *see Laudate Dominum In Sanctis Ejus

Sechs Marienmotettenlieder *see Das Nonnchen "Als Mich Mein Mutterlein Zum Nonnchen Macht"; Das Nonnlein Und Der Teufel "Ging Das Nonnlein Und Sucht Im Garten"; Die Liebste Als Schlangenkochin "Wo Bist Du Denn Gewesen?"; Giannetta "Sag Mir, Giannetta, Willst Du Wirklich Frein?" (S4315)

Sieben Neue Marienlieder *CC7U,BVM
3 eq voices MOSELER s.p. (S4316)

Verleih Uns Frieden Gnadiglich
wom cor,Bar solo, metallophone cor pts BREITKOPF-W CHB-4811 s.p. see also Drei Geistliche Konzerte (S4317)

STROKINE
Glory Be To God
(Tellep) SATB,acap oct BOOSEY 5036 $.30 (S4318)

STROMMEN
Peace On Earth *prayer
SAB (jazz) ALFRED 6519 $.40 (S4319)
SA (jazz) ALFRED 6546 $.40 (S4320)
SATB (jazz) ALFRED 6416 $.40 (S4321)
SSA (jazz) ALFRED 6219 $.40 (S4322)

What's The Use In Prayin'
SATB (jazz) ALFRED 6701 $.45 (S4323)

STRONG
Prayer Of Patriotism *Gen
SAB SCHMITT 5507 $.20 (S4324)

STRONG IS YOUR LOVE see Jillett, David, E Hehu Kerito

STRONG SON OF GOD see Filkins

STRONG SON OF GOD, IMMORTAL LOVE see Darst, S. Glen

STRONGHOLD SURE see Bach, Johann Sebastian

STRONGHOLD SURE, A see Bach, Johann Sebastian, Ein Feste Burg Ist Unser Gott

STRONGHOLD SURE, A see Bach, Johann Sebastian, Ein' Feste Burg Ist Unser Gott

STRONGHOLD SURE, THE see Bach, Johann Sebastian

STROPHIC ALLELUIAS see Young, Gordon

STROUSE
It's Just Like His Great Love
(Ferrin) SATB oct LILLENAS AN-1136 $.30 (S4325)

STRUBE, ADOLF
Arise, Sons Of The Kingdom *Adv
SAB,acap (easy) oct CONCORDIA 98-1112 $.20 (S4326)

Come, Your Hearts And Voices Raising *Xmas
SAB,acap (easy) oct CONCORDIA 99-1398 $.20 (S4327)

How Lovely Shines The Morning Star *Adv/Epiph/Gen
SAB,acap (med easy) oct CONCORDIA 98-1397 $.25 (S4328)

STRUBE, ADOLF (cont'd.)

O Christ, Our True And Only Light *Epiph/Gen
SAB,acap (easy) oct CONCORDIA 98-1109 $.20 (S4329)

Once He Came In Blessing *Adv/Epiph
SAB,acap (easy) oct CONCORDIA 98-1111 $.20 (S4330)

To Us A Child Of Hope Is Born *Xmas
SAB,acap (easy) oct CONCORDIA 98-1087 $.20 (S4331)

We All Rejoice On This Glad Day *Easter
SAB,acap (easy) oct CONCORDIA 98-1098 $.20 (S4332)

STRUTIUS, THOMAS (1621-1678)
Resonet In Laudibus *see Singet Frisch Und Wohlgemut

Singet Frisch Und Wohlgemut *Xmas
(Grusnick, Bruno) "Resonet In Laudibus" [Lat/Ger] 3pt,cont,2vln (easy) BAREN. BA 3519 sc s.p., cor pts s.p., ipa (S4333)

STUART
Let Us Praise The Lord
SATB oct PRO ART 1667 $.20 (S4334)

Sing And Rejoice
SATB oct PRO ART 1876 $.30 (S4335)

STUCKY, STEVEN
Ah, Holy Jesus *Easter/Lent
SATB WORD CS-2471 $.30 (S4336)

Almighty God, Give Us Grace
SATB WORD CS-2488 $.30 (S4337)

Psalm 149
SATB,trp oct WORD CS-2528 $.40 (S4338)

'Tis Midnight; And On Olive's Brow
SATB oct WORD CS-2522 $.30 (S4339)

STUDENT'S MASS see Lotti, Antonio, Mass In C

STUDER, HANS (1911-)
Drei Psalmen *Gen
[Ger] SATB,org (med diff) cor pts BAREN. BA 2774 $1.50, ipr
contains: Psalm 13; Psalm 143; Psalm 146 (S4340)

Es Kommt Ein Schiff, Geladen
SA LAUDINELLA LR 21 s.p. contains also: Macht Hoch Die Tur (SATB); Nun Komm Der Heiden Heiland (SAT/SAB); O Heiland, Reiss Die Himmel Auf (SAT/SAB) (S4341)

Ich Will Mich Freuen Des Herrn *Gen
[Ger] SSA,org (med diff) sc BAREN. BA 2415 $3.00, cor pts $1.00 (S4342)

In Dich Hab Ich Gehoffet, Herr *cant
[Ger] mix cor,B solo,org HUG s.p. (S4343)

Lasset Eure Lenden Umgurtet Sein *ECY,mot
[Ger] SATB,A solo,org (med diff) BAREN. BA 5403 $2.25 (S4344)

Macht Hoch Die Tur
see Studer, Hans, Es Kommt Ein Schiff, Geladen

Nun Komm Der Heiden Heiland
see Studer, Hans, Es Kommt Ein Schiff, Geladen

O Heiland, Reiss Die Himmel Auf
see Studer, Hans, Es Kommt Ein Schiff, Geladen

Psalm 13
see Drei Psalmen

Psalm 143
see Drei Psalmen

Psalm 146
see Drei Psalmen

Siehe, Der Tag Des Herrn Ist Nahe *ECY,cant
[Ger] SATB,A solo,org (med diff) BAREN. BA 3659 rental (S4345)

STUDY WAR NO MORE *spir
(De Cormier) SATB oct LAWSON 51477 $.30 (S4346)

STULTS, R.
Immortality *Easter
SA PRESSER $1.00 (S4347)

Just As I Am
SATB ALLANS 70 s.p. (S4348)

King Cometh *Xmas
SA PRESSER $.85 (S4349)
SATB PRESSER $1.25 (S4350)

Thy Way Not Mine O Lord
SATB ALLANS 75 s.p. (S4351)

STUNTZ, JOSEF HARTMANN (1793-1859)
Domine Deus *Fest,Offer
(Dite, L.) 4pt mix cor,org (contains also: Aiblinger, Johann Kaspar, Locus Iste) DOBLINGER voc sc s.p., cor pts s.p. see from DER KLEINE KIRCHENCHOR (S4352)

STURMER, BRUNO (1892-1958)
Alles Gab Euch Gott *Op.131, Gen
[Ger] 4 cor,acap (med) MULLER SM 2292 s.p. (S4353)

Dem Bruder Die Hand *hymn
men cor&opt treb cor,winds,timp voc sc TONGER s.p., ipa (S4354)

Die Hirten *Xmas
[Ger] SSATBB&jr cor,acap (med easy) MULLER MS 52 s.p. (S4355)

Drei Motetten *Op.133, CC3U,Gen,mot
[Ger] SATB,acap (med) sc MULLER SM 2327 s.p., cor pts s.p. (S4356)

Es Ist Ein Ros Entsprungen *Xmas
men cor TONGER s.p. (S4357)

Kommet, Ihr Hirten
see CHORE ZUR WEIHNACHT

STURMER, BRUNO (cont'd.)

Zwischen Ochs Und Eselein *Xmas
wom cor&jr cor TONGER s.p. (S4358)

STUTSMAN, G.M.
Wait's Carol *Xmas,carol
(Copes, V.E.; Young, C.R.) SATB oct KERBY
81275 $.30 (S4359)
(Copes, V.E.; Young, C.R.) SAB oct KERBY
6010C $.30 (S4360)
(Copes; Young) SAB/SATB,kbd oct KERBY 812
$.30 (S4361)

S'U SHEORIM see Naumbourg

S'U SH'ORIM see Altman, Ludwig

SUB TUUM see Boulay, J.

SUB TUUM see Claussmann, A.

SUB TUUM see Danjou, F.

SUB TUUM see Mendelssohn-Bartholdy, Felix

SUB TUUM see Saint-Saens, Camille

SUB TUUM see Schmitt, Florent

SUB TUUM PRAESIDIUM see Bottazzo, Luigi

SUB TUUM PRAESIDIUM see Chiti, G.

SUB TUUM PRAESIDIUM see Heidet, Le R. P.

SUB TUUM PRAESIDIUM see Mozart, Wolfgang
Amadeus

SUB VESPERUM see Lewkovitch, Bernhard

SUBDUE US BY THY GOODNESS see Bach, Johann
Sebastian

SUBDUE US THROUGH THY KINDNESS see Bach, Johann
Sebastian

SUBLIME ALLELUIA, A see Young

SUBMISSION see Wolf, Hugo, Ergebung

SUCH A SOLITARY STAR see Caldwell, Mary
[Elizabeth]

SUCH GOOD THINGS see Bock, Fred

SUCH LOVE see Harkness

SUCH, WER DA WILL see Hanssler, Friedrich

SUCH, WER DA WILL see Oertzen, Rudolf von

SUCH, WER DA WILL EIN ANDER ZIEL see Kurig,
Hans-Hermann

SUCH, WER DA WILL, EIN ANDER ZIEL see Stern,
Hermann

SUCH, WER DA WILL, EIN ANDER ZIEL see Stobaeus,
Johann

SUCH, WER DA WILL, EIN ANDER ZIEL see Zipp,
Friedrich

SUCHET DEN HERRN see Ruppel, Paul Ernst

SUCHET DEN HERRN, SO WERDET IHR LEBEN see
Weismann, Wilhelm

SUCHET GOTT, SO WERDET IHR LEBEN see Knorr,
Ernst Lother von

SUCHOFF, B.
Pageant Of Carols *CCU,Xmas,carol
BELWIN SA/TB $1.00; SAB $1.00; SATB $1.00
(S4362)

SUCHON, [EUGEN] (1908-)
Psalm Des Karpathenlandes *Op.12, Ger/Slav
cor pts UNIVER. 1170A-D (S4363)

SUDDENLY AFRAID see Forbes, Sebastian

SUDDENLY THERE CAME A SOUND see Fox, Gregory

SUDDENLY THERE CAME A SOUND FROM HEAVEN see
Aichinger, Gregor, Factus Est Repente

SUDDENLY THERE'S A VALLEY
see Great Choral Series
SSA/SATB BIG3 $.25 (S4364)

SUDERBURG, R.
Concert Mass
[Lat] SATB,acap PRESSER $1.25 (S4365)

First Nowell, The *Xmas
SATB oct PRESSER 312-40915 $.35 (S4366)

In Dulci Jubilo *Xmas
SATB oct PRESSER 312-40918 $.35 (S4367)

Joy To The World *Xmas
SATB oct PRESSER 312-40917 $.35 (S4368)

Lo, How A Rose A'er Blooming
SATB oct PRESSER 312-40918 $.30 (S4369)

O Little Town Of Bethlehem *Xmas
SATB oct PRESSER 312-40916 $.30 (S4370)

Recessional And Postlude
SATB oct PRESSER 312-40918 $.30 (S4371)

SUESSER TOD see Bach, Johann Sebastian, Susser
Trost, Mein Jesus Kommt

SUESSER TROST see Bach, Johann Sebastian,
Susser Trost, Mein Jesus Kommt

SUFFER THE LITTLE CHILDREN see Jordan, Alice

SUFFER THE LITTLE CHILDREN see Lynn, George

SUFFER THE LITTLE CHILDREN see Palmer, T.

SUITE OF UNISON ANTHEMS, A see Zaninelli, Luigi

SUITOR
Psalm 51 *mot
SATB FLAMMER A5298 $.30 (S4372)

SUITOR, M. LEE
Poverty *Xmas
SATB (med) ABINGDON APM-634 $.30 (S4373)

SULLIVAN, SIR ARTHUR SEYMOUR (1842-1900)
Christmas Meditation *Xmas
(Denton) SATB oct LORENZ B165 $.30 (S4374)

Come, Ye Faithful *Easter/Lent
(Wiley) SATB oct PRO ART 1414 $.25 (S4375)
(Wiley) SSA oct PRO ART 1835 $.20 (S4376)
(Wiley) SAB oct PRO ART 1836 $.25 (S4377)
(Wiley) 2pt oct PRO ART 1881 $.25 (S4378)

Come, Ye Faithful, Raise The Strain
(Cain) SATB FLAMMER A 5254 $.30 (S4379)
(Cain) SAB FLAMMER D5066 $.30 (S4380)

Glory To God (from Light Of The World) Xmas
SA CRAMER CO s.p. (S4381)

God Shall Wipe Away All Tears (from Light Of
The World) anthem
(Coleman) SATB,org CRAMER A 20 s.p. (S4382)
(Miller) 3pt wom cor,org/pno SCHIRM.G
10440 $.25 (S4383)
(Williams, A.) men cor,acap CRAMER B20 s.p. (S4384)

Golden Harps Are Sounding *Xmas
(Hadley) SATB oct PRO ART 1859 $.22 (S4385)

Hearken Unto Me, My People *Adv,anthem
mix cor oct NOVELLO 40.0417.05 s.p. (S4386)
SATB oct PRO ART 1701 $.22 (S4387)

Hosanna To The Son Of Davis (from Light Of
The World)
SSA CRAMER CO s.p. (S4388)

I Will Sing Of Thy Power *anthem
mix cor,T solo oct NOVELLO 40.0407.08 s.p. (S4389)
SSA oct STAFF 424 $.25 (S4390)
SATB oct STAFF 364 $.25 (S4391)

Lord Is Nigh, The (from Prodigal Son, The)
SATB,org SCHIRM.EC 2628 $.30 (S4392)

Lord, Open Thou Our Eyes
SATB oct LORENZ 9545 $.30 (S4393)

Lost Chord, The
SATB oct LORENZ 2140 $.30 (S4394)
(Macy, J.) SATB oct PRESSER 332-07975 $.25 (S4395)
(Page, N.) SATB oct PRESSER 332-13613 $.35 (S4396)
(Strickling) SSA oct SHAPIRO SCE 3503 $.35 (S4397)

My Soul Doth Magnify The Lord
(Brown, F.E.) cor oct HART s.p. (S4398)

Nature's Anthem Of Praise *anthem
SATB oct LORENZ 9185 $.30 (S4399)

O Gladsome Light (from Golden Legend) anthem
SATB,acap oct NOVELLO 34.0743.08 s.p. (S4400)
SA (easy) ALLANS 293 s.p. (S4401)

O Love The Lord *anthem
mix cor oct NOVELLO 28.0003.09 s.p. (S4402)
SATB ALLANS 323 s.p. (S4403)

O Taste And See How Gracious The Lord Is
*anthem
mix cor oct NOVELLO 40.0296.02 s.p. (S4404)

Oh! Say, But I'm Glad
(Ferrin) SATB oct LILLENAS AT-1035 $.30 (S4405)

Onward Christian Soldiers *hymn
(Hollis) SAB FLAMMER D5194 $.25 (S4406)
(Hustad, Don) SATB/SAB ALLANS 409 s.p. (S4407)
(Nilsen) SATB&SATB,pno/org,3brass WARNER
W2579 $.40 (S4408)
(Silverman) SA,band MARKS 4166 $.30, ipa (S4409)
(Simeone) SSA SHAWNEE B 135 $.30 (S4410)
(Simeone) TTBB SHAWNEE C64 $.30 (S4411)
(Simeone) TTBB SHAWNEE C64 $.30 (S4412)
(Simeone) SATB SHAWNEE A 7 $.35 (S4413)
(Smith) SATB,opt inst oct SHAPIRO SK 2064
$.30 (S4414)
(Wilson) SATB oct LORENZ 4422 $.30 (S4415)

Prodigal Son, The
cor,pno voc sc SCHIRM.G $1.75 (S4416)

Sing Hosanna
(Davies) SA/TB FLAMMER E5113 $.25 (S4417)
(Davies) SA/TB FLAMMER E5128 $.25 (S4418)

Son Of God Goes Forth To War, The *anthem
mix cor oct NOVELLO 40.0459.00 s.p. (S4419)

Thou, O Lord, Art Our Father (from Prodigal
Son, The)
SATB,pno SCHIRM.EC 1797 $.25, ipr (S4420)

Turn Thy Face From My Sins
SATB,org SCHIRM.EC 377 $.25 (S4421)

We Sing A Song Of Christmas-Time *Xmas,carol
unis CRAMER 23 s.p. (S4422)

Yea, Though I Walk
(Richardson, W.) SATB oct PRESSER 332-00249
$.30 (S4423)

SULLY
Come And Listen *Xmas,carol
SA,A solo,pno (easy) oct WILLIS 6422 $.12 (S4424)

SULTZBERGER, JOHANN ULRICH (1638-1701)
Jauchz, Erd Und Himmel, Juble Hell
SATB LAUDINELLA LR 27 s.p. contains also:
Komm, Schopfer Geist, Kehr Bei Uns Ein;
Nun Bitten Wir Den Heiligen Geist (S4425)

Komm, Schopfer Geist, Kehr Bei Uns Ein
see Sultzberger, Johann Ulrich, Jauchz, Erd
Und Himmel, Juble Hell

SULTZBERGER, JOHANN ULRICH (cont'd.)

Nun Bitten Wir Den Heiligen Geist
see Sultzberger, Johann Ulrich, Jauchz, Erd
Und Himmel, Juble Hell

SUMITE PSALMUM see Schutz, Heinrich

SUMITE PSALMUM, ET DATE TYMPANUM see Cruger,
Johann

SUMMA PASSIONIS VOM LEIDEN UND STERBEN UNSERES
HERRN JESU CHRISTI see Koch, Johannes H.E.

SUMMER ENDED see Wood, Charles

SUMMER IN WINTER see Roth, N.

SUMMER IN WINTER see Roth, R.N.

SUMMERLIN, ED.
Evensong-A Jazz Liturgy *liturg
cor,org,2trp,bvl,drums,gtr/pno,alto sax,
tenor sax, bass trombone MJQ rental (S4426)

SUMMERSIDE, FRANK
Christmas Caravan *Xmas,anthem
unis treb cor (easy) oct AUGSBURG 0509 $.22 (S4427)

SUMSION, HERBERT
Benedicite (Shortened Form)
SATB (B flat maj) oct NOVELLO 44.1340.07
s.p. (S4428)

Blessed Are They That Dwell In Thy House
mix cor LENGNICK s.p. (S4429)

Fear Not, O Land *Gen/Harv,anthem
mix cor oct NOVELLO 28.1430.07 s.p. (S4430)

Festival Benedicite In D
mix cor LENGNICK s.p. (S4431)

Holy Communion *Commun
SATB (F maj) oct NOVELLO 44.1333.04 s.p. (S4432)

Magnificat And Nunc Dimittis *Magnif/Nunc
unis/SS (G maj) NOVELLO 33.0090.00 s.p. (S4433)
SATB (G maj) oct NOVELLO 44.1284.02 s.p. (S4434)

Magnificat And Nunc Dimittis In A *Magnif/.
Nunc
oct ROYAL 115 s.p. (S4435)

Te Deum *Te Deum
SATB (G maj) oct NOVELLO 44.1420.09 s.p. (S4436)

Te Deum Laudamus *Te Deum
oct ROYAL 1014 s.p. (S4437)

SUN DON'T SET IN THE MORNING *spir
(Papp, A.) SAB,acap oct PRESSER 312-40574
$.25 (S4438)

SUN IS ON THE LAND AND SEA, THE see Lovelace,
Austin C.

SUN OF MY SOUL
see Jesus, The Very Thought Of Thee

SUN OF MY SOUL see Adams, Joseph

SUN OF MY SOUL see Barnes, H.W.S.

SUN OF MY SOUL see Crook, A.T.

SUN OF MY SOUL see Des Prez, Josquin

SUN OF MY SOUL see Gesangbuch

SUN OF MY SOUL see Martin, Warren

SUN OF MY SOUL see Turner, Edmund (Edmond)

SUN OF MY SOUL see Williams

SUN OF RIGHTEOUSNESS see Willan, Healey

SUN SHALL BE NO MORE see Woodward, H.H.

SUN SHALL BE NO MORE THY LIGHT see Greene

SUN SHALL BE NO MORE THY LIGHT BY DAY, THE see
Woodward, H.H.

SUN SHINES IN SPLENDOR, THE see Elliott

SUN SHINES IN SPLENDOUR see Warner, Richard

SUNBEAM OUT OF HEAVEN see Christiansen, F.
Melius

SUNDAY A.M. *CCUL,anthem
SATB voc sc WORD 37562 $1.95 (S4439)

SUNDAY AFTERNOON see Owens, Jimmy

SUNDAY CHOIR, THE *CC18L,Gen,anthem
(Grauert) unis/SA/SB/SAB/SSA/SATB PRO ART 999
$1.00 (S4440)

SUNDAY PSALTER, THE *liturg/Psalm
(Lindemann, H.; Powell, N.) cor,org CONCORDIA
97-6342 $3.00, ipa (S4441)

SUNDBERG, JOHN
Milde Jesu
mix cor NORDISKA 3436 s.p. (S4442)

SUNDBERG, OVE KR.
Klokkeklangen
mix cor MUSIKK 247 s.p. (S4443)

Pris Herren
mix cor MUSIKK 240 s.p. (S4444)

SUNDERREITER, G.
Mein Schonste Zier Und Kleinod Bist
see Lowenstern, Matthaus Appelles von, Ich
Hab Von Ferne, Herr, Deinen Thron

SUNDOWN *Ir
SATB oct LORENZ 1701 $.25 (S4445)

SUNDOWN see Hageman

SUNG VESPERS see Jurgens, Wm. A., Rev.

SUNRISE see Ackley

SUNRISE ALLELUIA see Bright, Houston

SUNRISE MOUNTAIN CHORUSES see Noe, J.T.

SUNRISE ON A HILL see Lorenz

SUNRISE ON EASTER MORNING see Olds

SUNRISE OVER CALVARY see Benson

SUNSET TO SUNRISE see Kliewer, Jonah

SUNSHINE IN MY SOUL see Sweney, J.

SUNT LACRIMAE RERUM see Orff, Carl

SUOGAN *Xmas,carol,Welsh
    (Smith, Gregg) 2pt wom cor oct SCHIRM.G 11714
    $.25   (S4446)

SUPER FLUMINA see Pergolesi, Giovanni Battista

SUPER FLUMINA BABYLONIS (Psalm 126)
    (Geveart, F.-A.) "U Assis Au Bord De Ce
    Superbe Fleuve" [Fr/Lat] 4pt mix cor,acap
    (easy) cor pts LEMOINE s.p. see from
    Collection De Choeurs, quatrieme Fascicule
                                            (S4447)

SUPER FLUMINA BABYLONIS see Gounod, Charles
    Francois

SUPER FLUMINA BABYLONIS see Lassus, Roland de
    (Orlandus)

SUPER FLUMINA BABYLONIS see Palestrina,
    Giovanni

SUPER FLUMINA BABYLONIS see Pergolesi, Giovanni
    Battista

SUPER FOLK FOR SUPER FOLKS see Wilson, John F.

SUPEREMINET OMNEM SCIENTIAM see Schutz,
    Heinrich

SUPPER TIME
    SATB/TTBB BIG3 $.25   (S4448)

SUPPLICATION *hymn,Fr,16th cent
    (Fuleihan) SAATB,acap oct SCHIRM.G 7992 $.20
                                            (S4449)

SUPPLICATION see Cowell, Henry Dixon

SUPPLICATION see Frielitz, C.

SUPPLICATION see Hedges

SUPPLICATION see Lokey

SUPPLICATION see Potter

SUPPLICATION see Rees

SUPPLICATION AND ALLELUIA see Butler

SUPPLICATIONES see Palestrina, Giovanni

SUPPLIEMUS JESU BONE see Wideen, Ivar

SUPPORT US O GOD see Morgan, Haydn

SUPREME SACRIFICE see Harris, Cuthbert

SUR LA NAISSANCE DE NOTRE SEIGNEUR see Roesgen-
    Champion, Marguerite

SUR TOUS REGRETZ see Gombert, Nicolas

SURDO, JOSEPH
    He Is Risen *Easter
    SATB,pno (diff) oct WILLIS 1917 $.18
                                            (S4450)

SURE THERE IS NO GOD OF LOVE see Tomkins,
    Thomas

SURELY GOD IS IN THIS PLACE see Price

SURELY GOD IS IN THIS PLACE see Priest, A

SURELY GOD IS IN THIS PLACE see Rasely

SURELY GOD IS IN THIS PLACE see Rasley

SURELY GOD IS IN THIS THE HOLY PLACE see Young,
    Robert H.

SURELY GOODNESS AND MERCY see Peterson, John W.

SURELY HE BORE OUR GRIEFS see Vidal, D. De

SURELY, HE BORE OUR SORROWS see Victoria, Tomas
    Luis de, Vere Languores

SURELY HE HAS BORNE OUR GRIEFS see Antes, John

SURELY HE HAS BORNE OUR GRIEFS see Hillert,
    Richard

SURELY HE HAS BORNE OUR GRIEFS see Hunnicutt,
    Judy

SURELY HE HAS BORNE OUR GRIEFS see Lotti,
    Antonio

SURELY HE HATH BORNE OUR BURDENS see Forsblad

SURELY, HE HATH BORNE OUR GRIEFS see Franck,
    Melchior, Fuhrwahr, Er Trug Uns're
    Krankheit

SURELY HE HATH BORNE OUR GRIEFS see Graun, E.H.

SURELY HE HATH BORNE OUR GRIEFS see Graun, Karl
    Heinrich

SURELY HE HATH BORNE OUR GRIEFS see Handel,
    George Frideric

SURELY HE HATH BORNE OUR GRIEFS see Lotti,
    Antonio, Vere Languores Nostros

SURELY HE HATH BORNE OUR GRIEFS see Roff,
    Joseph

SURELY HE HATH BORNE OUR GRIEFS see Rosewall,
    Richard B.

SURELY HE HATH BORNE OUR GRIEFS see Salathiel,
    Lyndon

SURELY HE HATH BORNE OUR GRIEFS see Whittredge

SURELY HE HATH BORNE OUR GRIEFS see Willan,
    Healey

SURELY HE HATH BOURNE OUR GRIEFS see Lotti,
    Antonio, Vere Languores Nostros

SURELY THE LORD IS IN THIS PLACE see Burnell,
    I.

SURELY THE LORD IS IN THIS PLACE see Coke,
    Norman

SURELY THE LORD IS IN THIS PLACE see Fannon,
    Daniel Stephen

SURELY THE LORD IS IN THIS PLACE see Moyer, J.
    Edward

SURELY THE LORD IS IN THIS PLACE see Mueller,
    Carl F.

SURELY THE LORD IS IN THIS PLACE see Powell

SURELY, YES, SURELY HE HAS BORNE OUR GRIEFS see
    Victoria, Tomas Luis de, Vere Languores
    Nostros

SUREXIT CHRISTUS HODIE *Easter
    (Geveart, F.-A.) "Pour Le Jour De Pacques"
    [Lat/Fr] 4pt mix cor,acap (easy) cor pts
    LEMOINE s.p. see from Collection De
    Choeurs, troisieme Fascicule   (S4451)

SUREXIT CHRISTUS HODIE see Bach, Johann
    Sebastian

SURGE ILLUMINARE see Byrd, William

SURGE, ILLUMINARE see Palestrina, Giovanni

SURGE ILLUMINARE HIERUSALEM see Palestrina,
    Giovanni

SURGE, ILLUMINARE JERUSALEM see Palestrina,
    Giovanni, Surge Illuminare Hierusalem

SURGE PROPERA see Lassus, Roland de (Orlandus)

SURGE QUI DORMIS see Stahmer, Klaus

SURGENS JESUS see Philips, Peter

SURIANO, FRANCESCO (1549-1621)
    Ave Regina
    mix cor ALSBACH&D sc s.p., cor pts s.p.
                                            (S4452)

    Ave Regina Caelorum
    see LA SCHOLA PALESTRINIENNE DEUXIEME
    CAHIER

    Fair Queen Of Heaven *see Regina Caeli

    Hail, Holy Queen
    see TWO MOTETS IN HONOR OF THE BLESSED
    VIRGIN

    Hail, Queen Of Heaven, Be Joyful *Renais
    (Ehret, Walter) SATB,acap PEER $.40 (S4453)

    Regina Caeli
    SATB,acap SCHIRM.EC $.16   (S4454)
    "Fair Queen Of Heaven" SATB oct SPRATT 2013
    $.25   (S4455)

    Regina Caeli Laetare *anti
    (Collins, H.B.) [Lat] SATB CHESTER s.p.
                                            (S4456)

    Sanctus And Hosanna *Sanctus
    (Knight, Gerald) SATB,acap oct FISCHER,C
    CM-7510 $.25   (S4457)

SURINACH, CARLOS (1915-   )
    Cantata Of St. John *cant
    [Eng/Span] SATBarB,2perc AMP A378 $1.50
                                            (S4458)
    Dark Night Of The Soul *see Noche Oscura Del
    Alma

    Delirio Del Alma Por Vera Dios
    "Soul Longing To See God, The" [Eng/Span]
    SATB,acap AMP A518 $.50 see from Songs Of
    The Soul   (S4459)

    Gozo A La Fe
    "Joy In The Faith" [Eng/Span] SATB,acap AMP
    A519 $.50 see from Songs Of The Soul
                                            (S4460)
    Joy In The Faith *see Gozo A La Fe

    Living Flame Of Love *see Llama De Amor Viva

    Llama De Amor Viva
    "Living Flame Of Love" [Eng/Span] SATB,acap
    AMP A517 $.40 see from Songs Of The Soul
                                            (S4461)
    Noche Oscura Del Alma
    "Dark Night Of The Soul" [Eng/Span] SATB,
    acap AMP A516 $.40 see from Songs Of The
    Soul   (S4462)

    Songs Of The Soul *see Delirio Del Alma Por
    Vera Dios, "Soul Longing To See God,
    The"; Gozo A La Fe, "Joy In The Faith";
    Llama De Amor Viva, "Living Flame Of
    Love"; Noche Oscura Del Alma, "Dark Night
    Of The Soul"   (S4463)

    Soul Longing To See God, The *see Delirio
    Del Alma Por Vera Dios

SUROVCHAK
    Master, What Shall I Do?
    SATB oct LORENZ C201 $.30   (S4464)

SURPLICE, [REGINALD] ALWYN (1906-   )
    I Will Lift Up Mine Eyes Unto The Hills
    SATB,org oct BOOSEY 5573 $.30   (S4465)

    Stork Carol, The *Xmas,carol
    oct ROYAL 345 s.p.   (S4466)

SURRENDER see Roe, Gloria [Ann]

SURREXIT CHRISTUS see Gabrieli, Giovanni

SURREXIT CHRISTUS see Scheidt, Samuel

SURREXIT CHRISTUS HODIE see Bodenschatz, Erhard

SURREXIT DOMINUS see Bresgen, Cesar

SURREXIT DOMINUS see Gallus, Jacobus

SURREXIT DOMINUS VERE see van Berchem, J.

SURREXIT HODIE see Kelly, Bryan

SURREXIT PASTON BONUS see Coloma

SURREXIT PASTOR BONUS see Arnaldi, Antonio

SURREXIT PASTOR BONUS see Bossi, Marco Enrico

SURREXIT PASTOR BONUS see Lassus, Roland de
    (Orlandus)

SURREXIT PASTOR BONUS see Mendelssohn-
    Bartholdy, Felix

SURREXIT PASTOR BONUS see Scheidt, Samuel

SURSUM CORDA *Commun
    cor,pno/org sc ROYAL s.p.
    contains: Lord's Prayer; Responses; Sursum
    Corda   (S4467)

SURSUM CORDA
    see Sursum Corda

SURSUM CORDA see Elgar, Edward

SURSUM CORDA see Piechler, Arthur

SURSUM CORDA see Shaw, Martin

SURSUM CORDA see Smith

SURSUM CORDA see Thalben-Ball, George [Thomas]

SURSUM CORDA VOL. 1 see Stein, C.

SURSUM CORDA VOL. 2 see Stein, C.

SURSUM CORDA VOL. 4 see Stein, C.

SURSUM CORDA VOL. 5 see Stein, C.

SURSUM CORDA VOL. 6 see Stein, C.

SUS, DEBOUT GENTILZ PASTEURS see Costeley,
    Guillaume

SUS, ESGAIONS AU SEIGNEUR see Goudimel, Claude

SUS LE PONT D'AVIGNON see Certon, [Pierre]

SUS, SUS, QU'ON SE DISPOSE DE LOUER LE SEIGNEUR
    see Lupi II, Didier

SUS: TOUS SES SERVANTES, BENISSEZ LA SEIGNEUR
    see Mauduit, Jacques

SUSANI *Xmas,17th cent
    (Bauernfeind, Hans) mix cor,acap oct
    DOBLINGER   (S4468)
    (Seitz, Rudiger) mix cor,acap oct DOBLINGER
    s.p. see from Zwei Weihnachtslieder (S4469)

SUSANI see Gordon, P.

SUSANI see Haus, Karl

SUSANINNE see Hensel, Walther

SUSANNE UN GIOUR see Merulo, Claudio

SUSANNE UN JOUR see Lassus, Roland de
    (Orlandus)

SUSANNI *Xmas,carol,Ger
    (Shaw; Parker) 4pt mix cor,acap oct SCHIRM.G
    10168 $.30   (S4470)

SUSANNI see Collins

SUSANNI see Ehret, Walter

SUSANNI see Newbold, David

SUSCEPIMUS see Quack, Erhard

SUSCEPIT ISRAEL see Bach, Johann Sebastian

SUSCIPE, CLEMENTISSIME DEUS see Gabrieli,
    Giovanni

SUSSER DIE GLOCKEN NIE KLINGEN see Weber,
    Bernhard

SUSSER TROST, MEIN JESUS KOMMT see Bach, Johann
    Sebastian

SUSSEX CAROL *carol
    (Hunter; Weale) SATB,acap oct LAWSON 51286
    $.30   (S4471)

SUSSEX CAROL see Wentworth

SUSSEX CAROL, THE *Xmas
    (Biss) unis,rec,pno,opt vln&vcl oct SCHIRM.G
    11630 $.30   (S4472)

SUSSMAYR, FRANZ XAVIER (1766-1803)
    Das Namensfest
    [Ger/Eng] jr cor,orch, children soloists
    BOOSEY voc sc $5.00, sc $9.50, ipa
                                            (S4473)

SUSTAINING POWER see Katter

SUTCLIFFE, JAMES H.
    Christmas Cradle Song *Xmas
    SATB,acap oct LAWSON 51350 $.30   (S4474)

SUTER, HERMANN (1870-1916)
    Le Laudi Di San Francesco D'Assisi
    [It/Ger] cor&jr cor,SATB soli,org,pic,2fl,
    2ob,2clar,2bsn,4horn,3trp,3trom,tuba,
    strings,timp,harp, English horn, bass
    clarinet celeste, contrabassoon HUG s.p.,
    ipr   (S4475)

SUTERMEISTER, HEINRICH (1910-)
Mass In E Flat *Mass
[Lat] SATB SCHOTT s.p. (S4476)

SUTHERLAND
Glory To God *Xmas
SATB oct LORENZ 1380 $.25 (S4477)

SUTHOFF-GROSS, RUDOLF (1930-)
Ach Bleib Mit Deiner Gnade
see Schlenker, Manfred, Allein Gott In Der Hoh Sei Ehr

Gesange Des Propriums Fur Den Erntedanktag *CCU,Harv/Thanks
mix cor HANSSLER 7.163 s.p. (S4478)

Halleluja! Der Herr Sendet Eine Erlosung
see Proprium Zu Jubilate

Jauchzet Gott, Alle Lande
see Proprium Zu Jubilate

Lobt Gott, Ihr Christen Alle Gleich
SATB HANSSLER 6.304 s.p. contains also: Nun Singet Und Seid Froh (S4479)

Mit Freuden Zart
see Proprium Zu Jubilate

Nun Singet Und Seid Froh
see Suthoff-Gross, Rudolf, Lobt Gott, Ihr Christen Alle Gleich

O Heiland, Reiss Die Himmel Auf
SAT/SAB HANSSLER 6.303 s.p. contains also: Wie Soll Ich Dich Empfangen (S4480)

Proprium Zu Jubilate
SAT/SAB HANSSLER 7.158 s.p.
contains: Halleluja! Der Herr Sendet Eine Erlosung; Jauchzet Gott, Alle Lande; Mit Freuden Zart; Wahrlich Ich Sage Euch: Ihr Werdet Weinen Und Heulen (S4481)

Wahrlich Ich Sage Euch: Ihr Werdet Weinen Und Heulen
see Proprium Zu Jubilate

Wie Soll Ich Dich Empfangen
see Suthoff-Gross, Rudolf, O Heiland, Reiss Die Himmel Auf

SVATA LUDMILA see Dvorak, Antonin

SVATOU DOBU JIZ TU MAME *Xmas,carol,Czech
"Now The Rarest Day" see Czech Christmas Carols
(Glaser, V.) "Now The Rarest Day" SATB,acap SCHIRM.EC 2601 $.25 (S4482)

SVEINSSON, GUNNAR REYNIR (1933-)
Mass *Mass
mix cor,STB soli,acap ICELAND s.p. (S4483)

Motet *mot
mix cor ICELAND s.p. (S4484)

Skald I Kirkjugaroi
[ICELANDIC] mix cor,Bar solo,org ICELAND s.p. (S4485)

Songs On English Medieval Texts *CCU
mix cor ICELAND s.p. (S4486)

SWAFFIELD, RONALD
Christmas Stars Are Shining Bright
2pt (easy) CRAMER 141 ipr (S4487)

Love Came Down At Christmas *Xmas
SSA CRAMER 139 s.p. (S4488)

O How Amiable Are Thy Dwellings *anthem
SATB CRAMER C 0 s.p. (S4489)

Our Lady In The Stable
2pt jr cor LEONARD-ENG 96 s.p. (S4490)

Rogation Carol *Harv,anthem
SATB,acap CRAMER C 43 s.p. (S4491)

SWAIN, FREDA (1902-)
Breathe On Me, Breath Of God
SATB&opt desc,acap oct FOX PS151 $.25 (S4492)

Gaelic Prayer, A
SATB,opt soli oct BOURNE 877 $.30 (S4493)

Holly And The Ivy, The
SATB oct BOURNE 856 $.25 (S4494)

SWAN
Eternal Heavenly King
SATB,acap oct BOOSEY 5156 $.30 (S4495)

Let The Shrill Trumpet's Warlike Voice
(McAfee) SATB oct BOURNE 847 $.30 (S4496)

Het Thy Soul Be Full Of Exceeding Gladness
SATB,acap oct BOOSEY 5266 $.30 (S4497)

Thy Most Radiant And Blessed Birth
SATB,acap oct BOOSEY 5265 $.30 (S4498)

SWANN
Clock Carol *Xmas,carol
unis oct GALLIARD 2.0701.1 $.30 (S4499)

Jesu Parvule *Xmas
SA oct GALAXY 1.2480.1 $.25 (S4500)

Jubilate Domino *Xmas
[Lat] SA oct GALAXY 1.2481.1 $.30 (S4501)

Sing Roung The Year *CCU,Xmas
unis pap GALLIARD 2.9057.1 $2.50 (S4502)

SWANN, DONALD
Benedictus *Bene/Bibl
see Festival Matins
4pt mix cor,org oct CURWEN 11808 $.35 (S4503)
"Blessed Be The Lord God Of Israel" 2pt jr cor/2pt wom cor CURWEN 72688 s.p. (S4504)
"Blessed Be The Lord God Of Israel" 2pt wom cor/2pt men cor/2pt mix cor,org/pno oct CURWEN 11791 $.30 (S4505)

SWANN, DONALD (cont'd.)

Blessed Be The Lord God Of Israel *see Benedictus

Creed, Lord's Prayer And Responses, The
see Festival Matins

Festival Matins
(Steinitz) mix cor CURWEN s.p.
contains: Benedictus (Bene); Creed, Lord's Prayer And Responses, The (Credo/prayer) (CC); Modern Te Deum, A (Te Deum); O Come Let Us Sing Unto The Lord (S4506)

Modern Te Deum, A *Te Deum
see Festival Matins
"We Praise Thee, O God" 2pt jr cor/2pt wom cor CURWEN 72690 s.p. (S4507)

O Come Let Us Sing Unto The Lord *see Venite

Requiem For The Living *cant/Req
mix cor voc sc CURWEN (S4508)
mix cor,narrator,Mez/B solo,pno,perc CURWEN s.p. (S4509)

Venite *Bibl
"O Come Let Us Sing Unto The Lord" see Festival Matins
"O Come Let Us Sing Unto The Lord" 2pt jr cor/2pt wom cor CURWEN 72689 s.p. (S4510)
(Steinitz) "O Come Let Us Sing Unto The Lord" 2pt wom cor/2pt men cor/2pt mix cor,org/pno oct CURWEN 11792 $.30 (S4511)
(Steinitz) "O Come Let Us Sing Unto The Lord" 4pt mix cor oct CURWEN 10771 $.30 (S4512)

We Praise Thee, O God *see Modern Te Deum, A

SWANN, [FREDERICK LEWIS] (1931-)
God Of All Love And Pity
SATB,org oct KERBY 5804 $.30 (S4513)
SATB oct KERBY 5804C $.30 (S4514)

SWEDISH DANCE CAROL *Xmas,carol,Swed
(Davis) SSA oct GALAXY 1.1187.1 $.40 (S4515)
(Davis) SATB oct GALAXY 1.2055.1 $.40 (S4516)

SWEELINCK, D.J.
Cecilia Lied En Oculus Non Vindit
(Sigtenhorst-Meyer, B.V.D.) mix cor ALSBACH&D sc s.p., cor pts s.p. (S4517)

SWEELINCK, JAN PIETERSZOON (1562-1621)
All People That On Earth Do Dwell *see Or Sus, Serviteurs

Alles, Was Odem Hat, Jauchze Dem Herrn (Psalm 150) Gen
(Holliger, Hans) [Ger] SAATB,acap (med) BAREN. BA 2808 $.65 see from Der Hugenottenpsalter (S4518)

Angelus Ad Pastores Ait
(Knight, Gerald) SATB,acap oct FISCHER,C CM-7499 $.25 (S4519)

Arise, O Ye Servants *see Or Sus, Serviteurs

Arise, O Ye Servants Of God
(Davison, A.) TTTBBB,acap SCHIRM.EC 76 $.22 (S4520)

Arise, Ye Who Serve The Lord
(Hilton, A.) SATB oct PRESSER 352-00447 $.30 (S4521)

Born To-Day! *see Hodie Christus Natus Est

Born Today *Xmas
2pt oct LORENZ 5745 $.30 (S4522)

Cantate Domino *Asc/Easter/Gen
see Cantiones Sacrae
"O Sing Ye To The Lord" SSATB,acap (med diff) oct CONCORDIA 98-1937 $.60 (S4523)
"O Sing Ye To The Lord" SATB oct WALTON 6029 $.35 (S4524)

Cantiones Sacrae
mix cor VOLK 132 s.p.
contains: Cantate Domino; Laudate Dominum; Venite, Exultemus Domino (S4525)

Chantez A Dieu
(Anderson, Terrance) SATB,acap FOSTER MF126 $.40 (S4526)

Chantez A Dieu Chanson Nouvelle (Psalm 96)
(Boepple, P.) SATB,acap oct PRESSER 352-00004 $.30 (S4527)
(Mishkin, H.) [Fr/Eng] TTBB,acap SCHIRM.EC 2111 $.30 (S4528)

Chantez Gayement A Dieu
(Anderson, Terrance) SSATTB,acap FOSTER MF127 $.45 (S4529)

Collected Works II: Psalms *CCU,Psalm
(Seifert, Max) cor GREGG ISBN 0:576 28008 9 s.p. (S4530)

Collected Works III: Psalms *CCU,Psalm
(Seiffert, Max) cor GREGG ISBN 0:576 28009 7 s.p. (S4531)

Collected Works IV: Psalms *CCU,Psalm
(Seifert, Max) cor GREGG ISBN 0:576 28010 0 s.p. (S4532)

Collected Works V: Psalms *CCU,Psalm
(Seifert, Max) cor GREGG ISBN 0:576 28011 9 s.p. (S4533)

Collected Works VI: Cantiones Sacrae *CCU, Psalm
(Seifert, Max) cor GREGG ISBN 0:576 28012 7 s.p. (S4534)

Come, Let Us Rejoice *see Venite, Exultemus Domino

Come, Praise Him *see Venite, Exultemus Domino

Der Herr Ist Konig (Psalm 93) Gen
(Holliger, Hans) [Ger] SATB,acap (med) BAREN. BA 2803 s.p. see from Der

SWEELINCK, JAN PIETERSZOON (cont'd.)

Hugenottenpsalter (S4535)

Der Herr Ist Mein Hirt (Psalm 23) Easter/Pent,mot
[Ger] SATB&SATTB&SSATTB,acap (med) BAREN. BA 2802 $1.50 (S4536)

Der Hugenottenpsalter *see Alles, Was Odem Hat, Jauchze Dem Herrn (Psalm 150); Der Herr Ist Konig (Psalm 93); Halleluja, Singt Neue Lieder (Psalm 149); Herr Gott, Erhore Mein Flehen (Psalm 102); Ich Erhebe Mein Gemute (Psalm 25); Ich Schau Nach Jenen Bergen Fern (Psalm 121); Ihr Pforten, Hebt Das Haupt Empor (Psalm 24); Mein Ganzes Herz Erhebet Dich (Psalm 138); Mein Gott, Mein Gott (Psalm 22); Mein Gott Und Herr, Du Bist Mein Hochstes Gut (Psalm 145); Straf Mich Nicht In Deinem Grimme (Psalm 38); Unendlicher, Dir Unserm Gott Und Konig (Psalm 8); Von Ganzem Herzen Dank Ich Dir (Psalm 9) (S4537)

Ecce Prandium
[Lat] SSATB BOSWORTH s.p. (S4538)

Halleluja, Lobet Den Herrn (Psalm 150) Bibl/mot
(Trubel) 8pt mix cor HANSSLER 1.491 s.p. (S4539)

Halleluja, Singt Neue Lieder (Psalm 149) Gen
(Anderson, T.) SATB FOSTER MF126 $.40 (S4540)
(Holliger, Hans) [Ger] SATB,acap (med) BAREN. BA 2809 s.p. see from Der Hugenottenpsalter (S4541)

Herr Gott, Erhore Mein Flehen (Psalm 102) Gen
(Boepple, P.) SATB,acap oct PRESSER 352-00005 $.30 (S4542)
(Holliger, Hans) [Ger] SATB,acap (med) BAREN. BA 2804 $.40 see from Der Hugenottenpsalter (S4543)

Hodie Christus Natus Est *Xmas,anthem/mot
[Ger] SSATB,org KISTNER sc s.p., cor pts s.p., ipa (S4544)
[Lat] SSATB oct NOVELLO 03.0125.06 s.p. (S4545)
[Lat] SSATB,acap (med) MULLER MS 80 s.p. (S4546)
"Born To-Day!" SATB,acap oct BELWIN 64048 $.35 (S4547)
"Born To-Day!" SATB oct BELWIN 64048 $.35 (S4548)
"Born To-Day!" SATB oct GRAY GCMR 1855 $.35 (S4549)
"Born To-Day!" SATB oct GRAY GCMR 1461 $.30 (S4550)
(Cain) SSATB oct FOX R133 $.40 (S4551)
(Cramer) [Eng/Lat] SSATB,acap MARKS 4301 $.50 (S4552)
(Funk, I.) SATB,acap oct PRESSER 312-40155 $.35 (S4553)
(Lefebvre) "Born To-Day!" [Lat/Eng] TTBB, acap oct COLOMBO 759 $.35 (S4554)
(Lloyd, C.H.) "Born To-Day" SSATB oct NOVELLO 28.0961.03 s.p. (S4555)
(Row) "Born To-Day" SATB oct FISCHER,C R-6128 $.30 (S4556)
(Schindler) "Born To-Day!" SSATB oct COLOMBO 338 $.30 (S4557)
(Tillinghast) SSA,acap WARNER W2903 $.35 (S4558)

How Brightly Beams
see SIX SEVENTEENTH CENTURY CAROLS FROM THE NETHERLANDS

Ich Erhebe Mein Gemute (Psalm 25) Gen
(Holliger, Hans) [Ger] SAATB,acap (med) BAREN. BA 2737 $.55 see from Der Hugenottenpsalter (S4559)

Ich Schau Nach Jenen Bergen Fern (Psalm 121) Gen
(Holliger, Hans) [Ger] SATB,acap (med) BAREN. BA 2805 $.40 see from Der Hugenottenpsalter (S4560)

Ihr Pforten, Hebt Das Haupt Empor (Psalm 24) Gen
(Holliger, Hans) [Ger] SATB,acap (med) BAREN. BA 2736 s.p. see from Der Hugenottenpsalter (S4561)

Jauchzt Alle Lande, Gott Zu Ehren *mot
(Hellmann) SATTB HANSSLER 1.108 s.p. (S4562)

Laudate Dominum
see Cantiones Sacrae
[Lat] SSATB BOSWORTH s.p. (S4563)

Mein Ganzes Herz Erhebet Dich (Psalm 138) Gen
(Holliger, Hans) [Ger] SATB,acap (med) BAREN. BA 2806 $.40 see from Der Hugenottenpsalter (S4564)

Mein Gott, Mein Gott (Psalm 22) Gen
(Holliger, Hans) [Ger] SATB,acap (med) BAREN. BA 2801 $.40 see from Der Hugenottenpsalter (S4565)

Mein Gott Und Herr, Du Bist Mein Hochstes Gut (Psalm 145) Gen
(Holliger, Hans) [Ger] SSATB,acap (med) BAREN. BA 2807 $.65 see from Der Hugenottenpsalter (S4566)

Mein Junges Leben Hat Ein End
see TROSTGESANG UND STERBELIED

Now Praise The Lord *see Or Soit Loue L'Eternel

O Gracious Lord Jesus Christ
(Richardson) SATB oct WORD CS-111 $.35 (S4567)

O Lord God To Thee Be Praise *see O Seigneur Loue Sera

O Most High And Holy God *Gen
(Riedel) SATB SCHMITT 1405 $.25 (S4568)

O Seigneur Loue Sera (Psalm 75)
"O Lord God To Thee Be Praise" [Eng/Fr] 4pt mix cor,acap oct SCHIRM.G 2620 $.35 (S4569)

SWEELINCK, JAN PIETERSZOON (cont'd.)

"O Lord God, To Thee Be Praise" SATB
SCHIRM.EC 2792 $.30 (S4570)

O Sing With Full Voice
(Anderson, Terrance) SSATTB FOSTER MF127
$.45 (S4571)

O Sing Ye To The Lord *see Cantate Domino

Or Soit Loue L'Eternel (Psalm 150)
[Lat] SSSAATB BOSWORTH s.p. (S4572)
"Now Praise The Lord" SSAATTBB SCHIRM.EC
2790 $.90 (S4573)

Or Sus, Serviteurs (Psalm 134)
"All People That On Earth Do Dwell" SATB
SCHIRM.EC 2791 $.30 (S4574)
"Arise, O Ye Servants" [Fr/Eng] SSATBB,acap
oct SCHIRM.G 2619 $.30 (S4575)

Praise Ye The Lord
(Anderson, T.) SATB,acap FOSTER MF126 $.40 (S4576)

Psalm 8 *see Unendlicher, Dir Unserm Gott
Und Konig

Psalm 9 *see Von Ganzem Herzen Dank Ich Dir

Psalm 22 *see Mein Gott, Mein Gott

Psalm 23 *see Der Herr Ist Mein Hirt

Psalm 24 *see Ihr Pforten, Hebt Das Haupt
Empor

Psalm 25 *see Ich Erhebe Mein Gemute

Psalm 38 *see Straf Mich Nicht In Deinem
Grimme

Psalm 75 *see O Seigneur, Loue Sera

Psalm 81
(Anderson, T.) SSATTB FOSTER MF127 $.45 (S4577)

Psalm 90
[Norw] SATB LYCHE 51 s.p. (S4578)
(Boepple, P.) SATB,acap oct PRESSER
352-00003 $.30 (S4579)

Psalm 93 *see Der Herr Ist Konig

Psalm 96 *see Chantez A Dieu Chanson
Nouvelle

Psalm 102 *see Herr Gott, Erhore Mein Flehen

Psalm 121 *see Ich Schau Nach Jenen Bergen
Fern

Psalm 134 *see Or Sus, Serviteurs

Psalm 138 *see Mein Ganzes Herz Erhebet Dich

Psalm 145 *see Mein Gott Und Herr, Du Bist
Mein Hochstes Gut

Psalm 149 *see Halleluja, Singt Neue Lieder

Psalm 150 *see Alles, Was Odem Hat, Jauchze
Dem Herrn

Psalm 150 *see Halleluja, Lobet Den Herrn

Psalm 150 *see Or Soit Loue L'Eternel

Straf Mich Nicht In Deinem Grimme (Psalm 38)
Gen
(Holliger, Hans) [Ger] SSATB,acap (med)
BAREN. BA 2811 $.40 see from Der
Hugenottenpsalter (S4580)

Unendlicher, Dir Unserm Gott Und Konig (Psalm
8) Gen
(Holliger, Hans) [Ger] SSATB,acap (med)
BAREN. BA 2810 s.p. see from Der
Hugenottenpsalter (S4581)

Venite Exsultemus Domino
(Kudlawiec) SSATB oct SUMMY 5517 $.70 (S4582)

Venite, Exultemus Domino *Epiph/Gen
see Cantiones Sacrae
"Come, Praise Him" SSATB,acap (med diff)
oct CONCORDIA 98-1938 $.50 (S4563)
(Payson, A.) "Come, Let Us Rejoice" SSATB
FRANK F-568 $.40 (S4584)

Von Ganzem Herzen Dank Ich Dir (Psalm 9) Gen
(Holliger, Hans) [Ger] SATB,acap (med)
BAREN. BA 2812 $.40 see from Der
Hugenottenpsalter (S4585)

SWEENY, JACK
Alleluia
TTBB oct FISCHER,J 9740 $.30 (S4586)

Psalm 134
SATB oct GALAXY 1.1853.1 $.30 (S4587)

SWEET ARE THE THOUGHTS see Amner

SWEET BABY KING see Comini

SWEET BABY, SLEEP see Vaughan Williams, Ralph

SWEET BE THY SLUMBER see Hardwicke

SWEET BELLS OF BETHLEHEM see Offer, Charles K.

SWEET CANAAN *spir
(Taylor) SATB,S solo,acap oct LAWSON 51210
$.35 (S4588)

SWEET DAY see Handel, George Frideric

SWEET DAY, SO COOL see Bliss, Sir Arthur

SWEET DREAMS see Prentice, Fred

SWEET HOLY CHILD see Caldwell, Mary [Elizabeth]

SWEET HOUR OF PRAYER
(Parker) TTBB,pno/gtr oct LAWSON 51359 $.30 (S4589)

SWEET HOUR OF PRAYER see Bradbury, William
Batchelder

SWEET HOUR OF PRAYER see Ellis, Mary

SWEET HOUR OF PRAYER see Landon

SWEET HOUR OF PRAYER see Wilson

SWEET HYMNS AND SONGS see Jordahl

SWEET IS THAT DYING see Palestrina, Giovanni,
Soave Fia Il Morir

SWEET IS THE HOUR see Findlay, George

SWEET IS THE NAME OF JESUS see Handel, George
Frideric

SWEET IS THE SUNLIGHT see Eggleston, John W.

SWEET IS THE WORK see Robson, R. Walker

SWEET IS THY MERCY see Barnby, Sir Joseph

SWEET IT IS TO PRAISE THE LORD see Hruby,
Delores

SWEET JESU, KING OF BLISS see Archer, Frederick

SWEET JESUS *anthem
SATB/SAB/SA/TB BIG3 $.30 (S4590)

SWEET JESUS IN THE MANGER see Waterman

SWEET JESUS IN THE MANGER see Waterman, Frances

SWEET LAMB see Ehret, Walter

SWEET LITTLE BOY JESUS see Niles, John Jacob

SWEET LITTLE JESUS BOY see MacGimsey, [Robert]

SWEET MARIE AND HER BABY see Niles, John Jacob

SWEET MARY, GUARD THY PRECIOUS CHILD see Ehret,
Walter

SWEET MARY ROCKS HER INFANT see Ehret, Walter

SWEET MARY SINGS HER BABE TO SLEEP *Xmas,
carol,Czech
(Ehret, Walter) SATB,opt inst oct WALTON 2502
$.30 (S4591)
(Ehret, Walter) SSA oct WALTON 2536 $.30 (S4592)

SWEET MARY TENDS HER NEWBORN SON see Ehret,
Walter

SWEET MARY TO THE TEMPLE FARES see Eccard,
Johannes

SWEET MUSIC IS KING *carol
(Sharpe, E) unis CRAMER 28 s.p. (S4593)

SWEET NIGHTINGALE, AWAKE *anthem/folk,Ger
(Near, Gerald) unis treb cor (easy) oct
AUGSBURG 0413 $.20 (S4594)

SWEET RIVERS (from Sacred Harp, The)
(Cram) 4pt mix cor,T solo,acap oct SCHIRM.G
11918 $.30 (S4595)

SWEET SAVIOUR, BLESS US ERE WE GO see Harwood,
Basil

SWEET SPIRIT COMFORT ME see Noble, Harold

SWEET SPIRIT COMFORT ME see Pitfield, Thomas
Baron

SWEET STORY OF OLD, THE see Jacobus, Dale Asher

SWEET STORY, THE see Filkins

SWEET SWEET SONG OF SALVATION see Norman

SWEET, SWEET SPIRIT
(Kaiser, Kurt) SATB oct WORD CS-2499 $.30 (S4596)

SWEET WAS THE SONG *Xmas
(Jenkins) SATB,acap oct FISCHER,C CM-7064
$.25 (S4597)

SWEET WAS THE SONG see Bielawa, Herbert

SWEET WAS THE SONG see Britten, Benjamin

SWEET WAS THE SONG see Diercks, John H.

SWEET WAS THE SONG see Dussek, Johann Ladislaus

SWEET WAS THE SONG see Raffman, Relly

SWEET WAS THE SONG see Wetzler

SWEET WAS THE SONG THE VIRGIN SANG (from Sacred
Harp, The) anthem/folk,US,17th cent
(Fitzgerald, J.) SSAA,acap SCHIRM.EC 1895
$.15 (S4598)
(Johnson, David N.) SATB (easy) oct AUGSBURG
0531 $.25 (S4599)
(Johnson, David N.) SSA (easy) oct AUGSBURG
0530 $.25 (S4600)

SWEET WAS THE SONG THE VIRGIN SANG see Arundel-
Timms, T.

SWEET WAS THE SONG THE VIRGIN SANG see Ballett,
William

SWEET WAS THE SONG THE VIRGIN SANG see
Berkeley, Lennox

SWEET WAS THE SONG THE VIRGIN SANG see Hawkey,
William

SWEET WAS THE SONG THE VIRGIN SANG see Holman,
Derek

SWEET WAS THE SONG THE VIRGIN SANG see Johnson,
David N.

SWEET WAS THE SONG THE VIRGIN SANG see Pearson

SWEET WAS THE SONG THE VIRGIN SUNG see Cowell,
Henry Dixon

SWEETER THE BELLS NEVER RING see Ohl, [Jeremiah
Franklin]

SWELL THE FULL CHORUS see Handel, George
Frideric

SWENEY, J.
Organ Score Anthems [Vol. 1] *CCU
(Kirkpatrick, W.) SATB oct PRESSER $3.50 (S4601)
Organ Score Anthems [Vol. 2] *CCU
(Kirkpatrick, W.) SATB oct PRESSER $3.50 (S4602)
Sunshine In My Soul
(Coates) SA/TB SHAWNEE E87 $.30 (S4603)
Tell Me The Story Of Jesus *hymn
(Whitsett) SATB oct LILLENAS AN-1616 $.30 (S4604)

SWENSON
Gloria *Gloria
SATB oct FISCHER,C CM-7793 $.35 (S4605)
I Believe In One God
SATB oct FISCHER,C CM-7794 $.40 (S4606)
My God, My God, Why Hast Thou Forsaken Me?
*Easter
SATB oct GALAXY 1.2475.1 $.30 (S4607)

SWIFT
Almighty God, Whose Love Profound
SATB oct PRO ART 1607 $.18 (S4608)
He Is Born *see Davis, Katherine K.
Heavenly Voices *Xmas
SSA oct PRO ART 1055 $.20 (S4609)

SWIFT, B.
Carol Of Hope, A
(Palmer, A.) SATB oct PRESSER G-4504 $.30 (S4610)
O Master, Let Me Walk With Thee
SATB SHAWNEE A 818 $.30 (S4611)

SWIFT, F. F.
Jordan Road, The *see Swift, R.A.
Junior Choir Album *CCU
SA BELWIN $1.00 (S4612)
Sing Praise To God
SATB BELWIN $1.00 (S4613)
Story Of Easter *Easter,cant
SATB BELWIN $1.00 (S4614)

SWIFT, GERTRUDE P.
In Heavenly Love Abiding
SATB,SA soli,pno (med) oct WILLIS 6319 $.15 (S4615)

SWIFT, R.A.
All Night, All Day *spir
2pt jr cor oct KENDOR $.25 (S4616)
SSA oct KENDOR $.25 (S4617)
Jordan Road, The (composed with Swift, F. F.)
SATB oct BOURNE 647 $.25 (S4618)

SWINBURNE
This Day Born Again *Xmas
(Roff) SAB oct BOURNE 3024 $.25 (S4619)

SWING DAT HAMMER! *spir
(Johnson) TTBBB,acap oct SCHIRM.G 10643 $.25 (S4620)

SWING LITTLE JESUS see Grime, William

SWING LOW *spir
see Four Negro Spirituals
(Whitman) SATB oct LILLENAS AN-3808 $.30 (S4621)

SWING LOW see Burroughs

SWING LOW, SWEET CHARIOT *spir,US
"Fahre Sanft, Schoner Wagen" see Sechs Negro
Spirituals, Blatt 3
(Bartholomew) TTBBB,B solo,acap oct SCHIRM.G
8915 $.25 (S4622)
(Billups) 4pt mix cor,S solo,acap oct
SCHIRM.G 8657 $.25 (S4623)
(Christiansen) SATB KJOS 72 $.30 (S4624)
(Clements, J.) SATB,opt A solo,pno, opt semi-
chorus PROWSE s.p. (S4625)
(Dawson) SATB KJOS T114 $.30 (S4626)
(Dawson) men cor KJOS T115 $.30 (S4627)
(Dawson) SSA KJOS T116 $.30 (S4628)
(Dexter, Harry) 2pt ENOCH TP266 s.p. (S4629)
(Durian, Tim) 4pt men cor,Bar solo,acap
BREITKOPF-W Z-39 s.p. see also Dreizehn
Negro- Spirituals (S4630)
(Geller) SATB MARKS 4196 $.25 (S4631)
(Huntley) 4pt mix cor,acap oct SCHIRM.G 7126
$.25 (S4632)
(Jonsson, Josef) men cor NORDISKA 2427 s.p. (S4633)
(Mittergradnegger, Gunther) [Ger] mix cor,
acap oct DOBLINGER s.p. see also Funf
Amerikanische Negro-Spirituals (S4634)
(Pens) SATB oct PRO ART 1353 $.25 (S4635)
(Ritz, James) SSA&SATB,T solo,acap oct WORLD
ESE-728-8 $.60 (S4636)
(Ritz, James) SSA,pno oct WESTWOOD ESE-1528-3
$.60 (S4637)
(Roberton) 4pt mix cor,acap oct CURWEN 8429
$.25 (S4638)
(Roberton) 3pt jr cor/3pt wom cor ROBERTON
72103 s.p. (S4639)
(Roberton) mix cor ROBERTON 61287 s.p. (S4640)
(Shaw; Parker) SATB,acap oct LAWSON 984 $.25 (S4641)
(Trant) SSA (med) OXFORD 83.034 $.25 (S4642)
(Widdicombe) 2pt jr cor/2pt wom cor CURWEN
72493 s.p. (S4643)

SWING LOW SWEET CHARIOT see Gerhold, Norbert

SWING LOW, SWEET CHARIOT see Ringwald, [Roy]

SWING LOW, SWEET CHARIOT see Westbrook, Francis
B.

SWING LOW, SWEET STAR see Jolley

SWISHER, CHARLES
Sleep, Baby Jesus *Xmas
SSA LEONARD-US 08060160 $.25   (S4644)

SWORD, A see Woodman, Raymond Huntington

SWORDS INTO PLOWSHAWS see Vernon, Knight

SYCAMORE TREE see Heseltine, Philip

SYCAMORE TREE, THE see Britten, Benjamin

SYDENHAM, E.A.
Great Is The Lord *anthem
mix cor oct NOVELLO 28.0813.07 s.p. (S4645)

SYDOW
Hosanna, Blessed Is He *Easter
SATB oct LORENZ C341 $.30   (S4646)

Promised One, The *Xmas,cant
SATB oct LORENZ $1.95   (S4647)

SYDOW, RALPH KARL
Sing Praise To God *CC11U,Gen
SATB oct WILLIS $1.50   (S4648)

SYKES
Child Of The World, The
SATB,acap (easy) OXFORD 84.041 $.25 (S4649)

SYMBOLUM see Bialas, Gunther

SYMFONI IV see Uppenbarelse, Johannes

SYMONS
Sing We Merrily *anthem
SS oct OXFORD 44.079 $.25   (S4650)

SYMPHONIAE JUCUNDAE, 1538 see Rhaw, Georg

SYMPHONIAE SACRAE II see Schutz, Heinrich

SYMPHONIAE SACRAE III *see Schutz, Heinrich,
Es Ging Ein Samann Aus, Zu Saen Seinen
Samen, SWV 408; Schutz, Heinrich, Komm
Heiliger Geist, SWV 417; Schutz, Heinrich,
Lasset Uns Doch Den Herren, Unsern Gott,
Loben, "Let Us Declare The Glory Of The
Lord, Our God", SWV 407; Schutz, Heinrich,
Meister, Wir Wissen, Dass Du Wahrhaftig
Bist, SWV 414; Schutz, Heinrich, O Herr,
Hilf, O Herr, Lass Wohl Gelingen, "O Save
Us, Lord", SWV 402; Schutz, Heinrich, Seid
Barmherzig, Wie Auch Euer Vater Barmherzig
Ist, "Be Ye Loving Even As Your Father Hath
Loved You", SWV 409; Schutz, Heinrich,
Siehe, Es Erschien Der Engel, "Behold,
There Appeared", SWV 403; Schutz, Heinrich,
Wo Der Herr Nicht Das Haus Bauet (Psalm
127) SWV 400   (S4651)

SYMPHONIAE SACRAE III see Schutz, Heinrich

SYMPHONISCHE KANTATE see Chemin-Petit, Hans

SYMPHONY OF EASTER, THE see Beethoven, Ludwig
van

SYMPHONY OF PSALMS see Stravinsky, Igor

SYNG FOR HERREN see Nystedt, Knut

SYNG OG LOV see Ukjent

SYNGER FOR GUD see Pachelbel, Johann

SZABO, [FERENC] (1902-1969)
Vallomas
[Hung] SATB,4trp,4horn,3trom,tuba,drums,
tamb,timp, cymbals (diff) BUDAPEST 5526
s.p.   (S4652)

SZADEK, TOMASZ
Dies Est Laetitiae *Pol
(Szweykowski, Z.M.) men cor POLSKIE WDMP33
s.p.   (S4653)

SZARZYNSKI, STANISLAW SILWESTER
Ad Hymnos, Ad Cantus *Pol
(Szweykowski) SSATB,cont,strings POLSKIE
WDMP26 s.p.   (S4654)

Litania Cursoria *Pol
(Szweykowski) cor,cont,strings POLSKIE
WDMP72 s.p.   (S4655)

SZIVUNKRE SZALL MA see Lotti, Antonio

SZMANOWSKI
Stabat Mater *Op.53
[Lat/Pol] voc sc UNIVER. 8743 $4.10, cor
pts UNIVER. 8742 $.75   (S4656)

SZOKALAY
Cantata Nigra *cant
mix cor,orch LEDUC rental   (S4657)

T

'T VIOOLTJE see Rennes, Cath. v.

TABERNACLE CHOIR NO.2 *CCU
mix cor oct AGAPE $2.25   (T1)

TABERNACLE CHOIR NO.3 *CCU
mix cor oct AGAPE $2.00   (T2)

TABERNACLE CHOIR NO.4 *CCU
mix cor oct AGAPE $2.00   (T3)

TABERNACLE OF GOD, THE see MacDonald

TACKSAGELSHYMN see Sorenson, Torsten

TAFFS, J.
Oh, Now Be Joyful All
SATB oct PRESSER 332-40091 $.30   (T4)

TAG SO GROSS UND FREUDENREICH see Waldbroel,
Wilhelm

TAGES- UND LEBENSLAUF
see Psalmen Und Geistliche Lieder Der
Christenheit

TAGESZEITEN see Bornefeld, Helmut

TAGG, LAWRENCE E.
Sing And Rejoice
SATB,acap oct WORLD CA-2087-8 $.60 (T5)

TAIT, JOHN
Lord Of All Power And Might
SATB ALLANS 177 s.p.   (T6)

TAKACS, JENO (1902-   )
Lamb, The *Op.71a
SSA,opt pno oct WORLD ESA-720-3 $.45 (T7)

Let Nothing Disturb Thee *Op.71c
SATB,acap oct WORLD ESA-722-8 $.30 (T8)

Meditation And Simple Requiem
SATB oct COLOMBO 2723 $.30   (T9)

Shepherd, Hark *Xmas
4pt mix cor,acap oct SCHIRM.G 10909 $.25
(T10)

TAKE, BELIEVE see Wetzler

TAKE FROM US, LORD see Berger, Jean

TAKE IT ON OVER see Martin, Gilbert M.

TAKE IT TO JESUS see Smith

TAKE IT TO THE LORD IN PRAYER see Lorenz

TAKE MY HAND *spir
(Geller) SATB MARKS 4225 $.25   (T11)

TAKE MY HAND, PRECIOUS LORD *anthem
see Great Choral Series
SAB/SA/TB BIG3 $.25   (T12)

TAKE MY LIFE, AND LET IT BE see Hintze, Jakob

TAKE MY LIFE AND LET IT BE see Hughes

TAKE MY LIFE AND LET IT BE see Kirk

TAKE MY LIFE AND LET IT BE see Malan

TAKE MY LIFE AND LET IT BE see Mozart, Wolfgang
Amadeus

TAKE MY LIFE, AND LET IT BE see Williams, David
H.

TAKE MY YOKE see Palestrina, Giovanni, Tollite
Jugum Meum

TAKE NOT THY HOLY SPIRIT FROM ME see Williams,
R.

TAKE, TAKE AND EAT see Ferguson, Howard

TAKE THOU OUR MINDS, DEAR LORD see Darst, W.
Glenn

TAKE TIME see Avery

TAKE TIME TO BE HOLY see Smith

TAKE TIME TO BE HOLY see Wolf

TAKE UP THY CROSS see Grant, Cecil

TAKE UP THY CROSS see Hughes

TAKE UP THY CROSS see Lovelace, Austin C.

TAKE UP THY CROSS see Wilson

TAKE UP THY CROSS see Young, Carlton R.

TAL, JOSEPH (1910-   )
Die Mutter Jubelt *cant,Heb
"Mother Rejoices, The" SATB,soli,pno,orch
ISRAELI 311 s.p.   (T13)

Mother Rejoices, The *see Die Mutter Jubelt

TALK ABOUT A CHILD *spir
(Roberts) SATB,acap oct LAWSON 51555 $.30
(T14)

TALK ABOUT A CHILD WHO DO LOVE JESUS *spir
(Alderfer) SATB oct SPRATT 129 $.30 (T15)

TALK WITH US, LORD see Ford, Virgil T.

TALK WITH US, LORD see Lovelace, Austin C.

TALL TOWER TALE see Fleisher, Simi

TALLIS CANON see Pitcher, Gladys

TALLIS' CANON see Tallis, Thomas

TALLIS, THOMAS (ca. 1505-1585)
All Hail Thou Noble Guest *Xmas,canon
(Wehr) SAB oct PRO ART 2284 $.25   (T16)

All People That On Earth Do Dwell *Thanks
SATB,acap SCHIRM.EC 1708 $.30   (T17)
(Wienandt) SATB,acap oct LAWSON 51424 $.30
(T18)

All People That On Earth Do Well
(Knight) 4pt jr cor/SATB (easy) FISCHER,C
CM 7579 $.30   (T19)

All Praise To Thee *anthem/canon
(Foltz-Shelly) SATB oct BELWIN 60099 $.30
(T20)
(Mueller) SATB oct SCHIRM.G 11163 $.30
(T21)
(Pooler) 2pt treb cor/3pt treb cor/4pt treb
cor (easy) oct AUGSBURG 1318 $.30   (T22)
(Stone, Leonard) SATB oct BELWIN 2223 $.30
(T23)

All Praise To Thee, My God, This Night *Gen
(Wienhorst, R.) SATB,acap (med easy) oct
CONCORDIA 98-1791 $.25 contains also:
Awake, My Soul, And With The Sun   (T24)

Almighty Word *Adv/Gen
(Scott, Anthony) SATB&cong,org (med easy)
oct OXFORD 42.955 $.35   (T25)

Audivi, Media Nocte *Adv/Gen
SATB,acap (med) oct OXFORD 43.327 $.30 (T26)

Audivi Vocem De Caelo
"I Heard A Voice" SATB,acap SCHIRM.EC 1637
$.16   (T27)

Awake, My Soul, And With The Sun
see Tallis, Thomas, All Praise To Thee, My
God, This Night

Before The Ending Of The Day *see Te Lucis
Ante Terminum

Benedicite
TTBarB,acap oct NOVELLO 40.1536.03 s.p.
(T28)

Benedictus *Bene
TTBB,acap oct NOVELLO s.p.   (T29)

Blessed Be The Lord
(Collins) TTBB,opt org AMP 30 $.25 (T30)

Blessed Be Thy Name *see Mihi Autem Nimis

Classic Anthems *CCU,anthem
SATB oct PRESSER 352-00060 $.40   (T31)

Deus Tuorum Militum *hymn
(Stevens) [Lat] SAATB,acap AMP N17 $.30 see
from Five Hymns   (T32)

Dum Transisset Sabbatum *mot
SATTB,acap SCHIRM.EC $.36   (T33)
(Collins, H.B.) [Lat] SATTB/SATBarB CHESTER
s.p.   (T34)

Festal Responses
SATBB (easy) oct OXFORD 40.909 $.25 (T35)

Fifteen Anthems Vol. 1 *CCU
mix cor,acap voc sc KALMUS 6700 $1.00 (T36)

Fifteen Anthems Vol. 2 *CCU,anthem
mix cor,acap voc sc KALMUS 6701 $1.00 (T37)

Five Hymns *see Deus Tuorum Militum; Jam
Christus Astra Ascenderat; Quod Chorus
Vatum; Salvator Mundi Domine; Sermone
Blando Angelus   (T38)

Five-Part Litany
SATBB (easy) oct OXFORD 40.913 $.65 (T39)

Gloria Patri
(Terry, R.R.) [Lat] mix cor oct NOVELLO
52.0007.05 s.p.   (T40)

Glory To Thee My God This Night *Xmas/Eve
(Brown, Kenneth) SATB (very easy) oct
OXFORD 40.922 $.25, ipr   (T41)
(Pfaff) SSA BOOSEY-CAN s.p.   (T42)

Hear The Voice And Prayer *Ded/Gen,anthem
SATB oct GRAY GCMR 2968 $.30   (T43)
SATB SCHIRM.EC 1638 $.20   (T44)
"Heare The Voyce And Prayer Of Thy
Servaunts" SSAA,acap (med diff) oct
CONCORDIA 98-1855 $.35   (T45)
(Doe, Paul) SATB/AATB oct NOVELLO
88.0018.09 s.p.   (T46)
(Doe, Paul) AATB oct NOVELLO 88.0018.09
s.p.   (T47)
(, Ehret) SATB oct ELKAN-V 362-1310 $.30
(T48)
(West, John E.) mix cor oct NOVELLO
28.0776.09 s.p.   (T49)

Heare The Voyce And Prayer Of Thy Servaunts
*see Hear The Voice And Prayer

Holy Communion *Commun
(Bevan, Maurice) SATB oct NOVELLO
44.1349.00 s.p.   (T50)

I Call And Cry To Thee *anthem
(Doe, Paul) SAATB oct NOVELLO 88.0026.10
s.p.   (T51)

I Heard A Voice *see Audivi Vocem De Caelo

I Heard The Voice Of Jesus *anthem
SATB (easy) oct AUGSBURG 1119 $.18 (T52)

If Ye Love Me *Fest/Gen/Lent/Pent/Whitsun,
anthem
TTBB,acap (med easy) oct CONCORDIA 98-1520
$.25   (T53)
mix cor oct OXFORD 42.601 $.35   (T54)
SATB (easy) oct OXFORD 42.601 $.25 (T55)
SATB oct FISCHER,C HO-500 $.25   (T56)
SATB oct GRAY GCMR 1629 $.30   (T57)
SATB (easy) ALLANS 321 s.p.   (T58)
SATB,acap PETERS H1476 $.40   (T59)
mix cor oct NOVELLO 40.0231.08 s.p. (T60)

If Ye Love Me, Keep My Commandments *Bibl
4pt mix cor,acap oct SCHIRM.G 10234 $.30
(T61)

TALLIS, THOMAS (cont'd.)

boy cor SOUTHERN $.25 (T62)
SATB,acap oct PRO ART 1728 $.30 (T63)
SATB,acap SCHIRM.EC 2269 $.30 (T64)
(Carlton) mix cor SOUTHERN $.30 (T65)
(Carlton) SATB,acap oct BOOSEY 5224 $.30 (T66)
(Clough-Leighter) mix cor SOUTHERN $.30 (T67)
(Glaser, V.) SAB,acap SCHIRM.EC 2406 $.25 (T68)

In Ieiunio Et Fletu *anthem
mix cor oct OXFORD 43.255 $.35 (T69)

In Jejunio Et Fletu *Lent
STTBB/SATTBB,acap SCHIRM.EC 1637 $.30 (T70)

In Manus Tuas
"Into Thy Hands" [Lat/Eng] SSATB/SSAATB, acap PETERS H1562 (T71)
"Into Thy Hands" SATB oct WALTON 6028 $.30 (T72)

Into Thy Hands *see In Manus Tuas

Jam Christus Astra Ascenderat *hymn
(Stevens) [Lat] SATTB,acap AMP N15 $.30 see from Five Hymns (T73)

Jesu Salvator Saeculi
"Jesus, The World's Redeeming Lord" SSATB/SAATB,acap PETERS H1507 $.50 (T74)

Jesus, Redeemer Of The World *see O Nata Lux De Lumine

Jesus, The World's Redeeming Lord *see Jesu Salvator Saeculi

Kyrie Eleison *mot
[Lat] TTBB RICORDI-ENG SY161 s.p. (T75)

Lamentations *Psntd,anthem
TTBB oct OXFORD 46.156 $3.60 (T76)
SATTB,acap (med diff) oct OXFORD 46.032 $1.65 (T77)
(Shore, Royle) mix cor oct NOVELLO s.p. (T78)

Lamentations Of Jeremiah, The *Bibl
(Woodworth) 5pt mix cor,acap oct SCHIRM.G 10523 $.35 (T79)

Laudate Dominum *mot
"O Praise The Lord On High" SAATB,acap SCHIRM.EC $.25 (T80)
(Collins, H.B.) "O Praise The Lord On High" [Eng/Lat] SAATB CHESTER s.p. (T81)

Litany With The Later Suffrages, The (Ferial)
(Shaw, Watkins) SATB oct NOVELLO 02.0076.10 s.p. (T82)

Lord, Teach Us How To Pray Aright *Gen/Lent
SATB,acap (easy) oct CONCORDIA 98-1983 $.25 (T83)

Magnificat And Nunc Dimittis *Magnif/Nunc
SATB oct PRESSER 352-00060 $.35 (T84)
SATB oct NOVELLO 44.0888.08 s.p. (T85)

Mass For Four Voices *Mass
4pt voc sc KALMUS 6693 $.30 (T86)

Hihi &qtem Nimis !Gen
"Blessed Be Thy Name" SAATB,acap (med easy) OXFORD 43.230 $.30 (T87)
"Blessed Be Thy Name" SATTB,acap (med) oct OXFORD 43.230 $.30 (T88)

Most Loving Saviour *see Salvator Mundi

My Lord, My Love
(Stephens) SATB oct FISCHER,J 9520 $.30 (T89)

Nineteen Anthems Vol. 1 *CCU
mix cor,acap voc sc KALMUS 6694 $1.35 (T90)

Nineteen Anthems Vol. 2 *CCU
mix cor,acap voc sc KALMUS 6695 $1.35 (T91)

Nineteen Anthems Vol. 3 *CCU
mix cor,acap voc sc KALMUS 6696 $1.35 (T92)

Nineteen Anthems Vol. 4 *CCU
mix cor,acap voc sc KALMUS 6697 $1.35 (T93)

O Born Of Light *see O Nata Lux De Lumine

O Light Of Light *see O Nata Lux

O Light Of Light *see O Nata Lux De Lumine

O Lord, Give Thy Holy Spirit *Whitsun
SATB,acap SCHIRM.EC 1718 $.25 (T94)
SATB oct GRAY GCMR 3044 $.30 (T95)
SATB (easy) oct OXFORD 42.237 $.25 (T96)
(Ehret) mix cor CHAPPELL 0024232-358 $.40 (T97)

O Lord, Give Thy Holy Spirit Into Our Hearts *anthem
(Harwood, Basil) mix cor oct NOVELLO 50.0133.01 s.p. (T98)

O Nata Lux *Gen
"O Light Of Light" SATTB,acap (easy) oct OXFORD 43.228 $.25 (T99)

O Nata Lux De Lumine
"Jesus, Redeemer Of The World" [Lat/Eng] SATBarB PETERS H1516 $.40 (T100)
"O Light Of Light" SATTB,acap (med) OXFORD 43.228 $.25 (T101)
(Harris) "O Born Of Light" [Eng/Lat] SATBB, acap oct SCHIRM.G 8644 $.25 (T102)
(Lynn) "O Shining Light" [Eng/Lat] SATTB oct SCHIRM.G 11704 $.25 (T103)

O Praise The Lord On High *see Laudate Dominum

O Sacrum Convivium *anthem
mix cor oct OXFORD 43.218 $.35 (T104)
(Doe, Paul) [Lat] SAATB oct NOVELLO 88.0026.10 s.p. (T105)

O Salutaris Hostia *Commun
SATBB,acap SCHIRM.EC $.25 (T106)

TALLIS, THOMAS (cont'd.)

O Saviour Of The World *see Salvator Mundi Domine

O Shining Light *see O Nata Lux De Lumine

Pour Forth Thy Spirit *Gen
(Pooler) SATB SCHMITT 8025 $.30 (T107)

Praise Be Unto The Father *anthem
(Terry, R.R.) mix cor oct NOVELLO 52.0007.05 s.p. (T108)

Preces And Responses
ATTB/TTBB,acap (easy) oct OXFORD 41.020 $.25 (T109)

Preces And Responses (Ferial)
(Shaw, Watkins) SATB oct NOVELLO 02.0004.02 s.p. (T110)

Purge Me, O Lord *Gen/Lent
see TRE ENGELSKA MOTETTER
SATB,opt inst (easy) oct OXFORD 43.382 $.25 (T111)
(Harris) SSA oct PLYMOUTH PCS-213 $.25 (T112)
(Harris) SAB oct PLYMOUTH PCS-405 $.25 (T113)

Quod Chorus Vatum *hymn
(Stevens) [Lat] SAATB,acap AMP N16 $.30 see from Five Hymns (T114)

Rise, God! Judge Thou The Earth In Might
(Woodworth) 4pt mix cor,org/pno oct SCHIRM.G 10480 $.35 (T115)

Salvator Mundi *Lent/Psntd
SATTB,acap SCHIRM.EC $.25 (T116)
"Most Loving Saviour" SATTB,acap (med diff) OXFORD 43.231 $.30 (T117)
"Most Loving Saviour" SATTB/SATBB,acap (med) oct OXFORD 43.231 $.30 (T118)

Salvator Mundi Domine *hymn
"O Saviour Of The World" [Lat/Eng] SSATB, acap PETERS H1508 $.50 (T119)
(Stevens) [Lat] SATBarB,acap AMP N14 $.30 see from Five Hymns (T120)

Salve Intemerata *Mass
mix cor,acap voc sc KALMUS 6692 $1.00 (T121)

Sermone Blando Angelus *hymn
(Stevens) [Lat] SAATB,acap AMP N13 $.25 see from Five Hymns (T122)

"Short" Evening Service *Eve
SATB,acap (med easy) oct OXFORD 43.325 $.30 (T123)

Sixteen Cantiones Sacrae (1575) Vol. 1 *CCU
mix cor,acap voc sc KALMUS 6698 $1.00 (T124)

Sixteen Cantiones Sacrae (1575) Vol. 2 *CCU
mix cor,acap voc sc KALMUS 6699 $1.00 (T125)

Sons And Daughters, Let Us Sing *Easter
SATB oct GALAXY 1.2311.1 $.30 (T126)

Spem In Alium Nunquam Habui *Gen
40pt (med) oct OXFORD 43.260 $3.00 (T127)

Tallis' Canon *Gen
see THREE FAMOUS CANONS
(Olds) SATB SCHMITT 1587 $.30 (T128)

Te Deum *Te Deum
SAATB,acap (med) oct OXFORD (T129)

Te Lucis Ante Terminum
"Before The Ending Of The Day" [Lat/Eng] SATTB,acap PETERS H1509 $.40 (T130)

That Virgin's Child *Xmas/Easter/Lent
(Marshall) mix cor SOUTHERN $.30 (T131)
(Marshall, Charles) SATB FRANK F-543 $.30 (T132)
(Shaw) 4pt mix cor,acap oct SCHIRM.G 9946 $.25 (T133)

This Is My Commandment *Psntd/Quinqua/Rembrnc/Whitsun,anthem
SSATB (easy) oct OXFORD 43.224 $.35 (T134)
TTBB oct OXFORD 41.025 $.30 (T135)

Verily, Verily, I Say Unto You
SATB (easy) oct OXFORD (T136)

When Shall My Sorrowful Sighing
SATB,acap PETERS H1510 $.40 (T137)

TALMADGE

Christmas Bells, The *Xmas
SATB oct SACRED S-124 $.35 (T138)

Psalm For The Cities *Psalm
SATB oct HERITAGE H71 $.35 (T139)

TALMADGE, CHARLES L.

Crucifixus *Lent
SATB oct GRAY GCMR 3079 $.30 (T140)

Jesus The Very Thought Of Thee
SATB oct SCHIRM.G 10276 $.25 (T141)

Jesus Thou Joy Of Loving Hearts
SATB oct GALAXY 1.2109.1 $.25 (T142)

Lord Jesus Think On Me
SATB oct GALAXY 1.2499.1 $.25 (T143)

Lord Of All Power And Might
4pt mix cor,org oct SCHIRM.G 11049 $.25 (T144)

Nowell *Xmas
SATB oct FISCHER,J 10038 $.25 (T145)

See The Destined Day Arise *Easter
SATB oct GALAXY 1.1825.1 $.25 (T146)

Sing Alleluia Forth
SATB oct GALAXY 1.1939.1 $.30 (T147)

Sing We Nowell *Xmas
SATB,acap oct PRESSER 312-40599 $.25 (T148)

TALMADGE, CHARLES L. (cont'd.)

Thou Art The Way
4pt mix cor,acap oct SCHIRM.G 11048 $.25 (T149)

We Love The Place, O God
SATB oct SCHIRM.G 10051 $.20 (T150)

TALSMANNEN DEN HELLIGE AND see Hovland, Egil

TAMAS, A. GREGORY

Missa Sancti Joannis A Capistrano *Mass
SATB LUDWIG $1.00, ipr (T151)

TAMBLYN, WILLIAM

Hail Mary
see Dawney, Michael, Lord's Prayer, The

Make We Joy *anthem
mix cor oct OXFORD 84.177 $.35 (T152)

Make We Joy Now In This Fest
SATB OXFORD (T153)

Parish Choir Book No. 11, The *see Hail Mary (T154)

You Are Peter
SATB,org/bvl oct BOOSEY 5824 $.30 (T155)

TAMQUAM AD LATRONEM see Victoria, Tomas Luis de

TAMQUAM AGNUS see Victoria, Tomas Luis de

TAN, TAN, TAN *Xmas,Span
(Nichols) SATB SCHMITT 8056 $.25 (T156)

TAN, TAN, THEY SAW A STAR see Staley

TANCNOTA see Weores, S.

TANDIS QUE LE SOMMEIL *Morn,hymn
(Racine, C.; Geveart, F.-A.) [Lat/Fr] 3pt wom cor,acap (med easy) cor pts LEMOINE s.p. see from Collection De Choeurs, premiere Facsimile (T157)

TANK ICKE PA MIN UNGDOMS SYNDER see Hammarstrom, Hugo

TANKARD, GEOFFREY

Bermuda Anthem, The *anthem
SATB oct NOVELLO 44.1412.08 s.p. (T158)

TANNER, PETER

Sing For Joy
SATB,org oct LAWSON 51266 $.35 (T159)

TANOUS

Let's Say A Rosary Each Day (composed with Smolin)
SATB PARAGON 1014 $.25 (T160)

TANQUAM AD LATRONEM see Victoria, Tomas Luis de

TANQUAM AGNUS see Victoria, Tomas Luis de

TANSMAN, ALEXANDER (1897-)

Prophet Isaiah, The
[Eng/Fr] cor pts UNIVER. 12076A-D $1.40 (T161)

TANS'UR, WILLIAM (ca. 1706-1783)

Come, Holy Spirit
(Cain) SAB FLAMMER D5084 $.25 (T162)

Passiontide Carol, A *Psntd
(Purvis) SA/TB FLAMMER E5145 $.30 (T163)

With Joy We Hail The Sacred Day
(Hutson) SATB SHAWNEE A 521 $.25 (T164)

TANTI AUGURI *Xmas,carol
(Malatesta, Gianni) 4pt men cor ZANIBON 4638 s.p.
contains: Adeste Fideles; Bimbo Bimbo Fai La Nanna "Piva, Piva"; Jingle Bells; Stille Nacht; Tanti Auguri; Tu Scendi Dalle Stelle (T165)

TANTI AUGURI
see Tanti Auguri

TANTUM ERGO see Asola, Giovanni Matteo

TANTUM ERGO see Aubanel, Georges

TANTUM ERGO see Bach, Johann Sebastian

TANTUM ERGO see Baroni, Giovanni

TANTUM ERGO see Baumann, Max

TANTUM ERGO see Bellini, Vincenzo

TANTUM ERGO see Bentivoglio, Giulio

TANTUM ERGO see Beobide, Jose Maria

TANTUM ERGO see Bernasconi, Luigi

TANTUM ERGO see Bezzi, Enrico

TANTUM ERGO see Boellmann, Leon

TANTUM ERGO see Bondeville, [Emmanuel de]

TANTUM ERGO see Bonneau, P.

TANTUM ERGO see Borsieri, C.

TANTUM ERGO see Bossi, Marco Enrico

TANTUM ERGO see Bottazzo, Luigi

TANTUM ERGO see Boulay, J.

TANTUM ERGO see Breville, Pierre-Onfroy de

TANTUM ERGO see Bush, Geoffrey

TANTUM ERGO see Busser, [Henri-Paul]

TANTUM ERGO see Cerquetelli, Giuseppe

TANTUM ERGO see Choisnel, G.

TANTUM ERGO see Claussmann, A.

TANTUM ERGO see Cline

TANTUM ERGO see Colonna, Giovanni Paolo

TANTUM ERGO see Delvincourt, Claude

TANTUM ERGO oee Demerath, F.

TANTUM ERGO see Dubois, Theodore

TANTUM ERGO see Dupre, Marcel

TANTUM ERGO see Durufle, Maurice

TANTUM ERGO see Etti, Karl

TANTUM ERGO see Faure, Gabriel-Urbain

TANTUM ERGO see Franck, Cesar

TANTUM ERGO see Franck, [Johann Wolfgang]

TANTUM ERGO see Franco

TANTUM ERGO see Gehring, A.

TANTUM ERGO see Gigout, [Eugene]

TANTUM ERGO see Gluck, Christoph Willibald
    Ritter von

TANTUM ERGO see Gounod, Charles Francois

TANTUM ERGO see Grassi, Ciro

TANTUM ERGO see Handel, George Frideric

TANTUM ERGO see Hartmann, Luigi

TANTUM ERGO see Heidet, Le R. P.

TANTUM ERGO see Kaufmann, Ferdinand

TANTUM ERGO see Lambiollotte, Louis

TANTUM ERGO see Lefebure-Wely, Louis James
    Alfred

TANTUM ERGO see Loss, Luigi

TANTUM ERGO see Maugeri, Giuseppe

TANTUM ERGO see Mendelssohn-Bartholdy, Felix

TANTUM ERGO see Mengelberg, Rudolf

TANTUM ERGO see Moioli, Romano

TANTUM ERGO see Mozart, Wolfgang Amadeus

TANTUM ERGO see Muller, J.

TANTUM ERGO see Muller, Giulio

TANTUM ERGO see Nicolosi, Salvatore

TANTUM ERGO oee Oltrassi, Giuseppe

TANTUM ERGO see Philipp, Franz

TANTUM ERGO see Pitoni, Giuseppe Ottavio

TANTUM ERGO see Ravanello, Oreste

TANTUM ERGO see Renzi, Angelo

TANTUM ERGO see Rinck, Johann Christian Hein.

TANTUM ERGO see Rodella, Sante

TANTUM ERGO see Roff, Joseph

TANTUM ERGO see Sacchetto, Guido

TANTUM ERGO see Saint-Saens, Camille

TANTUM ERGO see Schmitt, Florent

TANTUM ERGO see Schroeder, Hermann

TANTUM ERGO see Schubert, Franz (Peter)

TANTUM ERGO see Schumann, Robert (Alexander)

TANTUM ERGO see Sciammarello

TANTUM ERGO see Triembacher, Henriette

TANTUM ERGO see Victoria, Tomas Luis de

TANTUM ERGO see Volpi, Edoardo

TANTUM ERGO see Bottazzo, Luigi

TANTUM ERGO see Bottazzo, Luigi

TANTUM ERGO, EN FA see Faure, Gabriel-Urbain

TANTUM ERGO, EN LA MINEUR see Beethoven, Ludwig
    van

TANTUM ERGO, EN SI BEMOL see Bach, Johann
    Sebastian

TANTUM ERGO I see Ahrens, Joseph

TANTUM ERGO I see Heiller, Anton

TANTUM ERGO II see Ahrens, Joseph

TANTUM ERGO II see Heiller, Anton

TANTUM ERGO III see Ahrens, Joseph

TANTUM ERGO IN E FLAT see Schubert, Franz
    (Peter)

TANTUM ERGO IV see Ahrens, Joseph

TANTUM ERGO, MI MINEUR see Bach, Johann
    Sebastian

TANTUM ERGO SACRAMENTUM see Diepenbrock, Alfons

TANTUM ERGO SACRAMENTUM see Reger, Max

TANTUM ERGO SACRAMENTUM see Sandvold, Arild

TANTUM ERGO, TEIL 1 UND 2
(Pfannhauser, K.) 4pt mix cor,orch (CCU,
    contains works by: Bruckner, Anton;
    Diabelli, A.; Haydn, Michael; Kreutzer, C.;
    Schubert, Ferdinand; Schubert, Franz; and
    others) DOBLINGER voc sc s.p., cor pts
    s.p., ipa see from Osterreichische
    Kirchenmusik   (T166)

TANTUM ERGO, TEIL 3
(Pfannhauser, K.) 4pt mix cor,org (CCU,
    contains works by: Bruckner, Anton;
    Diabelli, A.; Haydn, Michael; Kreutzer, C.;
    Schubert, Ferdinand; Schubert, Franz; and
    others) DOBLINGER voc sc s.p., cor pts s.p.
    see from Osterreichische Kirchenmusik   (T167)

TANTUM ERGO see Mozart, Wolfgang Amadeus

TANTUM ERGO see Mozart, Wolfgang Amadeus,
    Tantum Ergo

TANTUM ERGO see Mozart, Wolfgang Amadeus

TANTUM ERGO see Mozart, Wolfgang Amadeus,
    Tantum Ergo

TANTUM ERGO see Bruckner, Anton

TAPSCOTT, CARL
    God Who Made The Earth
        unis,pno oct BERANDOL 910T5AA $.35   (T168)

    Three Canticles *CC3U
        SATB,acap oct BERANDOL 910T5AD $.35   (T169)

TARNER
    Seek And Ye Shall Find
        SATB oct LORENZ A506 $.25   (T170)

    Show Me A Window
        SATB oct LORENZ A533 $.25   (T171)

    Teach Me To Love Thee More
        SATB oct LORENZ A526 $.25   (T172)

TARNER, EVELYN F.
    Risen Lord, The *Easter,cant
        oct AGAPE $1.50   (T173)

    Saviour Has Come, The *Xmas,cant
        oct AGAPE $1.50   (T174)

    Saviour Has Come To Earth, The *Xmas
        SATB oct AGAPE GC 805 $.30   (T175)

    Show Me A Window *Gen,anthem
        SATB/SA (easy) oct LORENZ A533 $.25   (T176)

TARP, SVEND ERIK (1908-   )
    Te Deum *Op.33, Te Deum
        cor SAMFUNDET voc sc s.p., cor pts s.p.
                                              (T177)
        [Lat] mix cor,opt soli,orch FOG III, 86 voc
        sc s.p., cor pts s.p.   (T178)

TARRELL
    I'm Gonna Walk My Way To Heaven *spir
        SATB SCHMITT 1188 $.25   (T179)

TARRY IN THE GARDEN see Marshall

TARRY WITH ME see Mozart, Wolfgang Amadeus, Ave
    Verum Corpus

TARTARIN, A.
    Noel Blesois Avec Noel D'orleans *Xmas
        [Fr] mix cor,acap (med easy) cor pts
        LEMOINE s.p.   (T180)

TARTINI, GIUSEPPE (1692-1770)
    Down In Adoration Falling
        see THREE MOTETS IN HONOR OF THE BLESSED
        SACRAMENT

    Lord God, Hear My Prayer
        (Dieterich) SATB,acap oct BOOSEY 5039 $.30
                                              (T181)

TASTE AND SEE see Peloquin, C. Alexander

TASTE THE NEW WINE see Avery

TATE, TOBY
    City And The Tower, The
        SATB,acap oct LAWSON 51431 $.40   (T182)

    Prince Is Born, A
        SSA (med) OXFORD 83.043 $.35   (T183)

    Virgin And Child, The *Xmas
        SATB (med) OXFORD 84.159 $.35   (T184)

TATTON
    Babe Holds Court In Bethlehem , A *Xmas
        SATB,acap (easy) OXFORD 43.202 $.30 (T185)

TAUBERT, K.H.
    Gott So Wollen Wir Loben Und Ehren *Xmas
        SATB,TTBB soli TONGER s.p.   (T186)

TAUBLEIN WEISS see Brahms, Johannes

TAUET, HIMMEL, DEN GERECHTEN see Cruger, Johann

TAUET, HIMMEL, DEN GERECHTEN see Hessenberg,
    Kurt

TAUET, IHR HIMMEL see Callhoff, Herbert

TAVA SZI KANTATA see Halmos, Ladislas

TAVERNER, JOHN
    Benedictus
        (Pinkham) [Lat] SATTBarB,acap AMP A546 $.25
                                              (T187)

    Christe Jesu *anthem
        mix cor,acap voc sc KALMUS 6714 $1.00
        contains also: Gaude Plurimum; Mater
        Christi   (T188)
        "O Christ Jesus" SSATB,acap (med diff)
        OXFORD 43.225 $.35   (T189)
        "O Christ Jesus" mix cor OXFORD 43.225
        $.35   (T190)

    Christe Jesu, Pastor Bone *Gen/Royal
        "O Christ Jesus, Loving Shepherd" SSATB,
        acap (med) oct OXFORD 43.225 $.35 (T191)

TAVERNER, JOHN (cont'd.)

    Coplas
        [Lat] SATB,SATB soli,electronic tape
        CHESTER s.p.   (T192)

    Corona Spinea *Mass
        mix cor,acap voc sc KALMUS 6709 $1.00
                                              (T193)

    Dum Transisset Sabbatum *mot
        "When The Sabbath Was Past" SATBB STAINER
        CC560 s.p.   (T194)

    Five Anthems *CC5U,anthem
        mix cor,acap voc sc KALMUS 6712 $1.00
                                              (T195)

    Gaude Plurimum
        see Taverner, John, Christe Jesu

    Gloria Tibi Trinitas *Mass
        SATTBB STAINER CS355 s.p.   (T196)
        mix cor,acap voc sc KALMUS 6708 $1.00
                                              (T197)

    LeRoy Kyrie *Kyrie
        mix cor oct OXFORD 43.461 $.30   (T198)

    Magnificat *Magnif
        TTBB STAINER CC347 s.p.   (T199)

    Mater Christi *Mass
        see Taverner, John, Christe Jesu
        mix cor,acap voc sc KALMUS 6706 $1.00
                                              (T200)

    Nomine Jesu
        SSATTBB,5 narrators,Mez solo,org,2fl
        CHESTER s.p.   (T201)

    O Christ Jesus *see Christe Jesu

    O Christ Jesus, Loving Shepherd *see Christe
        Jesu, Pastor Bone

    O Michaeli *Mass
        mix cor,acap voc sc KALMUS 6710 $1.35
                                              (T202)

    Playn Song *Mass
        mix cor,acap voc sc KALMUS 6703 $.80 (T203)

    Seventeen Anthems *CC17U,anthem
        mix cor,acap voc sc KALMUS 6715 $1.50
                                              (T204)

    Sine Nomine *Mass
        mix cor,acap (English adaptation) voc sc
        KALMUS 6716 $1.00   (T205)
        mix cor,acap voc sc KALMUS 6704 $.80 (T206)

    Small Devotion *Mass
        mix cor,acap voc sc KALMUS 6705 $1.00
                                              (T207)
        mix cor,acap (English adaptation) voc sc
        KALMUS 6717 $1.00   (T208)

    Three Magnificats *CC3U,Magnif
        mix cor,acap voc sc KALMUS 6711 $1.00
                                              (T209)

    Twelve Anthems *CC12U,anthem
        mix cor,acap voc sc KALMUS 6713 $1.00
                                              (T210)

    Western Wind, The *Mass
        SATB STAINER CS326 s.p.   (T211)

    Western Wynde Mass, The
        SATB,acap SCHIRM.EC $1.80   (T212)

    Western Wynde, The *Mass
        mix cor,acap voc sc KALMUS 6702 $1.00
                                              (T213)
        (Collins) [Lat] SATB CHESTER s.p.   (T214)

    When The Sabbath Was Past *see Dum
        Transisset Sabbatum

TAYLOR
    Hymn Of Glory, A *Asc
        (Harris) SATB oct PRO ART 1871 $.25 (T215)

    King Of Love Is Dead, The *see Why?

    Lift Up Your Heads *see Coleridge

    Why?
        "King Of Love Is Dead, The" SATB oct FOX
        $.35   (T216)

TAYLOR, CLIFFORD
    Gloria *Scot
        SATB,pno/org oct LAWSON 759 $.25   (T217)

    Lettest Thou Thy Servant Depart In Peace
        *see Nunc Dimittis

    Nunc Dimittis *Nunc
        "Lettest Thou Thy Servant Depart In Peace"
        SATB,acap oct LAWSON 760 $.25   (T218)

    Sing To The Lord A New Song
        SATB,org oct LAWSON 803 $.25   (T219)

TAYLOR, COLIN
    Child's Prayer, A *Gen/Thanks
        unis (very easy) oct OXFORD 45.009 $.25
                                              (T220)

TAYLOR, DEEMS (JOSEPH) (1885-1966)
    Hymn To The Trinity
        SATB oct GRAY GCMR 57 $.25   (T221)

TAYLOR, DORTHY J.
    Carol Of The Littlest Angel *Xmas,carol
        2pt wom cor,opt S solo oct SCHIRM.G 9822
        $.20   (T222)

TAYLOR, H. STANLEY
    Carol *anthem
        SATB,acap CRAMER A 16 s.p.   (T223)

    Seven Joys Of Mary, The *canon
        2pt cor CURWEN   (T224)

TAYLOR, M.T.
    O Lawd Hear My Prayer (A Negro's Lament)
        SATB,Bar solo PARAGON 1031 $.30   (T225)

TAYLOR, MAUDE B.C.
    They Shall Run And Not Be Weary
        SATB,pno/org ELKAN,H $.30   (T226)

TAYLOR, P.
Men And Angels Share *Xmas
SATB oct ELKAN-V 362-1219 $.25 (T227)

TCHAIKOVSKY, PIOTR ILYITCH (1840-1893)
A L'eglise
(Lowell) SATB oct STAFF 118 $.25 (T228)

Blessed Angel Spirits *Trin,anthem/hymn
mix cor oct NOVELLO 40.0760.03 s.p. (T229)

Bow Down Thine Ear
(Douglas) SATB,acap oct PRO ART 1598 $.18 (T230)

Cherubic Hymn, The *hymn
(Hudson) mix cor CURWEN 61451 s.p. (T231)
(Hudson, F.) 4pt mix cor,acap oct CURWEN 10225 $.25 (T232)

Cherubim Song
mix cor oct SCHIRM.G 2561 $.25 (T233)
SATB,acap (E min) SCHIRM.EC 2227 $.30 (T234)
SATB,acap oct PRESSER 332-14567 $.30 (T235)
(Marting, E.) SSA,acap SCHIRM.EC 1817 $.25 (T236)

Child Jesus *Xmas
2pt ASHDOWN E.A.110 s.p. (T237)
(Geehl) SA BOOSEY-CAN s.p. (T238)

Christ, When A Child
(Davis, K.) SA,pno SCHIRM.EC 1553 $.25 (T239)

Christ, When A Child, A Garden Made
(Pisano) SATB oct PLYMOUTH PCS-58 $.25 (T240)

Credo *Credo
(McKinney) "I Believe In One God" SATB oct FISCHER,J 9768 $.30 (T241)

Crown Him King Of Glory
(Cain) SSAATTBB,acap oct BOOSEY 1813 $.30 (T242)

Fair Was The Garden
unis oct NOVELLO 48.1900.04 s.p. (T243)
(Ramsey, Basil) 4pt oct NOVELLO 51.0644.03 s.p. (T244)

For Thou Art Worthy To Be Praised
SATB,acap SCHIRM.EC 2624 $.30 (T245)
(Glaser, V.) SAB,acap SCHIRM.EC 2457 $.30 (T246)

Forever Worthy Is Thy Lamb
SATB,acap oct PRESSER 332-13415 $.25 (T247)
(Cramer) SATB,acap MARKS 4152 $.25 (T248)

From Darkness To Light *Easter,cant
SATB LORENZ $1.95 (T249)

Hear, Lord Our God
SATB oct FISCHER,J 4180 $.30 (T250)

Holy Blessed Trinity
SATB oct FISCHER,J 4181 $.30 (T251)

Holy, Holy, Holy *Trin,hymn/Sanctus
SATB oct STAFF 498 $.30 (T252)
SATB,acap SCHIRM.EC 1779 $.30 (T253)
(Chambers) SATB oct LESLIE 4062 (T254)
(Davis, K.) SSA SCHIRM.EC 1863 (T255)
(Davis, K.) TTBB,acap SCHIRM.EC 567 $.16 (T256)
(Davis, K.) SSAA,acap SCHIRM.EC 1837 $.16 (T257)

Holy, Holy, Holy! Lord God Almighty *Trin, anthem/hymn
(Ramsey, Basil) mix cor oct NOVELLO 28.1386.06 s.p. (T258)

Holy Lord Of Hosts *Gen
(Tkach) SATB SCHMITT 848 $.18 (T259)

How Blest Are They
SSAATTBB,acap SCHIRM.EC 1138 $.30 (T260)
SATB oct GRAY GCMR 1473 $.25 (T261)

Hymn Of Praise *Bibl
(Gibson) 8pt mix cor oct SCHIRM.G 4291 $.25 (T262)

Hymn Of The Cherubim
SATB BOSWORTH s.p. see from LAUDY COLLECTION OF MODERN PART SONGS (T263)

Hymn To The Trinity *Trin,hymn
(Wyton) SATB oct FISCHER,C CM-7694 $.30 (T264)

I Believe In One God *see Credo

Legend *Xmas/Easter/Lent
SATB,acap oct FISCHER,C CM-6358 $.25 (T265)
SAB oct FISCHER,C CM-6324 $.25 (T266)
SSA oct FISCHER,C CM-6325 $.25 (T267)
(Ehret) SATB,acap oct PRO ART 1487 $.25 (T268)
(Ehret) 2pt oct PRO ART 1629 $.25 (T269)
(Ehret) SSA oct PRO ART 1677 $.22 (T270)

Legend, A
SATB,acap SCHIRM.EC 2200 $.18 (T271)
(Baldwin) 4pt mix cor,acap oct SCHIRM.G 9038 $.25 (T272)
(David, K.) SSAA,acap SCHIRM.EC 1543 $.25 (T273)
(Deis) 2pt wom cor oct SCHIRM.G 9847 $.25 (T274)
(Deis) 4pt men cor,acap oct SCHIRM.G 10034 $.25 (T275)
(Deis) SAB oct SCHIRM.G 10035 $.30 (T276)

Legend (Christ In His Garden) *Op.54,No.5, anthem
mix cor oct NOVELLO 40.0934.07 s.p. (T277)
SATB,pno CHESTER s.p. (T278)

Legende
SATB oct LORENZ 9575 $.25 (T279)
SSA oct LORENZ 6246 $.30 (T280)
SA oct LORENZ 5325 $.25 (T281)
SAB oct LORENZ 7351 $.25 (T282)
(Ferrari) [Eng/Fr] 3pt wom cor oct SCHIRM.G 7157 $.25 (T283)

Iorning Prayer *Morn
(Lowell) SATB oct STAFF 119 $.25 (T284)

Nutcracker Suite *CCU
(Johnson; Rodby) SATB oct AGAPE $1.50 (T285)

TCHAIKOVSKY, PIOTR ILYITCH (cont'd.)

O Blessed And Ever Gracious Lord
SATB oct FISCHER,J 4364 $.30 (T286)

O Blessed Lord
(Gillman, W.) SATB,acap oct PRESSER G-4001 $.30 (T287)

O Holy Lord
(Cain) SSAA oct FOX R176 $.25 (T288)
(Manten) SSATB oct FOX R105 $.35 (T289)

O Lord, Our Lord
SATB oct WALTON 2109 $.25 (T290)

O Lord, Ruler Of All Nations
(Rodby) SATB oct PLYMOUTH WR-103 $.25 (T291)

O Praise The Lord
(Harris) SSA,acap,opt pno oct PRO ART 2544 $.30 (T292)

O Praise The Name
(Douglas) SATB oct GRAY GAC 6 $.30 (T293)

O Praise Ye God
(Goodrich) SATB,acap BOSTON 1682 $.35 (T294)

O Sing To God
(Christiansen) SATB,acap (med diff/diff) SOUTHERN $.35 (T295)

O Thou, From Whom All Blessings Come
SATB,acap SCHIRM.EC 1139 $.30 (T296)

Oh, Thou, From Whom All Blessings Come *Gen
(Andersen) SATB SCHMITT 1565 $.18 (T297)

Opening Litany And 2nd Antiphon (from Divine Liturgy Of St. John Chrysostom)
SSAA&TTBB&SATB SCHIRM.EC 3 $.25 (T298)

Our Father *see Pater Noster

Pater Noster *Bibl
"Our Father" [Eng/Lat] 4pt mix cor oct SCHIRM.G 3615 $.20 (T299)
(Luboff, Norman) SATB oct WALTON 3025 $.30 (T300)
(Montani) "Our Father" [Eng/Lat] 4pt mix cor oct SCHIRM.G 5475 $.25 (T301)

Praise Ye The Lord
SATB oct FISCHER,J 7032 $.30 (T302)
(Ehret) SAB oct AGAPE A 411 $.30 (T303)
(Whitford) TTBB oct FISCHER,J 6691 $.30 (T304)
(Whitford) SATB oct FISCHER,J 9701 $.30 (T305)

Praise Ye The Name Of The Lord
SATB oct FISCHER,J 6214 $.35 (T306)

See Amid The Winter's Snow *Xmas
(Kirk) SATB,acap,opt pno oct PRO ART 2460 $.25 (T307)

Sing Ye To The Lord
(Ehret) mix cor CHAPPELL 0024273-358 $.40 (T308)

To Thee We Call
SATB oct FISCHER,J 4186 $.30 (T309)

We Praise Thee
SATB oct FISCHER,J 4268 $.30 (T310)

When Jesus Was A Little Child *Easter
(Page, N.) SATB oct PRESSER 332-13334 $.30 (T311)

Ye Who The Longing Know
(Brown) SSAA HUNTZINGER 2008 $.12 (T312)

TCHEREPNIN, ALEXANDER (1899-)
Alleluia *Op.103
SATB,acap PETERS 66177F $.50 see from Six Liturgical Chants (T313)

Cherubim Song *Op.103
SATB,acap PETERS 66177A $.50 see from Six Liturgical Chants (T314)

Light So Tender *Op.103
SATB,acap PETERS 66177C $.30 see from Six Liturgical Chants (T315)

Mass *Mass
3 eq voices PETERS 66162 $.40 (T316)

Nativity Play *Op.74, Xmas,cant
SSTB,strings/5strings,perc cmplt ed BOOSEY rental (T317)
[Russ/Fr/Eng/Ger] SSTB,soli,5strings,perc voc sc BELAIEFF BEL313 $3.00, cor pts BELAIEFF BEL313A $.50 (T318)

O My God, I Cry To Thee *Op.103
SATB,acap PETERS 66177B $.50 see from Six Liturgical Chants (T319)

Prayer To The Holy Spirit *Op.103
SATB,acap PETERS 66177D $.25 see from Six Liturgical Chants (T320)

Six Liturgical Chants *see Alleluia, Op.103; Cherubim Song, Op.103; Light So Tender, Op.103; O My God, I Cry To Thee, Op.103; Prayer To The Holy Spirit, Op.103; Transfiguration, Op.103 (T321)

Transfiguration *Op.103
SATB,acap PETERS 661773 $.50 see from Six Liturgical Chants (T322)

TCHEREPNIN, NIKOLAY NIKOLAYEVITCH (1873-1945)
It Is Meet And Right In Truth To Bless Thee
SATB,acap SCHIRM.EC 1620 $.18 (T323)

Let Us, Representing Mystic'lly, The Cherubim
SATB,acap SCHIRM.EC 1619 $.25 (T324)

Praise Ye The Name Of The Lord
SSATTBB,acap SCHIRM.EC 1621 $.25 (T325)
(Bement, G.) PTBB,acap SCHIRM.EC 2130 $.30 (T326)
(Talmadge, A.) SSAA,acap SCHIRM.EC 1940 $.20 (T327)

TCHEREPNIN, NIKOLAY NIKOLAYEVITCH (cont'd.)

We Sing To Thee, O Lord
SATB,acap SCHIRM.EC 1622 $.20 (T328)

TCHESNOKOV, PAVEL GRIGORIEVITCH (1877-1944)
Angels' Song, The
(Ziemer) SATB oct AGAPE WR1005 $.30 (T329)

Cherubic Hymn
TTBB,acap SCHIRM.EC 77 $.25 (T330)

For God So Loved The World , %Also Contains Solo Work: Offertorio
(Cain) SSAATTBB,acap oct BOOSEY 1815 $.30 (T331)

Glory To God
(Ehret) SSAATTBB oct BOOSEY 5392 $.30 (T332)

Gracious Is The Lord
(Ehret) SATB oct BOURNE BL3039 $.25 (T333)

Great God, Our Strength
SATB oct WALTON 2110 $.25 (T334)

Let Thy Holy Presence
(Cain) SSATTBB oct SUMMY B 12 $.30 (T335)
(Ehret) TTBB,acap oct BOOSEY 5022 $.30 (T336)

O Lord God
SATB BOSTON 7723 $.35 (T337)

Praise Him
(Carlton) SATB,acap oct BOOSEY 5242 $.30 (T338)

Salvation Belongeth To Our God
(Davison, A.) TTBB,acap SCHIRM.EC 947 $.25 (T339)
(Glaser, V.) SATB,acap SCHIRM.EC 2483 $.30 (T340)
(Shand, D.) SSAA,acap SCHIRM.EC 1925 $.20 (T341)

Salvation Is Created
(Ehret) SAB oct BOURNE BL3043 $.30 (T342)
(Ehret) SSA oct BOURNE BL2804 $.25 (T343)

Sanctus
(Gorokhoff) SSAA oct GRAY GCMR 1150 $.25 (T344)

Thou Life Of Life
SSAATTBB,acap SCHIRM.EC 1720 (T345)

TE BETHLEHEM see Oosterzee, Cornelius van

TE DECET HYMNUS see Verdi, Giuseppe

TE DECET HYMNUS see Wildgans, Friedrich

TE DEUM *Fr
(Nevin) "O God, We Praise Thee" SATB,pno (easy) oct WILLIS 989 $.12 (T346)

TE DEUM see Alcock, Walter G.

TE DEUM see Andriselli, Ottavio Eugenio

TE DEUM see Aston, Hugo

TE DEUM see Badings, Henk

TE DEUM see Bairstow, Edward Cuthbert

TE DEUM see Barraud, Henry

TE DEUM see Berlioz, Hector

TE DEUM see Bruckner, Anton

TE DEUM see Burkhard Willy

TE DEUM see Byrd, William

TE DEUM see Cabena, Barrie

TE DEUM see Caldara, Antonio

TE DEUM see Campbell, Sydney S.

TE DEUM see Charpentier, Marc-Antoine

TE DEUM see Cimarosa, Domenico

TE DEUM see Clokey, Joseph Waddell

TE DEUM see Davies, Henry Walford

TE DEUM see Devreese, Godefroid

TE DEUM see Dvorak, Antonin

TE DEUM see Egerton, A.H.

TE DEUM see Fetler, Paul

TE DEUM see Fink, Michael

TE DEUM see Flagello, Nicholas

TE DEUM see Forbes, Sebastian

TE DEUM see Fouser, C.E.

TE DEUM see Fox

TE DEUM see Geiser, Walther

TE DEUM see Haas, Joseph

TE DEUM see Harker, Clifford

TE DEUM see Haydn, (Franz) Joseph

TE DEUM see Haydn, (Johann) Michael

TE DEUM see Hegedus, A.

TE DEUM see Heiller, Anton

TE DEUM see Hemel, Oscar van

TE DEUM see Hewitt-Jones, Tony

TE DEUM see Hofer, A.

TE DEUM see Howells, Herbert Norman

TE DEUM see Hure, [Jean]

TE DEUM see Ireland, John

TE DEUM see Jackson, William I

TE DEUM see Jenny, Albert

TE DEUM see Joubert, John

TE DEUM see Kayser, Leif

TE DEUM see Kitson, Charles Herbert

TE DEUM see Kodaly, Zoltan

TE DEUM see La Montaine, John

TE DEUM see Latham, [William P.]

TE DEUM see Le Fleming, Christopher (Kaye)

TE DEUM see Leighton, Kenneth

TE DEUM see Leonard, Clair

TE DEUM see Lully (Lulli), Jean-Baptiste

TE DEUM see Malmfors, Ake

TE DEUM see Marchant, Stanley R.

TE DEUM see Mellers, Wilfred

TE DEUM see Mendelssohn-Bartholdy, Felix

TE DEUM see Milner, Anthony

TE DEUM see Monnikendam, Marius

TE DEUM see Mozart, Wolfgang Amadeus

TE DEUM see Neilsen, Ludvig

TE DEUM see Nicolai, Otto

TE DEUM see Nourse, John

TE DEUM see Orlando

TE DEUM see Parry, Charles Hubert Hastings

TE DEUM see Peeters, Flor

TE DEUM see Persichetti, Vincent

TE DEUM see Pigani, Giovanni

TE DEUM see Purcell, Henry

TE DEUM see Raphael, Gunther

TE DEUM see Renzi, Angelo

TE DEUM see Rietz, Johannes

TE DEUM see Rubbra, Edmund

TE DEUM see Ryelandt, Joseph

TE DEUM see Schroeder, Hermann

TE DEUM see Schroth

TE DEUM see Schumann, William Howard

TE DEUM see Sigurbjornsson, Thorkell

TE DEUM see Smart, Henry Thomas

TE DEUM see Somervell, Arthur

TE DEUM see Stanford, Charles Villiers

TE DEUM see Stevens, Halsey

TE DEUM see Strategier, Herman

TE DEUM see Sumsion, Herbert

TE DEUM see Tallis, Thomas

TE DEUM see Tarp, Svend Erik

TE DEUM see Thalben-Ball, George [Thomas]

TE DEUM see Tomblings, Philip

TE DEUM see Tosar, Hector

TE DEUM see Troman, Thomas

TE DEUM see Verdi, Giuseppe

TE DEUM see Williamson, Malcolm

TE DEUM AND BENEDICTUS see Byrd, William

TE DEUM AND BENEDICTUS see Davies, Henry
   Walford

TE DEUM AND BENEDICTUS see Harwood, Basil

TE DEUM AND BENEDICTUS see Le Fleming,
   Christopher (Kaye)

TE DEUM AND BENEDICTUS see Shaw, Martin

TE DEUM AND BENEDICTUS see Vaughan Williams,
   Ralph

TE DEUM AND JUBILATE see Howells, Herbert
   Norman

TE DEUM AND JUBILATE see Langdon, Jonn

TE DEUM AND JUBILATE see Purcell, Henry

TE DEUM AND JUBILATE IN E see Walmisley, Thomas
   Attwood

TE DEUM FOR THE EMPRESS MARIA THERESA see
   Haydn, (Franz) Joseph, Te Deum [II]

TE DEUM FOR THE EMPRESS MARIE THERESA see
   Haydn, (Franz) Joseph

TE DEUM FUR DIE KAISERIN MARIE THERESA see
   Haydn, (Franz) Joseph, Tedeum

TE DEUM FUR FURST NICOLAUS ESTERHAZY see Haydn,
   (Franz) Joseph

TE DEUM FUR LITURG see Axenfeld, Fritz

TE DEUM - HALLELUJA see Goudimel, Claude

TE DEUM [II] see Haydn, (Franz) Joseph

TE DEUM IN C see Mozart, Wolfgang Amadeus

TE DEUM IN C-DUR see Vanhal, Johann Baptist

TE DEUM IN C-DUR see Werner, Gregor Joseph

TE DEUM IN C MAJOR see Britten, Benjamin

TE DEUM IN D see Purcell, Henry

TE DEUM, IN E FLAT see Woodward, H.H.

TE DEUM IN F see Jackson, William

TE DEUM IN G see Filkins

TE DEUM IN G see Jackson, Francis

TE DEUM IN G see Vaughan Williams, Ralph

TE DEUM JUBILAR see Bernal Jimenez, Miguel

TE DEUM, JUBILATE, AND BENEDICTUS see Rose,
   Bernard

TE DEUM LAUDAMUS *CCU
   2-6pt AMP A664 $2.50   (T347)

TE DEUM LAUDAMUS *Gen,anthem/folk,Neth
   (Bergen, C.) "We Praise Thee, O God" unis,kbd
   (easy) oct CONCORDIA 98-6205 $.75   (T348)
   (Johnson, David N.) "We Praise Thee, O God"
   SAB,opt trp (easy) oct AUGSBURG 1563 $.25
                                              (T349)

TE DEUM LAUDAMUS see Andriessen, Hendrik

TE DEUM LAUDAMUS see Bender, Jan

TE DEUM LAUDAMUS see Bottazzo, Luigi

TE DEUM LAUDAMUS see Braal, Andreas de

TE DEUM LAUDAMUS see Bright, Houston

TE DEUM LAUDAMUS see Bullock, Ernest

TE DEUM LAUDAMUS see Busarow, Donald

TE DEUM LAUDAMUS see Caldara, Antonio

TE DEUM LAUDAMUS see Cook, John

TE DEUM LAUDAMUS see Crone, R.

TE DEUM LAUDAMUS see Cuypers, H.

TE DEUM LAUDAMUS see Diepenbrock, Alfons

TE DEUM LAUDAMUS see Handel, George Frideric

TE DEUM LAUDAMUS see Hasse, Johann Adolph

TE DEUM LAUDAMUS see Haydn, (Franz) Joseph

TE DEUM LAUDAMUS see Jackson

TE DEUM LAUDAMUS see King, Harold C.

TE DEUM LAUDAMUS see Lalande, Michel Richard de

TE DEUM LAUDAMUS see Laub, Thomas

TE DEUM LAUDAMUS see Leighton, Kenneth

TE DEUM LAUDAMUS see Looren De Jong, E.D.

TE DEUM LAUDAMUS see Mellers, Wilfrid Howard

TE DEUM LAUDAMUS see Montani, Nicola A.

TE DEUM LAUDAMUS see Mozart, Wolfgang Amadeus

TE DEUM LAUDAMUS see Mul, Jan

TE DEUM LAUDAMUS see Noble, Harold

TE DEUM LAUDAMUS see Palestrina, Giovanni

TE DEUM LAUDAMUS see Pearson

TE DEUM LAUDAMUS see Pepping, Ernst

TE DEUM LAUDAMUS see Perosi, (Dom) Lorenzo

TE DEUM LAUDAMUS see Proctor, Charles

TE DEUM LAUDAMUS see Purcell, Henry

TE DEUM LAUDAMUS see Reda, Siegfried

TE DEUM LAUDAMUS see Scarlatti, Alessandro

TE DEUM LAUDAMUS see Shepherd, John

TE DEUM LAUDAMUS see Smart, Henry Thomas

TE DEUM LAUDAMUS see Sumsion, Herbert

TE DEUM LAUDAMUS see Thiman, Eric Harding

TE DEUM LAUDAMUS see Visona', Gino

TE DEUM LAUDAMUS see Wiesehahn, W.

TE DEUM LAUDAMUS see Willan, Healey

TE DEUM LAUDAMUS see Wills, Arthur

TE DEUM LAUDAMUS II see Andriessen, Hendrik

TE DEUM LAUDAMUS IN A FLAT see Reed, W.

TE DEUM LAUDAMUS IN C see Thalben-Ball, George
   [Thomas]

TE DEUM LAUDAMUS (TONE 5, NO. 2) see Viadana,
   Lodovico Grossi da

TE DEUM OF SANDOR SIK see Kodaly, Zoltan

TE DEUM PATREM see Gabrieli, Andrea

TE DEUM PATREM see Marenzio, Luca

TE DEUM SOLENNE see Arnaldi, Antonio

TE DEUM see Parsley, Osbert

TE DEUM see Parsley, Osbert

TE DEUM see Mozart, Wolfgang Amadeus

TE ERGO QUAESUMUS see Muller, Giulio

TE JOSEPH see Ascenso, Antonio

TE LUCIS ANTE TERMINUM see Davies, Peter
   Maxwell

TE LUCIS ANTE TERMINUM see Gardiner, Henry
   Balfour

TE LUCIS ANTE TERMINUM see Tallis, Thomas

TE SAECULORUM PRINCIPEM see Maessen, Antoon

TEACH ALL NATIONS see Thygerson

TEACH ME, FILL ME, USE ME, LORD see Ford

TEACH ME, MY GOD AND KING see Pritchard, Arthur
   J.

TEACH ME, O LORD
   2pt CHAPPELL 0018242-352 $.40   (T350)
   SSA CHAPPELL 0018242-354 $.40   (T351)
   SATB CHAPPELL 0018242-358 $.40   (T352)

TEACH ME, O LORD see Attwood, Thomas

TEACH ME, O LORD see Byrd, William

TEACH ME, O LORD see Hilton, John (The Younger)

TEACH ME, O LORD see Rogers

TEACH ME, O LORD see Rogers, Benjamin

TEACH ME O LORD see Sacco

TEACH ME, O LORD see White

TEACH ME, O LORD, THE WAY OF THY STATUTES see
   Attwood, Thomas

TEACH ME, O LORD, THY HOLY WAY see Fischer

TEACH ME THE MEASURE *hymn
   (Parker) SATB,acap oct LAWSON 51308 $.30
                                              (T353)

TEACH ME THE MEASURE OF MY DAYS see French,
   Jacob

TEACH ME THY PATHS see Nosse

TEACH ME THY WAY see Crook, A.T.

TEACH ME THY WAY see Wilson

TEACH ME THY WAY, O LORD see Crook, A.T.

TEACH ME THY WAY, O LORD see Hooper, Edmund

TEACH ME TO LOVE THEE MORE see Tarner

TEACH ME TO PRAY see Jewitt

TEACH ME TO PRAY see McPhail

TEACH US, GOOD LORD see Cranmer, Philip

TEACH US, GOOD LORD see Hopson, Hal H.

TEACH US, GOOD LORD see Nicholson, S.H.

TEACH US, GOOD LORD see Roff, Joseph

TEACH US LORD ABOUT TIME see Grime, William

TEACH US TO PRAY see Kempinski, Leo [A.]

TEACHING LITTLE CHILDREN TO PRAY see Grime

TEACHINGS OF JESUS, SERIES 1 see Grime, William

TEARES OR LAMENTATIONS OF A SORROWFUL SOUL, THE
   see Leighton

TEBALDINI, GIOVANNI (1864-1952)
   Ave Maria
      see CINQUE MOTECTA IN HON. B.V.M.

   Fortem Virili
      [Lat] 3pt mix cor,org ZANIBON 2731 s.p.
                                              (T354)

   Iste Confessor
      [Lat] 2 eq voices,org ZANIBON 2708 s.p.
                                              (T355)

   Nisi Dominus (Psalm 126)
      [Lat] 3pt mix cor,org ZANIBON 2582 s.p.
                                              (T356)

   Pange Lingua
      see QUATTRO MOTTETTI EUCARISTICI

   Psalm 126 *see Nisi Dominus

TECUM PRINCIPIUM see Fayrfax, Robert

TECUM PRINCIPIUM see Haydn, (Johann) Michael

TECUM PRINCIPIUM see Saint-Saens, Camille

TECUM PRINCIPUM see Haydn, (Johann) Michael

TECUM PRINCIPUM see Saint-Saens, Camille

TEDEUM see Schindler, Walter

TEDEUM see Haydn, (Franz) Joseph

TEE
   Magnify The Lord
      (Collins) SATB oct LILLENAS AT-1007 $.25
                                              (T357)

TEED, ROY (1928-)
Nativity At Night, The *Xmas,anthem
SATB CHESTER s.p. (T358)

TEEN SOUND, THE (BOOK 1) *CCUL
1-4pt,pno cmplt ed LILLENAS MB-206 $1.25 (T359)

TEEN SOUND, THE (BOOK 2) *CC9UL,spir
(Schubert, Myra) 2-4pt,pno cmplt ed LILLENAS MB-207 $1.25 (T360)

TEEN SOUND, THE (BOOK 3) *CC10UL
(Schubert, Myra) jr cor cmplt ed LILLENAS MB-208 $1.25 (T361)

TEEN TONE ECHOES *CCUL
(Widen, Svante) SATB cmplt ed LILLENAS MB-209 $1.25 (T362)

TEEN TONES *CC10UL
(Widen, Svante) SATB cmplt ed LILLENAS MB-210 $1.25 (T363)

TEENAGE VOICES (BOOK 1) *CC28UL
SAB Ympl t ed LILLENAS MB-203 $1.00 (T364)

TEENAGE VOICES (BOOK 2) *CC22UL
SAB cmplt ed LILLENAS MB-204 $1.00 (T365)

TEENAGE VOICES (BOOK 3) *CC21UL
SAB cmplt ed LILLENAS MB-205 $1.00 (T366)

TEGNER, ALICE
Betlehems Stjarna *Xmas
mix cor,pno NORDISKA 2690 s.p. (T367)
4pt wom cor/jr cor NORDISKA 4360 s.p. (T368)
men cor NORDISKA 4361 s.p. (T369)
(Conner, Herbert) wom cor,S solo,fl,vcl NORDISKA 5191 s.p. (T370)

Herdarna Spela For Barnet Jesus
3pt wom cor,pno NORDISKA 2696 s.p. (T371)

Julens Gava
3pt wom cor/3pt jr cor,acap NORDISKA 4844 s.p. (T372)

Tercentenary Hymn *hymn
men cor NORDISKA 1633 s.p. (T373)

TELEMANN, GEORG PHILIPP (1681-1767)
Also Hat Gott Die Welt Geliebt *mot
SA/SAT,cont,opt 2vln,vla,vcl HANSSLER 39.014 s.p. see also Biblische Spruche (T374)

Auf, Lobet Den Herren *see Laudate Jehovam

Auf, Lobet Den Herrn, Alle Heiden (Psalm 117)
[Lat/Dut/Ger] SATB,org,opt 2vln PETERS HU914 $1.50 (T375)

Beware Of False Prophets *cant
[Ger/Eng] SAB,S solo,cembalo,strings min sc PETERS E1072 $2.50, ipa (T376)

Biblische Spruche *Bibl/mot
SA/SAT,cont,opt 2vln,vla,vcl HANSSLER 39.101 s.p.
contains & see also: Also Hat Gott Die Welt Geliebt; Der Herr Ist Mein Hirte; Dies Ist Der Tag, Den Der Herr; Halt Im Gedachtnis Jesum Christum; Hosianna Dem Sohne David; Ich Habe Lust, Abzuscheiden; Ja, Selig Sind, Die Gottes Wort Horen; Jesus Christus Ist Kommen; Lob Und Ehre Und Wiesheit; Lobet Den Herrn, Alle Heiden; Meine Seele Erhebet Den Herrn; Siehe, Das Ist Gottes Lamm; Trachtet Am Ersten Nach Dem Reich Gottes; Und Das Wort Ward Fleisch; Wachset In Der Gnade; Wie Lieblich Sind Deine Wohnuegen (T377)

Cantata 682 *see Uns Ist Ein Kind Geboren

Come, All Ye Saints
SATB oct HERITAGE H2 $.35 (T378)

Danket Dem Herrn *mot
(Hobohm) SATB&TB,soli,cont cor pts MOSELER s.p. (T379)

Das Ist Je Gewisslich Wahr *Adv,cant
mix cor,ATB soli,org,2ob,strings,cembalo (previously attributed to Bach, J.S. (BWV 141)) voc pt BREITKOPF-L CHB-2181 r.p., voc sc BREITKOPF-L EB-7141 s.p., ipr (T380)

Der Herr Ist Mein Hirte *mot
SA/SAT,cont,opt 2vln&vla&vcl HANSSLER 39.012 s.p. see also Biblische Spruche (T381)

Didst Thou Suffer Shame? *Easter
SATB oct HERITAGE H5 $.35 (T382)

Dies Ist Der Tag, Den Der Herr *mot
SA/SAT,cont,opt 2vln&vla&vcl HANSSLER 39.010 s.p. see also Biblische Spruche (T383)

Du Aber Daniel, Gehe Hin *cant/funeral
(Fock, Gustav) [Ger] SATB,SB soli,org,cont, fl,ob,vln, 2 viola da gamba (med diff) BAREN. BA 3583 sc $7.75, cor pts $.65, ipa (T384)

Ehre Sei Gott In Der Hohe *Xmas,cant
(Fock, Gustav) [Ger] SATB,SATB soli,cont, 3trp,2vln,vla,drums (med diff) BAREN. BA 3467 sc s.p., cor pts s.p., ipa (T385)

Ein Feste Burg Ist Unser Gott *mot
SA/SAT,cont,opt 2vln&vla&vcl HANSSLER 39.001 s.p. (T386)

Ein Kindelein So Lobelich *Xmas,cant/Mass
[Lat] SAT,SATB soli,strings,org PETERS WM65 $2.50 (T387)
(Schultz; Hauser) [Ger] mix cor,SATB soli, org,strings VIEWEG voc sc s.p., cor pts s.p., ipa (T388)
(Schultz-Hauser, Karlheinz) [Ger] SATB,opt inst (med) MULLER SM 2248 s.p. (T389)

Four Sacred Canons *CC4U,canon
2pt,acap oct NOVELLO 53.0355.09 s.p. (T390)

TELEMANN, GEORG PHILIPP (cont'd.)

Gott Sei Mir Gnadig *cant
(Fedtke) SATB,SATB soli,cont,2vln,vla,vcl HANSSLER 10.186 sc s.p., voc sc s.p., ipa (T391)

Hallelujah
(Ehret) SATB SOUTHERN $.30 (T392)
(Ehret) SATB FLAMMER A 5602 $.30 (T393)

Halt Im Gedachtnis Jesum Christum *mot
SA/SAT,cont,opt 2vln&vla&vcl HANSSLER 39.005 s.p. see also Biblische Spruche (T394)

Heilig
(Schultz; Hauser) [Ger] 2pt men cor cor pts VIEWEG s.p. (T395)

Herr Gott, Dich Loben Wir
see Telemann, Georg Philipp, Lobt Gott, Ihr Christen Allzugleich

Hosianna Dem Sohne David *mot
SA/SAT,cont,opt 2vln&vla&vcl HANSSLER 39.008 s.p. see also Biblische Spruche (T396)

I Will Praise The Lord
(Harris) girl cor SOUTHERN $.35 (T397)
(Harris) SSA,acap BOSTON 13733 $.30 (T398)
(Harris) 3pt mix cor,acap oct SCHIRM.G 11875 $.30 (T399)

I Will Sing Praises
SATB oct HERITAGE H25 $.35 (T400)

Ich Habe Lust, Abzuscheiden *mot
SA/SAT,cont,opt 2vln&vla&vcl HANSSLER 39.011 s.p. see also Biblische Spruche (T401)

Ich Will Den Herren Loben Allezeit
see Stern, Hermann, Lobt Gott, Ihr Frommen Christen

In Dulci Jubilo *Xmas,cant
[Ger] SATB,ATB soli,org,2horn,strings sc PETERS EM922 $4.00, ipa, voc sc PETERS EM922 $1.00, ipa (T402)

Ja, Selig Sind, Die Gottes Wort Horen *mot
SA/SAT,cont,opt 2vln&vla&vcl HANSSLER 39.009 s.p. see also Biblische Spruche (T403)

Jesus Christus Ist Kommen *mot
SA/SAT,cont,opt 2vln&vla&vcl HANSSLER 39.006 s.p. see also Biblische Spruche (T404)

Laudate Jehovam (Psalm 117) Gen
mix cor,acap voc sc KALMUS 6454 $1.25 (T405)
(Valentin, Erich) "Auf, Lobet Den Herren" [Ger/Lat] SATB,cont,2vln (med) BAREN. BA 2900 sc $2.25, cor pts $.65, ipa (T406)

Laudate Jehovam, Omnes Gentes (Psalm 117)
"O Praise The Lord, All Ye Nations" SATB, 2vln,vcl,org (med easy) CONCORDIA 97-4838 $.85, ipa (T407)

Lob Und Ehre Und Wiesheit *mot
SA/SAT,cont,opt 2vln,vla,vcl HANSSLER 39.107 s.p. see also Biblische Spruche (T408)

Lobet Den Herrn, Alle Heiden *mot
SA/SAT,cont,opt 2vln&vla&vcl HANSSLER 39.007 s.p. see also Biblische Spruche (T409)

Lobt Gott, Ihr Christen Allzugleich *Xmas, cant
[Ger] SSAATTBB,STB soli,org,5trom/5ob, strings,timp sc PETERS EM910 $5.00, ipa, voc sc PETERS EM910 $.80, ipa contains also: Herr Gott, Dich Loben Wir (T410)

Lukas Passion, 1728 *Psntd
(Horner, Hans; Ruhnke, Martin) [Ger] SATB, STTBarBarBB soli,cont,fl,ob,bsn,strings (med diff) sc BAREN. BA 2965 $29.00, ipr (T411)

Lukaspassion *Psntd
(Schroeder) "St. Luke's Passion" [Eng/Ger] SATB,STB soli,cont,2ob,2vln,vla HANSSLER 10.210 sc $18.00, voc sc $2.00, ipa (T412)

Machet Die Tore Weit *cant
(Fedtke) SATB,STB soli,cont,2ob,bsn,vln,vla HANSSLER 10.183 sc $5.00, voc sc $.90, ipa (T413)

Markus-Passion *Psntd
(Redel, Kurt) mix cor,SATBarBar soli,org, cembalo,2fl,2ob,bsn,strings BREITKOPF-W rental (T414)

Matthaus-Passion *Psntd
mix cor,STBarBar soli,org,cembalo,2fl,2ob, bsn,strings BREITKOPF-W rental (T415)

Meine Seele Erhebet Den Herrn *mot
SA/SAT,cont,opt 2vln,vla,vcl HANSSLER 39.015 s.p. see also Biblische Spruche (T416)

O Come, Holy Spirit *anthem
(Nelson) unis treb cor,cont,vln (med) oct AUGSBURG 0314 $.30 (T417)

O Jesu Christ, Dein Kripplein *Xmas,cant
mix cor,strings HANSSLER 10.282 sc s.p., cor pts s.p., ipa (T418)

O Not To Us, Good Lord *anthem
(Nelson) unis treb cor,fl (med) oct AUGSBURG 0311 $.30 (T419)

O Praise The Lord, All Ye Nations *see Laudate Jehovam, Omnes Gentes

Our Father, Thou In Heaven Above
(Peek, R.) SA,org SCHIRM.EC 2516 $.25 (T420)

Psalm 117 *see Auf, Lobet Den Herrn, Alle Heiden

Psalm 117 *see Laudate Jehovam

Psalm 117 *see Laudate Jehovam, Omnes Gentes

Seihe, Das Ist Gottes Lamm *cant
(Hofmann, Klaus) SA/SAT/SAB,S/T,A/Mez/Bar soli,cont,2vln HANSSLER 10.193 sc s.p., voc sc s.p., ipa (T421)

TELEMANN, GEORG PHILIPP (cont'd.)

Siehe, Das Ist Gottes Lamm *mot
SA/SAT,cont,opt 2vln&vla&vcl HANSSLER 39.004 s.p. see also Biblische Spruche (T422)

St. Luke's Passion *see Lukaspassion

Trachtet Am Ersten Nach Dem Reich Gottes *mot
SA/SAT,cont,opt 2vln,vla,vcl HANSSLER 39.013 s.p. see also Biblische Spruche (T423)

Und Das Wort Ward Fleisch *mot
[Ger/Eng] SA/SAT,cont,opt 2vln&vla&vcl HANSSLER 39.002 $.50 see also Biblische Spruche (T424)

Uns Ist Ein Kind Geboren (Cantata 682) Xmas, cant
(Jaedtke, Helga) 4pt mix cor,ATB soli,cont, 2fl,2ob,strings (A min) MOSELER sc s.p., cor pts s.p., ipa (T425)

Vier Motetten *CC4U,mot
(Morgan) 3-4pt mix cor&8pt mix cor,cont MOSELER s.p. (T426)

Wachset In Der Gnade *mot
SA/SAT,cont,opt 2vln&vla&vcl HANSSLER 39.003 s.p. see also Biblische Spruche (T427)

Weiche, Lust Und Frohlichkeit *cant
mix cor,ob,strings HANSSLER 10.280 sc s.p., cor pts s.p., ipa (T428)

Werfet Panier Auf Im Lande
mix cor SOUTHERN $.30 (T429)

Wie Lieblich Sind Deine Wohnuegen *mot
SA/SAT,cont,opt 2vln,vla,vcl HANSSLER 39.016 s.p. see also Biblische Spruche (T430)

TELI HANGULAT see Mozart, Wolfgang Amadeus

TELL ABROAD HIS RISING see Butler, Eugene

TELL GOD O' MY TROUBLES *spir
(Morris) SATB,acap oct LAWSON 51543 $.35 (T431)

TELL IT LIKE IT IS see Kaiser, Kurt

TELL IT OUT see Handel, George Frideric

TELL IT OUT see Toolan, S. Suzanne

TELL IT OUT, THE STORY (from Piae Cantiones)
see Four Easter Carols

TELL ME, MY PEOPLE see Victoria, Tomas Luis de, Popule Meus

TELL ME, SHEPHERDS see Rasley

TELL ME, SHEPHERDS DEAR see Pasterze Mili

TELL ME THE STORY OF JESUS see Sweney, J.

TELL OUT MY SOUL see Wyton, Alec

TELL OUT THE NEWS see Curry

TELL THE BLESSED TIDINGS see Ford

TELL US, MARY see Guerrero, Francisco, Virgen Sancta

TELL US OF CHRISTMAS *Xmas/Pageant,cant
oct LORENZ $1.00 (T432)

TELL US, SHEPHERD MAIDS *Xmas
(Caldwell, Mary E.) SSA oct GRAY GCMR 2615 $.30 (T433)
(Caldwell, Mary E.) SAB oct GRAY GCM 2358 $.30 (T434)

TELLEP, LEO M.
Alleluia *Easter/Gen
SATB,acap oct PRESSER 312-40291 $.30 (T435)

Be Joyful, Be Merry
SATB,acap SHAWNEE A 479 $.30 (T436)

In Bethlehem *Xmas
SATB oct STAFF 371 $.30 (T437)

It Was A Night Of Wonder
SA/TB SHAWNEE E19 $.30 (T438)
SAB SHAWNEE A416 $.25 (T439)
SATB SHAWNEE A 416 $.25 (T440)

Praise Ye The Name Of The Lord
SSATBB,acap oct PRESSER MC411 $.35 (T441)

They Took My Saviour To Crucify *Lent
SATB oct BOURNE 799 $.25 (T442)

TELLER, MARCUS
Exurge Domine *mot
4pt,A solo,cont,strings HEUWEKE. 555 s.p. (T443)

TELPASI
Hashkivenu
[Heb] SATB MARKS 4581 $.40 (T444)

TEMA see Janson, Alfred

TEMPERANCE ANTHEM see Leslie, C.E.

TEMPLE, THE see Clokey, Joseph Waddell

TEMPLE ANTHEMS *CCU,anthem
SATB LORENZ $1.95 (T445)

TEMPLE OF GOD, THE see Bancroft, H. Hugh

TEMPLE OF HOLINESS, THE see Karvonen, Paul

TEMPLE OF THE LIVING GOD see Kirk

TEMPLE OF THE LORD, THE see Wilson

TEMPLE, S.
And The Waters Keep On Running Through My Mind *CC12U,Gen,folk/hymn,Contemp (easy) unis,gtr cmplt ed GIA G1629 $1.00; SATB,pno,gtr cmplt ed GIA G1628 $2.50

TEMPLE, S. (cont'd.)

God Is A Fire Of Love *CC12U,Gen/Pent,folk/
  hymn
  (easy) SATB,gtr cmplt ed GIA G1630 $2.00;
  unis,gtr cmplt ed GIA G1631 $1.00 (T447)

Happy The Man *CC12U,Gen,folk/hymn,Contemp
  unis,gtr (easy) cmplt ed GIA G1788 $1.00 (T448)

Sing! People Of God, Sing! *CC12U,Gen,folk/
  hymn,Contemp
  unis,gtr (easy) cmplt ed GIA G1787 $1.00 (T449)

Universe Is Singing, The *CC12U,Gen,folk
  unis,gtr (easy) cmplt ed GIA G1532 $1.00 (T450)

TEMPLE, THE see Robertson, Leroy

TEMPLES ETERNAL see Christiansen, F. Melius

TEMPLETON
  Alleluia, Sing Noel
  SATB FLAMMER A 5573 $.30 (T451)

TEMPO CHORAL PACKAGE NO. 1 *gospel
  (McLellan, Cyril) cor oct LILLENAS AT-3001
  $.30
  contains: Anonymous, Never Alone; Bliss,
  Paul, Hallelujah! 'Tis Done; Jones, Lean
  On His Arms; Lowry, [Robert], Nothing But
  The Blood (T452)

TEMPO CHORAL PACKAGE NO. 2
  (McLellan, Cyril) mix cor oct LILLENAS
  AT-3002 $.30
  contains: Anonymous, Jesus Is A Wonderful
  Saviour; Bradbury, William Batchelder,
  Oh, Sing Of His Mighty Love; Gabriel, He
  Lifted Me; Loveless, Since Jesus Took All
  My Sins Away (T453)

TEMPORAL CYCLE, THE see Laboure

TEMPORE PASCHALI see Gombert, Nicolas

TEMPTATION OF CHRIST, THE see Pfautsch, Lloyd

TEMPTATIONS OF CHRIST, THE see Thiman, Eric
  Harding

TEN ANTHEMS ABOUT PEACE see Zettervall, Howard

TEN CHORAL INVOCATIONS AND BENEDICTIONS
  *CC10U,Bene
  SATB oct LILLENAS AN-2374 $.30 (T454)

TEN CHORALE SETTINGS see Pepping, Ernst

TEN CHORALES see Bach, Johann Sebastian

TEN CHRISTMAS CAROLS *CC10U,Xmas
  (White, E.) unis/mix cor,acap oct PRESSER
  352-00059 $.40 (T455)

TEN CHRISTMAS CAROLS *CC10U,Xmas,carol
  (Cope) SSA,acap oct BOOSEY 1895 $.35 (T456)

TEN CHRISTMAS CAROLS FROM THE SOUTHERN
  APPALACHIAN MOUNTAINS *see See Jesus The
  Savior (T457)

TEN COMMANDMENTS *Bibl/folk/hymn,US
  SSA/SATB BIG3 $.25 (T458)
  (Terri) SATB,solo,acap oct LAWSON 51015 $.40 (T459)

TEN FAMOUS NEGRO SPIRITUALS *CC10U,spir
  (Boekel, Meindert) TTBB,acap LENGNICK s.p. (T460)

TEN FAMOUS NEGRO SPIRTUALS *CC10L,spir
  (Boekel, M.) SATB LENGNICK s.p. (T461)

TEN FAUX BOURDONS ON WELL-KNOWN HYMNS see
  Willan, Healey

TEN FOLKSONGS AND SPIRITUALS *sac/sec,CC10L
  (Johnson, David N.) unis/mix cor,kbd/fl/gtr
  AUGSBURG 11-9491 $1.15 (T462)

TEN FOUR-PART MOTETS FOR THE CHURCH'S YEAR see
  Palestrina, Giovanni

TEN MINIATURE ANTHEMS see Thiman, Eric Harding

TEN MORE PSALMS FROM THE "BECKER PSALTER" see
  Schutz, Heinrich

TEN MOTETS AND ANTHEMS FOR TWO-VOICE CHOIRS
  *CC10L,Gen,anthem/mot
  SA/TB/SB (easy) oct GIA G1577 $1.25 contains
  works by: Andrews; Isaac; Kreitmaier;
  Lambillotte; Mohr; Mozart; Palestrina;
  Remondi (T463)

TEN PSALMS FROM THE "BECKER PSALTER" see
  Schutz, Heinrich

TEN RENAISSANCE MOTETS IN ENGLISH-VOL. 2
  *CC10U,mot,Renais
  (Linduskey) mix cor SOUTHERN $1.50 (T464)

TEN SACRED CONCERTOS see Viadana, Lodovico
  Grossi da

TEN SCHEMELLI CHORALES see Bach, Johann
  Sebastian

TEN SELECT ANTHEMS see Hoffmann

TEN STANDARD ANTHEMS FOR MIXED VOICES *CC10U
  mix cor SCHMITT 59 $.45 (T465)

TEN THOUSAND ANGELS see Overholt

TEN TRADITIONAL CAROLS FOR CHRISTMAS *CC10U,
  Xmas,carol
  (Manney, A.) TTBB,acap oct PRESSER 332-13914
  $.35 (T466)

TENDER SHEPHERD see Ehret, Walter

TENDER SHEPHERD, THE see Lister, Mosie

TENDERLY HE WATCHES see Wiseman

TENEBRAE see Hamill

TENEBRAE see Leo, Leonardo

TENEBRAE FACTAE SUNT *Lent
  (Buszin) "Darkness, Gross Darkness Did Cover
  The Earth" SATB,kbd (med easy) oct
  CONCORDIA 98-1458 $.25 (T467)

TENEBRAE FACTAE SUNT see Biber, C.H.

TENEBRAE FACTAE SUNT see Christiansen, Olaf
  Christian

TENEBRAE FACTAE SUNT see Croce, Giovanni

TENEBRAE FACTAE SUNT see Davye

TENEBRAE FACTAE SUNT see Davye, John F.

TENEBRAE FACTAE SUNT see Haydn, (Franz) Joseph

TENEBRAE FACTAE SUNT see Haydn, (Johann)
  Michael

TENEBRAE FACTAE SUNT see Ingegneri, Marco
  Antonio

TENEBRAE FACTAE SUNT see Jean-Baptiiste, L.

TENEBRAE FACTAE SUNT see Nucius, Johannes

TENEBRAE FACTAE SUNT see Palestrina, Giovanni

TENEBRAE FACTAE SUNT see Poulenc, Francis

TENEBRAE FACTAE SUNT see Victoria, Tomas Luis
  de

TENEBRAE FACTAE SUNT see Weerbecke, Gaspar van

TENEBRAE IN E FLAT see Haydn, (Franz) Joseph

TENEBRAE NOCTURNES see Kelly, Bryan

TENERO
  Adoramus Te, Christe
  girl cor SOUTHERN $.25 (T468)

TENNE, ARNO
  Es Kommt Ein Schiff, Geladen *mot
  SSATB HANSSLER 7.104 s.p. (T469)

TENNEY, MILDRED
  Thy Way, Not Mine, O Lord
  4pt mix cor oct SCHIRM.G 9546 $.25 (T470)

TENTATIO JESU see Heiller, Anton

TENUISTI, IMPROPERIUM, GRADUALE UND OFFERTORIUM
  FUR DEN PALMSONNTAG see Sechter, Simon

TERCENTENARY HYMN see Tegner, Alice

TERRA DEI see Zbinden, Julien-Francois

TERRA TREMUIT see Andrews, C.T.

TERRA TREMUIT see Callhoff, Herbert

TERRA TREMUIT see Ferro, Stefano

TERRA TREMUIT see Gaburo, Kenneth

TERRA TREMUIT see Muller, A.M.

TERRA TREMUIT see Palestrina, Giovanni

TERRA TREMUIT see Volpi, Edoardo

TERRA TREMUIT see Wiltberger

TERRIBILIS EST see Waldbroel, Wilhelm

TERRY
  Richard De Castre's Prayer To Jesus *prayer
  mix cor SOUTHERN $.25 (T471)

TERRY, RICHARD RUNCIMAN (1865-1938)
  Good Day, Sir Christmas *Xmas
  4pt mix cor oct CURWEN 8636 $.25 (T472)
  mix cor CURWEN 80670 $.25 (T473)

  Joseph And The Angel *Xmas
  mix cor CURWEN 89002 s.p. (T474)

  Myn Lyking *Xmas
  mix cor CURWEN 89008 s.p. (T475)

  Richard De Castre's Prayer To Jesus *Xmas,
  prayer
  4pt mix cor,acap oct CURWEN 8624 $.25 (T476)
  mix cor CURWEN 89014 s.p. (T477)
  (Jacobson) 4pt men cor,acap oct CURWEN
  10204 $.25 (T478)
  (Jacobson) mix cor oct CURWEN 11066 $.25 (T479)

  So Blyssid Be The Tyme *Xmas
  mix cor CURWEN 89003 s.p. (T480)

  Twelve Christmas Carols By R.R. Terry
  *CC12L,Xmas,carol
  SATB/unis CURWEN 6281 s.p. (T481)

TESCHNER
  All Glory, Laud And Honor *see Wie Soll Ich
  Dich Empfangen

  O Lord, How Shall I Meet Thee?
  (Ehret) SATB,acap MARKS 4106 $.30 (T482)

  St. Theodulph's Hymn *Easter/Lent
  (Olds) SSA oct FISCHER,C CM-630 $.25 (T483)
  (Olds) SATB,opt 3trp oct FISCHER,C CM-600
  $.25, ipa (T484)
  (Olds) TTBB oct FISCHER,C CM-637 $.25 (T485)

  Wie Soll Ich Dich Empfangen *Easter/Lent/
  Palm,anthem/hymn
  "All Glory, Laud And Honor" see MUSIC FOR
  PALM SUNDAY
  (Archie) "All Glory, Laud, And Honor" SATB
  FLAMMER A5419 $.30 (T486)
  (Boersma) "All Glory, Laud And Honor" SA
  oct WORD CS-2331 $.25 (T487)
  (Cain) "All Glory, Laud And Honor" SAB
  FLAMMER D5100 $.35 (T488)
  (Cain) "All Glory, Laud And Honor" SATB
  FLAMMER A 5035 $.35 (T489)
  (Cain) "All Glory, Laud And Honor" SSA

TESCHNER (cont'd.)
  FLAMMER B 5137 $.30 (T490)
  (Douglas) "All Glory, Laud And Honor" SATB
  oct PRO ART 1949 $.25 (T491)
  (Douglas) "All Glory, Laud And Honor" SAB
  oct PRO ART 2261 $.25 (T492)
  (Ehret) "All Glory, Laud And Honor" SA oct
  SPRATT 600 $.25 (T493)
  (Frackenpohl) "All Glory, Laud And Honor"
  SATB&jr cor MARKS 4245 $.25 (T494)
  (Heller) "All Glory, Laud And Honor" SA
  SCHMITT 2556 $.20 (T495)
  (Kinsman) "All Glory, Laud And Honor" SATB
  oct PLYMOUTH HA-4 $.25 (T496)
  (Kirk) "All Glory, Laud And Honor" SAB
  SCHMITT 5515 $.35 (T497)
  (Mueller) "All Glory, Laud, And Honor" 3pt
  jr cor/SAB (easy) FISCHER,C CM 7207 $.25 (T498)
  (Mueller) "All Glory Laud And Honor" SA oct
  FISCHER,C CM-6380 $.25 (T499)
  (Mueller) "All Glory, Laud, And Honor" 2pt
  jr cor FISCHER,C CM 6380 $.25 (T500)
  (Mueller) "All Glory, Laud, And Honor" SAB
  oct FISCHER,C CM-7207 $.25 (T501)
  (Ohl) "All Glory, Laud And Honor" SATB oct
  PLYMOUTH FO-104 $.25 (T502)
  (Olds) "All Glory, Laud And Honor" SATB&jr
  cor SCHMITT 1574 $.45 (T503)
  (Wainrow) "All Glory, Laud And Honor" SA
  oct FOX R128 $.30 (T504)

TESORIERO
  Ave Maria
  SSA ALBERT s.p. (T505)

  Natale *Xmas,carol/folk,It
  [It] unis ALBERT s.p. (T506)

  Ninna Nonna *Xmas,carol,It
  [It/Eng] 2pt ALBERT s.p. (T507)

TESTI
  Stabat Mater
  cor,S solo,inst voc sc RICORDI-ENG 129568
  s.p. (T508)

TEUSCHER, HANS (1907-1961)
  Es Sungen Drei Engel *Xmas
  wom cor&jr cor TONGER s.p. contains also:
  Frohlich Soll Mein Herze Springen; O
  Heiland, Reiss Die Himmel Auf (T509)

  Frohlich Soll Mein Herze Springen
  see Teuscher, Hans, Es Sungen Drei Engel

  O Heiland, Reiss Die Himmel Auf
  see Teuscher, Hans, Es Sungen Drei Engel

T'FILAT SHEL Y'LADIM see Siegel, Benjamin

T'FILOT BETH EL see Tickton, Jason H.

TGETTIS, NICHOLAS
  Alleluia *Allelu
  SATB BRANDEN $.25 (T510)

  Amen
  SATB BRANDEN $.25 (T511)

  Long, Long Ago
  SATB BRANDEN $.25 (T512)

  Salutation Of The Dawn
  SATB BRANDEN $.40 (T513)

THALBEN-BALL, GEORGE [THOMAS] (1896-   )
  Benedictus In C
  SATB oct BOOSEY 5203 $.30 (T514)

  Comfort Ye My People *anthem
  mix cor,Bar solo oct NOVELLO 28.1311.04
  s.p. (T515)

  For All The Saints *CCU,ASD,anthem/hymn
  SATB oct NOVELLO 02.0079.04 s.p. (T516)

  Honour A Physician *anthem
  mix cor oct NOVELLO s.p. (T517)

  Jubilate *Jubil
  SATB (B flat maj) oct NOVELLO 40.1381.06
  s.p. (T518)

  Laudate Dominum (Book 1) *CC34L,Introit
  mix cor cmplt ed NOVELLO 03.0103.05 s.p. (T519)

  Laudate Dominum (Book 2) *CC34L,Introit
  mix cor cmplt ed NOVELLO 03.0104.05 s.p. (T520)

  Magnificat In C Major
  SATB oct BOOSEY 3266 $.30 (T521)

  O Be Joyful In The Lord *anthem
  mix cor oct NOVELLO 40.1381.06 s.p. (T522)

  Sursum Corda
  SATB BOSWORTH s.p. (T523)

  Te Deum *Te Deum
  SATB (B flat maj) oct NOVELLO 44.1376.08
  s.p. (T524)

  Te Deum Laudamus In C *Te Deum
  SATB oct BOOSEY 5200 $.35 (T525)

THANK AND PRAISE GOD, LAUD, EXTOL HIM see Bach,
  Johann Sebastian

THANK THEE, O LORD see Emig, Lois

THANK WE NOW THE LORD OF HEAVEN see Kechley,
  [Gerald]

THANK WE THE LORD see Davis, Katherine K.

THANK YE THE LORD see Geisler, Johan C.

THANK YOU, JESUS see Hallett, John C.

THANK YOU LORD see Dring, [Madeleine]

THANK YOU, THANK YOU see Avery

THANKED BE THOU, JESU, MY KING see Pasquet,
  Jean

THANKFUL PEOPLE, RAISE YOUR SONG see Elvey, George Job

THANKS BE FOR THE WONDERFUL THINGS see Bach

THANKS BE TO GOD see Clare, Edwyn A.

THANKS BE TO GOD see Coggin

THANKS BE TO GOD see Dickson

THANKS BE TO GOD see Dickson, Stanley

THANKS BE TO GOD see Haydn, (Franz) Joseph

THANKS BE TO GOD see Lowell

THANKS BE TO GOD see Mendelssohn-Bartholdy, Felix

THANKS BE TO GOD see Murton, T.

THANKS BE TO GOD see Pooler

THANKS BE TO GOD see Rogers, Vivienne R.

THANKS BE TO GOD see Schutz, Heinrich, Gott Sei Dank, Der Uns Den Sieg Gegebem Hat

THANKS BE TO GOD see Worthing, Richard

THANKS BE TO OUR GOD *Xmas
(Ehret, W.) SATB LEONARD-US 08064320 $.25
(T526)

THANKS BE TO OUR LORD see Schutz, Heinrich, Dank Sei Unserm Herrn

THANKS BE TO THEE see Giordano, Umberto

THANKS BE TO THEE see Handel, George Frideric, Dank Sei Dir, Herr

THANKS BE TO THEE see Leonard

THANKS BE TO THEE see Roff, Joseph

THANKS BE TO THEE, O LORD! see Handel, George Frideric

THANKS BE UNTO CHRIST see Dank Sei Unserm Heern

THANKS BE UNTO CHRIST see Schutz, Heinrich, Dank Sei Unserm Herrn

THANKS FROM EARTH TO HEAVEN see Eklund

THANKS, O LORD see Gordon

THANKS TO GOD FOR ALL HIS LOVE see Hadley

THANKS TO GOD FOR MY MOTHER see Loucks

THANKS TO GOD OUR FATHER see Brandon

THANKS TO GOD WHOSE WORD WAS SPOKEN see Lovelace, Austin C.

THANKS TO THEE, O LORD see Handel, George Frideric

THANKS TO THESE LONESOME VALES see Purcell, Henry

THANKS UNTO THE LORD see Beckhard

THANKSGIVING see Kraft, Leo

THANKSGIVING see Krenek, Ernst

THANKSGIVING see Titcomb, Everett

THANKSGIVING AND FOREFATHERS' DAY see Ives, Charles

THANKSGIVING CHORALE see La Mure, [Pierre]

THANKSGIVING DAY ODE, A see Woodman, Raymond Huntington

THANKSGIVING EXULTATION see Bartow

THANKSGIVING FOR VICTORY see Vaughan Williams, Ralph

THANKSGIVING HYMN, A see Butler

THANKSGIVING HYMN, A see Felts

THANKSGIVING PROCLAMATION see Elvey, George Job

THANKSGIVING PROCLAMATION AND HARVEST HYMN see Elvey, George Job

THANKSGIVING SONG see Davis, Katherine K.

THANKSGIVING SONG see Gearhart

THANKSGIVING SONGS *Gen/Thanks
oct RUBANK 2280-PL $.18, ipa
contains:
Prayer Of Thanksgiving (Johnson, Clair W.) (SATB,band) (prayer,Dut);
Elvey, George Job, Come, Ye Thankful People (SATB,band) (T527)

THANKSGIVING TO GOD FOR HIS HOUSE, A see Burnham, Cardon

THANKSGIVING WE GIVE TO GOD see Schutz, Heinrich, Dank Sagen Wir Alle Gott

THAT BETHLEHEM'S BABE see Butler, Eugene

THAT BLESSED EASTER MORN *Easter/Lent
(Caldwell, Mary E.) SA oct GRAY GMCR 2280 $.30 (T528)
(Caldwell, Mary E.) SATB oct GRAY GCMR 2405 $.20 (T529)

THAT BLESSED NIGHT see Livingstone

THAT CHILD SO DEAR see Rogers

THAT EASTER DAY WITH JOY WAS BRIGHT *anthem/ carol/chant,Ger
(Pooler, Marie) unis treb cor/SA (easy) oct AUGSBURG 1321 $.25 (T530)
(Wood, Dale) unis treb cor&opt desc (easy) oct AUGSBURG 1576 $.25 (T531)

THAT EASTER DAY WITH JOY WAS BRIGHT see Cruger, Johann

THAT EASTER DAY WITH JOY WAS BRIGHT see Goodman, Joseph

THAT EASTER MORN see Tisserand

THAT EASTER-TIDE WITH JOY WAS BRIGHT *Easter, 17th cent
(Ley, Henry G.) SATB (very easy) oct OXFORD 42.968 $.30 (T532)

THAT FIRST, BEST CHRISTMAS NIGHT see Rodgers, Irene

THAT FIRST CHRISTMAS MORN see Graham

THAT FIRST CHRISTMAS NIGHT see Ehret, Walter

THAT GOD DOTH LOVE THE WORLD, WE KNOW see Wadely, F.W.

THAT HOLY NIGHT see Hughes

THAT HOLY THING see Chadwyck

THAT I MAY SPEAK see Ramseth, Ann

THAT I MAY TOO ARISE see Patterson

THAT LONESOME VALLEY *spir
(Shaw; Parker) SATB,Bar solo,acap oct LAWSON 51103 $.30 (T533)

THAT OLD TIME RELIGION *CCU
(Carmichael, Ralph) SATB voc sc WORD 20020 $1.95 (T534)

THAT OLD TIME RELIGION see Murray, Lyn

THAT THE WORLD MAY KNOW see Johnson, Paul

THAT THEY ALL MAY BE ONE see Mueller, Carl F.

THAT THEY ALL MAY BE ONE see Roff, Joseph

THAT TINY CHILD see Van Wormer, G.

THAT VIRGIN'S CHILD see Johnston, Jack

THAT VIRGIN'S CHILD see Tallis, Thomas

THAT WONDROUS CHRISTMAS NIGHT *Xmas
(Hopkins, H.) SATB oct PRESSER 312-21466 $.30 (T535)

THAT WONDROUS NIGHT see Pasquet, Jean

THAT WONDROUS NIGHT OF CHRISTMAS EVE see Ward

THAT YOUR JOY MAY BE FULL see Moser, Rudolf

THATCHER, R.S.
Come, Ye Faithful *Easter
SAB/SATB (very easy) oct OXFORD 42.809 $.30 (T536)

THATE, ALBERT (1903-   )
Siebzehn Geistliche Kanons *CC17U,Gen,Bibl/ canon
[Ger] 2-4pt,acap (med diff) BAREN. BA 2177 s.p. (T537)

THAT'S FOR ME see Kaiser, Kurt

THAXTED MASS see Putterill, Jack

THAYER, PAT
If I Have Faith
2pt PROWSE s.p. (T538)

THE BABE IN BETHLEHEM'S MANGER LAID see Noel

THE DUTEOUS DAY KNOW CLOSETH see Bach, Johann Sebastian

THE SONG OF THE SHEPHERDS *carol,Ger
(Glaser, V.) "While By Our Sleeping Flocks We Lay" SAB,acap, echo chorus SCHIRM.EC 2235 $.30 (T539)
(Jungst, H.) "While By Our Sleeping Flocks We Lay" SATB,acap, echo chorus SCHIRM.EC 1685 $.30 (T540)

THEE ADORE see Pasquet, Jean

THEE, GOD THE FATHER see Marenzio, Luca, Te Deum Patrem

THEE GOD WE PRAISE *Gen,Russ
(Tkach) SATB SCHMITT 817 $.30 (T541)

THEE, HOLY FATHER, WE ADORE see Haugland

THEE, LORD, BEFORE THE CLOSE OF DAY see Gardiner, Henry Balfour, Te Lucis Ante Terminum

THEE WE ADORE see Bevan, Richard T.

THEE WE ADORE see Candlyn

THEE WE ADORE see Candlyn, T. Frederick H.

THEE WE ADORE see Dubois, Theodore

THEE WE ADORE see Holman, Derek

THEE WE ADORE see James

THEE WE ADORE see Martin

THEE WE ADORE see Palestrina, Giovanni

THEE WE ADORE see Warland, Dale

THEE WE ADORE see Westbrook, Francis B.

THEE WE ADORE, ETERNAL LORD see Bach, Johann Sebastian

THEE WE ADORE, O HIDDEN SAVIOR see Brown

THEE WE DO ADORE see Lassus, Roland de (Orlandus), Adoramus Te

THEE WE PRAISE see Lassus, Roland de (Orlandus)

THEE WILL I CHERISH see Roff, Joseph

THEE WILL I EXTOL see Palestrina, Giovanni, Exaltabo Te, Domine

THEE WILL I LOVE see Beethoven, Ludwig van

THEE WILL I LOVE see Gibbs, [Cecil] Armstrong

THEE WILL I LOVE see Howells, Herbert Norman

THEE WILL I LOVE see Pasquet, Jean

THEE WILL I LOVE, O LORD see Little, Leonard

THEE WITH TENDER CARE see Bach

THEE, WITH TENDER CARE see Bach, Johann Sebastian

THEIR SOUND IS GONE OUT see Wills, Arthur

THEMA WEIHNACHTEN see Blarr, Oskar Gottlieb

THEME see Janson, Alfred, Tema

THEME SUBLIME OF ENDLESS PRAISE see Handel, George Frideric

THEN CAME THE DISCIPLES TO JESUS see Vulpius, Melchior

THEN DAVID MOURNED see Tomkins, Thomas

THEN DID JESUS PRAY see McCormick

THEN DID PRIESTS MAKE OFFERING see Byrd, William, Sacerdotes Domini

THEN DID THE PRIESTS see Byrd, William, Sacerdotes Domini

THEN HOLY JOSEPH OF ARIMATHAEA see Lvov, Alexey Feodorovitch

THEN I KNOW see Martin, Gilbert M.

THEN I MET THE MASTER see Lister, Mosie

THEN ROUND ABOUT THE STARRY THRONE see Gallus, Jacobus

THEN ROUND ABOUT THE STARRY THRONE see Handel, George Frideric

THEN ROUND THE STARRY THRONE see Handel, George Frideric

THEN SHALL THE KING SAY UNTO THEM see Pasquet, Jean

THEN SHALL THE RIGHTEOUS SHINE FORTH see Mendelssohn-Bartholdy, Felix

THEN SHALL THEY KNOW see Handel, George Frideric

THEN SING WE ALL, NOWELL see Pearson

THEN SPAKE SOLOMON see Whettam, Graham

THEN THE GOOD SHEPHERD AROSE see Goodale, R.L.

THEN WERE MY EYELIDS VEILED WITH DARKNESS see Victoria, Tomas Luis de, Calagaverunt Oculi Mei

THEODORA see Handel, George Frideric

THEOPHANE, SISTER M. (HYTREK)
Come, Let Us Sing To The Lord *Gen/Proces, anthem
SATB (med easy) oct GIA G1297 $.30 (T542)

Elegit Eum Dominus *Gen,anthem
"Lord Has Chosen Him, The" [Eng/Lat] SATB (med) oct GIA G1294 $.40 (T543)
"Lord Has Chosen Him, The" [Eng/Lat] SSA/ TTB (med) oct GIA G1007 $.25 (T544)

Lord Has Chosen Him, The *see Elegit Eum Dominus

O Holy Banquet *Commun,anthem/Commun
SSAA (med) oct GIA G1293 $.30 (T545)
SATB (med) oct GIA G1291 $.30 (T546)

Psalm 22 *Gen,anthem
unis,org,fl (easy) oct GIA G1608 $.35 (T547)

THERE BE FOUR THINGS see Krenek, Ernst

THERE BE THREE THINGS see Krenek, Ernst

THERE CAME A STAR see Ouchterlony, David

THERE COMES A SHIP A-SAILING *carol
SATB (easy) OXFORD 08.090 $.15 (T548)

THERE COMES A TIME see Nichols, Ted

THERE DWELT IN OLD JUDEA see Ferguson, Howard

THERE GO I see Lister, Mosie

THERE IN THE STABLE *Xmas,carol,Pol
(Kinsman, F.) SATB oct PRESSER MC468 $.30 (T549)

THERE IS A BALM IN GILEAD *spir
(Coggin, R.) SAB oct PRESSER 312-40913 $.30 (T550)
(Dawson) SATB KJOS T105 $.30 (T551)
(Dawson) SSA KJOS T107 $.30 (T552)
(Dawson) men cor KJOS T106 $.30 (T553)
(Ehret) SATB oct FOX S126 $.30 (T554)
(Ehret) SSA oct FOX S158 $.30 (T555)
(Ehret) SAB oct FOX S157 $.30 (T556)
(Kirk) SATB,acap,opt pno oct PRO ART 1527 $.30 (T557)
(Kirk) SAB oct PRO ART 1718 $.30 (T558)
(Kirk) SSA oct PRO ART 1887 $.25 (T559)
(Kirk) TTBB,acap,opt pno oct PRO ART 2347 $.30 (T560)

THERE IS A BALM IN GILEAD see Brandon, George

THERE IS A BALM IN GILEAD see Howorth, Wayne

THERE IS A BALM IN GILEAD see Kemmer, [George W.]

THERE IS A CHILD see Er Is Ein Kindeke

THERE IS A GOD see Track, Gerhard

THERE IS A GREEN HILL see Gounod, Charles Francois

THERE IS A GREEN HILL see Somerset, H.

THERE IS A GREEN HILL see Stebbins

THERE IS A GREEN HILL see Wheeler, Alfred

THERE IS A GREEN HILL FAR AWAY
(Cornwall, J.S.) SAB PIONEER 4004 $.20 (T561)

THERE IS A GREEN HILL FAR AWAY see Gounod, Charles Francois

THERE IS A GREEN HILL FAR AWAY see Roberton, Hugh S.

THERE IS A LAMB IN THE STABLE see Graham, Robert [V.]

THERE IS A LAND see Lewis, John Leo

THERE IS A LAND OF PLEASURE see Burroughs, B.

THERE IS A LOVE see Lang

THERE IS A RIVER see Lewis

THERE IS A RIVER see Lynn, George

THERE IS A SPIRIT see Rubbra, Edmund

THERE IS A STAIRWAY THAT LEADS UP TO HEAVEN see Twohig

THERE IS BALM IN GILEAD
see Four Folksongs And Spirituals

THERE IS GLADNESS IN THE AIR see Brunsman, W.J.

THERE IS IN SOULS see Binkerd, [Gordon]

THERE IS MORE TO LIFE see Carmichael, Ralph

THERE IS NO EYE FOR SEEING see Franck, Cesar

THERE IS NO OTHER COMFORTER see Kastal

THERE IS NO OTHER GOD see Newbury

THERE IS NO PEACE
SATB BIG3 $.30 (T562)
CSA BIG3 $.25 (T563)

THERE IS NO ROSE *Xmas
(Boyd) SATB SCHMITT 888 $.30 (T564)

THERE IS NO ROSE see Britten, Benjamin

THERE IS NO ROSE see Childs, Barney

THERE IS NO ROSE see Davis, Carl

THERE IS NO ROSE see Kraehenbuehl, D.

THERE IS NO ROSE OF SUCH VIRTUE *Xmas,carol
(Garland, Hugh) SATB oct LESLIE 4056 see from Two Christmas Carols, Set 1 (T565)

THERE IS NO ROSE OF SUCH VIRTUE see Anonymous

THERE IS NO ROSE OF SUCH VIRTUE see Joubert, John

THERE IS NO ROSE OF SUCH VIRTUE see Spencer, W.

THERE IS NO ROSE OF SUCH VIRTUE see Tournier, Marcel

THERE IS NO ROSE OF SUCH VIRTUE see Wishart

THERE IS NOUGHT OF SOUNDNESS IN ALL MY BODY see Bach, Johann Sebastian, Es Ist Nichts Gesundes An Meinem Leibe

THERE IS ONE GOD AND ONE SAVIOUR see Geisler, Johan C.

THERE IS ONE GOD AND ONE SAVIOUR see Lotti, Antonio

THERE MIGHT HAVE BEEN A STRANGER see Lewis, John Leo

THERE SHALL A STAR see Mendelssohn-Bartholdy, Felix

THERE SHALL A STAR COME OUT OF JACOB see Mendelssohn-Bartholdy, Felix

THERE SHALL A STAR FROM JACOB see Christiansen, Olaf Christian

THERE SHALL A STAR FROM JACOB see Mendelssohn-Bartholdy, Felix

THERE SHALL BE ONE FOLD see Ford

THERE THE MOTHER STANDS see Schubert, Franz (Peter), Stabat Mater

THERE UPROSE A GREAT STRIFE see Bach, Johann Sebastian, Es Erhub Sich Ein Streit

THERE WAS A LITTLE BABY see Johnstone, A.

THERE WAS A LITTLE BABY KING see Sharpe, Evelyn

THERE WAS A MAN see Boyd, Jack

THERE WAS A PIG *Xmas
(Holst, Imogen) 3pt boy cor/3pt wom cor/3pt men cor,acap oct SCHIRM.G 11636 $.30 (T566)

THERE WAS CHRIST WITH GOD see Nichols

THERE WAS DARKNESS OVER THE EARTH see Willis

THERE WAS NO ROOM FOR THE CHRIST CHILD
(Tuttle, S.) SSAA,acap SCHIRM.EC 1914 $.30 (T567)

THERE WERE NINETY AND NINE see Lane, [Spencer]

THERE WERE SHEPHERDS see Statham, Heathcote (Dicken)

THERE WERE SHEPHERDS see Vincent, Charles John

THERE WERE SHEPHERDS see Wyton, Alex

THERE WERE SHEPHERDS IN THE FIELD see Vincent, Charles John

THERE WERE SHEPHERDS IN THE FIELDS see Alcock

THERE WERE THREE LIGHTS see Blake

THERE WERE TWO THIEVES see Wilson

THERE WITH HIS MOTHER IN A MANGER see Alain, A.

THEREFORE BE MERRY see Ehret, Walter

THEREFORE THEY ARE BEFORE THE THRONE OF GOD see Goemanne, Noel

THEREFORE WATCH THAT YE BE READY see Hammerschmidt, Andreas, Darum Wachet, Denn Ihr Wisset Weder Tag

THEREFORE WE see Roff, Joseph, Tantum Ergo

THEREFORE WE, BEFORE HIM BENDING see Beobide, Jose Maria, Tantum Ergo

THEREFORE WE, BEFORE HIM BENDING see Faure, Gabriel-Urbain, Tantum Ergo

THEREFORE WE BEFORE HIM BENDING see Franco, Tantum Ergo

THEREFORE WE, BEFORE HIM BENDING see Ratcliffe, Desmond

THERE'LL BE A PLACE IN THE VALLEY FOR ME see Great Choral Series

THERE'LL BE NO TOMORROW
see Great Choral Series

THERE'LL BE PEACE IN THE VALLEY FOR ME *anthem
SATB/SAB/SA/TB/TTBB BIG3 $.25 (T568)

THERE'S A CITY CALLED HEAVEN see Page, Robert E.

THERE'S A CROSS AT THE CROSSROADS see Kohlman

THERE'S A DIFFERENCE see Waters

THERE'S A GREAT CAMP MEETING
(Kinsman) SATB oct VOLKWEIN VB265 $.25 (T569)

THERE'S A LIGHT UPON THE MOUNTAINS see Walter, Samuel

THERE'S A LITTLE WHEEL A-TURNIN *spir
(Ehret) SSA FRANK F2072 $.35 (T570)

THERE'S A MAN GOIN' ROUN' TAKIN' NAMES see Kleinsinger, George

THERE'S A MEETING HERE TONIGHT *spir
(Dexter, Harry) 2pt ENOCH.TP271 s.p. (T571)
(Work, J.) TTBB,T solo,acap SCHIRM.EC 2150 $.28 (T572)

THERE'S A REASON FOR IT ALL see Owens, Jimmy

THERE'S A SONG IN THE AIR see Harrington

THERE'S A SONG IN THE AIR see Harrington, Karl P.

THERE'S A SONG IN THE AIR see Speaks, [Oley]

THERE'S A STAIRWAY THAT LEADS UP TO HEAVEN see Twohig

THERE'S A VOICE IN THE WILDERNESS see Lovelace, Austin C.

THERE'S A WIDENESS IN GOD'S MERCY see Goemanne, Noel

THERE'S A WIDENESS IN GOD'S MERCY see Tourjee

THERE'S NO HIDIN' PLACE DOWN HERE see Moffatt, James

THERE'S ROOM AT THE CROSS FOR YOU see Stanphill

THERESA see Haydn, (Franz) Joseph, Theresienmesse

THERESA MASS see Haydn, (Franz) Joseph, Theresienmesse

THERESE EST DANS LES CIEUX see Mercenier, P.

THERESIENMESSE see Haydn, (Franz) Joseph

THERMIGNON
Alma Redemptoris
see QUATTRO ANTIFONE MARIANE

THERON
O Lord, My God
(Kirk) SATB SHAWNEE A 5547 $.25 (T573)

THESAURI MUSICI, HEFT 1: CANTIONES SACRAE IN ADVENTU DOMINI *CCU,Renais
(Pass, Walter) 4-5pt mix cor,acap cmplt ed DOBLINGER s.p. contains works by: Regnart; Louis; Hollander (T574)

THESAURI MUSICI, HEFT 3: MISSA SALVA NOS see Isaac, Heinrich

THESAURI MUSICI, HEFT 4: LITANIA DEIPARAE VIRGINIS MARIAE see Regnart, Jacob

THESAURI MUSICI, HEFT 5: CANTIONES SACRAE IN ADVENTU DOMINI *CCU,Renais
(Pass, Walter) 4-5pt mix cor,acap cmplt ed DOBLINGER s.p. contains works by: Court; Zaphelius (T575)

THESAURI MUSICI, HEFT 7: MISSA DA REQUIEM see Sermisy, Claude de

THESAURI MUSICI, HEFT 8: VIER MARIENMOTETTEN *CC4U,BVM,mot,Renais
(Pass, Walter) 5pt mix cor cmplt ed DOBLINGER s.p. contains works by: Aichinger; Stuber; Bildstein; Zacharijs (T576)

THESAURI MUSICI, HEFT 9: MISSA "DEUS IN ADIUTORIUM" see Manchicourt, Pierre De

THESAURI MUSICI, HEFT 10: CANTIONES SACRAE DE NATIVITATE DOMINI *CCU,Xmas,Renais
(Pass, Walter) 4-5pt mix cor,acap cmplt ed DOBLINGER s.p. contains works by: Speiller; Regnart (T577)

THESAURI MUSICI, HEFT 11: CANTIO SACRA DE NATIVITATE DOMINI see Buissons

THESAURI MUSICI, HEFT 13: ZUM ADVENT *CCU,Adv, Renais
(Pass, Walter) 4-5pt mix cor,acap cmplt ed DOBLINGER s.p. contains works by: Praetorius; Gesius; Franck; Helder (T578)

THESE ARE THE BLOSSOMS see Lekberg, Sven

THESE ARE THEY see Bodycombe, [Aneurin]

THESE ARE THEY see Gaul, Alfred Robert

THESE ARE THEY see Stair, Patty

THESE ARE THY GLORIOUS WORKS see Thompson

THESE DROPS OF BLOOD see Lister, Mosie

THESE FORTY DAY see Hamill

THESE THINGS SHALL BE see Henderson

THESE THINGS SHALL BE see Krone

THESE THINGS SHALL BE see Krones

THESE THINGS SHALL BE see Peninger

THESE THINGS SHALL PASS see Hamblen

THEY ARE EVER BLESSED see Franck, Cesar

THEY ARE HAPPY WHOSE LIFE IS BLAMELESS see Anders, Charles

THEY ARE SLAVES see Kremenliev, Boris

THEY CALLED HER MOSES *cant
(De Cormier, Robert; McKayle, Donald) mix cor,soli,narrator,pno oct LAWSON $2.00 (T579)

THEY CALLED HIM JESUS see Pearson, Edith

THEY CAST THEIR NETS see Hourdeaux

THEY CAST THEIR NETS IN GALILEE see Draesel, Lederhouse

THEY CRUCIFIED MY LORD *spir
(Clements, J.) SATB PROWSE s.p. (T580)

THEY FOLLOWED THE STAR see Track

THEY FOUND HIM IN THE TEMPLE see Hart, A.W.

THEY HAVE TAKEN AWAY MY LORD see Stainer, John

THEY HAVE TAKEN AWAY THE LORD see Handel, George Frideric

THEY LED MY LORD AWAY see Johnson, Alfred H.

THEY SANG THAT NIGHT IN BETHLEHEM see Schubert, Franz (Peter)

THEY SAW THE LIGHT *carol
SATB (easy) OXFORD 08.164 $.15 (T581)

THEY SHALL MOUNT UP WITH WINGS see Knight, Vincent

THEY SHALL RUN AND NOT BE WEARY see Taylor, Maude B.C.

THEY SHALL SEE THE GLORY OF THE LORD! see Rhodes

THEY SHALL WALK see Bitgood

THEY SLUMBER NOT, NOR SLEEP see Praetorius, Michael

THEY THAT GO DOWN TO THE SEA IN SHIPS see Le Fleming, Christopher (Kaye)

THEY THAT KNOW THY NAME see Glarum, L. Stanley

THEY THAT KNOW THY NAME see Powell

THEY THAT PUT THEIR TRUST see Hartley, Walter [S.]

THEY THAT PUT THEIR TRUST IN THE LORD see Orr, Robin

THEY THAT SEEK THY TRUTH see Pasquet, Jean

THEY THAT SOW IN TEARS see Bach, Johann Ludwig, Die Mit Tranen Saen

THEY THAT SOW IN TEARS see Gaul, Alfred Robert

THEY THAT TRUST IN THE LORD see Adams, Stephen

THEY THAT WAIT UPON THE LORD
2pt CHAPPELL 0018259-352 $.40 (T582)
SSA CHAPPELL 0018259-354 $.40 (T583)

THEY THAT WAIT UPON THE LORD see Baldwin

THEY THAT WAIT UPON THE LORD see Berger, Jean

THEY THAT WAIT UPON THE LORD see Bullock, Ernest

THEY THAT WAIT UPON THE LORD see Nelson, Ronald A.

THEY TOOK MY SAVIOUR PO CRUCIFY see Tellep, Leo M.

THEY WHO CONSIDERETH THE DOOR SHALL BE BLEST see Morgan

THEY WHO GRIEVING SOWETH see Schein, Johann Hermann, Die Mit Tranen Saen

THEY'LL KNOW WE ARE CHRISTIANS see Scholtes

THEY'LL KNOW WE ARE CHRISTIANS BY OUR LOVE see Scholtes

THEY'LL KNOW WE ARE CHRISTIANS BY OUR LOVE see Scholtes, P.

THIELE
Lissa Brevis !Mass
mix cor,acap voc sc KALMUS 6455 $2.00 contains also: Bernhard, Missa Brevis (T584)

THIELE, SIEGFRIED (1934-)
Apokalypse (from Offenbarung Des Johannes) ECY,Bibl
[Ger] 4pt mix cor,S solo,brass,drums (med) cor pts DEUTSCHER DV 7071 s.p., ipr (T585)
[Ger] cor,S solo,brass,timp cor pts DEUTSCHER 7071 $1.50, ipa (T586)

Dieweil Auch Heuer Nach Advent *Adv
SA,org,2rec HANSSLER 5.045 s.p. (T587)

Gott Ist Liebe, Und Wer In Der Liebe
unis cor,org HANSSLER 5.083 s.p. contains also: Herr, Du Hast Worte Des Ewigen Lebens (T588)

Herr, Du Hast Worte Des Ewigen Lebens see Thiele, Siegfried, Gott Ist Liebe, Und Wer In Der Liebe

O Herr, Mache Mich Zum Werkzeug Deines Friedens *prayer
SATB,2fl HANSSLER 5.162 s.p. (T589)

Zwei Kurzmessen (composed with Bernhard, Christoph) *CC2U,Mass
(Gerber) 5pt mix cor MOSELER s.p. (T590)

THIEME, KARF (1909-)
Tu Der Volker Turen Auf *Gen,mot
[Ger] SATB,acap (med) sc MULLER SM 2358 s.p., cor pts s.p. (T591)

Wahlt Das Leben *Gen,mot
[Ger] 3-6pt mix cor,acap (med) MULLER SM 2370 s.p. (T592)

THIM, GUNTHER
Messe In A *Mass
[Ger] SATB,acap cor pts SIRIUS s.p. (T593)

THIMAN, ERIC HARDING (1900-)
Again, The Morn Of Gladness *anthem/hymn
SATB&unis oct NOVELLO 28.1356.04 s.p. (T594)

All My Heart This Night Rejoices *Xmas
SA oct GRAY GCMR 3068 $.30 (T595)

All That's Good And Great And True
4pt mix cor,org oct SCHIRM.G 10885 $.25 (T596)

Angels Holy, High And Lovely *Thanks
4pt jr cor/SATB (med) FISCHER,C PT 1637 $.25 (T597)

Angels, Holy, High And Lowly
SATB PATERSON 1637 s.p. (T598)

Annunciation Carol *carol
unis jr cor/unis wom cor CURWEN 72031 s.p. (T599)

Annunciation Carol, The (from Flower Of Bethlehem, The) Xmas,carol
unis oct CURWEN 11067 $.20 (T600)

As Pants The Hart
SATB,opt acap WARNER W2546 $.30 (T601)

Author Of Life Divine
SATB,opt acap WARNER W2545 $.30 (T602)

Blessed Jesus At Thy Word
SATB THOMP.G G-560 s.p. (T603)

Blest Are The Pure *anthem
mix cor oct NOVELLO 50.0276.01 s.p. (T604)

Book Of Stories, The
2pt boy cor oct SCHIRM.G 11134 $.25 (T605)

Breathe On Me, Breath Of God
SATB THOMP.G G-546 s.p. (T606)

Carol Of The Birds *carol
SATB,acap oct BOOSEY 5740 $.35 (T607)

Christ Being Raised *Easter
SATB oct GRAY GCMR 2738 $.25 (T608)

Christ Hath A Garden *anthem
mix cor oct NOVELLO 40.1061.02 s.p. (T609)

Christ Is Our Corner-Stone *anthem
SAT/SAB oct NOVELLO 28.1345.09 s.p. (T610)

Christ Is The World's Light *anthem
mix cor oct NOVELLO 29.0019.10 s.p. (T611)

Christ The Lord Is Risen Again *Easter, anthem
mix cor oct NOVELLO 40.1032.09 s.p. (T612)

Christ, Who Knows All His Sheep *anthem
SATB,acap SOUTHERN $.30 (T613)
4pt mix cor,acap oct SCHIRM.G 11545 $.25 (T614)
mix cor,acap oct NOVELLO 40.1485.05 s.p. (T615)
SATB,acap NOVELLO AP221 $.30 (T616)

Christ, Whose Glory Fills The Skies
4pt mix cor oct SCHIRM.G 11275 $.25 (T617)

Christmas Rhapsody, A *Xmas,carol
SSA,pno voc sc NOVELLO 20.0046.06 s.p. (T618)

THIMAN, ERIC HARDING (cont'd.)

Come, Holy Ghost *Whitsun,anthem
mix cor,S solo oct NOVELLO 28.1150.02 s.p. (T619)

Come Holy Spirit *Introit
SATB THOMP.G G-555 s.p. see from Two Introits (T620)

Come Kingdom Of Our God
SATB THOMP.G G-581 s.p. (T621)

Come, Lord, And Rule The Earth *Rembrnc
unis&desc,orch oct NOVELLO 48.1714.01 s.p., ipr (T622)
unis oct GRAY GCMR 1932 $.30 (T623)

Come, Ye Faithful, Raise The Strain *Easter, anthem
mix cor oct NOVELLO 29.0010.06 s.p. (T624)

Come Ye Fathful *Easter/Lent
SAB oct GRAY GCMR 3037 $.30 (T625)

Corde Natus *Adv/Xmas,anthem
(Thiman, Eric H.) "Of The Father's Love Begotten" mix cor oct NOVELLO 28.1184.07 s.p. (T626)

Draw Nigh And Take The Body Of The Lord *Commun,anthem
mix cor oct NOVELLO 40.1410.03 s.p. (T627)
SATB,org/pno NOVELLO AP216 $.30 (T628)
SATB SOUTHERN $.30 (T629)

Earth Does Not Hold *Rembrnc,anthem
mix cor oct NOVELLO 50.0256.07 s.p. (T630)

Earth Is The Lord's, The *Thanks,cant
SATB,MezBar soli,org voc sc NOVELLO s.p. (T631)

Easter Carol, An *Easter,carol
2pt oct NOVELLO 53.0321.04 s.p. (T632)

Eternal Ruler Of The Ceaseless Round
unis oct NOVELLO 40.1012.04 s.p. (T633)

Father, We Praise Thee *Gen/Trin,anthem
mix cor,S solo oct NOVELLO 40.1075.02 s.p. (T634)

Fight The Good Fight
unis oct GRAY GCMR 2055 $.30 (T635)
SATB oct GRAY GCMR 2051 $.30 (T636)

Fill Thou My Life, O Lord My God
mix cor CURWEN 80765 s.p. (T637)

Fill Thou My Light
unis ALLANS 306 s.p. (T638)

Flower Of Bethlehem, The *Xmas,cant
2pt,pno/strings voc sc CURWEN C03718 s.p., ipr (T639)

For The Beauty Of The Earth *hymn
mix cor CURWEN 80762 s.p. (T640)

Four Graces
unis/SATB oct CURWEN 10490 $.20 (T641)

Gifts, The
unis THOMP.G G-131 s.p. (T642)

Gloria In Excelsis
unis ALLANS 307 s.p. (T643)

Gloria In Excelsis Deo (from The Flower Of Bethlehem) Xmas,Gloria
4pt mix cor oct CURWEN 10596 $.30 (T644)
mix cor CURWEN 61438 s.p. (T645)
unis oct CURWEN 10823 $.25 (T646)
mix cor CURWEN 61438 s.p. (T647)
2pt jr cor/2pt wom cor CURWEN 72399 s.p. (T648)
unis jr cor/unis wom cor CURWEN 72032 s.p. (T649)

Glory To God In The Highest
4pt mix cor,org oct CURWEN 11022 $.20 (T650)
mix cor CURWEN 80850 s.p. (T651)
SATB ALLANS 459 s.p. (T652)

God Make My Life A Little Light
unis THOMP.G G-136 s.p. (T653)

God, That Madest Earth And Heaven
SATB THOMP.G G-570 s.p. (T654)

Good Christian Men, Rejoice *Easter,anthem
mix cor oct NOVELLO 28.1231.02 s.p. (T655)

Good Shepherd, The *anthem
mix cor oct NOVELLO 28.1299.01 s.p. (T656)

Grant Us Light
unis&desc ALLANS 308 s.p. (T657)
unis&desc oct CURWEN 10280 $.25 (T658)
unis jr cor/unis wom cor&desc CURWEN 72281 s.p. (T659)
(Sarson, M.) 4pt mix cor oct CURWEN 10228 $.25 (T660)

Hark! A Thrilling Voice Is Sounding *Adv, anthem
mix cor oct NOVELLO 40.0993.02 s.p. (T661)

Hark The Glad Sound *Xmas
4pt mix cor,org oct SCHIRM.G 11528 $.25 (T662)

Here Beauty Dwell And Holiness *anthem
mix cor,acap oct NOVELLO 40.1379.04 s.p. (T663)

How Beauteous Are Their Feet *Adv/Gen
4pt mix cor oct SCHIRM.G 11226 $.25 (T664)

How Lovely Are Thy Dwellings *anthem
mix cor oct NOVELLO 28.1298.03 s.p. (T665)
2pt oct NOVELLO 33.0078.01 s.p. (T666)

Hymn Of Consecration
SATB oct GRAY GCMR 2908 $.25 (T667)

Hymn Of Freedom, A
SS/SA oct GRAY GCMR 1885 $.25 (T668)
TTBB oct GRAY GCMR 1882 $.25 (T669)
SATB oct GRAY GCMR 1683 $.25 (T670)

THIMAN, ERIC HARDING (cont'd.)

Hymn Of Praise
SATB oct GRAY GCMR 2290 $.30 (T671)

I Praised The Earth
mix cor CURWEN 80847 s.p. (T672)

I Will Lay Me Down In Peace *anthem
mix cor oct NOVELLO 40.1215.01 s.p. (T673)

Immortal, Invisible *anthem
SATB BELWIN AP 5 $.35 (T674)
mix cor oct NOVELLO 28.1140.05 s.p. (T675)

Jesu, The Very Thought Of Thee *Gen/Lent
SATB PATERSON 1648 s.p. (T676)
SATB oct GRAY GCMR 1845 $.30 (T677)

Jesus Shall Reign Where E'er The Sun
(Diack) 4pt jr cor/SATB (easy) FISCHER,C PT 1642 $.25 (T678)

Jesus Shall Reign Where'er The Sun
SATB oct FISCHER,C PT-1642 $.25 (T679)
SATB PATERSON 1642 s.p. (T680)

King Of Glory, King Of Peace *anthem
mix cor oct NOVELLO 40.1049.03 s.p. (T681)
SATB BELWIN AP4 $.35 (T682)

Last Supper, The *Holywk,cant
SATB,SBar soli,org,fl,ob,clar,bsn,2horn, strings,timp voc sc NOVELLO s.p., ipr (T683)

Let All The World In Every Corner Sing *anthem
mix cor,opt S solo oct NOVELLO 28.1151.00 s.p. (T684)

Let Saints On Earth *anthem
mix cor oct NOVELLO 28.1176.06 s.p. (T685)

Let Us With A Gladsome Mind
SATB THOMP.G G-550 s.p. (T686)

Lift Up Your Heart
unis oct NOVELLO 40.1172.04 s.p. (T687)

Lord Jesus, Think On Me
SATB oct GRAY GCMR 2800 $.25 (T688)

Lord Of Our Life *anthem
mix cor oct NOVELLO 28.1260.06 s.p. (T689)

Lord, While For All Mankind We Pray
unis oct NOVELLO 40.1132.05 s.p. (T690)

Lord's Prayer, The *prayer
unis jr cor/unis wom cor CURWEN 72032 s.p. (T691)

Love Came Down At Christmas *Xmas
4pt mix cor,S solo oct SCHIRM.G 10677 $.20 (T692)
unis oct SCHIRM.G 10678 $.25 (T693)

Love Divine, All Loves Excelling *hymn
unis/SATB oct NOVELLO 44.1337.07 s.p. (T694)

Love's Redeeming Work Is Done *Easter
SATB oct GRAY GCMR 3042 $.40 (T695)

Magnificat And Nunc Dimittis *Magnif/Nunc
unis (G maj) NOVELLO 44.1234.06 s.p. (T696)

Mary's Nowell *Xmas
4pt mix cor,acap oct SCHIRM.G 11958 $.30 (T697)

Morning Prayer *Morn,prayer
SATB BELWIN AP7 $.35 (T698)

Morning Prayer, A *Morn,anthem/prayer
mix cor,acap oct NOVELLO 28.1428.05 s.p. (T699)

My God, And Is Thy Table Spread (from Last Supper, The) Commun/Easter/Psntd,anthem
SATB oct NOVELLO 50.0274.05 s.p. (T700)

My Soul, There Is A Country *anthem
mix cor oct NOVELLO 28.1341.06 s.p. (T701)
unis oct NOVELLO 40.1366.02 s.p. (T702)

Nativity, The *Xmas,cant
SATB,ST soli,org,opt strings voc sc NOVELLO s.p., ipr (T703)

O Christ, The Heavens' Eternal King *Easter, anthem
mix cor oct NOVELLO 28.1148.00 s.p. (T704)

O Gladsome Light *anthem
mix cor,orch oct NOVELLO 40.1269.00 s.p., ipr (T705)

O God Of Love
SATB oct GRAY GCMR 1731 $.30 (T706)

O Love How Deep
SATB oct GRAY GCMR 2953 $.25 (T707)

O Love Of God *anthem
SAB oct NOVELLO 40.1195.03 s.p. (T708)

O Praise Ye The Lord
SATB THOMP.G G-563 s.p. (T709)

O Sing The Glories Of Our Lord *Gen/Harv, anthem
SATB SOUTHERN $.30 (T710)
mix cor oct NOVELLO 40.1524.10 s.p. (T711)
SATB,org/pno NOVELLO AP226 $.30 (T712)

O Strength And Stay *anthem
mix cor oct NOVELLO 28.1139.01 s.p. (T713)

O That Men Would Praise The Lord *Gen/Harv, anthem
mix cor oct NOVELLO 40.1109.00 s.p. (T714)

O Thou, To Whom In Ancient Time
4pt mix cor&opt desc,opt S solo oct SCHIRM.G 10645 $.25 (T715)

Of The Father's Love Begotten *see Corde Natus

Parables, The *Bibl/cant
SATB,TBar soli,org voc sc NOVELLO s.p. (T716)

THIMAN, ERIC HARDING (cont'd.)

Pilgrims To Bethlehem *Xmas
2pt jr cor/2pt wom cor CURWEN 72691 s.p.
(T717)

Praise, Lord, For Thee In Zion Waits *anthem
unis oct NOVELLO 28.1306.08 s.p. (T718)
mix cor oct NOVELLO 40.1192.09 s.p. (T719)

Praise, O Praise The Lord Of Harvest *Harv/
Thanks,anthem
mix cor oct NOVELLO 40.1037.10 s.p. (T720)

Praise The Lord, His Glories Show *Fest/Gen,
4pt mix cor,org oct SCHIRM.G 11692 $.35
(T721)

Praise The Lord Of Heaven *Thanks
SATB oct GRAY GCMR 2028 $.30 (T722)

Praise The Lord, Ye Heavens
SATB oct GRAY GCMR 2963 $.25 (T723)

Praise The Lord, Ye Heavens Adore Him
SATB THOMP.G G-571 s.p. (T724)

Rejoice The Lord Is King *Asc/Easter/Gen,
anthem
mix cor oct NOVELLO 28.1379.03 s.p. (T725)

Rise Up O
en Of God
SATB oct GRAY GCMR 3101 $.25 (T726)

Round Me Falls The Night
2pt wom cor,org oct SCHIRM.G 10748 $.25
(T727)
4pt mix cor,S solo,org oct SCHIRM.G 10738
$.25 (T728)

Seasonal Thanksgiving, A *Thanks
unis oct SCHIRM.G 8740 $.25 (T729)

See What Love Hath The Father *Introit
SATB THOMP.G G-555 s.p. see from Two
Introits (T730)

Shepherd's Story, The
SATB,org/orch ROBERTON (T731)

Sing Alleluia Forth *anthem/hymn
mix cor oct NOVELLO 40.0989.04 s.p. (T732)

Sing, O Sing This Blessed Morn *Xmas
SATB oct GRAY GCMR 3106 $.30 (T733)

Sing Unto The Lord
SATB oct GRAY GCMR 2343 $.35 (T734)

Sing We Merrily Unto God
SATB oct GRAY GCMR 2590 $.25 (T735)

Sing We Triumphant
SATB oct GRAY GCMR 2741 $.25 (T736)

Six Hymns Of Courage And Praise *CC6U,hymn
cong,pno/org cmplt ed WEINBERGER $1.00
(T737)

Songs Of Praise The Angels Sang *Fest/Gen,
anthem
mix cor oct NOVELLO 40.1318.02 s.p. (T738)

Souls Of The Righteous, The *anthem/Bibl
unis/2pt oct CURWEN 10594 $.20 (T739)

Spacious Firmament, The
unis,orch oct NOVELLO 40.1079.05 s.p., ipr
(T740)

Spacious Firmament On High, The *anthem
SAT/SAB oct NOVELLO 28.1346.07 s.p. (T741)

Stand Up And Bless The Lord
SATB (med easy) SOUTHERN $.30 (T742)
SATB SOUTHERN $.30 (T743)

Stand Up! Stand Up For Jesus
unis oct NOVELLO 37.0020.08 s.p. (T744)

Strife Is O'er, The *Easter,anthem
mix cor oct NOVELLO 28.1153.07 s.p. (T745)

&e &eum Laudamus *Te Deum
unis oct CURWEN 10602 $.25 (T746)
SSA (C maj) NOVELLO 51.0637.00 s.p. (T747)

Temptations Of Christ, The *Lent,cant
mix cor,SBar,opt T soli,org voc sc CURWEN
$1.00 (T748)

Ten Miniature Anthems *CC10L,anthem
mix cor cmplt ed NOVELLO 03.0106.10 s.p.
(T749)

This Is The Day The Lord Hath Made
unis oct NOVELLO 28.1307.06 s.p. (T750)

Three Choral Songs Of Praise *CC3U
mix cor oct CURWEN 80770 s.p. (T751)

Thy Church, O God, Her Heart To Thee
Upraiseth *anthem
SATB BELWIN AP 14 $.30 (T752)
mix cor oct NOVELLO 40.2166.05 s.p. (T753)

Twenty-Four Introits And Introductory
Sentences *CC24U,Introit
mix cor cmplt ed NOVELLO 03.0105.01 s.p.
(T754)

Two Introits *see Come Holy Spirit; See What
Love Hath The Father (T755)

Two Short Anthems And The Lord's Prayer
*CC3UL,anthem/prayer
mix cor oct CURWEN 80888 s.p. (T756)

Two Short Anthems Or Introits For
Unaccompanied Singing *CC2U,anthem/
Introit
mix cor,acap CURWEN s.p. (T757)

Virgin's Lullaby, The *Xmas
2pt jr cor/2pt wom cor CURWEN 72243 s.p.
(T758)

We Give Immortal Praise
unis Yt NOVELLO 28.1308.04 s.p. (T759)

When The Lord Of Love
unis oct NOVELLO s.p. (T760)

THIMAN, ERIC HARDING (cont'd.)

While Shepherds Watched *Xmas,anthem
mix cor oct NOVELLO 40.1040.10 s.p. (T761)

Who Would True Valour See *anthem
unis oct NOVELLO 28.1335.01 s.p. (T762)
mix cor oct NOVELLO 40.1357.03 s.p. (T763)

Wilderness, The *anthem
mix cor,S solo oct NOVELLO 28.1474.09 s.p.
(T764)

Winter Nativity *Xmas
3pt wom cor,pno oct CURWEN 11819 $.25
(T765)

With Gladness We Worship
SATB THOMP.G G-575 s.p. (T766)

Ye Sons And Daughters Of The King *Easter
SATB oct PRESSER 332-14550 $.30 (T767)

Ye That Are To Mirth Inclined *Xmas,anthem
mix cor oct NOVELLO 28.1457.09 s.p. (T768)

Ye That Do Your Master's Will *anthem
mix cor,acap oct NOVELLO 91.0008.03 s.p.
(T769)

THINE ANGER WITHOLD see Bach, Johann Sebastian

THINE ARE THE HEAVENS see Wiltberger, Tui Sunt

Coeli

THINE BE THE MAJESTY see Hutson, Wihla

THINE FOREVER! GOD OF LOVE (from Nurnbergisches
Gesangbuch)
(Coggin) SATB,org BOSTON 13316 $.35 (T770)

THINE FOREVER, GOD OF LOVE see Roff, Joseph

THINE IS THE GLORY see Elgar

THINE IS THE GLORY see Handel, George Frideric

THINE IS THE GREATNESS see Bortniansky, Dimitri
Stepanovitch

THINE IS THE KINGDOM see Gaul, Alfred Robert

THINE, LORD, IS WISDOM, THINE ALONE see Tynan,
D. Jr.

THINE, O LORD see Diemer, Emma Lou

THINE, O LORD see Macfarlane, William Charles

THINE, O LORD, IS THE GREATNESS see Kent

THINE, O LORD, IS THE GREATNESS see Kent, J.

THINE, O LORD, IS THE GREATNESS see Kent, James

THINE THE GLORY *CCU,anthem
SATB LORENZ $1.95 (T771)

THINK ON ME *anthem
(Diack) SATB oct FISCHER,C PT-1540 $.25
(T772)

THINK ON ME see Scott

THINK ON ME see Scott, Lady John

THINK ON THESE THINGS see Fitch

THINK ON THESE THINGS see Mueller, Carl F.

THINK, THOU, ON ME, O LORD see Morgan

THIRD COMMUNION SERVICE see Gounod, Charles
Francois, Missa Paschalis

THIRD CONCORD ANTHEM BOOK, THE *CC30U
(Glaser, V.; Clough-Leighter, H.) SATB
SCHIRM.EC 1290 $3.50 (T773)

THIRD DAY, THE see London, Edwin

THIRD MASS see Haller, Michael

THIRD MASS OF CHRISTMAS see Binkerd, [Gordon]

THIRD MORNING STAR CHOIR BOOK, A *CC16L
(Thomas, P.) unis mix cor/unis men cor/unis
treb cor/unis jr cor,kbd, inst pts for 6
pieces CONCORDIA 97-4972 $2.00, ipa
contains works by: Ley; Greene; Bach;
Dvorak; Willan; Nystedt; Mayer; Koler;
Bender; Viadana; Micheelsen; Peter;
Telemann; Schein (T774)

THIRD SERVICE see Byrd, William

THIRD SERVICE see Byrd, William

THIRD SERVICE see Tomkins, Thomas

THIRD VERSE SERVICE see Batten, Adrian

THIRIET, [MAURICE] (1906-   )
Choer Final (from Son Et Lumiere)
4pt mix cor,org LEMOINE voc sc s.p., cor
pts s.p. (T775)

Je Vous Salue, Marie
cor LEMOINE s.p. (T776)

Trois Motets *CC3U,mot
men cor,acap LEMOINE s.p. (T777)

THIRTEEN ANTHEMS FOR SPECIAL OCCASIONS *CC13U,
anthem
SATB LORENZ $1.75 (T778)

THIRTEEN CHORALES see Bach, Johann Sebastian

THIRTEEN SPIRITUALS *CC13U,spir
(Hancock) 1 eq voices/2 eq voices,org/acap
GRAY $1.50 (T779)

THIRTIETH ODE OF SOLOMON see Hovhaness, Alan

THIRTY 20TH CENTURY HYMN TUNES *CC30U,hymn
cong,pno/org cmplt ed WEINBERGER $1.85
(T780)

THIRTY CHRISTMAS CAROLS *CC30L,Xmas,anthem/
carol
cor,opt pno oct HART s.p., ipa (T781)

THIRTY-EIGHT INTROITS AND RESPONSES see Fuller,
[Esther Mary]

THIRTY-FIVE ROUNDS AND CANONS FROM FOUR
CENTURIES *CC35U,canon/round
(Bristol, L.) mix cor oct KERBY 804 $.75
(T782)

THIRTY-FIVE SACRED ROUNDS AND CANONS FROM FOUR
CENTURIES see Bristol, Lee H., Jr.

THIRTY-FOUR HYMN DESCANTS see Williams, David
McK.

THIRTY LITTLE ANGELS *spir
(Ehret) SAB MARKS 4454 $.30 (T783)
(Ehret) SATB MARKS 4455 $.30 (T784)
(Ehret) SA MARKS 4412 $.25 (T785)
(Ehret) SSA MARKS 4361 $.25 (T786)

THIRTY TWO CANONS ON SACRED TEXTS *CC32U
(Buszin, Walter) [Eng/Lat] 2-7pt PETERS 66166
$.60 contains works by: Lassus;
Gumpeltzhaimer; Praetorius; Telemann;
Haydn; Cherubini; Mozart; Schubert; Brahms;
and others (T787)

THIS BE MY SONG see Peery

THIS BE MY SONG see Peery, [Rob Roy]

THIS BLESSED CHRISTMASTIDE see Hunt, Reginald

THIS BOOK OF THE LAW see Grieb, Herbert [C.]

THIS CHILD BEHOLD see Cashmore, Donald

THIS CHILD OF LIFE see Cox, A.

THIS CHILD WAS BORN TO MEN OF GOD *carol
SATB (med easy) OXFORD 08.029 $.20 (T788)

THIS CHRISTMAS NIGHT see Arnold, Malcolm

THIS CHRISTMASTIDE see Snyder, J.

THIS DAY see Maconchy, Elizabeth

THIS DAY see Palestrina, Giovanni, Haec Dies

THIS DAY see Vaughan Williams, Ralph, Hodie

THIS DAY A CHILD IS BORN see Hilton

THIS DAY BORN AGAIN see Swinburne

THIS DAY CHRIST IS BORN see Santa Cruz,
Domingo, Hodie Christus Natus Est

THIS DAY CHRIST WAS BORN see Byrd, William

THIS DAY HAS COME FOR US TO SING
see Five Dutch Carols

THIS DAY IS THE DAY WHICH THE LORD HATH MADE
see Maltzeff, A.

THIS DAY REJOICE see Milano, R.

THIS DAY WE HONOR see Williams

THIS ENDERS NIGHT (from Anthology Of Carols,
An) Xmas,carol
(Wulstan, David) ATB,T solo CHESTER s.p.
contains also: Behold A Simple Tender Babe
(SATB) (T789)

THIS ENDERS NYZGT *Xmas
(Kirk) "Other Night, The" SATB oct PRO ART
1658 $.25 (T790)

THIS ENDRIS NIGHT *carol
see Six Traditional Carols, Set II
SATB (easy) OXFORD 08.039 $.15 (T791)

THIS ENDRIS NIGHT see Gronquist, R.

THIS FIRST CHRISTMAS NIGHT *Xmas,Pol
(Assenmacher) 2pt jr cor oct LILLENAS AN-4001
$.25 (T792)

THIS GLAD DAY see Byrd, William, Haec Dies

THIS GLAD DAY see Lassus, Roland de (Orlandus),
Hodie Apparuit

THIS GLAD DAY see Palestrina, Giovanni, Haec
Dies

THIS GLAD DAY HE APPEARED see Lassus, Roland de
(Orlandus), Hodie Apparuit

THIS GLAD DAY TO US THE KING OF HEAVEN see
Nanini (Nanino), Giovanni Bernardino, Hodie
Nobis Coelorum Rex

THIS GLAD EASTER DAY *Easter,Norw
(Dickinson, C.) SATB oct GRAY GSC 104 $.30
(T793)

THIS GLORIOUS CHRISTMAS NIGHT see Yeh, Huai-Deh

THIS GREAT HOUR see Gibbs

THIS HAPPY MORNING WAS CHRIST THE LORD BORN see
Schutz, Heinrich, Heute Ist Christ, Der
Herr, Geboren

THIS HOLY DAY see Grieb, Herbert [C.], Noel!
Noel!

THIS HOUR WITH THEE see Ferguson, Howard

THIS HUMAN WAY see Thompson, Alan

THIS I SAW! see Martin

THIS IS CHRISTMAS see Burt, Alfred

THIS IS EASTER DAY see Marryott, Ralph E.

THIS IS HE OF WHOM IT IS WRITTEN see Hillert,
Richard

THIS IS INDEED THE PROPHET see Bender, Jan

THIS IS JESUS
(Price) SATB oct LORENZ C221 $.30 (T794)
(Price) SA/SAB oct LORENZ 7817 $.25 (T795)

THIS IS LIFE see Prine

THIS IS MY BELOVED SON see Nystedt, Knut

THIS IS MY COMMANDMENT see Morgan, Haydn

THIS IS MY COMMANDMENT see Tallis, Thomas

THIS IS MY COMMANDMENT see Trued

THIS IS MY FATHER'S WORLD
   see Three General Hymns

THIS IS MY FATHER'S WORLD see Hughes

THIS IS MY FATHER'S WORLD see Johnson

THIS IS MY FATHER'S WORLD see Kaiser, Kurt

THIS IS MY FATHER'S WORLD see Ringwald, [Roy]

THIS IS MY FATHER'S WORLD see Sheppard

THIS IS MY PRAYER
   (Huntley) SATB CHAPPELL 5970009-358 $.40
                             (T796)

THIS IS MY PRAYER see Newman

THIS IS MY SONG see Cram

THIS IS NOEL see Davis, Katherine K.

THIS IS OUR FATHER'S HOUSE see Grime, William

THIS IS OUR LAND see Williams, Ralph E.

THIS IS THE DAY
   see Almighty Lord And God Of Love

THIS IS THE DAY see Angell

THIS IS THE DAY see Anonymous

THIS IS THE DAY see Barker

THIS IS THE DAY see Beck, Thomas [Ludvigsen]

THIS IS THE DAY see Bell, L.R.

THIS IS THE DAY see Bortniansky, Dimitri Stepanovitch

THIS IS THE DAY see Byrd, William, Haec Dies

THIS HS THE DAY see Christiansen, Paul

THIS IS THE DAY see Cooke, S.C.

THIS IS THE DAY see Friedell, Harold W.

THIS IS THE DAY see Gallus, Jacobus, Haec East Dies

THIS IS THE DAY see Gallus, Jacobus, Haec Est Dies

THIS IS THE DAY see Garland, Hugh

THIS IS THE DAY see Kreutz, Robert E.

THIS IS THE DAY see Monaco, Richard A.

THIS HS THE DAY see Palestrina, Giovanni, Haec Dies Quam Fecit Dominus

THIS IS THE DAY see Peloquin, C. Alexander

THIS IS THE DAY see Roff, Joseph

THIS IS THE DAY see Schroth, Gerhard

THIS IS THE DAY OF LIGHT see Brandon

THIS IS THE DAY THAT THE LORD CREATED see Geisler, Johan C.

THIS IS THE DAY THE LORD HAS MADE see Lee, J.

THIS IS THE DAY THE LORD HAS MADE see Proulx, Richard

THIS IS THE DAY THE LORD HAS MADE see Sanders, Robert L.

THIS IS THE DAY THE LORD HATH MADE see Gibbons, Orlando

THIS IS THE DAY THE LORD HATH MADE see Near, Gerald

THIS IS THE DAY THE LORD HATH MADE see Thiman, Eric Harding

THIS IS THE DAY THE LORD HATH MADE see Wolff, S. Drummond

THIS IS THE DAY WHICH THE LORD HATH MADE see Bortniansky, Dimitri Stepanovitch

THIS IS THE DAY WHICH THE LORD HATH MADE see Dovenspike

THIS IS THE DAY WHICH THE LORD HATH MADE see Ford, Virgil T.

THIS IS THE DAY WHICH THE LORD HATH MADE see Kirk

THIS IS THE DAY WHICH THE LORD HATH MADE see Merkel, Gustav A.

THIS IS THE DAY WHICH THE LORD HATH MADE see Newbury, Kent A.

THIS IS THE DAY WHICH THE LORD HATH MADE see Peeters, Flor

THIS IS THE GARDEN see Blitzstein, Marc

THIS IS THE GARDEN see Persichetti, Vincent

THIS IS THE HOLY EVEN
   (Tuttle, S.) SSAA,acap SCHIRM.EC 1913 $.18
                             (T797)

THIS IS THE KING see Wilson

THIS IS THE LAND I LOVE see Hughes

THIS IS THE LORD'S OWN DAY see Kreutzer, Konradin

THIS IS THE MIGHTY PROPHET see Victoria, Tomas Luis de, Ecce Sacerdos Magnus

THIS IS THE RECORD OF JOHN see Gibbons, Orlando

THIS IS THE STORY OF JESUS see O'Hara, Geoffrey

THIS IS TRULY THE HOUSE OF GOD see Rubbra, Edmund, Haec Est Domus Domini

THIS IS WHAT WE ARE see Kimmel

THIS IS YOUR PRAYER see Lewy, Ron, VeHi Tehilatecha

THIS JOYFUL EASTER-TIDE *Easter/Lent,Dut
   cor/cong oct MOWBRAY 65025 5 s.p. see also
   Cowley Carol Book, The   (T798)
   (Carter) jr cor&sr cor,opt trp oct SPRATT 545
   $.25   (T799)
   (Fearing, John) SATB oct LESLIE 4104 (T800)
   (Somervell) unis oct BOOSEY 5223 $.30 (T801)

THIS JOYFUL EASTERTIDE *Easter,anthem/carol,
   Dut/Neth
   SATB oct BELWIN 64147 $.30   (T802)
   (Candlyn, T.F.H.) SATB oct FISCHER,J 8865
   $.35   (T803)
   (Greville; Cooke) SATB ALLANS 186 s.p. (T804)
   (Harris, William H.) mix cor oct NOVELLO
   28.1367.10 s.p.   (T805)
   (Shaw; Parker) 4pt mix cor,acap oct SCHIRM.G
   9941 $.30   (T806)
   (Wolff, S.D.) SAB,kbd (med easy) oct
   CONCORDIA 98-1147 $.20   (T807)
   (Wolff, S.D.) SS,kbd (easy) oct CONCORDIA
   98-2136 $.35   (T808)

THIS JOYFUL EASTERTIDE see Anonymous

THIS JOYFUL EASTERTIDE see Harvey

THIS JOYFUL EASTERTIDE see Ratcliffe, Desmond

THIS JOYFUL EASTERTIDE see Shaw, R.

THIS JOYFUL EASTERTIDE see Wyton, Alec

THIS JOYOUS DAY see Shaw, Martin

THIS LAND UNDER THEE see Wehr, David A.

THIS LITTLE BABE see Britten, Benjamin

THIS LITTLE BABE see Burroughs

THIS LITTLE BABE see Byrd, William

THIS LITTLE BABE see Roff, Joseph

THIS LITTLE BABE see Wetzler, Robert

THIS LITTLE LIGHT O MINE see Work

THIS LITTLE LIGHT OF MINE *spir
   (Christiansen, P.) SATB SCHMITT 918 $.35
                             (T809)
   (Ehret) SA,pno oct LAWSON 51637 $.30 (T810)
   (Ehret) SSA/SAA,pno oct LAWSON 51638 $.35
                             (T811)
   (Ehret) SATB,pno oct LAWSON 51639 $.30 (T812)
   (Ehret) 3pt mix cor oct LAWSON 51640 $.35
                             (T813)
   (Ehret) SSA SOUTHERN $.35   (T814)

THIS LITTLE PILGRIM see Sellew

THIS LOVE IS MINE see Lister, Mosie

THIS MAN see Victoria, Tomas Luis de, Hic Vir Despicians Mundum

THIS MORNING see Lorentzen, Bent

THIS NATION UNDER GOD see Youse

THIS NEW CHRISTMAS CAROL
   unis/SATB,opt inst (easy) OXFORD 08.029 $.20
                             (T815)

THIS NIGHT see Bach

THIS NIGHT see Konig

THIS NIGHT THERE COMES TO BETHLEHEM
   see Five Dutch Carols

THIS NOBLE TASK see Hughes

THIS, OUR PRAYER see Bodycombe, [Aneurin]

THIS OUR SONG OF PRAISE
   SATB HANSEN-US C291B $.40   (T816)

THIS PROUD HEART see Bach, Johann Sebastian

THIS SACRED DAY see Kroeger, Karl, Dies Sanctificatus

THIS SAME JESUS *CC10UL
   (Mickelson, Paul) cor,narrator,inst cmplt ed
   LILLENAS MB-211 $1.95 may be performed
   individually or as one choral program
                             (T817)

THIS SOUND OF SIGHING *Gen
   (Hokanson) SATB SCHMITT 920 $.35 (T818)

THIS TRAIN *spir
   (Ehret, W.) SA LEONARD-US 08065600 $.25
                             (T819)
   (Ehret, W.) SAB LEONARD-US 08065920 $.30
                             (T820)
   (Ehret, W.) SATB LEONARD-US 08066240 $.25
                             (T821)
   (Ehret, W.) SSA LEONARD-US 08065280 $.25
                             (T822)
   (Geller) SATB MARKS 4202 $.30   (T823)
   (Heath) 4pt men cor,T solo,acap oct SCHIRM.G
   11244 $.35   (T824)

THIS WAS THE DAY WHEN CHRIST WAS BORN see Andrews, C.T.

THIS WE GIVE see Hutson, Wihla

THIS WINTER'S NIGHT see Pasfield, W.R.

THIS WONDROUS WORLD see Fuller, [Esther Mary]

THIS WOULD I KEEP see Crowell, M.

THO' YOUR SINS BE AS SCARLET see Johnson, S.

THOMAS
   I Turn The Corner Of Prayer
   (Taylor) SATB oct BOURNE 795 $.25 (T825)

   Love Came Down At Christmas *Xmas
   SATB,opt inst (easy) OXFORD 84.093 $.20
                             (T826)

   Sleep, Holy Babe *Xmas
   SATB SCHMITT 1200 $.25   (T827)

THOMAS, CHRISTOPHER (1894-   )
   Father Of Us All
   SATB,acap (easy) oct WILLIS 6639 $.18
                             (T828)

THOMAS, J.
   Day By Day, Dear Lord
   SATB,acap oct PRESSER MC390 $.30 (T829)

THOMAS, KURT (1904-   )
   An Den Wassern Zu Babel (Psalm 137) Op.4
   dbl cor,acap cor pts BREITKOPF-L PB-3078
   s.p., voc pt BREITKOPF-L CHB-2478 s.p.
                             (T830)
   SATB&SATB,acap cor pts BREITKOPF-W PB-3078
   s.p.   (T831)

   Auferstehungs-Oratorium *Op.24, Easter,
   evang/ora
   4pt mix cor,fl,trp,2trom,3strings,opt bvl,
   org BREITKOPF-W rental   (T832)

   Aus Tiefer Not
   see Sechs Kleine Choralmotetten
   see Sechs Kleine Choralmotetten
   see Three Choral Settings

   Christ Fuhr Gen Himmel
   3pt wom cor/3pt jr cor,acap cor pts
   BREITKOPF-W CHB-3133 s.p.   (T833)

   Daran Ist Erschienen *Xmas,mot
   mix cor,S solo,vln sc BREITKOPF-L PB-3502
   s.p. see from Kleine Geistliche Chormusik
                             (T834)

   Der Tod Ist Verschlungen *Easter,mot
   mix cor,acap cor pts BREITKOPF-L PB-3507
   s.p. see from Kleine Geistliche Chormusik
                             (T835)

   Die Gnade Unsers Herrn *Trin,mot
   mix cor,acap cor pts BREITKOPF-L PB-3511
   s.p. see from Kleine Geistliche Chormusik
                             (T836)

   Ein' Feste Burg
   see Three Choral Settings

   Ein Feste Burg Ist Unser Gott
   see Sechs Kleine Choralmotetten

   Erhalt Uns, Herr, Bei Deinem Wort *Refm,mot
   mix cor,acap cor pts BREITKOPF-L PB-3513
   s.p. see from Kleine Geistliche Chormusik
                             (T837)

   Furchte Dich Nicht *Cnfrm,mot
   mix cor,acap cor pts BREITKOPF-L PB-3517
   s.p. see from Kleine Geistliche Chormusik
                             (T838)

   Furwahr, Er Trug Unsre Krankheit *Psntd,mot
   mix cor,acap cor pts BREITKOPF-L PB-3506
   s.p. see from Kleine Geistliche Chormusik
                             (T839)

   Gelobet Seist Du, Jesu Christ
   see Sechs Kleine Choralmotetten

   Gott Fahret Auf *Asc,mot
   mix cor,acap cor pts BREITKOPF-L PB-3508
   s.p. see from Kleine Geistliche Chormusik
                             (T840)

   Gott Wird Abwischen Alle Tranen *Ded/
   Rembrnc,mot
   mix cor,acap cor pts BREITKOPF-L PB-3515
   s.p. see from Kleine Geistliche Chormusik
                             (T841)

   Herr Gott, Dich Loben Alle Wir *ASD,mot
   mix cor,acap cor pts BREITKOPF-L PB-3519
   s.p. see from Kleine Geistliche Chormusik
                             (T842)

   Herr, Ich Habe Lieb Die Statte *Ded/Fest,mot
   mix cor,acap cor pts BREITKOPF-L PB-3516
   s.p. see from Kleine Geistliche Chormusik
                             (T843)

   Herr, Sei Mir Gnadig *mot
   mix cor,acap cor pts BREITKOPF-L PB-3514
   s.p. see from Kleine Geistliche Chormusik
                             (T844)

   Herr, Wie Du Willst
   see Three Choral Settings

   Herr, Wie Du Willst, So Schicks Mit Mir
   see Sechs Kleine Choralmotetten

   Ist Gott Fur Uns *mot
   mix cor,acap sc BREITKOPF-L PB-3503 s.p.
   see from Kleine Geistliche Chormusik
                             (T845)

   Jauchzet Gott, Alle Lande *Harv/Thanks
   mix cor,acap cor pts BREITKOPF-L PB-3512
   s.p. see from Kleine Geistliche Chormusik
                             (T846)

   Jerusalem, Du Hochgebaute Stadt *cant
   mix cor,SATB soli,org,2fl,2ob,2clar,2bsn,
   2trp,4horn,3trom,tuba,strings,perc,timp
   sc BREITKOPF-L PB-3265 s.p., ipr (T847)

   Kleine Geistliche Chormusik *see Daran Ist
   Erschienen; Der Tod Ist Verschlungen; Die
   Gnade Unsers Herrn; Erhalt Uns, Herr, Bei
   Deinem Wort; Furchte Dich Nicht; Furwahr,
   Er Trug Unsre Krankheit; Gott Fahret Auf;
   Gott Wird Abwischen Alle Tranen; Herr
   Gott, Dich Loben Alle Wir; Herr, Ich Habe
   Lieb Die Statte; Herr, Sei Mir Gnadig;
   Ist Gott Fur Uns; Jauchzet Gott, Alle
   Lande; Mache Dich Auf, Werde Licht;
   Machet Die Tore Weit; Niemand Hat
   Grossere Liebe; Nun Freut Euch, Liebe
   Christen; Schmucket Das Fest; Wenn Ich
   Mit Menschen Und Engelzungen Redete; Wir
   Wollen Singen   (T848)

THOMAS, KURT (cont'd.)

Kleine Weihnachtsmusik *Op.14c, Xmas
4pt mix cor,fl,vln,vla,vcl cor pts
BREITKOPF-W CHB-2595 s.p. (T849)

Komm, Heiliger Geist
2pt wom cor/2pt jr cor,acap cor pts
BREITKOPF-W CHB-3134 s.p. (T850)

Mache Dich Auf, Werde Licht *Adv/Epiph,mot
mix cor,acap cor pts BREITKOPF-L PB-3504
s.p. see from Kleine Geistliche Chormusik (T851)

Machet Die Tore Weit *Adv,mot
mix cor,acap cor pts BREITKOPF-L PB-3501
s.p. see from Kleine Geistliche Chormusik (T852)

Markus Passion *Op.6, Lent/Psntd
8pt mix cor,acap cor pts BREITKOPF-L
PB-3157 s.p., voc sc BREITKOPF-L CHB-2514
s.p. (T853)

Messe In a *Op.1, Mass
4pt mix cor&4pt mix cor,SATB soli,acap cor
pts BREITKOPF-W PB-3049 (T854)

Niemand Hat Grossere Liebe *mot
mix cor,S/T solo,org sc BREITKOPF-L PB-3505
s.p. see from Kleine Geistliche Chormusik (T855)

Nun Freut Euch, Liebe Christen *mot
mix cor,2vln sc BREITKOPF-L PB-3520 s.p.
see from Kleine Geistliche Chormusik (T856)

Passionsmusik Nach Dem Evangelisten Markus
*Op.6, Psntd,Bibl
SATB&SATB,acap cor pts BREITKOPF-W PB-3157
s.p. (T857)

Psalm 137 *see An Den Wassern Zu Babel

Schmucket Das Fest *Adv/Epiph,mot
mix cor,2vln sc BREITKOPF-L PB-3509 s.p.
see from Kleine Geistliche Chormusik (T858)

Sechs Kleine Choralmotetten *mot
cor pts BREITKOPF-W CHB-2594 s.p.
contains: Aus Tiefer Not (2 eq voices,
acap); Aus Tiefer Not (4pt mix cor,
acap); Ein Feste Burg Ist Unserott
(4pt mix cor,acap); Gelobet Seist Du,
Jesu Christ (4pt mix cor,acap); Herr,
Wie Du Willst, So Schicks Mit Mir (4pt
mix cor,acap); Verleih Uns Frieden
Gnadiglich (4pt mix cor,acap) (T859)

Three Choral Settings
[Ger] SATB,acap PETERS 4864 $.60
contains: Aus Tiefer Not; Ein' Feste
Burg; Herr, Wie Du Willst (T860)

Verleih Uns Frieden Gnadiglich
see Sechs Kleine Choralmotetten

Von Der Ewigen Liebe *Op.21, mot
6pt mix cor,acap cor pts BREITKOPF-L
PB-3429 s.p. (T861)

Weihnachts-Oratorium *Op.17, Xmas,ora
SSATBB,acap cor pts BREITKOPF-L PB-3350
s.p., voc pt BREITKOPF-L CHB-2696 s.p. (T862)

Weihnachtsoratorium *Xmas,ora
6pt mix cor,acap BREITKOPF-W rental (T863)

Wenn Ich Mit Menschen Und Engelzungen Redete
*funeral/mot
wom cor,Bar solo,org/pno sc BREITKOPF-L
PB-3518 s.p. see from Kleine Geistliche
Chormusik (T864)

Wir Wollen Singen *ASD,mot
mix cor,acap cor pts BREITKOPF-L PB-3510
s.p. see from Kleine Geistliche Chormusik (T865)

THOMAS, MANSEL
Carol For A New-Born King *Xmas,carol
unis jr cor/unis wom cor CURWEN 72656 s.p. (T866)

I Will Lift Up Mine Eyes *anthem
mix cor,acap oct NOVELLO 28.1419.06 s.p. (T867)

One Generation Passeth *anthem/mot
mix cor,acap oct NOVELLO 28.1424.02 s.p. (T868)

THOMAS, PAUL LINDSLEY
Fanfare And Alleluias *Easter
SATB oct GRAY GCMR 3076 $.30 (T869)

THOMAS, T.A.
O Come Let Us Worship
cor oct HART s.p. (T870)

THOMASCHKE, EDGAR (1913-)
Er Hat Den Frieden Verkundigen Lassen
SATB HANSSLER 7.157 s.p. (T871)

Kommt Her Zu Mir, Spricht Gottes Sohn *cant
SATB,ST soli,5brass,perc HANSSLER 10.131 sc
s.p., cor pts s.p. (T872)

THOMASI, [HENRI] (1901-1971)
Dio Vi Salvi Regina *hymn
3pt men cor/3pt wom cor,org LEMOINE voc sc
s.p., cor pts s.p. (T873)

THOMISSON, HANS
Den Danske Psalmebog 1569 *CCU,Psalm
[Dan] cor FOG 148 s.p. (T874)

THOMPSON
All Hail The Power Of Jesus' Name
SATB oct LORENZ 9911 $.35 (T875)

Am I A Soldier Of The Cross?
SATB oct LORENZ 9953 $.30 (T876)

Canticle Of Love, A
SATB oct LORENZ 9886 $.30 (T877)

Come, Ye Thankful People
SATB oct LORENZ 9845 $.30 (T878)

Deer Is Panting For The Stream
SATB oct SACRED E88 $.35 (T879)

THOMPSON (cont'd.)

Garden Hymn, The
SATB oct SACRED S-9949 $.35 (T880)

Glory To The King Of Kings *Xmas
SATB oct LORENZ 9145 $.30 (T881)
TTBB oct LORENZ 2849 $.30 (T882)
unis oct LORENZ 8543 $.25 (T883)

Go Forth To Life, O Child Of Earth
2pt oct LORENZ 5703 $.30 (T884)
SATB oct LORENZ 9523 $.30 (T885)

Go Ye And Teach All Nations
SATB oct LORENZ 9951 $.30 (T886)

God Is Love
SATB oct LORENZ 9976 $.30 (T887)

God Of Love My Shepherd Is, The
SATB oct LORENZ 9988 $.30 (T888)

Hosanna To The Living Lord *Easter
SATB oct LORENZ 9895 $.30 (T889)

How Firm A Foundation
SAB oct LORENZ 7384 $.30 (T890)
SATB oct LORENZ E9 $.30 (T891)

Hymn To The Godhead *hymn
SATB oct LORENZ E16 $.30 (T892)

Hymn To The Trinity *hymn
SATB oct LORENZ 9578 $.30 (T893)

I Have Quieted My Soul
SATB oct LORENZ C294 $.30 (T894)

I Heard The Voice Of Jesus Say
SATB oct LORENZ 9957 $.30 (T895)

Jesus Is All The World To Me *hymn
(Ferrin) SATB oct LILLENAS AN-1614 $.30 (T896)

Lead On, O King Eternal
SATB oct LORENZ 9787 $.30 (T897)

Living Light *Easter,cant
SATB LORENZ $1.95 (T898)

Lord Is Nigh, The
SATB oct LORENZ 9889 $.30 (T899)

Lord Of All Being
SATB oct SACRED S-18 $.35 (T900)

Man Of Sorrows *Easter,cant
SATB LORENZ $1.95 (T901)

Mass *Mass
2pt,perc oct MCA (T902)
2pt,perc oct MCA $.60 (T903)

More Love To Thee
SATB oct LORENZ C299 $.30 (T904)

O For A Thousand Tongues
SATB oct LORENZ 9705 $.30 (T905)

O God, Our Help In Ages Past
SATB oct LORENZ 9742 $.30 (T906)

O Gracious King
unis oct LORENZ 8864 $.25 (T907)
SATB oct LORENZ 9567 $.25 (T908)

O King Of Kings
SATB oct LORENZ 9294 $.30 (T909)

O Lord, Our Lord
SATB oct LORENZ 9769 $.30 (T910)

O Love Of God
SATB oct LORENZ 9974 $.30 (T911)

Onward, Christian Soldiers
SATB oct LORENZ 9718 $.30 (T912)

Praise God In His Holiness
SATB oct LORENZ 9785 $.30 (T913)

Praise The Lord Of Heaven
SATB oct LORENZ 9987 $.30 (T914)

Praise To The Lord, The Almighty
SATB oct LORENZ 9883 $.30 (T915)

Praised Be My Lord
SATB oct LORENZ 9978 $.30 (T916)

Psalm Of Gratitude, A *Psalm
SATB oct LORENZ C270 $.30 (T917)

Psalm Of Thanksgiving, A *Psalm
SATB oct LORENZ 9770 $.30 (T918)

Pueri Hebraeorium
girl cor SOUTHERN $.55 (T919)

Rose Of Christmas, The *Xmas,cant
SATB oct LORENZ $1.95 (T920)

Sing And Give Praise
SATB oct LORENZ C314 $.30 (T921)

Song Of The Angels, The *Xmas,cant
SATB oct LORENZ $1.95 (T922)

Stand Up For Jesus
SATB oct LORENZ C68 $.35 (T923)

These Are Thy Glorious Works
SATB oct LORENZ E18 $.30 (T924)

Thou Art The King Of Glory
SATB oct LORENZ 9898 $.30 (T925)

Thou Hope Of Every Contrite Heart
SATB oct LORENZ 9989 $.30 (T926)

When Love Came Down *Xmas,cant
SATB oct LORENZ $1.95 (T927)

When Love Was Born *Xmas,cant
SATB oct LORENZ $1.95 (T928)

THOMPSON (cont'd.)

When Morning Gilds The Skies
SATB oct LORENZ 9806 $.30 (T929)

THOMPSON, ALAN
Author Of Live Divine
SATB,acap oct BERANDOL 914T5AF $.35 (T930)

How They So Softly Rest
SATB,acap oct BERANDOL 914T5AG $.35 (T931)

I Was Glad When They Said Unto Me
SATB,org oct BERANDOL 914T5AI $.35 (T932)

In The Still Night
SATB,acap oct BERANDOL 914T5AH $.35 (T933)

This Human Way
SATB,acap oct BERANDOL 914T5AJ $.35 (T934)

THOMPSON, R.G.
What Of The Night? *Adv
SATB oct GRAY GCMR 410 $.30 (T935)

THOMPSON, RANDALL (1899-)
Agnus Dei (from Mass Of The Holy Spirit)
"O Lamb Of God" SATB,acap SCHIRM.EC 2469
$.35 (T936)

Alleluia *Fest
TTBB,acap SCHIRM.EC 2312 $.40 (T937)
SATB,acap SCHIRM.EC 1786 $.45 (T938)
SSAA,acap SCHIRM.EC 2593 $.40 (T939)

Amen And Amen, Alleluia (from Requiem)
dbl cor,acap SCHIRM.EC 2673 $1.00 (T940)

And The Child Grew (from Nativity According
To Saint Luke, The)
SATB,pno SCHIRM.EC 2644 $.75 (T941)

Benedictus (from Mass Of The Holy Spirit)
"Blessed Is He That Cometh" SATB,acap
SCHIRM.EC 2467 $.40 (T942)

Blessed Is He That Cometh *see Benedictus

But These Are They That Forsake The Lord
(from Peaceable Kingdom, The)
dbl cor,acap SCHIRM.EC 1752 $.45 (T943)

Call To Song, The
see Requiem

Credo (from Mass Of The Holy Spirit)
"I Believe In One God" SATB,acap SCHIRM.EC
2465 $.45 (T944)

Feast Of Praise, A *cant
SATB,pno/brass&harp SCHIRM.EC 2675 $.75,
ipa (T945)

Garment Of Praise, The (from Requiem)
see Requiem
dbl cor,acap SCHIRM.EC 2639 $1.75 (T946)
dbl cor,acap SCHIRM.EC 2639 $1.75 (T947)

Gate Of Heaven, The
SSAA,acap SCHIRM.EC 2531 $.50 (T948)
SATB,acap SCHIRM.EC 2490 $.50 (T949)
TTBB,acap SCHIRM.EC 2175 $.50 (T950)

Gloria (from Mass Of The Holy Spirit)
"Glory Be To God On High" SSAATTBB,acap
SCHIRM.EC 2464 $.50 (T951)

Glory Be To God On High *see Gloria

Glory To God In The Highest
SATB,acap SCHIRM.EC 2470 $.35 (T952)

Good Tidings To The Meek (from Requiem)
dbl cor,acap SCHIRM.EC 2638 $.75 (T953)

Have Ye Not Known (from Peaceable Kingdom,
The)
dbl cor,acap SCHIRM.EC 1753 $.65 contains
also: Ye Shall Have A Song (T954)

Holy, Holy, Holy *see Sanctus

Hosanna (from Mass Of The Holy Spirit)
SATB,acap SCHIRM.EC 2468 $.25 (T955)

Howl Ye (from Peaceable Kingdom, The)
dbl cor,acap SCHIRM.EC 1750 $.55 (T956)

I Believe In One God *see Credo

Kyrie (from Mass Of The Holy Spirit) Ger
SATB,acap SCHIRM.EC 2463 $.45 (T957)

Lamentations
see Requiem

Last Words Of David, The
TTBB,pno/orch SCHIRM.EC 2145 $.40, ipr, ipr (T958)
SATB,pno/orch SCHIRM.EC 2294 $.40, ipa, ipr (T959)

Leave-Taking, The
see Requiem

Lord Is My Shepherd, The (Psalm 23)
SSAA,pno,org/harp SCHIRM.EC 2578 $.75 (T960)
SATB,pno/org/harp SCHIRM.EC 2688 $.75, ipr (T961)

Lord Shall Be Unto Thee, The (from Requiem)
SATB,acap SCHIRM.EC 2641 $.50 (T962)

Lullaby (from Nativity According To Saint
Luke, The)
"Upon My Lap My Sov'reign Sits" opt cor,S
solo SCHIRM.EC 125 $.75 (T963)

Mass Of The Holy Spirit *Commun
4 cor&7 cor,acap SCHIRM.EC 2426 $2.50 (T964)
SATB,acap SCHIRM.EC 2426 $2.50 (T965)

Nativity According To Saint Luke, The
cor,soli,org,bells,orch SCHIRM.EC 622 voc
sc $6.00, cor pts $2.50, ipa, ipr (T966)

Nativity According To St. Luke, The
cor,soli,bells,org,orch SCHIRM.EC 622 voc
sc $7.50, cor pts $2.50, ipr, ipa (T967)

THOMPSON, RANDALL (cont'd.)

Noise Of A Multitude, The (from Peaceable
Kingdom, The)
SATB,acap SCHIRM.EC 1749 $.45   (T968)

Now I Lay Me Down To Sleep
SSA,acap SCHIRM.EC 1985 $.35   (T969)

Nowel (from Nativity According To Saint Luke,
The)
SSAA,pno SCHIRM.EC 2567 $.35   (T970)
TTBB,pno SCHIRM.EC 2300 $.35   (T971)

O Lamb Of God *see Agnus Dei

Paper Reeds By The Brook, The (from Peaceable
Kingdom, The)
SATB,acap SCHIRM.EC 1751 $.35   (T972)

Passion According To Saint Luke, The *ora
SATB,soli,pno/orch SCHIRM.EC 2695 $4.00,
ipr   (T973)

Peaceable Kingdom, The *CC8L,Bibl/cant
SATB&dbl cor,acap SCHIRM.EC 1730 $3.00 (T974)

Psalm 23 *see Lord Is My Shepherd, The

Pueri Hebraeorum *anti
dbl cor,acap SCHIRM.EC 492 $.60   (T975)

Quis Multa Gracilis (from Odes Of Horace)
TTBB,acap SCHIRM.EC 539 $.30   (T976)

Requiem
dbl cor,acap SCHIRM.EC 2459 $7.50
contains: Call To Song, The; Garment Of
Praise, The; Lamentations; Leave-
Taking, The; Triumph Of Faith, The
(T977)

Sanctus (from Mass Of The Holy Spirit)
"Holy, Holy, Holy" SAATTBB,acap SCHIRM.EC
2466 $.65   (T978)

Say Ye To The Righteous (from Peaceable
Kingdom, The)
SATB,acap SCHIRM.EC 1747 $.45   (T979)

Thou Hast Given Him (from Requiem)
SATB,acap SCHIRM.EC 2642 $.50   (T980)

Triumph Of Faith, The
see Requiem

Upon My Lap My Sov'reign Sits *see Lullaby

Woe Unto Them (from Peaceable Kingdom, The)
SATB,acap SCHIRM.EC 1748 $.40   (T981)

Ye Shall Have A Song (from Peaceable Kingdom,
The)
see Thompson, Randall, Have Ye Not Known

Ye Were Sometimes Darkness (from Requiem)
dbl cor,acap SCHIRM.EC 2640 $1.00   (T982)

THOMPSON, RONALD
Sacred Chorister *CCU
SAB BELWIN $1.00   (T983)

Worship In Song, Book 1
SA BELWIN $1.00   (T984)

Worship In Song, Book 2 *CCU
SA BELWIN $1.00   (T985)

THOMPSON, V.D.
Beloved, Het Qs Love
SATB oct GRAY GCMR 1518 $.25   (T986)

Blessing And Honor
SATB oct GRAY GCMR 2978 $.25   (T987)

Breathe On Me, Breath Of God
SATB oct GRAY GCMR 1137 $.30   (T988)

Choral Prayer
SATB oct GRAY GCMR 2977 $.30   (T989)

Dear Lord, Who Once Upon The Lake
4pt mix cor,S solo oct SCHIRM.G 7666 $.25
(T990)

Father, In Thy Mysterious Presence *Gen/Lent
SATB oct GRAY GCMR 1367 $.30   (T991)

Mercy And Truth *Bibl
mix cor,acap oct SCHIRM.G 7665 $.30   (T992)

Ride On, Ride On *Easter/Lent/Palm
SATB oct GRAY GCMR 1154 $.30   (T993)

THOMPSON, W.
Jesus Is All The World To Me *hymn
(Hustad, Don) SATB ALLANS 407 s.p.   (T994)

Softly And Tenderly
(Peery, R.) SA oct PRESSER 312-40529 $.30
(T995)

THOMPSON, WILL LAMARITNE (1847-1909)
Softly And Tenderly
SAB oct LORENZ 7327 $.25   (T996)
(Parker) TTBB,acap oct LAWSON 51358 $.30
(T997)

THOMSON
Ye Gates, Lift Up Your Heads
(Smith) SATB oct BOOSEY 5171 $.30   (T998)

THOMSON, DAVID CLEGHORN
Knight Of Bethlehem, The *Xmas,anthem
mix cor oct NOVELLO s.p.   (T999)

THOMSON, VIRGIL (1896-   )
De Profundis (Psalm 130)
"Out Of The Deep" SATB voc sc MUSIC   (T1000)
"Out Of The Depths" SATB MUSIC s.p.   (T1001)

Flight Into Egypt, The
see Scenes From The Holy Infancy (According
To St. Matthew)

Holly And The Ivy, The *Xmas
4pt mix cor,acap oct SCHIRM.G 11195 $.30
(T1002)

Holy Infant, So Tender And Mild
SATB,acap SHAWNEE A 677 $.25   (T1003)

THOMSON, VIRGIL (cont'd.)

Joseph And The Angel
see Scenes From The Holy Infancy (According
To St. Matthew)

Mass
[Lat] unis voc sc SCHIRM.G $.60   (T1004)

Mass (Two-Part)
[Lat] SATB,acap,perc voc sc MCA $1.00 (T1005)

Morning Star, The *Epiph
SATB oct GRAY GCCS 7 $.25   (T1006)

My Master Hath A Garden
3pt wom cor oct SCHIRM.G 11177 $.25   (T1007)
4pt mix cor oct SCHIRM.G 11176 $.25   (T1008)

Nativity As Sung By The Shepherds, The
4pt mix cor,pno voc sc SCHIRM.G $1.00
(T1009)

Out Of The Deep *see De Profundis

Out Of The Depths *see De Profundis

Psalm 130 *see De Profundis

Scenes From The Holy Infancy (According To
St. Matthew) *Xmas
4pt mix cor,acap oct SCHIRM.G 11680 $.35
contains: Flight Into Egypt, The; Joseph
And The Angel; Wise Men, The   (T1010)

Tribulatones Civitatum
SATB MUSIC s.p.   (T1011)

Wise Men, The
see Scenes From The Holy Infancy (According
To St. Matthew)

THORDARSON, SIGURDUR (1895-1969)
Psalms *Op.19, CCU,Psalm
mix cor,soli,pno ICELAND s.p.   (T1012)

Solemn Mass, A *Op.20, Mass
men cor,pno ICELAND s.p.   (T1013)

THORN-CROWNED KING see Holton

THORNE
Evening Prayer
SATB MARKS 4461 $.25   (T1014)

Kyrie Eleison *Kyrie
[Lat] SSA MARKS 4318 $.25   (T1015)

Thy Children, Lord
SSA,acap MARKS 4363 $.25   (T1016)

THORNE, FRANCIS (1922-   )
De Profundis
SATB,S solo GENERAL CH689 $.40   (T1017)

Thy Word Resound
SATB GENERAL CH690   (T1018)

THORNS AND PURPLE see Denton

THORPE, FRANK
Light Of Christmas, The *Xmas,carol
WEINBERGER s.p.   (T1019)

THORTON
Honor Thy Father And Thy Mother *Bibl
SA/2pt jr cor oct PRO ART 2077 $.25 (T1020)

THOSE WHO TRUST IN THE LORD see Zimmermann,
Heinz Werner

THOU ALL-TRANSCENDENT DEITY see Palestrina,
Giovanni, Jesu, Rex Admirabilis

THOU ARE MY SOUL'S DELIGHT see Palestrina,
Giovanni, Pars Mea Dominus

THOU ART ALL MY TREASURE THOU see Lekberg, Sven

THOU ART GREAT see Des Prez, Josquin

THOU ART HE see Pasquet, Jean

THOU ART JESUS, SAVIOR AND LORD see Schutz,
Heinrich

THOU ART MIGHTY see Haydn, (Johann) Michael,
Exultabunt Sancti

THOU ART MY GOD see Roff, Joseph

THOU ART MY LAMP see Paul

THOU ART MY LIFE see Norden, Hugo

THOU ART OUR BREAD AND WINE see Davis,
Katherine K.

THOU ART PETER see Palestrina, Giovanni, Tu Es
Petrus

THOU ART SO WEAK, SO FRAIL, SO HELPLESS *Xmas,
Fr
(Field, Robert) SA,pno,fl,fing.cym. (easy)
PRESSER $.35   (T1021)

THOU ART THE CHRIST see Hughes

THOU ART THE KING OF GLORY see Handel, George
Frideric

THOU ART THE KING OF GLORY see Klein

THOU ART THE KING OF GLORY see Thompson

THOU ART THE LIVING CHRIST see Wilson, Ira B.

THOU ART THE LORD OF HEAVEN see Harris, Jerry
Weseley

THOU ART THE QUEEN OF ALL HEAVEN see Lassus,
Roland de (Orlandus), Ave Regina Coelorum

THOU ART THE WAY see Gustafson, D.

THOU ART THE WAY see Mueller, Carl F.

THOU ART THE WAY see Peninger, David

THOU ART THE WAY see Richardson

THOU ART THE WAY see Roff, Joseph

THOU ART THE WAY see Steel, Christopher
[Charles]

THOU ART THE WAY see Talmadge, Charles L.

THOU ART THE WAY see Warner, Richard

THOU ART WORTHY see Pooler, Frank

THOU ART WORTHY OF PRAISE see Haydn, (Franz)
Joseph, Du Bist's Dem Ruhm Und Ehre
Gebuhret

THOU, BETHLEHEM see Wilson, Ira B.

THOU CROWNEST THE YEAR see Berridge, A.

THOU CROWNEST THE YEAR see Clare, Edwyn A.

THOU DOST KEEP HIM IN PERFECT PEACE see Young,
Robert H.

THOU GOD AND FATHER IN HEAVEN ABOVE see Schutz,
Heinrich

THOU GOD OF ALL see Moore, Robert

THOU GOEST TO JERUSALEM see Franck, Melchior

THOU GRACIOUS AND MOST HOLY LORD see Davis,
Katherine K.

THOU, GRACIOUS LORD, ART MY DEFENSE see
Gretchaninov, Alexander Tikhonovitch

THOU GUIDE see Bach, Johann Sebastian, Du Hirte
Israel, Hore

THOU GUIDE OF ISRAEL see Bach, Johann
Sebastian, Du Hirte Israel, Hore

THOU HALLOWED CHOSEN MORN see Lockwood, Normand

THOU HAST A WORK FOR ME TO DO see Robson, R.
Walker

THOU HAST BEEN GRACIOUS, LORD see Gabrieli,
Giovanni, Benedixisti, Domine

THOU HAST GIVEN ABUNDANCE TO THY SERVANT see
Berger, Jean

THOU HAST GIVEN HIM see Thompson, Randall

THOU HAST GIVEN US BREAD see Geisler, Johan C.

THOU HAST HEARD MY CRY see Kjelson

THOU HAST LOVED RIGHTEOUSNESS see Pinkham,
Daniel

THOU HAST MADE ME see Berkeley, Lennox

THOU HAST MADE ME see Harris, William Henry

THOU HAST MADE US FOR THYSELF see Roff, Joseph

THOU HIDDEN SOURCE see Bortniansky, Dimitri
Stepanovitch

THOU HOLY, LORD GOD see Kocher

THOU HOPE OF EVERY CONTRITE HEART see Thompson

THOU, JESU, SON OF GOD see Bach, Johann
Christoph, Dir, Jesu, Gottes Sohn

THOU KNOWEST, LORD see Purcell, Henry, Thou
Knowest, Lord, The Secrets Of Our Hearts

THOU KNOWEST, LORD THE SECRETS OF MY HEART see
Purcell, Henry

THOU KNOWEST LORD, THE SECRETS OF OUR HEARTS
see Morley, Thomas

THOU KNOWEST, LORD, THE SECRETS OF OUR HEARTS
see Purcell, Henry

THOU LIFE OF LIFE see Tchesnokov, Pavel
Grigorievitch

THOU LIFE OF OUR LIFE see Tschesnokoff, P.I.

THOU, LORD, ALL PRAISE AND HONOR COMMANDETH see
Haydn, (Franz) Joseph

THOU LORD, ART OUR SHEPHERD see Gregor

THOU, LORD, OF GLORY AND HONOUR ART WORTHY see
Haydn, (Franz) Joseph

THOU, LORD, OUR REFUGE see Mendelssohn-
Bartholdy, Felix

THOU, LORD, THE REFUGE OF THE MEEK see Des
Prez, Josquin

THOU LOVEDST ME see Freestone

THOU MARTYRED LAMB, IN DARKEST TOMB IMPRISONED
see Bach, Johann Sebastian

THOU MUST LEAVE THY LOWLY DWELLING see Berlioz,
Hector

THOU MUST LEAVE THY LOWLY DWELLING see Titcomb

THOU, O GOD, ART PRAISED IN SION see Corfe,
Joseph

THOU, O GOD, ART PRAISED IN SION see
Macpherson, Charles

THOU, O GOD, ART PRAISED IN ZION see Steel,
Christopher [Charles]

THOU O LORD see Nystedt, Knut

THOU, O LORD, ART MY SHEPHERD see Marcello,
Benedetto

THOU, O LORD, ART OUR FATHER see Sullivan, Sir
Arthur Seymour

THOU, O LORD, JOY OF MY HEART see Bach, Johann Sebastian, Jesu, Meines Herzens Freud'

THOU PREPAREST A TABLE see Hovhaness, Alan

THOU REFUGE OF THE DESTITUTE see Des Prez, Josquin, Tu Pauperum Refugium

THOU SANCTIFIED FIRE see Bach, Johann Sebastian, Du Heilige Brunst

THOU SHALT CALL HIS NAME JESUS see Posegate

THOU SHALT GUIDE ME see Roff, Joseph

THOU SHALT KEEP THE SABBATH HOLY see Fuhrer, Robert, Mass In C

THOU SHALT LOVE THE LORD, THY GOD see Amram, David Werner

THOU SHALT LOVE THE LORD THY GOD see Glarum, L. Stanley

THOU SHALT LOVE THE LORD THY GOD see Roff, Joseph

THOU SHALT NO MORE BE TERMED FORSAKEN see Ben-Haim, Paul

THOU SHALT REJOICE IN THE LORD see Paul

THOU SHEPHERD OF MY SOUL see Lovelace, Austin C.

THOU SPIRIT OF LOVE DIVINE see Chapman, Edward T.

THOU SPIRIT OF LOVE DIVINE see Mahler, Gustav

THOU THAT LIFE AND DEATH ORDAINST see Bach, Johann Sebastian, Herrscher Uber Tod Und Leben

THOU, THE ALL-HOLY see Gibbons, Orlando

THOU, THE TRUE AND ONLY LIGHT see Mendelssohn-Bartholdy, Felix

THOU VERY GOD AND DAVID'S SON see Bach, Johann Sebastian, Du Wahrer Gott Und Davids Sohn

THOU VISITEST THE EARTH see Greene

THOU VISITEST THE EARTH see Greene, Maurice

THOU VISITEST THE EARTH see Rowley

THOU VISITEST THE EARTH see Waters, Charles F.

THOU WEARY WORLD see Brahms, Johannes, Ach, Arme Welt

THOU, WHO ART ALL HOLY see Haydn, (Franz) Joseph

THOU WHO ART PEACE ETERNAL see Pasquet, Jean

THOU WHO ART THREE see Praetorius, Michael, Der Du Bist Drey

THOU WHO HAST TAUGHT US see Pasquet, Jean

THOU WHO LOVEST LITTLE CHILDREN see Emig, Lois

THOU WHO WAST GOD see Davis, Katherine K.

THOU WHOSE BIRTH ON EARTH see Pasfield, W.R.

THOU WHOSE REDEEMING SACRIFICE see Rossini, Gioacchino, O Salutaris Hostia

THOU WILT KEEP HIM see Peery

THOU WILT KEEP HIM see Schroth

THOU WILT KEEP HIM see Wesley, Samuel Sebastian Jr.

THOU WILT KEEP HIM IN PEACE see Kirk

THOU WILT KEEP HIM IN PERFECT PEACE see Bright, Houston

THOU WILT KEEP HIM IN PERFECT PEACE see Buck, Dudley

THOU WILT KEEP HIM IN PERFECT PEACE see Coggin, Elwood

THOU WILT KEEP HIM IN PERFECT PEACE see Frank, Rene

THOU WILT KEEP HIM IN PERFECT PEACE see Fryxell, Regina Holmen

THOU WILT KEEP HIM IN PERFECT PEACE see Holloway, Lorraine

THOU WILT KEEP HIM IN PERFECT PEACE see Hughes

THOU WILT KEEP HIM IN PERFECT PEACE see Kretz

THOU WILT KEEP HIM IN PERFECT PEACE see Matthews, H.

THOU WILT KEEP HIM IN PERFECT PEACE see Redman, Reginald

THOU WILT KEEP HIM IN PERFECT PEACE see Schutz, Heinrich

THOU WILT KEEP HIM IN PERFECT PEACE see Speaks, [Oley]

THOU WILT KEEP HIM IN PERFECT PEACE see Wesley, Samuel Sebastian Jr.

THOU WILT KEEP HIM IN PERFECT PEACE see Williams, Charles Lee

THOU WILT KEEP HIM IN PERFECT PEACE see Williams, Clifton

THOU WILT KEEP HIM IN PERFECT PEACE see Winans

THOU WILT KEEP HIM IN PERFECT PEACE see Young, Gordon

THOU WILT LIGHT MY CANDLE see Youse, Glad [Robinson]

THOU WRETCHED WORLD, DECEIVEST ME see Brahms, Johannes

THOUGH DEEP HAS BEEN MY FALLING see Lassus, Roland de (Orlandus), Aus Meiner Sunden Tiefe

THOUGH GREAT OUR SINS AND SORE OUR WOES see Bach, Johann Sebastian, Ob Bei Uns Is Der Sunden Viel

THOUGH I SPEAK WITH THE TONGUES OF MEN see Bairstow, Edward Cuthbert

THOUGH I SPEAK WITH THE TONGUES OF MEN see Read, Gardner

THOUGH I SPEAK WITH THE TONGUES OF MEN AND OF ANGELS see Rapley

THOUGH THE FIG TREE DO NOT BLOSSOM see Goldman, E.

THOUGH WORMS DESTROY MY BODY see Bach, Johann Sebastian, Der Leib Zwar In Der Erden

THOUGH YOUR SINS BE AS SCARLET see Doane, [William Howard]

THOUGH YOUR SINS BE AS SCARLET see McCluskey

THOUGH YOUR SINS BE AS SCARLET see Wilson

THOUGHT OF GOD, THE see Lovelace, Austin C.

THOUGHT OF JESUS, THE *Commun
(Harris) SATB oct PRO ART 2345 $.25   (T1022)

THOUGHTS ON A WONDEROUS EVENT see Stafford, Dave

THOUSAND STARS, A see Cavalieri

THREE "ADORAMUS TE" SETTINGS see Perti, Giacomo Antonio

THREE ADVENT CHORALES see Cruger, Johann

THREE ALLELUIAS FOR CHRISTMAS see Goodman, Joseph

THREE AMENS
4pt mix cor,acap oct SCHIRM.G 5313 $.20
    contains: Gibbons, Orlando, Threefold Amen,
    "Dresden Amen"; Stainer, John, Sevenfold
    Amen   (T1023)

THREE AMERICAN FOLK CAROLS *CC3U,Xmas,carol
(Hyde, Derek) SSA oct GRAY GCMR 2992 $.25
                                            (T1024)

THREE ANTHEMS see Merbecke, John

THREE ANTHEMS FOR BEGINNING CHOIRS see Leaf, Robert

THREE ANTHEMS FOR EASTER see Sterne, Colin

THREE ANTHEMS OF PRAISE see Wade, Walter

THREE ANTHEMS see Berger, Jean

THREE ANTHEMS see Reger, Max

THREE AUSTRIAN CAROLS see Track, Gerhard

THREE BACH CHORALES see Bach, Johann Sebastian

THREE BELL CAROLS FOR JUNIOR CHOIRS see Hadler

THREE BLESSINGS see Beckwith, John Christmas

THREE CALLS TO WORSHIP FOR JUNIORS see Caldwell

THREE CAMPAIGN SONGS see Noe, J.T.

THREE CANADIAN CAROLS see Garlick

THREE CANTICLES see Tapscott, Carl

THREE CANTICLES AND A MOTET FOR THE EASTER VIGIL SERVICE see Zgodava

THREE CANTICLES FOR CHORUS see Davidson

THREE CANTICLES FOR THE EASTER VIGIL see Doherty, Christopher

THREE CANTICLES FOR TREBLE VOICES see Liljestrand, Paul

THREE CANTICLES OF THOMAS A KEMPIS see Nevens, David

THREE CANZONCINE see Parodi, Lorenzo

THREE CAROLS FOR CHRISTMAS see Grundman

THREE CAROLS FOR CHRISTMAS see Ratcliffe, Desmond

THREE CAROLS FOR CHRISTMAS AND NEW YEAR *CC3U, Xmas,carol
SATB (easy) ABINGDON APM-137 $.20 contains
works by: Davies; Westbrook, Francis B.;
Frost   (T1025)

THREE CAROLS FOR CHRIST'S NATIVITY see Bennett, F. Roy

THREE CAROLS FOR SAB *Xmas,carol
(Aufdemberge, E.) SAB,acap (easy) oct
CONCORDIA 98-2132 $.30
    contains: Behold, A Branch Is Growing; From
    Heaven High, O Angels, Come; Maria Walks
    Amid The Thorn   (T1026)

THREE CAROLS FOR THE NATIVITY see Bennett, F. Roy

THREE CAROLS IN UNISON see Hall

THREE CAROLS OF THE NATIVITY see Rimmer, Frederick

THREE CAROLS ON OLD TEXTS see Childs, Barney

THREE CAROLS *carol
(Russell) SSA,acap (easy) OXFORD 83.009 $.25
    contains: Glory To God; He Smiles Within
    His Cradle; Mary, Flower Of Flowers   (T1027)

THREE CAROLS *see Balulalow; Balulalow (T1028)

THREE CAROLS see Heseltine, Philip

THREE CAROLS see Wishart

THREE CAROLS see Wishart

THREE CHORAL-MOTETTEN see Schumann, Georg

THREE CHORAL PSALMS see Schutz, Heinrich

THREE CHORAL SETTINGS see Thomas, Kurt

THREE CHORAL SONGS FOR CHRISTMAS see Praetorius, Michael

THREE CHORAL SONGS OF PRAISE see Thiman, Eric Harding

THREE CHORALES FOR EASTER AND ASCENSION see Schutz, Heinrich

THREE CHORALES FOR LENT AND HOLY WEEK see Praetorius, Michael

THREE CHORALES IN MODERN STYLE see Kirk, T.

THREE CHORALES, SET I see Bach, Johann Sebastian

THREE CHORALES, SET II see Bach, Johann Sebastian

THREE CHORALES see Bach, Johann Sebastian

THREE CHORALES see Bach, Johann Sebastian

THREE CHORALES see Bach, Johann Sebastian

THREE CHORALES see Bach, Johann Sebastian

THREE CHORALES see Bach, Johann Sebastian

THREE CHORALES *chorale
(Filkins) SSA oct PRO ART 1367 $.25
    contains: O Blessed Jesu; Sorrows Thou Art
    Bearing, The; When Life Begins To Fail Me
                                            (T1029)

THREE CHRISTMAS ANTHEMS see Ehret, Walter

THREE CHRISTMAS ANTHEMS FOR SA VOICES see Powell, Robert J.

THREE CHRISTMAS CAROLS, SET 1 *see Christ-Child Smiles, The; Come In, Dear Angels;
Dear Nightingale Awake   (T1030)

THREE CHRISTMAS CAROLS, SET 2 *see Carol Of
The Good Thief; O Gay Is The Day We Sing; O
Little Christ Sweet   (T1031)

THREE CHRISTMAS CAROLS see Brown

THREE CHRISTMAS CAROLS *Xmas,carol
(Willcocks) SATB,acap (med) OXFORD 43.340
$.30
    contains: Away In A Manger; I Saw Three
    Ships; Rocking   (T1032)

THREE CHRISTMAS CAROLS see Brown, J.

THREE CHRISTMAS CAROLS see Bennett, F. Roy

THREE CHRISTMAS CAROLS see Davis, Katherine K.

THREE CHRISTMAS CAROLS see Guerrero, Francisco

THREE CHRISTMAS CAROLS see Praetorius, Michael

THREE CHRISTMAS CAROLS *Xmas,carol
(Martin) 2pt oct PRO ART 2173 $.30
    contains: Angels We Have Heard On High;
    Bring A Torch Jeannette, Isabella; Holly
    And The Ivy, The   (T1033)

THREE CHRISTMAS CAROLS *Xmas,carol
(Whitehead) SATB ALLANS 213 s.p.
    contains: Christ Child Smiles; Come In,
    Dear Angels; Dear Nightingale Awake   (T1034)

THREE CHRISTMAS CAROLS *Xmas,carol
(Schultz, R.) SAB,acap (med easy) oct
CONCORDIA 98-1563 $.25
    contains: Away In A Manger; From Heaven
    Above To Earth I Come; Softly Sleep,
    Jesus   (T1035)

THREE CHRISTMAS CAROLS *CC3U,Xmas,carol
(Whitehead, Alfred) mix cor CURWEN 80744 s.p.
                                            (T1036)

THREE CHRISTMAS CAROLS *Xmas,carol
(Parker) SA,org/harp oct LAWSON 51539 $.40
    contains: Coverdale's Carol; Irish Carol;
    Wexford Carol   (T1037)

THREE CHRISTMAS CAROLS see Whitehead, Alfred

THREE CHRISTMAS HYMNS AND CAROLS *Xmas,carol/
hymn
SSA,acap (easy) oct CONCORDIA 98-1429 $.20
    contains: Markworth, Henry, Let Us All With
    Gladsome Voice; Stellhorn, August W.,
    Come, Your Hearts And Voices Raising;
    Stellhorn, August W., Hark, Now, O
    Shepherds   (T1038)

THREE CHRISTMAS LAUDE *It,15th cent
(Mishkin, H.) TTBB,acap SCHIRM.EC 2107 $.30
    contains: Dimmi, Dolce Maria; Ecco'l
    Messia; O Maria, Diana Stella   (T1039)

THREE CHRISTMAS SCENES see McCormick

THREE CHRISTMAS SETTINGS see Kaminski, Heinrich

THREE CHRISTMAS SONGS see Jerrett, Jack

THREE CHRISTMAS SPIRITUALS see Page, R.

THREE CONCERT MOTETS see Grandi, Alessandro

THREE CONTEMPORARY MADRIGALS see Butler, Eugene

THREE DESCANTS see Kohn

THREE DEVOTIONAL MOTETS see Giannini, V.

THREE DEVOTIONAL SONGS see Johnston, Jack

THREE EARLY AMERICAN ANTHEMS *CC3U,anthem,US
 (Wienandt) SATB oct AGAPE US 1770 $.45
   contains works by: Billings; Holden;
   Stickney   (T1040)

THREE EARLY AMERICAN CHRISTMAS CAROLS see
 Owens, Barbara

THREE EARLY AMERICAN CHRISTMAS SETTINGS see
 Young, Carlton R.

THREE EARLY CHRISTMAS CAROLS *Xmas,carol
 (Powell, R.J.) TTB,acap (easy) oct CONCORDIA
 98-1887 $.30
   contains: Coventry Carol; Make We Joy;
   Masters In This Hall (Fr)   (T1041)

THREE EARLY LITURGICAL SETTINGS see Anonymous

THREE EASTER CAROLS see Meek, Kenneth

THREE EASTER CAROLS see Whitehead, Alfred

THREE EASTER CAROLS (2ND SET) see Whitehead,
 Alfred

THREE EASTER CHORALES see Cruger, Johann

THREE EASTER HYMNS *Easter/Lent,hymn
 (Martin) 2pt oct PRO ART 2257 $.25
   contains: Now All Bells Are Ringing; See
   The Conqueror Mounts In Triumph; We
   Welcome Glad Easter   (T1042)

THREE EASY ANTHEMS see Crampton, T.

THREE FAMOUS CANONS *canon
 (Ritz, James) SAB,pno oct WESTWOOD SM-1367-7
 $.90
   contains: Anonymous, Dona Nobis Pacem;
   Byrd, William, Non Nobis Domine; Tallis,
   Thomas, Tallis' Canon   (T1043)

THREE FESTIVAL MUSIC LITURGY see Binder,
 Abraham Wolfe

THREE FESTIVE CAROLS see Pitfield, Thomas Baron

THREE FOR CHRISTMAS see Anderson, Marion

THREE FRENCH CAROLS *Xmas,carol,Fr
 (Hyde) SSA,acap,opt pno oct PRO ART 2565 $.30
   contains: Born Is He; Gabriel's Message;
   Masters In This Hall   (T1044)

THREE FRENCH CAROLS (NOELS) *Xmas,anthem/
 carol,Fr
 (Miller, M.R.) SATB (easy) oct GIA G1043 $.60
   contains: Good Shepherds; Joseph's Sorrow;
   Who's At The Door?   (T1045)

THREE FRENCH NOELS see Mc Graw

THREE FUGUING TUNES see Billings, William

THREE GENERAL CHORUSES *Gen
 (Barthelson) 2pt oct PRO ART 2382 $.30
   contains: Glory To The Father Give; Jesus,
   Tender Shepherd; Thy Word Is Like A
   Garden, Lord   (T1046)

THREE GENERAL HYMNS *Gen,hymn
 (Martin) 2pt oct PRO ART 2171 $.30
   contains: I Would Be True; Rejoice Ye Pure
   In Heart; This Is My Father's World   (T1047)

THREE GOOD CITIZENS see Martin

THREE GRADUALS FOR THE CHURCH YEAR see
 Bruckner, Anton

THREE HARVEST HOME CHORALES see Ives, Charles

THREE HEBREW PSALMS see Braz, M.

THREE HOLY KINGS, THE see Pablo, Juan

THREE HOLY WOMEN see Carol, N.

THREE HUNDRED AND EIGHT-NINE FOUR PART CHORALES
 see Bach, Johann Sebastian

THREE HUNDRED SEVENTEEN CHORALES AND SACRED
 ARIAS, VOL. 1, ONE HUNDRED NINETY FIVE
 CHORALES AND SACRED ARIAS see Bach, Johann
 Sebastian

THREE HUNDRED SEVENTEEN CHORALES AND SACRED
 ARIAS, VOL. 2, ONE HUNDRED TWENTY TWO
 CHORALES AND SACRED ARIAS see Bach, Johann
 Sebastian

THREE HYMN ARRANGEMENTS see Markworth, Henry

THREE HYMN ARRANGEMENTS see Markworth, Henry

THREE HYMN TUNE ANTHEMS see Jones, Hilton Kean

THREE HYMN TUNES (SET 1) see Beaumont, Rev.
 Geoffrey

THREE HYMN TUNES (SET 2) see Simpson, Reginald

THREE HYMN TUNES (SET 3) see Simpson, Reginald

THREE HYMNS IN MODERN STYLE see Palmer, Jane

THREE HYMNS OF THE CHURCH see Charpentier,
 Marc-Antoine

THREE HYMNS TO THE VIRGIN see Aston, Peter

THREE-IN-ONE-IN-THREE see Felciano, Richard

THREE INTRADAS FOR ADVENT AND CHRISTMAS see
 Altenburg

THREE INTROITS see Whitlock, Percy

THREE INTROITS FOR FESTIVAL WORSHIP see Scott,
 Sarah

THREE INTROITS see Berger, Jean

THREE JUNIOR CHOIR ANTHEMS see Dressler, John

THREE KINGS *Xmas,carol
 see Three Spanish Carols
 unis/SATB (easy) OXFORD 08.080 $.15   (T1048)
 (Romeu, L.) SATB,acap oct PRESSER 332-13267
 $.30   (T1049)

THREE KINGS see Barnes, [Edward Shippen]

THREE KINGS see Gallus, Jacobus, Omnes De Saba

THREE KINGS see Hoggard

THREE KINGS see Willan, Healey

THREE KINGS, THE see Gibbs, [Cecil] Armstrong

THREE KINGS FROM PERSIAN LANDS see Cornelius,
 Peter

THREE KINGS FROM PERSIAN LANDS AFAR *Xmas
 unis (med) OXFORD 08.190 $.20   (T1050)

THREE KINGS FROM PERSIAN LANDS AFAR see
 Cornelius, Peter

THREE KINGS IN GREAT GLORY *Xmas,carol
 unis/SATB (easy) OXFORD 08.194 $.15   (T1051)

THREE KINGS IN GREAT GLORY see Shaw

THREE KINGS OF ORIENT, THE *Xmas
 (Forcucci) SAB,acap,opt perc oct PRO ART 2712
 $.35   (T1052)
 (Forcucci) SSA,acap,opt perc oct PRO ART 2716
 $.35   (T1053)
 (Forcucci) SATB,opt perc oct PRO ART 2651
 $.35   (T1054)

THREE KINGS, THE *Xmas,carol/folk,Belg/Span
 see Belgian Christmas Songs, Set 2
 (Forbes) 4pt mix cor,acap oct SCHIRM.G 11137
 $.30   (T1055)
 (Kirk) SATB oct SHAPIRO SK 2072 $.30   (T1056)
 (Kirk) 2pt oct SHAPIRO SK 4021 $.25   (T1057)
 (Kirk) SAB oct SHAPIRO SK 5014 $.30   (T1058)
 (Kirk) SSA oct SHAPIRO SK 3025 $.30   (T1059)

THREE KINGS, THE see Cornelius

THREE KINGS, THE see Cornelius, Peter

THREE KINGS, THE see Dietrich, Fritz

THREE KINGS, THE see Ehret, Walter

THREE KINGS, THE see Gevaert, Francois Auguste

THREE KINGS, THE see Willan, Healey

THREE LENTEN AND EASTER HYMNS see Martini,
 Padre

THREE LENTEN CHORUSES see Udulutsch

THREE LENTEN POEMS OF RICHARD CRASHAW see
 Pinkham, Daniel

THREE LENTEN SCENES see Williams, David H.

THREE LILIES, THE see Gaul, Harvey Bartlet

[THREE] LITANIAE DOMINI see Palestrina,
 Giovanni

THREE LITTLE SACRED CONCERTOS see Schutz,
 Heinrich

THREE LITURGICAL AMENS see Berlinski, [Herman]

THREE LITURGICAL PRAYERS *CC3U,liturg
 (Ziemer, C.) oct AGAPE WR 1001 $.40 contains
 works by: Gretchaninov; Kalinnikov;
 Tchaikovsky   (T1060)

THREE MAGNIFICATS see Taverner, John

THREE MEDIEVAL LYRICS see Mathias, William

THREE MEDIEVAL SONGS see Hoddinott, Alun

THREE MENNONITE CHRISTMAS HYMNS *Xmas,hymn
 (Parker) SATB,acap oct LAWSON 51445 $.30
   contains: Song Of The Angel; Song Of The
   Virgin; Songs At The Stable   (T1061)

THREE MORAVIAN CAROLS *Xmas,carol,Morav
 (Tate) unis (easy) OXFORD 45.064 $.50 (T1062)

THREE MORE GENERAL CHORUSES *Gen
 (Barthelson) 2pt oct PRO ART 2384 $.30
   contains: Children Of The Heavenly Father;
   Jesus Called; Little Children, Praise The
   Saviour   (T1063)

THREE MOTETS FOR A CAPELLA see Nielsen, Carl

THREE MOTETS FOR BENEDICTION see Goodman,
 Joseph

THREE MOTETS FOR CHORUS AND SOLO see
 Mendelssohn-Bartholdy, Felix

THREE MOTETS FOR ORGAN see Howells, Herbert
 Norman

THREE MOTETS IN HONOR OF THE BLESSED SACRAMENT
 *Commun/Gen,anthem/Bene/mot
 (Lee, J.) SATB (easy) oct GIA G1515 $.60
   contains: Lee, Let Us Adore For All
   Eternity; Lee, Psalm 116; Schein, Johann
   Hermann, O Saving Victim; Tartini,
   Giuseppe, Down In Adoration Falling (T1064)

THREE MOTETS see Des Prez, Josquin

THREE MOTETS see Gabrieli, Giovanni

THREE MOTETS see Diemente, Edward

THREE MOTETS see De Wert

THREE MOTETS see Foss, Julius

THREE MOTETS see Fuller, [Esther Mary]

THREE MOTETS see Morley, Thomas

THREE MOTETS see Nystedt, Knut

THREE MOTETS see Rubbra, Edmund

THREE NATIVITY CAROLS *Xmas,carol
 (Hyde) SSA,acap,opt pno oct PRO ART 2392 $.25
   contains: Lute-Book Lullaby; Tyrolean
   Cradle Song; What Is That Fragrance (T1065)

THREE NOELS see Grundman

[THREE] OFFERTORIES see Schubert, Franz (Peter)

THREE OLD BOHEMIAN CHRISTMAS CAROLS *Xmas,
 carol,Boh
 (Riedel) mix cor,acap oct SCHIRM.G 2624 $.30
   contains: Angels And The Shepherds, The;
   Hail, All Hail The Glorious Morn; Let All
   Men Sing God's Praises   (T1066)

THREE OR FOUR OR MORE *CCU,anthem
 SSA/TTBB/SSATTBB LORENZ $1.50   (T1067)

THREE ORIGINAL CAROLS FOR JUNIOR CHOIR see
 Baker

THREE ORIGINAL CAROLS FOR JUNIOR CHOIR see
 Baker, Dwight B.

THREE PART ANTHEM BOOK see Mueller, Carl F.

THREE-PART CHORUSES FOR MALE VOICES *CCU
 3pt men cor SCHMITT 44 $.50   (T1068)

THREE-PART PSALMS see Le Jeune, Claude

THREE-PART TREBLE CHOIR NO. 1 *CCU,anthem
 3pt treb cor LORENZ $1.75   (T1069)

THREE-PART TREBLE CHOIR NO. 2 *CCU,anthem
 3pt treb cor LORENZ $1.75   (T1070)

THREE-PART TREBLE CHOIR NO. 3 *CCU,anthem
 3pt treb cor LORENZ $1.75   (T1071)

THREE PASSION CHORALES AND THEIR SECULAR
 ANCESTORS *CC3U,Psntd,chorale
 (Erb) [Eng/Lat] SATB,acap oct LAWSON 51573
 $.40   (T1072)

THREE PASSION MOTETS see Lassus, Roland de
 (Orlandus)

THREE POLISH CAROLS *Xmas,carol,Pol
 (Erhart) SATB,acap (very easy) OXFORD 43.048
 $.25
   contains: Cradle Song; Little Jesus; Star
                                        (T1073)

THREE POLISH CHRISTMAS CAROLS *CC3U,Xmas,
 carol,Pol
 (Hopkins, H.) SATB oct PRESSER 312-21227 $.30
                                        (T1074)

THREE PRAYERS FOR TODAY see Roff, Joseph

THREE PSALM MOTETS see Pinkham, Daniel

THREE PSALMS see Elmore, Robert [Hall]

[THREE] PSALMS see Des Prez, Josquin

THREE PSALMS OF DAVID see Milhaud, Darius

THREE PSALMS see Ben-Haim, Paul

THREE PSALMS see Des Prez, Josquin

THREE PSALMS see Lassus, Roland de (Orlandus)

THREE PSALMS see Mobach, E.

THREE PUERTO RICAN CAROLS see Pablo, Juan

THREE RESPONSORIES see Goodman, Joseph

THREE RIDERS, THE see Grieb

THREE SACRED CHORUSES [OP.37] see Brahms,
 Johannes

THREE SACRED CHORUSES [OP.37] see Brahms,
 Johannes

THREE SACRED CHORUSES see Brahms, Johannes

THREE SACRED CHORUSES see Brahms, Johannes

THREE SACRED CHORUSES see Martini, Padre

THREE SACRED CONCERTOS see Schutz, Heinrich

THREE SACRED MOTETS *CC3U,mot
 (Gardner) SATB oct STAFF 615 $.30   (T1075)

THREE SACRED MOTETS see Charpentier, Marc-
 Antoine

THREE SACRED PIECES see Krenek, Ernst

THREE SAYINGS OF JESUS see Merbecke, John

THREE SEASONAL ANTHEMS FOR JUNIOR CHOIR see
 Smart, David

THREE SEASONS see Newbury, Kent A.

THREE SETTINGS FROM THE BAY PSALM BOOK see
 Beeson, Jack Hamilton

THREE SETTINGS OF THE TWENTY THIRD PSALM see
 London, Edwin

THREE SHAKER SONGS *see O The Beautiful
 Treasure; Aks, Come To Zion, Sin Sick Souls
                                        (T1076)

THREE SHAKER SONGS see Aks

THREE SHEPHERD CAROLS see Freed

THREE SHORT ANTHEMS FOR BOY'S VOICES see
 Hurford, Peter

THREE SHORT HOLY WEEK ANTHEMS see Newbury, Kent A.

THREE SHORT PSALMS see Young, Gordon

THREE SIMPLE MELODIES see Zimmermann

THREE SONGS FOR CHRISTMAS *Xmas,carol
(Grundman) oct SA,band/orch BOOSEY 1963 $.30,
ipa; SSA,band/orch BOOSEY 1964 $.30, ipa;
SAB,band/orch BOOSEY 5410 $.30, ipa; SATB,
band/orch BOOSEY 1965 $.30, ipa; TTBB,band/
orch BOOSEY 1962 $.30, ipa
contains: Angels We Have Heard On High;
Bring A Torch; What Child Is This?
(T1077)

THREE SONGS FOR HANUKAH see Shur, Bonia

THREE SONGS OF MOURNING see Bach, Johann
Christoph

THREE SONGS OF PRAISE see Roy, Klaus George

THREE SONGS OF THE CRIB see Mac Nutt, Walter

THREE SONGS TO CHILDREN see Barnes, M.H.

THREE SPANISH CAROLS *Xmas,carol,Span
(Davies) unis oct CURWEN 11125 $.25
contains: Fum! Fum! Fum!; Shepherds, Come
Before Him; Three Kings
(T1078)

THREE SPANISH CHRISTMAS CAROLS *see E La Don,
Don, Sweet Virgin Mary; Riu, Riu, Chiu;
Sons Of Eve, Reward My Tidings
(T1079)

THREE SPIRITUALS see Zimmermann, Heinz Werner

[THREE] TANTUM ERGO see Schubert, Franz (Peter)

THREE THANKSGIVING HYMNS *Thanks,hymn
(Martin) 2pt oct PRO ART 2260 $.30
contains: Come Ye Thankful People Come; On
The First Thanksgiving Day; We Gather
Together
(T1080)

THREE TRAITORS *carol
SATB (med easy) OXFORD 08.161 $.15
(T1081)

THREE TREBLE CHOIR ANTHEMS see Powell, Robert J.

THREE VERNACULAR MOTETS see Crone, R.

THREE WEDDING MOTETS !Gen/Marriage,anthem/mot
(Dooner, A.) [Eng/Lat] unis/SA/TB (easy)
cmplt ed GIA G1347 $.75
contains: Arcadelt, Jacob, Ave Maria;
Franck, Cesar, Panis Angelicus; Mozart,
Wolfgang Amadeus, Ave Verum
(T1082)

THREE WISE KINGS see Cooke, Arnold

THREE WOMEN WENT FORTH see Matthews, H.

THREE YUGOSLAV FOLKSONGS *see Mary, Mary,
Maiden
(T1083)

THREEFOLD AMEN see Gibbons, Orlando

THRENI see Stravinsky, Igor

THRON'D HIGH IN HEAVEN see Handel, George
Frideric

THRONE OF GOD see Sowerby, Leo

THRONED UPON THAT AWFUL TREE see Sjolund, Paul

THRONED UPON THE AWEFUL TREE *anthem,Welsh
(Running, Arnold) SAB (easy) oct AUGSBURG
1370 $.25
(T1084)

THRONED UPON THE AWFUL TREE see Hopkins

THROUGH ALL THE CHANGING SCENES OF LIFE see
Hughes, Rita Mea

THROUGH ALL THE WORLD BELOW see McAfee

THROUGH THE DARK THE DREAMERS CAME see Daniels,
Mabel Wheeler

THROUGH THE DAY see Morley, Thomas

THROUGH THE DAY THY LOVE HAS SPARED US see
Bach, Johann Sebastian

THROUGH THE DAY THY LOVE HAS SPARED US see
Willan, Healey

THROUGH THE NIGHT OF DOUBT AND SORROW see Shaw,
Hartin

THRU A PRAYER
SATB BIG3 $.25
(T1085)

THUILLE, LUDWIG (WILHELM ANDREAS MARIA)
(1861-1907)
Lacrimae Christi *Op.23,No.1
(Baumbach, R.) men cor (med) oct LEUCKART
193 s.p.
(T1086)

THUNDER OF THE LORD see Mott

THUS AS MOSES see Schutz, Heinrich, Sicut Moses
Serpentem

THUS DID THE ANGEL SING
(Grant, Louise) SATB oct BELWIN 1706 $.25
(T1087)

THUS SAID THE LORD see Bernardi, Steffano,
Dixit Dominus Domino Meo

THUS SAITH GOD THE LORD see Harris, William
Henry

THUS SAITH THE HIGH, THE LOFTY ONE see
Billings, William

THUS SAITH THE LORD see Billings, William

THUS SAITH THE LORD see Geisler, Johan C.

THUS SAITH THE LORD see Mendelssohn-Bartholdy,
Felix

THUS SAITH THE LORD see Nystedt, Knut

THUS SAITH THE LORD OF HOSTS see Rogers, J.H.

THUS THEN, THE LAW see Bach, Johann Sebastian

THUS WAS HE BORN see Coleman, Jack

THY BLESSINGS, FATHER see Johnson

THY CHILDREN, LORD see Thorne

THY CHURCH, O GOD, HER HEART TO THEE UPRAISETH
see Thiman, Eric Harding

THY CROSS, O JESU, THOU DIDST BEAR *anthem
(Pooler, Frank) SATB&jr cor (easy) oct
AUGSBURG 1154 $.20
(T1088)
(Pooler, Frank) SA&SATB (easy) oct AUGSBURG
1154 $.20
(T1089)

THY CROSS, O JESUS THOU DIDST BEAR see Frylof,
[Harald Leonard]

THY FOLLOW ME see Sateren, Leland Bernhard

THY GIVING POWER see Carter, Elliott Cook, Jr.

THY GIVING POWER see Goodenough, F.

THY GLORIOUS NAME see Fitch

THY GLORY DAWNS, JERUSALEM, AWAKE see Davye,
John F.

THY GOD IS GREAT AND MIGHTY see Durante

THY GUIDING HAND see Reissiger

THY HAND, O GOD, HAS GUIDED see Sateren, Leland
Bernhard

THY HAND UPON MY HEART
SATB CHAPPELL 0017202-358 $.40
(T1090)

THY HOUSE FOREVER see Protheroe, Daniel

THY KING COMETH see Fletcher

THY KINGDOM COME see Berger, Jean

THY KINGDOM COME see Blair, Elizabeth

THY KINGDOM COME see Hopkins

THY KINGDOM COME see Johnson, David N.

THY KINGDOM COME see Pedrette

THY KINGDOM COME see Wood

THY KINGDOM COME, O GOD *hymn,Dut
oct ROYAL 342 s.p.
(T1091)

THY KINGDOM COME, O LORD see Christiansen, F.
Melius

THY KINGDOM COME, O LORD see Wehr, David A.

THY LAW IS AN EVERGREEN see Pasquet, Jean

THY LIFE WAS GIVEN FOR ME see Wienandt, Elwyn
A.

THY LIFE WAS GIVEN TO ME see Wienandt, Elwyn A.

THY LIGHT IS COME see Clough-Leighter, Henry

THY LITTLE ONES *Xmas
(Christiansen, P.) SATB SCHMITT 903 $.25
(T1092)

THY LITTLE ONES, DEAR LORD, ARE WE see Schulz,
Her Kommer Dine Arme Smaa

THY LITTLE ONES, DEAR LORD, ARE WE see Schutz,
Heinrich

THY LITTLE ONES, DEAR LORD, ARE WE see Track,
Gerhard

THY LOVE DECLARE see Roff, Joseph

THY LOVELY SAINTS see Bright

THY MAJESTIC GREATNESS see Brandon

THY MOST RADIANT AND BLESSED BIRTH see Swan

THY NAME WE BLESS see Vulpius, Melchior

THY NAME WE PRAISE see Angell

THY PRAISES SING see Malmin, Gunnar

THY REBUKE HATH BROKEN MY HEART see Goodman,
Joseph

THY SAVIOUR COMES see Williams, David H.

THY SPIRIT ASCENDING see Purcell, Henry

THY SPIRIT FLOWETH FREE see Handel, George
Frideric

THY STATUTES HAVE BEEN MY SONGS see Pinkham,
Daniel

THY TEMPLE IS NOT MADE WITH HANDS see Bitgood,
Roberta

THY TESTIMONIES ARE VERY SURE see Boeringer,
James

THY TRUTH WITHIN *anthem,17th cent
(Sateren, Leland) SATB (med diff) oct
AUGSBURG 1424 $.25
(T1093)

THY WAY NOT MINE O LORD see Stults, R.

THY WAY, NOT MINE, O LORD see Tenney, Mildred

THY WILL BE DONE *anthem
(Brandon) SATB (Maundy Thursday) oct BOURNE
864 $.30
(T1094)

THY WILL BE DONE see Bruckner, Anton

THY WILL BE DONE see Dieterich

THY WILL BE DONE! see Ford, Virgil T.

THY WILL BE DONE see Foster, Will

THY WILL BE DONE see Nelson, Paul

THY WILL BE DONE see Wolf

THY WILL, NOT MINE see Rachmaninoff, Sergey
Vassilievitch

THY WISDOM, LORD, ALL THOUGHT TRANSCENDETH see
Kol Slaven

THY WORD IS A LAMP see Glarum, L. Stanley

THY WORD IS A LAMP see Kirk

THY WORD IS A LAMP see Pasquet, Jean

THY WORD IS A LANTERN see Purcell, Henry

THY WORD IS A LIGHT see Morgan

THY WORD IS LIKE A GARDEN see Lanier, Gary

THY WORD IS LIKE A GARDEN, LORD
see Three General Choruses
(Barthelson) SAB oct PRO ART 2497 $.30
(T1095)

THY WORD IS TRUTH see Gibbs, Alan

THY WORD RESOUND see Thorne, Francis

THY WORD WITH ME SHALL ALWAYS STAY see Berger,
Jean

THY YEARS HAVE NO END see Sateren, Leland
Bernhard

THYGERSON
Child Jesus *Xmas
SATB (med easy) SOUTHERN $.35
(T1096)
SATB SCHMITT 1883 $.35
(T1097)

Consider The Lilies
SSA oct HERITAGE H6003 $.35
(T1098)

Crown Him Lord Of All
SATB oct LORENZ C235 $.30
(T1099)

Crown Him With Many Crowns *Easter
SATB oct SACRED S-50 $.40, ipa
(T1100)

Gloria To God On High *Xmas
SATB oct HERITAGE H62 $.40
(T1101)

How Still, How Still *Xmas
SATB,opt fl/vln SCHMITT 919 $.35
(T1102)

Jesus, The New Born Baby
SATB oct PLYMOUTH JR-165 $.35
(T1103)

Little Star On The Christmas Tree *Xmas
SATB oct HERITAGE H33 $.45
(T1104)

Long Ago In Bethlehem *Xmas
SATB SOUTHERN $.35
(T1105)
SATB oct HERITAGE H70 $.40
(T1106)

Make A Joyful Noise
SATB oct SACRED S-112 $.45
(T1107)

Marching Saints, The
SAT/SAB oct HERITAGE H6504 $.35
(T1108)

New Day, A
SATB oct HERITAGE H30 $.40
(T1109)

No Room In The Inn *Xmas
SATB oct LORENZ 9925 $.30
(T1110)

Praise God In His Sanctuary
SATB oct SACRED S-66 $.35
(T1111)

Right On With Number One!
SATB oct LORENZ 9996 $.35
(T1112)
SATB (med diff/diff) SOUTHERN $.35
(T1113)

Seven Long Days Was The Journey Of The Wise
Men *Xmas,anthem
mix cor HERITAGE H91 $.40
(T1114)

Sing And Rejoice *Xmas
SATB oct SACRED E38 $.40
(T1115)

Sing Merrily To God
SATB oct HERITAGE H67 $.40
(T1116)

Song Of The Shepherd Boy *see Hughes

Teach All Nations
SATB SOUTHERN $.30
(T1117)
SATB (med diff/diff) SOUTHERN $.30
(T1118)
SATB oct SACRED S-127 $.35
(T1119)

Time To Be Alone, A
SATB oct HERITAGE H32 $.40
(T1120)

Tiny Little Baby Boy *Xmas
SATB oct HERITAGE H15 $.40
(T1121)

THYGERSON, ROBERT
Mary's Journey
SATB oct AGAPE AD 1980 $.35
(T1122)

THYRESTAM, GUNNAR
Botpsalm
mix cor NORDISKA 1528 s.p.
(T1123)

Du Dotter Sion, Frojda Dig
mix cor NORDISKA 4504 s.p.
(T1124)

Himmelsfardssang
mix cor NORDISKA 3316 s.p.
(T1125)

Jesu, Gor Mig Angelagen
mix cor NORDISKA 4215 s.p.
(T1126)

Johannes Sag Sa Klar En Syn
mix cor NORDISKA 2418 s.p.
(T1127)

Kom, Helge Ande, Till Mig In *hymn
3pt mix cor NORDISKA 4503 s.p.
(T1128)

THYRESTAM, GUNNAR (cont'd.)

Lik Petrus Jag Pa Villans Stig
mix cor NORDISKA 5424 s.p.   (T1129)

Liten Massa
3pt mix cor NORDISKA 2115 s.p.   (T1130)

Lover Gud I Himmelshojd
(Ahlen, Waldemar) 2pt wom cor/2pt jr cor,
acap NORDISKA 4124 s.p.   (T1131)
(Ahlen, Waldemar) 2pt wom cor/2pt jr cor,
pno,inst NORDISKA 4123 s.p.   (T1132)

Lovsjungen Herren
3pt mix cor NORDISKA 4266 s.p.   (T1133)

Min Gud Och Fader Kare
mix cor NORDISKA 4904 s.p.   (T1134)

Nu Herren Ar Uppstanden
3pt mix cor NORDISKA 2741 s.p.   (T1135)

O Du, Var Herre Jesu Krist
3pt mix cor NORDISKA 2419 s.p.   (T1136)

O Gode Jesu
3pt mix cor NORDISKA 4212 s.p.   (T1137)

O Gud, Som Horer Allas Rost
mix cor NORDISKA 4211 s.p.   (T1138)

O Herre Gud, Gor Nad Med Mig
mix cor NORDISKA 4264 s.p.   (T1139)

O Herre Gud, Vi Bedja Dig
3pt mix cor NORDISKA 2740 s.p.   (T1140)

O, Hoge Konung
mix cor NORDISKA 4267 s.p.   (T1141)

O, Hur Salla Aro Ej De Fromma
mix cor NORDISKA 5270 s.p.   (T1142)

O Jesu Krist, Dig Till Oss Vand
mix cor NORDISKA 3616 s.p.   (T1143)

Oss Ar Fodd Immanuel
mix cor NORDISKA 4268 s.p.   (T1144)

Paskhymn *hymn
mix cor NORDISKA 3614 s.p.   (T1145)

Saliga Aro De, Som Hora Guds Ord
mix cor NORDISKA 3954 s.p.   (T1146)

Se, Detta Ar Guds Lamm
mix cor NORDISKA 2777 s.p.   (T1147)

TIBI LAUS see Lassus, Roland de (Orlandus)

TIBI LAUS, TIBI GLORIA see Philips, Peter

TIBUR see Diepenbrock, Alfons

TICKTON, JASON H.
P'filot Beth El *Sab-Eve
SATB TRANSCON. TCL 764 $1.50   (T1148)

TIDINGS OF COMFORT AND JOY *Xmas,carol
(Luboff, Norman) SATB,opt winds&perc oct
WALTON 2753 $.50, cmplt ed WALTON 2753A
$6.00
contains: First Nowell, The; God Rest Ye
Merry Gentlemen; Whence Comes This Rush
Of Wings   (T1149)

TIDINGS OF COMFORT AND JOY see Porter

TIDINGS OF JOY see Bampton, R.

TIDINGS OF JOY see Blomquist, R.

TIDINGS OF PEACE see Roff, Joseph

TIDINGS TRUE
see Musica Britannica Vol. 4: Set 8

TIENS TA LUMIERE, SOLDAT see Heav'n Boun,
Soldier

TIERCE see Klein, Lothar

TIERIE, J.F.
Lente
mix cor ALSBACH&D sc s.p., cor pts s.p.
(T1150)
Lente En Paaschlied
mix cor ALSBACH&D sc s.p., cor pts s.p.
(T1151)

TIL BORDS I GUDS RIKE see Hovland, Egil

TIL DIG HERRE, TAR JEG MIN TILFLUKT see
Slogedal, Bjarne

TIL DIG JAG ROPAR, HERRE KRIST see Lassus,
Roland de (Orlandus)

TIL MARIAE RENSELSESFEST (MARIA GAR SIN
TEMPELGANG) see Eccard, Johannes

TIL PASKEFESTEN (FOR DENNE PASKEMORGENS FRYD)
see Eccard, Johannes

TIL PINSEFESTEN (DEN HELLIGAND FRA HIMLEN KOM)
see Eccard, Johannes

'TIL THE STORM PASSES BY see Lister, Mosie

TILL DIG ALLENA JESU KRIST
(Vulpius, Melchior) [Swed] SATB,acap GEHRMANS
KRB 320   (T1152)

TILL DIG ALLENA, JESU KRIST see Calvisius,
Sethus

TILL DIG ALLENA, JESU KRIST see Praetorius,
Michael

TILL DIG, HERRE, UPPLYFTER JAG MIN SJAL see
Carlstedt, Gunnemar

TILL TEMPLET JESUSBARNET KOM see Eccard,
Johannes

TILLMAN
Old-Time Power
(Kirk) SATB oct LILLENAS AT-1001 $.30   (T1153)

TIME AND SPACE see Christiansen, Paul

TIME AS HE FLIES see Palestrina, Giovanni

TIME DRAWS NEAR, THE see Graham, Robert [V.]

TIME DRAWS NEAR THE BIRTH OF CHRIST, THE see
Lang, C.S.

TIME FOR ALL THINGS, A see Carpenter, S.M.

TIME FOR JOY, A see Besig

TIME FOR SINGING HAS COME, THE see Jordan,
Alice

TIME OUT! see Adams, J.T.

TIME TO BE ALONE, A see Thygerson

TIME TO BE BORN, A see Silver, Frederick

TIME TO BE GLAD, A see Oxtoby, Charles

TIME TO EVERY PURPOSE see Trythall, Gilbert

TIME TO SING, A *CCUL
(Spurr, Thurlow) SATB voc sc WORD 15012 $1.50
(T1154)

TIME TO SING SOME MORE, A *CCUL
(Spurr, Thurlow) SATB voc sc WORD 20028 $1.50
(T1155)

TIMETE DOMINUM see Brosig, Moritz

TIMETE DOMINUM see Haydn, (Johann) Michael

TIMETE DOMINUM see Skroup, Jan Nepomuk

TIMOR ET TREMOR see Gabrieli, Giovanni

TIMOR ET TREMOR VENERENT SUPER ME see Gabrieli,
Giovanni

TIMOR ET TREMOR VENERUNT SUPER ME see Poulenc,
Francis

TINCANI, ALCESTE
Fior Di Cielo *Xmas
unis/2pt,pno/org ZANIBON 3208 s.p.   (T1156)

TINCTORIS, JOHANNES (ca. 1436-ca. 1476)
Mass Dedicated To Ferdinand King Of Sicily
And Aragon *Mass
(Feldmann, Fritz) cor cmplt ed AM.INST.MUS.
$6.00 see from Opera Omnia Vol. I (T1157)

Opera Omnia Vol. I *see Mass Dedicated To
Ferdinand King Of Sicily And Aragon
(T1158)

TINDLEY
Nothing Between
(Winans) SATB oct LILLENAS AN-1615 $.30
(T1159)

TINEL, EDGAR (1854-1912)
Gelobt Sei Mein Herr Und Gott *Op.36 (from
Franziskus)
4pt mix cor,T solo,2fl,2ob,2clar,2bsn,
4horn,2trp,3trom,tuba,strings,timp
BREITKOPF-W rental   (T1160)

Judge Me, God Of My Salvation
(Lundquist, M.) SATB,acap SCHIRM.EC 2282
$.16   (T1161)

TINY BELLS RANG, THE see Procter, Leland

TINY KING see Eilers

TINY LITTLE BABY BOY see Thygerson

TIPPETT, MICHAEL (1905-   )
Child Of Our Time, A *ora
SATB,SATB soli,orch voc sc SCHOTT 10065
s.p., study sc SCHOTT 10899 s.p.   (T1162)

Epilogue (Non Nobis Domine)
SATB,orch voc sc SCHOTT 10912 s.p., ipr
(T1163)

Magnificat And Nunc Dimittis *Magnif
SATB,org SCHOTT s.p.   (T1164)

Plebs Angelica *mot
[Lat] SSAATTBB SCHOTT s.p.   (T1165)

Vision Of St. Augustine
cor,Bar solo,orch voc sc SCHOTT 10898 s.p.,
study sc SCHOTT 10897 s.p.   (T1166)

Weeping Babe, The *mot
SATB,S solo SCHOTT s.p.   (T1167)

TIRRO
American Jazz Mass *Mass,US
SATB voc sc SUMMY $1.75, ipa   (T1168)

'TIS CHRISTMAS see Roff, Joseph

'TIS CHRISTMAS THIS NIGHT see Hourdeaux

'TIS FINISHED (from Christian Psalmody) Easter,
hymn,Ger
(Shaw; Parker) 4pt mix cor,acap oct SCHIRM.G
9944 $.25   (T1169)

'TIS FINISHED see Shaw

'TIS FINISHED see Wentworth

'TIS FINISHED! SO THE SAVIOR CRIED see Gesius,
Bartholomaus

'TIS FINISHED, THE MESSIAH DIES see Butler,
Eugene

'TIS GOD WHO MADE US FREE see Grime, William

'TIS JESUS see Harkness, Robert

'TIS MARVELOUS AND WONDERFUL see Morris

'TIS ME, O LORD see Burleigh, Henry Thacker

'TIS MIDNIGHT see Bradbury, William Batchelder

'TIS MIDNIGHT; AND ON OLIVE'S BROW see Stucky,
Steven

'TIS NOW THE GLORIOUS EASTER MORN see Kirk, T.

'TIS SO SWEET TO TRUST IN JESUS see Kirkpatrick

'TIS SO SWEET TO TRUST IN JESUS see Nordman,
Chester

'TIS SO SWEET TO TRUST IN JESUS see Price

'TIS THE EVENING'S HOLY HOUR see Beethoven,
Ludwig van

'TIS THE GIFT TO BE SIMPLE *anthem
unis treb cor,kbd,gtr (very easy) oct
AUGSBURG 3004 $.10 contains also:
Brokering, Lois, Love, Love, Love   (T1170)

'TIS THE GIFT TO BE SIMPLE see Brokering, Lois

'TIS THE SPRING OF SOULS see Eldridge, Guy H.

'TIS THOU TO WHOM ALL HONOR see Haydn, (Franz)
Joseph

TISSERAND
Easter Carol, An *Easter,carol
(Hallstrom) SATB SHAWNEE A 697 $.25 (T1171)

That Easter Morn *Easter
(Richardson, D.) SATB oct KENDOR $.25
(T1172)

TITCOMB
Alleluia! O Come, Let Us Sing
SATB FLAMMER A 5085 $.30   (T1173)

Antiphon Of Spring *Easter
mix cor SOUTHERN $.25   (T1174)
SATB FLAMMER A 5240 $.30   (T1175)
SATB oct SOUTHERN $.30   (T1176)

Be Joyful In The Lord
SATB,acap oct FISCHER,C CM-6708 $.25   (T1177)

Be Joyful, O Daughter Of Zion
SATB,acap oct FISCHER,C CM-437 $.25 (T1178)

Benedictus Es, Domine
SATB oct FISCHER,C CM-509 $.30   (T1179)

Christ Our Passover *Easter/Lent
SATB oct FISCHER,C CM-439 $.25   (T1180)

Come, Ye Faithful
SATB oct BELWIN 64183 $.40   (T1181)

Communion Service *see Missa Salve Regina

Communion Service In D *Commun
SATB oct BELWIN 64200 $.50   (T1182)

Eternal Praise
SATB oct BELWIN 64217 $.35   (T1183)

Eyes Of All Wait Upon Thee, O Lord
SATB,acap oct FISCHER,C CM-7406 $.25
(T1184)

I Will Always Give Thanks
SATB FLAMMER A 5184 $.30   (T1185)
SAB SHAWNEE D5055 $.25   (T1186)

I Will Not Leave You Comfortless
mix cor SOUTHERN $.25   (T1187)
SATB,acap oct FISCHER,C CM-441 $.25 (T1188)

Jesu, Word Of God Incarnate
SATB oct SUMMY M 2860 $.35   (T1189)

Jesus! Name Of Wondrous Love
SAB oct BELWIN 64323 $.30   (T1190)
SA oct BELWIN 64275 $.30   (T1191)
SATB oct BELWIN 64207 $.30   (T1192)

Jesus, The Very Thought Of Thee
SATB oct BELWIN 64384 $.30   (T1193)

Lord Is My Strength, The
SATB FLAMMER A 5272 $.30   (T1194)

Magnificat And Nunc Dimittis *Magnif/Nunc
SATB oct FISCHER,C CM-543 $.35   (T1195)

Missa Salve Regina *Commun
"Communion Service" SATB,acap oct BELWIN
64137 $.30   (T1196)

My House Shall Be Called Of All Nations
SATB,acap oct FISCHER,C CM-443 $.25 (T1197)

Nowell *Xmas
SATB oct BELWIN 64212 $.30   (T1198)

O Be Joyful In The Lord
mix cor SOUTHERN $.25   (T1199)

O Bread Of Man's Delight
SA/SATB oct SUMMY M 2882 $.25   (T1200)

O Give Thanks Unto The Lord *Thanks
SATB,acap oct FISCHER,C CM-7407 $.25
(T1201)

O God, Our Help In Ages Past
SATB FLAMMER A 5181 $.30   (T1202)

Rejoice In The Lord, O Ye Righteous
SATB FLAMMER A 5349 $.30   (T1203)

Ride On, Ride On In Majesty *Easter/Lent/
Palm
SATB oct FISCHER,C CM-6468 $.25   (T1204)

Sing, O Sing, This Blessed Morn
SATB FLAMMER A 5145 $.30   (T1205)

Sing Ye To The Lord *Asc,anthem
mix cor SOUTHERN $.25   (T1206)
SATB oct FISCHER,C CM-440 $.25   (T1207)

Strain Upraise Of Joy And Praise, The
SATB&treb cor oct BELWIN 64266 $.35 (T1208)

Thou Must Leave Thy Lowly Dwelling *Xmas
SSA oct BELWIN 64199 $.30   (T1209)

Victory Te Deum
SATB oct BELWIN 64198 $.40   (T1210)

TITCOMB (cont'd.)

We Have Seen His Star *Xmas
SATB oct FISCHER,C CM-438 $.25   (T1211)

TITCOMB, EVERETT
Adeste Fidelis *anthem/hymn
"O Come All Ye Faithful" [Lat/Eng] SATB,S/T
solo,org/pno,opt 2trp&2trom PETERS 6399
$.30, ipa   (T1212)

Alleluia, All The Earth Doth Worship Thee
SAB oct BELWIN 64175 $.30   (T1213)

Behold Now, Praise The Lord
SA oct BELWIN 64196 $.30   (T1214)
TTBB oct BELWIN 64158 $.35   (T1215)
SATB oct BELWIN 64133 $.35   (T1216)

Christ The Lord Is Risen Today *Easter
SATB,org/pno,opt 2trp PETERS 6388 $.30, ipa
                                              (T1217)

Christmas Story *Xmas,cant
mix cor BELWIN $.50   (T1218)

Herald Of Good Tidings
SATB,org/pno,opt 2trp PETERS 6653 $.30, ipa
                                              (T1219)

Hosanna To The Son Of David
SATB oct FISCHER,J 8738 $.30   (T1220)

Lord's My Shepherd, The (from Crimond)
SATB oct GRAY GCMR 2809 $.30   (T1221)

O Come All Ye Faithful *see Adeste Fidelis

O For A Closer Walk With God
SA (easy) ABINGDON APM-209 $.24   (T1222)
SATB (easy) ABINGDON APM-237 $.24   (T1223)

O Love How Deep
SATB oct GRAY GCMR 2226 $.30   (T1224)

O People Of Syon *Adv
SATB,kbd (med easy) oct CONCORDIA 98-1084
$.25   (T1225)

Spirit Of The Lord, The
PTBB,acap (med) ABINGDON APM-207 $.26
                                              (T1226)

Thanksgiving *Thanks
SATB,org/pno,opt 2trp&2trom PETERS 6890
$.30, ipa   (T1227)

To Calvary *Lent,cant
BELWIN $1.50   (T1228)

To The Prince Of Peace
SATB,org/pno,opt 2trp&2trom PETERS 6987
$.30, ipa   (T1229)

TITTEL, ERNST (1910-1969)
Amen
men cor,acap oct DOBLINGER s.p. see from
Drei Gesange Aus Der Geheimen Offenbarung
                                              (T1230)

De Profundis
men cor,acap oct DOBLINGER s.p.   (T1231)

Dem, Der Uns Liebt
men cor,acap oct DOBLINGER s.p. see from
Drei Gesange Aus Der Geheimen Offenbarung
                                              (T1232)

Deutsche Festkreis-Proprien *see
Marienfeste; Ostern; Pfingsten;
Weihnachten   (T1233)

Deutsches Magnificat *Magnif
mix cor,org &OBLINGER r.p.   (T1234)

Deutsches Ordinarium *Op.79
4pt mix cor,org DOBLINGER voc sc s.p., cor
pts s.p.   (T1235)

Deutsches Proprium *ASD,Mass
3pt jr cor/3pt wom cor,org DOBLINGER voc sc
s.p., cor pts s.p.   (T1236)

Deutsches Requiem *Op.81, Req
4pt mix cor,acap DOBLINGER sc s.p., cor pts
s.p.   (T1237)

Drei Gesange Aus Der Geheimen Offenbarung
*see Amen; Dem, Der Uns Liebt; Gross Und
Wunderbar   (T1238)

Franziskusmesse *Op.78, Mass
4pt mix cor,org DOBLINGER voc sc s.p., cor
pts s.p.   (T1239)

Gegrusset Seist Du, Maria
mix cor,acap oct DOBLINGER s.p.   (T1240)

Gross Und Wunderbar
men cor,acap oct DOBLINGER s.p. see from
Drei Gesange Aus Der Geheimen Offenbarung
                                              (T1241)

Jubilate Deo *Op.74,No.2, Jubil
(Tittel, Ernst) mix cor,acap oct DOBLINGER
s.p.   (T1242)

Klosterneuburger Messe *see Goller, Vincent

Marienfeste *BVM
mix cor&cong,org DOBLINGER voc sc s.p., cor
pts s.p. see from Deutsche Festkreis-
Proprien   (T1243)

Missa Cum Jubilo *Op.66, Mass
4pt mix cor,acap DOBLINGER sc s.p., cor pts
s.p.   (T1244)

Ostern *Easter
mix cor&cong,org (contains also: Pfingsten;
Weihnachten) DOBLINGER voc sc s.p., cor
pts s.p. see from Deutsche Festkreis-
Proprien   (T1245)

Pfingsten *Pent
mix cor&cong,org (contains also: Ostern;
Weihnachten) DOBLINGER voc sc s.p., cor
pts s.p. see from Deutsche Festkreis-
Proprien   (T1246)

Weihnachten *Xmas
mix cor&cong,org (contains also: Ostern;
Pfingsten) DOBLINGER voc sc s.p., cor
pts s.p. see from Deutsche Festkreis-Proprien
                                              (T1247)

TKACH
Blessed Is The Nation
SATB KJOS 6512 $.30   (T1248)

Bow Down Thine Ear
SATB KJOS 6509 $.30   (T1249)

Come Thou, Holy Spirit
SATB KJOS 6521 $.30   (T1250)

Give Ear Unto Me
SAB KJOS 5704 $.30   (T1251)

Glory And Honor Are Before Him
SATB KJOS 5150 $.30   (T1252)

Hear Thou Our Prayer, O Lord *prayer
SAB KJOS 5717 $.30   (T1253)
boy cor SOUTHERN $.30   (T1254)
SSA KJOS 7752 $.30   (T1255)
men cor KJOS 7501 $.30   (T1256)

O Come, O Come, Emmanuel *Xmas
SAB KJOS 5705 $.30   (T1257)

O Most Precious Savior
SSAB KJOS 6511 $.30   (T1258)

To Thee We Sing
SAB KJOS 5709 $.30   (T1259)
SSA KJOS 7753 $.30   (T1260)
men cor KJOS 7500 $.30   (T1261)

We Sing Thy Praise
SAB KJOS 5719 $.30   (T1262)

While Shepherds Watched *Xmas
SATB KJOS 5109 $.30   (T1263)
SSA KJOS 6044 $.30   (T1264)

TKACH, D.
Blessing, Glory And Wisdom
SATB KJOS 5140 $.30   (T1265)

Give Thanks Unto The Lord
SATB KJOS 7050 $.30   (T1266)

Hallelujah, Amen
SATB KJOS 6531 $.30   (T1267)

Hear Me, O Lord
SATB KJOS 6542 $.30   (T1268)

We Praise Thee
SATB KJOS 5319 $.30   (T1269)

TKACH, HAZEL
Sing In Joy *Easter
SSA oct BOURNE 192 $.25   (T1270)

TKACH, P.
Glory Be To God
SATB KJOS 6528 $.30   (T1271)

Good News From Heaven
SATB KJOS 6514 $.30   (T1272)

Hear Thou Our Prayer, O Lord
SATB KJOS 6505 $.30   (T1273)

Laud His Name
SSA KJOS 7754 $.30   (T1274)

Sing God's Praise *CCU
SAB KJOS $1.25   (T1275)

We Thank Thee, Lord
SATB KJOS 6513 $.30   (T1276)
SAB KJOS 5720 $.30   (T1277)

TO A BABY *carol
(Sargent) SSAATTBB,acap (easy) OXFORD 43.092
$.25   (T1278)

TO A VIRGIN MEEK AND MILD *Xmas,carol,Span
(Glarum) SSAA SCHMITT 2563 $.30   (T1279)
(Glarum) SATB SCHMITT 1689 $.35   (T1280)

TO ADORE A TINY INFANT see Guerrero, Francisco,
A Un Nino Iiorando

TO ALL GENERATIONS see Ancis, Solomon, L'dor
Vodor

TO ALL, TO EACH see Schumann, William Howard

TO BE A PILGRIM see Cain, Noble

TO BETHLEHEM *Xmas,carol,So Am
(Wilson) SSA oct SPRATT 605 $.25   (T1281)
(Wilson) SA oct SPRATT 623 $.25   (T1282)

TO BETHLEHEM see Kozinski, [David B.]

TO BETHLEHEM see Williams, David McK.

TO BETHLEHEM SINGING
(Wilson) SATB,acap oct BOOSEY 5056 $.30
                                              (T1283)

TO BLESS THE EARTH see Lovelace, Austin C.

TO CALVARY see Titcomb, Everett

TO CALVARY'S SUMMIT see Black, Charles

TO COME, O LORD, TO THEE see Stevenson, F.

TO DAVID'S TOWN see Young

TO DO GOD'S WILL see Berger, Jean

TO EVERY THING THERE IS A SEASON
SATB oct STAFF 521 $.30   (T1284)

TO EVERYTHING THERE IS A SEASON see Derby,
Richard

TO EVERYTHING THERE IS A SEASON see Starer,
Robert

TO FACE THE WORLD see Lovelace, Austin C.

TO GIVE HIM PRAISE see Williams, David H.

TO GLORY I WILL GO
(Ferguson) SATB,pno/org oct LAWSON 51313 $.30
                                              (T1285)

TO GOD ALL GLORY *anthem,Heb
(Pooler, Frank) SATB&jr cor (med) oct
AUGSBURG 1136 $.20   (T1286)
(Pooler, Frank) SA&SATB (med) oct AUGSBURG
1136 $.20   (T1287)

TO GOD ALL PRAISE AND GLORY
SATB CHAPPELL 0017210-358 $.40   (T1288)

TO GOD ALL PRAISE AND GLORY see Darst, W. Glen

TO GOD ALL PRAISE AND GLORY see Nelson

TO GOD ALL PRAISE AND GLORY see Wilson

TO GOD ALL PRAISE AND GLORY AND THE LORD
ASCENDETH see Candlyn, T. Frederick H.

TO GOD BE PRAISE AND GLORY *anthem
(Davis, K.K.) SATB oct FISCHER,C CM-7720 $.25
                                              (T1289)

TO GOD BE THE GLORY *CCU,anthem
SATB LORENZ $1.75   (T1290)

TO GOD BE THE GLORY see Brahms, Johannes

TO GOD BE THE GLORY see Brown, Leon F.

TO GOD BE THE GLORY see Cram

TO GOD BE THE GLORY see Doane, [William Howard]

TO GOD BE THE GLORY see Hughes

TO GOD ON HIGH see Decius, Nicolaus

TO GOD ON HIGH see Mendelssohn-Bartholdy, Felix

TO GOD ON HIGH see Schubert, Franz (Peter)

TO GOD ON HIGH BE GLORY see Bach, Johann
Sebastian, Jesu, Nun Sei Gepreiset
[Chorale]

TO GOD ON HIGH BE THANKS AND PRAISE see Decius,
Nicolaus

TO GOD THE MIGHTY LORD see Phillips, C. Henry

TO GOD WITH HEART AND VOICE see Malin

TO GREET THE BABE SO HOLY see Kinsman, Elmer F.

TO HEAVEN ASCENDED CHRIST, OUR KING see Hirsch

TO HIM ALL GLORY GIVE see Diemer, Emma Lou

TO HIM BE GLORY see Keating, L.

TO HIM GIVE PRAISE see Fraser, Shena

TO HIM THAT OVERCOMETH see Christiansen, Paul

TO HIM THAT OVERCOMETH see Strimple, N.

TO HIM WE SING see Rubbra, Edmund

TO HIM WHO NEVER FAILETH see Altnikol, Befiehl
Du Deine Wege

TO JESUS CHRIST, OUR SOVEREIGN KING
see Recessional Hymns
(Keldermans) SATB&cong,opt S solo oct SUMMY
M 2572 $.45   (T1291)

TO JESUS FROM THE ENDS OF EARTH *Xmas/Epiph,
carol,US
(Jewell, K.W.) SATB,kbd (med easy) oct
CONCORDIA 98-1710 $.25   (T1292)

TO JESUS FROM THE ENDS OF THE EARTH see Jewell

TO JESUS ON HIS BIRTHDAY see Harris, A.

TO LIGHT THAT SHINES see Johnson

TO MAKE HIS COMING SWEET see Rinehart

TO MANY A WELL
see Musica Britannica Vol. 4: Set 2

TO MARY SING WE PRAISES *Span
(Glaser, V.) SSAA,acap SCHIRM.EC 1960 $.22
                                              (T1293)

TO MEN OF GOOD WILL see Jones, R.W.

TO MERCY, PITY, PEACE AND LOVE see Fast,
Willard S.

TO MERCY, PITY, PEACE AND LOVE see Joubert,
John

TO MUSIC see York, D.

TO MY FATHER'S HOUSE see Hawkins, Ed.

TO MY HEART ON CHRISTMAS DAY see Gibbs

TO MY HUMBLE SUPPLICATION see Jacob, Gordon

TO MY HUMBLE SUPPLICATION see Wolff

TO MY HUMBLE SUPPLICATION see Wolff, S.
Drummond

TO MY HUMBLE SUPPLICATION, LORD see Holst,
Gustav

TO OUR FATHERS AND THEE see Lynn, George

TO OUR GOD GIVE PRAISE see Carmichael, Ralph

TO OUR KING IMMORTAL see Leaf

TO OUR KING IMMORTAL see Leaf, Robert

TO OUR REDEEMER'S GLORIOUS NAME see Tye,
Christopher

TO REALMS OF GLORY see Blom, Oscar

TO SAINT CECILIA see Dello Joio, Norman

TO SALMETONER see Beck, Thomas [Ludvigsen]

TO SEE THE LORD see Martin

TO SHEPHERDS FAST ASLEEP see Davis, Katherine K.

TO SHEPHERDS IN COLD WINTER NIGHT see Haydn, (Franz) Joseph

TO SINGING AND DANCING see Biechteler, M.S., Ad Cantus, Ad Choros

TO SONG AND DANCE see Handel, George Frideric

TO THE BLESSED TRINITY see Johnson

TO THE BLESSED VIRGIN see Soderman, (Johan) August

TO THE FATHER see Soderman, (Johan) August

TO THE GOD OF PEACE see Pasquet, Jean

TO THE GOD WHO IS IN THE FIRE see Hovhaness, Alan

TO THE HILLS I LIFT MINE EYES see Fryxell, Regina Holmen

TO THE HOLY CHILD see Posegate

TO THE HOLY SPIRIT see Soderman, (Johan) August

TO THE LORD I CRY see Track, Gerhard

TO THE NAME OF OUR SALVATION see Howells, Herbert Norman

TO THE NAME OF OUR SALVATION see Scott

TO THE NAME OF OUR SALVATION see Stewart, C. Hylton

TO THE PRINCE OF PEACE see Titcomb, Everett

TO THE QUEEN OF HEAVEN see Dunhill, Thomas Frederick

TO THE SON see Soderman, (Johan) August

TO THE STABLE GATE see Guerrero, Francisco, Vamos Al Portal

TO THE TOWN OF BETHLEHEM see Peloquin, C. Alexander

TO THE WORK see Blakley

TO THEE ALONE BE GLORY see Bach, Johann Sebastian

TO THEE BE GLORY see Mozart, Wolfgang Amadeus

TO THEE BE PRAISE FOREVER see Bach, Johann Sebastian

TO THEE CHERUBIN see Handel, George Frideric

TO THEE, ETERNAL SPIRIT see Young, G.

TO THEE I LIFT UP see Brandon

TO THEE IN SONG *CC13L,Gen
(Douglas) 3pt/4pt PRO ART 680 $1.25   (T1294)

TO THEE, JEHOVAH see Bach, Johann Sebastian

TO THEE, JEHOVAH, I AM SINGING see Bach, Johann Sebastian, Dir, Dir, Jehova, Will Ich Singen

TO THEE, O CHRIST, WE SING see Grime

TO THEE, O JESU see Clokey, Joseph Waddell

TO THEE, O JESUS CHRIST, WE CRY see Brahms, Johannes

TO THEE, O LORD see Beethoven, Ludwig van

TO THEE, O LORD see Kalinnikoff, Paul

TO THEE, O LORD see Mendelssohn-Bartholdy, Felix

TO THEE O LORD see Rachmaninoff, Sergey Vassilievitch

TO THEE O LORD I LIFT MY SOUL see Trued, Clarence

TO THEE, O LORD, OUR HEARTS WE RAISE see Bach, Johann Sebastian

TO THEE, O LORD OUR HEARTS WE RAISE see Coleman, Henry

TO THEE, O LORD, OUR HEARTS WE RAISE see Darst, W. Glenn

TO THEE, O LORD, OUR HEARTS WE RAISE see Hughes

TO THEE, O LORD, OUR HEARTS WE RAISE see Ratcliffe, Desmond

TO THEE OUR GOD see Maunder, J.H.

TO THEE, OUR GOD, WE FLY see Clokey, Joseph Waddell

TO THEE, THE HOLY GHOST, WE NOW PRAY see Nun Bitten Wir Den Heiligen Geist

TO THEE WE CALL see Tchaikovsky, Piotr Ilyitch

TO THEE WE SING see Arkhangelsky, G.

TO THEE WE SING see Schvedov

TO THEE WE SING see Tkach

TO THEE WE TURN see Bach, Johann Sebastian

TO THEE WE TURN OUR EYES see Schutz, Heinrich, Oculi Omnium In Te Sperant, Domine

TO THEM HATH BEEN GIVEN see Casciolini, Claudio, Istorum Est

TO US A CHILD IS BORN see Bach, Johann Sebastian, Uns Ist Ein Kind Geboren

TO US A CHILD IS BORN see Schutz, Heinrich

TO US A CHILD IS BORN see Bach, Johann Sebastian, Es Ist Ein Kind Geboren [Chorale]

TO US A CHILD IS GIVEN see Bach, Johann Sebastian, Uns Ist Ein Kind Geboren

TO US A CHILD IS GIVEN see Graun, Karl Heinrich

TO US A CHILD OF HOPE IS BORN *Xmas
(Ehret) SATB oct PRO ART 2615 $.30   (T1295)

TO US A CHILD OF HOPE IS BORN see Strube, Adolf

TO US A LITTLE CHILD IS BORN see De Leeuw

TO US A SAVIOR see Graham, R.W.

TO US A SAVIOR [ANTHEM] see Graham, R.W.

TO US A SON IS GIVEN see Franck, Cesar

TO US IN BETHLEM CITY *Xmas,carol
SATB (easy) OXFORD 08.111 $.15   (T1296)

TO US IN BETHLEM CITY see Mc Cabe, John

TO US IS BORN see Praetorius, Michael

TO US IS BORN A LITTLE CHILD *Xmas,carol,Ger
(Ehret) SA MARKS 4074 $.30 contains also: I Saw Three Ships (Eng)   (T1297)

TO US IS BORN A LITTLE CHILD see Praetorius, Michael

TO US IS BORN EMMANUEL see Praetorius, Michael, Enatus Est Emmanuel

TO US IS BORN IMMANUEL see Praetorius, Michael

TO US, THERE COMES A LITTLE CHILD
(Malin) SATB,acap oct BELWIN 60635 $.25   (T1298)

TO WORSHIP, WORK AND WITNESS see Powell

TO YOU, BLESSED MARY see Bock, F.

TO YOU I LIFT UP MY SOUL see Track, Gerhard

TO YOU, MY BELOVED see Gottlieb, J., L'chah Dodi

TO YOU, O LORD see Peloquin, C. Alexander

TO YOU THIS NIGHT IS BORN A CHILD see Forster, Georg

TO ZION JESUS COMES see Williams, David H.

TOAST FOR THE NEW YEAR see Rossini, Gioacchino

TOBENDER STURM, SINKENDES SCHIFF see Schweizer, Rolf

TOBLER, J.H.
Ode An Gott
[Ger] men cor,acap (easy) HUG s.p.   (T1299)
[Ger] mix cor,acap (easy) HUG s.p.   (T1300)

TOCCATA-GLORIA see Widor, Charles-Marie

TOCCHI, [GIAN-LUCA] (1901-   )
Ave Maria
unis,pno RICORDI-ENG 128769 s.p.   (T1301)

Buona Pasqua A Renatina *Easter
jr cor CURCI 9427 s.p.   (T1302)

Due Cori
jr cor,pno RICORDI-ENG 128708 s.p.   (T1303)

Otto Canoni Antichi *CC8U,canon
jr cor CURCI 6530 s.p.   (T1304)

Tre Cori
jr cor,pno RICORDI-ENG 128707 s.p.   (T1305)

TOD IST EIN LANGER SCHLAF see Haydn, (Franz) Joseph

TOD UND EWIGKEIT see Bornefeld, Helmut

TOD UND LEBEN see Micheelsen, Hans Friedrich

TOD UND VERGANGLICHKEIT *Gd.Fri.
SATB,acap cmplt ed DOBLINGER s.p.
contains & see also: Agricola, Martin, Mit Fried Und Freud Ich Fahr Dahin; Bach, Johann Sebastian, Es Ist Genug!; Bach, Johann Sebastian, O Ewigkeit, Du Donnerwort; Bruck, Arnold von, Mitten Wir Im Leben Sind; Demantius, Christoph, Ich Hab Mein Sach; Dressler, Gallus, Ich Bin Die Auferstehung Und Das Leben; Franck, Melchior, Du Weiss, Dass Mein Erloser Lebt; Franck, Melchior, In Den Armen Dein; Franck, Melchior, Wenn Ich In Todesnoten Bin; Gallus, Jacobus, O Herre Gott; Gesius, Bartholomaus, Ich Bin Ein Gast Auf Erden; Gumpeltzhaimer, Adam, Wenn Mein Stundlein Vorhanden Ist; Lassus, Roland de (Orlandus), Justorum Animae; Praetorius, Michael, Herre, Nun Lassest Du Deinen Diener; Praetorius, Michael, O Welt, Ich Muss Dich Lassen; Rosenmuller, Johann, Welt Ade!; Schein, Johann Hermann, Die Mit Tranen Saen; Schutz, Heinrich, Selig Sind Die Toten; Schutz, Heinrich, So Fahr Ich Hin, SWV 379; Schutz, Heinrich, So Lehr Mich Doch, SWV 139a   (T1306)

TODAY ABOVE THE SKY HE SOARED see Vulpius, Melchior

TODAY AROSE CHRIST FROM THE GRAVE see Praetorius, Michael

TODAY CHRIST IS BORN see Bender, Jan, Hodie Christus Natus Est

TODAY CHRIST IS BORN see Church, Hodie

TODAY DID CHRIST ARISE see Whitehead, Alfred

TODAY IN BETHLEHEM *Xmas,carol
(Garland, Hugh) SATB oct LESLIE 4056 see from Two Christmas Carols, Set 1   (T1307)

TODAY IN BETHLEHEM see Powell, Robert J.

TODAY IS BORN A CHILD ON EARTH see Praetorius, Michael

TODAY IS BORN EMMANUEL see Praetorius, Michael

TODAY IS BORN THE KING OF HEAVEN see Marenzio, Luca, Hodie Christus Natus Est

TODAY IS RISEN CHRIST THE LORD see Vulpius, Melchior

TODAY THE PRINCE OF PEACE IS BORN see Mueller, Carl F.

TODAY THERE IS RINGING see Christiansen, F. Melius

TODD
God Rest You Merry
unis&SA&SATB (easy) OXFORD 84.132 $.35   (T1308)

TODD, M. FLORA
Alleluia! *Easter
3pt wom cor,opt pno (diff) oct WILLIS 6089 $.15   (T1309)
5pt mix cor,pno (diff) oct WILLIS 7043 $.22   (T1310)

Bow Down Thine Ear
SATB,pno (med) oct WILLIS 7242 $.25   (T1311)

Crossing The Bar
SATB,pno (easy) oct WILLIS 6619 $.18   (T1312)

Eternal King Of Day *Epiph/Gen
3-4pt mix cor,SAT soli,org (med) oct WILLIS 5552 $.20   (T1313)

Giver, The
3pt wom cor,S solo,pno (med) oct WILLIS 6238 $.15   (T1314)

King Of Peace, The
SATB,pno (med) oct WILLIS 7044 $.20   (T1315)

Out Of The Depths
3pt wom cor,A solo,pno (easy) oct WILLIS 6505 $.20   (T1316)

TODOS A CANTAR *sac/sec,CC32L
(Pahlen) [Span] 2-3pt jr cor,acap/pno RICORDI-ARG BA 12209 s.p. contains works by: Lasso; Beethoven; Mozart; Brahms; and others   (T1317)

TOEBOSCH, LOUIS (1916-   )
Psalm 37 *Op.41
[Dut] men cor,2fl,ob,2clar,bsn,2trp,4horn, 3trom,tuba,perc,timp DONEMUS min sc s.p., cor pts s.p.   (T1318)

Psalm 126 *Op.77
[Dut] mix cor,2fl,2ob,2clar,2bsn,3trp, 4horn,3trom,tuba,strings,perc,timp DONEMUS min sc s.p., cor pts s.p., voc sc s.p.   (T1319)

Psalm 131 *Op.53
[Dut] men cor,2fl,2ob,2clar,2bsn,2trp, 2horn,3trom,strings,timp DONEMUS min sc s.p., cor pts s.p.   (T1320)

TOEPLER, A.
Missa Gregoriana *Op.11, Mass
[Lat] SATB SCHOTT s.p.   (T1321)

TOGETHER IN UNITY see Williamson, Malcolm

TOGETHER WITH GOD see Ashton

TOKEN OF HIS LOVE, THE see Fraser

TOLLITE see Fux, Johann Joseph

TOLLITE HOSTIAS? see Saint-Saens, Camille

TOLLITE JUGUM MEUM see Palestrina, Giovanni

TOLMAGE, GERALD
In Dulce Jubilo
SATB oct STAFF 302 $.25   (T1322)

Promised Land, The
SATB oct STAFF 433 $.25   (T1323)

Streets Of Glory
SATB oct STAFF 448 $.25   (T1324)

Vesper Hymn *Eve,hymn
SATB oct STAFF 347 $.20   (T1325)

TOLV FEM-STEMMIGE SATSER see Pederson, Mogens

TOLV TOSTEMMIGE DANSKE MOTETTER see Jeppesen, Knud

TOMASI
Bergers, Bergeres *Xmas,Fr
[Fr] SATB cor pts LEDUC s.p.   (T1326)

La Jambe Me Fait Mal *Xmas,Fr
[Fr] SATB/SAT cor pts LEDUC s.p.   (T1327)

La Nuit Obscure De Saint-Jean De La Croix
[Fr] opt SATB,Mez solo,orch cor pts LEDUC rental   (T1328)

Le Cabanon De Bethleem *Xmas,Fr
[Fr] SATB cor pts LEDUC s.p.   (T1329)

Le Rossignolet *Fr
[Fr] 3pt jr cor&B/3pt wom cor&B cor pts LEDUC s.p.   (T1330)

Les Pastoureaux *Xmas,Fr
[Fr] SA/SAB/SATB cor pts LEDUC s.p.   (T1331)

Messe De La Nativite *Xmas,Mass,Fr
[Fr] 2pt/3pt,opt orch/org LEDUC voc sc s.p., voc pt s.p.   (T1332)

Patres Des Montagnes *Xmas,Fr
[Fr] 3pt wom cor/3pt jr cor cor pts LEDUC s.p.   (T1333)

TOMBELLE, FERDINAND DE LA
see LA TOMBELLE, FERNAND DE

TOMBLINGS, PHILIP
All From The Sun's Uprise *Gen/Thanks
SAB (very easy) oct OXFORD 42.810 $.25 (T1334)

Behold The Great Creator *carol
SATB ENOCH EC340 s.p. (T1335)

Benedicite
unis/SATB (very easy) oct OXFORD 40.310 $.20 (T1336)

Come, My Way, My Truth, My Life *Gen
SATB,acap (easy) oct OXFORD 42.007 $.25 (T1337)

Put Thou Thy Trust In God *Gen
SATB/unis (very easy) oct OXFORD 42.815 $.25 (T1338)

Seek The Lord *Gen
2pt/unis (very easy) oct OXFORD 44.802 $.25 (T1339)

Te Deum *Te Deum
SATB (C maj) oct NOVELLO 44.1402.00 s.p. (T1340)

TOMKINS, THOMAS (ca. 1572-1656)
Above The Stars *Gen
SAATB,kbd (med easy) cor pts CONCORDIA 98-1576 $.25 (T1341)
(Stevens, D.) SAATB,A/T solo,org,opt strings (verse anthem) sc CONCORDIA 97-6308 $1.90, cor pts CONCORDIA 98-1576 $.25, ipa (T1342)

Absalom
SAATB BROUDE BR. $.35 (T1343)
(Ehret) mix cor CHAPPELL 0023416-358 $.40 (T1344)

Almighty And Everlasting God (from Music Deo Sacra)
see Two Collects

Almighty God, The Fountain Of All Wisdom *anthem
(Still) SAATB,opt org SCHOTT s.p. (T1345)

Behold The Hour Cometh *anthem
(Rose) SATB,A solo,org SCHOTT 10608 s.p. (T1346)

Fifth Service
mix cor,acap voc sc KALMUS 6722 $1.35 (T1347)

First Service
mix cor,acap voc sc KALMUS 6718 $1.35 (T1348)

Fourth Service
mix cor,acap voc sc KALMUS 6721 $1.35 (T1349)

God, Who At This Time (from Music Deo Sacra)
see Two Collects

Great And Marvellous *Epiph/Gen
SSATB,acap (med) oct OXFORD 43.223 $.35 (T1350)

Have Mercy Upon Me, O God *Gen
SAB (med easy) oct OXFORD 43.361 $.25 (T1351)

Hear My Prayer, O Lord *anthem
(Rose) SATB,SBar soli,org SCHOTT s.p. (T1352)

Heavens Declare The Glory Of God, The *Xmas/Gen
TTBB,acap (diff) oct CONCORDIA 98-1432 $.30 (T1353)

Holy, Holy, Holy *anthem
(Rose) SSATB,org SCHOTT s.p. (T1354)

I Heard A Voice From Heaven *anthem
(Atkins, Ivor) mix cor,acap oct NOVELLO 40.0925.08 s.p. (T1355)

Magnificat And Nunc Dimittis (from First Service, The) Magnif/Nunc
(Rose, Bernard) SATB oct NOVELLO 88.0020.00 s.p. (T1356)

Magnificat And Nunc Dimittis (from Second Service, The) Magnif/Nunc
SATB (med) oct OXFORD 42.839 $.65 (T1357)

Magnificat And Nunc Dimittis (from Third Service) Magnif/Nunc
mix cor oct OXFORD 43.286 $2.00 (T1358)

Magnificat And Nunc Dimittis (from Fifth Service, The) Magnif/Nunc
SATB (med) oct OXFORD 42.817 $.70 (T1359)

Musica Deo Sacra 1 *CCU,Eng
cor STAINER 3.8205.8 $11.50 (T1360)

Musica Deo Sacra 2 *CCU,Eng
cor STAINER 3.8209.8 $15.50 (T1361)

My Beloved Spake Unto Me *anthem
(Rose) SATB,SSAB soli,org SCHOTT 10609 s.p. (T1362)

My Shepherd Is The Living Lord *Gen,anthem
SATB,ST soli,kbd (med easy) oct CONCORDIA 98-1416 $.30 (T1363)
SATB,org STAINER CC581 s.p. (T1364)

O Give Thanks Unto The Lord (Psalm 105) Gen/Thanks
ATTB,opt inst (med) oct OXFORD 41.003 $.30 (T1365)

O God, Wonderful Art Thou *Gen
SAATB,opt inst (med) oct OXFORD 43.254 $.35 (T1366)

O How Amiable (Psalm 84) Gen
ATTB (med) oct OXFORD 41.017 $.50 (T1367)

O Lord, I Have Loved (Psalm 26)
SAATB,org/pno PETERS 6068 $.30 (T1368)

O Praise The Lord
(Couraud) SSSAAATTTBBB oct SALABERT-US $2.00 (T1369)

O Praise The Lord All Ye Heathen *Fest/Gen/Thanks
SSSAAATTTBBB (med easy) oct OXFORD 43.229 $1.20 (T1370)

O Pray For The Peace Of Jerusalem *Ded/Gen, anthem
mix cor oct OXFORD 43.336 $.25 (T1371)

TOMKINS, THOMAS (cont'd.)

SSTB,acap (med easy) oct OXFORD 43.336 $.25 (T1372)
SATB,acap BROUDE BR. $.35 (T1373)

O Sing Unto The Lord A New Song *anthem
(Rose) SSAATBB,opt org SCHOTT 10610 s.p. (T1374)

Out Of The Deep *anthem
(Rose) SATB,SAB soli,org SCHOTT s.p. (T1375)

Praise The Lord *anthem
mix cor oct OXFORD 43.220 $.35 (T1376)

Praise The Lord, O My Soul *anthem
(Morehen, John) mix cor oct NOVELLO 88.0012.10 s.p. (T1377)

Psalm 26 *see O Lord, I Have Loved

Psalm 84 *see O How Amiable

Psalm 105 *see O Give Thanks Unto The Lord

Second Service
mix cor,acap voc sc KALMUS 6719 $1.35 (T1378)

Sing Unto God *anthem
SATTB,org STAINER CC712 s.p. (T1379)

Sure There Is No God Of Love
SSA STAINER s.p. (T1380)

Then David Mourned *anthem
SAATB,org/pno PETERS 6069 $.30 (T1381)
(Rose) SSATB,opt org SCHOTT 10611 s.p. (T1382)

Third Service
mix cor,acap voc sc KALMUS 6720 $2.00 (T1383)

Two Collects (from Music Deo Sacra)
PETERS $.40
contains: Almighty And Everlasting God (SATB,opt org); God, Who At This Time (SATB,org) (T1384)

When David Heard That Absalom Was Slain *anthem/Bibl
SAATB STAINER T18-19 s.p. (T1385)
(Simkins) 5pt mix cor,acap oct SCHIRM.G 11287 $.25 (T1386)

TOMLINS, GRETA
Balulalow *Xmas
3pt jr cor/3pt wom cor CURWEN 72649 s.p. (T1387)

Jubilate Deo *Jubil
3pt ASHDOWN V.T.61 s.p. (T1388)

TOMMASINI, VINCENZO (1878-1950)
Messa Da Requien
4pt mix cor,org sc SANTIS 754 s.p., cor pts SANTIS 755A-B s.p. (T1389)

TOMORROW CHRIST IS COMING see Lovelace, Austin C.

TOMORROW IS THE MARRIAGE DAY see Weelkes

TONADA DE RONDA see Benedito

TONE DUH BELL EASY *spir
(Terri) mix cor,opt soli,acap oct LAWSON 836 $.30 (T1390)

TONES OF PLAINSONG, THE, PART I
SCHIRM.EC 16 $1.00 (T1391)

TONES OF PLAINSONG, THE, PART II
SCHIRM.EC 19 $1.00 (T1392)

TONETTI, OTTONE
Canzoniere Mariano
unis,org RICORDI-ENG 129697 s.p. (T1393)

Messa In On. Di S. Romedio Eremita E Confessore *Mass
[Lat] TTB,org sc ZANIBON 4662 s.p., voc pt ZANIBON s.p. (T1394)

Sei Canti In Onore Di Maria Santissima *CC6U,BVM
[It] unis,org ZANIBON 4721 s.p. (T1395)

TONI PUISQUE J' AI PERDU see Lassus, Roland de (Orlandus), Missa VIII

TONIUTTI, VITTORIO
Missa In Hon. B.M.V. A Monte Sancto *BVM, Mass
[Lat] ATB,org sc ZANIBON 3551 s.p., voc pt ZANIBON s.p. (T1396)

TOOLAN, S. SUZANNE
Advent Glad Song *Adv,anthem
SATB (med easy) oct GIA G1689 $.25 (T1397)
SA (med easy) oct GIA G1672 $.25 (T1398)

Behold, I Stand At The Door *Gen,anthem
SATB (easy) oct GIA G1688 $.30 (T1399)

Behold I Stand At The Door And Knock *Gen, anthem
SSAA (easy) oct GIA G1671 $.30 (T1400)

Call, The *Gen,anthem
SSA (easy) oct GIA G1668 $.25 (T1401)
SATB (easy) oct GIA G1685 $.25 (T1402)

Ephesians Hymn I *Gen,anthem/Bibl
unis (easy) oct GIA G1675 $.25 (T1403)

Ephesians Hymn II *Gen,anthem/Bibl
unis (easy) oct GIA G1684 $.25 (T1404)

Friendship Hymn *Gen,anthem/Bibl
SSAA (easy) oct GIA G1678 $.25 (T1405)
SATB (easy) oct GIA G1694 $.25 (T1406)

Hymn Of Joy *Gen,anthem/Bibl
SSAA (med easy) oct GIA D1682 $.30 (T1407)
SATB (med easy) oct GIA G1697 $.30 (T1408)

Hymn Of Unity *Gen,anthem/Bibl
SSAA (easy) oct GIA G1681 $.25 (T1409)
SATB (easy) oct GIA G1696 $.25 (T1410)

TOOLAN, S. SUZANNE (cont'd.)

I Am The Bread Of Life *Commun,Allelu/anthem/Bibl
SSA (easy) oct GIA G1677 $.25 (T1411)
SATB (easy) oct GIA G1693 $.25 (T1412)

Living Spirit *CC17L,Gen,anthem/Bibl/hymn/Psalm
(med easy) cmplt ed SSA/SSAA GIA G1606 $2.50; SATB GIA G1625 $2.50 (T1413)

Living Spirit *Pent,anthem/Bibl
SSAA (easy) oct GIA G1683 $.35 (T1414)
SATB (easy) oct GIA G1698 $.35 (T1415)

Living Waters *Gen,anthem/Bibl
SSAA (easy) oct GIA G1676 $.25 (T1416)
SATB (easy) oct GIA G1692 $.25 (T1417)

Lobe Den Herren *Gen,anthem
"Praise To The Lord" [Eng/Ger] SATB (med) oct GIA G1710 $.40 (T1418)

Peace Hymn *Gen,anthem/Bibl
SSAA (easy) oct GIA G1670 $.30 (T1419)
SATB (easy) oct GIA G1687 $.30 (T1420)

Praise To The Lord *see Lobe Den Herren

Psalm 84 *Gen,anthem
SATB (med) oct GIA G1695 $.25 (T1421)
SSAA (med) oct GIA G1680 $.25 (T1422)

Psalm 139 *see Stilled And Quiet Is My Soul

Stilled And Quiet Is My Soul (Psalm 139) Gen, anthem
SATB (easy) oct GIA G1691 $.25 (T1423)
SSAA (easy) oct GIA G1674 $.25 (T1424)

Tell It Out *Gen,anthem
unis (easy) oct GIA G1679 $.25 (T1425)

Walk In Light *Gen,anthem/Bibl
SATB (med easy) oct GIA G1690 $.25 (T1426)
SSAA (med easy) oct GIA G1673 $.25 (T1427)

Word, The *Gen,anthem/Bibl
SATB (easy) oct GIA G1686 $.25 (T1428)
SSAA (easy) oct GIA G1669 $.25 (T1429)

TOPFF, J.
Angel To The Shepherds
mix cor SOUTHERN $.30 (T1430)

Angels To The Shepherds, The
(Ross) SSATB,acap AMP A158 $.30 (T1431)

TOQUEN ARPAS Y GUITARRAS see Santa Cruz, Domingo

TORAH SERVICE see Neumann, Richard J.

TORAS ADONOY T'MIMOH see Lewandowski, Louis

TORAT EMET. see Freed, Isadore

TORCH HAS BEEN PASSED, THE see McLin

TORLIND
Lucia
[Swed] 3pt wom cor LUNDQUIST 22 s.p. (T1432)

TORLIND, TORE
Jag Ar Uppstandelsen Och Livet *Bibl
[Swed] SATB,acap GEHRMANS KRB 297 (T1433)

TORRA
O Maria, Virgo Pia *BVM
[Lat] 2pt wom cor,org RICORDI-ARG BA 8068 s.p. (T1434)

TORRANCE, GEORGE WILLIAM (1835-1907)
Lord, I Have Loved The Habitation Of Thy House *anthem
mix cor oct NOVELLO 28.0722.10 s.p. (T1435)

Who Shall Roll Us Away The Stone *Easter, anthem
mix cor oct NOVELLO 40.0672.00 s.p. (T1436)

TORRANS, RICHARD
Dream Of Lace
SATB oct AGAPE CF 125 $.30 (T1437)

TORRES, EDUARDO (1872-)
Ave Regina Caelorum
"Queen Of The Heavens, We Hail Thee" SATB, acap SCHIRM.EC 1277 $.20 (T1438)

Magnificat (Tone 1, No. 7) *see Ripolles, Vincente

Magnificat (Tone 2, No. 2) *see Ripolles, Vincente

Magnificat (Tone 4, No. 1) *see Ripolles, Vincente

Magnificat (Tone 5, No. 1) *see Ripolles, Vincente

Magnificat (Tone 6) (composed with Ripolles, Vincente)
(Williams, Walter) mix cor SCHIRM.EC 1209 $.18 contains also: Nunc Dimittis (Tone 7, No. 5) (T1439)

Magnificat (Tone 7, No. 5) (composed with Ripolles, Vincente)
(Williams, Walter) mix cor SCHIRM.EC 1215 $.18 contains also: Nunc Dimittis (Tone 2, No. 1) (T1440)

Missa Breve
STB SCHIRM.EC 1216 $.60 (T1441)

Nunc Dimittis (Tone 2, No. 1) (composed with Ripolles, Vincente)
see Torres, Eduardo, Magnificat (Tone 7, No. 5)

Nunc Dimittis (Tone 4, No. 1, With Fauxbourdons) *see Ripolles, Vincente

Nunc Dimittis (Tone 5, No. 1) *see Ripolles, Vincente

TORRES, EDUARDO (cont'd.)

Nunc Dimittis (Tone 5, No. 3 With
    Fauxbourdons) *see Ripolles, Vincente

Nunc Dimittis (Tone 7, No. 5) (composed with
    Ripolles, Vincente)
    see Torres, Eduardo, Magnificat (Tone 6)

Nunc Dimittis (Tonus Peregrinus) *see
    Ripolles, Vincente

Queen Of The Heavens, We Hail Thee !see Ave
    Regina Caelorum

TORSTEN, STENIUS (1918-1964)
    Ave Maris Stella
        [Lat] mix cor oct FAZER s.p.   (T1442)

TORTOLANO, W.
    Nineteen Liturgical Rounds *CC19U,anthem/
        litug/round
        2-5pt (med easy) cmplt ed GIA G1600 $1.00
                                                (T1443)

TORTORELLA, HUIGI
    Padre Nostro *prayer
        [It] unis/2pt,org voc sc ZANIBON 4723 s.p.,
        cor pts ZANIBON 4724 s.p.   (T1444)

TOSAR, HECTOR (1923-   )
    Te Deum
        [Eng/Lat] mix cor,pno,3fl,3ob,3clar,3bsn,
        3trp,4horn,3trom,tuba,strings,harp,perc,
        timp cmplt ed BOOSEY rental   (T1445)

TOT WIEN ZULLEN WIJ HENENGAAN see Felderhof,
    Jan

TOTA PULCHRA see Bottazzo, Luigi

TOTA PULCHRA see Casals, Pablo

TOTA PULCHRA see Ceriana, Angelo

TOTA PULCHRA see Leoncini, Lorenzo

TOTA PULCHRA see Mariani, Eligio

TOTA PULCHRA see Martorell

TOTA PULCHRA see Moioli, Romano

TOTA PULCHRA see Muller, J.

TOTA PULCHRA see Ravanello, Oreste

TOTA PULCHRA see Volpi, Edoardo

TOTA PULCHRA ES see Durufle, Maurice

TOTA PULCHRA ES see Gletle, Johann Melchoir

TOTA PULCHRA ES see Palestrina, Giovanni

TOTA PULCHRA ES MARIA see Bruckner, Anton

TOTA PULCHRA ES MARIA see Putten, P. v.d.

TOTA PULCHRA EST see Bruckner, Anton

TOTENFEIER see Reger, Max

TOTENMOTETTEN oee Bresgen, Cesar

TOTENTANZ see Distler, Hugo

TOUCH OF GOD, THE see Lillenas, Haldor

TOUJOURS A TOI, SEIGNEUR see Gounod, Charles
    Francois

TOURJEE
    There's A Wideness In God's Mercy *hymn
        (Tucker) 2pt jr cor oct LILLENAS AN-4015
        $.25   (T1446)

TOURNAI MASS, THE see Gabrieli, Giovanni, Missa
    Tornacensis

TOURNIER, MARCEL
    There Is No Rose Of Such Virtue *Xmas
        SATB BELWIN AP22 $.30   (T1447)

TOURO-LOURO-LOURO *Xmas,carol,Fr
    (Wilson, Harry R.) SSA oct WALTON 5008 $.25
                                                (T1448)

TOURO-LOURO-LOURO see Saboly, Nicholas

TOURONT
    O Gloriosa Regina
        see MEISTERWERKE MITTELALTERLICHER MUSIK

TOURS
    Sing, O Heavens *Xmas/Gen
        SATB SCHMITT 1901 $.30   (T1449)
        (Ehret) SATB oct PRO ART 1502 $.30   (T1450)

    While The Earth Remaineth *Thanks
        SATB oct PRO ART 1723 $.22   (T1451)

TOURS, BERTHOLD (1838-1897)
    Benedictus *Bene
        unis (F maj) oct NOVELLO 06.0002.04 s.p.
                                                (T1452)

    Hail To The Lord's Anointed *Adv
        (Scholin) jr cor&sr cor (med easy) FISCHER,
        C CM 7065 $.20   (T1453)

    In Thee, O Lord, Have I Put My Trust
        (Stickles) 4pt mix cor oct SCHIRM.G 10570
        $.25   (T1454)

    Jubilate Deo *Bibl
        SATB oct HUNTZINGER 7050 $.25   (T1455)
        (Mueller) "O Be Joyful In The Lord" SABar
        oct SCHIRM.G 8698 $.25   (T1456)

    Jubilate, In F *Bibl
        [Eng] 4pt mix cor oct SCHIRM.G 4651 $.25
                                                (T1457)

    O Be Joyful In The Lord *see Jubilate Deo

    O Come Let Us Sing Good Tidings *Harv
        SATB ALLANS 264 s.p.   (T1458)

    O Zion That Bringeth Good Tidings
        SATB ALLANS 263 s.p.   (T1459)

TOURS, BERTHOLD (cont'd.)

    Sing, O Heavens *Xmas,Bibl
        SATB oct PRESSER 332-00291 $.30   (T1460)
        (Macfarlane) 4pt mix cor,S solo oct
        SCHIRM.G 4336 $.30   (T1461)

    While The Earth Remaineth *Harv
        SATB ALLANS 261 s.p.   (T1462)

TOUS LES BOURGEOIS DE CHASTRES
    see Five French Noels

TOUT CE QUI PREND NAISSANCE see Crawford, John

TOV L'HODOS see Rehfeld

TOVO LEFONECHO see Lewandowski, Louis

TOWARDS THE MOUNTAINS I LIFT MY EYES see
    Goudimel, C.W.

TOWER, A. WESLEY
    We Three Kings *Xmas
        SSAATTBB,acap (med) ABINGDON APM-289 $.18
                                                (T1463)

TOWER OF BABEL, THE see Bartow

TOWNE
    Easter Canticle, An *Easter
        (Kennedy) unis jr cor,opt strings oct
        BOURNE 2036 $.30   (T1464)

TOWNER, DANIEL B.
    At Calvary *Lent
        (Peterson) SATB oct SOUTHERN $.30   (T1465)

    Grace Greater Than Our Sin
        (Hustad) SATB oct AGAPE HA 111 $.30   (T1466)

    O Thou God Of My Salvation *hymn
        (Hustad, Don) SATB ALLANS 454 s.p.   (T1467)

TOWNSEND
    Forgive Me *Easter
        SATB oct LORENZ C317 $.30   (T1468)

TOWNSEND, JOHN
    Fall On Your Knees
        SATB oct JUSKO 253 $.25   (T1469)

    Fool Hath Said In His Heart, The
        SATB oct JUSKO 280 $.25   (T1470)

    Jesus So Tender
        SATB oct JUSKO 255 $.25   (T1471)

    Let Peace Fill My Heart
        SATB oct JUSKO 251 $.25   (T1472)

    Seek Ye The Master
        SATB oct JUSKO 252 $.25   (T1473)

    Shepherd And His Sheep, The
        SATB oct JUSKO 254 $.25   (T1474)

TOZER, FERRIS
    Way Of The Cross, The *Lent/Psntd,cant
        SATB,STBar soli,org voc sc NOVELLO s.p.
                                                (T1475)

TRACHTET AM ERSTEN NACH DEM REICH GOTTES see
    Franck, Melchior

TRACHTET AM ERSTEN NACH DEM REICH GOTTES see
    Hartmann, Heinrich

TRACHTET AM ERSTEN NACH DEM REICH GOTTES see
    Raselius, Andreas

TRACHTET AM ERSTEN NACH DEM REICH GOTTES see
    Telemann, Georg Philipp

TRACHTET AM ERSTEN NACH DEM REICH GOTTES see
    Vulpius, Melchior

TRACHTET AM ERSTEN NACH DEM REICHE GOTTES see
    Cruger, Johann

TRACK
    Lullaby For Christmas Night *Xmas
        SOUTHERN $.35   (T1476)

    Rejoice And Be Glad *Xmas
        SA (Carinthian carol) SCHMITT 219 $.35 (T1477)

    Sing To The Lord A New Song *Gen
        SATB SCHMITT 8024 $.35   (T1478)

    Sleep Child Sweet And Mild
        SA KJOS 6106 $.30   (T1479)

    They Followed The Star *Xmas
        SATB SCHMITT 6103 $.40   (T1480)
        SA SCHMITT 2573 $.25   (T1481)

TRACK, GERHARD (1934-   )
    All Men Seek God *Xmas,anthem/cant
        SAB,org,opt orch (med easy) oct GIA G1754
        $.75   (T1482)

    Bagpipers' Carol *Xmas,anthem/carol,It
        SA (easy) oct GIA G1584 $.25   (T1483)

    Christmas Bells *Xmas
        SSA SCHMITT 233 $.30   (T1484)

    Christmas Cradle Song *Xmas,cradle
        SATB KJOS 5450 $.30   (T1485)

    Dear Nightingale, Awake *Xmas
        SA SCHMITT 224 $.35   (T1486)

    Festliches Ordinarium *Fest,Mass
        [Eng/Ger/Lat] mix cor,org,opt strings
        DOBLINGER voc sc s.p., voc pt s.p.
                                                (T1487)
        [Ger/Eng/Lat] 4pt mix cor,org,opt strings
        DOBLINGER voc sc s.p., cor pts s.p., ipa
                                                (T1488)

    Gloria
        SATB,acap SHAWNEE A 672 $.25   (T1489)

    Glory To God In The Highest
        4pt mix cor,acap oct SCHIRM.G 11710 $.35
                                                (T1490)

    Icy December, The *Xmas,anthem/carol
        SSA (med) oct GIA G1531 $.30   (T1491)

TRACK, GERHARD (cont'd.)

    It Soon Will Be Evening *Xmas
        SA (Tyrolean carol) SCHMITT 220 $.25
                                                (T1492)
        SATB SCHMITT 8064 $.35   (T1493)

    Jubilate Deo *anthem/Jubil
        "Shout With Joy" SATB (med diff) oct
        AUGSBURG 1361 $.35   (T1494)

    Let All Mortal Flesh Keep Silence *Gen,
        anthem
        SAB (med easy) oct GIA G1716 $.40   (T1495)

    Let Us All With Gladsome Voice *Gen,anthem/
        chorale,16th cent
        SAB (med) oct GIA G1556 $.30   (T1496)

    Lullaby For Christmas Night *Xmas
        SA SCHMITT 223 $.35   (T1497)
        SATB SCHMITT 923 $.35   (T1498)

    Mass In C Minor *Gen,Mass
        SATB (med) voc sc GIA G1564 $1.00   (T1499)

    My Heart This Night Rejoices *Xmas
        SA SCHMITT 225 $.25   (T1500)

    O Come, Let Us Sing To The Lord (Psalm 95)
        Gen,anthem
        SATB (med easy) oct GIA G1715 $.40   (T1501)

    Praise Ye The Lord (Psalm 150) Gen,anthem
        TTBB,TB soli (med diff) oct GIA G1018 $.75
                                                (T1502)
        SATB,SB soli (med diff) oct GIA G1037 $.75
                                                (T1503)

    Psalm 95 *see O Come, Let Us Sing To The
        Lord

    Psalm 141 *see To The Lord I Cry

    Psalm 150 *see Praise Ye The Lord

    Seven Stars Of The Assiniboine *Gen,anthem/
        cant,Ind
        SSAA&TTBB,SBarB soli (med) voc sc GIA G1409
        $1.50   (T1504)

    Shout With Joy *see Jubilate Deo

    Star, A *Xmas,anthem
        SA,solo (med easy) oct GIA G1752 $.30
                                                (T1505)

    Still, Still *Xmas,anthem/carol,Ger,20th
        cent
        SSA (med) oct GIA G1530 $.30   (T1506)

    There Is A God *Gen,anthem/prayer
        SA/TB,solo (med) oct GIA G1484 $.40   (T1507)
        TTBB,B solo (med) oct GIA G1482 $.40
                                                (T1508)
        SATB,A/Bar solo (med easy) oct GIA G1483
        $.25   (T1509)

    Three Austrian Carols *CC3U,carol,Aus
        SATB SHAWNEE A 762 $.40   (T1510)

    Thy Little Ones, Dear Lord, Are We *Xmas,
        anthem/carol
        SA (med) oct GIA G1591 $.30   (T1511)

    To The Lord I Cry (Psalm 141) Gen,anthem
        (Burke, H.C.) SATB (med) oct GIA G 1036
        $.30   (T1512)

    To You I Lift Up My Soul
        (Prentiss) SSA oct SUMMY M 2908 $.25
                                                (T1513)

    Whence Art Thou, My Maiden *Xmas,anthem
        SA (med easy) oct GIA G1753 $.30   (T1514)

    Ye Sons And Daughters *Easter,anthem
        cor,org,opt 3trp (easy) oct GIA G1474 $.40
                                                (T1515)

TRADER, WILLI (1920-   )
    Kommet Ihr Hirten
        5pt mix cor MOSELER LB-66 s.p.   (T1516)

    Lasst Uns Das Kindelein Wiegen *Xmas
        4pt mix cor MOSELER LB-205 s.p.   (T1517)

    O Du Frohliche
        5pt mix cor MOSELER LB-394 s.p.   (T1518)

TRADIDERUNT ME see Goodman, Joseph

TRADIDERUNT ME see Victoria, Tomas Luis de

TRADITIONAL CHRISTMAS CAROLS *CCU,Xmas,carol
    SATB/unis LORENZ C214 $.35   (T1519)

TRAGET MICH ZU MEINEM GRABE
    (Steiner, Lois; Uray, Ernst L.) mix cor,acap
    oct DOBLINGER s.p. see from Vier
    Totenlieder Aus St. Lambrecht   (T1520)

TRAHE ME see Palestrina, Giovanni

TRAHE ME POST TE see Gallus, Jacobus

TRAHE ME POST TE, VIRGO MARIA see Guerrero,
    Francisco

TRAMPIN' *spir
    (Pittman) SATB oct SPRATT 136 $.25   (T1521)

TRAMPING *spir
    2pt oct LORENZ 5717 $.25   (T1522)

TRANGER I DOLDA DJUPEN NER see Erlandson, Ake

TRANSEAMUS see Erdlen, Hermann

TRANSFIGE DULCISSIME DOMINE see Bordi, Giovanni

TRANSFIGE DULCISSME DOMINE see Bordi, Giovanni

TRANSFIGURATION see Berglund

TRANSFIGURATION see Dixon

TRANSFIGURATION see Hovhaness, Alan

TRANSFIGURATION see Tcherepnin, Alexander

TRANSFIGURATION, THE see Back, Sven-Erick

TRANSITUS ANIMAE see Perosi, (Dom) Lorenzo

TRANSITUS DIV. ANTONII PAT. see Sacchetto, Guido

TRANSITUS S. ANTONII see Ravanello, Oreste

TRANT, BRIAN
Love Came Down At Christmas *Xmas
SSA (easy) OXFORD 44.034 $.35   (T1523)
SS/SA (med easy) OXFORD 82.038 $.25 (T1524)

Missa Brevis *Mass
SATB (easy) oct OXFORD 43.946 $.25 (T1525)

Spacious Firmament, The *anthem
mix cor oct NOVELLO 28.1264.09 s.p. (T1526)

TRAUER see Haydn, (Franz) Joseph

TRAUER-HYMNE see Handel, George Frideric

TRAUERCHORAL see Messner, Karl

TRAUERHYMNE see Handel, George Frideric

TRAUERMUSIK see Bach, Johann Sebastian

TRAUERMUSIK see Bach, Johann Sebastian, Lass, Furstin, Lass Noch Einen Strahl

TRAUFELT IHR HIMMEL VON OBEN see Mendelssohn, Arnold

TRAUUNGSGESANG
(Bamer, Alfred) wom cor,acap oct DOBLINGER
s.p. see also Sechs Geistliche Chore
(T1527)

TRAVAGLIA, SILVIO
Inno A S. Franceso D'Assisi *ASD,hymn
[It] unis sc ZANIBON 648 s.p., cor pts
ZANIBON 649 s.p.   (T1528)

La Preghiera Del Mattino
unis ZANIBON 1773 s.p.   (T1529)

L'Ave Maria
unis ZANIBON 1753 s.p.   (T1530)

Missa Angelica *Mass
[Lat] 2pt jr cor/2pt,org,opt strings sc
ZANIBON 1908 s.p., voc pt ZANIBON s.p.,
ipr   (T1531)

Missa Pastoralis *Mass
[Lat] unis,opt org (very easy) sc ZANIBON
4324 s.p., cor pts ZANIBON 4325 s.p.
(T1532)

Missa Solemnis *Mass
[Lat] ABar,org sc ZANIBON 3602 s.p., voc pt
ZANIBON s.p.   (T1533)

Padre Nostro
unis ZANIBON 1844 s.p.   (T1534)

Pater Noster *prayer
[Lat] 2 eq voices,org ZANIBON 3869 s.p.
(T1535)

TRAVELER, THE see Wood

TRAVER
Jesus Saviour
SATB,acap SHAWNEE A 1031 $.30   (T1536)

Lord Eternal, Almighty
SATB oct GALAXY 1.2472.1 $.20   (T1537)

Praise The Lord Our King
SATB oct GALAXY 1.2455.1 $.30   (T1538)

TRAVER, JAMES
Hymn Of Triumph *Easter
SATB oct PRESSER 312-40562 $.35   (T1539)

In Bethlehem Town *Xmas
SATB,acap (med easy) oct CONCORDIA 98-1951
$.30   (T1540)

TRAVERS, JOHN (ca. 1703-1758)
Ascribe Unto The Lord *anthem
mix cor,TB soli oct NOVELLO 28.0147.07 s.p.
(T1541)
Ascribe Unto The Lord(First Section) *anthem
mix cor,TB soli oct NOVELLO 28.2147.08 s.p.
(T1542)

O Worship The Lord *Gen,anthem
unis,opt pno (contains also: Love One
Another by Wesley, S.S.) oct ROYAL 245
s.p. see also ANTHEMS FOR UNISON OR TWO
PART SINGING   (T1543)

Psalm Of Praise, A *Psalm
(Graves) 2pt jr cor/2pt wom cor CURWEN
72293 s.p.   (T1544)

TRE BIBLISKA SCENER see Schutz, Heinrich

TRE CANTATE SULLA PASSIONE DI CRISTO see
Labroca, Mario

TRE CANTI A MARIA see Ascenso, Antonio

TRE CANTI AL SACRO CUORE DI GESU see Arnaldi,
Antonio

TRE CANTI AL SS. CUORE DI GESU see Magri,
Pietro

TRE CANTI DI ACCLAMAZIONE see Dalla Vecchia,
Wolfango

TRE CANTI EUCARISTICI see Ramella

TRE CANTI PEL NATALE see Magri, Pietro

TRE CANTI PER BAMBINI see Somma

TRE CANTICI AL S. CUORE DI GESU
[Lat] 2 eq voices,org ZANIBON 497 s.p.
contains: Bottazzo, Luigi, Discite A Me;
Cossetti, Gio. Batta., O Bone Jesu;
Nicolosi, Salvatore, Cor Jesu Flagrans
(T1545)

TRE CORI see Rossini, Gioacchino

TRE CORI see Tocchi, [Gian-Luca]

TRE ENGELSKA MOTETTER *mot
mix cor NORDISKA NMS-6205 s.p.
contains: Byrd, William, Ave Regina
Caelorum [Lat]; Tallis, Thomas, Purge Me,
O Lord [Eng]; Weelkes, Thomas, Let Thy
Merciful Ears, O Lord [Eng]   (T1546)

TRE INNI E CANTICI see Rodella, Sante

TRE INNI EUCARISTICI see Renzi, Angelo

TRE INNI EUCARISTICI see Rodella, Sante

TRE INVOCAZIONI A MARIA see Favero, Gino

TRE ISPIRAZIONI see Vergani, G.

TRE LATINSKA HYMNER see Moren, John

TRE LAUDI ALLA SS. VERGINE MARIA see Zuccoli,
Gastone

TRE MAGNIFICAT see Cavalli, Francesco

TRE MOTECTA IN HON. B.V.M. *BVM,mot
[Lat] 2 eq voices,org ZANIBON 2736 s.p.
contains: Bottazzo, Luigi, Ave Maria;
Fabiani, Angelo, Ave Maria; Volpi,
Edoardo, Tota Pulchra   (T1547)

TRE MOTECTA IN HON. B.V.M. see Volpi, Edoardo

TRE MOTECTA MARIANA see Fuser, Ireneo

TRE MOTETTER see Bach, Johann Michael

TRE MOTTETTI A S. GIUSEPPE *CC3U,ASD,mot
[Lat] unis,org ZANIBON 2721 s.p. contains
works by: Di Fausto; Firpo; Volpi (T1548)

TRE MOTTETTI EUCARISTICI see Cervi, Luigi

TRE MOTTETTI EUCARISTICI see Grassi, Ciro

TRE MOTTETTI EUCARISTICI see Oltrassi, Giuseppe

TRE MOTTETTI PEL S. NATALE see Volpi, Edoardo

TRE MOTTETTI PEL VENERDI SANTO see Bianchini,
Carlo

TRE MOTTETTI PER MESSA NOVELLA, INGRESSO E
FESTA PARROCCHIALE see Arnaldi, Antonio

TRE MOTTETTI PER VISITA PASTORALE ED INGRESSO
PARROCCHIALE see Rioda, Umberto

TRE PEZZI SACRI see Razzi, Fausto

TRE TANTUM ERGO see Zimarino, Settimio

TREAD SOFTLY, SHEPHERDS see Graham, George

TREASURES IN HEAVEN see Burroughs

TREASURES IN HEAVEN see Clokey

TREASURY OF ENGLISH CHURCH MUSIC, THE VOL.1:5
*CCU
(Knight, Gerald H.; Reed, William L.) BROUDE,
A. $40.00   (T1549)

TREASURY OF ENGLISH CHURCH MUSIC, THE VOL.1
*CCU
(Knight, Gerald H.; Reed, William L.) BROUDE,
A. $8.50   (T1550)

TREASURY OF ENGLISH CHURCH MUSIC, THE VOL.2
*CCU
(Knight, Gerald H.; Reed, William L.) BROUDE,
A. $8.50   (T1551)

TREASURY OF ENGLISH CHURCH MUSIC, THE VOL.3
*CCU
(Knight, Gerald H.; Reed, William L.) BROUDE,
A. $8.50   (T1552)

TREASURY OF ENGLISH CHURCH MUSIC, THE VOL.4
*CCU
(Knight, Gerald H.; Reed, William L.) BROUDE,
A. $8.50   (T1553)

TREASURY OF ENGLISH CHURCH MUSIC, THE VOL.5
*CCU
(Knight, Gerald H.; Reed, William L.) BROUDE,
A. $8.50   (T1554)

TREBLE CAROLER *CCU,Xmas
treb cor SCHMITT 9082 $1.25   (T1555)

TREBLE CAROLLING *sac/sec,CC11L,Xmas,carol
(Multer) SSA PRO ART 1151 $1.25   (T1556)

TREBLE CHOIR *CCU
treb cor SCHMITT 9150 $1.00   (T1557)

TREBLE CHOIR RESPONSES see Heller

TREBLE CLEF CHORISTER *CCU
treb cor SCHMITT 9151 $.90   (T1558)

TREE OF LIFE, THE see Nelson

TREE OF PEACE see Bock, F.

TREE SPRINGS TO LIFE, THE see Lovelace, Austin
C.

TREES AND THE MASTER, THE see Vorse, R.

TREE'S NEW YEAR'S, THE see Low, Leo, Rosh
Hashanah L'ilanot

TREGASKIS
Ring Out Wild Bells
SATB,org/pno PETERS H708 $.40   (T1559)

TREMBLING SEIZED THE EARTH see Wiltberger,
Terra Tremuit

TREMPER, FRED
God So Loved The World *Bibl
SATB,acap oct WORLD ESA-1852-8 $.45 (T1560)

TRENTETRE HYMNI ET CANTICA *CC33U,BVM/Fest/
Psntd/Proces,hymn
[Lat] unis,org/inst sc ZANIBON 293 s.p., cor

pts ZANIBON 292 s.p., ipa   (T1561)

TRENTUNO LITANIE LAURETANE *CC31U
[Lat] 2-3 eq voices,org (easy) ZANIBON 3100
s.p.   (T1562)

TRES CANTIONES SACRAE see Kelterborn, Rudolf

TRES SACRAE CANTIONES see Gesualdo, Don Carlo

TRES SUNT see Burkhart, Franz

TRES SUNT see Haydn, (Johann) Michael

TREUER WACHTER ISRAEL see Kubler, Emil

TREUER WACHTER ISRAEL, DES SICH FREUET see
Kubler, Emil

TREVISIOL, MARIO
Inno Missionario *hymn
[Lat] unis,pno/orch sc ZANIBON 4378 s.p.,
cor pts ZANIBON 4379 s.p., ipr   (T1563)

TREXLER, GEORG (1903-)
Adorate Deum *Epiph
[Ger] SATB,acap (med) MULLER SM 728 s.p.
(T1564)

Assumpta Est Maria *Fest,cant
[Lat] SSATB,soli,orch (med diff) MULLER
SM 1665 voc sc s.p., cor pts s.p., ipr
(T1565)

Ave Maria *Fest
[Lat] SAATBB,acap (med) MULLER MS 39 s.p.
(T1566)

Ecce Sacerdos Magnus
4pt mix cor&8pt mix cor,acap cor pts
BREITKOPF-L CHB-2918 s.p.   (T1567)

Exaudi, Domine *Pent
[Lat] SATB,acap (med) MULLER SM 729 s.p.
(T1568)

Extuli Electum De Populo *Gen
[Lat] SATB&SATB,acap (med diff) MULLER
MS 56 s.p.   (T1569)

Gnade Euch Und Friede
see Zwei Hymnen
cor pts BREITKOPF-L CHB-2932 s.p. see from
Zwei Hymnen   (T1570)

Ich Horte Etwas Wie Die Stimme Vielen Volkes
see Zwei Hymnen
cor pts BREITKOPF-L CHB-2933 s.p. see from
Zwei Hymnen   (T1571)

In Te Domine, Speravi *Mass
[Lat] SATB,org/winds (med diff) MULLER
SM 1959 voc sc s.p., cor pts s.p. (T1572)

Puer Natus Est *Xmas
[Lat] SATB,acap (med easy, appropriate for
third christmas mass) MULLER SM 702 s.p.
(T1573)

Salve Regina *Trin
[Lat] SAATBB,acap (med) MULLER MS 1 s.p.
(T1574)

Zwei Hymnen *see Gnade Euch Und Friede; Ich
Horte Etwas Wie Die Stimme Vielen Volkes
(T1575)

Zwei Hymnen *hymn
mix cor,org,2ob,2clar,3bsn,4horn,2trp,
3trom,tuba voc sc BREITKOPF-L EB-5791
s.p., sc BREITKOPF-L PB-4036 s.p.
contains: Gnade Euch Und Friede; Ich
Horte Etwas Wie Die Stimme Vielen
Volkes   (T1576)

TRIA COR JESU
[Lat] ZANIBON 2766 s.p.
contains: Mangone, Gioacchino, Cor Jesu (2
eq voices,org); Moioli, Romano, Cor Jesu
(2 eq voices,org); Volpi, Edoardo, Cor
Jesu (S/T,org)   (T1577)

TRIA MOTECTA see Volpi, Edoardo

TRIA MOTECTA IN FESTO SEPTEM DOL. B.V.M. *BVM,
mot
[Lat] ZANIBON 2747 s.p.
contains: Crispo, E., Sancta Mater (B,org);
Volpi, Edoardo, Cui Comparabo (A/B,org);
Volpi, Edoardo, Recordare (2 eq voices,
org)   (T1578)

TRIA MOTECTA NATALICIA see Bottazzo, Luigi

TRIA RESPONSORIA see Palestrina, Giovanni

TRIBULATIONES CIVITATUM see Gallus, Jacobus

TRIBULATONES CIVITATUM see Thomson, Virgil

TRIBUS MIRACULIS see Marenzio, Luca

TRIBUTE OF CAROLS, A see Gordon

TRIBUTE TO MOTHER, A *Aus
SATB oct LORENZ A276 $.25   (T1579)

TRIEMBACHER, HENRIETTE
Tantum Ergo
wom cor,acap oct DOBLINGER s.p.   (T1580)

TRILLER, VALENTIN
Fra Himlen Kom En Engel Klar *Xmas,16th
cent/17th cent
(Larsen, Jens Peter) [Dan] SATB (contains
also: Praetorius, Michael, Fra Himlen Kom
En Engel Klar) HANSEN-DEN 206 s.p. see
also JULESANGE   (T1581)
(Larsen, Jens Peter) [Dan] STB HANSEN-DEN
25768 s.p. see also JULESANGE   (T1582)

TRILOGY see Elaine, Sister M. (Gentemann)

TRILOGY FOR HOLY WEEK, A see Morgan

TRIMBLE, LESTER (1923-)
Var Gud Ei Med Oss Denne Tid
[Norw] mix cor LYCHE 11 s.p.   (T1583)

TRIONFA O SOLE! see Pagella, G.

TRIPLE AMEN, THE see Peloquin, C. Alexander

TRIPTYCH see Hovhaness, Alan

TRIPTYCH see Nagel

TRIPTYCHON see Graap, Lothar

TRIPTYCHON see Wolters, K.-H.

TRIPTYCHON ZU WORTEN DES ST. THOMAS see
Raphael, Gunther

TRIPYCHON see Matthes, Rene

TRIR AND GO see Simpson, Kenneth

TRISTE ESTABA EL REY DAVID see Rodrigo

TRISTESSE see Bach, Johann Sebastian

TRISTIS EST ANIMA MEA *Easter/Lent,16th cent
(Martens, Mason) "Sad Is My Soul" SATBct
WALTON 2053 $.25   (T1584)

TRISTIS EST ANIMA MEA see Haydn, (Johann)
Michael

TRISTIS EST ANIMA MEA see Ingegneri, Marco
Antonio

TRISTIS EST ANIMA MEA see Kuhnau, Johann

TRISTIS EST ANIMA MEA see Lassus, Roland de
(Orlandus)

TRISTIS EST ANIMA MEA see Martini, Padre

TRISTIS EST ANIMA MEA see Nasco

TRISTIS EST ANIMA MEA see Palestrina, Giovanni

TRISTIS EST ANIMA MEA see Rubbra, Edmund

TRISTIS EST ANIMAE MEA see Poulenc, Francis

TRIUMPH AND REJOICE IN THE LORD see Viadana,
Lodovico Grossi da, Exultate Justi In
Domino

TRIUMPH OF CHRIST, THE see Marth, Helen Jun

TRIUMPH OF FAITH, THE see Thompson, Randall

TRIUMPH OF THE CROSS, THE see Matthews, Harvey
Alexander

TRIUMPH-SONG, THE see Mueller, Carl F.

TRIUMPH! THANKSGIVING see Rachmaninoff, Sergey
Vassilievitch

TRIUMPH, TRIUMPH, VICTORIA see Hammerschmidt,
Andreas

TRIUMPHAL HYMN see Brahms, Johannes

TRIUMPHAL TE DEUM see Nelson, Ronald A.

TRIUMPHANT CHRIST, THE see Cain, Noble

TRIUMPHANT FANFARE see Zanton

TRIUMPHANT GLADNESS see Young, C.

TROENS TRIUMF see Nystedt, Knut

TROGET VID DITT KORS see Bengtsson, [Gustav
Adolf Tiburt]

TROIS ANTIENNES A LA SAINTE VIERGE see Busser,
[Henri-Paul]

TROIS CHANTS BEARNAIS see Vuillermoz, [Jean]

TROIS CHANTS D'EGLISE see Caplet, [Lucien]

TROIS LITURGIES JOYEUSES see Schmitt, Florent

TROIS MOTETS see Thiriet, [Maurice]

TROIS NOELS see Bonnal, Ermend

TROIS NOELS FRANCAIS see Favre, Georges

TROIS PIECES LITURGIQUES see Rosenthal, Manuel

TROIS ROIS SONT EN CAMPAGNE *Xmas,carol,Fr
(Tomasi) [Fr] 2pt/3pt,pno/orch LEDUC s.p. see
also Douze Noels De Saboly   (T1585)

TROISIEME MESSE SOLENNELLE see Cherubini, Luigi

TROISIEME SALUT see Heidet, Le R. P.

TROLL THE ANCIENT CAROL *Xmas,carol
(Luboff, Norman) SATB,opt winds&perc oct
WALTON 2752 $.50, cmplt ed WALTON 2752A
$6.00
contains: Baloo Lammy; Deck The Halls; Here
We Come A-Wassailing   (T1586)

TROMAN, THOMAS
Pax Dei
SATB oct NOVELLO s.p.   (T1587)

Te Deum *Te Deum
SATB (E flat maj) oct NOVELLO s.p. (T1588)

TROPHY OF HIS LOVE, A see Johnson, Paul

TROSET TROSET MEIN VOLK see Schutz, Heinrich

TROST see Schmid, Walter

TROST-ARIA see Gattermayer, Heinrich

TROST MICH, O HERR see Forster, Georg

TROSTE, TROSTE UNS GOTT see Pachelbel, Johann

TROSTER MITT FOLK see Palmer, C.

TROSTET, SPRICHT DER HERR see Weismann, Wilhelm

TROSTET, TROSTET MEIN VOLK see Schutz, Heinrich

"TROSTET, TROSTET", SPRICHT DER HERR see
Micheelsen, Hans Friedrich

TROSTGESANG UND STERBELIED
(Stern, A.) [Ger] wom cor,acap HUG s.p.
contains: Praetorius, Michael, Wenn Wir In

Hochsten Noten Sein; Sweelinck, Jan
Pieterszoon, Mein Junges Leben Hat Ein
End   (T1589)

TROSTLIED AM ABEND "IN JEDER NACHT, DIE MICH
BEDROHT" see Lohr, Ina

TROUBLE WILL BURY ME DOWN
(Lynn, G.) SATB,acap oct PRESSER 312-40352
$.25   (T1590)

TROXELL
Responses For Mixed Choir *CCU
SATB FLAMMER A 5517 $.30   (T1591)

TRUBEL, GERHARD (1917-   )
Abend Ward, Bald Kommt Die Nacht
see Trubel, Gerhard, So Wunsch Ich Euch Ein
Gute Nacht
SAT/SAB HANSSLER 6.270 s.p. contains also:
Spiele, Kleine Flote (SAT/SAB); Ich Hebe
Meine Augen Auf (3pt) (canon) (CC)
                                 (T1592)

Ach Wie Fluchtig, Ach Wie Nichtig
SATB HANSSLER 6.138 s.p. contains also:
Bach, Johann Sebastian, Ach Wie Fluchtig,
Ach Wie Nichtig [Chorale] (from Ach Wie
Fluchtig, Ach Wie Nichtig) (Trin,G min)
                                 (T1593)

Aus Meines Herzens Grunde *see Nun Jauchzet,
All Ihr Frommen

Christ Ist Erstanden Von Der Marter *Easter
SSATB/SSAT/SSAB HANSSLER 6.127 s.p. (T1594)

Dein Tod Gebietet Schweigen
see Bossler, Kurt, Fragst Du Nach Meiner
Sunde

Der Erste Psalm *Psalm
SSATTB,T solo,bvl,cembalo, opt metallophone
sc HANSSLER 10.203 rental   (T1595)

Der Mond Ist Aufgegangen
SATB HANSSLER 6.078 s.p. contains also:
Spiele, Kleine Flote (SATB,2rec); Mude
Bin Ich, Geh Zur Ruh (SAT/SAB/SATB)
                                 (T1596)

Der Morgenstern Ist Aufgedrungen
SAT/SAB/SST/SSB HANSSLER 6.091 s.p.
contains also: Anonymous, Wir Danken Dir,
Herr Jesu Christ (SATB)   (T1597)

Der Tag Geht Mud Von Hinnen
see Praetorius, Michael, Ich Dank Dir Schon
Durch Deinen Sohn

Die Guldne Sonne Voll Freud Und Wonne *cant
SAB/SAT HANSSLER 6.077 s.p. contains also:
Morgenglanz Der Ewigkeit (T1598)
SAB,2inst&opt vln/fl&opt vcl, triangle,
glockenspiel HANSSLER 10.073 sc s.p., cor
pts s.p.   (T1599)

Freut Euch, Ihr Lieben Christen *Xmas
SSAT/SSAB HANSSLER 6.264 s.p. contains
also: Praetorius, Michael, Ein Kind
Geborn Zu Bethlehem (SAT/SAB);
Praetorius, Michael, Seid Frohlich Und
Jubiliert (SSAT/SSAB); Praetorius,
Michael, Das Alte Jahr Ist Nun Dahin
(SSAT/SSAB)   (T1600)

Gott Des Himmels Und Der Erden
SAB/SAT HANSSLER 6.081 s.p. contains also:
Albert, Heinrich, Gott Des Himmels Und
Der Erden (SSATB)   (T1601)

Gott Rufet Noch, Sollt Ich Nicht
see Kubler, Emil, Treuer Wachter Israel

Gottes Sohn Ist Kommen
see Trubel, Gerhard, Nun Jauchzet, All Ihr
Frommen

Herr, Unser Herrscher
see Gumpeltzhaimer, Adam, O Lieber Gott Im
Hochsten Thron

Ich Hebe Meine Augen Auf
see Trubel, Gerhard, Abend Ward, Bald Kommt
Die Nacht

Jauchz, Erd Und Himmel
SAT/SAB HANSSLER 6.267 s.p. contains also:
Trubel, Gerhard, O Mensch, Bewein Dein
Sunde Gross (SAT/SAB); Schroter,
Leonhard, Allein Gott In Der Hoh (SSAT/
SSAB)   (T1602)

Jauchzt Alle Lande, Gott Zu Ehren
SAB/SAT HANSSLER 6.178 s.p.   (T1603)

Jesu, Meine Freude
SA,org/cembalo HANSSLER 5.047 s.p. (T1604)

Liebster Jesu, Wir Sind Hier
see Goudimel, Claude, Es Geht Daher Des
Tages Schein

Lobe Den Herren, Den Machtigen Konig
see Gumpeltzhaimer, Adam, Wir Danken Dir,
Gott, Fur Und Fur

Lobet Gott Mit Frohlichem Mund
see Goudimel, Claude, Es Geht Daher Des
Tages Schein

Lobt Gott, Ihr Christen Alle Gleich *Thanks
SAT/SAB HANSSLER 6.096 s.p. contains also:
Stern, Hermann, Der Tag, Der Ist So
Freudenreich (SATB)   (T1605)

Mit Freuden Zart Zu Dieser Fahrt (from
Matthaus-Passion)
see de la Rue, Pierre, Wir Danken Dir, O
Gottes Lamm

Morgenglanz Der Ewigkeit
see Trubel, Gerhard, Die Guldne Sonne Voll
Freud Und Wonne

Mude Bin Ich, Geh Zur Ruh
see Trubel, Gerhard, Der Mond Ist
Aufgegangen

Nun Bitten Wir Den Heiligen Geist
SAB/SAT HANSSLER 6.130 s.p. contains also:
Bach, Johann Sebastian, Komm, Gott

TRUBEL, GERHARD (cont'd.)

Schopfer, Heiliger Geist, S.370 (SATB)
                                 (T1606)

Nun Freut Euch, Lieben Christen Gmein *cant
SAB,3inst HANSSLER 10.053 sc s.p., cor pts
s.p.   (T1607)

Nun Jauchzet, All Ihr Frommen
"Aus Meines Herzens Grunde" SAT/SAB
HANSSLER 6.263 s.p. contains also: Gottes
Sohn Ist Kommen (3pt) (canon); Wie Soll
Ich Dich Empfangen (SAT/SAB)   (T1608)

Nun Komm, Der Heiden Heiland
see Eccard, Johannes, Nun Komm, Der Heiden
Heiland

O Mensch, Bewein Dein Sunde Gross
see Trubel, Gerhard, Jauchz, Erd Und Himmel

Sei Lob Und Ehr Dem Hochsten Gut
see Cruger, Johann, Sei Lob Und Ehr Dem
Hochsten Gut

So Wunsch Ich Euch Ein Gute Nacht *Eve
SATB HANSSLER 6.084 s.p. contains also:
Schein, Johann Hermann, Die Nacht Ist
Kommen, Drin Wir Ruhen; Trubel, Gerhard,
Abend Ward, Bald Kommt Die Nacht (T1609)

Sonne Der Gerechtigkeit, Gehe Auf
see Jeep, Johann, Ich Ruf Zu Dir, Herr Jesu
Christ

Spiele, Kleine Flote
see Trubel, Gerhard, Abend Ward, Bald Kommt
Die Nacht
see Trubel, Gerhard, Der Mond Ist
Aufgegangen

Vom Himmel Hoch, Da Komm Ich Her
see Trubel, Gerhard, Vom Himmel Kam Der
Engel Schar

Vom Himmel Kam Der Engel Schar *Xmas
SAB/SAT HANSSLER 6.092 s.p. contains also:
Vom Himmel Hoch, Da Komm Ich Her (SSATB/
SSAT/SSAB)   (T1610)

Wach Auf, Mein Herz, Und Singe *cant
SAA/TTB,org,3inst HANSSLER 10.052 sc s.p.,
cor pts s.p.   (T1611)
SSA/TTB,org,3inst HANSSLER 10.052 sc s.p.,
cor pts s.p.   (T1612)

War Gott Nicht Mit Uns Diese Zeit
see Bach, Johann Sebastian, War Gott Nicht
Mit Uns Diese Zeit

Wenn Mein Stundlein Vorhanden Ist
see Altenburg, Michael, Herr Gott, Nun
Schleuss Den Himmel Auf

Wie Soll Ich Dich Empfangen
see Trubel, Gerhard, Nun Jauchzet, All Ihr
Frommen

Wir Danken Dir, Herr Jesu Christ, Das Du
see Schutz, Heinrich, Aller Augen Warten
Auf Dich

Wir Wollen Alle Frohlich Sein (from Matthaus-
Passion)
see Metzger, Hans-Arnold, Christ Lag In
Todesbanden, Fur Unsre Sund
see Weber, Karl-Heinz, Erschienen Ist Der
Herrlich Tag

Wunderbarer Konig, Herrscher
SAT/SAB HANSSLER 6.152 s.p. contains also:
Wunderbarer Konig, Herrscher (SSTB/SSAB)
                                 (T1613)

Wunderbarer Konig, Herrscher
see Trubel, Gerhard, Wunderbarer Konig,
Herrscher

TRUE AND LIVING WAY see Simeone

TRUE FASTING see Brandon, George

TRUE-HEARTED, WHOLE-HEARTED see Lynn, George

TRUE LOVE'S THE GIFT see Chambers, H.A.

TRUE VINE, THE *hymn,US
(Terri) SATB,acap oct LAWSON 802 $.25 (T1614)

TRUED
Come Now To His Table
SATB,acap BOSTON 12869 $.35   (T1615)

Precious Child So Sweetly Sleeping *Xmas
SATB oct PRO ART 1691 $.22   (T1616)

Seek The Lord
SATB oct BELWIN 2192 $.30   (T1617)

This Is My Commandment
SATB oct SACRED S-21 $.35   (T1618)

While Jesus Lay Asleep
SATB oct BELWIN 2091 $.25   (T1619)

TRUED, CLARENCE
Come, Lord Of Life
cor HIGHLAND 4129 $.30   (T1620)

Eternal Trinity
4pt mix cor,acap oct SCHIRM.G 11393 $.30
                                 (T1621)

Father, The Hour Has Come *anthem
SATB oct FOX R199 $.25   (T1622)

Have Faith In God
SATB oct BELWIN 2193 $.25   (T1623)
SATB oct BELWIN 2146 $.25   (T1624)

He Is Risen
SATB oct BELWIN 2120 $.25   (T1625)

Hear Me, O Lord (Psalm 61)
SATB oct BELWIN 2196 $.30   (T1626)

Let Us Sing To The Lord A Song Of Joy
SATB oct BELWIN 2081 $.25   (T1627)

TRUED, CLARENCE (cont'd.)

My Sheep Hear My Voice
cor HIGHLAND 4126 $.30 (T1628)

O Clap Your Hands
SATB oct BELWIN 2048 $.35 (T1629)

O God Of Love
SATB (easy) ABINGDON APM-375 $.30 (T1630)

Psalm 61 *see Hear Me, O Lord

Rejoice, O Zion, Shout And Sing!
SATB oct FISCHER,J 9836 $.35 (T1631)

Remember Also Thy Creator
SATB,band/orch BELWIN $1.00, ipr (T1632)

To Thee O Lord I Lift My Soul
SATB oct BELWIN 2119 $.25 (T1633)

TRUED, S. CLARENCE (1895-)
Give Ear, O Lord
SATB,acap PEER $.35 (T1634)

Save Me, O Lord!
SATB,acap PEER $.40 (T1635)

TRULY I MUST PERISH see Monteverdi, Claudio

TRULY MY SOUL see Billings, William

TRULY MY SOUL WAITETH UPON GOD see Sacco, P.

TRULY MY SOUL WAITETH UPON GOD see Sanders

TRULY MY SOUL WAITETH UPON THE LORD see
Mueller, Carl F.

TRULY, TRULY, I SAY TO YOU see Krapf, Gerhard

TRULY WAS THE WORD MADE FLESH see Schein,
Johann Hermann, Verbum Caro Factum Est

TRULY WE SHALL BE IN PARADISE WITH HIM see
Neumann, Alfred

TRUMPET GLORIA see Dufay, Guillaume

TRUMPET GLORIA, A see Dressler, John

TRUMPET OF GOD see Barraclough

TRUMPET SHALL SOUND, THE see Handel, George
Frideric

TRUMPETERS AND SINGERS WERE AS ONE, THE see
Powell, Robert J.

TRUMPETS OF ZION see Christiansen, Olaf
Christian

TRUNK, [RICHARD] (1879-1968)
O Du Mein Trost
[Ger] mix cor,acap (med) HUG s.p. (T1636)

Scheiden Und Meiden *Op.43,No.2
men cor (med easy) oct LEUCKART 232 s.p.
(T1637)

TRUSLER
Gentle Jesus, Meek And Mild *Xmas
SATB oct PLYMOUTH TR-101 $.25 (T1638)

Lay Down Your Staffs *Xmas
SATB oct PLYMOUTH TR-107 $.25 (T1639)

Sing We All Noel *Xmas
SATB oct PLYMOUTH TR-108 $.25 (T1640)

TRUSLER, IVAN (1925-)
Angel And The Shepherds, The *Xmas
SATB (med) ABINGDON APM-817 $.40 (T1641)

TRUSSELLE, STANLEY
Christ Is Risen, Alleluia *Easter
SATB oct JUSKO 173 $.20 (T1642)

TRUST see Sibelius, Jean

TRUST, HEINZ-EWALD (1928-)
Ein Segen Hat Ergossen Sich
see Vier Weihnachtslieder

Furwahr, Er Trug Unsre Krankheit
SATB HANSSLER 6.293 s.p. contains also:
Siehe, Das Ist Gottes Lamm (T1643)

Hirten, Stehet Auf, Eilet Im Raschen Lauf
see Vier Weihnachtslieder

Hor, Bruder, Was Kundet Der Engel
see Vier Weihnachtslieder

Ich Hab Ein Herzlich Freud Und Gross
SATB HANSSLER 6.6106 s.p. (T1644)

Im Anfang War's Auf Erden
see Nother, Willi, Wir Danken, Herr, Fur
Brot Und Kleid

Siehe, Das Ist Gottes Lamm
see Trust, Heinz-Ewald, Furwahr, Er Trug
Unsre Krankheit

Vier Weihnachtslieder *Xmas
SATB HANSSLER 6.6107 s.p.
contains: Ein Segen Hat Ergossen Sich;
Hirten, Stehet Auf, Eilet Im Raschen
Lauf; Hor, Bruder, Was Kundet Der
Engel; Zu Bethlehem Geboren Ist Uns
(T1645)

Zu Bethlehem Geboren Ist Uns
see Vier Weihnachtslieder

TRUST IN HIM see Hamblen, [Bernard]

TRUST IN HIM see Rasley, [John M.]

TRUST IN THE LORD see Berger, Jean

TRUST IN THE LORD see Davis, Katherine K.

TRUST IN THE LORD see Eberlin, Johann Ernst,
Bonum Est Confiteri

TRUST IN THE LORD see Freestone, G.S.

TRUST IN THE LORD see Fuller, [Esther Mary]

TRUST IN THE LORD see Handel, George Frideric

TRUST IN THE LORD see McCormick

TRUST IN THE LORD see Nystedt, Knut

TRUST IN THE LORD AND DO GOOD see Ouchterlony,
David

TRUST IN THE WORD OF THE LORD see Brown,
William David

TRUST THOU IN GOD see Mendelssohn-Bartholdy,
Felix

TRUST YE IN THE LORD see Barnes, H.W.S.

TRUST YE IN THE LORD see Wilson, Ira B.

TRUTH ABOUT CHRISTMAS, THE see Burgstahler,
Elton

TRUTH OF THE LORD ENDURETH FOREVER, THE see
Lekberg, Sven

TRUTH SENT FROM ABOVE, THE
(Vaughn Williams, Ralph) SATB/unis,pno GALAXY
s.p. see also Eight Traditional Carols
(T1646)

TRY ME, O GOD see Greene, Maurice

TRY ME O GOD see Haydn, (Franz) Joseph

TRY ME, O GOD see Nares, James

TRYGGARE KAN INGEN VARA
see Klippa Du Som Brast For Mig

TRYGGHET HOS GUD see Olson, Daniel

TRYSTE NOEL see Klein, Ivy Frances

TRYTHALL, GILBERT
Time To Every Purpose
SATB&cong,electronic tape MARKS $.85, ipa
(T1647)

TSCHESNOKOFF, P.I.
Angel's Song, The *Xmas
(Krone) SATB,acap WARNER W2742 $.30 (T1648)

Bless The Lord
SATB oct FISCHER,J 4498 $.30 (T1649)

Bring Thy Glory To Us *Easter,liturg,Jew
(Hallagan, R.) SSAA,acap oct PRESSER
312-40786 $.30 (T1650)
(Hallagan, R.) SATB,acap oct PRESSER
312-40434 $.30 (T1651)

Come Thou Holy Spirit
boy cor SOUTHERN $.30 (T1652)
(Trusler) SAB,acap WARNER W3674 $.30
(T1653)

Glorious Is Thy Name
(Watson, R.) SSA&opt men cor,acap WARNER
G1640 $.30 (T1654)

Glory Be To Thee *Gen
(Honaas) SATTBB SCHMITT 1576 $.20 (T1655)

Let Thy Blessed Spirit
SATB oct FISCHER,J 4497 $.30 (T1656)

Let Thy Holy Presence
(Ehret) SAB,acap oct PRO ART 1600 $.30
(T1657)
(Ehret) SATB,opt kbd oct PRO ART 1514 $.30
(T1658)
(Ehret) 2pt oct PRO ART 2105 $.20 (T1659)
(Ehret) SSA,acap oct PRO ART 1687 $.30
(T1660)

Let Thy Holy Spirit Come Upon Us
(Lyall) SATB,acap oct LAWSON 660 $.30
(T1661)

Now Unto Thee
(Ehret) SATB oct BOURNE BL3034 $.25 (T1662)

O Light Divine
(Tkach) SATB oct BOURNE 775 $.25 (T1663)

Salvation Is Created *Gen,anthem
TTBB oct FISCHER,J 8381 $.30 (T1664)
SATB,opt band KJOS 7038 $.30 (T1665)
SATTBB oct FISCHER,J 4129 $.30 (T1666)
(Becker, A.C.) SATTBB (easy) oct GIA G1542
$.25 (T1667)
(Butts) SATB oct PLYMOUTH SC-30 $.35
(T1668)
(Ehret) TTBB oct BOURNE BL3044 $.25 (T1669)
(Ehret) SATB oct BOURNE BL2483 $.25 (T1670)
(McKinney) SSA oct FISCHER,J 9177 $.30
(T1671)
(McKinney) SATB oct FISCHER,J 9685 $.30
(T1672)
(McKinney) SAB oct FISCHER,J 9150 $.30
(T1673)
(White) 4pt mix cor,acap oct SCHIRM.G 10804
$.25 (T1674)

Sing We Now Thy Praise
(Carlyle) SATB oct PLYMOUTH SC-8 $.25
(T1675)

Spirit Of God
(Howorth) SATB,opt acap oct FOX PS179 $.30
(T1676)

Thou Life Of Our Life
(Ehret) SATB oct BOURNE BL3033 $.25 (T1677)

Wake, Ye Saints
(Ehret) SATB oct BOURNE BL3032 $.25 (T1678)

TSCHESNOKOFF, PAUL
see TCHESNOKOV, PAVEL GRIGORIEVITCH

TSCHESNOKOV
see TCHESNOKOV, PAVEL GRIGORIEVITCH

TTBB CHORALE BOOK, THE see Hoelty-Nickel,
Theodore

TU CHE NELL'ETERE VIVI BEATO see Ravanello,
Oreste

TU DER VOLKER TUREN AUF see Thieme, Karf

TU ES DEUS see Eberlin, Johann Ernst

TU ES PASTOR OVIUM see Byrd, William

TU ES PETRUS see Arnaldi, Antonio

TU ES PETRUS see Burkhart, Franz

TU ES PETRUS see Busser, [Henri-Paul]

TU ES PETRUS see Byrd, William

TU ES PETRUS see Clemens, Jacobus

TU ES PETRUS see Cornelius, Peter

TU ES PETRUS see Delvincourt, Claude

TU ES PETRUS see Dubois, Theodore

TU ES PETRUS see Durufle, Maurice

TU ES PETRUS see Faure, Gabriel-Urbain

TU ES PETRUS see Faure, Jean-Baptist

TU ES PETRUS see Hahn, Reynaldo

TU ES PETRUS see Lassus, Roland de (Orlandus)

TU ES PETRUS see Mendelssohn-Bartholdy, Felix

TU ES PETRUS see Mendelssohn-Bartholdy, Felix,
Verleih Uns Frieden

TU ES PETRUS see Paladilhe, [Emile]

TU ES PETRUS see Palestrina, Giovanni

TU ES PETRUS see Ravanello, Oreste

TU ES PETRUS see Renzi, Angelo

TU ES PETRUS see Rodella, Sante

TU ES PETRUS see Saint-Saens, Camille

TU ES PETRUS see Scarlatti, Alessandro

TU ES PETRUS see Schmitt, Florent

TU ES PETRUS see Stalin, G.

TU ES PETRUS see Victoria, Tomas Luis de

TU ES SACERDOS see Arnaldi, Antonio

TU ES SACERDOS see Bentivoglio, Giulio

TU ES SACERDOS see Bottazzo, Luigi

TU ES SACERDOS see Corradini, Vasco Lodovico

TU ES SACERDOS see Ferrari, Giuseppe

TU ES SACERDOS see Ferro, Stefano

TU ES SACERDOS see Giacomello, Pietro

TU ES SACERDOS see Pasini, Crescenzio

TU ES SACERDOS see Ravanello, Oreste

TU ES SACERDOS see Rioda, Umberto

TU ES SACERDOS see Volpi, Edoardo

TU, MENTIS DELECTATIO see Giovanelli, [Ruggero]

TU PAUPERUM REFUGIUM see Des Prez, Josquin

TU SCENDI DALLE STELLE *Xmas
see Tanti Auguri
(Comin, L.) unis/3pt,pno/org ZANIBON 3204
s.p. (T1679)

TU SCENDI DALLE STELLE see McKinney, Howard D.

TU SCENDI DALLE STELLE see Picchi, Luigi

TU SEI SACERDOTE see Leoni, Leonardo

TU SOLUS see Des Prez, Josquin

TU SOLUS QUI FACIS MIRABILLA see Des Prez,
Josquin

TU VIRGINUM CORONA see Mozart, Wolfgang Amadeus

TUBB, MONTE
Agnus Dei *Agnus
"Lamb Of God" [Eng/Lat] SATB,acap oct
LAWSON 51132 $.25 (T1680)

Free Me Lord *see Libera Me

Lamb Of God *see Agnus Dei

Libera Me
"Free Me Lord" [Eng/Lat] 2pt boy cor/SA oct
LAWSON 51406 $.30 (T1681)

TUCKER
Come, Worship The Child *Xmas
2pt jr cor oct LILLENAS AN-4014 $.25
(T1682)

Magnificat And Nunc Dimittis *see Cooke,
Arnold

TUCKER, IRENE
Happiest Christmas Day *Xmas
unis PROWSE s.p. (T1683)

TUE RECHNUNG see Bach, Johann Sebastian

TUE RECHNUNG, DONNERWORT see Bach, Johann
Sebastian

TUI SUNT COELI see Palestrina, Giovanni

TUI SUNT COELI see Picchi, Luigi

TUI SUNT COELI see Wiltberger

TULERUNT DOMINUM MEUM see Scheidt, Samuel

TULLAR
Face To Face
(McLellan) SSATB oct LILLENAS AT-1043 $.30
(T1684)

TUMA, FRANTISEK IGNAZ ANTONIN (1704-1774)
Stabat Mater *Psntd
mix cor,acap SUPRAPHON s.p.
(T1685)
[Lat/Eng] mix cor,T solo,org voc sc BOOSEY
$2.50
(T1686)
[Ger] SATB,org (med) ARTIA AP 1805 s.p.
(T1687)

TUNDER, FRANZ (1614-1667)
Eine Feste Burg Ist Unser Gott *anthem
[Ger] cor,org,strings KISTNER sc s.p., cor
pts s.p., ipa
(T1688)

Herr, Nun Lassest Du Deinen Diener
cor,inst voc sc HANSEN-DEN 29103 s.p.
(T1689)

Hosianna Dem Sohne Davids *cant
(Kruger) SSATB,B solo,cont,2vln,2vla
HANSSLER 10.047 sc s.p., voc sc s.p., ipa
(T1690)

Jesus Little One *Xmas
(Thompson, R.) SATB oct PRESSER 312-40106
$.30
(T1691)

Scatter Palm Branches *Palm
(Lillehaug, L.) SSATB,strings CONCORDIA
97-6406 $.45, ipa
(T1692)

Sions Vekter Hever Rosten
[Norw] cor,solo,org,strings LYCHE 53 s.p.
(T1693)

Wake, Awake, For Night Is Flying *Adv/ECY
unis,kbd (med easy) oct CONCORDIA 98-1816
$.20
(T1694)

TUNE ME, O LORD see Starer, Robert

TUNEFUL TEENS (BOOK 1) *CC20UL,spir
(Fisher, Marge) unis&2pt&SAB&SATB cmplt ed
LILLENAS MB-220 $1.00
(T1695)

TUNEFUL TEENS (BOOK 2) *CC18UL,spir
(Fisher, Marge) unis&2pt&SAB&SATB cmplt ed
LILLENAS MB-221 $1.00
(T1696)

TUNGER, ALBRECHT
Die Weihnachtsgeschichte *Xmas,cant
SATB&jr cor,S solo,2vln,vla,vcl,bvl
HANSSLER 10.108 sc s.p., cor pts s.p.,
ipa
(T1697)

TURBABOR see Schutz, Heinrich

TURBABOR, SED NON PERTUBABOR see Schutz,
Heinrich

TURBAE FOR THE PASSION ACCORDING TO ST. JOHN
see Milner, Anthony

TURBAE FOR THE PASSION ACCORDING TO ST. MATTHEW
see Milner, Anthony

TURE LURE LURE *Xmas,carol,Fr
(Dauly, G.) [Fr] 3pt wom cor LEMOINE s.p.
(T1698)
(Dauly, G.) [Fr] 2pt men cor (easy) voc sc
LEMOINE s.p.
(T1699)
(Tomasi) SMezA LEDUC s.p. see also Douze
Noels De Saboly
(T1700)

TURE, LURE, LURE see Dauly, G.

TURE-LURE-LURE see Saboly, Nicholas, Touro-
Louro-Louro

TURN AROUND *spir
(Gardner) SATB oct STAFF 559 $.30
(T1701)

TURN BACK O MAN see Bax, Sir Arnold

TURN BACK, O MAN see Bourgeois, Loys (Louis)

TURN BACK, O MAN see Copes, V. Earle

TURN BACK, O MAN see Gilbert, Norman

TURN BACK O MAN see Holst, Gustav

TURN BACK O MAN see Leyden

TURN BACK, O MAN see Schwartz, Stephen

TURN BACK O MAN see Sorce

TURN NOT THY FACE see Sateren, Leland Bernhard

TURN OUR CAPTIVITY, O LORD see Byrd, William

TURN THEE, AGAIN, O LORD see Attwood, Thomas

TURN THEE, O LORD see Croft, William

TURN THEE TO ME see Dvorak, Antonin

TURN THEE TO ME see Wink, Richard L.

TURN THOU TO ME see Morgan, Haydn

TURN THOU US, O GOOD LORD see Child, William

TURN THY FACE FROM MY SINS see Attwood, Thomas

TURN THY FACE FROM MY SINS see Locke, Matthew

TURN THY FACE FROM MY SINS see Sullivan, Sir
Arthur Seymour

TURN THY FACE FROM MY SINS see Wolff, S.
Drummond

TURN YE EVEN TO ME see Harker, F. Flaxington

TURN YE TO ME *Scot
(Stone, Norman) SATB,acap CRAMER B 29 s.p.
(T1702)

TURN YE TO ME see Cooper, Irvin

TURN YE TO ME see Ehret, Walter

TURN YE TO ME see Lawson

TURN YE, TURN YE see Ives, Charles

TURN YOUR THOUGHTS TO THOSE WHO'RE GONE see
Schubert, Franz (Peter)

TURNER
All Knew He Was There
(Maley, F.) SATB oct HUNTZINGER 4010 $.16
(T1703)

Joseph Dearest, Joseph Mine *Xmas
SSA BOOSEY-CAN s.p.
(T1704)

TURNER, C. KENNETH
O Trinity, Most Blessed Light *Eve/Trin
SATB (med easy) oct OXFORD 42.821 $.25
(T1705)

Stand Up And Bless The Lord *Gen
unis/2pt (easy) oct OXFORD 81.038 $.25
(T1706)

TURNER, E.
Benedict, Omnia Opera
cor orch HART s.p.
contains: Domini, Domini In D; Domini,
Domini In G
(T1707)

Domini, Domini In D
see Benedict, Omnia Opera

Domini, Domini In G
see Benedict, Omnia Opera

Goin' Home On A Cloud
SATB oct PRESSER 312-40545 $.30 (T1708)

TURNER, EDMUND (EDMOND)
At Even Ere The Sun *anthem
mix cor oct NOVELLO 28.1452.08 s.p. (T1709)

Christ Is Risen *Easter,anthem
mix cor oct NOVELLO s.p.
(T1710)

Gethsemane To Golgotha *Lent/Psntd,cant
SATB,STBar soli,org voc sc NOVELLO s.p.,
ipr
(T1711)

Great And Marvellous *Harv,anthem
mix cor oct NOVELLO 28.1414.05 s.p. (T1712)

O Clap Your Hands *anthem
mix cor oct NOVELLO 28.1421.08 s.p. (T1713)

Praise The Lord, Ye Heavens *Thanks,anthem
mix cor oct NOVELLO s.p.
(T1714)

Sun Of My Soul *anthem
mix cor oct NOVELLO 28.1408.00 s.p. (T1715)

TURNER, ELTHEA
Gentle Mother
SA oct WORD CS-2463 $.30
(T1716)

TURNER, LEE
Glory Hallelujah Jubilee
SATB oct WORD CS-2543 $.40
(T1717)

TURNER-MALEY, F.
Hark! What Mean Those Holy Voices *Xmas,Bibl
4pt mix cor oct SCHIRM.G 7794 $.25 (T1718)

TURNER, MICHAEL
Joseph Dearest, Joseph Mine *Xmas
3pt ASHDOWN V.T.63 s.p.
(T1719)

TURNER, OLIVE
Christmas Minstrel, The *Xmas
cor CRAMER 329 s.p.
(T1720)

TURTLE DOVES, THE see Brown, J.

TUT MIR AUF DIE SCHONE PFORTE see Muller,
Manfred

TUTTI VENITE ARMATI see Gastoldi, Giovanni
Giacomo

TUTTLE, STEPHEN (1908-1954)
Dormi, Jesu!
"Virgin's Cradle-Song, The" [Lat/Eng] SSAA,
S solo,pno SCHIRM.EC 1911 $.35 (T1721)

Virgin's Cradle-Song, The *see Dormi, Jesu!

TVA DOPVISOR
see Fem Korkoraler

TVA JULKONSERTER *Xmas
[Swed/Ger] mix cor NORDISKA NMS-6208 s.p.
contains: Scheidt, Samuel, Av Himlens Hojd
Oss Kommet Ar; Schein, Johann Hermann,
Lov Vare Dig, O Jesu Krist (T1722)

TVA NEGRO SPIRITUALS *spir
(Luboff, Norman) mix cor NORDISKA NMS-6413
s.p.
contains: Deep River; Wade In The Water
(T1723)

TWARDOWSKI, ROMUALD (1930-   )
Carmina De Mortuis *Pol
mix cor POLSKIE s.p.
(T1724)

T'WAS HERE A KING WAS BORN see Hughes, Nous
Voici Dans La Ville

'TWAS IN THE SILENT NIGHT HE CAME see Anderson,
[William H.]

'TWAS IN THE SILENT NIGHT HE CAME see Blanchard

'TWAS NIGHT O'ER LONELY OLIVET see Maunder,
J.H.

'TWAS ON A QUIET STARRY NIGHT see Duddy, [John
H.]

'TWAS ON ONE SUNDAY MORNING *Easter/Lent,spir
(Blaine, G.Gordon) SATB oct WALTON 2018 $.30
(T1725)

'TWAS ON ONE SUNDAY MORNING see Burkhart, C.

'TWAS ON ONE SUNDAY MORNING see Price, Benton

'TWAS ON ONE SUNDAY MORNING see Wilson

TWEE FRAGMENTEN UIT HET HOOGLIED see Horst,
Anthon van der

TWEE KERSTLIEDEREN see Appeldoorn, [Dina]

TWELFTH MASS see Mozart, Wolfgang Amadeus

TWELFTH NIGHT SONG *Xmas,carol,Russ
(De Cormier) SATB oct LAWSON 51481 $.35
(T1726)

TWELVE AMENS see Cronham

TWELVE ANTHEMS FOR SAB see Williams

TWELVE ANTHEMS FOR YOUNG SINGERS see Matthews,
H.

TWELVE ANTHEMS see Taverner, John

TWELVE BENEDICTION AMENS see Cabena, Barrie

TWELVE CHORAL HYMNS AND CAROLS see Edmunds,
John

TWELVE CHORAL RESPONSES see Mueller, Carl F.

TWELVE CHORALES see Bach, Johann Sebastian

TWELVE CHRISTMAS CAROLS BY R.R. TERRY see
Terry, Richard Runciman

TWELVE CHRISTMAS HYMNS see Praetorius, Michael

TWELVE COFFEE HOUSE SONGS see Ford

TWELVE DAYS OF CHRISTMAS see Lefebvre

TWELVE DAYS OF CHRISTMAS, THE *Xmas,carol,Eng
(James, Allen) SATB (med) ABINGDON APM-445
$.35
(T1727)
(Shaw, Parker) 4pt mix cor,12 soli,acap oct
SCHIRM.G 10197 $.50
(T1728)
(Smith, Gregg) 4pt mix cor,acap oct SCHIRM.G
10979 $.45
(T1729)

TWELVE FOLK HYMNS see Powell

TWELVE FOLKSONGS AND SPIRITUALS *sac/sec,CC12L
(Johnson, David N.) unis/mix cor,kbd/fl/gtr
AUGSBURG 11-9505 $1.00
(T1730)

TWELVE FRENCH CHRISTMAS CAROLS see Norman

TWELVE HYMN-ANTHEMS see Clokey, Joseph Waddell

TWELVE HYMN DESCANTS see Withrow, Scott

TWELVE HYMNS (from Our Parish Prays And Sings)
hymn
(Roff, Rev. Joseph) LITURGICAL $5.00 (T1731)

TWELVE MORAVIAN CHORALES see Antes, John

TWELVE MOTETS OF THE SPANISH GOLDEN AGE
*CC12L,mot,Span
(Lewkovitch, Bernhard) [Lat] mix cor CHESTER
s.p. contains works by: Esquivel; Guerau;
Guerrero; and others
(T1732)

TWELVE NEW HYMN TUNES see Williamson, Malcolm

TWELVE NEW HYMNS FOR CHILDREN see Boeringer,
James

TWELVE PRAYER AND CLOSING RESPONSES see
Salathiel, Lyndon

TWELVE RESPONSES AND SENTENCES see Whitney

TWELVE RESPONSES FOR GENERAL USE see Cain,
Noble

TWELVE SACRED DUETS FROM CANTATAS, VOL. 1 see
Bach, Johann Sebastian

TWELVE SACRED DUETS FROM CANTATAS, VOL. 2 see
Bach, Johann Sebastian

TWELVE SACRED DUETS FROM CANTATAS, VOL. 3 see
Bach, Johann Sebastian

TWELVE SACRED DUETS FROM CANTATAS, VOL. 4 see
Bach, Johann Sebastian

TWELVE SHORT INTROITS see Copley

TWELVE SHORT RESPONSES AND AMENS see Savage

TWELVE, THE see Walton, William

TWELVE TRADITIONAL CAROLS FROM HEREFORDSHIRE
*CC12L,carol,Eng
(Vaughn Williams, Ralph) SATB/unis,pno GALAXY
s.p.
see also: Angel Gabriel, The (T1733)

TWENTIETH CENTURY CHORAL MUSIC *sac/sec,CCU,
20th cent
(Bradley) mix cor SOUTHERN $2.50 (T1734)

TWENTIETH CENTURY EVENING SERVICE, A see Shaw,
Gerald

TWENTIETH CENTURY FOLK MASS see Beaumont

TWENTIETH CENTURY FOLK MASS see Beaumont, Rev.
Gerard

TWENTIETH CENTURY HYMN TUNES FOR YOUNG PEOPLE
see Simpson, Reginald

TWENTIETH CENTURY MERBECKE see Jackson

TWENTIETH-CENTURY MERBECKE see Jackson,
Nicholas

TWENTY AND ONE, THE *CC21L,Adv/Xmas/Easter/
Gen/Palm/Thanks
(Harris) unis jr cor/2pt jr cor PRO ART 528
$1.00
(T1735)

TWENTY CHORUSES *CC20U
mix cor/boy cor SCHMITT 52 $.50 (T1736)

TWENTY-EIGHT CHORALES, BOOK II see Bach, Johann
Sebastian

TWENTY-EIGHT SACRED CHORUSES FOR TREBLE VOICES
see Moore

TWENTY-FIVE ANTHEMS FROM THE RUSSIAN LITURGY
*CC25U,anthem,Russ
SATB BELWIN $2.50
(T1737)

TWENTY-FIVE ANTHEMS VOL. 1 see Gibbons, Orlando

TWENTY-FIVE ANTHEMS VOL. 2 see Gibbons, Orlando

TWENTY-FIVE ANTHEMS VOL. 3 see Gibbons, Orlando

TWENTY-FIVE ANTHEMS VOL. 4 see Gibbons, Orlando

TWENTY-FIVE CHORALES, BOOK I see Bach, Johann Sebastian

TWENTY-FIVE CHORALES, BOOK III see Bach, Johann Sebastian

TWENTY-FOUR CANONS see Cherubini, Luigi

TWENTY FOUR CANONS oee Haydn, (Franz) Joseph

TWENTY-FOUR INTROITS AND INTRODUCTORY SENTENCES see Thiman, Eric Harding

TWENTY FOUR RESPONSES AND AMENS see Walton

TWENTY INTROITS FOR GENERAL USE see Cashmore, Donald

TWENTY-ONE HYMN TUNES *CC21U,hymn
   cong,pno/org cmplt ed WEINBERGER $2.00
                                             (T1738)

TWENTY POPULAR ANTHEMS FOR GENERAL USE see Austin, R.

TWENTY RESPONSES FOR GENERAL WORSHIP *CCU,cor-resp
   SATB LORENZ 9285 $.30   (T1739)

TWENTY RESPONSES IN ELIZABETHAN STYLE see Ferguson

TWENTY-SEVEN 20TH CENTURY HYMNS *CC27U,hymn
   cong,pno/org cmplt ed WEINBERGER $2.00
                                             (T1740)

TWENTY-SEVEN CHORALES, BOOK IV see Bach, Johann Sebastian

TWENTY-SIX CHORALES, BOOK V see Bach, Johann Sebastian

TWENTY-THIRD PSALM see Harter, [Harry]

TWENTY-THIRD PSALM OF DAVID (Psalm 23) (from Bay Psalm Book)
   (Taylor) SATB,pno/org,opt strings oct LAWSON
   51599 $.25   (T1741)

TWENTY-THIRD PSALM, THE see Christiansen, Paul

TWENTY-THIRD PSALM, THE see Jacob, Gordon

TWENTY-THIRD PSALM, THE see Nordoff, Paul

TWENTY-THIRD PSALM, THE see Vaughan Williams, Ralph

TWENTY-THIRD PSALME, THE see Aschaffenburg, [Walter]

TWENTY-TWO ANTHEMS VOL. 1 see Byrd, William

TWENTY-TWO ANTHEMS VOL. 2 see Byrd, William

TWENTY-TWO ANTHEMS VOL. 3 see Byrd, William

TWENTY-TWO ANTHEMS VOL. 4 see Byrd, William

TWENTY-TWO CANZONETTES see Anerio, Felice

TWENTY TWO CHORALES see Bach, Johann Sebastian

TWENTY UNISON ANTHEMS FOR JUNIOR CHOIR see Barnes, [Edward Shippen]

TWILIGHT AND DAWN see Speaks, [Oley]

TWILIGHT IS FALLING, THE *Xmas,carol,Aus
   (Ehret, Walter) SATB,opt inst oct WALTON 2522
   $.30   (T1742)

TWO AIRS see Mendelssohn-Bartholdy, Felix

TWO ANGEL SONGS see Pitfield, Thomas Baron

TWO ANTHEMS see Barcrofte, Thomas

TWO ANTHEMS FOR CHILDREN'S VOICES see Caperton, Florence

TWO ANTHEMS FOR WHITSUNTIDE see King, Harold C.

TWO ANTHEMS FROM THE MORAVIANS *CC2U,anthem, Morav
   (Nolte, Ewald V.) SATB (med) ABINGDON APM-525
   $.40   (T1743)

TWO ANTHEMS see Amram, David Werner

TWO ANTHEMS oee Franck,Helchior

TWO ANTHEMS see Gibbons, Orlando

TWO ANTHEMS see Reger, Max

TWO ANTHEMS see Tye, Christopher

TWO ANTHEMS see Wishart, Campbell

TWO ANTHEMS see Wills, Arthur

TWO BACH CHORALES FOR CHRISTMAS see Bach, Johann Sebastian

[TWO] BASS ARIAS see Beethoven, Ludwig van

TWO BENEDICTIONS see Willan, Healey

TWO BESANCON CAROLS see Garland, Hugh

TWO CANTICLES see Hewitt-Jones, Tony

TWO CAROLS FOR CHRISTMAS see Olson

TWO CAROLS see Fricker, Peter Racine

TWO CAROLS *Xmas,carol
   (Willian) unis/TTBB/SATB (very easy) OXFORD
   94.314 $.20
   bontains: First Nowell; Great God   (T1744)

TWO CEREMONIAL PSALMS see Arnold

TWO CHORAL SONGS see Bach, Johann Sebastian

TWO CHORALES see Bach, Johann Sebastian

TWO CHORALES see Bach, Johann Sebastian

TWO CHORALES see Bach, Johann Sebastian

TWO CHORALES see Bach, Johann Sebastian

TWO CHORALES see Bach, Johann Sebastian

TWO CHORALES see Bach, Johann Sebastian

&WO CHORALES oee Bach, Johann Sebastian

TWO CHORALES see Bach, Johann Sebastian

TWO CHORALES see Bach, Johann Sebastian

TWO CHORALS see Vaughan Williams, Ralph

TWO CHORALS FROM "THIS DAY" see Vaughan Williams, Ralph

TWO CHORALS see Luvaas

TWO CHORUSES see Bach, Johann Sebastian

TWO CHORUSES FROM THE PASSION ACCORDING TO ST. LUKE see Penderecki, Krzysztof

TWO CHORUSES FROM THE RUSSIAN EASTER SERVICE *CC2U,Easter/Lent
   (Geer) SSA oct FISCHER,C CM-579 $.25   (T1745)

TWO CHRISTMAS ANTHEMS see Billings, William

TWO CHRISTMAS CAROLS IN TRADITIONAL STYLE see Musgrave, Thea

TWO CHRISTMAS CAROLS, SET 1 *see Bethlehem;
   Prince Of Peace   (T1746)

DWO CHRISTMAS CAROLS, SET 1 !see Carol O Ye
   Angels; Quiet Chamber, A   (T1747)

TWO CHRISTMAS CAROLS, SET 1 *see There Is No
   Rose Of Such Virtue; Today In Bethlehem   (T1748)

TWO CHRISTMAS CAROLS, SET 2 *see Cradle Hymn;
   Wassail Song, A   (T1749)

TWO CHRISTMAS CAROLS, SET 2 *see Carol Of The
   Northern Lights; Cradle Song   (T1750)

TWO CHRISTMAS CAROLS SET 3 *see Hark! All
   Around The Welkin Rings; Oh, Little
   Children Lead Us   (T1751)

TWO CHRISTMAS CAROLS see Kountz

TWO CHRISTMAS CAROLS see McAfee, Don

TWO CHRISTMAS CAROLS see Rogers, William Keith

TWO CHRISTMAS CAROLS *Xmas,carol
   (Willan) TTBB,acap (easy) OXFORD 94.101 $.15
   contains: God Rest You Merry; Mummers'
   Carol   (T1752)

TWO CHRISTMAS CAROLS
   (Praetorius, M.; Geer, E.) [Ger/Eng] SSAA,
   acap SCHIRM.EC 881 $.25
   contains: In Natali Domine; Psallite
   Unigenito   (T1753)

TWO CHRISTMAS CHORALES see Bach, Johann Sebastian

TWO CHRISTMAS CHORUSES see Christiansen, Larry A.

TWO CHRISTMAS MADRIGALS see Spencer, W.

TWO CHRISTMAS SONGS see Bissell, Keith

TWO CHRISTMAS SONGS FOR UNISON CHOIR *Xmas
   2pt oct WALTON 2954 $.35
   contains: Pooler, Frank, Christmas Lullaby;
   Pooler, Marie, December Song   (T1754)

TWO CHRISTMAS SONGS see Crosse, Gordon

TWO CHRISTMAS SONGS see Sibelius, Jean

TWO CHRISTMAS SPIRITUALS *Xmas,spir
   (Sargent) (easy) $.50 SATB,acap OXFORD
   84.119; TTBB,acap OXFORD 85.015
   contains: Mary Had A Baby; Virgin Mary, The
                                              (T1755)

TWO COLLECTS see Tomkins, Thomas

TWO DIALOGUES see Schutz, Heinrich

TWO DWELLINGS see Martin, Gilbert M.

TWO EASTER ANTHEMS see Billings, William

TWO EUROPEAN FOLK CAROLS
   (Graves) mix cor CURWEN 80882 s.p.
   contains: Carol Of The Holy Rose (carol,
   Span); Carol Of The Simple Shepherd
   (carol,Belg) (CC,Xmas)   (T1756)

TWO EXCERPTS FROM PENITENTIAL PSALM see Lassus, Roland de (Orlandus)

TWO EXCERPTS FROM THE PENITENTIAL PSALM NO. V
   see Lassus, Roland de (Orlandus)

TWO EXTANT MOTETS, THE see Carver, Robert

TWO EXTRACTS FROM THE SONGS OF SOLOMON see Johansson, Bengt

TWO FESTIVAL CHORALES see Bach, Johann Sebastian

TWO FESTIVAL INTROITS see Klein

TWO FOLK CAROLS *Xmas,carol/folk
   (Pitfield) SSA (easy) OXFORD 44.989 $.30
   contains: Ballad Of Jesus; Spanish Carol
                                              (T1757)

TWO FOLK CAROLS *Xmas,carol/folk
   (Sargent) SATB,acap (easy) OXFORD 84.050 $.25
   contains: Star In The East; Zither Carol
                                              (T1758)

TWO FOURTEENTH-CENTURY CAROLS *CC2U,carol,14th cent
   (Harrison, Frank) 2 eq voices,org oct FABER
   F0068 $.35   (T1759)

TWO FRIENDS see Wilson, Ira B.

TWO FUGING TUNES see Billings, William

TWO HEBREW PRAYERS see Wolfsohn, Georg

TWO HOLY SONGS see Rorem, Ned

TWO HYMNS IN THE DORIAN MODE *Op.71
   (Jenkins, Joseph Willcox) SATB,acap oct WORLD
   CA-1681-8 $.30
   contains: How Happy You, Who Fear The Lord;
   O Mary, Of All Women   (T1760)

TWO HYMNS ON POEMS OF CHRISTOPHER SMART see Escovada, R.

TWO INNI DI PENTECOSTE see Salieri, Antonio

TWO INTROITS see Hawkey

TWO INTROITS see Smith, H.

TWO INTROITS see Thiman, Eric Harding

TWO INTROITS see Atkinson

TWO INTROITS see Harker, Clifford

TWO INTROITS see Langlois, H.G.

TWO INTROITS see Wills, Arthur

TWO INTROITS see Wood, John

TWO KINGS see Clokey, Joseph Waddell

TWO LATIN CHORUSES see Christiansen

TWO LATIN HYMNS see Bush, Geoffrey

TWO LATIN MOTETS see Wills, Arthur

TWO LENTEN MEDITATIONS see Wetzler, Robert

[TWO] LITANIAE SACROSANCTAE EUCHARISTIAE see Palestrina, Giovanni

TWO LITANIES see Meyerowitz, Jan

TWO MADRIGALS FOR CHRISTMAS see Bolz

TWO MADRIGALS see Gabrieli, Giovanni

TWO MARIAN COMPOSITIONS see Bruckner, Anton

TWO MARIAN MOTETS see Des Prez, Josquin

TWO MASSES AND FRAGMENTS see Pergolesi, Giovanni Battista

TWO MEDIEVAL ALLELUIAS see Anonymous

TWO-MELODY ANTHEM SPECIALS NO. 1 *CCU,anthem
   SATB LORENZ $1.75   (T1761)

TWO-MELODY ANTHEM SPECIALS NO. 2 *CCU,anthem
   SATB LORENZ $1.75   (T1762)

TWO-MELODY ANTHEM SPECIALS NO. 3 *CCU,anthem
   SATB LORENZ $1.75   (T1763)

TWO-MELODY ANTHEM SPECIALS NO. 4 *CCU,anthem
   SATB LORENZ $1.75   (T1764)

TWO MEN BETOOK THEMSELVES TO PRAY IN THE TEMPLE
   see Schutz, Heinrich

TWO METRICAL PSALMS see Pitfield, Thomas Baron

TWO MEXICAN CAROLS *Xmas,carol,Mex
   (Sargent) SATB,acap (easy) OXFORD 84.111 $.35
   contains: Earth's Joy; Jesus Sleeps   (T1765)

TWO MISERERE see Pergolesi, Giovanni Battista

TWO MOTETS see Bruckner, Anton

TWO MOTETS FOR HOLY WEEK see Zgodava

TWO MOTETS "IN DIEM PACIS" see Mellers, Wilfrid Howard

TWO MOTETS IN HONOR OF THE BLESSED VIRGIN
   *ASD/BVM,anthem/mot
   (Lee, J.) SATB (easy) oct GIA G1386 $.35
   contains: Lotti, Antonio, Hail, Queen Of
   Heaven; Suriano, Francesco, Hail, Holy
   Queen   (T1766)

TWO MOTETS [OP.29] see Brahms, Johannes

TWO MOTETS [OP.74] see Brahms, Johannes

TWO MOTETS see Haydn, (Johann) Michael

TWO MOTETS see Brahms, Johannes

TWO MOTETS see Creston, Paul

TWO MOTETS see Correa, Carlos

TWO MOTETS see Deering, Richard

TWO MOTETS see Durante, Francesco

TWO MOTETS see Lang, Hans

TWO MOTETS see Lassus, Roland de (Orlandus)

TWO MOTETS see Monteverdi, Claudio

TWO MOTETS see Monteverdi, Claudio

TWO MOTETS see Pergolesi, Giovanni Battista

TWO NEGRO SPIRITUALS *spir
   (Trant) SATB,acap (easy) OXFORD 84.063 $.50
   contains: Deep River; Were You There?
                                              (T1767)

TWO NEGRO SPIRITUALS *spir
   (Parker) SATB,Bar solo,acap oct LAWSON 51254
   $.30
   contains: He's The Lily Of The Valley;

Seeking For A City   (T1768)
TWO NEGRO SPIRITUALS *spir
(Fjerstad) SATB SCHMITT 1878 $.30; SA SCHMITT
347 $.30
contains: God Is A God!; King Of Kings
(T1769)

TWO NOELS
(Pitfield) unis (very easy) OXFORD 81.095
$.30
contains: Go Forth; Sing We All   (T1770)

TWO OFFERTORIES see Graves

TWO OLD ENGLISH CHRISTMAS CAROLS *Xmas
(Butcher) unis oct SCHIRM.G 7465 $.20
contains: Boar's Head Carol, The; Come,
Follow, Follow, Follow, Me   (T1771)

TWO OLD FRENCH CAROLS *Xmas,carol,Fr
(Cockshott) unis (easy) OXFORD 45.024 $.35
contains: He Is Born; Virgin Mother (T1772)

TWO OLD GERMAN PARTSONGS see Hassler, Hans Leo

TWO PARABLES see McAfee, Don

TWO-PART ANTHEM BOOK see Mueller, Carl F.

TWO-PART CANONS ON CLASSIC HYMNS AND CHORALES,
SET I see Schalk, Carl

TWO-PART CANONS ON CLASSIC HYMNS AND CHORALES,
SET II see Schalk, Carl

TWO-PART CANONS ON CLASSIC HYMNS AND CHORALES,
SET III see Schalk, Carl

TWO-PART CHOIR NO. 1 *CCU,anthem
SA LORENZ $1.75   (T1773)

TWO-PART CHOIR NO. 3 *CCU,anthem
SA HORENZ $1.75   (T1774)

TWO-PART CHOIR NO. 4 *CCU,anthem
SA LORENZ $1.75   (T1775)

TWO-PART CHOIR NO. 5 *CCU,anthem
SA LORENZ $1.75   (T1776)

TWO-PART CHOIR NO. 6 *CCU,anthem
SA LORENZ $1.75   (T1777)

TWO-PART CHOIR NO. 7 *CCU,anthem
SA LORENZ $1.75   (T1778)

TWO-PART CHOIR NO. 8 *CCU,anthem
SA LORENZ $1.75   (T1779)

TWO-PART MASS IN ENGLISH see Bevenot, Laurence

TWO PART SONG ALBUM *sac/sec,CC17U
(Fearis) 2pt jr cor (easy) voc sc WILLIS $.60
(T1780)

TWO PART STYLINGS see Krieger

TWO-PART TREBLE CHORUSES *CCU
2pt treb cor SCHMITT 36 $.50   (T1781)

TWO PATREM FOR CHRISTMAS see Pekiel, Bertlomiej

TWO POLISH CAROLS *Xmas,carol,Pol
(Fraser) (very easy) $.30 SATB,acap OXFORD
84.046; SSA,opt inst OXFORD 83.032
contains: Lullaby Jesus; On The Day When
God Was Born   (T1782)

TWO POLISH PSALMS see Gomolka, Mikolaj

TWO PRAYER SONGS *prayer
SATB WEINBERGER s.p.
contains: Hardy, B. Edward, Keep Me Near
Thee; Janes, Oliver, My Jesus Who Loves
Me   (T1783)

TWO PRAYERS see Schickele, Peter

TWO PROCESSIONAL HYMNS *hymn
oct ROYAL 311 s.p.
contains: Church Triumphant, The (Tune Of
St.Magnus); Our Father's Home Eternal
(Tune Of Erfreut Euch)   (T1784)

TWO PROVERBS see Berger, Jean

TWO PSALM MOTETS see Adler, Samuel

TWO PSALMS AND A PROVERB see Rorem, Ned

TWO PSALMS AND A PROVERB see Rorem, Ned

TWO RESPONSES see Brahms, Johannes

TWO ROADS, THE
SATB CHAPPELL 0018309-358 $.40   (T1785)

TWO SACRED CONCERTOS see Schein, Johann Hermann

TWO SACRED PIECES see Ravenscroft, Thomas

TWO SACRED SETTINGS see Le Jeune, Claude

TWO SACRED SONGS IN FIVE PARTS see Byrd,
William

TWO SACRED SONGS see Byrd, William

[TWO] SALVE REGINAS see Schubert, Franz (Peter)

TWO SETTINGS OF THE TWENTY THIRD PSALM see
Goudimel, Claude

TWO SHAKER SONGS
(Ferguson) SATB,pno/org oct LAWSON 51352 $.30
contains: I Will Bow And Be Simple; Simple
Gifts   (T1786)

TWO SHORT ANTHEMS AND THE LORD'S PRAYER see
Thiman, Eric Harding

TWO SHORT ANTHEMS OR INTROITS FOR UNACCOMPANIED
SINGING see Thiman, Eric Harding

TWO SHORT INTROITS see Bullock, Ernest

TWO SHORT LITANIES see Pitfield, Thomas Baron

TWO SHORT MOTETS FOR EASTER see Clokey, Joseph
Waddell

TWO SHORT PSALMS see Schutz, Heinrich

TWO SONGS see Hubicki

TWO SONGS FOR THE CHRIST CHILD see Major,
Douglas

TWO SONGS FROM SOLOMON see Wilkinson

TWO SONGS OF HOPE see Adler, Samuel

TWO SONGS OF PRAISE
(Vree) unis&desc oct LAWSON 51292 $.25
contains: All Things Bright And Beautiful;
Song Of Praise   (T1787)

TWO SONGS OF SPRING see Heiden, Bernhard

TWO SONGS see Bach, Johann Sebastian

TWO SPIRITUALS *spir
(Martin) oct SATB PRO ART 2341 $.25; TTBB PRO
ART 1907 $.30   (T1788)

TWO SPIRITUALS see Gardner, Maurice

TWO SPIRITUALS see Martin

[TWO] STABAT MATER see Schubert, Franz (Peter)

TWO THOUSAND YEARS AGO see Firth, Rev. Peter

TWO TWO-PART BACH CHORALES see Bach, Johann
Sebastian

TWO UNISON ANTHEMS see Powell

TWO WASSAILS
(Johnston) SSA,acap (easy) OXFORD 83.064 $.35
contains: Gloucestershire Wassail; Wassail
Song   (T1789)

TWO WEDDING HYMNS *Marriage,hymn
oct ROYAL 249 s.p.
contains: Liebster Jesu, "Father, Thou
That Hearest Prayer"; Schmucke Dich,
"Bless, O God, This Glad Endeavor"   (T1790)

TWO WINGS *spir
SAB oct LORENZ 7366 $.25   (T1791)
(Chambers) SATB BOOSEY-CAN s.p.   (T1792)

TWO WITH GOD see Myers, G.

TWOHIG
All Things Are Full Of Thee, Lord
(Scarmolin) SATB oct PRO ART 1744 $.22
(T1793)
Not Built With Hands
(Scarmolin) SATB oct PRO ART 1739 $.22
(T1794)
There Is A Stairway That Leads Up To Heaven
(O'Hara) SSA oct BOURNE 190 $.25   (T1795)
There's A Stairway That Leads Up To Heaven
(O'Hara) SATB oct BOURNE 737 $.25   (T1796)

TY DU GLADER MIG, HERRE see Skagerburg, Einar

TYE, CHRISTOPHER (ca. 1497-1572)
Acts Of The Apostles, Volume I
SATB,acap PETERS H1529A   (T1797)
Acts Of The Apostles, Volume II
SATB,acap PETERS H1529B   (T1798)
Agnus Dei
(Knight, Gerald) SATB,acap oct FISCHER,C
CM-7498 $.25   (T1799)
Behold The Savior Of Mankind *Lent
SATB,kbd (med easy) oct CONCORDIA 98-1037
$.25   (T1800)
Christ Rising Again *anthem
mix cor oct OXFORD 43.469 $.65   (T1801)
Deliver Us, Good Lord *anthem
mix cor oct OXFORD 43.455 $.35   (T1802)
(McCarthy) SATB oct BOURNE 902 $.40 (T1803)
Drop Down Dew *Adv,anthem
(Diemente, E.) SATB oct GIA G1314 $.25
(T1804)
Drop Down Your Dew, Ye Heavens *see Rorate
Coeli
Eternal Gates Lift Up Their Heads
see Two Anthems
Evening Service *Magnif/Nunc
SATB,opt inst (med) oct OXFORD 43.291 $.50
(T1805)
Father Of All *anthem
SATB oct GRAY GCMR 3053 $.30   (T1806)
(West, John E.) mix cor oct NOVELLO
50.0135.08 s.p.   (T1807)
Give Almes Of Thy Goods *anthem
(Langdon, John) mix cor oct NOVELLO
88.0011.01 s.p.   (T1808)
Hail, Glorious Spirits *anthem
SATB oct ROYAL 221 s.p.   (T1809)
How Glorious Sion's Courts Appear
see Two Anthems
I Will Exalt Thee *Thanks,anthem
SATB,acap (med easy) oct OXFORD 45.258 $.65
contains also: Sing Unto The Lord (T1810)
SATB,acap (med) OXFORD 45.258 $.65 contains
also: Sing Unto The Lord   (T1811)
(Langdon, John) mix cor oct NOVELLO
88.0010.03 s.p.   (T1812)
Laudate Dominum Domini
"O Come, Ye Servants Of The Lord" SATB
ALLANS 354 s.p.   (T1813)
Laudate Nomen Domini *Gen,anthem/Introit/mot
SATB oct GRAY GCMR 1526 $.30   (T1814)
"O Come, Ye Servants Of The Lord" SATB
STAINER CC365 s.p.   (T1815)
"O Come Ye Servants Of The Lord" [Lat/Eng]
SATB oct HARRIS HC4017 $.20   (T1816)

TYE, CHRISTOPHER (cont'd.)
"O Come, Ye Servants Of The Lord" mix cor
oct NOVELLO 40.0094.03 s.p.   (T1817)
"O Come, Ye Servants Of The Lord" SATB oct
ROYAL 207 s.p.   (T1818)
"O Come, Ye Servants Of The Lord" TTBB,acap
(med easy) oct CONCORDIA 98-1995 $.30
(T1819)
(Greyson) "O Come Ye Servants Of The Lord"
SATB oct BOURNE ES23 $.25   (T1820)
(Greyson) "O Come Ye Servants Of The Lord"
mix cor SOUTHERN $.25   (T1821)
Lift Up The Everlasting Gates *anthem
(West, John E.) mix cor oct NOVELLO
50.0137.04 s.p.   (T1822)
Lord Is Good
mix cor SOUTHERN $.30   (T1823)
Lord Is Good, The
SATB oct LESLIE 4076   (T1824)
SATB oct BELWIN 60604 $.30   (T1825)
Lord Will Come, The *Adv,anthem
SATB oct ROYAL 226 s.p.   (T1826)
O Come Ye Servants Of The Lord *see Laudate
Dominum Domini
O Come Ye Servants Of The Lord *see Laudate
Nomen Domini
O God Be Merciful *Eve,anthem
SATB,acap (easy) oct OXFORD 43.222 $.25
(T1827)
mix cor,soli oct OXFORD 43.472 $.65 (T1828)
mix cor oct OXFORD 43.471 $.45   (T1829)
O God Of Bethel *anthem
(West, John E.) mix cor oct NOVELLO
50.0136.06 s.p.   (T1830)
O God Of Jacob, By Whose Hand *Gen
(Wolff, S.D.) TTBB,acap (med easy) oct
CONCORDIA 98-2117 $.30   (T1831)
O Holy Spirit, Lord Of Grace *Whitsun,anthem
SATB oct ROYAL 209 s.p.   (T1832)
O Jesus, King Most Wonderful *Epiph/Gen
SATB,acap (med easy) oct CONCORDIA 98-1470
$.25   (T1833)
O Lord Thy Word Endureth
(Ehret) SATB oct BOOSEY 5240 $.30   (T1834)
O Praise The Name Of Christ, The Lord
(Coggin) SATB,acap oct PRO ART 2567 $.25
(T1835)
Oh Come, Ye Servants Of The Lord
(Greyson) TTBB oct BOURNE ES23B $.25
(T1836)
Omnes Gentes Plaudite Manibus *Asc
SATBB,acap SCHIRM.EC $.30   (T1837)
Peccavimus Cum Patribus Nostris *mot
(Langdon, John) [Lat] SATTBarBB,acap oct
NOVELLO 40.1556.08 s.p.   (T1838)
Praise Ye The Lord, Ye Children (Psalm 113)
Fest/Thanks
SATB,acap (easy) oct OXFORD 43.241 $.35
(T1839)
Psalm 113 *see Praise Ye The Lord, Ye
Children
Rorate Coeli
(McCarthy) "Drop Down Your Dew, Ye Heavens"
SATB oct BOURNE 905 $.25   (T1840)
Rubum Quem Viderat Moyses
SATBB,acap SCHIRM.EC   (T1841)
Sing To The Lord *anthem
mix cor oct NOVELLO 50.0115.03 s.p. (T1842)
Sing Unto The Lord
see Tye, Christopher, I Will Exalt Thee
see Tye, Christopher, I Will Exalt Thee
Sound Of Angels, A
(Atkins) SATB,acap (med) OXFORD 43.937 $.25
(T1843)
To Our Redeemer's Glorious Name *Gen
SATB,acap (med easy) oct CONCORDIA 98-1040
$.25   (T1844)
Two Anthems *anthem
SATB oct ROYAL 210 s.p.
contains: Eternal Gates Lift Up Their
Heads (Asc); How Glorious Sion's Courts
Appear (Ded)   (T1845)
Western Wind, The *Mass
(Davison, Nigel) [Lat] SATB CHESTER s.p.
(T1846)

TYLER
Canticle Of St. Francis *Gen
SATB SCHMITT 8066 $.40   (T1847)

TYLER, DON
Come, Thou Long Expected Jesus *Xmas
SATB (med) ABINGDON APM-692 $.25   (T1848)

TYNAN, D. JR.
Thine, Lord, Is Wisdom, Thine Alone
SATB oct PRESSER 312-40555 $.30   (T1849)

TYRLEY, TYRLOW see Heseltine, Philip

TYROLEAN CRADLE SONG
see Three Nativity Carols

TZADIK KATOMOR see Roskin

TZSCHOPPE, EBERHART
Ach, Wie Fluchtig, Ach Wie Nichtig
2pt jr cor/SS sc HANSSLER 12.109 s.p.
contains also: Tzschoppe, Eberhart, Jesus
Lebte, Mit Ihm Auch Ich (2pt jr cor/SS);
Solter, Heinz, Allein Zu Dir Herr Jesu
Christ (2pt jr cor/SS); Tzschoppe,
Eberhart, Herzlich Lieb Hab Ich Dich O
Herr (3pt jr cor/SSA); Solter, Heinz,
Wenn Mein Stundlein Vorhanden Ist (2pt jr
cor/SA)   (T1850)

TZSCHOPPE, EBERHART (cont'd.)

Epiphanias-Kantate *Epiph,cant
jr cor,strings HANSSLER 12.214 sc s.p., voc
sc s.p., ipa (T1851)

As Ist Ein Kostlich Ding
2pt jr cor sc HANSSLER 12.102 s.p. contains
also: Kretzschmar, Gunther, Das Ist Meine
Freude, Dass Ich Mich Zu Gott (3pt jr
cor); Kretzschmar, Gunther, Jesu, Meine
Freude (2pt jr cor); Enders, Gottfried,
Befiehl Du Deine Wege (2pt jr cor);
Enders, Gottfried, Die Helle Sonn Leucht
(3pt jr cor); Kretzschmar, Gunther, Sonne
Der Gerechtigkeit (2pt jr cor) (T1852)

Herzlich Lieb Hab Ich Dich O Herr
see Tzschoppe, Eberhart, Ach, Wie Fluchtig,
Ach Wie Nichtig

Jauchzet, Alle Lande, Gott Zu Ehren
see Kretzschmar, Gunther, Pfingstruf

Jesus Lebte, Mit Ihm Auch Ich
see Tzschoppe, Eberhart, Ach, Wie Fluchtig,
Ach Wie Nichtig

Kleine Weihnachtskantate *Xmas,cant
2pt jr cor,S rec,A rec,vcl sc HANSSLER
12.203 s.p. contains also: Kretzschmar,
Gunther, Der Morgenstern Ist Aufgedrungen
(2pt jr cor,S rec,A rec,T rec,B rec,timp,
opt vcl, xylophones, glockenspiel,
triangle); Becker-Foss, Jurgen, Machet
Die Tore Weit (1-3pt jr cor/SSA,org,trp)
(T1853)

U

U ASSIS AU BORD DE CE SUPERBE FLEUVE see Super
Flumina Babylonis

U BID IK AAN, O MACHT DER LIEFDE see
Bortniansky, Dimitri Stepanovitch

UBER ALLE ERKENNTNIS ERHEBET SICH see Schutz,
Heinrich, Supereminet Omnem Scientiam

UBER EIN KLEINES, SO WERDET IHR MICH NICHT
SEHEN see Rohwer, Jens

UBERDENK ICH DIE ZEIT (from Evangelischen
Kirchentag 1965) CC12U,Gen
[Ger] unis,kbd (med) BOSSE BE 221 s.p. (U1)

UBERDENK ICH DIE ZEIT nee Blarr, Oskar Gottlieb

UBERFAHRT see Meister, G.

UBER'S GEBIRG MARIA GEHT see Eccard, Johannes

UBERS GEBIRG MARIA GEHT, HALT EINKEHR see
Eccard, Johannes

UBI CARITAS see Durufle, Maurice

UBI CARITAS ET AMOR DEI see Eben, Petr

UBI EST ABEL see Aichinger, Gregor

UBI EST ABEL FRATER TUUS see Aichinger, Gregor

UBIQUE EST OMNIAQUE INSPICIT DEUS see Bottcher,
Georg

UDULUTSCH
Three Lenten Choruses *CC3U,Lent
SSA&cong,cantor oct SUMMY M 2752 $.45 (U2)

UEBER ALLER DIESER DEINER TRAUER see Porena,
Boris

UFF'M BERGE, DA GEHET DER WIND see Holscher,
Bernhard

UGGEN
How Excellent Is Thy Name *Gen
SATB SCHMITT 821 $.25 (U3)

UHL
Let The Word Go Forth
unis,opt S solo oct HERITAGE H35 $.35 (U4)

UKJENT
Syng Og Lov
(Pratorius; Nielsen, Rolf) [Norw] LYCHE 8
s.p. (U5)

UKRAINIAN BELL CAROL see Leontovich, M.

UKRANIAN BELL CAROL see Leontovich, M.

ULTAN, L.
Rejoice In The Lord
(Mason, Vito) SATB oct WORD CS-2490 $.40
(U6)

UM DEIN GRAB SIND WIR GEGANGEN see Mendelssohn,
Arnold

UMIPNEY CHATOEYNU see Ancis, Solomon

UN ENFANT DU CIEL NOUS EST NE see Du Caurroy,
Francoise-Eustache

UN FLAMBEAU, JEANNETTE, ISABELLE *carol,Fr
(Wasner) "Bring Your Torches" SSA/SAT oct
SCHIRM.G 8791 $.35 (U7)

UNA HORA see Victoria, Tomas Luis de

UNA HORA NON POTUISTIS see Ingegneri, Marco
Antonio

UNA HORA NON POTUISTIS see Rubbra, Edmund

UNA SANCTA see Christiansen, Paul

UNCLOUDED DAY, THE see Attwood, Thomas

UNCOMMON CHRISTMAS CAROLS *CCU,Xmas
mix cor SCHMITT 54 $.50 (U8)

UND ALS DER SABBATH VERGANGEN WAR see Selle,
Thomas

UND ALSBALD WAR DA BEI DEM ENGEL see Vulpius,
Melchior

UND DA ACHT TAG UM WAREN see Vulpius, Melchior

UND DA ACHT TAGE UM WAREN see Vulpius, Melchior

UND DAS WORT WARD FLEISCH see Doppelbauer,
Josef Friedrich

UND DAS WORT WARD FLEISCH see Driessler,
Johannes

UND DAS WORT WARD FLEISCH see Telemann, Georg
Philipp

UND DER HERR LOBETE DEN UNGERECHTEN see
Vulpius, Melchior

UND DER HERR LOBTE DEN UNGERECHTEN HAUSHALTER
see Driessler, Johannes

UND DU BETHLEHEM IM JUDISCHEN LANDE see
&riessler, Johannes

UND ER ERHOB EIN WEIB SEINE see Vulpius,
Melchior

UND ER GEBOT IHNEN see Vulpius, Melchior

UND ER NAHM DIE SIEBEN BROTE see Driessler,
Johannes

UND ER WANDTE SICH ZU SEINEN JUNGERN see
Vulpius, Melchior

UND ES BEGAB SICH DANACH see David, Johann
Nepomuk

UND ES BEGAB SICH NACH DREIEN TAGEN see
Raselius, Andreas

UND ES ERHOB EIN WEIB SEINE STIMME see Vulpius,
Melchior

UND ES ERSCHIENEN DEN APOSTELN ZUNGEN see
Reger, Max

UND ES KAM SIE ALLE EINE FURCHT AN see
Driessler, Johannes

UND ES SOLL GESCHEHEN see Baudach, Ulrich

UND ES WAREN HIRTEN IN DERSELBEN GEGEND see
Eglin, Arthur

UND ES WIRD EIN REIS AUFGEHEN see Pepping,
Ernst

UND FRIED' DEN MENSCHEN AUF DER ERD see Lehner,
Walter

UND ICH HORTE EINE GROSSE STIMM see Franck,
Melchior

UND ICH SAGE EUCH AUCH: MACHET EUCH FREUNDE see
Raselius, Andreas

UND ICH SAH EINEN ENGEL see Reda, Siegfried

UND ICH SAH EINEN NEUEN HIMMEL see David,
Johann Nepomuk

UND ICH SAH EINEN NEUEN HIMMEL see Stockmeier,
Wolfgang

UND IHR HABT AUCH NUN TRAURIGKEIT see
Driessler, Johannes

UND JESUS TRAT ZU IHNEN see Schrader, Oswald

UND SIE KAMEN NACH BETHSAIDA see David, Johann
Nepomuk

UND SIEHE, EIN KANAANAISCH WEIB see Vulpius,
Melchior

UND SIEHE, EIN KANANAISCH WEIB see Raselius,
Andreas

UND UNSER LIEBEN FRAUEN *Adv,17th cent
(Bauernfeind, Hans) mix cor,acap oct
DOBLINGER s.p. see from Vier Adventlieder
(U9)

UND UNSER LIEBEN FRAUEN see Kubizek,
Augustinian

UND UNSER LIEBEN FRAUEN see Weiss, Ewald

UND UNSER LIEBEN FRAUEN TRAUM see Dangel,
Arthur

UND UNSERER LIEBEN FRAUE *Xmas,mot,17th cent
(Schiff, Helmut) [Ger] mix cor,acap oct
DOBLINGER s.p. see from Zwei Choralmotetten
(U10)

UND UNSRE LIEBEN FRAUEN see Brautigam, Helmut

UND WENN MIR GLEICH MEIN HERZ see Scheidt,
Samuel

UND WIE MOSE IN DER WUSTE see Raselius, Andreas

UND WIE MOSE IN DER WUSTE see Vulpius, Melchior

UND WIE MOSES IN DER WUSTEN see Demantius,
Christoph

UND WIEDER IST WIEHNACHT *Xmas
(Track) "Christmas Prayer, A" SA SCHMITT 335
$.25 (U11)

UND WO DIESE TAGE NICHT WURDEN VERKURZT see
Driessler, Johannes

UND WOLLTE ALLES WANKEN see Bach, Johann
Sebastian

UNDER HIS WINGS see Smith

UNDER THE EASTERN SKY see Nelson, Ronald A.

UNDER THE STARS see Brown

UNDERBAR EN STJARNA BLID see Nilsson, Christian

UNDERWOOD
I Know I Love Thee, Lord
SATB,acap AMP A658 $.30 (U12)

Sing For Joy!
SATB,acap AMP A660 $.35 (U13)

Spirit Of God
3pt jr cor/SSA (easy) FISCHER,C CM 7366
$.25 (U14)

Unto Thee, O Lord
SATB,org/pno AMP A598 $.25 (U15)

UNE CANTATE DE NOEL see Honegger, Arthur

UNE ETOILE see Saboly, Nicholas, Uno Estello

UNENDLICH MEER see Lissmann, Kurt

UNENDLICHER, DIR UNSERM GOTT UND KONIG see
Sweelinck, Jan Pieterszoon

UNFOLD, THOU FROZEN CHRIST see Silesius,
Angelus, Bluh Auf, Gefrorner Christ

UNFOLD, UNFOLD! TAKE IN HIS LIGHT see Powell,
Robert J.

UNFOLD, YE PORTALS see Gounod, Charles Francois

UNGDOMSPALM see Wessman, Sven A.

UNGER, HERMANN (1886-1958)
Christ Ist Erstanden *Easter
3pt wom cor,orch cor pts TONGER s.p., ipa
(U16)
mix cor,orch cor pts TONGER s.p., ipa (U17)

UNGER, HERMANN (cont'd.)

Dach Und Wiesen Sind Vom Frost Silbern
Uberzogen *hymn
men cor,winds voc sc TONGER s.p., ipa (U18)

UNGER, WALTER
Vom Himmel Hoch, O Engel Kommt
5pt mix cor MOSELER LB-389 s.p. (U19)

UNISON AND TWO-PART ANTHEMS see Pooler, Marie

UNISON ANTHEM BOOK see Barnes, [Edward Shippen]

UNISON ANTHEMS FOR YOUNG VOICES *CC15L,Gen
(Fuller) unis jr cor PRO ART 268 $.85 (U20)

UNISON ANTHEMS FROM MANY LANDS see Upshur

UNISON CHOIR NO. 3 *CCU,anthem
unis/SA LORENZ $1.75 (U21)

UNISON CHOIR NO. 4 *CCU,anthem
unis/SA LORENZ $1.75 (U22)

UNISON CHOIR NO. 5 *CCU,anthem
unis/SA LORENZ $1.75 (U23)

UNISON CHOIR NO. 6 *CCU,anthem
unis/SA LORENZ $1.75 (U24)

UNISON CHOIR NO. 7 *CCU,anthem
unis/SA LORENZ $1.75 (U25)

UNISON CHOIR NO. 8 *CCU,anthem
unis/SA LORENZ $1.75 (U26)

UNISON CHOIR RESPONSES *CCU,cor-resp
unis LORENZ 8608 $.25 (U27)

UNISON HYMNS WITH DESCANTS see Pooler, Marie

UNISON VERSICLES AND RESPONSES *CCU
unis pap ROYAL s.p. (U28)

UNITE TO PRAISE THY MAKER'S NAME see Webber,
Lloyd

UNIVERSAL HYMN oee Wagner

UNIVERSAL HYMNS *CC114UL
BIG3 $1.50 (U29)

UNIVERSAL LORD, THE see Lovelace, Austin C.

UNIVERSE IS SINGING, THE see Temple, S.

UNIVERSI QUI TE EXPECTANT see Haydn, (Johann)
Michael

UNKNOWN GOD, THE see Read, Gardner

UNKNOWN REGION, THE see Schumann, William
Howard

UNNEPI KANTATA see Erkel, Franz

UNNEPI ZENE see Gumpeltzhaimer, Adam

UNO ESTELLO see Saboly, Nicholas

UNRUHIG IST MEIN HERZ see Schieri, Fritz

UNS HAT GOTT DEN HELDEN HERGESANDT see Handel,
George Frideric

UNS, HERR, WIRST DU FRIEDEN SCHAFFEN see
Wenzel, Eberhard

UNS IST see Bach, Johann Sebastian, Uns Ist Ein
Kind Geboren

UNS IST EIN KIND GEBOREN *Xmas
SSATB HANSSLER 6.099 s.p. (U30)

UNS IST EIN KIND GEBOREN see Bach, Johann
Sebastian

UNS IST EIN KIND GEBOREN see Bartmus, Richard

UNS IST EIN KIND GEBOREN see Dedekind,
Constantine Christian

UNS IST EIN KIND GEBOREN see Franck, Melchior

UNS IST EIN KIND GEBOREN see Kuhnau, Johann

UNS IST EIN KIND GEBOREN see Micheelsen, Hans
Friedrich

UNS IST EIN KIND GEBOREN see Poos, Heinrich

UNS IST EIN KIND GEBOREN see Purvis, Richard

UNS IST EIN KIND GEBOREN see Stobaeus, Johann

UNS IST EIN KIND GEBOREN see Telemann, Georg
Philipp

UNS IST EIN KIND GEBOREN see Zimmermann, Heinz
Werner

UNS IST EIN KINDLEIN HEUT GEBORN see Bach,
Johann Sebastian

UNS IST EIN KINDLEIN HEUT GEBORN see Sorge,
Erich

UNS IST EIN KINDLEIN HEUT GEBORN see Zeuner,
Martin

UNS IST GEBOREN EIN AUSERKOREN see Lohr, Ina

UNS IST GEBOREN EIN KINDELEIN see Anonymous

UNS IST GEBOR'N EIN KINDELEIN see Pommer,
Helmut

UNS KOMMT EIN SCHIFF GELADEN *BVM,17th cent
(Dawidowicz, Anton) wom cor,acap oct
DOBLINGER s.p. see also Acht Marienleider
(U31)

UNSEEN PRESENCE, THE see Fryxell, Regina Holmen

UNSER ANFANG GESCHEHE IM NAMEN see Brunner,
Adolf

UNSER GLAUBE IST DER SIEG, DER DIE WELT
UBERWUNDEN HAT see Hufschmidt, Wolfgang

UNSER HERR IST GROSS UND VON GROSSER KRAFT see
Ruppel, Paul Ernst

UNSER HERR JESUS CHRISTUS see Schutz, Heinrich,
Unser Herr Jesus Christus, In Der Nacht, Da
Er Verraten Ward

UNSER HERR JESUS CHRISTUS, IN DER NACHT see
Koler, Martin

UNSER HERR JESUS CHRISTUS, IN DER NACHT, DA ER
VERRATEN WARD see Schutz, Heinrich

UNSER HERR JESUS CHRISTUS, IN DER NACHT, DA ER
VERRATEN WARD see Schutz, Heinrich

UNSER HERRGOTT HAT'S GEWOLLT see Weber,
Bernhard

UNSER KEINER LEBET IHM SELBER see Lohr, Ina

UNSER KEINER LEBET IHM SELBER see Schutz,
Heinrich

UNSER KEINER LEBT SICH see Stier, Alfred

UNSER LEBEN IST EIN SCHATTEN see Bach, Johann
(Hans)

UNSER LEBEN IST EIN SCHATTEN see Bach, Johann
Michael

UNSER LEBEN WAHRET SIEBENZIG JAHR see Bach,
Johann Michael

UNSER LEBEN WAHRET SIEBNZIG JAHR see Schein,
Johann Hermann

UNSER LEBEN WAHRET SIEBZIG JAHR see Calvisius,
Sethus

UNSER LIEBEN FRAUE TRAUM see Sendt, Willy

UNSER MUND SEI see Bach, Johann Sebastian,
Unser Mund Sei Voll Lachens

UNSER MUND SEI VOLL LACHENS see Bach, Johann
Sebastian

UNSER VATER, DER DU BIST IN DEN HIMMELN see
Heer, Emil

UNSER VATER IN DER HOHE see Schein, Johann
Hermann

UNSER WANDEL IST IM HIMMEL see Franck, Melchior

UNSER WANDEL IST IM HIMMEL see Micheelsen, Hans
Friedrich

UNSER WANDEL IST IM HIMMEL see Reda, Siegfried

UNSER WANDEL IST IM HIMMEL see Schutz, Heinrich

UNSER WANDEL IST IN HIMMEL see Schutz, Heinrich

UNSERE LIEBE FRAU *BVM
SATB,acap cmplt ed DOBLINGER s.p.
contains & see also: Alle Tage Sing Und
Sage (from Paradeisvogel Ingolstadt
1613); Ave Maria (from Bamberger
Gesangbuch 1628); Ave Maria, Du
Himmelskonigin (from Psalteriolum 1642);
Ave Maria Klare (from Psalteriolum 1642);
Dich, Frau Vom Himmel (from Psalteriolum
1642); Eine Jungfrau Zart (from
Psalteriolum 1642); Gegrusset Seist Du,
Edelste Konigin (from Psalteriolum 1642);
Ihr Christenmenschen Alle (from Bamberger
Gesangbuch 1628); Maria Jung Und Zart
(from Psalteriolum 1642); O Konigin,
Gnadigste Frau (from Psalteriolum 1642);
O Quam Decora (from Sirenes
Symphoniacae); Eccard, Johannes, Maria
Wallt Zum Heiligtum; Eccard, Johannes,
Ubers Gebirg Maria Geht; Palestrina,
Giovanni, Ave Maria Gratia Plena;
Praetorius, Michael, Als Der Gutige Gott;
Praetorius, Michael, Ein Engel Schon Aus
Gottes Thron; Praetorius, Michael, Freu
Dich, Du Himmelskonigin; Praetorius,
Michael, Hort Zu, Ihr Lieben Leute;
Praetorius, Michael, Maria Zart Von Edler
Art; Praetorius, Michael, Sie Ist Mir
Lieb (U32)

UNSERE SAAT, DIE WIR GESAET see Bach, Johann
Sebastian

UNSERE VATER HOFFTEN AUF DICH see Brahms,
Johannes

UNSERES HERZENS FREUDE HAT EIN ENDE see Franck,
Melchior

UNSERS HERZENS FREUDE see Bach, Johann
Christian

UNSPEAKABLE GIFT, THE see Dunford, Benjamin

UNSRE LIEBE FRAU
(Strobl, Otto) mix cor,acap oct DOBLINGER
s.p. contains also: Von Himmel Kam Der
Engel Schar (U33)

UNSRE TRUBSAL, DIE ZEITLICH see Michael, Tobias

UNSTERBLICH DUFTEN DIE LINDEN see Woll, Erna

UNTERMEYER
Prayer
(Kalmanoff) SATB oct BOURNE 804 $.30 (U34)

UNTIL I FOUND THE LORD see Lister, Mosie

UNTIL THE SHADOWS LENGTHEN see Bancroft, H.
Hugh

UNTITLED CHORAL COLLECTION *CC8L
jr cor/SS/SA sc HANSSLER 12.104 s.p. contains
works by: Ehlers; Schlenker; Albrecht;
Tzschoppe; Kretzschnar; Neubert (U35)

UNTITLED CHORAL COLLECTION *CC7L
jr cor/SA/SS/SSA sc HANSSLER 12.105 s.p.
contains works by: Kretzschmar; Ochs;

Neubert; Tzschoppe (U36)

UNTITLED CHORAL COLLECTION *CC7L
jr cor/SS/SA sc HANSSLER 12.106 s.p. contains
works by: Koch; Schulz; Enders; Albrecht;
Schlenker (U37)

UNTITLED CHORAL COLLECTION *CC8L
jr cor/SS/SSA sc HANSSLER 12.108 s.p.
contains works by: Rabsch; Kretzschmar;
Schulz; Schlenker (U38)

UNTITLED CHORAL COLLECTION *CC7L
jr cor/SA sc HANSSLER 12.110 s.p. contains
works by: Schlenker; Schulz (U39)

UNTITLED CHORAL COLLECTION *CC7L
jr cor/SS/SA/SSA sc HANSSLER 12, 111 s.p.
contains works by: Schlenker; Schulz;
Kretzschmar; Solter (U40)

UNTITLED CHORAL COLLECTION see Schlenker,
Manfred

UNTITLED CHORAL COLLECTION *CC7L
mix cor,inst sc HANSSLER 19.301 s.p. contains
works by: Ruppel, V.; Schwartz; Schwarz;
Schauss-Flake; Schweizer (U41)

UNTITLED CHORAL COLLECTION *CC8L
mix cor,kbd sc HANSSLER 19.305 s.p. contains
works by: Lotz; Ruppel; Schwarz ; Schweiser
(U42)

UNTITLED CHORAL COLLECTION *CC8L
2-4pt jr cor/SSA sc HANSSLER 12.103 s.p.
contains works by: Kretzschmar; Ehlers;
Tzschoppe; Becker-Foss (U43)

UNTITLED CHORAL COLLECTION *CC8L,canon
SATB/3pt HANSSLER 8.036 s.p. (U44)

UNTO CHRIST THE VICTIM see Byrd, William,
Victimae Paschali

UNTO HIS HOLY NAME SING PRAISES see Bach,
Johann Sebastian

UNTO JESUS' CROSS see Gambold

UNTO THE FATHER see Binkerd, [Gordon], Ad Te
Levavi

UNTO THE HILLS see Jolley, Florence [W.]

UNTO THE HILLS see Marshall

UNTO THE HILLS I LIFT MINE EYES see Peek,
Richard

UNTO THE LEAST OF THESE see Price, Milburn

UNTO THE SKY see Russell, Velma A.

UNTO THE WORLD THIS HAPPY MORN see Bach, Johann
Sebastian, Das Neugeborne Kindelein

UNTO THEE DO I LIFT UP MY SOUL see Bestor, C.

UNTO THEE DO WE CRY see Graves, [William]

UNTO THEE I LIFT MY PRAISES see Hiller

UNTO THEE I LIFT MY SPIRIT see Hiller

UNTO THEE LIFT I UP MINE EYES see Canavati

UNTO THEE LIFT I UP MINE EYES see Palestrina,
Giovanni, Ad Te Levavi Oculos Meos

UNTO THEE, O GOD see Hovhaness, Alan

UNTO THEE, O LORD (Psalm 25) Psalm
(Kirk) SATB,acap,opt pno oct PRO ART 2425
$.25 (U45)

UNTO THEE O LORD see Ashby, Bertrand

UNTO THEE O LORD see Aulbach

UNTO THEE, O LORD see Ford, Virgil T.

UNTO THEE O LORD see Lewis, J.

UNTO THEE, O LORD see Underwood

UNTO THEE, O LORD see Whitford

UNTO THEE, O LORD see Willis

UNTO THEE, O LORD, WILL I LIFT UP MY SOUL see
Young

UNTO THEE WE SING *CCU
mix cor SCHMITT 9153 $1.25 (U46)

UNTO THEE WILL I CALL see Chopin, Frederic

UNTO THEE WILL I CRY see Barnes

UNTO THEE WILL I CRY see Hovhaness, Alan

UNTO THEE WILL I SING see Glarum, L. Stanley

UNTO US A BOY IS BORN see Goemanne, Noel

UNTO US A BOY IS BORN see Hastings, Paul

UNTO US A BOY IS BORN see Hill, Harry

UNTO US A BOY IS BORN see Hutson

UNTO US A BOY IS BORN see Puer Nobis

UNTO US A CHILD IS BORN see Kennedy, John
Brodbin

UNTO US A CHILD IS BORN see Handel, George
Frideric

UNTO US A CHILD IS BORN see Moschetti,
[Giuseppe]

UNTO US A CHILD IS BORN see Purvis, Richard,
Uns Ist Ein Kind Geboren

UNTO US A CHILD IS BORN see Roberts

UNTO US IS BORN A SON
    see Six Traditional Carols, Set IV

UNTO US IS BORN A SON see Shaw, Geoffrey
    [Turton]

UNTO YOU IS BORN A SAVIOUR see Darst, W. Glenn

UNTO YOU, MY DAUGHTER see Hallett, Mrs. Robert,
    Jr.

UNUS EC DISCIPULIS see Rubbra, Edmund

UNUS EX DISCIPULIS MEIS see Ingegneri, Marco
    Antonio

UNUS EX DISCIPULIS MEIS see Victoria, Tomas
    Luis de

UNVEILED CHRIST, THE see Herrell

UNWORTHY see Roe

UNWORTHY see Roe, Gloria [Ann]

UP AND WAKE THEE, PETER LAD see Besancon

UP, GOOD CHRISTEN FOLK, AND LISTEN
    (Hinton) unis (easy) OXFORD 81.093 $.20, ipa
    (U47)

UP! GOOD CHRISTIAN FOLK, AND LISTEN *Xmas,
    carol
    cor/cong oct MOWBRAY 65024 7 s.p. see also
    Cowley Carol Book, The   (U48)

UP, MY NEIGHBOR, COME AWAY *carol
    SATB (easy) OXFORD 08.106 $.15   (U49)

UP, O MY SOUL see Rubbra, Edmund

UP, O SHEPHERDS *Xmas,carol,Aus
    (Schroeder, H.) SAT,inst (easy) oct CONCORDIA
    98-2066 $.25   (U50)

UP TO THE HILLS see Marzo, Eduardo

UP, UP, MY HEART see Cruger, Johann

UP, UP! MY HEART, WITH GLADNESS see Bach,
    Johann Sebastian, Auf, Auf! Mein Herz, Mit
    Freuden

UP WITH PEOPLE!
    (Thygerson, Robert W.) SATB,band oct HERITAGE
    H39 $4.50   (U51)

UPHOLD MY HEART WITH FAITH IN THEE see Bach,
    Johann Sebastian, Erhalt' Mein Herz Im
    Glauben Rein

UPON A NIGHT see Diercks, John H.

UPON MY LAP MY SOVERAIGNE SITS see Peerson,
    Martin

UPON MY LAP MY SOVEREIGN SITS see Peerson,
    Martin

UPON MY LAP MY SOV'REIGN SITS see Thompson,
    Randall, Lullaby

UPON THE MOUNT OF OLIVES see Palestrina,
    Giovanni, In Monte Oliveti

UPON THE MOUNT OF OLIVES see Schubert, Franz
    (Peter)

UPON THE MT. OF OLIVES see Croce, Giovanni, In
    Monte Oliveti

UPON THE ROCK OF FAITH see Boeringer, James

UPON THE ROCK OF FAITH see Reed, Robert B.

UPON THE SNOW-CLAD EARTH WITHOUT *Xmas,carol,
    US
    (Ehret) SAB,opt ob oct FOX CC8 $.30   (U52)
    (Ehret) SATB,opt ob oct FOX CC19 $.30   (U53)
    (Ehret, W.) SAB,opt ob PROWSE CC8 s.p.   (U54)

UPON THIS ROCK see Beck, John Ness

UPON THIS ROCK see Wilson, Harry [Robert]

UPPENBARELSE, JOHANNES
    Symfoni IV
    mix cor&speak cor,orch voc sc NORDISKA 3300
    s.p., cor pts NORDISKA 3157 s.p.   (U55)

UPPFAREN AR VAR HERRE KRIST see Berg, Gottfrid

UPPFAREN AR VAR HERRE KRIST see Franck,
    Melchior

UPPFAREN AR VAR HERRE KRIST see Gesius,
    Bartholomaus

UPPFAREN AR VAR HERRE KRIST see Norman, Rudolf

UPPFAREN AR VAR HERRE KRIST see Olson, Daniel

UPPFAREN AR VAR HERRE KRIST see Praetorius,
    Michael

UPPLAT VAR MUN TILL DITT NAMNS PRIS see Berg,
    Gottfrid

UPPSALA-MAGNIFICAT see Schutz, Heinrich,
    Magnificat Anima Mea Dominum

UPPSTANDELSE *Easter
    mix cor NORDISKA NMS-6292 s.p.
    contains: Bodenschatz, Erhard, Uppstanden
    Ar Var Herre Krist; Eccard, Johannes,
    Krist Ar Uppstanden; Hassler, Hans Leo,
    Krist Ar Uppstanden; Vulpius, Melchior,
    Uppstanden Ar Var Herre Krist   (U56)

UPPSTANDELSEN see Andrep-Nordin, Birger

UPPSTANDEN AR VAR HERRE KRIST
    (Lundborg, Gosta) [Swed] SATB,acap GEHRMANS
    KRB 101   (U57)

UPPSTANDEN AR VAR HERRE KRIST see Berg,
    Gottfrid

UPPSTANDEN AR VAR HERRE KRIST see Bodenschatz,
    Erhard

UPPSTANDEN AR VAR HERRE KRIST see Lundgren, Per

UPPSTANDEN AR VAR HERRE KRIST see Vulpius,
    Melchior

UPPVAKNEN, I KRISTNE ALLA see Allard, F.M.

UPSHUR
    Alleluia! Christ Is Risen
    SAB FLAMMER D5123 $.60   (U58)

    Easter Victory
    SAB FLAMMER D5187 $.85   (U59)

    Prophecy Fulfilled, The
    SAB FLAMMER D5195 $.80   (U60)

    Unison Anthems From Many Lands *CCU,anthem
    unis&desc FLAMMER GF5008 $1.10   (U61)

UPWARD GLANCE see Wolf, Hugo, Auflick

UR DJUPET ROPAR JAG see Olson, Daniel

URBS BEATA see Joubert, John

URHAN, CHRETIAN (1790-1845)
    In Speechless Prayer And Reverence *prayer
    (Davis, Katherine K.) SATB,pno/org oct
    FISCHER,C CM-7179 $.20   (U62)

USH'AVTEM MAYIM see Pugatchov, E.

UT QUEANT LAXIS see David, Johann Nepomuk

UT QUEANT LAXIS see Festa, Costanza

UT RE MI see Palestrina, Giovanni

UTRECHT JUBILATE see Handel, George Frideric

UTRECHT TE DEUM see Handel, George Frideric

UTRECHT TE DEUM & JUBILATE see Handel, George
    Frideric

UTTERMOST DAWN, THE see Ream, Albert

UTUR DJUPEN ROPAR JAG see Kullnes, Ake

UV' SHOFAR GADOL see Adler, Samuel

UVASHOFOR GODOL see Helfman, Max

UVERDIG ER JEG, HERRE see Soraas, Lars

UXOR TUA see Jolivet, Andre

V

VA-ANI S'FILOSI see Helfman, Max

VAAL, O. DE
    Aan De Stromen Babylon (Psalm 137)
    men cor ALSBACH&D sc s.p., cor pts s.p.
    (V1)

    Lentekonigin
    mix cor ALSBACH&D sc s.p., cor pts s.p.
    (V2)

    2pt wom cor,acap sc ALSBACH&D s.p.   (V3)

    Lentelied
    wom cor sc ALSBACH&D s.p.   (V4)

    Psalm 137 *see Aan De Stromen Babylon

VACILLAT PES MEUS see Kopelent, Marek

VAD KAN OSS SKILJA FRAN GUDS KARLEK see
    Buxtehude, Dietrich, Nichts Soll Uns
    Scheiden Von Der Liebe Gottes

VAD MIN GUD VILL, DET ALLTID SKER see Cruger,
    Johann

VAD MIN GUD VILL, DET ALLTID SKER see
    Praetorius, Michael

VADEMECUM PER LE FUNZIONI RELIGIOSE see
    Coronaro, Antonio

VAER IKKE BEKYMRET see Nystedt, Knut

VAER MEG NAER *folk
    (Sorass, Lars) mix cor MUSIKK 140 s.p. see
    from Religise Korsanger   (V5)

VAER TRO see Hovland, Egil

VAET, JACOBUS (1529-1567)
    O How Glorious *see O Quam Gloriosum

    O How Great And Glorious *see O Quam
    Gloriosum

    O Quam Gloriosum
    (Mattfeld, V.) "O How Great And Glorious"
    SATB,acap SCHIRM.EC 2445   (V6)
    (Payson, A.) "O How Glorious" SATB,acap
    FRANK F-566 $.30   (V7)

    Sechs Motetten *CC6U,mot
    (Meyer) [Ger/Lat] 4-6pt mix cor MOSELER
    s.p.   (V8)

    Six Motets *CC6U,mot
    mix cor,acap voc KALMUS 6466 $2.50   (V9)

VAGEN see Olsen, Sparre

VAGN OP MIN SJAEL see Valen, Fartein

VAIL
    I Will Magnify Thee
    SATB oct LORENZ 1437 $.30   (V10)

    King All-Glorious *Easter/Fest,hymn
    SAB oct LORENZ 7313 $.30   (V11)
    SA oct LORENZ 5364 $.30   (V12)
    SATB (easy) ALLANS 115 s.p.   (V13)
    TTBB oct LORENZ 2847 $.30   (V14)
    SATB (very easy) oct LORENZ 4420 $.35   (V15)
    SATB oct LORENZ 1624 $.30   (V16)
    (Wilson, Roger C.) SA ALLANS 358 s.p.   (V17)

    Lord Is Risen Today, The *Easter
    SAB oct LORENZ 7071 $.30   (V18)

VAK UPP, MIN SJAL, GIV ARA see Berg, Gottfrid

VAKNEN UPP HOR RUPET SKALLER see Bach, Johann
    Sebastian, Wachet Auf

VALE, CHARLES
    Christ's Carol *Xmas,carol
    SATB,acap ROBERTON   (V19)

VALEN
    Et Dices In Die Illa *Op.16,No.1, mot
    SATB,acap PETERS LY298 $1.50   (V20)

VALEN, FARTEIN (1887-1952)
    Deus Noster *mot
    [Lat] mix cor LYCHE LY414 s.p.   (V21)

    Et Dices In Die Illa *Op.16,No.1, mot
    [Norw] mix cor LYCHE LY298 s.p.   (V22)

    O Store Konge, Davids Son *mot
    [Norw] men cor LYCHE 38A s.p.   (V23)

    Vagn Op Min Sjael *mot
    [Norw] mix cor LYCHE LY415 s.p.   (V24)

VALENCIA CANTA see Serrano

VALENTE, A.
    Versi Spirituali *CCU,canon/Mass
    (Vecchi, Prof. Giuseppe) cor,org oct FORNI
    447 s.p.   (V25)

VALERIUS
    Des Himmels Gezelt
    (Zoll, Paul) jr cor&men cor (med easy) oct
    LEUCKART 47 s.p.   (V26)

    Prayer Of Thanksgiving *Thanks,prayer
    SATB oct FISCHER,C CM-4545 $.25   (V27)

VALIANT-FOR-TRUTH see Vaughan Williams, Ralph

VALIANTLY DOETH THE LORD'S RIGHT HAND see
    Geoffray, Cesar, Dextera Domini

VALINOFF
    Lord, Thou Art Mighty
    (Farnes) SATB FLAMMER A 5068 $.25   (V28)

VALKOMMEN, O JESU see Hahn, Gunner

VALLEY, JIM
Family *CCU
1-2pt voc sc WORD 37530 $1.95   (V29)

VALLOMAS see Szabo, [Ferenc]

VALOTTI
All Ye People
(Kingsbury, John) SATB ALFRED 6306 $.25   (V30)

VALSIGNA OSS, O HELGA AND
(Bjarnegard, Gustaf) [Swed] SATB,acap
GEHRMANS KRB 305   (V31)

VALSIGNAD GUD see Runback, Albert

VALSIGNAD VARE HAN see Nilsson, Torsten

VAMOS AL PORTAL see Guerrero, Francisco

VAMOS PASTORCITOS see Anonymous

VAN LIEFDEN COMT GROOT LIDEN see Rontgen,
[Julius]

VAN ALSTYNE
My Prayer For Today (composed with Arnold)
SAB WARNER W3440 $.30   (V32)
2pt WARNER W3363 $.30   (V33)
SSA WARNER 3323 $.30   (V34)

VAN BERCHEM, J.
All Ye People *see O Vos Omnes

Lord Has Risen *see Surrexit Dominus Vere

O Jesu Christe *Easter
see LA SCHOLA PALESTRINIENNE PREMIERE
CAHIER
SATB,acap oct PRESSER 352-00074 $.30   (V35)

O Vos Omnes
(Hardwicke) "All Ye People" SATB,acap oct
PRO ART 2395 $.25   (V36)

Surrexit Dominus Vere
(Payson, A.) "Lord Has Risen" SATB,acap
FRANK F-448 $.30   (V37)

VANCE
God Bless The King
SATB HANSEN-US C630 $.40   (V38)

I Am The Good Shepherd
SATB HANSEN-US C623 $.40   (V39)

VANCE, MARGARET SHELLEY
Alleluia
SSA oct BELWIN 2137 $.30   (V40)

God Of Abraham
SATB oct BELWIN 2233 $.30   (V41)

Sing To The Lord
SATB oct BELWIN 2169 $.25   (V42)

VAN DER HOECK
Love Divine *anthem
unis oct OXFORD 02.009 $.20   (V43)

My God, And Is Thy Table Spread *anthem
mix cor oct OXFORD 02.014 $.25   (V44)

VANDERVALK, BRUCE
Day Like Today, A
2pt,soli oct AGAPE CF 142 $.45   (V45)

VAN DE WATER, B.
Penitent, The
(Starke, F.) SATB oct PRESSER 332-15126
$.35   (V46)

Publican, The
(Starke, F.) SATB oct PRESSER 332-15049
$.35   (V47)

VANDRE, CARL W.
Famous Hymn-Tune Anthems, Vol. 1 *CCU,
anthem/hymn
SAB BELWIN $1.00   (V48)

Famous Hymn-Tune Anthems, Vol. 2 *CCU,
anthem/hymn
SAB BELWIN $1.00   (V49)

Love Came Down *Xmas,Bibl/cant/carol
cor voc sc LILLENAS MC-13 $1.50   (V50)

O Brother, Man
jr cor&unis oct FISCHER,J 9476 $.30   (V51)

Sing His Praise
SA BELWIN $1.00   (V52)

We Gather Together To Ask The Lord's Blessing
SAB oct BELWIN 1880 $.30   (V53)

VAN DYKE
Away In A Manger *Xmas
4pt mix cor,org oct SCHIRM.G 11363 $.25   (V54)

Babe Is Born In Bethlehem, A *Xmas
SATB FLAMMER A 5549 $.30   (V55)

Christmas Fanfare *Xmas
SATB oct PRO ART 2419 $.30   (V56)

Dost Thou In A Manger Lie?
4pt mix cor,Bar solo,org oct SCHIRM.G 10828
$.25   (V57)

Easter Alleluia *Easter
SATB FLAMMER A 5115 $.30   (V58)
SATB&jr cor&jr cor FLAMMER
A 5511 R(EAST), SAC .30   (V59)

Endless Alleluia
SATB oct FISCHER,C CM-7248 $.25   (V60)

Gloria In Excelsis Deo
SATB FLAMMER A 5605 $.30   (V61)

God Is Gone Up, Alleluia
SATB FLAMMER A 5544 $.40   (V62)

God Of All Grace *Lent
4pt mix cor,Bar solo,org oct SCHIRM.G 10890
$.25   (V63)

VAN DYKE (cont'd.)

I Praised The Earth In Beauty Seen
SATB FLAMMER A 5152 $.30   (V64)

I Saw Three Ships *Xmas,carol,Eng
4pt mix cor oct SCHIRM.G 11118 $.30   (V65)

Let Our Gladness Know No End
SATB FLAMMER A 5179 $.30   (V66)

Let Us With A Gladsome Mind *Thanks
jr cor&sr cor (med) FISCHER,C CM 7361 $.30   (V67)

Lord's My Shepherd, The (Psalm 23)
SATB oct PRO ART 2300 $.25   (V68)

Love Came Down At Christmas *Xmas
SATB oct FISCHER,C CM-7351 $.25   (V69)

Passion Of Christ *cant
SATB FLAMMER A5520 $1.25   (V70)

Peace Be Unto You
4pt mix cor,acap oct SCHIRM.G 11227 $.25   (V71)

Praise To The Lord, The Almighty
SATB FLAMMER A 5414 $.30   (V72)

Prayer For God's Blessing *Bibl
4pt mix cor oct SCHIRM.G 10857 $.25   (V73)

Psalm 23 *see Lord's My Shepherd, The

Sing, This Blessed Morn *Xmas
4pt mix cor,Bar solo,org oct SCHIRM.G 11039
$.25   (V74)

Sing We Noel *Xmas,carol,Fr
4pt mix cor oct SCHIRM.G 11119 $.30   (V75)

Sing With Joy
SATB (med easy) SOUTHERN $.30   (V76)
SATB FLAMMER A 5595 $.30   (V77)

Sleep, Sleep, Holy Babe
SATB FLAMMER A 5229 $.30   (V78)

VAN DYKE, MAY
Song For Christmas *Xmas,cant
mix cor BELWIN $1.00   (V79)

VAN ETTEN, ELEANOR
Old English Christmas, An (composed with Van
Etten, Elizabeth) *Pageant
SSA SCHIRM.EC 797 $.75   (V80)

VAN ETTEN, ELIZABETH
Old English Christmas, An *see Van Etten,
Eleanor

VANHAL, JAN KRITTEL
see WANHAL, JOHANN BAPTIST

VANHAL, JOHANN BAPTIST
Te Deum In C-Dur *Te Deum
(Eckhardt, M.P.) 4pt mix cor,org,2horn,vln,
vcl,bvl DOBLINGER sac s.p., voc sc s.p.,
cor pts s.p., ipa   (V81)

VAN HORN
Newborn Baby *Xmas
unis oct LORENZ 8865 $.25   (V82)

VAN HULSE
Give Praise To The Lord (Psalm 150) Bibl
SSA,org oct WORLD ESA-527 -3 $.60   (V83)
girl cor SOUTHERN $.35   (V84)

Lord, Almighty God
SATB KJOS 5845 $.30   (V85)

Psalm 150 *see Give Praise To The Lord

VAN IDERSTINE, A.P.
Christ, The Fleur-De-Lis *Xmas
SATB oct GALAXY 1.2391.1 $.40   (V86)

Fortress Of Hope
SATB,org/pno,3trp,opt timp STANDARD A23U1
$.45   (V87)

Garden Hymn *hymn
SATB,acap (med) ABINGDON APM-227 $.24   (V88)

God Rest Ye Merry, Gentlemen *Xmas
SATB (easy) ABINGDON APM-124 $.25   (V89)

King Of Kings
SATB STANDARD A12MX1 $.50   (V90)

O Lamb Of God
unis,S solo,pno/org,clar,gtr STANDARD A24U1
$.45   (V91)

O Praise The Lord
SATB,org,opt 4brass BOSTON 13686 $.35   (V92)

Oh God, Your World Is Wonderful
SATB STANDARD A22MX1 $.40   (V93)

Psalm Of Adoration *Psalm
SATB oct SACRED S-107 $.35   (V94)

Wondrous Love
SATB,acap (med) ABINGDON APM-193 $.25   (V95)

VANITY, VANITY, ALL IS VANITY see Wesley,
Samuel Sr., Carmen Funebrae

VAN LIER, BERTUS (1906-)
Het Hooglied *see Song Of Songs, The

Psalm 136
[Dut] mix cor&cong,Bar solo,3fl,2ob,2clar,
2bsn,2trp,4horn,3trom,strings,perc
DONEMUS min sc s.p., cor pts s.p.   (V96)

Song Of Songs, The
"Het Hooglied" [Dut/Eng] mix cor,STB soli,
fl,ob,clar,bsn,horn,strings,perc,timp,
harp DONEMUS min sc s.p., cor pts s.p.,
voc sc s.p.   (V97)

VANN, STANLEY
Behold How Good *anthem
mix cor oct OXFORD 43.473 $.25   (V98)

VANN, STANLEY (cont'd.)

Magnificat And Nunc Dimittis In E Minor
*Magnif/Nunc
SATB (easy) oct OXFORD 42.822 $.50   (V99)

VAN VACTOR, DAVID (1906-)
New Light, The *Xmas,Bibl
SATB,narrator,pno/org,orch AM.MUS.ED. sc
$4.50, voc sc $.75   (V100)

VAN VLIET, J.R.
O Taste And See *Bibl
4pt mix cor,S solo SCHIRM.G 7034 $.25   (V101)

VAN VOORHIS
Carol Berry Tree *Xmas
SATB SCHMITT 1880 $.35   (V102)

VAN WOERT
Christ Hath Won The Victory *Easter
SATB SCHMITT 1615 $.20   (V103)

He Lives Triumphant *Easter
SATB oct LORENZ B114 $.30   (V104)

Resurrection Morn *Easter
SATB oct LORENZ B38 $.30   (V105)

VAN WORMER, G.
Come To The Manger *Xmas
SATB KJOS 5877 $.30   (V106)

Make Ye Merry For Him That Is Come
SATB KJOS 5884 $.30   (V107)

That Tiny Child
SATB KJOS GC40 $.30   (V108)

VAN WYATT
O God, The Joy Of Our Life *anthem/pop
SATB,opt gtr oct PRO ART 2629 $.30   (V109)

What Is It All About? *anthem/pop
SATB,opt gtr oct PRO ART 2628 $.30   (V110)

VAR GUD AR OSS EN VALDIG BORG see Bach, Johann
Sebastian, Ein' Feste Burg Ist Unser Gott

VAR GUD AR OSS EN VALDIG BORG see Cruger,
Johann

VAR GUD EI MED OSS DENNE TID see Trimble,
Lester

VAR GUD HAN SIGNE NORGES LAND see Karlsen, Rolf

VAR KRISTTROGEN FROJDE SIG *Xmas,hymn
(Wikander, David) mix cor NORDISKA 964 s.p.   (V111)

VAR KRISTTROGEN FROJDE SIG see Hassler, Hans
Leo

VAR KRISTTROGEN FROJDE SIG see Runback, Albert

VAR MAN MA NU VAL GLADJA SIG see Berg, Gottfrid

VAR MIG NADIG, O GUD see Berg, Gottfrid

VAR SJAL VANTAR EFTER HERREN see Erlandson, Ake

VAR VALKOMMEN JESU KAR see Hammerschmidt,
Andreas

VAREN ICKE FORSKRACKTA see Nilsson, Torsten

VARHERRE HAN HVILTE I KRYBBEN SA TRANG see
Beck, Thomas [Ludvigsen]

VARIANTS FOR ST. ANNE see Coke, Norman

VARIANTS ON "A MIGHTY FORTRESS" see Darst, W.
Glenn

VARIANTS ON AN IRISH HYMN see Beck, John Ness

VARIATIONEN UBER DREI WEIHNACHTSLIEDER *Op.17,
Xmas
(Heroldt, Bruno) [Ger] 3-5pt mix cor,acap
(easy) DEUTSCHER DV 7623 s.p.   (V112)

VARIATIONEN UBER DREI WEIHNACHTSLIEDER see
Heroldt, Bruno

VARIATIONS ON "TWINKLE, TWINKLE" see Burroughs,
Bob

VARIOUS MIXED AND MENS' CHORUSES see Schubert,
Franz [Peter]

VARLDENS FRALSARE KOM HAR see Berg, Gottfrid

VARSALME see Islandsmoen, Sigurd

VART HJARTA LYFTA VI, O GUD see Blom, Oscar

VART HUS, O HERRE, FARDIGT STAR see Moren, John

VART PASKALAMM, O JESU KRIST see Berg, Gottfrid

VASINIS, GIUSSEPPE
Ave Maris Stella *BVM
[Lat] 3 eq voices,org ZANIBON 647 s.p.   (V113)

VASSEUR, HENRY
Rois Et Bergers
[Fr] 2 eq voices,pno/org HEUGEL voc sc
s.p., voc pt s.p.   (V114)

VATER ABRAHAM, ERBARM DICH MEIN see Raselius,
Andreas

VATER ABRAHAM, ERBARME DICH MEIN see Schutz,
Heinrich

VATER ABRAHAM, ERBARME DICH MEIN see Vulpius,
Melchior

VATER ALLES LEBENS see Ruppel, Paul Ernst

VATER DER GNADE see Handel, George Frideric,
Father Of Mercy

VATER, DER IN DEN HIMMELN IST see Schweizer,
Rolf

VATER IM HIMMEL HOCH see Donizetti, Gaetano

VATER IM HIMMEL, SIEH DAREIN see Rohwer, Jens

VATER IM HIMMEL, WIR RUFEN ZU DIR see Schweizer, Rolf

VATER UNSER see Blarr, Oskar Gottlieb

VATER UNSER see Hegar, Friedrich

VATER UNSER see Janacek, Leos

VATER UNSER see Kugelmann, Johann

VATER UNSER see Muller von Kulm, Walter

VATER UNSER see Raphael, Gunther

VATER UNSER see Reger, Max

VATER UNSER see Schein, Johann Hermann

VATER UNSER see Schutz, Heinrich

VATER UNSER see Schweizer, Rolf

VATER UNSER see Stockmeier, Wolfgang

VATER UNSER see Zimmermann, Heinz Werner

VATER UNSER, DER DU BIST see Schein, Johann Hermann

VATER UNSER, DER DU BIST IM HIMMEL see Blarr, Oskar Gottlieb

VATER UNSER, DER DU BIST IM HIMMEL see Schutz, Heinrich

VATER UNSER, DER DU BIST IN HIMMEL see Schutz, Heinrich

VATER UNSER IM HIMMEIREICH see Metzger, Hans-Arnold

VATER UNSER IM HIMMELREICH see Bach, Johann Sebastian

VATER UNSER IM HIMMELREICH see Bieske, Werner

VATER UNSER IM HIMMELREICH see Bruck, Arnold von

VATER UNSER IM HIMMELREICH see Ducis, Benedictus

VATER UNSER IM HIMMELREICH see Eccard, Johannes

VATER UNSER IM HIMMELREICH see Erythraus, Gotthard

VATER UNSER IM HIMMELREICH see Franck, Melchior

VATER UNSER IM HIMMELREICH see Hassler, Hans Leo

VATER UNSER IM HIMMELREICH see Heiller, Anton

VATER UNSER IM HIMMELREICH see Hufschmidt, Wolfgang

VATER UNSER IM HIMMELREICH see Kugelmann, Paul

VATER UNSER IM HIMMELREICH see Praetorius, Michael

VATER UNSER IM HIMMELREICH see Ruppel, Paul Ernst

VATER UNSER IM HIMMELREICH see Scheidt, Samuel

VATER UNSER IM HIMMELREICH see Schein, Johann Hermann

VATER UNSER IM HIMMELREICH see Stern, Hermann

VATER UNSER IM HIMMELREICH see Wagner, Alexander

VATER UNSER IM HIMMELREICH see Werner, Fritz

VATER UNSER IN HIMMELREICH see Franck, Melchior

VATER UNSER IN HIMMELREICH see Praetorius, Michael

VATER, VERGIB UNS see Rohwer, Jens

VAUGHAN
Christmas Lullaby *Xmas
SATB FLAMMER F 5001 $.30 (V115)

VAUGHAN, RODGER
I Will Lift Up Mine Eyes (V116)
SATB FOSTER MF119 $.35
Psalm 100 *Gen/Thanks
SATB,acap (med easy) oct OXFORD 94.319 $.35 (V117)

VAUGHAN WILLIAMS, RALPH (1872-1958)
All Hail The Power *Asc/Gen
SATB&cong,orch/org (med) oct OXFORD 42.230 $.65, ipr (V118)

Antiphon *anti
SATB oct STAINER 3.0900.1 $.30 (V119)

At The Name Of Jesus *Fest
SATB (easy) oct OXFORD 40.100 $.35 (V120)

Benedicite *Bene
SSA,S solo cor pts OXFORD $1.70 (V121)
SATB,S solo,orch (med) voc sc OXFORD 56.515 $1.75, ipr (V122)
(Storry) SSA (diff) voc sc OXFORD 56.516 $1.70, ipr (V123)

Blessed Son Of God
see Two Chorals From "This Day"

Children's Christmas Song *Xmas,folk
SA (med easy) cor pts OXFORD 44.063 $.25
see from Folksongs Of The Four Seasons (V124)

Choral Flourish, A (Psalm 33) Fest/Thanks
SATB,trp/org (med) oct OXFORD 43.934 $.35 (V125)

Christmas Hymn *Xmas,hymn
4pt mix cor oct CURWEN 10444 $.30 (V126)

VAUGHAN WILLIAMS, RALPH (cont'd.)

Communion Service In D Minor *Commun,Agnus/Bene/Credo/Gloria/Kyrie/Sanctus
SATB&cong (easy) oct OXFORD 42.120 $.95 (V127)

Dona Nobis Pacem *cant
mix cor,SB soli,orch (diff) voc sc OXFORD 56.602 $2.20, ipr (V128)

Easter Hymn *Easter,hymn
4pt mix cor oct CURWEN 10406 $.30 (V129)

Fantasia On Christmas Carols *Xmas,carol
SATB,Bar solo,orch cor pts STAINER 3.1223.1 $1.25 (V130)

Fantasia On The 'Old 104th' Psalm Tune (Psalm 104)
(Sternhold, Thomas; Hopkins, John) SATB, pno,orch (med) voc sc OXFORD rental (V131)

Festival Te Deum *Fest,Te Deum
SATB (med) oct OXFORD 42.110 $.75, ipr (V132)

First Nowell, The
SATB (med) voc sc OXFORD 46.509 $3.40, ipr (V133)

Folksongs Of The Four Seasons *see Children's Christmas Song; God Bless The Master; In Bethlehem City; Wassail Song (V134)

For All The Saints *see Sine Nomine

God Bless The Master *Xmas,folk
unis/desc (med easy) cor pts OXFORD 44.061 $.20 see from Folksongs Of The Four Seasons (V135)

He That Is Down Need Fear No Fall *Gen
unis (easy) oct OXFORD 81.050 $.25 (V136)

Hodie *Xmas,cant
"This Day" SATB (med) voc sc OXFORD 46.501 $3.85, ipr, cor pts OXFORD 46.502 $1.35 (V137)

Holy City, The *see Sancta Civitas

In Bethlehem City *Xmas,carol/folk
SSA,acap (med easy) cor pts OXFORD 44.060 $.30 see from Folksongs Of The Four Seasons (V138)
SSA,acap (med) OXFORD 44.060 $.30 see from FOLKSONGS OF THE FOUR SEASONS (V139)

It Is Nothing To You? *see O Vos Omnes

Let Us Now Praise Famous Men
unis jr cor/unis wom cor CURWEN 71619 s.p. (V140)
(Jacobson) mix cor CURWEN 61498 s.p. (V141)
(Jacobson) SAB CURWEN 61571 s.p. (V142)

Lord, Thou Has Been Our Refuge
mix cor&opt unis,opt Bar solo,orch/org oct CURWEN 9720 $.40 (V143)

Lord, Thou Hast Been Our Refuge
mix cor CURWEN 80592 s.p. (V144)

Magnificat *Bibl
see Magnificat And Nunc Dimittis
4pt mix cor oct CURWEN 8813 $.30 contains also: Nunc Dimittis (V145)
SSA,A solo,orch (med easy) voc sc OXFORD 46.200 $.65, ipr (V146)

Magnificat And Nunc Dimittis
mix cor CURWEN 80640 s.p.
contains: Magnificat (Magnif); Nunc Dimittis (Nunc) (V147)

Mass In G Minor *Mass
[Lat] 3 cor,SATB soli,opt org voc sc CURWEN $1.00 (V148)
dbl cor,SATB soli,opt org voc sc CURWEN C03642 s.p. (V149)

Morning Service In D Minor *Morn,Bene/Jubil/Te Deum
SATB&cong (med easy) oct OXFORD 42.119 $.90 (V150)

My Soul, Praise The Lord *Thanks
SATB (easy) oct OXFORD 44.710 $.25 (V151)

No Sad Thought
see Two Chorals From "This Day"

No Sad Thought His Soul Affright (from Hodie)
SATB,acap (easy) OXFORD 43.929 $.35 see from Two Chorals (V152)

Nsee Magnificat And Nunc Dimittis
see Vaughan Williams, Ralph, Magnificat

O Be Joyful In The Lord (Psalm 100)
SATB,orch STAINER 3.4011.1 $.50 (V153)
SATB,orch/org&strings oct STAINER 3.4011.1 $.50, ipr (V154)

O Clap Your Hands *mot
SATB,org,3trp,3trom,opt tuba,timp,opt perc voc sc STAINER 3.2222.1 $.50, ipr (V155)

O How Amiable *Ded/Gen
mix cor,band cmplt ed OXFORD 97.830-70 $24.00 (V156)
SATB (easy) oct OXFORD 42.056 $.30 (V157)

O Praise The Lord Of Heaven (Psalm 148)
dbl cor,acap, semi-chorus GALAXY s.p. (V158)

O Taste And See (Psalm 34) Commun/Gen
SSA,acap (very easy) oct OXFORD 44.415 $.20 (V159)
SSATB,acap (very easy) oct OXFORD 43.909 $.20 (V160)
mix cor SOUTHERN $.20 (V161)

O Vos Omnes
mix cor CURWEN 80594 s.p. (V162)
"It Is Nothing To You?" 8pt mix cor,A solo, acap oct CURWEN 10582 $.35 (V163)

Old Hundreth Psalm Tune, The *Thanks
SATB&cong (very easy) oct OXFORD 42.953 $.30 (V164)

VAUGHAN WILLIAMS, RALPH (cont'd.)

On Christmas Night *Xmas
SATB oct STAINER 3.2151.1 $.25 (V165)

Pilgrim's Journey *cant
SATB,STBar soli,orch/org (med) voc sc OXFORD 46.130 $3.10, ipr (V166)

Prayer To The Father Of Heaven *Gen
SATB,acap (med) oct OXFORD 40.003 $.50 (V167)

Psalm 23 *see Twenty-Third Psalm, The

Psalm 33 *see Choral Flourish, A

Psalm 34 *see O Taste And See

Psalm 100 *see O Be Joyful In The Lord

Psalm 104 *see Fantasia On The 'Old 104th' Psalm Tune

Psalm 148 *see O Praise The Lord Of Heaven

Sancta Civitas *Bibl/ora
"Holy City, The" cor,TBar soli,pno&strings/pno&org/pno&3fl&2ob&2clar&2bsn&4horn&3trp&tuba&strings&perc&harp voc sc CURWEN C03663 s.p., sc CURWEN rental, ipr (V168)
(Havergail, Brian) "Holy City, The" dbl cor,TBar soli,orch/pno voc sc CURWEN $1.50 (V169)

Sine Nomine *ASD
SATB oct FISCHER,C CM-6637 $.25 (V170)
TTBB oct FISCHER,C CM-7282 $.25 (V171)
(Bullock) "For All The Saints" SAB (easy) OXFORD 42.994 $.50 (V172)
(Bullock, Ernest) "For All The Saints" SAB (easy) oct OXFORD 42.994 $.50 (V173)
(Ley, Henry G.) "For All The Saints" SATB (med easy) oct OXFORD 40.002 $.50 (V174)
(Lorenz) "For All The Saints" SATB oct LORENZ 9864 $.30 (V175)
(Morgan, W.K.) "For All The Saints" SATB, kbd oct KERBY 6106 $.30 (V176)
(Morgan, W.K.) "For All The Saints" SATB oct KERBY 81878 $.30 (V177)
(Rosenberg) 3pt jr cor/SAB (med) FISCHER,C CM 7571 $.30 (V178)
(Shaw) "For All The Saints" 4pt mix cor, acap oct SCHIRM.G 9908 $.30 (V179)
(Shaw) "For All The Saints" SAB,acap oct SCHIRM.G 11642 $.25 (V180)

Song Of Jesus, A
(Williams) 4pt jr cor/SATB (easy) FISCHER,C CM 7171 $.25 (V181)

Song Of Thanksgiving, A *Thanks
SATB&jr cor,narrator,S solo,orch (med easy) voc sc OXFORD $1.00, ipr (V182)

Song Of Thansgiving *see Thanksgiving For Victory

Song Of The Tree Of Life
SA (easy) OXFORD 82.037 $.25 (V183)

Souls Of The Righteous, The (from Wisdom Of Solomon, The) ASD/Rembrnc
SATB,STB soli,acap (easy) oct OXFORD 42.800 $.25 (V184)

Sweet Baby, Sleep
(Peter) SATB,acap oct LAWSON 51134 $.25 (V185)
(Peter) 2pt boy cor/3pt boy cor,pno/org oct LAWSON 51344 $.30 (V186)

Te Deum And Benedictus *Bene/Te Deum
unis/SATB,opt org (easy) oct OXFORD 40.906 $.65 (V187)

Te Deum In G *Te Deum
SSAATTBB (med) oct OXFORD 42.178 $.50 (V188)

Thanksgiving For Victory *Thanks
"Song Of Thansgiving" SATB (med) OXFORD 56.700 $1.00 (V189)

This Day *see Hodie

Twenty-Third Psalm, The (Psalm 23) (from Pilgrim's Progress, The) Gen
(Churchill, John) SATB,opt S solo,acap (med) oct OXFORD 43.913 $.35 (V190)

Two Chorals *see No Sad Thought His Soul Affright (from Hodie) (V191)

TSATBhecaps(Faom)"OXFORDa43.929 $.35
contains: Blessed Son Of God; No Sad Thought (V192)

Valiant-For-Truth *Gen
SATB (med) oct OXFORD 42.240 $.50 (V193)

Vision Of Aeroplanes, A *Bibl/mot
mix cor,org (diff) voc sc OXFORD rental (V194)

Voice Out Of The Whirlwood, The (from Job) ASD/Thanks
SATB (med) oct OXFORD 40.012 $.75, ipr (V195)

Wassail Song *Xmas,folk
desc (med easy) cor pts OXFORD 54.235 $.25 see from Folksongs Of The Four Seasons (V196)
SATB oct STAINER 3.1563.1 $.50 (V197)

VAUGHN
Festival Anthem
SATB,acap SHAWNEE A 916 $.35 (V198)

We Shall See The King
(Decou) SATB oct LILLENAS AT-1006 $.30 (V199)

VAUGHN, LESLIE
Gospel Chorister, The *CCU
SATB oct AGAPE $1.25 (V200)

VAUTAZ, R.
Psalm 33
unis,org,2trp OUVRIERES sc s.p., cor pts s.p., ipa (V201)

VAY' CHULU see Gottlieb, J.

VAYECHULU HASHAMAYIM see Starer, Robert

VE DIG, KORASIN see Nilsson, Torsten

VECCHI
Come, Now Let Us Be Joyful
mix cor SOUTHERN $.25 (V202)

Missa In Resurrectione Domini *Mass
(Ruegge) 8pt MOSELER s.p. (V203)

O Dulcis Jesu *cant
SATB&ATTB,3trp,5trom MOSELER sc s.p., cor
pts s.p., ipa (V204)

VECCHI, ORAZIO (1550-1605)
Alleluja, Sing Praises *mot
(Bridge, Sir Fredk.) SATTB BOSWORTH s.p.
(V205)

Cantabo Domino *Gen
SATB,acap (med easy) MULLER MS 76 s.p.
(V206)

Cantate Domino
(Wilhelm) "Sing Unto The Lord" SATB oct
LAWSON 51633 $.35 (V207)

Erat Jesus Ejiciens *Lent/Psntd,mot
[Lat] mix cor,acap oct NOVELLO DM-14 s.p.
(V208)
[Lat] SATB,acap (med) MULLER M 14 s.p.
(V209)

Lord, Hear My Cry (Psalm 142)
SATB,acap SCHIRM.EC 2614 $.30 (V210)

Psalm 142 *see Lord, Hear My Cry

Sing Unto The Lord *see Cantate Domino

Velociter Exaudi Me *Gen,mot
SATB,acap (med) MULLER M 36 s.p. (V211)
[Lat] mix cor,acap oct NOVELLO DM-36 s.p.
(V212)

VECKRUISE
If My People
SATB FLAMMER A 5185 $.25 (V213)

VECNE EVANGELIUM see Janacek, Leos

VEDRASSI PRIMA see Palestrina, Giovanni

VEHI TEHILATECHA see Lewy, Ron

VEITCH, WILLIAM.
Christ Was Born On Christmas-Day *Xmas,carol
unis CRAMER 24 s.p. (V214)

Let Us All With Voices Sing *carol
unis CRAMER 10 (V215)

Lu Lulla Lay *carol
unis CRAMER 15 (V216)

On Christmas Day *Xmas,carol
unis CRAMER 13 (V217)

VELKOMMEN, HERRE JESUL IL see Lubeck,
Vincentius, Wilkommen, Susser Brautigam

VELOCITER EXAUDI ME see Vecchi, Orazio

VELONA
O Bambino *see Capra

VELSIGNET VAERE HAM see Nystedt, Knut

VELSIGNET VAERE JESU NAVN see Olsen, Sparre

VELSIGNET VARE JESU NAVN see Olsen, Sparre

VEN, OH SANTO ESPIRITU! see Benedito

VENE, RUGGERO (1897-1961)
doramus Te, Christe
[Lat] SATB,acap SCHIRM.EC 2265 $.18 (V218)

Ave Maria
"Father Almighty" TTBB,acap SCHIRM.EC 2137
$.18 (V219)
"Father Almighty, Grant Our Petition" SA,
pno SCHIRM.EC 1936 $.16 (V220)

Balulalow *cradle,13th cent
SSA oct COLOMBO 965 $.25 (V221)

Blow Ye The Trumpet In Zion *see Canite Tuba
In Sion

Canite Tuba In Sion
"Blow Ye The Trumpet In Zion" SATB,acap
SCHIRM.EC 2254 $.18 (V222)

Convertere Anima Mea
"Return, O My Soul" SATB,acap SCHIRM.EC
2255 $.18 (V223)

Father Almighty *see Ave Maria

Father Almighty, Grant Our Petition *see Ave
Maria

Judge Me, O Lord *see Judica Me, Domine

Judica Ie, Domine
"Judge Me, O Lord" SATB,acap SCHIRM.EC 2257
$.18 (V224)

Magnificat Anima Mea
[Lat] SATB,acap SCHIRM.EC 2264 $.18 (V225)

Return, O My Soul *see Convertere Anima Mea

VENERABILIS BARBA CAPUCINORUM see Lully
(Lulli), Jean-Baptiste

VENEZ, ENFANTS &U SEIGNEUR *Xmas,carol,Fr
(Tomasi) [Fr] 2pt/3pt,pno/orch LEDUC s.p. see
also Douze Noels De Saboly (V226)

VENEZIANI, VITTORE
Preghiera
TTBB sc ZANIBON 1562 s.p., voc pt ZANIBON
1562A-B-C-D s.p. (V227)

VENI CREATOR *Pent
(Geveart, F.-A.) "Pour La Fete De La
Pentecote" [Lat/Fr] 4pt mix cor,acap (easy)
cor pts LEMOINE s.p. see from Collection De

Choeurs, troisieme Fascicule (V228)

VENI CREATOR see Andriessen, Hendrik

VENI CREATOR see Arnaldi, Antonio

VENI CREATOR see Bach, Johann Sebastian

VENI CREATOR see Beethoven, Ludwig van

VENI CREATOR see Berlioz, Hector

VENI CREATOR see Demerath, F.

VENI CREATOR see Durand, F.L.

VENI CREATOR see Gehring, A.

VENI CREATOR see Gibbons, Orlando

VENI CREATOR see Monnikendam, Marius

VENI CREATOR see Ravanello, Oreste

VENI CREATOR see Schmitt, Florent

VENI CREATOR see Visona', Gino

VENI CREATOR see Vranken, Alph.

VENI CREATOR, EN UT see Saint-Saens, Camille

VENI CREATOR SPIRITUS see Bach, Johann
Sebastian

VENI, CREATOR SPIRITUS see Berlioz, Hector

VENI CREATOR SPIRITUS see Bernabei, Giuseppe
Antonio

VENI CREATOR SPIRITUS see Casciolini, Claudio

VENI CREATOR SPIRITUS see David, Johann Nepomuk

VENI CREATOR SPIRITUS see Diepenbrock, Alfons

VENI CREATOR SPIRITUS see Fast

VENI, CREATOR SPIRITUS see Gibbons, Orlando

VENI CREATOR SPIRITUS see Lenel, Ludwig

VENI CREATOR SPIRITUS see Orff, Carl

VENI CREATOR SPIRITUS see Palestrina, Giovanni

VENI CREATOR SPIRITUS see Praetorius, Michael

VENI, CREATOR SPIRITUS see Proctor, Charles

VENI CREATOR SPIRITUS see Rubbra, Edmund

VENI, DOMINE see Mendelssohn-Bartholdy, Felix

VENI DOMINE see Mielczewski, Marcin

VENI DOMINE, JESU see Graap, Lothar

VENI EMMANUEL *Adv/Xmas,hymn
"O Come, Emmanuel" cor&cong ROYAL s.p. (V229)
"O Come, Emmanuel" 1-2pt oct LORENZ 5736 $.30
(V230)
(Van Dyke) "O Come Emmanuel" 4pt mix cor&desc
oct SCHIRM.G 10659 $.35 (V231)

VENI EMMANUEL see Barnard, Parke S.

VENI EMMANUEL see McKinney

VENI JESU see Cherubini, Luigi

VENI JESUS see Cherubini, Luigi

VENI REDEMPTOR GENTIUM *Adv
(Geveart, F.-A.) "Pour Le Temps De L'avent"
[Lat/Fr] 4pt mix cor,acap (easy) cor pts
LEMOINE s.p. see from Collection De
Choeurs, troisieme Fascicule (V232)

VENI, REDEMPTOR GENTIUM see Praetorius, Michael

VENI, ROGO IN COR MEUM see Schutz, Heinrich

VENI SANCTE see Sherlaw-Johnson, Robert

VENI, SANCTE SPIRITUS (from Anthology Of
Carols, An)
see Immortal Babe

VENI SANCTE SPIRITUS see Allegri, Gregorio

VENI SANCTE SPIRITUS see Davies, Peter Maxwell

VENI, SANCTE SPIRITUS see Dunstable, John

VENI, SANCTE SPIRITUS see Haydn, (Johann)
Michael

VENI SANCTE SPIRITUS see Hieronim of
Koprzywnica

VENI SANCTE SPIRITUS see Johnson, Robert
Sherlaw

VENI SANCTE SPIRITUS see Kelly, Bryan

VENI SANCTE SPIRITUS see Kirk

VENI, SANCTE SPIRITUS see Monnikendam, Marius

VENI, SANCTE SPIRITUS see Moren, John

VENI SANCTE SPIRITUS see Mozart, Wolfgang
Amadeus

VENI, SANCTE SPIRITUS see Palestrina, Giovanni

VENI SANCTE SPIRITUS see Salieri, Antonio

VENI, SANCTE SPIRITUS see Scheidt, Samuel

VENI, SANCTE SPIRITUS see Schutz, Heinrich

VENI SANCTE SPIRITUS see Steigleder, Joh.
Ulrich

VENI SANCTE SPIRITUS see Stewart, H.C.

VENI SANCTE SPIRITUS ET EMITTE COELITUS see
Selle, Thomas

VENI SANCTIE SPIRITUS see Byrd, William

VENI SANCTIFICATOR see Krenek, Ernst

VENI SANCTUS SPIRITUS see Mozart, Wolfgang
Amadeus

VENI SPONSA CHRISTI see Arnaldi, Antonio

VENI SPONSA CHRISTI see Bottazzo, Luigi

VENI SPONSA CHRISTI see Dagand, Abbe J.

VENI SPONSA CHRISTI see Fabiani, Angelo

VENI SPONSA CHRISTI see Monteverdi, Claudio

VENI SPONSA CHRISTI see Palestrina, Giovanni

VENI SPONSA CHRISTI see Picchi, Luigi

VENI SPONSA CHRISTI see Victoria, Tomas Luis de

VENI SPONSA CHRISTI IN HON. BEATAE MARIAE
BERTILLAE BOSCARDON see Pasini, Crescenzio

VENI, VENI, EMMANUEL *Adv
(Kodaly, Z.) [Lat/Eng] SAB,acap oct BOOSEY
5564 $.35 (V233)

VENIAT DILECTUS MEUS see Grandi, Alessandro

VENITE see Byrd, William

VENITE see Leighton, Kenneth

VENITE see Swann, Donald

VENITE AD ME see Charpentier, Marc-Antoine

VENITE AD ME see Volpi, Edoardo

VENITE AD ME OMNES see Lassus, Roland de
(Orlandus)

VENITE ADOREMUS *Xmas,anthem/carol,Eng/Ir
"Snow Lay On The Ground, The" 2pt oct LORENZ
5728 $.25 (V234)
(Grant, Louise) SSA oct BELWIN 1698 $.25
(V235)
(Sowerby, Leo) "Snow Lay On The Ground, The"
SA oct GRAY GCMR 2819 $.35 (V236)
(Sowerby, Leo) "Snow Lay On The Ground, The"
SSA oct GRAY GCMR 2822 $.30 (V237)
(Sowerby, Leo) "Snow Lay On The Ground, The"
SAB oct GRAY GCMR 2318 $.30 (V238)
(Sowerby, Leo) "Snow Lay On The Ground, The"
SATB oct GRAY GCMR 2240 $.40 (V239)
(Sowerby, Leo) "Snow Lay On The Ground, The"
TTBB oct GRAY GCMR 2825 $.30 (V240)
(Sowerby, Leo) "Snow Lay On The Ground, The"
unis&desc oct GRAY GCMR 2238 $.30 (V241)
(Wetzler, Robert) "Snow Lay On The Ground,
The" SATB (easy) oct AUGSBURG 1520 $.30
(V242)

VENITE ADOREMUS see Field, R.

VENITE ADOREMUS see Wright, S.

VENITE ADOREMUS see Young

VENITE ADORIAMO see Bottazzo, Luigi

VENITE ET VIDETE *Lat
mix cor sc ALSBACH&D s.p. (V243)

VENITE, EXSULTEMUS DOMINO see Cammarota, Carlo

VENITE EXSULTEMUS DOMINO see Sweelinck, Jan
Pieterszoon

VENITE, EXULTEMUS DOMINO see Cruger, Johann

VENITE EXULTEMUS DOMINO see Heiberg

VENITE, EXULTEMUS DOMINO see King, Harold C.

VENITE, EXULTEMUS DOMINO see Roe, Betty

VENITE, EXULTEMUS DOMINO see Sweelinck, Jan
Pieterszoon

VENITE, FILII see Sandvold, Arild

VENITE POPULI see Bottazzo, Luigi

VENOSA, DA
see GESUALDO, DON CARLO

VENTEQUATRO NUOVE CANZONCINE SPIRITUALI see
Bas, Giulio

VENTI LITANIE LAURENTANE see Gorlatto, Giacomo

VENTO, IVO DE (ca. 1540-1575)
Gott Ist Mein Trost *mot
(Hellmann) SAB HANSSLER 1.241 s.p. (V244)

VENTOTTO LITANIE LAURETANE see Gubinelli,
Oderisio

VENTOTTO LITANIE LAURETANE see Zimarino,
Settimio

VER MISKUNNSAME see Hovland, Egil

VER SANCTUM see Olsen, Sparre

VER TOI J'AILEVE MES YEUX see DuBois, Pierre
Max

V'ERASTICH LI see Steinberg, Ben

VERBA MEA see Schutz, Heinrich

VERBA MEA AURIBUS PERCIPE see Schutz, Heinrich

VERBUM CARO see Geist, Christian

VERBUM CARO see Palestrina, Giovanni

VERBUM CARO FACTUM EST see Anonymous

VERBUM CARO FACTUM EST see Geist, Christian

VERBUM CARO FACTUM EST see Hassler, Hans Leo

VERBUM CARO FACTUM EST see Malmfors, Ake, Ordet Vordet Kott

VERBUM CARO FACTUM EST see Schein, Johann Hermann

VERBUM CARO IN A MINOR see Victoria, Tomas Luis de

VERBUM CARO IN G see Victoria, Tomas Luis de

VERBUM PATRIS (from Anthology Of Carols, An)
  Xmas,carol
  (Wulstan, David) STB/STBar CHESTER s.p.
    contains also: Salutation, The (unis)
    (Xmas); Nova! Nova! (unis) (Xmas,carol)
                                                    (V245)

VERBUM PATRIS HUMANATUR *Xmas,carol,13th cent
  (Stevens) 3pt boy cor/3pt wom cor/3pt men
    cor,acap SCHIRM.G 11628 $.25   (V246)
  (Stevens, Denis) [Lat] 3 eq voices FABER
    11628 $.25   (V247)

VERBUM SUPERNUM see Maggio, Giuseppe

VERBUM SUPERNUM PRODIENS see Reda, Siegfried

VERBUN INQUIM see Morales, Cristobal de

VERDANCK, JOHANN
  Lobe Den Herren
    TTB NORDISKA 4875 s.p.   (V248)

VERDANT MEADOWS see Handel, George Frideric

VERDELOT, PHILLIPPE (? -ca. 1550)
  Angelus Domini *Xmas,mot
    [Eng/Lat/Ger] PETERS V118 $.75 see also
      CHRISTMAS MOTETS OF PRE-PALESTRINA DAYS
                                        (V249)
    [Eng/Lat/Ger] SATB,acap PETERS V118 $.75
                                        (V250)
    (Egidi, A.) [Eng/Ger/Lat] mix cor cor pts
      VIEWEG s.p. see from SECHS
      WEIHNACHTSMOTETTEN   (V251)

  Opera Omnia Vol. I *CCU,hymn/Mass
    (Bragard, Anne-Marie) cor AM.INST.MUS.
    $15.00   (V252)

  Opera Omnia Vol. II *CCU
    (Bragard, Anne-Marie) cor AM.INST.MUS.
    $27.00 Motets From Iss Rome, Bibl.
    Vallicelliana E. II 55-60 And Florence,
    Opera Del Duomo 13 And 27   (V253)

VERDI, GIUSEPPE (1813-1901)
  Ave Maria
    see Quattro Pezzi Sacri
    [Lat] SATB,acap voc sc PETERS 4256A $.25
      see from Four Sacred Pieces   (V254)
    [Lat] SATB,acap MARKS 7 $.25   (V255)
    mix cor SOUTHERN $.25   (V256)
    [Lat] SATB,opt pno RICORDI-ENG 101468 s.p.
                                        (V257)
    (Davis) SSA oct GALAXY 1.1897.1 $.30 (V258)

  Father, Our Father *see Pater Noster

  Four Sacred Pieces *see Ave Maria; Laudi
    Alla Vergine Maria; Stabat Mater; Te Deum
                                        (V259)
  Four Sacred Pieces *CC4U
    SATB BELWIN $1.50   (V260)

  Hymn To The Virgin *see Laudi Alla Vergine
    Maria

  Lamb Of God (from Requiem)
    (Carlton) SATB oct BOOSEY 5276 $.35 (V261)

  Laudate Alla Virgine
    2pt wom cor oct KALMUS 6473 $.30   (V262)

  Laudi Alla Vergine Maria *BVM
    see Quattro Pezzi Sacri
    [Lat] SSAA,acap voc sc PETERS 4256C $.30
      see from Four Sacred Pieces   (V263)
    [Lat] SSAA PETERS 4256C $.30   (V264)
    4pt wom cor,pno RICORDI-ENG 101469 s.p.
                                        (V265)
    girl cor SOUTHERN $.30   (V266)
    4pt wom cor,acap RICORDI-ENG 100009 s.p.
                                        (V267)
    "Hymn To The Virgin" [It/Eng] SSAA,acap oct
      COLOMBO 1733 $.25   (V268)

  Manzoni Requiem (from Requiem) Mass/Req
    "Requiem" [Lat] SATB,SMezTB soli,orch voc
      sc PETERS 4251 $2.50, cloth PETERS 4251
      $7.50, sc PETERS 4250 $25.00, ipa, min sc
      PETERS E975 $6.00, min sc-cloth PETERS
      E975 $9.00   (V269)
    "Requiem" cor,opt orch oct KALMUS 6472
      $2.50, ipa   (V270)
    "Requiem" [Eng/Lat] cor,4 soli SCHIRM.G voc
      sc $2.50, cloth $3.50   (V271)
    "Requiem" cor KALMUS L391 $10.00   (V272)
    "Requiem" cor KALMUS $3.00   (V273)
    "Requiem" cor,orch sc KALMUS $10.00, ipa
                                        (V274)
    "Requiem" cor sc KALMUS $10.00   (V275)
    (Dunn) —Messa &i Requiem" .Lat/Eng] SATB
      s.p. voc sc RICORDI-ENG LD403, cor pts
      RICORDI-ENG SY164-67   (V276)
    (Rogers) "Requiem" SATB oct PRO ART 2055
      $.25   (V277)

  Messa Di Requiem *see Manzoni Requiem

  Messe De Requiem *Mass/Req
    SATB LEMOINE voc sc s.p., cor pts s.p.
                                        (V278)

  O Fair Zion (from Nabucco)
    (Strickling, G.) SATB ct PRESSER MC473
    $.35   (V279)

  Pater Noster
    "Father, Our Father" [Eng/Lat] SSATB,acap
      oct SCHIRM.G 8001 $.40   (V280)

  Praises To The Virgin Mary *BVM
    SSAA WEINBERGER s.p.   (V281)
    SSAA,acap MARKS 8 $.30   (V282)

VERDI, GIUSEPPE (cont'd.)

  Quattro Pezzi Sacri
    SATB,acap RICORDI-ENG 101729 s.p.
      contains: Ave Maria; Laudi Alla Vergine
      Maria; Stabat Mater; Te Deum   (V283)

  Requiem *Req
    [Lat/Eng] cor,soli,orch min sc INTERNAT.
    $4.00   (V284)

  Requiem *see Manzoni Requiem

  Requiem Aeternum (from Messa Di Requiem)
    SATB,acap RICORDI-ENG SY250 s.p.   (V285)

  Song Of The Gypsy Girls
    (Rodby) SA oct AGAPE SP 686 $.35   (V286)

  Stabat Mater
    see Quattro Pezzi Sacri
    [Lat] SATB,orch min sc sc PETERS 4256B 4257
      $.75 $6.00, ipa see from Four Sacred
      Pieces   (V287)
    cor oct KALMUS 6471 $.75   (V288)
    cor,orch sc KALMUS $6.00, ipa   (V289)
    cor sc KALMUS $6.00   (V290)
    [Lat/Eng] cor,pno s.p. voc sc RICORDI-ENG
      114637, cor pts RICORDI-ENG SY168-71
                                        (V291)

  Te Decet Hymnus (from Manzoni Requiem) Xmas
    (Craig; Mason) SATB oct PLYMOUTH FS-102
    $.30   (V292)
    (Craig; Mason) SATB oct PLYMOUTH FS-102
    $.30   (V293)

  Te Deum (from Four Sacred Pieces) Te Deum
    see Quattro Pezzi Sacri
    [Lat] SATB&SATB,orch min sc sc PETERS
      42560 $.75 see from Four Sacred Pieces
                                        (V294)
    [Lat] SATB&SATB,S solo,orch sc PETERS 4258
      $6.00, ipa see from FOUR SACRED PIECES
                                        (V295)
    SATB BELWIN $1.00   (V296)
    dbl cor,pno voc sc RICORDI-ENG 101470 s.p.
                                        (V297)
    cor,orch sc KALMUS $6.00, ipa   (V298)
    cor sc KALMUS $6.00   (V299)
    cor oct KALMUS 6470 $.75   (V300)

VERDONCK, CORNELIUS (1563-1625)
  Ave Gratia Plena *mot
    [Lat] 4pt mix cor SKAND. SMF5454 s.p.
      bontains also: Prome Novas, Hymenaee (6pt
      mix cor) (hymn)   (V301)

  Ave Maria *Fest,mot
    [Lat] SATB,acap cor (med easy) MULLER MS 26
    s.p.   (V302)
    (Steele, Jonathan) [Lat] SATB CHESTER s.p.
                                        (V303)

  Prome Novas, Hymenaee
    see Verdonck, Cornelius, Ave Gratia Plena

VERE LANGUORES see Victoria, Tomas Luis de

VERE LANGUORES see Volpi, Edoardo

VERE LANGUORES NOSTROS see Lotti, Antonio

VERE LANGUORES NOSTROS see Victoria, Tomas Luis
  de

VERESS, SANDOR (1907-   )
  Laudatio Musicae
    mix cor,S solo,orch voc sc ZERBONI 5536
    s.p., ipr   (V304)

  Sancti Augustini Psalmus *ASD,Psalm
    [Lat/Hung] mix cor,B solo,orch voc sc
    ZERBONI 4713 s.p., ipr   (V305)

VERETTI, ANTONIO (1900-   )
  &ue Mottetti *CC2U,mot
    [Lat] SATB RICORDI-ENG 131283 s.p. (V306)

  Sinfonia Sacra
    men cor,orch voc sc ZERBONI 4501 s.p., ipr
                                        (V307)

VERGANI, G.
  Tre Ispirazioni *CC3U,BVM
    [Lat] unis ZANIBON 2738 s.p.   (V308)

VERGEBLICHES STANDCHEN see Brahms, Johannes

VERGINE BELLA see Gandolfi

VERGINE CHIARA see Palestrina, Giovanni

VERGINE IL CUI FIGLIOL see Gabrieli, Giovanni

VERGINE TUTTO AMOR see Farina, G.

VERGNUGTE PLEISSENSTADT see Bach, Johann
  Sebastian

VERHAALEN, B.
  Panis Angelicus
    men cor ALSBACH&D sc s.p., cor pts s.p.
                                        (V309)

VERHEUL, W.P.
  Sanctus *Sanctus
    wom cor sc ALSBACH&D s.p.   (V310)

VERHEY, A.B.B.
  Lofzang Van Maria *see Magnificat

  Magnificat
    "Lofzang Van Maria" men cor ALSBACH&D sc
    s.p., cor pts s.p.   (V311)

VERILY, VERILY, I SAY UNTO YOU see Tallis,
  Thomas

VERITAS MEA see Bottigliero, Eduardo

VERITAS MEA see Magri, Pietro

VERITAS MEA see Polzer, Odo

VERITAS MEA see Ravanello, Oreste

VERITAS MEA see Volpi, Edoardo

VERKAAIK
  Children At Christmas *Xmas
    SATB oct HERITAGE H59 $.35   (V312)

VERKOUTERAN, ADRIAN
  Missa Brevis *Mass
    SATB oct GRAY GCMR 3122 $.35   (V313)

VERKUNDIGUNG DER GEBURT UNSERES HEILANDES see
  Reda, Siegfried

VERLANGEN NAAR GOD see Herwaarden, J.G.

VERLEIH UNS FRIEDEN see Mendelssohn-Bartholdy,
  Felix

VERLEIH UNS FRIEDEN see Micheelsen, Hans
  Friedrich

VERLEIH UNS FRIEDEN see Schweppe, Joachim

VERLEIH UNS FRIEDEN GNADIGLICH see Arfken,
  Ernst

VERLEIH UNS FRIEDEN GNADIGLICH see Bornefeld,
  Helmut

VERLEIH UNS FRIEDEN GNADIGLICH see Borris,
  Siegfried

VERLEIH UNS FRIEDEN GNADIGLICH see Distler,
  Hugo

VERLEIH UNS FRIEDEN GNADIGLICH see Eccard,
  Johannes

VERLEIH UNS FRIEDEN GNADIGLICH see Erythraus,
  Gotthard

VERLEIH UNS FRIEDEN GNADIGLICH see Othmayr,
  Kaspar

VERLEIH UNS FRIEDEN GNADIGLICH see Pepping,
  Ernst

VERLEIH UNS FRIEDEN GNADIGLICH see Praetorius,
  Michael

VERLEIH UNS FRIEDEN GNADIGLICH see Raphael,
  Gunther

VERLEIH UNS FRIEDEN GNADIGLICH see Resinarius,
  Balthasar

VERLEIH UNS FRIEDEN GNADIGLICH see Schutz,
  Heinrich

VERLEIH UNS FRIEDEN GNADIGLICH see Schweizer,
  Rolf

VERLEIH UNS FRIEDEN GNADIGLICH see Strohbach,
  Siegfried

VERLEIH UNS FRIEDEN GNADIGLICH see Thomas, Kurt

VERMULST, JAN
  Blessing Of Saint Francis *Bene
    2 eq voices,org oct WORLD ESA-540-2 $.30
                                        (V314)
  How Lovely Is Your Dwelling Place (Psalm 83)
    Bibl
    SA&cong,org oct WORLD ESA-1126-2 $.45
                                        (V315)
    SATB&cong,org oct WORLD ESA-1124-8 $.45
                                        (V316)
  Lord Is My Shepherd, The (Psalm 23) Bibl
    2 eq voices,org,opt fl oct WORLD ESA-745-2
    $.30   (V317)
    SATB/unis,org,opt fl oct WORLD ESA-608-1
    $.30   (V318)
    3 eq voices,org,opt fl oct WORLD ESA-746-3
    $.30   (V319)

  Mass For Christian Unity *Credo/Mass
    cong&opt cor,opt org oct ST.MARTIN SMP667
    s.p., ipa   (V320)

  Psalm 23 *see Lord Is My Shepherd, The

  Psalm 83 *see How Lovely Is Your Dwelling
    Place

  Psalm 150 *Bibl
    SATB&opt cong,org,opt 2trp oct WORLD
    ESA-699-8 $.30   (V321)
    2 eq voices&opt cong,org,opt 2trp oct WORLD
    ESA-748-2 $.30   (V322)

VERNEHMT DIE REDE see Kaufmann, Otto

VERNIMM, O GOTT, MEIN SCHREIEN see Mareschall,
  Samuel

VERNON, KNIGHT
  Swords Into Plowshaws
    4pt mix cor,acap oct SCHIRM.G 11921 $.35
                                        (V323)

VERNON, SISTER (VERHAALEN, M.)
  Hymn Of Praise *Gen,anthem
    SSA (med easy) oct GIA G1296 $.40   (V324)

VEROVIO, S.
  Diletto Spirituale
    (Vecchi, Prof. Giuseppe) 3-4pt quarto FORNI
    459 s.p.   (V325)

VERRALL, JOHN (1908-   )
  Carols And Songs For Christmastide *CCU,
    Xmas,carol
    unis/mix cor BOSTON 11239 $.75   (V326)

  Christmas Fantasy *Xmas
    SATB,band oct PRESSER 312-40083 $.35, ipr
                                        (V327)

VERREES, LEON
  I Do Not Ask, O Lord
    SATB,org SEESAW $1.50   (V328)

VERS LES MONTS (Psalm 120)
  (Geveart, F.-A.) [Fr] 4pt mix cor,acap (easy)
    cor pts LEMOINE s.p. see from Collection De
    Choeurs, troisieme Fascicule   (V329)

VERSE see Diemente, Edward

VERSE see Goehr, Alexander

VERSE ANTHEMS 1 see Gibbons, Orlando

VERSES FROM THE BOOK OF RUTH see Spies, Claudio

VERSI SPIRITUALI see Valente, A.

VERSICLES AND RESPONSES see Hewitt-Jones, Tony

VERSICLES AND RESPONSES see Rose, Bernard

VERSICLES AND RESPONSES FOR THREE TREBLE VOICES
  *CCU,Gen
  (Stevenson, Peter) 3pt treb cor oct ROYAL
  s.p.   (V330)

VERSICLES AND RESPONSES see Shaw, Gerald

VERSICLES AND RESPONSES *CCU
  pap ROYAL 326 s.p.   (V331)

VERSICLES, RESPONSES AND LORD'S PRAYER see
  Holman, Derek

VERSO, ANTONIO IL
  Mottetti E Ricercari *see Vinci, Pietro

VERTRAGET EINANDER IN DER LIEBE see Reda,
  Siegfried

VERTROUWEN (WAT GOD DOET IS WELGEDAAN) see
  Bach, Johann Sebastian

VERWEHT SIND WEG UND GRABEN see Schafer, Karl

VERWUNDERT EUCH NICHT, WENN EUCH DIE WELT HASST
  see Reda, Siegfried

VERWUNSCHTES FREUDENLICHT see Bach, Johann
  Sebastian

VERY BREAD, GOOD SHEPHERD see Willan, Healey

VERY FIRST CHRISTMAS, THE see Jenkins

VERY MERRY CHRISTMAS, A see Robinson, G.W.

VERZAGE NICHT, DU HAUFLEIN KLEIN see Altenburg,
  Michael

VERZAGE NICHT, DU HAUFLEIN KLEIN see Raphael,
  Gunther

VESPER see Zimmermann, Heinz Werner

VESPER *mot
  see Hebrew Benediction
  (Burkhart, Franz) mix cor,acap DOBLINGER s.p.
  see also In Seiner Handen   (V332)

VESPER see Anderson, [William H.]

VESPER BELL, THE see Engelhart, P.

VESPER BELLS
  (Tapscott, Carl) SA,pno oct BERANDOL 790T5AC
  $.35   (V333)

VESPER BELLS see Rubinstein, Anton

VESPER HYMN see Churchill

VESPER HYMN see Tolmage, Gerald

VESPER I see Bender, Jan

VESPER II "O WIE SELIG SEID IHR DOCH, IHR
  FROMMEN" see Bender, Jan

VESPERA IAM VENIT see Wenzel, Eberhard

VESPERAE BEATAE MARIAE VIRGINIS see Monteverdi,
  Claudio

VESPERAE BEATAE MARIAE VIRGINIS 1610 see
  Monteverdi, Claudio

VESPERAE DE DOMINICA see Mozart, Wolfgang
  Amadeus

VESPERAE DOMINICALES see Mielczewski, Marcin

VESPERAE SOLEMNES DE CONFESSORE see Mozart,
  Wolfgang Amadeus

VESPERAE SOLEMNES DEL CONFESSORE see Mozart,
  Wolfgang Amadeus

VESPERAE SOLENNES see Mozart, Wolfgang Amadeus

VESPERAE SOLENNES DE CONFESSORE see Mozart,
  Wolfgang Amadeus

VESPERARE SOLEMNES DE CONFESSORE see Mozart,
  Wolfgang Amadeus

VESPERARUM PRECUM OFFICIA, 1540 see Rhaw, Georg

VESPERE AUTEM SABBATI see Gallus, Jacobus

VESPERGESANG see Kampf, [Karl]

VESPERS see Monteverdi, Claudio

VESPERS NO. 3 see Haydn, (Johann) Michael

VESPERSANG see Bortniansky, Dimitri
  Stepanovitch, Jubilate Amen

VESPRI DELLA DOMENICA see Bottazzo, Luigi

VESPRO see Bottazzo, Luigi

VESPRO DELLA BEATA VERGINE see Monteverdi,
  Claudio

VESPRO DELLA DOMENICA see Bottazzo, Luigi

VESPRO DELLA DOMENICA see Bottazzo, Luigi,
  Vespri Della Domenica

VESPRO DOMENICALE see Firpo, Antonio

VESPRO DOMENICALE see Garbelotto, Antonio

VESTIVA I COLLI see Palestrina, Giovanni

VETTER
  Alt Er Ferdig (composed with Bach, Johann
  Sebastian)
  [Norw] unis,org LYCHE 65 s.p.   (V334)

VEXILLA REGIS see Arnaldi, Antonio

VEXILLA REGIS see Bortolan, C.

VEXILLA REGIS see Bottazzo, Luigi

VEXILLA REGIS see Bruckner, Anton

VEXILLA REGIS see Fabiani, Angelo

VEXILLA REGIS see Ferrari, Giovanni

VEXILLA REGIS see Muller, J.

VEXILLA REGIS see Pergolesi, Giovanni Battista

VEXILLA REGIS see Rodella, Sante

VEXILLA REGIS see Somers, Harry Stewart

VEXILLA REGIS PRODEUNT see Bruckner, Anton

VEXILLA REGIS PRODEUNT see Palestrina, Giovanni

VEXILLA REGIS PRODUENT see Wuensch

VI CHRISTUM LOVE see Vulpius, Melchior

VI PRISA DIG see Lindegren, Johan, Laudamus

VI PRISER DIG AF HJERTE see Distler, Hugo, Wir
  Bitten Dich Von Herzen

VI SJUNGA GUDS ARA see Wideen, Ivar

VI SJUNGER OCH SPELAR HAFTE 1 (from Sang Och
  Spel) CC11U
  (Norrman, Rudolf) wom cor/jr cor NORDISKA
  5116 s.p.   (V335)

VI SJUNGER OCH SPELAR HAFTE 2 *CC27U
  (Conner, Herbert) 2pt wom cor/3pt wom cor/2pt
  jr cor/3pt jr cor,fl NORDISKA 5115 s.p.   (V336)

VI SJUNGER OCH SPELAR HAFTE 3 *CCU,Xmas
  (Conner, Herbert) 2-4pt wom cor/2-4pt jr cor,
  fl/vln NORDISKA 5076 s.p.   (V337)

VI SJUNGER OCH SPELAR HAFTE 5 (from Skolkoren)
  CC15U
  (Norrman, Rudolph) wom cor/jr cor,inst
  NORDISKA 5527 s.p.   (V338)

VI SJUNGER OCH SPELAR HAFTE 4 *CC20U,Xmas
  (Conner, Herbert) wom cor/jr cor,opt inst
  NORDISKA 5283 s.p.   (V339)

VI TACKA DIG, GUD see Bach, Johann Sebastian

VI TACKA DIG, HERRE GUD see Schutz, Heinrich

VI TACKA DIG, O JESU GOD see Ahlen, Waldemar

VI TILLBEDJA DIG, KRISTE see Lundrik, Hildor

VI TRO ALLESAMMEN PA EN GUD see Pederson,
  Mogens

VI TRO PA EN ALLSMAKTIG GUD
  (Berg, Gottfrid) 3pt mix cor NORDISKA 3469
  s.p. see also Sacrae Cantiones   (V340)

VIA CRUCIS see Christopher, Cyril S.

VIA CRUCIS see Liszt, Franz

VIA CRUCIS E ADOREMUS TE CHRISTI see Mancini,
  Vincenzo

VIA DOLOROSA see Bjarnegard, Gustaf

VIA SACRA see Monnikendam, Marius

VIADANA, LODOVICO GROSSI DA (1564-1645)
  Adoramus Te, Christe *Easter/Lent
  (Martens, Mason J.) "We Adore Thee, O Lord
  Christ" [Lat/Eng] SATB,cont SCHIRM.EC
  2449   (V341)
  (Richardson) "We Adore Thee, Christ, Jesus"
  SATB oct SPRATT 2015 $.25   (V342)

  Ave Verum Corpus
  (Ehret) "Hail, True Body" [Lat/Eng] SATB
  oct COLOMBO 2383 $.25   (V343)

  Benedictus (from Cantato Domino)
  see Viadana, Lodovico Grossi da, Sanctus

  Cantabo Domino *Mass
  (Bauerle, Hermann) SATB,acap voc pt
  BREITKOPF-L CHB-2776 s.p.   (V344)

  Cantata Domino
  (Cramer) "Sing Ye Unto The Lord" [Eng/Lat]
  SATB,acap MARKS 4291 $.25   (V345)

  Christus Resurgens *Lat
  mix cor SOUTHERN $.25   (V346)
  (Martens) [Lat/Eng] SSB/SSAB,org oct MCA   (V347)

  Dieci Concerti Ecclesiastici *CC10U
  (Tonetti, O.) [Lat] 1-4pt,org ZANIBON 4868
  s.p.   (V348)

  Exsultate Iusti *Gen/Thanks
  voc pt DOBLINGER s.p. see also LOB UND DANK (V349)

  Exsultate Justi *mot
  mix cor SOUTHERN $.30   (V350)
  [Lat] SATB,acap MUSICUS 1030 $.25   (V351)
  [Lat] SATB,acap oct GIA G561 $.25   (V352)
  boy cor SOUTHERN $.20   (V353)
  (Borucchia) SATB oct SUMMY M 2304 $.45   (V354)
  (Vene) [Lat] TTBB,acap oct COLOMBO 1720
  $.25   (V355)

  Exsultate Justi *Easter/Gen
  SATB,acap (med easy) MULLER MS 31 s.p.   (V356)
  "Sing, Ye Righteous" SATB,acap (med diff)
  oct CONCORDIA 98-1527 $.30   (V357)

VIADANA, LODOVICO GROSSI DA (cont'd.)
  Exultate Justi In Domino
  (Martens, Mason) "Triumph And Rejoice In
  The Lord" SATB oct WALTON 2153 $.30
                                               (V358)

  Hail, O Hail True Body *Renais
  (Ehret, Walter) SATB,acap PEER $.40   (V359)

  Hail, True Body *see Ave Verum Corpus

  L'hora Passa *Mass
  (Katt, L.) 4pt mix cor,acap DOBLINGER sc
  s.p., cor pts s.p.   (V360)

  Missa L'Hora Passa *Mass
  mix cor BELWIN $1.00   (V361)

  Missa Sine Nomine *Mass
  mix cor,acap voc sc KALMUS 6492 $1.25   (V362)

  O Queen Of Heaven *see Regina Caeli

  O Sacrum Convivium *mot
  [Lat] TTBB,acap SCHIRM.EC 78 $.25   (V363)
  boy cor SOUTHERN $.25   (V364)
  (Collins, H.B.) [Lat] TTBarB,opt org
  CHESTER s.p.   (V365)
  (Ruiz) [Lat] 4pt men cor,acap RICORDI-ARG
  BA 10491 s.p.   (V366)

  Regina Caeli *Easter/Lent
  (Martens, Mason) "O Queen Of Heaven" SATB
  oct WALTON 6015 $.35   (V367)

  Renaissance Motets For Lent And Passiontide
  *CCU,Lent/Psntd,mot,Renais
  (Keeley) mix cor SOUTHERN $.80   (V368)

  Sanctus (from Cantato Domino) mot/Sanctus
  [Lat] SATB RICORDI-ENG SY192 s.p. contains
  also: Benedictus (Bene)   (V369)

  Sing, Ye Righteous *see Exultate Justi

  Sing Ye Unto The Lord *see Cantata Domino

  Te Deum Laudamus (Tone 5, No. 2)
  mix cor SCHIRM.EC 1278   (V370)

  Ten Sacred Concertos *Op.12
  [Lat] 2-4pt mix cor,S/T solo,org sc
  HINRICHSEN N4868 s.p.   (V371)

  Triumph And Rejoice In The Lord *see
  Exultate Justi In Domino

  We Adore Thee, Christ, Jesus *see Adoramus
  Te, Christe

  We Adore Thee, O Lord Christ *see Adoramus
  Te, Christe

VIADANA, TH. L.A.
  O Sacrum Convivium
  men cor sc ALSBACH&D s.p.   (V372)

VIANELLO, GINO
  Messa Conciliare *Mass
  [It] unis sc ZANIBON 4747 s.p., cor pts
  ZANIBON 4748 s.p.   (V373)

VIANELLO, LINO
  La Messa Dei Giovani (composed with Angelini,
  Lucio) *Mass
  [It] unis sc ZANIBON E.O.1223 s.p., cor pts
  ZANIBON E.O.1224 s.p.   (V374)

VIANELLO, PIERO
  Padre Nostro
  cor ZANIBON 1559 s.p.   (V375)

VIARDOT-GARCIA, PAULINE (1821-1910)
  Ave Maria *BVM
  [Lat] SA,solo ENOCH voc sc s.p., cor pts
  s.p.   (V376)

VICARI, CARLO
  Laudate Pueri Dominum *Op.45, Mass
  [Lat] unis,org ZANIBON 3573 s.p.   (V377)

VICK
  All That's Good And Great And True
  SA oct SACRED S-5390 $.35   (V378)

  Alleluia, Song Of Gladness
  SATB FLAMMER A 5556 $.30   (V379)

  Jesus, Thy Boundless Love To Me
  SATB oct SACRED E77 $.35   (V380)

  Now To The Lord A Noble Song
  SATB FLAMMER A 5611 $.30   (V381)

  O Blessed Day Of Motherhood
  SATB oct LORENZ 9966 $.30   (V382)

  O Lord, Thy Heavenly Grace Impart
  SATB oct SACRED S-54 $.35   (V383)

  Shepherd Of Tender Youth
  2pt oct PLYMOUTH SC-508 $.25   (V384)

VICK, BERYL, JR.
  Beautiful Saviour *Xmas,cant
  2pt jr cor,opt S rec,A rec,T rec cmplt ed
  PRO ART 1297 $.85, ipa   (V385)

  Blest Are The Pure In Heart
  SA oct WORD CS-2460 $.30   (V386)

  My God, Accept My Heart
  SATB (med) ABINGDON APM-602 $.25   (V387)

VICTIMAE PASCALI LAUDES see David, Johann
  Nepomuk

VICTIMAE PASCHALI see Bottazzo, Luigi

VICTIMAE PASCHALI see Byrd, William

VICTIMAE PASCHALI see Infantas, Fernando de las

VICTIMAE PASCHALI LAUDES see Biechteler,
  Sigismund

VICTIMAE PASCHALI LAUDES see Byrd, William

VICTIMAE PASCHALI LAUDES nee Mengelberg, Rudolf

VICTIMAE PASCHALI LAUDES see Pederson, Mogens

VICTIMAE PASCHALI LAUDES see Victoria

VICTORIA
Christians Praise The Paschal Victim *see Victimae Paschali Laudes

Jesu, Dulcis Memoria *Easter/Lent
(Greyson) "Jesu, The Very Thought Is Sweet" SATB nct BOURNE ES48 $.25 (V388)

Jesu, The Very Thought Is Sweet *see Jesu, Dulcis Memoria

Judas, Mercator Pessimus
mix cor SOUTHERN $.30 (V389)

Kyrie Eleison *Kyrie
mix cor SOUTHERN $.25 (V390)

O Sacrum Convivium
boy cor SOUTHERN $.30 (V391)

Sanctus *Sanctus
(Harris) SSA,acap SOUTHERN $.30 (V392)

Victimae Paschali Laudes *Easter
mix cor SOUTHERN $.40 (V393)
(Riedel) "Christians Praise The Paschal Victim" SATB SCHMITT 1412 $.40 (V394)

VICTORIA, TOMAS LUIS DE (ca. 1549-1611)
Aestimatus Sum *cor-resp
(Turner, Bruno) [Lat] SSAT/TTBarB CHESTER s.p. see also Responsories For Tenebrae (V395)
(Turner, Bruno) [Lat] TTBarB CHESTER s.p. (V396)

Agnus Dei *Easter/Lent,Agnus
"Lamb Of God" SATB oct WALTON 2131 $.25 (V397)
(McKelvy, J.) SATB&SATB,acap FOSTER MF408 $.25 (V398)
(Rider) [Eng/Lat] 5pt mix cor,acap oct LAWSON 925 $.25 (V399)

Album *CC17UL,hymn/mot
mix cor,acap voc sc KALMUS 6495 $1.50 (V400)

All Ye People *see O Vos Omnes

Alma Redemptoris !Mass
(McKelvy, J.) SATB&SATB,soli,acap FOSTER MF409 $2.00 (V401)

Amicus Meus *cor-resp
(Turner, Bruno) [Lat] SATB CHESTER s.p. see also Responsories For Tenebrae (V402)

Animam Meam Dilectam *cor-resp
(Ruiz) [Lat] SATB,acap RICORDI-ARG BA 10083 s.p. (V403)
(Turner, Bruno) [Lat] SATB CHESTER s.p. see also Responsories For Tenebrae (V404)

Antiphon III *BVM
SAATB/SATBB PETERS WM60 $1.50 see also ANTIPHONS IN HONOR OF THE BLESSED VIRGIN (V405)

&s A Lamb !see Tanquam Agnus

Astiterunt Reges *cor-resp
(Turner, Bruno) [Lat] SATB CHESTER s.p. see also Responsories For Tenebrae (V406)

Ave Maria *BVM/Xmas,mot,Lat
see LA SCHOLA PALESTRINIENNE DEUXIEME CAHIER
[Eng/Lat] 4pt mix cor,acap oct SCHIRM.G 11565 $.30 (V407)
[Lat] SATB,acap oct GIA G562 $.25 (V408)
boy bor SOUTHERN $.30 (V409)
[Lat] 4pt mix cor/4 eq voices UNION ESP. 18821 $.60 (V410)
SATB,acap oct PRESSER 352-00079 $.30 (V411)
[Lat] SKAND. SMF5566 s.p. (V412)
"Hail, Virgin Mary" [Lat/Eng] SATB,acap BROUDE BR. $.30 (V413)
(Cain) SAB oct FOX R173 $.30 (V414)
(Cain) TTBB oct FOX R174 $.30 (V415)
(Cain) SSAATTBB oct FOX R184 $.30 (V416)
(Gray) "Father In Heaven" SATB,acap oct PRO ART $.25 (V417)
(Krone) SATB,acap WARNER W2712 $.30 (V418)
(Lavater, H.) [Lat] wom cor,acap (med) HUG s.p. (V419)
(Lavater, H.) [Lat] men cor,acap (med) HUG s.p. (V420)
(Mattfeld, V.) "Hail, Virgin Mary" [Lat/Eng] SATB,acap SCHIRM.EC 1279 $.20 (V421)
(Schinelli, A.) [It/Eng/Ger] 4pt mix cor CURCI 6476 s.p. see also Collana Di Composizioni Polifoniche Vocali Sacre E Profane, Vol. 1 (V422)
(Scott) SSA oct FOX R106 $.30 (V423)
(Scott) SATB oct FOX R100 $.30 (V424)
(Steele, Jonathan) [Lat] SATB CHESTER s.p. (V425)
(Wilhousky) SATB,acap oct FISCHER,C CM-6581 $.25 (V426)

Ave Verum Corpus !Easter/Lent
(Richardson) "Hail, O Hail, True Body" SATB oct SPRATT 2005 $.30 (V427)

Be Not Afraid Mary *see Ne Timeas Maria

Be Strong In Battle *see Estote Fortes In Bello

Beati Immaculati
(Martens, Mason) "Blessed Are The Undefiled" SATB oct WALTON 6020 $.30 (V428)

Benedicam Dominum *Gen,mot
[Lat] SSAB,acap (med easy) MULLER M 34 s.p. (V429)
[Lat] SSABar,acap oct NOVELLO DM-34 s.p. (V430)

Benedictus fBene
girl cor SOUTHERN $.30 (V431)

Blessed Are All Men Who Name Thee Savior
(Coggin, E.) SATB,acap oct PRESSER 312-40741 $.30 (V432)

VICTORIA, TOMAS HUIS &E (cont'd.)

Blessed Are The Undefiled *see Beati Immaculati

Blessed Is He *Bene
(Castellazzi; Vene) [Lat/Eng] SSA/TTB,acap oct COLOMBO 2040 $.25 (V433)

Bread Of Heaven
(Ehret, W.) SATB,acap oct PRESSER 362-03120 $.30 (V434)

Bride Of Christ *see Veni Sponsa Christi

Calagaverunt Oculi Mei *Bibl
(Deis) "Then Were My Eyelids Veiled With Darkness" [Eng/Lat] 4pt mix cor,acap oct SCHIRM.G 8409 $.30 (V435)

Caligaverunt Oculi Me *cor-resp
(Turner, Bruno) [Lat] SATB CHESTER s.p. see also Responsories For Tenebrae (V436)

Caligaverunt Oculi Mei
(Payson, A.) "O See My Dark Eyes" SATB,acap FRANK F-442 $.30 (V437)
(Wilhousky) SATB,acap oct FISCHER,C CM-6579 $.25 (V438)

Collana Di Composizioni Polifoniche Vocali Sacre E Profane, Vol. 1 *see Ave Maria (V439)

Come To The Waters *see Sitientes, Venite Ad Aquas

Darkness Was Over All *Easter/Lent,Renais
(Ehret, Walter) SATB,acap PEER $.40 (V440)
(Richardson) SATB oct WORD CS-326 $.30 (V441)
(Richardson) SAB oct WORD CS-2445 $.30 (V442)

Domine, Non Sum Dignus *anthem
[Lat] TTBB oct NOVELLO 38.0131.04 s.p. (V443)
men cor sc ALSBACH&D s.p. (V444)

Domino Non Sum Dignus
(Zethelius, Gudrun) "Herre, Jag Ar Icke Vardig" mix cor NORDISKA 3719 s.p. (V445)

Dum Complerentur Dies Pentecostes *mot
(Petti, Anthony G.) "Now When The Day" [Eng/Lat] SSATB CHESTER s.p. (V446)

Dum Complerentur Dies Pentecotes *Whitsun
"When The Day Of Pentecost" SSATB,acap SCHIRM.EC 1281 $.30 (V447)

Dum Ergo Essent *mot
(Petti, Anthony G.) "When All Disciples" [Eng/Lat] SSATB CHESTER s.p. (V448)

Duo Seraphim
[Lat] SSAA CHESTER s.p. (V449)
4pt wom cor sc ALSBACH&D s.p. (V450)
(Candlyn) "Yea, Two Seraphim Cried Out" SATB,acap WARNER W3713 $.30 (V451)

Ecce Dominus Veniet *Adv,mot
SATTB,acap SCHIRM.EC $.35 (V452)
(Collins, H.B.) [Lat] SATTB CHESTER s.p. (V453)

Ecce Quomodo Moritur *cor-resp
(Turner, Bruno) [Lat] SATB CHESTER s.p. see also Responsories For Tenebrae (V454)

Ecce Sacerdos Magnus *mot
[Lat] SATB,acap oct GIA G559 $.25 (V455)
"This Is The Mighty Prophet" [Lat/Eng] SATB,acap BROUDE BR. $.30 see from Seven Motets (V456)
(Steele, Jonathan) [Lat] SATB CHESTER s.p. (V457)

Eine Stunde *see Una Hora

Eram Quasi Agnus *Holywk,cor-resp
"I Was Like An Innocent Lamb" SATB,acap SCHIRM.EC 1280 $.30 (V458)
(Knight, Gerald) SATB,acap oct FISCHER,C CM-7584 $.25 (V459)
(Turner, Bruno) [Lat] SATB CHESTER s.p. see also Responsories For Tenebrae (V460)

Estote Fortes In Bello *mot
"Be Strong In Battle" [Lat/Eng] SATB,acap BROUDE BR. $.35 see from Seven Motets (V461)
"Go Forth With Courage" [Eng/Lat] 4pt mix cor,acap oct SCHIRM.G 7688 $.30 (V462)

Father In Heaven *see Ave Maria

For Their Faith In The Lord *see Iste Sanctus

Four Motets *CC4U,mot
[Lat] 4-6pt,acap AMP A661 $1.25 (V463)

Funfzehn Motetten *CC15L,mot
(Bauerle, Hermann) SATB,acap cor pts BREITKOPF-L PB-1887 s.p., voc pt BREITKOPF-L CHB-1659 s.p. (V464)

Gaude Maria Virgo
(McKelvy, J.) SSATB FOSTER MF 153 $.25 (V465)

Gaudent In Caelis *mot
"Heav'n Doth Resound" [Lat/Eng] SATB,acap BROUDE BR. $.35 see from Seven Motets (V466)
(Talmadge, A.) SSAA,acap SCHIRM.EC 1941 $.16 (V467)

Gaudent In Coelis *mot
[Lat] SATB,acap oct GIA G553 $.25 (V468)

Gloria In Excelsis Deo
(McKelvy) SATB&SATB FOSTER MF404 $.45 (V469)

Glorious In Heaven Are The Souls Of All Saints *anthem
(Burgess, Francis) mix cor oct NOVELLO 28.1039.05 s.p. (V470)

Glory Be To God On High *Gen
(Ehret) SATB SCHMITT 1416 $.30 (V471)

VICTORIA, TOMAS LUIS DE (cont'd.)

Go Forth With Courage *see Estote Fortes In Bello

Gott, Dem Vater Und Dem Sohne
see Praetorius, Michael, Gott, Dem Vater Im Hochsten Thron

Hail, O Hail, True Body *see Ave Verum Corpus

Hail, Virgin Mary *see Ave Maria

Hear Me, O Lord God *see Salve Regina

Hear My Cry, O God
(Hornish) SSA,acap oct PRO ART 1015 $.20 (V472)

Hear Ye, My People *see O Vos Omnes

Heav'n Doth Resound *see Gaudent In Caelis

Herre, Jag Ar Icke Vardig *see Domino Non Sum Dignus

Hic Vir Despicians Mundum *mot
"This Man" [Lat/Eng] SATB,acap BROUDE BR. $.30 see from Seven Motets (V473)

Holy, Holy, Holy *see Sanctus

Holy Lord, God Of Nations
(Coggin) SATB,acap WARNER W7-1019 $.30 (V474)

Holy Spirit, Lord Of Glory
SATB,acap oct WORD CS-681 $.25 (V475)

Hosanna To The Son Of David *see Pueri Hebraeorum

Hosanna Unto David's Son *see Pueri Hebraeorum

Hosianna, Davids Sohn, Lob Sei Dem *mot
(Berger) SATB HANSSLER 1.117 s.p. contains also: Anonymous, Alta Trinita Beata (Hellmann) (V476)

Hosianna, Davids Son
mix cor NORDISKA 2431 s.p. (V477)

I Was Like An Innocent Lamb *see Eram Quasi Agnus

In Festo Corporis Christe *mot
SSAA STAINER 20727 s.p. (V478)

In Festo Natalis Domini
(Schmidt) [Eng/Lat] SATB,acap oct LAWSON 51516 $.40 (V479)

Is It Nothing To You? *see O Vos Omnes?

Iste Sanctus *mot
"For Their Faith In The Lord" [Lat/Eng] SATB,acap BROUDE BR. $.30 see from Seven Motets (V480)

Jesu Dulcis
see LA SCHOLA PALESTRINIENNE PREMIERE CAHIER

Jesu Dulcis Memoria *Commun/Easter/Gen, anthem/hymn/mot
[Lat] 4pt mix cor,acap UNION ESP. 19179 s.p. (V481)
SATB,acap oct PRESSER 332-13383 $.25 (V482)
mix cor ALSBACH&D sc s.p., cor pts s.p. (V483)
"Jesu, Sweet Are All Thoughts" [Lat/Eng] SATB,acap BROUDE BR. $.30 (V484)
"Jesu, The Very Thought Is Sweet" [Eng/Lat] SATB,acap oct BELWIN 64097 $.30 (V485)
"Jesu! The Very Thought Is Sweet" [Lat] mix cor,acap oct NOVELLO 40.0879.00 s.p. (V486)
"Jesu, The Very Thought Of Thee" SATB,opt inst (easy) oct OXFORD 42.004 $.25 (V487)
"O Thou Joy Of Loving Hearts" SATB,acap SCHIRM.EC 1125 $.25 (V488)
(Bridge, Sir Fredk.) "Jesu, The Very Thought Is Sweet" SATB BOSWORTH s.p. see from Motets (V489)
(Davids) mix cor SOUTHERN $.25 (V490)
(Davison, A.) [Lat] TTBB,acap SCHIRM.EC 79 $.20 (V491)
(Ehret, W.) "Jesu, The Very Thought Is Sweet" [Eng/Lat] SATB oct BELWIN 1759 $.30 (V492)
(Gray) SATB,acap oct PRO ART 1260 $.12 (V493)
(Montani) [Lat] 4pt mix cor,acap oct SCHIRM.G 5573 $.25 (V494)
(Woodworth, G.) SSAA,acap SCHIRM.EC 830 $.20 (V495)

Jesu, Sweet Are All Thoughts *see Jesu Dulcis Memoria

Jesu, The Very Thought Is Sweet *see Jesu Dulcis Memoria

Jesu, The Very Thought Of Thee *see Jesu, Dulcis Memoria

Jesum Tradidit Impius *cor-resp
(Turner, Bruno) [Lat] SSAT CHESTER s.p. see also Responsories For Tenebrae (V496)

Jesus Dulcis *mot
[Lat] SATB RICORDI-ENG SY144 s.p. (V497)

Judas, Mercator Pessimus *Lent,cor-resp
"Judas, Who Dealt Most Cruelly" [Eng/Lat] 4pt mix cor,acap oct SCHIRM.G 8486 $.30 (V498)
(Turner, Bruno) [Lat] SSAT CHESTER s.p. see also Responsories For Tenebrae (V499)

Judas, Who Dealt Most Cruelly *see Judas, Mercator Pessimus

Kristi Brud, Kom, Fryd Dig *see Veni Sponsa Christi

Kyrie Eleison *Kyrie
SATB oct SACRED E68 $.35 (V500)
(McKelvy, J.) SATB FOSTER MF151 $.25 (V501)

VICTORIA, TOMAS LUIS DE (cont'd.)

Lamb Of God *see Agnus Dei

Lauda Sion Salvatorem *mot
(Petti, Anthony G.) SATB&SATB,cont CHESTER s.p. (V502)

Laudate Dominum, Heft VIII, Part 3: Die Marianischen Antiphone *CC4U,BVM/Fest
(Hubsch, Hanns) [Ger] 5pt mix cor,acap (med) MULLER SM 1514C s.p. (V503)

Lord, Do Thou Have Mercy *anthem
(Rainbow, Bernarr) TTBB oct NOVELLO 38.0138.01 s.p. (V504)

Los Cincuenta Y Dos Motetes Cuaderno I *CC19L,mot
(Rubio) [Lat] 4-8pt mix cor,acap UNION ESP. 19907-1 $7.50 (V505)

Los Cincuenta Y Dos Motetes Cuaderno II *CC13L,mot
(Rubio) [Lat] 4-9pt mix cor,acap UNION ESP. 19907-2 $7.50 (V506)

Los Cincuenta Y Dos Motetes Cuaderno III *CC8L,mot
(Rubio) [Lat] 4-8pt mix cor,acap UNION ESP. 19907-3 $7.50 (V507)

Los Cincuenta Y Dos Motetes Cuaderno IV *CC11L,mot
(Rubio) [Lat] 4-8pt mix cor,acap UNION ESP. 19907-4 $.75 (V508)

Magnificat Primi Toni *Magnif
(Petti, Anthony G.) [Lat] SSAT&SATB,cont CHESTER s.p. (V509)

Miserere Mei, Domine *anthem
(Rainbow, Bernarr) .Lat]&TBB oct NOVELLO 38.0138.01 s.p. (V510)

Missa Gaudeamus *Mass
[Lat] SSATBB MCA voc sc $3.50, cor pts $.40 (V511)
mix cor VOLK 106 sc s.p., cor pts s.p. (V512)

Missa Pro Defunctis
mix cor,acap voc sc KALMUS 6496 $1.25 (V513)

Missa Pro Defunctus *Mass/Req
(Agey, C. Buell) "Requiem Mass" [Eng/Lat] 4pt mix cor,acap voc sc SCHIRM.G $1.25 (V514)

Missa Quarti Toni *Mass
(Bauerle) [Lat] 4pt mix cor,acap UNION ESP. 19641 $1.00 (V515)
(Bauerle, Hermann) SATB,acap cor pts BREITKOPF-L PB-2075 s.p., voc pt BREITKOPF-L CHB-2529 s.p. (V516)

Missa Simile Est Regnum *Mass
mix cor,acap voc sc KALMUS 6493 $1.25 (V517)

Motets *see Jesu, The Very Thought Is Sweet; O My People And Faithful Cross (V518)

Motetter Og Lauder Fra Det 16. Arhhundrede *see Veni Sponsa Christi, "Kristi Brud, Kom, Fryd Dig" (V519)

Ne Timeas Maria *mot
(Kirk) "Be Not Afraid Mary" SATB,opt kbd oct PRO ART 2188 $.30 (V520)
(Washington, Henry) [Lat] SATB CHESTER s.p. (V521)

Now When The Day *see Dum Complerentur Dies Pentecostes

O All Ye That Pass By *see O Vos Omnes

O All Ye That Pass By *see O Vos Omnes, Qui Transitis Per Viam

O Blessed Nativity *see O Magnum Mysterium

O Blessed People *see Populе Meus

O Domine *mot
[Lat] SSTTB,acap UNION ESP. 19176 $1.00 (V522)

O How Full Of Glory *see O Quam Gloriosum Est Regnum

O How Glorious *see O Quam Gloriosum

O Lord, Our God
(Kingsbury, John) SSATBB ALFRED 6405 $.30 (V523)

O Love Lost PerfZct !Easter/Lent
(Richardson) SATB oct WORD CS-314 $.30 (V524)
(Richardson) SAB oct WORD CS-2447 $.30 (V525)

O Lux Beata Trinitas
mix cor sc ALSBACH&D s.p. (V526)

O Magnum Mysterium *Xmas,Mass/mot
[Lat] SATB,acap (med easy) MULLER SM 78 s.p. (V527)
SATB,acap SCHIRM.EC 1177 $.35 (V528)
"O Wondrous Nativity" [Eng/Lat] 4pt mix cor,acap oct SCHIRM.G 7626 $.30 (V529)
(Glaser, V.) SSAA,acap SCHIRM.EC 1922 $.25 (V530)
(Graetzer) [Lat] SATB,acap RICORDI-ARG BA 9837 s.p. (V531)
(Greyson) "O Blessed Nativity" SATB oct BOURNE ES20 $.30 (V532)
(Hallagan, R.) SATB,acap oct PRESSER 312-40484 $.35 (V533)
(Hallagan, R.) SSAA,acap oct PRESSER 312-40737 $.35 (V534)
(Kirk) SATB,acap,opt pno oct PRO ART 2231 $.30 (V535)
(Rubio) [Lat] 4pt mix cor,acap UNION ESP. 19640 $3.50 (V536)
(Shaw; Parker) "O Wondrous Nativity" [Eng/Lat] 4pt mix cor,acap oct SCHIRM.G 10193 $.35 (V537)
(Washington, Henry) [Lat] SATB CHESTER s.p. (V538)
(William; Deis) "O Wondrous Nativity" [Eng/Lat] 4pt wom cor,acap oct SCHIRM.G 9882 $.30 (V539)

O My God I Am Not Worthy *anthem
TTBB oct NOVELLO 38.0131.04 s.p. (V540)

O My People And Faithful Cross *Gd.Fri.,mot
(Bridge, Sir Fredk.) SATB BOSWORTH s.p. see from Motets (V541)

O Quam Gloriosum *Easter,Mass/mot
[Lat] SATB RICORDI-ENG SY172 s.p. (V542)
[Lat] cor,acap UNION ESP. 19178 $1.50 (V543)
"O How Glorious" SATB,acap oct PRESSER 332-13448 $.30 (V544)
(Bauerle, Hermann) SATB,acap voc pt BREITKOPF-L CHB-2477 s.p. (V545)
(Washington, Henri) [Lat] SATB CHESTER s.p. (V546)

O Quam Gloriosum Est Regnum *ASD/ECY,anthem/Mass/mot
[Lat] SATB,acap (med) MULLER MS 65 s.p. (V547)
mix cor,acap voc sc KALMUS 6494 $1.25 (V548)
(Stewart, C.H.) "O How Full Of Glory" [Eng/Lat] mix cor,acap oct NOVELLO 28.1167.07 s.p. (V549)
(Washington, Henry) [Lat] SATB CHESTER s.p. (V550)

O Quam Metuendus *mot
(Steele, Jonathan) [Lat] SATB CHESTER s.p. (V551)

O Quam Metuendus Est *mot
"O Such Holiness" [Lat/Eng] SATB,acap BROUDE BR. $.30 see from Seven Motets (V552)

O Sacrum Convivium *Corpus
TTBarB,acap (easy) oct OXFORD 41.204 $.30 (V553)

O See My Dark Eyes *see Caligaverunt Oculi Mei

O Such Holiness *see O Quam Metuendus Est

O Thou Joy Of Loving Hearts *see Jesu Dulcis Memoria

O Vos Omnes (from Feria VI. In Parasceve) Easter/Lent,anthem/cor-resp/mot,16th cent
SATB oct SUMMY 5476 $.45 (V554)
[Lat] cor,acap UNION ESP. 19339 $.75 (V555)
SATB,acap SCHIRM.EC 1173 $.30 (V556)
"All Ye People" SATB oct WALTON 2134 2170 $.30 $.30 (V557)
"All Ye People" SSA oct WALTON 2134 $.30 (V558)
"Is It Nothing To You" mix cor SOUTHERN $.25 (V559)
"O All Ye That Pass By" SATB,acap oct PRESSER 332-13378 $.30 (V560)
"O Ye People" SSAA,acap SCHIRM.EC 871 $.25 (V561)
(Davison, A.) [Lat] TTBB,acap SCHIRM.EC 915 $.30 (V562)
(Haberl, Fr.X.) SATB,acap voc pt BREITKOPF-L CHB-1634 s.p. (V563)
(Klein, M.) "Is It Nothing To You?" [Eng/Lat] SATB (med) oct GIA G1525 $.30 (V564)
(Ruiz) [Lat] 4pt men cor,acap RICORDI-ARG BA 10492 s.p. (V565)
(Schnyder, P.) [Lat] men cor,acap (med) HUG s.p. (V566)
(Trusler) "Hear Ye, My People" SATB oct PLYMOUTH TR-118 $.25 (V567)
(Turner, Bruno) [Lat] SSAT CHESTER s.p. see also Responsories For Tenebrae (V568)

O Vos Omnes, Qui Transitis Per Viam *Lent, anthem
[Lat] 4pt mix cor HEUGEL s.p. see from LA MAITRISE (V569)
(Rainbow, Bernarr) [Lat] ATBB/TTBB oct NOVELLO 38.0137.03 s.p. (V570)
(Rainbow, Bernarr) "O All Ye That Pass By" ATTB oct NOVELLO 38.0137.03 s.p. (V571)
(Zanon; Vene) "Ye Who Pass Me" [Lat/Eng] SATB,acap oct COLOMBO 1875 $.25 (V572)

O Wondrous Nativity *see O Magnum Mysterium

O Ye People *see O Vos Omnes

Of The Glorious Body Telling *Commun,anthem
SATB,acap (easy) oct OXFORD 43.304 $.20 (V573)
(Sateren) SATB (med) oct AUGSBURG 1147 $.25 (V574)

Opera Omnia IV: Psalmi, Antiphoane Mariane, etc. *CCU
(Pedrell, Felipe) cor GREGG ISBN 0:576 28018 6 s.p. (V575)

Opera Omnia I: Motecta, Missarum Liber Primus *CCU
(Pedrell, Felipe) cor GREGG ISBN 0:576 28015 1 s.p. (V576)

Opera Omnia II: Cantica BVM Vulgo Magnificat, Canticum Seimeonis, Missarum Liber Secundus
(Pedrell, Felipe) cor GREGG ISBN 0:576 28016 X s.p. (V577)

Opera Omnia III: Hymni, Officium Hebdomadae Sanctae, Missarum Liber Tertius *CCU
(Pedrell, Felipe) cor GREGG ISBN 0:576 28017 8 s.p. (V578)

Pange Lingua *Pent/Whitsun
SATB,acap voc pt DOBLINGER s.p. see also PFINGSTEN UND EUCHARISTIE (V579)

Passion According To St. Matthew, The
(Lovelace) SATB,narrator oct SUMMY 1588 $1.00 (V580)

Popule Meus *Xmas/Easter/Psntd,mot
[Lat] men cor,acap (easy) HUG s.p. (V581)
[Lat] SATB RICORDI-ENG SY114 s.p. (V582)
[Lat] SATB,acap (med easy) MULLER MS 18 s.p. (V583)
(Greyson) "O Blessed People" SATB oct BOURNE ES92 $.25 (V584)
(Richter) "Tell Me, My People" [Lat/Eng] SATB,acap AMP A419 $.20 (V585)

Pueri Hebraeorum *Adv/Gen/Palm
[Lat] SATB,acap (med easy) MULLER MS 42 s.p. (V586)
"Hosanna To The Son Of David" SATB,kbd (med easy) oct CONCORDIA 98-1993 $.25 (V587)
(Wolff) "Hosanna To The Son Of David" SATB oct LESLIE 4089 (V588)
(Wolff) "Hosanna To The Son Of David" SATB, acap oct BELWIN 60636 $.30 (V589)
(Zanon; Vene) "Hosanna Unto David's Son" [Lat/Eng] SATB,acap oct COLOMBO 1879 $.25 (V590)

Recessit Pastor Noster *cor-resp
(Turner, Bruno) [Lat] SATB CHESTER s.p. see also Responsories For Tenebrae (V591)

Requiem Mass *see Missa Pro Defunctus

Responsories For Tenebrae *cor-resp
(Turner, Bruno) [Lat] CHESTER contains & see also: Aestimatus Sum; Amicus Meus; Animam Meam Dilectam; Astiterunt Reges; Caligaverunt Oculi Me; Ecce Quomodo Moritur; Eram Quasi Agnus; Jesum Tradidit Impius; Judas Mercator Pessimus; O Vos Omnes; Recessit Pastor Noster; Seniores Populi; Sepulto Domino; Tanquam Ad Latronem; Tenebrae Factae Sunt; Tradiderunt Me; Una Hora; Unus Ex Discipulis Meis (V592)

Salve Regina *mot
(Jarrett, Jack M.) "Hear Me, O Lord God" [Eng/Lat] 6pt mix cor,acap oct LAWSON $.75 (V593)
(Petti, Anthony G.) [Lat] SSABar&SATB,cont CHESTER s.p. (V594)

Sanctus (from O Magnum Mysterium) Easter/Lent,Sanctus
(Harris) "Holy, Holy, Holy" [Eng/Lat] 3pt wom cor,acap oct SCHIRM.G 11922 $.30 (V595)
(Hilton, Arthur) SATB,acap (med) PRESSER 352-00457 $.40 (V596)
(Marshall, Charles) "Holy, Holy, Holy" SATB FRANK F-604 $.30 (V597)

Sanctus And Benedictus *Bene/Sanctus
(McKelvy, J.) SATB&SATB,acap FOSTER MF 407 $.40 (V598)
(McKelvy, James) SATB&SATB,acap FOSTER MF 408 $.40 (V599)

Sechs Hymnen *CC6U,hymn
(Bauerle, Hermann) SATB,acap cor pts BREITKOPF-L PB-3143 s.p., voc pt BREITKOPF-L CHB-2794 s.p. (V600)

Senex Puerum Portabat *Fest,mot
[Lat] mix cor,acap oct NOVELLO DM-49 s.p. (V601)
[Lat] SATB,acap (med) MULLER M 49 s.p. (V602)

Seniores Populi *cor-resp
(Turner, Bruno) [Lat] SATB CHESTER s.p. see also Responsories For Tenebrae (V603)

Sepulto Domino *cor-resp
(Turner, Bruno) [Lat] SATB CHESTER s.p. see also Responsories For Tenebrae (V604)

Seven Motets *see Ecce Sacerdos Magnus, "This Is The Mighty Prophet"; Estote Fortes In Bello, "Be Strong In Battle"; Gaudent In Caelis, "Heav'n Doth Resound"; Hic Vir Despicians Mundum, "This Man"; Iste Sanctus, "For Their Faith In The Lord"; O Quam Metuendus Est, "O Such Holiness"; Veni Sponsa Christi, "Bride Of Christ" (V605)

Sitientes, Venite Ad Aquas
see DOS MOTETES
(Pahissa; Vene) "Come To The Waters" [Lat/Eng] SATB,acap oct COLOMBO 1854 $.30 (V606)

Surely, He Bore Our Sorrows *see Vere Languores

Surely, Yes, Surely He Has Borne Our Griefs *see Vere Languores Nostros

Tamquam Ad Latronem
(Ruiz) [Lat] 4pt men cor,acap RICORDI-ARG BA 10082 s.p. (V607)

Tamquam Agnus
SS,acap SCHIRM.EC 1507 (V608)

Tanquam Ad Latronem *cor-resp
(Turner, Bruno) [Lat] SATB CHESTER s.p. see also Responsories For Tenebrae (V609)

Tanquam Agnus
(Vene) "As A Lamb" [Lat/Eng] TTB/SSA,acap oct COLOMBO 2187 $.20 (V610)

Tantum Ergo *mot
[Lat] SATB RICORDI-ENG SY158 s.p. (V611)
[Lat] SATB,acap oct GIA G560 $.25 (V612)
SATB,acap oct PRESSER 352-00070 $.30 (V613)
SSATB,acap oct PRESSER 352-00069 $.30 (V614)

Tell Me, My People *see Popule Meus

Tenebrae Factae Sunt *cor-resp
(Ruiz) [Lat] 4pt men cor,acap RICORDI-ARG BA 10493 s.p. (V615)
(Turner, Bruno) [Lat] SSAT/TTBarB CHESTER s.p. see also Responsories For Tenebrae (V616)
(Turner, Bruno) [Lat] TTBarB CHESTER s.p. (V617)

Then Were My Eyelids Veiled With Darkness *see Calagaverunt Oculi Mei

This Is The Mighty Prophet *see Ecce Sacerdos Magnus

This Man *see Hic Vir Despicians Mundum

Tradiderunt Me *cor-resp
(Turner, Bruno) [Lat] SATB CHESTER s.p. see also Responsories For Tenebrae (V618)

VICTORIA, TOMAS LUIS DE (cont'd.)

Tu Es Petrus
(McKelvy, J.) SSATBB FOSTER MF152 $.25
(V619)

Una Hora *cor-resp
(Track, G.) "Eine Stunde" 4pt mix cor,acap
voc pt DOBLINGER s.p. (V620)
(Turner, Bruno) [Lat] SSAT CHESTER s.p. see
also Responsories For Tenebrae (V621)

Unus Ex Discipulis Meis *cor-resp
(Turner, Bruno) [Lat] SATB CHESTER s.p. see
also Responsories For Tenebrae (V622)

Veni Sponsa Christi *mot
"Bride Of Christ" [Lat/Eng] SATB,acap
BROUDE BR. $.35 see from Seven Motets
(V623)
(Sorensen, S.) [Dan/Lat] SATB CHESTER s.p.
(V624)
(Sorenson, Soren) "Kristi Brud, Kom, Fryd
Dig" [Lat/Dan] SATB,acap HANSEN-DEN 26882
s.p. see from Motetter Og Lauder Fra Det
16. Arhhundrede (V625)

Verbum Caro In A Minor *mot
[Lat] 3 eq voices,acap oct GIA G578 $.25
(V626)

Verbum Caro In G *mot
[Lat] 3 eq voices,acap oct GIA G581 $.25
(V627)

Vere Languores *Easter,mot
SATB,acap oct PRESSER 332-13380 $.30 (V628)
[Lat] cor,acap UNION ESP. 19180 $.60 (V629)
"Surely, He Bore Our Sorrows" SATB,acap
SCHIRM.EC 2217 $.30 (V630)
(Castellazzi) [Lat] SATB,acap RICORDI-ARG
BA 9891 s.p. (V631)

Vere Languores Nostros *Easter/Lent,mot
[Lat] SATB RICORDI-ENG SY196 s.p. (V632)
(Marshall) "Surely, Yes, Surely He Has
Borne Our Griefs" SATB oct SOUTHERN $.30
(V633)
(Marshall, Charles) "Surely, Yes, Surely He
Has Borne Our Griefs" SATB FRANK F-551
$.30 (V634)

When All Disciples *see Dum Ergo Essent

When The Day Of Pentecost *see Dum
Complerentur Dies Pentecotes

Ye Who Pass Me *see O Vos Omnes, Qui
Transitis Per Viam

Yea, Two Seraphim Cried Out *see Duo
Seraphim

VICTORIOUS CHRIST, THE see Lillenas, Haldor

VICTORIOUS CHRISTMAS see Bonneau, P.

VICTORY see Sanderson

VICTORY DIVINE see Marks, J.

VICTORY DIVINE see Norman

VICTORY, GERARD (1921-   )
Christ, Qui Lux Es Et Dies *Gen,hymn
[Lat] SSAATTBB,S solo,acap (med diff)
BAREN. BA 5407 $.25 (V635)

VICTORY TE DEUM see Titcomb

VID JESU KORS see Wideen, Ivar

VID MIN JESU SIDA see Runback, Albert

VIDA
Merry Christmas!, A *Xmas
SA SCHMITT 2103 $.20 (V636)

VIDAL, D. DE
Surely He Bore Our Griefs *Easter
SATB oct PRESSER G-129 $.35 (V637)

VIDAL, PAUL (1863-1931)
Chanson Des Anges *Xmas
(Klein) "Song Of The Angels" 3pt wom cor,S
solo,opt pno/harp SCHIRM.G 11484 $.35
(V638)
Song Of The Angels *see Chanson Des Anges

VIDENS DOMINUS see Willaert, Adrian

VIDENTES STELLAM see Palestrina, Giovanni

VIDENTES STELLAM see Poulenc, Francis

VIDENTES STELLAM MAGI see Goudimel, Claude

VIDERO, FINN
Kom Hedningers Frelsermand *Adv/Xmas,cant
SATB,strings HANSEN-DEN 25632 s.p., ipa
(V639)
Spirit, All Holy *anthem
SAT (med) oct AUGSBURG 1540 $.30 (V640)
We Come Unto Our Father's God *anthem
SA (med) oct AUGSBURG 1490 $.25 (V641)

VIDERUNT OMNES SEDERUNT see Perotin

VIDETE MANUS MEAS see Aston, Hugo

VIDI AQUAM *anthem/Greg
(Christiansen, Paul J.) SATB (easy) oct
AUGSBURG 0532 $.35 (V642)

VIDI AQUAM see Beadell, Robert M.

VIDI AQUAM see Christiansen, Paul

VIDI SPECIOSAM see Anerio, Felice

VIDI TURBAM MAGNAM see Porta, Costanzo

VIDIT JACOB SCALAM see Crecquillon, Thomas

VIDITQUE QUOD ESSET BONUM see Pezzati, Mauro

VIEL STERNE GLORIIEREN see Schnitzler, Heinrich

VIEL WERDEN KOMMEN VON MORGEN UND VON ABEND see
Schutz, Heinrich

VIEL WERDEN KOMMEN VON MORGEN UND VON AKEND see
Schutz, Heinrich

VIENE LA BEFANA see Visona', Gino

VIENI, VIENI, GESU BAMBINO see Somma

VIENS, JESUS, VIENS! see Bach, Johann Sebastian

VIER ADVENTLIEDER *see Macht Hoch Die Tur;
Maria Durch Ein Dornwald Ging; O Heiland,
Reiss Die Himmel Auf; Und Unser Lieben
Frauen (V643)

VIER ADVENTLIEDER UND DREI WEIHNACHTSLIEDER
*CC7U, Adv/Xmas
(Bauernfeind, Hans) mix cor,acap cmplt ed
DOBLINGER s.p. (V644)

VIER ADVENTSLIEDER see Kaufmann, Otto

VIER ALTE WEIHNACHTSLIEDER see Weber, Bernhard

VIER ANTHEMS see Batten, Adrian

VIER BAUERNGEDICHTE see Bella, R.

VIER DEUTSCHE MOTETTEN see Demantius, Christoph

VIER DEUTSCHE MOTETTEN see Hartmann

VIER EINLAGESATZEN DER ES-DUR FASSUNG see Bach,
Johann Sebastian

VIER FESTMOTETTEN see Goudimel, Claude

VIER GEESTELIJKE LIEDEREN see Badings, Henk

VIER GEISTLICHE CHORSATZE see Walter (Walther),
Johann

VIER GEISTLICHE LIEDER see Lehman, Siegfried

VIER GEISTLICHE MANNERCHORE see Gattermayer,
Heinrich

VIER GEISTLICHEN MINNELIEDERN see Meissner,
Gen. Frauenlob

VIER GEZANGEN UIT DE "MORNING SERVICE" see
King, Harold C.

VIER GLEICHNISSE VON DER GERECHTIGKEIT GOTTES
see Hufschmidt, Wolfgang

VIER HEITERE CHORE see Gebhard, Hans

VIER HUGENOTTENPSALMEN *CC4U,Psalm
(Wieruszowski, L.) [Ger] mix cor,acap (med)
HUG s.p. (V645)

VIER HYMNEN see Ahrens, Joseph

VIER KANONISCHE ADVENTSMOTETTEN see Kaufmann,
Otto

VIER KLEINE MOTETTEN see Doppelbauer, Josef
Friedrich

VIER KLEINE WEIHNACHTSMOTETTEN see Doppelbauer,
Josef Friedrich

VIER KLEINE WEIHNACHTSMOTETTEN see Brautigam,
Helmut

VIER LEITVERSE ZUM PSALM-SINGEN see Egermann,
Eberhard

VIER LIEDER FUR KAMMERCHOR UND MOETUS MICHAELIS
see Seitz, Rudiger

VIER LOBGESANGE *CC4U
(Calvisius, Seth) [Ger] 3pt mix cor BAREN.
EM 460 s.p. from the "tricinia", 1603
(V646)

VIER MARIENMOTETTEN see Isaac

VIER MOTETTEN see Lassus, Roland de (Orlandus)

VIER MOTETTEN DER BACHSCHULE *CC4U,mot
(Feder) 4-5pt mix cor,cont MOSELER s.p.
contains works by: Krebs; Kirnberger;
Homilius (V647)

VIER MOTETTEN see Des Prez, Josquin

VIER MOTETTEN see La Rue, Pierre de

VIER MOTETTEN see Nucius, Johannes

VIER MOTETTEN see Sayve

VIER MOTETTEN see Telemann, Georg Philipp

VIER NEUE LIEDER ZUM ADVENT see Heilbut, P.

VIER OSTERMOTETTEN *Easter,mot
HANSSLER 7.092 s.p.
contains: Marx, Karl, Auferstanden Bin Ich
(SAB); Marx, Karl, Halleluja, Der Herr
Ist Auferstanden (SATB); Wenzel,
Eberhard, Da Der Sabbat (SATB); Wenzel,
Eberhard, Was Suchet Ihr Den (SATB)
(V648)

VIER PSALM-MOTETTEN *mot/Psalm
HANSSLER 7.093 s.p.
contains: Beck, Conrad, Es Ist Ein Kostlich
Ding (SAB); Marx, Karl, Halleluja, Gott
Der Ist Herr Sonne (SATB); Marx, Karl,
Herr, Hore Meine Stimme, Wenn Ich (SAB);
Raphael, Gunther, Ich Rede Von Deinen
Zeugnissen (SAB) (V649)

VIER SANCTUS [BWV 237-240] see Bach, Johann
Sebastian

VIER SPRUCHMOTETTEN see Kern, Matthias

VIER TANTUM ERGO see Ahrens, Joseph

VIER TOTENLIEDER AUS ST. LAMBRECHT *see Ach,
Muss Ich Dann Allein Davon; All' Mussen Wir
Sterben; Jetzt Ist Mein Ganzes Leben Aus;
Traget Mich Zu Meinem Grabe (V650)

VIER TROSTLIEDER see Weber, Bernhard

VIER WEIHNACHTSCHORE UND DREI KANONS see
Werner, St.

VIER WEIHNACHTSKONZERTEN see Kretzschmar,
Gunther

VIER WEIHNACHTSLIEDER *Xmas
(Vogel, M.) [Ger] wom cor,acap HUG s.p.
contains: Kommet Ihr Hirten (Boh); O Du
Frohliche (folk,It); Gruber, Franz Xaver,
Stille Nacht, Heil'ge Nacht; Praetorius,
Michael, Es Ist Ein Ros' Entsprungen
(V651)

VIER WEIHNACHTSLIEDER see Praetorius, Michael

VIER WEIHNACHTSLIEDER see Trust, Heinz-Ewald

VIER WEIHNACHTSMOTETTEN see Calvisius, Sethus

VIERDANCK, JOHANN (ca. 1610-1646)
Lo I Bring Tidings *cant
(Kleeman) 2 eq voices BELWIN $.80 (V652)

Lobe Den Herren
"Lova Herren" wom cor/jr cor cor pts
NORDISKA 4875 s.p. (V653)

Lobe Den Herrn *Gen
(Erdmann, Hans) [Ger] 3pt treb cor,cont
(med easy) BAREN. BA 453 sc $2.50, cor
pts $.65 (V654)

Lova Herren *see Lobe Den Herren

Mein Herz Ist Bereit *Gen
(Erdmann, Hans) [Ger] 2pt treb cor,cont,
2vln (med easy) BAREN. BA 452 sc $2.50,
cor pts $.40 (V655)

Siehe, Wie Fein Und Lieblich Ists *Gen
(Engel, Hans) [Ger] 2pt men cor,cont,2vln/
2vla (med easy) sc BAREN. BA 687 $2.50,
ipa (V656)

Weihnachtskonzert *Xmas
(Engel, Hans) [Ger] SA,SA soli,cont,2vln
(med easy) BAREN. BA 468 sc $2.75, cor
pts $.55 (V657)

VIERNE, LOUIS (1870-1937)
Kyrie Eleison *Kyrie
(Huntington, Ronald) SATB,org FOSTER MF104
$.35 (V658)

VIERO, FRANCESCO
Hymnus Te Deum Laudamus *hymn/Te Deum
[Lat] 2pt men cor,org sc ZANIBON 2595 s.p.,
cor pts ZANIBON 2596 s.p. (V659)

Jesu Redemptor Omnium *Mass
[Lat] 2 eq voices,org sc ZANIBON 2590 s.p.,
voc pt ZANIBON 2590A-B s.p. (V660)

Miserere Mei Deus *Easter,Psalm
[Lat] 2 eq voices,org sc ZANIBON 2593 s.p.,
cor pts ZANIBON 2594 s.p. (V661)

Missa Pro Pace *Mass
[Lat] 2 eq voices,org sc ZANIBON 2591 s.p.,
cor pts ZANIBON 2592 s.p. (V662)

VIERRA
Out Of The Depths
SATB,acap oct BOOSEY 5302 $.35 (V663)

VIERSTIMMIGE CHORALE NR. 1-12 *chorale
[Ger] SATB cor pts KISTNER s.p. see from
Melodeyen-Gesangbuch (V664)

VIERSTIMMIGE CHORALE NR. 13-23 *chorale
[Ger] SATB cor pts KISTNER s.p. see from
Melodeyen-Gesangbuch (V665)

VIERSTIMMIGE CHORALE NR. 24-35 *chorale
[Ger] SATB cor pts KISTNER s.p. see from
Melodeyen-Gesangbuch (V666)

VIERSTIMMIGE CHORSAETZE ZU LIEDERN DES
EVANGELISCHEN KIRCHEN-GESANGBUCHES see
Schutz, Heinrich

VIERSTIMMIGE CHORSATZE ZU LIEDERN DES
EVANGELISCHES KIRCHENGESANGBUCH see Schutz,
Heinrich

VIERSTIMMIGE HYMNEN see Stadlmayr, Johann

VIERSTIMMIGE KIRCHENGESANGE see Bach, Johann
Sebastian

VIERTER NACHTRAG ZUR GESAMTAUSGABE-BAND XXXIII
see Palestrina, Giovanni

VIEW ME, LORD see Lloyd, Richard H.

VIGIL see Christiansen, F. Melius

VIGIL OF CHRISTMAS, THE (THE VIGIL OF LITTLE
JESUS) see Massenet, Jules

VIGILS OF MARY, THE see Ohlson

VIGORELLI, SANTE
Missa Secunda Facillima *Mass
[Lat] cong,opt org (very easy) sc ZANIBON
2577 s.p., cor pts ZANIBON 2577A s.p.
(V667)

VIJF GEESTELIJKE LIEDEREN see Sigtenhorst-
Meyer, [Bernhard van den]

VILLA-LOBOS, HEITOR (1887-   )
Bendita Sabedoria
[Lat] SATB,acap AMP $1.50 (V668)

Lord's Prayer, The
[Eng/Span] SATB,acap MARKS 30 $.25 (V669)

Mass In Honor Of Saint Sebastian *Mass
[Lat] SSA/TTB AMP A525 $1.00 (V670)
[Lat] SSATTB,acap AMP A525 $1.00 (V671)
girl cor SOUTHERN $1.00 (V672)

VILLAGE FIDDLER, THE see Rothstein, Arnold

VILLANCICO MONTANES see Benedito

VILLANCICO MURCIANO see Massotti Littel, M.

VILLANCICO POPULAR FRANCES see Benedito

VILLANCICOS. CUADERNO II see Escudero

VILLANCICOS. CUADERNO I see Escudero

VILLANCICOS TRADICIONALES *Xmas,carol
    (Gil) [Span] cor UNION ESP. 18603 s.p.
       contains: Camino De Belen; El Buen Rabadan;
       Esta Noche Los Pastores; Esta Noche Nace
       El Nino; La Virgen Lava Panales; La
       Virgen Y San Jose   (V673)

VILLANESCA see Guerrero, Francisco

VILLETTE, P.
    Adorate
       [Lat] 4pt mix cor,acap oct DURAND s.p.
                                                    (V674)

VILONI
    El Pastorcito De Belen
       (Kubik) [Span] 2 eq voices,opt pno (easy)
       sc cor pts RICORDI-ARG BA 8643 BA 8644B
       s.p. s.p.   (V675)
       (Kubik) [Span] SATB,Mez solo,opt pno sc cor
       pts RICORDI-ARG BA 8643 BA 8644A s.p.
       s.p.   (V676)

VINCENT, CHARLES JOHN (1852-1934)
    As It Began To Dawn *Easter/Lent,Bibl
       SATB,S solo,opt org (med) oct WILLIS 957
       $.16   (V677)
       SATB oct PRESSER 332-03905 $.30   (V678)
       (Collins) SSA oct PRO ART 1623 $.22   (V679)
       (Mueller) SABar oct SCHIRM.G 9745 $.30
                                                    (V680)
    Behold, I Bring You Good Tidings *Xmas
       SATB,org (med) oct WILLIS 1034 $.15   (V681)
    Hallelujah, Christ Is Risen *Easter
       SATB,org (med) oct WILLIS 1090 $.16   (V682)
    Saviour, Like A Shepherd Lead Us
       (Follett) SAB oct PRO ART 2177 $.25   (V683)
    There Were Shepherds *Xmas,anthem/Bibl
       4pt mix cor,S solo oct SCHIRM.G 4501 $.35
                                                    (V684)
       SATB,org (med) oct WILLIS 927 $.15   (V685)
       mix cor oct NOVELLO 28.0324.00 s.p.   (V686)
       SATB oct PRESSER 332-10456 $.35   (V687)
       (Ehret) SAB oct BELWIN 1638 $.25   (V688)
    There Were Shepherds In The Field *Xmas
       (Stevens) SSA oct PRO ART 1547 $.25   (V689)

VINCENTINO, NICOLA (1511-1576)
    Collected Works *sac/sec,CCU
       (Kaufmann, Henry H.) cor AM.INST.MUS.
       $22.00   (V690)

VINCI, PIETRO (1535-1584)
    Mottetti E Ricercari (composed with Verso,
       Antonio II) *CCU
       (Sciarrino, Salvatore; Carapezza, Paolo
       Emilio) 3pt SANTIS 1100 s.p.   (V691)

VINE THAT I HAVE CHOSEN AS MY OWN see Poulenc,
    Francis, Vinea Mea Electa

VINEA MEA ELECTA see Poulenc, Francis

VINEAM MEAM see Palestrina, Giovanni

VINGT MOTETS see Saint-Saens, Camille

VINGT NOELS, ANCIENS ET MODERNES *CC20L,Xmas,
    carol
    (Pierne, Paul) cor quarto CHOUDENS s.p.
                                                    (V692)

VINTER, GILBERT
    Christmas Fantasy, A
       SATB,pno/org,opt orch WEINBERGER s.p., ipr
       voc sc, cor pts   (V693)

VIOTTI, GIOVANNI BATTISTA (1755-1824)
    All Ye People
       (Ehret) SATB oct ELKAN-V 362-1314 $.30
                                                    (V694)

VIR FIDELIS see Ascenso, Antonio

VIRGA JESSE see Bruckner, Anton

VIRGA JESSE FLORUIT see Bruckner, Anton

VIRGEN SANCTA see Guerrero, Francisco

VIRGEN SANTISIMA see Benedito

VIRGILI, LAVINIO
    Canti Per La S. Messa Letta E Laudi Sacre
       Devozionale *CCU
       [It] unis,org ZANIBON 4722 s.p.   (V695)

VIRGIN AND CHILD, THE see Faure, Gabriel-Urbain

VIRGIN AND CHILD, THE see Tate, Toby

VIRGIN AND MOTHER, A see Merbecke, John

VIRGIN AND THE CHILD, THE see Brumby

VIRGIN AT THE CRADLE, THE see Franck, Cesar

VIRGIN BY THE MANGER see Franck, Cesar

VIRGIN BY THE MANGER, THE see Franck, Cesar

VIRGIN KNELT IN PRAYER, A see Birgina Gazte
    Hobat

VIRGIN MARY HAD A BABY BOY *Xmas
    (Bune) SATB SCHMITT 4003 $.50   (V696)
    (Ehret) SA oct BOOSEY 5526 $.30   (V697)
    (Ehret) SSA oct BOOSEY 5305 $.35   (V698)
    (Ehret) SAB oct BOOSEY 5475 $.35   (V699)
    (Ehret) SATB nct BOOSEY 5304 $.30   (V700)
    (Ehret) TTBB oct BOOSEY 5306 $.35   (V701)

VIRGIN MARY HAD A BABY, THE *Xmas
    (De Cormier) SATB,acap,bells oct LAWSON 51271
    $.40   (V702)

VIRGIN MARY HAD ONE SON *Xmas
    (Willumsen, E.) SATB oct PRESSER 312-40629
    $.30   (V703)

VIRGIN MARY-MOTHER BLESSED see Farrar, H.M.

VIRGIN MARY, THE
    see Two Christmas Spirituals

VIRGIN MARY'S LULLABY, THE
    see Christmas Song, A

VIRGIN MILD, WHOSE OWN DEAR SON see Gabrieli,
    Giovanni, Vergine Il Cui Figliol

VIRGIN MOST HOLY, A *Xmas
    ASHDOWN 36 s.p.   (V704)

VIRGIN MOST PURE
    see Six Two-Part Carols
    see Six Traditional Carols, Set I

VIRGIN MOST PURE, A see Arnatt, Ronald

VIRGIN MOST PURE, A *Xmas,carol,Eng
    SATB (easy) OXFORD 08.004 $.15   (V705)
    (Glaser, V.) SSAA,acap SCHIRM.EC 1910 $.20
                                                    (V706)
    (Halter, C.) SATB,kbd (med easy) oct
    CONCORDIA 98-1237 $.30   (V707)
    (Jesson) unis (easy) OXFORD 81.103 $.25
                                                    (V708)
    (Kranz) SATB SCHMITT 901 $.25   (V709)
    (Roseberry) unis oct SCHIRM.G 11633 $.30
                                                    (V710)
    (Vaughan Williams) TBB,acap (easy) OXFORD
    41.904 $.20 see from Nine Carols   (V711)
    (Vaughan Williams) SATB,acap (med easy)
    OXFORD 84.107 $.35   (V712)

VIRGIN MOST PURE, A see Gerrish, J.

VIRGIN MOST PURE, A see Kinsman

VIRGIN MOST PURE, A see Stevens, Halsey

VIRGIN MOST PURE, A *carol
    (Roseberry, Eric) unis,pno oct FABER 11633
    $.30 contains also: Virgin Most Pure, A
    (unis,pno)   (V713)

VIRGIN MOST PURE, A
    see Virgin Most Pure, A

VIRGIN MOTHER
    see Two Old French Carols

VIRGIN MOTHER see Roff, Joseph

VIRGIN SHALL CONCEIVE, A see Johnson, Sidney

VIRGIN UNSPOTTED see Jenkins, [Joseph Willcox]

VIRGIN UNSPOTTED, A *Xmas
    see Colonial Christmas Carols
    (Sharpe, E.) cor&acap CRAMER 24   (V714)
    (Wiley) SATB oct PRO ART 2064 $.22   (V715)

VIRGIN UNSPOTTED, A see Billings, William

VIRGIN UNSPOTTED, A see Dunhill

VIRGIN'S CRADLE HYMN see Rubbra, Edmund

VIRGIN'S CRADLE SONG
    see At The Manger

VIRGIN'S CRADLE-SONG, THE see Tuttle, Stephen,
    Dormi, Jesu!

VIRGIN'S LULLABY, THE see Thiman, Eric Harding

VIRGIN'S LULLABY, THE see A La Nanita Nana

VIRGIN'S LULLABY, THE see Glover, R.F., A La
    Nanita Nana

VIRGIN'S LULLABY, THE see Harvey

VIRGIN'S SLUMBER SONG, THE *Xmas,carol
    oct HART s.p.   (V716)

VIRGIN'S SLUMBER SONG, THE see Pfautsch, Lloyd

VIRGIN'S SLUMBER-SONG, THE see Reger, Max,
    Maria Wiegenlied

VIRGO FIDELIS see Amatucci, Paolo

VIRGO GLORIOSA see Schmitt, Florent

VIRGO MARIA see Werbecke, G. Von

VIRGO PARENS CHRISTI see Desderi, Ettore

VIRGO POTENS see Amatucci, Paolo

VIRGO PRUDENTISSIMA see Isaac, Heinrich

VIRGO SIMUL ET MATER see Palestrina, Giovanni

VIRI GALIALEI see Palestrina, Giovanni

VIRI GALILAEI see Waldbroel, Wilhelm

VIRI GALILAEI see Couillart

VIRIN MOST PURE, A *Xmas,carol
    cor/cong oct MOWBRAY 65026 3 s.p. see also
    Cowley Carol Book, The   (V717)

VIRTUE see Jacobson, Maurice

VIRTUTE MAGNA see Clemens, Jacobus

VIRTUTE MAGNA see Croce, Giovanni

VIRTUTE MAGNA see Palestrina, Giovanni

VISA FRAN LEKSAND see Bond, Anders

VISA MIG, HERRE DIN VAG see Eklof, Ejnar

VISE KONUNGARS TAG see Sjogren

VISION OF A PROPHET, THE see Ben-Haim, Paul,
    Die Vision Des Propheten

VISION OF AEROPLANES, A see Vaughan Williams,
    Ralph

VISION OF ISAIAH, THE see Adler, Samuel

VISION OF ISAIAH, THE see Bright

VISION OF ISAIAH, THE see Wyton, Alex

VISION OF PEACE see Berger, Jean

VISION OF SAINT JOAN see Haubiel, Charles

VISION OF SAINT JOHN, THE see Christiansen,
    Paul

VISION OF ST. AUGUSTINE see Tippett, Michael

VISION OF THE SHEPHERDS see Fink

VISION OF THE SHEPHERDS, THE see Fink

VISION OF THE SHEPHERDS, THE see Groff

VISION OF THE SHEPHERDS, THE see Pasquet, Jean

VISIONS OF ST. JOHN see Beck, John Ness

VISIT OF THE MAGI, THE see Sharpe, Evelyn

VISITATIO SEPULCHRI *Easter,12th cent
    (Smoldon, W.L.) [Eng/Lat] unis,soli,org,opt
    inst (med easy) sc OXFORD 46.135 $3.80,
    ipr, rental   (V718)

VISONA', GINO
    Ave Maris Stella
       see Piccolo Repertorio Per Le Figlie Di
       Maria
    Canto Antiblasfemo
       unis men cor ZANIBON 1534 s.p.   (V719)
    Jesu Corona, Virginum
       see Piccolo Repertorio Per Le Figlie Di
       Maria
    Laude Popol. A S. Agnese
       see Piccolo Repertorio Per Le Figlie Di
       Maria
    Litanie Lauretane
       see Per Il Mese Mariano
    Lodate Maria
       see Per Il Mese Mariano
       see Piccolo Repertorio Per Le Figlie Di
       Maria
    Magnificat VIII Tono
       see Piccolo Repertorio Per Le Figlie Di
       Maria
    Per Il Mese Mariano *BVM
       [Lat] unis (easy) ZANIBON 453 s.p.
       contains: Litanie Lauretane; Lodate Maria
                                                    (V720)
    Piccolo Repertorio Per Le Figlie Di Maria
       *BVM
       [Lat] 2pt,org (easy) cor pts ZANIBON 1324
       s.p., sc ZANIBON 1323 s.p.
       contains: Ave Maris Stella; Jesu Corona,
       Virginum; Laude Popol. A S. Agnese;
       Lodate Maria; Magnificat VIII Tono;
       Veni Creator   (V721)
    Te Deum Laudamus *Te Deum
       [Lat] 2 eq voices,org sc ZANIBON 325 s.p.,
       cor pts ZANIBON 326 s.p.   (V722)
    Veni Creator
       see Piccolo Repertorio Per Le Figlie Di
       Maria
    Viene La Befana
       2pt,Mez solo,pno ZANIBON 1533 s.p.   (V723)

VISSER, DICK
    Stabat Mater
       4pt mix cor HEUWEKE. 174 s.p.   (V724)

VISTOR, THE see Smith, Lani

VITAL SPARK OF HEAV'NLY FLAME see Read, Gardner

VITTORIA, LUDOVICO
    Ave Maria *mot
       (Mattfeld, V.) "Hail, Virgin Mary" [Lat/
       Eng] TTBB,acap SCHIRM.EC 2162 $.18   (V725)
    Hail, Virgin Mary *see Ave Maria
    Lord, Thou Gav'st Us Christ To Save Us *see
       Nobis Datus
    Nobis Datus
       "Lord, Thou Gav'st Us Christ To Save Us"
       SATB,acap SCHIRM.EC 2617 $.30   (V726)
    O King Of Heaven *see O Regem Coeli
    O Regem Coeli *Xmas,mot
       (Talmadge, A.; Mattfeld, V.) "O King Of
       Heaven" [Lat/Eng] SSAA,acap SCHIRM.EC
       2535 $.35   (V727)
    O Vos Omnes *Easter/Psntd
       SATB,acap voc pt DOBLINGER s.p. see also
       PASSION UND OSTERN   (V728)
    Popule Meus *Easter/Psntd
       SATB,acap voc pt DOBLINGER s.p. see also
       PASSION UND OSTERN   (V729)

VITTORIA, T.
    see VICTORIA, TOMAS LUIS DE

VIVA LA GALA, VIVA LA FLOR see Martin Pompey

VIVA LA MUSICA see Gabrieli, Giovanni

VIVALDI, ANTONIO (1678-1741)
    All Glory Be To God *see Gloria In Excelsis
       Deo
    Beatus Vir (Psalm 112)
       voc sc UNIVER. 27C001 $2.05   (V730)
       [Lat/Eng] dbl cor,SST soli,2orch (C maj)
       voc sc RICORDI-ENG s.p.   (V731)
       [Lat/Eng] cor,SSA soli,cont,strings (B flat
       maj) voc sc RICORDI-ENG s.p.   (V732)
       (Fussl) study sc UNIVER. PH. 901 $2.50

VIVALDI, ANTONIO (cont'd.)

   (V733)
   (Fussl) study sc UNIVER. 27A001 $4.05
                       (V734)
   (Pichierri, Louis) [Lat] dbl cor,org/pno
     voc sc SCHIRM.G $2.00   (V735)
   (Pichierri, Louis) dbl cor,SA soli,orch/pno
     oct LAWSON $2.50, ipr   (V736)

Beatus Vir (II)
   SATB voc sc BELWIN AP105 $1.00   (V737)

Chamber Mass *Mass
   (Aslanian, Vane) mix cor, SSAT soli oct
    LAWSON $2.50   (V738)

Credo *Xmas,Credo
   bor,orch nc KALMUS $12.00, ipa   (V739)
   cor oct KALMUS 6503 $1.75   (V740)
   SATB voc sc BELWIN AP 106 $1.25   (V741)
   voc sc UNIVER. 27C002 $2.05   (V742)
   [Lat/Eng] SATB,cont,strings voc sc RICORDI-
    ENG s.p.   (V743)
   (Fasano) study sc UNIVER. PH. 902 $2.50
                       (V744)
   (Fasano) study sc UNIVER. 27A002 $5.65
                       (V745)
   (Martens, Mason) SATB,cont,strings voc sc
    WALTON M 105 $1.75, ipr   (V746)

Crucifixus *anthem
   (Ehret) [Eng/Lat] SATB (med) oct AUGSBURG
    1633 $.30   (V747)

Cum Sancto Spiritu (from Gloria)
   (Casella) "For Thou Art Powerful" [Lat/Eng]
    SATB oct COLOMBO 2237 $.30   (V748)

Dixit
   SATB voc sc BELWIN 107 $2.50   (V749)
   (Pichierri) dbl cor,soli,pno/org oct LAWSON
    $3.00   (V750)

Dixit Dominus
   [Lat/Eng] dbl cor,SSATB soli,2orch voc sc
    RICORDI-ENG s.p.   (V751)

Domine *Xmas,Bibl
   (Martens, Mason) dbl cor,S solo,orch voc sc
    WALTON M 106 $1.75, ipr, sc WALTON rental
                       (V752)

Domine Deus (from Gloria)
   (Casella) "Lord God Almighty" [Lat/Eng]
    SATB,A solo oct COLOMBO 2236 $.30 (V753)

Domine Deus, Agnus Dei (from Gloria)
   (Martens, Mason) SATB oct WALTON 2046 $.30
                       (V754)

Domine Fili Unigenite (from Gloria)
   (Casella) "Honor And Glory" [Lat/Eng] SATB
    oct COLOMBO 2313 $.30   (V755)
   (Kjelson) SATB oct BELWIN 2086 $.35 (V756)
   (Martens, Mason) SATB oct WALTON 2045 $.30
                       (V757)

Esurientes Implevit
   (Harris) "He Hath Filled The Hungry" [Eng/
    Lat] SA oct LAWSON 51708 $.30 (V758)

Et In Terra Pax (from Gloria)
   (Martens, Mason) TTBB oct WALTON 9001 $.30 (V759)
   (Martens, Mason) SSA oct WALTON 5016 $.30
                       (V760)
   (Martens, Mason) SATB oct WALTON 2044 $.35
                       (V761)

Et In Terra Pax Hominibus (from Gloria)
   (Casella) "Peace On Earth" [Lat/Eng] SATB
    oct COLOMBO 2236 $.30   (V762)

Et Misericordia
   (Kjelson) SATB oct BELWIN 2236 $.25 (V763)

For Thou Art Powerful *see Cum Sancto
   Spiritu

Gloria *Xmas,Gloria
   [Eng/Lat] voc sc UNIVER. 14504 $4.35 (V764)
   [Lat] voc sc PETERS HU1412 $2.00, ipr
                       (V765)
   SATB oct STAFF 670 $.30   (V766)
   libor,soli,orch BELWIN $1.50, ipr (V767)
   cor min KALMUS 749 $1.30   (V768)
   cor KALMUS $1.50   (V769)
   cor sc KALMUS $14.00   (V770)
   cor,opt orch oct KALMUS 6497 $1.50, ipa
                       (V771)
   cor,4 soli,orch INTERNAT. s.p., ipr (V772)
   cor,orch/org sc KALMUS $14.00, ipa (V773)
   (Casella) [Lat/Eng] cor,SSA soli voc sc
    RICORDI-ENG s.p.   (V774)
   (Martens, Mason) SATB,org,cont,ob,bsn,trp,
    strings voc sc WALTON M 101 $1.75, ipr,
    sc WALTON rental   (V775)
   (Martens, Mason) SATB,soli,orch voc sc
    WALTON M 101 $1.75, ipr   (V776)
   (Pichierri) 3pt wom cor,soli,pno oct LAWSON
    $2.50   (V777)

Gloria In Excelsis (from Gloria)
   (Martens) TTBB oct WALTON 9000 $.30 (V778)
   (Martens) mix cor SOUTHERN $.30 (V779)
   (Martens, Mason) SSA oct WALTON 5015 $.30
                       (V780)
   (Martens, Mason) SATB oct WALTON 2043 $.30
                       (V781)

Gloria In Excelsis Deo (from Gloria)
   (Casella) "All Glory Be To God" [Lat/Eng]
    SATB oct COLOMBO 2235 $.30   (V782)

Hand Of God Doth Supply All Our Needs, The
   (Vree, M.) 2pt treb cor oct PRESSER
    312-40672 $.30   (V783)

He Hath Filled The Hungry *see Esurientes
   Implevit

Honor And Glory *see Domine Fili Unigenite

In Exitu Israel
   see Zwei Psalmen

Introduze Al Gloria E Gloria
   unis mix cor,SAT soli,2ob,trp,kbd,strings
    JOBERT sc s.p., voc sc s.p., ipr (V784)

Juditha Triumphans
   [Lat] SATB,SMezTBarB soli,orch voc sc
    HINRICHSEN SM10 s.p.   (V785)

VIVALDI, ANTONIO (cont'd.)

Juditha Triumphans Devicta Holofernis
   Barbarie *ora
   (Bianchi, Lino) cor,pno SANTIS 1106 rental
                       (V786)

Kyrie *Kyrie
   study sc UNIVER. PH. 903 $3.40 (V787)
   [Lat] SATB&SATB,SSAA soli,org,cembalo,2orch
    min sc PETERS E1090 $2.50, ipa (V788)
   [Lat] SATB&SATB,SSAA soli,org,hpsd,2orch
    min sc PETERS E1090 $2.50, ipa (V789)
   [Lat/Eng] dbl cor,2orch voc sc RICORDI-ENG
    s.p.   (V790)
   (Fussl) study sc UNIVER. 27A003 $6.75
                       (V791)

Laetatus (Psalm 122)
   (Pichierri) SATB oct LAWSON 51670 $.40 (V792)

Lauda Jerusalem
   [Lat] SATB&SATB,SS soli,org,cembalo,2orch
    min sc PETERS E1081 $2.50, ipa (V793)
   [Lat] SATB&SATB,SS soli,org,cembalo,2orch
    min sc PETERS E1081 $2.50, ipa (V794)

Laudamus Te (from Gloria)
   (Casella) "We Praise Thee, Lord" [Lat/Eng]
    SS oct COLOMBO 2312 $.30   (V795)
   (Martens) 2pt oct WALTON 5014 $.30 (V796)

Laudate Dominum
   see Zwei Psalmen
   (Pichierri) [Lat] SATB,pno/org oct LAWSON
    51617 $.30   (V797)

Laudate Pueri
   SATB voc sc BELWIN AP108 $1.25 (V798)

Lord God Almighty *see Domine Deus

Magnificat *Magnif
   [Lat] voc sc UNIVER. 13193 $2.95, cor pts
    UNIVER. 13194A-D $.30   (V799)
   [Lat] voc sc PETERS HU1698 $2.00, ipr
                       (V800)
   [Lat/Eng] cor,SSAT soli voc sc RICORDI-ENG
    s.p.   (V801)
   cor,orch/org sc KALMUS $12.00, ipa (V802)
   cor sc KALMUS $9.00   (V803)
   cor KALMUS $3.00   (V804)
   cor oct KALMUS 6498 $1.50   (V805)

Peace On Earth *see Et In Terra Pax
   Hominibus

Psalm 112 *see Beatus Vir

Psalm 122 *see Laetatus

Salve Regina
   SATB voc sc BELWIN AP109 $2.00 (V806)

Stabat Mater
   SATB voc sc BELWIN AP110 $1.00 (V807)
   study sc UNIVER. PH. 904 $2.50 (V808)
   voc sc UNIVER. 27C004 $2.05 (V809)
   (Fasano) study sc UNIVER. 27A004 $6.75
                       (V810)

We Praise Thee, Lord *see Laudamus Te

Zwei Psalmen *Psalm
   mix cor MOSELER s.p.
    contains: In Exitu Israel; Laudate
    Dominum   (V811)

VIVALO
   Campanas De Navidad *Xmas
    [Span] SATB,acap RICORDI-ARG BA 12169 s.p.
                       (V812)
   Duerme, Nino Mio
    4pt RICORDI-ARG BA 12374 s.p. (V813)

VIVET, A.
   Ecce Panis
    [Lat] 4pt,T/S solo,org,opt harp&2vln&vcl&
    bvl LEMOINE voc sc s.p., cor pts s.p.,
    ipa   (V814)

VIVO SIN VIVIR see Brindle, [Reginald Smith]

VLAD, ROMAN (1919-)
   De Profundis
    [Lat] mix cor,orch voc sc ZERBONI 5350
    s.p., ipr   (V815)

VLIEGH, C.C.A. DE
   Lentebloemen
    wom cor,pno sc ALSBACH&D s.p. (V816)

V'NATAN LANU TORAT EMET *Fest
   (Jospe, Erwin) "Joyful Torah Song" [Heb] SATB
    TRANSCON. TCL 704 $.25 (V817)

VOCAL ANTHOLOGY *sac/sec,CC7L,20th cent
   mix cor,inst EXPERIMENTAL s.p. contains
   sacred work by:Bryn Harris (V818)

VOCAL COMPANION TO BACH'S ORGELBUCHLEIN, A
   (BOOK 1) see Bach, Johann Sebastian

VOCAL COMPANION TO BACH'S ORGELBUCHLEIN, A
   (BOOK 2) see Bach, Johann Sebastian

VOCE MEA AD DOMINUM CLAMAVI see Lassus, Roland
   de (Orlandus)

VOCES CLAMANTIUM see Parry, Charles Hubert
   Hastings

VOCES TRISTES see Hanks

VOCHT, LODEWIJK DE (1887-)
   Communion Service In G Major *see Missa In
    Honorem Angelorum

   Missa In Honorem Angelorum
    "Communion Service In G Major" SAB
     SCHIRM.EC 1239 $.40   (V819)
    "Communion Service In G Major" SSA
     SCHIRM.EC 1239   (V820)
    "Communion Service In G Major" TTB
     SCHIRM.EC 1239 $.40   (V821)

VOGEL, HEINRICH (1902-)
   Lob Aus Der Stille *CC24U
    [Ger] unis/2-4pt mix cor BAREN. EM 770 s.p.
                       (V822)

VOGEL KUCKUCK see Csenki, I.

VOGEL, W.
   Alles, Was Ihr Tut *Epiph,mot
    [Ger] SATB,acap (med diff) BAREN. BA 5408
    $1.75   (V823)

VOGLER
   Holy Is The Lord, Our God
    (Barthelson) SAB oct PRO ART 2494 $.30
                       (V824)

VOGLER, GEORG JOSEPH (1749-1814)
   Do You Know The Love Of Jesus?
    (Ferguson) SATB oct LILLENAS AN-2365 $.30
                       (V825)

   Holy Is Thy Name, O Lord
    (Davies) SAB FLAMMER D5114 $.25 (V826)
    (Davies) SATB FLAMMER A 5150 $.30 (V827)

   Laudate *Gen,cant
    (Hessel, Eduard) [Ger] SATB,S/T solo,org,
    2clar,2trp,strings,drums (med) MULLER
    SM 663 sc s.p., cor pts s.p. (V828)

   Missa Pastoritia *Mass
    (St. Winter, Joseph) [Ger] SATB,org (med
    diff) MULLER SM 526 voc sc s.p., cor pts
    s.p.   (V829)

VOGT, HANS (1911-)
   Requiem *Bibl/Req
    mix cor,SB soli,2drums,4timp sc BREITKOPF-W
    s.p., cor pts BREITKOPF-W CHB-3530 s.p.,
    ipa   (V830)

VOICE IN THE WILDERNESS, A see Danielson, Davis
   G.

VOICE IN THE WILDERNESS, THE see Scott, John
   Prindle

VOICE OF A PSALM, THE see Fitch

VOICE OF FAITH, THE see Schwarz, Herman, Kol
   Emunah

VOICE OF JESUS, THE see Kodaly, Zoltan

VOICE OF JESUS, THE see Watson

VOICE OF JOY, THE see Nares, James

VOICE OF THE LORD SOUNDS UPON THE WATERS, THE
   see Schutz, Heinrich

VOICE OF THE LORD, THE see Wagner

VOICE OF WORSHIP *CCU,anthem
   LORENZ $1.95   (V831)

VOICE OUT OF THE WHIRLWOOD, THE see Vaughan
   Williams, Ralph

VOICE, THE see Herforth

VOICES FOR TODAY see Britten, Benjamin

VOICES IN PRAISE *CC16L,Gen
   (Kirby) SAB PRO ART 1104 $1.00 (V832)

VOICES IN PRAISE see Young, Gordon

VOICES IN WORSHIP see Delmonte

VOICES OF APPALACHIA *CC9L,folk/hymn,US
   (Grender, A.) SATB PRO ART 1240 $1.25 (V833)

VOICES OF GOD see Rhea, A.

VOICES OF THE ANGELS see Wilson, H. Lane

VOICES OF THE SKY see Matthews, Harvey
   Alexander

VOICES OF WORSHIP see Malin, Don

VOICI LA SAINT-JEAN see Aubanel, Georges

VOICI LE PERE AU DOUBLE FRONT see Crawford,
   John

VOICI LE SAINT TEMPS, MES FRERES see Darcieux,
   [F.]

VOICI LE SAINT TEMPS MES FRERES see Parozai,
   Gui

VOICI LES VACACES see Danhieux, G.

VOISIN, D'OUVENAIT CE GRAND BRUIT? see Gevaert,
   Francois Auguste

VOLGER, ABBE
   Hosianna
    (Lundivk, H.) men cor NORDISKA 1170 s.p.
                       (V834)
    (Wikander, David) mix cor,org NORDISKA 947
    s.p.   (V835)

VOLK VAN SION see Olman, Isr, J., Populus Sion

VOLK WILL LEBEN, HERR GOTT, HILF see Stier,
   Alfred

VOLKMANN, ROBERT (1815-1883)
   Er Ist Gewaltig Und Stark *Xmas,13th cent
    SSAAT,B solo,acap cor pts BREITKOPF-L
    rental   (V836)

VOLLENWYDER, H.
   Das Kind Ruht Aus
    (Eichendorff) [Ger] wom cor,acap (med) HUG
    s.p.   (V837)

VOLPI, EDOARDO
   Adoramus
    see Per La Settimana Santa

   Adoremus Te Christe
    see Per La Settimana Santa
    see Per La Via Crucis Solenne Del Venerdi
    Santo

   Adoro Te Devote *Commun
    [Lat] 2 eq voices ZANIBON 1965 s.p. (V838)

   Ave Maria
    see CINQUE MOTECTA IN HON. B.V.M.
    see CINQUE MOTECTA IN HON. B.V.M.

VOLPI, EDOARDO (cont'd.)

   see Tre Motecta In Hon. B.V.M.

Ave Maris Stella
   see Firpo, Antonio, Ave Maris Stella

Ave Verum *Commun
   [Lat] 2 eq voices ZANIBON 1779 s.p. (V839)

Beatus Vir
   [Lat] cor,org ZANIBON 2695 s.p.   (V840)

Caro Mea
   see SEI MOTTETTI EUCARISTICI

Christus
   see IN HEBDOMADA SANCTA

Cor Jesu
   see TRIA COR JESU

Cor Jesu Flagrens
   see CINQUE MOTTETTI

Cui Comparabo
   see TRIA MOTECTA IN FESTO SEPTEM DOL.
    B.V.M.

Deus Tuorum Militum
   oee &uo Hymni

Dextera Domini
   see Per La Settimana Santa

Disprezzator Magnanimo
   [Lat] 2 eq voices,org ZANIBON 32 s.p.
                         (V841)

Dixit Dominus
   [Lat] 2 eq voices,org ZANIBON 2697 s.p.
                         (V842)

Domine Ad Adjuvandum
   [Lat] 2 eq voices,org ZANIBON 2713 s.p.
                         (V843)

Domine Salvum Fac Pastorem Nostrum *mot
   [It] 2 eq voices,org ZANIBON 2707 s.p.
                         (V844)

Dormi Non Piangere *Xmas
   unis ZANIBON 2780 s.p.   (V845)

Due "Parce Domine"
   unis&2pt ZANIBON 2301 s.p.   (V846)

Duo Hymni *hymn
   [Lat] 2 eq voices,org ZANIBON 2714 s.p.
    contains: Deus Tuorum Militum; Jesu
    Corona Virginum   (V847)

Ecce Sacerdos
   see AD REC. EPISCOPUM

Gaudens Gaudebo *BVM
   [Lat] 3pt mix cor,org ZANIBON 2751 s.p.
                         (V848)

Haec Dies
   see PEL TEMPO PASQUALE

Hodie In Bethlehem
   see Tre Mottetti Pel S. Natale

Introibo Ad Altare Dei
   see Raccolta Di Sei Mottetti Eucaristici

Jesu Corona Virginum
   see Duo Hymni

Jesu Dulcis Memoria
   see Raccolta Di Sei Mottetti Eucaristici

Laudate Dominum
   [Lat] 2 eq voices,org ZANIBON 2712 s.p.
                         (V849)

Laudate Pueri
   [Lat] 2 eq voices,org ZANIBON 2698 s.p.
                         (V850)

Le Sette Parole Di Gesu Cristo In Croce
   *Gd.Fri./Holywk
   [Lat] 2 eq voices sc ZANIBON 2589 s.p., voc
   pt ZANIBON 2589A-B s.p.   (V851)

Libera Ie Domine
   see Volpi, Edoardo, Missa Pro Defunctis

Litaniae De S. Joseph *ASD
   [Lat] unis/2pt,org ZANIBON 30 s.p. (V852)

Litaniae SS. Cordis Jesu
   [Lat] 2 eq voices,org ZANIBON 29 s.p.
                         (V853)

Magnificat Solenne *Magnif
   [Lat] 2 eq voices,org ZANIBON 2585 s.p.
                         (V854)

Miserere
   see Per La Settimana Santa

Miserere Nostri
   see Per La Via Crucis Solenne Del Venerdi
    Santo

Missa Dominicalis Facilis *Mass
   unis,org sc ZANIBON 2578 s.p., cor pts
   ZANIBON 2578B s.p.   (V855)

Missa Pro Defunctis *Mass/Req
   [Lat] SA/TB,org sc ZANIBON 2960 s.p., cor
   pts ZANIBON s.p. contains also: Libera Me
   Domine   (V856)

O Esca Viatorum
   see Raccolta Di Sei Mottetti Eucaristici

O Sacrum Convivium
   see Raccolta Di Sei Mottetti Eucaristici
   see Tria Motecta

O Salutaris
   see Tria Motecta

O Vos Omnes
   see IN HEBDOMADA SANCTA

Panem Coelestem
   see Raccolta Di Sei Mottetti Eucaristici

Pei Defunti *mot/Req
   [Lat] 2 eq voices,acap ZANIBON 2773 s.p.
    contains: Pie Jesu; Requiem Aeternam
                         (V857)

VOLPI, EDOARDO (cont'd.)

Pel Mese Mariano *CC9U,BVM
   [Lat] 1-2 eq voices,org ZANIBON 2764 s.p.
                         (V858)

Per La Settimana Santa *Holywk
   [Lat] 2 eq voices,kbd&acap ZANIBON 2955
   s.p.
    contains: Adoramus; Adoremus Te Christe;
    Dextera Domini; Miserere; Terra
    Tremuit; Vere Languores   (V859)

Per La Via Crucis Solenne Del Venerdi Santo
   *Gd.Fri./Holywk
   [Lat] 2 eq voices,org ZANIBON 2947 s.p.
    contains: Adoremus Te Christe; Miserere
    Nostri; Santa Madre; Stabat Mater   (V860)

Pie Jesu
   see Pei Defunti

Psalmi Vespertini *CCU,Eve,Greg/Psalm
   [Lat] 2 eq voices,org ZANIBON 2692 s.p.
                         (V861)

Quam Amabilia
   see Raccolta Di Sei Mottetti Eucaristici

Raccolta Di Sei Mottetti Eucaristici
   *Commun,mot
   [Lat] 2pt,org ZANIBON 2627 s.p.
    contains: Introibo Ad Altare Dei; Jesu
    Dulcis Memoria; O Esca Viatorum; O
    Sacrum Convivium; Panem Coelestem; Quam
    Amabilia   (V862)

Recordare
   see TRIA MOTECTA IN FESTO SEPTEM DOL.
    B.V.M.

Requiem Aeternam
   see Pei Defunti

Resurrexi In Epiphanietate Paschali
   see PER LA SANTA PASQUA

Salve Regina
   see Tre Motecta In Hon. B.V.M.

Sanctus
   see Tre Mottetti Pel S. Natale

Santa Madre
   see Per La Via Crucis Solenne Del Venerdi
    Santo

Si Quaeris *ASD
   [Lat] unis,org ZANIBON 2723 s.p.   (V863)

Stabat Mater
   see Per La Via Crucis Solenne Del Venerdi
    Santo
   see QUATTRO STABAT MATER
   see QUATTRO STABAT MATER

Tantum Ergo
   see SEI MOTTETTI EUCARISTICI
   see Tria Motecta

Terra Tremuit
   see Per La Settimana Santa

Tota Pulchra
   see Tre Motecta In Hon. B.V.M.
   see TRE MOTECTA IN HON. B.V.M.

Tre Motecta In Hon. B.V.M. *BVM,mot
   [Lat] unis,org ZANIBON 2743 s.p.
    contains: Ave Maria; Salve Regina; Tota
    Pulchra   (V864)

Tre Mottetti Pel S. Natale *Xmas,mot
   [Lat] ZANIBON 2673 s.p. also contains solo
   work
    contains: Hodie In Bethlehem (2 eq
    voices,org); Sanctus (2 eq voices,org)
    (Sanctus) (Offer)   (V865)

Tria Motecta *Commun,mot
   [Lat] ATB,org ZANIBON 2689 s.p.
    contains: O Sacrum Convivium; O
    Salutaris; Tantum Ergo   (V866)

Tu Es Sacerdos
   see AD REC. EPISCOPUM
   [It] 3pt mix cor,org ZANIBON 2622 s.p.
                         (V867)

Venite Ad Me *mot
   [Lat] 2 eq voices ZANIBON 2956 s.p. (V868)

Vere Languores
   see Per La Settimana Santa

Veritas Mea *ASD,Offer
   [Lat] ABar ZANIBON 31 s.p.   (V869)

VOM AUFGANG DER SONNE BIS ZU IHREM NIEDERGANG
   *CC15U,Gen
   (Brodde, Otto) [Ger] 2pt/3pt,opt inst (easy)
   BAREN. BA 2722 $1.50   (V870)

VOM FRUHJAHR, OLTANK UND VOM FLIEGEN see Orff,
   Carl

VOM HIMMEL DURCH DIE WOLKEN EIN NEUES JAHR
   HERDRINGET see Lechner, Leonhard

VOM HIMMEL HOCH see Schlageter, Walter

VOM HIMMEL HOCH see Bach, Johann Sebastian

VOM HIMMEL HOCH see Krause, Chr.

VOM HIMMEL HOCH see Lang, Hans

VOM HIMMEL HOCH see Scandello

VOM HIMMEL HOCH see Schein

VOM HIMMEL HOCH see Schein, Johann Hermann

VOM HIMMEL HOCH see Weiss, Ewald

VOM HIMMEL HOCH, DA KOMM see Praetorius, Jakob

VOM HIMMEL HOCH, DA KOMM ICH HER *Xmas,cant
   (Dahmen Hermann Josef) [Ger] 2-4pt mix cor,
   org,brass,strings (med, from settings of
   old masters) MULLER SM 411 s.p.   (V871)

VOM HIMMEL HOCH, DA KOMM ICH HER see Bach,
   Johann Sebastian

VOM HIMMEL HOCH, DA KOMM ICH HER see Bender,
   Jan

VOM HIMMEL HOCH, DA KOMM ICH HER see Calvisius,
   Sethus

VOM HIMMEL HOCH, DA KOMM ICH HER see Cruger,
   Johann

VOM HIMMEL HOCH DA KOMM ICH HER see Eccard,
   Johannes

VOM HIMMEL HOCH, DA KOMM ICH HER see Forster,
   Georg

VOM HIMMEL HOCH, DA KOMM ICH HER see
   Gumpeltzhaimer, Adam

VOM HIMMEL HOCH, DA KOMM ICH HER see Lissmann,
   Kurt

VOM HIMMEL HOCH, DA KOMM ICH HER see
   Praetorius, Michael

VOM HIMMEL HOCH, DA KOMM ICH HER see Schop,
   Johann

VOM HIMMEL HOCH, DA KOMM ICH HER see Spitta,
   Heinrich

VOM HIMMEL HOCH, DA KOMM ICH HER see Trubel,
   Gerhard

VOM HIMMEL HOCH, DA KOMM ICH HER see Weber,
   Bernhard

VOM HIMMEL HOCH DA KOMM ICH HER see Werner,
   Fritz

VOM HIMMEL HOCH, IHR ENGLEIN KOMMT see Grofe

VOM HIMMEL HOCH, IHR ENGLEIN KOMMT see Weiss,
   Ewald

VOM HIMMEL HOCH, O ENGEL KOMMT see Unger,
   Walter

VOM HIMMEL HOCH, O ENGELEIN, KOMMT! see
   Holscher, Bernhard

VOM HIMMEL HOCH, O ENGLEIN KOMMT see Distler,
   Hugo

VOM HIMMEL HOCH, O ENGLEIN KOMMT see Knab,
   Armin

VOM HIMMEL HOCH, O ENGLEIN KOMMT see Raphael,
   Gunther

VOM HIMMEL KAM DER ENGEL SCHAR see Lohr, Ina

VOM HIMMEL KAM DER ENGEL SCHAR see Trubel,
   Gerhard

VOM HIMMEL KAM DER ENGEL SCHAR see Werner,
   Fritz

VOM HIMMEL KAM DER ENGEL SCHAR see Wolleb,
   Johann Jakob

VOM HIMMEL KOMMT see Praetorius, Michael

VOM JUNGSTEN GERICHT see Raphael, Gunther

VOM LEBEN see Lissmann, Kurt

VOM MORGEN BIS ZUM ABEND see Micheelsen, Hans
   Friedrich

VOM OLBERG ZEUCHT DAHER CHRISTUS see Burck,
   Joachim

VOM REICHE GOTTES see Bach, Johann Sebastian

VON ALL DEN TAUSEND KLANGEN see Schwartz, J.

VON DEINER GUT'O HERR see Haydn, (Franz) Joseph

VON DER AUFERSTEHUNG DER TOTEN see Schieri,
   Fritz

VON DER EWIGEN LIEBE see Thomas, Kurt

VON DER GEBURT JESU CHRISTI see Vulpius,
   Melchior

VON DER MUTTER UND DEM KIND see Rabsch, Edgar

VON DIR, DU GOTT DER EINIGKEIT see Bach, Johann
   Sebastian

VON EDLER ART see Ahrens, Joseph

VON EWIGKEIT ZU EWIGKEIT see Bach, Johann
   Sebastian

VON GANZEM HERZEN DANK ICH DIR see Sweelinck,
   Jan Pieterszoon

VON GOTT WILL ICH NICHT LASSEN see Rohwer, Jens

VON GOTT WILL ICH NICHT LASSEN see Schroter,
   Leonhard

VON GOTT WILL ICH NICHT LASSEN see Schutz,
   Heinrich

VON GOTTES GNADE BIN ICH see Reda, Siegfried

VON GUTEN MACHTEN see Breuer, Herbert

VON GUTEN MACHTEN TREU UND STILL UMGEBEN see
   Holsten, Martin

VON GUTEN MACHTEN WUNDERBAR GEBOREN see Eglin,
   Arthur

VON HIMMEL HOCH see Andrews, C.T.

VON HIMMEL HOCH see Calvisius, Sethus

VON HIMMEL HOCH DA KOMM ICH HER see Bach,
   Johann Sebastian

VON HIMMEL HOCH, DA KOMM ICH HER see Reger, Max

VON HIMMEL HOCH, DA KOMM ICH HER see Schein, Johann Hermann

VON HIMMEL KAM DER ENGEL SCHAR
see Unsre Liebe Frau

VON HIMMEL KAM DER ENGEL SCHAR see Praetorius, Michael

VOORJAARSHYMNE see Herwaarden, J.G.

VOPELIUS, GOTTFRIED (1635-1715)
Du Grosser Schmerzensmann (from Matthaus-Passion)
see Bach, Johann Sebastian, Herzliebster Jesu, Was Hast Du Verbrochen

VOR ALLEN GASTEN CHRISTUM see Jacobi, Samuel

VOR DEINEN THRON TRET ICH HIERMIT see Bach, Johann Sebastian

VOR DEM GROSSEN ELEFANTEN see Beckerath, Alfred von

VOR DIR IST FREUDE DIE FULLE see Reda, Siegfried

VOR GUD HAN ER SA FAST EN BORG see Jeppesen, Knud

VOR GUD HAN ER SA FAST EN BORG see Laub, Thomas

VOR GUD HAN ER SA FAST EN BORG see Pederson, Mogens

VOR HERRE KOM TIL JORDANS FLOD see Bach, Johann Sebastian, Christ Unser Herr Zum Jordan Kam

VOR SEINEM STERBEN SIMEON see Jacobi, Samuel

VORIS, W.R.
As Mary Walked In The Garden Green *Easter, carol
SSAA,S solo,org (med) oct WILLIS 5265 $.20
(V872)

Blessed Is He That Cometh *Easter/Palm
SATB oct GRAY GCMR 914 $.30   (V873)

God Is Love
SATB,acap (easy) oct WILLIS 5286 $.12
(V874)

VORISEK, JAN HUGO
see WORZISCHEK, JAN HUGO

VORSE, R.
Away In A Manger *Xmas,carol
SSAA/unis,pno (easy) oct WILLIS 5208 $.12
(V875)

Bread Of The World In Mercy Broken *Commun
SATB,org (easy) oct WILLIS 5205 $.15 (V876)

Over Slumb'ring Bethl'em Town *Xmas,carol
3pt wom cor,pno/org (easy) oct WILLIS 5206
$.16   (V877)

Trees And The Master, The *Gen/Lent
SATB,opt acap (easy) oct WILLIS 5207 $.16
(V878)

VOS MICHAEL see Isaac, Heinrich

VOS QUI SECUTI see Dufay, Guillaume

VOSS
Jesus Saviour
(Hustad) SATB oct AGAPE HA 118 $.30 (V879)

VOX DICENTIS: CLAMA see Clemens, Jacobus

VOX DICENTIS: CLAMA see Naylor, Edward Woodall

VOX DOMINI see Pasini, Crescenzio

VOX IN RAMA see Kirbye, George

VOX IN RAMA see Weinberg, Henry

VOX IN RAMA see Zielenski, Mikolaj

VOX IN RAMA AUDITA EST see Clemens, Jacobus

VOX IN ROMA AUDITA EST see Clemens, Jacobus

VOX ULTIMA CRUCIS see Harris, William Henry

VRANKEN, ALPH.
Anima Christi
"Ziel Van Christus" men cor ALSBACH&D sc
s.p., cor pts s.p.   (V880)

Dit Is De Dag *see Haec Dies

Drie Mannenkoren
men cor ALSBACH&D s.p. score and parts
separately published
contains: Exspectans Exspectavi Dominum;
Honum Est Confiteri Domino; Panis, Quem
Ego Dedero   (V881)

Exspectans Exspectavi Dominum
see Drie Mannenkoren

Haec Dies *Fest
wom cor ALSBACH&D sc s.p., cor pts s.p.
(V882)
mix cor ALSBACH&D sc s.p., cor pts s.p.
(V883)
"Dit Is De Dag" men cor ALSBACH&D sc s.p.,
cor pts s.p.   (V884)

Honum Est Confiteri Domino
see Drie Mannenkoren

In Nomine Jesu *mot
men cor ALSBACH&D sc s.p., cor pts s.p.
(V885)

In Paradisum *mot
men cor ALSBACH&D sc s.p., cor pts s.p.
(V886)

Panis, Quem Ego Dedero
see Drie Mannenkoren

Salve Regina
men cor ALSBACH&D sc s.p., cor pts s.p.
(V887)

VRANKEN, ALPH. (cont'd.)
Veni Creator
mix cor ALSBACH&D sc s.p., cor pts s.p.
(V888)

Ziel Van Christus *see Anima Christi

VREE
Christ The Lord Is Ris'n Today *Easter/Lent
SATB oct FISCHER,C CM-7671 $.25   (V889)
SAB oct FISCHER,C CM-7724 $.25   (V890)
SATB,org oct FISCHER,C CM-7671 $.25 (V891)

Lord Will Come, The
SAB SHAWNEE D118 $.30   (V892)

O Worship The King
SATB FLAMMER A 5589 $.35   (V893)

Praise To The Living God
SAB FLAMMER D5209 $.30   (V894)
SATB SHAWNEE A 874 $.35   (V895)

Ye Servants Of God
SATB SHAWNEE A 1075 $.25   (V896)
SAB SHAWNEE D87 $.30   (V897)

VRIES, TOM DE
Miserere Mihi
men cor ALSBACH&D sc s.p., cor pts s.p.
(V898)

VROLIJK KERSTFEEST see Zanen, P.

V'SHAMRU see Gottlieb, J.

V'SHOM'RU see Ancis, Solomon

V'SHOMRU see Freed, Isadore

V'SHOMRU see Jadlowker, Hermann

V'SHOMRU see Low, Leo

V'SHOM'RU see Weisgal, A.

V'SHOMRU NO 2 see Nowakowsky

VUILLERMOZ, [JEAN] (1906-1940)
Noel (D'andichon) *Xmas
[Fr] mix cor,acap (med) cor pts LEMOINE
s.p. see from Trois Chants Bearnais
(V899)

Trois Chants Bearnais *see Noel (D'andichon)
(V900)

VULNERASTI COR MEUM see Bouzignac, [Guillaume]

VULNERASTI COR MEUM see Palestrina, Giovanni

VULNERASTI COR MEUM see Schutz, Heinrich

VULPIUS, MELCHIOR (ca. 1560-1615)
Aber Das Wind Wuchs *mot
(Stern; Nitsche) SABB HANSSLER 1.201 s.p.
(V901)

Abide, O Dearest Jesus
(Dunsmore) SA SCHMITT 230 $.25   (V902)

After The People Had Seen The Sign *Gen/Lent
SATB,kbd (med diff) oct CONCORDIA 98-1658
$.30   (V903)

All Praise To God Who Reigns Above
(Kinsman) SATB oct PRO ART 1950 $.22 (V904)
(Kinsman) SSA oct PRO ART 2085 $.25 (V905)
(Kinsman) SAB oct PRO ART 2152 $.25 (V906)

Als Jesus Nahe Hinzukam *mot
(Stern; Nitsche) SATB HANSSLER 1.270 s.p.
(V907)

Also Wird Euch Mein Himmlischer Vater *mot
(Stern; Nitsche) SSSAT HANSSLER 1.282 s.p.
(V908)

Am Abend Aber Desselbigen Sabbats *mot
(Stern; Nitsche) SSAB HANSSLER 1.218 s.p.
(V909)

Angelus Ad Pastores *Gen
(Ehrhorn, Manfred) [Ger] SSATB&TTBB/SSATT&
ATBB,opt inst (med) BAREN BA 4395 s.p.
(V910)

Another Year Is Dawning
(Licht) SATB FLAMMER A 5407 $.25   (V911)

Ara Ske Gud, Sa Ock Hans Krist
mix cor NORDISKA 4945 s.p.   (V912)
(Moren, John) 3pt mix cor/unis wom cor/unis
jr cor,org NORDISKA 4229 s.p.   (V913)

Christ The Lord Is Risen Again *Easter/Lent
(Couper) SATB,hndbl oct FISCHER,C CM-7347
$.30   (V914)

Christus, Der Ist Mein Leben
SATB HANSSLER 6.252 s.p. contains also:
Hassler, Hans Leo, Wenn Mein Stundlein
Vorhanden Ist (from Christus Der Herr
Ist Mein Leben) (SATB) (Trin);
Bach, Johann Sebastian, Wenn Mein
Stundlein Vorhanden (SATB,vln) (CC)
(V915)
(Berger, H.L.) TTBB HANSSLER 6.5065 s.p.
contains also: Knecht, [Justin Heinrich],
Das Walte Gott, Der Helfen Kan   (V916)
(Schabasser, Josef) mix cor,acap oct
DOBLINGER s.p. see also CHRISTUS, DER
HERR   (V917)

Come, Holy Ghost, God And Lord
(Ehret) SATB,acap MARKS 4108 $.30 (V918)

Da Nun Jesus Ihren Glauben Sahe *mot
(Stern; Nitsche) SATTB HANSSLER 1.279 s.p.
(V919)

Da Traten Die Junger Zu Jesu *mot
(Stern; Nitsche) SATB HANSSLER 1.206 s.p.
(V920)

Dan Nun Die Menschen Das Zeichen *mot
(Stern; Nitsche) SATB HANSSLER 1.214 s.p.
(V921)

Darum Seid Barmherzig *mot
(Stern; Nitsche) SATB HANSSLER 1.264 s.p.
(V922)

Das Volk Aber, Das Voranging *Adv
(Eggebrecht, Hans Heinrich) [Ger] SATB,acap
(med easy, first Sunday in Adv) BAREN
BA 2578 $.40 see from Sonntagliche
Evangelienspruche Fur Das Kirchenjahr
(V923)

VULPIUS, MELCHIOR (cont'd.)
Das Volk Aber, Das Vorging *mot
(Stern; Nitsche) SATB HANSSLER 1.196 s.p.
(V924)

De Dina, Jesu, Narma Sig
mix cor NORDISKA 3971 s.p.   (V925)

De Profundis
see Vulpius, Melchior, Factum Est

Der Same Ist Das Wort Gottes *mot
(Stern; Nitsche) SATB HANSSLER 1.209 s.p.
(V926)

Der Tag Bricht An Und Zeiget Sich
see Vulpius, Melchior, Die Helle Sonn
Leucht Jetzt Herfur
SATB/SAB/SSA HANSSLER 8.030 s.p. contains
also: Schutz, Heinrich, Wohl Denen, Die
Da Wandeln, SWV 219 (SATB)   (V927)

Des Heilgen Geistes Gnade Gross
see Schutz, Heinrich, Dank Sei Unserm Herrn
Jesu Christo
see Kurig, Hans-Hermann, Ich Will Dem
Herren Singen

Det Volder Herren Jesuli *Xmas,17th cent
[Dan] SATB HANSEN-DEN 210 s.p. see also
JULESANGE   (V928)

Deutsche Sonntagliche Evangelienspruche 1612
*CC30U,Adv/Trin,mot
(Stern; Nitsche) SATB HANSSLER 2.012 s.p.
(V929)

Deutsche Sonntagliche Evangelienspruche 1614
*CC25U,Trin,mot
(Stern; Nitsche) 4-6pt HANSSLER 2.013 s.p.
(V930)

Deutsche Sonntagliche Evangelienspruche 1612
& 1614
(Stern; Nitsche) 4-7pt cloth HANSSLER 4.009
s.p.   (V931)

Die Helle Sonn Leucht' Jetzt Herfur
see Weber, Karl-Heinz, Abend Kommt, Der Tag
Sich Neiget
SATB HANSSLER 6.2506 s.p. contains also:
Vulpius, Melchior, Der Tag Bricht An Und
Zeiget Sich (SATB); Mozart, Wolfgang
Amadeus, Heil Dem Tag, Dem Die Nacht
Erlag (5pt); Anonymous, Sende Dein Licht
Und Deine Wahrheit (3pt)   (V932)

Die Hochzeit Ist Zwar Bereit *Marriage,mot
(Stern; Nitsche) SSAT&ATBB HANSSLER 1.280
s.p.   (V933)

Du Sollst Lieben Gott, Deinen Herren *mot
(Stern; Nitsche) SATB HANSSLER 1.278 s.p.
(V934)

Easter Hallelujah *Easter
(Dickinson, C.) SATB oct GRAY GSC 65 $.30
(V935)

Easter Hallelujah, An *Easter
(Davison, A.) anti cor,acap SCHIRM.EC 98
$.16   (V936)

Ein Feste Burg Ist Unser Gott
SAT/SAB LAUDINELLA LR 77 s.p. contains
also: Gib Frieden Unsrer Zeit, O Herr; In
Dich Hab Ich Gehoffet, Herr; Kommt Her Zu
Mir   (V937)

Ein Kind Geborn Zu Bethlehem
see Gesius, Bartholomaus, Ein Kind Geborn
Zu Bethlehem

Entsetzet Euch Nicht *Easter,mot
[Ger] SATB,acap (med easy) BAREN. BA 2587
$.40 see from Sonntagliche
Evangelienspruche Fur Das Kirchenjahr
(V938)
(Stern; Nitsche) SSAB HANSSLER 1.217 s.p.
(V939)

Erhalt Uns, Herr, Bei Deinem Wort *prayer
SSATB HANSSLER 6.149 s.p. contains also:
Bach, Johann Sebastian, Erhalt Uns
Herr, Bei Deinem Wort, S.416 (from
Bleib' Bei Uns Denn Es Will Abend
Werden) (SATB);
Bach, Johann Sebastian, Vater Unser Im
Himmelreich, S.416 (SATB)   (V940)

Erstanden Ist Der Heilig Christ *Easter,mot
see Bach, Johann Sebastian, Heut
Trimphieret Gottes Sohn
(Schmidt) dbl cor HANSSLER 1.223 s.p.
(V941)
(Stern; Nitsche) dbl cor HANSSLER 1.216
s.p.   (V942)

Es Ist Ein Grosser Prophet Unter Uns *Bibl/
mot
(Stern; Nitsche) SSATB HANSSLER 1.276 s.p.
(V943)

Es Ist Ein Ros Entsprungen *Xmas,canon
[Ger] 4pt,acap (easy) NAGELS NCH 208 s.p.
(V944)

Es Ist Euch Gut, Dass Ich Hingehe *Easter/
Pent,cant/mot
[Ger] SATB,acap (med easy) BAREN. BA 2588
$.40 see from Sonntagliche
Evangelienspruche Fur Das Kirchenjahr
(V945)
(Stern; Nitsche) SATB HANSSLER 1.221 s.p.
(V946)

Es Kommt Aber Die Zeit *mot
(Stern; Nitsche) SATB HANSSLER 1.223 s.p.
(V947)

Es Werden Nicht Alle, Die Zu Mir Sagen *mot
(Stern; Nitsche) SSATTB HANSSLER 1.269 s.p.
(V948)

Et Barn Er Fodt I Bethlehem *Xmas,17th cent
(Larsen, Jens Peter) [Dan] SSATB HANSEN-DEN
208 s.p. see also JULESANGE   (V949)
(Larsen, Jens Peter) [Dan] SATB HANSEN-DEN
208 s.p. see also JULESANGE   (V950)

Exaltabo Te, Domine
see Vulpius, Melchior, Exultent Et
Laetentur

Exultent Et Laetentur *Gen
(Ehrhorn, Manfred) [Lat] SSAT&ATBB,acap
(med) BAREN. BA 4392 s.p. contains also:
Exaltabo Te, Domine   (V951)

VULPIUS, MELCHIOR (cont'd.)

Factum Est *Gen,mot
(Ehrhorn, Manfred) [Lat] SSATTB,acap (med) BAREN. BA 4393 s.p. contains also: De Profundis (V952)

Fanfare For Easter *Easter
(Johnson) SATB&dbl cor oct SOUTHERN $.25 (V953)
(Johnson) SATB FLAMMER A 5206 $.25 (V954)

Freuet Euch Mit Mir *mot
(Stern; Nitsche) SSATB HANSSLER 1.263 s.p. (V955)

Gehe Aus Auf Die Landstrassen *mot
(Stern; Nitsche) SSTB HANSSLER 1.262 s.p. (V956)

Gelobt Sei Gott *Easter
see Hassler, Hans Leo, Erstanden Ist Der Heilig Christ
"Now God Be Praised In Heav'n Above" SATB, acap SCHIRM.EC 1693 $.30 (V957)
(Beveridge, L.) "Now God Be Praised In Heav'n Above" PTBB,acap SCHIRM.EC 2195 $.30 (V958)
(Davis, K.) "Praise We Our God" unis&desc, pno SCHIRM.EC 1573 $.20 (V959)
(Glaser, V.) "Now God Be Praised In Heav'n Above" SAB,acap SCHIRM.EC 2447 $.25 (V960)

Gelobt Sei Gott Im Hochsten Thron
see Praetorius, Michael, Halleluja Ist Ein Frohlich Gesang

Gib Frieden Unsrer Zeit, O Herr
oee Vulpius, Melchior, Ein Feste Burg Ist Unser Gott

Gleichwie Der Blitz Ausgehet *mot
(Stern; Nitsche) SSATB HANSSLER 1.285 s.p. (V961)

Gloria, Laus Et Honor *Gen,mot
(Ehrhorn, Manfred) [Lat] SSAT&SATB&ATBB, acap (med) BAREN. BA 4394 s.p. (V962)

God Is Mijn Licht
mix cor sc ALSBACH&D s.p. (V963)

God Loved The World So That He Gave
see Vulpius, Melchior, Radiant Sun Shines In The Skies, The

Good Christian Men, Rejoice And Sing *anthem
(Glarum) SATB (very easy) oct AUGSBURG 1106 $.25 (V964)
(Johnson) SAB,org,opt trp (easy) oct AUGSBURG 1517 $.30 (V965)

Gott Vater, Hore Unsre Bitt
SATB HANSSLER 6.169 s.p. contains also: Bach, Johann Sebastian, Schmucke Dich, O Liebe Seele (from Schmucke Dich, O Liebe Seele) (Trin) (V966)

Heb Dich Weg Von Mir, Satan! *Psntd
[Ger] SATB,acap (med easy, invocation) BAREN. BA 2585 s.p. see from Sonntagliche Evangeliensprue Fur Das Kirchenjahr (V967)

Hebe Dich Weg Von Mir, Satan *mot
(Stern; Nitsche) SATB HANSSLER 1.211 s.p. (V968)

Hedningar Alla, Loven Gud
mix cor NORDISKA 6114 s.p. (V969)

Herr, Ich Bin Nicht Wert *mot
(Stern; Nitsche) SATB HANSSLER 1.205 s.p. (V970)

Herr, Komm Hinab, Eh' Denn Mein Kind *mot
(Stern; Nitsche) SSATTB HANSSLER 1.281 s.p. (V971)

Het Daget In Den Oosten *Adv
mix cor sc ALSBACH&D s.p. (V972)

Hinunter Ist Der Sonnen Schein
see Schutz, Heinrich, Aller Augen Warten Auf Dich
see Bach, Johann Sebastian, Der Lieben Sonne Licht Und Pracht

Ich Bin Der Gute Hirte *Bibl/mot
(Stern; Nitsche) SATB HANSSLER 1.219 s.p. (V973)

Ich Bin Eine Stimme Eines Rufers *Adv,mot
(Eggebrecht, Hans Heinrich) [Ger] SATB,acap (med easy, fourth Sunday in Adv) BAREN. BA 2581 $.40 see from Sonntagliche Evangeliensprue Fur Das Kirchenjahr (V974)
(Stern; Nitsche) SSAB HANSSLER 1.199 s.p. (V975)

Ich Hab Mein Sach Gott Heimgestellt
SSAT/SSAB HANSSLER 6.268 s.p. contains also: Cruger, Johann, Lobet Den Herren, Alle Die Ihn Ehren (SAT/SAB) (V976)

Ich Sage Euch, Dieser Ging Hinab *mot
(Stern; Nitsche) SATB HANSSLER 1.271 s.p. (V977)

Ihr Heuchler, Was Versucht Ihr Mich? *mot
(Stern; Nitsche) SATB HANSSLER 1.283 s.p. (V978)

In Dich Hab Ich Gehoffet, Herr
see Vulpius, Melchior, Ein Feste Burg Ist Unser Gott

Isaiah, Mighty Seer *Gen/Trin
SSATTBB,acap (med easy) oct CONCORDIA 98-1533 $.30 (V979)

Jedermann Gibt Zuerst Den Guten Wein *mot
(Stern; Nitsche) SSAB HANSSLER 1.204 s.p. (V980)

Jedermann Gibt Zum Ersten Vom Guten Wein *Epiph
.Ger] SATB,acap (med easy) BAREN. BA 2584 $.40 see from Sonntagliche Evangeliensprue Fur Das Kirchenjahr (V981)

Jesus, I Will Ponder Now *Easter/Lent,Commun
(Harris) SATB oct PRO ART 2459 $.25 (V982)

Jesus, Our Lord Is Risen Today *Easter
(Ehret) SATB&SATB,4brass oct AGAPE F 929 $.30 (V983)

VULPIUS, MELCHIOR (cont'd.)

Jesus Said To The Blind Man *see Jesus Sprach Zu Dem Blinden

Jesus Sprach Zu Dem Blinden *Bibl/mot
"Jesus Said To The Blind Man" SATB,acap (diff) oct CONCORDIA 98-1027 $.30 (V984)
(Stern; Nitsche) SATB HANSSLER 1.210 s.p. (V985)

Kommt Her Zu Mir
see Vulpius, Melchior, Ein Feste Burg Ist Unser Gott

Lift Up Your Heads
(Lundquist, M.) SATB,acap SCHIRM.EC 2435 $.25 (V986)

Lobet Den Herrn, Ihr Heiden
see Bach, Johann Sebastian, Kommt, Seelen, Dieser Tag Muss Heilig

Matthaus-Passion 1613 *Psntd
(Ziebler, Karl) [Ger] SATB&SSATTB,TT soli, acap (med) BAREN. BA 695 $3.00 (V987)

Mein Freund, Ich Tue Dir Nicht *mot
(Stern; Nitsche) SATB HANSSLER 1.208 s.p. (V988)

Mein Sohn, Warum Hast Du Uns Das *mot
(Stern; Nitsche) SSAB HANSSLER 1.203 s.p. (V989)

Meister, Wir Haben Die Ganze Nacht Gearbeitet *mot
(Stern; Nitsche) SATB HANSSLER 1.265 s.p. (V990)

Mich Jammert Des Volks *mot
(Stern; Nitsche) SATB HANSSLER 1.267 s.p. (V991)

Now God Be Praised In Heav'n Above *see Gelobt Sei Gott

O Heiliger Geist, Du Gottlich Feur
see Goudimel, Claude, Jauchz, Erd Und Himmel, Juble Hell
SATB HANSSLER 6.016 s.p. contains also: Bach, Johann Sebastian, Du Lebensfurst, Herr Jesu Christ (V992)

O Hellige Treenighet
[Norw] LYCHE 60 s.p. (V993)

O Sing Ye To The Lord
(Kingsbury, John) SATB ALFRED 6409 $.30 (V994)

On The Wood His Arms Are Stretched *Easter
(Roff, J.) SATB oct PRESSER 332-40058 $.30 (V995)

Oppstanden Er Var Frelsermann
(Ludvig Neilson,) [Norw] dbl cor,inst LYCHE 37 s.p. (V996)

Our Lord And Christ Arose Today *Easter,mot
(Lundquist) SSAATTBB,acap (diff) oct WILLIS 6058 $.20 (V997)

Praise To The Lord Who Lives On High *Easter
(Olds) SATB&opt jr cor,opt SA soli WARNER W3244 $.30 (V998)

Praise We Our God *see Gelobt Sei Gott

Praise We The Lord In Highest Heaven *Easter/Thanks
SATB,acap (easy) oct CONCORDIA 98-1244 $.20 (V999)
mix cor SOUTHERN $.20 (V1000)

Praise Ye The Lord *anthem
SATB (very easy) oct AUGSBURG 0044 $.15 (V1001)

Radiant Sun Shines In The Skies, The *Gen
SATB,acap (easy) oct CONCORDIA 98-1249 $.18 contains also: God Loved The World So That He Gave (V1002)

Sammelt Zuvor Das Unkraut *mot
(Stern; Nitsche) SATB HANSSLER 1.207 s.p. (V1003)

Seed Is The Word Of God, The *Gen/Trin
SATB,acap (med diff) oct CONCORDIA 98-2089 $.40 (V1004)

Sei Willfahrig Deinem Widersacher Bald *mot
(Stern; Nitsche) SSTB HANSSLER 1.266 s.p. (V1005)

Siehe, Ein Weib, Das Zwolf Jahr *mot
(Stern; Nitsche) SSAB&ATTB HANSSLER 1.284 s.p. (V1006)

Siehe, Ich Sende Meinen Engel Vor Dir Her *Adv,mot
(Eggebrecht, Hans Heinrich) [Ger] SATB,acap (med easy, third Sunday in Adv) BAREN. BA 2580 $.40 see from Sonntagliche Evangeliensprue Fur Das Kirchenjahr (V1007)
(Stern; Nitsche) SATB HANSSLER 1.198 s.p. (V1008)

Sind Ihr' Nicht Zehn Rein Geworden *mot
(Stern; Nitsche) SATB HANSSLER 1.274 s.p. (V1009)

So Jemand Mein Wort Wird Halten *mot
(Stern; Nitsche) SATB HANSSLER 1.215 s.p. (V1010)

Sonntagliche Evangeliensprue Fur Das Kirchenjahr *see Das Volk Aber, Das Voranging; Entsetzet Euch Nicht; Es Ist Euch Gut, Dass Ich Hingehe; Heb Dich Weg Von Mir, Satan!; Ich Bin Eine Stimme Eines Rufers; Jedermann Gibt Zum Ersten Vom Guten Wein; Siehe, Ich Sende Meinen Engel Vor Dir Her; Und Alsbald War Da Bei Dem Engel; Und Da Acht Tage Um Waren; Und Es Erhob Ein Weib Seine Stimme; Wahrlich, Ich Sage Euch: Dies Geschlect Wird Nicht Vergehen; Wer Mich Liebet, Der Wird Mein Wort Halten (V1011)

Spiritus Sancti Gratia *Pent/Whitsun
SATB,acap voc pt DOBLINGER s.p. see also PFINGSTEN UND EUCHARISTIE (V1012)

Star Proclaims The King Is Here, The *Xmas/Epiph
(Metzler, F.) SATB,acap (med easy) oct CONCORDIA 98-1867 $.25 (V1013)

VULPIUS, MELCHIOR (cont'd.)

Strife Is O'er, The *Easter/Lent
SATB oct FISCHER,C CM-385 $.25 (V1014)
SATB,kbd (easy) oct CONCORDIA 98-1982 $.25 (V1015)

Then Came The Disciples To Jesus *Epiph/Gen
SATB,kbd (med easy) oct CONCORDIA 98-1574 $.35 (V1016)

Thy Name We Bless
(Lovelace) SATB FLAMMER A 5113 $.25 (V1017)
(Lovelace) SAB FLAMMER D5204 $.25 (V1018)

Today Above The Sky He Soared *Easter/Lent
(Follett) SATB oct PRO ART 2315 $.25 (V1019)

Today Is Risen Christ The Lord *Easter
dbl cor/SATB,brass (med easy) oct CONCORDIA 98-1900 $.25 (V1020)

Trachtet Am Ersten Nach Dem Reich Gottes *mot
(Stern; Nitsche) SSAB HANSSLER 1.275 s.p. (V1021)

Und Alsbald War Da Bei Dem Engel *Xmas,mot
[Ger] SATB,acap (med easy) BAREN. BA 2582 $.40 see from Sonntagliche Evangeliensprue Fur Das Kirchenjahr (V1022)
(Stern; Nitsche) SSAB HANSSLER 1.200 s.p. (V1023)

Und Da Acht Tag Um Waren *mot
(Stern; Nitsche) SATB HANSSLER 1.202 s.p. (V1024)

Und Da Acht Tage Um Waren *Xmas/ECY
[Ger] SATB,acap (med easy) BAREN. BA 2583 $.40 see from Sonntagliche Evangeliensprue Fur Das Kirchenjahr (V1025)

Und Der Herr Lobete Den Ungerechten *mot
(Stern; Nitsche) SSTB HANSSLER 1.268 s.p. (V1026)

Und Er Erhob Ein Weib Seine *mot
(Stern; Nitsche) SSAB HANSSLER 1.213 s.p. (V1027)

Und Er Gebot Ihnen *mot
(Stern; Nitsche) SSATTB HANSSLER 1.272 s.p. (V1028)

Und Er Wandte Sich Zu Seinen Jungern *mot
(Stern; Nitsche) SSAB HANSSLER 1.273 s.p. (V1029)

Und Es Erhob Ein Weib Seine Stimme *Psntd
[Ger] SATB,acap (med easy, Oculi) BAREN. BA 2586 $.40 see from Sonntagliche Evangeliensprue Fur Das Kirchenjahr (V1030)

Und Siehe, Ein Kanaanaisch Weib *mot
(Stern; Nitsche) SATB HANSSLER 1.212 s.p. (V1031)

Und Wie Mose In Der Wuste *Bibl/mot
(Stern; Nitsche) SATB HANSSLER 1.225 s.p. (V1032)

Uppstanden Ar Var Herre Krist
see UPPSTANDELSE

Vater Abraham, Erbarme Dich Mein *Bibl/mot
(Stern; Nitsche) SATB HANSSLER 1.261 s.p. (V1033)

Vi Christum Love *Xmas,17th cent
[Dan] SATB HANSEN-DEN 209 s.p. see also JULESANGE (V1034)

Von Der Geburt Jesu Christi *CC14U,Xmas, chorale
(Heyden, Reinhold) [Ger] 4pt mix cor/5pt mix cor,acap (med easy) BAREN. BA 1466 $2.50 (V1035)

Wahrlich, Ich Sage Euch: Dies Geschlecht Wird Nicht Vergehen *mot
(Stern; Nitsche) SSAB HANSSLER 1.197 s.p. (V1036)

Wahrlich, Ich Sage Euch: Dies Geschlect Wird Nicht Vergehen *Adv
(Eggebrecht, Hans Heinrich) [Ger] SATB,acap (med easy, second Sunday in Adv) BAREN. BA 2579 $.40 see from Sonntagliche Evangeliensprue Fur Das Kirchenjahr (V1037)

Wahrlich, Ich Sage Euch, Ihr Werdet Weinen *mot
(Stern; Nitsche) SATB HANSSLER 1.220 s.p. (V1038)

Wahrlich, Ich Sage Euch, So Ihr Den Vater Um Etwas Bitten Werdet *mot
(Stern; Nitsche) SSAB HANSSLER 1.222 s.p. (V1039)

We All Believe In One True God *Gen/Trin
SATB,acap (med easy) oct CONCORDIA 98-1042 $.25 (V1040)

Wer Mich Liebet *Pent,mot
(Mattfeld, V.) "Whoso Loves Me" [Ger/Eng] SATB,acap SCHIRM.EC 2444 $.35 (V1041)

Wer Mich Liebet, Der Wird Mein Wort Halten *Pent
[Ger] SATB,acap (med easy) BAREN. BA 2589 $.40 see from Sonntagliche Evangeliensprue Fur Das Kirchenjahr (V1042)

Wer Miche Liebet, Der Wird Mein Wort *mot
(Stern; Nitsche) SATB HANSSLER 1.224 s.p. (V1043)

Wer Sich Selbst Erhoht, Der Wird *mot
(Stern; Nitsche) SSATTB HANSSLER 1.277 s.p. (V1044)

When I Survey The Wondrous Cross *Lent
(Strube, A.) SAB,acap (easy) oct CONCORDIA 98-1097 $.18 (V1045)

Whoso Loves Me *see Wer Mich Liebet

Wir Danken Dir Fur Deinen Tod
see Anonymous, Wir Danken Dir, Herr Jesu Christ

Wo Gott Der Herr Nicht Bei Uns Halt *Trin
[Ger] SATB,acap (easy) BAREN. BA 1573 s.p. (V1046)

VUM VI VE VO
(Jacobson) 4pt boy cor/4pt wom cor oct SCHIRM.G 11600 $.35 (V1047)

W

W.B. OLDS CHORUSES FOR MIXED VOICES-NO. 1 see Olds, [William Benjamin]

W.B. OLDS CHORUSES FOR MIXED VOICES-NO. 2 see Olds, [William Benjamin]

W.B. OLDS MALE CHORUSES-NO. 1 see Olds, [William Benjamin]

W.B. OLDS MALE CHORUSES-NO. 2 see Olds, [William Benjamin]

W.B. OLDS TREBLE CHORUSES-NO. 1 see Olds, [William Benjamin]

WACH AUF see Hensel, Walther

WACH AUF! see Wagner, Richard

WACH AUF, DU DEUTSCHES LAND see Kurig, Hans-Hermann

WACH AUF, DU DEUTSCHES REICH see Distler, Hugo

WACH AUF, DU WERTE CHRISTENHEIT see Eccard, Johannes

WACH' AUF! ES NAHET GEN DEN TAG see Wagner, Richard

WACH AUF, MEIN HERZ, UND SINGE see Bach, Johann Sebastian

WACH AUF MEIN HERZ UND SINGE see Broechin, Ernst

WACH AUF, MEIN HERZ, UND SINGE! see Fischli, Fr.

WACH AUF, MEIN HERZ, UND SINGE see Trubel, Gerhard

WACH AUF, MEIN VOLK see Haug, [Hans]

WACH AUF, MEINS HERZENS SCHONE see Oechsler, Elias

WACH AUF, MEINS HERZENS SCHONE see Werner, Fritz

WACH AUF, O MENSCHENKIND see Lassus, Roland de (Orlandus)

WACH AUF, WACH AUF, DU DEUTSCHES LAND see Kurig, Hans-Hermann

WACH AUF, WACH AUF, DU DEUTSCHES LAND see Stern, Hermann

WACH AUF, WACH AUF, DU DEUTSCHES LAND see Walter (Walther), Johann

WACH AUF, WACH AUF, DU DEUTSCHES LAND see Zipp, Friedrich

WACH AUF, WACH AUF, 'S IST HOCHSTE ZEIT see Rohwer, Jens

WACH AUF, WACH AUF, S'IST HOHE ZEIT see Hofmann, Eberhard

WACH, NACHTIGALL, WACH AUF see Werner, St.

WACHET AUF see Bach, Johann Sebastian

WACHET AUF see Bach, Johann Sebastian, Wachet Auf, Ruft Uns Die Stimme

WACHET AUF! see Kaun, [Hugo]

WACHET AUF [CHORALE] see Bach, Johann Sebastian

WACHET AUF IHR CHRISTEN ALLE see Praetorius, Michael

WACHET AUF, RUFT UNS DIE STIMME see Praetorius, Michael

WACHET AUF, RUFT UNS DIE STIMME see Bach, Johann Sebastian

WACHET AUF, RUFT UNS DIE STIMME see Barbe, Helmut

WACHET AUF, RUFT UNS DIE STIMME see Beckerath, Alfred von

WACHET AUF, RUFT UNS DIE STIMME see Buxtehude, Dietrich

WACHET AUF, RUFT UNS DIE STIMME see Distler, Hugo

WACHET AUF, RUFT UNS DIE STIMME see Kappesser, Karl

WACHET AUF, RUFT UNS DIE STIMME see Nicolai, Philipp

WACHET AUF, RUFT UNS DIE STIMME see Praetorius, Michael

WACHET AUF RUFT UNS DIE STIMME see Proske, Erwin

WACHET AUF, RUFT UNS DIE STIMME see Stern, Hermann

WACHET AUF, RUFT UNS DIE STIMME see Zipp, Friedrich

WACHET AUF, RUFT UNS DIE STIMME [CHORALE] see Bach, Johann Sebastian

WACHET, BETET! see Bach, Johann Sebastian

WACHET, BETET see Bach, Johann Sebastian, Wachet, Betet, Seid Bereit Allezeit

WACHET, BETET, SEID BEREIT ALLEZEIT see Bach, Johann Sebastian

WACHET, DENN IHR WISSET NICHT TAG NOCH STUNDE see Brunner, Adolf

WACHET UND BETET see Fischer-Dieskau, Klaus

WACHSET IN DER GNADE see Telemann, Georg Philipp

WACHT AUF, ES TUT EUCH NOT "KLAGLICH ICH SCHREI" see Distler, Hugo

WACHT AUF IHR CHRISTEN ALLE see Praetorius, Michael

WACLAW OF SZAMOTULY
In Te, Domine, Speravi *mot,Pol (Szczepanska) mix cor,acap POLSKIE WDMP9 s.p. (W1)

WADDINGTON
Crown Him With Many Crowns *Easter/Lent (Douglas) SATB oct PRO ART 2160 $.25 (W2)

Father Of Mercies *Easter/Lent (Kraft) SSA oct PRO ART 1287 $.22 (W3)

WADE
First Noel, The *Xmas,carol (Porter) SATB oct SPRATT 310 $.25 (W4)

Live It Live SATB oct HERITAGE H75 $.40 (W5)

Lo, He Comes With Clouds Descending (Hastings) SATB oct BOURNE HA3 $.30 (W6)

O Come, All Ye Faithful *Xmas (Normand) SATB oct PLYMOUTH XM-108 $.25 (W7)

(Porter) SATB oct SPRATT 301 $.30 (W8)

WADE IN DE WATER *spir
SSA oct STAFF 375 $.25 (W9)
(Howorth) SATB,acap oct PRO ART 1012 $.20 (W10)
(Norman, Robert) SATB oct STAFF 323 $.30 (W11)

WADE IN THE WATER *spir
see Tva Negro Spirituals
(Cain) mix cor,acap oct SCHIRM.G 7697 $.30 (W12)
(Clark) SSA,acap MARKS 330 $.30 (W13)
(Clark) SATB,acap MARKS 830 $.30 (W14)
(Durian, Tim) 4pt men cor,ABar soli,acap BREITKOPF-W Z-42 s.p. see also Dreizehn Negro-Spirituals (W15)
(Hall) 4pt men cor,acap oct SCHIRM.G 8489 $.35 (W16)
(Love) SATB oct SPRATT 119 $.25 (W17)
(Luboff, Norman) SATB oct WALTON 3051 $.35 (W18)
(Papale, Henry) SATB&opt jr cor,opt S solo, pno oct WORLD ESE-772-8 $.90 (W19)
(Roberts) SATB,T solo,acap,opt perc oct LAWSON 51652 $.40 (W20)

WADE, WALTER
Christmas Fantasy, A *Xmas TTBB (med) ABINGDON APM-894 $.95 (W21)

Eye Hath Not Seen SATB,acap (diff) ABINGDON APM-189 $.26 (W22)

Four American Folk Hymns *CC4U,folk/hymn,US SA/unis (easy) ABINGDON APM-293 $.60 (W23)

Three Anthems Of Praise *CC3U,anthem SAB (med) ABINGDON APM-549 $.50 (W24)

What Wondrous Love *Lent,cant SATB,STB soli ABINGDON APM-504 $1.75 (W25)

WADELY, F.W.
At The Lamb's High Feast We Sing *Easter/Gen unis (very easy) oct OXFORD 45.013 $.25 (W26)

Christ Is Our Corner Stone *Fest,anthem mix cor oct NOVELLO s.p. (W27)

Christ Is Risen From The Dead *Easter,Bibl SATB,opt org (easy) oct OXFORD $.25 (W28)

Christians, Be Joyful *Xmas,anthem mix cor oct NOVELLO 28.1276.02 s.p. (W29)

Come, Thou Holy Spirit *Gen/Whitsun,anthem mix cor oct NOVELLO 40.1143.00 s.p. (W30)

Communion Service In G *Commun oct ROYAL 101 s.p. (W31)

Forth In Thy Name 2pt oct NOVELLO 33.0085.04 s.p. (W32)

Holy Birth, The *Xmas,cant SATB,7 narrators,STBar/STA soli,fl,2clar, bsn,2horn,2trp,strings (may be performed as Nativity play) voc sc NOVELLO s.p., ipr (W33)

I Will Lift Up Mine Eyes *anthem mix cor oct NOVELLO 40.1163.05 s.p. (W34)

If Ye Then Be Risen With Christ *Easter 2pt oct NOVELLO 33.0060.09 s.p. (W35)

Our Blest Redeemer *Gen/Whitsun,anthem mix cor oct NOVELLO 40.1071.10 s.p. (W36)

Sing We The Birth SATB (easy) OXFORD 42.990 $.25 (W37)

That God Doth Love The World, We Know *Easter/Gen SAB (easy) oct OXFORD 42.138 $.25 (W38)

WAGENER, GREGOR
Ach Herr, Strafe Mich Nicht (Psalm 38) mot (Haberl) SATB HANSSLER 1.230 s.p. (W39)

Die Toren Sprechen In Ihren (Psalm 14) mot (Haberl) SATTB HANSSLER 1.232 s.p. (W40)

Erzurne Dich Nicht Uber Die (Psalm 37) mot (Haberl) SATB HANSSLER 1.233 s.p. (W41)

WAGENER, GREGOR (cont'd.)
Freuet Euch Des Herren (Psalm 33) mot (Haberl) SATTB HANSSLER 1.231 s.p. (W42)

Gott Sei Mir Gnadig (Psalm 51) mot (Haberl) SSATB HANSSLER 1.235 s.p. (W43)

Ich Habe Mir Vorgesetzt (Psalm 39) mot (Haberl) SATB HANSSLER 1.234 s.p. (W44)

Jauchzet Dem Herren Alle Welt (Psalm 100) mot (Haberl) SAATB HANSSLER 1.236 s.p. (W45)

Psalm 14 *see Die Toren Sprechen In Ihren

Psalm 32 *see Wohl Dem, Dem Die Ubertretung

Psalm 33 *see Freuet Euch Des Herren

Psalm 37 *see Erzurne Dich Nicht Uber Die

Psalm 38 *see Ach Herr, Strafe Mich Nicht

Psalm 39 *see Ich Habe Mir Vorgesetzt

Psalm 51 *see Gott Sei Mir Gnadig

Psalm 100 *see Jauchzet Dem Herren Alle Welt

Wohl Dem, Dem Die Ubertretung (Psalm 32) mot (Haberl) SATB HANSSLER 1.229 s.p. (W46)

WAGENHEIM
Hymnus Choralis *hymn [Lat] voc sc PETERS 4844 $6.00, ipr (W47)

WAGNER
Blessing, Glory, And Wisdom
(Ehret) SSA oct BOOSEY 5292 $.30 (W48)
(Ehret) SATB oct BOOSEY 5090 $.30 (W49)

Psalm 75 *see Voice Of The Lord, The

Spacious Firmament On High SATB,org oct BOOSEY 5384 $.35 (W50)

Universal Hymn *hymn SATB,org oct BOOSEY 5383 $.35 (W51)

Voice Of The Lord, The (Psalm 75) TTBB oct MCA (W52)

WAGNER, ALEXANDER (1926-   )
Braunschweiger Liedmesse *Mass 5pt mix cor MOSELER s.p. (W53)

Der Herr Ist Mein Getreuer Hirt *Easter/Pent [Ger] 2-4pt mix cor,acap (med easy) BAREN. BA 792 s.p. (W54)

Ehre Sei Dir Christe see Kukuck, Felicitas, O Wir Armen Sunder

Es Wolle Gott Uns Gnadig Sein see Goudimel, Claude, Jauchzt, Alle Lande, Gott Zu Ehren

Freuet Euch, Ihr Christen Alle *Thanks SATB/SATBB HANSSLER 6.102 s.p. (W55)

Herr, Fur Dein Wort mix cor HANSSLER 14.145 s.p. contains also: Poser, Hans, Ach Bleib Bei Uns (W56)

Komm, Gott Schopfer, Heiliger Geist SAT/SAB,treb inst/bass inst HANSSLER 14.097 s.p. (W57)

Lobe Den Herren, O Meine Seele *Gen [Ger] 3pt mix cor,acap (med easy) BAREN. BA 792 s.p. (W58)

Macht Hoch Die Tur SAT/SAB,treb inst HANSSLER 14.006 s.p. (W59)

Nun Lob, Mein Seel mix cor HANSSLER 14.188 s.p. (W60)

O Traurigkeit, O Herzelied *mot SSATB HANSSLER 7.089 s.p. (W61)

Vater Unser Im Himmelreich *prayer SSB/SAB HANSSLER 6.145 s.p. contains also: Wenn Wir In Hochsten Noten Sein (SATB) (W62)

Wenn Wir In Hochsten Noten Sein see Wagner, Alexander, Vater Unser Im Himmelreich

WAGNER, DOUG
Psalm Of Praise *Psalm TTBB oct AGAPE MM 9008 $.30 (W63)

WAGNER, GEORG GOTTFRIED (1698-1756)
Alleluia, Amen (Harris) SSAA,acap oct LAWSON 51301 $.25 (W64)

Alleluia, Amen, And Chorale (Ziemer; Rodby) SATB,acap oct LAWSON 51180 $.30 (W65)

Blessing, Glory, Wisdom And Thanks (Ziemer; Rodby) SATB,acap oct LAWSON 51179 $.30 (W66)

Hallelujah, Amen, And Chorale *Gen SATB,acap (med diff) oct CONCORDIA 98-1154 $.25 (W67)

WAGNER, JOSEPH FREDERICK (1900-   )
How Are Thy Servants Blessed, O Lord SATB,org oct BOOSEY 5365 $.35 (W68)

WAGNER-REGENY, RUDOLF (1903-1969)
Cantica Davidi Regis [Lat] jr cor/wom cor,B solo,orch,opt pno BOTE voc sc s.p., cor pts s.p., min sc s.p. (W69)

Genesis *Bibl [Ger] mix cor,A solo,orch,opt pno BOTE voc sc s.p., cor pts s.p. (W70)

WAGNER, RICHARD (1813-1883)
All Praise To God, In Light Arrayed (from Lohengrin) (Cornell) 4pt mix cor,B solo oct SCHIRM.G 3384 $.25 (W71)

WAGNER, RICHARD (cont'd.)

Awake! *see Wach Auf!

Awake! Draws Nigh The Break Of Day *see
   Wach' Auf! Es Nahet Gen Den Tag

Das Liebesmahl Der Apostel *Gd.Fri.,Bibl
   men cor,3fl,2ob,2clar,4bsn,4trp,4horn,
   3trom,tuba,strings,timp, serpent
   BREITKOPF-L rental   (W72)

Deus Abraham *Gen,mot
   [Lat] SATBar oct DURAND s.p.   (W73)

Eucharist Music (from Parsifal) cant
   (Garden) mix cor BELWIN $2.00   (W74)

Festival Prelude (from Die Meistersinger)
   Fest
   (Krone) SATB,acap WARNER W2904 $.35 (W75)

Hail Bright Abode
   SATB oct PRESSER 332-04167 $.35 (W76)

Jesu Quem Velatum (from La Cene Des Apotres)
   (Brun, L'abbe F.) [Lat] 4pt men cor,acap
   oct DURAND s.p.   (W77)

Parsifal, Grande Scene Religieuse, Final Du
   Premier Acte (from Parsifal)
   (Doyen, A.) [Fr] SSAAATTTBB/SSSAAAATTTBBB,
   opt-pno,orch LEDUC CC29 voc sc s.p., cor
   pts s.p.   (W78)

Pilgrim's Chorus
   (Page, N.) SATB oct PRESSER 332-12286 $.30
         (W79)

Prayer (from Lohengrin)
   (Mead) TTBB oct GALAXY 1.1761.1 $.30 (W80)

Sing To God
   (Allum, C.) SATB oct PRESSER 332-13150 $.30
         (W81)

Wach Auf! (from Lohengrin)
   (Christiansen, O.) "Awake!" SATB,opt band
   KJOS 5104 $.30   (W82)

Wach' Auf! Es Nahet Gen Den Tag (from Die
   Meistersinger) chorale
   "Awake! Draws Nigh The Break Of Day" [Ger/
   Eng] SATB,pno SCHIRM.EC 1662 $.16, ipr
         (W83)
   "Awake! Draws Nigh The Break Of Day" SSA,
   pno SCHIRM.EC 1813 $.25, ipr   (W84)

When To Thee Our Savior Went (from Die
   Meistersinger)
   4pt mix cor oct SCHIRM.G 2428 $.25 (W85)

When To Thee Our Saviour Went (from Die
   Meistersinger)
   SATB oct PRO ART 1215 $.16   (W86)

WAGNER, VIOLA
   While Shepherds Watched *see Lillenas,
   Haldor

WAHLT DAS LEBEN see Thieme, Karf

WAHRLICH, ALL UNSRE QUALEN see Erk, Ludwig

WAHRLICH ICH SAGE EUCH see Driessler, Johannes

WAHRLICH, ICH SAGE EUCH, DIES GESCHLECHT see
   Raselius, Andreas

WAHRLICH, ICH SAGE EUCH: DIES GESCHLECHT WIRD
   NICHT VERGEHEN see Vulpius, Melchior

WAHRLICH, ICH SAGE EUCH: DIES GESCHLECT WIRD
   NICHT VERGEHEN see Vulpius, Melchior

WAHRLICH, ICH SAGE EUCH, IHR WERDET WEINEN see
   Vulpius, Melchior

WAHRLICH ICH SAGE EUCH: IHR WERDET WEINEN UND
   HEULEN see Suthoff-Gross, Rudolf

WAHRLICH, ICH SAGE EUCH: SO IHR DEN VATER ETWAS
   BITTEN WERDET see Franck, Melchior

WAHRLICH, ICH SAGE EUCH, SO IHR DEN VATER UM
   ETWAS BITTEN WERDET see Vulpius, Melchior

WAHRLICH, ICH SAGE EUCH, SO JEMAND MEIN WORT
   see Raselius, Andreas

WAHRLICH ICH SAGE EUCH, WAS IHR GETAN HABT see
   Driessler, Johannes

WAHRLICH, ICH SAGE EUCH: WENN IHR DEN VATER
   ETWAS BITTEN see Raselius, Andreas

WAHRLICH ICH SAGE EUCH, WER MEIN WORT HORET see
   Driessler, Johannes

WAHRLICH, WAHRLICH see Bach, Johann Sebastian,
   Wahrlich, Wahrlich, Ich Sage Euch

WAHRLICH, WAHRLICH, ICH SAGE EUCH see Bach,
   Johann Sebastian

WAHRLICH, WAHRLICH, ICH SAGE EUCH see
   Rosenmuller, Johann

WAILING, CRYING, MOURNING, SIGHING see Bach,
   Johann Sebastian, Weinen, Klagen, Sorgen,
   Zagen

WAIT 'TIL I GET ON MY ROBE see Rhea

WAIT 'TIL I GIT ON MY ROBE see Rhea

WAITIN' FOR THE KINGDOM *spir
   SATB oct STAFF 524 $.30   (W87)

WAIT'S CAROL see Stutsman, G.M.

WAKE, AWAKE see Mendelssohn-Bartholdy, Felix

WAKE, AWAKE see Nicolai, Philipp, Wachet Auf,
   Ruft Uns Die Stimme

WAKE, AWAKE, FOR NIGHT IS FLYING *Xmas
   (Fishburn) TTBB SCHMITT 3504 $.30 (W88)

WAKE, AWAKE, FOR NIGHT IS FLYING see Buxtehude,
   Dietrich, Wachet Auf, Ruft Uns Die Stimme

WAKE, AWAKE, FOR NIGHT IS FLYING see Lenel,
   Ludwig

WAKE, AWAKE FOR NIGHT IS FLYING see Mueller,
   Carl F.

WAKE, AWAKE, FOR NIGHT IS FLYING see Nicolai

WAKE, AWAKE, FOR NIGHT IS FLYING see
   Praetorius, Michael

WAKE, AWAKE, FOR NIGHT IS FLYING see Rohlig,
   Harald

WAKE, AWAKE, FOR NIGHT IS FLYING see Tunder,
   Franz

WAKE, AWAKE FOR NIGHT IS FLYING see Wood, Dale

WAKE, AWAKE, FOR NIGHT IS FLYING see Zipp,
   Friedrich

WAKE MY SOUL AND HAIL THE MORNING *carol,US
   (Ehret) SSA MARKS 4362 $.30   (W89)
   (Ehret) SATB MARKS 4526 $.35   (W90)
   (Ehret) SAB MARKS 4460 $.30   (W91)

WAKE, NIGHTINGALE, AWAKE *Xmas,carol,Ger
   (Klause, G.) SAB&desc (easy) oct CONCORDIA
   98-1114 $.25   (W92)

WAKE NOW, YE SHEPHERDS *Xmas
   (Winslow) SATB,acap oct FISCHER,C CM-609 $.25
         (W93)

WAKE NOW YE SHEPHERDS see Winslow

WAKE, O SHEPHERDS see Rameau, Jean-Philippe

WAKE, O WAKE! see Bach, Johann Sebastian,
   Wachet Auf, Ruft Uns Die Stimme [Chorale]

WAKE PSALTRY, AND HARP see Berger

WAKE, SHEPHERDS, AWAKE *Xmas,carol,Ger
   (Schroeder, H.) SAT,inst (med easy) oct
   CONCORDIA 98-2068 $.25   (W94)

WAKE SONS OF EARTH AWAKE see Burroughs, Bob

WAKE! THE WELCOME DAY APPEARETH see Bach,
   Johann Sebastian

WAKE UP, JACOB *spir
   (Papale, Henry) SATB&opt jr cor,opt SA soli,
   acap oct WORLD ESE-775-8 $.45 (W95)

WAKE UP! JACOB see Douglas

WAKE UP, WORLD! see McAfee, Don

WAKE YE AND JOIN THE SINGING see Schiedemann,
   Frisch Auf Und Lasst Uns Singen

WAKE, YE SAINTS see Tschesnokoff, P.I.

WAKE, YE SHEPHERDS *Xmas,carol,Morav
   (Salama) 4pt mix cor oct SCHIRM.G 74381 $.25
         (W96)

WAKE, YE SHEPHERDS see Salama, A.

WAKEN HAPPY PEOPLE see Murray

WAKEN, LITTLE SHEPHERD see Niles, John Jacob

WAKEN, O SHEPHERDS see Klein

WALCH
   O Zion, Haste *Gen
   (Olds) SATB SCHMITT 1865 $.22 (W97)

WALD, GEORGE
   All Hail This Resurrection Day *Easter
   SATB,opt 3trp oct JUSKO 116 $.25 (W98)

   God Who Art Peace Everlasting
   SATB oct GALAXY 1.1420.1 $.20 (W99)

WALDBROEL, WILHELM (1896-1952)
   Christmette *Xmas
   [Ger] SATB,acap (med, appropriate for first
   christmas mass) MULLER SM 782 s.p. (W100)

   Christus Factus Est *Psntd
   [Lat] SATB,acap (med) MULLER SM 493 sc
   s.p., cor pts s.p.   (W101)

   Ecce Sacerdos Magnus *Fest
   [Lat] SATB,org/brass (med easy) MULLER
   SM 898 s.p.   (W102)

   Exaudi Domine *Pent
   [Lat] SATB,acap (med easy) MULLER SM 928
   s.p.   (W103)

   Jesus Christus, Unser Heiland *Easter
   [Ger] SATB,acap (easy) MULLER MS 12 s.p.
      (W104)

   Misericordia Domini *Easter/Pent
   [Lat] SATB,acap (med) MULLER SM 923 s.p.
      (W105)

   Nun Danket Alle Gott *Easter
   [Ger] SAB,acap (med) MULLER MS 11 s.p. (W106)

   Psalm 97 *see Singet Dem Herrn Ein Neues
   Lied

   Salus Populi *Pent
   [Lat] SATB,acap (med) MULLER SM 922 s.p.
      (W107)

   Signum Magnum *BVM/Fest
   [Lat] SATB,acap (med) MULLER SM 720 s.p.
      (W108)

   Singet Dem Herrn Ein Neues Lied (Psalm 97)
   *Easter/Pent
   [Ger] SATB,Bar solo,orch (med diff) MULLER
   SM 944 voc sc s.p., cor pts s.p. (W109)

   Tag So Gross Und Freudenreich *Xmas
   [Ger] SATB,acap (med) MULLER MS 14 s.p.
      (W110)

   Terribilis Est *Ded/Fest
   [Ger] SATB,acap (med) MULLER SM 724 s.p.
      (W111)

   Viri Galilaei *Easter/Pent
   [Lat] SATB,acap (med) MULLER SM 710 s.p.
      (W112)

WALDIS, B.
   Pris Vare Gud
   mix cor NORDISKA 3037 s.p.   (W113)

WALK AS CHILDREN OF LIGHT see Roff, Joseph

WALK HUMBLY WITH THY GOD see Bach, Johann
   Sebastian

WALK HUMBLY WITH THY GOD see Darst, W. Glenn

WALK IN JERUSALEM see Owens

WALK IN JERUSALEM JUS' LIKE JOHN *spir,US
   (Aubanel, Georges) "Marche Dans Jerusalem"
   [Eng/Fr] 3pt mix cor OUVRIERES s.p. (W114)

WALK IN LIGHT see Toolan, S. Suzanne

WALK IN THE LIGHT see Lekberg, Sven

WALK IN THE LIGHT see Mueller, Carl F.

WALK INTO YOUR WORLD see Bancsi, Ruth

WALK TOGETHER, CHILDREN *spir
   (De Cormier) SATB,SB soli,acap oct LAWSON
   51273 $.35   (W115)
   (Schubert) SB oct LILLENAS AN-3820 $.30
      (W116)

WALK TOGETHER CHILDREN see Norman

WALK TOGETHER, CHILDREN see Rhea

WALK WITH ME
   (Gardner) SATB oct STAFF 463 $.25 (W117)

WALK WITH ME see Emig, Lois

WALK WITH ME see Murray

WALK WITH ME see Sjolund, Paul

WALK WITH US, LORD see Lokey

WALK WITH YOUR GOD see Bell

WALK WORTHY see Grieb, Herbert [C.]

WALKER
   Mary's Baby Boy *Xmas
   SATB oct PRO ART 2635 $.35   (W118)

   My Refuge Is The God Of Love
   (McAfee) SATB oct BOURNE 850 $.25 (W119)

   Wise Men From The East *Xmas
   SATB,S,T soli,opt gtr oct PRO ART 2725 $.35
      (W120)

WALKER, ALAN
   Lift Up Your Heads, Ye Mighty Gates *Palm
   unis/sr cor oct GRAY GCMR 2452 $.30 (W121)

WALKER, C.
   Shepherd Of Eager Youth
   unis oct PRESSER MC469 $.25   (W122)

WALKER, DAVID S.
   Little Cradle Rocks Tonight In Glory, The
   see Spiritual Quodlibet For Christmas, A

   Mary Had A Baby
   see Spiritual Quodlibet For Christmas, A

   O Mary, Where Is Your Baby?
   see Spiritual Quodlibet For Christmas, A

   Rise Up, Shepherd, And Follow
   see Spiritual Quodlibet For Christmas, A

   Spiritual Quodlibet For Christmas, A *Xmas
   SSSS,inst (med easy) oct CONCORDIA 98-2143
   $.50
      contains: Little Cradle Rocks Tonight In
      Glory, The; Mary Had A Baby; O Mary,
      Where Is Your Baby?; Rise Up, Shepherd,
      And Follow   (W123)

WALKER, ERNEST (1870-1949)
   I Will Lift Up Mine Eyes *anthem
   ATB oct NOVELLO 38.0127.06 s.p. (W124)

WALKER, GEORGE
   Gloria-In Memoriam
   SSA oct NEW VALLEY $.25   (W125)

WALKER, LINDA H.
   O Lord, I Have Trusted In Thee
   SSA PIONEER 1015 $.40   (W126)

WALKER, ROBIN
   Missa Brevis *Mass
   SATB (med) oct OXFORD 42.865 $.50 (W127)

WALKIN' IN GOD'S COUNTRY see Nordeen, La Juana

WALKING ALONG TO BETHLEHEM see Ehret, Walter

WALKING WITH GOD see Nichols

WALL OF HEAVEN, O SAVIOR, REND, THE see Brahms,
   Johannes, O Heiland, Reiss Die Himmel Auf

WALLACE
   Coventry Carol *Xmas,carol
   SATB STANDARD A9MX1 $.40   (W128)

   Immortal Love Forever Full *Gen
   (Olds) SATB SCHMITT 1855 $.20 (W129)

   Rise Up O Men Of God
   SATB STANDARD A8MX1 $.40   (W130)

WALLACE, G.
   Grant Us Thy Spirit *Easter
   SATB,opt soli oct SOUTHERN $.25 (W131)

   In A World That Needs Thy Love And Care
   SATB oct SOUTHERN $.25   (W132)

WALLACE, WILLIAM (1860-1940)
   Carol Of The Birds
   SATB,acap oct BERANDOL 910W2AA $.35 (W133)

   Cause Of Our Joy *BVM/Xmas,anthem
   SATB,acap oct HARRIS HC4003 $.25 (W134)

WALLACE, WILLIAM (cont'd.)

Dog's Carol, The *Xmas,anthem/carol
SATB,A solo,acap oct HARRIS HC4002 $.35 (W135)

Ox And The Donkey's Carol, The *Xmas,anthem/carol
SATB,acap oct HARRIS HC4001 $.35 (W136)

WALLIS, C.
Saviour, Like A Shepherd Lead Us
SATB,S/T,A/Bar soli,pno (easy) oct WILLIS 2683 $.12 (W137)

WALLS, DANA
Four Modern Anthems *CC4U,anthem
SATB (med) ABINGDON APM-619 $.65 (W138)

WALMISLEY, THOMAS ATTWOOD (1814-1856)
From All That Dwell *Gen,anthem
SATB oct ROYAL 216 s.p. (W139)
SA ALLANS 423 s.p. (W140)

From All That Dwell Below The Skies *anthem
mix cor oct NOVELLO 40.0431.00 s.p. (W141)
SATB BOSWORTH s.p. (W142)
(Davies) 2pt jr cor/2pt wom cor CURWEN 72681 s.p. (W143)

Magnificat And Nunc Dimittis *Magnif/Nunc
unis (D min) oct NOVELLO w2.0061.01 s.p. (W144)
SATB (D min) oct NOVELLO 02.0638.04 s.p. (W145)

Not Unto Us, O Lord
(Knight) 3pt mix cor oct CURWEN 11200 $.20 (W146)
(Knight, Vincent) SAB CURWEN 80872 s.p. (W147)

Ponder My Words *Gen,anthem
SSAA oct ROYAL 211 s.p. (W148)
(McLean) SA oct LESLIE 2040 (W149)

Te Deum And Jubilate In E *Jubil/Te Deum
SS (easy) oct OXFORD 44.211 $.35 (W150)

WALTE, WALTE NAH UND FERN see Stern, Hermann

WALTER
Child Of Bethlehem, The *Xmas,cant
SATB oct LORENZ $1.95 (W151)

Christ Lag In Todesbanden *Psntd
4pt mix cor MOSELER LB-87 s.p. (W152)

Christ Lay In Death's Dark Prison *Holywk/Psntd
(Warkentin, L.) SATB FOSTER MF111 $.25 (W153)

Christ The Lord Is Born *Xmas
SATB oct HORENZ A319 $.30 (W154)

Eternal God Is Your Dwelling Place, The
SATB FLAMMER A 5522 $.25 (W155)

Gelobet Seist Du Jesu Christ
4pt mix cor MOSELER LB-296 s.p. (W156)

Good Tidings Of Joy *Xmas,cant
SATB oct LORENZ $1.95 (W157)

Humbly I Adore Thee
SATB oct GALAXY 1.2012.1 $.30 (W158)

In Dulci Jubilo
see Praetorius, Michael, In Dulci Jubilo

Jerusalem, My Happy Home
SATB oct SACRED S-16 $.35 (W159)

Joseph, Lieber Joseph Mein *Xmas
5pt mix cor MOSELER LB-297 s.p. (W160)

Lord, Keep Us Steadfast *anthem
(Wunderlich) SATB (med) oct AUGSBURG 1352 $.20 (W161)

O Thou In All Thy Might So Far
SATB oct SACRED S-59 $.35 (W162)

Rise Up, O Men Of God *anthem
(Jennings) TTBB (easy) oct AUGSBURG 1535 $.25 (W163)
(Ottesen) SAB FLAMMER D5029 $.25 (W164)

WALTER (WALTHER), JOHANN (1496-1570)
All Morgan Ist Ganz Frisch Und Neu *Gen
[Ger] 3pt mix cor,acap (easy) BAREN. BCH 45 s.p. (W165)

Allein Auf Gottes Wort Will Ich
SATB HANSSLER 6.005 s.p. (W166)

Aus Tiefer Not *Gen
[Ger] SATB,acap (med easy) MULLER K 16 s.p. (W167)

Christum Wir Sollen Loben Schon *Xmas
[Ger] SATTB,acap (med) MULLER K 9 s.p. (W168)

Ein Feste Burg Ist Unser Gott *Fest
[Ger] SATB,acap (med easy) MULLER K 1 s.p. (W169)

Erhalt Uns, Herr, Bei Deinem Wort *Fest
[Ger] 4-5pt mix cor,acap (med easy) MULLER K 11 s.p. (W170)

Geistliches Gesangbuchlein Wittenburg 1551, Erster Teil *CC74U,Gen
(Schroder, Otto) [Ger] 3-6pt mix cor,acap (med) cor pts s.p. (W171)

Jesus Chrstus, Unser Heiland, Der Den Tod
see Staden, Johann, Danket Dem Herrn

Now Sing We, Now Rejoice *Xmas/Epiph
SATB,kbd (med easy) oct CONCORDIA 98-2049 $.30 (W172)

Vier Geistliche Chorsatze *CC4U,Gen
(Stalmann, Joachim) [Ger/Lat] 4-6pt mix cor,acap (med) BAREN. BA 4397 s.p. (W173)

Wach Auf, Wach Auf, Du Deutsches Land
see Schutz, Heinrich, Von Gott Will Ich Nicht Lassen
SATB HANSSLER 6.1466 s.p. (W174)
mix cor HANSSLER 6.2155 s.p. (W175)

WALTER (WALTHER), JOHANN (cont'd.)

War Gott Nicht Mit Uns Diese Zeit
SATB HANSSLER 6.2535 s.p. (W176)

Wohlauf, Wohlauf Mit Lauter Stimm
see Franck, Melchior, Aus Tiefer Not Schrei Ich Zu Dir

WALTER, KARL (1862-1929)
Festmesse *Fest,Mass
4pt mix cor,2trp,2horn,2trom,org DOBLINGER voc sc s.p., cor pts s.p., ipa (W177)

WALTER, SAMUEL
Blessed Are The Pure In Heart *Bibl
SATB,acap (diff) ABINGDON APM-190 $.24 (W178)

Christ Is The World's True Light
SAB (easy) ABINGDON APM-174 $.30 (W179)

Hearts To Heaven And Voices Raise *Easter
SATB (med) ABINGDON APM-403 $.55 (W180)

Holy, Holy, Holy *Commun
SATB (diff) ABINGDON APM-172 $.18 (W181)

How Firm A Foundation
SAB (easy) ABINGDON APM-125 $.25 (W182)

Lord, Have Mercy Upon Us *Commun
SATB (diff) ABINGDON APM-171 $.18 (W183)

Lord Reigneth, The
SA/SATB (med) ABINGDON APM-203 $.24 (W184)
SA/SATB (med) ABINGDON APM-203 $.24 (W185)

O Lamb Of God *Commun
SATT/SATB (diff) ABINGDON APM-173 $.22 (W186)

O Most Loving Father
SATB,acap (easy) ABINGDON APM-280 $.18 (W187)

Peace Be Unto You
SATB (med) ABINGDON APM-279 $.25 (W188)

There's A Light Upon The Mountains *ASD
SATB&unis (easy) ABINGDON APM-316 $.25 (W189)

WALTER, WILLIAM HENRY (1825-1893)
Rise Up, O Men Of God
(Shaw) mix cor oct LAWSON 755 $.30 (W190)

WALTERS
Easy Responses *CCU,cor-resp
SATB,acap oct FISCHER,C CM-7346 $.30 (W191)

WALTHER
Arise, Arise, This Day Rejoice
(Lundquist) SATB SCHMITT 1548 $.30 (W192)

Kristus Kom Selv Til Jordans Flod
[Norw] LYCHE 62 s.p. (W193)

WALTHER, JOHANN GOTTFREID (1684-1748)
Christ Ist Erstanden *Easter
[Ger] 3pt mix cor&4pt mix cor,acap (med) MULLER K 20 s.p. (W194)

Come, Holy Ghost, God And Lord!
SATB,acap oct PRESSER 312-40183 $.30 (W195)

En Salme Om Kristus *Psalm,16th cent
(Woldike, Mogens) [Dan] SATB HANSEN-DEN 80 s.p. see also SALMEMELODIER FRA REFORMATIONSTIDEN (W196)

Fum! Fum! Fum!
SATB oct BELWIN 60751 $.35 (W197)

Herre, Nu Lader Du Din Tjener Fare *Psalm, 16th cent
(Woldike, Mogens) [Dan] SATB (contains also: Praetorius, Michael, En Sang Om Den Hellige, Kristelige Kirke) HANSEN-DEN 82 s.p. see also SALMEMELODIER FRA REFORMATIONSTIDEN (W198)
(Woldike, Mogens) [Dan] SATB (contains also: Praetorius, Michael, Ensang Om Den Heilige, Kristelige Kirke) HANSEN-DEN 82 s.p. see also SALMEMELODIER FRA REFORMATIONSTIDEN (W199)

Joseph, Dearest Joseph Mild *see Joseph, Lieber Joseph Mein

Joseph, Lieber Joseph Mein
"Joseph, Dearest Joseph Mild" [Eng/Ger] SSATB,acap AMP A400 $.30 (W200)

Lov Vare Dig, O Jesu Krist
mix cor NORDISKA 3958 s.p. (W201)
(Berg, Gottfrid) mix cor NORDISKA 5046 s.p. (W202)

Mitten Wir Im Leben Sind *ECY
[Ger] SATTB,acap (med) MULLER K 15 s.p. (W203)

O Light Most Blessed *see O Lux Beata

O Lux Beata
(Granville) "O Light Most Blessed" SATB, acap oct FOX CM3 $.25 (W204)

We Now Implore God, The Holy Ghost
SATTB,acap oct PRESSER 312-40358 $.30 (W205)

WALTHEW, [RICHARD HENRY] (1872-1951)
December *Xmas
cor CRAMER 13 (W206)

WALTON
Angels Came Caroling *Xmas
SSA oct VOLKWEIN VB105 $.25 (W207)

Easter Fanfare *sac/sec,Easter/Lent
SATB,opt 3trp oct SPRATT 540 $.25 (W208)

Easter Lilies *Easter
SSA oct FOX PS56 $.25 (W209)
SATB oct FOX PS55 $.25 (W210)
SA oct FOX PS57 $.25 (W211)

Lord Give Us Faith
(Swift) SATB oct PRO ART 1178 $.20 (W212)
(Swift) SSA oct PRO ART 1093 $.25 (W213)

Make We Joy Now In This Fest
SATB,acap (easy) OXFORD 43.204 $.25 (W214)

WALTON (cont'd.)

Nineteen Responses And Amens *CC19U,cor-resp
SATB SCHMITT 15001 $.30 (W215)

O Lovely World Of Mine
SSA oct FISCHER,C CM-7615 $.25 (W216)

O Thou Who Hearest Every Heartfelt Prayer
SATB oct VOLKWEIN VB235 $.25 (W217)

Twenty Four Responses And Amens *CC24U,Gen
SATB SCHMITT 1762 $.35 (W218)

WALTON, KENNETH
Alleluia
SATB oct BOURNE K6 $.25 (W219)

Before The Paling Of The Stars *Xmas
SATB,SA/SB soli oct BOURNE K1 $.25 (W220)

Christmas Rite *Xmas
SATB oct BOURNE 791 $.25 (W221)

Fanfare For Easter *Easter
SATB KJOS 5234 $.30 (W222)

Praise Ye The Lord (Psalm 135)
SATB oct BOURNE K2 $.25 (W223)

Psalm 135 *see Praise Ye The Lord

Ye Servants Of The Lord
SATB oct BOURNE K3 $.25 (W224)

WALTON, WILLIAM (1902-)
Belshazzar's Feast *ora
[Ger] SATB,Bar solo,orch (diff) sc OXFORD 56.720 $8.75, ipr, voc sc OXFORD 56.713 $4.00 (W225)

Coronation Te Deum *Te Deum
[Lat] SSAATTBB,orch,org (diff) oct OXFORD 46.110 $1.25, rental (W226)

Gifting, The
(Ehret) SSA MARKS 341 $.25 (W227)

Gloria *Gloria
cor,ATB soli,orch (diff) voc sc OXFORD 46.128 $2.75, ipr (W228)

Litany, A *Gen/Psntd
SATB,acap (med easy) oct OXFORD 43.349 $.30 (W229)

Missa Brevis *Agnus/Bene/Gloria/Kyrie/Sanctus
SSAATTBB,org (med) oct OXFORD 46.512 $1.00 (W230)

Set Me As A Seal Upon Thine Heart *Gen
SATB,acap (med) oct OXFORD 43.043 $.25 (W231)

Twelve, The *Gen,anthem
SSAATTBB,org/orch (med) oct OXFORD 46.511 $1.80, ipr (W232)

Where Does The Uttered Music Go? *Ded/Fest
SATB,acap (diff) oct OXFORD 52.602 $.65 (W233)

WALTS GOTT, MEIN WERK ICH LASSE see Buxtehude, Dietrich

WALTS GOTT, MEIN WERK ICH LASSE see Schutz, Heinrich

WALTZ FOR TWO LEFT FEET, A see Rodby, Walter

WALTZ OF THE FLOWERS
(Johnson; Rodby) SSA oct AGAPE WR 1009 $.40 (W234)

WANDELT IM GEIST see Reda, Siegfried

WANDELT IN DER LIEBE see Reda, Siegfried

WANGENHEIM
Stabat Mater
[Lat] SSATTB PETERS 5908 $2.00 (W235)

WANGENHEIM, [VOLKER] (1928-)
Eile, Gott, Mich Zu Erretten (Psalm 70)
mix cor,acap TONGER s.p. (W236)

Ich Hebe Meine Augen Auf (Psalm 123)
mix cor,acap TONGER s.p. (W237)

Psalm 70 *see Eile, Gott, Mich Zu Erretten

Psalm 123 *see Ich Hebe Meine Augen Auf

WANN ICH EINMAL SOLL SCHEIDEN see Bach, Johann Sebastian

WANN IH WIEDER AUF'N TANZBODEN GEH see Lehner, F.X.

WANN UNSRE AUGEN SCHLAFEN EIN see Schutz, Heinrich

WANNENMACHER, JOHANNES (ca. 1485-1551)
An Wasserflussen Babylon
SS/TT LAUDINELLA LR 49 s.p. contains also: Es Woll Uns Gott Genadig Sein (W238)

Es Woll Uns Gott Genadig Sein
see Wannenmacher, Johannes, An Wasserflussen Babylon

WANNER, J.G.
Konfirmation *Cnfrm
[Ger] mix cor,acap (easy) HUG s.p. (W239)

Zur Konfirmation *Cnfrm
[Ger] mix cor,acap (easy) HUG s.p. (W240)

WAPEN, FRANCIS A.
Come, Let Us Bow Down (Psalm 94) Gen,anthem
SB/TB (med easy) oct GIA G1550 $.25 (W241)
SB/TB (med) oct GIA G1550 $.25 (W242)

Lord Reigns, The (Psalm 97) Op.15,No.1
SATB,trp,trom,timp,org CONCORDIA 97-5128 $.50, ipa (W243)

Psalm 94 *see Come, Let Us Bow Down

Psalm 97 *see Lord Reigns, The

WAPENHENSCH, W.
Christe, Du Schopfer Aller Welt *No.72,
Psntd
[Ger] 3pt mix cor,acap BAREN. EM 68 s.p.
see from Evangelisches Kirchengesangbuch
(W244)

Evangelisches Kirchengesangbuch *see
Christe, Du Schopfer Aller Welt, No.72
(W245)

WAR GOTT NICHT see Bach, Johann Sebastian, War'
Gott Nicht Mit Uns Diese Zeit

WAR GOTT NICHT MIT UNS see Bach, Johann
Sebastian

WAR GOTT NICHT MIT UNS see Rohwer, Jens

WAR GOTT NICHT MIT UNS see Zeuner, Martin

WAR' GOTT NICHT MIT UNS DIESE ZEIT see Bach,
Johann Sebastian

WAR GOTT NICHT MIT UNS DIESE ZEIT see
Buxtehude, Dietrich

WAR GOTT NICHT MIT UNS DIESE ZEIT see Franck,
Melchior

WAR GOTT NICHT MIT UNS DIESE ZEIT see
Praetorius, Michael

WAR GOTT NICHT MIT UNS DIESE ZEIT see Reda,
Siegfried

WAR GOTT NICHT MIT UNS DIESE ZEIT see Trubel,
Gerhard

WAR GOTT NICHT MIT UNS DIESE ZEIT see Walter
(Walther), Johann

WARD
America The Beautiful
(Whitman) SSATTBB oct LILLENAS AN-2223 $.30
(W246)
Be Thou My Vision
SATB oct FISCHER,C CM-7076 $.25 (W247)
Earth Shall Be Fair
SATB&opt jr cor,opt S solo,orch voc sc
HIGHLAND 7.0020.1 $2.00 (W248)
Father, We Praise Thee
SATB,brass MARKS 4037 $.35, ipr (W249)
Harvest Hymn
SATB THOMP.G G-552 s.p. (W250)
I'm In His Care
SATB FLAMMER A 5330 $.40 (W251)
Jesu, The Very Thought Of Thee
SATB THOMP.G G-536 s.p. (W252)
That Wondrous Night Of Christmas Eve *Xmas
SATB oct HIGHLAND 7.0006.1 $.40 (W253)
When Christ Rode Into Jerusalem *Easter
SATB oct HIGHLAND 7.0003.1 $.40 (W254)
Would Ye Be Glad And Wise
jr cor oct HIGHLAND 7.0107 $.25 (W255)
SATB oct HIGHLAND 7.0106.1 $.35 (W256)

WARD, JOHN (1571?-1641)
First Service, The *Magnif/Nunc
SAATB&SSAATBB (med) oct OXFORD 42.712 $1.90
(W257)
O Let Me Tread In The Right Path *Gen
SATB,acap (easy) oct OXFORD 43.354 $.25
(W258)

WARD, ROBERT (1917-)
Concord Hymn
SATB,acap oct PRESSER MC137 $.35 (W259)

WARD, RONA
Hymn To The Virgin, A
SATB,acap LENGNICK s.p. (W260)

WARD, WILLIAM R.
Listen, Lord
SATB,Bar solo,acap oct HAWSON 384 $.35
(W261)

WARE
O Holy, Holy Lord (composed with Edson,
[Lewis])
(Coggin) SAB oct BELWIN 64387 $.25 (W262)

WARING, PETER (1917-)
Blessed Is The Man (Psalm 1)
SATB,org SCHIRM.EC 2677 $.50 (W263)
God Be Merciful Unto Us (Psalm 67)
SATB,org SCHIRM.EC 2494 $.40 (W264)
Psalm 1 *see Blessed Is The Man
Psalm 67 *see God Be Merciful Unto Us

WARLAND, DALE
Be Joyful, O Earth *anthem
SATB (med) oct AUGSBURG 1348 $.22 (W265)
Benedictus
[Lat/Eng] SA,acap AMP A609 $.25 (W266)
Let All The World Now Hail Our Lord *anthem
SATB (med) oct AUGSBURG 1349 $.20 (W267)
Thee We Adore *Lent
SATB,acap (easy) ABINGDON APM-391 $.25
(W268)

WARLOCK, PETER
see HESELTINE, PHILIP

WARNER
All Good Gifts
SATB SHAWNEE A 532 $.30 (W269)
God Of My Shepherd Is, The
4pt jr cor/SATB (easy) FISCHER,C R 6013
$.25 (W270)
O Very God Of Very God
SATB SHAWNEE A 519 $.25 (W271)
Praise To God, Immortal Praise
SATB SHAWNEE A 501 $.25 (W272)

WARNER (cont'd.)
Psalm 98
SATB oct SACRED E32 $.35 (W273)

WARNER, LORRAINE D'OREMIEULX
Nativity, The *see Barney, Margaret
Higginson

WARNER, R.A.
Noel *Xmas
SATB,A solo,acap AMP A166 $.20 (W274)

WARNER, RICHARD
Christmas Eve Is Here *Xmas
2pt men cor oct SCHIRM.G 10759 $.25 (W275)
Come, Thou Long-Expected
SATB oct GRAY GCMR 2544 $.25 (W276)
Father Of Mercy
unis oct GRAY GCMR 3100 $.25 (W277)
Go, Labor On!
SATB oct GRAY GCMR 2654 $.25 (W278)
God Of Love My Shepherd Is, The (Psalm 23)
Bibl
mix cor,S solo,org oct FISCHER,C R-6013
$.25 (W279)
Holy Ghost, With Light Divine *Gen/Pent
SA,kbd (easy) oct CONCORDIA 98-1363 $.25
(W280)
How Firm A Foundation
SATB oct GRAY GCMR 2338 $.25 (W281)
Joyous Christmas Day, The
SA,opt hndbl oct GRAY GCMR 3112 $.30 (W282)
Lift Up Your Heads, Ye Mighty Gates *Adv/
Palm
SA oct GRAY GCMR 3102 $.25 (W283)
O Love How Deep
SATB oct GRAY GCMR 3089 $.30 (W284)
Offering Of Praise, An
unis&SA oct GRAY GCMR 3097 $.25 (W285)
Once In Royal David's City *Xmas
SATB oct GRAY GCMR 2946 $.25 (W286)
People, Look East *Adv
SATB/unis/2pt oct GRAY GCMR 2669 $.30
(W287)
Psalm 23 *see God Of Love My Shepherd Is,
The
Sing Praise To God
2pt men cor oct GRAY GCMR 3096 $.30 (W288)
Soldier Of Christ, Arise!
TTB (easy) ABINGDON APM-329 $.18 (W289)
SA/SAB (easy) ABINGDON APM-333 $.18 (W290)
Soldiers Of Christ, Arise!
SA/SAB (easy) ABINGDON APM-333 $.18 (W291)
Sun Shines In Splendour
SA/unis oct GRAY GCMR 2589 $.25 (W292)
Thou Art The Way *Gen
SAB,kbd (med easy) oct CONCORDIA 98-1579
$.25 (W293)
We Thank Thee, O God *Gen/Thanks
SATB&opt jr cor oct GRAY GCMR 2951 $.25
(W294)

WARNER, THEODORE
Funf Psalmengesange *CC5U,Psalm
cor,3strings sc MOSELER s.p., ipa (W295)
Missa Brevis *Mass
3pt mix cor,strings MOSELER sc s.p., cor
pts s.p., ipa (W296)

WARRELL
Bethlehem Night *Xmas
SATB,acap (med easy) OXFORD 43.906 $.30
(W297)

WARREN
Gate Of The Year, The
SATB FLAMMER A 5421 $.25 (W298)
God Is My Song
SATB,org oct BOOSEY 5430 $.35 (W299)
God Of Our Fathers *anthem/hymn
(De Pue) SATB oct PLYMOUTH BG-101 $.30
(W300)
(Ehret) SA MARKS 4075 $.25 (W301)
(Porter) SATB oct SPRATT 304 $.25 (W302)
(Townsend) SAB oct PRO ART 1441 $.30 (W303)
(Townsend) 2pt oct PRO ART 1931 $.25 (W304)
(Townsend) SATB oct PRO ART 1945 $.30
(W305)
(Townsend) SSA oct PRO ART 1636 $.30 (W306)
Heralds Of Christ
(Black) SATB oct FISCHER,J 9076 $.30 (W307)
Little Sheep Of Bethlehem *Xmas
SA HANSEN-US E9884 $.40 (W308)

WARREN, DAVID
Arise, Shine *Bibl
SATB LUDWIG L-1132 $.35 (W309)
Let All The Earth Sing Praise
SATB LUDWIG L-1127 $.30 (W310)

WARREN, ELINOR REMICK (1905-)
Awake, Put On Strength! *Ded/Gen/Refm
SATB,kbd (diff) oct CONCORDIA 98-1875 $.30
(W311)
Christmas Candle
mix cor,S solo,acap oct SCHIRM.G 9368 $.25
(W312)
God Be In My Heart
SATB,acap oct PRESSER 332-40053 $.30 (W313)
Hark! What Mean Those Holy Voices?
cor,S/T solo ENOCH EC58 s.p. (W314)
Holy, Holy *see Sanctus

WARREN, ELINOR REMICK (cont'd.)
My Heart Is Ready
SATB,org oct LAWSON 51393 $.30 (W315)
Requiem *Req
[Eng/Lat] mix cor,MezBar soli,pno/org/orch
LAWSON voc sc $3.50, sc rental, ipr
(W316)
Sanctus *Sanctus
"Holy, Holy" SATB,pno/org oct LAWSON 51263
$.40 (W317)

WARREN, GEORGE WILLIAM (1828-1902)
God Of Our Fathers *Gen,anthem
(Davies) SATB FLAMMER A 5452 $.25 (W318)
(Davies) TTBB FLAMMER C5024 $.30 (W319)
(Gearhart) TTBB SHAWNEE C80 $.40 (W320)
(Gearhart) SATB SHAWNEE A 111 $.40 (W321)
(Johnson, Clair W.) SATB,band/pno oct
RUBANK 2225-PL $.25, ipa (W322)
(Oatley) TTBB FLAMMER C5045 $.25 (W323)
(Pollack, Robert S.) SATB,acap oct WORLD
ESA-1904-8 $.45 (W324)
(Pollack, Robert S.) TTBB,opt pno/org oct
WORLD ESA-1911-4 $.45 (W325)
Magdalene *Easter/Lent
SATB oct FISCHER,C CM-6381 $.25 (W326)
(Booth) SSA,S solo oct FISCHER,C CM-6383
$.25 (W327)
(Fletcher) SA oct FISCHER,C CM-6382 $.25
(W328)
(Warren, R.H.) SSAA oct FISCHER,C CM-6384
$.25 (W329)

WARREN, J.
Even Me
SATB oct PRESSER 332-08272 $.30 (W330)

WARREN, JOHN C.
Even Me
SATB oct LESLIE 4038 (W331)

WARREN, RAYMOND (1928-)
Annunciation, The *Adv,cant
SATB,STB soli,org oct NOVELLO s.p.
(W332)
Come, Holy Ghost *Whitsun,anthem
mix cor oct NOVELLO 28.1331.09 s.p. (W333)
Earth Is Full Of Thy Riches, The *Harv,
anthem
mix cor,Bar solo oct NOVELLO 28.1434.10
s.p. (W334)
Holy, Holy, Holy *anthem
mix cor,acap oct NOVELLO 28.1332.07 s.p.
(W335)
Magnificat And Nunc Dimittis *Magnif/Nunc
unis (C maj) NOVELLO 44.1378.04 s.p. (W336)
Passion, The *Psntd,Bibl
SATB,TBar soli,pno,fl,ob,clar,bsn,horn,
strings,perc,timp voc sc NOVELLO s.p.,
ipr (W337)
Sea Change *Fest
2pt,solo,pno,fl,vln,perc,chimes,rec voc sc
NOVELLO 20.0022.09 s.p., ipa (W338)

WARRENTON
(Niles; Sheppard) 3pt wom cor oct SCHIRM.G
10709 $.25 (W339)
(Niles; Sheppard) 4pt mix cor oct SCHIRM.G
10973 $.25 (W340)

WARRENTON see Niles, John Jacob

WARST DU DORT? see Gerhold, Norbert, Were You
There?

WARST DU DORT see Were You There

WARUM BETRUBST DU DICH see Bach, Johann
Sebastian, Warum Betrubst Du Dich, Mein
Herz

WARUM BETRUBST DU DICH see Hassler, Hans Leo

WARUM BETRUBST DU DICH, MEIN HERZ see Bach,
Johann Sebastian

WARUM DENKET IHR SO ARGES IN EUREN see
Raselius, Andreas

WARUM DENKET IHR SO ARGS IN EUREM HERZEN? see
Franck, Melchior

WARUM HAST DU MICH GESCHLAGEN, GOTT? see
Muller, J.I.

WARUM IST DAS LICHT GEGEBAN see Brahms,
Johannes

WARUM IST DAS LICHT GEGEBEN see Brahms,
Johannes

WARUM IST DAS LICHT GEGEBEN DEM MUHSELIGEN? see
Brahms, Johannes

WARUM SOLLT ICH MICH DENN GRAMEN see Ebeling,
Johann Georg

WARUM SOLLT ICH MICH DENN GRAMEN see
Micheelsen, Hans Friedrich

WARUM SOLLT ICH MICH DENN GRAMEN see Oertzen,
Rudolf von

WARUM TOBEN DIE HEIDE see Koler, David

WARUM TOBEN DIE HEIDEN see Mendelssohn-
Bartholdy, Felix

WARUM TOBEN DIE HEIDEN see Schutz, Heinrich

WAS AUCH KOMMEN MAG see Mockel, Franz

WAS BETRUBST DU DICH MEINE SEELE see Handel,
George Frideric

WAS BETRUBST DU DICH, MEINE SEELE see Hartmann,
Heinrich

WAS BETRUBST DU DICH, MEINE SEELE see Lohr, Ina

WAS BETRUBST DU DICH, MEINE SEELE see Schein, Johann Hermann

WAS BETRUBST DU DICH, MEINE SEELE see Schutz, Heinrich

WAS BETRUEBST DU DICH, MEINE SEELE see Schutz, Heinrich

WAS ER DIR GEBEN MOGE, DU ZUNGE VOLL FALSCHHEIT see Schutz, Heinrich, Quid Detur Tibi

WAS FRAG ICH NACH DER WELT see Bach, Johann Sebastian

WAS FRAG' ICH NACH DER WELT see Buxtehude, Dietrich

WAS FRAG' ICH NCAH DER WELT see Buxtehude, Dietrich

WAS GOTT TUT DAS IST WOHLGETAN see Bach, Johann Sebastian

WAS GOTT TUT DAS IST WOHLGETAN see Gastorius, Severius

WAS GOTT TUT, DAS IST WOHLGETAN see Micheelsen, Hans Friedrich

WAS GOTT TUT, DAS IST WOHLGETAN see Pachelbel, Johann

WAS GOTT TUT, DAS IST WOHLGETAN see Stern, Hermann

WAS GOTT TUT, DAS IST WOHLGETAN see Bach, Johann Sebastian

WAS GOTT TUT, DAS IST WOHLGETAN see Bach, Johann Sebastian

WAS GOTT TUT, DAS IST WOHLGETAN see Bach, Johann Sebastian

WAS GOTT TUT, DAS IST WOHLGETAN [CHORALE] see Bach, Johann Sebastian

WAS GOTT TUT, DAS IST WOHLGETAN see Bach, Johann Sebastian

WAS GOTT TUT, DAS IST WOHLGETAN see Bach, Johann Sebastian

WAS GOTT TUT, DAS IST WOHLGETAN see Bach, Johann Sebastian

WAS GOTT TUT, DAS IST see Bach, Johann Sebastian, Was Gott Tut, Das Ist Wohlgetan

WAS GOTT TUT see Bach, Johann Sebastian, Was Gott Tut, Das Ist Wohlgetan

WAS GOTT TUT see Bach, Johann Sebastian, Was Gott Tut, Das Ist Wohlgetan

WAS HABE ICH DIR GETAN, MEIN VOLK see Palestrina, Giovanni

WAS HAST DU VERWIRKET see Schutz, Heinrich, Quid Commisisti

WAS IH MIR HEUT FRUH BEIM ABWASCH'N DENKT HAB see Lehner, F.X.

WAS IST DAS FUR EIN MENSCH see Driessler, Johannes

WAS IST DAS MENSCHENLEBEN see Staden

WAS IST FUR NEUE FREUD see Reda, Siegfried

WAS ISTS, DASS IHR MICH GESUCHT HABT see Driessler, Johannes

WAS JESUS IST see Lehman, Siegfried

WAS KEIN AUGE GESEHEN HAT see Zipp, Friedrich

WAS MEIN GOTT WILL see Bach, Johann Sebastian

WAS MEIN GOTT WILL see Bach, Johann Sebastian, Was Mein Gott Will, Das G'scheh' Allzeit

WAS MEIN GOTT WILL see Micheelsen, Hans Friedrich

WAS MEIN GOTT WILL see Raphael, Gunther

WAS MEIN GOTT WILL see Schutz, Heinrich

WAS MEIN GOTT WILL, DAS GESCHEH ALLZEIT see Gumpeltzhaimer, Adam

WAS MEIN GOTT WILL, DAS G'SCHEH' ALLZEIT see Bach, Johann Sebastian

WAS MEIN GOTT WILL, DAS GSCHEH ALLZEIT see Cruger, Johann

WAS MEIN GOTT WILL, DAS G'SCHEH ALLZEIT see Eccard, Johannes

WAS MEIN GOTT WILL, DAS GSCHEH ALLZEIT see Pahlitzsch, Wolfgang

WAS MEIN GOTT WILL, DAS GSCHEH ALLZEIT see Raphael, Gunther

WAS MEIN GOTT WILL, DAS GSCHEH ALLZEIT see Schutz, Heinrich

WAS MEIN GOTT WOLL, DAS GSCHEH ALLZEIT see Schutz, Heinrich

WAS MIR BEHAST, IST MUR DIE MUNTRE JAGD see Bach, Johann Sebastian

WAS SIND DAS FUR GROSSE SCHLOSSER see Bach, Johann Sebastian

WAS SOLL DAS BEDEUTEN? see Gresser, Hans

WAS SOLL DAS BEDEUTEN see Haus, Karl

WAS SOLL ICH AUS DIR MACHEN see Bach, Johann Sebastian

WAS SOLL ICH AUS DIR MACHEN, EPHRAIM? see Bach, Johann Sebastian

WAS SUCHET IHR DEN see Wenzel, Eberhard

WAS SUCHET IHR DEN LEBENDIGEN see Wenzel, Eberhard

WAS WILLST DU DICH BETRUBEN see Bach, Johann Sebastian

WASH ME, O LORD GOD see Pergolesi, Giovanni Battista

WASH ME THOROUGHLY FROM MY WICKEDNESS see Wesley, Samuel Sebastian Jr.

WASH ME THROUGHLY see Wesley, Samuel Sebastian Jr.

WASHBURN, ROBERT (1928-)
Child This Day Is Born, A
SATB SHAWNEE A 575 $.25 (W341)

Gloria !Gloria
mix cor,brass voc sc OXFORD 94.210 $.70, ipa (W342)
mix cor,brass sc OXFORD 94.210 $.70, ipa (W343)

Hymn Of Youth *hymn
SATB oct SHAPIRO SK 2080 $.30 (W344)

Praise The Lord
SATB,opt 2trp,horn,2trom,tuba oct SHAPIRO SK 2081 $.30, ipa (W345)

WASHINGTON, HENRY (1904-)
Ad Regias Agni Dapes
see Four Vesper Hymns

Audi, Benigne Conditor
see Four Vesper Hymns

Creator Alme Siderum
see Four Vesper Hymns

Four Vesper Hymns *hymn
[Lat] SATB CHESTER s.p.
contains: Ad Regias Agni Dapes; Audi, Benigne Conditor; Creator Alme Siderum; Lucis Creator Optime (W346)

Lucis Creator Optime
see Four Vesper Hymns

WASMUTH, JAN JURGEN (1938-)
Gott Ist Unsre Zuversicht Und Starke
SATB,cont HANSSLER 6.301 s.p. (W347)

WASNER, FRANZ
Children's Blessing *see Kindersegen

Christmas Nightingale, The *Xmas
3pt wom cor,A rec,T rec SCHIRM.G 10617 $.25 (W348)

Kindersegen
"Children's Blessing" [Eng/Ger] mix cor, acap oct SCHIRM.G 8795 $.25 (W349)

When Jesus In The Garden
SABar,acap oct SCHIRM.G 8822 $.25 (W350)

WASN'T THAT A MIGHTY DAY? *Xmas,spir
(Dett) SATBarB,opt ABar soli,acap oct SCHIRM.G 7712 $.30 (W351)

WASN'T THAT A MIGHTY DAY? see Dett, Robert Nathaniel

WASN'T THAT A MIGHTY DAY! see Ehret, Walter

WASSAIL CAROL see Mathias, William

WASSAIL SONG *Xmas,carol/folk,Eng
see Six Christmas Carols, Set III
see Two Wassails
SATB (med easy) OXFORD 08.015 $.15 (W352)
(Holst, Gustav) mix cor CURWEN 61278 s.p. (W353)
(Vaughn Williams, Ralph) SATB/unis,pno GALAXY s.p. see also Eight Traditional Carols (W354)
(Vaughn Williams, Ralph) TTBB,acap GALAXY s.p. (W355)

WASSAIL SONG see Finch, R.

WASSAIL SONG see Vaughan Williams, Ralph

WASSAIL SONG, A *Xmas,carol
(Anderson, W.H.) SATB oct LESLIE 4016 see from Two Christmas Carols, Set 2 (W356)

WASSAIL SONG, THE *Xmas
cor CRAMER s.p. (W357)
(Forrester) SAB SCHMITT 5538 $.25 (W358)

WASSAIL, WASSAIL, ALL OVER THE TOWN *Xmas, carol
SATB (easy) OXFORD 08.031 $.15 (W359)

WASSAIL, WASSAIL, ALL OVER THE TOWN! see Spencer, W.

WASTED ON ME see McWhertor

WAT DE SNEEUWVLOKKEN ZINGEN see Rontgen, [Julius]

WATCH AND PRAY
2pt CHAPPELL 0018317-352 $.40 (W360)
SSA CHAPPELL 0018317-354 $.40 (W361)
SAB CHAPPELL 0018317-356 $.40 (W362)
SATB CHAPPELL 0018317-358 $.40 (W363)

WATCH, O MASTER, O'ER US see Brandon, George

WATCH YE, PRAY YE see Bach, Johann Sebastian

WATCHMAN, TELL US see McAfee, Don

WATCHMAN, TELL US OF THE NIGHT see Cain, Noble

WATCHMAN, TELL US OF THE NIGHT see Emig, Lois

WATCHMAN, TELL US OF THE NIGHT see Gillam

WATCHMAN, TELL US OF THE NIGHT see Hastings

WATCHMAN, TELL US OF THE NIGHT see Hovhaness, Alan

WATCHMAN, TELL US OF THE NIGHT see Pfautsch, Lloyd

WATCHMAN, TELL US OF THE NIGHT see Wood, Dale

WATCHMAN, WHAT OF THE NIGHT? see Bright, Houston

WATCHMAN! WHAT OF THE NIGHT? see Sarjeant

WATER AND THE FIRE, THE see Milner, Anthony

WATER AND WINE see Haydn, (Franz) Joseph

WATER FOR A THIRSTY LAND see Johnson

WATER OF LIFE see Cain, Noble

WATER OF TYNE, THE
(Sharpe, E.) cor&desc CRAMER 51 (W364)

WATER PARTED FROM THE SEA see Arne, Thomas Augustine

WATERMAN
Sweet Jesus In The Manger *Xmas
SATB oct LORENZ 5765 $.30 (W365)

WATERMAN, FRANCES
Creation, The
SA oct LORENZ 5387 $.25 (W366)

David
unis oct LORENZ 8629 $.30 (W367)

Sweet Jesus In The Manger *Xmas,anthem/pop
SB oct LORENZ 5765 $.30 (W368)

Yes, I Know!
(Schubert) SB oct LILLENAS AN-1193 $.30 (W369)

WATERS
There's A Difference
(Collins) SATB oct LILLENAS AT-1016 $.25 (W370)

WATERS, CHARLES F.
Creator Spirit *Gen/Whitsun
SATB (easy) oct OXFORD 42.811 $.30 (W371)

Four Introits For Seasonal Use *CC4U,anthem/Introit
mix cor oct NOVELLO 44.1299.00 s.p. (W372)

Petition Carol
SATB,acap CRAMER C 42 s.p. (W373)

Psalm 65 *see Thou Visitest The Earth

Sing Alleluia Forth *anthem
SS oct ROYAL 206 s.p. (W374)

Thou Visitest The Earth (Psalm 65) Harv
SATB (easy) oct OXFORD $.35 (W375)

Whitsun Carol *Whitsun,carol
SATB,acap CRAMER C 44 s.p. (W376)

Ye Are Fellow-Citizens With The Saints *anthem
mix cor oct NOVELLO 86.0015.05 s.p. (W377)

WATERS OF THY LOVE, THE see O'Hara, Geoffrey

WATERS, PETER
Corpus Christi Mass *folk/Mass
unis,pno/org,fl/T rec,bvl,gtr ALBERT s.p. (W378)

Short Mass, A *Mass
unis,org ALBERT s.p. (W379)

WATKINSON, GERD (1915-)
Sag, Was Ist Geschehen? *CCU,Xmas
[Ger] SA&men cor,acap (med easy) BAREN. BA 3891 $1.75 new pastoral songs (W380)

WATKINSON, J.R.
Lift The Strain Of High Thanksgiving *anthem
mix cor oct NOVELLO 28.1213.04 s.p. (W381)

WATSON
Voice Of Jesus, The
SATB SHAWNEE A 744 $.25 (W382)

Ye Nations Praise The Lord
SATB SHAWNEE A 754 $.25 (W383)

WATSON, D.
Carol Of The Bells, A *Xmas
jr cor&sr cor oct GRAY GHCS 9 $.25 (W384)

WATSON, FRANK CAMPBELL
Missa Brevis *Mass
[Lat/Eng] SATB oct JUSKO 163 $.80 (W385)

WATSON, M.
Praise The Lord, O My Soul *Gen/Thanks, anthem/Bibl
4pt mix cor oct SCHIRM.G 3630 $.25 (W386)
(Mueller) SABar,Bar solo oct SCHIRM.G 8699 $.25 (W387)

Worship The Lord
SATB oct PRESSER 312-20394 $.30 (W388)

WATSON, MERLA
Make A Joyful Noise (Psalm 100) anthem/Bibl/round
SATB oct AGAPE CF 100 $.25 (W389)

Psalm 100 *see Make A Joyful Noise

WATSON, SYDNEY
Communion Service In F *Commun
unis (med easy) oct OXFORD 45.065 $.35 (W390)

Evening Service In E *Magnif/Nunc
SATB (med) oct OXFORD 42.097 $.35 (W391)

WATT
Alter Of God (from Mass Of San Antonio, The) CCU,folk
cor,pno,gtr ALBERT s.p. (W392)

WATTERS
Shepherd Song, The
(Collins) SATB oct LILLENAS AT-1064 $.30
(W393)

WATTS
I Sing The Mighty Power Of God (composed with
Handel, George Frideric)
(Ehret) SAB LUDWIG L-9137 $.35   (W394)

Joy To The World *Xmas
(Kuykendall) SATB oct PLYMOUTH JR-117 $.35
(W395)

Just Are Thy Ways, O Living God (composed
with Giroust)
(Ehret) SAB LUDWIG L-9140 $.35   (W396)

O Bless The Lord, My Soul!
(Avalos) SATB oct PRO ART 1355 $.25   (W397)

WATTS, HAROLD E.
God Of Abraham Praise, The *Gen/Harv,anthem
mix cor oct NOVELLO 40.0954.01 s.p.   (W398)

WATT'S NATIVITY CAROL see Shure, R. Deane

WATTS, W.
Come, Sound His Praise Abroad
(Rhea) SAB oct PLYMOUTH UIL-104 $.25   (W399)

From All That Dwell Below The Skies
(Rhea) TTBB oct PLYMOUTH UIL-107 $.25
(W400)

WAVE HIM ON see Schaefer, Christopher

WAY IN THE HEAVEN BYE AND BYE see Gerhold,
Norbert

WAY IS LONG AND DREARY see Rheinberger, Josef

WAY OF CHARITY, THE see Berger, Jean

WAY OF CHRIST, THE see Blake

WAY OF JEHOVAH, THE see Stevens, Halsey

WAY OF THE CROSS (from King Of Kings)
SATB BIG3 $.30   (W401)

WAY OF THE CROSS see Christopher, Cyril S., Via
Crucis

WAY OF THE CROSS LEADS HOME, THE see Gabriel

WAY OF THE CROSS, THE see Tozer, Ferris

WAY OUTSIDE YOU see Fields

WAY OVER IN BEULAH LAN' *spir
(Johnson, Hall) SATB,acap MARKS 4008 $.40
(W402)

WAY OVER IN EGYPT LAND see Work

WAY, THE LIFE, THE see Riego, Teresa del

WAY, THE TRUTH, AND THE LIFE, THE see Roff,
Joseph

WAY, THE TRUTH AND THE LIFE, THE see Williams,
Alice Crane

WAY TO JERUSALEM see Friedell, Harold W.

WAYFARING STRANGER *spir,US
(De Cormier) SATB,acap oct LAWSON 51625 $.30
(W403)
(De Cormier) 2pt boy cor/SA,acap oct LAWSON
51626 $.25   (W404)
(Mittergradnegger, Gunther) [Ger] mix cor,
acap oct &OBLINGER s.p. see also Funf
Amerikanische Negro-Spirituals   (W405)
(Niles) mix cor,acap oct SCHIRM.G 10040 $.35
(W406)

WAYFARING STRANGER see Niles, John Jacob

WAYS OF ZION DO MOURN, THE see Wise, Michael

WE ADORE THEE see Aichinger, Gregor, Adoramus
Te

WE ADORE THEE see Anerio, Giovanni Francesco,
Adoramus Te

WE ADORE THEE see Brahms, Johannes, Adoramus Te

WE ADORE THEE see Clement, Adoramus Te

WE ADORE THEE see Corsi, Giuseppe, Adoramus Te,
Christe

WE ADORE THEE see Gasparini, Adoramus Te

WE ADORE THEE see Gasparini, Francesco,
Adoramus Te

WE ADORE THEE see Gasparini, Quirino, Adoramus
Te

WE ADORE THEE see Lassus, Roland de (Orlandus)

WE ADORE THEE see Lotti, Antonio, Adoramus Te

WE ADORE THEE see Palestrina, Giovanni,
Adoramus Te

WE ADORE THEE see Palestrina, Giovanni,
Adoramus Te, Christe

WE ADORE THEE see Parthun, Paul, Adoramus Te
Christe

WE ADORE THEE see Perti, Giacomo Antonio,
Adoramus Te, Christe

WE ADORE THEE see Zielenski, Nicholas, Adoramus
Te

WE ADORE THEE, CHRIST, JESUS see Viadana,
Lodovico Grossi da, Adoramus Te, Christe

WE ADORE THEE, CHRIST OUR LORD see Jennings,
Kenneth L.

WE ADORE THEE, GRACIOUS LORD see Goodale, R.L.

WE ADORE THEE, LORD JESU see Palestrina,
Giovanni, Adoramus Te

WE ADORE THEE, O CHRIST see Dubois, Theodore,
Adoramus Te, Christe

WE ADORE THEE, O CHRIST see Lassus, Roland de
(Orlandus), Adoramus Te, Christe

WE ADORE THEE, O CHRIST see Rossello, Adoramus
Te

WE ADORE THEE, O CHRIST see Ruffo, [Vincenzo],
Adoramus Te, Christe

WE ADORE THEE, O LORD CHRIST see Viadana,
Lodovico Grossi da, Adoramus Te, Christe

WE ADORE YOU see Gasparini, Francesco, Adoramus
Te

WE ADORE YOU see Perti, Giacomo Antonio,
Adoramus Te, Christe

WE ADORE YOU, O CHRIST see Palestrina,
Giovanni, Laudate Dominum

WE ADORE YOU, O LORD JESUS CHRIST see Remondi,
R.

WE ALL BELIEVE IN ONE GOD see Reger, Max

WE ALL BELIEVE IN ONE TRUE GOD see Hassler,
Hans Leo

WE ALL BELIEVE IN ONE TRUE GOD see Mueller,
Carl F.

WE ALL BELIEVE IN ONE TRUE GOD see Vulpius,
Melchior

WE ALL BELIEVE IN ONE TRUE GOD see Wienhorst,
Richard

WE ALL BELIVE IN ONE GOD see Reger, Max

WE ALL NEED GOD see McCoy

WE ALL REJOICE ON THIS GLAD DAY see Praetorius,
Michael

WE ALL REJOICE ON THIS GLAD DAY see Strube,
Adolf

WE AM CLIM'IN JACOBS'S LADDER *spir,US
(Aubanel, Georges) "A L'echelle De Jacob"
[Eng/Fr] 4pt mix cor OUVRIERES s.p.   (W407)

WE ARE CLIMBING JACOB'S LADDER *spir
(Schubert) SATB oct LILLENAS AN-3819 $.25
(W408)

WE ARE GOING TO THE STABLE *Xmas,carol,Czech
(Ehret, Walter) SATB,opt inst oct WALTON 2504
$.30   (W409)
(Ehret, Walter) SSA,opt inst oct WALTON 2531
$.30   (W410)

WE ARE HIS PEOPLE see Peloquin, C. Alexander

WE ARE MORE THAN CONQUERORS see Carmichael

WE ARE ONE IN THE LORD see Wyatt

WE ARE SOLDIERS OF THE KING see Evans, Aubrey

WE ARE THY SERVANTS, O LORD see Kechley,
[Gerald]

WE ASK THEE, O LORD see Morgan

WE BEHOLD OUR DYING SAVIOUR see Rozell

WE BELIEVE THAT THOU SHALT COME see Handel,
George Frideric

WE BESEECH THEE see Graham, Robert [V.]

WE BESEECH THEE ALMIGHTY GOD see Batten, Adrian

WE BESEECH THEE ALMIGHTY GOD see Lavater, Louis

WE BLESS THE GOD OF HEAVEN see Fissinger, Edwin

WE BLESS THY HOLY NAME see Bach, Johann
Sebastian

WE BOW OUR HEADS see Fuller, [Esther Mary]

WE BRING OUR EAGER SOULS TO THEE see Beethoven,
Ludwig van

WE CALL TO THEE see O'Hara, Geoffrey

WE CHRISTIANS MAY REJOICE TODAY see Fuger, Wir
Christenleut

WE COME IN BRIGHT ARRAY see Handel, George
Frideric

WE COME TO PRAISE HIS NAME see Handel, George
Frideric

WE COME UNTO OUR FATHERS' GOD see Marshall

WE COME UNTO OUR FATHER'S GOD see Mendelssohn-
Bartholdy, Felix

WE COME UNTO OUR FATHERS' GOD see Mueller, Carl
F.

WE COME UNTO OUR FATHER'S GOD see Rohlig,
Harald

WE COME UNTO OUR FATHER'S GOD see Videro, Finn

WE COME WITH SONGS OF GLADNESS see Larson

WE DO ADORE THEE see Lassus, Roland de
(Orlandus)

WE DO WORSHIP THEE see Palestrina, Giovanni,
Adoremus Te, Christe

WE DO WORSHIP THEE see Pitoni, Giuseppe Ottavio

WE GATHER TOGETHER *Thanks,hymn
see Three Thanksgiving Hymns
(Clough-Leighter, H.) SATB,org SCHIRM.EC 306
$.25, ipr   (W411)
(Davis, K.) SATB&desc,acap SCHIRM.EC 1735
$.25   (W412)
(Davis, K.) SAB&desc,acap SCHIRM.EC 1737 $.22

(W413)
(Pottenger) SATB oct LILLENAS AN-2369 $.35
(W414)

WE GATHER TOGETHER see Hornibrook

WE GATHER TOGETHER TO ASK THE LORD'S BLESSING
see Vandre, Carl W.

WE GIVE IMMORTAL PRAISE see Thiman, Eric
Harding

WE GIVE THANKS see Bush, G.B.

WE GIVE THANKS TO THEE see Glarum, L. Stanley

WE GIVE THANKS TO THEE, O LORD see Palestrina,
Giovanni

WE GIVE THEE BUT THINE OWN
see Worship Responses
(Davis, K.) TBB,acap SCHIRM.EC 575 $.20
(W415)

WE GIVE THEE BUT THINE OWN see Elmore, Robert
[Hall]

WE GIVE THEE THANKS see Fuller, [Esther Mary]

WE GIVE THEE THANKS see Wetzler, Robert

WE GO TO CHURCH see Marshall, Jane M.

WE HASTEN, O JESU see Bach, Johann Sebastian

WE HASTEN, O MASTER see Bach, Johann Sebastian

WE HASTEN WITH EAGER, YET FALTERING FOOTSTEPS
see Bach, Johann Sebastian, Wir Eilen Mit
Schwachen, Doch Emsigen Schritten

WE HAVE A STRONG CITY see Gardner, John
[Linton]

WE HAVE A STRONG CITY see Harper, M.

WE HAVE BEEN A-RAMBLING *Xmas
(Imogen Holst) 3pt wom cor,acap oct SCHIRM.G
11635 $.25   (W416)

WE HAVE BUILDED AN HOUSE see Bohrnstedt, Wayne

WE HAVE HEARD THE WORDS see Nagel

WE HAVE SEEN HIS STAR see Mc Clintock, Donald

WE HAVE SEEN HIS STAR see Titcomb

WE HAVE SEEN HIS STAR IN THE EAST see Lipscomb,
Helen

WE HAVE WAITED FOR HIM see Roff, Joseph

WE HEAR see Handel, George Frideric

WE HEAR THE ANGEL GABRIEL see Ferguson, Howard

WE HOPE IN THEE, O GOD see Bach, Johann
Sebastian

WE KNOW THE PATHS see Hastings

WE LIFT OUR HEARTS TO THEE see Kempinski, Leo
[A.]

WE LIFT OUR HEARTS UNTO THE LORD see Graham,
Robert [V.]

WE LOVE THE PLACE O GOD see Bach

WE LOVE THE PLACE, O GOD see Monk

WE LOVE THE PLACE, O GOD see Powell

WE LOVE THE PLACE, O GOD see Robb, John

WE LOVE THE PLACE, O GOD see Talmadge, Charles
L.

WE LOVE THE PLACE WHERE THINE HONOUR DWELLS see
Brahms, Johannes

WE LOVE YOUR ALTAR HERE see Grime, William

WE MEET AROUND THE MANGER BED see Grime,
William

WE MUST THROUGH GREAT TRIBULATION see Bach,
Johann Sebastian, Wir Mussen Durch Viel
Trubsal

WE MUST VANISH LIKE A SHADOW see Bach, Johann
(Hans), Unser Leben Ist Ein Schatten

WE NEED THEE O LORD see Christiansen, Olaf
Christian

WE NEED THY LOVE see Darst, W. Glenn

WE NEVER WILL BOW DOWN see Handel, George
Frideric

WE NOW IMPLORE GOD THE HOLY GHOST see Lenel,
Ludwig

WE NOW IMPLORE GOD, THE HOLY GHOST see Walther,
Johann Gottfried

WE PAUSE BESIDE THIS DOOR see Ferguson, Edwin
Earle

WE PLOW THE FIELDS see Atkinson, Condit R.

WE PLOW THE FIELDS see Lockwood, Normand

WE PRAISE AND BLESS THEE see Gounod, Charles
Francois

WE PRAISE GOD see Leng, Deum Laudamus

WE PRAISE THEE see Buketoff, [Igor]

WE PRAISE THEE see Handel, George Frideric,
Chandos Te Deum

WE PRAISE THEE see Handel, George Frideric, Te
Deum Laudamus

WE PRAISE THEE see Mueller, Carl F., Laudamus
Te

WE PRAISE THEE see Pasquet, Jean

WE PRAISE THEE see Rachmaninoff, Sergey
    Vassilievitch

WE PRAISE THEE see Tchaikovsky, Piotr Ilyitch

WE PRAISE THEE see Tkach, D.

WE PRAISE THEE see Zhadanov

WE PRAISE THEE, LORD see Monaco, Richard A.

WE PRAISE THEE, LORD see Vivaldi, Antonio,
    Laudamus Te

WE PRAISE THEE, LORD, AND BLESS THY NAME
    (Ehret) SATB oct WORD CS-653 $.30   (W417)

WE PRAISE THEE, O GOD see Bach, Johann
    Sebastian

WE PRAISE THEE, O GOD see Busarow, Donald, Te
    Deum Laudamus

WE PRAISE THEE, O GOD see Crone, R., Te Deum
    Laudamus

WE PRAISE THEE, O GOD see Handel, George
    Frideric

WE PRAISE THEE, O GOD see Husband, [Edward]

WE PRAISE THEE, O GOD see Latrobe

WE PRAISE THEE, O GOD see Lipscomb, Helen

WE PRAISE THEE O GOD see Parton, K.

WE PRAISE THEE, O GOD see Sateren, Leland
    Bernhard

WE PRAISE THEE, O GOD see Swann, Donald, Modern
    Te Deum, A

WE PRAISE THEE, O GOD see Te Deum Laudamus

WE PRAISE THEE, O GOD see Willan, Healey, Te
    &eum Laudamus

WE PRAISE THEE, O GOD see Williams

WE PRAISE THEE, O LORD see McCowen

WE PRAISE THEE, PART I see Willan, Healey

WE PRAISE THEE, PART II see Willan, Healey

WE PRAY TO THEE see Palestrina, Giovanni

WE RENDER, LORD, THIS DAY see Young, Gordon

WE SANCTIFY THE NAME OF GOD see Gordon

WE SANCTIFY THY NAME see Berger

WE SAW A LIGHT SHINE OUT AFAR *Xmas
    (Stone) SSA oct PRO ART 1689 $.20   (W418)

WE SAW HIM SLEEPING see Booth

WE SAW HIS GLORY see Mauersberger, Erhard

WE SEEK NOT, GOD, OUR LORD, FOR GLORY see
    Haydn, (Franz) Joseph, Non Nobis, Domine

WE SHALL ALL BE CHANGED see Ashton

WE SHALL SEE HIS   HOVELY FACE see Roe, N.
    Clayton

WE SHALL SEE THE KING see Vaughn

WE SHALL WALK THROUGH THE VALLEY see Owens,
    Jimmy

WE SHALL WALK THROUGH THE VALLEY IN PEACE
    *spir
    (Appling, William) TTBB,acap oct WORLD CE2328
    $.30   (W419)

WE SHALL WALK THROUGH THE VALLEY IN PEACE see
    Hooper, William L.

WE SING A SONG OF CHRISTMAS-TIME see Sullivan,
    Sir Arthur Seymour

WE SING, IMMANUEL, THY PRAISE see Wolff, S.
    Drummond

WE SING OF GOD see Hayes

WE SING OF GOD, THE MIGHTY SOURCE see
    Boatwright, Howard

WE SING OUR PRAISES NOW TO THEE see Farrant,
    Richard

WE SING THE MIGHTY POWER OF GOD   !Gen
    (Pooler) SATB SCHMITT 8029 $.30   (W420)

WE SING THE PRAISE see Willan, Healey

WE SING THE PRAISE OF HIM see Schreck

WE SING THE PRAISE OF HIM WHO DIED see
    Gumpeltzhaimer, Adam

WE SING THE PRAISE OF HIM WHO DIED see
    Praetorius, Michael

WE SING THE PRAISE OF HIM WHO DIED see Schreck

WE SING THY PRAISE *CC10L,Gen
    SATB PRO ART 361 $1.25   (W421)

WE SING THY PRAISE see Bortniansky, Dimitri
    Stepanovitch

WE SING THY PRAISE see Tkach

WE SING TO LEARN see Marshall, Jane M.

WE SING TO THEE see Playford, John

WE SING TO THEE, O LORD see Tcherepnin, Nikolay
    Nikolayevitch

WE SING WITH REJOICING see Ritter, Christian,
    Gott Hat Jesum Erwecket

WE STRODE THROUGH THE WAVES see Chajes, Julius

WE THANK THEE
    2pt CHAPPELL 0018325-352 $.40   (W422)
    SSA CHAPPELL 0018325-354 $.40   (W423)
    SATB CHAPPELL 0018325-358 $.40   (W424)

WE THANK THEE see Byles

WE THANK THEE see Schein

WE THANK THEE, GOD see Bach, Johann Sebastian

WE THANK THEE, LORD see Bortniansky, Dimitri
    Stepanovitch

WE THANK THEE, LORD see Burroughs

WE THANK THEE LORD see Pritchard, Arthur J.

WE THANK THEE, LORD see Tkach, P.

WE THANK THEE, LORD, FOR GRACE OF HOME see
    Lovelace, Austin C.

WE THANK THEE, O FATHER see Williams, David H.

WE THANK THEE, O GOD see Christiansen

WE THANK THEE, O GOD see Warner, Richard

WE THANK THEE, O LORD see Price

WE THREE KINGS see Tower, A. Wesley

WE THREE KINGS OF ORIENT *Xmas,carol
    oct HART s.p.   (W425)

WE THREE KINGS OF ORIENT ARE *Xmas,carol
    SATB (easy) OXFORD 08.195 $.15   (W426)
    (Shaw; Parker) mix cor,acap oct LAWSON 738
    $.35   (W427)

WE TO THE LORD SING JOYFULLY see Carissimi,
    Giacomo, Cantemus Omnis Domina

WE TREAD UPON THY CARPETS see Gay, A.

WE TURN OUR EYES TO THEE see Praetorius,
    Michael

WE TURN TO THEE see Kirk

WE VENERATE THY CROSS see Goodman, Joseph,
    Crucem Tuam Adoramus

WE WAIT FOR THY LOVING KINDNESS see McKie,
    William

WE WALK THE EARTH AS PILGRIMS see Gesius,
    Bartholomaus, Ich Bin Ein Gast Auf Erden

WE WALK WITH GOD see Caldwell, Mary [Elizabeth]

WE WELCOME GLAD EASTER
    see Three Easter Hymns

WE WELCOME GLAD EASTER see Southbridge

WE WERE SLAVES see Adler, Hugo Ch., Avodim
    Hoyinu

WE, WHO MORTALS OF THIS CREATION see Lassus,
    Roland de (Orlandus), Nos Qui Sumus In Hoc
    Mundo

WE WILL CAROL JOYFULLY see Means, Claude

WE WILL CAROL JOYFULLY see Young

WE WILL NEVER BOW DOWN see Handel, George
    Frideric

WE WILL ROCK YOU see Pooler, Frank

WE WILL WALK IN THE NAME OF THE LORD see
    Mueller, Carl F.

WE WISH YOU A MERRY CHRISTMAS *Xmas,carol
    (Parker) SATB,acap oct LAWSON 750 $.35 (W428)

WE WORSHIP THEE see Lorenz

WE WORSHIP THEE, O CHRIST see Mozart, Wolfgang
    Amadeus, Adoramus Te, Christe

WE WORSHIP THEE, O CHRIST see Rosselli,
    Francesco, Adoramus Te

WE WORSHIP THY VIRGINITY see Des Prez, Josquin,
    Ave Vera Virginitas

WE WOULD OFFER THEE THIS DAY see Marshall

WE WOULD SEE JESUS see Brackett, F.H.

WE WOULD THANK THEE, ALMIGHTY FATHER see Wood

WEATHERSEED, J.J.
    O Lord, Our Heavenly Father
    SATB oct LESLIE 4086   (W429)

WEAVER
    Epiphany Alleluias *CCU,Epiph
    SATB,org oct BROWN 5683 $.30   (W430)

    Hail Jesu Bambino
    (Ades) SATB SHAWNEE A 969 $.25   (W431)

    He's My Jesus
    (Stubbs) SATB oct LILLENAS AT-1015 $.25
                                             (W432)
    I Love Thy Kingdom Lord
    SSA oct GALAXY 1.2247.1 $.30   (W433)
    SATB oct GALAXY 1.1799.1 $.30   (W434)

    I Walked In The Garden
    (Dilsner) SSA oct JUSKO 7043 $.20   (W435)

    One Star
    SATB oct LORENZ B96 $.25   (W436)

    Psalm 98
    (Raymond) TTBB oct PLYMOUTH JR-301 $.25
                                             (W437)
    (Raymond) SATB oct PLYMOUTH JR-115 $.25

WEAVER (cont'd.)

    Psalm 100   (W438)
    SATB,org oct BROWN 5336 $.35   (W439)

    Spirit Of God
    SATB oct GALAXY 1.0866.1 $.30   (W440)
    SAB oct GALAXY 1.1507.1 $.30   (W441)

    When Morning Gilds The Skies
    SATB oct GALAXY 1.1028.1 $.30   (W442)

WEAVER, H.
    Sing Alleluia *Easter
    SA oct PRESSER 312-40068 $.25   (W443)

WEAVER, MARION (1902-   )
    I Walked Into The Garden
    (Dilsnaer) SATB oct HUNTZINGER 7042 $.20
                                             (W444)
    Let's Bow Our Heads And Pray
    SATB oct HUNTZINGER 7041 $.20   (W445)

WEAVER, POWELL (1890-1951)
    Hear The Voice That Entreats You *Bibl
    SATB oct BELWIN 1793 $.25   (W446)

WEBB
    Choral Sentences For The Worship Service
    *CCU
    SATB SHAWNEE F 12 $1.00   (W447)

    Nine Short Responses For General Services
    *CC9U,cor-resp
    SATB HANSEN-US C266B $.40   (W448)

    O, For A Thousand Tongues To Sing
    SATB SHAWNEE F 10 $1.00   (W449)

    Stand Up For Jesus *hymn
    (Schubert) TTBB oct LILLENAS AN-1637 $.30
                                             (W450)
    Stand Up, Stand Up For Jesus
    (Hadley) SATB&desc oct PRO ART 1358 $.25
                                             (W451)
    Were You There?
    SSA FLAMMER B 5067 $.30   (W452)
                SAB FLAMMER D5063 $.25   (W453)

WEBBE
    Come, Ye Disconsolate
    (Hadley) SATB oct PRO ART 1416 $.25   (W454)

WEBBE, SAMUEL (1740-1816)
    Agnus Dei *Gen,Agnus/mot
    [Lat] 2 eq voices oct DURAND s.p.   (W455)

    Ave Regina *BVM,mot
    [Lat] 2 eq voices oct DURAND s.p.   (W456)

    Come Ye Disconsolate *Gen
    (Lockwood) SATB oct SOUTHERN $.25   (W457)

    O For A Heart To Praise My God
    2pt ASHDOWN E.A.252 s.p.   (W458)
    SATB ENOCH EC279 s.p.   (W459)

WEBBER
    Bethlehem *Xmas,carol
    SA/SS FRANCIS s.p.   (W460)

    O Lord, The Maker Of All Things
    SATB,org FRANCIS s.p.   (W461)

    Praise God For He Is Kind
    SATB FRANCIS s.p.   (W462)

    Saviour While My Heart Is Tender
    SATB,opt org FRANCIS s.p.   (W463)

    Ye Boundless Realms Of Joy
    SATB,org FRANCIS s.p.   (W464)

WEBBER, ANDREW
    Any Dream Will Do (from Joseph And The
    Amazing Technicolor Dreamcoat) (composed
    with Rice, Tim)
    (Sanford, Bill) mix cor,opt gtr&band&perc
    (jazz) BELWIN AP122 oct $.40, sc $2.00,
    ipa   (W465)

    Close Every Door To Me (from Joseph And The
    Amazing Technicolor Dreamcoat) (composed
    with Rice, Tim)
    (Sanford, Bill) mix cor,opt gtr&band&perc
    (jazz) BELWIN AP 121 oct $.40, sc $2.00,
    ipa   (W466)

    Joseph And The Amazing Technicolor Dreamcoat
    (composed with Rice, Tim) *Bibl/cant/pop
    unis&opt 2pt (abridged edition) voc sc
    NOVELLO 20.0122.05 s.p.   (W467)

    Joseph's Coat (from Joseph And The Amazing
    Technicolor Dreamcoat) (composed with
    Rice, Tim)
    (Sanford, Bill) mix cor,opt gtr&band&perc
    (jazz) BELWIN AP 123 oct $.40, sc $2.00,
    ipa   (W468)

    Pharaoh's Number Two (from Joseph And The
    Amazing Technicolor Dreamcoat) (composed
    with Rice, Tim)
    see Webber, Andrew, Song Of The King

    Song Of The King (from Joseph And The Amazing
    Technicolor Dreamcoat) (composed with
    Rice, Tim)
    (Sanford, Bill) mix cor,opt gtr&band&perc
    (jazz) BELWIN AP120 oct $.40, sc $2.00,
    ipa contains also: Pharaoh's Number Two
                                             (W469)

WEBBER, LLOYD
    Be Still, My Soul
    see Four Introits

    Beneath The Glory Of The Skies *Gen/Septua,
    anthem
    mix cor oct NOVELLO 28.1451.10 s.p.   (W470)

    Child My Choice, A *Xmas,anthem
    mix cor,acap oct NOVELLO 28.1470.06 s.p.
                                             (W471)
    Church With Joy Aclaims Her Lord, The
    *anthem
    mix cor oct NOVELLO 28.1385.08 s.p.   (W472)

WEBBER, LLOYD (cont'd.)

Come, Praise Your Lord And Saviour *anthem/
hymn
SATB&unis oct NOVELLO 28.1359.09 s.p.
(W473)

Festival Of Life, The *Easter,anthem
mix cor oct NOVELLO 28.1382.03 s.p. (W474)

Four Introits *anthem/Introit
mix cor oct NOVELLO 50.0349.00 s.p.
contains: Be Still, My Soul; Jesus,
Where're Thy People Meet; Let Your
Light So Shine; Lo, God Is Here (W475)

Glory And Praise And Dominion By Thine
*Palm,anthem
mix cor oct NOVELLO 28.1446.03 s.p. (W476)

God Is Good *anthem
mix cor,acap oct NOVELLO 50.0341.05 s.p.
(W477)

Good Samaritan, The *cant
SATB,B solo,org voc sc NOVELLO s.p. (W478)

Holy Communion *Commun
unis&desc (D min) NOVELLO 44.1407.01 s.p.
(W479)

Jesus, Where're Thy People Meet
see Four Introits

Just As I Am, Thine Own To Be *anthem/hymn
SATB&unis oct NOVELLO 28.1360.02 s.p.
(W480)

Let Your Light So Shine
see Four Introits

Lo, God Is Here
see Four Introits

Love Divine, All Loves Excelling *Marriage,
anthem
mix cor oct NOVELLO 28.1460.09 s.p. (W481)

Meeting Place, The *Xmas,meditation
SATB,Bar solo,pno/org voc sc NOVELLO s.p.
(W482)

Most Glorious Lord Of Life *Easter,anthem
mix cor oct NOVELLO 40.1391.03 s.p. (W483)

O For A Closer Walk With God *anthem
SAB oct NOVELLO 28.1349.01 s.p. (W484)

O Holy Spirit, Lord Of Grace *anthem
SAB oct NOVELLO 28.1351.03 s.p. (W485)

O Thou That Art The Light Eternal
4pt mix cor oct SCHIRM.G 11263 $.25 (W486)

Saviour, The *Psntd,meditation
SATB,TB soli,org voc sc NOVELLO s.p. (W487)

Sing, O Heavens *Harv,anthem
SAB oct NOVELLO 40.1372.07 s.p. (W488)

Sing The Life *Easter,anthem
mix cor,acap oct NOVELLO 28.1447.01 s.p.
(W489)

Unite To Praise Thy Maker's Name *Gen/
Thanks,anthem/hymn
SATB SOUTHERN $.30 (W490)
mix cor oct NOVELLO 40.1419.07 s.p. (W491)
SATB,org/pno NOVELLO AP218 $.30 (W492)

Winter Is Past, The *Easter,anthem
mix cor,acap oct NOVELLO 28.1448.10 s.p.
(W493)

WEBBER, W.S. LLOYD
Jesus, Dear Jesus *Xmas
unis ASHDOWN U.77 s.p. (W494)
unis BOOSEY-CAN s.p. (W495)

O Lovely Day *Easter
2pt ASHDOWN E.A.317 s.p. (W496)

Oh, Lord Spread Thy Wings O'er Me
SATB ENOCH EC290 s.p. (W497)

Oh, Lord Spread Thy Wings Over Me
2pt ENOCH TP202 s.p. (W498)

Reaper, The *Harv
2pt ASHDOWN E.A.323 s.p. (W499)

WEBER
Father, Lord Of All Creation
(Coggin) SATB KJOS 5858 $.30 (W500)

In Praise Of Song *see Preis Dir O Ton

Preis Dir O Ton
(Frank) "In Praise Of Song" SATB oct FOX
MM23 $.35 (W501)

WEBER, BERNHARD (1912-   )
Am Weihnachtsbaum Die Lichter Brennen
see Vier Alte Weihnachtslieder

Dona Nobis Pacem *Mass
[Ger] SATB,acap (med) MULLER SM 2480 s.p.
(W502)

Ein Kranzlein Zu Johanni
wom cor&jr cor,acap TONGER s.p. (W503)

Gott, Der Du Alles Wohl Bedacht
see Zwei Chorale Zur Trauung

Herr, Unser Herrscher (Psalm 8)
men cor,acap TONGER s.p. (W504)

Ich Danke Gott
mix cor,acap TONGER s.p. (W505)
men cor,acap TONGER s.p. (W506)

Ich Komm, Weiss Nicht Woher
see Vier Trostlieder

Jesu, Geh Voran
see Zwei Chorale Zur Trauung

Komm Nun Wieder, Stille Zeit *Xmas,cant
men cor&opt treb cor,org voc sc TONGER
s.p., ipa (W507)

Merkt Auf Die Zeit
see Vier Trostlieder

WEBER, BERNHARD (cont'd.)

Nicht Also Streng
see Vier Trostlieder

Psalm 8 *see Herr, Unser Herrscher

Susser Die Glocken Nie Klingen
see Vier Alte Weihnachtslieder

Unser Herrgott Hat's Gewollt
see Vier Trostlieder

Vier Alte Weihnachtslieder *Xmas
men cor&mix cor TONGER s.p.
contains: Am Weihnachtsbaum Die Lichter
Brennen; Susser Die Glocken Nie
Klingen; Vom Himmel Hoch, Da Komm Ich
Her; Zu Bethlehem Geboren (W508)

Vier Trostlieder
mix cor,acap TONGER s.p.
contains: Ich Komm, Weiss Nicht Woher;
Merkt Auf Die Zeit; Nicht Also Streng;
Unser Herrgott Hat's Gewollt (W509)

Vom Himmel Hoch, Da Komm Ich Her
see Vier Alte Weihnachtslieder

Zu Bethlehem Geboren
see Vier Alte Weihnachtslieder

Zu Ostern Liess Mir's Keine Ruh *Easter
wom cor&jr cor,acap TONGER s.p. (W510)

Zund An Das Licht *Xmas
men cor TONGER s.p. (W511)

Zwei Chorale Zur Trauung *chorale
men cor,acap TONGER s.p.
contains: Gott, Der Du Alles Wohl
Bedacht; Jesu, Geh Voran (W512)

WEBER, CARL MARIA VON (1786-1826)
Jubilee Cantata, The *Op.58,Harv,cant
SATB,SATB soli,2fl,2ob,2clar,2bsn,4horn,
2trp,3trom,strings,timp cor sc NOVELLO
s.p., ipr (W513)

Mass In G Major *Mass
(Kaplan, Abraham) mix cor,SATB soli,pno/org
oct LAWSON $2.50 (W514)

WEBER, DENNIS
Gentle Jesus Meek And Mild
jr cor,opt 2fl oct AGAPE F 913 $.30 (W515)

WEBER, HANNS JOACHIM
Nun Dieser Tag Ist Vergangen *Eve,cant
unis,inst sc MOSELER s.p., ipa (W516)

WEBER, HANS (1917-   )
Choralbuch Fur Kinderchor *CC78U,Gen
[Ger] 2 eq voices/3 eq voices,acap (easy)
BAREN. BA 3200 $4.00 (W517)

O Herr Jesu, Deine Leute *cant
TTBB,brass HANSSLER 10.211 sc s.p., cor pts
s.p. (W518)

WEBER, KARL-HEINZ (1927-   )
Abend Kommt, Der Tag Sich Neiget *Eve/Thanks
SATB HANSSLER 6.079 s.p. contains also:
Vulpius, Melchior, Die Helle Sonn Leucht'
Jetzt Herfur; Cruger, Johann, Lobet Den
Herren, Alle, Die Ihn Ehren (W519)

Erschienen Ist Der Herrlich Tag
SAT/SAB HANSSLER 6.266 s.p. contains also:
Trubel, Gerhard, Wir Wollen Alle Frohlich
Sein (W520)

Es Kommt Ein Schiff Geladen
see Weber, Karl-Heinz, O Heiland, Reiss Die
Himmel Auf

Lobe Den Herren, Den Machtigen Konig
see Gumpeltzhaimer, Adam, O Lieber Gott Im
Hochsten Thron

O Heiland, Reiss Die Himmel Auf
SATB HANSSLER 6.086 s.p. contains also: Es
Kommt Ein Schiff Geladen (W521)

WEBER, LUDWIG (1891-   )
Christgeburt *Xmas
wom cor&men cor,2 soli,orch MOSELER sc
s.p., voc sc s.p., cor pts s.p., ipa
(W522)

Ehre Sei Gott In Der Hohe
2 eq voices&2pt mix cor,opt inst MOSELER
LB-63 s.p. (W523)

Frohlich Soll Mein Herze Springen
SATB MOSELER sc s.p., voc pt s.p. (W524)

Herr Christe, Komm In Unsre Not
2pt mix cor MOSELER LB-64 s.p. contains
also: Lass Die Wurzel Unsres Handelns
(unis,inst); Segne Vater, Unser Essen
(unis,inst) (W525)

Hymnen *CCU,hymn
mix cor,inst MOSELER s.p. (W526)

Kommet, Ihr Hirten *Xmas
3 eq voices,opt inst MOSELER LB-124 s.p.
(W527)

Lass Die Wurzel Unsres Handelns
see Weber, Ludwig, Herr Christe, Komm In
Unsre Not

Segne Vater, Unser Essen
see Weber, Ludwig, Herr Christe, Komm In
Unsre Not

Zwei Geistliche Gesange *CC2U
SSAA,2vln,vla,vcl cor pts MOSELER s.p., ipa
(W528)

WEBER, VON
My Jesus, As Thou Wilt
(Miller) SATB oct PRO ART 2408 $.25 (W529)

WECKMANN, JAKOB
Wenn Der Herr Die Gefangenen Zions Erlosen
Wird (composed with Weckmann, Matthais)
*cant
(Kruger) SATB,cont,2vln,2vla HANSSLER
10.170 sc s.p., voc sc s.p., ipa (W530)

WECKMANN, JAKOB (cont'd.)

Wenn Der Herr Die Gefangenen Zu Zion *cant
[Ger] SATB,org,strings voc sc KISTNER s.p.,
ipa (W531)

WECKMANN, MATTHAIS (1919-1674)
Wenn Der Herr Die Gefangenen Zions Erlosen
Wird *see Weckmann, Jakob

Zion Spricht: Der Herr Hat Mich Verlassen
*mot
[Ger] cor,ATB soli,org,strings KISTNER sc
s.p., cor pts s.p., ipa (W532)

WEDDING ANTHEM see Handel, George Frideric,
Singt Unserm Gott, Ihr Reiche Aller Welt

WEDDING CANTATA see Bach, Johann Sebastian,
Vergnugte Pleissenstadt

WEDDING CANTATA see Pinkham, Daniel

WEDDING CHORUS see Handel, George Frideric

WEDDING PRAYER see Dunlap, Fern

WEDDING PSALM: PUT THOU THY TRUST IN THE LORD
see McKie, William

WEDDING RESPONSES see Smyth, William

WEED, MAURICE
Praise Ye The Lord
SATB,pno/org/brass oct LAWSON 51368 $.35
(W533)

WEEDEN
I Surrender All
(Boersma) SAB oct WORD CS-2339 $.25 (W534)

WEEGENHUISE, JOHAN (1910-   )
Domine Salvum Fac
[Lat] men cor,4horn,3trom,tuba min sc
DONEMUS s.p., voc sc BANK s.p. (W535)

WEELKES
Collected Anthems *CCU,anthem
cor STAINER 3.8923.8 $18.00 (W536)

Frag Nur Umher *ASD
"Hark, All Ye Lovely Saints" [Eng/Ger] 5pt
mix cor MOSELER LB-811 s.p. (W537)

Hark, All Ye Lovely Saints *see Frag Nur
Umher

Let Thy Merciful Ears, Lord
(Wolff) boy cor SOUTHERN $.30 (W538)

Lord, To Thee I Make My Moan
(Gronquist) SATB oct KERBY (W539)

Tomorrow Is The Marriage Day
(Richardson) SSA oct AGAPE SP 690 $.30
(W540)

WEELKES, THOMAS (ca. 1575-1623)
All People Clap Your Hands *Gen/Thanks,
anthem
SAATB (med) oct OXFORD 42.860 $.35 (W541)
SAATB,opt org STAINER MB23-1 s.p. (W542)

Alleluia, I Heard A Voice *ASD/Fest/Trin
SSTBB,acap (med) oct OXFORD 43.257 $.50
(W543)

David's Lament For Jonathan *anthem
SSAATB,acap oct NOVELLO 28.1435.08 s.p.
(W544)

Early Will I Seek Thee
(Richardson) SATB oct WORD CS-316 $.30
(W545)
(Richardson) SSA WORD CS-350 $.30 (W546)
(Richardson) SAB oct WORD CS-351 $.30 (W547)

Give The King Thy Judgements *anthem
SSAATB,org STAINER MB23-8 s.p. (W548)

Gloria In Excelsis *Easter/Gen,Gloria
SSAATB (med) oct OXFORD 43.337 $.50 (W549)

Gloria In Excelsis Deo *anthem
SSAATB STAINER MB23-4 s.p. (W550)

Hark, All Ye Lovely Saints Above
SSATB oct WALTON 8002 $.25 (W551)

Hosanna To The Son Of David *Adv/Palm,anthem
SSATBB STAINER MB23-3 s.p. (W552)
SSATBB,acap (med) oct OXFORD 43.237 $.30
(W553)
(Richardson) SATB oct WORD CS-323 $.30
(W554)

Let Thy Merciful Ears, O Lord *Gen/Trin
see TRE ENGELSKA MOTETTER
TTBB (med easy) oct CONCORDIA 98-1998
$.30 (W555)
SATB,acap SCHIRM.EC 1714 $.20 (W556)
SATB,acap oct PRESSER MC397 $.25 (W557)
SATB,acap (med) oct OXFORD 43.076 $.20
(W558)

Lord To Thee I Make My Moan *Lent
SAATB,acap (med easy) oct OXFORD 43.227
$.30 (W559)

Lord, When I Think
(Freed) SSA/SAB/TTB,acap oct FOX EA4 $.25
(W560)

Magnificat And Nunc Dimittis *Magnif/Nunc
SAATB,acap (med) oct OXFORD 43.292 $1.50
(W561)
SATB STAINER CS279 s.p. (W562)

Morning Canticles *CCU
SATB STAINER CS348 s.p. (W563)

Most Mightly And All-Knowing Lord *anthem
SATB STAINER CC715 s.p. contains also: O
Happy He Whom Thou Protect'st (SSATB)
(W564)

O Happy He Whom Thou Protect'st
see Weelkes, Thomas, Most Mightly And All-
Knowing Lord

O How Amiable (Psalm 84) Ded/Gen
SAATB (med) oct OXFORD 43.073 $.50 (W565)

O Jonathan *anthem
(Turner) SSATB SCHOTT s.p. (W566)

WEELKES, THOMAS (cont'd.)

O Lord Arise Into Thy Resting Place *Ember/
Fest
SSAATBB,acap (med) oct OXFORD 43.221 $.50
(W567)

O Lord God Almighty *Royal
SAATB (med) oct OXFORD 43.350 $.50   (W568)

O Lord Grant The King A Long Life *Royal
SSAATBB,acap (med) oct OXFORD 43.249 $.35
(W569)

O Mortal Man
(Eperson) mix cor CURWEN 80822 s.p.   (W570)

Psalm 84 *see O How Amiable

When David Heard *anthem/Bibl/mot
SSAATB STAINER MB23-2 s.p.   (W571)
SSAATB,acap oct NOVELLO 28.1316.05 s.p.
(W572)

WEEP NO MORE see Red, Buryl

WEEP, O MY SOUL see Young

WEEP YOU NO MORE, SAD FOUNTAINS see Butler,
Eugene

WEEPIN' MARY *spir
(Decoursey) SATB oct PRO ART 2029 $.25 (W573)

WEEPIN' MARY see Burleigh, Henry Thacker

WEEPING see Bach, Johann Sebastian, Weinen,
Klagen, Sorgen, Zagen

WEEPING BABE, THE see Tippett, Michael

WEEPING, CRYING, SORROW, SIGHING see Bach,
Johann Sebastian, Weinen, Klagen, Sorgen,
Zagen

WEEPING SAVIOR oee Clark, Keith

WEERBECKE, GASPAR VAN (ca. 1445- ?)
Tenebrae Factae Sunt *Holywk,16th cent
(Cartier, Anita; Carol, Henri; Gagnepain,
Bernard) [Lat] SATB OUVRIERES EO668 s.p.
(W574)

WEGENER, H.
Kommet, Ihr Hirten *Xmas
mix cor TONGER s.p.   (W575)

Lieb, Nachtigall, Wach Auf! *Xmas
mix cor TONGER s.p.   (W576)

WEH! WIR TRETEN AUF DEN DRACHEN see Bossler,
Kurt

WEHNERT, WOLFRAM
Lobet Den Herren, Ihr Seine Engel (Psalm 103)
unis sc HANSSLER 19.103 s.p. contains also:
Ruppel, Paul Ernst, Ich Hebe Meine Augen
Auf Zu Dir (Psalm 123) (SATB&cong,org);
Ruppel, Paul Ernst, Unser Herr Ist Gross
Und Von Grosser Kraft (Psalm 145) (unis,
gtr,treb inst)   (W577)

Psalm 103 *see Lobet Den Herren, Ihr Seine
Engel

WEHR
Child Of Faith   !Gen
SATB SCHMITT SD6101 $.30   (W578)

Father, O Hear Us *Lent
SATB SCHMITT 876 $.35   (W579)

Nearer, My God, To Thee
SATB oct SACRED E25 $.30   (W580)

WEHR, DAVID A. (1934-   )
Christ The Lord Is Risen *Easter
SATB,acap oct PRESSER 312-40634 $.30 (W581)

Dear Jesus Boy *Xmas
unis (easy) ABINGDON APM-821 $.30   (W582)

Father In Thy Mysterious Presence Kneeling
SATB oct FISCHER,J 10017 $.30   (W583)

Grant Us Wisdom, Grant Us Courage
SATB oct PRESSER 312-40563 $.30   (W584)

I Want Jesus To Walk With Me
SATB (easy) ABINGDON APM-292 $.25   (W585)

Jesu, Our Faithful Guide
SATB,acap oct PRESSER 312-40561 $.30 (W586)

Now Alien Tongues *Commun
SATB,acap (med) ABINGDON APM-144 $.20 (W587)

O God Of Peace
SATB oct PRESSER FH107 $.35   (W588)

O Jesus I Have Promised *anthem/hymn
SATB,org oct FISCHER,C R-6011 $.25   (W589)

Prophet Unwilling
mix cor&jr cor/mix cor&boy cor,narrator,
BarBar soli,org PRESSER $1.50   (W590)

Put Forth, O God, Thy Spirit's Might
SAB (med) ABINGDON APM-393 $.25   (W591)

This Land Under Thee
SAB oct PRESSER 312-40636 $.30   (W592)

Thy Kingdom Come, O Lord
unis (med easy) ABINGDON APM-340 $.20
(W593)

What God Has Promised
unis jr cor,org/pno FISCHER,J 10081 $.30
(W594)

When Jesus Walked Upon The Earth
unis jr cor oct AGAPE A 354 $.25   (W595)

WEIB, SIEHE, DAS IST DEIN SOHN see Driessler,
Johannes

WEIB, WAS WEINEST DU? see Schutz, Heinrich

WEICHE, LUST UND FROHLICHKEIT see Telemann,
Georg Philipp

WEICHET HINWEG VON MIR see Schutz, Heinrich,
Discedite A Me

WEICHT, IHR BERGE, FALLT, IHR HUGEL see
Neander, Joachim

WEIGENLIED DER HIRTEN see Breuer, Herbert

WEIGL, KARL (1881-1949)
Christmas Legend *Xmas
SATB oct GALLEON GCS1009   (W596)

WEIGL, VALLY
Saint Francis
SSA,pno,fl/vln SCHIRM.EC 1947 $.35   (W597)

WEIGLE
No One Ever Cared For Me
(Hughes) SATB oct WORD CS-2143 $.25 (W598)
(Jones) SATB oct WORD CS-1955 $.30 (W599)

WEIHE DES GESANGS see Mozart, Wolfgang Amadeus

WEIHE: TRETET NAHER see Bruckner, Anton

WEIHEGESANG see Schubert, Franz (Peter)

WEIHELIED see Pestalozza, Heinrich

WEIHELIED see Strobl, Otto

WEIHNACHT see Zimmermann, Heinz Werner

WEIHNACHT see Kaun, [Hugo]

WEIHNACHT IST DA *Ger
(Korda, Viktor) 2pt wom cor,acap oct s.p.
contains also: Als Dort Das Kind Zu
Bethlehem (It) (CC)   (W600)

WEIHNACHT, WEISS FEST DER LIEBE see Hartmann,
Br.

WEIHNACHT, WIE BIST DU SCHON *Xmas,Aus
(Schemitsch, Hans) [Ger] mix cor,acap oct
DOBLINGER s.p. see also Zehn Osterrichische
Weihnachtsleider   (W601)

WEIHNACHT, WIE BIST SO SCHON! see Czajanck,
[Victor]

WEIHNACHTEN see Tittel, Ernst

WEIHNACHTEN I: GEISTLICHE LIEDER (from
Cantionale Sacrum) CCU,Xmas
(Pass, Walter) 4-5pt DOBLINGER s.p. contains
works by: Aldenburger, M.; Helder, B.;
Vulpius, M.   (W602)

WEIHNACHTEN II: GEISTLICHE LIEDER (from
Cantionale Sacrum) CCU,Xmas
(Pass, Walter) 5pt DOBLINGER s.p. contains
works by: Aldenburger, M.; Vulpius, M.;
Anonymous   (W603)

WEIHNACHTLICHE CHORGEMEINSCHAFT see Krause,
Joach.

WEIHNACHTLICHE LIEDKANTATE see Spitta, Heinrich

WEIHNACHTLICHES KRIPPENLIED see Anonymous

WEIHNACHTLICHES TRIPTYCHON see Haus, Karl

WEIHNACHTS-HYMNUS see Rothschuh, F.

WEIHNACHTS MESSE see Gruben, Fr.

WEIHNACHTS-ORATORIUM see Kunz, Ernst

WEIHNACHTS-ORATORIUM see Schutz, Heinrich

WEIHNACHTS-ORATORIUM see Thomas, Kurt

WEIHNACHTSCHORALE see Bach, Johann Sebastian

WEIHNACHTSCHORALE-I see Bach, Johann Sebastian

WEIHNACHTSCHORALE-II see Bach, Johann Sebastian

WEIHNACHTSCHORALE-III see Bach, Johann
Sebastian

WEIHNACHTSCHORALE-IV see Bach, Johann Sebastian

WEIHNACHTSGESCHICTE see Schutz, Heinrich

WEIHNACHTSHYMNUS see Krause, Joach.

WEIHNACHTSHYMNUS see Krause, Joh. Chr.

WEIHNACHTSHYMNUS see Weismann, Wilhelm

WEIHNACHTSKANTATE see Buchner, Philipp
Friedrich

WEIHNACHTSKANTATE see Borris, Siegfried

WEIHNACHTSKANTATE see Erdmann, Dietrich

WEIHNACHTSKANTATE see Marks, Gunther

WEIHNACHTSKANTATE see Rebay, Ferd.

WEIHNACHTSKONZERT see Vierdanck, Johann

WEIHNACHTSKYRIE see Reda, Siegfried

WEIHNACHTSLIED see Heiller, Anton

WEIHNACHTSLIED see Sibelius, Jean

WEIHNACHTSLIED see Werner

WEIHNACHTSLIED AUF EINEN TEXT VON ILSE SCHNELL
see Zimmermann, Heinz Werner

WEIHNACHTSLIEDERBUCH see Freundt, Cornelius

WEIHNACHTSMOTETTE see Borris, Siegfried

WEIHNACHTSMOTETTE see Bruckner, Anton

WEIHNACHTSMUSIK see Bruckhorst, A.M.

WEIHNACHTSORATORIUM see Bach, Johann Sebastian

WEIHNACHTSORATORIUM see Thomas, Kurt

WEIHNACHTSPASTORELLA NACH BOHMISCHEN
VOLKSTEXTEN see Hurnik, Ilja

WEIHNACHTSSUITE see Gossec, Francois Joseph

WEIL DU "JA" ZU MIR SAGST *CC12U,Gen
[Ger] unis,kbd (med) BOSSE BE 218 s.p. (W604)

WEIL DU "JA" ZU MIR SAGST see Blarr, Oskar
Gottlieb

WEIL WIR WISSEN, DASS DER MENSCH see
Rosenmuller, Johann

WEILAND
Jauchzet Gott, Alle Lande
[Ger] voc sc PETERS HU1646 $1.00, ipr
(W605)

WEILL, KURT (1900-1950)
Berlin Requiem *Req
[Lat] (G maj) voc sc UNIVER. 9786 $4.05,
cor pts UNIVER. 13429A-D   (W606)

WEIMER
Children Of The Heavenly King
(Smith) SATB SHAWNEE A 694 $.25   (W607)

WEINACHTS-MOTETTE see Silcher, Friedrich

WEINACHTS-ORATORIUM see Schutz, Heinrich

WEINBERG, HENRY
Vox In Rama
SATB,acap oct PRESSER 312-40464 $.30 (W608)

WEINBERG, JACOB
Gettysburg Address, The
SATB TRANSCON. TCL 121 $.60, ipa   (W609)

Sabbath Eve Service *see Servizio
Pentatonico

Sabbath Service For Congregational Singing
*Sab-Eve
unis/2pt TRANSCON. TCL 335 $2.00   (W610)

Servizio Pentatonico *Sab-Eve
"Sabbath Eve Service" SATB TRANSCON.
TCL 864 $3.50   (W611)

Shabbat Ba-arets *Sab-Morn
SATB TRANSCON. TCL 859 $4.50   (W612)

WEINEIN, KLAGEN see Bach, Johann Sebastian,
Weinen, Klagen, Sorgen, Zagen

WEINEN, KLAGEN, SORGEN, ZAGEN see Bach, Johann
Sebastian

WEINER
Psalm Of Prayer And Praise, A
SATB SHAWNEE A 1056 $.25   (W613)

Sing Praise To God
SATB HANSEN-US C625 $.75   (W614)

WEINER, LAZAR (1897-   )
Shir L'yom Hashbos *Sab-Eve
cor,cantor TRANSCON. TCL 885 $4.00   (W615)

WEINREICH, WALTRAUT
Christ Lag In Todesbanden
see Osterchore

Christus Hat Dem Tode Die Macht Genommen
see Osterchore

Das Weihnachtsevangelium *Xmas,cant
dbl cor,org HANSSLER 10.063 sc s.p., voc sc
s.p.   (W616)

Den Fursten Des Lebens Habt Ihr Getotet
see Osterchore

Der Tod Ist Verschlungen In Den Sieg
see Osterchore

Es Ist In Keinem Andern Heil *cant
SATB&TTBB, TBarB soli,org,fl,ob,2trp,2vln,
vla,vcl,bvl,timp, English horn HANSSLER
10.069 rental   (W617)

Man Singt Mit Freuden Vom Sieg
see Osterchore

Osterchore *Easter
SSATB HANSSLER 7.103 s.p.
contains: Christ Lag In Todesbanden;
Christus Hat Dem Tode Die Macht
Genommen; Den Fursten Des Lebens Habt
Ihr Getotet; Der Tod Ist Verschlungen
In Den Sieg; Man Singt Mit Freuden Vom
Sieg   (W618)

WEINT NICHT UM MEINEN TOD see Bach, Johann
(Hans)

WEIS, FLEMMING (1898-   )
Liber Psalmorum (Psalm 38)
SATB oct WALTON 2908 $.35   (W619)

Psalm 38 *see Liber Psalmorum

WEISE MIR, HERR, DEINEN WEG see Lotz, Hans-
Georg

WEISER, WILLI (1916-   )
Si Digilis Me *Fest
[Lat] SATB,acap (med, for a papal festival)
MULLER SM 733 s.p.   (W620)

WEISGAL, A.
Bor'chenu *liturg,Jew
(Chaitman, A.) SATB,cantor oct PRESSER
MC557 $.30   (W621)

B'rosh Hashono *liturg,Jew
SATB,cantor,acap oct PRESSER MC517 $.35
(W622)

Echod Hu Elohenu *liturg,Jew
see Weisgal, A., K'vodo Vodo O Lom
SATB,cantor,acap (E maj) oct PRESSER MC558
$.25   (W623)
SATB,acap (G maj) oct PRESSER MC559 $.25
(W624)

Etz Chayim *liturg,Jew
SATB,cantor,acap oct PRESSER MC518 $.35
(W625)

Hashkivenu *liturg,Jew
SATB,cantor,acap (D min) oct PRESSER MC520
$.30   (W626)
SATB,cantor,acap (C min) oct PRESSER MC519

WEISGAL, A. (cont'd.)

$.35 (W627)
(Chaitman, A.) SATB,acap oct PRESSER 312-40771 $.30 (W628)

Kiddush For Passover *Passover
(Chaitman, A.) SATB,cantor,acap (med diff) PRESSER 312-40907 $.45 (W629)

K'vodo Vodo O Lom *liturg,Jew
SATB,cantor,acap oct PRESSER MC521 $.30
contains also: Echod Hu Elohenu (W630)

Sim Sholom *liturg,Heb
SATB,cantor,acap oct PRESSER MC522 $.35 (W631)

V'shom'ru *liturg,Heb
cor,cantor,acap (E min) oct PRESSER MC563 $.30 (W632)
SATB,acap oct PRESSER MC523 $.25 (W633)

Ya'ale *liturg,Heb
SATB,cantor,acap oct PRESSER MC524 $.30 (W634)

Y'hi Rotzon *liturg,Heb
SATB,cantor,acap oct PRESSER MC525 $.35 (W635)

WEISGALL, HUGO (1912-)
Evening Prayer For Peace *liturg,Jew
SATB,acap oct PRESSER 312-40515 $.25 (W636)

Fortress, Rock Of Our Salvation
SATB,acap oct PRESSER 342-40014 $.30 (W637)

God Is Due Praise *liturg,Jew
SATB,acap oct PRESSER 312-40510 $.35 (W638)

May The Words *see Yih'uy L'Rotzon

Praise Be Unto God *liturg,Jew
SATB,acap oct PRESSER 312-40508 $.35 (W639)

Psalm 29
[Eng/Heb] unis/2pt men cor/2pt wom cor/ SATB,pno (diff) PRESSER 312-40958 $.35 (W640)

So Spake Rabbi Akiba
SATB,acap oct PRESSER 312-40511 $.30 (W641)

When Israel Out Of Egypt Came *liturg,Heb
SATB,acap oct PRESSER 312-40509 $.30 (W642)

Who Is Like Unto Thee?
SATB oct PRESSER 312-40514 $.30 (W643)

Yih'uy L'Rotzon
"May The Words" SATB oct PRESSER 312-40507 $.30 (W644)

WEISMANN, WILHELM (1900-)
Alles Steht In Gottes Hand
see Dreissig Geistliche Lieder, Chorale, Und Hymnen-Heft 9

Christ Ist Erstanden
see Dreissig Geistliche Lieder, Chorale, Und Hymnen-Heft 4

Christmas Songs *CC8U,Xmas
[Ger] 3-4pt,opt pno/org/harmonium PETERS 4321 $2.50 (W645)

Da Jesus In Die Garten Ging
see Dreissig Geistliche Lieder, Chorale, Und Hymnen-Heft 2

Das Wessobrunner Gebet
see Zwei Hymnische Gesange

Der Herr Ist Mein Hirte (Psalm 23)
5pt mix cor cor pts BREITKOPF-L CHB-2941 s.p. (W646)

Die Auferstehung
see Dreissig Geistliche Lieder, Chorale, Und Hymnen-Heft 3

Die Auferstehung Christi *see Christ Ist Auferstanden; Es Gingen Drei Heilige Frauen; Fruhmorgens, Da Die Sohn Aufgeht (W647)

Die Verkundingung *mot
SATB HANSSLER 7.066 s.p. (W648)

Dreissig Geistliche Lieder, Chorale, Und Hymnen-Heft 1 *Adv/Xmas,chorale/hymn
mix cor,org cor pts BREITKOPF-L CHB-2905 s.p.
contains: Frohe Botschaft; Mit Schall Von Zungen; Trostet, Spricht Der Herr; Wir Haben Einen Stern Gesehen (W649)

Dreissig Geistliche Lieder, Chorale, Und Hymnen-Heft 2 *Psntd,chorale/hymn
mix cor,org cor pts BREITKOPF-L CHB-2906 s.p.
contains: Da Jesus In Die Garten Ging; Salve Mundi Salutare; Sieh, Ich Komme In Tranen (W650)

Dreissig Geistliche Lieder, Chorale, Und Hymnen-Heft 3 *Easter,chorale/hymn
mix cor,org cor pts BREITKOPF-L CHB-2907 s.p.
contains: Die Auferstehung; Jesus Christus Unser Heiland; Samanns Lied (W651)

Dreissig Geistliche Lieder, Chorale, Und Hymnen-Heft 4 *Easter,chorale/hymn
mix cor,org cor pts BREITKOPF-L CHB-2908 s.p.
contains: Christ Ist Erstanden; Ostersequenz (W652)

Dreissig Geistliche Lieder, Chorale, Und Hymnen-Heft 5 *Pent/Trin/Whitsun, chorale/hymn
mix cor,org cor pts BREITKOPF-L CHB-2909 s.p.
contains: Hymnus De Trinitate; Komm Uns Noch Einmal Segnen; Nun Bitten Wir Den Heil'gen Geist (W653)

Dreissig Geistliche Lieder, Chorale, Und Hymnen-Heft 6 *Harv/Thanks,chorale/hymn
mix cor,org cor pts BREITKOPF-L CHB-2910 s.p.
contains: Erntesegen: Die Wachtel Ruft;

WEISMANN, WILHELM (cont'd.)

Lobet Gott Mit Frohem Mund; Psalm 145; Psalm 148 (W654)

Dreissig Geistliche Lieder, Chorale, Und Hymnen-Heft 7 *Rembrnc,chorale/hymn
mix cor,org cor pts BREITKOPF-L CHB-2911 s.p.
contains: Geht Nun Hin; Wir Schritten Lange; Zum Totensonntag (W655)

Dreissig Geistliche Lieder, Chorale, Und Hymnen-Heft 8 *Gen,chorale/hymn
mix cor,org cor pts BREITKOPF-L CHB-2912 s.p.
contains: Marienlied; Morgenlied; Muttertreu Ist Unergrundlich; Sommerlied (W656)

Dreissig Geistliche Lieder, Chorale, Und Hymnen-Heft 9 *Gen,chorale/hymn
mix cor,org cor pts BREITKOPF-L CHB-2913 s.p.
contains: Alles Steht In Gottes Hand; Wie Wohl Ist Mir; Wir Dienen, Herr; Zum Tag Der Arbeit (W657)

Du Bist Als Stern Uns Aufgegangen *cant
mix cor,vln,org/pno sc BREITKOPF-L PB-3550 s.p., cor pts BREITKOPF-L CHB-2924 s.p. (W658)

Er Ist Gewaltig Und Ist Stark *mot
SATB HANSSLER 7.068 s.p. (W659)

Erntesegen: Die Wachtel Ruft
see Dreissig Geistliche Lieder, Chorale, Und Hymnen-Heft 6

Frohe Botschaft
see Dreissig Geistliche Lieder, Chorale, Und Hymnen-Heft 1

Gedenke, Herr, An Deine Barmherzigkeit *mot
SAB HANSSLER 7.045 s.p. (W660)

Geht Nun Hin
see Dreissig Geistliche Lieder, Chorale, Und Hymnen-Heft 7

Hoch Vom Himmel Komm Ich Her *mot
SATB HANSSLER 7.067 s.p. (W661)

Hymnus De Trinitate
see Dreissig Geistliche Lieder, Chorale, Und Hymnen-Heft 5

Jesus Christus Unser Heiland
see Dreissig Geistliche Lieder, Chorale, Und Hymnen-Heft 3

Komm Uns Noch Einmal Segnen
see Dreissig Geistliche Lieder, Chorale, Und Hymnen-Heft 5

Lobet Gott Mit Frohem Mund
see Dreissig Geistliche Lieder, Chorale, Und Hymnen-Heft 6

Marienlied
see Dreissig Geistliche Lieder, Chorale, Und Hymnen-Heft 8

Mein Seel Erhebt Den Herren Mein *Magnif
SATB HANSSLER 7.090 s.p. (W662)

Mit Schall Von Zungen
see Dreissig Geistliche Lieder, Chorale, Und Hymnen-Heft 1

Morgenlied
see Dreissig Geistliche Lieder, Chorale, Und Hymnen-Heft 8

Muttertreu Ist Unergrundlich
see Dreissig Geistliche Lieder, Chorale, Und Hymnen-Heft 8

Niemand Hat Grossere Liebe *mot
4pt mix cor,acap cor pts BREITKOPF-W CHB-3121 s.p. (W663)

Nun Bitten Wir Den Heil'gen Geist
see Dreissig Geistliche Lieder, Chorale, Und Hymnen-Heft 5

Ostersequenz
see Dreissig Geistliche Lieder, Chorale, Und Hymnen-Heft 4

Psalm 23 *see Der Herr Ist Mein Hirte

Psalm 71
6pt mix cor cor pts BREITKOPF-L PB-3549 s.p. (W664)

Psalm 76
[Lat] 8pt mix cor cor pts BREITKOPF-L PB-3956 s.p. (W665)

Psalm 145
see Dreissig Geistliche Lieder, Chorale, Und Hymnen-Heft 6

Psalm 148
see Dreissig Geistliche Lieder, Chorale, Und Hymnen-Heft 6

Salve Mundi Salutare
see Dreissig Geistliche Lieder, Chorale, Und Hymnen-Heft 2

Samanns Lied
see Dreissig Geistliche Lieder, Chorale, Und Hymnen-Heft 3

Sieh, Ich Komme In Tranen
see Dreissig Geistliche Lieder, Chorale, Und Hymnen-Heft 2

Sommerlied
see Dreissig Geistliche Lieder, Chorale, Und Hymnen-Heft 8

Suchet Den Herrn, So Werdet Ihr Leben *mot
SATB HANSSLER 7.085 s.p. (W666)

WEISMANN, WILHELM (cont'd.)

Trostet, Spricht Der Herr
see Dreissig Geistliche Lieder, Chorale, Und Hymnen-Heft 1

Weihnachtshymnus
see Zwei Hymnische Gesange

Wie Wohl Ist Mir
see Dreissig Geistliche Lieder, Chorale, Und Hymnen-Heft 9

Wir Dienen, Herr
see Dreissig Geistliche Lieder, Chorale, Und Hymnen-Heft 9

Wir Haben Einen Stern Gesehen
see Dreissig Geistliche Lieder, Chorale, Und Hymnen-Heft 1

Wir Schritten Lange
see Dreissig Geistliche Lieder, Chorale, Und Hymnen-Heft 7

Zum Tag Der Arbeit
see Dreissig Geistliche Lieder, Chorale, Und Hymnen-Heft 9

Zum Totensonntag
see Dreissig Geistliche Lieder, Chorale, Und Hymnen-Heft 7

Zwei Hymnische Gesange
sc BREITKOPF-L PB-3553 s.p.
contains: Das Wessobrunner Gebet (6pt mix cor,Bar solo,org/pno) (8th cent); Weihnachtshymnus (mix cor,org/pno,opt 2trp,2trom) (Xmas,hymn,13th cent) (W667)

WEISS, DONN
Service Responses (Set 2) *CCU
SATB FOSTER MF 202 $.25 (W668)

WEISS, EWALD
Deutsche Messe *Mass
SSATBB,acap HANSSLER 7.119 s.p. (W669)

Es Ist Ein Ros Entsprungen *Adv/Xmas
3pt wom cor/3pt jr cor,acap (contains also: Ich Steh An Deiner Krippen Hier) cor pts BREITKOPF-W CHB-3532E s.p. see also Zwolf Advents- Und Weihnachtslieder (W670)

Es Kommt Ein Schiff, Geladen *Adv/Xmas
3pt wom cor/3pt jr cor,acap (contains also: Und Unser Lieben Frauen) cor pts BREITKOPF-W CHB-3532B s.p. see also Zwolf Advents- Und Weihnachtslieder (W671)

Frohlich Soll Mein Herze Springen *Adv/Xmas
3pt wom cor/3pt jr cor,acap (contains also: Lobt Gott, Ihr Christen) cor pts BREITKOPF-W CHB-3532D s.p. see also Zwolf Advents- Und Weihnachtslieder (W672)

Gelobet Seist Du, Jesu Christ *Adv/Xmas
3pt wom cor/3pt jr cor,acap (contains also Vom Himmel Hoch) cor pts BREITKOPF-W CHB-3532C s.p. see also Zwolf Advents- Und Weihnachtslieder (W673)

Herzlich Lieb Hab Ich Dich *mot
4-6pt mix cor,acap cor pts BREITKOPF-W CHB-3479 s.p. (W674)

Hymnus
cor,Bar solo,orch voc sc UNIVER. 13423 $3.80, cor pts UNIVER. 13418A-D $.45 (W675)

Ich Steh An Deiner Krippen Hier *Adv/Xmas
3pt wom cor/3pt jr cor,acap (contains also: Es Ist Ein Ros Entsprungen) cor pts BREITKOPF-W CHB-3532E s.p. see also Zwolf Advents- Und Weihnachtslieder (W676)

In Dulci Jubilo *Adv/Xmas
3pt wom cor/3pt jr cor,acap (contains also: Vom Himmel Hoch, Ihr Englein Kommt) cor pts BREITKOPF-W CHB-3532F s.p. see also Zwolf Advents- Und Weihnachtslieder (W677)

Jauchz, Erd, Und Himmel, Juble Hell
SST/SSB,treb inst HANSSLER 14.100 s.p. (W678)

Lobt Gott, Ihr Christen *Adv/Xmas
3pt wom cor/3pt jr cor,acap (contains also: Frohlich Soll Mein Herze Springen) cor pts BREITKOPF-W CHB-3532D s.p. see also Zwolf Advents- Und Weihnachtslieder (W679)

Nun Komm, Der Heiden Heiland *Adv/Xmas
3pt wom cor/3pt jr cor,acap (contains also: O Heiland, Reiss Die Himmel Auf) cor pts BREITKOPF-W CHB-3532A s.p. see also Zwolf Advents- Und Weihnachtslieder (W680)

O Heiland, Reiss Die Himmel Auf *Adv/Xmas
3pt wom cor/3pt jr cor,acap (contains also: Nun Komm, Der Heiden Heiland) cor pts BREITKOPF-W CHB-3532A s.p. see also Zwolf Advents- Und Weihnachtslieder (W681)

Und Unser Lieben Frauen *Adv/Xmas
3pt wom cor/3pt jr cor,acap (contains also: Es Kommt Ein Schiff, Geladen) cor pts BREITKOPF-W CHB-3532B s.p. see also Zwolf Advents- Und Weihnachtslieder (W682)

Vom Himmel Hoch *Adv/Xmas
3pt wom cor/3pt jr cor,acap (contains also: Gelobet Seist Du, Jesu Christ) cor pts BREITKOPF-W CHB-3532C s.p. see also Zwolf Advents- Und Weihnachtslieder (W683)

Vom Himmel Hoch, Ihr Englein Kommt *Adv/Xmas
3pt wom cor/3pt jr cor,acap (contains also: In Dulci Jubilo) cor pts BREITKOPF-W CHB-3532F s.p. see also Zwolf Advents- Und Weihnachtslieder (W684)

Zwolf Advents- Und Weihnachtslieder *Adv/ Xmas
3pt wom cor/3pt jr cor,acap BREITKOPF-W
contains & see also: Es Ist Ein Ros Entsprungen; Es Kommt Ein Schiff, Geladen; Frohlich Soll Mein Herze Springen; Gelobet Seist Du, Jesu Christ; Ich Steh An Deiner Krippen

WEISS, EWALD (cont'd.)

Hier; In Dulci Jubilo; Lobt Gott, Ihr
Christen; Nun Komm, Der Heiden Heiland;
O Heiland, Reiss Die Himmel Auf; Und
Unser Lieben Frauen; Vom Himmel Hoch;
Vom Himmel Hoch, Ihr Englein Kommt
(W685)

WEISSER SONNTAG see Schieri, Fritz

WEITZ, GUY
O Vos Omnes
[Lat] SATB CHESTER s.p.   (W686)

WELCH FROHE BOTSCHAFT *Xmas,Czech/Eur
(Doppelbauer, Josef Friedrich) mix cor,acap
(contains also: Eja Slap Soting) DOBLINGER
s.p. see from Da Der Herr Geboren   (W687)

WELCHE DER GEIST GOTTES TREIBT see Reda,
Siegfried

WELCOME *Xmas
(Krumach) SA SCHMITT 339 $.25   (W688)

WELCOME see Cruft, Adrian

WELCOME AS THE CHEERFUL LIGHT (from Jephtha)
(Handel, G.) SA,pno SCHIRM.EC 1597 $.18
(W689)

WELCOME, GAY KOLYADA see Caldwell

WELCOME, GOOD SIR CHRISTEMAS see Johnston

WELCOME, HAPPY MORNING see Bowie, [William]

WELCOME, HAPPY MORNING see McCollin, Frances

WELCOME, HAPPY MORNING see Matthews, Harvey
Alexander

WELCOME, HAPPY MORNING see Olds, [William
Benjamin]

WELCOME, HAPPY MORNING see Williams

WELCOME, HAPPY MORNING see Wolff, S. Drummond

WELCOME HAPPY MORNING! AGE TO AGE SHALL SAY
*Easter/Lent
(Ehret) SATB oct WORD CS-662 $.30   (W690)

WELCOME HERE
see Four Songs For Christmas

WELCOME OUR MESSIAS see Roe, Christopher

WELCOME SONG, A see Mainville

WELCOME THOU KING OF GLORY see Lubeck,
Vincentius, Willkommen, Susser Brautigam

WELCOME, THOU VICTOR IN THE STRIFE
(Ehret, W.) SATB oct PRESSER 312-40602 $.30
(W691)

WELCOME TO ALL THE PLEASURES see Purcell, Henry

WELCOME, WELCOME CHRISTMAS MORN see Handel,
George Frideric

WELCOME, WELCOME, DEAR REDEEMER see Franck,
Cesar

WELCOME, WELCOME, JESU see Hobbs, C.M.

WELCOME, WELCOME JESUS see Hobbs, C.M.

WELCOME, YULE *carol
unis/SATB (easy) OXFORD 08.174 $.15   (W692)

WELCOME YULE see Kay, Ulysses Simpson

WELCOME YULE see Lewis, J.

WELCOME YULE see Spencer, W.

WELDON
O How Great Is The Lord Of All
(Coggin) SATB,acap oct PRO ART 2739 $.30
(W693)

WELDON, JOHN (1676-1736)
Hear My Crying (Psalm 61) Gen/Lent
SSATBB (med) oct OXFORD 42.221 $.65   (W694)

O Praise God
SATB,acap PETERS H1530   (W695)

O Praise God In His Holiness *Ded/Gen/Thanks
SAB,kbd (med easy) oct CONCORDIA 98-1787
$.25   (W696)

O Praise The Lord *Ded/Gen/Thanks
SAB,kbd (med easy) oct CONCORDIA 98-1786
$.20   (W697)

Psalm 61 *see Hear My Crying

WE'LL ALL PRAISE GOD TOGETHER see Brandon, G.

WELL DO I KNOW, MY LORD see Palestrina,
Giovanni, Ma So Ben, Signor Mio

WE'LL KEEP A WELCOME see Cundick, Robert

WE'LL KNEEL AT JESUS' FEET see Freeman, Charles

WELLESZ, EGON (1885-   )
Alleluia *Op.80, Allelu
[Lat] unis,opt high solo RONGWEN $.30
(W698)

(Tittel, Ernst) mix cor,acap DOBLINGER s.p.
see also Laus Nocturna   (W699)

Canticum Sapientiae *Op.104
mix cor,Bar solo,orch DOBLINGER voc sc
s.p., cor pts s.p., ipr   (W700)

Carmen Paschale *Easter
(Tittel, Ernst) mix cor,acap DOBLINGER s.p.
see also Laus Nocturna   (W701)

De Profundis
(Tittel, Ernst) mix cor,acap DOBLINGER s.p.
see also Laus Nocturna   (W702)

Dies Irae
(Tittel, Ernst) mix cor,acap DOBLINGER s.p.
see also Laus Nocturna   (W703)

WELLESZ, EGON (cont'd.)

Laus Nocturna *Op.88
(Tittel, Ernst) mix cor,acap cmplt ed
DOBLINGER s.p.
contains & see also: Alleluia; Carmen
Paschale; De Profundis; Dies Irae
(W704)

Messe In F-Moll *Op.51, Mass
4pt mix cor,org (F min) voc sc DOBLINGER
s.p.   (W705)

Mirabile Mysterium *Op.101
mix cor,soli,orch DOBLINGER voc sc s.p.,
cor pts s.p., ipr   (W706)

WELLS
Easter Introit *Easter/Lent,Introit
SATB,5brass oct FISCHER,C CM-6609 $.35, ipa
(W707)

Ending Of The Year *Xmas
SATB,acap oct FISCHER,C CM-7173 $.25 (W708)

Father, Hear Our Prayer
SATB oct LORENZ B6 $.25   (W709)

He Loves You *Xmas
(Wilson) SATB oct AGAPE CF 154 $.30   (W710)

How Real God Is
(Hustad) SATB oct AGAPE CF 155 $.30   (W711)

In Thy One Fold Of Love
(Brandon) SATB oct SHAPIRO SCE 2504 $.25
(W712)

Joyous Carol *Xmas
SATB,acap oct FISCHER,C CM-6317 $.30 (W713)

Lord Give Me Strength To Walk Thy Way
(Twohig) SATB oct PRO ART 1999 $.25   (W714)

Saviour, Lord, To Thee We Pray
SATBct PRO ART 1692 $.22   (W715)

With My Hand In Thine
SATB oct LORENZ B42 $.30   (W716)

WELLS, DANA F.
Anthem For Springtime *anthem
SATB (med) ABINGDON APM-501 $.18   (W717)

Let Us Now Praise Famous Men
SATB,acap (med) ABINGDON APM-483 $.35
(W718)

Noel *Xmas
SATB,acap oct PRESSER 312-40107 $.25 (W719)

WELSH
Praise, My Soul, The King Of Heaven
(Sheppard) TTBB,org/pno BOSTON 13622 $.35
(W720)

WELSH CAROL *carol,Welsh
SATB (very easy) OXFORD 08.034 $.15   (W721)

WELSH CHORAL see Reese

WELSH, W.A.
Ave Verum
"Jesu, Word Of God Incarnate" [Lat/Eng]
SATB,org AMP A606 $.30   (W722)

Jesu, Word Of God Incarnate *see Ave Verum

WELT ADE! see Rosenmuller, Johann

WELT ADE, ICH BIN DEIN MUDE see Bach, Johann
Sebastian

WELT ADE, ICH BIN DEIN MUDE see Rosenmuller,
Johann

WELTEN SINGEN DANK UND EHRE see Beethoven,
Ludwig van

WEM EIN TUGENDSAM WEIB BESCHERET IST see
Schein, Johann Hermann

WEM GOTT WILL RECHTE GUNST ERWEISEN see Jochum,
Otto

WEMAN, HENRY
Brollopsklader, Utan
mix cor,B solo,org voc sc NORDISKA 3860
s.p.   (W723)

WEN DENN SAHET IHR, HIRTEN? see Gabrieli,
Andrea

WEN DER TOD TRIFFT see Rohwer, Jens

WENDE DICH, HERR, WIEDER ZU MIR see Schein,
Johann Hermann

WENDE DICH ZU MIR see Planzer, Emanuel

WENDE, DU UNSER RICHTER see Schutz, Heinrich,
Reduc, Domine Deus Meus

WENDELBURG, NORMA
Create In Me A Clean Heart, O God
SATB&cong,inst oct AGAPE CY 3338 $.35
(W724)

WENN ABER DIESES ANFANGT see Driessler,
Johannes

WENN ABER JENER, DER GEIST DER WAHRHEIT see
Raphael, Gunther

WENN ABER JENER, DER GEIST DER WAHRHEIT KOMMEN
WIRD see Chemin-Petit, Hans

WENN ABER JENER GEIST DER WAHRHEIT KOMMEN WIRD
see Driessler, Johannes

WENN DER HERR DAS HAUS NICHT BAUT see
Romanovsky, Erich

WENN DER HERR DIE GEFANGENEN ZIONS see
Hartmann, Heinrich

WENN DER HERR DIE GEFANGENEN ZIONS see Raphael,
Gunther

WENN DER HERR DIE GEFANGENEN ZIONS ERLOSEN WIRD
see Micheelsen, Hans Friedrich

WENN DER HERR DIE GEFANGENEN ZIONS ERLOSEN WIRD
see Reda, Siegfried

WENN DER HERR DIE GEFANGENEN ZIONS ERLOSEN WIRD
see Weckmann, Jakob

WENN DER HERR DIE GEFANGENEN ZU ZION see
Weckmann, Jakob

WENN DER TROSTER KOMMEN WIRD see Driessler,
Johannes

WENN DES MENSCHEN SOHN KOMMEN WIRD see Rohwer,
Jens

WENN DIE ORGELN SPIELEN see Moyzes, Alexander

WENN DIE WEIHNACHTSNACHT WILL WERDEN see
Koerppen, Alfred

WENN DOCH AUCH DU ERKENNTEST see Driessler,
Johannes

WENN DU GELADEN WIRST, SO GEHE HIN see Franck,
Melchior

WENN DU GELADEN WIRST, SO GEHE HIN see
Raselius, Andreas

WENN EIN STARKER GEWAPPNETER see Brahms,
Johannes

WENN EINER, DER MIT MUHE KAUM see Hohlfeld,
Christoph

WENN ES MEINES GOTTES WILLE see Bach, Johann
Sebastian

WENN EURE SUNDE GLEICH see Zipp, Friedrich

WENN GOTT DAS HAUS see Biebl, Franz

WENN GOTT EINMAL ERLOSEN WIRD see Schutz,
Heinrich

WENN GOTT EINST LOSEN WIRD see Goudimel, Claude

WENN GOTT ES WILL *CC14U,Gen
[Ger] BOSSE BE 286 s.p.   (W725)

WENN ICH EINMAL SOLL SCHEIDEN see Bach, Johann
Sebastian

WENN ICH IN TODESNOTEN BIN see Franck, Melchior

WENN ICH MIT MENSCHEN UND ENGELZUNGEN REDETE
see Thomas, Kurt

WENN ICH MIT MENSCHEN - UND MIT ENGELSZUNGEN
REDETE see Reda, Siegfried

WENN ICH NUR DICH HAB see Harnisch, Otto
Siegfried

WENN ICH NUR HAB DICH, HERR see Lange, Gregor

WENN ICH SCHLAFEND RUH see Schutz, Heinrich,
Ego Dormio

WENN ICH ZU DIR EMPOR see Pezel, Johann
Christoph

WENN IHR NICHT ZEICHEN UND WUNDER SEHT see
Driessler, Johannes

WENN INS LAND DIE WETTER HANGEN see Lavater, H.

WENN JEMAND WEISS, WAS RECHT IST see
Hindermann, Walter Felix

WENN MEIN STUNDLEIN VORHANDEN see Bach, Johann
Sebastian

WENN MEIN STUNDLEIN VORHANDEN IST see Bach,
Johann Sebastian

WENN MEIN STUNDLEIN VORHANDEN IST see
Demantius, Christoph

WENN MEIN STUNDLEIN VORHANDEN IST see Franck,
Melchior

WENN MEIN STUNDLEIN VORHANDEN IST see
Gumpeltzhaimer, A.

WENN MEIN STUNDLEIN VORHANDEN IST see
Gumpeltzhaimer, Adam

WENN MEIN STUNDLEIN VORHANDEN IST see Hassler,
Hans Leo

WENN MEIN STUNDLEIN VORHANDEN IST see
Hufschmidt, Wolfgang

WENN MEIN STUNDLEIN VORHANDEN IST see Marx,
Karl

WENN MEIN STUNDLEIN VORHANDEN IST see
Praetorius, Michael

WENN MEIN STUNDLEIN VORHANDEN IST see Solter,
Heinz

WENN MEIN STUNDLEIN VORHANDEN IST see Trubel,
Gerhard

WENN MEINE SUND MICH KRANKEN see Gadsch,
Herbert

WENN MEINE SUND' MICH KRANKEN see Gesius,
Bartholomaus

WENN MEINE SUND MICH KRANKEN see Poser, Hans

WENN MEINE TRUBSAL ALS MIT see Bach, Johann
Sebastian

WENN MIR ANGST IST, SO RUF ICH DEN HERRN see
Hartmann, Heinrich

WENN TRUBSAL DA IST see Selle, Thomas

WENN WIR IN HOCHSTEN NOTEN SEIN see Brahms,
Johannes

WENN WIR IN HOCHSTEN NOTEN SEIN see Gesius,
Bartholomaus

WENN WIR IN HOCHSTEN NOTEN SEIN see Praetorius,
Michael

WENN WIR IN HOCHSTEN NOTEN SEIN see Raphael, Gunther

WENN WIR IN HOCHSTEN NOTEN SEIN see Schein, Johann Hermann

WENN WIR IN HOCHSTEN NOTEN SEIN see Schneidt, H.-M.

WENN WIR IN HOCHSTEN NOTEN SEIN see Wagner, Alexander

WENN WIR IN HOCHSTEN NOTEN SIND see Bach, Johann Sebastian

WENNERBERG, GUNNAR (1817-1901)
Goren Portarna Hoga (Psalm 24) Bibl
(Arrander, O.) [Swed] SATB,org GEHRMANS
KRB 301 s.p.   (W726)
(Sorensen, Heide) men cor,pno MUSIKK 113
s.p.   (W727)
(Wikander, David) mix cor NORDISKA 3869
s.p.   (W728)

Har Ar Gudagott Att Vara
4pt men cor NORDISKA 3866 s.p.   (W729)
TTB NORDISKA 3867 s.p.   (W730)
(Wikander, David) mix cor NORDISKA 3868
s.p.   (W731)

Hor Oss Svea *hymn
men cor NORDISKA 3913 s.p.   (W732)

Lord Of Hosts
SATB KJOS 5081 $.30   (W733)

Lover Gud I Hans Helgedom
[Swed] SATB,acap GEHRMANS KRB 355   (W734)

Min Sjal Langtar Och Trangtar (Psalm 84)
(Sorensen, Heide) men cor,pno MUSIKK 161
s.p.   (W735)
(Wikander, David) mix cor,solo,org NORDISKA
s.p., ipa   (W736)

Psalm 24 *see Goren Portarna Hoga

Psalm 84 *see Min Sjal Langtar Och Trangtar

Psalm 139
(Sorensen, Heide) men cor,pno MUSIKK 162
s.p.   (W737)

Psalm 150
(Sorensen, Heide) men cor,pno MUSIKK 114
s.p.   (W738)

WENTWORTH
Sussex Carol *Xmas,carol
SATB oct PLYMOUTH XM-111 $.25   (W739)

'Tis Finished
SATB oct PLYMOUTH SC-20 $.25   (W740)

WENZEL, EBERHARD (1896-   )
Da Der Sabbat
see VIER OSTERMOTETTEN

Da Der Sabbat Vergangen *Easter,mot
SATB HANSSLER 7.077 s.p.   (W741)

Da Jesus An Dem Kreuze Stund *CC3U,Easter
SA,treb inst,opt bass inst HANSSLER 14.502
s.p.   (W742)

Das Gleichnis Vom Saemann *evang/mot
4pt mix cor,S solo MOSELER s.p.   (W743)

Das Nizanische Glaubensbekenntnis *mot
SSATBB HANSSLER 7.037 s.p.   (W744)

Das Volk, So Im Finstern Wandelt *mot
SATB HANSSLER 7.065 s.p.   (W745)

Der Geist Des Herrn Erfullet Den Erdkreis
*Introit/mot
SATB HANSSLER 7.078 s.p.   (W746)

Der Herr Ward Aufgehoben Gen Himmel *mot
SAB HANSSLER 7.049 s.p.   (W747)

Der Michaelskampf *Fest,mot
[Ger] SATB,acap (med diff, michaelmas)
BAREN. BA 2869 $2.25   (W748)

Die Nacht Ist Virgeruckt
SAT/SAB,opt cantor HANSSLER 14.605 s.p.
                                          (W749)

Die Nacht Ist Vorgedrungen
SA,treb inst,bass inst HANSSLER 14.014 s.p.
                                          (W750)

Die Sieben Worte Am Kreuz *Gd.Fri.
SAT/SAB,opt cantor HANSSLER 14.603 s.p.
                                          (W751)

Du Hirte Israels, Hore *Bibl
SATB HANSSLER 7.169 s.p.   (W752)

Eins Bitte Ich Vom Herren *Gen
[Ger] 2 eq voices,acap (med easy) BAREN.
BA 4940 s.p. contains also: Herr, Hore
Meine Worte   (W753)

Einzug Jesu In Jerusalem *liturg
SAT/SAB,cantor/2 cantors HANSSLER 14.606
s.p.   (W754)

Er Kommt! *Adv
3pt mix cor,cantor,ob,vla,vcl,opt bvl,opt
xylophone HANSSLER 10.241 sc s.p., cor
pts s.p., ipa   (W755)

Erschienen Ist Der Herrlich Tag
see Linke, Norbert, Gelobt Sei Gott Im
Hochsten Thron

Frolich Soll Mein Herze Springen
see Koch, Johannes H.E., Es Ist Ein Ros
Etsprungen

Furwahr, Er Trug Unsre Krankheit
SAT/SAB HANSSLER 14.604 s.p.   (W756)

Gleichnis Vom Verlorenen Schaf Und Vom
Verlorenen Groschen
SAB HANSSLER 7.057 s.p.   (W757)

Gott Des Himmels Und Der Erden *Gen,cant
[Ger] SATB&opt cong,2trp,2trom,bvl (med)
BAREN. BA 3596 sc $3.00, cor pts $.40,

WENZEL, EBERHARD (cont'd.)
ipa   (W758)

Herr, Du Erforschest Mich *mot
SSAB,SS soli HANSSLER 7.035 s.p.   (W759)

Herr, Hore Meine Worte
see Wenzel, Eberhard, Eins Bitte Ich Vom
Herren

Herr, Lass Deiner Sich Freuen *Gen
[Ger] 2 eq voices,opt inst (med easy)
BAREN. BA 4939 s.p.   (W760)

Herzlich Lieb Habe Ich Dich *Introit/mot
SATB HANSSLER 7.081 s.p.   (W761)

Ipse Deus Sapiens
4pt mix cor MOSELER LB-420 s.p.   (W762)

Jesus Christus, Konig Und Herr
SA,org,2rec HANSSLER 5.054 s.p.   (W763)

Komm, Heiliger Geist, Herre Gott *Mass
4pt/5pt&cong,org HANSSLER 10.049 sc s.p.,
cor pts s.p.   (W764)

Lobe Den Herren, O Meine Seele *Gen,mot
[Ger] 2 eq voices&3pt mix cor&5pt mix cor&
2pt,acap (med easy) BAREN. BA 3262 s.p.
                                          (W765)

Markus-Passion *Psntd
[Ger] 3pt mix cor,cantor,acap BAREN. EM 438
sc s.p., cor pts s.p.   (W766)

Nec Tu Nate Dei
4pt mix cor MOSELER LB-421 s.p.   (W767)

Nun Freut Euch, Lieben Christen Gmein *cant
SAB,org,2trp,trom HANSSLER 10.035 sc s.p.,
cor pts s.p., ipa   (W768)

Nun Ist Der Himmel Aufgetan
SA,org,2rec HANSSLER 5.053 s.p.   (W769)

Ostermotette *Easter,Bibl,mot
[Ger] SATB,STB soli,acap (med diff) BAREN.
BA 2765 $2.50   (W770)

Psalm 84 *see Wie Lieblich Sind Deine

Psalm 121 *Bibl
4pt mix cor,S solo MOSELER s.p.   (W771)

Psalmkonzert *Gen
[Ger] SATB,S solo,org (med) MULLER SM 2470
sc s.p., cor pts s.p.   (W772)

Sehet Euch Vor Vor Den Falschen Propheten
*Trin,evang/mot
[Ger] SSATBB,acap (med diff) BAREN. BA 5401
$2.25   (W773)

Uns, Herr, Wirst Du Frieden Schaffen *Gen
[Ger] SA&men cor,acap (med diff) BAREN.
BA 4949 $.40   (W774)

Vespera Iam Venit
4pt mix cor MOSELER LB-423 s.p.   (W775)

Was Suchet Ihr Den
see VIER OSTERMOTETTEN

Was Suchet Ihr Den Lebendigen *Easter,mot
SAB HANSSLER 7.050 s.p.   (W776)

Wie Lieblich Sind Deine (Psalm 84)
SSATBB HANSSLER 7.019 s.p.   (W777)

Worte Des Propheten Jeremias *Bibl/cant
SSATB,Bar solo,2trp,3trom HANSSLER 10062 sc
s.p., cor pts s.p., ipa   (W778)

Zween Der Junger Gehn Mit Sehnen *cant
SAT/SAB,S solo,org,2vln HANSSLER 10.072 sc
s.p., voc sc s.p., ipa   (W779)

WEORES, S.
Kereztoltes
see KERESZTOLTES

Tancnota
see KERESZTOLTES

WER DA GLAUBET UND GETAUFT WIRD see Bach,
Johann Sebastian

WER DANK see Bach, Johann Sebastian, Wer Dank
Opfert, Der Preiset Mich

WER DANK OPFERT see Bach, Johann Sebastian, Wer
Dank Opfert, Der Preiset Mich

WER DANK OPFERT, DER PREISET MICH see Bach,
Johann Sebastian

WER DER HEIRSCH SCHREIET see Distler, Hugo

WER DU AUCH BIST see Keller, Wilhelm

WER GOTT LIEBT see Bruckner, Anton

WER GOTT VERTRAUEN TUT see Lassus, Roland de
(Orlandus)

WER GOTT VERTRAUEN TUT, DEN see Lassus, Roland
de (Orlandus)

WER GOTT VERTRAUT see Cruger, Johann

WER GOTTES MARTER IN EHREN HAT see Schutz,
Heinrich

WER HAT DICH SO GESCHLAGEN see Bloch, Waldemar

WER HEIMLICH SEINE WOHNESATT see Hagius, Conrad

WER IN DEM SCHUTZ DES HOCHSTEN IST see Othmayr,
Kaspar

WER IN DEM SCHUTZ DES HOCHSTEN IST see Reda,
Siegfried

WER IN DEM SCHUTZ DES HOCHSTEN SITZT see
Praetorius, Michael

WER IN MIR BLEIBET UND ICH IN IHM see Kurig,
Hans-Hermann

WER IST ES, DER DEN WELTENPLAN VERDUNKELT see
David, Thomas [Christian]

WER KANN DA KORN ANSCHAUEN see Meyer-Janson,
Burkhard

WER KANN DER TREU VERGESSEN see Schwartz,
Gerhard von

WER LEBEN WILL see Steffens

WER MICH LIEBET see Bach, Johann Sebastian, Wer
Mich Liebet, Der Wird Mein Wort Halten

WER MICH LIEBET see Driessler, Johannes

WER MICH LIEBET see Vulpius, Melchior

WER MICH LIEBET, DER WIRD MEIN WORT see
Raselius, Andreas

WER MICH LIEBET, DER WIRD MEIN WORT HALTEN see
Bach, Johann Sebastian

WER MICH LIEBET, DER WIRD MEIN WORT HALTEN see
Vulpius, Melchior

WER MICH LIEBET, DER WIRD MEIN WORT HALTEN see
Bach, Johann Sebastian

WER MICH LIEBET, DER WIRD MEIN WORT HALTEN see
Bach, Johann Sebastian

WER MICH LIEBET see Bach, Johann Sebastian, Wer
Mich Liebet, Der Wird Mein Wort Halten

WER MICHE LIEBET, DER WIRD MEIN WORT see
Vulpius, Melchior

WER MIR NACHFOLGEN WILL, DER VERLEUGNE SICH
SELBST see Brunner, Adolf

WER NICHT VON NEUEM GEBOREN WIRD see Buchtger,
Fritz

WER NUN DEN LIEBEN GOTT LASST WALTEN see
Schmidt, Wolfgang

WER NUN WEISS, GUTES ZU TUN see Lohr, Ina

WER NUR see Bach, Johann Sebastian, Wer Nur Den
Lieben Gott Lasst Walten

WER NUR DEN LIEBEN GOTT see Neumark, Georg

WER NUR DEN LIEBEN GOTT LAESST WALTEN see
Haydn, (Johann) Michael

WER NUR DEN LIEBEN GOTT LASST WALTEN see Bach,
Johann Sebastian

WER NUR DEN LIEBEN GOTT LASST WALTEN see
Burkhart, Franz

WER NUR DEN LIEBEN GOTT LASST WALTEN see
Doebler, Curt

WER NUR DEN LIEBEN GOTT LASST WALTEN see
Muller, Paul

WER NUR DEN LIEBEN GOTT LASST WALTEN see
Neumark, Georg

WER NUR DEN LIEBEN GOTT LASST WALTEN [CHORALE]
see Bach, Johann Sebastian

WER OHREN HAT ZU HOREN see Driessler, Johannes

WER OHREN HAT ZU HOREN, DER HORE see David,
Johann Nepomuk

WER SICH DIE MUSIK ERKIEST see Hindemith, Paul

WER SICH LASST DUNKEN, DASS ER FEST STEHE see
Reda, Siegfried

WER SICH SELBST ERHOHET see Bach, Johann
Sebastian

WER SICH SELBST ERHOHET see Bach, Johann
Sebastian, Wer Sich Selbst Erhohet

WER SICH SELBST ERHOHET, DER SOLL ERNIEDRIGET
WERDEN see Bach, Johann Sebastian

WER SICH SELBST ERHOHET, DER WIRD ERNIEDRIGT
see Raphael, Gunther

WER SICH SELBST ERHOHT, DER WIRD see Vulpius,
Melchior

WER UBERWINDET, DEM WILL ICH see Franck,
Melchior

WER UNTER DEM SCHIRM DES HOCHSTEN see Schein,
Johann Hermann

WER UNTER DEM SCHIRM DES HOCHSTEN see
Schlenker, Manfred

WER WALZET UNS DEN STEIN VON DES GRABES TUR see
Hammerschmidt, Andreas

WER WALZET UNS DEN STEIN VON DES GRABES TUR see
Hammerschmidt, Andreas

WER WEISS see Bach, Johann Sebastian, Wer
Weiss, Wie Nahe Mir Mein Ende

WER WEISS, WIE NAHE MIR MEIN ENDE see Bach,
Johann Sebastian

WER WILL UNS SCHEIDEN VON DER LIEBE GOTTES? see
Schutz, Heinrich

WER WOHLAUF IST UND GESUND see Stern, Hermann

WER WOHNT UNTERM SCHIRM DES HOCHSTEN see Blarr,
Oskar Gottlieb

WERBECKE, G. VON
Merciful Father *see Virgo Maria

O God Of Life Above *see Panis Angelicus

WERBECKE, G. VON (cont'd.)

Panis Angelicus
(Greyson) "O God Of Life Above" SATB oct
BOURNE ES111 $.25 (W780)

Virgo Maria
(Saar, L.) "Merciful Father" SSA oct
PRESSER 332-14212 $.25 (W781)

WERDET TATER AUS DEM WORT see Ruppel, Paul
Ernst

WE'RE ALL FOR THEE, LORD see Nourse, John

WE'RE GLAD JESUS GOT HOME see Grime, William

WE'RE HERE TO BE HAPPY AND GO AND BE HAPPY see
Avery

WERE I A BIRD see Hokanson

WE'RE MARCHING TO ZION see Lowry, [Robert]

WERE YOU THERE? *Easter/Lent,spir
see Two Negro Spirituals
"Warst Du Dort" see Sechs Negro Spirituals,
Blatt 2
SATB oct LORENZ 9710 $.25 (W782)
SATB (very easy) oct LORENZ A476 $.25 (W783)
SA oct LORENZ 5375 $.25 (W784)
unis oct LORENZ 8852 $.30 (W785)
(Bartholomew) 4pt men cor,A solo oct SCHIRM.G
9773 $.25 (W786)
(Clements, J.) SATB PROWSE s.p. (W787)
(Cook, C.A.) SATB CRESCENDO $.25 (W788)
(De Cormier) SATB,S/A solo,acap oct LAWSON
51613 $.30 (W789)
(Denton) SATB oct LILLENAS AN-3811 $.25 (W790)
(Frederick) SATB oct SHAPIRO SK 2008 $.25 (W791)
(Goemanne, Noel) SSA/TTB,acap oct WORLD
LE-1648-3 $.30 (W792)
(Heaton, W.) SATB oct PRESSER 312-40567 $.30 (W793)
(Johnson) mix cor,S/T solo,acap oct SCHIRM.G
10128 $.35 (W794)
(Luboff, Norman) SAATTBB oct WALTON 3048 $.30 (W795)
(McKelvy, J.) SATB FOSTER MF117 $.30 (W796)
(Mickelson) SATB oct LILLENAS AN-3806 $.25 (W797)
(Palmer) SSA ALFRED 6237 $.35 (W798)
(Parker) SATB,Mez solo,acap oct LAWSON 51249
$.30 (W799)
(Roberton) 3pt jr cor/3pt wom cor ROBERTON
72114 s.p. (W800)
(Roberton) TBB ROBERTON 50792 s.p. (W801)
(Roberton) mix cor ROBERTON 61286 s.p. (W802)
(Swift) SATB,acap oct PRO ART 1248 $.30 (W803)
(Swift) SSA,acap oct PRO ART 1240 $.25 (W804)
(Wagner, Terri) SATB,med solo,acap oct LAWSON
668 $.30 (W805)

WERE YOU THERE? see Brandon, George

WERE YOU THERE? see Burleigh, Henry Thacker

WERE YOU THERE? see Carr

WERE YOU THERE? see Christy

WERE YOU THERE? see Gerhold, Norbert

WERE YOU THERE? see Gillette

WERE YOU THERE? see Webb

WERE YOU THERE? see Westbrook, Francis B.

WERE YOU THERE? see Wilson

WERE YOU THERE WHEN THEY CRUCIFIED MY LORD? see
Ringwald, [Roy]

WERFET EUER VERTRAUEN NICHT WEG see Schrader,
Oswald

WERFET PANIER AUF IM LANDE see Telemann, Georg
Philipp

WERFT EUER HERZ IN DIE FLAMME see Rohwer, Jens

WERFT FORT DEN STEIN see Stier, Alfred

WERNER
Christmas Song *see Weihnachtslied

Missa Festivalis E Brevis *Fest,Mass
[Lat] SATB,org,2vln,vcl/bvl study sc PETERS
10005 $5.00, ipa, voc sc PETERS 10005
$2.00, ipa (W806)

Psalm 103 *Op.7
[Ger] SSAATTBB PETERS 5910 $1.25 (W807)

Weihnachtslied *Xmas
"Christmas Song" [Ger] SATB,org,strings min
sc PETERS E1084 $3.00, ipa (W808)

WERNER, FRITZ (1898-)
Christus, Der Uns Selig Macht
see Bach, Johann Sebastian, Christus, Der
Uns Selig Macht
SS/SA/SAB/SATB HANSSLER 8.019 s.p. (W809)

Der Herr Ist Mein Licht Und Mein Heil
see Sechs Motetten

Der Mensch Lebt Nicht Vom Brot Allein
see Evangelisches Kirchengesangbuch

Evangelisches Kirchengesangbuch *Psntd
[Ger] 3pt mix cor,acap BAREN. EM 16 s.p.
contains: Der Mensch Lebt Nicht Vom Brot
Allein; Gott Der Vater Wohn Uns Bei,
No.109; Herr Jesu Christ, Dich Zu Uns
Wend, No.126 (W810)

Freut Euch, Ihr Lieben Christen All
see Berger, Hans Ludwig, Frohlich Wir Nun
All Fangen An
SA/SAB/SATB HANSSLER 8.029 s.p. (W811)

Frohlich Wir Nun All
see Fiebig, Kurt, Frohlich Wir Nun All

WERNER, FRITZ (cont'd.)

Gott Der Vater Wohn Uns Bei
see Evangelisches Kirchengesangbuch
SAT/SAB,2treb inst/bass inst HANSSLER
14.109 s.p. contains also: Kukuck,
Felicitas, Heut Singt Die Liebe
Christenheit (SA/TB,treb inst) (W812)

Heilger Geist, Du Troster Mein *cant
SATB&cong,org,2ob,trp,2vln,vla,vcl,bvl
HANSSLER 10.087 sc s.p., voc sc s.p., ipa (W813)

Herr Christ, Der Enig Gotts Sohn
SAT/SAB,2treb inst HANSSLER 14.046 (W814)

Herr, Hore Meine Stimme, Wenn Ich Rufe
see Sechs Motetten

Herr Jesu Christ, Dich Zu Uns Wend
see Evangelisches Kirchengesangbuch

Lobt Gott Den Herrn, Ihr Heiden All *Thanks
unis/SAB/SATB,fl/vln HANSSLER 8.020 s.p. (W815)

Mit Freuden Zart *No.80, Easter,cant
[Ger] 3pt mix cor,3treb inst BAREN. EM 106
s.p. see from EVANGELISCHES
KIRCHENGESANGBUCH (W816)

Nun Sei Uns Willkommen, Herre Christ *cant
SSAT/SSAB,fl,ob,bsn,2vln,vla,bvl,cembalo
HANSSLER 10.159 sc s.p., voc sc s.p., ipa (W817)

Schaffe In Mir Gott Ein Reines Herze
see Sechs Motetten

Sechs Motetten *mot
HANSSLER 7.100 s.p.
contains: Der Herr Ist Mein Licht Und
Mein Heil (SSATBB); Herr, Hore Meine
Stimme, Wenn Ich Rufe (SSATBB); Schaffe
In Mir Gott Ein Reines Herze (SATB); So
Ziehet Nun An Als Die Auserwahlten
(SSATBB); Sollte Aber Gott Nicht Auch
Retten (SSATBB); Wo Der Herr Nicht Bei
Uns Ware (SSATBB) (W818)

Siegesfurste, Ehrenkonig
see Marx, Karl, Gen Himmel Aufgefahren Ist

So Ziehet Nun An Als Die Auserwahlten
see Sechs Motetten

Sollte Aber Gott Nicht Auch Retten
see Sechs Motetten

Vater Unser Im Himmelreich
see Eccard, Johannes, Vater Unser Im
Himmelreich

Vom Himmel Hoch Da Komm Ich Her
SAT/SAB,2treb inst HANSSLER 14.016 s.p.
contains also: Werner, Fritz, Vom Himmel
Kam Der Engel Schar (SAT/SAB,2treb inst);
Graap, Lothar, Wir Christenleut Habn
Jetzund Freud (SAT/SAB,treb inst) (W819)

Vom Himmel Kam Der Engel Schar
see Werner, Fritz, Vom Himmel Hoch Da Komm
Ich Her

Wach Auf, Meins Herzens Schone *folk
[Ger] men cor,acap (med) HUG s.p. (W820)

Wo Der Herr Nicht Bei Uns Ware
see Sechs Motetten

Wo Gott Der Herr Nicht Bei Uns Halt
SATB/SAB/SS/SA HANSSLER 8.028 s.p. (W821)

WERNER, GREGOR JOSEPH (1695-1766)
Auf, Auf, Ihr Hirten Allzugleich *Xmas,cant
(Schmid, Ernst Fritz) [Ger] SATB,STB soli,
cont,2ob,2vln (med easy) BAREN. BA 828 sc
$2.25, cor pts $.40, ipa (W822)

Der Tag, Der Ist So Freudenreich
SATB SATB,cont,vln HANSSLER 6.314 s.p.
contains also: Murschhauser, Franz Xaver
Anton, Lasst Uns Das Kindlein Wiegen (W823)

Good Christian Men Rejoice *Xmas
(Riedel) SATB SCHMITT 1424 $.25 (W824)

In Dulci Jubilo *Xmas
[Ger] SATB,cont (med easy) MULLER MS 35
s.p. (W825)

Puer Natus In Bethlehem *Xmas
[Ger] SATB,cont,vln (med easy) BAREN.
BA 786 s.p. (W826)

Requiem In G-Moll *Req
(Sulyok, I.) 4pt mix cor,soli,org,strings
(G min) DOBLINGER sc s.p., cor pts s.p.,
ipa (W827)

Te Deum In C-Dur *Te Deum
(Sulyok, I.) 4pt mix cor,org,2trp,vln,vcl,
bvl (C maj) DOBLINGER sc s.p., voc sc
s.p., cor pts s.p., ipa (W828)

WERNER, HANS
Lasst Uns Reisen *cant
2pt,fl,strings MOSELER sc s.p., cor pts
s.p., ipa (W829)

Musica, Himmlisch Gut *cant
4pt mix cor,fl,strings MOSELER sc s.p., cor
pts s.p., ipa (W830)

WERNER, ST.
Haben Engel Wir Vernommen
see Vier Weihnachtschore Und Drei Kanons

Lasst Uns Das Kindelein Wiegen
see Vier Weihnachtschore Und Drei Kanons

O Freudenreicher Tag
see Vier Weihnachtschore Und Drei Kanons

Vier Weihnachtschore Und Drei Kanons *Xmas,
canon
men cor TONGER s.p.
contains: Haben Engel Wir Vernommen;
Lasst Uns Das Kindelein Wiegen; O
Freudenreicher Tag; Wach, Nachtigall,
Wach Auf (W831)

WERNER, ST. (cont'd.)

Wach, Nachtigall, Wach Auf
see Vier Weihnachtschore Und Drei Kanons

WERNER, SVEN ERIK
Conditiones
dbl cor,acap sc SAMFUNDET s.p. (W832)

WERNICK
Chanukah Festival Overture
SATB&unis&2pt boy cor&2pt girl cor oct
BELWIN 60589 $.35 (W833)

WERT, GIACHES DE (1535-1596)
Drei Motetten *Gen,mot
(De Surcy, Bernard Bailly) [Lat] (med) PENN
STATE PSM 19 s.p.
contains: Egressus Jesus (SSSATBarB,
acap); Hoc Est Praeceptum Meum (SAATB,
acap); Quiescat Vox Tua (SATBarBarB,
acap) (W834)

Egressus Jesus
see Drei Motetten

Fourteenth-Century Mass Music In France
*CCU,Mass
(Stablein-Harder, H.) cor AM.INST.MUS.
$22.00 (W835)

Hoc Est Praeceptum Meum
see Drei Motetten

Opera Omnia vol. XI *CCU,mot
(Bernstein, Melvin) cor AM.INST.MUS. $17.00 (W836)

Opera Omnia vol. XIII; Second Book Of Motets
(1581) *CCU
(Bernstein, Melvin) 5pt cor AM.INST.MUS. $16.00 (W837)

Opera Omnia vol. XVI *CCU,mot
(Bernstein, Melvin) cor AM.INST.MUS. $18.00 (W838)

Quiescat Vox Tua
see Drei Motetten

WERT, JAKOB VAN
see WERT, GIACHES DE

WERTHEIM, S.L.
Jesu Dulcis Memoria
men cor ALSBACH&D sc s.p., cor pts s.p. (W839)

WERTHER, R.T.
Holy Of Holies, The
SATB ALLANS 470 s.p. (W840)

WES IST DAS BILD UND DIE UBERSCHRIFT see
Raselius, Andreas

WESLEY
Alleluia! King Eternal
(Wyatt) SAB oct PRO ART 2371 $.30 (W841)
(Wyatt) SATB oct PRO ART 1767 $.25 (W842)
(Wyatt) SSA oct PRO ART 2373 $.25 (W843)

Behold The Lamb Of God *Easter/Lent,Commun
(Kirk) SATB oct PRO ART 1581 $.25 (W844)

Blessed Are They
(Coggin) SAB WARNER R3491 $.30 (W845)

Blessed Are They That Alway Keep Judgement
(Douglas) SATB oct PRO ART 1778 $.18 (W846)

Brightest And Best *Xmas
(Stone) SATB oct PRO ART 2113 $.25 (W847)

Christ Whose Glory Fills The Skies
(Larson) SATB oct PRO ART 1851 $.22 (W848)

Church's One Foundation, The *hymn
(Williams) SATB oct LILLENAS AN-2331 $.30 (W849)

Gentle Jesus, Meek And Mild *Xmas/Gen
(Wilson) SA oct BOURNE HL2 $.30 (W850)

In Heavenly Love Abiding
(Gerig) SATB oct LILLENAS AN-2362 $.30 (W851)

Jesus Christ Is Risen *Easter
(Silver) SAB oct BOURNE 3031 $.35 (W852)

Lead Me Lord
SSA oct FISCHER,C CM-6945 $.25 (W853)
SATB oct FISCHER,C CM-6393 $.25 (W854)

O Thou Who Camest From Above
(Harris) SATB,S solo oct PRO ART 1660 $.20 (W855)

O Worship The Lord
(Roper) SSSATB (med diff) OXFORD 42.232
$.35 (W856)

Sing To The Great Jehovah's Praise
(Butler) SATB oct PRO ART 2193 $.25 (W857)

Where Shall My Wandering Soul Begin?
(Jordahl) SATB oct PLYMOUTH SC-34 $.35 (W858)

WESLEY, A.
Lead Me, Lord
(Warhurst, J.) SAB oct PRESSER 312-21444
$.25 (W859)

WESLEY, CHARLES (1757-1834)
Like As We Do Put Our Trust In Thee
(Greaves, Richard) SS oct NOVELLO
33.0095.01 s.p. (W860)

WESLEY, SAMUEL SEBASTIAN JR. (1810-1876)
Ascribe Unto The Lord *anthem
mix cor oct NOVELLO 28.0109.04 s.p. (W861)

Blessed Be The God And Father *Easter/Fest,
anthem
SATB,S solo ALLANS 56 s.p. (W862)
SSATB oct NOVELLO 28.0015.02 s.p. (W863)

Cast Me Not Away From Thy Presence *Gen/
Lent,anthem
SSATB oct NOVELLO 28.0975.03 s.p. (W864)

For This Mortal Must Put On Immortality (from
O Lord, Thou Art My God) Gen,Bibl
SSATB (med) oct OXFORD 42.708 $.35 (W865)

WESLEY, SAMUEL SEBASTIAN JR. (cont'd.)

Geloofd Zij God Den Vader
(Vaal, O. De) mix cor sc ALSBACH&D s.p. (W866)

Holsworthy Bells
SATB PROWSE s.p. (W867)

I Sing Of A Maiden *Xmas
SATB oct LESLIE 4096 (W868)

Jesu, The Very Thought Of Thee
(Easson) unis oct CURWEN 10966 $.20 (W869)

Lamb Of God
SATB oct WALTON 2029 $.25 (W870)

Lead Me Lord *Commun/Marriage,anthem/Bibl
SATB ALLANS 218 s.p. (W871)
4pt mix cor,SA soli oct SCHIRM.G 4913 $.25 (W872)
SA oct GRAY GCMR 1001 $.25 (W873)
SATB oct BELWIN 64054 $.25 (W874)
SA oct BELWIN 64016 $.25 (W875)
SATB oct PRESSER 332-12527 $.25 (W876)
SATB oct LESLIE 4033 contains also: Lord Of All Power (W877)
mix cor oct NOVELLO 50.0061.00 s.p. (W878)
SATB oct GRAY GCMR 3183 $.30 (W879)
(Chambers, H.A.) SA ALLANS 281 s.p. (W880)
(Mueller) SABar,SA soli oct SCHIRM.G 8700 $.25 (W881)
(Pitcher, Gladys) 3pt mix cor,pno (med) oct WILLIS 8493 $.20 (W882)
(Ratcliffe, Desmond) 2pt oct NOVELLO 33.0113.03 s.p. (W883)
(Strickling) SATB oct SPRATT 532 $.25 (W884)

Lead Me, Lord, In Thy Righteousness
SATB,org SCHIRM.EC 378 $.20 (W885)

Lead Me, O Lord
(Narvik) SATB KJOS 7048 $.30 (W886)

Lord Hath Been Mindful Of Us, The (from Ascribe Unto The Lord) anthem
mix cor oct NOVELLO 28.0477.08 s.p. (W887)

Lord Is My Shepherd, The *Commun/Fest/Lent/Marriage,anthem
SATB ALLANS 269 s.p. (W888)
mix cor oct NOVELLO 28.1195.02 s.p. (W889)

Lord Of All Power
see Wesley, Samuel Sebastian Jr., Lead Me Lord

Love One Another *Gen,anthem
unis,opt pno (contains also: O Worship The Lord by Travers, J.) oct ROYAL 245 s.p.
see also ANTHEMS FOR UNISON OR TWO PART SINGING (W890)

Might I In Thy Sight Appear *anthem
mix cor oct NOVELLO 40.1476.06 s.p. (W891)
unis oct NOVELLO 40.1476.06 s.p. (W892)

O Lord My God
SATB oct LESLIE 4019 (W893)
(Knight) 3pt mix cor oct CURWEN 11198 $.20 (W894)

O Lord, My God (Solomon's Prayer) *anthem/prayer
mix cor,orch oct NOVELLO 40.0314.04 s.p., ipr (W895)

Psalm 51 *see Wash Me Throughly

Thou Wilt Keep Him *Lent/Marriage/Rembrnc
SATB ALLANS 325 s.p. (W896)

Thou Wilt Keep Him In Perfect Peace *anthem
SATTB oct NOVELLO 28.0107.08 s.p. (W897)
SATB oct GRAY GCMR 1660 $.25 (W898)
(Palmer, P Spencer) 2pt oct NOVELLO 33.0082.10 s.p. (W899)
(Ramsey, Basil) SATB oct NOVELLO 28.1391.02 s.p. (W900)

Wash Me Thoroughly From My Wickedness
4pt mix cor,org oct SCHIRM.G 10403 $.30 (W901)

Wash Me Throughly (Psalm 51) anthem
SATB oct GRAY GCMR 2933 $.25 (W902)
SATB,S solo,org SCHIRM.EC 321 $.25 (W903)
mix cor oct NOVELLO 28.0186.08 s.p. (W904)

Wilderness, The *anthem
SATB,B solo,orch oct NOVELLO 28.0110.08 s.p., ipr (W905)

WESLEY, SAMUEL SR. (1766-1837)
Carmen Funebrae *funeral/mot
"Vanity, Vanity, All Is Vanity" [Eng/Lat] SATB,opt org/pno PETERS H230 $.60 (W906)

O How Amiable Are Thy Dwellings
(Bridge, Sir Fredk.) SATB BOSWORTH s.p. (W907)

O Lord, My God
(Knight) SAB CURWEN 80873 s.p. (W908)

Vanity, Vanity, All Is Vanity *see Carmen Funebrae

WESSEL, HENRY
Calvary *Easter/Lent,cant
mix cor,SAB soli,pno/org (med) oct WILLIS $.75 (W909)
3pt wom cor,SA/B soli,pno/org (med) voc sc WILLIS $.75 (W910)

Noel *Xmas,cant
mix cor,SATB soli,pno/org (med) oct WILLIS $.75 (W911)

WESSMAN, SVEN.
Ungdomspalm
wom cor/jr cor NORDISKA 5575 s.p. (W912)

WESSNITZER, WOLFGANG (ca. 1615-1697)
Das Ist Eine Sel'ge Stunde
see Bach, Johann Sebastian, O Jesulein Suss, O Jesulein Mild

WEST
Sing A Song Of Praise
(Spiro) SATB oct PRO ART 1507 $.16 (W913)

Woods And Every Sweetsmelling Tree, The *Thanks
SATB,S/T solo oct PRO ART 1309 $.18 (W914)

WEST, HAYDN
Church Service *hymn/Introit,Austral
SATB ALLANS 85 s.p. (W915)

WEST INDIAN CHRISTMAS CAROL *Xmas,carol,Carib
(Wilson, John F.) TTBB oct AGAPE JW 7774 $.30 (W916)

WEST, JOHN EBENEZER (1863-1929)
Father Of Mercies, God Of Love *Harv,anthem
2pt,S solo oct NOVELLO 33.0053.06 s.p. (W917)
mix cor oct NOVELLO 28.0671.01 s.p. (W918)

God Be Merciful Unto Us (from Seedtime And Harvest) anthem
SATB oct NOVELLO 40.0665.08 s.p. (W919)

Lord Is Exalted, The *Bibl
4pt mix cor oct SCHIRM.G 3963 $.25 (W920)
(Martin) SATB oct SPRATT 521 $.30 (W921)
(Mueller) SABar oct SCHIRM.G 8701 $.25 (W922)

O, How Amiable *Bibl
4pt mix cor oct SCHIRM.G 4364 $.25 (W923)

See Amid The Winter's Snow *Xmas
2pt&opt 3pt oct NOVELLO 33.0056.00 s.p. (W924)

Woods And Every Sweet-Smelling Tree, The *Thanks
4pt mix cor,ST soli oct SCHIRM.G 7297 $.35 (W925)

WESTBROOK, FRANCIS B.
Calvary *Easter/Psntd,cant
SATB,org GALLIARD 2.9062.1 $2.50 (W926)

Christ, From Whom All Blessings Flow *anthem
mix cor oct NOVELLO 91.0006.07 s.p. (W927)

Evening Hymn *Eve,hymn
SATB ENOCH EC216 s.p. (W928)

Faith Of Our Fathers *hymn
mix cor CURWEN 80908 s.p. (W929)

Lord, Thy Word Abideth *anthem
SATB ENOCH EC329 s.p. (W930)

Missa Brevis *Mass
"Short Communion Service, A" SATB,org PETERS H458 $.90 (W931)

Road To Calvary *Easter
SATB oct GALAXY 1.2358.1 $.30 (W932)

Short Communion Service, A *see Missa Brevis

Swing Low, Sweet Chariot
SATB (easy) ABINGDON APM-250 $.30 (W933)

Thee We Adore *anthem
SATB,org PETERS H855 $.40 (W934)

Were You There? *Lent
SATB (easy) ABINGDON APM-136 $.25 (W935)

WESTCOTT
Psalm For The Nations *Psalm,Contemp
SATB ALFRED 6570 $.35 (W936)

WESTERN ANTHEM BOOK *CC22L,anthem
cor oct LESLIE 10, 004 (W937)

WESTERN WIND, THE see Taverner, John

WESTERN WIND, THE see Tye, Christopher

WESTERN WYNDE MASS, THE see Taverner, John

WESTERN WYNDE, THE see Taverner, John

WESTHOFF, F.W.
King Of Love My Shepherd Is, The *anthem/hymn
SA,pno (easy) oct WILLIS 6325 $.15 (W938)

WESTMINSTER CAROL see Wilson

WESTMINSTER CAROL BOOK *CCU,Xmas,carol
oct HART s.p. (W939)

WESTNITZER, W.
Jezus' Lijden
mix cor sc ALSBACH&D s.p. (W940)

WESTOBY, C.F.
Preces And Responses (Festal)
SATB oct NOVELLO s.p. (W941)

WESTRUP, JACK ALLAN (1904-)
God Be Merciful Unto Us *anthem
mix cor oct NOVELLO 28.1427.07 s.p. (W942)

WETHERILL
Be Thou My Vision
SATB SHAWNEE A 1004 $.30 (W943)

Carol Of The Trees *Xmas/Gen/Lent,carol
SATB oct SACRED S-11 $.35 (W944)

Golgotha *Gd.Fri.
SATB oct SACRED S-62 $.35 (W945)

Hope Of The World
SATB FLAMMER A 5590 $.30 (W946)
SATB (med easy) SOUTHERN $.30 (W947)

Hymn Of Consecration *hymn
SATB SHAWNEE A 989 $.30 (W948)

I Will Lift Up Mine Eyes
SATB oct LORENZ 316 $.30 (W949)

Lord's Day, The
SATB FLAMMER A 5600 $.30 (W950)

Our Song Of Praise
unis jr cor oct LILLENAS AN-4026 $.25 (W951)

WETHERILL (cont'd.)

Prayer Of Humble Access, A
SATB oct SACRED E86 $.35 (W952)

WETTERER GESANGBUCH see Rhau, Johannes

WETTIG WEISSENBORN, E.
Lentesprookje
jr cor ALSBACH&D sc s.p., cor pts s.p. (W953)
wom cor ALSBACH&D sc s.p., cor pts s.p. (W954)

Psalm 150
mix cor ALSBACH&D sc s.p., cor pts s.p. (W955)

WETTON, H. DAVON
Come All Ye People, Hasten Near
SATB,org ROBERTON (W956)

WETTSTEIN, H.
Eidgenossischer Dank-, Buss- Und Bettag
[Ger] mix cor,acap (easy) HUG s.p. (W957)

WETZLER
Come And See The Christ Child *Xmas
unis/SA SOUTHERN $.35 (W958)

Lord Give New Tunes
SATB oct FISCHER,C CM-7772 $.35 (W959)

Lord, Remember Us
SATB SOUTHERN $.30 (W960)

Lord, Remember Us (God, Hurrah!)
SATB (med easy) SOUTHERN $.30 (W961)

Lord, Surround Us With Holy Symbols
SATB (med diff/diff) SOUTHERN $.35 (W962)

Sweet Was The Song *Xmas
SSA SCHMITT 2572 $.35 (W963)
SATB SCHMITT 6233 $.35 (W964)

Take, Believe
SATB/unis SOUTHERN $.35 (W965)

WETZLER, ROBERT
Abide With Us Our Saviour
SATB SCHMITT SD5903 $.30 (W966)

Ah, Dearest Jesu, Holy Child *anthem
unis/SATB (easy) oct AUGSBURG 1294 $.25 (W967)

All The Earth Doth Worship Thee
SATB oct AGAPE A 463 $.35 (W968)

Blessed City, Heavenly Salem *Adv/Palm
SATB,acap (med easy) oct CONCORDIA 98-1639 $.25 (W969)

Carol Of Thanksgiving *Thanks,carol
SATB,acap oct KERBY 6107C $.35 (W970)
SATB oct KERBY 6107 $.35 (W971)

Christ The Lord Is Risen Again *Easter
SATB SCHMITT SD5906 $.20 (W972)

Christmas Noel, A *Xmas
SAB SCHMITT 5528 $.25 (W973)
SATB SCHMITT SD6102 $.25 (W974)

Come And See The Christ Child *Xmas
SA/unis SCHMITT 247 $.35 (W975)

Crown Him Lord Of All *anthem
SATB (med) oct AUGSBURG 1334 $.30 (W976)

Dear Christians, One And All, Rejoice *anthem
SATB&opt cong/unis&opt cong,opt trp (med) oct AUGSBURG 1566 $.30 (W977)

Doxology *anthem/Doxol
unis treb cor (easy) oct AUGSBURG 1399 $.25 (W978)
unis (easy) oct AUGSBURG 1599 $.25 (W979)

Easter Dawning At The Tomb *Easter,anthem
SATB (easy) oct AUGSBURG 1278 $.20 (W980)

Go Ye Into All The World *anthem
2pt mix cor (easy) oct AUGSBURG 1346 $.30 (W981)

Hail Thee, Spirit, Lord Eternal *anthem
2pt mix cor (easy) oct AUGSBURG 1314 $.25 (W982)

Hark! A Thrilling Voice Is Sounding *anthem
SATB (easy) oct AUGSBURG 1297 $.25 (W983)

Hope Of The World *anthem
unis sr cor (easy) oct AUGSBURG 1366 $.25 (W984)

Introits, Part I *CCU,Adv/Xmas/Epiph
mix cor (med easy) oct AUGSBURG 11-9215 $.50 (W985)

Introits, Part II *CCU,Lent
mix cor (med easy) oct AUGSBURG 11-9216 $.50 (W986)

Introits, Part III *CCU,Easter/Pent
mix cor (med easy) oct AUGSBURG 11-9217 $.50 (W987)

Introits, Part IV *CCU,Trin
mix cor (med easy) oct AUGSBURG 11-9218 $.50 (W988)

Introits, Part V *CCU
mix cor (med easy) oct AUGSBURG 11-9219 $.50 (W989)

Look, Ye Saints, The Sight Is Glorious *anthem
SAB (med) oct AUGSBURG 1534 $.20 (W990)

Lord, A-Rock-A My Soul *spir
SATB SCHMITT 1877 $.35 (W991)

Lord, Make Me An Instrument Of Thy Peace *anthem
SATB,solo (easy) oct AUGSBURG 1522 $.20 (W992)

Lord, Remember Us (from God, Hurrah) anthem
SATB (med) oct AUGSBURG 1645 $.30 (W993)

WETZLER, ROBERT (cont'd.)

Lord, Surround Us With Holy Symbols (from God, Hurrah) anthem
SATB (med) oct AUGSBURG 1649 $.35 (W994)

Lord, We Praise You For The Rhythm (from God Hurrah) anthem
2pt mix cor (med) oct AUGSBURG 1624 $.35 (W995)

Mary, Mother Sweet And Mild *anthem
SATB,S solo (easy) oct AUGSBURG 1241 $.20 (W996)

Meditation On "Woodworth"
SATB,org (very easy) ABINGDON APM-260 cor pts $.18, sc ipa (W997)

Noel! The Savior Is Born *Xmas
mix cor oct AGAPE CF 165 $.30 (W998)

O Jesus, King Most Wonderful *anthem
SATB (easy) oct AUGSBURG 1452 $.20 (W999)

On Calvary's Hill *anthem
unis treb cor/SA (easy) oct AUGSBURG 1536 $.25 (W1000)

Onward Ye Saints *anthem
SATB (easy) oct AUGSBURG 1272 $.30 (W1001)

Praise The Lord
SATB oct GRAY GCMR 3019 $.30 (W1002)

Psalm 1960
SATB&SATB,opt inst oct WALTON 2906 $.35 (W1003)

Seek Ye The Lord *anthem
SATB (med diff) oct AUGSBURG 1457 $.30 (W1004)

Son Is Born Of Mary, A *anthem
SATB (easy) oct AUGSBURG 1381 $.25 (W1005)

This Little Babe *anthem
SATB,kbd/gtr (med easy) oct AUGSBURG 0536 $.30 (W1006)

Two Lenten Meditations *CC2U,Lent
SATB (easy) ABINGDON APM-347 $.25 (W1007)

We Give Thee Thanks *anthem
SATB (med) oct AUGSBURG 1359 $.35 (W1008)

What Shall I Render
SATB (easy) ABINGDON APM-395 $.25 (W1009)

Who Is The Child? *anthem
SATB (easy) oct AUGSBURG 1296 $.22 (W1010)

Winds Thru The Olive Trees *anthem
unis treb cor (easy) oct AUGSBURG 1570 $.20 (W1011)

WE'VE A STORY TO TELL TO THE NATION see Nichol, H. Ernest

WE'VE A STORY TO TELL TO THE NATIONS see Nichol

WE'VE BEEN A WHILE A'WANDERING see Christiansen, Olaf Christian

WE'VE GOT ONE HOUR, LORD see Prentice, Fred

WE'VE ONLY BEGUN see Newbury, Kent A.

WE'VE TRAVELED FAR see De Lejanas Tierras Venimos

WEXFORD CAROL
see Three Christmas Carols

WEYER, J.
Messe En L'honneur De Saint-Odile *Mass
2 eq voices/4pt mix cor,org LEMOINE voc sc s.p., cor pts s.p. (W1012)

WEYRAUCH, JOHANNES (1897-   )
Auf Das Christfest *cant
unis wom cor&SAB,org HANSSLER 10.033 sc s.p., cor pts s.p. (W1013)

Befiehl Du Deine Wege *mot
SATB HANSSLER 7.111 s.p. (W1014)

Der Herr Ward Gehorsam Bis Zum Tod *mot
SAB HANSSLER 7.046 s.p. (W1015)

Die Herrlichkeit Der Erden
SATB,org HANSSLER 5.082 s.p. (W1016)

Euch Ist Heute Der Heiland Geboren
SAT,org HANSSLER 10.197 sc s.p., cor pts s.p. (W1017)

Gott, Dem Ewigen Konige *Introit/mot
SATB HANSSLER 7.079 s.p. (W1018)

Herr, Neige Deine Ohren Und Erhore Mich *Introit/mot
SATB HANSSLER 7.082 s.p. (W1019)

Mein Seele Erhebet Den Herrn *Magnif
SATB,org HANSSLER 5.081 s.p. (W1020)

Passion Nach Dem Evangelium Des Johannes *cant
SAB,org HANSSLER 10.032 sc s.p., cor pts s.p. (W1021)

Siehe, Der Herr Wird Kommen Mit Feuer *Introit/mot
SATB HANSSLER 7.083 s.p. (W1022)

Zeit Ist Wie Ewigkeit
SA,org,2rec HANSSLER 5.044 s.p. (W1023)

WEYSE, CHRISTOPH ERNST FRIEDRICH (1774-1842)
Aftensang
mix cor MUSIKK 105 s.p. (W1024)

Christmas Is Here *Xmas
(Hansen) SSA SCHMITT 2579 $.25 (W1025)

High 'Bove The Starry Sky
(Stone) SAABar,acap oct WORD CRS-18 $.35 (W1026)

Jehovah's Might
SAABar,acap oct WORD CRS-19 $.35 (W1027)

WEYSE, CHRISTOPH ERNST FRIEDRICH (cont'd.)

Lord Of The Stars
SAABar,acap oct WORD CRS-20 $.35 (W1028)

O Day Full Of Grace *anthem
(Christiansen, F.M.) SATTBB (diff) oct AUGSBURG 0206 $.25 (W1029)
(Christiansen, Paul) SATB,med solo (med) oct AUGSBURG 1179 $.25 (W1030)
(Johnson) SAB (easy) oct AUGSBURG 1523 $.25 (W1031)
(Wetzler) TTBB (easy) oct AUGSBURG 1530 $.18 (W1032)

Reformationskantate *Refm,cant
[Dan] men cor,pno sc FOG I, 19 s.p. (W1033)

WHAT A FRIEND see Rasley

WHAT A FRIEND WE HAVE IN JESUS see Converse

WHAT A FRIEND WE HAVE IN JESUS see Converse, Charles Crozat

WHAT A FRIEND WE HAVE IN JESUS see Young, Gordon

WHAT ARE THESE? see Stainer, John

WHAT ARE THESE THAT ARE ARRAYED see Stainer, John

WHAT ARE THESE THAT ARE ARRAYED IN WHITE ROBES? see Stainer, John

WHAT CAN I DO FOR THEE? see Dexter, Harry

WHAT CAN I GIVE HIM
SSA/SATB BIG3 $.40 (W1034)

WHAT CAN I GIVE HIM? see Emery

WHAT CAN I GIVE HIM see Jones, Marjorie

WHAT CAN I GIVE HIM? see Rasley, [John M.]

WHAT CAN LIFE BE BUT A SHADOW? see Bach, Johann Michael, Unser Leben Ist Ein Schatten

WHAT CAN THIS MEAN? see Staley

WHAT CHEER? GOOD CHEER see Davies, Lawrence H.

WHAT CHEER? GOOD CHEER! see Gordon, Philip

WHAT CHEER? GOOD CHEER! see Heseltine, Philip

WHAT CHILD IS THIS? *Xmas,anthem/carol,Eng
see Many Moods Of Christmas, The, Suite Three
see Three Songs For Christmas
see From Heaven Above To Earth I Come
SATB&desc SCHIRM.EC 1764 $.25 (W1035)
SSA oct SPRATT 606 $.25 (W1036)
SA oct LORENZ 5383 $.30 (W1037)
(Barthelson) jr cor&sr cor oct BELWIN 693 $.25 (W1038)
(Bell) SATB oct BELWIN 60034 $.30 (W1039)
(Candlyn) SATB oct FISCHER,C CM-6566 $.25 (W1040)
(Candlyn) unis&desc oct FISCHER,C CM-6162 $.25 (W1041)
(Davis, K.) unis&SSA SCHIRM.EC 1882 $.25 (W1042)
(De Cormier) SATB,pno/org oct LAWSON 51437 $.35 (W1043)
(Gardner) SATB oct STAFF 337 $.20 (W1044)
(Glaser, V.) SSA,acap SCHIRM.EC 2550 $.30 (W1045)
(Heath) 4pt men cor,Bar solo,acap oct SCHIRM.G 10839 $.30 (W1046)
(Hughes) SATB oct LORENZ A463 $.30 (W1047)
(Ruggles, R. Brant) SATB (easy) oct AUGSBURG 1622 $.25 (W1048)
(Scarmolin) SATB oct PRO ART 1398 $.30 (W1049)
(Scarmolin) SAB oct PRO ART 1399 $.30 (W1050)
(Scarmolin) SAB oct PRO ART 1255 $.30 (W1051)
(Scholin) SSA oct BELWIN 1940 $.30 (W1052)
(Scholin) SATB oct BELWIN 1673 $.25 (W1053)
(Shaw; Parker) mix cor,acap oct SCHIRM.G 10199 $.30 (W1054)
(Swenson) SATB oct GALAXY 1.2474.1 $.20 (W1055)
(Van Koert, Han) SA&SATB,org,opt fl&vln&vla& vcl&harp oct WORLD AC-545-8 $.45, ipa (W1056)
(Warner) unis&desc oct SCHIRM.G 10758 $.30 (W1057)

WHAT CHILD IS THIS see Candlyn, T. Frederick H.

WHAT CHILD IS THIS see Christiansen, P.

WHAT CHILD IS THIS? see Escovada, R.

WHAT CHILD IS THIS? see Frackenpohl, Arthur

WHAT CHILD IS THIS? see Land

WHAT CHILD IS THIS? see Lowden

WHAT CHILD IS THIS? see Strickland

WHAT CHILD IS THIS see Williams

WHAT CHILD IS THIS? see Wilson

WHAT COLOR IS GOD'S SKIN? see Wilkes, T.

WHAT DID HE MEAN TO TELL US? see Nelson, Ronald A.

WHAT DID THE WISE MEN HEAR? see Grime, William

WHAT FEAR HAS DEATH FOR ME? see Bach, Johann Sebastian

WHAT FRAGRANCE THIS see Moschetti, [Giuseppe]

WHAT GAMES DID JESUS PLAY? see Grime, William

WHAT GOD DOES, THAT IS NOBLY DONE
SATB KJOS 2045 $.30 (W1058)

WHAT GOD DOTH, ONLY THAT IS RIGHT see Bach, Johann Sebastian, Was Mein Gott Will, Das G'scheh Allzeit

WHAT GOD HAS PROMISED see Wehr, David A.

WHAT GOD ORDAINS IS ALWAYS GOOD see Bach, Johann Sebastian

WHAT GOD ORDAINS IS ALWAYS GOOD see Pachelbel, Johann, Was Gott Tut, Das Ist Wohlgetan

WHAT GOD ORDAINS IS ALWAYS GOOD see Schutz, Heinrich

WHAT GOD ORDAINS IS BEST OF ALL see Bach, Johann Sebastian

WHAT HAPPENED TO CHRISTMAS *Xmas/Pageant
LORENZ $.75 (W1059)

WHAT HAVE THEY DONE? see White, Phil

WHAT IS IT ALL ABOUT? see Van Wyatt

WHAT IS MAN? see Glarum, L. Stanley

WHAT IS MAN see Le Jeune, Claude

WHAT IS MAN? see Nelson, Ronald A.

WHAT IS MAN see Sengstock

WHAT IS THAT FRAGRANCE
see Three Nativity Carols

WHAT IS THAT STRANGE NEW STAR?
(Ehret, Walter) SA oct AGAPE AD 1973 $.30 (W1060)

WHAT IS THE JOYFUL NEWS? see Gerhardt, Carl

WHAT IS THE PLEASANT FRAGRANCE? see Quelle Est Cette Odeur Agreable

WHAT IS THE WORLD TO ME see Buxtehude, Dietrich, Was Frag' Ich Nach Der Welt

WHAT IS THIS FRAGRANCE *Xmas,carol,Fr
(Grams, W.P.) SATB,kbd (med easy) oct CONCORDIA 98-1891 $.35 (W1061)
(Huston, J.) SATB oct GRAY GCMR 2541 $.30 (W1062)

WHAT IS THIS LOVE see Wilson, John F.

WHAT IS THIS LOVELY FRAGRANCE see Willan, Healey

WHAT IS THIS PERFUME SO APPEALING? *Xmas, carol,Fr
(Ehret, Walter) SATB,opt inst oct WALTON 2511 $.30 (W1063)
(Ehret, Walter) SSA,opt inst oct WALTON 2535 $.30 (W1064)

WHAT KIND OF KING? see Boeringer, James

WHAT MAKES THE WIND BLOW? see Avery

WHAT MAKES THE YELLOW STAR TO DANCE? see Bayley, Robert Charlton

WHAT MANNER OF LOVE see Ford, Virgil T.

WHAT MEANS THIS GLORY ROUND OUR FEET? see Mead, E.G.

WHAT MIRACLES OF BEAUTY see Hourdeaux

WHAT OF THE NIGHT? see Thompson, R.G.

WHAT OF THY FLOCKS, O SHEPHERD? see Geehl, Henry Ernest

WHAT PAIN OUR MASTER DIDST ENDURE see Schutz, Heinrich

WHAT RETURN SHALL I MAKE TO THE LORD see Roff, Joseph

WHAT SHALL I RENDER see Wetzler, Robert

WHAT SHALL I RENDER TO MY GOD see Lovelace, Austin C.

WHAT SHALL WE BRING see Kirk

WHAT SHALL WE CHILDREN BRING? see Agey

WHAT SHALL WE GIVE? see El Noi De La Mare?

WHAT SONGS WERE SUNG see Niles, John Jacob

WHAT SPLENDID RAYS see Antes, John

WHAT STAR IS THIS? see Beckhard

WHAT STAR IS THIS? see Blake, G.

WHAT STAR IS THIS? see Ehret, Walter

WHAT STAR IS THIS? see Harris

WHAT STAR IS THIS see Praetorius, Michael

WHAT STRANGERS ARE THESE? see Berger

WHAT SWEETER MUSIC see Clark, Keith

WHAT SWEETER MUSIC see Stevens, Halsey

WHAT TENDER NEWS YE BRING *Xmas
(Kozinski, D.) SATB,acap oct PRESSER 312-40319 $.30 (W1065)

WHAT THE FUTURE HATH see Brandon

WHAT TIDINGS? *Xmas,carol
SATB (easy) OXFORD 08.039 $.15 (W1066)

WHAT TIDINGS? see Hoddinott, Alun

WHAT TIDINGS BRINGEST THOU?
see Musica Britannica Vol. 4: Set 7

WHAT TONGUE CAN TELL THY GREATNESS, LORD see Bach

WHAT TONGUE CAN TELL THY GREATNESS, LORD see Bach, Johann Sebastian

WHAT TREES WERE IN GETHSEMANE see Caldwell

WHAT TREES WERE IN GETHSEMANE? see Caldwell, Mary [Elizabeth]

WHAT WAS THIS WONDROUS THING? see Giasson

WHAT WONDEROUS LOVE IS THIS see Harry, P.A.

WHAT WONDERS FILL THE HEAV'NS TONIGHT *Xmas
  (Wiley) SATB,acap,opt pno oct PRO ART 2528
  $.25   (W1067)

WHAT WONDROUS LOVE see Wade, Walter

WHAT WONDROUS LOVE IS THIS see Denton

WHAT WONDROUS LOVE IS THIS see Harry, P.A.

WHAT WONDROUS SACRIFICE see Haubiel, Charles

WHAT YOU GONNA CALL YO' PRETTY LITTLE BABY?
  *Xmas,spir
  (Ryder) 4pt men cor,acap oct SCHIRM.G 9501
  $.30   (W1068)

WHAT YOU GONNA CALL YO' PRETTY LITTLE BABY? see
  Ryder, Noah F.

WHAT YOU GONNA CALL YOUR PRETTY LITTLE BABY
  *Xmas
  (Ehret) SA SCHMITT 2584 $.35   (W1069)
  (Ehret) SAB SCHMITT 5525 $.45   (W1070)
  (Ehret) SATB SCHMITT 884 $.45   (W1071)
  (Ehret) SSA SCHMITT 334 $.45   (W1072)

WHAT YOU REALLY NEED IS JESUS see Landgrave,
  Phillip

WHATE'ER MY GOD ORDAINS IS RIGHT (from Weimar
  Gesangbuch)
  (Ehret) SATB BOSTON 13460 $.35   (W1073)

WHATE'ER MY GOD ORDAINS IS RIGHT see Pachelbel,
  Johann

WHAT'S THE USE IN PRAYIN' see Strommen

WHATSOE'ER YE DO see Buxtehude, Dietrich,
  Alles, Was Ihr Tut

WHATSOEVER THINGS see Curry, R.D.

WHATSOEVER YE SHALL ASK see Roff, Joseph

WHEAR, PAUL WILLIAM (1925-   )
  Forever Thy Word, Alleluia
  SATB,band/orch LUDWIG L-1103 $.30, ipa
                                                 (W1074)
  Glory To God
  SATB,brass LUDWIG L-1110 $.30, ipa   (W1075)

  Hosanna
  SATB LUDWIG L-1145 $.30   (W1076)

  Joyful-Jubilate
  cor,perc LUDWIG L-1141 oct $.50, ipa, sc
  $5.00   (W1077)

  Psalm 47 *see Psalms Of Celebration Part IV

  Psalm 92 *see Psalms Of Celebration Part II

  Psalm 133
         oee Whear,&aul William, Psalm 92

  Psalm 138 *see Psalms Of Celebration part I

  Psalms Of Celebration part I (Psalm 138)
  LUDWIG $.50   (W1078)

  Psalms Of Celebration Part IV (Psalm 47)
  LUDWIG $.50   (W1079)

  Psalms Of Celebration *Bibl
  cor,orch LUDWIG sc $1.50, study sc $2.00
                                                 (W1080)
  Psalms Of Celebration Part II (Psalm 92)
  LUDWIG $.50 contains also: Psalm 133
                                                 (W1081)

WHEEL IN THE MIDDLE OF THE WHEEL *spir
  (Ritz, James) SSA&SATB,acap oct WORLD
  ESE-730-8 $.60   (W1082)

WHEELER, ALFRED
  Be Thou My Guide *Austral
  SATB (easy) ALLANS 148 s.p.   (W1083)

  He Was Despised *Austral
  SATB (easy) ALLANS 68 s.p.   (W1084)

  I Am The Way *Austral
  SATB,S solo ALLANS 25 s.p.   (W1085)

  I Will Magnify *Austral
  SATB ALLANS 144 s.p.   (W1086)

  Lord Is My Light *Easter,Austral
  SATB (easy) ALLANS 28 s.p.   (W1087)

  Lord, Teach Us To Pray *Austral
  SATB (easy) ALLANS 32 s.p.   (W1088)

  Love Triumphant *Commun/Fest/Lent/Marriage,
  Austral
  SATB (easy) ALLANS 166 s.p.   (W1089)

  Loving Shepherd, Lead Me *Austral
  SATB (easy) ALLANS 47 s.p.   (W1090)

  O Gentle Savior *Austral
  SATB ALLANS 176 s.p.   (W1091)

  Our Father's Home *Austral
  SA ALLANS 251 s.p.   (W1092)

  Rejoice In The Lord *Easter/Fest,Austral
  SATB (easy) ALLANS 24 s.p.   (W1093)

  Sing To The Lord *Austral
  SATB ALLANS 120 s.p.   (W1094)

  There Is A Green Hill *Commun/Lent,Austral
  SATB (easy) ALLANS 67 s.p.   (W1095)

WHEELER, RUFUS
  Christmas Is Coming *see Siegmeister, Elie

WHEELWRIGHT, LORIN F.
  Deliverance
  SATB PIONEER 5056 $.18   (W1096)

  Garden Of My Lord, The
  SATB,T/S solo PIONEER 5053 $.20   (W1097)

  Go Forth Together Believing
  see Hymns For Teachers

  God Moves In A Mysterious Way
  see Wheelwright, Lorin F., Morning Breaks,
  The

  Help Me Teach With Inspiration
  see Hymns For Teachers

  Hymns For Teachers
  SATB PIONEER 6002 $.20
  contains: Go Forth Together Believing;
  Help Me Teach With Inspiration; O May
  My Soul Commune With Thee   (W1098)

  Hymns Of Joy *CC8L
  mix cor PIONEER $.25   (W1099)

  Morning Breaks, The
  SATB PIONEER 6001 $.20 contains also: God
  Moves In A Mysterious Way   (W1100)

  O May My Soul Commune With Thee
  see Hymns For Teachers

  O Men Of God
  unis PIONEER 7001 $.20   (W1101)
  TTBB PIONEER 7002 $.25   (W1102)

  Ode To Immortality
  SSA PIONEER $.20   (W1103)

  Star Bright
  SA PIONEER 1003 $.20   (W1104)

WHEN A STRONG MAN see Brahms, Johannes

WHEN ALL DISCIPLES see Palestrina, Giovanni,
  Dum Ergo Essent

WHEN ALL DISCIPLES see Victoria, Tomas Luis de,
  Dum Ergo Essent

WHEN ALL THY MERCIES, O MY GOD see Cole

WHEN AN ANGEL HOST ENTUNED see Jacques

WHEN AT CHRISTMAS see Quand Dieu Naquit A Noel

WHEN AT CHRISTMAS CHRIST WAS BORN *Xmas
  (Dalley; Scarlett) SATB,acap oct FISCHER,C
  CM-6938 $.25   (W1105)

WHEN BROTHERS DWELL IN UNITY see White, John

WHEN CHILDREN PRAY see Nordman, Chester

WHEN CHILDREN SING SONGS OF PRAISE see Schroth

WHEN CHRIST RODE INTO JERUSALEM see Ward

WHEN CHRIST THE CHILD CAME see Clokey

WHEN CHRIST WAS BORN see Gilbert, J.R.

WHEN CHRIST WAS BORN see Jacques

WHEN CHRIST WAS BORN see Lenel, Ludwig

WHEN CHRIST WAS BORN see Livingstone

WHEN CHRIST WAS BORN see Smith, Peter

WHEN CHRIST WAS BORN IN BETHLEHEM see Hammel,
  B.

WHEN CHRIST WAS BORN OF MARY FREE *Xmas,carol,
  Eng/Fr,16th cent
  (Barnes) SSATB/SATB,opt S solo,acap oct
  SCHIRM.G 7300 $.25   (W1106)
  (Coggin) 3pt mix cor,org/pno oct SCHIRM.G
  11325 $.25   (W1107)
  (Ehret) SA ALLANS 345 s.p.   (W1108)
  (Ehret) SATB ALLANS 330 s.p.   (W1109)
  (Field, Robert) SATB,pno,bells (easy) PRESSER
  $.35   (W1110)
  (Stone) SSA oct PRO ART 1549 $.22   (W1111)

WHEN CHRIST WAS BORN OF MARY FREE see Ehret,
  Walter

WHEN CHRIST WAS BORN OF MARY FREE see Hilton

WHEN CHRIST WAS BORN OF MARY FREE see Husted,
  B.

WHEN CHRIST WAS BORN OF MARY FREE see Morrison,
  Kenneth L.

WHEN CHRIST WAS BORN OF MARY FREE see Sellew

WHEN CHRISTMAS MORN IS DAWNING see Nar
  Juldagsmorgon Glimmar

WHEN CHRISTMAS MORN IS DAWNING see Pfust

WHEN DAVID FIRST HEARD THAT ABSALOM WAS SLAIN
  see East, Michael

WHEN DAVID HEARD see East, Michael

WHEN DAVID HEARD see Weelkes, Thomas

WHEN DAVID HEARD THAT ABSALOM WAS SLAIN see
  Ramsey, Robert

WHEN DAVID HEARD THAT ABSALOM WAS SLAIN see
  Tomkins, Thomas

WHEN DE STARS BEGIN TO FALL *spir
  (Roberton) 4pt mix cor ROBERTON 61384 s.p.
                                                 (W1112)
  (Roberton) men cor ROBERTON 50785 s.p.
                                                 (W1113)
  (Roberton) 3pt jr cor/3pt wom cor ROBERTON
  72107 s.p.   (W1114)

WHEN FEARS OF DEATH DO FRIGHT ME see Franck,
  Melchior

WHEN GOD OF OLD CAME DOWN FROM HEAVEN see Hall,
  E. Vine

WHEN GOD ON US HIS LOVE BESTOWS see Bach,
  Johann Sebastian, Ist Gott Versohnt Und
  Unser Freund

WHEN GOD SEES YOUR GARDEN see Hart, A.W.

WHEN GOD SPEAKS see Simpkins

WHEN HE COMETH see Bock, Fred

WHEN HE SHALL COME see Pearce

WHEN HIS LOUD VOICE see Handel, George Frideric

WHEN, HIS SALVATION BRINGING see Baumgartner,
  H. Leroy

WHEN HIS SALVATION BRINGING see Rasley, [John
  M.]

WHEN I CAN READ MY TITLE CLEAR *hymn
  (Parker) mix cor,acap oct LAWSON 51340 $.30
                                                 (W1115)

WHEN I CAN READ MY TITLE CLEAR see Coggin

WHEN I CONSIDER THE HEAVENS see Scott, John
  Prindle

WHEN I CONSIDER THY HEAVENS see Dalby, Martin

WHEN I MET THE MAN OF CALVARY see Moore

WHEN I NEED HIM see Smith

WHEN I RECALL THE HOUR see Regnart

WHEN I SEE MY SAVIOUR see Harkness

WHEN I STOOD AT CALVARY see McCluskey

WHEN I SURVEY THE WONDROUS CROSS *Easter/Lent
  SAB KJOS 8023 $.30   (W1116)
  (Kinsman) SATB oct PRO ART 2030 $.25 (W1117)

WHEN I SURVEY THE WONDROUS CROSS see
  Boatwright, Howard

WHEN I SURVEY THE WONDROUS CROSS see Copes, V.
  Earle

WHEN I SURVEY THE WONDROUS CROSS see Fawcett,
  J.

WHEN I SURVEY THE WONDROUS CROSS see Lenel,
  Ludwig

WHEN I SURVEY THE WONDROUS CROSS see Lovelace,
  Austin C.

WHEN I SURVEY THE WONDROUS CROSS see Markworth,
  Henry

WHEN I SURVEY THE WONDROUS CROSS see Martin, G.

WHEN I SURVEY THE WONDROUS CROSS see Mason

WHEN I SURVEY THE WONDROUS CROSS see Mason,
  Daniel Gregory

    WHEN I SURVEY THE WONDROUS CROSS see Mason,
  T.D.

WHEN I SURVEY THE WONDROUS CROSS see Ringwald,
  [Roy]

WHEN I SURVEY THE WONDROUS CROSS see Stanton,
  [Walter Kendall]

WHEN I SURVEY THE WONDROUS CROSS see Vulpius,
  Melchior

WHEN I SURVEY THE WONDROUS CROSS see William,
  Glan

WHEN I SURVEY THE WONDROUS CROSS see Williams,
  David H.

WHEN I SURVEY THE WONDROUS CROSS see Young,
  Gordon

WHEN I SURVEY THE WONDROUS CROSS see Young,
  Robert H.

WHEN I THINK OF CALVARY see Dieterich

WHEN I THINK UPON THY GOODNESS see Haydn,
  (Franz) Joseph

WHEN I TRUST THE SAVIOR see Johnson, Paul

WHEN I WAS IN TROUBLE see Le Fleming,
  Christopher (Kaye)

WHEN I WAS POOR AND IN HEAVINESS see Croce,
  Giovanni, Ego Sum Pauper Et Dolens

WHEN I WAS SINKIN' DOWN *hymn/spir,US
  (Ehret) SATB,S solo oct LAWSON 51182 $.25
                                                 (W1118)
  (Johnson) 4pt mix cor,acap oct SCHIRM.G 9559
  $.35   (W1119)

WHEN I'M FEELING LONELY see Avery

WHEN IN THE HOUR OF UTMOST NEED see Lundquist

WHEN ISRAEL CAME FORTH see Kraft, Leo

WHEN ISRAEL OUT OF EGYPT CAME see Weisgall,
  Hugo

WHEN I'VE DONE MY BEST
  SATB BIG3 $.25   (W1120)

WHEN JESUS CAME see Kirby

WHEN JESUS CAME TO LIVE WITH MEN see Hutson,
  Wihla

WHEN JESUS CHRIST, OUR LORD AND KING *Xmas,
  carol,Fr
  (Halter, C.) SATB,acap (easy) oct CONCORDIA
  98-1663 $.25   (W1121)

WHEN JESUS CHRIST WAS YET A CHILD *carol
   unis/SATB (very easy) OXFORD 08.197 $.15
                                              (W1122)
WHEN JESUS CHRIST WAS YET A CHILD see Foltz

WHEN JESUS IN THE GARDEN *Psntd,17th cent
   (Wasner) SABar,acap oct SCHIRM.G 8822 $.25
                                              (W1123)
WHEN JESUS IN THE GARDEN see Wasner, Franz

WHEN JESUS LEFT HIS FATHER'S THRONE *anthem/
   folk,US
   (Johnson, David N.) SATB (easy) oct AUGSBURG
   0515 $.20   (W1124)
   (Johnson, David N.) SSA oct AUGSBURG 0518
   $.22   (W1125)
WHEN JESUS LEFT HIS FATHER'S THRONE see Powell,
   Robert J.

WHEN JESUS LIVED IN GALILEE *Xmas,carol/folk
   (Niles) 3pt wom cor&unis jr cor,S solo,acap
   oct SCHIRM.G 9268   (W1126)
   (Niles) 4pt mix cor&unis jr cor,acap oct
   SCHIRM.G 9388   (W1127)
   (Niles) SATB&opt jr cor,opt S solo oct
   SCHIRM.G 9388 $.25   (W1128)
   (Niles) 3pt wom cor&jr cor,S solo oct
   SCHIRM.G 9268 $.25   (W1129)

WHEN JESUS LIVED IN GALILEE see Niles, John
   Jacob

WHEN JESUS WALKED UPON THE EARTH see Wehr,
   David A.

WHEN JESUS WAS A BOY, SERIES 1 see Grime,
   William

WHEN JESUS WAS A LITTLE CHILD see Tchaikovsky,
   Piotr Ilyitch

WHEN JESUS WAS BORN see Graham, Robert [V.]

WHEN JESUS WAS BORN see Matthews

WHEN JESUS WENT TO THE WELL see Grime, William

WHEN JESUS WEPT see Billings, William

WHEN JESUS WEPT see Kjelson

WHEN LIFE BEGINS TO FAIL ME
   see Three Chorales

WHEN LILACS LAST IN THE DOOR- YARD BLOOM'D see
   Hindemith, Paul

WHEN LOVE CAME DOWN see Thompson

WHEN LOVE WAS BORN see Thompson

WHEN MARY THROUGH THE GARDEN WENT see Judd,
   Percy

WHEN MORNING GILDS THE SKIES see Barnby

WHEN MORNING GILDS THE SKIES see Denton

WHEN MORNING GILDS THE SKIES see Dressler, John

WHEN MORNING GILDS THE SKIES see Hughes

WHEN MORNING GILDS THE SKIES see Schalk, Carl

WHEN MORNING GILDS THE SKIES see Thompson

WHEN MORNING GILDS THE SKIES see Weaver

WHEN MORNING GILDS THE SKY see Whitehead,
   Alfred

WHEN MY LAST HOUR IS CLOSE AT HAND see
   Gumpeltzhaimer, Adam

WHEN MY SAVIOR see Williams

WHEN ON MY SICK BED I LANGUISH see Purcell,
   Henry

WHEN ONE KNOWS THEE see Glarum, L. Stanley

WHEN OUR LORD WAS BORN *Xmas
   (Douglas) SSA oct PRO ART 2575 $.30   (W1130)

WHEN PEACE LIKE A RIVER see Boyd

WHEN RIGHTEOUS JOSEPH WEDDED WAS *carol
   SATB (very easy) OXFORD 08.041 $.15   (W1131)

WHEN SHALL MY SORROWFUL SIGHING see Tallis,
   Thomas

WHEN SIMEON CAME TO WORSHIP see Grime, William

WHEN THE DAY OF PENTECOST see Victoria, Tomas
   Luis de, Dum Complerentur Dies Pentecotes

WHEN THE HERDS WERE WATCHING see Andrews,
   Harold

WHEN THE HERDS WERE WATCHING see Redman,
   Reginald

WHEN THE INFANT JESUS   oee Hopkins, H.

WHEN THE LORD ENTERED see Schubert, Franz
   (Peter)

WHEN THE LORD OF LOVE see Thiman, Eric Harding

WHEN THE LORD TURNED AGAIN see Batten, Adrian

WHEN THE LORD TURNED AGAIN see Faning, Eaton

WHEN THE LORD TURNED AGAIN see Marshall, Philip

WHEN THE LORD WAS BORN see Peloquin, C.
   Alexander

WHEN THE PEOPLE SAW THE SIGN WHICH HE HAD DONE
   see Hillert, Richard

WHEN THE ROLL IS CALLED UP YONDER see Blancks,
   Edward

WHEN THE SABBATH WAS PAST see Taverner, John,
   Dum Transisset Sabbatum

WHEN THE SAINTS COME MARCHING IN *spir
   (Ehret) men cor oct SPRATT 197 $.30   (W1132)

WHEN THE SAINTS GO MARCHING IN
   see Folio Of Sacred Music (Volume 3)

WHEN THE SAVIOR CHRIST IS BORN see Gdy Sie
   Christus Rodzi

WHEN THE SAVIOR CHRIST IS BORN see Gdy Sie
   Chrystus Rodzi

WHEN THE SHEPHERDS HEARD THE ANGELS *Xmas
   (Follett) SATB oct PRO ART 2241 $.25   (W1133)

WHEN THE SON OF MAN SHALL COME see Harwood,
   Basil

WHEN THE SON OF MAN SHALL COME see Locke,
   Matthew

WHEN THE WORLD BEGAN TO WAKE see Hutson, Wihla

WHEN THEY FIRST SAW JESUS see Grime, William

WHEN THEY RING THE GOLDEN BELLS see De Marbelle

WHEN THOU ART NEAR see Bach, Johann Sebastian,
   Bist Du Bei Mir

WHEN THOU COMEST see Rossini, Gioacchino,
   Inflammatus

WHEN THOU COMEST TO THE JUDGMENT see Rossini,
   Gioacchino, Inflammatus Et Accensus

WHEN THOU PASSEST THROUGH THE WATERS see
   Austin, Ernest

WHEN THOU PASSEST THROUGH THE WATERS see
   Berger, Jean

WHEN THOU PRAYEST see Mueller, Carl F.

WHEN TO THE TEMPLE see Davies

WHEN TO THE TEMPLE MARY WENT see Eccard,
   Johannes

WHEN TO THEE OUR SAVIOR WENT see Wagner,
   Richard

WHEN TO THEE OUR SAVIOUR WENT see Wagner,
   Richard

WHEN WE COME TO WORSHIP see Grime, William

WHEN WE HEAR THE CHURCH BELLS see Grime,
   William

WHEN WE IN SPIRIT VIEW THY PASSION see Freydt

WHEN WE SEE SUNSET see Grime, William

WHEN WILL GOD RECALL MY SPIRIT? see Bach,
   Johann Sebastian, Liebster Gott, Wann Werd'
   Ich Sterben?

WHEN WILL GOD RECALL MY SPIRIT? see Bach,
   Johann Sebastian, Liebster Gott, Wann Werd'
   Ich Sterben [Chorale]

WHEN WILL HE COME see Matai Yavo

WHEN WILT THOU SAVE THE PEOPLE
   (Brandon) 2pt mix cor/3pt mix cor/4pt mix
   cor,pno/org oct LAWSON 51549 $.35   (W1134)

WHEN WILT THOU SAVE THE PEOPLE? see Mueller,
   Carl F.

WHEN YISRAEL LEFT MITZRAYIM see Chajes, Julius

WHENCE ART THOU, MY MAIDEN see Track, Gerhard

WHENCE COMES THIS FRAGRANCE? see Quelle Est
   Cette Odeur Agreable?

WHENCE COMES THIS RUSH OF WINGS *Xmas,carol,Fr
   see Tidings Of Comfort And Joy
   (Luboff, Norman) SATB oct WALTON 3029 $.30
                                          (W1135)
WHENCE COMES THIS RUSH OF WINGS AFAR? see
   Porter

WHERE CHARITY AND LOVE PREVAIL see Benoit, Dom
   Paul

WHERE COULD I GO BUT TO THE LORD
   SATB BIG3 $.25   (W1136)

WHERE CROSS THE CROWDED WAYS OF LIFE see
   Gardiner

WHERE CROSS THE CROWDED WAYS OF LIFE see
   Zeuner, Martin

WHERE DOES THE STAR SHINE BRIGHTLY see Harter,
   [Harry]

WHERE DOES THE UTTERED MUSIC GO? see Walton,
   William

WHERE HAS HE GONE? see Owens, Jimmy

WHERE HAVE YOU GONE, MY LONELY LORD? see Shea

WHERE HE LEADS ME see Davenport

WHERE IS HE BORN? see Mendelssohn-Bartholdy,
   Felix

WHERE IS MY DWELLING PLACE see Silesius,
   Angelus, Wo Ist Mein Aufenthalt

WHERE IS OLD ELIJAH see Gardner, Maurice

WHERE IS THE CHILD TODAY see Rhea, A.

WHERE IS THE NEWBORN KING? see Hammerschmidt,
   Andreas, Wo Ist Der Neugeborne Konig Der

WHERE LOVE MIGHT ENTER IN see Sateren, Leland
   Bernhard

WHERE NO ONE STANDS ALONE see Lister, Mosie

WHERE NOW ARE THE HEBREW CHILDREN *folk/hymn
   (Russell) TTBB,acap oct LAWSON 51506 $.25
                                          (W1137)
WHERE SHALL I FIND THE CHRIST CHILD? see Exner,
   Max

WHERE SHALL I GO? see Clary

WHERE SHALL I RUN? see Kaiser, Kurt

WHERE SHALL MY SOUL REPOSE? see Cantor, J.

WHERE SHALL MY WANDERING SOUL BEGIN? see Wesley

WHERE SHALL WISDOM BE FOUND? see Berger, Jean

WHERE SLEEPS THE INFANT JESUS *Xmas,carol,Mex
   (Ehret) SATB WARNER WB-138 $.30   (W1138)

WHERE THE RAINBOW ENDS see Smolover, R.

WHERE THOU REIGNEST see Schubert, Franz (Peter)

WHERE WERE YOU BORN, O HOLY CHILD? see Freed

WHERE WERE YOU, O SHEPHERD? see Burke, John

WHERE'ER HE LEADS ME
   SATB CHAPPELL 0017368-358 $.40   (W1139)

WHERE'ER I GO, WHATE'ER MY TASK see Hillert,
   Richard

WHERE'ER I ROAM OR LINGER see Handel, George
   Frideric

WHERE'ER THE CHRIST IS KNOWN see Harrington

WHERE'ER YOU WALK see Handel, George Frideric

WHEREFORE DO THE HEATHEN CLAMOR see Saint-
   Saens, Camille

WHEREFORE HATH THE LIGHT BEEN GIVEN see Brahms,
   Johannes, Warum Ist Das Licht Gegeben

WHEREFORE HATH THE LIGHT BEEN GRANTED see
   Brahms, Johannes, Warum Ist Das Licht
   Gegeben

WHEREFORE IS THE LIGHT BESTOWED see Brahms,
   Johannes, Warum Ist Das Licht Gegeban

WHEREFORE, O SAVIOUR, SO LONG IN RETURNING? see
   Bach, Johann Sebastian

WHEREVER HE LEADS I'LL GO see McKinney

WHETTAM, GRAHAM
   Magnificat And Nunc Dimittis
   SATB (med) oct OXFORD 42.852 $.65   (W1140)

   Mary Modyr, Cum And Se *Easter
   4pt mix cor oct SCHIRM.G 11256 $.30   (W1141)

   Missa Brevis
   SATB (med diff) oct OXFORD 42.862 $.65
                                          (W1142)
   Then Spake Solomon
   4pt mix cor oct SCHIRM.G 11264 $.35   (W1143)

WHILE ANGELS SING *anthem/folk,Mex
   (Christiansen, Paul) SATB/unis (very easy)
   oct AUGSBURG 1141 $.25   (W1144)

WHILE BY MY SHEEP *Xmas,hymn,17th cent
   see As Lately We Watched
   (Hallagan, R.) SATB,acap oct PRESSER
   312-40469 $.30   (W1145)
   (Jungst) 4pt mix cor,acap oct SCHIRM.G 2532
   $.30   (W1146)
   (Jungst) 4pt men cor,acap oct SCHIRM.G 1414
   $.20   (W1147)
   (Jungst; Deis) 3pt wom cor oct SCHIRM.G 9890
   $.20   (W1148)
   (Jungst; Deis) 3pt mix cor,acap oct SCHIRM.G
   9891 $.25   (W1149)
   (Jungst; Deis) 2pt boy cor oct SCHIRM.G 10214
   $.25   (W1150)

WHILE BY MY SHEEP see Junget

WHILE BY MY SHEEP see Jungst

WHILE BY MY SHEEP see Lowden

WHILE BY MY SHEEP I WATCHED AT NIGHT *anthem/
   carol,Ger,17th cent
   (Cassler, G. Winston) SA (easy) oct AUGSBURG
   1437 $.25   (W1151)

WHILE BY MY SHEEP I WATCHED AT NIGHT see Krapf,
   Gerhard

WHILE BY OUR SLEEPING FLOCK WE LAY *carol,Ger
   (Jungst, H.) SATB,acap, echo chorus SCHIRM.EC
   1685 $.30   (W1152)

WHILE BY OUR SLEEPING FLOCKS WE LAY see Jungst,
   Hugo

WHILE BY OUR SLEEPING FLOCKS WE LAY see The
   Song Of The Shepherds

   WHILE I DID WATCH MY SHEEP AT NIGHT *hymn,17th
   cent
   (Van Christy) SATB oct BELWIN 2189 $.30
                                          (W1153)
WHILE I SUP WITH THEE *CCU,anthem
   LORENZ $1.50   (W1154)

WHILE I SUP WITH THEE see Haxby

WHILE JESUS LAY ASLEEP see Trued

WHILE ORGANS MADE HARMONY see Philips, Peter

WHILE SHEPHERDS WATCHED *Xmas,carol
   see Five Christmas Carols
   (Reed) unis BOOSEY-CAN $.25   (W1155)
   (Sanders) SATB,acap oct PRO ART 1228 $.25
                                          (W1156)
   (Sanders) SSA,acap oct PRO ART 1296 $.16
                                          (W1157)
   (Warrell) SSAATBB,acap (easy) OXFORD 43.901
   $.35   (W1158)

WHILE SHEPHERDS WATCHED see Bliss, Paul

WHILE SHEPHERDS WATCHED see Cooke, Arnold

WHILE SHEPHERDS WATCHED see Lillenas, Haldor

WHILE SHEPHERDS WATCHED see Lockwood, Normand

WHILE SHEPHERDS WATCHED see Thiman, Eric
   Harding

WHILE SHEPHERDS WATCHED see Tkach

WHILE SHEPHERDS WATCHED THEIR FLOCKS see
   Bodycombe, [Aneurin]

WHILE SHEPHERDS WATCHED THEIR FLOCKS see
   Christiansen, Paul

WHILE SHEPHERDS WATCHED THEIR FLOCKS see
   Praetorius, Michael

WHILE SHEPHERDS WATCHED THEIR FLOCKS BY NIGHT
   *Xmas
   (Reynolds) SATB oct FISCHER,C CM-7712 $.25
                                          (W1159)
WHILE SHEPHERDS WATCHED THEIR FLOCKS BY NIGHT
   see Billings, William

WHILE SHEPHERDS WATCHED THEIR FLOCKS BY NIGHT
   see Praetorius, Michael

WHILE SHEPHERDS WATCHED THEIR SHEEP see Jungst

WHILE SHEPHERDS WERE WATCHING see Williams

WHILE STANDING AT THE CROSS see Carrier

WHILE STARS THEIR VIGIL KEEP see Luvaas

WHILE THE EARTH REMAINETH see Maunder, J.H.

WHILE THE EARTH REMAINETH see Powell, C.T.

WHILE THE EARTH REMAINETH see Tours

WHILE THE EARTH REMAINETH see Tours, Berthold

WHILE THE SHEPHERDS KEPT THEIR VIGIL *Xmas,
   carol
   oct HART s.p.   (W1160)

WHILE THE SHEPHERDS WERE WATCHING see Gibbs

WHINFIELD
   Let All The World In Ev'ry Corner Sing *Gen
   (Curry) SATB SCHMITT 1690 $.25   (W1161)

WHISPERING HOPE see Hawthorne

WHISPERING HOPE see Hawthorne, Alice

WHISPERS OF HEAVENLY DEATH see Kastle

WHITAKER
   Oh, What Can I Give To The Holy Child? *Xmas
   (Lowell; Wilson) SSA oct BOURNE 217 $.25
                                          (W1162)
WHITCOMB, MERVIN W.
   Dawn Has Come, The
   SATB oct BOURNE 666 $.25   (W1163)

WHITCOMB, R.
   Mighty One, The (Psalm 50)
   SATB oct ELKAN-V 362-1170 $.30   (W1164)

   Psalm 50 *see Mighty One, The

WHITE
   As A Child
   unis,opt fl SCHMITT 250 $.35   (W1165)

   God Loves Me *Gen
   unis SCHMITT 244 $.30   (W1166)

   Have You Ever Wondered Why? *Gen
   SA SCHMITT 2903 $.30   (W1167)

   Hear The Good News *spir
   TTBB oct COLOMBO 1929 $.25   (W1168)

   I Got My Religion In Time
   SATB oct HERITAGE H2148 $.35   (W1169)

   Omnes Gentes, Plaudite
   SA&SA oct SACRED S-6502 $.40   (W1170)

   Psalm 119 *see Teach Me, O Lord

   Rejoice Emmanuel Shall Come *Xmas
   SATB,inst GALAXY 1.2190.1 $2.00   (W1171)

   Search My Heart
   SATB oct FOX S119 $.25   (W1172)

   Teach Me, O Lord (Psalm 119)
   (Fuller) SATB oct PRO ART 1318 $.20   (W1173)

WHITE, DONALD H. (1921-   )
   Psalm
   SATB LUDWIG L-1120 $.40   (W1174)

WHITE DOVE, THE see Anderson, [William H.]

WHITE, JOHN (1855-1902)
   Canticle Of Brotherhood
   SATB,org oct LAWSON 51630 $.35   (W1175)

   He Dawns Upon Us *Epiph/Gen,Bibl
   SATB,pno/org oct LAWSON 51084 $.25   (W1176)

   Hosanna To Our King
   jr cor&opt mix cor oct LAWSON 51035 $.20
                                          (W1177)
   Our Blest Redeemer Ere He Breathed
   cor oct HART s.p.   (W1178)

   Solemn Mass, F Minor *Mass
   [Lat] cor,pno voc sc SCHIRM.G $2.50   (W1179)

   When Brothers Dwell In Unity
   SATB oct LAWSON 51209 $.35   (W1180)

WHITE, L.J.
   Communion Service *Commun,Agnus/Bene/Gloria/
   Kyrie/Sanctus
   unis (very easy) oct OXFORD 45.030 $.30
                                          (W1181)

WHITE, L.J. (cont'd.)
   Praise To The Risen Lord *Easter,cant
   BELWIN $.75   (W1182)

   Prayer Of St. Richard Of Chichester, A *Gen
   2pt (very easy) oct OXFORD 44.033 $.25
                                          (W1183)
WHITE LENT *Xmas
   SATB (easy) OXFORD 08.143 $.15   (W1184)

WHITE, LOUIE
   Hymn Of The World's Creator
   SATB oct GRAY GCMR 2707 $.30   (W1185)

   Jubilate Deo
   SATB (med) ABINGDON APM-177 $.30   (W1186)

   Prayer Of St. Francis Of Assisi *anthem
   SSAA,vcl,harp oct GRAY GCMR 3225 $.40
                                          (W1187)
WHITE, MATTHEW
   O Praise God In His Holiness (Psalm 150)
   Fest/Gen/Thanks
   SSAATTBB,opt inst (med) oct OXFORD 44.033
   $1.20   (W1188)

   Psalm 150 *see O Praise God In His Holiness

WHITE, MICHAEL (1931-   )
   Child's Prayer, A *prayer
   jr cor LEONARD-ENG 63 s.p.   (W1189)

   Goin' Home On A Cloud
   4pt mix cor,acap oct SCHIRM.G 11369 $.30
                                          (W1190)
   Magic Morning, The *Xmas
   2pt wom cor oct SCHIRM.G 11368 $.25   (W1191)

   Oh, Little Child Of Bethlehem *Xmas
   4pt mix cor,acap oct SCHIRM.G 10837 $.25
                                          (W1192)
   Silver Bells, The *Xmas
   4pt mix cor,acap oct SCHIRM.G 10838 $.25
                                          (W1193)
   Sleep, Little Lord *Xmas
   2pt boy cor/2pt wom cor oct SCHIRM.G 10936
   $.20   (W1194)

WHITE PATERNOSTER see Davies, Henry Walford

WHITE, PHIL
   Son Of A Carpenter
   SATB oct AGAPE CF 126 $.30   (W1195)

   What Have They Done?
   2pt oct AGAPE CF 127 $.25   (W1196)

WHITE, ROBERT (ca. 1530-1574)
   At Assembly (O Lord Of All) *anthem
   4pt oct NOVELLO 47.0363.04 s.p. contains
   also: Day Is Ending, The   (W1197)

   Christe, Qui Lux Es Et Dies *Eve/Gen/Lent
   SSATB/SSTBarB,opt inst (med) oct OXFORD
   43.393 $.50   (W1198)

   Day Is Ending, The
   see White, Robert, At Assembly (O Lord Of
   All)

   Domine Non Est Exaltatum
   mix cor,acap voc sc KALMUS 6726 $1.75
   contains also: Domine Qui Habitabit I;
   Domine Qui Habitabit II; Domine Qui
   Habitabit III   (W1199)

   Domine Qui Habitabit I
   see White, Robert, Domine Non Est Exaltatum

   Domine Qui Habitabit II
   see White, Robert, Domine Non Est Exaltatum

   Domine Qui Habitabit III
   see White, Robert, Domine Non Est Exaltatum

   Eight Anthems *CC8U,anthem
   mix cor,acap voc sc KALMUS 6728 $1.50
                                          (W1200)
   Four Anthems *CC4U,anthem
   mix cor,acap voc sc KALMUS 6725 $1.00
                                          (W1201)
   Lamentations
   5-6pt voc sc KALMUS 6724 $1.00   (W1202)

   Magnificat *Magnif
   mix cor,acap voc sc KALMUS 6723 $.90
                                          (W1203)
   Nine Anthems *CC9U,anthem
   mix cor,acap voc sc KALMUS 6727 $1.60
                                          (W1204)
   O How Glorious Art Thou *Gen/Thanks
   SAATB,opt inst (med) oct OXFORD 43.373 $.50
                                          (W1205)
   O Praise God In His Holiness (Psalm 150) Gen/
   Thanks
   SATB,acap (med) oct OXFORD 43.949 $.50
                                          (W1206)
   Precamur, Sancte Domine *Eve,hymn/mot
   SATBB,acap SCHIRM.EC $.25   (W1207)
   (Collins, H.B.) [Lat] SATBarB CHESTER s.p.
                                          (W1208)
   Psalm 150 *see O Praise God In His Holiness

WHITECOTTON, SHIRLEY
   Awake, My Soul
   unis oct AGAPE CH 653 $.25   (W1209)

   Christmas Carol, A *Xmas
   SSA SCHMITT 2902 $.35   (W1210)

   God Is Watching
   2pt oct AGAPE CF 136 $.30   (W1211)

   Michael
   SA oct AGAPE BR 2005 $.30   (W1212)

WHITEHEAD
   Hark The Song Of Jubilee
   SATB THOMP.G G-583 $.25   (W1213)

   Jesus, Bread Of Life, I Pray Thee
   SATB oct BELWIN 60745 $.25   (W1214)

WHITEHEAD, ALFRED
   Come, Holy Ghost, In Love *anthem
   SATB oct HARRIS HC4008 $.25   (W1215)

WHITEHEAD, ALFRED (cont'd.)
   Croon Carol, The *carol,Ger
   2pt jr cor FISCHER,C CM 6151 $.20   (W1216)

   God Of Mercy, God Of Grace *anthem
   SATB,org oct HARRIS HC4004 $.25   (W1217)

   King's Welcome, The *Easter
   SATB oct PRESSER 332-14659 $.35   (W1218)

   Let All The World In Every Corner Sing
   *anthem
   SATB,acap oct HARRIS HC4019 $.20   (W1219)

   Saviour Breathe An Evening Blessing *Eve
   SATB oct LESLIE 4002   (W1220)

   Shepherds' Hymn, The *Xmas
   SATB,acap oct GRAY GCMR 3212 $.30   (W1221)

   Three Christmas Carols *CC3U,Xmas
   SATB oct PRESSER 332-15095 $.30   (W1222)

   Three Easter Carols *CC3U,Easter
   SATB oct GRAY GCMR 1624 $.30   (W1223)

   Three Easter Carols (2nd Set) *CC3U,Easter
   SATB,acap oct PRESSER 332-40056 $.25
                                          (W1224)
   Today Did Christ Arise *Easter
   SATB,acap oct PRESSER 332-14548 $.35   (W1225)

   When Morning Gilds The Sky
   4pt mix cor,org oct SCHIRM.G 11480 $.25
                                          (W1226)
WHITESUNTIDE see Kodaly, Zoltan

WHITFORD
   Faith's Heritage
   SATB,org/pno BOSTON 13392 $.35   (W1227)

   Glory To God In The Highest *Xmas
   SSA SCHMITT 342 $.30   (W1228)
   TTBB SCHMITT 413 $.25   (W1229)
   SATB SCHMITT 1596 $.35   (W1230)
   SAB SCHMITT 5518 $.35   (W1231)

   O God, Enlighten My Mind
   SATB,org/pno BOSTON 12646 $.40   (W1232)

   Six Responses And Sanctus *CC6U
   SATB oct PRO ART 1754 $.22   (W1233)

   Unto Thee, O Lord
   SATB,org/pno BOSTON 13391 $.35   (W1234)

WHITHER BOUND, ST. JAMES see Hourdeaux

WHITHER SHALL I GO see Campbell

WHITHER SHALL I GO see Kreisler, A.von

WHITHER SHALL I GO FROM THY SPIRIT see Mueller,
   Carl F.

WHITHER THOU GOEST
   SSA/SATB BIG3 $.25   (W1235)

WHITIER
   O Brother Man, Fold To Thy Heart Thy Brother
   (Hopson) SATB,acap WARNER WB-172 $.30
                                          (W1236)
WHITLOCK, PERCY
   Be Still, My Soul *Commun/Gen,Introit
   SATB oct OXFORD 42.105 $.25 see from
   Three Introits   (W1237)

   He Is Risen *Easter
   SATB (easy) OXFORD 42.114 $.25   (W1238)
   SATB (easy) oct OXFORD 42.114 $.25   (W1239)

   Here, O My Lord, I See Thee Face To Face
   *Commun/Gen,Introit
   SATB (med) oct OXFORD 42.021 $.25 see from
   Three Introits   (W1240)

   Jesu, Grant Me This I Pray *Gen/Lent
   SATB,acap (med) oct OXFORD 42.706 $.30
                                          (W1241)
   O Living Bread, Who Once Didst Die *Commun/
   Gen,Introit
   SATB,acap (med) oct OXFORD 43.010 $.25 see
   from Three Introits   (W1242)

   Sing Praise To God Who Reigns Above *Fest/
   Gen
   SATB (med easy) oct OXFORD 42.010 $.30
                                          (W1243)
   Three Introits *see Be Still, My Soul; Here,
   O My Lord, I See Thee Face To Face; O
   Living Bread, Who Once Didst Die

WHITMAN
   Break Forth Into Joy
   SATB oct SUMMY 5524 $.20   (W1245)

   My God's A Mighty Maker *Gen
   SATB SCHMITT 1881 $.35   (W1246)

WHITMAN, DAVID
   Wondrous Love
   SATB oct AGAPE CH 615 $.25   (W1247)

WHITMAN, DON
   Lord Of Life *Easter,cant
   mix cor voc sc LILLENAS ME-31 $1.50   (W1248)

WHITMAN, MORRIS
   Let All The People Praise Thee
   SSATB oct LILLENAS AN-2327 $.30   (W1249)

WHITMER, THOMAS CARL (1873-1959)
   Annointing Of Solomon
   SATB,org,opt trp&timp oct AM.MUS.ED. $1.00
                                          (W1250)
   Anointing Of Solomon, The *Fest,Bibl/mot
   mix cor,org,opt trp,timp AM.MUS.ED. sc
   $4.00, voc sc $1.00   (W1251)

WHITNER, MARY ELIZABETH
   Cooper Square Chorister, The *CC15U,folk,US
   3pt jr cor/SAB/SAT FISCHER,C   (W1252)

   Joyous Carols *CC14U,Xmas,carol
   2pt jr cor oct FISCHER,C O-4004 $.75
                                          (W1253)

WHITNEY
Gloria In Excelsis Deo *Xmas
    SSA,acap WARNER W3800 $.35   (W1254)
    SATB,acap WARNER W3465   (W1255)

New Noel, A *Xmas
    unis/2pt WARNER W3708 $.30   (W1256)
    SATB WARNER W3706 $.30   (W1257)

Twelve Responses And Sentences *CC12U
    $.30 SAB,acap WARNER W3801; SATB,acap
    WARNER W3518   (W1258)

WHITNEY, M.
Angels, Roll The Stone Away *Easter
    SATB oct GRAY GCMR 2627 $.30   (W1259)

Blessed Is The Man
    SATB oct GRAY GCMR 2253 $.35   (W1260)

WHITNEY, MAURICE C. (1909-   )
Christ Child, The *Xmas
    SATB oct BOURNE 787 $.25   (W1261)

Christmas Night *Xmas
    SSA oct BOURNE 198 $.25   (W1262)

Easter Carol *Easter
    SATB oct FISCHER,J 8372 $.30   (W1263)

In The Lonely Midnight *Xmas
    SATB oct BOURNE 675 $.25   (W1264)

O God, Our Help
    SATB oct GRAY GCMR 2435 $.35   (W1265)

Palm Sunday *Palm
    SATB oct GRAY GCMR 2744 $.30   (W1266)

WHITSUN CAROL see Waters, Charles F.

WHITSUN MASS see Senator, Ronald

WHITTAKER, HOWARD
Oh, What Can I Give To The Holy Child?
    (Lowell) SATB oct BOURNE 802 $.25 (W1267)

WHITTIER
&ear Lord And Father Of Mankind
    (Rhea) SATB oct BOURNE 663 $.25   (W1268)

O Brother Man
    (Parry, Ehret) SATB LUDWIG L-1117 $.30
                                      (W1269)

WHITTLESEY
Bells Of Christmas
    SA/TB FLAMMER E5081 $.30   (W1270)

WHITTREDGE
Almighty God, Who Hast Given Us Grace
    SATB,acap BOSTON 2494 $.35   (W1271)

Christ Is Risen, Alleluia
    SSA KJOS 6062 $.30   (W1272)

Psalm 91 *Bibl
    SATB KJOS V-60 $1.50   (W1273)
    SATB KJOS $1.50   (W1274)

Surely He Hath Borne Our Griefs
    SATB KJOS 5181 $.30   (W1275)

WHO AM I? see Reid, Robert A.

WHO ARE THESE IN BRIGHT ARRAY? see Blake, G.

WHO ARE THESE THAT EARNEST KNOCK see Pelz,
    Walter L.

WHO ARE THESE THAT EARNEST KNOCK see Schroth,
    Godfrey

WHO ARE YOU TO DISAGREE? see Hanks

WHO AT MY DOOR IS STANDING? see Moffatt

WHO BUILT DE ARK? see Johnson

WHO CAN FIND A VIRTUOUS WOMAN? see Mechem,
    Kirke

WHO CAN TELL THE GLORY see Byrd, William, O
    Quam Gloriosum

WHO CRUCIFIED MY LORD? see Belcher, [Supply]

WHO DAT A-COMIN' OVAH YONDAH *spir,US
    (Aubanel, Georges) "O Qui Vient Donc De Si
    Loin" [Eng/Fr] 3pt mix cor OUVRIERES s.p.
                                      (W1276)

WHO HAS DELIVERED US? see Hovdesven, E.A.

WHO HAS SEEN THE WIND? see Grime, William

WHO HAS SEEN THE WIND? see Kunz

WHO HATH WOE? see Mechem, Kirke

WHO HS HE IN YONDER STALL see Resonet In
    Laudibus

WHO IS LIKE THEE
    (Norden, N. Lindsay) SATB oct GRAY GCMR 786
    $.30   (W1277)

WHO IS LIKE UNTO THEE? see Weisgall, Hugo

WHO IS LIKE UNTO THEE, O LORD see Berger, Jean

WHO IS LIKE UNTO YOU see Gottlieb, J., Mi
    Chamochah

WHO IS ON THE LORD'S SIDE *hymn,Ger
    (Lucky) SATB oct LILLENAS AN-2351 $.30
                                      (W1278)

WHO IS ON THE LORD'S SIDE? see Wilson

WHO IS THAT YONDER? *spir
    (Jessye) SATB oct SHAPIRO SK 2096 $.25
                                      (W1279)
    (Woollen, Russel) SSAA,A solo,acap oct WORLD
    ESE-705-4 $.30   (W1280)

WHO IS THE CHILD? see Wetzler, Robert

WHO IS THE KING OF GLORY see Williamson,
    Malcolm

WHO IS THIS BOY? see Gordon, A.

WHO IS THIS BOY? see Wilson, John F.

WHO IS THIS MAN OF GALILEE? see McWhertor

WHO IS THIS WHO COMES A-RIDING? see Davis,
    Katherine K.

WHO KNOWETH GOD see Glarum, L. Stanley

WHO KNOWS THE ANSWER? see Shea

WHO PASSES YONDER THROUGH THE THRONG see
    Williams, David H.

WHO PASSES YONDER THROUGH THE THRONG see Wood

WHO SHALL ABIDE see Pelz, Walter L.

WHO SHALL ASCEND see Christiansen, Olaf
    Christian

WHO SHALL ASCEND INTO THE HILL OF THE LORD see
    Mueller, Carl F.

WHO SHALL ASCEND INTO THE HILLS OF THE LORD?
    see Mueller, Carl F.

WHO SHALL ASCEND UNTO HIS HILL see Lassus,
    Roland de (Orlandus)

WHO SHALL COME? see Caldwell, Mary [Elizabeth]

WHO SHALL ROLL US AWAY THE STONE see Torrance,
    George William

WHO SHALL SEPARATE US FROM THE LOVE OF CHRIST
    see Lynn, George

WHO SHALL SEPARATE US FROM THE LOVE OF GOD? see
    Schutz, Heinrich, Wer Will Uns Scheiden Von
    Der Liebe Gottes?

WHO SHALL SEPARATE US FROM THE LOVE OF GOD? see
    York, D.

WHO SO DWELLETH see Goodenough, F.

WHO SO DWELLETH see Lamont

WHO TRUSTS IN GOD, A STRONG ABODE see
    Lundquist, Matthew Nathanael

WHO WAS BORN see Roff, Joseph

WHO WAS THE GUILTY see Boatwright, Howard

WHO WILL BOW AND BEND
    (Jacobson) 2pt boy cor oct SCHIRM.G 11598
    $.35   (W1281)

WHO WILL COME TO BETHELEHEM? *Xmas,carol,Span
    (Byles) 4pt mix cor oct SCHIRM.G 10664 $.25
                                      (W1282)
    (Byles) 3pt wom cor oct SCHIRM.G 10665 $.25
                                      (W1283)
    (Byles) unis oct SCHIRM.G 10668 $.20 (W1284)
    (Byles) 2pt boy cor/2pt wom cor oct SCHIRM.G
    10667 $.25   (W1285)
    (Byles) 3pt mix cor oct SCHIRM.G 10666 $.25
                                      (W1286)

WHO WILL GO? see Landgrave, Phillip

WHO WILL LIGHT MY LAMP? see Rasley

WHO WITH GRIEVING SOWETH see Schein, Johann
    Hermann

WHO WITH WEEPING SOWETH see Gambold

WHO WOULD TRUE VALOUR SEE see Thiman, Eric
    Harding

WHOEVER WOULD BE GREAT AMONG YOU see Nelson,
    Ronald A.

WHOLE BRIGHT WORLD, THE see Williams, David H.

WHOLE BRIGHT WORLD REJOICES NOW, THE see
    Frackenpohl, Arthur

WHOLE BRIGHT WORLD REJOICES, THE *carol
    SATB (very easy) OXFORD 08.095 $.15 (W1287)

WHOLE BRIGHT WORLD REJOICES, THE see Roff,
    Joseph

WHOLE WORLD COMES TO BETHLEHEM, THE see Miller

WHOM ALL MEN ADORE see Moore

WHOM ARE YOU SEEKING see Milano, R.

WHOM HAVE YOU SEEN, O SHEPHERDS? see Gallus,
    Jacobus, Quem Vidistis, Pastores?

WHOM HAVE YOU SEEN, SHEPHERDS? see Poulenc,
    Francis, Quem Vidistis Pastores Dicite

WHOM SHALL I SEND? see Berger, Jean

WHOM THESE HANDS HOLD see Sateren, Leland
    Bernhard

WHO'S AT THE DOOR?
    see Three French Carols (Noels)

WHO'S THAT GUY WITH THE BEARD? see Avery

WHOSO DOTH OFFER THANKS see Bach, Johann
    Sebastian

WHOSO DWELLETH see Moore, P.J.

WHOSO FINDETH A WIFE see Mechem, Kirke

WHOSO LOVES ME see Vulpius, Melchior, Wer Mich
    Liebet

WHY? see Hunkins, Eusebia Simpson

WHY? see Taylor

WHY AFFLICT THYSELF, OH MY SPIRIT see Schutz,
    Heinrich, Was Betruebst Du Dich, Meine
    Seele

WHY ARE THOU CAST DOWN, O MY SPIRIT see Bach,
    Johann Sebastian

WHY ART THOU CAST DOWN, MY SPIRIT see Schein,
    Johann Hermann

WHY ART THOU CAST DOWN, O MY SOUL? see Berger,
    Jean

WHY ART THOU HEAVY, O MY SOUL? see Gibbons,
    Orlando

WHY ART THOU SO CAST DOWN O MY SOUL see
    Pinkham, Daniel

WHY ART THOU SO HEAVY see Loosemore, Henry

WHY ART THOU SO HEAVY, O, MY SOUL? see Gibbons,
    Orlando

WHY ART THOU SO HEAVY, O MY SOUL? see Myers, G.

WHY DO BELLS FOR CHRISTMAS RING? see Roff,
    Joseph

WHY DO BELLS ON CHRISTMAS RING? see Rinehart

WHY DO I SING ABOUT JESUS? see Hustad, Donald
    P.

WHY DO I SING ABOUT JESUS see Ketchum, Albert

WHY DO THE BELLS OF CHRISTMAS RING? see Drynan,
    Margaret

WHY DO THE NATIONS RAGE? see Diercks, John H.

WHY HAST THOU CAST US OFF see Hovhaness, Alan

WHY HAST THOU FORSAKEN see Nemec

WHY NOT TRY PRAY'R see Lohr, Al

WHY, O LORD, DO YOU STAND ALOOF? see Peloquin,
    C. Alexander

WHY SEEK YE THE LIVING see Clare, Edwyn A.

WHY SEEK YE THE LIVING? see Cooke, S.C.

WHY SEEK YE THE LIVING? see Pasquet, Jean

WHY SHOULD HE LOVE ME SO? see Harkness

WHY SHOULD HE LOVE ME SO? see Wilson

WHY SHOULDST THOU BE AS A STRANGER IN THE LAND
    see Demarest, A.

WHY THE CHIMES RANG *Xmas/Pageant
    LORENZ $.75   (W1288)

WHY THE CHIMES RANG see Grauel, J.

WHY THEN HAS THE LIGHT BEEN GIVEN see Brahms,
    Johannes, Warum Ist Das Licht Gegeben

WHY THUS CRADLED HERE? see Lynn, George

WHYTE
O Praise God *see Psalm For A Coronation
    Year

Psalm For A Coronation Year *Psalm
    "O Praise God" SATB (diff) OXFORD 42.161
    $.50   (W1289)

WHYTE, ROBERT (ca. 1530-1574)
Christe, Qui Lux Es Et Dies
    "O Christ, Who Art The Light And Day" [Lat/
    Eng] SSATB PETERS H1502 $.40   (W1290)

Lord Bless Us, The
    SAATB PETERS H1500   (W1291)

O Christ, Who Art The Light And Day *see
    Christe, Qui Lux Es Et Dies

O Praise God In His Holiness *anthem
    dbl cor PETERS H1501 $.50   (W1292)
    (West, John E.) mix cor,acap oct NOVELLO
    28.1071.09 s.p.   (W1293)

WIANT, BLISS
Chinese Christmas Carol, A *Xmas,carol,Chin
    SATB oct GRAY GCMR 1870 $.30   (W1294)
    unis oct GRAY GCMR 1858 $.30   (W1295)

WICHMAN
Bell Carol *anthem/carol
    sr cor&jr cor oct OXFORD 94.004 $.40
                                      (W1296)

WICHMANN
I Lift Up My Eyes
    SATB oct VOLKWEIN VB177 $.25   (W1297)

O Lamb Of God *Commun
    SATB oct VOLKWEIN VB226 $.25   (W1298)

Responses And Amens *CCU,cor-resp
    SATB oct VOLKWEIN VB252 $.25   (W1299)

WICKENS, DENNIS [JOHN] (1926-   )
Jubilate Deo
    mix cor oct OXFORD 42.336 $.50   (W1300)

O Vos Omnes *Psntd,Bibl
    SATB,acap (med) oct OXFORD 43.394 $.25
                                      (W1301)

WICKHAM, B.
God Grant Us Peace
    SA BOSWORTH s.p.   (W1302)
    SATB BOSWORTH s.p.   (W1303)

WICKINS, F.
Bow Down Thine Ear, O Lord *anthem
    SATB BOSWORTH s.p.   (W1304)

WIDDICOMBE, TREVOR
Behold A Simple Tender Babe *Xmas
    cor CRAMER 243 s.p.   (W1305)

WIDDOES, LAWRENCE
Pied Beauty
    SATB (med diff) PRESSER 312-40998 $.40
                                      (W1306)

WIDEEN, IVAR
Blest Spirit
(Lundquist) SATB,acap (med) oct WILLIS 8400
$.18   (W1307)

Hymn Till Sangen *hymn
mix cor NORDISKA 3705 s.p.   (W1308)

Hymn Till Vastergotland *hymn
men cor NORDISKA 1791 s.p.   (W1309)

In Dulci Jubilo
"Nu Stige Jublets Ton" mix cor NORDISKA
4034 s.p.   (W1310)

Massa
mix cor,solo,org,vln voc sc NORDISKA 1568
s.p., ipa, cor pts NORDISKA 1632 s.p.   (W1311)

Nu Stige Jublets Ton *see In Dulci Jubilo

Pa Krubbans Stra *Xmas
men cor NORDISKA 4031 s.p.   (W1312)

Parafras Over O Kriste, Du Som Ljuset Ar
mix cor NORDISKA 3547 s.p.   (W1313)

Requiem *Req
mix cor,solo,org/pno,vln voc sc NORDISKA
2468 s.p., cor pts NORDISKA 2743 s.p.   (W1314)

Stabat Mater
mix cor,org NORDISKA 3511 s.p.   (W1315)

Suppliemus Jesu Bone *hymn
mix cor NORDISKA 3548 s.p.   (W1316)

Vi Sjunga Guds Ara
mix cor NORDISKA 2535 s.p.   (W1317)

Vid Jesu Kors *cant/chorale
mix cor,solo,org,vln voc sc NORDISKA 749
s.p., ipa, cor pts NORDISKA 792 s.p.   (W1318)

WIDERSTEHE see Bach, Johann Sebastian

WIDMER, A.
Zur Konfirmation *Cnfrm
[Ger] mix cor,acap (easy) HUG s.p.   (W1319)

WIDMUNG AN GOTT
(Etti, Karl) men cor,acap oct DOBLINGER s.p.
see from Drei Ernste Gesange   (W1320)

WIDOR, CHARLES-MARIE (1844-1937)
Da Pacem *Gen,mot
[Lat] 4pt mix cor oct DURAND s.p.   (W1321)

Les Pecheurs De Saint Jean *Xmas
[Fr] SA HEUGEL voc sc s.p., voc pt s.p.   (W1322)

Toccata-Gloria
(Young, G.) SATB oct PRESSER 312-40643 $.30
                                                  (W1323)

WIE BIN ICH DOCH SO HERZLICH FROH see Bach,
Johann Sebastian

WIE BIN ICH DOCH SO HERZLICH FROH see Brunner,
Adolf

WIE DER HIRSCH NACH FRISCHER QUELLE see
Pfiffner, Ernst

WIE DER HIRSCH SCHREIET NACH FRISCHEM WASSER
see Distler, Hugo

WIE DER HIRSCH SCHREIT see Mendelssohn-
Bartholdy, Felix

WIE DER HIRSCH SCHREIT NACH FRISCHEM WASSER see
Muller, Paul

WIE DER HIRSCH SCHREIT NACH FRISCHEM WASSER see
Reda, Siegfried

WIE EIN HIRSCH SCHREIT NACH FRISCHEM WASSER see
Schweizer, Rolf

WIE EINE ROSE UNTER DEN DORNEN see Selle,
Thomas

WIE GOTT WILL see Haug, G.

WIE GROSS IST DEINE LIEBE see Gerhold, Norbert,
Ride On, Conquering King

WIE HEILIG IST DIES STATTE see Stockmeier,
Wolfgang

WIE HEIMLICHER WEISE see Aeschbacher, C.

WIE HERRLICH GIBST DU, HERR, DICH ZU ERKENNEN
see Hindermann, Walter Felix

WIE ISTS SO LIEBLICH see Schutz, Heinrich

WIE LANG, O GOTT see Praetorius, Michael

WIE LANG, O GOTT, IN MEINER NOT see
Gumpeltzhaimer, Adam

WIE LANG SOLL SICH MEIN FEIND see Hartmann,
Heinrich

WIE LANG SOLL SICH MEIN FEIND see Scheidt,
Samuel

WIE LANGE NOCH, HERR see Schweizer, Rolf

WIE LIEBLICH IST DAS HAUS DE HERRN see Le
Jeune, Claude

WIE LIEBLICH IST DAS HAUS DES HERRN see Eglin,
Arthur

WIE LIEBLICH IST DER MAIEN see Kubler, Emil

WIE LIEBLICH IST DER MAIEN see Steurlein,
Johann

WIE LIEBLICH SIND DEINE see Wenzel, Eberhard

WIE LIEBLICH SIND DEINE WOHNUEGEN see Telemann,
Georg Philipp

WIE LIEBLICH SIND DEINE WOHNUNGEN see Burkhard
Willy

WIE LIEBLICH SIND DEINE WOHNUNGEN see
Hammerschmidt, Andreas

WIE LIEBLICH SIND DEINE WOHNUNGEN see Meyer-
Janson, Burkhard

WIE LIEBLICH SIND DEINE WOHNUNGEN see Ritter,
Christian

WIE LIEBLICH SIND DEINE WOHNUNGEN see Schutz,
Heinrich

WIE MAAR DEN GOEDEN GOD LAAT ZORGEN see Bach,
Johann Sebastian

WIE NACH EINER WASSERQUELLE
see Goudimel, Claude, Freu Dich Sehr, O Meine
Seele

WIE NACH EINER WASSERQUELLE see Goudimel,
Claude, Freu Dich Sehr, O Meine Seele

WIE NACH EINER WASSERQUELLE see Hartmann,
Heinrich

WIE OP GOD BETROUWT see Flipse, E.

WIE OP GOD BETROUWT see Oort, H.C.v.

WIE SCHOEN see Bach, Johann Sebastian, Wie
Schon Leuchtet Der Morgenstern

WIE SCHON IST'S DOCH, HERR JESU CHRIST, IM see
Bach, Johann Sebastian

WIE SCHON LEUCHTET UNS DER MORGENSTERN see Bach,
Johann Sebastian

WIE SCHON LEUCHT' UNS DER MORGENSTERN see
Distler, Hugo

WIE SCHON LEUCHT UNS DER MORGENSTERN see
Muller, Paul

WIE SCHON LEUCHT' UNS DER MORGENSTERN see
Nicolai, Philipp

WIE SCHON LEUCHT' UNS DIE MORGENSTERN see
Nicolai, Philipp

WIE SCHON LEUCHTET see Becker-Foss, Jurgen

WIE SCHON LEUCHTET DER MORGENSTERN see
Praetorius, Michael

WIE SCHON LEUCHTET DER MORGENSTERN *Xmas,
chorale,Ger
(Barrow, R.) "How Brightly Shines The Morning
Star" TTBB,acap SCHIRM.EC 2303   (W1324)
(Johnson) "How Brightly Shines The Morning
Star" SATB SCHMITT 15008 $.30   (W1325)

WIE SCHON LEUCHTET DER MORGENSTERN see Bach,
Johann Sebastian

WIE SCHON LEUCHTET DER MORGENSTERN see Brunner,
Adolf

WIE SCHON LEUCHTET DER MORGENSTERN see
Gottschick, Friedemann

WIE SCHON LEUCHTET DER MORGENSTERN see
Mendelssohn, Arnold

WIE SCHON LEUCHTET DER MORGENSTERN see
Praetorius, Michael

WIE SCHON LEUCHTET DER MORGENSTERN see Stern,
Hermann

WIE SCHON LEUCHTET DER MORGENSTERN [CHORALE]
see Bach, Johann Sebastian

WIE SCHON LEUCHTET DER MORGENSTERN [CHORALE]
see Nicolai, Philipp

WIE SCHON LEUCHT'T UNS DER MORGENSTERN see
Distler, Hugo

WIE SCHON SCHEINT DER MOND *BVM
(Dawidowicz, Anton) wom cor,acap (contains
also: Es Bluhen Drei Rosen) oct DOBLINGER
s.p. see also Acht Marienlieder   (W1326)

WIE SCHON SINGT UNS DER ENGEL SCHAR see
Freundt, Cornelius

WIE SCHWERLICH LASST SICH FLEISHCH UND BLUT see
Bach, Johann Sebastian

WIE SELIG SIND DIE TOTEN see Mendelssohn-
Bartholdy, Felix

WIE SICH EIN VATER ERBARMT see Kretzschmar,
Gunther

WIE SIE SO SANFT RUH'N see Beneken, Friedrich

WIE SOLL ICH DICH EMPFANGEN see Bach, Johann
Sebastian

WIE SOLL ICH DICH EMPFANGEN see Buxtehude,
Dietrich

WIE SOLL ICH DICH EMPFANGEN see Cruger, Johann

WIE SOLL ICH DICH EMPFANGEN see Horn, Paul

WIE SOLL ICH DICH EMPFANGEN see Koch, Heinz

WIE SOLL ICH DICH EMPFANGEN see Poser, Hans

WIE SOLL ICH DICH EMPFANGEN see Schreck, Gustav

WIE SOLL ICH DICH EMPFANGEN see Suthoff-Gross,
Rudolf

WIE SOLL ICH DICH EMPFANGEN see Teschner

WIE SOLL ICH DICH EMPFANGEN see Trubel, Gerhard

WIE SOLL ICH DICH EMPFANGEN [CHORALE] see Bach,
Johann Sebastian

WIE TEUER IST DEINE GUTE, GOTT see Hogner,
Friedrich

WIE WILL ICH MICH FREUEN see Bach, Johann
Sebastian

WIE WIRD ERNEUET, WIE WIRD ERFREUET see
Buxtehude, Dietrich

WIE WOHL IST MIR see Weismann, Wilhelm

WIEDER RAUNT IN ALLEN GASSEN see Niggli, F.

WIEGENLIED see Mozart, Wolfgang Amadeus

WIEGENLIED DER HIRTEN *Xmas,carol
(Davison, A.T.) "Cradle-Song Of The
Shepherds" SATB,acap SCHIRM.EC 1728 $.30
                                              (W1327)
(Kinsman) "Cradle Song Of The Shepherds" SATB
oct PRO ART 1937 $.25   (W1328)
(Kinsman) "Cradle Song Of The Shepherds" SSA
oct PRO ART 2103 $.25   (W1329)

WIEGENLIED DER HIRTEN see Glatz

WIEMER, WOLFGANG (1934-   )
Christe, Du Bist Der Helle Tag *cant
mix cor,SBar soli,strings cor pts
BREITKOPF-W CHB-3627 s.p., ipr, sc
BREITKOPF-W rental   (W1330)
mix cor,SBar soli,strings sc BREITKOPF-W
rental, cor pts BREITKOPF-W CHB-3627
s.p., ipr   (W1331)

Der Blinde Von Jericho "Es Geschah Aber, Als
Er Nahe An Jericho Kam" *evang/mot
4pt mix cor,acap cor pts BREITKOPF-W
CHB-3517 s.p.   (W1332)

Gott Vater Sohn, Und Heiliger Geist
see Wiemer, Wolfgang, O Here Gott, Dein
Gottlich Wort

Hinunter Ist Der Sonnen Schein *mot
3-6pt,acap cor pts BREITKOPF-W CHB-3513
s.p.   (W1333)

Jesu Kreuz, Leiden Und Pein
SAT/SAB, 2treb inst/bass inst HANSSLER
14.058 s.p.   (W1334)

Lobe Den Herren, O Meine
SA/SAT/SAB, 2treb inst,bass inst HANSSLER
14.198 s.p.   (W1335)

Nun Jauchzet, All Ihr Frommen
(Weise, Eigene) SAT/SAB,treb inst,bass inst
HANSSLER 14.006 s.p.   (W1336)

Nun Komm, Der Heiden Heiland *mot
4-6pt mix cor,acap cor pts BREITKOPF-W
CHB-3514 s.p.   (W1337)

O Here Gott, Dein Gottlich Wort
SS/T,treb inst HANSSLER 14.117 s.p.
contains also: Gott Vater Sohn, Und
Heiliger Geist   (W1338)

WIENANDT, ELWYN A.
I Will Extol Thee
SATB oct WORD CS-2502 $.30   (W1339)

Lift Up Your Heads *Xmas
SATB oct WORD CS-2527 $.30   (W1340)

Thy Life Was Given For Me
(Young, R.) SATB oct WORD CS-2469 $.30
                                               (W1341)

Thy Life Was Given To Me *Lent
(Young) SATB oct SOUTHERN $.30   (W1342)

WIENER MARIENLIED DER ZECHE UNSERER LIEBEN FRAU
ZU ST. PETER *15th cent
(Tittel, Ernst) mix cor,acap oct DOBLINGER
s.p.   (W1343)

WIENHORST, RICHARD
All Glory Be To God On High *Gen/Trin
SATB,acap (med easy) oct CONCORDIA 98-1350
$.25   (W1344)
SAB,acap (med easy) oct CONCORDIA 98-1465
$.22   (W1345)

Alleluia
see Four 18th-Century English Rounds

Behold, A Branch Is Growing
see Four Christmas Settings

Blessed Is He Who Cometh *Gen/Lent/Palm
SATB,acap (med diff) oct CONCORDIA 98-1055
$.25   (W1346)

Christ Jesus Lay In Death's Strong Bands
*Easter,cant
mix cor,org/strings CONCORDIA 97-6209 $.90,
ipa   (W1347)
SATB,acap (med easy) oct CONCORDIA 98-1348
$.18   (W1348)

Come, Holy Ghost, God And Lord *Ded/Gen/Pent
SAB,acap (med easy) oct CONCORDIA 98-1562
$.20   (W1349)

Come, Jesus Holy Child
see Four Christmas Settings

Come, Ye Children, Praise The Savior *Gen
SA,kbd (easy) oct CONCORDIA 98-1437 $.25
                                               (W1350)

Four Christmas Settings *Xmas
unis,kbd (easy) oct CONCORDIA 98-1498 $.25
contains: Behold, A Branch Is Growing;
Come, Jesus Holy Child; From Heaven
Above, Ye Angels All; Let The Earth Now
Praise The Lord   (W1351)

Four 18th-Century English Rounds *round,Eng,
18th cent
SATB, or any combination (med easy) oct
CONCORDIA 98-1668 $.30
contains: Alleluia (Xmas/Easter);
Jerusalem, Oh, That Thou Hadst Known;
Make Haste, O God, To Deliver Me; Oh,
Be Not Far From Helping Me (from
Sentence For The Passion Season)
                                               (W1352)

From Heaven Above, Ye Angels All
see Four Christmas Settings

WIENHORST, RICHARD (cont'd.)

Hear, O Lord
SATB,acap AMP A430 $.20 (W1353)

Hosanna Be The Children's Song *Adv/Gen/Palm
SA,kbd (easy) oct CONCORDIA 98-1359 $.25
(W1354)

I Know The Thoughts I Think
SATB,acap AMP A343 $.20 (W1355)

I Will Praise Thee With My Whole Heart (Psalm
138) Gen/Refm
SATB,acap (med easy) oct CONCORDIA 98-1792
$.25 (W1356)

Jerusalem, Oh, That Thou Hadst Known
see Four 18th-Century English Rounds

Lamb Goes Uncomplaining Forth, A *Lent
SAB,acap (med easy, or Ash Wednesday) oct
CONCORDIA 98-1464 $.25 (W1357)
SATB,acap (med easy, or Ash Wednesday) oct
CONCORDIA 98-1347 $.25 (W1358)

Let The Earth Now Praise The Lord
see Four Christmas Settings

Magnificat, The *Xmas/Gen
SATB,acap (med diff) oct CONCORDIA 98-1794
$.25 (W1359)

Make Haste, O God, To Deliver Me
see Four 18th-Century English Rounds

Missa Brevis *Mass
[Lat] SATB,acap AMP A457 $1.25 (W1360)

O Lord, Thine Enemies Roar
SATB,acap AMP A345 $.30 (W1361)

O Trinity, Most Blessed Light *Gen/Trin
unis men cor,kbd (easy) oct CONCORDIA
98-1665 $.20 (W1362)

Oh, Be Not Far From Helping Me (from Sentence
For The Passion Season)
see Four 18th-Century English Rounds

Once He Came In Blessing *Adv/Epiph
SATB,acap oct CONCORDIA 98-1344 $.20
(W1363)

Out Of The Depths
SA/TB,acap AMP 344 $.20 (W1364)

Praise Ye The Lord (Psalm 150) Ded/Gen
SATB,acap (med easy) oct CONCORDIA 98-1793
$.25 (W1365)

Psalm 138 *see I Will Praise Thee With My
Whole Heart

Psalm 150 *see Praise Ye The Lord

Quempas Carol, The *carol
unis jr cor&mix cor,2treb inst,org sc
CONCORDIA 97-4597 $1.25, cor pts
CONCORDIA 98-1653 $.25 (W1366)

Seven Words Of Christ From The Cross, The
mix cor,soli CONCORDIA 97-6269 $1.25 (W1367)

Sing Ye *Gen
SAB,acap (med diff) oct CONCORDIA 98-2074
$.40 (W1368)

We All Believe In One True God *Gen/Trin
SATB,2trp (med diff) oct CONCORDIA 98-1807
$.25 (W1369)

WIERUSZOWSKI, LILI (1900-   )
Danket Dem Herrn Und Ehret
SAT/SAB,winds,2-3trp,2trom LAUDINELLA LR 8
s.p. (W1370)

Hugenotten-Psalmen *CCU,Psalm
[Ger] 2-6pt mix cor,opt inst HUG s.p.
(W1371)

Psalm 47 *see Singt Mit Froher Stimm

Singt Mit Froher Stimm (Psalm 47) Bibl
SATB,trp HANSSLER 6.250 s.p. contains also:
Henking, Bernhard, Singt Mit Froher Stimm
(Psalm 47) (SATB) (W1372)

WIESEHAHN, W.
O Regina Coeli
men cor BROEKMANS 149 s.p. (W1373)

Te Deum Laudamus
men cor,org ALSBACH&D sc s.p., cor pts s.p.
(W1374)

WIJ BIDDEN U, O HEIL'GE GEEST
mix cor sc ALSBACH&D GEZ.79 s.p. (W1375)

WIKANDER, DAVID
Ad Perennis Vitae Fontem *hymn
mix cor NORDISKA 2776 s.p. (W1376)

Advensthymn *Adv,hymn
mix cor NORDISKA 2097 s.p. (W1377)

Gud Ar Var Tillflykt
men cor,Bar solo NORDISKA 2932 s.p. (W1378)

Gud Har Icke Skonat Sin Egen Son
mix cor NORDISKA 2102 s.p. (W1379)

Gud Har Uppvackt Kristus Jesu
mix cor NORDISKA 2105 s.p. (W1380)

Hojen Jubel Till Herren Alla Lander
mix cor,org,opt 2vln&vla&vcl&bvl voc sc
NORDISKA 910 s.p., ipa, cor pts NORDISKA
915 s.p. (W1381)

Koralmassa Pa Motiv Ur Reformationstidens
Svenska Tradition For Julen *Xmas
mix cor NORDISKA 1338 s.p. (W1382)

Kyrie Eleison *Kyrie
mix cor NORDISKA 5172 s.p. (W1383)

Massa
mix cor MUSIKAL. s.p. (W1384)

Missa Brevis In Festis Solemnibus *Mass
mix cor,acap NORDISKA 4009 s.p. (W1385)

WIKANDER, DAVID (cont'd.)

Misskundlig, Gud, Lat Nadens Sol Upprinna
3pt mix cor NORDISKA 2008 s.p. (W1386)

Nu Med Sang
wom cor&jr cor,pno NORDISKA 3658 s.p. see
from PIAE CANTIONES (W1387)

Om I Aren Uppstandna Med Kristus
mix cor NORDISKA 3350 s.p. (W1388)

Pris Vare Gud
mix cor NORDISKA 3037 s.p. (W1389)

Psalm 126 *see Psalm 126 I Psaltaren

Psalm 126 I Psaltaren (Psalm 126)
2-3pt wom cor,solo,org NORDISKA 3289 s.p.
(W1390)

Saliga De, Som Ifran Varldens Oden
men cor NORDISKA 2709 s.p. (W1391)

Sasom Hjorten Trangtar Till Vattubacker
mix cor,org,opt 2vln&vla&vcl&bvl voc sc
NORDISKA 907 s.p., ipa, cor pts NORDISKA
914 s.p. (W1392)

Se Detta Ar Dagen, Som Herren Oss Gor
mix cor NORDISKA 4417 s.p. (W1393)

WIKEHART, LEWIS E.
Love Of God, The
4pt mix cor,acap oct SCHIRM.G 11694 $.40
(W1394)

WIKLUND, GUSTAV
Ad Vesperas
[Lat] SAB,acap GEHRMANS TKS 67 (W1395)

WILAN, H.
see WILLAN, HEALY

WILBYE, JOHN (1574-1638)
Ye Restless Thoughts
(Field, Robert) SATB,acap (med) PRESSER
362-03138 $.35 (W1396)

WILD
Into The Woods My Master Went *Easter/Lent
SAB oct FISCHER,C CM-555 $.25 (W1397)

WILD, ERIC
Amazing Grace
see Hymn Sing (Volume 1)

Christ The Lord Is Risen
see Hymn Sing (Volume 1)

Come Sing To The Glory Of The Lord *anthem
SATB oct HARRIS $.35 (W1398)

Do Lord, Remember Me
see Hymn Sing (Volume 1)

Give Me That Old-Time Religion
see Hymn Sing (Volume 1)

Go Down Moses
see Hymn Sing (Volume 1)

Goodnight, God Bless You *anthem
SATB oct HARRIS $.35 (W1399)
SATB,acap oct BERANDOL 914W4AC $.35 (W1400)

He Is There! *anthem/hymn
SATB oct HARRIS HC4037 $.35 (W1401)

Hymn Sing (Volume 1) *anthem/spir
SATB HARRIS $1.95
contains: Amazing Grace; Christ The Lord
Is Risen; Do Lord, Remember Me; Give Me
That Old-Time Religion; Go Down Moses;
Let The Church Roll On (W1402)

I Stood At The Door Of My Lord *anthem/hymn
SATB,pno oct HARRIS HC4038 $.35 (W1403)

Let The Church Roll On
see Hymn Sing (Volume 1)

Sing! Sing! Ev'ryone Sing! *anthem
SATB oct HARRIS $.35 (W1404)
SATB,acap oct BERANDOL 914W4AB $.35 (W1405)

WILD, W.
Blow, Golden Trumpets *Easter
SATB oct GRAY GCMR 1550 $.25 (W1406)

Peace On Earth *Xmas
3pt jr cor/SAB (easy) FISCHER,C CM 534 $.20
(W1407)

WILDERNESS, THE see Goss, John

WILDERNESS, THE see Thiman, Eric Harding

WILDERNESS, THE see Wesley, Samuel Sebastian
Jr.

WILDGANS, FRIEDRICH (1913-   )
Betrubtes Herz *Op.47,No.2
mix cor,acap oct DOBLINGER s.p. see also
Drei Lieder Auf Texte Des Abraham A
Sancta Clara (W1408)

Des Hochsten Wort *Op.47,No.3
mix cor,acap oct DOBLINGER s.p. see also
Drei Lieder Auf Texte Des Abraham A
Sancta Clara (W1409)

Dilexisti Justitiam *mot
4pt mix cor,acap DOBLINGER sc s.p., cor pts
s.p. see from Drei Kleine Geistliche
Motetten (W1410)

Drei Kleine Geistliche Motetten *see
Dilexisti Justitiam; Laudate Dominum; Te
Decet Hymnus (W1411)

Drei Lieder Auf Texte Des Abraham A Sancta
Clara *CC3UL
mix cor,acap cmplt ed DOBLINGER s.p.
see also: Betrubtes Herz, Op.47,No.2; Des
Hochsten Wort, Op.47,No.3 (W1412)

Laudate Dominum *mot
4pt mix cor,acap DOBLINGER sc s.p., cor pts
s.p. see from Drei Kleine Geistliche
Motetten (W1413)

WILDGANS, FRIEDRICH (cont'd.)

Te Decet Hymnus *mot
4pt mix cor,acap DOBLINGER sc s.p., cor pts
s.p. see from Drei Kleine Geistliche
Motetten (W1414)

WILEY
Be Followers Of God
SATB,acap oct PRO ART 2527 $.30 (W1415)

Earth With Wonders Sweet And Fair
SATB oct PRO ART 2136 $.25 (W1416)

Glad Tidings Of Great Joy *Xmas
SATB oct PRO ART 1749 $.30 (W1417)

On Christmas Night *Xmas,folk
unis/2pt/SATB,opt bvl,perc,gtr (rock cant)
PRO ART 1159 $1.00 (W1418)

Songs Of Praise The Angels Sang *Xmas
SATB oct PRO ART 2191 $.25 (W1419)

WILHELM
Bethlehem Star *Xmas
SATB,acap SOUTHERN $.35 (W1420)

Bethlehem Star, The *Xmas
SATB,acap,opt pno oct PRO ART 2705 $.35
(W1421)

Easter Praises *Easter
SATB FLAMMER A 5621 $.30 (W1422)

Peace I Leave With You
SATB,acap oct PRO ART 2744 $.30 (W1423)

Sing We Noel *Xmas
SATB SCHMITT 7037 $.35 (W1424)

WILHOUSKY
Carol-Noel *Xmas
SATB,acap oct FISCHER,C CM-6520 $.30
(W1425)

WILKES
O'er All Nations God Alone
(Coggin, Elwood) SATB ALLANS 439 s.p.
(W1426)

Praise, O Praise Our God And King! *Thanks
(Harris) SATB oct PRO ART 1573 $.25 (W1427)
(Harris) SSA oct PRO ART 1879 $.25 (W1428)
(Harris) SAB oct PRO ART 2018 $.30 (W1429)
(Harris) 2pt oct PRO ART 1719 $.25 (W1430)

WILKES, R.W.
Incline Your Ear *Bibl
3pt wom cor oct SCHIRM.G 8201 $.25 (W1431)

Lo, The Earth *see Longfellow

WILKES, T.
What Color Is God's Skin? (composed with
Stevenson, D.)
SATB oct HERITAGE H40 $.45 (W1432)
SA oct HERITAGE H5003 $.45 (W1433)

WILKINSON
Blessed Are They
SATB oct FISCHER,C ZCM-105 $.30 (W1434)

Choral Meditations *CCU,meditation
SATB oct FISCHER,C ZCM-107 $.30 (W1435)

Halleluia, Sing! *Easter/Lent
SATB oct FISCHER,C ZCM-103 $.40 (W1436)

Psalm 119
SATB,acap oct FISCHER,C CM-7436 $.25
(W1437)

Puer Natus
SATB,acap (easy) OXFORD 84.095 $.25 (W1438)

Two Songs From Solomon *CC2U,anthem/Bibl
SATB oct FISCHER,C ZCM-104 $.40 (W1439)

WILKOMEN, SUSSER BRAUTIGAM see Lubeck,
Vincentius

WILKOMMEN, SUSSER BRAUTIGAM see Lubeck,
Vincentius

WILL IT MATTER THAT I WAS? see Landgrave,
Phillip

WILL OF GOD IS ALWAYS BEST see Praetorius,
Michael

WILLAERT, ADRIAN (ca. 1490-1562)
Ave Regina Caelorum *mot
[Lat] SATB RICORDI-ENG SY134 s.p. (W1440)
(Zanon, Vene) "Come, O Enlightening Spirit"
[Lat/Eng] SATB,acap oct COLOMBO 1887 $.30
(W1441)

Come, O Enlightening Spirit *see Ave Regina
Caelorum

Confiteanur Tibi *mot
[Lat] SSA,acap MUSICUS 1012 $.15 (W1442)

Consider The Lilies *see O Gemma Clarissima

Drei Motetten *CC3U,mot
(Gerstenberg) [Ger/Lat] 5pt mix cor MOSELER
s.p. (W1443)

Dulces Exuviae *mot
[Lat] SATB RICORDI-ENG SY142 s.p. (W1444)
(Zanon, Vene) "Jesu, Precious Lord" [Lat/
Eng] SATB,acap oct COLOMBO 1889 $.30
(W1445)

In Tua Patientia *mot
[Lat] SATB RICORDI-ENG SY147 s.p. (W1446)
(Zanon, Vene) "Lead Me In Ways Of Truth"
[Lat/Eng] SATB,acap oct COLOMBO 1888 $.30
(W1447)

Jesu, Precious Lord *see Dulces Exuviae

Lead Me In Ways Of Truth *see In Tua
Patientia

Magne Martyr Adriane *mot
[Lat] SATB RICORDI-ENG SY163 s.p. (W1448)
(Zanon, Vene) "O Ye Mighty" [Lat/Eng] SATB,
acap oct COLOMBO 1897 $.30 (W1449)

Memento Domine David (Psalm 131) Gen
(Long, Joan) [Lat] AATBar&STTB,acap (med)
PENN STATE PSM 20 s.p. (W1450)

WILLAERT, ADRIAN (cont'd.)

Mirabile Mysterium *Xmas,mot
[Eng/Lat/Ger] PETERS V116 $1.25 see also
CHRISTMAS MOTETS OF PRE-PALESTRINA DAYS
(W1451)
Lat/Ger] SATB,acap PETERS V116 $1.25
(W1452)
(Egidi, A.) [Eng/Ger/Lat] mix cor cor pts
VIEWEG s.p. see from SECHS
WEIHNACHTSMOTETTEN
(W1453)

Nazaraeus Vocabitur *mot
[Lat] SATB RICORDI-ENG SY153 s.p. (W1454)

Nazareus Vocabitur
(Zanon; Vene) "Ye Shall Call Him Emmanuel"
[Lat/Eng] SATB,acap oct COLOMBO 1881 $.30
(W1455)

O Blessed Nativity *see O Magnum Mysterium

O Domine Jesu Christe *16th cent
(Cartier, Anita; Carol, Henri; Gagnepain,
Bernard) [Lat] SATB OUVRIERES EO 529 s.p.
(W1456)

O Gemma Clarissima *mot
[Lat] SATB RICORDI-ENG SY177 s.p. (W1457)
(Zanon; Vene) "Consider The Lilies" [Lat/
Eng] SATB,acap oct COLOMBO 1898 $.30
(W1458)

O Magnum Mysterium *Xmas
(Richardson) "O Blessed Nativity" SATB oct
SPRATT 2016 $.30 (W1459)

O Ye Mighty *see Magne Martyr Adriane

Opera Omnia Vol. I *CCU,mot
(Zenck, H.) 4pt cmplt ed AM.INST.MUS.
$16.00 (W1460)

Opera Omnia Vol. II *CCU,mot
(Zenck, H.) 4pt cmplt ed AM.INST.MUS.
$16.00 (W1461)

Opera Omnia Vol. III *CCU,mot
(Zenck, H.) 5pt cmplt ed AM.INST.MUS.
$16.50 (W1462)

Opera Omnia Vol. IV *CCU,mot
(Zenck, H.) 6pt cmplt ed AM.INST.MUS.
$17.50 (W1463)

Opera Omnia Vol. V *CCU
(Gerstenberg) 4-7pt cmplt ed AM.INST.MUS.
$28.00 Motets of Musica Nova (W1464)

Opera Omnia vol. VII *CCU,hymn
(Gerstenberg) cor cmplt ed AM.INST.MUS.
$17.00 (W1465)

Opera Omnia Vol. VIII *CCU
(Gerstenberg) dbl cor cmplt ed AM.INST.MUS.
$23.00 Vesper Psalms, 1550 (W1466)

Psalm 131 *see Memento Domine David

Raising Of Lazarus, The !see Videns Dominus

Videns Dominus *mot
[Lat] SATB RICORDI-ENG SY131 s.p. (W1467)
(Zanon; Vene) "Raising Of Lazarus, The"
[Lat/Eng] SATB,acap oct COLOMBO 1873 $.30
(W1468)

Ye Shall Call Him Emmanuel *see Nazareus
Vocabitur

WILLAN, HEALEY (1880-1968)

Agnus Dei - O Christ, Thou Lamb Of God
*Commun/Lent
unis (easy) oct CONCORDIA 98-1824 $.20
(W1469)

Angels, Roll The Rock Away *Easter
SA&SSA,kbd (easy) oct CONCORDIA 98-1121
$.20 (W1470)

Angels Spirits Of Sleep
SSA (med) OXFORD 54.316 $.35 (W1471)

Anthem For The Centennial Of Canadian
Confederation
SATB,pno oct BERANDOL 91W28AF $.35 (W1472)

Apostrophe To The Heavenly Hosts, An *cant
SSAATTBB oct HARRIS HC4030 $1.00 (W1473)

Arise, Shine, For Thy Light Is Come *Epiph
SATB,kbd (med easy) oct CONCORDIA 98-1508
$.30 (W1474)

Ave Verum *anthem
"Hail, True Body" mix cor,T solo oct
NOVELLO 28.0945.01 s.p. (W1475)

Before Jehovah's Awefull Throne *anthem/hymn
SATB,org/pno PETERS 6239 $.30 (W1476)

Before The Ending Of The Day
SATB oct FISCHER,C CM-508 $.25 (W1477)

Behold The Lamb Of God *Lent
SATB,kbd (easy) oct CONCORDIA 98-1509 $.20
(W1478)

Behold, The Tabernacle Of God
SATB oct FISCHER,C CM-427 $.25 (W1479)

Benedicite (Shortened Form)
SATB (D maj) oct NOVELLO 44.0854.03 s.p.
(W1480)

Blessed Art Thou, O Lord *Ded/Fest
SATB (med) oct OXFORD 42.159 $.50 (W1481)

Carols For The Seasons *CC22L,carol
jr cor/treb cor CONCORDIA 97-6319 $1.25
(W1482)

Christ Hath Humbled Himself *Lent
SA,kbd (med easy) oct CONCORDIA 98-1768
$.20 (W1483)

Christ, Our Passover *Easter
SATB,acap (med diff) oct CONCORDIA 98-1009
$.25 (W1484)

Christ, Whose Glory Fills The Skies *Epiph/
Gen
SATB,kbd (med easy) oct CONCORDIA 98-2006
$.25 (W1485)

WILLAN, HEALEY (cont'd.)

Christmas Lullaby, A
SSA,Bar/T solo,acap oct BERANDOL 83W28AE
$.35 (W1486)

Christmas Praise *anthem
unis/SATB (easy) oct AUGSBURG 1207 $.16
(W1487)
unis treb cor/SA (easy) oct AUGSBURG 1207
$.16 (W1488)

Come, Holy Ghost *Gen/Pent
SATB,kbd (med easy) oct CONCORDIA 98-1552
$.25 (W1489)

Come, Jesus, Holy Child *Adv/Gen
unis&desc (easy) oct CONCORDIA 98-1091 $.20
(W1490)

Come, Ready Lyre
SSATB,acap oct BERANDOL 91W28AG $.35
(W1491)

Come Thou Beloved Of Christ
SSATB,acap oct BERANDOL 91W28AH $.50
(W1492)

Come, Thou Redeemer Of The Earth *Adv/Xmas
unis,strings (easy) cor pts CONCORDIA
98-1351 $.20, sc CONCORDIA 97-1394 s.p.
(W1493)

Communion Service *see Missa De Sancta Maria
Magdalena

Easy Communion Service, An *see Missa De
Sancto Albano In E Flat

Evening Canticles With Faux-Bourdons, No. 1
*CCU,Eve
SATB,acap (easy) oct OXFORD $.20 (W1494)

Evening Canticles With Faux-Bourdons, No. 3
*CCU,Eve
SATB,acap (easy) oct OXFORD $.20 (W1495)

Evening Canticles With Faux-Bourdons, No. 4
*CCU,Eve
SATB,acap (easy) oct OXFORD $.20 (W1496)

Evening Canticles With Faux-Bourdons, No. 5
*CCU,Eve
SATB,acap (easy) oct OXFORD $.20 (W1497)

Fair In Face *BVM,mot
SATB,acap (easy) oct OXFORD 94.307 $.25 see
from Liturgical Motets (W1498)

Fairest Lord Jesus *anthem/hymn
SS/TT,org/pno PETERS 6233 $.25 (W1499)

Father Of Heaven, Whose Love Profound *Gen/
SATB,kbd (med easy) oct CONCORDIA 98-2005
$.25 (W1500)

Father, We Praise Thee *anthem/hymn
SATB,org/pno PETERS 6125 $.30 (W1501)

Festival Te Deum *Te Deum
SATB,org/pno PETERS 6600 $.60 (W1502)

Five Hymn Tunes *CC5U,Gen
SATB (very easy) oct OXFORD 94.201 $.20
(W1503)

From Heaven High I Come To Earth *Xmas
SA&desc (easy) oct CONCORDIA 98-1645 $.25
(W1504)

Gloria Deo *mot
SSATB oct LESLIE 4084 (W1505)

Gloria Deo Per Immensa Saecula *mot
SSATB oct LESLIE 4084 (W1506)

Glory To God In The Highest *Xmas
SSA,kbd (med easy) oct CONCORDIA 98-1428
$.25 (W1507)

Glory To The Father Give *Gen/Trin
SA/SSA,kbd (easy) oct CONCORDIA 98-1382
$.22 (W1508)

God Is Gone Up With A Shout *Asc
SATB,kbd (med easy) oct CONCORDIA 98-1543
$.30 (W1509)

God Of Mercy *anthem/hymn
SATB,org/pno PETERS 6989 $.30 (W1510)

Grace Of The Lord Jesus, The
see Two Benedictions

Graduals For The Church Year *CCU,Gradual/
liturg
mix cor CONCORDIA 97-6312 $1.25 festival
half of church year and Trinity XIV,
Trinity XXI, and Trinity XXIII (W1511)

Grant Us Thy Light *Gen/Pent
SATB,acap (med diff) oct CONCORDIA 98-1014
$.25 (W1512)

Great Is The Lord *Ded/Fest,Psalm
SATB,acap (med) oct OXFORD 43.322 $.50
(W1513)

Great O Antiphons Of Advent, The *Adv,anti
SATB,acap (med easy) oct CONCORDIA 98-1446
$.35 (W1514)

Guide Me, O Thou Great Redeemer *anthem/hymn
SATB,org/pno PETERS 6157 $.25 (W1515)

Hail, True Body *see Ave Verum

Here Are We In Bethlehem *Xmas
SATB,acap (med) OXFORD 94.313 $.25 (W1516)

Hodie, Christus Natus Est *Xmas
SATB oct FISCHER,C CM-469 $.25 (W1517)

Holy, Holy, Holy Is The Lord *Gen/Trin
SATB,kbd (med easy) oct CONCORDIA 98-1553
$.30 (W1518)

Holy Spirit, Hear Us *Gen/Trin
SA,kbd (med easy) oct CONCORDIA 98-1120
$.20 (W1519)

Hosanna To The Living Lord *Adv/Gen
SATB,kbd (med easy) oct CONCORDIA 98-2004
$.25 (W1520)

WILLAN, HEALEY (cont'd.)

Hosanna To The Son Of David *Adv/Gen/Palm
SATB,acap (med diff) oct CONCORDIA 98-1016
$.30 (W1521)
SATB oct SOUTHERN $.30 (W1522)
SA/SSA,kbd (med easy) oct CONCORDIA 98-1118
$.25 (W1523)

I Beheld Her, Beautiful As A Dove *BVM/mot
SATB,acap (med) oct OXFORD 94.315 $.25 see
from Liturgical Motets (W1524)

I Looked, And Behold A White Cloud *Harv/
Thanks,anthem
mix cor oct NOVELLO 28.0903.06 s.p. (W1525)
SATB oct GRAY GCMR 1639 $.25 (W1526)

I Will Give Thanks *Gen/Thanks
SATB,kbd (med easy) oct CONCORDIA 98-1554
$.30 (W1527)

I Will Lay Me Down In Peace *Gen
SATB,kbd (med easy) oct CONCORDIA 98-1231
$.25 (W1528)
mix cor SOUTHERN $.25 (W1529)

I Will Lift Up Mine Eyes *Gen
SATB,acap (med diff) oct CONCORDIA 98-1017
$.25 (W1530)

In The Name Of Our God
SATB oct GRAY GCMR 466 $.35 (W1531)

Introit And Gradual For Dedication, The
*Ded/Gen,Gradual/Introit/liturg
SATB,kbd (med easy) oct CONCORDIA 98-1575
$.22 (W1532)
4pt CONCORDIA 98-1575 $.22 (W1533)

Introit And Gradual For Easter, The *Easter,
Gradual/Introit/liturg
SATB,kbd (med easy) oct CONCORDIA 98-1672
$.25 (W1534)
4pt CONCORDIA 98-1672 $.25 (W1535)

Introits *CC13L,Introit
cor oct LESLIE 4069 (W1536)

Introits *CCU
SATB oct BELWIN 60602 $.50 (W1537)

Introits And Graduals For The Church Year,
The *Gradual/Introit
cor cmplt ed CONCORDIA 97-4775 $3.25, pap
CONCORDIA 97-4853 $2.10 (W1538)

Introits For The Church Year, The *CC34U,
Ded/Easter/ECY,Introit/liturg
4pt CONCORDIA 97-7611 $1.00 festival half
of the church year (W1539)

Isaiah, Mighty Seer *Gen/Trin
SATB,kbd (med diff) oct CONCORDIA 98-1050
$.30 (W1540)

Jesus Good Above All The Others *anthem/hymn
SS/TT,org/pno PETERS 6676 $.25 (W1541)

Jesus, Lead Thou On *Cnfrm/Gen
SATB,kbd (med easy) oct CONCORDIA 98-2035
$.25 (W1542)

King Ascendeth Into Heaven, The *Asc/Gen
SA,kbd (med easy) oct CONCORDIA 98-1381
$.25 (W1543)

Lamb Of God, Pure And Holy *Lent
SA/SSA,kbd (easy) oct CONCORDIA 98-1383
$.25 (W1544)

Let All Mortal Flesh Keep Silence *anthem/
hymn
SATB,org/pno PETERS 6262 $.30 (W1545)

Let All The World In Every Corner Sing
SSA,org/pno PETERS 6677 $.25 (W1546)

Let Us Worship
SATB oct GRAY GCMR 717 $.25 (W1547)

Lift Up Your Heads, Ye Mighty Gates *Adv/Asc
SATB,kbd (med easy) oct CONCORDIA 98-2003
$.30 (W1548)

Like As The Hart *Gen
SATB,kbd (med easy) oct CONCORDIA 98-1230
$.25 (W1549)

Liturgical Motets *see Fair In Face; I
Beheld Her, Beautiful As A Dove; Lo, In
The Time Appointed; O King All Glorious;
O King Of Glory; Preserve Us, O Lord;
Rise Up, My Love (W1550)

Lo! He Comes With Clouds Descending *Adv
SATB,kbd (med easy) oct CONCORDIA 98-1592
$.30 (W1551)

Lo, In The Time Appointed *Adv,mot
SATB,acap (med easy) oct OXFORD 94.310 $.35 see
from Liturgical Motets (W1552)

Lo, The Star Which They Saw *Epiph
SA/SSA,kbd (med easy) oct CONCORDIA 98-1814
$.20 (W1553)

Lord Bless Thee, And Keep Thee, The
see Two Benedictions

Lord Of All Hopefulness *anthem/hymn
SATB,org/pno PETERS 6985 $.30 (W1554)

Lord, Thou Hast Been Our Refuge
SATB,org oct BERANDOL 91W28AI $.35 (W1555)

Lord Thou Hast Searched Me Out
SATB FLAMMER A 5062 $.30 (W1556)

Magnificat And Nunc Dimittis In E Flat
*Magnif/Nunc
SATB (med easy) oct OXFORD 42.971 $.35
(W1557)

Mass Of St. Teresa *Mass
unis mix cor,org (med) oct WILLIS $.35
(W1558)
unis jr cor,org (easy) oct WILLIS $.35
(W1559)

WILLAN, HEALEY (cont'd.)

Missa Brevis XIII
SATB,acap oct BERANDOL 91W28AJ $.35 (W1560)

Missa Brevis XIV
SATB,acap oct BERANDOL 91W28AK $.35 (W1561)

Missa De Sancta Maria Magdalena *Commun,
Agnus/Bene/Credo/Gloria/Kyrie/Sanctus
"Communion Service" unis oct OXFORD 45.200
$.65 (W1562)

Missa De Sancto Albano In E Flat *Agnus/
Bene/Credo/Gloria/Kyrie/Sanctus
"Easy Communion Service, An" SATB
oct OXFORD 42.402 $.65 (W1563)

Mystery Of Bethlehem fXmas,cant
BELWIN $1.25 (W1564)

Now Thank We All Our God *see Nun Danket
Alle Gott

Nun Danket Alle Gott *Thanks
"Now Thank We All Our God" SATB,org/pno
PETERS 6588 $.30 (W1565)

O Be Joyful In God *Bibl
SATB,S/T solo,org/pno PETERS 6073 $.40 (W1566)

O Be Joyful In The Lord (Psalm 100) Fest/
Thanks
SATB (easy) oct OXFORD 42.842 $.30 (W1567)

O Christ, Thou Lamb Of God *Lent
SA,kbd (easy) oct CONCORDIA 98-1122 $.22 (W1568)

O How Glorious
SATB oct GRAY GCMR 713 $.30 (W1569)

O How Sweet, O Lord
SATB oct GRAY GCMR 716 $.25 (W1570)

O King All Glorious *ASD,mot
SATB,acap (easy) oct OXFORD 94.308 $.20 see
from Liturgical Motets (W1571)

O King Of Glory *Asc,mot
SATB,acap (med) oct OXFORD 94.309 $.20 see
from Liturgical Motets (W1572)

O Lord Our Governor *anthem
mix cor oct NOVELLO 50.0315.06 s.p. (W1573)

O Praise The Lord *Bibl
SATB,org/pno PETERS 6464 $.40 (W1574)

O Sacred Feast
SATB oct GRAY GCMR 715 $.25 (W1575)

O Sing Unto The Lord A New Song
SATB,opt Bar solo,org/pno,opt 2trp&2trom
PETERS 6016 $.40, ipa (W1576)

O Strength And Stay *anthem/hymn
SATB,org/pno PETERS 6126 $.25 (W1577)

O Trinity Of Blessed Light *anthem/hymn
SATB,org/pno PETERS 6252 $.30 (W1578)

O What Their Joy And Their Glory Must Be
*anthem/hymn
SATB,org/pno PETERS 6066 $.30 (W1579)

Praise To The Lord *anthem/hymn
SATB,org/pno PETERS 6266 $.30 (W1580)

Prepare The Way, O Zion fAdv/Palm
SA,kbd (easy) oct CONCORDIA 98-1644 $.20 (W1581)

Preserve Us, O Lord *Eve,mot
SATB,acap (easy) oct OXFORD 94.312 $.20 see
from Liturgical Motets (W1582)

Psalm 100 *see O Be Joyful In The Lord

Rejoice Greatly, O Daughter Of Zion *Adv/Gen
SA,kbd (med easy) oct CONCORDIA 98-1113
$.25 (W1583)

Rejoice In The Lord Alway *Adv/Ded/Gen
SA,kbd (med easy) oct CONCORDIA 98-1815
$.20 (W1584)

Rejoice, O Jerusalem, Behold Thy King Cometh
*Adv
SATB,kbd (med easy) oct CONCORDIA 98-1506
$.25 (W1585)

Rejoice, O Land *anthem/hymn
SATB,org/pno PETERS 6986 $.30 (W1586)

Rejoice, Ye Pure In Heart *anthem/hymn
SATB,org/pno PETERS 6065 $.25 (W1587)

Responsaries For The Offices Of Tenebrae
SATB,acap oct BERANDOL 91W28AL $.35 (W1588)

Responsories For The Church Year, The *CCU,
liturg
cor (easy) CONCORDIA 97-6424 $.75 (W1589)

Responsory For Passiontide, The *Lent/Psntd
SA,kbd (easy) oct CONCORDIA 98-1770 $.20 (W1590)

Ring Out Ye Crystal Sphears
SSATB,acap oct BERANDOL 91W28AM $.35 (W1591)

Rise, Crowned With Light *Gen
SATB&desc (med easy) oct CONCORDIA 98-2001
$.25 (W1592)

Rise Up, My Love *Easter,mot
SATB,acap (med) oct OXFORD 94.306 $.25 see
from Liturgical Motets (W1593)

Sing Alleluya Forth In Duteous Praise
*anthem
SATB,org oct HARRIS HC4027 $.40 (W1594)

Sing To The Lord Of Harvest *Gen/Harv/Thanks
SA&desc (easy) oct CONCORDIA 98-1643 $.25 (W1595)
SSA,kbd (med easy) oct CONCORDIA 98-1450
$.25 (W1596)
SAB,kbd (med easy) oct CONCORDIA 98-1451
$.25 (W1597)
SATB&SA,kbd (med easy) oct CONCORDIA

WILLAN, HEALEY (cont'd.)

98-1454 $.25 (W1598)
SATB,kbd (med easy) oct CONCORDIA 98-2013
$.25 (W1599)

Sing We Triumphant Songs
SATB oct GRAY GCMR 2159 $.35 (W1600)

Spirit Of The Lord, The *Gen/Pent
SATB,acap (med diff) oct CONCORDIA 98-1013
$.30 (W1601)

Story Of Bethlehem, The *Xmas,Bibl
unis&SSA/unis&SSA,opt S solo,org CONCORDIA
97-7572 $.60 (W1602)

Strengthen For Service, Lord, The Hands
*anthem/hymn
SATB,org/pno PETERS 6510 $.30 (W1603)

Sun Of Righteousness
SSAATB oct BERANDOL 91W28AN $.35 (W1604)

Surely He Hath Borne Our Griefs *Lent
SA,kbd (med easy) oct CONCORDIA 98-1769
$.22 (W1605)

Te Deum Laudamus *Gen,liturg/Te Deum
cor/cong,org sc CONCORDIA 97-5083 $1.50,
Yor pts CONCORDIA 97-5084 $.12 (W1606)
"We Praise Thee, O God" SATB,kbd (med easy)
oct CONCORDIA 98-1126 $.30 (W1607)
"We Praise Thee, O God" unis,kbd (med easy,
abridged) oct CONCORDIA 98-1059 $.25 (W1608)

Ten Faux Bourdons On Well-Known Hymns
*CC10U,Gen
SATB (easy) oct OXFORD 94.002 $.15 (W1609)

Three Kings *Xmas
(Running) TTBB (med easy) OXFORD 41.023
$.25 (W1610)
(Running; Morris) SSA (med easy) OXFORD
83.077 $.25 (W1611)

Three Kings, The *Epiph
SSATB,acap (med easy) oct OXFORD 42.214
$.35 (W1612)
SSA (easy) oct OXFORD 83.077 $.25 (W1613)
TTBB (easy) oct OXFORD 41.023 $.25 (W1614)

Through The Day Thy Love Has Spared Us
*anthem/hymn
SATB,S/T solo,pno/org PETERS 6400 $.25 (W1615)

Two Benedictions *Bene
PETERS 6099 $.25
contains: Grace Of The Lord Jesus, The
(SATB,org/pno); Lord Bless Thee, And
Keep Thee, The (SATB,acap) (W1616)

Very Bread, Good Shepherd
SATB oct GRAY GCMR 714 $.25 (W1617)

We Praise Thee, O God *see Te Deum Laudamus

We Praise Thee, Part I *CC27L
unis treb cor&2pt treb cor&3pt treb cor
CONCORDIA 97-7564 $1.35 (W1618)

We Praise Thee, Part II *CC23L
unis treb cor&2pt treb cor&3pt treb cor
CONCORDIA 97-7610 $1.35 (W1619)

We Sing The Praise *anthem/hymn
SATB,org/pno PETERS 6224 $.25 (W1620)

What Is This Lovely Fragrance *Gen
SATB (easy) oct OXFORD 42.171 $.35 (W1621)

Worthy Art Thou, O Lord *Easter/Gen
SATB,acap (med diff) oct CONCORDIA 98-1015
$.25 (W1622)

Ye Shall Know That The Lord Will Come
SATB,opt soli,org/pno PETERS 6052 $.40 (W1623)

Ye Watchers And Ye Holy Ones *anthem/hymn
SATB,org/pno PETERS 6238 $.30 (W1624)

WILLCOXON, LARRY
Cross Was His Own, The
SATB oct AGAPE CF 139 $.35 (W1625)

Shout The Glad Tidings
SATB FLAMMER A 5583 $.30 (W1626)

WILLE
Lord, I Want To Be
(Andrews) TTBB oct GALAXY 1.0793.1 $.30 (W1627)

WILLIAM A.
Bells Ring Out At Christmas, The *Xmas
SATB oct LESLIE 4080 (W1628)

WILLIAM, DAVID
I Know Not Where The Road May Lead
SATB ABINGDON APM-869 $.35 (W1629)

WILLIAM, GLAN
When I Survey The Wondrous Cross
SATB oct LESLIE 4001 (W1630)

WILLIAMS
All Thy Mercies
SATB KJOS 5819 $.30 (W1631)

Alleluia *Allelu
SATB oct HERITAGE H72 $.35 (W1632)
SATB KJOS 5154 $.30 (W1633)

Alleluia! Alleluia! *Easter/Lent
(Richardson) SATB WORD CS-2411 $.30 (W1634)

Alleluia, Christ Is Born
SAB FLAMMER D5107 $.25 (W1635)
SATB FLAMMER A5138 $.25 (W1636)
SSA FLAMMER B 5064 $.30 (W1637)

And The Inn Was Full
SATB FLAMMER A 5159 $.30 (W1638)

Attend Our Prayers
SATB SCHMITT 858 $.30 (W1639)

Be Merciful Unto Me, O Lord
SATB SCHMITT 877 $.30 (W1640)

WILLIAMS (cont'd.)

Be Thou Exalted, O God
TTBB FLAMMER C5032 $.30 (W1641)
SAB FLAMMER D5154 $.25 (W1642)

Before The Paling Of The Stars
SATB FLAMMER A5153 $.25 (W1643)

Begin, My Tongue, Some Heavenly Theme
SATB oct LILLENAS AN-2350 $.30 (W1644)

Behold The Saviour Of Mankind
SAB FLAMMER D5080 $.25 (W1645)
SATB FLAMMER A 5094 $.25 (W1646)

Bells Of Joy
SATB oct LILLENAS AN-1128 $.35 (W1647)

Blest Are They
SATB KJOS 5838 $.30 (W1648)

Canticle From The Psalms
SATB FLAMMER A5096 $.30 (W1649)

Carillon Carol
SATB FLAMMER A 5387 $.30 (W1650)
SSA FLAMMER B 5152 $.30 (W1651)
SAB FLAMMER D5200 $.30 (W1652)

Cast Away All Your Transgressions
SATB FLAMMER A 5362 $.25 (W1653)

Chelsea Unison Choir Book, The *CCU
unis FLAMMER GF5003 $.95 (W1654)

Christ Is Risen *Easter
4pt jr cor/SATB (easy) FISCHER,C CM 7576
$.25 (W1655)

Christ, The Lord Is Born
SSA FLAMMER B 5103 $.25 (W1656)
SATB FLAMMER A 5107 $.30 (W1657)

Christ, The Risen Lord
SATB FLAMMER A5519 $.80 (W1658)

Christmas Canticle *Xmas
SATB FLAMMER A 5148 $.25 (W1659)
SAB FLAMMER D5028 $.25 (W1660)

Come Down, O Love Divine
SAB KJOS 5707 $.30 (W1661)

Come Unto Me, Ye Weary
SATB KJOS 5477 $.30 (W1662)

Dear Lord And Father Of Mankind
SATB (med easy) SOUTHERN $.30 (W1663)
2pt mix cor SOUTHERN $.30 (W1664)

Draw Nigh To Jerusalem *Palm
SATB oct SOUTHERN $.30 (W1665)

Easter Paean *Easter
SATB oct SOUTHERN $.30 (W1666)

Easter Story, The *CCU,Easter
SA/TB ALFRED 6101 $1.25 (W1667)

Eternal God Is Thy Refuge
SATB oct FISCHER,C CM-7648 $.25 (W1668)

Father Eternal *Gen
SATB SCHMITT 834 $.20 (W1669)

Festal Hymns *CCU
unis FLAMMER GF5005 $1.10 (W1670)

Fight The Good Fight
4pt jr cor/SATB (easy) FISCHER,C CM 6704
$.25 (W1671)
SATB oct FISCHER,C CM-6704 $.25 (W1672)

For A Closer Walk With God
SATB oct FISCHER,C CM-7546 $.25 (W1673)

For All The Saints
SATB oct LORENZ C342 $.30 (W1674)
(Barthelson) SATB oct PLYMOUTH HA-9 $.25 (W1675)

Forth In Thy Name, O Lord
SATB SHAWNEE A 728 $.30 (W1676)

Forty Days He Tarried Here
SATB FLAMMER A 5093 $.25 (W1677)
SAB FLAMMER D5042 $.25 (W1678)
SSA FLAMMER B 5082 $.25 (W1679)

From All Thy Saints In Warfare
(Rotermund) SATB (med easy) SOUTHERN $.25 (W1680)

Give Me Jesus
(Raymond) SATB oct PLYMOUTH JR-160 $.35 (W1681)

Give Thanks
SSA FLAMMER B 5055 $.25 (W1682)
SATB FLAMMER A 5055 $.30 (W1683)
SA/TB FLAMMER E5060 $.30 (W1684)
SAB FLAMMER D5061 $.30 (W1685)

Glory In His Holy Name
SA/TB FLAMMER E5137 $.25 (W1686)

Glory In Thy Perfect Love
SATB KJOS 5427 $.30 (W1687)

God Be Merciful Unto Us
SATB KJOS 5246 $.30 (W1688)

God Is Everywhere
SATB oct BELWIN 60233 $.30 (W1689)

Guide Us Thru The Night
SATB KJOS 5115 $.30 (W1690)

Hail The Day That Sees Him Rise *Asc
(Avalos) SATB oct PRO ART 1582 $.22 (W1691)
(Hastings) SATB oct BOURNE HA12 $.30 (W1692)

Hallelujah *spir
SATB oct PLYMOUTH JR-148 $.35 (W1693)

Have You Any Room For Jesus?
SATB oct LORENZ A301 $.30 (W1694)

He Lives Forevermore
SATB FLAMMER A 5450 $.30 (W1695)

WILLIAMS (cont'd.)

He Who Would Valiant Be
SATB FLAMMER A 5449 $.25   (W1696)

Hear My Prayer, O Lord   *Gen
SATB SCHMITT 829 $.30   (W1697)

Hear Ye, O Mountains
SAB FLAMMER D5148 $.30   (W1698)
SATB FLAMMER A 5377 $.30   (W1699)

His Praise Sing Forth
SATB FLAMMER A 5163 $.30   (W1700)

Holy Spirit, Truth Divine
SATB KJOS 5487 $.30   (W1701)

Hope Thou In God
SATB FLAMMER A 5530 $.30   (W1702)

Hymn For Thanksgiving, A   *Thanks,hymn
unis/SA oct SUMMY B 218 $.30   (W1703)
SATB oct SUMMY B 279 $.40   (W1704)

I Am The Resurrection And The Life
SATB oct SACRED E46 $.35   (W1705)

In Bethlehem's Lowly Manger
SATB&unis&SAB FLAMMER A 5418 $.30   (W1706)
SATB&unis FLAMMER A 5182 $.30   (W1707)
SA/TB FLAMMER E5054 $.30   (W1708)
SAB FLAMMER D5120 $.25   (W1709)

In The Beginning, God
(Frank) SATB,opt S solo oct FOX $.30   (W1710)

In The Highest, Glory
SAB FLAMMER D5132 $.25   (W1711)

Into The Woods My Master Went   *Lent
SATB oct SOUTHERN $.25   (W1712)

Jesus Before Pilate
SATB SHAWNEE A 556 $.25   (W1713)

Jesus, Born In Bethlehem   *Xmas
SATB KJOS 5461 $.30   (W1714)

Joyful Carol
SATB FLAMMER A 5375 $.30   (W1715)
SAB FLAMMER D5199 $.30   (W1716)
TTBB FLAMMER C5064 $.30   (W1717)

Junior Choir Anthems   *CCU,anthem
unis/SA SUMMY $2.25   (W1718)

Just A Closer Walk With Thee
(Raymond) SATB oct PLYMOUTH JR-162 $.30   (W1719)

King Aternal
SATB FLAMMER A5278 $1.10   (W1720)

Lenten Meditation   *Lent,cant
SATB FISCHER,C O-4148 $1.00   (W1721)

Let The People Praise Thee   *Gen
SATB SCHMITT 865 $.25   (W1722)

Little Christ Child, Sweet And Holy
SA/TB FLAMMER E5029 $.25   (W1723)

Lo! The Earth Is Ris'n Again
(Drake) SSA oct BELWIN 1982 $.25   (W1724)
(Drake) SAB oct BELWIN 1985 $.25   (W1725)

Lord, I Can't Turn Back
SATB oct GALAXY 1.2189.1 $.30   (W1726)

Love Must Rule In Man's Heart
SATB oct LORENZ C253 $.30   (W1727)

Most Holy Trinity
SAB KJOS 5706 $.30   (W1728)

Nine Choir Responses   *CC9U,Gen,cor-resp
SATB SCHMITT 1652 $.30   (W1729)

Now, Bright And Still
SAB FLAMMER D5106 $.25   (W1730)
SSA FLAMMER B 5100 $.25   (W1731)
SATB FLAMMER A 5149 $.30   (W1732)

O For A Closer Walk With God
4pt jr cor/SATB (easy) FISCHER,C CM 7546
$.25   (W1733)

O Give Thanks Unto The Lord
SATB KJOS 5436 $.30   (W1734)

O Lord Have Mercy   *Gen
SATB SCHMITT 819 $.30   (W1735)

O Lord, Hear My Voice
SATB KJOS $.30   (W1736)

O Man, Thy Grief And Sin Bemoan   *Gen
TTBB SCHMITT 412 $.25   (W1737)
SATB SCHMITT 814 $.35   (W1738)

O Taste And See
SATB oct LORENZ C285 $.25   (W1739)

On Jordan's Stormy Banks I Stand
SATB,opt fl&clar&bsn SOUTHERN $.30   (W1740)

Once To Every Man And Nation
(Stevens) SATB oct PRO ART 1772 $.30   (W1741)

Onward For God And My Country
SATB oct FOX $.30   (W1742)

Praise Song
SATB FLAMMER A 5070 $.30   (W1743)

Praise The Lord Who Reigns Above
SATB oct FISCHER,C CM-7747 $.25   (W1744)

Praise The Lord, Ye Heavens Adore Him
SATB FLAMMER A 5171 $.30   (W1745)
SAB FLAMMER D5074 $.30   (W1746)
SSA FLAMMER B 5029 $.30   (W1747)

Praise To God, Immortal Praise
SAB FLAMMER D5008 $.30   (W1748)
SATB FLAMMER A 5036 $.25   (W1749)
SA/TB FLAMMER E5039 $.25   (W1750)

WILLIAMS (cont'd.)

Praise Ye The Lord
SSATBB oct SUMMY 5273 $.65   (W1751)

Proclaim Liberty!
SATB oct HERITAGE H22 $.35   (W1752)
TTBB oct HERITAGE H2870 $.35   (W1753)

Psalm 100
SSATB oct SUMMY B 2047 $.45   (W1754)

Rejoice And Give Thanks
SATB KJOS 5132 $.30   (W1755)

Sing Praises To God
SA/TB FLAMMER E5031 $.30   (W1756)

Song Of Jesus   *anthem
SATB oct FISCHER,C CM-7171 $.25   (W1757)

Stars Shone Bright, The
SA/TB FLAMMER E5056 $.25   (W1758)
SATB FLAMMER A 5279 $.30   (W1759)

Sun Of My Soul   *Gen
SATB GALLEON GCS3002   (W1760)

This Day We Honor
SATB KJOS 5195 $.30   (W1761)

Twelve Anthems For SAB   *CC12U,anthem
SAB SUMMY $2.25   (W1762)

We Praise Thee, O God
SA/TB FLAMMER E5056 $.25   (W1763)

Welcome, Happy Morning
SATB FLAMMER A 5247 $.30   (W1764)

What Child Is This   *Xmas
SATB oct FISCHER,C CM-7737 $.25   (W1765)

When My Savior
(Raymond) SATB oct PLYMOUTH JR-159 $.30   (W1766)

While Shepherds Were Watching   *Xmas
SATB,acap SHAWNEE A 631 $.30   (W1767)

Worship Canticle
SATB FLAMMER A 5092 $.30   (W1768)

WILLIAMS, ALICE CRANE
Build The More Stately Mansions
SATB PARAGON 1027 $.25   (W1769)

Way, The Truth And The Life, The
SATB,A solo PARAGON 1018 $.25   (W1770)

Ye Are The Light
SATB PARAGON 1026 $.25   (W1771)

WILLIAMS, ARTHUR
Little Folk Mass Of Saint Philip, The
unis,org oct BERANDOL 914W7AA $.35, ipa   (W1772)

WILLIAMS, BECKET
Ring Out The Bells   *carol
unis CRAMER 48 s.p.   (W1773)

WILLIAMS, CHARLES LEE (1853-1935)
Thou Wilt Keep Him In Perfect Peace   *anthem
SATB oct GRAY GCMR 3171 $.30   (W1774)
TTBB oct NOVELLO 38.0106.03 s.p.   (W1775)
mix cor oct NOVELLO 28.0276.07 s.p.   (W1776)

WILLIAMS, CLIFTON
Thou Wilt Keep Him In Perfect Peace
4pt mix cor,acap oct SCHIRM.G 4915 $.25   (W1777)

WILLIAMS, D.
Easter Introit   *Easter
SATB,acap oct PRESSER 312-40940 $.30   (W1778)

Gloria
SATB,acap oct PRESSER 312-40669 $.30   (W1779)

Hosanna   *Easter
SATB,acap oct PRESSER 312-40493 $.25   (W1780)

How They So Softly Rest
SATB oct PRESSER 312-40488 $.30   (W1781)

WILLIAMS, D.M.
Pageant Of The Holy Nativity   *Xmas,cant
BELWIN $1.25   (W1782)

WILLIAMS, DAVID
O For A Thousand Tongues To Sing
mix cor,org PEER $.40   (W1783)

WILLIAMS, DAVID H.
As With Gladness   *Xmas
SATB oct GRAY GCMR 2891 $.25   (W1784)

Child Is Born In Bethlehem, A   *anthem
SATB (easy) oct AUGSBURG 1290 $.25   (W1785)

Child My Choice, A   *cant
mix cor BELWIN $1.25   (W1786)

Child Of Heaven, The   *Xmas,cant
unis BELWIN $.75   (W1787)

Christ Came To Bethlehem   *Xmas
SS/SA oct GRAY GCMR 2311 $.25   (W1788)
SATB oct GRAY GCMR 2300 $.30   (W1789)

Christ The Lord Is Risen   *Easter
SATB oct GRAY GCMR 2275 $.30   (W1790)

Christ The Lord Is Risen Again   *anthem
unis treb cor&SATB (easy) oct AUGSBURG 1256
$.22   (W1791)
SATB&jr cor oct AUGSBURG 1256 $.22   (W1792)

Christmas Song   *Xmas
unis oct AGAPE CF 151 $.30   (W1793)

Draw Nigh To Jerusalem   *Palm
SATB oct GRAY GCMR 2410 $.30   (W1794)

For Thy Sake   *Lent,cant
BELWIN $.60   (W1795)

Forth He Came   *Easter/Lent
SA oct GRAY GCMR 2523 $.30   (W1796)

WILLIAMS, DAVID H. (cont'd.)

Forth He Came At Easter   *Easter,Fr
SATB oct GRAY GCMR 2450 $.25   (W1797)

Gethsemane   *cant
mix cor BELWIN $1.25   (W1798)

How Far Is It To Bethlehem   *Xmas
SATB oct GRAY GCMR 2990 $.25   (W1799)

Hymn For Our Time
SATB oct GRAY GCMR 2268 $.25   (W1800)

Jesus Word Of God Incarnate   *Lent
SATB oct GRAY GCMR 2972 $.25   (W1801)

Lamb Of God   *Lent,cant
BELWIN $1.50   (W1802)

Let All The World
SATB oct FISCHER,J 9609 $.30   (W1803)

Let All Together Praise Our God   *Thanks,cant
BELWIN $1.25   (W1804)

Lo' He Comes   *Adv
SATB oct GRAY GCMR 2350 $.30   (W1805)

Mary's Wandering   *Lent
SATB oct GRAY GCMR 2794 $.30   (W1806)

O Come And Mourn   *Lent
SATB oct GRAY GCMR 2323 $.30   (W1807)

O Come, Emmanuel   *Adv
SATB oct GRAY GCMR 2440 $.25   (W1808)

O How Glorious
SATB oct GRAY GCMR 3098 $.30   (W1809)

O Lord, Where Now Is Bethlehem   *Xmas
SATB oct GRAY GCMR 2812 $.30   (W1810)

O My Dear Heart   *Xmas
SATB oct GRAY GCMR 3028 $.30   (W1811)

Of Christes Birth   *Xmas,cant
BELWIN $1.25   (W1812)

On The Passion Of Christ   *Lent,cant
BELWIN $1.25   (W1813)

On The Resurrection   *Easter,cant
BELWIN $1.50   (W1814)

Praise My Soul The King Of Heaven
SATB oct GRAY GCMR 2488 $.30   (W1815)

Puer Natus   *Xmas,cant
BELWIN $1.25   (W1816)

Shepherds Went Their Hasty Way, The   *Xmas
SATB (med) ABINGDON APM-923 $.30   (W1817)

Shout The Glad Tidings   *anthem
SS/SA (easy) oct AUGSBURG 1253 $.30   (W1818)

Sing Alleluia Forth
SATB oct GRAY GCMR 2390 $.30   (W1819)

Sing Today With One Accord   *Easter
SS/SA oct GRAY GCMR 3007 $.30   (W1820)
SATB oct GRAY GCMR 3004 $.30   (W1821)

Take My Life, And Let It Be
2pt oct GRAY GCMR 3048 $.30   (W1822)

Three Lenten Scenes   *CC3U,Lent,cant
BELWIN $1.25   (W1823)

Thy Saviour Comes   *Palm
SATB oct GRAY GCMR 2883 $.30   (W1824)

To Give Him Praise
unis jr cor oct FISCHER,J 9738 $.30   (W1825)

To Zion Jesus Comes   *Palm
SATB oct GRAY GCMR 2330 $.30   (W1826)

We Thank Thee, O Father   *Thanks
SATB oct GRAY GCMR 2345 $.25   (W1827)

When I Survey The Wondrous Cross   *Lent
SATB oct GRAY GCMR 2607 $.30   (W1828)

Who Passes Yonder Through The Throng   *Palm
SATB,org GRAY GCMR 3288 $.30   (W1829)

Whole Bright World, The   *Easter
SATB oct GRAY GCMR 2742 $.30   (W1830)
SA/wom cor oct GRAY GCMR 2522 $.30   (W1831)

WILLIAMS, DAVID MCK. (1887-)
Darst Thou Now
SATB oct GRAY GCMR 846 $.30   (W1832)

Hymn Of The Immortals   *hymn
mix cor,soli BELWIN $1.00   (W1833)

In The Year That King Uzziah Died
SATB oct GRAY GCMR 1356 $.40   (W1834)

King's Highway, The
SATB oct GRAY GCMR 1217 $.35   (W1835)
SAB oct GRAY GCMR 1458 $.25   (W1836)

Thirty-Four Hymn Descants   *CC34U,hymn
desc BELWIN $1.25   (W1837)

To Bethlehem   *Xmas
SATB oct GRAY GCMR 1478 $.25   (W1838)

WILLIAMS, DONALD O.
Christmas Carol Anthem, A   *Xmas,anthem/carol
jr cor&sr cor HIGHLAND 7100 $.25   (W1839)

Song Of Praise
cor HIGHLAND 4112 $.25   (W1840)

WILLIAMS, P.
King Of Glory, King Of Peace
cor oct HART s.p.   (W1841)

Lift Up Your Heads Ye Gates Of Brass
cor oct HART s.p.   (W1842)

WILLIAMS, P. (cont'd.)

Lord At First Did Adam Make, The
cor oct HART s.p.   (W1843)

WILLIAMS, R.
Christ, The Lord, Is Risen *Easter
(Peery, R.) SA oct PRESSER 312-40941 $.30
(W1844)

Come, Let Us Sing Unto The Lord
SATB KJOS 5411 $.30   (W1845)

Give Ear To My Words, O Lord
SATB KJOS 5442 $.30   (W1846)

Loving Shepherd Of Thy Sheep
SATB KJOS 5820 $.30   (W1847)

O Praise Him Alleluia
SATB KJOS 5868 $.30   (W1848)

Praise The Lord, His Glories Show *Easter/
Gen
(Vree, M.) SATB oct PRESSER 312-40565 $.30
(W1849)
(Vree, M.) SAB oct PRESSER 312-40788 $.30
(W1850)
(Vree, M.) SSA oct PRESSER 312-40673 $.30
(W1851)

Sing Unto The Lord
SATB KJOS 5252 $.30   (W1852)

Take Not Thy Holy Spirit From Me
SATB KJOS 5095 $.30   (W1853)

WILLIAMS, RALPH E.
Crib In Bethlehem, A *Xmas
SATB oct BOURNE 649 $.25   (W1854)

Good Earth
SATB KJOS 5443 $.30   (W1855)

Prince Of Peace
SATB KJOS 5837 $.30   (W1856)

This Is Our Land
SATB KJOS 5399 $.30   (W1857)

WILLIAMSON, INEZ MCCUNE
Lord's Prayer, The
SATB (easy) PRESSER G-202 $.35   (W1858)

WILLIAMSON, MALCOLM
Cantate Domino (Psalm 98) Bibl
SATB nct &RESSER 312-40793 $.45   (W1859)
SATB,org voc sc WEINBERGER s.p.   (W1860)

Carols Of King David *see I Will Lift Up
Mine Eyes (Psalm 121); King Of Love, The
(Psalm 23); O Jerusalem (Psalm 122);
Together In Unity (Psalm 133); Who Is The
King Of Glory (Psalm 24)   (W1861)

Christmas Carol, A *Xmas,carol
WEINBERGER s.p.   (W1862)

Come, Ye Thankful People, Come *Thanks
(Weinberger) 4pt mix cor,ST soli oct
SCHIRM.G 11252 $.40   (W1863)

Crown Him With Many Crowns
(Hutson) unis MARKS 4559 $.30   (W1864)

Easter Carol *Easter,carol
SATB oct SOUTHERN $.25   (W1865)
SATB,org WEINBERGER s.p.   (W1866)
(Weinberger) 4pt mix cor,S solo oct
SCHIRM.G 11249 $.30   (W1867)

Epiphany Carol *Xmas/Epiph,carol
WEINBERGER s.p.   (W1868)

I Will Lift Up Mine Eyes (Psalm 121) anthem/
Bibl
SATB&SATB,org WEINBERGER s.p. see from
Carols Of King David   (W1869)
SATB oct PRESSER 312-40787 $.30   (W1870)

In Dulci Jubilo
SATB,pno/org voc sc WEINBERGER s.p.   (W1871)

Jesu, Lover Of My Soul
dbl cor,SATB soli,org voc sc WEINBERGER
s.p.   (W1872)
dbl cor,SATB soli MARKS 4531 $.40   (W1873)
(Hutson) unis MARKS 4560 $.30   (W1874)

King Of Love, The (Psalm 23) Bibl
unis&cong,org WEINBERGER s.p. see from
Carols Of King David   (W1875)

Let Them Give Thanks *anthem
SATB nct &RESSER 312-40719 $.25   (W1876)
mix cor&unis,org voc sc WEINBERGER s.p.
(W1877)

Mass Of Saint Andrew
(Weinberger) 4pt mix cor oct SCHIRM.G 11250
$.40   (W1878)

Mass Of St. Andrew *Commun,Mass
cong,org voc sc WEINBERGER s.p.   (W1879)

Morning Of The Day Of Days *Easter,cant
cor,ST soli,org voc sc WEINBERGER s.p.
(W1880)

Morning Of The Day Of Days, The *Easter
(Weinberger) 4pt mix cor,ST soli oct
SCHIRM.G 11247 $.35   (W1881)

O Jerusalem (Psalm 122) Bibl
unis&cong,org WEINBERGER s.p. see from
Carols Of King David   (W1882)

O Sanctissima *Xmas,carol
SATB oct PRESSER JW $.35   (W1883)
SATB,pno/org WEINBERGER s.p.   (W1884)

Procession Of Palms *Easter/Psntd
SATB cor pts WEINBERGER s.p.   (W1885)
SATB,org voc sc WEINBERGER s.p.   (W1886)
SSA,org/pno voc sc WEINBERGER s.p.   (W1887)
(Weinberger) 4pt mix cor,SA soli oct
SCHIRM.G 11251 $.40   (W1888)

Psalm 23 *see King Of Love, The

Psalm 24 *see Who Is The King Of Glory

WILLIAMSON, MALCOLM (cont'd.)

Psalm 98 *see Cantate Domino

Psalm 121 *see I Will Lift Up Mine Eyes

Psalm 122 *see O Jerusalem

Psalm 133 *see Together In Unity

Psalm 148 *see Psalm Of Praise, A

Psalm Of Praise, A (Psalm 148) Bibl
unis,org voc sc WEINBERGER s.p.   (W1889)
unis oct PRESSER 312-40718 $.30   (W1890)
voc sc WEINBERGER s.p.   (W1891)

Six Christmas Songs *Xmas
(Weinberger) unis oct SCHIRM.G 11253 $.35
(W1892)

Six Christmas Songs For The Young *CC6U,Xmas
jr cor,perc cmplt ed WEINBERGER s.p., ipa
(W1893)

Six Evening Hymns *CC6U,hymn
cong,pno/org cmplt ed WEINBERGER s.p.   (W1894)

Six Evening Hymns
(Weinberger) unis oct SCHIRM.G 11278 $.25
(W1895)

Six Wesley Songs For The Young *CC6U
jr cor cmplt ed WEINBERGER s.p.   (W1896)

Six Wesley Songs For The Young *CC6U
unis jr cor SOUTHERN $.35   (W1897)

Sonnet
SATB,acap WEINBERGER s.p.   (W1898)

Sonnet (On Hearing The Dies Irae Sung In The
Sistine Chapel)
(Weinberger) 4pt mix cor,acap oct SCHIRM.G
11683 $.30   (W1899)

Te Deum *Bibl/Te Deum
unis MARKS 4530 $.35   (W1900)
cong WEINBERGER s.p. voc sc, cor pts   (W1901)
SATB,org,opt 3trp&3trom voc sc WEINBERGER
s.p., ipr   (W1902)
SATB,opt brass oct PRESSER 312-40947 $.45 (W1903)

Together In Unity (Psalm 133) Bibl
unis&cong,org WEINBERGER s.p. see from
Carols Of King David   (W1904)

Twelve New Hymn Tunes *CC12U,hymn
unis MARKS $1.25   (W1905)

Twelve New Hymn Tunes *CC12U,hymn
cong,pno/org cmplt ed WEINBERGER s.p.
(W1906)

Who Is The King Of Glory (Psalm 24) Bibl
unis&cong,org WEINBERGER s.p. see from
Carols Of King David   (W1907)

Wrestling Jacob *anthem
mix cor,S solo oct NOVELLO 40.1437.05 s.p.
(W1908)

WILLIAMSON, WARREN
Rock-A My Soul *spir
SA LEONARD-US 08054960 $.30   (W1909)

WILLIE BRING YOUR LITTLE DRUM see Rhea, Patapan

WILLIE, TAKE YOUR DRUM *Xmas
(Strickling) SATB SCHMITT 1071 $.35   (W1910)
(Strickling) SSAA SCHMITT 2070 $.30   (W1911)

WILLING
On Jordan's Banks *anthem
(George) SA (easy) oct AUGSBURG 1551 $.20
(W1912)

WILLIS
Be Thou My Judge, O Lord
SATB KJOS 5800 $.30   (W1913)

Blessed Be The Name Of The Lord
SATB KJOS 5499 $.35   (W1914)

It Came Upon A Midnight Clear
see Gruber, Franz Xaver, Silent Night

There Was Darkness Over The Earth
SATB oct SACRED S-5 $.35   (W1915)

Unto Thee, O Lord
SATB oct SACRED E59 $.35   (W1916)

Work Of Righteousness
SATB KJOS 5824 $.40   (W1917)

WILLIS, RICHARD STORRS (1819-1900)
It Came Upon The Midnight Clear *Xmas,carol
(Shaw; Parker) SATB,acap oct LAWSON 717
$.25   (W1918)

WILLKOMEN, SUSSER BRAUTIGAM see Hessenberg,
Kurt

WILLKOMMEN, SUESSER BRAEUTIGAM see Luebeck

WILLKOMMEN, SUSSER BRAUTIGAM see Lubeck,
Vincentius

WILLMINGTON
As For Man, His Days Are As Grass
SATB SCHMITT 1199 $.25   (W1919)

WILLMS, F.
Missa Brevis Super: Regina Caeli Et Tantum
Ergo *Mass
[Lat] SATB SCHOTT s.p.   (W1920)

WILLOUGHBY
Joseph Came Seeking A Resting Place *Xmas
SATB,acap oct FISCHER,C CM-564 $.25 (W1921)
SSAA oct FISCHER,C CM-563 $.25   (W1922)

WILLS
Hymn For Mankind *hymn
(Ades) SATB SHAWNEE A 849 $.30   (W1923)

It Came Upon The Midnight Clear *Xmas
(Stone) SATB oct PRO ART 1300 $.20   (W1924)
(Stone) SSA oct PRO ART 1371 $.20   (W1925)
(Stone) SAB oct PRO ART 1372 $.25   (W1926)

WILLS, ARTHUR
Ave Verum Corpus
see Two Latin Motets

Behold Now, Praise The Lord *Gen,anthem
SATB oct ROYAL 234 s.p.   (W1927)

Blessed Are All They That Fear The Lord
*Marriage,anthem
mix cor oct NOVELLO 50.0337.07 s.p. (W1928)

By The Waters Of Babylon
see Two Anthems

Carol Of King Canute, The *Xmas
4pt mix cor,acap oct SCHIRM.G 11544 $.25
(W1929)

Communion Service In C *Commun
cor&cong sc ROYAL 119 s.p.   (W1930)

From The Depths Of My Distress
unis oct NOVELLO 28.1465.10 s.p.   (W1931)

Jubilate *Jubil
unis oct NOVELLO 44.3426.10 s.p.   (W1932)
SATB&opt unis oct NOVELLO 44.1426.08 s.p.
(W1933)

Let God Arise *anthem/Bibl
mix cor,acap oct NOVELLO 28.1455.02 s.p.
(W1934)
4pt mix cor,acap oct SCHIRM.G 11360 $.30
(W1935)

Let This Mind Be In You *anthem
mix cor oct NOVELLO 28.1413.07 s.p.   (W1936)

Magnificat And Nunc Dimittis *Magnif/Nunc
ATB,acap (G min) oct NOVELLO 38.0143.08
s.p.   (W1937)
SATB (G min) oct NOVELLO 44.1408.10 s.p.
(W1938)

Missa Brevis *Mass
unis NOVELLO 44.1398.09 s.p.   (W1939)

Missa Eliensis *Mass
SATB (D min) oct NOVELLO 44.1381.04 s.p.
(W1940)

Missa Passionis Christi *Mass
SATB oct NOVELLO 44.1393.08 s.p.   (W1941)

O Lord, How Manifold Are Thy Works
see Two Introits

O Praise God In His Holiness *Thanks,anthem
mix cor oct NOVELLO 40.1452.09 s.p.   (W1942)

O Praise The Lord *Thanks,anthem
mix cor oct NOVELLO 86.0004.10 s.p.   (W1943)

O Praise The Lord Of Heaven
[Lat] 4pt,acap oct NOVELLO 33.0121.04 s.p.
(W1944)

O Quam Gloriosum
see Two Latin Motets

O Saviour Of The World
see Two Introits

Popular Psalm Settings *Bibl
unis oct SCHIRM.G 11771 $.30
contains: Psalm 24; Psalm 67; Psalm 121
(W1945)

Praises Of The Trinity, The *Gen/Trin,anthem
mix cor,acap oct NOVELLO 28.1445.05 s.p.
(W1946)

Preces And Responses
SATB oct NOVELLO 44.1435.07 s.p.   (W1947)

Psalm 24
see Popular Psalm Settings

Psalm 67
see Popular Psalm Settings

Psalm 121
see Popular Psalm Settings

Sing A New Song To The Lord
unis oct NOVELLO 28.1453.06 s.p.   (W1948)

Te Deum Laudamus *Te Deum
unis&opt desc NOVELLO 86.0016.03 s.p.
(W1949)

Their Sound Is Gone Out
see Two Anthems

Two Anthems *anthem/Bibl
ATB oct NOVELLO 38.0148.09 s.p.
contains: By The Waters Of Babylon; Their
Sound Is Gone Out   (W1950)

Two Introits *anthem/Introit
mix cor,acap oct NOVELLO 50.0344.10 s.p.
contains: O Lord, How Manifold Are Thy
Works; O Saviour Of The World   (W1951)

Two Latin Motets *mot
[Lat] 2pt oct NOVELLO 33.0114.01 s.p.
contains: Ave Verum Corpus; O Quam
Gloriosum   (W1952)

WILLSON
Mass Of The Bells
unis FRANK R-157 $.45   (W1953)

WILLUMSON, E.
Go Down Moses
SATB oct PRESSER 312-40651 $.30   (W1954)

WILM, NICOLAI VON (1834-1911)
Festal Song, A *carol
SATB BOSWORTH s.p.   (W1955)

WILSON
Abide With Me
SATB oct LORENZ C198 $.30   (W1956)

Agnus Dei *Easter/Lent,Agnus
SSAATTBB oct SPRATT 625 $.25   (W1957)

Alas! And Did My Savior Bleed *Lent
(Olds) SATB,A solo SCHMITT 1862 $.30
(W1958)

All Glory, Laud, And Honor *Easter
SATB oct LORENZ B162 $.30   (W1959)

All Hail The Power Of Jesus' Name
SATB oct LORENZ 9797 $.35   (W1960)

WILSON (cont'd.)

All Shall Be Well
SATB oct LORENZ C30 $.30 (W1961)

Animals Of Christmas, The *cant
SA FLAMMER E5014 $.75 (W1962)

"Are Ye Able", Said The Master
SATB oct LORENZ B12 $.30 (W1963)

At Calvary *Easter
SATB oct LORENZ A499 $.30 (W1964)

At The Cry Of The First Bird
SATB FLAMMER A 5211 $.30 (W1965)

Ave Maria
SSA,S solo,pno FRANK F-454 $.30 (W1966)

Balm In Gilead *spir
SSA oct BOURNE 215 $.25 (W1967)

Battle Hymn Of The Republic
SATB oct LORENZ 4424 $.30 (W1968)

Behold This Man *Easter,cant
SATB LORENZ $1.95 (W1969)

Beneath The Cross Of Jesus
SATB oct LORENZ 4387 $.30 (W1970)

Blessed Are The Meek
3pt jr cor/SSA (easy) FISCHER,C CM 6407 $.20 (W1971)

Blessed Assurance, Jesus Is Mine
SATB oct LORENZ 4472 $.30 (W1972)

Blessed Redeemer
SATB oct LORENZ B48 $.30 (W1973)

Carol Ye *Xmas
SATB oct LORENZ 9757 $.30 (W1974)

Cheer Up, Friends And Neighbors *Easter
SATB ALFRED 6322 $.30 (W1975)

Child Of Heaven *Xmas,cant
SATB oct LORENZ $1.95 (W1976)

Children Of God, The *Xmas,carol
SATB,acap oct COLOMBO 1411 $.30 (W1977)

Choral Service For Thanksgiving, A
SATB oct LORENZ B39 $.30 (W1978)

Choral Service For Watch Night, A
SATB oct LORENZ B40 $.30 (W1979)

Christ Everlasting *Easter,cant
SATB LORENZ $1.95 (W1980)

Christ Is Born!
SATB oct LORENZ C207 $.25 (W1981)

Christ Is Risen, Alleluia! *Easter
SATB oct LORENZ B146 $.30 (W1982)

Christ The Lord Is Risen Today *Easter
2pt oct LORENZ 5738 $.25 (W1983)

Create In Me A Clean Heart
SATB,acap oct BELWIN 60136 $.25 (W1984)

Cross Of Jesus *Easter
SATB oct SOUTHERN $.25 (W1985)

Crusade
SATB oct LORENZ A467 $.25 (W1986)

Crusader's Hymn
SATB oct LORENZ 4477 $.30 (W1987)

Desert Shall Rejoice, The
SATB oct LORENZ 9847 $.30 (W1988)

Did Jesus Weep For Me?
SATB oct LORENZ C333 $.25 (W1989)

Ding, Dong, Merrily On High *Xmas
SATB oct LORENZ A490 $.30 (W1990)

Direct Our Steps This Day
SATB oct GALAXY 1.2107.1 $.25 (W1991)

Does Jesus Care?
SATB oct LORENZ B122 $.30 (W1992)

Easter Alleluia, An *Easter
SATB FLAMMER A5194 $1.50 (W1993)
SATB oct LORENZ 9858 $.30 (W1994)

Festival Of Christmas *Xmas,cant
SATB oct LORENZ $1.95 (W1995)

Follow Me
SATB ALLANS 363 s.p. (W1996)
SAB oct LORENZ 7407 $.30 (W1997)
SATB oct LORENZ E14 $.30 (W1998)

Fum, Fum, Fum *Xmas,carol,Span
SA oct BOURNE HL6 $.25 (W1999)
SAB oct BOURNE T6 $.25 (W2000)

Git On Board, Little Children *spir
SA oct BOURNE HL10 $.25 (W2001)

God Be In My Head
SATB SHAWNEE A 587 $.25 (W2002)

God Of Our Fathers
SATB oct LORENZ 9817 $.30 (W2003)

God So Loved The World
SATB ALFRED 6343 $.30 (W2004)

Good News
SA/SAB oct LORENZ 7824 $.25 (W2005)

Hallelujah! What A Savior!
SATB oct LORENZ 4335 $.30 (W2006)

He Leadeth Me
SATB oct LORENZ B46 $.30 (W2007)

His Love All Around
2pt oct LORENZ 5740 $.30 (W2008)
SATB oct LORENZ A441 $.25 (W2009)

WILSON (cont'd.)

I Love To Tell The Story
SATB oct LORENZ A439 $.25 (W2010)

I Thought On The Lamb Of God
SATB oct VOLKWEIN VB191 $.25 (W2011)

I Will Extol Thee
SATB oct VOLKWEIN VB193 $.25 (W2012)

I Will Sing
SATB oct LORENZ A492 $.30 (W2013)

Immortal, Invisible
SATB oct LORENZ B117 $.30 (W2014)

In The Stillness Of The Night *Xmas
SAB oct SPRATT 104 $.30 (W2015)
SATB oct SPRATT 101 $.30 (W2016)
men cor oct SPRATT 622 $.30 (W2017)
SA oct SPRATT 103 $.30 (W2018)
SSA oct SPRATT 100 $.30 (W2019)

Jacob's Ladder *spir
SATB oct LORENZ 4374 $.30 (W2020)
SAB oct LORENZ 7340 $.30 (W2021)
2pt oct LORENZ 5704 $.25 (W2022)
unis oct LORENZ 8573 $.30 (W2023)
TTBB,acap oct COLOMBO 1680 $.35 (W2024)
SATB,acap oct COLOMBO 1476 $.30 (W2025)
SSA,acap oct COLOMBO 1629 $.25 (W2026)
(Vene) SAB oct COLOMBO 1809 $.30 (W2027)

Jesus Calls Us
SAB oct LORENZ 7369 $.25 (W2028)

Jesus, Lover Of My Soul
SATB oct LORENZ 4405 $.30 (W2029)

Just For You
SATB oct LORENZ 4345 $.30 (W2030)

King Of Love, The
SATB oct LORENZ 9907 $.25 (W2031)

Lead Me, Savior
SATB oct LORENZ A484 $.30 (W2032)

Let Earth Receive Her King *Xmas
SATB oct LORENZ A436 $.30 (W2033)

Lonesome Valley *Easter
SATB oct LORENZ B11 $.30 (W2034)
unis oct LORENZ 8589 $.25 (W2035)
SATB ALLANS 370 s.p. (W2036)
SAB oct LORENZ 7360 $.30 (W2037)

Magic Of Christmas, The *Xmas
SATB oct SPRATT 572 $.25 (W2038)

Mighty Fortress, A
SATB oct LORENZ A404 $.25 (W2039)

Moon Shines Bright, The *Xmas/Gen,carol,Eng
SAB oct BOURNE T8 $.25 (W2040)

More Holiness Give Me
SATB oct LORENZ B158 $.30 (W2041)

Mother's Prayer, A
SATB oct LORENZ 4345 $.30 (W2042)

My Lord, What A Morning *Easter
SATB oct LORENZ B75 $.30 (W2043)

My Shepherd Will Supply My Need
SATB oct LORENZ C166 $.30 (W2044)

Nativity, The *Xmas,cant
SATB oct LORENZ $1.95 (W2045)

O Brother Man
SAB oct LORENZ 7377 $.30 (W2046)
SATB oct LORENZ B116 $.30 (W2047)

O God, Thy Hands The Heavens Made
SATB oct LORENZ A525 $.30 (W2048)

O Sleep, My Fairest One *Xmas
SATB oct LORENZ A517 $.30 (W2049)

One God
SATB HANSEN-US C267B $.40 (W2050)
SSA HANSEN-US C267A $.40 (W2051)
SAB HANSEN-US C267E $.40 (W2052)
TTBB HANSEN-US C267D $.40 (W2053)
SA HANSEN-US C267C $.40 (W2054)

Praise To The Lord, The Almighty
SATB oct LORENZ 9955 $.30 (W2055)

Psalm 148 *Psalm
SATB oct LORENZ 9890 $.30 (W2056)

Rejoice Ye Pure In Heart
SATB oct GALAXY 1.2471.1 $.30 (W2057)

Rock-a My Soul *spir
SAB oct BOURNE T11 $.25 (W2058)

Sing We Now Of Christmas *Xmas
SA oct LORENZ A503 $.30 (W2059)

Somebody's Knocking At Your Door
SA oct LORENZ 5362 $.30 (W2060)
SATB oct LORENZ 4461 $.30 (W2061)
SAB oct LORENZ 7356 $.25 (W2062)

Song For Christmas, A *Xmas
SSA FLAMMER B 5086 $.25 (W2063)

Song Of Easter *Easter,cant
SATB LORENZ $1.95 (W2064)

Song Of The Holy Night *Xmas,cant
SATB oct LORENZ $1.95 (W2065)
SSA oct LORENZ $1.75 (W2066)

Song Of The Resurrection *Easter
SATB oct LORENZ B25 $.30 (W2067)

Spirit Of The Lord, The
SATB oct LORENZ 9844 $.30 (W2068)

Story Of Jesus, The *CCU,spir
SATB ALFRED 6102 $1.50 (W2069)

WILSON (cont'd.)

Sweet Hour Of Prayer
SATB oct LORENZ 4376 $.30 (W2070)

Take Up Thy Cross *Easter
SATB ALLANS 362 s.p. (W2071)
SATB oct LORENZ E1 $.30 (W2072)

Teach Me Thy Way
SATB oct LORENZ B57 $.30 (W2073)

Temple Of The Lord, The
SATB ALFRED 6437 $.35 (W2074)

There Were Two Thieves
SATB FLAMMER A 5345 $.30 (W2075)

This Is The King *Easter,cant
SATB LORENZ $1.95 (W2076)

Though Your Sins Be As Scarlet
SATB oct LORENZ A325 $.30 (W2077)

To God All Praise And Glory
SATB oct LORENZ B130 $.30 (W2078)

'Twas On One Sunday Morning *Easter
SATB ALFRED 6629 $.30 (W2079)

Were You There? *Easter,spir
SAB oct BOURNE T2 $.25 (W2080)
SA oct BOURNE HL7 $.25 (W2081)

Westminster Carol *Xmas,carol
SATB oct LORENZ B171 $.30 (W2082)

What Child Is This? *Xmas
SATB oct LORENZ C19 $.30 (W2083)

Who Is On The Lord's Side?
SATB oct LORENZ C177 $.30 (W2084)

Why Should He Love Me So? *Easter
SATB oct LORENZ A422 $.25 (W2085)

Within The Silence
SATB oct LORENZ C277 $.30 (W2086)

WILSON, CHARLES
Dona Nobis Pacem
SATB,org/brass THOMP.G s.p. (W2087)
SATB,org/brass THOMP.G E.I. 1013 s.p. (W2088)

WILSON, D.
Silent Stars Go By, The *Xmas
(Lynn, A.) SATB oct PRESSER 312-40666 $.30 (W2089)

WILSON, H.
A-Rockin All Night
SATB oct PRESSER 312-40109 $.30 (W2090)

Bells, The
SATB oct HERITAGE H10 $.35 (W2091)

Go, Song Of Mine!
SATB oct HERITAGE H7 $.35 (W2092)

Old Woman, The
SATB oct HERITAGE H11 $.30 (W2093)

WILSON, H. LANE
Voices Of The Angels
SATB ENOCH TP21 s.p. (W2094)

WILSON, HARRY [ROBERT] (1901-)
Fanfare For Easter *Easter
SATB oct BOURNE 705 $.25 (W2095)

Give Us Faith For Today
mix cor,acap,opt org/pno oct SCHIRM.G 10060 $.25 (W2096)
wom cor,acap,opt pno/org oct SCHIRM.G 10106 $.25 (W2097)

Let Not Your Heart Be Troubled *Bibl
SATB oct BOURNE 706 $.25 (W2098)

Let There Be Song
SSA oct ELKAN-V 362-3059 $.25 (W2099)

Mary And Martha
SSA oct ELKAN-V 362-3062 $.25 (W2100)
SA oct ELKAN-V 362-126 $.25 (W2101)

Prayer And Praise
SATB,opt band/orch KJOS 5300 $.30 (W2102)

Prince Of Peace, The *Xmas,Bibl
SSAATBB oct BOURNE 702 $.30 (W2103)

Psalm 23
SATB oct BOURNE 703 $.25 (W2104)

Res' My Shoes
SATB oct BOURNE 670 $.25 (W2105)
SAB oct BOURNE T1 $.25 (W2106)
SA oct BOURNE HL1 $.30 (W2107)

Upon This Rock *ora
cor,soli,orch voc sc SCHIRM.G $1.50 (W2108)

WILSON, IRA B. (1880-1950)
Alone In The Garden
SSA oct LORENZ 6241 $.30 (W2109)

And There Were Shepherds *Xmas
SATB oct LORENZ 928 $.30 (W2110)

Blessed Be The Lord
SATB oct LORENZ 1445 $.30 (W2111)

Christmas Song Of Songs *Xmas,cant
SATB oct LORENZ $1.95 (W2112)

Cross Triumphant *Easter,cant
SATB LORENZ $1.95 (W2113)

First Easter *Easter,cant
SATB LORENZ $1.95 (W2114)

Great And Marvelous
SATB oct LORENZ 9200 $.30 (W2115)

Hear Our Prayer
(Rubinstein) SA ALLANS 155 s.p. (W2116)

WILSON, IRA B. (cont'd.)

I Need Thee Every Hour
SATB oct LORENZ A271 $.25   (W2117)

King Eternal   *Easter,cant
SATB&ORENZ $1.95   (W2118)

Mother's Prayer, A
SATB oct LORENZ 4398 $.30   (W2119)

Music Of Christmas, The   *Xmas,cant
SATB oct LORENZ $1.95   (W2120)
SAB oct LORENZ $1.75   (W2121)

Night Of Holy Memories   *Xmas,cant
SATB oct LORENZ $1.95   (W2122)

O Night Of Holy Memory   *Xmas
SATB oct LORENZ 1012 $.30   (W2123)

Our Living Lord   *Easter,cant
SATB LORENZ $1.95   (W2124)

Stilling The Tempest
SATB oct LORENZ 1112 $.30   (W2125)

Thou Art The Living Christ   *Easter
SATB oct LORENZ 1999 $.30   (W2126)

Thou, Bethlehem   *Xmas
SATB oct LORENZ 9275 $.35   (W2127)

Trust Ye In The Lord
TTBB,pno (easy) oct WILLIS 6335 $.12   (W2128)

Two Friends
SA oct LORENZ 5374 $.25   (W2129)

Yuletide Memories   *Xmas,cant
SATB oct LORENZ $1.95   (W2130)

WILSON, IRENE
Music Of Christmas, The   *Xmas,cant
SA oct LORENZ 1.75   (W2131)

WILSON, JAMES R.
Give Unto The Lord   *Bibl
4pt mix cor,acap oct SCHIRM.G 11008 $.25   (W2132)

How Excellent Is Thy Name   *Bibl
4pt mix cor,acap oct SCHIRM.G 11046 $.20   (W2133)

Lord, Hear My Voice
4pt mix cor,acap oct SCHIRM.G 11237 $.25   (W2134)

WILSON, JOHN F.
Amen
SATB oct AGAPE CF 118 $.25   (W2135)

Arrow And The Song, The
SSA oct AGAPE SP 684 $.30   (W2136)

Blessed Is The Nation
SATB oct AGAPE CF 119 $.30   (W2137)

Choral Primer, The   *CCU
SATB oct AGAPE $1.75   (W2138)

Christ Is Risen! Alleluia!   *Easter
SATB oct AGAPE A 385 $.30   (W2139)

Christ Triumphant   *Easter,cant
oct AGAPE $1.50   (W2140)

Christmas Happening, A   *Xmas,folk
oct AGAPE $1.50   (W2141)

Come Unto Me
SATB oct AGAPE 302 $.25   (W2142)

Cross Of Jesus
SATB oct AGAPE CH 649 $.25   (W2143)

Crown Him With Many Crowns
SATB,brass oct AGAPE F 909 $.35   (W2144)

Easter Canticle Of Praise   *Easter
SATB oct AGAPE A 397 $.30   (W2145)

Go Little Song
SATB oct AGAPE SP 705 $.25   (W2146)

God Of Justice, Save Thy People
SATB oct AGAPE 408 $.30   (W2147)

Good Christian Men, Rejoice
SATB oct AGAPE CH 640 $.30   (W2148)

He Is Risen   *Easter,cant
jr cor oct AGAPE $1.25   (W2149)

He's Alive   *Easter,folk
oct AGAPE $1.95   (W2150)

Hosanna, Loud Hosanna
SATB&treb cor oct AGAPE F 910 $.30   (W2151)

I Got A Shoe
SATB oct AGAPE JW 7771 $.30   (W2152)

I'm Going Away
SATB oct AGAPE JW 7772 $.30   (W2153)

Junior Choir Praise   *CCU
jr cor oct AGAPE $1.50   (W2154)

Let Us With A Gladsome Mind
SSATB&treb cor/SATB&treb cor oct AGAPE
F 916 $.30   (W2155)

Lord Jehovah Reigns, The
SAB,opt 3trp oct AGAPE F 915 $.30   (W2156)

Loud Roar Of The Rocket
unis oct AGAPE CH 654 $.25   (W2157)

Man Alive   *Gen
oct AGAPE $1.95   (W2158)

New Creature, A
SATB oct AGAPE AG 7135 $.30   (W2159)

Noel   *Xmas
SATB oct AGAPE CF 128 $.30   (W2160)

O Lord, How Majestic Is Thy Name
SATB oct AGAPE A 400 $.30   (W2161)

WILSON, JOHN F. (cont'd.)

Praise, My Soul, The King Of Heaven
SATB,brass oct AGAPE F 928 $.35   (W2162)

Redeemer, Come
SATB oct AGAPE A 423 $.30   (W2163)

Shepherds, Rejoice   *Xmas,cant/folk
oct AGAPE $1.50   (W2164)

Sing Unto His Name
SSA oct AGAPE A 465 $.30   (W2165)
SATB oct AGAPE A 464 $.30   (W2166)

Son Of God, The   *Xmas,cant
oct AGAPE $1.50   (W2167)

Sounds Of A New Generation   *CCU
jr cor oct AGAPE $1.50   (W2168)

Super Folk For Super Folks   *CCU
jr cor oct AGAPE $1.50   (W2169)

What Is This Love
SATB oct AGAPE CF 158 $.30   (W2170)

Who Is This Boy?
(Hustad) SATB oct AGAPE CF 102 $.30   (W2171)

With Thankful Hearts
2pt mix cor/treb cor oct AGAPE CH 634 $.30 (W2172)

WILSON, KEITH E.
God Of Compassion
SAB,acap (easy) PRESSER G-125 $.30   (W2173)

WILSON, R.
Love Came Down At Christmas   *Xmas
SATB oct PRESSER MC295 $.30   (W2174)

WILSON, ROGER [C.] (1912-   )
Forty Days To Easter   *CC15U,Lent,anthem
SA/SATB (easy) LORENZ $1.75   (W2175)

He Shall Feed His Flock   *Adv/Xmas,anthem/
Bibl
SATB/SA,opt med solo (easy) oct LORENZ A528
$.30   (W2176)

Lord Is My Shepherd, The   *Gen,anthem/spir,US
SATB/SA (easy) oct LORENZ A534 $.30   (W2177)

Rejoice, The Lord Is King   *Gen,anthem
SATB oct LORENZ A537 $.30   (W2178)

WILT DU GEBEN SONNENSCHEIN see Bottcher, Georg

WILT NOT THOU TURN AGAIN? see Dietterich,
Philip R.

WILT THOU FORGIVE see Schiavone, John

WILT THOU NOT TURN AGAIN? see Powell, Robert J.

WILT THOU WALK BESIDE ME, LORD see Morgan

WILTBERGER
Confirma Hoc Deus
(Vene) "O God, Preserve The Work" [Lat/Eng]
TTBB oct COLOMBO 2010 $.25   (W2179)

Jubilate Deo
(Vene) "Sing To God" [Lat/Eng] TTBB oct
COLOMBO 2012 $.30   (W2180)

O God, Preserve The Work   *see Confirma Hoc
Deus

Sing To God   *see Jubilate Deo

Terra Tremuit
(Vene) "Trembling Seized The Earth" [Lat/
Eng] TTBB oct COLOMBO 2009 $.25   (W2181)

Thine Are The Heavens   *see Tui Sunt Coeli

Trembling Seized The Earth   *see Terra
Tremuit

Tui Sunt Coeli
(Vene) "Thine Are The Heavens" [Lat/Eng]
TTBB oct COLOMBO 2011 $.30   (W2182)

WINANS
Now I Lay Me Down To Sleep
2pt jr cor oct LILLENAS AN-4022 $.25   (W2183)

Thou Wilt Keep Him In Perfect Peace
SATB oct LORENZ C268 $.30   (W2184)

WINANS, WINIFRED LAMB
God So Loved   *Easter,cant
unis jr cor&2pt jr cor&opt 3pt jr cor,opt
soli voc sc LILLENAS ME-10 $1.25   (W2185)

WINCHESTER, E.C.
Cross, The
Xor HART oct s.p., pap s.p.   (W2186)

Ferial Responses   *CCU,Gen
cor oct HART s.p.   (W2187)

Festival Responses   *CCU,Fest
cor oct HART s.p.   (W2188)

Hallelujah Christ Is Risen
cor oct HART s.p.   (W2189)

Let Us Now Go Unto Bethlehem   *Xmas
cor oct HART s.p.   (W2190)

Magnificat   *Magnif/Nunc
cor oct HART s.p. contains also: Nunc
Dimittis   (W2191)

Nunc Dimittis
see Winchester, E.C., Magnificat

Preces And Responses   *CCU
cor oct HART s.p.   (W2192)

WINCHESTER, F.
Be Merciful After Thy Power   *Offer
cor oct HART s.p.   (W2193)

WIND THROUGH THE OLIVE TREES   *Xmas
(Butler) SATB,acap,opt pno oct PRO ART 2221
$.25   (W2194)

WIND THROUGH THE OLIVE TREES see Rinehart

WINDS AT BETHLEHEM, THE see Rogers, E.

WINDS OF TRUTH see Murray, Bain

WINDS THROUGH THE OLIVE TREES   *Xmas,carol,Ger
SSA oct STAFF 328 $.25   (W2195)
SATB oct STAFF 281 $.30   (W2196)
(Ehret) SA oct SPRATT 614 $.25   (W2197)
(Ehret) SAB oct SPRATT 608 $.25   (W2198)

WINDS THROUGH THE OLIVE TREES see Bampton, R.

WINDS THROUGH THE OLIVE TREES see Barker

WINDS THROUGH THE OLIVE TREES see Bayley,
Robert Charlton

WINDS THROUGH THE OLIVE TREES see Christiansen,
Paul

WINDS THROUGH THE OLIVE TREES see Pyle, Francis
[Johnson]

WINDS THROUGH THE OLIVE TREES see Rees

WINDS THROUGH THE OLIVE TREES   *Xmas,carol
(Rodgers, I.) SATB/SA,pno (easy) oct WILLIS
5871 $.10   (W2199)

WINDS THRU THE OLIVE TREES see Wetzler, Robert

WINDSOR MASS, THE   *Mass
(Simkins) [Eng/Lat] SATB STAINER F19 s.p.   (W2200)

WINE AND WATER see Parry, Charles Hubert
Hastings

WINGS OF MORNING, THE see Danhock, L.

WINK, RICHARD L.
Turn Thee To Me   *Psalm
SATB,acap oct WORLD CA-2114-8 $.45   (W2201)

WINSLOW
Mary's Lullaby
SA oct BELWIN 64192 $.30   (W2202)

Wake Now Ye Shepherds
jr cor&sr cor (med) FISCHER,C CM 609 $.20 (W2203)

WINSLOW, R.K.
Consider The Lilies
SATB oct ELKAN-V 362-1217 $.25   (W2204)

Creation Locked   *Xmas
SATB oct ELKAN-V 362-1235 $.25   (W2205)

I Call Heaven And Earth
SATB oct ELKAN-V 362-1216 $.25   (W2206)

WINTER see Sanders, Robert L.

WINTER BIRTH, A see Nicholson, Ralph

WINTER BIRTH, A see Nicholson

WINTER CAROL see Peek, Richard

WINTER CAROL, A see McAfee, Don

WINTER IS PAST, THE see Webber, Lloyd

WINTER, JOHN
Magnificat And Nunc Dimitis
4pt mix cor oct SCHIRM.G 11261 $.25 (W2207)

WINTER NATIVITY see Thiman, Eric Harding

WINTER PASSES OVER see Purvis, Richard

WINTERAUSTREIBEN see Spitta, Heinrich

WINTERTIDE HATH PASSED AWAY see Meek, Kenneth

WINTERTIME HATH PAST AWAY see Garlick, Anthony

WIR BITTEN DICH VON HERZEN see Distler, Hugo

WIR CHRISTENLEUT see Fuger

WIR CHRISTENLEUT HABN JETZUND FREUD see Graap,
Lothar

WIR CHRISTENLEUT HABN JETZUND FREUD see Kuhnau,
Johann

WIR CHRISTENLEUT HAN JETZUND FREUD see Bach,
Johann Sebastian

WIR DANKEN DIR see Bach, Johann Sebastian, Wir
Danken Dir, Gott, Wir Danken Dir

WIR DANKEN DIR FUR DEINEN TOD see Vulpius,
Melchior

WIR DANKEN DIR, GOTT see Bach, Johann Sebastian

WIR DANKEN DIR, GOTT, FUR UND FUR see
Gumpeltzhaimer, Adam

WIR DANKEN DIR, GOTT, WIR DANKEN DIR see Bach,
Johann Sebastian

WIR DANKEN DIR, HERR GOTT, HIMMLISCHER VATER
see Schutz, Heinrich

WIR DANKEN DIR, HERR GOTT VATER see
Gumpeltzhaimer, Adam

WIR DANKEN DIR, HERR JESU see Anonymous

WIR DANKEN DIR, HERR JESU CHRIST see Anonymous

WIR DANKEN DIR, HERR JESU CHRIST see Ehlers,
Erich

WIR DANKEN DIR, HERR JESU CHRIST see Gesius,
Bartholomaus

WIR DANKEN DIR, HERR JESU CHRIST see Horn, Paul

WIR DANKEN DIR, HERR JESU CHRIST see
Hufschmidt, Wolfgang

WIR DANKEN DIR, HERR JESU CHRIST see Schweppe,
Joachim

WIR DANKEN DIR, HERR JESU CHRIST, DAS DU see Trubel, Gerhard

WIR DANKEN DIR, HERR JESU CHRIST, DASS DU FUR UNS GESTORBEN BIS see Bornefeld, Helmut

WIR DANKEN DIR, O GOTTES LAMM see de la Rue, Pierre

WIR DANKEN GOTT FUR SEINE GABEN see Schmidt-Mannheim, Hans

WIR DANKEN GOTT FUR SEINE GABEN see Stern, Hermann

WIR DANKEN, HERR see Biebl, Franz

WIR DANKEN, HERR see Rein, Walter

WIR DANKEN, HERR, FUR BROT UND KLEID see Lahusen, Christian

WIR DANKEN, HERR, FUR BROT UND KLEID see Nother, Willi

WIR DIENEN, HERR see Weismann, Wilhelm

WIR EILEN MIT SCHWACHEN, DOCH EMSIGEN SCHRITTEN see Bach, Johann Sebastian

WIR ERMAHNEN AUCH ABER see Reda, Siegfried

WIR ESSEN UND WIR LEBEN WOHL see Bach, Johann Sebastian

WIR FAHR'N DAHIN, WIRF HELLES LICHT see Anonymous

WIR GALUBEN ALL AN EINEN GOTT see Schwartz, Gerhard von

WIR GINGEN ALLE IN DER IRRE see Reda, Siegfried

WIR GINGEN ALLE IN DIE IRRE, AUSGABE A see Zipp, Friedrich

WIR GINGEN ALLE IN DIE IRRE, AUSGABE B see Zipp, Friedrich

WIR GLAUBEN ALL AN EINEN see Barbe, Helmut

WIR GLAUBEN ALL AN EINEN GOTT see Bach, Johann Sebastian

WIR GLAUBEN ALL AN EINEN GOTT see Bruck, Arnold von

WIR GLAUBEN ALL AN EINEN GOTT see Hassler, Hans Leo

WIR GLAUBEN ALL AN EINEN GOTT see Praetorius, Michael

WIR GLAUBEN GOTT see Ruppel, Paul Ernst

WIR GLAUBEN GOTT IM HOCHSTEN THORN see Poos, Heinrich

WIR GRUSSEN DICH, HERR JESU CHRIST see Reda, Siegfried

WIR HABEN EINEN STERN GESEHEN see Weismann, Wilhelm

WIR HABEN IHN GESEHEN NACH DIESEM BERGE GEHEN see Beethoven, Ludwig van

WIR HABEN SO LANGE KRIEG GESEHN see Krietsch, Georg

WIR HARREN, CHRISTE see Kaufmann, Otto

WIR HEBEN AN ZU SINGEN see Kurig, Hans-Hermann

WIR KENNEN KEINEN ANDERN GOTT see Reger, Max

WIR LEBEN NICHT ALLEIN VOM BROT *CC12U,Gen
[Ger] unis,inst sc BOSSE BE 288 s.p.   (W2208)

WIR LEBEN NICHT ALLEIN VOM BROT see Puls, Hans

WIR LOBEN DEN VATER UND DEN SOHN see Reger, Max

WIR LOBEN DICH see Zillinger, Erwin

WIR LOBEN NOCH UND SINGEN see Rohwer, Jens

WIR MOCHTEN GERN DEIN KREUZ see Mendelssohn, Arnold

WIR MUSSEN see Bach, Johann Sebastian, Wir Mussen Durch Viel Trubsal

WIR MUSSEN DURCH VIEL TRUBSAL see Bach, Johann Sebastian

WIR MUSSEN DURCH VIEL TRUBSAL IN DAS REICH GOTTES EINGEHEN see Bach, Johann Sebastian

WIR PFLUGEN UND WIR STREUEN see Schulz, Peter

WIR PREISEN DEN HIMMELSGOTT see Heiller, Anton

WIR PREISEN DICH, O GOTT see Handel, George Frideric

WIR SAGEN DIR DANK see Seckinger, Konrad

WIR SCHRITTEN LANGE see Weismann, Wilhelm

WIR SIND NUR GAST AUF ERDEN   oee Strobl, Otto

WIR SINGEN ALL MIT FREUDENSCHALL see Eccard, Johannes

WIR SINGEN DIR, IMMANUEL see Hiltscher, Wolfgang

WIR SINGEN DIR IN DEINEM HEER see Bach, Johann Sebastian

WIR STEHEN IM DASEIN ALS KAMPFER DES LEBENS see Sehlbach, Oswald Erich

WIR WARTEN ABER EINES NEUEN HIMMELS see Graap, Lothar

WIR WISSEN NICHT, WAS KOMMT see Michel, Josep

WIR WOLLEN ALLE FROHLICH SEIN see Eglin, Arthur

WIR WOLLEN ALLE FROHLICH SEIN see Gadsch, Herbert

WIR WOLLEN ALLE FROHLICH SEIN see Gottschick, Friedemann

WIR WOLLEN ALLE FROHLICH SEIN see Graap, Lothar

WIR WOLLEN ALLE FROHLICH SEIN see Grabner, Hermann

WIR WOLLEN ALLE FROHLICH SEIN see Herbst, Wolfgang

WIR WOLLEN ALLE FROHLICH SEIN see Hessenberg, Kurt

WIR WOLLEN ALLE FROHLICH SEIN see Kubler, Emil

WIR WOLLEN ALLE FROHLICH SEIN see Marx, Karl

WIR WOLLEN ALLE FROHLICH SEIN see Micheelsen, Hans Friedrich

WIR WOLLEN ALLE FROHLICH SEIN see Poos, Heinrich

WIR WOLLEN ALLE FROHLICH SEIN see Praetorius, Michael

WIR WOLLEN ALLE FROHLICH SEIN see Trubel, Gerhard

WIR WOLLEN ALLE FROLICH SEIN see Neubert, Gottfried

WIR WOLLEN EUCH ABER, LIEBEN BRUDER, NICHT VERHALTEN VON DENEN, DIE DA SCHLAFEN see Reda, Siegfried

WIR WOLLEN SINGEN see Thomas, Kurt

WIR WOLLEN SING'N EIN LOBGESANG see Borris, Siegfried

WISDOM AND UNDERSTANDING see Newbury, Kent A.

WISDOM EXALTETH HER CHILDREN see Nowak, Lionel

WISDOM HATH BUILDED HER HOUSE see Berger

WISE AND FOOLISH BUILDERS, THE see Grime, William

WISE, JUDAH L.
God Of The World
SATB,pno/org PEER $.35   (W2209)

Hallelujah (Psalm 150)
[Heb/Eng] SATB,pno PEER $.35   (W2210)

Notre Dieu Est Roi
"Our God Is King" [Eng/Fr] 2pt treb cor,pno
PEER $.35   (W2211)

Our God Is King *see Notre Dieu Est Roi

Peace Be Unto You
SATB,pno/org PEER $.35   (W2212)

Psalm 150 *see Hallelujah

WISE MAY BRING THEIR LEARNING see Lynn, George

WISE MAY BRING THEIR   HEARNING, THE *Xmas
(Mueller) SA oct FISCHER,C CM-6302 $.25   (W2213)

WISE MAY BRING THEIR LEARNING, THE see Mueller, Carl F.

WISE MEN, BEHOLDING THE STAR, THE see Goudimel, Claude, Videntes Stellam Magi

WISE MEN CAME, THE see Bronson, Margaret

WISE MEN FROM THE EAST see Walker

WISE MEN, ON YOUR LONELY JOURNEY see Schaefer, Christopher

WISE MEN SEEKING JESUS see Bitgood

WISE MEN, THE see Daunton, Frank

WISE MEN, THE see Kozinski, [David B.]

WISE MEN, THE see Thomson, Virgil

WISE MEN'S CAROL see Musgrave, Thea

WISE, MICHAEL (ca. 1648-1687)
Magnificat And Nunc Dimittis *Magnif/Nunc
SATB (easy) oct OXFORD 42.146 $.35   (W2214)

Prepare Ye The Way Of The Lord *anthem/Bibl
SSAB&cor oct NOVELLO 28.0151.05 s.p.   (W2215)

Ways Of Zion Do Mourn, The *anthem
(Pinkham, D.) SATB,MezB soli,org SCHIRM.EC
2680 $.40   (W2216)

WISEMAN
Tenderly He Watches
(Ehret) SSA/SSAA oct MCA   (W2217)

WISHART
    Alleluya, A New Work
see Three Carols

I Sing Of A Maiden
see Three Carols

Lullay Lay, Lay
see Three Carols

Made We Merry
see Three Carols

Now Thrice Welcome Christmas
see Three Carols

There Is No Rose Of Such Virtue
see Three Carols

WISHART (cont'd.)

Three Carols *Xmas,carol
SATB,acap (med) OXFORD 43.914 $.65
contains: Alleluya, A New Work; Lullay
Lay, Lay; There Is No Rose Of Such
Virtue   (W2218)

Three Carols *Xmas,carol
SAB,acap (easy) OXFORD 43.083 $.35
contains: I Sing Of A Maiden; Made We
Merry; Now Thrice Welcome Christmas   (W2219)

WISHART, CAMPBELL
Two Anthems *CC2U
SATB,acap oct BERANDOL 910C4AA $.35 (W2220)

WISSET, DASS IHR DAZU BERUFEN SEID see Reda, Siegfried

WISSET, DASS IHR NICHT MIT VERGANGLICHEM see Ahle, Johann Rudolph

WISSET IHR NICHT see Reda, Siegfried

WISSET IHR NICHT, DASS ALLE, DIE WIR IN JESUM CHRISTUM GETAUFT SIND see Reda, Siegfried

WISSET IHR, WAS ICH EUCH GETAN HABE see Driessler, Johannes

WISSMER
Bete A Bon Dieu Fais Moi-T-Un Beau Dimanche
[Fr] jr cor/SSA,acap oct SALABERT-US $.65
see from Chants De Mars   (W2221)

C'est Pas Moi Que Suis Le Bon Dieu
[Fr] jr cor/SSA,acap oct SALABERT-US $.65
see from Chants De Mars   (W2222)

Chants De Mars *see Bete A Bon Dieu Fais
Moi-T-Un Beau Dimanche; C'est Pas Moi Que
Suis Le Bon Dieu; Comme Les Anges Au
Paradis   (W2223)

Comme Les Anges Au Paradis
[Fr] jr cor/SSA,acap oct SALABERT-US $.65
see from Chants De Mars   (W2224)

WISST IHR NOCH, WIE ES GESCHEHEN see Lahusen, Christian

WITH A JUBILANT SONG see Leaf, Robert

WITH A SONG see Martin

WITH A VOICE OF PRAISE see Handel, George Frideric

WITH A VOICE OF SINGING see Jennings

WITH A VOICE OF SINGING see Jennings, Kenneth L.

WITH A VOICE OF SINGING see Newbury, Kent A.

WITH A VOICE OF SINGING see Pritchard, Arthur J.

WITH A VOICE OF SINGING see Shaw, Martin

WITH ALL THINE HEART see Harris

WITH ALL WHO LOVE THY NAME, O LORD see Smith, Lani

WITH AN EVERLASTING LOVE see Roff, Joseph

WITH BROKEN HEART AND CONTRITE SIGH see Gomolka, Mikolaj

WITH BROKEN HEART AND CONTRITE SIGH see Slater

WITH CHEERFUL NOTEK see Handel, George Frideric

WITH CHEERFUL NOTES see Handel, George Frideric

WITH CHEERFUL NOTES LET ALL THE EARTH see Handel, George Frideric, As Pants The Hart

WITH CONTRITE HEARTS see Kilnarwick

WITH CONTRITE HEARTS RETURN *hymn,US
(Harter, H.) SATB oct BELWIN 2212 $.25   (W2225)

WITH GLADNESS WE WORSHIP see Knight, Vincent

WITH GLADNESS WE WORSHIP see Mead

WITH GLADNESS WE WORSHIP see Thiman, Eric Harding

WITH GOD THY GUIDE see Hancock, Norton

WITH GOD THY GUIDE see Norton, Hancock

WITH GRATEFUL HEART MY THANKS I BRING see Lundquist, Matthew Nathanael

WITH GRATEFUL HEARTS see Bach, Johann Sebastian

WITH GRATEFUL HEARTS see Bach, Johann Sebastian

WITH GRATEFUL HEARTS WE ALL ARE MET see Bach, Johann Sebastian, Wir Essen Und Wir Leben Wohl

WITH HAPPY VOICES RINGING see Stanton, [Walter] Kendall

WITH HAPPY VOICES SINGING *CCU
SA FLAMMER GE5007 $.60   (W2226)

WITH HARP AND VOICE OF PSALMS see Brandon, G.

WITH HEART AND VOICE *CCU,anthem
BELWIN $1.50   (W2227)

WITH HEART UPLIFTED
(Schvedov, C.; Davison, A.) TTBB,acap
SCHIRM.EC 74 $.22   (W2228)

WITH HIGH DELIGHT *CC13L
(Thomas, P.) mix cor CONCORDIA 97-5047 $1.50
contains works by: Bach; Hillert; Tye;
Pachelbel; Willan; Pelz; Vulpius;
Praetorius; Jewell; Gumpeltzhaimer;
Mendelssohn; Riegel; Chemin-Petit;
Praetorius   (W2229)

WITH HIGH &ELIGHT see Henel, Hudwig

WITH HIGH DELIGHT see Micheelsen, Hans Friedrich

WITH HIM FOR ALL ETERNITY see Roff, Joseph

WITH JESUS WILL I GO see Heussenstamm, George

WITH JOY I WELCOME THEE see Bach, Johann Sebastian, Ich Freue Mich In Dir

WITH JOY WE HAIL THE SACRED DAY see Tans'ur, William

WITH JOY WE MARCH ONWARD TO ZION see Bach, Johann Sebastian, So Lasset Uns Gehen In Salem

WITH JOYFUL SONG see Schvedov, Constantine

WITH LOUDEST REJOICING see Bach, Johann Sebastian, Ich Jauchze, Ich Lache

WITH MERRY HEART LET ALL REJOICE *Xmas,carol
SATB (very easy) OXFORD 08.030 $.15 (W2230)

WITH MY HAND IN THINE see Wells

WITH MY WHOLE HEART see Blakley, D.

WITH MY WHOLE HEART see Le Jeune, Claude

WITH MY WHOLE HEART I HAVE SOUGHT THEE see Lekberg, Sven

WITH ONE ACCORD see Brandon, George

WITH OTHER TONGUES SPAKE THE APOSTLES see Palestrina, Giovanni

WITH RUE MY HEART IS LADEN see Heussenstamm, George

WITH SHINING FACE AND BRIGHT ARRAY see Bouman, Paul

WITH SONG AND DANCE see Fritschel, James

WITH SONGS OF JOY see Garland, Hugh

WITH SWEETEST SONGS OF JOY see McKasson, M.

WITH THANKFUL HEARTS see Wilson, John F.

WITH VOICE OF MELODY see Byrd, William, Cantate Domino

WITH VOICES RAISED see Ehret, Walter

WITH WEEPING LIFE BEGINS see Bach, Johann Christoph

WITHER
Rocking Hymn, The *hymn
(Gordon) SSATB oct SHAPIRO SK 2121 $.30 (W2231)

WITHER THOU GOEST see Goldman

WITHIN A STABLE LOWLY *Xmas
(Krone, B.) SSA KJOS 6126 $.30 (W2232)

WITHIN THE SILENCE see Wilson

WITHIN THY GATES, O JERUSALEM
SATB CHAPPELL 0017376-367 $.40 (W2233)

WITHIN THY LIGHT see Orleans, Ilo

WITHOUT LOVE, NO FEELING see Martin

WITHOUT THE LOVE OF JESUS
SATB BIG3 $.30 (W2234)

WITHOUT WORDS see Berkowitz, S.

WITHROW, SCOTT
Twelve Hymn Descants *CC12U,hymn
unis,opt org (easy) ABINGDON APM-381 $.35, ipa (W2235)

WITNESS *spir
(Fissinger, Edwin) SATB,Bar solo,acap oct WORLD CA-2357-8 $.90 (W2236)

WITT, FRIEDRICH (1770-1837)
Ave Maria
(Vene) "Hymn To The Trinity" [Lat/Eng] SSAA,acap oct COLOMBO 2124 $.25 (W2237)
(Vene) "Hymn To The Trinity" [Lat/Eng] TTBB,acap oct COLOMBO 1890 $.25 (W2238)

Hymn To The Trinity *see Ave Maria

WITTE, GERD (1927-)
Allein Zu Dir, Herr Jesu Christ *mot
4-6pt,T solo HANSSLER 7.105 s.p. (W2239)

Jesu, Meines Lebens Leben
SAA/TBarB HANSSLER 14.065 s.p. (W2240)

Meditationen Zum Karsamstag *cant
SATB,org HANSSLER 10.235 sc s.p., cor pts s.p. (W2241)

Psalm 98 *see Singet Dem Herrn Ein Neues Lied

Singet Dem Herrn Ein Neues Lied (Psalm 98)
dbl cor HANSSLER 7.014 s.p. (W2242)

WITTMER, EBERHARD LUDWIG
Mass In D *Mass
[Lat] SATB SCHOTT s.p. (W2243)

WO DER HERR NICHT BEI UNS WARE see Driessler, Johannes

WO DER HERR NICHT BEI UNS WARE see Werner, Fritz

WO DER HERR NICHT DAS HAUS BAUET see Schroter, Leonhard

WO DER HERR NICHT DAS HAUS BAUET see Schutz, Heinrich

WO &ES SEES WELLEN GEHN nee Pfannenstiel, Ekkehart

WO FIND ICH DEINES VATERS HAUS see Rein, Walter

WO FIND ICH DENN DEIN'S VATERS HAUS see Franck, Cesar

WO GEHEST DU HIN? see Bach, Johann Sebastian

WO GEHST DU HIN see Bach, Johann Sebastian

WO GLAUBE, DA LIEBE see Biebl, Franz

WO GOTT DER HERR see Bach, Johann Sebastian, Wo Gott, Der Herr, Nicht Bei Uns Halt

WO GOTT, DER HERR, NICHT BEI UNS HALT see Bach, Johann Sebastian

WO GOTT DER HERR NICHT BEI UNS HALT see Franck, Melchior

WO GOTT DER HERR NICHT BEI UNS HALT see Marx, Karl

WO GOTT DER HERR NICHT BEI UNS HALT see Praetorius, Michael

WO GOTT DER HERR NICHT BEI UNS HALT see Reda, Siegfried

WO GOTT DER HERR NICHT BEI UNS HALT see Schein, Johann Hermann

WO GOTT DER HERR NICHT BEI UNS HALT see Vulpius, Melchior

WO GOTT DER HERR NICHT BEI UNS HALT see Werner, Fritz

WO GOTT ZU HAUS NIT GIBT SEIN GUNST see Distler, Hugo

WO GOTT ZUM HAUS see Biebl, Franz

WO GOTT ZUM HAUS NICHT GIBT SEIN GUNST see Franck, Melchior

WO GOTT ZUM HAUS NICHT GIBT SEIN GUNST see Hassler, Hans Leo

WO GOTT ZUM HAUS NICHT GIBT SEIN GUNST see Praetorius, Michael

WO GOTT ZUM HAUS NICHT GIBT SEIN GUNST see Reda, Siegfried

WO GOTT ZUM HAUS NICHT GIBT SEIN GUNST see Schein, Johann Hermann

WO IST DEIN STACHEL NUN, O TOD? see Eccard, Johannes

WO IST DER NEUGEBORNE KONIG DER JUDEN see Hammerschmidt, Andreas

WO IST EIN SO HERRLICH VOLK see Brahms, Johannes

WO IST MEIN AUFENTHALT see Silesius, Angelus

WO IST MEIN GOTT, DER HOHE, DER HEHRE see Schaefers, Anton

WO NEHMEN WIR DEN STERN HER see Blarr, Oskar Gottlieb

WO SOLL ICH FLIEHEN HIN see Bach, Johann Sebastian

WO SOLL ICH FLIEHEN HIN see Buxtehude, Dietrich

WO WILLST DU HIN, WEIL'S ABEND IST see Anger, Erhard

WO WILLST DU HIN, WEILS ABEND IST see Poos, Heinrich

WOCHEN- UND FESTTAGSSPRUCHE *CCU,evang
(Oertzen, Rudolf Von) [Ger] 2 eq voices/3pt mix cor BAREN. EM 332 s.p. (W2244)

WOE IS ME see Amner, John

WOE UNTO THEM see Thompson, Randall

WOEFULLY ARRAYED see Cornysh

WOEHL, WALDEMAR (1902-)
Freut Euch Des Herrn, Ihr Christen All
see Fiebig, Kurt, Sollt Ich Meinem Gott Nicht Singen

Sollt Ich Meinem Gott Nicht Singen
see Fiebig, Kurt, Sollt Ich Meinem Gott Nicht Singen

WOHIN SOLL ICH MICH WENDEN see Schubert, Franz (Peter)

WOHL DEM see Bach, Johann Sebastian, Wohl Dem, Der Sich Auf Seinen Gott

WOHL DEM, DEM DIE UBERTRETUNG see Wagener, Gregor

WOHL DEM, DER IN FURCHT GOTTES STEHT see Zeuner, Martin

WOHL DEM, DER NICHT DEM RAT DER GOTTLOSEN FOLGT see Klein, Richard Rudolf

WOHL DEM, DER NICHT WANDELT IM RAT DER GOTTLOSEN see Micheelsen, Hans Friedrich

WOHL DEM, DER NICHT WANDELT IM RAT DER GOTTLOSEN see Reda, Siegfried

WOHL DEM, DER SICH AUF SEINEN GOTT see Bach, Johann Sebastian

WOHL DEM, DER SICH AUF SEINEN GOTT [CHORALE] see Bach, Johann Sebastian

WOHL DEM MENSCHEN, DER WANDELT see Raselius, Andreas

WOHL DEN MENSCHEN, DIE DURCH FUR IHRE STA HALTEN see Gronostay, Uwe

WOHL DENEN, DIE DA WANDELN see Schmidt-Mannheim, Hans

WOHL DENEN, DIE DA WANDELN see Schutz, Heinrich

WOHL DENEN, DIE DA WANDELN see Schutz, Heinrich

WOHL DENEN, DIE DA WANDELN see Herbst, Wolfgang

WOHL DENEN, DIE OHNE TADEL LEBEN see Raphael, Gunther

WOHL DENEN, DIE OHNE TADEL LEBEN see Schutz, Heinrich

WOHL DIR, DU CHRISTENSCHAR see Schein, Johann Hermann

WOHL EINEM HAUS, DA JESUS CHRIST see Berger, Hans Ludwig

WOHL MIR, DAS ICH JESUM HABE see Bach, Johann Sebastian

WOHLAN, ALLE, DIE IHR DURSTIG SEID, KOMMET HER see Ruppel, Paul Ernst

WOHLAN! WIR FOLGEN GERN see Handel, George Frideric, We Come In Bright Array

WOHLAUF, DIE IHR HUNGRIG SEID see Pepping, Ernst

WOHLAUF, IHR CHRISTEN see Praetorius, Michael

WOHLAUF, IHR CHRISTEN, FREUET EUCH see Praetorius, Michael

WOHLAUF, IHR KLEIN WALDVOGELEIN see Hohlfeld, Christoph

WOHLAUF, WOHLAN ZUM LETZTEN GANG see Layer, J.

WOHLAUF, WOHLAUF MIT LAUTER STIMM see Walter (Walther), Johann

WOHLAUF, WOHLAUF ZU DIESER FRIST see Grimm, Heinrich

WOHLBERG, MAX
Kochve Voker *Sab-Morn
"Morning Stars" 3pt jr cor,cantor TRANSCON. TCL 343 $2.50 (W2245)

Morning Stars *see Kochve Voker

WOLCOTT, J.
How Beautiful Upon The Mountains *Xmas/Gen
SATB oct PRESSER 312-10119 $.35 (W2246)

How Lovely Are Thy Dwellings
SATB oct PRESSER 312-10168 $.35 (W2247)

More Love To Thee *Easter
SATB oct PRESSER 312-10883 $.30 (W2248)

WOLCUM YOLE see Britten, Benjamin

WOLCUM YOLE see Hand, Colin

WOLDER, DAVID
Die Ernt Ist Nun Zu Ende
(Berger, H.L.) TTBB HANSSLER 6.5071 s.p. (W2249)

WOLF
Blessed Assurance
SATB oct LORENZ B73 $.30 (W2250)

Give Praise To Him (composed with Churchill)
(Craig) SATB oct PLYMOUTH DC-103 $.25 (W2251)

Glory Be To Him *Easter,Morav
(Dickinson) SATB oct GRAY GMCM 11 $.30 (W2252)

Morgenhymne
(Frank) "Morning Hymn" SATB oct FOX MM11 $.30 (W2253)

Morning Hymn *see Morgenhymne

Take Time To Be Holy
SATB oct LORENZ A429 $.25 (W2254)

Thy Will Be Done
(Granville, Heiberg) SATB oct FOX R159 $.25 (W2255)

WOLF, FRIEDERICH
Deutsches Ordinarium
mix cor&cong,org,opt 2trp&2trom DOBLINGER voc sc s.p., cor pts s.p., ipa (W2256)

WOLF, HUGO (1860-1903)
Aufblick
(Richter, C.G.) "Looking Upwards" [Ger/Eng] SATB oct BOONIN 112 $.30 see from Six Sacred Songs (W2257)

Aufblick: Vergeht Mir Der Himmel
(Thomas, Eugen) [Eng/Ger] SATB voc sc BOTE s.p. see from Sechs Geistliche Lieder (W2258)

Auflick
(Boyd) "Upward Glance" [Eng/Ger] SATB,acap oct LAWSON 51672 $.25 see from Sechs Geistliche Lieder (W2259)

Christmas Night *Xmas
SATB,orch voc sc BROUDE BR. $.90, ipr (W2260)

Einklang
(Boyd) "Harmony" [Eng/Ger] SATB,acap oct LAWSON 51673 $.25 see from Sechs Geistliche Lieder (W2261)
(Richter, C.G.) "Harmony" [Ger/Eng] SATB oct BOONIN 113 $.35 see from Six Sacred Songs (W2262)

Einklang: Weil Jetzo Alles Stille Ist
(Thomas, Eugen) [Eng/Ger] SATB voc sc BOTE s.p. see from Sechs Geistliche Lieder (W2263)

Ergebung
(Boyd) "Submission" [Eng/Ger] SATB,acap oct LAWSON 51676 $.30 see from Sechs Geistliche Lieder (W2264)
(Richter, C.G.) "Submission" [Ger/Eng] SATB

WOLF, HUGO (cont'd.)

    oct BOONIN 116 $.50 see from Six Sacred
    Songs   (W2265)

Ergebung: Dein Wille, Herr Geschehe
  (Thomas, Eugen) [Eng/Ger] SATB voc sc BOTE
  s.p. see from Sechs Geistliche Lieder
                          (W2266)

Erhebung
  (Boyd) "Exaltation" [Eng/Ger] SATB,acap oct
  LAWSON 51677 $.30 see from Sechs
  Geistliche Lieder   (W2267)
  (Richter, C.G.) "Exaltation" [Ger/Eng] SATB
  oct BOONIN 117 $.35 see from Six Sacred
  Songs   (W2268)

Erhebung: So Lass Herein Nun Brechen
  (Thomas, Eugen) [Eng/Ger] SATB voc sc BOTE
  s.p. see from Sechs Geistliche Lieder
                          (W2269)

Exaltation *see Erhebung

Harmony *see Einklang

Last Prayer *see Letzte Bitte

Last Prayer, The *see Letzte Bitte

Letzte Bitte
  (Boyd) "Last Prayer, The" [Eng/Ger] SATB,
  acap oct LAWSON 51675 $.25 see from Sechs
  Geistliche Lieder   (W2270)
  (Richter, C.G.) "Last Prayer" [Ger/Eng]
  SATB oct BOONIN 115 $.30 see from Six
  Sacred Songs   (W2271)

Letzte Bitte: Wie Ein Todeswunder Streiter
  (Thomas, Eugen) [Eng/Ger] SATB voc sc BOTE
  s.p. see from Sechs Geistliche Lieder
                          (W2272)

Looking Upwards *see Aufblick

Resignation
  (Boyd) "Resignation" [Eng/Ger] SATB,acap
  oct LAWSON 51674 $.30 see from Sechs
  Geistliche Lieder   (W2273)
  (Richter, C.G.) "Resignation" [Ger/Eng]
  SATB oct BOONIN 114 $.40 see from Six
  Sacred Songs   (W2274)

Resignation *see Resignation

Resignation: Komm, Trost Der Welt, Du Stille
  Nacht
  (Thomas, Eugen) [Eng/Ger] SATB voc sc BOTE
  s.p. see from Sechs Geistliche Lieder
                          (W2275)

Sechs Geistliche Lieder *see Aufblick:
  Vergeht Mir Der Himmel; Auflick, "Upward
  Glance"; Einklang, "Harmony"; Einklang:
  Weil Jetzo Alles Stille Ist; Ergebung,
  "Submission"; Ergebung: Dein Wille, Herr
  Geschehe; Erhebung, "Exaltation";
  Erhebung: So Lass Herein Nun Brechen;
  Letzte Bitte, "Last Prayer, The"; Letzte
  Bitte: Wie Ein Todeswunder Streiter;
  Resignation, "Resignation"; Resignation:
  Komm, Trost Der Welt, Du Stille Nacht
                          (W2276)

Six Sacred Songs *see Aufblick, "Looking
  Upwards"; Einklang, "Harmony"; Ergebung,
  "Submission"; Erhebung, "Exaltation";
  Letzte Bitte, "Last Prayer"; Resignation
                          (W2277)

Submission *see Ergebung

Upward Glance *see Auflick

WOLFE
In A Stable Manger *Xmas
  SATB oct VOLKWEIN VB184 $.25   (W2278)

Jesus Christ Is Risen Today Alleluia *Easter
  SATB,trp oct SOUTHERN $.30   (W2279)

Prayer For Peace (composed with O'Hara,
  Geoffrey)
  (Frank) SATB oct BOURNE 622 $.30 (W2280)

WOLFE, JACQUES (1896-   )
British Children's Prayer
  4pt mix cor oct SCHIRM.G 8827 $.25 (W2281)

WOLFF
Awake My Soul
  SATB THOMP.G G-579 s.p.   (W2282)

Before The Lord We Bow
  SATB THOMP.G G-578 s.p.   (W2283)

Blessed Jesus, At Thy Word
  SATB THOMP.G G-577 s.p.   (W2284)

Christ The Lord Is Risen To-Day
  SATB THOMP.G M-3 s.p.   (W2285)

Come Let Us Join Our Cheerful Songs
  SATB THOMP.G M-7 s.p.   (W2286)

Draw Nigh And Take The Body Of The Lord
  SATB THOMP.G G-569 s.p.   (W2287)

Hosanna Loud Hosanna
  SA THOMP.G G-216 s.p.   (W2288)

Judge Eternal, Throned In Splendour
  SATB THOMP.G G-574 s.p.   (W2289)

Let Us With A Gladsome Mind
  SATB THOMP.G M-4 s.p.   (W2290)

May The Grace Of Christ Our Saviour
  SATB THOMP.G G-587 s.p.   (W2291)

O How Amiable Are Thy Dwellings
  SATB THOMP.G M-11 s.p.   (W2292)

O Praise God In His Holiness
  SATB THOMP.G M-2 s.p.   (W2293)

Only Begotten Word Of God Eternal
  SATB THOMP.G M-9 s.p.   (W2294)

Remember, O Lord
  SATB THOMP.G M-15 s.p.   (W2295)

WOLFF (cont'd.)

Rise Up, O Men Of God *Easter/Lent
  SATB oct WALTON 2150 $.30   (W2296)

Songs Of Praise The Angels Sang
  SATB THOMP.G G-568 s.p.   (W2297)

Stand Up And Bless The Lord
  SATB THOMP.G M-13 s.p.   (W2298)

To My Humble Supplication
  SATB (med diff/diff) SOUTHERN $.35 (W2299)
  SATB THOMP.G M-12 s.p.   (W2300)

WOLFF, A.
Ave Maria *BVM
  [Lat] SA/TB,org,vln,vcl,harp ENOCH s.p.
                          (W2301)

WOLFF, S. DRUMMOND
Abide, O Dearest Jesus *Gen
  SA,kbd (med easy) oct CONCORDIA 98-1730
  $.25   (W2302)

Above The Clear Blue Sky *Gen
  SS/SA,kbd (med easy) oct CONCORDIA 98-1912
  $.30   (W2303)

All Praise To God, Who Reigns Above *Gen
  SATB,kbd (med easy) oct CONCORDIA 98-1424
  $.30   (W2304)

Alleluia! Let Praises Ring! *Ded/Gen
  SATB,kbd (med easy) oct CONCORDIA 98-1911
  $.40   (W2305)

Almighty God, Thy Word Is Cast *Gen
  SAB,kbd (med easy) oct CONCORDIA 98-1952
  $.30   (W2306)

At Even When The Sun Did Set *Gen
  SAB,kbd (easy) oct CONCORDIA 98-1930 $.25
                          (W2307)

Awake, My Soul *Gen
  SAB,acap (easy) oct CONCORDIA 98-1749
  $.25   (W2308)

Be Merciful Unto Me, O Lord *Lent/Trin
  SATB,kbd (med easy) oct CONCORDIA 98-1903
  $.30   (W2309)

Behold The Savior Of Mankind *Gen/Lent
  SATB,kbd (med easy) oct CONCORDIA 98-1873
  $.25 contains also: Help Us To Help Each
  Other, Lord   (W2310)

Blest Are The Pure In Heart *Gen
  SAB,kbd (easy) oct CONCORDIA 98-2147 $.30
                          (W2311)

Built On The Rock, The Church Doth Stand
  *Ded/Gen/Refm
  SATB,kbd (med easy) oct CONCORDIA 98-1492
  $.30   (W2312)

Christ The Lord Is Risen Today *Easter
  SAB,acap (easy) oct CONCORDIA 98-1364 $.20
                          (W2313)

Christ, Whose Glory Fills The Skies *Epiph/
  Gen
  SAB,kbd (med easy) oct CONCORDIA 98-1905
  $.30   (W2314)

Christians, Sing Out With Exultation
  SATB,org PEER $.40   (W2315)

Come, Holy Spirit, Come *Gen/Pent
  SS,kbd (easy) oct CONCORDIA 98-1356 $.25
                          (W2316)

Come, Jesus, Holy Child, To Me *Adv/Gen
  SS,kbd (med easy) oct CONCORDIA 98-2103 $.30
                          (W2317)

Come, Ye Faithful, Raise The Strain *Easter
  SATB,opt trp (med easy) oct CONCORDIA
  98-2112 $.40   (W2318)

Draw Us To Thee *Asc/Gen
  SATB,kbd (med easy) oct CONCORDIA 98-1932
  $.30   (W2319)

Father, Son, And Holy Ghost *Cnfrm/Gen
  SATB,kbd (med easy) oct CONCORDIA 98-2021
  $.25   (W2320)

God, My Father, Loving Me *Gen
  SS,kbd (med easy) oct CONCORDIA 98-1679
  $.25   (W2321)

Help Us To Help Each Other, Lord
  see Wolff, S. Drummond, Behold The Savior
  Of Mankind

Hold Thou My Hands
  SATB oct LESLIE 4079   (W2322)

Holy, Holy, Holy, Lord God Almighty *Gen/
  Trin
  SATB&cong/SATB&jr cor,org,2trp (med easy)
  sc CONCORDIA 98-2129 $.40   (W2323)

How Sweet The Name Of Jesus Sounds *Circum/
  Cnfrm/Gen
  SS,kbd (easy) oct CONCORDIA 98-2073 $.30
                          (W2324)

Hymn Of Praise *hymn
  SATB&opt jr cor,opt solo,org FOSTER 451
  $.30   (W2325)

I Am The Resurrection
  SATB oct LESLIE 4082 see from Words Of
  Comfort   (W2326)

I Was Glad *Gen/Lent
  SATB,acap (med easy) oct CONCORDIA 98-1061
  $.25   (W2327)

If Ye Love Me *anthem
  mix cor oct NOVELLO 40.1230.05 s.p. (W2328)

Jesus Christ Is Risen Today, Alleluia!
  *Easter
  SATB,trp (med easy) oct CONCORDIA 98-2050
  $.30   (W2329)

Jesus, Grant Me This I Pray *Gen/Lent
  SATB,kbd (med easy) oct CONCORDIA 98-2012
  $.25   (W2330)

WOLFF, S. DRUMMOND (cont'd.)

Let Not Your Heart Be Troubled
  SATB oct LESLIE 4082 see from Words Of
  Comfort   (W2331)

Lord Is King! Lift Up Thy Voice, The
  *Easter/Gen
  SATB,kbd (med easy) oct CONCORDIA 98-2018
  $.30   (W2332)

Lord, My God, Be Praised, The *Gen
  SATB,kbd (med easy) oct CONCORDIA 98-1162
  $.30   (W2333)

Lord Of Our Life *Gen/Lent
  SATB,kbd (med easy) oct CONCORDIA 98-1480
  $.30   (W2334)

Love Of The Father *Gen/Pent
  SATB,kbd (med easy) oct CONCORDIA 98-1514
  $.30   (W2335)

Now Let Us All With One Accord *Easter/Gen
  SS,kbd (med easy) oct CONCORDIA 98-1678
  $.30   (W2336)

Now Thank We All Our God *Ded/Gen/Thanks/
  Trin
  SATB,kbd (med easy) oct CONCORDIA 98-1434
  $.30   (W2337)

O Gladsome Light *Xmas/Gen
  SATB,kbd (med diff) oct CONCORDIA 98-1755
  $.30   (W2338)

O Jesus So Sweet *Xmas/Gen
  SS,kbd (med easy) oct CONCORDIA 98-1939
  $.30   (W2339)

O Perfect Life Of Love *Lent
  SAB,kbd (med easy) oct CONCORDIA 98-1150
  $.25   (W2340)

O Praise Ye The Lord *Gen/Thanks
  SATB,kbd (med easy) oct CONCORDIA 98-1880
  $.30   (W2341)

O What Their Joy And Their Glory Must Be
  *ASD/Gen
  SATB,kbd (med diff) oct CONCORDIA 98-1750
  $.35   (W2342)

Our Lord Is Risen From The Dead *Easter
  SATB,kbd (med diff) oct CONCORDIA 98-1754
  $.30   (W2343)

Praise, Oh, Praise Our God And King *Gen/
  Thanks
  SATB,kbd (med easy) oct CONCORDIA 98-2009
  $.30   (W2344)

Praise The Lord Of Heaven *Gen/Thanks
  SATB,kbd (med easy) oct CONCORDIA 98-1731
  $.30   (W2345)

Rejoice, The Lord Is King
  SATB,org PEER $.40   (W2346)

Savior, Like A Shepherd Lead Us *Gen
  SA,kbd (easy) oct CONCORDIA 98-1358 $.25
                         (W2347)

Seek And Ye Shall Find
  SATB oct LESLIE 4082 see from Words Of
  Comfort   (W2348)

Sing Alleluia Forth
  SATB,org FOSTER MF116 $.30   (W2349)

Sing Praise To God, Who Reigns Above *Gen
  SATB,kbd (med easy) oct CONCORDIA 98-2113
  $.40   (W2350)

Sing To The Lord Of Harvest *Gen/Thanks
  SATB&cong/SATB&jr cor,org,2trp (med easy)
  oct CONCORDIA 98-2137 $.40   (W2351)

Soul, Adorn Thyself With Gladness *Commun
  SATB,kbd (med easy) oct CONCORDIA 98-1906
  $.30   (W2352)

Strife Is O'er, The *Easter/Gen
  SATB,kbd (med easy) oct CONCORDIA 98-2099
  $.35   (W2353)

This Is The Day The Lord Hath Made *Gen
  SATB,kbd (med easy) oct CONCORDIA 98-1881
  $.25   (W2354)

To My Humble Supplication *Gen/Lent
  SATB,kbd (med easy) oct CONCORDIA 98-2090
  $.35   (W2355)

Turn Thy Face From My Sins *Gen/Lent
  SATB,kbd (med easy) oct CONCORDIA 98-1691
  $.25   (W2356)

We Sing, Immanuel, Thy Praise
  SATB,pno/org oct LAWSON 51561 $.35 (W2357)

Welcome, Happy Morning *Easter
  SATB,kbd (med easy) oct CONCORDIA 98-1872
  $.30   (W2358)

Words Of Comfort *see I Am The Resurrection;
  Let Not Your Heart Be Troubled; Seek And
  Ye Shall Find   (W2359)

Ye Servants Of The Lord
  SATB oct WALTON 2066 $.25   (W2360)

Ye Sons And Daughters Of The King *Easter
  SA,kbd (med easy) oct CONCORDIA 98-1735
  $.25   (W2361)

Ye Watchers And Ye Holy Ones *ASD/Gen
  SATB,brass (med easy) oct CONCORDIA 98-1904
  $.30   (W2362)

WOLFORD, JULIE L.
Song Of Joy
  SSA PIONEER 1013 $.40   (W2363)

WOLFSOHN, GEORG
Two Hebrew Prayers *CC2U,prayer,Heb
  SATB,high solo,org/pno ISRAELI 213 s.p.
                          (W2364)

WOLL, E.
Ehre Sei Gott In Der Hohe
mix cor,acap ERDMANN 504 s.p.   (W2365)

Es Kommt Der Herr Der Herrlichkeit *cant
wom cor,S/T solo,strings,rec sc,cor pts
ERDMANN 543 s.p., ipa   (W2366)

WOLL, ERNA (1917-   )
Ave, Ave Maria, Dich Lobt Die Susse Musica
*CC7U
3pt mix cor,acap/inst,opt cont TONGER s.p.
          (W2367)

Fall Ab, Herz, Vom Baum Der Zeit
see Zeit, O Verkundigung

In Lauter Tranen Tropft Der Tag
see Zeit, O Verkundigung

Kind Und Gottessohn
3 eq voices MOSELER LB-167 s.p. contains
also: O Nacht, Du Bist Besiegt   (W2368)
3pt mix cor MOSELER LB-279 s.p. contains
also: O Nacht, Du Bist Besiegt   (W2369)

Komm, Susser Gast, O Musica *mot
mix cor,acap TONGER s.p.   (W2370)

Leiser Wird Nichts Verkundigt
see Zeit, O Verkundigung

Maria Im Advent *cant
eq voices/mix cor,acap/fl&strings cor pts
MOSELER s.p., ipa   (W2371)

O Nacht, Du Bist Besiegt
see Woll, Erna, Kind Und Gottessohn
see Woll, Erna, Kind Und Gottessohn

Unsterblich Duften Die Linden
see Zeit, O Verkundigung

Zauber Und Segen *CC6U,mot
4pt mix cor MOSELER s.p.   (W2372)

Zeit, O Verkundigung
mix cor,acap TONGER s.p.
contains: Fall Ab, Herz, Vom Baum Der
Zeit; In Lauter Tranen Tropft Der Tag;
Leiser Wird Nichts Verkundigt;
Unsterblich Duften Die Linden   (W2373)

Zur Heiligen Nacht *Xmas,cant
SATB,cantor,fl,2vln,vcl HANSSLER 10.232 sc
n.p.,cor pts s.p., ipa   (W2374)

WOLLE
For Me? O Lord *Gen/Lent,Morav
(Dickinson) SATB oct GRAY GMCM 7 $.30
          (W2375)

WOLLEB, JOHANN JAKOB (1613-1667)
Gott Ist Die Zuflucht Aller Frommen
SATB LAUDINELLA LR 47 s.p. contains also:
Herr, Hore Doch; Ich Freue Mich, So Oft
Man Spricht; Ihr Knechte Gottes   (W2376)

Herr, Hore Doch
see Wolleb, Johann Jakob, Gott Ist Die
Zuflucht Aller Frommen

Ich Freue Mich, So Oft Man Spricht
see Wolleb, Johann Jakob, Gott Ist Die
Zuflucht Aller Frommen

Ihr Knechte Gottes
see Wolleb, Johann Jakob, Gott Ist Die
Zuflucht Aller Frommen

Lob Gott, Du Werte Christenheit
SATB LAUDINELLA LR 9 s.p. contains also:
Singet Frisch Und Wohlgemut; Vom Himmel
Kam Der Engel Schar   (W2377)

Singet Frisch Und Wohlgemut
olleb, Johann Jakob, Lob Gott, &u
Werte Christenheit

Vom Himmel Kam Der Engel Schar
see Wolleb, Johann Jakob, Lob Gott, Du
Werte Christenheit

WOLLEN, P.
Praise The Lord From The Heavens
SSAATTBB oct PRESSER MC441 $.50   (W2378)

WOLLEN, RUSSELL
Lord Is My True Shepherd, The
(Bottenberg, Wolfgang) 3 eq voices,acap oct
WORLD ESA-725-3 $.30   (W2379)

One Fold, One Shepherd
2 eq voices/2pt mix cor,org oct WORLD
DSA-660-2 $.45   (W2380)

WOLTERS, GOTTFRIED (1910-   )
Ein Kind Geboren Zu Bethlehem Im Stall *Xmas
cor MOSELER LB-199 s.p. contains also:
Still, Wer Gott Erkennen Will   (W2381)
mix cor MOSELER LB-438 s.p. contains also:
Still, Wer Gott Erkennen Will   (W2382)

Ein Sternlein Ist Gekommen
see Wolters, Gottfried, Grunt Ein
Tannenbaum

Es Ist Fur Uns Eine Zeit Angekommen
(Kraft, H.) 5pt mix cor MOSELER LB-35 s.p.
contains also: Nun Kommt Fur Uns Die
Schone Zeit (4pt mix cor)   (W2383)
(Kraft, H.) 3 eq voices MOSELER LB-131 s.p.
contains also: Nun Kommt Fur Uns Die
Schone Zeit (3 eq voices); Lasst Uns Auf
Die Berge Gehn (3-4 eq voices)   (W2384)

Grunt Ein Tannenbaum *Xmas
men cor TONGER s.p.   (W2385)
wom cor&jr cor TONGER s.p. contains also:
Heut Ist Ein Sternlein Vom Himmel
Gefalln; Sing Und Jubiliere,
Weihnachtsnachtigall; Ein Sternlein Ist
Gekommen   (W2386)

Heut Hst Ein Sternlein Vom Himmel Gefalln
see Wolters, Gottfried, Grunt Ein
Tannenbaum

Inmitten Der Nacht *Xmas
mix cor TONGER s.p.   (W2387)

WOLTERS, GOTTFRIED (cont'd.)

Lasst Uns Auf Die Berge Gehn
see Wolters, Gottfried, Es Ist Fur Uns Eine
Zeit Angekommen

Maria Durch Ein Dornwald Ging *BVM
5pt mix cor MOSELER LB-206 s.p.   (W2388)

Nun Kommt Fur Uns Die Schone Zeit
see Wolters, Gottfried, Es Ist Fur Uns Eine
Zeit Angekommen
see Wolters, Gottfried, Es Ist Fur Uns Eine
Zeit Angekommen

O Du Stille Zeit
4pt mix cor MOSELER LB-310 s.p. contains
also: Sieh, Wie Der Abendstern (5pt mix
cor)   (W2389)

Sieh, Wie Der Abendstern
see Wolters, Gottfried, O Du Stille Zeit

Sing Und Jubiliere, Weihnachtsnachtigall
*Xmas
see Wolters, Gottfried, Grunt Ein
Tannenbaum
mix cor TONGER s.p.   (W2390)

Still, Wer Gott Erkennen Will
see Wolters, Gottfried, Ein Kind Geboren Zu
Bethlehem Im Stall
see Wolters, Gottfried, Ein Kind Geboren Zu
Bethlehem Im Stall

WOLTERS, K.-H.
Triptychon
men cor,S solo,2pno,perc,timp LEUCKART
s.p., ipr   (W2391)

WOM HIMMEL HOCH HERAB see Rossel, W.

WOMAN OF SAMARIA, THE see Bennett, Sir William
Sterndale

WOMAN OF VALOR, A see Adler, Hugo Ch.

WOMAN OF VALOR, A see Orleans, Ilo

WOMAN, WHY WEEPEST THOU? see Schutz, Heinrich,
Weib, Was Weinest Du?

WOMEN'S GET-TOGETHER SONGS *CCU,cor-resp
wom cor LORENZ $1.25   (W2392)

WOMEN'S GOSPEL QUARTETS *CCU
4pt wom cor LORENZ $1.50   (W2393)

WOMEN'S GOSPEL SONG ANTHEMS *CCU,anthem
SSA/SSAA LORENZ $1.75   (W2394)

WOMEN'S GOSPEL TRIOS NO. 1 *CCU
SSA/SSAA LORENZ $1.25   (W2395)

WOMEN'S GOSPEL TRIOS NO. 2 *CCU
SSA/SSAA LORENZ $1.25   (W2396)

WOMEN'S GOSPEL TRIOS NO. 4 *CCU
SSA/SSAA LORENZ $1.25   (W2397)

WOMEN'S NEW GOSPEL QUARTETS *CCU
4pt wom cor LORENZ $1.50   (W2398)

WONDER CHILD, THE see Reiff, S.T.

WONDER OF EASTER see Emig, Lois

WONDER OF EASTER, THE *Easter,Bibl/cant
(Silvey, Helen) jr cor,narrator,soli voc sc
LILLENAS ME-215 $1.00   (W2399)

WONDER OF IT ALL, THE see Martin

WONDER OF THE AGES see Hughes

WONDER OF THE AGES, THE see Hughes

WONDER OF THE STAR, THE see Carleton

WONDER THING, THE see Niles, John Jacob

WONDER TIDINGS
SATB (easy) OXFORD 08.039 $.15   (W2400)

WONDER TIDINGS see La Montaine, John

WONDER, WONDER see Kozinski, [David B.]

WONDERFUL see Lillenas, Haldor

WONDERFUL! A CHILD IS BORN see Johnson, Sidney

WONDERFUL INN, THE see Das Schlaraffenland

WONDERFUL LOVE see Ashton

WONDERFUL NEW TONIGHT, THE see Hovdesven, E.A.

WONDERFUL PEACE
(Carmichael) SATB oct WORD CS-301 $.30
          (W2401)
(Hughes, Robert J.) SATB ALLANS 446 s.p.
          (W2402)

WONDERFUL PEACE see Hughes

WONDERFUL PEACE see Lillenas, Haldor

WONDERFUL SAVIOR see Boalt

WONDERFUL SAVIOUR see Jenkins, M.

WONDERFUL STORY, A see Basham, Robert A.

WONDERFUL THING, A see Davis, Katherine K.

WONDERFUL WORDS OF LIFE see Landon

WONDEROUS MYSTERY, A see Bourdon

WONDERS OF EARTH, THE see Davis, Katherine K.

WONDROUS CHILD! *CC16U,Xmas,20th cent
3-6pt mix cor AMP A665 $2.00   (W2403)

WONDROUS CHILD see Schroth

WONDROUS CHILD DIVINE see Elmore, Robert [Hall]

WONDROUS CROSS, THE see Hunt, Reginald

WONDROUS CROSS, THE see Lorenz

WONDROUS CROSS, THE see Mason

WONDROUS DAY see Johnson, Sidney

WONDROUS IS THE LIFE IN HEAVEN see Schutz,
Heinrich, Unser Wandel Ist In Himmel

WONDROUS KINGDOM, THE (FLORA AND FAUNA) see
Bucci, [Mark]

WONDROUS LOVE *Easter/Lent,anthem/folk/hymn,US
(Christiansen, Paul) SATB (easy) oct AUGSBURG
1140 $.22   (W2404)
(Christiansen, Paul) SSAA (easy) oct AUGSBURG
1233 $.18   (W2405)
(Christiansen, Paul) TTBB (easy) oct AUGSBURG
1234 $.20   (W2406)
(Niles; Sheppard) 3pt men cor oct SCHIRM.G
10710 $.30   (W2407)
(Niles; Sheppard) 4pt mix cor oct SCHIRM.G
10972 $.25   (W2408)
(Niles; Sheppard) 3pt mix cor oct SCHIRM.G
10971 $.20   (W2409)
(Pooler, Marie) SAB (easy) oct AUGSBURG 1444
$.25   (W2410)
(Pooler, Marie) SA (easy) oct AUGSBURG 1445
$.25   (W2411)
(Pooler, Marie) unis treb cor (easy) oct
AUGSBURG 1385 $.25   (W2412)
(Price) SAB oct FISCHER,C CM-7733 $.25
          (W2413)
(Shaw; Parker) SATB,acap oct LAWSON 907 $.35
          (W2414)

WONDROUS LOVE see Christiansen

WONDROUS LOVE see Gardner, Maurice

WONDROUS LOVE see Groom, Lester H.

WONDROUS LOVE see Hunkins, Eusebia Simpson

WONDROUS LOVE see Landon

WONDROUS LOVE see Lynn, George

WONDROUS LOVE see Niles, John Jacob

WONDROUS LOVE see Pooler

WONDROUS LOVE see Van Iderstine, A.P.

WONDROUS LOVE see Whitman, David

WONDROUS NIGHT *Xmas
(Nyquist) SSA,acap (echo carol) oct PRO ART
1899 $.25   (W2415)
(Nyquist) SATB,acap (echo carol) oct PRO ART
1435 $.25   (W2416)

WONDROUS NIGHT, THE see Hoddinott, Alun

WONDROUS STORY, THE see Kountz

WOOD
At The Cross, Her Station Keeping
SATB FLAMMER A 5422 $.30   (W2417)

Bless O My Soul The Living God
SATB WARNER W7- 1025 $.30   (W2418)

Bound Upon The Accursed Tree
SATB FLAMMER A5329 $.30   (W2419)

Carol For The Home *Gen
SATB SCHMITT 8050 $.35   (W2420)
unis SCHMITT 238 $.35   (W2421)

Carol From An Irish Cabin *Xmas
SSA SCHMITT 353 $.30   (W2422)
SATB/unis SCHMITT 7033 $.35   (W2423)

Christ Is Made The Sure Foundation *Gen
SAB SCHMITT SD6208 $.35   (W2424)
SATB SCHMITT SD5904 $.35   (W2425)

Christmas Is Here *Xmas
SATB SCHMITT 7039 $.30   (W2426)

Expectans Expectavi
SATB oct SUMMY B 1147 $.40   (W2427)

Give Ear, O Ye Heavens *Gen
SATB SCHMITT SD6007 $.35   (W2428)

Hear Us, Holy Jesus
SATB FLAMMER A 5527 $.25   (W2429)

Highlands Of Heaven, The (from Sacred Harp)
SATB,acap WARNER R3312 $.30   (W2430)

Jubilate Deo *Jubil
SA SOUTHERN $.25   (W2431)
SA SOUTHERN $.25   (W2432)

O Come And Mourn With Me Awhile *Lent
SATB FLAMMER A 5231 $.30   (W2433)
SATB oct SOUTHERN $.25   (W2434)
SAB FLAMMER D5090 $.25   (W2435)

O Perfect Life Of Love *Lent
SATB oct SOUTHERN $.25   (W2436)

O Praise Ye The Lord
SATB FLAMMER A 5043 $.35   (W2437)

Service Of Darkness, A
SAB FLAMMER D5021 $1.25   (W2438)
SATB FLAMMER A5005 $1.25   (W2439)

Sing A Joyful Song In Praise *Gen
SSATBB SCHMITT 1710 $.25   (W2440)

Sing For Joy *Xmas
SATB SCHMITT 6231 $.35   (W2441)

Song Of Peace, A
SATB oct SACRED S-41 $.40   (W2442)
SATB oct HERITAGE H21 $.40   (W2443)

Thy Kingdom Come
SATB oct GALAXY 1.2491.1 $.25   (W2444)

Traveler, The *folk/hymn
SATB,acap WARNER R3374 $.30   (W2445)

WOOD (cont'd.)

We Would Thank Thee, Almighty Father *Gen
SATB SCHMITT SD6002 $.30   (W2446)

Who Passes Yonder Through The Throng *Palm
SATB FLAMMER A 5027 $.30   (W2447)
SATB&unis oct SOUTHERN $.30   (W2448)

World, Farewell
SATBB WARNER W7-1024 $.30   (W2449)

WOOD, CHARLES (1866-1926)
Communion Service In F *see Missa Sancti
Patricii

Glorious And Powerful God *anthem
mix cor oct NOVELLO s.p.   (W2450)

Latin Mass In F *Mass
[Lat] SATB oct ST.MARTIN s.p.   (W2451)

Magnificat And Nunc Dimittis *Magnif/Nunc
SATB (C min) oct NOVELLO 44.0486.06 s.p.
(W2452)
SATB (D maj) oct NOVELLO 44.0391.06 s.p.
(W2453)
unis (C min) oct NOVELLO 02.0063.08
s.p.   (W2454)
unis (E flat maj) oct NOVELLO 02.0065.04
s.p.   (W2455)
SATB (E flat maj) oct NOVELLO 44.0080.01
s.p.   (W2456)
unis (D maj) oct NOVELLO 02.0064.06
s.p.   (W2457)

Missa Sancti Patricii *Commun
"Communion Service In F" SATB (med) oct
OXFORD 43.941 $.65   (W2458)

Occuli Omnium
SATB,acap CRAMER C 30 s.p.   (W2459)

Summer Ended
4pt mix cor,org oct SCHIRM.G 11479 $.30
(W2460)

WOOD, DALE
Arise, My Soul, Arise!
SATB (easy) ABINGDON APM-251 $.25   (W2461)

Austrian Shepherd's Carol *anthem
SATB&opt unis/SATB&unis jr cor,opt solo
(easy) oct AUGSBURG 0414 $.30   (W2462)
unis treb cor (easy) oct AUGSBURG 0415 $.30
(W2463)

Choral Sentences For Worship
SATB oct SACRED S-141 $.40   (W2464)

Creator Of The Stars *Adv
SATB/unis oct GRAY GCMR 2889 $.30   (W2465)

Glory Of Our King, The *anthem
unis treb cor (easy) oct AUGSBURG 1644 $.25
(W2466)

Hymn Of Youth, A *anthem/hymn
2 eq voices (easy) oct AUGSBURG 1488 $.25
(W2467)

I Am The Good Shepherd *anthem
unis treb cor (med) oct AUGSBURG 1590 $.20
(W2468)

Jesus Had Not Where To Lay His Head *Xmas
SATB oct WORD CS-654 $.30   (W2469)

Jesus, The Very Thought Of Thee
SATB oct WORD CS-340 $.30   (W2470)

Jubilate Deo (Psalm 100) anthem/Jubil
SATB,org&perc/brass (med) sc AUGSBURG 1603
$.35, ipa   (W2471)
unis treb cor/SA (med) oct AUGSBURG 1646
$.25   (W2472)

Lamb, The *Lent
jr cor&sr cor (med) ABINGDON APM-206 $.25
(W2473)

Let The Whole Creation Cry
SATB oct WORD CS-666 $.25   (W2474)

New Settings Of Twenty Well-Known Hymntunes
*CC20L,hymn
treb cor,opt inst cor pts AUGSBURG 11-9294
$.50, voc sc AUGSBURG 11-9292 $2.75, ipa
(W2475)

O Fear The Lord, Ye His Saints *anthem
SATB (easy) oct AUGSBURG 1486 $.30   (W2476)

Psalm 100 *see Jubilate Deo

Slumber, O Holy Jesu *Xmas
jr cor&SATB,opt high solo/low solo (easy)
ABINGDON APM-147 $.22   (W2477)

Wake, Awake For Night Is Flying *Adv
SATB oct GRAY GCMR 2802 $.35   (W2478)

Watchman, Tell Us Of The Night *Adv/Epiph
SATB&jr cor,opt hndbl oct GRAY GCMR 2909
$.35   (W2479)

WOOD, F.C.
Shout On
(Parker) mix cor,Bar solo,acap oct LAWSON
51332 $.40   (W2480)

WOOD, JAMES H.
Only-Begotten Word Of God Eternal *Adv/Ded/
Gen
SATB,brass (med easy) oct CONCORDIA 98-1673
$.30, ipa   (W2481)

WOOD, JEFF
Side By Side
(Johnson, Paul) SATB (med) PRESSER G-123
$.35   (W2482)

WOOD, JOHN
Holy Father, Cheer Our Way *anthem
mix cor,acap oct NOVELLO 50.0330.10 s.p.
(W2483)

Lord, Be Thy Word My Rule *anthem
TBar oct NOVELLO 28.1357.02 s.p.   (W2484)
2pt oct NOVELLO 28.1357.02 s.p.   (W2485)

Magnificat And Nunc Dimittis *Magnif/Nunc
unis (G maj) NOVELLO 33.0099.04 s.p. (W2486)

My Soul Truly Waiteth Still Upon God
see Two Introits

WOOD, JOHN (cont'd.)
O Give Thanks Unto The Lord *Thanks,anthem
SABar oct NOVELLO 40.1550.09 s.p.   (W2487)

O God My Heart Is Ready
see Two Introits

Two Introits *anthem/Introit
mix cor oct NOVELLO 28.1388.02 s.p.
contains: My Soul Truly Waiteth Still
Upon God; O God My Heart Is Ready
(W2488)

WOOD, ROBIN
I Will Praise Thee *Austral
SATB ALLANS 468 s.p.   (W2489)

WOODBURY
By Cool Siloam's Shady Rill
(Rarig; Craig) SATB oct PLYMOUTH DC-112
$.25   (W2490)

WOODEN TOYS see Anderson, Marion

WOODGATE
First Christmas, The *Xmas
unis jr cor FISCHER,C PT 1759 $.24   (W2491)

WOODLAND HYMN see Posegate

WOODMAN, RAYMOND HUNTINGTON (1861-1943)
Lord Is My Rock, The *Bibl
4pt mix cor oct SCHIRM.G 3969 $.25   (W2492)

Love Of God, The *Gen
4pt mix cor oct SCHIRM.G 8488 $.25   (W2493)

Sword, A
(Dickinson) mix cor,Bar solo oct SCHIRM.G
9320 $.25   (W2494)

Thanksgiving Day Ode, A *Thanks
4pt mix cor,SBar,opt T soli oct SCHIRM.G
4231 $.25   (W2495)

WOODS AND EVERY SWEET-SMELLING TREE, THE see
West, John Ebenezer

WOODS AND EVERY SWEETSMELLING TREE, THE see
West

WOODS COLLECTION OF CHRISTMAS CAROLS *CCU,
Xmas,carol
oct SSA BELWIN 64187 $.35; SATB BELWIN 64115
$.75   (W2496)

WOODWARD
Ding, Dong, Merrily On High *Xmas
(Geehl) SA BOOSEY-CAN s.p.   (W2497)

Radiant Morn Hath Passed Away, The
(Stevens) SSA oct PRO ART 1627 $.20   (W2498)

Rejoice Greatly *Adv
SATB oct PRO ART 1726 $.30   (W2499)

WOODWARD, H.H.
Behold The Days Come
SATB ALLANS 425 s.p.   (W2500)

Comes, At Times, A Stillness *anthem
mix cor oct NOVELLO 28.0914.01 s.p.   (W2501)

Holy Communion *Commun
SATB (E flat maj) oct NOVELLO 44.1393.08
s.p.   (W2502)

Radiant Morn Hath Passed Away
SATB ALLANS 378 s.p.   (W2503)

Radiant Morn Hath Passed Away, The *anthem/
Bibl
SATB,pno (easy) oct WILLIS 6330 $.12
(W2504)
mix cor,orch oct NOVELLO 40.0472.08 s.p.,
ipr   (W2505)
4pt mix cor oct SCHIRM.G 3732 $.25   (W2506)

Rejoice Greatly *Adv,anthem/Bibl
mix cor oct NOVELLO 50.0014.09 s.p.   (W2507)
(Mueller) SABar oct SCHIRM.G 8702 $.20
(W2508)

Story Of The Cross *Easter/Lent
SATB ALLANS 217 s.p.   (W2509)

Sun Shall Be No More
SATB ALLANS 379 s.p.   (W2510)

Sun Shall Be No More Thy Light By Day, The
*Bibl
4pt mix cor oct SCHIRM.G 3896 $.25   (W2511)

Te Deum, In E Flat *Bibl
[Eng] 4pt mix cor oct SCHIRM.G 4652 $.25
(W2512)

WOOLEN, R.
Prayer Of St. Francis
SATB oct ELKAN-V 362-1182 $.30   (W2513)

WOOLER, A.
Consider And Hear Me
SATB oct PRESSER 332-13553 $.30   (W2514)

Give Me A Perfect Heart
SATB oct PRESSER 332-12736 $.30   (W2515)

Hail The Victor *Easter
SATB PRESSER $1.25   (W2516)

Hosanna In The Highest *Xmas
SATB PRESSER $.85   (W2517)

WOOLEY
Have You Had An Encounter With God? *anthem
(Whitman) SATB oct LILLENAS AN-1632 $.25
(W2518)

WOOLLEN
Evening Mass Of Holy Thursday *Eve/Holywk,
Mass
mix cor SOUTHERN $.30   (W2519)

Great Is The Lord
SSB oct SUMMY M 2838 $.35   (W2520)

WOOLLY LAMB AT THE MANGER see Campbell, Madge
E.

WORAN DENKST DU, MEIN CHRISTUS, JETZT, IM TODE?
see Burgmann, J. Hartmut

WORD, THE see Toolan, S. Suzanne

WORD BECAME FLESH, THE see Brandon, G.

WORD BECAME FLESH, THE see Ford

WORD MADE FLESH, THE see Clokey, Joseph Waddell

WORD MADE FLESH, THE see Davidson

WORD OF GOD, THE see Berger, Jean

WORD OF LIFE, MOST PURE AND STRONG see Jones

WORD OF TRUE FLESH see Palestrina, Giovanni,
Verbum Caro

WORD, THE see Jay

WORD WAS GOD, THE see Lanier

WORD WAS MADE FLESH, THE see Back, Sven-Erick,
Et Verbum Caro Factum Est

WORD WAS MADE FLESH, THE see Bender, Jan

WORD WAS MADE FLESH, THE see Dean, T.W.

WORDS FROM THE CROSS, THE see Fetler, Paul

WORDS FROM THE CROSS, THE see Schaffer, Jeanne
E.

WORDS OF COMFORT see Wolff, S. Drummond

WORDS OF COMFORT see Davies, Henry Walford

WORDS OF JESUS see Dean, T.W.

WORDS OF RUTH, THE see Ludlow

WORDS OF SAINT PETER see Felciano, Richard

WORDSWORTH, WILLIAM (1908-   )
De Profundis *anthem
mix cor oct NOVELLO 40.1460.10 s.p. (W2521)

Hymn Of Dedication
SATB,org LENGNICK s.p.   (W2522)

WORK
Alas, And Did My Saviour Bleed *Lent
SATB oct SOUTHERN $.35   (W2523)

Done Made My Vow To The Lord
SATB oct GALAXY 1.2110.1 $.30   (W2524)

Golgotha Is A Mountain
SATB oct GALAXY 1.2155.1 $.35   (W2525)

How Beautiful Upon The Mountains
SATB oct GALAXY 1.0633.1 $.30   (W2526)

I, John, Saw The Holy Number
SATB oct GALAXY 1.2236.1 $.35   (W2527)

I've Been Listening
SATB oct LORENZ C259 $.30   (W2528)

Jesus Lay Your Head In The Window *Xmas
SATB oct GALAXY 1.2166.1 $.35   (W2529)

Listen To The Angels Shouting *Xmas
SSA/SAA oct GALAXY 1.1649.1 $.25   (W2530)

Lord, I'm Out Here On Your Word
SATB oct GALAXY 1.1903.1 $.40   (W2531)

Processional Hymn
SATB SHAWNEE A 455 $.30   (W2532)

Rock, Mount Sinai
SATB oct GALAXY 1.2237.1 $.30   (W2533)

This Little Light O Mine
SATB oct GALAXY 1.1384.1 $.30   (W2534)

Way Over In Egypt Land
SATB oct GALAXY 1.1574.1 $.35   (W2535)

WORK, HENRY CLAY (1832-1884)
God Is A Spirit
SATB oct PRESSER 332-00988 $.30   (W2536)

WORK, JOHN [WESLEY] (1901-   )
Do Not I Love Thee, O My Lord?
(Doddridge, P.) SATB oct PRESSER 312-40041
$.30   (W2537)

Jesus, Thou Joy Of Loving Hearts
SATB oct ELKAN-V 362-1247 $.30   (W2538)

Sinner, Please Don't Let This Harvest Pass
SATB,acap oct PRESSER 322-40020 $.35
(W2539)

You May Bury Me In The East *spir
SSA,T solo,acap SCHIRM.EC 1971 $.25 (W2540)

WORK OF CONSOLATION see Brandon

WORK OF RIGHTEOUSNESS see Willis

WORKING ON THE BUILDING *spir
SATB oct STAFF 664 $.30   (W2541)

WORKS OF GOD, THE see Rowlands

WORKS WITH PERFORMANCE DIRECTIONS see Perotin

WORLD ABOUT ME, THE see Youse, Glad [Robinson]

WORLD, FAREWELL see Wood

WORLD IS CHARGED WITH THE GRANDEUR OF GOD, THE
see Bliss, Sir Arthur

WORLD ITSELF KEEPS EASTER DAY *Easter
(Ehret) SATB oct BOOSEY 5284 $.30   (W2542)

WORLD ITSELF KEEPS EASTER DAY see Davis,
Katherine K.

WORLD ITSELF KEEPS EASTER DAY, THE see Garlick,
Anthony

WORLD ITSELF KEEPS EASTER DAY, THE (from Piae
  Cantiones) anthem
  see Four Easter Carols
  (Pooler, Marie) unis treb cor oct AUGSBURG
  1386 $.20   (W2543)

WORLD ITSELF KEEPS EASTER DAY, THE see
  Frackenpohl, Arthur

WORLD REJOICE! *Xmas,carol
  (Phillips, John C.) 2pt&3pt,pno&strings&perc/
  pno&opt perc voc sc NOVELLO s.p., ipr (W2544)

WORLD WITHOUT LOVE, A see Skillings, Otis

WORLD'S DESIRE, THE *carol
  SATB (easy) OXFORD 08.143 $.15   (W2545)

WORLD'S REDEEMER, THE see Holton

WORP
  Give Thanks To God
  (Olds) SATB (old psalm tune) SCHMITT 1618
  $.35   (W2546)

WORSHIP see Shaw, G.

WORSHIP see Shaw, Geoffrey [Turton]

WORSHIP AND ADORE *CCU,anthem
  (Davis, K.K.) SSA/3pt WARNER $1.50   (W2547)

WORSHIP AND PRAISE *CCU,anthem
  LORENZ $1.95   (W2548)

WORSHIP CANTICLE see Williams

WORSHIP CHRIST THE NEWBORN KING *Xmas
  SATB oct STAFF 336 $.20   (W2549)

WORSHIP CHRIST, THE NEWBORN KING see Mueller,
  Carl F.

WORSHIP FOR TODAY see Mac Neil

WORSHIP HIM WITH SONG *CCU
  mix cor SCHMITT 9069 $1.50   (W2550)

WORSHIP IN SONG, BOOK 1 see Thompson, Ronald

WORSHIP IN SONG, BOOK 2 see Thompson, Ronald

WORSHIP OF GOD IN NATURE see Beethoven, Ludwig
  van

WORSHIP RESPONSES *anthem
  SATB (very easy) oct AUGSBURG 1120 $.15
  contains: All Things Come Of Thee; Create
  In Me A Clean Heart, O God; Hear Our
  Prayer; Lord Is In His Holy Temple, The;
  Sevenfold Amen; We Give Thee But Thine
  Own   (W2551)

WORSHIP SUPPLEMENT *CC93U,Commun,hymn/liturg
  cor,org cor pts CONCORDIA 3-1081 $1.25, cor
  pts CONCORDIA 3-1082 $1.25, sc CONCORDIA
  97-4945, USA $7.50, sc CONCORDIA
  97-5003, FOREIGN $7.50   (W2552)

WORSHIP THE CHRIST CHILD see Ball

WORSHIP THE LORD see Watson, M.

WORSHIP THE LORD IN THE BEAUTY OF HOLINESS see
  Smith

WORSHIP WE THE FATHER see Pasquet, Jean

WORT see Bornefeld, Helmut

WORTE DES PROPHETEN JEREMIAS see Wenzel,
  Eberhard

WORTHING, RICHARD
  Calm On The List'ning Ear *Xmas
  3pt wom cor,pno (easy) oct WILLIS 2788 $.12
                                         (W2553)
  Christ The Lord Is Risen Today *Easter
  3pt wom cor,acap (easy) oct WILLIS 2803
  $.10   (W2554)
  Emmanuel (God With Us) *Xmas,cant
  mix cor,SA soli,org (easy) voc sc WILLIS
  $.75   (W2555)
  Hark! Ten Thousand Voices Sounding
  see SIX EASTER CAROLS
  He Is Risen *Easter,cant
  mix cor,SATB soli,pno/org (med) voc sc
  WILLIS $1.00   (W2556)
  Holy, Holy, Holy Lord *Gen/Trin
  3pt wom cor,org (easy) oct WILLIS 1804 $.15
                                         (W2557)
  Thanks Be To God *Easter
  SATB,S solo,pno (med) oct WILLIS 2805 $.16
                                         (W2558)

WORTHY ART THOU see Clark, Henry A.

WORTHY ART THOU, O LORD see Pergolesi, Giovanni
  Battista

WORTHY ART THOU, O LORD see Willan, Healey

WORTHY ART THOU, O LORD GOD see Bruckner, Anton

WORTHY IS THE LAMB see Gallus, Jacobus

WORTHY IS THE LAMB see Hall, Regnal L.

WORTHY IS THE LAMB see Handel, George Frideric

WORTHY IS THE LAMB see Leddy

WORTHY IS THE LAMB, THAT WAS SLAIN see Handel,
  George Frideric

WORTHY THE LAMB see Bradshaw

WORTLEY, HOWARD [S.] (1916-   )
  Hallelu, Amen
  SATB oct STAFF 415 $.25   (W2559)

WOULD THAT I WERE THERE see Fleming

WOULD YE BE GLAD AND WISE see Ward

WOULD YOU see Red, Buryl

WOUNDS WITHOUT CAUSE see Rorem, Ned

WRAPPED IN SWADDLING CLOTHES THEY FOUND HIM
  *Xmas
  (Russell) SSA oct PRO ART 2436 $.25   (W2560)
  (Russell) 2pt oct PRO ART 2434 $.22   (W2561)

WREATH FOR WAITS see Kay, Ulysses Simpson

WREFORD
  Lord, While For All Mankind We Pray
  (Rhea) SSA oct PLYMOUTH UIL-100 $.25
                                         (W2562)

WRESTLING JACOB *Xmas
  (Tyler) SATB SCHMITT 1882 $.35   (W2563)

WRESTLING JACOB see Williamson, Malcolm

WRIGHT
  God's Handiwork
  SA/unis oct VOLKWEIN VB714 $.30   (W2564)
  He Can Open Doors
  (Wilson) SATB FLAMMER A 5398 $.25   (W2565)
  Mount Calvary *Easter
  SATB oct LORENZ B191 $.30   (W2566)
  O Worship The King
  SATB FLAMMER A 5271 $.30   (W2567)
  Prayer Of St. Francis *prayer
  SATB WARNER W3446 $.30   (W2568)
  Seven Choir Responses For The Worship Service
  *CC7U
  SATB,acap,opt pno oct PRO ART 2599 $.30
                                         (W2569)
  Spirit Divine, Attend Our Prayers
  SATB oct GALAXY 1.2272.1 $.75   (W2570)

WRIGHT, B.
  Let The People Praise Thee
  SATB oct SOUTHERN $.25   (W2571)
  O For A Thousand Tongues To Sing
  SATB oct SOUTHERN $.30   (W2572)

WRIGHT, EVELYN
  Flowers, The
  SA/SS CRAMER 138 s.p.   (W2573)

WRIGHT, G.
  Heaven-Bound Soldier
  (Cain) SATB FLAMMER A 5307 $.30   (W2574)

WRIGHT, NORMAN SORENG (1905-   )
  O Lord, As Thou Art Kind
  SATB CRITERION $.50   (W2575)
  Psalm 23
  SATB CRITERION $.50   (W2576)

WRIGHT, S.
  Green Blade Riseth, The *Easter,cant
  BELWIN $1.50   (W2577)
  Short Communion Service In D *Commun
  SATB oct KERBY 5101C $.35   (W2578)
  Venite Adoremus *Xmas
  SATB,acap oct KERBY 5110C $.30   (W2579)

WRIGHT, THOMAS
  Nesciens Mater
  TTBB,acap SCHIRM.EC $.25   (W2580)
  Nesciens Mater Virgo
  (Collins, H.B.) [Lat] TTBB/TTBarB CHESTER
  s.p.   (W2581)

WRITTEN IN DE HOLY BOOK *Xmas
  (Rodby) SATB SCHMITT 1876 $.30   (W2582)
  (Rodby) SSA SCHMITT 351 $.30   (W2583)

WUENSCH
  Vexilla Regis Produent *cant
  mix cor,soli,org (diff) oct WESTERN WIM 25
  $1.75   (W2584)

WUERFEL
  Adon Olom
  (Roskin) SATB HATIKVAH HCL 30 $.35   (W2585)

WUNDERBARBER GNADENTHRON, GOTTES UND MARIEN
  SCHON see Kubler, Emil

WUNDERBARER KONIG see Oertzen, Rudolf von

WUNDERBARER KONIG, HERRSCHER VON UNS ALLEN see
  Gruber, Erich

WUNDERBARER KONIG, HERRSCHER see Trubel,
  Gerhard

WUNDERBARER KONIG, HERRSCHER see Trubel,
  Gerhard

WUNDERLICH DING HAT SICH ERGANGEN see Pepping,
  Ernst

WUNDERLICH, HEINZ (1919-   )
  Die Weihnachtsgeschichte Nach Lukas *Xmas,
  Bibl
  [Ger] SATB,S/A solo,acap (med easy) BAREN.
  BA 3162 $1.25   (W2586)
  Es Kommt Ein Schiff, Geladen *Adv,cant
  [Ger] SA&men cor,fl,2vln,vcl (med) BAREN.
  BA 3165 sc s.p., cor pts s.p., ipa
                                         (W2587)
  Maranatha, Unser Herr Kommt *Easter/Gen,ora
  [Ger] SATB&SATB,narrator,SSATTBarBarB soli,
  orch (diff) BAREN. BA 2111 sc $9.75, cor
  pts $2.50, ipr   (W2588)
  Ship With Cargo Precious, A *Adv/Xmas,cant
  SAB,strings,A rec CONCORDIA 97-4767 $.35,
  ipa   (W2589)

WUNDERSCHONE PRACHTIGE see Muller, A.M.

WUNSCH, HERMANN (1884-1954)
  Die Kleine Passion *Psntd
  [Ger] SATB,S/T solo,3inst (med easy) MULLER
  SM 1043 sc s.p., cor pts s.p.   (W2590)

WURMAN, HANS
  Avodah L'ami *Sab-Eve/Sab-Morn
  SATB TRANSCON. TCL 854 $3.75   (W2591)
  SATB TRANSCON. TCL 854 $3.75   (W2592)

WYATT
  All Praise To Our Redeeming Lord
  SATB oct PRO ART 2749 $.30   (W2593)
  Come, Let Us Tune Our Loftiest Song
  SATB oct PRO ART 2735 $.30   (W2594)
  It's Christmas Time *Xmas
  SATB oct PRO ART 2740 $.30   (W2595)
  Let Us Sing The New Song *anthem/folk
  SATB oct PRO ART 2690 $.35   (W2596)
  SATB SOUTHERN $.35   (W2597)
  SATB (med easy) SOUTHERN $.35   (W2598)
  Make A Joyful Noise Unto The Lord (Psalm 66)
  SATB oct PRO ART 1601 $.22   (W2599)
  O Love Divine
  SATB oct PRO ART 1942 $.22   (W2600)
  Psalm 66 *see Make A Joyful Noise Unto The
  Lord
  We Are One In The Lord
  SATB oct PRO ART 2691 $.30   (W2601)
  SATB (med easy) SOUTHERN $.30   (W2602)

WYDLER, A.
  Bis Hieher Hat Mich Gott Gebracht
  [Ger] wom cor,acap (easy) HUG s.p.   (W2603)

WYETH
  Come, Thou Fount *hymn
  (Pottenger) SATB oct LILLENAS AN-2268 $.30
                                         (W2604)
  (Ralston; Dobbs) SAB oct LILLENAS AN-6003
  $.30   (W2605)
  Come, Thou Fount Of Every Blessing *Gen
  (Allen) SATB SCHMITT 897 $.25   (W2606)
  (Fuller) SAB oct PRO ART 1271 $.30   (W2607)

WYETH, JOHN
  Come, Thou Fount *anthem/hymn
  (Cram, James D.) SATB oct FISCHER,C
  SIG. 113 $.25   (W2608)

WYNER, [YEHUDI] (1929-   )
  Friday Evening Service
  [Heb] SATB,T solo,org AMP A479 $2.50
                                         (W2609)

WYRTZEN
  Seek Ye The Lord
  SATB oct SACRED S-9 $.35   (W2610)
  So Let Me Live
  SATB oct LORENZ B181 $.30   (W2611)
  Yesterday, Today And Tomorrow
  (Wilson) SATB oct AGAPE CF 138 $.30   (W2612)

WYTON
  Introits For The Church Year *CCU,Introit
  SATB oct FISCHER,C CM-7608 $.35   (W2613)

WYTON, ALEC (1921-   )
  Benedictus Es *Gen
  SSA/TTB,acap (easy) oct CONCORDIA 98-1729
  $.35 contains also: Jubilate Deo   (W2614)
  Hymn Of Brotherhood, A
  unis/2pt&opt SATB,opt band oct GRAY
  GCMR 3114 $.30, ipa   (W2615)
  Jubilate Deo
  see Wyton, Alec, Benedictus Es
  Magnificat *Magnif
  SATB oct AGAPE AG 7127 $.35   (W2616)
  People's Eucharist, A
  unis oct AGAPE A 449 $.45   (W2617)
  Sing Joyfully
  SA oct PRESSER MC457 $.30   (W2618)
  Tell Out My Soul
  2pt treb cor oct PRESSER MC435 $.30   (W2619)
  This Joyful Eastertide *Easter,Neth
  SATB oct GRAY GCMR 2970 $.30   (W2620)

WYTON, ALEX
  Behold Now, Praise The Lord
  unis oct PRESSER MC448 $.30   (W2621)
  Endless Alleluia, An *Gen/Thanks
  4pt jr cor/SATB (med easy) FISCHER,C
  CM 7374 $.25   (W2622)
  King Jesus Hath A Garden
  SATB FLAMMER A 5222 $.25   (W2623)
  Meditation Of St. Theresa, A
  treb cor oct PRESSER MC537 $.30   (W2624)
  There Were Shepherds
  SATB FLAMMER A 5243 $.25   (W2625)
  Vision Of Isaiah, The
  SATB oct PRESSER MC501 $.40   (W2626)

WZTOBIE LEZY *Xmas,carol,Pol
  (Bement, G.) "He Is Sleeping In A Manger"
  TTBB,acap SCHIRM.EC 2191   (W2627)
  (Glaser, V.) "He Is Sleeping In A Manger"
  SATB,acap SCHIRM.EC 2607 $.30   (W2628)

X

XERXES see Handel, George Frideric

Y

YA NO VA LA NINA see Martin Pompey

YA VIENE LA VIEJA *Xmas,carol,Span
(Shaw; Parker) [Eng/Span] 4pt mix cor,acap
oct SCHIRM.G 10200 $.25   (Y1)

YA'ALE see Weisgal, A.

YAHRES
Children Of God, Sing On
SATB oct VOLKWEIN VB126 $.30   (Y2)

Now We Sing Noel *Xmas
SATB oct VOLKWEIN VB218 $.30   (Y3)

Ode Of Thanksgiving *Thanks
SATB oct VOLKWEIN VB221 $.25   (Y4)

Small Song Of Gratitude
SATB oct VOLKWEIN VB258 $.30   (Y5)

YAMIM NORAIM VOL. II *Rosh Ha-Shanah/Sab-Morn/
Yiskor/Yom Kippur
(Adler, Samuel) SATB TRANSCON. TCL 877 $7.50
                                               (Y6)
YAMIN NOPAIM VOL. I *Rosh Ha-Shanah/Sab-Eve/
Yom Kippur
(Adler, Samuel) SATB oct TRANSCON. TCL 876
$6.50   (Y7)

YANCEY
Song Of David
SATB (med diff/diff) SOUTHERN $.30   (Y8)

Song Of David, The
SATB FLAMMER A 5596 $.30   (Y9)

YE ANGELS IN THE HEAVENS see McGraw, Cameron

YE ARE FELLOW-CITIZENS WITH THE SAINTS see
Waters, Charles F.

YE ARE NO MORE STRANGERS see Cruft, Adrian

YE ARE NOT OF THE FLESH see Bach, Johann
Sebastian

YE ARE NOT OF THE FLESH see Krone

YE ARE THE LIGHT see Williams, Alice Crane

YE BIRDS WITH OPEN THROAT see Meek, Kenneth

YE BOUNDLESS REALMS OF JOY see Webber

YE CHILDREN WHO DO PRAISE THE LORD (Psalm 113)
Scot
(Martens, J.) SATB,acap SCHIRM.EC 2452 $.30
                                              (Y10)
YE CHILDREN WHO DO SERVE THE LORD (Psalm 113)
Scot
(Ehret) SATB,acap,opt pno oct PRO ART 2349
$.25   (Y11)
(Martens, J.) SATB SCHIRM.EC 2452 $.30   (Y12)

YE CHOIR ABOVE see Dyson, George

YE CHOIRS OF NEW JERUSALEM see Davies, Ivor

YE CHOIRS OF NEW JERUSALEM see Hunt, Reginald

YE CHRISTIAN HERALDS! GO PROCLAIM see
Landgrave, Phillip

YE DAUGHTERS OF ZION see Aquilius, Jacobus,
Sions Dottre

YE FAIR GREEN HILLS OF GALILEE see Skeat,
William J.

YE FIELDS OF LIGHT, CELESTIAL PLAINS see
Franck, Cesar

YE FOLK AFAR see Ream, Albert

YE FOLLOWERS OF THE LAMB see Ferguson, Edwin
Earle

YE GATES LIFT UP YOUR HEADS see Smith

YE GATES, LIFT UP YOUR HEADS see Thomson

YE HEAVENS ADORE HIM see Durham

YE HOLY ANGELS BRIGHT see Clokey, Joseph
Waddell

YE HOLY ANGELS BRIGHT see Darst, W. Glenn

YE HOLY ANGELS BRIGHT see Darwall

YE HOLY ANGELS BRIGHT see Mead

YE HOLY ANGELS BRIGHT see Niles, John Jacob

YE KNOW THAT THE LORD IS GRACIOUS see Statham,
Heathcote (Dicken)

YE LANDS, TO THE LORD, MAKE A JUBILANT NOISE
*anthem
(Pooler, Marie) SSA&SATB (easy) oct AUGSBURG
1156 $.25   (Y13)

YE NATIONS BOW IN SACRED JOY see Schein

YE NATIONS PRAISE THE LORD see Watson

YE RESTLESS THOUGHTS see Wilbye, John

YE SAINTS AND SERVANTS OF THE LORD see
Herrmann, William

YE SERVANTS OF GOD *Fest/Gen
(Coleman, Henry) SATB (very easy) oct OXFORD
42.981 $.25   (Y14)

YE SERVANTS OF GOD see Angell, Warren M.

YE SERVANTS OF GOD see Burroughs, B.

YE SERVANTS OF GOD see Croft

YE SERVANTS OF GOD see Croft, W.

YE SERVANTS OF GOD see Knight, Vincent

YE SERVANTS OF GOD see Malin

YE SERVANTS OF GOD see Means, Claude

YE SERVANTS OF GOD see Newbury, Kent A.

YE SERVANTS OF GOD see Smith

YE SERVANTS OF GOD see Vree

YE SERVANTS OF GOD see Young, C.

YE SERVANTS OF GOD, YOUR MASTER PROCLAIM see
Schalk, Carl

YE SERVANTS OF THE LORD see Walton, Kenneth

YE SERVANTS OF THE LORD see Wolff, S. Drummond

YE SHALL BE WITNESSES see Kirk

YE SHALL CALL HIM EMMANUEL see Willaert,
Adrian, Nazareus Vocabitur

YE SHALL DWELL IN THE LAND see Stainer, John

YE SHALL GO OUT WITH JOY see Barnby, Sir Joseph

YE SHALL GO OUT WITH JOY see Beck

YE SHALL GO OUT WITH JOY see Berger, Jean

YE SHALL GO OUT WITH JOY see Gardner

YE SHALL HAVE A SONG see Barbe, Helmut

YE SHALL HAVE A SONG see Thompson, Randall

YE SHALL KNOW THAT THE LORD WILL COME see
Willan, Healey

YE SONS AND DAUGHTERS see Schroth

YE SONS AND DAUGHTERS see Track, Gerhard

YE SONS AND DAUGHTERS NOW SHALL SING see
Kjelson

YE SONS AND DAUGHTERS OF THE KING see Graver

YE SONS AND DAUGHTERS OF THE KING see Leisring

YE SONS AND DAUGHTERS OF THE KING see Leisring,
Volkmar, O Filii Et Filiae

YE SONS AND DAUGHTERS OF THE KING see Liszt,
Franz

YE SONS AND DAUGHTERS OF THE KING see Sjolund,
Paul

YE SONS AND DAUGHTERS OF THE KING see Thiman,
Eric Harding

YE SONS AND DAUGHTERS OF THE KING see Wolff, S.
Drummond

YE SONS AND DAUGHTERS OF THE LORD *Easter
(Lahmar, R.) SATB,acap oct PRESSER 312-40549
$.30   (Y15)

YE SONS OF GOD see Beck

YE SONS OF GOD see Beck, Theodore

YE SONS OF ISRAEL see Mendelssohn-Bartholdy,
Felix, Laudate Pueri

YE SONS OF ISRAEL see Mendelssohn-Bartholdy,
Felix, Laudate Pueri Dominum

YE SONS OF ISRAEL, NOW LAMENT see Handel,
George Frideric

YE SONS OF MEN, OH, HEARKEN see Cruger, Johann

YE THAT ARE TO MIRTH INCLINED see Thiman, Eric
Harding

YE THAT DO YOUR MASTER'S WILL
SATB oct STAFF 429 $.25   (Y16)

YE THAT DO YOUR MASTER'S WILL see Dyson, George

YE THAT DO YOUR MASTER'S WILL see Gibbons,
Orlando

YE THAT DO YOUR MASTER'S WILL see Thiman, Eric
Harding

YE THAT STAND IN THE HOUSE OF THE LORD see
Lanier

YE THAT STAND IN THE HOUSE OF THE LORD see
Spinney, W.

YE TRIBES OF ADAM JOIN
(Reynolds) SATB oct FISCHER,C CM-7709 $.25
                                              (Y17)

YE WATCHERS AND YE HOLY ONES see Coln

YE WATCHERS AND YE HOLY ONES see Lasst Uns
Erfreuen

YE WATCHERS AND YE HOLY ONES see Peters, J.V.

YE WATCHERS AND YE HOLY ONES see Willan, Healey

YE WATCHERS AND YE HOLY ONES see Wolff, S.
Drummond

YE WEARY AND BURDENED see Ream

YE WERE SOMETIMES DARKNESS see Thompson,
Randall

YE WHO HAVE FOLLOWED ME see Dufay, Guillaume,
Vos Qui Secuti

YE WHO NOW SORROW see Brahms, Johannes

YE WHO PASS BY see Lotti, Antonio

YE WHO PASS ME see Croce, Giovanni, O Vos Omnes

YE WHO PASS ME see Victoria, Tomas Luis de, O Vos Omnes, Qui Transitis Per Viam

YE, WHO SEEK THE TRUTH see Peery

YE WHO THE LONGING KNOW see Tchaikovsky, Piotr Ilyitch

YE WITH SORROW NOW ARE FILLED oee Brahms, Johannes, Ihr Habt Nun Traurigkeit

YEA, BLESSED SHALL YE BE see Croce, Giovanni, Beati Eritis

YEA THOUGH I WALK see Coggin

YEA, THOUGH I WALK see Sullivan, Sir Arthur Seymour

YEA, THOUGH I WANDER see Schumann

YEA, TWO SERAPHIM CRIED OUT see Victoria, Tomas Luis de, Duo Seraphim

YEAKLE, THOMAS
Bow Down Thine Ear, O Lord
SATB,ST soli,acap GRAY GCMR 3275 $.30 (Y18)

Sir Christemas *cant
SATB,harp GRAY $1.50 (Y19)

YEAMAN, W. HOLLIDAY
Praise The Lord, O My Soul *Bibl
4pt mix cor oct SCHIRM.G 11007 $.25 (Y20)

YEAR OF OUR LORD, THE see Graham, Robert [V.]

YEAR ROUND ANTHEM BOOK, THE see Hoffmann

YEH, HUAI-DEH
This Glorious Christmas Night *Xmas
4pt mix cor,acap oct SCHIRM.G 11454 $.30 (Y21)

YERUSHALAIM see Aznavour, [Charles]

YERUSHALAYIM see Ory, David

YES, GOD IS REAL see Landgrave, Phillip

YES, I KNOW! see Waterman, Frances

YES, I'LL SING see Hallett, John C.

YESTERDAY, TODAY AND TOMORROW see Wyrtzen

YESTERDAY'S BUBBLE see Idelsohn, Abraham Zevi

YET A LITTLE WHILE see Nystedt, Knut

Y'HI ROTZON see Weisgal, A.

YIELD NOT TO TEMPTATION see Palmer

YIH'UY L'ROTZON see Weisgall, Hugo

YISM' CHU NO. 1 see Freed, Isadore

YISM' CHU NO. 2 see Freed, Isadore

YLVISAKER, JOHN
Singing Catechism *CCU,folk
jr cor/sr cor,gtr,opt kbd cor pts AUGSBURG
11-9396 $.85, ipa (Y22)

YNO YN HWYRDDYDD EBRILL see Roberton, Hugh S.

YOLKOFF, ARTHUR
Shirat Atideinu *Sab-Eve
2pt jr cor/3pt jr cor,solo TRANSCON.
TCL 336 $2.50 (Y23)
GnEng/Heb] SATBDRANSCON. TCL 336 $2.50 (Y24)

YOM HA-SHABBAT see Adler, Samuel

YOM ZE MEKHUBAD see Jochsberger, T.

YON, PIETRO ALESSANDRO (1886-1943)
Eesu Bambino
(Ringwald) SATB SHAWNEE A 446 $.35 (Y25)

Gesu Bambino
jr cor oct FISCHER,J 4655 $.30 (Y26)
TTBB,acap oct FISCHER,J 4658 $.30 (Y27)
SSA oct FISCHER,J 4657 $.30 (Y28)
SA oct FISCHER,J 4656 $.30 (Y29)
(Ringwald) SSAB SHAWNEE D45 $.35 (Y30)

Messa Pastorale *Mass
"Pastoral Mass" .Lat] unis,solo voc sc
SCHIRM.G $.40 (Y31)

Our Paschal Joy *Easter
(Decker) SATB oct FISCHER,J 7833 $.30 (Y32)

Pastoral Mass *see Messa Pastorale

YONDA' COME DAY *spir
(Appling, William) SATB,acap oct WORLD
CE-2329 $.45 (Y33)

YONDER, YONDER see Gaines, S.

YORK
Do I Crucify My Savior?
SAB MARKS 423 $.25 (Y34)

For The Beauty Of The Earth
2pt jr cor FISCHER,C CM 549 $.20 (Y35)

Heavenly Choir, The
SSA MARKS 369 $.25 (Y36)

I Found My Savior
SSA MARKS 344 $.25 (Y37)

Keep Me Ever Close To Thee
SSA MARKS 348 $.25 (Y38)

Make Us Holy Thine
SATB MARKS 4099 $.25 (Y39)

Sinner's Soul, A
SSA MARKS 354 $.25 (Y40)

YORK, D.
Beatitudes, The
SSAATTB oct PRESSER MC389 $.35 (Y41)

Blessing And Honor
SATB,opt brass oct PRESSER 312-40948 $.30 (Y42)

Christ Is Made The Sure Foundation
SATB oct PRESSER 312-40761 $.30 (Y43)

Four Freedoms, The
SATB,Bar solo,acap oct PRESSER 312-40296 $.25 (Y44)

Go, Ye, Into All The World
SATB oct PRESSER 312-40538 $.35 (Y45)

Holy Spirit, Truth Divine
SATB oct PRESSER 312-40178 $.25 (Y46)

Jesus Calls Us O'er The Tumult
SATB oct PRESSER MC221 $.30 (Y47)

Lift Up Our Hearts
SATB,acap oct PRESSER 312-40392 $.30 (Y48)

Lord Jesus We Stand Afar *Easter
SSATB oct PRESSER MC325 $.30 (Y49)

Lord Make Me Thine Instrument
SATB,acap oct PRESSER 352-00199 $.30 (Y50)

New Covenant, The
SATB oct PRESSER 312-40640 $.35 (Y51)

O God Of Love
SSAATTBB,acap,trp oct PRESSER MC388 $.30 (Y52)

Once To Every Man And Nation *Easter
SATB oct PRESSER 312-40098 $.30 (Y53)
TTBB oct PRESSER 312-40170 $.30 (Y54)

Peace I Leave With You *Easter
SSATBB oct PRESSER MC300 $.25 (Y55)

Peace Of God, The
SATB,acap oct PRESSER MC301 $.25 (Y56)

Praise, My Soul, The King Of Heaven
SATB oct PRESSER 312-40179 $.30 (Y57)

Prayer
SATB,acap oct PRESSER 312-40212 $.30 (Y58)

Psalm 150
SATB oct PRESSER 312-40683 $.30 (Y59)

Rise Up, O Men Of God *Easter/Gen
SATB oct PRESSER MC239 $.30 (Y60)

To Music
SSATTBB,acap oct PRESSER 352-00320 $.25 (Y61)

Who Shall Separate Us From The Love Of God?
SATB,acap oct PRESSER 312-40637 $.30 (Y62)

YORK, D.S.
Blessed Art Thou Forever
SATB oct PRESSER 312-40796 $.25 (Y63)

YORK, W.W.
Collect For Peace, A
SSATB,acap AMP A600 $.25 (Y64)

YORKE, COLIN
Christ Is Born Of Maiden Fair *see Britten, Anthony

YOSHIOKA, EMMETT
In Amber Light *Xmas
SATB oct WALTON 2958 $.35 (Y65)

YOU ARE NOT FAR FROM THE KINGDOM OF GOD see McCormick

YOU ARE PETER see Tamblyn, William

YOU ARE RIGHTEOUS, O LORD see Lewis

YOU ARE THE LIGHT OF THE WORLD see Kirk

YOU ARE THE LIGHT OF THE WORLD see Newbury, Kent A.

YOU ARE THE SALT OF THE EARTH see Butler, Eugene

YOU BETTER MIND! see Burroughs, Bob

YOU BETTER MIND see Ehret, Walter

YOU BETTER MIND see Hairston, Jester

YOU CAN DIG MY GRAVE *spir
(Ehret, W.) SA LEONARD-US 08073600 $.25 (Y66)
(Ehret, W.) SSA LEONARD-US 08074240 $.25 (Y67)
(Ehret, W.) SAB LEONARD-US 08073920 $.30 (Y68)
(Ehret, W.) SATB LEONARD-US 08074560 $.25 (Y69)

YOU CAN DIG MY GRAVE see Hesch

YOU CAN DIG MY GRAVE see Siegmeister, Elie

YOU CAN EXPERIENCE see Skillings, Otis

YOU CAN TELL THE WORLD see Jonson, William

YOU CAN'T MAKE ME DOUBT HIM *anthem
SAB/SA/TB BIG3 $.25 (Y70)

YOU DID NOT MISS JERUSALEM see Fetler, Paul

YOU DON'T NEED A SWORD see Lewis

YOU GOT A RIGHT *spir,US
(Aubanel, Georges) "Moi, J'y Ai Droit" [Eng/
Fr] 3 eq voices OUVRIERES s.p. (Y71)

YOU GOT TO CROSS THAT LONESOME VALLEY *folk,US
(Niles) 3pt wom cor oct SCHIRM.G 9934 $.25 (Y72)

YOU GOT TO CROSS THAT LONESOME VALLEY see Niles, John Jacob

YOU GOT TO LIVE! see Phillips

YOU GOTTA CROSS THE RIVER WHEN YOU DIE
(Davis) 4pt mix cor,ST soli,acap oct SCHIRM.G
10601 $.25 (Y73)

YOU GOTTA CROSS THE RIVER WHEN YOU DIE see Davis, Elmer L.

YOU GREEN AND GLITTERING TREE *Xmas,carol,Swed
(Ehret Walter) SATB,opt inst oct WALTON 2520 $.30 (Y74)

YOU HAVE HEARD THAT IT WAS SAID see Krapf, Gerhard

YOU HEAR THE LAMBS A-CRYIN'?
(Scarmolin) SATB,acap,opt pno oct PRO ART
1335 $.18 (Y75)

YOU KNOW WHO! see Centrone

YOU MAY BURY ME IN THE EAST *spir
(Work, J.) SATB,A/Mez solo,acap SCHIRM.EC
2413 $.30 (Y76)
(Work, J.) TTBB,T solo,acap SCHIRM.EC 2149
$.30 (Y77)

YOU MAY BURY ME IN THE EAST see Work, John [Wesley]

YOU MUST BE BORN AGAIN see McCormick

YOU SHALL LOVE THE LORD see Ream

YOU SHALL LOVE THE LORD YOUR GOD see Hillert, Richard

YOU TAUGHT ME HOW TO PRAY see Marth

YOU THAT LIKE HEEDLESS STRANGERS PASS ALONG see Gibbons, Orlando

YOU'D BETTER RUN *spir
(Ehret) SA oct SPRATT 199 $.30 (Y78)

YOUNG
All People That On Earth Do Dwell
SATB FLAMMER A 5037 $.30 (Y79)

All Ye Servants Of The Lord
SATB oct SACRED E50 $.35 (Y80)

Alleluia *Easter,Allelu
SATB oct SACRED S-134 $.35 (Y81)

Alleluia, All Glory Be To God
SATB oct GALAXY 1.2265.1 $.30 (Y82)

Alleluia! Christ Is Born
SATB SHAWNEE A 755 $.30 (Y83)

Alleluia! Christ Is Risen *Easter
SATB oct SOUTHERN $.25 (Y84)
(Lowden) SAB FLAMMER D5201 $.30 (Y85)

Almighty And Everlasting God
SATB oct SACRED S-80 $.30 (Y86)

And The Lord Appeared To Solomon
SATB oct FISCHER,C CM-7731 $.25 (Y87)

Arise O God And Shine
SATB oct GALAXY 1.2232.1 $.30 (Y88)

Begin, My Tongue, Some Heavenly Theme
SATB (med easy) SOUTHERN $.30 (Y89)
SATB SOUTHERN $.30 (Y90)

Bell Song, The
SATB FLAMMER A 5015 $.25 (Y91)

Bless The Lord, O My Soul
SATB oct SACRED S-74 $.35 (Y92)
SATB FLAMMER A 5124 $.25 (Y93)

Bread Of The World, In Mercy Broken
SATB KJOS 5315 $.30 (Y94)

By The Waters Of Babylon
SATB FLAMMER A 5539 $.30 (Y95)

Canticle For Easter, A *Easter
SATB oct SACRED S-6 $.35 (Y96)

Canticle Of Creation, A
SATB FLAMMER A 5045 $.30 (Y97)

Children Of The Heavenly Father
SATB KJOS 5483 $.30 (Y98)

Christ Is Arisen *Easter
SATB oct SOUTHERN $.25 (Y99)

Christ's Sacrifice Complete *Easter/Lent, cant
SATB FISCHER,C O-4866 $1.50 (Y100)

Christus Resurrexit *Easter
SATB FLAMMER A 5009 $.30 (Y101)
mix cor SOUTHERN $.25 (Y102)
SAB FLAMMER D5022 $.30 (Y103)
SATB oct SOUTHERN $.30 (Y104)

Come Christians, Join To Sing
SATB oct GALAXY 1.2312.1 $.30 (Y105)

Come Let Us Sing Of His Glory
SATB,acap SHAWNEE A 815 $.30 (Y106)

Come, Praise The Lord
mix cor SOUTHERN $.25 (Y107)

Crucifixus *Lent
SATB oct SOUTHERN $.30 (Y108)
SATB FLAMMER A 5064 $.30 (Y109)
(Gilbert) SAB FLAMMER D5058 $.30 (Y110)

Doxology
SATB SOUTHERN $.35 contains also: Gloria
Patri (Y111)

Drop, Drop, Slow Tears *Lent
SATB oct SOUTHERE$.25 (Y107)
SATB FLAMMER A 5032 $.25 (Y113)
(Lowden) SAB FLAMMER D5009 $.30 (Y114)

Drums Of God, The
SATB oct HERITAGE H13 $.35 (Y115)

YOUNG (cont'd.)

Echo Alleluia *Easter,Allelu
SSATTB oct SACRED S-20 $.35   (Y116)

Fanfare For A Holy Day
SATB oct SACRED S-52 $.35   (Y117)

Forth In Thy Name
SATB oct SACRED S-9921 $.35   (Y118)

Fret Not Thyself
SATB FLAMMER A 5540 $.30   (Y119)

From All That Dwell Below The Skies
SATB oct GALAXY 1.2186.1 $.30   (Y120)
SSA oct GALAXY 1.2241.1 $.30   (Y121)

Gethsemane *Lent
SATB oct SOUTHERN $.30   (Y122)

Gloria Patri
see Young, Doxology

Glorious Forever
SATB FLAMMER A 5095 $.30   (Y123)

Glorious Is Thy Holy Name
SATB oct SACRED S-14 $.35   (Y124)

God Leads Us Along
(Williams) SSATB oct LILLENAS AN-1125 $.30
                                                (Y125)
God Of Mercy God Of Grace
SATB oct GALAXY 1.2183.1 $.30   (Y126)

Gonna Ride That Heavenly Train
SATB oct HERITAGE H2149 $.35   (Y127)

Grant Us Thy Peace
SATB oct SACRED S-65 $.35   (Y128)

Great Is The Lord
SATB oct LORENZ 9916 $.30   (Y129)

Hodie Christus Natus Est *Xmas
[Lat] SATB oct GALAXY 1.2308 $.30   (Y130)

Holy Child, The *cant
SATB FLAMMER A5034 $1.00   (Y131)

Holy Lord God Of Hosts
SATB FLAMMER A 5162 $.30   (Y132)

How Firm A Foundation
SATB FLAMMER A 5599 $.30   (Y133)

Hymn Of The Last Supper *Commun/hymn
SATB,acap,opt pno oct PRO ART 2125 $.30
                                                (Y134)
I Am The Good Shepherd
SATB oct FISCHER,C CM-7759 $.30   (Y135)

I Am The Way, The Truth, And The Life
SATB oct SACRED E40 $.35   (Y136)

I Believe
SATB oct SACRED E87 $.35   (Y137)

I Give Myself Unto Prayer
SATB oct SACRED S-89 $.30   (Y138)

I Love Thy Kingdom, Lord
SATB oct SACRED S-143 $.35   (Y139)

I Will Extol Thee
SATB FLAMMER A 5083 $.30   (Y140)

I Will Lift Up Mine Eyes
SATB FLAMMER A 5618 $.30   (Y141)

In Paths Of Beauty
SATB FLAMMER A 5537 $.30   (Y142)

Jesus, My Lord, My All
SATB FLAMMER A 5506 $.25   (Y143)

Jesus, Our Lord, Is Risen Today! *Easter
SATB oct SACRED E66 $.35   (Y144)

Jesus The Very Thought Of Thee
SATB FLAMMER A 5617 $.30   (Y145)

Jesus, Thou Blessed Name Of Mercy
SATB oct SACRED E81 $.35   (Y146)

Joyful Alleluia *Allelu
girl cor SOUTHERN $.25   (Y147)
SSAA,acap SHAWNEE B 266 $.25   (Y148)

Joyful Alleluia, A
SATB,acap SHAWNEE A 794 $.30   (Y149)

Jubilate Deo
SATB,acap SHAWNEE A 857 $.30   (Y150)
mix cor SOUTHERN $.25   (Y151)
SAB,acap SHAWNEE D91 $.30   (Y152)

Laud To The Trinity
SATB FLAMMER A 5029 $.30   (Y153)

Laudate Dominum
SATB FLAMMER A 5014 $.30   (Y154)

Let God Arise
SATB oct GALAXY 1.2409.1 $.35   (Y155)

Light Everlasting
SATB oct GALAXY 1.2310.1 $.30   (Y156)

Litany For Easter *Easter
SATB oct SOUTHERN $.18   (Y157)

Lord Is My Shepherd, The
SATB FLAMMER A 5536 $.30   (Y158)

Lord My Pasture Shall Prepare, The
SATB FLAMMER A 5140 $.25   (Y159)

Lord Of All Being
SATB FLAMMER A 5521 $.25   (Y160)

Lord Of The Worlds Above
SATB oct SACRED E37 $.35   (Y161)

Lord's My Shepherd, The
SATB oct SACRED E61 $.35   (Y162)

YOUNG (cont'd.)

Lord's Supper *Lent
SATB oct SOUTHERN $.25   (Y163)

Love Came Down At Christmas *Xmas
unis oct GALAXY 1.2187.1 $.25   (Y164)

Missa Exultate *Mass
[Lat] SATB,org GALAXY 1.2314.1 $1.25   (Y165)

My Master Was So Very Poor *Xmas
SATB oct GALAXY 1.2200.1 $.30   (Y166)

Not So In Haste, My Heart
4pt jr cor/SATB (very easy) FISCHER,C
CM7288 $.20   (Y167)

Now Let Us All Praise God And Sing
SSA oct GALAXY 1.2207.1 $.30   (Y168)
SATB oct GALAXY 1.2108.1 $.30   (Y169)

Now Praise We Great And Famous Men
SATB oct SACRED S-58 $.35   (Y170)

Now Sing We All Noel *Xmas
SATB oct SACRED S-120 $.35   (Y171)

Now Sing We Joyfully Unto God
SATB SHAWNEE A 651 $.30   (Y172)
SSAA SHAWNEE B 285 $.35   (Y173)

O Clap Your Hands *anthem
mix cor oct OXFORD 94.206 $.25   (Y174)

O Come And Mourn With Me
SATB FLAMMER A 5208 $.30   (Y175)

O God, Our Help In Ages Past
SATB oct LORENZ 9959 $.30   (Y176)

O Holy Savior
SATB SHAWNEE A 5431 $.25   (Y177)

O Holy Saviour
SATB,acap,opt pno oct PRO ART 2148 $.25
                                                (Y178)
O Jesus, Crucified For Man *Lent
SATB oct SOUTHERN $.25   (Y179)

O Lamb Of God Most Lowly
SATB oct GALAXY 1.2215.1 $.30   (Y180)

O Let The Light, The Truth
SATB SHAWNEE A 5077 $.25   (Y181)

O Lord, My God, Give Ear Unto My Prayer
  *prayer
SATB,acap,opt pno oct PRO ART 2307 $.20
                                                (Y182)
O Love, How Deep
SATB oct LORENZ 9982 $.25   (Y183)

O Love Of God Most Full
SATB oct PRO ART 2147 $.25   (Y184)

O Master, Let Me Walk With Thee
SATB oct BELWIN 64278 $.30   (Y185)

O Mortal Man *Lent
SATB oct SOUTHERN $.30   (Y186)

O Thou Who Hearest Our Prayers
SATB KJOS 5470 $.30   (Y187)

Oh, What Praises Shall We Render
SATB FLAMMER A 5434 $.25   (Y188)

Outburst For Easter, An *Easter
SATB FLAMMER A 5270 $.30   (Y189)

Peace Within Thy Walls
SATB oct SACRED S-106 $.35   (Y190)

Praise, My Soul, The King Of Heaven
SATB oct FISCHER,C CM-7020 $.25   (Y191)
4pt jr cor/SATB (easy) FISCHER,C CM 7020
  $.25   (Y192)

Praise Ye The Lord (Psalm 150) anthem
SATB FLAMMER A 5022 $.25   (Y193)
mix cor oct OXFORD 94.207 $.30   (Y194)

Prince Of Peace
SATB FLAMMER A5065 $1.25   (Y195)

Psalm 150 *see Praise Ye The Lord

Recessional
SATB oct SACRED E31 $.35   (Y196)

Ride On Ride On In Majesty
SATB oct GALAXY 1.2277.1 $.30   (Y197)

Rise Up, O Men Of God
SATB FLAMMER A 5192 $.30   (Y198)

Send Down Thy Truth O God
SATB FLAMMER A 5111 $.25   (Y199)

Shepherds In This Hall *Xmas
SATB oct GALAXY 1.2465.1 $.30   (Y200)

Shine On Our Souls, Eternal God
SATB FLAMMER A 5087 $.25   (Y201)

Sing To The Lord Of Harvest
SATB KJOS 5446 $.30   (Y202)

Sing To The Lord Of Hosts
SATB FLAMMER A 5082 $.30   (Y203)

Sing Unto God
SATB oct FISCHER,C CM-7303 $.25   (Y204)

Sing Unto The Lord A New Song
SATB FLAMMER A 5341 $.30   (Y205)

Sing We Noel *Xmas
SATB oct HERITAGE H14 $.35   (Y206)

Speak To Me, Lord Jesus Christ
SATB,acap,opt pno oct PRO ART 2124 $.30
                                                (Y207)
Stand In The Gate Of The Lord's House
SATB oct BELWIN 60765 $.30   (Y208)

YOUNG (cont'd.)

Stand Up For Jesus
unis,pno/org FRANCIS s.p.   (Y209)

Stand Up, Stand Up For Jesus
SATB oct SACRED E74 $.35   (Y210)

Sublime Alleluia, A
SATB oct SACRED S-137 $.40   (Y211)

To David's Town *Xmas,cant
SATB FISCHER,C O-4842 $1.25   (Y212)

Unto Thee, O Lord, Will I Lift Up My Soul
SATB FLAMMER A 5147 $.25   (Y213)

Venite Adoremus *Xmas
SA/SATB oct SACRED S-110 $.35   (Y214)

We Will Carol Joyfully
SATB FLAMMER A 5378 $.30   (Y215)
SAB FLAMMER D5033 $.25   (Y216)
(Webb) SA/TB FLAMMER E5038 $.30   (Y217)

Weep, O My Soul
SATB FLAMMER A 5529 $.25   (Y218)

YOUNG *CCUL
(Carmichael, Ralph) 1-6pt voc sc WORD 30069
$1.95   (Y219)

YOUNG, C.
All Nature's Works His Praise Declare
SATB oct KERBY 6203C $.30   (Y220)
SATB,kbd oct KERBY 6203 $.30   (Y221)

Be Thou My Vision
SATB KJOS 5254 $.30   (Y222)

Come Thou Fount Of Every Blessing
SATB KJOS 5291 $.30   (Y223)

Easter Anthem *Easter,anthem
SATB KJOS 5437 $.30   (Y224)

I Lay My Sins On Jesus
SATB KJOS 5290 $.30   (Y225)

Let Hearts Awake And Sing
SATB KJOS 5358 $.35   (Y226)

Sleep, Holy Child!
SATB KJOS 5334 $.30   (Y227)

Still, Still, Still
SATB KJOS 5370 $.30   (Y228)

Triumphant Gladness
SATB KJOS 5351 $.30   (Y229)

Ye Servants Of God
SATB KJOS 5277 $.30   (Y230)

YOUNG, CARLTON R.
Bless The Lord, All Works Of The Lord
SATB oct AGAPE A 393 $.25   (Y231)

Blessed Assurance
SATB oct AGAPE CY 3337 $.35   (Y232)

Bread Of Life, The *Commun
SATB (med) ABINGDON APM-877 $.30   (Y233)

Bring A Torch, Jeanette *Xmas,carol
SATB oct AGAPE A 401 $.30   (Y234)
SA oct AGAPE A 370 $.30   (Y235)

Christians And Pagans
2pt mix cor oct AGAPE AG 7111 $.35   (Y236)

Come, Lord Jesus!
mix cor oct AGAPE AG 7133 $.35   (Y237)

Come, Praise The Lord
SATB oct AGAPE A 403 $.25   (Y238)

Come Thou, O Lover Of My Soul
SATB oct AGAPE A 432 $.25   (Y239)

Come, Ye Sinners, Poor And Needy
SATB oct SACRED E53 $.35   (Y240)

Come, Ye That Love The Lord
SATB oct SACRED E80 $.35   (Y241)

Day By Day, Dear Lord
SATB oct AGAPE A 359 $.25   (Y242)

Fourteen Canticles And Responses *CC14U
cor&cong,inst oct AGAPE AG 7129 $.90 (Y243)

God Created Man
unis oct AGAPE CY 3333 $.30   (Y244)

God Is
cor&cong,inst oct AGAPE CY 3339 $.30 (Y245)

God Is Working His Purpose Out
SATB oct AGAPE CF 121 $.30   (Y246)

God, Roll That Rock
mix cor oct AGAPE AG 7124 $.35   (Y247)

Guide Me, O Thou Great Jehovah
SATB oct AGAPE CH 620 $.30   (Y248)

Hearts And Voices Raise *anthem
SATB,tamb,perc (easy) oct AUGSBURG 1658
$.25   (Y249)

I Sing Of A Maiden
TTBB oct AGAPE MM 9005 $.25   (Y250)

Let All The World In Every Corner Sing
SATB oct GALAXY 1.2342.1 $.30   (Y251)
SATB,acap (easy) ABINGDON APM-458 $.25
                                                (Y252)
Lord's Supper, The
SATB oct AGAPE A 367 $.30   (Y253)

My Jesus, I Love Thee
SATB oct AGAPE CH 614 $.30   (Y254)

O Lamb Of God
SATB oct AGAPE CY 3331 $.35   (Y255)

YOUNG, CARLTON R. (cont'd.)

O My Saviour
2pt mix cor oct AGAPE A 417 $.30   (Y256)

O Thou Diviner Mystery
SATB oct AGAPE A 399 $.25   (Y257)

Psalm 139
SATB,ob oct AGAPE CY 3332 $.30   (Y258)

Saints And Sinners
SATB oct AGAPE AG 7100 $.30   (Y259)

Snow Lay On The Ground, The
SATB&opt treb cor,opt hndbl oct AGAPE F 923
$.30   (Y260)

Take Up Thy Cross
SATB oct AGAPE CH 624 $.30   (Y261)

Three Early American Christmas Settings
*CC3U,Xmas,US
SATB oct AGAPE A 407 $.35   (Y262)

YOUNG, G.

All Hail The Power Of Jesus' Name
SA oct WORD CS-675 $.25   (Y263)

As The Hart Panteth
SATBct SACRED S-118 $.35   (Y264)

Christ Is Arisen *Easter
SATB KJOS 5439 $.30   (Y265)

Come Praise The Lord *Thanks
SATB oct VOLKWEIN VB136 $.25   (Y266)

Easter Chant, An *Easter
SATB KJOS 5409 $.30   (Y267)

Jesus, Our Savior Is Born
SATB KJOS 5408 $.30   (Y268)

Jesus, Thou Mighty King Of Heaven
SATB KJOS 5441 $.30   (Y269)

La Nativite *Xmas
SATB KJOS 5447 $.30   (Y270)

Lord, Send Thy Holy Spirit
SATB oct VOLKWEIN VB696 $.25   (Y271)

Lullay, My Jesus
SATB KJOS 5469 $.30   (Y272)

Sing Unto God
SATB KJOS 5414 $.30   (Y273)

Sing Unto God Loudly
SATB KJOS 5493 $.30   (Y274)

To Thee, Eternal Spirit
SATB KJOS 5468 $.30   (Y275)

YOUNG, GORDON (1919-   )

All Hail The Power Of Jesus' Name *Easter/
Gen
unis oct PRESSER 312-40466 $.30   (Y276)

Alleluia! Christ Is Risen *Easter/Lent
SATB FLAMMER A 5038 $.25   (Y277)
SATB,acap oct FISCHER,C CM-7401 $.25   (Y278)
4pt jr cor/SATB (easy) FISCHER,C CM 7401
$.25   (Y279)
SATB oct WALTON 2050 $.30   (Y280)

Alleluia, Hodie! *Xmas
SATB,acap nct PRESSER 312-40762 $.25   (Y281)

Autumn Reverie
SATB oct AGAPE SP 689 $.25   (Y282)

Awake, Psaltry And Harp *anthem
SATB (easy) oct AUGSBURG 0628 $.25   (Y283)

Begin My Tongue, Some Heavenly Theme
SATB oct FISCHER,C CM-7786 $.30   (Y284)

Bless Thou, The Lord, O My Soul
SATB nct BELWIN 64286 $.30   (Y285)

Build Thee More Stately Mansions
(Holmes, O.) SATB oct PRESSER 312-40405
$.30   (Y286)

Canticle Of Celebration
SATB,opt inst oct FISCHER,C CM-7792 $.35,
ipa   (Y287)

Carillon For Christmas *Xmas
SATB oct GRAY GCMR 3030 $.25   (Y288)

Come, Holy Spirit
unis oct PRESSER 312-40465 $.25   (Y289)

Easter Alleluia, An *Easter
SATB oct GRAY GCMR 2779 $.25   (Y290)

Fear Not, O Israel
SATB oct FISCHER,J 9610 $.30   (Y291)

Festive Alleluia
SATB,opt 4brass oct AGAPE F 926 $.30   (Y292)

Forth In Thy Name
SATB oct WORD CS-2437 $.30   (Y293)

Forth To Thy New Year
SATB oct WORD CS-678 $.25   (Y294)

Gethsemane (Blessed Jesu, Come To Me)
SATB oct BELWIN 64319 $.30   (Y295)

Hail To Thee, Eternal God
SATB oct PRESSER 312-40910 $.30   (Y296)

Ho, Everyone That Thirsteth
SATB oct GRAY GCMR 3055 $.25   (Y297)

House Of The Lord, The
SATB oct FISCHER,C CM-7732 $.40   (Y298)

In The Year That King Uzziah Died
unis (med) ABINGDON APM-530 $.25   (Y299)

Jesu, Our Blessed Hope Of Heaven *anthem
SATB (easy) oct AUGSBURG 1567 $.20   (Y300)

YOUNG, GORDON (cont'd.)

Jesus, The Very Thought Of Thee
SATB oct PRESSER 312-40406 $.30   (Y301)

King Of Love
SATB oct GRAY GCMR 2548 $.30   (Y302)

Laudate Dominum
SATB oct AGAPE A 410 $.30   (Y303)

Litany For Easter *Easter
SSAATTB,acap (med) ABINGDON APM-354 $.18   (Y304)

Lord, Hearken And Pity *Easter/Gen
SATB,acap oct PRESSER 312-40671 $.25   (Y305)

Make A Joyful Noise
SATB oct GRAY GCMR 3016 $.25   (Y306)
(Kjelson; Vance) SA/TB oct BELWIN 1899 $.30   (Y307)

Mighty Fortress, A
SATB oct PRESSER 312-40732 $.30   (Y308)

Moyst With One Drop Of Thy Blood *Commun
SATB (med) ABINGDON APM-230 $.25   (Y309)

My God, My King, Thy Praise I Sing
SATB (easy) ABINGDON APM-252 $.25   (Y310)

O Come, Let Us Sing
SATB oct GRAY GCMR 2913 $.30   (Y311)

O For A Closer Walk With God
SATB oct PRESSER 312-40390 $.30   (Y312)

O Lord Support Us All The Day Long
SATB (med) ABINGDON APM-166 $.24   (Y313)

O Men Of God, Fight On!
SATB oct PRESSER G-144 $.30   (Y314)

O Sorrow Deep
SATB oct WORD CS-2473 $.30   (Y315)

Praise
SATB oct PRESSER 312-50491 $.35   (Y316)

Praise Ye The Name Of The Lord
SATB oct WORD CS-307 $.30   (Y317)

Resurrection, The *Easter
SATB oct PRESSER 312-40449 $.35   (Y318)

Shout Ye! *Adv
SATB oct GRAY GCMR 3104 $.25   (Y319)

Sing To Our God Immortal Praise
SATB oct PRESSER 312-40646 $.25   (Y320)

Strophic Alleluias
SATB oct WORD CS-302 $.30   (Y321)

Thou Wilt Keep Him In Perfect Peace
SATB oct AGAPE A 458 $.30   (Y322)

Three Short Psalms *CC3U
SATB oct PRESSER 312-40467 $.30   (Y323)

Voices In Praise *CCU
SATB oct PRESSER $1.25   (Y324)

We Render, Lord, This Day
SATB oct PRESSER 312-40798 $.25   (Y325)
SAB,acap oct PRESSER 312-40798 $.25   (Y326)

What A Friend We Have In Jesus
SATB oct AGAPE CH 657 $.30   (Y327)

When I Survey The Wondrous Cross *Easter
SATB oct PRESSER 312-40440 $.30   (Y328)

YOUNG JOSEPH see Diamond, David

YOUNG, K.
Australian Carols *CC20U,Xmas,carol,Austral
SATB ALLANS 465 s.p.   (Y329)

YOUNG LIONS, THE see Beck, John Ness

YOUNG, P.
God Of The Earth
SATB oct SACRED E79 $.35   (Y330)

YOUNG PEOPLE'S CHOIR BOOK see Peery, Robert Roy

YOUNG, PETER
Hope And Pray
SATB PROWSE s.p.   (Y331)

YOUNG, PHILLIP
Let The Whole Creation Cry *anthem
unis treb cor (easy) oct AUGSBURG 1470 $.25   (Y332)
unis (easy) oct AUGSBURG 1470 $.25   (Y333)

Search Me, O God *anthem
SATB (easy) oct AUGSBURG 0621 $.25   (Y334)

Sing Ye Joyfully To The Lord *anthem
SA (easy) oct AUGSBURG 0620 $.25   (Y335)

YOUNG, ROBERT H.
Children Of The King
2pt/unis oct SOUTHERN $.25   (Y336)

Drop, Drop Slow Tears
SATB oct WORD CS-2390 $.30   (Y337)

Gabriel's Message *Fest
SATB,brass oct WORD CS-2493 $.35   (Y338)

Gentle Jesus, Meek And Mild
2pt/unis oct SOUTHERN $.25   (Y339)

Surely God Is In This The Holy Place
SATB oct SOUTHERN $.25   (Y340)

Thou Dost Keep Him In Perfect Peace
SATB oct SOUTHERN $.25   (Y341)

When I Survey The Wondrous Cross
SATB oct WORD CS-673 $.30   (Y342)

YOUNG SINGERS' CHOIR BOOK see Nightingale, Mae
[Wheeler]

YOUNG SOUND, THE see Mickelson, Paul

YOUNG VOICES FOR GOD *CCU
jr cor LORENZ $1.00   (Y343)

YOUNG WORLD see Skillings, Otis

YOUNGER CHOIR, THE-BOOK 1 *CC44U,spir
1-3pt&desc oct LILLENAS MB-230 $1.25   (Y344)

YOUNGER CHOIR, THE-BOOK 2 *CCU
(Latham, Joy) jr cor oct LILLENAS MB-231
$1.25   (Y345)

YOUNGER, JOHN B.
Be Known To Us *Commun,anthem
SATB,acap oct HARRIS HC4005 $.30   (Y346)

Lamb, The *anthem
unis/2pt,pno oct HARRIS HC2001 $.20   (Y347)
(Wild, Eric L.) SATB,pno, or celeste oct
HARRIS HC4020 $.30   (Y348)

My Song Is Love Unknown *Easter/Lent,anthem
SATB,solo,org oct HARRIS HC4026 $.35   (Y349)

O God Of Bethel! *anthem/Bibl/hymn
SSATB,solo,acap oct HARRIS HC4032 $.35   (Y350)

Praise Ye The Lord *Thanks,anthem
(Buononcini, G.) SATB,acap oct HARRIS
HC4022 $.25   (Y351)

YOUR CHILDREN'S CHOIR see Licht

YOUR LORD IS BORN TODAY *Xmas,carol,Eng
(Ehret) SAB oct FOX CC6 $.25   (Y352)
(Ehret, W.) SAB PROWSE CC6 s.p.   (Y353)

YOUR SSA CHOIR see Peery

YOUR TREASURES IN HEAVEN see Berger

YOUR VOICES RAISE see Handel, George Frideric,
As Pants The Hart

YOUR VOICES RAISE, YE CHERUBIM see Handel,
George Frideric

YOUR WORK WITH LOVE SURROUNDS YOU see Feltmate

YOUR YOUTH CHOIR see Licht

YOU'RE GOIN' TO REAP JUST WHAT YOU SOW
SATB oct STAFF 579 $.30   (Y354)

YOURS ARE THE HEAVENS see Lee, J.

YOURS ARE THE HEAVENS see Roff, Joseph

YOURS IS PRINCELY POWER see Schroth, Gerhard

YOUSE
Seek Ye The Lord
SATB oct BOURNE 781 $.25   (Y355)

This Nation Under God
SATB,narrator,band oct BOURNE 798 $.60, ipr   (Y356)

YOUSE, GLAD [ROBINSON] (1898-   )
Beloved *Bibl
SATB oct BOURNE 690 $.25   (Y357)

God Gave Us A Lovely World
SATB oct BOURNE 672 $.25   (Y358)

God's World
unis/2pt BELWIN $1.00   (Y359)

Hear Me Lord
SA oct BOURNE 2005 $.25   (Y360)
SSA oct BOURNE 122 $.30   (Y361)
(Wilson) SATB oct BOURNE 640 $.30   (Y362)

Little Children
SSA oct BOURNE 153 $.25   (Y363)

Thou Wilt Light My Candle
(Deis) 4pt mix cor oct SCHIRM.G 9431 $.25   (Y364)

World About Me, The
SSA oct BOURNE 218 $.25   (Y365)

YOUTH CHOIR ANTHEM BOOK 1 see Holler, John

YOUTH CHOIR ANTHEM BOOK 2 see Holler, John

YOUTH CHOIR ANTHEM BOOK 3 see Holler, John

YOUTH CHOIR ANTHEM BOOK 4 see Holler, John

YOUTH CHOIR ANTHEM BOOK 5 see Holler, John

YOUTH CHOIR CLASSICS *CCU,anthem
SAB/SA/unis LORENZ $1.75   (Y366)

YOUTH CHOIR, THE *CC19L,anthem/liturg
(Hadley) SA/SB/TB PRO ART 919 $1.50   (Y367)

YOUTH HYMN ANTHEMS NO. 1 *CCU,anthem
SAB/SA/unis LORENZ $1.75   (Y368)

YOUTH HYMN ANTHEMS NO. 2 *CC13U,anthem/hymn
(Martin, Gilbert M.) SAB/SA/unis LORENZ $1.75   (Y369)

YOUTH PRAISES see Hutson, Wihla

YUFFY
I Heard The Bells *Xmas
(Myrow) SATB CRESCENDO $.30   (Y370)

YULE LOG CAROL see Giasson

YULE SONG see Heaton, [Wallace]

YULE TIDINGS *CCU,Xmas,carol
(Ehret) SA MARKS $1.00   (Y371)

YULETIDE CAROL see Mac Dougall

YULETIDE CAROLS *CCU
TTBB,acap oct PRESSER 312-21180 $.40   (Y372)

YULETIDE CAROLS *CCU,Xmas,carol
(Malin; Morgan) SAB oct BELWIN 64302 $.35;
SSA oct BELWIN 64220 $.40   (Y373)

YULETIDE FOR TEENTIME see Cooper

YULETIDE MEMORIES see Wilson, Ira B.

YULETIME FOR TEENTIME see Cooper, Irvin

YUNG, ALF.
Ave Maria *BVM
[Lat] SA/TB (E flat maj) CHOUDENS s.p.
(Y374)

[Lat] SA/TB (B flat maj) CHOUDENS s.p.
(Y375)

[Lat] SA/TB (F maj) CHOUDENS s.p.
(Y376)

Cantique Pour Messe De Marriage *Marriage
opt cor,solo CHOUDENS s.p.   (Y377)

Les Chants Du Sanctuaire *CC70U,Mass/mot/
Psalm
cor,org/pno oct CHOUDENS s.p.   (Y378)

Messe *Mass
2 eq voices,pno/org (D maj) CHOUDENS s.p.
(Y379)

Messe Breve *Mass
unis,pno/org (F maj) CHOUDENS s.p. (Y380)

O Salutaris
[Lat] 2pt (E maj) CHOUDENS s.p.   (Y381)

Z

ZACCARIA, VITTORE
Adoro Te Devote
see Cinque Mottetti Eucaristici

Ave Verum
see Cinque Mottetti Eucaristici

Cinque Mottetti Eucaristici *Commun,mot
[Lat] unis,org ZANIBON 4497 s.p.
contains: Adoro Te Devote; Ave Verum;
Domine Non Sum Dignus; O Sacrum
Convivium; O Salutaris Hostia   (Z1)

Dodici Litanie Lauretane *CC12U
[Lat] 1-2 eq voices,org ZANIBON 4496 s.p.
(Z2)

Domine Non Sum Dignus
see Cinque Mottetti Eucaristici

O Sacrum Convivium
see Cinque Mottetti Eucaristici

O Salutaris Hostia
see Cinque Mottetti Eucaristici

ZACCARIIS, CAESAR DE (ca. 1550-ca. 1600)
Eile, Herr, Mir Zu Helfen *mot
(Hellmann) SATB HANSSLER 1.127 s.p. (Z3)

ZACCHEUS see Sherill, G.

ZACHAU
Come, Holy Spirit, God And Lord *anthem
(Pasquet) unis (easy) oct AUGSBURG 1431
$.30   (Z4)
(Pasquet) unis treb cor (easy) oct AUGSBURG
1431 $.30   (Z5)

Lord Have Mercy On Us
(Kingsbury, John) SATB ALFRED 6369 $.30
(Z6)

ZACHAUS, STEIG EILEND HERNIEDER see Driessler,
Johannes

ZACHER, GERD
Magnificat *cant
ST/SB, 4brass/org&timp HANSSLER 10.067 sc
s.p., voc sc s.p., ipa   (Z7)

ZACHOW, FRIEDRICH WILHELM (1663-1712)
Herr, Wenn Ich Nur Dich Habe *cant
[Ger] SATB,soli,org,cembalo,harp,strings
KISTNER sc s.p., cor pts s.p., ipa (Z8)

ZACK, O.V.
Herr, Schicke Was Du Willt
[Ger] mix cor,acap (med) HUG s.p.   (Z9)

ZADOK DER PRIESTER see Handel, George Frideric,
Zadok, The Priest

ZADOK THE PRIEST see Handel, George Frideric

ZAGATTI, FRANCESCO (ca. 1750?)
Gloria Patri
(Hellmann) "Lob Und Preis Sei Gott" [Lat/
Ger] SA,cont,2rec HANSSLER 5.058 sc s.p.,
cor pts s.p.   (Z10)

Lob Und Preis Sei Gott *see Gloria Patri

ZAGWIJN, [HENRI] (1878-1954)
Hoe Groot, O Heer
men cor ALSBACH&D sc s.p., cor pts s.p.
(Z11)

ZAMBITA DE NAVIDAD see Anonymous

ZANDONAI, RICCARDO (1883-1944)
Preghiera Alla Virgine
wom cor,inst ZANIBON 4069 s.p.   (Z12)
(Tonetti, O.) wom cor,org ZANIBON 4070 s.p.
(Z13)

ZANEN, P.
De Drie Koningen
see Drie Oud-Franse Kerstliederen

Drie Oud-Franse Kerstliederen
mix cor sc ALSBACH&D s.p. score and choral
parts separately published
contains: De Drie Koningen; Looft Hem;
Vrolijk Kerstfeest   (Z14)

Looft Hem
see Drie Oud-Franse Kerstliederen

Vrolijk Kerstfeest
see Drie Oud-Franse Kerstliederen

ZANGIUS, NIKOLAUS (ca. 1570-ca. 1618)
Angelus Ad Pastores Ait *Adv/Xmas
SSATBB,acap voc pt DOBLINGER s.p. see also
ADVENT UND WEIHNACHT, HEFT 2   (Z15)

Congratulamini *Adv/Xmas
SSATTB,acap voc pt DOBLINGER s.p. see also
ADVENT UND WEIHNACHT, HEFT 2   (Z16)

Geistliche Und Weltliche Lieder *sac/sec,CCU
[Ger] 5pt mix cor BAREN. EM 1081 s.p. (Z17)

Jesus Dulcis Memoria
(Schabasser, Josef) mix cor,acap oct
DOBLINGER s.p. see also CHRISTUS, DER
HERR   (Z18)

ZANINELLI, LUIGI
At The Gates Of Heaven
SATB SHAWNEE A 588 $.30   (Z19)

Give Thanks To The Lord
SATB oct WALTON 3403 $.75   (Z20)

Jubilate Deo
SATB,acap SHAWNEE A 919 $.40   (Z21)

Liturgical Suite
SATB SHAWNEE A 1043 $.40   (Z22)

Lord, Make Me An Instrument Of Thy Peace
SATB SHAWNEE A 1020 $.30   (Z23)

ZANINELLI, LUIGI (cont'd.)
Mass In Honor Of Pope John XXIII *Mass
SATB oct WALTON 3402 $.35   (Z24)

Now Is Christ Risen From The Dead
SATB SHAWNEE A 782 $.30   (Z25)

Oh God Of Love *hymn
SATB SHAWNEE A 702 $.25   (Z26)

Sing, Ye Choirs *CCU
S&SATB SHAWNEE G44 $1.50   (Z27)

Suite Of Unison Anthems, A *anthem
unis SHAWNEE A 764 $.40   (Z28)

ZANTON
Triumphant Fanfare
SATB oct SHAPIRO SCE 2510 $.30   (Z29)

ZARLINO, [GIOSEFFO] (1517-1590)
Drei Motetten Und Ein Geistliches Madrigal
*CC4U,madrigal/mot
(Flury) [Ger/It/Lat] 4-6pt mix cor MOSELER
s.p.   (Z30)

ZAUBER UND SEGEN see Woll, Erna

ZAUBER- UND SEGENSSPRUCHE see Krietsch, Georg

ZAUMEYER
Alleluia
SATB WARNER W3669 $.30   (Z31)

Holy Father
SATB WARNER W3787 $.30   (Z32)

Lord's Prayer *prayer
SSAATBB LEONARD-US 08040000 $.25   (Z33)

Psalm 25
SSAATBB LEONARD-US 08052800 $.30   (Z34)

Psalm 42
SATB LEONARD-US 08052960 $.25   (Z35)

Psalm 43
SATB LEONARD-US 08052970 $.25   (Z36)

ZBINDEN, JULIEN-FRANCOIS (1917-   )
Terra Dei *Op.41, ora
4pt mix cor,SATB soli,2fl,2ob,2clar,2bsn,
4horn,4trp,3trom,tuba,strings,perc,timp,
harp voc sc BREITKOPF-W EB-6573 s.p., sc
BREITKOPF-W rental   (Z37)

ZEBROWSKI, MARCIN JOZF
Magnificat *Pol
(Heising, R.; Sikorski, K.) cor,soli,cont,
inst POLSKIE WDMP64 s.p.   (Z38)

ZEHN NEGRO-SPIRITUALS see Gerhold, Norbert

ZEHN OSTERRICHISCHE WEIHNACHTSLEIDER *Xmas,Aus
(Schemitsch, Hans) [Ger] mix cor,acap cmplt
ed DOBLINGER s.p.
contains & see also: Als Ich Bei Meinen
Schafen Wacht'; Da Droben Vom Berge; Der
Heiland Ist Geboren; Grunet, Felder; Los,
Los, Mein Wolferl; O Jubel, O Freud;
Schlaf, Schlaf, Holdseliges Jesulein;
Still, O Himmel; Weihnacht, Wie Bist Du
Schon; Gruber, Franz Xaver, Stille Nacht,
Heil'ge Nacht   (Z39)

ZEISL, ERIC (1905-1959)
Psalm 92 *see Requiem Ebraico

Requiem Ebraico (Psalm 92)
[Eng/Heb] SATB TRANSCON. TCL 266 $2.00, ipa
(Z40)

ZEIT IST WIE EWIGKEIT see Weyrauch, Johannes

ZEIT, O VERKUNDIGUNG see Woll, Erna

ZEITGENOSSISCHE KIRCHENLIEDER see Hofmann,
Friedrich

ZEITGENOSSISCHE KIRCHENLIEDER see Hofmann,
Friedrich

ZELTER
Der Konig In Thule
(Buck) men cor BIRNBACH s.p.   (Z41)

ZELTER, CARL FRIEDRICH (1758-1832)
Der Mensch Lebt Und Besteht *mot
mix cor,acap TONGER s.p.   (Z42)

ZEMLINSKY, [ALEXANDER VON] (1871-1942)
Psalm 23
[Ger] voc sc UNIVER. 2861 $3.80   (Z43)

ZENTNER, JOHANNES (1903-   )
Hore Gott, Mein Schreien (Psalm 61)
[Ger] men cor&boy cor,org HUG s.p. (Z44)
[Ger] men cor&boy cor,orch HUG s.p. (Z45)

Psalm 61 *see Hore Gott, Mein Schreien

Psalm 92
[Ger] wom cor,org/orch (vocal score and
instrumental parts for rent) HUG s.p.
contains also: Psalm 131   (Z46)

Psalm 131
see Zentner, Johannes, Psalm 92

ZES OUD-NED. LIEDEREN see Rontgen, [Julius]

ZES VROUWENKOREN see Rontgen, [Julius]

ZETTERVALL, HOWARD
Make A Joyful Noise *CCU,anthem
mix cor SACRED $1.75   (Z47)

Ten Anthems About Peace *CC10U,anthem
SATB SACRED $1.75   (Z48)

ZEUCH AN DIE MACHT, DU ARM DES HERRN see
Geisel, Gustav

ZEUCH AN DIE MACHT, DU ARM DES HERRN see Kurig,
Hans-Hermann

ZEUCH EIN ZU DEINEN TOREN see Huth, Alfred

ZEUCH EIN ZU DEINEN TOREN see Marx, Karl

ZEUCH EIN ZU DEINEN TOREN see Rohwer, Jens

ZEUCH HIN, BETRUBTES JAHR see Haller, Hermann

ZEUNER, MARTIN (ca. 1600?)
Ach Gott, Vom Himmel Sieh Darein
SATTB LAUDINELLA LR 43 s.p. contains also:
Aus Tiefer Not (SATBB); War Gott Nicht
Mit Uns (SATBB); Wohl Dem, Der In Furcht
Gottes Steht (SATBB)   (Z49)

Aus Tiefer Not
see Zeuner, Martin, Ach Gott, Vom Himmel
Sieh Darein

Jesu, Deine Passion
see Praetorius, Michael, Christus, Der Uns
Selig Macht

Jesus, I Will Ponder Now *Easter
SAATB,acap oct PRESSER 312-40182 $.30 (Z50)

Uns Ist Ein Kindlein Heut Geborn *Xmas
[Ger] SATTB,acap (med easy) MULLER K 28
                                         (Z51)

War Gott Nicht Mit Uns
see Zeuner, Martin, Ach Gott, Vom Himmel
Sieh Darein

Where Cross The Crowded Ways Of Life
(Lynn) SATB oct SOUTHERN $.25   (Z52)

Wohl Dem, Der In Furcht Gottes Steht
see Zeuner, Martin, Ach Gott, Vom Himmel
Sieh Darein

ZGODAVA
Carol Of The Italian Pipers *carol
SSA SHAWNEE B 321 $.35   (Z53)

Three Canticles And A Motet For The Easter
Vigil Service *CC4U,Holywk,mot
SATB oct SUMMY M 2853 $.25   (Z54)

Two Motets For Holy Week *CC2U,Holywk,mot
SATB oct SUMMY M 2852 $.25   (Z55)

ZHADANOV
We Praise Thee
(Tellep) SATB,acap oct BOOSEY 5174 $.30 (Z56)

ZIEL VAN CHRISTUS see Vranken, Alph., Anima
Christi

ZIELENSKI, MIKOLAJ
Domus Mea *Commun,Pol
(Szczepanska, M.) 4pt mix cor,org POLSKIE
WDMP31 s.p.   (Z57)

In Monte Oliveti *Pol
(Szweykowski) 5pt mix cor,org POLSKIE
WDMP53 s.p.   (Z58)

Iustus Ut Palma Florebit *Offer,Pol
(Jachimecki, Z.) 7pt mix cor,org POLSKIE
WDMP41 s.p.   (Z59)

Vox In Rama *Commun,Pol
(Chybinski, A.) 4pt mix cor,org POLSKIE
WDMP12 s.p.   (Z60)

ZIELENSKI, NICHOLAS
Adoramus Te *Easter/Lent
(Martens, Mason) "We Adore Thee" SATB oct
WALTON 6021 $.30   (Z61)

We Adore Thee *see Adoramus Te

ZILCH
Is It Nothing To You?
(McLellan) SATB oct LILLENAS AT-1021 $.25 (Z62)

ZILCHER, HERMANN (1881-1948)
Du Aber, Herr, Bist Unser Vater *Gen,cant
[Ger] SATB,SATB soli,orch (diff) MULLER
SM 2277 voc sc s.p., cor pts s.p.   (Z63)

ZILLINGER, ERWIN (1893-   )
Dein Konig Kommt In Niedern Hullen
SAT/SAB,treb inst HANSSLER 14.012 s.p.
contains also: Micheelsen, Hans
Friedrich, "Trostet, Trostet", Spricht
Der Herr (SA)   (Z64)

Deutsche Messe Auf Bibelworte *Mass
SSATBB,S solo,acap HANSSLER 10.202 sc s.p.,
cor pts s.p.   (Z65)

O Traurigkeit, O Herzeleid
see Poser, Hans, Christe, Du Schopfer Aller
Welt

Wir Loben Dich *Doxol
[Ger] SATB,acap (med easy) NAGELS EN 1156
s.p.   (Z66)

ZIMARINO, SETTIMIO
A Sant'Antonio "La Canzoncina Dei Gigli"
[Lat] mix cor,org ZANIBON 1505 s.p. (Z67)

Inno A Sant'Antonio Di Padova *hymn
[Lat] unis mix cor,org ZANIBON 1504 s.p. (Z68)

Quatuor Pange Lingua *CC4U,Commun
[Lat] unis&eq voices&mix cor,org ZANIBON
1503 s.p.   (Z69)

Tre Tantum Ergo *CC3U,Commun
[Lat] S/T,org ZANIBON 1506 s.p.   (Z70)

Ventotto Litanie Lauretane *CC28U
[Lat] 2-3pt,org (easy) ZANIBON 2897 s.p. (Z71)

ZIMMERMANN
Three Simple Melodies *CC3U
unis oct FISCHER,C CM-7778 $.30   (Z72)

ZIMMERMANN, HEINZ WERNER (1930-   )
And The Word Became Flesh *Bibl/hymn/liturg
cor,org CONCORDIA 98-2177 $.25 see also
Five Hymns   (Z73)

ZIMMERMANN, HEINZ WERNER (cont'd.)

Chorvariationen Uber Ein Thema Von Hugo
Distler ("Nurnberger Grosses Gloria")
[Ger] SSATBB,opt T soli,acap (diff)
BAREN. BA 5412 $4.75   (Z74)

Crucifixion *spir
cor,acap (diff) oct AUGSBURG 11-9137 $1.50
see from Three Spirituals   (Z75)

Der Herr Ist Meine Macht Und Mein Psalm
(Psalm 118)
SSATB,hpsd,bvl, vibraphone (med diff)
BAREN. BA 4353 sc $4.50, cor pts $1.00
see from Vesper   (Z76)

Eile Gott, Mich Zu Erretten (Psalm 70) Proces
SSATB,hpsd,bvl, vibraphone (med diff)
BAREN. BA 4352 sc $3.50, cor pts $.40 see
from Vesper   (Z77)

Five Hymns *Bibl/hymn/liturg
cor,org cor pts CONCORDIA 98-2171 $.20, voc
sc CONCORDIA 97-5131 $.85
contains & see also: And The Word Became
Flesh; Have No Fear, Little Flock; Lord
Is My Light, The; Praise The Lord;
Those Who Trust In The Lord   (Z78)

Gelobet Sei Der Herr Taeglich *mot
[Ger] SATB,bvl PETERS EM478 $1.25, ipa (Z79)

Gott Ist Unsre Zuversicht (Psalm 46) hymn
SSATB,hpsd,bvl, vibraphone (med diff)
BAREN. BA 4354 sc $4.50, cor pts $1.00
see from Vesper   (Z80)
5pt mix cor,hpsd (med diff) BAREN. BA 4355
sc $2.00, cor pts $.40 see from Vesper
                                     (Z81)

Have No Fear, Little Flock *Bibl/hymn/liturg
cor,org CONCORDIA 98-2175 $.25 see also
Five Hymns   (Z82)

Herr, Mache Mich Zum Werkzeug Deines Friedens
*mot
[Ger] 6pt mix cor,bvl PETERS EM452 $1.50,
ipa   (Z83)

I Am Glad *spir
cor,acap (diff) oct AUGSBURG 11-9237 $1.50
see from Three Spirituals   (Z84)

In That Great Gettin' Up Mornin' *spir
cor,acap (diff) oct AUGSBURG 11-9234 $1.00
see from Three Spirituals   (Z85)

Kommt, Singt Unserem Herrn *Gen,Psalm
[Ger] SATB,bvl (diff) sc BAREN. BA 4347
$2.25, ipa   (Z86)

Lobet, Ihr Knechte Des Herrn *mot
[Ger] 5pt mix cor,bvl PETERS EM447 $1.25,
ipa   (Z87)

Lord Is My Light, The *Bibl/hymn/liturg
cor,org CONCORDIA 98-2174 $.30 see also
Five Hymns   (Z88)

Lord's Prayer, The
SSATTBB,bvl CONCORDIA 97-4906 $.50, ipa
                                     (Z89)

Meine Seele Erhebt Den Herrn *Magnif
SSATB,hpsd,bvl, vibraphone (med diff)
BAREN. BA 4356 sc $4.50, cor pts $1.00
see from Vesper   (Z90)

Mighty Fortress, A
mix cor,band (diff) cor pts AUGSBURG
11-9283 $.25, sc AUGSBURG 11-9282 $25.00,
ipr   (Z91)

Praise The Lord *Bibl/hymn/liturg
cor,org CONCORDIA 98-2176 $.25 see also
Five Hymns   (Z92)

Psalm 23 *anthem
SATB,org,bvl voc sc AUGSBURG 0638 $.30, ipa
                                     (Z93)

Psalm 46 *see Gott Ist Unsre Zuversicht

Psalm 70 *see Eile Gott, Mich Zu Erretten

Psalm 100 *anthem
SATB,org,bvl voc sc AUGSBURG 0640 $.40, ipa
                                     (Z94)

Psalm 118 *see Der Herr Ist Meine Macht Und
Mein Psalm

Psalmkonzert *Psalm
5pt mix cor&unis jr cor,Bar solo,3trp,bvl,
vibraphone sc CONCORDIA 97-4854 $2.50,
cor pts CONCORDIA 97-4866 $.90, ipa, cor
pts CONCORDIA 97-4886 $.10, ipa   (Z95)
[Ger] 5pt mix cor&unis&boy cor,B/Bar solo,
3trp,bvl,org, or Vibraphone sc PETERS
EM521 $6.50, ipa, voc sc PETERS EM521
$1.25, ipa, cor pts PETERS EM521 $.60,
ipa   (Z96)
[Ger] unis boy cor&5pt mix cor,B solo,org,
3trp,bvl, & vibraphone sc PETERS EM521
$6.50 voc sc PETERS EM521 $1.25, voc pt
PETERS EM521 $.60, ipa   (Z97)

Siehe, Wir Ziehen Hinauf Gen Jerusalem
*Psntd,mot
[Ger] SSAATTBB,bvl (med diff) sc BAREN.
BA 4350 s.p., ipa   (Z98)

Those Who Trust In The Lord *Bibl/hymn/
liturg
cor,org CONCORDIA 98-2178 $.25 see also
Five Hymns   (Z99)

Three Spirituals *see Crucifixion; I Am
Glad; In That Great Gettin' Up Mornin'
                                     (Z100)

Uns Ist Ein Kind Geboren *mot
[Ger] 5pt mix cor,bvl PETERS EM448 $1.25,
ipa   (Z101)

Vater Unser
[Ger] 7pt mix cor,bvl PETERS EM451 $1.50,
ipa   (Z102)

Vesper *see Der Herr Ist Meine Macht Und
Mein Psalm (Psalm 118); Eile Gott, Mich
Zu Erretten (Psalm 70); Gott Ist Unsre
Zuversicht (Psalm 46); Meine Seele Erhebt

ZIMMERMANN, HEINZ WERNER (cont'd.)

Den Herrn   (Z103)

Weihnacht *CC4U,Xmas,mot
[Ger] SATB,bvl PETERS EM474 $2.50, ipa (Z104)

Weihnachtslied Auf Einen Text Von Ilse
Schnell *CCU,Xmas
[Ger] SSATB&unis wom cor,hpsd,bvl,opt perc,
vibraphone (med) BAREN. BA 4348 sc $2.50,
cor pts $.40, ipa   (Z105)

ZINGARELLI, NICOLA ANTONIO (1752-1837)
Be Not Far From Me
SAB oct LORENZ 7400 $.30   (Z106)

Christus E Miserere (from Christus E
Miserere) Easter/Gen/Lent,anthem/Bibl/mot
"Go Not Far From Me, O God" SATB,acap oct
BELWIN 1029 $.25   (Z107)
"Go Not Far From Me, O God" SATB,acap oct
PRO ART 1085 $.30   (Z108)
"Go Not Far From Me, O God" SATB,acap oct
HARRIS HC 4018 $.30   (Z109)
(Carlson) "Go Not Far From Me, O God" SATB
oct SPRATT 500 $.30   (Z110)
(Carlson) "Go Not Far From Me, O God" SSA
oct SPRATT 631 $.30   (Z111)
(Christy) "Go Not Far From Me, O God" SSAA
SCHMITT 2531 $.45   (Z112)
(Ehret, Walter) "Go Not Far From Me, O God"
SATB,acap oct BELWIN 1029 $.25   (Z113)
(Ehret, Walter) "Go Not Far From Me, O God"
SAB,acap oct BELWIN 1584 $.30   (Z114)
(Holler) "Go Not Far From Me, O God" SATB
oct GRAY GCMR 1464 $.30   (Z115)
(Hullah; Harker) "Go Not Far From Me, O
God" 4pt mix cor,acap oct SCHIRM.G 4889
$.30   (Z116)
(Perry) "Go Not Far From Me, O God" SSA
FLAMMER B 5065 $.30   (Z117)
(Riegger) "Go Not Far From Me, O God" SAB
FLAMMER D5103 $.30   (Z118)
(Riegger) "Go Not Far From Me, O God" SATB
FLAMMER A 5215 $.35   (Z119)
(Stickles) "Go Not Far From Me, O God" 2pt
boy cor/2pt men cor/2pt mix cor oct
SCHIRM.G 10334 $.25   (Z120)
(Stickles) "Go Not Far From Me, O God" 3pt
mix cor oct SCHIRM.G 10335 $.30   (Z121)
(Stone) "Go Not Far From Me, O God" SSA,
acap oct PRO ART 1238 $.25   (Z122)

Christus Factus Est *Bibl/Lat
(Kaplan) "Jesus For Us Became Obedient"
[Eng/Lat] SATB,acap oct LAWSON 51428 $.30
                                     (Z123)

Go Not Far From Me, O God *see Christus E
Miserere

Jesus For Us Became Obedient *see Christus
Factus Est

ZINGG, JULIUS C.
May The Words *Purim
[Eng] TTBB TRANSCON. TCL 772 $.15   (Z124)

Shirey B'nai Jeshurun *Sab-Eve
SATB TRANSCON. TCL 767 $1.50   (Z125)

ZION HEARS HER WATCHMEN'S VOICES see Bach,
Johann Sebastian

ZION HEARS THE WATCHMEN SINGING see Buxtehude,
Dietrich, Zion Hort Die Wachter Singen

ZION HORT DIE WACHTER SINGEN see Buxtehude,
Dietrich

ZION SPEAKS see Schein, Johann Hermann, Zion
Spricht

ZION SPEAKS: I AM BY GOD FORSAKEN see Schein,
Johann Hermann

ZION SPRICHT see Schein, Johann Hermann

ZION SPRICHT: ACH, MEIN HERR UND GOTT see
Hartmann, Heinrich

ZION SPRICHT: DER HERR HAT MICH see
Hammerschmidt, Andreas

ZION SPRICHT: DER HERR HAT MICH see Scheidt,
Samuel

ZION SPRICHT: DER HERR HAT MICH see Staden,
Johann

ZION SPRICHT: DER HERR HAT MICH VERLASSEN see
Calvisius, Sethus

ZION SPRICHT: DER HERR HAT MICH VERLASSEN see
Dulichius, Philippus

ZION SPRICHT: DER HERR HAT MICH VERLASSEN see
Scheidt, Samuel

ZION SPRICHT: DER HERR HAT MICH VERLASSEN see
Schein, Johann Hermann

ZION SPRICHT: DER HERR HAT MICH VERLASSEN see
Schutz, Heinrich

ZION SPRICHT: DER HERR HAT MICH VERLASSEN see
Weckmann, Matthais

ZION'S CHILDREN *spir
see Eight Negro Spirituals: Book I
(Holloway) SA oct SPRATT 210 $.25   (Z126)

ZIONS KLAGE UND TROSTUNG see Staempfli, Edward

ZION'S LAMENT AND CONSOLATION see Staempfli,
Edward, Zions Klage Und Trostung

ZION'S SOLDIER
(Shaw; Parker) mix cor,acap oct LAWSON 908
$.30   (Z127)

ZION'S WALLS see Dawson

ZIPP, FRIEDRICH (1914-   )
Aber Des Herrn Wort Bleibt
see Kleine Spruchmotte

ZIPP, FRIEDRICH (cont'd.)

Alle Eure Sorge Werfet Auf Ihn
  see Kleine Spruchmotte

Allein Gott In Der Hoh
  oee Zipp, Friedrich, Herr Jesu Christ, Dich
  Zu Uns Wend

Come, Hasten, Ye Shepherds *Xmas,cant
  jr cor/treb cor,3rec/3fl,opt bells,
  triangle sc CONCORDIA 97-4727 $1.50, cor
  pts CONCORDIA 97-4762 $.30, ipa (Z128)

Da Jesus In Den Garten Ging *Psntd
  [Ger] SATB,acap (med) MULLER MS 13 s.p.
                                      (Z129)

Darum Spricht Der Herr, Herr
  see Sechs Motetten-Heft 1

Das Volk, So Im Finstern Wandelt *mot
  SAB HANSSLER 7.015 s.p.   (Z130)

Der Geist Des Herrn Erfullet Den Erdkreis
  SAB HANSSLER .028 s.p.   (Z131)

Des Menschen Sohn Ist Nicht Gekommen
  SAB HANSSLER 7.038 s.p.   (Z132)

Die Weihnachtsgeschichte *Xmas
  [Ger] SA/jr cor,2fl,vcl, xylophone or
  glockenspiel, triangle (easy) BAREN.
  BA 2894 sc $2.75, cor pts $1.00, ipa
                                      (Z133)

Erhore Uns Nach Der Wunderbaren Gerechtigkeit
  see Sechs Motetten-Heft 1

Erneure Mich, O Ewigs Licht
  SAA/SAT HANSSLER 6.012 s.p. contains also:
  Gruber, Erich, Wunderbarer Konig,
  Herrscher Von Uns Allen   (Z134)

Erschienen Ist Der Herrlich Tag *cant
  SAB,org/4brass HANSSLER 10.059 sc s.p., voc
  sc s.p.   (Z135)

Es Ist Vollbracht *Psntd
  [Ger] SATB,acap (med easy) MULLER
  SM 1162, 1163 s.p.   (Z136)

Es Kommt Ein Schiff Geladen *Xmas
  wom cor&jr cor TONGER s.p.   (Z137)

Freue Dich Sehr, Du Tochter Zion *mot
  SATB HANSSLER   3.064 s.p. (Z138)

Freut Euch, Ihr Lieben Christen
  see Gumpeltzhaimer, Adam, Nun Freuet Euch,
  Ihr Arm Und Reich

Frolocket Mit Handen, Alle Volker *mot
  SATB HANSSLER 7.016 s.p.   (Z139)

Geh Aus, Mein Herz, Und Suche Freud *Gen
  [Ger] mix cor&jr cor,fl,perc,inst (med
  easy) MULLER SM 1275 sc s.p., cor pts
  s.p.   (Z140)

Gelobet Seist Du, Jesu Christ *cant
  SATB,cont&org/4brass HANSSLER 10.058 sc
  s.p., cor pts s.p.   (Z141)

Gott Ist Liebe
  see Kleine Spruchmotte

Herr, Die Wasserstrome Erheben Sich
  see Sechs Motetten-Heft 1

Herr Gott, Durch Deine Speis
  SS/TT,org HANSSLER 7.029 s.p.   (Z142)

Herr Jesu Christ, Dich Zu Uns Wend
  SA/SAB/SATB/SA&SATB,org HANSSLER 6.019 s.p.
  contains also: Allein Gott In Der Hoh
  (SA/SATB/SATB,org)   (Z143)

Ist Gott Fur Mich *cant
  SSATTB&SATB&cong,ST soli,org,brass,timp
  HANSSLER 10.100 sc s.p., voc sc s.p., ipa
                                      (Z144)

Ist Gott Fur Mich, So Trete *cant
  SATB&cong,4-6brass,opt timp HANSSLER 10.107
  sc s.p., cor pts s.p.   (Z145)

Ist Gott Fur Uns, Wer Mag Wider Uns Sein
  see Sechs Motetten-Heft 2

Kleine Spruchmotte *mot
  SSA HANSSLER 7.027 s.p.
  contains: Aber Des Herrn Wort Bleibt;
  Alle Eure Sorge Werfet Auf Ihn; Gott
  Ist Liebe   (Z146)

Konig, Dem Kein Konig Gleichet *Gen,mot
  [Ger] SATB,2vln,vcl (med) BAREN. BA 3394
  s.p.   (Z147)
  [Ger] 2 eq voices/unis men cor,opt 2inst
  (med) BAREN. BA 3394 s.p.   (Z148)

Lob Gott Getrost Mit Singen *No.205, cant
  [Ger] 3pt mix cor,org,2vln,vcl BAREN.
  EM 127 sc s.p., cor pts s.p., ipa see
  from EVANGELISCHES KIRCHENGESANGBUCH
                                      (Z149)

  Hobet Den Herrn, Alle Heiden
  2-5pt/SATB,inst HANSSLER 7.030 s.p. (Z150)

Machet Die Tore Weit *Adv,cant/mot
  SAB HANSSLER 7.017 s.p.   (Z151)
  mix cor/eq voices,org/pno,fl,strings GERIG
  381 sc s.p., voc sc s.p., ipa   (Z152)

Mein Herz, Was Dir Begegnen *Gen
  [Ger] SATB,acap (easy) MULLER SM 1162, 63
  s.p.   (Z153)

Iit Freuden Zart
  [Ger] TTBB,acap (med easy) MULLER SM 499
  s.p. see from Zwei Osterlieder   (Z154)

Nehmt Wahr Das Licht *Nunc
  SATB HANSSLER 7.091 s.p.   (Z155)

O Tod, Wo Ist Dein Stachel Nun
  [Ger] TTBB,acap (med easy) MULLER SM 498
  s.p. see from Zwei Osterlieder   (Z156)

ZIPP, FRIEDRICH (cont'd.)

Praise The Almighty, My Soul, Adore Him *Gen
  SAB,acap (easy) oct CONCORDIA 98-1086 $.25
                                      (Z157)

Sechs Motetten-Heft 1 *mot
  SATB HANSSLER 7.109 s.p.
  contains: Darum Spricht Der Herr, Herr;
  Erhore Uns Nach Der Wunderbaren
  Gerechtigkeit; Herr, Die Wasserstrome
  Erheben Sich   (Z158)

Sechs Motetten-Heft 2 *mot
  SATB HANSSLER 7.110 s.p.
  contains: Ist Gott Fur Uns, Wer Mag Wider
  Uns Sein; Sei Nur Stille Zu Gott, Meine
  Seele; Was Kein Auge Gesehen Hat   (Z159)

Sei Lob Und Ehr Dem Hochsten Gut *cant
  SATB&cong,org,5brass,strings HANSSLER
  10.083 sc $6.00, cor pts $.80, ipa (Z160)

Sei Nur Stille Zu Gott, Meine Seele
  see Sechs Motetten-Heft 2

Singet Frisch Und Wohlgemut *Xmas
  wom cor&jr cor TONGER s.p.   (Z161)

Such, Wer Da Will, Ein Ander Ziel *Epiph,
  cant
  [Ger] SATB&cong,4trp,2trom,opt drums (med)
  BAREN. BA 2633 sc $3.50, cor pts $.65,
  ipa   (Z162)

Wach Auf, Wach Auf, Du Deutsches Land *cant
  SATB&cong,5-7brass HANSSLER 10.119 sc s.p.,
  cor pts s.p.   (Z163)

Wachet Auf, Ruft Uns Die Stimme *ECY
  [Ger] 3pt mix cor/4pt mix cor,org,trp,opt
  2trp&2trom BAREN. BA 3176 $1.00   (Z164)

Wake, Awake, For Night Is Flying *Adv/ECY/
  Gen
  SAB,acap (med easy) oct CONCORDIA 98-1104
  $.25   (Z165)

Was Kein Auge Gesehen Hat
  see Sechs Motetten-Heft 2

Wenn Eure Sunde Gleich
  mix cor HANSSLER 5.172 s.p.   (Z166)

Wir Gingen Alle In Die Irre, Ausgabe A
  *Psntd,Bibl
  [Ger] 2 eq voices,org BAREN. EM 130 s.p.
                                      (Z167)

Wir Gingen Alle In Die Irre, Ausgabe B
  *Psntd,Bibl
  [Ger] 2 eq voices,org,strings BAREN.
  EM 130A s.p.   (Z168)

Zwei Osterlieder *see Mit Freuden Zart; O
  Tod, Wo Ist Dein Stachel Nun   (Z169)

ZITHER CAROL
  see Two Folk Carols

ZOCHARTI LOCH see Lewandowski, Louis

ZOETE KINDETJE, WEET GIJ WEL see Appeldoorn,
  [Dina]

ZOLL, PAUL (1907-   )
  Herr Der Welten-Herr Der Menschen *Gen,cant
  [Ger] cor&men cor,A/Bar solo,org,brass,opt
  strings,drums (med) MULLER SM 2566 s.p.
                                      (Z170)

ZOLLER, ALFRED HANS (1928-   )
  Erd Und Himmel Sollen Singen *Gen,spir
  [Ger] unis,acap (easy) BOSSE BE 257 s.p.
                                      (Z171)

  Gott Ist Da (Ich Habe Lange Verzweifelt
  Gefragt) *Gen
  [Ger] unis,acap (easy) BOSSE BE 257 s.p.
                                      (Z172)

  Herr, Lass Uns Dich Loben *Gen
  [Ger] 1-3pt,acap BOSSE BE 262 s.p. (Z173)

  Lass Uns Spuren, Dass Du Bist *Gen
  [Ger] unis,acap (easy) BOSSE BE 251 s.p.
                                      (Z174)

  Stern Uber Bethlehem *Xmas
  [Ger] SATB,fl,bvl (easy) BOSSE BE 245 s.p.
                                      (Z175)

ZONDAG see Rontgen, [Julius]

ZOOALS 'T HERT DORST see Mendelssohn-Bartholdy,
  Felix

ZORITA, NICOSIA (? -ca. 1589)
  Children Of The Hebrews, The *see Pueri
  Hebraeorum

  Pueri Hebraeorum *Easter/Lent
  (Martens, Mason) "Children Of The Hebrews,
  The" SATB oct WALTON 2100 $.30   (Z176)

ZU BETHLEHEM GEBOREN *Xmas
  (Track) "In Bethlehem Love Is Born" 2pt oct
  PRO ART 2479 $.25   (Z177)

ZU BETHLEHEM GEBOREN see Anonymous

    ZU BETHLEHEM GEBOREN see Barthel, Ursula

ZU BETHLEHEM GEBOREN see Cybinski, J.

ZU BETHLEHEM GEBOREN see Pepping, Ernst

ZU BETHLEHEM GEBOREN see Raphael, Gunther

ZU BETHLEHEM GEBOREN see Rein, Walter

ZU BETHLEHEM GEBOREN see Weber, Bernhard

ZU BETHLEHEM GEBOREN IST UNS see Trust, Heinz-
  Ewald

ZU DEN FUSSEN JESU see Ruppel, Paul Ernst

ZU DIESER OSTERLICHEN ZEIT see Eccard, Johannes

ZU DIESER OSTERLICHEN ZEIT see Grimm, Heinrich

ZU DIESER OSTERLICHEN ZEIT see Eccard, Johannes

ZU DIESER OSTERLICHEN ZEIT see Eccard, Johannes

ZU DIR HEB ICH DIE AUGEN AUF see Schwarz,
  Jochen

ZU DIR ICH MEIN HERZ ERHEBE see Praetorius,
  Michael

ZU DIR VON HERZENSGRUNDE RUF ICH see Lassus,
  Roland de (Orlandus)

ZU GOTTES EHRE MEIN SAITENSPIEL see Ruppel,
  Paul Ernst

ZU GUTER NACHT *CC10U,Gen
  (Ameln, Konrad; Thomas, Wilhelm) [Ger] SATB,
  acap (easy) BAREN. BA 415 $1.50 evening
  songs by: Schutz; Heugel; Osiander; Schein;
  Calvisius; Steier; Altenburg   (Z178)

ZU OSTERN LIESS MIR'S KEINE RUH see Weber,
  Bernhard

ZU SANG UND TANZ see Handel, George Frideric,
  To Song And Dance

ZU SEINEN ZEITEN see Dedekind, Constantine
  Christian

ZUCCHINI, GREGORIO
  Haec Dies
  (Wilhelm) SATB oct LAWSON 51657 $.30 (Z179)

ZUCCOLI, GASTONE
  Canto Di Natale *Xmas
  unis ZANIBON 1322 s.p.   (Z180)

  Missa S. Francisci Assisiensis *Mass
  [Lat] SATB,org sc ZANIBON 4821 s.p., voc pt
  ZANIBON 4822-4825 s.p.   (Z181)

  Sanctus Et Benedictus (from Messa Mater
  Divinae Gratiae) Bene/Sanctus
  [Lat] SATB,org sc ZANIBON 2304 s.p., voc pt
  ZANIBON 2304-A-B-C-D s.p.   (Z182)

  Tre Laudi Alla SS. Vergine Maria *CC3U,BVM
  [Lat] unis mix cor,org ZANIBON 3295 s.p.
                                      (Z183)

ZUCHINO
  Ave Maria
  (Hunter) [Lat] dbl cor,acap MARKS 4425 $.35
                                      (Z184)

ZULETZT, MEINE BRUDER, SEID STARK IN DEM HERRN
  see Reda, Siegfried

ZUM BETTAG see Mader, Rud

ZUM JAHRRESSCHLUSS
  (Bamer, Alfred) wom cor,acap oct DOBLINGER
  s.p. see also Sechs Geistliche Chore (Z185)

ZUM JUBILAUM EINES GEISTLICHEN ODER LEHRERS see
  Nagler, F.

ZUM NEUEN JAHR see Jacot, Andre

ZUM OFFERTORIUM see Schubert, Franz (Peter)

ZUM PALMSONNTAG see Schieri, Fritz

ZUM PASSIONSSONNTAG see Schieri, Fritz

ZUM SANCTUS see Schubert, Franz (Peter), Helig,
  Helig, Helig

ZUM SEHEN GEBOREN see Lissmann, Kurt

ZUM TAG DER ARBEIT see Weismann, Wilhelm

ZUM TOTENSONNTAG see Weismann, Wilhelm

ZUND AN DAS LICHT see Weber, Bernhard

ZUNDEL, [JOHN] (1815-1882)
  Love Divine
  (Cain) SATB FLAMMER A 5132 $.30   (Z186)
  (Kay) SATB,org oct MCA   (Z187)

  Love Divine, All Love Excelling
  (De Vito) SSA oct PRO ART 1671 $.20 (Z188)

ZUR EINWEISUNG EINES GEISTLICHEN ODER LEHRERS
  see Nagler, F.

ZUR GLOCKENWEIHE see Messner, Karl

ZUR HEILIGEN NACHT see Woll, Erna

ZUR KOMMUNION
  see Die Einsetzungsworte

ZUR KONFIRMATION see Aeschbacher, Walther

ZUR KONFIRMATION see Schmid, Walter

ZUR KONFIRMATION see Wanner, J.G.

ZUR KONFIRMATION see Widmer, A.

ZUR STILLEN NACHT see Lahusen, Christian

ZUTPHEN, TH. V.
  Psalm 46
  men cor ALSBACH&D sc s.p., cor pts s.p.
                                      (Z189)
  mix cor ALSBACH&D sc s.p., cor pts s.p.
                                      (Z190)

ZUVERSICHT see Kirschnereit, Kurt

ZWANZIG RESPONSORIEN-HEFT 1 see Reger, Max

ZWANZIG RESPONSORIEN-HEFT 2 see Reger, Max

ZWANZIG RESPONSORIEN-HEFT 3 see Reger, Max

ZWANZIG RESPONSORIEN-HEFT 4 see Reger, Max

ZWANZIG RESPONSORIEN-HEFT 5 see Reger, Max

ZWART, JAN
  Kerstcantata *cant
  jr cor,Mez solo,org ALSBACH&D sc s.p., cor
  pts s.p.   (Z191)

  O Gij Mijn Troost *hymn
  wom cor,4 soli ALSBACH&D sc s.p., cor pts
  s.p.   (Z192)
  wom cor,4 soli ALSBACH&D sc s.p., cor pts

ZWART, JAN (cont'd.)

    s.p.   (Z193)

ZWEEN DER JUNGER GEHN MIT SEHNEN see Wenzel,
    Eberhard

ZWEERS, [BERNARD] (1854-1924)
    De Kosmos (Psalm 104)
      mix cor,kbd ALSBACH&D sc s.p., cor pts s.p.
                            (Z194)

    Psalm 104 *see De Kosmos

ZWEI ABENDLIEDER see Schnitzler, Heinrich

ZWEI ALTE WEIHNACHTSLIEDER *see Alttiroler
    Weihnachtslied; Slowakisches Weihnachtslied
                            (Z195)

ZWEI ALTOSTERREICHISCHE WEIHNACHTSLIEDER see
    Liebe, Kurt Maria

ZWEI AUGEN HAT DIE SEEL see Hohlfeld, Christoph

ZWEI CHORALE ZUR TRAUUNG see Weber, Bernhard

ZWEI CHORALE see Muller, Paul

ZWEI CHORALMOTETTEN see Burkhart, Franz

ZWEI CHORALMOTETTEN *see Da Jesus In Den
    Garten Ging; Und Unserer Lieben Fraue
                            (Z196)

ZWEI CHORALSATZE FUR ADVENT UND WEIHNACHTEN see
    Kaufmann, Diethelm

ZWEI CHORE ZUR WEIHNACHT see Barthel, Ursula

ZWEI CHORE ZUR WEIHNACHT see Giefer, Willy

ZWEI DER SERAPHIM SIE RIEFEN see Gallus,
    Jacobus

ZWEI DEUTSCHE PSALMEN see Romanovsky, Erich

ZWEI EINFACHE GRABGESANGE see Flemming, F.

ZWEI ERNSTE GESANGE see Sendt, Willy

ZWEI GEISTLICHE CHORE see Bauernfiend, Hans

ZWEI GEISTLICHE CHORE see Kratochwill, Heinrich

ZWEI GEISTLICHE CHORE see Mendelssohn-
    Bartholdy, Felix

ZWEI GEISTLICHE GESANGE see Weber, Ludwig

ZWEI GESANGE VON GOTT see Muller, Paul

ZWEI GRABCHORALE see Hollfelder, Waldram

ZWEI HOCHZEITSLIEDER see Burkhart, Franz

ZWEI HYMNEN see Trexler, Georg

ZWEI HYMNEN see Trexler, Georg

ZWEI HYMNISCHE GESANGE see Weismann, Wilhelm

ZWEI KIRCHLICHE LIEDER see Schmid, Walter

ZWEI KLEINE CHORALMOTETTEN see Heilmann, Harald

ZWEI KLEINE OSTERKONZERTE see Grimm, Heinrich

ZWEI KLEINE SPRUCHMOTETTEN see Stahmer, Klaus

ZWEI KLEINE WEIHNACHTSKONZERTE see Grimm,
    Heinrich

ZWEI KLEINE WEIHNACHTSMOTETTEN see Mendelssohn,
    Arnold

ZWEI KREUZE see Krenger, R.

ZWEI KURZMESSEN see Selle, Thomas

ZWEI KURZMESSEN see Thiele, Siegfried

ZWEI LIEDER NACH CHORALSATZEN see Bach, Johann
    Sebastian

ZWEI LIEDER ZUM HEILIGEN CHRISTFEST see
    Schrenk, Johannes

ZWEI MARIENLIEDER see Muller, A.M.

ZWEI MARIENLIEDER see Muller, A.M.

ZWEI MARIENMOTETTEN see Senfl, Ludwig

ZWEI MESSEN see Haydn, (Johann) Michael

ZWEI MOTETTEN see David, Johann Nepomuk

ZWEI MOTETTEN [OP.29] see Brahms, Johannes

ZWEI MOTETTEN [OP.74] see Brahms, Johannes

ZWEI MOTETTEN see Bach, Johann Ludwig

ZWEI MOTETTEN see David, Johann Nepomuk

ZWEI NEGRO-SPIRITUALS *see Deep River; Go Tell
    It On The Mountains   (Z197)

ZWEI OSTER-MOTETTEN see Schaper, Heinz-
    Christian

ZWEI OSTERLICHE ZWIEGESANGE
    (Stern, A.) [Lat] wom cor,acap HUG s.p.
      contains: Hassler, Hans Leo, Crucifixus
        Etiam; Praetorius, Michael, Benedicamus
        Domino
      see also: Hassler, Hans Leo, Crucifixus;
        Praetorius, Michael, Benedicamus (Z198)

ZWEI OSTERLIEDER see Zipp, Friedrich

ZWEI PASSIONMOTETTEN see Kropfreiter,
    Augustinius Franz

ZWEI PASSIONS-MOTETTEN see Spar, Otto

ZWEI PASSIONSLIEDER AUS FRANKEN see Mockel,
    Franz

ZWEI PSALM-MOTETTEN see Bornefeld, Helmut

ZWEI PSALMEN see Des Prez, Josquin

ZWEI PSALMEN see Holtz, J.

ZWEI PSALMEN see Schmid, Walter

ZWEI PSALMEN see Stockmeier, Wolfgang

ZWEI PSALMEN see Vivaldi, Antonio

ZWEI QUODLIBETS see Grofe

ZWEI SCHLESISCHE WEIHNACHTSLIEDER see Haus,
    Karl

ZWEI SPRUCHTEXTE AUF DAS EVANGELIUM see Jacobi,
    Samuel

ZWEI TAG HAT ER GELEGEN see Peter, Herbert

ZWEI TRAUERCHORALE see Lang, Hans

ZWEI TRAUERCHORALE see Lang, Hans

ZWEI WEIHNACHTLICHE LIEDKANTATEN see Fegers,
    Karl

ZWEI WEIHNACHTSLEIDER see Katt, Leopold

ZWEI WEIHNACHTSLIEDER *see Josef, Lieber Josef
    Mein; Kindelein Zart   (Z199)

ZWEI WEIHNACHTSLIEDER see Cadow, Paul

ZWEI WEIHNACHTSLIEDER oee Nitsche, Paul

ZWEI WEIHNACHTSLIEDER see Rothschuh, F.

ZWEI WEIHNACHTSLIEDER *see Die Hirten; Susani
                            (Z200)

ZWEI WEIHNACHTSMOTETTEN see Stockmeier,
    Wolfgang

ZWEIERLEI BITT ICH VON DIR see Hammerschmidt,
    Andreas

ZWEITER NACHTRAG ZUR GESAMTUSGABE-BAND XXXI see
    Palestrina, Giovanni

ZWIEGESANGE, HEFT 1: DER JAHRESKREIS see
    Praetorius, Michael

ZWIEGESANGE, HEFT 2: DER TAGES KREIS see
    Praetorius, Michael

ZWIERZCHOWSKI, MATEUSZ
    Requiem *Pol
      (Dabrowski, F.) 4pt mix cor,soli,cont,inst
      POLSKIE ZHMP14 s.p.   (Z201)

ZWINGLI
    Lord, We Cry To Thee *Gen/Lent
      (Dickinson) SATB oct GRAY GSC 212 $.25
                            (Z202)

ZWINGLI, HULDREICH (1484-1531)
    Herr, Nun Selbst Den Wagen Halt
      see Praetorius, Michael, Sie Ist Mir Lieb,
      Die Werte Magd

ZWINGLI-LIEDER *CCU
    (Stern, Alfred) [Ger] 2-4pt mix cor HUG s.p.
                            (Z203)

ZWINGT DIE SAITEN IN CYTHARA see Bach, Johann
    Sebastian

ZWISCHEN OCHS UND ESELEIN see Lissmann, Kurt

ZWISCHEN OCHS UND ESELEIN see Sturmer, Bruno

ZWOLF ADVENTS- UND WEIHNACHTSLIEDER see Weiss,
    Ewald

ZWOLF ALTDEUTSCHE WEIHNACHTSLIEDER see
    Mendelssohn, Arnold

ZWOLF GEISTLICHE GESANGE see Schutz, Heinrich

ZWOLF GEISTLICHE GESANGE-1657 see Schutz,
    Heinrich

ZWOLF GEISTLICHE LIEDER PAUL GERHARDTS see
    Ebeling, Johann Georg

ZWOLF GEISTLICHE UND WELTLICHE WERKE see Dufay,
    Guillaume

ZWOLF HEILIGE DINGE see Noble, Felix de

ZWOLF KANONISCHE CHORALE see Reda, Siegfried

ZWOLF MUTTERGOTTESLIEDER see Schabasser, Joseph

ZWOLF SPRUCHMOTETTEN see Raphael, Gunther

ZWOLF WEIHNACHTLICHE KANONS see Jochum, Otto

ZWOLF WURZELN UND ZWOLF FRUCHTE see Beckerath,
    Alfred von

ZWYSSIG, [ALBERICH] (1808-1854)
    Schweizerpsalm
      [Ger] mix cor,acap (easy) HUG s.p. (Z204)

Publishers and Addresses

The list of publishers which follows contains the code assigned for each publisher, the name and address of the publisher, and agents who distribute their publications. The list is for Volume I and Volume II of *Choral Music In Print*.

Code	Publisher	Agent
ABINGDON	Abingdon Press 201 Eighth Ave. S. Nashville, TN 37202	
AGAPE	Agape 380 S. Main Place Carol Stream, IL 60187	
ALBERSEN	Muziekhandel Albersen & Co.	DONEMUS
ALBERT	J. Albert & Son Pty. Ltd. 139 King Street Sydney, N.S.W. Australia 2000	
ALCOVE	Alcove Music	WESTERN
ALFRED	Alfred Publishing Co., Inc. 75 Channel Drive Port Washington, NY 11050	
ALLANS	Allans Music Pty. Ltd. 276 Collins Street Melbourne, Australia	
ALLYN	Allyn & Bacon, Inc. Boston, MA 02210	
ALPHENAAR	W. Alphenaar	DONEMUS
ALSBACH	G. Alsbach & Co.	DONEMUS
ALSBACH & D	Alsbach & Doyer	PETERS
AM. INST. MUS.	American Institute of Musiology	HANSSLER
AM. MUS. ED.	American Music Edition	BOONIN
AMP	AMP 609 Fifth Avenue New York, NY 10017	
AMICI	Gli Amici della Musica da Camera Via Bocca di Leone 25 Rome, Italy	
AMPHION	Editions Amphion	BELWIN
APOGEE	Apogee Press, Inc.	WORLD
ARCO	Arco Music Publishers	WESTERN
ARION	Coleccion Arion	MEXICANAS
ARNOLD	Edward Arnold Series	NOVELLO
ARS NOVA	Ars Nova	DONEMUS
ARTIA	Artia	BOOSEY-CAN
ARTRANSA	Artransa Music	WESTERN
ASHDOWN	Edwin Ashdown Ltd.	BOOSEY-CAN
	Associated Music Publishers see AMP	
AUGSBURG	Augsburg Publishing House 426 S. Fifth Street Minneapolis, MN 55415	
AVANT	Avant Music	WESTERN
BANK	Annie Bank	DONEMUS
BAREN.	Bärenreiter Verlag Heinrich-Schütz-Allee 29 3500 Kassel-Wilhelmshöhe Germany	BOONIN MAGNAMUSIC
BASART	Les Editions Internationales Basart	GENERAL
BELAIEFF	M.P. Belaieff	PETERS
BELMONT	Belmont Music Publishers P.O. Box 49961 Los Angeles, CA 90049	
BELWIN	Belwin-Mills Publishing Corp. Melville, NY 11746	
BERANDOL	Berandol Music Ltd.	AMP
BERBEN	Edizioni Musicali Berben	PRESSER
BERGMANS	W. Bergmans	DONEMUS
BERLIN	Irving Berlin Music Corp. 1290 Avenue of the Americas New York, NY 10019	
BERNOUILLI	Ed. Bernouilli	DONEMUS
BEZIGE BIJ	De Bezige Bij	DONEMUS
BIG 3	Big 3 Music Corp. 1350 Avenue of the Americas New York, NY 10019	
BIRNBACH	Richard Birnbach Dürerstrasse 28a 1 Berlin-Lichterfelde-West Germany	
BOMART	Bomart Music Publications	AMP
BOONIN	Joseph Boonin, Inc. P.O. Box 2124 S. Hackensack, NJ 07606	
BOOSEY	Boosey & Hawkes, Inc. Oceanside, NY 11572	
BOOSEY CAN	Boosey & Hawkes Ltd. 279 Yorkland Blvd. Willowdale, Ontario Canada	BOOSEY
BOOSEY-ENG	Boosey & Hawkes	BOOSEY
BOOSE	Gustav Bosse Verlag Postfach 417 84 Regensbury 2 Germany	MAGNAMUSIC
BOSTON	Boston Music Company	FRANK
BOSWORTH	Bosworth & Company, Ltd. 14/18 Heddon Street Regent Street London, W.1, England	

Code	Publisher	Agent
BOTE	Bote & Bock	AMP
BOURNE	Bourne Co. 136 West 52 Street New York, NY 10019	
BRANDEN	Branden Press, Inc. 221 Columbus Avenue Boston, MA 02116	
BREITKOPF-L	Breitkopf & Härtel, Leipzig	AMP
BREITKOPF-W	Breitkopf & Härtel, Wiesbaden	AMP
BRIGHT STAR	Bright Star Music Pubications	WESTERN
BRODT	Brodt Music Co. P.O. Box 1207 Charlotte, NC 28201	
BROEKMANS	Broekmans & Van Poppel	PETERS
BROGNEAUX	Editions Musicales Brogneaux	ELKAN, H
BROUDE, A.	Alexander Broude, Inc. 225 West 57 Street New York, NY 10019	
BROUDE BR.	Broude Brothers Ltd. 56 West 45 Street New York, NY 10036	
BROWN	Brown University Choral Series	BOOSEY
BUDAPEST	Editio Musica Budapest P.O.B. 322 Budapest, Hungary	BOOSEY-CAN
CAILLET	Lucien Cailliet	SOUTHERN
CAPELLA	Capella Music, Inc.	BOURNE
CARISH	Carisch S.p.A. Via General Fara, 39 20124 Milan, Italy	BAREN.
CARLTON	Carlton Musikverlag	GERIG
CBDM	Centre Belge De Documentation Musicale	ELKAN, H
CHANT	Editions Le Chant Du Monde 64, rue Ampere Paris, France	
CHAPPELL	Chappell & Co., Inc. 609 Fifth Avenue New York, NY 10017	
CHAPPELL-FR	Chappell S.A. 25, rue d'Hauteville Paris, France	
CHARTER	Charter Publications, Inc. Valley Forge, PA 19481	
CHESTER	J. & W. Chester, Ltd.	SCHIRM. G
CHOUDENS	Choudens	PETERS
CHURCH	John Church Co.	PRESSER
COLE	M. M. Cole Publishing Co. 251 East Grand Avenue Chicago, IL 60611	
COLOMBO	Franco Colombo Publications	BELWIN
COMP/PERF	Composer/Performer Edition 2101 22 Street Sacramento, CA 95818	
CONCERT	Concert Music Publishing Co.	BOURNE
CONCORD	Concord Music Publishing Co.	ELKAN, H

Code	Publisher	Agent
CONCORDIA	Concordia Publishing House 3558 S. Jefferson Avenue St. Louis, MO 63118	
CONSORTIUM	Consortium Musical	ELKAN-V
CRAMER	J.B. Cramer & Co., Ltd.	LESLIE
CRES.-NETH	Uitg. Crescendo	DONEMUS
CRESCENDO	Crescendo Music Sales Co. Box 395 Naperville, IL 60540	
CRITERION	Criterion Music Corp. 6124 Selma Avenue Hollywood, CA 90028	
CURCI	Edizioni Curci Galleria del Corso 4 20122 Milan, Italy	
CURWEN	J. Curwen & Sons	SCHIRM. G
CZECH	Czechoslovak Music Information Centre Besedni 3 Prague 1, Czechoslovakia	
DA CAPO	Da Capo Press, Inc. 227 West 17 Street New York, NY 10011	
DELRIEU	Georges Delrieu & Cie	GALAXY
DEUTSCHER	Deutscher Verlag für Musik	AMP
DITSON	Oliver Ditson Co.	PRESSER
DOBLINGER	Ludwig Doblinger Verlag	AMP
DONEMUS	Stichting Donemus	PETERS
DRUSTVO	Drustvo Slovenskih Skladateljev	
DRZAVNA	Drzavna Zalozba Slovenije	DRUSTVO
DURAND	Durand & Cie	ELKAN-V
ECK	Van Eck & Zn.	DONEMUS
EIGEN UITGAVE	Eigen Uitgave van de Componist	DONEMUS
ELKAN, H	Henri Elkan Music Publisher 1316 Walnut Street Philadelphia, PA 19107	
ELKAN-V	Elkan-Vogel, Inc. Presser Place Bryn Mawr, PA 19010	
ELKIN	Elkin & Co. Ltd.	GALAXY
ENOCH	Enoch & Cie	AMP
ERDMANN	Rudolf Erdmann, Musikverlag Adolfsallee 34 62 Wiesbaden, Germany	
ESCHIG	Editions Max Eschig	AMP
ESSO	Van Esso & Co.	DONEMUS
EULENBURG	Edition Eulenburg	PETERS
EXPERIMENTAL	Experimental Music Catalogue 208 Ladbroke Grove London, W.10, England	
FABER	Faber Music Ltd.	SCHIRM. G
FAR WEST	Far West Music	WESTERN
FAZER	Musik Fazer Aleksanterinkatu 11 Helsinki 11, Finland	

Code	Publisher	Agent
FEMA	Fema Music Publications	CRESCENDO
FISCHER, C	Carl Fischer 56-62 Cooper Square New York, NY 10003	
FISCHER, J	J. Fischer & Bro.	BELWIN
FLAMMER	Harold Flammer, Inc. Delaware Water Gap, PA 18327	
FOG	Dan Fog Musikforlag	PETERS
FORLIVESI	A. Forlivesi & C. Via Roma 4 Florence, Italy	
FORNI	Arnaldo Forni Editore Via Triumvirato 7 40132 Bologna, Italy	
FOSTER	Mark Foster Music Co. Box 4012 Champaign, IL 61820	
FOSTER-HALL	Foster-Hall Publications	PRESSER
FOX	Sam Fox Music Sales Corp. 1540 Broadway New York, NY 10036	
FRANCIS	Francis, Day & Hunter, Ltd.	ALBERT
FRANK	Frank Distributing Corp. 116 Boylston Street Boston, MA 02116	
GALAXY	Galaxy Music Corp. 2121 Broadway New York, NY 10023	
GALLEON	Galleon Press 94 Greenwich Ave. New York, NY 10011	
GALLIARD	Galliard, Ltd.	GALAXY
GEHRMANS	Carl Gehrmans Musikförlag Postbox 505 10126 Stockholm, Sweden	
GENERAL	General Music Publishing Co. P.O. Box 267 Hastings-on-Hudson, NY 10706	
GENTRY	Gentry Publications	PRESSER
GERIG	Musikverlag Hans Gerig Drususgasse 7-11 5 Köln, Germany	
GIA	GIA Publications 7404 S. Mason Avenue Chicago, IL 60638	
GILLMAN	Gillman Publications	PRESSER
GORNSTON	David Gornston	FOX
GRAY	H. W. Gray Co., Inc.	BELWIN
GREENWOOD	Greenwood Press	WORLD
GREGG	Gregg International Publishers 1 Westmead, Farnborough, Hants England	
	Gregorian Institute of America see GIA	
HAMELLE	Hamelle & Cie	ELKAN-V
HANSEN-DEN	Wilhelm Hansen Edition	SCHIRM. G

Code	Publisher	Agent
HANSEN-ENG	Hansen, London	ALBERT
HANSEN-US	Hansen Press 1842 West Avenue Miami Beach, FL 33139	
HANSSLER	Hänssler-Verlag	PETERS
HARMONIA	Harmonia Uitgave	PETERS
HARRIS	Frederick Harris Music Co., Ltd. P.O. Box 670 Oakville, Ontario Canada	
HART	F. Pitman Hart	LESLIE
HATIKVAH	Hatikvah Publications	TRANSCON.
HEIDELBERGER	Heidelberger	BAREN.
HEINRICH.	Heinrichshofen's Verlag	PETERS
HENLE	G. Henle Verlag Schongauerstrasse 24 8 Munich 70, Germany	
HERITAGE	Heritage Music Press	LORENZ
HEUGEL	Heugel & Cie	PRESSER
HEUWEKE.	Edition Heuwekemeijer	PETERS
HIGHGATE	Highgate Press	GALAXY
HIGHLAND	Highland Music Co. 1311 N. Highland Avenue Hollywood, CA 90028	
HINRICHSEN	Hinrichsen Edition, Ltd.	PETERS
HOFMEISTER	Friedrich Hofmeister	AMP
HOLLY-PIX	Holly-Pix Music Publishing Co.	WESTERN
HONOUR	Honour Publications	WESTERN
HUG	Hug & Company	PETERS
HUNTZINGER	R. L. Huntzinger Publications	WILLIS
ICELAND	Iceland Music Information Centre	ELKAN, H
INTERNAT.	International Music Co. 511 Fifth Avenue New York, NY 10017	
INTERNAT. S.	International Music Service Box 66, Ansonia Station New York, NY 10023	
ISRAELI	Israeli Music Publications P.O. Box 6011 Tel-Aviv, Israel	
JAPAN	Japan Federation of Composers Ohminato Building 14, Suga-Cho Shinjuku-ku Tokyo, Japan	
JEANNETTE	Ed. Jeannette	DONEMUS
JEHLE	Jehle	HANSSLER
JOBERT	Editions Jean Jobert	ELKAN-V
JOHNSON	Johnson Reprint Corp. 111 Fifth Avenue New York, NY 10003	
JUSKO	Jusko Publications	WILLIS
KALMUS	Edwin F. Kalmus Miami-Dade Industrial Park P.O. Box 1007 Opa-Locka, FL 33054	

Code	Publisher	Agent
KENDOR	Kendor Music, Inc. Delevan, NY 14042	
KENYON	Kenyon Publications	PLYMOUTH
KERBY	E. C. Kerby, Ltd.	BOONIN
KISTNER	Kistner & Siegel	TONGER
KJOS	Neil A. Kjos Music Co. 525 Busse Hwy. Park Ridge, IL 60068	
KON BOND	Kon Bond van Chr. Zangen Oratoriumverenigingen	DONEMUS
KONINKLIJK	Koninklijk Nederlands Zangersverbond	DONEMUS
KRENN	Ludwig Krenn Reindorfgasse 42 1150 Wien 15, Austria	
KROMPHOLZ	Krompholz & Co. Spitalgasse 28 3001 Bern, Switzerland	
KRUSEMAN	Ed. Philip Kruseman	DONEMUS
LAND	A. Land Ezn, Muziekuitgevers	DONEMUS
LAUDINELLA	Laudinella Reihe	HANSSLER
LAWSON	Lawson-Gould	SCHIRM. G
LEDUC	Alphonse Leduc 175, rue Saint-Honore Paris, France	
LEMOINE	Henry Lemoine & Cie	ELKAN-V
LENGNICK	Alfred Lengnick & Co., Ltd.	HARRIS
LEONARD-ENG	Leonard, Gould & Bolttler	LESLIE
LEONARD-US	Hal Leonard Music 64 E. Second Street Winona, MN 55987	
LESLIE	Leslie Music Supply	BRODT
LEUCKART	F.E.C. Leuckart	AMP
LICHTENAUER	W. F. Lichtenauer	DONEMUS
LIENAU	Robert Lienau, Musikverlag	PETERS
LILLENAS	Lillenas Publishing Co.	BELWIN
LITURGICAL	Liturgical Press St. Johns Abbey Collegeville, MN 56321	
LORENZ	Lorenz Industries 501 E. Third Street Dayton, OH 45401	
LUDWIG	Ludwig Music Publishing Co. 557-67 E. 140 Street Cleveland, OH 44110	
LUNDQUIST	Abr. Lundquist AB Katarina Bangata 17 116 25 Stockholm, Sweden	
LYCHE	Harald Lyche	PETERS
MAGNAMUSIC	Magnamusic-Baton, Inc. 6390 Delmar Blvd. St. Louis, MO 63130	
MARCHAND	Marchand, Paap en Strooker	DONEMUS
MARKS	Edward B. Marks Music Corp.	BELWIN
MCA	MCA Music	BELWIN

Code	Publisher	Agent
MCAFEE	McAfee Music Corp.	LORENZ
MEDIA	Media Press Box 895 Champaign, IL 61820	
MERCURY	Mercury Music Corp.	PRESSER
MERION	Merion Music, Inc.	PRESSER
MERRYMOUNT	Merrymount Music, Inc.	PRESSER
MEXICANAS	Ediciones Mexicanas De Musica Avenida Juarez 18 Mexico City, Mexico	
MJQ	MJQ Music, Inc.	FOX
MOECK	Hermann Moeck Verlag	BELWIN
MORAVIAN	Moravian Music Foundation	ABINGDON BELWIN BOOSEY BRODT PETERS
MOSELER	Möseler Verlag Postfach 460 3340 Wolfenbüttel Germany	
MOWBRAY	A. R. Mowbray & Co., Ltd.	PRESSER
MULLER	Willy Müller	PETERS
MUNSTER	Van Munster Editie	DONEMUS
MURPHY	Spud Murphy Publications	WESTERN
MUSIC	Music Sales Corp. 33 West 60 Street New York, NY 10023	
MUSICO	Musico Muziekuitgeverij	DONEMUS
MUSICUS	Edition Musicus P.O. Box 1341 Stamford, CT 06904	
MUSIKAL.	Musikaliska Konstföreningen	NORDISKA
MUSIKHOJ	Musikhojskolens Forlag	BOONIN
MUSIKK	Musikk-Huset A/S	PETERS
MUSIKWISS.	Musikwissenschaftlicher Verlag	BAREN. DOBLINGER
NAGELS	Nagels Verlag	AMP
NEW VALLEY	New Valley Music Press of Smith College Sage Hall 3 Northampton, MA 01060	
NIEUWE	De Nieuwe Musiekhandel	DONEMUS
NOORDHOFF	P. Noordhoff	DONEMUS
NORDISKA	AB Nordiska Musikförlaget Drottninggatan 37 Stockholm, Sweden	SCHIRM. G WALTON
NORSK	Norsk Musikforlag A/S Karl Johans Gate 39 P.O. Box 1499 Vika Oslo, Norway	
NORTON	W. W. Norton & Co., Inc. 55 Fifth Avenue New York, NY 10003	
NOSKE	A. A. Noske	DONEMUS
NOVELLO	Novello & Co., Ltd.	BELWIN

Code	Publisher	Agent
OSTARA	Ostara Press, Inc.	WESTERN
AMP	Österreichischer Bundesverlag	OSTER
OUVRIERES	Les Editions Ouvrieres	GALAXY
OXFORD	Oxford University Press 200 Madison Avenue New York, NY 10019	
PANTON	Panton	GENERAL
PARAGON	Paragon Music Publishers 71 Fourth Avenue New York, NY 10003	
PARIS	Uitgeverij H.J. Paris	DONEMUS
PATERSON	Paterson's Publications, Ltd.	FISCHER, C
PAXTON	Paxton Publications	NOVELLO
PEER	Peer-Southern Organization 1740 Broadway New York, NY 10019	
PENN STATE	Pennsylvania State University Press 215 Wagner Building University Park, PA 16802	
PETERS	C. F. Peters Corp. 373 Park Avenue South New York, NY 10016	
PHILIPPO	Editions Philippo	ELKAN-V
PILLIN	Pillin Music	WESTERN
PIONEER	Pioneer Music Press 975 SW Temple Street Salt Lake City, UT 84101	
PLENUM	Plenum Publishing Corp. 227 West 17 Street New York, NY 10011	
PLYMOUTH	Plymouth Music Co., Inc. 17 West 60 Street New York, NY 10023	
POLSKIE	Polskie Wydawnictwo Muzyczne Krakowskie Przedmiescie 7 Warsaw, Poland	
POLYPHON	Polyphon Musikverlag	GERIG
PRESSER	Theodore Presser Co. Presser Place Bryn Mawr, PA 19010	
PRIMAVERA	Editions Primavera	GENERAL
PRO ART	Pro Art Publications, Inc. 469 Union Avenue Westbury, NY 11590	
PROSVETNI	Prosvetni Servis	DRUSTVO
PROWSE	Keith Prowse Music Publishing Co. 21 Denmark Street London, W.C.2, England	
RICORDI-ARG	Ricordi Americana S.A.	BELWIN
RICORDI-ENG	G. Ricordi & Company, Ltd.	BELWIN
RICORDI-FR	Societe Anonyme des Editions Ricordi	BELWIN
RIDEAU	Les Editions Rideau Rouge	ELKAN-V
ROBBINS	Robbins Music Corp.	BIG 3
ROBERTON	Roberton Publications The Windmill Wendover, Aylesbury, Bucks England	BOOSEY-CAN
ROCHESTER	Rochester Music Publishers, Inc. 358 Aldrich Road Fairport, NY 14450	
RONGWEN	Rongwen Music, Inc.	BROUDE BR.
ROSSUM	Wed. J. R. van Rossum	DONEMUS
ROUART	Rouart-Lerolle & Cie	SALABERT-US
ROYAL	Royal School of Church Music Addington Place Croydon, Surrey England	
ROZSAVO.	Rozsavölgyi & Co.	DONEMUS
RUBANK	Rubank, Inc. 16215 N.W. 15 Avenue Miami, FL 33169	
SACRED	Sacred Music Press	LORENZ
SALABERT-FR	Francis Salabert Editions 22 rue Chauchat Paris 9, France	
SALABERT-US	Edition Salabert, Inc. 575 Madison Avenue New York, NY 10022	
SAMFUNDET	Samfundet til udgivelse af dansk Musik	PETERS
SANTIS	Edizioni de Santis Via Cassia 13 00191 Rome, Italy	
SCHIRM. EC	E. C. Schirmer Music Co. 112 South Street Boston, MA 02111	
SCHIRM. G	G. Schirmer, Inc. 609 Fifth Avenue New York, NY 10017	
SCHMITT	Schmitt, Hall & McCreary Co. 110 N. Fifth Street Minneapolis, MN 55403	
SCHOTT	Schott & Co., Ltd.	BELWIN
SCHOTTS	B. Schotts Söhne	BELWIN
SCHWEIZER.	Schweizerischen Kirchengesangsbundes	HANSSLER
SCOTT	G. Scott Music Publishing Co.	WESTERN
SCREEN	Screen Gems P.O. Box 488 6744 N.E. Fourth Avenue Miami, FL 33138	
SEESAW	Seesaw Music Corporation 177 East 87 Street New York, NY 10028	
SENART	Ed. Maurice Senart	SALABERT-US
SHAPIRO	Shapiro, Bernstein & Co.	PLYMOUTH
SHAWNEE	Shawnee Press	FLAMMER
SHEPPARD	John Sheppard Music Press	BOONIN
SIFLER	Paul J. Sifler 3947 Fredonia Drive Hollywood, CA 90028	

Code	Publisher	Agent	Code	Publisher	Agent
SIKORSKI	Hans Sikorski Verlag	BELWIN	UNIV. CAL	University of California Press 2223 Fulton Street Berkeley, CA 94720	
SIMROCK	N. Simrock, A. Benjamin, D. Rahter	AMP	UNIV. CH	University of Chicago Press 5801 S. Ellis Avenue Chicago, IL 60637	
SIRIUS	Sirius-Verlag	PETERS	UNIV. NC	University of North Carolina Press Box 2288 Chapel Hill, NC 27514	
SKAND.	Skandinavisk Musikforlag Gothersgade 9-11, 1123 Copenhagen, Denmark		UNIVER.	Universal Edition	PRESSER
SLOV. AKA.	Slovenska akademija znanosti in umetnosti	DRUSTVO	UP WITH	Up With People Music	LORENZ
SLOV. MAT.	Slovenska Matica	DRUSTVO	VALANDO	Valando Music, Inc.	PLYMOUTH
SOUTHERN	Southern Music Co. 1100 Broadway San Antonio, TX 78292		VIEWEG	Chr. Friedrich Vieweg	PETERS
			VOLK	Arno Volk Verlag	GERIG
SPIRE	Spire Editions	BOONIN WORLD	VOLKWEIN	Volkwein Brothers, Inc. 117 Sandusky Street Pittsburgh, PA 15212	
SPRATT	Spratt Music Company	PLYMOUTH	WAGENAAR	J. A. H. Wagenaar	ELKAN, H
ST. GREG.	St. Gregory Publishing Co. 4 West Hill Road Hoddesdon, Hertfordshire England		WALTON	Walton Music Corp.	PLYMOUTH
ST. MARTIN	St. Martin Music Co., Inc.	ROYAL	WARNER	Warner Brothers Publications 1230 Avenue of the Americas New York, NY 10020	
STAFF	Staff Music Publishing Co., Inc.	PLYMOUTH	WEINBERGER	Josef Weinberger, Ltd.	PRESSER
STAINER	Stainer & Bell, Ltd.	GALAXY	WESTCOAST	West Coast Publications, Inc. 4423 W. Jefferson Blvd. Los Angeles, CA 90016	
STANDARD	Standard Music Publishing, Inc. P.O. Box 1043 Whitman Square Turnersville, NJ 08012		WESTERN	Western International Music 2859 Holt Avenue Los Angeles, CA 90034	
SUMMY	Summy-Birchard Co. 1834 Ridge Avenue Evanston, IL 60204		WESTPORT	Westport	WESTCOAST
			WESTWOOD	Westwood Press	WORLD
SUPRAPHON	Editio Supraphon	BAREN.	WILHELM.	Wilhelmiana Musikverlag Eschersheimer Landstrasse 12 Frankfurt/Main, Germany	
THOMP.	Thompson Music House P.O. Box 12463 Nashville, TN 37212		WILLIS	Willis Music Company 7380 Industrial Highway Florence, KY 41042	
THOMP. G	Gordon V. Thompson, Ltd. 29 Birch Avenue Toronto, Ontario Canada		WOLF	Wolf-Mills Music	WESTERN
			WORD	Word, Incorporated 4800 W. Waco Drive Waco, TX 76703	
TIEROLFF	Tierolff Muziek Centrale Markt 90-92 Roosendaal, Netherlands		WORLD	World Library Publications, Inc. 2145 Central Parkway Cincinnati, OH 45214	
TONGER	P. J. Tonger, Musikverlag	PETERS	YORKE	Yorke Edition	GALAXY
TOORTS	Uit. De Toorts	DONEMUS	ZANIBON	G. Zanibon Edition Company	PETERS
TRANSAT.	Editions Transatlantiques	PRESSER	ZENEM.	Zenemükiado Vallalat	GENERAL
TRANSCON.	Transcontinental Music Publications 1674 Broadway New York, 10019		ZERBONI	Suvini Zerboni Galleria de Corso 4 Milan, Italy	
TRO	Tro Songways Service, Inc.	PLYMOUTH			
UNION ESP.	Union Musical Espanola	AMP	ZIMMER.	Wilhelm Zimmermann, Musikverlag	PETERS

Publishers' Advertisements